PERIODIC TABLE OF THE ELEMENTS

W9-BNV-120

KEY TO CHART

50	+2 +4	→ Oxidation States
Sn		← Symbol
118.69		← Atomic Weight
18 18 4		← Electron Configuration

Atomic Number → 50; Symbol → Sn; Atomic Weight → 118.69

Transition Elements — Group 8

Each entry below lists: **Atomic Number**, *Oxidation States*, **Symbol**, Atomic Weight, Electron Configuration (Orbit)

1a	2a	3b	4b	5b	6b	7b	8	8	8	1b	2b	3a	4a	5a	6a	7a	0
1 H +1 −1; 1.0079																	**2 He** 0; 4.00260; 2
3 Li +1; 6.94; 2-1	**4 Be** +2; 9.01218; 2-2											**5 B** +3; 10.81; 2-3	**6 C** +2 +4 −4; 12.011; 2-4	**7 N** +1+2+3+4+5 −3; 14.0067; 2-5	**8 O** −2; 15.9994; 2-6	**9 F** −1; 18.99840; 2-7	**10 Ne** 0; 20.179; 2-8
11 Na +1; 22.98977; 2-8-1	**12 Mg** +2; 24.305; 2-8-2											**13 Al** +3; 26.98154; 2-8-3	**14 Si** +2 +4 −4; 28.086; 2-8-4	**15 P** +1+3+5 −3; 30.97376; 2-8-5	**16 S** +4+6 −2; 32.06; 2-8-6	**17 Cl** +1+5+7 −1; 35.453; 2-8-7	**18 Ar** 0; 39.948; 2-8-8
19 K +1; 39.09₈; -8-8-1	**20 Ca** +2; 40.08; -8-8-2	**21 Sc** +3; 44.9559; -8-9-2	**22 Ti** +2+3+4; 47.90; -8-10-2	**23 V** +2+3+4+5; 50.941₄; -8-11-2	**24 Cr** +2+3+6; 51.996; -8-13-1	**25 Mn** +2+3+4+6+7; 54.9380; -8-13-2	**26 Fe** +2+3; 55.847; -8-14-2	**27 Co** +2+3; 58.9332; -8-15-2	**28 Ni** +2+3; 58.71; -8-16-2	**29 Cu** +1+2; 63.546; -8-18-1	**30 Zn** +2; 65.38; -8-18-2	**31 Ga** +3; 69.72; -8-18-3	**32 Ge** +2+4; 72.59; -8-18-4	**33 As** +3+5 −3; 74.9216; -8-18-5	**34 Se** +4+6 −2; 78.96; -8-18-6	**35 Br** +1+5 −1; 79.904; -8-18-7	**36 Kr** 0; 83.80; -8-18-8
37 Rb +1; 85.467₈; -18-8-1	**38 Sr** +2; 87.62; -18-8-2	**39 Y** +3; 88.905₉; -18-9-2	**40 Zr** +4; 91.22; -18-10-2	**41 Nb** +3+5; 92.9064; -18-12-1	**42 Mo** +6; 95.94; -18-13-1	**43 Tc** +4+6+7; 98.9062; -18-13-2	**44 Ru** +3; 101.07; -18-15-1	**45 Rh** +3; 102.9055; -18-16-1	**46 Pd** +2+4; 106.4; -18-18-0	**47 Ag** +1; 107.868; -18-18-1	**48 Cd** +2; 112.40; -18-18-2	**49 In** +3; 114.82; -18-18-3	**50 Sn** +2+4; 118.69; -18-18-4	**51 Sb** +3+5 −3; 121.75; -18-18-5	**52 Te** +4+6 −2; 127.60; -18-18-6	**53 I** +1+5+7 −1; 126.9045; -18-18-7	**54 Xe** 0; 131.30; -18-18-8
55 Cs +1; 132.9054; -18-8-1	**56 Ba** +2; 137.34; -18-8-2	**57* La** +3; 138.9055; -18-9-2	**72 Hf** +4; 178.49; -32-10-2	**73 Ta** +5; 180.947₉; -32-11-2	**74 W** +6; 183.85; -32-12-2	**75 Re** +4+6+7; 186.2; -32-13-2	**76 Os** +3+4; 190.2; -32-14-2	**77 Ir** +3+4; 192.22; -32-15-2	**78 Pt** +2+4; 195.09; -32-16-2	**79 Au** +1+3; 196.9665; -32-18-1	**80 Hg** +1+2; 200.59; -32-18-2	**81 Tl** +1+3; 204.37; -32-18-3	**82 Pb** +2+4; 207.2; -32-18-4	**83 Bi** +3+5; 208.9808; -32-18-5	**84 Po** +2+4; (209); -32-18-6	**85 At** −1; (210); -32-18-7	**86 Rn** 0; (222); -32-18-8
87 Fr +1; (223); -18-8-1	**88 Ra** +2; 226.0254; -18-8-2	**89** La** +3; (227); -18-9-2	**104** +4; (261); -32-10-2	**105** (262); -32-11-2	**106** (263); -32-12-2												

*Lanthanides

3b	4b	5b	6b	7b	8	8	8	1b	2b	3a	4a	5a	6a
58 Ce +3+4; 140.12; -20-8-2	**59 Pr** +3; 140.9077; -21-8-2	**60 Nd** +3; 144.24; -22-8-2	**61 Pm** +3; (145); -23-8-2	**62 Sm** +2+3; 150.4; -24-8-2	**63 Eu** +2+3; 151.96; -25-8-2	**64 Gd** +3; 157.25; -25-9-2	**65 Tb** +3; 158.9254; -27-8-2	**66 Dy** +3; 162.50; -28-8-2	**67 Ho** +3; 164.9304; -29-8-2	**68 Er** +3; 167.26; -30-8-2	**69 Tm** +3; 168.9342; -31-8-2	**70 Yb** +2+3; 173.04; -32-8-2	**71 Lu** +3; 174.97; -32-9-2

**Actinides

3b	4b	5b	6b	7b	8	8	8	1b	2b	3a	4a	5a	6a
90 Th +4; 232.0381; -18-10-2	**91 Pa** +4+5; 231.0359; -20-9-2	**92 U** +3+4+5+6; 238.029; -21-9-2	**93 Np** +3+4+5+6; 237.0482; -22-9-2	**94 Pu** +3+4+5+6; (244); -24-8-2	**95 Am** +3+4+5+6; (243); -25-8-2	**96 Cm** +3; (247); -25-9-2	**97 Bk** +3+4; (247); -27-8-2	**98 Cf** +3; (251); -28-8-2	**99 Es** +3; (254); -29-8-2	**100 Fm** +3; (257); -30-8-2	**101 Md** +2+3; (258); -31-8-2	**102 No** +2+3; (259); -32-8-2	**103 Lr** +3; (260); -32-9-2

Orbit key: K; K-L; K-L-M; -L-M-N; -M-N-O; -N-O-P; O P Q; N O P; O Q

Numbers in parentheses are mass numbers of most stable isotope of that element.

Handbook

OF

Chemistry and Physics

A Ready-Reference Book of Chemical and Physical Data

HANDBOOK OF CHEMISTRY AND PHYSICS
1975-1976
56th
EDITION
CRC PRESS, INC.

EDITOR

ROBERT C. WEAST, Ph.D.

Vice President, Research, Consolidated Natural Gas Service Company, Inc.
Formerly Professor of Chemistry at Case Institute of Technology

In collaboration with a large number of professional chemists and physicists
whose assistance is acknowledged in the list of general collaborators and in
connection with the particular tables or sections involved.

Published by

18901 Cranwood Parkway · Cleveland, Ohio 44128

PREFACE TO THE 56th EDITION

In keeping with the established policy, the *CRC Handbook of Chemistry and Physics* has again been revised in order to afford students and research men the latest, most reliable, and complete data possible. An attempt has been made to include material on all branches of chemistry and physics and the closely allied sciences that would be likely to find any extended use. However, in order to retain the convenience of moderate dimensions while at the same time allow for natural growth of the book due to extension of knowledge in these sciences and logical additions along lines already developed, it has seemed necessary to exclude types of material whose use at this time would be only in certain specialized lines of work. Included in the new material are some data dealing with cryogenics, some with solar radiation, and some with thermodynamics. New information in this present edition includes:

Thermodynamic Properties of Alkane Hydrocarbons

Vapor Pressure of Elements that are Gaseous at Standard Conditions

Heats of Vaporization of Organic Compounds

Data for ten additional compounds in the table, "Concentrative Properties of Aqueous Solutions"

Primary Fixed Points of International Practical Temperature Scale-68 (IPTS-68)

Standard Atmosphere

Solubility Parameters of Organic Compounds

Total Monthly Solar Radiation in a Cloudless Sky

Thermal Conductivity of Compressed Oxygen

Transport Properties of Oxygen at Saturation

Viscosity and Thermal Conductivity of Nitrogen at Cryogenic Temperatures

Viscosity and Thermal Conductivity of Oxygen as a Function of Temperature

The following information and tables appearing in earlier editions have been largely revised:

Efficacies of Illuminants

The Elements

Key Values for Thermodynamics

Melting and Boiling Points, and Atomic Weights of the Elements

Recommended Consistent Values of the Fundamental Physical Constants

Selected Values of Superconductive Elements

Surface Tension of Liquid Halogens

Tables of Particle Properties

Certain tables have been reset in order that they may be more easily read. Still further, all errors brought to our attention have been corrected. Sincere gratitude is expressed to all who have written regarding these errors or who have made suggestions for further improvement of the book.

Robert C. Weast
April 1, 1975

Physics Editorial Board

Collaborators and Contributors

L. ALBERTS, Ph.D.
Department of Physics
Rand Afrikaans University
Johannesburg, South Africa

C. J. ALLEN
Illuminating Engineer
General Electric Company
Nela Park
Cleveland, Ohio 44112

W. A. ANDERSON, Ph.D.
Analytical Instrument Research
Varian Associates
611 Hansen Way
Palo Alto, California 94303

W. J. ARMENTO
Research Chemist
Babcock & Wilcox
Alliance, Ohio 44601

J. ASKILL, Ph.D.
Chairman, Physics Department
Millikin University
Decatur, Illinois 62522

J. C. BAILAR, JR., Ph.D.
Professor of Inorganic Chemistry
University of Illinois
Urbana, Illinois 61801

R. A. BAXTER, M.S.
Professor of Chemistry
Colorado School of Mines
Golden, Colorado 80401

J. A. BEARDEN, Ph.D.
Department of Physics
Johns Hopkins University
Baltimore, Maryland 21218

A. H. BENADE, Ph.D.
Department of Physics
Case Western Reserve University
Cleveland, Ohio 44106

F. F. BENTLEY
Air Force Materials Laboratory
Wright Patterson Air Force Base, Ohio 45433

J. H. BILLMAN, Ph.D.
Professor of Chemistry
Indiana University
Bloomington, Indiana 47401

A. L. BLOOM, Ph.D.
Spectra-Physics, Inc.
1255 Terra Bella Avenue
Mountain View, California 94040

J. A. BRADLEY, Ph.D.
Dean, Newark College of Engineering
323 High Street
Newark, New Jersey 07102

B. H. BROWN, Ph.D.
Dartmouth College
Hanover, New Hampshire 03755

J. E. BROWN
Eastman Kodak Company
Rochester, New York 14650

A. B. BURG, Ph.D.
Department of Chemistry
University of Southern California
Los Angeles, California 90007

G. P. BURNS, Ph.D.
Department of Physics
Mary Washington College
Fredericksburg, Virginia 22401

A. F. BURR, Ph.D.
Department of Physics
New Mexico State University
Las Cruces, New Mexico 88001

R. K. CARLETON, Ph.D.
213 Plymouth Street
Whitman, Massachusetts 02382

J. P. CATCHPOLE, Ph.D.
Admiralty Materials Laboratory
Holton Heath
Dorset, England

E. RICHARD COHEN, Ph.D.
Associate Director
Science Center/Aerospace and Systems Group
North American Rockwell Corporation
Thousand Oaks, California 91360

M. DAVIES, Ph.D.
Edward Davies Chemical Laboratories
University of Wales
Aberystwyth, Wales

COLLABORATORS AND CONTRIBUTORS

J. DE MENT, D. SC.
Dement Laboratories
4847 S.E. Division St.
Portland, Oregon 97206

H. G. DEMING, Ph.D.
2316 Tuttle Terrace
Sarasota, Florida 33580

E. DICYAN, Ph.D.
Consulting Chemist
420 Lexington Ave
New York, New York 10017

HANS DOLEZALEK
Department of the Navy
Office of Naval Research
Arlington, Virginia 22217

A. P. DUNLOP, Ph.D.
Director of Chemical Research
and Development
John Stuart Research Laboratories
The Quaker Oats Company
Barrington, Illinois 60010

M. S. DUNN, Ph.D.
Professor of Biochemistry
University of California
Los Angeles, California 90024

L. M. FOSTER, Ph.D.
Thomas J. Watson Research Center
International Business Machines Corp.
Yorktown Heights, New York 10598

J. L. FRANKLIN, Ph.D.
Welch Professor of Chemistry
William Marsh Rice University
Houston, Texas 77001

G. FULFORD, Ph.D.
Assistant Professor of Chemical
Engineering
University of Waterloo
Waterloo, Ontario, Canada

GLADYS H. FULLER
NBS Institute of Science and Technology
National Bureau of Standards
Washington, D.C. 20234

E. F. FURTSCH, Ph.D.
Department of Chemistry
Virginia Polytechnic Institute
Blacksburg, Virginia 24060

R. J. GETTENS, M. A.
Head Curator
Freer Gallery Laboratory
Smithsonian Institution
Washington, D.C. 20560

L. A. GILLETTE, Ph.D.
Manager, Product Development
Pennsalt Chemicals Corporation
Philadelphia, Pennsylvania 19102

H. GILMAN, Ph.D.
Department of Chemistry
Iowa State University
Ames, Iowa 50010

B. GIRLING, M.Sc., F.I.M.A.
Department of Mathematics
The City University
London E.C.1, England

E. C. GREGG, Ph.D.
School of Medicine
Case Western Reserve University
Cleveland, Ohio 44106

C. R. HAMMOND
Emhart Corporation
Hartford, Connecticut 06102

W. E. HARRIS
Professor of Chemistry
University of Alberta
Edmonton, Alberta, Canada

H. J. HARWOOD, Ph.D.
Head, Durkee Famous Foods
Organic Chemistry Division
Glidden Company
Chicago, Illinois 60647

R. L. HEATH
Atomic Energy Division
Phillips Petroleum Co.
Idaho Falls, Idaho 83401

R. W. HOFFMAN, Ph.D.
Department of Physics
Case Western Reserve University
Cleveland, Ohio 44106

JESSE F. HUNSBERGER
Research Chemist
Kawecki Chemical Company
Boyertown, Pennsylvania 19512

COLLABORATORS AND CONTRIBUTORS

C. D. HURD, Ph.D.
Chemical Laboratory
Northwestern University
Evanston, Illinois 60201

J. L. KASSNER, Ph.D.
Department of Physics
The University of Missouri-Rolla
Rolla, Missouri 65401

OLGA KENNARD, Ph.D.
University Chemical Laboratory
Cambridge, England

T. G. KENNARD, Ph.D.
20747 E. Palm Drive
Glendora, California 91740

J. A. KERR, Ph.D.
Chemistry Department
The University of Birmingham
Haworth Building
Birmingham 15, England

A. L. KING, Ph.D.
Department of Physics
Dartmouth College
Hanover, New Hampshire 03755

C. R. KINNEY, Ph.D.
1318 27th Street
Des Moines, Iowa 50311

R. KRETZ, Ph.D.
Department of Science
    and Engineering
University of Ottawa
Ottawa, Ontario, Canada K1N 6N5

G. LANG, DIPL. ING.
A–4963
St. Peter am Hart
Austria

D. F. LAWDEN, Sc.D.
Department of Mathematics
University of Aston
Birmingham, England

K. LEE, Ph.D.
IBM Research Laboratory
San Jose, California 95114

A. P. LEVITT
75 Lovett Road
Newton Center, Massachusetts 02159

M. M. MACMASTERS, Ph.D.
Department of Grain Science and
    Industry
Kansas State University
Manhattan, Kansas 66502

W. MAHLIG
Assistant Sales Manager
Laboratory Equipment Division
The W. S. Tyler Company
Cleveland, Ohio 44114

C. J. MAJOR, Ph.D.
Department of Chemical Engineering
University of Akron
Akron, Ohio 44304

J. C. MCGOWAN, Ph.D., D.Sc.
"Quantock"
13 Moreton Avenue
Harpenden, Herts AL5 2EU, England

L. MEITES, Ph.D.
Head, Department of Chemistry
Clarkson College of Technology
Potsdam, New York 13676

M. G. MELLON, Ph.D.
Professor Emeritus, Analytical Chemistry
Purdue University
West Lafayette, Indiana 47906

H. B. MICHAELSON
International Business Machines Corporation
590 Madison Avenue
New York, New York 10022

KARL Z. MORGAN, Ph.D.
Director, Health Physics Division
Oak Ridge National Laboratory
Oak Ridge, Tennessee 37830

W. M. MORGAN, Ph.D.
Professor Emeritus
Mount Union College
Alliance, Ohio 44601

R. R. NIMMO, Ph.D.
Professor of Physics
University of Otago
Dunedin, New Zealand

F. J. NORTON, Ph.D.
General Electric Company
1133 Eastern Avenue
Schenectady, New York 12308

COLLABORATORS AND CONTRIBUTORS

F. M. PAGE
Department of Chemistry
The University of Aston
Birmingham B4 7ET, England

B. R. PAMPLIN, Ph.D.
Scientific Advisers
15 Park Lane
Bath A1 2XH, England

W. PARKER, Ph.D.
Department of Physics
University of California
Irvine, California 92664

W. G. PARKS, Ph.D.
University of Rhode Island
Kingston, Rhode Island 02881

M. J. PARSONAGE
Chemistry Department
The University of Birmingham
Birmingham 15, England

SAUL PATAI, Ph.D.
Department of Organic Chemistry
Hebrew University of Jerusalem
Jerusalem, Israel

I. A. PEARL, Ph.D.
The Institute of Paper Chemistry
Appleton, Wisconsin 54911

R. F. PEART, Ph.D.
The Plessey Co. Ltd.
Allen Clark Research Centre
Northampton, England

A. C. PEED, JR.
Eastman Kodak Company
243 State Street
Rochester, New York 14614

R. PEPINSKY, Ph.D.
Department of Physics and Astronomy
University of Florida
Gainesville, Florida 32601

H. A. POUL, Ph.D.
Professor of Physics
Oklahoma State University
Stillwater, Oklahoma 74074

RICHARD L. PRATT
Staff Analyst
Data Corporation
Dayton, Ohio

H. J. PREBLUDA, Ph.D.
Consulting Biochemist
3 Belmont Circle
Trenton, New Jersey 08618

I. B. PRETTYMAN, M.S.
The Firestone Tire and Rubber Co.
1200 Firestone Parkway
Akron, Ohio 44301

ZVI RAPPOPORT, Ph.D.
Department of Organic Chemistry
Hebrew University of Jerusalem
Jerusalem, Israel

E. H. RATCLIFFE
Water Research Centre
Stevenage Laboratory
Elder Way
Stevenage, Hertfordshire SG1 1TH, England

M. C. REED, Ph.D.
1368 Wood Valley Road
Mountainside, New Jersey 07092

B. W. ROBERTS, Ph.D.
General Electric Research Laboratory
Schenectady, New York 12305

R. C. ROBERTS, Ph.D.
Professor Emeritus of Chemistry
Colgate University
Hamilton, New York 13346

R. A. ROBINSON
School of Chemistry
The University
Newcastle-upon-Tyne NE1 7RU, England

R. J. ROSEN
Consulting Chemist
9301 Parkhill Drive
Los Angeles, California 90045

A. H. ROSENFELD, Ph.D.
Lawrence Radiation Laboratory
University of California
Berkeley, California 94720

GORDON D. ROWE
Specialist Lighting of GE Properties
General Electric Company
Cleveland, Ohio 44112

A. L. ROZEK
Velsicol Chemical Corporation
Chicago, Illinois 60607

COLLABORATORS AND CONTRIBUTORS

S. I. SALEM, Ph.D.
Professor, Department of Physics and Astronomy
California State College
Long Beach, California 90840

GERT G. SCHLESSINGER, Ph.D.
Technical Service Supervisor
General Science Corporation
Bridgeport, Connecticut

JANET D. SCOTT, M.S.
600 Lakewood Road
Hendersonville, North Carolina 28739

G. T. SEABORG, Ph.D.
Lawrence Berkeley Laboratory
University of California
Berkeley, California 94720

R. S. SHANKLAND, Ph.D.
Department of Physics
Case Western Reserve University
Cleveland, Ohio 44106

R. SHAW
Chemical Physicist
Physical Organic Program
Stanford Research Institute
Menlo Park, California 94025

J. R. SHELTON, Ph.D.
Department of Chemistry
Case Western Reserve University
Cleveland, Ohio 44106

G. W. SMITH, Ph.D.
General Motors Corporation
Research Laboratories
Warren, Michigan 48090

J. M. SMITH, B.S.E.E.
Product Planning Large Lamp
Department
General Electric Company
Cleveland, Ohio 44112

L. D. SMITHSON
Air Force Materials Laboratory
Wright-Patterson Air Force Base, Ohio 45433

F. H. SPEDDING
Director, Ames Laboratory
Iowa State University
Ames, Iowa 50010

R. H. STOKES, Ph.D.
Department of Chemistry
The University of New England
Armidale, N.S.W., Australia

D. R. STULL
Research Scientist
Dow Chemical Company
Midland, Michigan

DONALD F. SWINEHART, Ph.D.
Department of Chemistry
University of Oregon
Eugene, Oregon 97043

A. TARPINIAN
Army Materials and
Mechanics Research Center
Arsenal Street
Watertown, Massachusetts 02172

B. N. TAYLOR, Ph.D.
A-247-Metrology
National Bureau of Standards
Washington, D.C. 20234

D. H. TOMLIN, Ph.D.
Department of Physics
University of Reading
Reading, Berkshire, England

A. F. TROTMAN-DICKENSON, Ph.D.
University Institute of Technology
Cardiff CF1 3NU, Wales

H. B. VICKERY, Ph.D.
Connecticut Agricultural Experimental
Station
112 Huntington Street
New Haven, Connecticut 06511

W. W. WENDLANDT, Ph.D.
Professor of Chemistry
University of Houston
Houston, Texas 77004

N. R. WHETTEN, Ph.D.
Research and Development Center
General Electric Company
P.O. Box 8
Schenectady, New York 12305

COLLABORATORS AND CONTRIBUTORS

J. H. YOE, Ph.D.
Professor Emeritus of Chemistry
University of Virginia
Charlottesville, Virginia 22294

G. R. YOHE, Ph.D.
Illinois State Geological Survey
University of Illinois Campus
Urbana, Illinois 61801

T. F. YOUNG, Ph.D.
Division of Chemical Engineering
Argonne National Laboratory
Argonne, Illinois 60439

J. ZABICKY, Ph.D.
Department of Biophysics
The Weizmann Institute of Science
Rehovoth, Israel

S. ZUFFANTI, A.M.
Professor of Chemistry
Northeastern University
Boston, Massachusetts 02115

The Publishers and Editors will be grateful to readers of this Handbook who will call their attention to errors that may be discovered. Suggestions for improvement are also welcome.

TABLE OF CONTENTS

USE OF LOGARITHMS

LAWS OF EXPONENTS

For a any real number and m a positive integer, the exponential a^m is defined as

$$\underbrace{a \cdot a \cdot a \cdot \ldots \cdot a}_{m \text{ terms}}$$

Using this definition, it is easy to show that the following three *laws of exponents* hold:

I. $a^m \cdot a^n = a^{m+n}$

II. $\dfrac{a^m}{a^n} = \begin{cases} a^{m-n} & \text{if } m > n \\ 1 & \text{if } m = n \\ \dfrac{1}{a^{n-m}} & \text{if } m < n \end{cases}$

III. $(a^m)^n = a^{mn}$

The n-th root function is defined as the inverse of the n-th power function; that is, if

$$b^n = a, \quad \text{then} \quad b = \sqrt[n]{a}.$$

If n is odd, there will be a unique real number satisfying the above definition for $\sqrt[n]{a}$, for any real value of a. If n is even, for positive values of a there will be two real values for $\sqrt[n]{a}$, one positive and one negative. By convention, the symbol $\sqrt[n]{a}$ is understood to mean the positive value in this case. If n is even and a is negative, there are no real values for $\sqrt[n]{a}$.

If we now attempt to extend the definition of the exponential a^t to all rational values of the exponent t, in such a way that the three laws of exponents continue to hold, it is easily shown that the required definitions are:

$$a^0 = 1$$

$$a^{p/q} = \sqrt[q]{a^p}$$

$$a^{-t} = \frac{1}{a^t}$$

In order to avoid difficulties with imaginary numbers and division by zero, a must now be restricted to be positive.

With this extended definition, it is possible to restate the second law of exponents in a simpler form:

II'. $\dfrac{a^m}{a^n} = a^{m-n}$

It is shown in advanced calculus that this definition may be further extended so that the exponent may be any real number, and the laws of exponents continue to hold. When the quantity a^x thus defined is viewed as a function of the exponent x, with the base a held constant, it is a continuous function. Also, if $a > 1$, the exponential function is monotone increasing, and if $0 < a < 1$, it is monotone decreasing.

Any monotone function has a single-valued inverse function, which is also monotone. Furthermore, if the original function is continuous, so is the inverse. Therefore, the inverse function to the exponential function a^x exists for all positive values of a, except $a = 1$. This function is given the name *logarithm to the base a*, abbreviated $\log_a$. That is, if

$$x = a^y, \quad \text{then} \quad y = \log_a x.$$

This function is defined and continuous for all positive values of x. It is monotone increasing if $a > 1$, and monotone decreasing if $a < 1$.

If the laws of exponents are rewritten in terms of logarithms, they become the *laws of logarithms*:

I. $\log_a (xy) = \log_a x + \log_a y$

II. $\log_a \left(\dfrac{x}{y}\right) = \log_a x - \log_a y$

III. $\log_a (x^n) = n \log_a x$

Logarithms derive their main usefulness in computation from the above laws, since they allow multiplication, division, and exponentiation to be replaced by the simpler operations of addition, subtraction, and multiplication, respectively. See the examples which follow.

Further recourse to the definition of logarithm leads to the following formula for change of base

$$\log_a x = \log_b x / \log_b a = (\log_b x) \cdot (\log_a b)$$

Two numbers are commonly used as bases for logarithms. Logarithms to the base 10 are most convenient for use in computation. These logarithm are called common or Briggsian logarithms.

The other usual base for logarithms is an irrational number denoted by e, whose value is approximately 2.71828 .... These logarithms are called natural, Naperian, or hyperbolic logarithms, and occur in many formulas of higher mathematics. The abbreviation ln is frequently used for the natural logarithm function.

Other bases for logarithms, such as 2 and 3, occur in certain applications. These applications are so infrequent that separate tables for these bases are usually not given. Instead, the formulas for change of base are applied to common or natural logarithms.

If the formulas for change of base are applied to the two usual bases, the following formulas result:

$$\log_{10} x = \log_e x / \log_e 10 = (\log_{10} e)(\log_e x) = M \log_e x$$
$$= 0.43429 \; 44819 \log_e x$$

$$\log_e x = \log_{10} x / \log_{10} e = (\log_e 10)(\log_{10} x) = \frac{1}{M} \log_{10} x$$
$$= 2.30258 \; 50930 \log_{10} x$$

The following remarks apply to common logarithms.

Since most numbers are irrational powers of ten, a common logarithm, in general, consists of an integer, which is called the characteristic, and an endless decimal, the mantissa.

It is to be observed that the common logarithms of all numbers expressed by the same figures in the same order with the decimal point in different positions have different characteristics but the same mantissa. To illustrate:—if the decimal point stands after the first figure of a number, counting from the left, the characteristic is 0; if after two figures, it is 1; if after three figures, it is 2; and so forth. If the decimal point stands before the first significant figure the characteristic is -1, usually written $\bar{1}$; if there is one zero between the decimal point and the first significant figure it is $\bar{2}$, and so on. For example: log 256 = 2.40824, log 2.56 = 0.40824, log 0.256 = $\bar{1}$.40824, log 0.00256 = $\bar{3}$.40824. The two latter are often written log 0.256 = 9.40824 $-$ 10, log 0.00256 = 7.40824 $-$ 10.

Notice that, although the common logarithm of a number less than one is a negative number, it is customarily written as a negative characteristic and a *positive* mantissa, since the mantissas are usually given in tables as positive numbers. This is the reason that the negative sign is written above the characteristic, since it does not apply to the mantissa. Thus log 0.00256 = $\bar{3}$.40824 = 7.40824 $-$ 10 = -2.59176.

A method of determining characteristics of logarithms is to write the number with one figure to the left of the decimal point multiplied by the appropriate power of 10. The characteristic is then the exponent used. For example:

$$256\ 000\ 000 = 2.56 \times 10^8 \qquad \log = 8.40824$$
$$0.000\ 000\ 256 = 2.56 \times 10^{-7} \qquad \log = \bar{7}.40824 \quad \text{or} \quad 3.40824 - 10$$

Inasmuch as the characteristic may be determined by inspection, the mantissas only are given in tables of common logarithms.

USE OF LOGARITHM TABLES

To find the common logarithm of a number:

(*Note:* This description and examples refer specifically to the table entitled "Five-Place Logarithms." For the other tables, there will be minor differences from this description. Most of these differences are obvious. Notes with the individual tables explain any differences which are not immediately obvious.)

For a number of four figures, take out the tabular mantissa on a line with the first three figures of the number and under its fourth figure. The characteristic is determined as previously explained.

For a number of less than four figures, supply zeros to make a four figure number and take the value of the mantissa from the tables as before. For example: log 2 = log 2.000 = 0.30103.

(Notice that in some of the tables not all of the digits of the logarithm are given for every value. For example, in the table of five-place common logarithms, the first two digits of each mantissa are given only once for each line. The remaining three digits of each mantissa are given in the correct place in the table. When the leading two digits are not given on a line, they should be taken from the last line above it on which they do appear. When a mantissa is marked with an asterisk, it indicates that the value for the leading digits is to be taken from the *next* line instead of the present line. Similar remarks apply to the other tables in which this method of presenting the values are used.)

For a number of more than four figures, interpolation must be used. There are several precautions that must be observed when interpolating:

1. Linear interpolation, as described below, may only be used to add one extra digit to the argument (i.e., in the present case, for a four-digit argument).

2. Even though the mantissas given in the table are accurate to five decimal places, interpolated values are accurate only to the same number of places as in the argument, i.e. four places.

3. Because of the rapidly changing values in this region of the table, interpolation is not accurate if the first two digits of the argument are 11 or 12. For this reason, the table has been extended at the end so that such values may be read directly from the table with five-digit arguments, without interpolation. (The four-place table is not so extended. If interpolation is required in this section of the four-place table, the value should be read instead from the five-place table without interpolation.)

If the above precautions cannot be observed, then higher order interpolation should be used.

Where applicable, linear interpolation is carried out as follows:

Take the tabular value of the mantissa for the first four figures; find the difference between the mantissa and the next greater tabular mantissa and multiply the difference so found by the remaining figures of the number as a decimal and add the product to the mantissa of the first four figures. For example, to find log 46.762:

$$\log 46.76 = 1.66987$$

Tabular difference between this mantissa and that for 4677 is .00010

$$\therefore \log 46.762 = 1.66987 + .2 \times .00010$$
$$= 1.66987 + .00002$$
$$= 1.66989$$

In the four-place logarithm table, a column of proportional parts is given at the end of each line. The number in the column under the fourth digit of the argument is the amount that must be added to any mantissa in that line to interpolate for the fourth digit. This number is to be added to the last place of the mantissa. These numbers are averages for the entire line, so may be off by 1 in the last place.

For example, to find log 33.74

$$\log 33.7 = 1.5276$$
$$\text{proportional part for } 4 = \underline{\quad 5}$$
$$\therefore \log 33.74 = 1.5281$$

To find the number corresponding to a given logarithm:

(*Note:* This number is called the antilogarithm, and is denoted by $\log^{-1}$. Since the logarithm function is the inverse of the exponential function, $\log_a^{-1} x = a^x$. Therefore, any procedure or table which calculates antilogarithms may also be used to calculate exponentials, and vice-versa. In particular, tables of e^x may be used to compute antilogarithms to the base e.)

The procedure given below refers to the five-place logarithm table. As before, any significant deviation for other tables will be noted.

If the mantissa is found exactly in the table, join the figure at the top which is directly above the given mantissa to the three figures on the line at the left and place the decimal point according to the characteristic of the logarithm. For example,

$$\log^{-1} 3.39967 = \text{antilog } 3.39967 = 2510.$$

If the mantissa is not found exactly in the table it is necessary to interpolate. For example, to find antilog 3.40028, we find in the table

$$\text{antilog } 3.40019 = 2513.$$
$$\text{antilog } \underline{3.40037 = 2514.}$$
$$\text{tabular difference} \quad 18$$

A-4

The required difference is 9, so we must add $\frac{9}{18} = .5$.

$$\therefore \text{antilog } 3.40028 = 2513.5$$

The same precautions must be observed for interpolation in finding antilogarithms as in finding logarithms.

Tables of natural logarithms are used in the same way as tables of common logarithms, except that they contain both the characteristics and the mantissas of the logarithms.

Examples of the use of logarithms in computation follow. Almost all computation with logarithms is done with common logarithms, since the computation of the characteristic is simpler, and since only the significant digits of the argument need be given in the table, without regard for the decimal point location. These examples all use the table of five-place common logarithms.

1. $52600 \times 0.00381 \times 2.74 = 549.11$

log 52600	= 4.72099	
log 0.00381	= $\bar{3}$.58092*	*For numbers less than one, the characteristic is negative whereas the mantissa is positive.
log 2.74	= 0.43775	
adding	= 2.73966	
antilog	= 549.11	

The sum is the logarithm of the product, the mantissa of which is 73966. On looking up this mantissa in the logarithm tables we see that it corresponds to the digits 54911. The characteristic is 2, hence there are three figures before the decimal point. The number corresponding to the logarithm, called the antilogarithm, is 549.11.

2. $0.00123 \div 52.7 = 0.000\ 023\ 34$ An alternative method:

log 0.00123	= $\bar{3}$.08991		log 0.00123	= 7.08991 − 10
log 52.7	= 1.72181		log 52.7	= 1.72181
subtracting	= $\bar{5}$.36810			5.36810 − 10
antilog	= 0.000 023 34			

The characteristic $\bar{5}(5. - 10)$ shows four zeros after the decimal point before the first significant figure.

3. $\dfrac{273 \times 780}{292 \times 760} \times 15 \times 0.09 = 1.2954$

log 273	= 2.43616		log 292	= 2.46538
log 780	= 2.89209		log 760	= 2.88081
log 15	= 1.17609		log denominator	= 5.34619
log 0.09	= $\bar{2}$.95424			
log numerator	= 5.45858			

log numerator	= 5.45858
log denominator	= 5.34619
subtracting	= 0.11237
antilog	= 1.2954

As division may be accomplished by multiplying by the reciprocal of a number, the above may be considerably simplified. The logarithm of the reciprocal of a number, called the cologarithm, is readily obtained from the table by subtracting the logarithm of the number from zero. This may be readily read off from the table of mantissas. Change the sign of the charactreristic algebraically adding to it − 1, then mentally subtract each figure of the mantissa from 9 proceeding from left to right, the last figure being subtracted from 10. The example then is:

$$
\begin{aligned}
\log 273 &= 2.43616 \\
\log 780 &= 2.89209 \\
\log 15 &= 1.17609 \\
\log 0.09 &= \overline{2}.95424 \\
\text{colog } 292 &= \overline{3}.53462 \\
\text{colog } 760 &= \overline{3}.11919 \\
\hline
&\ 0.11239
\end{aligned}
$$

4. $(0.00098)^4 = 9.224 \times 10^{-13}$ An alternative method:

$$
\begin{array}{ll}
\log 0.00098 = \overline{4}.99123 & \log 0.00098 = 6.99123 - 10 \\
\ 4 & \ 4 \\
\hline
\ 3.96492 \ (a) & \ 27.96492 - 40 \\
\overline{4} \times 4 = \overline{16}. \quad (b) & \text{or } 7.96492 - 20 \\
\log (0.00098)^4 = \overline{13}.96492 \ (c) & \text{or } \overline{13}.96492 \\
\text{antilog} = 9.224 \times 10^{-13} & \text{antilog} = 9.224 \times 10^{-13}
\end{array}
$$

In the above it will be noted that the mantissa is always positive, hence the multiplication of the mantissa shown at (a), while (b) shows the multiplication of the characteristic. (c) is the algebraic sum.

5. $\sqrt[5]{492} = 3.4546$
   $\log 492 = 2.69197$

Dividing the logarithm by 5 gives as the logarithm of the root 0.53839 the antilogarithm of which is 3.4546 both characteristic and mantissa being positive. When the characteristic is negative and not evenly divisible by the root to be taken, a modification of the logarithm is necessary, as the following example shows:

6. $\sqrt[3]{0.000372} = 0.07192$
   $\log 3.72 \times 10^{-4} = \overline{4}.57054$ \hfill (a)
   $\phantom{\log 3.72 \times 10^{-4} } = 26.57054 - 30$ \hfill (b)

Dividing (b) by 3 gives 8.85685 − 10 which may be written $\overline{2}.85685$ and is the logarithm of the root sought, the antilogarithm of which is 0.07191.

7. $(0.000\ 372)^{1.2} = 0.000\ 076\ 672$

$$
\begin{aligned}
\log 0.000\ 372 &= \overline{4}.57054 \\
\text{or } &\ 6.57054 - 10 \\
&\ 1.2 \\
\hline
&\ 7.884648 - 12 \\
\text{antilog} &= 0.000\ 076\ 672
\end{aligned}
$$

8. $(0.000372)^{-1.32} = 33642$

$$
\begin{aligned}
\text{colog } 0.000372 &= 3.42946 \\
&\ 1.32 \\
\hline
&\ 4.52689 \\
\text{antilog} &= 33642
\end{aligned}
$$

N	0	1	2	3	4	5	6	7	8	9	Proportional Parts								
											1	2	3	4	5	6	7	8	9
10	0000	0043	0086	0128	0170	0212	0253	0294	0334	0374	*4	8	12	17	21	25	29	33	37
11	0414	0453	0492	0531	0569	0607	0645	0682	0719	0755	4	8	11	15	19	23	26	30	34
12	0792	0828	0864	0899	0934	0969	1004	1038	1072	1106	3	7	10	14	17	21	24	28	31
13	1139	1173	1206	1239	1271	1303	1335	1367	1399	1430	3	6	10	13	16	19	23	26	29
14	1461	1492	1523	1553	1584	1614	1644	1673	1703	1732	3	6	9	12	15	18	21	24	27
15	1761	1790	1818	1847	1875	1903	1931	1959	1987	2014	*3	6	8	11	14	17	20	22	25
16	2041	2068	2095	2122	2148	2175	2201	2227	2253	2279	3	5	8	11	13	16	18	21	24
17	2304	2330	2355	2380	2405	2430	2455	2480	2504	2529	2	5	7	10	12	15	17	20	22
18	2553	2577	2601	2625	2648	2672	2695	2718	2742	2765	2	5	7	9	12	14	16	19	21
19	2788	2810	2833	2856	2878	2900	2923	2945	2967	2989	2	4	7	9	11	13	16	18	20
20	3010	3032	3054	3075	3096	3118	3139	3160	3181	3201	2	4	6	8	11	13	15	17	19
21	3222	3243	3263	3284	3304	3324	3345	3365	3385	3404	2	4	6	8	10	12	14	16	18
22	3424	3444	3464	3483	3502	3522	3541	3560	3579	3598	2	4	6	8	10	12	14	15	17
23	3617	3636	3655	3674	3692	3711	3729	3747	3766	3784	2	4	6	7	9	11	13	15	17
24	3802	3820	3838	3856	3874	3892	3909	3927	3945	3962	2	4	5	7	9	11	12	14	16
25	3979	3997	4014	4031	4048	4065	4082	4099	4116	4133	2	3	5	7	9	10	12	14	15
26	4150	4166	4183	4200	4216	4232	4249	4265	4281	4298	2	3	5	7	8	10	11	13	15
27	4314	4330	4346	4362	4378	4393	4409	4425	4440	4456	2	3	5	6	8	9	11	13	14
28	4472	4487	4502	4518	4533	4548	4564	4579	4594	4609	2	3	5	6	8	9	11	12	14
29	4624	4639	4654	4669	4683	4698	4713	4728	4742	4757	1	3	4	6	7	9	10	12	13
30	4771	4786	4800	4814	4829	4843	4857	4871	4886	4900	1	3	4	6	7	9	10	11	13
31	4914	4928	4942	4955	4969	4983	4997	5011	5024	5038	1	3	4	6	7	8	10	11	12
32	5051	5065	5079	5092	5105	5119	5132	5145	5159	5172	1	3	4	5	7	8	9	11	12
33	5185	5198	5211	5224	5237	5250	5263	5276	5289	5302	1	3	4	5	6	8	9	10	12
34	5315	5328	5340	5353	5366	5378	5391	5403	5416	5428	1	3	4	5	6	8	9	10	11
35	5441	5453	5465	5478	5490	5502	5514	5527	5539	5551	1	2	4	5	6	7	9	10	11
36	5563	5575	5587	5599	5611	5623	5635	5647	5658	5670	1	2	4	5	6	7	8	10	11
37	5682	5694	5705	5717	5729	5740	5752	5763	5775	5786	1	2	3	5	6	7	8	9	10
38	5798	5809	5821	5832	5843	5855	5866	5877	5888	5899	1	2	3	5	6	7	8	9	10
39	5911	5922	5933	5944	5955	5966	5977	5988	5999	6010	1	2	3	4	5	7	8	9	10
40	6021	6031	6042	6053	6064	6075	6085	6096	6107	6117	1	2	3	4	5	6	8	9	10
41	6128	6138	6149	6160	6170	6180	6191	6201	6212	6222	1	2	3	4	5	6	7	8	9
42	6232	6243	6253	6263	6274	6284	6294	6304	6314	6325	1	2	3	4	5	6	7	8	9
43	6335	6345	6355	6365	6375	6385	6395	6405	6415	6425	1	2	3	4	5	6	7	8	9
44	6435	6444	6454	6464	6474	6484	6493	6503	6513	6522	1	2	3	4	5	6	7	8	9
45	6532	6542	6551	6561	6571	6580	6590	6599	6609	6618	1	2	3	4	5	6	7	8	9
46	6628	6637	6646	6656	6665	6675	6684	6693	6702	6712	1	2	3	4	5	6	7	7	8
47	6721	6730	6739	6749	6758	6767	6776	6785	6794	6803	1	2	3	4	5	5	6	7	8
48	6812	6821	6830	6839	6848	6857	6866	6875	6884	6893	1	2	3	4	4	5	6	7	8
49	6902	6911	6920	6928	6937	6946	6955	6964	6972	6981	1	2	3	4	4	5	6	7	8
50	6990	6998	7007	7016	7024	7033	7042	7050	7059	7067	1	2	3	3	4	5	6	7	8
51	7076	7084	7093	7101	7110	7118	7126	7135	7143	7152	1	2	3	3	4	5	6	7	8
52	7160	7168	7177	7185	7193	7202	7210	7218	7226	7235	1	2	2	3	4	5	6	7	7
53	7243	7251	7259	7267	7275	7284	7292	7300	7308	7316	1	2	2	3	4	5	6	6	7
54	7324	7332	7340	7348	7356	7364	7372	7380	7388	7396	1	2	2	3	4	5	6	6	7
N	0	1	2	3	4	5	6	7	8	9	1	2	3	4	5	6	7	8	9

* Interpolation in this section of the table is inaccurate.

N	0	1	2	3	4	5	6	7	8	9	Proportional Parts								
											1	2	3	4	5	6	7	8	9
55	7404	7412	7419	7427	7435	7443	7451	7459	7466	7474	1	2	2	3	4	5	5	6	7
56	7482	7490	7497	7505	7513	7520	7528	7536	7543	7551	1	2	2	3	4	5	5	6	7
57	7559	7566	7574	7582	7589	7597	7604	7612	7619	7627	1	2	2	3	4	5	5	6	7
58	7634	7642	7649	7657	7664	7672	7679	7686	7694	7701	1	1	2	3	4	4	5	6	7
59	7709	7716	7723	7731	7738	7745	7752	7760	7767	7774	1	1	2	3	4	4	5	6	7
60	7782	7789	7796	7803	7810	7818	7825	7832	7839	7846	1	1	2	3	4	4	5	6	6
61	7853	7860	7868	7875	7882	7889	7896	7903	7910	7917	1	1	2	3	4	4	5	6	6
62	7924	7931	7938	7945	7952	7959	7966	7973	7980	7987	1	1	2	3	3	4	5	6	6
63	7993	8000	8007	8014	8021	8028	8035	8041	8048	8055	1	1	2	3	3	4	5	5	6
64	8062	8069	8075	8082	8089	8096	8102	8109	8116	8122	1	1	2	3	3	4	5	5	6
65	8129	8136	8142	8149	8156	8162	8169	8176	8182	8189	1	1	2	3	3	4	5	5	6
66	8195	8202	8209	8215	8222	8228	8235	8241	8248	8254	1	1	2	3	3	4	5	5	6
67	8261	8267	8274	8280	8287	8293	8299	8306	8312	8319	1	1	2	3	3	4	5	5	6
68	8325	8331	8338	8344	8351	8357	8363	8370	8376	8382	1	1	2	3	3	4	4	5	6
69	8388	8395	8401	8407	8414	8420	8426	8432	8439	8445	1	1	2	2	3	4	4	5	6
70	8451	8457	8463	8470	8476	8482	8488	8494	8500	8506	1	1	2	2	3	4	4	5	6
71	8513	8519	8525	8531	8537	8543	8549	8555	8561	8567	1	1	2	2	3	4	4	5	5
72	8573	8579	8585	8591	8597	8603	8609	8615	8621	8627	1	1	2	2	3	4	4	5	5
73	8633	8639	8645	8651	8657	8663	8669	8675	8681	8686	1	1	2	2	3	4	4	5	5
74	8692	8698	8704	8710	8716	8722	8727	8733	8739	8745	1	1	2	2	3	4	4	5	5
75	8751	8756	8762	8768	8774	8779	8785	8791	8797	8802	1	1	2	2	3	3	4	5	5
76	8808	8814	8820	8825	8831	8837	8842	8848	8854	8859	1	1	2	2	3	3	4	5	5
77	8865	8871	8876	8882	8887	8893	8899	8904	8910	8915	1	1	2	2	3	3	4	4	5
78	8921	8927	8932	8938	8943	8949	8954	8960	8965	8971	1	1	2	2	3	3	4	4	5
79	8976	8982	8987	8993	8998	9004	9009	9015	9020	9025	1	1	2	2	3	3	4	4	5
80	9031	9036	9042	9047	9053	9058	9063	9069	9074	9079	1	1	2	2	3	3	4	4	5
81	9085	9090	9096	9101	9106	9112	9117	9122	9128	9133	1	1	2	2	3	3	4	4	5
82	9138	9143	9149	9154	9159	9165	9170	9175	9180	9186	1	1	2	2	3	3	4	4	5
83	9191	9196	9201	9206	9212	9217	9222	9227	9232	9238	1	1	2	2	3	3	4	4	5
84	9243	9248	9253	9258	9263	9269	9274	9279	9284	9289	1	1	2	2	3	3	4	4	5
85	9294	9299	9304	9309	9315	9320	9325	9330	9335	9340	1	1	2	2	3	3	4	4	5
86	9345	9350	9355	9360	9365	9370	9375	9380	9385	9390	1	1	2	2	3	3	4	4	5
87	9395	9400	9405	9410	9415	9420	9425	9430	9435	9440	0	1	1	2	2	3	3	4	4
88	9445	9450	9455	9460	9465	9469	9474	9479	9484	9489	0	1	1	2	2	3	3	4	4
89	9494	9499	9504	9509	9513	9518	9523	9528	9533	9538	0	1	1	2	2	3	3	4	4
90	9542	9547	9552	9557	9562	9566	9571	9576	9581	9586	0	1	1	2	2	3	3	4	4
91	9590	9595	9600	9605	9609	9614	9619	9624	9628	9633	0	1	1	2	2	3	3	4	4
92	9638	9643	9647	9652	9657	9661	9666	9671	9675	9680	0	1	1	2	2	3	3	4	4
93	9685	9689	9694	9699	9703	9708	9713	9717	9722	9727	0	1	1	2	2	3	3	4	4
94	9731	9736	9741	9745	9750	9754	9759	9763	9768	9773	0	1	1	2	2	3	3	4	4
95	9777	9782	9786	9791	9795	9800	9805	9809	9814	9818	0	1	1	2	2	3	3	4	4
96	9823	9827	9832	9836	9841	9845	9850	9854	9859	9863	0	1	1	2	2	3	3	4	4
97	9868	9872	9877	9881	9886	9890	9894	9899	9903	9908	0	1	1	2	2	3	3	4	4
98	9912	9917	9921	9926	9930	9934	9939	9943	9948	9952	0	1	1	2	2	3	3	4	4
99	9956	9961	9965	9969	9974	9978	9983	9987	9991	9996	0	1	1	2	2	3	3	3	4
N	0	1	2	3	4	5	6	7	8	9	1	2	3	4	5	6	7	8	9

N	0	1	2	3	4	5	6	7	8	9
.10	−1.000	− .9957	− .9914	− .9872	− .9830	− .9788	− .9747	− .9706	− .9666	− .9626
.11	− .9586	− .9547	− .9508	− .9469	− .9431	− .9393	− .9355	− .9318	− .9281	− .9245
.12	− .9208	− .9172	− .9136	− .9101	− .9066	− .9031	− .8996	− .8962	− .8928	− .8894
.13	− .8861	− .8827	− .8794	− .8761	− .8729	− .8697	− .8665	− .8633	− .8601	− .8570
.14	− .8539	− .8508	− .8477	− .8447	− .8416	− .8386	− .8356	− .8327	− .8297	− .8268
.15	− .8239	− .8210	− .8182	− .8153	− .8125	− .8097	− .8069	− .8041	− .8013	− .7986
.16	− .7959	− .7932	− .7905	− .7878	− .7852	− .7825	− .7799	− .7773	− .7747	− .7721
.17	− .7696	− .7670	− .7645	− .7620	− .7595	− .7570	− .7545	− .7520	− .7496	− .7471
.18	− .7447	− .7423	− .7399	− .7375	− .7352	− .7328	− .7305	− .7282	− .7258	− .7235
.19	− .7212	− .7190	− .7167	− .7144	− .7122	− .7100	− .7077	− .7055	− .7033	− .7011
.20	− .6990	− .6968	− .6946	− .6925	− .6904	− .6882	− .6861	− .6840	− .6819	− .6799
.21	− .6778	− .6757	− .6737	− .6716	− .6696	− .6676	− .6655	− .6635	− .6615	− .6596
.22	− .6576	− .6556	− .6536	− .6517	− .6498	− .6478	− .6459	− .6440	− .6421	− .6402
.23	− .6383	− .6364	− .6345	− .6326	− .6308	− .6289	− .6271	− .6253	− .6234	− .6216
.24	− .6198	− .6180	− .6162	− .6144	− .6126	− .6108	− .6091	− .6073	− .6055	− .6038
.25	− .6021	− .6003	− .5986	− .5969	− .5952	− .5935	− .5918	− .5901	− .5884	− .5867
.26	− .5850	− .5834	− .5817	− .5800	− .5784	− .5768	− .5751	− .5735	− .5719	− .5702
.27	− .5686	− .5670	− .5654	− .5638	− .5622	− .5607	− .5591	− .5575	− .5560	− .5544
.28	− .5528	− .5513	− .5498	− .5482	− .5467	− .5452	− .5436	− .5421	− .5406	− .5391
.29	− .5376	− .5361	− .5346	− .5331	− .5317	− .5302	− .5287	− .5272	− .5258	− .5243
.30	− .5229	− .5214	− .5200	− .5186	− .5171	− .5157	− .5143	− .5129	− .5114	− .5100
.31	− .5086	− .5072	− .5058	− .5045	− .5031	− .5017	− .5003	− .4989	− .4976	− .4962
.32	− .4949	− .4935	− .4921	− .4908	− .4895	− .4881	− .4868	− .4855	− .4841	− .4828
.33	− .4815	− .4802	− .4789	− .4776	− .4763	− .4750	− .4737	− .4724	− .4711	− .4698
.34	− .4685	− .4672	− .4660	− .4647	− .4634	− .4622	− .4609	− .4597	− .4584	− .4572
.35	− .4559	− .4547	− .4535	− .4522	− .4510	− .4498	− .4486	− .4473	− .4461	− .4449
.36	− .4437	− .4425	− .4413	− .4401	− .4389	− .4377	− .4365	− .4353	− .4342	− .4330
.37	− .4318	− .4306	− .4295	− .4283	− .4271	− .4260	− .4248	− .4237	− .4225	− .4214
.38	− .4202	− .4191	− .4179	− .4168	− .4157	− .4145	− .4134	− .4123	− .4112	− .4101
.39	− .4089	− .4078	− .4067	− .4056	− .4045	− .4034	− .4023	− .4012	− .4001	− .3990
.40	− .3979	− .3969	− .3958	− .3947	− .3936	− .3925	− .3915	− .3904	− .3893	− .3883
.41	− .3872	− .3862	− .3851	− .3840	− .3830	− .3820	− .3809	− .3799	− .3788	− .3778
.42	− .3768	− .3757	− .3747	− .3737	− .3726	− .3716	− .3706	− .3696	− .3686	− .3675
.43	− .3665	− .3655	− .3645	− .3635	− .3625	− .3615	− .3605	− .3595	− .3585	− .3575
.44	− .3565	− .3556	− .3546	− .3536	− .3526	− .3516	− .3507	− .3497	− .3487	− .3478
.45	− .3468	− .3458	− .3449	− .3439	− .3429	− .3420	− .3410	− .3401	− .3391	− .3382
.46	− .3372	− .3363	− .3354	− .3344	− .3335	− .3325	− .3316	− .3307	− .3298	− .3288
.47	− .3279	− .3270	− .3261	− .3251	− .3242	− .3233	− .3224	− .3215	− .3206	− .3197
.48	− .3188	− .3179	− .3170	− .3161	− .3152	− .3143	− .3134	− .3125	− .3116	− .3107
.49	− .3098	− .3089	− .3080	− .3072	− .3063	− .3054	− .3045	− .3036	− .3028	− .3019
.50	− .3010	− .3002	− .2993	− .2984	− .2976	− .2967	− .2958	− .2950	− .2941	− .2933
.51	− .2924	− .2916	− .2907	− .2899	− .2890	− .2882	− .2874	− .2865	− .2857	− .2848
.52	− .2840	− .2832	− .2823	− .2815	− .2807	− .2798	− .2790	− .2782	− .2774	− .2765
.53	− .2757	− .2749	− .2741	− .2733	− .2725	− .2716	− .2708	− .2700	− .2692	− .2684
.54	− .2676	− .2668	− .2660	− .2652	− .2644	− .2636	− .2628	− .2620	− .2612	− .2604

* This table gives the logarithms of the decimal fractions which are negative numbers.

For example log 0.61 = −0.2147 = 9.7853 − 10. It should be noted that the entries as given can be used conveniently to find cologarithms of positive numbers. Every positive number N = P · (10)^k, where $0 < P \leq 1$. Since colog N = − log N, it follows that colog N = − log P − k.

For example colog 0.61 = − log 0.61 = 0.2147; colog 61 = 0.2147 − 2; and colog 0.00061 = 3.2147.

N	0	1	2	3	4	5	6	7	8	9
.55	−.2596	−.2588	−.2581	−.2573	−.2565	−.2557	−.2549	−.2541	−.2534	−.2526
.56	−.2518	−.2510	−.2503	−.2495	−.2487	−.2480	−.2472	−.2464	−.2457	−.2449
.57	−.2441	−.2434	−.2426	−.2418	−.2411	−.2403	−.2396	−.2388	−.2381	−.2373
.58	−.2366	−.2358	−.2351	−.2343	−.2336	−.2328	−.2321	−.2314	−.2306	−.2299
.59	−.2291	−.2284	−.2277	−.2269	−.2262	−.2255	−.2248	−.2240	−.2233	−.2226
.60	−.2218	−.2211	−.2204	−.2197	−.2190	−.2182	−.2175	−.2168	−.2161	−.2154
.61	−.2147	−.2140	−.2132	−.2125	−.2118	−.2111	−.2104	−.2097	.2090	−.2083
.62	−.2076	−.2069	−.2062	−.2055	−.2048	−.2041	−.2034	−.2027	−.2020	−.2013
.63	−.2007	−.2000	−.1993	−.1986	−.1979	−.1972	−.1965	−.1959	−.1952	−.1945
.64	−.1938	−.1931	−.1925	−.1918	−.1911	−.1904	−.1898	−.1891	−.1884	−.1878
.65	−.1871	−.1864	−.1858	−.1851	−.1844	−.1838	−.1831	−.1824	−.1818	−.1811
.66	−.1805	−.1798	−.1791	−.1785	−.1778	−.1772	−.1765	−.1759	−.1752	−.1746
.67	−.1730	.1733	−.1726	−.1720	−.1713	−.1707	−.1701	−.1694	−.1688	−.1681
.68	−.1675	−.1669	−.1662	−.1656	−.1649	−.1643	−.1637	−.1630	−.1624	−.1618
.69	−.1612	−.1605	−.1599	−.1593	−.1586	−.1580	−.1574	−.1568	−.1561	−.1555
.70	−.1549	−.1543	−.1537	−.1530	−.1524	−.1518	−.1512	−.1506	−.1500	−.1494
.71	−.1487	−.1481	−.1475	−.1469	−.1463	−.1457	−.1451	−.1445	−.1439	−.1433
.72	−.1427	−.1421	−.1415	−.1409	−.1403	−.1397	−.1391	−.1385	−.1379	−.1373
.73	−.1307	−.1361	−.1355	−.1349	−.1343	−.1337	−.1331	−.1325	−.1319	−.1314
.74	−.1308	−.1302	−.1296	−.1290	−.1284	−.1278	−.1273	−.1267	−.1261	−.1255
.75	−.1249	−.1244	−.1238	−.1232	−.1226	−.1221	−.1215	−.1209	−.1203	−.1198
.76	−.1192	−.1186	−.1180	−.1175	−.1169	−.1163	−.1158	−.1152	−.1146	−.1141
.77	−.1135	−.1129	−.1124	−.1118	−.1113	−.1107	−.1101	−.1096	−.1090	−.1085
.78	−.1079	−.1073	−.1068	−.1062	−.1057	−.1051	−.1046	−.1040	−.1035	−.1029
.79	−.1024	−.1018	−.1013	−.1007	−.1002	−.0996	−.0991	−.0985	−.0980	−.0975
.80	−.0969	−.0964	−.0958	−.0953	−.0947	−.0942	−.0937	−.0931	−.0926	−.0921
.81	−.0915	−.0910	−.0904	−.0899	−.0894	−.0888	−.0883	−.0878	−.0872	−.0867
.82	−.0862	−.0857	−.0851	−.0846	−.0841	−.0835	−.0830	−.0825	−.0820	−.0814
.83	−.0809	−.0804	−.0799	−.0794	−.0788	−.0783	−.0778	−.0773	−.0768	−.0762
.84	−.0757	−.0752	−.0747	−.0742	−.0737	−.0731	−.0726	−.0721	−.0716	−.0711
.85	−.0706	−.0701	−.0696	−.0691	−.0685	−.0680	−.0675	−.0670	−.0665	−.0660
.86	−.0655	−.0650	−.0645	−.0640	−.0635	−.0630	−.0625	−.0620	−.0615	−.0610
.87	−.0605	−.0600	−.0595	−.0590	−.0585	−.0580	−.0575	−.0570	−.0565	−.0560
.88	−.0555	−.0550	−.0545	−.0540	−.0535	−.0531	−.0526	−.0521	−.0516	−.0511
.89	−.0506	−.0501	−.0496	−.0491	−.0487	−.0482	−.0477	−.0472	−.0467	−.0462
.90	−.0458	−.0453	−.0448	−.0443	−.0438	−.0434	−.0429	−.0424	−.0419	−.0414
.91	−.0410	−.0405	−.0400	−.0395	−.0391	−.0386	−.0381	−.0376	−.0372	−.0367
.92	−.0362	−.0357	−.0353	.0348	−.0343	−.0339	−.0334	−.0329	−.0325	−.0320
.93	−.0315	−.0311	−.0306	−.0301	−.0297	−.0292	−.0287	−.0283	−.0278	−.0273
.94	−.0269	−.0264	−.0259	−.0255	−.0250	−.0246	−.0241	−.0237	−.0232	−.0227
.95	−.0223	−.0218	−.0214	−.0209	−.0205	−.0200	−.0195	−.0191	−.0186	−.0182
.96	−.0177	−.0173	−.0168	−.0164	−.0159	−.0155	−.0150	−.0146	−.0141	−.0137
.97	−.0132	−.0128	−.0123	−.0119	−.0114	−.0110	−.0106	−.0101	−.0097	−.0092
.98	−.0088	−.0083	−.0079	−.0074	−.0070	−.0066	−.0061	−.0057	−.0052	−.0048
.99	−.0044	−.0039	−.0035	−.0031	−.0026	−.0022	−.0017	−.0013	−.0009	−.0004

*See footnote page A-9.

N.	0	1	2	3	4	5	6	7	8	9	Proportional parts		
100	00 000	043	087	130	173	217	260	303	346	389	**44**	**43**	**42**
101	432	475	518	561	604	647	689	732	775	817	1 4.4	4.3	4.2
102	860	903	945	988	*030	*072	*115	*157	*199	*242	2 8.8	8.6	8.4
103	01 284	326	368	410	452	494	536	578	620	662	3 13.2	12.9	12.6
104	703	745	787	828	870	912	953	995	*036	*078	4 17.6	17.2	16.8
105	02 119	160	202	243	284	325	366	407	449	490	5 22.0	21.5	21.0
106	531	572	612	653	694	735	776	816	857	898	6 26.4	25.8	25.2
107	938	979	*019	*060	*100	*141	*181	*222	*262	*302	7 30.8	30.1	29.4
108	03 342	383	423	463	503	543	583	623	663	703	8 35.2	34.4	33.6
109	743	782	822	862	902	941	981	*021	*060	*100	9 39.6	38.7	37.8
110	04 139	179	218	258	297	336	376	415	454	493	**41**	**40**	**39**
111	532	571	610	650	689	727	766	805	844	883	1 4.1	4.0	3.9
112	922	961	999	*038	*077	*115	*154	*192	*231	*269	2 8.2	8.0	7.8
113	05 308	346	385	423	461	500	538	576	614	652	3 12.3	12.0	11.7
114	690	729	767	805	843	881	918	956	994	*032	4 16.4	16.0	15.6
115	06 070	108	145	183	221	258	296	333	371	408	5 20.5	20.0	19.5
116	446	483	521	558	595	633	670	707	744	781	6 24.6	24.0	23.4
117	819	856	893	930	967	*004	*041	*078	*115	*151	7 28.7	28.0	27.3
118	07 188	225	262	298	335	372	408	445	482	518	8 32.8	32.0	31.2
119	555	591	628	664	700	737	773	809	846	882	9 36.9	36.0	35.1
120	918	954	990	*027	*063	*099	*135	*171	*207	*243	**38**	**37**	**36**
121	08 279	314	350	386	422	458	493	529	565	600	1 3.8	3.7	3.6
122	636	672	707	743	778	814	849	884	920	955	2 7.6	7.4	7.2
123	991	*026	*061	*096	*132	*167	*202	*237	*272	*307	3 11.4	11.1	10.8
124	09 342	377	412	447	482	517	552	587	621	656	4 15.2	14.8	14.4
125	691	726	760	795	830	864	899	934	968	*003	5 19.0	18.5	18.0
126	10 037	072	106	140	175	209	243	278	312	346	6 22.8	22.2	21.6
127	380	415	449	483	517	551	585	619	653	687	7 26.6	25.9	25.2
128	721	755	789	823	857	890	924	958	992	*025	8 30.4	29.6	28.8
129	11 059	093	126	160	193	227	261	294	327	361	9 34.2	33.3	32.4
130	394	428	461	494	528	561	594	628	661	694	**35**	**34**	**33**
131	727	760	793	826	860	893	926	959	992	*024	1 3.5	3.4	3.3
132	12 057	090	123	156	189	222	254	287	320	352	2 7.0	6.8	6.6
133	385	418	450	483	516	548	581	613	646	678	3 10.5	10.2	9.9
134	710	743	775	808	840	872	905	937	969	*001	4 14.0	13.6	13.2
135	13 033	066	098	130	162	194	226	258	290	322	5 17.5	17.0	16.5
136	354	386	418	450	481	513	545	577	609	640	6 21.0	20.4	19.8
137	672	704	735	767	799	830	862	893	925	956	7 24.5	23.8	23.1
138	988	*019	*051	*082	*114	*145	*176	*208	*239	*270	8 28.0	27.2	26.4
139	14 301	333	364	395	426	457	489	520	551	582	9 31.5	30.6	29.7
140	613	644	675	706	737	768	799	829	860	891	**32**	**31**	**30**
141	922	953	983	*014	*045	*076	*106	*137	*168	*198	1 3.2	3.1	3.0
142	15 229	259	290	320	351	381	412	442	473	503	2 6.4	6.2	6.0
143	534	564	594	625	655	685	715	746	776	806	3 9.6	9.3	9.0
144	836	866	897	927	957	987	*017	*047	*077	*107	4 12.8	12.4	12.0
145	16 137	167	197	227	256	286	316	346	376	406	5 16.0	15.5	15.0
146	435	465	495	524	554	584	613	643	673	702	6 19.2	18.6	18.0
147	732	761	791	820	850	879	909	938	967	997	7 22.4	21.7	21.0
148	17 026	056	085	114	143	173	202	231	260	289	8 25.6	24.8	24.0
149	319	348	377	406	435	464	493	522	551	580	9 28.8	27.9	27.0
150	609	638	667	696	725	754	782	811	840	869			
N.	0	1	2	3	4	5	6	7	8	9	Proportional parts		

N.	0	1	2	3	4	5	6	7	8	9	Proportional parts	
150	17 609	638	667	696	725	754	782	811	840	869	**29**	**28**
151	898	926	955	984	*013	*041	*070	*099	*127	*156	1 2.9	2.8
152	18 184	213	241	270	298	327	355	384	412	441	2 5.8	5.6
153	469	498	526	554	583	611	639	667	696	724	3 8.7	8.4
154	752	780	808	837	865	893	921	949	977	*005	4 11.6	11.2
155	19 033	061	089	117	145	173	201	229	257	285	5 14.5	14.0
156	312	340	368	396	424	451	479	507	535	562	6 17.4	16.8
157	590	618	645	673	700	728	756	783	811	838	7 20.3	19.6
158	866	893	921	948	976	*003	*030	*058	*085	*112	8 23.2	22.4
159	20 140	167	194	222	249	276	303	330	358	385	9 26.1	25.2
160	412	439	466	493	520	548	575	602	629	656	**27**	**26**
161	683	710	737	763	790	817	844	871	898	925	1 2.7	2.6
162	952	978	*005	*032	*059	*085	*112	*139	*165	*192	2 5.4	5.2
163	21 219	245	272	299	325	352	378	405	431	458	3 8.1	7.8
164	484	511	537	564	590	617	643	669	696	722	4 10.8	10.4
165	748	775	801	827	854	880	906	932	958	985	5 13.5	13.0
166	22 011	037	063	089	115	141	167	194	220	246	6 16.2	15.6
167	272	298	324	350	376	401	427	453	479	505	7 18.9	18.2
168	531	557	583	608	634	660	686	712	737	763	8 21.6	20.8
169	789	814	840	866	891	917	943	968	994	*019	9 24.3	23.4
170	23 045	070	096	121	147	172	198	223	249	274	**25**	
171	300	325	350	376	401	426	452	477	502	528	1 2.5	
172	553	578	603	629	654	679	704	729	754	779	2 5.0	
173	805	830	855	880	905	930	955	980	*005	*030	3 7.5	
174	24 055	080	105	130	155	180	204	229	254	279	4 10.0	
175	304	329	353	378	403	428	452	477	502	527	5 12.5	
176	551	576	601	625	650	674	699	724	748	773	6 15.0	
177	797	822	846	871	895	920	944	969	993	*018	7 17.5	
178	25 042	066	091	115	139	164	188	212	237	261	8 20.0	
179	285	310	334	358	382	406	431	455	479	503	9 22.5	
180	527	551	575	600	624	648	672	696	720	744	**24**	**23**
181	768	792	816	840	864	888	912	935	959	983	1 2.4	2.3
182	26 007	031	055	079	102	126	150	174	198	221	2 4.8	4.6
183	245	269	293	316	340	364	387	411	435	458	3 7.2	6.9
184	482	505	529	553	576	600	623	647	670	694	4 9.6	9.2
185	717	741	764	788	811	834	858	881	905	928	5 12.0	11.5
186	951	975	998	*021	*045	*068	*091	*114	*138	*161	6 14.4	13.8
187	27 184	207	231	254	277	300	323	346	370	393	7 16.8	16.1
188	416	439	462	485	508	531	554	577	600	623	8 19.2	18.4
189	646	669	692	715	738	761	784	807	830	852	9 21.6	20.7
190	875	898	921	944	967	989	*012	*035	*058	*081	**22**	**21**
191	28 103	126	149	171	194	217	240	262	285	307	1 2.2	2.1
192	330	353	375	398	421	443	466	488	511	533	2 4.4	4.2
193	556	578	601	623	646	668	691	713	735	758	3 6.6	6.3
194	780	803	825	847	870	892	914	937	959	981	4 8.8	8.4
195	29 003	026	048	070	092	115	137	159	181	203	5 11.0	10.5
196	226	248	270	292	314	336	358	380	403	425	6 13.2	12.6
197	447	469	491	513	535	557	579	601	623	645	7 15.4	14.7
198	667	688	710	732	754	776	798	820	842	863	8 17.6	16.8
199	885	907	929	951	973	994	*016	*038	*060	*081	9 19.8	18.9
200	30 103	125	146	168	190	211	233	255	276	298		
N.	0	1	2	3	4	5	6	7	8	9	Proportional parts	

N.	0	1	2	3	4	5	6	7	8	9
200	30 103	125	146	168	190	211	233	255	276	298
201	320	341	363	384	406	428	449	471	492	514
202	535	557	578	600	621	643	664	685	707	728
203	750	771	792	814	835	856	878	899	920	942
204	963	984	*006	*027	*048	*069	*091	*112	*133	*154
205	31 175	197	218	239	260	281	302	323	345	366
206	387	408	429	450	471	492	513	534	555	576
207	597	618	639	660	681	702	723	744	765	785
208	806	827	848	869	890	911	931	952	973	994
209	32 015	035	056	077	098	118	139	160	181	201
210	222	243	263	284	305	325	346	366	387	408
211	428	449	469	490	510	531	552	572	593	613
212	634	654	675	695	715	736	756	777	797	818
213	838	858	879	899	919	940	960	980	*001	*021
214	33 041	062	082	102	122	143	163	183	203	224
215	244	264	284	304	325	345	365	385	405	425
216	445	465	486	506	526	546	566	586	606	626
217	646	666	686	706	726	746	766	786	806	826
218	846	866	885	905	925	945	965	985	*005	*025
219	34 044	064	084	104	124	143	163	183	203	223
220	242	262	282	301	321	341	361	380	400	420
221	439	459	479	498	518	537	557	577	596	616
222	635	655	674	694	713	733	753	772	792	811
223	830	850	869	889	908	928	947	967	986	*005
224	35 025	044	064	083	102	122	141	160	180	199
225	218	238	257	276	295	315	334	353	372	392
226	411	430	449	468	488	507	526	545	564	583
227	603	622	641	660	679	698	717	736	755	774
228	793	813	832	851	870	889	908	927	946	965
229	984	*003	*021	*040	*059	*078	*097	*116	*135	*154
230	36 173	192	211	229	248	267	286	305	324	342
231	361	380	399	418	436	455	474	493	511	530
232	549	568	586	605	624	642	661	680	698	717
233	736	754	773	791	810	829	847	866	884	903
234	922	940	959	977	996	*014	*033	*051	*070	*088
235	37 107	125	144	162	181	199	218	236	254	273
236	291	310	328	346	365	383	401	420	438	457
237	475	493	511	530	548	566	585	603	621	639
238	658	676	694	712	731	749	767	785	803	822
239	840	858	876	894	912	931	949	967	985	*003
240	38 021	039	057	075	093	112	130	148	166	184
241	202	220	238	256	274	292	310	328	346	364
242	382	399	417	435	453	471	489	507	525	543
243	561	578	596	614	632	650	668	686	703	721
244	739	757	775	792	810	828	846	863	881	899
245	917	934	952	970	987	*005	*023	*041	*058	*076
246	39 094	111	129	146	164	182	199	217	235	252
247	270	287	305	322	340	358	375	393	410	428
248	445	463	480	498	515	533	550	568	585	602
249	620	637	655	672	690	707	724	742	759	777
250	794	811	829	846	863	881	898	915	933	950

| N. | 0 | 1 | 2 | 3 | 4 | 5 | 6 | 7 | 8 | 9 |

Proportional parts

	22	21
1	2.2	2.1
2	4.4	4.2
3	6.6	6.3
4	8.8	8.4
5	11.0	10.5
6	13.2	12.6
7	15.4	14.7
8	17.6	16.8
9	19.8	18.9

	20
1	2.0
2	4.0
3	6.0
4	8.0
5	10.0
6	12.0
7	14.0
8	16.0
9	18.0

	19
1	1.9
2	3.8
3	5.7
4	7.6
5	9.5
6	11.4
7	13.3
8	15.2
9	17.1

	18
1	1.8
2	3.6
3	5.4
4	7.2
5	9.0
6	10.8
7	12.6
8	14.4
9	16.2

	17
1	1.7
2	3.4
3	5.1
4	6.8
5	8.5
6	10.2
7	11.9
8	13.6
9	15.3

N.	0	1	2	3	4	5	6	7	8	9
250	39 794	811	829	846	863	881	898	915	933	950
251	967	985	*002	*019	*037	*054	*071	*088	*106	*123
252	40 140	157	175	192	209	226	243	261	278	295
253	312	329	346	364	381	398	415	432	449	466
254	483	500	518	535	552	569	586	603	620	637
255	654	671	688	705	722	739	756	773	790	807
256	824	841	858	875	892	909	926	943	960	976
257	993	*010	*027	*044	*061	*078	*095	*111	*128	*145
258	41 162	179	196	212	229	246	263	280	296	313
259	330	347	363	380	397	414	430	447	464	481
260	497	514	531	547	564	581	597	614	631	647
261	664	681	697	714	731	747	764	780	797	814
262	830	847	863	880	896	913	929	946	963	979
263	996	*012	*029	*045	*062	*078	*095	*111	*127	*144
264	42 160	177	193	210	226	243	259	275	292	308
265	325	341	357	374	390	406	423	439	455	472
266	488	504	521	537	553	570	586	602	619	635
267	651	667	684	700	716	732	749	765	781	797
268	813	830	846	862	878	894	911	927	943	959
269	975	991	*008	*024	*040	*056	*072	*088	*104	*120
270	43 136	152	169	185	201	217	233	249	265	281
271	297	313	329	345	361	377	393	409	425	441
272	457	473	489	505	521	537	553	569	584	600
273	616	632	648	664	680	696	712	727	743	759
274	775	791	807	823	838	854	870	886	902	917
275	933	949	965	981	996	*012	*028	*044	*059	*075
276	44 091	107	122	138	154	170	185	201	217	232
277	248	264	279	295	311	326	342	358	373	389
278	404	420	436	451	467	483	498	514	529	545
279	560	576	592	607	623	638	654	669	685	700
280	716	731	747	762	778	793	809	824	840	855
281	871	886	902	917	932	948	963	979	994	*010
282	45 025	040	056	071	086	102	117	133	148	163
283	179	194	209	225	240	255	271	286	301	317
284	332	347	362	378	393	408	423	439	454	469
285	484	500	515	530	545	561	576	591	606	621
286	637	652	667	682	697	712	728	743	758	773
287	788	803	818	834	849	864	879	894	909	924
288	939	954	969	984	*000	*015	*030	*045	*060	*075
289	46 090	105	120	135	150	165	180	195	210	225
290	240	255	270	285	300	315	330	345	359	374
291	389	404	419	434	449	464	479	494	509	523
292	538	553	568	583	598	613	627	642	657	672
293	687	702	716	731	746	761	776	790	805	820
294	835	850	864	879	894	909	923	938	953	967
295	982	997	*012	*026	*041	*056	*070	*085	*100	*114
296	47 129	144	159	173	188	202	217	232	246	261
297	276	290	305	319	334	349	363	378	392	407
298	422	436	451	465	480	494	509	524	538	553
299	567	582	596	611	625	640	654	669	683	698
300	712	727	741	756	770	784	799	813	828	842

Proportional parts

	18		17		16		15		14
1	1.8		1.7		1.6		1.5		1.4
2	3.6		3.4		3.2		3.0		2.8
3	5.4		5.1		4.8		4.5		4.2
4	7.2		6.8		6.4		6.0		5.6
5	9.0		8.5		8.0		7.5		7.0
6	10.8		10.2		9.6		9.0		8.4
7	12.6		11.9		11.2		10.5		9.8
8	14.4		13.6		12.8		12.0		11.2
9	16.2		15.3		14.4		13.5		12.6

| N. | 0 | 1 | 2 | 3 | 4 | 5 | 6 | 7 | 8 | 9 | Proportional parts |

N.	0	1	2	3	4	5	6	7	8	9	Proportional parts	
300	47 712	727	741	756	770	784	799	813	828	842		**15**
301	857	871	885	900	914	929	943	958	972	986	1	1.5
302	48 001	015	029	044	058	073	087	101	116	130	2	3.0
303	144	159	173	187	202	216	230	244	259	273	3	4.5
304	287	302	316	330	344	359	373	387	401	416	4	6.0
305	430	444	458	473	487	501	515	530	544	558	5	7.5
306	572	586	601	615	629	643	657	671	686	700	6	9.0
307	714	728	742	756	770	785	799	813	827	841	7	10.5
308	855	869	883	897	911	926	940	954	968	982	8	12.0
309	996	*010	*024	*038	*052	*066	*080	*094	*108	*122	9	13.5
310	49 136	150	164	178	192	206	220	234	248	262		
311	276	290	304	318	332	346	360	374	388	402		
312	415	429	443	457	471	485	499	513	527	541		
313	554	568	582	596	610	624	638	651	665	679		**14**
314	693	707	721	734	748	762	776	790	803	817	1	1.4
315	831	845	859	872	886	900	914	927	941	955	2	2.8
316	969	982	996	*010	*024	*037	*051	*065	*079	*092	3	4.2
317	50 106	120	133	147	161	174	188	202	215	229	4	5.6
318	243	256	270	284	297	311	325	338	352	365	5	7.0
319	379	393	406	420	433	447	461	474	488	501	6	8.4
											7	9.8
320	515	529	542	556	569	583	596	610	623	637	8	11.2
321	651	664	678	691	705	718	732	745	759	772	9	12.6
322	786	799	813	826	840	853	866	880	893	907		
323	920	934	947	961	974	987	*001	*014	*028	*041		
324	51 055	068	081	095	108	121	135	148	162	175		
325	188	202	215	228	242	255	268	282	295	308		
326	322	335	348	362	375	388	402	415	428	441		**13**
327	455	468	481	495	508	521	534	548	561	574	1	1.3
328	587	601	614	627	640	654	667	680	693	706	2	2.6
329	720	733	746	759	772	786	799	812	825	838	3	3.9
											4	5.2
330	851	865	878	891	904	917	930	943	957	970	5	6.5
331	983	996	*009	*022	*035	*048	*061	*075	*088	*101	6	7.8
332	52 114	127	140	153	166	179	192	205	218	231	7	9.1
333	244	257	270	284	297	310	323	336	349	362	8	10.4
334	375	388	401	414	427	440	453	466	479	492	9	11.7
335	504	517	530	543	556	569	582	595	608	621		
336	634	647	660	673	686	699	711	724	737	750		
337	763	776	789	802	815	827	840	853	866	879		
338	892	905	917	930	943	956	969	982	994	*007		**12**
339	53 020	033	046	058	071	084	097	110	122	135	1	1.2
											2	2.4
340	148	161	173	186	199	212	224	237	250	263	3	3.6
341	275	288	301	314	326	339	352	364	377	390	4	4.8
342	403	415	428	441	453	466	479	491	504	517	5	6.0
343	529	542	555	567	580	593	605	618	631	643	6	7.2
344	656	668	681	694	706	719	732	744	757	769	7	8.4
345	782	794	807	820	832	845	857	870	882	895	8	9.6
346	908	920	933	945	958	970	983	995	*008	*020	9	10.8
347	54 033	045	058	070	083	095	108	120	133	145		
348	158	170	183	195	208	220	233	245	258	270		
349	283	295	307	320	332	345	357	370	382	394		
350	407	419	432	444	456	469	481	494	506	518		
N.	0	1	2	3	4	5	6	7	8	9	Proportional parts	

N.	0	1	2	3	4	5	6	7	8	9	Proportional parts	
350	54 407	419	432	444	456	469	481	494	506	518		
351	531	543	555	568	580	593	605	617	630	642		
352	654	667	679	691	704	716	728	741	753	765		
353	777	790	802	814	827	839	851	864	876	888		**13**
354	900	913	925	937	949	962	974	986	998	*011	1	1.3
355	55 023	035	047	060	072	084	096	108	121	133	2	2.6
356	145	157	169	182	194	206	218	230	242	255	3	3.9
357	267	279	291	303	315	328	340	352	364	376	4	5.2
358	388	400	413	425	437	449	461	473	485	497	5	6.5
359	509	522	534	546	558	570	582	594	606	618	6	7.8
											7	9.1
360	630	642	654	666	678	691	703	715	727	739	8	10.4
361	751	763	775	787	799	811	823	835	847	859	9	11.7
362	871	883	895	907	919	931	943	955	967	979		
363	991	*003	*015	*027	*038	*050	*062	*074	*086	*098		
364	56 110	122	134	146	158	170	182	194	205	217		
365	229	241	253	265	277	289	301	312	324	336		**12**
366	348	360	372	384	396	407	419	431	443	455	1	1.2
367	467	478	490	502	514	526	538	549	561	573	2	2.4
368	585	597	608	620	632	644	656	667	679	691	3	3.6
369	703	714	726	738	750	761	773	785	797	808	4	4.8
											5	6.0
370	820	832	844	855	867	879	891	902	914	926	6	7.2
371	937	949	961	972	984	996	*008	*019	*031	*043	7	8.4
372	57 054	066	078	089	101	113	124	136	148	159	8	9.6
373	171	183	194	206	217	229	241	252	264	276	9	10.8
374	287	299	310	322	334	345	357	368	380	392		
375	403	415	426	438	449	461	473	484	496	507		
376	519	530	542	553	565	576	588	600	611	623		
377	634	646	657	669	680	692	703	715	726	738		**11**
378	749	761	772	784	795	807	818	830	841	852	1	1.1
379	864	875	887	898	910	921	933	944	955	967	2	2.2
											3	3.3
380	978	990	*001	*013	*024	*035	*047	*058	*070	*081	4	4.4
381	58 092	104	115	127	138	149	161	172	184	195	5	5.5
382	206	218	229	240	252	263	274	286	297	309	6	6.6
383	320	331	343	354	365	377	388	399	410	422	7	7.7
384	433	444	456	467	478	490	501	512	524	535	8	8.8
385	546	557	569	580	591	602	614	625	636	647	9	9.9
386	659	670	681	692	704	715	726	737	749	760		
387	771	782	794	805	816	827	838	850	861	872		
388	883	894	906	917	928	939	950	961	973	984		
389	995	*006	*017	*028	*040	*051	*062	*073	*084	*095		**10**
											1	1.0
390	59 106	118	129	140	151	162	173	184	195	207	2	2.0
391	218	229	240	251	262	273	284	295	306	318	3	3.0
392	329	340	351	362	373	384	395	406	417	428	4	4.0
393	439	450	461	472	483	494	506	517	528	539	5	5.0
394	550	561	572	583	594	605	616	627	638	649	6	6.0
395	660	671	682	693	704	715	726	737	748	759	7	7.0
396	770	780	791	802	813	824	835	846	857	868	8	8.0
397	879	890	901	912	923	934	945	956	966	977	9	9.0
398	988	999	*010	*021	*032	*043	*054	*065	*076	*086		
399	60 097	108	119	130	141	152	163	173	184	195		
400	206	217	228	239	249	260	271	282	293	304		

N.	0	1	2	3	4	5	6	7	8	9	Proportional parts

N.	0	1	2	3	4	5	6	7	8	9
400	60 206	217	228	239	249	260	271	282	293	304
401	314	325	336	347	358	369	379	390	401	412
402	423	433	444	455	466	477	487	498	509	520
403	531	541	552	563	574	584	595	606	617	627
404	638	649	660	670	681	692	703	713	724	735
405	746	756	767	778	788	799	810	821	831	842
406	853	863	874	885	895	906	917	927	938	949
407	959	970	981	991	*002	*013	*023	*034	*045	*055
408	61 066	077	087	098	109	119	130	140	151	162
409	172	183	194	204	215	225	236	247	257	268
410	278	289	300	310	321	331	342	352	363	374
411	384	395	405	416	426	437	448	458	469	479
412	490	500	511	521	532	542	553	563	574	584
413	595	606	616	627	637	648	658	669	679	690
414	700	711	721	731	742	752	763	773	784	794
415	805	815	826	836	847	857	868	878	888	899
416	909	920	930	941	951	962	972	982	993	*003
417	62 014	024	034	045	055	066	076	086	097	107
418	118	128	138	149	159	170	180	190	201	211
419	221	232	242	252	263	273	284	294	304	315
420	325	335	346	356	366	377	387	397	408	418
421	428	439	449	459	469	480	490	500	511	521
422	531	542	552	562	572	583	593	603	613	624
423	634	644	655	665	675	685	696	706	716	726
424	737	747	757	767	778	788	798	808	818	829
425	839	849	859	870	880	890	900	910	921	931
426	941	951	961	972	982	992	*002	*012	*022	*033
427	63 043	053	063	073	083	094	104	114	124	134
428	144	155	165	175	185	195	205	215	225	236
429	246	256	266	276	286	296	306	317	327	337
430	347	357	367	377	387	397	407	417	428	438
431	448	458	468	478	488	498	508	518	528	538
432	548	558	568	579	589	599	609	619	629	639
433	649	659	669	679	689	699	709	719	729	739
434	749	759	769	779	789	799	809	819	829	839
435	849	859	869	879	889	899	909	919	929	939
436	949	959	969	979	988	998	*008	*018	*028	*038
437	64 048	058	068	078	088	098	108	118	128	137
438	147	157	167	177	187	197	207	217	227	237
439	246	256	266	276	286	296	306	316	326	335
440	345	355	365	375	385	395	404	414	424	434
441	444	454	464	473	483	493	503	513	523	532
442	542	552	562	572	582	591	601	611	621	631
443	640	650	660	670	680	689	699	709	719	729
444	738	748	758	768	777	787	797	807	816	826
445	836	846	856	865	875	885	895	904	914	924
446	933	943	953	963	972	982	992	*002	*011	*021
447	65 031	040	050	060	070	079	089	099	108	118
448	128	137	147	157	167	176	186	196	205	215
449	225	234	244	254	263	273	283	292	302	312
450	321	331	341	350	360	369	379	389	398	408

N.	0	1	2	3	4	5	6	7	8	9

Proportional parts

	11
1	1.1
2	2.2
3	3.3
4	4.4
5	5.5
6	6.6
7	7.7
8	8.8
9	9.9

	10
1	1.0
2	2.0
3	3.0
4	4.0
5	5.0
6	6.0
7	7.0
8	8.0
9	9.0

	9
1	0.9
2	1.8
3	2.7
4	3.6
5	4.5
6	5.4
7	6.3
8	7.2
9	8.1

N.	0	1	2	3	4	5	6	7	8	9	Proportional parts	
450	65 321	331	341	350	360	369	379	389	398	408		
451	418	427	437	447	456	466	475	485	495	504		
452	514	523	533	543	552	562	571	581	591	600		
453	610	619	629	639	648	658	667	677	686	696		
454	706	715	725	734	744	753	763	772	782	792		
455	801	811	820	830	839	849	858	868	877	887		
456	896	906	916	925	935	944	954	963	973	982		
457	992	*001	*011	*020	*030	*039	*049	*058	*068	*077		**10**
458	66 087	096	106	115	124	134	143	153	162	172	1	1.0
459	181	191	200	210	219	229	238	247	257	266	2	2.0
											3	3.0
460	276	285	295	304	314	323	332	342	351	361	4	4.0
461	370	380	389	398	408	417	427	436	445	455	5	5.0
462	464	474	483	492	502	511	521	530	539	549	6	6.0
463	558	567	577	586	596	605	614	624	633	642	7	7.0
464	652	661	671	680	689	699	708	717	727	736	8	8.0
465	745	755	764	773	783	792	801	811	820	829	9	9.0
466	839	848	857	867	876	885	894	904	913	922		
467	932	941	950	960	969	978	987	997	*006	*015		
468	67 025	034	043	052	062	071	080	089	099	108		
469	117	127	136	145	154	164	173	182	191	201		
470	210	219	228	237	247	256	265	274	284	293		
471	302	311	321	330	339	348	357	367	376	385		
472	394	403	413	422	431	440	449	459	468	477		
473	486	495	504	514	523	532	541	550	560	569		**9**
474	578	587	596	605	614	624	633	642	651	660	1	0.9
475	669	679	688	697	706	715	724	733	742	752	2	1.8
476	761	770	779	788	797	806	815	825	834	843	3	2.7
477	852	861	870	879	888	897	906	916	925	934	4	3.6
478	943	952	961	970	979	988	997	*006	*015	*024	5	4.5
479	68 034	043	052	061	070	079	088	097	106	115	6	5.4
											7	6.3
480	124	133	142	151	160	169	178	187	196	205	8	7.2
481	215	224	233	242	251	260	269	278	287	296	9	8.1
482	305	314	323	332	341	350	359	368	377	386		
483	395	404	413	422	431	440	449	458	467	476		
484	485	494	502	511	520	529	538	547	556	565		
485	574	583	592	601	610	619	628	637	646	655		
486	664	673	681	690	699	708	717	726	735	744		
487	753	762	771	780	789	797	806	815	824	833		
488	842	851	860	869	878	886	895	904	913	922		**8**
489	931	940	949	958	966	975	984	993	*002	*011	1	0.8
											2	1.6
490	69 020	028	037	046	055	064	073	082	090	099	3	2.4
491	108	117	126	135	144	152	161	170	179	188	4	3.2
492	197	205	214	223	232	241	249	258	267	276	5	4.0
493	285	294	302	311	320	329	338	346	355	364	6	4.8
494	373	381	390	399	408	417	425	434	443	452	7	5.6
495	461	469	478	487	496	504	513	522	531	539	8	6.4
496	548	557	566	574	583	592	601	609	618	627	9	7.2
497	636	644	653	662	671	679	688	697	705	714		
498	723	732	740	749	758	767	775	784	793	801		
499	810	819	827	836	845	854	862	871	880	888		
500	897	906	914	923	932	940	949	958	966	975		
N.	0	1	2	3	4	5	6	7	8	9	Proportional parts	

N.	0	1	2	3	4	5	6	7	8	9	Proportional parts	
500	69 897	906	914	923	932	940	949	958	966	975		
501	984	992	*001	*010	*018	*027	*036	*044	*053	*062		
502	70 070	079	088	096	105	114	122	131	140	148		
503	157	165	174	183	191	200	209	217	226	234		
504	243	252	260	269	278	286	295	303	312	321		
505	329	338	346	355	364	372	381	389	398	406		
506	415	424	432	441	449	458	467	475	484	492		
507	501	509	518	526	535	544	552	561	569	578		**9**
508	586	595	603	612	621	629	638	646	655	663	1	0.9
509	672	680	689	697	706	714	723	731	740	749	2	1.8
											3	2.7
510	757	766	774	783	791	800	808	817	825	834	4	3.6
511	842	851	859	868	876	885	893	902	910	919	5	4.5
512	927	935	944	952	961	969	978	986	995	*003	6	5.4
513	71 012	020	029	037	046	054	063	071	079	088	7	6.3
514	096	105	113	122	130	139	147	155	164	172	8	7.2
515	181	189	198	206	214	223	231	240	248	257	9	8.1
516	265	273	282	290	299	307	315	324	332	341		
517	349	357	366	374	383	391	399	408	416	425		
518	433	441	450	458	466	475	483	492	500	508		
519	517	525	533	542	550	559	567	575	584	592		
520	600	609	617	625	634	642	650	659	667	675		
521	684	692	700	709	717	725	734	742	750	759		**8**
522	767	775	784	792	800	809	817	825	834	842	1	0.8
523	850	858	867	875	883	892	900	908	917	925	2	1.6
524	933	941	950	958	966	975	983	991	999	*008	3	2.4
525	72 016	024	032	041	049	057	066	074	082	090	4	3.2
526	099	107	115	123	132	140	148	156	165	173	5	4.0
527	181	189	198	206	214	222	230	239	247	255	6	4.8
528	263	272	280	288	296	304	313	321	329	337	7	5.6
529	346	354	362	370	378	387	395	403	411	419	8	6.4
											9	7.2
530	428	436	444	452	460	469	477	485	493	501		
531	509	518	526	534	542	550	558	567	575	583		
532	591	599	607	616	624	632	640	648	656	665		
533	673	681	689	697	705	713	722	730	738	746		
534	754	762	770	779	787	795	803	811	819	827		
535	835	843	852	860	868	876	884	892	900	908		
536	916	925	933	941	949	957	965	973	981	989		
537	997	*006	*014	*022	*030	*038	*046	*054	*062	*070		
538	73 078	086	094	102	111	119	127	135	143	151		
539	159	167	175	183	191	199	207	215	223	231		**7**
											1	0.7
540	239	247	255	263	272	280	288	296	304	312	2	1.4
541	320	328	336	344	352	360	368	376	384	392	3	2.1
542	400	408	416	424	432	440	448	456	464	472	4	2.8
543	480	488	496	504	512	520	528	536	544	552	5	3.5
544	560	568	576	584	592	600	608	616	624	632	6	4.2
545	640	648	656	664	672	679	687	695	703	711	7	4.9
546	719	727	735	743	751	759	767	775	783	791	8	5.6
547	799	807	815	823	830	838	846	854	862	870	9	6.3
548	878	886	894	902	910	918	926	933	941	949		
549	957	965	973	981	989	997	*005	*013	*020	*028		
550	74 036	044	052	060	068	076	084	092	099	107		

N.	0	1	2	3	4	5	6	7	8	9	Proportional parts

N.	0	1	2	3	4	5	6	7	8	9	Proportional parts	
550	74 036	044	052	060	068	076	084	092	099	107		
551	115	123	131	139	147	155	162	170	178	186		
552	194	202	210	218	225	233	241	249	257	265		
553	273	280	288	296	304	312	320	327	335	343		
554	351	359	367	374	382	390	398	406	414	421		
555	429	437	445	453	461	468	476	484	492	500		
556	507	515	523	531	539	547	554	562	570	578		
557	586	593	601	609	617	624	632	640	648	656		
558	663	671	679	687	695	702	710	718	726	733		
559	741	749	757	764	772	780	788	796	803	811		
560	819	827	834	842	850	858	865	873	881	889		**8**
561	896	904	912	920	927	935	943	950	958	966	1	0.8
562	974	981	989	997	*005	*012	*020	*028	*035	*043	2	1.6
563	75 051	059	066	074	082	089	097	105	113	120	3	2.4
564	128	136	143	151	159	166	174	182	189	197	4	3.2
565	205	213	220	228	236	243	251	259	266	274	5	4.0
566	282	289	297	305	312	320	328	335	343	351	6	4.8
567	358	366	374	381	389	397	404	412	420	427	7	5.6
568	435	442	450	458	465	473	481	488	496	504	8	6.4
569	511	519	526	534	542	549	557	565	572	580	9	7.2
570	587	595	603	610	618	626	633	641	648	656		
571	664	671	679	686	694	702	709	717	724	732		
572	740	747	755	762	770	778	785	793	800	808		
573	815	823	831	838	846	853	861	868	876	884		
574	891	899	906	914	921	929	937	944	952	959		
575	967	974	982	989	997	*005	*012	*020	*027	*035		
576	76 042	050	057	065	072	080	087	095	103	110		
577	118	125	133	140	148	155	163	170	178	185		
578	193	200	208	215	223	230	238	245	253	260		
579	268	275	283	290	298	305	313	320	328	335		
580	343	350	358	365	373	380	388	395	403	410		**7**
581	418	425	433	440	448	455	462	470	477	485	1	0.7
582	492	500	507	515	522	530	537	545	552	559	2	1.4
583	567	574	582	589	597	604	612	619	626	634	3	2.1
584	641	649	656	664	671	678	686	693	701	708	4	2.8
585	716	723	730	738	745	753	760	768	775	782	5	3.5
586	790	797	805	812	819	827	834	842	849	856	6	4.2
587	864	871	879	886	893	901	908	916	923	930	7	4.9
588	938	945	953	960	967	975	982	989	997	*004	8	5.6
589	77 012	019	026	034	041	048	056	063	070	078	9	6.3
590	085	093	100	107	115	122	129	137	144	151		
591	159	166	173	181	188	195	203	210	217	225		
592	232	240	247	254	262	269	276	283	291	298		
593	305	313	320	327	335	342	349	357	364	371		
594	379	386	393	401	408	415	422	430	437	444		
595	452	459	466	474	481	488	495	503	510	517		
596	525	532	539	546	554	561	568	576	583	590		
597	597	605	612	619	627	634	641	648	656	663		
598	670	677	685	692	699	706	714	721	728	735		
599	743	750	757	764	772	779	786	793	801	808		
600	815	822	830	837	844	851	859	866	873	880		
N.	0	1	2	3	4	5	6	7	8	9	Proportional parts	

N.	0	1	2	3	4	5	6	7	8	9
600	77 815	822	830	837	844	851	859	866	873	880
601	887	895	902	909	916	924	931	938	945	952
602	960	967	974	981	988	996	*003	*010	*017	*025
603	78 032	039	046	053	061	068	075	082	089	097
604	104	111	118	125	132	140	147	154	161	168
605	176	183	190	197	204	211	219	226	233	240
606	247	254	262	269	276	283	290	297	305	312
607	319	326	333	340	347	355	362	369	376	383
608	390	398	405	412	419	426	433	440	447	455
609	462	469	476	483	490	497	504	512	519	526
610	533	540	547	554	561	569	576	583	590	597
611	604	611	618	625	633	640	647	654	661	668
612	675	682	689	696	704	711	718	725	732	739
613	746	753	760	767	774	781	789	796	803	810
614	817	824	831	838	845	852	859	866	873	880
615	888	895	902	909	916	923	930	937	944	951
616	958	965	972	979	986	993	*000	*007	*014	*021
617	79 029	036	043	050	057	064	071	078	085	092
618	099	106	113	120	127	134	141	148	155	162
619	169	176	183	190	197	204	211	218	225	232
620	239	246	253	260	267	274	281	288	295	302
621	309	316	323	330	337	344	351	358	365	372
622	379	386	393	400	407	414	421	428	435	442
623	449	456	463	470	477	484	491	498	505	511
624	518	525	532	539	546	553	560	567	574	581
625	588	595	602	609	616	623	630	637	644	650
626	657	664	671	678	685	692	699	706	713	720
627	727	734	741	748	754	761	768	775	782	789
628	796	803	810	817	824	831	837	844	851	858
629	865	872	879	886	893	900	906	913	920	927
630	934	941	948	955	962	969	975	982	989	996
631	80 003	010	017	024	030	037	044	051	058	065
632	072	079	085	092	099	106	113	120	127	134
633	140	147	154	161	168	175	182	188	195	202
634	209	216	223	229	236	243	250	257	264	271
635	277	284	291	298	305	312	318	325	332	339
636	346	353	359	366	373	380	387	393	400	407
637	414	421	428	434	441	448	455	462	468	475
638	482	489	496	502	509	516	523	530	536	543
639	550	557	564	570	577	584	591	598	604	611
640	618	625	632	638	645	652	659	665	672	679
641	686	693	699	706	713	720	726	733	740	747
642	754	760	767	774	781	787	794	801	808	814
643	821	828	835	841	848	855	862	868	875	882
644	889	895	902	909	916	922	929	936	943	949
645	956	963	969	976	983	990	996	*003	*010	*017
646	81 023	030	037	043	050	057	064	070	077	084
647	090	097	104	111	117	124	131	137	144	151
648	158	164	171	178	184	191	198	204	211	218
649	224	231	238	245	251	258	265	271	278	285
650	291	298	305	311	318	325	331	338	345	351

Proportional parts

	8		7		6
1	0.8	1	0.7	1	0.6
2	1.6	2	1.4	2	1.2
3	2.4	3	2.1	3	1.8
4	3.2	4	2.8	4	2.4
5	4.0	5	3.5	5	3.0
6	4.8	6	4.2	6	3.6
7	5.0	7	4.9	7	4.2
8	6.4	8	5.6	8	4.8
9	7.2	9	6.3	9	5.4

N.	0	1	2	3	4	5	6	7	8	9	Proportional parts

N.	0	1	2	3	4	5	6	7	8	9	Proportional parts	
650	81 291	298	305	311	318	325	331	338	345	351		
651	358	365	371	378	385	391	398	405	411	418		
652	425	431	438	445	451	458	465	471	478	485		
653	491	498	505	511	518	525	531	538	544	551		
654	558	564	571	578	584	591	598	604	611	617		
655	624	631	637	644	651	657	664	671	677	684		
656	690	697	704	710	717	723	730	737	743	750		
657	757	763	770	776	783	790	796	803	809	816		
658	823	829	836	842	849	856	862	869	875	882		
659	889	895	902	908	915	921	928	935	941	948		
											7	
660	954	961	968	974	981	987	994	*000	*007	*014		
661	82 020	027	033	040	046	053	060	066	073	079	1	0.7
662	086	092	099	105	112	119	125	132	138	145	2	1.4
663	151	158	164	171	178	184	191	197	204	210	3	2.1
664	217	223	230	236	243	249	256	263	269	276	4	2.8
665	282	289	295	302	308	315	321	328	334	341	5	3.5
666	347	354	360	367	373	380	387	393	400	406	6	4.2
667	413	419	426	432	439	445	452	458	465	471	7	4.9
668	478	484	491	497	504	510	517	523	530	536	8	5.6
669	543	549	556	562	569	575	582	588	595	601	9	6.3
670	607	614	620	627	633	640	646	653	659	666		
671	672	679	685	692	698	705	711	718	724	730		
672	737	743	750	756	763	769	776	782	789	795		
673	802	808	814	821	827	834	840	847	853	860		
674	866	872	879	885	892	898	905	911	918	924		
675	930	937	943	950	956	963	969	975	982	988		
676	995	*001	*008	*014	*020	*027	*033	*040	*046	*052		
677	83 059	065	072	078	085	091	097	104	110	117		
678	123	129	136	142	149	155	161	168	174	181		
679	187	193	200	206	213	219	225	232	238	245		
											6	
680	251	257	264	270	276	283	289	296	302	308		
681	315	321	327	334	340	347	353	359	366	372	1	0.6
682	378	385	391	398	404	410	417	423	429	436	2	1.2
683	442	448	455	461	467	474	480	487	493	499	3	1.8
684	506	512	518	525	531	537	544	550	556	563	4	2.4
685	569	575	582	588	594	601	607	613	620	626	5	3.0
686	632	639	645	651	658	664	670	677	683	689	6	3.6
687	696	702	708	715	721	727	734	740	746	753	7	4.2
688	759	765	771	778	784	790	797	803	809	816	8	4.8
689	822	828	835	841	847	853	860	866	872	879	9	5.4
690	885	891	897	904	910	916	923	929	935	942		
691	948	954	960	967	973	979	985	992	998	*004		
692	84 011	017	023	029	036	042	048	055	061	067		
693	073	080	086	092	098	105	111	117	123	130		
694	136	142	148	155	161	167	173	180	186	192		
695	198	205	211	217	223	230	236	242	248	255		
696	261	267	273	280	286	292	298	305	311	317		
697	323	330	336	342	348	354	361	367	373	379		
698	386	392	398	404	410	417	423	429	435	442		
699	448	454	460	466	473	479	485	491	497	504		
700	510	516	522	528	535	541	547	553	559	566		
N.	0	1	2	3	4	5	6	7	8	9	Proportional parts	

N.	0	1	2	3	4	5	6	7	8	9	Proportional parts	
700	84 510	516	522	528	535	541	547	553	559	566		
701	572	578	584	590	597	603	609	615	621	628		
702	634	640	646	652	658	665	671	677	683	689		
703	696	702	708	714	720	726	733	739	745	751		
704	757	763	770	776	782	788	794	800	807	813		
705	819	825	831	837	844	850	856	862	868	874		
706	880	887	893	899	905	911	917	924	930	936		
707	942	948	954	960	967	973	979	985	991	997		**7**
708	85 003	009	016	022	028	034	040	046	052	058	1	0.7
709	065	071	077	083	089	095	101	107	114	120	2	1.4
											3	2.1
710	126	132	138	144	150	156	163	169	175	181	4	2.8
711	187	193	199	205	211	217	224	230	236	242	5	3.5
712	248	254	260	266	272	278	285	291	297	303	6	4.2
713	309	315	321	327	333	339	345	352	358	364	7	4.9
714	370	376	382	388	394	400	406	412	418	425	8	5.6
715	431	437	443	449	455	461	467	473	479	485	9	6.3
716	491	497	503	509	516	522	528	534	540	546		
717	552	558	564	570	576	582	588	594	600	606		
718	612	618	625	631	637	643	649	655	661	667		
719	673	679	685	691	697	703	709	715	721	727		**6**
											1	0.6
720	733	739	745	751	757	763	769	775	781	788	2	1.2
721	794	800	806	812	818	824	830	836	842	848	3	1.8
722	854	860	866	872	878	884	890	896	902	908	4	2.4
723	914	920	926	932	938	944	950	956	962	968	5	3.0
724	974	980	986	992	998	*004	*010	*016	*022	*028	6	3.6
725	86 034	040	046	052	058	064	070	076	082	088	7	4.2
726	094	100	106	112	118	124	130	136	141	147	8	4.8
727	153	159	165	171	177	183	189	195	201	207	9	5.4
728	213	219	225	231	237	243	249	255	261	267		
729	273	279	285	291	297	303	308	314	320	326		
730	332	338	344	350	356	362	368	374	380	386		**5**
731	392	398	404	410	415	421	427	433	439	445	1	0.5
732	451	457	463	469	475	481	487	493	499	504	2	1.0
733	510	516	522	528	534	540	546	552	558	564	3	1.5
734	570	576	581	587	593	599	605	611	617	623	4	2.0
735	629	635	641	646	652	658	664	670	676	682	5	2.5
736	688	694	700	705	711	717	723	729	735	741	6	3.0
737	747	753	759	764	770	776	782	788	794	800	7	3.5
738	806	812	817	823	829	835	841	847	853	859	8	4.0
739	864	870	876	882	888	894	900	906	911	917	9	4.5
740	923	929	935	941	947	953	958	964	970	976		
741	982	988	994	999	*005	*011	*017	*023	*029	*035		
742	87 040	046	052	058	064	070	075	081	087	093		
743	099	105	111	116	122	128	134	140	146	151		
744	157	163	169	175	181	186	192	198	204	210		
745	216	221	227	233	239	245	251	256	262	268		
746	274	280	286	291	297	303	309	315	320	326		
747	332	338	344	349	355	361	367	373	379	384		
748	390	396	402	408	413	419	425	431	437	442		
749	448	454	460	466	471	477	483	489	495	500		
750	506	512	518	523	529	535	541	547	552	558		
N.	0	1	2	3	4	5	6	7	8	9	Proportional parts	

N.	0	1	2	3	4	5	6	7	8	9	Proportional parts	
750	87 506	512	518	523	529	535	541	547	552	558		
751	564	570	576	581	587	593	599	604	610	616		
752	622	628	633	639	645	651	656	662	668	674		
753	679	685	691	697	703	708	714	720	726	731		
754	737	743	749	754	760	766	772	777	783	789		
755	795	800	806	812	818	823	829	835	841	846		
756	852	858	864	869	875	881	887	892	898	904		
757	910	915	921	927	933	938	944	950	955	961		
758	967	973	978	984	990	996	*001	*007	*013	*018		
759	88 024	030	036	041	047	053	058	064	070	076		
760	081	087	093	098	104	110	116	121	127	133		**6**
761	138	144	150	156	161	167	173	178	184	190	1	0.6
762	195	201	207	213	218	224	230	235	241	247	2	1.2
763	252	258	264	270	275	281	287	292	298	304	3	1.8
764	309	315	321	326	332	338	343	349	355	360	4	2.4
765	366	372	377	383	389	395	400	406	412	417	5	3.0
766	423	429	434	440	446	451	457	463	468	474	6	3.6
767	480	485	491	497	502	508	513	519	525	530	7	4.2
768	536	542	547	553	559	564	570	576	581	587	8	4.8
769	593	598	604	610	615	621	627	632	638	643	9	5.4
770	649	655	660	666	672	677	683	689	694	700		
771	705	711	717	722	728	734	739	745	750	756		
772	762	767	773	779	784	790	795	801	807	812		
773	818	824	829	835	840	846	852	857	863	868		
774	874	880	885	891	897	902	908	913	919	925		
775	930	936	941	947	953	958	964	969	975	981		
776	986	992	997	*003	*009	*014	*020	*025	*031	*037		
777	89 042	048	053	059	064	070	076	081	087	092		
778	098	104	109	115	120	126	131	137	143	148		
779	154	159	165	170	176	182	187	193	198	204		
780	209	215	221	226	232	237	243	248	254	260		**5**
781	265	271	276	282	287	293	298	304	310	315	1	0.5
782	321	326	332	337	343	348	354	360	365	371	2	1.0
783	376	382	387	393	398	404	409	415	421	426	3	1.5
784	432	437	443	448	454	459	465	470	476	481	4	2.0
785	487	492	498	504	509	515	520	526	531	537	5	2.5
786	542	548	553	559	564	570	575	581	586	592	6	3.0
787	597	603	609	614	620	625	631	636	642	647	7	3.5
788	653	658	664	669	675	680	686	691	697	702	8	4.0
789	708	713	719	724	730	735	741	746	752	757	9	4.5
790	763	768	774	779	785	790	796	801	807	812		
791	818	823	829	834	840	845	851	856	862	867		
792	873	878	883	889	894	900	905	911	916	922		
793	927	933	938	944	949	955	960	966	971	977		
794	982	988	993	998	*004	*009	*015	*020	*026	*031		
795	90 037	042	048	053	059	064	069	075	080	086		
796	091	097	102	108	113	119	124	129	135	140		
797	146	151	157	162	168	173	179	184	189	195		
798	200	206	211	217	222	227	233	238	244	249		
799	255	260	266	271	276	282	287	293	298	304		
800	309	314	320	325	331	336	342	347	352	358		
N.	0	1	2	3	4	5	6	7	8	9	Proportional parts	

N.	0	1	2	3	4	5	6	7	8	9	Proportional parts
800	90 309	314	320	325	331	336	342	347	352	358	
801	363	369	374	380	385	390	396	401	407	412	
802	417	423	428	434	439	445	450	455	461	466	
803	472	477	482	488	493	499	504	509	515	520	
804	526	531	536	542	547	553	558	563	569	574	
805	580	585	590	596	601	607	612	617	623	628	
806	634	639	644	650	655	660	666	671	677	682	
807	687	693	698	703	709	714	720	725	730	736	
808	741	747	752	757	763	768	773	779	784	789	
809	795	800	806	811	816	822	827	832	838	843	
810	849	854	859	865	870	875	881	886	891	897	**6**
811	902	907	913	918	924	929	934	940	945	950	1 0.6
812	956	961	966	972	977	982	988	993	998	*004	2 1.2
813	91 009	014	020	025	030	036	041	046	052	057	3 1.8
814	062	068	073	078	084	089	094	100	105	110	4 2.4
815	116	121	126	132	137	142	148	153	158	164	5 3.0
816	169	174	180	185	190	196	201	206	212	217	6 3.6
817	222	228	233	238	243	249	254	259	265	270	7 4.2
818	275	281	286	291	297	302	307	312	318	323	8 4.8
819	328	334	339	344	350	355	360	365	371	376	9 5.4
820	381	387	392	397	403	408	113	418	424	429	
821	434	440	445	450	455	461	466	471	477	482	
822	487	492	498	503	508	514	519	524	529	535	
823	540	545	551	556	561	566	572	577	582	587	
824	593	598	603	609	614	619	624	630	635	640	
825	645	651	656	661	666	672	677	682	687	693	
826	698	703	709	714	719	724	730	735	740	745	
827	751	756	761	766	772	777	782	787	793	798	
828	803	808	814	819	824	829	834	840	845	850	
829	855	861	866	871	876	882	887	892	897	903	
830	908	913	918	924	929	934	939	944	950	955	**5**
831	960	965	971	976	981	986	991	997	*002	*007	1 0.5
832	92 012	018	023	028	033	038	044	049	054	059	2 1.0
833	065	070	075	080	085	091	096	101	106	111	3 1.5
834	117	122	127	132	137	143	148	153	158	163	4 2.0
835	169	174	179	184	189	195	200	205	210	215	5 2.5
836	221	226	231	236	241	247	252	257	262	267	6 3.0
837	273	278	283	288	293	298	304	309	314	319	7 3.5
838	324	330	335	340	345	350	355	361	366	371	8 4.0
839	376	381	387	392	397	402	407	412	418	423	9 4.5
840	428	433	438	443	449	454	459	464	469	474	
841	480	485	490	495	500	505	511	516	521	526	
842	531	536	542	547	552	557	562	567	572	578	
843	583	588	593	598	603	609	614	619	624	629	
844	634	639	645	650	655	660	005	670	675	681	
845	686	691	696	701	706	711	716	722	727	732	
846	737	742	747	752	758	763	768	773	778	783	
847	788	793	799	804	809	814	819	824	829	834	
848	840	845	850	855	860	865	870	875	881	886	
849	891	896	901	906	911	916	921	927	932	937	
850	942	947	952	957	902	967	973	978	983	988	
N.	0	1	2	3	4	5	6	7	8	9	Proportional parts

N.	0	1	2	3	4	5	6	7	8	9	Proportio
850	92 942	947	952	957	962	967	973	978	983	988	
851	993	998	*003	*008	*013	*018	*024	*029	*034	*039	
852	93 044	049	054	059	064	069	075	080	085	090	
853	095	100	105	110	115	120	125	131	136	141	
854	146	151	156	161	166	171	176	181	186	192	
855	197	202	207	212	217	222	227	232	237	242	
856	247	252	258	263	268	273	278	283	288	293	
857	298	303	308	313	318	323	328	334	339	344	
858	349	354	359	364	369	374	379	384	389	394	
859	399	404	409	414	420	425	430	435	440	445	
860	450	455	460	465	470	475	480	485	490	495	
861	500	505	510	515	520	526	531	536	541	546	
862	551	556	561	566	571	576	581	586	591	596	
863	601	606	611	616	621	626	631	636	641	646	
864	651	656	661	666	671	676	682	687	692	697	
865	702	707	712	717	722	727	732	737	742	747	
866	752	757	762	767	772	777	782	787	792	797	
867	802	807	812	817	822	827	832	837	842	847	
868	852	857	862	867	872	877	882	887	892	897	
869	902	907	912	917	922	927	932	937	942	947	
870	952	957	962	967	972	977	982	987	992	997	
871	94 002	007	012	017	022	027	032	037	042	047	
872	052	057	062	067	072	077	082	086	091	096	
873	101	106	111	116	121	126	131	136	141	146	
874	151	156	161	166	171	176	181	186	191	196	
875	201	206	211	216	221	226	231	236	240	245	
876	250	255	260	265	270	275	280	285	290	295	
877	300	305	310	315	320	325	330	335	340	345	
878	349	354	359	364	369	374	379	384	389	394	
879	399	404	409	414	419	424	429	433	438	443	
880	448	453	458	463	468	473	478	483	488	493	
881	498	503	507	512	517	522	527	532	537	542	
882	547	552	557	562	567	571	576	581	586	591	
883	596	601	606	611	616	621	626	630	635	640	
884	645	650	655	660	665	670	675	680	685	689	
885	694	699	704	709	714	719	724	729	734	738	
886	743	748	753	758	763	768	773	778	783	787	
887	792	797	802	807	812	817	822	827	832	836	
888	841	846	851	856	861	866	871	876	880	885	
889	890	895	900	905	910	915	919	924	929	934	
890	939	944	949	954	959	963	968	973	978	983	
891	988	993	998	*002	*007	*012	*017	*022	*027	*032	
892	95 036	041	046	051	056	061	066	071	075	080	
893	085	090	095	100	105	109	114	119	124	129	
894	134	139	143	148	153	158	163	168	173	177	
895	182	187	192	197	202	207	211	216	221	226	
896	231	236	240	245	250	255	260	265	270	274	
897	279	284	289	294	299	303	308	313	318	323	
898	328	332	337	342	347	352	357	361	366	371	
899	376	381	386	390	395	400	405	410	415	419	
900	424	429	434	439	444	448	453	458	463	468	
N.	0	1	2	3	4	5	6	7	8	9	Proportional parts

Proportional parts:

6

1	0.6
2	1.2
3	1.8
4	2.4
5	3.0
6	3.6
7	4.2
8	4.8
9	5.4

5

1	0.5
2	1.0
3	1.5
4	2.0
5	2.5
6	3.0
7	3.5
8	4.0
9	4.5

4

1	0.4
2	0.8
3	1.2
4	1.6
5	2.0
6	2.4
7	2.8
8	3.2
9	3.6

N.	0	1	2	3	4	5	6	7	8	9	Proportional parts	
900	95 424	429	434	439	444	448	453	458	463	468		
901	472	477	482	487	492	497	501	506	511	516		
902	521	525	530	535	540	545	550	554	559	564		
903	569	574	578	583	588	593	598	602	607	612		
904	617	622	626	631	636	641	646	650	655	660		
905	665	670	674	679	684	689	694	698	703	708		
906	713	718	722	727	732	737	742	746	751	756		
907	761	766	770	775	780	785	789	794	799	804		
908	809	813	818	823	828	832	837	842	847	852		
909	856	861	866	871	875	880	885	890	895	899		
												5
910	904	909	914	918	923	928	933	938	942	947		
911	952	957	961	966	971	976	980	985	990	995	1	0.5
912	999	*004	*009	*014	*019	*023	*028	*033	*038	*042	2	1.0
913	96 047	052	057	061	066	071	076	080	085	090	3	1.5
914	095	099	104	109	114	118	123	128	133	137	4	2.0
915	142	147	152	156	161	166	171	175	180	185	5	2.5
916	190	194	199	204	209	213	218	223	227	232	6	3.0
917	237	242	246	251	256	261	265	270	275	280	7	3.5
918	284	289	294	298	303	308	313	317	322	327	8	4.0
919	332	336	341	346	350	355	360	365	369	374	9	4.5
920	379	384	388	393	398	402	407	412	417	421		
921	426	431	435	440	445	450	454	459	464	468		
922	473	478	483	487	492	497	501	506	511	515		
923	520	525	530	534	539	544	548	553	558	562		
924	567	572	577	581	586	591	595	600	605	609		
925	614	619	624	628	633	638	642	647	652	656		
926	661	666	670	675	680	685	689	694	699	703		
927	708	713	717	722	727	731	736	741	745	750		
928	755	759	764	769	774	778	783	788	792	797		
929	802	806	811	816	820	825	830	834	839	844		
												4
930	848	853	858	862	867	872	876	881	886	890		
931	895	900	904	909	914	918	923	928	932	937	1	0.4
932	942	946	951	956	960	965	970	974	979	984	2	0.8
933	988	993	997	*002	*007	*011	*016	*021	*025	*030	3	1.2
934	97 035	039	044	049	053	058	063	067	072	077	4	1.6
935	081	086	090	095	100	104	109	114	118	123	5	2.0
936	128	132	137	142	146	151	155	160	165	169	6	2.4
937	174	179	183	188	192	197	202	206	211	216	7	2.8
938	220	225	230	234	239	243	248	253	257	262	8	3.2
939	267	271	276	280	285	290	294	299	304	308	9	3.6
940	313	317	322	327	331	336	340	345	350	354		
941	359	364	368	373	377	382	387	391	396	400		
942	405	410	414	419	424	428	433	437	442	447		
943	451	456	460	465	470	474	479	483	488	493		
944	497	502	506	511	516	520	525	529	534	539		
945	543	548	552	557	562	566	571	575	580	585		
946	589	594	598	603	607	612	617	621	626	630		
947	635	640	644	649	653	658	663	667	672	676		
948	681	685	690	695	699	704	708	713	717	722		
949	727	731	736	740	745	749	754	759	763	768		
950	772	777	782	786	791	795	800	804	809	813		
N.	0	1	2	3	4	5	6	7	8	9	Proportional parts	

N.	0	1	2	3	4	5	6	7	8	9	Proportional parts	
950	97 772	777	782	786	791	795	800	804	809	813		
951	818	823	827	832	836	841	845	850	855	859		
952	864	868	873	877	882	886	891	896	900	905		
953	909	914	918	923	928	932	937	941	946	950		
954	955	959	964	968	973	978	982	987	991	996		
955	98 000	005	009	014	019	023	028	032	037	041		
956	046	050	055	059	064	068	073	078	082	087		
957	091	096	100	105	109	114	118	123	127	132		
958	137	141	146	150	155	159	164	168	173	177		
959	182	186	191	195	200	204	209	214	218	223		
												5
960	227	232	236	241	245	250	254	259	263	268		
961	272	277	281	286	290	295	299	304	308	313	1	0.5
962	318	322	327	331	336	340	345	349	354	358	2	1.0
963	363	367	372	376	381	385	390	394	399	403	3	1.5
964	408	412	417	421	426	430	435	439	444	448	4	2.0
965	453	457	462	466	471	475	480	484	489	493	5	2.5
966	498	502	507	511	516	520	525	529	534	538	6	3.0
967	543	547	552	556	561	565	570	574	579	583	7	3.5
968	588	592	597	601	605	610	614	619	623	628	8	4.0
969	632	637	641	646	650	655	659	664	668	673	9	4.5
970	677	682	686	691	695	700	704	709	713	717		
971	722	726	731	735	740	744	749	753	758	762		
972	767	771	776	780	784	789	793	798	802	807		
973	811	816	820	825	829	834	838	843	847	851		
974	856	860	865	869	874	878	883	887	892	896		
975	900	905	909	914	918	923	927	932	936	941		
976	945	949	954	958	963	967	972	976	981	985		
977	989	994	998	*003	*007	*012	*016	*021	*025	*029		
978	99 034	038	043	047	052	056	061	065	069	074		
979	078	083	087	092	096	100	105	109	114	118		
												4
980	123	127	131	136	140	145	149	154	158	162		
981	167	171	176	180	185	189	193	198	202	207	1	0.4
982	211	216	220	224	229	233	238	242	247	251	2	0.8
983	255	260	264	269	273	277	282	286	291	295	3	1.2
984	300	304	308	313	317	322	326	330	335	339	4	1.6
985	344	348	352	357	361	366	370	374	379	383	5	2.0
986	388	392	396	401	405	410	414	419	423	427	6	2.4
987	432	436	441	445	449	454	458	463	467	471	7	2.8
988	476	480	484	489	493	498	502	506	511	515	8	3.2
989	520	524	528	533	537	542	546	550	555	559	9	3.6
990	564	568	572	577	581	585	590	594	599	603		
991	607	612	616	621	625	629	634	638	642	647		
992	651	656	660	664	669	673	677	682	686	691		
993	695	699	704	708	712	717	721	726	730	734		
994	739	743	747	752	756	760	765	769	774	778		
995	782	787	791	795	800	804	808	813	817	822		
996	826	830	835	839	843	848	852	856	861	865		
997	870	874	878	883	887	891	896	900	904	909		
998	913	917	922	926	930	935	939	944	948	952		
999	957	961	965	970	974	978	983	987	991	996		
1000	00 000	004	009	013	017	022	026	030	035	039		
N.	0	1	2	3	4	5	6	7	8	9	Proportional parts	

N.		0	1	2	3	4	5	6	7	8	9	d.
1000	000	0000	0434	0869	1303	1737	2171	2605	3039	3473	3907	434
1001		4341	4775	5208	5642	6076	6510	6943	7377	7810	8244	434
1002		8677	9111	9544	9977	*0411	*0844	*1277	*1710	*2143	*2576	433
1003	001	3009	3442	3875	4308	4741	5174	5607	6039	6472	6905	433
1004		7337	7770	8202	8635	9067	9499	9932	*0364	*0796	*1228	432
1005	002	1661	2093	2525	2957	3389	3821	4253	4685	5116	5548	432
1006		5980	6411	6843	7275	7706	8138	8569	9001	9432	9863	431
1007	003	0295	0726	1157	1588	2019	2451	2882	3313	3744	4174	431
1008		4605	5036	5467	5898	6328	6759	7190	7620	8051	8481	431
1009		8912	9342	9772	*0203	*0633	*1063	*1493	*1924	*2354	*2784	430
1010	004	3214	3644	4074	4504	4933	5363	5793	6223	6652	7082	430
1011		7512	7941	8371	8800	9229	9659	*0088	*0517	*0947	*1376	429
1012	005	1805	2234	2663	3092	3521	3950	4379	4808	5237	5666	429
1013		6094	6523	6952	7380	7809	8238	8666	9094	9523	9951	429
1014	006	0380	0808	1236	1664	2092	2521	2940	3377	3805	4233	428
1015		4660	5088	5516	5944	6372	6799	7227	7655	8082	8510	428
1016		8937	9365	9792	*0219	*0647	*1074	*1501	*1928	*2355	*2782	427
1017	007	3210	3637	4064	4490	4917	5344	5771	6198	6624	7051	427
1018		7478	7904	8331	8757	9184	9610	*0037	*0463	*0889	*1316	426
1019	008	1742	2168	2594	3020	3446	3872	4298	4724	5150	5576	426
1020		6002	6427	6853	7279	7704	8130	8556	8981	9407	9832	426
1021	009	0257	0683	1108	1533	1959	2384	2809	3234	3659	4084	425
1022		4509	4934	5359	5784	6208	6633	7058	7483	7907	8332	425
1023		8756	9181	9605	*0030	*0454	*0878	*1303	*1727	*2151	*2575	424
1024	010	3000	3424	3848	4272	4696	5120	5544	5967	6391	6815	424
1025		7239	7662	8086	8510	8933	9357	9780	*0204	*0627	*1050	424
1026	011	1474	1897	2320	2743	3166	3590	4013	4436	4859	5282	423
1027		5704	6127	6550	6973	7396	7818	8241	8664	9086	9509	423
1028		9931	*0354	*0776	*1198	*1621	*2043	*2465	*2887	*3310	*3732	422
1029	012	4154	4576	4998	5420	5842	6264	6685	7107	7529	7951	422
1030		8372	8794	9215	9637	*0059	*0480	*0901	*1323	*1744	*2165	422
1031	013	2587	3008	3429	3850	4271	4692	5113	5534	5955	6376	421
1032		6797	7218	7639	8059	8480	8901	9321	9742	*0162	*0583	421
1033	014	1003	1424	1844	2264	2685	3105	3525	3945	4365	4785	420
1034		5205	5625	6045	6465	6885	7305	7725	8144	8564	8984	420
1035		9403	9823	*0243	*0662	*1082	*1501	*1920	*2340	*2759	*3178	420
1036	015	3598	4017	4436	4855	5274	5693	6112	6531	6950	7369	419
1037		7788	8206	8625	9044	9462	9881	*0300	*0718	*1137	*1555	419
1038	016	1974	2392	2810	3229	3647	4065	4483	4901	5319	5737	418
1039		6155	6573	6991	7409	7827	8245	8663	9080	9498	9916	418
1040	017	0333	0751	1168	1586	2003	2421	2838	3256	3673	4090	417
1041		4507	4924	5342	5759	6176	6593	7010	7427	7844	8260	417
1042		8677	9094	9511	9927	*0344	*0761	*1177	*1594	*2010	*2427	417
1043	018	2843	3259	3676	4092	4508	4925	5341	5757	6173	6589	416
1044		7005	7421	7837	8253	8669	9084	9500	9916	*0332	*0747	416
1045	019	1163	1578	1994	2410	2825	3240	3656	4071	4486	4902	415
1046		5317	5732	6147	6562	6977	7392	7807	8222	8637	9052	415
1047		9467	9882	*0296	*0711	*1126	*1540	*1955	*2369	*2784	*3198	415
1048	020	3613	4027	4442	4856	5270	5684	6099	6513	6927	7341	414
1049		7755	8169	8583	8997	9411	9824	*0238	*0652	*1066	*1479	414
1050	021	1893	2307	2720	3134	3547	3961	4374	4787	5201	5614	413

N.		0	1	2	3	4	5	6	7	8	9	d.

N.		0	1	2	3	4	5	6	7	8	9	d.
1050	021	1893	2307	2720	3134	3547	3961	4374	4787	5201	5614	413
1051		6027	6440	6854	7267	7680	8093	8506	8919	9332	9745	413
1052	022	0157	0570	0983	1396	1808	2221	2634	3046	3459	3871	413
1053		4284	4696	5109	5521	5933	6345	6758	7170	7582	7994	412
1054		8406	8818	9230	9642	*0054	*0466	*0878	*1289	*1701	*2113	412
1055	023	2525	2936	3348	3759	4171	4582	4994	5405	5817	6228	411
1056		6639	7050	7462	7873	8284	8695	9106	9517	9928	*0339	411
1057	024	0750	1161	1572	1982	2393	2804	3214	3625	4036	4446	411
1058		4857	5267	5678	6088	6498	6909	7319	7729	8139	8549	410
1059		8960	9370	9780	*0190	*0600	*1010	*1419	*1829	*2239	*2649	410
1060	025	3059	3468	3878	4288	4697	5107	5516	5926	6335	6744	410
1061		7154	7563	7972	8382	8791	9200	9609	*0018	*0427	*0836	409
1062	026	1245	1654	2063	2472	2881	3289	3698	4107	4515	4924	409
1063		5333	5741	6150	6558	6967	7375	7783	8192	8600	9008	408
1064		9416	9824	*0233	*0641	*1049	*1457	*1865	*2273	*2680	*3088	408
1065	027	3496	3904	4312	4719	5127	5535	5942	6350	6757	7165	408
1066		7572	7979	8387	8794	9201	9609	*0016	*0423	*0830	*1237	407
1067	028	1644	2051	2458	2865	3272	3679	4086	4492	4899	5306	407
1068		5713	6119	6526	6932	7339	7745	8152	8558	8964	9371	406
1069		9777	*0183	*0590	*0996	*1402	*1808	*2214	*2620	*3026	*3432	406
1070	029	3833	4244	4649	5055	5461	5867	6272	6678	7084	7489	406
1071		7895	8300	8706	9111	9516	9922	*0327	*0732	*1138	*1543	405
1072	030	1948	2353	2758	3163	3568	3973	4378	4783	5188	5592	405
1073		5997	6402	6807	7211	7616	8020	8425	8830	9234	9638	405
1074	031	0043	0447	0851	1256	1660	2064	2468	2872	3277	3681	404
1075		4085	4489	4893	5296	5700	6104	6508	6912	7315	7719	404
1076		8123	8526	8930	9333	9737	*0140	*0544	*0947	*1350	*1754	403
1077	032	2157	2560	2963	3367	3770	4173	4576	4979	5382	5785	403
1078		6188	6590	6993	7396	7799	8201	8604	9007	9409	9812	403
1079	033	0214	0617	1019	1422	1824	2226	2629	3031	3433	3835	402
1080		4238	4640	5042	5444	5846	6248	6650	7052	7453	7855	402
1081		8257	8659	9060	9462	9864	*0265	*0667	*1068	*1470	*1871	402
1082	034	2273	2674	3075	3477	3878	4279	4680	5081	5482	5884	401
1083		6285	6686	7087	7487	7888	8289	8690	9091	9491	9892	401
1084	035	0293	0693	1094	1495	1895	2296	2696	3096	3497	3897	400
1085		4297	4698	5098	5498	5898	6298	6698	7098	7498	7898	400
1086		8298	8698	9098	9498	9898	*0297	*0697	*1097	*1496	*1896	400
1087	036	2295	2695	3094	3494	3893	4293	4692	5091	5491	5890	399
1088		6289	6688	7087	7486	7885	8284	8683	9082	9481	9880	399
1089	037	0279	0678	1076	1475	1874	2272	2671	3070	3468	3867	399
1090		4265	4663	5062	5460	5858	6257	6655	7053	7451	7849	398
1091		8248	8646	9044	9442	9839	*0237	*0635	*1033	*1431	*1829	398
1092	038	2226	2624	3022	3419	3817	4214	4612	5009	5407	5804	398
1093		6202	6599	6996	7393	7791	8188	8585	8982	9379	9776	397
1094	039	0173	0570	0967	1364	1761	2158	2554	2951	3348	3745	397
1095		4141	4538	4934	5331	5727	6124	6520	6917	7313	7709	397
1096		8106	8502	8898	9294	9690	*0086	*0482	*0878	*1274	*1670	396
1097	040	2066	2462	2858	3254	3650	4045	4441	4837	5232	5628	396
1098		6023	6419	6814	7210	7605	8001	8396	8791	9187	9582	395
1099		9977	*0372	*0767	*1162	*1557	*1952	*2347	*2742	*3137	*3532	395
1100	041	3927	4322	4716	5111	5506	5900	6295	6690	7084	7479	395
N.		0	1	2	3	4	5	6	7	8	9	d.

N.		0	1	2	3	4	5	6	7	8	9	d.
1100	041	3927	4322	4716	5111	5506	5900	6295	6690	7084	7479	395
1101		7873	8268	8662	9056	9451	9845	*0239	*0633	*1028	*1422	394
1102	042	1816	2210	2604	2998	3392	3786	4180	4574	4968	5361	394
1103		5755	6149	6543	6936	7330	7723	8117	8510	8904	9297	394
1104		9691	*0084	*0477	*0871	*1264	*1657	*2050	*2444	*2837	*3230	393
1105	043	3623	4016	4409	4802	5195	5587	5980	6373	6766	7159	393
1106		7551	7944	8337	8729	9122	9514	9907	*0299	*0692	*1084	393
1107	044	1476	1869	2261	2653	3045	3437	3829	4222	4614	5006	392
1108		5398	5790	6181	6573	6965	7357	7749	8140	8532	8924	392
1109		9315	9707	*0099	*0490	*0882	*1273	*1664	*2056	*2447	*2839	392
1110	045	3230	3621	4012	4403	4795	5186	5577	5968	6359	6750	391
1111		7141	7531	7922	8313	8704	9095	9485	9876	*0267	*0657	391
1112	046	1048	1438	1829	2219	2610	3000	3391	3781	4171	4561	390
1113		4952	5342	5732	6122	6512	6902	7292	7682	8072	8462	390
1114		8852	9242	9632	*0021	*0411	*0801	*1190	*1580	*1970	*2359	390
1115	047	2749	3138	3528	3917	4306	4696	5085	5474	5864	6253	389
1116		6642	7031	7420	7809	8198	8587	8976	9365	9754	*0143	389
1117	048	0532	0921	1309	1698	2087	2475	2864	3253	3641	4030	389
1118		4418	4806	5195	5583	5972	6360	6748	7136	7525	7913	388
1119		8301	8689	9077	9465	9853	*0241	*0629	*1017	*1405	*1792	388
1120	049	2180	2568	2956	3343	3731	4119	4506	4894	5281	5669	388
1121		6056	6444	6831	7218	7606	7993	8380	8767	9154	9541	387
1122		9929	*0316	*0703	*1090	*1477	*1863	*2250	*2637	*3024	*3411	387
1123	050	3798	4184	4571	4958	5344	5731	6117	6504	6890	7277	387
1124		7663	8049	8436	8822	9208	9595	9981	*0367	*0753	*1139	386
1125	051	1525	1911	2297	2683	3069	3455	3841	4227	4612	4998	386
1126		5384	5770	6155	6541	6926	7312	7697	8083	8468	8854	386
1127		9239	9624	*0010	*0395	*0780	*1166	*1551	*1936	*2321	*2706	385
1128	052	3091	3476	3861	4246	4631	5016	5400	5785	6170	6555	385
1129		6939	7324	7709	8093	8478	8862	9247	9631	*0016	*0400	385
1130	053	0784	1169	1553	1937	2321	2706	3090	3474	3858	4242	384
1131		4626	5010	5394	5778	6162	6546	6929	7313	7697	8081	384
1132		8464	8848	9232	9615	9999	*0382	*0766	*1149	*1532	*1916	384
1133	054	2299	2682	3066	3449	3832	4215	4598	4981	5365	5748	383
1134		6131	6514	6896	7279	7662	8045	8428	8811	9193	9576	383
1135		9959	*0341	*0724	*1106	*1489	*1871	*2254	*2636	*3019	*3401	382
1136	055	3783	4166	4548	4930	5312	5694	6077	6459	6841	7223	382
1137		7605	7987	8369	8750	9132	9514	9896	*0278	*0659	*1041	382
1138	056	1423	1804	2186	2567	2949	3330	3712	4093	4475	4856	381
1139		5237	5619	6000	6381	6762	7143	7524	7905	8287	8668	381
1140		9049	9429	9810	*0191	*0572	*0953	*1334	*1714	*2095	*2476	381
1141	057	2856	3237	3618	3998	4379	4759	5140	5520	5900	6281	381
1142		6661	7041	7422	7802	8182	8562	8942	9322	9702	*0082	380
1143	058	0462	0842	1222	1602	1982	2362	2741	3121	3501	3881	380
1144		4260	4640	5019	5399	5778	6158	6537	6917	7296	7676	380
1145		8055	8434	8813	9193	9572	9951	*0330	*0709	*1088	*1467	379
1146	059	1846	2225	2604	2983	3362	3741	4119	4498	4877	5256	379
1147		5634	6013	6391	6770	7148	7527	7905	8284	8662	9041	379
1148		9419	9797	*0175	*0554	*0932	*1310	*1688	*2066	*2444	*2822	378
1149	060	3200	3578	3956	4334	4712	5090	5468	5845	6223	6601	378
1150		6978	7356	7734	8111	8489	8866	9244	9621	9999	*0376	378
N.		0	1	2	3	4	5	6	7	8	9	d.

N.		0	1	2	3	4	5	6	7	8	9	d.
1150	060	6978	7356	7734	8111	8489	8866	9244	9621	9999	*0376	378
1151	061	0753	1131	1508	1885	2262	2639	3017	3394	3771	4148	377
1152		4525	4902	5279	5656	6032	6409	6786	7163	7540	7916	377
1153		8293	8670	9046	9423	9799	*0176	*0552	*0929	*1305	*1682	377
1154	062	2058	2434	2811	3187	3563	3939	4316	4692	5068	5444	376
1155		5820	6196	6572	6948	7324	7699	8075	8451	8827	9203	376
1156		9578	9954	*0330	*0705	*1081	*1456	*1832	*2207	*2583	*2958	376
1157	063	3334	3709	4084	4460	4835	5210	5585	5960	6335	6711	375
1158		7086	7461	7836	8211	8585	8960	9335	9710	*0085	*0460	375
1159	064	0834	1209	1584	1958	2333	2708	3082	3457	3831	4205	375
1160		4580	4954	5329	5703	6077	6451	6826	7200	7574	7948	374
1161		8322	8696	9070	9444	9818	*0192	*0566	*0940	*1314	*1688	374
1162	065	2061	2435	2809	3182	3556	3930	4303	4677	5050	5424	374
1163		5797	6171	6544	6917	7291	7664	8037	8410	8784	9157	373
1164		9530	9903	*0276	*0649	*1022	*1395	*1768	*2141	*2514	*2886	373
1165	066	3259	3632	4005	4377	4750	5123	5495	5868	6241	6613	373
1166		6986	7358	7730	8103	8475	8847	9220	9592	9964	*0336	372
1167	067	0709	1081	1453	1825	2197	2569	2941	3313	3685	4057	372
1168		4428	4800	5172	5544	5915	6287	6659	7030	7402	7774	372
1169		8145	8517	8888	9259	9631	*0002	*0374	*0745	*1116	*1487	371
1170	068	1859	2230	2601	2972	3343	3714	4085	4456	4827	5198	371
1171		5569	5940	6311	6681	7052	7423	7794	8164	8535	8906	371
1172		9276	9647	*0017	*0388	*0758	*1129	*1499	*1869	*2240	*2610	370
1173	069	2980	3350	3721	4091	4461	4831	5201	5571	5941	6311	370
1174		6681	7051	7421	7791	8160	8530	8900	9270	9639	*0009	370
1175	070	0379	0748	1118	1487	1857	2226	2596	2965	3335	3704	369
1176		4073	4442	4812	5181	5550	5919	6288	6658	7027	7396	369
1177		7765	8134	8503	8871	9240	9609	9978	*0347	*0715	*1084	369
1178	071	1453	1822	2190	2559	2927	3296	3664	4033	4401	4770	369
1179		5138	5506	5875	6243	6611	6979	7348	7716	8084	8452	368
1180		8820	9188	9556	9924	*0292	*0660	*1028	*1396	*1763	*2131	368
1181	072	2499	2867	3234	3602	3970	4337	4705	5072	5440	5807	368
1182		6175	6542	6910	7277	7644	8011	8379	8746	9113	9480	367
1183		9847	*0215	*0582	*0949	*1316	*1683	*2050	*2416	*2783	*3150	367
1184	073	3517	3884	4251	4617	4984	5351	5717	6084	6450	6817	367
1185		7184	7550	7916	8283	8649	9016	9382	9748	*0114	*0481	366
1186	074	0847	1213	1579	1945	2311	2677	3043	3409	3775	4141	366
1187		4507	4873	5239	5605	5970	6336	6702	7068	7433	7799	366
1188		8164	8530	8895	9261	9626	9992	*0357	*0723	*1088	*1453	365
1189	075	1819	2184	2549	2914	3279	3644	4010	4375	4740	5105	365
1190		5470	5835	6199	6564	6929	7294	7659	8024	8388	8753	365
1191		9118	9482	9847	*0211	*0576	*0940	*1305	*1669	*2034	*2398	364
1192	076	2763	3127	3491	3855	4220	4584	4948	5312	5676	6040	364
1193		6404	6768	7132	7496	7860	8224	8588	8952	9316	9680	364
1194	077	0043	0407	0771	1134	1498	1862	2225	2589	2952	3316	364
1195		3679	4042	4406	4769	5133	5496	5859	6222	6585	6949	363
1196		7312	7675	8038	8401	8764	9127	9490	9853	*0216	*0579	363
1197	078	0942	1304	1667	2030	2393	2755	3118	3480	3843	4206	363
1198		4568	4931	5293	5656	6018	6380	6743	7105	7467	7830	362
1199		8192	8554	8916	9278	9640	*0003	*0365	*0727	*1089	*1451	362
1200	079	1812	2174	2536	2898	3260	3622	3983	4345	4707	5068	362
N.		0	1	2	3	4	5	6	7	8	9	d.

NATURAL OR NAPERIAN LOGARITHMS
0.000–0.499

N	0	1	2	3	4	5	6	7	8	9
0.00	− ∞	−6‡ .90776	−6 .21461	−5 .80914	−5 .52146	−5 .29832	−5 .11600	−4 .96185	−4 .82831	−4 .71053
.01	−4.60517	.50986	.42285	.34281	.26870	.19971	.13517	.07454	.01738	*.96332
.02	−3.91202	.86323	.81671	.77226	.72970	.68888	.64966	.61192	.57555	.54046
.03	.50656	.47377	.44202	.41125	.38139	.35241	.32424	.29684	.27017	.24419
.04	.21888	.19418	.17009	.14656	.12357	.10109	.07911	.05761	.03655	.01593
.05	−2.99573	.97593	.95651	.93746	.91877	.90042	.88240	.86470	.84731	.83022
.06	.81341	.79688	.78062	.76462	.74887	.73337	.71810	.70306	.68825	.67365
.07	.65926	.64508	.63109	.61730	.60369	.59027	.57702	.56395	.55105	.53831
.08	.52573	.51331	.50104	.48891	.47694	.46510	.45341	.44185	.43042	.41912
.09	.40795	.39690	.38597	.37516	.36446	.35388	.34341	.33304	.32279	.31264
0.10	−2.30259	.29263	.28278	.27303	.26336	.25379	.24432	.23493	.22562	.21641
.11	.20727	.19823	.18926	.18037	.17156	.16282	.15417	.14558	.13707	.12863
.12	.12026	.11196	.10373	.09557	.08747	.07944	.07147	.06357	.05573	.04794
.13	.04022	.03256	.02495	.01741	.00992	.00248	*.99510	*.98777	*.98050	*.97328
.14	−1.96611	.95900	.95193	.94491	.93794	.93102	.92415	.91732	.91054	.90381
.15	.89712	.89048	.88387	.87732	.87080	.86433	.85790	.85151	.84516	.83885
.16	.83258	.82635	.82016	.81401	.80789	.80181	.79577	.78976	.78379	.77786
.17	.77196	.76609	.76026	.75446	.74870	.74297	.73727	.73161	.72597	.72037
.18	.71480	.70926	.70375	.69827	.69282	.68740	.68201	.67665	.67131	.66601
.19	.66073	.65548	.65026	.64507	.63990	.63476	.62964	.62455	.61949	.61445
0.20	−1.60944	.60445	.59949	.59455	.58964	.58475	.57988	.57504	.57022	.56542
.21	.56065	.55590	.55117	.54646	.54178	.53712	.53248	.52786	.52326	.51868
.22	.51413	.50959	.50508	.50058	.49611	.49165	.48722	.48281	.47841	.47403
.23	.46968	.46534	.46102	.45672	.45243	.44817	.44392	.43970	.43548	.43129
.24	.42712	.42296	.41882	.41469	.41059	.40650	.40242	.39837	.39433	.39030
.25	.38629	.38230	.37833	.37437	.37042	.36649	.36258	.35868	.35480	.35093
.26	.34707	.34323	.33941	.33560	.33181	.32803	.32426	.32051	.31677	.31304
.27	.30933	.30564	.30195	.29828	.29463	.29098	.28735	.28374	.28013	.27654
.28	.27297	.26940	.26585	.26231	.25878	.25527	.25176	.24827	.24479	.24133
.29	.23787	.23443	.23100	.22758	.22418	.22078	.21740	.21402	.21066	.20731
0.30	−1.20397	.20065	.19733	.19402	.19073	.18744	.18417	.18091	.17766	.17441
.31	.17118	.16796	.16475	.16155	.15836	.15518	.15201	.14885	.14570	.14256
.32	.13943	.13631	.13320	.13010	.12701	.12393	.12086	.11780	.11474	.11170
.33	.10866	.10564	.10262	.09961	.09661	.09362	.09064	.08767	.08471	.08176
.34	.07881	.07587	.07294	.07002	.06711	.06421	.06132	.05843	.05555	.05268
.35	−1.04982	.04697	.04412	.04129	.03846	.03564	.03282	.03002	.02722	.02443
.36	.02165	.01888	.01611	.01335	.01060	.00786	.00512	.00239	*.99967	*.99696
.37	−0.99425	.99155	.98886	.98618	.98350	.98083	.97817	.97551	.97286	.97022
.38	.96758	.96496	.96233	.95972	.95711	.95451	.95192	.94933	.94675	.94418
.39	.94161	.93905	.93649	.93395	.93140	.92887	.92634	.92382	.92130	.91879
0.40	−0.91629	.91379	.91130	.90882	.90634	.90387	.90140	.89894	.89649	.89404
.41	.89160	.88916	.88673	.88431	.88189	.87948	.87707	.87467	.87227	.86988
.42	.86750	.86512	.86275	.86038	.85802	.85567	.85332	.85097	.84863	.84630
.43	.84397	.84165	.83933	.83702	.83471	.83241	.83011	.82782	.82554	.82326
.44	.82098	.81871	.81645	.81419	.81193	.80968	.80744	.80520	.80296	.80073
.45	.79851	.79629	.79407	.79186	.78966	.78746	.78526	.78307	.78089	.77871
.46	.77653	.77436	.77219	.77003	.76787	.76572	.76357	.76143	.75929	.75715
.47	.75502	.75290	.75078	.74866	.74655	.74444	.74234	.74024	.73814	.73605
.48	.73397	.73189	.72981	.72774	.72567	.72361	.72155	.71949	.71744	.71539
.49	.71335	.71131	.70928	.70725	.70522	.70320	.70118	.69917	.69716	.69515

‡ Note that the whole number values are given above the decimal values for the first line. In the second and following lines they are given at the left.

N	0	1	2	3	4	5	6	7	8	9
0.50	−0.69315	.69115	.68916	.68717	.68518	.68320	.68122	.67924	.67727	.67531
.51	.67334	.67139	.66934	.66748	.66553	.66359	.66165	.65971	.65778	.65585
.52	.65393	.65201	.65009	.64817	.64626	.64436	.64245	.64055	.63866	.63677
.53	.63488	.63299	.63111	.62923	.62736	.62549	.62362	.62176	.61990	.61804
.54	.61619	.61434	.61249	.61065	.60881	.60697	.60514	.60331	.60148	.59966
.55	.59784	.59602	.59421	.59240	.59059	.58879	.58699	.58519	.58340	.58161
.56	.57982	.57803	.57625	.57448	.57270	.57093	.56916	.56740	.56563	.56387
.57	.56212	.56037	.55862	.55687	.55513	.55339	.55165	.54991	.54818	.54645
.58	.54473	.54300	.54128	.53957	.53785	.53614	.53444	.53273	.53103	.52933
.59	.52763	.52594	.52425	.52256	.52088	.51919	.51751	.51584	.51416	.51249
0.60	−0.51083	.50916	.50750	.50584	.50418	.50253	.50088	.49923	.49758	.49594
.61	.49430	.49266	.49102	.48939	.48776	.48613	.48451	.48289	.48127	.47965
.62	.47804	.47642	.47482	.47321	.47160	.47000	.46840	.46681	.46522	.46362
.63	.46204	.46045	.45887	.45728	.45571	.45413	.45256	.45099	.44942	.44785
.64	.44629	.44473	.44317	.44161	.44006	.43850	.43696	.43541	.43386	.43232
.65	.43078	.42925	.42771	.42618	.42465	.42312	.42159	.42007	.41855	.41703
.66	.41552	.41400	.41249	.41098	.40947	.40797	.40647	.40497	.40347	.40197
.67	.40048	.39899	.39750	.39601	.39453	.39304	.39156	.39008	.38861	.38713
.68	.38566	.38419	.38273	.38126	.37980	.37834	.37688	.37542	.37397	.37251
.69	.37106	.36962	.36817	.36673	.36528	.36384	.36241	.36097	.35954	.35810
0.70	−0.35667	.35525	.35382	.35240	.35098	.34956	.34814	.34672	.34531	.34390
.71	.34249	.34108	.33968	.33827	.33687	.33547	.33408	.33268	.33129	.32989
.72	.32850	.32712	.32573	.32435	.32296	.32158	.32021	.31883	.31745	.31608
.73	.31471	.31334	.31197	.31061	.30925	.30788	.30653	.30517	.30381	.30246
.74	.30111	.29975	.29841	.29706	.29571	.29437	.29303	.29169	.29035	.28902
.75	.28768	.28635	.28502	.28369	.28236	.28104	.27971	.27839	.27707	.27575
.76	.27444	.27312	.27181	.27050	.26919	.26788	.26657	.26527	.26397	.26266
.77	.26136	.26007	.25877	.25748	.25618	.25489	.25360	.25231	.25103	.24974
.78	.24846	.24718	.24590	.24462	.24335	.24207	.24080	.23953	.23826	.23699
.79	.23572	.23446	.23319	.23193	.23067	.22941	.22816	.22690	.22565	.22439
0.80	−0.22314	.22189	.22065	.21940	.21816	.21691	.21567	.21433	.21319	.21196
.81	.21072	.20949	.20825	.20702	.20579	.20457	.20334	.20212	.20089	.19967
.82	.19845	.19723	.19601	.19480	.19358	.19237	.19116	.18995	.18874	.18754
.83	.18633	.18513	.18392	.18272	.18152	.18032	.17913	.17793	.17674	.17554
.84	.17435	.17316	.17198	.17079	.16960	.16842	.16724	.16605	.16487	.16370
.85	−0.16252	.16134	.16017	.15900	.15782	.15665	.15548	.15432	.15315	.15199
.86	.15082	.14966	.14850	.14734	.14618	.14503	.14387	.14272	.14156	.14041
.87	.13926	.13811	.13697	.13582	.13467	.13353	.13239	.13125	.13011	.12897
.88	.12783	.12670	.12556	.12443	.12330	.12217	.12104	.11991	.11878	.11766
.89	.11653	.11541	.11429	.11317	.11205	.11093	.10981	.10870	.10759	.10647
0.90	−0.10536	.10425	.10314	.10203	.10093	.09982	.09872	.09761	.09651	.09541
.91	.09431	.09321	.09212	.09102	.08992	.08883	.08744	.08665	.08556	.08447
.92	.08338	.08230	.08121	.08013	.07904	.07796	.07688	.07580	.07472	.07365
.93	.07257	.07150	.07042	.06935	.06828	.06721	.06614	.06507	.06401	.06294
.94	.06188	.06081	.05975	.05869	.05763	.05657	.05551	.05446	.05340	.05235
.95	.05129	.05024	.04919	.04814	.04709	.04604	.04500	.04395	.04291	.04186
.96	.04082	.03978	.03874	.03770	.03666	.03563	.03459	.03356	.03252	.03149
.97	.03046	.02943	.02840	.02737	.02634	.02532	.02429	.02327	.02225	.02122
.98	.02020	.01918	.01816	.01715	.01613	.01511	.01410	.01309	.01207	.01106
.99	.01005	.00904	.00803	.00702	.00602	.00501	.00401	.00300	.00200	.00100

NATURAL OR NAPERIAN LOGARITHMS (Continued)

To find the natural logarithm of a number which is $\frac{1}{10}$, $\frac{1}{100}$, $\frac{1}{1000}$, etc. of a number whose logarithm is given, subtract from the given logarithm $\log_e 10$, $2 \log_e 10$, $3 \log_e 10$, etc.

To find the natural logarithm of a number which is 10, 100, 1000, etc. times a number whose logarithm is given, add to the given logarithm $\log_e 10$, $2 \log_e 10$, $3 \log_e 10$, etc.

$\log_e 10 = 2.30258\ 50930$	$6 \log_e 10 = 13.81551\ 05580$
$2 \log_e 10 = 4.60517\ 01860$	$7 \log_e 10 = 16.11809\ 56510$
$3 \log_e 10 = 6.90775\ 52790$	$8 \log_e 10 = 18.42068\ 07440$
$4 \log_e 10 = 9.21034\ 03720$	$9 \log_e 10 = 20.72326\ 58369$
$5 \log_e 10 = 11.51292\ 54650$	$10 \log_e 10 = 23.02585\ 09299$

See preceding table for logarithms for numbers between 0.000 and 0.999.

1.00–4.99

N	0	1	2	3	4	5	6	7	8	9
1.0	0.00000	.00995	.01980	.02956	.03922	.04879	.05827	.06766	.07696	.08618
.1	.09531	.10436	.11333	.12222	.13103	.13976	.14842	.15700	.16551	.17395
.2	.18232	.19062	.19885	.20701	.21511	.22314	.23111	.23902	.24686	.25464
.3	.26236	.27003	.27763	.28518	.29267	.30010	.30748	.31481	.32208	.32930
.4	.33647	.34359	.35066	.35767	.36464	.37156	.37844	.38526	.39204	.39878
.5	.40547	.41211	.41871	.42527	.43178	.43825	.44469	.45108	.45742	.46373
.6	.47000	.47623	.48243	.48858	.49470	.50078	.50682	.51282	.51879	.52473
.7	.53063	.53649	.54232	.54812	.55389	.55962	.56531	.57098	.57661	.58222
.8	.58779	.59333	.59884	.60432	.60977	.61519	.62058	.62594	.63127	.63658
.9	.64185	.64710	.65233	.65752	.66269	.66783	.67294	.67803	.68310	.68813
2.0	0.69315	.69813	.70310	.70804	.71295	.71784	.72271	.72755	.73237	.73716
.1	.74194	.74669	.75142	.75612	.76081	.76547	.77011	.77473	.77932	.78390
.2	.78846	.79299	.79751	.80200	.80648	.81093	.81536	.81978	.82418	.82855
.3	.83291	.83725	.84157	.84587	.85015	.85442	.85866	.86289	.86710	.87129
.4	.87547	.87963	.88377	.88789	.89200	.89609	.90016	.90422	.90826	.91228
.5	.91629	.92028	.92426	.92822	.93216	.93609	.94001	.94391	.94779	.95166
.6	.95551	.95935	.96317	.96698	.97078	.97456	.97833	.98208	.98582	.98954
.7	.99325	.99695	*.00063	*.00430	*.00796	*.01160	*.01523	*.01885	*.02245	*.02604
.8	1.02962	.03318	.03674	.04028	.04380	.04732	.05082	.05431	.05779	.06126
.9	.06471	.06815	.07158	.07500	.07841	.08181	.08519	.08856	.09192	.09527
3.0	1.09861	.10194	.10526	.10856	.11186	.11514	.11841	.12168	.12493	.12817
.1	.13140	.13462	.13783	.14103	.14422	.14740	.15057	.15373	.15688	.16002
.2	.16315	.16627	.16938	.17248	.17557	.17865	.18173	.18479	.18784	.19089
.3	.19392	.19695	.19996	.20297	.20597	.20896	.21194	.21491	.21788	.22083
.4	.22378	.22671	.22964	.23256	.23547	.23837	.24127	.24415	.24703	.24990
.5	.25276	.25562	.25846	.26130	.26413	.26695	.26976	.27257	.27536	.27815
.6	.28093	.28371	.28647	.28923	.29198	.29473	.29746	.30019	.30291	.30563
.7	.30833	.31103	.31372	.31641	.31909	.32176	.32442	.32708	.32972	.33237
.8	.33500	.33763	.34025	.34286	.34547	.34807	.35067	.35325	.35584	.35841
.9	.36098	.36354	.36609	.36864	.37118	.37372	.37624	.37877	.38128	.38379
4.0	1.38629	.38879	.39128	.39377	.39624	.39872	.40118	.40364	.40610	.40854
.1	.41099	.41342	.41585	.41828	.42070	.42311	.42552	.42792	.43031	.43270
.2	.43508	.43746	.43984	.44220	.44456	.44692	.44927	.45161	.45395	.45629
.3	.45862	.46094	.46326	.46557	.46787	.47018	.47247	.47476	.47705	.47933
.4	.48160	.48387	.48614	.48840	.49065	.49290	.49515	.49739	.49962	.50185
.5	.50408	.50630	.50851	.51072	.51293	.51513	.51732	.51951	.52170	.52388
.6	.52606	.52823	.53039	.53256	.53471	.53687	.53902	.54116	.54330	.54543
.7	.54756	.54969	.55181	.55393	.55604	.55814	.56025	.56235	.56444	.56653
.8	.56862	.57070	.57277	.57485	.57691	.57898	.58104	.58309	.58515	.58719
.9	.58924	.59127	.59331	.59534	.59737	.59939	.60141	.60342	.60543	.60744

N	0	1	2	3	4	5	6	7	8	9
5.0	1.60944	.61144	.61343	.61542	.61741	.61939	.62137	.62334	.62531	.62728
.1	.62924	.63120	.63315	.63511	.63705	.63900	.64094	.64287	.64481	.64673
.2	.64866	.65058	.65250	.65441	.65632	.65823	.66013	.66203	.66393	.66582
.3	.66771	.66959	.67147	.67335	.67523	.67710	.67896	.68083	.68269	.68455
.4	.68640	.68825	.69010	.69194	.69378	.69562	.69745	.69928	.70111	.70293
.5	.70475	.70656	.70838	.71019	.71199	.71380	.71560	.71740	.71919	.72098
.6	.72277	.72455	.72633	.72811	.72988	.73166	.73342	.73519	.73695	.73871
.7	.74047	.74222	.74397	.74572	.74746	.74920	.75094	.75267	.75440	.75613
.8	.75786	.75958	.76130	.76302	.76473	.76644	.76815	.76985	.77156	.77326
.9	.77495	.77665	.77834	.78002	.78171	.78339	.78507	.78675	.78842	.79009
6.0	1.79176	.79342	.79509	.79675	.79840	.80006	.80171	.80336	.80500	.80665
.1	.80829	.80993	.81156	.81319	.81482	.81645	.81808	.81970	.82132	.82294
.2	.82455	.82616	.82777	.82938	.83098	.83258	.83418	.83578	.83737	.83896
.3	.84055	.84214	.84372	.84530	.84688	.84845	.85003	.85160	.85317	.85473
.4	.85630	.85786	.85942	.86097	.86253	.86408	.86563	.86718	.86872	.87026
.5	.87180	.87334	.87487	.87641	.87794	.87947	.88099	.88251	.88403	.88555
.6	.88707	.88858	.89010	.89160	.89311	.89462	.89612	.89762	.89912	.90061
.7	.90211	.90360	.90509	.90658	.90806	.90954	.91102	.91250	.91398	.91545
.8	.91692	.91839	.91986	.92132	.92279	.92425	.92571	.92716	.92862	.93007
.9	.93152	.93297	.93442	.93586	.93730	.93874	.94018	.94162	.94305	.94448
7.0	1.94591	.94734	.94876	.95019	.95161	.95303	.95445	.95586	.95727	.95869
.1	.96009	.96150	.96291	.96431	.96571	.96711	.96851	.96991	.97130	.97269
.2	.97408	.97547	.97685	.97824	.97962	.98100	.98238	.98376	.98513	.98650
.3	.98787	.98924	.99061	.99198	.99334	.99470	.99606	.99742	.99877	*.00013
.4	2.00148	.00283	.00418	.00553	.00687	.00821	.00956	.01089	.01223	.01357
.5	.01490	.01624	.01757	.01890	.02022	.02155	.02287	.02419	.02551	.02683
.6	.02815	.02946	.03078	.03209	.03340	.03471	.03601	.03732	.03862	.03992
.7	.04122	.04252	.04381	.04511	.04640	.04769	.04898	.05027	.05156	.05284
.8	.05412	.05540	.05668	.05796	.05924	.06051	.06179	.06306	.06433	.06560
.9	.06686	.06813	.06939	.07065	.07191	.07317	.07443	.07568	.07694	.07819
8.0	2.07944	.08069	.08194	.08318	.08443	.08567	.08691	.08815	.08939	.09063
.1	.09186	.09310	.09433	.09556	.09679	.09802	.09924	.10047	.10169	.10291
.2	.10413	.10535	.10657	.10779	.10900	.11021	.11142	.11263	.11384	.11505
.3	.11626	.11746	.11866	.11986	.12106	.12226	.12346	.12465	.12585	.12704
.4	.12823	.12942	.13061	.13180	.13298	.13417	.13535	.13653	.13771	.13889
.5	.14007	.14124	.14242	.14359	.14476	.14593	.14710	.14827	.14943	.150€0
.6	.15176	.15292	.15409	.15524	.15640	.15756	.15871	.15987	.16102	.16217
.7	.16332	.16447	.16562	.16677	.16791	.16905	.17020	.17134	.17248	.17361
.8	.17475	.17589	.17702	.17816	.17929	.18042	.18155	.18267	.18380	.18493
.9	.18605	.18717	.18830	.18942	.19054	.19165	.19277	.19389	.19500	.19611
9.0	2.19722	.19834	.19944	.20055	.20166	.20276	.20387	.20497	.20607	.20717
.1	.20827	.20937	.21047	.21157	.21266	.21375	.21485	.21594	.21703	.21812
.2	.21920	.22029	.22138	.22246	.22354	.22462	.22570	.22678	.22786	.22894
.3	.23001	.23109	.23216	.23324	.23431	.23538	.23645	.23751	.23858	.23965
.4	.24071	.24177	.24284	.24390	.24496	.24601	.24707	.24813	.24918	.25024
.5	.25129	.25234	.25339	.25444	.25549	.25654	.25759	.25863	.25968	.26072
.6	.26176	.26280	.26384	.26488	.26592	.26696	.26799	.26903	.27006	.27109
.7	.27213	.27316	.27419	.27521	.27624	.27727	.27829	.27932	.28034	.28136
.8	.28238	.28340	.28442	.28544	.28646	.28747	.28849	.28950	.29051	.29152
.9	.29253	.29354	.29455	.29556	.29657	.29757	.29858	.29958	.30058	.30158

EXPONENTIAL FUNCTIONS

x	e^x	$\text{Log}_{10}(e^x)$	e^{-x}	x	e^x	$\text{Log}_{10}(e^x)$	e^{-x}
0.00	1.0000	0.00000	1.000000	**0.50**	1.6487	0.21715	0.606531
0.01	1.0101	.00434	0.990050	0.51	1.6653	.22149	.600496
0.02	1.0202	.00869	.980199	0.52	1.6820	.22583	.594521
0.03	1.0305	.01303	.970446	0.53	1.6989	.23018	.588605
0.04	1.0408	.01737	.960789	0.54	1.7160	.23452	.582748
0.05	1.0513	0.02171	0.951229	**0.55**	1.7333	0.23886	0.576950
0.06	1.0618	.02606	.941765	0.56	1.7507	.24320	.571209
0.07	1.0725	.03040	.932394	0.57	1.7683	.24755	.565525
0.08	1.0833	.03474	.923116	0.58	1.7860	.25189	.559898
0.09	1.0942	.03909	.913931	0.59	1.8040	.25623	.554327
0.10	1.1052	0.04343	0.904837	**0.60**	1.8221	0.26058	0.548812
0.11	1.1163	.04777	.895834	0.61	1.8404	.26492	.543351
0.12	1.1275	.05212	.886920	0.62	1.8589	.26926	.537944
0.13	1.1388	.05646	.878095	0.63	1.8776	.27361	.532592
0.14	1.1503	.06080	.869358	0.64	1.8965	.27795	.527292
0.15	1.1618	0.06514	0.860708	**0.65**	1.9155	0.28229	0.522046
0.16	1.1735	.06949	.852144	0.66	1.9348	.28663	.516851
0.17	1.1853	.07383	.843665	0.67	1.9542	.29098	.511709
0.18	1.1972	.07817	.835270	0.68	1.9739	.29532	.506617
0.19	1.2092	.08252	.826959	0.69	1.9937	.29966	.501576
0.20	1.2214	0.08686	0.818731	**0.70**	2.0138	0.30401	0.496585
0.21	1.2337	.09120	.810584	0.71	2.0340	.30835	.491644
0.22	1.2461	.09554	.802519	0.72	2.0544	.31269	.486752
0.23	1.2586	.09989	.794534	0.73	2.0751	.31703	.481909
0.24	1.2712	.10423	.786628	0.74	2.0959	.32138	.477114
0.25	1.2840	0.10857	0.778801	**0.75**	2.1170	0.32572	0.472367
0.26	1.2969	.11292	.771052	0.76	2.1383	.33006	.467666
0.27	1.3100	.11726	.763379	0.77	2.1598	.33441	.463013
0.28	1.3231	.12160	.755784	0.78	2.1815	.33875	.458406
0.29	1.3364	.12595	.748264	0.79	2.2034	.34309	.453845
0.30	1.3499	0.13029	0.740818	**0.80**	2.2255	0.34744	0.449329
0.31	1.3634	.13463	.733447	0.81	2.2479	.35178	.444858
0.32	1.3771	.13897	.726149	0.82	2.2705	.35612	.440432
0.33	1.3910	.14332	.718924	0.83	2.2933	.36046	.436049
0.34	1.4049	.14766	.711770	0.84	2.3164	.36481	.431711
0.35	1.4191	0.15200	0.704688	**0.85**	2.3396	0.36915	0.427415
0.36	1.4333	.15635	.697676	0.86	2.3632	.37349	.423162
0.37	1.4477	.16069	.690734	0.87	2.3869	.37784	.418952
0.38	1.4623	.16503	.683861	0.88	2.4109	.38218	.414783
0.39	1.4770	.16937	.677057	0.89	2.4351	.38652	.410656
0.40	1.4918	0.17372	0.670320	**0.90**	2.4596	0.39087	0.406570
0.41	1.5068	.17806	.663650	0.91	2.4843	.39521	.402524
0.42	1.5220	.18240	.657047	0.92	2.5093	.39955	.398519
0.43	1.5373	.18675	.650509	0.93	2.5345	.40389	.394554
0.44	1.5527	.19109	.644036	0.94	2.5600	.40824	.390628
0.45	1.5683	0.19543	0.637628	**0.95**	2.5857	0.41258	0.386741
0.46	1.5841	.19978	.631284	0.96	2.6117	.41692	.382893
0.47	1.6000	.20412	.625002	0.97	2.6379	.42127	.379083
0.48	1.6161	.20846	.618783	0.98	2.6645	.42561	.375311
0.49	1.6323	.21280	.612626	0.99	2.6912	.42995	.371577
0.50	1.6487	0.21715	0.606531	**1.00**	2.7183	0.43429	0.367879

x	e^x	$\text{Log}_{10}(e^x)$	e^{-x}	x	e^x	$\text{Log}_{10}(e^x)$	e^{-x}
1.00	2.7183	0.43429	0.367879	**1.50**	4.4817	0.65144	0.223130
1.01	2.7456	.43864	.364219	1.51	4.5267	.65578	.220910
1.02	2.7732	.44298	.360595	1.52	4.5722	.66013	.218712
1.03	2.8011	.44732	.357007	1.53	4.6182	.66447	.216536
1.04	2.8292	.45167	.353455	1.54	4.6646	.66881	.214381
1.05	2.8577	0.45601	0.349938	**1.55**	4.7115	0.67316	0.212248
1.06	2.8864	.46035	.346456	1.56	4.7588	.67750	.210136
1.07	2.9154	.46470	.343009	1.57	4.8066	.68184	.208045
1.08	2.9447	.46904	.339596	1.58	4.8550	.68619	.205975
1.09	2.9743	.47338	.336216	1.59	4.9037	.69053	.203926
1.10	3.0042	0.47772	0.332871	**1.60**	4.9530	0.69487	0.201897
1.11	3.0344	.48207	.329559	1.61	5.0028	.69921	.199888
1.12	3.0649	.48641	.326280	1.62	5.0531	.70356	.197899
1.13	3.0957	.49075	.323033	1.63	5.1039	.70790	.195930
1.14	3.1268	.49510	.319819	1.64	5.1552	.71224	.193980
1.15	3.1582	0.49944	0.316637	**1.65**	5.2070	0.71659	0.192050
1.16	3.1899	.50378	.313486	1.66	5.2593	.72093	.190139
1.17	3.2220	.50812	.310367	1.67	5.3122	.72527	.188247
1.18	3.2544	.51247	.307279	1.68	5.3656	.72961	.186374
1.19	3.2871	.51681	.304221	1.69	5.4195	.73396	.184520
1.20	3.3201	0.52115	0.301194	**1.70**	5.4739	0.73830	0.182684
1.21	3.3535	.52550	.298197	1.71	5.5290	.74264	.180866
1.22	3.3872	.52984	.295230	1.72	5.5845	.74699	.179066
1.23	3.4212	.53418	.292293	1.73	5.6407	.75133	.177284
1.24	3.4556	.53853	.289384	1.74	5.6973	.75567	.175520
1.25	3.4903	0.54287	0.286505	**1.75**	5.7546	0.76002	0.173774
1.26	3.5254	.54721	.283654	1.76	5.8124	.76436	.172045
1.27	3.5609	.55155	.280832	1.77	5.8709	.76870	.170333
1.28	3.5966	.55590	.278037	1.78	5.9299	.77304	.168638
1.29	3.6328	.56024	.275271	1.79	5.9895	.77739	.166960
1.30	3.6693	0.56458	0.272532	**1.80**	6.0496	0.78173	0.165299
1.31	3.7062	.56893	.269820	1.81	6.1104	.78607	.163654
1.32	3.7434	.57327	.267135	1.82	6.1719	.79042	.162026
1.33	3.7810	.57761	.264477	1.83	6.2339	.79476	.160414
1.34	3.8190	.58195	.261846	1.84	6.2965	.79910	.158817
1.35	3.8574	0.58630	0.259240	**1.85**	6.3598	0.80344	0.157237
1.36	3.8962	.59064	.256661	1.86	6.4237	.80779	.155673
1.37	3.9354	.59498	.254107	1.87	6.4883	.81213	.154124
1.38	3.9749	.59933	.251579	1.88	6.5535	.81647	.152590
1.39	4.0149	.60367	.249075	1.89	6.6194	.82082	.151072
1.40	4.0552	0.60801	0.246597	**1.90**	6.6859	0.82516	0.149569
1.41	4.0960	.61236	.244143	1.91	6.7531	.82950	.148080
1.42	4.1371	.61670	.241714	1.92	6.8210	.83385	.146607
1.43	4.1787	.62104	.239309	1.93	6.8895	.83819	.145148
1.44	4.2207	.62538	.236928	1.94	6.9588	.84253	.143704
1.45	4.2631	0.62973	0.234570	**1.95**	7.0287	0.84687	0.142274
1.46	4.3060	.63407	.232236	1.96	7.0993	.85122	.140858
1.47	4.3492	.63841	.229925	1.97	7.1707	.85556	.139457
1.48	4.3929	.64276	.227638	1.98	7.2427	.85990	.138069
1.49	4.4371	.64710	.225373	1.99	7.3155	.86425	.136695
1.50	4.4817	0.65144	0.223130	**2.00**	7.3891	0.86859	0.135335

x	e^x	$\text{Log}_{10}(e^x)$	e^{-x}	x	e^x	$\text{Log}_{10}(e^x)$	e^{-x}
2.00	7.3891	0.86859	0.135335	**2.50**	12.182	1.08574	0.082085
2.01	7.4633	.87293	.133989	2.51	12.305	1.09008	.081268
2.02	7.5383	.87727	.132655	2.52	12.429	1.09442	.080460
2.03	7.6141	.88162	.131336	2.53	12.554	1.09877	.079659
2.04	7.6906	.88596	.130029	2.54	12.680	1.10311	.078866
2.05	7.7679	0.89030	0.128735	**2.55**	12.807	1.10745	0.078082
2.06	7.8460	.89465	.127454	2.56	12.936	1.11179	.077305
2.07	7.9248	.89899	.126186	2.57	13.066	1.11614	.076536
2.08	8.0045	.90333	.124930	2.58	13.197	1.12048	.075774
2.09	8.0849	.90768	.123687	2.59	13.330	1.12482	.075020
2.10	8.1662	0.91202	0.122456	**2.60**	13.464	1.12917	0.074274
2.11	8.2482	.91636	.121238	2.61	13.599	1.13351	.073535
2.12	8.3311	.92070	.120032	2.62	13.736	1.13785	.072803
2.13	8.4149	.92505	.118837	2.63	13.874	1.14219	.072078
2.14	8.4994	.92939	.117655	2.64	14.013	1.14654	.071361
2.15	8.5849	0.93373	0.116484	**2.65**	14.154	1.15088	0.070651
2.16	8.6711	.93808	.115325	2.66	14.296	1.15522	.069948
2.17	8.7583	.94242	.114178	2.67	14.440	1.15957	.069252
2.18	8.8463	.94676	.113042	2.68	14.585	1.16391	.068563
2.19	8.9352	.95110	.111917	2.69	14.732	1.16825	.067881
2.20	9.0250	0.95545	0.110803	**2.70**	14.880	1.17260	0.067206
2.21	9.1157	.95979	.109701	2.71	15.029	1.17694	.066537
2.22	9.2073	.96413	.108609	2.72	15.180	1.18128	.065875
2.23	9.2999	.96848	.107528	2.73	15.333	1.18562	.065219
2.24	9.3933	.97282	.106459	2.74	15.487	1.18997	.064570
2.25	9.4877	0.97716	0.105399	**2.75**	15.643	1.19431	0.063928
2.26	9.5831	.98151	.104350	2.76	15.800	1.19865	.063292
2.27	9.6794	.98585	.103312	2.77	15.959	1.20300	.062662
2.28	9.7767	.99019	.102284	2.78	16.119	1.20734	.062039
2.29	9.8749	.99453	.101266	2.79	16.281	1.21168	.061421
2.30	9.9742	0.99888	0.100259	**2.80**	16.445	1.21602	0.060810
2.31	10.074	1.00322	.099261	2.81	16.610	1.22037	.060205
2.32	10.176	1.00756	.098274	2.82	16.777	1.22471	.059606
2.33	10.278	1.01191	.097296	2.83	16.945	1.22905	.059013
2.34	10.381	1.01625	.096328	2.84	17.116	1.23340	.058426
2.35	10.486	1.02059	0.095369	**2.85**	17.288	1.23774	0.057844
2.36	10.591	1.02493	.094420	2.86	17.462	1.24208	.057269
2.37	10.697	1.02928	.093481	2.87	17.637	1.24643	.056699
2.38	10.805	1.03362	.092551	2.88	17.814	1.25077	.056135
2.39	10.913	1.03796	.091630	2.89	17.993	1.25511	.055576
2.40	11.023	1.04231	0.090718	**2.90**	18.174	1.25945	0.055023
2.41	11.134	1.04665	.089815	2.91	18.357	1.26380	.054476
2.42	11.246	1.05099	.088922	2.92	18.541	1.26814	.053934
2.43	11.359	1.05534	.088037	2.93	18.728	1.27248	.053397
2.44	11.473	1.05968	.087161	2.94	18.916	1.27683	.052866
2.45	11.588	1.06402	0.086294	**2.95**	19.106	1.28117	0.052340
2.46	11.705	1.06836	.085435	2.96	19.298	1.28551	.051819
2.47	11.822	1.07271	.084585	2.97	19.492	1.28985	.051303
2.48	11.941	1.07705	.083743	2.98	19.688	1.29420	.050793
2.49	12.061	1.08139	.082910	2.99	19.886	1.29854	.050287
2.50	12.182	1.08574	0.082085	**3.00**	20.086	1.30288	0.049787

x	e^x	$\text{Log}_{10}(e^x)$	e^{-x}	x	e^x	$\text{Log}_{10}(e^x)$	e^{-x}
3.00	20.086	1.30288	0.049787	**3.50**	33.115	1.52003	0.030197
3.01	20.287	1.30723	.049292	3.51	33.448	1.52437	.029897
3.02	20.491	1.31157	.048801	3.52	33.784	1.52872	.029599
3.03	20.697	1.31591	.048316	3.53	34.124	1.53306	.029305
3.04	20.905	1.32026	.047835	3.54	34.467	1.53740	.029013
3.05	21.115	1.32460	0.047359	**3.55**	34.813	1.54175	0.028725
3.06	21.328	1.32894	.046888	3.56	35.163	1.54609	.028439
3.07	21.542	1.33328	.046421	3.57	35.517	1.55043	.028156
3.08	21.758	1.33763	.045959	3.58	35.874	1.55477	.027876
3.09	21.977	1.34197	.045502	3.59	36.234	1.55912	.027598
3.10	22.198	1.34631	0.045049	**3.60**	36.598	1.56346	0.027324
3.11	22.421	1.35066	.044601	3.61	36.966	1.56780	.027052
3.12	22.646	1.35500	.044157	3.62	37.338	1.57215	.026783
3.13	22.874	1.35934	.043718	3.63	37.713	1.57649	.026516
3.14	23.104	1.36368	.043283	3.64	38.092	1.58083	.026252
3.15	23.336	1.36803	0.042852	**3.65**	38.475	1.58517	0.025991
3.16	23.571	1.37237	.042426	3.66	38.861	1.58952	.025733
3.17	23.807	1.37671	.042004	3.67	39.252	1.59386	.025476
3.18	24.047	1.38106	.041586	3.68	39.646	1.59820	.025223
3.19	24.288	1.38540	.041172	3.69	40.045	1.60255	.024972
3.20	24.533	1.38974	0.040762	**3.70**	40.447	1.60689	0.024724
3.21	24.779	1.39409	.040357	3.71	40.854	1.61123	.024478
3.22	25.028	1.39843	.039955	3.72	41.264	1.61558	.024234
3.23	25.280	1.40277	.039557	3.73	41.679	1.61992	.023993
3.24	25.534	1.40711	.039164	3.74	42.098	1.62426	.023754
3.25	25.790	1.41146	0.038774	**3.75**	42.521	1.62860	0.023518
3.26	26.050	1.41580	.038388	3.76	42.948	1.63295	.023284
3.27	26.311	1.42014	.038006	3.77	43.380	1.63729	.023052
3.28	26.576	1.42449	.037628	3.78	43.816	1.64163	.022823
3.29	26.843	1.42883	.037254	3.79	44.256	1.64598	.022596
3.30	27.113	1.43317	0.036883	**3.80**	44.701	1.65032	0.022371
3.31	27.385	1.43751	.036516	3.81	45.150	1.65466	.022148
3.32	27.660	1.44186	.036153	3.82	45.604	1.65900	.021928
3.33	27.938	1.44620	.035793	3.83	46.063	1.66335	.021710
3.34	28.219	1.45054	.035437	3.84	46.525	1.66769	ª .021494
3.35	28.503	1.45489	0.035084	**3.85**	46.993	1.67203	0.021280
3.36	28.789	1.45923	.034735	3.86	47.465	1.67638	.021068
3.37	29.079	1.46357	.034390	3.87	47.942	1.68072	.020858
3.38	29.371	1.46792	.034047	3.88	48.424	1.68506	.020651
3.39	29.666	1.47226	.033709	3.89	48.911	1.68941	.020445
3.40	29.964	1.47660	0.033373	**3.90**	49.402	1.69375	0.020242
3.41	30.265	1.48094	.033041	3.91	49.899	1.69809	.020041
3.42	30.569	1.48529	.032712	3.92	50.400	1.70243	.019841
3.43	30.877	1.48963	.032387	3.93	50.907	1.70678	.019644
3.44	31.187	1.49397	.032065	3.94	51.419	1.71112	.019448
3.45	31.500	1.49832	0.031746	**3.95**	51.935	1.71546	0.019255
3.46	31.817	1.50266	.031430	3.96	52.457	1.71981	.019063
3.47	32.137	1.50700	.031117	3.97	52.985	1.72415	.018873
3.48	32.460	1.51134	.030807	3.98	53.517	1.72849	.018686
3.49	32.786	1.51569	.030501	3.99	54.055	1.73283	.018500
3.50	33.115	1.52003	0.030197	**4.00**	54.598	1.73718	0.018316

x	e^x	$\log_{10}(e^x)$	e^{-x}	x	e^x	$\log_{10}(e^x)$	e^{-x}
4.00	54.598	1.73718	0.018316	**4.50**	90.017	1.95433	0.011109
4.01	55.147	1.74152	.018133	4.51	90.922	1.95867	.010998
4.02	55.701	1.74586	.017953	4.52	91.836	1.96301	.010889
4.03	56.261	1.75021	.017774	4.53	92.759	1.96735	.010781
4.04	56.826	1.75455	.017597	4.54	93.691	1.97170	.010673
4.05	57.397	1.75889	0.017422	**4.55**	94.632	1.97604	0.010567
4.06	57.974	1.76324	.017249	4.56	95.583	1.98038	.010462
4.07	58.557	1.76758	.017077	4.57	96.544	1.98473	.010358
4.08	59.145	1.77192	.016907	4.58	97.514	1.98907	.010255
4.09	59.740	1.77626	.016739	4.59	98.494	1.99341	.010153
4.10	60.340	1.78061	0.016573	**4.60**	99.484	1.99775	0.010052
4.11	60.947	1.78495	.016408	4.61	100.48	2.00210	.009952
4.12	61.559	1.78929	.016245	4.62	101.49	2.00644	.009853
4.13	62.178	1.79364	.016083	4.63	102.51	2.01078	.009755
4.14	62.803	1.79798	.015923	4.64	103.54	2.01513	.009658
4.15	63.434	1.80232	0.015764	**4.65**	104.58	2.01947	0.009562
4.16	64.072	1.80667	.015608	4.66	105.64	2.02381	.009466
4.17	64.715	1.81101	.015452	4.67	106.70	2.02816	.009372
4.18	65.366	1.81535	.015299	4.68	107.77	2.03250	.009279
4.19	66.023	1.81969	.015146	4.69	108.85	2.03684	.009187
4.20	66.686	1.82404	0.014996	**4.70**	109.95	2.04118	0.009095
4.21	67.357	1.82838	.014846	4.71	111.05	2.04553	.009005
4.22	68.033	1.83272	.014699	4.72	112.17	2.04987	.008915
4.23	68.717	1.83707	.014552	4.73	113.30	2.05421	.008826
4.24	69.408	1.84141	.014408	4.74	114.43	2.05856	.008739
4.25	70.105	1.84575	0.014264	**4.75**	115.58	2.06290	0.008652
4.26	70.810	1.85009	.014122	4.76	116.75	2.06724	.008566
4.27	71.522	1.85444	.013982	4.77	117.92	2.07158	.008480
4.28	72.240	1.85878	.013843	4.78	119.10	2.07593	.008396
4.29	72.966	1.86312	.013705	4.79	120.30	2.08027	.008312
4.30	73.700	1.86747	0.013569	**4.80**	121.51	2.08461	0.008230
4.31	74.440	1.87181	.013434	4.81	122.73	2.08896	.008148
4.32	75.189	1.87615	.013300	4.82	123.97	2.09330	.008067
4.33	75.944	1.88050	.013168	4.83	125.21	2.09764	.007987
4.34	76.708	1.88484	.013037	4.84	126.47	2.10199	.007907
4.35	77.478	1.88918	0.012907	**4.85**	127.74	2.10633	0.007828
4.36	78.257	1.89352	.012778	4.86	129.02	2.11067	.007750
4.37	79.044	1.89787	.012651	4.87	130.32	2.11501	.007673
4.38	79.838	1.90221	.012525	4.88	131.63	2.11936	.007597
4.39	80.640	1.90655	.012401	4.89	132.95	2.12370	.007521
4.40	81.451	1.91090	0.012277	**4.90**	134.29	2.12804	0.007447
4.41	82.269	1.91524	.012155	4.91	135.64	2.13239	.007372
4.42	83.096	1.91958	.012034	4.92	137.00	2.13673	.007299
4.43	83.931	1.92392	.011914	4.93	138.38	2.14107	.007227
4.44	84.775	1.92827	.011796	4.94	139.77	2.14541	.007155
4.45	85.627	1.93261	0.011679	**4.95**	141.17	2.14976	0.007083
4.46	86.488	1.93695	.011562	4.96	142.59	2.15410	.007013
4.47	87.357	1.94130	.011447	4.97	144.03	2.15844	.006943
4.48	88.235	1.94564	.011333	4.98	145.47	2.16279	.006874
4.49	89.121	1.94998	.011221	4.99	146.94	2.16713	.006806
4.50	90.017	1.95433	0.011109	**5.00**	148.41	2.17147	0.006738

x	e^x	$\text{Log}_{10}(e^x)$	e^{-x}	x	e^x	$\text{Log}_{10}(e^x)$	e^{-x}
5.00	148.41	2.17147	0.006738	**5.50**	244.69	2.38862	0.0040868
5.01	149.90	2.17582	.006671	5.55	257.24	2.41033	.0038875
5.02	151.41	2.18016	.006605	5.60	270.43	2.43205	.0036979
5.03	152.93	2.18450	.006539	5.65	284.29	2.45376	.0035175
5.04	154.47	2.18884	.006474	5.70	298.87	2.47548	.0033460
5.05	156.02	2.19319	0.006409	**5.75**	314.19	2.49719	0.0031828
5.06	157.59	2.19753	.006346	5.80	330.30	2.51891	.0030276
5.07	159.17	2.20187	.006282	5.85	347.23	2.54062	.0028799
5.08	160.77	2.20622	.006220	5.90	365.04	2.56234	.0027394
5.09	162.39	2.21056	.006158	5.95	383.75	2.58405	.0026058
5.10	164.02	2.21490	0.006097	**6.00**	403.43	2.60577	0.0024788
5.11	165.67	2.21924	.006036	6.05	424.11	2.62748	.0023579
5.12	167.34	2.22359	.005976	6.10	445.86	2.64920	.0022429
5.13	169.02	2.22793	.005917	6.15	468.72	2.67091	.0021335
5.14	170.72	2.23227	.005858	6.20	492.75	2.69263	.0020294
5.15	172.43	2.23662	0.005799	**6.25**	518.01	2.71434	0.0019305
5.16	174.16	2.24096	.005742	6.30	544.57	2.73606	.0018363
5.17	175.91	2.24530	.005685	6.35	572.49	2.75777	.0017467
5.18	177.68	2.24965	.005628	6.40	601.85	2.77948	.0016616
5.19	179.47	2.25399	.005572	6.45	632.70	2.80120	.0015805
5.20	181.27	2.25833	0.005517	**6.50**	665.14	2.82291	0.0015034
5.21	183.09	2.26267	.005462	6.55	699.24	2.84463	.0014301
5.22	184.93	2.26702	.005407	6.60	735.10	2.86634	.0013604
5.23	186.79	2.27136	.005354	6.65	772.78	2.88806	.0012940
5.24	188.67	2.27570	.005300	6.70	812.41	2.90977	.0012309
5.25	190.57	2.28005	0.005248	**6.75**	854.06	2.93149	0.0011709
5.26	192.48	2.28439	.005195	6.80	897.85	2.95320	.0011138
5.27	194.42	2.28873	.005144	6.85	943.88	2.97492	.0010595
5.28	196.37	2.29307	.005092	6.90	992.27	2.99663	.0010078
5.29	198.34	2.29742	.005042	6.95	1043.1	3.01835	.0009586
5.30	200.34	2.30176	0.004992	**7.00**	1096.6	3.04006	0.0009119
5.31	202.35	2.30610	.004942	7.05	1152.9	3.06178	.0008674
5.32	204.38	2.31045	.004893	7.10	1212.0	3.08349	.0008251
5.33	206.44	2.31479	.004844	7.15	1274.1	3.10521	.0007849
5.34	208.51	2.31913	.004796	7.20	1339.4	3.12692	.0007466
5.35	210.61	2.32348	0.004748	**7.25**	1408.1	3.14863	0.0007102
5.36	212.72	2.32782	.004701	7.30	1480.3	3.17035	.0006755
5.37	214.86	2.33216	.004654	7.35	1556.2	3.19206	.0006426
5.38	217.02	2.33650	.004608	7.40	1636.0	3.21378	.0006113
5.39	219.20	2.34085	.004562	7.45	1719.9	3.23549	.0005814
5.40	221.41	2.34519	0.004517	**7.50**	1808.0	3.25721	0.0005531
5.41	223.63	2.34953	.004472	7.55	1900.7	3.27892	.0005261
5.42	225.88	2.35388	.004427	7.60	1998.2	3.30064	.0005005
5.43	228.15	2.35822	.004383	7.65	2100.6	3.32235	.0004760
5.44	230.44	2.36256	.004339	7.70	2208.3	3.34407	.0004528
5.45	232.76	2.36690	0.004296	**7.75**	2321.6	3.36578	0.0004307
5.46	235.10	2.37125	.004254	7.80	2440.6	3.38750	.0004097
5.47	237.46	2.37559	.004211	7.85	2565.7	3.40921	.0003898
5.48	239.85	2.37993	.004169	7.90	2697.3	3.43093	.0003707
5.49	242.26	2.38428	.004128	7.95	2835.6	3.45264	.0003527
5.50	244.69	2.38862	0.004087	**8.00**	2981.0	3.47436	0.0003355

x	e^x	$\mathrm{Log}_{10}(e^x)$	e^{-x}
8.00	2981.0	3.47436	0.0003355
8.05	3133.8	3.49607	.0003191
8.10	3294.5	3.51779	.0003035
8.15	3463.4	3.53950	.0002887
8.20	3641.0	3.56121	.0002747
8.25	3827.6	3.58293	0.0002613
8.30	4023.9	3.60464	.0002485
8.35	4230.2	3.62636	.0002364
8.40	4447.1	3.64807	.0002249
8.45	4675.1	3.66979	.0002139
8.50	4914.8	3.69150	0.0002035
8.55	5166.8	3.71322	.0001935
8.60	5431.7	3.73493	.0001841
8.65	5710.1	3.75665	.0001751
8.70	6002.9	3.77836	.0001666
8.75	6310.7	3.80008	0.0001585
8.80	6634.2	3.82179	.0001507
8.85	6974.4	3.84351	.0001434
8.90	7332.0	3.86522	.0001364
8.95	7707.9	3.88694	.0001297
9.00	8103.1	3.90865	0.0001234
9.05	8518.5	3.93037	.0001174
9.10	8955.3	3.95208	.0001117
9.15	9414.4	3.97379	.0001062
9.20	9897.1	3.99551	.0001010
9.25	10405	4.01722	0.0000961
9.30	10938	4.03894	.0000914
9.35	11499	4.06065	.0000870
9.40	12088	4.08237	.0000827
9.45	12708	4.10408	.0000787
9.50	13360	4.12580	0.0000749
9.55	14045	4.14751	.0000712
9.60	14765	4.16923	.0000677
9.65	15522	4.19094	.0000644
9.70	16318	4.21266	.0000613
9.75	17154	4.23437	0.0000583
9.80	18034	4.25609	.0000555
9.85	18958	4.27780	.0000527
9.90	19930	4.29952	.0000502
9.95	20952	4.32123	0.0000477
10.00	22026	4.34294	0.0000454

HYPERBOLIC FUNCTIONS AND THEIR COMMON LOGARITHMS

The logarithms given below show the mantissa only. The proper characteristic must be added.

x	Sinh x Value	$\log_{10}$	Cosh x Value	$\log_{10}$	Tanh x Value	$\log_{10}$	Coth x Value	$\log_{10}$
0.00	0.00000	$-\infty$	1.00000	.00000	0.00000	$-\infty$	∞	∞
0.01	.01000	.00001	1.00005	.00002	.01000	.99999	100.003	.00001
0.02	.02000	.30106	1.00020	.00009	.02000	.30097	50.007	.69903
0.03	.03000	.47719	1.00045	.00020	.02999	.47699	33.343	.52301
0.04	.04001	.60218	1.00080	.00035	.03998	.60183	25.013	.39817
0.05	0.05002	.69915	1.00125	.00054	0.04996	.69861	20.017	.30139
0.06	.06004	.77841	1.00180	.00078	.05993	.77763	16.687	.22237
0.07	.07006	.84545	1.00245	.00106	.06989	.84439	14.309	.15561
0.08	.08009	.90355	1.00320	.00139	.07983	.90216	12.527	.09784
0.09	.09012	.95483	1.00405	.00176	.08976	.95307	11.141	.04693
0.10	0.10017	.00072	1.00500	.00217	0.09967	.99856	10.0333	.00144
0.11	.11022	.04227	1.00606	.00262	.10956	.03965	9.1275	.96035
0.12	.12029	.08022	1.00721	.00312	.11943	.07710	8.3733	.92290
0.13	.13037	.11517	1.00846	.00366	.12927	.11151	7.7356	.88849
0.14	.14046	.14755	1.00982	.00424	.13909	.14330	7.1895	.85670
0.15	0.15056	.17772	1.01127	.00487	0.14889	.17285	6.7166	.82715
0.16	.16068	.20597	1.01283	.00554	.15865	.20044	6.3032	.79956
0.17	.17082	.23254	1.01448	.00625	.16838	.22629	5.9389	.77371
0.18	.18097	.25762	1.01624	.00700	.17808	.25062	5.6154	.74938
0.19	.19115	.28136	1.01810	.00779	.18775	.27357	5.3263	.72643
0.20	0.20134	.30392	1.02007	.00863	0.19738	.29529	5.0665	.70471
0.21	.21155	.32541	1.02213	.00951	.20697	.31590	4.8317	.68410
0.22	.22178	.34592	1.02430	.01043	.21652	.33549	4.6186	.66451
0.23	.23203	.36555	1.02657	.01139	.22603	.35416	4.4242	.64584
0.24	.24231	.38437	1.02894	.01239	.23550	.37198	4.2464	.62802
0.25	0.25261	.40245	1.03141	.01343	0.24492	.38902	4.0830	.61098
0.26	.26294	.41986	1.03399	.01452	.25430	.40534	3.9324	.59466
0.27	.27329	.43663	1.03667	.01564	.26362	.42099	3.7933	.57901
0.28	.28367	.45282	1.03946	.01681	.27291	.43601	3.6643	.56399
0.29	.29408	.46847	1.04235	.01801	.28213	.45046	3.5444	.54954
0.30	0.30452	.48362	1.04534	.01926	0.29131	.46436	3.4327	.53564
0.31	.31499	.49830	1.04844	.02054	.30044	.47775	3.3285	.52225
0.32	.32549	.51254	1.05164	.02187	.30951	.49067	3.2309	.50933
0.33	.33602	.52637	1.05495	.02323	.31852	.50314	3.1395	.49686
0.34	.34659	.53981	1.05836	.02463	.32748	.51518	3.0536	.48482
0.35	0.35719	.55290	1.06188	.02607	0.33638	.52682	2.9729	.47318
0.36	.36783	.56564	1.06550	.02755	.34521	.53809	2.8968	.46191
0.37	.37850	.57807	1.06923	.02907	.35399	.54899	2.8249	.45101
0.38	.38921	.59019	1.07307	.03063	.36271	.55956	2.7570	.44044
0.39	.39996	.60202	1.07702	.03222	.37136	.56980	2.6928	.43020
0.40	0.41075	.61358	1.08107	.03385	0.37995	.57973	2.6319	.42027
0.41	.42158	.62488	1.08523	.03552	.38847	.58936	2.5742	.41064
0.42	.43246	.63594	1.08950	.03723	.39693	.59871	2.5193	.40129
0.43	.44337	.64677	1.09388	.03897	.40532	.60780	2.4672	.39220
0.44	.45434	.65738	1.09837	.04075	.41364	.61663	2.4175	.38337
0.45	0.46534	.66777	1.10297	.04256	0.42190	.62521	2.3702	.37479
0.46	.47640	.67797	1.10768	.04441	.43008	.63355	2.3251	.36645
0.47	.48750	.68797	1.11250	.04630	.43820	.64167	2.2821	.35833
0.48	.49865	.69779	1.11743	.04822	.44624	.64957	2.2409	.35043
0.49	.50984	.70744	1.12247	.05018	.45422	.65726	2.2016	.34274

x	Sinh x		Cosh x		Tanh x		Coth x	
	Value	$\log_{10}$	Value	$\log_{10}$	Value	$\log_{10}$	Value	$\log_{10}$
0.50	0.52110	.71692	1.12763	.05217	0.46212	.66475	2.1640	.33525
0.51	.53240	.72624	1.13289	.05419	.46995	.67205	2.1279	.32795
0.52	.54375	.73540	1.13827	.05625	.47770	.67916	2.0934	.32084
0.53	.55516	.74442	1.14377	.05834	.48538	.68608	2.0602	.31392
0.54	.56663	.75330	1.14938	.06046	.49299	.69284	2.0284	.30716
0.55	0.57815	.76204	1.15510	.06262	0.50052	.69942	1.9979	.30058
0.56	.58973	.77065	1.16094	.06481	.50798	.70584	1.9686	.29416
0.57	.60137	.77914	1.16690	.06703	.51536	.71211	1.9404	.28789
0.58	.61307	.78751	1.17297	.06929	.52267	.71822	1.9133	.28178
0.59	.62483	.79576	1.17916	.07157	.52990	.72419	1.8872	.27581
0.60	0.63665	.80390	1.18547	.07389	0.53705	.73001	1.8620	.26999
0.61	.64854	.81194	1.19189	.07624	.54413	.73570	1.8378	.26430
0.62	.66049	.81987	1.19844	.07861	.55113	.74125	1.8145	.25875
0.63	.67251	.82770	1.20510	.08102	.55805	.74667	1.7919	.25333
0.64	.68459	.83543	1.21189	.08346	.56490	.75197	1.7702	.24803
0.65	0.69675	.84308	1.21879	.08593	0.57167	.75715	1.7493	.24285
0.66	.70897	.85063	1.22582	.08843	.57836	.76220	1.7290	.23780
0.67	.72126	.85809	1.23297	.09095	.58498	.76714	1.7095	.23286
0.68	.73363	.86548	1.24025	.09351	.59152	.77197	1.6906	.22803
0.69	.74607	.87278	1.24765	.09609	.59798	.77669	1.6723	.22331
0.70	0.75858	.88000	1.25517	.09870	0.60437	.78130	1.6546	.21870
0.71	.77117	.88715	1.26282	.10134	.61068	.78581	1.6375	.21419
0.72	.78384	.89423	1.27059	.10401	.61691	.79022	1.6210	.20978
0.73	.79659	.90123	1.27849	.10670	.62307	.79453	1.6050	.20547
0.74	.80941	.90817	1.28652	.10942	.62915	.79875	1.5895	.20125
0.75	0.82232	.91504	1.29468	.11216	0.63515	.80288	1.5744	.19712
0.76	.83530	.92185	1.30297	.11493	.64108	.80691	1.5599	.19309
0.77	.84838	.92859	1.31139	.11773	.64693	.81086	1.5458	.18914
0.78	.86153	.93527	1.31994	.12055	.65271	.81472	1.5321	.18528
0.79	.87478	.94190	1.32862	.12340	.65841	.81850	1.5188	.18150
0.80	0.88811	.94846	1.33743	.12627	0.66404	.82219	1.5059	.17781
0.81	.90152	.95498	1.34638	.12917	.66959	.82581	1.4935	.17419
0.82	.91503	.96144	1.35547	.13209	.67507	.82935	1.4813	.17065
0.83	.92863	.96784	1.36468	.13503	.68048	.83281	1.4696	.16719
0.84	.94233	.97420	1.37404	.13800	.68581	.83620	1.4581	.16380
0.85	0.95612	.98051	1.38353	.14099	0.69107	.83952	1.4470	.16048
0.86	.97000	.98677	1.39316	.14400	.69626	.84277	1.4362	.15723
0.87	.98398	.99299	1.40293	.14704	.70137	.84595	1.4258	.15405
0.88	.99806	.99916	1.41284	.15009	.70642	.84906	1.4156	.15094
0.89	1.01224	.00528	1.42289	.15317	.71139	.85211	1.4057	.14789
0.90	1.02652	.01137	1.43309	.15627	0.71630	.85509	1.3961	.14491
0.91	1.04090	.01741	1.44342	.15939	.72113	.85801	1.3867	.14199
0.92	1.05539	.02341	1.45390	.16254	.72590	.86088	1.3776	.13912
0.93	1.06998	.02937	1.46453	.16570	.73059	.86368	1.3687	.13632
0.94	1.08468	.03530	1.47530	.16888	.73522	.86642	1.3601	.13358
0.95	1.09948	.04119	1.48623	.17208	0.73978	.86910	1.3517	.13090
0.96	1.11440	.04704	1.49729	.17531	.74428	.87173	1.3436	.12827
0.97	1.12943	.05286	1.50851	.17855	.74870	.87431	1.3356	.12569
0.98	1.14457	.05864	1.51988	.18181	.75307	.87683	1.3279	.12317
0.99	1.15983	.06439	1.53141	.18509	.75736	.87930	1.3204	.12070

x	Sinh x Value	Sinh x log₁₀	Cosh x Value	Cosh x log₁₀	Tanh x Value	Tanh x log₁₀	Coth x Value	Coth x log₁₀
1.00	1.17520	.07011	1.54308	.18839	0.76159	.88172	1.3130	.11828
1.01	1.19069	.07580	1.55491	.19171	.76576	.88409	1.3059	.11591
1.02	1.20630	.08146	1.56689	.19504	.76987	.88642	1.2989	.11358
1.03	1.22203	.08708	1.57904	.19839	.77391	.88869	1.2921	.11131
1.04	1.23788	.09268	1.59134	.20176	.77789	.89092	1.2855	.10908
1.05	1.25386	.09825	1.60379	.20515	0.78181	.89310	1.2791	.10690
1.06	1.26996	.10379	1.61641	.20855	.78566	.89524	1.2728	.10476
1.07	1.28619	.10930	1.62919	.21197	.78946	.89733	1.2667	.10267
1.08	1.30254	.11479	1.64214	.21541	.79320	.89938	1.2607	.10062
1.09	1.31903	.12025	1.65525	.21886	.79688	.90139	1.2549	.09861
1.10	1.33565	.12569	1.66852	.22233	0.80050	.90336	1.2492	.09664
1.11	1.35240	.13111	1.68196	.22582	.80406	.90529	1.2437	.09471
1.12	1.36929	.13649	1.69557	.22931	.80757	.90718	1.2383	.09282
1.13	1.38631	.14186	1.70934	.23283	.81102	.90903	1.2330	.09097
1.14	1.40347	.14720	1.72329	.23636	.81441	.91085	1.2279	.08915
1.15	1.42078	.15253	1.73741	.23990	0.81775	.91262	1.2229	.08738
1.16	1.43822	.15783	1.75171	.24346	.82104	.91436	1.2180	.08564
1.17	1.45581	.16311	1.76618	.24703	.82427	.91607	1.2132	.08393
1.18	1.47355	.16836	1.78083	.25062	.82745	.91774	1.2085	.08226
1.19	1.49143	.17360	1.79565	.25422	.83058	.91938	1.2040	.08062
1.20	1.50946	.17882	1.81066	.25784	0.83365	.92099	1.1995	.07901
1.21	1.52764	.18402	1.82584	.26146	.83668	.92256	1.1952	.07744
1.22	1.54598	.18920	1.84121	.26510	.83965	.92410	1.1910	.07590
1.23	1.56447	.19437	1.85676	.26876	.84258	.92561	1.1868	.07439
1.24	1.58311	.19951	1.87250	.27242	.84546	.92709	1.1828	.07291
1.25	1.60192	.20464	1.88842	.27610	0.84828	.92854	1.1789	.07146
1.26	1.62088	.20975	1.90454	.27979	.85106	.92996	1.1750	.07004
1.27	1.64001	.21485	1.92084	.28349	.85380	.93135	1.1712	.06865
1.28	1.65930	.21993	1.93734	.28721	.85648	.93272	1.1676	.06728
1.29	1.67876	.22499	1.95403	.29093	.85913	.93406	1.1640	.06594
1.30	1.69838	.23004	1.97091	.29467	0.86172	.93537	1.1605	.06463
1.31	1.71818	.23507	1.98800	.29842	.86428	.93665	1.1570	.06335
1.32	1.73814	.24009	2.00528	.30217	.86678	.93791	1.1537	.06209
1.33	1.75828	.24509	2.02276	.30594	.86925	.93914	1.1504	.06086
1.34	1.77860	.25008	2.04044	.30972	.87167	.94035	1.1472	.05965
1.35	1.79909	.25505	2.05833	.31352	0.87405	.94154	1.1441	.05846
1.36	1.81977	.26002	2.07643	.31732	.87639	.94270	1.1410	.05730
1.37	1.84062	.26496	2.09473	.32113	.87869	.94384	1.1381	.05616
1.38	1.86166	.26990	2.11324	.32495	.88095	.94495	1.1351	.05505
1.39	1.88289	.27482	2.13196	.32878	.88317	.94604	1.1323	.05396
1.40	1.90430	.27974	2.15090	.33262	0.88535	.94712	1.1295	.05288
1.41	1.92591	.28464	2.17005	.33647	.88749	.94817	1.1268	.05183
1.42	1.94770	.28952	2.18942	.34033	.88960	.94919	1.1241	.05081
1.43	1.96970	.29440	2.20900	.34420	.89167	.95020	1.1215	.04980
1.44	1.99188	.29926	2.22881	.34807	.89370	.95119	1.1189	.04881
1.45	2.01427	.30412	2.24884	.35196	0.89569	.95216	1.1165	.04784
1.46	2.03686	.30896	2.26910	.35585	.89765	.95311	1.1140	.04689
1.47	2.05965	.31379	2.28958	.35976	.89958	.95404	1.1116	.04596
1.48	2.08265	.31862	2.31029	.36367	.90147	.95495	1.1093	.04505
1.49	2.10586	.32343	2.33123	.36759	.90332	.95584	1.1070	.04416

x	Sinh x Value	Sinh x $\log_{10}$	Cosh x Value	Cosh x $\log_{10}$	Tanh x Value	Tanh x $\log_{10}$	Coth x Value	Coth x $\log_{10}$
1.50	2.12928	.32823	2.35241	.37151	0.90515	.95672	1.1048	.04328
1.51	2.15291	.33303	2.37382	.37545	.90694	.95758	1.1026	.04242
1.52	2.17676	.33781	2.39547	.37939	.90870	.95842	1.1005	.04158
1.53	2.20082	.34258	2.41736	.38334	.91042	.95924	1.0984	.04076
1.54	2.22510	.34735	2.43949	.38730	.91212	.96005	1.0963	.03995
1.55	2.24961	.35211	2.46186	.39126	0.91379	.96084	1.0943	.03916
1.56	2.27434	.35686	2.48448	.39524	.91542	.96162	1.0924	.03838
1.57	2.29930	.36160	2.50735	.39921	.91703	.96238	1.0905	.03762
1.58	2.32449	.36633	2.53047	.40320	.91860	.96313	1.0886	.03687
1.59	2.34991	.37105	2.55384	.40719	.92015	.96386	1.0868	.03614
1.60	2.37557	.37577	2.57746	.41110	0.92167	.96457	1.0850	.03543
1.61	2.40146	.38048	2.60135	.41520	.92316	.96528	1.0832	.03472
1.62	2.42760	.38518	2.62549	.41921	.92462	.96597	1.0815	.03403
1.63	2.45397	.38987	2.64990	.42323	.92606	.96664	1.0798	.03336
1.64	2.48059	.39456	2.67457	.42725	.92747	.96730	1.0782	.03270
1.65	2.50746	.39923	2.69951	.43129	0.92886	.96795	1.0766	.03205
1.66	2.53459	.40391	2.72472	.43532	.93022	.96858	1.0750	.03142
1.67	2.56196	.40857	2.75021	.43937	.93155	.96921	1.0735	.03079
1.68	2.58959	.41323	2.77596	.44341	.93286	.96982	1.0720	.03018
1.69	2.61748	.41788	2.80200	.44747	.93415	.97042	1.0705	.02958
1.70	2.64563	.42253	2.82832	.45153	.93541	.97100	1.0691	.02900
1.71	2.67405	.42717	2.85491	.45559	.93665	.97158	1.0676	.02842
1.72	2.70273	.43180	2.88180	.45966	.93786	.97214	1.0663	.02786
1.73	2.73168	.43643	2.90897	.46374	.93906	.97269	1.0649	.02731
1.74	2.76091	.44105	2.93643	.46782	.94023	.97323	1.0636	.02677
1.75	2.79041	.44567	2.96419	.47191	0.94138	.97376	1.0623	.02624
1.76	2.82020	.45028	2.99224	.47600	.94250	.97428	1.0610	.02572
1.77	2.85026	.45488	3.02059	.48009	.94361	.97479	1.0598	.02521
1.78	2.88061	.45948	3.04925	.48419	.94470	.07529	1.0585	.02471
1.79	2.91125	.46408	3.07821	.48830	.94576	.97578	1.0574	.02422
1.80	2.94217	.46867	3.10747	.49241	0.94681	.97626	1.0562	.02374
1.81	2.97340	.47325	3.13705	.49652	.94783	.97673	1.0550	.02327
1.82	3.00492	.47783	3.16694	.50064	.94884	.97719	1.0539	.02281
1.83	3.03674	.48241	3.19715	.50476	.94983	.97764	1.0528	.02236
1.84	3.06886	.48698	3.22768	.50889	.95080	.97809	1.0518	.02191
1.85	3.10129	.49154	3.25853	.51302	0.95175	.97852	1.0507	.02148
1.86	3.13403	.49610	3.28970	.51716	.95268	.97895	1.0497	.02105
1.87	3.16709	.50066	3.32121	.52130	.95359	.97936	1.0487	.02064
1.88	3.20046	.50521	3.35305	.52544	.95449	.97977	1.0477	.02023
1.89	3.23415	.50976	3.38522	.52959	.95537	.98017	1.0467	.01983
1.90	3.26816	.51430	3.41773	.53374	0.95624	.98057	1.0458	.01943
1.91	3.30250	.51884	3.45058	.53789	.95709	.98095	1.0448	.01905
1.92	3.33718	.52338	3.48378	.54205	.95792	.98133	1.0439	.01867
1.93	3.37218	.52791	3.51733	.54621	.95873	.98170	1.0430	.01830
1.94	3.40752	.53244	3.55123	.55038	.95953	.98206	1.0422	.01794
1.95	3.44321	.53696	3.58548	.55455	0.96032	.98242	1.0413	.01758
1.96	3.47923	.54148	3.62009	.55872	.96109	.98276	1.0405	.01724
1.97	3.51561	.54600	3.65507	.56290	.96185	.98311	1.0397	.01689
1.98	3.55234	.55051	3.69041	.56707	.96259	.98344	1.0389	.01656
1.99	3.58942	.55502	3.72611	.57126	.96331	.98377	1.0381	.01623

x	Sinh x Value	Sinh x $\log_{10}$	Cosh x Value	Cosh x $\log_{10}$	Tanh x Value	Tanh x $\log_{10}$	Coth x Value	Coth x $\log_{10}$
2.00	3.62686	.55953	3.76220	.57544	0.96403	.98409	1.0373	.01591
2.01	3.66466	.56403	3.79865	.57963	.96473	.98440	1.0366	.01560
2.02	3.70283	.56853	3.83549	.58382	.96541	.98471	1.0358	.01529
2.03	3.74138	.57303	3.87271	.58802	.96609	.98502	1.0351	.01498
2.04	3.78029	.57753	3.91032	.59221	.96675	.98531	1.0344	.01469
2.05	3.81958	.58202	3.94832	.59641	0.96740	.98560	1.0337	.01440
2.06	3.85926	.58650	3.98671	.60061	.96803	.98589	1.0330	.01411
2.07	3.89932	.59099	4.02550	.60482	.96865	.98617	1.0324	.01383
2.08	3.93977	.59547	4.06470	.60903	.96926	.98644	1.0317	.01356
2.09	3.98061	.59995	4.10430	.61324	.96986	.98671	1.0311	.01329
2.10	4.02186	.60443	4.14431	.61745	0.97045	.98697	1.0304	.01303
2.11	4.06350	.60890	4.18474	.62167	.97103	.98723	1.0298	.01277
2.12	4.10555	.61337	4.22558	.62589	.97159	.98748	1.0292	.01252
2.13	4.14801	.61784	4.26685	.63011	.97215	.98773	1.0286	.01227
2.14	4.19089	.62231	4.30855	.63433	.97269	.98798	1.0281	.01202
2.15	4.23419	.62677	4.35067	.63856	0.97323	.98821	1.0275	.01179
2.16	4.27791	.63123	4.39323	.64278	.97375	.98845	1.0270	.01155
2.17	4.32205	.63569	4.43623	.64701	.97426	.98868	1.0264	.01132
2.18	4.36663	.64015	4.47967	.65125	.97477	.98890	1.0259	.01110
2.19	4.41165	.64460	4.52356	.65548	.97526	.98912	1.0254	.01088
2.20	4.45711	.64905	4.56791	.65972	0.97574	.98934	1.0249	.01066
2.21	4.50301	.65350	4.61271	.66396	.97622	.98955	1.0244	.01045
2.22	4.54936	.65795	4.65797	.66820	.97668	.98975	1.0239	.01025
2.23	4.59617	.66240	4.70370	.67244	.97714	.98996	1.0234	.01004
2.24	4.64344	.66684	4.74989	.67668	.97759	.99016	1.0229	.00984
2.25	4.69117	.67128	4.79657	.68093	0.97803	.99035	1.0225	.00965
2.26	4.73937	.67572	4.84372	.68518	.97846	.99054	1.0220	.00946
2.27	4.78804	.68016	4.89136	.68943	.97888	.99073	1.0216	.00927
2.28	4.83720	.68459	4.93948	.69368	.97929	.99091	1.0211	.00909
2.29	4.88684	.68903	4.98810	.69794	.97970	.99109	1.0207	.00891
2.30	4.93696	.69346	5.03722	.70219	0.98010	.99127	1.0203	.00873
2.31	4.98758	.69789	5.08684	.70645	.98049	.99144	1.0199	.00856
2.32	5.03870	.70232	5.13697	.71071	.98087	.99161	1.0195	00839
2.33	5.09032	.70675	5.18762	.71497	.98124	.99178	1.0191	.00822
2.34	5.14245	.71117	5.23878	.71923	.98161	.99194	1.0187	.00806
2.35	5.19510	.71559	5.29047	.72349	0.98197	.99210	1.0184	.00790
2.36	5.24827	.72002	5.34269	.72776	.98233	.99226	1.0180	.00774
2.37	5.30196	.72444	5.39544	.73203	.98267	.99241	1.0176	.00759
2.38	5.35618	.72885	5.44873	.73630	.98301	.99256	1.0173	.00744
2.39	5.41093	.73327	5.50256	.74056	.98335	.99271	1.0169	.00729
2.40	5.46623	.73769	5.55695	.74484	0.98367	.99285	1.0166	.00715
2.41	5.52207	.74210	5.61189	.74911	.98400	.99299	1.0163	.00701
2.42	5.57847	.74652	5.66739	.75338	.98431	.99313	1.0159	.00687
2.43	5.63542	.75093	5.72346	.75766	.98462	.99327	1.0156	.00673
2.44	5.69294	.75534	5.78010	.76194	.98492	.99340	1.0153	.00660
2.45	5.75103	.75975	5.83732	.76621	0.98522	.99353	1.0150	.00647
2.46	5.80969	.75415	5.89512	.77049	.98551	.99366	1.0147	.00634
2.47	5.86893	.76856	5.95352	.77477	.98579	.99379	1.0144	.00621
2.48	5.92876	.77296	6.01250	.77906	.98607	.99391	1.0141	.00609
2.49	5.98918	.77737	6.07209	.78334	.98635	.99403	1.0138	.00597

x	Sinh x Value	Sinh x log$_{10}$	Cosh x Value	Cosh x log$_{10}$	Tanh x Value	Tanh x log$_{10}$	Coth x Value	Coth x log$_{10}$
2.50	6.05020	.78177	6.13229	.78762	0.98661	.99415	1.0136	.00585
2.51	6.11183	.78617	6.19310	.79191	.98688	.99426	1.0133	.00574
2.52	6.17407	.79057	6.25453	.79619	.98714	.99438	1.0130	.00562
2.53	6.23692	.79497	6.31658	.80048	.98739	.99449	1.0128	.00551
2.54	6.30040	.79937	6.37927	.80477	.98764	.99460	1.0125	.00540
2.55	6.36451	.80377	6.44259	.80906	0.98788	.99470	1.0123	.00530
2.56	6.42926	.80816	6.50656	.81335	.98812	.99481	1.0120	.00519
2.57	6.49464	.81256	6.57118	.81764	.98835	.99491	1.0118	.00509
2.58	6.56068	.81695	6.63646	.82194	.98858	.99501	1.0115	.00499
2.59	6.62738	.82134	6.70240	.82623	.98881	.99511	1.0113	.00489
2.60	6.69473	.82573	6.76901	.83052	0.98903	.99521	1.0111	.00479
2.61	6.76276	.83012	6.83629	.83482	.98924	.99530	1.0109	.00470
2.62	6.83146	.83451	6.90426	.83912	.98946	.99540	1.0107	.00460
2.63	6.90085	.83890	6.97292	.84341	.98966	.99549	1.0104	.00451
2.64	6.97092	.84329	7.04228	.84771	.98987	.99558	1.0102	.00442
2.65	7.04169	.84768	7.11234	.85201	0.99007	.99566	1.0100	.00434
2.66	7.11317	.85206	7.18312	.85631	.99026	.99575	1.0098	.00425
2.67	7.18536	.85645	7.25461	.86061	.99045	.99583	1.0096	.00417
2.68	7.25827	.86083	7.32683	.86492	.99064	.99592	1.0094	.00408
2.69	7.33190	.86522	7.39978	.86922	.99083	.99600	1.0093	.00400
2.70	7.40626	.86960	7.47347	.87352	0.99101	.99608	1.0091	.00392
2.71	7.48137	.87398	7.54791	.87783	.99118	.99615	1.0089	.00385
2.72	7.55722	.87836	7.62310	.88213	.99136	.99623	1.0087	.00377
2.73	7.63383	.88274	7.69905	.88644	.99153	.99631	1.0085	.00369
2.74	7.71121	.88712	7.77578	.89074	.99170	.99638	1.0084	.00362
2.75	7.78935	.89150	7.85328	.89505	0.99186	.99645	1.0082	.00355
2.76	7.86828	.89588	7.93157	.89936	.99202	.99652	1.0080	.00348
2.77	7.94799	.90026	8.01065	.90367	.99218	.99659	1.0079	.00341
2.78	8.02849	.90463	8.09053	.90798	.99233	.99666	1.0077	.00334
2.79	8.10980	.90901	8.17122	.91229	.99248	.99672	1.0076	.00328
2.80	8.19192	.91339	8.25273	.91660	0.99263	.99679	1.0074	.00321
2.81	8.27486	.91776	8.33506	.92091	.99278	.99685	1.0073	.00315
2.82	8.35862	.92213	8.41823	.92522	.99292	.99691	1.0071	.00309
2.83	8.44322	.92651	8.50224	.92953	.99306	.99698	1.0070	.00302
2.84	8.52867	.93088	8.58710	.93385	.99320	.99704	1.0069	.00296
2.85	8.61497	.93525	8.67281	.93816	0.99333	.99709	1.0067	.00291
2.86	8.70213	.93963	8.75940	.94247	.99346	.99715	1.0066	.00285
2.87	8.79016	.94400	8.84686	.94679	.99359	.99721	1.0065	.00279
2.88	8.87907	.94837	8.93520	.95110	.99372	.99726	1.0063	.00274
2.89	8.96887	.95274	9.02444	.95542	.99384	.99732	1.0062	.00268
2.90	9.05956	.95711	9.11458	.95974	0.99396	.99737	1.0061	.00263
2.91	9.15116	.96148	9.20564	.96405	.99408	.99742	1.0060	.00258
2.92	9.24368	.96584	9.29761	.96837	.99420	.99747	1.0058	.00253
2.93	9.33712	.97021	9.39051	.97269	.99431	.99752	1.0057	.00248
2.94	9.43149	.97458	9.48436	.97701	.99443	.99757	1.0056	.00243
2.95	9.52681	.97895	9.57915	.98133	0.99454	.99762	1.0055	.00238
2.96	9.62308	.98331	9.67490	.98565	.99464	.99767	1.0054	.00233
2.97	9.72031	.98768	9.77161	.98997	.99475	.99771	1.0053	.00229
2.98	9.81851	.99205	9.86930	.99429	.99485	.99776	1.0052	.00224
2.99	9.91770	.99641	9.96798	.99861	.99496	.99780	1.0051	.00220

x	Sinh x Value	Sinh x $\log_{10}$	Cosh x Value	Cosh x $\log_{10}$	Tanh x Value	Tanh x $\log_{10}$	Coth x Value	Coth x $\log_{10}$
3.0	10.0179	.00078	10.0677	.00293	0.99505	.99785	1.0050	.00215
3.1	11.0765	.04440	11.1215	.04616	.99595	.99824	1.0041	.00176
3.2	12.2459	.08799	12.2866	.08943	.99668	.99856	1.0033	.00144
3.3	13.5379	.13155	13.5748	.13273	.99728	.99882	1.0027	.00118
3.4	14.9654	.17509	14.9987	.17605	.99777	.99903	1.0022	.00097
3.5	16.5426	.21860	16.5728	.21940	0.99818	.99921	1.0018	.00079
3.6	18.2855	.26211	18.3128	.26275	.99851	.99935	1.0015	.00065
3.7	20.2113	.30559	20.2360	.30612	.99878	.99947	1.0012	.00053
3.8	22.3394	.34907	22.3618	.34951	.99900	.99957	1.0010	.00043
3.9	24.6911	.39254	24.7113	.39290	.99918	.99964	1.0008	.00036
4.0	27.2899	.43600	27.3082	.43629	0.99933	.99971	1.0007	.00029
4.1	30.1619	.47946	30.1784	.47970	.99945	.99976	1.0005	.00024
4.2	33.3357	.52291	33.3507	.52310	.99955	.99980	1.0004	.00020
4.3	36.8431	.56636	36.8567	.56652	.99963	.99984	1.0004	.00016
4.4	40.7193	.60980	40.7316	.60993	.99970	.99987	1.0003	.00013
4.5	45.0030	.65324	45.0141	.65335	0.99975	.99989	1.0002	.00011
4.6	49.7371	.69668	49.7472	.69677	.99980	.99991	1.0002	.00009
4.7	54.9690	.74012	54.9781	.74019	.99983	.99993	1.0002	.00007
4.8	60.7511	.78355	60.7593	.78361	.99986	.99994	1.0001	.00006
4.9	67.1412	.82699	67.1486	.82704	.99989	.99995	1.0001	.00005
5.0	74.2032	.87042	74.2099	.87046	0.99991	.99996	1.0001	.00004
5.1	82.008	.91386	82.014	.91389	.99993	.99997	1.0001	.00003
5.2	90.633	.95729	90.639	.95731	.99994	.99997	1.0001	.00003
5.3	100.17	.00072	100.17	.00074	.99995	.99998	1.0000	.00002
5.4	110.70	.04415	110.71	.04417	.99996	.99998	1.0000	.00002
5.5	122.34	.08758	122.35	.08760	0.99997	.99999	1.0000	.00001
5.6	135.21	.13101	135.22	.13103	.99997	.99999	1.0000	.00001
5.7	149.43	.17444	149.44	.17445	.99998	.99999	1.0000	.00001
5.8	165.15	.21787	165.15	.21788	.99998	.99999	1.0000	.00001
5.9	182.52	.26130	182.52	.26131	.99998	.99999	1.0000	.00001
6.0	201.71	.30473	201.72	.30474	0.99999	.00000	1.0000	.00000
6.1	222.93	.34817	222.93	.34817	.99999	.00000	1.0000	.00000
6.2	246.37	.39159	246.38	.39161	.99999	.00000	1.0000	.00000
6.3	272.29	.43503	272.29	.43503	.99999	.00000	1.0000	.00000
6.4	300.92	.47845	300.92	.47845	.99999	.00000	1.0000	.00000
6.5	332.57	.52188	332.57	.52188	1.0000	.00000	1.0000	.00000
6.6	367.55	.56532	367.55	.56532	1.0000	.00000	1.0000	.00000
6.7	406.20	.60874	406.20	.60874	1.0000	.00000	1.0000	.00000
6.8	448.92	.65217	448.92	.65217	1.0000	.00000	1.0000	.00000
6.9	496.14	.69560	496.14	.69560	1.0000	.00000	1.0000	.00000
7.0	548.32	.73903	548.32	.73903	1.0000	.00000	1.0000	.00000
7.1	605.98	.78246	605.98	.78246	1.0000	.00000	1.0000	.00000
7.2	669.72	.82589	669.72	.82589	1.0000	.00000	1.0000	.00000
7.3	740.15	.86932	740.15	.86932	1.0000	.00000	1.0000	.00000
7.4	817.99	.91275	817.99	.91275	1.0000	.00000	1.0000	.00000
7.5	904.02	.95618	904.02	.95618	1.0000	.00000	1.0000	.00000
7.6	999.10	.99961	999.10	.99961	1.0000	.00000	1.0000	.00000
7.7	1104.2	.04305	1104.2	.04305	1.0000	.00000	1.0000	.00000
7.8	1220.3	.08647	1220.3	.08647	1.0000	.00000	1.0000	.00000
7.9	1348.6	.12988	1348.6	.12988	1.0000	.00000	1.0000	.00000

x	Sinh x		Cosh x		Tanh x		Coth x	
	Value	$\log_{10}$	Value	$\log_{10}$	Value	$\log_{10}$	Value	$\log_{10}$
8.0	1490.5	.17333	1490.5	.17333	1.0000	.00000	1.0000	.00000
8.1	1647.2	.21675	1647.2	.21675	1.0000	.00000	1.0000	.00000
8.2	1820.5	.26019	1820.5	.26019	1.0000	.00000	1.0000	.00000
8.3	2011.9	.30360	2011.9	.30360	1.0000	.00000	1.0000	.00000
8.4	2223.5	.34704	2223.5	.34704	1.0000	.00000	1.0000	.00000
8.5	2457.4	.39048	2457.4	.39048	1.0000	.00000	1.0000	.00000
8.6	2715.8	.43390	2715.8	.43390	1.0000	.00000	1.0000	.00000
8.7	3001.5	.47734	3001.5	.47734	1.0000	.00000	1.0000	.00000
8.8	3317.1	.52076	3317.1	.52076	1.0000	.00000	1.0000	.00000
8.9	3666.0	.56419	3666.0	.56419	1.0000	.00000	1.0000	.00000
9.0	4051.5	.60762	4051.5	.60762	1.0000	.00000	1.0000	.00000
9.1	4477.6	.65105	4477.6	.65105	1.0000	.00000	1.0000	.00000
9.2	4948.6	.69448	4948.6	.69448	1.0000	.00000	1.0000	.00000
9.3	5469.0	.73791	5469.0	.73791	1.0000	.00000	1.0000	.00000
9.4	6044.2	.78134	6044.2	.78134	1.0000	.00000	1.0000	.00000
9.5	6679.9	.82477	6679.9	.82477	1.0000	.00000	1.0000	.00000
9.6	7382.4	.86820	7382.4	.86820	1.0000	.00000	1.0000	.00000
9.7	8158.8	.91163	8158.8	.91163	1.0000	.00000	1.0000	.00000
9.8	9016.9	.95506	9016.9	.95506	1.0000	.00000	1.0000	.00000
9.9	9965.2	.99849	9965.2	.99849	1.0000	.00000	1.0000	.00000
10.0	11013.2	.04191	11013.2	.04191	1.0000	.00000	1.0000	.00000

NATURAL TRIGONOMETRIC FUNCTIONS

′	Sin	Tan	Cot	Cos	Sec	Csc	′
0	.00000	.00000	———	1.0000	1.0000	———	60
1	.00029	.00029	3437.7	1.0000	1.0000	3437.7	59
2	.00058	.00058	1718.9	1.0000	1.0000	1718.9	58
3	.00087	.00087	1145.9	1.0000	1.0000	1145.9	57
4	.00116	.00116	859.44	1.0000	1.0000	859.44	56
5	.00145	.00145	687.55	1.0000	1.0000	687.55	55
6	.00175	.00175	572.96	1.0000	1.0000	572.96	54
7	.00204	.00204	491.11	1.0000	1.0000	491.11	53
8	.00233	.00233	429.72	1.0000	1.0000	429.72	52
9	.00262	.00262	381.97	1.0000	1.0000	381.97	51
10	.00291	.00291	343.77	1.0000	1.0000	343.78	50
11	.00320	.00320	312.52	.99999	1.0000	312.52	49
12	.00349	.00349	286.48	.99999	1.0000	286.48	48
13	.00378	.00378	264.44	.99999	1.0000	264.44	47
14	.00407	.00407	245.55	.99999	1.0000	245.55	46
15	.00436	.00436	229.18	.99999	1.0000	229.18	45
16	.00465	.00465	214.86	.99999	1.0000	214.86	44
17	.00495	.00495	202.22	.99999	1.0000	202.22	43
18	.00524	.00524	190.98	.99999	1.0000	190.99	42
19	.00553	.00553	180.93	.99998	1.0000	180.93	41
20	.00582	.00582	171.89	.99998	1.0000	171.89	40
21	.00611	.00611	163.70	.99998	1.0000	163.70	39
22	.00640	.00640	156.26	.99998	1.0000	156.26	38
23	.00669	.00669	149.47	.99998	1.0000	149.47	37
24	.00698	.00698	143.24	.99998	1.0000	143.24	36
25	.00727	.00727	137.51	.99997	1.0000	137.51	35
26	.00756	.00756	132.22	.99997	1.0000	132.22	34
27	.00785	.00785	127.32	.99997	1.0000	127.33	33
28	.00814	.00815	122.77	.99997	1.0000	122.78	32
29	.00844	.00844	118.54	.99996	1.0000	118.54	31
30	.00873	.00873	114.59	.99996	1.0000	114.59	30
31	.00902	.00902	110.89	.99996	1.0000	110.00	29
32	.00931	.00931	107.43	.99996	1.0000	107.43	28
33	.00960	.00960	104.17	.99995	1.0000	104.18	27
34	.00989	.00989	101.11	.99995	1.0000	101.11	26
35	.01018	.01018	98.218	.99995	1.0001	98.223	25
36	.01047	.01047	95.489	.99995	1.0001	95.495	24
37	.01076	.01076	92.908	.99994	1.0001	92.914	23
38	.01105	.01105	90.463	.99994	1.0001	90.469	22
39	.01134	.01135	88.144	.99994	1.0001	88.149	21
40	.01164	.01164	85.940	.99993	1.0001	85.946	20
41	.01193	.01193	83.844	.99993	1.0001	83.849	19
42	.01222	.01222	81.847	.99993	1.0001	81.853	18
43	.01251	.01251	79.943	.99992	1.0001	79.950	17
44	.01280	.01280	78.126	.99992	1.0001	78.133	16
45	.01309	.01309	76.390	.99991	1.0001	76.397	15
46	.01338	.01338	74.729	.99991	1.0001	74.736	14
47	.01367	.01367	73.139	.99991	1.0001	73.146	13
48	.01396	.01396	71.615	.99990	1.0001	71.622	12
49	.01425	.01425	70.153	.99990	1.0001	70.160	11
50	.01454	.01455	68.750	.99989	1.0001	68.757	10
51	.01483	.01484	67.402	.99989	1.0001	67.409	9
52	.01513	.01513	66.105	.99989	1.0001	66.113	8
53	.01542	.01542	64.858	.99988	1.0001	64.866	7
54	.01571	.01571	63.657	.99988	1.0001	63.665	6
55	.01600	.01600	62.499	.99987	1.0001	62.507	5
56	.01629	.01629	61.383	.99987	1.0001	61.391	4
57	.01658	.01658	60.306	.99986	1.0001	60.314	3
58	.01687	.01687	59.266	.99986	1.0001	59.274	2
59	.01716	.01716	58.261	.99985	1.0001	58.270	1
60	.01745	.01746	57.290	.99985	1.0002	57.299	0
′	Cos	Cot	Tan	Sin	Csc	Sec	′

′	Sin	Tan	Cot	Cos	Sec	Csc	′
0	.01745	.01746	57.290	.99985	1.0002	57.299	60
1	.01774	.01775	56.351	.99984	1.0002	56.359	59
2	.01803	.01804	55.442	.99984	1.0002	55.451	58
3	.01832	.01833	54.561	.99983	1.0002	54.570	57
4	.01862	.01862	53.709	.99983	1.0002	53.718	56
5	.01891	.01891	52.882	.99982	1.0002	52.892	55
6	.01920	.01920	52.081	.99982	1.0002	52.090	54
7	.01949	.01949	51.303	.99981	1.0002	51.313	53
8	.01978	.01978	50.549	.99980	1.0002	50.558	52
9	.02007	.02007	49.816	.99980	1.0002	49.826	51
10	.02036	.02036	49.104	.99979	1.0002	49.114	50
11	.02065	.02066	48.412	.99979	1.0002	48.422	49
12	.02094	.02095	47.740	.99978	1.0002	47.750	48
13	.02123	.02124	47.085	.99977	1.0002	47.096	47
14	.02152	.02153	46.449	.99977	1.0002	46.460	46
15	.02181	.02182	45.829	.99976	1.0002	45.840	45
16	.02211	.02211	45.226	.99976	1.0002	45.237	44
17	.02240	.02240	44.639	.99975	1.0003	44.650	43
18	.02269	.02269	44.066	.99974	1.0003	44.077	42
19	.02298	.02208	43.508	.99974	1.0003	43.520	41
20	.02327	.02328	42.964	.99973	1.0003	42.976	40
21	.02356	.02357	42.433	.99972	1.0003	42.445	39
22	.02385	.02386	41.916	.99972	1.0003	41.928	38
23	.02414	.02415	41.411	.99971	1.0003	41.423	37
24	.02443	.02444	40.917	.99970	1.0003	40.930	36
25	.02472	.02473	40.436	.99969	1.0003	40.448	35
26	.02501	.02502	39.965	.99969	1.0003	39.978	34
27	.02530	.02531	39.506	.99968	1.0003	39.519	33
28	.02560	.02560	39.057	.99967	1.0003	39.070	32
29	.02589	.02589	38.618	.99966	1.0003	38.631	31
30	.02618	.02619	38.188	.99966	1.0003	38.202	30
31	.02647	.02648	37.769	.99965	1.0004	37.782	29
32	.02676	.02677	37.358	.99964	1.0004	37.371	28
33	.02705	.02706	36.956	.99963	1.0004	36.970	27
34	.02734	.02735	36.563	.99963	1.0004	36.576	26
35	.02763	.02764	36.178	.99962	1.0004	36.191	25
36	.02792	.02793	35.801	.99961	1.0004	35.815	24
37	.02821	.02822	35.431	.99960	1.0004	35.445	23
38	.02850	.02851	35.070	.99959	1.0004	35.084	22
39	.02879	.02881	34.715	.99959	1.0004	34.730	21
40	.02908	.02910	34.368	.99958	1.0004	34.382	20
41	.02938	.02939	34.027	.99957	1.0004	34.042	19
42	.02967	.02968	33.694	.99956	1.0004	33.708	18
43	.02996	.02997	33.366	.99955	1.0004	33.381	17
44	.03025	.03026	33.045	.99954	1.0005	33.060	16
45	.03054	.03055	32.730	.99953	1.0005	32.746	15
46	.03083	.03084	32.421	.99952	1.0005	32.437	14
47	.03112	.03114	32.118	.99952	1.0005	32.134	13
48	.03141	.03143	31.821	.99951	1.0005	31.836	12
49	.03170	.03172	31.528	.99950	1.0005	31.544	11
50	.03199	.03201	31.242	.99949	1.0005	31.258	10
51	.03228	.03230	30.960	.99948	1.0005	30.976	9
52	.03257	.03259	30.683	.99947	1.0005	30.700	8
53	.03286	.03288	30.412	.99946	1.0005	30.428	7
54	.03316	.03317	30.145	.99945	1.0006	30.161	6
55	.03345	.03346	29.882	.99944	1.0006	29.899	5
56	.03374	.03376	29.624	.99943	1.0006	29.641	4
57	.03403	.03405	29.371	.99942	1.0006	29.388	3
58	.03432	.03434	29.122	.99941	1.0006	29.139	2
59	.03461	.03463	28.877	.99940	1.0006	28.894	1
60	.03490	.03492	28.636	.99939	1.0006	28.654	0
′	Cos	Cot	Tan	Sin	Csc	Sec	′

2° (182°)   (357°) 177°

'	Sin	Tan	Cot	Cos	Sec	Csc	'
0	.03490	.03492	28.636	.99939	1.0006	28.654	60
1	.03519	.03521	28.399	.99938	1.0006	28.417	59
2	.03548	.03550	28.166	.99937	1.0006	28.184	58
3	.03577	.03579	27.937	.99936	1.0006	27.955	57
4	.03606	.03609	27.712	.99935	1.0007	27.730	56
5	.03635	.03638	27.490	.99934	1.0007	27.508	55
6	.03664	.03667	27.271	.99933	1.0007	27.290	54
7	.03693	.03696	27.057	.99932	1.0007	27.075	53
8	.03723	.03725	26.845	.99931	1.0007	26.864	52
9	.03752	.03754	26.637	.99930	1.0007	26.655	51
10	.03781	.03783	26.432	.99929	1.0007	26.451	50
11	.03810	.03812	26.230	.99927	1.0007	26.249	49
12	.03839	.03842	26.031	.99926	1.0007	26.050	48
13	.03868	.03871	25.835	.99925	1.0007	25.854	47
14	.03897	.03900	25.642	.99924	1.0008	25.661	46
15	.03926	.03929	25.452	.99923	1.0008	25.471	45
16	.03955	.03958	25.264	.99922	1.0008	25.284	44
17	.03984	.03987	25.080	.99921	1.0008	25.100	43
18	.04013	.04016	24.898	.99919	1.0008	24.918	42
19	.04042	.04046	24.719	.99918	1.0008	24.739	41
20	.04071	.04075	24.542	.99917	1.0008	24.562	40
21	.04100	.04104	24.368	.99916	1.0008	24.388	39
22	.04129	.04133	24.196	.99915	1.0009	24.216	38
23	.04159	.04162	24.026	.99913	1.0009	24.047	37
24	.04188	.04191	23.859	.99912	1.0009	23.880	36
25	.04217	.04220	23.695	.99911	1.0009	23.716	35
26	.04246	.04250	23.532	.99910	1.0009	23.553	34
27	.04275	.04279	23.372	.99909	1.0009	23.393	33
28	.04304	.04308	23.214	.99907	1.0009	23.235	32
29	.04333	.04337	23.058	.99906	1.0009	23.079	31
30	.04362	.04366	22.904	.99905	1.0010	22.926	30
31	.04391	.04395	22.752	.99904	1.0010	22.774	29
32	.04420	.04424	22.602	.99902	1.0010	22.624	28
33	.04449	.04454	22.454	.99901	1.0010	22.476	27
34	.04478	.04483	22.308	.99900	1.0010	22.330	26
35	.04507	.04512	22.164	.99898	1.0010	22.187	25
36	.04536	.04541	22.022	.99897	1.0010	22.044	24
37	.04565	.04570	21.881	.99896	1.0010	21.904	23
38	.04594	.04599	21.743	.99894	1.0011	21.766	22
39	.04623	.04628	21.606	.99893	1.0011	21.629	21
40	.04653	.04658	21.470	.99892	1.0011	21.494	20
41	.04682	.04687	21.337	.99890	1.0011	21.360	19
42	.04711	.04716	21.205	.99889	1.0011	21.229	18
43	.04740	.04745	21.075	.99888	1.0011	21.098	17
44	.04769	.04774	20.946	.99886	1.0011	20.970	16
45	.04798	.04803	20.819	.99885	1.0012	20.843	15
46	.04827	.04833	20.693	.99883	1.0012	20.717	14
47	.04856	.04862	20.569	.99882	1.0012	20.593	13
48	.04885	.04891	20.446	.99881	1.0012	20.471	12
49	.04914	.04920	20.325	.99879	1.0012	20.350	11
50	.04943	.04949	20.206	.99878	1.0012	20.230	10
51	.04972	.04978	20.087	.99876	1.0012	20.112	9
52	.05001	.05007	19.970	.99875	1.0013	19.995	8
53	.05030	.05037	19.855	.99873	1.0013	19.880	7
54	.05059	.05066	19.740	.99872	1.0013	19.766	6
55	.05088	.05095	19.627	.99870	1.0013	19.653	5
56	.05117	.05124	19.516	.99869	1.0013	19.541	4
57	.05146	.05153	19.405	.99867	1.0013	19.431	3
58	.05175	.05182	19.296	.99866	1.0014	19.322	2
59	.05205	.05212	19.188	.99864	1.0014	19.214	1
60	.05234	.05241	19.081	.99863	1.0014	19.107	0
'	Cos	Cot	Tan	Sin	Csc	Sec	'

3° (183°)   (356°) 176°

'	Sin	Tan	Cot	Cos	Sec	Csc	'
0	.05234	.05241	19.081	.99863	1.0014	19.107	60
1	.05263	.05270	18.976	.99861	1.0014	19.002	59
2	.05292	.05299	18.871	.99860	1.0014	18.898	58
3	.05321	.05328	18.768	.99858	1.0014	18.794	57
4	.05350	.05357	18.666	.99857	1.0014	18.692	56
5	.05379	.05387	18.564	.99855	1.0014	18.591	55
6	.05408	.05416	18.464	.99854	1.0015	18.492	54
7	.05437	.05445	18.366	.99852	1.0015	18.393	53
8	.05466	.05474	18.268	.99851	1.0015	18.295	52
9	.05495	.05503	18.171	.99849	1.0015	18.198	51
10	.05524	.05533	18.075	.99847	1.0015	18.103	50
11	.05553	.05562	17.980	.99846	1.0015	18.008	49
12	.05582	.05591	17.886	.99844	1.0016	17.914	48
13	.05611	.05620	17.793	.99842	1.0016	17.822	47
14	.05640	.05649	17.702	.99841	1.0016	17.730	46
15	.05669	.05678	17.611	.99839	1.0016	17.639	45
16	.05698	.05708	17.521	.99838	1.0016	17.549	44
17	.05727	.05737	17.431	.99836	1.0016	17.460	43
18	.05756	.05766	17.343	.99834	1.0017	17.372	42
19	.05785	.05795	17.256	.99833	1.0017	17.285	41
20	.05814	.05824	17.169	.99831	1.0017	17.198	40
21	.05844	.05854	17.084	.99829	1.0017	17.113	39
22	.05873	.05883	16.999	.99827	1.0017	17.028	38
23	.05902	.05912	16.915	.99826	1.0017	16.945	37
24	.05931	.05941	16.832	.99824	1.0018	16.862	36
25	.05960	.05970	16.750	.99822	1.0018	16.779	35
26	.05989	.05999	16.668	.99821	1.0018	16.698	34
27	.06018	.06029	16.587	.99819	1.0018	16.618	33
28	.06047	.06058	16.507	.99817	1.0018	16.538	32
29	.06076	.06087	16.428	.99815	1.0019	16.459	31
30	.06105	.06116	16.350	.99813	1.0019	16.380	30
31	.06134	.06145	16.272	.99812	1.0019	16.303	29
32	.06163	.06175	16.195	.99810	1.0019	16.226	28
33	.06192	.06204	16.119	.99808	1.0019	16.150	27
34	.06221	.06233	16.043	.99806	1.0019	16.075	26
35	.06250	.06262	15.969	.99804	1.0020	16.000	25
36	.06279	.06291	15.895	.99803	1.0020	15.926	24
37	.06308	.06321	15.821	.99801	1.0020	15.853	23
38	.06337	.06350	15.748	.99799	1.0020	15.780	22
39	.06366	.06379	15.676	.99797	1.0020	15.708	21
40	.06395	.06408	15.605	.99795	1.0021	15.637	20
41	.06424	.06438	15.534	.99793	1.0021	15.566	19
42	.06453	.06467	15.464	.99792	1.0021	15.496	18
43	.06482	.06496	15.394	.99790	1.0021	15.427	17
44	.06511	.06525	15.325	.99788	1.0021	15.358	16
45	.06540	.06554	15.257	.99786	1.0021	15.290	15
46	.06569	.06584	15.189	.99784	1.0022	15.222	14
47	.06598	.06613	15.122	.99782	1.0022	15.155	13
48	.06627	.06642	15.056	.99780	1.0022	15.089	12
49	.06656	.06671	14.990	.99778	1.0022	15.023	11
50	.06685	.06700	14.924	.99776	1.0022	14.958	10
51	.06714	.06730	14.860	.99774	1.0023	14.893	9
52	.06743	.06759	14.795	.99772	1.0023	14.829	8
53	.06773	.06788	14.732	.99770	1.0023	14.766	7
54	.06802	.06817	14.669	.99768	1.0023	14.703	6
55	.06831	.06847	14.606	.99766	1.0023	14.640	5
56	.06860	.06876	14.544	.99764	1.0024	14.578	4
57	.06889	.06905	14.482	.99762	1.0024	14.517	3
58	.06918	.06934	14.421	.99760	1.0024	14.456	2
59	.06947	.06963	14.361	.99758	1.0024	14.395	1
60	.06976	.06993	14.301	.99756	1.0024	14.336	0
'	Cos	Cot	Tan	Sin	Csc	Sec	'

NATURAL TRIGONOMETRIC FUNCTIONS (*Continued*)

4° (184°) (355°) 175°

′	Sin	Tan	Cot	Cos	Sec	Csc	′
0	.06976	.06993	14.301	.99756	1.0024	14.336	60
1	.07005	.07022	14.241	.99754	1.0025	14.276	59
2	.07034	.07051	14.182	.99752	1.0025	14.217	58
3	.07063	.07080	14.124	.99750	1.0025	14.159	57
4	.07092	.07110	14.065	.99748	1.0025	14.101	56
5	.07121	.07139	14.008	.99746	1.0025	14.044	55
6	.07150	.07168	13.951	.99744	1.0026	13.987	54
7	.07179	.07197	13.894	.99742	1.0026	13.930	53
8	.07208	.07227	13.838	.99740	1.0026	13.874	52
9	.07237	.07256	13.782	.99738	1.0026	13.818	51
10	.07266	.07285	13.727	.99736	1.0027	13.763	50
11	.07295	.07314	13.672	.99734	1.0027	13.708	49
12	.07324	.07344	13.617	.99731	1.0027	13.654	48
13	.07353	.07373	13.563	.99729	1.0027	13.600	47
14	.07382	.07402	13.510	.99727	1.0027	13.547	46
15	.07411	.07431	13.457	.99725	1.0028	13.494	45
16	.07440	.07461	13.404	.99723	1.0028	13.441	44
17	.07469	.07490	13.352	.99721	1.0028	13.389	43
18	.07498	.07519	13.300	.99719	1.0028	13.337	42
19	.07527	.07548	13.248	.99716	1.0028	13.286	41
20	.07556	.07578	13.197	.99714	1.0029	13.235	40
21	.07585	.07607	13.146	.99712	1.0029	13.184	39
22	.07614	.07636	13.096	.99710	1.0029	13.134	38
23	.07643	.07665	13.046	.99708	1.0029	13.084	37
24	.07672	.07695	12.996	.99705	1.0030	13.035	36
25	.07701	.07724	12.947	.99703	1.0030	12.985	35
26	.07730	.07753	12.898	.99701	1.0030	12.937	34
27	.07759	.07782	12.850	.99699	1.0030	12.888	33
28	.07788	.07812	12.801	.99696	1.0030	12.840	32
29	.07817	.07841	12.754	.99694	1.0031	12.793	31
30	.07846	.07870	12.706	.99692	1.0031	12.745	30
31	.07875	.07899	12.659	.99689	1.0031	12.699	29
32	.07904	.07929	12.612	.99687	1.0031	12.652	28
33	.07933	.07958	12.566	.99685	1.0032	12.606	27
34	.07962	.07987	12.520	.99683	1.0032	12.560	26
35	.07991	.08017	12.474	.99680	1.0032	12.514	25
36	.08020	.08046	12.429	.99678	1.0032	12.469	24
37	.08049	.08075	12.384	.99676	1.0033	12.424	23
38	.08078	.08104	12.339	.99673	1.0033	12.379	22
39	.08107	.08134	12.295	.99671	1.0033	12.335	21
40	.08136	.08163	12.251	.99668	1.0033	12.291	20
41	.08165	.08192	12.207	.99666	1.0034	12.248	19
42	.08194	.08221	12.163	.99664	1.0034	12.204	18
43	.08223	.08251	12.120	.99661	1.0034	12.161	17
44	.08252	.08280	12.077	.99659	1.0034	12.119	16
45	.08281	.08309	12.035	.99657	1.0034	12.076	15
46	.08310	.08339	11.992	.99654	1.0035	12.034	14
47	.08339	.08368	11.950	.99652	1.0035	11.992	13
48	.08368	.08397	11.909	.99649	1.0035	11.951	12
49	.08397	.08427	11.867	.99647	1.0035	11.909	11
50	.08426	.08456	11.826	.99644	1.0036	11.868	10
51	.08455	.08485	11.785	.99642	1.0036	11.828	9
52	.08484	.08514	11.745	.99639	1.0036	11.787	8
53	.08513	.08544	11.705	.99637	1.0036	11.747	7
54	.08542	.08573	11.664	.99635	1.0037	11.707	6
55	.08571	.08602	11.625	.99632	1.0037	11.668	5
56	.08600	.08632	11.585	.99630	1.0037	11.628	4
57	.08629	.08661	11.546	.99627	1.0037	11.589	3
58	.08658	.08690	11.507	.99625	1.0038	11.551	2
59	.08687	.08720	11.468	.99622	1.0038	11.512	1
60	.08716	.08749	11.430	.99619	1.0038	11.474	0
′	Cos	Cot	Tan	Sin	Csc	Sec	′

94° (274°) (265°) 85°

5° (185°) (354°) 174°

′	Sin	Tan	Cot	Cos	Sec	Csc	′
0	.08716	.08749	11.430	.99619	1.0038	11.474	60
1	.08745	.08778	11.392	.99617	1.0038	11.436	59
2	.08774	.08807	11.354	.99614	1.0039	11.398	58
3	.08803	.08837	11.316	.99612	1.0039	11.360	57
4	.08831	.08866	11.279	.99609	1.0039	11.323	56
5	.08860	.08895	11.242	.99607	1.0039	11.286	55
6	.08889	.08925	11.205	.99604	1.0040	11.249	54
7	.08918	.08954	11.168	.99602	1.0040	11.213	53
8	.08947	.08983	11.132	.99599	1.0040	11.176	52
9	.08976	.09013	11.095	.99596	1.0041	11.140	51
10	.09005	.09042	11.059	.99594	1.0041	11.105	50
11	.09034	.09071	11.024	.99591	1.0041	11.069	49
12	.09063	.09101	10.988	.99588	1.0041	11.034	48
13	.09092	.09130	10.953	.99586	1.0042	10.998	47
14	.09121	.09159	10.918	.99583	1.0042	10.963	46
15	.09150	.09189	10.883	.99580	1.0042	10.929	45
16	.09179	.09218	10.848	.99578	1.0042	10.894	44
17	.09208	.09247	10.814	.99575	1.0043	10.860	43
18	.09237	.09277	10.780	.99572	1.0043	10.826	42
19	.09266	.09306	10.746	.99570	1.0043	10.792	41
20	.09295	.09335	10.712	.99567	1.0043	10.758	40
21	.09324	.09365	10.678	.99564	1.0044	10.725	39
22	.09353	.09394	10.645	.99562	1.0044	10.692	38
23	.09382	.09423	10.612	.99559	1.0044	10.659	37
24	.09411	.09453	10.579	.99556	1.0045	10.626	36
25	.09440	.09482	10.546	.99553	1.0045	10.593	35
26	.09469	.09511	10.514	.99551	1.0045	10.561	34
27	.09498	.09541	10.481	.99548	1.0045	10.529	33
28	.09527	.09570	10.449	.99545	1.0046	10.497	32
29	.09556	.09600	10.417	.99542	1.0046	10.465	31
30	.09585	.09629	10.385	.99540	1.0046	10.433	30
31	.09614	.09658	10.354	.99537	1.0047	10.402	29
32	.09642	.09688	10.322	.99534	1.0047	10.371	28
33	.09671	.09717	10.291	.99531	1.0047	10.340	27
34	.09700	.09746	10.260	.99528	1.0047	10.309	26
35	.09729	.09776	10.229	.99526	1.0048	10.278	25
36	.09758	.09805	10.199	.99523	1.0048	10.248	24
37	.09787	.09834	10.168	.99520	1.0048	10.217	23
38	.09816	.09864	10.138	.99517	1.0049	10.187	22
39	.09845	.09893	10.108	.99514	1.0049	10.157	21
40	.09874	.09923	10.078	.99511	1.0049	10.128	20
41	.09903	.09952	10.048	.99508	1.0050	10.098	19
42	.09932	.09981	10.019	.99506	1.0050	10.068	18
43	.09961	.10011	9.9893	.99503	1.0050	10.039	17
44	.09990	.10040	9.9601	.99500	1.0050	10.010	16
45	.10019	.10069	9.9310	.99497	1.0051	9.9812	15
46	.10048	.10099	9.9021	.99494	1.0051	9.9525	14
47	.10077	.10128	9.8734	.99491	1.0051	9.9239	13
48	.10106	.10158	9.8448	.99488	1.0051	9.8955	12
49	.10135	.10187	9.8164	.99485	1.0052	9.8672	11
50	.10164	.10216	9.7882	.99482	1.0052	9.8391	10
51	.10192	.10246	9.7601	.99479	1.0052	9.8112	9
52	.10221	.10275	9.7322	.99476	1.0053	9.7834	8
53	.10250	.10305	9.7044	.99473	1.0053	9.7558	7
54	.10279	.10334	9.6768	.99470	1.0053	9.7283	6
55	.10308	.10363	9.6493	.99467	1.0054	9.7010	5
56	.10337	.10393	9.6220	.99464	1.0054	9.6739	4
57	.10366	.10422	9.5949	.99461	1.0054	9.6469	3
58	.10395	.10452	9.5679	.99458	1.0054	9.6200	2
59	.10424	.10481	9.5411	.99455	1.0055	9.5933	1
60	.10453	.10510	9.5144	.99452	1.0055	9.5668	0
′	Cos	Cot	Tan	Sin	Csc	Sec	′

95° (275°) (264°) 84°

6° (186°)   **(353°) 173°**

′	Sin	Tan	Cot	Cos	Sec	Csc	′
0	.10453	.10510	9.5144	.99452	1.0055	9.5668	60
1	.10482	.10540	9.4878	.99449	1.0055	9.5404	59
2	.10511	.10569	9.4614	.99446	1.0056	9.5141	58
3	.10540	.10599	9.4352	.99443	1.0056	9.4880	57
4	.10569	.10628	9.4090	.99440	1.0056	9.4620	56
5	.10597	.10657	9.3831	.99437	1.0057	9.4362	55
6	.10626	.10687	9.3572	.99434	1.0057	9.4105	54
7	.10655	.10716	9.3315	.99431	1.0057	9.3850	53
8	.10684	.10746	9.3060	.99428	1.0058	9.3596	52
9	.10713	.10775	9.2806	.99424	1.0058	9.3343	51
10	.10742	.10805	9.2553	.99421	1.0058	9.3092	50
11	.10771	.10834	9.2302	.99418	1.0059	9.2842	49
12	.10800	.10863	9.2052	.99415	1.0059	9.2593	48
13	.10829	.10893	9.1803	.99412	1.0059	9.2346	47
14	.10858	.10922	9.1555	.99409	1.0059	9.2100	46
15	.10887	.10952	9.1309	.99406	1.0060	9.1855	45
16	.10916	.10981	9.1065	.99402	1.0060	9.1612	44
17	.10945	.11011	9.0821	.99399	1.0060	9.1370	43
18	.10973	.11040	9.0579	.99396	1.0061	9.1129	42
19	.11002	.11070	9.0338	.99393	1.0061	9.0890	41
20	.11031	.11099	9.0098	.99390	1.0061	9.0652	40
21	.11060	.11128	8.9860	.99386	1.0062	9.0415	39
22	.11089	.11158	8.9623	.99383	1.0062	9.0179	38
23	.11118	.11187	8.9387	.99380	1.0062	8.9944	37
24	.11147	.11217	8.9152	.99377	1.0063	8.9711	36
25	.11176	.11246	8.8919	.99374	1.0063	8.9479	35
26	.11205	.11276	8.8686	.99370	1.0063	8.9248	34
27	.11234	.11305	8.8455	.99367	1.0064	8.9019	33
28	.11263	.11335	8.8225	.99364	1.0064	8.8790	32
29	.11291	.11364	8.7996	.99360	1.0064	8.8563	31
30	.11320	.11394	8.7769	.99357	1.0065	8.8337	30
31	.11349	.11423	8.7542	.99354	1.0065	8.8112	29
32	.11378	.11452	8.7317	.99351	1.0065	8.7888	28
33	.11407	.11482	8.7093	.99347	1.0066	8.7665	27
34	.11436	.11511	8.6870	.99344	1.0066	8.7444	26
35	.11465	.11541	8.6648	.99341	1.0066	8.7223	25
36	.11494	.11570	8.6427	.99337	1.0067	8.7004	24
37	.11523	.11600	8.6208	.99334	1.0067	8.6786	23
38	.11552	.11629	8.5989	.99331	1.0067	8.6569	22
39	.11580	.11659	8.5772	.99327	1.0068	8.6353	21
40	.11609	.11688	8.5555	.99324	1.0068	8.6138	20
41	.11638	.11718	8.5340	.99320	1.0068	8.5924	19
42	.11667	.11747	8.5126	.99317	1.0069	8.5711	18
43	.11696	.11777	8.4913	.99314	1.0069	8.5500	17
44	.11725	.11806	8.4701	.99310	1.0069	8.5289	16
45	.11754	.11836	8.4490	.99307	1.0070	8.5079	15
46	.11783	.11865	8.4280	.99303	1.0070	8.4871	14
47	.11812	.11895	8.4071	.99300	1.0070	8.4663	13
48	.11840	.11924	8.3863	.99297	1.0071	8.4457	12
49	.11869	.11954	8.3656	.99293	1.0071	8.4251	11
50	.11898	.11983	8.3450	.99290	1.0072	8.4047	10
51	.11927	.12013	8.3245	.99286	1.0072	8.3843	9
52	.11956	.12042	8.3041	.99283	1.0072	8.3641	8
53	.11985	.12072	8.2838	.99279	1.0073	8.3439	7
54	.12014	.12101	8.2636	.99276	1.0073	8.3238	6
55	.12043	.12131	8.2434	.99272	1.0073	8.3039	5
56	.12071	.12160	8.2234	.99269	1.0074	8.2840	4
57	.12100	.12190	8.2035	.99265	1.0074	8.2642	3
58	.12129	.12219	8.1837	.99262	1.0074	8.2446	2
59	.12158	.12249	8.1640	.99258	1.0075	8.2250	1
60	.12187	.12278	8.1443	.99255	1.0075	8.2055	0
′	Cos	Cot	Tan	Sin	Csc	Sec	′

96° (276°)   **(263°) 83°**

7° (187°)   **(352°) 172°**

′	Sin	Tan	Cot	Cos	Sec	Csc	′
0	.12187	.12278	8.1443	.99255	1.0075	8.2055	60
1	.12216	.12308	8.1248	.99251	1.0075	8.1861	59
2	.12245	.12338	8.1054	.99248	1.0076	8.1668	58
3	.12274	.12367	8.0860	.99244	1.0076	8.1476	57
4	.12302	.12397	8.0667	.99240	1.0077	8.1285	56
5	.12331	.12426	8.0476	.99237	1.0077	8.1095	55
6	.12360	.12456	8.0285	.99233	1.0077	8.0905	54
7	.12389	.12485	8.0095	.99230	1.0078	8.0717	53
8	.12418	.12515	7.9906	.99226	1.0078	8.0529	52
9	.12447	.12544	7.9718	.99222	1.0078	8.0342	51
10	.12476	.12574	7.9530	.99219	1.0079	8.0156	50
11	.12504	.12603	7.9344	.99215	1.0079	7.9971	49
12	.12533	.12633	7.9158	.99211	1.0079	7.9787	48
13	.12562	.12662	7.8973	.99208	1.0080	7.9604	47
14	.12591	.12692	7.8789	.99204	1.0080	7.9422	46
15	.12620	.12722	7.8606	.99200	1.0081	7.9240	45
16	.12649	.12751	7.8424	.99197	1.0081	7.9059	44
17	.12678	.12781	7.8243	.99193	1.0081	7.8879	43
18	.12706	.12810	7.8062	.99189	1.0082	7.8700	42
19	.12735	.12840	7.7882	.99186	1.0082	7.8522	41
20	.12764	.12869	7.7704	.99182	1.0082	7.8344	40
21	.12793	.12899	7.7525	.99178	1.0083	7.8168	39
22	.12822	.12929	7.7348	.99175	1.0083	7.7992	38
23	.12851	.12958	7.7171	.99171	1.0084	7.7817	37
24	.12880	.12988	7.6996	.99167	1.0084	7.7642	36
25	.12908	.13017	7.6821	.99163	1.0084	7.7469	35
26	.12937	.13047	7.6647	.99160	1.0085	7.7296	34
27	.12966	.13076	7.6473	.99156	1.0085	7.7124	33
28	.12995	.13106	7.6301	.99152	1.0086	7.6953	32
29	.13024	.13136	7.6129	.99148	1.0086	7.6783	31
30	.13053	.13165	7.5958	.99144	1.0086	7.6613	30
31	.13081	.13195	7.5787	.99141	1.0087	7.6444	29
32	.13110	.13224	7.5618	.99137	1.0087	7.6276	28
33	.13139	.13254	7.5449	.99133	1.0087	7.6109	27
34	.13168	.13284	7.5281	.99129	1.0088	7.5942	26
35	.13197	.13313	7.5113	.99125	1.0088	7.5776	25
36	.13226	.13343	7.4947	.99122	1.0089	7.5611	24
37	.13254	.13372	7.4781	.99118	1.0089	7.5446	23
38	.13283	.13402	7.4615	.99114	1.0089	7.5282	22
39	.13312	.13432	7.4451	.99110	1.0090	7.5119	21
40	.13341	.13461	7.4287	.99106	1.0090	7.4957	20
41	.13370	.13491	7.4124	.99102	1.0091	7.4795	19
42	.13399	.13521	7.3962	.99098	1.0091	7.4635	18
43	.13427	.13550	7.3800	.99094	1.0091	7.4474	17
44	.13456	.13580	7.3639	.99091	1.0092	7.4315	16
45	.13485	.13609	7.3479	.99087	1.0092	7.4156	15
46	.13514	.13639	7.3319	.99083	1.0093	7.3998	14
47	.13543	.13669	7.3160	.99079	1.0093	7.3840	13
48	.13572	.13698	7.3002	.99075	1.0093	7.3684	12
49	.13600	.13728	7.2844	.99071	1.0094	7.3527	11
50	.13629	.13758	7.2687	.99067	1.0094	7.3372	10
51	.13658	.13787	7.2531	.99063	1.0095	7.3217	9
52	.13687	.13817	7.2375	.99059	1.0095	7.3063	8
53	.13716	.13846	7.2220	.99055	1.0095	7.2900	7
54	.13744	.13876	7.2066	.99051	1.0096	7.2757	6
55	.13773	.13906	7.1912	.99047	1.0096	7.2604	5
56	.13802	.13935	7.1759	.99043	1.0097	7.2453	4
57	.13831	.13965	7.1607	.99039	1.0097	7.2302	3
58	.13860	.13995	7.1455	.99035	1.0097	7.2152	2
59	.13889	.14024	7.1304	.99031	1.0098	7.2002	1
60	.13917	.14054	7.1154	.99027	1.0098	7.1853	0
′	Cos	Cot	Tan	Sin	Csc	Sec	′

97° (277°)   **(262°) 82°**

8° (188°)   (351°) 171°   9° (189°)   (350°) 170°

′	Sin	Tan	Cot	Cos	Sec	Csc	′		′	Sin	Tan	Cot	Cos	Sec	Csc	′
0	.13917	.14054	7.1154	.99027	1.0098	7.1853	**60**		**0**	.15643	.15838	6.3138	.98769	1.0125	6.3925	**60**
1	.13946	.14084	7.1004	.99023	1.0099	7.1705	59		1	.15672	.15868	6.3019	.98764	1.0125	6.3807	59
2	.13975	.14113	7.0855	.99019	1.0099	7.1557	58		2	.15701	.15898	6.2901	.98760	1.0126	6.3691	58
3	.14004	.14143	7.0706	.99015	1.0100	7.1410	57		3	.15730	.15928	6.2783	.98755	1.0126	6.3574	57
4	.14033	.14173	7.0558	.99011	1.0100	7.1263	56		4	.15758	.15958	6.2666	.98751	1.0127	6.3458	56
5	.14061	.14202	7.0410	.99006	1.0100	7.1117	**55**		**5**	.15787	.15988	6.2549	.98746	1.0127	6.3343	**55**
6	.14090	.14232	7.0264	.99002	1.0101	7.0972	54		6	.15816	.16017	6.2432	.98741	1.0127	6.3228	54
7	.14119	.14262	7.0117	.98998	1.0101	7.0827	53		7	.15845	.16047	6.2316	.98737	1.0128	6.3113	53
8	.14148	.14291	6.9972	.98994	1.0102	7.0683	52		8	.15873	.16077	6.2200	.98732	1.0128	6.2999	52
9	.14177	.14321	6.9827	.98990	1.0102	7.0539	51		9	.15902	.16107	6.2085	.98728	1.0129	6.2885	51
10	.14205	.14351	6.9682	.98986	1.0102	7.0396	**50**		**10**	.15931	.16137	6.1970	.98723	1.0129	6.2772	**50**
11	.14234	.14381	6.9538	.98982	1.0103	7.0254	49		11	.15959	.16167	6.1856	.98718	1.0130	6.2659	49
12	.14263	.14410	6.9395	.98978	1.0103	7.0112	48		12	.15988	.16196	6.1742	.98714	1.0130	6.2546	48
13	.14292	.14440	6.9252	.98973	1.0104	6.9971	47		13	.16017	.16226	6.1628	.98709	1.0131	6.2434	47
14	.14320	.14470	6.9110	.98969	1.0104	6.9830	46		14	.16046	.16256	6.1515	.98704	1.0131	6.2323	46
15	.14349	.14499	6.8969	.98965	1.0105	6.9690	**45**		**15**	.16074	.16286	6.1402	.98700	1.0132	6.2211	**45**
16	.14378	.14529	6.8828	.98961	1.0105	6.9550	44		16	.16103	.16316	6.1290	.98695	1.0132	6.2100	44
17	.14407	.14559	6.8687	.98957	1.0105	6.9411	43		17	.16132	.16346	6.1178	.98690	1.0133	6.1990	43
18	.14436	.14588	6.8548	.98953	1.0106	6.9273	42		18	.16160	.16376	6.1066	.98686	1.0133	6.1880	42
19	.14464	.14618	6.8408	.98948	1.0106	6.9135	41		19	.16189	.16405	6.0955	.98681	1.0134	6.1770	41
20	.14493	.14648	6.8269	.98944	1.0107	6.8998	**40**		**20**	.16218	.16435	6.0844	.98676	1.0134	6.1661	**40**
21	.14522	.14678	6.8131	.98940	1.0107	6.8861	39		21	.16246	.16465	6.0734	.98671	1.0135	6.1552	39
22	.14551	.14707	6.7994	.98936	1.0108	6.8725	38		22	.16275	.16495	6.0624	.98667	1.0135	6.1443	38
23	.14580	.14737	6.7856	.98931	1.0108	6.8589	37		23	.16304	.16525	6.0514	.98662	1.0136	6.1335	37
24	.14608	.14767	6.7720	.98927	1.0108	6.8454	36		24	.16333	.16555	6.0405	.98657	1.0136	6.1227	36
25	.14637	.14796	6.7584	.98923	1.0109	6.8320	**35**		**25**	.16361	.16585	6.0296	.98652	1.0137	6.1120	**35**
26	.14666	.14826	6.7448	.98919	1.0109	6.8186	34		26	.16390	.16615	6.0188	.98648	1.0137	6.1013	34
27	.14695	.14856	6.7313	.98914	1.0110	6.8052	33		27	.16419	.16645	6.0080	.98643	1.0138	6.0906	33
28	.14723	.14886	6.7179	.98910	1.0110	6.7919	32		28	.16447	.16674	5.9972	.98638	1.0138	6.0800	32
29	.14752	.14915	6.7045	.98906	1.0111	6.7787	31		29	.16476	.16704	5.9865	.98633	1.0139	6.0694	31
30	.14781	.14945	6.6912	.98902	1.0111	6.7655	**30**		**30**	.16505	.16734	5.9758	.98629	1.0139	6.0589	**30**
31	.14810	.14975	6.6779	.98897	1.0112	6.7523	29		31	.16533	.16764	5.9651	.98624	1.0140	6.0483	29
32	.14838	.15005	6.6646	.98893	1.0112	6.7392	28		32	.16562	.16794	5.9545	.98619	1.0140	6.0379	28
33	.14867	.15034	6.6514	.98889	1.0112	6.7262	27		33	.16591	.16824	5.9439	.98614	1.0141	6.0274	27
34	.14896	.15064	6.6383	.98884	1.0113	6.7132	26		34	.16620	.16854	5.9333	.98609	1.0141	6.0170	26
35	.14925	.15094	6.6252	.98880	1.0113	6.7003	**25**		**35**	.16648	.16884	5.9228	.98604	1.0142	6.0067	**25**
36	.14954	.15124	6.6122	.98876	1.0114	6.6874	24		36	.16677	.16914	5.9124	.98600	1.0142	5.9963	24
37	.14982	.15153	6.5992	.98871	1.0114	6.6745	23		37	.16706	.16944	5.9019	.98595	1.0143	5.9860	23
38	.15011	.15183	6.5863	.98867	1.0115	6.6618	22		38	.16734	.16974	5.8915	.98590	1.0143	5.9758	22
39	.15040	.15213	6.5734	.98863	1.0115	6.6490	21		39	.16763	.17004	5.8811	.98585	1.0144	5.9656	21
40	.15069	.15243	6.5606	.98858	1.0116	6.6363	**20**		**40**	.16792	.17033	5.8708	.98580	1.0144	5.9554	**20**
41	.15097	.15272	6.5478	.98854	1.0116	6.6237	19		41	.16820	.17063	5.8605	.98575	1.0145	5.9452	19
42	.15126	.15302	6.5350	.98849	1.0116	6.6111	18		42	.16849	.17093	5.8502	.98570	1.0145	5.9351	18
43	.15155	.15332	6.5223	.98845	1.0117	6.5986	17		43	.16878	.17123	5.8400	.98565	1.0146	5.9250	17
44	.15184	.15362	6.5097	.98841	1.0117	6.5861	16		44	.16906	.17153	5.8298	.98561	1.0146	5.9150	16
45	.15212	.15391	6.4971	.98836	1.0118	6.5736	**15**		**45**	.16935	.17183	5.8197	.98556	1.0147	5.9049	**15**
46	.15241	.15421	6.4846	.98832	1.0118	6.5612	14		46	.16964	.17213	5.8095	.98551	1.0147	5.8950	14
47	.15270	.15451	6.4721	.98827	1.0119	6.5489	13		47	.16992	.17243	5.7994	.98546	1.0148	5.8850	13
48	.15299	.15481	6.4596	.98823	1.0119	6.5366	12		48	.17021	.17273	5.7894	.98541	1.0148	5.8751	12
49	.15327	.15511	6.4472	.98818	1.0120	6.5243	11		49	.17050	.17303	5.7794	.98536	1.0149	5.8652	11
50	.15356	.15540	6.4348	.98814	1.0120	6.5121	**10**		**50**	.17078	.17333	5.7694	.98531	1.0149	5.8554	**10**
51	.15385	.15570	6.4225	.98809	1.0120	6.4999	9		51	.17107	.17363	5.7594	.98526	1.0150	5.8456	9
52	.15414	.15600	6.4103	.98805	1.0121	6.4878	8		52	.17136	.17393	5.7495	.98521	1.0150	5.8358	8
53	.15442	.15630	6.3980	.98800	1.0121	6.4757	7		53	.17164	.17423	5.7396	.98516	1.0151	5.8261	7
54	.15471	.15660	6.3859	.98796	1.0122	6.4637	6		54	.17193	.17453	5.7297	.98511	1.0151	5.8164	6
55	.15500	.15689	6.3737	.98791	1.0122	6.4517	**5**		**55**	.17222	.17483	5.7199	.98506	1.0152	5.8067	**5**
56	.15529	.15719	6.3617	.98787	1.0123	6.4398	4		56	.17250	.17513	5.7101	.98501	1.0152	5.7970	4
57	.15557	.15749	6.3496	.98782	1.0123	6.4279	3		57	.17279	.17543	5.7004	.98496	1.0153	5.7874	3
58	.15586	.15779	6.3376	.98778	1.0124	6.4160	2		58	.17308	.17573	5.6906	.98491	1.0153	5.7778	2
59	.15615	.15809	6.3257	.98773	1.0124	6.4042	1		59	.17336	.17603	5.6809	.98486	1.0154	5.7683	1
60	.15643	.15838	6.3138	.98769	1.0125	6.3925	**0**		**60**	.17365	.17633	5.6713	.98481	1.0154	5.7588	**0**
′	Cos	Cot	Tan	Sin	Csc	Sec	′		′	Cos	Cot	Tan	Sin	Csc	Sec	′

98° (278°)   (261°) 81°   99° (279°)   (260°) 80°

10° (190°) (349°) **169°**

′	Sin	Tan	Cot	Cos	Sec	Csc	′
0	.17365	.17633	5.6713	.98481	1.0154	5.7588	60
1	.17393	.17663	5.6617	.98476	1.0155	5.7493	59
2	.17422	.17693	5.6521	.98471	1.0155	5.7398	58
3	.17451	.17723	5.6425	.98466	1.0156	5.7304	57
4	.17479	.17753	5.6329	.98461	1.0156	5.7210	56
5	.17508	.17783	5.6234	.98455	1.0157	5.7117	55
6	.17537	.17813	5.6140	.98450	1.0157	5.7023	54
7	.17565	.17843	5.6045	.98445	1.0158	5.6930	53
8	.17594	.17873	5.5951	.98440	1.0158	5.6838	52
9	.17623	.17903	5.5857	.98435	1.0159	5.6745	51
10	.17651	.17933	5.5764	.98430	1.0160	5.6653	50
11	.17680	.17963	5.5671	.98425	1.0160	5.6562	49
12	.17708	.17993	5.5578	.98420	1.0161	5.6470	48
13	.17737	.18023	5.5485	.98414	1.0161	5.6379	47
14	.17766	.18053	5.5393	.98409	1.0162	5.6288	46
15	.17794	.18083	5.5301	.98404	1.0162	5.6198	45
16	.17823	.18113	5.5209	.98399	1.0163	5.6107	44
17	.17852	.18143	5.5118	.98394	1.0163	5.6017	43
18	.17880	.18173	5.5026	.98389	1.0164	5.5928	42
19	.17909	.18203	5.4936	.98383	1.0164	5.5838	41
20	.17937	.18233	5.4845	.98378	1.0165	5.5749	40
21	.17966	.18263	5.4755	.98373	1.0165	5.5660	39
22	.17995	.18293	5.4665	.98368	1.0166	5.5572	38
23	.18023	.18323	5.4575	.98362	1.0166	5.5484	37
24	.18052	.18353	5.4486	.98357	1.0167	5.5396	36
25	.18081	.18384	5.4397	.98352	1.0168	5.5308	35
26	.18109	.18414	5.4308	.98347	1.0168	5.5221	34
27	.18138	.18444	5.4219	.98341	1.0169	5.5134	33
28	.18166	.18474	5.4131	.98336	1.0169	5.5047	32
29	.18195	.18504	5.4043	.98331	1.0170	5.4960	31
30	.18224	.18534	5.3955	.98325	1.0170	5.4874	30
31	.18252	.18564	5.3868	.98320	1.0171	5.4788	29
32	.18281	.18594	5.3781	.98315	1.0171	5.4702	28
33	.18309	.18624	5.3694	.98310	1.0172	5.4617	27
34	.18338	.18654	5.3607	.98304	1.0173	5.4532	26
35	.18367	.18684	5.3521	.98299	1.0173	5.4447	25
36	.18395	.18714	5.3435	.98294	1.0174	5.4362	24
37	.18424	.18745	5.3349	.98288	1.0174	5.4278	23
38	.18452	.18775	5.3263	.98283	1.0175	5.4194	22
39	.18481	.18805	5.3178	.98277	1.0175	5.4110	21
40	.18509	.18835	5.3093	.98272	1.0176	5.4026	20
41	.18538	.18865	5.3008	.98267	1.0176	5.3943	19
42	.18567	.18895	5.2924	.98261	1.0177	5.3860	18
43	.18595	.18925	5.2839	.98256	1.0178	5.3777	17
44	.18624	.18955	5.2755	.98250	1.0178	5.3695	16
45	.18652	.18986	5.2672	.98245	1.0179	5.3612	15
46	.18681	.19016	5.2588	.98240	1.0179	5.3530	14
47	.18710	.19046	5.2505	.98234	1.0180	5.3449	13
48	.18738	.19076	5.2422	.98229	1.0180	5.3367	12
49	.18767	.19106	5.2339	.98223	1.0181	5.3286	11
50	.18795	.19136	5.2257	.98218	1.0181	5.3205	10
51	.18824	.19166	5.2174	.98212	1.0182	5.3124	9
52	.18852	.19197	5.2092	.98207	1.0183	5.3044	8
53	.18881	.19227	5.2011	.98201	1.0183	5.2963	7
54	.18910	.19257	5.1929	.98196	1.0184	5.2883	6
55	.18938	.19287	5.1848	.98190	1.0184	5.2804	5
56	.18967	.19317	5.1767	.98185	1.0185	5.2724	4
57	.18995	.19347	5.1686	.98179	1.0185	5.2645	3
58	.19024	.19378	5.1606	.98174	1.0186	5.2566	2
59	.19052	.19408	5.1526	.98168	1.0187	5.2487	1
60	.19081	.19438	5.1446	.98163	1.0187	5.2408	0
′	Cos	Cot	Tan	Sin	Csc	Sec	′

100° (200°) (259°) **79°**

11° (191°) (348°) **168°**

′	Sin	Tan	Cot	Cos	Sec	Csc	′
0	.19081	.19438	5.1446	.98163	1.0187	5.2408	60
1	.19109	.19468	5.1366	.98157	1.0188	5.2330	59
2	.19138	.19498	5.1286	.98152	1.0188	5.2252	58
3	.19167	.19529	5.1207	.98146	1.0189	5.2174	57
4	.19195	.19559	5.1128	.98140	1.0189	5.2097	56
5	.19224	.19589	5.1049	.98135	1.0190	5.2019	55
6	.19252	.19619	5.0970	.98129	1.0191	5.1942	54
7	.19281	.19649	5.0892	.98124	1.0191	5.1865	53
8	.19309	.19680	5.0814	.98118	1.0192	5.1789	52
9	.19338	.19710	5.0736	.98112	1.0192	5.1712	51
10	.19366	.19740	5.0658	.98107	1.0193	5.1636	50
11	.19395	.19770	5.0581	.98101	1.0194	5.1560	49
12	.19423	.19801	5.0504	.98096	1.0194	5.1484	48
13	.19452	.19831	5.0427	.98090	1.0195	5.1409	47
14	.19481	.19861	5.0350	.98084	1.0195	5.1333	46
15	.19509	.19891	5.0273	.98079	1.0196	5.1258	45
16	.19538	.19921	5.0197	.98073	1.0197	5.1183	44
17	.19566	.19952	5.0121	.98067	1.0197	5.1109	43
18	.19595	.19982	5.0045	.98061	1.0198	5.1034	42
19	.19623	.20012	4.9969	.98056	1.0198	5.0960	41
20	.19652	.20042	4.9894	.98050	1.0199	5.0886	40
21	.19680	.20073	4.9819	.98044	1.0199	5.0813	39
22	.19709	.20103	4.9744	.98039	1.0200	5.0739	38
23	.19737	.20133	4.9669	.98033	1.0201	5.0666	37
24	.19766	.20164	4.9594	.98027	1.0201	5.0593	36
25	.19794	.20194	4.9520	.98021	1.0202	5.0520	35
26	.19823	.20224	4.9446	.98016	1.0202	5.0447	34
27	.19851	.20254	4.9372	.98010	1.0203	5.0375	33
28	.19880	.20285	4.9298	.98004	1.0204	5.0302	32
29	.19908	.20315	4.9225	.97998	1.0204	5.0230	31
30	.19937	.20345	4.9152	.97992	1.0205	5.0159	30
31	.19965	.20376	4.9078	.97987	1.0205	5.0087	29
32	.19994	.20406	4.9006	.97981	1.0206	5.0016	28
33	.20022	.20436	4.8933	.97975	1.0207	4.9944	27
34	.20051	.20466	4.8860	.97969	1.0207	4.9873	26
35	.20079	.20497	4.8788	.97963	1.0208	4.9803	25
36	.20108	.20527	4.8716	.97958	1.0209	4.9732	24
37	.20136	.20557	4.8644	.97952	1.0209	4.9662	23
38	.20165	.20588	4.8573	.97946	1.0210	4.9591	22
39	.20193	.20618	4.8501	.97940	1.0210	4.9521	21
40	.20222	.20648	4.8430	.97934	1.0211	4.9452	20
41	.20250	.20679	4.8359	.97928	1.0212	4.9382	19
42	.20279	.20709	4.8288	.97922	1.0212	4.9313	18
43	.20307	.20739	4.8218	.97916	1.0213	4.9244	17
44	.20336	.20770	4.8147	.97910	1.0213	4.9175	16
45	.20364	.20800	4.8077	.97905	1.0214	4.9106	15
46	.20393	.20830	4.8007	.97899	1.0215	4.9037	14
47	.20421	.20861	4.7937	.97893	1.0215	4.8969	13
48	.20450	.20891	4.7867	.97887	1.0216	4.8901	12
49	.20478	.20921	4.7798	.97881	1.0217	4.8833	11
50	.20507	.20952	4.7729	.97875	1.0217	4.8765	10
51	.20535	.20982	4.7659	.97869	1.0218	4.8697	9
52	.20563	.21013	4.7591	.97863	1.0218	4.8630	8
53	.20592	.21043	4.7522	.97857	1.0219	4.8563	7
54	.20620	.21073	4.7453	.97851	1.0220	4.8496	6
55	.20649	.21104	4.7385	.97845	1.0220	4.8429	5
56	.20677	.21134	4.7317	.97839	1.0221	4.8362	4
57	.20706	.21164	4.7249	.97833	1.0222	4.8296	3
58	.20734	.21195	4.7181	.97827	1.0222	4.8229	2
59	.20763	.21225	4.7114	.97821	1.0223	4.8163	1
60	.20791	.21256	4.7046	.97815	1.0223	4.8097	0
′	Cos	Cot	Tan	Sin	Csc	Sec	′

101° (281°) (258°) **78°**

12° (192°) (347°) 167° 13° (193°) (346°) 166°

′	Sin	Tan	Cot	Cos	Sec	Csc	′		′	Sin	Tan	Cot	Cos	Sec	Csc	′
0	.20791	.21256	4.7046	.97815	1.0223	4.8097	60		0	.22495	.23087	4.3315	.97437	1.0263	4.4454	60
1	.20820	.21286	4.6979	.97809	1.0224	4.8032	59		1	.22523	.23117	4.3257	.97430	1.0264	4.4398	59
2	.20848	.21316	4.6912	.97803	1.0225	4.7966	58		2	.22552	.23148	4.3200	.97424	1.0264	4.4342	58
3	.20877	.21347	4.6845	.97797	1.0225	4.7901	57		3	.22580	.23179	4.3143	.97417	1.0265	4.4287	57
4	.20905	.21377	4.6779	.97791	1.0226	4.7836	56		4	.22608	.23209	4.3086	.97411	1.0266	4.4231	56
5	.20933	.21408	4.6712	.97784	1.0227	4.7771	55		5	.22637	.23240	4.3029	.97404	1.0266	4.4176	55
6	.20962	.21438	4.6646	.97778	1.0227	4.7706	54		6	.22665	.23271	4.2972	.97398	1.0267	4.4121	54
7	.20990	.21469	4.6580	.97772	1.0228	4.7641	53		7	.22693	.23301	4.2916	.97391	1.0268	4.4066	53
8	.21019	.21499	4.6514	.97766	1.0228	4.7577	52		8	.22722	.23332	4.2859	.97384	1.0269	4.4011	52
9	.21047	.21529	4.6448	.97760	1.0229	4.7512	51		9	.22750	.23363	4.2803	.97378	1.0269	4.3956	51
10	.21076	.21560	4.6382	.97754	1.0230	4.7448	50		10	.22778	.23393	4.2747	.97371	1.0270	4.3901	50
11	.21104	.21590	4.6317	.97748	1.0230	4.7384	49		11	.22807	.23424	4.2691	.97365	1.0271	4.3847	49
12	.21132	.21621	4.6252	.97742	1.0231	4.7321	48		12	.22835	.23455	4.2635	.97358	1.0271	4.3792	48
13	.21161	.21651	4.6187	.97735	1.0232	4.7257	47		13	.22863	.23485	4.2580	.97351	1.0272	4.3738	47
14	.21189	.21682	4.6122	.97729	1.0232	4.7194	46		14	.22892	.23516	4.2524	.97345	1.0273	4.3684	46
15	.21218	.21712	4.6057	.97723	1.0233	4.7130	45		15	.22920	.23547	4.2468	.97338	1.0273	4.3630	45
16	.21246	.21743	4.5993	.97717	1.0234	4.7067	44		16	.22948	.23578	4.2413	.97331	1.0274	4.3576	44
17	.21275	.21773	4.5928	.97711	1.0234	4.7004	43		17	.22977	.23608	4.2358	.97325	1.0275	4.3522	43
18	.21303	.21804	4.5864	.97705	1.0235	4.6942	42		18	.23005	.23639	4.2303	.97318	1.0276	4.3469	42
19	.21331	.21834	4.5800	.97698	1.0236	4.6879	41		19	.23033	.23670	4.2248	.97311	1.0276	4.3415	41
20	.21360	.21864	4.5736	.97692	1.0236	4.6817	40		20	.23062	.23700	4.2193	.97304	1.0277	4.3362	40
21	.21388	.21895	4.5673	.97686	1.0237	4.6755	39		21	.23090	.23731	4.2139	.97298	1.0278	4.3309	39
22	.21417	.21925	4.5609	.97680	1.0238	4.6693	38		22	.23118	.23762	4.2084	.97291	1.0278	4.3256	38
23	.21445	.21956	4.5546	.97673	1.0238	4.6631	37		23	.23146	.23793	4.2030	.97284	1.0279	4.3203	37
24	.21474	.21986	4.5483	.97667	1.0239	4.6569	36		24	.23175	.23823	4.1976	.97278	1.0280	4.3150	36
25	.21502	.22017	4.5420	.97661	1.0240	4.6507	35		25	.23203	.23854	4.1922	.97271	1.0281	4.3098	35
26	.21530	.22047	4.5357	.97655	1.0240	4.6446	34		26	.23231	.23885	4.1868	.97264	1.0281	4.3045	34
27	.21559	.22078	4.5294	.97648	1.0241	4.6385	33		27	.23260	.23916	4.1814	.97257	1.0282	4.2993	33
28	.21587	.22108	4.5232	.97642	1.0241	4.6324	32		28	.23288	.23946	4.1760	.97251	1.0283	4.2941	32
29	.21616	.22139	4.5169	.97636	1.0242	4.6263	31		29	.23316	.23977	4.1706	.97244	1.0283	4.2889	31
30	.21644	.22169	4.5107	.97630	1.0243	4.6202	30		30	.23345	.24008	4.1653	.97237	1.0284	4.2837	30
31	.21672	.22200	4.5045	.97623	1.0243	4.6142	29		31	.23373	.24039	4.1600	.97230	1.0285	4.2785	29
32	.21701	.22231	4.4983	.97617	1.0244	4.6081	28		32	.23401	.24069	4.1547	.97223	1.0286	4.2733	28
33	.21729	.22261	4.4922	.97611	1.0245	4.6021	27		33	.23429	.24100	4.1493	.97217	1.0286	4.2681	27
34	.21758	.22292	4.4860	.97604	1.0245	4.5961	26		34	.23458	.24131	4.1441	.97210	1.0287	4.2630	26
35	.21786	.22322	4.4799	.97598	1.0246	4.5901	25		35	.23486	.24162	4.1388	.97203	1.0288	4.2579	25
36	.21814	.22353	4.4737	.97592	1.0247	4.5841	24		36	.23514	.24193	4.1335	.97196	1.0288	4.2527	24
37	.21843	.22383	4.4676	.97585	1.0247	4.5782	23		37	.23542	.24223	4.1282	.97189	1.0289	4.2476	23
38	.21871	.22414	4.4615	.97579	1.0248	4.5722	22		38	.23571	.24254	4.1230	.97182	1.0290	4.2425	22
39	.21899	.22444	4.4555	.97573	1.0249	4.5663	21		39	.23599	.24285	4.1178	.97176	1.0291	4.2375	21
40	.21928	.22475	4.4494	.97566	1.0249	4.5604	20		40	.23627	.24316	4.1126	.97169	1.0291	4.2324	20
41	.21956	.22505	4.4434	.97560	1.0250	4.5545	19		41	.23656	.24347	4.1074	.97162	1.0292	4.2273	19
42	.21985	.22536	4.4373	.97553	1.0251	4.5486	18		42	.23684	.24377	4.1022	.97155	1.0293	4.2223	18
43	.22013	.22567	4.4313	.95747	1.0251	4.5428	17		43	.23712	.24408	4.0970	.97148	1.0294	4.2173	17
44	.22041	.22597	4.4253	.97541	1.0252	4.5369	16		44	.23740	.24439	4.0918	.97141	1.0294	4.2122	16
45	.22070	.22628	4.4194	.97534	1.0253	4.5311	15		45	.23769	.24470	4.0867	.97134	1.0295	4.2072	15
46	.22098	.22658	4.4134	.97528	1.0253	4.5253	14		46	.23797	.24501	4.0815	.97127	1.0296	4.2022	14
47	.22126	.22689	4.4075	.97521	1.0254	4.5195	13		47	.23825	.24532	4.0764	.97120	1.0297	4.1973	13
48	.22155	.22719	4.4015	.97515	1.0255	4.5137	12		48	.23853	.24562	4.0713	.97113	1.0297	4.1923	12
49	.22183	.22750	4.3956	.97508	1.0256	4.5079	11		49	.23882	.24593	4.0662	.97106	1.0298	4.1873	11
50	.22212	.22781	4.3897	.97502	1.0256	4.5022	10		50	.23910	.24624	4.0611	.97100	1.0299	4.1824	10
51	.22240	.22811	4.3838	.97496	1.0257	4.4964	9		51	.23938	.24655	4.0560	.97093	1.0299	4.1774	9
52	.22268	.22842	4.3779	.97489	1.0258	4.4907	8		52	.23966	.24686	4.0509	.97086	1.0300	4.1725	8
53	.22297	.22872	4.3721	.97483	1.0258	4.4850	7		53	.23995	.24717	4.0459	.97079	1.0301	4.1676	7
54	.22325	.22903	4.3662	.97476	1.0259	4.4793	6		54	.24023	.24747	4.0408	.97072	1.0302	4.1627	6
55	.22353	.22934	4.3604	.97470	1.0260	4.4736	5		55	.24051	.24778	4.0358	.97065	1.0302	4.1578	5
56	.22382	.22964	4.3546	.97463	1.0260	4.4679	4		56	.24079	.24809	4.0308	.97058	1.0303	4.1529	4
57	.22410	.22995	4.3488	.97457	1.0261	4.4623	3		57	.24108	.24840	4.0257	.97051	1.0304	4.1481	3
58	.22438	.23026	4.3430	.97450	1.0262	4.4566	2		58	.24136	.24871	4.0207	.97044	1.0305	4.1432	2
59	.22467	.23056	4.3372	.97444	1.0262	4.4510	1		59	.24164	.24902	4.0158	.97037	1.0305	4.1384	1
60	.22495	.23087	4.3315	.97437	1.0263	4.4454	0		60	.24192	.24933	4.0108	.97030	1.0306	4.1336	0
′	Cos	Cot	Tan	Sin	Csc	Sec	′		′	Cos	Cot	Tan	Sin	Csc	Sec	′

102° (282°) (257°) 77° 103° (283°) (256°) 76°

14° (194°)   (345°) 165°   15° (195°)   (344°) 164°

′	Sin	Tan	Cot	Cos	Sec	Csc	′
0	.24192	.24933	4.0108	.97030	1.0306	4.1336	60
1	.24220	.24964	4.0058	.97023	1.0307	4.1287	59
2	.24249	.24995	4.0009	.97015	1.0308	4.1239	58
3	.24277	.25026	3.9959	.97008	1.0308	4.1191	57
4	.24305	.25056	3.9910	.97001	1.0309	4.1144	56
5	.24333	.25087	3.9861	.96994	1.0310	4.1096	55
6	.24362	.25118	3.9812	.96987	1.0311	4.1048	54
7	.24390	.25149	3.9763	.96980	1.0311	4.1001	53
8	.24418	.25180	3.9714	.96973	1.0312	4.0954	52
9	.24446	.25211	3.9665	.96966	1.0313	4.0906	51
10	.24474	.25242	3.9617	.96959	1.0314	4.0859	50
11	.24503	.25273	3.9568	.96952	1.0314	4.0812	49
12	.24531	.25304	3.9520	.96945	1.0315	4.0765	48
13	.24559	.25335	3.9471	.96937	1.0316	4.0718	47
14	.24587	.25366	3.9423	.96930	1.0317	4.0672	46
15	.24615	.25397	3.9375	.96923	1.0317	4.0625	45
16	.24644	.25428	3.9327	.96916	1.0318	4.0579	44
17	.24672	.25459	3.9279	.96909	1.0319	4.0532	43
18	.24700	.25490	3.9232	.96902	1.0320	4.0486	42
19	.24728	.25521	3.9184	.96894	1.0321	4.0440	41
20	.24756	.25552	3.9136	.96887	1.0321	4.0394	40
21	.24784	.25583	3.9089	.96880	1.0322	4.0348	39
22	.24813	.25614	3.9042	.96873	1.0323	4.0302	38
23	.24841	.25645	3.8995	.96866	1.0324	4.0256	37
24	.24869	.25676	3.8947	.96858	1.0324	4.0211	36
25	.24897	.25707	3.8900	.96851	1.0325	4.0165	35
26	.24925	.25738	3.8854	.96844	1.0326	4.0120	34
27	.24954	.25769	3.8807	.96837	1.0327	4.0075	33
28	.24982	.25800	3.8760	.96829	1.0327	4.0029	32
29	.25010	.25831	3.8714	.96822	1.0328	3.9984	31
30	.25038	.25862	3.8667	.96815	1.0329	3.9939	30
31	.25066	.25893	3.8621	.96807	1.0330	3.9894	29
32	.25094	.25924	3.8575	.96800	1.0331	3.9850	28
33	.25122	.25955	3.8528	.96793	1.0331	3.9805	27
34	.25151	.25986	3.8482	.96786	1.0332	3.9760	26
35	.25179	.26017	3.8436	.96778	1.0333	3.9716	25
36	.25207	.26048	3.8391	.96771	1.0334	3.9672	24
37	.25235	.26079	3.8345	.96764	1.0334	3.9627	23
38	.25263	.26110	3.8299	.96756	1.0335	3.9583	22
39	.25291	.26141	3.8254	.96749	1.0336	3.9539	21
40	.25320	.26172	3.8208	.96742	1.0337	3.9495	20
41	.25348	.26203	3.8163	.96734	1.0338	3.9451	19
42	.25376	.26235	3.8118	.96727	1.0338	3.9408	18
43	.25404	.26266	3.8073	.96719	1.0339	3.9364	17
44	.25432	.26297	3.8028	.96712	1.0340	3.9320	16
45	.25460	.26328	3.7983	.96705	1.0341	3.9277	15
46	.25488	.26359	3.7938	.96697	1.0342	3.9234	14
47	.25516	.26390	3.7893	.96690	1.0342	3.9190	13
48	.25545	.26421	3.7848	.96682	1.0343	3.9147	12
49	.25573	.26452	3.7804	.96675	1.0344	3.9104	11
50	.25601	.26483	3.7760	.96667	1.0345	3.9061	10
51	.25629	.26515	3.7715	.96660	1.0346	3.9018	9
52	.25657	.26546	3.7671	.96653	1.0346	3.8976	8
53	.25685	.26577	3.7627	.96645	1.0347	3.8933	7
54	.25713	.26608	3.7583	.96638	1.0348	3.8890	6
55	.25741	.26639	3.7539	.96630	1.0349	3.8848	5
56	.25769	.26670	3.7495	.96623	1.0350	3.8806	4
57	.25798	.26701	3.7451	.96615	1.0350	3.8763	3
58	.25826	.26733	3.7408	.96608	1.0351	3.8721	2
59	.25854	.26764	3.7364	.96600	1.0352	3.8679	1
60	.25882	.26795	3.7321	.96593	1.0353	3.8637	0
′	Cos	Cot	Tan	Sin	Csc	Sec	′

104° (284°)   (255°) 75°

′	Sin	Tan	Cot	Cos	Sec	Csc	′
0	.25882	.26795	3.7321	.96593	1.0353	3.8637	60
1	.25910	.26826	3.7277	.96585	1.0354	3.8595	59
2	.25938	.26857	3.7234	.96578	1.0354	3.8553	58
3	.25966	.26888	3.7191	.96570	1.0355	3.8512	57
4	.25994	.26920	3.7148	.96562	1.0356	3.8470	56
5	.26022	.26951	3.7105	.96555	1.0357	3.8428	55
6	.26050	.26982	3.7062	.96547	1.0358	3.8387	54
7	.26079	.27013	3.7019	.96540	1.0358	3.8346	53
8	.26107	.27044	3.6976	.96532	1.0359	3.8304	52
9	.26135	.27076	3.6933	.96524	1.0360	3.8263	51
10	.26163	.27107	3.6891	.96517	1.0361	3.8222	50
11	.26191	.27138	3.6848	.96509	1.0362	3.8181	49
12	.26219	.27169	3.6806	.96502	1.0363	3.8140	48
13	.26247	.27201	3.6764	.96494	1.0363	3.8100	47
14	.26275	.27232	3.6722	.96486	1.0364	3.8059	46
15	.26303	.27263	3.6680	.96479	1.0365	3.8018	45
16	.26331	.27294	3.6638	.96471	1.0366	3.7978	44
17	.26359	.27326	3.6596	.96463	1.0367	3.7937	43
18	.26387	.27357	3.6554	.96456	1.0367	3.7897	42
19	.26415	.27388	3.6512	.96448	1.0368	3.7857	41
20	.26443	.27419	3.6470	.96440	1.0369	3.7817	40
21	.26471	.27451	3.6429	.96433	1.0370	3.7777	39
22	.26500	.27482	3.6387	.96425	1.0371	3.7737	38
23	.26528	.27513	3.6346	.96417	1.0372	3.7697	37
24	.26556	.27545	3.6305	.96410	1.0372	3.7657	36
25	.26584	.27576	3.6264	.96402	1.0373	3.7617	35
26	.26612	.27607	3.6222	.96394	1.0374	3.7577	34
27	.26640	.27638	3.6181	.96386	1.0375	3.7538	33
28	.26668	.27670	3.6140	.96379	1.0376	3.7498	32
29	.26696	.27701	3.6100	.96371	1.0377	3.7459	31
30	.26724	.27732	3.6059	.96363	1.0377	3.7420	30
31	.26752	.27764	3.6018	.96355	1.0378	3.7381	29
32	.26780	.27795	3.5978	.96347	1.0379	3.7341	28
33	.26808	.27826	3.5937	.96340	1.0380	3.7302	27
34	.26836	.27858	3.5897	.96332	1.0381	3.7263	26
35	.26864	.27889	3.5856	.96324	1.0382	3.7225	25
36	.26892	.27921	3.5816	.96316	1.0382	3.7186	24
37	.26920	.27952	3.5776	.96308	1.0383	3.7147	23
38	.26948	.27983	3.5736	.96301	1.0384	3.7108	22
39	.26976	.28015	3.5696	.96293	1.0385	3.7070	21
40	.27004	.28046	3.5656	.96285	1.0386	3.7032	20
41	.27032	.28077	3.5616	.96277	1.0387	3.6993	19
42	.27060	.28109	3.5576	.96269	1.0388	3.6955	18
43	.27088	.28140	3.5536	.96261	1.0388	3.6917	17
44	.27116	.28172	3.5497	.96253	1.0389	3.6879	16
45	.27144	.28203	3.5457	.96246	1.0390	3.6840	15
46	.27172	.28234	3.5418	.96238	1.0391	3.6803	14
47	.27200	.28266	3.5379	.96230	1.0392	3.6765	13
48	.27228	.28297	3.5339	.96222	1.0393	3.6727	12
49	.27256	.28329	3.5300	.96214	1.0394	3.6689	11
50	.27284	.28360	3.5261	.96206	1.0394	3.6652	10
51	.27312	.28391	3.5222	.96198	1.0395	3.6614	9
52	.27340	.28423	3.5183	.96190	1.0396	3.6575	8
53	.27368	.28454	3.5144	.96182	1.0397	3.6539	7
54	.27396	.28486	3.5105	.96174	1.0398	3.6502	6
55	.27424	.28517	3.5067	.96166	1.0399	3.6465	5
56	.27452	.28549	3.5028	.96158	1.0400	3.6427	4
57	.27480	.28580	3.4989	.96150	1.0400	3.6390	3
58	.27508	.28612	3.4951	.96142	1.0401	3.6353	2
59	.27536	.28643	3.4912	.96134	1.0402	3.6316	1
60	.27564	.28675	3.4874	.96126	1.0403	3.6280	0
′	Cos	Cot	Tan	Sin	Csc	Sec	′

105° (285°)   (254°) 74°

NATURAL TRIGONOMETRIC FUNCTIONS (*Continued*)

′	Sin	Tan	Cot	Cos	Sec	Csc	′	′	Sin	Tan	Cot	Cos	Sec	Csc	′
0	.27564	.28675	3.4874	.96126	1.0403	3.6280	60	0	.29237	.30573	3.2709	.95630	1.0457	3.4203	60
1	.27592	.28706	3.4836	.96118	1.0404	3.6243	59	1	.29265	.30605	3.2675	.95622	1.0458	3.4171	59
2	.27620	.28738	3.4798	.96110	1.0405	3.6206	58	2	.29293	.30637	3.2641	.95613	1.0459	3.4138	58
3	.27648	.28769	3.4760	.96102	1.0406	3.6169	57	3	.29321	.30669	3.2607	.95605	1.0460	3.4106	57
4	.27676	.28801	3.4722	.96094	1.0406	3.6133	56	4	.29348	.30700	3.2573	.95596	1.0461	3.4073	56
5	.27704	.28832	3.4684	.96086	1.0407	3.6097	55	5	.29376	.30732	3.2539	.95588	1.0462	3.4041	55
6	.27731	.28864	3.4646	.96078	1.0408	3.6060	54	6	.29404	.30764	3.2506	.95579	1.0463	3.4009	54
7	.27759	.28895	3.4608	.96070	1.0409	3.6024	53	7	.29432	.30796	3.2472	.95571	1.0463	3.3977	53
8	.27787	.28927	3.4570	.96062	1.0410	3.5988	52	8	.29460	.30828	3.2438	.95562	1.0464	3.3945	52
9	.27815	.28958	3.4533	.96054	1.0411	3.5951	51	9	.29487	.30860	3.2405	.95554	1.0465	3.3913	51
10	.27843	.28990	3.4495	.96046	1.0412	3.5915	50	10	.29515	.30891	3.2371	.95545	1.0466	3.3881	50
11	.27871	.29021	3.4458	.96037	1.0413	3.5879	49	11	.29543	.30923	3.2338	.95536	1.0467	3.3849	49
12	.27899	.29053	3.4420	.96029	1.0413	3.5843	48	12	.29571	.30955	3.2305	.95528	1.0468	3.3817	48
13	.27927	.29084	3.4383	.96021	1.0414	3.5808	47	13	.29599	.30987	3.2272	.95519	1.0469	3.3785	47
14	.27955	.29116	3.4346	.96013	1.0415	3.5772	46	14	.29626	.31019	3.2238	.95511	1.0470	3.3754	46
15	.27983	.29147	3.4308	.96005	1.0416	3.5736	45	15	.29654	.31051	3.2205	.95502	1.0471	3.3722	45
16	.28011	.29179	3.4271	.95997	1.0417	3.5700	44	16	.29682	.31083	3.2172	.95493	1.0472	3.3691	44
17	.28039	.29210	3.4234	.95989	1.0418	3.5665	43	17	.29710	.31115	3.2139	.95485	1.0473	3.3659	43
18	.28067	.29242	3.4197	.95981	1.0419	3.5629	42	18	.29737	.31147	3.2106	.95476	1.0474	3.3628	42
19	.28095	.29274	3.4160	.95972	1.0420	3.5594	41	19	.29765	.31178	3.2073	.95467	1.0475	3.3596	41
20	.28123	.29305	3.4124	.95964	1.0421	3.5559	40	20	.29793	.31210	3.2041	.95459	1.0476	3.3565	40
21	.28150	.29337	3.4087	.95956	1.0421	3.5523	39	21	.29821	.31242	3.2008	.95450	1.0477	3.3534	39
22	.28178	.29368	3.4050	.95948	1.0422	3.5488	38	22	.29849	.31274	3.1975	.95441	1.0478	3.3502	38
23	.28206	.29400	3.4014	.95940	1.0423	3.5453	37	23	.29876	.31306	3.1943	.95433	1.0479	3.3471	37
24	.28234	.29432	3.3977	.95931	1.0424	3.5418	36	24	.29904	.31338	3.1910	.95424	1.0480	3.3440	36
25	.28262	.29463	3.3941	.95923	1.0425	3.5383	35	25	.29932	.31370	3.1878	.95415	1.0480	3.3409	35
26	.28290	.29495	3.3904	.95915	1.0426	3.5348	34	26	.29960	.31402	3.1845	.95407	1.0481	3.3378	34
27	.28318	.29526	3.3868	.95907	1.0427	3.5313	33	27	.29987	.31434	3.1813	.95398	1.0482	3.3347	33
28	.28346	.29558	3.3832	.95898	1.0428	3.5279	32	28	.30015	.31466	3.1780	.95389	1.0483	3.3317	32
29	.28374	.29590	3.3796	.95890	1.0429	3.5244	31	29	.30043	.31498	3.1748	.95380	1.0484	3.3286	31
30	.28402	.29621	3.3759	.95882	1.0429	3.5209	30	30	.30071	.31530	3.1716	.95372	1.0485	3.3255	30
31	.28429	.29653	3.3723	.95874	1.0430	3.5175	29	31	.30098	.31562	3.1684	.95363	1.0486	3.3224	29
32	.28457	.29685	3.3687	.95865	1.0431	3.5140	28	32	.30126	.31594	3.1652	.95354	1.0487	3.3194	28
33	.28485	.29716	3.3652	.95857	1.0432	3.5106	27	33	.30154	.31626	3.1620	.95345	1.0488	3.3163	27
34	.28513	.29748	3.3616	.95849	1.0433	3.5072	26	34	.30182	.31658	3.1588	.95337	1.0489	3.3133	26
35	.28541	.29780	3.3580	.95841	1.0434	3.5037	25	35	.30209	.31690	3.1556	.95328	1.0490	3.3102	25
36	.28569	.29811	3.3544	.95832	1.0435	3.5003	24	36	.30237	.31722	3.1524	.95319	1.0491	3.3072	24
37	.28597	.29843	3.3509	.95824	1.0436	3.4969	23	37	.30265	.31754	3.1492	.95310	1.0492	3.3042	23
38	.28625	.29875	3.3473	.95816	1.0437	3.4935	22	38	.30292	.31786	3.1460	.95301	1.0493	3.3012	22
39	.28652	.29906	3.3438	.95807	1.0438	3.4901	21	39	.30320	.31818	3.1429	.95293	1.0494	3.2981	21
40	.28680	.29938	3.3402	.95799	1.0439	3.4867	20	40	.30348	.31850	3.1397	.95284	1.0495	3.2951	20
41	.28708	.29970	3.3367	.95791	1.0439	3.4833	19	41	.30376	.31882	3.1366	.95275	1.0496	3.2921	19
42	.28736	.30001	3.3332	.95782	1.0440	3.4799	18	42	.30403	.31914	3.1334	.95266	1.0497	3.2891	18
43	.28764	.30033	3.3297	.95774	1.0441	3.4766	17	43	.30431	.31946	3.1303	.95257	1.0498	3.2861	17
44	.28792	.30065	3.3261	.95766	1.0442	3.4732	16	44	.30459	.31978	3.1271	.95248	1.0499	3.2831	16
45	.28820	.30097	3.3226	.95757	1.0443	3.4699	15	45	.30486	.32010	3.1240	.95240	1.0500	3.2801	15
46	.28847	.30128	3.3191	.95749	1.0444	3.4665	14	46	.30514	.32042	3.1209	.95231	1.0501	3.2772	14
47	.28875	.30160	3.3156	.95740	1.0445	3.4632	13	47	.30542	.32074	3.1178	.95222	1.0502	3.2742	13
48	.28903	.30192	3.3122	.95732	1.0446	3.4598	12	48	.30570	.32106	3.1146	.95213	1.0503	3.2712	12
49	.28931	.30224	3.3087	.95724	1.0447	3.4565	11	49	.30597	.32139	3.1115	.95204	1.0504	3.2683	11
50	.28959	.30255	3.3052	.95715	1.0448	3.4532	10	50	.30625	.32171	3.1084	.95195	1.0505	3.2653	10
51	.28987	.30287	3.3017	.95707	1.0449	3.4499	9	51	.30653	.32203	3.1053	.95186	1.0506	3.2624	9
52	.29015	.30319	3.2983	.95698	1.0450	3.4465	8	52	.30680	.32235	3.1022	.95177	1.0507	3.2594	8
53	.29042	.30351	3.2948	.95690	1.0450	3.4432	7	53	.30708	.32267	3.0991	.95168	1.0508	3.2565	7
54	.29070	.30382	3.2914	.95681	1.0451	3.4399	6	54	.30736	.32299	3.0961	.95159	1.0509	3.2535	6
55	.29098	.30414	3.2879	.95673	1.0452	3.4367	5	55	.30763	.32331	3.0930	.95150	1.0510	3.2506	5
56	.29126	.30446	3.2845	.95664	1.0453	3.4334	4	56	.30791	.32363	3.0899	.95142	1.0511	3.2477	4
57	.29154	.30478	3.2811	.95656	1.0454	3.4301	3	57	.30819	.32396	3.0868	.95133	1.0512	3.2448	3
58	.29182	.30509	3.2777	.95647	1.0455	3.4268	2	58	.30846	.32428	3.0838	.95124	1.0513	3.2419	2
59	.29209	.30541	3.2743	.95639	1.0456	3.4236	1	59	.30874	.32460	3.0807	.95115	1.0514	3.2390	1
60	.29237	.30573	3.2709	.95630	1.0457	3.4203	0	60	.30902	.32492	3.0777	.95106	1.0515	3.2361	0
′	Cos	Cot	Tan	Sin	Csc	Sec	′	′	Cos	Cot	Tan	Sin	Csc	Sec	′

NATURAL TRIGONOMETRIC FUNCTIONS (*Continued*)

18° (198°)   (341°) 161°

′	Sin	Tan	Cot	Cos	Sec	Csc	′
0	.30902	.32492	3.0777	.95106	1.0515	3.2361	60
1	.30929	.32524	3.0746	.95097	1.0516	3.2332	59
2	.30957	.32556	3.0716	.95088	1.0517	3.2303	58
3	.30985	.32588	3.0686	.95079	1.0518	3.2274	57
4	.31012	.32621	3.0655	.95070	1.0519	3.2245	56
5	.31040	.32653	3.0625	.95061	1.0520	3.2217	55
6	.31068	.32685	3.0595	.95052	1.0521	3.2188	54
7	.31095	.32717	3.0565	.95043	1.0522	3.2159	53
8	.31123	.32749	3.0535	.95033	1.0523	3.2131	52
9	.31151	.32782	3.0505	.95024	1.0524	3.2102	51
10	.31178	.32814	3.0475	.95015	1.0525	3.2074	50
11	.31206	.32846	3.0445	.95006	1.0526	3.2045	49
12	.31233	.32878	3.0415	.94997	1.0527	3.2017	48
13	.31261	.32911	3.0385	.94988	1.0528	3.1989	47
14	.31289	.32943	3.0356	.94979	1.0529	3.1960	46
15	.31316	.32975	3.0326	.94970	1.0530	3.1932	45
16	.31344	.33007	3.0296	.94961	1.0531	3.1904	44
17	.31372	.33040	3.0267	.94952	1.0532	3.1876	43
18	.31399	.33072	3.0237	.94943	1.0533	3.1848	42
19	.31427	.33104	3.0208	.94933	1.0534	3.1820	41
20	.31454	.33136	3.0178	.94924	1.0535	3.1792	40
21	.31482	.33169	3.0149	.94915	1.0536	3.1764	39
22	.31510	.33201	3.0120	.94906	1.0537	3.1736	38
23	.31537	.33233	3.0090	.94897	1.0538	3.1708	37
24	.31565	.33266	3.0061	.94888	1.0539	3.1681	36
25	.31593	.33298	3.0032	.94878	1.0540	3.1653	35
26	.31620	.33330	3.0003	.94869	1.0541	3.1625	34
27	.31648	.33363	2.9974	.94860	1.0542	3.1598	33
28	.31675	.33395	2.9945	.94851	1.0543	3.1570	32
29	.31703	.33427	2.9916	.94842	1.0544	3.1543	31
30	.31730	.33460	2.9887	.94832	1.0545	3.1515	30
31	.31758	.33492	2.9858	.94823	1.0546	3.1488	29
32	.31786	.33524	2.9829	.94814	1.0547	3.1461	28
33	.31813	.33557	2.9800	.94805	1.0548	3.1433	27
34	.31841	.33589	2.9772	.94795	1.0549	3.1406	26
35	.31868	.33621	2.9743	.94786	1.0550	3.1379	25
36	.31896	.33654	2.9714	.94777	1.0551	3.1352	24
37	.31923	.33686	2.9686	.94768	1.0552	3.1325	23
38	.31951	.33718	2.9657	.94758	1.0553	3.1298	22
39	.31979	.33751	2.9629	.94749	1.0554	3.1271	21
40	.32006	.33783	2.9600	.94740	1.0555	3.1244	20
41	.32034	.33816	2.9572	.94730	1.0556	3.1217	19
42	.32061	.33848	2.9544	.94721	1.0557	3.1190	18
43	.32089	.33881	2.9515	.94712	1.0558	3.1163	17
44	.32116	.33913	2.9487	.94702	1.0559	3.1137	16
45	.32144	.33945	2.9459	.94693	1.0560	3.1110	15
46	.32171	.33978	2.9431	.94684	1.0561	3.1083	14
47	.32199	.34010	2.9403	.94674	1.0563	3.1057	13
48	.32227	.34043	2.9375	.94665	1.0564	3.1030	12
49	.32254	.34075	2.9347	.94656	1.0565	3.1004	11
50	.32282	.34108	2.9319	.94646	1.0566	3.0977	10
51	.32309	.34140	2.9291	.94637	1.0567	3.0951	9
52	.32337	.34173	2.9263	.94627	1.0568	3.0925	8
53	.32364	.34205	2.9235	.94618	1.0569	3.0898	7
54	.32392	.34238	2.9208	.94609	1.0570	3.0872	6
55	.32419	.34270	2.9180	.94599	1.0571	3.0846	5
56	.32447	.34303	2.9152	.94590	1.0572	3.0820	4
57	.32474	.34335	2.9125	.94580	1.0573	3.0794	3
58	.32502	.34368	2.9097	.94571	1.0574	3.0768	2
59	.32529	.34400	2.9070	.94561	1.0575	3.0742	1
60	.32557	.34433	2.9042	.94552	1.0576	3.0716	0
′	Cos	Cot	Tan	Sin	Csc	Sec	′

108° (288°)   (251°) 71°

19° (199°)   (340°) 160°

′	Sin	Tan	Cot	Cos	Sec	Csc	′
0	.32557	.34433	2.9042	.94552	1.0576	3.0716	60
1	.32584	.34465	2.9015	.94542	1.0577	3.0690	59
2	.32612	.34498	2.8987	.94533	1.0578	3.0664	58
3	.32639	.34530	2.8960	.94523	1.0579	3.0638	57
4	.32667	.34563	2.8933	.94514	1.0580	3.0612	56
5	.32694	.34596	2.8905	.94504	1.0582	3.0586	55
6	.32722	.34628	2.8878	.94495	1.0583	3.0561	54
7	.32749	.34661	2.8851	.94485	1.0584	3.0535	53
8	.32777	.34693	2.8824	.94476	1.0585	3.0509	52
9	.32804	.34726	2.8797	.94466	1.0586	3.0484	51
10	.32832	.34758	2.8770	.94457	1.0587	3.0458	50
11	.32859	.34791	2.8743	.94447	1.0588	3.0433	49
12	.32887	.34824	2.8716	.94438	1.0589	3.0407	48
13	.32914	.34856	2.8689	.94428	1.0590	3.0382	47
14	.32942	.34889	2.8662	.94418	1.0591	3.0357	46
15	.32969	.34922	2.8636	.94409	1.0592	3.0331	45
16	.32997	.34954	2.8609	.94399	1.0593	3.0306	44
17	.33024	.34987	2.8582	.94390	1.0594	3.0281	43
18	.33051	.35020	2.8556	.94380	1.0595	3.0256	42
19	.33079	.35052	2.8529	.94370	1.0597	3.0231	41
20	.33106	.35085	2.8502	.94361	1.0598	3.0206	40
21	.33134	.35118	2.8476	.94351	1.0599	3.0181	39
22	.33161	.35150	2.8449	.94342	1.0600	3.0156	38
23	.33189	.35183	2.8423	.94332	1.0601	3.0131	37
24	.33216	.35216	2.8397	.94322	1.0602	3.0106	36
25	.33244	.35248	2.8370	.94313	1.0603	3.0081	35
26	.33271	.35281	2.8344	.94303	1.0604	3.0056	34
27	.33298	.35314	2.8318	.94293	1.0605	3.0031	33
28	.33326	.35346	2.8291	.94284	1.0606	3.0007	32
29	.33353	.35379	2.8265	.94274	1.0607	2.9982	31
30	.33381	.35412	2.8239	.94264	1.0608	2.9957	30
31	.33408	.35445	2.8213	.94254	1.0610	2.9933	29
32	.33436	.35477	2.8187	.94245	1.0611	2.9908	28
33	.33463	.35510	2.8161	.94235	1.0612	2.9884	27
34	.33490	.35543	2.8135	.94225	1.0613	2.9859	26
35	.33518	.35576	2.8109	.94215	1.0614	2.9835	25
36	.33545	.35608	2.8083	.94206	1.0615	2.9811	24
37	.33573	.35641	2.8057	.94196	1.0616	2.9786	23
38	.33600	.35674	2.8032	.94186	1.0617	2.9762	22
39	.33627	.35707	2.8006	.94176	1.0618	2.9738	21
40	.33655	.35740	2.7980	.94167	1.0619	2.9713	20
41	.33682	.35772	2.7955	.94157	1.0621	2.9689	19
42	.33710	.35805	2.7929	.94147	1.0622	2.9665	18
43	.33737	.35838	2.7903	.94137	1.0623	2.9641	17
44	.33764	.35871	2.7878	.94127	1.0624	2.9617	16
45	.33792	.35904	2.7852	.94118	1.0625	2.9593	15
46	.33819	.35937	2.7827	.94108	1.0626	2.9569	14
47	.33846	.35969	2.7801	.94098	1.0627	2.9545	13
48	.33874	.36002	2.7776	.94088	1.0628	2.9521	12
49	.33901	.36035	2.7751	.94078	1.0629	2.9498	11
50	.33929	.36068	2.7725	.94068	1.0631	2.9474	10
51	.33956	.36101	2.7700	.94058	1.0632	2.9450	9
52	.33983	.36134	2.7675	.94049	1.0633	2.9426	8
53	.34011	.36167	2.7650	.94039	1.0634	2.9403	7
54	.34038	.36199	2.7625	.94029	1.0635	2.9379	6
55	.34065	.36232	2.7600	.94019	1.0636	2.9355	5
56	.34093	.36265	2.7575	.94009	1.0637	2.9332	4
57	.34120	.36298	2.7550	.93999	1.0638	2.9308	3
58	.34147	.36331	2.7525	.93989	1.0640	2.9285	2
59	.34175	.36364	2.7500	.93979	1.0641	2.9261	1
60	.34202	.36397	2.7475	.93969	1.0642	2.9238	0
′	Cos	Cot	Tan	Sin	Csc	Sec	′

109° (289°)   (250°) 70°

20° (200°)   (339°) **159°**   21° (201°)   (338°) **158°**

′	Sin	Tan	Cot	Cos	Sec	Csc	′		′	Sin	Tan	Cot	Cos	Sec	Csc	′
0	.34202	.36397	2.7475	.93969	1.0642	2.9238	**60**		**0**	.35837	.38386	2.6051	.93358	1.0711	2.7904	**60**
1	.34229	.36430	2.7450	.93959	1.0643	2.9215	59		1	.35864	.38420	2.6028	.93348	1.0713	2.7883	59
2	.34257	.36463	2.7425	.93949	1.0644	2.9191	58		2	.35891	.38453	2.6006	.93337	1.0714	2.7862	58
3	.34284	.36496	2.7400	.93939	1.0645	2.9168	57		3	.35918	.38487	2.5983	.93327	1.0715	2.7841	57
4	.34311	.36529	2.7376	.93929	1.0646	2.9145	56		4	.35945	.38520	2.5961	.93316	1.0716	2.7820	56
5	.34339	.36562	2.7351	.93919	1.0647	2.9122	**55**		**5**	.35973	.38553	2.5938	.93306	1.0717	2.7799	**55**
6	.34366	.36595	2.7326	.93909	1.0649	2.9099	54		6	.36000	.38587	2.5916	.93295	1.0719	2.7778	54
7	.34393	.36628	2.7302	.93899	1.0650	2.9075	53		7	.36027	.38620	2.5893	.93285	1.0720	2.7757	53
8	.34421	.36661	2.7277	.93889	1.0651	2.9052	52		8	.36054	.38654	2.5871	.93274	1.0721	2.7736	52
9	.34448	.36694	2.7253	.93879	1.0652	2.9029	51		9	.36081	.38687	2.5848	.93264	1.0722	2.7715	51
10	.34475	.36727	2.7228	.93869	1.0653	2.9006	**50**		**10**	.36108	.38721	2.5826	.93253	1.0723	2.7695	**50**
11	.34503	.36760	2.7204	.93859	1.0654	2.8983	49		11	.36135	.38754	2.5804	.93243	1.0725	2.7674	49
12	.34530	.36793	2.7179	.93849	1.0655	2.8960	48		12	.36162	.38787	2.5782	.93232	1.0726	2.7653	48
13	.34557	.36826	2.7155	.93839	1.0657	2.8938	47		13	.36190	.38821	2.5759	.93222	1.0727	2.7632	47
14	.34584	.36859	2.7130	.93829	1.0658	2.8915	46		14	.36217	.38854	2.5737	.93211	1.0728	2.7612	46
15	.34612	.36892	2.7106	.93819	1.0659	2.8892	**45**		**15**	.36244	.38888	2.5715	.93201	1.0730	2.7591	**45**
16	.34639	.36925	2.7082	.93809	1.0660	2.8869	44		16	.36271	.38921	2.5693	.93190	1.0731	2.7570	44
17	.34666	.36958	2.7058	.93799	1.0661	2.8846	43		17	.36298	.38955	2.5671	.93180	1.0732	2.7550	43
18	.34694	.36991	2.7034	.93789	1.0662	2.8824	42		18	.36325	.38988	2.5649	.93169	1.0733	2.7529	42
19	.34721	.37024	2.7009	.93779	1.0663	2.8801	41		19	.36352	.39022	2.5627	.93159	1.0734	2.7509	41
20	.34748	.37057	2.6985	.93769	1.0665	2.8779	**40**		**20**	.36379	.39055	2.5605	.93148	1.0736	2.7488	**40**
21	.34775	.37090	2.6961	.93759	1.0666	2.8756	39		21	.36406	.39089	2.5583	.93137	1.0737	2.7468	39
22	.34803	.37123	2.6937	.93748	1.0667	2.8733	38		22	.36434	.39122	2.5561	.93127	1.0738	2.7447	38
23	.34830	.37157	2.6913	.93738	1.0668	2.8711	37		23	.36461	.39156	2.5539	.93116	1.0739	2.7427	37
24	.34857	.37190	2.6889	.93728	1.0669	2.8688	36		24	.36488	.39190	2.5517	.93106	1.0740	2.7407	36
25	.34884	.37223	2.6865	.93718	1.0670	2.8666	**35**		**25**	.36515	.39223	2.5495	.93095	1.0742	2.7386	**35**
26	.34912	.37256	2.6841	.93708	1.0671	2.8644	34		26	.36542	.39257	2.5473	.93084	1.0743	2.7366	34
27	.34939	.37289	2.6818	.93698	1.0673	2.8621	33		27	.36569	.39290	2.5452	.93074	1.0744	2.7346	33
28	.34966	.37322	2.6794	.93688	1.0674	2.8599	32		28	.36596	.39324	2.5430	.93063	1.0745	2.7325	32
29	.34993	.37355	2.6770	.93677	1.0675	2.8577	31		29	.36623	.39357	2.5408	.93052	1.0747	2.7305	31
30	.35021	.37388	2.6746	.93667	1.0676	2.8555	**30**		**30**	.36650	.39391	2.5386	.93042	1.0748	2.7285	**30**
31	.35048	.37422	2.6723	.93657	1.0677	2.8532	29		31	.36677	.39425	2.5365	.93031	1.0749	2.7265	29
32	.35075	.37455	2.6699	.93647	1.0678	2.8510	28		32	.36704	.39458	2.5343	.93020	1.0750	2.7245	28
33	.35102	.37488	2.6675	.93637	1.0680	2.8488	27		33	.36731	.39492	2.5322	.93010	1.0752	2.7225	27
34	.35130	.37521	2.6652	.93626	1.0681	2.8466	26		34	.36758	.39526	2.5300	.92999	1.0753	2.7205	26
35	.35157	.37554	2.6628	.93616	1.0682	2.8444	**25**		**35**	.36785	.39559	2.5279	.92988	1.0754	2.7185	**25**
36	.35184	.37588	2.6605	.93606	1.0683	2.8422	24		36	.36812	.39593	2.5257	.92978	1.0755	2.7165	24
37	.35211	.37621	2.6581	.93596	1.0684	2.8400	23		37	.36839	.39626	2.5236	.92967	1.0757	2.7145	23
38	.35239	.37654	2.6558	.93585	1.0685	2.8378	22		38	.36867	.39660	2.5214	.92956	1.0758	2.7125	22
39	.35266	.37687	2.6534	.93575	1.0687	2.8356	21		39	.36894	.39694	2.5193	.92945	1.0759	2.7105	21
40	.35293	.37720	2.6511	.93565	1.0688	2.8334	**20**		**40**	.36921	.39727	2.5172	.92935	1.0760	2.7085	**20**
41	.35320	.37754	2.6488	.93555	1.0689	2.8312	19		41	.36948	.39761	2.5150	.92924	1.0761	2.7065	19
42	.35347	.37787	2.6464	.93544	1.0690	2.8291	18		42	.36975	.39795	2.5129	.92913	1.0763	2.7046	18
43	.35375	.37820	2.6441	.93534	1.0691	2.8269	17		43	.37002	.39829	2.5108	.92902	1.0764	2.7026	17
44	.35402	.37853	2.6418	.93524	1.0692	2.8247	16		44	.37029	.39862	2.5086	.92892	1.0765	2.7006	16
45	.35429	.37887	2.6395	.93514	1.0694	2.8225	**15**		**45**	.37056	.39896	2.5065	.92881	1.0766	2.6986	**15**
46	.35456	.37920	2.6371	.93503	1.0695	2.8204	14		46	.37083	.39930	2.5044	.92870	1.0768	2.6967	14
47	.35484	.37953	2.6348	.93493	1.0696	2.8182	13		47	.37110	.39963	2.5023	.92859	1.0769	2.6947	13
48	.35511	.37936	2.6325	.93483	1.0697	2.8161	12		48	.37137	.39997	2.5002	.92849	1.0770	2.6927	12
49	.35538	.38020	2.6302	.93472	1.0698	2.8139	11		49	.37164	.40031	2.4981	.92838	1.0771	2.6908	11
50	.35565	.38053	2.6279	.93462	1.0700	2.8117	**10**		**50**	.37191	.40065	2.4960	.92827	1.0773	2.6888	**10**
51	.35592	.38086	2.6256	.93452	1.0701	2.8096	9		51	.37218	.40098	2.4939	.92816	1.0774	2.6869	9
52	.35619	.38120	2.6233	.93441	1.0702	2.8075	8		52	.37245	.40132	2.4918	.92805	1.0775	2.6849	8
53	.35647	.38153	2.6210	.93431	1.0703	2.8053	7		53	.37272	.40166	2.4897	.92794	1.0777	2.6830	7
54	.35674	.38186	2.6187	.93420	1.0704	2.8032	6		54	.37299	.40200	2.4876	.92784	1.0778	2.6811	6
55	.35701	.38220	2.6165	.93410	1.0705	2.8010	**5**		**55**	.37326	.40234	2.4855	.92773	1.0779	2.6791	**5**
56	.35728	.38253	2.6142	.93400	1.0707	2.7989	4		56	.37353	.40267	2.4834	.92762	1.0780	2.6772	4
57	.35755	.38286	2.6119	.93389	1.0708	2.7968	3		57	.37380	.40301	2.4813	.92751	1.0782	2.6752	3
58	.35782	.38320	2.6096	.93379	1.0709	2.7947	2		58	.37407	.40335	2.4792	.92740	1.0783	2.6733	2
59	.35810	.38353	2.6074	.93368	1.0710	2.7925	1		59	.37434	.40369	2.4772	.92729	1.0784	2.6714	1
60	.35837	.38386	2.6051	.93358	1.0711	2.7904	**0**		**60**	.37461	.40403	2.4751	.92718	1.0785	2.6695	**0**
′	Cos	Cot	Tan	Sin	Csc	Sec	′		′	Cos	Cot	Tan	Sin	Csc	Sec	′

110° (290°)   (249°) **69°**   111° (291°)   (248°) **68°**

22° (202°)   (337°) **157°**

′	Sin	Tan	Cot	Cos	Sec	Csc	′
0	.37461	.40403	2.4751	.92718	1.0785	2.6695	60
1	.37488	.40436	2.4730	.92707	1.0787	2.6675	59
2	.37515	.40470	2.4709	.92697	1.0788	2.6656	58
3	.37542	.40504	2.4689	.92686	1.0789	2.6637	57
4	.37569	.40538	2.4668	.92675	1.0790	2.6618	56
5	.37595	.40572	2.4648	.92664	1.0792	2.6599	55
6	.37622	.40606	2.4627	.92653	1.0793	2.6580	54
7	.37649	.40640	2.4606	.92642	1.0794	2.6561	53
8	.37676	.40674	2.4586	.92631	1.0796	2.6542	52
9	.37703	.40707	2.4566	.92620	1.0797	2.6523	51
10	.37730	.40741	2.4545	.92609	1.0798	2.6504	50
11	.37757	.40775	2.4525	.92598	1.0799	2.6485	49
12	.37784	.40809	2.4504	.92587	1.0801	2.6466	48
13	.37811	.40843	2.4484	.92576	1.0802	2.6447	47
14	.37838	.40877	2.4464	.92565	1.0803	2.6429	46
15	.37865	.40911	2.4443	.92554	1.0804	2.6410	45
16	.37892	.40945	2.4423	.92543	1.0806	2.6391	44
17	.37919	.40979	2.4403	.92532	1.0807	2.6372	43
18	.37946	.41013	2.4383	.92521	1.0808	2.6354	42
19	.37973	.41047	2.4362	.92510	1.0810	2.6335	41
20	.37999	.41081	2.4342	.92499	1.0811	2.6316	40
21	.38026	.41115	2.4322	.92488	1.0812	2.6298	39
22	.38053	.41149	2.4302	.92477	1.0814	2.6279	38
23	.38080	.41183	2.4282	.92466	1.0815	2.6260	37
24	.38107	.41217	2.4262	.92455	1.0816	2.6242	36
25	.38134	.41251	2.4242	.92444	1.0817	2.6223	35
26	.38161	.41285	2.4222	.92432	1.0819	2.6205	34
27	.38188	.41319	2.4202	.92421	1.0820	2.6186	33
28	.38215	.41353	2.4182	.92410	1.0821	2.6168	32
29	.38241	.41387	2.4162	.92399	1.0823	2.6150	31
30	.38268	.41421	2.4142	.92388	1.0824	2.6131	30
31	.38295	.41455	2.4122	.92377	1.0825	2.6113	29
32	.38322	.41490	2.4102	.92366	1.0827	2.6095	28
33	.38310	.41524	2.4083	.92355	1.0828	2.6076	27
34	.38376	.41558	2.4063	.92343	1.0829	2.6058	26
35	.38403	.41592	2.4043	.92332	1.0830	2.6040	25
36	.38430	.41626	2.4023	.92321	1.0832	2.6022	24
37	.38456	.41660	2.4004	.92310	1.0833	2.6003	23
38	.38483	.41694	2.3984	.92299	1.0834	2.5985	22
39	.38510	.41728	2.3964	.92287	1.0836	2.5967	21
40	.38537	.41763	2.3945	.92276	1.0837	2.5949	20
41	.38564	.41797	2.3925	.92265	1.0838	2.5931	19
42	.38591	.41831	2.3906	.92254	1.0840	2.5913	18
43	.38617	.41865	2.3886	.92243	1.0841	2.5895	17
44	.38644	.41899	2.3867	.92231	1.0842	2.5877	16
45	.38671	.41933	2.3847	.92220	1.0844	2.5859	15
46	.38698	.41968	2.3828	.92209	1.0845	2.5841	14
47	.38725	.42002	2.3808	.92198	1.0846	2.5823	13
48	.38752	.42036	2.3789	.92186	1.0848	2.5805	12
49	.38778	.42070	2.3770	.92175	1.0849	2.5788	11
50	.38805	.42105	2.3750	.92164	1.0850	2.5770	10
51	.38832	.42139	2.3731	.92152	1.0852	2.5752	9
52	.38859	.42173	2.3712	.92141	1.0853	2.5734	8
53	.38886	.42207	2.3693	.92130	1.0854	2.5716	7
54	.38912	.42242	2.3673	.92119	1.0856	2.5699	6
55	.38939	.42276	2.3654	.92107	1.0857	2.5681	5
56	.38966	.42310	2.3635	.92096	1.0859	2.5663	4
57	.38993	.42345	2.3616	.92085	1.0860	2.5646	3
58	.39020	.42379	2.3597	.92073	1.0861	2.5628	2
59	.39046	.42413	2.3578	.92062	1.0862	2.5611	1
60	.39073	.42447	2.3559	.92050	1.0864	2.5593	0
′	Cos	Cot	Tan	Sin	Csc	Sec	′

112° (292°)   (247°) **67°**

23° (203°)   (336°) **156°**

′	Sin	Tan	Cot	Cos	Sec	Csc	′
0	.39073	.42447	2.3559	.92050	1.0864	2.5593	60
1	.39100	.42482	2.3539	.92039	1.0865	2.5576	59
2	.39127	.42516	2.3520	.92028	1.0866	2.5558	58
3	.39153	.42551	2.3501	.92016	1.0868	2.5541	57
4	.39180	.42585	2 3483	92005	1.0869	2.5523	56
5	.39207	.42619	2.3464	.91994	1.0870	2.5506	55
6	.39234	.42654	2.3445	.91982	1.0872	2.5488	54
7	.39260	.42688	2.3426	.91971	1.0873	2.5471	53
8	.39287	.42722	2.3407	.91959	1.0874	2.5454	52
9	.39314	.42757	2.3388	.91948	1.0876	2.5436	51
10	.39341	.42791	2.3369	.91936	1.0877	2.5419	50
11	.39367	.42826	2.3351	.91925	1.0878	2.5402	49
12	.39394	.42860	2.3332	.91914	1.0880	2.5384	48
13	.39421	.42894	2.3313	.91902	1.0881	2.5367	47
14	.39448	.42929	2.3294	.91891	1.0883	2.5350	46
15	.39474	.42963	2.3276	.91879	1.0884	2.5333	45
16	.39501	.42998	2.3257	.91868	1.0885	2.5316	44
17	.39528	.43032	2.3238	.91856	1.0887	2.5299	43
18	.39555	.43067	2.3220	.91845	1.0888	2.5282	42
19	.39581	.43101	2.3201	.91833	1.0889	2.5264	41
20	.39608	.43136	2.3183	.91822	1.0891	2.5247	40
21	.39635	.43170	2.3164	.91810	1.0892	2.5230	39
22	.39661	.43205	2.3146	.91799	1.0893	2.5213	38
23	.39688	.43239	2.3127	.91787	1.0895	2.5196	37
24	.39715	.43274	2.3109	.91775	1.0896	2.5180	36
25	.39741	.43308	2.3090	.91764	1.0898	2.5163	35
26	.39768	.43343	2.3072	.91752	1.0899	2.5146	34
27	.39795	.43378	2.3053	.91741	1.0900	2.5129	33
28	.39822	.43412	2.3035	.91729	1.0902	2.5112	32
29	.39848	.43447	2.3017	.91718	1.0903	2.5095	31
30	.39875	.43481	2.2998	.91706	1.0904	2.5078	30
31	.39902	.43516	2.2980	.91694	1.0906	2.5062	29
32	.39928	.43550	2.2962	.91683	1.0907	2.5045	28
33	.39955	.43585	2.2944	.91671	1.0909	2.5028	27
34	.39982	.43620	2.2925	.91660	1.0910	2.5012	26
35	.40008	.43654	2.2907	.91648	1.0911	2.4995	25
36	.40035	.43689	2.2889	.91636	1.0913	2.4978	24
37	.40062	.43724	2.2871	.91625	1.0914	2.4962	23
38	.40088	.43758	2.2853	.91613	1.0915	2.4945	22
39	.40115	.43793	2.2835	.91601	1.0917	2.4928	21
40	.40141	.43828	2.2817	.91590	1.0918	2.4912	20
41	.40168	.43862	2.2799	.91578	1.0920	2.4895	19
42	.40195	.43897	2.2781	.91566	1.0921	2.4879	18
43	.40221	.43932	2.2763	.91555	1.0922	2.4862	17
44	.40248	.43966	2.2745	.91543	1.0924	2.4846	16
45	.40275	.44001	2.2727	.91531	1.0925	2.4830	15
46	.40301	.44036	2.2709	.91519	1.0927	2.4813	14
47	.40328	.44071	2.2691	.91508	1.0928	2.4797	13
48	.40355	.44105	2.2673	.91496	1.0929	2.4780	12
49	.40381	.44140	2.2655	.91484	1.0931	2.4764	11
50	.40408	.44175	2.2637	.91472	1.0932	2.4748	10
51	.40434	.44210	2.2620	.91461	1.0934	2.4731	9
52	.40461	.44244	2.2602	.91449	1.0935	2.4715	8
53	.40488	.44279	2.2584	.91437	1.0936	2.4699	7
54	.40514	.44314	2.2566	.91425	1.0938	2.4683	6
55	.40541	.44349	2.2549	.91414	1.0939	2.4667	5
56	.40567	.44384	2.2531	.91402	1.0941	2.4650	4
57	.40594	.44418	2.2513	.91390	1.0942	2.4634	3
58	.40621	.44453	2.2496	.91378	1.0944	2.4618	2
59	.40647	.44488	2.2478	.91366	1.0945	2.4602	1
60	.40674	.44523	2.2460	.91355	1.0946	2.4586	0
′	Cos	Cot	Tan	Sin	Csc	Sec	′

113° (293°)   (246°) **66°**

24° (204°) (335°) 155° 25° (205°) (334°) 154°

′	Sin	Tan	Cot	Cos	Sec	Csc	′	′	Sin	Tan	Cot	Cos	Sec	Csc	′
0	.40674	.44523	2.2460	.91355	1.0946	2.4586	60	0	.42262	.46631	2.1445	.90631	1.1034	2.3662	60
1	.40700	.44558	2.2443	.91343	1.0948	2.4570	59	1	.42288	.46666	2.1429	.90618	1.1035	2.3647	59
2	.40727	.44593	2.2425	.91331	1.0949	2.4554	58	2	.42315	.46702	2.1413	.90606	1.1037	2.3633	58
3	.40753	.44627	2.2408	.91319	1.0951	2.4538	57	3	.42341	.46737	2.1396	.90594	1.1038	2.3618	57
4	.40780	.44662	2.2390	.91307	1.0952	2.4522	56	4	.42367	.46772	2.1380	.90582	1.1040	2.3603	56
5	.40806	.44697	2.2373	.91295	1.0953	2.4506	55	5	.42394	.46808	2.1364	.90569	1.1041	2.3588	55
6	.40833	.44732	2.2355	.91283	1.0955	2.4490	54	6	.42420	.46843	2.1348	.90557	1.1043	2.3574	54
7	.40860	.44767	2.2338	.91272	1.0956	2.4474	53	7	.42446	.46879	2.1332	.90545	1.1044	2.3559	53
8	.40886	.44802	2.2320	.91260	1.0958	2.4458	52	8	.42473	.46914	2.1315	.90532	1.1046	2.3545	52
9	.40913	.44837	2.2303	.91248	1.0959	2.4442	51	9	.42499	.46950	2.1299	.90520	1.1047	2.3530	51
10	.40939	.44872	2.2286	.91236	1.0961	2.4426	50	10	.42525	.46985	2.1283	.90507	1.1049	2.3515	50
11	.40966	.44907	2.2268	.91224	1.0962	2.4411	49	11	.42552	.47021	2.1267	.90495	1.1050	2.3501	49
12	.40992	.44942	2.2251	.91212	1.0963	2.4395	48	12	.42578	.47056	2.1251	.90483	1.1052	2.3486	48
13	.41019	.44977	2.2234	.91200	1.0965	2.4379	47	13	.42604	.47092	2.1235	.90470	1.1053	2.3472	47
14	.41045	.45012	2.2216	.91188	1.0966	2.4363	46	14	.42631	.47128	2.1219	.90458	1.1055	2.3457	46
15	.41072	.45047	2.2199	.91176	1.0968	2.4348	45	15	.42657	.47163	2.1203	.90446	1.1056	2.3443	45
16	.41098	.45082	2.2182	.91164	1.0969	2.4332	44	16	.42683	.47199	2.1187	.90433	1.1058	2.3428	44
17	.41125	.45117	2.2165	.91152	1.0971	2.4316	43	17	.42709	.47234	2.1171	.90421	1.1059	2.3414	43
18	.41151	.45152	2.2148	.91140	1.0972	2.4300	42	18	.42736	.47270	2.1155	.90408	1.1061	2.3400	42
19	.41178	.45187	2.2130	.91128	1.0974	2.4285	41	19	.42762	.47305	2.1139	.90396	1.1062	2.3385	41
20	.41204	.45222	2.2113	.91116	1.0975	2.4269	40	20	.42788	.47341	2.1123	.90383	1.1064	2.3371	40
21	.41231	.45257	2.2096	.91104	1.0976	2.4254	39	21	.42815	.47377	2.1107	.90371	1.1066	2.3356	39
22	.41257	.45292	2.2079	.91092	1.0978	2.4238	38	22	.42841	.47412	2.1092	.90358	1.1067	2.3342	38
23	.41284	.45327	2.2062	.91080	1.0979	2.4222	37	23	.42867	.47448	2.1076	.90346	1.1069	2.3328	37
24	.41310	.45362	2.2045	.91068	1.0981	2.4207	36	24	.42894	.47483	2.1060	.90334	1.1070	2.3314	36
25	.41337	.45397	2.2028	.91056	1.0982	2.4191	35	25	.42920	.47519	2.1044	.90321	1.1072	2.3299	35
26	.41363	.45432	2.2011	.91044	1.0984	2.4176	34	26	.42946	.47555	2.1028	.90309	1.1073	2.3285	34
27	.41390	.45467	2.1994	.91032	1.0985	2.4160	33	27	.42972	.47590	2.1013	.90296	1.1075	2.3271	33
28	.41416	.45502	2.1977	.91020	1.0987	2.4145	32	28	.42999	.47626	2.0997	.90284	1.1076	2.3257	32
29	.41443	.45538	2.1960	.91008	1.0988	2.4130	31	29	.43025	.47662	2.0981	.90271	1.1078	2.3242	31
30	.41469	.45573	2.1943	.90996	1.0989	2.4114	30	30	.43051	.47698	2.0965	.90259	1.1079	2.3228	30
31	.41496	.45608	2.1926	.90984	1.0991	2.4099	29	31	.43077	.47733	2.0950	.90246	1.1081	2.3214	29
32	.41522	.45643	2.1909	.90972	1.0992	2.4083	28	32	.43104	.47769	2.0934	.90233	1.1082	2.3200	28
33	.41549	.45678	2.1892	.90960	1.0994	2.4068	27	33	.43130	.47805	2.0918	.90221	1.1084	2.3186	27
34	.41575	.45713	2.1876	.90948	1.0995	2.4053	26	34	.43156	.47840	2.0903	.90208	1.1085	2.3172	26
35	.41602	.45748	2.1859	.90936	1.0997	2.4038	25	35	.43182	.47876	2.0887	.90196	1.1087	2.3158	25
36	.41628	.45784	2.1842	.90924	1.0998	2.4022	24	36	.43209	.47912	2.0872	.90183	1.1089	2.3144	24
37	.41655	.45819	2.1825	.90911	1.1000	2.4007	23	37	.43235	.47948	2.0856	.90171	1.1090	2.3130	23
38	.41681	.45854	2.1808	.90899	1.1001	2.3992	22	38	.43261	.47984	2.0840	.90158	1.1092	2.3115	22
39	.41707	.45889	2.1792	.90887	1.1003	2.3977	21	39	.43287	.48019	2.0825	.90146	1.1093	2.3101	21
40	.41734	.45924	2.1775	.90875	1.1004	2.3961	20	40	.43313	.48055	2.0809	.90133	1.1095	2.3088	20
41	.41760	.45960	2.1758	.90863	1.1006	2.3946	19	41	.43340	.48091	2.0794	.90120	1.1096	2.3074	19
42	.41787	.45995	2.1742	.90851	1.1007	2.3931	18	42	.43366	.48127	2.0778	.90108	1.1098	2.3060	18
43	.41813	.46030	2.1725	.90839	1.1009	2.3916	17	43	.43392	.48163	2.0763	.90095	1.1099	2.3046	17
44	.41840	.46065	2.1708	.90826	1.1010	2.3901	16	44	.43418	.48198	2.0748	.90082	1.1101	2.3032	16
45	.41866	.46101	2.1692	.90814	1.1011	2.3886	15	45	.43445	.48234	2.0732	.90070	1.1102	2.3018	15
46	.41892	.46136	2.1675	.90802	1.1013	2.3871	14	46	.43471	.48270	2.0717	.90057	1.1104	2.3004	14
47	.41919	.46171	2.1659	.90790	1.1014	2.3856	13	47	.43497	.48306	2.0701	.90045	1.1106	2.2990	13
48	.41945	.46206	2.1642	.90778	1.1016	2.3841	12	48	.43523	.48342	2.0686	.90032	1.1107	2.2976	12
49	.41972	.46242	2.1625	.90766	1.1017	2.3826	11	49	.43549	.48378	2.0671	.90019	1.1109	2.2962	11
50	.41998	.46277	2.1609	.90753	1.1019	2.3811	10	50	.43575	.48414	2.0655	.90007	1.1110	2.2949	10
51	.42024	.46312	2.1592	.90741	1.1020	2.3796	9	51	.43602	.48450	2.0640	.89994	1.1112	2.2935	9
52	.42051	.46348	2.1576	.90729	1.1022	2.3781	8	52	.43628	.48486	2.0625	.89981	1.1113	2.2921	8
53	.42077	.46383	2.1560	.90717	1.1023	2.3766	7	53	.43654	.48521	2.0609	.89968	1.1115	2.2907	7
54	.42104	.46418	2.1543	.90704	1.1025	2.3751	6	54	.43680	.48557	2.0594	.89956	1.1117	2.2894	6
55	.42130	.46454	2.1527	.90692	1.1026	2.3736	5	55	.43706	.48593	2.0579	.89943	1.1118	2.2880	5
56	.42156	.46489	2.1510	.90680	1.1028	2.3721	4	56	.43733	.48629	2.0564	.89930	1.1120	2.2866	4
57	.42183	.46525	2.1494	.90668	1.1029	2.3706	3	57	.43759	.48665	2.0549	.89918	1.1121	2.2853	3
58	.42209	.46560	2.1478	.90655	1.1031	2.3692	2	58	.43785	.48701	2.0533	.89905	1.1123	2.2839	2
59	.42235	.46595	2.1461	.90643	1.1032	2.3677	1	59	.43811	.48737	2.0518	.89892	1.1124	2.2825	1
60	.42262	.46631	2.1445	.90631	1.1034	2.3662	0	60	.43837	.48773	2.0503	.89879	1.1126	2.2812	0
′	Cos	Cot	Tan	Sin	Csc	Sec	′	′	Cos	Cot	Tan	Sin	Csc	Sce	′

114° (294°) (245°) 65° 115° (295°) (244°) 64°

26° (206°)   (333°) **153°**

′	Sin	Tan	Cot	Cos	Sec	Csc	′
0	.43837	.48773	2.0503	.89879	1.1126	2.2812	60
1	.43863	.48809	2.0488	.89867	1.1128	2.2798	59
2	.43889	.48845	2.0473	.89854	1.1129	2.2785	58
3	.43916	.48881	2.0458	.89841	1.1131	2.2771	57
4	.43942	.48917	2.0443	.89828	1.1132	2.2757	56
5	.43968	.48953	2.0428	.89816	1.1134	2.2744	55
6	.43994	.48989	2.0413	.89803	1.1136	2.2730	54
7	.44020	.49026	2.0398	.89790	1.1137	2.2717	53
8	.44046	.49062	2.0383	.89777	1.1139	2.2703	52
9	.44072	.49098	2.0368	.89764	1.1140	2.2690	51
10	.44098	.49134	2.0353	.89752	1.1142	2.2677	50
11	.44124	.49170	2.0338	.89739	1.1143	2.2663	49
12	.44151	.49206	2.0323	.89726	1.1145	2.2650	48
13	.44177	.49242	2.0308	.89713	1.1147	2.2636	47
14	.44203	.49278	2.0293	.89700	1.1148	2.2623	46
15	.44229	.49315	2.0278	.89687	1.1150	2.2610	45
16	.44255	.49351	2.0263	.89674	1.1151	2.2596	44
17	.44281	.49387	2.0248	.89662	1.1153	2.2583	43
18	.44307	.49423	2.0233	.89649	1.1155	2.2570	42
19	.44333	.49459	2.0219	.89636	1.1156	2.2556	41
20	.44359	.49495	2.0204	.89623	1.1158	2.2543	40
21	.44385	.49532	2.0189	.89610	1.1159	2.2530	39
22	.44411	.49568	2.0174	.89597	1.1161	2.2517	38
23	.44437	.49604	2.0160	.89584	1.1163	2.2504	37
24	.44464	.49640	2.0145	.89571	1.1164	2.2490	36
25	.44490	.49677	2.0130	.89558	1.1166	2.2477	35
26	.44516	.49713	2.0115	.89545	1.1168	2.2464	34
27	.44542	.49749	2.0101	.89532	1.1169	2.2451	33
28	.44568	.49786	2.0086	.89519	1.1171	2.2438	32
29	.44594	.49822	2.0072	.89506	1.1172	2.2425	31
30	.44620	.49858	2.0057	.89493	1.1174	2.2412	30
31	.44646	.49894	2.0042	.89480	1.1176	2.2399	29
32	.44672	.49931	2.0028	.89467	1.1177	2.2385	28
33	.44698	.49967	2.0013	.89454	1.1179	2.2372	27
34	.44721	.50004	1.9999	.89441	1.1180	2.2359	26
35	.44750	.50040	1.9984	.89428	1.1182	2.2346	25
36	.44776	.50076	1.9970	.89415	1.1184	2.2333	24
37	.44802	.50113	1.9955	.89402	1.1185	2.2320	23
38	.44828	.50149	1.9941	.89389	1.1187	2.2308	22
39	.44854	.50185	1.9926	.89376	1.1189	2.2295	21
40	.44880	.50222	1.9912	.89363	1.1190	2.2282	20
41	.44906	.50258	1.9897	.89350	1.1192	2.2269	19
42	.44932	.50295	1.9883	.89337	1.1194	2.2256	18
43	.44958	.50331	1.9868	.89324	1.1195	2.2243	17
44	.44984	.50368	1.9854	.89311	1.1197	2.2230	16
45	.45010	.50404	1.9840	.89298	1.1198	2.2217	15
46	.45036	.50441	1.9825	.89285	1.1200	2.2205	14
47	.45062	.50477	1.9811	.89272	1.1202	2.2192	13
48	.45088	.50514	1.9797	.89259	1.1203	2.2179	12
49	.45114	.50550	1.9782	.89245	1.1205	2.2166	11
50	.45140	.50587	1.9768	.89232	1.1207	2.2153	10
51	.45166	.50623	1.9754	.89219	1.1208	2.2141	9
52	.45192	.50660	1.9740	.89206	1.1210	2.2128	8
53	.45218	.50696	1.9725	.89193	1.1212	2.2115	7
54	.45243	.50733	1.9711	.89180	1.1213	2.2103	6
55	.45269	.50769	1.9697	.89167	1.1215	2.2090	5
56	.45295	.50806	1.9683	.89153	1.1217	2.2077	4
57	.45321	.50843	1.9669	.89140	1.1218	2.2065	3
58	.45347	.50879	1.9654	.89127	1.1220	2.2052	2
59	.45373	.50916	1.9640	.89114	1.1222	2.2039	1
60	.45399	.50953	1.9626	.89101	1.1223	2.2027	0
′	Cos	Cot	Tan	Sin	Csc	Sec	′

27° (207°)   (332°) **152°**

′	Sin	Tan	Cot	Cos	Sec	Csc	′
0	.45399	.50953	1.9626	.89101	1.1223	2.2027	60
1	.45425	.50989	1.9612	.89087	1.1225	2.2014	59
2	.45451	.51026	1.9598	.89074	1.1227	2.2002	58
3	.45477	.51063	1.9584	.89061	1.1228	2.1989	57
4	.45503	.51099	1.9570	.89048	1.1230	2.1977	56
5	.45529	.51136	1.9556	.89035	1.1232	2.1964	55
6	.45554	.51173	1.9542	.89021	1.1233	2.1952	54
7	.45580	.51209	1.9528	.89008	1.1235	2.1939	53
8	.45606	.51246	1.9514	.88995	1.1237	2.1927	52
9	.45632	.51283	1.9500	.88981	1.1238	2.1914	51
10	.45658	.51319	1.9486	.88968	1.1240	2.1902	50
11	.45684	.51356	1.9472	.88955	1.1242	2.1890	49
12	.45710	.51393	1.9458	.88942	1.1243	2.1877	48
13	.45736	.51430	1.9444	.88928	1.1245	2.1865	47
14	.45762	.51467	1.9430	.88915	1.1247	2.1852	46
15	.45787	.51503	1.9416	.88902	1.1248	2.1840	45
16	.45813	.51540	1.9402	.88888	1.1250	2.1828	44
17	.45839	.51577	1.9388	.88875	1.1252	2.1815	43
18	.45865	.51614	1.9375	.88862	1.1253	2.1803	42
19	.45891	.51651	1.9361	.88848	1.1255	2.1791	41
20	.45917	.51688	1.9347	.88835	1.1257	2.1779	40
21	.45942	.51724	1.9333	.88822	1.1259	2.1766	39
22	.45968	.51761	1.9319	.88808	1.1260	2.1754	38
23	.45994	.51798	1.0306	.88705	1.1262	2.1742	37
24	.46020	.51835	1.9292	.88782	1.1264	2.1730	36
25	.46046	.51872	1.9278	.88768	1.1265	2.1718	35
26	.46072	.51909	1.9265	.88755	1.1267	2.1705	34
27	.46097	.51946	1.9251	.88741	1.1269	2.1693	33
28	.46123	.51983	1.9237	.88728	1.1270	2.1681	32
29	.46149	.52020	1.9223	.88715	1.1272	2.1669	31
30	.46175	.52057	1.9210	.88701	1.1274	2.1657	30
31	.46201	.52094	1.9196	.88688	1.1276	2.1645	29
32	.46226	.52131	1.9183	.88674	1.1277	2.1633	28
33	.46252	.52168	1.9169	.88661	1.1279	2.1621	27
34	.46278	.52205	1.9155	.88647	1.1281	2.1609	26
35	.46304	.52242	1.9142	.88634	1.1282	2.1596	25
36	.46330	.52279	1.9128	.88620	1.1284	2.1584	24
37	.46355	.52316	1.9115	.88607	1.1286	2.1572	23
38	.46381	.52353	1.0101	.88593	1.1288	2.1560	22
39	.46407	.52390	1.9088	.88580	1.1289	2.1549	21
40	.46433	.52427	1.9074	.88566	1.1291	2.1537	20
41	.46458	.52464	1.9061	.88553	1.1293	2.1525	19
42	.46484	.52501	1.9047	.88539	1.1294	2.1513	18
43	.46510	.52538	1.9034	.88526	1.1296	2.1501	17
44	.46536	.52575	1.9020	.88512	1.1298	2.1489	16
45	.46561	.52613	1.9007	.88499	1.1300	2.1477	15
46	.46587	.52650	1.8993	.88485	1.1301	2.1465	14
47	.46613	.52687	1.8980	.88472	1.1303	2.1453	13
48	.46639	.52724	1.8967	.88458	1.1305	2.1441	12
49	.46664	.52761	1.8953	.88445	1.1307	2.1430	11
50	.46690	.52798	1.8940	.88431	1.1308	2.1418	10
51	.46716	.52836	1.8927	.88417	1.1310	2.1406	9
52	.46742	.52873	1.8913	.88404	1.1312	2.1394	8
53	.46767	.52910	1.8900	.88390	1.1313	2.1382	7
54	.46793	.52947	1.8887	.88377	1.1315	2.1371	6
55	.46819	.52985	1.8873	.88363	1.1317	2.1359	5
56	.46844	.53022	1.8860	.88349	1.1319	2.1347	4
57	.46870	.53059	1.8847	.88336	1.1320	2.1336	3
58	.46896	.53096	1.8834	.88322	1.1322	2.1324	2
59	.46921	.53134	1.8820	.88308	1.1324	2.1312	1
60	.46047	.53171	1.8807	.88295	1.1326	2.1301	0
′	Cos	Cot	Tan	Sin	Csc	Sec	′

28° (208°)   (331)° 151°

′	Sin	Tan	Cot	Cos	Sec	Csc	′
0	.46947	.53171	1.8807	.88295	1.1326	2.1301	**60**
1	.46973	.53208	1.8794	.88281	1.1327	2.1289	59
2	.46999	.53246	1.8781	.88267	1.1329	2.1277	58
3	.47024	.53283	1.8768	.88254	1.1331	2.1266	57
4	.47050	.53320	1.8755	.88240	1.1333	2.1254	56
5	.47076	.53358	1.8741	.88226	1.1334	2.1242	**55**
6	.47101	.53395	1.8728	.88213	1.1336	2.1231	54
7	.47127	.53432	1.8715	.88199	1.1338	2.1219	53
8	.47153	.53470	1.8702	.88185	1.1340	2.1208	52
9	.47178	.53507	1.8689	.88172	1.1342	2.1196	51
10	.47204	.53545	1.8676	.88158	1.1343	2.1185	**50**
11	.47229	.53582	1.8663	.88144	1.1345	2.1173	49
12	.47255	.53620	1.8650	.88130	1.1347	2.1162	48
13	.47281	.53657	1.8637	.88117	1.1349	2.1150	47
14	.47306	.53694	1.8624	.88103	1.1350	2.1139	46
15	.47332	.53732	1.8611	.88089	1.1352	2.1127	**45**
16	.47358	.53769	1.8598	.88075	1.1354	2.1116	44
17	.47383	.53807	1.8585	.88062	1.1356	2.1105	43
18	.47409	.53844	1.8572	.88048	1.1357	2.1093	42
19	.47434	.53882	1.8559	.88034	1.1359	2.1082	41
20	.47460	.53920	1.8546	.88020	1.1361	2.1070	**40**
21	.47486	.53957	1.8533	.88006	1.1363	2.1059	39
22	.47511	.53995	1.8520	.87993	1.1365	2.1048	38
23	.47537	.54032	1.8507	.87979	1.1366	2.1036	37
24	.47562	.54070	1.8495	.87965	1.1368	2.1025	36
25	.47588	.54107	1.8482	.87951	1.1370	2.1014	**35**
26	.47614	.54145	1.8469	.87937	1.1372	2.1002	34
27	.47639	.54183	1.8456	.87923	1.1374	2.0991	33
28	.47665	.54220	1.8443	.87909	1.1375	2.0980	32
29	.47690	.54258	1.8430	.87896	1.1377	2.0969	31
30	.47716	.54296	1.8418	.87882	1.1379	2.0957	**30**
31	.47741	.54333	1.8405	.87868	1.1381	2.0946	29
32	.47767	.54371	1.8392	.87854	1.1383	2.0935	28
33	.47793	.54409	1.8379	.87840	1.1384	2.0924	27
34	.47818	.54446	1.8367	.87826	1.1386	2.0913	26
35	.47844	.54484	1.8354	.87812	1.1388	2.0901	**25**
36	.47869	.54522	1.8341	.87798	1.1390	2.0890	24
37	.47895	.54560	1.8329	.87784	1.1392	2.0879	23
38	.47920	.54597	1.8316	.87770	1.1393	2.0868	22
39	.47946	.54635	1.8303	.87756	1.1395	2.0857	21
40	.47971	.54673	1.8291	.87743	1.1397	2.0846	**20**
41	.47997	.54711	1.8278	.87729	1.1399	2.0835	19
42	.48022	.54748	1.8265	.87715	1.1401	2.0824	18
43	.48048	.54786	1.8253	.87701	1.1402	2.0813	17
44	.48073	.54824	1.8240	.87687	1.1404	2.0802	16
45	.48099	.54862	1.8228	.87673	1.1406	2.0791	**15**
46	.48124	.54900	1.8215	.87659	1.1408	2.0779	14
47	.48150	.54938	1.8202	.87645	1.1410	2.0768	13
48	.48175	.54975	1.8190	.87631	1.1412	2.0757	12
49	.48201	.55013	1.8177	.87617	1.1413	2.0747	11
50	.48226	.55051	1.8165	.87603	1.1415	2.0736	**10**
51	.48252	.55089	1.8152	.87589	1.1417	2.0725	9
52	.48277	.55127	1.8140	.87575	1.1419	2.0714	8
53	.48303	.55165	1.8127	.87561	1.1421	2.0703	7
54	.48328	.55203	1.8115	.87546	1.1423	2.0692	6
55	.48354	.55241	1.8103	.87532	1.1424	2.0681	**5**
56	.48379	.55279	1.8090	.87518	1.1426	2.0670	4
57	.48405	.55317	1.8078	.87504	1.1428	2.0659	3
58	.48430	.55355	1.8065	.87490	1.1430	2.0648	2
59	.48456	.55393	1.8053	.87476	1.1432	2.0637	1
60	.48481	.55431	1.8040	.87462	1.1434	2.0627	**0**
′	Cos	Cot	Tan	Sin	Csc	Sec	′

118° (298°)   (241°) 61°

29° (209°)   (330)° 150°

′	Sin	Tan	Cot	Cos	Sec	Csc	′
0	.48481	.55431	1.8040	.87462	1.1434	2.0627	**60**
1	.48506	.55469	1.8028	.87448	1.1435	2.0616	59
2	.48532	.55507	1.8016	.87434	1.1437	2.0605	58
3	.48557	.55545	1.8003	.87420	1.1439	2.0594	57
4	.48583	.55583	1.7991	.87406	1.1441	2.0583	56
5	.48608	.55621	1.7979	.87391	1.1443	2.0573	**55**
6	.48634	.55659	1.7966	.87377	1.1445	2.0562	54
7	.48659	.55697	1.7954	.87363	1.1446	2.0551	53
8	.48684	.55736	1.7942	.87349	1.1448	2.0540	52
9	.48710	.55774	1.7930	.87335	1.1450	2.0530	51
10	.48735	.55812	1.7917	.87321	1.1452	2.0519	**50**
11	.48761	.55850	1.7905	.87306	1.1454	2.0508	49
12	.48786	.55888	1.7893	.87292	1.1456	2.0498	48
13	.48811	.55926	1.7881	.87278	1.1458	2.0487	47
14	.48837	.55964	1.7868	.87264	1.1460	2.0476	46
15	.48862	.56003	1.7856	.87250	1.1461	2.0466	**45**
16	.48888	.56041	1.7844	.87235	1.1463	2.0455	44
17	.48913	.56079	1.7832	.87221	1.1465	2.0445	43
18	.48938	.56117	1.7820	.87207	1.1467	2.0434	42
19	.48964	.56156	1.7808	.87193	1.1469	2.0423	41
20	.48989	.56194	1.7796	.87178	1.1471	2.0413	**40**
21	.49014	.56232	1.7783	.87164	1.1473	2.0402	39
22	.49040	.56270	1.7771	.87150	1.1474	2.0392	38
23	.49065	.56309	1.7759	.87136	1.1476	2.0381	37
24	.49090	.56347	1.7747	.87121	1.1478	2.0371	36
25	.49116	.56385	1.7735	.87107	1.1480	2.0360	**35**
26	.49141	.56424	1.7723	.87093	1.1482	2.0350	34
27	.49166	.56462	1.7711	.87079	1.1484	2.0339	33
28	.49192	.56501	1.7699	.87064	1.1486	2.0329	32
29	.49217	.56539	1.7687	.87050	1.1488	2.0318	31
30	.49242	.56577	1.7675	.87036	1.1490	2.0308	**30**
31	.49268	.56616	1.7663	.87021	1.1491	2.0297	29
32	.49293	.56654	1.7651	.87007	1.1493	2.0287	28
33	.49318	.56693	1.7639	.86993	1.1495	2.0276	27
34	.49344	.56731	1.7627	.86978	1.1497	2.0266	26
35	.49369	.56769	1.7615	.86964	1.1499	2.0256	**25**
36	.49394	.56808	1.7603	.86949	1.1501	2.0245	24
37	.49419	.56846	1.7591	.86935	1.1503	2.0235	23
38	.49445	.56885	1.7579	.86921	1.1505	2.0225	22
39	.49470	.56923	1.7567	.86906	1.1507	2.0214	21
40	.49495	.56962	1.7556	.86892	1.1509	2.0204	**20**
41	.49521	.57000	1.7544	.86878	1.1510	2.0194	19
42	.49546	.57039	1.7532	.86863	1.1512	2.0183	18
43	.49571	.57078	1.7520	.86849	1.1514	2.0173	17
44	.49596	.57116	1.7508	.86834	1.1516	2.0163	16
45	.49622	.57155	1.7496	.86820	1.1518	2.0152	**15**
46	.49647	.57193	1.7485	.86805	1.1520	2.0142	14
47	.49672	.57232	1.7473	.86791	1.1522	2.0132	13
48	.49697	.57271	1.7461	.86777	1.1524	2.0122	12
49	.49723	.57309	1.7449	.86762	1.1526	2.0112	11
50	.49748	.57348	1.7437	.86748	1.1528	2.0101	**10**
51	.49773	.57386	1.7426	.86733	1.1530	2.0091	9
52	.49798	.57425	1.7414	.86719	1.1532	2.0081	8
53	.49824	.57464	1.7402	.86704	1.1533	2.0071	7
54	.49849	.57503	1.7391	.86690	1.1535	2.0061	6
55	.49874	.57541	1.7379	.86675	1.1537	2.0051	**5**
56	.49899	.57580	1.7367	.86661	1.1539	2.0040	4
57	.49924	.57619	1.7355	.86646	1.1541	2.0030	3
58	.49950	.57657	1.7344	.86632	1.1543	2.0020	2
59	.49975	.57696	1.7332	.86617	1.1545	2.0010	1
60	.50000	.57735	1.7321	.86603	1.1547	2.0000	**0**
′	Cos	Cot	Tan	Sin	Csc	Sec	′

119° (299°)   (240°) 60°

30° (210°)   (329°) **149°**

′	Sin	Tan	Cot	Cos	Sec	Csc	′
0	.50000	.57735	1.7321	.86603	1.1547	2.0000	**60**
1	.50025	.57774	1.7309	.86588	1.1549	1.9990	59
2	.50050	.57813	1.7297	.86573	1.1551	1.9980	58
3	.50076	.57851	1.7286	.86559	1.1553	1.9970	57
4	.50101	.57890	1.7274	.86544	1.1555	1.9960	56
5	.50126	.57929	1.7262	.86530	1.1557	1.9950	**55**
6	.50151	.57968	1.7251	.86515	1.1559	1.9940	54
7	.50176	.58007	1.7239	.86501	1.1561	1.9930	53
8	.50201	.58046	1.7228	.86486	1.1563	1.9920	52
9	.50227	.58085	1.7216	.86471	1.1565	1.9910	51
10	.50252	.58124	1.7205	.86457	1.1566	1.9900	**50**
11	.50277	.58162	1.7193	.86442	1.1568	1.9890	49
12	.50302	.58201	1.7182	.86427	1.1570	1.9880	48
13	.50327	.58240	1.7170	.86413	1.1572	1.9870	47
14	.50352	.58279	1.7159	.86398	1.1574	1.9860	46
15	.50377	.58318	1.7147	.86384	1.1576	1.9850	**45**
16	.50403	.58357	1.7136	.86369	1.1578	1.9840	44
17	.50428	.58396	1.7124	.86354	1.1580	1.9830	13
18	.50453	.58435	1.7113	.86340	1.1582	1.9821	42
19	.50478	.58474	1.7102	.86325	1.1584	1.9811	41
20	.50503	.58513	1.7090	.86310	1.1586	1.9801	**40**
21	.50528	.58552	1.7079	.86295	1.1588	1.9791	39
22	.50553	.58591	1.7067	.86281	1.1590	1.9781	38
23	.50578	.58631	1.7056	.86266	1.1592	1.9771	37
24	.50603	.58670	1.7045	.86251	1.1594	1.9762	36
25	.50628	.58709	1.7033	.86237	1.1596	1.9752	**35**
26	.50654	.58748	1.7022	.86222	1.1598	1.9742	34
27	.50679	.58787	1.7011	.86207	1.1600	1.9732	33
28	.50704	.58826	1.6999	.86192	1.1602	1.9722	32
29	.50729	.58865	1.6988	.86178	1.1604	1.9713	31
30	.50754	.58905	1.6977	.86163	1.1606	1.9703	**30**
31	.50779	.58944	1.6965	.86148	1.1608	1.9693	29
32	.50804	.58983	1.6954	.86133	1.1610	1.9684	28
33	.50829	.59022	1.6943	.86119	1.1612	1.9674	27
34	.50854	.59061	1.6932	.86104	1.1614	1.9664	26
35	.50879	.59101	1.6920	.86089	1.1616	1.9654	**25**
36	.50904	.59140	1.6909	.86074	1.1618	1.9645	24
37	.50929	.59179	1.6898	.86059	1.1620	1.9635	23
38	.50054	.59218	1.6887	.86045	1.1622	1.9625	22
39	.50979	.50258	1.6875	.86030	1.1624	1.9616	21
40	.51004	.59297	1.6864	.86015	1.1626	1.9606	**20**
41	.51029	.59336	1.6853	.86000	1.1628	1.9597	19
42	.51054	.59376	1.6842	.85985	1.1630	1.9587	18
43	.51079	.59415	1.6831	.85970	1.1632	1.9577	17
44	.51104	.59454	1.6820	.85956	1.1634	1.9568	16
45	.51129	.59494	1.6808	.85941	1.1636	1.9558	**15**
46	.51154	.59533	1.6797	.85926	1.1638	1.9549	14
47	.51179	.59573	1.6786	.85911	1.1640	1.9539	13
48	.51204	.59612	1.6775	.85896	1.1642	1.9530	12
49	.51229	.59651	1.6764	.85881	1.1644	1.9520	11
50	.51254	.59691	1.6753	.85866	1.1646	1.9511	**10**
51	.51279	.59730	1.6742	.85851	1.1648	1.9501	9
52	.51304	.59770	1.6731	.85836	1.1650	1.9492	8
53	.51329	.59809	1.6720	.85821	1.1652	1.9482	7
54	.51354	.59849	1.6709	.85806	1.1654	1.9473	6
55	.51379	.59888	1.6698	.85792	1.1656	1.9463	**5**
56	.51404	.59928	1.6687	.85777	1.1658	1.9454	4
57	.51429	.59967	1.6676	.85762	1.1660	1.9444	3
58	.51454	.60007	1.6665	.85747	1.1002	1.9435	2
59	.51479	.60046	1.6654	.85732	1.1664	1.9425	1
60	.51504	.60086	1.6643	.85717	1.1666	1.9416	**0**
′	Cos	Cot	Tan	Sin	Csc	Sec	′

120° (300°)   (239°) **59°**

31° (211°)   (328°) **148°**

′	Sin	Tan	Cot	Cos	Sec	Csc	′
0	.51504	.60086	1.6643	.85717	1.1666	1.9416	**60**
1	.51529	.60126	1.6632	.85702	1.1668	1.9407	59
2	.51554	.60165	1.6621	.85687	1.1670	1.9397	58
3	.51579	.60205	1.6610	.85672	1.1672	1.9388	57
4	.51604	.60245	1.6599	.85657	1.1675	1.9379	56
5	.51628	.60284	1.6588	.85642	1.1677	1.9369	**55**
6	.51653	.60324	1.6577	.85627	1.1679	1.9360	54
7	.51678	.60364	1.6566	.85612	1.1681	1.9351	53
8	.51703	.60403	1.6555	.85597	1.1683	1.9341	52
9	.51728	.60443	1.6545	.85582	1.1685	1.9332	51
10	.51753	.60483	1.6534	.85567	1.1687	1.9323	**50**
11	.51778	.60522	1.6523	.85551	1.1689	1.9313	49
12	.51803	.60562	1.6512	.85536	1.1691	1.9304	48
13	.51828	.60602	1.6501	.85521	1.1693	1.9295	47
14	.51852	.60642	1.6490	.85506	1.1695	1.9285	46
15	.51877	.60681	1.6479	.85491	1.1697	1.9276	**45**
16	.51902	.60721	1.6469	.85476	1.1699	1.9267	44
17	.51927	.60761	1.6458	.85461	1.1701	1.9258	43
18	.51952	.60801	1.6447	.85446	1.1703	1.9249	42
19	.51977	.60841	1.6436	.85431	1.1705	1.9239	41
20	.52002	.60881	1.6426	.85416	1.1707	1.9230	**40**
21	.52026	.60921	1.6415	.85401	1.1710	1.9221	39
22	.52051	.60960	1.6404	.85385	1.1712	1.9212	38
23	.52076	.61000	1.6393	.85370	1.1714	1.9203	37
24	.52101	.61040	1.6383	.85355	1.1716	1.9194	36
25	.52126	.61080	1.6372	.85340	1.1718	1.9184	**35**
26	.52151	.61120	1.6361	.85325	1.1720	1.9175	34
27	.52175	.61160	1.6351	.85310	1.1722	1.9166	33
28	.52200	.61200	1.6340	.85294	1.1724	1.9157	32
29	.52225	.61240	1.6329	.85279	1.1726	1.9148	31
30	.52250	.61280	1.6319	.85264	1.1728	1.9139	**30**
31	.52275	.61320	1.6308	.85249	1.1730	1.9130	29
32	.52299	.61360	1.6297	.85234	1.1732	1.9121	28
33	.52324	.61400	1.6287	.85218	1.1735	1.9112	27
34	.52349	.61440	1.6276	.85203	1.1737	1.9103	26
35	.52374	.61480	1.6265	.85188	1.1739	1.9094	**25**
36	.52399	.61520	1.6255	.85173	1.1741	1.9084	24
37	.52423	.61561	1.6244	.85157	1.1743	1.9075	23
38	.52448	.61601	1.6234	.85142	1.1745	1.9066	22
39	.52473	.61611	1.6223	.85127	1.1747	1.0057	21
40	.52498	.61681	1.6212	.85112	1.1749	1.9048	**20**
41	.52522	.61721	1.6202	.85096	1.1751	1.9039	19
42	.52547	.61761	1.6191	.85081	1.1753	1.9031	18
43	.52572	.61801	1.6181	.85066	1.1756	1.9022	17
44	.52597	.61842	1.6170	.85051	1.1758	1.9013	16
45	.52621	.61882	1.6160	.85035	1.1760	1.9004	**15**
46	.52646	.61922	1.6149	.85020	1.1762	1.8995	14
47	.52671	.61962	1.6139	.85005	1.1764	1.8986	13
48	.52696	.62003	1.6128	.84989	1.1766	1.8977	12
49	.52720	.62043	1.6118	.84974	1.1768	1.8968	11
50	.52745	.62083	1.6107	.84959	1.1770	1.8959	**10**
51	.52770	.62124	1.6097	.84943	1.1773	1.8950	9
52	.52794	.62164	1.6087	.84928	1.1775	1.8941	8
53	.52819	.62204	1.6076	.84913	1.1777	1.8933	7
54	.52844	.62245	1.6066	.84897	1.1779	1.8924	6
55	.52869	.62285	1.6055	.84882	1.1781	1.8915	**5**
56	.52893	.62325	1.6045	.84866	1.1783	1.8906	4
57	.52918	.62366	1.6034	.84851	1.1785	1.8897	3
58	.52943	.62406	1.0024	.84836	1.1788	1.8888	2
59	.52967	.62446	1.6014	.84820	1.1790	1.8880	1
60	.52992	.62487	1.6003	.84805	1.1792	1.8871	**0**
′	Cos	Cot	Tan	Sin	Csc	Sec	′

121° (301°)   (238°) **58°**

32° (212°)   (327°) 147°   33° (213°)   (326°) 146°

′	Sin	Tan	Cot	Cos	Sec	Csc	′	′	Sin	Tan	Cot	Cos	Sec	Csc	′
0	.52992	.62487	1.6003	.84805	1.1792	1.8871	60	0	.54464	.64941	1.5399	.83867	1.1924	1.8361	60
1	.53017	.62527	1.5993	.84789	1.1794	1.8862	59	1	.54488	.64982	1.5389	.83851	1.1926	1.8353	59
2	.53041	.62568	1.5983	.84774	1.1796	1.8853	58	2	.54513	.65024	1.5379	.83835	1.1928	1.8344	58
3	.53066	.62608	1.5972	.84759	1.1798	1.8844	57	3	.54537	.65065	1.5369	.83819	1.1930	1.8336	57
4	.53091	.62649	1.5962	.84743	1.1800	1.8836	56	4	.54561	.65106	1.5359	.83804	1.1933	1.8328	56
5	.53115	.62689	1.5952	.84728	1.1803	1.8827	55	5	.54586	.65148	1.5350	.83788	1.1935	1.8320	55
6	.53140	.62730	1.5941	.84712	1.1805	1.8818	54	6	.54610	.65189	1.5340	.83772	1.9137	1.8312	54
7	.53164	.62770	1.5931	.84697	1.1807	1.8810	53	7	.54635	.65231	1.5330	.83756	1.1939	1.8303	53
8	.53189	.62811	1.5921	.84681	1.1809	1.8801	52	8	.54659	.65272	1.5320	.83740	1.1942	1.8295	52
9	.53214	.62852	1.5911	.84666	1.1811	1.8792	51	9	.54683	.65314	1.5311	.83724	1.1944	1.8287	51
10	.53238	.62892	1.5900	.84650	1.1813	1.8783	50	10	.54708	.65355	1.5301	.83708	1.1946	1.8279	50
11	.53263	.62933	1.5890	.84635	1.1815	1.8775	49	11	.54732	.65397	1.5291	.83692	1.1949	1.8271	49
12	.53288	.62973	1.5880	.84619	1.1818	1.8766	48	12	.54756	.65438	1.5282	.83676	1.1951	1.8263	48
13	.53312	.63014	1.5869	.84604	1.1820	1.8757	47	13	.54781	.65480	1.5272	.83660	1.1953	1.8255	47
14	.53337	.63055	1.5859	.84588	1.1822	1.8749	46	14	.54805	.65521	1.5262	.83645	1.1955	1.8247	46
15	.53361	.63095	1.5849	.84573	1.1824	1.8740	45	15	.54829	.65563	1.5253	.83629	1.1958	1.8238	45
16	.53386	.63136	1.5839	.84557	1.1826	1.8731	44	16	.54854	.65604	1.5243	.83613	1.1960	1.8230	44
17	.53411	.63177	1.5829	.84542	1.1828	1.8723	43	17	.54878	.65646	1.5233	.83597	1.1962	1.8222	43
18	.53435	.63217	1.5818	.84526	1.1831	1.8714	42	18	.54902	.65688	1.5224	.83581	1.1964	1.8214	42
19	.53460	.63258	1.5808	.84511	1.1833	1.8706	41	19	.54927	.65729	1.5214	.83565	1.1967	1.8206	41
20	.53484	.63299	1.5798	.84495	1.1835	1.8697	40	20	.54951	.65771	1.5204	.83549	1.1969	1.8198	40
21	.53509	.63340	1.5788	.84480	1.1837	1.8688	39	21	.54975	.65813	1.5195	.83533	1.1971	1.8190	39
22	.53534	.63380	1.5778	.84464	1.1830	1.8680	38	22	.54999	.65854	1.5185	.83517	1.1974	1.8182	38
23	.53558	.63421	1.5768	.84448	1.1842	1.8671	37	23	.55024	.65896	1.5175	.83501	1.1976	1.8174	37
24	.53583	.63462	1.5757	.84433	1.1844	1.8663	36	24	.55048	.65938	1.5166	.83485	1.1978	1.8166	36
25	.53607	.63503	1.5747	.84417	1.1846	1.8654	35	25	.55072	.65980	1.5156	.83469	1.1981	1.8158	35
26	.53632	.63544	1.5737	.84402	1.1848	1.8646	34	26	.55097	.66021	1.5147	.83453	1.1983	1.8150	34
27	.53656	.63584	1.5727	.84386	1.1850	1.8637	33	27	.55121	.66063	1.5137	.83437	1.1985	1.8142	33
28	.53681	.63625	1.5717	.84370	1.1852	1.8629	32	28	.55145	.66105	1.5127	.83421	1.1987	1.8134	32
29	.53705	.63666	1.5707	.84355	1.1855	1.8620	31	29	.55169	.66147	1.5118	.83405	1.1990	1.8126	31
30	.53730	.63707	1.5697	.84339	1.1857	1.8612	30	30	.55194	.66189	1.5108	.83389	1.1992	1.8118	30
31	.53754	.63748	1.5687	.84324	1.1859	1.8603	29	31	.55218	.66230	1.5099	.83373	1.1994	1.8110	29
32	.53779	.63789	1.5677	.84308	1.1861	1.8595	28	32	.55242	.66272	1.5089	.83356	1.1997	1.8102	28
33	.53804	.63830	1.5667	.84292	1.1863	1.8586	27	33	.55266	.66314	1.5080	.83340	1.1999	1.8094	27
34	.53828	.63871	1.5657	.84277	1.1866	1.8578	26	34	.55291	.66356	1.5070	.83324	1.2001	1.8086	26
35	.53853	.63912	1.5647	.84261	1.1868	1.8569	25	35	.55315	.66398	1.5061	.83308	1.2004	1.8078	25
36	.53877	.63953	1.5637	.84245	1.1870	1.8561	24	36	.55339	.66440	1.5051	.83292	1.2006	1.8070	24
37	.53902	.63994	1.5627	.84230	1.1872	1.8552	23	37	.55363	.66482	1.5042	.83276	1.2008	1.8062	23
38	.53926	.64035	1.5617	.84214	1.1875	1.8544	22	38	.55388	.66524	1.5032	.83260	1.2011	1.8055	22
39	.53951	.64076	1.5607	.84198	1.1877	1.8535	21	39	.55412	.66566	1.5023	.83244	1.2013	1.8047	21
40	.53975	.64117	1.5597	.84182	1.1879	1.8527	20	40	.55436	.66608	1.5013	.83228	1.2015	1.8039	20
41	.54000	.64158	1.5587	.84167	1.1881	1.8519	19	41	.55460	.66650	1.5004	.83212	1.2018	1.8031	19
42	.54024	.64199	1.5577	.84151	1.1883	1.8510	18	42	.55484	.66692	1.4994	.83195	1.2020	1.8023	18
43	.54049	.64240	1.5567	.84135	1.1886	1.8502	17	43	.55509	.66734	1.4985	.83179	1.2022	1.8015	17
44	.54073	.64281	1.5557	.84120	1.1888	1.8494	16	44	.55533	.66776	1.4975	.83163	1.2025	1.8007	16
45	.54097	.64322	1.5547	.84104	1.1890	1.8485	15	45	.55557	.66818	1.4966	.83147	1.2027	1.8000	15
46	.54122	.64363	1.5537	.84088	1.1892	1.8477	14	46	.55581	.66860	1.4957	.83131	1.2029	1.7992	14
47	.54146	.64404	1.5527	.84072	1.1895	1.8468	13	47	.55605	.66902	1.4947	.83115	1.2032	1.7984	13
48	.54171	.64446	1.5517	.84057	1.1897	1.8460	12	48	.55630	.66944	1.4938	.83098	1.2034	1.7976	12
49	.54195	.64487	1.5507	.84041	1.1899	1.8452	11	49	.55654	.66986	1.4928	.83082	1.2036	1.7968	11
50	.54220	.64528	1.5497	.84025	1.1901	1.8443	10	50	.55678	.67028	1.4919	.83066	1.2039	1.7960	10
51	.54244	.64569	1.5487	.84009	1.1903	1.8435	9	51	.55702	.67071	1.4910	.83050	1.2041	1.7953	9
52	.54269	.64610	1.5477	.83994	1.1906	1.8427	8	52	.55726	.67113	1.4900	.83034	1.2043	1.7945	8
53	.54293	.64652	1.5468	.83978	1.1908	1.8419	7	53	.55750	.67155	1.4891	.83017	1.2046	1.7937	7
54	.54317	.64693	1.5458	.83962	1.1910	1.8410	6	54	.55775	.67197	1.4882	.83001	1.2048	1.7929	6
55	.54342	.64734	1.5448	.83946	1.1912	1.8402	5	55	.55799	.67239	1.4872	.82985	1.2050	1.7922	5
56	.54366	.64775	1.5438	.83930	1.1915	1.8394	4	56	.55823	.67282	1.4863	.82969	1.2053	1.7914	4
57	.54391	.64817	1.5428	.83915	1.1917	1.8385	3	57	.55847	.67324	1.4854	.82953	1.2055	1.7906	3
58	.54415	.64858	1.5418	.83899	1.1919	1.8377	2	58	.55871	.67366	1.4844	.82936	1.2057	1.7898	2
59	.54440	.64899	1.5408	.83883	1.1921	1.8369	1	59	.55895	.67409	1.4835	.82920	1.2060	1.7891	1
60	.54464	.64941	1.5399	.83867	1.1924	1.8361	0	60	.55919	.67451	1.4826	.82904	1.2062	1.7883	0
′	Cos	Cot	Tan	Sin	Csc	Sec	′	′	Cos	Cot	Tan	Sin	Csc	Sec	′

122° (302°)   (237°) 57°   123° (303°)   (236°) 56°

34° (214°)   (325°) 145°

′	Sin	Tan	Cot	Cos	Sec	Csc	′
0	.55919	.67451	1.4826	.82904	1.2062	1.7883	60
1	.55943	.67493	1.4816	.82887	1.2065	1.7875	59
2	.55968	.67536	1.4807	.82871	1.2067	1.7868	58
3	.55992	.67578	1.4798	.82855	1.2069	1.7860	57
4	.56016	.67620	1.4788	.82839	1.2072	1.7852	56
5	.56040	.67663	1.4779	.82822	1.2074	1.7844	55
6	.56064	.67705	1.4770	.82806	1.2076	1.7837	54
7	.56088	.67748	1.4761	.82790	1.2079	1.7829	53
8	.56112	.67790	1.4751	.82773	1.2081	1.7821	52
9	.56136	.67832	1.4742	.82757	1.2084	1.7814	51
10	.56160	.67875	1.4733	.82741	1.2086	1.7806	50
11	.56184	.67917	1.4724	.82724	1.2088	1.7799	49
12	.56208	.67960	1.4715	.82708	1.2091	1.7791	48
13	.56232	.68002	1.4705	.82692	1.2093	1.7783	47
14	.56256	.68045	1.4696	.82675	1.2096	1.7776	46
15	.56280	.68088	1.4687	.82659	1.2098	1.7768	45
16	.56305	.68130	1.4678	.82643	1.2100	1.7761	44
17	.56329	.68173	1.4669	.82626	1.2103	1.7753	43
18	.56353	.68215	1.4659	.82610	1.2105	1.7745	42
19	.56377	.68258	1.4650	.82593	1.2108	1.7738	41
20	.56401	.68301	1.4641	.82577	1.2110	1.7730	40
21	.56425	.68343	1.4632	.82561	1.2112	1.7723	39
22	.56449	.68386	1.4623	.82544	1.2115	1.7715	38
23	.56473	.68429	1.4614	.82528	1.2117	1.7708	37
24	.56497	.68471	1.4605	.82511	1.2120	1.7700	36
25	.56521	.68514	1.4596	.82495	1.2122	1.7693	35
26	.56545	.68557	1.4586	.82478	1.2124	1.7685	34
27	.56569	.68600	1.4577	.82462	1.2127	1.7678	33
28	.56593	.68642	1.4568	.82446	1.2129	1.7670	32
29	.56617	.68685	1.4559	.82429	1.2132	1.7663	31
30	.56641	.68728	1.4550	.82413	1.2134	1.7655	30
31	.56665	.68771	1.4541	.82396	1.2136	1.7648	29
32	.56689	.68814	1.4532	.82380	1.2139	1.7640	28
33	.56713	.68857	1.4523	.82363	1.2141	1.7633	27
34	.56736	.68900	1.4514	.82347	1.2144	1.7625	26
35	.56760	.68942	1.4505	.82330	1.2146	1.7618	25
36	.56784	.68985	1.4496	.82314	1.2149	1.7610	24
37	.56808	.69028	1.4487	.82297	1.2151	1.7603	23
38	.56832	.69071	1.4478	.82281	1.2154	1.7596	22
39	.56856	.69114	1.4469	.82264	1.2156	1.7588	21
40	.56880	.69157	1.4460	.82248	1.2158	1.7581	20
41	.56904	.69200	1.4451	.82231	1.2161	1.7573	19
42	.56928	.69243	1.4442	.82214	1.2163	1.7566	18
43	.56952	.69286	1.4433	.82198	1.2166	1.7559	17
44	.56976	.69329	1.4424	.82181	1.2168	1.7551	16
45	.57000	.69372	1.4415	.82165	1.2171	1.7544	15
46	.57024	.69416	1.4406	.82148	1.2173	1.7537	14
47	.57047	.69459	1.4397	.82132	1.2176	1.7529	13
48	.57071	.69502	1.4388	.82115	1.2178	1.7522	12
49	.57095	.69545	1.4379	.82098	1.2181	1.7515	11
50	.57119	.69588	1.4370	.82082	1.2183	1.7507	10
51	.57143	.69631	1.4361	.82065	1.2185	1.7500	9
52	.57167	.69675	1.4352	.82048	1.2188	1.7493	8
53	.57191	.69718	1.4344	.82032	1.2190	1.7485	7
54	.57215	.69761	1.4335	.82015	1.2193	1.7478	6
55	.57238	.69804	1.4326	.81999	1.2195	1.7471	5
56	.57262	.69847	1.4317	.81982	1.2198	1.7463	4
57	.57286	.69891	1.4308	.81965	1.2200	1.7456	3
58	.57310	.69934	1.4299	.81949	1.2203	1.7449	2
59	.57334	.69977	1.4290	.81932	1.2205	1.7442	1
60	.57358	.70021	1.4281	.81915	1.2208	1.7434	0
′	Cos	Cot	Tan	Sin	Csc	Sec	′

124° (304°)   (235°) 55°

35° (215°)   (324°) 144°

′	Sin	Tan	Cot	Cos	Sec	Csc	′
0	.57358	.70021	1.4281	.81915	1.2208	1.7434	60
1	.57381	.70064	1.4273	.81899	1.2210	1.7427	59
2	.57405	.70107	1.4264	.81882	1.2213	1.7420	58
3	.57429	.70151	1.4255	.81865	1.2215	1.7413	57
4	.57453	.70194	1.4246	.81848	1.2218	1.7406	56
5	.57477	.70238	1.4237	.81832	1.2220	1.7398	55
6	.57501	.70281	1.4229	.81815	1.2223	1.7391	54
7	.57524	.70325	1.4220	.81798	1.2225	1.7384	53
8	.57548	.70368	1.4211	.81782	1.2228	1.7377	52
9	.57572	.70412	1.4202	.81765	1.2230	1.7370	51
10	.57596	.70455	1.4193	.81748	1.2233	1.7362	50
11	.57619	.70499	1.4185	.81731	1.2235	1.7355	49
12	.57643	.70542	1.4176	.81714	1.2238	1.7348	48
13	.57667	.70586	1.4167	.81698	1.2240	1.7341	47
14	.57691	.70629	1.4158	.81681	1.2243	1.7334	46
15	.57715	.70673	1.4150	.81664	1.2245	1.7327	45
16	.57738	.70717	1.4141	.81647	1.2248	1.7320	44
17	.57762	.70760	1.4132	.81631	1.2250	1.7312	43
18	.57786	.70804	1.4124	.81614	1.2253	1.7305	42
19	.57810	.70848	1.4115	.81597	1.2255	1.7298	41
20	.57833	.70891	1.4106	.81580	1.2258	1.7291	40
21	.57857	.70935	1.4097	.81563	1.2260	1.7284	39
22	.57881	.70979	1.4089	.81546	1.2263	1.7277	38
23	.57904	.71023	1.4080	.81530	1.2265	1.7270	37
24	.57928	.71066	1.4071	.81513	1.2268	1.7263	36
25	.57952	.71110	1.4063	.81496	1.2271	1.7256	35
26	.57976	.71154	1.4054	.81479	1.2273	1.7249	34
27	.57999	.71198	1.4045	.81462	1.2276	1.7242	33
28	.58023	.71242	1.4037	.81445	1.2278	1.7235	32
29	.58047	.71285	1.4028	.81428	1.2281	1.7228	31
30	.58070	.71329	1.4019	.81412	1.2283	1.7221	30
31	.58094	.71373	1.4011	.81395	1.2286	1.7213	29
32	.58118	.71417	1.4002	.81378	1.2288	1.7206	28
33	.58141	.71461	1.3994	.81361	1.2291	1.7199	27
34	.58165	.71505	1.3985	.81344	1.2293	1.7192	26
35	.58189	.71549	1.3976	.81327	1.2296	1.7185	25
36	.58212	.71593	1.3968	.81310	1.2299	1.7179	24
37	.58236	.71637	1.3959	.81293	1.2301	1.7172	23
38	.58260	.71681	1.3951	.81276	1.2304	1.7165	22
39	.58283	.71725	1.3942	.81259	1.2306	1.7158	21
40	.58307	.71769	1.3934	.81242	1.2309	1.7151	20
41	.58330	.71813	1.3925	.81225	1.2311	1.7144	19
42	.58354	.71857	1.3916	.81208	1.2314	1.7137	18
43	.58378	.71901	1.3908	.81191	1.2317	1.7130	17
44	.58401	.71946	1.3899	.81174	1.2319	1.7123	16
45	.58425	.71990	1.3891	.81157	1.2322	1.7116	15
46	.58449	.72034	1.3882	.81140	1.2324	1.7109	14
47	.58472	.72078	1.3874	.81123	1.2327	1.7102	13
48	.58496	.72122	1.3865	.81106	1.2329	1.7095	12
49	.58519	.72167	1.3857	.81089	1.2332	1.7088	11
50	.58543	.72211	1.3848	.81072	1.2335	1.7081	10
51	.58567	.72255	1.3840	.81055	1.2337	1.7075	9
52	.58590	.72299	1.3831	.81038	1.2340	1.7068	8
53	.58614	.72344	1.3823	.81021	1.2342	1.7061	7
54	.58637	.72388	1.3814	.81004	1.2345	1.7054	6
55	.58661	.72432	1.3806	.80987	1.2348	1.7047	5
56	.58684	.72477	1.3798	.80970	1.2350	1.7040	4
57	.58708	.72521	1.3789	.80953	1.2353	1.7033	3
58	.58731	.72565	1.3781	.80936	1.2355	1.7027	2
59	.58755	.72610	1.3772	.80919	1.2358	1.7020	1
60	.58779	.72654	1.3764	.80902	1.2361	1.7013	0
′	Cos	Cot	Tan	Sin	Csc	Sec	′

125° (305°)   (234°) 54°

36° (216°)   (323°) **143°**   **37° (217°)**   (322°) **142°**

′	Sin	Tan	Cot	Cos	Sec	Csc	′	′	Sin	Tan	Cot	Cos	Sec	Csc	′
0	.58779	.72654	1.3764	.80902	1.2361	1.7013	**60**	**0**	.60182	.75355	1.3270	.79864	1.2521	1.6616	**60**
1	.58802	.72699	1.3755	.80885	1.2363	1.7006	59	1	.60205	.75401	1.3262	.79846	1.2524	1.6610	59
2	.58826	.72743	1.3747	.80867	1.2366	1.6999	58	2	.60228	.75447	1.3254	.79829	1.2527	1.6604	58
3	.58849	.72788	1.3739	.80850	1.2369	1.6993	57	3	.60251	.75492	1.3246	.79811	1.2530	1.6597	57
4	.58873	.72832	1.3730	.80833	1.2371	1.6986	56	4	.60274	.75538	1.3238	.79793	1.2532	1.6591	56
5	.58896	.72877	1.3722	.80816	1.2374	1.6979	**55**	**5**	.60298	.75584	1.3230	.79776	1.2535	1.6584	**55**
6	.58920	.72921	1.3713	.80799	1.2376	1.6972	54	6	.60321	.75629	1.3222	.79758	1.2538	1.6578	54
7	.58943	.72966	1.3705	.80782	1.2379	1.6966	53	7	.60344	.75675	1.3214	.79741	1.2541	1.6572	53
8	.58967	.73010	1.3697	.80765	1.2382	1.6959	52	8	.60367	.75721	1.3206	.79723	1.2543	1.6565	52
9	.58990	.73055	1.3688	.80748	1.2384	1.6952	51	9	.60390	.75767	1.3198	.79706	1.2546	1.6559	51
10	.59014	.73100	1.3680	.80730	1.2387	1.6945	**50**	**10**	.60414	.75812	1.3190	.79688	1.2549	1.6553	**50**
11	.59037	.73144	1.3672	.80713	1.2390	1.6939	49	11	.60437	.75858	1.3182	.79671	1.2552	1.6546	49
12	.59061	.73189	1.3663	.80696	1.2392	1.6932	48	12	.60460	.75904	1.3175	.79653	1.2554	1.6540	48
13	.59084	.73234	1.3655	.80679	1.2395	1.6925	47	13	.60483	.75950	1.3167	.79635	1.2557	1.6534	47
14	.59108	.73278	1.3647	.80662	1.2397	1.6918	46	14	.60506	.75996	1.3159	.79618	1.2560	1.6527	46
15	.59131	.73323	1.3638	.80644	1.2400	1.6912	**45**	**15**	.60529	.76042	1.3151	.79600	1.2563	1.6521	**45**
16	.59154	.73368	1.3630	.80627	1.2403	1.6905	44	16	.60553	.76088	1.3143	.79583	1.2566	1.6515	44
17	.59178	.73413	1.3622	.80610	1.2405	1.6898	43	17	.60576	.76134	1.3135	.79565	1.2568	1.6508	43
18	.59201	.73457	1.3613	.80593	1.2408	1.6892	42	18	.60599	.76180	1.3127	.79547	1.2571	1.6502	42
19	.59225	.73502	1.3605	.80576	1.2411	1.6885	41	19	.60622	.76226	1.3119	.79530	1.2574	1.6496	41
20	.59248	.73547	1.3597	.80558	1.2413	1.6878	**40**	**20**	.60645	.76272	1.3111	.79512	1.2577	1.6489	**40**
21	.59272	.73592	1.3588	.80541	1.2416	1.6871	39	21	.60668	.76318	1.3103	.79494	1.2579	1.6483	39
22	.59295	.73637	1.3580	.80524	1.2419	1.6865	38	22	.60691	.76364	1.3095	.79477	1.2582	1.6477	38
23	.59318	.73681	1.3572	.80507	1.2421	1.6858	37	23	.60714	.76410	1.3087	.79459	1.2585	1.6471	37
24	.59342	.73726	1.3564	.80489	1.2424	1.6852	36	24	.60738	.76456	1.3079	.79441	1.2588	1.6464	36
25	.59365	.73771	1.3555	.80472	1.2427	1.6845	**35**	**25**	.60761	.76502	1.3072	.79424	1.2591	1.6458	**35**
26	.59389	.73816	1.3547	.80455	1.2429	1.6838	34	26	.60784	.76548	1.3064	.79406	1.2593	1.6452	34
27	.59412	.73861	1.3539	.80438	1.2432	1.6832	33	27	.60807	.76594	1.3056	.79388	1.2596	1.6446	33
28	.59436	.73906	1.3531	.80420	1.2435	1.6825	32	28	.60830	.76640	1.3048	.79371	1.2599	1.6439	32
29	.59459	.73951	1.3522	.80403	1.2437	1.6818	31	29	.60853	.76686	1.3040	.79353	1.2602	1.6433	31
30	.59482	.73996	1.3514	.80386	1.2440	1.6812	**30**	**30**	.60876	.76733	1.3032	.79335	1.2605	1.6427	**30**
31	.59506	.74041	1.3506	.80368	1.2443	1.6805	29	31	.60899	.76779	1.3024	.79318	1.2608	1.6421	29
32	.59529	.74086	1.3498	.80351	1.2445	1.6799	28	32	.60922	.76825	1.3017	.79300	1.2610	1.6414	28
33	.59552	.74131	1.3490	.80334	1.2448	1.6792	27	33	.60945	.76871	1.3009	.79282	1.2613	1.6408	27
34	.59576	.74176	1.3481	.80316	1.2451	1.6785	26	34	.60968	.76918	1.3001	.79264	1.2616	1.6402	26
35	.59599	.74221	1.3473	.80299	1.2453	1.6779	**25**	**35**	.60991	.76964	1.2993	.79247	1.2619	1.6396	**25**
36	.59622	.74267	1.3465	.80282	1.2456	1.6772	24	36	.61015	.77010	1.2985	.79229	1.2622	1.6390	24
37	.59646	.74312	1.3457	.80264	1.2459	1.6766	23	37	.61038	.77057	1.2977	.79211	1.2624	1.6383	23
38	.59669	.74357	1.3449	.80247	1.2462	1.6759	22	38	.61061	.77103	1.2970	.79193	1.2627	1.6377	22
39	.59693	.74402	1.3440	.80230	1.2464	1.6753	21	39	.61084	.77149	1.2962	.79176	1.2630	1.6371	21
40	.59716	.74447	1.3432	.80212	1.2467	1.6746	**20**	**40**	.61107	.77196	1.2954	.79158	1.2633	1.6365	**20**
41	.59739	.74492	1.3424	.80195	1.2470	1.6739	19	41	.61130	.77242	1.2946	.79140	1.2636	1.6359	19
42	.59763	.74538	1.3416	.80178	1.2472	1.6733	18	42	.61153	.77289	1.2938	.79122	1.2639	1.6353	18
43	.59786	.74583	1.3408	.80160	1.2475	1.6726	17	43	.61176	.77335	1.2931	.79105	1.2641	1.6346	17
44	.59809	.74628	1.3400	.80143	1.2478	1.6720	16	44	.61199	.77382	1.2923	.79087	1.2644	1.6340	16
45	.59832	.74674	1.3392	.80125	1.2480	1.6713	**15**	**45**	.61222	.77428	1.2915	.79069	1.2647	1.6334	**15**
46	.59856	.74719	1.3384	.80108	1.2483	1.6707	14	46	.61245	.77475	1.2907	.79051	1.2650	1.6328	14
47	.59879	.74764	1.3375	.80091	1.2486	1.6700	13	47	.61268	.77521	1.2900	.79033	1.2653	1.6322	13
48	.59902	.74810	1.3367	.80073	1.2489	1.6694	12	48	.61291	.77568	1.2892	.79016	1.2656	1.6316	12
49	.59926	.74855	1.3359	.80056	1.2491	1.6687	11	49	.61314	.77615	1.2884	.78998	1.2659	1.6310	11
50	.59949	.74900	1.3351	.80038	1.2494	1.6681	**10**	**50**	.61337	.77661	1.2876	.78980	1.2661	1.6303	**10**
51	.59972	.74946	1.3343	.80021	1.2497	1.6674	9	51	.61360	.77708	1.2869	.78962	1.2664	1.6297	9
52	.59995	.74991	1.3335	.80003	1.2499	1.6668	8	52	.61383	.77754	1.2861	.78944	1.2667	1.6291	8
53	.60019	.75037	1.3327	.79986	1.2502	1.6661	7	53	.61406	.77801	1.2853	.78926	1.2670	1.6285	7
54	.60042	.75082	1.3319	.79968	1.2505	1.6655	6	54	.61429	.77848	1.2846	.78908	1.2673	1.6279	6
55	.60065	.75128	1.3311	.79951	1.2508	1.6649	**5**	**55**	.61451	.77895	1.2838	.78891	1.2676	1.6273	**5**
56	.60089	.75173	1.3303	.79934	1.2510	1.6642	4	56	.61474	.77941	1.2830	.78873	1.2679	1.6267	4
57	.60112	.75219	1.3295	.79916	1.2513	1.6636	3	57	.61497	.77988	1.2822	.78855	1.2682	1.6261	3
58	.60135	.75264	1.3287	.79899	1.2516	1.6629	2	58	.61520	.78035	1.2815	.78837	1.2684	1.6255	2
59	.60158	.75310	1.3278	.79881	1.2519	1.6623	1	59	.61543	.78082	1.2807	.78819	1.2687	1.6249	1
60	.60182	.75355	1.3270	.79864	1.2521	1.6616	**0**	**60**	.61566	.78129	1.2799	.78801	1.2690	1.6243	**0**
′	Cos	Cot	Tan	Sin	Csc	Sec	′	′	Cos	Cot	Tan	Sin	Csc	Sec	′

126° (306°)   (233°) **53°**   **127° (307°)**   (232°) **52°**

38° (218°)   (321°) 141°

′	Sin	Tan	Cot	Cos	Sec	Csc	′
0	.61566	.78129	1.2799	.78801	1.2690	1.6243	60
1	.61589	.78175	1.2792	.78783	1.2693	1.6237	59
2	.61612	.78222	1.2784	.78765	1.2696	1.6231	58
3	.61635	.78269	1.2776	.78747	1.2699	1.6225	57
4	.61658	.78316	1.2769	.78729	1.2702	1.6219	56
5	.61681	.78363	1.2761	.78711	1.2705	1.6213	55
6	.61704	.78410	1.2753	.78694	1.2708	1.6207	54
7	.61726	.78457	1.2746	.78676	1.2710	1.6201	53
8	.61749	.78504	1.2738	.78658	1.2713	1.6195	52
9	.61772	.78551	1.2731	.78640	1.2716	1.6189	51
10	.61795	.78598	1.2723	.78622	1.1719	1.6183	50
11	.61818	.78645	1.2715	.78604	1.2722	1.6177	49
12	.61841	.78692	1.2708	.78586	1.2725	1.6171	48
13	.61864	.78739	1.2700	.78568	1.2728	1.6165	47
14	.61887	.78786	1.2693	.78550	1.2731	1.6159	46
15	.61909	.78834	1.2685	.78532	1.2734	1.6153	45
16	.61932	.78881	1.2677	.78514	1.2737	1.6147	44
17	.61955	.78928	1.2670	.78496	1.2740	1.6141	43
18	.61978	.78975	1.2662	.78478	1.2742	1.6135	42
19	.62001	.79022	1.2655	.78460	1.2745	1.6129	41
20	.62024	.79070	1.2647	.78442	1.2748	1.6123	40
21	.62046	.79117	1.2640	.78424	1.2751	1.6117	39
22	.62069	.79164	1.2632	.78405	1.2754	1.6111	38
23	.62092	.79212	1.2624	.78387	1.2757	1.6105	37
24	.62115	.79259	1.2617	.78369	1.2760	1.6099	36
25	.62138	.79306	1.2609	.78351	1.2763	1.6093	35
26	.62160	.79354	1.2602	.78333	1.2766	1.6087	34
27	.62183	.79401	1.2594	.78315	1.2769	1.6082	33
28	.62206	.79449	1.2587	.78297	1.2772	1.6076	32
29	.62229	.79496	1.2579	.78279	1.2775	1.6070	31
30	.62251	.79544	1.2572	.78261	1.2778	1.6064	30
31	.62274	.79591	1.2564	.78243	1.2781	1.6058	29
32	.62297	.79639	1.2557	.78225	1.2784	1.6052	28
33	.62320	.79686	1.2549	.78206	1.2787	1.6046	27
34	.62342	.79734	1.2542	.78188	1.2790	1.6040	26
35	.62365	.79781	1.2534	.78170	1.2793	1.6035	25
36	.62388	.79829	1.2527	.78152	1.2796	1.6029	24
37	.62411	.79877	1.2519	.78134	1.2799	1.6023	23
38	.62433	.79924	1.2512	.78116	1.2802	1.6017	22
39	.62456	.79972	1.2504	.78098	1.2804	1.6011	21
40	.62479	.80020	1.2497	.78079	1.2807	1.6005	20
41	.62502	.80067	1.2489	.78061	1.2810	1.6000	19
42	.62524	.80115	1.2482	.78043	1.2813	1.5994	18
43	.62547	.80163	1.2475	.78025	1.2816	1.5988	17
44	.62570	.80211	1.2467	.78007	1.2819	1.5982	16
45	.62592	.80258	1.2460	.77988	1.2822	1.5976	15
46	.62615	.80306	1.2452	.77970	1.2825	1.5971	14
47	.62638	.80354	1.2445	.77952	1.2828	1.5965	13
48	.62660	.80402	1.2437	.77934	1.2831	1.5959	12
49	.62683	.80450	1.2430	.77916	1.2834	1.5953	11
50	.62706	.80498	1.2423	.77897	1.2837	1.5948	10
51	.62728	.80546	1.2415	.77879	1.2840	1.5942	9
52	.62751	.80594	1.2408	.77861	1.2843	1.5936	8
53	.62774	.80642	1.2401	.77843	1.2846	1.5930	7
54	.62796	.80690	1.2393	.77824	1.2849	1.5925	6
55	.62819	.80738	1.2386	.77806	1.2852	1.5919	5
56	.62842	.80786	1.2378	.77788	1.2855	1.5913	4
57	.62864	.80834	1.2371	.77769	1.2859	1.5907	3
58	.62887	.80882	1.2364	.77751	1.2862	1.5902	2
59	.62909	.80930	1.2356	.77733	1.2865	1.5896	1
60	.62932	.80978	1.2349	.77715	1.2868	1.5890	0
′	Cos	Cot	Tan	Sin	Csc	Sec	′

128° (308°)   (231°) 51°

39° (219°)   (320°) 140°

′	Sin	Tan	Cot	Cos	Sec	Csc	′
0	.62932	.80978	1.2349	.77715	1.2868	1.5890	60
1	.62955	.81027	1.2342	.77696	1.2871	1.5884	59
2	.62977	.81075	1.2334	.77678	1.2874	1.5879	58
3	.63000	.81123	1.2327	.77660	1.2877	1.5873	57
4	.63022	.81171	1.2320	.77641	1.2880	1.5867	56
5	.63045	.81220	1.2312	.77623	1.2883	1.5862	55
6	.63068	.81268	1.2305	.77605	1.2886	1.5856	54
7	.63090	.81316	1.2298	.77586	1.2889	1.5850	53
8	.63113	.81364	1.2290	.77568	1.2892	1.5845	52
9	.63135	.81413	1.2283	.77550	1.2895	1.5839	51
10	.63158	.81461	1.2276	.77531	1.2898	1.5833	50
11	.63180	.81510	1.2268	.77513	1.2901	1.5828	49
12	.63203	.81558	1.2261	.77494	1.2904	1.5822	48
13	.63225	.81606	1.2254	.77476	1.2907	1.5816	47
14	.63248	.81655	1.2247	.77458	1.2910	1.5811	46
15	.63271	.81703	1.2239	.77439	1.2913	1.5805	45
16	.63293	.81752	1.2232	.77421	1.2916	1.5800	44
17	.63316	.81800	1.2225	.77402	1.2919	1.5794	43
18	.63338	.81849	1.2218	.77384	1.2923	1.5788	42
19	.63361	.81898	1.2210	.77366	1.2926	1.5783	41
20	.63383	.81946	1.2203	.77347	1.2929	1.5777	40
21	.63406	.81995	1.2196	.77329	1.2932	1.5771	39
22	.63428	.82044	1.2189	.77310	1.2935	1.5766	38
23	.63451	.82092	1.2181	.77292	1.2938	1.5760	37
24	.63473	.82141	1.2174	.77273	1.2941	1.5755	36
25	.63496	.82190	1.2167	.77255	1.2944	1.5749	35
26	.63518	.82238	1.2160	.77236	1.2947	1.5744	34
27	.63540	.82287	1.2153	.77218	1.2950	1.5738	33
28	.63563	.82336	1.2145	.77199	1.2953	1.5732	32
29	.63585	.82385	1.2138	.77181	1.2957	1.5727	31
30	.63608	.82434	1.2131	.77162	1.2960	1.5721	30
31	.63630	.82483	1.2124	.77144	1.2963	1.5716	29
32	.63653	.82531	1.2117	.77125	1.2966	1.5710	28
33	.63675	.82580	1.2109	.77107	1.2969	1.5705	27
34	.63698	.82629	1.2102	.77088	1.2972	1.5699	26
35	.63720	.82678	1.2095	.77070	1.2975	1.5694	25
36	.63742	.82727	1.2088	.77051	1.2978	1.5688	24
37	.63765	.82776	1.2081	.77033	1.2981	1.5683	23
38	.63787	.82825	1.2074	.77014	1.2985	1.5677	22
39	.63810	.82874	1.2066	.76996	1.2988	1.5672	21
40	.63832	.82923	1.2059	.76977	1.2991	1.5666	20
41	.63854	.82972	1.2052	.76959	1.2994	1.5661	19
42	.63877	.83022	1.2045	.76940	1.2997	1.5655	18
43	.63899	.83071	1.2038	.76921	1.3000	1.5650	17
44	.63922	.83120	1.2031	.76903	1.3003	1.5644	16
45	.63944	.83169	1.2024	.76884	1.3007	1.5639	15
46	.63966	.83218	1.2017	.76866	1.3010	1.5633	14
47	.63989	.83268	1.2009	.76847	1.3013	1.5628	13
48	.64011	.83317	1.2002	.76828	1.3016	1.5622	12
49	.64033	.83366	1.1995	.76810	1.3019	1.5617	11
50	.64056	.83415	1.1988	.76791	1.3022	1.5611	10
51	.64078	.83465	1.1981	.76772	1.3026	1.5606	9
52	.64100	.83514	1.1974	.76754	1.3029	1.5601	8
53	.64123	.83564	1.1967	.76735	1.3032	1.5596	7
54	.64145	.83613	1.1960	.76717	1.3035	1.5590	6
55	.64167	.83662	1.1953	.76698	1.3038	1.5584	5
56	.64190	.83712	1.1946	.76679	1.3041	1.5579	4
57	.64212	.83761	1.1939	.76661	1.3045	1.5573	3
58	.64234	.83811	1.1932	.76642	1.3048	1.5568	2
59	.64256	.83860	1.1925	.76623	1.3051	1.5563	1
60	.64279	.83910	1.1918	.76604	1.3054	1.5557	0
′	Cos	Cot	Tan	Sin	Csc	Sec	′

129° (309°)   (230°) 50°

40° (220°)   (319°) 139°   41° (221°)   (318°) 138°

′	Sin	Tan	Cot	Cos	Sec	Csc	′		′	Sin	Tan	Cot	Cos	Sec	Csc	′
0	.64279	.83910	1.1918	.76604	1.3054	1.5557	60		0	.65606	.86929	1.1504	.75471	1.3250	1.5243	60
1	.64301	.83960	1.1910	.76586	1.3057	1.5552	59		1	.65628	.86980	1.1497	.75452	1.3253	1.5237	59
2	.64323	.84009	1.1903	.76567	1.3060	1.5546	58		2	.65650	.87031	1.1490	.75433	1.3257	1.5232	58
3	.64346	.84059	1.1896	.76548	1.3064	1.5541	57		3	.65672	.87082	1.1483	.75414	1.3260	1.5227	57
4	.64368	.84108	1.1889	.76530	1.3067	1.5536	56		4	.65694	.87133	1.1477	.75395	1.3264	1.5222	56
5	.64390	.84158	1.1882	.76511	1.3070	1.5530	55		5	.65716	.87184	1.1470	.75375	1.3267	1.5217	55
6	.64412	.84208	1.1875	.76492	1.3073	1.5525	54		6	.65738	.87236	1.1463	.75356	1.3270	1.5212	54
7	.64435	.84258	1.1868	.76473	1.3076	1.5520	53		7	.65759	.87287	1.1456	.75337	1.3274	1.5207	53
8	.64457	.84307	1.1861	.76455	1.3080	1.5514	52		8	.65781	.87338	1.1450	.75318	1.3277	1.5202	52
9	.64479	.84357	1.1854	.76436	1.3083	1.5509	51		9	.65803	.87389	1.1443	.75299	1.3280	1.5197	51
10	.64501	.84407	1.1847	.76417	1.3086	1.5504	50		10	.65825	.87441	1.1436	.75280	1.3284	1.5192	50
11	.64524	.84457	1.1840	.76398	1.3089	1.5498	49		11	.65847	.87492	1.1430	.75261	1.3287	1.5187	49
12	.64546	.84507	1.1833	.76380	1.3093	1.5493	48		12	.65869	.87543	1.1423	.75241	1.3291	1.5182	48
13	.64568	.84556	1.1826	.76361	1.3096	1.5488	47		13	.65891	.87595	1.1416	.75222	1.3294	1.5177	47
14	.64590	.84606	1.1819	.76342	1.3099	1.5482	46		14	.65913	.87646	1.1410	.75203	1.3297	1.5172	46
15	.64612	.84656	1.1812	.76323	1.3102	1.5477	45		15	.65935	.87698	1.1403	.75184	1.3301	1.5167	45
16	.64635	.84706	1.1806	.76304	1.3105	1.5472	44		16	.65956	.87749	1.1396	.75165	1.3304	1.5162	44
17	.64657	.84756	1.1799	.76286	1.3109	1.5466	43		17	.65978	.87801	1.1389	.75146	1.3307	1.5156	43
18	.64679	.84806	1.1792	.76267	1.3112	1.5461	42		18	.66000	.87852	1.1383	.75126	1.3311	1.5151	42
19	.64701	.84856	1.1785	.76248	1.3115	1.5456	41		19	.66022	.87904	1.1376	.75107	1.3314	1.5146	41
20	.64723	.84906	1.1778	.76229	1.3118	1.5450	40		20	.66044	.87955	1.1369	.75088	1.3318	1.5141	40
21	.64746	.84956	1.1771	.76210	1.3122	1.5445	39		21	.66066	.88007	1.1363	.75069	1.3321	1.5136	39
22	.64768	.85006	1.1764	.76192	1.3125	1.5440	38		22	.66088	.88059	1.1356	.75050	1.3325	1.5131	38
23	.64790	.85057	1.1757	.76173	1.3128	1.5435	37		23	.66109	.88110	1.1349	.75030	1.3328	1.5126	37
24	.64812	.85107	1.1750	.76154	1.3131	1.5429	36		24	.66131	.88162	1.1343	.75011	1.3331	1.5121	36
25	.64834	.85157	1.1743	.76135	1.3135	1.5424	35		25	.66153	.88214	1.1336	.74992	1.3335	1.5116	35
26	.64856	.85207	1.1736	.76116	1.3138	1.5419	34		26	.66175	.88265	1.1329	.74973	1.3338	1.5111	34
27	.64878	.85257	1.1729	.76097	1.3141	1.5413	33		27	.66197	.88317	1.1323	.74953	1.3342	1.5107	33
28	.64901	.85308	1.1722	.76078	1.3144	1.5408	32		28	.66218	.88369	1.1316	.74934	1.3345	1.5102	32
29	.64923	.85358	1.1715	.76059	1.3148	1.5403	31		29	.66240	.88421	1.1310	.74915	1.3348	1.5097	31
30	.64945	.85408	1.1708	.76041	1.3151	1.5398	30		30	.66262	.88473	1.1303	.74896	1.3352	1.5092	30
31	.64967	.85458	1.1702	.76022	1.3154	1.5392	29		31	.66284	.88524	1.1296	.74876	1.3355	1.5087	29
32	.64989	.85509	1.1695	.76003	1.3157	1.5387	28		32	.66306	.88576	1.1290	.74857	1.3359	1.5082	28
33	.65011	.85559	1.1688	.75984	1.3161	1.5382	27		33	.66327	.88628	1.1283	.74838	1.3362	1.5077	27
34	.65033	.85609	1.1681	.75965	1.3164	1.5377	26		34	.66349	.88680	1.1276	.74818	1.3366	1.5072	26
35	.65055	.85660	1.1674	.75946	1.3167	1.5372	25		35	.66371	.88732	1.1270	.74799	1.3369	1.5067	25
36	.65077	.85710	1.1667	.75927	1.3171	1.5366	24		36	.66393	.88784	1.1263	.74780	1.3373	1.5062	24
37	.65100	.85761	1.1660	.75908	1.3174	1.5361	23		37	.66414	.88836	1.1257	.74760	1.3376	1.5057	23
38	.65122	.85811	1.1653	.75889	1.3177	1.5356	22		38	.66436	.88888	1.1250	.74741	1.3380	1.5052	22
39	.65144	.85862	1.1647	.75870	1.3180	1.5351	21		39	.66458	.88940	1.1243	.74722	1.3383	1.5047	21
40	.65166	.85912	1.1640	.75851	1.3184	1.5345	20		40	.66480	.88992	1.1237	.74703	1.3386	1.5042	20
41	.65188	.85963	1.1633	.75832	1.3187	1.5340	19		41	.66501	.89045	1.1230	.74683	1.3390	1.5037	19
42	.65210	.86014	1.1626	.75813	1.3190	1.5335	18		42	.66523	.89097	1.1224	.74664	1.3393	1.5032	18
43	.65232	.86064	1.1619	.75794	1.3194	1.5330	17		43	.66545	.89149	1.1217	.74644	1.3397	1.5027	17
44	.65254	.86115	1.1612	.75775	1.3197	1.5325	16		44	.66566	.89201	1.1211	.74625	1.3400	1.5023	16
45	.65276	.86166	1.1606	.75756	1.3200	1.5320	15		45	.66588	.89253	1.1204	.74606	1.3404	1.5018	15
46	.65298	.86216	1.1599	.75738	1.3203	1.5314	14		46	.66610	.89306	1.1197	.74586	1.3407	1.5013	14
47	.65320	.86267	1.1592	.75719	1.3207	1.5309	13		47	.66632	.89358	1.1191	.74567	1.3411	1.5008	13
48	.65342	.86318	1.1585	.75700	1.3210	1.5304	12		48	.66653	.89410	1.1184	.74548	1.3414	1.5003	12
49	.65364	.86368	1.1578	.75680	1.3213	1.5299	11		49	.66675	.89463	1.1178	.74528	1.3418	1.4998	11
50	.65386	.86419	1.1571	.75661	1.3217	1.5294	10		50	.66697	.89515	1.1171	.74509	1.3421	1.4993	10
51	.65408	.86470	1.1565	.75642	1.3220	1.5289	9		51	.66718	.89567	1.1165	.74489	1.3425	1.4988	9
52	.65430	.86521	1.1558	.75623	1.3223	1.5283	8		52	.66740	.89620	1.1158	.74470	1.3428	1.4984	8
53	.65452	.86572	1.1551	.75604	1.3227	1.5278	7		53	.66762	.89672	1.1152	.74451	1.3432	1.4979	7
54	.65474	.86623	1.1544	.75585	1.3230	1.5273	6		54	.66783	.89725	1.1145	.74431	1.3435	1.4974	6
55	.65496	.86674	1.1538	.75566	1.3233	1.5268	5		55	.66805	.89777	1.1139	.74412	1.3439	1.4969	5
56	.65518	.86725	1.1531	.75547	1.3237	1.5263	4		56	.66827	.89830	1.1132	.74392	1.3442	1.4964	4
57	.65540	.86776	1.1524	.75528	1.3240	1.5258	3		57	.66848	.89883	1.1126	.74373	1.3446	1.4959	3
58	.65562	.86827	1.1517	.75509	1.3243	1.5253	2		58	.66870	.89935	1.1119	.74353	1.3449	1.4954	2
59	.65584	.86878	1.1510	.75490	1.3247	1.5248	1		59	.66891	.89988	1.1113	.74334	1.3453	1.4950	1
60	.65606	.86929	1.1504	.75471	1.3250	1.5243	0		60	.66913	.90040	1.1106	.74314	1.3456	1.4945	0
′	Cos	Cot	Tan	Sin	Csc	Sec	′		′	Cos	Cot	Tan	Sin	Csc	Sec	′

130° (310°)   (229°) 49°   131° (311°)   (228°) 48°

42° (222°)   (317°) **137°**

'	Sin	Tan	Cot	Cos	Sec	Csc	'
0	.66913	.90040	1.1106	.74314	1.3456	1.4945	60
1	.66935	.90093	1.1100	.74295	1.3460	1.4940	59
2	.66956	.90146	1.1093	.74276	1.3463	1.4935	58
3	.66978	.90199	1.1087	.74256	1.3467	1.4930	57
4	.66999	.90251	1.1080	.74237	1.3470	1.4925	56
5	.67021	.90304	1.1074	.74217	1.3474	1.4921	55
6	.67043	.90357	1.1067	.74198	1.3478	1.4916	54
7	.67064	.90410	1.1061	.74178	1.3481	1.4911	53
8	.67086	.90463	1.1054	.74159	1.3485	1.4906	52
9	.67107	.90516	1.1048	.74139	1.3488	1.4901	51
10	.67129	.90569	1.1041	.74120	1.3492	1.4897	50
11	.67151	.90621	1.1035	.74100	1.3495	1.4892	49
12	.67172	.90674	1.1028	.74080	1.3499	1.4887	48
13	.67194	.90727	1.1022	.74061	1.3502	1.4882	47
14	.67215	.90781	1.1016	.74041	1.3506	1.4878	46
15	.67237	.90834	1.1009	.74022	1.3510	1.4873	45
16	.67258	.90887	1.1003	.74002	1.3513	1.4868	44
17	.67280	.90940	1.0996	.73983	1.3517	1.4863	43
18	.67301	.90993	1.0990	.73963	1.3520	1.4859	42
19	.67323	.91046	1.0983	.73944	1.3524	1.4854	41
20	.67344	.91099	1.0977	.73924	1.3527	1.4849	40
21	.67366	.91153	1.0971	.73904	1.3531	1.4844	39
22	.67387	.91206	1.0964	.73885	1.3535	1.4840	38
23	.67409	.91259	1.0958	.73865	1.3538	1.4835	37
24	.67430	.91313	1.0951	.73846	1.3542	1.4830	36
25	.67452	.91366	1.0945	.73826	1.3545	1.4825	35
26	.67473	.91419	1.0939	.73806	1.3549	1.4821	34
27	.67495	.91473	1.0932	.73787	1.3553	1.4816	33
28	.67516	.91526	1.0926	.73767	1.3556	1.4811	32
29	.67538	.91580	1.0919	.73747	1.3560	1.4807	31
30	.67559	.91633	1.0913	.73728	1.3563	1.4802	30
31	.67580	.91687	1.0907	.73708	1.3567	1.4797	29
32	.67602	.91740	1.0900	.73688	1.3571	1.4792	28
33	.67623	.91794	1.0894	.73669	1.3574	1.4788	27
34	.67645	.91847	1.0888	.73649	1.3578	1.4783	26
35	.67666	.91901	1.0881	.73629	1.3582	1.4778	25
36	.67688	.91955	1.0875	.73610	1.3585	1.4774	24
37	.67709	.92008	1.0869	.73590	1.3589	1.4769	23
38	.67730	.92062	1.0862	.73570	1.3592	1.4764	22
39	.67752	.92116	1.0856	.73551	1.3596	1.4760	21
40	.67773	.92170	1.0850	.73531	1.3600	1.4755	20
41	.67795	.92224	1.0843	.73511	1.3603	1.4750	19
42	.67816	.92277	1.0837	.73491	1.3607	1.4746	18
43	.67837	.92331	1.0831	.73472	1.3611	1.4741	17
44	.67859	.92385	1.0824	.73452	1.3614	1.4737	16
45	.67880	.92439	1.0818	.73432	1.3618	1.4732	15
46	.67901	.92493	1.0812	.73413	1.3622	1.4727	14
47	.67923	.92547	1.0805	.73393	1.3625	1.4723	13
48	.67944	.92601	1.0799	.73373	1.3629	1.4718	12
49	.67965	.92655	1.0793	.73353	1.3633	1.4713	11
50	.67987	.92709	1.0786	.73333	1.3636	1.4709	10
51	.68008	.92763	1.0780	.73314	1.3640	1.4704	9
52	.68029	.92817	1.0774	.73294	1.3644	1.4699	8
53	.68051	.92872	1.0768	.73274	1.3647	1.4695	7
54	.68072	.92926	1.0761	.73254	1.3651	1.4690	6
55	.68093	.92980	1.0755	.73234	1.3655	1.4686	5
56	.68115	.93034	1.0749	.73215	1.3658	1.4681	4
57	.68136	.93088	1.0742	.73195	1.3662	1.4677	3
58	.68157	.93143	1.0736	.73175	1.3666	1.4672	2
59	.68179	.93197	1.0730	.73155	1.3670	1.4667	1
60	.68200	.93252	1.0724	.73135	1.3673	1.4663	0
'	Cos	Cot	Tan	Sin	Csc	Sec	'

132° (312°)   (227°) **47°**

43° (223°)   (316°) **136°**

'	Sin	Tan	Cot	Cos	Sec	Csc	'
0	.68200	.93252	1.0724	.73135	1.3673	1.4663	60
1	.68221	.93306	1.0717	.73116	1.3677	1.4658	59
2	.68242	.93360	1.0711	.73096	1.3681	1.4654	58
3	.68264	.93415	1.0705	.73076	1.3684	1.4649	57
4	.68285	.93469	1.0699	.73056	1.3688	1.4645	56
5	.68306	.93524	1.0692	.73036	1.3692	1.4640	55
6	.68327	.93578	1.0686	.73016	1.3696	1.4635	54
7	.68349	.93633	1.0680	.72996	1.3699	1.4631	53
8	.68370	.93688	1.0674	.72976	1.3703	1.4626	52
9	.68391	.93742	1.0668	.72957	1.3707	1.4622	51
10	.68412	.93797	1.0661	.72937	1.3711	1.4617	50
11	.68434	.93852	1.0655	.72917	1.3714	1.4613	49
12	.68455	.93906	1.0649	.72897	1.3718	1.4608	48
13	.68476	.93961	1.0643	.72877	1.3722	1.4604	47
14	.68497	.94016	1.0637	.72857	1.3726	1.4599	46
15	.68518	.94071	1.0630	.72837	1.3729	1.4595	45
16	.68539	.94125	1.0624	.72817	1.3733	1.4590	44
17	.68561	.94180	1.0618	.72797	1.3737	1.4586	43
18	.68582	.94235	1.0612	.72777	1.3741	1.4581	42
19	.68603	.94290	1.0606	.72757	1.3744	1.4577	41
20	.68624	.94345	1.0599	.72737	1.3748	1.4572	40
21	.68645	.94400	1.0593	.72717	1.3752	1.4568	39
22	.68666	.94455	1.0587	.72697	1.3756	1.4563	38
23	.68688	.94510	1.0581	.72677	1.3759	1.4559	37
24	.68709	.94565	1.0575	.72657	1.3763	1.4554	36
25	.68730	.94620	1.0569	.72637	1.3767	1.4550	35
26	.68751	.94676	1.0562	.72617	1.3771	1.4545	34
27	.68772	.94731	1.0556	.72597	1.3775	1.4541	33
28	.68793	.94786	1.0550	.72577	1.3778	1.4536	32
29	.68814	.94841	1.0544	.72557	1.3782	1.4532	31
30	.68835	.94896	1.0538	.72537	1.3786	1.4527	30
31	.68857	.94952	1.0532	.72517	1.3790	1.4523	29
32	.68878	.95007	1.0526	.72497	1.3794	1.4518	28
33	.68899	.95062	1.0519	.72477	1.3797	1.4514	27
34	.68920	.95118	1.0513	.72457	1.3801	1.4510	26
35	.68941	.95173	1.0507	.72437	1.3805	1.4505	25
36	.68962	.95229	1.0501	.72417	1.3809	1.4501	24
37	.68983	.95284	1.0495	.72397	1.3813	1.4496	23
38	.69004	.95340	1.0489	.72377	1.3817	1.4492	22
39	.69025	.95395	1.0483	.72357	1.3820	1.4487	21
40	.69046	.95451	1.0477	.72337	1.3824	1.4483	20
41	.69067	.95506	1.0470	.72317	1.3828	1.4479	19
42	.69088	.95562	1.0464	.72297	1.3832	1.4474	18
43	.69109	.95618	1.0458	.72277	1.3836	1.4470	17
44	.69130	.95673	1.0452	.72257	1.3840	1.4465	16
45	.69151	.95729	1.0446	.72236	1.3843	1.4461	15
46	.69172	.95785	1.0440	.72216	1.3847	1.4457	14
47	.69193	.95841	1.0434	.72196	1.3851	1.4452	13
48	.69214	.95897	1.0428	.72176	1.3855	1.4448	12
49	.69235	.95952	1.0422	.72156	1.3859	1.4443	11
50	.69256	.96008	1.0416	.72136	1.3863	1.4439	10
51	.69277	.96064	1.0410	.72116	1.3867	1.4435	9
52	.69298	.96120	1.0404	.72095	1.3871	1.4430	8
53	.69319	.96176	1.0398	.72075	1.3874	1.4426	7
54	.69340	.96232	1.0392	.72055	1.3878	1.4422	6
55	.69361	.96288	1.0385	.72035	1.3882	1.4417	5
56	.69382	.96344	1.0379	.72015	1.3886	1.4413	4
57	.69403	.96400	1.0373	.71995	1.3890	1.4409	3
58	.69424	.96457	1.0367	.71974	1.3894	1.4404	2
59	.69445	.96513	1.0361	.71954	1.3898	1.4400	1
60	.69466	.96569	1.0355	.71934	1.3902	1.4396	0
'	Cos	Cot	Tan	Sin	Csc	Sec	'

133° (313°)   (226°) **46°**

44° (224°)   (315°) 135°

′	Sin	Tan	Cot	Cos	Sec	Csc	′
0	.69466	.96569	1.0355	.71934	1.3902	1.4396	**60**
1	.69487	.96625	1.0349	.71914	1.3906	1.4391	59
2	.69508	.96681	1.0343	.71894	1.3909	1.4387	58
3	.69529	.96738	1.0337	.71873	1.3913	1.4383	57
4	.69549	.96794	1.0331	.71853	1.3917	1.4378	56
5	.69570	.96850	1.0325	.71833	1.3921	1.4374	**55**
6	.69591	.96907	1.0319	.71813	1.3925	1.4370	54
7	.69612	.96963	1.0313	.71792	1.3929	1.4365	53
8	.69633	.97020	1.0307	.71772	1.3933	1.4361	52
9	.69654	.97076	1.0301	.71752	1.3937	1.4357	51
10	.69675	.97133	1.0295	.71732	1.3941	1.4352	**50**
11	.69696	.97189	1.0289	.71711	1.3945	1.4348	49
12	.69717	.97246	1.0283	.71691	1.3949	1.4344	48
13	.69737	.97302	1.0277	.71671	1.3953	1.4340	47
14	.69758	.97359	1.0271	.71650	1.3957	1.4335	46
15	.69779	.97416	1.0265	.71630	1.3961	1.4331	**45**
16	.69800	.97472	1.0259	.71610	1.3965	1.4327	44
17	.69821	.97529	1.0253	.71590	1.3969	1.4322	43
18	.69842	.97586	1.0247	.71569	1.3972	1.4318	42
19	.69862	.97643	1.0241	.71549	1.3976	1.4314	41
20	.69883	.97700	1.0235	.71529	1.3980	1.4310	**40**
21	.69904	.97756	1.0230	.71508	1.3984	1.4305	39
22	.69925	.97813	1.0224	.71488	1.3988	1.4301	38
23	.69946	.97870	1.0218	.71468	1.3992	1.4297	37
24	.69966	.97927	1.0212	.71447	1.3996	1.4293	36
25	.69987	.97984	1.0206	.71427	1.4000	1.4288	**35**
26	.70008	.98041	1.0200	.71407	1.4004	1.4284	34
27	.70029	.98098	1.0194	.71386	1.4008	1.4280	33
28	.70049	.98155	1.0188	.71366	1.4012	1.4276	32
29	.70070	.98213	1.0182	.71345	1.4016	1.4271	31
30	.70091	.98270	1.0176	.71325	1.4020	1.4267	**30**
31	.70112	.98327	1.0170	.71305	1.4024	1.4263	29
32	.70132	.98384	1.0164	.71284	1.4028	1.4259	28
33	.70153	.98441	1.0158	.71264	1.4032	1.4255	27
34	.70174	.98499	1.0152	.71243	1.4036	1.4250	26
35	.70195	.98556	1.0147	.71223	1.4040	1.4246	**25**
36	.70215	.98613	1.0141	.71203	1.4044	1.4242	24
37	.70236	.98671	1.0135	.71182	1.4048	1.4238	23
38	.70257	.98728	1.0129	.71162	1.4052	1.4234	22
39	.70277	.98786	1.0123	.71141	1.4057	1.4229	21
40	.70298	.98843	1.0117	.71121	1.4061	1.4225	**20**
41	.70319	.98901	1.0111	.71100	1.4065	1.4221	19
42	.70339	.98958	1.0105	.71080	1.4069	1.4217	18
43	.70360	.99016	1.0099	.71059	1.4073	1.4213	17
44	.70381	.99073	1.0094	.71039	1.4077	1.4208	16
45	.70401	.99131	1.0088	.71019	1.4081	1.4204	**15**
46	.70422	.99189	1.0082	.70998	1.4085	1.4200	14
47	.70443	.99247	1.0076	.70978	1.4089	1.4196	13
48	.70463	.99304	1.0070	.70957	1.4093	1.4192	12
49	.70484	.99362	1.0064	.70937	1.4097	1.4188	11
50	.70505	.99420	1.0058	.70916	1.4101	1.4183	**10**
51	.70525	.99478	1.0052	.70896	1.4105	1.4179	9
52	.70546	.99536	1.0047	.70875	1.4109	1.4175	8
53	.70567	.99594	1.0041	.70855	1.4113	1.4171	7
54	.70587	.99652	1.0035	.70834	1.4118	1.4167	6
55	.70608	.99710	1.0029	.70813	1.4122	1.4163	**5**
56	.70628	.99768	1.0023	.70793	1.4126	1.4159	4
57	.70649	.99826	1.0017	.70772	1.4130	1.4154	3
58	.70670	.99884	1.0012	.70752	1.4134	1.4150	2
59	.70690	.99942	1.0006	.70731	1.4138	1.4146	1
60	.70711	1.0000	1.0000	.70711	1.4142	1.4142	**0**
′	Cos	Cot	Tan	Sin	Csc	Sec	′

134° (314°)   (225°) 45°

NATURAL TRIGONOMETRIC FUNCTIONS

FOR ANGLES IN x RADIANS

x	Sin	Tan	Cot	Cos	x	Sin	Tan	Cot	Cos
.00	.00000	.00000	∞	1.00000	**.50**	.47943	.54630	1.8305	.87758
.01	.01000	.01000	99.997	0.99995	.51	.48818	.55936	1.7878	.87274
.02	.02000	.02000	49.993	.99980	.52	.49688	.57256	1.7465	.86782
.03	.03000	.03001	33.323	.99955	.53	.50553	.58592	1.7067	.86281
.04	.03999	.04002	24.987	.99920	.54	.51414	.59943	1.6683	.85771
.05	.04998	.05004	19.983	.99875	.55	.52269	.61311	1.6310	.85252
.06	.05996	.06007	16.647	.99820	.56	.53119	.62695	1.5950	.84726
.07	.06994	.07011	14.262	.99755	.57	.53963	.64097	1.5601	.84190
.08	.07991	.08017	12.473	.99680	.58	.54802	.65517	1.5263	.83646
.09	.08988	.09024	11.081	.99595	.59	.55636	.66956	1.4935	.83094
.10	.09983	.10033	9.9666	.99500	**.60**	.56464	.68414	1.4617	.82534
.11	.10978	.11045	9.0542	.99396	.61	.57287	.69892	1.4308	.81965
.12	.11971	.12058	8.2933	.99281	.62	.58104	.71391	1.4007	.81388
.13	.12963	.13074	7.6489	.99156	.63	.58914	.72911	1.3715	.80803
.14	.13954	.14092	7.0961	.99022	.64	.59720	.74454	1.3431	.80210
.15	.14944	.15114	6.6166	.98877	.65	.60519	.76020	1.3154	.79608
.16	.15932	.16138	6.1966	.98723	.66	.61312	.77610	1.2885	.78999
.17	.16918	.17166	5.8256	.98558	.67	.62099	.79225	1.2622	.78382
.18	.17903	.18197	5.4954	.98384	.68	.62879	.80866	1.2366	.77757
.19	.18886	.19232	5.1997	.98200	.69	.63654	.82534	1.2116	.77125
.20	.19867	.20271	4.9332	.98007	**.70**	.64422	.84229	1.1872	.76484
.21	.20846	.21314	4.6917	.97803	.71	.65183	.85953	1.1634	.75836
.22	.21823	.22362	4.4719	.97590	.72	.65938	.87707	1.1402	.75181
.23	.22798	.23414	4.2709	.97367	.73	.66687	.89492	1.1174	.74517
.24	.23770	.24472	4.0864	.97134	.74	.67429	.91309	1.0952	.73847
.25	.24740	.25534	3.9163	.96891	.75	.68164	.93160	1.0734	.73169
.26	.25708	.26602	3.7591	.96639	.76	.68892	.95045	1.0521	.72484
.27	.26673	.27676	3.6133	.96377	.77	.69614	.96967	1.0313	.71791
.28	.27636	.28755	3.4776	.96106	.78	.70328	.98926	1.0109	.71091
.29	.28595	.29841	3.3511	.95824	.79	.71035	1.0092	.99084	.70385
.30	.29552	.30934	3.2327	.95534	**.80**	.71736	1.0296	.97121	.69671
.31	.30506	.32033	3.1218	.95233	.81	.72429	1.0505	.95197	.68950
.32	.31457	.33139	3.0176	.94924	.82	.73115	1.0717	.93309	.68222
.33	.32404	.34252	2.9195	.94604	.83	.73793	1.0934	.91455	.67488
.34	.33349	.35374	2.8270	.94275	.84	.74464	1.1156	.89635	.66746
.35	.34290	.36503	2.7395	.93937	.85	.75128	1.1383	.87848	.65998
.36	.35227	.37640	2.6567	.93590	.86	.75784	1.1616	.86091	.65244
.37	.36162	.38786	2.5782	.93233	.87	.76433	1.1853	.84365	.64483
.38	.37092	.39941	2.5037	.92866	.88	.77074	1.2097	.82668	.63715
.39	.38019	.41105	2.4328	.92491	.89	.77707	1.2346	.80998	.62941
.40	.38942	.42279	2.3652	.92106	**.90**	.78333	1.2602	.79355	.62161
.41	.39861	.43463	2.3008	.91712	.91	.78950	1.2864	.77738	.61375
.42	.40776	.44657	2.2393	.91309	.92	.79560	1.3133	.76146	.60582
.43	.41687	.45862	2.1804	.90897	.93	.80162	1.3409	.74578	.59783
.44	.42594	.47078	2.1241	.90475	.94	.80756	1.3692	.73034	.58979
.45	.43497	.48306	2.0702	.90045	.95	.81342	1.3984	.71511	.58168
.46	.44395	.49545	2.0184	.89605	.96	.81919	1.4284	.70010	.57352
.47	.45289	.50797	1.9686	.89157	.97	.82489	1.4592	.68531	.56530
.48	.46178	.52061	1.9208	.88699	.98	.83050	1.4910	.67071	.55702
.49	.47063	.53339	1.8748	.88233	.99	.83603	1.5237	.65631	.54869
.50	.47943	.54630	1.8305	.87758	**1.00**	.84147	1.5574	.64209	.54030
Rad.	Sin	Tan	Cot	Cos	Rad.	Sin	Tan	Cot	Cos

x	Sin	Tan	Cot	Cos	x	Sin	Tan	Cot	Cos
1.00	.84147	1.5574	.64209	.54030	1.50	.99749	14.101	.07091	.07074
1.01	.84683	1.5922	.62806	.53186	1.51	.99815	16.428	.06087	.06076
1.02	.85211	1.6281	.61420	.52337	1.52	.99871	19.670	.05084	.05077
1.03	.85730	1.6652	.60051	.51482	1.53	.99917	24.498	.04082	.04079
1.04	.86240	1.7036	.58699	.50622	1.54	.99953	32.461	.03081	.03079
1.05	.86742	1.7433	.57362	.49757	1.55	.99978	48.078	.02080	.02079
1.06	.87236	1.7844	.56040	.48887	1.56	.99994	92.621	.01080	.01080
1.07	.87720	1.8270	.54734	.48012	1.57	1.00000	1255.8	.00080	.00080
1.08	.88196	1.8712	.53441	.47133	1.58	.99996	−108.65	−.00920	−.00920
1.09	.88663	1.9171	.52162	.46249	1.59	.99982	−52.067	−.01921	−.01920
1.10	.89121	1.9648	.50897	.45360	1.60	.99957	−34.233	−.02921	−.02920
1.11	.89570	2.0143	.49644	.44466	1.61	.99923	−25.495	−.03922	−.03919
1.12	.90010	2.0660	.48404	.43568	1.62	.99879	−20.307	−.04924	−.04918
1.13	.90441	2.1198	.47175	.42666	1.63	.99825	−16.871	−.05927	−.05917
1.14	.90863	2.1759	.45959	.41759	1.64	.99761	−14.427	−.06931	−.06915
1.15	.91276	2.2345	.44753	.40849	1.65	.99687	−12.599	−.07937	−.07912
1.16	.91680	2.2958	.43558	.39934	1.66	.99602	−11.181	−.08944	−.08909
1.17	.92075	2.3600	.42373	.39015	1.67	.99508	−10.047	−.09953	−.09904
1.18	.92461	2.4273	.41199	.38092	1.68	.99404	− 9.1208	−.10964	−.10899
1.19	.92837	2.4979	.40034	.37166	1.69	.99290	− 8.3492	−.11977	−.11892
1.20	.93204	2.5722	.38878	.36236	1.70	.99166	− 7.6966	−.12993	−.12884
1.21	.93562	2.6503	.37731	.35302	1.71	.99033	− 7.1373	−.14011	−.13875
1.22	.93910	2.7328	.36593	.34365	1.72	.98889	− 6.6524	−.15032	−.14865
1.23	.94249	2.8198	.35463	.33424	1.73	.98735	− 6.2281	−.16056	−.15853
1.24	.94578	2.9119	.34341	.32480	1.74	.98572	− 5.8535	−.17084	−.16840
1.25	.94898	3.0096	.33227	.31532	1.75	.98399	− 5.5204	−.18115	−.17825
1.26	.95209	3.1133	.32121	.30582	1.76	.98215	− 5.2221	−.19149	−.18808
1.27	.95510	3.2236	.31021	.29628	1.77	.98022	− 4.9534	−.20188	−.19789
1.28	.95802	3.3413	.29928	.28672	1.78	.97820	− 4.7101	−.21231	−.20768
1.29	.96084	3.4672	.28842	.27712	1.79	.97607	− 4.4887	−.22278	−.21745
1.30	.96356	3.6021	.27762	.26750	1.80	.97385	− 4.2863	−.23330	−.22720
1.31	.96618	3.7471	.26687	.25785	1.81	.97153	− 4.1005	−.24387	−.23693
1.32	.96872	3.9033	.25619	.24818	1.82	.96911	− 3.9294	−.25449	−.24663
1.33	.97115	4.0723	.24556	.23848	1.83	.96659	− 3.7712	−.26517	−.25631
1.34	.97348	4.2556	.23498	.22875	1.84	.96398	− 3.6245	−.27590	−.26596
1.35	.97572	4.4552	.22446	.21901	1.85	.96128	− 3.4881	−.28669	−.27559
1.36	.97786	4.6734	.21398	.20924	1.86	.95847	− 3.3608	−.29755	−.28519
1.37	.97991	4.9131	.20354	.19945	1.87	.95557	− 3.2419	−.30846	−.29476
1.38	.98185	5.1774	.19315	.18964	1.88	.95258	− 3.1304	−.31945	−.30430
1.39	.98370	5.4707	.18279	.17981	1.89	.94949	− 3.0257	−.33051	−.31381
1.40	.98545	5.7979	.17248	.16997	1.90	.94630	− 2.9271	−.34164	−.32329
1.41	.98710	6.1654	.16220	.16010	1.91	.94302	− 2.8341	−.35284	−.33274
1.42	.98865	6.5811	.15195	.15023	1.92	.93965	− 2.7463	−.36413	−.34215
1.43	.99010	7.0555	.14173	.14033	1.93	.93618	− 2.6632	−.37549	−.35153
1.44	.99146	7.6018	.13155	.13042	1.94	.93262	− 2.5843	−.38695	−.36087
1.45	.99271	8.2381	.12139	.12050	1.95	.92896	− 2.5095	−.39849	−.37018
1.46	.99387	8.9886	.11125	.11057	1.96	.92521	− 2.4383	−.41012	−.37945
1.47	.99492	9.8874	.10114	.10063	1.97	.92137	− 2.3705	−.42185	−.38868
1.48	.99588	10.983	.09105	.09067	1.98	.91744	− 2.3058	−.43368	−.39788
1.49	.99674	12.350	.08097	.08071	1.99	.91341	− 2.2441	−.44562	−.40703
1.50	.99749	14.101	.07091	.07074	2.00	.90930	− 2.1850	−.45766	−.41615
Rad.	Sin	Tan	Cot	Cos	Rad.	Sin	Tan	Cot	Cos

NATURAL TRIGONOMETRIC FUNCTIONS
SECANTS AND COSECANTS
FOR ANGLES IN RADIANS

x	sec x	csc x	x	sec x	csc x	x	sec x	csc x
0.00	1.00000	∞	0.55	1.17299	1.91319	1.10	2.20460	1.12207
0.01	1.00005	100.00167	0.56	1.18028	1.88258	1.11	2.24890	1.11645
0.02	1.00020	50.00333	0.57	1.18779	1.85311	1.12	2.29525	1.11099
0.03	1.00045	33.33833	0.58	1.19551	1.82474	1.13	2.34379	1.10569
0.04	1.00080	25.00667	0.59	1.20346	1.79739	1.14	2.39467	1.10055
0.05	1.00125	20.00834	0.60	1.21163	1.77103	1.15	2.44806	1.09557
0.06	1.00180	16.67667	0.61	1.22004	1.74560	1.16	2.50413	1.09075
0.07	1.00246	14.29739	0.62	1.22868	1.72107	1.17	2.56311	1.08607
0.08	1.00321	12.51334	0.63	1.23758	1.69738	1.18	2.62519	1.08154
0.09	1.00406	11.12613	0.64	1.24673	1.67449	1.19	2.69063	1.07716
0.10	1.00502	10.01669	0.65	1.25615	1.65238	1.20	2.75970	1.07292
0.11	1.00608	9.10927	0.66	1.26583	1.63101	1.21	2.83271	1.06881
0.12	1.00724	8.35337	0.67	1.27580	1.61034	1.22	2.90997	1.06485
0.13	1.00851	7.71402	0.68	1.28605	1.59035	1.23	2.99188	1.06102
0.14	1.00988	7.16624	0.69	1.29660	1.57100	1.24	3.07885	1.05732
0.15	1.01136	6.69173	0.70	1.30746	1.55227	1.24	3.17136	1.05376
0.16	1.01294	6.27675	0.71	1.31863	1.53413	1.26	3.26993	1.05032
0.17	1.01463	5.91078	0.72	1.33013	1.51657	1.27	3.37518	1.04701
0.18	1.01642	5.58567	0.73	1.34197	1.49954	1.28	3.48778	1.04382
0.19	1.01833	5.29496	0.74	1.35415	1.48305	1.29	3.60853	1.04076
0.20	1.02034	5.03349	0.75	1.36670	1.46705	1.30	3.73833	1.03782
0.21	1.02246	4.79709	0.76	1.37962	1.45154	1.31	3.87822	1.03500
0.22	1.02470	4.58233	0.77	1.39293	1.43650	1.32	4.02941	1.03230
0.23	1.02705	4.38640	0.78	1.40664	1.42191	1.33	4.19329	1.02971
0.24	1.02951	4.20694	0.79	1.42077	1.40775	1.34	4.37153	1.02724
0.25	1.03209	4.04197	0.80	1.43532	1.39401	1.35	4.56607	1.02488
0.26	1.03478	3.88983	0.81	1.45033	1.38067	1.36	4.77923	1.02264
0.27	1.03759	3.74909	0.82	1.46580	1.36772	1.37	5.01379	1.02050
0.28	1.04052	3.61853	0.83	1.48175	1.35514	1.38	5.27313	1.01848
0.29	1.04358	3.49709	0.84	1.49821	1.34293	1.39	5.56133	1.01657
0.30	1.04675	3.38386	0.85	1.51519	1.33106	1.40	5.88349	1.01477
0.31	1.05005	3.27806	0.86	1.53271	1.31954	1.41	6.24593	1.01307
0.32	1.05348	3.17898	0.87	1.55080	1.30834	1.42	6.65666	1.01148
0.33	1.05704	3.08601	0.88	1.56949	1.29746	1.43	7.12598	1.00999
0.34	1.06072	2.99862	0.89	1.58878	1.28688	1.44	7.66732	1.00862
0.35	1.06454	2.91632	0.90	1.60873	1.27661	1.45	8.29856	1.00734
0.36	1.06849	2.83870	0.91	1.62934	1.26662	1.46	9.04406	1.00617
0.37	1.07258	2.76537	0.92	1.65065	1.25691	1.47	9.93782	1.00510
0.38	1.07682	2.69600	0.93	1.67271	1.24747	1.48	11.02881	1.00414
0.39	1.08119	2.63027	0.94	1.69552	1.23830	1.49	12.39028	1.00327
0.40	1.08570	2.56793	0.95	1.71915	1.22938	1.50	14.13683	1.00251
0.41	1.09037	2.50872	0.96	1.74362	1.22072	1.51	16.45850	1.00185
0.42	1.09518	2.45242	0.97	1.76897	1.21229	1.52	19.69493	1.00129
0.43	1.10015	2.39882	0.98	1.79526	1.20410	1.53	24.51881	1.00083
0.44	1.10528	2.34775	0.99	1.82252	1.19614	1.54	32.47654	1.00047
0.45	1.11056	2.29903	1.00	1.85082	1.18840	1.55	48.08888	1.00022
0.46	1.11601	2.25252	1.01	1.88010	1.18087	1.56	92.62580	1.00006
0.47	1.12162	2.20806	1.02	1.91071	1.17356	1.57	+1255.76599	1.00000
0.48	1.12740	2.16554	1.03	1.94243	1.16645	1.58	− 108.65381	1.00004
0.49	1.13336	2.12483	1.04	1.97542	1.15955	1.59	− 52.07657	1.00018
0.50	1.13949	2.08583	1.05	2.00976	1.15284	1.60	− 34.24714	1.00043
0.51	1.14581	2.04844	1.06	2.04552	1.14632			
0.52	1.15231	2.01256	1.07	2.08279	1.13999			
0.53	1.15901	1.97811	1.08	2.12166	1.13384			
0.54	1.16590	1.94501	1.09	2.16223	1.12787			
0.55	1.17299	1.91319	1.10	2.20460	1.12207			

NATURAL TRIGONOMETRIC FUNCTIONS
SINE, TANGENT, COTANGENT, COSINE
FOR ANGLES IN π RADIANS

x		Sin (πx)	Tan (πx)	Cot (πx)	Cos (πx)
.00 or 1.00		.00000	.00000	inf	1.00000
.01	.99	.03141	.03143	31.821	.99951
.02	.98	.06279	.06291	15.895	.99803
.03	.97	.09411	.09453	10.579	.99556
.04	.96	.12533	.12633	7.9158	.99211
.05	.95	.15643	.15838	6.3138	.98769
.06	.94	.18738	.19076	5.2422	.98229
.07	.93	.21814	.22353	4.4737	.97592
.08	.92	.24869	.25676	3.8947	.96858
.09	.91	.27899	.29053	3.4420	.96029
.10	.90	.30902	.32492	3.0777	.95106
.11	.89	.33874	.36002	2.7776	.94088
.12	.88	.36812	.39593	2.5257	.92978
.13	.87	.39715	.43274	2.3109	.91775
.14	.86	.42578	.47056	2.1251	.90483
.15	.85	.45399	.50953	1.9626	.89101
.16	.84	.48175	.54975	1.8190	.87631
.17	.83	.50904	.59140	1.6909	.86074
.18	.82	.53583	.63462	1.5757	.84433
.19	.81	.56208	.67960	1.4715	.82708
.20	.80	.58779	.72654	1.3764	.80902
.21	.79	.61291	.77568	1.2892	.79016
.22	.78	.63742	.82727	1.2088	.77051
.23	.77	.66131	.88162	1.1343	.75011
.24	.76	.68455	.93906	1.0649	.72897
.25	.75	.70711	1.0000	1.0000	.70711
.26	.74	.72897	1.0649	.93906	.68455
.27	.73	.75011	1.1343	.88162	.66131
.28	.72	.77051	1.2088	.82727	.63742
.29	.71	.79016	1.2892	.77568	.61291
.30	.70	.80902	1.3764	.72654	.58779
.31	.69	.82708	1.4715	.67960	.56208
.32	.68	.84433	1.5757	.63462	.53583
.33	.67	.86074	1.6909	.59140	.50904
.34	.66	.87631	1.8190	.54975	.48175
.35	.65	.89101	1.9626	.50953	.45399
.36	.64	.90483	2.1251	.47056	.42578
.37	.63	.91775	2.3109	.43274	.39715
.38	.62	.92978	2.5257	.39593	.36812
.39	.61	.94088	2.7776	.36002	.33874
.40	.60	.95106	3.0777	.32492	.30902
.41	.59	.96029	3.4420	.29053	.27899
.42	.58	.96858	3.8947	.25676	.24869
.43	.57	.97592	4.4737	.22353	.21814
.44	.56	.98229	5.2422	.19076	.18738
.45	.55	.98769	6.3138	.15838	.15643
.46	.54	.99211	7.9158	.12633	.12533
.47	.53	.99556	10.579	.09453	.09411
.48	.52	.99803	15.895	.06291	.06279
.49	.51	.99951	31.821	.03143	.03141
.50	.50	1.0000	inf	.00000	.00000

These functions are useful in the solution of wave equations such as the displacement equation of a sound wave in the form:

$$y = A \sin 2\pi n x$$

without the necessity of reducing the angular rotation either to radians or to degrees in order to find the value of the function.

The algebraic sign of the function follows the familiar Quadrant Law for the particular function desired. Thus a numerical value of 9.13π radians becomes (by the subtraction of the greatest multiple of 2π radians) 1.13π radians. This is the same as $.13\pi$ radians in the **3rd** Quadrant, which would give, from the tables above, a value of the sine function of $-.39715$.

Submitted by J. A. Blythe Jr.

SINE AND COSINE FUNCTIONS FOR SPECIAL MULTIPLES OF π RADIANS

k	$\sin\dfrac{2\pi k}{m}$	$\cos\dfrac{2\pi k}{m}$	$\sin\dfrac{2\pi k}{m}$	$\cos\dfrac{2\pi k}{m}$	$\sin\dfrac{2\pi k}{m}$	$\cos\dfrac{2\pi k}{m}$
	$m = 3$		$m = 4$		$m = 5$	
1	0.86603	−0.50000	1.00000	+0.00000	0.95106	+0.30902
2			0.00000	−1.00000	0.58779	−0.80902
	$m = 6$		$m = 7$		$m = 8$	
1	0.86603	+0.50000	0.78183	+0.62349	0.70711	0.70711
2	0.86603	−0.50000	0.97493	−0.22252	1.00000	+0.00000
3	0.00000	−1.00000	0.43388	−0.90097	0.70711	+0.70711
4					0.00000	−1.00000
	$m = 9$		$m = 10$		$m = 11$	
1	0.64279	0.76604	0.58779	0.80902	0.54064	0.84125
2	0.98481	+0.17365	0.95106	+0.30902	0.90963	+0.41542
3	0.86603	−0.50000	0.95106	−0.30902	0.98982	−0.14231
4	0.34202	−0.93969	0.58779	−1.80902	0.75575	−0.65486
5			0.00000	−1.00000	0.28173	−0.95949
	$m = 12$		$m = 13$		$m = 14$	
1	0.50000	0.86603	0.46472	0.88546	0.43388	0.90097
2	0.86603	0.50000	0.82289	0.56806	0.78183	0.62349
3	1.00000	+0.00000	0.99271	+0.12054	0.97493	+0.22252
4	0.86603	−0.50000	0.93502	−0.35460	0.97493	−0.22252
5	0.50000	−0.86603	0.66312	−0.74851	0.78183	−0.62349
6	0.00000	−1.00000	0.23932	−0.97904	0.43388	−0.90097
7					0.00000	−1.00000
	$m = 15$		$m = 16$		$m = 17$	
1	0.40674	0.91355	0.38268	0.92388	0.36124	0.93247
2	0.74314	0.66913	0.70711	0.70711	0.67370	0.73901
3	0.95106	+0.30902	0.92388	0.38268	0.89516	0.44574
4	0.99452	−0.10453	1.00000	+0.00000	0.99573	+0.09227
5	0.86603	−0.50000	0.92388	−0.38268	0.96183	−0.27366
6	0.58779	−0.80902	0.70711	−0.70711	0.79802	−0.60263
7	0.20791	−0.97815	0.38268	−0.92388	0.52643	−0.85022
8			0.00000	−1.00000	0.18375	−0.98297
	$m = 18$		$m = 19$		$m = 20$	
1	0.34202	0.93969	0.32402	0.94582	0.30902	0.95106
2	0.64279	0.76604	0.61421	0.78914	0.58779	0.80902
3	0.86603	0.50000	0.83717	0.54695	0.80902	0.58779
4	0.98481	+0.17365	0.96940	+0.24549	0.95106	0.30902
5	0.98481	−0.17365	0.99658	−0.08258	1.00000	+0.00000
6	0.86603	−0.50000	0.91577	−0.40170	0.95106	−0.30902
7	0.64279	−0.76604	0.73572	−0.67728	0.80902	−0.58779
8	0.34202	−0.93969	0.47595	−0.87947	0.58779	−0.80902
9	0.00000	−1.00000	0.16459	−0.98636	0.30902	−0.95106
10					0.00000	−1.00000
	$m = 21$		$m = 22$		$m = 23$	
1	0.29476	0.95557	0.28173	0.95949	0.26980	0.96292
2	0.56332	0.82624	0.54064	0.84125	0.51958	0.85442
3	0.78183	0.62349	0.75575	0.65486	0.73084	0.68255
4	0.93087	0.36534	0.90963	0.41542	0.88789	0.46007
5	0.99720	+0.07473	0.98982	+0.14231	0.97908	+0.20346
6	0.97493	−0.22252	0.98982	−0.14231	0.99767	−0.06824
7	0.86603	−0.50000	0.90963	−0.41542	0.94226	−0.33488
8	0.68017	−0.73305	0.75575	−0.65486	0.81697	−0.57668
9	0.43388	−0.90097	0.54064	−0.84125	0.63109	−0.77571
10	0.14904	−0.98883	0.28173	−0.95949	0.39840	−0.91721
11			0.00000	−1.00000	0.13617	−0.99069
	$m = 24$		$m = 25$			
1	0.25882	0.96593	0.24869	0.96858		
2	0.50000	0.86603	0.48175	0.87631		
3	0.70711	0.70711	0.68455	0.72897		
4	0.86603	0.50000	0.84433	0.53583		
5	0.96593	0.25882	0.95106	0.30902		
6	1.00000	+0.00000	0.99803	+0.06279		
7	0.96593	−0.25882	0.98229	−0.18738		
8	0.86603	−0.50000	0.90483	−0.42578		
9	0.70711	−0.70711	0.77051	−0.63742		
10	0.50000	−0.86603	0.58779	−0.80902		
11	0.25882	−0.96593	0.36812	−0.92978		
12	0.00000	−1.00000	0.12533	−0.99211		

SQUARES, CUBES AND ROOTS

Roots of numbers other than those given directly may be found by the following relations:

$$\sqrt{100n} = 10\sqrt{n}; \quad \sqrt{1000n} = 10\sqrt{10n}; \quad \sqrt{\frac{1}{10}n} = \frac{1}{10}\sqrt{10n}; \quad \sqrt{\frac{1}{100}n} = \frac{1}{10}\sqrt{n}, \quad \sqrt{\frac{1}{1000}n} =$$

$$\frac{1}{100}\sqrt{10n}; \quad \sqrt[3]{1000n} = 10\sqrt[3]{n}; \quad \sqrt[3]{10,000n} = 10\sqrt[3]{10n}; \quad \sqrt[3]{100,000n} = 10\sqrt[3]{100n}; \quad \sqrt[3]{\frac{1}{10}n} = \frac{1}{10}\sqrt[3]{100n};$$

$$\sqrt[3]{\frac{1}{100}n} = \frac{1}{10}\sqrt[3]{10n}; \quad \sqrt[3]{\frac{1}{1000}n} = \frac{1}{10}\sqrt[3]{n}.$$

n	n^2	$\sqrt{n}$	$\sqrt{10n}$	n^3	$\sqrt[3]{n}$	$\sqrt[3]{10n}$	$\sqrt[3]{100n}$
1	1	1.000 000	3.162 278	1	1.000 000	2.154 435	4.641 589
2	4	1.414 214	4.472 136	8	1.259 921	2.714 418	5.848 035
3	9	1.732 051	5.477 226	27	1.442 250	3.107 233	6.694 330
4	16	2.000 000	6.324 555	64	1.587 401	3.419 952	7.368 063
5	25	2.236 068	7.071 068	125	1.709 976	3.684 031	7.937 005
6	36	2.449 490	7.745 967	216	1.817 121	3.914 868	8.434 327
7	49	2.645 751	8.366 600	343	1.912 931	4.121 285	8.879 040
8	64	2.828 427	8.944 272	512	2.000 000	4.308 869	9.283 178
9	81	3.000 000	9.486 833	729	2.080 084	4.481 405	9.654 894
10	100	3.162 278	10.00000	1 000	2.154 435	4.641 589	10.00000
11	121	3.316 625	10.48809	1 331	2.223 980	4.791 420	10.32280
12	144	3.464 102	10.95445	1 728	2.289 428	4.932 424	10.62659
13	169	3.605 551	11.40175	2 197	2.351 335	5.065 797	10.91393
14	196	3.741 657	11.83216	2 744	2.410 142	5.192 494	11.18689
15	225	3.872 983	12.24745	3 375	2.466 212	5.313 293	11.44714
16	256	4.000 000	12.64911	4 096	2.519 842	5.428 835	11.69607
17	289	4.123 106	13.03840	4 913	2.571 282	5.539 658	11.93483
18	324	4.242 641	13.41641	5 832	2.620 741	5.646 216	12.16440
19	361	4.358 899	13.78405	6 859	2.668 402	5.748 897	12.38562
20	400	4.472 136	14.14214	8 000	2.714 418	5.848 035	12.59921
21	441	4.582 576	14.49138	9 261	2.758 924	5.943 922	12.80579
22	484	4.690 416	14.83240	10 648	2.802 039	6.036 811	13.00591
23	529	4.795 832	15.16575	12 167	2.843 867	6.126 926	13.20006
24	576	4.898 979	15.49193	13 824	2.884 499	6.214 465	13.38866
25	625	5.000 000	15.81139	15 625	2.924 018	6.299 605	13.57209
26	676	5.099 020	16.12452	17 576	2.962 496	6.382 504	13.75069
27	729	5.196 152	16.43168	19 683	3.000 000	6.463 304	13.92477
28	784	5.291 503	16.73320	21 952	3.036 589	6.542 133	14.09460
29	841	5.385 165	17.02939	24 389	3.072 317	6.619 106	14.26043
30	900	5.477 226	17.32051	27 000	3.107 233	6.694 330	14.42250
31	961	5.567 764	17.60682	29 791	3.141 381	6.767 899	14.58100
32	1 024	5.656 854	17.88854	32 768	3.174 802	6.839 904	14.73613
33	1 089	5.744 563	18.16590	35 937	3.207 534	6.910 423	14.88806
34	1 156	5.830 952	18.43909	39 304	3.239 612	6.979 532	15.03695
35	1 225	5.916 080	18.70829	42 875	3.271 066	7.047 299	15.18294
36	1 296	6.000 000	18.97367	46 656	3.301 927	7.113 787	15.32619
37	1 369	6.082 763	19.23538	50 653	3.332 222	7.179 054	15.46680
38	1 444	6.164 414	19.49359	54 872	3.361 975	7.243 156	15.60491
39	1 521	6.244 998	19.74842	59 319	3.391 211	7.306 144	15.74061
40	1 600	6.324 555	20.00000	64 000	3.419 952	7.368 063	15.87401
41	1 681	6.403 124	20.24846	68 921	3.448 217	7.428 959	16.00521
42	1 764	6.480 741	20.49390	74 088	3.476 027	7.488 872	16.13429
43	1 849	6.557 439	20.73644	79 507	3.503 398	7.547 842	16.26133
44	1 936	6.633 250	20.97618	85 184	3.530 348	7.605 905	16.38643
45	2 025	6.708 204	21.21320	91 125	3.556 893	7.663 094	16.50964
46	2 116	6.782 330	21.44761	97 336	3.583 048	7.719 443	16.63103
47	2 209	6.855 655	21.67948	103 823	3.608 826	7.774 980	16.75069
48	2 304	6.928 203	21.90890	110 592	3.634 241	7.829 735	16.86865
49	2 401	7.000 000	22.13594	117 649	3.659 306	7.883 735	16.98499
50	2 500	7.071 068	22.36068	125 000	3.684 031	7.937 005	17.09976

n	n^2	$\sqrt{n}$	$\sqrt{10n}$	n^3	$\sqrt[3]{n}$	$\sqrt[3]{10n}$	$\sqrt[3]{100n}$
50	2 500	7.071 068	22.36068	125 000	3.684 031	7.937 005	17.09976
51	2 601	7.141 428	22.58318	132 651	3.708 430	7.989 570	17.21301
52	2 704	7.211 103	22.80351	140 608	3.732 511	8.041 452	17.32478
53	2 809	7.280 110	23.02173	148 877	3.756 286	8.092 672	17.43513
54	2 916	7.348 469	23.23790	157 464	3.779 763	8.143 253	17.54411
55	3 025	7.416 198	23.45208	166 375	3.802 952	8.193 213	17.65174
56	3 136	7.483 315	23.66432	175 616	3.825 862	8.242 571	17.75808
57	3 249	7.549 834	23.87467	185 193	3.848 501	8.291 344	17.86316
58	3 364	7.615 773	24.08319	195 112	3.870 877	8.339 551	17.96702
59	3 481	7.681 146	24.28992	205 379	3.892 996	8.387 207	18.06969
60	3 600	7.745 967	24.49490	216 000	3.914 868	8.434 327	18.17121
61	3 721	7.810 250	24.69818	226 981	3.936 497	8.480 926	18.27160
62	3 844	7.874 008	24.89980	238 328	3.957 892	8.527 019	18.37091
63	3 969	7.937 254	25.09980	250 047	3.979 057	8.572 619	18.46915
64	4 096	8.000 000	25.29822	262 144	4.000 000	8.617 739	18.56636
65	4 225	8.062 258	25.49510	274 625	4.020 726	8.662 391	18.66256
66	4 356	8.124 038	25.69047	287 496	4.041 240	8.706 588	18.75777
67	4 489	8.185 353	25.88436	300 763	4.061 548	8.750 340	18.85204
68	4 624	8.246 211	26.07681	314 432	4.081 655	8 793 659	18.94536
69	4 761	8.306 624	26.26785	328 509	4.101 566	8.836 556	19.03778
70	4 900	8.366 600	26.45751	343 000	4.121 285	8.879 040	19.12931
71	5 041	8.426 150	26.64583	357 911	4.140 818	8.921 121	19.21997
72	5 184	8.485 281	26.83282	373 248	4.160 168	8.962 809	19.30979
73	5 329	8.544 004	27.01851	389 017	4.179 339	9.004 113	19.39877
74	5 476	8.602 325	27.20294	405 224	4.198 336	9.045 042	19.48695
75	5 625	8.660 254	27.38613	421 875	4.217 163	9.085 603	19.57434
76	5 776	8.717 798	27.56810	438 976	4.235 824	9.125 805	19.66095
77	5 929	8.774 964	27.74887	456 533	4.254 321	9.165 656	19.74681
78	6 084	8.831 761	27.92848	474 552	4.272 659	9.205 164	19.83192
79	6 241	8.888 194	28.10694	493 039	4.290 840	9.244 335	19.91632
80	6 400	8.944 272	28.28427	512 000	4.308 869	9.283 178	20.00000
81	6 561	9.000 000	28.46050	531 441	4.326 749	9.321 698	20.08299
82	6 724	9.055 385	28.63564	551 368	4.344 481	9.359 902	20.16530
83	6 889	9.110 434	28.80972	571 787	4.362 071	9.397 796	20.24694
84	7 056	9.165 151	28.98275	592 704	4.379 519	9.435 388	20.32793
85	7 225	9.219 544	29.15476	614 125	4.396 830	9.472 682	20.40828
86	7 396	9.273 618	29.32576	636 056	4.414 005	9.509 685	20.48800
87	7 569	9.327 379	29.49576	658 503	4.431 048	9.546 403	20.56710
88	7 744	9.380 832	29.66479	681 472	4.447 960	9.582 840	20.64560
89	7 921	9.433 981	29.83287	704 969	4.464 745	9.619 002	20.72351
90	8 100	9.486 833	30.00000	729 000	4.481 405	9.654 894	20.80084
91	8 281	9.539 392	30.16621	753 571	4.497 941	9.690 521	20.87759
92	8 464	9.591 663	30.33150	778 688	4.514 357	9.725 888	20.95379
93	8 649	9.643 651	30.49590	804 357	4.530 655	9.761 000	21.02944
94	8 836	9.695 360	30.65942	830 584	4.546 836	9.795 861	21.10454
95	9 025	9.746 794	30.82207	857 375	4.562 903	9.830 476	21.17912
96	9 216	9.797 959	30.98387	884 736	4.578 857	9.864 848	21.25317
97	9 409	9.848 858	31.14482	912 673	4.594 701	9.898 983	21.32671
98	9 604	9.899 495	31.30495	941 192	4.610 436	9.932 884	21.39975
99	9 801	9.949 874	31.46427	970 299	4.626 065	9.966 555	21.47229
100	10 000	10.00000	31.62278	1 000 000	4.641 589	10.00000	21.54435

n	n^2	$\sqrt{n}$	$\sqrt{10n}$	n^3	$\sqrt[3]{n}$	$\sqrt[3]{10n}$	$\sqrt[3]{100n}$
100	10 000	10.00000	31.62278	1 000 000	4.641 589	10.00000	21.54435
101	10 201	10.04988	31.78050	1 030 301	4.657 010	10.03322	21.61592
102	10 404	10.09950	31.93744	1 061 208	4.672 329	10.06623	21.68703
103	10 609	10.14889	32.09361	1 092 727	4.687 548	10.09902	21.75767
104	10 816	10.19804	32.24903	1 124 864	4.702 669	10.13159	21.82786
105	11 025	10.24695	32.40370	1 157 625	4.717 694	10.16396	21.89760
106	11 236	10.29563	32.55764	1 191 016	4.732 623	10.19613	21.96689
107	11 449	10.34408	32.71085	1 225 043	4.747 459	10.22809	22.03575
108	11 664	10.39230	32.86335	1 259 712	4.762 203	10.25986	22.10419
109	11 881	10.44031	33.01515	1 295 029	4.776 856	10.29142	22.17220
110	12 100	10.48809	33.16625	1 331 000	4.791 420	10.32280	22.23980
111	12 321	10.53565	33.31666	1 367 631	4.805 896	10.35399	22.30699
112	12 544	10.58301	33.46640	1 404 928	4.820 285	10.38499	22.37378
113	12 769	10.63015	33.61547	1 442 897	4.834 588	10.41580	22.44017
114	12 996	10.67708	33.76389	1 481 544	4.848 808	10.44644	22.50617
115	13 225	10.72381	33.91165	1 520 875	4.862 944	10.47690	22.57179
116	13 456	10.77033	34.05877	1 560 896	4.876 999	10.50718	22.63702
117	13 689	10.81665	34.20526	1 601 613	4.890 973	10.53728	22.70189
118	13 924	10.86278	34.35113	1 643 032	4.904 868	10.56722	22.76638
119	14 161	10.90871	34.49638	1 685 159	4.918 685	10.59699	22.83051
120	14 400	10.95445	34.64102	1 728 000	4.932 424	10.62659	22.89428
121	14 641	11.00000	34.78505	1 771 561	4.946 087	10.65602	22.95770
122	14 884	11.04536	34.92850	1 815 848	4.959 676	10.68530	23.02078
123	15 129	11.09054	35.07136	1 860 867	4.973 190	10.71441	23.08350
124	15 376	11.13553	35.21363	1 906 624	4.986 631	10.74337	23.14589
125	15 625	11.18034	35.35534	1 953 125	5.000 000	10.77217	23.20794
126	15 876	11.22497	35.49648	2 000 376	5.013 298	10.80082	23.26967
127	16 129	11.26943	35.63706	2 048 383	5.026 526	10.82932	23.33107
128	16 384	11.31371	35.77709	2 097 152	5.039 684	10.85767	23.39214
129	16 641	11.35782	35.91657	2 146 689	5.052 774	10.88587	23.45290
130	16 900	11.40175	36.05551	2 197 000	5.065 797	10.91393	23.51335
131	17 161	11.44552	36.19392	2 248 091	5.078 753	10.94184	23.57348
132	17 424	11.48913	36.33180	2 299 968	5.091 643	10.96961	23.63332
133	17 689	11.53256	36.46917	2 352 637	5.104 469	10.99724	23.69285
134	17 956	11.57584	36.60601	2 406 104	5.117 230	11.02474	23.75208
135	18 225	11.61895	36.74235	2 460 375	5.129 928	11.05209	23.81102
136	18 496	11.66190	36.87818	2 515 456	5.142 563	11.07932	23.86966
137	18 769	11.70470	37.01351	2 571 353	5.155 137	11.10641	23.92803
138	19 044	11.74734	37.14835	2 628 072	5.167 649	11.13336	23.98610
139	19 321	11.78983	37.28270	2 685 619	5.180 101	11.16019	24.04390
140	19 600	11.83216	37.41657	2 744 000	5.192 494	11.18689	24.10142
141	19 881	11.87434	37.54997	2 803 221	5.204 828	11.21346	24.15867
142	20 164	11.91638	37.68289	2 863 288	5.217 103	11.23991	24.21565
143	20 449	11.95826	37.81534	2 924 207	5.229 322	11.26623	24.27236
144	20 736	12.00000	37.94733	2 985 984	5.241 483	11.29243	24.32881
145	21 025	12.04159	38.07887	3 048 625	5.253 588	11.31851	24.38499
146	21 316	12.08305	38.20995	3 112 136	5.265 637	11.34447	24.44092
147	21 609	12.12436	38.34058	3 176 523	5.277 632	11.37031	24.49660
148	21 904	12.16553	38.47077	3 241 792	5.289 572	11.39604	24.55202
149	22 201	12.20656	38.60052	3 307 949	5.301 459	11.42165	24.60719
150	22.500	12.24745	38.72983	3 375 000	5.313 293	11.44714	24.66212

n	n^2	$\sqrt{n}$	$\sqrt{10n}$	n^3	$\sqrt[3]{n}$	$\sqrt[3]{10n}$	$\sqrt[3]{100n}$
150	22 500	12.24745	38.72983	3 375 000	5.313 293	11.44714	24.66212
151	22 801	12.28821	38.85872	3 442 951	5.325 074	11.47252	24.71680
152	23 104	12.32883	38.98718	3 511 808	5.336 803	11.49779	24.77125
153	23 409	12.36932	39.11521	3 581 577	5.348 481	11.52295	24.82545
154	23 716	12.40967	39.24283	3 652 264	5.360 108	11.54800	24.87942
155	24 025	12.44990	39.37004	3 723 875	5.371 685	11.57295	24.93315
156	24 336	12.49000	39.49684	3 796 416	5.383 213	11.59778	24.98666
157	24 649	12.52996	39.62323	3 869 893	5.394 691	11.62251	25.03994
158	24 964	12.56981	39.74921	3 944 312	5.406 120	11.64713	25.09299
159	25 281	12.60952	39.87480	4 019 679	5.417 502	11.67165	25.14581
160	25 600	12.64911	40.00000	4 096 000	5.428 835	11.69607	25.19842
161	25 921	12.68858	40.12481	4 173 281	5.440 122	11.72039	25.25081
162	26 244	12.72792	40.24922	4 251 528	5.451 362	11.74460	25.30298
163	26 569	12.76715	40.37326	4 330 747	5.462 556	11.76872	25.35494
164	26 896	12.80625	40.49691	4 410 944	5.473 704	11.79274	25.40668
165	27 225	12.84523	40.62019	4 492 125	5.484 807	11.81666	25.45822
166	27 556	12.88410	40.74310	4 574 296	5.495 865	11.84048	25.50954
167	27 889	12.92285	40.86563	4 657 463	5.506 878	11.86421	25.56067
168	28 224	12.96148	40.98780	4 741 632	5.517 848	11.88784	25.61158
169	28 561	13.00000	41.10961	4 826 809	5.528 775	11.91138	25.66230
170	28 900	13.03840	41.23106	4 913 000	5.539 658	11.93483	25.71282
171	29 241	13.07670	41.35215	5 000 211	5.550 499	11.95819	25.76313
172	29 584	13.11488	41.47288	5 088 448	5.561 298	11.98145	25.81326
173	29 929	13.15295	41.59327	5 177 717	5.572 055	12.00463	25.86319
174	30 276	13.19091	41.71331	5 268 024	5.582 770	12.02771	25.91292
175	30 625	13.22876	41.83300	5 359 375	5.593 445	12.05071	25.96247
176	30 976	13.26650	41.95235	5 451 776	5.604 079	12.07362	26.01183
177	31 329	13.30413	42.07137	5 545 233	5.614 672	12.09645	20.06100
178	31 684	13.34166	42.19005	5 639 752	5.625 226	12.11918	26.10999
179	32 041	13.37909	42.30839	5 735 339	5.635 741	12.14184	26.15879
180	32 400	13.41641	42.42641	5 832 000	5.646 216	12.16440	26.20741
181	32 761	13.45362	42.54409	5 929 741	5.656 653	12.18689	26.25586
182	33 124	13.49074	42.66146	6 028 568	5.667 051	12.20929	26.30412
183	33 489	13.52775	42.77850	6 128 487	5.677 411	12.23161	26.35221
184	33 856	13.56466	42.89522	6 229 504	5.687 734	12.25385	26.40012
185	34 225	13.60147	43.01163	6 331 625	5.698 019	12.27601	26.44786
186	34 596	13.63818	43.12772	6 434 856	5.708 267	12.29809	26.49543
187	34 969	13.67479	43.24350	6 539 203	5.718 479	12.32009	26.54283
188	35 344	13.71131	43.35897	6 644 672	5.728 654	12.34201	26.59006
189	35 721	13.74773	43.47413	6 751 269	5.738 794	12.36386	26.63712
190	36 100	13.78405	43.58899	6 859 000	5.748 897	12.38562	26.68402
191	36 481	13.82027	43.70355	6 967 871	5.758 965	12.40731	26.73075
192	36 864	13.85641	43.81780	7 077 888	5.768 998	12.42893	26.77732
193	37 249	13.89244	43.93177	7 189 057	5.778 997	12.45047	26.82373
194	37 636	13.92839	44.04543	7 301 384	5.788 960	12.47194	26.86997
195	38 025	13.96424	44.15880	7 414 875	5.798 890	12.49333	26.91606
196	38 416	14.00000	44.27189	7 529 536	5.808 786	12.51465	26.96199
197	38 809	14.03567	44.38468	7 645 373	5.818 648	12.53590	27.00777
198	39 204	14.07125	44.49719	7 762 392	5.828 477	12.55707	27.05339
199	39 601	14.10674	44.60942	7 880 599	5.838 272	12.57818	27.09886
200	40 000	14.14214	44.72136	8 000 000	5.848 035	12.59921	27.14418

SQUARES, CUBES AND ROOTS (Continued)

n	n^2	$\sqrt{n}$	$\sqrt{10n}$	n^3	$\sqrt[3]{n}$	$\sqrt[3]{10n}$	$\sqrt[3]{100n}$
200	40 000	14.14214	44.72136	8 000 000	5.848 035	12.59921	27.14418
201	40 401	14.17745	44.83302	8 120 601	5.857 766	12.62017	27.18934
202	40 804	14.21267	44.94441	8 242 408	5.867 464	12.64107	27.23436
203	41 209	14.24781	45.05552	8 365 427	5.877 131	12.66189	27.27922
204	41 616	14.28286	45.16636	8 489 664	5.886 765	12.68265	27.32394
205	42 025	14.31782	45.27693	8 615 125	5.896 369	12.70334	27.36852
206	42 436	14.35270	45.38722	8 741 816	5.905 941	12.72396	27.41295
207	42 849	14.38749	45.49725	8 869 743	5.915 482	12.74452	27.45723
208	43 264	14.42221	45.60702	8 998 912	5.924 992	12.76501	27.50138
209	43 681	14.45683	45.71652	9 129 329	5.934 472	12.78543	27.54538
210	44 100	14.49138	45.82576	9 261 000	5.943 922	12.80579	27.58924
211	44 521	14.52584	45.93474	9 393 931	5.953 342	12.82609	27.63296
212	44 944	14.56022	46.04346	9 528 128	5.962 732	12.84632	27.67655
213	45 369	14.59452	46.15192	9 663 597	5.972 093	12.86648	27.72000
214	45 796	14.62874	46.26013	9 800 344	5.981 424	12.88659	27.76331
215	46 225	14.66288	46.36809	9 938 375	5.990 726	12.90663	27.80649
216	46 656	14.69694	46.47580	10 077 696	6.000 000	12.92661	27.84953
217	47 089	14.73092	46.58326	10 218 313	6.009 245	12.94653	27.89244
218	47 524	14.76482	46.69047	10 360 232	6.018 462	12.96638	27.93522
219	47 961	14.79865	46.79744	10 503 459	6.027 650	12.98618	27.97787
220	48 400	14.83240	46.90416	10 648 000	6.036 811	13.00591	28.02039
221	48 841	14.86607	47.01064	10 793 861	6.045 944	13.02559	28.06278
222	49 284	14.89966	47.11688	10 941 048	6.055 049	13.04521	28.10505
223	49 729	14.93318	47.22288	11 089 567	6.064 127	13.06477	28.14718
224	50 176	14.96663	47.32864	11 239 424	6.073 178	13.08427	28.18919
225	50 625	15.00000	47.43416	11 390 625	6.082 202	13.10371	28.23108
226	51 076	15.03330	47.53946	11 543 176	6.091 199	13.12309	28.27284
227	51 529	15.06652	47.64452	11 697 083	6.100 170	13.14242	28.31448
228	51 984	15.09967	47.74935	11 852 352	6.109 115	13.16169	28.35600
229	52 441	15.13275	47.85394	12 008 989	6.118 033	13.18090	28.39739
230	52 900	15.16575	47.95832	12 167 000	6.126 926	13.20006	28.43867
231	53 361	15.19868	48.06246	12 326 391	6.135 792	13.21916	28.47983
232	53 824	15.23155	48.16638	12 487 168	6.144 634	13.23821	28.52086
233	54 289	15.26434	48.27007	12 649 337	6.153 449	13.25721	28.56178
234	54 756	15.29706	48.37355	12 812 904	6.162 240	13.27614	28.60259
235	55 225	15.32971	48.47680	12 977 875	6.171 006	13.29503	28.64327
236	55 696	15.36229	48.57983	13 144 256	6.179 747	13.31386	28.68384
237	56 169	15.39480	48.68265	13 312 053	6.188 463	13.33264	28.72430
238	56 644	15.42725	48.78524	13 481 272	6.197 154	13.35136	28.76464
239	57 121	15.45962	48.88763	13 651 919	6.205 822	13.37004	28.80487
240	57 600	15.49193	48.98979	13 824 000	6.214 465	13.38866	28.84499
241	58 081	15.52417	49.09175	13 997 521	6.223 084	13.40723	28.88500
242	58 564	15.55635	49.19350	14 172 488	6.231 680	13.42575	28.92489
243	59 049	15.58846	49.29503	14 348 907	6.240 251	13.44421	28.96468
244	59 536	15.62050	49.39636	14 526 784	6.248 800	13.46263	29.00436
245	60 025	15.65248	49.49747	14 706 125	6.257 325	13.48100	29.04393
246	60 516	15.68439	49.59839	14 886 936	6.265 827	13.49931	29.08339
247	61 009	15.71623	49.69909	15 069 223	6.274 305	13.51758	29.12275
248	61 504	15.74802	49.79960	15 252 992	6.282 761	13.53580	29.16199
249	62 001	15.77973	49.89990	15 438 249	6.291 195	13.55397	29.20114
250	62 500	15.81139	50.00000	15 625 000	6.299 605	13.57209	29.24018

n	n^2	$\sqrt{n}$	$\sqrt{10n}$	n^3	$\sqrt[3]{n}$	$\sqrt[3]{10n}$	$\sqrt[3]{100n}$
250	62 500	15.81139	50.00000	15 625 000	6.299 605	13.57209	29.24018
251	63 001	15.84298	50.09990	15 813 251	6.307 994	13.59016	29.27911
252	63 504	15.87451	50.19960	16 003 008	6.316 360	13.60818	29.31794
253	64 009	15.90597	50.29911	16 194 277	6.324 704	13.62616	29.35667
254	64 516	15.93738	50.39841	16 387 064	6.333 026	13.64409	29.39530
255	65 025	15.96872	50.49752	16 581 375	6.341 326	13.66197	29.43383
256	65 536	16.00000	50.59644	16 777 216	6.349 604	13.67981	29.47225
257	66 049	16.03122	50.69517	16 974 593	6.357 861	13.69760	29.51058
258	66 564	16.06238	50.79370	17 173 512	6.366 097	13.71534	29.54880
259	67 081	16.09348	50.89204	17 373 979	6.374 311	13.73304	29.58693
260	67 600	16.12452	50.99020	17 576 000	6.382 504	13.75069	29.62496
261	68 121	16.15549	51.08816	17 779 581	6.390 677	13.76830	29.66289
262	68 644	16.18641	51.18594	17 984 728	6.398 828	13.78586	29.70073
263	69 169	16.21727	51.28353	18 191 447	6.406 959	13.80337	29.73847
264	69 696	16.24808	51.38093	18 399 744	6.415 069	13.82085	29.77611
265	70 225	16.27882	51.47815	18 609 625	6.423 158	13.83828	29.81366
266	70 756	16.30951	51.57519	18 821 096	6.431 228	13.85566	29.85111
267	71 289	16.34013	51.67204	19 034 163	6.439 277	13.87300	29.88847
268	71 824	16.37071	51.76872	19 248 832	6.447 306	13.89030	29.92574
269	72 361	16.40122	51.86521	19 465 109	6.455 315	13.90755	29.96292
270	72 900	16.43168	51.96152	19 683 000	6.463 304	13.92477	30.00000
271	73 441	16.46208	52.05766	19 902 511	6.471 274	13.94194	30.03699
272	73 984	16.49242	52.15362	20 123 648	6.479 224	13.95906	30.07389
273	74 529	16.52271	52.24940	20 346 417	6.487 154	13.97615	30.11070
274	75 076	16.55295	52.34501	20 570 824	6.495 065	13.99319	30.14742
275	75 625	16.58312	52.44044	20 796 875	6.502 957	14.01020	30.18405
276	76 176	16.61325	52.53570	21 024 576	6.510 830	14.02716	30.22060
277	76 729	16.64332	52.63079	21 253 933	6.518 684	14.04408	30.25705
278	77 284	16.67333	52.72571	21 484 952	6.526 519	14.06096	30.29342
279	77 841	16.70329	52.82045	21 717 639	6.534 335	14.07780	30.32970
280	78 400	16.73320	52.91503	21 952 000	6.542 133	14.09460	30.36589
281	78 961	16.76305	53.00943	22 188 041	6.549 912	14.11136	30.40200
282	79 524	16.79286	53.10367	22 425 768	6.557 672	14.12808	30.43802
283	80 089	16.82260	53.19774	22 665 187	6.565 414	14.14476	30.47395
284	80 656	16.85230	53.29165	22 906 304	6.573 138	14.16140	30.50981
285	81 225	16.88194	53.38539	23 149 125	6.580 844	14.17800	30.54557
286	81 796	16.91153	53.47897	23 393 656	6.588 532	14.19456	30.58126
287	82 369	16.94107	53.57238	23 639 903	6.596 202	14.21109	30.61686
288	82 944	16.97056	53.66563	23 887 872	6.603 854	14.22757	30.65238
289	83 521	17.00000	53.75872	24 137 569	6.611 489	14.24402	30.68781
290	84 100	17.02939	53.85165	24 389 000	6.619 106	14.26043	30.72317
291	84 681	17.05872	53.94442	24 642 171	6.626 705	14.27680	30.75844
292	85 264	17.08801	54.03702	24 897 088	6.634 287	14.29314	30.79363
293	85 849	17.11724	54.12947	25 153 757	6.641 852	14.30944	30.82875
294	86 436	17.14643	54.22177	25 412 184	6.649 400	14.32570	30.86378
295	87 025	17.17556	54.31390	25 672 375	6.656 930	14.34192	30.89873
296	87 616	17.20465	54.40588	25 934 336	6.664 444	14.35811	30.93361
297	88 209	17.23369	54.49771	26 198 073	6.671 940	14.37426	30.96840
298	88 804	17.26268	54.58938	26 463 592	6.679 420	14.39037	31.00312
299	89 401	17.29162	54.68089	26 730 899	6.686 883	14.40645	31.03776
300	90 000	17.32051	54.77226	27 000 000	6.694 330	14.42250	31.07233

n	n^2	$\sqrt{n}$	$\sqrt{10n}$	n^3	$\sqrt[3]{n}$	$\sqrt[3]{10n}$	$\sqrt[3]{100n}$
300	90 000	17.32051	54.77226	27 000 000	6.694 330	14.42250	31.07233
301	90 601	17.34935	54.86347	27 270 901	6.701 759	14.43850	31.10681
302	91 204	17.37815	54.95453	27 543 608	6.709 173	14.45447	31.14122
303	91 809	17.40690	55.04544	27 818 127	6.716 570	14.47041	31.17556
304	92 416	17.43560	55.13620	28 094 464	6.723 951	14.48631	31.20982
305	93 025	17.46425	55.22681	28 372 625	6.731 315	14.50218	31.24400
306	93 636	17.49286	55.31727	28.652 616	6.738 664	14.51801	31.27811
307	94 249	17.52142	55.40758	28 934 443	6.745 997	14.53381	31.31214
308	94 864	17.54993	55.49775	29 218 112	6.753 313	14.54957	31.34610
309	95 481	17.57840	55.58777	29 503 629	6.760 614	14.56530	31.37999
310	96 100	17.60682	55.67764	29 791 000	6.767 899	14.58100	31.41381
311	96 721	17.63519	55.76737	30 080 231	6.775 169	14.59666	31.44755
312	97 344	17.66352	55.85696	30 371 328	6.782 423	14.61229	31.48122
313	97 969	17.69181	55.94640	30 664 297	6.789 661	14.62788	31.51482
314	98 596	17.72005	56.03570	30 959 144	6.796 884	14.64344	31.54834
315	99 225	17.74824	56.12486	31 255 875	6.804 092	14.65897	31.58180
316	99 856	17.77639	56.21388	31 554 496	6.811 285	14.67447	31.61518
317	100 489	17.80449	56.30275	31 855 013	6.818 462	14.68993	31.64850
318	101 124	17.83255	56.39149	32 157 432	6.825 624	14.70536	31.68174
319	101 761	17.86057	56.48008	32 461 759	6.832 771	14.72076	31.71492
320	102 400	17.88854	56.56854	32 768 000	6.839 904	14.73613	31.74802
321	103 041	17.91647	56.65686	33 076 161	6.847 021	14.75146	31.78106
322	103 684	17.94436	56.74504	33 386 248	6.854 124	14.76676	31.81403
323	104 329	17.97220	56.83309	33 698 267	6.861 212	14.78203	31.84693
324	104 976	18.00000	56.92100	34 012 224	6.868 285	14.79727	31.87976
325	105 625	18.02776	57.00877	34 328 125	6.875 344	14.81248	31.91252
326	106 276	18.05547	57.09641	34 645 976	6.882 389	14.82766	31.94522
327	106 929	18.08314	57.18391	34 965 783	6.889 419	14.84280	31.97785
328	107 584	18.11077	57.27128	35 287 552	6.896 434	14.85792	32.01041
329	108 241	18.13836	57.35852	35 611 289	6.903 436	14.87300	32.04291
330	108 900	18.16590	57.44563	35 937 000	6.910 423	14.88806	32.07534
331	109 561	18.19341	57.53260	36 264 691	6.917 396	14.90308	32.10771
332	110 224	18.22087	57.61944	36 594 368	6.924 356	14.91807	32.14001
333	110 889	18.24829	57.70615	36 926 037	6.931 301	14.93303	32.17225
334	111 556	18.27567	57.79273	37 259 704	6.938 232	14.94797	32.20442
335	112 225	18.30301	57.87918	37 595 375	6.945 150	14.96287	32.23653
336	112 896	18.33030	57.96551	37 933 056	6.952 053	14.97774	32.26857
337	113 569	18.35756	58.05170	38 272 753	6.958 943	14.99259	32.30055
338	114 244	18.38478	58.13777	38 614 472	6.965 820	15.00740	32.33247
339	114 921	18.41195	58.22371	38 958 219	6.972 683	15.02219	32.36433
340	115 600	18.43909	58.30952	39 304 000	6.979 532	15.03695	32.39612
341	116 281	18.46619	58.39521	39 651 821	6.986 368	15.05167	32.42785
342	116 964	18.49324	58.48077	40 001 688	6.993 191	15.06637	32.45952
343	117 649	18.52026	58.56620	40 353 607	7.000 000	15.08104	32.49112
344	118 336	18.54724	58.65151	40 707 584	7.006 796	15.09568	32.52267
345	119 025	18.57418	58.73670	41 063 625	7.013 579	15.11030	32.55415
346	119 716	18.60108	58.82176	41 421 736	7.020 349	15.12488	32.58557
347	120 409	18.62794	58.90671	41 781 923	7.027 106	15.13944	32.61694
348	121 104	18.65476	58.99152	42 144 192	7.033 850	15.15397	32.64824
349	121 801	18.68154	59.07622	42 508 549	7.040 581	15.16847	32.67948
350	122 500	18.70829	59.16080	42 875 000	7.047 299	15.18294	32.71066

n	n^2	$\sqrt{n}$	$\sqrt{10n}$	n^3	$\sqrt[3]{n}$	$\sqrt[3]{10n}$	$\sqrt[3]{100n}$
350	122 500	18.70829	59.16080	42 875 000	7.047 299	15.18294	32.71066
351	123 201	18.73499	59.24525	43 243 551	7.054 004	15.19739	32.74179
352	123 904	18.76166	59.32959	43 614 208	7.060 697	15.21181	32.77285
353	124 609	18.78829	59.41380	43 986 977	7.067 377	15.22620	32.80386
354	125 316	18.81489	59.49790	44 361 864	7.074 044	15.24057	32.83480
355	126 025	18.84144	59.58188	44 738 875	7.080 699	15.25490	32.86569
356	126 736	18.86796	59.66574	45 118 016	7.087 341	15.26921	32.89652
357	127 449	18.89444	59.74948	45 499 293	7.093 971	15.28350	32.92730
358	128 164	18.92089	59.83310	45 882 712	7.100 588	15.29775	32.95801
359	128 881	18.94730	59.91661	46 268 279	7.107 194	15.31198	32.98867
360	129 600	18.97367	60.00000	46 656 000	7.113 787	15.32619	33.01927
361	130 321	19.00000	60.08328	47 045 881	7.120 367	15.34037	33.04982
362	131 044	19.02630	60.16644	47 437 928	7.126 936	15.35452	33.08031
363	131 769	19.05256	60.24948	47 832 147	7.133 492	15.36864	33.11074
364	132 496	19.07878	60.33241	48 228 544	7.140 037	15.38274	33.14112
365	133 225	19.10497	60.41523	48 627 125	7.146 569	15.39682	33.17144
366	133 956	19.13113	60.49793	49 027 896	7.153 090	15.41087	33.20170
367	134 689	19.15724	60.58052	49 430 863	7.159 599	15.42489	33.23191
368	135 424	19.18333	60.66300	49 836 032	7.166 096	15.43889	33.26207
369	136 161	19.20937	60.74537	50 243 409	7.172 581	15.45286	33.29217
370	136 900	19.23538	60.82763	50 653 000	7.179 054	15.46680	33.32222
371	137 641	19.26136	60.90977	51 064 811	7.185 516	15.48073	33.35221
372	138 384	19.28730	60.99180	51 478 848	7.191 966	15.49462	33.38215
373	139 129	19.31321	61.07373	51 895 117	7.198 405	15.50849	33.41204
374	139 876	19.33908	61.15554	52 313 624	7.204 832	15.52234	33.44187
375	140 625	19.36492	61.23724	52 734 375	7.211 248	15.53616	33.47165
376	141 376	19.39072	61.31884	53 157 376	7.217 652	15.54996	33.50137
377	142 129	19.41649	61.40033	53 582 633	7.224 045	15.56373	33.53105
378	142 884	19.44222	61.48170	54 010 152	7.230 427	15.57748	33.56067
379	143 641	19.46792	61.56298	54 439 939	7.236 797	15.59121	33.59024
380	144 400	19.49359	61.64414	54 872 000	7.243 156	15.60491	33.61975
381	145 161	19.51922	61.72520	55 306 341	7.249 505	15.61858	33.64922
382	145 924	19.54482	61.80615	55 742 968	7.255 842	15.63224	33.67863
383	146 689	19.57039	61.88699	56 181 887	7.262 167	15.64587	33.70800
384	147 456	19.59592	61.96773	56 623 104	7.268 482	15.65947	33.73731
385	148 225	19.62142	62.04837	57 066 625	7.274 786	15.67305	33.76657
386	148 996	19.64688	62.12890	57 512 456	7.281 079	15.68661	33.79578
387	149 769	19.67232	62.20932	57 960 603	7.287 362	15.70014	33.82494
388	150 544	19.69772	62.28965	58 411 072	7.293 633	15.71366	33.85405
389	151 321	19.72308	62.36986	58 863 869	7.299 894	15.72714	33.88310
390	152 100	19.74842	62.44998	59 319 000	7.306 144	15.74061	33.91211
391	152 881	19.77372	62.52999	59 776 471	7.312 383	15.75405	33.94107
392	153 664	19.79899	62.60990	60 236 288	7.318 611	15.76747	33.96999
393	154 449	19.82423	62.68971	60 698 457	7.324 829	15.78087	33.99885
394	155 236	19.84943	62.76942	61 162 984	7.331 037	15.79424	34.02766
395	156 025	19.87461	62.84903	61 629 875	7.337 234	15.80759	34.05642
396	156 816	19.89975	62.92853	62 099 136	7.343 420	15.82092	34.08514
397	157 609	19.92486	63.00794	62 570 773	7.349 597	15.83423	34.11381
398	158 404	19.94994	63.08724	63 044 792	7.355 762	15.84751	34.14242
399	159 201	19.97498	63.16645	63 521 199	7.361 918	15.86077	34.17100
400	160 000	20.00000	63.24555	64 000 000	7.368 063	15.87401	34.19952

n	n^2	$\sqrt{n}$	$\sqrt{10n}$	n^3	$\sqrt[3]{n}$	$\sqrt[3]{10n}$	$\sqrt[3]{100n}$
400	160 000	20.00000	63.24555	64 000 000	7.368 063	15.87401	34.19952
401	160 801	20.02498	63.32456	64 481 201	7.374 198	15.88723	34.22799
402	161 604	20.04994	63.40347	64 964 808	7.380 323	15.90042	34.25642
403	162 409	20.07486	63.48228	65 450 827	7.386 437	15.91360	34.28480
404	163 216	20.09975	63.56099	65 939 264	7.392 542	15.92675	34.31314
405	164 025	20.12461	63.63961	66 430 125	7.398 636	15.93988	34.34143
406	164 836	20.14944	63.71813	66 923 416	7.404 721	15.95299	34.36967
407	165 649	20.17424	63.79655	67 419 143	7.410 795	15.96607	34.39786
408	166 464	20.19901	63.87488	67 917 312	7.416 860	15.97914	34.42601
409	167 281	20.22375	63.95311	68 417 929	7.422 914	15.99218	34.45412
410	168 100	20.24846	64.03124	68 921 000	7.428 959	16.00521	34.48217
411	168 921	20.27313	64.10928	69 426 531	7.434 994	16.01821	34.51018
412	169 744	20.29778	64.18723	69 934 528	7.441 019	16.03119	34.53815
413	170 569	20.32240	64.26508	70 444 997	7.447 034	16.04415	34.56607
414	171 396	20.34699	64.34283	70 957 944	7.453 040	16.05709	34.59395
415	172 225	20.37155	64.42049	71 473 375	7.459 036	16.07001	34.62178
416	173 056	20.39608	64.49806	71 991 296	7.465 022	16.08290	34.64956
417	173 889	20.42058	64.57554	72 511 713	7.470 999	16.09578	34.67731
418	174 724	20.44505	64.65292	73 034 632	7.476 966	16.10864	34.70500
419	175 561	20.46949	64.73021	73 560 059	7.482 924	16.12147	34.73266
420	176 400	20.49390	64.80741	74 088 000	7.488 872	16.13429	34.76027
421	177 241	20.51828	64.88451	74 618 461	7.494 811	16.14708	34.78783
422	178 084	20.54264	64.96153	75 151 448	7.500 741	16.15986	34.81535
423	178 929	20.56696	65.03845	75 686 967	7.506 661	16.17261	34.84283
424	179 776	20.59126	65.11528	76 225 024	7.512 572	16.18534	34.87027
425	180 625	20.61553	65.19202	76 765 625	7.518 473	16.19806	34.89766
426	181 476	20.63977	65.26868	77 308 776	7.524 365	16.21075	34.92501
427	182 329	20.66398	65.34524	77 854 483	7.530 248	16.22343	34.95232
428	183 184	20.68816	65.42171	78 402 752	7.536 122	16.23608	34.97958
429	184 041	20.71232	65.49809	78 953 589	7.541 987	16.24872	35.00680
430	184 900	20.73644	65.57439	79 507 000	7.547 842	16.26133	35.03398
431	185 761	20.76054	65.65059	80 062 991	7.553 689	16.27393	35.06112
432	186 624	20.78461	65.72671	80 621 568	7.559 526	16.28651	35.08821
433	187 489	20.80865	65.80274	81 182 737	7.565 355	16.29906	35.11527
434	188 356	20.83267	65.87868	81 746 504	7.571 174	16.31160	35.14228
435	189 225	20.85665	65.95453	82 312 875	7.576 985	16.32412	35.16925
436	190 096	20.88061	66.03030	82 881 856	7.582 787	16.33662	35.19618
437	190 969	20.90454	66.10598	83 453 453	7.588 579	16.34910	35.22307
438	191 844	20.92845	66.18157	84 027 672	7.594 363	16.36156	35.24991
439	192 721	20.95233	66.25708	84 604 519	7.600 139	16.37400	35.27672
440	193 600	20.97618	66.33250	85 184 000	7.605 905	16.38643	35.30348
441	194 481	21.00000	66.40783	85 766 121	7.611 663	16.39883	35.33021
442	195 364	21.02380	66.48308	86 350 888	7.617 412	16.41122	35.35689
443	196 249	21.04757	66.55825	86 938 307	7.623 152	16.42358	35.38354
444	197 136	21.07131	66.63332	87 528 384	7.628 884	16.43593	35.41014
445	198 025	21.09502	66.70832	88 121 125	7.634 607	16.44826	35.43671
446	198 916	21.11871	66.78323	88 716 536	7.640 321	16.46057	35.46323
447	199 809	21.14237	66.85806	89 314 623	7.646 027	16.47287	35.48971
448	200 704	21.16601	66.93280	89 915 392	7.651 725	16.48514	35.51616
449	201 601	21.18962	67.00746	90 518 849	7.657 414	16.49740	35.54257
450	202 500	21.21320	67.08204	91 125 000	7.663 094	16.50964	35.56893

n	n^2	$\sqrt{n}$	$\sqrt{10n}$	n^3	$\sqrt[3]{n}$	$\sqrt[3]{10n}$	$\sqrt[3]{100n}$
450	202 500	21.21320	67.08204	91 125 000	7.663 094	16.50964	35.56893
451	203 401	21.23676	67.15653	91 733 851	7.668 766	16.52186	35.59526
452	204 304	21.26029	67.23095	92 345 408	7.674 430	16.53406	35.62155
453	205 209	21.28380	67.30527	92 959 677	7.680 086	16.54624	35.64780
454	206 116	21.30728	67.37952	93 576 664	7.685 733	16.55841	35.67401
455	207 025	21.33073	67.45369	94 196 375	7.691 372	16.57056	35.70018
456	207 936	21.35416	67.52777	94 818 816	7.697 002	16.58269	35.72632
457	208 849	21.37756	67.60178	95 443 993	7.702 625	16.59480	35.75242
458	209 764	21.40093	67.67570	96 071 912	7.708 239	16.60690	35.77848
459	210 681	21.42429	67.74954	96 702 579	7.713 845	16.61897	35.80450
460	211 600	21.44761	67.82330	97 336 000	7.719 443	16.63103	35.83048
461	212 521	21.47091	67.89698	97 972 181	7.725 032	16.64308	35.85642
462	213 444	21.49419	67.97058	98 611 128	7.730 614	16.65510	35.88233
463	214 369	21.51743	68.04410	99 252 847	7.736 188	16.66711	35.90820
464	215 296	21.54066	68.11755	99 897 344	7.741 753	16.67910	35.93404
465	216 225	21.56386	68.19091	100 544 625	7.747 311	16.69108	35.95983
466	217 156	21.58703	68.26419	101 194 696	7.752 861	16.70303	35.98559
467	218 089	21.61018	68.33740	101 847 563	7.758 402	16.71497	36.01131
468	219 024	21.63331	68.41053	102 503 232	7.763 936	16.72689	36.03700
469	219 961	21.65641	68.48357	103 161 709	7.769 462	16.73880	36.06265
470	220 900	21.67948	68.55655	103 823 000	7.774 980	16.75069	36.08826
471	221 841	21.70253	68.62944	104 487 111	7.780 490	16.76256	36.11384
472	222 784	21.72556	68.70226	105 154 048	7.785 993	16.77441	36.13938
473	223 729	21.74856	68.77500	105 823 817	7.791 488	16.78625	36.16488
474	224 676	21.77154	68.84766	106 496 424	7.796 975	16.79807	36.19035
475	225 625	21.79449	68.92024	107 171 875	7.802 454	16.80988	36.21578
476	226 576	21.81742	68.99275	107 850 176	7.807 925	16.82167	36.24118
477	227 529	21.84033	69.06519	108 531 333	7.813 389	16.83344	36.26654
478	228 484	21.86321	69.13754	109 215 352	7.818 846	16.84519	36.29187
470	229 411	21.88607	69.20983	109 902 239	7.824 294	16.85693	36.31716
480	230 400	21.90890	69.28203	110 592 000	7.829 735	16.86865	36.34241
481	231 361	21.93171	69.35416	111 284 641	7.835 169	16.88036	36.36763
482	232 324	21.95450	69.42622	111 980 168	7.840 595	16.89205	36.39282
483	233 289	21.97726	69.49820	112 678 587	7.846 013	16.90372	36.41797
484	234 256	22.00000	69.57011	113 379 904	7.851 424	16.91538	36.44308
485	235 225	22.02272	69.64194	114 084 125	7.856 828	16.92702	36.46817
486	236 196	22.04541	69.71370	114 791 256	7.862 224	16.93865	36.49321
487	237 169	22.06808	69.78539	115 501 303	7.867 613	16.95026	36.51822
488	238 144	22.09072	69.85700	116 214 272	7.872 994	16.96185	36.54320
489	239 121	22.11334	69.92853	116 930 169	7.878 368	16.97343	36.56815
490	240 100	22.13594	70.00000	117 649 000	7.883 735	16.98499	36.59306
491	241 081	22.15852	70.07139	118 370 771	7.889 095	16.99654	36.61793
492	242 064	22.18107	70.14271	119 095 488	7.894 447	17.00807	36.64278
493	243 049	22.20360	70.21396	119 823 157	7.899 792	17.01959	36.66758
494	244 036	22.22611	70.28513	120 553 784	7.905 129	17.03108	36.69236
105	345 025	22.24800	70.35624	121 287 375	7.910 460	17.04257	36.71710
496	246 016	22.27106	70.42727	122 023 936	7.915 783	17.05404	36.74181
497	247 009	22.29350	70.49823	122 763 473	7.921 099	17.06549	36.76649
498	248 004	22.31591	70.56912	123 505 992	7.926 408	17.07693	36.79113
499	249 001	22.33831	70.63993	124 251 499	7.931 710	17.08835	36.81574
500	250 000	22.36068	70.71068	125 000 000	7.937 005	17.09976	36.84031

n	n^2	$\sqrt{n}$	$\sqrt{10n}$	n^3	$\sqrt[3]{n}$	$\sqrt[3]{10n}$	$\sqrt[3]{100n}$
500	250 000	22.36068	70.71068	125 000 000	7.937 005	17.09976	36.84031
501	251 001	22.38303	70.78135	125 751 501	7.942 293	17.11115	36.86486
502	252 004	22.40536	70.85196	126 506 008	7.947 574	17.12253	36.88937
503	253 009	22.42766	70.92249	127 263 527	7.952 848	17.13389	36.91385
504	254 016	22.44994	70.99296	128 024 064	7.958 114	17.14524	36.93830
505	255 025	22.47221	71.06335	128 787 625	7.963 374	17.15657	36.96271
506	256 036	22.49444	71.13368	129 554 216	7.968 627	17.16789	36.98709
507	257 049	22.51666	71.20393	130 323 843	7.973 873	17.17919	37.01144
508	258 064	22.53886	71.27412	131 096 512	7.979 112	17.19048	37.03576
509	259 081	22.56103	71.34424	131 872 229	7.984 344	17.20175	37.06004
510	260 100	22.58318	71.41428	132 651 000	7.989 570	17.21301	37.08430
511	261 121	22.60531	71.48426	133 432 831	7.994 788	17.22425	37.10852
512	262 144	22.62742	71.55418	134 217 728	8.000 000	17.23548	37.13271
513	263 169	22.64950	71.62402	135 005 697	8.005 205	17.24669	37.15687
514	264 196	22.67157	71.69379	135 796 744	8.010 403	17.25789	37.18100
515	265 225	22.69361	71.76350	136 590 875	8.015 595	17.26908	37.20509
516	266 256	22.71563	71.83314	137 388 096	8.020 779	17.28025	37.22916
517	267 289	22.73763	71.90271	138 188 413	8.025 957	17.29140	37.25319
518	268 324	22.75961	71.97222	138 991 832	8.031 129	17.30254	37.27720
519	269 361	22.78157	72.04165	139 798 359	8.036 293	17.31367	37.30117
520	270 400	22.80351	72.11103	140 608 000	8.041 452	17.32478	37.32511
521	271 441	22.82542	72.18033	141 420 761	8.046 603	17.33588	37.34902
522	272 484	22.84732	72.24957	142 236 648	8.051 748	17.34696	37.37290
523	273 529	22.86919	72.31874	143 055 667	8.056 886	17.35804	37.39675
524	274 576	22.89105	72.38784	143 877 824	8.062 018	17.36909	37.42057
525	275 625	22.91288	72.45688	144 703 125	8.067 143	17.38013	37.44436
526	276 676	22.93469	72.52586	145 531 576	8.072 262	17.39116	37.46812
527	277 729	22.95648	72.59477	146 363 183	8.077 374	17.40218	37.49185
528	278 784	22.97825	72.66361	147 197 952	8.082 480	17.41318	37.51555
529	279 841	23.00000	72.73239	148 035 889	8.087 579	17.42416	37.53922
530	280 900	23.02173	72.80110	148 877 000	8.092 672	17.43513	37.56286
531	281 961	23.04344	72.86975	149 721 291	8.097 759	17.44609	37.58647
532	283 024	23.06513	72.93833	150 568 768	8.102 839	17.45704	37.61005
533	284 089	23.08679	73.00685	151 419 437	8.107 913	17.46797	37.63360
534	285 156	23.10844	73.07530	152 273 304	8.112 980	17.47889	37.65712
535	286 225	23.13007	73.14369	153 130 375	8.118 041	17.48979	37.68061
536	287 296	23.15167	73.21202	153 990 656	8.123 096	17.50068	37.70407
537	288 369	23.17326	73.28028	154 854 153	8.128 145	17.51156	37.72751
538	289 444	23.19483	73.34848	155 720 872	8.133 187	17.52242	37.75091
539	290 521	23.21637	73.41662	156 590 819	8.138 223	17.53327	37.77429
540	291 600	23.23790	73.48469	157 464 000	8.143 253	17.54411	37.79763
541	292 681	23.25941	73.55270	158 340 421	8.148 276	17.55493	37.82095
542	293 764	23.28089	73.62065	159 220 088	8.153 294	17.56574	37.84424
543	294 849	23.30236	73.68853	160 103 007	8.158 305	17.57654	37.86750
544	295 936	23.32381	73.75636	160 989 184	8.163 310	17.58732	37.89073
545	297 025	23.34524	73.82412	161 878 625	8.168 309	17.59809	37.91393
546	298 116	23.36664	73.89181	162 771 336	8.173 302	17.60885	37.93711
547	299 209	23.38803	73.95945	163 667 323	8.178 289	17.61959	37.96025
548	300 304	23.40940	74.02702	164 566 592	8.183 269	17.63032	37.98337
549	301 401	23.43075	74.09453	165 469 149	8.188 244	17.64104	38.00646
550	302 500	23.45208	74.16198	166 375 000	8.193 213	17.65174	38.02952

n	n^2	$\sqrt{n}$	$\sqrt{10n}$	n^3	$\sqrt[3]{n}$	$\sqrt[3]{10n}$	$\sqrt[3]{100n}$
550	302 500	23.45208	74.16198	166 375 000	8.193 213	17.65174	38.02952
551	303 601	23.47339	74.22937	167 284 151	8.198 175	17.66243	38.05256
552	304 704	23.49468	74.29670	168 196 608	8.203 132	17.67311	38.07557
553	305 809	23.51595	74.36397	169 112 377	8.208 082	17.68378	38.09854
554	306 916	23.53720	74.43118	170 031 464	8.213 027	17.69443	38.12149
555	308 025	23.55844	74.49832	170 953 875	8.217 966	17.70507	38.14442
556	309 136	23.57965	74.56541	171 879 616	8.222 899	17.71570	38.16731
557	310 249	23.60085	74.63243	172 808 693	8.227 825	17.72631	38.19018
558	311 364	23.62202	74.69940	173 741 112	8.232 746	17.73691	38.21302
559	312 481	23.64318	74.76630	174 676 879	8.237 661	17.74750	38.23584
560	313 600	23.66432	74.83315	175 616 000	8.242 571	17.75808	38.25862
561	314 721	23.68544	74.89993	176 558 481	8.247 474	17.76864	38.28138
562	315 844	23.70654	74.96666	177 504 328	8.252 372	17.77920	38.30412
563	316 969	23.72762	75.03333	178 453 547	8.257 263	17.78973	38.32682
564	318 096	23.74868	75.09993	179 406 144	8.262 149	17.80026	38.34950
565	319 225	23.76973	75.16648	180 362 029	8.267 029	17.81077	38.37215
566	320 356	23.79075	75.23297	181 321 496	8.271 904	17.82128	38.39478
567	321 489	23.81176	75.29940	182 284 263	8.276 773	17.83177	38.41737
568	322 624	23.83275	75.36577	183 250 432	8.281 635	17.84224	38.43995
569	323 761	23.85372	75.43209	184 220 009	8.286 493	17.85271	38.46249
570	324 900	23.87467	75.49834	185 193 000	8.291 344	17.86316	38.48501
571	326 041	23.89561	75.56454	186 169 411	8.296 190	17.87360	38.50750
572	327 184	23.91652	75.63068	187 149 248	8.301 031	17.88403	38.52997
573	328 329	23.93742	75.69676	188 132 517	8.305 865	17.89444	38.55241
574	329 476	23.95830	75.76279	189 119 224	8.310 694	17.90485	38.57482
575	330 625	23.97916	75.82875	190 109 375	8.315 517	17.91524	38.59721
576	331 776	24.00000	75.89466	191 102 976	8.320 335	17.92562	38.61958
577	332 929	24.02082	75.96052	192 100 033	8.325 148	17.93599	38.64191
578	334 084	24.04163	76.02631	193 100 552	8.329 954	17.94634	38.66422
579	335 241	24.06242	76.09205	194 104 539	8.334 755	17.95669	38.68651
580	336 400	24.08319	76.15773	195 112 000	8.339 551	17.96702	38.70877
581	337 561	24.10394	76.22336	196 122 941	8.344 341	17.97734	38.73100
582	338 724	24.12468	76.28892	197 137 368	8.349 126	17.98765	38.75321
583	339 889	24.14539	76.35444	198 155 287	8.353 905	17.99794	38.77539
584	341 056	24.16609	76.41989	199 176 704	8.358 678	18.00823	38.79755
585	342 225	24.18677	76.48529	200 201 625	8.363 447	18.01850	38.81968
586	343 396	24.20744	76.55064	201 230 056	8.368 209	18.02876	38.84179
587	344 569	24.22808	76.61593	202 262 003	8.372 967	18.03901	38.86387
588	345 744	24.24871	76.68116	203 297 472	8.377 719	18.04925	38.88593
589	346 921	24.26932	76.74634	204 336 469	8.382 465	18.05947	38.90796
590	348 100	24.28992	76.81146	205 379 000	8.387 207	18.06969	38.92996
591	349 281	24.31049	76.87652	206 425 071	8.391 942	18.07989	38.95195
592	350 464	24.33105	76.94154	207 474 688	8.396 673	18.09008	38.97390
593	351 649	24.35159	77.00649	208 527 857	8.401 398	18.10026	38.99584
594	352 836	24.37212	77.07140	209 584 584	8.406 118	18.11043	39.01774
595	354 025	24.39262	77.13624	210 644 875	8.410 833	18.12059	39.03963
596	355 216	24.41311	77.20104	211 708 736	8.415 542	18.13074	39.06149
597	356 409	24.43358	77.26578	212 776 173	8.420 246	18.14087	39.08332
598	357 604	24.45404	77.33046	213 847 192	8.424 945	18.15099	39.10513
599	358 801	24.47448	77.39509	214 921 799	8.429 638	18.16111	39.12692
600	360 000	24.49490	77.45967	216 000 000	8.434 327	18.17121	39.14868

n	n^2	$\sqrt{n}$	$\sqrt{10n}$	n^3	$\sqrt[3]{n}$	$\sqrt[3]{10n}$	$\sqrt[3]{100n}$
600	360 000	24.49490	77.45967	216 000 000	8.434 327	18.17121	39.14868
601	361 201	24.51530	77.52419	217 081 801	8.439 010	18.18130	39.17041
602	362 404	24.53569	77.58866	218 167 208	8.443 688	18.19137	39.19213
603	363 609	24.55606	77.65307	219 256 227	8.448 361	18.20144	39.21382
604	364 816	24.57641	77.71744	220 348 864	8.453 028	18.21150	39.23548
605	366 025	24.59675	77.78175	221 445 125	8.457 691	18.22154	39.25712
606	367 236	24.61707	77.84600	222 545 016	8.462 348	18.23158	39.27874
607	368 449	24.63737	77.91020	223 648 543	8.467 000	18.24160	39.30033
608	369 664	24.65766	77.97435	224 755 712	8.471 647	18.25161	39.32190
609	370 881	24.67793	78.03845	225 866 529	8.476 289	18.26161	39.34345
610	372 100	24.69818	78.10250	226 981 000	8.480 926	18.27160	39.36497
611	373 321	24.71841	78.16649	228 099 131	8.485 558	18.28158	39.38647
612	374 544	24.73863	78.23043	229 220 928	8.490 185	18.29155	39.40795
613	375 769	24.75884	78.29432	230 346 397	8.494 807	18.30151	39.42940
614	376 996	24.77902	78.35815	231 475 544	8.499 423	18.31145	39.45083
615	378 225	24.79919	78.42194	232 608 375	8.504 035	18.32139	39.47223
616	379 456	24.81935	78.48567	233 744 896	8.508 642	18.33131	39.49362
617	380 689	24.83948	78.54935	234 885 113	8.513 243	18.34123	39.51498
618	381 924	24.85961	78.61298	236 029 032	8.517 840	18.35113	39.53631
619	383 161	24.87971	78.67655	237 176 659	8.522 432	18.36102	39.55763
620	384 400	24.89980	78.74008	238 328 000	8.527 019	18.37091	39.57892
621	385 641	24.91987	78.80355	239 483 061	8.531 601	18.38078	39.60018
622	386 884	24.93993	78.86698	240 641 848	8.536 178	18.39064	39.62143
623	388 129	24.95997	78.93035	241 804 367	8.540 750	18.40049	39.64265
624	389 376	24.97999	78.99367	242 970 624	8.545 317	18.41033	39.66385
625	390 625	25.00000	79.05694	244 140 625	8.549 880	18.42016	39.68503
626	391 876	25.01999	79.12016	245 314 376	8.554 437	18.42998	39.70618
627	393 129	25.03997	79.18333	246 491 883	8.558 990	18.43978	39.72731
628	394 384	25.05993	79.24645	247 673 152	8.563 538	18.44958	39.74842
629	395 641	25.07987	79.30952	248 858 189	8.568 081	18.45937	39.76951
630	396 900	25.09980	79.37254	250 047 000	8.572 619	18.46915	39.79057
631	398 161	25.11971	79.43551	251 239 591	8.577 152	18.47891	39.81161
632	399 424	25.13961	79.49843	252 435 968	8.581 681	18.48867	39.83263
633	400 689	25.15949	79.56130	253 636 137	8.586 205	18.49842	39.85363
634	401 956	25.17936	79.62412	254 840 104	8.590 724	18.50815	39.87461
635	403 225	25.19921	79.68689	256 047 875	8.595 238	18.51788	39.89556
636	404 496	25.21904	79.74961	257 259 456	8.599 748	18.52759	39.91649
637	405 769	25.23886	79.81228	258 474 853	8.604 252	18.53730	39.93740
638	407 044	25.25866	79.87490	259 694 072	8.608 753	18.54700	39.95829
639	408 321	25.27845	79.93748	260 917 119	8.613 248	18.55668	39.97916
640	409 600	25.29822	80.00000	262 144 000	8.617 739	18.56636	40.00000
641	410 881	25.31798	80.06248	263 374 721	8.622 225	18.57602	40.02082
642	412 164	25.33772	80.12490	264 609 288	8.626 706	18.58568	40.04162
643	413 449	25.35744	80.18728	265 847 707	8.631 183	18.59532	40.06240
644	414 736	25 37716	80.24961	267 089 984	8.635 655	18.60495	40.08316
645	416 025	25.39685	80.31189	268 336 125	8.640 123	18.61458	40.10390
646	417 316	25.41653	80.37413	269 586 136	8.644 585	18.62419	40.12461
647	418 609	25.43619	80.43631	270 840 023	8.649 044	18.63380	40.14530
648	419 904	25.45584	80.49845	272 097 792	8.653 497	18.64340	40.16598
649	421 201	25.47548	80.56054	273 359 449	8.657 947	18.65298	40.18663
650	422 500	25.49510	80.62258	274 625 000	8.662 391	18.66256	40.20726

n	n^2	$\sqrt{n}$	$\sqrt{10n}$	n^3	$\sqrt[3]{n}$	$\sqrt[3]{10n}$	$\sqrt[3]{100n}$
650	422 500	25 49510	80.62258	274 625 000	8.662 391	18.66256	40.20726
651	423 801	25.51470	80.68457	275 894 451	8.666 831	18.67212	40.22787
652	425 104	25.53429	80.74652	277 167 808	8.671 266	18.68168	40.24845
653	426 409	25.55386	80.80842	278 445 077	8.675 697	18.69122	40.26902
654	427 716	25.57342	80.87027	279 726 264	8.680 124	18.70076	40.28957
655	429 025	25 59297	80.93207	281 011 375	8.684 546	18.71029	40.31009
656	430 336	25.61250	80.99383	282 300 416	8.688 963	18.71980	40.33059
657	431 649	25.63201	81.05554	283 593 393	8.693 376	18.72931	40.35108
658	432 964	25.65151	81.11720	284 890 312	8.697 784	18.73881	40.37154
659	434 281	25.67100	81.17881	286 191 179	8.702 188	18.74830	40.39198
660	435 600	25.69047	81.24038	287 496 000	8.706 588	18.75777	40.41240
661	436 921	25.70992	81.30191	288 804 781	8.710 983	18.76724	40.43280
662	438 244	25.72936	81.36338	290 117 528	8.715 373	18.77670	40.45318
663	439 569	25.74879	81.42481	291 434 247	8.719 760	18.78615	40.47354
664	440 896	25.76820	81.48620	292 754 944	8.724 141	18.79559	40.49388
665	442 225	25.78759	81.54753	294 079 625	8.728 519	18.80502	40.51420
666	443 556	25.80698	81.60882	295 408 296	8.732 892	18.81444	40.53449
667	444 889	25.82634	81.67007	296 740 963	8.737 260	18.82386	40.55477
668	446 224	25.84570	81.73127	298 077 632	8.741 625	18.83326	40.57503
669	447 561	25.86503	81.79242	299 418 309	8.745 985	18.84265	40.59526
670	448 900	25.88436	81.85353	300 763 000	8.750 340	18.85204	40.61548
671	150 241	25.90367	81.91459	302 111 711	8.754 691	18.86141	40.63568
672	451 584	25.92296	81.97561	303 464 448	8.759 038	18.87078	40.65585
673	452 929	25.94224	82.03658	304 821 217	8.763 381	18.88013	40.67601
674	454 276	25.96151	82.09750	306 182 024	8.767 719	18.88948	40.69615
675	455 625	25.98076	82.15838	307 546 875	8.772 053	18.89882	40.71626
676	456 976	26.00000	82.21922	308 915 776	8.776 383	18.90814	40.73636
677	458 329	26.01922	82.28001	310 288 733	8.780 708	18.91746	40.75644
678	459 684	26.03843	82.34076	311 665 752	8.785 030	18.92677	40.77650
679	461 041	26.05763	82.40146	313 046 839	8.789 347	18.93607	40.79653
680	462 400	26.07681	82.46211	314 432 000	8.793 659	18.94536	40.81655
681	463 761	26.09598	82.52272	315 821 241	8.797 968	18.95465	40.83655
682	465 124	26.11513	82.58329	317 214 568	8.802 272	18.96392	40.85653
683	466 489	26.13427	82.64381	318 611 987	8.806 572	18.97318	40.87649
684	467 856	26.15339	82.70429	320 013 504	8.810 868	18.98244	40.89643
685	469 225	26.17250	82.76473	321 419 125	8.815 160	18.99169	40.91635
686	470 596	26.19160	82.82512	322 828 856	8.819 447	19.00092	40.93625
687	471 969	26.21068	82.88546	324 242 703	8.823 731	19.01015	40.95613
688	473 344	26.22975	82.94577	325 660 672	8.828 010	19.01937	40.97599
689	474 721	26.24881	83.00602	327 082 769	8.832 285	19.02858	40.99584
690	476 100	26.26785	83.06624	328 509 000	8.836 556	19.03778	41.01566
691	477 481	26.28688	83.12641	329 939 371	8.840 823	19.04698	41.03546
692	478 864	26.30589	83.18654	331 373 888	8.845 085	19.05616	41.05525
693	480 249	26.32489	83.24662	332 812 557	8.849 344	19.06533	41.07502
694	481 636	26.34388	83.30666	334 255 384	8.853 599	19.07450	41.09476
695	483 025	26.36285	83.36666	335 702 375	8.857 849	19.08366	41.11449
696	484 416	26.38181	83.42661	337 153 536	8.862 095	19.09281	41.13420
697	485 809	26.40076	83.48653	338 608 873	8.866 338	19.10195	41.15389
698	487 204	26.41969	83.54639	340 068 392	8.870 576	19.11108	41.17357
699	488 601	26.43861	83.60622	341 532 099	8.874 810	19.12020	41.19322
700	490 000	26.45751	83.66600	343 000 000	8.879 040	19.12931	41.21285

n	n^2	$\sqrt{n}$	$\sqrt{10n}$	n^3	$\sqrt[3]{n}$	$\sqrt[3]{10n}$	$\sqrt[3]{100n}$
700	490 000	26.45751	83.66600	343 000 000	8.879 040	19.12931	41.21285
701	491 401	26.47640	83.72574	344 472 101	8.883 266	19.13842	41.23247
702	492 804	26.49528	83.78544	345 948 408	8.887 488	19.14751	41.25207
703	494 209	26.51415	83.84510	347 428 927	8.891 706	19.15660	41.27164
704	495 616	26.53300	83.90471	348 913 664	8.895 920	19.16568	41.29120
705	497 025	26.55184	83.96428	350 402 625	8.900 130	19.17475	41.31075
706	498 436	26.57066	84.02381	351 895 816	8.904 337	19.18381	41.33027
707	499 849	26.58947	84.08329	353 393 243	8.908 539	19.19286	41.34977
708	501 264	26.60827	84.14274	354 894 912	8.912 737	19.20191	41.36926
709	502 681	26.62705	84.20214	356 400 829	8.916 931	19.21095	41.38873
710	504 100	26.64583	84.26150	357 911 000	8.921 121	19.21997	41.40818
711	505 521	26.66458	84.32082	359 425 431	8.925 308	19.22899	41.42761
712	506 944	26.68333	84.38009	360 944 128	8.929 490	19.23800	41.44702
713	508 369	26.70206	84.43933	362 467 097	8.933 669	19.24701	41.46642
714	509 796	26.72078	84.49852	363 994 344	8.937 843	19.25600	41.48579
715	511 225	26.73948	84.55767	365 525 875	8.942 014	19.26499	41.50515
716	512 656	26.75818	84.61678	367 061 696	8.946 181	19.27396	41.52449
717	514 089	26.77686	84.67585	368 601 813	8.950 344	19.28293	41.54382
718	515 524	26.79552	84.73488	370 146 232	8.954 503	19.29189	41.56312
719	516 961	26.81418	84.79387	371 694 959	8.958 658	19.30084	41.58241
720	518 400	26.83282	84.85281	373 248 000	8.962 809	19.30979	41.60168
721	519 841	26.85144	84.91172	374 805 361	8.966 957	19.31872	41.62093
722	521 284	26.87006	84.97058	376 367 048	8.971 101	19.32765	41.64016
723	522 729	26.88866	85.02941	377 933 067	8.975 241	19.33657	41.65938
724	524 176	26.90725	85.08819	379 503 424	8.979 377	19.34548	41.67857
725	525 625	26.92582	85.14693	381 078 125	8.983 509	19.35438	41.69775
726	527 076	26.94439	85.20563	382 657 176	8.987 637	19.36328	41.71692
727	528 529	26.96294	85.26429	384 240 583	8.991 762	19.37216	41.73606
728	529 984	26.98148	85.32292	385 828 352	8.995 883	19.38104	41.75519
729	531 441	27.00000	85.38150	387 420 489	9.000 000	19.38991	41.77430
730	532 900	27.01851	85.44004	389 017 000	9.004 113	19.39877	41.79339
731	534 361	27.03701	85.49854	390 617 891	9.008 223	19.40763	41.81247
732	535 824	27.05550	85.55700	392 223 168	9.012 329	19.41647	41.83152
733	537 289	27.07397	85.61542	393 832 837	9.016 431	19.42531	41.85056
734	538 756	27.09243	85.67380	395 446 904	9.020 529	19.43414	41.86959
735	540 225	27.11088	85.73214	397 065 375	9.024 624	19.44296	41.88859
736	541 696	27.12932	85.79044	398 688 256	9.028 715	19.45178	41.90758
737	543 169	27.14774	85.84870	400 315 553	9.032 802	19.46058	41.92655
738	544 644	27.16616	85.90693	401 947 272	9.036 886	19.46938	41.94551
739	546 121	27.18455	85.96511	403 583 419	9.040 966	19.47817	41.96444
740	547 600	27.20294	86.02325	405 224 000	9.045 042	19.48695	41.98336
741	549 081	27.22132	86.08136	406 869 021	9.049 114	19.49573	42.00227
742	550 564	27.23968	86.13942	408 518 488	9.053 183	19.50449	42.02115
743	552 049	27.25803	86.19745	410 172 407	9.057 248	19.51325	42.04002
744	553 536	27.27636	86.25543	411 830 784	9.061 310	19.52200	42.05887
745	555 025	27.29469	86.31338	413 493 625	9.065 368	19.53074	42.07771
746	556 516	27.31300	86.37129	415 160 936	9.069 422	19.53948	42.09653
747	558 009	27.33130	86.42916	416 832 723	9.073 473	19.54820	42.11533
748	559 504	27.34959	86.48699	418 508 992	9.077 520	19.55692	42.13411
749	561 001	27.36786	86.54479	420 189 749	9.081 563	19.56563	42.15288
750	562 500	27.38613	86.60254	421 875 000	9.085 603	19.57434	42.17163

n	n^2	$\sqrt{n}$	$\sqrt{10n}$	n^3	$\sqrt[3]{n}$	$\sqrt[3]{10n}$	$\sqrt[3]{100n}$
750	562 500	27.38613	86.60254	421 875 000	9.085 603	19.57434	42.17163
751	564 001	27.40438	86.66026	423 564 751	9.089 639	19.58303	42.19037
752	565 504	27.42262	86.71793	425 259 008	9.093 672	19.59172	42.20909
753	567 009	27.44085	86.77557	426 957 777	9.097 701	19.60040	42.22779
754	568 516	27.45906	86.83317	428 661 064	9.101 727	19.60908	42.24647
755	570 025	27.47726	86.89074	430 368 875	9.105 748	19.61774	42.26514
756	571 536	27.49545	86.94826	432 081 216	9.109 767	19.62640	42.28379
757	573 049	27.51363	87.00575	433 798 093	9.113 782	19.63505	42.30243
758	574 564	27.53180	87.06320	435 519 512	9.117 793	19.64369	42.32105
759	576 081	27.54995	87.12061	437 245 479	9.121 801	19.65232	42.33965
760	577 600	27.56810	87.17798	438 976 000	9.125 805	19.66095	42.35824
761	579 121	27.58623	87.23531	440 711 081	9.129 806	19.66957	42.37681
762	580 644	27.60435	87.29261	442 450 728	9.133 803	19.67818	42.39536
763	582 169	27.62245	87.34987	444 194 947	9.137 797	19.68679	42.41390
764	583 696	27.64055	87.40709	445 943 744	9.141 787	19.69538	42.43242
765	585 225	27.65863	87.46428	447 697 125	9.145 774	19.70397	42.45092
766	586 756	27.67671	87.52143	449 455 096	9.149 758	19.71256	42.46941
767	588 289	27.69476	87.57854	451 217 663	9.153 738	19.72113	42.48789
768	589 824	27.71281	87.63561	452 984 832	9.157 714	19.72970	42.50634
769	591 361	27.73085	87.69265	454 756 609	9.161 687	19.73826	42.52478
770	592 900	27.74887	87.74964	456 533 000	9.165 656	19.74681	42.54321
771	594 441	27.76689	87.80661	458 314 011	9.169 623	19.75535	42.56162
772	595 984	27.78489	87.86353	460 099 648	9.173 585	19.76389	42.58001
773	597 529	27.80288	87.92042	461 889 917	9.177 544	19.77242	42.59839
774	599 076	27.82086	87.97727	463 684 824	9.181 500	19.78094	42.61675
775	600 625	27.83882	88.03408	465 484 375	9.185 453	19.78946	42.63509
776	602 176	27.85678	88.09086	467 288 576	9.189 402	19.79797	42.65342
777	603 729	27.87472	88.14760	469 097 433	9.193 347	19.80647	42.67174
778	605 284	27.89265	88.20431	470 910 952	9.197 290	19.81496	42.69004
779	606 841	27.91057	88.26098	472 729 139	9.201 229	19.82345	42.70832
780	608 400	27.92848	88.31761	474 552 000	9.205 164	19.83192	42.72659
781	609 961	27.94638	88.37420	476 379 541	9.209 096	19.84040	42.74484
782	611 524	27.96426	88.43076	478 211 768	9.213 025	19.84886	42.76307
783	613 089	27.98214	88.48729	480 048 687	9.216 950	19.85732	42.78129
784	614 656	28.00000	88.54377	481 890 304	9.220 873	19.86577	42.79950
785	616 225	28.01785	88.60023	483 736 625	9.224 791	19.87421	42.81769
786	617 796	28.03569	88.65664	485 587 656	9.228 707	19.88265	42.83586
787	619 369	28.05352	88.71302	487 443 403	9.232 619	19.89107	42.85402
788	620 944	28.07134	88.76936	489 303 872	9.236 528	19.89950	42.87216
789	622 521	28.08914	88.82567	491 169 069	9.240 433	19.90791	42.89029
790	624 100	28.10694	88.88194	493 039 000	9.244 335	19.91632	42.90840
791	625 681	28.12472	88.93818	494 913 671	9.248 234	19.92472	42.92650
792	627 264	28.14249	88.99438	496 793 088	9.252 130	19.93311	42.94458
793	628 849	28.16026	89.05055	498 677 257	9.256 022	19.94150	42.96265
794	630 436	28.17801	89.10668	500 566 184	9.259 911	19.94987	42.98070
795	632 025	28.19574	89.16277	502 459 875	9.263 797	19.95825	42.99874
796	633 616	28.21347	89.21883	504 358 336	9.267 680	19.96661	43.01676
797	635 209	28.23119	89.27486	506 261 573	9.271 559	19.97497	43.03477
798	636 804	28.24889	89.33085	508 169 592	9.275 435	19.98332	43.05276
799	638 401	28.26659	89.38680	510 082 399	9.279 308	19.99166	43.07073
800	640 000	28.28427	89.44272	512 000 000	9.283 178	20.00000	43.08869

n	n^2	$\sqrt{n}$	$\sqrt{10n}$	n^3	$\sqrt[3]{n}$	$\sqrt[3]{10n}$	$\sqrt[3]{100n}$
800	640 000	28.28427	89.44272	512 000 000	9.283 178	20.00000	43.08869
801	641 601	28.30194	89.49860	513 922 401	9.287 044	20.00833	43.10664
802	643 204	28.31960	89.55445	515 849 608	9.290 907	20.01665	43.12457
803	644 809	28.33725	89.61027	517 781 627	9.294 767	20.02497	43.14249
804	646 416	28.35489	89.66605	519 718 464	9.298 624	20.03328	43.16039
805	648 025	28.37252	89.72179	521 660 125	9.302 477	20.04158	43.17828
806	649 636	28.39014	89.77750	523 606 616	9.306 328	20.04988	43.19615
807	651 249	28.40775	89.83318	525 557 943	9.310 175	20.05816	43.21400
808	652 864	28.42534	89.88882	527 514 112	9.314 019	20.06645	43.23185
809	654 481	28.44293	89.94443	529 475 129	9.317 860	20.07472	43.24967
810	656 100	28.46050	90.00000	531 441 000	9.321 698	20.08299	43.26749
811	657 721	28.47806	90.05554	533 411 731	9.325 532	20.09125	43.28529
812	659 344	28.49561	90.11104	535 387 328	9.329 363	20.09950	43.30307
813	660 969	28.51315	90.16651	537 367 797	9.333 192	20.10775	43.32084
814	662 596	28.53069	90.22195	539 353 144	9.337 017	20.11599	43.33859
815	664 225	28.54820	90.27735	541 343 375	9.340 839	20.12423	43.35633
816	665 856	28.56571	90.33272	543 338 496	9.344 657	20.13245	43.37406
817	667 489	28.58321	90.38805	545 338 513	9.348 473	20.14067	43.39177
818	669 124	28.60070	90.44335	547 343 432	9.352 286	20.14889	43.40947
819	670 761	28.61818	90.49862	549 353 259	9.356 095	20.15710	43.42715
820	672 400	28.63564	90.55385	551 368 000	9.359 902	20.16530	43.44481
821	674 041	28.65310	90.60905	553 387 661	9.363 705	20.17349	43.46247
822	675 684	28.67054	90.66422	555 412 248	9.367 505	20.18168	43.48011
823	677 329	28.68798	90.71935	557 441 767	9.371 302	20.18986	43.49773
824	678 976	28.70540	90.77445	559 476 224	9.375 096	20.19803	43.51534
825	680 625	28.72281	90.82951	561 515 625	9.378 887	20.20620	43.53294
826	682 276	28.74022	90.88454	563 559 976	9.382 675	20.21436	43.55052
827	683 929	28.75761	90.93954	565 609 283	9.386 460	20.22252	43.56809
828	685 584	28.77499	90.99451	567 663 552	9.390 242	20.23066	43.58564
829	687 241	28.79236	91.04944	569 722 789	9.394 021	20.23880	43.60318
830	688 900	28.80972	91.10434	571 787 000	9.397 796	20.24694	43.62071
831	690 561	28.82707	91.15920	573 856 191	9.401 569	20.25507	43.63822
832	692 224	28.84441	91.21403	575 930 368	9.405 339	20.26319	43.65572
833	693 889	28.86174	91.26883	578 009 537	9.409 105	20.27130	43.67320
834	695 556	28.87906	91.32360	580 093 704	9.412 869	20.27941	43.69067
835	697 225	28.89637	91.37833	582 182 875	9.416 630	20.28751	43.70812
836	698 896	28.91366	91.43304	584 277 056	9.420 387	20.29561	43.72556
837	700 569	28.93095	91.48770	586 376 253	9.424 142	20.30370	43.74299
838	702 244	28.94823	91.54234	588 480 472	9.427 894	20.31178	43.76041
839	703 921	28 96550	91.59694	590 589 719	9.431 642	20.31986	43.77781
840	705 600	28.98275	91.65151	592 704 000	9.435 388	20.32793	43.79519
841	707 281	29.00000	91.70605	594 823 321	9.439 131	29.33599	43.81256
842	708 964	29.01724	91.76056	596 947 688	9.442 870	20.34405	43.82992
843	710 649	29.03446	91.81503	599 077 107	9.446 607	20.35210	43.84727
844	712 336	29.05168	91.86947	601 211 584	9.450 341	20.36014	43.86460
845	714 025	29.06888	91.92388	603 351 125	9.454 072	20.36818	43.88191
846	715 716	29.08608	91.97826	605 495 736	9.457 800	20.37621	43.89922
847	717 409	29.10326	92.03260	607 645 423	9.461 525	20.38424	43.91651
848	719 104	29.12044	92.08692	609 800 192	9.465 247	20.39226	43.93378
849	720 801	29.13760	92.14120	611 960 049	9.468 966	20.40027	43.95105
850	722 500	29.15476	92.19544	614 125 000	9.472 682	20.40828	43.96830

n	n^2	$\sqrt{n}$	$\sqrt{10n}$	n^3	$\sqrt[3]{n}$	$\sqrt[3]{10n}$	$\sqrt[3]{100n}$
850	722 500	29.15476	92.19544	614 125 000	9.472 682	20.40828	43.96830
851	724 201	29.17190	92.24966	616 295 051	9.476 396	20.41628	43.98553
852	725 904	29.18904	92.30385	618 470 208	9.480 106	20.42427	44.00275
853	727 609	29.20616	92.35800	620 650 477	9.483 814	20.43226	44.01996
854	729 316	29.22328	92.41212	622 835 864	9.487 518	20.44024	44.03716
855	731 025	29.24038	92.46621	625 026 375	9.491 220	20.44821	44.05434
856	732 736	29.25748	92.52027	627 222 016	9.494 919	20.45618	44.07151
857	734 449	29.27456	92.57429	629 422 793	9.498 615	20.46415	44.08866
858	736 164	29.29164	92.62829	631 628 712	9.502 308	20.47210	44.10581
859	737 881	29.30870	92.68225	633 839 779	9.505 998	20.48005	44.12293
860	739 600	29.32576	92.73618	636 056 000	9.509 685	20.48800	44.14005
861	741 321	29.34280	92.79009	638 277 381	9.513 370	20.49593	44.15715
862	743 044	29.35984	92.84396	640 503 928	9.517 052	20 50387	44.17424
863	744 769	29.37686	92.89779	642 735 647	9.520 730	20.51179	44.19132
864	746 496	29.30388	92.95160	644 972 544	9.524 406	20.51971	44.20838
865	748 225	29.41088	93.00538	647 214 625	9.528 079	20.52762	44.22543
866	749 956	29.42788	93.05912	649 461 896	9.531 750	20.53553	44.24246
867	751 689	29.44486	93.11283	651 714 363	9.535 417	20.54343	44.25949
868	753 424	29.46184	93.16652	653 972 032	9.539 082	20.55133	44.27650
869	755 161	29.47881	93.22017	656 234 909	9.542 744	20.55922	44.29349
870	756 900	29.49576	93.27379	658 503 000	9.546 403	20.56710	44.31048
871	758 641	29.51271	93.32738	660 776 311	9.550 059	20.57498	44.32745
872	760 384	29.52965	93.38094	663 054 848	9.553 712	20.58285	44.34440
873	762 129	29.54657	93.43447	665 338 617	9.557 363	20.59071	44.36135
874	763 876	29.56349	93.48797	667 627 624	9.561 011	20.59857	44.37828
875	765 625	29.58040	93.54143	669 921 875	9.564 656	20.60643	44.39520
876	767 376	29.59730	93.59487	672 221 376	9.568 298	20.61427	44.41211
877	769 129	29.61419	93.64828	674 526 133	9.571 938	20.62211	44.42900
878	770 884	29.63106	93.70165	676 836 152	9.575 574	20.62995	44.44588
879	772 641	29.64793	93.75500	679 151 439	9.579 208	20.63778	14.40275
880	774 400	29.66479	93.80832	681 472 000	9.582 840	20.64560	44.47960
881	776 161	29.68164	93.86160	683 797 841	9.586 468	20.65342	44.49644
882	777 924	29.69848	93.91486	686 128 968	9.590 094	20.66123	44.51327
883	779 689	29.71532	93.96808	688 465 387	9.593 717	20.66904	44.53009
884	781 456	29.73214	94.02127	690 807 104	9.597 337	20.67684	44.54689
885	783 225	29.74895	94.07444	693 154 125	9.600 955	20.68463	44.56368
886	784 996	29.76575	94.12757	695 506 456	9.604 570	20.69242	44.58046
887	786 769	29.78255	94.18068	697 864 103	9.608 182	20.70020	44.59723
888	788 544	29.79933	94.23375	700 227 072	9.611 791	20.70798	44.61398
889	790 321	29.81610	94.28680	702 595 369	9.615 398	20.71575	44.63072
890	792 100	29.83287	94.33981	704 969 000	9.619 002	20.72351	44.64745
891	793 881	29.84962	94.39280	707 347 971	9.622 603	20.73127	44.66417
892	795 664	29.86637	94.44575	709 732 288	9.626 202	20 73902	44.68087
893	797 449	29.88311	04.49868	712 121 957	9.629 797	20.74677	44.69756
894	799 236	29.89983	94.55157	714 516 984	9.633 391	20.75451	44.71424
895	801 025	29.91655	94.60444	716 917 375	9.636 981	20.76225	44.73090
896	802 816	29.93326	94.65728	719 323 136	9.640 569	20.76998	44.74756
897	804 609	29.94996	94.71008	721 734 273	9.644 154	20.77770	44.76420
898	806 404	29.96665	94.76286	724 150 792	9.647 737	20.78542	44.78083
899	808 201	29.98333	94.81561	726 572 699	9.651 317	20.79313	44.79744
900	810 000	30.00000	94.86833	729 000 000	9.654 894	20.80084	44.81405

n	n^2	$\sqrt{n}$	$\sqrt{10n}$	n^3	$\sqrt[3]{n}$	$\sqrt[3]{10n}$	$\sqrt[3]{100n}$
900	810 000	30.00000	94.86833	729 000 000	9.654 894	20.80084	44.81405
901	811 801	30.01666	94.92102	731 432 701	9.658 468	20.80854	44.83064
902	813 604	30.03331	94.97368	733 870 808	9.662 040	20.81623	44.84722
903	815 409	30.04996	95.02631	736 314 327	9.665 610	20.82392	44.86379
904	817 216	30.06659	95.07891	738 763 264	9.669 176	20.83161	44.88034
905	819 025	30.08322	95.13149	741 217 625	9.672 740	20.83929	44.89688
906	820 836	30.09983	95.18403	743 677 416	9.676 302	20.84696	44.91341
907	822 649	30.11644	95.23655	746 142 643	9.679 860	20.85463	44.92993
908	824 464	30.13304	95.28903	748 613 312	9.683 417	20.86229	44.94644
909	826 281	30.14963	95.34149	751 089 429	9.686 970	20.86994	44.96293
910	828 100	30.16621	95.39392	753 571 000	9.690 521	20.87759	44.97941
911	829 921	30.18278	95.44632	756 058 031	9.694 069	20.88524	44.99588
912	831 744	30.19934	95.49869	758 550 528	9.697 615	20.89288	45.01234
913	833 569	30.21589	95.55103	761 048 497	9.701 158	20.90051	45.02879
914	835 396	30.23243	95.60335	763 551 944	9.704 699	20.90814	45.04522
915	837 225	30.24897	95.65563	766 060 875	9.708 237	20.91576	45.06164
916	839 056	30.26549	95.70789	768 575 296	9.711 772	20.92338	45.07805
917	840 889	30.28201	95.76012	771 095 213	9.715 305	20.93099	45.09445
918	842 724	30.29851	95.81232	773 620 632	9.718 835	20.93860	45.11084
919	844 561	30.31501	95.86449	776 151 559	9.722 363	20.94620	45.12721
920	846 400	30.33150	95.91663	778 688 000	9.725 888	20.95379	45.14357
921	848 241	30.34798	95.96874	781 229 961	9.729 411	20.96138	45.15992
922	850 084	30.36445	96.02083	783 777 448	9.732 931	20.96896	45.17626
923	851 929	30.38092	96.07289	786 330 467	9.736 448	20.97654	45.19259
924	853 776	30.39737	96.12492	788 889 024	9.739 963	20.98411	45.20891
925	855 625	30.41381	96.17692	791 453 125	9.743 476	20.99168	45.22521
926	857 476	30.43025	96.22889	794 022 776	9.746 986	20.99924	45.24150
927	859 329	30.44667	96.28084	796 597 983	9.750 493	21.00680	45.25778
928	861 184	30.46309	96.33276	799 178 752	9.753 998	21.01435	45.27405
929	863 041	30.47950	96.38465	801 765 089	9.757 500	21.02190	45.29030
930	864 900	30.49590	96.43651	804 357 000	9.761 000	21.02944	45.30655
931	866 761	30.51229	96.48834	806 954 491	9.764 497	21.03697	45.32278
932	868 624	30.52868	96.54015	809 557 568	9.767 992	21.04450	45.33900
933	870 489	30.54505	96.59193	812 166 237	9.771 485	21.05203	45.35521
934	872 356	30.56141	96.64368	814 780 504	9.774 974	21.05954	45.37141
935	874 225	30.57777	96.69540	817 400 375	9.778 462	21.06706	45.38760
936	876 096	30.59412	96.74709	820 025 856	9.781 946	21.07456	45.40377
937	877 969	30.61046	96.79876	822 656 953	9.785 429	21.08207	45.41994
938	879 844	30.62679	96.85040	825 293 672	9.788 909	21.08956	45.43609
939	881 721	30.64311	96.90201	827 936 019	9.792 386	21.09706	45.45223
940	883 600	30.65942	96.95360	830 584 000	9.795 861	21.10454	45.46836
941	885 481	30.67572	97.00515	833 237 621	9.799 334	21.11202	45.48448
942	887 364	30.69202	97.05668	835 896 888	9.802 804	21.11950	45.50058
943	889 249	30.70831	97.10819	838 561 807	9.806 271	21.12697	45.51668
944	891 136	30.72458	97.15966	841 232 384	9.809 736	21.13444	45.53276
945	893 025	30.74085	97.21111	843 908 625	9.813 199	21.14190	45.54883
946	894 916	30.75711	97.26253	846 590 536	9.816 659	21.14935	45.56490
947	896 809	30.77337	97.31393	849 278 123	9.820 117	21.15680	45.58095
948	898.704	30.78961	97.36529	851 971 392	9.823 572	21.16424	45.59698
949	900 601	30.80584	97.41663	854 670 349	9.827 025	21.17168	45.61301
950	902 500	30.82207	97.46794	857 375 000	9.830 476	21.17912	45.62903

n	n^2	$\sqrt{n}$	$\sqrt{10n}$	n^3	$\sqrt[3]{n}$	$\sqrt[3]{10n}$	$\sqrt[3]{100n}$
950	902 500	30.82207	97.46794	857 375 000	9.830 476	21.17912	45.62903
951	904 401	30.83829	97.51923	860 085 351	9.833 924	21.18655	45.64503
952	906 304	30.85450	97.57049	862 801 408	9.837 369	21.19397	45.66102
953	908 209	30.87070	97.62172	865 523 177	9.840 813	21.20139	45.67701
954	910 116	30.88689	97.67292	868 250 664	9.844 254	21.20880	45.69298
955	912 025	30.90307	97.72410	870 983 875	9.847 692	21.21621	45.70894
956	913 936	30.91925	97.77525	873 722 816	9.851 128	21.22361	45.72489
957	915 849	30.93542	97.82638	876 467 493	9.854 562	21.23101	45.74082
958	917 764	30.95158	97.87747	879 217 912	9.857 993	21.23840	45.75675
959	919 681	30.96773	97.92855	881 974 079	9.861 422	21.24579	45.77267
960	921 600	30.98387	97.97959	884 736 000	9.864 848	21.25317	45.78857
961	923 521	31.00000	98.03061	887 503 681	9.868 272	21.26055	45.80446
962	925 444	31.01612	98.08160	890 277 128	9.871 694	21.26792	45.82035
963	927 369	31.03224	98.13256	893 056 347	9.875 113	21.27529	45.83622
964	929 296	31.04835	98.18350	895 841 344	9.878 530	21.28265	45.85208
965	931 225	31.06445	98.23441	898 632 125	9.881 945	21.29001	45.86793
966	933 156	31.08054	98.28530	901 428 696	9.885 357	21.29736	45.88376
967	935 089	31.09662	98.33616	904 231 063	9.888 767	21.30470	45.89959
968	937 024	31.11270	98.38699	907 039 232	9.892 175	21.31204	45.91541
969	938 961	31.12876	98.43780	909 853 209	9.895 580	21.31938	45.93121
970	940 900	31.14482	98.48858	912 673 000	9.898 983	21.32671	45.94701
971	942 841	31.16087	98.53933	915 498 611	9.902 384	21.33404	45.96279
972	944 784	31.17691	98.59006	918 330 048	9.905 782	21.34136	45.97857
973	946 729	31.19295	98.64076	921 167 317	9.909 178	21.34868	45.99433
974	948 676	31.20897	98.69144	924 010 424	9.912 571	21.35599	46.01008
975	950 625	31.22499	98.74209	926 859 375	9.915 962	21.36329	46.02582
976	952 576	31.24100	98.79271	929 714 176	9.919 351	21.37059	46.04155
977	954 529	31.25700	98.84331	932 574 833	9.922 738	21.37789	46.05727
978	956 484	31.27299	98.89388	935 441 352	9.926 122	21.38518	46.07298
979	958 441	31.28898	98.94443	938 313 739	9.929 504	21.39247	46.08868
980	960 400	31.30495	98.99495	941 192 000	9.932 884	21.39975	46.10436
981	962 361	31.32092	99.04544	944 076 141	9.936 261	21.40703	46.12004
982	964 324	31.33688	99.09591	946 966 168	9.939 636	21.41430	46.13571
983	966 289	31.35283	99.14636	949 862 087	9.943 009	21.42156	46.15136
984	968 256	31.36877	99.19677	952 763 904	9.946 380	21.42883	46.16700
985	970 225	31.38471	99.24717	955 671 625	9.949 748	21.43608	46.18264
986	972 196	31.40064	99.29753	958 585 256	9.953 114	21.44333	46.19826
987	974 169	31.41656	99.34787	961 504 803	9.956 478	21.45058	46.21387
988	976 144	31.43247	99.39819	964 430 272	9.959 839	21.45782	46.22948
989	978 121	31.44837	99.44848	967 361 669	9.963 198	21.46506	46.24507
990	980 100	31.46427	99.49874	970 299 000	9.966 555	21.47229	46.26065
991	982 081	31.48015	99.54898	973 242 271	9.969 910	21.47952	46.27622
992	984 064	31.49603	99.59920	976 191 488	9.973 262	21.48674	46.29178
993	986 049	31.51190	99.64939	979 146 657	9.976 612	21.49396	46.30733
994	988 036	31.52777	99.69955	982 107 784	9.979 960	21.50117	46.32287
995	990 025	31.54362	99.74969	985 074 875	9.983 305	21.50838	46.33840
996	992 016	31.55947	99.79980	988 047 936	9.986 649	21.51558	46.35392
997	994 009	31.57531	99.84989	991 026 973	9.989 990	21.52278	46.36943
998	996 004	31.59114	99.89995	994 011 992	9.993 329	21.52997	46.38492
999	998 001	31.60696	99.94999	997 002 999	9.996 666	21.53716	46.40041
1000	1 000 000	31.62278	100.00000	1 000 000 000	10.000 000	21.54435	46.41589

DEGREES, MINUTES, AND SECONDS TO RADIANS

Units in degrees, minutes or seconds	Degrees to Radians	Minutes to Radians	Seconds to Radians
10	0.174 5329	0.002 9089	0.000 0485
20	0.349 0659	0.005 8178	0.000 0970
30	0.523 5988	0.008 7266	0.000 1454
40	0.698 1317	0.011 6355	0.000 1939
50	0.872 6646	0.014 5444	0.000 2424
60	1.047 1976	0.017 4533	0.000 2909
70	1.221 7305	(0.020 3622)	(0.000 3394)
80	1.396 2634	(0.023 2711)	(0.000 3879)
90	1.570 7963	(0.026 1800)	(0.000 4364)
100	1.745 3293	....	....
200	3.490 6585	....	....
300	5.235 9878	....	....

where n = 1, 2, 3, 4, etc. n (100°) = n (1.745 3293)

*RADIANS TO DEGREES, MINUTES, AND SECONDS

Radians	1.0	0.1	0.01	0.001	0.0001
1	57° 17′ 44.8″	5° 43′ 46.5″	0° 34′ 22.6″	0° 03′ 26.3″	0° 00′ 20.6″
2	114° 35′ 29.6″	11° 27′ 33.0″	1° 08′ 45.3″	0° 06′ 52.5″	0° 00′ 41.3″
3	171° 53′ 14.4″	17° 11′ 19.4″	1° 43′ 07.9′	0° 10′ 18.8″	0° 01′ 01.9″
4	229° 10′ 59.2″	22° 55′ 05.9″	2° 17′ 30.6″	0° 13′ 45.1′	0° 01′ 22.5″
5	286° 28′ 44.0″	28° 38′ 52.4″	2° 51′ 53.2″	0° 17′ 11.3″	0° 01′ 43.1″
6	343° 46′ 28.8″	34° 22′ 38.9″	3° 26′ 15.9″	0° 20′ 37.6″	0° 02′ 03.8″
7	401° 04′ 13.6″	40° 06′ 25.4″	4° 00′ 38.5″	0° 24′ 03.9″	0° 02′ 24.4″
8	458° 21′ 58.4″	45° 50′ 11.8″	4° 35′ 01.2″	0° 27′ 30.1″	0° 02′ 45.0″
9	515° 39′ 43.3″	51° 33′ 58.3″	5° 09′ 23.8″	0° 30′ 56.4″	0° 03′ 05.6″

*If 3.214 is desired in degrees, minutes and seconds it is obtained as follows:

$$3 = 171° 53′ 14.4″$$
$$.2 = 11° 27′ 33.0″$$
$$.01 = 0° 34′ 22.6″$$
$$.004 = 0° 13′ 45.1″$$
$$\overline{3.214 = 184° 8′ 55.1″}$$

MILS—RADIANS—DEGREES

1 mil = 0.00098175 radians = 0.05625° = 3.375′ = 202.5″
1000 mils = 0.98175 radians = 56.25°
6400 mils = 360° = 2π radians
1 radian = 1018.6 mils
1° = 17.777778 mils
1′ = 0.296296 mils
1″ = 0.0049382 mils

DEGREES—RADIANS

1 radian =   57° 17′ 44.08625″

		log
1 radian = 57.29577 95131 degrees		1.75812 26324
1 radian = 3437.74677 07849 minutes		3.53627 38828
1 radian = 206264.80625 seconds		5.31442 51332
1 degree = 0.01745 32925 19943 radians		8.24187 73676—10
1 minute = 0.00029 08882 08666 radians		6.46372 61172—10
1 second = 0.00000 48481 36811 radians		4.68557 48668—10

MINUTES AND SECONDS TO DECIMAL PARTS OF A DEGREE

MINUTES AND SECONDS TO DECIMAL PARTS OF A DEG.				DECIMAL PARTS OF A DEGREE TO MINUTES AND SECONDS					
Min.	Degrees	Sec.	Degrees	Deg.	'	"	Deg.	'	"
0	0.00000	**0**	0.00000	**0.00**	0	00	**0.60**	36	
1	.01667	1	.00028	.01	0	36	.61	36	36
2	.03333	2	.00056	.02	1	12	.62	37	12
3	.05	3	.00083	.03	1	48	.63	37	48
4	.06667	4	.00111	.04	2	24	.64	38	24
5	.08333	5	.00139	.05	3		.65	39	
6	.10	6	.00167	.06	3	36	.66	39	36
7	.11667	7	.00194	.07	4	12	.67	40	12
8	.13333	8	.00222	.08	4	48	.68	40	48
9	.15	9	.0025	.09	5	24	.69	41	24
10	0.16667	**10**	0.00278	**0.10**	6		**0.70**	42	
11	.18333	11	.00306	.11	6	36	.71	42	36
12	.20	12	.00333	.12	7	12	.72	43	12
13	.21667	13	.00361	.13	7	48	.73	43	48
14	.23333	14	.00389	.14	8	24	.74	44	24
15	.25	15	.00417	.15	9		.75	45	
16	.26667	16	.00444	.16	9	36	.76	45	36
17	.28333	17	.00472	.17	10	12	.77	46	12
18	.30	18	.005	.18	10	48	.78	46	48
19	.31667	19	.00528	.19	11	24	.79	47	24
20	0.33333	**20**	0 00556	**0.20**	12		**0.80**	48	
21	.35	21	.00583	.21	12	36	.81	48	36
22	.36667	22	.00611	.22	13	12	.82	49	12
23	.38333	23	.00639	.23	13	48	.83	49	48
24	.40	24	.00667	.24	14	24	.84	50	24
25	.41667	25	.00694	.25	15		.85	51	
26	.43333	26	.00722	.26	15	36	.86	51	36
27	.45	27	.0075	.27	16	12	.87	52	12
28	.46667	28	.00778	.28	16	48	.88	52	48
29	.48333	29	.00806	.29	17	24	.89	53	24
30	0.50	**30**	0.00833	**0.30**	18		**0.90**	54	
31	.51667	31	.00861	.31	18	36	.91	54	36
32	.53333	32	.00889	.32	19	12	.92	55	12
33	.55	33	.00917	.33	19	48	.93	55	48
34	.56667	34	.00944	.34	20	24	.94	56	24
35	.58333	35	.00972	.35	21		.95	57	
36	.60	36	.01	.36	21	36	.96	57	36
37	.61667	37	.01028	.37	22	12	.97	58	12
38	.63333	38	.01056	.38	22	48	.98	58	48
39	.65	39	.01083	.39	23	24	.99	59	24
40	0.66667	**40**	0.01111	**0.40**	24		**1.00**	60	
41	.68333	41	.01139	.41	24	36			
42	.70	42	.01167	.42	25	12			
43	.71667	43	.01194	.43	25	48			
44	.73333	44	.01222	.44	26	24			
45	.75	45	.0125	.45	27		Deg.	Sec.	
46	.76667	46	.01278	.46	27	36	**0.000**	0.0	
47	.78333	47	.01306	.47	28	12	.001	3.6	
48	.80	48	.01333	.48	28	48	.002	7.2	
49	.81667	49	.01361	.49	29	24	.003	10.8	
50	0.83333	**50**	0.01389	**0.50**	30		.004	14.4	
51	.85	51	.01417	.51	30	36	.005	18.	
52	.86667	52	.01444	.52	31	12	.006	21.6	
53	.88333	53	.01472	.53	31	48	.007	25.2	
54	.90	54	.015	.54	32	24	.008	28.8	
55	.91667	55	.01528	.55	33		.009	32.4	
56	.93333	56	.01556	.56	33	36	**0.010**	36.	
57	.95	57	.01583	.57	34	12			
58	.96667	58	.01611	.58	34	48			
59	.98333	59	.01639	.59	35	24			
60	1.00	**60**	0.01667	**0.60**	36				

*Derivatives

In the following formulas u, v, w represent functions of x, while a, c, n represent fixed real numbers. All arguments in the trigonometric functions are measured in radians, and all inverse trigonometric and hyperbolic functions represent principal values.

1. $\dfrac{d}{dx}(a) = 0$

2. $\dfrac{d}{dx}(x) = 1$

3. $\dfrac{d}{dx}(au) = a\dfrac{du}{dx}$

4. $\dfrac{d}{dx}(u + v - w) = \dfrac{du}{dx} + \dfrac{dv}{dx} - \dfrac{dw}{dx}$

5. $\dfrac{d}{dx}(uv) = u\dfrac{dv}{dx} + v\dfrac{du}{dx}$

6. $\dfrac{d}{dx}(uvw) = uv\dfrac{dw}{dx} + vw\dfrac{du}{dx} + uw\dfrac{dv}{dx}$

7. $\dfrac{d}{dx}\left(\dfrac{u}{v}\right) = \dfrac{v\dfrac{du}{dx} - u\dfrac{dv}{dx}}{v^2} = \dfrac{1}{v}\dfrac{du}{dx} - \dfrac{u}{v^2}\dfrac{dv}{dx}$

8. $\dfrac{d}{dx}(u^n) = nu^{n-1}\dfrac{du}{dx}$

9. $\dfrac{d}{dx}(\sqrt{u}) = \dfrac{1}{2\sqrt{u}}\dfrac{du}{dx}$

10. $\dfrac{d}{dx}\left(\dfrac{1}{u}\right) = -\dfrac{1}{u^2}\dfrac{du}{dx}$

11. $\dfrac{d}{dx}\left(\dfrac{1}{u^n}\right) = -\dfrac{n}{u^{n+1}}\dfrac{du}{dx}$

12. $\dfrac{d}{dx}\left(\dfrac{u^n}{v^m}\right) = \dfrac{u^{n-1}}{v^{m+1}}\left(nv\dfrac{du}{dx} - mu\dfrac{dv}{dx}\right)$

13. $\dfrac{d}{dx}(u^n v^m) = u^{n-1}v^{m-1}\left(nv\dfrac{du}{dx} + mu\dfrac{dv}{dx}\right)$

14. $\dfrac{d}{dx}[f(u)] = \dfrac{d}{du}[f(u)]\cdot\dfrac{du}{dx}$

* Let $y = f(x)$ and $\dfrac{dy}{dx} = \dfrac{d[f(x)]}{dx} = f'(x)$ define respectively a function and its derivative for any value x in their common domain. The differential for the function at such a value x is accordingly defined as

$$dy = d[f(x)] = \frac{dy}{dx}dx = \frac{d[f(x)]}{dx}dx = f'(x)\,dx$$

Each derivative formula has an associated differential formula. For example, formula 6 above has the differential formula

$$d(uvw) = uv\,dw + vw\,du + uw\,dv$$

15. $\dfrac{d^2}{dx^2}[f(u)] = \dfrac{df(u)}{du} \cdot \dfrac{d^2u}{dx^2} + \dfrac{d^2f(u)}{du^2} \cdot \left(\dfrac{du}{dx}\right)^2$

16. $\dfrac{d^n}{dx^n}[uv] = \dbinom{n}{0} v \dfrac{d^n u}{dx^n} + \dbinom{n}{1} \dfrac{dv}{dx} \dfrac{d^{n-1}u}{dx^{n-1}} + \dbinom{n}{2} \dfrac{d^2v}{dx^2} \dfrac{d^{n-2}u}{dx^{n-2}}$

$$+ \cdots + \dbinom{n}{k} \dfrac{d^k v}{dx^k} \dfrac{d^{n-k}u}{dx^{n-k}} + \cdots + \dbinom{n}{n} u \dfrac{d^n v}{dx^n}$$

where $\dbinom{n}{r} = \dfrac{n!}{r!(n-r)!}$ the binomial coefficient, n non-negative integer and $\dbinom{n}{0} = 1$.

17. $\dfrac{du}{dx} = \dfrac{1}{\dfrac{dx}{du}} \qquad$ if $\dfrac{dx}{du} \neq 0$

18. $\dfrac{d}{dx}(\log_a u) = (\log_a e)\dfrac{1}{u}\dfrac{du}{dx}$

19. $\dfrac{d}{dx}(\log_e u) = \dfrac{1}{u}\dfrac{du}{dx}$

20. $\dfrac{d}{dx}(a^u) = a^u(\log_e a)\dfrac{du}{dx}$

21. $\dfrac{d}{dx}(e^u) = e^u\dfrac{du}{dx}$

22. $\dfrac{d}{dx}(u^v) = vu^{v-1}\dfrac{du}{dx} + (\log_e u)u^v\dfrac{dv}{dx}$

23. $\dfrac{d}{dx}(\sin u) = \dfrac{du}{dx}(\cos u)$

24. $\dfrac{d}{dx}(\cos u) = -\dfrac{du}{dx}(\sin u)$

25. $\dfrac{d}{dx}(\tan u) = \dfrac{du}{dx}(\sec^2 u)$

26. $\dfrac{d}{dx}(\cot u) = -\dfrac{du}{dx}(\csc^2 u)$

27. $\dfrac{d}{dx}(\sec u) = \dfrac{du}{dx}\sec u \cdot \tan u$

28. $\dfrac{d}{dx}(\csc u) = -\dfrac{du}{dx}\csc u \cdot \cot u$

29. $\dfrac{d}{dx}(\text{vers } u) = \dfrac{du}{dx}\sin u$

30. $\dfrac{d}{dx}(\text{arc sin } u) = \dfrac{1}{\sqrt{1-u^2}}\dfrac{du}{dx}, \qquad \left(-\dfrac{\pi}{2} \leq \text{arc sin } u \leq \dfrac{\pi}{2}\right)$

31. $\dfrac{d}{dx}(\text{arc cos } u) = -\dfrac{1}{\sqrt{1-u^2}}\dfrac{du}{dx},$ $\quad (0 \leq \text{arc cos } u \leq \pi)$

32. $\dfrac{d}{dx}(\text{arc tan } u) = \dfrac{1}{1+u^2}\dfrac{du}{dx},$ $\quad \left(-\dfrac{\pi}{2} < \text{arc tan } u < \dfrac{\pi}{2}\right)$

33. $\dfrac{d}{dx}(\text{arc cot } u) = -\dfrac{1}{1+u^2}\dfrac{du}{dx},$ $\quad (0 \leq \text{arc cot } u \leq \pi)$

34. $\dfrac{d}{dx}(\text{arc sec } u) = \dfrac{1}{u\sqrt{u^2-1}}\dfrac{du}{dx},$ $\quad \left(0 \leq \text{arc sec } u < \dfrac{\pi}{2}, -\pi \leq \text{arc sec } u < -\dfrac{\pi}{2}\right)$

35. $\dfrac{d}{dx}(\text{arc csc } u) = -\dfrac{1}{u\sqrt{u^2-1}}\dfrac{du}{dx},$ $\quad \left(0 < \text{arc csc } u \leq \dfrac{\pi}{2}, -\pi < \text{arc csc } u \leq -\dfrac{\pi}{2}\right)$

36. $\dfrac{d}{dx}(\text{arc vers } u) = \dfrac{1}{\sqrt{2u-u^2}}\dfrac{du}{dx},$ $\quad (0 \leq \text{arc vers } u \leq \pi)$

37. $\dfrac{d}{dx}(\sinh u) = \dfrac{du}{dx}(\cosh u)$

38. $\dfrac{d}{dx}(\cosh u) = \dfrac{du}{dx}(\sinh u)$

39. $\dfrac{d}{dx}(\tanh u) = \dfrac{du}{dx}(\text{sech}^2 u)$

40. $\dfrac{d}{dx}(\coth u) = -\dfrac{du}{dx}(\text{csch}^2 u)$

41. $\dfrac{d}{dx}(\text{sech } u) = -\dfrac{du}{dx}(\text{sech } u \cdot \tanh u)$

42. $\dfrac{d}{dx}(\text{csch } u) = -\dfrac{du}{dx}(\text{csch } u \cdot \coth u)$

43. $\dfrac{d}{dx}(\sinh^{-1} u) = \dfrac{d}{dx}[\log(u + \sqrt{u^2+1})] = \dfrac{1}{\sqrt{u^2+1}}\dfrac{du}{dx}$

44. $\dfrac{d}{dx}(\cosh^{-1} u) = \dfrac{d}{dx}[\log(u + \sqrt{u^2-1})] = \dfrac{1}{\sqrt{u^2-1}}\dfrac{du}{dx},$ $\quad (u > 1, \cosh^{-1} u > 0)$

45. $\dfrac{d}{dx}(\tanh^{-1} u) = \dfrac{d}{dx}\left[\dfrac{1}{2}\log\dfrac{1+u}{1-u}\right] = \dfrac{1}{1-u^2}\dfrac{du}{dx},$ $\quad (u^2 < 1)$

46. $\dfrac{d}{dx}(\coth^{-1} u) = \dfrac{d}{dx}\left[\dfrac{1}{2}\log\dfrac{u+1}{u-1}\right] = \dfrac{1}{1-u^2}\dfrac{du}{dx},$ $\quad (u^2 > 1)$

47. $\dfrac{d}{dx}(\text{sech}^{-1} u) = \dfrac{d}{dx}\left[\log\dfrac{1+\sqrt{1-u^2}}{u}\right] = -\dfrac{1}{u\sqrt{1-u^2}}\dfrac{du}{dx},$ $\quad (0 < u < 1, \text{sech}^{-1} u > 0)$

48. $\dfrac{d}{dx}(\text{csch}^{-1} u) = \dfrac{d}{dx}\left[\log\dfrac{1+\sqrt{1+u^2}}{u}\right] = -\dfrac{1}{|u|\sqrt{1+u^2}}\dfrac{du}{dx}$

49. $\dfrac{d}{dq} \displaystyle\int_p^q f(x)\,dx = f(q),$ [p constant]

50. $\dfrac{d}{dp} \displaystyle\int_p^q f(x)\,dx = -f(p),$ [q constant]

51. $\dfrac{d}{da} \displaystyle\int_p^q f(x, a)\,dx = \int_p^q \dfrac{\partial}{\partial a}[f(x, a)]\,dx + f(q, a)\dfrac{dq}{da} - f(p, a)\dfrac{dp}{da}$

INTEGRATION

The following is a brief discussion of some integration techniques. A more complete discussion can be found in a number of good text books. However, the purpose of this introduction is simply to discuss a few of the important techniques which may be used, in conjunction with the integral table which follows, to integrate particular functions.

No matter how extensive the integral table, it is a fairly uncommon occurrence to find in the table the exact integral desired. Usually some form of transformation will have to be made. The simplest type of transformation, and yet the most general, is substitution. Simple forms of substitution, such as $y = ax$, are employed almost unconsciously by experienced users of integral tables. Other substitutions may require more thought. In some sections of the tables, appropriate substitutions are suggested for integrals which are similar to, but not exactly like, integrals in the table. Finding the right substitution is largely a matter of intuition and experience.

Several precautions must be observed when using substitutions:

1. Be sure to make the substitution in the dx term, as well as everywhere else in the integral.
2. Be sure that the function substituted is one-to-one and continuous. If this is not the case, the integral must be restricted in such a way as to make it true. See the example following.
3. With definite integrals, the limits should also be expressed in terms of the new dependent variable. With indefinite integrals, it is necessary to perform the reverse substitution to obtain the answer in terms of the original independent variable. This may also be done for definite integrals, but it is usually easier to change the limits.

Example:

$$\int \frac{x^4}{\sqrt{a^2 - x^2}} dx$$

Here we make the substitution $x = |a| \sin \theta$. Then $dx = |a| \cos \theta \, d\theta$, and

$$\sqrt{a^2 - x^2} = \sqrt{a^2 - a^2 \sin^2 \theta} = |a|\sqrt{1 - \sin^2 \theta} = |a \cos \theta|$$

Notice the absolute value signs. It is very important to keep in mind that a square root radical always denotes the positive square root, and to assure the sign is always kept positive. Thus $\sqrt{x^2} = |x|$. Failure to observe this is a common cause of errors in integration.

Notice also that the indicated substitution is not a one-to-one function, that is, it does not have a unique inverse. Thus we must restrict the range of θ in such a way as to make the function one-to-one. Fortunately, this is easily done by solving for θ

$$\theta = \sin^{-1} \frac{x}{|a|}$$

and restricting the inverse sine to the principal values, $-\frac{\pi}{2} \leq \theta \leq \frac{\pi}{2}$.

Thus the integral becomes

$$\int \frac{a^4 \sin^4 \theta |a| \cos \theta \, d\theta}{|a| |\cos \theta|}$$

Now, however, in the range of values chosen for θ, $\cos \theta$ is always positive. Thus we may remove the absolute value signs from $\cos \theta$ in the denominator. (This is one of the reasons that the principal values of the inverse trigonometric functions are defined as they are.)

Then the $\cos \theta$ terms cancel, and the integral becomes

$$a^4 \int \sin^4 \theta \, d\theta$$

By application of integral formulas 299 and 296, we integrate this to

$$-a^4 \frac{\sin^3 \theta \cos \theta}{4} - \frac{3a^4}{8} \cos \theta \sin \theta + \frac{3a^4}{8} \theta + C$$

We now must perform the inverse substitution to get the result in terms of x. We have

$$\theta = \sin^{-1} \frac{x}{|a|}$$

$$\sin \theta = \frac{x}{|a|}$$

Then

$$\cos \theta = \pm \sqrt{1 - \sin^2 \theta} = \pm \sqrt{1 - \frac{x^2}{a^2}} = \pm \frac{\sqrt{a^2 - x^2}}{|a|}.$$

Because of the previously mentioned fact that $\cos \theta$ is positive, we may omit the $\pm$ sign. The reverse substitution then produces the final answer

$$\int \frac{x^4}{\sqrt{a^2 - x^2}} \, dx = -\tfrac{1}{4} x^3 \sqrt{a^2 - x^2} - \tfrac{3}{8} a^2 x \sqrt{a^2 - x^2} + \frac{3a^4}{8} \sin^{-1} \frac{x}{|a|} + C.$$

Any rational function of x may be integrated, if the denominator is factored into linear and irreducible quadratic factors. The function may then be broken into partial fractions, and the individual partial fractions integrated by use of the appropriate formula from the integral table. See the section on partial fractions for further information.

Many integrals may be reduced to rational functions by proper substitutions. For example,

$$z = \tan \frac{x}{2}$$

will reduce any rational function of the six trigonometric functions of x to a rational function of z. (Frequently there are other substitutions which are simpler to use, but this one will always work. See integral formula number 484.)

Any rational function of x and $\sqrt{ax + b}$ may be reduced to a rational function of z by making the substitution

$$z = \sqrt{ax + b}.$$

Other likely substitutions will be suggested by looking at the form of the integrand.

The other main method of transforming integrals is integration by parts. This involves applying formula number 5 or 6 in the accompanying integral table. The critical factor in this method is the choice of the functions u and v. In order for the method to be successful, $v = \int dv$ and $\int v \, du$ must be easier to integrate than the original integral. Again, this choice is largely a matter of intuition and experience.

Example:

$$\int x \sin x \, dx$$

Two obvious choices are $u = x$, $dv = \sin x \, dx$, or $u = \sin x$, $dv = x \, dx$. Since a preliminary mental calculation indicates that $\int v \, du$ in the second choice would be more, rather than less, complicated than the original integral (it would contain x^2), we use the first choice.

$$u = x \qquad\qquad du = dx$$

$$dv = \sin x \, dx \qquad\qquad v = -\cos x$$

$$\int x \sin x \, dx = \int u \, dv = uv - \int v \, du = -x \cos x + \int \cos x \, dx$$

$$= \sin x - x \cos x$$

Of course, this result could have been obtained directly from the integral table, but it provides a simple example of the method. In more complicated examples the choice of u and v may not be so obvious, and several different choices may have to be tried. Of course, there is no guarantee that any of them will work.

Integration by parts may be applied more than once, or combined with substitution. A fairly common case is illustrated by the following example.

Example:

$$\int e^x \sin x \, dx$$

Let

$$u = e^x \qquad \text{Then} \quad du = e^x \, dx$$

$$dv = \sin x \, dx \qquad\qquad v = -\cos x$$

$$\int e^x \sin x \, dx = \int u \, dv = uv - \int v \, du = -e^x \cos x + \int e^x \cos x \, dx$$

In this latter integral,

$$\text{let} \quad u = e^x \qquad \text{Then} \quad du = e^x \, dx$$

$$dv = \cos x \, dx \qquad\qquad v = \sin x$$

$$\int e^x \sin x \, dx = -e^x \cos x + \int e^x \cos x \, dx = -e^x \cos x + \int u \, dv$$

$$= -e^x \cos x + uv - \int v \, du$$

$$= -e^x \cos x + e^x \sin x - \int e^x \sin x \, dx$$

This looks as if a circular transformation has taken place, since we are back at the same integral we started from. However, the above equation can be solved algebraically for the required integral:

$$\int e^x \sin x \, dx = \tfrac{1}{2}(e^x \sin x - e^x \cos x)$$

In the second integration by parts, if the parts had been chosen as $u = \cos x$, $dv = e^x \, dx$, we would indeed have made a circular transformation, and returned to the starting place. In general, when doing repeated integration by parts, one should never choose the function u at any stage to be the same as the function v at the previous stage, or a constant times the previous v.

The following rule is called the extended rule for integration by parts. It is the result of $n + 1$ successive applications of integration by parts.

If

$$g_1(x) = \int g(x)\,dx, \qquad g_2(x) = \int g_1(x)\,dx,$$

$$g_3(x) = \int g_2(x)\,dx, \ldots, g_m(x) = \int g_{m-1}(x)\,dx, \ldots,$$

then

$$\int f(x) \cdot g(x)\,dx = f(x) \cdot g_1(x) - f'(x) \cdot g_2(x) + f''(x) \cdot g_3(x) - + \cdots$$

$$+ (-1)^n f^{(n)}(x) g_{n+1}(x) + (-1)^{n+1} \int f^{(n+1)}(x) g_{n+1}(x)\,dx.$$

A useful special case of the above rule is when $f(x)$ is a polynomial of degree n. Then $f^{(n+1)}(x) = 0$, and

$$\int f(x) \cdot g(x)\,dx = f(x) \cdot g_1(x) - f'(x) \cdot g_2(x) + f''(x) \cdot g_3(x) - + \cdots + (-1)^n f^{(n)}(x) g_{n+1}(x) + C$$

Example:

If $f(x) = x^2$, $g(x) = \sin x$

$$\int x^2 \sin x\,dx = -x^2 \cos x + 2x \sin x + 2 \cos x + C$$

Another application of this formula occurs if

$$f''(x) = af(x) \quad \text{and} \quad g''(x) = bg(x),$$

where a and b are unequal constants. In this case, by a process similar to that used in the above example for $\int e^x \sin x\,dx$, we get the formula

$$\int f(x)g(x)\,dx = \frac{f(x) \cdot g'(x) - f'(x) \cdot g(x)}{b - a} + C$$

This formula could have been used in the example mentioned. Here is another example.

Example:

If $f(x) = e^{2x}$, $g(x) = \sin 3x$, then $a = 4, b = -9$, and

$$\int e^{2x} \sin 3x\,dx = \frac{3\,e^{2x} \cos 3x - 2\,e^{2x} \sin 3x}{-9 - 4} + C = \frac{e^{2x}}{13}(2 \sin 3x - 3 \cos 3x) + C$$

The following additional points should be observed when using this table.

1. A constant of integration is to be supplied with the answers for indefinite integrals.
2. Logarithmic expressions are to base $e = 2.71828\ldots$, unless otherwise specified, and are to be evaluated for the absolute value of the arguments involved therein.
3. All angles are measured in radians, and inverse trigonometric and hyperbolic functions represent principal values, unless otherwise indicated.
4. If the application of a formula produces either a zero denominator or the square root of a negative number in the result, there is usually available another form of the answer which avoids this difficulty. In many of the results, the excluded values are specified, but when such are omitted it is presumed that one can tell what these should be, especially when difficulties of the type herein mentioned are obtained.
5. When inverse trigonometric functions occur in the integrals, be sure that any replacements made for them are strictly in accordance with the rules for such functions. This causes

little difficulty when the argument of the inverse trigonometric function is positive, since then all angles involved are in the first quadrant. However, if the argument is negative, special care must be used. Thus if $u > 0$,

$$\sin^{-1} u = \cos^{-1}\sqrt{1 - u^2} = \csc^{-1}\frac{1}{u}, \text{ etc.}$$

However, if $u < 0$,

$$\sin^{-1} u = -\cos^{-1}\sqrt{1 - u^2} = -\pi - \csc^{-1}\frac{1}{u}, \text{ etc.}$$

See the section on inverse trigonometric functions for a full treatment of the allowable substitutions.

6. In integrals 340–345 and some others, the right side includes expressions of the form

$$A \tan^{-1}[B + C \tan f(x)].$$

In these formulas, the $\tan^{-1}$ does not necessarily represent the principal value. Instead of always employing the principal branch of the inverse tangent function, one must instead use that branch of the inverse tangent function upon which $f(x)$ lies for any particular choice of x.

Example:

$$\int_0^{4\pi} \frac{dx}{2 + \sin x} = \frac{2}{\sqrt{3}}\tan^{-1}\frac{2\tan\frac{x}{2} + 1}{\sqrt{3}} \Bigg]_0^{4\pi}$$

$$= \frac{2}{\sqrt{3}}\left[\tan^{-1}\frac{2\tan 2\pi + 1}{\sqrt{3}} - \tan^{-1}\frac{2\tan 0 + 1}{\sqrt{3}}\right]$$

$$= \frac{2}{\sqrt{3}}\left[\frac{13\pi}{6} - \frac{\pi}{6}\right] = \frac{4\pi}{\sqrt{3}} = \frac{4\sqrt{3}\pi}{3}$$

Here

$$\tan^{-1}\frac{2\tan 2\pi + 1}{\sqrt{3}} = \tan^{-1}\frac{1}{\sqrt{3}} = \frac{13\pi}{6},$$

since $f(x) = 2\pi$; and

$$\tan^{-1}\frac{2\tan 0 + 1}{\sqrt{3}} = \tan^{-1}\frac{1}{\sqrt{3}} = \frac{\pi}{6},$$

since $f(x) = 0$.

INTEGRALS

ELEMENTARY FORMS

1. $\int a\,dx = ax$

2. $\int a \cdot f(x)\,dx = a \int f(x)\,dx$

3. $\int \phi(y)\,dx = \int \dfrac{\phi(y)}{y'}\,dy,$ where $y' = \dfrac{dy}{dx}$

4. $\int (u + v)\,dx = \int u\,dx + \int v\,dx,$ where u and v are any functions of x

5. $\int u\,dv = u \int dv - \int v\,du = uv - \int v\,du$

6. $\int u \dfrac{dv}{dx}\,dx = uv - \int v \dfrac{du}{dx}\,dx$

7. $\int x^n\,dx = \dfrac{x^{n+1}}{n+1},$ except $n = -1$

8. $\int \dfrac{f'(x)\,dx}{f(x)} = \log f(x),$ $(df(x) = f'(x)\,dx)$

9. $\int \dfrac{dx}{x} = \log x$

10. $\int \dfrac{f'(x)\,dx}{2\sqrt{f(x)}} = \sqrt{f(x)},$ $(df(x) = f'(x)\,dx)$

11. $\int e^x\,dx = e^x$

12. $\int e^{ax}\,dx = e^{ax}/a$

13. $\int b^{ax}\,dx = \dfrac{b^{ax}}{a \log b},$ $(b > 0)$

14. $\int \log x\,dx = x \log x - x$

15. $\int a^x \log a\,dx = a^x,$ $(a > 0)$

16. $\int \dfrac{dx}{a^2 + x^2} = \dfrac{1}{a} \tan^{-1} \dfrac{x}{a}$

17. $\displaystyle\int \frac{dx}{a^2 - x^2} = \begin{cases} \dfrac{1}{a}\tanh^{-1}\dfrac{x}{a} \\ \quad\text{or} \\ \dfrac{1}{2a}\log\dfrac{a + x}{a - x}, \quad (a^2 > x^2) \end{cases}$

18. $\displaystyle\int \frac{dx}{x^2 - a^2} = \begin{cases} -\dfrac{1}{a}\coth^{-1}\dfrac{x}{a} \\ \quad\text{or} \\ \dfrac{1}{2a}\log\dfrac{x - a}{x + a}, \quad (x^2 > a^2) \end{cases}$

19. $\displaystyle\int \frac{dx}{\sqrt{a^2 - x^2}} = \begin{cases} \sin^{-1}\dfrac{x}{|a|} \\ \quad\text{or} \\ -\cos^{-1}\dfrac{x}{|a|}, \quad (a^2 > x^2) \end{cases}$

20. $\displaystyle\int \frac{dx}{\sqrt{x^2 \pm a^2}} = \log\left(x + \sqrt{x^2 \pm a^2}\right)$

21. $\displaystyle\int \frac{dx}{x\sqrt{x^2 - a^2}} = \frac{1}{|a|}\sec^{-1}\frac{x}{a}$

22. $\displaystyle\int \frac{dx}{x\sqrt{a^2 \pm x^2}} = -\frac{1}{a}\log\left(\frac{a + \sqrt{a^2 \pm x^2}}{x}\right)$

FORMS CONTAINING $(a + bx)$

For forms containing $a + bx$, but not listed in the table, the substitution $u = \dfrac{a + bx}{x}$ may prove helpful.

23. $\displaystyle\int (a + bx)^n \, dx = \frac{(a + bx)^{n+1}}{(n + 1)b}, \quad (n \neq -1)$

24. $\displaystyle\int x(a + bx)^n \, dx$

$$= \frac{1}{b^2(n + 2)}(a + bx)^{n+2} - \frac{a}{b^2(n + 1)}(a + bx)^{n+1}, \quad (n \neq -1, -2)$$

25. $\displaystyle\int x^2(a + bx)^n \, dx = \frac{1}{b^3}\left[\frac{(a + bx)^{n+3}}{n + 3} - 2a\frac{(a + bx)^{n+2}}{n + 2} + a^2\frac{(a + bx)^{n+1}}{n + 1}\right]$

26. $\displaystyle \int x^m(a + bx)^n\, dx = \begin{cases} \dfrac{x^{m+1}(a + bx)^n}{m + n + 1} + \dfrac{an}{m + n + 1}\displaystyle\int x^m(a + bx)^{n-1}\, dx \\[2mm] \qquad\qquad\qquad\qquad \text{or} \\[2mm] \dfrac{1}{a(n + 1)}\left[-x^{m+1}(a + bx)^{n+1} \right. \\[4mm] \left. \qquad\qquad\qquad + (m + n + 2)\displaystyle\int x^m(a + bx)^{n+1}\, dx \right] \\[4mm] \qquad\qquad\qquad\qquad \text{or} \\[2mm] \dfrac{1}{b(m + n + 1)}\left[x^m(a + bx)^{n+1} - ma\displaystyle\int x^{m-1}(a + bx)^n\, dx \right] \end{cases}$

27. $\displaystyle \int \frac{dx}{a + bx} = \frac{1}{b}\log(a + bx)$

28. $\displaystyle \int \frac{dx}{(a + bx)^2} = -\frac{1}{b(a + bx)}$

29. $\displaystyle \int \frac{dx}{(a + bx)^3} = -\frac{1}{2b(a + bx)^2}$

30. $\displaystyle \int \frac{x\, dx}{a + bx} = \begin{cases} \dfrac{1}{b^2}[a + bx - a\log(a + bx)] \\[3mm] \qquad\qquad \text{or} \\[3mm] \dfrac{x}{b} - \dfrac{a}{b^2}\log(a + bx) \end{cases}$

31. $\displaystyle \int \frac{x\, dx}{(a + bx)^2} = \frac{1}{b^2}\left[\log(a + bx) + \frac{a}{a + bx} \right]$

32. $\displaystyle \int \frac{x\, dx}{(a + bx)^n} = \frac{1}{b^2}\left[\frac{-1}{(n - 2)(a + bx)^{n-2}} + \frac{a}{(n - 1)(a + bx)^{n-1}} \right], \qquad n \neq 1, 2$

33. $\displaystyle \int \frac{x^2\, dx}{a + bx} = \frac{1}{b^3}\left[\frac{1}{2}(a + bx)^2 - 2a(a + bx) + a^2\log(a + bx) \right]$

34. $\displaystyle \int \frac{x^2\, dx}{(a + bx)^2} = \frac{1}{b^3}\left[a + bx - 2a\log(a + bx) - \frac{a^2}{a + bx} \right]$

35. $\displaystyle \int \frac{x^2\, dx}{(a + bx)^3} = \frac{1}{b^3}\left[\log(a + bx) + \frac{2a}{a + bx} - \frac{a^2}{2(a + bx)^2} \right]$

36. $\displaystyle \int \frac{x^2\, dx}{(a + bx)^n} = \frac{1}{b^3}\left[\frac{-1}{(n - 3)(a + bx)^{n-3}} \right.$

$$\left. + \frac{2a}{(n - 2)(a + bx)^{n-2}} - \frac{a^2}{(n - 1)(a + bx)^{n-1}} \right], \qquad n \neq 1, 2, 3$$

37. $\displaystyle\int \frac{dx}{x(a + bx)} = -\frac{1}{a}\log\frac{a + bx}{x}$

38. $\displaystyle\int \frac{dx}{x(a + bx)^2} = \frac{1}{a(a + bx)} - \frac{1}{a^2}\log\frac{a + bx}{x}$

39. $\displaystyle\int \frac{dx}{x(a + bx)^3} = \frac{1}{a^3}\left[\frac{1}{2}\left(\frac{2a + bx}{a + bx}\right)^2 + \log\frac{x}{a + bx}\right]$

40. $\displaystyle\int \frac{dx}{x^2(a + bx)} = -\frac{1}{ax} + \frac{b}{a^2}\log\frac{a + bx}{x}$

41. $\displaystyle\int \frac{dx}{x^3(a + bx)} = \frac{2bx - a}{2a^2x^2} + \frac{b^2}{a^3}\log\frac{x}{a + bx}$

42. $\displaystyle\int \frac{dx}{x^2(a + bx)^2} = -\frac{a + 2bx}{a^2x(a + bx)} + \frac{2b}{a^3}\log\frac{a + bx}{x}$

FORMS CONTAINING $c^2 \pm x^2$, $x^2 - c^2$

43. $\displaystyle\int \frac{dx}{c^2 + x^2} = \frac{1}{c}\tan^{-1}\frac{x}{c}$

44. $\displaystyle\int \frac{dx}{c^2 - x^2} = \frac{1}{2c}\log\frac{c + x}{c - x}, \qquad (c^2 > x^2)$

45. $\displaystyle\int \frac{dx}{x^2 - c^2} = \frac{1}{2c}\log\frac{x - c}{x + c}, \qquad (x^2 > c^2)$

46. $\displaystyle\int \frac{x\,dx}{c^2 \pm x^2} = \pm\frac{1}{2}\log(c^2 \pm x^2)$

47. $\displaystyle\int \frac{x\,dx}{(c^2 \pm x^2)^{n+1}} = \mp\frac{1}{2n(c^2 \pm x^2)^n}$

48. $\displaystyle\int \frac{dx}{(c^2 \pm x^2)^n} = \frac{1}{2c^2(n - 1)}\left[\frac{x}{(c^2 \pm x^2)^{n-1}} + (2n - 3)\int \frac{dx}{(c^2 \pm x^2)^{n-1}}\right]$

49. $\displaystyle\int \frac{dx}{(x^2 - c^2)^n} = \frac{1}{2c^2(n - 1)}\left[-\frac{x}{(x^2 - c^2)^{n-1}} - (2n - 3)\int \frac{dx}{(x^2 - c^2)^{n-1}}\right]$

50. $\displaystyle\int \frac{x\,dx}{x^2 - c^2} = \frac{1}{2}\log(x^2 - c^2)$

51. $\displaystyle\int \frac{x\,dx}{(x^2 - c^2)^{n+1}} = -\frac{1}{2n(x^2 - c^2)^n}$

FORMS CONTAINING $a + bx$ and $c + dx$

$$u = a + bx, \qquad v = c + dx, \qquad k = ad - bc$$

If $k = 0$, then $v = \dfrac{c}{a}u$

52. $\displaystyle \int \frac{dx}{u \cdot v} = \frac{1}{k} \cdot \log\left(\frac{v}{u}\right)$

53. $\displaystyle \int \frac{x\,dx}{u \cdot v} = \frac{1}{k}\left[\frac{a}{b}\log(u) - \frac{c}{d}\log(v)\right]$

54. $\displaystyle \int \frac{dx}{u^2 \cdot v} = \frac{1}{k}\left(\frac{1}{u} + \frac{d}{k}\log\frac{v}{u}\right)$

55. $\displaystyle \int \frac{x\,dx}{u^2 \cdot v} = \frac{-a}{bku} - \frac{c}{k^2}\log\frac{v}{u}$

56. $\displaystyle \int \frac{x^2\,dx}{u^2 \cdot v} = \frac{a^2}{b^2ku} + \frac{1}{k^2}\left[\frac{c^2}{d}\log(v) + \frac{a(k - bc)}{b^2}\log(u)\right]$

57. $\displaystyle \int \frac{dx}{u^n \cdot v^m} = \frac{1}{k(m-1)}\left[\frac{-1}{u^{n-1} \cdot v^{m-1}} - (m+n-2)b\int \frac{dx}{u^n \cdot v^{m-1}}\right]$

58. $\displaystyle \int \frac{u}{v}\,dx = \frac{bx}{d} + \frac{k}{d^2}\log(v)$

59. $\displaystyle \int \frac{u^m\,dx}{v^n} = \begin{cases} \dfrac{-1}{k(n-1)}\left[\dfrac{u^{m+1}}{v^{n-1}} + b(n-m-2)\displaystyle\int \dfrac{u^m}{v^{n-1}}\,dx\right] \\[1ex] \qquad\qquad \text{or} \\[1ex] \dfrac{-1}{d(n-m-1)}\left[\dfrac{u^m}{v^{n-1}} + mk\displaystyle\int \dfrac{u^{m-1}}{v^n}\,dx\right] \\[1ex] \qquad\qquad \text{or} \\[1ex] \dfrac{-1}{d(n-1)}\left[\dfrac{u^m}{v^{n-1}} - mb\displaystyle\int \dfrac{u^{m-1}}{v^{n-1}}\,dx\right] \end{cases}$

FORMS CONTAINING $(a + bx^n)$

60. $\displaystyle \int \frac{dx}{a + bx^2} = \frac{1}{\sqrt{ab}}\tan^{-1}\frac{x\sqrt{ab}}{a}, \qquad (ab > 0)$

61. $\displaystyle \int \frac{dx}{a + bx^2} = \begin{cases} \dfrac{1}{2\sqrt{-ab}}\log\dfrac{a + x\sqrt{-ab}}{a - x\sqrt{-ab}}, \qquad (ab < 0) \\[1ex] \qquad\qquad \text{or} \\[1ex] \dfrac{1}{\sqrt{-ab}}\tanh^{-1}\dfrac{x\sqrt{-ab}}{a}, \qquad (ab < 0) \end{cases}$

62. $\displaystyle\int \frac{dx}{a^2 + b^2 x^2} = \frac{1}{ab}\tan^{-1}\frac{bx}{a}$

63. $\displaystyle\int \frac{x\,dx}{a + bx^2} = \frac{1}{2b}\log(a + bx^2)$

64. $\displaystyle\int \frac{x^2\,dx}{a + bx^2} = \frac{x}{b} - \frac{a}{b}\int \frac{dx}{a + bx^2}$

65. $\displaystyle\int \frac{dx}{(a + bx^2)^2} = \frac{x}{2a(a + bx^2)} + \frac{1}{2a}\int \frac{dx}{a + bx^2}$

66. $\displaystyle\int \frac{dx}{a^2 - b^2 x^2} = \frac{1}{2ab}\log\frac{a + bx}{a - bx}$

67. $\displaystyle\int \frac{dx}{(a + bx^2)^{m+1}} = \begin{cases} \dfrac{1}{2ma}\dfrac{x}{(a + bx^2)^m} + \dfrac{2m-1}{2ma}\displaystyle\int \dfrac{dx}{(a + bx^2)^m} \\[2ex] \qquad\qquad\text{or} \\[2ex] \dfrac{(2m)!}{(m!)^2}\left[\dfrac{x}{2a}\displaystyle\sum_{r=1}^{m}\dfrac{r!(r-1)!}{(4a)^{m-r}(2r)!(a+bx^2)^r} + \dfrac{1}{(4a)^m}\displaystyle\int\dfrac{dx}{a+bx^2}\right] \end{cases}$

68. $\displaystyle\int \frac{x\,dx}{(a + bx^2)^{m+1}} = -\frac{1}{2bm(a + bx^2)^m}$

69. $\displaystyle\int \frac{x^2\,dx}{(a + bx^2)^{m+1}} = \frac{-x}{2mb(a + bx^2)^m} + \frac{1}{2mb}\int \frac{dx}{(a + bx^2)^m}$

70. $\displaystyle\int \frac{dx}{x(a + bx^2)} = \frac{1}{2a}\log\frac{x^2}{a + bx^2}$

71. $\displaystyle\int \frac{dx}{x^2(a + bx^2)} = -\frac{1}{ax} - \frac{b}{a}\int \frac{dx}{a + bx^2}$

72. $\displaystyle\int \frac{dx}{x(a + bx^2)^{m+1}} = \begin{cases} \dfrac{1}{2am(a + bx^2)^m} + \dfrac{1}{a}\displaystyle\int \dfrac{dx}{x(a + bx^2)^m} \\[2ex] \qquad\qquad\text{or} \\[2ex] \dfrac{1}{2a^{m+1}}\left[\displaystyle\sum_{r=1}^{m}\dfrac{a^r}{r(a + bx^2)^r} + \log\dfrac{x^2}{a + bx^2}\right] \end{cases}$

73. $\displaystyle\int \frac{dx}{x^2(a + bx^2)^{m+1}} = \frac{1}{a}\int \frac{dx}{x^2(a + bx^2)^m} - \frac{b}{a}\int \frac{dx}{(a + bx^2)^{m+1}}$

74. $\displaystyle\int \frac{dx}{a + bx^3} = \frac{k}{3a}\left[\frac{1}{2}\log\frac{(k + x)^3}{a + bx^3} + \sqrt{3}\tan^{-1}\frac{2x - k}{k\sqrt{3}}\right], \quad \left(k = \sqrt[3]{\frac{a}{b}}\right)$

75. $\displaystyle\int \frac{x\,dx}{a + bx^3} = \frac{1}{3bk}\left[\frac{1}{2}\log\frac{a + bx^3}{(k + x)^3} + \sqrt{3}\tan^{-1}\frac{2x - k}{k\sqrt{3}}\right], \quad \left(k = \sqrt[3]{\frac{a}{b}}\right)$

76. $\displaystyle\int \frac{x^2\,dx}{a+bx^3} = \frac{1}{3b}\log(a+bx^3)$

77. $\displaystyle\int \frac{dx}{a+bx^4} = \frac{k}{2a}\left[\frac{1}{2}\log\frac{x^2+2kx+2k^2}{x^2-2kx+2k^2} + \tan^{-1}\frac{2kx}{2k^2-x^2}\right],$

$$\left(ab>0,\; k=\sqrt[4]{\frac{a}{4b}}\right)$$

78. $\displaystyle\int \frac{dx}{a+bx^4} = \frac{k}{2a}\left[\frac{1}{2}\log\frac{x+k}{x-k} + \tan^{-1}\frac{x}{k}\right], \qquad \left(ab<0,\; k=\sqrt[4]{-\frac{a}{b}}\right)$

79. $\displaystyle\int \frac{x\,dx}{a+bx^4} = \frac{1}{2bk}\tan^{-1}\frac{x^2}{k}, \qquad \left(ab>0,\; k=\sqrt{\frac{a}{b}}\right)$

80. $\displaystyle\int \frac{x\,dx}{a+bx^4} = \frac{1}{4bk}\log\frac{x^2-k}{x^2+k}, \qquad \left(ab<0,\; k=\sqrt{-\frac{a}{b}}\right)$

81. $\displaystyle\int \frac{x^2\,dx}{a+bx^4} = \frac{1}{4bk}\left[\frac{1}{2}\log\frac{x^2-2kx+2k^2}{x^2+2kx+2k^2} + \tan^{-1}\frac{2kx}{2k^2-x^2}\right],$

$$\left(ab>0,\; k=\sqrt[4]{\frac{a}{4b}}\right)$$

82. $\displaystyle\int \frac{x^2\,dx}{a+bx^4} = \frac{1}{4bk}\left[\log\frac{x-k}{x+k} + 2\tan^{-1}\frac{x}{k}\right], \qquad \left(ab<0,\; k=\sqrt[4]{-\frac{a}{b}}\right)$

83. $\displaystyle\int \frac{x^3\,dx}{a+bx^4} = \frac{1}{4b}\log(a+bx^4)$

84. $\displaystyle\int \frac{dx}{x(a+bx^n)} = \frac{1}{an}\log\frac{x^n}{a+bx^n}$

85. $\displaystyle\int \frac{dx}{(a+bx^n)^{m+1}} = \frac{1}{a}\int \frac{dx}{(a+bx^n)^m} - \frac{b}{a}\int \frac{x^n\,dx}{(a+bx^n)^{m+1}}$

86. $\displaystyle\int \frac{x^m\,dx}{(a+bx^n)^{p+1}} = \frac{1}{b}\int \frac{x^{m-n}\,dx}{(a+bx^n)^p} - \frac{a}{b}\int \frac{x^{m-n}\,dx}{(a+bx^n)^{p+1}}$

87. $\displaystyle\int \frac{dx}{x^m(a+bx^n)^{p+1}} = \frac{1}{a}\int \frac{dx}{x^m(a+bx^n)^p} - \frac{b}{a}\int \frac{dx}{x^{m-n}(a+bx^n)^{p+1}}$

88. $\displaystyle\int x^m(a + bx^n)^p\,dx = \begin{cases} \dfrac{1}{b(np + m + 1)}\left[x^{m-n+1}(a + bx^n)^{p+1}\right. \\ \qquad\qquad \left. - a(m - n + 1)\displaystyle\int x^{m-n}(a + bx^n)^p\,dx\right] \\[4pt] \text{or} \\[4pt] \dfrac{1}{np + m + 1}\left[x^{m+1}(a + bx^n)^p\right. \\ \qquad\qquad \left. + anp\displaystyle\int x^m(a + bx^n)^{p-1}\,dx\right] \\[4pt] \text{or} \\[4pt] \dfrac{1}{a(m + 1)}\left[x^{m+1}(a + bx^n)^{p+1}\right. \\ \qquad\qquad \left. - (m + 1 + np + n)b\displaystyle\int x^{m+n}(a + bx^n)^p\,dx\right] \\[4pt] \text{or} \\[4pt] \dfrac{1}{an(p + 1)}\left[-x^{m+1}(a + bx^n)^{p+1}\right. \\ \qquad\qquad \left. + (m + 1 + np + n)\displaystyle\int x^m(a + bx^n)^{p+1}\,dx\right] \end{cases}$

FORMS CONTAINING $c^3 \pm x^3$

89. $\displaystyle\int \frac{dx}{c^3 \pm x^3} = \pm\frac{1}{6c^2}\log\frac{(c \pm x)^3}{c^3 \pm x^3} + \frac{1}{c^2\sqrt{3}}\tan^{-1}\frac{2x \mp c}{c\sqrt{3}}$

90. $\displaystyle\int \frac{dx}{(c^3 \pm x^3)^2} = \frac{x}{3c^3(c^3 \pm x^3)} + \frac{2}{3c^3}\int\frac{dx}{c^3 \pm x^3}$

91. $\displaystyle\int \frac{dx}{(c^3 \pm x^3)^{n+1}} = \frac{1}{3nc^3}\left[\frac{x}{(c^3 \pm x^3)^n} + (3n - 1)\int\frac{dx}{(c^3 \pm x^3)^n}\right]$

92. $\displaystyle\int \frac{x\,dx}{c^3 \pm x^3} = \frac{1}{6c}\log\frac{c^3 \pm x^3}{(c \pm x)^3} \pm \frac{1}{c\sqrt{3}}\tan^{-1}\frac{2x \mp c}{c\sqrt{3}}$

93. $\displaystyle\int \frac{x\,dx}{(c^3 \pm x^3)^2} = \frac{x^2}{3c^3(c^3 \pm x^3)} + \frac{1}{3c^3}\int\frac{x\,dx}{c^3 \pm x^3}$

94. $\displaystyle\int \frac{x\,dx}{(c^3 \pm x^3)^{n+1}} = \frac{1}{3nc^3}\left[\frac{x^2}{(c^3 \pm x^3)^n} + (3n - 2)\int\frac{x\,dx}{(c^3 \pm x^3)^n}\right]$

95. $\displaystyle\int \frac{x^2\,dx}{c^3 \pm x^3} = \pm\frac{1}{3}\log(c^3 \pm x^3)$

96. $\int \dfrac{x^2\, dx}{(c^3 \pm x^3)^{n+1}} = \mp \dfrac{1}{3n(c^3 \pm x^3)^n}$

97. $\int \dfrac{dx}{x(c^3 \pm x^3)} = \dfrac{1}{3c^3} \log \dfrac{x^3}{c^3 \pm x^3}$

98. $\int \dfrac{dx}{x(c^3 \pm x^3)^2} = \dfrac{1}{3c^3(c^3 \pm x^3)} + \dfrac{1}{3c^6} \log \dfrac{x^3}{c^3 \pm x^3}$

99. $\int \dfrac{dx}{x(c^3 \pm x^3)^{n+1}} = \dfrac{1}{3nc^3(c^3 \pm x^3)^n} + \dfrac{1}{c^3} \int \dfrac{dx}{x(c^3 \pm x^3)^n}$

100. $\int \dfrac{dx}{x^2(c^3 \pm x^3)} = -\dfrac{1}{c^3 x} \mp \dfrac{1}{c^3} \int \dfrac{x\, dx}{c^3 \pm x^3}$

101. $\int \dfrac{dx}{x^2(c^3 \pm x^3)^{n+1}} = \dfrac{1}{c^3} \int \dfrac{dx}{x^2(c^3 \pm x^3)^n} \mp \dfrac{1}{c^3} \int \dfrac{x\, dx}{(c^3 \pm x^3)^{n+1}}$

FORMS CONTAINING $c^4 \pm x^4$

102. $\int \dfrac{dx}{c^4 + x^4} = \dfrac{1}{2c^3\sqrt{2}} \left[\dfrac{1}{2} \log \dfrac{x^2 + cx\sqrt{2} + c^2}{x^2 - cx\sqrt{2} + c^2} + \tan^{-1} \dfrac{cx\sqrt{2}}{c^2 - x^2} \right]$

103. $\int \dfrac{dx}{c^4 - x^4} = \dfrac{1}{2c^3} \left[\dfrac{1}{2} \log \dfrac{c + x}{c - x} + \tan^{-1} \dfrac{x}{c} \right]$

104. $\int \dfrac{x\, dx}{c^4 + x^4} = \dfrac{1}{2c^2} \tan^{-1} \dfrac{x^2}{c^2}$

105. $\int \dfrac{x\, dx}{c^4 - x^4} = \dfrac{1}{4c^2} \log \dfrac{c^2 + x^2}{c^2 - x^2}$

106. $\int \dfrac{x^2\, dx}{c^4 + x^4} = \dfrac{1}{2c\sqrt{2}} \left[\dfrac{1}{2} \log \dfrac{x^2 - cx\sqrt{2} + c^2}{x^2 + cx\sqrt{2} + c^2} + \tan^{-1} \dfrac{cx\sqrt{2}}{c^2 - x^2} \right]$

107. $\int \dfrac{x^2\, dx}{c^4 - x^4} = \dfrac{1}{2c} \left[\dfrac{1}{2} \log \dfrac{c + x}{c - x} - \tan^{-1} \dfrac{x}{c} \right]$

108. $\int \dfrac{x^3\, dx}{c^4 \pm x^4} = \pm \dfrac{1}{4} \log (c^4 \pm x^4)$

FORMS CONTAINING $(a + bx + cx^2)$

$$X = a + bx + cx^2 \text{ and } q = 4ac - b^2$$

If $q = 0$, then $X = c\left(x + \dfrac{b}{2c}\right)^2$, and formulas starting with 23 should be used in place of these.

109. $\int \dfrac{dx}{X} = \dfrac{2}{\sqrt{q}} \tan^{-1} \dfrac{2cx + b}{\sqrt{q}}, \qquad (q > 0)$

110. $\displaystyle\int \frac{dx}{X} = \begin{cases} \dfrac{-2}{\sqrt{-q}} \tanh^{-1} \dfrac{2cx+b}{\sqrt{-q}} \\[4mm] \qquad\qquad \text{or} \\[4mm] \dfrac{1}{\sqrt{-q}} \log \dfrac{2cx+b-\sqrt{-q}}{2cx+b+\sqrt{-q}}, \qquad (q<0) \end{cases}$

111. $\displaystyle\int \frac{dx}{X^2} = \frac{2cx+b}{qX} + \frac{2c}{q}\int \frac{dx}{X}$

112. $\displaystyle\int \frac{dx}{X^3} = \frac{2cx+b}{q}\left(\frac{1}{2X^2} + \frac{3c}{qX}\right) + \frac{6c^2}{q^2}\int \frac{dx}{X}$

113. $\displaystyle\int \frac{dx}{X^{n+1}} = \begin{cases} \dfrac{2cx+b}{nqX^n} + \dfrac{2(2n-1)c}{qn}\displaystyle\int \dfrac{dx}{X^n} \\[4mm] \qquad\qquad \text{or} \\[4mm] \dfrac{(2n)!}{(n!)^2}\left(\dfrac{c}{q}\right)^n\left[\dfrac{2cx+b}{q}\displaystyle\sum_{r=1}^{n}\left(\dfrac{q}{cX}\right)^r\left(\dfrac{(r-1)!\,r!}{(2r)!}\right) + \displaystyle\int \dfrac{dx}{X}\right] \end{cases}$

114. $\displaystyle\int \frac{x\,dx}{X} = \frac{1}{2c}\log X - \frac{b}{2c}\int \frac{dx}{X}$

115. $\displaystyle\int \frac{x\,dx}{X^2} = -\frac{bx+2a}{qX} - \frac{b}{q}\int \frac{dx}{X}$

116. $\displaystyle\int \frac{x\,dx}{X^{n+1}} = -\frac{2a+bx}{nqX^n} - \frac{b(2n-1)}{nq}\int \frac{dx}{X^n}$

117. $\displaystyle\int \frac{x^2}{X}\,dx = \frac{x}{c} - \frac{b}{2c^2}\log X + \frac{b^2-2ac}{2c^2}\int \frac{dx}{X}$

118. $\displaystyle\int \frac{x^2}{X^2}\,dx = \frac{(b^2-2ac)x+ab}{cqX} + \frac{2a}{q}\int \frac{dx}{X}$

119. $\displaystyle\int \frac{x^m\,dx}{X^{n+1}} = -\frac{x^{m-1}}{(2n-m+1)cX^n} - \frac{n-m+1}{2n-m+1}\cdot\frac{b}{c}\int \frac{x^{m-1}\,dx}{X^{n+1}}$

$$+ \frac{m-1}{2n-m+1}\cdot\frac{a}{c}\int \frac{x^{m-2}\,dx}{X^{n+1}}$$

120. $\displaystyle\int \frac{dx}{xX} = \frac{1}{2a}\log \frac{x^2}{X} - \frac{b}{2a}\int \frac{dx}{X}$

121. $\displaystyle\int \frac{dx}{x^2X} = \frac{b}{2a^2}\log \frac{X}{x^2} - \frac{1}{ax} + \left(\frac{b^2}{2a^2} - \frac{c}{a}\right)\int \frac{dx}{X}$

122. $\displaystyle\int \frac{dx}{xX^n} = \frac{1}{2a(n-1)X^{n-1}} - \frac{b}{2a}\int \frac{dx}{X^n} + \frac{1}{a}\int \frac{dx}{xX^{n-1}}$

123. $\displaystyle\int \frac{dx}{x^m X^{n+1}} = -\frac{1}{(m-1)ax^{m-1}X^n} - \frac{n+m-1}{m-1}\cdot\frac{b}{a}\int \frac{dx}{x^{m-1}X^{n+1}}$

$$-\frac{2n+m-1}{m-1}\cdot\frac{c}{a}\int \frac{dx}{x^{m-2}X^{n+1}}$$

FORMS CONTAINING $\sqrt{a+bx}$

124. $\displaystyle\int \sqrt{a+bx}\,dx = \frac{2}{3b}\sqrt{(a+bx)^3}$

125. $\displaystyle\int x\sqrt{a+bx}\,dx = -\frac{2(2a-3bx)\sqrt{(a+bx)^3}}{15b^2}$

126. $\displaystyle\int x^2\sqrt{a+bx}\,dx = \frac{2(8a^2-12abx+15b^2x^2)\sqrt{(a+bx)^3}}{105b^3}$

127. $\displaystyle\int x^m\sqrt{a+bx}\,dx = \begin{cases} \dfrac{2}{b(2m+3)}\left[x^m\sqrt{(a+bx)^3} - ma\int x^{m-1}\sqrt{a+bx}\,dx\right] \\[4mm] \quad\text{or} \\[2mm] \dfrac{2}{b^{m+1}}\sqrt{a+bx}\sum_{r=0}^{m}\dfrac{m!(-a)^{m-r}}{r!(m-r)!(2r+3)}(a+bx)^{r+1} \end{cases}$

128. $\displaystyle\int \frac{\sqrt{a+bx}}{x}\,dx = 2\sqrt{a+bx} + a\int \frac{dx}{x\sqrt{a+bx}}$

129. $\displaystyle\int \frac{\sqrt{a+bx}}{x^2}\,dx = -\frac{\sqrt{a+bx}}{x} + \frac{b}{2}\int \frac{dx}{x\sqrt{a+bx}}$

130. $\displaystyle\int \frac{\sqrt{a+bx}}{x^m}\,dx = -\frac{1}{(m-1)a}\left[\frac{\sqrt{(a+bx)^3}}{x^{m-1}} + \frac{(2m-5)b}{2}\int \frac{\sqrt{a+bx}}{x^{m-1}}\,dx\right]$

131. $\displaystyle\int \frac{dx}{\sqrt{a+bx}} = \frac{2\sqrt{a+bx}}{b}$

132. $\displaystyle\int \frac{x\,dx}{\sqrt{a+bx}} = -\frac{2(2a-bx)}{3b^2}\sqrt{a+bx}$

133. $\displaystyle\int \frac{x^2\,dx}{\sqrt{a+bx}} = \frac{2(8a^2-4abx+3b^2x^2)}{15b^3}\sqrt{a+bx}$

134. $\displaystyle\int \frac{x^m\,dx}{\sqrt{a+bx}} = \begin{cases} \dfrac{2}{(2m+1)b}\left[x^m\sqrt{a+bx} - ma\displaystyle\int \dfrac{x^{m-1}\,dx}{\sqrt{a+bx}}\right] \\[2ex] \text{or} \\[1ex] \dfrac{2(-a)^m\sqrt{a+bx}}{b^{m+1}}\displaystyle\sum_{r=0}^{m}\dfrac{(-1)^r m!(a+bx)^r}{(2r+1)r!(m-r)!a^r} \end{cases}$

135. $\displaystyle\int \frac{dx}{x\sqrt{a+bx}} = \frac{1}{\sqrt{a}}\log\left(\frac{\sqrt{a+bx}-\sqrt{a}}{\sqrt{a+bx}+\sqrt{a}}\right), \qquad (a>0)$

136. $\displaystyle\int \frac{dx}{x\sqrt{a+bx}} = \frac{2}{\sqrt{-a}}\tan^{-1}\sqrt{\frac{a+bx}{-a}}, \qquad (a<0)$

137. $\displaystyle\int \frac{dx}{x^2\sqrt{a+bx}} = -\frac{\sqrt{a+bx}}{ax} - \frac{b}{2a}\int \frac{dx}{x\sqrt{a+bx}}$

138. $\displaystyle\int \frac{dx}{x^n\sqrt{a+bx}} = \begin{cases} -\dfrac{\sqrt{a+bx}}{(n-1)ax^{n-1}} - \dfrac{(2n-3)b}{(2n-2)a}\displaystyle\int \dfrac{dx}{x^{n-1}\sqrt{a+bx}} \\[2ex] \text{or} \\[1ex] \dfrac{(2n-2)!}{[(n-1)!]^2}\left[-\dfrac{\sqrt{a+bx}}{a}\displaystyle\sum_{r=1}^{n-1}\dfrac{r!(r-1)!}{x^r(2r)!}\left(-\dfrac{b}{4a}\right)^{n-r-1}\right. \\[2ex] \qquad\qquad\left. + \left(-\dfrac{b}{4a}\right)^{n-1}\displaystyle\int \dfrac{dx}{x\sqrt{a+bx}}\right] \end{cases}$

139. $\displaystyle\int (a+bx)^{\pm\frac{n}{2}}\,dx = \frac{2(a+bx)^{\frac{2\pm n}{2}}}{b(2\pm n)}$

140. $\displaystyle\int x(a+bx)^{\pm\frac{n}{2}}\,dx = \frac{2}{b^2}\left[\frac{(a+bx)^{\frac{4\pm n}{2}}}{4\pm n} - \frac{a(a+bx)^{\frac{2\pm n}{2}}}{2\pm n}\right]$

141. $\displaystyle\int \frac{dx}{x(a+bx)^{\frac{m}{2}}} = \frac{1}{a}\int \frac{dx}{x(a+bx)^{\frac{m-2}{2}}} - \frac{b}{a}\int \frac{dx}{(a+bx)^{\frac{m}{2}}}$

142. $\displaystyle\int \frac{(a+bx)^{\frac{n}{2}}\,dx}{x} = b\int (a+bx)^{\frac{n-2}{2}}\,dx + a\int \frac{(a+bx)^{\frac{n-2}{2}}}{x}\,dx$

143. $\displaystyle\int f(x,\sqrt{a+bx})\,dx = \frac{2}{b}\int f\left(\frac{z^2-a}{b},z\right)z\,dz, \qquad (z=\sqrt{a+bx})$

FORMS CONTAINING $\sqrt{a + bx}$ and $\sqrt{c + dx}$

$$u = a + bx \qquad v = c + dx \qquad k = ad - bc$$

If $k = 0$, then $v = \dfrac{c}{a}u$, and formulas starting with 124 should be used in place of these.

144. $\displaystyle\int \frac{dx}{\sqrt{uv}} = \begin{cases} \dfrac{2}{\sqrt{bd}}\tanh^{-1}\dfrac{\sqrt{bduv}}{bv} \\[2mm] \text{or} \\[2mm] \dfrac{1}{\sqrt{bd}}\log\dfrac{bv + \sqrt{bduv}}{bv - \sqrt{bduv}} \\[2mm] \text{or} \\[2mm] \dfrac{1}{\sqrt{bd}}\log\dfrac{(bv + \sqrt{bduv})^2}{v}, \quad (bd > 0) \end{cases}$

145. $\displaystyle\int \frac{dx}{\sqrt{uv}} = \begin{cases} \dfrac{2}{\sqrt{-bd}}\tan^{-1}\dfrac{\sqrt{-bduv}}{bv} \\[2mm] \text{or} \\[2mm] -\dfrac{1}{\sqrt{-bd}}\sin^{-1}\left(\dfrac{2bdx + ad + bc}{|k|}\right), \quad (bd < 0) \end{cases}$

146. $\displaystyle\int \sqrt{uv}\,dx = \frac{k + 2bv}{4bd}\sqrt{uv} - \frac{k^2}{8bd}\int\frac{dx}{\sqrt{uv}}$

147. $\displaystyle\int \frac{dx}{v\sqrt{u}} = \begin{cases} \dfrac{1}{\sqrt{kd}}\log\dfrac{d\sqrt{u} - \sqrt{kd}}{d\sqrt{u} + \sqrt{kd}} \\[2mm] \text{or} \\[2mm] \dfrac{1}{\sqrt{kd}}\log\dfrac{(d\sqrt{u} - \sqrt{kd})^2}{v}, \quad (kd > 0) \end{cases}$

148. $\displaystyle\int \frac{dx}{v\sqrt{u}} = \frac{2}{\sqrt{-kd}}\tan^{-1}\frac{d\sqrt{u}}{\sqrt{-kd}}, \quad (kd < 0)$

149. $\displaystyle\int \frac{x\,dx}{\sqrt{uv}} = \frac{\sqrt{uv}}{bd} - \frac{ad + bc}{2bd}\int\frac{dx}{\sqrt{uv}}$

150. $\displaystyle\int \frac{dx}{v\sqrt{uv}} = \frac{-2\sqrt{uv}}{kv}$

151. $\displaystyle \int \frac{v\,dx}{\sqrt{uv}} = \frac{\sqrt{uv}}{b} - \frac{k}{2b} \int \frac{dx}{\sqrt{uv}}$

152. $\displaystyle \int \sqrt{\frac{v}{u}}\,dx = \frac{v}{|v|} \int \frac{v\,dx}{\sqrt{uv}}$

153. $\displaystyle \int v^m \sqrt{u}\,dx = \frac{1}{(2m+3)d}\left(2v^{m+1}\sqrt{u} + k \int \frac{v^m\,dx}{\sqrt{u}}\right)$

154. $\displaystyle \int \frac{dx}{v^m \sqrt{u}} = -\frac{1}{(m-1)k}\left(\frac{\sqrt{u}}{v^{m-1}} + \left(m - \frac{3}{2}\right)b \int \frac{dx}{v^{m-1}\sqrt{u}}\right)$

155. $\displaystyle \int \frac{v^m\,dx}{\sqrt{u}} = \begin{cases} \dfrac{2}{b(2m+1)}\left[v^m\sqrt{u} - mk \displaystyle\int \dfrac{v^{m-1}}{\sqrt{u}}\,dx\right] \\ \qquad\text{or} \\ \dfrac{2(m!)^2\sqrt{u}}{b(2m+1)!} \displaystyle\sum_{r=0}^{m}\left(-\dfrac{4k}{b}\right)^{m-r}\dfrac{(2r)!}{(r!)^2}v^r \end{cases}$

FORMS CONTAINING $\sqrt{x^2 \pm a^2}$

156. $\displaystyle \int \sqrt{x^2 \pm a^2}\,dx = \tfrac{1}{2}[x\sqrt{x^2 \pm a^2} \pm a^2 \log(x + \sqrt{x^2 \pm a^2})]$

157. $\displaystyle \int \frac{dx}{\sqrt{x^2 \pm a^2}} = \log(x + \sqrt{x^2 \pm a^2})$

158. $\displaystyle \int \frac{dx}{x\sqrt{x^2 - a^2}} = \frac{1}{|a|}\sec^{-1}\frac{x}{a}$

159. $\displaystyle \int \frac{dx}{x\sqrt{x^2 + a^2}} = -\frac{1}{a}\log\left(\frac{a + \sqrt{x^2 + a^2}}{x}\right)$

160. $\displaystyle \int \frac{\sqrt{x^2 + a^2}}{x}\,dx = \sqrt{x^2 + a^2} - a\log\left(\frac{a + \sqrt{x^2 + a^2}}{x}\right)$

161. $\displaystyle \int \frac{\sqrt{x^2 - a^2}}{x}\,dx = \sqrt{x^2 - a^2} - |a|\sec^{-1}\frac{x}{a}$

162. $\displaystyle \int \frac{x\,dx}{\sqrt{x^2 \pm a^2}} = \sqrt{x^2 \pm a^2}$

163. $\displaystyle \int x\sqrt{x^2 \pm a^2}\,dx = \tfrac{1}{3}\sqrt{(x^2 \pm a^2)^3}$

164. $\int \sqrt{(x^2 \pm a^2)^3}\, dx = \dfrac{1}{4}\left[x\sqrt{(x^2 \pm a^2)^3} \pm \dfrac{3a^2 x}{2}\sqrt{x^2 \pm a^2} \right.$

$$\left. + \dfrac{3a^4}{2}\log\left(x + \sqrt{x^2 \pm a^2}\right) \right]$$

165. $\int \dfrac{dx}{\sqrt{(x^2 \pm a^2)^3}} = \dfrac{\pm x}{a^2 \sqrt{x^2 \pm a^2}}$

166. $\int \dfrac{x\, dx}{\sqrt{(x^2 \pm a^2)^3}} = \dfrac{-1}{\sqrt{x^2 \pm a^2}}$

167. $\int x\sqrt{(x^2 \pm a^2)^3}\, dx = \frac{1}{5}\sqrt{(x^2 \pm a^2)^5}$

168. $\int x^2\sqrt{x^2 \pm a^2}\, dx = \dfrac{x}{4}\sqrt{(x^2 \pm a^2)^3} \mp \dfrac{a^2}{8}x\sqrt{x^2 \pm a^2} - \dfrac{a^4}{8}\log\left(x + \sqrt{x^2 \pm a^2}\right)$

169. $\int x^3\sqrt{x^2 + a^2}\, dx = (\frac{1}{5}x^2 - \frac{2}{15}a^2)\sqrt{(a^2 + x^2)^3}$

170. $\int x^3\sqrt{x^2 - a^2}\, dx = \dfrac{1}{5}\sqrt{(x^2 - a^2)^5} + \dfrac{a^2}{3}\sqrt{(x^2 - a^2)^3}$

171. $\int \dfrac{x^2\, dx}{\sqrt{x^2 \pm a^2}} = \dfrac{x}{2}\sqrt{x^2 \pm a^2} \mp \dfrac{a^2}{2}\log\left(x + \sqrt{x^2 \pm a^2}\right)$

172. $\int \dfrac{x^3\, dx}{\sqrt{x^2 \pm a^2}} = \dfrac{1}{3}\sqrt{(x^2 \pm a^2)^3} \mp a^2\sqrt{x^2 \pm a^2}$

173. $\int \dfrac{dx}{x^2\sqrt{x^2 \pm a^2}} = \mp \dfrac{\sqrt{x^2 \pm a^2}}{a^2 x}$

174. $\int \dfrac{dx}{x^3\sqrt{x^2 + a^2}} = -\dfrac{\sqrt{x^2 + a^2}}{2a^2 x^2} + \dfrac{1}{2a^3}\log\dfrac{a + \sqrt{x^2 + a^2}}{x}$

175. $\int \dfrac{dx}{x^3\sqrt{x^2 - a^2}} = \dfrac{\sqrt{x^2 - a^2}}{2a^2 x^2} + \dfrac{1}{2|a^3|}\sec^{-1}\dfrac{x}{a}$

176. $\int x^2\sqrt{(x^2 \pm a^2)^3}\, dx = \dfrac{x}{6}\sqrt{(x^2 \pm a^2)^5} \mp \dfrac{a^2 x}{24}\sqrt{(x^2 \pm a^2)^3} - \dfrac{a^4 x}{16}\sqrt{x^2 \pm a^2}$

$$\mp \dfrac{a^6}{16}\log\left(x + \sqrt{x^2 \pm a^2}\right)$$

177. $\int x^3\sqrt{(x^2 \pm a^2)^3}\, dx = \dfrac{1}{7}\sqrt{(x^2 \pm a^2)^7} \mp \dfrac{a^2}{5}\sqrt{(x^2 \pm a^2)^5}$

178. $\displaystyle \int \frac{\sqrt{x^2 \pm a^2}\, dx}{x^2} = -\frac{\sqrt{x^2 \pm a^2}}{x} + \log\left(x + \sqrt{x^2 \pm a^2}\right)$

179. $\displaystyle \int \frac{\sqrt{x^2 + a^2}}{x^3}\, dx = -\frac{\sqrt{x^2 + a^2}}{2x^2} - \frac{1}{2a}\log\frac{a + \sqrt{x^2 + a^2}}{x}$

180. $\displaystyle \int \frac{\sqrt{x^2 - a^2}}{x^3}\, dx = -\frac{\sqrt{x^2 - a^2}}{2x^2} + \frac{1}{2|a|}\sec^{-1}\frac{x}{a}$

181. $\displaystyle \int \frac{\sqrt{x^2 \pm a^2}}{x^4}\, dx = \mp\frac{\sqrt{(x^2 \pm a^2)^3}}{3a^2 x^3}$

182. $\displaystyle \int \frac{x^2\, dx}{\sqrt{(x^2 \pm a^2)^3}} = \frac{-x}{\sqrt{x^2 \pm a^2}} + \log\left(x + \sqrt{x^2 \pm a^2}\right)$

183. $\displaystyle \int \frac{x^3\, dx}{\sqrt{(x^2 \pm a^2)^3}} = \sqrt{x^2 \pm a^2} \pm \frac{a^2}{\sqrt{x^2 \pm a^2}}$

184. $\displaystyle \int \frac{dx}{x\sqrt{(x^2 + a^2)^3}} = \frac{1}{a^2\sqrt{x^2 + a^2}} - \frac{1}{a^3}\log\frac{a + \sqrt{x^2 + a^2}}{x}$

185. $\displaystyle \int \frac{dx}{x\sqrt{(x^2 - a^2)^3}} = -\frac{1}{a^2\sqrt{x^2 - a^2}} - \frac{1}{|a^3|}\sec^{-1}\frac{x}{a}$

186. $\displaystyle \int \frac{dx}{x^2\sqrt{(x^2 \pm a^2)^3}} = -\frac{1}{a^4}\left[\frac{\sqrt{x^2 \pm a^2}}{x} + \frac{x}{\sqrt{x^2 \pm a^2}}\right]$

187. $\displaystyle \int \frac{dx}{x^3\sqrt{(x^2 + a^2)^3}} = -\frac{1}{2a^2 x^2\sqrt{x^2 + a^2}} - \frac{3}{2a^4\sqrt{x^2 + a^2}}$

$$+ \frac{3}{2a^5}\log\frac{a + \sqrt{x^2 + a^2}}{x}$$

188. $\displaystyle \int \frac{dx}{x^3\sqrt{(x^2 - a^2)^3}} = \frac{1}{2a^2 x^2\sqrt{x^2 - a^2}} - \frac{3}{2a^4\sqrt{x^2 - a^2}} - \frac{3}{2|a^5|}\sec^{-1}\frac{x}{a}$

189. $\displaystyle \int \frac{x^m}{\sqrt{x^2 \pm a^2}}\, dx = \frac{1}{m}x^{m-1}\sqrt{x^2 \pm a^2} \mp \frac{m-1}{m}a^2\int \frac{x^{m-2}}{\sqrt{x^2 \pm a^2}}\, dx$

190. $\displaystyle \int \frac{x^{2m}}{\sqrt{x^2 \pm a^2}}\, dx = \frac{(2m)!}{2^{2m}(m!)^2}\left[\sqrt{x^2 \pm a^2}\sum_{r=1}^{m}\frac{r!(r-1)!}{(2r)!}(\mp a^2)^{m-r}(2x)^{2r-1}\right.$

$$\left. + (\mp a^2)^m \log\left(x + \sqrt{x^2 \pm a^2}\right)\right]$$

191. $\displaystyle \int \frac{x^{2m+1}}{\sqrt{x^2 \pm a^2}}\, dx = \sqrt{x^2 \pm a^2}\sum_{r=0}^{m}\frac{(2r)!(m!)^2}{(2m+1)!(r!)^2}(\mp 4a^2)^{m-r}x^{2r}$

192. $\displaystyle\int \frac{dx}{x^m\sqrt{x^2 \pm a^2}} = \mp \frac{\sqrt{x^2 \pm a^2}}{(m-1)a^2 x^{m-1}} \mp \frac{(m-2)}{(m-1)a^2}\int \frac{dx}{x^{m-2}\sqrt{x^2 \pm a^2}}$

193. $\displaystyle\int \frac{dx}{x^{2m}\sqrt{x^2 \pm a^2}} = \sqrt{x^2 \pm a^2}\sum_{r=0}^{m-1} \frac{(m-1)!\,m!\,(2r)!\,2^{2m-2r-1}}{(r!)^2(2m)!(\mp a^2)^{m-r}x^{2r+1}}$

194. $\displaystyle\int \frac{dx}{x^{2m+1}\sqrt{x^2 + a^2}} = \frac{(2m)!}{(m!)^2}\left[\frac{\sqrt{x^2 + a^2}}{a^2}\sum_{r=1}^{m}(-1)^{m-r+1}\frac{r!(r-1)!}{2(2r)!(4a^2)^{m-r}x^{2r}}\right.$

$$\left. + \frac{(-1)^{m+1}}{2^{2m}a^{2m+1}}\log \frac{\sqrt{x^2 + a^2} + a}{x}\right]$$

195. $\displaystyle\int \frac{dx}{x^{2m+1}\sqrt{x^2 - a^2}} = \frac{(2m)!}{(m!)^2}\left[\frac{\sqrt{x^2 - a^2}}{a^2}\sum_{r=1}^{m}\frac{r!(r-1)!}{2(2r)!(4a^2)^{m-r}x^{2r}}\right.$

$$\left. + \frac{1}{2^{2m}|a|^{2m+1}}\sec^{-1}\frac{x}{a}\right]$$

196. $\displaystyle\int \frac{dx}{(x-a)\sqrt{x^2 - a^2}} = -\frac{\sqrt{x^2 - a^2}}{a(x-a)}$

197. $\displaystyle\int \frac{dx}{(x+a)\sqrt{x^2 - a^2}} = \frac{\sqrt{x^2 - a^2}}{a(x+a)}$

198. $\displaystyle\int f(x, \sqrt{x^2 + a^2})\,dx = a\int f(a\tan u, a\sec u)\sec^2 u\,du, \quad \left(u = \tan^{-1}\frac{x}{a}, a > 0\right)$

199. $\displaystyle\int f(x, \sqrt{x^2 - a^2})\,dx = a\int f(a\sec u, a\tan u)\sec u\tan u\,du, \quad \left(u = \sec^{-1}\frac{x}{a},\right.$

$$\left. a > 0\right)$$

FORMS CONTAINING $\sqrt{a^2 - x^2}$

200. $\displaystyle\int \sqrt{a^2 - x^2}\,dx = \frac{1}{2}\left[x\sqrt{a^2 - x^2} + a^2\sin^{-1}\frac{x}{|a|}\right]$

201. $\displaystyle\int \frac{dx}{\sqrt{a^2 - x^2}} = \begin{cases} \sin^{-1}\dfrac{x}{|a|} \\ \text{or} \\ -\cos^{-1}\dfrac{x}{|a|} \end{cases}$

202. $\displaystyle\int \frac{dx}{x\sqrt{a^2 - x^2}} = -\frac{1}{a}\log\left(\frac{a + \sqrt{a^2 - x^2}}{x}\right)$

203. $\int \dfrac{\sqrt{a^2 - x^2}}{x} \, dx = \sqrt{a^2 - x^2} - a \log\left(\dfrac{a + \sqrt{a^2 - x^2}}{x}\right)$

204. $\int \dfrac{x \, dx}{\sqrt{a^2 - x^2}} = -\sqrt{a^2 - x^2}$

205. $\int x\sqrt{a^2 - x^2} \, dx = -\frac{1}{3}\sqrt{(a^2 - x^2)^3}$

206. $\int \sqrt{(a^2 - x^2)^3} \, dx = \dfrac{1}{4}\left[x\sqrt{(a^2 - x^2)^3} + \dfrac{3a^2 x}{2}\sqrt{a^2 - x^2} + \dfrac{3a^4}{2}\sin^{-1}\dfrac{x}{|a|}\right]$

207. $\int \dfrac{dx}{\sqrt{(a^2 - x^2)^3}} = \dfrac{x}{a^2\sqrt{a^2 - x^2}}$

208. $\int \dfrac{x \, dx}{\sqrt{(a^2 - x^2)^3}} = \dfrac{1}{\sqrt{a^2 - x^2}}$

209. $\int x\sqrt{(a^2 - x^2)^3} \, dx = -\frac{1}{5}\sqrt{(a^2 - x^2)^5}$

210. $\int x^2\sqrt{a^2 - x^2} \, dx = -\dfrac{x}{4}\sqrt{(a^2 - x^2)^3} + \dfrac{a^2}{8}\left(x\sqrt{a^2 - x^2} + a^2 \sin^{-1}\dfrac{x}{|a|}\right)$

211. $\int x^3\sqrt{a^2 - x^2} \, dx = (-\frac{1}{5}x^2 - \frac{2}{15}a^2)\sqrt{(a^2 - x^2)^3}$

212. $\int x^2\sqrt{(a^2 - x^2)^3} \, dx = -\dfrac{1}{6}x\sqrt{(a^2 - x^2)^5} + \dfrac{a^2 x}{24}\sqrt{(a^2 - x^2)^3}$

$$+ \dfrac{a^4 x}{16}\sqrt{a^2 - x^2} + \dfrac{a^6}{16}\sin^{-1}\dfrac{x}{|a|}$$

213. $\int x^3\sqrt{(a^2 - x^2)^3} \, dx = \dfrac{1}{7}\sqrt{(a^2 - x^2)^7} - \dfrac{a^2}{5}\sqrt{(a^2 - x^2)^5}$

214. $\int \dfrac{x^2 \, dx}{\sqrt{a^2 - x^2}} = -\dfrac{x}{2}\sqrt{a^2 - x^2} + \dfrac{a^2}{2}\sin^{-1}\dfrac{x}{|a|}$

215. $\int \dfrac{dx}{x^2\sqrt{a^2 - x^2}} = -\dfrac{\sqrt{a^2 - x^2}}{a^2 x}$

216. $\int \dfrac{\sqrt{a^2 - x^2}}{x^2} \, dx = -\dfrac{\sqrt{a^2 - x^2}}{x} - \sin^{-1}\dfrac{x}{|a|}$

217. $\int \dfrac{\sqrt{a^2 - x^2}}{x^3} \, dx = -\dfrac{\sqrt{a^2 - x^2}}{2x^2} + \dfrac{1}{2a}\log\dfrac{a + \sqrt{a^2 - x^2}}{x}$

218. $\int \dfrac{\sqrt{a^2 - x^2}}{x^4} \, dx = -\dfrac{\sqrt{(a^2 - x^2)^3}}{3a^2 x^3}$

219. $\displaystyle\int \frac{x^2\,dx}{\sqrt{(a^2-x^2)^3}} = \frac{x}{\sqrt{a^2-x^2}} - \sin^{-1}\frac{x}{|a|}$

220. $\displaystyle\int \frac{x^3\,dx}{\sqrt{a^2-x^2}} = -\frac{2}{3}(a^2-x^2)^{\frac{3}{2}} - x^2(a^2-x^2)^{\frac{1}{2}} = -\frac{1}{3}\sqrt{a^2-x^2}(x^2+2a^2)$

221. $\displaystyle\int \frac{x^3\,dx}{\sqrt{(a^2-x^2)^3}} = 2(a^2-x^2)^{\frac{1}{2}} + \frac{x^2}{(a^2-x^2)^{\frac{1}{2}}} = \frac{a^2}{\sqrt{a^2-x^2}} + \sqrt{a^2-x^2}$

222. $\displaystyle\int \frac{dx}{x^3\sqrt{a^2-x^2}} = -\frac{\sqrt{a^2-x^2}}{2a^2x^2} - \frac{1}{2a^3}\log\frac{a+\sqrt{a^2-x^2}}{x}$

223. $\displaystyle\int \frac{dx}{x\sqrt{(a^2-x^2)^3}} = \frac{1}{a^2\sqrt{a^2-x^2}} - \frac{1}{a^3}\log\frac{a+\sqrt{a^2-x^2}}{x}$

224. $\displaystyle\int \frac{dx}{x^2\sqrt{(a^2-x^2)^3}} = \frac{1}{a^4}\left[-\frac{\sqrt{a^2-x^2}}{x} + \frac{x}{\sqrt{a^2-x^2}} \right]$

225. $\displaystyle\int \frac{dx}{x^3\sqrt{(a^2-x^2)^3}} = -\frac{1}{2a^2x^2\sqrt{a^2-x^2}} + \frac{3}{2a^4\sqrt{a^2-x^2}}$

$$-\frac{3}{2a^5}\log\frac{a+\sqrt{a^2-x^2}}{x}$$

226. $\displaystyle\int \frac{x^m}{\sqrt{a^2-x^2}}\,dx = -\frac{x^{m-1}\sqrt{a^2-x^2}}{m} + \frac{(m-1)a^2}{m}\int \frac{x^{m-2}}{\sqrt{a^2-x^2}}\,dx$

227. $\displaystyle\int \frac{x^{2m}}{\sqrt{a^2-x^2}}\,dx = \frac{(2m)!}{(m!)^2}\left[-\sqrt{a^2-x^2}\sum_{r=1}^{m}\frac{r!(r-1)!}{2^{2m-2r+1}(2r)!}a^{2m-2r}x^{2r-1} \right.$

$$\left. +\frac{a^{2m}}{2^{2m}}\sin^{-1}\frac{x}{|a|} \right]$$

228. $\displaystyle\int \frac{x^{2m+1}}{\sqrt{a^2-x^2}}\,dx = -\sqrt{a^2-x^2}\sum_{r=0}^{m}\frac{(2r)!(m!)^2}{(2m+1)!(r!)^2}(4a^2)^{m-r}x^{2r}$

229. $\displaystyle\int \frac{dx}{x^m\sqrt{a^2-x^2}} = -\frac{\sqrt{a^2-x^2}}{(m-1)a^2x^{m-1}} + \frac{m-2}{(m-1)a^2}\int \frac{dx}{x^{m-2}\sqrt{a^2-x^2}}$

230. $\displaystyle\int \frac{dx}{x^{2m}\sqrt{a^2-x^2}} = -\sqrt{a^2-x^2}\sum_{r=0}^{m-1}\frac{(m-1)!m!(2r)!2^{2m-2r-1}}{(r!)^2(2m)!a^{2m-2r}x^{2r+1}}$

231. $\displaystyle\int \frac{dx}{x^{2m+1}\sqrt{a^2-x^2}} = \frac{(2m)!}{(m!)^2}\left[-\frac{\sqrt{a^2-x^2}}{a^2}\sum_{r=1}^{m}\frac{r!(r-1)!}{2(2r)!(4a^2)^{m-r}x^{2r}} \right.$

$$\left. +\frac{1}{2^{2m}a^{2m+1}}\log\frac{a-\sqrt{a^2-x^2}}{x} \right]$$

232. $\displaystyle\int \frac{dx}{(b^2 - x^2)\sqrt{a^2 - x^2}} = \frac{1}{2b\sqrt{a^2 - b^2}} \log \frac{(b\sqrt{a^2 - x^2} + x\sqrt{a^2 - b^2})^2}{b^2 - x^2},$

$$(a^2 > b^2)$$

233. $\displaystyle\int \frac{dx}{(b^2 - x^2)\sqrt{a^2 - x^2}} = \frac{1}{b\sqrt{b^2 - a^2}} \tan^{-1} \frac{x\sqrt{b^2 - a^2}}{b\sqrt{a^2 - x^2}}, \quad (b^2 > a^2)$

234. $\displaystyle\int \frac{dx}{(b^2 + x^2)\sqrt{a^2 - x^2}} = \frac{1}{b\sqrt{a^2 + b^2}} \tan^{-1} \frac{x\sqrt{a^2 + b^2}}{b\sqrt{a^2 - x^2}}$

235. $\displaystyle\int \frac{\sqrt{a^2 - x^2}}{b^2 + x^2} dx = \frac{\sqrt{a^2 + b^2}}{|b|} \sin^{-1} \frac{x\sqrt{a^2 + b^2}}{|a|\sqrt{x^2 + b^2}} - \sin^{-1} \frac{x}{|a|}$

236. $\displaystyle\int f(x, \sqrt{a^2 - x^2})\, dx = a \int f(a \sin u, a \cos u) \cos u\, du, \quad \left(u = \sin^{-1} \frac{x}{a}, a > 0 \right)$

FORMS CONTAINING $\sqrt{a + bx + cx^2}$

$$X = a + bx + cx^2, q = 4ac - b^2, \text{ and } k = \frac{4c}{q}$$

If $q = 0$, then $\sqrt{X} = \sqrt{c}\, \left| x + \dfrac{b}{2c} \right|$

237. $\displaystyle\int \frac{dx}{\sqrt{X}} = \begin{cases} \dfrac{1}{\sqrt{c}} \log\left(2\sqrt{cX} + 2cx + b\right) \\[2mm] \text{or} \\[2mm] \dfrac{1}{\sqrt{c}} \sinh^{-1} \dfrac{2cx + b}{\sqrt{q}}, \quad (c > 0) \end{cases}$

238. $\displaystyle\int \frac{dx}{\sqrt{X}} = -\frac{1}{\sqrt{-c}} \sin^{-1} \frac{2cx + b}{\sqrt{-q}}, \quad (c < 0)$

239. $\displaystyle\int \frac{dx}{X\sqrt{X}} = \frac{2(2cx + b)}{q\sqrt{X}}$

240. $\displaystyle\int \frac{dx}{X^2\sqrt{X}} = \frac{2(2cx + b)}{3q\sqrt{X}} \left(\frac{1}{X} + 2k \right)$

241. $\displaystyle\int \frac{dx}{X^n\sqrt{X}} = \begin{cases} \dfrac{2(2cx + b)\sqrt{X}}{(2n - 1)qX^n} + \dfrac{2k(n - 1)}{2n - 1} \displaystyle\int \frac{dx}{X^{n-1}\sqrt{X}} \\[2mm] \text{or} \\[2mm] \dfrac{(2cx + b)(n!)(n - 1)!4^n k^{n-1}}{q[(2n)!]\sqrt{X}} \displaystyle\sum_{r=0}^{n-1} \frac{(2r)!}{(4kX)^r(r!)^2} \end{cases}$

242. $\displaystyle \int \sqrt{X}\, dx = \frac{(2cx + b)\sqrt{X}}{4c} + \frac{1}{2k}\int \frac{dx}{\sqrt{X}}$

243. $\displaystyle \int X\sqrt{X}\, dx = \frac{(2cx + b)\sqrt{X}}{8c}\left(X + \frac{3}{2k}\right) + \frac{3}{8k^2}\int \frac{dx}{\sqrt{X}}$

244. $\displaystyle \int X^2\sqrt{X}\, dx = \frac{(2cx + b)\sqrt{X}}{12c}\left(X^2 + \frac{5X}{4k} + \frac{15}{8k^2}\right) + \frac{5}{16k^3}\int \frac{dx}{\sqrt{X}}$

245. $\displaystyle \int X^n\sqrt{X}\, dx = \begin{cases} \dfrac{(2cx + b)X^n\sqrt{X}}{4(n + 1)c} + \dfrac{2n + 1}{2(n + 1)k}\displaystyle\int X^{n-1}\sqrt{X}\, dx \\[2mm] \qquad\qquad\text{or} \\[2mm] \dfrac{(2n + 2)!}{[(n + 1)!]^2(4k)^{n+1}}\left[\dfrac{k(2cx + b)\sqrt{X}}{c}\displaystyle\sum_{r=0}^{n}\dfrac{r!(r + 1)!(4kX)^r}{(2r + 2)!}\right. \\[4mm] \qquad\qquad\qquad\qquad\qquad\qquad\qquad\qquad \left. + \displaystyle\int \dfrac{dx}{\sqrt{X}}\right] \end{cases}$

246. $\displaystyle \int \frac{x\, dx}{\sqrt{X}} = \frac{\sqrt{X}}{c} - \frac{b}{2c}\int \frac{dx}{\sqrt{X}}$

247. $\displaystyle \int \frac{x\, dx}{X\sqrt{X}} = -\frac{2(bx + 2a)}{q\sqrt{X}}$

248. $\displaystyle \int \frac{x\, dx}{X^n\sqrt{X}} = -\frac{\sqrt{X}}{(2n - 1)cX^n} - \frac{b}{2c}\int \frac{dx}{X^n\sqrt{X}}$

249. $\displaystyle \int \frac{x^2\, dx}{\sqrt{X}} = \left(\frac{x}{2c} - \frac{3b}{4c^2}\right)\sqrt{X} + \frac{3b^2 - 4ac}{8c^2}\int \frac{dx}{\sqrt{X}}$

250. $\displaystyle \int \frac{x^2\, dx}{X\sqrt{X}} = \frac{(2b^2 - 4ac)x + 2ab}{cq\sqrt{X}} + \frac{1}{c}\int \frac{dx}{\sqrt{X}}$

251. $\displaystyle \int \frac{x^2\, dx}{X^n\sqrt{X}} - \frac{(2b^2 - 4ac)x + 2ab}{(2n - 1)cqX^{n-1}\sqrt{X}} + \frac{4ac + (2n - 3)b^2}{(2n - 1)cq}\int \frac{dx}{X^{n-1}\sqrt{X}}$

252. $\displaystyle \int \frac{x^3\, dx}{\sqrt{X}} = \left(\frac{x^2}{3c} - \frac{5bx}{12c^2} + \frac{5b^2}{8c^3} - \frac{2a}{3c^2}\right)\sqrt{X} + \left(\frac{3ab}{4c^2} - \frac{5b^3}{16c^3}\right)\int \frac{dx}{\sqrt{X}}$

253. $\displaystyle \int \frac{x^n\, dx}{\sqrt{X}} = \frac{1}{nc}x^{n-1}\sqrt{X} - \frac{(2n - 1)b}{2nc}\int \frac{x^{n-1}\, dx}{\sqrt{X}} - \frac{(n - 1)a}{nc}\int \frac{x^{n-2}\, dx}{\sqrt{X}}$

254. $\int x\sqrt{X}\,dx = \dfrac{X\sqrt{X}}{3c} - \dfrac{b(2cx+b)}{8c^2}\sqrt{X} - \dfrac{b}{4ck}\int \dfrac{dx}{\sqrt{X}}$

255. $\int xX\sqrt{X}\,dx = \dfrac{X^2\sqrt{X}}{5c} - \dfrac{b}{2c}\int X\sqrt{X}\,dx$

256. $\int xX^n\sqrt{X}\,dx = \dfrac{X^{n+1}\sqrt{X}}{(2n+3)c} - \dfrac{b}{2c}\int X^n\sqrt{X}\,dx$

257. $\int x^2\sqrt{X}\,dx = \left(x - \dfrac{5b}{6c}\right)\dfrac{X\sqrt{X}}{4c} + \dfrac{5b^2-4ac}{16c^2}\int \sqrt{X}\,dx$

258. $\int \dfrac{dx}{x\sqrt{X}} = -\dfrac{1}{\sqrt{a}}\log\dfrac{2\sqrt{aX}+bx+2a}{x}, \quad (a>0)$

259. $\int \dfrac{dx}{x\sqrt{X}} = \dfrac{1}{\sqrt{-a}}\sin^{-1}\left(\dfrac{bx+2a}{|x|\sqrt{-q}}\right), \quad (a<0)$

260. $\int \dfrac{dx}{x\sqrt{X}} = -\dfrac{2\sqrt{X}}{bx}, \quad (a=0)$

261. $\int \dfrac{dx}{x^2\sqrt{X}} = -\dfrac{\sqrt{X}}{ax} - \dfrac{b}{2a}\int \dfrac{dx}{x\sqrt{X}}$

262. $\int \dfrac{\sqrt{X}\,dx}{x} = \sqrt{X} + \dfrac{b}{2}\int \dfrac{dx}{\sqrt{X}} + a\int \dfrac{dx}{x\sqrt{X}}$

263. $\int \dfrac{\sqrt{X}\,dx}{x^2} = -\dfrac{\sqrt{X}}{x} + \dfrac{b}{2}\int \dfrac{dx}{x\sqrt{X}} + c\int \dfrac{dx}{\sqrt{X}}$

FORMS INVOLVING $\sqrt{2ax-x^2}$

264. $\int \sqrt{2ax-x^2}\,dx = \dfrac{1}{2}\left[(x-a)\sqrt{2ax-x^2} + a^2\sin^{-1}\dfrac{x-a}{|a|}\right]$

265. $\int \dfrac{dx}{\sqrt{2ax-x^2}} = \begin{cases} \cos^{-1}\dfrac{a-x}{|a|} \\ \text{or} \\ \sin^{-1}\dfrac{x-a}{|a|} \end{cases}$

266. $\int x^n \sqrt{2ax - x^2}\, dx = \begin{cases} -\dfrac{x^{n-1}(2ax - x^2)^{\frac{3}{2}}}{n+2} + \dfrac{(2n+1)a}{n+2} \int x^{n-1}\sqrt{2ax - x^2}\, dx \\[2mm] \quad\text{or} \\[2mm] \sqrt{2ax - x^2}\left[\dfrac{x^{n+1}}{n+2} - \displaystyle\sum_{r=0}^{n} \dfrac{(2n+1)!(r!)^2 a^{n-r+1}}{2^{n-r}(2r+1)!(n+2)!n!} x^r\right] \\[4mm] \qquad\qquad\qquad + \dfrac{(2n+1)!a^{n+2}}{2^n n!(n+2)!}\sin^{-1}\dfrac{x-a}{|a|} \end{cases}$

267. $\int \dfrac{\sqrt{2ax - x^2}}{x^n}\, dx = \dfrac{(2ax - x^2)^{\frac{3}{2}}}{(3 - 2n)ax^n} + \dfrac{n-3}{(2n-3)a}\int \dfrac{\sqrt{2ax - x^2}}{x^{n-1}}\, dx$

268. $\int \dfrac{x^n\, dx}{\sqrt{2ax - x^2}} = \begin{cases} \dfrac{-x^{n-1}\sqrt{2ax - x^2}}{n} + \dfrac{a(2n-1)}{n}\int \dfrac{x^{n-1}}{\sqrt{2ax - x^2}}\, dx \\[2mm] \quad\text{or} \\[2mm] -\sqrt{2ax - x^2}\displaystyle\sum_{r=1}^{n}\dfrac{(2n)!r!(r-1)!a^{n-r}}{2^{n-r}(2r)!(n!)^2}x^{r-1} \\[4mm] \qquad\qquad\qquad + \dfrac{(2n)!a^n}{2^n(n!)^2}\sin^{-1}\dfrac{x-a}{|a|} \end{cases}$

269. $\int \dfrac{dx}{x^n\sqrt{2ax - x^2}} = \begin{cases} \dfrac{\sqrt{2ax - x^2}}{a(1 - 2n)x^n} + \dfrac{n-1}{(2n-1)a}\int \dfrac{dx}{x^{n-1}\sqrt{2ax - x^2}} \\[2mm] \quad\text{or} \\[2mm] -\sqrt{2ax - x^2}\displaystyle\sum_{r=0}^{n-1}\dfrac{2^{n-r}(n-1)!n!(2r)!}{(2n)!(r!)^2 a^{n-r}x^{r+1}} \end{cases}$

270. $\int \dfrac{dx}{(2ax - x^2)^{\frac{3}{2}}} = \dfrac{x-a}{a^2\sqrt{2ax - x^2}}$

271. $\int \dfrac{x\, dx}{(2ax - x^2)^{\frac{3}{2}}} = \dfrac{x}{a\sqrt{2ax - x^2}}$

MISCELLANEOUS ALGEBRAIC FORMS

272. $\int \dfrac{dx}{\sqrt{2ax + x^2}} = \log\left(x + a + \sqrt{2ax + x^2}\right)$

273. $\int \sqrt{ax^2 + c}\, dx = \dfrac{x}{2}\sqrt{ax^2 + c} + \dfrac{c}{2\sqrt{a}}\log\left(x\sqrt{a} + \sqrt{ax^2 + c}\right), \quad (a > 0)$

274. $\int \sqrt{ax^2 + c}\, dx = \dfrac{x}{2}\sqrt{ax^2 + c} + \dfrac{c}{2\sqrt{-a}}\sin^{-1}\left(x\sqrt{-\dfrac{a}{c}}\right), \quad (a < 0)$

275. $\int \sqrt{\dfrac{1+x}{1-x}}\,dx = \sin^{-1} x - \sqrt{1-x^2}$

276. $\int \dfrac{dx}{x\sqrt{ax^n + c}} = \begin{cases} \dfrac{1}{n\sqrt{c}} \log \dfrac{\sqrt{ax^n + c} - \sqrt{c}}{\sqrt{ax^n + c} + \sqrt{c}} \\[3mm] \text{or} \\[3mm] \dfrac{2}{n\sqrt{c}} \log \dfrac{\sqrt{ax^n + c} - \sqrt{c}}{\sqrt{x^n}}, \quad (c > 0) \end{cases}$

277. $\int \dfrac{dx}{x\sqrt{ax^n + c}} = \dfrac{2}{n\sqrt{-c}} \sec^{-1} \sqrt{-\dfrac{ax^n}{c}}, \quad (c < 0)$

278. $\int \dfrac{dx}{\sqrt{ax^2 + c}} = \dfrac{1}{\sqrt{a}} \log (x\sqrt{a} + \sqrt{ax^2 + c}), \quad (a > 0)$

279. $\int \dfrac{dx}{\sqrt{ax^2 + c}} = \dfrac{1}{\sqrt{-a}} \sin^{-1}\left(x\sqrt{-\dfrac{a}{c}}\right), \quad (a < 0)$

280. $\int (ax^2 + c)^{m+\frac{1}{2}}\,dx = \begin{cases} \dfrac{x(ax^2 + c)^{m+\frac{1}{2}}}{2(m+1)} + \dfrac{(2m+1)c}{2(m+1)} \int (ax^2 + c)^{m-\frac{1}{2}}\,dx \\[3mm] \text{or} \\[3mm] x\sqrt{ax^2 + c} \displaystyle\sum_{r=0}^{m} \dfrac{(2m+1)!(r!)^2 c^{m-r}}{2^{2m-2r+1}m!(m+1)!(2r+1)!}(ax^2 + c)^r \\[3mm] \qquad + \dfrac{(2m+1)!c^{m+1}}{2^{2m+1}m!(m+1)!} \displaystyle\int \dfrac{dx}{\sqrt{ax^2 + c}} \end{cases}$

281. $\int x(ax^2 + c)^{m+\frac{1}{2}}\,dx = \dfrac{(ax^2 + c)^{m+\frac{3}{2}}}{(2m+3)a}$

282. $\int \dfrac{(ax^2 + c)^{m+\frac{1}{2}}}{x}\,dx = \begin{cases} \dfrac{(ax^2 + c)^{m+\frac{1}{2}}}{2m+1} + c \displaystyle\int \dfrac{(ax^2 + c)^{m-\frac{1}{2}}}{x}\,dx \\[3mm] \text{or} \\[3mm] \sqrt{ax^2 + c} \displaystyle\sum_{r=0}^{m} \dfrac{c^{m-r}(ax^2 + c)^r}{2r+1} + c^{m+1} \displaystyle\int \dfrac{dx}{x\sqrt{ax^2 + c}} \end{cases}$

283. $\int \dfrac{dx}{(ax^2 + c)^{m+\frac{1}{2}}} = \begin{cases} \dfrac{x}{(2m-1)c(ax^2 + c)^{m-\frac{1}{2}}} + \dfrac{2m-2}{(2m-1)c} \displaystyle\int \dfrac{dx}{(ax^2 + c)^{m-\frac{1}{2}}} \\[3mm] \text{or} \\[3mm] \dfrac{x}{\sqrt{ax^2 + c}} \displaystyle\sum_{r=0}^{m-1} \dfrac{2^{2m-2r-1}(m-1)!m!(2r)!}{(2m)!(r!)^2 c^{m-r}(ax^2 + c)^r} \end{cases}$

284. $\displaystyle\int \frac{dx}{x^m\sqrt{ax^2+c}} = -\frac{\sqrt{ax^2+c}}{(m-1)cx^{m-1}} - \frac{(m-2)a}{(m-1)c}\int \frac{dx}{x^{m-2}\sqrt{ax^2+c}}$

285. $\displaystyle\int \frac{1+x^2}{(1-x^2)\sqrt{1+x^4}}\,dx = \frac{1}{\sqrt{2}}\log\frac{x\sqrt{2}+\sqrt{1+x^4}}{1-x^2}$

286. $\displaystyle\int \frac{1-x^2}{(1+x^2)\sqrt{1+x^4}}\,dx = \frac{1}{\sqrt{2}}\tan^{-1}\frac{x\sqrt{2}}{\sqrt{1+x^4}}$

287. $\displaystyle\int \frac{dx}{x\sqrt{x^n+a^2}} = -\frac{2}{na}\log\frac{a+\sqrt{x^n+a^2}}{\sqrt{x^n}}$

288. $\displaystyle\int \frac{dx}{x\sqrt{x^n-a^2}} = -\frac{2}{na}\sin^{-1}\frac{a}{\sqrt{x^n}}$

289. $\displaystyle\int \sqrt{\frac{x}{a^3-x^3}}\,dx = \frac{2}{3}\sin^{-1}\left(\frac{x}{a}\right)^{\frac{3}{2}}$

FORMS INVOLVING TRIGONOMETRIC FUNCTIONS

290. $\displaystyle\int (\sin ax)\,dx = -\frac{1}{a}\cos ax$

291. $\displaystyle\int (\cos ax)\,dx = \frac{1}{a}\sin ax$

292. $\displaystyle\int (\tan ax)\,dx = -\frac{1}{a}\log\cos ax = \frac{1}{a}\log\sec ax$

293. $\displaystyle\int (\cot ax)\,dx = \frac{1}{a}\log\sin ax = -\frac{1}{a}\log\csc ax$

294. $\displaystyle\int (\sec ax)\,dx = \frac{1}{a}\log(\sec ax + \tan ax) = \frac{1}{a}\log\tan\left(\frac{\pi}{4}+\frac{ax}{2}\right)$

295. $\displaystyle\int (\csc ax)\,dx = \frac{1}{a}\log(\csc ax - \cot ax) = \frac{1}{a}\log\tan\frac{ax}{2}$

296. $\displaystyle\int (\sin^2 ax)\,dx - -\frac{1}{2a}\cos ax\sin ax + \frac{1}{2}x = \frac{1}{2}x - \frac{1}{4a}\sin 2ax$

297. $\displaystyle\int (\sin^3 ax)\,dx = -\frac{1}{3a}(\cos ax)(\sin^2 ax + 2)$

298. $\displaystyle\int (\sin^4 ax)\,dx = \frac{3x}{8} - \frac{\sin 2ax}{4a} + \frac{\sin 4ax}{32a}$

299. $\displaystyle\int (\sin^n ax)\,dx = -\frac{\sin^{n-1} ax\cos ax}{na} + \frac{n-1}{n}\int (\sin^{n-2} ax)\,dx$

300. $\displaystyle\int (\sin^{2m} ax)\, dx = -\frac{\cos ax}{a} \sum_{r=0}^{m-1} \frac{(2m)!(r!)^2}{2^{2m-2r}(2r+1)!(m!)^2} \sin^{2r+1} ax + \frac{(2m)!}{2^{2m}(m!)^2} x$

301. $\displaystyle\int (\sin^{2m+1} ax)\, dx = -\frac{\cos ax}{a} \sum_{r=0}^{m} \frac{2^{2m-2r}(m!)^2(2r)!}{(2m+1)!(r!)^2} \sin^{2r} ax$

302. $\displaystyle\int (\cos^2 ax)\, dx = \frac{1}{2a}\sin ax \cos ax + \frac{1}{2}x = \frac{1}{2}x + \frac{1}{4a}\sin 2ax$

303. $\displaystyle\int (\cos^3 ax)\, dx = \frac{1}{3a}(\sin ax)(\cos^2 ax + 2)$

304. $\displaystyle\int (\cos^4 ax)\, dx = \frac{3x}{8} + \frac{\sin 2ax}{4a} + \frac{\sin 4ax}{32a}$

305. $\displaystyle\int (\cos^n ax)\, dx = \frac{1}{na}\cos^{n-1} ax \sin ax + \frac{n-1}{n}\int (\cos^{n-2} ax)\, dx$

306. $\displaystyle\int (\cos^{2m} ax)\, dx = \frac{\sin ax}{a} \sum_{r=0}^{m-1} \frac{(2m)!(r!)^2}{2^{2m-2r}(2r+1)!(m!)^2} \cos^{2r+1} ax + \frac{(2m)!}{2^{2m}(m!)^2} x$

307. $\displaystyle\int (\cos^{2m+1} ax)\, dx = \frac{\sin ax}{a} \sum_{r=0}^{m} \frac{2^{2m-2r}(m!)^2(2r)!}{(2m+1)!(r!)^2} \cos^{2r} ax$

308. $\displaystyle\int \frac{dx}{\sin^2 ax} = \int (\csc^2 ax)\, dx = -\frac{1}{a}\cot ax$

309. $\displaystyle\int \frac{dx}{\sin^m ax} = \int (\csc^m ax)\, dx = -\frac{1}{(m-1)a}\cdot\frac{\cos ax}{\sin^{m-1} ax} + \frac{m-2}{m-1}\int \frac{dx}{\sin^{m-2} ax}$

310. $\displaystyle\int \frac{dx}{\sin^{2m} ax} = \int (\csc^{2m} ax)\, dx = -\frac{1}{a}\cos ax \sum_{r=0}^{m-1} \frac{2^{2m-2r-1}(m-1)!m!(2r)!}{(2m)!(r!)^2 \sin^{2r+1} ax}$

311. $\displaystyle\int \frac{dx}{\sin^{2m+1} ax} = \int (\csc^{2m+1} ax)\, dx =$

$\displaystyle\qquad -\frac{1}{a}\cos ax \sum_{r=0}^{m-1} \frac{(2m)!(r!)^2}{2^{2m-2r}(m!)^2(2r+1)!\sin^{2r+2} ax} + \frac{1}{a}\cdot\frac{(2m)!}{2^{2m}(m!)^2}\log\tan\frac{ax}{2}$

312. $\displaystyle\int \frac{dx}{\cos^2 ax} = \int (\sec^2 ax)\, dx = \frac{1}{a}\tan ax$

313. $\displaystyle\int \frac{dx}{\cos^n ax} = \int (\sec^n ax)\, dx = \frac{1}{(n-1)a}\cdot\frac{\sin ax}{\cos^{n-1} ax} + \frac{n-2}{n-1}\int \frac{dx}{\cos^{n-2} ax}$

314. $\displaystyle\int \frac{dx}{\cos^{2m} ax} = \int (\sec^{2m} ax)\, dx = \frac{1}{a}\sin ax \sum_{r=0}^{m-1} \frac{2^{2m-2r-1}(m-1)!m!(2r)!}{(2m)!(r!)^2 \cos^{2r+1} ax}$

315. $\displaystyle\int \frac{dx}{\cos^{2m+1} ax} = \int (\sec^{2m+1} ax)\,dx =$

$$\frac{1}{a}\sin ax \sum_{r=0}^{m-1} \frac{(2m)!(r!)^2}{2^{2m-2r}(m!)^2(2r+1)!\cos^{2r+2} ax}$$

$$+ \frac{1}{a}\cdot\frac{(2m)!}{2^{2m}(m!)^2}\log(\sec ax + \tan ax)$$

316. $\displaystyle\int (\sin mx)(\sin nx)\,dx = \frac{\sin(m-n)x}{2(m-n)} - \frac{\sin(m+n)x}{2(m+n)}, \qquad (m^2 \neq n^2)$

317. $\displaystyle\int (\cos mx)(\cos nx)\,dx = \frac{\sin(m-n)x}{2(m-n)} + \frac{\sin(m+n)x}{2(m+n)}, \qquad (m^2 \neq n^2)$

318. $\displaystyle\int (\sin ax)(\cos ax)\,dx = \frac{1}{2a}\sin^2 ax$

319. $\displaystyle\int (\sin mx)(\cos nx)\,dx = -\frac{\cos(m-n)x}{2(m-n)} - \frac{\cos(m+n)x}{2(m+n)}, \qquad (m^2 \neq n^2)$

320. $\displaystyle\int (\sin^2 ax)(\cos^2 ax)\,dx = -\frac{1}{32a}\sin 4ax + \frac{x}{8}$

321. $\displaystyle\int (\sin ax)(\cos^m ax)\,dx = -\frac{\cos^{m+1} ax}{(m+1)a}$

322. $\displaystyle\int (\sin^m ax)(\cos ax)\,dx = \frac{\sin^{m+1} ax}{(m+1)a}$

323. $\displaystyle\int (\cos^m ax)(\sin^n ax)\,dx = \begin{cases} \dfrac{\cos^{m-1} ax\,\sin^{n+1} ax}{(m+n)a} \\[2ex] \qquad + \dfrac{m-1}{m+n}\displaystyle\int (\cos^{m-2} ax)(\sin^n ax)\,dx \\[2ex] \text{or} \\[2ex] -\dfrac{\sin^{n-1} ax\,\cos^{m+1} ax}{(m+n)a} \\[2ex] \qquad + \dfrac{n-1}{m+n}\displaystyle\int (\cos^m ax)(\sin^{n-2} ax)\,dx \end{cases}$

324. $\displaystyle\int \frac{\cos^m ax}{\sin^n ax}\,dx = \begin{cases} -\dfrac{\cos^{m+1} ax}{(n-1)a\,\sin^{n-1} ax} - \dfrac{m-n+2}{n-1}\displaystyle\int \dfrac{\cos^m ax}{\sin^{n-2} ax}\,dx \\[2ex] \text{or} \\[2ex] \dfrac{\cos^{m-1} ax}{a(m-n)\sin^{n-1} ax} + \dfrac{m-1}{m-n}\displaystyle\int \dfrac{\cos^{m-2} ax}{\sin^n ax}\,dx \end{cases}$

325. $\displaystyle\int \frac{\sin^m ax}{\cos^n ax}\,dx = \begin{cases} \dfrac{\sin^{m+1} ax}{a(n-1)\cos^{n-1} ax} + \dfrac{m-n+2}{n-1}\displaystyle\int \dfrac{\sin^m ax}{\cos^{n-2} ax}\,dx \\[4mm] \text{or} \\[4mm] -\dfrac{\sin^{m-1} ax}{a(m-n)\cos^{n-1} ax} - \dfrac{m-1}{m-n}\displaystyle\int \dfrac{\sin^{m-2} ax}{\cos^n ax}\,dx \end{cases}$

326. $\displaystyle\int \frac{\sin ax}{\cos^2 ax}\,dx = \frac{1}{a\cos ax} = \frac{\sec ax}{a}$

327. $\displaystyle\int \frac{\sin^2 ax}{\cos ax}\,dx = -\frac{1}{a}\sin ax + \frac{1}{a}\log\tan\left(\frac{\pi}{4} + \frac{ax}{2}\right)$

328. $\displaystyle\int \frac{\cos ax}{\sin^2 ax}\,dx = -\frac{1}{a\sin ax} = -\frac{\csc ax}{a}$

329. $\displaystyle\int \frac{dx}{(\sin ax)(\cos ax)} = \frac{1}{a}\log\tan ax$

330. $\displaystyle\int \frac{dx}{(\sin ax)(\cos^2 ax)} = \frac{1}{a}\left(\sec ax + \log\tan\frac{ax}{2}\right)$

331. $\displaystyle\int \frac{dx}{(\sin ax)(\cos^n ax)} = \frac{1}{a(n-1)\cos^{n-1} ax} + \int \frac{dx}{(\sin ax)(\cos^{n-2} ax)}$

332. $\displaystyle\int \frac{dx}{(\sin^2 ax)(\cos ax)} = -\frac{1}{a}\csc ax + \frac{1}{a}\log\tan\left(\frac{\pi}{4} + \frac{ax}{2}\right)$

333. $\displaystyle\int \frac{dx}{(\sin^2 ax)(\cos^2 ax)} = -\frac{2}{a}\cot 2ax$

334. $\displaystyle\int \frac{dx}{\sin^m ax \cos^n ax} = \begin{cases} -\dfrac{1}{a(m-1)(\sin^{m-1} ax)(\cos^{n-1} ax)} \\[4mm] \qquad\qquad + \dfrac{m+n-2}{m-1}\displaystyle\int \dfrac{dx}{(\sin^{m-2} ax)(\cos^n ax)} \\[4mm] \text{or} \\[4mm] \dfrac{1}{a(n-1)\sin^{m-1} ax \cos^{n-1} ax} \\[4mm] \qquad\qquad - \dfrac{m+n-2}{n-1}\displaystyle\int \dfrac{dx}{\sin^m ax \cos^{n-2} ax} \end{cases}$

335. $\displaystyle\int \sin(a+bx)\,dx = -\frac{1}{b}\cos(a+bx)$

336. $\displaystyle\int \cos(a+bx)\,dx = \frac{1}{b}\sin(a+bx)$

337. $\displaystyle\int \frac{dx}{1 \pm \sin ax} = \mp\frac{1}{a}\tan\left(\frac{\pi}{4} \mp \frac{ax}{2}\right)$

338. $\displaystyle\int \frac{dx}{1 + \cos ax} = \frac{1}{a}\tan\frac{ax}{2}$

339. $\displaystyle\int \frac{dx}{1 - \cos ax} = -\frac{1}{a}\cot\frac{ax}{2}$

*340. $\displaystyle\int \frac{dx}{a + b\sin x} = \begin{cases} \dfrac{2}{\sqrt{a^2 - b^2}}\tan^{-1}\dfrac{a\tan\dfrac{x}{2} + b}{\sqrt{a^2 - b^2}} \\[2em] \text{or} \\[1em] \dfrac{1}{\sqrt{b^2 - a^2}}\log\dfrac{a\tan\dfrac{x}{2} + b - \sqrt{b^2 - a^2}}{a\tan\dfrac{x}{2} + b + \sqrt{b^2 - a^2}} \end{cases}$

*341. $\displaystyle\int \frac{dx}{a + b\cos x} = \begin{cases} \dfrac{2}{\sqrt{a^2 - b^2}}\tan^{-1}\dfrac{\sqrt{a^2 - b^2}\tan\dfrac{x}{2}}{a + b} \\[2em] \text{or} \\[1em] \dfrac{1}{\sqrt{b^2 - a^2}}\log\left(\dfrac{\sqrt{b^2 - a^2}\tan\dfrac{x}{2} + a + b}{\sqrt{b^2 - a^2}\tan\dfrac{x}{2} - a - b}\right) \end{cases}$

*342. $\displaystyle\int \frac{dx}{a + b\sin x + c\cos x}$

$= \begin{cases} \dfrac{1}{\sqrt{b^2 + c^2 - a^2}}\log\dfrac{b - \sqrt{b^2 + c^2 - a^2} + (a - c)\tan\dfrac{x}{2}}{b + \sqrt{b^2 + c^2 - a^2} + (a - c)\tan\dfrac{x}{2}}, \quad \text{if } a^2 < b^2 + c^2, a \neq c \\[2.5em] \text{or} \\[1em] \dfrac{2}{\sqrt{a^2 - b^2 - c^2}}\tan^{-1}\dfrac{b + (a - c)\tan\dfrac{x}{2}}{\sqrt{a^2 - b^2 - c^2}}, \quad \text{if } a^2 > b^2 + c^2 \\[2.5em] \text{or} \\[1em] \dfrac{1}{a}\left[\dfrac{a - (b + c)\cos x - (b - c)\sin x}{a - (b - c)\cos x + (b + c)\sin x}\right], \quad \text{if } a^2 = b^2 + c^2, a \neq c. \end{cases}$

*343. $\displaystyle\int \frac{\sin^2 x\, dx}{a + b\cos^2 x} = \frac{1}{b}\sqrt{\frac{a + b}{a}}\tan^{-1}\left(\sqrt{\frac{a}{a + b}}\tan x\right) - \frac{x}{b}, \qquad (ab > 0, \text{ or } |a| > |b|)$

*See note p. 110.

*344. $\int \dfrac{dx}{a^2 \cos^2 x + b^2 \sin^2 x} = \dfrac{1}{ab} \tan^{-1} \left(\dfrac{b \tan x}{a} \right)$

*345. $\int \dfrac{\cos^2 cx}{a^2 + b^2 \sin^2 cx} \, dx = \dfrac{\sqrt{a^2 + b^2}}{ab^2 c} \tan^{-1} \dfrac{\sqrt{a^2 + b^2} \tan cx}{a} - \dfrac{x}{b^2}$

346. $\int \dfrac{\sin cx \cos cx}{a \cos^2 cx + b \sin^2 cx} \, dx = \dfrac{1}{2c(b - a)} \log (a \cos^2 cx + b \sin^2 cx)$

347. $\int \dfrac{\cos cx}{a \cos cx + b \sin cx} \, dx = \int \dfrac{dx}{a + b \tan cx} =$

$$\dfrac{1}{c(a^2 + b^2)} [acx + b \log (a \cos cx + b \sin cx)]$$

348. $\int \dfrac{\sin cx}{a \sin cx + b \cos cx} \, dx = \int \dfrac{dx}{a + b \cot cx} =$

$$\dfrac{1}{c(a^2 + b^2)} [acx - b \log (a \sin cx + b \cos cx)]$$

*349. $\int \dfrac{dx}{a \cos^2 x + 2b \cos x \sin x + c \sin^2 x} = \begin{cases} \dfrac{1}{2\sqrt{b^2 - ac}} \log \dfrac{c \tan x + b - \sqrt{b^2 - ac}}{c \tan x + b + \sqrt{b^2 - ac}}, \\ \qquad\qquad\qquad\qquad\qquad (b^2 > ac) \\ \text{or} \\ \dfrac{1}{\sqrt{ac - b^2}} \tan^{-1} \dfrac{c \tan x + b}{\sqrt{ac - b^2}}, \quad (b^2 < ac) \\ \text{or} \\ -\dfrac{1}{c \tan x + b}, \qquad (b^2 = ac) \end{cases}$

350. $\int \dfrac{\sin ax}{1 \pm \sin ax} \, dx = \pm x + \dfrac{1}{a} \tan \left(\dfrac{\pi}{4} \mp \dfrac{ax}{2} \right)$

351. $\int \dfrac{dx}{(\sin ax)(1 \pm \sin ax)} = \dfrac{1}{a} \tan \left(\dfrac{\pi}{4} \mp \dfrac{ax}{2} \right) + \dfrac{1}{a} \log \tan \dfrac{ax}{2}$

352. $\int \dfrac{dx}{(1 + \sin ax)^2} = -\dfrac{1}{2a} \tan \left(\dfrac{\pi}{4} - \dfrac{ax}{2} \right) - \dfrac{1}{6a} \tan^3 \left(\dfrac{\pi}{4} - \dfrac{ax}{2} \right)$

353. $\int \dfrac{dx}{(1 - \sin ax)^2} = \dfrac{1}{2a} \cot \left(\dfrac{\pi}{4} - \dfrac{ax}{2} \right) + \dfrac{1}{6a} \cot^3 \left(\dfrac{\pi}{4} - \dfrac{ax}{2} \right)$

354. $\int \dfrac{\sin ax}{(1 + \sin ax)^2} \, dx = -\dfrac{1}{2a} \tan \left(\dfrac{\pi}{4} - \dfrac{ax}{2} \right) + \dfrac{1}{6a} \tan^3 \left(\dfrac{\pi}{4} - \dfrac{ax}{2} \right).$

*See note p. 110.

355. $\displaystyle\int \frac{\sin ax}{(1 - \sin ax)^2}\,dx = -\frac{1}{2a}\cot\left(\frac{\pi}{4} - \frac{ax}{2}\right) + \frac{1}{6a}\cot^3\left(\frac{\pi}{4} - \frac{ax}{2}\right)$

356. $\displaystyle\int \frac{\sin x\,dx}{a + b\sin x} = \frac{x}{b} - \frac{a}{b}\int \frac{dx}{a + b\sin x}$

357. $\displaystyle\int \frac{dx}{(\sin x)(a + b\sin x)} = \frac{1}{a}\log\tan\frac{x}{2} - \frac{b}{a}\int \frac{dx}{a + b\sin x}$

358. $\displaystyle\int \frac{dx}{(a + b\sin x)^2} = \frac{b\cos x}{(a^2 - b^2)(a + b\sin x)} + \frac{a}{a^2 - b^2}\int \frac{dx}{a + b\sin x}$

359. $\displaystyle\int \frac{\sin x\,dx}{(a + b\sin x)^2} = \frac{a\cos x}{(b^2 - a^2)(a + b\sin x)} + \frac{b}{b^2 - a^2}\int \frac{dx}{a + b\sin x}$

*360. $\displaystyle\int \frac{dx}{a^2 + b^2\sin^2 cx} = \frac{1}{ac\sqrt{a^2 + b^2}}\tan^{-1}\frac{\sqrt{a^2 + b^2}\,\tan cx}{a}$

*361. $\displaystyle\int \frac{dx}{a^2 - b^2\sin^2 cx} = \begin{cases} \dfrac{1}{ac\sqrt{a^2 - b^2}}\tan^{-1}\dfrac{\sqrt{a^2 - b^2}\,\tan cx}{a}, & (a^2 > b^2) \\[2mm] \text{or} \\[2mm] \dfrac{1}{2ac\sqrt{b^2 - a^2}}\log\dfrac{\sqrt{b^2 - a^2}\,\tan cx + a}{\sqrt{b^2 - a^2}\,\tan cx - a}, & (a^2 < b^2) \end{cases}$

362. $\displaystyle\int \frac{\cos ax}{1 + \cos ax}\,dx = x - \frac{1}{a}\tan\frac{ax}{2}$

363. $\displaystyle\int \frac{\cos ax}{1 - \cos ax}\,dx = -x - \frac{1}{a}\cot\frac{ax}{2}$

364. $\displaystyle\int \frac{dx}{(\cos ax)(1 + \cos ax)} = \frac{1}{a}\log\tan\left(\frac{\pi}{4} + \frac{ax}{2}\right) - \frac{1}{a}\tan\frac{ax}{2}$

365. $\displaystyle\int \frac{dx}{(\cos ax)(1 - \cos ax)} = \frac{1}{a}\log\tan\left(\frac{\pi}{4} + \frac{ax}{2}\right) - \frac{1}{a}\cot\frac{ax}{2}$

366. $\displaystyle\int \frac{dx}{(1 + \cos ax)^2} = \frac{1}{2a}\tan\frac{ax}{2} + \frac{1}{6a}\tan^3\frac{ax}{2}$

367. $\displaystyle\int \frac{dx}{(1 - \cos ax)^2} = -\frac{1}{2a}\cot\frac{ax}{2} - \frac{1}{6a}\cot^3\frac{ax}{2}$

368. $\displaystyle\int \frac{\cos ax}{(1 + \cos ax)^2}\,dx = \frac{1}{2a}\tan\frac{ax}{2} - \frac{1}{6a}\tan^3\frac{ax}{2}$

369. $\displaystyle\int \frac{\cos ax}{(1 - \cos ax)^2}\,dx = \frac{1}{2a}\cot\frac{ax}{2} - \frac{1}{6a}\cot^3\frac{ax}{2}$

*See note p. 110.

370. $\displaystyle\int \frac{\cos x \, dx}{a + b \cos x} = \frac{x}{b} - \frac{a}{b} \int \frac{dx}{a + b \cos x}$

371. $\displaystyle\int \frac{dx}{(\cos x)(a + b \cos x)} = \frac{1}{a} \log \tan \left(\frac{x}{2} + \frac{\pi}{4}\right) - \frac{b}{a} \int \frac{dx}{a + b \cos x}$

372. $\displaystyle\int \frac{dx}{(a + b \cos x)^2} = \frac{b \sin x}{(b^2 - a^2)(a + b \cos x)} - \frac{a}{b^2 - a^2} \int \frac{dx}{a + b \cos x}$

373. $\displaystyle\int \frac{\cos x}{(a + b \cos x)^2} \, dx = \frac{a \sin x}{(a^2 - b^2)(a + b \cos x)} - \frac{b}{a^2 - b^2} \int \frac{dx}{a + b \cos x}$

*374. $\displaystyle\int \frac{dx}{a^2 + b^2 - 2ab \cos cx} = \frac{2}{c(a^2 - b^2)} \tan^{-1}\left(\frac{a + b}{a - b} \tan \frac{cx}{2}\right)$

*375. $\displaystyle\int \frac{dx}{a^2 + b^2 \cos^2 cx} = \frac{1}{ac\sqrt{a^2 + b^2}} \tan^{-1} \frac{a \tan cx}{\sqrt{a^2 + b^2}}$

*376. $\displaystyle\int \frac{dx}{a^2 - b^2 \cos^2 cx} - \begin{cases} \dfrac{1}{ac\sqrt{a^2 - b^2}} \tan^{-1} \dfrac{a \tan cx}{\sqrt{a^2 - b^2}}, & (a^2 > b^2) \\[2ex] \text{or} \\[2ex] \dfrac{1}{2ac\sqrt{b^2 - a^2}} \log \dfrac{a \tan cx - \sqrt{b^2 - a^2}}{a \tan cx + \sqrt{b^2 - a^2}}, & (b^2 > a^2) \end{cases}$

377. $\displaystyle\int \frac{\sin ax}{1 \pm \cos ax} \, dx = \mp \frac{1}{a} \log (1 \pm \cos ax)$

378. $\displaystyle\int \frac{\cos ax}{1 \pm \sin ax} \, dx = \pm \frac{1}{a} \log (1 \pm \sin ax)$

379. $\displaystyle\int \frac{dx}{(\sin ax)(1 \pm \cos ax)} = \pm \frac{1}{2a(1 \pm \cos ax)} + \frac{1}{2a} \log \tan \frac{ax}{2}$

380. $\displaystyle\int \frac{dx}{(\cos ax)(1 \pm \sin ax)} = \mp \frac{1}{2a(1 \pm \sin ax)} + \frac{1}{2a} \log \tan \left(\frac{\pi}{4} + \frac{ax}{2}\right)$

381. $\displaystyle\int \frac{\sin ax}{(\cos ax)(1 \pm \cos ax)} \, dx = \frac{1}{a} \log (\sec ax \pm 1)$

382. $\displaystyle\int \frac{\cos ax}{(\sin ax)(1 \pm \sin ax)} \, dx = -\frac{1}{a} \log (\csc ax \pm 1)$

383. $\displaystyle\int \frac{\sin ax}{(\cos ax)(1 \pm \sin ax)} \, dx = \frac{1}{2a(1 \pm \sin ax)} \pm \frac{1}{2a} \log \tan \left(\frac{\pi}{4} + \frac{ax}{2}\right)$

384. $\displaystyle\int \frac{\cos ax}{(\sin ax)(1 \pm \cos ax)} \, dx = -\frac{1}{2a(1 \pm \cos ax)} \pm \frac{1}{2a} \log \tan \frac{ax}{2}$

*See note p. 110.

385. $\displaystyle\int \frac{dx}{\sin ax \pm \cos ax} = \frac{1}{a\sqrt{2}} \log \tan\left(\frac{ax}{2} \pm \frac{\pi}{8}\right)$

386. $\displaystyle\int \frac{dx}{(\sin ax \pm \cos ax)^2} = \frac{1}{2a} \tan\left(ax \mp \frac{\pi}{4}\right)$

387. $\displaystyle\int \frac{dx}{1 + \cos ax \pm \sin ax} = \pm\frac{1}{a} \log\left(1 \pm \tan\frac{ax}{2}\right)$

388. $\displaystyle\int \frac{dx}{a^2 \cos^2 cx - b^2 \sin^2 cx} = \frac{1}{2abc} \log\frac{b \tan cx + a}{b \tan cx - a}$

389. $\displaystyle\int x(\sin ax)\,dx = \frac{1}{a^2} \sin ax - \frac{x}{a} \cos ax$

390. $\displaystyle\int x^2(\sin ax)\,dx = \frac{2x}{a^2} \sin ax - \frac{a^2x^2 - 2}{a^3} \cos ax$

391. $\displaystyle\int x^3(\sin ax)\,dx = \frac{3a^2x^2 - 6}{a^4} \sin ax - \frac{a^2x^3 - 6x}{a^3} \cos ax$

392. $\displaystyle\int x^m \sin ax\,dx = \begin{cases} -\dfrac{1}{a} x^m \cos ax + \dfrac{m}{a} \displaystyle\int x^{m-1} \cos ax\,dx \\[2mm] \text{or} \\[2mm] \cos ax \displaystyle\sum_{r=0}^{\left[\frac{m}{2}\right]} (-1)^{r+1} \dfrac{m!}{(m-2r)!} \cdot \dfrac{x^{m-2r}}{a^{2r+1}} \\[4mm] + \sin ax \displaystyle\sum_{r=0}^{\left[\frac{m-1}{2}\right]} (-1)^r \dfrac{m!}{(m-2r-1)!} \cdot \dfrac{x^{m-2r-1}}{a^{2r+2}} \end{cases}$

Note: $[s]$ means greatest integer $\le s$; $[3\tfrac{1}{2}] = 3$, $[\tfrac{1}{2}] = 0$, etc.

393. $\displaystyle\int x(\cos ax)\,dx = \frac{1}{a^2} \cos ax + \frac{x}{a} \sin ax$

394. $\displaystyle\int x^2(\cos ax)\,dx = \frac{2x \cos ax}{a^2} + \frac{a^2x^2 - 2}{a^3} \sin ax$

395. $\displaystyle\int x^3(\cos ax)\,dx = \frac{3a^2x^2 - 6}{a^4} \cos ax + \frac{a^2x^3 - 6x}{a^3} \sin ax$

396. $\displaystyle\int x^m(\cos ax)\,dx = \begin{cases} \dfrac{x^m \sin ax}{a} - \dfrac{m}{a} \displaystyle\int x^{m-1} \sin ax\,dx \\[2mm] \text{or} \\[2mm] \sin ax \displaystyle\sum_{r=0}^{\left[\frac{m}{2}\right]} (-1)^r \dfrac{m!}{(m-2r)!} \cdot \dfrac{x^{m-2r}}{a^{2r+1}} \\[4mm] + \cos ax \displaystyle\sum_{r=0}^{\left[\frac{m-1}{2}\right]} (-1)^r \dfrac{m!}{(m-2r-1)!} \cdot \dfrac{x^{m-2r-1}}{a^{2r+2}} \end{cases}$

See note integral 392.

397. $\displaystyle\int \frac{\sin ax}{x}\,dx = \sum_{n=0}^{\infty} (-1)^n \frac{(ax)^{2n+1}}{(2n+1)(2n+1)!}$

398. $\displaystyle\int \frac{\cos ax}{x}\,dx = \log x + \sum_{n=1}^{\infty} (-1)^n \frac{(ax)^{2n}}{2n(2n)!}$

399. $\displaystyle\int x(\sin^2 ax)\,dx = \frac{x^2}{4} - \frac{x \sin 2ax}{4a} - \frac{\cos 2ax}{8a^2}$

400. $\displaystyle\int x^2(\sin^2 ax)\,dx = \frac{x^3}{6} - \left(\frac{x^2}{4a} - \frac{1}{8a^3}\right)\sin 2ax - \frac{x \cos 2ax}{4a^2}$

401. $\displaystyle\int x(\sin^3 ax)\,dx = \frac{x \cos 3ax}{12a} - \frac{\sin 3ax}{36a^2} - \frac{3x \cos ax}{4a} + \frac{3 \sin ax}{4a^2}$

402. $\displaystyle\int x(\cos^2 ax)\,dx = \frac{x^2}{4} + \frac{x \sin 2ax}{4a} + \frac{\cos 2ax}{8a^2}$

403. $\displaystyle\int x^2(\cos^2 ax)\,dx = \frac{x^3}{6} + \left(\frac{x^2}{4a} - \frac{1}{8a^3}\right)\sin 2ax + \frac{x \cos 2ax}{4a^2}$

404. $\displaystyle\int x(\cos^3 ax)\,dx = \frac{x \sin 3ax}{12a} + \frac{\cos 3ax}{36a^2} + \frac{3x \sin ax}{4a} + \frac{3 \cos ax}{4a^2}$

405. $\displaystyle\int \frac{\sin ax}{x^m}\,dx = -\frac{\sin ax}{(m-1)x^{m-1}} + \frac{a}{m-1}\int \frac{\cos ax}{x^{m-1}}\,dx$

406. $\displaystyle\int \frac{\cos ax}{x^m}\,dx = -\frac{\cos ax}{(m-1)x^{m-1}} - \frac{a}{m-1}\int \frac{\sin ax}{x^{m-1}}\,dx$

407. $\displaystyle\int \frac{x}{1 \pm \sin ax}\,dx = \mp \frac{x \cos ax}{a(1 \pm \sin ax)} + \frac{1}{a^2}\log(1 \pm \sin ax)$

408. $\displaystyle\int \frac{x}{1 + \cos ax}\,dx = \frac{x}{a}\tan\frac{ax}{2} + \frac{2}{a^2}\log\cos\frac{ax}{2}$

409. $\displaystyle\int \frac{x}{1 - \cos ax}\,dx = -\frac{x}{a}\cot\frac{ax}{2} + \frac{2}{a^2}\log\sin\frac{ax}{2}$

410. $\displaystyle\int \frac{x + \sin x}{1 + \cos x}\,dx = x \tan\frac{x}{2}$

411. $\displaystyle\int \frac{x - \sin x}{1 - \cos x}\,dx = -x \cot\frac{x}{2}$

412. $\displaystyle\int \sqrt{1 - \cos ax}\,dx = -\frac{2 \sin ax}{a\sqrt{1 - \cos ax}}$

413. $\displaystyle\int \sqrt{1 + \cos ax}\,dx = \frac{2 \sin ax}{a\sqrt{1 + \cos ax}}$

414. $\int \sqrt{1 + \sin x}\, dx = \pm 2\left(\sin\dfrac{x}{2} - \cos\dfrac{x}{2}\right),$

[use $+$ if $(8k - 1)\dfrac{\pi}{2} < x \le (8k + 3)\dfrac{\pi}{2}$, otherwise $-$; k an integer]

415. $\int \sqrt{1 - \sin x}\, dx = \pm 2\left(\sin\dfrac{x}{2} + \cos\dfrac{x}{2}\right),$

[use $+$ if $(8k - 3)\dfrac{\pi}{2} < x \le (8k + 1)\dfrac{\pi}{2}$, otherwise $-$; k an integer]

416. $\int \dfrac{dx}{\sqrt{1 - \cos x}} = \pm \sqrt{2} \log \tan \dfrac{x}{4},$

[use $+$ if $4k\pi < x < (4k + 2)\pi$, otherwise $-$; k an integer]

417. $\int \dfrac{dx}{\sqrt{1 + \cos x}} = \pm \sqrt{2} \log \tan\left(\dfrac{x + \pi}{4}\right),$

[use $+$ if $(4k - 1)\pi < x < (4k + 1)\pi$, otherwise $-$; k an integer]

418. $\int \dfrac{dx}{\sqrt{1 - \sin x}} = \pm \sqrt{2} \log \tan\left(\dfrac{x}{4} - \dfrac{\pi}{8}\right),$

[use $+$ if $(8k + 1)\dfrac{\pi}{2} < x < (8k + 5)\dfrac{\pi}{2}$, otherwise $-$; k an integer]

419. $\int \dfrac{dx}{\sqrt{1 + \sin x}} = \pm \sqrt{2} \log \tan\left(\dfrac{x}{4} + \dfrac{\pi}{8}\right),$

[use $+$ if $(8k - 1)\dfrac{\pi}{2} < x < (8k + 3)\dfrac{\pi}{2}$, otherwise $-$; k an integer]

420. $\int (\tan^2 ax)\, dx = \dfrac{1}{a} \tan ax - x$

421. $\int (\tan^3 ax)\, dx = \dfrac{1}{2a} \tan^2 ax + \dfrac{1}{a} \log \cos ax$

422. $\int (\tan^4 ax)\, dx = \dfrac{\tan^3 ax}{3a} - \dfrac{1}{a} \tan x + x$

423. $\int (\tan^n ax)\, dx = \dfrac{\tan^{n-1} ax}{a(n - 1)} - \int (\tan^{n-2} ax)\, dx$

424. $\int (\cot^2 ax)\, dx = -\dfrac{1}{a} \cot ax - x$

425. $\int (\cot^3 ax)\, dx = -\dfrac{1}{2a} \cot^2 ax - \dfrac{1}{a} \log \sin ax$

426. $\int (\cot^4 ax)\, dx = -\dfrac{1}{3a} \cot^3 ax + \dfrac{1}{a} \cot ax + x$

427. $\int (\cot^n ax)\, dx = -\dfrac{\cot^{n-1} ax}{a(n-1)} - \int (\cot^{n-2} ax)\, dx$

428. $\int \dfrac{x}{\sin^2 ax}\, dx = \int x(\csc^2 ax)\, dx = -\dfrac{x \cot ax}{a} + \dfrac{1}{a^2} \log \sin ax$

429. $\int \dfrac{x}{\sin^n ax}\, dx = \int x(\csc^n ax)\, dx = -\dfrac{x \cos ax}{a(n-1)\sin^{n-1} ax}$

$$-\dfrac{1}{a^2(n-1)(n-2)\sin^{n-2} ax} + \dfrac{(n-2)}{(n-1)} \int \dfrac{x}{\sin^{n-2} ax}\, dx$$

430. $\int \dfrac{x}{\cos^2 ax}\, dx = \int x(\sec^2 ax)\, dx = \dfrac{1}{a} x \tan ax + \dfrac{1}{a^2} \log \cos ax$

431. $\int \dfrac{x}{\cos^n ax}\, dx = \int x(\sec^n ax)\, dx = \dfrac{x \sin ax}{a(n-1)\cos^{n-1} ax}$

$$-\dfrac{1}{a^2(n-1)(n-2)\cos^{n-2} ax} + \dfrac{n-2}{n-1} \int \dfrac{x}{\cos^{n-2} ax}\, dx$$

432. $\int \dfrac{\sin ax}{\sqrt{1 + b^2 \sin^2 ax}}\, dx = -\dfrac{1}{ab} \sin^{-1} \dfrac{b \cos ax}{\sqrt{1 + b^2}}$

433. $\int \dfrac{\sin ax}{\sqrt{1 - b^2 \sin^2 ax}}\, dx = -\dfrac{1}{ab} \log (b \cos ax + \sqrt{1 - b^2 \sin^2 ax})$

434. $\int (\sin ax)\sqrt{1 + b^2 \sin^2 ax}\, dx = -\dfrac{\cos ax}{2a} \sqrt{1 + b^2 \sin^2 ax}$

$$-\dfrac{1 + b^2}{2ab} \sin^{-1} \dfrac{b \cos ax}{\sqrt{1 + b^2}}$$

435. $\int (\sin ax)\sqrt{1 - b^2 \sin^2 ax}\, dx = -\dfrac{\cos ax}{2a} \sqrt{1 - b^2 \sin^2 ax}$

$$-\dfrac{1 - b^2}{2ab} \log (b \cos ax + \sqrt{1 - b^2 \sin^2 ax})$$

436. $\int \dfrac{\cos ax}{\sqrt{1 + b^2 \sin^2 ax}}\, dx = \dfrac{1}{ab} \log (b \sin ax + \sqrt{1 + b^2 \sin^2 ax})$

437. $\int \dfrac{\cos ax}{\sqrt{1 - b^2 \sin^2 ax}}\, dx = \dfrac{1}{ab} \sin^{-1} (b \sin ax)$

438. $\int (\cos ax)\sqrt{1 + b^2 \sin^2 ax}\, dx = \dfrac{\sin ax}{2a} \sqrt{1 + b^2 \sin^2 ax}$

$$+\dfrac{1}{2ab} \log (b \sin ax + \sqrt{1 + b^2 \sin^2 ax})$$

439. $\int (\cos ax)\sqrt{1 - b^2 \sin^2 ax}\, dx = \dfrac{\sin ax}{2a}\sqrt{1 - b^2 \sin^2 ax} + \dfrac{1}{2ab}\sin^{-1}(b \sin ax)$

440. $\int \dfrac{dx}{\sqrt{a + b \tan^2 cx}} = \dfrac{\pm 1}{c\sqrt{a - b}}\sin^{-1}\left(\sqrt{\dfrac{a - b}{a}}\sin cx\right), \qquad (a > |b|)$

$\left[\text{use} + \text{ if } (2k - 1)\dfrac{\pi}{2} < x \le (2k + 1)\dfrac{\pi}{2}, \text{ otherwise} -; k \text{ an integer}\right]$

FORMS INVOLVING INVERSE TRIGONOMETRIC FUNCTIONS

441. $\int (\sin^{-1} ax)\, dx = x \sin^{-1} ax + \dfrac{\sqrt{1 - a^2 x^2}}{a}$

442. $\int (\cos^{-1} ax)\, dx = x \cos^{-1} ax - \dfrac{\sqrt{1 - a^2 x^2}}{a}$

443. $\int (\tan^{-1} ax)\, dx = x \tan^{-1} ax - \dfrac{1}{2a}\log(1 + a^2 x^2)$

444. $\int (\cot^{-1} ax)\, dx = x \cot^{-1} ax + \dfrac{1}{2a}\log(1 + a^2 x^2)$

445. $\int (\sec^{-1} ax)\, dx = x \sec^{-1} ax - \dfrac{1}{a}\log(ax + \sqrt{a^2 x^2 - 1})$

446. $\int (\csc^{-1} ax)\, dx = x \csc^{-1} ax + \dfrac{1}{a}\log(ax + \sqrt{a^2 x^2 - 1})$

447. $\int \left(\sin^{-1}\dfrac{x}{a}\right) dx = x \sin^{-1}\dfrac{x}{a} + \sqrt{a^2 - x^2}, \qquad (a > 0)$

448. $\int \left(\cos^{-1}\dfrac{x}{a}\right) dx = x \cos^{-1}\dfrac{x}{a} - \sqrt{a^2 - x^2}, \qquad (a > 0)$

449. $\int \left(\tan^{-1}\dfrac{x}{a}\right) dx = x \tan^{-1}\dfrac{x}{u} - \dfrac{a}{2}\log(a^2 + x^2)$

450. $\int \left(\cot^{-1}\dfrac{x}{a}\right) dx = x \cot^{-1}\dfrac{x}{a} + \dfrac{a}{2}\log(a^2 + x^2)$

451. $\int x[\sin^{-1}(ax)]\, dx = \dfrac{1}{4a^2}[(2a^2 x^2 - 1)\sin^{-1}(ax) + ax\sqrt{1 - a^2 x^2}]$

452. $\int x[\cos^{-1}(ax)]\, dx = \dfrac{1}{4a^2}[(2a^2 x^2 - 1)\cos^{-1}(ax) - ax\sqrt{1 - a^2 x^2}]$

453. $\displaystyle\int x^n[\sin^{-1}(ax)]\,dx = \frac{x^{n+1}}{n+1}\sin^{-1}(ax) - \frac{a}{n+1}\int\frac{x^{n+1}\,dx}{\sqrt{1-a^2x^2}}, \qquad (n \neq -1)$

454. $\displaystyle\int x^n[\cos^{-1}(ax)]\,dx = \frac{x^{n+1}}{n+1}\cos^{-1}(ax) + \frac{a}{n+1}\int\frac{x^{n+1}\,dx}{\sqrt{1-a^2x^2}}, \qquad (n \neq -1)$

455. $\displaystyle\int x(\tan^{-1}ax)\,dx = \frac{1+a^2x^2}{2a^2}\tan^{-1}ax - \frac{x}{2a}$

456. $\displaystyle\int x^n(\tan^{-1}ax)\,dx = \frac{x^{n+1}}{n+1}\tan^{-1}ax - \frac{a}{n+1}\int\frac{x^{n+1}}{1+a^2x^2}\,dx$

457. $\displaystyle\int x(\cot^{-1}ax)\,dx = \frac{1+a^2x^2}{2a^2}\cot^{-1}ax + \frac{x}{2a}$

458. $\displaystyle\int x^n(\cot^{-1}ax)\,dx = \frac{x^{n+1}}{n+1}\cot^{-1}ax + \frac{a}{n+1}\int\frac{x^{n+1}}{1+a^2x^2}\,dx$

459. $\displaystyle\int\frac{\sin^{-1}(ax)}{x^2}\,dx = a\log\left(\frac{1-\sqrt{1-a^2x^2}}{x}\right) - \frac{\sin^{-1}(ax)}{x}$

460. $\displaystyle\int\frac{\cos^{-1}(ax)\,dx}{x^2} = -\frac{1}{x}\cos^{-1}(ax) + a\log\frac{1+\sqrt{1-a^2x^2}}{x}$

461. $\displaystyle\int\frac{\tan^{-1}(ax)\,dx}{x^2} = -\frac{1}{x}\tan^{-1}(ax) - \frac{a}{2}\log\frac{1+a^2x^2}{x^2}$

462. $\displaystyle\int\frac{\cot^{-1}ax}{x^2}\,dx = -\frac{1}{x}\cot^{-1}ax - \frac{a}{2}\log\frac{x^2}{a^2x^2+1}$

463. $\displaystyle\int(\sin^{-1}ax)^2\,dx = x(\sin^{-1}ax)^2 - 2x + \frac{2\sqrt{1-a^2x^2}}{a}\sin^{-1}ax$

464. $\displaystyle\int(\cos^{-1}ax)^2\,dx = x(\cos^{-1}ax)^2 - 2x - \frac{2\sqrt{1-a^2x^2}}{a}\cos^{-1}ax$

465. $\displaystyle\int(\sin^{-1}ax)^n\,dx = \begin{cases} x(\sin^{-1}ax)^n + \dfrac{n\sqrt{1-a^2x^2}}{a}(\sin^{-1}ax)^{n-1} \\ \qquad\qquad\qquad\qquad - n(n-1)\displaystyle\int(\sin^{-1}ax)^{n-2}\,dx \\ \qquad\qquad\text{or} \\ \displaystyle\sum_{r=0}^{\left[\frac{n}{2}\right]}(-1)^r\frac{n!}{(n-2r)!}x(\sin^{-1}ax)^{n-2r} \\ \qquad + \displaystyle\sum_{r=0}^{\left[\frac{n-1}{2}\right]}(-1)^r\frac{n!\sqrt{1-a^2x^2}}{(n-2r-1)!a}(\sin^{-1}ax)^{n-2r-1} \end{cases}$

Note: $[s]$ means greatest integer $\leq s$. Thus $[3.5]$ means 3; $[5] = 5$, $[\tfrac{1}{2}] = 0$.

466. $\displaystyle\int (\cos^{-1} ax)^n \, dx =$
$$
\begin{cases}
x(\cos^{-1} ax)^n - \dfrac{n\sqrt{1 - a^2x^2}}{a}(\cos^{-1} ax)^{n-1} \\[2ex]
\qquad\qquad\qquad\qquad -n(n-1)\displaystyle\int (\cos^{-1} ax)^{n-2}\, dx \\[2ex]
\qquad\qquad \text{or} \\[2ex]
\displaystyle\sum_{r=0}^{\left[\frac{n}{2}\right]} (-1)^r \dfrac{n!}{(n-2r)!} x(\cos^{-1} ax)^{n-2r} \\[2ex]
\qquad - \displaystyle\sum_{r=0}^{\left[\frac{n-1}{2}\right]} (-1)^r \dfrac{n!\sqrt{1 - a^2x^2}}{(n-2r-1)!\,a}(\cos^{-1} ax)^{n-2r-1}
\end{cases}
$$

467. $\displaystyle\int \frac{1}{\sqrt{1 - a^2x^2}}(\sin^{-1} ax)\, dx = \frac{1}{2a}(\sin^{-1} ax)^2$

468. $\displaystyle\int \frac{x^n}{\sqrt{1 - a^2x^2}}(\sin^{-1} ax)\, dx = -\frac{x^{n-1}}{na^2}\sqrt{1 - a^2x^2}\,\sin^{-1} ax + \frac{x^n}{n^2a}$
$$
+ \frac{n-1}{na^2}\int \frac{x^{n-2}}{\sqrt{1 - a^2x^2}}\sin^{-1} ax\, dx
$$

469. $\displaystyle\int \frac{1}{\sqrt{1 - a^2x^2}}(\cos^{-1} ax)\, dx = -\frac{1}{2a}(\cos^{-1} ax)^2$

470. $\displaystyle\int \frac{x^n}{\sqrt{1 - a^2x^2}}(\cos^{-1} ax)\, dx = -\frac{x^{n-1}}{na^2}\sqrt{1 - a^2x^2}\,\cos^{-1} ax - \frac{x^n}{n^2a}$
$$
+ \frac{n-1}{na^2}\int \frac{x^{n-2}}{\sqrt{1 - a^2x^2}}\cos^{-1} ax\, dx
$$

471. $\displaystyle\int \frac{\tan^{-1} ax}{a^2x^2 + 1}\, dx = \frac{1}{2a}(\tan^{-1} ax)^2$

472. $\displaystyle\int \frac{\cot^{-1} ax}{a^2x^2 + 1}\, dx = -\frac{1}{2a}(\cot^{-1} ax)^2$

473. $\displaystyle\int x \sec^{-1} ax\, dx = \frac{x^2}{2}\sec^{-1} ax - \frac{1}{2a^2}\sqrt{a^2x^2 - 1}$

474. $\displaystyle\int x^n \sec^{-1} ax\, dx = \frac{x^{n+1}}{n+1}\sec^{-1} ax - \frac{1}{n+1}\int \frac{x^n\, dx}{\sqrt{a^2x^2 - 1}}$

475. $\displaystyle\int \frac{\sec^{-1} ax}{x^2}\, dx = -\frac{\sec^{-1} ax}{x} + \frac{\sqrt{a^2x^2 - 1}}{x}$

476. $\displaystyle\int x \csc^{-1} ax\, dx = \frac{x^2}{2}\csc^{-1} ax + \frac{1}{2a^2}\sqrt{a^2x^2 - 1}$

477. $\displaystyle\int x^n \csc^{-1} ax\, dx = \frac{x^{n+1}}{n+1}\csc^{-1} ax + \frac{1}{n+1}\int \frac{x^n\, dx}{\sqrt{a^2x^2 - 1}}$

478. $\displaystyle\int \frac{\csc^{-1} ax}{x^2}\, dx = -\frac{\csc^{-1} ax}{x} - \frac{\sqrt{a^2 x^2 - 1}}{x}$

FORMS INVOLVING TRIGONOMETRIC SUBSTITUTIONS

479. $\displaystyle\int f(\sin x)\, dx = 2 \int f\left(\frac{2z}{1+z^2}\right) \frac{dz}{1+z^2}, \qquad \left(z = \tan\frac{x}{2}\right)$

480. $\displaystyle\int f(\cos x)\, dx = 2 \int f\left(\frac{1-z^2}{1+z^2}\right) \frac{dz}{1+z^2}, \qquad \left(z = \tan\frac{x}{2}\right)$

*481. $\displaystyle\int f(\sin x)\, dx = \int f(u) \frac{du}{\sqrt{1-u^2}}, \qquad (u = \sin x)$

*482. $\displaystyle\int f(\cos x)\, dx = - \int f(u) \frac{du}{\sqrt{1-u^2}}, \qquad (u = \cos x)$

*483. $\displaystyle\int f(\sin x, \cos x)\, dx = \int f(u, \sqrt{1-u^2}) \frac{du}{\sqrt{1-u^2}}, \qquad (u = \sin x)$

484. $\displaystyle\int f(\sin x, \cos x)\, dx = 2 \int f\left(\frac{2z}{1+z^2}, \frac{1-z^2}{1+z^2}\right) \frac{dz}{1+z^2}, \qquad \left(z = \tan\frac{x}{2}\right)$

LOGARITHMIC FORMS

485. $\displaystyle\int (\log x)\, dx = x \log x - x$

486. $\displaystyle\int x(\log x)\, dx = \frac{x^2}{2} \log x - \frac{x^2}{4}$

487. $\displaystyle\int x^2(\log x)\, dx = \frac{x^3}{3} \log x - \frac{x^3}{9}$

488. $\displaystyle\int x^n(\log ax)\, dx = \frac{x^{n+1}}{n+1} \log ax - \frac{x^{n+1}}{(n+1)^2}$

489. $\displaystyle\int (\log x)^2\, dx = x(\log x)^2 - 2x \log x + 2x$

490. $\displaystyle\int (\log x)^n\, dx = \begin{cases} x(\log x)^n - n \displaystyle\int (\log x)^{n-1}\, dx, & (n \neq -1) \\[2mm] \quad\text{or} \\[2mm] (-1)^n n!\, x \displaystyle\sum_{r=0}^{n} \frac{(-\log x)^r}{r!} \end{cases}$

---

* The square roots appearing in these formulas may be plus or minus, depending on the quadrant of x. Care must be used to give them the proper sign.

491. $\displaystyle\int \frac{(\log x)^n}{x}\, dx = \frac{1}{n+1}(\log x)^{n+1}$

492. $\displaystyle\int \frac{dx}{\log x} = \log(\log x) + \log x + \frac{(\log x)^2}{2 \cdot 2!} + \frac{(\log x)^3}{3 \cdot 3!} + \cdots$

493. $\displaystyle\int \frac{dx}{x \log x} = \log(\log x)$

494. $\displaystyle\int \frac{dx}{x(\log x)^n} = -\frac{1}{(n-1)(\log x)^{n-1}}$

495. $\displaystyle\int \frac{x^m\, dx}{(\log x)^n} = -\frac{x^{m+1}}{(n-1)(\log x)^{n-1}} + \frac{m+1}{n-1}\int \frac{x^m\, dx}{(\log x)^{n-1}}$

496. $\displaystyle\int x^m(\log x)^n\, dx = \begin{cases} \dfrac{x^{m+1}(\log x)^n}{m+1} - \dfrac{n}{m+1}\displaystyle\int x^m(\log x)^{n-1}\, dx \\[4mm] \text{or} \\[2mm] (-1)^n\dfrac{n!}{m+1}x^{m+1}\displaystyle\sum_{r=0}^{n}\dfrac{(-\log x)^r}{r!(m+1)^{n-r}} \end{cases}$

497. $\displaystyle\int \sin(\log x)\, dx = \tfrac{1}{2}x \sin(\log x) - \tfrac{1}{2}x \cos(\log x)$

498. $\displaystyle\int \cos(\log x)\, dx = \tfrac{1}{2}x \sin(\log x) + \tfrac{1}{2}x \cos(\log x)$

499. $\displaystyle\int [\log(ax+b)]\, dx = \frac{ax+b}{a}\log(ax+b) - x$

500. $\displaystyle\int \frac{\log(ax+b)}{x^2}\, dx = \frac{a}{b}\log x - \frac{ax+b}{bx}\log(ax+b)$

501. $\displaystyle\int x^m[\log(ax+b)]\, dx = \frac{1}{m+1}\left[x^{m+1} - \left(-\frac{b}{a}\right)^{m+1}\right]\log(ax+b)$

$$-\frac{1}{m+1}\left(-\frac{b}{a}\right)^{m+1}\sum_{r=1}^{m+1}\frac{1}{r}\left(-\frac{ax}{b}\right)^r$$

502. $\displaystyle\int \frac{\log(ax+b)}{x^m}\, dx = -\frac{1}{m-1}\frac{\log(ax+b)}{x^{m-1}} + \frac{1}{m-1}\left(-\frac{a}{b}\right)^{m-1}\log\frac{ax+b}{x}$

$$+\frac{1}{m-1}\left(-\frac{a}{b}\right)^{m-1}\sum_{r=1}^{m-2}\frac{1}{r}\left(-\frac{b}{ax}\right)^r, \quad (m > 2)$$

503. $\displaystyle\int \left[\log\frac{x+a}{x-a}\right] dx = (x+a)\log(x+a) - (x-a)\log(x-a)$

504. $\displaystyle\int x^m\left[\log\frac{x+a}{x-a}\right] dx = \frac{x^{m+1} - (-a)^{m+1}}{m+1}\log(x+a) - \frac{x^{m+1} - a^{m+1}}{m+1}\log(x-a)$

$$+\frac{2a^{m+1}}{m+1}\sum_{r=1}^{\left[\frac{m+1}{2}\right]}\frac{1}{m-2r+2}\left(\frac{x}{a}\right)^{m-2r+2}$$

505. $\int \dfrac{1}{x^2}\left[\log \dfrac{x+a}{x-a}\right] dx = \dfrac{1}{x}\log \dfrac{x-a}{x+a} - \dfrac{1}{a}\log \dfrac{x^2-a^2}{x^2}$

506. $\int (\log X)\, dx =$
$$
\begin{cases}
\left(x + \dfrac{b}{2c}\right)\log X - 2x + \dfrac{\sqrt{4ac-b^2}}{c}\tan^{-1}\dfrac{2cx+b}{\sqrt{4ac-b^2}}, \\
\hspace{7cm} (b^2 - 4ac < 0) \\[4pt]
\text{or} \\[4pt]
\left(x + \dfrac{b}{2c}\right)\log X - 2x + \dfrac{\sqrt{b^2-4ac}}{c}\tanh^{-1}\dfrac{2cx+b}{\sqrt{b^2-4ac}}, \\
\hspace{7cm} (b^2 - 4ac > 0) \\[4pt]
\text{where} \\[4pt]
X = a + bx + cx^2
\end{cases}
$$

507. $\int x^n(\log X)\, dx = \dfrac{x^{n+1}}{n+1}\log X - \dfrac{2c}{n+1}\int \dfrac{x^{n+2}}{X}\, dx - \dfrac{b}{n+1}\int \dfrac{x^{n+1}}{X}\, dx$

$$\text{where } X = a + bx + cx^2$$

508. $\int [\log (x^2 + a^2)]\, dx = x\log (x^2 + a^2) - 2x + 2a\tan^{-1}\dfrac{x}{a}$

509. $\int [\log (x^2 - a^2)]\, dx = x\log (x^2 - a^2) - 2x + a\log \dfrac{x+a}{x-a}$

510. $\int x[\log (x^2 \pm a^2)]\, dx = \tfrac{1}{2}(x^2 \pm a^2)\log (x^2 \pm a^2) - \tfrac{1}{2}x^2$

511. $\int [\log (x + \sqrt{x^2 \pm a^2})]\, dx = x\log (x + \sqrt{x^2 \pm a^2}) - \sqrt{x^2 \pm a^2}$

512. $\int x[\log (x + \sqrt{x^2 \pm a^2})]\, dx = \left(\dfrac{x^2}{2} \pm \dfrac{a^2}{4}\right)\log (x + \sqrt{x^2 \pm a^2}) - \dfrac{x\sqrt{x^2 \pm a^2}}{4}$

513. $\int x^m[\log (x + \sqrt{x^2 \pm a^2})]\, dx = \dfrac{x^{m+1}}{m+1}\log (x + \sqrt{x^2 \pm a^2})$

$$- \dfrac{1}{m+1}\int \dfrac{x^{m+1}}{\sqrt{x^2 \pm a^2}}\, dx$$

514. $\int \dfrac{\log (x + \sqrt{x^2 + a^2})}{x^2}\, dx = -\dfrac{\log (x + \sqrt{x^2 + a^2})}{x} - \dfrac{1}{a}\log \dfrac{a + \sqrt{x^2 + a^2}}{x}$

515. $\int \dfrac{\log (x + \sqrt{x^2 - a^2})}{x^2}\, dx = -\dfrac{\log (x + \sqrt{x^2 - a^2})}{x} + \dfrac{1}{|a|}\sec^{-1}\dfrac{x}{a}$

516. $\displaystyle\int x^n \log(x^2 - a^2)\, dx = \frac{1}{n+1}\bigg[x^{n+1} \log(x^2 - a^2) - a^{n+1} \log(x - a)$

$$-(-a)^{n+1} \log(x + a) - 2 \sum_{r=0}^{\left[\frac{n}{2}\right]} \frac{a^{2r} x^{n-2r+1}}{n - 2r + 1}\bigg]$$

EXPONENTIAL FORMS

517. $\displaystyle\int e^x\, dx = e^x$

518. $\displaystyle\int e^{-x}\, dx = -e^{-x}$

519. $\displaystyle\int e^{ax}\, dx = \frac{e^{ax}}{a}$

520. $\displaystyle\int x\, e^{ax}\, dx = \frac{e^{ax}}{a^2}(ax - 1)$

521. $\displaystyle\int x^m e^{ax}\, dx = \begin{cases} \dfrac{x^m e^{ax}}{a} - \dfrac{m}{a} \displaystyle\int x^{m-1} e^{ax}\, dx \\[2mm] \qquad\qquad \text{or} \\[2mm] e^{ax} \displaystyle\sum_{r=0}^{m} (-1)^r \dfrac{m!\, x^{m-r}}{(m-r)!\, a^{r+1}} \end{cases}$

522. $\displaystyle\int \frac{e^{ax}\, dx}{x} = \log x + \frac{ax}{1!} + \frac{a^2 x^2}{2 \cdot 2!} + \frac{a^3 x^3}{3 \cdot 3!} + \cdots$

523. $\displaystyle\int \frac{e^{ax}}{x^m}\, dx = -\frac{1}{m-1} \frac{e^{ax}}{x^{m-1}} + \frac{a}{m-1} \int \frac{e^{ax}}{x^{m-1}}\, dx$

524. $\displaystyle\int e^{ax} \log x\, dx = \frac{e^{ax} \log x}{a} - \frac{1}{a} \int \frac{e^{ax}}{x}\, dx$

525. $\displaystyle\int \frac{dx}{1 + e^x} = x - \log(1 + e^x) = \log \frac{e^x}{1 + e^x}$

526. $\displaystyle\int \frac{dx}{a + be^{px}} = \frac{x}{a} - \frac{1}{ap} \log(a + be^{px})$

527. $\displaystyle\int \frac{dx}{ae^{mx} + be^{-mx}} = \frac{1}{m\sqrt{ab}} \tan^{-1}\left(e^{mx} \sqrt{\frac{a}{b}} \right), \qquad (a > 0, b > 0)$

528. $\displaystyle\int \frac{dx}{ae^{mx} - be^{-mx}} = \begin{cases} \dfrac{1}{2m\sqrt{ab}} \log \dfrac{\sqrt{a}\, e^{mx} - \sqrt{b}}{\sqrt{a}\, e^{mx} + \sqrt{b}} \\[3mm] \qquad\qquad \text{or} \\[3mm] \dfrac{-1}{m\sqrt{ab}} \tanh^{-1}\left(\sqrt{\dfrac{a}{b}}\, e^{mx} \right), \qquad (a > 0, b > 0) \end{cases}$

529. $\displaystyle\int (a^x - a^{-x})\, dx = \frac{a^x + a^{-x}}{\log a}$

530. $\displaystyle\int \frac{e^{ax}}{b + ce^{ax}}\, dx = \frac{1}{ac}\log (b + ce^{ax})$

531. $\displaystyle\int \frac{x\, e^{ax}}{(1 + ax)^2}\, dx = \frac{e^{ax}}{a^2(1 + ax)}$

532. $\displaystyle\int x\, e^{-x^2}\, dx = -\tfrac{1}{2}\, e^{-x^2}$

533. $\displaystyle\int e^{ax}\,[\sin (bx)]\, dx = \frac{e^{ax}[a \sin (bx) - b \cos (bx)]}{a^2 + b^2}$

534. $\displaystyle\int e^{ax}\,[\sin (bx)]\,[\sin (cx)]\, dx = \frac{e^{ax}[(b - c) \sin (b - c)x + a \cos (b - c)x]}{2[a^2 + (b - c)^2]}$

$$-\frac{e^{ax}[(b + c) \sin (b + c)x + a \cos (b + c)x]}{2[a^2 + (b + c)^2]}$$

535. $\displaystyle\int e^{ax}[\sin (bx)]\,[\cos (cx)]\, dx = \begin{cases} \dfrac{e^{ax}[a \sin (b - c)x - (b - c) \cos (b - c)x]}{2[a^2 + (b - c)^2]} \\[2ex] \quad + \dfrac{e^{ax}[a \sin (b + c)x - (b + c) \cos (b + c)x]}{2[a^2 + (b + c)^2]} \\[2ex] \qquad\qquad \text{or} \\[1.5ex] \dfrac{e^{ax}}{\rho}[(a \sin bx - b \cos bx)[\cos (cx - \alpha)] \\[1.5ex] \qquad\qquad\qquad - c(\sin bx) \sin (cx - \alpha)] \\[1.5ex] \text{where} \\[1.5ex] \rho = \sqrt{(a^2 + b^2 - c^2)^2 + 4a^2 c^2}, \\[1.5ex] \rho \cos \alpha = a^2 + b^2 - c^2, \qquad \rho \sin \alpha = 2ac \end{cases}$

536. $\displaystyle\int e^{ax}[\sin (bx)]\,[\sin (bx + c)]\, dx$

$$= \frac{e^{ax} \cos c}{2a} - \frac{e^{ax}[a \cos (2bx + c) + 2b \sin (2bx + c)]}{2(a^2 + 4b^2)}$$

537. $\displaystyle\int e^{ax}[\sin (bx)]\,[\cos (bx + c)]\, dx$

$$= \frac{-e^{ax} \sin c}{2a} + \frac{e^{ax}[a \sin (2bx + c) - 2b \cos (2bx + c)]}{2(a^2 + 4b^2)}$$

538. $\displaystyle\int e^{ax}[\cos (bx)]\, dx = \frac{e^{ax}}{a^2 + b^2}[a \cos (bx) + b \sin (bx)]$

539. $\int e^{ax}[\cos(bx)][\cos(cx)]\,dx = \dfrac{e^{ax}[(b-c)\sin(b-c)x + a\cos(b-c)x]}{2[a^2 + (b-c)^2]}$

$$+ \dfrac{e^{ax}[(b+c)\sin(b+c)x + a\cos(b+c)x]}{2[a^2 + (b+c)^2]}$$

540. $\int e^{ax}[\cos(bx)][\cos(bx+c)]\,dx$

$$= \dfrac{e^{ax}\cos c}{2a} + \dfrac{e^{ax}[a\cos(2bx+c) + 2b\sin(2bx+c)]}{2(a^2 + 4b^2)}$$

541. $\int e^{ax}[\cos(bx)][\sin(bx+c)]\,dx$

$$= \dfrac{e^{ax}\sin c}{2a} + \dfrac{e^{ax}[a\sin(2bx+c) - 2b\cos(2bx+c)]}{2(a^2 + 4b^2)}$$

542. $\int e^{ax}[\sin^n bx]\,dx = \dfrac{1}{a^2 + n^2 b^2}\bigg[(a\sin bx - nb\cos bx)e^{ax}\sin^{n-1}bx$

$$+ n(n-1)b^2 \int e^{ax}[\sin^{n-2}bx]\,dx\bigg]$$

543. $\int e^{ax}[\cos^n bx]\,dx = \dfrac{1}{a^2 + n^2 b^2}\bigg[(a\cos bx + nb\sin bx)e^{ax}\cos^{n-1}bx$

$$+ n(n-1)b^2 \int e^{ax}[\cos^{n-2}bx]\,dx\bigg]$$

544. $\int x^m e^x \sin x\,dx = \dfrac{1}{2}x^m e^x(\sin x - \cos x) - \dfrac{m}{2}\int x^{m-1}e^x \sin x\,dx$

$$+ \dfrac{m}{2}\int x^{m-1}e^x \cos x\,dx$$

545. $\int x^m e^{ax}[\sin bx]\,dx = \begin{cases} x^m e^{ax}\dfrac{a\sin bx - b\cos bx}{a^2 + b^2} \\[2mm] \qquad - \dfrac{m}{a^2 + b^2}\int x^{m-1}e^{ax}(a\sin bx - b\cos bx)\,dx \\[2mm] \qquad\qquad \text{or} \\[2mm] e^{ax}\displaystyle\sum_{r=0}^{m}\dfrac{(-1)^r m!\,x^{m-r}}{\rho^{r+1}(m-r)!}\sin[bx - (r+1)\alpha] \\[2mm] \qquad\qquad \text{where} \\[2mm] \rho = \sqrt{a^2 + b^2}, \qquad \rho\cos\alpha = a, \qquad \rho\sin\alpha = b \end{cases}$

546. $\int x^m e^x \cos x\,dx = \dfrac{1}{2}x^m e^x(\sin x + \cos x)$

$$- \dfrac{m}{2}\int x^{m-1}e^x \sin x\,dx - \dfrac{m}{2}\int x^{m-1}e^x \cos x\,dx$$

547. $\int x^m e^{ax} \cos bx \, dx = $
$$\begin{cases} x^m e^{ax} \dfrac{a \cos bx + b \sin bx}{a^2 + b^2} \\[2mm] \qquad\qquad - \dfrac{m}{a^2 + b^2} \int x^{m-1} e^{ax}(a \cos bx + b \sin bx) \, dx \\[2mm] \text{or} \\[2mm] e^{ax} \displaystyle\sum_{r=0}^{m} \dfrac{(-1)^r m! x^{m-r}}{\rho^{r+1}(m-r)!} \cos\left[bx - (r+1)\alpha\right] \\[2mm] \text{where} \\[2mm] \rho = \sqrt{a^2 + b^2}, \qquad \rho \cos \alpha = a, \qquad \rho \sin \alpha = b \end{cases}$$

548. $\int e^{ax}(\cos^m x)(\sin^n x) \, dx = $
$$\begin{cases} \dfrac{e^{ax} \cos^{m-1} x \sin^n x [a \cos x + (m+n)\sin x]}{(m+n)^2 + a^2} \\[2mm] \qquad - \dfrac{na}{(m+n)^2 + a^2} \int e^{ax}(\cos^{m-1} x)(\sin^{n-1} x) \, dx \\[2mm] \qquad + \dfrac{(m-1)(m+n)}{(m+n)^2 + a^2} \int e^{ax}(\cos^{m-2} x)(\sin^n x) \, dx \\[2mm] \text{or} \\[2mm] \dfrac{e^{ax} \cos^m x \sin^{n-1} x [a \sin x - (m+n)\cos x]}{(m+n)^2 + a^2} \\[2mm] \qquad + \dfrac{ma}{(m+n)^2 + a^2} \int e^{ax}(\cos^{m-1} x)(\sin^{n-1} x) \, dx \\[2mm] \qquad + \dfrac{(n-1)(m+n)}{(m+n)^2 + a^2} \int e^{ax}(\cos^m x)(\sin^{n-2} x) \, dx \\[2mm] \text{or} \\[2mm] \dfrac{e^{ax}(\cos^{m-1} x)(\sin^{n-1} x)(a \sin x \cos x + m \sin^2 x - n \cos^2 x)}{(m+n)^2 + a^2} \\[2mm] \qquad + \dfrac{m(m-1)}{(m+n)^2 + a^2} \int e^{ax}(\cos^{m-2} x)(\sin^n x) \, dx \\[2mm] \qquad + \dfrac{n(n-1)}{(m+n)^2 + a^2} \int e^{ax}(\cos^m x)(\sin^{n-2} x) \, dx \\[2mm] \text{or} \\[2mm] \dfrac{e^{ax}(\cos^{m-1} x)(\sin^{n-1} x)(a \cos x \sin x + m \sin^2 x - n \cos^2 x)}{(m+n)^2 + a^2} \\[2mm] \qquad + \dfrac{m(m-1)}{(m+n)^2 + a^2} \int e^{ax}(\cos^{m-2} x)(\sin^{n-2} x) \, dx \\[2mm] \qquad + \dfrac{(n-m)(n+m-1)}{(m+n)^2 + a^2} \int e^{ax}(\cos^m x)(\sin^{n-2} x) \, dx \end{cases}$$

549. $\int x e^{ax}(\sin bx)\,dx = \dfrac{x e^{ax}}{a^2 + b^2}(a \sin bx - b \cos bx)$

$$-\dfrac{e^{ax}}{(a^2 + b^2)^2}[(a^2 - b^2)\sin bx - 2ab \cos bx]$$

550. $\int x e^{ax}(\cos bx)\,dx = \dfrac{x e^{ax}}{a^2 + b^2}(a \cos bx + b \sin bx)$

$$-\dfrac{e^{ax}}{(a^2 + b^2)^2}[(a^2 - b^2)\cos bx + 2ab \sin bx]$$

551. $\int \dfrac{e^{ax}}{\sin^n x}\,dx = -\dfrac{e^{ax}[a \sin x + (n - 2)\cos x]}{(n - 1)(n - 2)\sin^{n-1} x} + \dfrac{a^2 + (n - 2)^2}{(n - 1)(n - 2)}\int \dfrac{e^{ax}}{\sin^{n-2} x}\,dx$

552. $\int \dfrac{e^{ax}}{\cos^n x}\,dx = -\dfrac{e^{ax}[a \cos x - (n - 2)\sin x]}{(n - 1)(n - 2)\cos^{n-1} x} + \dfrac{a^2 + (n - 2)^2}{(n - 1)(n - 2)}\int \dfrac{e^{ax}}{\cos^{n-2} x}\,dx$

553. $\int e^{ax}\tan^n x\,dx = e^{ax}\dfrac{\tan^{n-1} x}{n - 1} - \dfrac{a}{n - 1}\int e^{ax}\tan^{n-1} x\,dx - \int e^{ax}\tan^{n-2} x\,dx$

HYPERBOLIC FORMS

554. $\int (\sinh x)\,dx = \cosh x$

555. $\int (\cosh x)\,dx = \sinh x$

556. $\int (\tanh x)\,dx = \log \cosh x$

557. $\int (\coth x)\,dx = \log \sinh x$

558. $\int (\operatorname{sech} x)\,dx = \tan^{-1}(\sinh x)$

559. $\int \operatorname{csch} x\,dx = \log \tanh\left(\dfrac{x}{2}\right)$

560. $\int x(\sinh x)\,dx = x \cosh x - \sinh x$

561. $\int x^n(\sinh x)\,dx = x^n \cosh x - n \int x^{n-1}(\cosh x)\,dx$

562. $\int x(\cosh x)\,dx = x \sinh x - \cosh x$

563. $\int x^n(\cosh x)\,dx = x^n \sinh x - n \int x^{n-1}(\sinh x)\,dx$

564. $\displaystyle\int (\text{sech } x)(\tanh x)\, dx = -\text{sech } x$

565. $\displaystyle\int (\text{csch } x)(\coth x)\, dx = -\text{csch } x$

566. $\displaystyle\int (\sinh^2 x)\, dx = \frac{\sinh 2x}{4} - \frac{x}{2}$

567. $\displaystyle\int (\sinh^m x)(\cosh^n x)\, dx = \begin{cases} \dfrac{1}{m+n}(\sinh^{m+1} x)(\cosh^{n-1} x) \\[2mm] \qquad + \dfrac{n-1}{m+n}\displaystyle\int (\sinh^m x)(\cosh^{n-2} x)\, dx \\[2mm] \qquad\qquad \text{or} \\[2mm] \dfrac{1}{m+n}\sinh^{m-1} x \cosh^{n+1} x \\[2mm] \qquad - \dfrac{m-1}{m+n}\displaystyle\int (\sinh^{m-2} x)(\cosh^n x)\, dx, \quad (m+n \neq 0) \end{cases}$

568. $\displaystyle\int \frac{dx}{(\sinh^m x)(\cosh^n x)} = \begin{cases} -\dfrac{1}{(m-1)(\sinh^{m-1} x)(\cosh^{n-1} x)} \\[2mm] \qquad - \dfrac{m+n-2}{m-1}\displaystyle\int \dfrac{dx}{(\sinh^{m-2} x)(\cosh^n x)}, \quad (m \neq 1) \\[2mm] \qquad\qquad \text{or} \\[2mm] \dfrac{1}{(n-1)\sinh^{m-1} x \cosh^{n-1} x} \\[2mm] \qquad + \dfrac{m+n-2}{n-1}\displaystyle\int \dfrac{dx}{(\sinh^m x)(\cosh^{n-2} x)}, \quad (n \neq 1) \end{cases}$

569. $\displaystyle\int (\tanh^2 x)\, dx = x - \tanh x$

570. $\displaystyle\int (\tanh^n x)\, dx = -\frac{\tanh^{n-1} x}{n-1} + \int (\tanh^{n-2} x)\, dx, \quad (n \neq 1)$

571. $\displaystyle\int (\text{sech}^2 x)\, dx = \tanh x$

572. $\displaystyle\int (\cosh^2 x)\, dx = \frac{\sinh 2x}{4} + \frac{x}{2}$

573. $\displaystyle\int (\coth^2 x)\, dx = x - \coth x$

574. $\displaystyle\int (\coth^n x)\, dx = -\frac{\coth^{n-1} x}{n-1} + \int \coth^{n-2} x\, dx, \quad (n \neq 1)$

575. $\int (\operatorname{csch}^2 x)\, dx = -\operatorname{ctnh} x$

576. $\int (\sinh mx)(\sinh nx)\, dx = \dfrac{\sinh (m + n)x}{2(m + n)} - \dfrac{\sinh (m - n)x}{2(m - n)},\qquad (m^2 \neq n^2)$

577. $\int (\cosh mx)(\cosh nx)\, dx = \dfrac{\sinh (m + n)x}{2(m + n)} + \dfrac{\sinh (m - n)x}{2(m - n)},\qquad (m^2 \neq n^2)$

578. $\int (\sinh mx)(\cosh nx)\, dx = \dfrac{\cosh (m + n)x}{2(m + n)} + \dfrac{\cosh (m - n)x}{2(m - n)},\qquad (m^2 \neq n^2)$

579. $\int \left(\sinh^{-1} \dfrac{x}{a}\right) dx = x \sinh^{-1} \dfrac{x}{a} - \sqrt{x^2 + a^2},\qquad (a > 0)$

580. $\int x\left(\sinh^{-1} \dfrac{x}{a}\right) dx = \left(\dfrac{x^2}{2} + \dfrac{a^2}{4}\right) \sinh^{-1} \dfrac{x}{a} - \dfrac{x}{4}\sqrt{x^2 + a^2},\qquad (a > 0)$

581. $\int x^n(\sinh^{-1} x)\, dx = \dfrac{x^{n+1}}{n + 1} \sinh^{-1} x - \dfrac{1}{n + 1} \int \dfrac{x^{n+1}}{(1 + x^2)^{\frac{1}{2}}}\, dx,\qquad (n \neq -1)$

582. $\int \left(\cosh^{-1} \dfrac{x}{a}\right) dx = \begin{cases} x \cosh^{-1} \dfrac{x}{a} - \sqrt{x^2 - a^2}, & \left(\cosh^{-1} \dfrac{x}{a} > 0\right) \\[2mm] \qquad\qquad \text{or} \\[2mm] x \cosh^{-1} \dfrac{x}{a} + \sqrt{x^2 - a^2}, & \left(\cosh^{-1} \dfrac{x}{a} < 0\right), \end{cases}\qquad (a > 0)$

583. $\int x\left(\cosh^{-1} \dfrac{x}{a}\right) dx = \dfrac{2x^2 - a^2}{4} \cosh^{-1} \dfrac{x}{a} - \dfrac{x}{4}(x^2 - a^2)^{\frac{1}{2}}$

584. $\int x^n(\cosh^{-1} x)\, dx = \dfrac{x^{n+1}}{n + 1} \cosh^{-1} x - \dfrac{1}{n + 1} \int \dfrac{x^{n+1}}{(x^2 - 1)^{\frac{1}{2}}}\, dx,\qquad (n \neq -1)$

585. $\int \left(\tanh^{-1} \dfrac{x}{a}\right) dx = x \tanh^{-1} \dfrac{x}{a} + \dfrac{a}{2} \log (a^2 - x^2),\qquad \left(\left|\dfrac{x}{a}\right| < 1\right)$

586. $\int \left(\coth^{-1} \dfrac{x}{a}\right) dx = x \coth^{-1} \dfrac{x}{a} + \dfrac{a}{2} \log (x^2 - a^2),\qquad \left(\left|\dfrac{x}{a}\right| > 1\right)$

587. $\int x\left(\tanh^{-1} \dfrac{x}{a}\right) dx = \dfrac{x^2 - a^2}{2} \tanh^{-1} \dfrac{x}{a} + \dfrac{ax}{2},\qquad \left(\left|\dfrac{x}{a}\right| < 1\right)$

588. $\int x^n\left(\tanh^{-1} x\right) dx = \dfrac{x^{n+1}}{n + 1} \tanh^{-1} x - \dfrac{1}{n + 1} \int \dfrac{x^{n+1}}{1 - x^2}\, dx,\qquad (n \neq -1)$

589. $\int x\left(\coth^{-1} \dfrac{x}{a}\right) dx = \dfrac{x^2 - a^2}{2} \coth^{-1} \dfrac{x}{a} + \dfrac{ax}{2},\qquad \left(\left|\dfrac{x}{a}\right| > 1\right)$

590. $\int x^n(\coth^{-1} x)\, dx = \dfrac{x^{n+1}}{n + 1} \coth^{-1} x + \dfrac{1}{n + 1} \int \dfrac{x^{n+1}}{x^2 - 1}\, dx,\qquad (n \neq -1)$

591. $\int (\operatorname{sech}^{-1} x)\, dx = x \operatorname{sech}^{-1} x + \sin^{-1} x$

592. $\int x \operatorname{sech}^{-1} x\, dx = \dfrac{x^2}{2} \operatorname{sech}^{-1} x - \dfrac{1}{2}(1 - x^2)$

593. $\int x^n \operatorname{sech}^{-1} x\, dx = \dfrac{x^{n+1}}{n+1} \operatorname{sech}^{-1} x + \dfrac{1}{n+1} \int \dfrac{x^n}{(1 - x^2)^{\frac{1}{2}}}\, dx,$ $(n \neq -1)$

594. $\int \operatorname{csch}^{-1} x\, dx = x \operatorname{csch}^{-1} x + \dfrac{x}{|x|} \sinh^{-1} x$

595. $\int x \operatorname{csch}^{-1} x\, dx = \dfrac{x^2}{2} \operatorname{csch}^{-1} x + \dfrac{1}{2} \dfrac{x}{|x|} \sqrt{1 + x^2}$

596. $\int x^n \operatorname{csch}^{-1} x\, dx = \dfrac{x^{n+1}}{n+1} \operatorname{csch}^{-1} x + \dfrac{1}{n+1} \dfrac{x}{|x|} \int \dfrac{x^n}{(x^2 + 1)^{\frac{1}{2}}}\, dx,$ $(n \neq -1)$

DEFINITE INTEGRALS

597. $\displaystyle\int_0^\infty x^{n-1} e^{-x}\, dx = \int_0^1 \left(\log \dfrac{1}{x}\right)^{n-1} dx = \dfrac{1}{n} \prod_{m=1}^\infty \dfrac{\left(1 + \dfrac{1}{m}\right)^n}{1 + \dfrac{n}{m}}$

$$= \Gamma(n),\, n \neq 0, -1, -2, -3, \ldots \quad \text{(Gamma Function)}$$

598. $\displaystyle\int_0^\infty t^n p^{-t}\, dt = \dfrac{n!}{(\log p)^{n+1}}, \quad (n = 0, 1, 2, 3, \ldots \text{ and } p > 0)$

599. $\displaystyle\int_0^\infty t^{n-1} e^{-(a+1)t}\, dt = \dfrac{\Gamma(n)}{(a+1)^n}, \quad (n > 0, a > -1)$

600. $\displaystyle\int_0^1 x^m \left(\log \dfrac{1}{x}\right)^n dx = \dfrac{\Gamma(n+1)}{(m+1)^{n+1}}, \quad (m > -1, n > -1)$

601. $\Gamma(n)$ is finite if $n > 0$, $\Gamma(n+1) = n\Gamma(n)$

602. $\Gamma(n) \cdot \Gamma(1 - n) = \dfrac{\pi}{\sin n\pi}$

603. $\Gamma(n) = (n - 1)!$ if $n = $ integer > 0

604. $\Gamma(\tfrac{1}{2}) = 2 \displaystyle\int_0^\infty e^{-t^2}\, dt = \sqrt{\pi} = 1.7724538509 \cdots = (-\tfrac{1}{2})!$

605. $\Gamma(n + \tfrac{1}{2}) = \dfrac{1 \cdot 3 \cdot 5 \ldots (2n - 1)}{2^n} \sqrt{\pi} \quad n = 1, 2, 3, \ldots$

606. $\Gamma(-n + \tfrac{1}{2}) = \dfrac{(-1)^n 2^n \sqrt{\pi}}{1 \cdot 3 \cdot 5 \ldots (2n - 1)} \quad n = 1, 2, 3, \ldots$

607. $\displaystyle\int_0^1 x^{m-1}(1-x)^{n-1}\,dx = \int_0^\infty \frac{x^{m-1}}{(1+x)^{m+n}}\,dx = \frac{\Gamma(m)\Gamma(n)}{\Gamma(m+n)} = B(m,n)$

(Beta function)

608. $B(m,n) = B(n,m) = \dfrac{\Gamma(m)\Gamma(n)}{\Gamma(m+n)}$, where m and n are any positive real numbers.

609. $\displaystyle\int_a^b (x-a)^m(b-x)^n\,dx = (b-a)^{m+n+1}\frac{\Gamma(m+1)\cdot\Gamma(n+1)}{\Gamma(m+n+2)},$

$$(m > -1, n > -1, b > a)$$

610. $\displaystyle\int_1^\infty \frac{dx}{x^m} = \frac{1}{m-1}, \qquad [m > 1]$

611. $\displaystyle\int_0^\infty \frac{dx}{(1+x)x^p} = \pi\csc p\pi, \qquad [p < 1]$

612. $\displaystyle\int_0^\infty \frac{dx}{(1-x)x^p} = -\pi\cot p\pi, \qquad [p < 1]$

613. $\displaystyle\int_0^\infty \frac{x^{p-1}\,dx}{1+x} = \frac{\pi}{\sin p\pi}$

$$- B(p, 1-p) - \Gamma(p)\Gamma(1-p), \qquad [0 < p < 1]$$

614. $\displaystyle\int_0^\infty \frac{x^{m-1}\,dx}{1+x^n} = \frac{\pi}{n\sin\dfrac{m\pi}{n}}, \qquad [0 < m < n]$

615. $\displaystyle\int_0^\infty \frac{x^a\,dx}{(m+x^b)^c} = \frac{m^{\frac{a+1}{b}-c}}{b}\left[\frac{\Gamma\!\left(\dfrac{a+1}{b}\right)\Gamma\!\left(c-\dfrac{a+1}{b}\right)}{\Gamma(c)}\right]$

$$\left(a > -1, b > 0, m > 0, c > \frac{a+1}{b}\right)$$

616. $\displaystyle\int_0^\infty \frac{dx}{(1+x)\sqrt{x}} = \pi$

617. $\displaystyle\int_0^\infty \frac{a\,dx}{a^2+x^2} = \frac{\pi}{2}, \text{ if } a > 0 ; 0, \text{ if } a = 0 ; -\frac{\pi}{2}, \text{ if } a < 0$

618. $\displaystyle\int_0^a (a^2-x^2)^{\frac{n}{2}}\,dx = \frac{1}{2}\int_{-a}^a (a^2-x^2)^{\frac{n}{2}}\,dx = \frac{1\cdot 3\cdot 5\ldots n}{2\cdot 4\cdot 6\ldots(n+1)}\cdot\frac{\pi}{2}\cdot a^{n+1} \qquad (n \text{ odd})$

619. $\displaystyle\int_0^a x^m(a^2-x^2)^{\frac{n}{2}}\,dx = \begin{cases} \dfrac{1}{2}a^{m+n+1}B\!\left(\dfrac{m+1}{2}, \dfrac{n+2}{2}\right) \\[2mm] \text{or} \\[2mm] \dfrac{1}{2}a^{m+n+1}\dfrac{\Gamma\!\left(\dfrac{m+1}{2}\right)\Gamma\!\left(\dfrac{n+2}{2}\right)}{\Gamma\!\left(\dfrac{m+n+3}{2}\right)} \end{cases}$

620. $\int_0^{\pi/2} (\sin^n x)\, dx = \begin{cases} \int_0^{\pi/2} (\cos^n x)\, dx \\[1em] \text{or} \\[1em] \dfrac{1\cdot 3\cdot 5\cdot 7\ldots(n-1)}{2\cdot 4\cdot 6\cdot 8\ldots(n)}\dfrac{\pi}{2}, & (n \text{ an even integer, } n \neq 0) \\[1em] \text{or} \\[1em] \dfrac{2\cdot 4\cdot 6\cdot 8\ldots(n-1)}{1\cdot 3\cdot 5\cdot 7\ldots(n)}, & (n \text{ an odd integer, } n \neq 1) \\[1em] \text{or} \\[1em] \dfrac{\sqrt{\pi}}{2}\dfrac{\Gamma\left(\dfrac{n+1}{2}\right)}{\Gamma\left(\dfrac{n}{2}+1\right)}, & (n > -1) \end{cases}$

621. $\int_0^\infty \dfrac{\sin mx\, dx}{x} = \dfrac{\pi}{2}$, if $m > 0$; 0, if $m = 0$; $-\dfrac{\pi}{2}$, if $m < 0$

622. $\int_0^\infty \dfrac{\cos x\, dx}{x} = \infty$

623. $\int_0^\infty \dfrac{\tan x\, dx}{x} = \dfrac{\pi}{2}$

624. $\int_0^\pi \sin ax \cdot \sin bx\, dx = \int_0^\pi \cos ax \cdot \cos bx\, dx = 0,$ $\quad (a \neq b; a, b \text{ integers})$

625. $\int_0^{\pi/a} [\sin(ax)][\cos(ax)]\, dx = \int_0^\pi [\sin(ax)][\cos(ax)]\, dx = 0$

626. $\int_0^\pi [\sin(ax)][\cos(bx)]\, dx = \dfrac{2a}{a^2 - b^2}$, if $a - b$ is odd, or 0 if $a - b$ is even

627. $\int_0^\infty \dfrac{\sin x \cos mx\, dx}{x}$

$$= 0, \text{ if } m < -1 \text{ or } m > 1; \frac{\pi}{4}, \text{ if } m = \pm 1; \frac{\pi}{2}, \text{ if } m^2 < 1$$

628. $\int_0^\infty \dfrac{\sin ax \sin bx}{x^2}\, dx = \dfrac{\pi a}{2}, \quad (a \leq b)$

629. $\int_0^\pi \sin^2 mx\, dx = \int_0^\pi \cos^2 mx\, dx = \dfrac{\pi}{2}$

630. $\int_0^\infty \dfrac{\sin^2(px)}{x^2}\, dx = \dfrac{\pi p}{2}$

631. $\displaystyle\int_0^\infty \frac{\sin x}{x^p}\,dx = \frac{\pi}{2\Gamma(p)\sin(p\pi/2)}, \qquad 0 < p < 1$

632. $\displaystyle\int_0^\infty \frac{\cos x}{x^p}\,dx = \frac{\pi}{2\Gamma(p)\cos(p\pi/2)}, \qquad 0 < p < 1$

633. $\displaystyle\int_0^\infty \frac{1 - \cos px}{x^2}\,dx = \frac{\pi p}{2}$

634. $\displaystyle\int_0^\infty \frac{\sin px \cos qx}{x}\,dx = \left\{ 0, \quad q > p > 0; \quad \frac{\pi}{2}, \quad p > q > 0; \quad \frac{\pi}{4}, \quad p = q > 0 \right\}$

635. $\displaystyle\int_0^\infty \frac{\cos(mx)}{x^2 + a^2}\,dx = \frac{\pi}{2|a|}e^{-|m\,a|}$

636. $\displaystyle\int_0^\infty \cos(x^2)\,dx = \int_0^\infty \sin(x^2)\,dx = \frac{1}{2}\sqrt{\frac{\pi}{2}}$

637. $\displaystyle\int_0^\infty \sin ax^n\,dx = \frac{1}{na^{1/n}}\Gamma(1/n)\sin\frac{\pi}{2n}, \qquad n > 1$

638. $\displaystyle\int_0^\infty \cos ax^n\,dx = \frac{1}{na^{1/n}}\Gamma(1/n)\cos\frac{\pi}{2n}, \qquad n > 1$

639. $\displaystyle\int_0^\infty \frac{\sin x}{\sqrt{x}}\,dx = \int_0^\infty \frac{\cos x}{\sqrt{x}}\,dx = \sqrt{\frac{\pi}{2}}$

640. $\displaystyle\int_0^\infty \frac{\sin^3 x}{x^2}\,dx = \frac{3}{4}\log 3$

641. $\displaystyle\int_0^\infty \frac{\sin^3 x}{x^3}\,dx = \frac{3\pi}{8}$

642. $\displaystyle\int_0^\infty \frac{\sin^4 x}{x^4}\,dx = \frac{\pi}{3}$

643. $\displaystyle\int_0^{\pi/2} \frac{dx}{1 + a\cos x} = \frac{\cos^{-1}a}{\sqrt{1 - a^2}}, \qquad (a < 1)$

644. $\displaystyle\int_0^\pi \frac{dx}{a + b\cos x} = \frac{\pi}{\sqrt{a^2 - b^2}}, \qquad (a > b \geq 0)$

645. $\displaystyle\int_0^{2\pi} \frac{dx}{1 + a\cos x} = \frac{2\pi}{\sqrt{1 - a^2}}, \qquad (a^2 < 1)$

646. $\displaystyle\int_0^\infty \frac{\cos ax - \cos bx}{x}\,dx = \log\frac{b}{a}$

647. $\displaystyle\int_0^{\pi/2} \frac{dx}{a^2\sin^2 x + b^2\cos^2 x} = \frac{\pi}{2ab}$

648. $\displaystyle\int_0^{\pi/2} \frac{dx}{(a^2 \sin^2 x + b^2 \cos^2 x)^2} = \frac{\pi(a^2 + b^2)}{4a^3 b^3}, \qquad (a, b > 0)$

649. $\displaystyle\int_0^{\pi/2} \sin^{n-1} x \cos^{m-1} x\, dx = \frac{1}{2} \mathrm{B}\left(\frac{n}{2}, \frac{m}{2}\right), \qquad m \text{ and } n \text{ positive integers}$

650. $\displaystyle\int_0^{\pi/2} (\sin^{2n+1} \theta)\, d\theta = \frac{2 \cdot 4 \cdot 6 \ldots (2n)}{1 \cdot 3 \cdot 5 \ldots (2n + 1)}, \qquad (n = 1, 2, 3 \ldots)$

651. $\displaystyle\int_0^{\pi/2} (\sin^{2n} \theta)\, d\theta = \frac{1 \cdot 3 \cdot 5 \ldots (2n - 1)}{2 \cdot 4 \ldots (2n)} \left(\frac{\pi}{2}\right), \qquad (n = 1, 2, 3 \ldots)$

652. $\displaystyle\int_0^{\pi/2} \frac{x}{\sin x}\, dx = 2\left\{\frac{1}{1^2} - \frac{1}{3^2} + \frac{1}{5^2} - \frac{1}{7^2} + \cdots\right\}$

653. $\displaystyle\int_0^{\pi/2} \frac{dx}{1 + \tan^m x} = \frac{\pi}{4}$

654. $\displaystyle\int_0^{\pi/2} \sqrt{\cos \theta}\, d\theta = \frac{(2\pi)^{\frac{3}{2}}}{[\Gamma(\frac{1}{4})]^2}$

655. $\displaystyle\int_0^{\pi/2} (\tan^h \theta)\, d\theta = \frac{\pi}{2 \cos\left(\dfrac{h\pi}{2}\right)}, \qquad (0 < h < 1)$

656. $\displaystyle\int_0^{\infty} \frac{\tan^{-1}(ax) - \tan^{-1}(bx)}{x}\, dx = \frac{\pi}{2} \log \frac{a}{b}, \qquad (a, b > 0)$

657. The area enclosed by a curve defined through the equation $x^{\frac{b}{c}} + y^{\frac{b}{c}} = a^{\frac{b}{c}}$ where $a > 0$, c a positive odd integer and b a positive even integer is given by

$$\frac{\left[\Gamma\left(\dfrac{c}{b}\right)\right]^2}{\Gamma\left(\dfrac{2c}{b}\right)} \left(\frac{2ca^2}{b}\right)$$

658. $\displaystyle I = \iiint_R x^{h-1} y^{m-1} z^{n-1}\, dv$, where R denotes the region of space bounded by

the co-ordinate planes and that portion of the surface $\left(\dfrac{x}{a}\right)^p + \left(\dfrac{y}{b}\right)^q + \left(\dfrac{z}{c}\right)^k = 1$,

which lies in the first octant and where h, m, n, p, q, k, a, b, c, denote positive real numbers is given by

$$\int_0^a x^{h-1}\, dx \int_0^{b\left[1 - \left(\frac{x}{a}\right)^p\right]^{\frac{1}{q}}} y^m\, dy \int_0^{c\left[1 - \left(\frac{x}{a}\right)^p - \left(\frac{y}{b}\right)^q\right]^{\frac{1}{k}}} z^{n-1}\, dz$$

$$= \frac{a^h b^m c^n}{pqk} \frac{\Gamma\left(\dfrac{h}{p}\right) \Gamma\left(\dfrac{m}{q}\right) \Gamma\left(\dfrac{n}{k}\right)}{\Gamma\left(\dfrac{h}{p} + \dfrac{m}{q} + \dfrac{n}{k} + 1\right)}$$

659. $\displaystyle\int_0^\infty e^{-ax}\,dx = \frac{1}{a}$, $\quad (a > 0)$

660. $\displaystyle\int_0^\infty \frac{e^{-ax} - e^{-bx}}{x}\,dx = \log\frac{b}{a}$, $\quad (a, b > 0)$

661. $\displaystyle\int_0^\infty x^n e^{-ax}\,dx = \begin{cases} \dfrac{\Gamma(n+1)}{a^{n+1}}, & (n > -1, a > 0) \\ \qquad\text{or} \\ \dfrac{n!}{a^{n+1}}, & (a > 0, n \text{ positive integer}) \end{cases}$

662. $\displaystyle\int_0^\infty x^n \exp(-ax^p)\,dx = \frac{\Gamma(k)}{pa^k}$, $\quad \left(n > -1, p > 0, a > 0, k = \frac{n+1}{p}\right)$

663. $\displaystyle\int_0^\infty e^{-a^2 x^2}\,dx = \frac{1}{2a}\sqrt{\pi} = \frac{1}{2a}\Gamma\left(\frac{1}{2}\right)$, $\quad (a > 0)$

664. $\displaystyle\int_0^\infty x e^{-x^2}\,dx = \tfrac{1}{2}$

665. $\displaystyle\int_0^\infty x^2 e^{-x^2}\,dx = \frac{\sqrt{\pi}}{4}$

666. $\displaystyle\int_0^\infty x^{2n} e^{-ax^2}\,dx = \frac{1\cdot 3\cdot 5\ldots(2n-1)}{2^{n+1}a^n}\sqrt{\frac{\pi}{a}}$

667. $\displaystyle\int_0^\infty x^{2n+1} e^{-ax^2}\,dx = \frac{n!}{2a^{n+1}}$, $\quad (a > 0)$

668. $\displaystyle\int_0^1 x^m e^{-ax}\,dx = \frac{m!}{a^{m+1}}\left[1 - e^{-a}\sum_{r=0}^m \frac{a^r}{r!}\right]$

669. $\displaystyle\int_0^\infty e^{\left(-x^2 - \frac{a^2}{x^2}\right)}\,dx = \frac{e^{-2a}\sqrt{\pi}}{2}$, $\quad (a \geq 0)$

670. $\displaystyle\int_0^\infty e^{-nx}\sqrt{x}\,dx = \frac{1}{2n}\sqrt{\frac{\pi}{n}}$

671. $\displaystyle\int_0^\infty \frac{e^{-nx}}{\sqrt{x}}\,dx = \sqrt{\frac{\pi}{n}}$

672. $\displaystyle\int_0^\infty e^{-ax}(\cos mx)\,dx = \frac{a}{a^2 + m^2}$, $\quad (a > 0)$

673. $\displaystyle\int_0^\infty e^{-ax}(\sin mx)\,dx = \frac{m}{a^2 + m^2}$, $\quad (a > 0)$

674. $\displaystyle\int_0^\infty x\,e^{-ax}[\sin(bx)]\,dx = \frac{2ab}{(a^2+b^2)^2}, \qquad (a > 0)$

675. $\displaystyle\int_0^\infty x\,e^{-ax}[\cos(bx)]\,dx = \frac{a^2-b^2}{(a^2+b^2)^2}, \qquad (a > 0)$

676. $\displaystyle\int_0^\infty x^n e^{-ax}[\sin(bx)]\,dx = \frac{n![(a+ib)^{n+1} - (a+ib)^{n+1}]}{2i(a^2+b^2)^{n+1}}, \qquad (i^2 = -1, a > 0)$

677. $\displaystyle\int_0^\infty x^n e^{-ax}[\cos(bx)]\,dx = \frac{n![(a-ib)^{n+1} + (a+ib)^{n+1}]}{2(a^2+b^2)^{n+1}}, \qquad (i^2 = -1, a > 0)$

678. $\displaystyle\int_0^\infty \frac{e^{-ax}\sin x}{x}\,dx = \cot^{-1} a, \qquad (a > 0)$

679. $\displaystyle\int_0^\infty e^{-a^2x^2}\cos bx\,dx = \frac{\sqrt{\pi}}{2a}\exp\left(-\frac{b^2}{4a^2}\right), \qquad (ab \neq 0)$

680. $\displaystyle\int_0^\infty e^{-t\cos\phi}\,t^{b-1}\sin(t\sin\phi)\,dt = [\Gamma(b)]\sin(b\phi), \qquad \left(b > 0, -\frac{\pi}{2} < \phi < \frac{\pi}{2}\right)$

681. $\displaystyle\int_0^\infty e^{-t\cos\phi}\,t^{b-1}[\cos(t\sin\phi)]\,dt = [\Gamma(b)]\cos(b\phi), \qquad \left(b > 0, -\frac{\pi}{2} < \phi < \frac{\pi}{2}\right)$

682. $\displaystyle\int_0^\infty t^{b-1}\cos t\,dt = [\Gamma(b)]\cos\left(\frac{b\pi}{2}\right), \qquad (0 < b < 1)$

683. $\displaystyle\int_0^\infty t^{b-1}(\sin t)\,dt = [\Gamma(b)]\sin\left(\frac{b\pi}{2}\right), \qquad (0 < b < 1)$

684. $\displaystyle\int_0^1 (\log x)^n\,dx = (-1)^n \cdot n!$

685. $\displaystyle\int_0^1 \left(\log\frac{1}{x}\right)^{\frac{1}{2}}\,dx = \frac{\sqrt{\pi}}{2}$

686. $\displaystyle\int_0^1 \left(\log\frac{1}{x}\right)^{-\frac{1}{2}}\,dx = \sqrt{\pi}$

687. $\displaystyle\int_0^1 \left(\log\frac{1}{x}\right)^n\,dx = n!$

688. $\displaystyle\int_0^1 x\log(1-x)\,dx = -\tfrac{3}{4}$

689. $\displaystyle\int_0^1 x\log(1+x)\,dx = \tfrac{1}{4}$

690. $\displaystyle\int_0^1 x^m(\log x)^n\,dx = \frac{(-1)^n n!}{(m+1)^{n+1}}, \qquad m > -1, n = 0, 1, 2, \ldots$

If $n \neq 0, 1, 2, \ldots$ replace $n!$ by $\Gamma(n+1)$.

691. $\displaystyle\int_0^1 \frac{\log x}{1 + x}\, dx = -\frac{\pi^2}{12}$

692. $\displaystyle\int_0^1 \frac{\log x}{1 - x}\, dx = -\frac{\pi^2}{6}$

693. $\displaystyle\int_0^1 \frac{\log(1 + x)}{x}\, dx = \frac{\pi^2}{12}$

694. $\displaystyle\int_0^1 \frac{\log(1 - x)}{x}\, dx = -\frac{\pi^2}{6}$

695. $\displaystyle\int_0^1 (\log x)[\log(1 + x)]\, dx = 2 - 2\log 2 - \frac{\pi^2}{12}$

696. $\displaystyle\int_0^1 (\log x)[\log(1 - x)]\, dx = 2 - \frac{\pi^2}{6}$

697. $\displaystyle\int_0^1 \frac{\log x}{1 - x^2}\, dx = -\frac{\pi^2}{8}$

698. $\displaystyle\int_0^1 \log\left(\frac{1 + x}{1 - x}\right) \cdot \frac{dx}{x} = \frac{\pi^2}{4}$

699. $\displaystyle\int_0^1 \frac{\log x\, dx}{\sqrt{1 - x^2}} = -\frac{\pi}{2}\log 2$

700. $\displaystyle\int_0^1 x^m \left[\log\left(\frac{1}{x}\right)\right]^n dx = \frac{\Gamma(n + 1)}{(m + 1)^{n+1}}, \qquad \text{if } m + 1 > 0, n + 1 > 0$

701. $\displaystyle\int_0^1 \frac{(x^p - x^q)\, dx}{\log x} = \log\left(\frac{p + 1}{q + 1}\right), \qquad (p + 1 > 0, q + 1 > 0)$

702. $\displaystyle\int_0^1 \frac{dx}{\sqrt{\log\left(\dfrac{1}{x}\right)}} = \sqrt{\pi}$

703. $\displaystyle\int_0^\infty \log\left(\frac{e^x + 1}{e^x - 1}\right) dx = \frac{\pi^2}{4}$

704. $\displaystyle\int_0^{\pi/2} (\log \sin x)\, dx = \int_0^{\pi/2} \log \cos x\, dx = -\frac{\pi}{2}\log 2$

705. $\displaystyle\int_0^{\pi/2} (\log \sec x)\, dx = \int_0^{\pi/2} \log \csc x\, dx = \frac{\pi}{2}\log 2$

706. $\displaystyle\int_0^{\pi} x(\log \sin x)\, dx = -\frac{\pi^2}{2}\log 2$

707. $\displaystyle\int_0^{\pi/2} (\sin x)(\log \sin x)\, dx = \log 2 - 1$

708. $\displaystyle\int_0^{\pi/2} (\log \tan x)\, dx = 0$

709. $\displaystyle\int_0^{\pi} \log\,(a \pm b \cos x)\, dx = \pi \log \left(\frac{a + \sqrt{a^2 - b^2}}{2} \right), \qquad (a \geq b)$

710. $\displaystyle\int_0^{\pi} \log\,(a^2 - 2ab \cos x + b^2)\, dx = \begin{cases} 2\pi \log a, & a \geq b > 0 \\ 2\pi \log b, & b \geq a > 0 \end{cases}$

711. $\displaystyle\int_0^{\infty} \frac{\sin ax}{\sinh bx}\, dx = \frac{\pi}{2b} \tanh \frac{a\pi}{2b}$

712. $\displaystyle\int_0^{\infty} \frac{\cos ax}{\cosh bx}\, dx = \frac{\pi}{2b} \operatorname{sech} \frac{a\pi}{2b}$

713. $\displaystyle\int_0^{\infty} \frac{dx}{\cosh ax} = \frac{\pi}{2a}$

714. $\displaystyle\int_0^{\infty} \frac{x\, dx}{\sinh ax} = \frac{\pi^2}{4a^2}$

715. $\displaystyle\int_0^{\infty} e^{-ax}(\cosh bx)\, dx = \frac{a}{a^2 - b^2}, \qquad (0 \leq |b| < a)$

716. $\displaystyle\int_0^{\infty} e^{-ax}(\sinh bx)\, dx = \frac{b}{a^2 - b^2}, \qquad (0 \leq |b| < a)$

717. $\displaystyle\int_0^{\infty} \frac{\sinh ax}{e^{bx} + 1}\, dx = \frac{\pi}{2b} \csc \frac{a\pi}{b} - \frac{1}{2a}$

718. $\displaystyle\int_0^{\infty} \frac{\sinh ax}{e^{bx} - 1}\, dx = \frac{1}{2a} - \frac{\pi}{2b} \cot \frac{a\pi}{b}$

719. $\displaystyle\int_0^{\pi/2} \frac{dx}{\sqrt{1 - k^2 \sin^2 x}} = \frac{\pi}{2} \left[1 + \left(\frac{1}{2}\right)^2 k^2 + \left(\frac{1 \cdot 3}{2 \cdot 4}\right)^2 k^4 \right.$
$$\left. + \left(\frac{1 \cdot 3 \cdot 5}{2 \cdot 4 \cdot 6}\right)^2 k^6 + \cdots \right], \text{if } k^2 < 1$$

720. $\displaystyle\int_0^{\pi/2} \sqrt{1 - k^2 \sin^2 x}\, dx = \frac{\pi}{2} \left[1 - \left(\frac{1}{2}\right)^2 k^2 - \left(\frac{1 \cdot 3}{2 \cdot 4}\right)^2 \frac{k^4}{3} \right.$
$$\left. - \left(\frac{1 \cdot 3 \cdot 5}{2 \cdot 4 \cdot 6}\right)^2 \frac{k^6}{5} - \cdots \right], \text{if } k^2 < 1$$

721. $\displaystyle\int_0^{\infty} e^{-x} \log x\, dx = -\gamma = -0.5772157\ldots$

722. $\displaystyle\int_0^{\infty} e^{-x^2} \log x\, dx = -\frac{\sqrt{\pi}}{4}(\gamma + 2 \log 2)$

723. $\int_0^\infty \left(\dfrac{1}{1 - e^{-x}} - \dfrac{1}{x} \right) e^{-x}\, dx = \gamma = 0.5772157\ldots$ [Euler's Constant]

724. $\int_0^\infty \dfrac{1}{x} \left(\dfrac{1}{1 + x} - e^{-x} \right) dx = \gamma = 0.5772157\ldots$

FOURIER SERIES

1. If $f(x)$ is a bounded periodic function of period $2L$ (i.e. $f(x+2L)=f(x)$), and satisfies the *Dirichlet conditions*:

   a) In any period $f(x)$ is continuous, except possibly for a finite number of jump discontinuities.

   b) In any period $f(x)$ has only a finite number of maxima and minima.

Then $f(x)$ may be represented by the *Fourier series*

$$\frac{a_0}{2} + \sum_{n=1}^{\infty} \left(a_n \cos \frac{n\pi x}{L} + b_n \sin \frac{n\pi x}{L} \right),$$

where a_n and b_n are as determined below. This series will converge to $f(x)$ at every point where $f(x)$ is continuous, and to

$$\frac{f(x^+) + f(x^-)}{2}$$

(i.e. the average of the left-hand and right-hand limits) at every point where $f(x)$ has a jump discontinuity.

$$a_n = \frac{1}{L} \int_{-L}^{L} f(x) \cos \frac{n\pi x}{L} \, dx, \quad n = 0, 1, 2, 3, \ldots;$$

$$b_n = \frac{1}{L} \int_{-L}^{L} f(x) \sin \frac{n\pi x}{L} \, dx, \quad n = 1, 2, 3, \ldots$$

We may also write

$$a_n = \frac{1}{L} \int_{\alpha}^{\alpha+2L} f(x) \cos \frac{n\pi x}{L} \, dx \text{ and } b_n = \frac{1}{L} \int_{\alpha}^{\alpha+2L} f(x) \sin \frac{n\pi x}{L} \, dx,$$

where α is any real number. Thus if $\alpha = 0$,

$$a_n = \frac{1}{L} \int_{0}^{2L} f(x) \cos \frac{n\pi x}{L} \, dx, \quad n = 0, 1, 2, 3, \ldots;$$

$$b_n = \frac{1}{L} \int_{0}^{2L} f(x) \sin \frac{n\pi x}{L} \, dx, \quad n = 1, 2, 3, \ldots$$

2. If in addition to the above restrictions, $f(x)$ is even (i.e. $f(-x) = f(x)$), the Fourier series reduces to

$$\frac{a_0}{2} + \sum_{n=1}^{\infty} a_n \cos \frac{n\pi x}{L}.$$

That is, $b_n = 0$. In this case, a simpler formula for a_n is

$$a_n = \frac{2}{L} \int_{0}^{L} f(x) \cos \frac{n\pi x}{L} \, dx, \quad n = 0, 1, 2, 3, \ldots$$

3. If in addition to the restrictions in (1), $f(x)$ is an odd function (i.e. $f(-x) = -f(x)$), then the Fourier series reduces to

$$\sum_{n=1}^{\infty} b_n \sin \frac{n\pi x}{L}.$$

That is, $a_n = 0$. In this case, a simpler formula for the b_n is

$$b_n = \frac{2}{L} \int_{0}^{L} f(x) \sin \frac{n\pi x}{L} \, dx, \quad n = 1, 2, 3, \ldots$$

4. If in addition to the restrictions in (2) above, $f(x) = -f(L - x)$, then a_n will be 0 for all even values of n, including $n = 0$. Thus in this case, the expansion reduces to

$$\sum_{m=1}^{\infty} a_{2m-1} \cos \frac{(2m - 1) \pi x}{L}.$$

5. If in addition to the restrictions in (3) above, $f(x) = f(L - x)$, then b_n will be 0 for all even values of n. Thus in this case, the expansion reduces to

$$\sum_{m=1}^{\infty} b_{2m-1} \sin \frac{(2m - 1) \pi x}{L}.$$

(The series in (4) and (5) are known as *odd-harmonic series*, since only the odd harmonics appear. Similar rules may be stated for even-harmonic series, but when a series appears in the even-harmonic form, it means that $2L$ has not been taken as the smallest period of $f(x)$. Since any integral multiple of a period is also a period, series obtained in this way will also work, but in general computation is simplified if $2L$ is taken to be the smallest period.)

6. If we write the Euler definitions for $\cos \theta$ and $\sin \theta$, we obtain the complex form of the Fourier Series known either as the "Complex Fourier Series" or the "Exponential Fourier Series" of $f(x)$. It is represented as

$$f(x) = \tfrac{1}{2} \sum_{n=-\infty}^{n=+\infty} c_n e^{i\omega_n x},$$

where

$$c_n = \frac{1}{L} \int_{-L}^{L} f(x) e^{-i\omega_n x} dx, \quad n = 0, \pm 1, \pm 2, \pm 3, \ldots$$

with $\omega_n = \dfrac{n\pi}{L}, \quad n = 0, \pm 1, \pm 2, \ldots$

The set of coefficients $\{c_n\}$ is often referred to as the Fourier spectrum.

7. If both sine and cosine terms are present and if $f(x)$ is of period $2L$ and expandable by a Fourier series, it can be represented as

$$f(x) = \frac{a_0}{2} + \sum_{n=1}^{\infty} c_n \sin\left(\frac{n\pi x}{L} + \phi_n\right), \text{ where } a_n = c_n \sin \phi_n,$$

$$b_n = c_n \cos \phi_n, \quad c_n = \sqrt{a_n^2 + b_n^2}, \quad \phi_n = \arctan\left(\frac{a_n}{b_n}\right)$$

It can also be represented as

$$f(x) = \frac{a_0}{2} + \sum_{n=1}^{\infty} c_n \cos\left(\frac{n\pi x}{L} + \phi_n\right), \text{ where } a_n = c_n \cos \phi_n,$$

$$b_n = -c_n \sin \phi_n, \quad c_n = \sqrt{a_n^2 + b_n^2}, \quad \phi_n = \arctan\left(-\frac{b_n}{a_n}\right)$$

where ϕ_n is chosen so as to make a_n, b_n, and c_n hold.

8. The following table of trigonometric identities should be helpful for developing Fourier Series.

	n	n even	n odd	$n/2$ odd	$n/2$ even
$\sin n\pi$	0	0	0	0	0
$\cos n\pi$	$(-1)^n$	$+1$	-1	$+1$	$+1$
*$\sin \dfrac{n\pi}{2}$		0	$(-1)^{(n-1)/2}$	0	0
*$\cos \dfrac{n\pi}{2}$		$(-1)^{n/2}$	0	-1	$+1$
$\sin \dfrac{n\pi}{4}$		$\dfrac{\sqrt{2}}{2}(-1)^{(n^2+4n+11)/8}$		$(-1)^{(n-2)/4}$	0

*A useful formula for $\sin \dfrac{n\pi}{2}$ and $\cos \dfrac{n\pi}{2}$ is given by

$$\sin \frac{n\pi}{2} = \frac{(i)^{n+1}}{2}[(-1)^n - 1] \text{ and } \cos \frac{n\pi}{2} = \frac{(i)^n}{2}[(-1)^n + 1], \text{ where } i^2 = -1.$$

AUXILIARY FORMULAS FOR FOURIER SERIES

$$1 = \frac{4}{\pi}\left[\sin \frac{\pi x}{k} + \frac{1}{3}\sin \frac{3\pi x}{k} + \frac{1}{5}\sin \frac{5\pi x}{k} + \cdots\right] \qquad [0 < x < k]$$

$$x = \frac{2k}{\pi}\left[\sin \frac{\pi x}{k} - \frac{1}{2}\sin \frac{2\pi x}{k} + \frac{1}{3}\sin \frac{3\pi x}{k} - \cdots\right] \qquad [-k < x < k]$$

$$x = \frac{k}{2} - \frac{4k}{\pi^2}\left[\cos \frac{\pi x}{k} + \frac{1}{3^2}\cos \frac{3\pi x}{k} + \frac{1}{5^2}\cos \frac{5\pi x}{k} + \cdots\right] \qquad [0 < x < k]$$

$$x^2 = \frac{2k^2}{\pi^3}\left[\left(\frac{\pi^2}{1} - \frac{4}{1}\right)\sin \frac{\pi x}{k} - \frac{\pi^2}{2}\sin \frac{2\pi x}{k} + \left(\frac{\pi^2}{3} - \frac{4}{3^3}\right)\sin \frac{3\pi x}{k}\right.$$

$$\left. - \frac{\pi^2}{4}\sin \frac{4\pi x}{k} + \left(\frac{\pi^2}{5} - \frac{4}{5^3}\right)\sin \frac{5\pi x}{k} + \cdots\right] [0 < x < k]$$

$$x^2 = \frac{k^2}{3} - \frac{4k^2}{\pi^2}\left[\cos \frac{\pi x}{k} - \frac{1}{2^2}\cos \frac{2\pi x}{k} + \frac{1}{3^2}\cos \frac{3\pi x}{k} - \frac{1}{4^2}\cos \frac{4\pi x}{k} + \cdots\right]$$

$$[-k < x < k]$$

$$1 - \frac{1}{3} + \frac{1}{5} - \frac{1}{7} + \cdots = \frac{\pi}{4}$$

$$1 + \frac{1}{2^2} + \frac{1}{3^2} + \frac{1}{4^2} + \cdots = \frac{\pi^2}{6}$$

$$1 - \frac{1}{2^2} + \frac{1}{3^2} - \frac{1}{4^2} + \cdots = \frac{\pi^2}{12}$$

$$1 + \frac{1}{3^2} + \frac{1}{5^2} + \frac{1}{7^2} + \cdots = \frac{\pi^2}{8}$$

$$\frac{1}{2^2} + \frac{1}{4^2} + \frac{1}{6^2} + \frac{1}{8^2} + \cdots = \frac{\pi^2}{24}$$

DIFFERENTIAL EQUATIONS

SPECIAL FORMULAS

Certain types of differential equations occur sufficiently often to justify the use of formulas for the corresponding particular solutions. The following set of tables I to XIV covers all first, second and nth order ordinary linear differential equations with constant coefficients for which the right members are of the form $P(x)e^{rx}\sin sx$ or $P(x)e^{rx}\cos sx$, where r and s are constants and $P(x)$ is a polynomial of degree n.

When the right member of a reducible linear partial differential equation with constant coefficients is not zero, particular solutions for certain types of right members are contained in tables XV to XXI. In these tables both F and P are used to denote polynomials, and it is assumed that no denominator is zero. In any formula the roles of x and y may be reversed throughout, changing a formula in which x dominates to one in which y dominates. Tables XIX, XX, XXI are applicable whether the equations are reducible or not. The symbol $\binom{m}{n}$ stands for $\dfrac{m!}{(m-n)!n!}$ and is the $n+1$ st coefficient in the expansion of $(a+b)^m$. Also $0! = 1$ by definition.

The tables as herewith given are those contained in the text *Differential Equations* by Ginn and Company (1955) and are published with their kind permission and that of the author, Professor Frederick H. Steen.

Solution of Linear Differential Equations with Constant Coefficients

Any linear differential equation with constant coefficients may be written in the form

$$p(D)y = R(x),$$

where D is the differential operation

$$Dy = \frac{dy}{dx},$$

$p(D)$ is a polynomial in D,
y is the dependent variable,
x is the independent variable,
$R(x)$ is an arbitrary function of x.

A power of D represents repeated differentiation, that is

$$D^n y = \frac{d^n y}{dx^n}.$$

For such an equation, the general solution may be written in the form

$$y = y_c + y_p,$$

where y_p is any particular solution, and y_c is called the *complementary function*. This complementary function is defined as the general solution of the *homogeneous equation*, which is the original differential equation with the right side replaced by zero, i.e.

$$p(D)y = 0$$

The complementary function y_c may be determined as follows:

1. Factor the polynomial $p(D)$ into real and complex linear factors, just as if D were a variable instead of an operator.

2. For each non-repeated linear factor of the form $(D - a)$, where a is real, write down a term of the form

$$ce^{ax},$$

where c is an arbitrary constant.

3. For each repeated real linear factor of the form $(D - a)^n$, write down n terms of the form

$$c_1e^{ax} + c_2xe^{ax} + c_3x^2e^{ax} + \cdots + c_nx^{n-1}e^{ax},$$

where the c_i's are arbitrary constants.

4. For each non-repeated conjugate complex pair of factors of the form $(D - a + ib)(D - a - ib)$, write down 2 terms of the form

$$c_1e^{ax}\cos bx + c_2e^{ax}\sin bx$$

5. For each repeated conjugate complex pair of factors of the form $(D - a + ib)^n(D - a - ib)^n$, write down $2n$ terms of the form

$$c_1e^{ax}\cos bx + c_2e^{ax}\sin bx + c_3xe^{ax}\cos bx + c_4xe^{ax}\sin bx + \cdots$$
$$+ c_{2n-1}x^{n-1}e^{ax}\cos bx + c_{2n}x^{n-1}e^{ax}\sin bx$$

6. The sum of all the terms thus written down is the complementary function y_c.

To find the particular solution y_p, use the following tables, as shown in the examples. For cases not shown in the tables, there are various methods of finding y_p. The most general method is called *variation of parameters*. The following example illustrates the method:

Find y_p for $(D^2 - 4)y = e^x$.

This example can be solved most easily by use of equation 63 in the tables following. However it is given here as an example of the method of variation of parameters.

The complementary function is

$$y_c = c_1e^{2x} + c_2e^{-2x}$$

To find y_p, replace the constants in the complementary function with unknown functions,

$$y_p = ue^{2x} + ve^{-2x}.$$

We now prepare to substitute this assumed solution into the original equation. We begin by taking all the necessary derivatives:

$$y_p = ue^{2x} + ve^{-2x}$$
$$y_p' = 2ue^{2x} - 2ve^{-2x} + u'e^{2x} + v'e^{-2x}$$

For each derivative of y_p except the highest, we set the sum of all the terms containing u' and v' to 0. Thus the above equation becomes

$$u'e^{2x} + v'e^{-2x} = 0 \quad \text{and} \quad y_p' = 2ue^{2x} - 2ve^{-2x}$$

Continuing to differentiate, we have

$$y_p'' = 4ue^{2x} + 4ve^{-2x} + 2u'e^{2x} - 2v'e^{-2x}$$

When we substitute into the original equation, all the terms not containing u' or v' cancel out. This is a consequence of the method by which y_p was set up.

Thus all that is necessary is to write down the terms containing u' or v' in the highest order derivative of y_p, multiply by the constant coefficient of the highest power of D in $p(D)$, and set it equal to $R(x)$. Together with the previous terms in u' and v' which were set equal to 0, this gives us as many linear equations in the first derivatives of the unknown functions as there are unknown functions. The first derivatives may then be solved for by algebra, and the unknown functions found by integration. In the present example, this becomes

$$u'e^{2x} + v'e^{-2x} = 0$$
$$2u'e^{2x} - 2v'e^{-2x} = e^x.$$

We eliminate v' and u' separately, getting

$$4u'e^{2x} = e^x$$
$$4v'e^{-2x} = -e^x.$$

Thus

$$u' = \tfrac{1}{4}e^{-x}$$
$$v' = -\tfrac{1}{4}e^{3x}.$$

Therefore, by integrating

$$u = -\tfrac{1}{4}e^{-x}$$
$$v = -\tfrac{1}{12}e^{3x}.$$

A constant of integration is not needed, since we need only one particular solution. Thus

$$y_p = ue^{2x} + ve^{-2x} = -\tfrac{1}{4}e^{-x}e^{2x} - \tfrac{1}{12}e^{3x}e^{-2x}$$
$$= -\tfrac{1}{4}e^x - \tfrac{1}{12}e^x = -\tfrac{1}{3}e^x,$$

and the general solution is

$$y = y_c + y_p = c_1e^{2x} + c_2e^{-2x} - \tfrac{1}{3}e^x.$$

The following examples illustrate the use of the tables.

Example 1. Solve $(D^2 - 4)y = \sin 3x$.

Substitution of $q = -4, s = 3$ in formula 24 gives

$$y_p = \frac{\sin 3x}{-9 - 4},$$

wherefore the general solution is

$$y = c_1e^{2x} + c_2e^{-2x} - \frac{\sin 3x}{13}.$$

Example 2. Obtain a particular solution of $(D^2 - 4D + 5)y = x^2e^{3x}\sin x$.

Applying formula 40 with $a = 2, b = 1, r = 3, s = 1, P(x) = x^2, s + b = 2, s - b = 0, a - r = -1, (a - r)^2 + (s + b)^2 = 5, (a - r)^2 + (s - b)^2 = 1$, we have

$$y_p = \frac{e^{3x}\sin x}{2}\left[\left(\frac{2}{5} - \frac{0}{1}\right)x^2 + \left(\frac{2(-1)2}{25} - \frac{2(-1)0}{1}\right)2x \right.$$
$$\left. + \left(\frac{3\cdot1\cdot2 - 2^3}{125} - \frac{3\cdot1\cdot0 - 0}{1}\right)2\right]$$
$$- \frac{e^{3x}\cos x}{2}\left[\left(\frac{-1}{5} - \frac{-1}{1}\right)x^2 + \left(\frac{1 - 4}{25} - \frac{1 - 0}{1}\right)2x \right.$$
$$\left. + \left(\frac{-1 - 3(-1)4}{125} - \frac{-1 - 3(-1)0}{1}\right)2\right]$$
$$= (\tfrac{1}{5}x^2 - \tfrac{4}{25}x - \tfrac{2}{125})e^{3x}\sin x + (-\tfrac{2}{5}x^2 + \tfrac{28}{25}x - \tfrac{136}{125})e^{3x}\cos x.$$

The special formulas effect a very considerable saving of time in problems of this type.

Example 3.   Obtain a particular solution of $(D^2 - 4D + 5)y = x^2 e^{2x} \cos x$. (Compare with Example 2.)

Formula 40 is not applicable here since for this equation $r = a$, $s = b$, wherefore the denominator $(a - r)^2 + (s - b)^2 = 0$. We turn instead to formula 44.   Substituting $a = 2, b = 1, P(x) = x^2$ and replacing sin by cos, cos by $-\sin$, we obtain

$$y_p = \frac{e^{2x} \cos x}{4} (x^2 - \tfrac{2}{4}) + \frac{e^{2x} \sin x}{2} \int (x^2 - \tfrac{1}{2})\,dx$$

$$= \left(\frac{x^2}{4} - \frac{1}{8}\right) e^{2x} \cos x + \left(\frac{x^3}{6} - \frac{x}{4}\right) e^{2x} \sin x,$$

which is the required solution.

Example 4.   Find z_p for $(D_x - 3D_y)z = \ln(y + 3x)$.

Referring to Table XV we note that formula 69 (not 68) is applicable. This gives

$$z_p = x \ln(y + 3x).$$

It is easily seen that $-\dfrac{y}{3} \ln(y + 3x)$ would serve equally well.

Example 5.   Solve $(D_x + 2D_y - 4)z = y \cos(y - 2x)$.

Since R in formula 76 contains a polynomial in x, not y, we rewrite the given equation in the form

$$(D_y + \tfrac{1}{2}D_x - 2)z = \tfrac{1}{2} y \cos(y - 2x).$$

Then

$$z_c = e^{2y} F(x - \tfrac{1}{2}y) = e^{2y} f(2x - y),$$

and by the formula

$$z_p = -\tfrac{1}{2} \cos(y - 2x) \cdot \left(\frac{y}{2} + \frac{\frac{1}{2}}{2}\right)$$

$$= -\tfrac{1}{8}(2y + 1) \cos(y - 2x).$$

Example 6.   Find z_p for $(D_x + 4D_y)^3 z = (2x - y)^2$.

Using formula 79, we obtain

$$z_p = \frac{\int\int\int u^2 du^3}{[2 + 4(-1)]^3} = \frac{u^5}{5 \cdot 4 \cdot 3 \cdot (-8)} = -\frac{(2x - y)^5}{480}.$$

Example 7.   Find z_p for $(D_x^3 + 5D_x^2 D_y - 7D_x + 4)z = e^{2x+3y}$.

By formula 87

$$z_p = \frac{e^{2x+3y}}{2^3 + 5 \cdot 2^2 \cdot 3 - 7 \cdot 2 + 4} = \frac{e^{2x+3y}}{58}.$$

Example 8.   Find z_p for

$$(D_x^4 + 6D_x^3 D_y + D_x D_y + D_y^2 + 9)z = \sin(3x + 4y).$$

Since every term in the left member is of *even* degree in the two operators D_x and D_y, formula 90 is applicable.

It gives

$$z_p = \frac{\sin(3x + 4y)}{(-9)^2 + 6(-9)(-12) + (-12) + (-16) + 9}$$

$$= \frac{\sin(3x + 4y)}{710}.$$

TABLE I: $(D-a)y = R$

R	y_p
1. e^{rx}	$\dfrac{e^{rx}}{r-a}$
2. $\sin sx$*	$-\dfrac{a\sin sx + s\cos sx}{a^2+s^2} = -\dfrac{1}{\sqrt{a^2+s^2}}\sin\left(sx+\tan^{-1}\dfrac{s}{a}\right)$
3. $P(x)$	$-\dfrac{1}{a}\left[P(x) + \dfrac{P'(x)}{a} + \dfrac{P''(x)}{a^2} + \cdots + \dfrac{P^{(n)}(x)}{a^n}\right]$
4. $e^{rx}\sin sx$*	Replace a by $a-r$ in formula 2 and multiply by e^{rx}.
5. $P(x)e^{rx}$	Replace a by $a-r$ in formula 3 and multiply by e^{rx}.

6. $P(x)\sin sx$*

$$-\sin sx\left[\dfrac{a}{a^2+s^2}P(x) + \dfrac{a^2-s^2}{(a^2+s^2)^2}P'(x) + \dfrac{a^3-3as^2}{(a^2+s^2)^3}P''(x) + \cdots + \dfrac{a^k - \binom{k}{2}a^{k-2}s^2 + \binom{k}{4}a^{k-4}s^4 - \cdots}{(a^2+s^2)^k}P^{(k-1)}(x) + \cdots\right]$$

$$-\cos sx\left[\dfrac{s}{a^2+s^2}P(x) + \dfrac{2as}{(a^2+s^2)^2}P'(x) + \dfrac{3a^2s-s^3}{(a^2+s^2)^3}P''(x) + \cdots + \dfrac{\binom{k}{1}a^{k-1}s - \binom{k}{3}a^{k-3}s^3 + \cdots}{(a^2+s^2)^k}P^{(k-1)}(x) + \cdots\right]$$

R	y_p
7. $P(x)e^{rx}\sin sx$*	Replace a by $a-r$ in formula 6 and multiply by e^{rx}.
8. e^{ax}	xe^{ax}
9. $e^{ax}\sin sx$*	$-\dfrac{e^{ax}\cos sx}{s}$
10. $P(x)e^{ax}$	$e^{ax}\displaystyle\int P(x)\,dx$

11. $P(x)e^{ax}\sin sx$*

$$\dfrac{e^{ax}\sin sx}{s}\left[P(x) - \dfrac{P''(x)}{s^2} + \dfrac{P^{iv}(x)}{s^4} - \cdots\right] - \dfrac{e^{ax}\cos sx}{s}\left[\dfrac{P'(x)}{s^3} - \dfrac{P'''(x)}{s^3} + \dfrac{P^v(x)}{s^5} - \cdots\right]$$

* For $\cos sx$ in R replace "sin" by "cos" and "cos" by "$-$ sin" in y_p.

$$D^n = \dfrac{d^n}{dx^n} \qquad \binom{m}{n} = \dfrac{m!}{(m-n)!\,n!} \qquad 0! = 1$$

TABLE II: $(D - a)^2 y = R$

R	y_p
12. e^{rx}	$\dfrac{e^{rx}}{(r-a)^2}$
13. $\sin sx$*	$\dfrac{1}{(a^2+s^2)^2}[(a^2-s^2)\sin sx + 2as\cos sx] = \dfrac{1}{a^2+s^2}\sin\left(sx+\tan^{-1}\dfrac{2as}{a^2-s^2}\right)$
14. $P(x)$	$\dfrac{1}{a^2}\left[P(x)+\dfrac{2P'(x)}{a}+\dfrac{3P''(x)}{a^2}+\cdots+\dfrac{(n+1)P^{(n)}(x)}{a^n}\right]$
15. $e^x\sin sx$*	Replace a by $a-r$ in formula 13 and multiply by e^{rx}.
16. $P(x)e^{rx}$	Replace a by $a-r$ in formula 14 and multiply by e^{rx}.

17. $P(x)\sin sx$*

$$\sin sx\left[\dfrac{a^2-s^2}{(a^2+s^2)^2}P(x)+2\dfrac{a^3-3as^2}{(a^2+s^2)^3}P'(x)+3\dfrac{a^4-6a^2s^2+s^4}{(a^2+s^2)^4}P''(x)+\cdots\right.$$
$$\left.+(k-1)\dfrac{a^k-\binom{k}{2}a^{k-2}s^2+\binom{k}{4}a^{k-4}s^4-\cdots}{(a^2+s^2)^k}P^{(k-2)}(x)+\cdots\right]$$
$$+\cos sx\left[\dfrac{2as}{(a^2+s^2)^2}P(x)+2\dfrac{3a^2s-s^3}{(a^2+s^2)^3}P'(x)+3\dfrac{4a^3s-4as^3}{(a^2+s^2)^4}P''(x)+\cdots\right.$$
$$\left.+(k-1)\dfrac{\binom{k}{1}a^{k-1}s-\binom{k}{3}a^{k-3}s^3+\cdots}{(a^2+s^2)^k}P^{(k-2)}(x)+\cdots\right]$$

R	y_p
18. $P(x)e^{rx}\sin sx$*	Replace a by $a-r$ in formula 17 and multiply by e^{rx}.
19. e^{ax}	$\tfrac{1}{2}x^2 e^{ax}$
20. $e^{ax}\sin sx$*	$-\dfrac{e^{ax}\sin sx}{s^2}$
21. $P(x)e^{ax}$	$e^{ax}\displaystyle\iint P(x)\,dx\,dx$

22. $P(x)e^{ax}\sin sx$*

$$-\dfrac{e^{ax}\sin sx}{s^2}\left[P(x)-\dfrac{3P''(x)}{s^2}+\dfrac{5P^{iv}(x)}{s^4}-\dfrac{7P^{vi}(x)}{s^6}+\cdots\right]$$
$$-\dfrac{e^{ax}\cos sx}{s^2}\left[\dfrac{2P'(x)}{s}-\dfrac{4P'''(x)}{s^3}+\dfrac{6P^v(x)}{s^5}-\cdots\right]$$

* For $\cos sx$ in R replace "sin" by "cos" and "cos" by "$-$sin" in y_p.

TABLE III: $(D^2 + q)y = R$

R	y_p
23. e^{rz}	$\dfrac{e^{rz}}{r^2 + q}$
24. $\sin sx$*	$\dfrac{\sin sx}{-s^2 + q}$
25. $P(x)$	$\dfrac{1}{q}\left[P(x) - \dfrac{P''(x)}{q} + \dfrac{P^{iv}(x)}{q^2} - \cdots + (-1)^k\dfrac{P^{(2k)}(x)}{q^k}\cdots\right]$

26. $e^{rz}\sin sx$*

$$\frac{(r^2 - s^2 + q)e^{rz}\sin sx - 2rse^{rz}\cos sx}{(r^2 - s^2 + q)^2 + (2rs)^2} = \frac{e^{rz}}{\sqrt{(r^2-s^2+q)^2+(2rs)^2}}\sin\left[sx - \tan^{-1}\frac{2rs}{r^2 - s^2 + q}\right]$$

27. $P(x)e^{rz}$

$$\frac{e^{rz}}{r^2+q}\left[P(x) - \frac{2r}{r^2+q}P'(x) + \frac{3r^2-q}{(r^2+q)^2}P''(x) - \frac{4r^3 - 4qr}{(r^2+q)^3}P'''(x)\right.$$
$$\left. + \cdots + (-1)^{k-1}\frac{\binom{k}{1}r^{k-1} - \binom{k}{3}r^{k-3}q + \binom{k}{5}r^{k-5}q^2 - \cdots}{(r^2+q)^{k-1}}P^{(k-1)}(x) + \cdots\right]$$

28. $P(x)\sin sx$*

$$\frac{\sin sx}{(-s^2+q)}\left[P(x) - \frac{3s^2+q}{(-s^2+q)^2}P''(x) + \frac{5s^4+10s^2q+q^2}{(-s^2+q)^4}P^{iv}(x) + \cdots\right.$$
$$\left. + (-1)^k\frac{\binom{2k+1}{1}s^{2k} + \binom{2k+1}{3}s^{2k-2}q + \binom{2k+1}{5}s^{2k-4}q^2 + \cdots}{(-s^2+q)^{2k}}P^{(2k)}(x) + \cdots\right]$$
$$- \frac{s\cos sx}{(-s^2+q)}\left[\frac{2P'(x)}{(-s^2+q)} - \frac{4s^2+4q}{(-s^2+q)^3}P'''(x) - \cdots\right.$$
$$\left. + (-1)^{k+1}\frac{\binom{2k}{1}s^{2k-2} + \binom{2k}{3}s^{2k-4}q + \cdots}{(-s^2+q)^{2k-1}}P^{(2k-1)}(x) + \cdots\right]$$

TABLE IV: $(D^2 + b^2)y = R$

R	y_p
29. $\sin bx$*	$-\dfrac{x\cos bx}{2b}$

30. $P(x)\sin bx$*

$$-\frac{\sin bx}{(2b)^2}\left[P(x) - \frac{P''(x)}{(2b)^2} + \frac{P^{iv}(x)}{(2b)^4} - \cdots\right] - \frac{\cos bx}{2b}\int\left[P(x) - \frac{P''(x)}{(2b)^2} + \cdots\right]dx$$

* For cos sx in R replace "sin" by "cos" and "cos" by "− sin" in y_p.

TABLE V: $(D^2 + pD + q)y = R$

R	y_p
31. e^{rz}	$\dfrac{e^{rz}}{r^2 + pr + q}$
32. $\sin sx$*	$\dfrac{(q - s^2)\sin sx - ps\cos sx}{(q - s^2)^2 + (ps)^2} = \dfrac{1}{\sqrt{(q - s^2)^2 + (ps)^2}}\sin\left(sx - \tan^{-1}\dfrac{ps}{q - s^2}\right)$
33. $P(x)$	$\dfrac{1}{q}\left[P(x) - \dfrac{p}{q}P'(x) + \dfrac{p^2 - q}{q^2}P''(x) - \dfrac{p^3 - 2pq}{q^3}P'''(x) + \cdots \right.$ $\left. + (-1)^n\dfrac{p^n - \binom{n-1}{1}p^{n-2}q + \binom{n-2}{2}p^{n-4}q^2 - \cdots}{q^n}\,P^{(n)}(x)\right]$
34. $e^{rz}\sin sx$*	Replace p by $p + 2r$, q by $q + pr + r^2$ in formula 32 and multiply by e^{rz}.
35. $P(x)e^{rz}$	Replace p by $p + 2r$, q by $q + pr + r^2$ in formula 33 and multiply by e^{rz}.

TABLE VI: $(D - b)(D - a)y = R$

R	y_p
36. $P(x)\sin sx$*	$\dfrac{\sin sx}{b - a}\left[\left(\dfrac{a}{a^2 + s^2} - \dfrac{b}{b^2 + s^2}\right)P(x) + \left(\dfrac{a^2 - s^2}{(a^2 + s^2)^2} - \dfrac{b^2 - s^2}{(b^2 + s^2)^2}\right)P'(x)\right.$ $\left. + \left(\dfrac{a^3 - 3as^2}{(a^2 + s^2)^3} - \dfrac{b^3 - 3bs^2}{(b^2 + s^2)^3}\right)P''(x) + \cdots\right]$ $+ \dfrac{\cos sx}{b - a}\left[\left(\dfrac{s}{a^2 + s^2} - \dfrac{s}{b^2 + s^2}\right)P(x) + \left(\dfrac{2as}{(a^2 + s^2)^2} - \dfrac{2bs}{(b^2 + s^2)^2}\right)P'(x)\right.$ $\left. + \left(\dfrac{3a^2s - s^3}{(a^2 + s^2)^3} - \dfrac{3b^2s - s^3}{(b^2 + s^2)^3}\right)P''(x) + \cdots\right]$†
37. $P(x)e^{rz}\sin sx$*	Replace a by $a - r$, b by $b - r$ in formula 36 and multiply by e^{rz}.
38. $P(x)e^{az}$	$\dfrac{e^{az}}{a - b}\left[\displaystyle\iint P(x)\,dx + \dfrac{P(x)}{b - a} + \dfrac{P'(x)}{(b - a)^2} + \dfrac{P''(x)}{(b - a)^3} + \cdots + \dfrac{P^{(n)}(x)}{(b - a)^{n+1}}\right]$

* For $\cos sx$ in R replace "sin" by "cos" and "cos" by "$-$ sin" in y_p.

† For additional terms, compare with formula 6.

TABLE VII: $(D^2 - 2aD + a^2 + b^2)y = R$

R	y_p

39. $P(x) \sin sx^*$

$$\frac{\sin sx}{2b}\left[\left(\frac{s+b}{a^2+(s+b)^2} - \frac{s-b}{a^2+(s-b)^2}\right)P(x) + \left(\frac{2a(s+b)}{[a^2+(s+b)^2]^2} - \frac{2a(s-b)}{[a^2+(s-b)^2]^2}\right)P'(x)\right.$$
$$+ \left(\frac{3a^2(s+b)-(s+b)^3}{[a^2+(s+b)^2]^3} - \frac{3a^2(s-b)-(s-b)^3}{[a^2+(s-b)^2]^3}\right)P''(x) + \cdots\right]$$
$$- \frac{\cos sx}{2b}\left[\left(\frac{a}{a^2+(s+b)^2} - \frac{a}{a^2+(s-b)^2}\right)P(x) + \left(\frac{a^2-(s+b)^2}{[a^2+(s+b)^2]^2} - \frac{a^2-(s-b)^2}{[a^2+(s-b)^2]^2}\right)P'(x)\right.$$
$$+ \left(\frac{a^3-3a(s+b)^2}{[a^2+(s+b)^2]^3} - \frac{a^3-3a(s-b)^2}{[a^2+(s-b)^2]^3}\right)P''(x) + \cdots\right]^\dagger$$

40. $P(x)e^{rx} \sin sx^*$ Replace a by $a - r$ in formula 39 and multiply by e^{rx}.

41. $P(x)e^{ax}$

$$\frac{e^{ax}}{b^2}\left[P(x) - \frac{P''(x)}{b^2} + \frac{P^{iv}(x)}{b^4} - \cdots\right]$$

42. $e^{ax} \sin sx^*$

$$\frac{e^{ax}\sin sx}{-s^2+b^2}$$

43. $e^{ax} \sin bx^*$

$$-\frac{xe^{ax}\cos bx}{2b}$$

44. $P(x)e^{ax} \sin bx^*$

$$\frac{e^{ax}\sin bx}{(2b)^2}\left[P(x) - \frac{P''(x)}{(2b)^2} + \frac{P^{iv}(x)}{(2b)^4} - \cdots\right] - \frac{e^{ax}\cos bx}{2b}\int\left[P(x) - \frac{P''(x)}{(2b)^2} + \frac{P^{iv}(x)}{(2b)^4} - \cdots\right]dx$$

* For $\cos sx$ in R replace "sin" by "cos" and "cos" by "$-$sin" in y_p.

† For additional terms, compare with formula 6.

TABLE VIII: $f(D)y = [D^n + a_{n-1}D^{n-1} + \cdots + a_1 D + a_0]y = R$

R	y_p
45. e^{rx}	$\dfrac{e^{rx}}{f(r)}$
46. $\sin sx^*$	$\dfrac{[a_0 - a_2 s^2 + a_4 s^4 - \cdots]\sin sx - [a_1 s - a_3 s^3 + a_5 s^5 + \cdots]\cos sx}{[a_0 - a_2 s^2 + a_4 s^4 - \cdots]^2 + [a_1 s - a_3 s^3 + a_5 s^5 - \cdots]^2}$

TABLE IX: $f(D^2)y = R$

47. $\sin sx^*$	$\dfrac{\sin sx}{f(-s^2)} = \dfrac{\sin sx}{a_0 - a_2 s^2 + \cdots \pm s^{2n}}$

TABLE X: $(D-a)^n y = R$

48. e^{rx}	$\dfrac{e^{rx}}{(r-a)^n}$
49. $\sin sx^*$	$\dfrac{(-1)^n}{(a^2+s^2)^n}\left\{\left[a^n - \binom{n}{2}a^{n-2}s^2 + \binom{n}{4}a^{n-4}s^4 - \cdots\right]\sin sx + \left[\binom{n}{1}a^{n-1}s - \binom{n}{3}a^{n-3}s^3 + \cdots\right]\cos sx\right\}$
50. $P(x)$	$\dfrac{(-1)^n}{a^n}\left[P(x) + \binom{n}{1}\dfrac{P'(x)}{a} + \binom{n+1}{2}\dfrac{P''(x)}{a^2} + \binom{n+2}{3}\dfrac{P'''(x)}{a^3} + \cdots\right]$
51. $e^{rx}\sin sx^*$	Replace a by $a - r$ in formula 49 and multiply by e^{rx}.
52. $e^{rx}P(x)$	Replace a by $a - r$ in formula 50 and multiply by e^{rx}.

*For $\cos sx$ in R replace "sin" by "cos" and "cos" by "− sin" in y_p.

53. $P(x) \sin sx$*

$(-1)^n \sin sx[A_n P(x) + \binom{n}{1} A_{n+1} P'(x) + \binom{n+1}{2} A_{n+2}P''(x) + \binom{n+2}{3} A_{n+3}P'''(x) + \cdots]$
$+ (-1)^n \cos sx[B_n P(x) + \binom{n}{1} B_{n+1}P'(x) + \binom{n+1}{2} B_{n+2}P''(x) + \binom{n+2}{3} B_{n+3}P'''(x) + \cdots]$

$A_1 = \dfrac{a}{a^2+s^2}, \quad A_2 = \dfrac{a^2-s^2}{(a^2+s^2)^2}, \quad \cdots, \quad A_k = \dfrac{a^k - \binom{k}{2}a^{k-2}s^2 + \binom{k}{4}a^{k-4}s^4 - \cdots}{(a^2+s^2)^k}$

$B_1 = \dfrac{s}{a^2+s^2}, \quad B_2 = \dfrac{2as}{(a^2+s^2)^2}, \quad \cdots, \quad B_k = \dfrac{\binom{k}{1}a^{k-1}s - \binom{k}{3}a^{k-3}s^3 + \cdots}{(a^2+s^2)^k}$

54. $P(x)e^{ax} \sin sx$*   Replace a by $a - r$ in formula 53 and multiply by e^{rx}.

55. $e^{ax}P(x)$ $e^{ax}\displaystyle\int\int \cdots \int P(x)dx^n$

56. $P(x)e^{ax} \sin sx$*

$\dfrac{(-1)^{\frac{n-1}{2}} e^{ax}\sin sx}{s^n}\left[\binom{n}{n-1}\dfrac{P'(x)}{s} - \binom{n+2}{n-1}\dfrac{P'''(x)}{s^3} + \binom{n+4}{n-1}\dfrac{P^{v}(x)}{s^5} - \cdots\right]$
$+ \dfrac{(-1)^{\frac{n+1}{2}} e^{ax}\cos sx}{s^n}\left[\binom{n-1}{n-1}P(x) - \binom{n+1}{n-1}\dfrac{P''(x)}{s^2} + \binom{n+3}{n-1}\dfrac{P^{iv}(x)}{s^4} - \cdots\right]$ (n odd)

$\dfrac{(-1)^{\frac{n}{2}} e^{ax}\sin sx}{s^n}\left[\binom{n-1}{n-1}P(x) - \binom{n+1}{n-1}\dfrac{P''(x)}{s^2} + \binom{n+3}{n-1}\dfrac{P^{iv}(x)}{s^4} - \cdots\right]$
$+ \dfrac{(-1)^{\frac{n}{2}} e^{ax}\cos sx}{s^n}\left[\binom{n}{n-1}\dfrac{P'(x)}{s} - \binom{n+2}{n-1}\dfrac{P'''(x)}{s^3} + \binom{n+4}{n-1}\dfrac{P^{v}(x)}{s^5} - \cdots\right]$ (n even)

TABLE XI: $(D - a)^n f(D)y = R$

57. e^{ax} $\dfrac{x^n}{n!} \cdot \dfrac{e^{ax}}{f(a)}$

* For $\cos sx$ in R replace "sin" by "cos" and "cos" by "− sin" in y_p.

TABLE XII: $(D^2 + q)^n y = R$

R	y_p
58. e^{rx}	$e^{rx}/(r^2 + q)^n$
59. $\sin sx$*	$\sin sx/(q - s^2)^n$
60. $P(x)$	$\dfrac{1}{q^n}\left[P(x) - \binom{n}{1}\dfrac{P''(x)}{q} + \binom{n+1}{2}\dfrac{P^{iv}(x)}{q^2} - \binom{n+2}{3}\dfrac{P^{vi}(x)}{q^3} + \cdots\right]$
61. $e^{rx}\sin sx$*	$\dfrac{e^{rx}}{(A^2 + B^2)^n}\left\{\left[A^n - \binom{n}{2}A^{n-2}B^2 + \binom{n}{4}A^{n-4}B^4 - \cdots\right]\sin sx - \left[\binom{n}{1}A^{n-1}B - \binom{n}{3}A^{n-3}B^3 + \cdots\right]\cos sx\right\}$

$$A = r^2 - s^2 + q, \qquad B = 2rs$$

TABLE XIII: $(D^2 + b^2)^n y = R$

62. $\sin bx$*	$(-1)^{\frac{n+1}{2}}\dfrac{x^n \cos bx}{n!(2b)^n}$ (n odd), $\quad (-1)^{\frac{n}{2}}\dfrac{x^n \sin bx}{n!(2b)^n}$ (n even)

TABLE XIV: $(D^n - q)y = R$

63. e^{rx}	$e^{rx}/(r^n - q)$
64. $P(x)$	$-\dfrac{1}{q}\left[P(x) + \dfrac{P^{(n)}(x)}{q} + \dfrac{P^{(2n)}(x)}{q^2} + \cdots\right]$
65. $\sin sx$*	$-\dfrac{q\sin sx + (-1)^{\frac{n-1}{2}}s^n\cos sx}{q^2 + s^{2n}}$ (n odd), $\quad \dfrac{\sin sx}{(-s^2)^{n/2} - q}$ (n even)
66. $e^{rx}\sin sx$*	$\dfrac{Ae^{rx}\sin sr - Be^{rx}\cos sx}{A^2 + B^2} = \dfrac{e^{rx}}{\sqrt{A^2 + B^2}}\sin\left(sx - \tan^{-1}\dfrac{B}{A}\right)$

$$A = \left[r^n - \binom{n}{2}r^{n-2}s^2 + \binom{n}{4}r^{n-4}s^4 - \cdots\right] - q, \qquad B = \left[\binom{n}{1}r^{n-1}s - \binom{n}{3}r^{n-3}s^3 + \cdots\right]$$

* For cos sx in R replace "sin" by "cos" and "cos" by "− sin" in y_p.

TABLE XV: $(D_x + mD_y)z = R$

R	z_p
67. e^{ax+by}	$\dfrac{e^{ax+by}}{a+mb}$
68. $f(ax+by)$	$\dfrac{\int f(u)du}{a+mb}$, $u = ax + by$
69. $f(y-mx)$	$xf(y-mx)$
70. $\phi(x,y)f(y-mx)$	$f(y-mx)\int \phi(x, a+mx)dx$ $\quad(a = y - mx$ after integration)

TABLE XVI: $(D_x + mD_y - k)z = R$

71. e^{ax+by}	$\dfrac{e^{ax+by}}{a+mb-k}$
72. $\sin(ax+by)$*	$-\dfrac{(a+bm)\cos(ax+by)+k\sin(ax+by)}{(a+bm)^2+k^2}$
73. $e^{\alpha x+\beta y}\sin(ax+by)$*	Replace k in 72 by $k - \alpha - m\beta$ and multiply by $e^{\alpha x+\beta y}$
74. $e^{kx}f(ax+by)$	$\dfrac{e^{kx}\int f(u)du}{a+mb}$, $u = ax + by$
75. $f(y-mx)$	$-\dfrac{f(y-mx)}{k}$
76. $P(x)f(y-mx)$	$-\dfrac{1}{k}f(y-mx)\left[P(x) + \dfrac{P'(x)}{k} + \dfrac{P''(x)}{k^2} + \cdots + \dfrac{P^{(n)}(x)}{k^n}\right]$
77. $e^{kx}f(y-mx)$	$xe^{kx}f(y-mx)$

* For cos $(ax + by)$ replace "sin" by "cos," and "cos" by "$-$sin" in z_p.

$$D_x = \frac{\partial}{\partial x}; \qquad D_y = \frac{\partial}{\partial y}; \qquad D_x{}^k D_y{}^r = \frac{\partial^{k+r}}{\partial_x{}^k \partial_y{}^r}$$

TABLE XVII: $(D_z + mD_y)^n z = R$

R	z_p
78. e^{ax+by}	$\dfrac{e^{ax+by}}{(a+mb)^n}$
79. $f(ax+by)$	$\dfrac{\int\int \cdots \int f(u)du^n}{(a+mb)^n},\ u = ax+by$
80. $f(y-mx)$	$\dfrac{x^n}{n!}f(y-mx)$
81. $\phi(x,y)f(y+mx)$	$f(y-mx)\int\int \cdots \int \phi(x,\ a+mx)dx^n \quad (a = y - mx$ after integration)

TABLE XVIII: $(D_z + mD_y - k)^n z = R$

82. e^{ax+by}	$\dfrac{e^{ax+by}}{(a+mb-k)^n}$
83. $f(y-mx)$	$\dfrac{(-1)^n f(y-mx)}{k^n}$
84. $P(x)f(y-mx)$	$\dfrac{(-1)^n}{k^n}f(y-mx)\left[P(x) + \binom{n}{1}\dfrac{P'(x)}{k} + \binom{n+1}{2}\dfrac{P''(x)}{k^2} + \binom{n+2}{3}\dfrac{P'''(x)}{k^3} + \cdots\right]$
85. $e^{kx}f(ax+by)$	$\dfrac{e^{kx}\int\int\cdots\int f(u)du^n}{(a+mb)^n},\ u = ax + by$
86. $e^{kx}f(y-mx)$	$\dfrac{x^n}{n!}e^{kx}f(y-mx)$

TABLE XIX: $[D_x^n + a_1 D_x^{n-1} D_y + a_2 D_x^{n-2} D_y^2 + \cdots + a^n D_y^n]z = R$

87. e^{ax+by} $\dfrac{e^{ax+by}}{a + a_1 a^{n-1} b + a_2 a^{n-2} b^2 + \cdots + a_n b^n}$

88. $f(ax + by)$ $\dfrac{\int\!\int \cdots \int f(u)du^n}{a^n + a_1 a^{n-1} b + a_2 a^{n-2} b^2 + \cdots + a^n b^n}$, $(u = ax + by)$

TABLE XX: $F(D_x, D_y)z = R$

89. e^{ax+by} $\dfrac{e^{ax+by}}{F(a, b)}$

TABLE XXI: $F(D_x^2, D_x D_y, D_y^2)z = R$

90. $\sin(ax + by)$* $\dfrac{\sin(ax + by)}{F(-a^2, -ab, -b^2)}$

* For $\cos(ax + by)$ replace "sin" by "cos", and "cos" by "−sin", in z_v.

x	$J_0(x)$	$J_1(x)$	x	$J_0(x)$	$J_1(x)$	x	$J_0(x)$	$J_1(x)$
0.0	1.0000	.0000	5.0	−.1776	−.3276	10.0	−.2459	.0435
0.1	.9975	.0499	5.1	−.1443	−.3371	10.1	−.2490	.0184
0.2	.9900	.0995	5.2	−.1103	−.3432	10.2	−.2496	−.0066
0.3	.9776	.1483	5.3	−.0758	−.3460	10.3	−.2477	−.0313
0.4	.9604	.1960	5.4	−.0412	−.3453	10.4	−.2434	−.0555
0.5	.9385	.2423	5.5	−.0068	−.3414	10.5	−.2366	−.0789
0.6	.9120	.2867	5.6	.0270	−.3343	10.6	−.2276	−.1012
0.7	.8812	.3290	5.7	.0599	−.3241	10.7	−.2164	−.1224
0.8	.8463	.3688	5.8	.0917	−.3110	10.8	−.2032	−.1422
0.9	.8075	.4059	5.9	.1220	−.2951	10.9	−.1881	−.1603
1.0	.7652	.4401	6.0	.1506	−.2767	11.0	−.1712	−.1768
1.1	.7196	.4709	6.1	.1773	−.2559	11.1	−.1528	−.1913
1.2	.6711	.4983	6.2	.2017	−.2329	11.2	−.1330	−.2039
1.3	.6201	.5220	6.3	.2238	−.2081	11.3	−.1121	−.2143
1.4	.5669	.5419	6.4	.2433	−.1816	11.4	−.0902	−.2225
1.5	.5118	.5579	6.5	.2601	−.1538	11.5	−.0677	−.2284
1.6	.4554	.5699	6.6	.2740	−.1250	11.6	−.0446	−.2320
1.7	.3980	.5778	6.7	.2851	−.0953	11.7	−.0213	−.2333
1.8	.3400	.5815	6.8	.2931	−.0652	11.8	.0020	−.2323
1.9	.2818	.5812	6.9	.2981	−.0349	11.9	.0250	−.2290
2.0	.2239	.5767	7.0	.3001	−.0047	12.0	.0477	−.2234
2.1	.1666	.5683	7.1	.2991	.0252	12.1	.0697	−.2157
2.2	.1104	.5560	7.2	.2951	.0543	12.2	.0908	−.2060
2.3	.0555	.5399	7.3	.2882	.0826	12.3	.1108	−.1943
2.4	.0025	.5202	7.4	.2786	.1096	12.4	.1296	−.1807
2.5	−.0484	.4971	7.5	.2663	.1352	12.5	.1469	−.1655
2.6	−.0968	.4708	7.6	.2516	.1592	12.6	.1626	−.1487
2.7	−.1424	.4416	7.7	.2346	.1813	12.7	.1766	−.1307
2.8	−.1850	.4097	7.8	.2154	.2014	12.8	.1887	−.1114
2.9	−.2243	.3754	7.9	.1944	.2192	12.9	.1988	−.0912
3.0	−.2601	.3391	8.0	.1717	.2346	13.0	.2069	−.0703
3.1	−.2921	.3009	8.1	.1475	.2476	13.1	.2129	−.0489
3 2	−.3202	.2613	8.2	.1222	.2580	13.2	.2167	−.0271
3.3	−.3443	.2207	8.3	.0960	.2657	13.3	.2183	−.0052
3.4	−.3643	.1792	8.4	.0692	.2708	13.4	.2177	.0166
3.5	−.3801	.1374	8.5	.0419	.2731	13.5	.2150	.0380
3.6	−.3918	.0955	8.6	.0146	.2728	13.6	.2101	.0590
3.7	−.3992	.0538	8.7	−.0125	.2697	13.7	.2032	.0791
3.8	−.4026	.0128	8.8	−.0392	.2641	13.8	.1943	.0984
3.9	−.4018	−.0272	8.9	−.0653	.2559	13.9	.1836	.1165
4.0	−.3971	−.0660	9.0	−.0903	.2453	14.0	.1711	.1334
4.1	−.3887	−.1033	9.1	−.1142	.2324	14.1	.1570	.1488
4.2	−.3766	−.1386	9.2	−.1367	.2174	14.2	.1414	.1626
4.3	−.3610	−.1719	9.3	−.1577	.2004	14.3	.1245	.1747
4.4	−.3423	−.2028	9.4	−.1768	.1816	14.4	.1065	.1850
4.5	−.3205	−.2311	9.5	−.1939	.1613	14.5	.0875	.1934
4.6	−.2961	−.2566	9.6	−.2090	.1395	14.6	.0679	.1999
4.7	−.2693	−.2791	9.7	−.2218	.1166	14.7	.0476	.2043
4.8	−.2404	−.2985	9.8	−.2323	.0928	14.8	.0271	.2066
4.9	−.2097	−.3147	9.9	−.2403	.0684	14.9	.0064	.2069

BESSEL FUNCTIONS FOR SPHERICAL COORDINATES

$$j_n(x) = \sqrt{\frac{\pi}{2x}}\, J_{(n+\frac{1}{2})}(x), \quad y_n(x) = \sqrt{\frac{\pi}{2x}}\, Y_{(n+\frac{1}{2})}(x) = (-1)^{n+1}\sqrt{\frac{\pi}{2x}}\, J_{-(n+\frac{1}{2})}(x)$$

x	$j_0(x)$	$y_0(x)$	$j_1(x)$	$y_1(x)$	$j_2(x)$	$y_2(x)$
0.0	1.0000	$-\infty$	0.0000	$-\infty$	0.0000	$-\infty$
0.1	0.9983	-9.9500	0.0333	-100.50	0.0007	-3005.0
0.2	0.9933	-4.9003	0.0664	-25.495	0.0027	-377.52
0.4	0.9735	-2.3027	0.1312	-6.7302	0.0105	-48.174
0.6	0.9411	-1.3756	0.1929	-3.2337	0.0234	-14.793
0.8	0.8967	-0.8709	0.2500	-1.9853	0.0408	-6.5740
1.0	0.8415	-0.5403	0.3012	-1.3818	0.0620	-3.6050
1.2	0.7767	-0.3020	0.3453	-1.0283	0.0865	-2.2689
1.4	0.7039	-0.1214	0.3814	-0.7906	0.1133	-1.5728
1.6	0.6247	$+0.0182$	0.4087	-0.6133	0.1416	-1.1682
1.8	0.5410	0.1262	0.4268	-0.4709	0.1703	-0.9111
2.0	0.4546	0.2081	0.4354	-0.3506	0.1984	-0.7340
2.2	0.3675	0.2675	0.4345	-0.2459	0.2251	-0.6028
2.4	0.2814	0.3072	0.4245	-0.1534	0.2492	-0.4990
2.6	0.1983	0.3296	0.4058	-0.0715	0.2700	-0.4121
2.8	0.1196	0.3365	0.3792	$+0.0005$	0.2867	-0.3359
3.0	$+0.0470$	0.3300	0.3457	0.0630	0.2986	-0.2670
3.2	-0.0182	0.3120	0.3063	0.1157	0.3054	-0.2035
3.4	-0.0752	0.2844	0.2622	0.1588	0.3066	-0.1442
3.6	-0.1229	0.2491	0.2150	0.1921	0.3021	-0.0890
3.8	-0.1610	0.2081	0.1658	0.2158	0.2919	-0.0378
4.0	-0.1892	0.1634	0.1161	0.2301	0.2763	$+0.0091$
4.2	-0.2075	0.1167	0.0673	0.2353	0.2556	0.0514
4.4	-0.2163	0.0698	$+0.0207$	0.2321	0.2304	0.0884
4.6	-0.2160	$+0.0244$	-0.0226	0.2213	0.2013	0.1200
4.8	-0.2075	-0.0182	-0.0615	0.2037	0.1691	0.1456
5.0	-0.1918	-0.0567	-0.0951	0.1804	0.1347	0.1650
5.2	-0.1698	-0.0901	-0.1228	0.1526	0.0991	0.1781
5.4	-0.1431	-0.1175	-0.1440	0.1213	0.0631	0.1850
5.6	-0.1127	-0.1385	-0.1586	0.0880	$+0.0277$	0.1856
5.8	-0.0801	-0.1527	-0.1665	0.0538	-0.0060	0.1805
6.0	-0.0466	-0.1600	-0.1678	$+0.0199$	-0.0373	0.1700
6.2	-0.0134	-0.1607	-0.1629	-0.0125	-0.0654	0.1547
6.4	$+0.0182$	-0.1552	-0.1523	-0.0425	-0.0896	0.1353
6.6	0.0472	-0.1440	-0.1368	-0.0690	-0.1094	0.1126
6.8	0.0727	-0.1278	-0.1172	-0.0915	-0.1243	0.0875
7.0	0.0939	-0.1077	-0.0943	-0.1092	-0.1343	0.0609
7.2	0.1102	-0.0845	-0.0692	-0.1220	-0.1391	0.0337
7.4	0.1215	-0.0593	-0.0429	-0.1295	-0.1388	$+0.0068$
7.6	0.1274	-0.0331	-0.0163	-0.1317	-0.1338	-0.0189
7.8	0.1280	-0.0069	$+0.0095$	-0.1289	-0.1244	-0.0427
8.0	0.1237	$+0.0182$	0.0336	-0.1214	-0.1111	-0.0637

Taken from Vibration and Sound with the permission of Philip Morse, author, and McGraw-Hill Book Company, Inc., publisher.

HYPERBOLIC BESSEL FUNCTIONS

$$I_m(x) = i^{-m} J_m(ix)$$

x	$I_0(x)$	$I_1(x)$	$I_2(x)$
0.0	1.0000	0.0000	0.0000
0.1	1.0025	0.0501	0.0012
0.2	1.0100	0.1005	0.0050
0.4	1.0404	0.2040	0.0203
0.6	1.0920	0.3137	0.0464
0.8	1.1665	0.4329	0.0844
1.0	1.2661	0.5652	0.1357
1.2	1.3937	0.7147	0.2026
1.4	1.5534	0.8861	0.2875
1.6	1.7500	1.0848	0.3940
1.8	1.9896	1.3172	0.5260
2.0	2.2796	1.5906	0.6889
2.2	2.6291	1.9141	0.8891
2.4	3.0493	2.2981	1.1342
2.6	3.5533	2.7554	1.4337
2.8	4.1573	3.3011	1.7994
3.0	4.8808	3.9534	2.2452
3.2	5.7472	4.7343	2.7883
3.4	6.7848	5.6701	3.4495
3.6	8.0277	6.7927	4.2540
3.8	9.5169	8.1404	5.2325
4.0	11.302	9.7595	6.4222
4.2	13.442	11.70o	7.8684
4.4	16.010	14.046	9.6258
4.6	19.093	16.863	11.761
4.8	22.794	20.253	14.355
5.0	27.240	24.336	17.506
5.2	32.584	29.254	21.332
5.4	39.009	35.182	25.978
5.6	46.738	42.328	31.620
5.8	56.039	50.946	38.470
6.0	67.234	61.342	46.787
6.2	80.718	73.886	56.884
6.4	96.962	89.026	69.141
6.6	116.54	107.30	84.021
6.8	140.14	129.38	102.08
7.0	168.59	156.04	124.01
7.2	202.92	188.25	150.63
7.4	244.34	227.17	182.94
7.6	294.33	274.22	222.17
7.8	354.68	331.10	269.79
8.0	427.56	399.87	327.60

Taken from Vibration and Sound with the permission of Philip Morse, author, and McGraw-Hill Book Company, Inc., publisher.

GAMMA FUNCTION*

Values of $\Gamma(n) = \int_0^\infty e^{-x} x^{n-1} dx$; $\Gamma(n+1) = n\Gamma(n)$

n	$\Gamma(n)$	n	$\Gamma(n)$	n	$\Gamma(n)$	n	$\Gamma(n)$
1.00	1.00000	1.25	.90640	1.50	.88623	1.75	.91906
1.01	.99433	1.26	.90440	1.51	.88659	1.76	.92137
1.02	.98884	1.27	.90250	1.52	.88704	1.77	.92376
1.03	.98355	1.28	.90072	1.53	.88757	1.78	.92623
1.04	.97844	1.29	.89904	1.54	.88818	1.79	.92877
1.05	.97350	1.30	.89747	1.55	.88887	1.80	.93138
1.06	.96874	1.31	.89600	1.56	.88964	1.81	.93408
1.07	.96415	1.32	.89464	1.57	.89049	1.82	.93685
1.08	.95973	1.33	.89338	1.58	.89142	1.83	.93969
1.09	.95546	1.34	.89222	1.59	.89243	1.84	.94261
1.10	.95135	1.35	.89115	1.60	.89352	1.85	.94561
1.11	.94739	1.36	.89018	1.61	.89468	1.86	.94869
1.12	.94359	1.37	.88931	1.62	.89592	1.87	.95184
1.13	.93993	1.38	.88854	1.63	.89724	1.88	.95507
1.14	.93642	1.39	.88785	1.64	.89864	1.89	.95838
1.15	.93304	1.40	.88726	1.65	.90012	1.90	.96177
1.16	.92980	1.41	.88676	1.66	.90167	1.91	.96523
1.17	.92670	1.42	.88636	1.67	.90330	1.92	.96878
1.18	.92373	1.43	.88604	1.68	.90500	1.93	.97240
1.19	.92088	1.44	.88580	1.69	.90678	1.94	.97610
1.20	.91817	1.45	.88565	1.70	.90864	1.95	.97988
1.21	.91558	1.46	.88560	1.71	.91057	1.96	.98374
1.22	.91311	1.47	.88563	1.72	.91258	1.97	.98768
1.23	.91075	1.48	.88575	1.73	.91466	1.98	.99171
1.24	.90852	1.49	.88595	1.74	.91683	1.99	.99581
						2.00	1.00000

* For large positive values of x, $\Gamma(x)$ approximates the asymptotic series

$$x^x e^{-x} \sqrt{\frac{2\pi}{x}} \left[1 + \frac{1}{12x} + \frac{1}{288x^2} - \frac{139}{51840x^3} - \frac{571}{2488320x^4} + \cdots \right].$$

π CONSTANTS

π = 3.14159 26535 89793 23846 26433 83279 50288 41971 69399 37511
$1/\pi$ = 0.31830 98861 83790 67153 77675 26745 02872 40689 19291 48091
π^2 = 9.86960 44010 89358 61883 44909 99876 15113 53136 99407 24079
$\log_e \pi$ = 1.14472 98858 49400 17414 34273 51353 05871 16472 94812 91531
$\log_{10} \pi$ = 0.49714 98726 94133 85435 12682 88290 89887 36516 78324 38044
$\log_{10} \sqrt{2\pi}$ = 0.39908 99341 79057 52478 25035 91507 69595 02099 34102 92128

CONSTANTS INVOLVING e

e = 2.71828 18284 59045 23536 02874 71352 66249 77572 47093 69996
$1/e$ = 0.36787 94411 71442 32159 55237 70161 46086 74458 11131 03177
e^2 = 7.38905 60989 30650 22723 04274 60575 00781 31803 15570 55185
$M = \log_{10} e$ = 0.43429 44819 03251 82765 11289 18916 60508 22943 97005 80367
$1/M = \log_e 10$ = 2.30258 50929 94045 68401 79914 54684 36420 76011 01488 62877
$\log_{10} M$ = 9.63778 43113 00536 78912 29674 98645 $- 10$

π^e AND e^π CONSTANTS

π^e = 22.45915 77183 61045 47342 71522
e^π = 23.14069 26327 79269 00572 90864
$e^{-\pi}$ = 0.04321 39182 63772 24977 44177
$e^{\frac{1}{2}\pi}$ = 4.81047 73809 65351 65547 30357
$i^i = e^{-\frac{1}{2}\pi}$ = 0.20787 95763 50761 90854 69556

NUMERICAL CONSTANTS

$\sqrt{2}$ = 1.41421 35623 73095 04880 16887 24209 69807 85696 71875 37695
$\sqrt[3]{2}$ = 1.25992 10498 94873 16476 72106 07278 22835 05702 51464 70151
$\log_e 2$ = 0.69314 71805 59945 30941 72321 21458 17656 80755 00134 36026
$\log_{10} 2$ = 0.30102 99956 63981 19521 37388 94724 49302 67681 89881 46211
$\sqrt{3}$ = 1.73205 08075 68877 29352 74463 41505 87236 69428 05253 81039
$\sqrt[3]{3}$ = 1.44224 95703 07408 38232 16383 10780 10958 83918 69253 49935
$\log_e 3$ = 1.09861 22886 68109 69139 52452 36922 52570 46474 90557 82275
$\log_{10} 3$ = 0.47712 12547 19662 43729 50279 03255 11530 92001 28864 19070

OTHER CONSTANTS

Euler's Constant γ = 0.57721 56649 01532 86061
$\log_e \gamma$ = -0.54953 93129 81644 82234
Golden Ratio ϕ = 1.61803 39887 49894 84820 45868 34365 63811 77203 09180

MELTING AND BOILING POINTS, AND ATOMIC WEIGHTS OF THE ELEMENTS

Based on the Assigned Relative Atomic Mass of $^{12}C = 12$

The following values apply to elements as they exist in materials of terrestrial origin and to certain artificial elements. When used with the footnotes, they are reliable to ±1 in the last digit, or ±3 if that digit is in small type.

Name	Symbol	Atomic number	Atomic weight	Melting point, °C	Boiling point, °C
Actinum	Ac	89	(227)	1,050	3,200 ± 300
Aluminum	Al	13	26.98154[a]	660.37	2,467
Americium	Am	95	(243)	994 ± 4	2,607
Antimony	Sb	51	121.75	630.74	1,750
Argon	Ar	18	39.948[b,c,d,g]	−189.2	−185.7
Arsenic (gray)	As	33	74.9216[a]	817(28 atm)	613(sub.)
Astatine	At	85	~210	302	337
Barium	Ba	56	137.34	725	1,640
Berkelium	Bk	97	(247)	—	—
Beryllium	Be	4	9.01218[a]	1,278 ± 5	2,970(5 mm)
Bismuth	Bi	83	208.9808[a]	271.3	1,560 ± 5
Boron	B	5	10.81[c,d,e]	2,300	2,550(sub.)
Bromine	Br	35	79.904[c]	−7.2	58.78
Cadmium	Cd	48	112.40	320.9	765
Calcium	Ca	20	40.08	839 ± 2	1,484
Californium	Cf	98	(251)	—	—
Carbon	C	6	12.011[b,d]	~3,550	4,827
Cerium	Ce	58	140.12	798 ± 3	3,257
Cesium	Cs	55	132.9054[c]	28.40 ± 0.01	678.4
Chlorine	Cl	17	35.453[c]	−100.98	−34.6
Chromium	Cr	24	51.996[c]	1,857 + 20	2,672
Cobalt	Co	27	58.9332[a]	1,495	2,870
Copper	Cu	29	63.546[c,d]	1,083.4 ± 0.2	2,567
Curium	Cm	96	(247)	1,340 ± 40	
Dysprosium	Dy	66	162.50	1,409	2,335
Einsteinium	Es	99	(254)	—	
Erbium	Er	68	167.26	1,522	2,510
Europium	Eu	63	151.96	822 ± 5	1,597
Fermium	Fm	100	(257)	—	
Fluorine	F	9	18.99840[a]	−219.62	−188.14
Francium	Fr	87	(223)	(27)	(677)
Gadolinium	Gd	64	157.25	1,311 ± 1	3,233
Gallium	Ga	31	69.72	29.78	2,403
Germanium	Ge	32	72.59	937.4	2,830
Gold	Au	79	196.9665[a]	1,064.43	2,807
Hafnium	Hf	72	178.49	2,227 ± 20	4,602
Helium	He	2	4.00260[b]	−272.2[26] atm	−268.934
Holmium	Ho	67	164.9304[a]	1,470	2,720
Hydrogen	H	1	1.0079[b,d]	−259.14	−252.87
Indium	In	49	114.82	156.61	2,080
Iodine	I	53	126.9045[a]	113.5	184.35
Iridium	Ir	77	192.22	2,410	4,130
Iron	Fe	26	55.847	1,535	2,750
Krypton	Kr	36	83.80	−156.6	−152.30 ± 0.10
Lanthanum	La	57	138.9055[b]	920 ± 5	3,454
Lawrencium	Lr	103	(260)	—	—
Lead	Pb	82	207.2[d,g]	327.502	1,740
Lithium	Li	3	6.941[c,d,e]	180.54	1,347
Lutetium	Lu	71	174.97	1,656 ± 5	3,315
Magnesium	Mg	12	24.305[c]	648.8 ± 0.5	1,090
Manganese	Mn	25	54.9380[a]	1,244 ± 3	1,962
Mendelevium	Md	101	(258)		
Mercury	Hg	80	200.59	−38.87	356.58
Molybdenum	Mo	42	95.94	2,617	4,612

Note: See end of table for footnotes.

Name	Symbol	Atomic number	Atomic weight	Melting point, °C	Boiling point, °C
Neodymium	Nd	60	144.24	1,010	3,127
Neon	Ne	10	20.179[c]	−248.67	−246.048
Neptunium	Np	93	237.0482[b]	640 ± 1	3,902
Nickel	Ni	28	58.71	1,453	2,732
Niobium (Columbium)	Nb	41	92.9064[a]	2.468 ± 10	4,742
Nitrogen	N	7	14.0067[b,c]	−209.86	−195.8
Nobelium	No	102	(259)	−	−
Osmium	Os	76	190.2	3,045 ± 30	5,027 ± 100
Oxygen	O	8	15.9994[b,c,d]	−218.4	−182.962
Palladium	Pd	46	106.4	1,552	3,140
Phosphorus	P	15	30.97376	44.1 (white)	280 (white)
Platinum	Pt	78	195.09	1,772	3,827 ± 100
Plutonium	Pu	94	(244)	641	3,232
Polonium	Po	84	(~210)	254	962
Potassium	K	19	39.098	63.65	774
Praeseodymium	Pr	59	140.9077[a]	931 ± 4	3,212
Promethium	Pm	61	(145)	~1,080	2,460(?)
Protactinium	Pa	91	231.0359[a]	<1,600	−
Radium	Ra	88	226.0254[a,f,g]	700	1,140
Radon	Rn	86	(~222)	−71	−61.8
Rhenium	Re	75	186.2	3,180	5,627(est.)
Rhodium	Rh	45	102.9055[a]	1,966 ± 3	3,727 ± 100
Rubidium	Rb	37	85.4678[c]	38.89	688
Ruthenium	Ru	44	101.07	2,310	3,900
Samarium	Sm	62	150.4	1,072 ± 5	1,778
Scandium	Sc	21	44.9559[a]	1,539	2,832
Selenium	Se	34	78.96[c]	217	684.9 ± 1.0
Silicon	Si	14	28.086[d]	1,410	2,355
Silver	Ag	47	107.868[c]	961.93	2,212
Sodium	Na	11	22.9898[a]	97.81 ± 0.03	882.9
Strontium	Sr	38	87.62[g]	769	1,384
Sulfur	S	16	32.06[d]	112.8	444.674
Tantalum	Ta	73	180.9479[b]	2,996	5,425 ± 100
Technetium	Tc	43	98.9062[f]	2,172	4,877
Tellurium	Te	52	127.60	449.5 ± 0.3	989.8 ± 3.8
Terbium	Tb	65	158.9254[a]	1,360 ± 4	3,041
Thallium	Tl	81	204.37	303.5	1,457 ± 10
Thorium	Th	90	232.0381[a]	1,750	~4,790
Thulium	Tm	69	168.9342[a]	1,545 ± 15	1,727
Tin	Sn	50	118.69	231.9681	2.270
Titanium	Ti	22	47.90	1,660 ± 10	3,287
Tungsten	W	74	183.85	3,410 ± 20	5,660
Uranium	U	92	238.029[b,c,e]	1,132.3 ± 0.8	3,818
Vanadium	V	23	50.9414[b,c]	1,890 ± 10	3,380
Wolfram (see Tungsten)					
Xenon	Xe	54	131.30	−111.9	−107.1 ± 3
Ytterbium	Yb	70	173.04	824 ± 5	1,193
Yttrium	Y	39	88.9059[a]	1,523 ± 8	3,337
Zinc	Zn	30	65.38	419.58	907
Zirconium	Zr	40	91.22	1,852 ± 2	4,377

[a] Mononuclidic element.

[b] Element with one predominant isotope (about 99 to 100% abundance).

[c] Element for which the atomic weight is based on calibrated measurements.

[d] Element for which variation in isotropic abundance in terrestrial samples limits the precision of the atomic weight given.

[e] Element for which users are cautioned against the possibility of large variations in atomic weight due to inadvertent or undisclosed artificial isotropic separation in commercially available materials.

[f] Most commonly available long-lived isotope.

[g] In some geological specimens this element has a highly anomalous isotropic composition, corresponding to an atomic weight significantly different from that given.

ELECTRONIC CONFIGURATION OF THE ELEMENTS

By Laurence S. Foster

References: F. H. Spedding and A. H. Daane, Editors, *The Rare Earths*, John Wiley and Sons, Inc. Publishers, New York, 1961. R. F. Gould, Editor, *Lanthanide–Actinide Chemistry*, Advances in Chemistry Series, No. 71, American Chemical Society, Washington, D.C., 1967: Paper No. 14, Mark Fred, *Electronic Structure of the Actinide Elements.*

Atomic No.	Element	K (1s)	L (2 s p)	M (3 s p d)	N (4 s p d f)	O (5 s p d f)	P (6 s p d f)	Q (7 s p d f)
1	H	1						
2	He	2						
3	Li	2	1					
4	Be	2	2					
5	B	2	2 1					
6	C	2	2 2					
7	N	2	2 3					
8	O	2	2 4					
9	F	2	2 5					
10	Ne	2	2 6					
11	Na	2	2 6	1				
12	Mg	2	2 6	2				
13	Al	2	2 6	2 1				
14	Si	2	2 6	2 2				
15	P	2	2 6	2 3				
16	S	2	2 6	2 4				
17	Cl	2	2 6	2 5				
18	Ar	2	2 6	2 6				
19	K	2	2 6	2 6 ..	1			
20	Ca	2	2 6	2 6 ..	2			
21	Sc	2	2 6	2 6 1	2			
22	Ti	2	2 6	2 6 2	2			
23	V	2	2 6	2 6 3	2			
24	Cr	2	2 6	2 6 5*	1			
25	Mn	2	2 6	2 6 5	2			
26	Fe	2	2 6	2 6 6	2			
27	Co	2	2 6	2 6 7	2			
28	Ni	2	2 6	2 6 8	2			
29	Cu	2	2 6	2 6 10*	1			
30	Zn	2	2 6	2 6 10	2			
31	Ga	2	2 6	2 6 10	2 1			
32	Ge	2	2 6	2 6 10	2 2			
33	As	2	2 6	2 6 10	2 3			
34	Se	2	2 6	2 6 10	2 4			
35	Br	2	2 6	2 6 10	2 5			
36	Kr	2	2 6	2 6 10	2 6			
37	Rb	2	2 6	2 6 10	2 6 ..	1		
38	Sr	2	2 6	2 6 10	2 6 ..	2		
39	Y	2	2 6	2 6 10	2 6 1	2		
40	Zr	2	2 6	2 6 10	2 6 2 ..	2		
41	Nb	2	2 6	2 6 10	2 6 4*..	1		
42	Mo	2	2 6	2 6 10	2 6 5 ..	1		
43	Tc	2	2 6	2 6 10	2 6 6 ..	1		
44	Ru	2	2 6	2 6 10	2 6 7 ..	1		
45	Rh	2	2 6	2 6 10	2 6 8 ..	1		
46	Pd	2	2 6	2 6 10	2 6 10*..	0		
47	Ag	2	2 6	2 6 10	2 6 10 ..	1		
48	Cd	2	2 6	2 6 10	2 6 10 ..	2		
49	In	2	2 6	2 6 10	2 6 10 ..	2 1		
50	Sn	2	2 6	2 6 10	2 6 10 ..	2 2		
51	Sb	2	2 6	2 6 10	2 6 10 ..	2 3		
52	Te	2	2 6	2 6 10	2 6 10 ..	2 4		
53	I	2	2 6	2 6 10	2 6 10 ..	2 5		
54	Xe	2	2 6	2 6 10	2 6 10 ..	2 6		
55	Cs	2	2 6	2 6 10	2 6 10 ..	2 6 ...	1	
56	Ba	2	2 6	2 6 10	2 6 10 ..	2 6 ...	2	
57	La	2	2 6	2 6 10	2 6 10 ..	2 6 1 ..	2	
58	Ce	2	2 6	2 6 10	2 6 10 2*	2 6 ...	2	
59	Pr	2	2 6	2 6 10	2 6 10 3	2 6 ...	2	
60	Nd	2	2 6	2 6 10	2 6 10 4	2 6 ...	2	
61	Pm	2	2 6	2 6 10	2 6 10 5	2 6 ...	2	
62	Sm	2	2 6	2 6 10	2 6 10 6	2 6 ...	2	
63	Eu	2	2 6	2 6 10	2 6 10 7	2 6 ...	2	
64	Gd	2	2 6	2 6 10	2 6 10 7	2 6 1 ..	2	
65	Tb	2	2 6	2 6 10	2 6 10 9*	2 6 ...	2	
66	Dy	2	2 6	2 6 10	2 6 10 10	2 6 ...	2	
67	Ho	2	2 6	2 6 10	2 6 10 11	2 6 ...	2	
68	Er	2	2 6	2 6 10	2 6 10 12	2 6 ...	2	
69	Tm	2	2 6	2 6 10	2 6 10 13	2 6 ...	2	
70	Yb	2	2 6	2 6 10	2 6 10 14	2 6 ...	2	
71	Lu	2	2 6	2 6 10	2 6 10 14	2 6 1 ..	2	
72	Hf	2	2 6	2 6 10	2 6 10 14	2 6 2 ..	2	
73	Ta	2	2 6	2 6 10	2 6 10 14	2 6 3 ..	2	
74	W	2	2 6	2 6 10	2 6 10 14	2 6 4 ..	2	
75	Re	2	2 6	2 6 10	2 6 10 14	2 6 5 ..	2	
76	Os	2	2 6	2 6 10	2 6 10 14	2 6 6 ..	2	
77	Ir	2	2 6	2 6 10	2 6 10 14	2 6 7 ..	2	
78	Pt	2	2 6	2 6 10	2 6 10 14	2 6 9 ..	1	
79	Au	2	2 6	2 6 10	2 6 10 14	2 6 10 ..	1	
80	Hg	2	2 6	2 6 10	2 6 10 14	2 6 10 ..	2	
81	Ti	2	2 6	2 6 10	2 6 10 14	2 6 10 ..	2 1	
82	Pb	2	2 6	2 6 10	2 6 10 14	2 6 10 ..	2 2	
83	Bi	2	2 6	2 6 10	2 6 10 14	2 6 10 ..	2 3	
84	Po	2	2 6	2 6 10	2 6 10 14	2 6 10 ..	2 4	
85	At	2	2 6	2 6 10	2 6 10 14	2 6 10 ..	2 5	
86	Rn	2	2 6	2 6 10	2 6 10 14	2 6 10 ..	2 6	
87	Fr	2	2 6	2 6 10	2 6 10 14	2 6 10 ..	2 6.. ..	1
88	Ra	2	2 6	2 6 10	2 6 10 14	2 6 10 ..	2 6.. ..	2
89	Ac	2	2 6	2 6 10	2 6 10 14	2 6 10 ..	2 6 1 ..	2
90	Th	2	2 6	2 6 10	2 6 10 14	2 6 10 ..	2 6 2 ..	2
91	Pa	2	2 6	2 6 10	2 6 10 14	2 6 10 2*	2 6 1 ..	2
92	U	2	2 6	2 6 10	2 6 10 14	2 6 10 3	2 6 1 ..	2
93	Np	2	2 6	2 6 10	2 6 10 14	2 6 10 4	2 6 1 ..	2
94	Pu	2	2 6	2 6 10	2 6 10 14	2 6 10 6	2 6.. ..	2
95	Am	2	2 6	2 6 10	2 6 10 14	2 6 10 7	2 6.. ..	2
96	Cm	2	2 6	2 6 10	2 6 10 14	2 6 10 7	2 6 1 ..	2
97	Bk	2	2 6	2 6 10	2 6 10 14	2 6 10 9*	2 6.. ..	2
98	Cf	2	2 6	2 6 10	2 6 10 14	2 6 10 10	2 6.. ..	2
99	Es	2	2 6	2 6 10	2 6 10 14	2 6 10 11	2 6.. ..	2
100	Fm	2	2 6	2 6 10	2 6 10 14	2 6 10 12	2 6.. ..	2
101	Md	2	2 6	2 6 10	2 6 10 14	2 6 10 13	2 6.. ..	2
102	No	2	2 6	2 6 10	2 6 10 14	2 6 10 14	2 6.. ..	2
103	Lr	2	2 6	2 6 10	2 6 10 14	2 6 10 14	2 6 1 ..	2
104	—	2	2 6	2 6 10	2 6 10 14	2 6 10 14	2 6 2 ..	2

* Note irregularity.

PERIODIC TABLE OF THE ELEMENTS

KEY TO CHART

```
Atomic Number → 50   +2  ← Oxidation States
       Symbol → Sn   +4
Atomic Weight → 118.69
                18 18 4  ← Electron Configuration
```

Transition Elements — Group 8

Z	Symbol	Group	Oxidation States	Atomic Weight	Electron Configuration
1	H	1a	+1, −1	1.0079	1
2	He	0	0	4.00260	2
3	Li	1a	+1	6.94	2-1
4	Be	2a	+2	9.01218	2-2
5	B	3a	+3	10.81	2-3
6	C	4a	+2, +4, −4	12.011	2-4
7	N	5a	+1, +2, +3, +4, +5, −1, −3	14.0067	2-5
8	O	6a	−2	15.9994	2-6
9	F	7a	−1	18.99840	2-7
10	Ne	0	0	20.179	2-8
11	Na	1a	+1	22.98977	2-8-1
12	Mg	2a	+2	24.305	2-8-2
13	Al	3a	+3	26.98154	2-8-3
14	Si	4a	+2, +4, −4	28.086	2-8-4
15	P	5a	+3, +5, −3	30.97376	2-8-5
16	S	6a	+4, +6, −2	32.06	2-8-6
17	Cl	7a	+1, +5, +7, −1	35.453	2-8-7
18	Ar	0	0	39.948	2-8-8
19	K	1a	+1	39.098	2-8-8-1
20	Ca	2a	+2	40.08	2-8-8-2
21	Sc	3b	+3	44.9559	2-8-9-2
22	Ti	4b	+2, +3, +4	47.90	2-8-10-2
23	V	5b	+2, +3, +4, +5	50.9414	2-8-11-2
24	Cr	6b	+2, +3, +6	51.996	2-8-13-1
25	Mn	7b	+2, +3, +4, +7	54.9380	2-8-13-2
26	Fe	8	+2, +3	55.847	2-8-14-2
27	Co	8	+2, +3	58.9332	2-8-15-2
28	Ni	8	+2, +3	58.71	2-8-16-2
29	Cu	1b	+1, +2	63.546	2-8-18-1
30	Zn	2b	+2	65.38	2-8-18-2
31	Ga	3a	+3	69.72	2-8-18-3
32	Ge	4a	+2, +4	72.59	2-8-18-4
33	As	5a	+3, +5, −3	74.9216	2-8-18-5
34	Se	6a	+4, +6, −2	78.96	2-8-18-6
35	Br	7a	+1, +5, −1	79.904	2-8-18-7
36	Kr	0	0	83.80	2-8-18-8
37	Rb	1a	+1	85.467₆	2-8-18-8-1
38	Sr	2a	+2	87.62	2-8-18-8-2
39	Y	3b	+3	88.9059	2-8-18-9-2
40	Zr	4b	+4	91.22	2-8-18-10-2
41	Nb	5b	+3, +5	92.9064	2-8-18-12-1
42	Mo	6b	+6	95.94	2-8-18-13-1
43	Tc	7b	+4, +6, +7	98.9062	2-8-18-13-2
44	Ru	8	+3	101.07	2-8-18-15-1
45	Rh	8	+3	102.9055	2-8-18-16-1
46	Pd	8	+2, +4	106.4	2-8-18-18-0
47	Ag	1b	+1	107.868	2-8-18-18-1
48	Cd	2b	+2	112.40	2-8-18-18-2
49	In	3a	+3	114.82	2-8-18-18-3
50	Sn	4a	+2, +4	118.69	2-8-18-18-4
51	Sb	5a	+3, +5, −3	121.75	2-8-18-18-5
52	Te	6a	+4, +6, −2	127.60	2-8-18-18-6
53	I	7a	+1, +5, +7, −1	126.9045	2-8-18-18-7
54	Xe	0	0	131.30	2-8-18-18-8
55	Cs	1a	+1	132.9054	2-8-18-18-8-1
56	Ba	2a	+2	137.34	2-8-18-18-8-2
57	La*	3b	+3	138.9055	-18-9-2
72	Hf	4b	+4	178.49	-32-10-2
73	Ta	5b	+5	180.9479	-32-11-2
74	W	6b	+6	183.85	-32-12-2
75	Re	7b	+4, +6, +7	186.2	-32-13-2
76	Os	8	+3, +4	190.2	-32-14-2
77	Ir	8	+3, +4	192.22	-32-15-2
78	Pt	8	+2, +4	195.09	-32-16-2
79	Au	1b	+1, +3	196.9665	-32-18-1
80	Hg	2b	+1, +2	200.59	-32-18-2
81	Tl	3a	+1, +3	204.37	-32-18-3
82	Pb	4a	+2, +4	207.2	-32-18-4
83	Bi	5a	+3, +5	208.9808	-32-18-5
84	Po	6a	+2, +4	(209)	-32-18-6
85	At	7a		(210)	-32-18-7
86	Rn	0	0	(222)	-32-18-8
87	Fr	1a	+1	(223)	-18-8-1
88	Ra	2a	+2	226.0254	-18-8-2
89	Ac**	3b	+3	(227)	-18-9-2
104		4b	+4	(261)	-32-10-2
105		5b		(262)	-32-11-2
106		6b		(263)	-32-12-2

*Lanthanides

Z	Symbol	Oxidation States	Atomic Weight	Electron Configuration
58	Ce	+3, +4	140.12	-20-8-2
59	Pr	+3	140.9077	-21-8-2
60	Nd	+3	144.24	-22-8-2
61	Pm	+3	(145)	-23-8-2
62	Sm	+2, +3	150.4	-24-8-2
63	Eu	+2, +3	151.96	-25-8-2
64	Gd	+3	157.25	-25-9-2
65	Tb	+3	158.9254	-27-8-2
66	Dy	+3	162.50	-28-8-2
67	Ho	+3	164.9304	-29-8-2
68	Er	+3	167.26	-30-8-2
69	Tm	+3	168.9342	-31-8-2
70	Yb	+2, +3	173.04	-32-8-2
71	Lu	+3	174.97	-32-9-2

**Actinides

Z	Symbol	Oxidation States	Atomic Weight	Electron Configuration
90	Th	+4	232.0381	-18-10-2
91	Pa	+4, +5	231.0359	-20-9-2
92	U	+3, +4, +5, +6	238.029	-21-9-2
93	Np	+3, +4, +5, +6	237.0482	-22-9-2
94	Pu	+3, +4, +5, +6	(244)	-24-8-2
95	Am	+3, +4, +5, +6	(243)	-25-8-2
96	Cm	+3	(247)	-25-9-2
97	Bk	+3, +4	(247)	-27-8-2
98	Cf	+3	(251)	-28-8-2
99	Es	+3	(254)	-29-8-2
100	Fm	+3	(257)	-30-8-2
101	Md	+2, +3	(258)	-31-8-2
102	No	+2, +3	(259)	-32-8-2
103	Lr	+3	(260)	-32-9-2

Orbit legend: K; K-L; K-L-M; L-M-N; M-N-O; N-O-P; O-P-Q

Numbers in parentheses are mass numbers of most stable isotope of that element.

The Elements

C. R. Hammond

One of the most striking facts about the elements is their unequal distribution and occurrence in nature. Present knowledge of the chemical composition of the universe, obtained from the study of the spectra of stars and nebulae, indicates that hydrogen is by far the most abundant element and may account for more than 90% of the atoms or about 75% of the mass of the universe. Helium atoms make up most of the remainder. All of the other elements together contribute only slightly to the total mass.

The chemical composition of the universe is undergoing continuous change. Hydrogen is being converted into helium, and helium is being changed into heavier elements. As time goes on, the ratio of heavier elements increases relative to hydrogen. Presumably, the process is not reversible.

Burbridge, Burbridge, Fowler, and Hoyle have studied the synthesis of elements in stars. To explain all of the features of the nuclear abundance curve — obtained by studies of the composition of the earth, meteorites, stars, etc. — it is necessary to postulate that the elements were originally formed by at least eight different processes: (1) hydrogen burning, (2) helium burning, (3) α process, (4) e process, (5) s process, (6) r process, (7) p process, and (8) the χ process. The χ process is thought to account for the existence of light nuclei such as D, Li, Be, and B. Common metals such as Fe, Cr, Ni, Cu, Ti, Zn, etc., were likely produced early in the history of our galaxy. It is also probable that most of the heavy elements on earth and elsewhere in the universe were originally formed in supernovae, or in the hot interior of stars.

Studies of the solar spectrum have led to the identification of 67 elements in the sun's atmosphere; however all elements cannot be identified with the same degree of certainty. Other elements may be present in the sun, although they have not yet been detected spectroscopically. The element helium was discovered on the sun before it was found on earth. Some elements such as scandium are relatively more plentiful in the sun and stars than here on earth.

Minerals in lunar rocks brought back from the moon on the Apollo missions consist predominantly of *plagioclase* [(Ca, Na) (Al, Si)O_4O_8] and *pyroxene* [(Ca, Mg, Fe)$_2$Si$_2$O$_6$] — two minerals common in terrestrial volcanic rock. No new elements have been found on the moon that cannot be accounted for on earth; however, two minerals, *armalcolite* [(Fe, Mg)Ti$_2$O$_5$] and *pyroxferroite,* [CaFe$_6$ (SiO$_3$)$_7$] are new. The oldest known terrestrial rocks are about 3.5 billion years old. One rock, known as the "Genesis Rock," brought back from the Apollo 15 Mission, is about 4.15 billion years old. This is only about one-half billion years younger than the supposed age of the moon and solar system. Lunar rocks appear to be relatively enriched in refractory elements such as chromium, titanium, zirconium, and the rare earths, and impoverished in volatile elements such as the alkali metals, in chlorine, and in noble metals such as nickel, platinum, and gold.

F. W. Clarke and others have carefully studied the composition of rocks making up the crust of the earth. Oxygen accounts for about 47% of the crust, by weight, while silicon comprises about 28%, and aluminum about 8%. These elements, plus iron, calcium, sodium, potassium, and magnesium, account for about 99% of the composition of the crust.

Many elements such as tin, copper, zinc, lead, mercury, silver, platinum, antimony, arsenic, and gold, which are so essential to our needs and civilization, are among some of the rarest elements in the earth's crust. These are made available to us only by the processes of concentration in ore bodies. Some of the so-called *rare-earth* elements have been found to be much more plentiful than originally thought and are about as abundant as uranium, mercury, lead, or bismuth. The least abundant rare-earth or *lanthanide* element, thulium, is now believed to be more plentiful on earth than silver, cadmium, gold, or iodine, for example. Rubidium, the 16th most abundant element, is more plentiful than chlorine, while its compounds are little known in chemistry and commerce.

Ninety-one elements occur naturally on earth. Minute traces of plutonium-244 were recently discovered in rocks mined in southern California. This discovery supports the theory that heavy elements were produced during creation of the solar system. While technetium and promethium have not yet been found naturally on earth, they have been found to be present in stars. Technetium has been identified in the spectra of certain "late" type stars, and promethium lines have been identified in the spectra of a faintly visible star HR465 in Andromeda. Promethium must have been made very recently near the star's surface for no known isotope of this element has a half-life longer than 17.7 years.

It has been suggested that californium is present in certain stellar explosions known as supernovae; however, this has not been proved. At present no elements are found elsewhere in the universe that cannot be accounted for here on earth.

All atomic mass numbers from 1 to 238 are found naturally on earth except for masses 5 and 8. About 280 stable and 67 naturally radioactive isotopes occur on earth, totalling 347. In addition, the neutron, technetium, promethium, and the transuranic elements (lying beyond uranium) up to Element 105 have been produced artificially. Laboratory processes have now extended the radioactive mass numbers beyond 238 to about 260. Each element from atomic number 1 to 106 is known to have at least one radioactive isotope. About 1,700 different nuclides (the name given to different kinds of nuclei, whether they are of the same or different elements), are now recognized. Many stable and radioactive isotopes are now produced and distributed by the Oak Ridge National Laboratory, Oak Ridge, Tenn., U.S.A., to customers licensed by the U.S. Atomic Energy Commission.

The available evidence leads to the conclusion that elements 89 (actinium) through 103 (lawrencium) are chemically similar to the rare-earth or lanthanide elements (elements 57 to 71, inclusive). These elements therefore have been named *actinides* after the first member of this series. Those elements beyond uranium that have been produced artificially have the following names and symbols: neptunium, 93 (Np); plutonium, 94 (Pu); americium, 95 (Am); curium, 96 (Cm); berkelium, 97 (Bk); californium, 98 (Cf); einsteinium, 99 (Es); fermium, 100 (Fm); mendelevium, 101 (Md); nobelium, 102 (No); and lawrencium 103 (Lr). It is now claimed that Elements 104, 105, and 106 have been produced and positively identified. Element 104 is expected to have chemical properties similar to those of hafnium and would not be a member of the actinide series. Element 105 should have properties similar to those of tantalum, and Element 106 properties similar to tungsten.

There is presently some reason for optimism in producing elements beyond Element 106 either by bombardment of heavy isotopic targets with heavy ions, or by the irradiation of uranium or transuranic elements with the instantaneous high flux of neutrons produced by underground nuclear explosions. The limit will be set by the yields of the nuclear reactions and by the half-lives of radioactive decay. It has been suggested that Elements 102 and 103 have abnormally short lives only because they are in a pocket of instability, and that this region of instability might begin to "heal" around Element 105. If so, it may be possible to produce heavier isotopes with longer half-lives. It has also been suggested that Element 114, with a mass number of 298, and Element 126, with a mass number of 310, may be sufficiently stable to make discovery and identification possible. Calculations indicate that Element 110, a homolog of platinum, may have a half-life of as long as 100 million years. Searches have already been made by workers in a number of laboratories for Element 110 and its neighboring elements in naturally occurring platinum.

There are many claims in the literature of the existence of various allotropic modifications of the elements, some of which are based on doubtful or incomplete evidence. Also, the physical properties of an element may change drastically by the presence of small amounts of impurities. With new methods of purification, which are now able to produce elements with 99.9999+% purity, it has been necessary to restudy the properties of the elements. For example, the melting point of thorium changes by several hundred degrees by the presence of a small percentage of ThO_2 as an impurity. Ordinary commercial tungsten is brittle and can be worked only with difficulty. Pure tungsten, however, can be cut with a hacksaw, forged, spun, drawn, or extruded. In general, the value of physical properties given here applies to the pure element, when it is known.

ACTINIUM (Gr. *aktis, aktinos*, beam or ray), Ac; at. wt. (227); at. no. 89; m.p. 1050°C; b.p. 3200°C $\pm$ 300°C (est.); sp. gr. 10.07 (calc.). Discovered by Andre Debierne in 1899 and independently by F. Giesel in 1902. Occurs naturally in association with uranium minerals. Actinium-227, a decay product of uranium-235, is a beta emitter with a 21.6-yr. half-life. Its principal decay products are thorium-227 (18.5-day half-life), radium-223 (11.4-day half-life), and a number of short-lived products including radon, bismuth, polonium, and lead isotopes. In equilibrium with its decay products, it is a powerful source of alpha rays. Actinium metal has been prepared by the reduction of actinium fluoride with lithium vapor at about 1100–1300°C. The chemical behavior of actinium is similar to that of the rare earths, particularly lanthanum. Purified actinium comes into equilibrium with its decay products at the end of 185 days, and then decays according to its 21.6-yr. half-life. It is about 150 times as active as radium, making it of value in the production of neutrons.

ALUMINUM (L. *alumen, alum*), Al; at. wt. 26.98154; at. no. 13; m.p. 660.37°C; b.p. 2467°C; sp. gr. 2.6989 (20°C); valence 3. The ancient Greeks and Romans used *alum* in medicine as an astringent, and as a mordant in dyeing. In 1761 de Morveau proposed the name *alumine* for the base in alum, and Lavoisier, in 1787, thought this to be the oxide of a still undiscovered metal. Wöhler is generally credited with having isolated the metal in 1827, although an impure form was prepared by Oersted two years earlier. In 1807 Davy proposed the name *aluminum* for the metal, undiscovered at that time, and later agreed to change it to *aluminum*. Shortly thereafter, the name *aluminium* was adopted to conform with the "ium" ending of most elements, and this spelling is now in use elsewhere in the world. *Aluminium* was also the accepted spelling in the U.S. until 1925 at which time the American Chemical Society officially decided to use the name *aluminum* thereafter in their publications. The method of obtaining aluminum metal by the electrolysis of alumina dissolved in *cryolite* was discovered in 1886 by Hall in the U.S. and about the same time by Heroult in France. Cryolite, a natural ore found in Greenland, is no longer widely used in commercial production, but has been replaced by an artificial mixture of sodium, aluminum, and calcium fluorides. *Bauxite*, an impure hydrated oxide ore, is found in large deposits in Arkansas, Jamaica, and elsewhere. The Bayer process is most commonly used today to refine bauxite so it can be accommodated in the Hall-Heroult refining process, used to produce most aluminum. Aluminum can now be produced from clay, but the process is not economically feasible at present. Aluminum is the most abundant metal to be found in the earth's crust (8.1 %), but is never found free in nature. In addition to the minerals mentioned above, it is found in feldspars, granite, and in many other common minerals. Pure aluminum, a silvery-white metal, possesses many desirable characteristics. It is light, nontoxic, has a pleasing appearance, can easily be formed, machined, or cast, has a high thermal conductivity, and has excellent corrosion resistance. It is nonmagnetic and nonsparking, stands second among metals in the scale of malleability, and sixth in ductility. It is extensively used for kitchen utensils, outside building decoration, and in thousands of industrial applications where a strong, light, easily constructed material is needed. Although its electrical conductivity is only about 60% that of copper per area of cross section, it is used in electrical transmission lines because of its light weight. Pure aluminum is soft and lacks strength, but it can be alloyed with small amounts of copper, magnesium, silicon, manganese, and other elements to impart a variety of useful properties. These alloys are of vital importance in the construction of modern aircraft and rockets. Aluminum, evaporated in a vacuum, forms a highly reflective coating for both visible light and radiant heat. These coatings soon form a thin layer of the protective oxide and do not deteriorate as do silver coatings. They have found application in coatings for telescope mirrors, in making decorative paper, packages, toys, and in many other uses. The compounds of greatest importance are aluminum oxide, the sulfate, and the soluble sulfate with potassium (alum). The oxide, alumina, occurs naturally as ruby, sapphire, corundum, and emery, and is used in glassmaking. Synthetic ruby and sapphire have found application in the construction of lasers for producing coherent light. In 1852, the price of aluminum was about $545 a pound, and just before Hall's discovery in 1886, about $11.00. The price rapidly dropped to 30¢ and has been as low as 15¢/lb.

AMERICIUM (the Americas), Am; at. wt. (243); at. no. 95; m.p. $994 \pm 4°C$; b.p. 2607°C; sp. gr. 13.67 (20°C); valence 2, 3, 4, 5, or 6. Americium was the fourth transuranium element to be discovered; the isotope Am^{241} was identified by Seaborg, James, Morgan and Ghiorso late in 1944 at the wartime Metallurgical Laboratory (now the Argonne National Laboratory) of the University of Chicago as the result of successive neutron capture reactions by plutonium isotopes in a nuclear reactor:

$$Pu^{239}(n, \gamma)Pu^{240}(n, \gamma)Pu^{241} \xrightarrow{\beta} Am^{241}$$

Since the isotope Am^{241} can be prepared in relatively pure form by extraction as a decay product over a period of years from strongly neutron-bombarded plutonium Pu^{241}, this isotope is used for much of the chemical investigation of this element. Better suited is the isotope Am^{243} due to its longer half-life (8.8×10^3 years as compared to 470 years for Am^{241}). A mixture of the isotopes Am^{241}, Am^{242}, and Am^{243} can be prepared by intense neutron irradiation of Am^{241} according to the reactions $Am^{241}(n, \gamma)$ $Am^{242}(n, \gamma)$ Am^{243}. Nearly isotopically pure Am^{243} can be prepared by a sequence of neutron bombardments and chemical separations as follows: neutron-bombardment of Am^{241} yields Pu^{242} by the reactions $Am^{241}(n, \gamma)$ $Am^{242} \xrightarrow{EC} Pu^{242}$; after chemical separation the Pu^{242} can be transformed to Am^{243} via the reactions $Pu^{242}(n, \gamma)Pu^{243} \xrightarrow{\beta} Am^{243}$, and the Am^{243} can be chemically separated. Fairly pure Pu^{242} can be prepared more simply by very intense neutron irradiation of Pu^{239} as the result of successive neutron-capture reactions. Americium metal has been prepared by reducing the trifluoride with barium vapor at 1000°-1200°C or the dioxide by lanthanum metal. The luster of freshly prepared americium metal is whiter and more silvery than plutonium or neptunium prepared in the same manner. It appears to be more malleable than uranium or neptunium and tarnishes slowly in dry air at room temperature. Americium is thought to exist in two forms: an alpha form which has a double hexagonal close-packed structure, and a loose-packed cubic beta form. Americium must be handled with great care to avoid personal contamination. As little as 0.02 microgram of Am^{241} is the allowable body burden (bone). The alpha activity from Am^{241} is about three times that of radium. When gram quantities of Am^{241} are handled, the intense gamma activity makes exposure a serious problem. Americium dioxide, AmO_2, is the most important oxide. AmF_3, AmF_4, $AmCl_3$, $AmBr_3$, and AmI_3, and other compounds have been prepared. The isotope Am^{241} has been used as a portable source for gamma radiography. It has also been used as a radioactive glass thickness gage for the flat glass industry. Americium-241 is available from the A.E.C. at a cost of $150/gm. and Americium-243 at a cost of $100/mg.

ANTIMONY (L. *antimonium*), Sb, (L. *stibium*, mark); at. wt. 121.75; at. no. 51; m.p. 630.74°C; b.p. 1750°C; sp. gr. 6.691 (20°C); valence 0, -3, $+3$, or $+5$. Antimony was recognized in compounds by the ancients and was known as a metal at the beginning of the 17th century and possibly much earlier. It is not abundant, but is found in over 100 mineral species. It is sometimes found native, but more frequently as the sulfide, *stibnite* (Sb_2S_3); it is also found as antimonides of the heavy metals, and as oxides. It is extracted from the sulfide by roasting to the oxide, which is reduced by salt and scrap iron; from its oxides it is also prepared by reduction with carbon. Two allotropic forms of antimony exist: the normal stable, metallic form, and the amorphous gray form. The so-called explosive antimony is an ill-defined material always containing an appreciable amount of halogen; therefore it no longer warrants consideration as a separate allotrope. The yellow form, obtained by oxidation of *stibine*, SbH_3, is probably impure, and is not a distinct form. Metallic antimony is an extremely brittle metal of a flaky, crystalline texture. It is bluish-white and has a metallic luster. It is not acted on by air at room temperature, but burns brilliantly when heated with the formation of white fumes of Sb_2O_3. It is a poor conductor of heat and electricity, and has a hardness of 3 to 3.5. Antimony, available commercially with a purity of 99.999 + %, is finding use in semiconductor technology, for making infrared detectors, diodes, and Hall-effect devices. Commercial-grade antimony is widely used in alloys with percentages ranging from one to twenty. It greatly increases the hardness and mechanical strength of lead. Batteries, antifriction alloys, type metal, cable sheathing, and minor products use about half the metal produced. Compounds taking up the other half are oxides, sulfides, sodium antimonate, and antimony trichloride. These are used in manufacturing flame-proofing compounds, paints, ceramic enamels, glass and pottery. Tartar emetic (hydrated potassium antimonyl-tartate) is used as a medicine. Antimony and many of its compounds are toxic. The maximum allowable concentration of antimony dust in the air is recommended to be 0.5 mg/cubic meter. Atmospheric concentrations of *stibine* should not exceed 0.1 ppm.

ARGON (Gr. *argos*, inactive), Ar; at. wt. 39.948; at. no. 18; freezing pt. $-189.2°C$; b.p. $-185.7°C$; density 1.7837 gm/l. Its presence in air was suspected by Cavendish in 1785; discovered by Lord Rayleigh and Sir William Ramsay in 1894. The gas is prepared by fractionation of liquid air, the atmosphere containing 0.94% argon. It is $2\frac{1}{2}$ times as soluble in water as nitrogen, having about the same solubility as oxygen; best recognized by the characteristic lines in the red end of the spectrum. It is used in electric light bulbs and in fluorescent tubes at a pressure of about 3 mm, and in filling photo tubes, glow tubes, etc. Argon is also used as an inert gas shield for arc welding and cutting, as a blanket for the production of titanium and other reactive elements, and as a protective atmosphere for growing silicon and germanium crystals. Argon is colorless and odorless, both as a gas and liquid. It is available in high-purity form. Commercial argon is available at a cost of about 10 cents per cu. ft. Argon is considered to be a very inert gas and is not now known to form true chemical compounds, as do krypton, xenon, and radon. However, it does form a hydrate having a dissociation pressure of 105 atm. at 0°C. Ion molecules, such as $(ArKr)^+$, $(ArXe)^+$, $(NeAr)^+$, have been observed spectroscopically. Argon also forms a clathrate with β hydroquinone. This clathrate is stable and can be stored for a considerable time, but a true chemical bond does not exist. Van der Waals' forces act to hold the argon. Naturally occurring argon is a mixture of three isotopes. Five other radioactive isotopes are now known to exist.

ARSENIC (L. *arsenicum*, Gr. *arsenikon*, yellow orpiment –identified with *arsenikos*, male, from the belief that metals were different sexes—Arab. *az-zernikh*, the orpiment from Persian *zerni-zar*. gold), As; at. wt. 74.9216; at. no. 33; valence -3, 0, $+3$ or $+5$. Elemental arsenic occurs in two solid modifications: yellow, and gray or metallic, with specific gravities of 1.97, and 5.73, respectively. Gray arsenic, the ordinary stable form, has a m.p. of 817°C (28 atm.) and sublimes at 613°C. Several other allotropic forms of arsenic are reported in the literature. It is believed that Albertus Magnus obtained the element in 1250 A.D. In 1649 Schroeder published two methods of preparing the element. It is found native, in the sulfides *realgar* and *orpiment*, as arsenides and sulfarsenides of heavy metals, as the oxide, and as arsenates. *Mispickel* or arsenopyrite (FeSAs) is the most common mineral, from which on heating the arsenic sublimes leaving ferrous sulfide. The element is a steel gray, very brittle, crystalline, semi-metallic solid; it tarnishes in air, and when heated is rapidly oxidized to arsenous oxide (As_2O_3) with the odor of garlic. Arsenic and its compounds are poisonous. The maximum allowable concentration of arsenic is recommended to be 0.5 mg/cu. meter of air. Arsenic is also used in bronzing, pyrotechny, and for hardening and improving the sphericity of shot. The most important compounds are white arsenic (As_2O_3), the sulfide, Paris green $3Cu(AsO_2)_2 \cdot Cu(C_2H_3O_2)_2$, calcium arsenate, and lead arsenate, the last three being used as agricultural insecticides and poisons. Marsh's test makes use of the formation and ready decomposition of arsine (AsH_3). Arsenic is available in high-purity form. It is finding increasing uses as a doping agent in solid-state devices, such as transistors. Gallium arsenide is used as a laser material to convert electricity directly into coherent light.

ASTATINE (Gr. *astatos*, unstable), At; at. wt. ~210; at. no. 85; m.p. 302°C; b.p. 337°C; valence probably 1, 3, 5, or 7. Synthesized in 1940 by D. R. Corson, K. R. MacKenzie, and E. Segré at the University of California by bombarding bismuth with alpha particles. The longest-lived isotope, At^{210}, has a half-life of only 8.3 hr. Twenty isotopes are now known. Minute quantities of At^{215}, At^{218}, and At^{219} exist in equilibrium in nature with naturally occurring uranium and thorium isotopes, and traces of At^{217} are in equilibrium with U^{233} and Np^{239} resulting from interaction of thorium and uranium with naturally produced neutrons. The total amount of astatine present in the earth's crust, however, totals less than 1 oz. Astatine can be produced by bombarding bismuth with energetic alpha particles to obtain the relatively long-lived $At^{209-211}$, which can be distilled from the target by heating it in air. Only about 0.05 μg of astatine have been prepared to date. The "time of flight" mass spectrometer has been used to confirm that this highly radioactive halogen behaves chemically very much like other halogens, particularly iodine. The inter-halogen compounds AtI, AtBr, and AtCl are known to form, but it is not yet known if astatine forms diatomic astatine molecules. HAt and CH_3At (methyl astatide) have been detected. Astatine is said to be more metallic than iodine, and, like iodine, it probably accumulates in the thyroid gland. Workers at the Brookhaven National Laboratory have recently used reactive scattering in crossed molecular beams to identify and measure elementary reactions involving astatine.

BARIUM (Gr. *barys*, heavy), Ba; at. wt. 137.34; at. no. 56; m.p. 725°C; b.p. 1640°C; sp. gr. 3.5 (20°C); valence 2. Baryta was distinguished from lime by Scheele in 1774; the element was discovered by Sir Humphry Davy in 1808. It is found only in combination with other elements chiefly in *barite* or *heavy spar* (sulfate) and *witherite* (carbonate) and is prepared by electrolysis of the chloride. Barium is a metallic element, soft, and when pure is silvery-white like lead; it belongs to the alkaline earth group, resembling calcium chemically. The metal oxidizes very easily and should be kept under petroleum or other suitable oxygen-free liquids to exclude air. It is decomposed by water or alcohol. The metal is used as a "getter" in vacuum tubes. The most important compounds are the peroxide (BaO_2), chloride, sulfate, carbonate, nitrate and chlorate. Lithopone, a pigment containing barium sulfate and zinc sulfide, has good covering power, and does not darken in the presence of sulfides. The sulfate, as permanent white or *blanc fixé*, is also used in paint, in x-ray diagnostic work, and in glassmaking. *Barite* is extensively used as a wetting agent in oilwell drilling fluids, and also in making rubber. The carbonate is used as a rat poison, while the nitrate and chlorate give colors in pyrotechny. The impure sulfide phosphoresces after exposure to the light. The compounds and the metal are not expensive. Barium metal (99.5 + %, pure) costs about $20.00/lb. All barium compounds that are water or acid soluble are poisonous. Natural-occurring barium is a mixture of seven stable isotopes. Thirteen other radioactive isotopes are known to exist.

BERKELIUM (*Berkeley*, home of Univ. of Calif.), Bk; at. wt. (247); at. no. 97; valence 3 or 4; sp. gr. 14 (est.). Berkelium, the eighth member of the actinide transition series, was discovered in December 1949 by Thompson, Ghiorso, and Seaborg, and was the fifth transuranium element synthesized. It was produced by cyclotron bombardment of milligram amounts of Am^{241} with helium ions at Berkeley, California. The first isotope produced had a mass number of 243 and decayed with a half-life of 4.6 hrs. Eight isotopes are now known and have been synthesized. The existence of Bk^{249}, with a half-life of 314 days, makes it feasible to isolate berkelium in weighable amounts so that its properties can be investigated with macroscopic quantities. One of the first visible amounts of a pure berkelium compound—berkelium chloride—was produced in 1962. It weighed 3 billionth of a gram. Berkelium has not yet been prepared in elemental form, but it is expected to be a silvery metal, easily soluble in dilute mineral acids, and readily oxidized by air or oxygen at elevated temperatures to form the oxide. X-ray diffraction methods have been used to identify the following compounds: BkO_2, Bk_2O_3, BkF_3, $BkCl_3$, and BkOCl. As with other actinide elements, berkelium tends to accumulate in the skeletal system. The maximum permissible body burden of Bk^{249} in the human skeleton is about 0.0004 μgm. (micrograms). Because of its rarity, berkelium presently has no commercial or technological use.

BERYLLIUM (Gr. *berryllos*, *beryl*; also called Glucinium or Glucinum, Gr. *glykys*, sweet;), Be; at. wt. 9.01218; at. no. 4; m.p. 1278 $\pm$ 5°C; b.p. 2970°C; sp. gr. 1.848 (20°C); valence 2. Discovered as the oxide by Vauquelin in beryl and in emeralds in 1798. The metal was isolated in 1828 by Wöhler and by Bussy independently by the action of potassium on beryllium chloride. Beryllium is found in some 30 mineral species, the most important of which are: *beryl*, *chrysoberyl*, and *phenacite*. *Aquamarine* and *emerald* are precious forms of *beryl*. Beryl ($3BeO \cdot Al_2O_3 \cdot 6SiO_2$) is the most important commercial source of the element and its compounds. Most of the metal is now prepared by reducing beryllium fluoride with magnesium metal. Beryllium metal did not become readily available to industry until 1957. The metal, steel gray in color, has many desirable properties. It is one of the lightest of all metals, and has one of the highest melting points of the light metals. Its modulus of elasticity is about one-third greater than that of steel. It resists attack by concentrated nitric acid, has excellent thermal conductivity, and is nonmagnetic. It has a high permeability to x-rays, and when bombarded by alpha particles, as from radium or polonium, neutrons are produced in the ratio of about 30 neutrons/million alpha particles. At ordinary temperatures beryllium resists oxidation in air, although its ability to scratch glass is probably due to the formation of a thin layer of the oxide. Beryllium is used as an alloying agent in producing beryllium copper, which is extensively used for springs, electrical contacts, spot-welding electrodes, and nonsparking tools. It is finding application as a structural material for high-speed aircraft, missiles, and spacecraft. It is used in nuclear reactors as a reflector or moderator for it has a low thermal neutron absorption cross section. It is used in gyroscopes, computer parts, and inertial guidance instruments where lightness, stiffness, and dimensional stability are required. The oxide has a very high melting point and is also used in nuclear work and ceramic applications. Beryllium and its salts are toxic and should be handled with the greatest of care. Beryllium and its compounds should not be tasted to verify the sweetish nature of beryllium (as did early experimenters). The metal, its alloys, and its salts can be handled safely if certain work codes are observed, but no attempt should be made to work with beryllium before becoming familiar with proper safeguards. The maximum allowable concentration of beryllium dust in an 8-hr. day is recommended to be about 2μ gms./cu. meter in working areas. The average monthly concentration should not exceed 0.01 μ gms./cu. meter in non-working areas. Beryllium metal in vacuum cast billet form is priced roughly at \$70/lb. Fabricated forms are more expensive.

BISMUTH (Ger. *Weisse Masse*, white mass; later *Wismuth* and *Bisemutum*), Bi; at. wt. 208.9808; at. no. 83; m.p. 271.3°C; b.p. 1560 ± 5°C; sp. gr. 9.747 (20°C); valence 3 or 5. In early times bismuth was confused with tin and lead. Claude Geoffroy the Younger showed it to be distinct from lead in 1753. It is a white, crystalline, brittle metal with a pinkish tinge. It occurs native. The most important ores are *bismuthinite* or *bismuth glance* (Bi_2S_3) and *bismite* (Bi_2O_3). Peru, Japan, Mexico, Bolivia, and Canada are major bismuth producers. Much of the bismuth produced in the U.S. is obtained as a by-product in refining lead, copper, tin, silver, and gold ores. Bismuth is the most diamagnetic of all metals, and the thermal conductivity is lower than any metal, except mercury. It has a high electrical resistance, and has the highest Hall effect of any metal (i.e., greatest increase in electrical resistance when placed in a magnetic field). "Bismanol" is a permanent magnet of high coercive force, made of MnBi, by the U.S. Naval Ordnance Laboratory. Bismuth expands 3.32% on solidification. This property makes bismuth alloys particularly suited to the making of sharp castings of objects subject to damage by high temperatures. With other metals, such as tin, cadmium, etc., bismuth forms low-melting alloys which are extensively used for safety devices used in fire detection and extinguishing

systems. Bismuth is used in producing malleable irons and is finding use as a catalyst for making acrylic fibers. When bismuth is heated in air it burns with a blue flame forming yellow fumes of the oxide. The metal is also used as a thermocouple material (has highest negativity known), and has found application as a carrier for U^{235} or U^{233} fuel in atomic reactors. Its soluble salts are characterized by forming insoluble basic salts on the addition of water a property sometimes used in detection work. Bismuth oxychloride is used extensively in cosmetics. Bismuth subnitrate and subcarbonate are used in medicine. High-purity bismuth metal costs about \$4/lb.

BORON (Ar. *Büraq*, Pers. *Būrah*), B; at. wt. 10.81; at. no. 5; m.p. 2300°C; b.p. sublimes 2550°C; sp. gr. of crystals 2.34, of amorphous variety 2.37; valence 3. Boron compounds have been known for thousands of years, but the element was not discovered until 1808 by Sir Humphry Davy and by Gay Lussac and Thenard. The element is not found free in nature, but occurs as orthoboric acid usually in certain volcanic spring waters and as borates in *borax* and *colemanite*. *Ulexite*, another boron mineral, is interesting as it is nature's own version of "fiber optics." By far the most important source of boron is the mineral *rasorite*, also known as *kernite*, found in the Mojave desert of California. Extensive *borax* deposits are also found in Turkey. Boron exists naturally as 19.78% $_5B^{10}$ isotope and 80.22% $_5B^{11}$ isotope. High-purity crystalline boron may be prepared by the vapor phase reduction of boron trichloride or tribromide with hydrogen on electrically heated filaments. The impure, or amorphous boron, a brownish-black powder, can be obtained by heating the trioxide with magnesium powder. Boron of 99.9999% purity has been produced and is available commercially. Elemental boron has an energy band gap of 1.50 to 1.56 electron volts, which is higher than that of either silicon or germanium. It has interesting optical characteristics, transmitting portions of the infrared, and is a poor conductor of electricity at room temperature, but a good conductor at high temperature. Amorphous boron is used in pyrotechnic flares to provide a distinctive green color, and in rockets as an igniter. The most important compounds of boron are boric, or boracic acid widely used as a mild antiseptic, and borax ($Na_2B_4O_7 \cdot 10H_2O$), which serves as a cleansing flux in welding and as a water softener in washing powders. Boron compounds are used in production of enamels for covering steel of refrigerators, washing machines, and like products. Boron compounds are also extensively used in the manufacture of borosilicate glasses. The isotope boron 10 is used as a control for nuclear reactors, as a shield for nuclear radiation, and in instruments used for detecting neutrons. Boron nitride has remarkable properties and can be used to make a material as hard as diamond. The nitride also behaves like an electrical insulator but conducts heat like a metal. It also has lubricating properties similar to graphite. The hydrides are easily oxidized with considerable energy liberation, and are being studied for use as rocket fuels. Demand is increasing for boron filaments, a high-strength, lightweight material chiefly employed for advanced aerospace structures. Amorphous boron (90%–92% grade) costs about \$12 to \$30/lb. depending on quantity ordered. Elemental boron is not considered to be a poison, but assimilation of its compounds has a cumulative poisonous effect.

BROMINE (Gr. *bromos*, stench), Br; at. wt. 79.904; at. no. 35; m.p. –7.2°C; b.p. 58.78°C; density of gas 7.59 g/l, liquid 3.12 (20°C); valence 1, 3, 5, or 7.

Discovered by Balard in 1826, but not prepared in quantity until 1860. A member of the halogen group of elements, it is obtained from natural brines from wells in Michigan and West Virginia and from sea water by displacement with chlorine; electrolysis might be used. Bromine is the only liquid nonmetallic element. It is a heavy, mobile, reddish-brown liquid, volatilizing readily at room temperature to a red vapor with a strong disagreeable odor, resembling chlorine, and having a very irritating effect on the eyes and throat; it is readily soluble in water or carbon disulfide, forming a red solution; it is less active than chlorine but more so than iodine; it unites readily with many elements and has a bleaching action; when spilled on the skin it produces painful sores. It presents a serious health hazard, and maximum safety precautions should be taken when handling it. Much of the bromine output in the U.S. is used in the production of ethylene dibromide, a lead scavenger used in making gasoline antiknock compounds. Lead in gasoline, however, is presently being drastically reduced, due to environmental considerations. This will greatly affect future production of bromine. Bromine is also used in making fumigants, flameproofing agents, water purification compounds, dyes, medicinals, sanitizers, inorganic bromides for photography, etc. Organic bromides are also important.

CADMIUM (L. *cadmia;* Gr. *kadmeia* — ancient name for calamine, zinc carbonate), Cd; at. wt. 112.40; at. no. 48; m.p. 320.9°C; b.p. 765°C; sp. gr. 8.65 (20°C); valence 2. Discovered by Stromeyer in 1817 from an impurity in zinc carbonate. Cadmium most often occurs in small quantities associated with zinc ores, such as *sphalerite* (ZnS). *Greenockite* (CdS) is the only mineral of any consequence bearing cadmium. Almost all cadmium is obtained as a by-product in the treatment of zinc, copper, and lead ores. It is a soft, bluish-white metal which is easily cut with a knife. It is similar in many respects to zinc. It is a component of some of the lowest melting alloys; it is used in bearing alloys with low coefficients of friction and great resistance to fatigue; it is used extensively in electroplating, which accounts for about 60% of its use. It is also used in many types of solder, for standard E.M.F. cells, for batteries, and as a barrier to control atomic fission. Cadmium compounds are used in black and white television phosphors and in blue and green phosphors for color TV tubes. It forms a number of salts of which the sulfate is the most common; the sulfide is used as a yellow pigment. Cadmium and solutions of its compounds are toxic. Failure to appreciate the toxic properties of cadmium may cause workers to be unwittingly exposed to dangerous fumes. Silver solder, for example, which contains cadmium, should be handled with care. Serious toxicity problems have been found from long-term exposure and work with cadmium plating baths. The recommended maximum allowable (8-hr day) concentration of cadmium vapor in air is 0.1 mg/m³. The current price of cadmium is about $2.50/lb. It is available in high purity form.

CALCIUM (L. *calx*, lime), Ca; at. wt. 40.08; at. no. 20; m.p. 839 ± 2°C; b.p. 1484°C; sp. gr. 1.55 (20°C); valence 2.

Though lime was prepared by the Romans in the first century under the name calx, not until 1808 was the metal discovered. After learning that Berzelius and Pontin prepared calcium amalgam by electrolyzing lime in mercury, Davy was able to isolate the impure metal. Calcium is a metallic element, fifth in abundance in the earth's crust, of which it forms more than three per cent. It is an essential constituent of leaves, bones, teeth and shells. Never found in nature uncombined, it occurs abundantly as *limestone* ($CaCO_3$), *gypsum* ($CaSO_4 \cdot 2H_2O$) and *fluorite* (CaF_2); *apatite* is the fluophosphate or chlorophosphate of calcium. The metal has a silvery color, is rather hard, and is prepared by electrolysis of the fused chloride to which calcium fluoride is added to lower the melting point. Chemically it is one of the alkaline earth elements; it readily forms a white coating of nitride in air, reacts with water, burns with a yellow red flame, forming largely the nitride. The metal is used as a reducing agent in preparing other metals, such as thorium, uranium, zirconium, etc., and is used as a deoxidizer, desulfurizer, or decarburizer for various ferrous and nonferrous alloys. It is also used as an alloying agent for aluminum, beryllium, copper, lead and magnesium alloys, and serves as a "getter" for residual gases in vacuum tubes, etc. Its natural and prepared compounds are widely used. Quicklime (CaO), made by heating limestone and changed into slaked lime by the careful addition of water, is the great cheap base of chemical industry with countless uses. Mixed with sand it hardens as mortar and plaster by taking up carbon dioxide from the air. Calcium from limestone is an important element in Portland cement. The solubility of the carbonate in water containing carbon dioxide causes the formation of caves with stalactites and stalagmites and hardness in water. Other important compounds are the carbide (CaC_2), chloride ($CaCl_2$), cyanamide ($Ca(CN_2)$), hypochlorite ($Ca(OCl)_2$), nitrate ($Ca(NO_3)_2$), and sulfide (CaS).

CALIFORNIUM (State and University of California; Cf; at. wt. (251); at. no. 98). Californium, the sixth transuranium element to be discovered, was produced by Thompson, Street, Ghiorso, and Seaborg in 1950 by bombarding microgram quantities of Cm^{242} with 35 MeV helium ions in the Berkeley 60-inch cyclotron. Californium (III) is the only ion stable in aqueous solutions, all attempts to reduce or oxidize californium (III) having failed. The isotope Cf^{249} results from the beta decay of Bk^{249} while the heavier isotopes are produced by intense neutron irradiation by the reactions:

$$Bk^{249}(n, \gamma) Bk^{250} \xrightarrow{\beta^-} Cf^{250} \quad \text{and} \quad Cf^{249}(n, \gamma)Cf^{250}$$

followed by

$$Cf^{250}(n, \gamma) Cf^{251}(n, \gamma)Cf^{252}$$

The existence of the isotopes Cf^{249}, Cf^{250}, Cf^{251} and Cf^{252} makes it feasible to isolate californium in weighable amounts so that its properties can be investigated with macroscopic quantities. Californium-252 is a very strong neutron emitter. One microgram releases 170 million neutrons per minute which presents biological hazards. In 1960 a few tenths of a microgram of californium trichloride $CfCl_3$, californium oxychloride, CfOCl, and californium oxide. Cf_2O_3, were first prepared. Reduction of californium to its metallic state has not yet been accomplished. Because californium is a very efficient source of neutrons, many new uses are expected for it. It has already found use in neutron moisture gages and in well-logging (the determination of water and oil-bearing layers). It is also being used as a portable neutron source for discovery of metals, such as gold or silver, by on-the-spot activation analysis. Cf^{252} is now being offered for sale by the A.E.C. at a cost of $100 per 0.1 microgram. It has been suggested that californium may be produced in certain stellar explosions, called *supernovae*, for the radioactive decay of Cf^{254} (55-day half-life) agrees with the characteristics of the light curves of such explosions observed through telescopes. This suggestion, however, is questioned.

CARBON (L. *carbo*, charcoal), C; at. wt. 12 exactly (C^{12}); at. wt. (natural carbon) 12.011; at. no. 6; m.p. $\sim 3550°C$, graphite sublimes at $3367 \pm 25°C$; b.p. 4827°C; sp. gr. amorphous 1.8–2.1, graphite 1.9–2.3, diamond 3.15–3.53 (depending on variety); gem diamond 3.513 (25°C); valence 2, 3, or 4. Carbon, an element of prehistoric discovery, is very widely distributed in nature. It is found in abundance in the sun, stars, comets, and atmospheres of most planets. Carbon in the form of microscopic diamonds is found in some meteorites. Natural diamonds are found in *kimberlite* of ancient volcanic "pipes," such as found in South Africa, Arkansas, and elsewhere. Diamonds are now also being recovered from the ocean floor off the Cape of Good Hope. About 30% of all industrial diamonds used in the U.S. are now made synthetically. The energy of the sun and stars can be attributed at least in part to the well-known carbon-nitrogen cycle. Carbon is found free in nature in three allotropic forms: amorphous, graphite, and diamond. A fourth form, known as "white" carbon, is now thought to exist. Graphite is one of the softest known materials while diamond is one of the hardest. Graphite exists in two forms: alpha and beta. These have identical physical properties, except for their crystal structure. Naturally-occurring graphites are reported to contain as much as 30% of the rhombohedral (beta) form, whereas synthetic materials contain only the alpha form. The hexagonal alpha type can be converted to the beta by mechanical treatment, and the beta form reverts to the alpha on heating it above 1000°C. In 1969 a new allotropic form of carbon was produced during the sublimation of pyrolytic graphite at low pressures. Under free-vaporization conditions above $\sim 2550°K$, "white" carbon forms as small transparent crystals on the edges of the basal planes of graphite. The interplanar spacings of "white" carbon are identical to those of a carbon form noted in the graphitic gneiss from the Ries (meteoritic) Crater of Germany. "White" carbon is a transparent birefringent material. Little information is presently available about this allotrope. In combination, carbon is found as carbon dioxide in the atmosphere of the earth and dissolved in all natural waters. It is a component of great rock masses in the form of carbonates of calcium (limestone), magnesium, and iron. Coal, petroleum, and natural gas are chiefly hydrocarbons. Carbon is unique among the elements in the vast number and variety of compounds it can form. With hydrogen, oxygen, and nitrogen, and other elements, it forms a very large number of compounds, carbon atom often being linked to carbon atom. There are upwards of a million or more known carbon compounds, many thousands of which are vital to organic and life processes. Without carbon, the basis for life would be impossible. While it has been thought that silicon might take the place of carbon in forming a host of similar compounds, it is now not possible to form stable compounds with very long chains of silicon atoms. Some of the most important compounds of carbon are: carbon dioxide (CO_2), carbon monoxide (CO), carbon disulfide (CS_2), chloroform ($CHCl_3$), carbon tetrachloride (CCl_4), methane (CH_4), ethylene (C_2H_4), acetylene (C_2H_2), benzene (C_6H_6), ethyl alcohol (C_2H_5OH), acetic acid (CH_3COOH), and their derivatives. Carbon has seven isotopes. In 1961 the International Union of Pure and Applied Chemistry adopted the isotope carbon-12 as the basis for atomic weights. Carbon-14, an isotope with a half-life of 5730 yrs, has been widely used to date such materials as wood, archeological specimens, etc. Carbon-13 is now commercially available at a cost of $700/gm.

CERIUM (named for the asteroid *Ceres*, which was discovered in 1801 only two years before the element), Ce; at. wt. 140.12; at. no. 58; m.p. 799 C; b.p. 3426 C; sp. gr. 6.657(25°C); valence 3 or 4. Discovered in 1803 by Klaproth and by Berzelius and Hisinger; metal prepared by Hillebrand and Norton in 1875. Cerium is the most abundant of the metals of the so-called rare earths; it is found in a number of minerals including *allanite* (also known as *orthite*), *monazite*, *bastnasite*, *cerite*, and *samarskite*. Monazite and bastnasite are presently the two most important sources of cerium. Large deposits of monazite found on the beaches of Travancore, India, in river sands in Brazil, and deposits of *allanite* in the Western United States, and *bastnasite* in Southern California will supply cerium, thorium and the other rare-earth metals for many years to come. Metallic cerium is prepared by metallothermic reduction techniques, such as by reducing cerous fluoride with calcium, or by electrolysis of molten cerous chloride or other cerous halides. The metallothermic technique is used to produce high-purity cerium. Cerium is especially interesting because of its variable electronic structure. The energy of the inner 4f level is nearly the same as that of the outer or valence electrons, and only small amounts of energy are required to change the relative occupancy of these electronic levels. This gives rise to dual valency states. For example, a volume change of about 10% occurs when cerium is subjected to high pressures or low temperatures. It appears that the valence changes from about 3 to 4 when it is cooled or compressed. The low temperature behavior of cerium is complex. Four allotropic modifications are thought to exist: cerium at room temperature and at atmospheric pressure is known as γ cerium. Upon cooling to $-23°C$, γ cerium changes to β cerium. The remaining γ cerium starts to change to α cerium when cooled to $-158°C$, and the transformation is complete at 196°C. α cerium has a density of 8.24. δ cerium exists above 726°C. At atmospheric pressure, liquid cerium is more dense than its solid form at the melting point. Cerium is an iron-gray lustrous metal. It is malleable, and oxidizes very readily at room temperature, especially in moist air. Except for europium, cerium is the most reactive of the "rare-earth" metals. It slowly decomposes in cold water, and rapidly in hot water. Alkali solutions and dilute and concentrated acids attack the metal rapidly. The pure metal is likely to ignite if scratched with a knife. Ceric salts are orange-red or yellowish; cerous salts are usually white. Cerium is a component of misch metal, which is extensively used in the manufacture of pyrophoric alloys for cigarette lighters, etc. While cerium is not radioactive, the impure commercial grade may contain traces of thorium, which is radioactive. The oxide is an important constituent of incandescent gas mantles and it is emerging as a hydrocarbon catalyst in "self-cleaning" ovens. In this application it can be incorporated into oven walls to prevent the collection of cooking residues. As ceric sulfate it finds extensive use as a volumetric oxidizing agent in quantitative analysis. Cerium compounds are used in the manufacture of glass, both as a component and as a decolorizer. The oxide is finding increased use as a glass polishing agent instead of rouge, for it is much faster than rouge in polishing glass surfaces. Cerium, with other rare earths, is used in carbon-arc lighting, especially in the motion picture industry. It is also finding use as an important catalyst in petroleum refining and in metallurgical and nuclear applications. Commercial cerium metal costs about $75/lb. In small lots, 99.9% cerium costs about 65¢/gm.

CESIUM (L. *caesius*, skyblue), Cs; at. wt. 132.9054; at. no. 55; m.p. 28.40 ± 0.01°C; b.p. 678.4°C; sp. gr. 1.873 (20°C); valence 1. Cesium was discovered spectroscopically by Bunsen and Kirchhoff in 1860 in mineral water from Dürkheim. Cesium, an alkali metal, occurs in *lepidolite*, *pollucite* (a hydrated silicate of aluminum and cesium) and in other sources. One of the world's richest sources of cesium is located at Bernic Lake, Manitoba. The deposits are estimated to contain 300,000 tons of pollucite, averaging 20% cesium. It can be isolated by electrolysis of the fused cyanide and by a number of other methods. Very pure, gas-free cesium can be prepared by thermal decomposition of cesium azide. The metal is characterized by a spectrum containing two bright lines in the blue along with several others in the red, yellow and green. It is silvery-white, soft, and ductile. It is the most electropositive and most alkaline element. Cesium, gallium and mercury are the only three metals that are liquid at room temperature. Cesium reacts explosively with cold water, and reacts with ice at temperatures above −116°C. Cesium hydroxide, the strongest base known, attacks glass. Because of its great affinity for oxygen the metal is used as a "getter" in radio tubes. It is also used in photoelectric cells, as well as a catalyst in the hydrogenation of certain organic compounds. The metal has recently found application in ion propulsion systems. Although these are not usable in the earth's atmosphere, 1 lb. of cesium in outer space theoretically will propel a vehicle 140 times as far as the burning of the same amount of any known liquid or solid. Cesium is used in atomic clocks, which are accurate to 5 sec. in 300 yrs. Its chief compounds are the chloride and the nitrate. The present price of cesium is about $100 to $150/lb., depending on quantity and purity.

CHLORINE (Gr. *chloros*, greenish-yellow), Cl; at. wt. 35.453; at. no. 17; f.p. −100.98°C; b.p. −34.6°C; density 3.214 g/l; sp. gr. 1.56 (−33.6°C); valence 1, 3, 5, or 7. Discovered in 1774 by Scheele, who thought it contained oxygen; named in 1810 by Davy, who insisted it was an element. In nature it is found in the combined state only, chiefly with sodium as common salt ($NaCl$), *carnallite* ($KMgCl_3 \cdot 6H_2O$), and *sylvite* (KCl). It is a member of the halogen (salt forming) group of elements and is obtained from chlorides by the action of oxidizing agents and more often by electrolysis; it is a greenish-yellow gas, combining directly with nearly all elements. At 10°C one volume of water dissolves 3.10 volumes of chlorine; at 30°C only 1.77 volumes. Chlorine is widely used in making many every-day products. It is used for producing safe drinking water the world over. Even the smallest water supplies are now usually chlorinated. It is also extensively used in the production of paper products, dyestuffs, textiles, petroleum products, medicines, antiseptics, insecticides, foodstuffs, solvents, paints, plastics, and many other consumer products. Most of the chlorine produced is used in the manufacture of chlorinated compounds for sanitation, pulp bleaching, disinfectants, and textile processing. Further use is in the manufacture of chlorates, chloroform, carbon tetrachloride and in the extraction of bromine. Organic chemistry demands much from chlorine, both as an oxidizing agent and in substitution, since it often brings desired properties in an organic compound when substituted for hydrogen, as in one form of synthetic rubber. Chlorine is a respiratory irritant. The gas irritates the mucous membranes and the liquid burns the skin. As little as 3.5 ppm. can be detected as an odor, and

1000 ppm. is likely to be fatal after a few deep breaths. It was used as a war gas in 1915. The recommended maximum allowable concentration in air is about 1 ppm. for prolonged exposure.

CHROMIUM (Gr. *chroma*, color), Cr; at. wt. 51.996; at. no. 24; m.p. 1857 ± 20°C; b.p. 2672°C; sp. gr. 7.18–7.20 (20°C); valence chiefly 2, 3, or 6. Discovered in 1797 by Vauquelin, who prepared the metal the next year. Chromium is a steel gray, lustrous, hard metal that takes a high polish. The principal ore is *chromite* ($FeO \cdot Cr_2O_3$), which is found in Southern Rhodesia, U.S.S.R., Transvaal, Turkey, Iran, Albania, Finland, Malagasy, and the Philippines. The metal is usually produced by reducing the oxide with aluminum. Chromium is used to harden steel, to manufacture stainless steel, and to form many very useful alloys. Much is used in plating to produce a hard, beautiful surface and to prevent corrosion. Chromium is used to give glass an emerald green color. It finds wide use as a catalyst. All compounds of chromium are colored; the most important are the chromates of sodium and potassium (K_2CrO_4) and the dichromates ($K_2Cr_2O_7$) and the potassium and ammonium chrome alums, as $KCr(SO_4)_2 \cdot 12H_2O$. The dichromates are used as oxidizing agents in quantitative analysis, also in tanning leather. Other compounds are of industrial value; lead chromate is chrome yellow, a valued pigment. Chromium compounds are used in the textile industry as mordants, and by the aircraft and other industries for anodizing aluminum. The refractory industry has found chromite useful for forming bricks and shapes, as it has a high melting point, moderate thermal expansion, and stability of crystalline structure. Hexavalent chromium compounds are toxic. The recommended maximum allowable concentration of dusts and mists in air, measured as CrO_3, is 0.1 mg./cu.m for daily 8-hr. exposure. Chromium is available in high-purity form.

COBALT (*Kobold*, from the German, goblin or evil spirit, *cobalos*, Greek, mine), Co; at. wt. 58.9332; at. no. 27; m.p. 1,495°C; b.p. 2,870°C; sp. gr. 8.9 (20°C); valence 2 or 3. Discovered by Brandt about 1735. Cobalt occurs in the minerals *cobaltite*, *smaltite*, and *erythrite*, and is often associated with nickel, silver, lead, copper, and iron ores, from which it is most frequently obtained as a by-product. It is also present in meteorites. Important ore deposits are found in Zaire, Morocco, and Canada. Cobalt is a brittle, hard metal, closely resembling iron and nickel in appearance. It has a magnetic permeability of about two-thirds that of iron. Cobalt tends to exist as a mixture of two allotropes over a wide temperature range; the β-form predominates below 400°C, and the α above that temperature. The transformation is sluggish and accounts in part for the wide variation in reported data on physical properties of cobalt. It is alloyed with iron, nickel, and other metals to make Alnico, an alloy of unusual magnetic strength with many important uses. Stellite alloys, containing cobalt, chromium, and tungsten, are used for high-speed, heavy-duty, high-temperature cutting tools, and for dies. Cobalt is also used in other magnet steels and stainless steels, and in alloys used in jet turbines and gas turbine generators. The metal is used in electroplating because of its appearance, hardness, and resistance to oxidation. The salts have been used for centuries for the production of brilliant and permanent blue colors in porcelain, glass, pottery, tiles, and enamels. It is the principal ingredient in Serves and Thénard's blue. A solution of the chloride ($CoCl_2 \cdot 6H_2O$) is used as sympathetic ink. The cobalt ammines are of interest; the oxide and the nitrate are important. Cobalt carefully used in the form of the chloride, sulfate, acetate, or nitrate has been found effective in correcting a certain mineral deficiency disease in animals. Soils should contain 0.13 to 0.30 ppm of cobalt for proper animal nutrition. Cobalt-60, an artificial isotope, is an important gamma ray source, and is extensively used as a tracer and a radiotherapeutic agent. Single compact sources of Cobalt-60 are readily available and have an equivalent gamma ray output equal to thousands of grams of radium. The cost of Cobalt-60 varies from about 40¢ to $7.00/curie, depending on quantity and specific activity.

COLUMBIUM (see Niobium).

COPPER (L. *cuprum*, from the island of Cyprus). Cu; at. wt. 63.546; at. no. 29; m.p. $1083.4 \pm 0.2°C$; b.p. 2567°C; sp. gr. 8.96 (20°C); valence 1 or 2. The discovery of copper dates from prehistoric times; it is said to have been mined for more than 5000 years. It is one of man's most important metals. Copper is reddish-colored, takes on a bright metallic luster and is malleable, ductile, and a good conductor of heat and electricity (second only to silver in electrical conductivity). The electrical industry is one of the greatest users of copper. Copper occasionally occurs native, and is found in many minerals, such as *cuprite*, *malachite*, *azurite*, *chalcopyrite*, and *bornite*. Large copper ore deposits are found in the U.S., Chile, Zambia, Zaire, Peru, and Rhodesia. The most important copper ores are the sulfides, oxides, and carbonates. From these copper is obtained by smelting, leaching and by electrolysis. Its alloys, brass and bronze, long used, are still very important; all American coins are now copper alloys; monel and gun metals also contain copper. The most important compounds are the oxide and the sulfate, blue vitriol; the latter has wide use as an agricultural poison and as an algicide in water purification. Copper compounds are widely used in analytical chemistry, such as Fehling's solution in tests for sugar. High-purity copper (99.999 + %) is available commercially.

CURIUM (Pierre and Marie Curie). Cm; at. wt. (247); at. no. 96; m.p. $1340 \pm 40°C$; sp. gr. 13.51 (calc.); valence 3 and 4. Although curium follows americium in the periodic system, it was actually known before americium and was the third transuranium element to be discovered. It was identified by Seaborg, James, and Ghiorso in 1944 at the wartime Metallurgical Laboratory in Chicago as a result of helium-ion bombardment of Pu^{239} in the Berkeley, California, 60-inch cyclotron. Visible amounts (30 micrograms) of Cm^{242}, in the form of the hydroxide, were first isolated by Werner and Perlman of the University of California in 1947. In 1950, Crane, Wallmann, and Cunningham found that the magnetic susceptibility of microgram samples of CmF_3 was of the same magnitude as that of GdF_3. This provided direct experimental evidence for assigning a $5f^7$ electronic configuration to Cm^{+3}. In 1951, the same workers prepared curium in its elemental form for the first time. Thirteen isotopes of curium are now known. The most stable, Cm^{247}, with a half-life of 16 million years, is so short compared to the earth's age that any primordial curium must have disappeared long ago from the natural scene. Minute amounts of curium probably exist in natural deposits of

uranium, as a result of a sequence of neutron captures and β decays sustained by the very low flux of neutrons naturally present in uranium ores. The presence of natural curium, however, has never been detected. Cm^{242} and Cm^{244} are available in multigram quantities. Cm^{248} has been produced only in milligram amounts. Curium is similar in some regards to gadolinium, its rare-earth homolog, but it has a more complex crystal structure. Curium is silver in color, is chemically reactive, and is more electropositive than aluminum. CmO_2, Cm_2O_3, CmF_3, CmF_4, $CmCl_3$, $CmBr_3$, and CmI_3 have been prepared. Most compounds of trivalent curium are faintly yellow in color. The A.E.C. is attempting to produce several kilograms of Cm^{244}, an isotope with a 17.6 yr. half-life, by neutron irradiation of plutonium in a nuclear reactor. Ultimately, it is possible that it may be produced in ton quantities by converting a number of plutonium production reactors to the manufacture of Cm^{244}. Cm^{242} generates about three thermal watts of energy/gm. This compares to one-half thermal watt/gm of Pu^{238}. This suggests use for curium as an isotopic power source. Cm^{244} is now offered for sale by the A.E.C at $100 milligram. Curium absorbed into the body accumulates in the bones, and is therefore very toxic as its radiation destroys the red-cell forming mechanism. The maximum permissible body burden of Cm^{244} in a human being is 0.002 micrograms.

DEUTERIUM, an isotope of hydrogen see Hydrogen.

DYSPROSIUM (Gr. *dysprositos*, hard to get at). Dy; at. wt. 162.50; at. no. 66; m.p. 1412 C; b.p. 2562 C; sp. gr. 8.550 (25°C); valence 3. Dysprosium was discovered in 1886 by Lecoq de Boisbaudran, but not isolated. Neither the oxide nor the metal was available in relatively pure form until the development of ion-exchange separation and metallographic reduction techniques by Spedding and associates about 1950. Dysprosium occurs along with other so-called rare-earth or lanthanide elements in a variety of minerals, such as *xenotime*, *fergusonite*, *gadolinite*, *euxenite*, *polycrase*, and *blomstrandine*. The most important sources, however, are from *monazite* and *bastnasite*. Dysprosium can be prepared by reduction of the trifluoride with calcium. The element has a metallic, bright silver luster. It is relatively stable in air at room temperature, and is readily attacked and dissolved, with the evolution of hydrogen, by dilute and concentrated mineral acids. The metal is soft enough to be cut with a knife and can be machined without sparking if overheating is avoided. Small amounts of impurities can greatly affect its physical properties. While dysprosium has not yet found many applications, its thermal neutron absorption cross-section and high melting point suggest metallurgical uses in nuclear control applications for alloying with special stainless steels. A dysprosium oxide–nickel cermet has found use in cooling nuclear reactor control rods. This cermet absorbs neutrons readily without swelling or contracting under prolonged neutron bombardment. In combination with vanadium and other rare earths, dysprosium has been used in making laser materials. Dysprosium-cadmium calcogenides, as sources of infrared radiation, have been used for studying chemical reactions. The cost of dysprosium metal has dropped in recent years since the development of ion-exchange and solvent extraction techniques, and the discovery of large ore bodies. The metal is still expensive, however, and costs about 70¢/gm. or $190/lb. in purities of 99 + %.

EINSTEINIUM (Albert Einstein). Es; at. wt. (254); at. no. 99. Einsteinium, the seventh transuranic element of the actinide series to be discovered, was identified by Ghiorso and coworkers at Berkeley in Dec. 1952 in debris from the first large thermonuclear or "hydrogen" bomb explosion, which took place in the Pacific in Nov. 1952. The isotope produced was the 20-day Es^{253} isotope. In 1961 a sufficient amount of einsteinium was produced to permit separation of a macroscopic amount of Es^{253}. This sample weighed about 0.01 microgram. A special magnetic-type balance was used in making this determination. Es^{253} so produced was used to produce mendelevium (Element 101). Recently, about three micrograms of einsteinium were produced at Oak Ridge National Laboratories by irradiating for several years kilogram quantities of Pu^{239} in a reactor to produce Pu^{242}. This was then fabricated into pellets of plutonium oxide and aluminum powder, and loaded into target rods for an initial one-year irradiation at the A.E.C.'s Savannah River Plant, followed by irradiation in a HFIR (High Flux Isotopic Reactor). After four months in the HFIR the targets were removed for chemical separation of the einsteinium from californium. Eleven isotopes of einsteinium are now recognized. Es^{254} has the longest half-life (276 days). Tracer studies using Es^{253} show that einsteinium has chemical properties typical of a heavy trivalent, actinide element.

ELEMENT 104. In 1964, workers of the Joint Nuclear Research Institute at Dubna (U.S.S.R.) bombarded plutonium with accelerated 113–115 MeV. neon ions. By measuring fission tracks in a special glass with a microscope, they detected an isotope that decays by spontaneous fission. They suggested that this isotope, which had a half-line of 0.3 ± 0.1 sec. might be 104^{260}, produced by the following reaction:

$$_{94}Pu^{242} + _{10}Ne^{22} \rightarrow 104^{260} + 4n.$$

Element 104, the first *transactinide* element, is expected to have chemical properties similar to those of hafnium. It would, for example, form a relatively volatile compound with chlorine (a tetrachloride). The Soviet scientists have performed experiments aimed at chemical identification, and have attempted to show that the 0.3-sec. activity is more volatile than that of the relatively nonvolatile actinide trichlorides. This experiment does not fulfill the test of chemically separating the new element from all others, but it provides important evidence for evaluation. New data, reportedly issued by Soviet scientists, have reduced the half-life of the isotope they worked with from 0.3 sec. to 0.15 sec. The Dubna scientists suggest the name *kurchatovium* and symbol *Ku* for Element 104, in honor of Igor Vasilevich Kurchatov (1903–1960), late Head of Soviet Nuclear Research. In 1969, Ghiorso, Nurmia, Harris, K. A. Y. Eskola and P. L. Eskola, of the Univ. of Calif. at Berkeley, reported they had positively identified two and possibly three, isotopes of Element 104. The Group also indicated that after repeated attempts, so far they have been unable to produce isotope 104^{260} reported by the Dubna Group in 1964. The discoveries at Berkeley were made by bombarding a target of Cf^{249} with C^{12} nuclei of 71 MeV, and C^{13} nuclei of 69 MeV. The combination of C^{12} with Cf^{249} followed by instant emission of four neutrons, produced Element 104^{257}. This isotope has a half-life of 4 to 5 secs., decaying by emitting an alpha particle into No^{253}, with a half-life of 105 secs. The same reaction, except with the emission of three neutrons, was thought to have produced 104^{258}, with a half-life of about 1/100 sec. Element 104^{259} is formed by the merging of a C^{13} nuclei with Cf^{249}, followed by emission of three neutrons. This isotope has a half-life of 3

to 4 secs., and decays by emitting an alpha particle into No^{255}, which has a half-life of 185 secs. Thousands of atoms of 104^{257} and 104^{259} have been detected. The Berkeley Group believe their identification of 104^{258} is correct, but they do not attach the same degree of confidence to this work as to their work on 104^{257} and 104^{259}. The Berkeley Group proposes for the new element the name *rutherfordium* (Symbol *Rf*), in honor of Ernest R. Rutherford, New Zealand physicist. The claims for discovery and the naming of Element 104 are still in question.

ELEMENT 105. In 1967 G. N. Flerov reported that a Soviet team working at the Jt. Inst. for Nuclear Research at Dubna may have produced a few atoms of 105^{260} and 105^{261} by bombarding Am^{243} with Ne^{22}. Their evidence was based on time-coincidence measurements of alpha energies. More recently it was reported that early in 1970 Dubna scientists synthesized Element 105 and that by the end of April 1970 "had investigated all the types of decay of the new element and had determined its chemical properties." The Soviet Group have not proposed a name for Element 105. In late April 1970, it was announced that Ghiorso, Nurmia, Harris, K. A. Y. Eskola, and P. L. Eskola, working at the Univ. of Calif. at Berkeley, had positively identified Element 105. The discovery was made by bombarding a target of Cf^{249} with a beam of 84 MeV nitrogen nuclei in the Heavy Ion Linear Accelerator (HILAC). When a N^{15} nuclei is absorbed by a Cf^{249} nucleus, four neutrons are emitted and a new atom of 105^{260} with a half-life of 1.6 secs., is formed. While the first atoms of Element 105 are said to have been detected conclusively on March 5, 1970, there is evidence that Element 105 had been formed in Berkeley experiments a year earlier by the method described. Ghiorso and his associates have attempted to confirm Soviet findings by more sophisticated methods without success. The Berkeley Group proposes the name *hahnium*, after the late German scientist Otto Hahn (1879–1968), and *Ha*, for the chemical symbol.

More recently, in October 1971, it was announced that two new isotopes of Element 105 were synthesized with the heavy ion linear accelerator by A. Ghiorso and coworkers at Berkeley. Element 105^{261} was produced both by bombarding Cf^{250} with N^{15} and by bombarding Bk^{249} with O^{16}. The isotope emits 8.93-MeV α particles and decays to Lr^{257} with a half-life of about 1.8 secs. Element 105^{262} was produced by bombarding Bk^{249} with O^{18}. It emits 8.45 MeV α particles and decays to Lr^{258} with a half-life of about 40 secs.

ELEMENT 106. In June 1974, members of the Joint Institute for Nuclear Research in Dubna, U.S.S.R., reported their discovery of Element 106, which they claim to have synthesized. In September 1974, workers of the Lawrence Berkeley and Livermore Laboratories also reported creation of Element 106 "without any scientific doubt." The LBL and LLL Group used the SuperHILAC to accelerate O^{18} ions onto a Cf^{249} target. Element 106 was created by the reaction Cf^{249} $(O^{18}4n)$ $_{106}X^{263}$, which decayed by α emission to rutherfordium, and then by α emission to nobelium, which in turn further decayed by α emission. An elaborate detection system not only looked for correlations between the new element and its daughter, but also between daughter and granddaughter. The element so identified had α energies of 9.06 and 9.25 MeV with a half-life of 0.9 ± 0.2 sec. At Dubna, 280-MeV ions of Cr^{54} from the 310-cm cyclotron were used to strike targets of Pb^{206}, Pb^{207}, and Pb^{208}, in separate runs. Foils exposed to a rotating target disc were used to detect spontaneous fission activities, the foils being etched and examined microscopically to detect the number of fission tracts and the half-life of the fission activity. Other experiments were made to aid in confirmation of the discovery. Neither the Dubna team nor the Berkeley-Livermore Group has proposed a name as yet for Element 106.

ERBIUM (*Ytterby*, a town in Sweden). Er; at. wt. 167.26; at. no. 68; m.p. 1529 C; b.p. 2863 C; sp. gr. 9.066 (25°C); valence 3. Erbium, one of the so-called rare-earth elements of the lanthanide series, is found in the minerals mentioned under dysprosium above. In 1842 Mosander separated "yttria", found in the mineral *gadolinite*, into three fractions which he called *yttria*, *erbia*, and *terbia*. The names *erbia* and *terbia* became confused in this early period. After 1860, Mosander's *terbia* was known as *erbia*, and after 1877, the earlier known *erbia* became *terbia*. The *erbia* of this period was later shown to consist of five oxides, now known as *erbia*, *scandia*, *holmia*, *thulia*, and *ytterbia*. By 1905 Urbain and James independently succeeded in isolating fairly pure Er_2O_3. Klemm and Bommer first produced reasonably pure erbium metal in 1934 by reducing the anhydrous chloride with potassium vapor. The pure metal is soft and malleable and has a bright, silvery, metallic luster. As with other rare-earth metals, its properties depend to a certain extent on the impurities present. The metal is fairly stable in air and does not oxidize as rapidly as some of the other rare-earth metals. Natural-occurring erbium is a mixture of six isotopes, all of which are stable. Nine radioactive isotopes of erbium are also recognized. Recent production techniques, using ion-exchange reactions, have resulted in much lower prices of the rare-earth metals and their compounds in recent years. The cost of 99 + "₀ erbium metal is about $1.00 per gram, in small quantities. Erbium is finding nuclear and metallurgical uses. Added to vanadium, for example, erbium lowers the hardness and improves workability. Most of the rare-earth oxides have sharp absorption bands in the visible, ultraviolet, and near infrared. This property, associated with the electronic structure, gives beautiful pastel colors to many of the rare-earth salts. Erbium oxide gives a pink color and has been used as a colorant in glasses and porcelain enamel glazes.

EUROPIUM (Europe). Eu; at. wt. 151.96; at. no. 63; m.p. 822 C; b.p. 1597°C; sp. gr. 5.243 (25°C); valence 2 or 3. In 1890 Boisbaudran obtained basic fractions from samarium-gadolinium concentrates which had spark spectral lines not accounted for by samarium or gadolinium. These lines subsequently have been shown to belong to europium. The discovery of europium is generally credited to Demarcay, who separated the earth in reasonably pure form in 1901. The pure metal was not isolated until recent years. Europium is now prepared by mixing Eu_2O_3 with a 10"₀-excess of lanthanum metal and heating the mixture in a tantalum crucible under high vacuum. The element is collected as a silvery-white metallic deposit on the walls of the crucible. As with other rare-earth metals, except for lanthanum, europium ignites in air at about 150° to 180°C. Europium is about as hard as lead and is quite ductile. It is the most reactive of the rare-earth metals, quickly oxidizing in air. It resembles calcium in its reaction with water. *Bastnasite* and *monazite* are the principal ores containing europium. Europium has been identified spectroscopically in the sun and certain stars. Seventeen isotopes are now

recognized. Europium isotopes are good neutron absorbers and are being studied for use in nuclear control applications. Europium oxide is now widely used as a phosphor activator, and europium-activated yttrium vanadate is in commercial use as the red phosphor in color TV tubes. Europium-doped plastic has been used as a laser material. With the development of ion-exchange techniques and special processes, the cost of the metal has been greatly reduced in recent years. Europium is one of the rarest and most costly of the rare-earth metals. It is priced at about $11 to $15 gm., or $4000 lb.

FERMIUM (Enrico Fermi). Fm; at. wt. (257); at. no. 100. Fermium, the eighth transuranium element of the actinide series to be discovered, was identified by Ghiorso and co-workers in 1952 in the debris from a thermonuclear explosion in the Pacific in work involving the University of California Radiation Laboratory, the Argonne National Laboratory, and the Los Alamos Scientific Laboratory. The isotope produced was the 20-hour Fm^{255}. During 1953 and early 1954, while discovery of elements 99 and 100 was withheld from publication for security reasons, a group from the Nobel Institute of Physics in Stockholm bombarded U^{238} with O^{16} ions, and isolated a 30-min. α-emitter, which they ascribed to 100^{250}, without claiming discovery of the element. This isotope has since been identified positively, and the 30-min. half-life confirmed. The chemical properties of fermium have been studied solely with tracer amounts, and in normal aqueous media only the (III) oxidation state appears to exist. The isotope Fm^{254} and heavier isotopes can be produced by intense neutron irradiation of lower elements, such as plutonium, by a process of successive neutron capture interspersed with beta decays until these mass numbers and atomic numbers are reached. Ten isotopes of fermium are known to exist. Fm^{257}, with a half-life of about 80 days, is the longest lived. Fm^{250}, with a half-life of 30 min., has been shown to be a product of decay of Element 102^{254}. It was by chemical identification of Fm^{250} that it was certain that Element 102 (Nobelium) had been produced.

FLUORINE (L. and F. *fluere*, flow, or flux). F; at. wt. 18.99840; at. no. 9; m.p. $-219.62°C$ (1 atm.); b.p. $-188.14°C$ (1 atm.); density 1.696 g/l (0°C, 1 atm.); sp. gr. of liquid 1.108 at b.p.; valence 1. In 1529, Georgius Agricola described the use of fluorspar as a flux, and as early as 1670 Schwandhard found that glass was etched when exposed to fluorspar treated with acid. Scheele and many later investigators, including Davy, Gay-Lussac, Lavoisier, and Thenard, experimented with hydrofluoric acid, some experiments ending in tragedy. The element was finally isolated in 1886 by Moisson after nearly 74 years of continuous effort. Fluorine occurs chiefly in *fluorspar* (CaF_2) and *cryolite* (Na_2AlF_6), but is rather widely distributed in other minerals. It is a member of the halogen family of elements, and obtained by electrolyzing a solution of potassium hydrogen fluoride in anhydrous hydrogen fluoride in a vessel of metal or transparent fluorspar. Modern commercial production methods are essentially variations on the procedures first used by Moisson. Fluorine is the most electronegative and reactive of all elements. It is a pale yellow, corrosive gas, which reacts with practically all organic and inorganic substances. Finely divided metals, glass, ceramics, carbon, and even water burn in fluorine with a bright flame. Until World War II, there was no commercial production of elemental fluorine. The atom-bomb project and nuclear energy applications, however, made it necessary to produce large quantities. Safe handling techniques have now been developed and it is possible at present to transport liquid fluorine by the ton. Fluorine and its compounds are used in producing uranium (from the hexafluoride) and more than 100 commercial fluorochemicals, including many well-known high-temperature plastics. Hydrofluoric acid is extensively used for etching the glass of light bulbs, etc. Fluorochloro hydrocarbons are extensively used in air conditioning and refrigeration. It has been suggested that fluorine can be substituted for hydrogen wherever it occurs in organic compounds, which could lead to an astronomical number of new fluorine compounds. The presence of fluorine as a soluble fluoride in drinking water to the extent of 2 ppm may cause mottled enamel in teeth, when used by children acquiring permanent teeth; in smaller amounts, however, fluorides are said to be beneficial and used in water supplies to prevent dental cavities. Elemental fluorine is being studied as a rocket propellant as it has an exceptionally high specific impulse value. Compounds of fluorine with rare gases have now been confirmed. Fluorides of xenon, radon, and krypton are among those reported. Elemental fluorine and the fluoride ion are highly toxic. The free element has a characteristic pungent odor, detectable in concentrations as low as 20 parts per billion, which is below the safe working level. The recommended maximum allowable concentration for a daily 8-hr. exposure is 0.1 ppm.

FRANCIUM (France), Fr; at. no. 87; at. wt. (223); m.p. (27°C); b.p. (677°C); valence 1. Discovered in 1939 by Mlle. Marguerite Perey of the Curie Institute, Paris. Francium, the heaviest known member of the alkali metal series, occurs as a result of an alpha disintegration of actinium. It can also be made artificially by bombarding thorium with protons. While it occurs naturally in uranium minerals, there is probably less than an ounce of francium at any time in the total crust of the earth. It has the highest equivalent weight of any element, and is the most unstable of the first 101 elements of the periodic system. Twenty isotopes of francium are recognized. The longest lived, $Fr^{223}(AcK)$ a daughter of Ac^{227}, has a half-life of 22 minutes. This is the only isotope of francium occurring in nature. Because all known isotopes of francium are highly unstable, knowledge of the chemical properties of this element comes from radiochemical techniques. No weighable quantity of the element has been prepared or isolated. The chemical properties of francium most closely resemble cesium.

GADOLINIUM (*gadolinite*—a mineral named for Gadolin, a Finnish chemist), Gd; at. wt. 157.25; at. no. 64; m.p. 1313± 1°C; b.p. 3266 C; sp. gr.7.9004(25°C); valence 3. Gadolinia, the oxide of gadolinium, was separated by Marignac in 1880 and Lecoq de Boisbaudran independently isolated the element from Mosander's "yttria" in 1886. The element was named for the mineral *gadolinite* from which this rare earth was originally obtained. Gadolinium is found in several other minerals, including *monazite* and *bastnasite*, which are of commercial importance. The element has been isolated only in recent years. With the development of ion-exchange and solvent extraction techniques, the availability and price of gadolinium and the other rare-earth metals have greatly improved. Seventeen isotopes of gadolinium are now recognized. Seven occur naturally. The metal can be prepared by the reduction of the anhydrous fluoride with metallic calcium. As with other related rare-earth metals, it is silvery-white, has a metallic luster, and is malleable and ductile. At room temperature, gadolinium crystallizes in the hexagonal, close-packed α form. Upon heating to 1262°C α gadolinium transforms into the β

form, which has a body-centered cubic structure. The metal is relatively stable in dry air, but in moist air, it tarnishes with the formation of a loosely adhering oxide film which spalls off and exposes more surface to oxidation. The metal reacts slowly with water and is soluble in dilute acid. Gadolinium has the highest thermal neutron capture cross-section of any known element (49,000 barns). Natural gadolinium is a mixture of seven isotopes. Two of these, Gd^{155} and Gd^{157} have excellent capture characteristics, but they are present naturally in low concentrations. As a result, gadolinium has a very fast burnout rate and has limited use as a nuclear control rod material. It has been used in making gadolinium yttrium garnets, which have microwave applications. Compounds of gadolinium are used in making phosphors for color TV tubes. The metal has unusual superconductive properties. As little as 1% gadolinium has been found to improve the workability and resistance of iron, chromium, and related alloys to high temperatures and oxidation. Gadolinium ethyl sulfate has extremely low noise characteristics and may find use in duplicating the performance of h.f. amplifiers, such as the maser. The metal is ferromagnetic. Gadolinium is unique for its high magnetic moment and for its special Curie temperature (above which ferromagnetism vanishes) lying just at room temperature. This suggests uses as a magnetic component that senses hot and cold. The price of the metal is $1.25/gm. or $250/lb.

GALLIUM (L. *Gallia*, France), Ga; at. wt. 69.72; at. no. 31; m.p. 29.78°C; b.p. 2403°C; sp. gr. 5.904 (29.6°C) solid; sp. gr. 6.095 (29.8°C) liquid; valence 2 or 3. Predicted and described by Mendeleev as ekaaluminum, and discovered spectroscopically by Lecoq de Boisbaudran in 1875, who in the same year obtained the free metal by electrolysis of a solution of the hydroxide in KOH. Gallium is often found as a trace element in *diaspore*, *sphalerite*, *germanite*, *bauxite*, and *coal*. Some flue dusts from burning coal have been shown to contain as much as 1.5% gallium. It is the only metal, except for mercury, cesium, and rubidium, which can be liquid near room temperatures; this makes possible its use in high-temperature thermometers. It has one of the longest liquid ranges of any metal and has a low vapor pressure even at high temperatures. There is a strong tendency for gallium to supercool below its freezing point. Therefore seeding may be necessary to initiate solidification. Ultra-pure gallium has a beautiful, silvery appearance and the solid metal exhibits a conchoidal fracture similar to glass. The metal expands 3.1% on solidifying; therefore, it should not be stored in glass or metal containers as they may break as the metal solidifies. Gallium wets glass or porcelain, and forms a brilliant mirror when it is painted on glass. It has found recent use in doping semiconductors and producing solid-state devices, such as transistors. High-purity gallium is attacked only slowly by mineral acids. Magnesium gallate containing divalent impurities, such as Mn^{+2}, is finding use in commercial ultraviolet activated powder phosphors. Gallium arsenide is capable of converting electricity directly into coherent light. Gallium readily alloys with most metals, and has been used as a component in low-melting alloys. Its toxicity appears to be of a low order, but should be handled with care until more data are forthcoming. The metal can be supplied in ultra-pure form (99.99999 + %).

GERMANIUM (L. *Germania*, Germany), Ge; at. wt. 72.59; at. no. 32; m.p. 937.4°C; b.p. 2,830°C; sp. gr. 5.323 (25°C); valence 2 and 4. Predicted by Mendeleev in 1871 as ekasilicon, and discovered by Winkler in 1886.

The metal is found in *argyrodite,* a sulfide of germanium and silver; in *germanite,* which contains 8% of the element; in zinc ores; in coal; and in other minerals. The element is frequently obtained commercially from flue dusts of smelters processing zinc ores, and has been recovered from the by-products of combustion of certain coals. Its presence in coal insures a large reserve of the element in the years to come. Germanium can be separated from other metals by fractional distillation of its volatile tetrachloride. The tetrachloride may then be hydrolyzed to give GeO_2; then the dioxide can be reduced with hydrogen to give the metal. Recently developed zone-refining techniques permit the production of germanium of ultra-high purity. The element is a gray-white metalloid, and in its pure state is crystalline and brittle, retaining its luster in air at room temperature. It is a very important semiconductor material. Zone-refining techniques have led to production of crystalline germanium for semiconductor use with an impurity of only one part in 10^{10}. Doped with arsenic, gallium, or other elements, it is used as a transistor element in thousands of electronic applications. Transistors now provide the largest use for the element, but germanium is also finding many other applications including use as an alloying agent, as a phosphor in fluorescent lamps, and as a catalyst. Germanium and germanium oxide are transparent to the infrared and are used in infrared spectroscopes and other optical equipment, including extremely sensitive infrared detectors. Germanium oxide's high index of refraction and dispersion has made it useful as a component of glasses used in wide-angle camera lenses and microscope objectives. The field of organogermanium chemistry is becoming increasingly important. Certain germanium compounds have a low mammalian toxicity, but a marked activity against certain bacteria, which makes them of interest as chemotherapeutic agents. The cost of germanium is about 50¢/gram for 99.9+% purity in small lots.

GOLD (Sanskrit *Jval;* Anglo-Saxon *gold*), Au (L. *aurum,* shining dawn); at. wt. 196.9665; at. no. 79; m.p. 1,064.43°C; b.p. 2,807°C; sp. gr. 19.32 (20°C); valence 1 or 3. Known and highly valued from earliest times. Gold is found in nature as the free metal and in tellurides; it is very widely distributed and is almost always associated with quartz or pyrite. It occurs in veins and alluvial deposits, and is often separated from rocks and other minerals by sluicing or panning operations. About two-thirds of the world's gold output now comes from South Africa, and about two thirds of the total U.S. production comes from South Dakota and Nevada. The metal is recovered from its ores by cyaniding, amalgamating, and smelting processes. Refining is also frequently done by electrolysis. Gold occurs in sea water to the extent of 0.1 to 2 mg/ton, depending on the location where the sample is taken. As yet no method has been found for recovering gold from sea water profitably. It is estimated that all the gold in the world, so far refined, could be placed in a single cube 50 ft on a side. Of all the elements, gold in its pure state is undoubtedly the most beautiful. It is metallic, having a yellow color when in a mass, but when finely divided it may be black, ruby, or purple. The Purple of Cassius is a delicate test for auric gold. It is the most malleable and ductile metal; 1 oz of gold can be beaten out to 300 ft². It is a soft metal and is usually alloyed to give it more strength. It is a good conductor of heat and electricity, and is unaffected by air and most reagents. It is used in coinage and is a standard for monetary systems in many countries. It is also extensively used for jewelry, decoration, dental work, and for plating. It is used for coating certain space satellites, as it is a good reflector of infrared and is inert. Gold, like other precious metals, is measured in troy weight; when alloyed with other metals, the term *carat* is used to express the amount of gold present, 24 carats being pure gold. For many years the value of gold was set by the U.S. at $20.67/troy ounce; in 1934 this value was fixed by law at $35.00/troy ounce, 9/10th fine. On March 17, 1968, because of a gold crisis, a two-tiered pricing system was established whereby gold was still used to settle international accounts at the old $35.00/troy ounce price while the price of gold on the private market would be allowed to fluctuate. Since this time, the price of gold on the free market has fluctuated widely. On March 19, 1968, President Johnson signed into law a bill removing the last statutory requirement for a gold backing against U.S. currency. On August 15, 1971, President Nixon announced an embargo on U.S. gold to settle international accounts, and on May 18, 1972, U.S. monetary gold was revalued at $38/troy ounce. In February 1973 the U.S. in effect devalued the dollar by another 10%, decreasing the dollar in relation to gold from $38.00 to $42.22/troy ounce. On September 21, 1973, President Nixon signed a bill ratifying the action taken earlier in February; the bill also restored to private U.S. citizens the right to own gold after December 31, 1973 (private possession, except for gold in the form of jewelry, certain coins, etc., had been prohibited since 1933 when the U.S. went off the gold standard). The final version of the bill gave the President discretion to lift the ban when he determined that private ownership would not impair the monetary position during this period of instability. President Ford signed final legislation on August 14, 1974, lifting the 41-year ban, to be effective after December 31, 1974. By this date the price of gold on the free market had reached an all-time high of about $200/troy ounce. The most common gold compounds are auric chloride ($AuCl_3$) and chlorauric acid ($HAuCl_4$), the latter being used in photography for toning the silver image. Gold has 18 isotopes; Au^{198}, with a half-life of 2.7 days, is used for treating cancer and other diseases. Disodium aurothiomalate is administered intramuscularly as a treatment for arthritis. A mixture of one part nitric acid with three of hydrochloric acid is called *aqua regia* (because it dissolved gold, the King of Metals). Gold is available commercially with a purity of 99.999 + %. For many years the temperature assigned to the freezing point of gold has been 1,063.0°C; this has served as a calibration point for the International Temperature Scales (ITS-27 and ITS-48) and the International Practical Temperature Scale (ITPS-48). In 1968 a new International Practical Temperature Scale (ITPS-68) was adopted, which demands that the freezing point of gold be changed to 1,064.43°C. Although workers in precision temperature measurement should adopt IPTS-68 immediately, many of the scale changes are of minor significance to the routine user. IPTS-68 has defined several other fixed temperature points, among which are the boiling points of hydrogen, neon, oxygen, and sulfur, and the freezing points of zinc, silver, tin, lead, antimony, and aluminum.

HAFNIUM (*Hafnia*, Latin name for Copenhagen), Hf; at. wt. 178.49; at. no. 72; m.p. 2227 $\pm$ 20°C; b.p. 4602°C; sp. gr. 13.31 (20°C); valence 4. Hafnium was thought to be present in various minerals and concentrations many years prior to its discovery, in 1923, credited to D. Coster and G. von Hevesey. On the basis of the Bohr theory, the new element was expected to be associated with zirconium. It was finally identified in *zircon* from Norway, by means of X-ray spectroscopic analysis. It was named in honor of the city in which the discovery was made. Most zirconium minerals contain 1 to 5% hafnium. It was originally separated from zirconium by repeated recrystallization of the double ammonium or potassium fluorides by von Hevesey and Jantzen. Metallic hafnium was first prepared by van Arkel and deBoer by passing the vapor of the tetra-iodide over a heated tungsten filament. Almost all hafnium metal now produced is made by reducing the tetrachloride with magnesium or with sodium (Kroll Process). Hafnium is a ductile metal with a brilliant silver luster. Its properties are considerably influenced by the impurities of zirconium present. Of all the elements, zirconium and hafnium are the two of the most difficult to separate. Their chemistry is almost identical; however the density of zirconium is about half that of hafnium. Very pure hafnium has been produced with zirconium being the major impurity. Because hafnium has a good absorption cross section for thermal neutrons (almost 600 times that of zirconium), has excellent mechanical properties, and is extremely corrosion resistant, it is used for reactor control rods. Such rods are used in nuclear submarines. Hafnium has been successfully alloyed with iron, titanium, niobium, tantalum, and other metals. Hafnium carbide is the most refractory binary composition known, and the nitride is the most refractory of all known metal nitrides (m.p. 3310°C). Hafnium is used in gas-filled and incandescent lamps, and is an efficient "getter" for scavenging oxygen and nitrogen. Finely divided hafnium is pyrophoric and can ignite spontaneously in air. Care should be taken when machining the metal or when handling hot sponge hafnium. At 700°C hafnium rapidly absorbs hydrogen to form the composition $HfH_{1.86}$. Hafnium is resistant to concentrated alkalis, but at elevated temperatures reacts with oxygen, nitrogen, carbon, boron, sulfur, and silicon. Halogens react directly to form tetrahalides. The price of the metal is in the broad range of $30 to $175/lb., depending on purity and quantity. The yearly demand for hafnium in the U.S. is now in excess of 60,000 lbs.

HAHNIUM (See Element 105)

HELIUM (Gr. *helios*, the sun), He; at. wt. 4.00260; at. no. 2; m.p. below −272.2°C (26 atm); b.p. −268.934°C; density 0.1785 gm/l (0°C, 1 atm.); liquid density 7.62 lb./cu. ft. at b.p.; valence usually 0. Evidence of the existence of helium was first obtained by Janssen during the solar eclipse of 1868 when he detected a new line in the solar spectrum; Lockyer and Frankland suggested the name *helium* for the new element; in 1895 Ramsay discovered helium in the uranium mineral *clevite*, and it was independently discovered in clevite by the Swedish chemists Cleve and Langlet about the same time. Rutherford and Royds in 1907 demonstrated that α particles are helium nuclei. Except for hydrogen, helium is the most abundant element found throughout the universe. It has been detected spectroscopically in great abundance, especially in the hotter stars, and it is an important component in both the proton-proton reaction and the carbon cycle, which account for the energy of the sun and stars. The fusion of hydrogen into helium provides the energy of the hydrogen bomb. The helium content of the atmosphere is about 1 part in 200,000. While it is present in various radioactive minerals as a decay product, the bulk of the Free World's supply is obtained from wells in Texas, Oklahoma, and Kansas. The only helium plant in the Free World outside the U.S. is near Swift River, Saskatchewan. The cost of helium fell from $2500/cu. ft. in 1915 to 1.5 cent/cu. ft. in 1940. The U.S. Bureau of Mines has set the price of Grade A helium at $35/1000 cu. ft. Helium has the lowest m.p. of any element and has found wide use in cryogenic research as its b.p. is close to absolute zero. Its use in the study of superconductivity is vital. Using liquid helium, Kurti and co-workers, and others, have succeeded in obtaining temperatures of a few microdegrees Kelvin, by the adiabatic demagnetization of copper nuclei, starting from about 0.01°K. Five isotopes of helium are known. Liquid helium (He^4) exists in two forms: He^4 I and He^4 II, with a sharp transition point at 2.174°K (3.83 cm Hg). He^4 I (above this temperature) is a normal liquid, but He^4 II (below it) is unlike any other known substance. It expands on cooling; its conductivity for heat is enormous; and neither its heat conduction nor viscosity obey normal rules. It has other peculiar properties. Helium is the only liquid that cannot be solidified by lowering the temperature. It remains liquid down to absolute zero at ordinary pressures, but it can readily be solidified by increasing the pressure. Solid He^3 and He^4 are unusual in that both can readily be changed in volume by more than 30% by application of pressure. The specific heat of helium gas is unusually high. The density of helium vapor at the normal boiling point is also very high, with the vapor expanding greatly when heated to room temperature. Containers filled with helium gas at 5 to 10°K should be treated as though they contained liquid helium due to the large increase in pressure resulting from warming the gas to room temperature. While helium normally has a 0 valence, it seems to have a weak tendency to combine with certain other elements. Means of preparing helium difluoride are being studied, and species, such as HeNe and the molecular ions He_2^+ and He_2^{++} have been investigated. Helium is widely used as an inert gas shield for arc welding; as a protective gas in growing silicon and germanium crystals, and in titanium and zirconium production; as a cooling medium for nuclear reactors; and as a gas for supersonic wind tunnels. A mixture of 80% helium and 20% oxygen is used as an artificial atmosphere for divers and others working under pressure. Helium is extensively used for filling balloons as it is a much safer gas than hydrogen. While its density is almost twice that of hydrogen, it has about 98% of the lifting power of hydrogen. At sea level, 1000 cu. ft. of helium lifts 68.5 lb. One of the recent largest uses for helium has been for pressuring liquid fuel rockets. A Saturn booster, such as used on the Apollo lunar missions, requires about 13 million cubic feet of helium for a firing, plus more for checkouts.

HOLMIUM (L. *Holmia*, for Stockholm), Ho; at. wt. 164.9304; at. no. 67; m.p. 1474 C; b.p. 2695 C; sp. gr. 8.795 (25°C); valence +3. The spectral absorption bands of holmium were noticed in 1878 by the Swiss chemists Delafontaine and Soret, who announced the existence of an

"Element X". Cleve, of Sweden, later independently discovered the element while working on erbia earth. The element is named after Cleve's native city. Pure holmia, the yellow oxide, was prepared by Homberg in 1911. Holmium occurs in *gadolinite*, *monazite*, and in other rare-earth minerals. It is commercially obtained from *monazite*, occurring in that mineral to the extent of about 0.05%. It has been isolated in pure form only in recent years. It can be separated from other rare earths by ion-exchange and solvent extraction techniques, and isolated by the reduction of its anhydrous chloride or fluoride with calcium metal. Pure holmium has a metallic to bright silver luster. It is relatively soft and malleable, and is stable in dry air at room temperature, but rapidly oxidizes in moist air and at elevated temperatures. The metal has unusual magnetic properties. Few uses have yet been found for the element. The element, as with other rare earths, seems to have a low acute toxic rating. The price of 99 + % holmium metal is about $1.50/gm. or $500/lb.

HYDROGEN (Gr. *hydro*, water, and *genes*, forming), H; at. wt. (natural) 1.0079; at. wt. (H^1) 1.007822; at. no. 1; m.p. $-259.14°C$; b.p. $-252.87°C$; density 0.08988 g/l; density (liquid) 70.8 g/l ($-253°C$); density (solid) 70.6 g/l ($-262°C$); valence 1. Hydrogen was prepared many years before it was recognized as a distinct substance by Cavendish in 1766. It was named by Lavoisier. Hydrogen is the most abundant of all elements in the universe, and it is thought that the heavier elements were, and still are, being built from hydrogen and helium. It has been estimated that hydrogen makes up more than 90% of all the atoms or three-quarters of the mass of the universe. It is found in the sun and most stars, and plays an important part in the proton-proton reaction and carbon-nitrogen cycle, which accounts for the energy of the sun and stars. It is thought that hydrogen is a major component of the planet Jupiter and that at some depth in the planet's interior the pressure is so great that solid molecular hydrogen is converted into solid metallic hydrogen. In 1973, it was reported that a group of Russian experimenters may have produced metallic hydrogen at a pressure of 2.8 megabars. At the transition the density changed from 1.08 to 1.3 g/cm^3. Earlier, in 1972, a Livermore (California) group also reported on a similar experiment in which they observed a pressure-volume point centered at 2 megabars. It has been predicted that metallic hydrogen may be metastable; others have predicted it would be a superconductor at room temperature. On earth, hydrogen occurs chiefly in combination with oxygen in water, but it is also present in organic matter such as living plants, petroleum, coal, etc. It is present as the free element in the atmosphere, but only to the extent of less than 1 ppm, by volume. It is the lightest of all gases, and combines with other elements, sometimes explosively, to form compounds. Great quantities of hydrogen are required commercially for the fixation of nitrogen from the air in the Haber ammonia process and for the hydrogenation of fats and oils. It is also used in large quantities in methanol production, in hydrodealkylation, hydrocracking, and hydrodesulfurization. It is also used as a rocket fuel, for welding, for production of hydrochloric acid, for the reduction of metallic ores, and for filling balloons. The

lifting power of 1 ft^3 of hydrogen gas is about 0.076 lb at 0°C, 760 mm pressure. Production of hydrogen in the U.S. alone now amounts to hundreds of millions of cubic feet per day. It is prepared by the action of steam on heated carbon, by decomposition of certain hydrocarbons with heat, by the electrolysis of water, or by the displacement from acids by certain metals. It is also produced by the action of sodium or potassium hydroxide on aluminum. Liquid hydrogen is important in cryogenics and in the study of superconductivity as its melting point is only a few degrees above absolute zero. The ordinary isotope of hydrogen, $_1H^1$, is known as *protium*. In 1932, Urey announced the preparation of a stable isotope, deuterium ($_1H^2$ or D) with an atomic weight of 2. Two years later an unstable isotope, tritium ($_1H^3$), with an atomic weight of 3 was discovered. Tritium has a half-life of about 12.5 years. One part deuterium is found to be about 6,000 ordinary hydrogen atoms. Tritium atoms are also present but in much smaller proportion. Tritium is readily produced in nuclear reactors and is used in the production of the hydrogen bomb. It is also used as a radioactive agent in making luminous paints, and as a tracer. The current price of tritium, to authorized personnel, is about $2/curie; deuterium gas is readily available, without permit, at about $1/liter. Heavy water, deuterium oxide (D_2O), which is used as a moderator to slow down neutrons, is available without permit at a cost of 6¢ to $1/gram, depending on quantity and purity. Quite apart from isotopes, it has been shown that hydrogen gas under ordinary conditions is a mixture of two kinds of molecules, known as *ortho*- and *para*-hydrogen, which differ from one another by the spins of their electrons and nuclei. Normal hydrogen at room temperature contains 25% of the *para* form and 75% of the *ortho* form. The *ortho* form cannot be prepared in the pure state. Since the two forms differ in energy, the physical properties also differ. The melting and boiling points of *para*-hydrogen are about 0.1°C lower than those of normal hydrogen.

INDIUM (from the brilliant indigo line in its spectrum), In; at. wt. 114.82; at. no. 49; m.p. 156.61°C; b.p. 2080°C; sp. gr. 7.31 (20°C); valence 1, 2, or 3. Discovered by Reich and Richter, who later isolated the metal. Indium is most frequently associated with zinc minerals, and it is from these that most commercial indium is now obtained; however, it is also found in iron, lead, and copper ores. Until 1924, a gram or so constituted the world's supply of this element in isolated form. It is probably about as abundant as silver. One to 1½ million troy ounces of indium are now produced annually in the Free World. Japan is presently producing more than 250,000 troy oz. annually. The present cost of indium is about $1.50 to $5.00/troy oz., depending on quantity and purity. It is available in ultrapure form. Indium is a very soft, silvery-white metal with a brilliant luster. The pure metal gives a high-pitched "cry" when bent. It wets glass, as does gallium. It has found application in making low-melting alloys; an alloy of 24% indium–76% gallium is liquid at room temperature. It is used in making bearing alloys, germanium transistors, rectifiers, thermistors, and photoconductors. It can be plated onto metal and evaporated onto glass forming a mirror as good as that made with silver, but with more resistance to atmospheric corrosion. There is evidence that indium has a low order of toxicity. Normal hygienic precautions should provide adequate protection.

IODINE (Gr. *iodes*, violet), I; at. wt. 126.9045; at. no. 53; m.p. 113.5°C; b.p. 184.35°C; density of the gas 11.27 g/l; sp. gr. solid 4.93 (20°C): valence 1, 3, 5, or 7. Discovered by Courtois in 1811. Iodine, a halogen, occurs sparingly in the form of iodides in sea water from which it is assimilated by seaweeds, in Chilean saltpeter and nitrate-bearing earth, known as *caliche*, in brines from old sea deposits, and in brackish waters from oil and salt wells. Ultrapure iodine can be obtained from the reaction of potassium iodide with copper sulfate. Several other methods of isolating the element are known. Iodine is a bluish-black, lustrous solid, volatilizing at ordinary temperatures into a blue-violet gas with an irritating odor; it forms compounds with many elements, but is less active than the other halogens, which displace it from iodides. Iodine exhibits some metallic-like properties. It dissolves readily in chloroform, carbon tetrachloride, or carbon disulfide to form beautiful purple solutions. It is only slightly soluble in water. Iodine compounds are important in organic chemistry and very useful in medicine. Twenty-three isotopes are recognized. Only one stable isotope, I^{127}, is found in nature. The artificial radioisotope I^{131}, with a half-life of 8 days, has been used in treating the thyroid gland. The most common compounds are the iodides of sodium and potassium (KI) and the iodates (KIO_3). Lack of iodine is the cause of goiter. The iodide, and thyroxin which contains iodine, are used internally in medicine, and a solution of KI and iodine in alcohol is used for external wounds. Potassium iodide finds use in photography. The deep blue color with starch solution is characteristic of the free element. Care should be taken in handling and using iodine as contact with the skin can cause lesions; iodine vapor is intensely irritating to the eyes and mucous membranes. The recommended maximum allowable concentration in air is 1 mg/cu. meter.

IRIDIUM (L. *iris*, rainbow), Ir; at. wt. 192.22; at. no. 77; m.p. 2410°C; b.p. 4130°C; sp. gr. 22.42 (17°C); valence 3 or 4. Discovered in 1803 by Tennant in the residue left when crude platinum is dissolved by aqua regia. The name iridium is appropriate, for its salts are highly colored. Iridium, a metal of the platinum family, is white, similar to platinum, but with a slight yellowish cast. It is very hard and brittle, making it very hard to machine, form, or work. It is the most corrosion-resistant metal known, and was used in making the standard meter bar of Paris, which is a 90% platinum–10% iridium alloy. This meter bar has since been replaced as a fundamental unit of length (see under Krypton). Iridium occurs uncombined in nature with platinum and other metals of this family in alluvial deposits. It is recovered as a byproduct from the nickel mining industry. Iridium has found use in making crucibles and apparatus for use at high temperatures. It is also used for electrical contacts. Its principal use is as a hardening agent for platinum. With osmium, it forms an alloy which is used for tipping pens and compass bearings. The specific gravity of iridium is only very slightly lower than that of osmium, which has been generally credited as being the heaviest known element. Calculations of the densities of iridium and osmium from the space lattices give values of 22.65 and 22.61 gms./cu. cm., respectively. These values may be more reliable than actual physical measurements. At present, therefore, we know that either iridium or osmium is the densest known element, but the data do not yet allow selection between the two. Iridium costs about $160 to $190/troy ounce.

IRON (Anglo-Saxon, *iron*) Fe, (L, *ferrum*); at. wt. 55.847; at. no. 26; m.p. 1535°C; b.p. 2750°C; sp. gr. 7.874 (20°C); valence 2, 3, 4, or 6. The use of iron is prehistoric. Genesis mentions that Tubal-Cain, seven generations from Adam, was "an instructer of every artificer in brass and iron." A remarkable iron pillar, dating to about A.D. 400, remains standing today in Delhi, India. This solid shaft of wrought iron is about $7\frac{1}{4}$ meters high by 40 cm. in diameter. Corrosion to the pillar has been minimal although it has been exposed to the weather since its erection. Iron is a relatively abundant element in the universe. It is found in the sun and many types of stars in considerable quantity. Its nuclei are very stable. Iron is found native as a principal component of a class of meteorites known as *siderites*, and is a minor constituent of the other two classes. The core of the earth, 2150 miles in radius, is thought to be largely composed of iron with about 10% occluded hydrogen. The metal is the fourth most abundant element, by weight, making up the crust of the earth. The most common ore is *hematite* (Fe_2O_3), from which the metal is obtained by reduction with carbon. Iron is found in other widely distributed minerals, such as *magnetite* which is frequently seen as *black sands* along beaches and banks of streams. *Taconite* is becoming increasingly important as a commercial ore. Common iron is a mixture of four isotopes. Six other isotopes are known to exist. Iron is a vital constituent of plant and animal life, and appears in hemoglobin. The pure metal is not often encountered in commerce, but is usually alloyed with carbon or other metals. The pure metal is very reactive chemically, and rapidly corrodes especially in moist air or at elevated temperatures. It has four allotropic forms, or ferrites, known as α, β, γ, and δ, with transition points at 770°, 928°, and 1530°C. The α form is magnetic but when transformed into the β form, the magnetism disappears although the lattice remains unchanged. The relations of these forms are peculiar. Pig iron is an alloy containing about 3% carbon with varying amounts of S, Si, Mn, and P. It is hard, brittle, fairly fusible, and is used to produce other alloys, including steel. Wrought iron contains only a few tenths of per cent of carbon, is tough, malleable, less fusible, and has usually a "fibrous" structure. Carbon steel is an alloy of iron with carbon, with small amounts of Mn, S, P, and Si. Alloy steels are carbon steels with other additives, such as nickel, chromium, vanadium, etc. Iron is the cheapest and most abundant, useful, and important of all metals.

KRYPTON (Gr. *kryptos*, hidden), Kr; at. wt. 83.80; at. no. 36; m.p. -156.6°C; b.p. -152.30 ± 0.10°C; density 3.733 g/l (0°C); valence usually 0. Discovered in 1898 by Ramsay and Travers in the residue left after liquid air had nearly boiled away. Krypton is present in the air to the extent of about 1 part per million. It is one of the "noble" gases. It is characterized by its brilliant green and orange spectral lines. Naturally-occurring krypton contains six stable isotopes. Fifteen other unstable isotopes are now recognized. The spectral lines of krypton are easily produced and some are very sharp. In 1960 it was internationally agreed that the fundamental unit of length, the meter, should be defined in terms of the orange-red spectral line of Kr^{86}, corresponding to the transition $5p[O_{1/2}]_1–6d[O_{1/2}]_1$, as follows: *1 meter = 1,650,763.73 wavelengths (in vacuo) of the orange-red line of Kr^{86}.* This replaces the standard meter of Paris, which was defined in terms of a bar made of a platinum-iridium alloy. Solid krypton is a white crystalline substance with a face-centered cubic structure which is common to all the "rare gases". While krypton is generally thought of as a rare gas that normally does not combine with other elements to form compounds, it now appears that the existence of some krypton compounds is established. Krypton difluoride has been prepared in gram quantities and can be made by several methods. A higher fluoride of krypton and a salt of an oxyacid of krypton also have been reported. Molecule ions of $ArKr^+$ and KrH^+ have been identified and investigated, and evidence is provided for the formation of KrXe or $KrXe^+$. Krypton clathrates have been prepared with hydroquinone and phenol. Kr^{85} has found recent application in chemical analysis. By imbedding the isotope in various solids, *kryptonates* are formed. The activity of these kryptonates is sensitive to chemical reactions at the surface. Estimates of the concentration of reactants is therefore made possible. Krypton is used commercially with argon as a low-pressure filling gas for fluorescent lights. It is used in certain photographic flash lamps for high-speed photography. Uses thus far have been limited because of its high cost. Krypton gas presently costs about $20/liter.

KURCHATOVIUM (see Element 104).

LANTHANUM (Gr. *lanthanein*, to lie hidden). La; at. wt. 138.9055; at. no. 57; m.p. 921°C, b.p. 3457°C, sp. gr. 6.145(25°C); valence 3. Mosander in 1839 extracted a new earth, *lanthana*, from impure cerium nitrate, and recognized the new element. Lanthanum is found in rare-earth minerals, such as *cerite, monazite, allanite,* and *bastnasite*. Monazite and bastnasite are principal ores in which lanthanum occurs in percentages up to 25% and 38%, respectively. Misch metal, used in making lighter flints, contains about 25% lanthanum. Lanthanum was isolated in relatively pure form in 1923. Ion-exchange and solvent extraction techniques have led to much easier isolation of the so-called "rare-earth" elements. The availability of lanthanum and other rare earths has improved greatly in recent years. The metal can be produced by reducing the anhydrous fluoride with calcium. Lanthanum is silvery-white, malleable, ductile, and soft enough to be cut with a knife. It is one of the most reactive of the rare-earth metals. It oxidizes rapidly when exposed to air. Cold water attacks lanthanum slowly, and hot water attacks it much more rapidly. The metal reacts directly with elemental carbon, nitrogen, boron, selenium, silicon, phosphorus, sulfur, and with halogens. At 310°C, lanthanum changes from a hexagonal to a face-centered cubic structure, and at 865°C it again transforms into a body-centered cubic structure. Natural lanthanum is a mixture of two stable isotopes, La^{138} and La^{139}. Seventeen other radioactive isotopes are recognized. Rare-earth compounds containing lanthanum are extensively used in carbon lighting applications, especially by the motion picture industry for studio lighting and projection. This application consumes about 25% of the rare-earth compounds produced. La_2O_3 improves the alkali resistance of glass, and is used in making special optical glasses. Small amounts of lanthanum, as an additive, can be used to produce nodular cast iron. Lanthanum and its compounds have a low to moderate acute toxicity rating; therefore care should be taken in handling them. The price of 99.9% La_2O_3 is about $8/lb. The metal costs about $70/lb.

LAWRENCIUM (Ernest O. Lawrence, inventor of the cyclotron), Lr; at. no. 103; at. mass no. 257; valence +3(?). This member of the 5f transition elements (actinide series) was discovered in March 1961 by A. Ghiorso, T. Sikkeland, A. E. Larsh, and R. M. Latimer. A 3 µg californium target, consisting of a mixture of isotopes of mass number 249, 250, 251, and 252, was bombarded with either B^{10} or B^{11}. The electrically charged transmutation nuclei recoiled with an atmosphere of helium and were collected on a thin copper conveyor tape which was then moved to place collected atoms in front of a series of solid-state detectors. The isotope of element 103 produced in this way decayed by emitting an 8.6-MeV alpha particle with a half-life of 8 sec. Flerov and associates of the Dubna Laboratory, in 1967, reported their inability to detect an alpha emitter with a half-life of 8 sec which was assigned by the Berkeley Group to 103^{257}. This assignment has been changed to Lr^{258} or Lr^{259}. In 1965, the Dubna workers found a longer-lived lawrencium isotope, Lr^{256}, with a half-life of 35 sec. In 1968, Ghiorso and associates at Berkeley were able to use a few atoms of this isotope to study the oxidation behavior of lawrencium. Using solvent extraction techniques and working very rapidly, they extracted lawrencium ions from a buffered aqueous solution into an organic solvent, completing each extraction in about 30 sec. It was found that lawrencium behaves differently from dipositive nobelium and more like the tripositive elements earlier in the actinide series.

LEAD (Anglo-Saxon *lead*) Pb (L. *plumbum*); at. wt. 207.2; at. no. 82; m.p. 327.502°C; b.p. 1,740°C; sp. gr. 11.35 (20°C); valence 2 or 4. Long known, mentioned in Exodus. The alchemists believed lead to be the oldest metal and associated it with the planet Saturn. Native lead occurs in nature, but it is rare. Lead is obtained chiefly from *galena* (PbS) by a roasting process. *Anglesite* ($PbSO_4$), *cerrusite* ($PbCO_3$), and *minim* (Pb_3O_4) are other common lead minerals. Lead is a bluish-white metal of bright luster, is very soft, highly malleable, ductile, and a poor conductor of electricity. It is very resistant to corrosion; lead pipes bearing the insignia of Roman emperors, used as drains from the baths, are still in service. It is used in containers for corrosive liquids (such as in sulfuric acid chambers) and may be toughened by the addition of a small percentage of antimony or other metals. Natural lead is a mixture of four stable isotopes: Pb^{204} (1.48%), Pb^{206} (23.6%), Pb^{207} (22.6%), and Pb^{208} (52.3%). Lead isotopes are the end products of each of the three series of naturally occurring radioactive elements: Pb^{206} for the uranium series, Pb^{207} for the actinium series, and Pb^{208} for the thorium series. Seventeen other isotopes of lead, all of which are radioactive, are recognized. Its alloys include solder, type metal, and various antifriction metals. Great quantities of lead, both as the metal and as the dioxide, are used in storage batteries. Much metal also goes into cable covering, plumbing, ammunition, and in the manufacture of lead tetraethyl, used as an anti-knock compound in gasoline. The metal is very effective as a sound absorber, is used as a radiation shield around X-ray equipment and nuclear reactors, and is used to absorb vibration. White lead, the basic carbonate, sublimed white lead ($PbSO_4$), chrome yellow ($PbCrO_4$), red lead (Pb_3O_4), and other lead compounds are used extensively in paints, although in recent years the use of lead in paints has been drastically curtailed to eliminate or reduce health hazards. Lead oxide is used in producing fine "crystal glass" and "flint glass" of a high index of refraction for achromatic lenses. The nitrate and the acetate are soluble salts. Lead salts such as lead arsenate have been used as insecticides, but their use in recent years has been practically eliminated in favor of less harmful organic compounds. Care must be used in handling lead as it is a cumulative poison. Environmental concern with lead poisoning has resulted in a national program to reduce the concentration of lead in gasoline.

LITHIUM (Gr. *lithos*, stone) Li; at. wt. 6.941; at. no. 3; m.p. 180.54°C; b.p. 1347°C; sp. gr. 0.534 (20°C); valence 1. Discovered by Arfvedson in 1817. Lithium is the lighest of all metals, with a density only about half that of water. It does not occur free in nature; combined it is found in small amounts in nearly all igneous rocks and in the waters of many mineral springs. *Lepidolite*, *spodumene*, *petalite*, and *amblygonite* are the more important minerals containing it. Lithium is presently being recovered from brines of Searles Lake, in California, and from the Great Salt Lake, Utah. Large deposits are found in Nevada and North Carolina. The metal is produced electrolytically from the fused chloride. Lithium is silvery in appearance much like Na and K, other members of the alkali metal series. It reacts with water, but not as vigorously as sodium. Lithium imparts a beautiful crimson color to a flame, but when the metal burns strongly the flame is a dazzling white. Since World War II, the production of lithium metal and its compounds has increased greatly. Because the metal has the highest specific heat of any solid element, it has found use in heat transfer applications; however it is corrosive and requires special handling. The metal has been used as an alloying agent, is of interest in synthesis of organic compounds, and it has nuclear applications. It ranks as a leading contender as a battery anode material as it has a high electrochemical potential. Lithium is used in special glasses and ceramics. The glass for the 200-inch telescope at Mt. Palomar contains lithium as a minor ingredient. Lithium chloride is one of the most hygroscopic materials known, and it, as well as lithium bromide, is used in air conditioning and industrial drying systems. Lithium stearate is used as an all-purpose and high-temperature lubricant. Other lithium compounds are used in dry cells and storage batteries. The metal is priced at about $8/lb.

LUTETIUM (*Lutetia*, ancient name for Paris sometimes called *cassiopeium* by the Germans). Lu; at. wt. 174.97; at. no. 71; m.p. 1663°C; b.p. 3395°C; sp. gr. 9.840(25°C); valence 3. In 1907 Urbain described a process by which Marignac's ytterbium (1879) could be separated into the two elements, ytterbium (neoytterbium) and lutetium. These elements were identical with "aldebaranium" and "cassiopeium" independently discovered by von Welsbach about the same time. Charles James of the University of New Hampshire also independently prepared the very pure oxide, *lutecia*, at this time. The spelling of the element was changed from *lutecium* to *lutetium* in 1949. Lutetium occurs in very small amounts in nearly all minerals containing yttrium, and is present in *monazite* to the extent of about 0.003%, which is a commercial source. The pure metal has been isolated only in recent years and is one of the most difficult to prepare. It can be prepared by the reduction of anhydrous $LuCl_3$ or LuF_3 by an alkali or alkaline earth metal. The metal is silvery-white and relatively stable in air. While new techniques, including ion-exchange reactions, have been developed to separate the various rare-earth elements, lutetium is still the most costly of all naturally-occurring rare earths. It is slightly more abundant than thulium. It is now priced at about $26/gm. or $8000/lb. Lu^{176} occurs naturally (2.6%) with Lu^{175} (97.4%). It is radioactive with a half-life of about 3×10^{10} yrs. Stable lutetium nuclides, which emit pure beta radiation after thermal neutron activation, can be used as a catalyst in cracking, alkylation, hydrogenation, and polymerization. Virtually no other commercial uses have been found yet for lutetium, as it is still one of the most costly natural elements. Lutetium, like other rare-earth metals, has a low toxicity rating. It should be handled with care.

MAGNESIUM (*Magnesia*, district in Thessaly), Mg; at. wt. 24.305; at. no. 12; m.p. 648.8 ± 0.5°C; b.p. 1090°C; sp. gr. 1.738 (20°C); valence 2. Compounds of magnesium have long been known. Black recognized magnesium as an element in 1755. It was isolated by Davy in 1808, and prepared in coherent form by Bussy in 1831. Magnesium is the eighth most abundant element in the earth's crust. It does not occur uncombined, but is found in large deposits in the form of *magnesite*, *dolomite*, and other minerals. The metal is now principally obtained in the U.S. by electrolysis of fused magnesium chloride derived from brines, from wells and from sea water. Magnesium is a light, silvery-white, and fairly tough metal. It tarnishes slightly in air, and finely divided magnesium readily ignites upon heating in air and burns with a dazzling white flame. It is used in flash-light photography, flares, and pyrotechnics, including incendiary bombs. It is one-third lighter than aluminum, and in alloys is essential for airplane and missile construction. The metal improves the mechanical, fabrication, and welding characteristics of aluminum, when used as an alloying agent. Magnesium is used in producing nodular graphite in cast iron, and is used as an additive to conventional propellants. It is also used as a reducing agent in the production of pure uranium and other metals from their salts. The hydroxide (*Milk of Magnesia*), chloride, sulfate (*Epsom Salts*), and citrate are used in medicine. Dead-burned magnesite is employed for refractory purposes, such as brick and liners in furnaces and converters. Organic magnesium compounds (Grignard's reaction) are important. Magnesium is an important element in both plant and animal life. Chlorophylls are magnesium-centered porphyrins. The adult daily requirement of magnesium is about 300 mgm./day, but this is affected by various factors. Great care should be taken in handling magnesium metal, especially in the finely divided state, as serious fires can occur. Water should not be used on burning magnesium or on magnesium fires.

MANGANESE (L. *magnes*, magnet from magnetic properties of pyrolusite; It. *manganese*, corrupt form of *magnesia*). Mn; at. wt. 54.9380; at. no. 25; m.p. 1244 ± 3°C; b.p. 1962°C; sp. gr. 7.21 to 7.44, depending on allotropic form; valence 1, 2, 3, 4, 6, or 7. Recognized by Scheele, Bergman, and others as an element and isolated by Gahn in 1774 by reduction of the dioxide with carbon. Manganese minerals are widely distributed; oxides, silicates, and carbonates are the most common. The recent discovery of large quantities of manganese nodules on the floor of the oceans appears promising as a new source of manganese. These nodules contain about 24% manganese together with many other elements in lesser abundance. Large deposits of nodules, extending over many square miles, have been found in Lake Michigan and Lake Superior. *Pyrolusite* (MnO_2) and *rhodochrosite* ($MnCO_3$) are common ores. The metal is obtained by reduction of the oxide with sodium, magnesium, aluminum, or by electrolysis. It is gray-white, resembling iron, but is harder and very brittle. The metal is reactive chemically, and decomposes cold water slowly. Manganese is used to form many important alloys. In steel, manganese improves the rolling and forging qualities, strength, toughness, stiffness, wear resistance, hardness, and hardenability. With aluminum and antimony, especially with small amounts of copper, it forms highly ferromagnetic alloys. Manganese metal is ferromagnetic only after special treatment. The pure metal exists in four allotropic forms. The alpha form is stable at ordinary temperature; gamma manganese, which changes to alpha at ordinary temperatures, is said to be flexible, soft, easily cut, and capable of being bent. The dioxide (pyrolusite) is used as a depolarizer in dry cells, and is used to "decolorize" glass that is colored green by impurities of iron. Manganese by itself colors glass an amethyst color, and is responsible for the color of true amethyst. The dioxide is also used in the preparation of oxygen, chlorine, and in drying black paints. The permanganate is a powerful oxidizing agent and is used in quantitative analysis and in medicine. Manganese is widely distributed throughout the animal kingdom. It is an important trace element and may be essential for utilization of vitamin B_1

MENDELEVIUM (Dmitri Mendeleev), Md; at. wt. (256); at. no. 101; valence +2, +3. Mendelevium, the ninth transuranium element of the actinide series to be discovered, was first identified by Ghiorso, Harvey, Choppin, Thompson, and Seaborg early in 1955 as a result of the bombardment of the isotope Es^{253} with helium ions in the Berkeley 60-inch cyclotron. The isotope produced was Md^{256}, which has a half-life of 77 minutes. This first identification was notable in that Md^{256} was synthesized on a one-atom-at-a-time basis. Four isotopes are now recognized. Md^{258} has a half-life of two months. This isotope has been produced by the bombardment of an isotope of einsteinium with ions of helium. It now appears possible that eventually enough Md^{258} can be made so that some of its physical properties can be determined. Md^{256} has been used to elucidate some of the chemical properties of mendelevium in aqueous solution. Experiments seem to show that the element possesses a moderately stable dipositive (II) oxidation state in addition to the tripositive (III) oxidation state, which is characteristic of actinide elements.

MERCURY (Planet *Mercury*). Hg (*hydragyrum*, liquid silver); at. wt. 200.59; at. no. 80; m.p. −38.87°C; b.p. 356.58°C; sp. gr. 13.546 (20°C); valence 1 or 2. Known to ancient Chinese and Hindus; found in Egyptian tombs of 1500 B.C. Mercury is the only common metal liquid at ordinary temperatures. It only rarely occurs free in nature. The chief ore is *cinnabar* (HgS). Spain and Italy produce about 50", of the world's supply of the metal. The commercial unit for handling mercury is the "flask," which weighs 76 lbs. The metal is obtained by heating cinnabar in a current of air and by condensing the vapor. It is a heavy, silvery-white metal; a rather poor conductor of heat, as compared with other metals; and a fair conductor of electricity. The metal is widely used in laboratory work for making thermometers, barometers, diffusion pumps, and many other instruments. It is used in making mercury-vapor lamps and advertising signs, etc., and is used in mercury switches and other electrical apparatus. Other uses are for making pesticides, mercury cells for caustic-chlorine production, dental preparations, anti-fouling paint, batteries, and catalysts. The most important salts are mercuric chloride ($HgCl_2$, corrosive sublimate—a violent poison), mercurous chloride Hg_2Cl_2 (calomel—occasionally still used in med-

icine), mercury fulminate ($Hg(ONC)_2$, a detonator widely used in explosives), and mercuric sulfide (HgS, vermillion, a high-grade paint pigment). Organic mercury compounds are important. It has been found that an electrical discharge causes mercury vapor to combine with neon, argon, krypton, and xenon. These products, held together with van der Waals' forces, correspond to HgNe, HgAr, HgKr, and HgXe. It is not generally appreciated that mercury is a virulent poison and is readily absorbed through the respiratory tract, the gastrointestinal tract, or through unbroken skin. It acts as a cumulative poison since only small amounts of the element can be eliminated at a time by the human organism. The present adopted threshold limit value for mercury in air (except for alkyl compounds) is 0.05 mg/cu. meter. Since mercury is a very volatile element, dangerous levels are readily attained in air. Air saturated with mercury vapor at 20°C contains a concentration which exceeds the toxic limit by more than 100 times. The danger increases at higher temperatures. *It is therefore important that mercury be handled with utmost care.* Containers of mercury should be securely covered and spillage should be avoided. If it is necessary to heat mercury or mercury compounds, it should be done in a well-ventilated hood. Methyl mercury is a dangerous pollutant and is now widely found in water and streams.

MOLYBDENUM (Gr. *molybdos*, lead). Mo; at. wt. 95.94; at. no. 42; m.p. 2617°C; b.p. 4612°C; sp. gr. 10.22 (20°C); valence 2, 3, 4?, 5?, or 6. Before Scheele recognized molybdenite as a distinct ore of a new element in 1778, it was confused with graphite and lead ore. The metal was prepared in an impure form in 1782 by Hjelm. Molybdenum does not occur native, but is obtained principally from *molybdenite* (MoS_2). *Wulfenite* ($PbMoO_4$) and *powellite* ($Ca(MoW)O_4$) are also minor commercial ores. Molybdenum is also recovered as a byproduct of copper and tungsten mining operations. The metal is prepared from the powder made by the hydrogen reduction of purified molybdic trioxide or ammonium molybdate. The metal is silvery-white, very hard, but is softer and more ductile than tungsten. It has a high elastic modulus, and only tungsten and tantalum, of the more readily available metals, have higher melting points. It is a valuable alloying agent, as it contributes to the hardenability and toughness of quenched and tempered steels. It also improves the strength of steel at high temperatures. It is used in certain nickel-based alloys, such as the "Hastelloys," which are heat-resistant and corrosion-resistant to chemical solutions. Molybdenum oxidizes at elevated temperatures. The metal has found recent application as electrodes for electrically heated glass furnaces and forehearths. The metal is also used in nuclear energy applications and for missile and aircraft parts. Molybdenum wire is valuable for use as a filament material for metal evaporation work, and as a filament, grid, and screen material for electronic tubes. Molybdenum is an essential trace element in plant nutrition. Some lands are barren for lack of this element in the soil. Molybdenum sulfide is useful as a lubricant, especially at high temperatures where oils would decompose. Almost all ultra-high strength steels with minimum yield points up to 300,000 psi (lb./sq. in.) contain molybdenum in amounts from 0.25 % to 8 %. Molybdenum powder is priced at about $4 lb., and bars rolled from arc-cast ingots cost about $15 lb.

NEODYMIUM (Gr. *neos*, new, and *didymos*, twin). Nd; at. wt. 144.24; at. no. 60; m.p. 1021 C; b.p. 3068 C; sp. gr. 6.80 and 7.007 depending on allotropic form; valence 3

In 1841 Mosander extracted from *cerite* a new rose-colored oxide, which he believed to contain a new element. He named the element *didymium*, as it was "an inseparable twin brother of lanthanum." In 1885 von Welsbach separated didymium into two new elemental components, *neodymia* and *praseodymia*, by repeated fractionation of ammonium didymium nitrate. While the free metal is in *misch metal*, long known and used as a pyrophoric alloy for lighter flints, the element was not isolated in relatively pure form until 1925. Neodymium is present in misch metal to the extent of about 18%. It is present in the minerals *monazite* and *bastnasite*, which are principal sources of rare-earth metals. The element may be obtained by separating neodymium salts from other rare earths by ion exchange or solvent extraction techniques, and by reducing anhydrous halides, such as NdF_3, with calcium metal. Other separation techniques are possible. The metal has a bright silvery metallic luster. Neodymium is one of the more reactive rare-earth metals and quickly tarnishes in air, forming an oxide that spalls off and exposes metal to oxidation. The metal, therefore, should be kept under light mineral oil or sealed in a plastic material. Neodymium exists in two allotropic forms, with a transformation from a double hexagonal to a body-centered cubic structure taking place at 860°C. Natural neodymium is a mixture of seven stable isotopes. Seven other radioactive isotopes are recognized. Didymium, of which neodymium is a component, is used for coloring glass to make welder's goggles. By itself, neodymium colors glass delicate shades ranging from pure violet through wine-red and warm gray. Light transmitted through such glass shows unusually sharp absorption bands. The glass is useful in astronomical work to produce sharp bands by which spectral lines may be calibrated. Glass containing neodymium can be used as a laser material in place of ruby to produce coherent light. Neodymium salts are also used as a colorant for enamels. The price of the metal is about 50¢/gm. or $120/lb. Neodymium has a low-to-moderate acute toxic rating. As with other rare earths, neodymium should be handled with care.

NEON (Gr. *neos* new), Ne; at. wt. 20.179; at. no. 10; m.p. −248.67°C; b.p. −246.048°C (1 atm); density of gas 0.89990 gm l (1 atm. 0°C); density of liquid at b.p. 1.207 gm cm³; valence 0. Discovered by Ramsay and Travers in 1898. Neon is a rare gaseous element present in the atmosphere to the extent of 1 part in 65,000 of air. It is obtained by liquefaction of air and separated from the other gases by fractional distillation. Natural neon is a mixture of three isotopes. Five other unstable isotopes are known. It is a very inert element; however it is said to form a compound with fluorine. It is still questionable if true compounds of neon exist, but evidence is mounting in favor of their existence. The following ions are known from optical and mass spectrometric studies: Ne_2^+, $(NeAr)^+$, $(NeH)^+$, and $(HeNe)^+$. Neon also forms an unstable hydrate. In a vacuum discharge tube, neon glows reddish-orange. Of all the rare gases, the discharge of neon is the most intense at ordinary voltages and currents. Neon is used in making the common neon advertising signs, which accounts for its largest use. It is also used to make high-voltage indicators, lightning arrestors, wave meter tubes, and TV tubes. Neon and helium are used in making gas lasers. Liquid neon is now commercially available and is finding important application as an economical cryogenic refrigerant. It has over 40 times more refrigerating capacity per unit volume than liquid helium and more than three times that of liquid hydrogen. It is compact, inert, and is less expensive than helium when it meets refrigeration requirements. Neon gas costs about $1.50 liter.

NEPTUNIUM (Planet *Neptune*), Np; at. wt. 237.0482; at. no. 93; m.p. 640 ± 1°C; b.p. 3902°C (est.); sp. gr. 20.25 (20°C); valence 3, 4, 5, and 6. Neptunium was the first synthetic transuranium element of the actinide series discovered; the isotope Np^{239} was produced by McMillan and Abelson in 1940 at Berkeley, California, as the result of bombarding uranium with cyclotron-produced neutrons. The isotope Np^{237} (half-life of 2.14×10^6 years) is currently obtained in gram quantities as a by-product from nuclear reactors in the production of plutonium. Trace quantities of the element are actually found in nature due to transmutation reactions in uranium ores produced by the neutrons which are present. Neptunium is prepared by the reduction of NpF_3 with barium or lithium vapor at about 1200°C. Neptunium metal has a silvery appearance, is chemically reactive, and exists in at least three structural modifications: α-neptunium, orthorhombic, density—20.25 gm./cm³; β-neptunium (above 280°C), tetragonal, density (313°C)—19.36 gm/cm³; γ-neptunium (above 577°C), cubic, density (600°C) 18.0 gm./cm³. Neptunium has four ionic oxidation states in solution: Np^{+3} (pale purple), analogous to the rare earth ion Pm^{+3}, Np^{+4} (yellow green), NpO_2^- (green blue), and NpO_2^{++} (pale pink). These latter oxygenated species are in contrast to the rare earths which exhibit only simple ions of the (II), (III), and (IV) oxidation states in aqueous solution. The element forms tri- and tetrahalides such as NpF_3, NpF_4, $NpCl_4$, $NpBr_3$, NpI_3, and oxides of various compositions such as are found in the uranium-oxygen system, including Np_3O_8 and NpO_2. Thirteen isotopes of neptunium are now recognized. The A.E.C. has Np^{237} available for sale to its licensees and for export. This isotope can be used as a component in neutron detection instruments. It is offered at a price of $225/gm. or $0.25/mg for quantities less than 1 gram.

NICKEL (Ger. *Nickel,* Satan or "Old Nick," and from *kupfernickel,* Old Nick's copper), Ni; at. wt. 58.71; at. no. 28; m.p. 1,453°C; b.p. 2,732°C; sp. gr. 8.902 (25°C); valence 0, 1, 2, 3. Discovered by Cronstedt in 1751 in kupfernickel (*niccolite*). Nickel is found as a constituent in most meteorites and often serves as one of the criteria for distinguishing a meteorite from other minerals. Iron meteorites, or *siderites,* may contain iron alloyed with from 5 to nearly 20% nickel. Nickel is obtained commercially from *pentlandite* and *pyrrhotite* of the Sudbury region of Ontario, a district that produces about 60% of the nickel for the free world. Other deposits are found in New Caledonia, Australia, Cuba, Japan, and elsewhere. Nickel is silvery-white and takes on a high polish. It is hard, malleable, ductile, somewhat ferromagnetic, and a fair conductor of heat and electricity. It belongs to the iron-cobalt group of metals and is chiefly valuable for the alloys it forms. It is extensively used for making stainless steel and other corrosion-resistant alloys such as Invar®, Monel®, Inconel®, and the Hastelloys®. Tubing made of a copper-nickel alloy is extensively used in making desalination plants for converting sea water into fresh water. Nickel is also now used extensively in coinage and in making nickel steel for armor plate and burglar-proof vaults, and is a component in Nichrome®, permalloy, and constantan. Nickel added to glass gives a green color. Nickel plating is often used to provide a protective coating for other metals, and finely divided nickel is a catalyst for hydrogenating vegetable oils. It is also used in ceramics, in the manufacture of Alnico magnets, and in the Edison® storage battery. The sulfate and the oxides are important compounds. Natural nickel is a mixture of five stable isotopes; seven other unstable isotopes are known.

NIOBIUM (*Niobe*, daughter of Tantalus), Nb; or **COLUMBIUM** (*Columbia*, name for America), Cb; at. wt. 92.9064; at. no. 41, m.p. 2468 ± 10°C; b.p. 4742°C; sp. gr. 8.57 (20°C); valence 2, 3, 4?, 5. Discovered in 1801 by Hatchett in an ore sent to England more than a century before by John Winthrop the Younger, first governor of Connecticut. The metal was first prepared in 1864 by Blomstrand, who reduced the chloride by heating it in a hydrogen atmosphere. The name "niobium" was adopted by the International Union of Pure and Applied Chemistry in 1950 after 100 years of controversy. Many leading chemical societies and government organizations refer to it by this name. Most metallurgists, leading metal societies, and all but one of the leading U.S. commercial producers, however, still refer to the metal as "columbium." The element is found in *niobite* (or *columbite*), *niobite-tantalite*, *pyrochlore*, and *euxenite*. Large deposits of niobium have been found associated with *carbonatites* (carbon-silicate rocks), as a constituent of *pyrochlore*. Extensive ore reserves are found in Canada, Brazil, Nigeria, Zaire and the U.S. The metal can be isolated from tantalum, and prepared in several ways. It is a shiny, white, soft, and ductile metal, and takes on a bluish cast when exposed to air at room temperatures for a long time. The metal starts to oxidize in air at 200°C, and when processed at even moderate temperatures must be placed in a protective atmosphere. It is used as an alloying agent in carbon and alloy steels and in nonferrous metals. These alloys have improved strength and other desirable properties. The metal has a low capture cross-section for thermal neutrons. It is used in arc-welding rods for stabilized grades of stainless steel. Thousands of pounds of niobium have been used in advanced air frame systems, such as was used in the Gemini space program. The element has superconductive properties; superconductive magnets have been made with Nb-Zr wire, which retains its superconductivity in strong magnetic fields. This type of application offers hope of direct large-scale generation of electric power. Sixteen isotopes of niobium are known. Niobium metal (99.5% pure) is priced at about $15/lb.

NITROGEN (L. *nitrum*, Gr. *nitron*, native soda; genes, *forming*), N; at. wt. 14.0067; at. no. 7; m.p. −209.86°C; b.p. −195.8°C; density 1.2506 gm./l; sp. gr. liquid 0.808 (−195.8°C), solid 1.026 (−252°C); valence 3 or 5. Discovered by Daniel Rutherford in 1772, but Scheele, Cavendish, Priestley and others about the same time studied "burnt or dephlogisticated air," as air without oxygen was then called. Nitrogen makes up 78% of the air, by volume. The estimated amount of this element in the atmosphere is more than 4000 billion tons. From this inexhaustible source it can be obtained by liquefaction and fractional distillation. Nitrogen molecules give the orange-red, blue-green, blue-violet, and deep violet shades to the aurora. The element is so inert that Lavoisier named it *azote*, meaning without life, yet its compounds are so active as to be most important in foods, poisons, fertilizers, and explosives. Nitrogen can be also easily prepared by heating a water solution of ammonium nitrite. Nitrogen, as a gas, is colorless, odorless, and a generally inert element. As a liquid it is also colorless and odorless, and is similar in appearance to water. Two allotropic forms of solid nitrogen exist, with the transition from

the α to the β form taking place at −237°C. When nitrogen is heated, it combines directly with magnesium, lithium, or calcium; when mixed with oxygen and subjected to electric sparks, it forms first nitric oxide (NO) and then the dioxide (NO_2); when heated under pressure with a catalyst with hydrogen, ammonia is formed (Haber process). The ammonia thus formed is of the utmost importance as it is used in fertilizers, and it can be oxidized to nitric acid (Ostwald process). The ammonia industry is the largest consumer of nitrogen. Large amounts of the gas are also used by the electronics industry, which uses the gas as a blanketing medium during production of such components as transistors, diodes, etc. The drug industry also uses large quantities. Nitrogen is used as a refrigerant both for the immersion freezing of food products and for transportation of foods. Liquid nitrogen is also used in missile work as a purge for components, insulators for space chambers, etc., and by the oil industry to build up great pressures in wells to force crude oil upward. Sodium and potassium nitrates are formed by the decomposition of organic matter with compounds of the metals present. In certain dry areas of the world these saltpeters are found in quantity. Ammonia, nitric acid, the nitrates, the five oxides (N_2O, NO, N_2O_3, NO_2, and N_2O_5), TNT, the cyanides, etc., are but a few of the important compounds. Nitrogen gas prices vary from 2¢ to $2.75 per 100 cu. ft., depending on purity, etc. Production of nitrogen in the U.S. is more than 160 billion cubic feet per year.

NOBELIUM (Alfred Nobel, discoverer of dynamite), No; at. no. 102; valence +2, +3. Nobelium was unambiguously discovered and identified in April 1958 at Berkeley by A. Ghiorso, T. Sikkeland, J. R. Walton, and G. T. Seaborg, who used a new double-recoil technique. A heavy-ion linear accelerator (HILAC) was used to bombard a thin target of curium (95% Cm^{244} and 4.5% Cm^{246}) with C^{12} ions to produce 102^{254} according to the Cm^{246} (C^{12}, 4n) reaction. Earlier in 1957 workers of the U.S., Britain, and Sweden announced the discovery of an isotope of element 102 with a 10-min. half-life at 8.5 MeV, as a result of bombarding Cm^{244} with C^{13} nuclei. On the basis of this experiment the name *nobelium* was assigned and accepted by the Commission on Atomic Weights of the International Union of Pure and Applied Chemistry. The acceptance of the name was premature, for both Russian and American efforts now completely rule out the possibility of any isotope of element 102 having a half-life of 10 minutes in the vicinity of 8.5 MeV. Early work in 1957 on the search for this element, in Russia at the Kurchatov Institute, was marred by the assignment of 8.9 ± 0.4 MeV alpha radiation with a half-life of 2 to 40 secs., which was too indefinite to support claim to discovery. Confirmatory experiments at Berkeley in 1966 have shown the existence of 102^{254} with a 55-sec. half-life, 102^{252} with a 2.3-sec. half-life, and 102^{257} with a 23-sec. half-life. Four other isotopes are now recognized, one of which—102^{255}—has a half-life of 3 min. In view of the discoverer's traditional right to name an element, the Berkeley Group, in 1967, suggested that the hastily given name *nobelium*, along with the symbol No be retained.

OSMIUM (Gr. *osme*, a smell), Os; at. wt. 190.2, at. no. 76; m.p. 3045 ± 30°C; b.p. 5027 ± 100°C; sp. gr. 22.57; valence 0 to +8, more usually +3, +4, +6, and +8. Discovered in 1803 by Tennant in the residue left when crude platinum is dissolved by aqua regia. Osmium occurs in *iridosmine* and in platinum-bearing river sands of the Urals, North America, and South America. It is also found in the nickel-bearing ores of the Sudbury, Ontario, region along with other platinum metals. While the quantity of platinum

THE ELEMENTS—(Continued)

metals in these ores is very small, the large tonnages of nickel ores processed make commercial recovery possible. The metal is lustrous, bluish-white, extremely hard, and brittle even at high temperatures. It has the highest melting point and lowest vapor pressure of the platinum group. The metal is very difficult to fabricate, but the powder can be sintered in a hydrogen atmosphere at a temperature of 2000°C. The solid metal is not affected by air at room temperature, but the powdered or spongy metal slowly gives off osmium tetroxide, which is a powerful oxidizing agent and has a strong smell. The tetroxide is highly toxic, and boils at 130°C (760 mm). Concentrations in air as low as 10^{-7} gm./cu. meter can cause lung congestion, skin damage, or eye damage. The tetroxide has been used to detect fingerprints and to stain fatty tissue for microscope slides. The metal is almost entirely used to produce very hard alloys, with other metals of the platinum group, for fountain pen tips, instrument pivots, phonograph needles, and electrical contacts. The price of 99% pure osmium powder—the form usually supplied commercially—is about $5/gm. or $300 to $450/troy ounce, depending on quantity and supplier. The measured densities of iridium and osmium seem to indicate that osmium is slightly more dense than iridium; so osmium has generally been credited with being the heaviest known element. Calculations of the density from the space lattice, which may be more reliable for these elements than actual measurements, however, give a density of 22.65 for iridium compared to 22.61 for osmium. At present, therefore, we know either iridium or osmium is the heaviest element, but the data do not allow selection between the two.

OXYGEN (Gr. *oxys,* sharp, acid, and *genes,* forming; acid former), O; at. wt. (natural) 15.9994; at. no. 8; m.p. -218.4°C; b.p. -182.962°C; density 1.429 g/l (0°C); sp. gr. liquid 1.14 (-182.96°C); valence 2. For many centuries, workers occasionally realized air was composed of more than one component. The behavior of oxygen and nitrogen as components of air led to the advancement of the phlogiston theory of combustion, which captured the minds of chemists for a century. Oxygen was prepared by several workers, including Bayen and Borch, but they did not know how to collect it, did not study its properties, and did not recognize it as an elementary substance. Priestley is generally credited with its discovery, although Scheele also discovered it independently. Oxygen is the third most abundant element found in the sun, and it plays a part in the carbon-nitrogen cycle, one process thought to give the sun and stars their energy. Oxygen under excited conditions is responsible for the bright red and yellow-green colors of the aurora. Oxygen, as a gaseous element, forms 21% of the atmosphere by volume from which it can be obtained by liquefaction and fractional distillation. The element and its compounds make up 49.2%, by weight, of the earth's crust. About two-thirds of the human body and nine-tenths of water is oxygen. In the laboratory it can be prepared by the electrolysis of water or by heating potassium chlorate with manganese dioxide as a catalyst. The gas is colorless, odorless, and tasteless. The liquid and solid forms are a pale blue color and are strongly paramagnetic. Ozone (O_3), a highly active allotropic form of oxygen, is formed by the action of an electrical discharge or ultraviolet light on oxygen. Ozone's presence in the atmosphere (amounting to the equivalent of a layer

3 mm thick at ordinary pressures and temperatures) is of vital importance in preventing ultraviolet rays from the sun from reaching the earth's surface and destroying life on earth. There has been recent concern that aerosols in the atmosphere may have a detrimental effect on this ozone layer. Undiluted ozone has a bluish color. Liquid ozone is bluish black, and solid ozone is violet-black. Oxygen is very reactive and capable of combining with most elements. It is a component of hundreds of thousands of organic compounds. It is essential for respiration of all plants and animals and for practically all combustion. In hospitals it is frequently used to aid respiration of patients. Its atomic weight was used as a standard of comparison for each of the other elements until 1961 when the International Union of Pure and Applied Chemistry adopted Carbon 12 as the new basis. Oxygen has eight isotopes. Natural oxygen is a mixture of three isotopes. Oxygen 18 occurs naturally, is stable, and is available commercially. Water (H_2O with 1.5% O^{18}) is also available. Commerical oxygen consumption in the U.S. is estimated at more than 350 billion ft^3/year, and the demand is expected to increase substantially in the next few years. Oxygen enrichment of steel blast furnaces accounts for the greatest use of the gas. Large quantities are also used in making synthesis gas for ammonia and methanol, ethylene oxide, and for oxy-acetylene welding. Air separation plants produce about 99% of the gas; electrolysis plants about 1%. The gas costs 2.5¢/cubic foot in small quantities, and from $6 to $12/ton in large quantities.

PALLADIUM (named after the asteroid *Pallas,* discovered about the same time; Gr. *Pallas,* goddess of wisdom), Pd; at. wt. 106.4; at. no. 46; m.p. 1552°C; b.p. 3140°C; sp. gr. 12.02 (20°C); valence, 2, 3, or 4. Discovered in 1803 by Wollaston. Palladium is found along with platinum and other metals of the platinum group in placer deposits of the U.S.S.R., South and North America, Ethiopia, and Australia. It is also found associated with the nickel-copper deposits of South Africa and Ontario. Its separation from the platinum metals depends upon the type of ore in which it is found. It is a steel-white metal, does not tarnish in air, and is the least dense and lowest melting of the platinum group of metals. When annealed, it is soft and ductile; cold working greatly increases its strength and hardness. Palladium is attacked by nitric and sulfuric acid. At room temperatures the metal has the unusual property of absorbing up to 900 times its own volume of hydrogen, possibly forming Pd_2H. It is not yet clear if this is a true compound. Hydrogen readily diffuses through heated palladium and this provides a means of purifying the gas. Finely divided palladium is a good catalyst and is used for hydrogenation and dehydrogenation reactions. It is alloyed and used in jewelry trades. White gold is an alloy of gold decolorized by the addition of palladium. Like gold, palladium can be beaten into leaf as thin as 1/250,000 inch. The metal is used in dentistry, watchmaking, and in making surgical instruments and electrical contacts. The metal sells for about $40/troy ounce.

PHOSPHORUS (Gr. *phosphoros,* light-bearing; ancient name for the planet Venus when appearing before sunrise), P; at. wt. 30.97376; at. no. 15; m.p. (white) 44.1°C; b.p. (white) 280°C; sp. gr. (white) 1.82, (red) 2.20, (black) 2.25

to 2.69; valence 3 or 5. Discovered in 1669 by Brand, who prepared it from urine. Phosphorus exists in four or more allotropic forms: white (or yellow), red, and black (or violet). White phosphorus has two modifications: α and β with a transition temperature at $-3.8°C$. Never found free in nature, it is widely distributed in combination with minerals. *Phosphate* rock, which contains the mineral *apatite*—an impure tri-calcium phosphate—is an important source of the element. Large deposits are found in the U.S.S.R., in Morocco, and in Florida, Tennessee, Utah, Idaho, and elsewhere. Phosphorus is an essential ingredient of all cell protoplasm, nervous tissue, and bones. Ordinary phosphorus is a waxy white solid; when pure it is colorless and transparent. It is insoluble in water, but soluble in carbon disulfide. It takes fire spontaneously in air, burning to the pentoxide. It is very poisonous—50 mg constituting an approximate fatal dose. The maximum recommended allowable concentration in air is 0.1 mg/cubic meter. White phosphorus should be kept under water as it is dangerously reactive in air, and it should be handled with forceps, as contact with the skin may cause severe burns. When exposed to sunlight or when heated in its own vapor to 250°C, it is converted to the red variety, which does not phosphoresce in air as does the white variety. This form does not ignite spontaneously and it is not as dangerous as white phosphorus. It should, however, be handled with care as it does convert to the white form at some temperatures and it emits highly toxic fumes of the oxides of phosphorus when heated. The red modification is fairly stable, sublimes with a vapor pressure of 1 atm. at 417°C, and is used in the manufacture of safety matches, pyrotechnics, pesticides, incendiary shells, smoke bombs, tracer bullets, etc. White phosphorus may be made by several methods. By one process, tri-calcium phosphate, the essential ingredient of phosphate rock, is heated in the presence of carbon and silica in an electric furnace or fuel-fired blast furnace. Elementary phosphorus is liberated as vapor and may be collected under water. If desired, the phosphorus vapor and carbon monoxide produced by the reaction can be oxidized at once in the presence of moisture or water to produce phosphoric acid—an important compound in making super-phosphate fertilizers. In recent years, concentrated phosphoric acids, which may contain as much as 70 to 75% P_2O_5 content, have become of great importance to agriculture and farm production. World-wide demand for fertilizers has caused record phosphate production in recent years. Phosphates are used in the production of special glasses, such as those used for sodium lamps. Bone-ash, calcium phosphate, is also used to produce fine chinaware and to produce mono-calcium phosphate used in baking powder. Phosphorus is also important in the production of steels, phosphor bronze, and many other products. Trisodium phosphate is important as a cleaning agent, as a water-softener, and for preventing boiler scale and corrosion of pipes and boiler tubes. Organic compounds of phosphorus are important.

PLATINUM (Sp. *platina,* silver), Pt; at. wt. 195.09; at. no. 78; m.p. 1,772°C; b.p. 3,827 ± 100°C; sp. gr. 21.45 (20°C); valence 1?, 2, 3, or 4. Discovered in South America by Ulloa, in 1735 and by Wood in 1741. The metal was used by pre-Columbian Indians. Platinum occurs native, accompanied by small quantities of iridium, osmium, palladium, ruthenium, and rhodium, all belonging to the same group of metals. These are found in the alluvial deposits of the Ural mountains, of Columbia, and of certain western American states. *Sperrylite* ($PtAs_2$), occurring with the nickel-bearing deposits of Sudbury,

Ontario, is the source of a considerable amount of the metal. The large production of nickel offsets there being only one part of the platinum metals in two million parts of ore. Platinum is a beautiful silvery-white metal, when pure, and is malleable and ductile. It has a coefficient of expansion almost equal to that of soda-lime-silica glass, and is therefore used to make sealed electrodes in glass systems. The metal does not oxidize in air at any temperature, but is corroded by halogens, cyanides, sulfur, and caustic alkalis. It is insoluble in hydrochloric and nitric acid, but dissolves when they are mixed as *aqua regia*, forming chloroplatinic acid (H_2PtCl_6), an important compound. The metal is extensively used in jewelry, wire, and vessels for laboratory use, and in many valuable instruments including thermocouple elements. It is also used for electrical contacts, corrosion-resistant apparatus, and in dentistry. Platinum-cobalt alloys have magnetic properties. One such alloy made of 76.7% Pt and 23.3% Co, by weight, is an extremely powerful magnet that offers a B-H (max) almost twice that of Alnico V. Platinum resistance wires are used for constructing high-temperature electric furnaces. The metal is used for coating missile nose cones, jet engine fuel nozzles, etc., which must perform reliably for long periods of time at high temperatures. The metal, like palladium, absorbs large volumes of hydrogen, retaining it at ordinary temperatures but giving it up at red heat. In the finely divided state platinum is an excellent catalyst, having long been used in the contact process for producing sulfuric acid. It is also used as a catalyst in cracking petroleum products. There is also much current interest in the use of platinum as a catalyst in fuel cells and in antipollution devices for automobiles. Fine platinum wire will glow red hot when placed in the vapor of methyl alcohol. It acts here as a catalyst, converting the alcohol to formaldehyde. This phenomenon has been used commercially to produce cigarette lighters and hand warmers. Hydrogen and oxygen explode in the presence of platinum. The price of platinum has varied widely; more than a century ago it was used to adulterate gold. It was nearly eight times as valuable as gold in 1920; the present price is about $175/troy ounce.

PLUTONIUM (Planet *pluto*), Pu; at. no. 94; isotopic mass Pu^{239} 239.13 (physical scale); sp. gr. (α modification) 19.84 (25°C); m.p. 641°C; b.p. 3232°C; valence 3, 4, 5, or 6. Plutonium was the second transuranium element of the actinide series to be discovered. The isotope Pu^{238} was produced in 1940 by Seaborg, McMillan, Kennedy, and Wahl by deuteron bombardment of uranium in the 60-inch cyclotron at Berkeley, California. Plutonium also exists in trace quantities in naturally-occurring uranium ores. It is formed in much the same manner as neptunium, by irradiation of natural uranium with the neutrons which are present. By far of greatest importance is the isotope Pu^{239}, with a half-life of 24,360 years, produced in extensive quantities in nuclear reactors from natural uranium:

$$U^{238} (n, \gamma) U^{239} \xrightarrow{\beta} Np^{239} \xrightarrow{\beta} Pu^{239}$$

Fifteen isotopes of plutonium are known. Plutonium has assumed the position of dominant importance among the transuranium elements because of its successful use as an explosive ingredient in nuclear weapons and the place which it holds as a key material in the development of industrial use of nuclear power. One pound is equivalent to about ten million kilowatt hours of heat energy. Its importance depends on the nuclear property of being readily fissionable with neutrons and its availability in quantity. The various nuclear applications of plutonium are well known. Pu^{238} has been used in the Apollo lunar missions to power seismic and other equipment on the lunar surface. As with neptunium and uranium, plutonium metal can be prepared by reduction of the trifluoride with alkaline-earth metals. The metal has a silvery appearance and takes on a yellow tarnish when slightly oxidized. It is chemically reactive. A relatively large piece of plutonium is warm to the touch because of the energy given off in alpha decay. Larger pieces will produce enough heat to boil water. The metal readily dissolves in concentrated hydrochloric acid, hydroiodic acid, or perchloric acid with formation of the Pu^{+3} ion. The metal exhibits six allotropic modifications having various crystalline structures. The densities of these vary from 16.00 to 19.86 gm./cu. cm. Plutonium also exhibits four ionic valence states in aqueous solutions: Pu^{+3} (blue lavender), Pu^{+4} (yellow brown), PuO_2^+ (pink?), and PuO_2^{+2} (pink orange). The ion PuO_2^+ is unstable in aqueous solutions, disproportionating into Pu^{+4} and PuO_2^{+2}; the Pu^{+4} thus formed, however, oxidizes the PuO_2^+ into PuO_2^{+2}, itself being reduced to Pu^{+3}, giving finally Pu^{+3} and PuO_2^{+2}. Plutonium forms binary compounds with oxygen: PuO, PuO_2, and intermediate oxides of variable composition; with the halides: PuF_3, PuF_4, $PuCl_3$, $PuBr_3$, PuI_3; with carbon, nitrogen, and silicon: PuC, PuN, $PuSi_2$. Oxyhalides are also well known: $PuOCl$, $PuOBr$, $PuOI$. Because of the high rate of emission of alpha particles and the element being specifically absorbed by bone marrow, plutonium, as well as all of the other transuranium elements except neptunium, are radiological poisons and must be handled with special equipment and precautions. The maximum permissible body burden, or the amount that can be maintained indefinitely in an adult without producing significant body injury, for Pu^{239} is now set at 0.04 microcurie (0.6 micrograms). It is recommended that the concentration of plutonium in air not exceed 0.00003 micrograms per cubic meter. Plutonium, therefore, is one of the most dangerous poisons known. Precautions must also be taken to prevent the unintentional formation of a critical mass. Plutonium in liquid solution is more likely to become critical than solid plutonium. The shape of the mass must also be considered where criticality is concerned. Plutonium-238 is available from the A.E.C. at a cost of about \$700/gm. (80 to 89% enriched).

POLONIUM (Poland, native country of Mme. Curie), Po; at. mass. (~ 210); at. no. 84; m.p. 254°C; b.p. 962°C; sp. gr. (alpha modification) 9.32; valence $-2, 0, +2, +3(?)$, $+4$, and $+6$. Polonium was the first element discovered by Mme. Curie, in 1898, while seeking the cause of radioactivity of pitchblende from Joachimsthal, Bohemia. The electroscope showed it separating with bismuth. Polonium is also called Radium F. Polonium is a very rare natural element. Uranium ores contain only about 100 micrograms of the element per ton. Its abundance is only about 0.2% of that of radium. In 1934 it was found that when natural bismuth (Bi^{209}) was bombarded by neutrons, Bi^{210}, the parent of polonium, was obtained. Milligram amounts of polonium may now be prepared this way, by using the high neutron fluxes of nuclear reactors. Polonium-210 is a low-melting, fairly volatile metal, 50% of which is vaporized in air in 45 hours at 55°C. It is an alpha emitter with a half-life of 138.39 days. A milligram emits as many alpha particles as 5 grams of radium. The energy released by its decay is so large (27.5 calories per curie per day or 140 watts/gm.) that a capsule containing about half a gram reaches a temperature above 500°C. The capsule also presents a contact gamma-ray dose rate of 1.2 roentgens per hour. A few curies of polonium exhibit a blue glow, caused by excitation of the surrounding gas. Because almost all alpha radiation is stopped within the solid source and its container, giving up its energy, polonium has attracted attention for uses as a light-weight heat source for thermoelectric power in space satellites. Polonium has more isotopes than any other element. Twenty-seven isotopes of polonium are known, with atomic masses ranging from 192 to 218. Polonium-210 is the most readily available. Isotopes of mass 209 (half-life of 103 yrs.) and mass 208 (half-life 2.9 yrs.) can be prepared by alpha, proton, or deuteron bombardment of lead or bismuth in a cyclotron, but these are expensive to produce. Metallic polonium has been prepared from polonium hydroxide and some other polonium compounds in the presence of concentrated aqueous or anhydrous liquid ammonia. Two allotropic modifications are known to exist. Polonium is readily dissolved in dilute acids, but is only slightly soluble in alkalis. Polonium salts of organic acids char rapidly; halide ammines are reduced to the metal. Polonium can be mixed or alloyed with beryllium to provide a source of neutrons. It has been used in devices for eliminating static charges in textile mills, etc.; however, beta sources are more commonly used and are less dangerous. It is also used on brushes for removing dust from photographic films. The polonium for these is carefully sealed and controlled, minimizing hazards to the user. Polonium-210 is very dangerous to handle in even milligram or microgram amounts and special equipment and strict control is necessary. Damage arises from the complete adsorption of the energy of the alpha particle into tissue. The maximum permissible body-burden for ingested polonium is only 0.03 microcuries, which represents a particle weighing only 6.8×10^{-12} grams. Weight-for-weight it is about 2.5×10^{11} times as toxic as hydrocyanic acid. The maximum allowable concentration for soluble polonium compounds in air is about 2×10^{-11} microcuries/cc. Polonium is available commercially on special order with an A.E.C. permit from the Oak Ridge National Laboratory.

POTASSIUM (English, *potash*—pot ashes; L. *kalium*; Arab. *qali*, alkali), K; at. wt. 39.09_8; at. no. 19; m.p. 63.65°C; b.p. 774°C; sp. gr. 0.862 (20°C); valence 1. Discovered in 1807 by Davy, who obtained it from caustic potash (KOH); this was the first metal isolated by electrolysis. The metal is the seventh most abundant and makes up about 2.4% by weight of the earth's crust. Most potassium minerals are insoluble and the metal is obtained from them only with great difficulty. Certain minerals, however, such as *sylvite*, *carnallite*, *langbeinite*, and *polyhalite* are found in ancient lake and sea beds and form rather extensive deposits from which potassium and its salts can readily be obtained. Potash is mined in Germany, New Mexico, California, Utah, and elsewhere. Large deposits of potash, found at a depth of some 3000 ft. in Saskatchewan, promise to be important in coming years. Potassium is also found in the ocean, but is present only in relatively small amounts, compared to sodium. The greatest demand for potash has been in its use for fertilizers. Potassium is an essential constituent for plant growth and it is found in most soils. Potassium is never found free in nature, but is obtained by electrolysis of the hydroxide, much in the same manner as prepared by Davy. Thermal methods also are commonly used to produce potassium (such as by reduction of potassium compounds with CaC_2, C, Si, or Na). It is one of the most reactive and electropositive of metals; except for lithium, it is the lightest known metal. It is soft, easily cut with a knife, and is silvery in appearance immediately after a fresh surface is exposed. It rapidly oxidizes in air and must be preserved in a mineral oil, such as kerosene. As with other metals of the alkali group, it decomposes in water with the evolution of hydrogen. It catches fire spontaneously on water. Potassium and its salts impart a violet color to flames. Nine isotopes of potassium are known. Ordinary potassium is composed of three isotopes, one of which is K^{40} (0.00118%), a radioactive isotope with a half-life of 1.28×10^9 yrs. The radioactivity presents no appreciable hazard. An alloy of sodium and potassium (NaK) is used as a heat-transfer medium. Many potassium salts are of utmost importance. These include the hydroxide, nitrate, carbonate, chloride, chlorate, bromide, iodide, cyanide, sulfate, chromate, and dichromate. Metallic potassium is available commercially for about $2/lb. in quantity.

PRASEODYMIUM (Gr. *prasios*, green, and *didymos*, twin), Pr; at. wt. 140.9077; at. no. 59; m.p. 931°C; b.p. 3512 C; sp. gr. (α) 6.773 (β) 6.64; valence 3 or 4. In 1841 Mosander extracted the rare earth *didymia* from *lanthana*; in 1879 Lecoq de Boisbaudran isolated a new earth, *samaria*, from didymia obtained from the mineral *samarskite*. Six years later, in 1885, von Welsbach separated didymia into two other earths, *praseodymia* and *neodymia*, which gave salts of different colors. As with other rare earths, compounds of these elements in solution have distinctive sharp spectral absorption bands or lines, some of which are only a few Ångstroms wide. The element occurs along with other rare-earth elements in a variety of minerals. *Monazite* and *bastnasite* are the two principal commercial sources of the rare-earth metals. Ion-exchange and solvent extraction techniques have led to much easier isolation of the rare earths and the cost has dropped greatly in the past few years. Praseodymium can be prepared by several methods, such as by calcium reduction of the anhydrous chloride or fluoride. Misch metal, used in making cigarette lighters, contains about 5% praseodymium metal. Praseodymium is soft, silvery, malleable, and ductile. It was prepared in relatively pure form in 1931. It is somewhat more resistant to corrosion in air than europium, lanthanum, cerium or neodymium, but it does develop a green oxide coating that spalls off, when exposed to air. As with other rare-earth metals it should be kept under a light mineral oil, or sealed in plastic. The rare-earth oxides, including Pr_2O_3, are among the most refractory substances known. Along with other rare earths, it is widely used as a core material for carbon arcs used by the motion picture industry for studio lighting and projection. Salts of praseodymium are used to color glasses and enamels; when mixed with certain other materials, praseodymium produces an intense and unusually clean yellow color in glass. Didymium glass, of which praseodymium is a component, is a colorant for welder's goggles. The metal (99 + % pure) is priced at about $2.00/gm.

PROMETHIUM (*Prometheus*, who, according to mythology, stole fire from heaven), Pm; at. no. 61; m.p. ∼ 1080°C; b.p. 2460°C(?); sp. gr. ...; valence 3. In 1902 Branner predicted the existence of an element between neodymium and samarium, and this was confirmed by Moseley in 1914. In 1941, workers at Ohio State University irradiated neodymium and praseodymium with neutrons, deuterons, and alpha particles, resp., and produced several new radioactivities, which most likely were those of Element 61. Wu and Segrè, and Bethe, in 1942, confirmed the formation; however chemical proof of the production of Element 61

was lacking because of the difficulty in separating the rare earths from each other at that time. In 1945, Marinsky, Glendenin, and Coryell made the first chemical identification by use of ion-exchange chromatography. Their work was done by fission of uranium and by neutron bombardment of neodymium. Searches for the element on earth have been fruitless, and it now appears that promethium is completely missing from the earth's crust. Promethium, however, has been identified in the spectrum of the star HR^{465} in Andromeda. This element is being formed recently near the star's surface, for no known isotope of promethium has a half-life longer than 17.7 yrs. Thirteen isotopes of promethium, with atomic masses from 141 to 154, are now known. Promethium–147, with a half-life of 2.5 yrs., is the most generally useful. Promethium–145 is the longest lived, and has a specific activity of 940 curies per gram. It is a soft beta emitter; although no gamma rays are emitted, x-radiation can be generated when beta particles impinge on elements of a high atomic number, and great care must be taken in handling it. Promethium salts luminesce in the dark with a pale blue or greenish glow, due to their high radioactivity. Ion-exchange methods led to the preparation of about 10g of promethium from atomic reactor fuel processing wastes in early 1963. Little is yet generally known about the properties of metallic promethium. Two or more allotropic modifications are thought to exist. The element has applications as a beta source for thickness gages, and it can be absorbed by a phosphor to produce light. Light produced in this manner can be used for signs or signals that require dependable operation; it can be used as a nuclear-powered battery by capturing light in photocells which convert it into electric current. Such a battery, using Pm^{147}, would have a useful life of about 5 years. Promethium shows promise as a portable x-ray unit, and it may become useful as a heat source to provide auxiliary power for space probes and satellites. More than thirty promethium compounds have been prepared. Most are colored. Promethium–147 is available to A.E.C. licensees at a cost of about 50¢ per curie.

PROTACTINIUM (Gr. *protos*, first), Pa; at. wt. 231.0359; at. no. 91; m.p. < 1600°C; b.p. ...; sp. gr. 15.37 (calc.); valence 4 or 5. The first isotope of Element 91 to be discovered was Pa^{234m}, also known as UX_2, a short-lived member of the naturally occurring U^{238} decay series. It was identified by K. Fajans and O. H. Göhring in 1913 and they named the new element *brevium*. When the longer-lived isotope Pa^{231} was identified by Hahn and Meitner in 1918, the name protoactinium was adopted as being more consistent with the characteristics of the most abundant isotope. Soddy, Cranston, and Fleck were also active in this work. The name *protoactinium* was shortened to *protactinium* in 1949. In 1927 Grosse prepared 2 mg. of a white powder, which was shown to be Pa_2O_5. Later, in 1934, from 0.1 gm. of pure Pa_2O_5 he isolated the element by two methods, one of which was by converting the oxide to an iodide and "cracking" it in a high vacuum by an electrically heated filament by the reaction

$$2PaI_5 \rightarrow 2Pa + 5I_2.$$

Protactinium has a bright metallic luster which it retains for sometime in air. The element occurs in *pitchblende* to the extent of about 1 part Pa^{231} to 10 million of ore. Ores from the Congo have about 3 ppm. Protactinium has thirteen isotopes, the most common of which is Pr^{231} with a half-life of 32,500 yrs. A number of protactinium compounds are known, some of which are colored. The element is superconductive below 1.4°K. An indirect measurement indicates that protactinium has a vapor pressure of 5.1×10^{-5} at 1927°C. The element is a dangerous toxic material and requires precautions similar to those used when handling plutonium. In 1959 and 1961, it was announced that the Great Britain Atomic Energy Authority extracted by a 12-stage process 125 gms of 99.9% protactinium, the world's only stock of the metal for many years to come. The extraction was made from 60 tons of waste material at a cost of about $500,000. Protactinium is one of the rarest and most expensive natural-occurring elements. It was reported that this stock was being distributed to laboratories around the world at a cost of about $2800/gm. The element is an alpha emitter (5.0 MeV), and is a radiological hazard similar to polonium.

RADIUM (L. *radius*, ray) Ra; at. wt. 226.0254; at. no. 88; m.p. 700°C; b.p. 1140°C; sp. gr. 5?; valence 2. Radium was discovered in 1898 by M. and Mme. Curie in the *pitchblende* or *uraninite* of North Bohemia, in which it occurs. There is about 1 gm. of radium in 7 tons of pitchblende. The element was isolated in 1911 by Mme. Curie and Debierne by the electrolysis of a solution of pure radium chloride, employing a mercury cathode; on distillation in an atmosphere of hydrogen this amalgam yielded the pure metal. Originally, radium was obtained from the rich pitchblende ore found at Joachimsthal, Bohemia. The *carnotite* sands of Colorado furnish some radium, but richer ores are found in the Democratic Republic of Congo and the Great Bear Lake region of Canada. Radium is present in all uranium minerals, and could be extracted, if desired, from the extensive wastes of uranium processing. Large uranium deposits are located in Ontario, New Mexico, Utah, Australia, and elsewhere. Radium is obtained commercially as the bromide or chloride; it is doubtful if any appreciable stock of the isolated element now exists. The pure metal is brilliant white when freshly prepared, but blackens on exposure to air, probably due to formation of the nitride. It exhibits luminescence, as do its salts; it decomposes in water and is somewhat more volatile than barium. It is a member of the alkaline-earth group of metals. Radium imparts a carmine red color to a flame. Radium emits alpha, beta, and gamma rays and when mixed with beryllium produces neutrons. One gram of Ra^{226} undergoes 3.7×10^{10} disintegrations per sec. The *curie* is defined as that amount of radioactivity which has the same disintegration rate as 1 gm. of Ra^{226}. Sixteen isotopes are now known; radium 226, the common isotope, has a half-life of 1620 yrs. One gram of radium produces about 0.0001 milliliter (stp) of emanation, or radon gas, per day. This is pumped from the radium and sealed in minute tubes, which are used in the treatment of cancer and other diseases. One gram of radium yields about 1000 calories per year. Radium is used in producing self-luminous paints, neutron sources, and in medicine for the treatment of disease. Some of the more recently discovered radioisotopes, such as Co^{60}, are now being used in place of radium. Some of these sources are much more powerful, and others are safer to use. Radium loses about 1% of its activity in 25 yrs., being transformed into elements of lower atomic weight. Lead is a final product of disintegration. The study of radium has greatly altered our ideas of the structure of the atom. Radium is a radiological hazard. (Stored radium should be ventilated to prevent build-up of radon.) Inhalation, injection, or body exposure to radium can cause cancer and other body disorders. The recommended maximum allowable concentration for total body content is 0.1 microgram and exposure to 2 roentgens/mo.

RADON (from *radium*; called *niton* at first, L. *nitens*,

shining), Rn; at. wt. (~222); at. no. 86; m.p. −71°C; b.p. −61.8°C; density of gas 9.73 gms/l; sp. gr. liquid 4.4 at −62°C, solid 4; valence usually 0. The element was discovered in 1900 by Dorn, who called it *radium emanation*. In 1908 Ramsay and Gray, who named it *niton*, isolated the element and determined its density, finding it to be the heaviest known gas. It is essentially inert and occupies the last place in the zero group of gases in the Periodic Table. Since 1923, it has been called radon. Twenty isotopes are known. Radon-222, coming from radium, has a half-life of 3.823 days and is an alpha emitter; radon-220, emanating naturally from thorium and called *thoron*, has a half-life of 54.5 seconds and is also an alpha emitter. Radon-219, emanates from actinium and is called *actinon*. It has a half-life of 3.92 seconds and is also an alpha emitter. It is estimated that every square mile of soil to a depth of 6 inches contains about 1 gm. of radium, which releases radon in tiny amounts to the atmosphere. Radon is present in some spring waters, such as those at Hot Springs, Arkansas. On the average, one part of radon is present to 1 sextillion parts of air. At ordinary temperatures radon is a colorless gas; when cooled below the freezing point, radon exhibits a brilliant phosphorescence which becomes yellow as the temperature is lowered and orange-red at the temperature of liquid air. It has been reported that fluorine reacts with radon, forming radon fluoride. Radon clathrates have also been reported. Radon is still produced for therapeutic use by a few hospitals by pumping it from a radium source and sealing it in minute tubes, called seeds or needles, for application to patients. This practice is now largely discontinued as hospitals can order the seeds directly from suppliers, who make up the seeds with the desired activity for the day of use. Radon is available at a cost of about $4/millicurie. Care must be taken in handling radon, as with other radioactive materials. The main hazard is from inhalation of the element and its solid daughters, which are collected on dust in the air. The maximum permissible level in air has been given at 10^{-8} microcuries/milliliter. Good ventilation should be provided where radium, thorium, or actinium is stored to prevent buildup of this element. Radon buildup is also a health consideration in uranium mines.

RHENIUM (L. *Rhenus*, Rhine), Re; at. wt. 186.2; at. no. 75; m.p. 3180°C; b.p. 5627°C (est.); sp. gr. 21.02 (20°C); valence −1, 2, 3, 4, 5, 6, 7. Discovery of rhenium is generally attributed to Noddack, Tacke, and Berg, who announced in 1925 they had detected the element in platinum ores and *columbite*. They also found the element in *gadolinite* and *molybdenite*. By working up 660 kg. of molybdenite they were able in 1928 to extract 1 gm. of rhenium. The price in 1928 was $10,000/gm. Rhenium does not occur free in nature or as a compound in a distinct mineral species. It is, however, widely spread throughout the earth's crust to the extent of about 0.001 ppm. Commercial rhenium in the U.S. today is obtained from molybdenite roaster-flue dusts obtained from copper-sulfide ores mined in the vicinity of Miami, Arizona, and elsewhere in Arizona and Utah. Some molybdenites contain from 0.002 to 0.2% rhenium. More than 120,000 troy ounces of rhenium are now being produced yearly in the United States. The total estimated free-world reserve of rhenium metal is 100 tons. Natural rhenium is a mixture of two stable isotopes. Sixteen other unstable isotopes are recognized. Rhenium metal is prepared by reducing ammonium perrhenate with hydrogen at elevated temperatures. The element is silvery-white with a metallic luster; its density is exceeded only by that of platinum, iridium, and osmium, and its melting point is exceeded only by that of tungsten and carbon. It has other useful properties. The usual commercial form of the element is a powder, but it can be consolidated by pressing and resistance-sintering in a vacuum or hydrogen atmosphere. This produces a compact shape in excess of 90% of the density of the metal. Annealed rhenium is very ductile, and can be bent, coiled, or rolled. Rhenium is used as an additive to tungsten and molybdenum-based alloys to impart useful properties. It is widely used for filaments for mass spectrographs and ion gages. Rhenium-molybdenum alloys are superconductive at 10°K. Rhenium is also used as an electrical contact material as it has good wear resistance and withstands arc corrosion. Thermocouples made of Re-W are used for measuring temperatures up to 2200°C, and rhenium wire is used in photoflash lamps for photography. Rhenium catalysts are exceptionally resistant to poisoning from nitrogen, sulfur, and phosphorus, and are used for hydrogenation of fine chemicals, hydrocracking, reforming, and the disproportionation of olefins. Rhenium costs about $40/troy ounce. Little is known of its toxicity; therefore it should be handled with care until more data are available.

RHODIUM (Gr. *rhodon*, rose), Rh; at. wt. 102.9055; at. no. 45; m.p. $1966 \pm 3°C$; b.p. $3727 \pm 100°C$; sp. gr. 12.41 (20°C); valence 2, 3, 4, 5, and 6. Wollaston discovered rhodium in 1803–4 in crude platinum ore he presumably obtained from South America. Rhodium occurs native with other platinum metals in river sands of the Urals and in North and South America. It is also found with other platinum metals in the copper-nickel sulfide ores of the Sudbury, Ontario, region. Although the quantity occurring here is very small, the large tonnages of nickel processed makes the recovery commercially feasible. The annual world production of rhodium is only two or three tons. The metal is silvery-white and at red heat slowly changes in air to the sesquioxide. At higher temperatures it converts back to the element. Rhodium has a higher melting point and lower density than platinum. Its major use is as an alloying agent to harden platinum and palladium. Such alloys are used for furnace windings, thermocouple elements, bushings for glass fiber production, electrodes for aircraft spark plugs, and laboratory crucibles. It is useful as an electrical contact material as it has a low electrical resistance, a low and stable contact resistance, and is highly resistant to corrosion. Plated rhodium, produced by electroplating or evaporation, is exceptionally hard and is used for optical instruments. It has a high reflectance and is hard and durable. Rhodium is also used for jewelry, for decoration, and as a catalyst. Rhodium in small quantities costs about $9/gm. or $225/troy ounce.

RUBIDIUM (L. *rubidius*, deepest red), Rb; at. wt. 85.4678; at. no. 37; m.p. 38.89°C; b.p. 688°C; sp. gr. (solid) 1.532 (20°C), (liquid) 1.475 (39°C); valence 1, 2, 3, 4. Discovered in 1861 by Bunsen and Kirchoff in the mineral *lepidolite* by use of the spectroscope. The element is much more abundant than was thought several years ago. It is now considered to be the 16th most abundant element in the earth's crust. Rubidium occurs in *pollucite*, *carnallite*, *leucite*, and *zinnwaldite*, which contains traces up to 1%, in the form of the oxide. It is found in lepidolite to the extent of about 1.5%, and is recovered commercially from this source. Potassium minerals, such as those found at Searles Lake, California, and potassium chloride recovered from brines in Michigan also contain the element and are commercial sources. It is also found along with cesium in the extensive deposits of *pollucite* at Bernic Lake, Manitoba. Rubidium can be liquid at room temperature. It is a soft,

silvery-white metallic element of the alkali group and is the second most electropositive and alkaline element. It ignites spontaneously in air and reacts violently in water, setting fire to the liberated hydrogen. As with other alkali metals, it forms amalgams with mercury and it alloys with gold, cesium, sodium, and potassium. It colors a flame yellowish-violet. Rubidium metal can be prepared by reducing rubidium chloride with calcium, and by a number of other methods. It must be kept under a dry mineral oil or in a vacuum or inert atmosphere. Seventeen isotopes of rubidium are known. Natural-occurring rubidium is made of two isotopes Rb^{85} and Rb^{87}. Rubidium-87 is present to the extent of 27.85% in natural rubidium and is a beta emitter with a half-life of 5×10^{11} yrs. Ordinary rubidium is sufficiently radioactive to expose a photographic film in about 30 to 60 days. Rubidium forms four oxides: Rb_2O, Rb_2O_2, Rb_2O_3, Rb_2O_4. Because rubidium can be easily ionized, it is being considered for use in "ion engines" for space vehicles; however cesium is somewhat more efficient for this purpose. It is also proposed for use as a working fluid for vapor turbines and for use in a thermoelectric generator using the magnetohydrodynamic principle where rubidium ions are formed by heat at high temperature and passed through a magnetic field. These conduct electricity and act like an armature of a generator and cause electricity to be generated. Rubidium is used as a getter in vacuum tubes and as a photocell component. It has been used in making special glasses. $RbAg_4I_5$ is important as it has the highest room conductivity of any known ionic crystal. At 20°C its conductivity is about the same as dilute sulfuric acid. This suggests use in thin film batteries and other applications. The present cost in small quantities is about $10/gm. (99.9%), or $300/lb.

RUTHENIUM (L. *Ruthenia*, Russia), Ru; at. wt. 101.07; at. no. 44; m.p. 2310°C; b.p. 3900°C; sp. gr. 12.41 (20°C); valence 0, 1, 2, 3, 4, 5, 6, 7, 8. Berzelius and Osann in 1827 examined the residues left after dissolving crude platinum from the Ural Mts. in *aqua regia*. While Berzelius found no unusual metals, Osann thought he found three new metals, one of which he named ruthenium. In 1844 Klaus, generally recognized as the discoverer, showed that Osann's ruthenium oxide was very impure and that it contained a new metal. Klaus obtained 6 gm. of ruthenium from the portion of crude platinum that is insoluble in aqua regia. A member of the platinum group, ruthenium occurs native with other members of the group in ores found in the Ural Mts. and in North and South America. It is also found along with other platinum metals in small but commercial quantities in *pentlandite* of the Sudbury, Ontario, nickel-mining region, and in *pyroxinite* deposits of South Africa. The metal is isolated commercially by a complex chemical process, the final stage of which is the hydrogen reduction of ammonium ruthenium chloride, which yields a powder. The powder is consolidated by powder metallurgy techniques or by argon-arc welding. Ruthenium is a hard, white metal and has four crystal modifications. It does not tarnish at room temperatures, but oxidizes in air at about 800°C. The metal is not attacked by hot or cold acids or aqua regia, but when potassium chlorate is added to the solution, it oxidizes explosively. It is attacked by halogens, hydroxides, etc. Ruthenium can be plated by electrodeposition or by thermal decomposition methods. The metal is one of the most effective hardeners for platinum and palladium, and is alloyed with these metals to make electrical contacts for severe wear resistance. A ruthenium-molybdenum alloy is said to be superconductive at 10.6°K. The corrosion resistance of titanium is improved a hundredfold by addition of 0.1% ruthenium. It is a versatile catalyst. Compounds in at least eight oxidation states have been found, but of these, the $+2$, $+3$, and $+4$ states are the most common. Ruthenium tetroxide, like osmium tetroxide, is highly toxic. Ruthenium compounds show a marked resemblance to those of osmium. The metal is priced at about $4/gm. or $60/troy ounce.

RUTHERFORDIUM (See Element 104)

SAMARIUM (*Samarskite*, a mineral), Sm; at. wt. 150.4; at. no. 62; m.p. $1077 \pm 5°C$; b.p. 1791 C; sp. gr. (α) 7.520 (β) 7.40; valence 2 or 3. Discovered spectroscopically by its sharp absorption lines in 1879 by Lecoq de Boisbaudran in the mineral *samarskite*, named in honor of a Russian mine official, Col. Samarski. Samarium is found along with other members of the rare-earth elements in many minerals, including *monazite* and *bastnasite*, which are commercial sources. It occurs in monazite to the extent of 2.8%. While *misch metal*, containing about 1% of samarium metal, has long been used, samarium has not been isolated in relatively pure form until recent years. Ion-exchange and solvent extraction techniques have recently simplified separation of the rare earths from one another; more recently, electrochemical deposition, using an electrolytic solution of lithium citrate and a mercury electrode, is said to be a simple, fast, and highly specific way to separate the rare earths. Samarium metal can be produced by reducing the oxide with barium or lanthanum. Samarium has a bright silver luster and is reasonably stable in air. Two crystal modifications of the metal exist, with a transformation point at 917°C. The metal ignites in air at about 150°C. Sixteen isotopes of samarium exist. Natural samarium is a mixture of seven isotopes, three of which are unstable with long half-lives. Samarium, along with other rare earths, is used for carbon-arc lighting for the motion-picture industry. The sulfide has excellent high-temperature stability and good thermoelectric efficiencies up to 1100°C. $SmCo_5$ has been used in making a new permanent magnet material with the highest resistance to demagnetization of any known material. It is said to have an intrinsic coercive force as high as 28,000 oersteds. Samarium oxide has been used in optical glass to absorb the infrared. Samarium is used to dope calcium fluoride crystals for use in optical masers or lasers. Compounds of the metal act as sensitizers for phosphors excited in the infrared; the oxide exhibits catalytic properties in the dehydration and dehydrogenation of ethyl alcohol. It is used in infrared absorbing glass and as a neutron absorber in nuclear reactors. The metal is priced at about $1/gm or $250/lb. Little is known of the toxicity of samarium; therefore it should be handled carefully.

SCANDIUM (L. *Scandia*, Scandinavia), Sc; at. wt. 44.9559; at. no. 21; m.p. 1541°C; b.p. 2831°C; sp. gr. 2.989 (25°C); valence 3. On the basis of the Periodic System, Mendeleev predicted the existence of *ekaboron*, which would have an atomic weight between 40 of calcium and 48 of titanium. The element was discovered by Nilson in 1876 in the minerals *euxenite* and *gadolinite*, which had not yet been found anywhere except in Scandinavia. By processing 10 kg of euxenite and other residues of rare-earth minerals, Nilson was able to prepare about 2 gms of scandium oxide of high purity. Cleve later pointed out that Nilson's scandium was identical with Mendeleev's ekaboron. Scandium is apparently a much more abundant element in the sun and certain stars than here on earth. It is about the 23rd most abundant element in the sun compared to the 50th most abundant on earth. It is widely distributed on earth, occurring in very minute quantities in over 800 mineral species. The blue color of beryl (aquamarine variety) is said to be due to scandium. It occurs as a principal component in the rare mineral *thortveitite*, found in Scandinavia and Malagasy. It is also found in the residues remaining after the extraction of tungsten from Zinnwald *wolframite*, and in *wiikite* and *bazzite*. Most scandium is presently being recovered from *thortveitite* or as a by-product of the extraction of uranium from *davidite*, which contains about 0.02% Sc_2O_3. Metallic scandium was first prepared in 1937 by Fischer, Brunger, and Grieneisen, who electrolyzed a eutectic melt of potassium, lithium, and scandium chlorides at 700–800°C. Tungsten wire and a pool of molten zinc served as the electrodes in a graphite crucible. Methods of producing the metal are now somewhat more complicated. The production of the first pound of 99% pure scandium metal was announced in 1960 as having been made under a U.S. Air Force contract. Scandium is a silvery-white metal which develops a slightly yellowish or pinkish cast upon exposure to air. It is relatively soft, and is reported to resemble yttrium and the rare-earth metals more than it resembles aluminum or titanium. It is a very light metal and has a higher melting point than aluminum, making it of interest to designers of space missiles. Scandium is not attacked by a 1:1 mixture of conc. HNO_3 and 48%HF. This mixture can be used to dissolve tantalum from scandium. Scandium reacts rapidly with many acids. Eleven isotopes of scandium are recognized. The metal is still expensive, costing about $20 to $60 or more per gram, or about $7500 per pound with a purity of about 99.9%. It has been reported that several hundred pounds of scandium have now been produced (1970). Scandium oxide costs about $8/gm. Little is yet known about the toxicity of scandium; therefore it should be handled with care.

SELENIUM (Gr. *Selene*, moon), Se; at. wt. 78.96; at. no. 34; m.p. (gray) 217°C; b.p. (gray) $684.9 \pm 1.0°C$; sp. gr. (gray) 4.79, (vitreous) 4.28; valence -2, $+4$, or $+6$. Discovered by Berzelius in 1817, who found it associated with tellurium, named for the earth. Selenium is found in a few rare minerals, such as *crooksite* and *clausthalite*. In years past it has been obtained from flue dusts remaining from processing copper sulfide ores, but the anode muds from electrolytic copper refineries now provide the source of most of the world's selenium. Selenium is recovered by roasting the muds with soda or sulfuric acid, or by smelting them with soda and niter. Selenium exists in several allotropic forms. Three are generally recognized, but as many as six have been claimed. Selenium can be prepared with either an amorphous or crystalline structure. The color of amorphous selenium is either red, in powder form, or black, in vitreous form. Crystalline monoclinic selenium is a deep red; crystalline hexagonal selenium, the most stable variety, is a metallic gray. Natural selenium contains six stable isotopes. Fourteen other nuclides and isomers have been characterized. The element is a member of the sulfur family and resembles sulfur both in its various forms and in its compounds. Selenium exhibits both photovoltaic action, where light is converted directly into electricity, and photoconductive action, where the electrical resistance decreases with increased illumination. These properties make selenium useful in the production of photocells and exposure meters for photographic use, as well as solar cells. Selenium is also able to convert a.c. electricity to d.c., and is extensively used in rectifiers. Below its melting point selenium is a p-type semiconductor, and is finding many uses in electronic and solid-state applications. It is used in Xerography for reproducing and copying documents, letters, etc. It is used by the glass industry to decolorize glass and to make ruby-colored glasses and enamels. It is also used as a photographic toner, and as an additive to stainless steel. Elemental selenium has been said to be practically nontoxic; however, hydrogen selenide and other selenium compounds are extremely toxic, and resemble arsenic in its physiological reactions. Hydrogen selenide in a concentration of 1.5 ppm. is intolerable to man. Selenium occurs in some soils in amounts sufficient to produce serious effects on animals feeding on plants, such as locoweed, grown in such soils. The maximum allowable concentration of selenium compounds in air has been recommended to be 0.1 mg/cu meter. Selenium is priced at about $5/lb. It is also available in high-purity form at a somewhat higher cost.

SILICON (L. *silex, silicis,* flint), Si; at. wt. 28.086; at. no. 14; m.p. 1410°C; b.p. 2355°C; sp. gr. 2.33 (25°C); valence 4. Davy in 1800 thought silica to be a compound and not an element; later in 1811, Gay Lussac and Thenard probably prepared impure amorphous silicon by heating potassium with silicon tetrafluoride. Berzelius, generally credited with the discovery, in 1824 succeeded in preparing amorphous silicon by the same general method as used earlier, but he purified the product by removing the fluosilicates by repeated washings. Deville in 1854 first prepared crystalline silicon, the second allotropic form of the element. Silicon is present in the sun and stars and is a principal component of a class of meteorites known as *aerolites.* It is also a component of *tektites,* a natural glass of uncertain origin, but believed by some to be ejected lunar material from the crater *Tycho.* Silicon makes up 25.7% of the earth's crust, by weight, and is the second most abundant element, being exceeded only by oxygen. Silicon is not found free in nature, but occurs chiefly as the oxide, and as silicates. *Sand, quartz, rock crystal, amethyst, agate, flint, jasper,* and *opal* are some of the forms in which the oxide appears. *Granite, hornblende, asbestos, feldspar, clay, mica,* etc. are but a few of the numerous silicate minerals. Silicon is prepared commercially by heating silica and carbon in an electric furnace, using carbon electrodes. Several other methods can be used for preparing the element. Amorphous silicon can be prepared as a brown powder, which can be easily melted or vaporized. Crystalline silicon has a metallic luster and grayish color. The Czochralski process is commonly used to produce single crystals of silicon used for solid-state or semiconductor devices. Hyper-pure silicon can be prepared by the thermal decomposition of ultra-pure trichlorosilane in a hydrogen atmosphere, and by a vacuum float zone process. This product can be doped with boron, gallium, phosphorus, or arsenic, etc. to produce silicon for use in transistors, solar cells, rectifiers, and other solid-state devices which are used extensively in the electronics and space-age industries. Silicon is a relatively inert element, but it is attacked by halogens and dilute alkali. Most acids, except hydrofluoric, do not affect it. Silicones are important products of silicon. They may be prepared by hydrolyzing a silicon organic chloride, such as dimethyl silicon chloride. Hydrolysis and condensation of various substituted chlorosilanes can be used to produce a very great number of polymeric products, or silicones, ranging from liquids to hard, glass-like solids with many useful properties. Elemental silicon transmits more than 95% of all wavelengths of infrared, from 1.3 to 6.7 microns. Silicon is one of man's most useful elements. In the form of sand and clay it is used to make concrete and brick; it is a useful refractory material for high-temperature work, and in the form of silicates it is used in making enamels, pottery, etc. Silica, as sand, is a principal ingredient of glass, one of the most inexpensive of materials with excellent mechanical, optical, thermal, and electrical properties. Glass can be made in a very great variety of shapes, and is used as containers, window glass, insulators, and thousands of other uses. Silicon tetrachloride can be used to iridize glass. Silicon is important in plant and animal life. Diatoms in both fresh and salt water extract silica from the water to build up their cell walls. Silica is present in ashes of plants and in the human skeleton. Silicon is an important ingredient in steel; silicon carbide is one of the most important abrasives and has been used in lasers to produce coherent light of 4560 Å. Regular grade silicon (97%) costs about 20 cents/lb. Silicon 99.7% pure costs about $7/lb.; hyper-pure silicon may cost as much as $100/lb. Miners, stonecutters, and others engaged in work where siliceous dust is breathed in large quantities often develop a serious lung disease known as *silicosis.*

SILVER (Anglo-Saxon, *Seolfor siolfur*), Ag (L. argentum; at. wt. 107.868; at. no. 47; m.p. 961.93°C; b.p. 2,212°C; sp. gr. 10.50 (20°C); valence 1, 2. Silver has been known since ancient times. It is mentioned in Genesis. Slag dumps in Asia Minor and on islands in the Aegean Sea indicate that man learned to separate silver from lead as early as 3,000 B.C. Silver occurs native and in ores such as *argentite* (Ag_2S) and *horn silver* (AgCl); lead, lead-zinc, copper, gold, and copper-nickel ores are principal sources. Mexico, Canada, Peru, and the United States are the principal silver producers in the Western Hemisphere. Silver is also recovered during electrolytic refining of copper. Commercial fine silver contains at least 99.9% silver. Purities of 99.999+% are available commercially. Pure silver has a brilliant white metallic luster. It is a little harder than gold and is very ductile and malleable, being exceeded only by gold and perhaps palladium. Pure silver has the highest electrical and thermal conductivity of all metals, and possesses the lowest contact resistance. It is stable in pure air and water, but tarnishes when exposed to ozone, hydrogen sulfide, or air containing sulfur. The alloys of silver are important. Sterling silver is used for jewelry, silverware, etc. where appearance is paramount. This alloy contains 92.5% silver, the remainder being copper or some other metal. Silver is of utmost importance in photography, about 30% of the U.S. industrial consumption going into this application. It is used for dental alloys. Silver is used in making solder and brazing alloys, electrical contacts, and high capacity silver-zinc and silver-cadmium batteries. Silver paints are used for making printed circuits. It is used in mirror production and may be deposited on glass or metals by chemical deposition, electrodeposition, or by evaporation. When freshly deposited, it is the best reflector of visible light known, but it rapidly tarnishes and loses much of its reflectance. It is a poor reflector of ultraviolet. Silver fulminate ($Ag_2C_2N_2O_2$), a powerful explosive, is sometimes formed during the silvering process. Silver iodide is used in seeding clouds to produce rain. Silver chloride has interesting optical properties as it can be made transparent; it also is a cement for glass. Silver nitrate, or *lunar caustic,* the most important silver compound, is used extensively in photography. While silver itself is not considered to be toxic, most of its salts are poisonous due to the anions present. Silver compounds can be absorbed in the circulatory system and reduced silver deposited in the various tissues of the body. A condition, known as *argyria*, results with a greyish pigmentation of the skin and mucous membranes. Silver has germicidal effects and kills many lower organisms effectively without harm to higher animals. Silver for centuries has been used traditionally for coinage by many countries of the world. In recent times, however, consumption of silver has greatly exceeded the output. In 1939, the price of silver was fixed by the U.S. Treasury at 71¢/troy oz., and at 90.5¢/troy oz. in 1946. In November 1961 the U.S. Treasury suspended sales of nonmonetized silver, and the price stabilized for a time at about $1.29, the melt-down value of silver U.S. coins. The Coinage Act of 1965 authorized a change in the metallic composition of the three U.S. subsidiary denominations to clad or composite type coins. This was the first change in U.S. coinage since the monetary system was established in 1792. Clad dimes and quarters are made of an outer layer of 75% Cu and 25% Ni bonded to a central core of pure Cu. The clad half dollars, with an overall silver content of 40%, contain an outer layer of 80% Ag and 20% Cu bonded to an inner core of about 20% Ag and 80% Cu. The U.S. Treasury has minted, as of 1970, about 1¼ billion of these half dollars and placed them into circulation. The composition of the one-cent and five-cent pieces remains unchanged. One-cent coins are 95% Cu and 5% Zn. Five-cent coins are 75% Cu and 25% Ni. Old silver dollars are 90% Ag and 10% Cu. Earlier subsidiary coins of 90% Ag and 10% Cu officially are to circulate alongside the clad coins; however, in practice they have largely disappeared (Gresham's Law), as the value of the silver is now greater than their exchange value. Silver coins of other countries have largely been replaced with coins made of other metals. On June 24, 1968, the U.S. Government ceased to redeem U.S. Silver Certificates with silver. Since that time, the price of silver has fluctuated widely; as of December 31, 1974, the price was about $4.75/troy ounce. The U.S. Government discontinued selling silver to domestic users and foreign buyers on November 10, 1970.

SODIUM (English, *soda*; Medieval Latin, *sodanum*, headache remedy), Na (L. *natrium*); at. wt. 22.9898; at. no. 11; m.p. 97.81 ± 0.03°C; b.p. 882.9°C; sp. gr. 0.971 (20°C); valence 1. Long recognized in compounds, sodium was first isolated by Davy in 1807 by electrolysis of caustic soda. Sodium is present in fair abundance in the sun and stars. The D lines of sodium are among the most prominent in the solar spectrum. Sodium is the sixth most abundant element on earth, comprising about 2.6% of the earth's crust; it is the most abundant of the alkali group of metals of which it is a member. The most common compound is sodium chloride, but it occurs in many other minerals, such as *soda niter*, *cryolite*, *amphibole*, *zeolite*, *sodalite*, etc. It is a very reactive element and is never found free in nature. It is now obtained commercially by the electrolysis of absolutely dry fused sodium chloride. This method is much cheaper than that of electrolyzing sodium hydroxide, as was used several years ago. Sodium is a soft, bright, silvery metal which floats on water, decomposing it with the evolution of hydrogen and the formation of the hydroxide. It may or may not ignite spontaneously on water, depending on the amount of oxide and metal exposed to the water. It normally does not ignite in air at temperatures below 115°C. Sodium should be handled with respect as it can be dangerous when improperly handled. Metallic sodium is vital in the manufacture of sodamide and sodium cyanide, sodium peroxide, and sodium hydride. It is used in preparing tetraethyl lead, in the reduction of organic esters, and in the preparation of organic compounds. The metal may be used to improve the structure of certain alloys, to descale metal, to purify molten metals, and as a heat transfer agent. An alloy of sodium with potassium, NaK, is also an important heat transfer agent. Sodium compounds are important to the paper, glass, soap, textile, petroleum, chemical and metal industries. Soap is generally a sodium salt of certain fatty acids. The importance of common salt to animal nutrition has been recognized since prehistoric times. Among the many compounds that are of the greatest industrial importance are: common salt ($NaCl$), soda ash (Na_2CO_3), baking soda ($NaHCO_3$), caustic soda ($NaOH$), Chile saltpeter ($NaNO_3$), di- and trisodium phosphates, sodium thiosulfate (hypo, $Na_2S_2O_3 \cdot 5H_2O$), and borax ($Na_2B_4O_7 \cdot 10H_2O$). Seven isotopes of sodium are recognized. Metallic sodium is priced at about 15 to 20¢/lb. in quantity. On a per cubic inch basis, it is the cheapest of all metals. Sodium metal should be handled with great care. It should be maintained in an inert atmosphere and contact with water and other substances with which sodium reacts should be avoided.

STRONTIUM (*Strontian*, town in Scotland), Sr; at. wt. 87.62; at. no. 38; m.p. 769°C; b.p. 1384°C; sp. gr. 2.54; valence 2. Discovered by Davy by electrolysis in 1808. Strontium is found chiefly as *celestite* ($SrSO_4$) and *strontianite* ($SrCO_3$). The metal can be prepared by electrolysis of the fused chloride mixed with potassium chloride, or is made by reducing strontium oxide with aluminum in a vacuum at a temperature at which strontium distills off. Three allotropic forms of the metal exist, with transition points at 235°C and 540°C. Strontium is softer than calcium and decomposes water more vigorously. It does not absorb nitrogen below 380°C. It should be kept under kerosene to prevent oxidation. Freshly cut strontium has a silvery appearance, but rapidly turns a yellowish color with the formation of the oxide. The finely divided metal ignites spontaneously in air. Volatile strontium salts impart a beautiful crimson color to flames, and these salts are used in pyrotechnics. Natural strontium is a mixture of four stable isotopes. Twelve other unstable isotopes are known to exist. Of greatest importance is Sr^{90} with a half-life of 28 yrs. It is a product of nuclear fallout and presents a health problem. This isotope is one of the best long-lived high-energy beta emitters known, and is used in SNAP devices (Systems for Nuclear Auxiliary Power). These devices hold promise for use in space vehicles, remote weather stations, navigational buoys, etc., where a lightweight, long-lived, nuclear-electric power source is needed. Strontium hydroxide, has been used in sugar refining; however lime is replacing its use as it is cheaper. Strontium titanate is an interesting optical material as it has an extremely high refractive index and an optical dispersion greater than that of diamond. It has been used as a gemstone, but it is very soft. It does not occur naturally. The applications of strontium are similar to those of barium and calcium, but there are few advantages and the cost is much higher. Strontium metal costs about $6 to $8/lb.

SULFUR (Sanskrit, *sulvere*; L. *sulphurium*), S; at. wt. 32.06; at. no. 16; m.p. (rhombic) 112.8°C, (monoclinic) 119.0°C; b.p. 444.674°C; sp. gr. (rhombic) 2.07, (monoclinic) 1.957 (20°C); valence 2, 4, or 6. Known to the ancients;

referred to in Genesis as *brimstone*. Sulfur is found in meteorites. A dark area near the crater Aristarchus on the moon has been studied by R. W. Wood with ultraviolet light. This study suggests strongly that it is a sulfur deposit. Sulfur occurs native in the vicinity of volcanoes and hot springs. It is widely distributed in nature as *iron pyrites*, *galena*, *sphalerite*, *cinnabar*, *stibnite*, *gypsum*, *epsom salts*, *celestite*, *barite*, etc. Sulfur is commercially recovered from wells sunk into the salt domes along the Gulf Coast of the U.S. It is obtained from these wells by the Frasch process, which forces heated water into the wells to melt the sulfur that is then brought to the surface. Sulfur also occurs in natural gas and petroleum crudes and must be removed from these products. Formerly this was done chemically, which wasted the sulfur. New processes now permit recovery, and these sources promise to be very important. Large amounts of sulfur are being recovered from Alberta gas fields. Sulfur is a pale yellow, odorless, brittle solid, which is insoluble in water, but soluble in carbon disulfide. In every state, whether gas, liquid, or solid, elemental sulfur occurs in more than one allotropic form or modification; these present a confusing multitude of forms whose relations are not yet fully understood. Amorphous or "plastic" sulfur is obtained by fast cooling of the crystalline form. X-ray studies indicate that amorphous sulfur may have a helical structure with eight atoms per spiral. Crystalline sulfur seems to be made of rings, each containing eight sulfur atoms, which fit together to give a normal x-ray pattern. Ten isotopes of sulfur exist. Four occur in natural sulfur, none of which is radioactive. A finely divided form of sulfur, known as *flowers of sulfur*, is obtained by sublimation. Sulfur readily forms sulfides with many elements. Sulfur is a component of black gunpowder, is used in the vulcanization of natural rubber, and is used as a fungicide. It is also used extensively in making phosphatic fertilizers. A tremendous tonnage is used to produce sulfuric acid, the most important manufactured chemical. It is used in making sulfite paper and other papers, is used as a fumigant, and in the bleaching of dried fruits. The element is a good electrical insulator. Organic compounds containing sulfur are very important. Calcium sulfate, ammonium sulfate, carbon disulfide, sulfur dioxide, and hydrogen sulfide are but a few of the other many important compounds of sulfur. Sulfur is essential to life. It is a minor constituent of fats, body fluids, and skeletal minerals. Carbon disulfide, hydrogen sulfide, and sulfur dioxide should be handled carefully. Hydrogen sulfide in small concentrations can be metabolized, but in higher concentrations it quickly can cause death by respiratory paralysis. It is insidious in that it quickly deadens the sense of smell. Sulfur dioxide is a dangerous component in atmospheric air pollution. High-purity sulfur is commercially available in purities of 99.999 + %

TANTALUM (Gr. *Tanalos*, mythological character, father of *Niobe*), Ta; at. wt. 180.9479; at. no. 73; m.p. 2,996°C; b.p. 5,425 ± 100°C; sp. gr. 16.654; valence 2?, 3, 4?, or 5. Discovered in 1802 by Ekeberg, but many chemists thought niobium and tantalum were identical elements until Rose, in 1844, and Marignac, in 1866, indicated and showed that niobic and tantalic acids were two different acids. The early investigators only isolated the impure metal. The first relatively pure ductile tantalum was produced by von Bolton in 1903. Tantalum occurs principally in the mineral *columbite-tantalite* (Fe, Mn) (Nb, Ta)$_2$O$_6$. Tantalum ores are found in the

People's Republic of the Congo, Brazil, Mozambique, Thailand, Portugal, Nigeria, and Canada. The new mine at Bernic Lake, Manitoba, has reserves of more than a million tons of ore averaging about one-fourth% tantalum oxide. Separation of tantalum from niobium requires several complicated steps. Several methods are used to commercially produce the element, including electrolysis of molten potassium fluotantalate, reduction of potassium fluotantalate with sodium, or reacting tantalum carbide with tantalum oxide. Sixteen isotopes of tantalum are known to exist. Natural tantalum contains two isotopes; one of these, Ta^{180}, is present in very small quantity (0.0123%) and is unstable with a very long half-life of >10^{13} years. Tantalum is a gray, heavy, and very hard metal. When pure, it is ductile and can be drawn into fine wire, which is used as a filament for evaporating metals such as aluminum. Tantalum is almost completely immune to chemical attack at temperatures below 150°C, and is attacked only by hydrofluoric acid, acidic solutions containing the fluoride ion, and free sulfur trioxide. Alkalis attack it only slowly. At higher temperatures, tantalum becomes much more reactive. The element has a melting point exceeded only by tungsten and rhenium. Tantalum is used to make a variety of alloys with desirable properties such as high-melting point, high strength, good ductility, etc. The metal has good "gettering" ability at high temperatures, and tantalum oxide films are stable and have good rectifying and dielectric properties. Tantalum is used to make electrolytic capacitors and vacuum furnace parts, which account for about 70% of its use. The metal is also widely used to fabricate chemical process equipment, nuclear reactors, and aircraft and missile parts. Tantalum is completely immune to body liquids and is a nonirritating metal. It has, therefore, found wide use in making surgical appliances. Tantalum oxide is used to make special glass with a high index of refraction for camera lenses. The metal has many other uses. In powdered form it costs about $35/pound. Sheet tantalum and fabricated forms are more expensive.

TECHNETIUM (Gr. *technetos*, artificial), Tc; at. wt. 98.9062; at. no. 43; m.p. 2172°C; b.p. 4877°C; sp. gr. 11.50 (calc.); valence 0, +2, +4, +5, +6, and +7. Element 43 was predicted on the basis of the periodic table, and was erroneously reported as having been discovered in 1925, at which time it was named *masurium*. The element was actually discovered by Perrier and Segrè in Italy in 1937. It was found in a sample of molybdenum, which was bombarded by deuterons in the Berkeley cyclotron, and which E. Lawrence sent to these investigators. Technetium was the first element to be produced artificially. Since its discovery, searches for the element in terrestrial materials have been made without success. If it does exist, the concentration must be very small. Surprisingly, it has been found in the spectrum of S, M, and N type stars, and its presence in stellar matter is leading to new theories of the production of heavy elements in the stars. Sixteen isotopes of technetium, with atomic masses ranging from 92 to 107, are known. Tc^{97} has a half-life of 2.6 × 10^6 yrs. Tc^{98} has a half-life of 1.5 × 10^6 yrs. The isomeric isotope Tc^{95m}, with a half-life of 61 days, is useful for tracer work, as it produces energetic gamma rays. Technetium metal has been produced in kilogram quantities. The metal was first prepared by passing hydrogen gas at 1100°C over Tc_2S_7. It is now conveniently prepared by the reduction of ammonium pertechnetate with hydrogen. Technetium is a silvery-gray metal that tarnishes slowly in moist air. Until 1960, technetium was available only in small amounts and the price was as high as $2800 per gm. It is now offered commercially to holders of A.E.C. permits at a price of $90 to $100/gm. The chemistry of technetium is said to be similar to that of rhenium. Technetium dissolves in nitric acid, aqua regia, and conc. sulfuric acid, but is not soluble in hydrochloric acid of any strength. The element is a remarkable corrosion inhibitor for steel. It is reported that mild carbon steels may be effectively protected by as little as 5 ppm of $KTcO_4$ in aerated distilled water at temperatures up to 250°C. This corrosion protection is limited to closed systems, since technetium is radioactive and must be confined. Tc^{99} has a specific activity of 6.2×10^8 disintegrations per sec./gm. Activity of this level must not be allowed to spread. Tc^{99} is a contamination hazard and should be handled in a glove box. The metal is an excellent superconductor at 11°K and below.

TELLURIUM (L. *tellus*, earth), Te; at. wt. 127.60; at. no. 52; m.p. $449.5 \pm 0.3°C$; b.p. $989.8 \pm 3.8°C$; sp. gr. 6.24 (20°C); valence 2, 4, or 6. Discovered by Müller von Reichenstein in 1782; named by Klaproth who isolated it in 1798. Tellurium is occasionally found native, but is more often found as the telluride of gold (*calaverite*), and combined with other metals. It is recovered commercially from the anode muds produced during the electrolytic refining of blister copper. The U.S., Canada, Peru, and Japan are the largest Free World producers of the element. Crystalline tellurium has a silvery-white appearance, and when pure exhibits a metallic luster. It is brittle and easily pulverized. Amorphous tellurium is formed by precipitating tellurium from a solution of telluric or tellurous acid. Whether this form is truly amorphous, or made of minute crystals, is open to question. Tellurium is a p-type semiconductor, and shows greater conductivity in certain directions, depending on alignment of the atoms. Its conductivity increases slightly with exposure to light. It can be doped with silver, copper, gold, tin, or other elements. In air, tellurium burns with a greenish-blue flame, forming the dioxide. Molten tellurium corrodes iron, copper, and stainless steel. Tellurium and its compounds are probably toxic and should be handled with care. Workmen exposed to as little as 0.01 mg/cu meter of air, or less, develop "tellurium breath", which has a garlic-like odor. Twenty-one isotopes of tellurium are known, with atomic masses ranging from 115 to 135. Natural tellurium consists of eight isotopes, one of which, Te^{127}, is unstable. It is present to the extent of 0.87% and has a half-life of 1.2×10^{13} years. Tellurium improves the machinability of copper and stainless steel, and its addition to lead decreases the corrosive action of sulfuric acid to lead and improves its strength and hardness. Tellurium is used as a basic ingredient in blasting caps, and is added to cast iron for chill control. Tellurium is used in ceramics. Bismuth telluride has been used in thermoelectric devices. One such device, using two Bi-Te semiconductors, is reportedly capable of freezing or boiling water in seconds with the power from two flash-light batteries. The unit is said to be capable of bringing the temperature down to $-75°C$, using only two amperes of current. Tellurium with a purity of 99.7% costs about $6/lb. It is also available with purities of 99.999 + % at a cost of $20 to $30/lb.

TERBIUM (*Ytterby*, village in Sweden), Tb; at. wt. 158.9254; at. no. 65; m.p. 1356°C, b.p. 3123°C; sp. gr. 8.229; valence 3, 4. Discovered by Mosander in 1843. Terbium is a member of the lanthanide or "rare earth" group of elements. It is found in *cerite*, *gadolinite*, and other minerals along with other rare earths. It is recovered commercially from *monazite* in which it is present to the extent of 0.03%, from *xenotime*, and from *euxenite*, a complex oxide containing 1% or more of terbia. Terbium has been isolated only in recent years with the development of ion-exchange techniques for separating the rare-earth elements. As with other rare earths, it can be produced by reducing the anhydrous chloride or fluoride with calcium metal in a tantalum crucible. Calcium and tantalum impurities can be removed by vacuum remelting. Other methods of isolation are possible. Terbium is reasonably stable in air. It is a silvery-gray metal, and is malleable, ductile and soft enough to be cut with a knife. Two crystal modifications exist, with a transformation temperature of 1315°C. Nineteen isotopes with atomic masses ranging from 147 to 164 are recognized. The oxide is a chocolate or dark maroon color. Sodium terbium borate is used as a laser material and emits coherent light at 5460 Å. Terbium is used to dope calcium fluoride, calcium tungstate, and strontium molybdate, used in solid-state devices. The oxide has potential application as an activator for green phosphors used in color T.V. tubes. It can be used with ZrO_2 as a crystal stabilizer of fuel cells which operate at elevated temperature. Few other uses have been found. The element is priced at about $3/gm. or $750/lb. Little is known of the toxicity of terbium. It should be handled with care, as with other lanthanide elements.

THALLIUM (Gr. *thallos*, a green shoot or twig), Tl; at. wt. 204.37; at. no. 81; m.p. 303.5°C; b.p. $1457 \pm 10°C$; sp. gr. 11.85 (20°C); valence 1 or 3. Discovered spectroscopically in 1861 by Crookes. The element was named after the beautiful green spectral line, which identified the element. The metal was isolated both by Crookes and Lamy in 1862 about the same time. Thallium occurs in *crooksite*, *lorandite*, *and hutchinsonite*. It is also present in *pyrites* and is recovered from the roasting of this ore in connection with the production of sulfuric acid. It is also obtained from the smelting of lead and zinc ores. Extraction is somewhat complex and depends on the source of the thallium. When freshly exposed to air thallium exhibits a metallic luster, but soon develops a bluish-gray tinge, resembling lead in appearance. A heavy oxide builds up on thallium if left in air, and in the presence of water the hydroxide is formed. The metal is very soft and malleable. It can be cut with a knife. Twenty isotopic forms of thallium, with atomic masses ranging from 191 to 210 are recognized. Natural thallium is a mixture of two isotopes. The element and its compounds are toxic and should be carefully handled. Contact of the metal with the skin is dangerous, and when melting the metal, adequate ventilation should be provided. The maximum allowable concentration of soluble thallium compounds in air is 0.1 mg/cu meter. Thallium sulfate is widely employed as a rodenticide and ant killer. It is odorless and tasteless, giving no warning of its presence. The electrical conductivity of thallium sulfide changes with exposure to infrared light and this compound is used in photocells. Thallium bromide-iodide crystals have been used as infrared detectors. Thallium has been used, with sulfur or selenium and arsenic, to produce low melting glasses which become fluid between 125 and 150°C. These glasses have properties at room temperatures similar to ordinary glasses and are said to be durable and insoluble in water. Thallium oxide has been used to produce glasses with a high index of refraction. A mercury–thallium alloy, which forms a eutectic at 8.5%

thallium, is reported to freeze at −60°C, some 20°C below the freezing point of mercury. Commercial thallium metal costs about $8/lb. It is available also in high-purity form at a cost of about $4/oz.

THORIUM (*Thor*, Scandinavian god of war), Th; at. wt. 232.0381; at. no. 90; m.p. 1750°C; b.p. ~4790°C; sp. gr. 11.72; valence +2(?), +3(?), +4. Discovered by Berzelius in 1828. Thorium occurs in *thorite* ($ThSiO_4$) and in *thorianite* ($ThO_2 + UO_2$). Large deposits of thorium minerals have been reported in New England and elsewhere, but these have not yet been exploited. Thorium is now thought to be about three times as abundant as uranium and about as abundant as lead or molybdenum. The metal is a source of nuclear power. There is probably more energy available for use from thorium in the minerals of the earth's crust than from both uranium and fossil fuels. Any sizable demand for thorium as a nuclear fuel is still a decade or more in the future; however work is progressing with several thorium cycle converter-reactor systems. Several prototypes, including the HTGR (High-temperature gas-cooled reactor) and MSRE (Molten salt converter reactor experiment), have operated successfully. Thorium is recovered commercially from the mineral *monazite*, which contains from 3 to 9% ThO_2 along with most rare-earth minerals. Much of the internal heat of the earth has been attributed to thorium and uranium. Several methods are available for producing thorium metal; it can be obtained by reducing thorium oxide with calcium; by electrolysis of anhydrous thorium chloride in a fused mixture of sodium and potassium chlorides; by calcium reduction of thorium tetrachloride mixed with anhydrous zinc chloride; and by reduction of thorium tetrachloride with an alkali metal. Thorium was originally assigned a position in Group IV of the periodic table. Because of its atomic weight, valence, etc., it is now considered to be the second member of the *actinide* series of elements. When pure, thorium is a silvery-white metal which is air-stable and retains its luster for several months. When contaminated with the oxide, thorium slowly tarnishes in air, becoming gray, and finally black. The physical properties of thorium are greatly influenced by the degree of contamination with the oxide. The purest specimens often contain several tenths of a per cent of the oxide. High-purity thorium has been made. Pure thorium is soft, very ductile, and can be cold-rolled, swaged, and drawn. Thorium is dimorphic, changing at 1400°C from a cubic to a body-centered cubic structure. Thorium oxide has a melting point of 3300°C, which is the highest of all oxides. Only a few elements, such as tungsten, and a few compounds, such as tantalum carbide, have higher melting points. Thorium is slowly attacked by water, but does not dissolve readily in most common acids, except hydrochloric. Powdered thorium metal is often pyrophoric and should be carefully handled. When heated in air, thorium turnings ignite and burn brilliantly with a white light. The principal use of thorium has been in the preparation of the Welsbach mantle, used for portable gas lights. These mantles, consisting of thorium oxide with about 1% cerium oxide and other ingredients, glow with a dazzling light when heated in a gas flame. Thorium is an important alloying element in magnesium, imparting high strength and creep resistance at elevated temperatures. Because thorium has a low work-function and high electron emission, it is used to coat tungsten wire used in electronic equipment. The oxide is also used to control the grain size of tungsten used for electric lamps; it is also used for high-temperature laboratory crucibles. Glasses containing thorium oxide have a high refractive index and low dispersion. Consequently, they find application in high quality lenses for cameras and scientific instruments. Thorium oxide has also found use as a catalyst in the conversion of ammonia to nitric acid, in petroleum cracking, and in producing sulfuric acid. Twelve isotopes of thorium are known with atomic masses ranging from 223 to 234. All are unstable. Th^{232} occurs naturally and has a half-life of 1.41×10^{10} yrs. It is an alpha emitter. Th^{232} goes through six alpha and four beta decay steps before becoming the stable isotope Pb^{208}. Th^{232} is sufficiently radioactive to expose a photographic plate in a few hours. Thorium disintegrates with the production of thoron (radon^{220}), which is an alpha emitter and presents a radiation hazard. Good ventilation of areas where thorium is stored or handled is therefore recommended. Thorium and its compounds are subject to licensing and control by the U.S. Atomic Energy Commission. Thorium metal in pellet or powder form costs about 25¢/gm. or $15/lb.

THULIUM (*Thule*, the earliest name for Scandinavia), Tm; at. wt. 168.9342; at. no. 69; m.p. 1,545 ± 15°C; b.p. 1,947°C; sp. gr. 9.321(25°); valence 2, 3. Discovered in 1879 by Cleve. Thulium occurs in small quantities along with other rare earths in a number of minerals. It is obtained commercially from *monazite*, which contains about 0.007% of the element. Thulium is the least abundant of the rare-earth elements, but with new sources recently discovered, it is now considered to be about as rare as silver, gold, or cadmium. Ion-exchange and solvent extraction techniques have recently permitted much easier separation of the rare earths, with much lower costs. Only a few years ago, thulium metal was not obtainable at any cost; in 1950 the oxide sold for $450/gram. Thulium metal now costs from $3 to $20/gram, depending on the purity, quantity, and supplier. Thulium can be isolated by reduction of the oxide with lanthanum metal or by calcium reduction of the anhydrous fluoride. The pure metal has a bright, silvery luster. It is reasonably stable in air, but the metal should be protected from moisture in a closed container. The element is silver-gray, soft, malleable, and ductile, and can be cut with a knife. Sixteen isotopes are known, with atomic masses ranging from 161 to 176. Natural thulium, Tm^{169}, is stable. Because of the relatively high price of the metal, thulium has not yet found many practical applications. Tm^{169} bombarded in a nuclear reactor can be used as a radiation source in portable X-ray equipment. Tm^{171} is potentially useful as an energy source. Natural thulium also has possible use in *ferrites* (ceramic magnetic materials) used in microwave equipment. As with other lanthanides, thulium has a low-to-moderate acute toxic rating. It should be handled with care.

TIN (Anglo-Saxon, *tin*), Sn (L. *stannum*); at. wt. 118.69; at. no. 50; m.p. 231.9681°C; b.p. 2,270°C; sp. gr. (gray) 5.75, (white) 7.31; valence, 2, 4. Known to the ancients. Tin is found chiefly in *cassiterite* (SnO_2). Most of the world's supply comes from Malaya, Boliva, Indonesia, Zaire, Thailand, and Nigeria. The U.S. produces almost none, although occurrences have been found in Alaska and California. Tin is obtained by reducing the ore with coal in a reverberatory furnace. Ordinary tin is composed of nine stable isotopes; 13

unstable isotopes are also known. Ordinary tin is a silvery-white metal, is malleable, somewhat ductile, and has a highly crystalline structure. Due to the breaking of these crystals, a "tin cry" is heard when a bar is bent. The element has two or perhaps three allotropic forms. On warming, gray, or α tin, with a cubic structure, changes at 13.2°C into white, or β tin, the ordinary form of the metal. White tin has a tetragonal structure. Some authorities believe a γ form exists between 161°C and the melting point; however, other authorities discount its existence. When tin is cooled below 13.2°C, it changes slowly from white to gray. This change is affected by impurities such as aluminum and zinc, and can be prevented by small additions of antimony or bismuth. This change from the α to β form is called the tin pest. There are few if any uses for gray tin. Tin takes a high polish and is used to coat other metals to prevent corrosion or other chemical action. Such tin plate over steel is used in the so-called tin can for preserving food. Alloys of tin are very important. Soft solder, type metal, fusible metal, pewter, bronze, bell metal, Babbitt metal, White metal, die casting alloy, and phosphor bronze are some of the important alloys using tin. Tin resists distilled, sea, and soft tap water, but is attacked by strong acids, alkalis, and acid salts. Oxygen in solution accelerates the attack. When heated in air, tin forms SnO_2, which is feebly acid, forming stannate salts with basic oxides. The most important salt is the chloride ($SnCl_2 \cdot H_2O$), which is used as a reducing agent and as a mordant in calico printing. Tin salts sprayed onto glass are used to produce electrically conductive coatings on the glass. These have been used for panel lighting and for frost-free wind shields. Of recent interest is a crystalline tin-niobium alloy that is superconductive at very low temperatures. This promises to be important in the construction of superconductive magnets that generate enormous field strengths but use practically no power. Such magnets, made of tin-niobium wire, weigh but a few pounds and produce magnetic fields, when started with a small battery, that are comparable to that of a 100-ton electromagnet operated continuously with a large power supply. The small amount of tin used in canned foods is quite harmless. The agreed limit of tin content in U.S. foods is 300 mg/kg. The trialkyl and triaryl tin compounds are used as biocides and must be handled carefully. Over the past 25 years the price of tin has varied from 50¢/pound to its present price of $3.50/pound.

TITANIUM (L. *Titans*, the first sons of the Earth, myth.), Ti; at. wt. 47.90; at. no. 22; m.p. 1660 ± 10°C; b.p. 3287°C; sp. gr. 4.54; valence 2, 3, or 4. Discovered by Gregor in 1791; named by Klaproth in 1795. Impure titanium was prepared by Nilson and Pettersson in 1887; however the pure metal (99.9%) was not made until 1910 by Hunter by heating $TiCl_4$ with sodium in a steel bomb. Titanium is present in meteorites and in the sun. Rocks obtained during the Apollo 11 lunar mission showed presence of 7 to 12% TiO_2. Analyses of rocks obtained during later Apollo missions show lower percentages. Titanium oxide bands are prominent in the spectra of M Type stars. The element is the ninth most abundant in the crust of the earth. Titanium is almost always present in igneous rocks and in the sedi-

ments derived from them. It occurs in the minerals *rutile*, *ilmenite*, and *sphene*, and is present in titanates and in many iron ores. Titanium is present in the ash of coal, in plants, and in the human body. The metal was a laboratory curiosity until Kroll, in 1946, showed that titanium could be produced commercially by reducing titanium tetrachloride with magnesium. This method is largely used for producing the metal today. The metal can be purified by decomposing the iodide. Titanium, when pure, is a lustrous, white metal. It has a low density, good strength, is easily fabricated, and has excellent corrosion resistance. It is ductile only when it is free of oxygen. The metal burns in air and is the only element that burns in nitrogen. Titanium is resistant to dilute sulfuric and hydrochloric acid, most organic acids, moist chlorine gas, and chloride solutions. Natural titanium consists of five isotopes with atomic masses from 46 to 50. All are stable. Four other unstable isotopes are known. Natural titanium is reported to become very radioactive after bombardment with deuterons. The emitted radiations are mostly positrons and hard gamma rays. The metal is dimorphic. The hexagonal α form changes to the cubic β form very slowly at about 880°C. The metal combines with oxygen at red heat, and with chlorine at 550°C. Titanium is important as an alloying agent with aluminum, molybdenum, manganese, iron, and other metals. Alloys of titanium are principally used for aircraft and missiles where lightweight strength, and ability to withstand extremes of temperature are important. Titanium is as strong as steel, but 45% lighter. It is 60% heavier than aluminum, but twice as strong. The A-11 jet plane, which flies at 2000 miles/hr., is largely constructed of titanium. Each SST jet plane is expected to consume 600,000 lbs. Titanium has potential use in desalination plants for converting sea water into fresh water. The metal has excellent resistance to sea water and is used for propeller shafts, rigging, and other parts of ships exposed to salt water. A titanium anode, coated with platinum has been used to provide cathodic protection from corrosion by salt water. Titanium metal is considered to be physiologically inert. When pure, titanium dioxide is relatively clear and has an extremely high index of refraction with an optical dispersion higher than diamond. It is produced artificially for use as a gemstone, but it is relatively soft. Star sapphires and rubies exhibit their asterism as a result of the presence of TiO_2. Titanium dioxide is extensively used for both house paint and artist's paint, as it is permanent and has good covering power. Titanium paint is an excellent reflector of infrared, and is extensively used in solar observatories where heat causes poor seeing conditions. Titanium tetrachloride is used to iridize glass. This compound fumes strongly in air and is used to produce smoke screens. The price of titanium mill products is about $6/lb. Its use is growing rapidly, and by 1978, it is expected that 10 million pounds of the metal will be used.

TUNGSTEN (Swedish, *tung sten*, heavy stone); also known as WOLFRAM (from *wolframite*, said to be named from *wolf rahm* or *spumi lupi*, because the ore interfered with the smelting of tin and was supposed to devour the tin). W; at. wt. 183.85; at. no. 74; m.p. 3410 ± 20°C; b.p. 5660°C; sp. gr. 19.3 (20°C); valence 2, 3, 4, 5, or 6. In 1779 Peter Woulfe examined the mineral now known as *wolframite* and concluded it must contain a new substance. Scheele, in 1781, found that a new acid could be made from *tung sten* (a name first applied about 1758 to a mineral now known as *scheelite*). Scheele and Bergman suggested the possibility of obtaining a new metal by reducing this acid. The de Elhuyar brothers found an acid in *wolframite* in 1783 that was identical to the acid of *tung sten* (tungstic acid) of Scheele, and in that year they succeeded in obtaining the element by reduction of this acid with charcoal. Tungsten occurs in *wolframite*, $(Fe, Mn)WO_4$; *scheelite*, $CaWO_4$; *huebnerite*, $MnWO_4$; and *ferberite*, $FeWO_4$. Important deposits of tungsten occur in California, North Carolina, South Korea, Bolivia, U.S.S.R., and Portugal. China is reported to have about 75% of the world's tungsten resources. Natural tungsten contains five stable isotopes. Twelve other unstable isotopes are recognized. The metal is obtained commercially by reducing tungstic oxide with hydrogen or carbon. Pure tungsten is a steel gray to tin-white metal. Very pure tungsten can be cut with a hacksaw, and can be forged, spun, drawn, and extruded. The impure metal is brittle and can be worked only with difficulty. Tungsten has the highest melting point and lowest vapor pressure of all metals, and at temperatures over 1650°C has the highest tensile strength. The metal oxidizes in air and must be protected at elevated temperatures. It has excellent corrosion resistance and is attacked only slightly by most mineral acids. The thermal expansion is about the same as borosilicate glass, which makes the metal useful for glass-to-metal seals. Tungsten and its alloys are used extensively for filaments for electric lamps, electron and television tubes, and for metal evaporation work; for electrical contact points for automobile distributors; x-ray targets; windings and heating elements for electrical furnaces; and for numerous space missile and high-temperature applications. High-speed tool steels, Hastelloys, Stellite, and many other alloys contain tungsten. Tungsten carbide is of great importance to the metalworking, mining, and petroleum industries. Calcium and magnesium tungstates are widely used in fluorescent lighting; other salts of tungsten are used in the chemical, and tanning industries. Tungsten disulfide is a dry, high-temperature lubricant, stable to 500°C. Tungsten bronzes and other tungsten compounds are used in paints. Hydrogen-reduced tungsten powder costs about $5/lb.

URANIUM (Planet *Uranus*), U; at. wt. 238.029; at. no. 92; m.p. 1132.3 ± 0.8°C; b.p. 3818°C; sp. gr. ~ 18.95; valence 2, 3, 4, 5, or 6. Yellow-colored glass, containing more than 1% uranium oxide and dating back to 79 A.D., has been found near Naples, Italy. Klaproth recognized an unknown element in *pitchblende* and attempted to isolate the metal in 1789. The metal apparently was first isolated in 1841 by Peligot, who reduced the anhydrous chloride with potassium. Uranium is not as rare as it was once thought. It is now considered to be more plentiful than mercury, antimony, silver, or cadmium, and is about as abundant as molybdenum or arsenic. It occurs in numerous minerals, such as *pitchblende, uraninite, carnotite, autunite, uranophane, davidite*, and *tobernite*. It is also found in *phosphate rock, lignite, monazite sands*, and can be recovered commercially from these sources. The A.E.C. purchases uranium in the form of acceptable U_3O_8 concentrates. This incentive program has greatly increased the known uranium reserves. Uranium can be prepared by reducing uranium halides with alkali or alkaline earth metals or by reducing uranium oxides by calcium, aluminum, or carbon at high temperatures. The metal can also be produced by electrolysis of KUF_5 or UF_4, dissolved in a molten mixture of $CaCl_2$, $NaCl$. High-purity uranium can be prepared by the thermal decomposition of uranium halides on a hot filament. Uranium exhibits three crystallographic modifications as follows:

$$\alpha \xrightarrow{667°C} \beta \xrightarrow{772°C} \gamma$$

Uranium is a heavy, silvery-white metal, which is pyrophoric when finely divided. It is a little softer than steel, and is attacked by cold water in a finely divided state. It is malleable, ductile, and slightly paramagnetic. In air, the metal becomes coated with a layer of oxide. Acids dissolve the metal, but it is unaffected by alkalis. Uranium has fourteen isotopes, all of which are radioactive. Naturally-occurring uranium nominally contains 99.2830% by weight U^{238}, 0.7110% U^{235}, and 0.0054% U^{234}. Studies show that the percentage weight of U^{235} in natural uranium varies by as much as 0.1%, depending on the source. The A.E.C. has adopted the value of 0.711 as being their "official" percentage of U^{235} in natural uranium. Natural uranium is sufficiently radioactive to expose a photographic plate in an hour or so. Much of the internal heat of the earth is thought to be attributable to the presence of uranium and thorium. U^{238}, with a half-life of 4.51×10^9 years, has been used to estimate the age of igneous rocks. The origin of uranium, the highest member of the natural-occurring elements—except perhaps for traces of neptunium or plutonium, is not clearly understood, although it may be presumed that uranium is a decay product of elements of higher atomic weight, which may have once been present on earth or elsewhere in the universe. These original elements may have been created as a result of a primordial "creation", known as "*the big bang*," in a supernovae, or in some other stellar processes. Uranium is of great importance as a nuclear fuel. U^{238} can be converted into fissionable plutonium by the following reactions:

$$U^{238}(n, \gamma)U^{239} \xrightarrow{\beta-} Np^{239} \xrightarrow{\beta-} Pu^{239}.$$

This nuclear conversion can be brought about in "breeder" reactors where it is possible to produce more new fissionable material than the fissionable material used in maintaining the chain reaction. U^{235} is of even greater importance, for it is the key to the utilization of uranium. U^{235}, while occurring in natural uranium to the extent of only 0.71%, is so fissionable with slow neutrons that a self-sustaining fission chain reaction can be made to occur in a reactor constructed from natural uranium and a suitable moderator, such as heavy water or graphite, alone. U^{235} can be concentrated by gaseous diffusion and other physical processes, if desired, and used directly as a nuclear fuel, instead of natural uranium, or used as an explosive. Natural uranium, slightly enriched with U^{235} by a small percentage is used to fuel nuclear power reactors for the generation of electricity. Natural thorium can be irradiated with neutrons as follows to produce the important isotope U^{233}:

$$Th^{232}(n, \gamma)Th^{233} \xrightarrow{\beta-} Pa^{233} \xrightarrow{\beta-} U^{233}.$$

While thorium itself is not fissionable, U^{233} is, and in this way may be used as a nuclear fuel. One pound of completely fissioned uranium has the fuel value of over 1500 tons of coal. The uses of nuclear fuels to generate electrical power, to make isotopes for peaceful purposes, and to make explosives are well known. The estimated world-wide capacity of nuclear power reactors in 1970 amounted to about 25 million kW and is expected to grow to between 200 and 250 million kW by 1980. Uranium in the U.S.A. is controlled by the Atomic Energy Commission. New uses are being found for "depleted" uranium (i.e. uranium with the percentage of U^{235} lowered to about 0.2%). It has found use in inertial guidance devices, gyro compasses, counterweights for aircraft control surfaces, as ballast for missile reentry vehicles, and as a shielding material. Uranium metal is used for x-ray targets for production of high-energy x-rays; the nitrate has been used as photographic toner; and the acetate is used in analytical chemistry.

Crystals of uranium nitrate are triboluminescent. Uranium salts have also been used for producing yellow "vaseline" glass and glazes. Uranium and its compounds are highly toxic, both from a chemical and radiological standpoint. Finely divided uranium metal, being pyrophoric, presents a fire hazard. The maximum recommended allowable concentration of soluble uranium compounds in air (based on chemical toxicity) is 0.05 mg/cu meter; for insoluble compounds the concentration is set at 0.25 mg/cu meter of air. The permissible body level of natural uranium (based on radiotoxicity) is 0.2 microcurie for soluble compounds; for insoluble compounds the level is 0.009 microcurie, or in air 1.7×10^{-11} microcurie per milliliter.

VANADIUM (Scandinavian goddess, *Vanadis*), V; at. wt. 50.9414; at. no. 23; m.p. 1890° $\pm$ 10°C; b.p. 3380°C; sp. gr. 6.11 (18.7°C); valence 2, 3, 4, or 5. Vanadium was first discovered by del Rio in 1801. Unfortunately a French chemist incorrectly declared del Rio's new element was only impure chromium; del Rio thought himself to be mistaken and accepted the French chemist's statement. The element was rediscovered in 1830 by Sefström who named the element in honor of the Scandinavian goddess *Vanadis* because of its beautiful multi-colored compounds. It was isolated in nearly pure form by Roscoe, in 1867, who reduced the chloride with hydrogen. Vanadium of 99.3 to 99.8% purity was not produced until 1927. Vanadium is found in about 65 different minerals among which are *carnotite*, *roscoelite*, *vanadinite*, and *patronite*—important sources of the metal. Vanadium is also found in phosphate rock, certain iron ores, and is present in some crude oils in the form of organic complexes. It is also found in small percentages in meteorites. Commercial production from petroleum ash holds promise as an important source of the element. High-purity ductile vanadium can be obtained by reduction of vanadium trichloride with magnesium or with magnesium-sodium mixtures. Much of the vanadium metal being produced is now made by calcium reduction of V_2O_5 in a pressure vessel, an adaption of a process developed by McKechnie and Seybolt. Natural vanadium is a mixture of two isotopes V^{50} (0.24%) and V^{51} (99.76%). V^{50} is slightly radioactive, having a half-life of 6×10^{15} yrs. Seven other unstable isotopes are recognized. Pure vanadium is a bright white metal, and is soft and ductile. It has good corrosion resistance to alkalis, sulfuric and hydrochloric acid, and salt waters, but the metal oxidizes readily above 660°C. The metal has good structural strength and a low-fission neutron cross section, making it useful in nuclear applications. Vanadium is used in producing rust-resistant, spring, and high-speed tool steels. It is an important carbide stabilizer in making steels. About 80% of the vanadium now produced is used as ferro-vanadium or as a steel additive. Vanadium foil is used as a bonding agent in cladding titanium to steel. Vanadium pentoxide is used in ceramics and as a catalyst. It is also used as a mordant in dyeing and printing fabrics and in the manufacture of aniline black. Vanadium and its compounds are toxic and should be handled with care. It has been reported that small doses of vanadium salts have reversed hardening of arteries in experimental animals, and that workers engaged in vanadium mining and milling operations have a lower serum cholesterol than unexposed workers in the same area. The threshold limit value of vanadium (V_2O_5 fume) as V has been suggested to be 0.05 mg./cu. meter. Ductile vanadium is commercially available at a cost of about $40/lb. Commercial vanadium metal, of about 95% purity, costs about $5/lb.

WOLFRAM (see Tungsten)

XENON (Gr. *xenon*, stranger), Xe; at. wt. 131.30; at. no. 54; m.p. −111.9°C; b.p. −107.1±3°C; density (gas) 5.887±0.009 g/l, sp. gr. (liquid) 3.52 (−109°C); valence usually 0. Discovered by Ramsay and Travers in 1898 in the residue left after evaporating liquid air components. Xenon is a member of the so-called noble or "inert" gases. It is present in the atmosphere to the extent of about one part in twenty million. The element is found in the gases evolved from certain mineral springs, and is commercially obtained by extraction from liquid air. Natural xenon is composed of nine stable isotopes. In addition to these, twenty-two unstable nuclides and isomers have been characterized. Until recently, xenon has been considered inert and unable to form compounds with other elements. Those compounds that were occasionally reported in the literature were considered not to be true compounds. Evidence has been mounting in the past few years that xenon, as well as other members of the zero valence elements, do form compounds. Among the "compounds" of xenon now reported are xenon hydrate, sodium perxenate, xenon deuterate, difluoride, tetrafluoride, hexafluoride, and $XePtF_6$ and $XeRhF_6$. More recently, xenon trioxide, which is highly explosive, has been prepared. The structure of these substances is still open to question. Xenon in a vacuum tube produces a beautiful blue glow when excited by an electrical discharge. The gas is used in making electron tubes, stroboscopic lamps, bactericidal lamps, and lamps used to excite ruby lasers for generating coherent light. Xenon is used in the atomic energy field in bubble chambers, probes, and other applications where its high molecular weight is of value. It is also potentially useful as a gas for ion engines. The perxenates are used in analytical chemistry as oxidizing agents. Xe^{133} and Xe^{135} are produced by neutron irradiation in air-cooled nuclear reactors. Xe^{133} has useful applications as a radioisotope. The element is available in sealed glass containers for about $20/liter of gas at standard pressure. Xenon is not toxic, but its compounds are highly toxic because of their strong oxidizing characteristics.

YTTERBIUM (*Ytterby*, village in Sweden), Yb; at. wt. 173.04; at. no. 70; m.p. 819°C; b.p. 1194°C; sp. gr. (α) 6.965 (β) 6.54; valence 2, 3. Marignac in 1878 discovered a new component, which he called *ytterbia*, in the earth then known as *erbia*. In 1907, Urbain separated ytterbia into two components, which he called *neoytterbia* and *lutecia*. The elements in these earths are now known as *ytterbium* and *lutetium*, respectively. These elements are identical with *aldebaranium and cassiopeium* discovered independently and at about the same time by von Welsbach. Ytterbium occurs along with other rare earths in a number of rare minerals. It is commercially recovered principally from *monazite sand*, which contains about 0.03%. Ion-exchange and solvent extraction techniques developed in recent years have greatly simplified the separation of the rare earths from one another. The element was first prepared by Klemm and Bonner in 1937 by reducing ytterbium trichloride with potassium. Their metal was mixed, however, with KCl. Daane, Dennison, and Spedding prepared a much purer form in 1953 from which the chemical and physical properties of the element could be determined. Ytterbium has a bright silvery luster, is soft, malleable, and quite ductile. While the element is fairly stable, it should be kept in closed containers to protect it from air and moisture. Ytterbium is readily attacked and dissolved by dilute and concentrated mineral acids and reacts slowly with water. Ytterbium normally has two allotropic forms with a transformation point at 798°C. The alpha form is a room-temperature, face-centered, cubic modification, while the high-temperature beta form is a body-centered cubic form. Another body-centered cubic phase has recently been found to be stable at high pressures at room temperatures. The alpha form ordinarily has metallic-type conductivity, but becomes a semiconductor when the pressure is increased above 16,000 atm. The electrical resistance increases tenfold as the pressure is increased to 39,000 atm and drops to about 80% of its standard temperature-pressure resistivity at a pressure of 40,000 atm. Natural ytterbium is a mixture of seven stable isotopes. Seven other unstable isotopes are known. Ytterbium metal has possible use in improving the grain refinement, strength, and other mechanical properties of stainless steel. One isotope is reported to have been used as a radiation source as a substitute for a portable x-ray machine where electricity is unavailable. Few other uses have been found. Ytterbium metal is commercially available with a purity of about 99 + % for about $1.50/gm, or $300/lb. Ytterbium has a low acute toxic rating.

YTTRIUM (*Ytterby*, village in Sweden near Vauxholm), Y; at. wt. 88.9059; at. no. 39; m.p. 1522 ± 8°C; b.p. 3338 C; sp. gr. 4.469 (25°C); valence 3. *Yttria*, which is an earth containing yttrium, was discovered by Gadolin in 1794. *Ytterby* is the site of a quarry which yielded many unusual minerals containing rare earths and other elements. This small town, near Stockholm, bears the honor of giving names to *erbium*, *terbium*, and *ytterbium*, as well as *yttrium*. In 1843 Mosander showed that yttria could be resolved into the earths of three elements. The name yttria was reserved for the most basic one; the others were named *erbia* and *terbia*. Yttrium occurs in nearly all of the rare-earth minerals. Preliminary analysis of lunar rock samples obtained during the Apollo 11 mission showed a relatively high yttrium content. It is recovered commercially from *monazite sand*, which contains about 3%, and from *bastnasite*, which contains about 0.2%. Wöhler obtained the impure element in 1828 by reduction of the anhydrous chloride with potassium. The metal is now produced commercially by reduction of the fluoride with calcium metal. It can also be prepared by other techniques. Yttrium has a silvery-metallic luster and is relatively stable in air. Turnings of the metal, however, ignite in air if their temperature exceeds 400°C, and finely divided yttrium is very unstable in air. Yttrium oxide is one of the most important compounds of yttrium and accounts for the largest use. It is widely used in making YVO_4:Europium, and Y_2O_3:Europium phosphors to give the red color in color television tubes. Many hundreds of thousands of pounds are now used in this application. Yttrium oxide also is used to produce yttrium-iron-garnets, which are very effective microwave filters. Yttrium iron, aluminum, and gadolinium garnets, with formulas such as $Y_3Fe_5O_{12}$ and $Y_3Al_5O_{12}$, have interesting magnetic properties. Yttrium iron garnet is also exceptionally efficient as both a transmitter and transducer of acoustic energy. Yttrium aluminum garnet, with a hardness of 8.5, is also finding use as a gemstone (simulated diamond) Small amounts of yttrium (0.1 to 0.2%) can be used to reduce the grain size in chromium, molybdenum, zirconium, and titanium, and to increase strength of aluminum and magnesium alloys. Alloys with other useful properties can be obtained by using yttrium as an additive. The metal can be used as a deoxidizer for vanadium and other nonferrous metals. The metal has a low cross section for nuclear capture. Y^{90}, one of the isotopes of yttrium, exists in equilibrium with its parent Sr^{90}, a product of atomic explosions. Yttrium has been considered for use as a nodulizer for producing nodular cast iron, in which the graphite forms compact nodules instead of the usual flakes. Such iron has increased ductility. Yttrium is also finding application in laser systems and as a catalyst for ethylene polymerization. It has also potential use in ceramic and glass formulas as the oxide has a high melting point and imparts shock resistance and low expansion characteristics to glass. Natural yttrium contains but one isotope, Y^{89}. Twenty other unstable nuclides and isomers have been characterized. Yttrium metal of 99 + % purity is commercially available at a cost of about $1/gm or $200/lb.

ZINC (Ger. *Zink*, of obscure origin), Zn; at. wt. 65.38; at. no. 30; m.p. 419.58°C; b.p. 907°C; sp. gr. 7.133 (25°C); valence 2. Centuries before zinc was recognized as a distinct element, zinc ores were used for making brass. Tubal-Cain, seven generations from Adam, is mentioned as being an "instructor in every artificer in brass and iron." An alloy containing 87% zinc has been found in prehistoric ruins in Transylvania. Metallic zinc was produced in the 13th Century A.D. in India by reducing calamine with organic substances such as wool. The metal was rediscovered in Europe by Marggraf in 1746, who showed that it could be obtained by reducing *calamine* with charcoal. The principal ores of zinc are *sphalerite* or *blende* (sulfide), *smithsonite* (carbonate), *calamine* (silicate), and *franklinite* (zinc, manganese, iron oxide). Zinc can be obtained by roasting its ores to form the oxide and by reduction of the oxide with coal or carbon, with subsequent distillation of the metal. Other methods of extraction are possible. Naturally occurring zinc contains five stable isotopes. Ten other unstable nuclides and isomers are recognized. Zinc is a bluish-white, lustrous metal. It is brittle at ordinary temperatures but malleable at 100 to 150°C. It is a fair conductor of electricity, and burns in air at high red heat with evolution of white clouds of the oxide. The metal is employed to form numerous alloys with other metals. Brass, nickel silver, typewriter metal, commercial bronze, spring brass, German silver, soft solder, and aluminum solder are some of the more important alloys. Large quantities of zinc are used to produce die castings, used extensively by the automotive, electrical, and hardware industries. An alloy called *Prestal*, consisting of 78% zinc and 22% aluminum is reported to be almost as strong as steel, but as easy to mold as plastic. It is said to be so plastic that it can be molded into form by relatively inexpensive die casts made of ceramics and cement. It exhibits superplasticity. Zinc is also extensively used to galvanize other metals such as iron to prevent corrosion. Neither zinc nor zirconium is ferromagnetic, but $ZrZn_2$ exhibits ferromagnetism at temperatures below 35 K. Zinc oxide is a unique and very useful material to modern civilization. It is widely used in the manufacture of paints, rubber products, cosmetics, pharmaceuticals, floor coverings, plastics, printing inks, soap, storage batteries, textiles, electrical equipment, and other products. It has unusual electrical, thermal, optical, and solid-state properties that have not yet been fully investigated. Lithopone, a mixture of zinc sulfide and barium sulfate, is an important pigment. Zinc sulfide is used in making luminous dials, X-ray and TV screens, and fluorescent lights. The chloride and chromate are also important compounds. Zinc is an essential element in the growth of human beings and animals. Tests show that zinc-deficient animals require 50% more food to gain the same weight of an animal supplied with sufficient zinc. Zinc is not considered to be toxic, but when freshly formed ZnO is inhaled a disorder known as the *oxide shakes* or *zinc chills* sometimes occurs. It is recommended that where zinc oxide is encountered good ventilation be provided to avoid concentrations exceeding 5 mg of zinc oxide/m³ over an 8-hr exposure. Zinc costs roughly 40¢/pound.

ZIRCONIUM (Arabic *zargun*, gold color), Zr; at. wt. 91.22; at. no. 40; m.p. $1852 \pm 2°C$; b.p. 4377°C; sp. gr. 6.506 (20°C); valence $+2$, $+3$, and $+4$. The name *zircon* probably originated from the arabic word *zargun*, which describes the color of the gemstone now known as *zircon*, *jargon*, *hyacinth*, *jacinth*, or *ligure*. This mineral, or its variations, is mentioned in biblical writings. The mineral was not known to contain a new element until Klaproth, in 1789, analyzed a jargon from Ceylon and found a new earth, which Werner named zircon (*silex circonius*), and Klaproth called *Zirkonerde* (*zirconia*). The impure metal was first isolated by Berzelius in 1824 by heating a mixture of potassium and potassium zirconium fluoride in a small iron tube. Pure zirconium was first prepared in 1914. Very pure zirconium was first produced in 1925 by van Arkel and de Boer by an iodide decomposition process they developed. Zirconium is found in abundance in S-type stars, and has been identified in the sun and meteorites. Analyses of lunar rock samples obtained during the various Apollo missions to the moon show a surprisingly high zirconium oxide content, compared with terrestrial rocks. Naturally-occurring zirconium contains five isotopes, one of which, Zr^{96} (abundant to the extent of 2.80%), is unstable with a very long half-life of $> 3.6 \times 10^{17}$ yrs. Fifteen other unstable nuclides and isomers of zirconium have been characterized. Zircon, $ZrSiO_4$, the principal ore, is found in deposits in Florida, South Carolina, Australia, and Brazil. *Baddeleyite*, found in Brazil, is an important zirconium mineral. It is principally pure ZrO_2 in crystalline form having a hafnium content of about 1%. Zirconium also occurs in some 30 other recognized mineral species. Zirconium is produced commercially by reduction of the chloride with magnesium (the Kroll Process), and by other methods. It is a grayish-white lustrous metal. When finely divided, the metal may ignite spontaneously in air, especially at elevated temperatures. The solid metal is much more difficult to ignite. The inherent toxicity of zirconium compounds is low. Hafnium is invariably found in zirconium ores, and the separation is difficult. Commercial-grade zirconium contains from 1 to 3% hafnium. Zirconium has a low absorption cross section for neutrons, and is therefore used for nuclear energy applications, such as for cladding fuel elements. Zirconium has been found to be extremely resistant to the corrosive environment inside atomic reactors, and it allows neutrons to pass through the internal zirconium construction material without appreciable absorption of energy. Reactors of the size now being made may use as much as a half-million lineal feet of zirconium alloy tubing. Reactor-grade zirconium is essentially free of hafnium. *Zircaloy* is an important alloy developed specifically for nuclear applications. Zirconium is exceptionally resistant to corrosion by many common acids and alkalis, by sea water, and by other agents. It is used extensively by the chemical industry where corrosive agents are employed. Zirconium is used as a getter in vacuum tubes, as an alloying agent in steel, in making surgical appliances, photoflash bulbs, explosive primers, rayon spinnerets, lamp filaments etc. It is used in poison ivy lotions in the form of the carbonate as it combines with *urushiol*. With niobium, zirconium is superconductive at low temperatures and is used to make superconductive magnets, which offer hope of direct large-scale generation of electric power. Alloyed with zinc, zirconium becomes magnetic at temperatures below 35°K. Zirconium oxide (zircon) has a high index of refraction and is used as a gem material. The impure oxide, zirconia, is used for laboratory crucibles that will withstand heat shock, for linings of metallurgical furnaces, and by the glass and ceramic industries as a refractory material. Its use as a refractory material accounts for a large share of all zirconium consumed. Commercial zirconium metal sponge is priced at about $5/lb. Fabricated zirconium parts are higher in cost.

NOMENCLATURE OF INORGANIC CHEMISTRY

AMERICAN VERSION*

By permission of the Committee on Publications of the International Union of Pure and Applied Chemistry.

INDEX TO IUPAC INORGANIC RULES

*This is the United States presentation of these IUPAC Inorganic Rules as published in J. Am. Chem. Soc., 82, 5525 (1960)

1. ELEMENTS

1.1. Names and Symbols of the Elements

1.11.—The elements should have the symbols given in the following table (Table I). It is desirable that the names should differ as little as possible among the different languages, but as complete uniformity is hard to achieve, separate lists have been drawn up in English and in French. The English list only is reproduced here.

TABLE I

ELEMENTS

Name	Symbol	Atomic number	Name	Symbol	Atomic number	Name	Symbol	Atomic number
Actinium	Ac	89	Gold (Aurum)	Au	79	Praseodymium	Pr	59
Aluminum	Al	13	Hafnium	Hf	72	Promethium	Pm	61
Americium	Am	95	Helium	He	2	Protactinium	Pa	91
Antimony	Sb	51	Holmium	Ho	67	Radium	Ra	88
Argon	Ar	18	Hydrogen	H	1	Radon	Rn	86
Arsenic	As	33	Indium	In	49	Rhenium	Re	75
Astatine	At	85	Iodine	I	53	Rhodium	Rh	45
Barium	Ba	56	Iridium	Ir	77	Rubidium	Rb	37
Berkelium	Bk	97	Iron (Ferrum)	Fe	26	Ruthenium	Ru	44
Beryllium	Be	4	Krypton	Kr	36	Samarium	Sm	62
Bismuth	Bi	83	Lanthanum	La	57	Scandium	Sc	21
Boron	B	5	Lead (Plumbum)	Pb	82	Selenium	Se	34
Bromine	Br	35	Lithium	Li	3	Silicon	Si	14
Cadmium	Cd	48	Lutetium	Lu	71	Silver (Argentum)	Ag	47
Calcium	Ca	20	Magnesium	Mg	12	Sodium	Na	11
Californium	Cf	98	Manganese	Mn	25	Strontium	Sr	38
Carbon	C	6	Mendelevium	Md	101	Sulfur	S	16
Cerium	Ce	58	Mercury	Hg	80	Tantalum	Ta	73
Cesium	Cs	55	Molybdenum	Mo	42	Technetium	Tc	43
Chlorine	Cl	17	Neodymium	Nd	60	Tellurium	Te	52
Chromium	Cr	24	Neon	Ne	10	Terbium	Tb	65
Cobalt	Co	27	Neptunium	Np	93	Thallium	Tl	81
Copper (Cuprum)	Cu	29	Nickel	Ni	28	Thorium	Th	90
Curium	Cm	96	Niobium	Nb	41	Thulium	Tm	69
Dysprosium	Dy	66	Nitrogen	N	7	Tin (Stannum)	Sn	50
Einsteinium	Es	99	Nobelium	No	102	Titanium	Ti	22
Erbium	Er	68	Osmium	Os	76	Tungsten (Wolfram)	W	74
Europium	Eu	63	Oxygen	O	8	Uranium	U	92
Fermium	Fm	100	Palladium	Pd	46	Vanadium	V	23
Fluorine	F	9	Phosphorus	P	15	Xenon	Xe	54
Francium	Fr	87	Platinum	Pt	78	Ytterbium	Yb	70
Gadolinium	Gd	64	Plutonium	Pu	94	Yttrium	Y	39
Gallium	Ga	31	Polonium	Po	84	Zinc	Zn	30
Germanium	Ge	32	Potassium	K	19	Zirconium	Zr	40

◆The committees reaffirm the name niobium for element 41 in spite of the fact that many in the United States, particularly outside of chemical circles, still retain the name columbium.

1.12.—The names placed in parentheses (after the trivial names) in the list in Table I shall always be used when forming names derived from those of the elements, *e.g.*, aurate, ferrate, wolframate and not goldate, ironate, tungstate.

For some compounds of sulfur, nitrogen, and antimony, derivatives of the Greek name θεῖον, the French name *azote*, and the Latin name *stibium*, respectively, are used.

Although the name nickel agrees with the chemical symbol, it is essentially a trivial name and is spelled so differently in various languages (niquel, nikkel, *etc.*) that it is recommended that names of derivatives be formed from the Latin name *niccolum, e.g.*, niccolate instead of nickelate. The name mercury should be used as the root name also in languages where the element has another name (mercurate, *not* hydrargyrate).

In the cases in which different names have been used, the Commission has selected one based upon considerations of prevailing usage and practicability. It should be emphasized that their selection carries no implication regarding priority of discovery.

◆Tungstate and nickelate are both so well established in American practice that the committees object to changing them to wolframate and niccolate.

1.13.—Any new metallic elements should be given names ending in -ium. Molybdenum and a few other elements have long been spelled without an "i" in most languages, and the Commission hesitates to insert it.

1.14.—All new elements shall have two-letter symbols.

1.15.—All isotopes of an element should have the same name. For hydrogen the isotope names protium, deuterium, and tritium may be retained, but it is undesirable to assign isotopic names instead of numbers to other elements. They should be designated by mass numbers as, for example, "oxygen-18."

◆The list in 3.21 implies that D is an acceptable symbol for deuterium, whereas ^{2}H is used in 1.32. It is recommended that D and T be allowed for deuterium and tritium, respectively. *Cf.* comments made at 1.31, 1.32.

1.2. Names for Groups of Elements and their Subdivisions

1.21.—The use of the collective names: halogens (F, Cl, Br, I, and At), chalcogens (O, S, Se, Te, and Po), and halides and chalcogenides for their compounds, alkali metals (Li to Fr), alkaline earth metals (Ca to Ra), and inert gases may be continued. The name rare earth metals may be used for the elements Sc, Y, and La to Lu inclusive; the name lanthanum series for the elements no. 57–71 (La to Lu inclusive), and the name lanthanides for the elements 58–71 (Ce to Lu inclusive) are recommended. Elements no. 89 (Ac) to 103 form the actinium series, and the name actinides is reserved for the elements in which the $5f$ shell is being filled. The name transuranium elements is also approved for the elements following uranium.

◆The collective term halogenides used in the Rules has been replaced in this version by halides, which is almost universally used in English and is unambiguous.

The inclusion of Sc with the rare earths is questioned by some. No need is seen for the terms lanthanum series and actinium series, particularly since the latter term is used for a radioactive series. The use of a collective term for elements 58–71 is approved, although it is suggested that lanthan*oid* is preferable to lanthan*ide* because of the use of -ide for binary compounds; similarly, actin*oid* is preferable to actin*ide*. Definition by means of atomic numbers is recommended in both cases rather than on the basis of interpretation (*e.g.*, filling of $5f$ shells).

1.22.—The word metalloid should not be used to denote nonmetals.

1.3. Indication of Mass, Charge, etc., on Atomic Symbols

1.31.—The mass number, atomic number, number of atoms, and ionic charge of an element may be indicated by means of four indices placed around the symbol. The positions are to be occupied thus

left upper index	right lower index	mass number	number of atoms
left lower index	right upper index	atomic number	ionic charge

Ionic charge should be indicated by A^{n+} rather than by A^{+n}.

Example: $^{32}_{16}S_2^{2+}$ represents a doubly ionized molecule containing two atoms of sulfur, each of which has the atomic number 16 and mass number 32.

The following is an example of an equation for a nuclear reaction

$$^{26}_{12}Mg + ^{4}_{2}He = ^{29}_{13}Al + ^{1}_{1}H$$

◆Although the practice of American chemists and physicists in general has been to put the mass number at the upper right of the symbol, the committees recognize the advantage of putting it at the upper left so that the upper right is available for the ionic charge as needed.

1.32.—Isotopically labeled compounds may be described by adding to the name of the compounds the symbol of the isotope in parentheses.

Examples:

$^{32}PCl_3$ phosphorus(^{32}P) trichloride (spoken: phosphorus-32 trichloride)

$H^{36}Cl$ hydrogen chloride^{36}(Cl) (spoken: hydrogen chloride-36)

$^{15}NH_3$ ammonia(^{15}N) (spoken: ammonia nitrogen-15)

The position of the labeled atom may be indicated by placing the isotope symbol immediately after the locant (name of the group concerned).

Example: $^{2}H^{35}SO_4$ sulfuric(^{35}S) acid(^{2}H)

If this method gives names which are ambiguous or difficult to pronounce, the whole group containing the labeled atom may be indicated.

Examples:

$HOSO_2^{35}SH$	thiosulfuric(^{35}SH) acid
$^{15}NO_2NH_2$	nitramide($^{15}NO_2$), not nitr(^{15}N)amide
$NO_2^{15}NH_2$	nitramide($^{15}NH_2$)
$HO_3S^{18}O-^{18}OSO_3H$	peroxo($^{18}O_2$)disulfuric acid

1.4. Allotropes

If systematic names for gaseous and liquid modifications are required, they should be based on the size of the molecule, which can be indicated by Greek numerical prefixes (listed in 2.251). If the number of atoms is large and unknown, the prefix poly may be used. To indicate ring and chain structures the prefixes cyclo and catena may be used.

Examples:

Symbol	Trivial Name	Systematic Name
H	atomic hydrogen	monohydrogen
O_2	(common) oxygen	dioxygen
O_3	ozone	trioxygen
P_4	white phosphorus (yellow phosphorus)	tetraphosphorus
S_8	λ-sulfur	cyclooctasulfur or octasulfur
S_n	μ-sulfur	catenapolysulfur or polysulfur

For the nomenclature of solid allotropic forms the rules in Section 8 may be applied.

◆The use of prefixes to indicate ring and chain structures is favored by the committees, but it should be pointed out that ino (not catena) has been used by mineralogists for indicating chain structures in silicates, along with cyclo and other prefixes (neso, phyllo, tecto, soro) denoting structure, all used without italics or hyphens (*e.g.*, inosilicates). *Cf.* use of catena in 7.42 for chains of alternating, not self-linking, atoms.

2. FORMULAS AND NAMES OF COMPOUNDS IN GENERAL

Many chemical compounds are essentially binary in nature and can be regarded as combinations of ions or radicals; others may be treated as such for the purpose of nomenclature.

Some chemists have expressed the opinion that the name of a compound should indicate whether it is ionic or covalent. Such a distinction is made in some languages (*e.g.*, in German: Natriumchlorid *but* Chlorwasserstoff), but it has not been made consistently, and indeed it seems impossible to introduce this distinction into a consistent system of nomenclature, because the line of demarcation between these two categories is not sharp. In these rules a system of nomenclature has been built on the basis of the endings -ide and -ate, and it should be emphasized that these are intended to be applied both to ionic and covalent compounds. If it is desired to avoid such endings for neutral molecules, names can be given as coördination compounds in accordance with **2.24** and Section **7**.

2.1. Formulas

2.11.—Formulas provide the simplest and clearest method of designating inorganic compounds. They are of particular importance in chemical equations and in descriptions of chemical procedure. However, their general use in text is not recommended, although in some cases a formula, on account of its compactness, may be preferable to a cumbersome and awkward name.

2.12.—The *empirical formula* is formed by juxtaposition of the atomic symbols to give the *simplest possible* formula expressing the stoichiometric composition of the compound in question. The empirical formula may be supplemented by indication of the crystal structure—see Section **8**.

2.13.—For compounds consisting of discrete molecules the *molecular formula*, *i.e.*, a formula corresponding with the correct molecular weight of the compound, should be used, *e.g.*, S_2Cl_2 and $H_4P_2O_6$ and not SCl and H_2PO_3. When the molecular weight varies with temperature, *etc.*, the simplest possible formula generally may be chosen, *e.g.*, S, P, and NO_2 instead of S_8, P_4, and N_2O_4, unless it is desirable to indicate the molecular complexity.

2.14.—In the *structural formula* the sequence and spatial arrangement of the atoms in a molecule are indicated.

2.15.—In formulas the *electropositive constituent* (cation) should always be placed first, *e.g.*, KCl, $CaSO_4$.

This also applies in Romance languages even though the electropositive constituent is placed last in the *name*, *e.g.*, KCl, chlorure de potassium.

If the compound contains more than one electropositive or more than one electronegative constituent, their sequence is determined by Rules **6.32** and **6.33**.

2.16.—In the case of binary compounds between nonmetals that constituent should be placed first which appears earlier in the sequence: B, Si, C, Sb, As, P, N, H, Te, Se, S, At, I, Br, Cl, O, F.

Examples: NH_3, H_2S, N_4S_4, S_2Cl_2, Cl_2O, OF_2

◆Because N_4S_4 is definitely a nitride, not a sulfide, the committees prefer to write the formula S_4N_4, name it sulfur nitride, and cite it as an exception rather than as an example.

2.161.—For compounds containing three or more elements, however, the sequence should in general follow the order in which the atoms are actually bound in the molecule or ion, *e.g.*, NCS^-, not CNS^-, HOCN (cyanic acid), and HONC (fulminic acid).

Although formulas such as HNO_3, $HClO_4$, H_2SO_4, do not agree with this rule and HNO_3 does not even follow the main rule in **2.16**, the Commission does not at this time wish to break the old custom of putting the central atom immediately after the hydrogen atom in such cases (*cf* Section **5**). The formula for hypochlorous acid may be written HCNO or HClO.

2.17.—In intermetallic compounds the constituents should be placed in the order

Fr, Cs, Rb, K, Na, Li	Pt, Ir, Os, Pd, Rh, Ru, Ni, Co, Fe
Ra, Ba, Sr, Ca, Mg, Be	Au, Ag, Cu
103, No, Md, Fm, Es, Cf, Bk, Cm, Am, Pu,	Hg, Cd, Zn
Np, U, Pa, Th, Ac, Lu–La, Y, Sc	Tl, In, Ga, Al
Hf, Zr, Ti	Pb, Sn, Ge
Ta, Nb, V	Bi, Sb
W, Mo, Cr	Po
Re, Tc, Mn	

Nonmetals (except Sb) in the order given in **2.16**.

Deviations from this order may be allowed, *e.g.*, when compounds with analogous structures are compared (AgZn and AgMg).

2.18.—The number of identical atoms or atomic groups in a formula is indicated by means of Arabic numerals, placed below and to the right of the symbol or symbols in parentheses ( ) or brackets [ ] to which they refer. Water of crystallization and similar loosely bound molecules, however, are designated by means of Arabic numerals before their formulas.

$$\text{Examples:} \quad CaCl_2 \text{ not } CaCl^2$$
$$[Co(NH_3)_6]Cl_3 \text{ not } [Co6NH_3]Cl_3$$
$$[Co(NH_3)_6]_2(SO_4)_3$$
$$Na_2SO_4.10H_2O$$

2.19.—The prefixes *cis*, *trans*, *sym*, *asym* may be used in their usual senses. The prefixes may be connected with the formula by a hyphen and it is recommended that they be italicized.

Example: *cis*-$[PtCl_2(NH_3)_2]$

NOMENCLATURE OF INORGANIC CHEMISTRY (Continued)

2.2. Systematic Names

Systematic names of compounds are formed by indicating the constituents and their proportions according to the following rules. (For the order of the constituents see also the later sections.)

2.21.—The name of the *electropositive constituent* (or that treated as such according to **2.16**) will not be modified (see, however, **2.2531**).

In Germanic languages the electropositive constituent is placed first, but in Romance languages it is customary to place the electronegative constituent first.

2.22.—If the *electronegative constituent* is monatomic its name is modified to end in -ide. For binary compounds of the nonmetals the name of the element standing later in the sequence in **2.16** is modified to end in -ide.

Examples: Sodium chloride, calcium sulfide, lithium nitride, arsenic selenide, calcium phosphides, nickel arsenide, aluminum borides, iron carbides, boron hydrides, phosphorus hydrides, hydrogen chloride, hydrogen sulfide, silicon carbide, carbon disulfide, sulfur hexafluoride, chlorine dioxide, oxygen difluoride.

Certain polyatomic groups are also given the ending -ide—see **3.22**.

In the Romance languages the endings -ure, -uro, and -eto are used instead of -ide. In some languages the word *oxyde* is used, whereas the ending -ide is used in the names of other binary compounds; it is recommended that the ending -ide be universally adopted in these languages.

◆Nitrogen sulfide has been taken out of the examples. *Cf.* comment at 2.16.

2.23.—If the electronegative constituent is polyatomic it should be designated by the termination -ate. In certain exceptional cases the terminations -ide and -ite are used—see **3.22**.

2.24.—In inorganic compounds it is generally possible in a polyatomic group to indicate a *characteristic atom* (as in ClO^-) or a *central atom* (as in ICl_4^-). Such a polyatomic group is designated a *complex*, and the atoms, radicals, or molecules bound to the characteristic or central atom are termed *ligands*.

In this case the name of a negatively charged complex should be formed from the name of the characteristic or central element (as indicated in **1.12**) modified to end in -ate.

Anionic ligands are indicated by the termination -o. Further details concerning the designation of ligands, the definition of "central atom," *etc.*, appear in Section 7.

Although the terms sulfate, phosphate, *etc.*, were originally the names of the anions of particular oxo acids, the names sulfate, phosphate, *etc.*, should now designate quite generally a negative group containing sulfur or phosphorus, respectively, as the central atom, irrespective of its oxidation state (the designation of the oxidation state is discussed in later rules) and the number and nature of the ligands. The complex is indicated by brackets [ ], but this is not always necessary.

Examples:

$Na_2[SO_4]$	sodium tetraoxosulfate	$Na_3[PS_4]$	sodium tetrathiophosphate
$Na_2[SO_3]$	sodium trioxosulfate	$Na[PCl_6]$	sodium hexachlorophosphate
$Na_2[S_2O_3]$	sodium trioxothiosulfate	$K[PO_2F_2]$	potassium dioxodifluorophosphate
$Na[SO_3F]$	sodium trioxofluorosulfate	$K[POCl_2(NH)]$	potassium oxodichloroimidophosphate
$Na_3[PO_4]$	sodium tetraoxophosphate		

In many cases these names may be abbreviated, *e.g.*, sodium sulfate, sodium thiosulfate (see **2.26**), and in other cases trivial names may be used (*cf.* **2.3**, **3.224**, and Section 5). It should be pointed out, however, that the principle is quite generally applicable, to compounds containing organic ligands also, and its use is recommended in all cases where trivial names do not exist.

The coördination principle applied in this rule may also be applied to complexes which are positive or neutral (*cf.* **3.1** and Section 7). However, neutral complexes which are as a rule considered as binary compounds are given names according to **2.22**, **2.16**. Thus, SO_3, sulfur trioxide, not trioxosulfur.

◆In the examples it would seem that full coördination-type names should be given, *e.g.*, either sodium tetraoxosulfate (VI) or disodium tetraoxosulfate. *Cf.* 7.32 and comment at 7.312.

2.25.—Indication of the Proportions of the Constituents.

2.251.—The *stoichiometric proportions* may be denoted by means of Greek numerical prefixes (mono, di, tri, tetra, penta, hexa, hepta, octa, ennea, deca, hendeca, and dodeca) preceding without hyphen the names of the elements to which they refer. It may be necessary in some languages to supplement these numerals with hemi ($^1/_2$) and the Latin sesqui ($^3/_2$).

The prefix mono may generally be omitted. Beyond 12, Greek prefixes are replaced by Arabic numerals (with or without hyphen according to the custom of the language), because they are more readily understood.

This system is applicable to all types of compounds and is especially suitable for binary compounds of the nonmetals.

When it is required to indicate the number of entire groups of atoms, particularly when the name includes a numerical prefix with a different significance, the multiplicative numerals (Latin bis, Greek tris, tetrakis, *etc.*) are used and the whole group to which they refer may be placed in parentheses if necessary.

Examples:

N_2O	dinitrogen oxide	Fe_3O_4	triiron tetraoxide
NO_2	nitrogen dioxide	U_3O_8	triuranium octaoxide
N_2O_4	dinitrogen tetraoxide	MnO_2	manganese dioxide
N_2S_5	dinitrogen pentasulfide	$Ca_3[PO_4]_2$	tricalcium diorthophosphate
S_2Cl_2	disulfur dichloride	$Ca[PCl_6]_2$	calcium bis(hexachlorophosphate)

In indexes it may be convenient to italicize a numerical prefix at the beginning of the name and connect it to the rest of the name with a hyphen, but this is not desirable in text, *e.g.*, *tri*-Uranium octaoxide.

Since the degree of polymerization of many substances varies with temperature, state of aggregation, *etc.*, the name to be used should normally be based upon the simplest possible formula of the substance except when it is required specifically to draw attention to the degree of polymerization.

Example: The name nitrogen dioxide may be used for the equilibrium mixture of NO_2 and N_2O_4. Dinitrogen tetraoxide means specifically N_2O_4.

◆In accordance with the organic nomenclature rules and well-established practice, it is recommended that "or Latin" be inserted between "Greek" and "numerical prefixes" in the first sentence and that "nona" replace "ennea," and "undeca" replace "hendeca."

Extreme caution is advised in the omission of numerical prefixes, including mono (*cf.* second set of examples in 5.23), because of the frequent use of names such as chloroplatinate (*cf.* 2.26 and the last sentence in 5.24).

2.252.—The proportions of the constituents also may be indicated indirectly by *Stock's system*, that is, by Roman numerals representing the oxidation number or stoichiometric valence of the element, placed in parentheses immediately following the name. For zero the Arabic 0 will be used. When used in conjunction with symbols the Roman numeral may be placed above and to the right.

The Stock notation can be applied to both cations and anions, but preferably should *not* be applied to compounds between nonmetals.

In employing the Stock notation, use of the Latin names of the elements (or Latin roots) is considered advantageous.

Examples:

$FeCl_2$	iron(II) chloride or ferrum(II) chloride
$FeCl_3$	iron(III) chloride or ferrum(III) chloride
MnO_2	manganese(IV) oxide
BaO_2	barium(II) peroxide
$Pb^{II}_2Pb^{IV}O_4$	dilead(II) lead(IV) oxide or trilead tetraoxide
$K_4[Ni(CN)_4]$	potassium tetracyanonicollate(0)
$K_4[Fe(CN)_6]$	potassium hexacyanoferrate(II)
$Na_2[Fe(CO)_4]$	sodium tetracarbonylferrate(—II)

◆While the committees favor the extended use of the Stock notation, they suggest that in some cases the system of Ewens and Bassett (designation of the aggregate charge of a complex ion by an Arabic numeral in parentheses following the name, similar to the use as superior notations with formulas) is advantageous and should be allowed as an alternate (*cf.* 3.17 and comment at 7.323). Mixed use of the two systems, while not desirable in any one context, does not affect indexing and should not lead to confusion. See comment at 1.12.

2.253.—The following systems are in use but are not recommended:

2.2531.—The system of indicating valence by means of the suffixes *-ous* and *-ic* added to the root of the name of the cation may be retained for elements exhibiting not more than two valences.

2.2532.—"*Functional*" nomenclature (such as "nitric anhydride" for N_2O_5) is not recommended apart from the name *acid* to designate the acid function (Section 5).

◆Apparently there is no objection to acid anhydride as a class name (*cf.* 5.32). Other functional derivatives of acids are named as such in the Rules (5.3).

2.26.—In systematic names it is not always necessary to indicate stoichiometric proportions. In many instances it is permissible to omit the numbers of atoms, oxidation numbers, *etc.*, when they are not required in the particular circumstances. For instance, these indications are not generally necessary with elements of essentially constant valence.

Examples:

> sodium sulfate instead of sodium tetraoxosulfate
> aluminum sulfate instead of aluminum(III) sulfate
> potassium chloroplatinate(IV) instead of potassium hexachloroplatinate(IV)
> potassium cyanoferrate(III) instead of potassium hexacyanoferrate(III)
> phosphorus pentaoxide instead of diphosphorus pentaoxide

2.3. Trivial Names

Certain well-established trivial names for oxo acids (Section 5) and for hydrogen compounds (water, ammonia, hydrazine) are still acceptable. For some other hydrogen compounds these names are approved:

B_2H_6	diboran	PH_3	phosphine	SbH_3	stibine	P_2H_4	diphosphine
SiH_4	silane	AsH_3	arsine	Si_2H_6	disilane, *etc.*	As_2H_4	diarsine

In some languages names of the type "Chlorwasserstoff" are in use and may be retained if national nomenclature committees so wish.

Purely trivial names, free from false scientific implications, such as soda, Chile saltpeter, quicklime, are harmless in industrial and popular literature; but old incorrect scientific names such as sulfate of magnesia, Natronhydrat, sodium muriate, carbonate of lime, should be avoided under all circumstances, and they should be eliminated from technical and patent literature.

◆For BH_3 (omitted in the Rules) borane rather than the previously used borine has been recommended by the Advisory Committee on the Nomenclature of Organic Boron Compounds of the ACS in a report not yet published.

Because soda is an ambiguous term, it is suggested that it be replaced by soda ash.

3. NAMES FOR IONS AND RADICALS

3.1. Cations

3.11.—Monatomic cations should be named like the corresponding element, without change or suffix, except as provided by **2.2531**.

Examples:

Cu^+ the copper(I) ion Cu^{2+} the copper(II) ion I^+ the iodine cation

◆For I^+, iodide(I) cation is more consistent with recommended practice. *Cf.* 3.21.

3.12.—The preceding principle should apply also to polyatomic cations corresponding to radicals for which special names are given in **3.32**, *i.e.*, these names should be used without change or suffix.

Examples: NO^+ the nitrosyl cation NO_2^+ the nitryl cation

◆Polyatomic here and in 3.13, 3.14, 3.223, 3.32, and 5.2 seems to be limited to more than one *kind* of atom, and hence heteratomic would be a more precise term. It is agreed that nitryl and not nitronium should be used in all cases (*cf.* 3.151).

3.13.—Polyatomic cations formed from monatomic cations by the addition of other ions or neutral atoms or molecules (ligands) will be regarded as complex and will be named according to the rules given in Section **7**.

Examples:

$[Al(H_2O)_6]^{3+}$ the hexaaquoaluminum ion $[CoCl(NH_3)_5]^{2+}$ the chloropentamminecobalt ion

For some important polyatomic cations which fall in this section, radical names given in **3.32** may be used alternatively, *e.g.*, for UO_2^{2+} the name uranyl(VI) ion in place of dioxouranium(VI) ion.

3.14.—Names for polyatomic cations derived by addition of protons to monatomic anions are formed by adding the ending -onium to the root of the name of the anion element.

Examples: phosphonium, arsonium, stibonium, oxonium, sulfonium, selenonium, telluronium, and iodonium ions.

Organic ions derived by substitution in these parent cations should be named as such, whether the parent itself is a known compound or not: for example $(CH_3)_4Sb^+$, the tetramethylstibonium ion.

The ion H_3O^+, which is in fact the monohydrated proton, is to be known as the oxonium ion when it is believed to have this constitution, as for example in $H_3O^+ClO_4^-$, oxonium perchlorate. The widely used term hydronium should be kept for the cases where it is wished to denote an indefinite degree of hydration of the proton, as, for example, in aqueous solution. If, however, the hydration is of no particular importance to the matter under consideration, the simpler term hydrogen ion may be used. The latter also may be used for the indefinitely solvated proton in nonaqueous solvents; but definite ions such as $CH_3OH_2^+$ and $(CH_3)_2OH^+$ should be named as derivatives of the oxonium ion, *i.e.*, as methyl- and dimethyloxonium ions, respectively.

◆The committees concur in oxonium for the ion H_3O^+, but see little reason for encouraging retention of the term hydronium ion because hydrogen ion adequately designates an indeterminate degree of hydration.

3.15.—Ions from Nitrogen Bases.

3.151.—The name ammonium for the ion NH_4^+ does not conform to **3.14**, but should be retained. This decision does *not* release the word nitronium for other uses: this would lead to inconsistencies when the rules are applied to other elements.

3.152.—Substituted ammonium ions derived from nitrogen bases with names ending in -amine will receive names formed by changing -amine to -ammonium. For example, $HONH_3^+$, the hydroxylammonium ion.

3.153.—When the nitrogen base is known by a name ending otherwise than in -amine, the cation name is to be formed by adding the ending -ium to the name of the base (if necessary omitting a final -e or other vowel).

Examples: hydrazinium, anilinium, glycinium, pyridinium, guanidinium, imidazolium.

The names uronium and thiouronium, though inconsistent with this rule, may be retained.

3.16.—Cations formed by adding protons to nonnitrogenous bases may also be given names formed by adding -ium to the name of the compound to which the proton is added.

Examples: dioxanium, acetonium.

In the case of cations formed by adding protons to acids, however, their names are to be formed by adding the word acidium to the name of the corresponding anion, and not that of the acid itself. For example, $H_2NO_3^+$, the nitrate acidium ion; $H_2NO_2^+$, the nitrite acidium ion; and $CH_3COOH_2^+$, the acetate acidium ion. Note, however, that when the anion of the acid is monatomic **3.14** will apply; for example, FH_2^+ is the fluoronium ion.

◆In accord with present practice, nitric acidium ion, *etc.*, are preferred to nitrate acidium ion, *etc.* $CH_3COOH_2^+$ is organic.

3.17.—Where more than one ion is derived from one base, as, for example, $N_2H_5^+$ and $N_2H_6^{2+}$, their charges may be indicated in their names as the hydrazinium(1+) and the hydrazinium(2+) ion, respectively.

◆*Cf.* comment at 2.252 and the use of Stock notation with ions or radicals in 3.13 and 3.32.

3.2. Anions

3.21.—The names for monatomic anions shall consist of the name (sometimes abbreviated) of the element, with the termination -ide. Thus

H^-	hydride ion	Br^-	bromide ion	Se^{2-}	selenide ion	As^{3-}	arsenide ion
D^-	deuteride ion	I^-	iodide ion	Te^{2-}	telluride ion	Sb^{3-}	antimonide ion
F^-	fluoride ion	O^{2-}	oxide ion	N^{3-}	nitride ion	C^{4-}	carbide ion
Cl^-	chloride ion	S^{2-}	sulfide ion	P^{3-}	phosphide ion	Si^{4-}	silicide ion
		B^{3-}	boride ion				

Expressions of the type "chlorine ion" are used particularly in connection with crystal structure work and spectroscopy; the Commission recommends that whenever the charge corresponds with that indicated above, the termination -ide should be used.

◆*Cf.* comments at 1.15 and 1.32 regarding ^{2}H and D.

3.22. Polyatomic Anions.

3.221.—Certain polyatomic anions have names ending in -ide. These are

OH^-	hydroxide ion	I_3^-	triiodide ion	$NHOH^-$	hydroxylamide ion
O_2^{2-}	peroxide ion	HF_2^-	hydrogen difluoride ion	$N_2H_3^-$	hydrazide ion
O_2^-	hyperoxide ion	N_3^-	azide ion	CN^-	cyanide ion
O_3^-	ozonide ion	NH^{2-}	imide ion	C_2^{2-}	acetylide ion
S_2^{2-}	disulfide ion	NH_2^-	amide ion		

Names for other polysulfide, polyhalide, *etc.*, ions may be formed in analogous manner. The OH^- ion should not be called the hydroxyl ion. The name hydroxyl is reserved for the OH group when neutral or positively charged, whether free or as a substituent (*cf.* **3.12** and **3.32**).

◆Superoxide is well established in English for O_2^- and no advantage is seen in changing to hyperoxide.

3.222.—Ions such as SH^- and O_2H^- will be called the hydrogen sulfide ion and the hydrogen peroxide ion, respectively. This agrees with **6.2**, and names such as hydrosulfide are not needed.

◆*Cf.* comment at 6.2. All "fused" names (as hydrogensulfide here and methylisocyanide in 5.33) in the original version have been written as two words in this version. For a rule on the written form of the names of compounds see *J. Chem. Education*, 8, 1336–8 (1931).

3.223.—The names for other polyatomic anions shall consist of the name of the central atom with the termination -ate, which is used quite generally for complex anions. Atoms and groups attached to the central atom shall generally be treated as ligands in a complex (*cf.* **2.24** and Section 7) as, for example, $[Sb(OH)_6]^-$, the hexahydroxoantimonate(V) ion.

This applies also when the exact composition of the anion is not known; *e.g.*, by solution of aluminum hydroxide or zinc hydroxide in sodium hydroxide, aluminate and zincate ions are formed.

3.224.—It is quite practicable to treat oxygen in the same manner as other ligands (**2.24**), but it has long been customary to ignore the name of this element altogether in anions and to indicate its presence and proportion by means of a series of prefixes (hypo-, per-, *etc.*, see Section 5) and sometimes also by the suffix -ite in place of -ate.

The termination -ite has been used to denote a lower oxidation state and may be retained in trivial names in these cases

NO_2^-	nitrite	$PH_2O_2^-$	hypophosphite	$S_2O_2^{2-}$	thiosulfite
$N_2O_2^{2-}$	hyponitrite	AsO_3^{3-}	arsenite	SeO_3^{2-}	selenite
NOO_2^-	peroxonitrite	SO_3^{2-}	sulfite	ClO_2^-	chlorite
PHO_3^{2-}	phosphite	$S_2O_5^{2-}$	disulfite (pyrosulfite)	ClO^-	hypochlorite
$P_2H_2O_5^{2-}$	diphosphite (pyrophosphite)	$S_2O_4^{2-}$	dithionite		

(and correspondingly for the other halogens)

The Commission does not recommend the use of any such names other than those listed. A number of other names ending in -ite have been used, *e.g.*, antimonite, tellurite, stannite, plumbite, ferrite, manganite, but in many cases such compounds are known in the solid state to be double oxides and are to be treated as such (*cf.* **6.5**), *e.g.*, $Cu(CrO_2)_2$ copper(II) chromium(III) oxide, not copper chromite. Where there is reason to believe that a definite salt with a discrete anion exists, the name is formed in accordance with **2.24**. By dissolving, for example, Sb_2O_3, SnO, or PbO in sodium hydroxide an antimonate(III), a stannate(II), or a plumbate(II) is formed in the solution.

Concerning the use of prefixes hypo-, per-, *etc.*, see the list of acids (table in **5.214**). For all new compounds and even for the less common ones listed in the table in **3.224** or derived from the acids listed in the table in **5.214**, it is preferable to use the system given in **2.24** and in Sections 5 and 7.

◆For phosphite names see comment at 6.2.

3.3. Radicals

3.31.—A radical is here regarded as a group of atoms which occurs repeatedly in a number of different compounds. Sometimes the same radical fulfils different functions in different cases, and accordingly different names often have been assigned to the same group. The Commission considers it desirable to reduce this diversity and recommends that formulas or systematic names be used to denote all new radicals, instead of introducing new trivial names. The list of names for ions and radicals on page B-169 gives an extensive selection of radical names at present in use in inorganic chemistry.

◆The list of names for ions and radicals following the Rules is very useful and can be made more so by additions (as of dithio, nitrilo, and azido in the last column) and by greater attempt at uniformity with organic usage. Some of the terms (as nitride and amide) listed as anions are used also of covalent compounds. A single atom may function like a radical as defined above and may be named similarly, as chloro and oxo.

3.32.—Certain radicals containing oxygen or other chalcogens have special names ending in -yl, and the Commission approves the provisional retention of

HO	hydroxyl	S_2O_5	pyrosulfuryl	PO	phosphoryl	ClO_2	chloryl
CO	carbonyl	SeO	seleninyl	VO	vanadyl	ClO_3	perchloryl
NO	nitrosyl	SeO_2	selenonyl	PuO_2	plutonyl		(and similarly
SO	sulfinyl	CrO_2	chromyl		(similarly for		for other
	(thionyl)	UO_2	uranyl		other actinide		halogens)
SO_2	sulfonyl	NpO_2	neptunyl		elements)		
	(sulfuryl)	NO_2	nitryl[1]	ClO	chlorosyl		

[1]The name nitroxyl should not be used for this group since the name nitroxylic acid has been used for H_2NO_2. Although the word nitryl is firmly established in English, nitroyl may be a better model for many other languages.

Names such as the above should be used only to designate compounds containing these discrete groups. The use of thionyl and sulfuryl should be restricted to the halides. Names such as bismuthyl and antimonyl are not approved because the compounds do not contain BiO and SbO groups, respectively; such compounds are to be designated as oxide halides (**6.4**).

Radicals analogous to the above containing other chalcogens in place of oxygen are named by adding the prefixes thio-, seleno-, *etc.*

Examples:

PS   thiophosphoryl   CSe   selenocarbonyl

In cases where radicals may have different valences, the oxidation number of the characteristic element should be indicated by means of the Stock notation. For example, the uranyl group UO_2 may refer either to the ion UO_2^{2+} or to the ion UO_2^+; these can be distinguished as uranyl(VI) and uranyl(V), respectively. In like manner, VO may be vanadyl(V), vanadyl(IV), and vanadyl(III).

These polyatomic radicals always are treated as forming the positive part of the compound.

Examples:

$COCl_2$	carbonyl chloride	$NO_2HS_2O_7$	nitryl hydrogen disulfate
NOS	nitrosyl sulfide	S_2O_5ClF	pyrosulfuryl chloride fluoride
PON	phosphoryl nitride	$SO_2(N_3)_2$	sulfonyl azide
$PSCl_3$	thiophosphoryl chloride	SO_2NH	sulfonyl imide
POCl	phosphoryl(III) chloride	IO_2F	iodyl fluoride

By using the same radical names regardless of unknown or controversial polarity relationships, names can be formed without entering into any controversy. Thus, for example, the compounds NOCl and $NOClO_4$ are quite unambiguously denoted by the names nitrosyl chloride and nitrosyl perchlorate, respectively.

◆Caution is urged in the use of some of these radical names: Vanadyl, for example, has been used for VO_2 as well as for VO (*cf.* also the naming of $VOSO_4$ in 6.42). Most of these radical names (except hydroxyl and thionyl) can be regarded as derived from the names of acids which have lost all of their hydroxyls (analogous to -yl or -oyl organic acid radical names) by the use of -yl and -osyl for radicals from -ic and -ous acids, respectively; this is implied in the footnote about nitroxyl. The use of the Stock notation in only one example (phosphoryl(III) chloride) seems confusing. It might be clearer to indicate stoichiometric proportions, *e.g.*, phosphoryl (mono)chloride, thiophosphoryl trichloride (*cf.* phosphoryl triamide in 5.34) or to use phosphorosyl for phosphoryl(III).

The restriction of the use of thionyl and sulfuryl to the halides was agreed upon at a joint meeting of the inorganic and organic nomenclature commissions of the IUPAC in 1951.

3.33.—It should be noted that the same radical may have different names in inorganic and organic chemistry. To draw attention to such differences the prefix names of radicals as substituents in organic compounds have been listed together with the inorganic names in the list of names printed at the end of the Rules. Names of purely organic compounds, of which many are important in the chemistry of coördination compounds (Section 7), should agree with the nomenclature of organic chemistry.

Organic chemical nomenclature is to a large extent based on the principle of substitution, *i.e.*, replacement of hydrogen atoms by other atoms or groups. Such "substitutive names" are extremely rare in inorganic chemistry; they are used, *e.g.*, in the following cases: NH_2Cl is called chloramine, and $NHCl_2$ dichloramine. These names may be retained in the absence of better terms. Other substitutive names (derived from "sulfonic acid" as a name for HSO_3H) are fluoro- and chlorosulfonic acid, aminosulfonic acid, iminodisulfonic acid, and nitrilotrisulfonic acid. These names should preferably be replaced by the following

FSO_3H	fluorosulfuric acid	$NH(SO_3H)_2$	imidodisulfuric acid
$ClSO_3H$	chlorosulfuric acid	$N(SO_3H)_3$	nitridotrisulfuric acid
NH_2SO_3H	amidosulfuric acid		

Names such as chlorosulfuric acid and amidosulfuric acid might be considered to be substitutive names derived by substitution of *hydroxyl* groups in sulfuric acid. From a more fundamental point of view, however (see **2.24**), such names are formed by adding hydroxyl, amide, imide, *etc.*, groups together with oxygen atoms to a sulfur atom, "sulfuric acid" in this connection standing as an abbreviation for "trioxosulfuric acid."

Another organic-chemical type of nomenclature, the formation of "conjunctive names," is also met in only a few cases in inorganic chemistry, *e.g.*, the hydrazine- and hydroxylaminesulfonic acids. According to the principles of inorganic chemical nomenclature these compounds should be called hydrazido- and hydroxylamidosulfuric acid.

◆These are not true "conjunctive names" since sulfonic acid is not a compound. For the naming of partial amides *cf.* also 5.34.

NOMENCLATURE OF INORGANIC CHEMISTRY (Continued)

4. CRYSTALLINE PHASES OF VARIABLE COMPOSITION

Isomorphous replacement, interstitial solutions, intermetallic compounds, and other nonstoichiometric compounds (berthollides)

4.1.—If an intermediate crystalline phase occurs in a two-component (or more complex) system, it may obey the law of constant composition very closely, as in the case of sodium chloride, or it may be capable of varying in composition over an appreciable range, as occurs for example with FeS. A substance showing such a variation is called a *berthollide*.

In connection with the berthollides the concept of a characteristic or ideal composition is frequently used. A unique definition of this concept seems to be lacking. In one case it may be necessary to use a definition based upon lattice geometry and in another to base it on the ratio of valence electrons to atoms. Sometimes one can state several characteristic compositions, and at other times it is impossible to say whether a phase corresponds to a characteristic composition or not.

In spite of these difficulties it seems that the concept of a characteristic composition can be used in its present undefined form for establishing a system of notation for phases of variable composition. It also seems possible to use the concept even if the characteristic composition is not included in the known homogeneity range of the phase.

4.2.—For the present, mainly formulas should be used for berthollides and solid solutions, since strictly logical names tend to become inconveniently cumbersome. The latter should be used only when unavoidable (*e.g.*, for indexing), and may be written in the style of iron(II) sulfide (iron-deficient); molybdenum dicarbide (excess carbon), or the like. Mineralogical names should be used only to designate actual minerals and not to define chemical composition; thus the name calcite refers to a particular mineral (contrasted with other minerals of similar composition) and is not a term for the chemical compound whose composition is properly expressed by the name calcium carbonate. (The mineral name may, however, be used to indicate the structure type—see **6.52.**)

4.3.—A general notation for the berthollides, which can be used even when the mechanism of the variation in composition is unknown, is to put the sign $\sim$ (read as *circa*) before the formula. (In special cases it may also be printed above the formula.)

$$\text{Examples:} \quad \sim\text{FeS}, \qquad \overset{\sim}{\text{CuZn}}$$

The direction of the deviation may be indicated when required:

$$\sim\text{FeS (iron-deficient)}; \qquad \sim\text{MoC}_2 \text{ (excess carbon)}$$

4.4.—For a phase where the variable composition is solely or partially caused by replacement, atoms or atomic groups which replace each other are separated by a comma and placed together between parentheses.

If possible the formula ought to be written so that the limits of the homogeneity range are represented when one or other of the two atoms or groups is lacking. For example the symbol (Ni,Cu) denotes the complete range from pure Ni to pure Cu; likewise K(Br,Cl) comprises the range from pure KBr to pure KCl. If only part of the homogeneity range is referred to, the major constituent should be placed first.

Substitution accompanied by the appearance of vacant positions (combination of substitutional and interstitial solution) receives an analogous notation. For example, $(\text{Li}_2,\text{Mg})\text{Cl}_2$ denotes the homogeneous phase from LiCl to MgCl_2 where the anion lattice structure remains the same but one vacant cation position appears for every substitution of 2Li^+ by Mg^{2+}.

The formula $(\text{Mg}_3,\text{Al}_2)\text{Al}_6\text{O}_{12}$ represents the homogeneous phase from the spinel MgAl_2O_4 ($= \text{Mg}_3\text{Al}_6\text{O}_{12}$) to the spinel form of Al_2O_3 ($= \text{Al}_2\text{Al}_6\text{O}_{12}$).

The solid solutions between CaF_2 and YF_3, where cation substitution is accompanied by interstitial addition of F^-, would be represented by the formula $(\text{Ca},\text{YF})\text{F}_2$. It is important to note that this formula is based purely on considerations of composition, and it does not imply that YF^{2+} takes over the actual physical position of Ca^{2+}. On the same basis a notation for the plagioclases would be $(\text{NaSi},\text{CaAl})\text{Si}_2\text{AlO}_8$.

4.5.—A still more complete notation, which should always be used in more complex cases, may be constructed by indicating in a formula the variables that define the composition. Thus, a phase involving simple substitution may be written A_xB_{1-x}.

$$\text{Examples:} \quad \text{Ni}_x\text{Cu}_{1-x} \text{ and } \text{KBr}_x\text{Cl}_{1-x}$$

This shows immediately that the total number of atoms in the lattice is constant. Combined substitutional and interstitial or subtractive solution can be shown in an analogous way. The commas and parentheses called for in **4.4** are not required in this case.

For example, the homogeneous phase between LiCl and MgCl_2 becomes $\text{Li}_{2x}\text{Mg}_{1-x}\text{Cl}_2$ and the phase between MgAl_2O_4 and Al_2O_3 can be written $\text{Mg}_{3x}\text{Al}_{2(1-x)}\text{Al}_6\text{O}_{12}$, which shows that it cannot contain more Mg than that corresponding to MgAl_2O_4 ($x = 1$). The other examples given in **4.4** will be given the formulas $\text{Ca}_x\text{Y}_{1-x}\text{F}_{3-x}$ and $\text{Na}_x\text{Ca}_{1-x}\text{Si}_{2+x}\text{Al}_{2-x}\text{O}_8$. In the case of the γ-phase of the Ag–Cd system, which has the characteristic formula Ag_5Cd_8, the Ag and Cd atoms can replace one another to some extent and the notation would be $\text{Ag}_{5\pm x}\text{Cd}_{8\mp x}$.

Further examples:

$$\text{Fe}_{1-x}\text{Sb} \quad \text{Fe}_{1-x}\text{O} \quad \text{Fe}_{1-x}\text{S} \quad \text{Cu}_{2-x}\text{O} \qquad \text{Na}_{1-x}\text{WO}_3 \text{ (sodium tungsten bronzes)}$$

For $x = 0$ each of these formulas corresponds to a characteristic composition. If it is desired to show that the variable denoted by x can attain only small values, this may be done by substituting ϵ for x.

Likewise a solid solution of hydrogen in palladium can be written as PdH_x, and a phase of the composition M which has dissolved a variable amount of water can be written $\text{M}(\text{H}_2\text{O})_x$.

When this notation is used, a particular composition can be indicated by stating the actual value of the variable x. Probably the best way of doing this is to put the value in parentheses after the general formula. For example, $Li_{4-x}Fe_{3x}Ti_{2(1-x)}O_6$ ($x = 0.35$). If it is desired to introduce the value of x into the formula itself, the mechanism of solution is more clearly understood if one writes $Li_{4-0.35}Fe_{3\times0.35}Ti_{2(1-0.35)}O_6$ instead of $Li_{3.65}Fe_{1.05}Ti_{1.30}O_6$.

5. ACIDS

Many of the compounds which now according to some definitions are called acids do not fall into the classical province of acids. In other parts of inorganic chemistry functional names are disappearing and it would have been most satisfactory to abolish them also for those compounds generally called acids. Names for these acids may be derived from the names of the anions as in Section 2, e.g., hydrogen sulfate instead of sulfuric acid. The nomenclature of acids has, however, a long history of established custom, and it appears impossible to systematize acid names without drastic alteration of the accepted names of many important and well-known substances.

The present rules are aimed at preserving the more useful of the older names while attempting to guide further development along directions which should allow new compounds to be named in a more systematic manner.

5.1. Binary and Pseudobinary Acids

Acids giving rise to the -ide anions defined by 3.21 and 3.221 will be named as binary and pseudobinary compounds of hydrogen, e.g., hydrogen chloride, hydrogen sulfide, hydrogen cyanide.

For the compound HN_3 the name hydrogen azide is recommended in preference to hydrazoic acid.

5.2. Acids Derived from Polyatomic Anions

Acids giving rise to anions bearing names ending in -ate or in -ite may also be treated as in 5.1, but names more in accordance with custom are formed by using the terminations -ic acid and -ous acid corresponding with the anion terminations -ate and -ite, respectively. Thus chloric acid corresponds to chlorate, sulfuric acid to sulfate, and phosphorous acid to phosphite.

This nomenclature may also be used for less common acids, e.g., hexacyanoferric acids correspond to hexacyanoferrate ions. In such cases, however, systematic names of the type hydrogen hexacyanoferrate are preferable.

Most of the common acids are oxo acids, i.e., they contain only oxygen atoms bound to the characteristic atom. It is a long-established custom not to indicate these oxygen atoms. It is mainly for these acids that long-established names will have to be retained. Most other acids may be considered as coördination compounds and be named as such.

◆Polyatomic means heteratomic here, as opposed to pseudobinary. Cf. comment at 3.12.

5.21. Oxo Acids.—For the oxo acids the ous–ic notation to distinguish between different oxidation states is applied in many cases. The -ous acid names are restricted to acids corresponding to the -ite anions listed in the table in 3.224.

Further distinction between different acids with the same characteristic element is in some cases effected by means of prefixes. This notation should not be extended beyond the cases listed below.

5.211.—The prefix hypo- is used to denote a lower oxidation state, and may be retained in these cases

$H_4B_2O_4$	hypoboric acid	HPH_2O_2	hypophosphorous acid
$H_2N_2O_2$	hyponitrous acid	$HOCl$	hypochlorous acid (and similarly for the other halogens)
$H_4P_2O_6$	hypophosphoric acid		

5.212.—The prefix per- is used to designate a higher oxidation state and may be retained for $HClO_4$, perchloric acid, and similarly for the other elements in Group VII.

The prefix per- should not be confused with the prefix peroxo- (see 5.22).

5.213.—The prefixes ortho- and meta- have been used to distinguish acids differing in "water content." These names are approved

H_3BO_3	orthoboric acid	H_5IO_6	orthoperiodic acid	$(H_2SiO_3)_n$	metasilicic acids
H_4SiO_4	orthosilicic acid	H_6TeO_6	orthotelluric acid	$(HPO_3)_n$	metaphosphoric acids
H_3PO_4	orthophosphoric acid	$(HBO_2)_n$	metaboric acids		

For the acids derived by removing water from orthoperiodic or orthotelluric acid, the systematic names should be used, e.g., HIO_4 tetraoxoiodic(VII) acid.

The prefix pyro- has been used to designate an acid formed from two molecules of an ortho acid minus one molecule of water. Such acids can now generally be regarded as the simplest cases of isopoly acids (cf. 7.5). The prefix pyro- may be retained for pyrosulfurous and pyrosulfuric acids and for pyrophosphorous and pyrophosphoric acids, although in these cases also the prefix di- is preferable.

◆The use of orthoperiodic acid and orthotelluric acid is approved, but the question of names for HIO_4, etc., needs further study because of confusion in the literature.

5.214.—The accompanying Table II contains the accepted names of the oxo acids (whether known in the free state or not) and some of their thio and peroxo derivatives (5.22 and 5.23).

For the less common of these acids systematic names would seem preferable, for example

H_2MnO_4	manganic(VI) acid, to distinguish it from H_3MnO_4, manganic(V) acid
$HReO_4$	tetraoxorhenic(VII) acid, to distinguish it from H_3ReO_5, pentaoxorhenic(VII) acid
H_2ReO_4	tetraoxorhenic(VI) acid, to distinguish it from $HReO_3$, trioxorhenic(V) acid; H_3ReO_4, tetraoxorhenic(V) acid; and $H_4Re_2O_7$, heptaoxodirhenic(V) acid
H_2NO_2	dioxonitric(II) acid instead of nitroxylic acid

Trivial names should not be given to such acids as HNO, $H_2N_2O_3$, $H_2N_2O_4$, of which salts have been described. These salts are to be designated systematically as oxonitrates(I), trioxodinitrates(II), tetraoxodinitrates(III), respectively.

The names germanic acid, stannic acid, antimonic acid, bismuthic acid, vanadic acid, niobic acid, tantalic acid, telluric acid, molybdic acid, wolframic acid, and uranic acid may be used for substances with indefinite "water content" and degree of polymerization.

◆Unless trivial names clash with good nomenclature practices or are ambiguous, retention of well-established ones or the use of formulas is urged (especially for HNO, $H_2N_2O_3$, etc.) until structures are known. Systematic coordination-type names in the case of these nitrogen acids, for example, imply a structure that is ruled out by our present state of knowledge.

If hexahydroxoantimonic acid is considered a trivial name, hexahydroxy- might be preferable (cf. the systematic name hexahydroxoantimonate(V) ion in 3.223). For the analogous use of peroxo and peroxy, see comment at 5.22.

TABLE II
NAMES FOR OXO ACIDS

H_3BO_3	orthoboric acid or (mono)boric acid	H_2SO_4	sulfuric acid
$(HBO_2)_n$	metaboric acids	$H_2S_2O_7$	disulfuric or pyrosulfuric acid
$(HBO_2)_3$	trimetaboric acid	H_2SO_5	peroxo(mono)sulfuric acid
$H_4B_2O_4$	hypoboric acid	$H_2S_2O_8$	peroxodisulfuric acid
H_2CO_3	carbonic acid	$H_2S_2O_3$	thiosulfuric acid
HOCN	cyanic acid	$H_2S_2O_6$	dithionic acid
HNCO	isocyanic acid	H_2SO_3	sulfurous acid
HONC	fulminic acid	$H_2S_2O_5$	disulfurous or pyrosulfurous acid
H_4SiO_4	orthosilicic acid	$H_2S_2O_2$	thiosulfurous acid
$(H_2SiO_3)_n$	metasilicic acids	$H_2S_2O_4$	dithionous acid
HNO_3	nitric acid	H_2SO_2	sulfoxylic acid
HNO_4	peroxonitric acid	$H_2S_xO_6 \; (x = 3,4...)$	polythionic acids
HNO_2	nitrous acid	H_2SeO_4	selenic acid
HOONO	peroxonitrous acid	H_2SeO_3	selenious acid
H_2NO_2	nitroxylic acid	H_6TeO_6	(ortho)telluric acid
$H_2N_2O_2$	hyponitrous acid	H_2CrO_4	chromic acid
H_3PO_4	(ortho)phosphoric acid	$H_2Cr_2O_7$	dichromic acid
$H_4P_2O_7$	diphosphoric or pyrophosphoric acid	$HClO_4$	perchloric acid
$H_5P_3O_{10}$	triphosphoric acid	$HClO_3$	chloric acid
$H_{n+2}P_nO_{3n+1}$	polyphosphoric acids	$HClO_2$	chlorous acid
$(HPO_3)_n$	metaphosphoric acids	HClO	hypochlorous acid
$(HPO_3)_3$	trimetaphosphoric acid	$HBrO_3$	bromic acid
$(HPO_3)_4$	tetrametaphosphoric acid	$HBrO_2$	bromous acid
H_3PO_5	peroxo(mono)phosphoric acid	HBrO	hypobromous acid
$H_4P_2O_8$	peroxodiphosphoric acid	H_5IO_6	(ortho)periodic acid
$(HO)_2OP-PO(OH)_2$	hypophosphoric acid	HIO_3	iodic acid
$(HO)_2P-O-PO(OH)_2$	diphosphoric(III,V) acid	HIO	hypoiodous acid
H_2PHO_3	phosphorous acid	$HMnO_4$	permanganic acid
$H_4P_2O_5$	diphosphorous or pyrophosphorous acid	H_2MnO_4	manganic acid
		$HTcO_4$	pertechnetic acid
HPH_2O_2	hypophosphorous acid	H_2TcO_4	technetic acid
H_3AsO_4	arsenic acid	$HReO_4$	perrhenic acid
H_3AsO_3	arsenious acid	H_2ReO_4	rhenic acid
$HSb(OH)_6$	hexahydroxoantimonic acid		

5.22. Peroxo Acids.—The prefix peroxo, when used in conjunction with the trivial names of acids, indicates substitution of –O– by –O–O– (cf. 7.312).

Examples: HNO_4 peroxonitric acid H_2SO_5 peroxosulfuric acid
          H_3PO_5 peroxophosphoric acid $H_2S_2O_8$ peroxodisulfuric acid
          $H_4P_2O_8$ peroxodiphosphoric acid

◆Peroxy, as recommended in the 1940 Rules (inorganic), is more acceptable than peroxo to organic chemists. It is not necessary that the use with trivial names conform with the use of peroxo denoting a coördinated ligand; e.g., peroxysulfuric acid or trioxoperoxosulfuric(VI) acid.

5.23. Thio Acids.—Acids derived from oxo acids by replacement of oxygen by sulfur are called *thio acids* (cf. 7.312).

Examples: $H_2S_2O_2$ thiosulfurous acid $H_2S_2O_3$ thiosulfuric acid   HSCN thiocyanic acid

When more than one oxygen atom can be replaced by sulfur the number of sulfur atoms generally should be indicated

          H_3PO_3S monothiophosphoric acid H_3AsS_3 trithioarsenious acid
          $H_3PO_2S_2$ dithiophosphoric acid H_3AsS_4 tetrathioarsenic acid
          H_2CS_3 trithiocarbonic acid

The prefixes seleno- and telluro- may be used in a similar manner.

5.24. Chloro Acids, etc.—Acids containing ligands other than oxygen and sulfur are generally designated according to the rules in Section 7.

Examples:

$HAuCl_4$	hydrogen tetrachloraurate(III) or tetrachloroauric(III) acid
H_2PtCl_4	hydrogen tetrachloroplatinate(II) or tetrachloroplatinic(II) acid
H_2PtCl_6	hydrogen hexachloroplatinate(IV) or hexachloroplatinic(IV) acid
$H_4Fe(CN)_6$	hydrogen hexacyanoferrate(II) or hexacyanoferric(II) acid
$H[PHO_2F]$	hydrogen hydridodioxofluorophosphate or hydridodioxofluorophosphoric acid
HPF_6	hydrogen hexafluorophosphate or hexafluorophosphoric acid
H_2SiF_6	hydrogen hexafluorosilicate or hexafluorosilicic acid
H_2SnCl_6	hydrogen hexachlorostannate(IV) or hexachlorostannic(IV) acid
HBF_4	hydrogen tetrafluoroborate or tetrafluoroboric acid
$H[B(OH)_2F_2]$	hydrogen dihydroxodifluoroborate or dihydroxodifluoroboric acid
$H[B(C_6H_5)_4]$	hydrogen tetraphenylborate or tetraphenylboric acid

It is preferable to use names of the type hydrogen tetrachloroaurate(III).

For some of the more important acids of this type abbreviated names may be used, *e.g.*, chloroplatinic acid, fluorosilicic acid.

◆For the use of hydrido in the fifth example see comment at 7.312.

5.3. Functional Derivatives of Acids

Functional derivatives of acids are compounds formed from acids by substitution of OH and sometimes also O by other groups. In this borderline between organic and inorganic chemistry organic-chemical nomenclature principles prevail.

◆The intention of the statement "organic-chemical nomenclature principles prevail" is not clear, since most of the examples given in the sections immediately following are not named according to organic practice. *Cf.* 3.33.

5.31. Acid Halides.—The names of acid halides are formed from the name of the corresponding acid radical if this has a special name, *e.g.*, sulfuryl chloride, phosphoryl chloride.

In other cases these compounds are named as oxide halides according to rule **6.41**, *e.g.*, MoO_2Cl_2, molybdenum dioxide dichloride.

5.32. Acid Anhydrides.—Anhydrides of inorganic acids generally should be given names as oxides, *e.g.*, N_2O_5 dinitrogen pentaoxide, *not* nitric anhydride or nitric acid anhydride.

5.33. Esters.—Esters of inorganic acids are given names in the same way as the salts, *e.g.*, dimethyl sulfate, diethyl hydrogen phosphate.

If, however, it is desired to specify the constitution of the compound, a name based on the nomenclature for coördination compounds should be used.

Example:

$(CH_3)_4[Fe(CN)_6]$	tetramethyl hexacyanoferrate(II)
or	or
$[Fe(CN)_2(CH_3NC)_4]$	dicyanotetrakis(methyl isocyanide)iron(II)

◆According to common organic practice for esters (ethers, sulfides, *etc.*) and to the naming of inorganic salts (*e.g.*, sodium sulfate, not disodium sulfate), methyl sulfate would be used instead of dimethyl sulfate. However, no objection is seen to the more specific name. Such names as methyl sulfate are better for alphabetic listing, as in indexes.

5.34. Amides.—The names for amides may be derived from the names of acids by replacing acid by amide, or from the names of the acid radicals.

Examples:

$SO_2(NH_2)_2$	sulfuric diamide or sulfonyl diamide
$PO(NH_2)_3$	phosphoric triamide or phosphoryl triamide

If not all hydroxyl groups of the acid have been replaced by NH_2 groups, names ending in -amidic acid may be used: this is an alternative to naming the compounds as complexes.

Examples:

NH_2SO_3H	amidosulfuric acid or sulfamidic acid
$NH_2PO(OH)_2$	amidophosphoric acid or phosphoramidic acid
$(NH_2)_2PO(OH)$	diamidophosphoric acid or phosphorodiamidic acid

Abbreviated names (sulfamide, phosphamide, sulfamic acid) are often used but are not recommended.

◆The use of adjectives from names of inorganic acids may lead to confusion because an -ic or -ous adjective (as chromic) may refer to a higher- or lower-valent form of the element as well as to the acid (a possibility that does not arise, of course, with adjectives from names of organic acids).

Names of the type phosphoramidic acid are recommended in the report of the Advisory Committee on the Nomenclature of Organic Phosphorus Compounds of the Division of Organic Chemistry of the ACS published in 1952, but are not as acceptable to the inorganic nomenclature committees as a whole as the amido- or coördination-type names. *Cf.* 3.33.

The retention of sulfamic acid and sulfamide as trivial names is favored by the committees. An acceptable systematic name for NH_2SO_3H would be ammonia-sulfur trioxide, in keeping with its probable structure.

5.35. Nitriles.—The suffix -nitrile has been used in the names of a few inorganic compounds, *e.g.* $(PNCl_2)_3$, trimeric phosphonitrilo chloride. According to **2.22** such compounds can be designated as nitrides, *e.g.*, phosphorus nitride dichloride. Accordingly there seems to be no reason for retention of the name nitrile (and nitrilo, *c.f.* **3.33**) in inorganic chemistry.

◆Nitrilo is used in organic chemistry, though not given in the list at the end of the Rules.

6. SALTS AND SALT-LIKE COMPOUNDS

Among salts particularly there persist many old names which are bad and misleading, and the Commission wishes to emphasize that any which do not conform to these Rules should be discarded.

6.1. Simple Salts

Simple salts fall under the broad definition of binary compounds given in Section **2**, and their names are formed from those of the constituent ions (given in Section **3**) in the manner set out in Section **2**.

6.2. Salts Containing Acid Hydrogen ("Acid" Salts[1])

Names are formed by adding the word hydrogen, to denote the replaceable hydrogen present, immediately in front of the name of the anion.

The nonacidic hydrogen present, *e.g.*, in the phosphite ion, is included in the name of the anion and is not explicitly cited (*e.g.*, Na_2PHO_3, sodium phosphite).

Examples:

$NaHCO_3$	sodium hydrogen carbonate
NaH_2PO_4	sodium dihydrogen phosphate
$NaH[PHO_3]$	sodium hydrogen phosphite

◆The use of "fused" hydrogen names (as hydrogencarbonate in the original version) is not acceptable in English; the present practice of running hydrogen as a separate word is preferred and has been followed throughout this version. *Cf.* 3.222, 6.324, 6.333. If necessary for clarity, parentheses can be used, as in naming ligands, *e.g.*, (hydrogen carbonato). The use of hydro (as in hydrocarbonato) is not acceptable because of conflicts with organic usage, where hydro denotes addition of hydrogen to unsaturated compounds.

It seems safer to cite even nonacidic hydrogen present in an anion like $PHO_3{}^{2-}$ (unless the ion has a specific name), because of current usage. (*Cf.* triethyl phosphite in 7.412, seventh example).

6.3. Double Salts, Triple Salts, etc.

6.31.—In formulas all the cations shall precede the anions; in names the principles embodied in Section 2 shall be applied. In those languages where cation names are placed after anion names the adjectives double, triple, *etc.* (their equivalents in the language concerned) may be added immediately after the anion name. The number so implied concerns the number of *kinds* of cation present and *not* the total number of such ions.

[1]For "basic" salts see 6.4.

6.32.—Cations.

6.321.—Cations shall be arranged in order of increasing valence (except hydrogen, *cf.* **6.2** and **6.324**).

6.322. The cations of each valence group shall be arranged in order of decreasing atomic number, with the polyatomic radical ions (*e.g.*, ammonium) at the end of their appropriate group.

◆Alphabetical order would be simpler here and even for 6.321.

6.323. Hydration of Cations.—Owing to the prevalence of hydrated cations, many of which are in reality complex, it seems unnecessary to disturb the cation order in order to allow for this; but if it is necessary to draw attention specifically to the presence of a particular hydrated cation this may be done by writing, for example, "hexaaquo" or "tetraaquo" before the name of the simple ion. Apart from this exception, however, all complex ions should be placed after simple ones in the appropriate valence group.

◆*Cf.* comment at 7.322.

6.324. Acidic Hydrogen.—When hydrogen is considered to be present as a cation its name shall be cited last among the cations. Actually acidic hydrogen will in most cases be bound to an anion and shall be cited together with this (**6.2**). If the salt contains only one anion, acidic hydrogen shall be cited in the same place whichever view is taken of the function of this hydrogen. Nonacidic hydrogen shall be either not explicitly cited (*cf.* **6.2**) or designated hydrido (*cf.* **5.24** and **7.311**). For salts with more than one anion see **6.333**.

Examples:

$KMgF_3$	potassium magnesium fluoride
$TlNa(NO_3)_2$	thallium(I) sodium nitrate or thallium sodium dinitrate
$KNaCO_3$	potassium sodium carbonate
$NH_4MgPO_4.6H_2O$	ammonium magnesium phosphate hexahydrate
$NaZn(UO_2)_3(C_2H_3O_2)_9.6H_2O$	sodium zinc triuranyl acetate hexahydrate
$Na[Zn(H_2O)_6](UO_2)_3(C_2H_3O_2)_9$	sodium hexaaquozinc triuranyl acetate
$NaNH_4HPO_4.4H_2O$	sodium ammonium hydrogen phosphate tetrahydrate

◆*Cf.* comments at 6.2, 7.312. In the fifth and sixth examples, either triuranyl(VI) or nonaacetate should be specified. *Cf.* 3.32, 6.34.

6.33.—Anions.

6.331.—Anions are to be cited in this group order

1. H^-
2. O_2^- and OH^- (in that order)
3. Simple (*i.e.*, one element only) inorganic anions, other than H^- and O^{2-}
4. Inorganic anions containing two or more elements, other than OH^-
5. Anions of organic acids and organic substances exerting an acid function

◆The committees consider it preferable to cite H^- last in accordance with usage.

6.332.—Within group 3 the ions shall be cited in the order given in **2.16**, the inclusion of O in that list being taken as referring to all oxygen anions apart from O^{2-} (*i.e.*, O_2^{2-}, *etc.*).

Within group 4, anions containing the smallest number of atoms shall be cited first, and in the case of two ions containing the same number of atoms they shall be cited in order of decreasing atomic number of the central atoms. Thus CO_3^{2-} should precede CrO_4^{2-}, and the latter should precede SO_4^{2-}.

Within group 5 the anions shall be cited in alphabetical order.

◆Again alphabetical order would be simpler, within groups 3 and 4 as well as 5. *Cf.* comment at 7.251.

6.333.—Acidic hydrogen should be cited together with the anion to which it is attached. If it is not known to which anion the hydrogen is bound, it should be cited last among the cations.

◆*Cf.* comment at 6.2.

6.34.—The stoichiometric method is the most practicable for indicating the proportions of the constituents. It is not always essential to give the numbers of all the anions, provided the valences of all the cations are either known or indicated.

Examples:

$NaCl.NaF.2Na_2SO_4$ or $Na_6ClF(SO_4)_2$	(hexa)sodium chloride fluoride (bis)sulfate
$Ca_5F(PO_4)_3$	(penta)calcium fluoride (tris)phosphate

The parentheses in these cases mean that numerical prefixes may not be necessary. The multiplicative numerical prefixes bis, tris, *etc.*, should be used in connection with anions, because disulfate, triphosphate, *etc.*, designate isopoly anions.

6.4. Oxide and Hydroxide Salts ("Basic" salts formerly oxy and hydroxy salts)

6.41.—For the purposes of nomenclature, these should be regarded as double salts containing O^{2-} and OH^- anions, and Section **6.3** may be applied in its entirety.

6.42. Use of the Prefixes Oxy and Hydroxy.—In some languages the citation in full of all the separate anion names presents no trouble and is strongly recommended (*e.g.*, copper oxide chloride), to the exclusion of the oxy form wherever possible. In some other languages, however, such names as "oxyde et chlorure double de cuivre" are so far removed from current practice that the present system of using oxy- and hydroxy-, *e.g.*, oxychlorure de cuivre, may be retained in such cases.

Examples:

$Mg(OH)Cl$	magnesium hydroxide chloride
$BiOCl$	bismuth oxide chloride
$LaOF$	lanthanum oxide fluoride
$VOSO_4$	vanadium(IV) oxide sulfate
$CuCl_2.3Cu(OH)_2$ or $Cu_2(OH)_3Cl$	dicopper trihydroxide chloride
$ZrOCl_2.8H_2O$	zirconium oxide (di)chloride octahydrate

6.5. Double Oxides and Hydroxides

The terms "mixed oxides" and "mixed hydroxides" are not recommended. Such substances preferably should be named double, triple, *etc.*, oxides or hydroxides as the case may be.

Many double oxides and hydroxides belong to several distinct groups, each having its own characteristic structure type, which is sometimes named after some well-known mineral of the same group (*e.g.*, perovskite, ilmenite, spinel). Thus, $NaNbO_3$, $CaTiO_3$, $CaCrO_3$, $CuSnO_3$, $YAlO_3$, $LaAlO_3$, and $LaGaO_3$ all have the same structure as perovskite, $CaTiO_3$. Names such as calcium titanate may convey false implications and it is preferable to name such compounds as double oxides and double hydroxides unless there is clear and generally accepted evidence of cations and oxo or hydroxo anions in the structure. This does not mean that names such as titanates or aluminates should always be abandoned, because such substances may exist in solution and in the solid state (*cf.* **3.223**).

♣"Multiple" has been used in English as a class term including double, triple, etc. (oxides or the like).

6.51.—In the double oxides and hydroxides the metals shall be named in the same order as for double salts (**6.32**).

6.52.—When required the structure type may be added in parentheses and in italics after the name, except that when the type name is also the mineral name of the substance itself then the italics should not be used (*cf.* **4.2**).

Examples:

$NaNbO_3$	sodium niobium trioxide (*perovskite* type)
$MgTiO_3$	magnesium titanium trioxide (*ilmenite* type)
$FeTiO_3$	iron(II) titanium trioxide (ilmenite)
$4CaO.Al_2O_3.nH_2O$ or $Ca_2Al(OH)_7.nH_2O$	dicalcium aluminum hydroxide hydrate
but $Ca_3[Al(OH)_6]_2$	(tri)calcium (bis)-[hexahydroxoaluminate]
$LiAl(OH)_4.2MnO_2$ or $LiAlMn^{IV}_2O_4(OH)_4$	lithium aluminum dimanganese(IV) tetraoxide tetrahydroxide

NOMENCLATURE OF INORGANIC CHEMISTRY (Continued)

7. COÖRDINATION COMPOUNDS

7.1. Definitions

In its oldest sense the term *coördination compound* is taken as referring to molecules or ions in which there is an atom (A) to which are attached other atoms (B) or groups (C) to a number in excess of that corresponding to the oxidation number of the atom A. However, the system of nomenclature originally evolved for the compounds within this narrow definition has proved useful for a much wider class of compounds, and for the purposes of nomenclature the restriction "in excess . . . oxidation number" is to be omitted. Any compound formed by addition of one or several ions and/or molecules to one or more ions or/and molecules may be named according to the same system as strict coördination compounds.

The effect of this is to bring many simple and well-known compounds under the same nomenclature rules as accepted coördination compounds; the result is to reduce the diversity of names and avoid many controversial issues, because it should be understood that there is no intention of implying that any structural analogy necessarily exists between different compounds merely on account of a common system of nomenclature. The system extends also to many addition compounds.

In the rules which follow certain terms are used in the senses here indicated: the atom referred to above as (A) is known as the *central* or *nuclear* atom, and all other atoms which are directly attached to A are known as *coördinating atoms*. Atoms (B) and groups (C) are called *ligands*. A group containing more than one *potential* coördinating atom is termed a *multidentate* ligand, the number of potential coördinating atoms being indicated by the terms *unidentate, bidentate, etc.* A *chelate* ligand is a ligand *attached* to *one* central atom through *two or more* coördinating atoms, while a *bridging group* is attached to *more than one* atom. The whole assembly of one or more central atoms with their attached ligands is referred to as a *complex*, which may be an uncharged molecule or an ion of either polarity. A *polynuclear complex* is a complex which contains *more than one* nuclear atom, their number being designated by the terms *mononuclear, dinuclear, etc.*

◆Some dissatisfaction with the definition of coördination compounds was expressed, though the broad definition (last sentence of first paragraph) was generally approved.

Central atom or *center of coördination* is to be preferred to *nuclear* atom because of other senses of nucleus, especially of an atom. Possible replacements for polynuclear, etc., are polycentric, *etc.*, or bridged complex since bridging group is in common use.

In the United States the Greek-Latin hybrid terms polydentate and monodentate seem to be used more than the all-Latin multidentate and unidentate.

7.2. Formulas and Names for Complex Compounds in General

7.21. Central Atoms.—In *formulas* the symbol for the central atom(s) should be placed *first* (except in formulas which are primarily structural), the anionic and neutral, *etc.*, ligands following as prescribed in **7.25**, and the formula for the whole complex entity (ion or molecule) should be placed in brackets [ ].

In *names* the central atom(s) should be placed *after* the ligands.

◆It is considered preferable to place the whole complex in brackets, especially when more than one central atom is present, but not essential with only one central atom or with complex ions or nonionic complexes, because brackets may be needed sometimes for indicating concentrations.

7.22. Indication of Valence and Proportion of Constituents.—The oxidation number of the central atom is indicated by means of the Stock notation (**2.252**). Alternatively the proportion of constituents may be given by means of stoichiometric prefixes (**2.251**).

7.23.—Formulas and names may be supplemented with the prefixes *cis, trans, etc.* (**2.19**).

7.24. Terminations.—Complex anions shall be given the termination -ate (*cf.* **2.23, 2.24** and **3.223**). Complex cations and neutral molecules are given no distinguishing termination. For further details concerning the names of ligands see **7.3**.

7.25. Order of Citation of Ligands in Complexes.—

first: anionic ligands
next: neutral and cationic ligands

7.251.—The anionic ligands shall be cited in the order

1. H^-
2. O^{2-}, OH^- (in that sequence)
3. Other simple anions (*i.e.*, one element only)
4. Polyatomic anions
5. Organic anions in alphabetical order

The sequence within categories 3 and 4 should be that given in **6.332**.

◆H^- is preferably named last, not first (*cf.* comment at 6.331). Alphabetical order is strongly recommended for simplicity at least within 3 and 4, where only rare uses are involved. The intention seems to be to include under 3 monatomic ions (*i.e.*, one *atom*—rather than one *element*—only), in other words to exclude N_3, I_3, etc. Under 4 the insertion of "inorganic" between "Polyatomic" and "anions" is recommended.

7.252.—Neutral and cationic ligands shall be cited in the order given

first: water, ammonia (in that sequence)
then: other inorganic ligands in the sequence in which their coördinating elements appear in the list given in **2.16**
last: organic ligands in alphabetical order.

◆For the inorganic ligands alphabetical order again is recommended. The use of parentheses wherever there is any possibility of ambiguity should be stressed, as illustrated in examples under 7.321: potassium trichloro(ethylene)platinate(II), where parentheses are given in the Rules, and tetra(pyridine)platinum(II) tetrachloroplatinate(II), where they have been added in this version. Parentheses might also be helpful with "thiocyanato" preceded by a numerical prefix (see last example in 7.311) and are definitely required with two-word names for ligands recommended instead of the fused names of the original version (6.2), as in the seventh example in 7.412: di-μ-carbonyl-bis|carbonyl(triethyl phosphite)cobalt|. Since brackets denote complexes, braces can be used in formulas or names where needed in order to avoid the use of two sets of parentheses (braces were so used in some but not all such cases in the original version).

7.3. Names for Ligands

7.31.—Anionic Ligands.

7.311.—The names for anionic ligands, whether inorganic or organic, end in -o (see, however, **7.324**). In general, if the anion name ends in -ide, -ite, or -ate, the final -e is replaced by -o, giving -ido, -ito, and -ato, respectively.

Examples:

$Li[AlH_4]$	lithium tetrahydridoaluminate
$Na[BH_4]$	sodium tetrahydridoborate
$K_2[OsNCl_5]$	potassium nitridopentachloroösmate(VI)
$[Co(NH_2)_2(NH_3)_4]OC_2H_5$	diamidotetraamminecobalt(III) ethanolate
$[CoN_3(NH_3)_5]SO_4$	azidopentaamminecobalt(III) sulfate
$Na_3[Ag(S_2O_3)_2]$	sodium bis(thiosulfato)argentate(I)
$[Ru(HSO_3)_2(NH_3)_4]$	bis(hydrogen sulfito)tetraammineruthenium
(II) $NH_4[Cr(SCN)_4(NH_3)_2]$	ammonium tetrathiocyanatodiamminechromate (III)

◆For "ethanolate" in the fourth example "ethoxide" may be preferred.

7.312.—These anions do not follow exactly the above rule; modified forms have become established:

F^-	fluoride	fluoro (*not* fluo)	O_2^{2-}	peroxide	peroxo
Cl^-	chloride	chloro	HS^-	hydrogen sulfide	thiolo
Br^-	bromide	bromo	S^{2-}	sulfide	thio[1] (sulfido)
I^-	iodide	iodo	(but:S_2^{2-}	disulfide	disulfido)
O^{2-}	oxide	oxo	CN^-	cyanide	cyano
OH^-	hydroxide	hydroxo			

[1]The name thio has long been used to denote the ligand S^{2-} when it can be regarded as replacing O^{2-} in an oxo acid or its anion. The general use of this name will prevent confusion between the two interpretations of disulfido as S_2^{2-} or two S^{2-} ligands.

By analogy with hydroxo, CH_3O^-, *etc.*, are called methoxo, *etc.* For CH_3S^-, *etc.*, the systematic names methanethiolato, *etc.*, are used.

Examples:

$K[AgF_4]$	potassium tetrafluoroargentate(III)
$K_2[NiF_6]$	potassium hexafluoroniccolate(IV)
$Ba[BrF_4]_2$	barium tetrafluorobromate(III)
$Na[AlCl_4]$	sodium tetrachloroaluminate
$Cs[ICl_4]$	cesium tetrachloroiodate(III)
$K[Au(OH)_4]$	potassium tetrahydroxoaurate(III)
$K[CrOF_4]$	potassium oxotetrafluorochromate(V)
$K_2[Cr(O)_2O_2(CN)_2(NH_3)]$	potassium dioxoperoxodicyanoamminechromate(VI)
$Na[BH(OCH_3)_3]$	sodium hydridotrimethoxoborate
$K_2[Fe_2S_2(NO)_4]$	dipotassium dithiotetranitrosyldiferrate

◆It is strongly recommended on the basis of past and present usage, analogy with chloro, *etc.*, and euphony that hydro be added to the list of modified forms of names for anionic ligands and that hydrido be abandoned (*cf.* also examples in 7.311).

While the Subcommittee on Coördination Compounds recognizes the usefulness of the invariable -o ending for anionic ligands, some members of the general committees do not see a sharp enough distinction between such ligands and the same groups in organic compounds to justify a departure from organic usage by using hydroxo, methoxo, *etc.*, instead of hydroxy, methoxy, *etc.* These members therefore favor adding hydroxy, methoxy, *etc.*, to the hydrocarbon radicals excepted from the rule of -o endings for anions (7.324). For the use of peroxo, see comment at 5.22.

The -o of a negative ligand should not be elided before another vowel (chloroösmate, chloroiodo). This agrees with organic practice. *Cf.* comment at 7.322.

It should be pointed out here as well as in the list of names for ions and radicals at the end of the Rules that the approved organic name for unsubstituted HS is mercapto (not thiol, as also given in the list) and for the alkyl- and aryl-substituted radicals methylthio, *etc.*

7.313.—Ligands derived from organic compounds not normally called acids, but which function as such in complex formation by loss of a proton, should be treated as anionic and given the ending -ato. If, however, no proton is lost, the ligand must be treated as neutral—see **7.32**.

Examples:

$[Ni(C_4H_7N_2O_2)_2]$ bis(dimethylglyoximato)nickel(II) $[Cu(C_5H_7O_2)_2]$ bis(acetylacetonato)copper(II)

bis(8-quinolinolato)silver(II)   bis(4-fluorosalicylaldehydato)copper(II)   *N,N'*-ethylenebis(salicylideneiminato)cobalt(II)

◆Although according to 3.33 the name for the ligand in the second example should be derived from the systematic name 2,4-pentanedione instead of from acetylacetone, acetylacetonato perhaps conveys better the idea that it is the enol form that is involved. However, the coördination subcommittee questions the use of the termination -ato rather than plain -o especially in cases where the -ate terms (as dimethylglyoximate) are not accepted organic practice. Such -ato terms are especially misleading in the last two examples, where the -ato belongs with the hydroxyl part of the name, not the aldehyde or imine part to which it is attached.

7.32.—Neutral and Cationic Ligands.

7.321.—The name of the coördinated molecule or cation is to be used without change, except in the special cases provided for in **7.322.**

Examples:

$[CoCl_2(C_4H_8N_2O_2)_2]$	dichlorobis(dimethylglyoxime)cobalt(II) (*cf.* nickel derivative given in **7.313**)
cis-$[PtCl_2(Et_3P)_2]$	*cis*-dichlorobis(triethylphosphine)platinum(II)
$[CuCl_2(CH_3NH_2)_2]$	dichlorobis(methylamine)copper(II)
$[Pt\ py_4]\ [PtCl_4]$	tetra(pyridine)platinum(II) tetrachloroplatinate(II)
$[Fe(dipy)_3]Cl_2$	tris(dipyridyl)iron(II) chloride
$[Co\ en_3]_2(SO_4)_3$	tris(ethylenediamine)cobalt(III) sulfate
$[Zn\{NH_2CH_2CH(NH_2)CH_2NH_2\}_2]I_2$	bis(1,2,3-triaminopropane)zinc iodide
$K[PtCl_3(C_2H_4)]$	potassium trichloro(ethylene)platinate(II) or potassium trichloromonoethyleneplatinate(II)
$[PtCl_2\{H_2NCH_2CH(NH_2)CH_2NH_3\}]Cl$	dichloro(2,3 - diaminopropylammonium)platinum(II) chloride
$[Cr(C_6H_5NC)_6]$	hexakis(phenyl isocyanide)chromium

◆In the fifth example, bipyridine is preferred to dipyridyl in organic practice, and in the seventh example 1,2,3-propanetriamine to 1,2,3-triaminopropane.

7.322.—Water and ammonia as neutral ligands in coördination complexes are called "aquo" and "ammine," respectively.

In the tentative rules it was proposed to change the old-established "aquo" to "aqua," thus keeping the -o termination consistently for anionic ligands alone. However, as the old form is so widely used, many regarded the change as too pedantic, and the Commission has decided to retain "aquo" as an exception.

Examples:

$[Cr(H_2O)_6]Cl_3$	hexaaquochromium(III) chloride or hexaaquochromium trichloride
$[Al(OH)(H_2O)_5]^{++}$	the hydroxopentaaquoaluminum ion
$[Co(NH_3)_6]ClSO_4$	hexaamminecobalt(III) chloride sulfate
$[CoCl(NH_3)_5]Cl_2$	chloropentaamminecobalt(III) chloride
$[CoCl_3(NH_3)_2\{(CH_3)_2NH\}]$	trichlorodiammine(dimethylamine)cobalt(III)

◆Hexaquo, pentaquo, *etc.*, are used in the examples in the original version, but have been changed in this version to hexaaquo, *etc.*, for conformity with the latest approved organic practice. (*Cf.* hexaammonium, given with two a's separated by a hyphen in 7.6, second example, in the original version.)

7.323.—The groups NO, NS, CO, and CS, when linked directly to a metal atom, are to be called nitrosyl, thionitrosyl, carbonyl, and thiocarbonyl, respectively. In computing the oxidation number these radicals are treated as neutral.

Examples:

$Na_2[Fe(CN)_5NO]$	disodium pentacyanonitrosylferrate
$K_3[Fe(CN)_5CO]$	tripotassium pentacyanocarbonylferrate
$K[Co(CN)(CO)_2(NO)]$	potassium cyanodicarbonylnitrosylcobaltate(0)
$HCo(CO)_4$	hydrogen tetracarbonylcobaltate(−I)
$[Ni(CO)_2(Ph_3P)_2]$	dicarbonylbis(triphenylphosphine)nickel(0)
$[Fe\ en_3]\ [Fe(CO)_4]$	tris(ethylenediamine)iron(II) tetracarbonylferrate (−II)
$Mn_2(CO)_{10}$ or $[CO_5]Mn-Mn(CO)_5]$	decacarbonyldimanganese(0) or bis(pentacarbonylmanganese)

◆The necessity of arbitrarily considering these groups as always neutral can be avoided by not using the oxidation number but instead the stoichiometric proportions (as in some of these examples) or the Ewens-Bassett system (*cf.* comment at 2.252). Thus the anion in the last example in 7.312 (where NO is known to be positive) would by this system be named dithiotetranitrosyldiferrate (2−).

7.324.—Anions derived from hydrocarbons are given radical names without -o, but are counted as negative when computing the oxidation number.

The consistent introduction of the ending -o would in this case lead to unfamiliar names, *e.g.*, phenylato or phenido for $C_6H_5^-$. On the other hand, if the radicals were counted as neutral ligands, the central atom would have to be given an unusual oxidation number, *e.g.*, −I for boron in $K[B(C_6H_5)_4]$, instead of III.

Examples:

$K[B(C_6H_5)_4]$	potassium tetraphenylborate
$K[SbCl_5C_6H_5]$	potassium pentachloro(phenyl)antimonate(V)
$K_2[Cu(C_2H)_3]$	potassium triethynylcuprate(I)
$K_4[Ni(C_2C_6H_5)_4]$	potassium tetrakis(phenylethynyl)niccolate(0)
$[Fe(CO)_4(C_2C_6H_5)_2]$	tetracarbonylbis(phenylethynyl)iron(II)
$Fe(C_5H_5)_2$	bis(cyclopentadienyl)iron(II)
$[Fe(C_5H_5)_2]Cl$	bis(cyclopentadienyl)iron(III) chloride
$[Ni(NO)(C_5H_5)]$	nitrosylcyclopentadienylnickel

◆The use of radical names such as cyclopentadienyl in the examples does not seem consistent with the use of Stock notations; for the sixth example ("ferrocene"), iron(II) cyclopentadienide is preferred by some. This matter is presumably part of the whole organometallic problem to be dealt with by the new IUPAC joint organic-inorganic subcommittee.

For niccolate, see comment at 1.12.

7.33.—Alternative Modes of Linkage of Some Ligands.—Where ligands are capable of attachment by different atoms this may be denoted by adding the symbol for the atom by which attachment occurs at the end of the name of the ligand. Thus the dithioöxalato group may be attached through S or O, and these are distinguished as dithioöxalato-*S,S'* and dithioöxalato-*O,O'*, respectively.

In some cases different names are already in use for alternative modes of attachment, as, for example, thiocyanato (−SCN) and isothiocyanato (−NCS), nitro (−NO₂), and nitrito (−ONO). In these cases existing custom may conveniently be retained.

Examples:

$$K_2\left[Ni \begin{pmatrix} S—CO \\ | \\ S—CO \end{pmatrix}_2 \right]$$

potassium bis(dithioöxalato-*S,S'*)niccolate(II)

dichloro(2-*N,N*-dimethylaminoethyl 2-aminoethyl sulfide-*N',S*)platinum(II)

$K_2[Pt(NO_2)_4]$	potassium tetranitroplatinate(II)
$Na_3[Co(NO_2)_6]$	sodium hexanitrocobaltate(III)
$[Co(NO_2)_3(NH_3)_3]$	trinitrotriamminecobalt(III)
$[Co(ONO)(NH_3)_5]SO_4$	nitritopentaamminecobalt(III) sulfate
$[Co(NCS)(NH_3)_5]Cl_2$	isothiocyanatopentaamminecobalt(III) chloride

◆Thioöxalato in the original version has been changed to dithioöxalato.

7.4. Di- and Polynuclear Compounds

7.41.—Bridging Groups.

7.411.—A bridging group shall be indicated by adding the Greek letter μ immediately before its name and separating this from the rest of the complex by a hyphen. Two or more bridging groups of the same kind are indicated by di-μ-, etc.

7.412.—If the number of central atoms bound by one bridging group exceeds two, the number shall be indicated by adding a subscript numeral to the μ.

This system of notation allows simply of distinction between, for example, μ-disulfido (one S₂ bridge) and di-μ-sulfido (two S bridges). It is also capable of extension to much more complex and unsymmetrical structures by use of the conventional prefixes *cis, trans, asym,* and *sym* where necessary.

Examples:

$[(NH_3)_5Cr–OH–Cr(NH_3)_5]Cl_5$
μ-hydroxo-bis{pentaamminechromium(III)}chloride

di-μ-chloro-dichlorobis(triethylarsine)diplatinum (II) (three possible isomers: *asym, sym-cis,* and *sym-trans;* the last is shown)

di-μ-thiocyanato-dithiocyanatobis(tripropylphosphine)diplatinum(II)

$[(CO)_3Fe(CO)_3Fe(CO)_3]$	tri-μ-carbonyl-bis(tricarbonyliron)
$[(CO)_3Fe(SEt)_2Fe(CO)_3]$	di-μ-ethanethiolato-bis(tricarbonyliron)
$[(C_5H_5)(CO)Fe(CO)_2Fe(CO)(C_5H_5)]$	di-μ-carbonyl-bis(carbonylcyclopentadienyliron)
$[(CO)\{P(OEt)_3\}Co(CO)_2Co(CO)\{P(OEt)_3\}]$	di-μ-carbonyl-bis{carbonyl(triethyl phosphite)-cobalt}
$[Au(CN)(C_3H_7)_2]_4$	cyclo-tetra μ cyano-tetrakis(dipropylgold)
$[CuI(Et_3As)]_4$	tetra-μ₃-iodo-tetrakis{triethylarsinecopper(I)}
$[Be_4O(CH_3COO)_6]$	μ₄-oxo-hexa-μ-acetato-tetraberyllium

7.42. Extended Structures.—Where bridging causes an indefinite extension of the structure it is best to name compounds primarily on the basis of their over-all composition; thus the compound having the composition represented by the formula $CsCuCl_3$ has an anion with the structure:

$$\left[\ldots Cl - \underset{\underset{Cl}{|}}{\overset{\overset{Cl}{|}}{Cu}} - Cl - \underset{\underset{Cl}{|}}{\overset{\overset{Cl}{|}}{Cu}} - Cl - \underset{\underset{Cl}{|}}{\overset{\overset{Cl}{|}}{Cu}} - Cl - \underset{\underset{Cl}{|}}{\overset{\overset{Cl}{|}}{Cu}} \ldots \right]^{n-}$$

This may be expressed in the formula $(Cs^+)_n$ $[(CuCl_3)_n]^{n-}$ which leads to the simple name cesium catena-μ-chloro-dichlorocuprate(II). If the structure were in doubt, however, the substance would be called cesium copper(II) chloride (as a double salt).

◆ *Cf.* comment on *catena* at 1.4.

7.5. Isopoly Anions

The structure of many complicated isopoly anions has now been cleared up by X-ray work and it turns out that the indication of the several μ-oxo and oxo atoms in the name does not convey any clear picture of the structure and is therefore of little value.

For the time being it is sufficient to indicate the number of atoms by Greek prefixes, at least until isomers are found. When all atoms have their "normal" oxidation states (*e.g.*, W^{VI}), it is not necessary to give the numbers of the oxygen atoms, if all the others are indicated.

Examples:

$K_2S_2O_7$	dipotassium disulfate
$K_2S_3O_{10}$	dipotassium trisulfate
$Na_5P_3O_{10}$	pentasodium triphosphate
$K_2Cr_4O_{13}$	dipotassium tetrachromate
$Na_2B_4O_7$	disodium tetraborate
NaB_5O_8	sodium pentaborate
$Ca_3Mo_7O_{24}$	tricalcium heptamolybdate
$Na_7HNb_6O_{19}.15H_2O$	heptasodium monohydrogen hexaniobate-15-water
$K_2Mg_2V_{10}O_{28}.16H_2O$	dipotassium dimagnesium decavanadate-16-water

7.6. Heteropoly Anions

The central atom or atoms should be cited last in the name and first in the formula of the anion (*cf.* **7.21**), *e.g.*, wolframophosphate, *not* phosphowolframate.

If the oxidation number has to be given, it may be necessary to place it immediately after the atom referred to and not after the ending -ate, in order to avoid ambiguity.

The method formerly recommended for naming iso- and heteropoly anions by giving the number of atoms in parentheses is not practicable in more complicated cases.

Examples:

$(NH_4)_3PW_{12}O_{40}$	triammonium dodecawolframophosphate
$(NH_4)_6TeMo_6O_{24}.7H_2O$	hexaammonium hexamolybdotellurate heptahydrate
$Li_3HSiW_{12}O_{40}.24H_2O$	trilithium (mono)hydrogen dodecawolframosilicate-24-water
$K_6Mn^{IV}Mo_9O_{32}$	hexapotassium enneamolybdomanganate(IV)
$Na_6P^V_2Mo_{18}O_{62}$	hexasodium 18-molybdodiphosphate(V)
$Na_4P^{III}_2Mo_{12}O_{41}$	tetrasodium dodecamolybdodiphosphate(III)
$K_7Co^{II}Co^{III}W_{12}O_{42}.16H_2O$	heptapotassiumdodecawolframocobalt(II)-cobalt(III)ate-16-water
$K_3PV_2Mo_{10}O_{39}$	tripotassium decamolybdodivanadophosphate

◆ The coördination subcommittee would prefer not to have sections 7.5 and 7.6 included under 7 and recommends that they should be studied by a special subcommittee. Some cyclic isomers are already known, and isopoly cations also are being investigated.

Cf. comment at 1.12 for stand on wolframate and wolframo, and 2.251 for nona instead of ennea (fourth example).

Isopoly and heteropoly are not separate words in the original version.

7.7. Addition Compounds

The ending -ate is now the accepted ending for *anions* and should generally not be used for addition compounds. Alcoholates are the *salts* of alcohols and this name should not be used to indicate alcohol of crystallization. Analogously addition compounds containing ether, ammonia, *etc.*, should *not* be termed etherates, ammoniates, *etc.*

However, one exception has to be recognized. According to the commonly accepted meaning of the ending -ate, "hydrate" would be, and was formerly regarded as, the name for a *salt* of water, *i.e.*, what is now known as a hydroxide; the name hydrate has now a very firm position as the name of a compound containing water of crystallization and is allowed also in these Rules to designate water bound in an unspecified way; it is considered to be preferable even in this case to avoid the ending -ate by using the name "water" (or its equivalent in other languages) when possible.

The names of addition compounds may be formed by connecting the names of individual compounds by hyphens (short dashes) and indicating the number of molecules by Arabic numerals. When the added molecules are organic, however, it is recommended to use multiplicative numeral prefixes (bis, tris, tetrakis, *etc.*) instead of Arabic figures to avoid confusion with the organic-chemical use of Arabic figures to indicate position of substituents.

Examples:

$CaCl_2.6H_2O$	calcium chloride–6-water (or calcium chloride hexahydrate)
$3CdSO_4.8H_2O$	3-cadmium sulfate–8-water
$Na_2CO_3.10H_2O$	sodium carbonate–10-water (or sodium carbonate decahydrate)
$AlCl_3.4C_2H_5OH$	aluminum chloride–4-ethanol or –tetrakisethanol
$BF_3.(C_2H_5)_2O$	boron trifluoride–diethyl ether
$BF_3.2CH_3OH$	boron trifluoride–bismethanol
$BF_3.H_3PO_4$	boron trifluoride–phosphoric acid
$BiCl_3.3PCl_5$	bismuth trichloride–3-(phosphorus pentachloride)
$TeCl_4.2PCl_5$	tellurium tetrachloride–2-(phosphorus pentachloride)
$(CH_3)_4NAsCl_4.2AsCl_3$	tetramethylammonium tetrachloroarsenate(III)–2-(arsenic trichloride)
$CaCl_2.8NH_3$	calcium chloride–8-ammonia
$8H_2S.46H_2O$	8-(hydrogen sulfide)–46-water
$8Kr.46H_2O$	8-krypton–46-water
$6Br_2.46H_2O$	6-dibromine–46-water
$8CHCl_3.16H_2S.136H_2O$	8-chloroform–16-(hydrogen sulfide)–136-water

These names are not very different from a pure verbal description which may in fact be used, *e.g.*, calcium chloride with 6 water, compound of aluminum chloride with 4 ethanol, *etc.*

If it needs to be shown that added molecules form part of a complex, the names are given according to **7.2** and **7.3**.

Examples:

$FeSO_4.7H_2O$ or $[Fe(H_2O)_6]SO_4.H_2O$	iron(II) sulfate heptahydrate or hexaaquoiron(II) sulfate monohydrate
$PtCl_2.2PCl_3$ or $[PtCl_2(PCl_3)_2]$	platinum(II) chloride 2-(phosphorus trichloride) or dichlorobis(phosphorus trichloride)-platinum(II)
$AlCl_3.NOCl$ or $NO[AlCl_4]$	aluminum chloride–nitrosyl chloride or nitrosyl tetrachloroaluminate
$BF_3.Et_3N$ or $[BF_3(Et_3N)]$	boron trifluoride–triethylamine or trifluoro(triethylamine)boron

◆Only some so-called "addition compounds" are known to be coordination compounds, and the formulas and names can show such structures. Those that are lattice compounds and those of unknown structure do not really belong in 7.

The committees like hydrate and ammoniate and see no particular advantage in dropping them (*cf.* the use of hydrate terms in examples in 6.324; 6-hydrate, *etc.*, as well as hexahydrate, *etc.*, are considered acceptable).

No reason can be seen for deviating here from usual organic practice by using multiplicative prefixes with simple names: tetraethanol is just as clear as tetrakisethanol, and dimethanol as bismethanol. Parentheses can always be used if there is danger of any ambiguity.

The use of short dashes ("en" dashes) instead of hyphens between the names (as in the examples here, but not in the original version) makes for greater ease in reading.

It is considered preferable by some to place the electron donor first in both the formulas and name: $(C_2H_5)_2O.BF_3$, diethyl ether–boron trifluoride (note that organic usage favors ethyl ether over diethyl ether).

8. POLYMORPHISM

Minerals occurring in nature with similar compositions have different names according to their crystal structures; thus, zinc blende, wurtzite; quartz, tridymite, and cristobalite. Chemists and metallographers have designated polymorphic modifications with Greek letters or with Roman numerals (α-iron, ice-I, *etc.*). The method is similar to the use of trivial names, and is likely to continue to be of use in the future in cases where the existence of polymorphism is established, but not the structures underlying it. Regrettably there has been no consistent system, and some investigators have designated as α the form stable at ordinary temperatures, while others have used α for the form stable immediately below the melting point, and some have even changed an already established usage and renamed α-quartz β-quartz, thereby causing confusion. If the α–β nomenclature is used for two substances A and B, difficulties are encountered when the binary system A–B is studied.

LIST OF NAMES FOR IONS AND RADICALS

In inorganic chemistry substitutive names seldom are used, but the organic-chemical names are shown to draw attention to certain differences between organic and inorganic nomenclature.

Atom or group	—————————————————Name—————————————————			
	as neutral molecule	as cation or cationic radical[1]	as anion	as ligand	as prefix for substituent in organic compounds
H	monohydrogen	hydrogen	hydride	hydrido	
F	monofluorine		fluoride	fluoro	fluoro
Cl	monochlorine	chlorine	chloride	chloro	chloro
Br	monobromine	bromine	bromide	bromo	bromo
I	monoiodine	iodine	iodide	iodo	iodo
I$_3$			triiodide		
ClO		chlorosyl	hypochlorite	hypochlorito	
ClO$_2$	chlorine dioxide	chloryl	chlorite	chlorito	
ClO$_3$		perchloryl	chlorate	chlorato	
ClO$_4$			perchlorate		
IO		iodosyl	hypoiodite		iodoso
IO$_2$		iodyl			iodyl or iodoxy
O	monoöxygen		oxide	oxo	oxo or keto
O$_2$	dioxygen		O$_2{}^{2-}$: peroxide	peroxo	peroxy
			O$_2{}^-$: hyperoxide		
HO	hydroxyl		hydroxide	hydroxo	hydroxy
HO$_2$	(perhydroxyl)		hydrogen peroxide	hydrogen peroxo	hydroperoxy
S	monosulfur		sulfide	thio (sulfido)	thio
HS	(sulfhydryl)		hydrogen sulfide	thiolo	thiol or mercapto
S$_2$	disulfur		disulfide	disulfido	
SO	sulfur monoxide	sulfinyl (thionyl)			sulfinyl
SO$_2$	sulfur dioxide	sulfonyl (sulfuryl)	sulfoxylate		sulfonyl
SO$_3$	sulfur trioxide		sulfite	sulfito	
HSO$_3$			hydrogen sulfite	hydrogen sulfito	
S$_2$O$_3$			thiosulfate	thiosulfato	
SO$_4$			sulfate	sulfato	
Se	selenium		selenide	seleno	seleno
SeO		seleninyl			seleninyl
SeO$_2$		selenonyl			selenonyl
SeO$_3$	selenium trioxide		selenite	selenito	
SeO$_4$			selenate	selenato	
Te	tellurium		telluride	telluro	telluro
CrO$_2$		chromyl			
UO$_2$		uranyl			
NpO$_2$		neptunyl			
PuO$_2$		plutonyl			
AmO$_2$		americyl			
N	mononitrogen		nitride	nitrido	
N$_3$			azide	azido	
NH			imide	imido	imino
NH$_2$			amide	amido	amino
NHOH			hydroxylamide	hydroxylamido	hydroxylamino
N$_2$H$_3$			hydrazide	hydrazido	hydrazino
NO	nitrogen oxide	nitrosyl		nitrosyl	nitroso
NO$_2$	nitrogen dioxide	nitryl		nitro	nitro
ONO			nitrite	nitrito	
NS		thionitrosyl			
(NS)$_n$		thiazyl (*e.g.*, trithiazyl)			
NO$_3$			nitrate	nitrato	
N$_2$O$_3$			hyponitrite	hyponitrito	
P	phosphorus		phosphide	phosphido	
PO		phosphoryl			
PS		thiophosphoryl			phosphoroso
PH$_2$O$_3$			hypophosphite	hypophosphito	
PHO$_3$			phosphite	phosphito	
PO$_4$			phosphate	phosphato	
AsO$_4$			arsenate	arsenato	
VO		vanadyl			
CO	carbon monoxide	carbonyl		carbonyl	carbonyl
CS		thiocarbonyl			
CH$_3$O	methoxyl		methanolate	methoxo	methoxy
C$_2$H$_5$O	ethoxyl		ethanolate	ethoxo	ethoxy
CH$_3$S			methanethiolate	methanethiolato	methylthio
C$_2$H$_5$S			ethanethiolate	ethanethiolato	ethylthio
CN		cyanogen	cyanide	cyano	cyano
OCN			cyanate	cyanato	cyanato
SCN			thiocyanate	thiocyanato and isothiocyanato	thiocyanato and isothiocyanato
SeCN			selenocyanate	selenocyanato	selenocyanato
TeCN			tellurocyanate	tellurocyanato	
CO$_3$			carbonate	carbonato	
HCO$_3$			hydrogen carbonate	hydrogen carbonato	
CH$_3$CO$_2$			acetate	acetato	acetoxy
CH$_3$CO	acetyl	acetyl			acetyl
C$_2$O$_4$			oxalate	oxalato	

[1]If necessary, oxidation state is to be given by Stock notation.

◆Although some additions might be made to this list, especially in the last column, and a few changes suggested, no attempt has been made to do so at this time. *Cf.* comments at such rules as 3.31, 3.32, 5.35, 6.2, and 7.312.

A rational system should be based upon crystal structure, and the designations α, β, γ, etc., should be regarded as provisional, or as trivial names. The designations should be as short and understandable as possible, and convey a maximum of information to the reader. The rules suggested here have been framed as a basis for future work, and it is hoped that experience in their use may enable more specific rules to be formulated at a later date.

8.1.—For chemical purposes (i.e., when particular mineral occurrences are not under consideration) polymorphs should be indicated by adding the crystal system after the name or formula. For example, zinc sulfide(cub.) or ZnS(cub.) corresponds to zinc blende or sphalerite, and ZnS(hex.) to wurtzite. The Commission considers that these abbreviations might with advantage be standardized internationally:

cub.	=	cubic	hex.	=	hexagonal
c.	=	body-centered	trig.	=	trigonal
f.	=	face-centered	mon.	=	monoclinic
tetr.	=	tetragonal	tric.	=	triclinic
o-rh.	=	orthorhombic			

Slightly distorted lattices may be indicated by use of the *circa* sign, $\sim$. Thus, for example, a slightly distorted face-centered cubic lattice would be expressed as $\sim$f.cub.

8.2.—Crystallographers may find it valuable to add the space-group; it is doubtful whether this system would commend itself to chemists where **8.1** is sufficient.

8.3.—Simple well-known structures may also be designated by giving the type-compound in italics in parentheses; but this system often breaks down because many structures are not referable to a type in this way. Thus, AuCd above 70° may be written as AuCd(cub.) or as AuCd(*CsCl-type*); but at low temperature only as AuCd(o-rh.), as its structure cannot be referred to a type.

◆*Cf.* 6.5 and 6.52.

ABBREVIATIONS USED IN TABLE OF PHYSICAL CONSTANTS
OF INORGANIC COMPOUNDS

a	acid	fus	fused	prop	properties
abs	absolute	fxd	fixed	purp	purple
ac. a	acetic acid	gel., gelat	gelatinous	pyr	pyridine
acet	acetone	gl	glass	quad	quadrilateral
act	active	glac	glacial	quest	questioned
al	alcohol	glit	glittering	rect	rectangular
alk	alkali	glob	globular	redsh	reddish
amm	ammonium	glyc	glycerin	reg	regular
amor	amorphous	gran	granular	rhbdr	rhombohedral
anh	anhydrous	greas	greasy	rhomb	rhombic, ortho-
appr	approximately	grn	green		rhombic
aq	aqua, water	h	hot	s	soluble
aq. reg	aqua regia	hex	hexagonal	satd	saturated
asym	asymmetrical	ht	heat	sld	solid
atm	atmospheres	hyd	hydrolyzed	sensit	sensitive
bipyr	bipyramidal	hydx	hydroxides	sc	scales
bl	blue	hyg	hygroscopic	sec	secondary
blk	black	i	insoluble	silv	silver
boil	boiling	ign	ignites	sl	slightly
br., brn	brown	ind	indigo	sly	slowly
brnsh	brownish	indef	indefinite	sm	small
bz	benzene	infl., inflam	inflammable	sod	sodium
c	cold	infus	infusible	soln	solution
calc	calculated	irid	iridescent	solv	solvents
carb	carbon	leaf	leaflets	spont	spontaneous
caust	caustic	lem	lemon	st	steel
chl	chloroform	lgr	ligroin	stab	stable
choc	chocolate	lng	long	subl	sublimes
cit. a	citric acid	lq., liq	liquid	suffoc	suffocating
col	colorless	lt	light	sulfd	sulfides
coll	colloidal	lum	luminous	sulf	sulfur
com'l	commercial	lust	lustrous	sym	symmetrical
comp	compounds	me., meth	methyl	tabl	tablets
compl	completely	met	metal or metal-	tart. a	tartaric acid
conc	concentrated		lic	tetr	tetragonal
const	constant	micr	microscopic	tetrah	tetrahedral
cont	contains	min	mineral	tol	toluene
corros	corrosive	misc	miscible	trac	trace, traces
cr	crystalline	mixt	mixture	trans	transparent
cub	cubic	mod	modifications	translu	translucent
d., dec	decomposes	monbas	monobasic	tri., trig	trigonal
deliq	deliquescent	mon-H	monohydrogen	tribas	tribasic
deriv	derivative	monocl	monoclinic	tricl	triclinic
dibas	dibasic	near	nearly	trim	trimetric
di-H	dihydrogen	need	needles	tr	transition point
dil	dilute	nit	nitrate	turp	turpentine
dimorph	dimorphous	oct	octahedral	unpleas	unpleasant
disg	disagreeable	odorl	odorless	unst	unstable
dk	dark	offen	offensive	v	very
doubt	doubtful	olv	olive	vac	vacuum
duct	ductile	opt	optical or	var	various
effl	efflorescent		optically	viol	violent,
em	emerald	or	orange		violence
eth	ether	ord	ordinary	visc	viscous
ev	evolves	org	organic	vitr	vitreous
evln	evolution	oxal	oxalate or	vlt	violet
ex	excess		oxalic	volt., volat	volatizes
exist	existence	pa	pale	wh	white
exp	explodes	pet	petroleum	wh. lt	white light
extr	extreme(ly)	pl	plates	yel	yellow
f., fr	from	pois	poisonous	yelsh	yellowish
feath	feathery	polymorph	polymorphous	∞	soluble in all pro-
fl	flakes	powd	powder		portions
floc	flocculent	ppt	precipitate	>	above
fluo, fluores	fluorescent	pr	prisms	<	below
form	formic	press	pressure		
fum	fuming	prob	probably		

No.	Name	Synonyms and Formulae	Mol. wt.	Crystalline form, properties and index of refraction	Density or spec. gravity	Melting point, °C	Boiling point, °C	Solubility, in grams per 100 cc Cold water	Hot water	Other solvents
	Actinium									
a1	Actinium	Ac	227	silv wh met, cub		1050	3200 ± 300	d to $Ac(OH)_3$		
a2	bromide	$AcBr_3$	466.73	wh, hex	5.85	subl 800		s		
a3	chloride, tri-	$AcCl_3$	333.36	wh cr, hex	4.81	subl 960				
a4	fluoride, tri-	AcF_3	284	wh cr, hex	7.88			i	i	
a5	hydroxide	$Ac(OH)_3$	278.02					i		
a6	iodide	AcI_3	607.71	wh		subl 700–800		s		
a7	oxalate	$Ac_2(C_2O_4)_3$	718.06					i		
a8	oxide, sesqui-	Ac_2O_3	502	wh cr, hex	9.10			i		
a9	sulfide, sesqui-	Ac_2S_3	550.19	dk, cub	6.75					
a10	**Aluminum**	Al	26.98154	silv wh duct met, cub	2.702	660.37	2467	i	i	s alk, HCl, H_2SO_4; i conc HNO_3, h ac a
a11	acetate, tri-	$Al(C_2H_3O_2)_3$	204.12	wh solid		d		v sl s	d	
a12	acetylacetonate	$Al(C_5H_7O_2)_3$	324.31	col, monocl	1.27	193, subl vac	314	i	i	v s al; s eth, bz
a13	orthoarsenate	$AlAsO_4.8H_2O$	310.02	wh powd	3.001	$-H_2O$		i	i	sl s a
a14	benzoate	$Al(C_7H_5O_2)_3$	390.33	wh cr powd				v sl s		
a15	benzyloxide	Aluminum benzylate. $Al(C_7H_7O)_3$	348.38			59–60	$283–284^{0.5}$			
a16	boride	AlB_{12}	156.71	dk red-blk, monocl	2.55^{18}_4			i		s hot HNO_3; i a, alk
a17	boride, di-	AlB_2	48.60	copper red, hex	3.19					
a18	bromate	$Al(BrO_3)_3.9H_2O$	572.84	wh cr, hygr		62.3	d 100	s	s	sl s a
a19	bromide	$AlBr_3$ (or Al_2Br_6)	266.71	col, rhomb pl, deliq	2.64^{19} (fused)	97.5	263.3^{747}	s with viol	d	s al, acet, CS_2
a20	bromide, hexahydrate	$AlBr_3.6H_2O$	374.80	col-yelsh need, deliq	2.54	93	d 135	s	d	s al, amyl al; sl s CS_2
a21	bromide, pentadecylhydrate	$AlBr_3.15H_2O$	536.94	col need		-7.5	d 7	s	s	s al
a22	butoxide, tert-	$Al(C_4H_9O)_3$	246.33	wh cr	1.0251^{20}_0	subl 180, m.p >300, sealed tube.				v s org solv
a23	carbide	Al_4C_3	143.96	yel-grn, hex	2.36	stab to 1400	$d 2200^{400}$	d to CH_4		d dil a; i acet
a24	chlorate	$Al(ClO_3)_3.6H_2O$	385.43	col, rhbdr, deliq		d		vs	vs	s dil HCl
a25	perchlorate	$Al(ClO_4)_3.6H_2O$	433.43	col, hygr	2.020	82	$-6H_2O, 178$ d 262	s	s	
a26	chloride	$AlCl_3$ (or Al_2Cl_6)	133.34	wh to col, hex, odor HCl, v deliq	fus 2.44^{25} liq 1.31^{200}	$190^{2.5}$ atm	182.7^{752} subl. 177.8	69.9^{15} with viol	s d	$100^{12.5}$ abs al; 0.072^{25} chl; sCCl_4, eth sl s bz
a27	chloride, hexahydrate	$AlCl_3.6H_2O$	241.43	col, rhomb, deliq, 1.6	2.398	d 100		s	v s ev HCl	50 abs al; s eth; sl s HCl
a28	chloride, hexammine	$AlCl_3.6NH_3$	235.52	col cr, hygr	1.412^{25}_4	d		s		
a29	diethylmalonate deriv	$Al(C_7H_{11}O_4)_3$	504.47		1.084^{100}	98		i		s org solv
a30	ethoxide	$Al(C_2H_5O)_3$	162.14	wh cr	1.142^{20}_0	134	205^{14}	d	s	v sl s al, eth
a31	α-ethylacetoacetate deriv	$Al(C_6H_9O_3)_3$	414.39	wh cr	1.101^{90}	78–79	$190–200^{11}$	s		s lgr
a32	ferrocyanide	$Al_4[Fe(CN)_6]_3.17H_2O$	1050.05	br powd				sl s	sl s	s dil a
a33	fluoride	AlF_3	83.98	col, tricl	2.882^{25}_4	1291 subl^{760}		0.559^{25}	s	i a, alk, al, acet
a34	fluoride	$AlF_3.3\frac{1}{2}H_2O$	147.03	wh cr powd	1.914^{25}_4	$-2H_2O 100$	anhydr 250	i	sl s	d ac a
a35	fluoride, monohydrate	Nat. fluellite. $AlF_3.H_2O$	101.00	col, rhomb, 1.473, 1.490, 1.511	2.17			sl s	sl s	
a36	fluosilicate	Nat topaz. $2AlFO.SiO_2$	184.04	rhomb, 1.619, 1.620, 1.627	3.58			i	i	
a37	hydroxide	Nat. boehmite. $AlO(OH)$	59.99	wh, orthorhomb microcr	3.01	$-H_2O$, trans to γ-Al_2O_3		i	i	s h a, h alk
a38	hydroxide	Nat. diaspore. $AlO(OH)$	59.99	col, rhomb cr	3.3–3.5	$-H_2O$, trans to Al_2O_3		i	i	s h a, h alk
a39	hydroxide	$Al(OH)_3$	78.00	wh, monocl	2.42	$-H_2O, 300$		i	i	s a, alk; i al
a40	iodide	AlI_3 (or Al_2I_6)	407.69	br pl, cont free I_2, deliq	3.98^{25}	191	360	s d	s	s al, eth, CS_2, liq NH_3
a41	iodide, hexahydrate	$AlI_3.6H_2O$	515.79	wh-yel cr, hygr	2.63	d 185	d	v s	v s	s al, CS_2
a42	isopropoxide	$Al(C_3H_5O)_3$	204.25	wh cr	$1.0346^{20}_{?}$	118.5	140.5^{8}	d		s al, bz, chl
a43	lactate	$Al(C_3H_5O_3)_3$	294.20	wh-yelsh powd				v s		

No.	Name	Synonyms and Formulae	Mol. wt.	Crystalline form, properties and index of refraction	Density or spec. gravity	Melting point, °C	Boiling point, °C	Solubility, in grams per 100 cc		
								Cold water	Hot water	Other solvents
	Aluminum									
a44	nitrate	$Al(NO_3)_3.9H_2O$	375.13	col, rhomb, deliq, 1.54	....	73.5	d 150	63.7^{25}	v s d	100 al; s alk, acet, HNO_3. a
a45	nitride	AlN	40.99	wh cr, hex	3.26	>2200 (in N_2)	subl 2000	d (NH_3)	d	d a; alk
a46	oleate (com'l)	$Al(C_{18}H_{33}O_2)_3(?)$	871.37	wh powd, existence doubted except as basic salt				d	s	i al; v sl s bz
a47	oxalate	$Al_2(C_2O_4)_3.4H_2O$	390.08	wh powd	....			i	i	i al; s a
a48	oxide	Al_2O_3	101.96	col, hex, 1.768, 1.760	3.965^{25}	2045	2980	i		v sl s a, alk
a49	oxide	α-Alumina. nat. corundum. Al_2O_3	101.96	col, rhomb cr, 1.765	3.97	2015 ± 15	2980 ± 60	0.000098^{29}	i	v sl s a, alk
a50	oxide	γ-Alumina. Al_2O_3	101.96	wh micr cr, 1.7	3.5–3.9	tr to α		i	i	sl s a, alk
a51	oxide, monohydrate	$Al_2O_3.H_2O$	119.98	col, rhomb, 1.624 ± 0.003	3.014			i	i	....
a52	oxide, trihydrate	Nat. gibbsite, hydra-argilite. $Al_2O_3.3H_2O$	156.01	wh monocl cr, 1.577, 1.577, 1.595	2.42	tr to $Al_2O_3.H_2O$ (Boehmite)		i	i	s h a, alk
a53	oxide, trihydrate	Nat. bayerite. $Al_2O_3.3H_2O$	156.01	wh micr cr, 1.583	2.53	tr to $Al_2O_3H_2O$ (Boehmite)	....	i	i	s hot a, alk
a54	*meta*phosphate	$Al(PO_3)_3$	263.90	col, tetr	2.779			i	i	i a
a55	palmitate, mono- (com'l)	$Al(OH)_2C_{16}H_{31}O_2$	316.41	wh	1.095	200		i		s alk, hydrocarb
a56	1-phenol-4-sulfonate	$Al(C_6H_5O_4S)_3$	546.49	redsh-wh powd	....			s		s al, glyc
a57	phenoxide	$Al(C_6H_5O)_3$	306.27	grayish-wh cr mass	1.23	d 265		d		s al, eth, chl
a58	*ortho*phosphate	$AlPO_4$	121.95	wh rhomb pl, 1.546, 1.556, 1.578	2.566	>1500		i	i	s a, alk, al
a59	propoxide	$Al(C_3H_7O)_3$	204.25	wh cr	1.0578^{20}_0	106	248^{14}	d	d	s al
a60	salicylate	$Al(C_7H_5O_3)_3$	438.33	redsh-wh powd	....			i		i al; s alk
a61	selenide	Al_2Se_3	290.84	lt brn powd, unstable in air	3.437^{15}_4			d	d	d a
a62	silicate	Nat. sillimanite, andalusite, cyanite. $Al_2O_3.SiO_2$	162.04	wh, rhomb, 1.66	3.247	1545 tr to $Al_2O_3.2SiO_2$	>1545	i	i	d HF; i HCl; s fus alk
a63	silicate	Nat. mullite. $3Al_2O_3.2SiO_2$	426.05	col, rhomb, 1.638, 1.642, 1.653	3.156	1920	....	i	i	i a, HF
a64	stearate, tri-	$Al(C_{18}H_{35}O_2)_3$	877.42	wh powd	1.010	103		i		s al, bz, turp, alk
a65	sulphate	$Al_2(SO_4)_3$	342.15	wh powd, 1.47	2.71	d 770		31.3^0	98.1^{100}	s dil a; sl s al
a66	sulfate, hydrate	Nat. alunogenite. $Al_2(SO_4)_3.18H_2O$	666.43	col, monocl, 1.474, 1.467, 1.483	1.69^{17}	d 86.5		86.9^0	1104^{100}	i al
a67	sulfide	Al_2S_3	150.16	yel, hex, odor H_2S, d moist air	2.02^{13}	1100	subl 1500 (N_2)	d		s a; i acet
a68	thallium sulfate	Aluminum thallium alum. $AlTl(SO_4)_2.12H_2O$	639.66	col, oct, 1.50112	2.325^{20}_4	91	....	4.84^0	65.19^{60}	
a69	**Americium**	Am	243.13	silvery, hex	....	994 ± 4	2607 (extrap)			s dil a
a70	bromide	$AmBr_3$	482.86	wh, orthorhomb		subl		s		
a71	chloride	$AmCl_3$	349.49	pink, hex	5.78	subl 850		s		
a72	fluoride	AmF_3	300.12	pink, hex	9.53			i		
a73	iodide	AmI_3	623.84	yel, orthoromb	6.9			s		
a74	oxide	Am_2O_3	534.26	redsh-brn, cub or tan, or hex	....					s min a
a75	oxide, di-	AmO_2	275.13	blk, cub	11.68					s min a
a76	**Ammonia**	NH_3	17.03	col gas; liq, 0.817^{-79}, $1.325^{16.5}$	0.7710 g/l 760 mm	−77.7	−33.35	89.9	7.4^{100}	13.20^{20} al; s eth, org solv
a77	Ammonia-d₃	Trideuterio ammonia. ND_3	20.05	....	....	−74	−30.9			
	Ammonium									
v78	acetate	$NH_4C_2H_3O_2$	77.08	wh cr, hygr	1.17^{20}_4	114	d	148^4	d	7.89^{15} MeOH; s al; sl s acet
a79	acetate, hydrogen	$(NH_4)H(C_2H_3O_2)_2$	137.14	col need, deliq	....	66		s		s al
a80	aluminum chloride	$NH_4Cl.AlCl_3$	186.83	wh cr	....	304		s		
a81	aluminum sulfate	$NH_4Al(SO_4)_2$	237.14	col, hex	2.45^{20}			s		s glyc; i al

No.	Name	Synonyms and Formulae	Mol. wt.	Crystalline form, properties and index of refraction	Density or spec. gravity	Melting point, °C	Boiling point, °C	Solubility, in grams per 100 cc		
								Cold water	Hot water	Other solvents
	Ammonium									
a82	aluminum sulfate, hydrate	Nat. tschernigite. $NH_4Al(SO_4)_2.12H_2O$	453.33	col, cub, 1.459....	1.64	93.5	$-10H_2O$, 120	15^{20}	v s	s dil a; i al
a83	orthoarsenate........	$(NH_4)_3AsO_4.3H_2O$..	247.08	rhomb cr........		d, $-NH_3$	....	sl s		
a84	orthoarsenate, di-H..	$NH_4H_2AsO_4$........	158.98	col, tetr, 1.577, 1.522	2.311^9	d, $-NH_3^{300}$	....	33.74^0	122.4^{90}	
a85	orthoarsenate mono-H	$(NH_4)_2HAsO_4$	176.00	col, monocl, odor NH_3	1.989	d	....	s	d	i al
a86	metaarsenite........	NH_4AsO_2	124.96	col, rhomb pr, hygr				v s	d	i al, acet; sl s NH_4OH
a87	azide...........	NH_4N_3	60.06	col pl........	1.346	160	subl 134 expl	20.16^{20}	27.04^{40}	1.06^{20} 80 % al; i eth, bz
a88	benzene sulfonate....	$NH_4C_6H_5SO_3$	175.21	rhomb........	1.342	d 271-275		98	320	19 c al; i eth, bz
a89	benzoate........	$NH_4C_7H_5O_2$	139.16	col, rhomb........	1.260	d 198	subl 160	$19.6^{14.5}$	83.3^{100}	1.63^{25} al; s glyc; i eth
a90	pentaborate........	Ammonium decaborate. $NH_4B_5O_8.4H_2O$	272.15	....				7.03^{18}		
a91	peroxyborate........	$NH_4BO_3.\frac{1}{2}H_2O$........	85.86	wh cr........		d		$1.55^{17.5}$		i al
a92	tetraborate	Ammonium biborate. $(NH_4)_2B_4O_7.4H_2O$	263.38	col, tetr........		d		7.27^{18}	52.68^{90}	sl s acet; i al
a93	bromate........	NH_4BrO_3	145.95	col, hex........		expl		v s	vs	
a94	bromide........	NH_4Br	97.95	cub, coll hygr, 1.712^{25}	2.429	subl 452	235 vac	97^{25}	145.6^{100}	10^{78} al; s acet, eth, NH_3
a95	dibromoiodide.......	NH_4IBr_2	304.75	met-grn pr, hygr		198		v s	s	s eth
a96	bromoplatinate......	$(NH_4)_2PtBr_6$	710.62	red-brn cub........	4.265^{24}	d 145		0.59^{20}	0.36^{100}	
a97	bromoselenate......	$(NH_4)_2SeBr_6$	594.49	red, oct cr	3.326	d		d	d	sl s eth
a98	bromostannate......	$(NH_4)_2SnBr_6$	634.22	col, cub........	3.50	d		v s		
a99	cadmium chloride....	$4NH_4Cl.CdCl_2$	397.27	col, rhomb, 1.6038	2.01			s		
a100	calcium arsenate....	$NH_4CaAsO_4.6H_2O$	305.13	col, monocl........	1.905^{15}	d 140		0.02	s	s NH_4Cl, i NH_4OH
a101	calcium phosphate...	$NH_4CaPO_4.7H_2O$	279.20	1.561^{15}........		d		i	d	s a
a102	carbamate........	$NH_4NH_2CO_2$	78.07	col, rhomb........		subl 60		v s	d	v s NH_4OH; sl s al; i acet
a103	carbamate acid carbonate	Sal volatile. $NH_4NH_2CO_2.NH_4HCO_3$	157.13	wh cr........		subl		25^{15}	67^{65}	d al; s glyc; i acet
a104	carbonate........	$(NH_4)_2CO_3.H_2O$	114.10	col, cub........		d 58		100^{15}	d	i al, NH_3, CS_2; s dil MeOH
a105	carbonate, hydrogen.	Ammonium bicarbonate. NH_4HCO_3	79.06	col, rhomb or monocl, 1.423, 1.536, 1.555	1.58	107.5 (d 36-60)	subl	11.9^0	d	i al, acet
a106	cerium nitrate(ic)....	$(NH_4)_2Ce(NO_3)_6$	548.23	or, monocl........				141^{25}	227^{80}	s HNO_3, al
a107	cerium nitrate(ous)	$2NH_4NO_3.Ce(NO_3)_3.4H_2O$	558.28	monocl........		74		318.20	817.4^{65}	
a108	cerium sulfate(ous)..	$(NH_4)_2SO_4.Ce_2(SO_4)_3.8H_2O$	844.69	monocl........	2.523	$-6H_2O$, 100	$-8H_2O$, 150	3.29^{49} (anhydr)	....	
a109	chlorate........	NH_4ClO_3	101.49	col, monocl need.	1.80	102 expl		28.7^0	115^{75}	sl s al
a110	perchlorate........	NH_4ClO_4	117.49	col, rhomb, 1.482	1.95	d		10.74^0	42.45^{85}	s acet; sl s al
a111	chloride........	Sal ammoniac. NH_4Cl	53.49	col, cub, 1.642.	1.527	subl 340	520	29.7^0	75.8^{100}	0.6^{19} al; s liq NH_3; i acet, eth
a112	chloroaurate.......	NH_4AuCl_4	356.82	yel, monocl or rhomb			520	s		sl s al
a113	chloroaurate, hydrate	$(NH_4AuCl_4)_4.5H_2O$	1517.35	yel, monocl........		$-5H_2O$, 100		s	....	s al
a114	chlorogallate.......	NH_4GaCl_4	229.57	wh cr........		275		v s	v s	s al; i pet eth
a115	chloroiridate.......	$(NH_4)_2IrCl_6$	441.00	red-blk, cub......	2.856	d		0.69^{14}	4.38^{50}	i al; s HCl
a116	chloroiridite.......	$(NH_4)_3IrCl_6.1\frac{1}{2}H_2O$	486.06	....				s		
a117	chloroosmate.......	$(NH_4)_2OsCl_6$	439.00	cub........	2.93					
a118	chloropalladate.....	$(NH_4)_2PdCl_6$	355.20	red-brn, cub......	2.418	d		sl s		
a119	chloropalladite.....	$(NH_4)_2PdCl_4$	284.29	olive grn, tetr........	2.17	d		s		i al
a120	hexachloroplatinate..	$(NH_4)_2PtCl_6$	443.89	yel, cub, 1.8..	3.065	d		0.7^{15}	1.25^{100}	0.005 al; i eth, conc HCl
a121	chloroplatinite	$(NH_4)_2PtCl_4$........	372.98	red, rhomb (tetr)	2.936	d 140-150		s	s	i al
a122	chloroplumbate.....	$(NH_4)_2PbCl_6$	455.98	yel, cub........	2.925	d 120		sl s	d	s a
a123	chlorostannate......	$(NH_4)_2SnCl_6$	367.49	wh, cub........	2.4	d		$33.^{14.5}$	v s	
a124	tetrachlorozincate..	$ZnCl_2.2NH_4Cl$	243.26	wh pl, rhomb, hygr	1.879	d 150		v s		
a125	chromate........	$(NH_4)_2CrO_4$	152.08	yel, monocl........	1.91^{12}	d 180		40.5^{30}	d	i al; sl s NH_3, acet
a126	dichromate........	$(NH_4)_2Cr_2O_7$	252.06	or, monocl........	2.15^{25}	d 170		30.8^{15}	89^{30}	s al; i acet
a127	peroxychromate.....	$(NH_4)_3CrO_8$	234.11	red-brn, cub........		d 40	expl 50	sl s	d	i al, eth, sl s NH_3; expl H_2SO_4
a129	chromium sulfate(ic).	$(NH_4)Cr(SO_4)_2.12H_2O$	478.34	grn or vlt, cub; 1.4842	1.72	94, $-9H_2O$, 100		21.2^{25}	32.8^{40}	s al, dil a
a130	citrate, di(sec.).....	$(NH_4)_2HC_6H_5O_7$	226.19	wh gran or powd.	1.48			100		sl s al
a131	citrate, tri(tert.)....	$(NH_4)_3C_6H_5O_7$	243.22	wh cr, deliq........		d		v s		i al, eth, acet
a132	cobalt orthophosphate(ous)	$(NH_4)CoPO_4.H_2O$	189.96	vlt cr powd........				i	d	s a

No.	Name	Synonyms and Formulae	Mol. wt.	Crystalline form, properties and index of refraction	Density or spec. gravity	Melting point, °C	Boiling point, °C	Cold water	Hot water	Other solvents
	Ammonium									
a133	cobalt (II)-selenate	$(NH_4)_2SeO_4 \cdot CoSO_4 \cdot 6H_2O$	489.02	ruby-red, monocl, 1.526, 1.532, 1.541	2.228_4^{20}					
a134	cobalt sulfate(ous)	$(NH_4)_2SO_4 \cdot CoSO_4 \cdot 6H_2O$.	395.23	ruby-red, monocl, 1.490, 1.495, 1.503	1.902			20.5^{20}	45.4^{80}	i al
a135	copper chloride(ic)	$2NH_4Cl \cdot CuCl_2 \cdot 2H_2O$	277.46	blue, tetrag, 1.744, 1.724	1.993	d 110		33.8^0	99.3^{80}	s a, al; sl s NH_3
a136	copper iodide(ous)	$NH_4I \cdot CuI \cdot H_2O$	353.40	rhomb pl				d	d	s NH_4I
a137	cyanate	NH_4OCN	60.06	wh cr	1.342^{20}	d 60		v s	d	sl s al; i eth
a138	cyanide	NH_4CN	44.06	col, cub	1.02^{100}	d 36	subl 40	v s	d	v s al
a139	cyanaurate	$NH_4Au(CN)_4 \cdot H_2O$	337.09	col pl		d 200		v s		v s al; i eth
a140	cyanaurite	$NH_4Au(CN)_2$	267.04	col, cub		d 100		v s	v s	s al: i eth
a141	cyanoplatinite	$(NH_4)_2Pt(CN)_4 \cdot H_2O$	353.61	yel cr				s		
a142	ethylsulfate	$NH_4C_2H_5SO_4$	143.16			99		s		
a143	ferricyanide	$(NH_4)_3Fe(CN)_6$	266.06	red cr, rhomb		d		v s		
a144	ferrocyanide	$(NH_4)_4Fe(CN)_6 \cdot 3H_2O$.	338.15	yel, monocl, turns bl in air		d		s	d	i al
a145	fluoantimonite	$(NH_4)_2SbF_5$	252.84	col, rhomb		d, subl		108		
a146	fluoborate	NH_4BF_4	104.84	wh, rhomb	1.871^{15}	subl		25^{16}	97^{100}	s NH_4OH
a147	fluogallate	$(NH_4)_3GaF_6$	237.83	wh oct cr		d >250– GaF_3			sl s	
a148	fluogermanate	$(NH_4)_2GeF_6$	222.66	col hex pr and bipyram, 1.428, 1.425	2.564_{25}^{25}			s		i al, MeOH
a149	fluophosphate, di-	$NH_4PO_2F_2$	119.01	col, rhomb		213		s	s	s al, acet
a150	fluophosphate, hexa.	NH_4PF_6	163.00	col, pl	2.180^{18}	d		s	s	s al, acet
a151	fluoride	NH_4F	37.04	col, hex, deliq	1.009^{25}	subl		100^0	d	s al; i NH_3
a152	fluoride, hydrogen	NH_4HF_2	57.04	rhomb or tetr, deliq, 1.390	1.50	125.6		v s	v s	sl s al
a153	fluorosulfonate	NH_4FSO_3	117.10	wh need		d 245		v s	v s	sl s al; s MeOH
a154	fluosilicate	α-Nat. cryptohalite. $(NH_4)_2SiF_6$	178.14	α oct, β hex, col α 1.3696	α 2.011 β 2.152	d		18.6^{17}	55.5^{100}	sl s al; i acet
a155	fluosulfonate	NH_4SO_3F	117.10	col, need		244.7		s	s	sl s al; s MeOH; d NH_4OH
a156	fluotitanate	$(NH_4)_2TiF_6$	197.97	hex pr		d		s	s	i al, eth
a157	fluozirconate	$(NH_4)_2ZrF_6$	241.29	rhomb, hex	1.154					
a158	fluozirconate	$(NH_4)_3ZrF_7$	278.32	col, cub	1.433			sl s		
a159	formate	NH_4CHO_2.	63.06	wh, monocl, deliq.	1.280	116	d 180	102^0	531^{80}	s al, eth, NH_3
a160	gallium sulfate	Ammonium gallium alum. $Ga(NH_4)(SO_4)_2 \cdot 12H_2O$	496.07	cub, 1.468	1.777			30.84^{25}		0.0087 5 25 70% EtOH
a161	trihydrogen paraperiodate	$(NH_4)_2H_3IO_6$	262.00	col, rhomb	2.85					
a162	hydroxide	NH_4OH	35.05	at ord temp in sol only		−77		s		
a163	iodate	NH_4IO_3	192.94	col, rhomb or monocl	3.309^{21}	d 150		2.06^{15}	14.5^{101}	
a164	iodide	NH_4I	144.94	col, cub, hygr, 1.7031	2.514^{25}	subl 551	220 vac	154.2^0	250.3^{100}	v s al, acet, NH_3; sl s eth
a165	triiodide	NH_4I_3	398.75	dk br, rhomb	3.749	d 175		s d	d	
a166	iodoplatinate	$(NH_4)_2PtI_4$	992.59	blk, cub	4.61					i al
a167	iridium chloride (III)	$(NH_4)_3IrCl_6 \cdot H_2O$	477.05	grn-br-bl, cub		d 350		10.5^{19}		
a168	iridium sulfate	$NH_4Ir(SO_4)_2 \cdot 12H_2O$	618.54	yel-red cr		106		s		
a169	iron (III) chloride	$2NH_4Cl \cdot FeCl_3 \cdot H_2O$	287.20	ruby-red, rhomb, hygr, 1.78	1.99	234f		v s	v s	
a170	iron (III) fluoride	$3NH_4F \cdot FeF_3$	223.95	col to lt yel, oct	1.96			sl s	sl s	
a171	iron (II) selenate	$(NH_4)_2SeO_4 \cdot FeSO_4 \cdot 6H_2O$	485.93	lt grn, monocl, 1.5226, 1.5260, 1.5334	2.191_4^{20}					
a172	iron (III) sulfate	$(NH_4)_2SO_4 \cdot Fe_2(SO_4)_3$	532.02	wh, hex	2.49^{22}	d 420		44.15^{25}		
a173	iron sulfate(ic)	$NH_4Fe(SO_4)_2 \cdot 12H_2O$	482.19	vlt, cub oct, 1.4854	1.71	39–41	−12H_2O, 230	124.0^{25}	400^{100}	i al; s dil a
a174	iron sulfate(ous)	$(NH_4)_2SO_4 \cdot FeSO_4 \cdot 6H_2O$	392.14	grn, monocl, 1.487, 1.492, 1.499	1.864_4^{20}	d 100–110		26.9^{20}	73.0^{80}	i al
a175	lactate	$NH_4C_2H_5O_3$	107.11	col-yelsh liq	$1.19–1.21^{15}$			∞		∞ al
a176	laurate, acid (mixt.)	$NH_4C_{12}H_{23}O_2 \cdot C_{12}H_{24}O_2$.	417.68	wh		75	d	s	s	4.8^7 al; sl s eth, acet
a177	magnesium arsenate	$NH_4MgAsO_4 \cdot 6H_2O$	289.36	col, tetrg, 1.608	1.932^{15}	d		0.038^{20}	0.024^{80}	s a; i al
a178	magnesium carbonate	$(NH_4)_2CO_3 \cdot MgCO_3 \cdot 4H_2O$ 252.47		wh				s	v s	s a; i al

No.	Name	Synonyms and Formulae	Mol. wt.	Crystalline form, properties and index of refraction	Density or spec. gravity	Melting point, °C	Boiling point, °C	Cold water	Hot water	Other solvents
	Ammonium									
a179	magnesium chloride	$NH_4Cl.MgCl_2.6H_2O$	256.80	col, rhomb, deliq	1.456	$-2H_2O$, 100 d		16.7	....	d al
a180	magnesium chromate	$(NH_4)_2CrO_4.MgCrO_4.6H_2O$	400.51	yel, monocl, 1.636, 1.637, 1.653	1.84	d	....	v s	v s	
a181	magnesium phosphate	Guanite, struvite $NH_4MgPO_4.6H_2O$	245.41	col, rhomb, 1.495, 1.496, 1.504	1.711	d		0.0231^0	0.0195^{50}	v s dil a; i al
a182	magnesium selenate	$(NH_4)_2SeO_4.MgSeO_4.6H_2O$	454.40	col monocl pr, 1.507, 1.509, 1.517	2.058_4^{20}	....	....	sl s		
a183	magnesium sulfate	Nat. boussingaulite. $(NH_4)_2SO_4.MgSO_4.6H_2O$	360.60	col, monocl, 1.472, 1.473, 1.479	1.723	>120	d 250	17.92^0	64.7^{100} (anhydr)	....
a184	l-malate, hydrogen	$NH_4HC_4H_4O_5$	151.08	col, rhomb	1.5	161	d	$32.2^{15.7}$		
a185	permanganate	NH_4MnO_4	136.97	rhomb	2.208^{10}	d 110	....	7.9^{15}	d	
a186	manganese phosphate(ic)	$NH_4MnPO_4.H_2O$	185.96	wh cr				0.0031	0.05	i al, NH_4 salts
a187	manganese sulfate(ous)	$(NH_4)_2SO_4.MnSO_4.6H_2O$	391.23	pa red, monocl, 1.480, 1.484, 1.491	1.83			51.3^{25}	v s	
a188	molybdate	$(NH_4)_2MoO_4$	196.01	col, monocl pr	2.276_4^{25}	d		s, d	d	s a; i al, NH_3, acet
a189	paramolybdate	"Molybdic acid" com'l. $(NH_4)_6Mo_7O_{24}.4H_2O$	1235.86	col-yelsh, monocl	2.498	$-H_2O$, 90	d 190	43	d	i al; s a, alk
a190	permolybdate	$3(NH_4)_2O.5MoO_3.2MoO_4.6H_2O$	608.17	lt yel monocl pr	2.975	d 170		v s	v s	sl s al
a191	molybdotellurate	$(NH_4)_6TeMo_6O_{24}.7H_2O$	1321.56	col, rhomb	2.78	d 550	d	s	s	
a192	myristate, acid (mixt.)	$NH_4C_{14}H_{27}O_2.C_{14}H_{28}O_2$	473.78	wh solid		75–90	d	sl s	s	s al; i eth
a193	nickel chloride	$NH_4Cl.NiCl_2.6H_2O$	291.20	grn, monocl, deliq	1.654			v s	v s	
a194	nickel sulfate	Double nickel salt. $(NH_4)_2SO_4.NiSO_4.6H_2O$	395.00	dk bl-grn, monocl, 1.495, 1.501, 1.508	1.923			10.4^{20}	30^{80}	i al; s $(NH_4)_2SO_4$
a195	nitrate	NH_4NO_3	80.04	col, rhomb, (monocl >32.1^0)	1.725^{25}	169.6	210^{11}	118.3^0	871^{100}	3.8^{20} al; 17.1^{20} MeOH s acet, NH_3; i eth
a196	nitratocerate	$(NH_4)_2Ce(NO_3)_6$	548.23	yel-red, monocl				142.6^{18}	232^{90}	s al; sl s HNO_3
a197	nitrite	NH_4NO_2	64.04	wh-yelsh cr	1.69	60–70 expl	30 subl vac	v s	d	s dil al; i eth
a198	oleate, acid (mixt.)	$NH_4C_{18}H_{33}O_2.C_{18}H_{34}O_2$	581.97	wh powd		d 78		s	s	80^{50} al; 13.3^{15} eth
a199	osmium chloride	$(NH_4)_2OsCl_6$	439.00	blk, oct	2.93^{25}	subl 170		d	d	s HCl
a200	oxalate	$(NH_4)_2C_2O_4.H_2O$	142.11	col, rhomb, 1.439, 1.546, 1.594	1.50	d		2.54^0	11.8^{50}	i NH_3
a201	oxalate, acid	Ammonium binoxalate. $NH_4HC_2O_4.H_2O$	125.08	col, rhomb	1.556	$-H_2O$, 170	....	s		i eth, bz
a202	oxalatoferrate (III)	$(NH_4)_3Fe(C_2O_4)_3.3H_2O$	428.07	grn, monocl	1.78	d 165		42.7^0	345^{100}	....
a203	palladium (II)-chloride	$(NH_4)_2PdCl_4$	284.29	grnsh-yel, tetr	2.17	d		v s	v s	s dil al; i abs al
a204	palladium (IV)-chloride	$(NH_4)_2PdCl_6$	355.20	red oct cr	2.418	d $-Cl$		sl s	sl s	
a205	palmitate, (acid)- (mixt.)	$NH_4C_{16}H_{31}O_2.C_{16}H_{22}O_2$	529.90	yelsh soapy mass or yel powd		>100	d	sl s	s	8.8^{50} al; 0.23^{15} eth
a206	metaperiodate	NH_4IO_4	208.94	col, tetr	3.056^{18}	expl		2.7^{16}		
a207	hypophosphate	$(NH_4)_2H_2P_2O_6$	196.04	col cr		170		7^{25}	25^{100}	
a208	orthophosphate	$(NH_4)_3PO_4.3H_2O$	203.13	wh pr				26.1^{25}	....	sl s dil NH_4OH; i NH_3, acet
a209	orthophosphate, di-H	$NH_4H_2PO_4$	115.03	col, tetr, 1.525, 1.479	1.803^{19}	190		22.7^0	173.2^{100}	i acet
a210	orthophosphate-mono-H	$(NH_4)_2HPO_4$	132.05	col, monocl, 1.52	1.619	d 155	d	57.5^{10}	106.0^{70}	i al, acet, NH_3
a211	hypophosphite	$NH_4H_2PO_2$	83.03	rhomb tabl	1.634	200	d 240	s	s	s al, NH_3, i acet
a212	orthophosphite, di-H	$NH_4H_2PO_3$	99.03	col, monocl pr		123	d 145	171^0	260^{31}	i al
a213	phosphofluoride, hexa-	NH_4PF_6	163.00	col, cub	2.180_4^{18}	d		74.8^{20}		s al, acet; d h a
a214	phosphomolybdate	Ammonium molybdo phosphate. $(NH_4)_3P(Mo_3O_{10})_4$	1876.35	yel powd		d		sl s	sl s	s alk; i al, HNO_3
a215	phosphotungstate	$(NH_4)_3P(W_3O_{10})_4$	2931.27	wh				sl s	sl s	
a216	picramate	$NH_4C_6H_4N_3O_5$	216.15	redsh-brn cr powd				s		
a217	picrate	$NH_4C_6H_2N_3O_7$	246.14	red or yel, rhomb	1.719	d	expl 423	1.1^{20}	s	sl s al
a219	praseodymium sulfate	$(NH_4)_2SO_4.Pr_2(SO_4)_3.8H_2O$	846.26	cr	$2.531^{16.5}$	$-8H_2O$, 170		sl s		
a220	propionate	$NH_4C_3H_5O_2$	91.11	pr, deliq	1.108^{25}	45		v s	....	s al, ac a
a221	perrhenate	NH_4ReO_4	268.24	wh, hex pl	3.97	d	d	6.1^{20}	32.34^{80}	....

No.	Name	Synonyms and Formulae	Mol. wt.	Crystalline form, properties and index of refraction	Density or spec. gravity	Melting point, °C	Boiling point, °C	Cold water	Hot water	Other solvents
	Ammonium									
a222	rhodanid	NH_4NCS	76.12	monocl cr, to rhomb at 92, ~1.685	1.305	149.6	d 170	128[0]	347[60]	v s al; s MeOH, acet; i $CHCl_3$
a223	rhodium chloride	$(NH_4)_3RhCl_6.H_2O$	387.75	dk red rhomb need		−H₂O, 140		s	s	sl s al; s dil NH_4Cl
a224	rhodium sulfate	Ammonium rhodium alum. $Rh(NH_4)(SO_4)_2.12H_2O$	529.25	orange, 1.5150		102				
a225	d-saccharate, hydrogen	$NH_4HC_6H_9O_8$	227.17	wh need or monocl pr				1.22[15]	24.35[100]	i c al; s h al
a226	salicylate	$NH_4C_7H_8O_3$	155.15	col, monocl			subl	111[25]	v s	28.8[25] al
a227	selenate	$(NH_4)_2SeO_4$	179.03	col, monocl, 1.561, 1.563, 1.585	2.194_4^{20}	d		117[7]	197[100]	i al, acet, NH_3
a228	selenate, hydrogen	NH_4HSeO_4	162.00	rhomb	2.162	d				
a229	selenide	$(NH_4)_2Se$	115.04	col, or wh cr		d		s		
a230	sodium phosphate, hydrate	Microsmic salt. $NH_4NaHPO_4.4H_2O$	209.07	col, monocl, 1.439, 1.442, 1.469	1.574	d 97				
a231	stearate, acid (mixt.)	$NH_4C_{18}H_{35}O_2.C_{18}H_{36}O_2$	586.00	wh cr		d 110		v s		0.3[25] al; 0.19[25] eth; 0.08[25] acet
a232	succinate	$(NH_4)_2.C_4H_4O_4$	152.15	col cr	1.37			s		sl s al
a233	sulfamate	$NH_4NH_2SO_3$	114.12	large, pl, deliq		125	d 160	166.6[10]	357[50]	i al
a234	sulfate	Nat. mascagnite. $(NH_4)_2SO_4$	132.14	col, rhomb, 1.521, 1.523, 1.533	1.769^{50}	d 235		70.6[0]	103.8[100]	i al, acet, NH_3
a235	sulfate, hydrogen	Ammonium bisulfate. NH_4HSO_4	115.11	col, rhomb, 1.473	1.78	146.9	d	100	v s	sl s al; i acet
a236	peroxydisulfate	$(NH_4)_2S_2O_8$	228.18	col, monocl, 1.498, 1.502, 1.587	1.982	d 120		58.2[0]	v s	
a237	sulfide, hydro-	NH_4HS	51.11	wh rhomb, 1.74	1.17	118[150atm]	88.4[19atm]	128.1[0]	d	s al; NH_3
a238	sulfide, mono-	$(NH_4)_2S$	68.14	col yel cr (> −18), hygr		d		v s	d	s al; v s NH_3
a239	sulfide, penta-	$(NH_4)_2S_5$	196.40	yel pr		d 115		v s		s al, i eth, CS_2
a240	sulfite	$(NH_4)_2SO_3.H_2O$	134.15	col, monocl, 1.515	1.41[25]	d 60–70	subl 150	32.4[0]	60.4[100]	sl s al; i acet
a241	sulfite, hydrogen	Ammonium bisulfite. NH_4HSO_3	99.10	rhomb pr, deliq	2.03	subl 150 (in N₂)		71.8[0]	84.7[60]	
a242	dl-tartrate	$(NH_4)_2C_4H_4O_6$	184.15	col, monocl, d, α 1.55, β 1.581	1.601	d		58.01[15]	81.17[60]	sl s al
a243	dl-tartrate, hydrogen	$NH_4HC_4H_4O_6$	167.12	col, monocl pr, 1.561, 1.591	1.636	d		2.35[15]	3.24[25]	i al, s a, alk
a244	tellurate	$(NH_4)_2TeO_4$	227.67	wh powd	$3.024^{24.5}$	d		s	s	i al; s dil a
a245	thallium chloride	$3NH_4Cl.TlCl_3.2H_2O$	507.23	col	2.39			s		
a246	thioantimonate	$(NH_4)_3SbS_4.4H_2O$	376.18	yel pr		d		71.2[0]	d	i al, eth
a247	thiocarbamate	$NH_4CS_2NH_2$	110.20	yel cr		d 50		v s		s al; sl s eth
a248	thiocarbonate, tri-	$(NH_4)_2CS_3$	144.28	yel cr, hygr		subl		v s	d	sl s al, eth
a249	thiocyanate	NH_4SCN	76.12	col, monocl, deliq	1.305	149.6	d 170	128[0]	v s	s al, acet, NH_3
a250	dithionate	$(NH_4)_2S_2O_6.\frac{1}{2}H_2O$	205.21	col, monocl	1.704	d 130		135[0]	v s	i al
a251	thiosulfate	$(NH_4)_2S_2O_3$	148.20	col, monocl, hygr	1.679	d 150		v s	103.3[100]	i al; sl s acet
a252	titanium oxalate, basic	$(NH_4)_2TiO(C_2O_4)_2.H_2O$	294.03					v s		
a253	uranylcarbonate	$2(NH_4)_2CO_3.UO_2CO_3.2H_2O$	558.24	yel, monocl	2.773	d 100		5.8[19]	d	s$(NH_4)_2CO_3$, aq.SO_2
a254	uranylfluoride, penta-	$(NH_4)_3UO_2F_5$	419.14	tetr cr, 1.495	3.186	subl		s		
a255	valerate	$NH_4C_5H_9O_2$	119.16	col or wh cr		d		v s		s al, eth
a256	metavanadate	NH_4VO_3	116.98	wh-yelsh or col cr	2.326	d 200		0.52[15]	6.95[96], d	
a257	vanadium sulfate	$NH_4V(SO_4)_2.12H_2O$	477.28	red to bl	1.687	49		28.45[20]		
a258	zinc sulfate	$(NH_4)_2SO_4.ZnSO_4.6H_2O$	401.66	wh monocl, 1.489, 1.493, 1.499	1.931	d		7[0] (anhydr)	42[80] (anhydr)	
a259	**Antimony**	Sb	121.75	silv wh met, hex	6.684^{25}	630.74	1750	i	i	s hot conc H_2SO_4, aq reg
a260	bromide, tri-	$SbBr_3$	361.48	col rhomb, 1.74	4.148^{23}	96.6	280	d		s HCl, HBr, CS_2, NH_3, al, acet
a261	chloride, penta-	$SbCl_5$	299.02	wh liq or monocl, 1.601^{14}	liq 2.336_4^{20}	2.8	79[22]	d	d	s HCl, tarta, $CHCl_3$
a262	chloride, tri-	Butter of antimony. $SbCl_3$	228.11	col, rhomb, deliq	3.140^{25}	73.4	283	601.6[0]	∞[80]	s abs al, HCl, tart a, $CHCl_3$, bz, acet
a263	fluoride, penta-	SbF_5	216.74	col oily liq	2.99^{23} liq	7	149.5	s		s KF
a264	fluoride, tri-	SbF_3	178.75	col, rhomb	$4.379^{20.9}$	292	subl 319	384.7[0]	5.636[30]	i NH_3
a265	hydride	SbH_3	124.77	inflamm gas	gas 4.36^{15}; liq 2.26^{-25}	−88	−17.1[75']	0.41[0]		1500 ml A; 2500 ml CS_2
a266	iodide, penta-	SbI_5	756.27	br		79	400.6			
a267	iodide, tri-	SbI_3	502.46	ruby-red, hex, 2.78Li, 2.36Li	4.917^{17}	170	401	d	d	i al; s CS_2, bz, HI, HCl
a268	iodosulfide	SbSI	280.72	dk red		392	d	i	i	d conc HCl; i CS_2

No.	Name	Synonyms and Formulae	Mol. wt.	Crystalline form, properties and index of refraction	Density or spec. gravity	Melting point, °C	Boiling point, °C	Solubility, in grams per 100 cc		
								Cold water	Hot water	Other solvents
	Antimony									
a269	mercaptoacetamide	Antimony thiogly-colamide. Sb(C₂H₄NOS)₃	392.12	wh cr		139		200		
a270	nitrate, basic	2Sb₂O₃.N₂O₅(?)	691.01	wh glossy cr		d		d		d a; v sl s conc HNO₃
a271	nitride	SbN	135.76	or powd		d		d		
a272	oxide, penta-	Sb₂O₅ (or Sb₄O₁₀)	323.50	yel powd	3.80 (dep on temp)	−O, 380 −O₂, 930		v sl s	v sl s	v sl s KOH, HCl, HI
a273	oxide, tetra-	Nat. cervantite. Sb₂O₄ (or Sb₂O₃.Sb₂O₅)	307.50	wh powd, 2.00	5.82	−O, 930		v sl s	v sl s	v sl s KOH, HCl, HI
a274	oxide, tri-	Nat. senarmontite. Sb₂O₃ (or Sb₄O₆)	291.50	wh, cub, 2.087	5.2	656	1550 subl	v sl s	sl s	s KOH HCl(3%), 0.03²⁰ tart a, ac a
a275	oxide, tri-	Nat. valentinite. Sb₂O₃(or Sb₄O₆)	291.50	col, rhomb, 2.18, 2.35, 2.35	5.67	656	1550	v sl s	sl s	s KOH, HCl, tart, a, ac a
a276	III oxychloride(ous)	SbOCl	173.20	wh monocl		d 170		i	d	s acet, HCl, CS₂; i al, eth, CHCl₃
a277	III oxychloride(ous)	Sb₄O₅Cl₂	637.90	monocl	5.01	d 320		i	d	s HCl; i al, eth
a278	oxyhydrate	H₄Sb₂O₇	359.13	wh, amorph		−H₂O, 200		sl s	sl s	s alk
a279	III oxysulfate, di-(ous)	Sb₂O₂SO₄	371.56	wh	4.89			d	d	s, H₂SO₄
a280	potassium tartrate	Tartar emetic. K(SbO)C₄H₄O₆.½H₂O	333.93	col cr	2.6	−½H₂O, 100		8.3	33.3	i al; 6.7 glyc
a281	selenide	Sb₂Se₃	480.38	gray cr		611		v sl s		s conc HCl
a282	III sulfate	Sb₂(SO₄)₃	531.68	wh powd, deliq	3.625⁴	d		i	d	s a
a283	sulfide, penta-	Sb₂S₅	403.82	yel powd, prism	4.120	d 75		i	i	i al; s HCl, alk, NH₄HS.
a284	sulfide, tri-	Nat. stibnite. Sb₂S₃	339.69	blk, rhomb, 3.194, 4.064, 4.303	4.64	550	ca 1150	0.000175¹⁸		s al, NH₄HS. K₂S, HCl; i ac a
a285	sulfide, tri-	Sb₂S₃	339.69	yel-red, amorph	4.12	550	ca 1150	0.000175¹⁸		s al, NH₄SH, K₂S, HCl; i ac a
a286	d-tartrate	Sb₂(C₄H₄O₆)₃.6H₂O	795.81	wh cr powd				s		
a287	telluride, tri-	Sb₂Te₃	626.30	gray	6.50¹³	629				s HNO₃, aq reg
a288	**Argon**	Ar	39.948	col inert gas, cr: 1.65⁻²³³, liq: 1.40⁻¹⁸⁶	1.784⁰g/l	−189.2	−185.7	5.6⁰ cm³	3.01⁵⁰ cm³	
a289	**Arsenic**	As	74.9216	gray met, hex-rhomb	5.727¹⁴	817 (28 atm.)	613 subl	i	i	s HNO₃
a290	**Arsenic**	As₄	299.69	yel, cub	2.026¹⁸	d 358		i	i	s CS₂, bz
a291	**Arsenic acid,** meta-	HAsO₃	123.93	wh, hygr		d	forms ortho-arsenic acid	d		
a292	ortho-	H₃AsO₄.½H₂O	150.95	wh translu hygr cr	2.0–2.5	35.5	−H₂O 160	302¹²·⁵		s al, alk, glyc
a293	pyro-	H₄As₂O₇	265.87	col pr			forms ortho-arsenic acid 206 d			
	Arsenic									
a294	bromide, tri-	AsBr₃	314.65	col-yel hygr pr	3.54²⁵	32.8	221	d	d	s HCl, HBr, CS₂
a295	chloride, tri-	AsCl₃	181.28	oily liq or need, 1.621¹⁴_F	liq 2.163²⁰	−8.5	130.2	d	d	s HBr, HCl, PCl₃, al, eth
a296	fluoride, penta-	AsF₅	169.91	col gas	7.71 g/l	−80	−53	s		s alk, al, eth, bz
a297	fluoride, tri-	AsF₃	131.92	oily liq	liq 2.666	−8.5	−63⁷⁵²	d	d	s al, eth, bz, NH₄OH
a298	hydride	Arsine. AsH₃	77.95	col gas	gas 2.695 liq 1.689⁸⁴·⁹	−116.3	−55 (d 300)	20 ml		s CHCl₃, bz
a299	iodide, di-	AsI₂	328.73	red pr		d 136		d		s al, eth, CHCl₃, bz, CS₂
a300	iodide, penta-	AsI₅	709.44		3.93	76				
a301	iodide, tri-	AsI₃	455.64	red hex, ca. 2.59, ca. 2.23	4.39¹³	146	403	6²⁵	30 d	5.2 CS₂; s al, eth, bz, CHCl₃
a302	oxide, pent-	As₂O₅	229.84	wh amor, deliq	4.32	d 315		150¹⁶	76.7¹⁰⁰	s al, a, alk
a303	oxide, tri-	As₂O₃	197.84	amor or vitreous	3.738	315		3.7²⁰	10.14¹⁰⁰	s alk, alk carb, HCl
a304	oxide, tri-	Nat. arsenolite. As₂O₃ (or As₄O₆)	197.84	col, cub or hbr, 1.755	3.865²⁵	subl 193		1.1¹⁷	11.46¹⁰⁰	s al, alk, HCl
a305	oxide, tri-	Nat. claudetite. As₂O₃ (or As₄O₆)	197.84	col, monocl, 1.871, 1.92, 2.01	4.15	193, subl 315	457.2	1.2²	11.46¹⁰⁰	s al, alk, HCl
a306	(III)oxychloride(ous)	AsOCl	126.37	brnsh		d		d	d	
a307	phosphide, mono-	AsP	105.90	br-red powd		subl, d		d	d	sl s CS₂; s H₂SO₄, HCl; i al, eth, CHCl₃
a308	selenide	As₂Se₃	386.72	br cr	4.75	ca. 360		1	d	s alk
a309	sulfide, di-	Nat. realgar. As₂S₂	213.97	red-br monocl, 2.46, 2.59, 2.61 α 3.506¹⁹ β 3.254¹⁹		α tr 267 β 307	565	i	i	s K₂S, NaHCO₃
a310	sulfide, penta-	As₂S₅	310.16	yel		subl, d 500		0.000136⁰	i	s alk, alk sulf, HNO₃

No.	Name	Synonyms and Formulae	Mol. wt.	Crystalline form, properties and index of refraction	Density or spec. gravity	Melting point, °C	Boiling point, °C	Solubility, in grams per 100 cc		
								Cold water	Hot water	Other solvents
	Arsenic									
a311	sulfide, tri-	Nat. orpiment. As_2S_3	246.04	yel or red, monocl, 2.4, 2.81, 3.02 (Li)	3.43	300	707	0.00005[18]	sl s	s al, alk, alk carb
	Auric or Aurous	*See* **Gold**								
b1	**Barium**	Ba	137.34	yel-silv met	3.51[20]	725	1640	d, ev H_2	d	s al; i bz
b2	acetate	$Ba(C_2H_3O_2)_2$	255.43	col cr	2.468			58.8[0]	75[100]	
b3	acetate, hydrate	$Ba(C_2H_3O_2)_2 \cdot H_2O$	273.45	col, tricl, 1.500, 1.517, 1.525	2.19	$-H_2O$, 150		76.4[26]	75[100]	sl s al
b4	amide	$Ba(NH_2)_2$	169.39	gray-wh cr		280		d	d	i liq NH_3
b5	orthoarsenate	$Ba_3(AsO_4)_2$	689.86		5.10	1605		0.055		s a, NH_4Cl
b6	orthoarsenate, mono-H	$BaHAsO_4 \cdot H_2O$	295.28	col, rhomb or monocl, 1.635	1.93[15]	$-H_2O$, 150		sl s		s HCl
b7	arsenide	Ba_3As_2	561.86	br	4.1[15]			d		d Cl_2, F_2, Br_2
b8	azide	$Ba(N_3)_2$	221.38	monocl pr	2.936	$-N_2$, 120	expl	17.3[17]		abs al 0.017[16]; i eth
b9	azide, hydrate	$Ba(N_3)_2 \cdot H_2O$	239.40	tricl, 1.7		expl		v s	v s	sl s al; i eth
b10	benzoate	$Ba(C_7H_5O_2)_2 \cdot 2H_2O$	415.60	col, nacreous leaf		$-2H_2O$, 100		s		sl s al
b11	boride, hexa-	BaB_6	202.21	met-blk, cub	4.36[15]	2270		i	i	s HNO_3; i HCl
b12	bromate	$Ba(BrO_3)_2 \cdot H_2O$	411.16	col, monocl	3.99[15]	d 260		0.3[0]	5.67[100]	i al; s acet
b13	bromide	$BaBr_2$	297.16	col cr, 1.75	4.781[24]	850	d	104.1[20]	149[100]	v s al, MeOH
b14	bromide, dihydrate	$BaBr_2 \cdot 2H_2O$	333.19	col, monocl, 1.713, 1.727, 1.744	3.58[24]	880, ($-H_2O$, 75)	$-2H_2O$, 120	151[20]	204[100]	v s MeOH, s al
b15	bromofluoride	$BaBr_2 \cdot BaF_2$	472.49	col pl	4.96[15]			d	d	i al; s conc HCl, conc HNO_3
b16	bromoplatinate	$BaPtBr_6 \cdot 10H_2O$	992.04	monocl	3.71					
b17	butyrate	$Ba(C_4H_7O_2)_2 \cdot 2H_2O$	347.57	col	3.75			37.42[0]	42.12[80]	d a
b18	carbide	BaC_2	161.36	gray, tetr	3.75			d to C_2H_2		d a
b19	carbonate(α)	$BaCO_3$	197.35	wh, hex	4.43	1740[90 atm]	d	0.002[20]	0.006[100]	s a, NH_4Cl; i al
b20	carbonate(β)	$BaCO_3$	197.35			tr to α, 982		0.0022[18]	0.0065[100]	s a, NH_4Cl; i al
b21	carbonate(γ)	Nat. witherite. $BaCO_3$	197.35	wh rhomb, 1.529, 1.676, 1.677	4.43	to β, 811	d 1450	0.0022[18]	0.0065[100]	s a, NH_4Cl; i al
b22	chlorate	$Ba(ClO_3)_2 \cdot H_2O$	322.26	col monocl, 1.5622, 1.577, 1.635	3.18	414 ($-H_2O$, 120)	$-O$, 250	27.4[15]	111.2[100]	sl s al, acet, HCl
b23	perchlorate	$Ba(ClO_4)_2$	336.24	col, hex	3.2	505		198.5[25]	562.3[100]	v s al
b24	perchlorate, hydrate	$Ba(ClO_4)_2 \cdot 3H_2O$	390.29	col, hex, 1.533	2.74	d 400		198[33]	s	al 124[62]
b25	chloride α	$BaCl_2$	208.25	col, monocl, 1.7303, 1.7367, 1.7420	3.856[24]	tr to cub 962	1560	37.5[26]	59[100]	sl s HCl, HNO_3; v sl s al
b26	chloride β	$BaCl_2$	208.25	col, cub	3.917	963	1560			v sl s al
b27	chloride, hydrate	$BaCl_2 \cdot 2H_2O$	244.28	col, monocl, 1.629, 1.642, 1.658 n_D^{26}	3.097[24]	$-2H_2O$, 113	35.7[20]	58.7[100]	sl s HCl, HNO_3; v sl s al
b28	hypochlorite	$Ba(ClO)_2 \cdot 2H_2O$	276.28	col cr		d				
b29	chlorofluoride	$BaCl_2 \cdot BaF_2$	383.58	col, tetr, 1.640	4.51[18]			d	d	i al; s conc HCl, HNO_3
b30	chloroplatinate	$BaPtCl_6 \cdot 6H_2O$	653.24	or-yel, monocl	2.868	$-5H_2O$, 70	d	s		d a, al; i MeOH, eth
b31	chloroplatinite	$BaPtCl_4 \cdot 3H_2O$	528.35	dk red pr	2.868	$-3H_2O$, 150		v s		s al
b32	chromate	$BaCrO_4$	253.33	yel, rhomb	4.498[15]			0.00034[16]	0.00044[28]	s min a
b33	dichromate	$BaCr_2O_7$	353.33	red, monocl				sl s		s h conc H_2SO_4
b34	dichromate, hydrate	$BaCr_2O_7 \cdot 2H_2O$	389.36	bright red-yel need		$-2H_2O$, 120		d		s conc CrO_3 soln
b35	chromite	$BaO \cdot 4Cr_2O_3$	761.30	grn-blk, hex	5.4[15]			i	i	s a, fus carb
b26	citrate	$Ba_3(C_6H_5O_7)_2 \cdot 7H_2O$	916.33	wh powd		$-7H_2O$, 150		0.0406[18]	0.0572[25]	sl s al; s HCl
b37	cyanide	$Ba(CN)_2$	189.38	wh cr powd				80[14]		18[14] 70 % al
b38	cyanoplatinite	$BaPt(CN)_4 \cdot 4H_2O$	508.56	(a) monocl, yel, α 1.6704 (b) grn, rhomb	a) 2.076 b) 2.085	$-2H_2O$, 100		3[16]	25[100]	i al
b39	dithionate	$Ba(S_2O_6)_2 \cdot 2H_2O$	333.50	col, rhomb or monocl, 1.586, 1.595, 1.607	4.536[18.5]	d 120		24.75[18]	90.9[100]	sl s al
b40	ethylsulfate	$Ba(C_2H_5SO_4)_2 \cdot 2H_2O$	423.62	wh lust leaf				s		sl s al
b41	ferrocyanide	$Ba_2Fe(CN)_6 \cdot 6H_2O$	594.73	yel, monocl	2.666	$-H_2O$, 40		0.17[15]	0.9[100]	i al
b42	fluogallate	$Ba_3(GaF_6)_2 \cdot H_2O$	797.46	wh cr	4.06	$-\frac{1}{2}H_2O$, 110; $-\frac{1}{2}H_2O$, 230		i		s HF
b43	fluoride	BaF_2	175.34	col, cub, 1.4741 n_D^{26}	4.89	1355	2137	0.12[25]	sl s	s a, NH_4Cl
b44	fluoroiodide	$BaF_2 \cdot BaI_2$	566.49	pl	5.21[18]			d	d	i al; s conc HCl, conc NHO_3

No.	Name	Synonyms and Formulae	Mol. wt.	Crystalline form, properties and index of refraction	Density or spec. gravity	Melting point, °C	Boiling point, °C	Solubility, in grams per 100 cc		
								Cold water	Hot water	Other solvents
	Barium									
b45	fluosilicate.........	BaSiF₆	279.42	rhomb need....	4.29²¹₄	d 300	....	0.026¹⁷	0.09¹⁰⁰	i al; sl s a, NH₄Cl
b46	formate...........	Ba(CHO₂)₂	227.38	col, rhomb, 1.573, 1.597, 1.636	3.21	d	....	27.76⁰	39.71⁸⁰	i al, eth
b47	gluconate.........	Ba(C₆H₁₁O₇)₂.3H₂O....	581.69	pr or rhomb leaf..		−3H₂O, 100; d 120		3.3¹⁵·⁵	....	i al
b48	hydride..........	BaH₂	139.36	gray cr.........	4.21⁰	d 675	1400(?)	d to Ba(OH)₂ +H₂	....	d a
b49	hydroxide........	Ba(OH)₂.8H₂O.....	315.48	col, monocl, 1.471, 1.502, 1.50	2.18¹⁶	78	−8H₂O, 780	5.6¹⁵	94.7⁷⁸	sl s al; i acet
b50	hyponitrite.......	BaN₂O₂.4H₂O......	269.41	wh cr powd....	2.742²⁵					
b51	iodate............	Ba(IO₃)₂	487.15	monocl........	4.998	d	....	0.008⁰	197¹⁰⁰	s HNO₃, HCl
b52	iodate, hydrate.....	Ba(IO₃)₂.H₂O.....	505.17	col, monocl....	4.657¹⁵	−H₂O, 200		v sl s	sl s	s HNO₃, HCl; i al, acet, H₂SO₄
b53	iodide............	BaI₂	391.15	col cr..........	5.15²⁵₄	740		170⁰	....	al 77²⁰
b54	iodide, hydrate.....	BaI₂.2H₂O........	427.18	col rhomb, deliq..	5.15	−H₂O, 98.9; −2H₂O, 539; d 740	200¹⁵	269¹⁰⁰	....	1.07¹⁵ al; s acet
b55	iodide, hydrate....	BaI₂.6H₂O........	499.24	col, hex........		25.7	....	410⁰	v s	v s al
b56	laurate...........	Ba(C₁₂H₂₃O₂)₂	535.97	wh leaf cr......		260		0.008¹⁵·⁸	0.011⁵⁰	0.008²⁵ al; 0.006²⁵ eth
b57	l-malate..........	BaC₄H₄O₅	269.41	col............				0.883²⁰	1.044⁸⁰	....
b58	malonate.........	BaC₃H₂O₄.H₂O....	257.40	col............				0.143⁰	0.326⁸⁰	....
b59	manganate........	BaMnO₄	256.28	gray-grn, hex...	4.85			v sl s		s a
b60	per-manganate....	Ba(MnO₄)₂	375.21	br-vlt cr.......	3.77	d 200		62.5¹¹	75.4²⁵	d al
b61	methylsulfate......	Ba(CH₃SO₄)₂.2H₂O...	395.56	col effl cr......				s		s al
b62	molybdate........	BaMoO₄	297.28	wh powd......	4.65	1480		0.0058²³		sl s a
b63	myristate.........	Ba(C₁₄H₂₇O₂)₂	592.08					0.007¹⁵	0.010⁵⁰	0.009²⁵ al; 0.003²⁵ eth 0.046¹⁵ MeOH
b64	nitrate...........	Nitrobarite. Ba(NO₃)₂	261.35	col cub, 1.572...	3.24²³	592	d	8.7²⁰	34.2¹⁰⁰	i al; sl s a
b65	nitride...........	Ba₃N₂	440.03	yel-br........	4.783²⁵₄		1000 vac	d	d	
b66	nitrite...........	Ba(NO₂)₂	229.35	col, hex........	3.23²¹	d 217	....	67.5²⁰	300¹⁰⁰	sl s al
b67	nitrite, hydrate....	Ba(NO₂)₂.H₂O....	247.37	col-yelsh, hex....	3.173²⁰	d 115		63²⁰	109.6⁸⁰	1.6 al; v s HCl; i acet
b68	oxalate...........	BaC₂O₄	225.36	cr............	2.658	d 400		0.0093¹⁸	0.0228¹⁰⁰	i al; s NH₄Cl, a
b69	oxide............	BaO	153.34	col, cub, wh-yelsh powd, 1.98	5.72	1923	ca 2000	3.48²⁰	90.8¹⁰⁰	s dil a, al; i acet, NH₃
b70	oxide, per-.......	BaO₂	169.34	wh-gray powd....	4.96	450	−O, 800	v sl s	d	s dil a; i acet
b71	oxide, per-, hydrate .	BaO₂8H₂O.......	313.46	col, hex........	2.292	−8H₂O, 100		0.168	d	s dil a; i al, eth, acet
b72	palmitate.........	Ba(C₁₆H₃₁O₂)₂	648.19	wh cr powd.....		d		0.004¹⁵	0.007⁵⁰	0.008¹⁶·⁵ al; 0.001¹⁵ eth
b73	hypophosphate.....	BaPO₂	216.31	need..........				sl s	....	s al; v sl s ac a
b74	orthophosphate di-...	BaHPO₄	233.32	wh, rhomb, 1.635, 1.617	4.165¹⁵	d 410⁷¹⁰		0.01−0.02		s a, NH₄Cl
b75	orthophosphate, mono-	Ba(H₂PO₄)₂	331.31	tricl..........	2.9⁴			d	d	s a
b76	orthophosphate, tri-.	Ba₃(PO₄)₂	601.96	wh, cub.......	4.1¹⁶			i	i	s a
b77	pyrophosphate.....	Ba₂P₂O₇	448.62	wh, rhomb.....	3.9²⁰			0.01	sl s	s a, NH₄ salts
b78	hypophosphite.....	Ba(H₂PO₂)₂.H₂O...	285.33	wh, monocl.....	2.90¹⁷₄	d 100−150		30¹⁵	33¹⁰⁰	i al
b79	propionate........	Ba(C₃H₅O₂)₂.H₂O...	301.50	rhomb, β 1.518....		d 300		48⁰	67.9⁸⁰	0.08 al
b80	salycylate........	Ba(C₇H₅O₃)₂.H₂O...	437.65	wh need.......				s		s al
b81	selenate..........	BaSeO₄	280.30	wh, rhomb.....	4.75	d		0.0118	0.138¹⁰⁰	s HCl; i HNO₃
b82	selenide..........	BaSe	216.30	wh cub disc, n_D, 2.268	5.02			d	d	d HCl
b83	metasilicate.......	BaSiO₃	213.42	col, rhomb, 1.673, 1.674, 1.678	4.399	1604		i	d	s HCl
b84	metasilicate, hydrate.	BaSiO₃.6H₂O.....	351.52	rhomb, 1.542, 1.548, 1.548	2.59			0.17	d	....
b85	stearate..........	Ba(C₁₈H₃₅O₂)₂	704.13	wh powd......				0.004¹⁵	0.006⁵⁰	0.005¹⁶·⁵ al, 0.008²⁵ al, 0.001²⁵ eth
b86	succinate.........	BaC₄H₄O₄	253.37	wh powd......				0.421⁰	0.237⁸⁰	sl s al
b87	sulfate...........	Nat. barite, prec. blanc fixe. BaSO₄	233.40	wh, rhomb (monocl), 1.637, 1.638, 1.649	4.50¹⁵	1580	tr 1149 monocl	0.000222¹⁸ 0.000246²⁵	0.000336⁵⁰ 0.000413¹⁰⁰	0.006 s 3 % HCl; sl s H₂SO₄
b88	peroxydisulfate.....	BaS₂O₈.4H₂O.....	401.52	wh, monocl.....		d	....	52.2⁰	d	d al
b89	sulfide, hydro-.....	Ba(HS)₂.4H₂O....	275.56	wh, rhomb.....		d 50		s		i al
b90	sulfide, mono....	BaS	169.40	col, cub, n_D 2.155	4.25¹⁵	1200		d	d	i al
b91	sulfide, tetra-......	BaS₄.H₂O......	283.61	red or yel, rhomb.	2.988	d 300		41¹⁵	v s	l al, CS₂
b92	sulfide, tri-......	BaS₃	233.53	yel-grn cr......		d 554		s	s	....

No.	Name	Synonyms and Formulae	Mol. wt.	Crystalline form, properties and index of refraction	Density or spec. gravity	Melting point, °C	Boiling point, °C	Solubility, in grams per 100 cc		
								Cold water	Hot water	Other solvents
	Barium									
b93	sulfite	BaSO₃	217.40	col, cub hex		d		0.02²⁰	0.002⁸⁰	v s HCl
b94	tartrate	BaC₄H₄O₆.H₂O	303.52	wh cr	2.980²⁰·⁵			0.026¹⁸	0.058²⁰	0.032¹⁸ al
b95	tellurate	BaTeO₄.3H₂O	383.07	volum wh	4.2²⁰⁰	d >200		sl s	sl s	s HCl, NHO₃
b96	*pyro*tellurate, hydrogen	Ba(HTe₂O₇)₂.H₂O	891.76	volum ppt; hot: yel; cold: wh				s	s	s a
b97	telluride	BaTe	264.94	yel-wh, cub, disc, n_D 2.440	5.13					d a
b98	thiocarbonate	BaCS₃	245.54	yel, hex		d		1.08⁰	d	i al
b99	thiocyanate	Ba(SCN)₂.2H₂O	289.53	need, deliq	2.286¹⁸	−H₂O, 160		4.3²⁰	s	35²⁰ al
b100	thiosulfate	BaS₂O₃	249.47	wh, rhomb		d 220		0.2		
b101	thiosulfate, hydrate	BaS₂O₃.H₂O	267.48	wh, rhomb	3.5¹⁸	d 100		0.208²⁰		i al
b102	titanate	BaTiO₃	233.24	tetr and hex, 2.40	tetr 6.017, hex 5.806					
b103	tungstate	BaWO₄	385.19	col, tetr	5.04			sl s	sl s	d a
b104	*pyro*vanadate	Ba₂V₂O₇	488.56	wh cr		863				
b105	**Beryllium**	Glucinum. Be	9.0122	grey met, hex	1.85²⁰	1278±5	2970(5mm)	i	sl s, d	s dil a, alk; i Hg
b106	acetate	Be(C₂H₃O₂)₂	127.10	col pl		d 300		i		i al, eth, CCl₄
b107	acetate, basic	BeO(C₂H₃O₂)₆	406.32	oct	1.36⁴	284	331	sl d	d	s chl, ac a; sl s al, eth
b108	acetate propionate, basic	Be₄O(C₂H₃O₂)₄.(C₃H₅O₂)₂	448.40			127	330			
b109	aluminate	Nat. chrysoberyl. BeAl₂O₄	126.97	rhomb, 1.747, 1.748, 1.757	3.76	1870				i a
b110	aluminum silicate	Nat. beryl. Be₃Al₂(SiO₃)₆	537.51	transp, hex, col, 1.580, 1.547	2.66	1410±100				i a
b111	aluminum silicate	Nat. euclase. Be₂Al₂(SiO₄)₂.(OH)₂	290.17	monocl, 1.652, 1.655, 1.671	3.1					
b112	benzenesulfonate	Be(C₆H₅O₃S)₂	323.35	monocl				v s	v s	v s al, acet, ac a; i eth, bz, CS₂, CCl₄
b113	*ortho*borate, basic	Nat. hambergite. Be₂(OH)BO₃	93.84	rhomb, 1.560, 1.591, 1.631	2.35					
b114	bromide	BeBr₂	168.83	wh need, deliq	3.465²⁵	490±10 subl	520	s	v s	s al, eth; i bz; 18.56 pyr
b115	butyrate, basic	Be₄O(C₄H₇O₂)₆	574.64			239¹⁹				
b116	carbide	Be₂C	30.04	yel, hex	1.90¹⁵	>2100 d		d	d	s a; d alk
b117	carbonate, basic	BeCO₃+Be(OH)₂	112.05	wh powd				i	d	s a, alk
b118	chloride	BeCl₂	79.92	col need, deliq	1.899²⁵	405	520 (488)	v s	v s, d	v s al, eth, pyr; sl s bz, chl, CS₂; i NH₃, acet
b119	fluoride	BeF₂	47.01	col, amorph, <1.33	1.986²⁵	subl 800		∞	∞	sl s al; s H₂SO₄
b120	hydride	BeH₂	11.03	wh cr		d 125		d	d	i eth, tol
b121	iodide	BeI₂	262.82	col need	4.325²⁵	510±10	590	d	d	s al, eth, CS₂
b122	nitrate	Be(NO₃)₂.3H₂O	187.07	wh-yel cr, deliq	1.557	60	142	v s	v s	v s al
b123	nitride	Be₃N₂	55.05	col, cub		2200±100	d 2240	d	d	d a, conc alk; i al
b124	oxalate	BeC₂O₄.3H₂O	151.08	rhomb, β 1.487		−H₂O, 100; −3H₂O, 220	d 350	38.22²⁵		
b125	oxide	Nat. bromellite. BeO	25.01	wh hex, 1.719, 1.733	3.01	2530±30	ca 3900	0.00002³⁰		s conc H₂SO₄, fus KOH
b126	oxide	BeO.xH₂O		wh amorph powd or gel		d		i	i	s a, alk, (NH₄)₂CO₃
b127	2,4-pentanedione deriv	Beryllium acetyl-acetonate Be(C₅H₇O₂)₂	207.23	wh, monocl	1.168⁴	108	270	sl s	d	s al, eth, a
b128	*ortho*phosphate	Be₃(PO₄)₂.3H₂O	271.03			−H₂O, 100		s	s	s ac a
b129	propionate basic	Be₄O(C₃H₅O₂)₆	490.43			120				
b130	selenate	BeSeO₄.4H₂O	224.03	col, rhomb, 1.466, 1.501, 1.503	2.03	−2H₂O, 100; −4H₂O, 300		56.7²⁵	s	v s al
b131	*di*-silicate	Nat. bertrandite. Be₄Si₂O₇(OH)₂	238.23	rhomb, 1.591, 1.605, 1.604	2.6					
b132	*ortho*silicate	Nat. phenazite. Be₂SiO₄	110.11	tricl, col, 1.654, 1.670	3.0					i a
b133	stearate (com'l)	Be(C₁₈H₃₅O₂)₂	575.97	wh, waxy		45		i	i	i al; s eth, CCl₄
b134	sulfate	BeSO₄	105.07		2.443	d 550–600		i	d to BeSO₄ 4H₂O	
b135	sulfate, hydrate	BeSO₄.4H₂O	177.14	col, tetr, 1.472, 1.440	1.713¹⁰·⁵	−2H₂O, 100	−4H₂O, 400	42.5²⁵	100¹⁰⁰	sl s conc H₂SO₄; i al
b136	sulfide	BeS	41.08	reg	2.36			d	d	
b137	**Bismuth**	Bi	208.9808	rhomb silver-wh or redsh met	9.80	271.3	1560±5⁷⁶⁰	i	i	s h H₂SO₄, HNO₃ aq, reg; sl s h HCl
b138	acetate	Bi(C₂H₃O₂)₃	386.12	wh cr		d		i	i	s ac a

No.	Name	Synonyms and Formulae	Mol. wt.	Crystalline form, properties and index of refraction	Density or spec. gravity	Melting point, °C	Boiling point, °C	Solubility, in grams per 100 cc		
								Cold water	Hot water	Other solvents
	Bismuth									
b139	orthoarsenate	$BiAsO_4$	347.90	wh, monocl, 2.14, 2.15, 2.18	7.14		i	i	i	sl s h conc HNO_3
b140	benzoate	$Bi(C_7H_5O_2)_3$	572.33	wh powd						s a; i eth
b141	bromide, tri-	$BiBr_3$	448.71	yel cr powd, deliq	5.72_4^{25}	218	453	d to BiOBr	d	i al; s HCl, HBr, eth; v s liq NH_3
b142	carbonate, basic	Bismuth oxycarbonate. $Bi_2O_2CO_3$	509.97	wh powd	6.86		d	i	i	s a
b143	chloride, tetra-	$BiCl_4$	350.79	col cr		226				
b144	chloride, tri-	$BiCl_3$	315.34	wh cr, deliq	4.75_4^{25}	230–232	447	d to BiOCl	d	s a, al, eth, acet
b145	dichromate, basic	$(BiO)_2.Cr_2O_7$	665.94	yel-or-red cr				i	i	s a; i alk
b146	citrate	$BiC_6H_5O_7$	398.08	wh cr	3.458	d		sl s	sl s	sl s al; s NH_4OH
b147	fluoride, tri-	BiF_3	265.98	gray cr, cub, 1.74	5.32^{20}	727		i		s inorg a; i liq NH_3, al
b148	gallate, basic	Com'l dermatol. $Bi(OH_2)C_7H_5O_5$ (appr)	412.11	yel, amorph		d		i		i al, eth
b149	hydroxide	$Bi(OH)_3$ (appr)	260.00	wh amorph powd.	4.36	$-H_2O$, 100; d 415	$-1\frac{1}{2}H_2O$, 400	0.00014	d	s a; i or sl s conc alk
b150	iodate	$Bi(IO_3)_3$	733.69	wh				i		i HNO_3
b151	iodide, di-	BiI_2	462.79	red need, rhomb		d 400	subl vac	s		s al, MeOH
b152	iodide, tri-	BiI_3	589.69	redsh, hex	5.778^{15}	408	ca 500	i	d	3.5^{20} al; i a; sl s NH_3; s HCl, HI
b153	lactate, dl	$Bi(C_3H_5O_3)_3.7H_2O$	512.22	pr, need				14.4^{25}		i al
b154	molybdate	$Bi_2(MoO_4)_3$	897.78	yel-wh tetr need	6.07	643		v s a		
b155	nitrate	$Bi(NO_3)_3.5H_2O$	485.07	col tricl, sl hygr	2.83	d 30	$-5H_2O$, 80	d	d	v s HNO_3; s a, glyc; i al, 42^{19} acet
b156	nitrate, basic	$BiONO_3.H_2O$	305.00	hex leaf	4.928^{18}	$-H_2O$, 105	$-HNO_3$, 260	i	i	s a; i al
b157	oxalate	$Bi_2(C_2O_4)_3.7H_2O$	808.73	wh powd		$-6H_2O$, ca 130		d		s inorg a; i al, eth
b158	oxide, mono-	BiO	224.97	dk-gray powd	7.15^{19}	d ca 180 (Bi_2O_2)		sl d	d	d dil a; s dil KOH
b159	oxide, pent-	Bi_2O_5	497.96	dk red or br	5.10	$-O$, 150	$-2O$, 357	i	i	s KOH
b160	oxide, tetr-	$Bi_2O_4.2H_2O$	517.99	br powd	5.6	$-H_2O$, 110	$-2H_2O$, 180	i	i	s a
b161	oxide, tri-	Bi_2O_3	465.96	yel, rhomb	8.9	820	1890 (?)	i	i	s a
b162	oxide, tri-	Bi_2O_3	465.96	gray-blk, cub	8.20	tr 704		i	i	s a
b163	oxide, tri-	Bi_2O_3	465.96	wh-lt yel, rhomb, 1.91	8.55	860		i	i	sl s a
b164	oxybromide	BiOBr	304.89	col cr or wh powd	8.082^{15}	d red ht		i	i	i al; s a
b165	oxychloride	BiOCl	260.43	wh cr or powd, 2.15	7.72^{15}	red ht.		i	i	s a; i NH_3, tart a, acet
b166	oxyfluoride	BiOF	243.98	wh cr or powd	7.5_{20}^{20}	d red ht		i	i	s a
b167	oxyiodide	BiOI	351.88	red cr, tetr	7.922	d red ht		i	i	s a; i al, $CHCl_3$
b168	orthophosphate	$BiPO_4$	303.95	wh, monocl	6.323^{15}	d		i	i	s HCl; i al, dil HNO_3
b169	propionate, basic	$BiOC_3H_5O_2$	297.97	wh powd				i		v s dil HCl; i al
b170	salicylate, basic	Bismuth subsalicylate. $Bi(C_7H_5O_3)_3.Bi_2O_3$ (appr)	1086.29	wh micr cr (variable comp)				i		s a, alk; i al, eth
b171	selenide, tri-	Nat. guanajuatite. Bi_2Se_3	654.84	blk, rhomb	6.82	710	d	i		i alk
b172	silicate	Nat. eulytite. $2Bi_2O_3.3SiO_2$	1112.17	yel, cub, 2.05	6.11			i	i	s, d HCl, HNO_3
b173	sulfate	$Bi_2(SO_4)_3$	706.14	wh need	5.08^{15}	d 405		d	d	s a
b174	mono-sulfide,	BiS	241.04	dk gray powd	7.6–7.8	680 (in CO_2)	d	v sl s		
b175	sulfide, tri-	Nat. bismuthinite. bismuthglance. Bi_2S_3	514.15	br-blk, rhomb, 1.340, 1.456, 1.459	7.39	d 685		0.000018^{18}		s HNO_3; i dil al
b176	tartrate	$Bi_2(C_4H_4O_6)_3.6H_2O$	970.27	wh powd	2.595_4^{25}	$-3H_2O$, 105		i	i	s a, alk; i al
b177	tellurate	Montanite. $Bi_2TeO_6.2H_2O$	677.59	biaxial, β: 2.09	3.79					
b178	telluride, tri-	Nat. tetradymite. Bi_2Te_3	800.76	gray, rhbdr	7.7_4^{20}	573				d HNO_3
b179	vandate	Nat. pucherite. $Bi_2O_3.V_2O_5$	647.84	red-grn, rhomb, 2.41, 2.50, 2.51 (Li)	6.25^{25}					
b180	**Bismuthic acid**	$HBiO_3$	257.99	red	5.75	$-H_2O$, 120	$-2O$, 357	i	i	s a, KOH
b181	**Borazole**	$B_3N_3H_6$	80.50	col liq	1^{00}, 0.8014^{00}	-58	53	sl d	d	
b182	**Boric Acid**, meta-	HBO_2	43.82	wh cr, cub, 1.619	2.486	236 ± 1		v sl s	sl s	

No.	Name	Synonyms and Formulae	Mol. wt.	Crystalline form, properties and index of refraction	Density or spec. gravity	Melting point, °C	Boiling point, °C	Solubility, in grams per 100 cc		
								Cold water	Hot water	Other solvents
	Boric acid									
b183	ortho-............	Boracic acid. H_3BO_3...	61.83	col, tricl, 1.337, 1.461, 1.462	1.435^{15}	169 ± 1 tr to HBO_2	$-1\frac{1}{2}H_2O$, 300	6.35^{30}	27.6^{100}	28^{20} glyc; 0.0078 eth; 5.56 al; 20. 20^{25} MeOH; 1.92^{25} liq NH_3; sl s acet
b184	tetra- (pyro-)......	$H_2B_4O_7$...........	157.26	vitr or wh powd....				s	s	s al
b185	fluo-..............	HBF_4...........	87.81	col liq............			d 130	∞	∞	s al
b186	**Borinoaminoborine.**	B_2H_7N........	42.68	col liq............		−66.5	76.2			s triborine tri- amine
b187	**Boron.**...........	B................	10.811	yel monocl or br amorph powd	2.34, 2.37 amorph	2300	2550 (sub)	i	i	v sl s HNO_3
b188	arsenate...........	$BAsO_4$..........	149.73	wh cr tetrag, 1.681, 1.690	3.64	subl ca 700	....	v sl s	1.4^{100}	i al; s inorg a
b189	bromide, tri-.......	BBr_3............	250.54	col fum liq, $n_D^{16.3}$ 1.5312	$2.6431^{18.4}_4$	−46	91.3 ± 0.25	d	....	s al, CCl_4
b190	bromide, di-, iodide..	BBr_2I..........	297.53	col liq.........			125	d	d	....
b191	bromide, mono-, diiodide	$BBrI_2$..........	344.53	col liq.........			180	d	d	....
b192	(di-) bromide, mono-, pentahydride	B_2H_5Br.......	106.67	col gas.........		−104	ca 10	hyd to HBO_2, $HBr +$ H_2		....
b193	(tetra-) carbide.....	B_4C	55.26	blk rhbdr.......	2.52	2350	>3500	i	i	i a; s fus alk
b194	chloride, tri-.......	BCl_3	117.17	col fum liq, $1.4195^{5.7}$ α line H_2	1.349^{11}_4	−107.3	12.5	....	d to HCl $+ H_3BO_3$	d al
b195	fluoride, tri-.......	BF_3	67.81	col gas.........	2.99 g/l	−126.7	−99.9	106 (762 mm)	d	d al; s conc H_2SO_4
b196	fluoride dihydrate...	$BF_3.2H_2O$	103.84	col liq; n_{HE}^{20} 1.31498	1.6316^{20}_4	6	....	d	d	s eth, dioxan
b197	hydride...........	Diborane, boroethane. B_2H_6	27.67	col gas.........	liq: 0.447^{-11} sol: 0.577^{-183}	−165.5	−92.5	sl s d to H_3BO_3 $+ H_2$		d 1.6^0 al; s NH_4OH, conc H_2SO_4
b198	hydride...........	Dihydrotetraborane, borobutane. B_4H_{10}	53.32	col gas, pois.....	0.56^{-35}	−120.8	16	sl s, d		s bz; d al
b199	hydride...........	Pentaborane. B_5H_9	63.13	col liq.........	0.66^0	−46.82	58.4	d		....
b200	hydride...........	Hexaborane. B_6H_{10}......	74.95	col liq.........	0.69^0	−65	0^{72}	d		....
b201	hydride...........	Decaborane. $B_{10}H_{14}$	122.22	wh cr.........	0.94^{25}	99.5	213	sl s	d	v s CS_2; s al, eth bz
b202	iodide, tri-........	BI_3	391.52	col pl, hygr......	3.35^{50}	49.9	210	d	d	d al; v s CS_2, bz, CCl_4
b203	nitride............	BN................	24.82	wh, hex.........	2.25	subl ca 3000	....	i	sl d	sl s h a
b204	oxide.............	B_2O_3........	69.62	rhomb cr, 1.64, 1.61	2.46 ± 0.01	460	ca 1860	sl s	s	....
b205	oxide glass........	B_2O_3........	69.62	col, vitr 1.485....	1.812^{25}_4	ca 450		1.1^0	15.7^{100}	s al, a
b206	phosphide........	BP	41.78	maroon powd....		ign 200		i	i	i all solv
b207	*triselenide*........	B_2Se_3	258.50	yel-gray powd....				d	d	....
b208	(hexa-) silicide.....	B_6Si	92.95	blk cr.........	2.47			i		s HNO_3; d H_2SO_4; i KOH
b209	(tri-) silicide......	B_3Si	60.52	blk rhomb.......	2.52			i		sl s HNO_3; d H_2SO_4, KOH
b210	sulfide, penta-......	B_2S_5	181.94	col, tetrag.......	1.85	390		d		d al
b211	sulfide, tri-.......	B_2S_3	117.81	wh cr or vitr....	1.55	310		d		sl s PCl_3, SCl_2; d al
b212	**Borotungstic acid...**	$H_8BW_{12}O_{40}.30H_2O$......	3402.49	tetr, cr.........	3	45–51		s		s al, eth
b213	**Bromic acid.**........	$HBrO_3$........	128.92	known in sol only, col or yelsh		d 100		v s	d	....
b214	**Bromine.**...........	Br_2........	159.808	dk red liq, 1.661..	2.928^{50}, 3.119^{20}	−7.2	58.78	4.17^0, 3.58^{20}	3.52^{50}	v s al, eth, chl, CS_2
b215	azide............	Bromoazide. BrN_3.....	121.93	cr, red liq.....		ca 45	exp			s eth, KI; sl s bz, ligr
b216	chloride..........	BrCl	115.36	red-col liq or gas..		ca −66 d 10	ca 5	s d		s eth, CS_2
b217	fluoride, mono-.....	BrF	98.91	red-br gas.......		d −33	−20			....
b218	fluoride, penta-.....	BrF_5	174.90	col liq.........	2.466^{25}	−61.3	40.5	d	d	....
b219	fluoride, tri-.......	BrF_3	136.90	col-gray-yel liq....	2.49^{135}	(−2) 8.8	135	d viol. to O_2, HOBr, HF, $HBrO_3$		d alk
b220	hydrate...........	$Br_2.10H_2O$	339.97	red oct.........	1.49	d 6.8	....	s		
b221	oxide, di-.........	BrO_2	111.91	lt yel..........		d 0				
b222	oxide, mon-........	Br_2O	175.82	dk br..........		−17 to −18				s, d CCl_4
b223	(tri-) oxide, oct-....	Br_3O_8(or Br_2O_3)$_n$........	367.72	wh............		stable at −40				

No.	Name	Synonyms and Formulae	Mol. wt.	Crystalline form, properties and index of refraction	Density or spec. gravity	Melting point, °C	Boiling point, °C	Solubility, in grams per 100 cc		
								Cold water	Hot water	Other solvents
	Bromauric acid									
b224	Bromauric acid	$HAuBr_4.5H_2O$	607.69	red-br cr		27		v s		s al
b225	Bromous acid, hypo-	$HBrO$	96.92	known only in soln, col-yel		40 (vac)		s	s d	s al, eth, chl
b226	Bromoplatinic acid	$H_2PtBr_6.9H_2O$	838.70	red monocl, deliq		d −100		v s	v s	
c1	Cadmium	Cd	112.40	hex silv-wh malleable met	8.642	320.9	765	i	i	s a, NH_4NO_3, h H_2SO_4
c2	acetate	$Cd(C_2H_3O_2)_2$	230.50	col	2.341	256	d	v s		s MeOH
c3	acetate, hydrate	$Cd(C_2H_3O_2)_2.2H_2O$	266.54	col monocl, odor ac a	2.01	− H_2O, 130		v s	v s	v s al
c4	amide	$Cd(NH_2)_2$	144.45		3.05^{25}	d 120				
c5	ammonium chloride	$CdCl_2.NH_4Cl$	236.79	col need, rhomb	2.93	289		33.45^{16}	$43.99^{63.8}$	s al, MeOH
c6	ammonium sulfate	$Cd(NH_4)_2(SO_4)_2.6H_2O$	448.69	col monocl pr	2.061^{20}_4	100 d − H_2O		s	s	
c7	arsenate, hydrogen	$CdHAsO_4.H_2O$	270.34		4.164^{15}_4	>120				
c8	arsenide	Cd_3As_2	487.04	dk gray cub	6.21^{15}_4	721		i	i	sl s HCl; s HNO_3; i aq reg
c9	benzoate	$Cd(C_7H_5O_2)_2.2H_2O$	390.66					3.34^{20}		sl s al
c10	borate	$Cd(BO_2)_2.H_2O$	248.03	wh rhomb	3.758	d		125^{17}		i al
c11	borotungstate	$Cd_5(BW_{12}O_{40}).18H_2O$	6600.25	yel tricl		75		1250^{19}	v s	
c12	bromide	$CdBr_2$	272.22	yel cr	5.192^{25}	567	863	57^{10}	162^{104}	26.6^{15} al; 0.4^{15} eth; s HCl; 1.6^{18} acet
c13	bromide, tetrahydrate	$CdBr_2.4H_2O$	344.28	sm wh need, effl		tr 36		121^{10}	v s	25 al; s acet; sl s eth
c14	carbonate	$CdCO_3$	172.41	wh, trig	4.258^4	d <500		i	i	s a, KCN, NH_4 salts; i NH_3
c15	chlorate	$Cd(ClO_3)_2.2H_2O$	315.33	col pr, deliq	2.28^{18}	80		298^0	487^{65}	s al, a, acet
c16	chloride	$CdCl_2$	183.32	col, hex	4.047^{25}	568	960	140^{20}	150^{100}	1.52^{15} al; $1.7^{15.5}$ MeOH; i acet, eth
c17	chloride	$CdCl_2.2\frac{1}{2}H_2O$	228.35	col monocl, 1.6513	3.327	tr 34		168^{20}	180^{100}	2.05^{15} MeOH; sl s al
c18	chloroacetate, di-	$Cd(C_2HCl_2O_2)_2.2H_2O$	386.29	need	2.132^{15}					
c19	chloroacetate mono-	$Cd(C_2H_2ClO_2)_2.6H_2O$	407.47		1.942^{25}					
c20	chloroacetate, tri-	$Cd(C_2Cl_3O_2)_2.1\frac{1}{2}H_2O$	461.18	rhomb	2.093^{25}					
c21	chloroplatinate	$CdPtCl_6.3H_2O$	574.25	yel trig need	2.882	− H_2O, 170, d		s	s	
c23	chromite	$CdCr_2O_4$	280.39	grn to blk, cub	5.79^{17}			i	i	i a
c24	cyanide	$Cd(CN)_2$	164.44	cr		dec >200		1.7^{15}	s	s a, KCN, NH_4OH; i al
c25	ferrocyanide	$Cd_2Fe(CN)_6.xH_2O$	403.22	col cr, 1.45	2.79	− $5H_2O$, 110		i	i	s HCl
c26	fluogallate	$[Cd(H_2O)_6].[GaF_6H_2O]$	403.22	col cr, 1.45	2.79	− $5H_2O$, 110		v s		
c27	fluoride	CdF_2	150.40	wh cub, 1.56	6.64	1100	1758	4.35^{25}		s a, HF; i al, NH_3
c28	fluosilicate	$CdSiF_6.6H_2O$	362.57	col hex				s	s	s 50 % al
c29	formate	$Cd(CHO_2)_2.2H_2O$	238.47	monocl	2.44	d		v s		
c30	fumarate	$Cd(C_4H_2O_4)$	226.48					0.9^{30}		
c31	hydroxide	$Cd(OH)_2$	146.41	wh, trig or amorph	4.79^{15}	d 300		0.00026^{25}		s a, NH_4 salts; i alk
c32	iodate	$Cd(IO_3)_2$	462.21	wh cr	6.43	d		s		s HNO_3; $NH_4.OH$
c33	iodide	CdI_2	366.21	grn-yel powd	5.670^{30}_4	387	796	86.2^{25}	125^{100}	110.5^{20} al; 41^{25} acet; sl s NH_3; 206.7^{25} MeOH
c34	lactate	$Cd(C_3H_5O_3)_2$	290.54	need				10	12.5	i al
c35	maleate	$Cd(C_4H_2O_4).2H_2O$	262.49					0.66^{30}		
c36	permanganate	$Cd(MnO_4)_2.6H_2O$	458.36		2.81	d 95		v s	v s	
c37	molybdate	$CdMoO_4$	272.34	yel pl	5.347			sl s		s a, NH_4OH, KCN
c38	nitrate	$Cd(NO_3)_2$	236.41	col		350		109^0	326^{60} 682^{100}	v s a; s et ac
c39	nitrate, tetrahydrate	$Cd(NO_3)_2.4H_2O$	308.47	wh pr, need, hygr	2.455^{17}_4	59.4	132	215		s al, NH_3; i HNO_3
c40	nitrocobaltate (III)	Cadmium cobaltinitrite. $Cd[Co(NO_2)_6]_2$	1007.13	yel		d 175		sl s	v s	d a, alk, org solv
c41	oxalate	CdC_2O_4	200.42	col cr	3.32^{18}_4	d 340				s a; i al
c42	oxalate, trihydrate	$CdC_2O_4.3H_2O$	254.45	col cr		d		0.005^{18}	0.009	
c43	oxide	CdO	128.40	br, amorph	6.95	<1426	d 900−1000	i	i	s a, NH_4 salts; i alk
c44	oxide	CdO	128.40	br cub, 2.49 (Li)	8.15	d 900	subl 1559	i	i	s a, NH_4 salts; i alk
c45	orthophosphate	$Cd_3(PO_4)_2$	527.14	col, amorph		1500		i		s a, NH_4 salts

No.	Name	Synonyms and Formulae	Mol. wt.	Crystalline form, properties and index of refraction	Density or spec. gravity	Melting point, °C	Boiling point, °C	Solubility, in grams per 100 cc		
								Cold water	Hot water	Other solvents
	Cadmium									
c46	*pyrophosphate*	$Cd_2P_2O_7$	398.74	wh cr leaf	4.965^{15}	above red heat		sl s	s	s a, NH_3
c47	phosphate, dihydrogen	$Cd(H_2PO_4)_2.2H_2O$	342.41	col, tricl	2.74^{15}_4	d 100				i al, eth; s HCl
c48	phosphide	Cd_3P_2	399.15	grn, tetr need	5.60	700				s d HCl; s exp conc HNO_3
c49	potassium cyanide	$Cd(CN)_2.2KCN$	294.68	col, glossy, oct	1.847			33.3	100	i al
c50	potassium sulfate	$CdK_2(SO_4)_2.2H_2O$	322.69	tricl col tab	2.922^{16}			42.89^{15}	47.40^{40}	
c51	salycilate	$Cd(C_7H_5O_3)_2.H_2O$	404.65	wh need		sl s			s	s al, eth, glycerol a, NH_4OH
c52	selenate	$CdSeO_4.2H_2O$	291.39	rhomb	3.63	$-1H_2O$, 100; $-2H_2O$, 170		v s		
c53	selenide	$CdSe$	191.36	grn-br or red powd, hex	5.81^{15}_4	>1350		i		d a
c54	*metasilicate*	$CdSiO_3$	188.48	col, rhomb, 1.739	4.93	1242		v sl s		
c55	sulfate	$CdSO_4$	208.46	wh, rhomb	4.691^{20}_4	1000		75.5^0	60.8^{100}	i al, acet, NH_3
c56	sulfate, hydrate	$CdSO_4.H_2O$	226.48	monocl	3.79^{20}	tr 108		s	s	i al
c57	sulfate, hydrate	$CdSO_4.7H_2O$	334.57	col, monocl	2.48	tr 4		s		i al
c58	sulfate, hydrate	$3CdSO_4.8H_2O$	769.50	col, monocl, 1.565	3.09	tr 41.5		113^0	s	
c59	sulfide	Nat. greenockite. CdS	144.46	yel-or, hex, 2.506, 2.529	4.82	1750^{100atm}	subl in N_2, 980	0.00013^{18}	colloid	s a; v sl s NH_4OH
c60	sulfite	$CdSO_3$	192.46			d		sl s		i al; s a, NH_4OH
c61	tartrate	$CdC_4H_4O_6$	260.47	wh cr powd				sl s		s a, NH_4OH
c62	telluride	$CdTe$	240.00	blk, cub	6.20^{15}	1041		i		i a; d HNO_3
c63	tungstate	$CdWO_4$	360.25	yel cr				0.05		s NH_4OH
	Cadmium complexes									
c64	tetramminecadmium perrhenate	$[Cd(NH_3)_4](ReO_4)_2$	681.16		3.714^{25}_4					0.037 conc NH_4OH
c65	tetrapyridine cadmiumfluosilicate	$[Cd(C_5H_5N)_4]SiF_6$	570.89	wh, tricl	2.282					
c66	**Calcium**	Ca	40.08	silv wh soft met, cub	1.54	839 ± 2	1484	d to H_2+ $Ca(OH)_2$	d	s a, liq NH_3; sl s al; i bz
c67	acetate	$Ca(C_2H_3O_2)_2$	158.17	col cr; 1.55, 1.56, 1.57		d		37.4^0	29.7^{100}	sl s al
c68	acetate, dihydrate	$Ca(C_2H_3O_2)_2.2H_2O$	194.21	col need		$-1H_2O$, 84		34.7^{20}	33.5^{80}	
c69	acetate, monohydrate	$Ca(C_2H_3O_2)_2.H_2O$	176.19	col need		d		43.6^0	34.3^{100}	sl s al
c70	aluminate	$CaAl_2O_4$ (or $CaO.Al_2O_3$)	158.04	wh monocl, tricl or rhomb; 1.643, 1.665, 1.663	2.981^{25}	1600		d		s HCl; i HNO_3, H_2SO_4
c71	(tri-)aluminate	$Ca_3Al_2O_6$ (or $3CaO.Al_2O_3$)	270.20	wh, cub, 1.710	3.038^{25}	d 1535		i		s a
c72	(tri-)aluminate hexahydrate	$3CaO.Al_2O_3.6H_2O$	378.29	col, oct, 1.603	2.52^{20}	d 700–800		d		
c73	aluminosilicate	$2Ca.Al_2O_3.SiO_2$	274.20	col, tetr, 1.669, 1.658	3.048	1590 ± 2				d a
c74	aluminosilicate	Nat. anorthite. $CaAl_2.Si_2O_8$ (or $CaO.Al_2O_3.2SiO_2$)	278.21	wh, tricl, 1.5832	2.765	1551				
c75	*ortho*arsenate	$Ca_3(AsO_4)_2$	398.08	col amorph powd	3.620			0.013^{25}		
c76	arsenate, trihydrate	Nat. haidingerite. $2CaO.As_2O_5.3H_2O$	396.04	col, rhomb, 1.590, 1.602, 1.638	2.967					
c77	arsenide	Ca_3As_2	270.08	red cr	3.031^{25}	d		d	d	d a; s h HNO_3
c78	azide	$Ca(N_3)_2$	124.12	col, rhomb, hyg		$-3H_2O$, 110; exp 144–156		38.1^0	45^{15}	0.211^{16} al; i eth
c79	benzoate	$Ca(C_7H_5O_2)_2.3H_2O$	336.36	col, rhomb	1.436	$-3H_2O$, 110		2.7^0	8.3^{80}	
c80	*metaborate*	$Ca(BO_2)_2$	125.70	col, flat rhomb pr, 1.550, 1.660, 1.680		1154		sl s		s a, NH_4 salts; sl s ac a
c81	*metaborate*, hexahydrate	$Ca(BO_2)_2.6H_2O$	233.79	col, tetr, 1.520, 1.502	1.88			0.25^{20}		
c82	*tetraborate*	CaB_4O_7	195.32	readily vitrified		986				
c83	boride	CaB_6	104.95	blk, cub	2.3^{20}	2235		i	i	s HNO_3; sl s conc H_2SO_4
c84	bromide	$CaBr_2$	199.90	col, rhomb need, deliq	3.353^{25}	sl d 730	806–812	142^{20}	312^{105}	s al, acet, a; sl s NH_3, MeOH
c85	bromate	$Ca(BrO_3)_2.H_2O$	313.91	monocl cr	3.329	$-H_2O$, 180		v s	v s	
c86	bromide, hexahydrate	$CaBr_2.6H_2O$	307.99	col, hex cr	2.295	38.2	149	594^0	1360^{85}	s al, acet, a

No.	Name	Synonyms and Formulae	Mol. wt.	Crystalline form, properties and index of refraction	Density or spec. gravity	Melting point, °C	Boiling point, °C	Solubility, in grams per 100 cc		
								Cold water	Hot water	Other solvents
	Calcium									
c87	butyrate	$Ca(C_4H_7O_2)_2.3H_2O$	268.32	col cr				s	sl s	
c88	carbide	CaC_2	64.10	col, tetr, 1.75	2.22	stab 25–447	2300	d	d	
c89	carbonate	Nat. aragonite. $CaCO_3$	100.09	col, rhomb, 1.530, 1.681, 1.685	2.930	tr to calcite 520	d 825	0.00153[25]	0.00190[75]	s a, NH₄Cl
c90	carbonate	Nat. calcite. $CaCO_3$	100.09	col, rhomb or hex, 1.6583, 1.4864	2.710[18]	1339[1025]	d 898.6	0.0014[25]	0.0018[75]	s a, NH₄Cl
c91	carbonate, hexahydrate	$CaCO_3.6H_2O$	208.18	col, monocl, 1.460, 1.535, 1.545	1.771[0]					
c92	chlorate	$Ca(ClO_3)_2$	206.99	wh cr, hyg		340 ± 10 (−some O)		s	s	s al, acet
c93	chlorate, dihydrate	$Ca(ClO_3)_2.2H_2O$	243.01	wh-yelsh, rhomb, or monocl, deliq	2.711	− H₂O, 100		177.7[8]	v s	s al, acet
c94	*perchlorate*	$(CaClO_4)_2$	238.98	col cr	2.651	d 270		188.6[25]	v s	166.2[$_{18}^{25}$] al; 237.4 MeOH
c95	chloride	$CaCl_2$	110.99	col, cub, deliq 1.52	2.15[$_4^{25}$]	782	>1600	74.5[20]	159[100]	s al, acet, ace a
c96	chloride aluminate	$3CaO.Al_2O_3.CaCl_2.10H_2O$	561.33	col, monocl or hex, hex, 1.550, 1.535	1.892[14]	− H₂O, 105	−8H₂O, 350	sl s	d	s a
c97	chloride, dihydrate	$CaCl_2.2H_2O$	147.02	col cr	0.835			97.7[0]	326[60]	50[80] al
c98	chloride, hexahydrate	$CaCl_2.6H_2O$	219.08	col, trig, deliq, 1.417, 1.393	1.71[25]	29.92	−4H₂O, 30, −6H₂O, 200	279[0]	536[20]	s al
c99	chloride, monohydrate	$CaCl_2.H_2O$	129.00	col cr, deliq		260		76.8[0]	249[100]	s al; i acet
c100	chloride fluoride *orthophosphate*	$3Ca_3(PO_4)_2.CaClF$	1025.08	col cr, 1.634, 1.631	3.14	1270		v sl s		
c101	chlorite	$Ca(ClO_2)_2$	174.98	wh, cub	2.71			d	d	i al
c102	hypochlorite	$Ca(ClO)_2$	142.98	wh powd or flat pl, 1.545, 1.69	2.35	d 100		s		i al
c103	chlorite, basic	$Ca(ClO)_2.2Ca(OH)_2$	257.16	wh, hex, 1.51, 1.585	2.10			sl s solns with 5–6 % avail Cl	d	d a
c104	*hypochlorite, basic*	Bleaching powder, chlorinated lime. $Ca(ClO)_2.CaCl_2.xCa(OH)_2.xH_2O$	comp varies	wh powd strong Cl odor		d		d evln Cl		d a
c105	*hypochlorite, trihydrate*	$Ca(ClO)_2.3H_2O$	197.03	tetr pl, 1.535, 1.63	2.1	−3H₂O, 60				
c106	chromate	$CaCrO_4.2H_2O$	192.09	yel. monocl pr		−2H₂O, 200		16.3[20]	18.2[45]	s a, al
c107	chromite	$CaCr_2O_4$	208.07	ol grn, cub need	4.8[18]	2090		i		i a; s fus K₂CO₃
c108	cinnamate	$Ca(C_9H_7O_2)_2.3H_2O$	388.44	col cr				0.22[2]	1.34[100]	
c109	citrate	$Ca_3(C_6H_5O_7)_2.4H_2O$	570.51	wh need		−4H₂O, 120		0.085[18]	0.096[23]	0.0065[18] al
c110	cyanamide	$CaCN_2$	80.10	col, hex, rhbdr		1300 subl >1150		d evl NH₃	d	
c111	cyanide	$Ca(CN)_2$	92.12	wh powd		d >350		d	d	
c112	cyanoplatinite	$CaPt(CN)_4.5H_2O$	429.31	yel-grn fluoresc, rhomb, 1.6226		−5H₂O, 100		s		
c113	ferricyanide	$Ca_3[Fe(CN)_6]_2.12H_2O$	760.42	red need, deliq				v s	v s	
c114	ferrite, mono-	$CaO.Fe_2O_3$	215.77	dk redsh r, rhomb, 2.58, 2.43 (Na)	5.08	1250		i	i	v sl s a
c115	ferrocyanide	$Ca_2Fe(CN)_6.11$ or $12H_2O$	490.28	yel tricl, 1.570, 1.582, 1.596	1.68	d		86.8[25]	115[65]	i al
c116	fluosilicate	$CaSiF_6$	182.16	col, tetr	2.66[18]			sl s		s al, HF, HCl
c117	fluoride	Nat. fluorite. CaF_2	78.08	col, cub luminisc w heat, 1.434	3.180	1423	ca 2500	0.0016[18]	0.0017[26]	s NH₄ salts; sl s a; i acet
c118	fluosilicate, dihydrate	$CaSiF_6.2H_2O$	218.19	col, tetrag	2.251			sl s al		s HCl, HF; i al
c119	formate	$Ca(CHO_2)_2$	130.12	col, rhomb, 1.510, 1.514, 1.578	2.015	d		16.2[0]	18.4[100]	i al
c120	fumarate	$CaC_4H_2O_4.3H_2O$	208.18	col, rhomb				2.11[30]		
c121	d-gluconate	$Ca(C_6H_{11}O_7)_2.H_2O$	448.40	wh cr powd, need		−H₂O, 120		3.3[15]		v sl s al
c122	glycerophosphate	$CaC_3H_7(OH)_2PO_4$	210.16	wh cr powd, hyg		d 170		2[25]	sl s	i al
c123	hydride	CaH_2	42.10	wh, rhomb cr	1.9	816 (in H₂) d ca 600		d H₂ + Ca(OH)₂		d a
c124	hydroxide	$Ca(OH)_2$	74.09	col, hex, 1.574, 1.545	2.24	−H₂O, 580	d	0.185[0]	0.077[100]	s NH₄ salts, a; i al
c125	hyponitrite	$CaN_2O_2.4H_2O$	172.15	wh cr	1.834	d 320			0.67[90]	d dil a
c126	iodate	Nat. lautarite. $Ca(IO_3)_2$	389.89	col, monocl	4.519[15]	d 540		0.20[15]		s HNO₃; i al
c127	iodate, hexahydrate	$Ca(IO_3)_2.6H_2O$	497.98	col, rhomb		d 35		0.13[0]	1.22[100]	s HNO₃
c128	iodide	CaI_2	293.89	yelsh-wh, hex, deliq	3.956[$_4^{25}$]	784	ca 1100	209[20]	426[100]	126[20] MeOH; s al, acet, a

No.	Name	Synonyms and Formulae	Mol. wt.	Crystalline form, properties and index of refraction	Density or spec. gravity	Melting point, °C	Boiling point, °C	Cold water	Hot water	Other solvents
								Solubility, in grams per 100 cc		
	Calcium									
c129	iodide, hexahydrate	$CaI_2.6H_2O$	401.98	yel, hex need	2.55	d 42	160	757^0	1680^{30}	s a, al, acet
c130	iron (III) aluminate	Calcium (tetra-) alumino-ferite, nat. celite. $4CaO.Fe_2O_3.Al_2O_3$	485.97	brn, rhomb, 1.98, 2.05, 2.08 all for λ	3.77	1418		3		
c131	isobutyrate	$Ca(C_4H_7O_2)_2.5H_2O$	304.35	col powd				20	sl s	
c132	lactate	$Ca(C_3H_5O_3)_2.5H_2O$	308.30	wh need, effl		$-3H_2O$, 100		3.1^0	7.9^{30}	sl s a; i al, eth
c133	laurate	$Ca(C_{12}H_{23}O_2)_2.H_2O$	456.73	wh need, effl		182–183		0.004^{15}	0.055^{100}	0.059^{15}, 1.72^{78} al
c134	linoleate	$Ca(C_{18}H_{31}O_2)_2$	598.97	wh amorph powd				i		s al, eth
c135	magnesium carbonate	Nat. dolomite. $CaCO_3.MgCO_3$	184.41	col, trig, 1.6817, 1.5026	2.872	d 730–760		0.032^{18}		
c136	magnesium *metasilicate*	Nat. diopside. $CaO.MgO.2SiO_2$	216.56	col, monocl, 1.665, 1.672, 1.695	3.275	1391		i	i	i HCl
c137	magnesium *orthosilicate*	Nat. mervinite. $3CaO.MgO.SiO_2$	328.72	col to pa grn, monocl, 1.708, 1.711, 1.718	3.150					
c138	dl-malate	$CaC_4H_4O_5.3H_2O$	226.20	col, rhomb, 1.545, 1.555, 1.575				0.321^0	$0.451^{37.5}$	i al
c139	*l*-malate	$CaC_4H_4O_5.2H_2O$	208.18	col				0.812^0	$1.224^{37.5}$	s al
c140	malate, dihydrogen	$Ca(HC_4H_4O_5)_2.6H_2O$	414.33	rhomb, or wh cr powd, 1.493, 1.507, 1.545				sl s		
c141	maleate	$CaC_4H_2O_4.H_2O$	172.15	col rhomb, 1.495, 1.575, 1.640				2.89^{25}	3.21^{40}	
c142	malonate	$CaC_3H_2O_4.4H_2O$	214.19					0.44^0	0.72^{100}	
c143	*permanganate*	$Ca(MnO_4)_2.5H_2O$	368.03	purp cr	2.4	d		331^{14}	338^{25}	s NH_4OH
c144	α-methylbutyrate	Calvium ethylmethyl-acetate. $Ca(C_5H_9O_2)_2$	242.34					24.24^0	25.65^{70}	
c145	molybdate	Nat. pawellite. $CaMoO_4$	200.01	col, tetr, 1.967, 1.978	4.38–4.53			i	d	s a i al, eth
c146	nitrate	$Ca(NO_3)_2$	164.09	col, cub, hyg	2.504^{18}	561		121.2^{18}	376^{100}	14^{15} al; s MeOH, liq NH_3, acet; i eth
c147	nitrate, tetrahydrate	$Ca(NO_3)_2.4H_2O$	236.15	col, monocl, deliq, 1.465, 1.498, 1.504	α 1.896, β 1.82	α 42.7, β 39.7	d 132	266^0	660^{30}	s al, acet
c148	nitrate, trihydrate	$Ca(NO_3)_2.3H_2O$	218.14	col, tricl		51.1				
c149	nitride	Ca_3N_2	148.25	brn cr, hex	2.63^{17}	1195		d	d	s dil a; d abs al
c150	nitrite	$Ca(NO_2)_2.H_2O$	150.11	col-yelsh, hex, deliq	2.23^{34}	$-H_2O$, 100		45.9^0	89.6^{91}	sl s al
c151	nitrite, tetrahydrate	$Ca(NO_2)_2.4H_2O$	204.15	col cr, tetr	1.674^0_4	$-2H_2O$, 44		74.9^0	106^{42}	s al
c152	oleate	$Ca(C_{18}H_{33}O_2)_2$	603.01	wh wax-like cr		83–84		0.04^{25}	0.03^{50}	sl s eth
c153	oxalate	CaC_2O_4	128.10	col, cub	2.2^4	d		0.00067^{20}	0.0014^{95}	s a; i ac a
c154	oxalate, hydrate	$CaC_2O_4.H_2O$	146.12	col	2.2	$-H_2O$, 200		i	i	s a; i ac a
c155	oxide	Lime, calcia. CaO	56.08	col, cub, 1.838	3.25–3.38	2580	2850	0.131^{10} d	0.07^{80} d	s a
c156	oxide, per-	CaO_2	72.08	wh, tetr, 1.895	2.92^{25}_4	d 275		sl s		s a
c157	oxide, per-octahydrate	$CaO_2.8H_2O$	216.20	wh, tetr, pearly	1.70	$-8H_2O$, 200 d 275 expl		sl s	d	s a, NH_4 salts; i al, eth
c158	palmitate	$Ca(C_{16}H_{31}O_2)_2$	550.93	wh or yelsh, wh fatty powd				0.003^{25}		v sl s al; 0.008^{25} eth
c159	1-phenol-4 sulfonate(p-)	$Ca[C_6H_4(OH)SO_3]_2.H_2O$	404.43	wh to pinkish powd				s		s al
c160	phenoxide	$Ca(OC_6H_5)_2$	226.29	redsh powd				sl s		sl s al
c161	*hypophosphate*	$Ca_2P_2O_6.2H_2O$	274.13	gel				i		s HCl
c162	*metaphosphate*	$Ca(PO_3)_2$	198.02	col, 1.588, 1.595	2.82	975		i	i	i a
c163	*orthophosphate*, di-(sec)	Nat. brushite. $CaHPO_4.2H_2O$	172.09	wh, tricl, 1.5576, 1.5457, 1.5392	2.306^{18}	$-H_2O$, 109		0.0316^{25}	0.075^{100}	i al, s a
c164	*orthophosphate*, mono-(prim.)	$Ca(H_2PO_4)_2.H_2O$	252.07	col, tricl, deliq, 1.5292, 1.5176, 1.4392	2.220^{18}	$-H_2O$, 109	d 203	1.8^{30}	d	s a
c165	*orthophosphate*, tri-(tert.)	Nat. whitlockite. $Ca_3(PO_4)_2$	310.18	wh amorph powd, 1.629, 1.626	3.14	1670		0.002	d	i al; s a
c166	*pyrophosphate*	$Ca_2P_2O_7$	254.10	col, biax, 1.585, 1.604	3.09	1230		i		s a
c167	*pyrophosphate*, pentahydrate	$Ca_2P_2O_7.5H_2O$	344.18	col, monocl, 1.539, 1.545, 1.551	2.25			sl s		s a; i NH_4Cl
c168	phosphide	Ca_3P_2	182.19	gray lumps	2.51	ca 1600		d ev PH_3		s a; i al, eth, bz
c169	*hypophosphite*	$Ca(H_2PO_2)_2$	170.06	wh-gray, monocl		d		15.4^{25}	12.5^{100}	i al
c170	*orthophosphite*, di-	$2CaHPO_3.3H_2O$	294.17					sl s	d	s NH_4Cl
c171	*orthoplumbate*	Ca_2PbO_4	351.35	red-br cr	5.71	d		i		s a
c172	propionate	$Ca(C_3H_5O_2)_2.H_2O$	204.24	col, monocl tabl				49^0	55.8^{100}	i al
c173	*l*-quinate	$Ca(C_7H_{11}O_6)_2.10H_2O$	602.56	rhomb leaf		50, $-10H_2O$ 120		16^{18}		i al

No.	Name	Synonyms and Formulae	Mol. wt.	Crystalline form, properties and index of refraction	Density or spec. gravity	Melting point, °C	Boiling point, °C	Solubility, in grams per 100 cc		
								Cold water	Hot water	Other solvents
	Calcium									
c174	salicylate	$Ca(C_7H_5O_3)_2.2H_2O$	350.34	wh, oct		$-2H_2O$, 120		4^{25}	s	s al
c175	selenate	$CaSeO_4$	183.04	col	2.88			7.9^6	5.4^{67}	
c176	selenate, dihydrate	$CaSeO_4.2H_2O$	219.07	col, monocl	2.68					
c177	selenide	CaSe	119.04	cub, 2.274	3.57					
c178	metasilicate(α)	Nat. pseudowollastonite. $CaSiO_3$	116.16	col, monocl, 1.610, 1.611, 1.664	2.905	1540		0.0095^{17}		s HCl
c179	metasilicate(β)	Nat. wollastonite. $CaSiO_3$	116.16	col, monocl, 1.616, 1.629, 1.631	2.5	tr 1200				
c180	di-orthosilicate (I)	Ca_2SiO_4	172.24	col, monocl, 1.717, 1.735	3.27	2130				
c181	di-orthosilicate (II)	Ca_2SiO_4	172.24	col, rhomb, 1.717, 1.735	3.28	tr to (I) 1420				
c182	di-orthosilicate (III)	Ca_2SiO_4	172.24	col, monocl, 1.642, 1.645, 1.654	2.97	tr to 675				
c183	(tri-)silicate	Nat. alite. Ca_3SiO_5 or ($3CaO.SiO_2$)	228.32	col, monocl, α 1.718, β 1.724		1900 (incngr)				
c184	silicide	$CaSi_2$	96.25		2.5			i	d	s a, alk
c185	stearate	$Ca(C_{18}H_{35}O_2)_2$	607.04	cr powd		179–180		0.004^{15}		i al, eth
c186	succinate	$CaC_4H_4O_4.3H_2O$	212.22	col, 1.460, 1.540, 1.610				0.193^{10}	0.89^{80}	
c187	sulfate	Nat. anhydrite. $CaSO_4$	136.14	col, rhomb, or monocl, 1.569, 1.575, 1.613	2.960	monocl 1450	rhomb tr to monocl 1193	0.209^{30}	0.1619^{100}	s a, NH_4 salts, $Na_2S_2O_3$, glyc
c188	sulfate	Soluble anhydrite. $CaSO_4$	136.14	col, hex or tricl, 1.505, 1.548	2.61	tr to rhomb >200				
c189	sulfate half-hydrate	Plaster of Paris. $CaSO_4.\frac{1}{2}H_2O$	145.15	wh powd		$-\frac{1}{2}H_2O$, 163		0.3^{20}	sl s	s a, NH_4 salts, $Na_2S_2O_3$, glyc
c190	sulfate dihydrate	Nat. gypsum. $CaSO_4.2H_2O$	172.17	col, monocl, 1.521, 1.523, 1.530	2.32	$-1\frac{1}{2}H_2O$, 128	$-2H_2O$, 163	0.241	0.222^{100}	s a, NH_4 salts, $Na_2S_2O_3$, glyc
c191	sulfide	Nat. oldhamite. CaS	72.14	col, cub, 2.137	2.5	d		0.0211^{15} d	0.048^{60} d	d a
c192	sulfide, hydro-	$Ca(HS)_2.6H_2O$	214.32	col pr		d 15–18		v s		s al,
c193	sulfite	$CaSO_3.2H_2O$	156.17	col, hex		$-2H_2O$, 100		0.0043^{18}	0.0011^{100}	s H_2SO_3
c194	sulfite, dihydrogen	$Ca(HSO_3)_2$	202.22	yelsh liq, strong SO_2 odor				s		s a
c195	d-tartrate	$CaC_4H_4O_6.4H_2O$	260.21	col, rhomb, 1.525, 1.535, 1.550		d		0.0266^0	$0.0689^{37.5}$	sl s al
c196	dl-tartrate	$CaC_4H_4O_6.4H_2O$	260.21	tricl, powd or need		$-4H_2O$, 200		0.0032^0	$0.0078^{37.5}$	s HCl; i ac, a
c197	mesotartrate	$CaC_4H_4O_6.3H_2O$	242.20	wh, monocl or tricl pr		$-3H_2O$ <170		i	0.16^{100}	0.28^{18}, 0.85^{100} ac a
c198	telluride	CaTe	167.68	cub, 2.51, 2.58	4.873					
c199	tellurite	$CaTeO_3$	215.68	wh fl		>960		sl s	s	s a
c200	thiocarbonate, tri-	$CaCS_3$	148.28	yel cr				s		i al
c201	thiocyanate	$Ca(SCN)_2.3H_2O$	210.29	wh cr, deliq				v s	v s	v s al
c202	di-thionate	$Ca(SO_3)_2.4H_2O$	272.27	col, trig, 1.5496	2.176			16^0	30^{30}	
c203	thiosulfate	$CaS_2O_3.6H_2O$	260.30	tricl	1.872	d		100^3	d	s al
c204	metatitanate	Nat. perovskite. $CaTiO_3$	135.98	col, cub, rhomb, β 2.34	4.10	1975				
c205	tungstate	$CaWO_4$	287.93	wh, tetr, 1.9263, 1.9107	6.062^{20}			0.00064^{15}	0.00012^{100}	
c206	tungstate	Nat. scheelite. $CaWO_4$	287.93	col or w sc, tetr, 1.918, 1.934	6.06			0.2		i al, a; s NH_4Cl
c207	metatungstate	$Ca_2H_4[H_2(W_2O_7)_6].27H_2O$	3500.96	col, tric		$-7H_2O$, 105	$-10H_2O$, d			d a
c208	valerate	$Ca(C_5H_9O_2)_2$	242.33					8.28^0	7.39^{100}	
c209	metazirconate	$CaZrO_3$	179.30	col, monocl	4.78	2550				
c210	**Carbon**	Diamond. C	12.01	col, cub, 2.4173	3.51	>3550	4827	i	i	i a, alk
c211	carbon	Graphite. C	12.01	blk, hex	2.25^{20}	subl 3652–97	4827	i	i	s liq Fe; i a, alk
c212	carbon, amorphous	C	12.01	amorph, blk	1.8–2.1	subl 3652–97	4827	i	i	i a, alk
c213	(di-)bromide, hexa-	Hexabromomethane. C_2Br_6	503.48	rhomb pr, 1.740, 1.847, 1.863	3.823	148–149 d	210	i		s CS_2; v sl s al, eth
c214	bromide, tetra-	Tetrabromomethane. CBr_4	331.65	col, monocl or oct	3.42	tr to oct 48.4; m.p. 90.1	189.5	0.024^{30}		s al, eth, chl
c215	(di-)bromide, tetra-	Tetrabromethylene. C_2Br_4	343.66			57.5	227			
c216	(di-)chloride, hexa-	Hexachloro ethane. C_2Cl_6	236.74	col, rhmb, tricl or cub	2.091	subl 187		i		s al, eth, oils
c217	chloride, tetra-	Tetrachloromethane. CCl_4	153.81	col liq, 1.4601	1.5867^{20}_{20}	-23	76.8		v sl s	s al, bs, chl, eth
c218	(di-)chloride, tetra-	Tetrachloroethylene. C_2Cl_4	165.83	col liq, eth odor, 1.5055	1.6311^{15}_4	-22.4	120.8			s al, eth

No.	Name	Synonyms and Formulae	Mol. wt.	Crystalline form, properties and index of refraction	Density or spec. gravity	Melting point, °C	Boiling point, °C	Solubility, in grams per 100 cc		
								Cold water	Hot water	Other solvents
	Carbon									
c219	fluoride, tetra-	Tetrafluoromethane. CF_4	87.99	col gas	1.96^{-184}	-184	-128	sl s		
c220	iodide, tetra-	Tetraiodomethane. CI_4	519.63	dk red, cub	4.34^{20}	d 171		i	d	s al, CS_2, eth, MeOH, bz
c221	oxide, di-	CO_2	44.01	col gas or col liq	1.977^0g/l, liq 1.101^{-37}, solid 1.56^{-79}	$-56.6^{5.2atm}$	-78.5 subl	171.3^0 cm³ 0.348^0g 0.145^{25}g	90.1^{20} cm³ 0.097^{60} g 0.058^{60}g	31^{15} cm³ al, s acet
c222	oxide, mon-	CO	28.01	col odorl pois gas	1.250^0g/l liq 0.793	-199	-191.5	3.5^0 cm	2.32^{20} cm³	s al, bz, ac a, Cu_2Cl_2
c223	oxide, sub-	C_3O_2	68.03	col gas or liq, 1.4538	liq 1.114^0	-111.3	7	d		
c224	oxysulfide	COS	60.07	col gas, pois	gas 1.073 g/l⁰ liq 1.24^{-87}	-138.2	-50.2	54^{20} ml		s al; v s CS_2
c225	selenide, di-	CSe_2	169.93	golden yel liq, 1.845^{20}	2.6626^{26}_4	-45.5	125–126	i		d al; s CS_2, tol
c226	selenide, sulfide	$CSeS$	123.04	yel oily liq	1.9874	-85	84.5	i	i	sl s al; s CS_2
c227	sulfide, di-	CS_2	76.14	col liq, inflamm, 1.62950^{18}	1.261^{22}_{20}	-110.8	46.3	0.22^{22}	0.14^{50}	s al, eth
c228	sulfide, mono-	CS	44.08	red powd	1.66	d 200		i		i al; s eth, CS_2
c229	sulfide, sub-	C_3S_2	100.16	red liq	1.274	-0.5	d 90			
c230	sulfide telluride	$CSTe$	171.68	yel-red liq	2.9^{-50}	-54	d > -54			s CS_2, bz
c231	sulfochloride	Thiophosgene. $CSCl_2$	114.98	yel-red liq	1.509^{15}		73.5			
c232	**Carbonic acid**	H_2CO_3	62.03	exists in solution only				s		
c233	**Carbonyl bromide**	Carbon oxybromide. $COBr_2$	187.83	col liq			64.5			
c234	**Carbonyl chloride**	Phosgene, carbon oxychloride, $COCl_2$	98.92	col gas, pois	1.392	-104	8.3	d		d al, a; v s bz, tol s ac a
c235	**Carbonyl fluoride, di-**	COF_2	66.01	col gas, hyg	sol 1.388^{-190} liq 1.139^{-114}	-114	-83.1	d		
c236	**Carbonyl selenide**	$COSe$	106.97	col gas, very pois	liq $1.812^{4.1}$	-124.4	-21.7	d		s $COCl_2$
c237	**Cerium**	Ce	140.12	gray met, cub or hex	hex 6.657 cub 6.757	799	3426	sl d	d	s dil min a, i alk
c238	(III) acetate	$Ce(C_2H_3O_2)_3$	317.26	col		d 308		20^{15}	12^{75}	
c239	(III) acetate hydrate	$Ce(C_2H_3O_2)_3.1\frac{1}{2}H_2O$	344.28	wh–redsh cr powd		$-1\frac{1}{2}H_2O$, 115	d	26.5^{15}	16.2^{75}	
c240	boride, hexa-	CeB_6	204.98	blue met, cub		2190	d	i	i	i HCl
c241	boride, tetra-	CeB_4	183.36	tetr	5.74					
c242	III bromate	$Ce(BrO_3)_3.9H_2O$	685.98	redsh-wh, hex		49		s		
c243	bromide	$CeBr_3.H_2O$	397.86	col need, deliq		d		v s	v s	v s al
c244	carbide	CeC_2	164.14	red, hex	5.23			d	d	s a
c245	carbonate	$Ce_2(CO_3)_3.5H_2O$	550.37	wh cr				i		s a; sl s $(NH_4)_2CO_3$
c246	carbonate fluoride	Nat. bastnaesite. $CeFCO_3$	219.13	hex, 1.717, 1.817	5					
c247	chloride	$CeCl_3$	246.48	col cr, deliq	3.92^0	848	1727	100	d	30 al; s acet
c248	citrate	$Ce(C_6H_5O_7).3\frac{1}{2}H_2O$	392.28	wh powd				i		s dil min a
c249	(III) cyanoplatinite	$Ce_2[Pt(CN)_4]_3.18H_2O$	1502.00	yel-bl lust, monocl	2.657	$-13\frac{1}{2}H_2O$ 100–110	d	s		
c250	(III) fluoride	CeF_3	197.12	wh, hex	6.16	1460	2300	i		
c251	(IV) fluoride	$CeF_4.H_2O$	234.13	col microcr, 1.614	4.77	ca 650	d	i		s a
c252	hydride	CeH_3	143.14	dk bl amorph powd		ign		d		
c253	(III) hydroxide	$Ce(OH)_3$	191.14	wh gelat ppt						s a, $(NH_4)_2CO_3$; i alk
c254	(IV) iodate	$Ce(IO_3)_4$	839.73	yel cr				0.015^{20}		
c255	(III) iodate	$Ce(IO_3)_3.2H_2O$	700.86	cr				0.16^{25}		s HNO_3
c256	(III) iodide	$CeI_3.9H_2O$	682.97	wh or redsh-wh cr		752	1397	v s		v s al
c257	(III) molybdate	$Ce_2(MoO_4)_3$	760.05	yel, tetr, 2.019, 2.007	4.83	973				
c258	(III) nitrate	$Ce(NO_3)_3.6H_2O$	434.23	col or redsh cr (trac La, Di), deliq		$-3H_2O$, 150	d 200	v s	v s	50 al; s acet
c259	(IV) nitrate, basic	$Ce(OH)(NO_3)_3.3H_2O$	397.07	long red need				s		
c260	(III) oxalate	$Ce_2(C_2O_4)_3.9H_2O$	706.44	yel-wh cr		d		v sl s		s H_2SO_4, HCl; i $H_2C_2O_4$, alk, eth, al
c261	(IV) oxide	$CeO_2.xH_2O$		yelsh gelat ppt						s a; sl s alk carb, i alk
c262	(III) oxide	Ce_2O_3	328.24	gray-grn, trig	6.86	1692, ign 200		i	i	s H_2SO_4, i HCl

No.	Name	Synonyms and Formulae	Mol. wt.	Crystalline form, properties and index of refraction	Density or spec. gravity	Melting point, °C	Boiling point, °C	Solubility, in grams per 100 cc		
								Cold water	Hot water	Other solvents
	Cerium									
c263	(IV) oxide(di-)	Ceria. CeO_2	172.12	brn-wh, cub	7.132^{23}	ca 2600		i	i	s H_2SO_4, HNO_3; i dil a
c264	oxychloride	CeOCl	191.57	purp leaf				i		s dil a
c265	(III) 2,4-pentanedione	Cerium acetylacetonate. $Ce(C_5H_7O_2)_3.3H_2O$	491.50	lt yel cr ppt		131–132		d		v s al
c266	(III) metophosphate	$Ce(PO_3)_3$	377.04	micr need	3.272					i a
c267	(III) orthophosphate	Nat. monazite. $CePO_4$	235.09	red, monocl or yel, rhomb, 1.795	5.22			i	i	s a; i al
c268	(III) salicylate	$Ce(C_7H_5O_3)_3$	551.47	wh-redsh wh powd				i		i al
c269	(III) selenate	$Ce_2(SeO_4)_3$	709.11	rhomb	4.456			39.55^0	2.513^{100}	
c270	silicide	$CeSi_2$	196.29		5.67^{17}			i		
c271	(IV) sulfate	$Ce(SO_4)_2$	332.24	deep yel cr	3.91^{18}	d 195		sl d, forms basic salts		
c272	(III) sulfate	$Ce_2(SO_4)_3$	568.42	col to grn, monocl or rhomb	3.912	$d\ 920^{746}$		10.1^0	2.25^{100}	
c273	(IV) sulfate, dihydrate	$Ce(SO_4)_2.4H_2O$	404.31	yel, rhomb				v s d		s dil H_2SO_4
c274	(III) sulfate, monohydrate	$Ce_2(SO_4)_3.9H_2O$	730.56	hex need	2.831			11.87^{15}	0.42^{30}	
c275	(III) sulfate, octahydrate	$Ce_2(SO_4)_3.8H_2O$	712.54	pink cr, tricl	2.886^{17}	$-8H_2O$, 630		12^{20}	6^{50}	
c276	(III) sulfate, pentahydrate	$Ce_2(SO_4)_3.5H_2O$	658.50	monocl	3.17			3.90^{50}	0.514^{100}	
c277	(III) sulfide	Ce_2S_3	376.43	red cr, br-dk powd, purp	5.020^{11}	d 2100 (vac)		i	d	s dil a
c278	(III) tungstate	$Ce_2(WO_4)_3$	1023.78	yel, tetr	6.77^{17}	1089				
	Cerium complexes									
c280	hexaantipyrinecerium perchlorate	$[Ce(C_{11}H_{12}N_2O)_6].(ClO_4)_3$	1567.86	col, hex cr		d 295–300		1.08^{20}		
c281	hexaantipyrinecerium iodide (III)	$[Ce(C_{11}H_{12}N_2O)_6].I_3$	1650.22	large yel cr		268–270		15.10^{20}		
c282	**Cesium**	Cs	132.9054	silv met cr hex	1.8785^{15}	28.40 ± 0.01	678.4	d		s liq NH_3
c283	acetate	$CsC_2H_3O_2$	191.95	deliq		194		$945.1^{-2.5}$	$1345.5^{88.5}$	
c284	aluminum sulfate	$CsAl(SO_4)_2.12H_2O$	568.19	col, cub, 1.4587	1.97	117		0.34^0	42.54^{100}	s dil al
c285	amide	$CsNH_2$	148.93	wh need	3.44^{25}_4	262 ± 1		d		s liq NH_3
c286	azide	CsN_3	174.93	col need, deliq		310		224.2^0		1.037^{16} al; i eth
c287	benzoate	$CsC_7H_5O_2$	254.02					294.5^0	398.5^{100}	
c288	borofluoride	$CsBF_4$	219.71	rhomb, 1.350	3.20	550 d		1.6^{17}	ca 30^{100}	s dil NH_3
c289	borohydride	$CsBH_4$	147.75	wh, cub, 1.498	2.404			v s		sl s al; i eth, bz
c290	bromate	$CsBrO_3$	260.81	hex, ca 2.15	4.109^{16}	ca 420 d		3.66^{25}	5.32^{35}	
c291	bromide, mono-	CsBr	212.81	col, cub, 1.6984	4.44, liq 3.04^{700}	636	1300	124.3^{25}	v s	s a
c292	bromide, tri-	$CsBr_3$	372.63	rhomb		180				
c293	dibromochloride	$CsBr_2Cl$	328.18	yel-red, rhomb		191	$150, -Br_2$	s		d al, acet
c294	bromochloride iodide	CsIBrCl	375.17	yel-red, rhomb		235	d 290	s		s al
c295	bromoiodide di-	$CsIBr_2$	419.63	rhomb	1.25	248	d 320	4.61^{20}		s al
c296	carbonate	Cs_2CO_3	325.82	col cr, deliq		d 610		260.5^{15}	v s	11^{19} al; s eth
c297	carbonate, hydrogen	$CsHCO_3$	193.92	rhomb		$175-\frac{1}{2}H_2O$		209.3^{15}	v s	s al
c298	chlorate	$CsClO_3$	216.36	sm cr	3.57			$6.28^{19.8}$	76.5^{90}	s al
c299	perchlorate	$CsClO_4$	232.36	rhomb, at 219 cub, 1.4752, 1.4788, 1.4804	3.327^4	d 250		2.00^{25}	28.57^{99}	0.093^{25} al; 0.7878^{25} al; 0.150^{25} acet
c300	chlorobromide	$CsBrCl_2$	283.72	glossy-yel, rhomb		205		s		d al, eth
c301	chloride	CsCl	168.36	col, cub, deliq, 1.6418	3.988	645	1290	$162.22^{0.7}$	$259.56^{89.5}$	33.7^{25} MeOH; v s al; i acetone
c302	chloroiodide	$CsICl_2$	330.74	or, trig	3.86	230	d 290	s		s al
c303	chloroaurate	$CsAuCl_4$	471.68	yel, monocl				0.5^{10}	27.5^{100}	s al
c304	chlorobromide, di-	$CsBrCl_2$	283.72			205				
c305	chlorodibromide	$CsBr_2Cl$	328.18	yel		191				
c306	chloroiodide, di-	$CsICl_2$	330.72	pa or, rhomb	3.68	230	d 290	s		s al
c307	chloroplatinate	Cs_2PtCl_6	673.62	yel, cub	4.197 ± 0.004	d 570		0.024^0	0.377^{100}	i al
c309	chlorostannate	Cs_2SnCl_6	597.22	wh, cub	3.33					
c310	chromate	Cs_2CrO_4	381.80	yel pr, rhomb	4.237			71.4^{13}	95.5^{90}	
c311	chromium sulfate	Cesium chromium alum. $Cs_2[Cr(H_2O)_6](SO_4)_2.6H_2O$	593.21	vlt cr	2.064	116		9.4^{25}		
c312	cyanide	CsCN	158.92	very sm wh cr	2.93			v s	v s	
c313	fluoride	CsF	151.90	cub, deliq, 1.478 ± 0.005^{18}	4.115	682	1251	367^{18}		191^{18} MeOH; i Diox, Pyr
c314	fluoride	$CsF, 1\frac{1}{2}H_2O$	178.93			703		366.5^{18}		
c315	fluorogermanate	Cs_2GeF_6	452.39	isotrop cr, reg oct	4.10			sl s	v s	sl s a
c316	fluosilicate	Cs_2SiF_6	407.89	wh, cub	3.372^{17}			60^{17}	sl s	i al
c317	fluotellurite	$CsTeF_5$	355.50	col need				d	d	s HF soln
c318	formate	$CsCHO_2$	172.92		1.0169^{21}_4				$2012^{96.4}$	

No.	Name	Synonyms and Formulae	Mol. wt.	Crystalline form, properties and index of refraction	Density or spec. gravity[16]	Melting point, °C	Boiling point, °C	Cold water	Hot water	Other solvents
	Cesium									
c319	formate.........	CsCHO₂.H₂O	195.94			41, −H₂O		4.14²⁵		
c320	gallium selenate.....	CsGa(SeO₄)₂.2H₂O....	704.72	col cr				4.14²⁵		
c321	gallium sulfate.....	CsGa(SO₄)₂.12H₂O....	610.93	col cub, 1.46495....	2.113			1.21²⁵		0.0035²⁵ 75 % al
c322	hydride.......	CsH	133.91	wh cr, cub.......	3.41	d		d	d	d a; i org solv
c323	hydrofluoride.......	CsF.HF	171.91	need, deliq		160		v s		v s a; i al
c324	hydrogencarbide....	CsHC₂	157.94	trsp cr		300		d		
c325	hydroxide.......	CsOH	149.91	lt yel, deliq.....	3.675	272.3		395.5¹⁵		s al
c326	iodate........	CsIO₃	307.81	wh, monocl.....	4.85			2.6²⁴		
c327	*meta*periodate......	CsIO₄	323.81	wh rhomb pl....	4.259¹⁵			2.15¹⁵	s	
c328	iodide........	CsI	259.81	rhomb, deliq, 1.7876	4.510²⁵/₄	626	1280	44⁰	160⁶¹	s al
c329	iodide, penta-.....	CsI₅	767.43	bl, tricl.....		73				
c330	iodide, tri-........	CsI₃	513.62	blk, rhomb......	4.47	207.5		sl s	sl s	s al
c331	iodotetrachloride....	CsICl₄	401.62	pale or needles....	3.374⁻¹⁰	228	d	sl s	sl s	
c332	iron (II) sulfate.....	Cs₂SO₄.FeSO₄.6H₂O....	621.87	lt grn, monocl, 1.500, 1.504, 1.509	2.791²⁰/₄	ca 70		101.1²⁵ (anhyd)		
c333	iron (III) sulfate.....	CsFe(SO₄)₂.12H₂O.....	597.06	pa-vlt cr, 1.484	2.061²⁰	ca 90		s	s	
c334	magnesium sulfate...	Cs₂SO₄.MgSO₄.6H₂O....	590.34	col, monocl, 1.486, 1.452	2.676²⁰/₄					
c335	*per*manganate......	CsMnO₄	251.84		3.597	d 320		0.097¹	1.27⁵⁹	
c336	mercury bromide(ic).	CsBr.2HgBr₂........	933.63	rhomb......				0.807¹⁷		sl s al
c337	mercury chloride(ic).	CsCl.HgCl₂........	439.85	col, cub or rhomb, 1.792				1.44¹⁷		i abs al
c338	nitrate........	CsNO₃	194.91	col, hex or cub, 1.55, 1.56	3.685 liq 2.71⁵⁰⁰	414	d	9.16⁰	196.8¹⁰⁹	s acet, sl s al
c339	nitrate, hydrogen....	CsNO₃.NHO₃	257.92	oct........		100				
c340	nitrate, dihydrogen..	CsNO₃.2HNO₃	320.92	col pl.....		32–36				
c341	nitrate.........	CsNO₂	178.91	yel cr......				v s	v s	
c342	oxalate........	Cs₂C₂O₄	353.82		3.230¹⁵			v s		
c343	oxide........	Cs₂O	281.81	or need.....	4.25	d 400; m.p. 490 (in N₂)		v s	d	s a
c344	oxide, per-.......	Cs₂O₂	297.81	pa yel need.....	4.25	400	650. −O₂	s	d	s a
c345	oxide, tri-.......	Cesium oxide, sesqui- Cs₂O₃	313.81	choc br cr, cub.....	4.25	400		d		s a
c346	phthalate, hydrogen	CsHC₈H₄O₄.......	298.03	rhomb......	2.178					
c347	polonium chloride...	Cs₂PoCl₆.......	688.53	cub, 1.86.....	3.82					
c348	rhodium sulfate....	CsRh(SO₄)₂.12H₂O....	644.12	yel, oct......	2.238	110–111		sl s		
c349	rhodium sulfate.....	CsRh(SO₄)₂.12H₂O....	644.12	or cr......	2.22²⁰/₄	111		sl s	s	
c350	salicylate.........	CsC₇H₅O₃	270.02					196.2⁰	1522¹⁰⁰	
c351	selenate.........	Cs₂SeO₄	408.77	rhomb, deliq, 1.5950, 1.5060, 1.5964	4.4528²⁰/₄			244.8¹²		
c352	sulfate.........	Cs₂SO₄	361.87	col rhomb, or hex, 1.560, 1.564, 1.566	4.243	1010	tr hex 600	167⁰	220¹⁰⁰	i al, acet
c353	sulfate, hydrogen....	CsHSO₄.......	229.97	col rhomb pr.....	3.352¹⁶	d		s		
c354	sulfide........	Cs₂S.4H₂O	369.94	wh cr, deliq.....				v s	v s	
c355	sulfide, di-......	Cs₂S₂	329.94	dk red, amorph.....		460	>800	hgr		
c356	sulfide, di-......	Cs₂S₂.H₂O	347.95	tetr........				s		
c357	sulfide, hexa-.....	Cs₂S₆	458.19	br red.....		186				
c358	sulfide, penta-.....	Cs₂S₅	426.13		2.806¹⁵	210				
c359	sulfide, tetra-.....	Cs₂S₄	394.06	yel.....		d 160				
c360	sulfide, tri-......	Cs₂S₃	362.00	yel leaf.....		217	780			
c361	tartrate, hydrogen...	CsHC₄H₄O₆.......	281.99	wh, rhomb cr.....				9.7²⁵	98¹⁰⁰	
c362	*l*-tartrate......	Cs₂C₄H₄O₆.......	413.88	col, trig......	3.03¹⁴			v s d	v s	
c363	vanadium sulfate....	Cesium vanadium alum· VCs(SO₄)₂.12H₂O	592.15	red, cub, 1.4780	2.033²⁰/₄	82	−12H₂O, 230; d 300	0.464¹⁰	sl s	
c364	**Chloramine, mono-.**	NH₂Cl	51.48	yel liq.....		−66		s		s al, eth; v sl s CCl₄, bz
c365	**Chloric acid**.......	HClO₃.7H₂O	210.57	known only as col sol	1.282¹⁴·²	< −20	d 40	v s		
c366	**Chloric acid, per-**....	HClO₄	100.46	col liq unstable...	1.764²²	−112	39⁵⁵	∞		
c367	**Chloric acid, per-**....	Hydronium perchlorate. HClO₄.H₂O or (H₃O)⁺(ClO₄)⁻	118.47	need, fairly stab	1.88, liq 1.776⁵⁰	50	exp 110	v s	v s	
c368	per-, dihydrate......	HClO₄.2HO........	136.49	stab liq.........	1.65	−17.8	200	v s	v s	s al

No.	Name	Synonyms and Formulae	Mol. wt.	Crystalline form, properties and index of refraction	Density or spec. gravity	Melting point, °C	Boiling point, °C	Solubility, in grams per 100 cc		
								Cold water	Hot water	Other solvents
	Chlorine									
c369	**Chlorine**	Cl_2	70.906	grnsh-yel gas, or liq, or rhomb cr; gas 1.000768, liq 1.367	3.214^0	−100.98	−34.6	310^{10} cm³ 1.46^0 g	177^{90} cm³ 0.57^{80} g	s alk
c370	azide	chlor(o)azide ClN_3	77.48	gas, expl				sl s		d alk
c371	fluoride, mono-	ClF	54.45	col gas	1.62^{-100}	−154 ± 5	−100.8	d	d	
c372	fluoride, tri-	ClF_3	92.45	col gas	1.77^{11}	−83	11.3	d	d	
c373	hydrate	$Cl_2 \cdot 8H_2O$	215.03	lt yel, rhomb	1.23	d 9.6		i		s alk
c374	oxide, di-	ClO_2	67.45	yel red gas, or red cr, expl	3.09^{11} g/l	−59.5	9.9^{731} exp	2000^4 cm³	d to $HClO_2$, Cl_2, O_2	s alk, H_2SO_4
c375	oxide, hept-	Cl_2O_7	182.90	col oil		−91.5	82	s d		s bz
c376	oxide, mono-	Cl_2O	86.91	yel-red gas, or red-br liq	3.89^0 g/l	−20	3.8^{766} exp	200 cm³	d to $HOCl$	s alk, H_2SO_4
c377	oxide, tetr-	ClO_4 or Cl_2O_8	99.45				d	s d		s bz
c378	chloroauric acid	$HAuCl_4 \cdot 4H_2O$	411.85	brt yel need, deliq	d			s	v s	s al, eth
c379	chloroplatinic acid	$H_2PtCl_6 \cdot 6H_2O$	517.92	red br pr, deliq	2.431	60		v s	v s	s al, eth
c380	chlorostannic acid	$H_2SnCl_6 \cdot 6H_2O$	441.52	col leaf	1.93	9		s		
c381	**Chlorosulfonic acid**	$ClSO_3H$	116.52	col fum liq, 1.437¹⁴	1.766^{18}	−80	158	d to H_2SO_4 + HCl		d al, a; i CS_2
c382	**Chlorotetroxy fluoride**	ClO_4F	118.45	col gas, v exp		−167.3	−15.9			
c383	**Chloryl (per-)fluoride**	ClO_3F	102.45	gas	1.392^{25}	−146	−46.8			
c384	**Chromium**	Cr	51.996	steel gray, cub v hard	7.20^{28}	1857 ± 20	2672	i	i	s dil H_2SO_4, HCl; i HNO_3, aq reg
c385	(II) acetate	$Cr(C_2H_3O_2)_2$	170.00	red cr				sl s	s	sl s al
c386	(III) acetate	$Cr(C_2H_3O_2)_3 \cdot H_2O$	247.15	gray-grn powd or blsh-grn pasty mass				s		i al
c387	arsenide, mon-	$CrAs$	126.92	gray, hex	6.35^{16}			i	i	i a
c388	boride, mono-	CrB	62.81	silv cr, orthorhomb	6.17	2760(?)		i	i	s fus Na_2O_2
c389	(II) bromide	$CrBr_2$	211.81	wh cr	4.356	842		s	s	s al
c390	(III) bromide	$CrBr_3$	291.72	olv gr, hex	4.250^{25}_4	subl		i	s	v s al; d alk
c391	bromide, hexahydrate	$[CrBr_2(H_2O)_4]Br \cdot 2H_2O$	399.81	grn cr, deliq				s	s tr to vlt	s al; i eth
c392	bromide, hexahydrate	$[Cr(H_2O)_6]Br_3$	399.81	blsh gray to vlt	5.4^{17}			v s	v s	i al
c393	(tri-)carbide, di-	Cr_2C_2	180.02	gray, rhomb	6.68	1890	3800	i	i	
c394	carbonyl	$Cr(CO)_6$	220.06	col, orthorhomb	1.77	d 110	210 exp	i	i	i al, eth, ac a; sl s CHl_3, CCl_4
c395	(II) chloride	$CrCl_2$	122.90	wh need, deliq	2.878^{25}	824		v s	v s	i al, eth
c396	(III) chloride	$CrCl_3$	158.35	vlt, trig	2.76^{15}	ca 1150	subl 1300	i	sl s	i al, acet, MeOH, eth
c397	chloride, hexahydrate	$[Cr(H_2O)_4Cl_2] \cdot 2H_2O$	266.45	vlt, monocl	1.76	83		58.5^{25}	s	s al; i eth; sl s acet
c398	(II) fluoride	CrF_2	89.99	grn, cr, monocl	4.11	1100	>1300	sl s		i al; s h HCl
c399	(III) fluoride	CrF_3	108.99	grn, rhomb	3.8	>1000	subl 1100 − 1200	i		i al, NH_3; sl s a; s HF
c400	(II) hydroxide	$Cr(OH)_2$	86.01	yel-br		v		d		s a
c401	iodate, hydrate	$[Cr(H_2O)_6]I_3 \cdot 3H_2O$	594.85	dk vlt cr, hygro	4.915^{25}_4	41 − HI		v s	v s	s al, acet; i CHl_3
c402	(II) iodide	CrI_2	305.80	graysh powd	5.196	856	subl vac 800	s		
c403	(III) iodide	CrI_3	432.71	shiny blk cr	4.915^{25}_4	>600	− I_2, vac 350			
c404	(III) nitrate	$Cr(NO_3)_3 \cdot 7\frac{1}{2}H_2O$	373.13	br, monocl		100	d	s	s	
c405	(III) nitrate	$Cr(NO_3)_3 \cdot 9H_2O$	400.15	purple, monocl		60	d 100	s	s	s a, alk, al, acet
c406	nitride, mono-	CrN	66.00	cub or amorph	5.9	d 1700		i	i	sl s aq reg
c407	(II) oxalate	$CrC_2O_4 \cdot H_2O$	158.03	yel cr powd	2.468			sl s	s	s dil a
c408	(III) oxalate	$Cr_2(C_2O_4)_3 \cdot 6H_2O$	476.14	red, amorph, hyg		120, − H_2O tr to grn		v s (red) al, eth; i (grn) al		
c409	oxide, di-	CrO_2	84.00	br-blk powd		300, − O		i		s HNO_3
c410	(II) oxide, mon-	CrO	68.00	blk powd				i	i	i dil HNO_3
c411	(III) oxide, sesqui-	Cr_2O_3	151.99	grn, hex, 2.551	5.21	2435	4000	i	i	i a, alk, al
c412	(III) oxide, sesqui-	$Cr_2O_3 \cdot xH_2O$	varies	vlt, amorph or bl-gray grn gel				i	i	s a, alk; sl s NH_4OH
c413	oxide, tri-	Chromic anhydride, "chromic acid", CrO_3	99.99	red, rhomb, deliq	2.70	196	d	61.7^0	67.45^{100}	d al, eth; s H_2SO_4 HNO_3
c414	oxychloride	CrO_2Cl_2	154.90	dk red liq	1.911	−96.5	117	d	d	d al; s eth, ac a
c415	2,4-pentandione	Chromium acetyl-acetonate, $Cr(C_5H_7O_2)_3$	349.33			216	340	i		s org solv; i lgr

No.	Name	Synonyms and Formulae	Mol. wt.	Crystalline form, properties and index of refraction	Density or spec. gravity	Melting point, °C	Boiling point, °C	Solubility, in grams per 100 cc		
								Cold water	Hot water	Other solvents
	Chromium									
c416	(III) *orthophosphate*	$CrPO_4.2H_2O$	183.00	vlt cr	$2.42^{32.5}$			sl s		s a, alk; i ac a
c417	(III) *orthophosphate*	$CrPO_4.6H_2O$	255.06	vlt, tricl, 1.568, 1.591, 1.699	2.121^{14}	100				
c418	*pyrophosphate*	$Cr_4(P_2O_7)_3$	729.81	pa grn, monocl	3.2			i	i	s alk
c419	phosphide, mono-	CrP	82.97	gray-blk cr	5.7^{15}			i		s HNO_3, HF
c420	silicide	Cr_3Si_2	212.17	gray, tetr pr	5.5^0			i	i	s HCl, HF; i H_2SO_4, HNO_3
c421	(II) sulfate	$CrSO_4.7H_2O$	274.17	bl cr				12.35^0	d	s ls al; s NH_4OH
c422	(III) sulfate	$Cr_2(SO_4)_3$	392.18	vlt or red powd	3.012			i, s*		sl s al; i a
c423	(III) sulfate	$Cr_2(SO_4)_3.15H_2O$	662.41	vlt, amorph sc	1.867^{17}	100	$-10H_2O$, 100	s	d 67	i al
c424	(III) sulfate	$Cr_2(SO_4)_3.18H_2O$	716.45	bl vlt, cub oct, 1.564	1.7^{22}	$-12H_2O$, 100		120^{20}	s	s al
c425	(II) sulfide, mono-	CrS	84.06	blk powd, hex	4.85	1550		i		v s a
c426	(III) sulfide, sesqui-	Cr_2S_3	200.18	brn-blk powd	3.77^{19}	$-S$, 1350		i, d	i	s HNO_3; d al
c427	(III) sulfite	$Cr_2(SO_3)_3$	344.18	grnsh-wh	2.2	d				
c428	(II) tartrate	$CrC_4H_4O_6$	200.07	bl powd	2.33			i	i	sl s a; i ac a
c429	**Chromium complexes**									
	*hex*ammine chromium-(III) chloride	$[Cr(NH_3)_6]Cl_3.H_2O$	278.55	yel cr	1.585			s		
c430	*hex*aureachromium-(III) fluosilicate	$[Cr(CON_2H_4)_6]_2.[SiF_6]_3.3H_2O$	1304.94	lt grn leaf				0.522^{20}		i al
c431	*hex*aureachromium-(III) *per*rhenate	$[C_2(CON_2H_4)_6].(ReO_4)_3$	1162.92	grn need	2.652^{25}_4			1.786		0.667 al
c432	chloropentammine chromium chloride	$[Cr(NH_3)_5Cl]Cl_2$	243.51	red, oct	1.696			0.65^{16}		i HCl
c433	**Cobalt**	Co	58.933	silv gray met, cub	8.9	1495	2870	i	i	s a
c434	(III) acetate	$Co(C_2H_3O_2)_3$	236.07	grn, oct		d 100		hydr readily		s a, glac ac a
c435	(II) acetate	$Co(C_2H_3O_2)_2.4H_2O$	249.08	red-vlt, monocl, deliq, 1.542	1.705^{19}	$-4H_2O$, 140		s	s	s a, al
c436	aluminate	(approx) Thenard's blue. $CoAl_2O_4$	176.89	bl, cub				i	i	
c437	(II) *ortho*arsenate	$Co_3(AsO_4)_2.8H_2O$	598.75	vlt-red, monocl, 1.626, 1.661, 1.669	3.178^{15}	d				s dil a, NH_4OH
c438	arsenic sulfide	Nat. cobaltite. CoAsS	156.92	gray-redsh	6.2–6.3	d		i	i	i HCl, H_2SO_4; s HNO_3, aq reg
c439	arsenide	Co_2As	192.79	cr powd	8.28	950		i	i	
c440	(II) benzoate	$Co(C_7H_5O_2)_2.4H_2O$	373.23	gray red leaf		$-4H_2O$, 115		v s		s HNO_3, aq reg
c441	boride, mono-	CoB	69.74	pr	7.25^{18}			d	d	s NH_4OH
c442	(II) bromate	$Co(BrO_3)_2.6H_2O$	422.84	red, oct				45.5^{17}		
c443	(II) bromide	$CoBr_2$	218.75	grn, hex, deliq	4.909^{25}_4	678 (in N_2)		66.7^{59}	68.1^{97}	77.1^{20} al; 58.6^{30} MeOH; s eth, acet
c444	(II) bromide hexahydrate	$CoBr_2.6H_2O$	326.84	red-vlt pr, deliq	2.46	47–48, $-4H_2O$ 100	$-6H_2O$, 130	s red color	153.2^{97}	s blk color, al, a, eth
c445	bromoplatinate	$CoPtBr_6.12H_2O$	949.66	trig	2.762					
c446	carbonate	Nat. spherocobaltite. $CoCO_3$	118.94	red, trig, 1.855, 1.60	4.13	d		i	i	s a; i NH_3
c447	(II) carbonate, basic	$2CoCO_3.Co(OH)_2.H_2O$	534.74	vlt-red pr				i	d	s a, $(NH_4)_2CO_3$
c448	carbonyl tetra-	Dicobalt octacarbonyl. $[Co(CO)_4]_2$ or $Co_2(CO)_8$	341.95	or cr or dk br, microcr	1.73^{18}	51	d 52	i	i	sl s al; s CS_2, eth
c449	carbonyl, tri-	Tetracobalt dodeca-carbonyl. $[Co(CO)_3]_4$ or $Co_4(CO)_{12}$	571.86	blk cr				sl s		s bz; d Br
c450	(II) chlorate	$Co(ClO_3)_2.6H_2O$	333.93	red, cub, deliq, 1.55	1.92	50	d 100	558.3^0	v s	s al
c451	(II) perchlorate	$Co(ClO_4)_2$	257.83	red need 1.510, 1.490	3.327			100^0	115^{45}	s al, acet
c452	(II) perchlorate	$Co(ClO_4)_2.5H_2O$	347.88	red, hex		143		100.13^0	115.10^{65}	v s al, acet i $CHCl_3$
c453	*perchlorate*	$Co(ClO_4)_2.6H_2O$	365.93	red pr		d 1534	d	259^{18}		s al, acet
c454	(II) perchlorate	$Co(ClO_4)_2.6H_2O$	365.93	red, oct, deliq, 1.55		d 182		255^{18}		s al, acet
c455	(II) chloride	$CoCl_2$	129.84	bl, hex, hygr	3.356^{25}_4	724 (in HCl gas)	1049	45^7	105^{96}	54.4 al; 8.6 acet; 38.5 MeOH; sl s eth
c456	(III) chloride	$CoCl_3$	165.29	red cr or yel cr	2.94	subl		s		

* Several chromic salts exist in two forms, a soluble and insoluble modification.

No.	Name	Synonyms and Formulae	Mol. wt.	Crystalline form, properties and index of refraction	Density or spec. gravity	Melting point, °C	Boiling point, °C	Solubility, in grams per 100 cc		
								Cold water	Hot water	Other solvents
	Cobalt									
c457	(II) chloride, dihydrate	$CoCl_2.2H_2O$	165.87	red-vlt, monocl or tricl, 1.625, 1.671, 1.67	2.477_{25}^{25}			s	s	v sl s eth
c458	(II) chloride, hexahydrate	$CoCl_2.6H_2O$	237.93	red, monocl	1.924_{25}^{25}	86	$-6H_2O$, 110	76.7^0	190.7^{100}	v s (bl col) al; s acet; 0.29 eth
c459	chloroplatinate	$CoPtCl_6.6H_2O$	574.83	trig	2.699	d				
c460	chlorostannate	$CoSnCl_6.6H_2O$	498.43	rhomb or trig		d 100				
c461	(II) chromate	$CoCrO_4$	174.93	gray blk cr		d		i	d	s a, NH_4OH
c462	(II) citrate	$Co_3(C_6H_5O_7)_2.2H_2O$	591.04	rose-red		$-2H_2O$, 150		0.8		
c463	(II) cyanide dihydrate	$Co(CN)_2.2H_2O$	147.00	buff anhydr bl-vlt powd	anhydr 1.872²⁵	$2H_2O$, 280	d 300	0.00418^{18}		s KCN, HCl, NH_4OH
c464	(II) cyanide, trihydrate	$Co(CN)_2.3H_2O$	165.01	red-gray powd, amorph		$-3H_2O$, 250		i		s KCN
c465	(II) ferricyanide	$Co_3[Fe(CN)_6]_2$	600.71	red need				i		s NH_4OH; i HCl
c466	(II) ferrocyanide	$Co_2Fe(CN)_6.xH_2O$		gray-grn				i		s KCN; i HCl
c467	(II) fluogallate	$[Co(H_2O)_6][GaF_5.H_2O]$	349.75	pink cr, monocl (?), 1.4̣	2.35	$-5H_2O$, 110		sl s		d a
c468	(II) fluoride	CoF_2	96.93	pink monocl	4.46_4^{25}	ca 1200	1400	1.5^{25}	s	sl s a; i al, eth, bz
c469	(III) fluoride	CoF_3	115.93	br, hex	3.88		d to $Co(OH)_3$			i, al, eth, bz
c470	fluoride	$Co_2F_5.7H_2O$	357.96	grn powd	2.314²⁵			d		s H_2SO_4
c471	(II) fluoride, tetrahydrate	$CoF_2.4H_2O$	168.99	α: red, rhomb oct, β: rose cr powd	2.192_4^{25}	d 200		s	s	i al
c472	fluosilicate	$CoSiF_6.6H_2O$	309.10	pink trig, 1.382, 1.387	2.113¹⁹			$118.1^{21.5}$		
c473	(II) formate	$Co(CHO_2)_2.2H_2O$	185.00	red cr	2.129²²	$-2H_2O$, 110	d 175	5.03^{20}		
c474	(II) hydroxide	$Co(OH)_2$	92.95	rose-red, rhomb	3.597¹⁵	d		0.00032		s a, NH_4 salts; i alk
c475	(III) hydroxide	$Co_2O_3.3H_2O$	219.91	blk-brn powd	4.46	d	$-H_2O$, 100	0.00032		s a; i al
c476	(II) iodate	$Co(IO_3)_2$	408.74	bl-vlt need	5.008¹⁸	d 200		0.45^{18}	1.33^{100}	s HCl, HNO_3. h H_2SO_4
c477	(II) iodate, hexahydrate	$Co(IO_3)_2.6H_2O$	516.83	red, oct	3.689²¹	d 61	$-4H_2O$, 135	s		
c478¹	(II) iodide (α) stable	CoI_2	312.74	blk hex, hyg	5.68	515(vac)	570 (vac)	159^0	420^{100}	v s al, acet
c478²	(II) iodide (β)	CoI_2	312.74	yel need, unstab	5.45²⁵	d 400		s		
c479	(II) iodide, dihydrate	$CoI_2.2H_2O$	348.77	grn, deliq		d 100		376.2^{45}	s	
c480	(II) iodide, hexahydrate	$CoI_2.6H_2O$	420.83	br-red hex, hygr	2.90	d 27, $-6H_2O$, 130		s	s	s al, eth, chl
c481	iodoplatinate	$CoPtI_6.9H_2O$	1177.59	trig	3.618					
c482	linoleate	$Co(C_{18}H_{31}O_2)_2$	617.83	br, amorph				i		s al, eth, acet
c483	(II) nitrate	$Co(NO_3)_2.6H_2O$	291.04	red, monocl, 1.52.	1.87_4^{25}	55–56	$-3H_2O$, 55	133.8^0	217^{80}	$100.0^{12.5}$ al; s acet; sl s NH_3
c484	nitrosylcarbonyl	$Co(NO)(CO)_3$	172.97	cherryred liq		-1.05	48.6; d 55	i		s al, eth, acet, bz
c485	(II) oleate	$Co(C_{18}H_{32}O_2)_2$	621.86	br, amorph				i		s al, eth, oils, bz
c486	(II) oxalate	CoC_2O_4	146.95	wh or redsh	3.021²⁵	d 250		i		s a, NH_4OH
c487	oxalate, dihydrate	$CoC_2O_4.2H_2O$	182.98	pink cr		$-H_2O$, ca 190		v sl s	sl s	v sl s a; s NH_4OH
c488	(II) oxide	CoO	74.93	grn-brn cub	6.45	1935		i	i	s a; i al, NH_4OH
c489	(III) oxide	Co_2O_3	165.86	blk-gray, hex, or rhomb	5.18	d 895		i	i	s a; i al
c490	(II, III) oxide	Co_3O_4	240.80	blk, cub	6.07	tr to CoO 900–950		i	i	v sl s a; i aq reg
c491	palmitate	$Co(C_{16}H_{31}O_2)_2$	569.78			70.5				s pyr, hot CS_2, CCl_4; sl s eth; i MeOH, acet
c492	(II) orthophosphate	$Co_3(PO_4)_2$	366.74	redsh cr	2.587²⁵			i	i	s H_3PO_4, NH_4OH
c493	(II) orthophosphate, dihydrate	$Co_3(PO_4)_2.2H_2O$	402.77	pink powd				i		s H_3PO_4
c494	(II) orthophosphate, octahydrate	$Co_3(PO_4)_2.8H_2O$	510.87	redsh powd	2.769²⁵	$-8H_2O$, 200		sl s		s min a, H_3PO_4; i al
c495	phosphide	Co_2P	148.84	gray need	6.4¹⁵	1386		i	i	s HNO_3, aq reg
c496	(II) propionate	$Co(C_3H_5O_2)_2.3H_2O$	250.12	dk-red cr		ca 250		anh 33.5¹¹		v s al
c497	(II) perrhenate	$Co(ReO_4)_2.5H_2O$	649.41	dk pink		d		d		
c498	(II) selenate, heptahydrate	$CoSeO_4.7H_2O$	328.00	monocl	2.135					
c499	selenate, hexahydrate	$CoSeO_4.6H_2O$	309.98	red, monocl, 1.5225	2.25¹⁷			s	s	
c500	(II) selenate, pentahydrate	$CoSeO_4.5H_2O$	291.97	ruby red, tricl	2.512	d		v s		

No.	Name	Synonyms and Formulae	Mol. wt.	Crystalline form, properties and index of refraction	Density or spec. gravity	Melting point, °C	Boiling point, °C	Solubility, in grams per 100 cc		
								Cold water	Hot water	Other solvents
	Cobalt									
c501	selenide, mono-	CoSe	137.89	yel, hex	7.65	red heat				s HNO_3, aq reg; i alk
c502	(II) orthosilicate	Co_2SiO_4	209.95	vlt cr, rhomb	4.63	1345		i	i	s dil HCl
c503	silicide	CoSi	87.03	rhomb		1395				s HCl; i HNO_3, H_2SO_4
c504	silicide, di-	$CoSi_2$	115.11	rhomb	5.3	1277				
c505	(di-)silicide	Co_2Si	145.95	gray cr	7.28^0	1327				d a
c506	(II) orthostannate	Co_2SnO_4	300.55	grnsh-bl, cub	6.30^{18}					i H_2SO_4; s h HCl
c507	(II) sulfate	$CoSO_4$	155.00	dk blsh, cub	3.71^{25}_{25}	d 735		36.2^{20}	83^{100}	1.04^{18} MeOH; i NH_3
c508	(II) sulfate, hepta-hydrate	Nat. bieberite. $CoSO_4.7H_2O$	281.10	red-pink, monocl, 1.477, 1.483, 1.489	1.948^{25}_{25}	96.8	$-7H_2O$, 420	60.4^3	67^{70}	2.5^3 al; 54.5^{18} MeOH
c509	(II) sulfate, hexa-hydrate	$CoSO_4.6H_2O$	263.09	red, monocl, 1.531 1.549, 1.552	2.019^{18}_{15}	$-2H_2O$, 95				
c510	(II) sulfate, mono-hydrate	$CoSO_4.H_2O$	173.01	red cr, 1.603, 1.639, 1.683	3.075^{25}	d		s	s	
c511	(III) sulfate	$Co_2(SO_4)_3.18H_2O$	730.33	bl-grn		d 35		s d		s H_2SO_4; i pyr
c512	sulfide, di-	CoS_2	123.06	blk, cub	4.269			i		s HNO_3, aq reg
c513	sulfide, mono-	Nat. sycoporite. CoS	91.00	redsh, silv-wh, oct	5.45^{18}	>1116		0.00038^{18}		sl s a
c514	(III) sulfide, sesqui-	Co_2S_3	214.06	blk cr	4.8					d a, aq reg
c515	(tri-) sulfide	Cobalt sulfide, tetra-(ous, ic) Nat. linneite. Co_3S_4	305.06	dk gray, cub	4.86	d 480				
c516	(II) sulfite	$CoSO_3.5H_2O$	229.07	red				i		s H_2SO_3
c517	tartrate	$CoC_4H_4O_6$	207.01	redsh, monocl				sl s		s dil a
c518	thiocyanate	$Co(SCN)_2.3H_2O$	229.14	vlt, rhomb		$-3H_2O$, 105		s		s al, MeOH, eth
c519	orthotitanate	Co_2TiO_4	229.76	grnsh-blk, cub	5.07-5.12					s conc HCl; sl s dil HCl
c520	(II) tungstate	$CoWO_4$	306.78	bl-grn, monocl	8.42			i		s h conc a; sl s c dil a
	Cobalt complexes									
c521	hexammine cobalt (II) bromide	$CoBr_2.6NH_3$	320.93	dk pink cr	1.871^{25}_4	d 258		d		
c522	diamminecobalt (II) chloride [α]	$CoCl_2.2NH_3$	163.90	rose cr	2.097	273				
c523	diamminecobalt (II) chloride(β)	$CoCl_2.2NH_3$	163.90	bl-vlt	2.073	tr to α, 210 (in NH_3)				
c524	hexamminecobalt (II) chloride	$[Co(NH_3)_6]Cl_2$	232.02	rose red, oct	1.497	d		d		s NH_4OH; i abs al
c525	hexamminecobalt (III) chloride	$Co(NH_3)_6Cl_3$	267.46	wine-red, monocl	1.710^{25}_4	$-1NH_3$, 215		5.9^{10}	$12.74^{46.6}$	s conc HCl; i al, NH_4OH
c526	hexamminecobalt (II) iodide	$CoI_2.6NH_3$	414.93	dk pink, cub	2.096^{25}_4	141^{100mm}				
c527	hexamminecobalt (III) nitrate	$Co(NH_3)_6.(NO_2)_3$	347.13	yel, tetr	1.804^{25}			1.7^{25}	v s	v sl s dil a
c528	hexamminecobalt (III) perrhenate	$[Co(NH_3)_6](ReO_4)_3.2H_2O$	947.74	or-yel pr	3.329^{25}			0.0469		
c529	hexamminecobalt (II) sulfate	$CoSO_4.6NH_3$	257.18	pink powd	1.654^{25}_4	d 116^{760}		d		v s dil NH_3
c530	hexamminecobalt (III) sulfate	$[Co(NH_3)_6]_2(SO_4)_3.5H_2O$	700.50	dk yel, monocl	1.797^{25} anhydr	$-4H_2O$, 100	$-5H_2O$, 150	$1.4^{17.4}$		
c531	ammonium tetra-nitrodiammine (III) cobaltate	Erdmann's salt. $NH_4[Co(NH_3)_2(NO_2)_4]$	295.12	redsh-pa brn, rhomb, 1.78, 1.78. 1.74	1.876^{25}					
c532	aquapentammine-cobalt (III) chloride (roseo)	$[Co(NH_3)_5.H_2O]Cl_3$	268.45	brick red cr	1.7^{25}	d 100		24.87^{25}		sl s HCl; i al
c533	aquapentammine-cobalt (III)-sulfate (roseo)	$[Co(NH_3)_5H_2O]_2(SO_4)_3.2H_2O$	638.34	red, tetr	1.854^{20}	$-3H_2O$, 99	d 110	$1^{17.2}$	1.72^{27}	s H_2SO_4
c534	cis-chloroaquo-tetramminecobalt (III) chloride	$[Co(NH_3)_4(H_2O)Cl]Cl_2$	251.42	vlt, rhomb	1.847	d		1.4^0		s a; i al
c535	chloropentammine cobalt-(III) chloride (purpureo)	$[Co(NH_3)_5Cl]Cl_2$	250.45	dk red-vlt, rhomb	1.819^{25}_{25}	d		0.4^{25}	$1.03^{46.6}$	s conc H_2SO_4; i al

No.	Name	Synonyms and Formulae	Mol. wt.	Crystalline form, properties and index of refraction	Density or spec. gravity	Melting point, °C	Boiling point, °C	Solubility, in grams per 100 cc		
								Cold water	Hot water	Other solvents
	Cobalt complexes									
c536	triethylenediaminecobalt-(III) chloride	$Co[C_2H_4(NH_2)_2]_3Cl_3.3H_2O$	399.64	br pr	1.542^{17}	256; $-3H_2O$, 100		v s		
c537	trinitrotriamminecobalt	$Co(NH_3)_3(NO_2)_3$	248.04	yel, rhomb pl or leaf	1.992^{25}_4	d 158	exp 164	$0.177^{16.5}$	0.28^{25}	
c538	trinitrotetramminecobalt-(III) nitrate	$[Co(NH_3)_4(NO_2)_2]NO_3$	265.07	yel, rhomb	1.922^{17}			3^{20}		
c539	potassium tetranitrodiamminecobaltate (III)	$K[Co(NH_3)_2(NO_2)_4]$	316.12	yel, rhomb	2.076^{15}			$1.758^{16.5}$		
	Colombium	see Niobium.								
c540	**Copper**	Cu	63.546	redsh met, cub	8.92	1083.4 ± 0.2	2567	i	i	s HNO_3, h H_2SO_4; v sl s HCl, NH_4OH
c541	acetate, basic	Blue verdigris. $Cu(C_2H_3O_2)_2.CuO.6H_2O$	369.26	grnsh-bl powd				sl s		s dil a, NH_4OH; sl s al
c542	(II) acetate	Neutral verdigris. $Cu(C_2H_3O_2)_2.H_2O$	199.65	dk grn powd, 1.545, 1.550	1.882, anhydr 1.93	115	d 240	7.2	20	7.14 al; s eth
c543	(II) acetate meta-arsenate	Paris green. $Cu(C_2H_3O_2)_2.3Cu(AsO_2)_2$ (approx)	1013.77	em grn powd				i		s a, NH_4OH; i al
c544	(III) acetylide	Cu_2C_2	151.10	red, amorph, expl.		exp		v sl s		s a, KCN
c545	amine azide	$Cu(NH_3)(N_3)_2$	181.64	dk grn cr, exp		d 100–105	exp 202	i	d	d a; i MeOH
c546	(II) diammine-chloride, di-	$Cu(NH_3)_2Cl_2$	168.51	grn cr	2.32^{25}_4	260–270	d 300	i		s NH_4OH; i abs a
c547	(II) hexammine-chloride, di-	$Cu(NH_3)_6Cl_2$	236.63	bl, cub	1.48^{25}_4			v s		
c548	tetrammine dithionate	$[Cu(NH_3)_4]S_2O_6$	291.79	vlt-bl cr		d 160		s	d	
c549	(II) tetrammine nitrate	$[Cu(NH_3)_4](NO_3)_2$	255.67	dk-bl, oct	1.91^{25}_4	d 210 exp		s		
c550	(II) amine nitrate	$[Cu(NH_3)_4](NO_2)_2$	223.61	vlt-bl, tetr		$-2NH_3$ 97		v s		
c551	tetrammine sulfate	Cuprum ammoniacale. $[Cu(NH_3)_4]SO_4.H_2O$	245.74	dk-bl, rhomb, unstab	1.79^{25}_4	$-NH_3.H_2O$, 30		$18.05^{21.5}$		
c552	(tri-)antimonide	Cu_3Sb	312.37	gray	8.51	687				
c553	(II) orthoarsenate	$Cu_3(AsO_4)_2.4H_2O$	540.52	blsh-grn				i	i	s a, NH_4OH
c554	(II) orthoarsenate, di-H	$Cu_3H_2(AsO_4)_4.2H_2O$	911.42	bl				i		s a, NH_4OH
c555	arsenide	Cu_5As_2	467.54	bl, oct	7.56			i	i	s a, NH_4OH
c556	tri-arsenide	Nat. domeykite. Cu_3As	265.54	hex	8.0	830				
c557	(II) orthoarsenite, hydrogen(?)	Scheele's green. $CuHAsO_3(?)$	187.47	grn powd		d				s a, NH_4OH; i al
c558	(I) azide	CuN_3	105.56	col cr, v exp	3.26			0.00075^{20}		d conc H_2SO_4; s NH_4Cl
c559	(II) azide	$Cu(N_3)_2$	147.58	brn-red or brn-yel cr, exp	2.604	exp 215		0.008^{20}		v s dil a
c560	(II) benzoate	$Cu(C_7H_5O_2)_2.2H_2O$	341.80	lt bl cr powd		$-H_2O$, 110		sl s		s dil a; sl s al
c561	(II) metaborate	$Cu(BO_2)_2$	149.16	blsh grn cr powd	3.859			s		
c562	boride	Cu_3B_2	212.24	yel	8.116					
c563	(II) bromate	$Cu(BrO_3)_2.6H_2O$	427.45	bl-grn, cub	2.583	d 180	$-6H_2O$, 200	v s		s NH_4OH
c564	(I) bromide	$CuBr$ (or Cu_2Br_2)	143.45	wh, cub, 2.116	4.98	492	1345	v sl s	d	s HBr, HCl, HNO_3, NH_4OH; i acet
c565	(II) bromide	$CuBr_2$	223.31	blk, monocl, deliq	4.77^{25}_4	498		v s		s al, acet, NH_3, pyr; i bz
c566	trioxybromide	$CuBr_2.3Cu(OH)_2$	516.02	em grn, rhomb	4.00	$-H_2O$, 210–215	d 240–250	i	d	s dil min a, NH_4OH; v s ac a
c567	(II) butyrate	$Cu(C_4H_7O_2)_2.2H_2O$	273.77	dk grn cr				v sl s		s al, eth, NH_4OH, dil a
c568	(I) carbonate	Cu_2CO_3	187.09	yel	4.40	d		i	i	s a, NH_4OH
c569	(II) carbonate, basic	Nat. malachite. $CuCO_3.Cu(OH)_2$	221.11	dk grn, monocl, 1.655, 1.875, 1.909	4.0	d 200		i	d	0.026 aq CO_2; s a, NH_4OH, KCN; i al
c570	(II) carbonate, basic	Nat. azurite, chessylite. $2CuCO_3.Cu(OH)_2$	344.65	bl, monocl, 1.730, 1.758, 1.838	3.88	d 220		i	d	s NH_4OH, h $NaHCO_3$
c571	(II) chlorate	$Cu(ClO_3)_2.6H_2O$	338.53	grn, cub, deliq		65	d 100	$?070$	v s	s al, acet
c572	(II) chlorate, basic	$Cu(ClO_3)_2.3Cu(OH)_2$	523.11	grn cr or amorph	3.55	d		i	i	s dil a

No.	Name	Synonyms and Formulae	Mol. wt.	Crystalline form, properties and index of refraction	Density or spec. gravity	Melting point, °C	Boiling point, °C	Solubility, in grams per 100 cc		
								Cold water	Hot water	Other solvents
	Copper									
c573	perchlorate	$Cu(ClO_4)_2$	262.43	monocl, 1.495, 1.505, 1.522	2.225^{23}	82.3		s	s	
c574	perchlorate, hexahydrate	$Cu(ClO_4)_2.6H_2O$	370.53	lt bl, tricl, deliq, 1.505	2.225^{25}_4	82	d 120	v s		s al, eth
c575	(I) chloride(ous)	Nat. nantokite. $CuCl$ (or Cu_2Cl_2)	98.99	wh, cub, 1.93	4.14	430	1490	0.0062		s HCl, NH_4OH, eth; i al
c576	(II) chloride	$CuCl_2$	134.44	br, yel powd, hygr	3.386^{25}_4	620	993 d to CuCl	70.6^0	107.9^{100}	53^{15} al; 68^{15} MeOH; s h H_2SO_4, acet
c577	(II) chloride, basic	$CuCl_2.Cu(OH)_2$	232.00	yel-grn, hex	3.78	$-H_2O$, 250	d red heat	d	d	
c578	(II) chloride, dihydrate	Nat. eriochaleite. $CuCl_2.2H_2O$	170.47	bl-grn, rhomb, deliq. 1.644, 1.683, 1.731	2.54	$-2H_2O$, 100	d	110.4^0	192.4^{100}	s al, NH_4OH
c579	chloride, thioureate	$CuCl.3[CS(NH_2)_2]$	327.35	col pr, 1.758, 1.17719	1.73	168		v s		
c580	(II) chromate, basic	$CuCrO_4.2CuO.2H_2O$	374.64	yel br		$-2H_2O$, 260		i		s dil a, NH_4OH; i al
c581	(II) dichromate	$CuCr_2O_7.2H_2O$	315.56	blk cr, deliq	2.283	$-2H_2O$, 100		v s	d	s a, NH_4OH, al
c582	(I) chromite	$Cu_2Cr_2O_4$	295.07	gray blk cub pl	5.24^{20}			i	i	s HNO_3
c583	(II) citrate	$2Cu_3C_6H_4O_7.5H_2O$	720.43	blsh grn powd		$-H_2O$, 100		i	i	s a, NH_4OH
c584	(I) cyanide	$CuCN$	89.56	wh, monocl pr	2.92	473 (in N_2)	d	i	i	s HCl, KCN, NH_4OH; sl s liq NH_3
c585	(II) cyanide	$Cu(CN)_2$	115.58	yel-grn powd		d		i		s a, alk, KCN, pyr
c586	ethylacetoacetate	$Cu(C_6H_9O_3)_2$	321.81	grn need		192–193	subl	i		v s al, eth; 10^{80} bz
c587	(I) ferricyanide	$Cu_3Fe(CN)_6$	402.57	br red				i		i HCl; s NH_4OH
c588	(II) ferricyanide	$Cu_3[Fe(CN)_6]_2.14H_2O$	866.74	yel-grn				i		i HCl; s NH_4OH
c589	(II) ferrocyanide	Hatchett's brown. $Cu_2Fe(CN)_6.xH_2O$		red brn				i	i	i a, NH_3; s NH_4OH
c590	(I) fluogallate	$[Cu(H_2O)_4][GaF_5.H_2O]$	354.36	pa bl, monocl(?), 1.45	2.20	$-5H_2O$, 110		sl s		s HF
c591	(I) fluoride	CuF (or Cu_2F_2)	82.54	red cr, (exist?)		908	subl, 1100	i		s HCl, HF; d HNO_3; i al
c592	(II) fluoride	CuF_2	101.54	wh, tricl	4.23	d 950		4.7^{20}	s	s dil min a; i al
c593	(II) fluoride dihydrate	$CuF_2.2H_2O$	137.57	bl, monocl	2.93^{25}_4	d		4.7^{20}	d	s HCl, HF, HNO_3, al; i acet, NH_3
c594	(I) fluosilicate	Cu_2SiF_6	269.16	red powd		d to SiF_4			d 100	
c595	(II) fluosilicate	$CuSiF_6.4H_2O$	277.68	monocl pr	2.158			42.8		
c596	(II) fluosilicate hexahydrate	$CuSiF_6.6H_2O$	313.71	bl, rhomb, deliq, 1.409, 1.408	2.207			232^{17}		0.16^{20} 92 % al
c597	(II) formate	$Cu(CHO_2)_2$	153.55	bl, monocl	1.831			12.5	d	0.25 al
c598	(II) formate tetrahydrate	$Cu(CHO_2)_2.4H_2O$	225.61	bl cr	1.81	$-H_2O$, 130		6.2		s alk; sl s al
c599	(II) glycerine deriv	$Cu(C_2H_4NO_2)_2.H_2O$	229.67	bl need		$-H_2O$, 130		0.57^{15}		s alk
c600	hydride	CuH (or Cu_2H_2)	64.55	red-brn, (exist?)	6.38	d sl 55–60		i	d 65	d HCl
c601	(II) hydroxide	$Cu(OH)_2$	97.56	bl gel cr powd	3.368	$-H_2O$, d		i	d	s a, NH_4OH, KCN
c602	(II) trihydroxychloride	γ: Paratacamite δ: atacamite $CuCl_2.3Cu(OH)_2$	427.11	γ: grn, hex, δ: grn rhomb; γ: 1.743, 1.849, δ:1.861, 1.861, 1.880, grn lt	(γ)3.75	$-H_2O$, 250		i		v s a
c603	(II) trihydroxynitrate	$Cu(NO_3)_2.3Cu(OH)_2$	480.27	dk grn, rhomb or moncl	rhomb, 3.41 monocl, 3.378	$-H_2O$ ~400		i	d	v s a
c604	(II) iodate	$Cu(IO_3)_2$	413.35	grn, moncl	5.241^{15}	d		0.1364^{15}	i	s dil HNO_3, dil H_2SO_4
c605	(II) iodate, basic	$Cu(OH)IO_3$	255.45	grn, rhomb	4.873	d 290		i	i	s dil H_2SO_4
c606	(II) iodate, monohydrate	Nat. bellingerite. $Cu(IO_3)_2.H_2O$	431.36	bl, tricl	4.872	$-H_2O$, 248	d 290	0.33^{15}	0.65^{100}	s dil H_2SO_4, NH_4OH; i al, dil HNO_3
c607	paraperiodate	Cu_2HIO_6	350.00	grn cr powd		d 110		i	i	s HNO_3, NH_4OH
c608	(I) iodide	Nat. marshite. CuI (or Cu_2I_2)	190.44	wh or brnsh-wh, cub, 2.346	5.62	605	1290	0.0008^{18}		s dil HCl, KI, KCN, conc H_2SO_4, liq NH_3
c609	(II) lactate	$Cu(C_3H_5O_3)_2.2H_2O$	277.71	dk bl, monocl				16.7	45^{100}	s NH_4OH; sl s al
c610	(II) laurate	$Cu(C_{12}H_{23}O_2)_2$	462.17	lt bl powd		111–113		sl s	sl s	
c611	mercury iodide (α)	Cu_2HgI_4	835.29	red, tetr	6.116	tr ca 67		i		
c612	mercury iodide (β)	Cu_2HgI_4	835.29	choc, cub	6.102			i		

No.	Name	Synonyms and Formulae	Mol. wt.	Crystalline form, properties and index of refraction	Density or spec. gravity	Melting point, °C	Boiling point, °C	Solubility, in grams per 100 cc		
								Cold water	Hot water	Other solvents
	Copper									
c613	(II) nitrate, hexahydrate	$Cu(NO_3)_2.6H_2O$	295.64	bl cr, deliq	2.074	$-3H_2O$, 26.4		243.7^0	∞	s al
c614	(II) nitrate, trihydrate	$Cu(NO_3)_2.3H_2O$	241.60	bl cr, deliq	2.32^{25}_4	114.5	$-HNO_3$, 170	137.8^0	1270^{100}	$100^{12.5}$ al; v s liq NH_3
c615	nitride	Cu_3N	204.63	dk grn powd	5.84^{25}_4	d 300		d		d a
c616	(II) nitrite, basic	$Cu(NO_2)_2.3Cu(OH)_2$	448.22	grn powd		d 120		i	d	v s dil a; sl s al; s NH_4OH
c617	(II) hyponitrite, basic	$Cu(NO)_2.Cu(OH)_2$	221.11	pea grn amorph, hygr		d<100		i		s dil a; v s NH_4OH; d NaOH
c618	(II) nitroprusside	$CuFe(CN)_5NO.2H_2O$	315.51	wh-grnsh powd				i		s alk; i al
c619	(II) oleate	$Cu(C_{18}H_{33}O_2)_2$	626.47	br powd or grn-bl mass, pois				i	i	s eth
c620	(II) oxalate	$CuC_2O_4.\frac{1}{2}H_2O$	160.57	bl wh				0.00253^{25}		s NH_4OH; l a c a
c621	(I) oxide	Nat. cuprite. Cu_2O	143.08	red, oct cub, 2.705	6.0	1235	$-O$, 1800	i	i	s HCl, NH_4Cl, NH_4OH; sl s HNO_3; i al
c622	(II) oxide	Nat. tenorite. CuO	79.54	blk, monocl, β 2.63	6.3–6.49	1326		i	i	s a, NH_4Cl, KCN
c623	oxide, per-	$CuO_2.H_2O$	113.55	br or brnsh-blk cr		d 60		i		i al, s d a
c624	oxide, sub-	Cu_4O	270.16	olv grn, (exist?)		d		i		d a
c625	(II) oxychloride	Nat. atacamite. $Cu_2(OH)_3Cl$ (or $CuCl_2.3Cu(OH)_2$)	213.56	grn, orthorhomb	3.76–3.78					
c626	(II) oxychloride	Brunswick green. $CuCl_2.3CuO.4H_2O(?)$	445.13	grn powd, or em grn to grnsh-blk, rhomb		$-3H_2O$, 140			d 100	s a, NH_4OH
c627	(II) palmitate	$Cu(C_{16}H_{31}O_2)_2$	574.39	grn-bl powd		120		i		s h bz, CS_2, CCl_4; sl s al, eth; i MeOH, acet
c628	2,4-pentanedione	Copper acetylacetonate. $Cu(C_5H_7O_2)_2$	261.76	bl cr		>230	subl	i		sl s al; s chl
c629	(I) phenyl	C_6H_5Cu	140.65	col powd		d 80		d	d	i al, CS_2; s pyr
c630	(II) orthophosphate	$Cu_3(PO_4)_2.3H_2O$	434.61	bl, rhomb		d		i	sl s	s a, NH_4OH, H_3PO_4; i NH_3
c631	(tri-) phosphide	Cu_3P	221.59	gray-blk	6.4–6.8	d		i		s HNO_3; i HCl
c632	(di-) pyridine chloride(di)	$Cu(C_5H_5N)_2Cl_2$	316.67	grn-bluish, monocl, 1.60, 1.75	1.76	d 263		s	d	sl s c al, chl
c633	(II) salicylate	$Cu(C_7H_5O_3)_2.4H_2O$	409.83	bl-grn need				v s		v s al, NH_4OH
c634	(II) selenate	$CuSeO_4.5H_2O$	296.57	bl, tricl, 1.56	2.559	$-4H_2O$, 50–100	$-5H_2O$, 150	25.7^{15}	d	s a, NH_4OH; v sl s acet; i a
c635	(I) selenide	Cu_2Se	206.04	blk, cub	6.749^{30}_4	1113				d HCl
c636	(II) selenide	$CuSe$	142.50	grn-blk hex pl, unstab	5.99	d red heat		i	i	sl s HCl, NH_4OH; s h HNO_3
c637	selenite	$CuSeO_3.2H_2O$	226.53	bl-grn, rhomb	3.31^{25}_4	$-H_2O$, 100		i	i	
c638	silicide	Cu_4Si	282.25	wh met	7.53	850				i HCl; d HNO_3
c639	(II) stearate	$Cu(C_{18}H_{35}O_2)_2$	630.50	lt grn-bl amorph powd		125		i		s eth, h bz, chl, turp; sl s pyr; i MeOH, acet
c640	(I) sulfate	Cu_2SO_4	223.14	gray powd, 1.724, 1.733, 1.739	3.605	$+O$, 200		d		s conc HCl, NH_3 glac ac a
c641	(II) sulfate	Nat. hydrocyanite. $CuSO_4$	159.60	grn, wh, rhomb, 1.733	3.603	sl d above 200	d 650 to CuO	14.3^0	75.4^{100}	1.04^{18} MeOH; i al
c642	(II) sulfate, basic	Nat. brochantite. $CuSO_4.3Cu(OH)_2$	452.27	grn, monocl, 1.728, 1.771, 1.800	3.78	d 300		i	i	s a, NH_4OH
c643	(II) sulfate, pentahydrate	Blue vitriol, nat. chalcanthite. $CuSO_4.5H_2O$	249.68	bl, tricl, 1.514, 1.537, 1.543	2.284	$-4H_2O$, 110	$-5H_2O$, 150	31.6^0	203.3^{100}	15.6^{18} MeOH; i al
c644	(I) sulfide	Nat. chalcocite. Cu_2S	159.14	blk, rhomb	5.6	1100		$\times 10^{-14}$		s HNO_3, NH_4OH; i acet
c645	(II) sulfide	Nat. covellite. CuS	95.60	blk, monocl or hex, 1.45	4.6	tr 103	d 220	0.000033^{18}		s HNO_3, KCN, h HCl, H_2SO_4; i al, alk
c646	(I) sulfite, monohydrate	$Cu_2SO_3.H_2O$	225.16	red pr	4.46^{15}			i		d dil a; s NH_4OH
c647	(I) sulfite, monohydrate	$Cu_2SO_3.H_2O$	225.16	wh, hex	3.83^{15}	d		sl s		s HCl, NH_4OH; i al, eth
c648	(I, II) sulfite, dihydrate	Chevreul's salt. $Cu_2SO_3.CuSO_3.2H_2O$	386.78	red cr	3.57	d 200		i	i	s HCl, NH_4OH, sl s HNO_3
c649	(II) tartrate	$CuC_4H_4O_6$	211.61	lt bl powd				v sl s		s a, alk
c650	(II) tartrate, trihydrate	$CuC_4H_4O_6.3H_2O$	265.66	lt gray-bl powd		d		0.02^{15}	0.14^{85}	s a, alk

No.	Name	Synonyms and Formulae	Mol. wt.	Crystalline form, properties and index of refraction	Density or spec. gravity	Melting point, °C	Boiling point, °C	Solubility, in grams per 100 cc		
								Cold water	Hot water	Other solvents
	Copper									
c651	telluride	Cu_2Te	254.68	bl-blk, oct	7.27					s $Br + H_2O$; i HCl, H_2SO_4
c652	telluride	Nat. rickardite. Cu_4Te_3	636.96	purp, tetr	7.54					
c653	tellurite	$CuTeO_3$	239.10	blk glass				i	i	s conc HCl
c654	(I) thiocyanate	$CuSCN$	121.62	wh	2.843	1084		0.0005^{18}		s NH_4OH; sl s ac a; i al; d min a
c655	(II) thiocyanate	$Cu(SCN)_2$	179.70	blk		d 100		d	d	s a, NH_4OH
c656	(II) tungstate	$CuWO_4.2H_2O$	347.42	lt-grn, oct		red heat		0.1^{15}		s NH_4OH; sl s ac a; i al; d min a
c657	xanthate	Copper ethylxanthogenate. $Cu(C_3H_5OS_2)_2$	305.94	yel ppt		d		i		s NH_4OH; v sl s al; i CS_2
	Copper complexes									
c658	diamminecopper (II) acetate	$Cu(C_2H_3O_2)_2.2NH_3$	215.69	vlt bl cr		d ca 175		s d		s ac a, NH_4OH; i al
c659	tetrammine copper (II) sulfate	$[Cu(NH_3)_4]SO_4.H_2O$	245.74	bl, rhomb	1.81	d 150		$18.5^{21.5}$	d	i al
c660	tetrapyridine copper (II) fluosilicate	$[Cu(C_5H_5N)_4]SiF_6$	522.03	purp-bl, rhomb	2.108					
c661	tetrapyridine copper-(II) *perrhenate*	$[Cu(C_5H_5N)_4](ReO_4)_2$	880.34	bl cr, monocl	2.338			0.5555		
c662	**Cyanic acid** isocyanic acid	$HOCN$	43.03	liq	1.14^{20}_4			s d		s eth, bz, tol
c663	**Cyanoauric acid**	$HAu(CN)_4.3H_2O$	356.09	tab		50	d	s		s al, eth
c664	**Cobalticyanic acid**	$[H_3Co(CN)_6]_2.H_2O$	454.14	col need, deliq		d 100		s		s al, HCl, dil HNO_3, dil H_2SO_4
c665	**Cyanogen**	$(CN)_2$	52.04	col gas, pungent odor v pois	2.335 g/l, liq: $0.9577^{-21.17}$	−27.9	−20.7	4.50^{20} cm³		230 cm³ al, 500 cm³ eth
c666	**Cyanogen compounds**	See organic tables								
d1	**Deuterium**	Heavy hydrogen. D_2	4.032	col gas	llg $0.169^{-250.9}$	−254.6	−249.7	sl s		s a
d2	deuterium chloride	DCl	37.47	gas		−114.8	−81.6	24.1 cm³ 11.9^{25} cm³	8.4⁴⁰ cm³ 7.12^{50} cm³	
d3	deuterium oxide	Heavy water. D_2O	20.031	col liq or hex cr, 1.33844^{20}	1.105^{20}_4	3.82	101.42^{760}			
d4	**Dysprosium**	Dy	162.50	met, hex	8.5500	1412	2562	i	i	s a
d5	acetate	$Dy(C_2H_3O_2)_3.4H_2O$	411.64	yel need		d 120		s		v sl s al
d6	bromate	$Dy(BrO_3)_3.9H_2O$	708.36	yel hex need		78	−6H_2O, 110	v s		sl s al
d7	bromide	$DyBr_3$	402.23	col cr		881	1480	s	s	
d8	carbonate	$Dy_2(CO_3)_3.4H_2O$	577.06			−3H_2O, 15		i		
d9	chloride	$DyCl_3$	268.85	shining yel pl	3.67^0_4	718	1500	s	s	
d10	chromate	$Dy_2(CrO_4)_3.10H_2O$	853.13	yel cr		−3½H_2O, 150	d		1.002^{25}	
d11	fluoride	DyF_3	219.50	col cr		1360	>2200	i	i	i dil a
d12	iodide	DyI_3	543.21	yelsh grn cr		955	1320	s	s	
d13	nitrate	$Dy(NO_3)_3.5H_2O$	438.58	yel cr		88.6		s		
d14	oxalate	$Dy_2(C_2O_4)_3.10H_2O$	769.21	wh pr		−H_2O, 40		i	i	s dil a
d15	oxide	Dysprosia. Dy_2O_3	373.00	wh powd	7.81^{27}	2340 ± 10		i		grn soln a
d16	*ortho*phosphate	$DyPO_4.5H_2O$	347.55	yelsh-wh powd		−5H_2O> 200		i		s dil a, ac a
d17	selenate	$Dy_2(SeO_4)_3.8H_2O$	898.00	yel need		−8H_2O, 200		v s		i al
d18	sulfate	$Dy_2(SO_4)_3.8H_2O$	757.31	bril yel cr		stab 110	−8H_2O, 360	5.072^{20}	3.34^{40}	
e1	**Erbium**	Er	167.28	dk gray powd	9.006	1529	2863	i	i	s a
e2	acetate	$Er(C_2H_3O_2)_3.4H_2O$	416.48	wh cr, tricl	2.114					
e3	bromide	$ErBr_3.9H_2O$	569.15	vlt-rose cr		950	1460	s	s	
e4	chloride	$ErCl_3.6H_2O$	381.73	pink cr, deliq		774	1500	s	s	s al
e5	fluoride	ErF_3	224.28	rose cr		1350	2200	i	i	i dil a
e6	iodide	ErI_3	547.99	vlt-red cr		1020	1280	s	s	
e7	nitrate	$Er(NO_3)_3.5H_2O$	443.37	redsh cr		−4H_2O, 130		s		s al, eth, acet
e8	oxalate	$Er_2(C_2O_4)_3.10H_2O$	778.77	redsh micr powd	2.64(?)	d 575		i	i	i dil a
e9	oxide	Erbia. Er_2O_3	382.56	rose red powd, tr to cub at 1300	8.640	infus		0.00049^{24}		sl s min a
e10	sulfate	$Er_2(SO_4)_3$	622.74	wh powd, hygr	3.678	d 630		43^0		
e11	sulfate, octahydrate	$Er_2(SO_4)_3.8H_2O$	766.87	rose red, monocl	3.217	−8H_2O, 400		16^{20}	6.53^{40}	
e12	**Europium**	Eu	151.96	steel gray met, cub	5.2434	822	1597	i	i	
e13	(II) bromide	$EuBr_2$	311.78			677	1880	s	s	
e14	(III) bromide	$EuBr_3$	391.69			702	d	s	s	
e15	(II) chloride	$EuCl_2$	222.87	wh, amorph		727	>2000	s	s	s a
e16	(III) chloride	$EuCl_3$	258.32	yel need	4.89^{20}	850		s	s	
e17	(II) fluoride	EuF_2	189.96	brt yel	6.495	1380	>2400	i	i	
e18	(III) fluoride	EuF_3	208.96	col		1390	2280	i	i	i dil a

No.	Name	Synonyms and Formulae	Mol. wt.	Crystalline form, properties and index of refraction	Density or spec. gravity	Melting point, °C	Boiling point, °C	Solubility, in grams per 100 cc Cold water	Hot water	Other solvents
	Europium									
e19	(II) iodide	EuI₂	405.77	br to olv grn cr	5.50_4^{25}	527	1580	s	s	
e20	(III) iodide	EuI₃	532.68			877	d	s	s	
e21	(III) nitrate	Eu(NO₃)₃.6H₂O	446.07	col		85 (sealed tube)		v s	v s	
e22	oxide	Eu₂O₃	351.92	pa rose powd	7.42					
e23	(II) sulfate	EuSO₄	248.02	col, orthorhomb	4.989^{20}			i	i	i dil a
e24	(III) sulfate	Eu₂(SO₄)₃.8H₂O	736.23	pa rose cr	4.95 (anh)	−8H₂O, 375		2.563^{20}	1.93^{40}	
—	**Ferric or ferrous**	See *Iron*								
f1	**Ferricyanic acid**	H₃Fe(CN)₆	214.98	grn-brn need, deliq		d		s	s	s al
f2	**Ferrocyanic acid**	H₄Fe(CN)₆	215.99	wh need, bl in moist air		d		s	s	s al; i eth
f3	**Fluoboric acid**	HBF₄	87.81	col liq		d 130		∞	s	∞ al
f4	**Fluorophosphoric acid, di-**	HPO₂F₂	101.98	col fum liq	1.583_4^{25}	−75	116	s		
f5	**Fluorophosphoric acid, hexa-**	HPF₆	145.97	col fum liq	ca 1.65 (65 %)	31 (6H₂O)				
f6	**Fluorophosphonic acid, mono-**	H₂PO₃F	99.99	col visc liq	1.818_4^{25}			∞		
f7	**Fluorine**	F	18.99840	grn yel gas, pois, 1.000195	1.69^{15}g/1 1.51^{-188}	−219.62	−188.14	HF+O₂	d	
f8	(di-)oxide	F₂O	54.00	col gas or yel brn liq	liq 1.65^{-190}	−223.8	−144.8	sl s d	i	sl s alk, a
f9	oxide, di-	Dioxygen fluoride. F₂O₂	70.00	brn gas, red liq, orange solid	sol 1.912^{-165} liq 1.45^{-57}	−163.5	−57			
f10	**Fluosilicic acid**	H₂SiF₆.xH₂O	hydr (not known)	col fum coros liq, 1.3465^{25} (60.97 % soln)	1.4634^{18} (60.97 % soln)		d	s	s	sl s alk
f11	dihydrate	H₂SiF₆.2H₂O	180.12	wh cr, fum, deliq		d		s	s	s alk
f12	**Fluosulfonic acid**	HSO₃F	100.07	col liq	1.743^{15}	−87.3	165.5	s		
g1	**Gadolinium**	Gd	157.25	col or lt yel met, hex	7.9004	1313	3266	i	i	s a
g2	acetate tetrahydrate	Gd(C₂H₃O₂)₃.4H₂O	406.45	col, tricl	1.611			11.6^{25}		
g3	acetylacetonate, trihydrate	Gd[CH(COCH₃)₂]₃.3H₂O	508.63			143.5–145		i	i	
g4	bromide, hexahydrate	GdBr₃.6H₂O	505.07	rhomb pl	2.844^{16}			s	s	s HBr
g5	chloride	GdCl₃	263.61	col monocl, pr	4.52^0	609		s	s	
g6	chloride, hexahydrate	GdCl₃.6H₂O	371.70	wh pr, deliq	2.424^0			s	s	
g7	iodide	GdI₃	537.96	citr yel		926	1340	s	s	
g8	fluoride	GdF₃	214.25					i		sl s h HF
g9	dimethylphosphate	Gd[(CH₃)₂PO₄]₃	532.37					23.0^{25}	6.7^{100}	
g10	nitrate, hexahydrate	Gd(NO₃)₃.6H₂O	451.36	tricl, deliq	2.332	91		v s	v s	s al
g11	nitrate, pentahydrate	Gd(NO₃)₃.5H₂O	433.34	pr	2.406^{15}	92		i	i	v sl s conc HNO₃
g12	oxalate	Gd₂(C₂O₄)₃.10H₂O	758.71	monocl		−6H₂O, 110		i		s HNO₃; v sl s H₂SO₄
g13	oxide	Gadolinia. Gd₂O₃	362.50	wh amorph powd, hygr	7.407^{15}			v sl s		s a
g14	selenate	Gd₂(SeO₄)₃.8H₂O	887.50	monocl, pearly	3.309	−8H₂O, 130		s	s	
g15	sulfate	Gd₂(SO₄)₃	602.68	col	$4.139^{14.5}$	d 500		3.98^0	$2.26^{34.4}$	
g16	sulfate, octahydrate	Gd₂(SO₄)₃.8H₂O	746.81	col, monocl	$3.010^{14.6}$			3.28^{20}	2.54^{40}	
g17	sulfide	Gd₂S₃	410.69	yel mass, hyg	3.8			d		d a
g18	**Gallium**	Ga	69.72	gray-blk orthorhomb, tendency to undercool	sol $5.904^{29.6}$ liq $6.095^{29.8}$	29.78	2403	i	i	s a, i alk
g19	acetate, basic	4Ga(C₂H₃O₂)₃. 2Ga₂O₃.5H₂O	1452.37	wh micro cr		d 160		s d	d	i ac a
g20	acetylacetonate	2,4-Pentanedione deriv. Ga(C₅H₇O₂)₃	367.05	monocl or pl, rhomb or pyram, rhomb pyram	1.42, 1.41	194–195	subl 140^{10}	s		s acet
g21	arsenide	GaAs	144.64	dk-gray cub cr		1239				
g22	bromide, tri-	GaBr₃	309.45	wh cr	3.69_4^{75}	121.5±0.6	278.8	s	s	sl s NH₃
g23	bromide, tri-, hexammine	GaBr₃.6NH₃	411.63	wh powd		d		d	d	sl s NH₃
g24	bromide, tri-, monammine	GaBr₃.NH₃	326.48	wh powd	3.112^{25}	124		d	d	sl s NH₃
g25	perchlorate	Ga(ClO₄)₃.6H₂O	476.16			d 175		v s		v s al
g26	chloride, di-	GaCl₂	140.63	wh cr, deliq		164	535	d	d	s bz
g27	chloride, tri-	GaCl₃	176.03	wh need, deliq	2.47_4^{25} liq 2.36_{30}^{30}	77.9±02	201.3	v s	v s	s bz, CCl₄, CS₂

No.	Name	Synonyms and Formulae	Mol. wt.	Crystalline form, properties and index of refraction	Density or spec. gravity	Melting point, °C	Boiling point, °C	Solubility, in grams per 100 cc		
								Cold water	Hot water	Other solvents
	Gallium									
g28	chloride, tri-, hexammine	$GaCl_3.6NH_3$	278.26					d	d	s NH_3
g29	chloride, tri-, monoammine	$GaCl_3.NH_3$	193.11	wh powd	2.189^{25}	124		d	d	s NH_3
g30	ferrocyanide	$Ga_4[Fe(CN)_6]_3$	914.74		d			d	d	i conc HCl
g31	fluoride, tri-	GaF_3	126.72	wh powd	4.47±0.01	subl 800 (in N_2)	ca 1000	0.002	i	v sl s dil a; s HF
g32	fluoride, tri-, trihydrate	$GaF_3.3H_2O$	180.76	wh powd		−H_2O(vac) 140		i	sl s	sl s dil H_2F_2; v s dil HCl
g33	fluoride, tri-, triammine	$GaF_3.3NH_3$	177.81	wh powd		−NH_3, 100		d	d	
g34	hydride	Digallane, galloethane. Ga_2H_6	145.49	col liq		−21.4	139, d>130	d	d	d a, alk
g35	hydroxide	$Ga(OH)_3$	120.74	wh		d 440		i	i	s dil a
g36	hydroxyquinoline deriv.	$Ga(C_9H_6NO)_3$	502.18	grn-yel cr		>150	subl vac	0.0001	0.0012	s a, alk; sl s al
g37	iodide, tri-	GaI_3	450.43	lt yel cr	4.15^{25}_4	212±1	subl 345		d	
g38	iodide, tri-, hexammine	$GaI_3.6HN_3$	552.62	wh powd				d	d	
g39	iodide, tri-, monoammine	$GaI_3.NH_3$	467.46	wh powd	3.635^{25}_4			d	d	
g40	nitrate	$Ga(NO_3)_3.xH_2O$		wh cr, deliq		d 110	d to Ga_2O_3 200	v s	v s	s abs al; i eth
g41	nitride	GaN	83.73	dk gray powd	6.1	subl 800		i	i	i dil a; sl s h conc H_2SO_4, h conc NaOH
g42	oxide, sesqui-(α)	Ga_2O_3	187.44	wh, hex, rhomb, 1.92, 1.95	6.44	1900;tr to β 600		i	i	s alk; v sl s h a
g43	oxide, sesqui-(β)	Ga_2O_3	187.44	monocl, rhomb	5.88	1900(1740)		i	i	s alk; v sl s ha a
g44	oxide, sesqui-, monohydrate	$Ga_2O_3.H_2O$	205.45	wh micr cr, orthorhom, 1.84	5.2	−H_2O, 400 tr to Ga_2O_3		i	i	sl s a; s alk
g45	oxide, sub-	Ga_2O	155.44	blk brn powd	4.77^{25}_4	>660	subl >500	i	i	s a, alk
g46	oxalate	$Ga_2(C_2O_4)_3.4H_2O$	475.56	wh micro cr, hygr		−4H_2O, 180	d 200	0.4		
g47	oxychloride	$6GaOCl.14H_2O$	979.25	oct				i		v s KOH; i dil HNO_3; s acet
g48	selenate	$Ga_2(Se_4O)_3.16H_2O$	856.56	col, monocl or tricl cr				57.5^{25}	v s	
g49	selenide, mono-	$GaSe$	148.68	dk red-br greasy leaf	5.03^{25}_4	960±10				
g50	selenide, sesqui-	Ga_2Se_3	376.32	rdsh-bl brittle, hard	4.92^{25}_4	>1020±10				
g51	selenide, sub-	Ga_2Se	218.40	bl	5.02^{25}_4					
g52	sulfate	$Ga_2(SO_4)_3$	427.62	wh powd		diss 690^{760}		v s	v s	s al; i eth
g53	sulfate, hydrate	$Ga_2(SO_4)_3.18H_2O$	751.90	oct cr				v s	v s	s 60 % al; i eth
g54	sulfide, mono-	GaS	101.78	yel cr	3.86^{25}_4	965±10		i	d	s a, alk
g55	sulfide, sesqui-	Ga_2S_3	235.63	yel cr, or wh amorph	3.65^{25}	1255±10		d	d	s a, alk
g56	sulfide, sub-	Ga_2S	171.50	dk gray	4.18^{25}_4	d vac 800		d	d	s a, alk
g57	telluride, mono-	$GaTe$	197.32	blk soft cr	5.44^{25}_4	824±2				
g58	telluride, sesqui-	Ga_2Te_3	522.24	blk brittle cr	5.57^{25}_4	790±2				
	Germane									
g59	bromo-	GeH_3Br	155.52	col liq	$2.34^{29.5}$	−32	52	d	d	i al; d alk
g60	chloro-	GeH_3Cl	111.07	col liq	1.75^{-25}	−52	28.0	d	d	i al; d alk
g61	chloro trifluoro-	GeF_3Cl	165.04	col gas		−66.2	−20.63	d	d	s abs al
g62	dibromo-	GeH_2Br_2	234.42		2.80^0	−15.0	89.0	d	d	i al; d alk
g63	dichloro-	GeH_2Cl_2	145.51	col liq	1.90^{-68}	−68.0	69.5	d	d	i al; d alk
g64	dichlorodifluoro-	$GeCl_2F_2$	181.49	col gas		−51.8	−2.8	d	d	s abs al
g65	tribromo-	Germanium bromoform $GeHBr_3$	313.33	col liq		−24	d	d	d	d alk
g66	trichloro-	Germanium chloroform. $GeHCl_3$	179.96	col liq	1.93^0	−71	75.2 d	d	d	d alk
g67	trichlorofluoro-	$GeCl_3F$	197.95	col liq		−49.8	37.5	d		s abs al
g68	**Germanium**	Ge	72.59	gray-wh met-cub	5.35^{20}_{20}	937.4	2830	i	i	s h H_2SO_4, aq reg; i alk

No.	Name	Synonyms and Formulae	Mol. wt.	Crystalline form, properties and index of refraction	Density or spec. gravity	Melting point, °C	Boiling point, °C	Solubility, in grams per 100 cc		
								Cold water	Hot water	Other solvents
	Germanium									
g69	bromide, di-	GeBr₂	232.41	col need or pl		122	d	d	d	s a, GeBr₄, al; i bz
g70	bromide, tetra-	GeBr₄	392.23	gray-wh oct, 1.6269	3.132_{29}^{29}	26.1	186.5	d	d	s abs al, eth, bz; i conc H₂SO₄
g71	chloride, di-	GeCl₂	143.50	wh powd		d to Ge + GeCl₄		d	d	s GeCl₄; i al, chl
g72	chloride, tetra-	GeCl₄	214.41	col liq, 1.464	1.8443^{30}	−49.5	84	d	d	s al, eth; v s dil HCl; i conc HCl conc H₂SO₄
g73	fluoride, di-	GeF₂	110.59	wh cr, hygr		d>350	subl	s	v s	
g74	fluoride, tetra-	GeF₄	148.58	col gas or liq, not liq at atm press	$2.46^{-36.5}$	subl −37		d to GeO + H₂GeF₆		
g75	fluoride, tetra-	GeF₄.3H₂O	202.63	wh cr, deliq		d		s	s	
g76	hydride	Digermane. Ge₂H₆	151.23	liq	1.98^{-100}	−109	29; d 215	s		s liq NH₃
g77	hydride	Trigermane. Ge₃H₈	225.83	col liq	2.2^{20}	−105.6	110.5; d 195	i	i	s CCl₄
g78	hydride, tetra-	Germane. GeH₄	76.62	col gas	1.523^{-142}	−165	−88.5; d 350	i	i	s liq NH₃, NaOCl; sl s h HCl
g79	imide	Ge(NH)₂	102.62	wh amorph powd		d 150			d to NH₃ + GeO₂	
g80	iodide, di-	GeI₂	326.40	or hex pl	5.37	d	subl vac 240	s	s d	s conc HI, dil a; sl s CCl₄, chl; i CS₂
g81	iodide, tetra-	GeI₄	580.21	red-or, cub	4.322_{26}^{26}	144	d 440	s d		s al, acet; s CS₂, CCl₄, bz, MeOH
g82	(tri-) nitride, di-	Ge₃N₂	245.78	blk cr			subl 650			
g83	(tri-) nitride, tetra-	Ge₃N₄	273.80	wh-lt brn powd	5.25_4^{25}	d 450		i	i	i a, alk
g84	oxide, d-(insoluble)	GeO₂	104.59	tetr	6.239	1086 ± 5		i		sl s NaOH; i HCl
g85	oxide, di-(soluble)	GeO₂	104.59	col, hex, 1.650	4.228^{25}	1115.0 ± 4		0.447^{25}	1.07^{100}	s a, alk; i HCl, HF; one form NaOH, NH₄OH; one form
g86	oxide, mono-	GeO	88.59	blk cr powd, 1.607		subl 710		i	i	s Cl₂ water, H₂O₂ + NH₄OH; i a, alk
g87	oxychloride	GeOCl₂	159.50	col liq		−56	d>20	d	d	i all solv
g88	selenide	GeSe₂	230.51	orange, rhomb(?)	4.56^{85}	707 ± 3	d	i	i	v sl s a; sl s alk
g89	sulfide, di-	GeS₂	136.72	wh powd, or wh, orthorhomb	2.94^{14}	ca 800	subl >600	0.45 d	d to GeO₂ + H₂S	s alk, alk sulf; i al, eth, a; 3.112 liq NH₃
g90	sulfide, mono-	GeS	104.65	yel-red amorph, or rhomb bipyram, blk	amorph: 3.31 rhomb:4.01	530	subl 430	0.24	i	s HCl, alk or alk sulf; sl s NH₄OH; 0.0473 liq NH₃
	Glucinum	See Beryllium								
g91	**Gold**	Au	196.967	yel duct met, cub, coll blue-viol	19.3 liq 17.0^{1063}	1064.43	2807	i	i	s aq reg, KCN, h H₂SeO₄; ia
g92	(I) bromide	AuBr	276.88	yel-gray mass, or cr powd	7.9	d 115		i	i	d a; s NaCN
g93	(III) bromide	AuBr₃	436.69	gray powd, or br cr		97.5−Br, 160		sl s		s eth, al
g94	(I) chloride	AuCl	232.42	yel cr	7.4	170 d to AuCl₃	d 289.5	v sl s d	d	s HCl, HBr
g95	(III) chloride	AuCl₃ or Au₂Cl₆	303.33	claret-red cr pr	3.9	d 254	subl 265	68	v s	s al, eth; sl s NH₃; i CS₂
g96	(I) cyanide	AuCN	222.98	lt yel cr powd	7.12^{25}	d		v sl s	v sl s	s KCN, NH₄OH; i eth, alk
g97	(III) cyanide	Cyanoauric acid. Au(CN)₃.3H₂O or HAu(CN)₄.3H₂O	329.07	col pl, hygr		d 50		v s	d, v s	s al, eth
g98	(I) iodide	AuI	323.87	grnsh-yel powd	8.25	d 120		v sl s	sl s d	s KI
g99	(III) iodide	AuI₃	577.68	dk grn		i	d	i	d	s iodides
g100	(III) nitrate, hydrogen	Nitratoauric acid. AuH(NO₃)₄.3H₂O or H[Au(NO₃)₄].3H₂O	500.04	yel, tricl, oct	2.84	d 72		s, d		s HNO₃
g101	(III) oxide	Au₂O₃	441.93			−O, 160	−3O, 250	i	l	s HCl, conc HNO₃, NaCN
g102	(III) oxide	Au₂O₃.xH₂O				−1½H₂O, 250		$5.7×10^{-11}$ 25		s HCl, NaCN, conc HNO₃
g103	phosphide	Au₂P₃	486.86	gray	6.67		d			i HCl, dil HNO₃
g104	selenide	Au₂Se₃	630.81		4.65^{22}					
g105	(I) sulfide	Au₂S	426.00	br blk powd		d 240		i fresh sol	ppt coll	s aq reg, KCN; i a
g106	(III) sulfide	Au₂S₃	490.13	br blk powd	8.754	d 197		i		i al, eth, s Na₂S

No.	Name	Synonyms and Formulae	Mol. wt.	Crystalline form, properties and index of refraction	Density or spec. gravity	Melting point, °C	Boiling point, °C	Solubility, in grams per 100 cc		
								Cold water	Hot water	Other solvents
	Gold									
g107	telluride, di-	Nat. krennerite. $AuTe_2$	452.16	1) rhomb, 2) monocl, 3) tricl yel earthy to massive	8.2–9.3	d 472		i	i	
h1	**Hafnium**	Hf	178.49	hex	13.31^{20}	2227±20	4602	i	i	s HF
h2	bromide	$HfBr_4$	498.13	wh		subl 420				
h3	carbide	HfC	190.54		12.20	ca 3890		i		
h4	chloride	$HfCl_4$	320.30	wh		subl 319		d		s MeOH, acet
h5	fluoride	HfF_4	254.48	monocl, 1.56						
h6	iodide	HfI_4	686.11				400 subl vac			
h7	nitride	HfN	192.50	yel-brn, cub		3305				
h8	oxide	Hafnia. HfO_2	210.49	wh, cub	9.68^{20}	2812	~5400(?)	i	i	
h9	oxychloride	$HfOCl_2.8H_2O$	409.52	col				s		
h10	**Helium**	He	4.0026	col gas, inert odorless	0.1785^0 g/l liq $0.147^{-270.3}$	−272.2^{26atm}	268.934	0.94^0 cm³ 0.94^{25} cm³	1.05^{60} cm³ 1.21^{75} cm³	i al; absorbed by Pt
h11	**Holmium**	Ho	164.9304	met, hex	8.7947	1474	2695	i	i	
h12	bromide	$HoBr_3$	404.66	lt yel		914	1470	s	s	
h13	chloride	$HoCl_3$	271.29	lt yel		718	1500	s	s	
h14	iodide	HoI_3	545.64	lt yel		989	1300	s	s	
h15	fluoride	HoF_3	221.93	lt yel		1143	>2200	i	i	i dil a
h16	oxalate	$Ho_2(C_2O_4)_3.10H_2O$	774.10	pa tan		− H_2O, 40	d	i	i	i dil a
h17	oxide	Holmia. Ho_2O_3	377.86	tan				i	i	s a
h18	**Hydrazine**	NH_2NH_2	32.05	col liq or wh cr, 1.470^{22}	liq 1.011^{15}	1.4	113.5	v s		s al
h19	azide	$N_2H_4.HN_3$	75.07	wh pr, deliq, 1.53, 1.76		75.4		v s	v s	1.2^{23} al; 6.1^{23} MeOH; i CS_2 bz
h20	fluogermanate	$2N_2H_4.H_2GeF_6$	252.80	monocl pr, 1.452, 1.460, 1.464	2.406^{25}_{25}			s		
h21	fluosilicate	$N_2H_4.H_2SiF_6$	176.14	cr		d 186		v s		sl s al
h22	formate	$N_2H_4.2CH_2O_2$	124.10			128		s		
h23	hydrate	$N_2H_4.H_2O$	50.07	col fum liq or cub cr, 1.42842	1.03^{21}	−40	118.5^{740}	∞	∞	s al; i eth, chl
h24	hydrochloride, di-	$N_2H_4.2HCl$	104.97	col vitr, oct	1.42	198, −HCl	d 200	27.2^{32}	v s	sl s al
h25	hydrochloride, mono-	$N_2H_4.HCl$	68.51	wh need		89	d 240	v s		v sl s al; v s liq NH_3
h26	hydroiodide	Hydrazine monoiodide. $N_2H_4.HI$	159.98	col pr		124–126		s		
h27	nitrate, di-	$N_2H_4.2HNO_3$	158.07	col cr		104 (rapid heat); d 80 (slow heat)		v s	d	
h28	nitrate, mono-	$N_2H_4.HNO_3$	95.06	col dimorph need (α, β)		α70.71; β62.09	subl 140	174.9^{10}	2127^{60}	sl s al
h29	oxalate	$2N_2H_4.H_2C_2O_4$	154.14	wh need		148		200^{25}		0.0003^{22} al; i eth
h30	perchlorate	$N_2H_4.HClO_4.\frac{1}{2}H_2O$	141.51	exp	1.939	137	d 145	d		s al; i eth, bz, chl, CS_2
h31	hypophosphate	$N_2H_4.2H_3PO_3$	194.03			152				
h32	orthophosphate	$N_2H_4.H_3PO_4$	130.05	cr, hygr		82		v s		
h33	orthophosphite	$N_2H_4.2H_3PO_3$	196.06			82				
h34	orthophosphite	$N_2H_4.H_3PO_3$	114.05			36		v s		
h35	picrate	$N_2H_4.HC_6H_2N_3O_7.\frac{1}{2}H_2O$	270.16			201.3		s	s	
h36	selenate	$N_2H_4.H_2SeO_4$	177.02	col cr powd, unstab		exp		v sl s	v s	
h37	sulfate	$N_2H_4.H_2SO_4$	130.13	col, rhomb	1.37	254	d	3.415^{25}	14.39^{60}	i al
h38	sulfate	$(N_2H_4)_2.H_2SO_4$	162.18	col cr, hygr		85		202.2^{25}	554.4^{60}	i al
h39	tartrate	$(N_2H_4)_2C_4H_2O_6$	182.13	col cr; $[\alpha]_4^{20}+22.5$		182–183		6.0^0		
h40	**Hydroazoic acid**	Azoimide. HN_3	43.03	col liq	1.09^{25}_4	−80	37	∞	∞	s al, alk, eth
h41	**Hydrogen**	H_2	1.0079	col gas, cub sol	gas 0.0899 g/l liq 0.070	−259.14	−252.87	2.14^0 cm³ 1.91^{25} cm³	0.85^{60} cm³ 1.89^{60} cm³	6.925^0 cm³ al
h42	antimonide	Stibine H_3Sb	124.77	col gas, pois	gas 5.30^0 g/l liq 2.26^{-25}	−88.5	−17	20 cm³	4 cm³	1500 cm³ al; 2500 cm³ CS_2
h43	arsenide	Arsine H_3As	77.95	col gas, pois	3.484 g/l	−113.5	−55, d 230	20 cm³	sl s	sl s al, alk
h44	arsenide (solid)	H_2As_2	151.86	br powd		d 200		i	d	i al, eth, CS_2, alk; s HNO_3
h45	bismuthide	Bismuthine. H_3Bi	212.00	liq, v unstab			22			
h46	bromide	Hydrobromic acid. HBr	80.92	col gas or pa yel liq, 1.325	gas 3.5^0 g/l liq 2.77^{-67}	−88.5	−67.0	221^0	130^{100}	s al
h47	bromide (const. boiling)	HBr(47%) + H_2O		col liq	1.49	−11	126			
h48	bromide, dihydrate	$HBr.2H_2O$	116.95	wh cr, col liq	2.11^{-15}	−11		s	s	

No.	Name	Synonyms and Formulae	Mol. wt.	Crystalline form, properties and index of refraction	Density or spec. gravity	Melting point, °C	Boiling point, °C	Solubility, in grams per 100 cc		
								Cold water	Hot water	Other solvents
	Hydrogen									
h49	bromide, monohydrate	$HBr.H_2O$	98.93	col liq	1.78	stab	−3.6 to −15.5 between 1–2.5 atm			
h50	chloride	Hydrochloric acid. HCl.	36.46	col gas or col liq, pois	$1.187^{-84.9}$ gas 1.00045 g/l	−114.8	−84.9	82.3^0	56.1^{60}	327 cm³ al; s eth, bz
h51	chloride (const. boiling)	$HCl(20.24\%)+H_2O$		col liq	1.097		110			
h52	chloride, dihydrate	$HCl.2H_2O$	72.49	col liq	$1.46^{18.3}$	−17.7	d	d	∞	s al
h53	chloride, monohydrate	$HCl.H_2O$	54.48	col liq	1.48	−15.35		∞	∞	s al
h54	chloride, trihydrate	$HCl.3H_2O$	90.51	col liq		−24.4	d	∞		s al
h55	cyanide	Hydrocyanic acid. HCN	27.03	col liq or gas, pois, liq 1.2675^{10}	gas 0.901 g/l liq 0.699^{22}	−14	26	∞	∞	∞ al; s eth
h56	fluoride	Hydrofluoric acid. HF	20.01	col fum cor liq, or gas; gas 1.90	$0.991^{19.44}$ liq 0.987	−83.1	19.54	∞	v s	
h57	fluoride (const. boiling)	$HF(35.35\%)+H_2O$		col liq			120			
h58	iodide	Hydroiodic acid. HI.	127.91	col gas, or pa yel liq, $n_D^{16.6}$ 1.466	gas 5.66 g/l liq $2.85^{-4.7}$	−50.8	$−35.38^4$ atm	42.5^0 cm³	v s	s al
h59	iodide (const. boiling)	$HI(57\%)+H_2O$		col or pa yel fum liq	1.70^{15}		127^{774}			
h60	iodide, dihydrate	$HI.2H_2O$	163.94	col liq		−43		∞		
h61	iodide, tetrahydrate	$HI.4H_2O$	199.97	col liq		−36.5		∞		
h62	iodide, trihydrate	$HI.3H_2O$	181.96	col liq		−48		∞		
h63	oxide	Water. H_2O	18.0153	col liq or hex cr, liq 1.333, sol 1.309, 1.313	1.000^4_4	0.000	100.000			∞ al
h64	oxide, per-	H_2O_2	34.01	col liq; 1.414^{22}	1.442^{25}	−0.41	150.2^{750}	∞		s al, eth; i pet eth
h65	phosphide	Phosphine. H_3P	34.00	col pois inflam gas or col liq, 1.317 liq	gas 1.529 g/l liq 0.746^{-90}	−133.5	−87.4	26^{17} cm³	i	s al, eth, Cu_2Cl_2
h66	phosphide	H_4P_2	65.98	col liq	1.012	−90	57.5^{736}	i	i	s al, turp
h67	phosphide	$(H_2P_4)_3$	377.73	yel solid	1.83^{19}	ign 160	d	i	i	i al; s P, P_2H_4
h68	sulfide	H_2S	34.08	col gas, infl, liq 1.374	1.539 g/l	−85.5	−60.7	437^0 cm³	186^{40} cm³	9.54^{20} cm³ al; s CS_2
h69	sulfide, di-	H_2S_2	66.14	yel oil, 1.885	1.334^{20}	−89.6	70.7^{760}	d		s bz, eth, CS_2; i al
h70	sulfide, penta-	H_2S_5	162.34	clear yel oil	1.67^{16}	−50	50^4			s bz, eth, CS_2; i al
h71	sulfide, tetra-	H_2S_4	130.27	lt yel liq	1.588^{16}	−85				
h72	sulfide, tri-	H_2S_3	98.21	brt yel liq, 1.705^{18}	1.496^{18}	−52	d 90			s bz, eth, CS_2; i al
h73	telluride	H_2Te	129.62	col gas or yel need	gas 5.81 g/l liq 2.57^{-20}	−49	−2	s unstab		s al, alk
h74	**Hydroxylamine**	NH_2OH	33.03	wh need or col liq, deliq	1.204	33.05	56.5	s	d	s a, al, MeOH; v sl s eth, chl, bz, CS_2
h75	acetate	$NH_2OH.CH_3CO_2$	92.08	col cr		87	subl 90	v s		
h76	bromide	$NH_2OH.HBr$	113.95	wh, monocl	2.35^{22}_4			v s	v s	i eth
h77	fluogermanate	$(NH_2OH)_2.H_2GeF_6.2H_2O$	290.69	monocl pr, 1.418, 1.438, 1.443	2.229^{25}			s		s abs al
h78	fluosilicate	$(NH_2OH)_2.H_2SiF_6.2H_2O$	246.18	scales				v s		i al
h79	formate	$NH_2OH.HCO_2$	78.05	col need		76	d 80	v s	d	s h al; i eth
h80	hydrochloride	$NH_2OH.HCl$	69.49	col, monocl	1.67^{17}	151	d	83^{17}	v s	4.43^{20} al; 16.4^{20} MeOH; s gluc; i eth
h81	iodide	$NH_2OH.HI$	160.94	col need, hygr		83–84 exp		v s	d	v s MeOH; sl s eth
h82	nitrate	$NH_2OH.HNO_3$	96.04	wh		48	d <100	v s	d	v s al
h83	orthophosphate	$(NH_2OH)_3.H_3PO_4$	197.09			148 exp		1.9^{20}	16.6^{90}	
h84	sulfate	$(NH_2OH)_2.H_2SO_4$	164.14	col, monocl		d 170	d	32.9^0	66.5^{88}	sl s al; s eth
i1	**Indium**	In	114.80	soft silv wh met, tetr	7.30^{20}	155.61	2080	i	i	s a; v sl s NaOH
i2	antimonide	InSb	236.57	cr		535				
i3	arsenide	InAs	189.74	met cr		943				i a
i4	bromide, di-	$InBr_2$	274.64	pa yel solid	4.22^{25}	235	632 subl	d		s a
i5	bromide, mono-	InBr	194.73	red br solid	4.96^{25}	220	662 subl	d		s a
i6	bromide, tri-	$InBr_3$	354.55	wh to yel need, deliq	4.74^{25}	436 ± 2	subl	v s		
i7	perchlorate	$In(ClO_4)_3.8H_2O$	557.29	col cr, deliq		ca 800	d 200	v s	d	s abs al; sl s eth
i8	chloride, di-	$InCl_2$	185.73	wh rhomb, deliq	3.655^{25}	235	550–570	d	d	
i9	chloride, mono-	InCl	150.27	1) yel or 2) dk red, deliq	4.19^{25} yel 4.18^{25} red	225 ± 1	608	d	d	s a

No.	Name	Synonyms and Formulae	Mol. wt.	Crystalline form, properties and index of refraction	Density or spec. gravity	Melting point, °C	Boiling point, °C	Solubility, in grams per 100 cc		
								Cold water	Hot water	Other solvents
	Indium									
i10	chloride, tri-	$InCl_3$	221.18	wh pl, deliq	3.46_4^{25}	586 subl 300	volat 600	v s	v s	sl s al, eth
i11	cyanide	$In(CN)_3$	192.87	wh ppt			unstab			i dil a; s HCN; v sl s NaOH
i12	fluoride	InF_3	171.82	col	$4.39^{25} \pm 1$	1170 ± 10	>1200	0.040^{25}		
i13	fluoride, trihydrate	$InF_3.3H_2O$	225.86	cr		$-3H_2O$, 100		8.49^{22}		s a; i al, eth
i14	fluoride, nonahydrate	$InF_3.9H_2O$	333.95	wh need		d		sl s	d	s HCl, HNO_3; i al, eth
i15	hydroxide	$In(OH)_3$	165.84	wh ppt		$-H_2O < 150$		i		s a; v sl s NaOH; i NH_4OH
i16	iodate	$In(IO_3)_3$	639.53	wh cr			d	0.067^{20}		s dil HNO_3, dil H_2SO_4; s d HCl
i17	iodide, di-	InI_2	368.63		4.71^{25}	212				s a
i18	iodide, mono-	InI	241.72	br red solid	5.31	351	711–715		sl d	i al, eth, chl; s dil a
i19	iodide, tri-	InI_3	495.53	carmine red, or yel cr	4.69	210		v unstable	s	s a, chl, bz yxl
i20	methylate	$In(CH_3)_3$	159.93	col cr	1.568_{19}^{19}		d			d al, MeOH; s liq NH_3, eth; v s acet, bz
i21	nitrate	$In(NO_3)_3.3H_2O$	354.88	pl, deliq		$-2H_2O$, 100	d	v s		s al
i22	nitrate	$In(NO_3)_3.4\frac{1}{2}H_2O$	381.90	need, deliq		$-4\frac{1}{2}H_2O$	d	v s		s al
i23	oxide, mon-	InO	130.81	wh gray				i		s a
i24	oxide, sesqui-	In_2O_3	277.64	red brn, (h) pa yel (c) amorph and trig	7.179		volat 850	i		amorph s a; cr i a
i25	oxide, sub-	In_2O	245.64	blk cr	6.99_4^{25}	subl vac 565–700				s HCl
i26	phosphide	InP	145.79	brittle mass met		1070				v sl s min a
i27	selenate	$In_2(SeO_4)_3.10H_2O$	838.67	cr, deliq				v s		
i28	selenide, sesqui-	In_2Se_3	466.52	blk cr, or soft dk scales	5.67_4^{25}	890 ± 10				s, d conc a
i29	sulfate	$In_2(SO_4)_3$	517.83	wh gray powd, monocl pr, hygr	3.438			s	v s	
i30	sulfate	$In_2(SO_4)_3.9H_2O$	679.96	wh powd, hygr	3.44	d 250		v s		
i31	sulfate, dihydrate	$In_2(SO_4)_3.H_2SO_4.7H_2O$	742.01	rhomb cr		$-7H_2O$, $-H_2SO_4$, ca 250				
i32	sulfide, mono-	InS	146.88	dk	5.18^{25}	692 ± 5	subl vac 850			s HCl, HNO_3
i33	sulfide, sesqui-	In_2S_3	325.83	red cr or yel ppt	4.90	1050	subl ca 850 in high vac	i		s a; sl s Na_2S
i34	sulfide, sub-	In_2S	261.70	yel or blk need	5.87^{25}	653 ± 5				
i35	sulfite, basic	$2In_2O_3.3SO_2.8H_2O$	891.59	wh cr		$-3H_2O$, 100	$-8H_2O$, 260	i		
i36	telluride, sesqui-	InTe	242.42	dk met, shiny	6.29_4^{25}	696 ± 2				i HCl, s HNO_3
i37	telluride	In_2Te_3	612.44	bl brittle cr	5.78	667				
i38	**Iodic acid**	HIO_3	175.91	col or pa yel cr powd, rhomb	4.629^0	d 110		286^0 310^{16}	473^{80} 576^{101}	v s 87 % al; sl s HNO_3; i abs al, eth, chl
i39	metaper-	HIO_4	191.91	col		subl 110	d 138	v s, d		
i40	orthoparaper-	H_5IO_6 or $HIO_4.2H_2O$	227.94	wh monocl, deliq			d 140	113	v s	s al, eth
i41	**Iodine**	I_2	253.809	vlt blk met lust, rhomb, 3.34	4.93	113.5	184.35^{atm}	0.029^{20} 0.030^{25}	0.078^{50}	20.5^{15} al; 16.46^{25} bz 20.6^{17} eth; s chl glyc, KI; 24^{25} eth 23^{25} MeOH 20.15^{25} CS_2; 2.91^{25} CCl_4
i42	azide	Iod(o)azide. IN_3	168.92	yel, exp				s d		s $Na_2S_2O_3$
i43	bromide, mono-	IBr	206.81	dk gray cr	4.4157°	(42) subl 50	d 116	s d		s al, eth, chl, CS_2
i44	bromide, tri-	IBr_3	366.63	br liq				s d		s al
i45	chloride, mono-(α)	ICl	162.36	dk-red need, cub, red br oily liq	3.1822^0	27.2	97.4	d to HIO_3 +Cl		s al, eth, CS_2, HCl
i46	chloride, mono-(β)	ICl	162.36	brn red, rhombic 6 sided pl	liq 3.24^{24}	13.92	97.4; d 100	d		s al, eth, HCl
i47	chloride, tri-	ICl_3	233.26	yel brn, rhomb, red liq	3.117^{15}	101^{16atm}	d 77	s d		s al, eth, CCl_4, ac a, bz
i48	cyanide	ICN	152.92	wh cr				sl s	sl s	s al, eth
i49	fluoride, hepta-	IF_7	259.89	col cr or liq	liq 2.8^6	5.5	4.5 subl	v s, d	d	d a, alk
i50	fluoride, penta-	IF_5	221.90	col liq	3.75	9.6	98	d	d	d a, ak
i51	oxide, di- (or tetra-)	IO_2 or I_2O_4	158.90	lem-yel cr	4.2_{10}^{10}	d slow 75 rap 130		d to HIO_3+I_2		s H_2SO_4; sl s acet; i al, eth

No.	Name	Synonyms and Formulae	Mol. wt.	Crystalline form, properties and index of refraction	Density or spec. gravity	Melting point, °C	Boiling point, °C	Solubility, in grams per 100 cc		
								Cold water	Hot water	Other solvents

Iodine

No.	Name	Synonyms and Formulae	Mol. wt.	Crystalline form	Density	Melting	Boiling	Cold water	Hot water	Other solvents
i52	oxide, pent-	I_2O_5	333.81	wh trim	4.799_4^{25}	d 300 350		187.4^{13}	v s	i abs al, eth, chl, CS_2; sl s dil a
i53	(tetra-) oxide non-	I_4O_9	651.61	yel powd, hygr			d 75			
i54	Iodo platinic acid	$H_2PtI_6.9H_2O$	1120.67	blk, monocl, deliq		>100		v s, d	d	
i55	Iodous acid, hypo-	Iodine hydroxide. HOI	143.91	only in sol, yel to grayish				d	d	
i56	Iridium	Ir	192.20	silv wh met, cub	22.421	2410	4130	i	i	sl s aq reg; i a, alk
i57	bromide, tetra-	$IrBr_4$	511.84	blk, deliq		d		s d		s al
i58	bromide, tri-	$IrBr_3.4H_2O$	503.99	olv-grn cr		$-3H_2O$, 100		v s		i al
i59	carbonyl	$Ir_2(CO)_8$	608.48	yel cr		subl 160 (in CO_2)				s CCl_4
i60	carbonyl	$Ir_4(CO)_{12}$	1104.93	yel cr		subl 250 (in CO_2)				i CCl_4
i61	carbonyl chloride	$Ir(CO)_2Cl_2$	319.13	col need		d 140		d		d HCl, KOH
i62	chloride, di-	$IrCl_2$	263.11	blk gray cr (exist ?)		d 773		s		i a, alk
i63	chloride, tetra-	$IrCl_4$	334.01	dk-brn, amorph, hygr		d		s	d	s al, dil HCl
i64	chloride, tri-	$IrCl_3$	298.56	olv-grn hex, or trig	5.30	d 763		i	i	i a, alk
i65	fluoride, hexa-	IrF_6	306.19	yel glass or tetr	6.0	44.4^{30}	53	d	d	
i66	iodide, tetra-	IrI_4	699.82	blk		d 100		i	i	i al, s KI
i67	iodide, tri-	IrI_3	572.91	grn		d		sl s	s	sl s al
i68	oxalic acid	$H_2[Ir(C_2O_4)_2.xH_2O$		pa yel cr				v s	v s	sl s al; i eth
i69	oxide, di-	IrO_2	224.20	blk tetr or bl cr	11.665	d 1100		0.0002^{20}		i a, alk
i70	oxide, di- hydrate	$IrO_2.2H_2O$ or $Ir(OH)_4$	260.23	indigo bl cr		$-2H_2O$, 350		i	i	s HCl
i71	oxide, sesqui-	Ir_2O_3	432.40	bl-blk (exist ?)		$-O$, 400		i		s H_2SO_4, h HCl; i alk
i72	oxide, sesqui-	$Ir_2O_3.xH_2O$		olive green		d		i		s a, alk
i73	phosphor chloride	IrP_3Cl_{12} or $IrCl_3.3PCl_3$	710.56	yel pr		d 250		sl s	d 100	sl s, d al
i74	selenide	$IrSe_2$	350.12	dk gray cr powd		d 600–700 (in CO_2)				sl s aq reg; i a
i75	sulfate	$Ir_2(SO_4)_3.xH_2O$		yel pr		d		s		
i76	sulfide, di	IrS_2	256.33	br-blk	8.43_4^{25}	d 300		i		s aq reg; i a
i77	sulfide, hydro-	$Ir(HS)_4.2H_2O$	327.45	choc br		d		i		s HNO_3
i78	sulfide, mono-	IrS	224.26	bl-blk		d		i		s K_2S, i a
i79	sulfide, sesqui-	Ir_2S_3	480.59	br-blk	9.64_4^{25}	d		sl s		s K_2S, HNO_3
i80	telluride	$IrTe_2$	575.00	dk gray cr	9.5_4^{25}			i	i	i a; s h aq reg

Iridium complexes

No.	Name	Synonyms and Formulae	Mol. wt.	Crystalline form	Density	Melting	Boiling	Cold water	Hot water	Other solvents
i81	aquopentammine iridium-chloride	$[Ir(NH_3)_5H_2(H_2O)]Cl_3$	402.54	wh micro cr	2.474_4^{15}	$-H_2O$, 100		ca 75^{25}	d	i al, eth
i82	chloropentammine iridiumchloride	$[Ir(NH_3)_5Cl]Cl_2$	383.71	pa yel, rhomb	$2.681_4^{15.5}$	d		sl s	s	i HCl
i83	hexammine iridium chloride	$[Ir(NH_3)_6]Cl_3$	400.74	col, rhomb	$2.434_4^{15.5}$			20		
i84	hexammine iridium nitrate	$[Ir(NH_3)_6](NO_3)_3$	408.40	col, tetr micro cr	2.395_1^{15}			1.7^{14}		
i85	nitratopentammine iridium nitrate	$[Ir(NH_3)_5(NO_3)](NO_3)_2$	463.37	wh micro cr	2.515_4^{15}	heat exp		0.28	2.5^{100}	
i86	Iron	Fe	55.847	silv met, cub	7.86	1535	2750	i	i	s a; i alk, al, eth
i87	(II) acetate	$Fe(C_2H_3O_2)_2.4H_2O$	246.00	lt grn need, monocl		d		v s		
i88	(III) acetate, basic	$FeOH(C_2H_3O_2)_2$	190.94	br-red powd				i		s a, al
i89	(III) acetylacetonate	$Fe(C_5H_7O_2)_3$	353.18	rubyred, rhomb	1.33	184		sl s	sl s	s al, acet, bz, chl
i90	(II) orthoarsenate	$Fe_3(AsO_4)_2.6H_2O$	553.47	grn amorph powd		d		i	i	s dil HCl; sl s NH_4OH
i91	(III) orthoarsenate	Nat. scorodite. $FeAsO_4.2H_2O$	230.80	grn, rhomb, 1.765, 1.774, 1.797	3.18	d		i	i	s HCl; i HNO_3
i92	(III) orthoarsenite, basic	$2FeAsO_3.Fe_2O_3.5H_2O$	607.30	br-yel powd		d		sl s		s a, alk
i93	(II) pyroarsenite	$Fe_2As_2O_5$	341.53	grn-wh				i		s NH_4OH
i94	arsenide	FeAs	130.77	wh	7.83	1020		v sl s		
i95	arsenide, di-	Arsenoferrite. $FeAs_2$	205.69	silv gray, cub	7.4	990				sl s HNO_3 ; i HCl
i96	(III) benzoate	$Fe(C_7H_5O_2)_3$	419.20	br powd				i		s h al, h eth
i97	boride	FeB	66.66	gray cr	7.15^{18}			i		s HNO_3, h conc H_2SO_4

No.	Name	Synonyms and Formulae	Mol. wt.	Crystalline form, properties and index of refraction	Density or spec. gravity	Melting point, °C	Boiling point, °C	Solubility, in grams per 100 cc		
								Cold water	Hot water	Other solvents
	Iron									
i98	(II) bromide	$FeBr_2$	215.67	grn-yel, hex	4.636[25]	d 684 (?)		109[10]	170[95]	s al; sl s bz
i99	(III) bromide	$FeBr_3$ or Fe_2Br_6	295.57	dk red-brn, rhomb (?) deliq		subl d		s	s	s al, eth, sl s NH_3
i100	(III) bromide-, hexahydrate	$FeBr_3.6H_2O$	403.68	dk grn		27		v s	v s	s al, eth
i101	(III) cacodylate	$Fe[(CH_3)_2AsO_2]_3$	466.82	yelsh amorph powd				6.67		sl s al
i102	carbide	Fe_3C	179.55	gray, cub	7.694	1837		i	i	s a
i103	(II) carbonate	Nat. siderite. $FeCO_3$	115.85	gray, trig, 1.875, 1.633	3.8	d		0.0067[25]		s CO_2 sol
i104	(II) carbonate, hydrate	$FeCO_3.H_2O$	133.86	amorph		d		sl s		s a, CO_2 sol
i105	carbonyl, ennea-	$Fe_2(CO)_9$	363.79	yel met cr, hex	2.085[18]	d 80		i	i	v sl s al, MeOH; d HNO_3; i a
i106	carbonyl, penta-	$Fe(CO)_5$	195.90	visc yel liq	liq 1.457[21]	−21	102.8[749]	i		s al, eth, bz, alk, conc H_2SO_4
i107	carbonyl, tetra-	$Fe(CO)_4$	167.89	dk grn lust cr, tetr	1.996[18]	d 140–150		i		s org solv, conc HNO_3 h H_2SO_4
i108	(II) perchlorate	$Fe(ClO_4)_2$	254.75	wh or grnsh-wh need, hygr		d>100		v s		
i109	(II) perchlorate hexahydrate	$Fe(ClO_4)_2.6H_2O$	362.84	grn, 1.493, 1.478		d>100		97.8[0]	116.1[50]	86.5[20] al; s $HClO_4$
i110	oxychloride	$FeOCl$	107.30	brn, rhomb	3.1	d 200				
i111	(II) chloride	Nat. lawrencite. $FeCl_2$	126.75	grn to yel, hex deliq, 1.567	3.16[25/4]	670–674	subl	64.4[10]	105.7[100]	100 al; s acet; i eth
i112	(II) chloride, dihydrate	$FeCl_2.2H_2O$	162.78	grn, monocl	2.358					
i113	(II) chloride, tetrahydrate	$FeCl_2.4H_2O$	198.81	bl-grn, monocl, deliq	1.93			160.1[10]	415.5[100]	s al; sl s acet
i114	(III) chloride	Nat. molysite. $FeCl_3$ or Fe_2Cl_6	162.21	blk-brn hex	2.898[25/4]	306	d 315	74.4[0]	535.7[100]	v s al, MeOH, eth; 63[18] acet
i115	(III) chloride, hydrate	$FeCl_3.2\frac{1}{2}H_2O$	207.24	dk yel-red, rhomb, deliq		56		v s	v s	v s al, eth
i116	(III) chloride, hexahydrate	$FeCl_3.6H_2O$	270.30	br yel cr mass, v deliq		37	280–285	91.9[20]	∞	s al, eth
i117	(II) chloride, hexammine	$FeCl_2.6NH_3$	228.94	wh powd	1.928[25/4]					
i118	(II) chloroplatinate	$FePtCl_6.6H_2O$	571.75	yel, hex	2.714	d		v s	v s	
i119	(III) dichromate	$Fe_2(Cr_2O_7)_3$	759.66	red-brn gran				s		s a
i120	(II) chromite	$FeCr_2O_4$	223.84	brn-blk, cub	4.97[20]			i	i	sl s a
i121	(II) citrate	$FeC_6H_6O_7.H_2O$	263.97	wh micr, rhomb		d 350 (in H_2)		sl s		s NH_4OH
i122	(III) citrate	$FeC_6H_6O_7.5H_2O$	335.03	red-brn scales				sl s	s	i al
i123	hydroxide	Nat. goethite. $FeO(OH)$	88.85	brn, blksh, rhomb, 2.260, 2.394, 2.400	4.28	−½H_2O, 136				s HCl
i124	(II) ferricyanide	$Fe_3[Fe(CN)_6]_2(?)$	591.45	deep bl		d		i		i al, dil a
i125	(III) ferricyanide	Berlin green. $Fe[Fe(CN)_6]$	267.80	cub						
i126	(II) ferrocyanide	$Fe_2[Fe(CN)_6]$	323.65	bl-wh, amorph	1.601[25/4]	d 100	d 430 (vac)	i		
i127	(III) ferrocyanide	$Fe_4[Fe(CN)_6]_3$	859.25	dk bl cr		d		i	i	s HCl, H_2SO_4; i al, eth
i128	(II) fluoride	FeF_2	93.84	wh, rhomb	4.09[25]	>1000 (?)		sl s		s a; i al, eth
i129	(II) fluoride, octahydrate	$FeF_2.8H_2O$	237.97	grn-bl	4.20 (anh)	−8H_2O, 100		sl s	s	s HF, a; i al, eth
i130	(II) fluoride, tetrahydrate	$FeF_2.4H_2O$	165.91	wh, rhomb	2.095	d		v sl s		s a; sl s al, eth
i131	(III) fluoride	FeF_3 or Fe_2F_6	112.84	grn, rhomb	3.52	>1000		sl s	s	s a; i al, eth
i132	(III) fluoride, tetrahydrate	$FeF_3.4\frac{1}{2}H_2O$	193.91	yel cr		−3H_2O, 100 d		sl s	s	i al
i133	(II) fluosilicate	$FeSiF_6.6H_2O$	306.01	col, trig, 1.361, 1.385	1.961			128.2		
i134	(III) fluosilicate	$Fe_2(SiF_6)_3$ (exist ?)	537.92	flesh col, gel				s	s, d	
i135	(III) formate	$Fe(CHO_2)_3.H_2O$	208.92	red cr or powd				s		v sl s al
i136	(III) glycerophosphate	$Fe_2[C_3H_5(OH)_2.PO_4]_3$	621.39	yelsh-grn sc or powd				50[25]		i al
i137	(II) hydrogen cyanide	$H_4[Fe(CN)_6]$	215.99	wh, rhomb	1.536[25/4]	d 190		s	s	v s al; s a; i acet
i138	(III) hydrogen cyanide	$H_3[Fe(CN)_6]$	214.98	brn-yel need		d 50–60		s	s	v s al; i eth

No.	Name	Synonyms and Formulae	Mol. wt.	Crystalline form, properties and index of refraction	Density or spec. gravity	Melting point, °C	Boiling point, °C	Solubility, in grams per 100 cc		
								Cold water	Hot water	Other solvents
	Iron									
i139	(II) hydroxide	$Fe(OH)_2$	89.86	pa grn hex, or wh amorph	3.4	d		0.00015^{18}		s a, NH_4Cl; i alk
i140	(III) hydrosulfate	Iron(ic) tetrasulfate. Nat. rhomboklas. $Fe_2O_3.4SO_3.9H_2O$	642.08	wh to pink powd, 1.533, 1.550, 1.635	2.172	$-6H_2O$, 80		a		sl s abs al
i141	(III) iodate	$Fe(IO_3)_3$	580.55	grn yel powd	4.80^{20}_4	d 130		sl s		i dil HNO_3
i142	(II) iodide	FeI_2	309.66	gray hex, hygr	5.315	red heat		s	s	s al, acet
i143	(II) iodide, tetra-hydrate	$FeI_2.4H_2O$	381.72	gray blk cr, deliq	2.873	d 90–98		v s	d	s al, eth
i144	(II) lactate	$Fe(C_3H_5O_3)_2.3H_2O$	287.96	grn-wh cr or powd		d		2.1^{10}	8.5^{100}	s alk citrate; v sl s al; i eth
i145	(III) lactate	$Fe(C_3H_5O_3)_3$	323.06	br, amorph, deliq				s	v s	i eth
i146	(III) malate	$Fe_2(C_4H_4O_5)_3$	507.91	br scales, hygr				s		s al
i147	methanoarsenate	$Fe(CH_3AsO_3)_3$	525.60	redsh br lustr scales				50		i al, eth
i148	(II) nitrate	$Fe(NO_3)_2.6H_2O$	287.95	grn, rhomb		60.5		83.5^{20}	166.7^{61}	
i149	(III) nitrate	$Fe(NO_3)_3.6H_2O$	349.95	cub		35	d	150^0	∞	
i150	(III) nitrate	$Fe(NO_3)_3.9H_2O$	404.02	col-pa vlt, monocl, deliq	1.684	47.2	d 125	s	s	s al, acet; sl s HNO_3
i151	nitride	Fe_4N	237.39		6.57(?)					
i152	nitride	Fe_2N or Fe_4N_2	125.70	gray	6.35	d 200		i		s HCl, H_2SO_4
i153	nitrosyl carbonyl	$Fe(NO)_2(CO)_2$	171.88	dk red cr	1.56	18.5	d 50, 110	i		s org solv
i154	(III) oleate	$Fe(C_{18}H_{33}O_2)_3$	900.23	br-red fatty lumps				i		s a, al, eth
i155	(II) oxalate	$FeC_2O_4.2H_2O$	179.90	pa yel, rhomb	2.28	d 190		0.022	0.026	s a
i156	(III) oxalate	$Fe_2(C_2O_4)_3.5H_2O$	465.83	yel micro cr powd		d 100		v s	v s	s a; i al
i157	(II) oxide	Nat. wuestite. FeO	71.85	blk, cub, 2.32	5.7	1420		i	i	s a; i al, alk
i158	(III) oxide	Nat. hematite. Fe_2O_3	159.69	red-brn to blk, trig, 3.01, 2.94(Li)	5.24	1565		i	i	s HCl, H_2SO_4; sl s HNO_3
i159	oxide	Iron ferrosoferric, nat. magnetite. Fe_3O_4	231.54	blk, cub or red-blk powd, 2.42	5.18	d 1538		i	i	s conc a; i al, eth
i160	(III) oxide, hydrate	$Fe_2O_3.xH_2O$		red-brn amorph powd or gelat	2.44–3.60	all H_2O, 350–400		i	i	s a; i al, eth
i161	(II) orthophosphate	Nat. vivianite. $Fe_3(PO_4)_2.8H_2O$	501.61	wh-bl, monocl, 1.579, 1.603, 1.633	2.58			i	i	s a; i ac a
i162	(III) orthophosphate	$FePO_4.2H_2O$	186.85	pink, monocl	2.74	d		v sl s	0.67^{100}	s HCl, H_2SO_4; i HNO_3
i163	(III) pyrophosphate	$Fe_4(P_2O_7)_3.9H_2O$	907.36	yel-wh powd				i		s a, alk citr
i164	phosphide, mono-	FeP	86.82	rhomb	6.07 (5.2²⁰)			i		
i165	(di-)phosphide	Fe_2P	142.67	bl-gray cr or powd	6.56	1290		i	i	s aq reg, HNO_3+HF; i dil a
i166	(tri-)phosphide	Fe_3P	198.51	gray	6.74	1100		i		
i167	(III) hypophosphite	$Fe(H_2PO_2)_3$	250.81	wh or gray-wh powd		d		0.043^{25}	0.083^{100}	s alk citr
i168	(II) metasilicate	Nat. gruenerite. $FeSiO_3$	131.93	gray-grn, rhomb, 1.672, 1.697, 1.717	3.5	1146		i		
i169	orthosilicate	Nat. fayalite. Fe_2SiO_4	203.78	col, rhomb	4.34	1503 (?)		i	i	d HCl
i170	silicide	$FeSi$	83.93	yel-gray, oct	6.1			i	i	i aq reg
i171	(II) sulfate	Nat. szomolnikite. $FeSO_4.H_2O$	169.96	off-wh, monocl	2.970^{25}			sl s	s	
i172	(III) sulfate	$Fe_2(SO_4)_3$	399.87	yel rhomb, hygr, 1.814	3.097^{18}	d 480		sl s	d	i H_2SO_4, NH_3
i173	(II) sulfate, hepta-hydrate	Nat. melanterite. $FeSO_4.7H_2O$	278.05	bl-grn, monocl, 1.471, 1.478, 1.486	1.898	$64-6H_2O$, 90	$-7H_2O$, 300	15.65	48.6^{50}	sl s al; s abs MeOH
i174	(II) sulfate, penta-hydrate	Nat siderotil. $FeSO_4.5H_2O$	242.02	wh, tricl, 1.526, 1.536, 1.542	2.2	$-5H_2O$, 300		s	s	i al
i175	(II) sulfate, tetra-hydrate	$FeSO_4.4H_2O$	224.01	grn monocl pr, 1.533, 1.535	2.23–2.29					
i176	(III) sulfate, enneahydrate	Nat. coquimbite. $Fe_2(SO_4)_3.9H_2O$	562.01	rhomb, deliq, 1.552, 1.558	2.1	$-7H_2O$, 175		440	d	s abs al
i177	sulfide, di-	Nat. pyrite. FeS_2	119.98	yel, cub	5.0	1171		0.00049		d HNO_3. dil a
i178	sulfide, di-	Nat. marcasite. FeS_2	119.98	yel, rhomb	4.87	tr 450	d	0.00049		d HNO_3, i dil a
i179	(II) sulfide	Nat. troilite. FeS	87.91	blk-brn, hex	4.74	1193–1199	d	0.00062^{18}	d	s d a; i NH_3
i180	(III) sulfide	Fe_2S_3	207.87	yel-grn	4.3	d		sl d	d FeS+S	d a
i181	(II) sulfite	$FeSO_3.3H_2O$	189.96	grnsh or wh cr		d 250		v sl s		s SO_2 sol; i al
i182	tantalate	Nat. tapiolite. $Fe(TaO_3)_2$	513.73	lt brn, tetr, 2.27, 2.42 (Li)	7.33					
i183	d-tartrate	$FeC_4H_4O_6$	203.92	wh cr				0.877^{16}	v sl s	v s min a; s NH_4OH
i184	(II) thiocyanate	$Fe(SCN)_2.3H_2O$	226.06	grn, rhomb		d		v s		s al, eth, acet
i185	(III) thiocyanate	$Fe(SCN)_3$ or $Fe_2(SCN)_6$	230.09	blk-red, cub, deliq				v s	d	s al, eth, acet

No.	Name	Synonyms and Formulae	Mol. wt.	Crystalline form, properties and index of refraction	Density or spec. gravity	Melting point, °C	Boiling point, °C	Solubility, in grams per 100 cc		
								Cold water	Hot water	Other solvents
	Iron									
i186	(II) thiosulfate	FeS₂O₃.5H₂O	258.05	grn cr, deliq				v s	d	v s al
i187	tungstate	Nat. ferberite. FeWO₄	303.69	tetr, 2.40 (Li)	6.64					s a; i al
i188	*meta*vanadate	Fe(VO₃)₃	352.67	grayish-brn powd						s a; i al
k1	**Krypton**	Kr	83.80	inert gas	gas 3.736g/l liq 2.155 at −152.9	−156.6	−152.30 ± 0.10	11.0⁰ cm³ 6.0²⁵ cm³	4.67⁶⁰ cm³	
l1	**Lanthanum**	La	138.91	wh met, tarnish in air, α: hex, β: cub above 350	α 6.1453, β 6.17	921	3457	d	d	s min a; i conc H₂SO₄
l2	acetate	La(C₂H₃O₂)₃.1½H₂O	343.07					16.88²⁵		
l3	boride, hexa-	LaB₆	203.78	purp met cub	2.61	2210	d	i	i	i HCl
l4	bromate	La(BrO₃)₃.9H₂O	684.77	hex pr		37.5	−7H₂O, 100	28.5¹⁵		i al
l5	bromide	LaBr₃.7H₂O	504.74	col cr	5.057²⁵ anh	783 ± 3 anh	1577	v s	d	v s al; i eth
l6	carbide	LaC₂	162.93	yel cr	5.02			d	d	s H₂SO₄; i conc HNO₃
l7	carbonate	La₂(CO₃)₃.8H₂O	601.97	wh	2.6–2.7			i	i	s dil a; sl s aq CO₂; i acet
l8	chloride	LaCl₃	245.27	wh cr, deliq	3.842²⁵	860	>1000	v s	d	v s al, pyr; i eth, bz
l9	chloride, hepta-hydrate	LaCl₃.7H₂O	371.38	wh, tricl, hygr		d 91		v s	v s	v s al
l10	hexantipyrin *per*chlorate	[La(C₁₁H₁₂N₂O)].(ClO₄)₃	1566.65	col, hex cr		d 290–295		1.50²⁰		
l11	hydroxide	La(OH)₃	189.93	wh powd		d		i		s a
l12	iodate	La(IO₃)₃	663.62	col, cr				1.7²⁵		
l13	iodide	LaI₃	519.62	gray-wh, rhomb, hygr	5.63	772		v s		s acet
l14	molybdate	La₂(MoO₄)₃	757.63	tetr	4.77¹⁶	1181		0.00179²⁵	0.0033⁵⁵	
l15	nitrate	La(NO₃)₃.6H₂O	433.02	col cr, deliq, tricl		40	d 126	151.1²⁵	v s	v s al; s acet
l16	oxalate	La₂(C₂O₄)₃.9H₂O	704.02	wh cr		d		0.00008²⁵		s min a
l17	oxide	Lanthana. La₂O₃	325.82	wh rhomb, or amorph	6.51¹⁵	2315	4200	0.0004²⁹	d	s a, NH₄Cl; i acet
l18	sulfate	La₂(SO₄)₃	566.00	wh powd, hygr	3.60¹⁵	d 1150		3.0	0.69¹⁰⁰	sl s al; i acet
l19	sulfate, hydrate	La₂(SO₄)₃.9H₂O	728.14	col hex, 1.564	2.821	d white heat		3.8⁰	0.87¹⁰⁰	sl s HCl; i al
l20	sulfide	La₂S₃	374.01	red-yel cr, hex	4.911¹¹	2100–2150 vac		d	d	s a
l21	**Lead**	Pb	207.19	silv-blsh wh soft met, cub, 2.01	11.3437¹⁶ Ra-Pb 11.288²⁰₂₀ UPb 11.2960¹⁶	327.502	1740	i	i	s HNO₃, h conc H₂SO₄
l22	abietate	Pb(C₂₀H₂₉O₂)₂	810.10	brn lumps or yelsh-wh powd				i		
l23	acetate	Pb(C₂H₃O₂)₂	325.28	wh cr	3.25²⁰₄	280		44.3²⁰	221⁵⁰	s glyc; v sl s al
l24	acetate, basic	Pb₂(OH)(C₂H₃O₂)₃	608.52	wh				v s		sl s al
l25	acetate, basic	Pb(C₂H₃O₂)₂.3PbO.H₂O	1012.86	wh powd						
l26	acetate, basic	Pb(C₂H₃O₂)₂.Pb(OH)₂.H₂O	584.50	wh, monocl				v s		v s al
l27	acetate, decahydrate	Pb(C₂H₃O₂)₂.10H₂O	505.44	wh, rhomb cr	1.69	22		s	s	i al
l28	acetate, trihydrate	Sugar of lead. Pb(C₂H₃O₂)₂.3H₂O	379.33	wh, monocl, β 1.567	2.55	−H₂O, 75	d 200	45.61¹⁵	200¹⁰⁰	i al
l29	acetate, tetra-	Pb(C₂H₃O₂)₄	443.37	col, monocl	2.228¹⁷	175		d		d al; s chl, h ac a
l30	*di*antimonate	Pb₂Sb₂O₇	769.88	dk yel powd	6.72			i	i	v sl s HCl
l31	*ortho*antimonate	Pb₃(SbO₄)₂	993.07	or-yel powd	6.58²⁰₄			i	i	v sl s HCl
l32	*ortho*antimonate	Nat. monimolite. Pb₃(SbO₄)₂	993.07	orange powd	6.58²⁰₄			i		i dil a
l33	*meta*arsenate	Pb(AsO₃)₂	453.03	hex tabl	6.42¹⁵			d	d	s HNO₃
l34	*ortho*arsenate	Pb₃(AsO₄)₂	899.41	wh cr, v pois	7.80	1042, sl d 1000		v sl s		s HNO₃
l35	*ortho*arsenate, di-	Nat. schultenite. PbHAsO₄	347.12	monocl leaf, α 1.90, γ 1.97	5.79	d 720	−H₂O, 220	i	sl s	s HNO₃, caust alk
l36	*ortho*arsenate, mono-	Pb(H₂AsO₄)₂	489.06	tricl, 1.74, 1.82	4.46¹⁵	d 140		d		s HNO₃
l37	*pyro*arsenate	Pb₂As₂O₇	676.22	rhomb, β 2.03	6.85¹⁵₁₅	802		i	d	s HCl, HNO₃; i ac a
l38	*meta*arsenite	Pb(AsO₂)₂	421.03	wh powd	5.85			i		s HNO₃
l39	*ortho*arsenite	Pb₃(AsO₃)₂.xH₂O	585.05	wh powd	5.85			i		s alk, HNO₃
l40	azide	Pb(N₃)₂	291.23	col need, or powd			expl 350	0.023¹⁸	0.09⁷⁰	v s s ac a; i NH₄OH
l41	*meta*borate	Pb(BO₂)₂.H₂O	310.82	wh cr powd	5.598, anhydr	−H₂O, 160		i	i	s a; i alk

No.	Name	Synonyms and Formulae	Mol. wt.	Crystalline form, properties and index of refraction	Density or spec. gravity	Melting point, °C	Boiling point, °C	Cold water	Hot water	Other solvents
	Lead									
142	borofluoride	$Pb(BF_4)_2$	380.80	cr pr				d		d al
143	bromate	$Pb(BrO_3)_2.H_2O$	481.02	col, monocl	5.53	d 180		1.38^{20}	sl s	sl s
144	bromide	$PbBr_2$	367.01	wh, rhomb	6.66	373	916	0.4554^0 0.8441^{20}	4.71^{100}	s a, KBr; sl s NH_3; i al
145	butyrate	$Pb(C_4H_7O_2)_2$	381.39	col scales, pois		90		i	i	s dil HNO_3
146	caprate	$Pb(C_{10}H_{19}O_2)_2$	549.71			103–104		i	0.0029^{20} eth	
147	caproate	$Pb(C_6H_{11}O_2)_2$	437.50			73–74				1.09^{25} eth
148	caprylate	Lead octoate. $Pb(C_8H_{15}O_2)_2$	493.60	wh leaf		83.5–84.5		i	i	s al; 0.0938 eth
149	carbonate	Nat. cerussite. $PbCO_3$	267.20	col, rhomb, 1.804, 2.076, 2.078	6.6	d 315		0.00011^{20}	d	s a, alk; i NH_3, al
150	carbonate, basic	White lead, hydrocerussite. $2PbCO_3.Pb(OH)_2$	775.60	wh powd, or hex	6.14	d 400		i	i	sl s aq CO_2; s HNO_3; i al
151	cerotate	$Pb(C_{26}H_{51}O_2)_2$	998.57	wh need		113		i		i al, eth; s bz
152	chlorate	$Pb(ClO_3)_2$	374.09	wh monocl, deliq	3.89	d 230		v s		s al
153	chlorate, hydrate	$Pb(ClO_3)_2.H_2O$	392.11	wh, monocl, deliq	4.037	d 110		151.3^{18}	171^{80}	s al
154	*perchlorate*	$Pb(ClO_4)_2.3H_2O$	460.14	wh, rhomb	2.6	d 100		499.7^{25}		s al
155	chloride	Nat. cotunite. $PbCl_2$	278.10	wh, rhomb, 2.199, 2.217, 2.260	5.85	501	950^{760}	0.99^{20}	3.34^{100}	sl s dil HCl, NH_3; i al; s NH_4 salts
156	chloride, tetra-	$PbCl_4$	349.01	yel oily liq	3.18^0	−15	expl 105	d (Cl_2)	d	s conc HCl
157	chloride, sulfide	$PbCl_2.3PbS$	995.86	red				i	d	d a, alk; i dil a
158	chlorite	$Pb(ClO_2)_2$	342.09	yel, monocl		expl 126		0.095^{20}	0.42^{100}	s KOH
159	chromate	Nat. crocoite, chrome yellow. $PbCrO_4$	323.18	yel, monocl, 2.31, 2.37(Li), 2.66	6.12^{15}	844	d	0.0000058^{20}	i	s a, alk; i ac a, NH_3
160	chromate, basic	Chrome red. $PbCrO_4.PbO$	546.37	red cr powd	6.63			i	i	s a, alk
161	chromate, basic	$Pb_2(OH)_2CrO_4$	564.39	red amorph or cr	6.63	920		i	i	s KOH
162	*dichromate*	$PbCr_2O_7$	423.18	red cr				d		s a, alk
163	citrate	$Pb_3(C_6H_5O_7)_2.3H_2O$	1053.82	wh cr powd				s		v sl s al
164	cyanate	$Pb(OCN)_2$	291.22	wh need		d		i	sl s	
165	cyanide	$Pb(CN)_2$	259.23	yelsh-wh powd, pois				sl s	s	s KCN
166	enanthate	$Pb(C_7H_{13}O_2)_2$	465.55	wh leaf		91.5		sl s		i al
167	ethylsulfate	$Pb(C_2H_5SO_4)_2.2H_2O$	493.57	col liq, pois				s		
168	ferricyanide	$Pb_3[Fe(CN)_6]_2.5$ (or 6) H_2O	1135.55	blk-brn to red, monocl pr		−H_2O, 110–120 d		sl s	s, d 100	s alk, HNO_3
169	ferrite	$PbFe_2O_4$	382.88	hex		1530 d, 725				
170	ferrocyanide	$Pb_2Fe(CN)_6.3H_2O$	680.38	yelsh-wh powd		−H_2O, 100		i		sl s H_2SO_4
171	fluoride	PbF_2	245.19	col, rhomb, pois	8.24	855	1290	0.064^{20}		s HNO_3; i acet, NH_3
172	fluorochloride	Nat. matlockite. PbFCl	261.64	wh, tetr, 2.145, 2.006	7.05	601		0.037^{25}	0.1081^{100}	
173	fluosilicate	$PbSiF_6.2H_2O$	385.30	col, monocl		d		s	v s	
174	fluosilicate, tetrahydrate	$PbSiF_6.4H_2O$	421.33	col, monocl		d<100				
175	formate	$Pb(CHO_2)_2$	297.23	wh, rhomb, lust, 1.789, 1.852, 1.877	4.63	d 190		1.6^{15}	20^{100}	i al
176	hydride, di-	PbH_2	209.21	gray powd		d				
177	hydroxide	$Pb(OH)_2$	241.20	wh, amorph		d 145		0.0155^{20}	sl s	s a, alk; i ac a
178	hydroxide	$Pb_2O(OH)_2$ or $2PbO.H_2O$	464.39	wh cub, or amorph powd, pois	7.592	d 145		0.014	sl s	s alk, ac a, HNO_3
179	iodate	$Pb(IO_3)_2$	557.00	wh	6.155^{20}	d 300		0.0012^2	0.003^{25}	sl s HNO_3; i NH_3
180	*paraperiodate*	$PbHIO_5$	415.10	wh cr		d 130		i	i	s dil HNO_3
181	*paraperiodate*, hydrate	$PbHIO_5.H_2O$	433.11	amorph		−H_2O, 110		i	i	sl s dil HNO_3
182	iodide, basic	$PbI_2.PbO.H_2O$	702.20	rhomb cr	6.83^{20}	d 100		i	i	
183	iodide, di-	PbI_2	461.00	yel hex powd, pois	6.16	402	954	0.044^0 0.063^{20}	0.41^{100}	s alk, KI; i al
184	iodide, mono-	PbI	334.09	pa yel		d 300		0.1		
185	isobutyrate	$Pb(C_4H_7O_2)_2$	381.39	wh pr		<100		9.1^{15}		
186	lactate	$Pb(C_3H_5O_3)_2$	385.33	wh cr powd				s		s h al
187	laurate	$Pb(C_{12}H_{23}O_2)_2$	605.82	chalky wh powd		104.7		0.009^{35}		0.008^{50} al; $0.007^{14.5}$ eth
188	lignocerate	$Pb(C_{24}H_{47}O_2)_2$	942.47	wh powd		117		i		v s h bz; sl s al; i eth
189	malate	$Pb(C_4H_4O_5).3H_2O$	393.31	wh powd				sl s		v sl s al
190	melissate	$Pb(C_{31}H_{61}O_2)_2$	1138.85	wh powd		115–116		i	i	s boil tol, ac a; sl s h bz, chl; i al, eth
191	molybdate	Nat. wulfenite. $PbMoO_4$	367.13	col-lt yel, tetr pl	6.92^{25}_4	1060–1070			i	d conc H_2SO_4; s a, KOH; i al
192	myristate	$Pb(C_{14}H_{27}O_2)_2$	661.93	wh powd		107		0.005^{35}	0.006^{50}	0.004^{25} al; $0.010^{14.5}$ eth

No.	Name	Synonyms and Formulae	Mol. wt.	Crystalline form, properties and index of refraction	Density or spec. gravity	Melting point, °C	Boiling point, °C	Solubility, in grams per 100 cc		
								Cold water	Hot water	Other solvents
	Lead									
193	2-naphthalene-sulfonate	$Pb(C_{10}H_7SO_3)_2$	621.65	wh cr powd, pois				i		s al
194	nitrate	$Pb(NO_3)_2$	331.20	col, cub or monocl, pois, 1.782	4.53^{20}	d 470		37.65^0 56.5^0	127^{100}	8.77^{22} 43 % al; s alk, NH_3
195	nitrate, basic	$Pb(OH)NO_3$	286.20	wh rhomb cr	5.93	d 180		19.4^{19}	s	s a
196	nitrite	$3PbO.N_2O_3.H_2O$	763.60	lt yel powd				v s		s dil HNO_3
197	oleate	$Pb(C_{18}H_{33}O_2)_2$	770.12					i		6.46^{20} eth; s pet eth; sl s al
198	oxalate	PbC_2O_4	295.21	wh powd	5.28	d 300		0.00016^{18}		s HNO_3; i al
199	oxide-, di-	Plattnerite. PbO_2	239.19	bz, tetr, ω 2.3(Li)	9.375	d 290	i	i		s dil HCl; sl s ac a; i al
1100	oxide, mono-	Litharge. PbO	223.19	yel, tetr	9.53	888		0.0017^{20}		s HNO_3, alk, Pb acet, NH_4Cl, $CaCl_2$, $SrCl_2$
1101	oxide, mono-	Massicot. PbO	223.19	yel, rhomb, 2.51, 2.61(Li), 2.71	8.0			0.0023^{22}	i	s alk
1102	oxide, red	Minium. Pb_3O_4	685.57	red cr sc, or amorph powd	9.1	d 500	i	i		s HCl, acet a; i al
1103	oxide, sesqui-	Pb_2O_3	462.38	or-yel powd, amorph		d 370		i	d	d a
1104	oxide, sub-	Pb_2O	430.38	blk, amorph	8.342	d		i	i	s a, alk
1105	oxychloride	$PbCl_2.3PbO$	947.66	yel				0.0056^{18}	0.07^{74}	
1106	oxychloride	Cassel yellow. $PbCl_2.7PbO$	1840.42	yel cr, or powd				i		
1107	oxychloride	Fiedlerite. $2PbCl_2.PbO.H_2O$	797.40	monocl, 1.816, 2.1023, 2.026	5.88^{20}	d 150				s HNO_3
1108	oxychloride	Nat. laurionite. $PbCl_2.Pb(OH)_2$	519.29	rhomb	6.24	d 142				
1109	oxychloride	Matlockite. $PbCl_2.PbO$	501.29				i			s alkalies, hot conc HCl
1110	oxychloride	Nat. matlockite. $PbCl_2.Pb(OH)_2$	519.29	wh, tetrag, 2.04, 2.15, 2.15	7.21	d 524		0.0095^{18}		s alk
1111	oxychloride	Nat. mendipite. $PbCl_2.2PbO$	724.47	yel, rhomb, 2.24, 2.27, 2.31	7.08	693	i	i		s alk
1112	oxychloride	Nat. paralaurionite. $PbCl_2.PbO.H_2O$	519.29	col or wh, monocl pr, 2.146	6.05^{15}	d 150				
1113	palmitate	$Pb(C_{16}H_{31}O_2)_2$	718.04	wh powd		112.3		0.005^{35}	0.007^{50}	s al; 0.148^{20} eth
1114	phenolate	Lead phenate, lead carbolate. $Pb(OH)OC_6H_5$	317.30	yelsh-wh powd				i		
1115	phenolsulfonate	Lead sulfocarbolate. $Pb[C_6H_4(OH)SO_3]_2.5H_2O$	643.60	wh lustr need				s		s al
1116	metaphosphate	$Pb(PO_3)_2$	365.13	col cr		800(?)			v sl s	
1117	orthophosphate	$Pb_3(PO_4)_2$	811.51	col or wh powd, hex, 1.970, 1.936	6.9–7.3	1014		0.000014^{20}	i	s HNO_3, alk; i ac a, al
1118	orthophosphate, di-	$PbHPO_4$	303.17	rhomb	5.661^{15}	d				s HNO_3, alk, NH_4Cl
1119	orthophosphate, mono-	$Pb(H_2PO_4)_2$	401.16	need						s alk, dil HNO_3; h conc HCl; i acet a
1120	phosphide	PbP_5	362.06	blk unstable, inflam		d 400 (vac)		d	d	d dil a
1122	orthophosphite	$PbHPO_3$	287.17	wh, powd		d		i		s HNO_3
1123	picrate	$Pb(C_6H_2N_3O_7)_2.H_2O$	681.45	yel, need	2.831^{20}	$-H_2O$, 130	expl	0.88^{15}		
1124	proprionate, tetra-	$Pb(C_3H_5O_2)_4$	499.48	solid		132				
1125	pyrophosphate	$Pb_2P_2O_7$	588.32	wh, rhomb	5.8^{20}	824		i	i	s HNO_3, KOH
1126	pyrophosphate, hydrate	$Pb_2P_2O_7.H_2O$	606.34	wh, rhomb		806 anhydr		i	d	s HNO_3, KOH, $Na_4P_2O_7$
1127	selenate	$PbSeO_4$	350.17	wh, rhomb	6.37^{20}_4	d		i	i	s conc a
1128	selenide	Nat. clausthalite. PbSe	286.15	gray, cub	8.10^{15}	1065		i		s HNO_3
1129	metasilicate	Nat. alamosite. $PbSiO_3$	283.27	col or wh monocl	6.49	766		i		d a
1130	orthosilicate, di-	Nat. barysilite. $Pb_3Si_2O_7$	582.55	wh, trig, 2.070, 2.050	6.707			i	i	
1131	stearate	$Pb(C_{18}H_{35}O_2)_2$	774.15	wh powd		115.7		0.05^{35}	0.06^{50}	$0.005^{14.5}$ eth; i al
1132	sulfate	Nat. anglesite. $PbSO_4$	303.25	wh, monocl, or rhomb, 1.877, 1.822, 1.894	6.2	1170		0.00425^{25}	0.00564^0	s NH_4 salts; sl s conc H_2SO_4; i a
1133	sulfate, basic	Nat. lanarkite. $PbSO_4.PbO$	526.44	wh, monocl, 1.93, 1.99, 2.02	6.92	977		0.0044^0	v sl s	sl s H_2SO_4
1134	sulfate, hydrogen	$Pb(HSO_4)_2.H_2O$	419.34	wh cr		d		0.0001^{18} d		sl s H_2SO_4
1135	peroxydisulfate	$PbS_2O_8.3H_2O$	453.36	deliq				v s		
1136	sulfide	Nat. galena. PbS	239.25	bl met cub, 3.921	7.5	1114		0.0000086^{11}		s a; i al, KOH
1137	sulfite	$PbSO_3$	287.25	wh powd		d		i	i	s HNO_3
1138	tartrate, dl-	$PbC_4H_4O_6$	355.26	wh cr powd	2.53^{19}			0.0025^{20}	0.0074^{100}	s HNO_3, KOH; i al, ac a, NH_4 ac

No.	Name	Synonyms and Formulae	Mol. wt.	Crystalline form, properties and index of refraction	Density or spec. gravity	Melting point, °C	Boiling point, °C	Solubility, in grams per 100 cc		
								Cold water	Hot water	Other solvents
	Lead									
1139	dithionate	$PbS_2O_6.4H_2O$	439.38	trig, 1.635, 1.653	3.22	d		115.0^{90}		
1140	thiosulfate	PbS_2O_3	319.32	wh cr	5.18	d		0.03		s a, $Na_2S_2O_3$
1141	metatitanate	$PbTiO_3$	303.09	yel, rhomb-pyr	7.52			i	i	
1142	telluride	Nat. altaite. PbTe	334.79	wh, cub	8.164_4^{20}	917				i a
1143	thiocyanate	$Pb(SCN)_2$	323.35	wh, monocl	3.82	d 190		0.05^{20}	0.2^{100}	s KCNS, HNO_3
1144	tungstate	Nat. stolzite. $PbWO_4$	455.04	tetr, 2.269, 2.182	8.23			i		i HNO_3, s KOH
1145	tungstate	Nat. raspite. $PbWO_4$	455.04	col, monocl, 2.27, 2.27, 2.30		1123		0.03		d a; i al
1146	metavanadate	$Pb(VO_3)_2$	405.07	yel powd				sl s		d HCl; s dil HNO_3
1147	**Lithium**	Li	6.939	silver white, soft	0.534^{20}	180.54	1347	d		
1148	acetate	$LiC_2H_3O_2.2H_2O$	102.01	wh, rhomb, α 1.40, β 1.50		70	d	300^{15}	v s	21.5 al
1149	acetylsalicylate	$LiC_9H_7O_4$	186.09	wh powd hygr, d in moist air				100		25 al
1150	metaaluminate	$LiAlO_2$ (or $Li_2Al_2O_4$)	65.92	wh, rhomb, 1.604, 1.614	2.55_4^{25}	1900–2000		i		
1151	aluminum hydride	$LiAlH_4$	37.95	wh cr powd	0.917	d 125		d		ca 30 eth
1152	amide	$LiNH_2$	22.96	col need, cub	$1.178^{17.5}$	380–400	d 750–200 subl	s	d	sl s liq NH_3, al; i eth, bz
1153	antimonide	Li_3Sb	142.57		3.2^{17}	>950		d	d	d a
1154	orthoarsenate	Li_3AsO_4	159.74	wh powd, rhomb	3.07^{15}			v sl s		s dil ac a; i pyr
1155	azide	LiN_3	48.96	col cr, hygr		d 115–298		66.41^{16}		20.26^{16} abs al; i eth
1156	benzoate	$LiC_7H_5O_2$	128.06	wh cr or powd				33^{25}	40^{100}	7.7^{25} al, 10^{75} al
1157	metaborate	$LiBO_2$	49.75	wh, tricl	$1.397^{41.7}$	845		2.57^{20}	11.83^{80}	
1158	metaborate	$LiBO_2.8H_2O$	193.87	col, trig	$1.38^{14.9}$	47				
1159	pentaborate	$Li_2B_{10}O_{16}.8H_2O$	522.10	wh	1.72	300–350 –8H_2O		36.3^{45}	194^{100}	3.9^{30} al; 22^{53} glycerine; i bz
1160	tetraborate	$Li_2B_4O_7$	169.11	wh cr		930		2.89^{20}	5.45^{100}	i org solv
1161	borohydride	$LiBH_4$	21.78	rhomb cr	0.66	d 279		s d		s eth
1162	borohydride	$LiBH_4$	21.78	wh, orthorhomb	0.666	275 d		v sl s		d al; 2.5 eth
1163	bromide	LiBr	86.85	wh, cub, deliq, 1.784	3.464^{25}	550	1265	145^4	254^{90}	73^{40} al; 8 MeOH; s al, eth; sl s pyrid
1164	bromide, dihydrate	$LiBr.2H_2O$	122.28	wh cr		$-1H_2O$; 44		246.0^{20}	v s	s al
1165	carbide	Li_2C_2	37.90	wh cr or powd	1.65^{18}			d	d	s a
1166	carbonate	Li_2CO_3	73.89	wh, monocl, 1.428, 1.567, 1.572	2.11	723	d 1310^{760}	1.54^0	0.72^{100}	i al; acet
1167	carbonate, acid	Lithium bicarbonate. $LiHCO_3$	67.96	wh				5.5^{13}		
1168	chlorate	$LiClO_3$	90.39	col, rhomb need, deliq, α 1.63, γ 1.64 (18 %Soln)	1.1190_4^{18}	127.6	300 d	500^{27}		v s al; 0.142^{25} acetone
1169	chlorate	$LiClO_3.\frac{1}{2}H_2O$ (or $\frac{1}{4}H_2O$)	99.39	wh, tetr, deliq		65(?)	$-\frac{1}{2}H_2O$, 90 d 290	v s	v s	v s al
1170	perchlorate	$LiClO_4$	106.39	wh	2.428	236	430 d	60.0^{25}	150^{89}	152^{25} al; 182^{25} MeOH; 114^{25} eth; 137^{25} acetone
1171	perchlorate, trihydrate	$LiClO_4.3H_2O$	160.44	wh, hex	1.841	95 deliq 236 (anhydr)	d 100 $-2H_2O$	130^{25}		72.9^{25} al; 156^{25} MeOH; 96.2^{25} acetone; 0.096^{25} eth
1172	chloride	LiCl	42.39	wh, cub, 1.662	2.068^{25}	605	1325–1360	63.7^0	130^{95}	25.10^{30} al; 42.36^{25} MeOH; 4.11^{25} acetone; $0.538^{23.9}$ NH_4OH
1173	chloride, monohydrate	$LiCl.H_2O$	60.41	wh cr, hygr	1.78	$-H_2O>98$		86.2^{30}	s	s HCl
1174	chloroplatinate	$Li_2PtCl_6.6H_2O$	529.70	or prism		$-6H_2O$, 180		v s	v s	v s al; i eth
1175	bichromate, dihydrate	$Li_2Cr_2O_7.2H_2O$	265.90	orange-red cr, deliq	2.34^{30}	187 d	$-2H_2O$	197^{90}	27^{100}	s react al
1176	dichromate	$Li_2Cr_2O_7.2H_2O$	265.90	blk-brn cr, deliq		$-2H_2O$, 130 d		151^{30}		
1177	citrate	$Li_3C_6H_5O_7.4H_2O$	281.98	col cr or powd, deliq		$-4H_2O$, 105		74.5^{25}	66.7^{100}	sl s al, eth
1178	fluoride	LiF	25.94	wh, cub, 1.3915	2.635^{20}	845	1676	0.27^{18}		i al; s HF
1179	fluosilicate	$Li_2SiF_6.2H_2O$	191.99	wh, monocl, 1.300, 1.296	2.33^{12}	$-2H_2O$, 100 d		73^{17}		s al; i eth, acet
1180	fluosulfonate	$LiSO_3F$	106.00	wh powd		360		v s	s	v s al, eth, acet; i ligorin
1181	formate, monohydrate	$H.COOLi.H_2O$	69.97	wh, rhomb	1.46	$-H_2O$, 94	d 230	27.85^{18}	57.05^{98}	sl s al, acet; i bz
1182	gallium hydride	$LiGaH_4$	80.69	wh cr		d	d	d	d	s eth
1183	gallium nitride	$LiGaN_2$	118.55	lt gr powd	3.35	d 800		d	d	s a, alk
1184	metagermanate	Li_2GeO_3	134.47	monocl, 1.7	3.53^{21}	1239		0.85^{25}		s a

No.	Name	Synonyms and Formulae	Mol. wt.	Crystalline form, properties and index of refraction	Density or spec. gravity	Melting point, °C	Boiling point, °C	Solubility, in grams per 100 cc		
								Cold water	Hot water	Other solvents
	Lithium									
1185	hydride	LiH	7.95	wh cr	0.82	680		d		v sl s a
1186	hydroxide	LiOH	23.95	wh tetr, 1.464, 1.452	1.46	450	d 924	12.8[20]	17.5[100]	sl s al
1187	hydroxide, mono- hydrate	LiOH.H₂O	41.96	wh monocl, 1.460, 1.524	1.51			22.3[10]	26.8[80]	sl s al; i eth
1188	iodate	LiIO₃	181.84	wh, hex, hygr	4.502$_4^{82}$			80.3[18]		i al
1189	iodide	LiI	133.84	wh, cub, 1.955 ± 0.003	3.494 ± 0.015	449	1180 ± 10	165[20]	433[80]	250.8[20] al; 42.6[18] acet 343.4[20] MeOH; v s NH₄OH
1190	iodide, trihydrate	LiI.3H₂O	187.89	col-yelsh, hex, hygr	3.48	73 − H₂O	−2H₂O, 80 −H₂O, 300	151[0]	201.2[60]	s abs al, acet
1191	laurate	LiC₁₂H₂₃O₂	206.25	wh powd		229.2−229.8		0.154[16.3]	0.178[25]	0.322[15] al; 0.008[15.3] eth; 0.240[25] acet
1192	permanganate	LiMnO₄.3H₂O	179.92	cub	2.06	d 190		71.43[16]		d alk
1193	molybdate	Li₂MoO₄	173.82	wh trig, hygr	2.66	705		v s		
1194	myristate	LiC₁₄H₂₇O₂	234.31			223.6−224.2		0.027[16.3] 0.036[25]	0.062[80]	0.010[15.3] eth; 0.331[15] acet; 0.155[20] al
1195	nitrate	LiNO₃	68.94	wh, trig, 1.735, 1.735	2.38	264	d 600	89.8[27.55]	234[100]	s NH₄OH, al; 37.15 pyridine
1196	nitrate, trihydrate	LiNO₃.3H₂O	122.99	col need		−2½H₂O, 29.9	−3H₂O, 61.1	34.8[0]	57.48[29.6]	s al, MeOH, acet
1197	nitride	Li₃N	34.82	red-brn amorph, or blk-gray cr, cub		tr 840−850 (in N₂)				
1198	nitrite	LiNO₂.H₂O	70.96	col flat need	1.615[0]	>100	d	125[0]	459[80]	v s abs al
1199	oxalate	Li₂C₂O₄	101.90	col, rhomb, 1.465, 1.53, 1.696	2.121[17.5]	d		8[19.5]		i al, eth
1200	oxalate, acid	LiHC₂O₄.H₂O	113.99			d		8[17]		
1201	oxide	Li₂O	29.88	wh cr, cub, n_D 1.644	2.013[25.2]	>1700	1200[600]	6.67[0] d	10.02[100]	
1202	palmitate	LiC₁₆H₃₁O₂	262.36	wh powd		224.5		0.01[18]	0.015[25]	0.347[15] acet; 0.077[20] al; 0.005[15.3] eth
1203	metaphosphate	LiPO₃	85.91	col pl	2.461	red heat		i	i	s a
1204	orthophosphate	Li₃PO₄	115.79	col, rhomb	2.537[17.5]	837		0.039[18]		s a, NH₄OH; i acet
1205	orthophosphate	Li₃PO₄.½H₂O	124.80	wh cr powd	2.41	−½H₂O, 100		0.04[25]		s a
1206	phosphate, di- H	LiH₂PO₄	103.93	col cr, hygr	2.461	>100				
1207	potassium sulfate	LiKSO₄	142.10	col, hex; n_D 1.4723, 1.4717	2.393[20]			s	s	
1208	potassium dl-tartrate	LiKC₄H₄O₆.H₂O	212.13	col, monocl, β 1.523 (red)	1.610			s		
1209	salicylate	LiC₇H₅O₃	144.06	wh, powd, deliq		d		133.3		50 al
1210	selenide	Li₂Se.9H₂O	254.98	col, rhomb, deliq				d		
1211	metasilicate	Li₂SiO₃	89.96	col, rhomb; α 1.584, γ 1.604	2.52$_4^{25}$	1204		i	s d	s dil HCl
1212	orthosilicate	Li₄SiO₄	119.84	col, rhomb; α 1.594, γ 1.614	2.392$_4^{25}$	1256		i	d	d a
1213	silicide	Li₂Si₂	97.81	bl cr, hygr	ca. 1.12	d 600 (vac)		d	d	d a; i NH₃ turp
1214	sodium fluoaluminate	Li₃Na₃(AlF₆)₂	371.73	cub cr, 1.3395	2.774	710		0.074[18]		
1215	stearate	LiC₁₈H₃₅O₂	290.41	wh cr		220.5−221.5		0.010[18]		0.010[25] al; 0.040[18] eth; 0.457[15] acet
1216	sulfate	Li₂SO₄	109.94	α monocl; β hex or rhomb, γ cub 500°C; β 1.465	2.221	845		26.1[0]	23[100]	i abs al, acet
1217	sulfate, hydrogen	LiHSO₄	104.01	col pr	2.123[13]	120		d		
1218	sulfate, mono- hydrate	Li₂SO₄.H₂O	127.95	col cr, monocl, 1.465, 1.477, 1.488		880		34.9[25]	29.2[100]	11.5[20] al + H₂O (23.9 % alco); i acet, pryidine
1219	sulfide	Li₂S	45.94	wh-yel, cub, deliq	1.66	900−975		v s	v s	v s al
1220	sulfide, hydro-	LiHS	40.01	wh powd, hygr				s	s	s al
1221	sulfite, monohydrate	Li₂SO₃.H₂O	111.96	wh need, α 1.53, γ 1.59		455 d	140 − H₂O	24.9[20]	22[90]	i org solv
1222	tartrate	Li₂C₄H₄O₆.H₂O	179.97	wh cr powd				s		
1223	thallium dl-tartrate	LiTlC₄H₄O₆.2H₂O	395.41	tricl	3.144					
1224	thiocyanate	LiSCN	65.02	wh cr, deliq, n_D 1.333				v s		s methylacet
1225	dithionate	Li₂S₂O₆.2H₂O	210.03	col, rhomb, 1.5602	2.158	d		v s		
1226	tungstate	Li₂WO₄	261.73	col, trig	3.71	742		v s	v s	d a; i al
1227	**Lutetium**	Cassiopeium. Lu	174.97	met, hex	9.8404	1663	3395			

No.	Name	Synonyms and Formulae	Mol. wt.	Crystalline form, properties and index of refraction	Density or spec. gravity	Melting point, °C	Boiling point, °C	Solubility, in grams per 100 cc		
								Cold water	Hot water	Other solvents
	Lutetium									
1228	bromide..........	LuBr₃............	414.70			1025	1400........	s	s	....
1229	chloride..........	LuCl₃............	281.33	col cr..........	3.98	905	subl 750	s		....
1230	fluoride..........	LuF₃............	231.97			1182	2200	i	i	....
1231	iodide..........	LuI₃............	555.68			1050	1200	s	s	....
1232	oxalate..........	Lu₂(C₂O₄)₃.6H₂O......	722.09	wh cr		50 (−H₂O)	....	i	i	i dil a
1233	oxide..........	Lu₂O₃..........	397.94	cub cr..........	9.42					....
1234	sulfate..........	Lu₂(SO₄)₃.8H₂O......	782.25	col cr				42.27²⁰	16.93⁴⁰	....
m1	**Magnesium**......	Mg............	24.312	silv wh met, hex .	1.74⁵	648.8	1090	i	d to Mg(OH)₂	s min a, conc. HF; NH₄ salts; i CrO₃, alk.
m2	acetate..........	Mg(C₂H₃O₂)₂.......	142.40	wh cr..........	1.42	323 d		v s	v s	5.25¹⁵ MeOH
m3	acetate, tetra-hydrate	Mg(C₂H₃O₂)₂.4H₂O......	214.46	col, monocl deliq, β 1.491	1.454	80		120¹⁵	∞	v s al
m4	aluminate..........	Nat. spinel. MgAl₂O₄..	142.27	col, cub, 1.723....	3.6	2135				al s H₂SO₄; v al s dil HCl; i HNO₃
m5	amide..........	Mg(NH₂)₂	56.36	gray powd........		d 350–400	d	d	v al s liq NH₃; d al
m6	antimonate..........	MgO.Sb₂O₅.12H₂O......	579.99	hex or tricl cr....	2.60 (hex)	−12H₂O, 200		v al s		d HCl
m7	antimonide..........	Mg₃Sb₂............	316.44	met hex pl........	4.088²⁵₄	961		i		....
m8	orthoarsenate........	Nat. hoernesite. Mg₃(AsO₄)₂.8H₂O.	494.90	wh monocl........	2.60–2.61					....
m9	orthoarsenate........	Mg₃(AsO₄)₂.22H₂O......	747.11	wh cr........	1.788	−17H₂O, 100	−21H₂O, 220	i	i	s a, NH₄Cl
m10	orthoarsenate, mono-H	Nat. roesslerite. MgHAsO₄.7H₂O	290.35	monocl..........	1.943¹⁵	−5H₂O, 100		d		....
m11	arsenide..........	Mg₃As₂............	222.78	brn-red, cub....	3.148²⁵₄	800		d	d	d dil a, al
m12	orthoarsenite........	Mg₃(AsO₃)₂	318.78	wh..........				s	v s	s a, NH₄Cl; i NH₄OH
m13	benzoate..........	Mg(C₇H₅O₂)₂.3H₂O....	320.59	wh powd........		−3H₂O, 110	d 200	6.16¹⁵	19.6¹⁰⁰	s al
m14	bismuthide..........	Mg₃Bi₂............	490.90	met, hex........	5.945²⁵₄	823				....
m15	bismuth nitrate......	3Mg(NO₃)₂.2Bi(NO₃)₃.24H₂O 1543.31		col cr, deliq....	2.32¹⁶₁₆	71		d	d	s HNO₃
m16	diborate..........	Nat. ascharite. Mg₂B₂O₄.H₂O	168.26	orthorhmb, 1.54..	2.60–2.70					....
m17	metaborate..........	Nat. pinnoite........ Mg(BO₂)₂.3H₂O	163.98	yel, tetr, pyram, 1.565, 1.575	2.27–2.30					....
m18	metaborate, octahydrate	Mg(BO₂)₂.8H₂O.......	254.05	col, tetr, 1.565, 1.575	2.30			i	v al s	s a
m19	orthoborate..........	Mg₃(BO₃)₂	190.55	col, rhomb, 1.6527, 1.6537, 1.6548	2.99²¹			i	i	s min a; i ac a
m20	boride..........	MgB₆............	89.18	bl............		d 1200 (vac)		d	v s	al s a
m21	bromate..........	Mg(BrO₃)₂.6H₂O......	388.22	col, cub, 1.514....	2.29	−6H₂O, 200	d	42¹⁸	v s	i al
m22	bromide..........	MgBr₂	184.13	wh hex cr, deliq	3.72²⁵₄	711		101.50²⁰	125.6¹⁰⁰	6.9 al; 21.8²⁰ MeOH
m23	bromide, hexahydrate	MgBr₂.6H₂O......	292.22	col, hex pr or need, hygr, fluo in x-rays	2.00	172.4		316⁰	v s	s al, acet; al s NH₃
m24	bromoplatinate......	MgPtBr₆.12H₂O......	915.04	trig..........	2.802					....
m25	carbonate..........	Nat. magnesite. MgCO₃	84.32	wh, trig, 1.717, 1.515	2.958	d 350	−CO₂, 900	0.0106		s a, aq +CO₂; i acet, NH₃
m26	carbonate, basic artinite	Nat. artinite. MgCO₃.Mg(OH)₂.3H₂O	196.69	wh, rhomb, 1.489, 1.534, 1.557	2.02²⁰					....
m27	carbonate, basic.....	Nat. hydromagnesite. 3MgCO₃.Mg(OH)₂.3H₂O	365.34	wh, rhomb, 1.527, 1.530, 1.540	2.16	d		0.04	0.011	s a, NH₄ salts
m28	carbonate, pentahydrate	Nat. lansfordite. MgCO₃.5H₂O	174.40	wh, monocl, 1.456 1.476, 1.502	1.73	d in air		0.176⁷	0.375⁹⁰	s HCl, MgSO₄ soln
m29	carbonate, trihydrate	Nat. nesquehonite. MgCO₃.3H₂O	138.37	col, rhomb need, 1.495, 1.501, 1.526	1.850	165		0.179¹⁶	d	s a; 1,4 aq +CO₂
m30	chlorate..........	Mg(ClO₃)₂.6H₂O......	299.31	wh, rhomb need, deliq	1.80²⁵	35	d 120	128.6¹⁸	v s	s al
m31	perchlorate..........	Mg(ClO₄)₂	223.21	deliq	2.21¹⁵	d 251		99.3²⁵	v s	23.96²⁵ al
m32	perchlorate, hexahydrate	Mg(ClO₄)₂.6H₂O.......	331.31	wh, rhomb cr, 1.482, 1.458	1.98	185–190		v s	v s	....
m33	perchlorate, hexammine	Mg(ClO₄)₂.6NH₃......	325.40	wh, cub..........	1.41²⁰₄					s liq NH₃; s d al
m34	chloride..........	MgCl₂............	95.22	wh, lustr hex cr, 1.675, 1.59	2.316–2.33	714	1412	54.25²⁰	72.7¹⁰⁰	7.40²⁰ al

No.	Name	Synonyms and Formulae	Mol. wt.	Crystalline form, properties and index of refraction	Density or spec. gravity	Melting point, °C	Boiling point, °C	Solubility, in grams per 100 cc		
								Cold water	Hot water	Other solvents
	Magnesium									
m35	chloride, hexahydrate	Nat. bischofite. $MgCl_2.6H_2O$	203.31	col, monocl, deliq, 1.495, 1.507 1.528	1.569	d 116–118	d	167	367	s al
m36	chloropalladate	$MgPdCl_4.6H_2O$	451.52	hex	2.12	d				
m37	chloroplatinate	$MgPtCl_6.6H_2O$	540.21	yel, trig	2.692	$-H_2O$, 180		s	s	
m38	chlorostannate	$MgSnCl_6.6H_2O$	463.81	tricl	2.08	d 100				
m39	chromate	$MgCrO_4.7H_2O$	266.41	yel, rhomb, 1.521, 1.550, 1.568	1.695		211.5[18]	v s		
m40	chromite	$MgCr_2O_4$	192.30	dk-grn or red, cub	4.6[20]			i	i	s conc H_2SO_4; i dl a, dil alk
m41	citrate, nono-H	$MgHC_6H_5O_7.5H_2O$	304.50	wh gran powd				20[25]	s	s a; i al
m42	cyanide	$Mg(CN)_2$	76.35			d 300 to $MgCN_2$	d 600	s	d	
m43	cyanoplatinite	$MgPt(CN)_4.7H_2O$	449.58	red, pr	2.185[16]	$-H_2O$, 45		v s	v s	i al, eth
m44	ferrite	$MgFeO_4$	200.00	blk, oct, 2.35	4.44–4.60	1750 ± 25				s conc HCl; i dil a, h HNO_3, al
m45	ferrocyanide	$Mg_2Fe(CN)_6.12H_2O$	476.76	pa yel cr		d ca 200		33		i al
m46	fluoride	Nat. sellaite. MgF_2	62.31	col, tetr, faint vlt, lumin, 1.378, 1.390; 3.14		1261	2239	0.0076[18]	i	s HNO_3; sl s a; i al
m47	fluosilicate	$MgSiF_6$	166.39	wh, cr or powd				65		
m48	fluosilicate, hexahydrate	$MgSiF_6.6H_2O$	274.48	wh, trig	1.788	d 120		64.8[17.5]		i al
m49	formate	$Mg(CHO_2)_2.2H_2O$	150.38	col, rhomb		$-2H_2O$, 100		14[0] (anh)	24[100] (anh)	i al, eth
m50	orthogermanate	Mg_2GeO_4	185.21	wh ppt				0.0016[25]		s a; i alk
m51	germanide	Mg_2Ge	121.21			1115				
m52	hydride	MgH_2	26.33	wh tetr cr or mass		d 280 (vac)		d viol		i eth
m53	hydroxide	Nat. brucite. $Mg(OH)_2$	58.33	col, hex pl, 1.559, 1.580	2.36	$-H_2O$, 350		0.0009[18]	0.004[100]	s a, NH_4 salts
m54	iodate	$Mg(IO_3)_2.4H_2O$	446.18	wh, monocl	3.3[18.5]	$-4H_2O$, 210	d	10.2[20]	19.3[100]	
m55	iodide	MgI_2	278.12	wh, hex, deliq	4.43[25/4]	d < 637		148[18]	164.9[110]	s al, eth, NH_3
m56	iodide, octahydrate	$MgI_2.8H_2O$	422.24	wh powd, deliq		d 41		81[20]	90.3[80]	s al, eth
m57	lactate	$Mg(C_3H_5O_3)_2.3H_2O$	256.50	wh cr powd, v bitter taste				3.3	16.7[100]	i al, eth
m58	laurate	$Mg(C_{12}H_{23}O_2)_2.2H_2O$	458.97	wh lumps		150.4		0.007[25]	0.041[100]	0.415[15] al; 0.012[25] eth
m59	permanganate	$Mg(MnO_4)_2.6H_2O$	370.27	dk purp need, deliq	2.18(?)	d		v s	d	s MeOH, ac a
m60	molybdate	$MgMoO_4$	184.25	rhomb, tricl	2.208			13.7[25]		
m61	myristate	$Mg(C_{14}H_{27}O_2)_2$	479.05	wh powd		131.6		0.006[15]	0.014[60]	0.189[25] al; 0.007[25] eth
m62	nitrate, dihydrate	$Mg(NO_3)_2.2H_2O$	184.35	col pr	2.0256[25]	129		s	s	s al, liq NH_3; sl s conc HNO_3
m63	nitrate, hexahydrate	$Mg(NO_3)_2.6H_2O$	256.41	col, monocl, deliq	1.6363[25/4]	89	d 330	125	v s	s al, liq NH_3
m64	nitride	Mg_3N_2	100.95	grn-yel, powd or mass	2.712[25/4]	d 800	subl 700 (vac)	d	d	s a; i al
m65	nitrite, trihydrate	$Mg(NO_2)_2.3H_2O$	170.37	wh pr, hygr		d 100		s		s al
m66	oleate	$Mg(C_{18}H_{33}O_2)_2$	587.24	yel powd or mass				0.024[25]		6.64[20] al; s linseed oil; sl s eth
m67	oxalate	$MgC_2O_4.2H_2O$	148.36	wh powd	2.45	d 150		0.07[16]	0.08[100]	s alk, a, oxalate
m68	oxide	Nat. periclase. MgO	40.31	col, cub, 1.736	3.58[25]	2800	3600	0.00062	0.0086[30]	s a, NH_4 salts; i al
m69	oxide, per-	MgO_2	56.31	wh powd				i	i	s a
m70	palmitate	$Mg(C_{16}H_{31}O_2)_2$	535.16	wh cr need or lumps		121.5		0.008[25]	0.009[60]	0.047[25] al; 0.003[25] eth
m71	orthophosphate	$Mg_3(PO_4)_2$	262.88	rhomb pl, iridisc		1184		i	i	s NH_4 salts, i liq NH_3
m72	orthophosphate	$Mg_3(PO_4)_2.22H_2O$	659.22	col, monocl pr	1.640[15]	$-18H_2O$, 100	d 200	v sl s		d a
m73	orthophosphate, mono-H	Nat. newberyite. $MgHPO_4.3H_2O$	174.34	wh, rhomb, 1.514, 1.518, 1.533	2.123[15]	$-H_2O$, 205	d 550–650	sl s		s a
m74	orthophosphate, mono-H, heptahydrate	$MgHPO_4.7H_2O$	246.40	wh, monocl need	1.728[15]	$-4H_2O$, 100	d 550–650	0.3	0.2	s a; i al
m75	orthophosphate, octahydrate	Nat. bobierite. $Mg_3(PO_4)_2.8H_2O$	407.00	wh, monocl pl, 1.510, 1.520, 1.543	2.195[15]	$-5H_2O$, 150	$-8H_2O$, 400	v sl s		s NH_4 citrate
m76	orthophosphate, tetrahydrate	$Mg_3(PO_4)_2.4H_2O$	334.97	monocl	1.64[15]			0.0205		s a; i NH_4 salts
m77	phosphide	Mg_3P_2	134.88	yel-grn cub cr	2.055			d	d	d dil min a; sl d conc H_2SO_4

No.	Name	Synonyms and Formulae	Mol. wt.	Crystalline form, properties and index of refraction	Density or spec. gravity	Melting point, °C	Boiling point, °C	Solubility, in grams per 100 cc		
								Cold water	Hot water	Other solvents
	Magnesium									
m78	*hypo*phosphite	Mg(H$_2$PO$_2$)$_2$.6H$_2$O	262.38	wh, ditetrag	1.59$_4^{12.5}$	−5H$_2$O, 100	−6H$_2$O, 180	20^{25}		i al, eth
m79	*ortho*phosphite	MgHPO$_3$.3H$_2$O	158.34						0.25	s a
m80	pyrophosphate	Mg$_2$P$_2$O$_7$	222.57	col, tab monocl, 1.602, 1.604, 1.615	2.559, (3.06)	1383		i	i	s a; i al
m81	platinocyanide	MgPt(CN)$_4$.7H$_2$O	449.58	red cr, 1.561	2.185^{16}	−2H$_2$O, 45		s	s	s al; i eth
m82	salicylate	Mg(C$_7$H$_5$O$_3$)$_2$.4H$_2$O	370.61	col or sl redsh cr powd, effl				s		s al
m83	selenate	MgSeO$_4$.6H$_2$O	275.36	col, monocl, 1.468, 1.489, 1.491	1.928			v s	v s	
m84	selenide	MgSe	103.27	lght gray powd or cr, 2.44	4.21			d	d	d a
m85	*meta*silicate	Nat. clinoenstatite. MgSiO$_3$	100.40	wh, monocl, α 1.651, γ 1.660	3.192$_4^{25}$	d 1557		i	i	v sl s HF
m86	*ortho*silicate	Nat. forstérite. Mg$_2$SiO$_4$	140.71	wh, orthorhmb, 1.65, 1.66, 1.67	3.21	1910		i		d h HCl
m87	(di-) silicide	Mg$_2$Si	76.71	blue cub	1.94	1102		i	d	s a, NH$_4$Cl, HCl
m88	silicofluoride	MgSiF$_6$.6H$_2$O	274.48	wh hex-rhomb, 1.3439, 1.3602	1.788	d 100		00^{31}	5	s dil a, v sl s HF; i al
m89	stannide	Mg$_2$Sn	167.31	blsh-wh met		778		s		s dil HCl
m90	stearate	Mg(C$_{18}$H$_{35}$O$_2$)$_2$	591.27	wh powd or lumps		86-88		0.003^{15} 0.004^{25}	0.008^{50}	0.020^{25} al; 0.003^{25} eth
m91	sulfate	MgSO$_4$	120.37	col, rhomb cr, 1.56	2.66	d 1124		26^0	73.8^{100}	s al, glyc; 1.16^{18} eth; i acet
m92	sulfate, heptahydrate	Epsom salt, nat. epsomite. MgSO$_4$.7H$_2$O	246.48	col, rhomb or monocl, 1.433, 1.455, 1.461	1.68	−6H$_2$O, 150	−7H$_2$O, 200	71^{20}	91^{40}	sl s al, glyc
m93	sulfate, monohydrate	Nat. kieserite, MgSO$_4$.H$_2$O	138.39	col, monocl pr, 1.523, 1.535, 1.586	2.445				68.4^{100}	
m94	sulfide	MgS	56.38	pa red-brn, cub, phosph, 2.271	2.84	d >2000		d	d	s a, PCl$_3$
m95	sulfite	MgSO$_3$.6H$_2$O	212.47	wh, rhomb or hex, 1.511, 1.464 (hex)	1.725	−6H$_2$O, 200	d	1.25	s	i al, NH$_3$
m96	*d*-tartrate	MgC$_4$H$_4$O$_6$.5H$_2$O	262.46	wh, rhomb	1.67	−4H$_2$O, 100	−5H$_2$O, 200	0.8^{18}	1.44^{90}	s min a; i al, NH$_3$
m97	*d*-tartrate, hydrogen	Mg(HC$_4$H$_4$O$_6$)$_2$.4H$_2$O	394.54	wh, rhomb	1.72				1.893^{100}	
m98	telluride	MgTe	151.91	wh, hex cr	3.86			d		d a
m99	thiosulfate	MgS$_2$O$_3$.6H$_2$O	244.53	col, rhomb pr	1.818^{24}	−3H$_2$O, 170	d	v s	v s	i al
m100	thiotellurite	Mg$_2$TeS$_3$	360.86	pa yel cr mass				s	s	s al
m101	tungstate	MgWO$_4$	272.16	col, monocl	5.66			i		d a; i al
m102	**Manganese**	Mn	54.938	gray-pink met, cub or tetr	7.20	1244 ± 3	1962	d	d	s dil a
m103	(II) acetate	Mn(C$_2$H$_3$O$_2$)$_2$	173.02	brn cr	1.74			s, d		s al
m104	acetate, tetrahydrate	Mn(C$_2$H$_3$O$_2$)$_2$.4H$_2$O	245.08	pa red, monocl	1.589			s		s al
m105	arsenide, mono-	MnAs	129.86	blk, hex	6.17-6.20 (5.55)	d 400		i	i	s HCl, aq reg
m106	arsenide, di-	MnAs$_2$	184.80			1400		i	i	s aq reg
m107	arsenide, tri-	Mn$_2$As$_2$	314.66	magnetic, (exist ?)				i	i	s aq reg
m108	(II) benzoate	Mn(C$_7$H$_5$O$_2$)$_2$.4H$_2$O	369.23	pa red pr				6.55^{15}		
m109	boride, di-	MnB$_2$	76.56	gray-vlt cr	6.9			d	d	s a
m110	boride, mono-	MnB	65.75	cr powd	6.2^{18}					
m111	bromide, di-	MnBr$_2$	214.76	rose cr	4.385$_4^{25}$	d		127.3^0	228^{100}	i NH$_3$
m112	bromide, di-, tetrahydrate	MnBr$_2$.4H$_2$O	286.82	α stable, rose monocl, deliq β labile, col, rhomb		d 64.3		296.7^0		
m113	carbide	Mn$_3$C	176.83	tetr	6.89^{17}			d	d	s a
m114	(II) carbonate	Nat rodochrosite. MnCO$_3$	114.95	rose, rhomb, lt brn in air	3.125	d		0.0065^{25}		s dil a, aq CO$_2$; i al, NH$_3$
m115	chloride, di-	Scacchite. MnCl$_2$	125.84	pink, cub cr, deliq	2.977$_4^{25}$	650	1190	72.3^{31}	123.8^{100}	s al; i eth, NH$_3$
m116	chloride, di-, tetrahydrate	MnCl$_2$.4H$_2$O	197.91	rose, monocl, deliq	2.01	58	−H$_2$O, 106; −4H$_2$O, 198	151^8	656^{100}	s al; i eth
m117	chloride, tri-	MnCl$_3$	161.30	brn cr or grnsh-blk		d sl				s abs al
m118	chloroplatinate	MnPtCl$_6$.6H$_2$O	570.84	trig	2.692	d				i a
m119	chromite	MnCr$_2$O$_4$	222.93	gray-blk, cub	4.97^{20}			i	i	i a
m120	(II) citrate	Mn$_3$(C$_6$H$_5$O$_7$)$_2$	543.02	wh-redsh powd				v sl s		s Na-citr sol
m121	(II) ferrocyanide	Mn$_2$Fe(CN)$_6$.7H$_2$O	447.94	grnsh-wh powd				i		s HCl; i NH$_4$ salts
m122	fluogallate	[Mn(H$_2$O)$_6$][GaF$_5$.H$_2$O]	345.76	pink, orthorhomb, 1.45	2.22	d 230		v s		s HF
m123	fluosilicate	MnSiF$_6$.6H$_2$O	305.11	rose, hex pr, 1.357, 1.374	1.903	d		140^{18}	v s	s al

No.	Name	Synonyms and Formulae	Mol. wt.	Crystalline form, properties and index of refraction	Density or spec. gravity	Melting point, °C	Boiling point, °C	Solubility, in grams per 100 cc		
								Cold water	Hot water	Other solvents
	Manganese									
m124	fluoride, di-	MnF_2	92.93	red, tetr, or redsh powd	3.98	856		0.66^{40}	0.48^{100}	s a; i al, eth
m125	fluoride, tri-	MnF_3	111.93	red cr	3.54	d		d	d	s a
m126	formate	$Mn(CHO_2)_2.2H_2O$	181.00	rhomb	1.953	d		s	s	
m127	(II) glycerophosphate	$MnC_3H_7O_6P$	225.00	wh or sl red powd				sl s		s a, citr a; i al
m128	hydroxide	$MnO(OH)_2$	104.95	blk-brn, amorph (exist ?)	2.58			v sl s		
m129	(II) hydroxide	Nat. pyrochroite. $Mn(OH)_2$	88.95	wh-pink, trig 1.723, 1.681	3.258^{13}	d		0.0002^{18}		s a, NH_4 salts; i alk
m130	(III) hydroxide	Magnanite. $MnO(OH)$	87.94	br-blk, rhomb. 2.24, 2.24, 2.53 (Li)	4.2–4.4	d		i	i	s HCl, h H_2SO_4
m131	iodide, di-	MnI_2	308.75	pink, hex cr, deliq, br. in air	5.0^1	638 (vac) d ca 80	subl vac 500	s	s	0.02^{25} NH_3
m132	iodide, di-, tetrahydrate	$MnI_2.4H_2O$	380.81	rose, monocl, deliq		d		s	v s	
m133	*hexaiodoplatinate*	$MnPtI_6.9H_2O$	1173.59	trig	3.604^{20}_4	d				
m134	(II) nitrate	$Mn(NO_3)_2.4H_2O$	251.01	col, or rose, monocl	1.82	25.8	129.4	426.4^0	∞	v s al
m135	(II) lactate	$Mn(C_3H_5O_3)_2.3H_2O$	287.04	pa red, monocl		d		10	v s	s al
m136	(II) oxalate	MnC_2O_4	142.96	wh cr powd	$2.43^{21.7}$	d 150		i	i	s a, NH_4Cl
m137	(II) oxalate, dihydrate	$MnC_2O_4.2H_2O$	178.98	redsh-wh oct cr powd		$-2H_2O$, 100	d	0.0312^{25}	0.037^{36}	
m138	(II) oxalate, trihydrate	$MnC_2O_4.3H_2O$	197.00	pink, tricl		$-H_2O$, 25				
m139	(II, III) oxide	Nat. hausmannite. Mn_3O_4	228.81	blk, tetr (rhomb), 2.46, (Li) 2.15 (Li)	4.856	1705		i	i	s HCl
m140	oxide, di-	Nat. pyrolusite. MnO_2	86.94	blk, rhomb, or brn-blk powd	5.026	$-O$, 535		i	i	s HCl; i HNO_3, acet
m141	oxide, hept-	Mn_2O_7	221.87	dk red oil, hyg, exp	2.396^{20}_4	5.9	d 55, exp 95	v s	d	s H_2SO_4
m142	(II) oxide, mon-	Nat. manganosite, MnO	70.94	grn, cub, 2.16	5.43–5.46 (3.7–3.9)			i	i	s a, NH_4Cl
m143	(III) oxide, sesqui-	Nat. braunite. Mn_2O_3	157.87	blk, cub (tetr)	4.50	$-O$, 1080		i	i	s a; i ac a
m144	oxide, tri-	MnO_3	102.94	redsh, deliq (exist ?)		d		s	d	s alk, H_2SO_4
m145	(III) *meta*phosphate	$Mn_2(PO_3)_6.2H_2O$	619.74					sl s	s	
m146	(II) *ortho*phosphate	Nat. reddingite. $Mn_3(PO_4)_2.3H_2O$	408.80	rose or yelsh-wh rhomb, 1.651, 1.656, 1.683	3.102					
m147	(III) *ortho*phosphate	$MnPO_4.H_2O$	167.92	gray cr powd		$-H_2O$, 300	d	i		s h conc H_2SO_4, conc HCl, molten H_3PO_4
m148	(II) *ortho*phosphate, di-H	$Mn(H_2PO_4)_2.2H_2O$	284.94			$-H_2O$, >100		s		i al
m149	(II) *ortho*phosphate mono-H	$MnHPO_4.3H_2O$	204.97	red, rhomb or pink powd, 1.656				sl s	d	s a; i al
m150	(II) *pyro*phosphate	$Mn_2P_2O_7$	283.82	br-pink, monocl, 1.695, 1.704, 1.710	3.707^{25}	1196		i		s a
m151	(II) *pyro*phosphate, trihydrate	$Mn_2P_2O_7.3H_2O$	337.87	wh, amorph powd				i		s $K_2P_2O_7$ sol, H_2SO_3 i acet
m152	phosphide, mono-	MnP	85.91	dk gray	5.39^{21}	1190		i	i	sl s HNO_3
m153	(tri-)phosphide, di-	Mn_3P_2	226.76	dk gray	5.12^{18}	1095		i	i	sl s dil HNO_3
m154	(II) *hypo*phosphite	$Mn(H_2PO_2)_2.H_2O$	202.93	rose cr or powd		$-H_2O$, >150		12.5	16.7	i al
m155	(II) *ortho*phosphite	$MnHPO_3.H_2O$	152.93	redsh		$-H_2O$, 200		sl s		s $MnSO_4$, $MnCl_2$
m156	selenate, dihydrate	$MnSeO_4.2H_2O$	233.93	rhomb	2.95–3.01			s	s	
m157	selenate, penta-hydrate	$MnSeO_4.5H_2O$	287.97	pa red, trig	2.33–2.39					
m158	selenide	$MnSe$	133.90	gray, cub	5.55^{15}			i		d dil a
m159	selenite	$MnSeO_3.2H_2O$	217.93	monocl cr				v sl s	v sl s	
m160	(II) *meta*silicate	Nat. rhodonite. $MnSiO_3$	131.02	red, tricl, 1.733, 1.740, 1.744	3.72^{25}	1323		i		i HCl
m161	silicide, di-	$MnSi_2$	111.11	gray, oct	5.24^{13}			i	i	s HF, alk; i HNO_3, H_2SO_3
m162	silicide, mono-	$MnSi$	83.02	tetrah	5.90^{15}	1280		i	i	s HF; v sl s a
m163	(di-)silicide,	Mn_2Si	137.96	quadr pr	6.20^{15}	1316		i	i	s HCl, NaOH; i HNO_3
m164	(II) sulfate	$MnSO_4$	151.00	redsh	3.25	700	d 850	52^5	70^{70}	s al; i eth
m165	(III) sulfate	$Mn_2(SO_4)_3$	398.06	grn cr, deliq, hex	3.24	d 160		d	d	s HCl, dil H_2SO_4; i conc. H_2SO_4, HNO_3

No.	Name	Synonyms and Formulae	Mol. wt.	Crystalline form, properties and index of refraction	Density or spec. gravity	Melting point, °C	Boiling point, °C	Solubility, in grams per 100 cc		
								Cold water	Hot water	Other solvents
	Manganese									
m166	(II) sulfate, dihydrate	$MnSO_4.2H_2O$	187.03	(exist ?)	2.526^{15}	stab 57–117		85.27^{35}	106.8^{55}	
m167	(II) sulfate, heptahydrate	$MnSO_4.7H_2O$	277.11	red monocl or rhomb	2.09	$-7H_2O$, 280; stab $+9$		172	118^{13}	i al
m168	(II) sulfate, hexahydrate	$MnSO_4.6H_2O$	259.09	(exist?)		stab $+5$ to $+8$		147.4	1.345^{38}	
m169	(II) sulfate, monohydrate	Nat. szmikite. $MnSO_4.H_2O$	169.01	pa pink monocl, 1.562, 1.595, 1.632	2.95	stab 57–117		98.47^{48}	79.8^{100}	
m170	(II) sulfate, pentahydrate	$MnSO_4.5H_2O$	241.08	rose, tricl 1.495, 1.508, 1.514	2.103^{15}	stab 9–26		124^0	142^{54}	
m171	(II) sulfate, tetrahydrate	Common form. $MnSO_4.4H_2O$	223.06	pink, monocl or rhomb effl, 1.508, 1.522	2.107	stab 26–27		105.3^0	111.2^{54}	i al
m172	(II) sulfate, tri-hydrate	$MnSO_4.3H_2O$	205.05	(exist?)	2.356^{15}	stab 30–40		74.22^5	99.31^{57}	
m173	(II) sulfide	Nat. alabandite. MnS	87.00	grn cub or pink amorph, 2.70 (Li)	3.99	d		0.00047^{18}		s dil a, al; i $(NH_4)_2S$
m174	(II) sulfide	$3MnS.H_2O$	279.05	gray-pink		d		0.0006	i	s dil a; i $(NH_4)_2$ S
m175	(IV) sulfide	Nat. hauerite. MnS_2	119.07	blk cub, 2.69 (Li)	3.463	d		i	i	d HCl
m176	(II) tantalate	$Mn(TaO_3)_2$	512.83	blk, rhomb, 2.22, 2.25, 2.29	7.03					
m177	(II) tartrate	$MnC_4H_4O_6$	203.01	wh powd				v sl s		s dil a
m178	(II) thiocyanate	$Mn(SCN)_2.3H_2O$	225.16	deliq		$-3H_2O$, 160–170		s	v s	v s al
m179	(II) dithionate	$Mn(SO_3)_2$	215.06	tricl cr	1.757			s	v s	
m180	(II) titanate	Nat. pyrophanite. $MnTiO_3$	150.84	yel, trig, 2.481, 2.210	4.54	1360				
m181	(II) valerate	$Mn(C_5H_9O_2)_2.2H_2O$	293.22	br powd				s		
m182	**Manganic acid, per-**	$HMnO_4$	119.94					v s	d	
m183	**Manganocyanic acid**	$H_4Mn(CN)_6$	215.08			d		i		v s al; i eth
m184	**Mercury**	Quicksilver. Hg	200.59	silv wh met, liq	13.5939^{20}_4	-38.87	356.58	i	i	s HNO_3; i dil HCl, HBr, HI cold H_2SO_4
m185	(I) acetate	$Hg_2(C_2H_3O_2)_2$	519.27	micaceous plates		d		0.75^{12}		s HNO_3, H_2SO_4; i al, eth
m186	(II) acetate	$Hg(C_2H_3O_2)_2$	318.76	wh, sc or powd	3.270	d		25^{10}	100^{100}	s al, ac a
m187	(II) acetylide	$3HgC_2.H_2O$	691.85	wh powd	5.3	expl		i	i	i al
m188	(II) orthoarsenate	$Hg_3(AsO_4)_2$	879.61	yel				v sl s		s HCl, HNO_3
m189	(I) orthoarsenate mono-H	Hg_2HAsO_4	541.11					i		s HNO_3; i ac a, NH_4OH
m190	(I) azide	$Hg_2(N_3)_2$	485.22	wh cr		expl, d by light		0.025		
m191	(II) benzoate	$Hg(C_7H_5O_2)_2.H_2O$	460.84	wh cr powd		165		1.2^{15}	2.5^{100}	s al, NaCl, NH_4Cl, bz
m192	(I) bromate	$Hg_2(BrO_3)_2$	656.99	cr		d		d		sl s HNO_3
m193	(II) bromate	$Hg(BrO_3)_2.2H_2O$	492.44	cr		d 130–140		0.15	1.6	s HCl, HNO_3, $Hg(NO_3)_2$
m194	(I) bromide	Hg_2Br_2	561.00	wh, yel, tetr	7.307	subl 345		$0.00000 4^{25}$		s a; i al, eth
m195	(II) bromide	$HgBr_2$	360.41	col rhomb	6.109^{25} 5.12^{240}	236	322	0.61^{25}	4.0^{100}	15^0 al; s MeOH; v sl s eth
m196	bromide iodide	HgBrI	407.40	yel, rhomb		229	360			s al, eth
m197	(I) carbonate	Hg_2CO_3	461.19	yel br cr		d 130		0.0000045	d	s NH_4Cl; i al
m198	(II) carbonate, basic	$HgCO_3.2HgO$	693.78	br red				i		s NH_4Cl, aq CO_2
m199	(I) chlorate	$Hg_2(ClO_3)_2$	568.08	wh, rhomb	6.409	d 250		s	d	s al, ac a
m200	(II) chlorate	$Hg(ClO_3)_2$	367.49	wh need	4.998	d		25		
m201	(I) chloride	Calomel. Hg_2Cl_2	472.09	wh. tetr, 1.973, 2.656	7.150	subl 400		0.00020^{25}	0.001^{43}	s aq reg, Hg $(NO_3)_2$; sl s HCl, h HNO_3; i al, eth
m202	(II) chloride	Corrosive sublimate. $HgCl_2$	271.50	col, rhomb or wh powd pois, 1.859	5.44^{25}, liq 4.44^{280}	276	302	6.9^{20}	48^{100}	33^{25} al; 4 eth; s ac a, pyr
m203	(I) chromate	Hg_2CrO_4	517.17	red need, or powd		d		v sl s	sl s	s HCN, HNO_3; i al, ac
m204	(II) chromate	$HgCrO_4$	316.58	red, rhomb		d		sl s, d	d	s HN_4Cl; d a; i acet
m205	(II) cyanide	$Hg(CN)_2$	252.63	col, tetr, or wh powd pois, 1.645	3.996	d		9.3^{14}	33^{100}	$25^{19.5}$ MeOH; 8 al; s NH_3, glyc; i bz
m206	(I) fluoride	Hg_2F_2	439.18	yel, cub	8.73^{15}	570	d	d to Hg_2O		
m207	(II) fluoride	HgF_2	238.59	col, cub	8.95^{15}	d 645	650	d		s HF, dil HNO_3
m208	(I) fluosilicate	$Hg_2SiF_6.2H_2O$	579.29	col pr	2.134			sl s		i HCl

No.	Name	Synonyms and Formulae	Mol. wt.	Crystalline form, properties and index of refraction	Density or spec. gravity	Melting point, °C	Boiling point, °C	Solubility, in grams per 100 cc		
								Cold water	Hot water	Other solvents
	Mercury									
m209	(II) fluosilicate	$HgSiF_6.6H_2O$	450.76	col, rhomb, deliq		d easily				
m210	(I) formate	$Hg_2(CHO_2)_2$	491.22	glist scales		d		0.4^{17}	d	i al
m211	(II) fulminate	$Hg(CNO)_2$	284.62	wh, cub	4.42	expl		sl s	s	s al, NH_4OH
m212	(I) iodate	$Hg_2(IO_3)_2$	750.99	yelsh		d 250		i	i	s dil HCl, conc HNO_3
m213	(II) iodate	$Hg(IO_3)_2$	550.48	wh, amorph powd				i		s HCl, NH_4Cl, NaCl, KI; i HNO_3
m214	(I) iodide	Hg_2I_2	654.99	yel, tetr or amorph powd	7.70	subl 140	d 290	v sl s		s KI, NH_4OH; i al, eth
m215	(II) iodide (α)	HgI_2	454.90	red, tetr	6.36^{25}_4	tr 127		0.01^{25}		3.18^{25} acet; 2.23^{25} al; s chl; d NH_4OH
m216	(II) iodide (β)	HgI_2	454.90	yel, rhomb cr or powd	6.094^{127}_4	259	354	v sl s	sl s	s eth, KI, $Na_2S_2O_3$; v sl s al
m217	(I) nitrate	$Hg_2(NO_3)_2.2H_2O$	561.22	col, monocl, effl	4.79^4	70		d	s, d	s dil HNO_3; i NH_4OH
m218	(II) nitrate	$Hg(NO_3)_2.\frac{1}{2}H_2O$	333.61	wh-yelsh cr or powd, deliq	4.39	79	d	v s	d	s acet, HNO_3, NH_3; i al
m219	(II) nitrate	$Hg(NO_3)_2.H_2O$	342.61	col cr or wh powd, deliq	4.3			s		s HNO_3; i al
m220	(I) nitrite	$Hg_2(NO_2)_2$	493.19	yel	7.33	d 100		d		
m221	nitride	Hg_3N_2	629.78	br powd		expl		d		s NH_4OH, NH_4 salts; d a
m222	(I) oxalate	$Hg_2C_2O_4$	489.20					i	i	sl s HNO_3
m223	(II) oxalate	HgC_2O_4	288.61			d		0.0107^{20}		s HCl; sl s HNO_3
m224	(I) oxide	Hg_2O	417.18	blk or brnish-blk powd	9.8	d 100		i	i	s HNO_3
m225	(II) oxide	Nat. montroydite. HgO	216.59	yel or red, rhomb, 2.37, 2.5, 2.65	11.14	d 500		0.0053^{25}	0.0395^{100}	s a; i al, eth, acet, alk, NH_3
m226	(II) oxybromide	$HgBr_2.3HgO$	1010.17	yel cr				i	sl s	v s al
m227	(II) oxychloride	$HgCl_2.2HgO$	704.67	red hex, or blk monocl	red 8.16–8.43 blk 8.53					
m228	(II) oxychloride	$HgCl_2.3HgO$	921.26	yel, hex	7.93	d 260		i	d	
m229	(II) oxycyanide	$Hg(CN)_2.HgO$	469.22	wh need or cr powd	4.437^{19}	expl		1.25	s	
m230	(II) oxyfluoride	$HgF_2.HgO.H_2O$	473.19	yel cr		d 100		d		s dil HNO_3
m231	(II) oxyiodide	$HgI_2.3HgO$	1104.17	yel br				d		s HI
m232	(II) selenide	Nat. tiemannite. HgSe	279.55	gray plates	8.266	vac subl		i		s aq reg
m233	(I) sulfate	Hg_2SO_4	497.24	col monocl, wh-yelsh powd	7.56	d	d	0.06^{25}	0.09^{100}	s HNO_3, H_2SO_4
m234	(II) sulfate	$HgSO_4$	296.65	col rhomb or wh powd	6.47	d		d		s a, NaCl; i al, acet, NH_3
m235	(II) sulfate, basic	$HgSO_4.2HgO$	729.83	lem yel powd	6.44		volat	0.003^{16}	sl s	s a; i al
m236	(I) sulfide	Hg_2S	433.24	blk		d		i		i al, $(NH_4)_2$ S
m237	(II) sulfide (α)	Cinnabar, vermillion. HgS	232.65	red cr hex, or powd, 2.854, 3.201	8.10	subl 583.5		0.000001^{18}		s aq reg, Na_2S; i al, HNO_3
m238	(II) sulfide (β)	Metacinnabar. HgS	232.65	blk, cub or amorph powd	7.73	583.5		i		s aq reg, Na_2S, alk; i al, HNO_3
m239	(I) tartrate	$Hg_2C_4H_4O_6$	549.25	yelsh-wh cr powd		d 20		i		i a
m240	(I) orthotellurate	HgH_4TeO_6	428.22	trans, orthorhomb		d 20		slow d	rapid d	
m241	(II) orthotellurate	Hg_3TeO_6	825.37	amber, cub		unalt at 140		i	i	s HCl, HNO_3
m242	(I) thiocyanate	$Hg_2(SCN)_2$	517.34			d		i		s HCl, KCNS
m243	(II) thiocyanate	$Hg(SCN)_2$	316.75	wh powd, pois		d		0.07^{25}	s	s NH_4 salts, HCl, NH_3, KCN; sl s al, eth
m244	(I) tungstate	Hg_2WO_4	649.03	yel, amorph		d		i	i	d a; i al
m245	(II) tungstate	$HgWO_4$	448.44	yel		d		i	d	d a; i al
	Mercury nitrogen compounds									
m246	mercury (II) bromide, ammono-basic	$Hg(NH_2)Br$	296.52	wh powd		d		d		s NH_4OH; i al
m247	mercury (II) bromide, diammine	$Hg(NH_3)_2Br_2$	394.47	wh powd		180		d		s NH_4Cl, NH_4Br, NH_4I
m248	mercury (II) chloride ammonobasic	Infusible ppt. $Hg(NH_2)Cl$	252.07	wh powd or sm pr	5.70	infus		0.14	d 100	d a; i al
m249	mercury (II) chloride, aquobasic ammonobasic	Chloride of Millon's base. OHg_2NH_2Cl	468.66	pa yel or wh powd		d >120		sl s		s HCl, HNO_3
m250	mercury (II) chloride, diammine	Fusible white ppt. $Hg(NH_3)_2Cl_2$	305.56	rhombd		300		i	d	s a, KI

No.	Name	Synonyms and Formulae	Mol. wt.	Crystalline form, properties and index of refraction	Density or spec. gravity	Melting point, °C	Boiling point, °C	Cold water	Hot water	Other solvents
	Mercury nitrogen compounds									
m251	mercury (II) iodide, ammonobasic	$Hg(NH_2)I$	353.52							i eth
m252	mercury (II) iodide aquobasic ammono-basic	Iodide of Millon's base. OHg_2NH_2I	560.11	yel to brn		>128	expl	i		s d, HCl, KI soln
m253	mercury (II) iodide, diammine	$Hg(NH_3)_2I_2$	488.48	col or pa yel powd or need				d		s NH_4OH
m254	**Millons's base**	$(HO)_2Hg_2NH_2OH$	468.22		4.083[18]					
m255	**Molybdenum**	Mo	95.94	silv-wh met, or gray-blk powd, cub	10.2	2617	4612	i	i	s h conc HNO_3, h conc H_2SO_4, aq reg; sl s HCl; i HF, NH_3
m256	boride, (di-)	MoB_2	117.56	rhomb	7.12					
m257	boride, (mono-)	MoB	106.75	tetr	8.65					
m258	(di-) boride	Mo_2B	202.69	tetr	9.26					
m259	bromide, di-	$MoBr_2$ (or Mo_2Br_4)	255.76	yel red, amorph	4.88[17.5]			i	i	s alk; i a, aq reg
m260	bromide, tetra-	$MoBr_4$	415.58	blk need, deliq	d	volat		v s		d alk
m261	bromide, tri-	$MoBr_3$	335.67	dk-grn need	d				i	d alk, NH_3; i a
m262	carbide, mono-	MoC	107.95	gray, hex	8.20[20]	2692		i	i	sl s HNO_3, HF, h H_2SO_4, HCl; i alk hydr
m263	carbide(di-)	Mo_2C	203.89	wh, hex pr	8.9	2687		i		sl s HNO_3, HF h H_2SO_4, aq reg, HCl; i alk
m264	carbonyl	$Mo(CO)_6$	264.00	wh cr, rhomb diamagnet	1.96	d 150, without meltg	156.4[766]	i	i	s bz; sl s eth
m265	carbonyl, tri pyridine, tri-	$Mo(CO)_3(C_5H_5N)_3$	287.08	yel-brn cr	d					
m266	chloride, di-	$MoCl_2$ (or Mo_2Cl_4)	166.85	yel, amorph	3.714[25]	d		i	i	s HCl, H_2SO_4, alk, NH_4OH, al, acet
m267	chloride, penta-	$MoCl_5$	273.21	grn-blk cr, trig, deliq	2.928	194	268	d	d	s conc min a, liq NH_3, CCl_4, chl; s d al, eth
m268	chloride, tetra-	$MoCl_4$	237.75	brn powd or cr, deliq	d		vol	d	d	s conc min a; d al, eth
m269	chloride, tri-	$MoCl_3$	202.30	dk red need or powd	3.578[25][4]	d		i	sl d	s conc H_2SO_4, conc HNO_3; v sl s al, eth; i HCl; d alk
m270	fluoride, hexa-	MoF_6	209.93	col cr	liq 2.55[17.5]	17.5[406]	35[760]	s d	d	s NH_4OH, alk
m271	hydrotetrachloro hydroxide, di-	$[Mo_2Cl_4(H_2O)_2](OH)_2 \cdot 6H_2O$	607.77	lt yel cr		−H_2O, 35–300		i	i	i a, al
m272	hydroxide	$Mo(OH)_3$ (or $Mo_2O_3 \cdot 3H_2O$)	146.96	blk powd	d				0.2	sl s H_2SO_4, HCl; s 30% H_2O_2
m273	hydroxide	$MoO(OH)_3$ (or $Mo_2O_5 \cdot 3H_2O$)	162.96	br to blk powd					0.2 (coll)	s a, alk carb; i alk hydr
m274	(VI) hydroxide	$MoO_2 \cdot 2H_2O$	179.97	lt yel, monocl pr	3.124[15]				0.05[15]	s dil H_2O_2, alk hydr; sl s a
m275	hydroxytetra-bromide, di-	$Mo_2Br_4(OH)_2$	641.47	red powd						s alk
m276	hydroxytetra-bromide, diocta-hydrate	$Mo_2Br_4(OH)_2 \cdot 8H_2O$	785.59	golden yel cr	d	d				s HCl; d alk, HNO_3
m277	hydroxytetra-chloride, di-	$Mo_2Cl_4(OH)_2 \cdot 2H_2O$	499.68	pa yel, amorph					i	s conc a; i al
m278	iodide, di-	MoI_2	349.75	brn powd	5.278[25.4]			i	d	v sl s a
m279	iodide, tetra-	MoI_4	603.56	blk cr	d 100					
m280	oxide, di-	MoO_2	127.94	lead gray, tetr or monocl	6.47			i	i	sl s h conc H_2SO_4; i alk, HCl, HF
m281	oxide, pent-	Mo_2O_5	271.88	vlt-bl powd (exist?)						s h H_2SO_4, h HCl
m282	oxide, pent-	"Molybd. blue" $Mo_2O_5 \cdot xH_2O$ (variations in Mo and O)		dk blue coll or powd	3.6[18]	d				s a, MeOH; i acet, bz, chl
m283	oxide, sesqui-	Mo_2O_3	239.88	blk, opaque (exist?)				i	i	i a, alk, NH_4OH
m284	oxide, tri-	Molybdic anhydride. Nat. Molybdite. MoO_3	143.94	col or wh-yel, rhomb	4.692[21]	795	subl 1155[760]	0.1066[18]	2.055[70]	s a, alk sulf, NH_4OH
m285	oxydibromide, di-	MoO_2Br_2	287.76	yel-red tabl, deliq				s		

No.	Name	Synonyms and Formulae	Mol. wt.	Crystalline form, properties and index of refraction	Density or spec. gravity	Melting point, °C	Boiling point, °C	Solubility, in grams per 100 cc		
								Cold water	Hot water	Other solvents
	Molybdenum									
m286	oxy*tetra*chloride	$MoOCl_4$	253.75	grn cr, deliq		subl		s		
m287	oxytrichloride	$MoOCl_3$	218.30	grn cr		subl 100		d		
m288	oxydichloride, di-	MoO_2Cl_2	198.84	yelsh wh scaly cr	3.31^{17}	subl		s	s	s al, eth
m289	oxydichloride, dihydrate	$MoO_2Cl_2.H_2O$	216.86	pa yel cr		subl		s	s	sl s al, acet, eth
m290	oxy*hexa*chloride, tri-	$Mo_2O_2Cl_6$	452.60	rubyred or dk vlt cr		d		d		s eth
m291	oxy*penta*chloride, tri-	$Mo_2O_2Cl_5$	417.14	dk brn-blk cr, deliq		melts easily	subl	s	s	
m292	oxychloride acid	$MoO(OH)_2Cl_2$	216.63	wh need, deliq		d 160		v s		s al, eth, acet
m293	oxydifluoride, di-	MoO_2F_2	165.94	wh cr, hygr	3.494^{25}	subl 270		v s	v s	s al, MeOH; i eth, chl, tol
m294	oxy*tetra*fluoride	$MoOF_4$	187.93	col-wh, deliq	3.001^{25}	98	180	s		s al, eth, CCl_4, s d H_2SO_4; v sl s bz
m295	*meta*phosphate	$Mo(PO_3)_4$	569.77	yel powd	3.28^0			i	i	sl s h aq reg; i HCL, HNO_3, H_2SO_4
m296	phosphide	MoP (or Mo_2P_2)	126.93	gray-grn cr powd	6.167					s h HNO_3
m297	phosphide	MoP_2	157.89	blk powd	5.35^{25}					s HNO_3, h conc H_2SO_4, aq reg; i conc HCl
m298	silicide	$MoSi_2$	152.11	gray, met, tetr	$6.31^{20.5}$					i a, aq reg; v s $HF+HNO_3$
m299	sulfide, di-	Nat. molybdenite. MoS_2	160.07	blk luster, hex	4.80^{14}	1185	subl 450, d in air	i	i	s h H_2SO_4, aq reg, HNO_3; i dil a, conc H_2SO_4
m300	sulfide, penta-	$Mo_2S_5.3H_2O$	406.25	dk br powd		$-H_2O$, 135 d		i	i	s NH_4OH, alk, sulfides
m301	sulfide, sesqui-	Mo_2S_3	288.07	steel gray need	5.91^{15}	d 1100	vol 1200			i conc HCl; d h HNO_3
m302	sulfide, tetra-	MoS_4	224.20	brn powd		d		i	i	i a; s h H_2SO_4, alk sulfide
m303	sulfide, tri-	MoS_3	192.13	blk pl		d	d	sl s	s	s alk sulf, conc KOH
m304	**Molybdic acid**	$H_2MoO_4.H_2O$ (or $MoO_3.2H_2O$)	179.97	yel, monocl	3.124^{15}	$-H_2O$, 70	d	0.133^{18}	2.568^{70}	s alk hydr, alk carb; sl s a
m305	anhydrous	H_2MoO_4 (or $MoO_3.H_2O$)	161.95	wh or sl yelsh, hex	3.112	$-H_2O$, 70		sl s	sl s	s alk, NH_4OH, H_2SO_4; i NH_3
m306	**Molybdic arsenic acid**	$As_2O_5.6MoO_3.18H_2O$	1475.75	col, trig	$2.493^{19.8}$	$-15H_2O$, 150		v s		s abs al; i chl, CS_2
m307	**Molybdic phosphoric acid**	$H_7[P(Mo_2O_7)_6].28H_2O$	2365.71	yel, oct	2.53	78		d		
m308	**Molybdic silicic acid**	$H_8[Si(Mo_2O_7)_6].28H_2O$	2363.83	yel, tetr		45	d 100	600^{14}		s dil a; i bz, chl, CS_2
n1	**Neodymium**	Nd	144.24	silv-wh to yelsh met, hex to m.p. 868, cub from 868	hex 7.007 cub 6.80	1021	3068	d		
n2	acetate	$Nd(C_2H_3O_2)_3.H_2O$	339.39					26.2		
n3	acetylacetonate	$Nd[CH(COCH_3)_2]_3$	441.57	pink cr	1.618	150–152				
n4	*hexa*antipyrin perchlorate	$[Nd(C_{11}H_{12}N_2O)_6].(ClO_4)_3$	1571.99	rose, hex cr		d 285–289		0.99^{20}		
n5	bromate	$Nd(BrO_3)_3.9H_2O$	690.10	red, hex		66.7	$-9H_2O$, 150	151^{25}		
n6	bromide	$NdBr_3$	383.97	grn cr		684	1540	sl s		
n7	carbide	NdC_2	168.26	yel, hex leaf	5.15	d		d	d	s dil a; i conc HNO_3
n8	chloride	$NdCl_3$	250.60	rose-vlt pr	4.134^{25}	784	1600	96.7^{13}	140^{100}	44.5 al; i eth, chl
n9	chloride, hexahydrate	$NdCl_3.6H_2O$	358.69	red, rhomb		124	$-6H_2O$, 160	246^{13}	511^{100}	v s al
n10	chromate	$Nd_2(CrO_4)_3.8H_2O$	780.58	yel cr				0.027		
n11	fluoride	NdF_3	201.24	pa lilac		1410	2300	i	i	
n12	iodide	NdI_3	524.95	grn powd		775 ± 3	1370	s	s	
n13	kojate	$Nd(C_6H_5O_4)_3$	567.60	lt choc		d 275		i		
n14	manganous nitrate	$2Nd(NO_3)_3.3Mn(NO_3)_2.24H_2O$	1629.72	vlt-red	2.114	77		77.4^{20}		
n15	magnesium nitrate	$2Nd(NO_3)_3.3Mg(NO_3)_2.24H_2O$	1537.84	vlt-red	2.020	109		69.5^{20}		
n16	dimethylphosphate	$Nd[(CH_3)_2PO_4]_3$	519.35	pa lilac, hex pl				56.1^{25}	22.3^{100}	
n17	molybdate	$Nd_2(MoO_4)_3$	768.29	tetr, 2.005	5.14^{18}	1176				
n18	nickel nitrate	$2Nd(NO_3)_3.3Ni(NO_3)_2.24H_2O$	1641.04	blsh-grn	2.202	105.6		71.5^{20}		
n19	nitrate	$Nd(NO_3)_3.6H_2O$	438.35	tricl				152.9^{25}		s al, acet
n20	nitride	NdN	158.25	blk powd				d		
n21	oxalate	$Nd_2(C_2O_4)_3.10H_2O$	732.69	rose cr				0.000074^{25}		
n22	oxide	Neodymia. Nd_2O_3	336.48	lt bl powd, red fluores	7.24	~1900		0.00019^{29}	0.003^{75}	s a

No.	Name	Synonyms and Formulae	Mol. wt.	Crystalline form, properties and index of refraction	Density or spec. gravity	Melting point, °C	Boiling point, °C	Solubility, in grams per 100 cc		
								Cold water	Hot water	Other solvents
	Neodymium									
n23	sulfate	$Nd_2(SO_4)_3.8H_2O$	720.79	red, monocl, 1.41, 1.551, 1.562	2.85	1176	....	8[20]	5.4[40]	....
n24	sulfide	Nd_2S_3	384.67	oliv grn powd	5.179[11]	d	....	i	d	s dil a
n25	Neon	Ne	20.183	inert gas col sol, cub	gas: 0.9002[0] g/l; liq: 1.204[-245.9]	−248.67	−246.048_	1.47[20] cm³	....	s liq O_2
n26	Neptunium	Np	237.00	α: orthorhomb silvery β: tetr (above 278) γ: cub (above 500)	α: 20.45 β: 19.36[313] γ: 18.0[600]	640 ± 1 278 ± 5 stab 278– 570	3902			s HCl
n27	bromide, tri-	$NpBr_3$	476.73	α: hex β: grn orthorhomb	α 6.92	subl ca 800		s		
n28	chloride, tetra-	$NpCl_4$	378.81	red-brn tetr	4.92	538		s		
n29	chloride, tri-	$NpCl_3$	343.36	wh, hex	5.38	ca 800		s		
n30	fluoride, hexa-	NpF_6	350.99	brn, orthorhomb.		53	d	d		
n31	fluoride, tetra-	NpF_4	312.99	grn, monocl	6.8			i		i conc HNO_3
n32	fluoride, tri-	NpF_3	294.00	purple, hex	9.12			i		
n33	iodide, tri-	NpI_3	617.71	brn, orthorhomb.	6.82			s		
n34	oxide, di-	NpO_2	269.00	apple grn, cub	11.11			i		s conc a
n35	(tri-) oxide, octa-	Np_8O_8	839.00	brn, cub		d 500		i		s HNO_3
n36	**Nickel**	Ni	58.71	silv met, cub	8.90	1453	2732	i	i	s dil HNO_3; al s HCl, H_2SO_4; i NH_3
n37	acetate	$Ni(C_2H_3O_2)_2$	176.80	grn pr	1.798	d		16.6		i al
n38	acetate, tetrahydrate	$Ni(C_2H_3O_2)_2.4H_2O$	248.86	grn pr	1.744	d	16	s		s dil al
n39	antimonide	Nat. breithauptite. NiSb	180.46	lt copper red, hex	7.54	1158	d 1400			
n40	*ortho*arsenate, octa-hydrate	$Ni_3(AsO_4)_2.8H_2O$	598.09	yelsh-grn powd	4.98			i		s a
n41	arsenide	Nat. niccolite. NiAs	133.63	hex	7.57[0]	968		i	i	s aq reg
n42	*ortho*arsenite, acid	$Ni_3H_2(AsO_3)_4.H_2O$	691.87	grn-wh		d		i		s a, alk
n43	benzenesulfonate	$Ni(C_6H_5SO_3)_2.6H_2O$	481.10	grn, monocl, 1.628[25]		−H_2O	d	14.3[18]	51.5[82]	5.9 al; 4.5 eth
n44	boride	NiB	69.52	pr	7.39[18]			d	d	s aq reg, HNO_3
n45	bromate	$Ni(BrO_3)_2.6H_2O$	422.62	monocl	2.575	d		28		
n46	bromide	$NiBr_2$	218.53	yel brn, deliq	5.098[27]	963		112.8[0]	155.1[100]	s al, eth, NH_4OH
n47	bromide, trihydrate	$NiBr_2.3H_2O$	272.57	yelsh-grn need, deliq		−3H_2O, 300		199[0]	315.7[100]	s al, eth, NH_4OH
n48	bromoplatinate	$NiPtBr_6.6H_2O$	841.35	trig	3.715					
n49	di-*N*-butyldithio-carbamate	(NBC).$Ni[(C_4H_9)_2NCSS]_2$	467.47	dk olive grn powd	1.29	89–90		i	i	sl s bz, pet comp; i al
n50	carbide	Ni_3C	188.14	dk gray powd	7.957[25]					
n51	carbonate	$NiCO_3$	118.72	lt grn, rhomb		d		0.0093[25]	i	s a
n52	carbonate, basic	$2NiCO_3.3Ni(OH)_2.4H_2O$	587.67	lt grn cr or brn powd		d		i	d	s a, NH_4 salts
n53	carbonate, basic	Zaratite. $NiCO_3.$ $2Ni(OH)_2.4H_2O(?)$	376.23	emerald grn, cub, 1.56–1.61	2.6			i	i	s h dil HCl, NH_4OH
n54	carbonyl	$Ni(CO)_4$	170.75	col, volat, inflamm, liq, or need	1.32[17]	−25	43	0.018[9.8]	....	s aq reg, al, eth, bz, HNO_3; i dil a, dil alk
n55	chlorate	$Ni(ClO_3)_2.6H_2O$	333.70	dk red	2.07	d 80		0.9[27]		
n56	perchlorate	$Ni(ClO_4)_2.6H_2O$	365.70	grn, hex need, 1.518, 1.498		140		222.5[0]	273.7[45]	s al, acet, chl
n57	chloride	$NiCl_2$	129.62	yel sc, deliq	3.55	1001	subl 973	64.2[20]	87.6[100]	s al, NH_4OH; i NH_3
n58	chloride, hexahydrate	$NiCl_2.6H_2O$	237.70	grn, monocl, deliq ~1.57				254[20]	599[100]	v s al
n59	chloropalladate	$NiPdCl_6.6H_2O$	485.92	hex	2.353					
n60	chloroplatinate	$NiPtCl_6.6H_2O$	574.61	trig	2.798					
n61	cyanide	$Ni(CN)_2$	110.75	yel-brn				i	i	s KCN
n62	cyanide, tetrahydrate	$Ni(CN)_2.4H_2O$	182.81	lt grn pl or powd pois		−4H_2O, 200	d	i	i	s KCN, NH_4OH, alk; sl s dil a
n63	ferrocyanide	$Ni_2Fe(CN)_6.xH_2O$		grn-wh	1.892(?)			i		s KCN, NH_4OH; i HCl
n64	fluogallate	$[Ni(H_2O)_6][GaF_5.H_2O]$	349.53	pa grn, monocl(?), 1.45	2.45	−5H_2O, 110		sl s		s HF
n65	fluoride	NiF_2	96.71	grn, tetr	4.63	subl 1000 (in HF)		4[25]		s a, alk, eth, NH_3
n66	fluosilicate	$NiSiF_6.6H_2O$	308.88	grn, trig, 1.391, 1.407	2.134	d				
n67	formate, dihydrate	$Ni(CHO_2)_2.2H_2O$	184.78	grn cr	2.154	d		s	....	
n68	(II) hydroxide	$Ni(OH)_2$ (or $NiO.xH_2O$)	92.72	grn cr, or amorph	4.15(3.65)	d 230		0.013		s a, NH_4OH
n69	iodate	$Ni(IO_3)_2$	408.52	yel need	5.07			1.1[20]	1.0[90]	
n70	iodate, tetrahydrate	$Ni(IO_3)_2.4H_2O$	480.59	hex		d 100		1.4[20]	1.1[90]	
n71	iodide	NiI_2	312.52	blk cr, deliq	5.834	797		124.2[0]	188.2[100]	s al

No.	Name	Synonyms and Formulae	Mol. wt.	Crystalline form, properties and index of refraction	Density or spec. gravity	Melting point, °C	Boiling point, °C	Solubility, in grams per 100 cc		
								Cold water	Hot water	Other solvents
	Nickel									
n72	dimethylglyoxime	$Ni(HC_2H_6N_2O_2)_2$	288.94	scarlet red cr		subl 250		i	i	s a, abs al; i a ac, NH_4OH
n73	nitrate, hexahydrate	$Ni(NO_3)_2.6H_2O$	290.81	grn, monocl, deliq	2.05	56.7	136.7	238.5⁰	v s	s al, NH_4OH
n74	oleate	$Ni(C_{18}H_{33}O_2)_2$	621.64	grn oil		18–20				
n75	oxalate	$NiC_2O_4.2H_2O$	182.76	lt grn powd				i		s a, NH_4 salts; v sl s oxal a
n76	oxide, mono-	Nat. bunsenite. NiO	74.71	grn-blk, cub, 2.1818(red)	6.67	1990		i	i	s a, NH_4OH
n77	orthophosphate	$Ni_3(PO_4)_2.8H_2O$	510.20	apple grn pl or emerald cr gran		d		i	i	s a, NH_4 salts; i me acet. et acet
n78	pyrophosphate	$Ni_2P_2O_7.xH_2O$		grn	3.93 (anhydr)					s a, NH_4OH
n79	(di-)phosphide	Ni_2P	148.39	gray cr	6.31¹⁵	1112		i		s HNO_3+HF; i a
n80	(penta)phosphide, (di-)	Ni_5P_2	355.50	need or tabl cr		1185				
n81	(tri-)phosphide, (di-)	Ni_2P_3	238.08	dk grn-blk	5.99			i	i	s HNO_3; i HCl
n82	hypophosphite	$Ni(H_2PO_2)_2.6H_2O$	296.78	grn	1.82¹⁹·⁵	d 100		s		
n83	selenate	$NiSeO_4.6H_2O$	309.76	grn, tetr, 1.5393	2.314			s		
n84	selenide	NiSe	137.67	wh or gray, cub	8.46	red heat		i		s aq reg, HNO_3; i a, HCl
n85	silicide	Ni_2Si	145.51		7.2¹⁷	1309		i		i a
n86	stearate	$Ni(C_{18}H_{35}O_2)_2$	625.67	grn powd		100		i		s CCl_4, pyr; sl s acet; i MeOH, eth
n87	sulfate	$NiSO_4$	154.78	yel, cub	3.68	d 848⁷⁶⁰		29.3⁰	83.7¹⁰⁰	i al, eth, acet
n88	sulfate, heptahydrate	Morenosite. $NiSO_4.7H_2O$	280.88	grn, rhomb, 1.467, 1.489, 1.492	1.948	99; −H_2O 31.5	−6H_2O, 103	75.6¹⁵·⁵	475.8¹⁰⁰	s al
n89	sulfate, hexahydrate	Single nickel salt. $NiSO_4.6H_2O$	262.86	α: bl, tetr β: grn, monocl, 1.511, 1.487	2.07	tr: 53.3	−6H_2O, 103	62.52⁰	340.7¹⁰⁰	12.5 MeOH; v s al, NH_4OH
n90	sulfide, mono-	Nat. millerite. NiS	90.77	blk; trig or amorph	5.3–5.65	797		0.00036¹⁸		s aq reg, HNO_3, KHS; sl s a
n91	sulfide, sub-	Heazlewoodite. Ni_3S_2	240.26	pa yelsh bronze met, lust	5.82	790		i		s HNO_3
n92	(II, III) sulfide	Poydomite. Ni_3S_4	304.39	gray-blk, cub	4.7			i		s HNO_3
n93	sulfite	$NiSO_3.6H_2O$	246.86	grn, tetrah				i		s HCl, H_2SO_4
n94	dithionate	$NiS_2O_6.6H_2O$	326.93	grn, tricl	1.908	d				
	Nickel Complexes									
n95	diaquotetrammine nickel (II) nitrate	$[Ni(NH_3)_4(H_2O)_2].(NO_3)_2$	286.87	grn cr				s		i al
n96	hexamminenickel (II) bromide	$[Ni(NH_3)_6]Br_2$	320.71	vlt powd	1.837			v s	d	
n97	hexamminenickel (II) chlorate	$[Ni(NH_3)_6](ClO_3)_2$	327.80		1.52	180		d to $Ni(NH_3)_4$		
n98	hexamminenickel (II) chloride	$[Ni(NH_3)_6]Cl_2$	231.80	blsh, cub	1.468²⁵			s	d	s NH_4OH; i al
n99	hexamminenickel (II) iodide	$[Ni(NH_3)_6]I_2$	414.70	pa bl, cub	2.101	d		d		s NH_4OH
n100	hexamminenickel (II) nitrate	$[Ni(NH_3)_6](NO_3)_2$	284.90	bl, oct or cub				4.46		
n101	tetrapyridinnickel (II) fluosilic	$[Ni(C_5H_5N)_4]SiF_6$	517.20	bl grn, rhomb	2.307					
n102	**Niobium**	Columbium. Nb	92.906	steel gray, lustr met cub, 1.80	8.57	2468 ± 10	4742	i	i	s fus alk; i HCl, HNO_3, aq reg
n103	boride	NbB_2	114.53	hex	6.97	2900(?)				
n104	bromide, penta-	$NbBr_5$	492.46	purp red		265.2	361.6	d		s al, ethyl bromide
n105	carbide	NbC	104.92	blk, cub or lavender-gray powd	7.6	3500		i		s HNO_3, HF
n106	chloride, penta-	$NbCl_5$	270.17	yel-wh, deliq	2.75	204.7	254	d		s al, HCl, CCl_4
n107	fluoride, penta-	NbF_5	187.90	col, monocl pr, hygr	3.293	72–73	236	d		s al; sl s chl, CS_2, H_2SO_4
n108	hydride	NbH	93.91	gray powd	6.6	infus				s HF, conc H_2SO_4; i HCl, alk, HNO_3
n109	nitride	NbN	106.91	blk, cub	8.4	2573		i		s HF+HNO_3; i HNO_3
n110	oxalate, hydrogen	$Nb(HC_2O_4)_5$	538.05	col, monocl		d	d	d	d	s $H_2C_2O_4$; d al
n111	oxide, di-	NbO_2	124.90	blk	5.9			i	i	sl s alk; i a
n112	oxide, mon- (or di-)	NbO (or Nb_2O_2)	108.91	blk, cub	7.30			i	i	s a, alk; i al, NHO_3
n113	oxide, pent-	Nb_2O_5	265.81	wh, rhomb	4.47	1460		i	i	s HF, alk; i a
n114	oxide, pent-, hydrate	$Nb_2O_5.xH_2O$				d		i		s conc H_2SO_4, conc HCl, HF, alk; i NH_3
n115	oxide, tri-(sesqui)	Nb_2O_3	233.81	bl-blk		1780				

No.	Name	Synonyms and Formulae	Mol. wt.	Crystalline form, properties and index of refraction	Density or spec. gravity	Melting point, °C	Boiling point, °C	Cold water	Hot water	Other solvents
	Niobium									
n116	oxybromide	$NbOBr_3$	348.63	yel cr		subl		d		s a
n117	oxychloride	$NbOCl_3$	215.26	col need		subl 400		s, d	d	s al, H_2SO_4; i HCl
n118	potassium fluoride	$NbOF_3.2KF.H_2O$	300.12	monocl leaf, lustr fatty				7.8	v s	
n119	**Nitric acid**	HNO_3	63.01	col liq, corr, pois, 1.5027_4^{25} $1.397^{16.4}$		-42	83	∞	∞	d al, viol; s eth
n120	const boil	68 % HNO_3 + 32 % H_2O		col liq	1.41_4^{20}		120.5	∞	∞	
n121	**Nitrogen**	N_2	28.0134	col gas, col liq, sol cub cr	gas 1.2506 g/l liq $0.8081^{-195.8}$ sol $1.026^{-252.5}$	-209.86	-195.8	2.33^0 cm³	1.42^{40} cm³	sl s al
n122	chloride, tri-	NCl_3	120.37	yel oil or rhomb cr	1.653	<-40	<71, expl 95	i	d	s chl, bz, CCl_4, CS_2, PCl_3
n123	fluoride, tri-	NF_3	71.00	col gas	liq: 1.537^{-129}	-206.60	-128.8	v sl s		
n124	iodide, tri-	NI_3	394.72	blk, expl		expl	subl vac	i	d	s KCNS, $Na_2S_2O_3$
n125	iodide, tri-, monoammine	$NI_3.NH_3$	411.75	dk red, rhomb	3.5	d > 20	expl	i	d	s HCl, KCNS, $Na_2S_2O_3$; i abs al
n126	oxide(ic)	NO	30.01	col gas, bl liq, sol liq 1.330^{-90}	gas 1.3402 g/l liq: $1.269^{-150.2}$	-163.6	-151.8	7.34^0 cm³	2.37^{60} cm³	3.4 cm³ H_2SO_4; 26.6 cm³ al; s $FeSO_4$, CS_2
n127	oxide(ous)	N_2O	44.01	col gas or liq or cub cr, 1.0005_{760}^{20}	1.977_{760}^0 g/l	-90.8	-88.5	130^0 cm³	56.7^{25} cm³	s al, eth, H_2SO_4
n128	oxide, pent-	Nitric anhydride. N_2O_5	108.01	wh, rhomb or hex	1.642^{18}	30	d 47	s	d to HNO_3	s chl
n129	oxide, tri-	NO_3	62.00	blsh gas		d at ord temp				s eth
n130	peroxide	Nitrogen oxide, di-. NO_2	46.01	col sol, yel liq or brn gas, 1.40^{20}	1.4494_{20}^{20}	-11.20	21.2	s, d		s alk, CS_2, chl
n131	(di-) oxide(tri-)	Nitrous anhydride. N_2O_3	76.01	red-brn gas, bl sol or liq	1.447^2	-102	d 3.5	s	d	s eth, a, alk
n132	oxi (tri-) fluoride	NO_3F	81.06	col gas expl	liq: $1.507^{-45.9}$ sol $1.951^{-193.2}$	-175	-45.9			s acet; expl al, eth
n133	sulfide, penta-	N_2S_5	188.33	gray cr		10–11	d	d	d	s CS_2, eth; i bz, al
n134	sulfide, tetra-	Tetranitrogen tetrasulfide sulfur-nitride. N_4S_4	184.28	yel cr, 2.046	2.24^{18}	d 178				s al, bz, CS_2
n135	**Nitrosyl bromide**	NOBr	109.92	br gas or dk br liq	> 1.0	-55.5	-2	d	d	s alk
n136	perchlorate	$NOClO_4.H_2O$	147.47	rhomb, deliq	2.169	d 100		d		expl al, eth
n137	chloride	NOCl	65.46	yel gas or yel-red liq or cr	gas: 2.99 g/l liq: 1.417^{-12}	-64.5	-5.5	d	d	s fum H_2SO_4
n138	fluoborate	$NOBF_4$	116.81	col, rhomb cr, hygr	2.185_4^{25}	subl $250^{0.01}$		d		
n139	fluoride	NOF	49.00	col gas	2.176 g/l	-134	-56			d to HNO_2 + HF
n140	**Nitrosylsulfuric acid**	Chamber crystals. $NOHSO_4$	127.08	col, rhomb		d 73.5		d		s H_2SO_4
n141	**Nitrosylsulfuric anhydride**	$(NOSO_3)_2O$	236.14	tetr		217	360	d		s H_2SO_4
n142	**Nitrous acid**	HNO_2	47.01	only in sol (pa bl)				d		
n143	hypo-	$H_2N_2O_2$	62.03	wh, sol		expl		s		
n144	**Nitryl chloride**	NO_2Cl	81.46	pa yel-br gas	gas: 2.57 g/l liq: 1.32^{14}	<-31	5	d		
n145	fluoride	NO_2F	65.00	col gas, col sol	2.90 g/l	-139	-63.5	d		d al, eth, chl
o1	**Osmium**	Os	190.20	gray-blsh met, hex	22.48^{20}	2045	5067±100	i	i	sl s aq reg, HNO_3; i NH_3
o2	carbonyl chloride	$Os(CO)_3Cl_2$	345.14	col pr		269–273	d 280	i	i	s NaOH; i a
o3	chloride, di-	$OsCl_2$	261.11	dk brn, deliq	d			d	sl d	s al, eth, HNO_3; sl s alk
o4	chloride, tetra-	$OsCl_4$	332.01	red br need		subl		sl s, d		i al
o5	chloride, tri-	$OsCl_3$	296.56	br, cub		d 500–600		v s		s alk, al, a; sl s eth
o6	chloride, tri-, tri-hydrate	$OsCl_3.3H_2O$	350.61	dk gr cr		d		v s		s al
o7	fluoride, hexa-	OsF_6	304.19	grn cr		32.1	45.9	d	d	
o8	fluoride, tetra-	OsF_4	266.19	br powd				d	d	
o9	iodide	OsI_4	697.82	vlt-blk, hygr met, lust				v s	d	s al

No.	Name	Synonyms and Formulae	Mol. wt.	Crystalline form, properties and index of refraction	Density or spec. gravity	Melting point, °C	Boiling point, °C	Solubility, in grams per 100 cc		
								Cold water	Hot water	Other solvents
	Osmium									
o10	oxide, di-, brown	OsO_2	222.20	brn cr	$11.37^{21.4}$	30 % tr to OsO_4, 500		i	i	i a
o11	oxide, di-, black	OsO_2	222.20	blk powd	7.71^{21}	tr to br 350–400		i	i	s dil HCl
o12	oxide, mon-	OsO	206.20	blk				i	i	
o13	oxide, sesqui-	Os_2O_3	428.40	dk brn		d		i	i	i a
o14	oxide, tetra-	OsO_4	254.10	a) col, monocl b) yel mass	4.906^{22}	a) 39.5 b) 41.0	130	5.70^{10}	6.23^{25}	250 ± 10^{20} CCl₄; s al, eth, NH₄OH, POCl₃
o15	sulfide, di-	OsS_2	254.33	blk, cub	9.47	d		i	i	s HNO₃; i alk
o16	sulfide, tetra-	OsS_4	318.46	br blk (exist?)		d		i		s dil HNO₃; i (NH₄)₂ S
o17	sulfite	$OsSO_3$	270.26	bl blk		d		i		s dil HCl, alk
o18	telluride	$OsTe_2$	445.40	gray-blk cr		ca 600				i a; d dil HNO₃
o19	**Oxygen**	O_2	31.9988	col gas, sol hex cr	gas: 1.429^0 g/l, liq: 1.149^{-183} sol: $1.426^{-252.5}$	−218.4	−182.962	4.89^0 cm³ 3.16^{25} cm³	2.46^{40} cm³ 2.30^{100} cm³ 3	2.78^{25} al
o20	fluoride	OF_2	54.00	col gas, unst	liq: $1.90^{-223.8}$	−223.8	−144.8	sl s, d	i	sl s a, alk
o21	**Ozone**	O_3	47.9982	col gas, or dk bl liq, or bl-blk cr, liq: 1.2226	gas: 2.144^0 g/l liq: $1.614^{-195.4}$ g/l	−192.7 ± 2 1.0	−111.9	49^0 cm³		s alk sol, oils
p1	**Palladium**	Pd	106.40	silv wh, met, cub	12.02^{20} $11.40^{22.5}$	1552	3140	i	i	s aq reg, h HNO₃, H₂SO₄; sl s HCl
p2	bromide	$PbBr_2$	266.22	red br	5.173^{16}	d		i	i	s HBr
p3¹	chloride	$PdCl_2$	177.31	dk red, cub need, deliq	4.0^{18}	d 500		s	s	s HBr; acet
p3²	chloride, dihydrate	$PdCl_2.2H_2O$	213.34	br pr, deliq		d		v s	v s	s HCl, acet
p4	cyanide	$Pd(CN)_2$	158.44	yelsh-wh		d		i	i	s KCN, NH₄OH; i dil a
p5	fluoride, di-	PdF_2	144.40	br, tetr	5.80	volat	d red heat	sl s, d		s HF
p6	fluoride, tri-	PdF_3	163.40	blk, rhomb	5.06	d	d	d	d	s HF
p7	hydride	Pd_2H (or Pd_4H_2)	213.81	silv met (exist?)	10.76	d				
p8	iodide	PdI_2	360.21	blk powd	6.003^{18}	d 350		i	i	s KI; i al, eth, dil HCl
p9	nitrate	$Pd(NO_3)_2$	230.41	br yel, rhomb, deliq		d		s, d		s HNO₃
p10	oxide, di-	$PdO_2.xH_2O$		dull red		d—H₂O, −O		i	i,d	s a, alk
p11	oxide, mon-	PdO	122.40	grnsh-bl or amber mass, or blk powd	8.70^{20}_4	870		i	i	i aq reg
p12	oxide, mon-, hydrate	$PdO.xH_2O$		yel to brn		d		i	i	s a, NH₃, NH₄Cl
p13	selenate	$PdSeO_4$	249.36	dk brn-red, rhomb, deliq	6.5	d red heat		v s	v s	i al, eth, alk; s NH₃
p14	selenide	$PdSe$	185.36	dk gray		<960		i		s aq reg
p15	selenide, di-	$PdSe_2$	264.32	olive gray, hex		<1000		i	i	v s aq reg; v sl s HNO₃; i alk
p16	silicide	$PdSi$	134.49	cr	7.31^{15}			i		
p17	sulfate	$PdSO_4.2H_2O$	238.50	red-br cr, deliq		d		v s	d	
p18	sulfide, di-	PdS_2	170.53	dk br cr	$4.7–4.8^{25}_4$	d		i	i	s aq reg, (NH₄)₂S
p19	sulfide, mono-	PdS	138.46	brn-blk tetr	6.6^{25}_4	d 950		i	i	sl s HNO₃, aq reg; i HCl, (NH₄)₂S
p20	sulfide, sub-	Pd_2S	244.86	grn gray (exist?)	7.303^{15}	d 800		i	i	sl s a, aq reg
p21	telluride, di-	$PdTe_2$	361.60	silvery cr, hex				i	i	v s aq reg; s HNO₃; i alk
	Palladium Complexes									
p22	diamminepalladium (II) hydroxide	$Pd(NH_3)_2(OH)_2$	174.48	yel micr cr		>105		v s	d	
p23	dichlorodiamminepalladium (II) *trans* (or α)	$Pd(NH_3)_2.Cl_2$	211.37	yel, tetr	2.5	d		0.304^{10}	s, d	s, d a; s NH₄OH; i chl, acet
p24	tetramminepalladium (II) chloride	$Pd(NH_3)_4Cl_2.H_2O$	263.44	col, tetr	1.91^{18}	d 120		v s		
p25	tetramminepalladium tetrachloropalladate	Vauquelin's salt. $Pd(NH_3)_4.PdCl_4$	422.73	pink powd or need	2.489^{21}	tr yel 184 d above 192		i	sl s	sl s dil HCl; s KOH
p26	**Phospham**	PN_2H	60.00	wh, amorph		infus		i	d	s conc H₂SO₄, alk; i a
p27	**Phosphomolybdic acid**	Molybdophosphoric acid $H_3[P(Mo_3O_{10})_4]$		yel, tetr		78–90		s	s	

No.	Name	Synonyms and Formulae	Mol. wt.	Crystalline form, properties and index of refraction	Density or spec. gravity	Melting point, °C	Boiling point, °C	Solubility, in grams per 100 cc		
								Cold water	Hot water	Other solvents
	Phosphonium									
	Phosphonium									
p28	bromide	PH_4Br	114.91	col, cub	gas: 2.464 g/l	subl ca 30	38.8[794]	d	d	
p29	chloride	PH_4Cl	70.46	col, cub		28[46 atm]	subl	d		
p30	iodide	PH_4I	161.91	col, tetr, deliq	2.86	18.5, subl 61.8	80	d		d, s a, alk
p31	sulfate	$(PH_4)_2SO_4$	166.07					d		
p32	**Phosphoramide**	Phosphorylamide. $PO(NH_2)_3$	95.04	wh, amorph		d		i	i	s al; i a
	Phosphoric acid									
p33	difluoro-	$H_2PO_2F_2$	102.99	col, fum liq	1.583_4^{25}	-96.5 ± 0.1	115.9 sl d			
p34	hypo-	$H_4P_2O_6.2H_2O$	198.01	col, rhomb deliq		70	d 100	d to $H_3PO_3 + HPO_3$		
p35	meta-	HPO_3	79.98	col, vitrous, deliq	2.2–2.5	subl		d to H_3PO_4 d		s al; i liq CO_2
p36	monofluo-	H_2PO_3F	99.99	oily, col liq	1.818	-80				
p37	ortho-	H_3PO_4	98.00	col, liq, or rhomb cr, deliq	1.834[18]	42.35	$-\frac{1}{2}H_2O$, 213	548	v s	s al
p38	ortho-	$2H_3PO_4.H_2O$	214.01	col, hex pr deliq		29.32	d	v s		
p39	pyro-	$H_4P_2O_7$	177.98	col, need or liq, hygr		61	709[23]	d to H_3PO_4	v s al, eth	
p40	**Phosphorus, black**	P_4	30.97376	blk, incombust	2.70			i CS_2, conc H_2SO_4		
p41	red	P_4	30.97376	redsh-brn, cub, or amorph powd, (mix of col and vlt?)	2.34	590[43 atm]	ign 200 280	v sl s	i	s abs al; i CS_2, eth, NH_3
p42	violet	P_4	30.97376	vlt, monocl	2.36	590				i org solv
p43	yellow	Phosphorus, white. P_4	30.97376	yel (or wh) cub or wax like solid, 2.144	1.82[20]	44.1	280	0.0003[15]	sl s	0.3 al; 880[18]CS_2; s bz, NH_3, alk, eth, chl, tol
p44	bromide, penta-	PBr_5	430.52	yel, rhomb		d < 100	d 106	d		s CS_2, CCl_4, bz
p45	bromide, tri-	PBr_3	270.70	col, fum liq, 1.697[26.6]	2.852[15]	-40	172.9	d		d al; s eth, chl, CS_2, CCl_4
p46	bromide(di-) chloride, tri-	PBr_2Cl_3	297.15	or cr		d 35		d		
p47	bromide(hepta-) chloride, di-	PBr_7Cl_2	661.24	pr				d		s PCl_3, PCl_5
p48	bromide(mono-) chloride, tetra-	$PBrCl_4$	252.69	yel cr				d		
p49	bromide(octa-) chloride, tri-	PBr_8Cl_3	776.60	brn need		25		d		
p50	bromide(di-) fluoride, tri-	PBr_2F_3	247.79	pa yel liq		20	d 15	d		d glass
p51	bromide nitride	$(PNBr_2)_3$	614.40	col, rhomb		190	subl v 150	i		s eth; sl s chl, CS_2
p52	chloride, di-	PCl_2 (or P_2Cl_4 ?)	101.88	col liq		-28	180	hydr		
p53	chloride, penta-	PCl_5	208.24	yelsh-wh, tetr, fum	gas: 4.65[14] g/l	d 166.8 (press)	subl 162	d		d a; s CS_2, CCl_4
p54	chloride, tri-	PCl_3	137.33	col, fum liq, 1.516[14]	1.574[21]	-112	75.5[749]	d	d	s eth, bz, chl, CS_2, CCl_4
p55	chloride(di-) fluoride, tri-	PCl_2F_3	158.88	col liq	5.4 g/l	-8	10			
p56	chloride(tri-)iodide, di-	PCl_3I_2	391.14	red, hex		d 259		d		s CS_2
p57	chloride(di-)nitride	$(PNCl_2)_3$	347.66	rhomb	1.98	114	256.5	i	d	s al, eth, bz, chl, a ac, CS_2
p58	chloride(di-)nitride	$(PNCl_2)_4$	463.55		2.18_{24}^{24}	123.5	328.5			
p59	chloride(di-)nitride	$(PNCl_2)_5$	579.43			41	224[13], polym >250			
p60	chloride(di-)nitride	$(PNCl_2)_6$	695.32			90	262[13], polym >250			
p61	cyanide	$P(CN)_3$	109.03	wh need		subl 130		d		v s eth; sl s h bz
p62	fluoride, penta-	PF_5	125.97	col gas	5.805 g/l	-83	-75	d		
p63	fluoride, tri-	PF_3	87.97	col gas	3.907 g/l	-151.5	-101.5	d		s al; d alk
p64	hydride, tri-	Phosphine. PH_3	34.00	col gas, pois		-133	-87.7	0.26 vol 20		
p65	iodide, di-	P_2I_4	569.57	or, tricl		110		d	d	s CS_2
p66	iodide, tri-	PI_3	411.68	red, hex, deliq	4.18	61	d	d	d	v s CS_2
p67	oxide, pent-	Phosphoric anhydride. P_2O_5 (or P_4O_{10})	141.94	wh, monocl or powd, v deliq	2.39	580–585	subl 300	d to H_3PO_4		s H_2SO_4; i acet, NH_3
p68	oxide, sesqui-	Phosphorus trioxide. P_4O_6 (or P_2O_3)	219.89	col, or wh powd, monocl cr, deliq	2.135[21]	23.8	175.4	d to H_3PO_3	d	s chl, bz, eth, CS_2
p69	oxide, tetra-	P_2O_4	125.95	col, rhomb, deliq	2.54[87]	>100	180 vac	v a to H_3PO_3		
p70	oxide, tri-	P_2O_3 (or P_4O_6)	109.95	col, or wh powd, or monocl, deliq	2.135[21]	23.8	173.8 (in N_2)	d to H_3PO_3	d	s CS_2, eth, chl, bz,

No.	Name	Synonyms and Formulae	Mol. wt.	Crystalline form, properties and index of refraction	Density or spec. gravity	Melting point, °C	Boiling point, °C	Solubility, in grams per 100 cc		
								Cold water	Hot water	Other solvents
	Phosphorus									
p71	oxybromide	$POBr_3$	286.70	col pl	2.822	56	189.5	d		s H_2SO_4, CS_2, eth, bz, chl
p72	oxy*di*bromide chloride	$POBr_2Cl$	242.27	sol or liq	liq: 2.45^{50}	30	165	d		
p73	oxybromide chloride, di	$POBrCl_2$	197.79	tabl or liq	liq: 2.104^{14}	13	137.6			
p74	oxychloride	$POCl_3$	153.33	col, fum liq, $1.460^{25.1}$	1.675	2	105.3	d	d	d al, a
p75	oxychloride	$P_2O_3Cl_4$	251.76	col fum liq	liq: 1.58^7	< −50	212	d		
p76	oxyfluoride	POF_3	103.97	col gas	4.69 g/l	−68	−39.8	d		d al
p77	oxynitride	PON	60.98	wh, amorph		red heat		i	i	i a, alk
p78	oxysulfide	$P_4O_6S_4$	348.15	wh, tetr, deliq		102	295	d		50 CS_2
p79	selenide, penta-	P_2Se_5	456.75	dk red-blk need	d			d		s CCl_4; i CS_2
p80	(tetra-)selenide, tri-	P_4Se_3	360.78	or red cr	1.31	242	360–400			
p81	(tetra-)sulfide, hepta-	P_4S_7	348.34	lt yel cr	2.19^{17}	310	523			sl s CS_2
p82	sulfide, penta-	P_2S_5 (or P_4S_{10})	222.27	gray-yel cr, deliq	2.03	286–90	514	i	d	0.22 CS_2; s alk
p83	sesquisulfide	Tetraphosphorus trisulfide. P_4S_3	220.09	yel, rhomb	2.03^{17}	174	408	i	d	100^{17} CS_2; 11.1^{20} bz
p84	thiobromide	$PSBr_3$	302.76	yel, oct	2.85^{17}	38	d 212	s		s eth, CS_2, PCl_3
p85	thiochloride	$PSCl_3$	169.40	col, fum liq	1.668	−35	125	sl d	d	s CS_2
p86	thiocyanate	$P(SCN)_3$	205.22	liq	1.625^{18}	ca −4	265	d		s al, eth, bz, CS_2
	Phosphorous acid									
p87	hypo-	$H(H_2PO_2)$	66.00	col oily liq or deliq cr	1.493^{19}	26.5	d 130	s	v s	v s al, eth
p88	meta-	HPO_2	63.98	feather like cr			d			
p89	ortho-	$H_2(HPO_3)$	82.00	col-yel cr, deliq	$1.651^{21.2}$	73.6	d 200	309^0	694^{40}	s al
p90	pyro-	$H_4P_2O_5$	145.98	need		38	d 120	d		
p91	**Phosphotungstic acid**	Tungstophosphoric acid $H_3[P(W_3O_{10})_4].14H_2O$	3132.39	yel-grn, tricl	d			s		s al, eth
p92	phosphotungstic acid	Dodecatungto-phosphoric acid. $H_3[P(W_3O_{10})_4].24H_2O$	3312.54	trig		89		s		
p93	**Platinic acid,** *hexachloro*	$H_2PtCl_6.6H_2O$	517.92	red, brn, deliq	2.431	60		v s	v s	s al, eth
p94	*tetracyano*	$H_2Pt(CN)_4$	301.18		d 100			v s	v s	v s al, eth, chl
p95	*hexahydroxy-*	$H_2Pt(OH)_6$	299.15	yel need		−2H_2O, 100	−3H_2O, 120	i	v sl s	s H_2SiF_6, dil a, alk
p96	*hexaiodo-*	$H_2PtI_6.9H_2O$	1120.67	blk-red, deliq						
p97	**Platinum**	Pt	195.09	silv met, cub	21.45^{20}	1772	3827 ± 100			s aq reg, fus alk
p98	arsenide	Nat. sperrylith. $PtAs_2$	344.93	gray, cub	11.8	d >800		sl d	sl d	v sl s a
p99	bromic acid	$H_2PtBr_6.9H_2O$	838.70	br-red, monocl, hygr				v s	v s	v s al, eth
p100	(II) bromide, di-	$PtBr_2$	354.91	br	6.65^{25}_4	d 250		i	i	i al; s HBr, KBr, aq Br
p101	(IV) bromide, tetra-	$PtBr_4$	514.73	dk cr	5.69^{25}_4	d 180		0.41^{20}	sl s	v s al, eth, HBr
p102	carbonyl bromide	$[Pt_2(CO)_2]Br_4$	765.84	lt red, need, hygr.	5.115^{25}_4	d 180		s d		s abs al, CCl_4, bz
p103	carbonyl chloride, di-	$Pt(CO)Cl_2$	294.00	yel need	4.2346^{25}_4	195, subl 240 in CO_2	d 300	d	d	s conc HCl, H_2SO_4, al
p104	dicarbonyl chloride, di-	$Pt(CO)_2Cl_2$	322.02	lt yel need	3.4882^{25}_4	142	−CO, 210	d	d	d HCl; s CCl_4
p105	*di*platinum dicarbonyl tetrachloride	$Pt_2(CO)_2Cl_4$	588.01	or-yel need	4.235^{25}_4	195	subl 240 (in CO_2)	d		d HCl
p106	*di*platinum tricarbonyl tetrachloride	$Pt_2(CO)_3Cl_4$	616.02	or-yel need		130	d 250	d		s h CCl_4, d al
p107	carbonyl diiodide	PtI_2CO	476.91	red cr	5.257	d 140–150		d		s d, al; s bz
p108	carbonyl sulfide	$Pt(CO)S$	255.16	br-blk		d 300–400		d		d alk, al
p109	chloric acid	$H_2PtCl_6.6H_2O$	517.92	brn-red cr, hygr	2.431	60	d >115	s	s	s abs al, acet; v s eth
p110	(II) chloride, di-	$PtCl_2$	266.00	olive grn, hex	6.05	d 581 (in Cl_2)		v sl s		i al, eth; s HCl, NH_4OH
p111	(IV) chloride, tetra-	$PtCl_4$	336.90	br-red cr	4.303^{25}_4	d 370 (in Cl_2)		58.7^{25}	v s	sl s al, NH_3; s acet; i eth
p112	(IV) chloride, tetra-, hydrate	$PtCl_4.5H_2O$	426.98	red, monocl	2.43	−H_2O, 100		v s	v s	s al, eth
p113	chloride, tri-	$PtCl_3$	301.45	grnsh-blk	5.256^{25}	435		sl s	s	s h HCl; v sl s conc HCl

No.	Name	Synonyms and Formulae	Mol. wt.	Crystalline form, properties and index of refraction	Density or spec. gravity	Melting point, °C	Boiling point, °C	Solubility, in grams per 100 cc		
								Cold water	Hot water	Other solvents
	Platinum									
p114	*dichlorocarbonyl, dichloride*	$Pt(COCl_2)Cl_2$	364.91	yel cr		d		v s		sl s al; v sl s CCl_4
p115	(II) cyanide, di-	$Pt(CN)_2$	247.13	yel-br cr				i	i	i al, a, alk; s KCN
p116	(II) fluoride, di-	PtF_2	233.09	yelsh-grn				i	i	
p117	fluoride, hexa-	PtF_6	309.08	dk red solid, very unstable		57.6				
p118	(IV) fluoride, tetra-	PtF_4	271.08	deep red, fused, or yel-lt brn cr, deliq		d red heat		s d	v s	s a, alk
p119	(II) hydroxide	$Pt(OH)_2$	229.10	blk		d		i	i	s HCl, HBr, alk; i H_2SO_4, dil HNO_3
p120	(II) hydroxide, hydrate	$Pt(OH)_2.2H_2O$	265.14			$-2H_2O$, 100		i	i	s conc a
p121	*monohydroxy chloric acid*	$H_2[PtCl_6(OH)].H_2O$	409.39	red-brn cr, hygr						
p122	(II) iodide, di-	PtI_2	448.90	blk powd	6.403_4^{25}	d 360		i	i	i eth, a; s HI; sl s Na_2SO_3
p123	(IV) iodide, tetra-	PtI_4	702.71	brn, amorph, or blk cr	6.064_4^{25}	d 130		s d		s al, acet, alk, HI, KI, liq NH_3
p124	iodide, tri-	PtI_3	575.80	blk, like graphite	7.414_4^{25}	d 270		i	i	i al, eth; s KI
p125	(II) oxide, mon-	PtO	211.09	vlt-blk	14.9^{15}	d 550		i	i	s HCl; i a, aq reg
p126	(II) oxide, mon-, dihydrate	$PtO.2H_2O$	247.12			$-2H_2O$, 140–150		i	i	s conc HCl, conc H_2SO_4, conc HNO_3
p127	(IV) oxide, di-	PtO_2	227.03	blk	10.2	450		i	i	i a, aq reg
p128	(IV) oxide, di-, dihydrate	Platinic hydroxide. $PtO_2.2H_2O$ or $Pt(OH)_4$	263.12			$-2H_2O$, 100		i	i	s HCl, aq reg, KOH
p129	(IV) oxide, di-, hydrate	$PtO_2.H_2O$	245.10					i	i	i aq reg, ac a, HCl; sl s NaOH
p130	(IV) oxide, di-, trihydrate	$PtO_2.3H_2O$	281.13	ochre		d 300		i	i	i aq reg, HCl
p131	(IV) oxide, di-, tetrahydrate	Hydroxoplatinic acid. $PtO_2.4H_2O$ or $H_2Pt(OH)_6$	299.15	yel need		$-2H_2O$, 100	$-3H_2O$, 120	i	i	s a, dil alk
p132	(II, IV) oxide,	Pt_3O_4	649.27			d		i	i	i a, aq reg
p133	oxide, sesqui,	$Pt_2O_3.3H_2O$	492.22			$-H_2O$, 100		i	i	s conc H_2SO_4, caust alk
p134	oxide, tri-	PtO_3	243.09	redsh-brn powd						s HCl, H_2SO_3; sl s HNO_3, H_2SO_4
p135	*pyrophosphate*	PtP_2O_7	369.03	grn-yel	4.85	d 600		v sl s		
p136	phosphide	PtP_2	257.04	met shine	9.01_4^{25}	ca 1500		i	i	i a; v sl s aq reg
p137	selenide, di-	$PtSe_2$	353.01	blk or gray cr or amorph	7.65	d when dry				s aq reg; sl s HNO_3, H_2SO_4
p138	selenide, tri-	$PtSe_3$	431.97	bl flakes	7.15	d 140		i	i	i conc a, CS_2; s aq reg
p139	sulfate	$Pt(SO_4)_2.4H_2O$	459.27	yel pl				s	d	s al, eth, a
p140	(IV) sulfide, di-	PtS_2	259.22	blk-brn powd	7.66_4^{25}	d 225–250		i	i	s HCl, HNO_3; i $(NH_4)_2S$
p141	(II) sulfide, mono-	PtS	227.15	blk, tetr	10.04_4^{25}	d		i	i	s $(NH_4)_2$ S; i a, alk
p142	sulfide, sesqui-	Pt_2S_3	486.37	gray (exist ?)	5.52	d		i	i	sl s aq reg; i a
p143	(III) sulfuric acid	$H_2[Pt_2(SO_4)_4(H_2O)_9].9\frac{1}{2}H_2O$	983.62	or, red, tricl		d 150		s	s	d alk
p144	telluride	$PtTe_2$	450.29	gray, hex		1200–1300				sl s Na_2S, $(NH_4)_2S$
	Platinum complexes									
p145	tetramine platinum (II) chloride	$[Pt(NH_3)_4]Cl_2.H_2O$	352.13	col, tetr, 1.672, 1.667	2.737	250, $-H_2O$, 100				
p146	tetramineplatinum (II) chloroplatinite	Magnus, salt. $[Pt(NH_3)_4]PtCl_4$	600.11	grn or red, tetr	<4.1	d		sl s	sl s	
p147	tetrachlorodiammine platinum (IV), *trans-*	$[Pt(NH_3)_2]Cl_4$	370.96		3.3	200–216				
p148	tetrachlorodiammine platinum (IV), *cis-*	$[Pt(NH_3)_2]Cl_4$	370.96	or-yel, rhomb or hexag pl or need		240				
p149	**Plumbous, plumbic**	see Lead								
p150	**Plutonium** α	Pu	242.00	sil wh, monocl	19.84	641	3232			s HCl; i HNO_3, conc H_2SO_4

No.	Name	Synonyms and Formulae	Mol. wt.	Crystalline form, properties and index of refraction	Density or spec. gravity	Melting point, °C	Boiling point, °C	Solubility, in grams per 100 cc		
								Cold water	Hot water	Other solvents
	Plutonium									
p151	β	Pu	239.05	monocl	17.70	stab 122 ± 2 to 206 ± 3				
p152	γ	Pu	239.05	orthorhomb	17.14	stab 206 ± 3 to 319 ± 5				
p153	δ	Pu	239.05	cub	15.92	stab 319 ± 5 to 451 ± 4				
p154	δ'	Pu	239.05	tetrag	16.00	stab 451 ± 4 to 476 ± 5				
p155	ε	Pu	239.05	cub	16.51	stab 476 ± 5 to 639.5 ± 2				
p156	bromide, tri-	$PuBr_3$	481.73	grn, orthorhomb	6.69	681		s		s dil a
p157	chloride, tri-	$PuCl_3$	348.36	emerald grn, hex	5.70	760		s		s dil a
p158	fluoride, hexa-	PuF_6	355.99	redsh-brn, orthorhomb		50.75	62.3	d		
p159	fluoride, tetra-	PuF_4	317.99	pa brn, monocl	7.0 ± 0.2	1037				
p160	fluoride, tri-	PuF_3	299.00	purple, hex	9.32	1425(± 3)		i		
p161	iodide, tri-	PuI_3	622.71	bright grn, orthorhomb	6.92	777		s		
p162	nitride	PuN	256.01	blk, cub	14.25			hydrol		s HCl, H_2SO_2
p163	oxalate	$Pu(C_2O_4)_2.6H_2O$	526.13	yel-grn				i		
p164	oxide, di-	PuO_2	274.00	yelsh-grn, cub	11.46					sl s h conc H_2SO_4, HNO_3, HF
p165	sulfate	$Pu(SO_4)_2$	434.12	light pink						s dil min a
p166	sulfate, tetrahydrate	$Pu(SO_4)_2.4H_2O$	506.18	coral pink		d 280				s dil min a
p167	**Polonium**	Po	210.05	α-Po: simple cub; β-Po: rhbr	9.4 (for β-Po)	254	962	sl s		s dil min a; v sl s dil KOH
p168	ammonium chloride	$(NH_4)_2PoCl_6$	458.85		2.76					
p169	*tetra*bromide	$PoBr_4$	529.67	bright red, cub		330 (in Br atm)	360^{200}			s al, acet; i bz, CCl_4
p170	*di*chloride	$PoCl_2$	280.96	ruby red, orthorhomb	6.50	subl 190				s dil HNO_3
p171	*tetra*chloride	$PoCl_4$	351.86	yel, monocl or tric		300 (in Cl atm)	390	s, d		s HCl; sl s al, acet
p172	*tetra*iodide	PoI_4	717.67	blk cr		200 (in N atm subl)				sl s al, acet; i bz, CCl_4
p173	*di*oxide	PoO_2	242.05	red, tetr		d 500				s dil HCl
p174	selenate	$2PoO_2.SeO_3$	611.06	wh powd		>400				s dil HCl
p175	sulfate, basic	$2PoO_2.SO_3$	564.16	wh powd		>400, d 550				i al; v s dil HCl
p176	*di*sulfate	$Po(SO_4)_2$	402.17	purp		d 550				i al; sl s dil HCl
p177	monosulfide	PoS	242.11	blk		d 275				
p178	**Potassium**	Kalium. K	39.09_8	cub silv met	0.86^{20}	63.65	774	d to KOH	d	d al; s a, Hg, NH_3
p179	acetate	$KC_2H_3O_2$	98.15	wh, lust powd, deliq	1.57^{25}	292		253^{20}	492^{62}	33 al; 24.24¹⁵ MeOH; s liq NH_3; i eth, acet
p180	acetate, acid	$K_2C_2H_3O_2.HC_2H_3O_2$	158.20	col, need or pl, hygr		148	d 200	d	d	s al, acet
p181	acetyl salicylate	$KC_9H_7O_4.2H_2O$	254.29			65				
p182	*meta*aluminate	$K_2Al_2O_4.3H_2O$	250.22	col cr				v s, d	v s, d	s alk; i al
p183	aluminosilicate	Nat. orthoclase. $KAlSi_3O_8$ (or $K_2O.Al_2O_3.6SiO_2$)	278.34	wh, monocl, 1.518, 1.524, 1.526	2.56	ca 1200				
p184	aluminosilicate	Nat. microcline. $KAlSi_3O_8$ (or $K_2O.Al_2O_3.6SiO_2$)	278.34	wh, tricl, 1.522, 1.526, 1.530	2.54–2.57	1140–1300				
p185	aluminosilicate	Nat. muscovite, white mica. $KAl_3Si_3O_{10}$.(OH)₂ (or $K_2O.3Al_2O_3.6SiO_2.2H_2O$)	398.31	col, monocl, 1.551, 1.587, 1.581	2.76–2.80	d		i		
p186	aluminum *meta*silicate	Nat. leucite. $KAlSi_2O_6$	218.25	col cr, 1.508	2.47	1686 ± 5		i	i	d a
p187	aluminum *ortho*silicate	Nat. kaliophilite. $KAlSiO_4$	158.17	col, hex or rhomb (hex→rhomb 1540°) hex: 1.532, 1.572; rhomb: 1.528, 1.536	2.5	ca 1800 (rhomb)				
p188	aluminum sulfate	Nat. kalinite. $KAl(SO_4)_2.12H_2O$	474.39	col, cub, oct or monocl, cub: 1.454, 1.4564; hex: 1.456, 1.429	1.757^{20}_{14}	92.5 −9H₂O, 64.5	−12H₂O, 200	11.4^{20}	v s	i al, acet; s dil a
p189	amide	Potassamide. KNH_2	55.12	col-wh, or yel-grn, hygr		335	subl 400	d	d	d al; s liq NH_3
p190	*peroxy*lammine sulfonate	$(KSO_3)_2NO$	268.39	yel cr, expl				0.62², d	6.6²⁹, d	i al

No.	Name	Synonyms and Formulae	Mol. wt.	Crystalline form, properties and index of refraction	Density or spec. gravity	Melting point, °C	Boiling point, °C	Solubility, in grams per 100 cc		
								Cold water	Hot water	Other solvents
	Potassium									
p191	ammonium tartrate	$KNH_4C_4H_4O_6$	205.21	wh, cr powd				v s		
p192	antimonate, hydroxo-	"Pyro"-antimonate. $KSb(OH)_6.\frac{1}{2}H_2O$	271.90	wh gran or cr powd				2.82^{20}	s	
p193	antimonide	K_3Sb	239.06	yel-grn		812		d		d air
p194	antimony tartrate	$KSbC_4H_4O_7.\frac{1}{2}H_2O$	333.93	col, rhomb, 1.620, 1.636, 1.638	2.607	$-H_2O$, 100		$5.26^{2.7}$	35.7^{100}	i al; 6.67^{25} glyc
p195	orthoarsenate	K_3AsO_4	256.23	col need, deliq		1310		18.87	v s	4 al
p196	orthoarsenate, di-H	KH_2AsO_4	180.04	col, tetr, 1.567, 1.518	2.867	288		19^6	v s	i al; s NH_3, a; 52.5 glyc
p197	ortharsenate, mono H	K_2HAsO_4	218.13	col monocl pr		d 300		18.86^6	s	i al
p198	metaarsenite	$KAsO_2$	146.02	wh powd, hygr				s	s	sl s al
p199	orthoarsenite	K_3AsO_3	240.23	col need				v s	s	s al
p200	metaarsenite, acid	$KH(AsO_2)_2.H_2O$	271.97					s		sl s al
p201	aurate	$KAuO_2.3H_2O$ (or $2H_2O$)	322.11	lt yel need		d		s	d	s al
p202	azide	KN_3	81.12	col, tetr	2.04	350 (vac)		49.6^{17}	105.7^{100}	s al; i eth
p203	benzoate	$KC_7H_5O_2.3H_2O$	214.26	wh cr powd		$-3H_2O$, 110	d	52^{25}	112^{100}	s al
p204	diborane	Diboranidex. $K_2B_2H_6$	105.87	wh, cub cr, 1.493	1.18	subl 400, vac		d		
p205	pentaborate	Pentaboranidex. $K_2B_5H_9$	141.32	wh powd		d <180		s, d	d	
p206	diborane, dihydroxy-	$K_2B_2H_6O_2$	137.87	col, cub cr	1.39	$d \rightarrow K$, 400–500		s, d		s al; d a
p207	metaborate	KBO_2 (or $K_2B_2O_4$)	81.91	col, hex 1.526, 1.450		950		71^{20}	v s	i al, eth
p208	pentaborate	$KB_5O_8.4H_2O$	293.21	col, rhomb		780		0.007^0		
p209	peroxyborate	$KBO_3.\frac{1}{2}H_2O$	106.92	wh cr		$-O_2$, 100	d 150	1.22^0		i al, eth
p210	tetraborate	$K_2B_4O_7.8H_2O$	377.57	col, monocl	1.74 (anhydr)	d		26.7^{20}	v s	
p211	borohydride	KBH_4	53.94	wh, cub, 1.494	1.178	d 500		19.3^{20}	v s	0.25 al; 0.56 MeOH; i eth
p213	boroxalate	$KHC_2O_4.HBO_2.2H_2O$	207.98			$-H_2O$, 110		v s	v s	i, d al
p214	borotartrate	Solution: cream of tartar. $KC_4H_4BO_7$	213.99	wh cr powd	1.832			v s		i al, eth, chl
p215	bromate	$KBrO_3$	167.01	col, trig	$3.27^{17.5}$	434 d 370		13.3^{40}	49.75^{100}	sl s al; i acet
p216	bromide	KBr	119.01	col, cub, sl hygr, 1.559	2.75^{25}	734	1435	53.48^0	102^{100}	0.142 al; sl s eth; s glyc
p217	bromoaurate	$K[AuBr_4]$	555.71	red-brn, rhomb		d 120		sl s		s al
p218	bromoaurate, dihydrate	$K[AuBr_4].2H_2O$	591.74	vlt, monocl cr	4.08			19.5^{15}	204^{67}	s al, KBr; d eth
p219	bromoiodide, di-	$KIBr_2$	325.82	red, rhomb		60	d 180	v s		
p220	hexabromoplatinate	$K_2[PtBr_6]$	752.75	dk red-brn, cub	4.66^{24}	d>400		2.02^{20}	10^{100}	i al
p221	tetrabromoplatinite	$K_2[PtBr_4]$	592.93	br, rhomb				v s	v s	
p222	bromoplatinite, dihydrate	$K_2[PtBr_4].2H_2O$	628.96	blk, rhomb	3.747^{25}_4	$-H_2O$, vac		v s	v s	
p223	bromostannate	$K_2[SnBr_6]$	676.35	wh cr	3.783					
p224	cacodylate	$K[(CN_2)_2AsO_2].H_2O$	194.10	wh cr				s		sl s al; i eth
p225	cadmium cyanide	$K_2[Cd(CN)_4]$	294.68	col, oct	1.846	450		33.3	100^{100}	s al
p226	cadmium iodide	$2KI.CdI_2.2H_2O$	734.25	wh-yelsh cr powd, deliq	3.359			137^{15}		s a, al, eth
p227	calcium chloride	Chlorocalcite. $KCl.CaCl_2$	185.54	col cub, β 1.52		754		s		
p228	calcium magnesium sulfate	Polyhalite. $K_2Ca_2Mg(SO_4)_4.2H_2O$	602.95	wh, trig, 1.548, 1.562, 1.567	2.775					
p228	calcium magnesium sulfate	Krugite $K_2Ca_4Mg(SO_4)_6.2H_2O$	875.24	gray cr	2.801					
p229	calcium sulfate	Kalussite, syngenite. $K_2Ca(SO_4)_2.H_2O$	328.42	col, monocl, 1.500, 1.517, 1.518	2.60	1004		0.25	d	i al; s a
p230	d-camphorate	$K_2C_{10}H_{14}O_4.5H_2O$	366.50	col, need cluster, hygr		$-5H_2O$, 110		260^{14}		s al
p231	carbide	KHC_2	64.13	col, rhomb cr	1.37					
p232	carbonate	K_2CO_3	138.21	col, monocl, hygr, 1.531	2.428^{19}	891	d	112^{20}	156^{100}	i al, acet
p233	peroxycarbonate	$K_2C_2O_6.H_2O$	216.22			200–300		s		
p234	carbonate, dihydrate	$K_2CO_3.2H_2O$	174.24	col, monocl, hygr, 1.380, 1.432, 1.573	2.043	$-H_2O$, 130		146.9	331^{100}	
p235	carbonate, hydrogen	$KHCO_3$	100.12	col, monocl, 1.482	2.17	d 100–200		22.4	60^{60}	i al
p236	carbonate, trihydrate	$2K_2CO_3.3H_2O$	330.47	col, monocl, 1.380, 1.482, 1.573	2.043			129.4	268.3^{100}	i al, conc HN_4OH
p237	carbonyl	$(KCO)_6$	402.68	gray-red		expl		expl		d al
p238	chlorate	$KClO_3$	122.55	col, monocl, 1.409, 1.517, 1.524	2.32	356	d 400	7.1^{20}	57^{100}	14.1^{100} 50 % al; sl s glyc, liq NH_3; i acet; s alk
p239	perchlorate	$KClO_4$	138.55	col, rhomb, 1.4717, 1.4724, 1.476	2.52^{19}	610 ± 10	d 400	0.75^0	21.8^{100}	v sl s al; i eth

No.	Name	Synonyms and Formulae	Mol. wt.	Crystalline form, properties and index of refraction	Density or spec. gravity	Melting point, °C	Boiling point, °C	Solubility, in grams per 100 cc		
								Cold water	Hot water	Other solvents
	Potassium									
p240	chloride............	Nat. sylvite. KCl......	74.56	cub, col 1.490....	1.984	770	subl 1500	34.7²⁰	56.7¹⁰⁰	al s al; s eth, glyc, alk
p241	*hypo*chlorite.......	KClO.............	90.55	in sol only..........		d		v s	v s	
p242	chloroaquoruthenate (III) penta-	K₂[Ru(H₂O)Cl₅].......	374.55	rose pr...........		−H₂O, 200		s	s	sl s al
p243¹	chloroaurate.......	K[AuCl₄]...........	377.88	yel, monocl......	3.75	d 357		61.8²⁰	80.2⁶⁰	25 al; s a
p243²	chloroaurate, dihydrate	K[AuCl₄].2H₂O........	413.91	yel , rhomb pl......				s	s	s al, eth
p244	chlorochromate.....	Peligot's salt. KCrO₃Cl.	174.55	red, monocl......	2.497	d		s, d	....	s a
p245	chlorohydroxo-ruthenate	K₂[Ru(OH)Cl₅].......	373.55	brn-red cr.......		d		s, d	d	i al
p246	chloroiodate (III)...	KICl₄.............	307.82	yel, rhomb........	1.76⁴⁵	d		d	....	d eth
p247	chloroiodide, di-..	KICl₂.............	236.91	col, monocl.......		60	d 215	d	....	
p248	chloroiridate......	K₂[IrCl₆]..........	483.22	blk, cub........	3.546	d		125¹⁹	6.67	i al, KCl, HN₄OH
p249	chloronitrosyl-ruthenate (III) penta-	K₂Ru(NO)Cl₅.......	386.55	dk red, rhomb.....		d		12²⁵	80⁶⁰	i al
p250	chloroösmate (III)...	K₃[OsCl₆].3H₂O........	574.27	dk red cr........		−3H₂O, 150		v s		s a; i eth
p251	chloroösmate (IV)...	K₂OsCl₆..........	481.12	red, cub.........	2.738	d		sl s	s	i al; s dil HCl
p252	chloropalladate.....	K₂[PdCl₆]..........	397.32	red, cub.........	2.738	d		sl s, d	d	i al; sl s HCl
p253	chloropalladite......	K₂PdCl₄..........	326.42	red-brn, tetr (yel cub)	2.67	d 105		s	v s	s KCl, HN₄OH; i al
p254	*hexa*chloroplatinate..	K₂[PtCl₆]..........	486.01	yel, cub, ~ 1.825	3.499²⁴	d 250		0.481²	5.22¹⁰⁰	i al, eth
p255	*tetra*chloroplatinite...	K₂[PtCl₄]..........	415.11	red-brn, tetr, 1.64, 1.67	3.38	d		0.93¹⁶	5.3¹⁰⁰	i al
p256	chloroplumbate.....	K₂[PbCl₆]..........	498.11	lt yel, cub......		d 190		d		s h HCl
p257	chlororhenate (IV)..	K₂ReCl₆..........	477.12	yel-grn, oct......	3.34	0.8	d	d	d alk; sl s HCl
p258	chlororhenate (V)...	K₂ReOCl₅.........	457.67	grn hex pl.......		d		d	d	s a; i al, eth
p259	chlororhodate, hexa-	K₃RhCl₆.3H₂O.......	486.98	red, tricl........	3.291	d		d		sl s al, KCl
p260	chlororhodite, penta-	K₂RhCl₅..........	358.37	red, rhomb......		d		sl s	d	i al
p261	chlororuthenate (IV)	K₂RuCl₆..........	391.99	blk, cub........		d		s, d		i al
p262	chlorostannate.....	K₂SnCl₆..........	409.63	col, cub, 1.657....	2.71			s	s	i al
p263	chlorotellurate......	K₂TeCl₆..........	418.52	pale yel, octa-hedral		d		d	d	s HCl
p264	chromate..........	Nat. tarapacaite. K₂CrO₄	194.20	yel, rhomb, β 1.74	2.732¹⁸	968.3		62.9²⁰	79.2¹⁰⁰	i al
p265	*di*chromate........	K₂Cr₂O₇..........	294.19	red, monocl or tricl, 1.738	2.676²⁵	tricl→ monocl 241.6 m.p. 398	d 500	4.9⁰	102¹⁰⁰	i al
p266	*peroxy*chromate.....	K₃CrO₈..........	297.30	brn-red, cub....		d 170		sl s		i a, al, eth
p267	chromium sulfate....	Potassium chromium alum. K[Cr(SO₄)₂].12H₂O	499.41	vlt-ruby red, cub, oct, 1.4814	1.826²⁵	89	−10H₂O, 100 −12H₂O, 400	24.39²⁵	50	i al; s dil a
p268	chromium chromate, basic	K₂CrO₄.2[Cr(OH).CrO₄]	564.19	vlt brn amorph powd	2.28¹⁴	300		i		i al, acet a
p269	citrate...........	K₃C₆H₅O₇.H₂O......	324.42	wh cr...........	1.98	d 230		167¹⁵	199.7⁸¹	sl s al; s glyc
p270	citrate, monobasic...	KH₂C₆H₅O₇........	230.22	wh cr powd......				s		
p271	cobalt carbonate, hydrogen(ous)	KHCO₃.CoCO₃.4H₂O.	291.12	rose need........				d		
p272	cobalt (II) cyanide..	K₄[Co(CN)₆].......	371.45	redsh-brn cr, deliq	2.039²⁵			v s	v s	d a; i al, eth, CHCl₃
p273	cobalt (III) cyanide..	K₃[CO(CN)₆].........	332.35	wh-yel, monocl pr	1.878²⁵			sl s	sl s	s dil HCl, dil HNO₃; sl s al
p274	cobaltinitrite.......	Fischer's salt. K₃[Co(NO₂)₆]	452.27	yel pr, cub......				0.9¹⁷	d	i al
p275	cobaltinitrite, hydrate	K₃[Co(NO₂)₆].H₂O...	470.29	yel cr powd......				i	s, d	s min a; sl s ac a; i al, eth
p276	cobaltinitrite, hydrate	K₃[Co(NO₂)₆].1½H₂O..	479.30	yel, tetr........		d 200		0.089¹⁷	sl s	i al, meth
p277	cobaltmalonate (II)..	K₂[Co(C₃H₂O₄)₂]......	341.23		2.234					
p278	cobalt sulfate (II)...	K₂SO₄.CoSO₄.6H₂O..	437.36	red pr, monocl, 1.481, 1.487, 1.500	2.218			25.5⁰	108.4⁴⁰	
p279	copperchloride.....	KCl.CuCl₂.........	209.00	red need........	2.86			s	s	i al
p280	cyanate..........	KOCN............	81.12	col, tetrag......	2.056³⁰	d 700–900		75²⁵	s	
p281	cyanide..........	KCN.............	65.12	col, cub, wh gran, deliq, very pois, 1.410	1.52¹⁶	634.5		50	100	0.88¹⁹·⁵ al; 4.91¹⁹·⁵ MeOH; s glyc
p282	cyanoargentate (I).	Potassium argento-cyanide. K[Ag(CN)₂]	199.01	cub, 1.625	2.36			25²⁰	100	4.85 % al; i a
p283	cyanoaurate.......	K[Au(CN)₂].........	288.10	col, rhomb......	3.45			14.3	200	sl s al; i eth
p284	cyanoaurate (III)...	K[Au(CN)₄].1½H₂O...	367.16	col tabl........		d 200		s	v s	s al

No.	Name	Synonyms and Formulae	Mol. wt.	Crystalline form, properties and index of refraction	Density or spec. gravity	Melting point, °C	Boiling point, °C	Solubility, in grams per 100 cc		
								Cold water	Hot water	Other solvents
	Potassium									
p285	cyanocadmate	$K_2[Cd(CN)_4]$	294.68	col, cub	1.85			33	100^{100}	sl s al
p286	cyanochromate (III)	$K_3[Cr(CN)_6]$	325.41	yel, rhomb	1.71			30.9^{20}		i al
p287	cyanocobaltate (II)	$K_4[Co(CN)_6]$	371.42					s	s	i al, eth
p288	cyanocobaltate (III)	$K_3[Co(CN)_6]$	332.32	yel, monocl	1.906	d		s	s	i al; sl s NH₃
p289	cyanocuprate (I)	$K_3[Cu(CN)_4]$	284.92	col, rhbdr		d		v s		
p290	cyanomanganate (II)	$K_4[Mn(CN)_6].3H_2O$	421.50	deep bl, tetr				s	d	
p291	cyanomanganate (III)	$K_3[Mn(CN)_6]$	328.35	red, rhomb, 1.553, 1.555, 1.571 (Li)				s		
p292	cyanomercurate	$K_2[Hg(CN)_4]$	382.87	col, cr pois				s		s al
p293	cyanomolybdate	$K_4[Mo(CN)_8].2H_2O$	496.52	yel, rhomb	2.337$^{25}_4$ (anhyd)	−H₂O, 105−110		v s	v s	i eth; 0.0017^{20} al
p294	cyanonickelate (II)	$K_2[Ni(CN)_4].H_2O$	259.00	red-yel, monocl cr or powd	1.875^{11}	−H₂O, 100		s		d a
p295	cyanoosmite	$K_4[Os(CN)_6].6H_2O$	556.76	col, yel, monocl, β 1.607	d			sl s	s	i al, eth
p296	cyanoplatinite	$K_2[Pt(CN)_4].3H_2O$	431.10	col, yel, rhomb, blue fluor, deliq	2.455^{16}	−3H₂O, 100	d 400−600	sl s	s	sl s al, eth, H₂SO₄
p297	cyanotungstate (IV)	$K_4[W(CN)_8].2H_2O$	584.43	lt yel- grn cr powd	1.989$^{25}_4$ (anhydr)	−2H₂O, 115		130^{18}	s	i al, eth
p298	ethylsulfate	$KC_2H_5SO_4$	164.23	wh, monocl	1.843			s		s al
p299	ferricyanide	$K_3Fe(CN)_6$	329.26	red, monocl, 1.566, 1.569, 1.583	1.85^{25}	d		33^4	77.5^{100}	i al; s acet
p300	ferrocyanide	Yellow prussate of potash. $K_4Fe(CN)_6.3H_2O$	422.41	lem yel, monocl, β 1.577	1.85^{17}	−3H₂O, 70	d	27.8^{12} anhydr 14.5^0	90.6$^{96.3}$ anhydr 74^{96}	s acet; i al, eth, NH₃
p301	fluoberyllate	K_2BeF_4	163.21	col, rhomb		red heat		2^{20}	5.26^{100}	
p302	fluoborate	Nat. avogadrite. KBF_4	125.91	col, rhomb or cub, 1.324, 1.325, 1.325	2.498^{20}	d 350	d	0.44^{20}	6.27^{100}	sl s al, eth; i alk
p303	fluogermanate	K_2GeF_6	264.78	wh, hex		730	ca 835	0.542^{18}	2.58^{130}	
p304	fluomanganate (IV)	K_2MnF_6	247.13	yel, hex, tab		d	d	d	d	s conc HCl
p305	fluoniobate, penta-	Potassium oxyniobate. $K_2NbOF_5.H_2O$	300.12	col, monocl pl or leaf				7.69	s	s d conc HF
p306	fluorescein deriv	$K_2C_{20}H_{10}O_5$	408.50	yelsh-red powd						
p307	fluoride	KF	58.10	col, cub deliq, 1.363	2.48	.858	1505	92.3^{18}	v s	s HF, NH₃; i al
p308	fluoride, acid	KHF_2	78.11	col, cub, deliq	2.37	d ca 225	d	41^{21}	v s	s KC₂H₃O₂; i al
p309	fluoride, dihydrate	$KF.2H_2O$	94.13	col, monocl pr, deliq, 1.352	2.454	41	156	349.3^{18}	v s	s HF; i al
p310	hexafluorophosphate	KPF_6	184.07			ca 575	d	9.3^{25}	20.6^{50}	
p311	fluorotungstate	$2KF.WO_2F_2.H_2O$	388.06	monocl		−H₂O, red heat		6^{17}	s	
p312	fluosilicate	Nat, hieratite. K_2SiF_6	220.25	col, cub or hex 1.3991	hex 3.08 cub 2.665^{17}	d		0.12$^{17.5}$ 6.9^{19}	0.954^{100}	s HCl; i NH₃; v sl s al
p313	fluostannate	$K_2SnF_6.H_2O$	328.90	monocl pr	3.053			3.7^{18}	33.3^{100}	i al, NH₃
p314	fluosulfonate	$KFSO_3$	138.16	short, thick pr		311		6.9^{19}		
p315	fluotantalate	K_2TaF_7	392.14	col, rhomb	4.56; 5.24			sl s, d		sl s HF
p316	fluotellurate, di-	$K_2TeO_2F_3.3H_2O$	345.84	micros oct, monocl		d		sl s	sl s	s HF
p317	fluothorate	$K_2ThF_6.4H_2O$	496.29	col		d		2.15	6.6	d a; i al
p318	fluotitanate	$K_2TiF_6.H_2O$	258.11	col, monocl lust leaf		−H₂O, 32 m.p. 780	d	0.556^0	1.27^{21}	sl s min a; i NH₃
p319	fluozirconate	K_2ZrF_6	283.41	col, monocl, 1.466, 1.455	3.48			0.781^2	25^{100}	i NH₃
p320	formate	$KCHO_2$	84.12	col, rhomb deliq	1.91	167.5	d	331^{18}	657^{80}	s al; i eth
p321	gadolinium sulfate	$K_2SO_4.Gd_2(SO_4)_3.2H_2O$	812.98	cr	3.503^{16}			s		s K₂SO₄
p322	gallium sulfate	$KGa(SO_4)_2.12H_2O$	517.13	col cr	1.805			s		
p323	digermanate	$K_2Ge_2O_5$	303.38	wh cr	4.31$^{21.5}$	>83		s	s a
p324	metagermanate	K_2GeO_3	198.79	wh cr	3.40$^{21.5}$	823		s	s a
p325	tetragermanate	$K_2Ge_4O_9$	512.55	wh cr	4.12$^{21.5}$	1083		s	s a
p326	glycerophosphate	$K_2C_3H_7PO_6$	248.26	col-sl yelsh mass, hygr				v s	v s	s al
p327	hydride	KH	40.11	wh need 1.453	1.47	d		d	d	i CS₂, eth, bz
p328	hydroxide	KOH	56.11	wh, rhomb deliq	2.044	360.4 ± 0.7	1320−1324	107^{15}	178^{100}	v s al; i eth, NH₃
p329	(tri-)hydroxyl- ammine trisulfonate	$(KSO_3)_3.NO.1\frac{1}{2}H_2O$	414.52	col, monocl pr		−H₂O, 100−200		4^{18}	sl d	
p330	hexahydroxyplatinate	$K_2[Pt(OH)_6]$	375.34	yel, rhomb	5.18	d 160		s	s	i al
p331	imidosulfonate	$(KSO_3)_2NH$	253.34	col, monocl	2.515	d 170−180	d 360−440, vac	1.3^{22}	d	i HNO₃
p332	iodate	KIO_3	214.00	col, monocl	3.93$^{22}_4$	560	d>100	4.74^0	32.3^{100}	s KI; i al, NH₃
p333	iodate, acid	$KIO_3.HIO_3$	389.92	col, monocl				1.33^{18}		i al

No.	Name	Synonyms and Formulae	Mol. wt.	Crystalline form, properties and index of refraction	Density or spec. gravity	Melting point, °C	Boiling point, °C	Solubility, in grams per 100 cc		
								Cold water	Hot water	Other solvents
	Potassium									
p334	iodate, acid	$KIO_3.2HIO_3$	565.83	col, tricl				4.15		
p335	*meta*periodate	KIO_4	230.00	col, tetr, 1.6205	3.618_4^{15}	582	$-O$, 300	0.66^{13}	s	v sl s KOH
p336	iodide	KI	166.01	col or wh, cub or gran, 1.677	3.13	681	1330	127.5^0	208^{100}	1.88^{25} al; 1.31^{25} acet; sl s eth; s NH_3
p337	iodide, tri-	$KI_3.\frac{1}{2}H_2O$	428.82	dk bl, monocl, deliq	3.498	31	d 225	v s		s al, KI
p338	iodoaurate	$KAuI_4$	743.69	blk lust cr		d 150		s, d		s dil KI sol
p339	iodoiridite	K_3IrI_6	1070.93	gr cr		d		i	i	i al
p340	iodomercurate (II) tetra-	K_2HgI_4 (or $KI.HgI_2$)	786.41	yel cr, deliq				v s		i al
p341	iodomercurate (II) tri-	Potassium mercury iodide. $KHgI_3$ (or $KI.HgI_2$)	620.47	yel pr, deliq		105		v s		341^{34} al; s KI sol, ac a, eth
p342	iodoplatinate	K_2PtI_6	1034.72	blk, rect	4.96_4^{25}			s	s, d	i al
p343	iridium chloride	Potassium hexachloro iridate. K_2IrCl_6	483.12	redsh-blk, cub	3.549	d		1.12^{20}	s	i al
p344	iridium oxalate	$K_3[Ir(C_2O_4)_3].4H_2O$	645.63	orange, tricl cr	2.510^{19}	$-H_2O$, 120	d 160	s	v s	i al, eth
p345	iron chloride, (III)	Nat. erythrosiderite. $2KCl.FeCl_3.H_2O$	329.33	red, orthorhomb	2.372					
p346	iron chloride (II)	Rinneite. $3KCl.NaCl.FeCl_2$	408.86	rhbdr, 1.589, 1.590	2.3					
p347	iron (III) oxalate	$K_3Fe(C_2O_4)_3.3H_2O$	491.26	emerald grn, monocl, 1.5019, 1.5558, 1.5960	2.133_4^{20}	$-3H_2O$, 100	d 230	4.7^0	118^{100}	i al
p348	iron sulfate (III)	$KFe(SO_4)_2.12H_2O$	599.32	vlt, cub oct, 1.452	1.83	33		$20^{12.5}$	v s	i al
p349	iron sulfate (III)	Nat. krausite. $K_2SO_4.Fe_2(SO_4)_3.24H_2O$	1006.51	pa yel-grn, monocl, 1.482	1.806	28	d 33			
p350	iron sulfate (II)	$K_2SO_4.FeSO_4.6H_2O$	434.27	grn pr, monocl, 1.476, 1.482, 1.497	2.169	d		s		
p351	iron sulfide	$KFeS_2$	159.08	purp, hex	2.563			d		
p352	lactate	$KC_3H_5O_3.xH_2O$		amorph				s		s al; i eth
p353	laurate	$KC_{12}H_{23}O_2$	238.42	amorph				4.5^{18} al		
p354	laurate, acid (mixt.)	$KC_{12}H_{23}O_2.C_{12}H_{24}O_2$	438.74	wh, wax like sol		160		$0.904^{12.5}$ al		
p355	lead chloride	Nat. pseudocotunnite. $2KCl.PbCl_2$	427.21	yel		490		s		
p356	magnesium carbonate, hydrogen	$KHCO_3.MgCO_3.4H_2O$	256.50	col, tricl or rhomb	2.98			d		
p357	magnesium chloride	Nat. carnalite. $KCl.MgCl_2.6H_2O$	277.86	col, rhomb, deliq, 1.466, 1.475, 1.494	1.61	265		64.5^{19}	d	d al
p358	magnesium chloride sulfate	Nat. kainite. $KCl.MgSO_4.3H_2O$	248.98	col, monocl	2.131			79.56^{18}		i al, eth
p359	magnesium chromate	$K_2CrO_4.MgCrO_4.2H_2O$	370.53	tricl	2.59					
p360	magnesium phosphate, hexahydrate	$KMgPO_4.6H_2O$	266.48	wh, rhomb cr		$-5H_2O$, 110		d		
p361	magnesium selenate	$K_2SeO_4.MgSeO_4.6H_2O$	496.52	col, monocl, 1.497, 1.499, 1.514	2.3645_4^{20}	$-2H_2O$, 33		s	s	
p362	magnesium sulfate	Nat. langbeinite. $K_2SO_4.2MgSO_4$	415.01	tetrah	2.829	927				
p363	magnesium sulfate	Nat. leonite. $K_2SO_4.MgSO_4.4H_2O$	366.70	col, monocl, 1.483, 1.487, 1.490	2.201^{20}			v s		
p364	magnesium sulfate	$K_2SO_4.MgSO_4.6H_2O$	402.73	col, monocl, 1.461, 1.463, 1.476	2.15	d 72		19.26^0 25^{20}	59.8^{75}	
p365	malate	$K_2C_4H_4O_5$	210.28	col, viscid mass				s		
p366	manganate	K_2MnO_4	197.14	grn, rhomb		d 190		d	d	s KOH
p367	*per*manganate	$KMnO_4$	158.04	purple rhomb, 1.59	2.703	d < 240		6.38^{20}	25^{65}	d al; v s MeOH, acet; s H_2SO_4
p368	manganese chloride(ous)	Chloromanganokalite. $4KCl.MnCl_2$	424.06	trig. 1.50	2.31			s	s	
p369	manganese sulfate(ic)	$KMn(SO_4)_2.12H_2O$	502.35	vlt, cub, (oct)				d		
p370	manganese sulfate(ous)	Manganolongbeinite. $K_2SO_4.2MnSO_4$	476.20	rose, tetrah, 1.572	3.02	850				
p371	mercury tartrate(ous)	$KHgC_4O_6$	387.76	wh cr powd				i		i al
p372	methionate	Potassium methanedisulfonate. $K_2CH_2(SO_3)_2$	252.36	monocl, β 1.539	2.376			s		
p373	methylsulfate	$2KCH_3SO_4.H_2O$	318.41	wh cr				s		s al

No.	Name	Synonyms and Formulae	Mol. wt.	Crystalline form, properties and index of refraction	Density or spec. gravity	Melting point, °C	Boiling point, °C	Cold water	Hot water	Other solvents
	Potassium									
p374	molybdate	K_2MoO_4	238.14	wh powd or 4-sid pr, deliq	2.91^{18}	919	d 1400	184.6^{25}	v s	i al
p375	permolybdate	$K_2O.3MoO_4.3H_2O$	596.06	lt yel cr, monocl		d 180		sl s	s	v sl s al
p376	trimolybdate	$K_2O.3MoO_4.3H_2O$	580.06	wh need		571 (anhydr)		0.22^{15}	s	
p377	molybdenum cyanate	$K_4[Mo(CN)_8].2H_2O$	496.52	yel, rhomb	2.337^{25}_4 (anhydr)	$-2H_2O$, 105–110		v s	v s	0.0017^{20} abs al; i eth; d HCl, H_2SO_4
p378	myristate, acid (mixt)	$KC_{14}H_{27}O_2.C_{14}H_{28}O_2$	494.85	wh, waxlike sol		153				$0.453^{13.5}$ al
p379	naphthalene—1,5-disulfonate	$K_2C_{10}H_6(SO_2)_2.2H_2O$	400.53	monocl, 1.485, 1.669, 1.697	1.797			s		
p380	nickelsulfate	$K_2SO_4.NiSO_4.6H_2O$	437.13	bl, monocl, 1.484, 1.492, 1.505	2.124	d < 100		7^0	60.8^{75}	
p381	nitrate	Saltpeter. KNO_3	101.11	col, rhomb or trig, 1.335, 1.5056, 1.5064	2.109^{16}	tr-trig 129 m.p. 334	d 400	13.3^0	247^{100}	i dil al, eth; s liq NH_3, glyc
p382	nitride	K_3N	131.31	grnsh-blk		d		d		
p383	nitrite	KNO_2	85.11	wh-yelsh pr, deliq	1.915	440	d	281^0	413^{100}	s hot al; v s liq NH_3
p384	m-nitrophenoxide	$KOC_6H_4NO_2.2H_2O$	213.24	flat or need	1.691^{20}	$-H_2O$, 130 d		16.3^{15}		s al
p385	p-nitrophenoxide	$KOC_6H_4NO_2.2H_2O$	213.24	yel leaf	1.652^{20}	$-2H_2O$, 130 d		7.5^{15}		sl s al
p386	nitroplatinite	$K_2Pt(NO_2)_4$	457.32	col, monocl				3.8^{15}	s	
p387	nitroprusside	$K_2[Fe(NO)(CN)_5].2H_2O$	330.18	red, monocl, hygr				100^{16}		s al
p388	nitrososulfate	$K_2SO_4(NO)_2$	218.28	col need		d 127, expl		$12^{14.5}$, d		i al
p389	oleate	$KC_{18}H_{33}O_2$	320.56	yelsh or brnsh soft mass or cr, 1.452				25	s	$4.315^{13.5}$ al; 100^{60} al; 3.5^{25} eth
p390	oleate, acid (mixt)	$KC_{18}H_{33}O_2.C_{18}H_{34}O_2$	603.03	wh, wax-like solid		95		s	s	$5.2^{13.5}$ al
p391	osmate	$K_2OsO_4.2H_2O$	368.43	vlt, cub, hygr		$-H_2O$, >100		sl s	s, d	i al, eth
p392	osmiumchloride	K_2OsCl_6	481.12	blk, oct	3.42^{16}	d 600		s	s	i al; s HCl
p393	osmylchloride	$K_2OsO_2Cl_4$	442.21	red, tetr	3.42	d 200 (in H atm)		s	s	
p394	osmyloxalate	$K_2[OsO_2(C_2O_4)_2].2H_2O$	512.47	brn need, tricl		$-H_2O$, 80	d 180	0.75^{15}	3.0^{15}	
p395	oxalate	$K_2C_2O_4.H_2O$	184.24	wh, monocl, 1.440, 1.485, 1.550	$2.127^{3.9}$	$-H_2O$, 100			33^{16}	
p396	oxalate, hydrogen	KHC_2O_4	128.11	col, monocl, 1.382, 1.553, 1.573	2.044	d		2.5	16.7^{100}	i al, eth
p396	oxalate, hydrogen, monohydrate	$KHC_2O_4.H_2O$	146.13	rhomb	$2.044^{3.9}$					
p398	oxalate, tetra-	$KHC_2O_4.H_2C_2O_4.2H_2O$	254.20	col, tricl, 1.415, 1.536, 1.560	1.836	d		1.8^{13}		d al
p399	oxaloferrate (II)	$K_2[Fe(C_2O_4)_2].2H_2O$	346.12	gold need		d		s	s	
p400	oxaloferrate (II)	$K_2[Fe(C_2O_4)_2].2\frac{1}{2}H_2O$	316.03	br cr		d		92^{21}	d	i al
p401	oxaloferrate (III)	$K_3[Fe(C_2O_4)_3].3H_2O$	491.25	grn, monocl		$-3H_2O$, 100	d 230	4.7^0	117.7^{100}	i al, NH_3; s acet
p402	oxalatoplatinate	$K_2[Pt(C_2O_4)_2].2H_2O$	485.36	col, monocl pr	3.04^{12}	$-H_2O$, 100		sl s	s	
p403	oxalatouranate (IV)	$K_4[U(C_2O_4)_4].5H_2O$	836.59	yel, monocl	2.563					
p404	oxide, mon-	K_2O	94.20	col, cub, hygr	2.32^0	d 350		v s	v s	s al, eth
p405	peroxide	K_2O_2	110.20	wh, amorph, deliq		490	d			
p406	oxide, super-	KO_2	71.10	yel, cub leaf	2.14	380	d	v s, d		d al
p407	oxide, tri- (sesqui-)	K_2O_3	126.20	red		430		ev O_2		d dil H_2SO_4
p408	palladium chloride	$K_2(PdCl_4)$	326.42	yel-grnsh-br cr, tetr, 1.710, 1.523	2.67	524		s	s	sl s^{80} al
p409	palladium chloride	$K_2(PdCl_6)$	397.32	lt red, oct	2.738	d 170		v sl s	sl s	s HCl; i al
p110	palladium oxalate	$K_2[Pd(C_2O_4)_2].4H_2O$	432.71	yel need		dec in air, $-4H_2O$, 80		0.833^{27}	$9.98^{52.9}$	
p411	palmitate, acid (mixt)	$KC_{16}H_{31}O_2.C_{16}H_{32}O_2$	550.96	wh, fatty sol		138				0.198^{13} al
p412	1-phenol 2-sulfonate (o-)	$KC_6H_4(OH)SO_3.H_2O$	230.29	rhomb, 1.527, 1.568, 1.647	1.87	400		s		s al
p413	1-phenol-4-sulfonate (p-)	$KC_6H_4(OH)SO_3$	212.27	rhomb, 1.571, 1.608, 1.694	1.87	>260		s		
p414	phenylsulfate	$KC_6H_5SO_4$	212.27	rhomb leaf		d 150–160	d	14^{15}		v sl s al
p415	metaphosphate, hexa-	$(KPO_3)_6$	708.44	col mass, hygr	2.107	810	1320	s	s	i al
p416	metaphosphate, tetra-	$(KPO_3)_4.2H_2O$	508.33	col cr		$-2H_2O$, 100		100^{15}	s	
p417	orthophosphate	K_3PO_4	212.28	col, rhomb, deliq	2.564^{17}	1340		90^{20}	s	i al
p418	orthophosphate, di-H	KH_2PO_4	136.09	col, tetr, deliq, 1.510, 1.4864	2.338	252.6		33^{25}	83.5^{90}	i al
p419	orthophosphate, mono-H	K_2HPO_4	174.18	wh, amorph, deliq		d		167^{20}	v s	v s al
p420	pyrophosphate	$K_4P_2O_7.3H_2O$	384.40	col, deliq	2.33	$-2H_2O$, 180	$-3H_2O$, 300	s	v s	i al
p421	subphosphate	$K_4P_2O_6.4H_2O$	229.24	col, rhomb		40	$4H_2O$, 150	v s	v s	

No.	Name	Synonyms and Formulae	Mol. wt.	Crystalline form, properties and index of refraction	Density or spec. gravity	Melting point, °C	Boiling point, °C	Solubility, in grams per 100 cc		
								Cold water	Hot water	Other solvents
	Potassium									
p422	*hypo*phosphite	KH_2PO_2	104.09	wh, hex, deliq		d		200^{25}	330	v sl s abs al, NH_3; i eth; 11.1^{25} chl
p423	*ortho*phosphite, di-H.	KH_2PO_3	120.09	wh cr, deliq		d		220^{20}	v s	i al
p424	phthalate, hydrogen	$KHC_8H_4O_4$	204.23	col, rhomb	1.636			10^{25}	33^{100}	
p425	picrate	$KC_6H_2N_3O_7$	267.20	yel-redsh or grnsh, rhomb, 1.527, 1.903, 1.952	1.852	expl 310		0.5^{15}	25^{100}	0.184^{25} al
p426	piperate	$KC_{12}H_9O_4$	256.31	lt yel cr powd				sl s	v s	
p427	platinate, hydroxo-	$K_2Pt(OH)_6$	375.34	yel, rhomb		d 160		s		i al
p428	platinorhodanide	$K_2[Pt(CNS)_6].2H_2O$	657.82	red, rhomb				s	8^{60}	s h al
p429	platinum iodide, hexa-	K_2PtI_6	1034.72	blk, cub	4.963^{25}_4			s		sl s al
p430	plumbate, hydroxo-	$K_2Pb(OH)_6$	387.44	col, rhomb		d	d			s KOH
p431	praseodymium sulfate	$3K_2SO_4.Pr_2(SO_4)_3.H_2O$	1110.81	cr	3.275^{16}			sl s		s HCl, HNO_3
p432	propionate	$KC_3H_5O_2.H_2O$	130.19	wh cr, hygr, or wh leaf, deliq		$-H_2O$, 120		207^{15}	359	22.2^{13} 95 % al
p433	propyl sulfate	$KC_3H_7SO_4$	178.25	wh cr powd				v s		
p434	*per*rhenate	$KReO_4$	289.30	wh, tetr, 1.643	4.887	550	1360–1370	1.21^{20}	14.0^{100}	v sl s al
p435	rhenium (IV) chloride	$K_2[ReCl_6]$	477.12	yel-grn cr, oct	3.34	d		s	s	s a; i conc H_2SO_4; d h H_2SO_4
p437	rhenium (V) oxychloride	$K_2[ReOCl_4]$	457.67	yel-grn cr, rhomb or monocl, 1.52				s		sl s HCl; H_2SO_4; i al, eth
p438	rhenium oxycyanide	$K_3[ReO_2(CN)_4]$	439.58	red cr, monocl	2.70^{25}_4	d 300–400, vac		s	s	v sl s al; i alk
p439	rhodium cyanide	$K_3[Rh(CN)_6]$	376.32	pa yel, monocl, 1.5498, 1.5513, 1.5634				v s	v s	
p440	rhodium oxalate	$K_3[Rh(C_2O_4)_3].4\frac{1}{2}H_2O$	565.34	col, tricl	2.171^{20}_4	$-4\frac{1}{2}H_2O$, 190		v s	v s	
p441	rhodium sulfate	$KRh(SO_4)_2.12H_2O$	646.38	yel, cub	2.23			s		
p442	ruthenate	$K_2RuO_4.H_2O$	261.29	blk, tetr		$-H_2O$, 200	d 400 vac	v s	d	d a, al
p443	*per*ruthenate	$KRuO_4$	204.17	blk, tetr		d 44		sl s	s, d	
p444	d-saccharate, acid	$KHC_6H_9O_8$	248.24	rhomb need				1.1^6	s	
p445	salicylate	$KC_7H_5O_3$	176.22	wh powd				s		s al
p446	santoninate	$KC_{15}H_{19}O_4$	302.42	wh cr powd, deliq				s		s al
p447	selenate	K_2SeO_4	221.16	col, rhomb, hygr, 1.535, 1.539, 1.545	3.066			110.5^0	122.2^{100}	
p448	selenide	K_2Se	157.16	wh cub, reddens in air, hygr	2.851^{15}			s d	s	
p449	selenite	K_2SeO_3	205.16	wh, deliq		d 875		s		sl s al
p450	selenocyanate	$KSeCN$	144.08	need, deliq	2.347	d 100		s	s	d a; s al
p451	selenocyanoplatinate	$K_2Pt(SeCN)_6$	903.16	rhomb	$3.378^{12.5}$	d 80		s		
p452	selenothionate	$K_2SeS_2O_6$	317.29	col, monocl pr		d 250		s, d		
p453	*di*silicate	$K_2Si_2O_5$	214.37	col, rhomb, 1.502, 1.513	2.456^{25}_4	1015 ± 10		s	s	
p454	*meta*silicate	K_2SiO_3	154.29	col, rhomb (?), 1.520, 1.528		976		s	s	i al
p455	*tetra*silicate	$K_2Si_4O_9.H_2O$	352.56	wh, rhomb, α 1.495, β 1.535	2.417	d 400		s	s	i al
p456	*di*silicate, hydrogen	$KHSi_2O_5$	176.28	wh, rhomb, 1.480, 1.530	2.417^{15}_4	515				d HCl
p457	silicotungstate	$K_4SiW_{12}O_{40}.18H_2O$	3354.95	col, hex		$-17H_2O$, 100		33.3^{20}	v s	v s acet; s MeOH; sl s al; eth, bz
p458	silver carbonate	$KAgCO_3$	206.98	rect pl	3.769	d		d	d	
p459	silver nitrate	$KNO_3.AgNO_3$	270.98	monocl	3.219	125		v s	v s	
p460	sodium antimony tartrate	$KNaSbC_4H_2O_7$	346.97	wh, scales or powd				s		
p461	sodium carbonate	$KNaCO_3.6H_2O$	230.19	monocl, hygr, effl	$1.61-1.63^{14}$	$-6H_2O$, 100		185.2^{15}		
p462	sodium ferricyanide	$K_2Na[Fe(CN)_6]$	313.15	or-red, monocl		d		50^{25}	80^{60}	
p463	sodium nitrocobaltate (III)	$K_2Na[Co(NO_2)_6].H_2O$	454.18	yel cr	1.633	135		0.07^{25}		i al
p464	sodium sulfate	$3K_2SO_4.Na_2SO_4$	664.84	col, rhbdr	2.7			s	s	
p465	sodium tartrate	Rochelle salt, seignette salt. $KNaC_4H_4O_6.4H_2O$	282.23	col, rhomb, 1.492, 1.493, 1.496	1.790	70–80	$-4H_2O$, 215	26^0	66^{26}	v sl s al
p466	sorbate	$KC_6H_7O_2$	150.22	col cr	1.363^{25}_{20}	d 270		58.5^{25}		sl s MeOH

No.	Name	Synonyms and Formulae	Mol. wt.	Crystalline form, properties and index of refraction	Density or spec. gravity	Melting point, °C	Boiling point, °C	Solubility, in grams per 100 cc		
								Cold water	Hot water	Other solvents
	Potassium									
p467	stannate, hydroxo-	$K_2Sn(OH)_6$	298.94	col, trig	3.197			85^{10}	110.5^{20}	sl s KOH; i al, acet
p468	stearate	$KC_{18}H_{35}O_2$	322.58	wh cr powd					s	$0.145^{13.5}$ al; i eth, chl, CS_2
p469	stearate, acid (mixt)	$KC_{18}H_{35}O_2.C_{18}H_{36}O_2$	607.07	wh powd		153		s	s	$0.091^{13.5}$ al
p470	strontium chromium oxalate(ic)	$KSrCr(C_2O_4)_3.6H_2O$	550.87	grnsh blk cr	2.155^{13}					
p471	styphnate	$KC_6H_2N_3O_8.H_2O$	301.22	yel, monocl pr		$-H_2O$, 120	expl	1.54^{20}		v sl s al
p472	succinate	$K_2C_4H_4O_4.3H_2O$	248.32	rhomb, hygr	1.564			s		
p473	succinate, hydrogen	$KHC_4H_4O_4$	156.18	monocl	1.767	d 242				
p474	succinate, hydrogen, dihydrate	$KHC_4H_4O_4.2H_2O$	192.21	rhomb, 1.417, 1.530, 1.533	1.616			s		s al
p475	succinate, hydrogen	$KHC_4H_4O_4.C_4H_6O_4$	274.27	monocl	1.56	162				
p476	sulfate	Nat. arcanite. K_2SO_4	174.27	col, rhomb or hex, 1.494, 1.495, 1.497	2.662	tr 588 m. p. 1069	1689	12^{25}	24.1^{100}	i al, acet, CS_2
p477	peroxydisulfate	$K_2S_2O_8$	270.33	col, tricl, 1.461, 1.467, 1.566	2.477	d <100		1.75^0	5.3^{20}	i al
p478	pyrosulfate	$K_2S_2O_7$	254.33	col, need	2.512_4^{25}	>300	d	s	d	
p479	sulfate, hydrogen	Nat. mercallite, misenite. $KHSO_4$	136.17	col, rhomb, deliq 1.480	2.322	214	d	36.3^0	121.6^{100}	i al, acet
p480	sulfide, di-	K_2S_2	142.33	red-yel cr		470		s	d	s al
p481	sulfide, hydro-	KHS	72.17	yel, rhomb deliq	1.68–1.70	455		d	d	s al
p482	sulfide, mono-	K_2S	110.27	yel-br, cub, deliq	1.805^{14}	840		s	v s	s al, glyc; i eth
p483	sulfide, mono-, pentahydrate	$K_2S.5H_2O$	200.34	col, rhomb		60	$-3H_2O$, 150	s		s al, glyc; i eth
p484	sulfide, penta-	K_2S_5	238.52	or cr, hygr		206	d 300	v s	v s	sl s al
p485	sulfide, tetra-	K_2S_4	206.46	red-brn cr		145	d 850	s	s	s al
p486	sulfide, tetra-dihydrate	$K_2S_4.2H_2O$	242.49	yel				s	s	sl s al
p487	sulfide, tri-	K_2S_3	174.40	br-yel cr		252		s	d	s al
p488	sulfide, di-, trihydrate	$K_2S_2.3H_2O$	196.38	yel				v s	v s	s al
p489	sulfite	$K_2SO_3.2H_2O$	194.30	wh-yelsh, hex		d		100	<100	sl s al; i NH_3; d dil a
p490	pyrosulfite	Potassium metabisulphite. $K_2S_2O_5$	222.33	col, monocl pl	2.34	d 190		sl s		sl s al; i eth
p491	sulfite, hydrogen	$KHSO_3$	120.17	col cr		d 190		s	s	i al
p492	d-tartrate	$K_2C_4H_4O_6.\frac{1}{2}H_2O$	235.28	col, monocl, β 1.526	1.98_4^{20}	$-H_2O$, 155	d 200–220	150^{14}	278^{100}	sl s al
p493	dl-tartrate	$K_2C_4H_4O_6.2H_2O$	262.31	col, monocl	1.984	$-2H_2O$, 100		100^{25}		s a
p494	d-tartrate, hydrogen	$KHC_4H_4O_6$	188.18	col, rhomb, 1.511, 1.550, 1.590	1.984^{16}			0.37	6.1^{100}	s a, alk; i al, ac s
p495	dl-tartrate, hydrogen	$KHC_4H_4O_6$	188.18	col, monocl	1.954			0.42^{15}	7.0^{100}	i al; s min a
p496	metatellurate	K_2TeO_4	269.80	soft glutinous mass		d 200		d		i al; sl s KOH
p497	orthotellurate	$K_2H_4TeO_6.3H_2O$	359.88	col, rhomb, deliq		$-H_2O$	$-O$, 300	sl s	s	i al; sl s KOH
p498	telluride	K_2Te	205.80	col, cub, hygr	2.51			s, d	s	
p499	tellurite	K_2TeO_3	253.80	wh cr, deliq		d 460–470		v s	v s	s h K_2CO_3, KOH
p500	tellurium chloride	K_2TeCl_6	418.52	yel, oct, hygr	2.645			s d,		s, d al; s dil HCl
p501	thioantimonate	$2K_3SbS_4.4\frac{1}{2}H_2O$	815.68	yel cr, deliq				300^0	400^{80}	i al
p502	thioarsenate	K_3AsS_4	320.48	wh cr, deliq			d	v s		i al
p503	thioarsenite	K_3AsS_3	288.42			d		s		i al
p504	thiocarbonate, tri-	K_2CS_3	186.41	yel-red-brn cr, deliq		d		v s	s	s NH_3; sl s al; i eth
p505	thiocyanate	$KNCS$	97.18	col, rhomb pr, deliq	1.886^{14}	173.2	d 500	177.2^0	217^{20}	s al; 20.75^{22} acet; 0.18^{13} amyl al; v s liq NH_3
p506	dithionate	$K_2S_2O_6$	238.32	col, trig, 1.455, 1.515	2.278	d		6	66^{100}	i al
p507	pentathionate	$K_2S_5O_6.1\frac{1}{2}H_2O$	361.55	col, rhomb, -1.63	2.113	d		s	d	i al
p508	tetrathionate	$K_2S_4O_6$	302.46	col, monocl, 1.605	2.296			v s		i al
p509	trithionate	$K_2S_3O_6$	270.39	col, rhomb, 1.475, 1.480, 1.487	2.304	d 30–40		s	d	i al
p510	thioplatinate	$K_2Pt_2S_6$	1050.95	bl-gray cr	6.44^{15}	d, ign		i		d HCl
p511	thiosulfate, penta-hydrate	$3K_2S_2O_3.5H_2O$	661.07	col, rhomb		d		$150.2^{17.2}$		
p512	metathiostannate	$K_2SnS_3.3H_2O$	347.13	dk brn oil	1.847^{18}	$-3H_2O$, 100		s		i al
p513	thiosulfate	$K_2S_2O_3\frac{1}{2}.H_2O$	196.34	col, monocl, deliq	2.590 anhydr 2.23	$-H_2O$, 200	d	96.1^0	312^{90}	i al
p514	tungstate	$K_2WO_4.2H_2O$	362.08	col, monocl, deliq	3.113	tr 388, 921		51.5	151.5	d a; i al
p515	metatungstate	$K_6[H_2W_{12}O_{40}].18H_2O$	3407.08	hex		ca 930		s	v s	d a
p516	metauranate	K_2UO_4	380.23	or-yel, rhomb				i		v s a
p517	uranyl acetate	$KUO_2(C_2H_3O_2)_3.H_2O$	504.28	tetr	3.296^{16} ($\frac{1}{2}H_2O$)	$-H_2O$, 275		s		
p518	uranyl carbonate	$2K_2CO_3.UO_2CO_3$	606.46	yel, hex		$-CO_2$		7.4^{15}	d	s K_2CO_3 sol; i a

No.	Name	Synonyms and Formulae	Mol. wt.	Crystalline form, properties and index of refraction	Density or spec. gravity	Melting point, °C	Boiling point, °C	Solubility, in grams per 100 cc		
								Cold water	Hot water	Other solvents
	Potassium									
p519	uranyl sulfate	$K_2SO_4.UO_2SO_4.2H_2O$	576.39	yel, monocl	$3.363^{19.1}$	$-2H_2O$, 120		s		
p520	urate, acid	$KHC_5H_2N_4O_3$	206.21	wh powd				sl s		
p521	*metavanadate*	KVO_3	138.04	col cr				sl s	s	sl s KOH; i al
p522	vanadium sulfate	Potassium vanadium alum. $KV(SO_4)_2.12H_2O$	498.35	violet cubic	1.783_4^{20}	20	$-12H_2O$, 230	1984^{10}		
p523	*ethylxanthate*	KC_2H_5OCSS	160.30	wh to pa yel cr or cr powd	$1.558^{21.5}$	d>200		v s	d	s al; i eth
p524	**Praseodymium** (α form)	Pr	140.907	pa yel, met, hex up to 798	6.773	931	3512	d		s a
p525	(β form)	Pr	140.907	cub	6.64	935	3127	d		s a
p526	acetate	$Pr(C_2H_3O_2)_3.3H_2O$	372.09	grn need				v s		
p527	acetylacetonate	$Pr(C_5H_7O_2)_3$	438.24	cr ppt		146				s CS_2
p528	bromate	$Pr(BrO_3)_3.9H_2O$	686.77	grn, hex		56.5	$-7H_2O$, 170	196^{25}		
p529	bromide	$PrBr_3$	380.63	grn cr powd		691	1547	d, sl s		
p530	carbide	PrC_2	164.93	yel cr	5.10	d		d	d	s dil a
p531	carbonate	$Pr_2(CO_3)_3.8H_2O$	605.96	grn silky pl		$-6H_2O$, 100		i		s a
p532	chloride	$PrCl_3$	247.27	bl grn need	4.02^{25}	786	1700	103.9^{13}	$∞^{100}$	v s al; 2.4 pyr; i chl, eth
p533	chloride, heptahydrate	$PrCl_3.7H_2O$	373.37	grn, tricl	2.25^{17}	115		334^{13}	$∞^{100}$	s al, HCl
p534	hexantipyrine *perchlorate*	$[Pr(C_{11}H_{12}N_2O)_6].(ClO_4)_3$	1568.65	grn, hex leaf		d 286–291				
p535	iodide	PrI_3	521.62	gr cr, hygr		737		v s		
p536	molybdate	$Pr_2(MoO_4)_3$	761.63	grass-green tetr	4.84	1030				
p537	oxalate	$Pr_2(C_2O_4)_3.10H_2O$	726.03	lt grn cr				i		s a
p538	oxide, di-	PrO_2	172.91	br-bl powd	6.82	>350 tr to Pr_6O_{10}				
p539	oxide, sesqui-	Praseodymia. Pr_2O_3	329.81	yel-grn, amorph	7.07	d		0.000020^{29}		s a
p540	selenate	$Pr_2(SeO_4)_3$	710.69		4.30^{15}			36^9	3^{72}	
p541	sulfate	$Pr_2(SO_4)_3$	570.00	lt grn powd	3.72^{16}			23.7^0 17.7^{30}	1.02^{95}	
p542	sulfate, octahydrate	$Pr_2(SO_4)_3.8H_2O$	714.12	grn, monocl, 1.540, 1.549, 1.561	$2.827^{14.3}$			17.4^{20}	sl s	
p543	sulfate, pentahydrate	$Pr_2(SO_4)_3.5H_2O$	660.08	monocl pr	3.176^{16}				1.85^{85}	
p544	sulfide	Pr_2S_3	378.01	br powd	5.042^{11}	d		i	d	s dil a
p545	**Protactinium**	Pa	231.10	gray met, tetrag	15.37	<1600				
p546	chloride	$PaCl_4$	372.91	yel-grn, tetrag		subl 400 in vac		s		s dil HCl
p547	fluoride	PaF_4	307.09	monocl				i		
p548	oxide, di-	PaO_2	263.10	blk, cub						
p549	oxide, pent-	Pa_2O_5	542.20	wh, cub						s dil HF
r1	**Radium**	Ra	226.0254	silver wh met	5(?)	700	<1140	d, ev H_2O		d a
r2	bromide	$RaBr_2$	385.82	col-yelsh, monocl	5.79	728	subl 900	s	s	s al
r3	bromide dihydrate	$RaBr_2.2H_2O$	421.85	wh, monocl		$-2H_2O$, 100		s		
r4	carbonate	$RaCO_3$	286.01	wh, or sl brnsh, monocl				i		d a
r5	chloride	$RaCl_2$	296.91	col-yelsh, monocl	4.91	1000		s	s	s al
r6	chloride, dihydrate	$RaCl_2.2H_2O$	332.94	wh, monocl, discol		$-2H_2O$, 100		s		s HCl
r7	iodate	$Ra(IO_3)_2$	575.81					0.0175^9	0.170^{100}	
r8	nitrate	$Ra(NO_3)_2$	350.01	cr				13.9^{20}		
r9	sulfate	$RaSO_4$	322.06	col, rhomb				0.000002^{25}	0.000005^{55}	i a
r10	**Radon**	Niton, Radium emanation. Rn	222.00	col gas, opaque cr	gas 9.73 g/l liq 4.4^{-62} sol 4.0	-71	-61.8	51.0^0 cm³ 22.4^{25} cm³	13.0^{60} cm³	sl s al, org liqu
r11	**Rhenium**	Re	186.2	met lust, hex	20.53	3180	5627 (est)	i	i	s dil HNO_3, H_2O_2; sl s H_2SO_4; i HCl
r12	bromide	$ReBr_3$	425.93	grn-blk cr		subl 500, vac				s dil H_2SO_4, HBr, liq NH_3
r13	carbonyl, penta-	$[Re(CO)_5]_2$	652.51	col, cub cr		d 250				v sl s org solv
r14	chloride, penta-	$ReCl_5$	363.47	dk grn to blk	4.9	d	d	d	d	s HCl, alk
r15	chloride, tetra-	$ReCl_4$	328.01	blk (exist. ?)			500	s, d	s, d	s HCl
r16	chloride, tri-	$ReCl_3$	292.56	dk red, hex			>550	s	s	s a, alk, liq NH_3 al; sl s eth
r17	fluoride	ReF_4	262.19	dk grn	5.383^{20}	124.5	d 500	d		s a
r18	fluoride, hexa-	ReF_6	300.19	pa yel, v hygr	liq 6.1573, sld $3.616^{18.5}$	18.8	47.6	s, d	s, d	d HNO_3, H_2SO_4
r19	iodide pentacarbonyl	$ReI.5CO$	453.16	yel, rhombd		200	d 400, subl vac 90	i		s bz
r20	oxide, di-	ReO_2	218.20	blk	11.4_4^{25}	d 1000		i	i	s conc HCl, H_2O_2
r21	oxide, hept-	Re_2O_7	484.40	yel pl or hex or powd, hygr	6.103	ca 297	subl 250	v s	v s	v s al; s alk, a
r22	oxide, per-	$Re_2O_8(?)$	500.40	wh	8.4	145		v s	v s	s alk; sl s eth

No.	Name	Synonyms and Formulae	Mol. wt.	Crystalline form, properties and index of refraction	Density or spec. gravity	Melting point, °C	Boiling point, °C	Solubility, in grams per 100 cc		
								Cold water	Hot water	Other solvents
	Rhenium									
r23	oxide, sesqui-	Dirhenium trioxide $Re_2O_3.xH_2O$		unstable				d, ev H_2		
r24	oxide, tri-	ReO_2	234.20	red, blue, cub.	6.9–7.4		d 400	i	i	s H_2O_2, HNO_3
r25	oxybromide, tri-	ReO_3Br	314.11	wh		39.5	163			
r26	oxychloride, tri-	ReO_3Cl	269.65	col liq	3.867_4^{20}	4.5	131^{760}	d	d	s CCl_4
r27	oxytetrachloride	$ReOCl_4$	344.01	or need		29.3	223.00	d	d	
r28	oxytetrafluoride	$ReOF_4$	278.19	wh	lq 3.717 sol 4.032	39.7	62.7			
r29	oxydifluoride, di-	ReO_2F_2	256.20	col		156				
r30	sulfide, di-	ReS_2	250.33	blk tr leaf	7.506_4^{20}		d	i	i	s HNO_3; i al, alk, HCl
r31	sulfide, hepta-	Re_2S_7	596.85	blk powd	4.866		d	i	i	s HNO_3, H_2O_2, alk; i HCl
r32	**Rhodium**	Rh	102.905	gray-wh, cub.	12.4	1966 ± 3	3727 ± 100	i	i	s H_2SO_4+HCl, conc H_2SO_4; sl s a, aq reg
r33	amminechloride, hexa-	$[Rh(NH_3)_6]Cl_3$	311.45	rhomb pl	2.008_4^{25}	−NH_3 210, d		12.5^8	s	
r34	carbonylchloride, basic	$RhCl_2.RhO.3CO$	376.75	ruby red need		subl 125.5		sl s	d	s CCl_4, ac a, bz
r35	chloride, tri-	$RhCl_3$	209.26	br-red powd, deliq		d 450–500	subl 800	i	i	i a, aq reg
r36	chloride, tri-	$RhCl_3.xH_2O$		dk red, deliq		d 100		v s	s	s al, HCl; i eth
r37	fluoride, tri-	RhF_3	159.90	red, rhomb	5.38	>600 subl		i	i	i a, alk
r38	iodide, tri-	RhI_3	483.62	blk				i		
r39	nitrate	$Rh(NO_3)_3.2H_2O$	324.93	red, deliq				s	s	i al
r40	oxide, di-	RhO_2	134.90	br				i		i a, alk
r41	oxide, di- dihydrate	$RhO_2.2H_2O$	170.93	olive grn		d		i	i	s HCl, acet a, alk
r42	oxide, sesqui-	Rh_2O_3	253.81	gray cr or amorph	8.20	d 1100–1150		i	i	i a, aq reg, KOH
r43	oxide, sesqui-, pentahydrate	$Rh_2O_3.5H_2O$	343.88	yel ppt		d		i	s	s a
r44	sulfate	$Rh_2(SO_4)_3.4H_2O$	566.05	red		d		s	s	
r45	sulfate	$Rh_2(SO_4)_3.12H_2O$	710.18	lt yel cr		d		v s	d	i al
r46	sulfate	$Rh_2(SO_4)_3.15H_2O$	764.22	pa yel cr		d		v s	d	i al, eth
r47	sulfide, hydro-	$Rh(HS)_3$	202.12	blk		d		i	d	s aq reg, aq Br; i Na_2S
r48	sulfide, mono-	RhS	134.97	gray-blk cr		d		i	i	i a, aq reg
r49	sulfide, sesqui-	Rh_2S_3	302.00	blk	6.40_4^{25}	d		i	i	i a, aq reg, aq Br
r50	sulfite	$Rh_2(SO_3)_3.6H_2O$	554.09	yel cr		d		s	s	i al
r51	**Rubidium**	Rb	85.47	soft, silver wh met	1.532 liq: $1.475^{38.5}$	38.89	688	d	d	d al; s a
r52	acetate	$RbC_2H_3O_2$	144.52	col, nacreous leaf, hygr		246		$86^{44.7}$	$89.3^{99.4}$	
r53	aluminium sulfate	$RbAl(SO_4)_2.12H_2O$	520.76	col, cub, oct, 1.457, 1.45232, 1.46618	1.867^0	99		2.59^{20}	43.25^{80}	
r54	azide	RbN_3	127.49	col need or plates	2.7876	d ca 310		107.1^{16}		0.182^{16} al; i eth
r55	borofluoride	$RbBF_4$	172.27	very sm rhomb cr, 1.333	2.820^{20}	590	d 500	0.6^{17}	10^{100}	
r56	borohydride	$RbBH_4$	100.31	white, cubic	1.920	1.487		v s		sl s al, i ether, bz
r57	bromate	$RbBrO_3$	213.38	cub	3.68	430		2.93^{25}	5.08^{40}	
r58	bromide	RbBr	165.38	col, cub, 1.5530	3.35 liq: 2.79^{730}	693	1340	98^8	$205.2^{113.5}$	i al, sl s acet
r59	bromide, tri-	$RbBr_3$	325.20	red, rhomb		d 140				
r60	bromochloroiodide	RbIBrCl	327.74	rhomb		d 200				s al, d eth
r61	bromoiodide, di-	$RbIBr_2$	372.13	red, rhomb	3.84	225	d 265	s		s al, d eth
r62	carbonate	Rb_2CO_3	230.95	col cr, deliq		837	d 740	450^{20}	s	0.7 abs al
r63	carbonate, acid	$RbHCO_3$	146.49	wh, rhomb		d 175		53.73^{20}		2.0 al
r64	chlorate	$RbClO_3$	168.92	trim	3.19			5.0^{19}	62.8^{100}	
r65	perchlorate	$RbClO_4$	184.92	rhomb, 1.4701	2.80	fus	d	0.5^0	18^{100}	0.009^{25} al, 0.06^{25} MeOH
r66	chloride	RbCl	120.92	col, cub, 1.493^{25}	2.80; liq: 2.088^{750}	718	1390	77^0	138.9^{100}	0.08^{25} al, 1.41^{25} MeOH; v al s NH_3
r67	chlorobromide, di-	$RbBrCl_2$	236.29	rhomb		d 110				
r68	chlorodibromide	$RbBr_2Cl$	280.74			76				
r69	chloroiodide, di-	$RbICl_2$	283.28	dk orange, rhomb		180–200	d 265	v s	v s	
r70	chloroplatinate	Rb_2PtCl_6	578.75	yel, cub	$3.94^{17.5}$	d		0.184^0	0.634^{100}	i al
r71	chloroplatinate, hexa-	$Rb_2[PtCl_6]$	578.75	yel, cub	$3.94^{17.5}$	d		0.014^0	0.33^{100}	i al
r72	chromate	Rb_2CrO_4	286.93	yel, rhomb, ~1.71	3.518			62^0	95.7^{80}	
r73	dichromate	$Rb_2Cr_2O_7$	386.93	tricl or monocl, >1.95, 1.70	3.02 monocl 3.125 tricl		tricl: monocl:	4.96^{16} 5.42^{15}	27.3^{80} 28.1^{90}	
r74	chromiumsulfate	$RbCr(SO_4)_2.12H_2O$	545.77	vlt cub, 1.482	1.946	107		43.4^{25}		

No.	Name	Synonyms and Formulae	Mol. wt.	Crystalline form, properties and index of refraction	Density or spec. gravity	Melting point, °C	Boiling point, °C	Solubility, in grams per 100 cc		
								Cold water	Hot water	Other solvents
	Rubidium									
r75	cobalt (II) sulfate	RbSO₄.CoSO₄.6H₂O	449.22	rubyred, monocl, 1.486, 1.491, 1.501	2.56[15]			9.3[25]	s	
r76	coppersulfate	Rb₂SO₄.CuSO₄.6H₂O	534.70	monocl, 1.489, 1.491, 1.504	2.57			10.28[25]		
r77	cyanide	RbCN	111.49	col cr powder	2.32			s	s	i al, eth
r78	galliumsulfate	RbGa(SO₄)₂.12H₂O	563.50	col cr, 1.46579	1.962			s		
r79	fluoride	RbF	104.47	col, cubic, 1.398	3.557	795	1410	130.6[18]		s dil HF; i al, eth, NH₃
r80	fluorogermanate	Rb₂GeF₆	357.52	wh cr				sl s	v s	
r81	fluosilicate	Rb₂SiF₆	313.02	cub, oct	3.332[20]			0.16[20]	1.35[100]	s a, i al
r82	fluosulfonate	RbFSO₃	184.53	need		304				
r83	iodate	RbIO₃	260.37	monocl or cub	4.33[19.5]	d		2.1[23]		v s HCl
r84	*meta*periodate	RbIO₄	276.37	tetr	3.918[16]			0.65[13]		
r85	iodide	RbI	212.37	col, cub, 1.6474	3.55; liq: 2.87[825]	647	1300	152[17]	163[25]	s liq NH₃; 0.674[25] acet
r86	iodide, tri-	RbI₃	466.18	blk, rhomb	4.03[22]	190		s		
r87	iodide, cmpd. with SO₂	RbI.4SO₂	468.63	lemon yel		13.5				
r88	iron (II) selenate	Rb₂SeO₄.FeSeO₄.6H₂O	620.79	blue-grn monocl, prism, 1.513, 1.520, 1.532	2.819					
r89	iron (III) selenate	RbFe(SeO₄)₂.12H₂O	643.42	cub, 1.507[18]	2.31[11]	45	−12H₂O, 100			
r90	iron (II) sulfate	Rb₂SO₄.FeSO₄.6H₂O	527.00	gr monocl, prism, 1.4815, 1.4874, 1.4977	2.516	d 60		24.2[25] (anhydr)		
r91	iron (III) sulfate	RbFe(SO₄)₂.12H₂O	549.62	cub, 1.4823	1.91–1.95	48–53	4.55[6.6]	52.6[90]	d	d a
r92	hydride	RbH	86.48	col need	2.60	d 300				d a
r93	hydroxide	RbOH	102.48	gray-wh, deliq	3.203[11]	301 ± 0.9		180[15]	v s	s al
r94	neodymium nitrate	2(?)RbNO₃.Nd(NO₃)₃.4H₂O	697.26	redsh-vlt pl	2.56	47	−4H₂O, 60			
r95	nitrate	RbNO₃	147.47	col, hex cub, rhomb or tricl, hygr, 1.51, 1.52, 1.524	3.11; liq: 2.395[100]	tr cub 161.4 m.p. 310	tricl rhom 219	44.28[16]	452[100]	sl s acet; v s HNO₃
r96	nitrate, hydrogen	RbNO₃.HNO₃	210.49	tetr		62				
r97	nitrate, hydrogen	RbNO₃.2HNO₃	273.50	col need		45				
r98	magnesium sulfate	Rb₂SO₄.MgSO₄.6H₂O	495.47	col, monocl, 1.467, 1.469, 1.478	2.386[20/4]			20.2[25] (anhydr)		
r99	permanganate	RbMnO₄	204.41	cr	3.235[10.4]	d 295		0.5[0]	4.7[60]	
r100	oxide, mon-	Rb₂O	186.94	col-yel, cub	3.72	d 400		s d	s d	s liq NH₃
r101	oxide, per-	Rb₂O₂	202.94	yel, cub	3.65[0]	570	d 1011[760 mm]	dec to RbOH +H₂		
r102	oxide, super-	RbO₂, unstable	117.47	yel plates	3.80	432	d 1157[1 atm]			
r103	oxide (tetr-)	Rb₂O₄	234.94	dk orange cr, deliq		dec 500 vac				
r104	oxide, tri- (sesqui)	Rb₂O₃ (or Rb₄O₆)	218.94	blk cub	3.53[0]	489		s d		
r105	praseodymium nitrate	2RbNO₃.Pr(NO₃)₃.4H₂O	693.93	grnsh, monocl, need hygr	2.50	63.5	−4H₂O, 60			
r106	selenate	Rb₂SeO₄	313.90	col, rhomb, 1.5515, 1.5537, 1.5582	3.90			159[12]		
r107	silicofluoride	Rb₂SiF₆	313.02	col, oct or hex	3.3383[20/4]			sl s	s	s a, i al
r108	sulfate	Rb₂SO₄	267.00	col, rhomb hex, 1.513, 1.513, 1.514	3.613[20/4]; liq 2.53[1100]	1060 trig 653	ca 1700	42.4[10]	81.8[100]	i acet; sl s NH₃
r109	sulfate, hydrogen	RbHSO₄	182.54	rhomb, 1.473	2.892[16]	< red heat				
r110	sulfide, di-	Rb₂S₂	235.07	dk red		420	volat >850			
r111	sulfide, hexa-	Rb₂S₆	363.32	brn-red		201				
r112	sulfide, mono-	Rb₂S	203.00	wh-pale yel	2.912	530 d vac		v s	v s	
r113	sulfide, mono-tetrahydrate	Rb₂S.4H₂O	275.07	cr, deliq				v s	v s	
r114	sulfide, penta-	Rb₂S₅	331.26	red, rhomb, deliq	2.618[15]	225		d		s 70 % al; i eth, chl
r115	sulfide, tri-	Rb₂S₃	267.13	redsh yel		213				
r116	tartrate, d & l	Rb₂C₄H₄O₆	319.01	trig	2.658[20/4]			200[25]		i toluol
r117	*dl*-tartrate, hydrogen	RbHC₄H₄O₆	234.55	trim pr	2.282	201 d		1.18[25]	11.7[100]	
r118	vanadium sulfate	Rubidium vanadium alum. RbV(SO₄)₂.12H₂O	544.72	yellow, cubic, 1.4689	1.915[20/4]	64	230 −12H₂O, 300 dec	2.56[10]		

No.	Name	Synonyms and Formulae	Mol. wt.	Crystalline form, properties and index of refraction	Density or spec. gravity	Melting point, °C	Boiling point, °C	Solubility, in grams per 100 cc		
								Cold water	Hot water	Other solvents
	Ruthenium									
r119	**Ruthenium**	Ru	101.07	gray-wh or silv brittle met, hex	12.30	2310	3900	i	i	i aq reg, a, al; s fus alk
r120	carbonyl, penta-	Ru(CO)$_5$	241.12	col liq		−22				s al, bz
r121	chloride, tetra-	RuCl$_4$.5H$_2$O	332.96	rdsh-br cr, hygr		d		s		s al
r122	chloride, tri-	RuCl$_3$	207.43	br cr, deliq	3.11	d >500		i	d	sl s al; s HCl; i CS$_2$
r123	fluoride, penta-	RuF$_5$	196.06	dk grn cr	2.963[18.5]	101	250	d	d	
r124	hydroxide	Ru(OH)$_3$	152.09	blk powd				v sl s		s a; i alk
r125	oxide, di-	RuO$_2$	133.07	dk bl, tetr	6.97	d		i		s a; s fus alk
r126	oxide, tetr-	RuO$_4$	165.07	yel, rhomb need	3.29[21]	25.5	d 108	2.033[20]	2.249[74]	s al, a, alk, CCl$_4$
r127	oxychloride ammoniated	Ruthenium red. Ru$_2$(OH)$_7$Cl$_4$.7NH$_3$.3H$_2$O	551.19	brn-red powd				s		
r128	silicide	RuSi	129.16	met pr	5.40[4]			i	i	s HNO$_3$+HF
r129	sulfide	Nat. laurite. RuS$_2$	165.20	gray-blk, cub	6.99	d 1000		i	i	s a; s fus alk
s1	**Samarium**	Sm	150.35	wh-gray met, hex	7.520	1077	1791	i	i	s a
s2	acetate	Sm(C$_2$H$_3$O$_2$)$_3$.3H$_2$O	381.53		1.94			15[25]		
s3	acetylacetonate	Sm(C$_5$H$_7$O$_2$)$_3$	447.68	cr mass		146−147		i		
s4	benzylacetonate	Sm(C$_{10}$H$_9$O$_2$)$_3$.2H$_2$O	669.92	straw color		103−105		i		s org solv
s5	bromate	Sm(BrO$_3$)$_3$.9H$_2$O	696.21	yel, hex		75	−9H$_2$O, 150	114[25]		v sl s al
s6	(II) bromide	SmBr$_2$	310.17	dk brn	5.1	508	1880	d		
s7	(III) bromide	SmBr$_3$.6H$_2$O	498.17	yel cr, deliq	2.971[22]	640				
s8	carbide	SmC$_2$	174.37	yel, hex	5.86			d	d	s, d a
s9	(II) chloride	SmCl$_2$	221.26	red-brn cr	4.56[4]	740		s, d		i al, CS$_2$
s10	(III) chloride	SmCl$_3$	256.71	yelsh-wh cr, hygr	4.46[15]	678 ± 2	d	92.4[10]	99.9[40]	v s al; 6.4[25] pyr
s11	(III) chloride, hexahydrate	SmCl$_3$.6H$_2$O	364.80	grn-yel, tricl, hygr	2.383	−5H$_2$O, 110				
s12	chromate	Sm$_2$(CrO$_4$)$_3$.8H$_2$O	792.80	yel				0.043[25]		
s13	(II) fluoride	SmF$_2$	188.35			1306	>2400	i	i	
s14	(III) fluoride	SmF$_3$	207.35			1306	2323	i	i	
s15	hydroxide	Sm(OH)$_3$	201.37	pa yel powd				i		s a; i alk
s16	(II) iodide	SmI$_2$	404.16	dk brn		527	1580	d		
s17	(III) iodide	SmI$_3$	531.06	or-yel cr		850				
s18	kojate	Sm(C$_6$H$_5$O$_4$)$_3$	573.66			d 275		i		
s19	(III) methyl-phosphate, di	Sm[(CH$_3$)$_2$PO$_4$]$_3$	525.47	cream col, hex pr				35.2[25]	10.8[25]	
s20	(III) molybdate	Sm$_2$(MoO$_4$)$_3$	780.51	vlt, rhomb oct	5.36			v s		
s21	(III) nitrate	Sm(NO$_3$)$_3$.6H$_2$O	444.46	pa yel, tricl	2.375	78−79		v s		
s22	(III) oxalate	Sm$_2$(C$_2$O$_4$)$_3$.10H$_2$O	744.91	wh cr				0.000054		s H$_2$SO$_4$
s23	oxide, sesqui-	Samaria. Sm$_2$O$_3$	348.70	wh-yelsh powd	8.347			i		v s a
s24	(III) sulfate	Sm$_2$(SO$_4$)$_3$.8H$_2$O	733.01	lt yel, monocl, 1.543, 1.552, 1.563	2.930	−8H$_2$O, 450		2.67[20] 4.4[25]	1.99[40]	
s25	(III) sulfide	Sm$_2$S$_3$	396.89	yelsh-pink	5.729	1900			d	d dil a
s26	sulfate, basic	Sm$_2$O$_3$SO$_4$	428.76	yel powd		d 1100		i		i dil H$_2$SO$_4$
s27	**Scandium**	Sc	44.956	silv met, cubic or hex	2.9890	1541	2831	d, ev H$_2$		
s28	acetylacetonate	Sc(C$_5$H$_7$O$_2$)$_3$	342.29	col pl		187.5	subl 210−215			s al, bz, chl
s29	bromide	ScBr$_3$	284.68		3.914	subl >1000				
s30	chloride	ScCl$_3$	151.32	col cr	2.39[25/4]	939	subl 800−850	v s	v s	i abs al
s31	hydroxide	Sc(OH)$_3$	95.98	col amorph				i		s dil a
s32	nitrate	Sc(NO$_3$)$_3$	230.97	col, deliq		150		s		s al
s33	nitrate, tetrahydrate	Sc(NO$_3$)$_3$.4H$_2$O	303.03	col, pr, deliq		−4H$_2$O, 100		v s		
s34	oxalate	Sc$_2$(C$_2$O$_4$)$_3$.5H$_2$O	444.05	cr		−4H$_2$O, 140				
s35	oxide	Scandia. Sc$_2$O$_3$	137.91	wh powd	3.864			i	i	s h a
s36	sulfate	Sc$_2$(SO$_4$)$_3$	378.10	col cr	2.579	d		10.3[25]	v s	
s37	sulfate, hexahydrate	Sc$_2$(SO$_4$)$_3$.6H$_2$O	486.19			−4H$_2$O, 100 −6H$_2$O, 250		v s		
s38	sulfate, pentahydrate	Sc$_2$(SO$_4$)$_3$.5H$_2$O	468.17		2.519	−3H$_2$O, 100		54.6[25]		
s39	**Selenic acid**	H$_2$SeO$_4$	144.97	wh, hex prism, hygr	3.004[15/4]	58 eas undercools	d 260	1300[30]	∞[60]	s H$_2$SO$_4$; d al; i NH$_3$
s40	monohydrate	H$_2$SeO$_4$.H$_2$O	162.99	wh, need	2.627[15/4] liq 2.3564[15/4]	26 eas undercools	205	v s	v s	
s41	tetrahydrate	H$_2$SeO$_4$.4H$_2$O	217.03	col liq		51.7 eas undercools	−H$_2$O, 172[25]	∞		s H$_2$SO$_4$; d org solv
s42	**Selenium**	Se	78.96	blsh-gray, met hex	4.81[20/4]	217	684.9 ± 1.0	i	i	s H$_2$SO$_4$, CHCl$_3$; i al; v sl s CS$_2$
s43	"	Se	78.96	red, monocl prism	4.50	170−180 trsf to hex	684.8	i	i	0.1[46.6] CS$_2$; s H$_2$SO$_4$, HNO$_3$
s44	"	Se	78.96	red amorph, blk vitr	red 4.26 blk 4.28	tr to hex, 60−80	684.8	i	i	s H$_2$SO$_4$, CS$_2$, bz

No.	Name	Synonyms and Formulae	Mol. wt.	Crystalline form, properties and index of refraction	Density or spec. gravity	Melting point, °C	Boiling point, °C	Solubility, in grams per 100 cc		
								Cold water	Hot water	Other solvents
	Selenium									
s45	bromide, "mono-"	Diselenium dibromide. Se_2Br_2	317.74	dk red liq	3.604^{15}		227 d	d	d	d al; s CS_2, $CHCl_3$, C_2H_5Br
s46	bromide, tetra-	$SeBr_4$	398.60	or-red-brn cr		d 75		d	d	s CS_2, chl, C_2H_5Br, HCl
s47	bromide (mono-) chloride, tri-,	$SeBrCl_3$	265.23	yel br cr		190				i CS_2
s48	bromide (tri-) chloride	$SeBr_3Cl$	354.14	or cr, hygr		d				v sl s CS_2
s49	carbide	SeC_2	102.98	yel liq, 1.845	2.682^{20}_4	45.5	$125-126^{760}$	i		s CS_2, eth, CCl_4, bz, al
s50	chloride "mono"-	Diselenium dichloride. Se_2Cl_2	228.83	br red liq, 1.596	2.77^{25}_4	−85	d 130	d	d	d al, eth; s CS_2, chl, CCl_4, bz
s51	chloride, tetra-	$SeCl_4$	220.77	wh-yel, cub, deliq. 1.807	$3.78-3.85^{260}$	305, subl 170−196	d 288	d	d	i al, eth, CS_2; s $POCl_3$; d a, alk
s52	fluoride, hexa-	SeF_6	192.95	col gas, 1.895	3.25^{-28} g/l	−39, subl −46.6	−34.5	s d		
s53	fluoride, tetra-	SeF_4	154.95	col liq or wh cr		m.p. −13.8 frz −90	>100	d	d	
s54	hydride	H_2Se	80.98	col gas, pois	gas 3.664^{760} air; liq: $2.004^{-41.5}$	−60.4	−41.5	3.77^4	$270^{22.5}$	s CS_2, $COCl_2$
s55	iodide, "mono"-	Diselenium diiodide. Se_2I_2	411.73	steelgray cr (exist ?)		68−70	d 100	d	d	
s56	nitride, or	Se_4N_4	371.87	amorph, or yel-brickred, hygr		expl 160−200	d	i	sl d	i al, eth; v sl s acet ac, bz
s57	oxide, di-	SeO_2	110.96	wh, monocl, col, tetr, pois, >1.76	3.95^{15}_{15}	340−350 subl 315−317		38.4^{14}	82.5^{65}	6.67^{14} al; $4.35^{15.3}$ acet; $1.11^{13.9}$ ac a; s bz
s58	oxide, tri-	SeO_3	126.96	pa yel cub or fibre, deliq	3.6	118	d 180	d, v s	d, v s	s al, conc H_2SO_4; i eth, bz, chl, CCl_4
s59	oxybromide	Selenyl bromide. $SeOBr_2$	254.78	red yel cr	liq 3.38^{50}	41.6	217^{710} d	d		s CS_2, CCl_4, chl, H_2SO_4, bz
s60	oxychloride	$SeOCl_2$	165.87	col-yel, liq 1.651^{20}	2.42^{22}	8.5	176.4	d		s CS_2, CCl_4, chl, bz
s61	sulfur oxy*tetra*chloride	$SeSO_2Cl_4$	300.83	hex pr		165	183	d		
s62	oxyfluoride	Selenyl fluoride. $SeOF_2$	132.96	col liq	2.67	4.6	124	d		s al, CCl_4
s63	sulfide, di-	SeS_2	143.09	br red-yel		<100	d	i		d aq reg, HNO_3; s $(NH_4)_2S$
s64	sulfide, "mono"-	SeS	111.02	or-yel tabl or powd	3.056^0	d 118−119		i	i	s CS_2; i eth; d al
s65	sulfur oxide	$SeSO_3$	159.02	grn pr or yel powd		−SO_2, 40		d, 118		s H_2SO_4; i SO_3
s67	**Selenious acid**	H_2SeO_3	128.97	col, hex, deliq	3.004^{15}_4	d 70	−H_2O	167^{20}	v s	v s al; i NH_3
s68	**Silane**, bromo-	SiH_3Br	111.02	col gas, expl in air	1.72^{-80} 1.533^0	−94	1.9			
s69	bromotrichloro-	$SiBrCl_3$	214.35	col liq	1.826	−62	80.3	d	d	
s70	chloro-	SiH_3Cl	66.56	col gas	gas: 3.033 g/l liq: 1.145^{-112}	−118.1	−30.4			
s71	dibromo-	SiH_2Br_2	189.92	col liq, inflam	2.17^0	−70.1	66	d	d	d alk
s72	dibromo-	Silicobromoform. $SiHBr_3$	268.82	col liq, inflam	2.7^{17}	−73	109	d	d	d NH_3
s73	dibromodichloro-	$SiBr_2Cl_2$	258.81	col liq	2.172^{25}_4	−45.5	104	d	d	
s74	dichloro-	SiH_2Cl_2	101.01	gas	gas 4.599 g/l liq 1.42^{-122}	−122	8.3	d	d	
s75	dichloro difluoro-	$SiCl_2F_2$	136.99	gas	6.2784 g/l	−144 ± 2	−31.7 ± 0.2	d	d	
s76	(hexa-)hexaoxocyclo-	Siloxane. $Si_6O_9H_6$	222.56	wh, pl	1.32^{20}	d 140, inflam		sl d	d	
s77	monochloro trifluoro-	$SiClF_3$	120.53	gas	5.455 g/l	−138.0 ± 2	−70.0 ± 0.2	d	d	
s78	monoiodo-	SiH_3I	158.01	col liq	$2.035^{14.8}$	−57.0	45.5	d		
s79	(tri-)nitrilo-	Silicylamine, tri-$(SiH_3)_3N$	107.34	col inflam liq	0.895^{-106}	−105.6				
s81	tribromochloro-	$SiBr_3Cl$	303.27	col liq	2.497^{25}_4	−20.8 ± 1	126−128	d	d	
s82	trichloro-	Silicochloroform. $SiHCl_3$	135.45	col liq	1.34	−126.5	33^{788} mm	d	d	s CS_2, CCl_4, chl, bz
s83	trichloroiodo-	$SiCl_3I$	261.35	col liq		>−60	113.5	d		
s84	trifluoro-	Silicofluoroform. $SiHF_3$	86.09	col gas	3.86^0 g/l	−131.4	ca −95	d		d al, eth, alk; s tol
s85	triiodo-	Silicoiodoform. $SiHI_3$	409.81	red liq	3.314^{20}	8	220	d		s CS_2, bz

No.	Name	Synonyms and Formulae	Mol. wt.	Crystalline form, properties and index of refraction	Density or spec. gravity	Melting point, °C	Boiling point, °C	Solubility, in grams per 100 cc		
								Cold water	Hot water	Other solvents
	Silicane cyanate									
s86	**Silicane cyanate**	$Si(OCN)_4$	196.16	sol or liq	1.414_4^{20}	34.5 ± 0.5	247.2 ± 0.5 0.5^{760}	d		
s87	diimide	$Si(NH)_2$	58.12	wh powd		d 900				
s88	isocyanate	$Si(NCO)_4$	196.16	sol or liq	1.434_4^{25}	26.0 ± 0.5	185.6 ± 0.3^{760}	d		i acet; s bz, CCl_4, CS_2
s89	**Silicic acid, di-**	H_2SiO_5	138.18	col cr		d 150		i	i	s NH_3, HF
s90	meta-	H_2SiO_3	78.10	col, amorph		d room temp		i	i	s NH_3, HF, h alk
s91	**Silicon**	Si	28.086	steel gray, large to micr cr, cub	2.32–2.34	1410	2355	i	i	s $HF+HNO_3$; i HF
s92	acetate, tetra-	$Si(C_2H_3O_2)_4$	264.27	col cr, hygr		subl 110 d 160–170	148^6 mm	d		d al; sl s acet, bz
s93	bromide, tetra-	Tetrabromosilane. $SiBr_4$	347.72	col fum liq, sol cub	liq: 2.7715_4^{25} sol: 3.292^{-79}	5.4	154	d	d	d H_2SO_4
s94	(di-)bromide, hexa-	Si_2Br_6	535.62	wh, rhomb		95	240	d	d	s CS_2; d KOH
s95	bromide(di-) sulfide	$SiSBr_2$	219.97	col pl		93	$150^{18.7}$ mm	d	d	s bz, CS_2
s96	carbide	SiC	40.10	col-blk, hex or cub, 2.654, 2.697	3.217	~2700, subl, d		i	i	i a; s fus KOH
s97	chloride, tetra-	Tetrachlorosilane. $SiCl_4$	169.90	col fum liq	liq: 1.483^{20}, sol: 1.90^{-97} gas: 7.59 g/l	-70	57.57	d	d	d al
s98	(di-)chloride, hexa-	Hexachlorodisilane. Si_2Cl_6	268.89	col liq, 1.4748^{18}	1.58^0	-1	145^{769}	d	d	d al
s99	chloride(di-) sulfide	$SiSCl_2$	131.06	col pr		75	$92^{22.5}$	d	d	s CCl_4, CS_2 bz
s100	chloride(tri-) sulfide, hydro-	$SiCl_3HS$	167.52	col liq	1.45		96–100	d	d	d al
s101	fluoride, tetra-	Tetrafluorosilane. SiF_4	104.08	col gas	gas: 4.69 g/l^{760} liq: 1.66^{-95}	-90.2	-86	d	d	s abs al, HF; i eth
s102	(di-)fluoride, hexa	Hexa-fluorodisilane. Si_2F_6	170.16	gas	7.759 g/l	-18.7	-18.5	d	d	
s103	hydride	Silane, silicane. SiH_4	32.12	col gas	liq: 0.68^{-85} gas: 1.44 g/l	-185	-111.8^{760} mm	i		d KOH
s104	hydride	Disilane, disilicane. Si_2H_6	62.22	col gas	gas: 2.865 g/l liq: 0.686^{-20}	-132.5	-14.5	sl d		s al, bz, CS_2
s105	hydride	Trisilane, trisilanepropane. Si_3H_8	92.32	col liq	liq: 0.743^0; gas: 4.15 g/l^0_{760}	-117.4	52.9	d	d	d CCl_4
s106	hydride	Tetrasilane, tetrasilane butane. Si_4H_{10}	122.42	col liq	liq: 0.79^0 gas 5.48 g/l^0_{760}	-108	84.3	d		
s107	iodide, tetra-	Tetraiodosilane. SiI_4	535.70	col, cub	4.198	120.5	287.5	d		2.2^{27} CS_2
s108	(di-)iodide, hexa-	Hexaiodosilane. Si_2I_6	817.60	col, hex		d 250		d	d	19^{19} CS_2
s109	nitride	Si_3N_4	140.28	gray-wh amorph powd	3.44	1900 press		i	i	s HF
s110	oxide, di-	Nat. cristobalite. SiO_2	60.08	col, cub or tetr, 1.487, 1.484	2.32	1713 ± 5	2230 (2590)	i	i	s HF; v sl s alk
s111	oxide, di-	Nat. lechatelierite. SiO_2	60.08	col, amorph, vitr, 1.4588	2.19		2230 (2590)	i	i	s HF; v sl s alk
s112	oxide, di-	Nat. opal. $SiO_2.xH_2O$		col, amorph 1.41–1.46	2.17–2.20	>1600		i	i	s HF; v sl s alk
s113	oxide, di-	Nat. tridymite. SiO_2	60.08	col, rhomb, 1.469, 1.470, 1.471	2.26_4^{25}	1703	2230 (2590)	i	i	s HF; v sl s alk
s114	oxide, di-	Nat. quartz. SiO_2	60.08	col, hex, 1.544, 1.553	2.635–2.660	1610	2230 (2590)	i	i	s HF; v sl s alk
s115	oxide, mon-	SiO	44.09	wh, cub	2.13	>1702	1880	i	i	s dil $HF+HNO_3$
s116	oxychloride	Chlorosiloxane. Si_2OCl_6	284.89	col liq		28.1 ± 0.2	137	d		∞ CS_2, CCl_4
s117	oxyfluoride	Si_2OF_6	186.16	col gas	1.358 liq	-47.8 ± 0.5	-23.3	d	d	d alk
s118	sulfide, di-	SiS_2	92.21	wh need, rhomb	2.02	subl 1090	white heat	d		d al, liq NH_3; s dil alk; i bz
s119	sulfide, mono-	SiS	60.15	yel need	1.853^{15}	subl 940^{20}		d	d	d al, alk
s120	thiocyanate	$Si(CNS)_4$	260.41	wh, rhomb need	1.409_4^{20}	143.8	314.2	d		d al, a, alk; i eth, CS_2, $CHCl_3$
s121	**Silicotungstic acid**	$H_4[Si(W_3O_{10})_4]\cdot 26H_2O$	3346.47	wh-sl yel cr, deliq				v s	v s	v s al
s122	**Silicyl oxide**	Disiloxane. $(SiH_3)_2O$	78.22	col gas	gas: 3.491 g/l liq: 0.881^{-80}	144	15.2	v sl s	sl d	

No.	Name	Synonyms and Formulae	Mol. wt.	Crystalline form, properties and index of refraction	Density or spec. gravity	Melting point, °C	Boiling point, °C	Solubility, in grams per 100 cc		
								Cold water	Hot water	Other solvents
	Siloxane									
s123	**Siloxane, (di-), oxide.**	$[H(O)Si]_2.O$	106.19	wh volum subst		expl ca 300		sl s		s, d HF; d al
s124	**Silver**	Ag	107.868	wh met, cub 0.54.	10.5^{20}	961.93	2212	i	i	s HNO₃, h H₂SO₄, KCN; i alk
s125	acetate	$AgC_2H_3O_2$	166.92	wh pl	3.259^{15}	d		1.02^{20}	2.52^{80}	s dil HNO₃
s126	acetylide	Ag_2C_2	239.76	wh ppt		expl		i		s a; sl s al
s127	orthoarsenate	Ag_3AsO_4	462.53	dk red, cub	6.657^{25}	d		0.00085^{20}		s NH₄OH, ac a
s128	orthoarsenite	Ag_3AsO_3	446.53	yel, powd		d 150		0.00115^{20}	i	s ac a, NH₄OH, HNO₃; i al
s129	azide	AgN_3	149.89	wh rhomb pr, expl		252	297	i	0.01^{100}	s KCN, dil HNO₃; sl s NH₄OH
s130	benzoate	$AgC_7H_5O_2$	228.99	wh powd				0.262^{25}	s	0.017 al
s131	tetraborate	$Ag_2B_4O_7.2H_2O$	407.01	wh cr				sl s		s a
s132	bromate	$AgBrO_3$	235.78	col, tetr, 1.874, 1.920	5.206	d		0.196^{25}	1.33^{90}	s NH₄OH; sl s HNO₃
s133	bromide	Bromyrite: $AgBr$	187.78	pa yel, 2.253	6.473^{25}	432	d>1300	8.4×10^{-6}	0.00037^{100}	s KCN, Na₂S₂O₃, NaCl sol; sl s NH₄OH; i al
s134	carbonate	Ag_2CO_3	275.75	yel powd	6.077	d 218		0.0032^{20}	0.05^{100}	s NH₄OH, Na₂S₂O₃; i al
s135	chlorate	$AgClO_3$	191.32	wh, tetr	4.430^{20}_4	230	d 270	10^{15}	50^{80}	sl s al
s136	perchlorate	$AgClO_4$	207.32	wh, cr, deliq	2.806^{25}	d 486		557^{25}	s	s al; 101 tol; 5.28 bz
s137	chloride	Nat. cerargyrite. $AgCl$	143.32	wh, cub, 2.071	5.56	455	1550	0.000089^{10}	0.0021^{100}	s NH₄OH, Na₂S₂O₃, KCN
s138	chlorite	$AgClO_2$	175.32	yel cr		105 expl		0.45^{25}	2.13^{100}	
s139	chromate	Ag_2CrO_4	331.73	red, monocl	5.625			0.0014^0	0.008^{70}	s NH₄OH, KCN
s140	dichromate	$Ag_2Cr_2O_7$	431.72	red, tricl	4.770	d		0.0083^{15}	d	s a, NH₄OH, KCN
s141	citrate	$Ag_3C_6H_5O_7$	512.71	wh need		d		0.028^{18}	sl s	s a, NH₄OH, KCN, Na₂S₂O₃
s142	cyanate	$AgOCN$	149.89	col	4.00	d		sl s	s	s KCN, HNO₃, NH₄OH
s143	cyanide	$AgCN$	133.84	wh, hex	3.95	d 320		0.000023^{20}		s HNO₃, NH₄OH, KCN, Na₂S₂O₃
s144	ferricyanide	$Ag_3Fe(CN)_6$	535.56					0.000066^{20}		i a; s NH₄OH, h (NH₄)₂CO₃
s145	ferrocyanide	$Ag_4Fe(CN)_6.H_2O$	661.45	wh				i	i	s KCN; i a, NH₄ salts, NH₄OH
s146	fluogallate	$Ag_3[GaF_6].10H_2O$	687.47	col, orthorhomb cr, 1.493	2.90			v s		i al
s147	fluoride	AgF	126.87	yel, cub, deliq	$5.852^{15.5}$	435	ca 1159	$182^{15.5}$	205^{108}	sl s NH₄OH
s148	fluoride, di-	AgF_2	145.87	brn, rhomb	4.57–4.58	690	d 700	d	d	
s149	(di-)fluoride	Ag_2F	234.74	yel, hex	8.57	d 90		d		
s150	fluosilicate	$Ag_2SiF_6.4H_2O$	429.88	wh powd or col cr, deliq		>100	d	v s		
s151	fulminate	$Ag_2C_2N_2O_2$	299.77	need		expl		0.075^{13}	s	i NHO₃; s NH₄OH
s152	iodate	$AgIO_3$	282.77	col, rhomb	$5.525^{16.5}$	>200	d	0.003^{10}	0.019^{60}	s HNO₃, NH₄OH, KI
s153	periodate	$AgIO_4$	298.77	or yel, tetrag	5.57	d 180		d		s HNO₃
s154	iodide(α)	Nat. iodyrite. AgI	234.77	yel, hex 2.21, 2.22	5.683^{30}_4	tr 146 to β		$2.8 \times 10^{-7.25}$	$2.5 \times 10^{-6.60}$	s KCN, Na₂S₂O₃, KI; sl s NH₄OH
s155	iodide (β)	AgI	234.77	or, cub	$6.010^{14.6}_4$	558	1506			
s156	iodomercurate (α)	Ag_2HgI_4	923.95	yel, tetrag	6.02	tr to β 50.7		i		s KI, KCN; i dil a
s157	iodomercurate (β)	Ag_2HgI_4	923.95	red, cub	5.90	d 158		i		s KI, KCN; i dil a
s158	hydrogen(tri-) paraperiodate	$Ag_2H_3IO_6$	441.69	yel, rhomb	5.68^{25}	60 d		1.68^{25}		s HNO₃
s159	hyponitrite	$Ag_2N_2O_2$	275.75	yel	5.75^{30}	d 110		v sl s		d HNO₃, H₂SO₄
s160	lactate	$AgC_3H_5O_3.H_2O$	214.96	wh or sl gray cr, powd				ca 7.7		
s161	laurate	$AgC_{12}H_{23}O_2$	307.19	wh, greasy powd		212.5				0.007^{25} al; 0.008^{15} eth
s162	levunilate	$AgC_5H_7O_3$	222.98	leaf		d		0.67^{17}	d	
s163	permanganate	$AgMnO_4$	226.81	dk vlt, monocl	4.27^{25}	d		0.55^0	$1.69^{28.5}$	d al
s164	mercury iodide (α)	Ag_2HgI_4	923.98	yel, tetrag	6.02	trst 50.7		i		
s165	mercury iodide (β)	Ag_2HgI_4	923.98	red, cub	5.90	158 d		i		
s166	myristate	$AgC_{14}H_{27}O_2$	335.24			211		0.007^{25}		0.006^{25} al; 0.007^{15} eth
s167	nitrate	$AgNO_3$	169.87	col, rhomb, 1.729, 1.744, 1.788	4.352^{19}	212	d 444	122^0	952^{190}	s eth, glyc; v sl s abs al

No.	Name	Synonyms and Formulae	Mol. wt.	Crystalline form, properties and index of refraction	Density or spec. gravity	Melting point, °C	Boiling point, °C	Solubility, in grams per 100 cc		
								Cold water	Hot water	Other solvents
	Silver									
s168	nitrite	$AgNO_2$	153.88	wh, rhomb	4.453^{26}	d 140		0.155^0	1.363^{60}	s ac a, NH_4OH; i al
s169	nitroplatinite	$Ag_2[Pt(NO_2)_4]$	594.85	yel-brn monocl pr		d 100		sl s	s	
s170	nitroprusside	$Ag_2[FeNO(CN)_5]$	431.68	lt pink				i		s NH_4OH; i al, HNO_3
s171	oxalate	$Ag_2C_2O_4$	303.76	col cr powd	5.029^4	expl 140		0.00339^{18}		s KCN, NH_4OH, a
s172	oxide	Ag_2O	231.74	br-blk, cub	$7.143^{16.6}$	d 300		0.0013^{20}	0.0053^{80}	s a, KCN, NH_4OH, al
s173	oxide, per	Ag_2O_2 (or AgO)	247.74	gray-blk, cub	7.44	d >100		i		s H_2SO_4, HNO_3, NH_4OH
s174	palmitate	$AgC_{16}H_{31}O_2$	363.29	wh, greasy powd		209		0.0012^{20}	0.006^{25}	0.0071^5 eth; 0.006^{25} al
s175	metaphosphate	$AgPO_3$	186.84	wh, amorph	6.37	ca 482		i		s HNO_3, NH_4OH
s176	orthophosphate	Ag_3PO_4	418.58	yel, cub	6.370^{25}	849		$0.00065^{19.5}$		s a, KCN, NH_4OH, NH_3
s177	orthophosphate, mono-H	Ag_2HPO_4	311.75	wh, trig	1.8036	d 110				
s178	pyrophosphate	$Ag_4P_2O_7$	605.42	wh	$5.306^{7.5}$	585		i	i	s a, NH_4OH, KCN, ac a
s179	propionate	$AgC_3H_5O_2$	180.94	wh leaf or need	2.687^{25}_4			0.842^{20}	2.04^{80}	
s180	perrhenate	$AgReO_4$	358.07	wh cr, tetrag or rhomb	7.05	430		0.32^{20}		
s181	salicylate	$AgC_7H_5O_3$	244.99	wh to redsh-wh cr				sl s		s al
s182	selenate	Ag_2SeO_4	358.73	wh, orthorhomb cr	5.72			0.118^{20}		
s183	selenide	Ag_2Se	294.70	thin gray pl, cub	8.0	880	d	i		s NH_4OH, h HNO_3
s184	stearate	$AgC_{18}H_{35}O_2$	391.35	wh powd amorph		205		0.006^{20}		0.006^{25} al; 0.006^{25} eth
s185	sulfate	Ag_2SO_4	311.80	wh, rhomb, 1.7583, 1.7748, 1.7852	$5.45^{29.2}$	652	d 1085	0.57^0	1.41^{100}	s a, NH_4OH; i al
s186	sulfide	Nat. acanthite. Ag_2S	247.80	gray-blk, rhomb	7.326	tr 175	d		v sl s	s KCN, conc H_2SO_4, HNO_3
s187	sulfide	Nat. argentite. Ag_2S	247.80	blk, cub	7.317	825	d	8.4×10^{-15}		s KCN, a
s188	sulfite	Ag_2SO_3	295.80	wh cr		d 100		v sl s		s a, NH_4OH, KCN; i HNO_3
s189	d-tartrate	$Ag_2C_4H_4O_6$	363.81	wh, scales	3.423^{15}	d		0.2^{18}	0.203^{25}	s a, KCN, NH_4OH
s190	orthotellurate, tetra-H	$Ag_2H_4TeO_6$	443.40	straw yel, rhomb bipyr		d >200		i	i	s KCN, NH_4OH
s191	telluride	Nat. hessite, Ag_2Te	343.31	gray, cub	8.5	955		i	i	s KCN, NH_4OH
s192	tellurite	Ag_2TeO_3	391.36	yel-wh ppt		250-bl 450-pa yel		i	i	s KCN, NH_3
s193¹	thioantimonite	Nat. pyrargyrite. Ag_3SbS_3	541.55	red, trig, 3.084 2.881 (Li)	5.76	486		i		s HNO_3
s193²	thioarsenite	Nat. proustite. Ag_3AsS_3	494.72	scarlet red, trig, 3.088, 2.792	5.49	490		i	i	s HNO_3
s194	thiocyanate	$AgSCN$	165.95	col cr		d		0.000021^{25}	0.00064^{100}	s NH_4OH; i a
s195	di-thionate	$Ag_2S_2O_6.2H_2O$	411.90	rhomb cr, ~1.662	3.61					
s196	thiosulfate	$Ag_2S_2O_3$	327.87	wh cr		d		sl s		s $Na_2S_2O_3$, NH_4OH
s197	tungstate	Ag_2WO_4	463.59	pa yel cr				0.05^{15}		s KCN, NH_4OH, HNO_3
	Silver complex									
s198	diamminesilver perrhenate	$[Ag(NH_3)_2]ReO_4$	392.13	col monocl cr	3.901					1.618 conc NH_4OH
s199	**Sodium**	Na	22.9898	silv, met cub, 4.22	0.97	97.81 ± 0.03	882.9	d to $NaOH + H_2$		d al; i eth, bz
s200	acetate	$NaC_2H_3O_2$	82.03	wh gr powd, monocl, 1.464	1.528	324		119^0	170.15^{100}	sl s al
s201	acetate trihydrate	$NaC_2H_3O_2.3H_2O$	136.08	col, monocl pr, effl, β 1.464	1.45	58	123, −3H₂O, 120	76.2^0	138.8^{50}	2.1^{18} al; s
s202	alumina trisilicate	Nat. albite. $NaAlSi_3O_8$ (or $Na_2O.Al_2O_3.6SiO_2$)	262.22	col, tricl, 1.525, 1.529, 1.536	2.61	1100			sl d	s HCl; d dil al
s203	metaaluminate	$NaAlO_2$	81.97	wh amorph powd, hygr, 1.566, 1.595, 1.580		1800		s	v s	i al
s204	aluminum chloride	$NaCl.AlCl_3$	191.78	wh-yelsh cr powd, hygr		185		s	s	
s205	aluminum meta-silicate	Nat. jadeite. $Na_2O.Al_2O_3.4SiO_2$	401.28	col, monocl	3.3	1000-1060		i	i	d HCl

No.	Name	Synonyms and Formulae	Mol. wt.	Crystalline form, properties and index of refraction	Density or spec. gravity	Melting point, °C	Boiling point, °C	Solubility, in grams per 100 cc		
								Cold water	Hot water	Other solvents
	Sodium									
s206	aluminum ortho-silicate	Nat. nephelite. $Na_2O.Al_2O_3.2SiO_2$	284.11	col, hex, 1.537 ± 0.002	2.619[21]	1526	....	i	d	d a
s207	aluminum sulfate	$NaAl(SO_4)_2.12H_2O$	458.28	col, cub oct, 1.4388	1.6754[20]	61	....	110[15] (anhydr)	146[30] (anhydr)	
s208	amide	Sodamide. $NaNH_2$	39.01	wh, conchoid fract	....	210	400	d	d	d hot al; 0.1 liq NH_3
s209	ammonium phosphate	Microcosmic salt, stercorite. $NaNH_4HPO_4.4H_2O$	209.07	col, monoc, 1.439, 1.441, 1.469	1.554	d 79	....	16.7	100	i al, acet
s210	ammonium sulfate	$NaNH_4SO_4.2H_2O$	173.12	wh, rhomb	1.63[15]	d 80	....	s	s	
s211	ammonium tartrate	$NaNH_4C_4H_4O_6.4H_2O$	261.16	wh, rhomb	1.590			21.09[0]		s Na_2S sol
s212	metaantimonate	Leuconine. $NaSbO_3$	192.74	wh powd				i	s	s Na_2S sol
s213	antimonate, hydroxy	"Pyroantimonate". $NaSb(OH)_6$	246.78	pseudo cub				0.03[12.5]	0.3[100]	sl s al
s214	pyroantimonate, dihydro-	$Na_2H_2Sb_2O_7.6H_2O(?)$	511.58	wh, tetrag		d 280		i	0.28[100], d	....
s215	antimonide	Na_3Sb	190.72	blk powd or bl cr, inflamm		856		d		sl s NH_3
s216	metaantimonite	$NaSbO_2.3H_2O$	230.78	col, rhomb	2.864	d		d		
s217	metaarsenate	$NaAsO_3$	145.91	rhomb, effl, 1.479, 1.502, 1.527	2.301	615		v s		
s218	orthoarsenate	$Na_3AsO_4.12H_2O$	423.93	col, trig or hex prism, 1.457, 1.466	1.752-1.804	86.3		38.9[15.5]		1.67 al; 50[15] glyc
s219	orthoarsenate, di-H	$NaH_2AsO_4.H_2O$	181.94	col, rhomb or monocl, 1.583, 1.553, 1.507	2.53	130, −H_2O, 100	d 200-280	s		
s220	orthoarsenate, mono-H	$Na_2HAsO_4.7H_2O$	312.01	col, monocl, pois, 1.462, 1.466, 1.478	1.88	130, −5H_2O, 50	d 180	5.46[0]	100[100]	s glyc; sl s al
s221	orthoarsenate, mono-H	$Na_2HAsO_4.12H_2O$	402.09	col, monocl, effl, 1.445, 1.466, 1.451	1.736	28	−12H_2O, 100	56[14]	140.7[30]	sl s al; i liq Cl
s222	pyroarsenate	$Na_4As_2O_7$	353.79	wh cr	2.205	850	d 1000	v s		....
s223	arsenate fluoride	$2Na_3AsO_4.NaF.19H_2O$	800.06	wh, cub, 1.4657, 1.4693, 1.4726	2.849[25]	....		10[75]		
s224	arsenite	Sodium metaarsenite (?) (com'l) $NaAsO_2$ (or mixt with Na_3AsO_3)	129.91	gray-wh powd, pois	1.87			v s	v s	sl s al
s225	arsenotartrate	$Na(AsO)C_4H_4O_6.2\frac{1}{2}H_2O$	307.02	shiny cr, pois		−2\frac{1}{2}H_2O, 275	d 275	6.5[19]		i al
s226	azide	NaN_3	65.01	col, hex	1.846[20]	d Na+N	d in vac	41.7[17]		0.314[15] al; s liq NH_3, i eth
s227	barbital	$NaC_8H_{11}N_2O_3$	206.18	wh powd				20[25]	40[100]	sl s al; i eth
s228	benzenesulfonate	$NaC_6H_5SO_3$	180.16	wh cr				35.8[30]	v s	
s229	benzoate	$NaC_7H_5O_2$	144.11	col cr, or wh amorph, or gran powd				66[20]	74.2[100]	1.64[25] al
s230	metabismuthate	$NaBiO_3$	279.97	yel-brn powd (com'l), yel (pure)				i	d	d a
s231	metaborate	$NaBO_2$	65.80	col, hex pr	2.464	966	1434	26[20]	36[35]	....
s232	metaborate, tetrahydrate	$NaBO_2.4H_2O$	137.86	tricl, coll		57	−H_2O, 120	v s	v s	
s233	metaborate, peroxyhydrate	Sodium perborate (com'l). $NaBO_2.H_2O_2.3H_2O$	153.86	col, monocl		63.0	−H_2O, 130-150	2.55[15]	3.75[22]	s a, al, glyc
s234	tetraborate	$Na_2B_4O_7$	201.22	cr, 1.5010	2.367	741	d 1575	1.06[0]	8.79[40]	i al
s235	tetraborate, decahydrate	Borax. $Na_2B_4O_7.10H_2O$	381.37	col, monocl, effl, 1.447, 1.469, 1.472	1.73	75, −8H_2O, 60	−10H_2O, 320	2.01[0]	170[100]	v sl s al; s glyc; i a
s236	tetraborate, pentahydrate	$Na_2B_4O_7.5H_2O$	291.30	col, cub or hex, deliq, 1.461	1.815	−H_2O, 120		22.65[55] (anhydr)	52.3[100]	
s237	borohydride	$NaBH_4$	37.83	white cub, 1.542	1.074	400 dec		55[25]	v s	4 al; 16.4 MeO s pyr; i eth
s238	bromate	$NaBrO_3$	150.90	col, cub, 1.594	3.339[17.5]	381		27.5[0]	90.9[100]	i al
s239	bromide	$NaBr$	102.90	col, cub, hygr, 1.6412	3.203[$\frac{25}{4}$]	747	1390	116.0[50]	121[100]	sl s al
s240	bromide, dihydrate	$NaBr.2H_2O$	138.93	col, monocl pr	2.176	−2H_2O, 51		79.5[0]	118.6[80.5]	2.31[15] al; s liq NH_3; 17.42[15] MeOH
s241	bromoaurate	$NaAuBr_4.2H_2O$	575.62	br-blk cr				s	....	
s242	bromoiridite	$Na_2IrBr_6.12H_2O$	956.81	dk grn, rhomb, effl		100	−H_2O, 150			s NH_4OH

No.	Name	Synonyms and Formulae	Mol. wt.	Crystalline form, properties and index of refraction	Density or spec. gravity	Melting point, °C	Boiling point, °C	Solubility, in grams per 100 cc		
								Cold water	Hot water	Other solvents
	Sodium									
s243	bromoplatinate......	$Na_2PtBr_6.6H_2O$	828.62	dk red, tricl	3.323	d 150	....	v s	v s	v s al
s244	cacodylate..........	$Na[(CH_3)_2AsO_2].3H_2O$	214.03	wh	....	ca 60	$-H_2O$, 120	200^{15-20}	....	40^{25} al; 100^{15-20} 90 % al
s245	calcium sulfate......	$Na_2Ca(SO_4)_2.2H_2O$	314.21	col, monocl need.	2.64	$-2H_2O$, 80	....	d	d	
s246	d-camphorate......	$Na_2C_{10}H_{14}O_4.3H_2O$	298.25	wh need, hygr....	....	$-3H_2O$, 100	....	122^{14}		s al
s247	carbide...........	Na_2C_2	70.00	wh powd	1.575^{15}	ca 700	....	d	d	s a; d al
s248	carbonate..........	Na_2CO_3	105.99	wh powd, hygr, 1.535	2.532	851	d	7.1^0	45.5^{100}	sl s abs al; i acet
s249	carbonate, deca-hydrate	Washing soda. $Na_2CO_3.10H_2O$	286.14	wh, monocl, 1.405, 1.425, 1.440	1.44^{15}	32.5–34.5	$-H_2O$, 33.5	21.5^{20}	421^{104}	i al
s250	carbonate, hepta-hydrate	$Na_2CO_3.7H_2O$	232.10	rhomb bipyr, effl	1.51	$-H_2O$, 32	....	16.90	33.9^{35}	....
s251	carbonate, mono-hydrate	Crystal carbonate, thermonatrite. $Na_2CO_3.H_2O$	124.00	col, rhomb, deliq, 1.506, 1.509	2.25	$-H_2O$, 100	....	33	52.08	14^{25} glyc; i al, eth
s252	carbonate, sesqui-...	$Na_2CO_3.NaHCO_3.2H_2O$	226.03	col, monocl, 1.5073	2.112	d	....	13^0	42^{100}	
s253	carbonate hydrogen...	$NaHCO_3$	84.00	wh, monocl pr, 1.500	2.159	$-CO_2$, 270	....	6.9^0	16.4^{60}	sl s al
s254	chlorate...........	$NaClO_3$	106.44	col, cub or trig, 1.513	2.490^{15}	248–261	d	79^0	230^{100}	s al, liq NH_3, glyc
s255	perchlorate........	$NaClO_4$	122.44	wh, rhomb, deliq, 1.4606, 1.4617, 1.4731		d 482	d	s	v s	s al
s256	perchlorate, hydrate.	$NaClO_4.H_2O$	140.46	col rhbdr, deliq	2.02	130	d 482	209^{15}	284^{50}	s al
s257	chloride...........	Common salt, nat. halite. $NaCl$	58.44	col, cub, 1.5442.	2.165^{25}_4	801	1413	35.7^0	39.12^{100}	sl s al, liq, NH_3; s glyc; i HCl
s258	chlorite...........	$NaClO_2$	90.44	wh, cr, hygr	....	d 180–200	....	39^{17}	55^{60}	....
s259	chlorite, penta-hydrate	$NaOCl.5H_2O$	164.52	col	....	24.5	....	29.3^0	94.2^{21}	....
s260	hypochlorite........	$NaOCl$	74.44	in solution only.			....			
s261	hypochlorite, dihydrate	$NaOCl.2\frac{1}{2}H_2O$	119.48	col, hygr	....	57.5	....	v s		
s262	chloroaurate.......	$NaAuCl_4.2H_2O$	397.80	yel, rhomb, ω 1.545 ϵ>1.75	....	d 100	....	150^{10}	990^{60}	v s al, eth
s263	chloroiridate.......	$Na_2IrCl_6.6H_2O$	558.99	dull red-blk, tricl	....	d 600	....	v s	v s	sl s al
s264	chloroiridite.......	$Na_3IrCl_6.12H_2O$	690.07	dk grn cr	....	$-H_2O$, 50	....	31.46^{15}	307.26^{85}	
s265	chloroosmate.......	$Na_2OsCl_6.2H_2O$	484.93	or-red, rhomb pr	....		....	v s		s al
s266	chloropalladite.....	$Na_2PdCl_4.3H_2O$	348.24	br-red cr, deliq	....		....	v s		s al
s267	chloroplatinate.....	Na_2PtCl_6	453.79	or-yel powd, hygr	....	tr 150–160	....	s	v s	s al
s268	hexachloroplatinate..	$Na_2PtCl_6.6H_2O$	561.88	or-red, tricl	2.500	$-6H_2O$, 100	....	66^{15}	v s	11.9 al, MeOH; i eth
s269	chloroplatinite.....	$Na_2PtCl_4.4H_2O$	454.98	red pr	....	100	$-H_2O$, 150	s	....	s al
s270	chlororhodite, hexa-.	Na_3RhCl_6	384.59	red, tricl	....	d>550	....	v s		
s271	chlororhodite, hexa-, hydrate	$Na_3RhCl_6.18H_2O$	708.87	garnet red, oct, effl	....	d 904, effl	....	v s		i al
s272	chromate...........	Na_2CrO_4	161.97	yel, rhomb bipyram	2.710–2.736		....	87.3^{30}	....	sl s al; s MeOH
s273	chromate decahydrate	$Na_2CrO_4.10H_2O$	342.13	yel, monocl, deliq	1.483	19.92	....	50^{10}	126^{100}	sl s al; i ac a
s274	dichromate........	$Na_2Cr_2O_7.2H_2O$	298.00	red, monocl pr, deliq, 1.661, 1.699, 1.751	2.52^{13}	$-2H_2O$, 100 356.7 (anhydr)	d 400 (anhydr)	238^0 (anhydr) 180^{20}	508^{80} (anhydr) 433^{98}	i al
s275	peroxychromate.....	Na_3CrO_8	248.96	or pl	....	d 115	....	sl s	....	i al, eth
s276	cinnamate.........	$NaC_9H_7O_2$	170.14	wh cr powd	....		....	9.1	5^{100}	0.625 90 % al; s glyc
s277	citrate, dihydrate ...	$Na_3C_6H_5O_7.2H_2O$	294.10	wh cr, gran or powd	....	$-2H_2O$, 150	....	72^{25}	167^{100}	0.625 90 % al; s glyc
s278	citrate, pentahydrate	$Na_3C_6H_5O_7.5(or 5\frac{1}{2})H_2O$	348.15	wh, rhomb	$1.857^{22.5}$	$-5H_2O$, 150	d	92.6^{25}	250^{100}	sl s al
s279	cobaltinitrite.......	$Na_3Co(NO_2)_6$	403.94	yelsh-brush cr powd	....		....	v s, d		sl s al; d min a; i dil ac a
s280	cyanamide, mono-...	$NaHCN_2$	64.02	wh cr powd, hygr	....		....	v s		
s281	cyanate...........	$NaOCN$	65.01	col need	1.937^{20}	d 700 vac	....	s	s	v sl s eth, bz
s282	cyanide...........	$NaCN$	49.01	col, cub, deliq, pois, 1.452	....	563.7	1496	48^{10}	82^{35}	sl s al; s NH_3
s283	cyanoaurite........	Sodium aurocyanide. $NaAu(CN)_2$	271.99		....		....	s		
s284	cyanocuprate (I)....	$NaCu(CN)_2$	138.57		1.013^{20}	d 100	....	s		
s285	cyanoplatinite.....	$Na_2[Pt(CN)_4].3H_2O$	399.19	col, tricl	2.646	$-3H_2O$, 120–125	....	s	s	s al
s286	enanthate.........	Sodium heptanoate. $NaC_7H_{13}O_2$	152.17	wh cr powd or leaf	....	240–350	....	s		s al
s287	ethyl acetoacetate...	$NaC_6H_9O_3$	152.13	need	....	d	....	d		s oth
s288	ethyl sulfate......	$NaC_2H_5SO_4.H_2O$	166.13	wh, hex pl, deliq	....	d	....	164^{17}		d alk, H_2SO_4; 142 al

Sodium

No.	Name	Synonyms and Formulae	Mol. wt.	Crystalline form, properties and index of refraction	Density or spec. gravity	Melting point, °C	Boiling point, °C	Cold water	Hot water	Other solvents
s289	ferrate (III)	Ferrite. $Na_2Fe_2O_4$	221.67	br, hex pl or need	4.05			d		v s dil HCl
s290	ferricyanide	$Na_3Fe(CN)_6.H_2O$	298.92	red cr, deliq				18.9^0	67^{100}	i al
s291	ferrocyanate	Yellow prussiate of soda. $Na_4Fe(CN)_6.10H_2O$	484.04	pa yel, monocl, 1.519, 1.530 1.544	1.458			31.85^{20}	156.5^{98}	i al
s292	fluoaluminate	Na_3AlF_6	209.94	col, monocl, β 1.364	2.90	1000		sl s		i HCl,; d alk
s293	fluoantimonate	$NaSbF_6$	258.73	rhomb	3.375^{18}	<1360		128.6^{20}		s al, acet
s294	fluoberyllate	Na_2BeF_4	130.99	wh, rhomb or monocl		d		1.47^{18}	2.94^{100}	
s295	fluoborate	$NaBF_4$	109.79	wh, rhomb	2.47^{20}	sl d 384	d	108^{26}	210^{100}	sl s al; d H_2SO_4
s296	fluoride	Nat. villiaumite. NaF	41.99	col, cub or tetr, 1.336	2.558^{41}	993	1695	4.22^{18}		s HF; v sl s al
s297	fluoride, hydrogen	$NaF.HF$	61.99	col, or wh cr powd, rhdr	2.08			s	s	
s298	fluoride *ortho*phosphate	$NaF.Na_3PO_4.12H_2O$	422.11		2.2165			12^{25}	57.5^{50}	
s299	fluoroacetate, mono-	$NaC_2H_2FO_2$	100.02	wh powd		200		111^{25}		1.4^{25} al; 5^{25} MeOH; 0.04^{25} acet; 0.0049^{25} CCl$_4$
s300	fluorophosphate, hexa-	$NaPF_6.H_2O$	185.97		2.369^{19}			103.2^0		
s301	fluorophosphate, mono-	Na_2PO_3F	143.95	col		ca 625		25		
s302	fluosilicate	Na_2SiF_6	188.06	col, hex, 1.312, 1.309	2.679	d		0.652^{17}	2.46^{100}	i al
s303	fluosulfonate	$NaSO_3F$	122.05	shiny leaf, hygr		d red heat		s		s al, acet; i eth
s304	formaldehyde-sulfoxylate	$NaHSO_2.CH_2O.2H_2O$	154.12	rhomb pr, hygr		64	d	v s		d a; s al, alk
s305	formate	$NaCHO_2$	68.01	col, monocl, deliq	1.92^{20}	253	d	97.2^{20}	160^{100}	sl s al; i eth
s306	2-furanacrylate	$NaC_7H_5O_3$	160.10	lt brn powd	1.919	d		s	s	sl s al; i eth
s307	*meta*germanate	Na_2GeO_3	166.57	wh, monocl, deliq, 1.59	3.31^{22}	1083			d	s a
s308	*meta*germanate, heptahydrate	$Na_2GeO_3.7H_2O$	292.68	col, rhomb		83		24.6^0 45.5^{25}		s a
s309	(mono-) *d*-glutamate	$NaC_5H_8NO_4$	169.11	wh cr		d		v s		sl s al
s310	glycerophosphate, monohydrate	$Na_2C_3H_7O_6P.H_2O$	234.05	yelsh visc liq; wh cr or powd				s		s al
s311	glycerophosphate, pentahydrate	$Na_2C_3H_7O_6P.5\frac{1}{2}H_2O$	315.12	wh pl, sc or powd		>130		v s		i al
s312	gold sulfide	$NaAuS.4H_2O$	324.08	col, monocl		d		s		s al
s313	hydride	NaH	24.00	silver need, 1.470	0.92	d 800		d	d	s molten Na; i CS_2, CCl_4, NH_3, bz
s314	hydroxide	$NaOH$	40.00	wh, deliq, 1.3576	2.130	318.4	1390	42^0	347^{100}	v s al, glyc; i acet, eth
s315	iodate	$NaIO_3$	197.89	wh, rhomb	$4.277^{17.5}$	d		9^{20}	34^{100}	i al; s ac a
s316	*meta*periodate	$NaIO_4$	213.89	col, tetr	4.174	d 300		14.44^{25}	$38.9^{51.5}$	s H_2SO_4, HNO_3, ac a
s317	*meta*periodate, trihydrate	$NaIO_4.3H_2O$	267.94	col, rhombdsh, effl	3.219^{18}_4	d 175		18.78^{25}	$36.4^{34.5}$	
s318	*para*periodate	Na_5IO_6	337.85			800 d		d		
s319	(tri-)*para*periodate	$Na_3H_2IO_6$	293.88	col, hexag				sl s		s con NaOH sol
s320	iodide	NaI	149.89	col, cub, 1.7745	3.667^{25}_4	661	1304	184^{25}	302^{100}	42.57^{25} al; 39.9^{25} acet; s glyc
s321	iodide, dihydrate	$NaI.2H_2O$	185.92	col, monocl	$2.448^{20.8}$	752		317.9^0	1550^{100}	v s NH_3
s322	iodoplatinate	$Na_2PtI_6.6H_2O$	1110.59	brn, monocl	3.707			v s		s al
s323	iridium chloride	Sodium hexachloroiridate. $Na_3IrCl_6.12H_2O$	690.07	olive cr, rhomb or trig-rhomb		50		s	s	i al
s324	iron (III) nitrosopentacyanide	$Na_2[Fe(CN)_5NO].2H_2O$	297.95	ruby red, rhomb, 1.605, 1.575, 1.56	1.687^{25}	$-H_2O$, 100	d 160	40^{16}		
s325	iron (III) oxalate	$Na_3[Fe(C_2O_4)_3].5\frac{1}{2}H_2O$	487.96	grn, monocl	$1.973^{17.5}$	$-4H_2O$	d 300	32^0	182^{100}	
s326	iron (III) sulfate	$3Na_2SO_4.Fe_2(SO_4)_3.6H_2O$	934.09	wh, trig, 1.558, 1.613	2.5	$-6H_2O$, 100		d v sl		i al
s327	lactate	$NaC_3H_5O_3$	112.06	col or yelsh liq, very hygr		17	d 140	v s		s al; i eth
s328	lithium sulfate	$Na_2Li(SO_4)_2.6H_2O$	376.12	col, ditrig	2.009	$-6H_2O$, 50		s	s	
s329	magnesium carbonate	$Na_2CO_3.MgCO_3$	190.31	wh, rhomb	2.729^{15}	677 CO_2 1240/atm		d	d	
s330	magnesium sulfate	Nat. bloedite. $Na_2SO_4.MgSO_4.4H_2O$	334.48	col, monocl, 1.486, 1.488, 1.489	2.23			s		
s331	magnesium tartrate	$Na_2Mg(C_4H_4O_6)_2.10H_2O$	546.59	wh, monocl pr or powd				s	s	

No.	Name	Synonyms and Formulae	Mol. wt.	Crystalline form, properties and index of refraction	Density or spec. gravity	Melting point, °C	Boiling point, °C	Solubility, in grams per 100 cc		
								Cold water	Hot water	Other solvents
	Sodium									
s332	manganate	$Na_2MnO_4.10H_2O$	345.07	grn, monocl		17		s	d	
s333	*per*manganate	$NaMnO_4$	141.93	red cr, deliq		d		v s	v s	
s334	*per*manganate, trihydrate	$NaMnO_4.3H_2O$	195.97	purp cr, deliq	2.47	d 170		v s	v s	s NH_3; d alk
s335	methanearsenate	$Na_2CH_3AsO_3.6H_2O$	292.03	wh cr powd		130–140		ca 100		sl s al; i bz, eth, oils
s336	methoxide	$CH_3ONa.2CH_3OH$	118.11	wh powd		d, $-CH_3OH$		s, d		s CH_3OH
s337	methylsulfate	$NaCH_3SO_4.H_2O$	152.10	col cr, hygr				s, d		s al
s338	molybdate	Na_2MoO_4	205.92	opaque wh	3.28^{18}	687		s 44.3'	84^{100}	
s339	molybdate, dihydrate	$Na_2MoO_4.2H_2O$	241.95	wh, rhbdr	3.28(?)	$-2H_2O$, 100		56.2^{0}	115.5^{100}	i meth acet
s340	*deca*molybdate	$Na_2Mo_{10}O_{31}.21H_2O$	1879.68	wh, monocl pr				sl s	0.842^{100}	
s341	*di*molybdate	$Na_2Mo_2O_7$	349.86	wh need		612		sl s	sl s	
s342	*octa*molybdate	$Na_2Mo_8O_{25}.17H_2O$	1519.75	monocl cr		$-H_2O$, 20		v s	v s	
s343	*para*molybdate	$Na_6Mo_7O_{24}.22H_2O$	1589.84	col, monocl, effl		$700 -H_2O$, 100–120		117.9^{30} (anhydr)	s	
s344	*tetra*molybdate	$Na_2Mo_4O_{13}.6H_2O$	745.82	yel need				39.8^{21}	v s	
s345	*tri*molybdate	$Na_2Mo_3O_{10}.7H_2O$	619.96	need acicular		$528 -6H_2O$, 100		3.878^{20}	13.7^{100}	
s346	*meta*niobate	$Na_2Nb_2O_6.7H_2O$	453.90	pseudo-cub	4.512 1.559	$-H_2O$, 100		s		
s347	nitrate	Soda niter. $NaNO_3$	84.99	col, trig or rhbdr, 1.587, 1.336	2.261	306.8	d 380	92.1^{25}	180^{100}	s al, MeOH; v s NH_3; v sl s acet; sl s glyc
s348	nitride	Na_3N	82.98	dk gray		d 300		d		
s349	nitrite	$NaNO_2$	69.00	col-yel, rhomb pr, hygr	2.168^{0}	271	d 320	81.5^{15}	163^{100}	0.3^{20} eth; 4.4^{20} MeOH; 3 abs al; v s NH_3
s350	*hypo*nitrite	$Na_2N_2O_2$	105.99		1.728^{25}	d 300		d		i al
s351	*p*-nitrophenoxide	$NaOC_6H_4NO_2.4H_2O$	233.15	yel, monocl pr		$-2H_2O$, 36 $-4H_2O$, 120	d	5.97^{25}		sl s al
s352	nitroplatinite	$Na_2Pt(NO_2)_4$	425.09	pa yel rhomb or monocl pr, effl				s	s	
s353	nitroprusside	$Na_2[Fe(NO)(CN)_5].2H_2O$	297.95	red, rhomb	1.72			40^{16}		s al
s354	oleate	$NaC_{18}H_{33}O_2$	304.45	wh cr, or yel amorph gran		232–235		10^{12}		s al; sl s eth
s355	oxalate	$Na_2C_2O_4$	134.00	col cr, or wh powd	2.34	d 250–270		3.7^{20}	6.33^{100}	i al, eth
s356	oxalate, hydrogen	$NaHC_2O_4.H_2O$	130.03	wh, monocl		$-H_2O$, 100	d 200	1.7^{15}	21^{100}	
s357	oxalatoferrate (III)	$Na_3[Fe(C_2O_4)_3].xH_2O$	365.89 $+xH_2O$	grn, monocl cr	$1.973^{17.5}$	$-H_2O$, 100–120		32.5	182^{100}	
s358	oxide, mon-	Na_2O	61.98	wh-gray, deliq	2.27	subl 1275		d	d	d al
s359	oxide, per-	Na_2O_2	77.98	yel-wh powd	2.805	d 460	d 657	s	d	d al, NH_3; s dil a; i alk
s360	oxide, per-, octahydrate	$Na_2O_2.8H_2O$	222.10	wh, hex		d 30	d	s	d	i al
s361	palmitate	$NaC_{16}H_{31}O_2$	278.41	wh cr		270				
s362	pentobarbital	$NaC_{11}H_{17}N_2O_3$	248.26					s	s, d	s al
s363	phenobarbital	$NaC_{12}H_{11}N_2O_3$	254.22	wh				v s		s al; i eth, chl
s364	1-phenol-4-sulfonate(*p*-)	$NaC_6H_4(OH)SO_3.2H_2O$	232.19	col, monocl or gran, sl effl		d		23.8^{25}	125^{100}	0.75^{25} al; 20^{25} glyc
s365	phenoxide	$NaOC_6H_5$	116.10	wh cr need, deliq				v s		s al, acet; d a
s366	phenylcarbonate	$NaC_7H_5O_3$	160.11	col powd		d 120		d		d acet
s367	*hypo*phosphate	$Na_4P_2O_6.10H_2O$	430.06	col, monocl, 1.477, 1.482, 1.504	1.823	d		1.49^{25}	5.46^{50}	
s368	*hypo*phosphate, di-H	$Na_2H_2P_2O_6.6H_2O$	314.03	col, monocl, 1.468, 1.490, 1.504	1.849	250 (anhydr)	$-6H_2O$, 100	2.35	25	s dil H_2SO_4, NH_4OH; i al
s369	*meta*phosphate, hexa-	Graham's salt. $(NaPO_3)_6$	611.17	col glass, 1.482 ± 0.002				v s		
s370	*meta*phosphate, tri-, hexahydrate	Knorre's salt. $(NaPO_3)_3.6H_2O$	413.98	col, tricl, effl, 1.433, 1.442, 1.446		53; $-6H_2O$, 50		s		
s371	*ortho*phosphate	$Na_3PO_4.10H_2O$	344.09	col, oct	$2.536^{17.5}$ (anhydr)	100		8.8 (anhydr)		
s372	*ortho*phosphate	$Na_3PO_4.12H_2O$	380.12	col, trig, 1.446, 1.452	1.62^{20}	d 73.3–76.7	$-12H_2O$, 100	1.5^{0}	157^{70}	i CS_2, al
s373	*ortho*phosphate, di-H	$NaH_2PO_4.H_2O$	137.99	col, rhomb, 1.456, 1.458, 1.487	2.040	$-H_2O$, 100	d 204	59.9^{0}	427^{100}	v sl s eth, chl, tol; i al
s374	*ortho*phosphate, di-H	$NaH_2PO_4.2H_2O$	156.01	col, rhomb, 1.4629	1.91	60		v s	v s	.—.
s375	*ortho*phosphate, mono-H	Sörensen's sodium phosphate. $Na_2HPO_4.2H_2O$	177.99	rhomb bispheroidal, 1.463	2.066^{16}	$-2H_2O$, 95		100^{50}	117^{80}	
s376	*ortho*phosphate, mono-H	$Na_2HPO_4.7H_2O$	268.07	col, monocl pr, 1.442	1.679	$-5H_2O$, 48.1		104^{40}		i al
s377	*ortho*phosphate, mono-H	$Na_2HPO_4.12H_2O$	358.14	col, rhomb or monocl, eff, wh powd, 1.432, 1.436, 1.437	1.52	$-5H_2O$, 35.1	$-12H_2O$, 100	1.15	87.4^{34}	i al

No.	Name	Synonyms and Formulae	Mol. wt.	Crystalline form, properties and index of refraction	Density or spec. gravity	Melting point, °C	Boiling point, °C	Solubility, in grams per 100 cc		
								Cold water	Hot water	Other solvents
	Sodium									
s378	pyrophosphate	$Na_4P_2O_7$	265.90	wh cr, 1.425	2.534	880		3.16^0	40.26^{100}	
s379	pyrophosphate	$Na_4P_2O_7.10H_2O$	446.06	col, monocl, 1.450, 1.453, 1.460	1.815–1.836	$-H_2O$, 93.8 m.p. 880		5.41^0	93.11^{100}	i al, NH_3
s380	pyrophosphate, di-H	$Na_2H_2P_2O_7.6H_2O$	330.03	monocl, 1.4599, 1.4645, 1.4649	1.85	$-H_2O$, 220		6.9^0	35^{40}	
s381	phosphide	Na_3P	99.94	red		d		d, PH_3		
s382	hypophosphite	$NaH_2PO_2.H_2O$	105.99	col, monocl, deliq		d viol		100^{25}	667^{100}	v s al; s glyc; sl s NH_3, NH_4OH
s383	orthophosphite, di-H	$NaH_2PO_3.2\frac{1}{2}H_2O$	149.01	col, monocl, 1.419, 1.431, 1.449		42	$-2\frac{1}{2}H_2O$, 100	56^0	193^{42}	
s384	orthophosphite, mono-H	$Na_2HPO_3.5H_2O$	216.04	wh, rhomb deliq, β, 1.443		53	d 200–250	s	v s	i al, NH_4OH
s385	triphosphate	Sodium tripolyphosphate. $Na_5P_3O_{10}$	367.86	powd and gran				14.5^{25}	32.5^{100}	
s386	phthalate	$Na_2C_8H_4O_4$	210.10	wh powd or pearly pl		$-H_2O$, 150				
s387	platinate, hydroxo-	$Na_2Pt(OH)_6$	343.11	yel or red-brn, hex		$-3H_2O$, 150–170	d	s		i al; sl s HCl
s388	platinum cyanide	$Na_2[Pt(CN)_4].3H_2O$	399.19	col, tricl	2.646	$-H_2O$, 120–125		s		s al
s389	plumbate, hydroxo-	$Na_2Pb(OH)_6$	355.21	yel-wh lumps, hygr				d to PbO_2		d a; s alk
s390	potassium(dl)-tartrate	$NaKC_4H_4O_6$	210.14	col, tricl		90–100	d 200	47.4^6 (anhydr)	v s	
s391	propionate	$NaC_3H_5O_2$	96.06	wh, gran powd				s		s al
s392	perrhenate	$NaReO_4$	273.19	col, hex pl, hygr	5.39	300 (in O_2) d 440 (vac)		100^{20}		s al
s393	pyrohyporhenate	$Na_4Re_2O_7.H_2O$	594.37	sandy yel cr				0.004		
s394	rhodiumchloride	$Na_3RhCl_6.12H_2O$	600.78	dk red cr, monocl pr		$-12H_2O$, 120		v s	v s	i al
s395	rhodiumnitrite	$Na_3[Rh(NO_2)_6]$	447.91	wh cr		d 360		40^{17}		i al; d a
s396	perruthenate	$NaRuO_4.H_2O$	206.07	blk cr, lamellar		d 440 vac		v s	d	
s397	salicylate	$NaC_7H_5O_3$	160.11	wh cr powd				111^{15}	125^{25}	17^{15} al; 25 glyc
s398	selenate	Na_2SeO_4	188.94	col, rhomb	$3.213^{17.4}$			84^{35}	72.8^{100}	
s399	selenate, decahydrate	$Na_2SeO_4.10H_2O$	369.09	col, monocl	1.603–1.620	ca 32 trans		43.5^{20}	340^{100}	
s400	selenide	Na_2Se	124.94	wh to red, cr, deliq	2.625^{10}	>875		d		i NH_3
s401	selenite	$Na_2SeO_3.5H_2O$	263.01	wh cr, tetrag				s	s	i al
s402	silicate	Waterglass. $Na_2O.xSiO_2(x=3-5)$		col, amorph, deliq				s	s	i al, K and Na salts
s403	disilicate	$Na_2Si_2O_5$	182.15	rhomb pearly luster 1.500, 1.510		874		s	s	
s404	metasilicate	Na_2SiO_3	122.06	col, monocl, α 1.518, γ 1.527	2.4	1088		s	s, d	i al, K and Na salts
s405	metasilicate	$Na_2SiO_3 \cdot 9H_2O$	284.20	col, rhomb bipyramid, effl		40–48	$-6H_2O$, 100	v s	v s	s dil NaOH; i al, a
s406	orthosilicate	Na_4SiO_4	184.04	col, hex, 1.530		1018		s	s	
s407	silicotungstate, dodeca-	$Na_4[Si(W_3O_{10})_4].20H_2O$ Sodium tungstosilicate	3326.53	col, tricl		$-7H_2O$, 100	d	v s	v s	s a, sl s al
s408	stannate, hydroxo-	$Na_2Sn(OH)_6$	266.71	col, hex or wh powd, or lumps		$-3H_2O$, 140		$61.3^{15.5}$	50^{100}	i al, acet
s409	stearate	$NaC_{18}H_{35}O_2$	306.47	wh fatty powd				s	s	s h al
s410	succinate	$Na_2C_4H_4O_4.6H_2O$	270.15	wh, gran or powd		$-6H_2O$, 120		21.45^0	86.63^{75}	v sl s al
s411	succinate, tetrahydroxy-	Sodium dihydroxy tartrate. $Na_2C_4H_4O_6.3H_2O$	280.10			d		0.032^0	d	d min a; i al, eth
s412	sulfanilate	$NaC_6H_4(NH_2)SO_3$	195.17	wh lust cr leaf				s		
s413	sulfate, anhydr	Na_2SO_4	142.04	monocl (between ca 160–185), 1.480		884; tr to hex ca 241			$42-5^{100}$	s HI
s414	sulfate, anhydr	Nat. thenardite. Na_2SO_4	142.04	orthorhomb, 1.484, 1.477, 1.471	2.68			4.76^0	42.7^{100}	s glyc; i al
s415	sulfate, decahydrate	Glauber's salt, mirabilite. $Na_2SO_4.10H_2O$	322.19	col, monocl, effl, 1.394, 1.396, 1.398	1.464	32.38	$-10H_2O$, 100	11^0	92.7^{30}	i al
s416	sulfate, heptahydrate	$Na_2SO_4.7H_2O$	268.15	wh, rhomb or tetrag		tr to anhydr 24.4		19.5^0	44^{30}	i al
s417	pyrosulfite	Sodium metabisulfite. $Na_2S_2O_5$	190.10	wh powd or cr ($+7H_2O$)	1.4	>d 150		54^{20}	81.7^{100}	sl s al; s glyc
s418	pyrosulfate	$Na_2S_2O_7$	222.16	wh, transluc cr, deliq	2.658^{25}	400.9	d 460	s		s fum H_2SO_4
s419	sulfate hydrogen	$NaHSO_4$	120.06	col, tricl	2.435^{13}	>315	d	28.6^{25}	100^{100}	sl s al; i NH_3
s420	sulfate hydrogen, monohydrate	$NaHSO_4.H_2O$	138.07	col, monocl, deliq ~1.46	$2.103^{18.5}_{4}$	58.54±0.5		ca 67, d	d	d al
s421	sulfide, hydro-	$NaHS$	56.06	col, rhomb or wh gran cr, deliq		350		v s		s al

No.	Name	Synonyms and Formulae	Mol. wt.	Crystalline form, properties and index of refraction	Density or spec. gravity	Melting point, °C	Boiling point, °C	Solubility, in grams per 100 cc		
								Cold water	Hot water	Other solvents
	Sodium									
s422	sulfide, hydrodi-hydrate	$NaHS.2H_2O$	92.09	col need, deliq		d		s	s	d a; s al
s423	sulfide, mono-	Na_2S	78.04	wh cr, deliq	1.856^{14}	1180		15.4^{10}	57.2^{90}	d a; sl s al; i eth
s424	sulfide, mono-hydrate	$Na_2S.9H_2O$	240.18	col, tetr, deliq	1.427^{16}_4	d 920		47.5^{10}	96.7^{10}	d, sl s al
s425	sulfide, penta-	Na_2S_5	206.30	yel (exist ?)		251.8		s	s	s al
s426	sulfide, tetra-	Na_2S_4	174.24	yel, cub, hygr		275	d	s		s al
s427	sulfide, hydro-trihydrate	$NaHS.3H_2O$	110.11	col, lust rhomb cr		22	d	s	s	s al
s428	sulfite	Na_2SO_3	126.04	wh powd or hex, prism 1.565, 1.515	$2.633^{15.4}$	d red heat	d	12.54^0	28.3^{80}	sl s al; i liq Cl_2, NH_3
s429	sulfite hydrate	$Na_2SO_3.7H_2O$	252.15	col, monocl, effl	1.539^{15}	$-7H_2O$, 150	d	32.8^0	196^{40}	sl s al
s430	hydrosulfite	Dithionite, hyposulfate $Na_2S_2O_4.2H_2O$	210.14	col, monocl(?) cr, or yel-wh powd		d 52		25.4^{20}	d	d a; s alk; i al
s431	sulfite, hydrogen	$NaHSO_3$	104.06	wh, monocl, yel in sol, 1.526	1.48	d		v s	v s	sl s al
s432	d(& l)-tartrate	$Na_2C_4H_4O_6.2H_2O$	230.08	col, rhomb, 1.545, 1.49	1.818	$-2H_2O$, 150		29^6	66^{43}	i al
s433	d-tartrate, hydrogen	$NaHC_4H_4O_6.H_2O$	190.09	wh cr powd, rhomb, 1.53, 1.54, 1.60		$-H_2O$, 100	d 234	6.7^{19}	9.2^{90}	
s434	dl-tartrate hydrogen	$NaHC_4H_4O_6.H_2O$	190.09	col, monocl or tricl, 1.53, 1.54, 1.60		$-H_2O$, 100	d 219	8.9^{19}		
s435	orthotellurate, tetra-H	$Na_2H_4TeO_6$	273.61	col, hex pl		d	d	0.77^{18}	2^{100}	s h dil HNO_3; i NaOH
s436	telluride	Na_2Te	173.58	wh cr powd very hygr, d in air	2.90	953		v s, d	v s, d	
s437	tellurite	Na_2TeO_3	221.58	wh, rhomb pr				sl s	s	
s438	thioantimonate	Schlippe's salt. $Na_3SbS_4.9H_2O$	481.11	pa yel, cub	1.806	87	d 234	20.15^0	100^{100}	i al, eth
s439	thioarsenate	$Na_3AsS_4.8H_2O$	416.27	yel, monocl, β 1.6802		d		v s	d	i al
s440	thiocarbonate, tri	$Na_2CS_3.H_2O$	172.20	yel need, deliq		d 75		s	d	s al; i eth, bz
s441	thiocyanate	$NaSCN$	81.07	col, rhomb deliq pois, ~1.625		287		$139.31^{21.3}$	225^{100}	v s al, acet
s442	dithionate	$Na_2S_2O_6.2H_2O$	242.13	col, rhomb, 1.482, 1.495, 1.519	2.189	$-2H_2O$, 110	$-SO_2$, 267	47.6^{16}	90.9^{100}	s HCl; i al
s443	thiosulfate	$Na_2S_2O_3$	158.11	col, monocl	1.667			50	231^{100}	i al
s444	thiosulfate, pentahydrate	"Hypo", sodium hyposulfite. $Na_2S_2O_3.5H_2O$	248.18	col, monocl, effle, 1.489, 1.508, 1.536	1.729^{17}	40–45 d 48	$-5H_2O$, 100	79.4^0	291.1^{45}	s NH_3; i al
s445	thiosulfoaurate (I)	$Na_3[Au(S_2O_3)_2].2H_2O$	526.22	wh cr, monocl	3.09	$-H_2O$, 150	d	50		i al
s446	trititanate	$Na_2Ti_3O_7$	301.68	wh need, monocl	3.35–3.50	1128		i		s h HCl
s447	tungstate	Na_2WO_4	293.83	wh, rhomb	4.179	698		57.5^0 73.2^{21}	96.9^{100}	
s448	tungstate, dihydrate	$Na_2WO_4.2H_2O$	329.86	col pl, rhomb, 1.5533	3.23–3.25	$-2H_2O$, 100 anhydr 698		41^0	123.5^{100}	sl s NH_3; i al, a
s449	metatungstate	$Na_2O.4WO_3.10H_2O$	1169.53	col, oct		706.6		s	v s	i a
s450	paratungstate	$Na_6W_7O_{24}.16H_2O$	2097.12	col, tricl	3.987	$-12H_2O$, 100; $-16H_2O$, 300		8	d	
s451	metauranate	Na_2UO_4	348.01	gr yel or red pl, rhomb pr				i	i	s dil a, alk carb
s452	uranyl acetate	$NaUO_2(C_2H_3O_2)_3$	470.15	yel, tetr pr, 1.501	2.56					
s453	uranyl carbonate	$2Na_2CO_3.UO_2CO_3$	542.02	yel cr		d 400		sl s		i al
s454	urate	$Na_2C_5H_2N_4O_3.H_2O$	230.09	wh gran powd or hard cr nodules					1.3^{100}	v sl s 90 % al
s455	urate, acid	$NaHC_5H_2N_4O_3$	190.09	wh gran powd				0.083	0.8^{100}	
s456	valerate	$NaC_5H_9O_2$	124.12	wh cr or mass, hygr		140		s		s al
s457	metavanadate	$NaVO_3$	121.93	col, monocl pr		630		21.1^{75}	38.8^{75}	
s458	orthovanadate	Na_3VO_4	183.94	col, hex pr		850–866		s		i al
s459	orthovanadate, decahydrate	$Na_3VO_4.10H_2O$	364.06	wh, cub or hex cr, 1.5305, 1.5398, 1.5475				s	s	
s460	orthovanadate, hexadecylhydrate	$Na_3VO_4.16H_2O$	472.15	col need		866 (anhydr)		v s	d	i al
s461	pyrovanadate	$Na_4V_2O_7$	305.84	col, hex		632–654		s	s	i al
s462	ethylxanthate	NaC_2H_5OCSS	144.19	yelsh powd				s		s al
s463	zinc uranyl acetate	$NaZn(UO_2)_3(C_2H_3O_2)_9.9H_2O$	1591.98	monocl cr, α 1.475, γ 1.480				i		s al
	Stannous	See under tin								
	Stannic	See under tin								

No.	Name	Synonyms and Formulae	Mol. wt.	Crystalline form, properties and index of refraction	Density or spec. gravity	Melting point, °C	Boiling point, °C	Solubility, in grams per 100 cc		
								Cold water	Hot water	Other solvents
	Strontium									
s464	Strontium	Sr	87.62	silv wh to pa yel met	2.6[30]	769	1384	d	d	s a, al, liq NH$_3$
s465	acetate	Sr(C$_2$H$_3$O$_2$)$_2$	205.71	wh cr	2.099	d		36.9	36.4[97]	0.26[15] MeOH
s466	acetate	Sr(C$_2$H$_3$O$_2$)$_2$.$\frac{1}{2}$H$_2$O	214.72	wh cr powd		$-\frac{1}{2}$H$_2$O, 150		s		sl s al
s467	orthoarsenate, acid	SrHAsO$_4$.H$_2$O	245.56	rhomb, need	3.606[15]; 4.035 (anhydr)	$-$H$_2$O, 125		0.284[15.5]	d	s a
s468	orthoarsenite	Sr$_3$(AsO$_3$)$_2$.4H$_2$O	580.76	cr, or wh powd				sl s		s a; sl s al
s469	borate, tetra-	SrB$_4$O$_7$.4H$_2$O	314.92						77[100]	s HNO$_3$; NH$_4$ salts
s470	boride, hexa-	SrB$_6$	152.49	blk, cub	3.39[15]	2235		i	i	s HNO$_3$; i HCl
s471	bromate	Sr(BrO$_3$)$_2$.H$_2$O	361.45	col yelsh, monocl, hygr	3.773	$-$H$_2$O, 120	d 240	33[16]		
s472	bromide	SrBr$_2$	247.44	wh, hex need, hygr, 1.575	4.216[24]	643	d	100[20]	222.5[100]	s al, amyl al
s473	bromide, hexahydrate	SrBr$_2$.6H$_2$O	355.53	col, hex, hygr	2.386[$\frac{25}{4}$]	tr to 2H$_2$O, 88.6	$-$6H$_2$O, >180	204.2[0]	∞	63.9[30] al; 113.4[30] MeOH; 0.6[30] acet; i eth
s474	carbide	SrC$_2$	111.64	blk, tetr	3.2	>1700		d	d	d a
s475	carbonate	Nat. strontianite. SrCO$_3$	147.63	col, rhomb, or wh powd trfrs to $-$hex at 926, 1.516, 1.664, 1.666	3.70	1497[69atm]	$-$CO$_2$, 1340	0.0011[18]	0.065[100]	0.12 aq CO$_2$; s a, NH$_4$ salts
s476	chlorate	Sr(ClO$_3$)$_2$	254.52	col, rhomb, or wh powd, 1.516, 1.605, 1.626	3.152	d 120		174.9[18]	v s	s dil al; i abs al
s477	perchlorate	Sr(ClO$_4$)$_2$	286.52	col cr, hygr				310[25]	v s	212 MeOH; 181 al; i eth
s478	chloride	SrCl$_2$	158.53	col, cub 1.650[25]	3.052	875	1250	53.8[20]	100.8[100]	v sl s abs al, acet; i NH$_3$
s479	chloride, dihydrate	SrCl$_2$.2H$_2$O	194.56	transp leaf, 1.594, 1.595, 1.617	2.6715[25]					
s480	chloride, fluoride	SrCl$_2$.SrF$_2$	284.14	col, tetr, 1.651, 1.627	4.18	962		d	d	s conc HNO$_3$, conc HCl, i al
s481	chloride, hexahydrate	SrCl$_2$.6H$_2$O	266.62	col, trig, 1.536, 1.487	1.93	115, $-$4H$_2$O, 60	$-$6H$_2$O, 100	106.2[0]	205.8[40]	3.8[6] al
s482	chromate	SrCrO$_4$	203.61	yel, monocl	3.895[15]			0.12[15]	3[100]	s HCl, HNO$_3$, ac a, NH$_4$ salts
s483	cyanide	Sr(CN)$_2$.4H$_2$O	211.72	wh, rhomb, deliq		d		v s		
s484	cyanoplatinite	Sr[Pt(CN)$_4$].5H$_2$O	476.86	col, monocl pr, 1.696		$-$5H$_2$O, 150				s abs al
s485	glycerophosphate	SrC$_3$H$_7$O$_6$P	257.68	wh powd				sl s		i al
s486	ferrocyanide	Sr$_2$Fe(CN)$_6$.15H$_2$O	657.42	yel, monocl				50	100	
s487	fluoride	SrF$_2$	125.62	col, cub or wh powd, 1.442	4.24	1473	2489[760]	0.011[0]	0.012[27]	s hot HCl; i HF, al, acet
s488	fluosilicate	SrSiF$_6$.2H$_2$O	265.73	monocl	2.99[17.5]	d		3.2[15]	v s	s HCl; 0.065[15] 50 % al
s489	formate	Sr(CHO$_2$)$_2$	177.66	col, rhomb, 1.559, 1.547, 1.598	2.693	71.9		9.1[0]	34.4[100]	i al, eth
s490	formate, dihydrate	Sr(CHO$_2$)$_2$.2H$_2$O	213.69	col, rhomb, 1.484, 1.521, 1.538	2.25	d, $-$2H$_2$O, 100		11.62[25.6]	26.57[100]	i al, eth
s491	hydride	SrH$_2$(?)	89.64	wh, rhomb, hygr	3.72	d 675	subl 1000 (in H$_2$)	d	d	d al
s492	hydroxide	Sr(OH)$_2$	121.63	wh, deliq	3.625	375 (in H$_2$)	$-$H$_2$O, 710	0.41[0]	21.83[100]	s a, NH$_4$Cl
s493	hydroxide, octahydrate	Sr(OH)$_2$.8H$_2$O	265.76	col, tetr, deliq, 1.499, 1.476	1.90	$-$8H$_2$O, 100		0.90[0]	47.71[100]	s a, NH$_4$Cl; i acet
s494	iodate	Sr(IO$_3$)$_2$	437.43	tricl	5.045[15]			0.03[15]	0.8[100]	
s495	iodide	SrI$_2$	341.43	col pl	4.549[$\frac{25}{4}$]	515	d	165.3[0]	383[100]	4.5[30] al; 0.31[0] NH$_4$OH; s MeOH
s496	iodide, hexahydrate	SrI$_2$.6H$_2$O	449.52	col-yelsh, hex, deliq	2.672[25]	d 90		448.9[0]	∞	s al; i eth
s497	lactate	Sr(C$_3$H$_5$O$_3$)$_2$.3H$_2$O	319.81	wh cr or gran powd		$-$3H$_2$O, 120		25	200[100]	sl s al
s498	permanganate	Sr(MnO$_4$)$_2$.3H$_2$O	379.54	purpl, cub	2.75	d 175		270[0]	291[18]	
s499	molybdate	SrMoO$_4$	247.56	col, tetr ~1.91	4.54[$\frac{25}{25}$]	d		0.0104[17]		s a
s500	nitrate	Sr(NO$_3$)$_2$	211.63	col, cub	2.986	570		70.9[18]	100[90]	0.012 abs al; v s NH$_3$; sl s acet
s501	nitrate, tetrahydrate	Sr(NO$_3$)$_2$.4H$_2$O	283.69	col, monocl	2.2	$-$4H$_2$O, 100	1100 tr SrO	60.43[0]	206.5[100]	s liq NH$_3$; v sl s abs al, acet; i HNO$_3$

No.	Name	Synonyms and Formulae	Mol. wt.	Crystalline form, properties and index of refraction	Density or spec. gravity	Melting point, °C	Boiling point, °C	Solubility, in grams per 100 cc		
								Cold water	Hot water	Other solvents
	Strontium									
s502	nitride........	Sr_3N_2	290.87					d	d	s HCl
s503	nitrite........	$Sr(NO_2)_2.H_2O$	197.65	col, hex, 1.588...	2.408_0^0	$-H_2O>100$	d 240	58.9^0	182^{100}	0.42^{20} 90% al
s504	hyponitrite......	$SrN_2O_2.5H_2O$	237.71	wh need......	2.173_4^{25}			v sl s	sl s	v sl s NH_3
s505	oxalate.........	$SrC_2O_4.H_2O$	193.64	col cr.....		$-H_2O, 150$		0.0051^{18}	5^{100}	s HCl, HNO_3
s506	oxide..........	SrO	103.62	gray-wh, cub, 4.7 1.810		2430	~ 3000	0.69^{20}	22.85^{100}	30 fus KOH; sl s al; i eth, acet
s507	oxide, per-.....	SrO_2	119.62	wh powd....	4.56	d 215^{760}		0.018^{20}	d	v s al, NH_4Cl; i acet
s508	oxide, per-, octahydrate	$SrO_2.8H_2O$	263.74	col cr......	1.951	$-8H_2O, 100$	d	0.018^{20}	d	s NH_4Cl; i al, acet, NH_4OH
s509	orthophosphate, di-	$SrHPO_4$	183.60	col, rhomb....	3.544^{15}	1.62		i	i	s a, NH_4 salts
s510	salicylate.......	$Sr(C_7H_5O_3)_2.2H_2O$	397.88	col cr......	d			5.6^{25}	28.6^{100}	1.5^{25}, 9.5^{78} al
s511	selenate........	$SrSeO_4$	230.58	col, rhomb....	4.23			i	i	s hot HCl; i HNO_3
s512	selenide........	$SrSe$	166.58	wh, cub, 2.220....	1.38			d	d	s HCl
s513	metasilicate.....	$SrSiO_3$	163.70	col, pr monocl, 1.599, 1.637	3.65	1580		i	i	s HCl
s514	orthosilicate....	$SrSiO_4$	179.70	monocl, 1.728, 1.732, 1.758	3.84	>1750				
s515	sulfate.........	Nat. celestite. $SrSO_4$...	183.68	col, rhomb, 1.622, 1.624, 1.631	3.96	1605		0.0113^0	0.014^{30}	sl s a; i al, dil H_2SO_4
s516	sulfate, hydrogen....	$Sr(HSO_4)_2$	281.76	col......	d			d	d	$14^{70} H_2SO_4$
s517	sulfide, hydro	$Sr(HS)_2$	153.76	col, cub need, 2.107	d			s	d	
s518	sulfide, mono......	SrS	119.68	col, lt gray, cub, 2.107	3.70^{15}	>2000		i	d	d a
s519	sulfide, tetra-	$SrS_4.6H_2O$	323.97	redsh cr, hygr....		25	$-4H_2O, 100$	s	s	s al
s520	sulfite.........	$SrSO_3$	167.68	col cr.....	d			0.0033^{17}		v s H_2SO_4; s a, HCl
s521	tartrate........	$SrC_4H_4O_6.4H_2O$	307.75	wh, monocl....	1.966			0.112^0	0.755^{85}	s dil HCl, dil HNO_3
s522	telluride........	$SrTe$	215.22	wh, cub, 2.408...	4.83					
s523	thiocyanate......	$Sr(SCN)_2.3H_2O$	257.83	deliq.....		$-3H_2O, 100$	d 160–170	v s		v s al
s524	thiosulfate......	$SrS_2O_3.5H_2O$	289.82	monocl need.....	2.17^{17}	$-4H_2O, 100$		2.5^{13}	57^{100}	i al
s525	dithionate.......	$SrS_2O_6.4H_2O$	319.81	trig, 1.530, 1.525	2.373	$-4H_2O, 78$		22^{16}	67^{100}	i al
s526	tungstate.......	$SrWO_4$	335.47	col, tetr........	6.187	d		0.14^{15}	d	i al
s527	**Sulfamic acid**......	Amidosulfuric, amino-sulfonic acid. NH_2SO_3H	97.09	col, rhomb.....	2.126^{25}	200 d	d	14.68	47.08^{80}	v sl s al, eth, acet; i CS_2, CCl_4
s528	**Sulfamide**........	Sulfuryl amide. $SO_2(NH_2)_2$	96.11	rhomb pl......	1.611	91.5	d 250	s		s al
s529	**Sulfur**(α)........	S_8	256.512	yel, rhomb, 1.957.	2.07^{20}	112.8 95.5 (revers.) 444.6	444.674	i	i	$23^0 CS_2$; sl s tol, al, bz, eth, liq NH_3; s CCl_4
s530	(β)............	S_8	256.512	pa yel, monocl...	1.96	119.0	444.674	i	i	$70 CS_2$; s al, bz
s531	(γ)............	S_8	256.512	pa yel, amorph....	1.92	ca 120	444.6	i	i	i CS_2
s532	bromide, mono-...	S_2Br_2	223.95	red liq, 1.730.....	2.63	-40	$54^{0.2}$	d	d	s CS_2
s533	chloride, di-.....	SCl_2	102.97	dk red liq, 1.557^{11}.	1.621_{15}^{15}	-78	d 59			s CCl_4, bz; d al, eth
s534	chloride, mono-...	S_2Cl_2	135.03	yel-red liq, 1.666^{14}	1.678	-80	135.6	d	d	s bz, eth, CS_2
s535	chloride, tetra-....	SCl_4	173.88	yel-br liq......		-30	d -15	d	d	
s536	fluoride, hexa-....	SF_6	146.05	col gas........	gas 6.602 g/l liq $1.88^{-50.5}$	-50.5	-63.8 (subl)	sl s	sl s	s al, KOH
s537	fluoride, mono-....	S_2F_2	102.12	col gas........	liq 1.5^{-100}	-120.5	-38.4	d	d	d KOH
s538	fluoride, tetra-....	SF_4	108.06	gas (exist ?).....		-124	-40	d	d	
s539	(di) fluoride, deca-	S_2F_{10}	254.11	col liq........	2.08_4^0	-92	29			d fus caust
s540	(tetra-) nitride, di-	S_4N_2	156.27	red liq or gray solid	1.901^{18}	23	d 100 expl	i		s eth; sl s al, CS_2
s541	(tetra-) nitride, tetra-	S_4N_4	184.28	or red, monocl....	2.22^{15}	subl 179	expl 160			s CS_2, chl, bz, NH_3; sl s al, eth
s542	(tri-)dinitrogen dioxide	$S_3N_2O_2$	156.20	pa yel cr.....		100.7	d	i		s al, bz
s543	oxide, di-.......	SO_2	64.06	col gas or liq suffoc odor	gas 2.927 g/l liq 1.434	-72.7	-10	22.8^0	0.58^{90}	s al, ac a, H_2SO_4
s544	oxide, hept-....	Sulfur oxide, per- S_2O_7	176.12	visc liq, or need....	0		subl 10	d	d	s H_2SO_4
s545	oxide, mono-.....	SO (or S_2O_2)	48.06	col gas.......		d	d	d		
s546	oxide, sesqui-.....	S_2O_3	112.13	bl-grn cr......		d 70–95		d		s al, eth, fum H_2SO_4
s547	oxide, tetra-......	Sulfurperoxide, SO_4....	96.06	wh........		d 0–3		s, d		d dil H_2SO_4
s548	oxide, tri-(α)......	SO_3	80.06	silky fibr need, stable modific	1.97^{20}	16.83	44.8	d	d	forms fum H_2SO_4
s549	oxide, tri-(β)......	$(SO_3)_2$	160.12	asbestos like fibre, metastable		62.4	50 (subl)	d	d	forms fum H_2SO_4

No.	Name	Synonyms and Formulae	Mol. wt.	Crystalline form, properties and index of retraction	Density or spec. gravity	Melting point, °C	Boiling point, °C	Solubility, in grams per 100 cc		
								Cold water	Hot water	Other solvents
	Sulfur(α)									
s550	oxide, tri-(γ)........	SO_3.............	80.06	vitreous, orthorhomb, metastable	liq 1.920_4^{20} sld 2.29^{-10}	16.8	44.8	d	d	forms fum H_2SO_4
s551	oxytetrachloride, mono-	S_2OCl_4.............	221.94	dk red liq.......	1.656^0		60	d	d	d al
s552	oxytetrachloride, tri-.	$S_2O_2Cl_4$.............	253.94	wh, rhomb need or pl	d 57			d	d	d al
s553	trithiazyl chloride....	S_4N_3Cl.............	205.73	pa yel cr.........		d 170 (vac)		d		....
s554	**Sulfuric acid**........	H_2SO_4.............	98.08	col liq...........	1.841 (96–98 %)	10.36 (100 %) 3.0 (98 %)	338 (98.3 %)	∞ ev heat	∞	d al
s555	dihydrate.........	$H_2SO_4.2H_2O$.......	134.11	col liq, 1.405....	1.650^0	−38.9	167	∞	∞	d al, eth
s556	hexahydrate........	$H_2SO_4.6H_2O$.......	206.17	liq............		−54		v s	v s	
s557	monohydrate.......	$H_2SO_4.H_2O$........	116.09	col liq or monocl cr, 1.438	1.788	8.62	290	∞	∞	d al
s558	octahydrate........	$H_2SO_4.8H_2O$.......	242.20	liq............		−62		v s	v s	
s559	peroxidi-..........	Per(di-)sulfuric acid. $H_2S_2O_8$	194.14	hygr cr...........		d 65	d	d	d	s al, eth, H_2SO_4
s560	peroximono-.......	Permonosulfuric acid. Caro's acid H_2SO_5	114.08	....		d 45		d		s H_3PO_4
s561	pyro-............	$H_2S_2O_7$...........	178.14	col cr, hygr......	1.9^{20}	35	d	d	d	d al
s562	tetrahydrate.......	$H_2SO_4.4H_2O$.......	170.14	....		−27		∞	∞	d al, eth
s563	**Sulfurous acid**......	H_2SO_3.............	82.08	in sol only.......	ca 1.03			s		s al, eth, ac a
s564	**Sulfuryl** chloride.....	SO_2Cl_2.............	134.97	col liq, 1.444.....	1.6674_4^{20}	−54.1	69.1	d	d	s bz, ac a
s565	chloride fluoride.....	SO_2ClF.............	118.52	col gas..........	1.623^0 g/l	−124.7	7.1	d		
s566	fluoride..........	SO_2F_2.............	102.06	col gas..........	gas 3.72 g/l liq 1.7	−136.7	−55.4	10^9		s al, CCl_4; sl s alk
s567	pyro-, chloride......	$S_2O_5Cl_2$...........	215.03	col liq, 1.937^{20}...	gas 9.6 g/l liq 1.818_4^{11}	−39 to −37	152.5	d	d	d a
t1	**Tantalum**..........	Ta.............	180.948	gray black hard metal, cub or powd	met 16.6 powd 14.401	2996	5425 ± 100	i	i	s HF, fus alk; i a
t2	boride, di-.........	TaB_2.............	202.57		11.15	3000(?)	....			....
t3	bromide..........	$TaBr_5$.............	580.49	yel cr..........	4.67	265	348.8	d	d	s abs al, eth
t4	carbide..........	TaC.............	192.96	blk, cub.........	13.9	3880	5500	i	i	sl s H_2SO_4. HF
t5	chloride, penta-....	$TaCl_5$.............	358.21	lt yel, vitr cr powd	3.68^{27}	216	242	d		s abs al, H_2SO_4
t6	fluoride..........	TaF_5.............	275.94	col, tetrag, deliq..	4.74	96.8	229.5	s		s HF, eth
t7	nitride...........	TaN.............	194.95	br bronze or blk, hex	16.30	3360 ± 50		i	i	sl s aq reg, HF, HNO_3
t8	oxide, pent-.......	Ta_2O_5.............	441.89	col, rhomb.......	8.2	1800	....	i	i	s fus $KHSO_4$, HF; i a
t9	oxide, pent- hydrate	Tantalic acid $Ta_2O_5.xH_2O$	......	col gel..........				s		s alk, exc conc HNO_3; i a
t10	oxide, tetr-.......	Ta_2O_4 (or TaO_2).......	425.89	dk gray powd......		oxidizes	....	i	i	i a
t11	sulfide..........	Ta_2S_4 (or TaS_2).......	490.15	blk powd or cr....		>1300	....	i	i	sl s HF+HNO_3; i HCl
t12	**Telluric acid, ortho-**.	$Te(OH)_6$ or $H_2TeO_4.2H_2O$	229.64	wh, monocl pr....	3.071	136	....	s	s	sl s dil a, HNO_3; i abs al, acet, eth
t13	**Telluric acid**,......	$Te(OH)_6$ or H_6TeO_6...	229.64	wh, cub.........	3.158	136		s	s	sl s dil a, HNO_3; i abs al, acet, eth
t14	**Tellurium**..........	Te.............	127.60	br blk, amorph, 1.0025	6.00	449.5 ± 0.3	989.8 ± 3.8	i	i	s H_2SO_4, HNO_3, aq reg, KCN, KOH; i HCl, CS_2
t15	**Tellurium**..........	Te.............	127.60	rhomb silv wh met, 1.0025	6.25	452	1390	i	i	s H_2SO_4, HNO_3, aq reg, KCN KOH; i HCl, CS_2
t16	bromide, di-.......	$TeBr_2$.............	287.42	brn to gray grn, need, unstable	....	210	339	d	....	s eth; sl s a; d NaOH
t17	bromide, tetra-.....	$TeBr_4$.............	447.27	or cr..........	4.31_4^{15}	380 ± 6	d 421	sl s	d	s eth, a, tart a, NaOH
t18	chloride, di-.......	$TeCl_2$.............	198.50	blk cr or amorph, unstable	7.05	209 ± 5	327	d	d	s min a, tart a; d NaOH
t19	chloride, tetra......	$TeCl_4$.............	269.41	wh to yel cr, deliq	3.26^{18} 2.559^{222}	224	380^{760}	s d	s d	s HCl, bz, al, chl, CCl_4; i CS_2
t20	ethoxide.........	$Te(OC_2H_5)_4$........	307.85			20	$107–107.5^{5.5}$			
t21	fluoride, hexa-.....	TeF_6.............	241.59	col gas unpleas odor	sol 4.006^{-191} liq 2.56^{-35}	−36	+35.5	d	d	d a, alk
t22	fluoride, tetra-.....	TeF_4.............	203.59	wh cr hygr.......		subl	>97	d	d	....
t23	hydride..........	H_2Te.............	129.62	col gas pois......	4.49	−48.9	$−2.2^{760}$	v s	s	d al

No.	Name	Synonyms and Formulae	Mol. wt.	Crystalline form, properties and index of refraction	Density or spec. gravity	Melting point, °C	Boiling point, °C	Solubility, in grams per 100 cc		
								Cold water	Hot water	Other solvents
	Tellurium									
t24	iodide, di-	TeI_2	381.41	blk cr (exist ?)		subl		i	i	
t25	iodide, tetra,-	TeI_4	635.22	blk cr	5.403^{15}_4	280	d	sl s	d	s alk, aq NH_3, HI
t26	methoxide	$Te(OCH_3)_4$	251.74	solid		123–124				
t27	oxide, di-	Tellurite. TeO_2	159.60	wh, tetr or rhomb, 2.00, 2.18(Li), 2.35	tetr 5.67^{15} rhomb 5.91^0	733	1245	i	i	s HCl, hot HNO_3, alk; i NH_4OH
t28	oxide, mon-	TeO	143.60	blk, amorph (exist ?)	5.682	d 370 (in CO_2)	d	i	i	s dil a, H_2SO_4, KOH
t29	oxide, tri-	TeO_3	175.60	α yel amorph β gray cr	α 5.075^{105}_4 β 6.21	d 395		i	i	d conc HCl; s hot KOH; i a, al
t30	sulfide	TeS_2	191.72	red-blk powd amorph (exist ?)				i		i a; s alk sulf
t31	sulfoxide	$TeSO_3$	207.66	deep red amorph		d 30	d	d	d	s H_2SO_4
t32	**Tellurous acid**	H_2TeO_3(?)	177.61	wh flocks, indef not isolated	3.05	d 40	d	0.00067	d	s a, NaOH; sl s NH_4OH; i al
t33	**Terbium**	Tb	158.924	silv-gray met, hex	8.2294	1360±4	3123	i	i	s a
t34	bromide	$TbBr_3$	398.65			827	1490	s	s	
t35	chloride hexa-hydrate	$TbCl_3.6H_2O$	373.38	col pr cr, deliq	4.35 (anhydr)	588 (anhydr)	$-H_2O$, 180–200 (in HCl gas)	v s		
t36	fluoride	TbF_3	215.92			1172	2280(?)	i	i	i dil a
t37	iodide	TbI_3	539.64			946	>1300	s	s	
t38	dimethylphosphate	$Tb[(CH_3)_2PO_4]_3$	534.05					12.6^{25}	8.07^{40}	
t39	nitrate	$Tb(NO_3)_3.6H_2O$	153.03	col, monocl cr		893		s		
t40	oxalate	$Tb_2(C_2O_4)_3.10H_2O$	762.06	wh cr	2.60	$-H_2O$, 40		i	i	i dil a
t41	oxide	Terbia. Tb_2O_3	365.85	wh solid				i		s dil a
t42	oxide, per-	Tb_4O_7	747.69	dk-brn or blk solid		$-O_2$		i	i	s hot conc a
t43	sulfate	$Tb_2(SO_4)_3.8H_2O$	750.16	wh cr		$-8H_2O$, 360		3.561^{20}	2.51^{40}	
t44	**Thallium**	Tl	204.37	bl-wh met, tetr	11.85	303.5	1457 ± 10	i	i	s HNO_3, H_2SO_4; sl s HCl
t45	acetate	$TlC_2H_3O_2$	263.42	silk wh cr, deliq	3.765^{137}	131		v s		v s al, $CHCl_3$; i acet
t46	aluminium sulfate	$TlAl(SO_4)_2.12H_2O$	639.66	oct, 1.488	2.306^{20}	91		11.78^{25}		
t47	azide	TlN_3	246.39	yel, tetr		330 (vac)		0.1712^0	0.3^{16}	i al, eth
t48	bromate	$TlBrO_3$	332.28	col, need				0.35^{20}	s	s dil al
t49	bromide, di-	Bromothallate(ous). Tl_2Br_4 or $Tl^I_2[Tl^{III}Br_4]$	728.38	yel need		d	d	d	d	
t50	bromide, mono-	$TlBr$	284.28	yel-wh, cub, 2.4–2.8	$7.557^{17.5}$	480	815	0.05^{25}	0.25^{68}	s al; i HB_2, acet
t51	bromide, tri-	$TlBr_3$	444.10	yel, deliq, unstable		d		s	v s	v s al
t52	carbonate	Tl_2CO_3	468.75	col, monocl	7.11	273		$4.03^{15.5}$	27.2^{100}	i abs al, eth, acet
t53	chlorate	$TlClO_3$	287.82	need (rhomb ?)	5.047^9			2^0	57.31^{100}	
t54	perchlorate	$TlClO_4$	303.82	col, rhomb	4.89	501	d	20.5^{30}	167^{100}	sl s al
t55	chloride	$TlCl$	239.82	wh reg discol in air, 2.247	7.004^{20}_4	430	720	$0.29^{15.5}$	$2.41^{99.35}$	i al, acet; d a
t56	chloride, tri-	$TlCl_3$	310.73	hex pl, hygr		25	d	v s		s al, eth
t57	chloride, tri-	$TlCl_3.H_2O$	328.74	col, need		$-H_2O$, 60	d 100	v s		v s al, eth
t58	chloride, tri-	$TlCl_3.4H_2O$	382.79	col, need		37	$-4H_2O$, 100	86.2^{17}	d	s al, eth
t59	chloroplatinate	Tl_2PtCl_6	816.55	pale or cr	5.76^{17}			0.0064^{15}	0.05^{100}	
t60	chromate	Tl_2CrO_4	524.73	yel				0.03^{60}	0.2^{100}	sl s a, alk; i ac a
t61	dichromate	$Tl_2Cr_2O_7$	624.73	red				i		d a
t62	chromium sulfate	Thallium chromium alum. $Tl[Cr(H_2O)_6](SO_4)_2.6H_2O$	664.67	vlt cr	2.394	92		163.8^{25}		
t63	cyanate	$TlCNO$	246.39	col, need	5.487^{20}_4			s	v s	sl s al
t64	cyanide	$TlCN$	230.39	tabl	6.523	d		$16.8^{28.5}$		s a
t65	ethoxide	$(TlOC_2H_5)_4$	997.73	col liq	3.522	-3	d 80	s d		9.11^{25} al; s bz; i liq NH_3
t66	ethylate	$TlOC_2H_5$	249.43	liq, 1.6714^{20}	3.493^{20}	-3	d 130	sl s al; s eth		
t67	ferrocyanide	$Tl_4Fe(CN)_6.2H_2O$	1065.46	yel, tricl	4.641			0.37^{18}	3.93^{101}	
t68	fluogallate	$Tl_3(GaF_6.H_2O)$	591.47	col, orthorhomb	6.44			s		
t69	fluoride, mono-	TlF	223.37	col, cub, oct	8.23^4	327	655	78.6^{15}	d	sl s al
t70	fluoride, tri-	TlF_3	261.37	olive grn	8.36^{25}	d 550		d		i conc HCl
t71	fluosilicate	$Tl_2SiF_6.2H_2O$	586.85	hex pl	5.72			v s		
t72	formate	$TlHCO_2$	249.39	col, need, hygr	4.967^{104}	101		500^{10}		v s MeOH, sl s al; i $CHCl_3$

No.	Name	Synonyms and Formulae	Mol. wt.	Crystalline form, properties and index of refraction	Density or spec. gravity	Melting point, °C	Boiling point, °C	Solubility, in grams per 100 cc		
								Cold water	Hot water	Other solvents
	Thallium									
t73	(I) hydroxide	TlOH	221.38	pa yel, need		d 139		25.9^0	52^{40}	s al
t74	iodate	TlIO₃	379.27	wh need		tr to (β) 170		0.058^{20}	sl s	sl s HNO₃
t75	iodide (α)	TlI	331.27	yel, rhomb	7.29	tr to (β) 170		0.0006^{20}	0.12^{100}	s liq NH₃
t76	iodide (β)	TlI	331.27	red, cub	$7.098^{14.7}$	440	823	i	i	i al
t77	iodide, tri-	TlI₃	585.08	blk, lust rhomb		d		s		
t78	iron (III) sulfate	TlFe(SO₄)₂.12H₂O	668.52	pink, oct, n_D^{17} 1.524	2.351^{15}	$-H_2O$, ca 100		36.15^{25} (anhydr)		
t79	magnesium sulfate	Tl₂SO₄.MgSO₄.6H₂O	733.26	wh dull cr, 1.5660, 1.5836, 1.5900	3.573^{20}_4	$-6H_2O$, 40		d 0		
t80	methoxide	TlOCH₃	235.40	wh cr powd		d>120		s d		1.70^{25} CH₃OH; 3.16^{25} bz
t81	molybdate	Tl₂MoO₄	568.68	wh powd or cr		vol red heat		i	v sl s	i al; s alk carb, conc NH₄OH, HF
t82	myristate	TlC₁₄H₂₇O₂	431.74	wh powd		120–3				0.52^{25} 50 % al
t83	(I) nitrate (α)	TlNO₃	266.37	cubic		206	430	9.55^{20}	4.13^{100}	i al, s acet
t84	(I) nitrate (β)	TlNO₃	266.37	trig		tr 145 to (α)				
t85	(I) nitrate (γ)	TlNO₃	266.37	rhomb, α 1.817	$5.556^{21.4}$	tr 75 to (β)		3.91^0	414^{100}	i al; s acet
t86	(III) nitrate	Tl(NO₃)₃	390.38	cr				s		
t87	(III) nitrate	Tl(NO₃)₃.3H₂O	444.43	col, rhomb, deliq			s 100	d	d	i a
t88	nitrite	TlNO₂	250.38	yel micro cr		182		32.10^{15}	95.78^{96}	i a
t89	oleate	TlC₁₈H₃₃O₂	485.83	wh cr clusters		131–2		0.05^{15}	0.3^{80}	3.0^{25} al
t90	oxalate	Tl₂C₂O₄	496.76	monocl pr	6.31			1.48^{15}	9.02^{100}	
t91	oxalate, tetra-	TlH₃(C₂O₄)₂.2H₂O	419.46	tricl, leaf, 1.5097, 1.6319, 1.6538	2.992^{17}	d 100		76.9^{23}	v s	i cold al; s hot al
t92	(I) oxide	Tl₂O	424.74	blk, deliq	9.52^{16}	300	$1080^{760}-O$, 1865	v s d to TlOH		s a, al
t93	(III) oxide	Tl₂O₃	456.74	col, amorph pr, hex	hex 10.19^{22} am 9.65^{21}	717 ± 5	$-2O$, 875	i	i	s a; i alk
t94	palmitate	TlC₁₆H₃₁O₂	459.79	cr need		115–117		0.01^{15}	0.07^{60}	1.04^{45} al
t95	phenoxide	TlOC₆H₅	297.48	wh cr		233–5		d		s hot bz; sl s lgr
t96	orthophosphate	Tl₃PO₄	708.08	col, need	6.89^{10}			0.5^{15}	0.67^{100}	i al, s NH₄ salts
t97	orthophosphate, (di)-β	TlH₂PO₄	301.36	monocl	4.726	ca 190		sl s	sl s	i al
t98	pyrophosphate	Tl₄P₂O₇	991.42	monocl pr	6.786^{20}	>120		40		
t99	picrate	TlC₆H₂N₃O₇	432.47	red, monocl or yel tricl	red 3.164^{17} yel 2.993^{17}	expl 723–725		0.135^0	2.43^{70}	0.40 CH₃OH
t100	rhodanide	TlCNS	262.45	glossy leaflets, rhomb, tetr cr	4.954^{30}_4	d low temp		0.393^{25}		0.024^0 liq SO₂; i acet; s MeOH
t101	selenate	Tl₂SeO₄	551.70	rhomb need, 1.949, 1.959, 1.964		>400		2.13^{10}	8.5^{50}	i al, eth
t102	selenide	Tl₂Se	487.70	gray leaf	9.05^{25}_4	340		i		s a; i acet a
t103	silver nitrate	TlNO₃.AgNO₃	436.25	wh cr powd		75		s		
t104	stearate	TlC₁₈H₃₅O₂	487.85	need		119		0.005^{15}	0.095^{75}	0.18^{15} al, 0.60^{60} al
t105	(I) sulfate	Tl₂SO₄	504.80	col, rhomb, 1.860, 1.867, 1.885	6.77	632	d	4.87^{20}	19.14^{100}	
t106	(I) sulfate hydrogen	TlHSO₄	301.44	pr need		120 d				v sl s dil H₂SO₄
t107	(III) sulfate	Tl₂(SO₄)₃.7H₂O	823.03	col leaf		$-6H_2O$, 220		d	d	s dil H₂SO₄
t108	(I) sulfide	Tl₂S	440.80	bl-blk tetr	8.46	448.5	d	0.02^{20}	sl s	s a; i alk, acet
t109	(III) sulfide	Tl₂S₃	504.93	blk, amorph		260 (in N₂)	d	i		s hot H₂SO₄
t110	sulfite	Tl₂SO₃	488.80	wh cr	6.427			3.34^{15}	v s	i al
t111	tartrate(dl)	Tl₂C₄H₄O₆	556.81	monocl	4.659	d 165		13.3^{15}		
t112	metatellurate	Tl₂TeO₄	600.34	heavy wh ppt	$6.760^{17.6}$	red heat		sl s	sl s	
t113	thiocyanate	TlSCN	262.45	col, tetr	4.956^{20}			0.315^{20}	0.727^{40}	i al
t114	dithionate	Tl₂S₂O₆	568.86	monocl	5.57^{20}_4	d		41.8^{19}		
t115	thiosulfate	Tl₂S₂O₃	520.87	wh rhomb cr		d 130		sl s	v s	
t116	metavanadate	TlVO₃	303.41	gray cr	6.09^{17}	424		0.87^{11}	0.21^{100}	
t117	pyrovanadate	Tl₄V₂O₇	1031.36	light yel	8.21^{19}	454		0.2^{14}	0.26^{100}	
t118	**Thiocarbonyl chloride**	Thiophosgene. CSCl₂	114.98	red yel liq, 1.5442	1.509^{15}		73.5	d		d al; s eth
t119	**Thiocarbonyl chloride, tetra-**	CSCl₄	185.89	yel	1.712^{15}	146–147			d	
t120	**Thiocyanic acid(iso)**	HSCN (HNCS)	59.09	col mass or gas		>−110	polym to solid −90	v s		v s al, eth, bz
t121	**Thiocyanogen**	(SCN)₂	116.16	liq, or yel solid		−2 to −3		d		s al, eth, CS₂, CCl₄

No.	Name	Synonyms and Formulae	Mol. wt.	Crystalline form, properties and index of refraction	Density or spec. gravity	Melting point, °C	Boiling point, °C	Cold water	Hot water	Other solvents
	Thionyl bromide									
t122	Thionyl bromide....	$SOBr_2$.............	207.88	or, yel liq........	2.68^{18}	−52	138^{773}, 68^{40}	d	d	s bz, chl, CS_2, CCl_4
t123	chloride........	$SOCl_2$.............	118.97	col, or yel liq; 1.527^{10}	1.655^{10}_{4}	−105	78.8^{746} d 140	d	d	d a, al, alk; s bz, chl
s124	chloride fluoride.....	$SOClF$......	102.51	gas........		−139.5	12.2	....	....	....
t125	fluoride...........	SOF_2.............	86.06	col, gas.......	gas 2.93 g/l liq 1.780^{-100}	−110.5	−43.8	d	d	s eth, bz, chl, acet, $AsCl_3$
t126	Thiophosphoramide.	Thiophosphorylamide. $PS(NH_2)_3$	111.11	yel wh amorph...	1.7^{18}	d 200	....	sl s	d	....
t127	Thiophosphoryl bromide	$PSBr_3$.............	302.76	yel, cub........	2.85^{17}	37.8	125^{25}	d		s eth, CS_2, PCl_3
t128	thiophosphoryl bromide, hydrate	$PSBr_3.H_2O$	320.78	yel cr........	2.794^{15}	35				
t129	thiophosphoryl bromide (mono-) chloride, di-	$PSBrCl_2$	213.85	yel liq.........	2.12^{0}	−30	d 150	d		
t130	thiophosphoryl bromide (di-) chloride	$PSBr_2Cl$.......	258.31	pa grn fum liq...	2.48^{0}	−60	95^{60}			
t131	thiophosphoryl chloride	$PSCl_3$...........	169.40	col liq, 1.563 (e)..	1.635	−35	125	d		s bz, CS_2, CCl_4
t132	thiophosphoryl fluoride	PSF_3...........	120.03	gas.........	$3.87^{b.p.atm}$		d	sl s d		s eth; i bz, CS_2
t133	Thiosulfuric acid....	$H_2S_2O_3$........	114.14	in sol only......			....	s		
t134	Thorium........	Th...........	232.038	gray, cub radioactive	11.7			i	i	s HCl, H_2SO_4, aq reg; sl s HNO_3
t135	boride, hexa-.......	ThB_6...........	296.92	dk viol-blk met, cub	6.4^{18}	2195	....	i	i	s HNO_3; i H_2SO_4, HCl, HF, aq alk
t136	boride, tetra........	ThB_4...........	275.28	tetr pr.........	7.5^{18}			i	i	s HNO_3 HCl, hot H_2SO_4
t137	bromide..........	$ThBr_4$...........	551.67	col cr, hygr......	5.67	subl 610	725	s	s	
t138	carbide........	ThC_2.........	256.06	yel, tetr........	8.96^{18}	2655 ± 25	ca 5000 (?)	d		v sl s conc a
t139	carbonate........	$Th(CO_3)_2$.......	352.06	exist?........				i	d	s conc Na_2CO_3
t140	chloride.........	$ThCl_4$...........	373.85	wh, rhomb, deliq.	4.59	770 ± 2 subl 820	d 928	v s	v s	s al, a, KCl; sl s eth
t142	tetracyanoplatinate..	$Th[Pt(CN)_4]_2.16H_2O$.	1118.61	yel-grn, rhomb...	2.460			sl s	s	....
t143	fluoride.........	ThF_4...........	308.03	wh cub powd....	6.32^{24}	>900				sl d dil H_2SO_4, HCl; i conc H_2SO_4
t144	fluoride.........	$ThF_4.4H_2O$.......	380.09	cr...........		−H_2O, 100	−$2H_2O$, 140−200	0.017^{25}		i HF
t145	hydroxide........	$Th(OH)_4$........	300.02	wh gelat.......		d		i	i	s a; i alk, HF
t146	iodate..........	$Th(IO_3)_4$........	931.65	....				i	i d	s dil H_2SO_4; i dil HNO_3
t147	iodide, tetra-.......	ThI_4...........	739.66	yel...........		566	839	s		....
t148	nitrate..........	$Th(NO_3)_4$.......	480.06	plates, deliq.....		d 500		v s		s al
t149	nitrate..........	$Th(NO_3)_4.4H_2O$.......	552.12	col cr.........		swells		v s		v s al; sl s acet; 36.9 eth
t150	nitrate..........	$Th(NO_3)_4.12H_2O$.......	696.24	col leaf, deliq...		d		v s		v s al, a
t151	nitride..........	Th_3N_4.........	752.14	dk brn powd, or blk cr				sl d	d	s HCl
t152	oxalate..........	$Th(C_2O_4)_2$........	408.08	wh cr.........	4.637^{16}	d		0.0017^{17}	0.0017^{60}	s h aq $(NH_4)_2C_2O_4$; sl s a
t153	oxalate..........	$Th(C_2O_4)_2.6H_2O$	516.17	wh amorph powd				i		s Na_2CO_3, $(NH_4)_2C_2O_4$ sol; i HNO_3
t154	oxide, di-........	Thorianite. ThO_2...	264.04	wh cub, 2.20 (liq)	9.86	3050	4400	i	i	s hot H_2SO_4; i dil a, alk
t155	oxysulfide........	$ThOS$.........	280.10	yel cr.........	6.44^{0}	d			i	s aq reg; sl s HNO_3
t156	2,4-pentanedione....	Thorium acetylacetonate. $Th(C_5H_7O_2)_4$	628.48	col cr.........		171 subl 160^{10}	$260-270^{10}$	sl s		v s al, chl; s eth
t157	hypophosphate......	$ThP_2O_6.11H_2O$.......	588.15	wh amorph ppt...		−$11H_2O$, 160		i	i	i a, alk
t158	metaphosphate......	$Th(PO_3)_4$.......	547.93	col rhomb pr.....	$4.08^{16.4}$					
t159	orthophosphate......	$Th_3(PO_4)_4.4H_2O$........	1148.06	wh gelat.......			i	i		s 30° HCl; i a
t160	picrate..........	$Th(C_6H_2N_3O_7)_4.10H_2O$.	1324.59	....				0.305^{25}		
t161	selenate.........	$Th(SeO_4)_2.9H_2O$.......	680.09	col, monocl.....	3.026	−$8H_2O$, 200	d 1500	0.5^{0}	2.0^{100}	
t162	orthosilicate.......	Thorite $ThSiO_4$.....	324.12	col, tetr, 1.80, 1.81	6.82^{18}			v sl s		i a
t163	silicide..........	$ThSi_2$........	288.21	blk, tetr........	7.96^{16}					s hot HCl; sl s H_2SO_4
t164	sulfate..........	$Th(SO_4)_2$.......	424.16	wh cr, hygr......	4.225^{17}			s	s	i a; v s $NH_4C_2H_3O_2$
t165	sulfate..........	$Th(SO_4)_2.4H_2O$.......	496.22	wh need, or cr powd		−$4H_2O$, 400		9.41^{17} (anhydr)	2.54^{50} (anhydr)	i a

No.	Name	Synonyms and Formulae	Mol. wt.	Crystalline form, properties and index of refraction	Density or spec. gravity	Melting point, °C	Boiling point, °C	Cold water	Hot water	Other solvents

Thorium

No.	Name	Synonyms and Formulae	Mol. wt.	Crystalline form	Density	M.p.	B.p.	Cold water	Hot water	Other solvents
t166	sulfate	$Th(SO_4)_2.6H_2O$	532.26			$-4H_2O$, 42		1.63^{15}	6.64^{60}	i a
t167	sulfate	$Th(SO_4)_2.8H_2O$	568.29	monocl, prism, 1.5168		$-4H_2O$, 42		1.88^{25}	3.71^{44}	i a
t168	sulfate	$Th(SO_4)_2.9H_2O$	586.31	wh monocl	2.77	$-9H_2O$, 400		1.57^{20}	6.67^{55}	i a
t169	sulfide	ThS_2	296.17	dk brn-blk cr	7.30^{25}_4	1925 ± 50 (vac)		i	d 200	s hot aq reg; sl s a
t170	pyrovanadate	$ThV_2O_7.6H_2O$	554.01	yel				i	i	s conc a
t171	**Thulium**	Tm	168.934	silv wh met, hex	9.3208	1545	1947	i	i	
t172	bromide	$TmBr_3$	408.66			952	1440	s	s	
t173	chloride	$TmCl_3.7H_2O$	401.40	grn cr, deliq		824	1440	v s		v s al
t174	fluoride	TmF_3	225.93			1158	>2200	i	i	s dil a
t175	iodide	TmI_3	549.65	brt yel cr		1015	1260	s	s	
t176	oxalate	$Tm_2(C_2O_4)_3.6H_2O$	710.02	grn-wh ppt		$-H_2O$, 50		i		s alk oxal sol; i dil a
t177	oxide	Thulia. Tm_2O_3	385.87	grn-wh powd						sl s min a
t178	**Tin gray**	Sn	118.69	gray, cub	5.75	231.9681	2270	i	i	s HCl, H_2SO_4, aq reg, alk; sl s dil HNO_3
t179	**Tin white**	Sn	118.69	wh met, tetr	7.28	231.88 stable 13.2—161	2260	i	i	s HCl, H_2SO_4, aq reg, alk; sl s dil HNO_3
t180	**Tin brittle**	Sn	118.69	wh, rhomb	6.52—56	231.89 stable >161	2260	i	i	s HCl, H_2SO_4, aq reg, alk; sl s dil HNO_3
t181	(II) acetate	$Sn(C_2H_3O_2)_2$	236.78	yelsh powd		182	240	d		s dil HCl
t182	pyroarsenate	$Sn_2As_2O_7$	499.22	flocculent ppt		d As_2O_3 + SnO_2		i	i	i conc ac a
t183	(II) bromide	$SnBr_2$	278.51	pa yel, rhomb	5.117^{17}	215.5	620	85.2^0	222.5^{100}	s al, eth, acet
t184	(IV) bromide	$SnBr_4$	438.33	col, rhomb pyr, deliq	liq 3.34^{35}	31	202^{784}	s d	d	s acet, PCl_3, $AsBr_3$
t185	bromide chloride(tri-)	$SnBrCl_3$	304.96	col liq	2.51^{13}	-31	50^{30}			
t186	bromide(di-) chloride(di-)	$SnBr_2Cl_2$	349.41		2.82^{13}	-20	65^{30} d 191	d	d	
t187	bromide(tri-) chloride	$SnBr_3Cl$	393.87	liq	3.12^{13}	1	73^{30}			
t188	bromide(di-) iodode(di-)	$SnBr_2I_2$	532.32	or-red, hex pl	3.631^{15}	50	225	s	d<80	
t189	(II) chloride	$SnCl_2$	189.60	wh, rhomb	3.95^{25}_4	246	652	83.9^0	269.8^{15} d	s al, eth, acet, et acet, me acet, pyr
t190	(II) chloride dihydrate	$SnCl_2.2H_2O$	225.63	wh, monocl	$2.710^{15.5}$	37.7	d	d	d	s al, eth, acet, glac ac a
t191	(IV) chloride	$SnCl_4$	260.50	col liq, solid cub, 1.512	liq 2.226	-33	114.1	s	d	s eth
t192	(IV) chloride pentahydrate	$SnCl_4.5H_2O$	350.58	monocl cr		stable 19–56		s		
t193	(IV) chloride tetrahydrate	$SnCl_4.4H_2O$	332.56	opaque			stable 56–83	s		
t194	(IV) chloride trihydrate	$SnCl_4.3H_2O$	314.55	col, monocl cr		80	stable 64–83	s		
t195	(IV) chloride diammine	$SnCl_4.2NH_3$	294.56	cr				s		d HCl
t196	chloride(tri-) bromide	$SnCl_3Br$	304.96	col liq	2.51^{13}	-31	50^{30}			
t197	chloride (di-) iodide(di-)	$SnCl_2I_2$	443.40	red mobile liq	3.287^{15}		297	s	d	s chl, bz CS_2
t198	(IV) chloride nitrosyl-chloride	$SnCl_4.2NOCl$	391.42	pa yel, oct cr	2.60	180		d		
t199	(IV) chromate	$Sn(CrO_4)_2$	350.68	br yel cr powd	d			s		
t200	(II) ferricyanide	$Sn_3[Fe(CN)_6]_2$	779.98	wh	d			i	i	s HCl
t201	(II) ferrocyanide	$Sn_2Fe(CN)_6$	449.33	wh gel				i	i	d HCl
t202	(IV) ferrocyanide	$SnFe(CN)_6$	330.64					i	i	d h HCl
t203	(II) fluoride	Fluoristan. SnF_2	156.69	wh, monocl cr				s		
t204	(IV) fluoride	SnF_4	194.68	wh, monocl cr, hygr	4.780^{19}	705 subl		v s	d	
t205	hydride	Stannane. SnH_4	122.72	gas		d -150	-52			s $AgNO_3$, $HgCl_2$, conc alk, conc H_2SO_4
t206	iodide	SnI_2	372.50	yelsh-red to red monocl need	5.285	320	717	0.98^{20}	4.03^{100}	v s NH_4OH, HI soln
t207	(IV) iodide	SnI_4	626.31	or red cub, 2.106	4.473^0	144.5	364.5	s	d	141.1^{15} CS_2; 6.03^{15} CCl_4; 17.88^{25} bz

No.	Name	Synonyms and Formulae	Mol. wt.	Crystalline form, properties and index of refraction	Density or spec. gravity	Melting point, °C	Boiling point, °C	Solubility, in grams per 100 cc		
								Cold water	Hot water	Other solvents
	Tin									
t208	(II) nitrate	$Sn(NO_3)_2.20H_2O$	603.07	col leaf		−20		d	d	d HNO_3
t209	(II) nitrate, basic	$SnO.Sn(NO_3)_2$	377.39	wh cr mass		d >100 expl		d	d	
t210	(IV) nitrate	$Sn(NO_3)_4$	366.71	silky need		d 50		d		
t211	(II) oxide, mon-	SnO	134.69	blk, cub (tetr)	6.446^0	d 1080^{600}		i	i	s a, alk; sl s NH_4Cl
t212	oxide, mon-hydrate	$SnO.xH_2O$		wh powd or yellow-brn cr				d to SnO		d a; alk; s alk carb; i NH_4OH
t213	(IV) oxide, di-	Nat. cussiterite. SnO_2	150.69	wh, tetr, (also hex or rhomb), 1.997, 2.093	6.95	1127	subl 1800–1900	i	i	d KOH, NaOH; i aq reg
t214	oxide, di-hydrate	α-Stannic acid or "ordinary" stannic acid. $SnO_2.xH_2O$		amorph or gel				i	i	s a, alk, K_2CO_3
t215	oxide, di-hydrate	β-Stannic acid or "meta" stannic acid. $SnO_2.xH_2O$		wh, amorph or gel				i	i	i a, K_2CO_3; sol alk
t216	(II) *meta*phosphate	$Sn(PO_3)_2$	276.63	amorph mass	$3.380^{22.8}$			i		
t217	(II) *ortho*phosphate	$Sn_3(PO_4)_2$	546.01	wh, amorph	3.823^{17}			i	i	d a, alk
t218	(II) *ortho*phosphate, di-H	$Sn(H_2PO_4)_2$	312.66	wh, rhomb cr	$3.167^{98.9}$	d	d		d	
t219	(II) *ortho*phosphate, mono-H	$SnHPO_4$	214.67	cr	$3.476^{15.5}$	stabl >100	d	i	i	s dil min a
t220	(II) *pyro*phosphate	$Sn_2P_2O_7$	411.32	amorph powd	$4.009^{15.4}$			i	i	s conc a
t221	phosphide, mono-	SnP	149.66	silv wh	6.56	d	d	i	i	s HCl; i HNO_3
t222	phosphide, tri-	SnP_3	211.61	cr	4.10^0	<415 d to Sn_4P_3		i	i	d HNO_3; i HCl
t223	*tetra*phosphide, tri-	Sn_4P_3	567.68	wh cr	5.181	d <480		i	i	d fixed alk hydr, HCl
t224	phosphorus chloride	$SnCl_4.PCl_5$	468.74	col cr		subl 200		d	d	
t225	(II) selenide	SnSe	197.65	steelgray cr	6.179^0	861		i	i	d HCl, HNO_3, aq reg, alk sulf
t226	(II) sulfate	$SnSO_4$	214.75	wh-yelsh cr powd		>360 (SO_2)		33^{25}		s H_2SO_4
t227	(IV) sulfate	$Sn(SO_4)_2.2H_2O$	346.84	wh, hex pr, deliq				v s	d	s eth, dil H_2SO_4, HCl
t228	(II) sulfide	SnS	150.75	gray-blk cub, monocl	5.22^{25}	882	1230	0.00002^{18}		d HCl, alk, $(NH_4)_2S$
t229	(IV) sulfide	Mosaic gold. SnS_2	182.82	gold yel, hex	4.5	d 600		0.0002^{18}		d alk sulf, aq reg, alk hydr, PCl_5, $SnCl_2$; i a
t230	(IV) sulfur chloride	$SnCl_4.2SCl_4$	608.25	yel cr		37	d <40	d	d	s eth, bz, CS_2, ethyl acet; d HNO_3
t231	tartrate	$SnC_4H_4O_6$	266.76	heavy wh powd				s		v s dil HCl
t232	(II) telluride	SnTe	246.29	gray cr	6.48	780		i	i	d alk sulf
t233	(IV) telluride	$SnTe_2$	373.89	blk, flocc ppt				i	i	d dil a, alk
t234	**Titanic acid, ortho-**	α Titanic acid. H_2TiO_4	113.91	wh		d		v sl s d		s dil HCl, dil H_2SO_4, conc alk
t235	**Titanium**	Ti	47.90	α hex, tr β cub 838, silv gray	4.5^{20}	1660±10	3287	i	i	s dil a
t236	boride, di-	TiB_2	69.52	hex	4.50	2900				
t237	bromide, di-	$TiBr_2$	207.72	blk powd	4.31	d >500		s ev H_2		
t238	bromide, tetra-	$TiBr_4$	367.54	or yel, deliq	2.6	39	230	d		s abs al, abs eth
t239	bromide, tri-	$TiBr_3.6H_2O$	395.72	redsh-viol or dk blue cr, deliq		115	d 400	v s		v s al, acet
t240	carbide	TiC	59.91	gr met, cub	4.93	3140±90	4820	i	i	s aq reg, HNO_3
t241	chloride, di-	$TiCl_2$	118.81	lt br-blk, hex, deliq	3.13	subl H_2	d 475 vac	d		s al, i eth, chl, CS_2
t242	chloride, tetra-	$TiCl_4$	189.71	lt yel liq, $1.61^{10.5}$	liq 1.726 sol 2.06^{-79}	−25	136.4	s	d	s dil HCl, al
t243	chloride, tri-	$TiCl_3$	154.26	dk viol, deliq	2.64	d 440	660^{108}	s	s	v s al; s HCl; i eth
t244	fluoride, tetra	TiF_4	123.89	wh powd, hygr	$2.798^{99.5}$	>100 (pressure)	284 (subl.)	s d		s H_2SO_4, al, C_5H_5N; i eth
t245	fluoride, tri-	TiF_3	104.90	purp-red or vlt	3.40	1200	1400	red s vlt i		
t246	hydride	TiH_2	49.92	gray powd	3.91^2	d 400		i	i	
t247	iodide, di-	TiI_2	301.71	blk, hygr	4.99	600	1000	d		d alk; s conc HF, conc HCl
t248	iodide, tetra-	TiI_4	555.52	red, cub	4.3	150	377.1	v s	d	
t249	nitride	TiN	61.91	yel-bronze, cub	5.22	2930		i	i	sl s hot aq reg +HF
t250	oxalate	$Ti_2(C_2O_4)_3.10H_2O$	540.01	yel pr				s	s	i al, eth
t251	oxide, di-	Nat. brookite. TiO_2	79.90	wh, rhomb, 2.583, 2.586, 2.741	4.17	1825		i	i	s H_2SO_4, alk; i a
t252	oxide, di-	Nat. octahedrite, anatase. TiO_2	79.90	br-blk, tetr, 2.554, 2.493	3.84			i	i	s H_2SO_4, alk; i a

No.	Name	Synonyms and Formulae	Mol. wt.	Crystalline form, properties and index of refraction	Density or spec. gravity	Melting point, °C	Boiling point, °C	Solubility, in grams per 100 cc		
								Cold water	Hot water	Other solvents
	Titanium									
t253	oxide, di-	Nat. rutile. TiO_2	79.90	col, tetr, 2.616, 2.903	4.26	1830–1850	2500–3000	i	i	s H_2SO_4, alk; i a
t254	oxide, mon-	TiO	63.90	yel blk, pr	4.93	1750	>3000			s dil H_2SO_4; i HNO_3
t255	oxide, sesqui-	Ti_2O_3	143.80	vlt blk, trig	4.6	2130 d		i	i	s H_2SO_4; i HCl, HNO_3
t256	phosphide	TiP	78.87	gray, met	3.95^{25}			i	i	i a
t257	sulfate	$Ti_2(SO_4)_3$	383.98	green powd				i	i	s dil a; i al, eth, conc H_2SO_4
t258	sulfate, basic	$TiOSO_4$	159.96	wh or sl yelsh powd, 1.80–1.89				d		
t259	sulfide, di-	TiS_2	112.03	yel sc	3.22^{20}			hyd sl	d in steam	d HCl; s dil HNO_3, H_2SO_4
t260	sulfide, mono-	TiS	79.96	redsh solid	4.12					s conc H_2SO_4; i HCl, HF, dil H_2SO_4
t261	sulfide, sesqui	Ti_2S_3	191.99	grayish-blk cr	3.584			i	i	s conc H_2SO_4, conc HNO_3; i dil H_2SO_4, dil HCl
t262	**Tungsten**	Wolfram. W	183.85	gray-blk, cub	19.35^{20}_4	3410 ± 20	5660	i	i	v sl s HNO_3, H_2SO_4, aq reg; s HNO_3+HF, fus NaOH+ $NaNO_2$; i HF, KOH
t263	arsenide	WAs_2	333.69	blk cr	6.9^{18}	d red heat		i		d hot HNO_3, hot H_2SO_4
t264	boride, di-	WB_2	205.47	silvery, oct	10.77	ca 2900		i	i	s aq reg
t265	bromide, di-	WBr_2	343.67	bl-blk need		d 400		d		
t266	bromide, penta-	WBr_5	583.40	vlt-brn need, hygr		276	333	d		s abs al, chl, eth, alk
t267	bromide, hexa-	WBr_6	663.30	bl-blk, need	6.9	232		i	d	s abs a, eth, CS_2, NH_4OH
t268	carbide	WC	195.86	blk, hex	15.63^{18}	2870 ± 50	6000	i		s HNO_3+HF, aq reg
t269	(di-)carbide	W_2C	379.71	blk, hex	17.15	2860	6000	i		s HNO_3+HCl
t270	carbonyl	$W(CO)_6$	351.91	col, rhomb cr	2.65	d~150	175^{766}	i	i	s fum HNO_3; v sl s al, eth, bz
t271	chloride, di-	WCl_2	254.76	gray, amorph	5.436			d		
t272	chloride, hexa-	WCl_6	396.57	dk bl, cub	3.52^{25}_4	275	346.7		d^{60}	s al, eth, bz, CCl_4; v s CS_2, POCl
t273	chloride, penta-	WCl_5	361.12	blk, deliq	3.875^{25}_4	248	275.6		d to W_2O_5	v sl s CS_2
t274	chloride, tetra-	WCl_4	325.66	gray, deliq	4.624^{25}_4	d		d		
t275	fluoride, hexa-	WF_6	297.84	col gas, or lt yel liq	liq 3.44 gas 12.9 g/l	2.5^{420}	17.5	d	d	s alk
t276	iodide, di-	WI_2	437.66	br-gr, amorph	6.799^{25}_4	d		i	d	s alk; i al CS_2
t277	iodide, tetra-	WI_4	691.47	blk, cr	5.2^{18}	d		i	d	s abs al; i eth, chl, turp
t278	nitride, di-	WN_2	211.86	brn, cub		above 400 (vac)		d	d	
t279	oxide, di-	WO_2	215.85	br, cub	12.11	1500–1600 (in N_2)	ca 1430 subl 800	i	i	s a, KOH
t280	oxide, pent-	Mineral blue. W_2O_5 or W_4O_{11}	447.70 or 911.39	blue-vlt, tricl		subl 800–900	ca 1530 d 2000	i	i	i a
t281	oxide, tri-	Nat. wolframite. WO_3	231.85	yel, rhomb, or yel-or powd	7.16	1473		i	i	s hot alk; sl s HF; i a
t282	oxydibromide, di-	WO_2Br_2	375.67	red, prism		d				
t283	oxytetrabromide	$WOBr_4$	519.49	blk, deliq		277	327	d	d	
t284	oxytetrachloride	$WOCl_4$	341.66	red, need		211	227.5	d	d	s CS_2, S_2Cl_2, bz
t285	oxydichloride, di-	WO_2Cl_2	286.75	lt yel tabl		266		s	d	i al; s NH_4OH, alk
t286	oxytetrafluoride-	WOF_4	275.84	col pl, hygr		110	187.5	d		sl s CS_2; i CCl_4
t287	phosphide	WP	214.82	gray, prism	8.5			i		s HNO_3+HF; i alk, HCl
t288	phosphide	WP_2	245.80	blk cr	5.8	d		i	i	s HNO_3+HF, aq reg; i al, eth
t289	phosphide	W_2P	398.67	dk gray prism	5.21	d				s fus Na_2CO_3+ $NaNO_3$; i a, aq reg

No.	Name	Synonyms and Formulae	Mol. wt.	Crystalline form, properties and index of refraction	Density or spec. gravity	Melting point, °C	Boiling point, °C	Solubility, in grams per 100 cc		
								Cold water	Hot water	Other solvents
	Tungsten									
t290	silicide	WSi_2	240.02	blue, gray, tetrag	9.4	above 900		i	i	s HNO_3+HF; i aq reg
t291	sulfide, di-	Nat. tungstenite. WS_2	247.98	dk gray, hexag	7.5[10]	d 1250		i		s HNO_3+HF, fus alk; i al
t292	sulfide, tri-	WS_3	280.04	choc brn powd				sl s	s	s alk
t293	**Tungstic acid, meta-**	$H_2W_4O_{13}.9H_2O$	1107.55	col, tetrag	3.93	d 50		88.57[22]	111.87[43.5]	110.76[24.3] eth; s al
t294	**Tungstic acid, ortho-**	H_2WO_4	249.86	yel powd, 2.24	5.5	−H_2O, 100	1473	i	sl s	s alk, HF, NH_3; i most a
t295	**Tungstic acid, ortho-**	$H_2WO_4.H_2O$	267.88	wh		$H_2W_2O_7$ at 100		sl s		s alk
u1	**Uranic acid meta-**	Uranyl hydroxide. H_2UO_4(or $UO_2(OH)_2$)	304.04	yel, rhomb, or powd	5.926	−H_2O 250−300		i	i	s a, alk carb
u2	**Uranium**	U	238.03	silvery, cubic, radioactive	19.05±0.02[25]	1132.3±0.8	3818	i	i	s a; i alk, al
u3	boride, di-	UB_2	259.65	hex	12.70	2365				
u4	bromide tetra-	UBr_4	557.67	br leaf, deliq	5.35	516	792[760]	v s	v s	s d al, MeOH; i bz; s liq NH_3
u5	bromide tri-	UBr_3	477.76	dk brn need, hygr	6.53	730	volat	s		s d al
u6	dicarbide	UC_2	262.05	met cr	11.28[16]	2350−2400	4370[760]	d	d	i al; d dil inorg a
u7	chloride, penta-	UCl_5	415.30	dk green, gray need, red by trans light, hydr	3.81(?)	d 300		d		s abs als, a acet, NH_4Cl; d ac a; i bz, eth
u8	chloride, tetra-	UCl_4	379.84	dk grn met, cub oct, hygr	4.87	590±1	792[760]	v s	s	s al, acet, ac a; i eth, $CHCl_3$
u9	chloride, tri-	UCl_3	344.39	dk red need, hygr	5.44[25/4]	842±5		s	s	s MeOH, acet, glac acet a; i eth
u10	fluoride, hexa-	UF_6	352.02	col cr, deliq, monocl	4.68[21]	64.5−64.8	56.2[65]	d		d al, eth; s CCl_4, chl; i CS_2
u11	fluoride, tetra	UF_4	314.02	green, tricl need	6.70±0.10	960±5		v sl s		i dil a, alk; s conc a, conc alk
u12	fluoride, tri-	UF_3	295.03	blk cr or fused		d above 1000		sl d		v sl s dil inorg a
u13	hydride	UH_3	241.05	blk-brn powd	10.95			i	i	i al, acet, liq NH_3; sl s dil HCl; d HNO_3
u14	hydride	UH_3	241.05	blk powd, cub	11.4					
u15	iodide, tetra-	UI_4	745.65	blk, need	5.6[15]	506	759	s	s d	
u16	nitride, mono-	UN	252.04	br powd	14.31	ca 2630±50				i HCl, H_2SO_4
u17	oxide, di-	UO_2	270.03	br-blk rhomb, or cub	10.96	2500		i	i	s HNO_3, conc H_2SO_4
u18	oxide, per-	$UO_4.2H_2O$	338.06	pa yel cr, hygr		d 115		0.0006[20]	0.008[90]	d HCl
u19	oxide, tri-	Uranyl oxide. UO_3	286.03	yel-red powd	7.29	d		i	i	s HNO_3, HCl
u20	tri-oxide, oct-	U_3O_8	842.09	olive green-blk	8.30	d 1300 to UO_2		i	i	s HNO_3, H_2SO_4
u21	(IV) sulfate	$U(SO_4)_2.4H_2O$	502.21	grn, rhomb		−$4H_2O$, 300		23[11]	9[63] (anhydr)	s dil a
u22	(IV) sulfate	$U(SO_4)_2.8H_2O$	574.28			d 90		11.3[18]	58.2[63]	i al; s dil a
u23	(IV) sulfate	$U(SO_4)_2.9H_2O$	592.29	grnsh, monocl		−$7H_2O$, 230	−$9H_2O$ red heat oxidizes			s dil H_2SO_4
u24	sulfide, di-	US_2	302.16	gray-blk, tetr	7.96[25]	>1100		sl d		s conc HCl; d HNO_3 v s al
u25	sulfide, mono-	US	270.09	blk amorph powd	10.87	above 2000				i HCl, HNO_3
u26	sulfide, sesqui-	U_2S_3	572.25	gray blk, rhomb need		ign				s+O aq reg conc HNO_3; i dil a
u27	**Uranyl acetate**	$UO_2(C_2H_3O_2)_2.2H_2O$	422.19	yel, rhomb	2.893[15]	−$2H_2O$, 110	d 275	7.694[15]	d	v s al
u28	benzoate	$UO_2(C_7H_5O_2)_2$	512.26	yel powd				sl s		sl s al
u29	bromide	UO_2Br_2	429.85	grn-yel need, hygr				s d		s al, eth
u30	perchlorate	$UO_2(ClO_4)_2.6H_2O$	577.02	yel cr, deliq, rhomb		90 d 110				
u31	chloride	UO_2Cl_2	340.93	yel, deliq		578	d	320[18]	v s	s al, amyl al, eth
u32	formate	$UO_2(CHO_2)_2.H_2O$	378.08	yel, oct	3.695[19]	−H_2O, 110		7.9[18]		sl s form a; 0.74[18] MeOH, 2.37[15] acet
u33	iodate	$UO_2(IO_3)_2$	619.83	yel, rhomb	5.2	d 250		s	s	i HNO_3
u34	iodate	$UO_2(IO_3)_2.H_2O$	637.85	α prismatic, stable, β pyramidal	α 5.220[18] β 5.052[18]			α 0.1049[18] β 0.1214[18]		
u35	iodide	UO_2I_2	523.84	red, deliq		d in air				s al, eth, bz
u36	nitrate	$UO_2(NO_3)_2.6H_2O$	502.13	yel, rhomb, deliq, 1.4967	2.807[13]	60.2 d 100	118		∞ 60	v s al, eth, ac a, acet, MeOH
u37	oxalate	$UO_2C_2O_4.3H_2O$	412.09	yel cr		−H_2O, 110		0.8[14]	3.3[100]	s inorg a, alk, oxal a
u38	phosphate, mono-H	$UO_2HPO_4.4H_2O$	438.07	yel pl, tetr				i	i	s HNO_3, aq Na_2CO_3; i ac a
u39	potassium carbonate	$UO_2CO_3.2K_2CO_3$	606.46	yel cr		−CO_2, 300		7.4[15]	d	i al

No.	Name	Synonyms and Formulae	Mol. wt.	Crystalline form, properties and index of refraction	Density or spec. gravity	Melting point, °C	Boiling point, °C	Solubility, in grams per 100 cc		
								Cold water	Hot water	Other solvents
	Uranyl									
u40	sodium carbonate...	$UO_2CO_3.2Na_2CO_3$	542.02	yel cr				sl s		i al
u41	sulfate	$UO_2SO_4.3H_2O$	420.14	yel-grn cr	$3.28^{16.5}$	d 100		$20.5^{15.5}$	22.2^{100}	24.3^{12} conc H_2SO_4; 30^{13} conc HCl
u42	sulfate	$2(UO_2SO_4).7H_2O$	858.29	yel		anh 300		sl s		s H_2SO_3
u43	sulfide	UO_2S	302.09	brn-blk, tetr		d 40-50		sl s	s d	s dil a, dil al, $(NH_4)_2CO_3$; i abs al
u44	sulfite	$UO_2SO_3.4H_2O$	422.15	pa-gr cr						s H_2SO_3
v1	**Vanadic acid, meta-**	HVO_3	99.95	yel sc				i		s a, alk; i NH_4OH
v2	tetra-	$H_2V_4O_{11}$	381.78	br amorph				i		s a, alk, NH_4OH
v3	**Vanadium**	V	50.942	lt gray met, cub, 3.03	5.96	1890 ± 10	3380	i	i	s aq reg, HNO_3, H_2SO_4, HF; i HCl, alk
v4	boride, di-	VB_2	72.56	hex	5.10					
v5¹	bromide, tri-	VBr_3	290.67	grn-blk, deliq	4.00^{18}	d		s		s al, eth; i HBr
v5²	carbide	VC	62.95	blk, cub	5.77	2810	3900	i		s HNO_3, fus KNO_3; i HCl, H_2SO_4
v6	chloride, di-	VCl_2	121.85	grn, hex, deliq	3.23^{18}			s d	s d	s al, eth
v7	chloride, tetra-	VCl_4	192.75	red-br liq	1.816^{30}	-28 ± 2	148.5^{755}	s d		s abs al, eth, chl, acet a
v8	chloride, tri-	VCl_3	157.30	pink cr, deliq	3.00^{18}	d		s d	s d	s abs al, eth
v9	fluoride, penta-	VF_5	145.93		2.177^{19}		111.2^{755}			s al
v10	fluoride, tetra-	VF_4	126.94	br yel	2.975^{23}	d 325		s		s acet; sl s al, chl
v11	fluoride, tri-	VF_3	107.94	grn, rhomb	3.363^{19}	>800	subl	i		s al, chl, CS_2
v12	fluoride, tri-	$VF_3.3H_2O$	161.98	dk gr, rhomb		$-3H_2O, 100$		s	v s d	i abs al
v13	iodide, di-	VI_2	304.71	vlt-rose, hex	5.44	750-800 subl vac		s		i al, CCl_4, CS_2, bs
v14	iodide, tri-	$VI_3.6H_2O$	539.75	gr cr, deliq		d		v s		s al
v15	nitride	VN	64.95	blk, cub	6.13	2320		i		sl s aq reg
v16	oxide	VO (or V_2O_2)	66.94	lt gray cr	5.758^{14}	ign		i	i	s a
v17	oxide, di- (or tetr)-	VO_2 (or V_2O_4)	82.94	bl cr	4.339	1967		i	i	s a, alk
v18	oxide, pent-	V_2O_5	181.88	yel-red, rhomb, 1.46, 1.52, 1.76	3.357^{18}	690	d 1750	0.8^{20}		s a, alk; i abs al
v19	oxide, sesqui-	Vanadium trioxide. V_2O_3	149.88	blk cr	4.87^{18}_{4}	1970		sl s	s	s HNO_3, HF, alk
v20	oxybromide	VOBr	146.85	vlt, oct	4.00^{18}	d 480		v sl s		s acet, anhydr eth, acet
v21	oxy di-bromide	$VOBr_2$	226.76	br powd, deliq		d 180		s		
v22	oxytribromide	$VOBr_3$	306.67	red liq	$2.933^{14.5}$	d 180	130^{100}	s		
v23	oxychloride	VOCl	102.39	yel brn powd	2.824, 3.64^{20}		127	i		v s HNO_3
v24	oxydichloride	$VOCl_2$	137.85	grn, deliq	2.88^{12}			d		s dil HNO_3
v25	oxytrichloride	$VOCl_3$	173.30	yel liq	1.829	-77 ± 2	126.7	s d		s al, eth, ac a
v26	oxydifluoride	VOF_2	104.94	yel	3.396^{19}	d				sl s acet
v27	oxytrifluoride	VOF_3	123.94	yel-wh, hygr	2.459^{19}	300	480	i		s HF; i al, eth, a
v28	silicide, di-	VSi_2	107.11	met pr	4.42			i	i	s HF; i al, eth, a
v29	(dl-)silicide	V_3Si	129.97	silv wh pr	5.48^{17}			i	i	s HF; i al, eth, a
v30	sulfate (hypovanadous)	$VSO_4.7H_2O$	273.11	vlt, monocl		d in air				
v31	sulfide, mono- or (di-)	VS (or V_2S_2)	83.01	blk pl (exist ?)	4.20	d				s hot H_2SO_4, HNO_3; sl s KSH; i HCl, alk
v32	sulfide, penta-	V_2S_5	262.20	blk-grn powd	3.0	d		i		s HNO_3, alk sulf, alk
v33	sulfide, sesqui- or (tri-)	V_2S_3	198.08	grn-blk pl, or powd	4.72^{21}	d>600		i		s alk sulf; sl s, alk, HCl, HNO_3, H_2SO_4
v34	**Vanadyl sulfate**	$VOSO_4$	163.00	bl				v s		
w1	**Water**	H_2O	18.01534	col liq, or col hex cr	liq 1.000^4 sld 0.9168^0	0.00	100.00			s al
w2	**Water heavy**	Deuterium oxide. D_2O	20.03	col liq or hex cr, 1.33844^{20}	1.105^{20}_{4}	3.82	101.42	∞	∞	∞ al; sl s eth
w3	**Wolfram**	See tungsten								
x1	**Xenon**	Xe	131.30	col inert gas	gas 5.887 g/l ± 0.009 liq 3.52^{-109} solid 2.7^{-140}	-111.9	-107.1 ± 3	24.1^0 cm³, 11.9^{25} cm³	8.4^{50}, 7.12^{90}	
y1	**Ytterbium**	Yb	173.04	cub	6.9654 up to 789 6.54 above 789	819 ± 5	1194	i		s a
y2	(III) acetate	$Yb(C_2H_3O_2)_3.4H_2O$	422.24	hex pl	2.09	$-4H_2O, 100$		v s	v s	
y3	(II) bromide	$YbBr_2$	332.86		5.91^{25}_{4}	677	1800	s	s	s dil a

No.	Name	Synonyms and Formulae	Mol. wt.	Crystalline form, properties and index of refraction	Density or spec. gravity	Melting point, °C	Boiling point, °C	Solubility, in grams per 100 cc		
								Cold water	Hot water	Other solvents
	Ytterbium									
y4	(III) bromide	$YbBr_3$	412.77	col cr		956	d	s	s	
y5	(II) chloride	$YbCl_2$	243.95	grn-yel cr	5.08	702	1900	s	s	s dil a
y6	(III) chloride	$YbCl_3.6H_2O$	387.49	grn, rhomb cr, deliq	2.575	865 $-6H_2O$, 180		v s	v s	s abs al
y7	(II) fluoride	YbF_2	211.04			1052	2380	i	i	
y8	fluoride	YbF_3	230.04			1157	2200	i	i	i dil a
y9	(II) iodide	YbI_2	426.85	lt yel, hex cr	5.40_4^{25}	780 ± 4	1300 d(700) vac	s	s	s dil a
y10	(III) iodide	YbI_3	553.75	gold yel cr		d 700		s	s	s dil a
y11	(III) oxalate	$Yb_2(C_2O_4)_3.10H_2O$	790.29	col cr	2.644			0.00033^{25}		sl s dil a
y12	(III) oxide	Ytterbia. Yb_2O_3	394.08	col	9.17			i	i	s h dil a
y13	(III) selenate	$Yb_2(SeO_4)_3.8H_2O$	919.08	hex pl	3.30			s d	s	
y14	(III) selenite	$Yb_2(SeO_3)_3$	726.95					i		
y15	(III) sulfate	$Yb_2(SO_4)_3$	634.26	col cr	3.793	d 900		44.2^0	4.7^{100}	
y16	(III) sulfate, octohydrate	$Yb_2(SO_4)_3.8H_2O$	778.39	prism	3.286			35.9^{24}	21.1^{40}	
y17	**Yttrium**	Y	88.905	gray-blk met, hex	4.4689	1522	3338	sl d	d	v s dil a; s h KOH
y18	acetate	$Y(C_2H_3O_2)_3.4H_2O$	338.10	col, tricl					9.03^{25}	
y19	bromate	$Y(BrO_3)_3.9H_2O$	634.76	hex pr		74	$-6H_2O$, 100	168^{25}		sl s al; i eth
y20	bromide	YBr_3	328.63	deliq		904		v s		s al; i eth
y21	bromide hydrate	$YBr_3.9H_2O$	490.77	col tabl, deliq				v s		sl s al; i eth
y22	carbide	YC_2	112.93	yel, microcr	4.13^{18}			d		
y23	carbonate	$Y_2(CO_3)_3.3H_2O$	411.88	wh-redsh powd						s dil min a, $(NH_4)_2$ CO_2; sl s aq CO_2; i al, eth
y24	chloride	YCl_3	195.26	shiny wh leaf	2.67	721	1507	78^{10}	82^{50}	60.1^{15} al; 60.6^{15} pyr
y25	chloride, hexahydrate	$YCl_3.6H_2O$	303.36	redsh-wh, rhomb, deliq	2.18^{18}	$-5H_2O$, 100		217^{20}	235^{50}	s al; i eth
y26	chloride, monohydrate	$YCl_3.H_2O$	213.28	col cr		$-H_2O$, 160		v s		
y27	fluoride	YF_3	145.90	gelat	4.01	1387		i		v sl s dil a
y28	hydroxide	$Y(OH)_3$	139.93	wh-yel gelat or powd		d		i	i	s a, NH_4Cl; i alk
y29	iodide	YI_3	469.62	wh, cr, deliq		1004	$650-700^{0.02}$	v s		s al, acet; sl s eth
y30	molybdate	$Y_2(MoO_4)_3.4H_2O$	729.68	grayish or yelsh, tetr pl, 2.03	4.79_{18}^{18}	1347				
y31	nitrate, hexahydrate	$Y(NO_3)_3.6H_2O$	383.01	col, redsh cr, deliq	2.68	$-3H_2O$, 100		$134.7^{22.5}$		v s al, eth, HNO_3
y32	nitrate, tetrahydrate	$Y(NO_3)_3.4H_2O$	346.98	redsh-wh pr	2.682			s		s al, HNO_3
y33	oxalate	$Y_2(C_2O_4)_3.9H_2O$	604.01	wh cr powd		d		0.0001		sl s HCl
y34	oxide	Yttria. Y_2O_3	225.81	col-yelsh, cub or powd	5.01	2410		0.00018²⁹		s a; i alk
y35	sulfate	$Y_2(SO_4)_3$	465.99	wh powd	2.52	d 1000		5.38^{25}	s	s sat K_2SO_4 sol
y36	sulfate, octahydrate	$Y_2(SO_4)_3.8H_2O$	610.12	col-redsh, monocl, 1.543, 1.549, 1.576	2.558	$-8H_2O$, 120	d 700	7.47^{15} (anhydr)	1.99^{95} (anhydr)	i al, alk; s conc H_2SO_4
y37	sulfide	Y_2S_3	273.99	yel-gr powd						d a
y38	**Yttrium hexanti-** pyrine *perchlorate*	$[Y(C_{11}H_{12}N_2O)_6](ClO_4)_3$	1516.60	col, hex cr		d 293-296		0.55^{20}		
y39	hexaantipyrine iodide	$[Y(C_{11}H_{12}N_2O)_6]I_3$	1598.96	col cr		280-282		4.65^{20}		
z1	**Zinc**	Zn	65.38	bluish-wh met, hex	7.14	419.58	907	i	i	s a, alk, ac a
z2	acetate	$Zn(C_2H_3O_2)_2$	183.46	col, monocl	1.84	d 200	subl vac	30^{20}	44.6^{100}	2.8^{25} dil; 166.79^{75} al
z3	acetate, dihydrate	$Zn(C_2H_3O_2)_2.2H_2O$	219.49	col, monocl, β 1.494	1.735	237	$-2H_2O$, 100	31.1^{20}	66.6^{100}	2 al
z4	acetylacetonate	$Zn(C_5H_7O_2)_2$	263.59	need		138	subl	v s d		v s bz, acet; s al
z5	aluminate	Nat. gahnite. $ZnAl_2O_4$	183.33	cub, grn 1.78	4.58			i	i	i a; sl s alk
z6	amide	$Zn(NH_2)_2$	97.42	wh powd, amorph	2.13^{25}	d 200 vac		d	d	i al, eth
z7	antimonide	$ZnSb_2$	439.61	silv wh, rhomb pr	6.33	570		d		
z8	*ortho*arsenate	Nat. koettixite. $Zn_3(AsO_4)_2.8H_2O$	610.00	monocl, 1.662, 1.683, 1.717	3.309^{15}	$-1H_2O$, 100		i	i	s HNO_3, H_3PO_4, alk
z9	*ortho*arsenate, basic	Nat. adamite. $Zn_3(AsO_4)_2.Zn(OH)_2$	573.34	col, rhomb	4.475^{15}	d 250				
z10	*ortho*arsenate, hydrogen	$ZnHAsO_4.4H_2O$	277.36	wh, rhomb		$-H_2O$, 327		d	d	
z11	arsenide	Zn_3As_2	345.95	met-gray, tetr	5.528	1015		i		d a
z12	benzoate	$Zn(C_7H_5O_2)_2$	307.60	wh powd				2.46^{20}	1.44^{20}	
z13	borate	$3ZnO.2B_2O_3$	383.35	wh tricl cr, or amorph powd	cr 4.22 powd 3.64	980		s		cr i HCl; amorph; s HCl
z14	bromate	$Zn(BrO_3)_2.6H_2O$	429.23	wh, cub, 1.5452	2.566	100	$-6H_2O$, 200	v s	∞	
z15	bromide	$ZnBr_2$	225.19	col, rhomb, hygr n_D^{18} 1.5452	4.201_7^{25}	394	650	447^{20}	675^{100}	v s al, eth, acet; s NH_4OH

No.	Name	Synonyms and Formulae	Mol. wt.	Crystalline form, properties and index of refraction	Density or spec. gravity	Melting point, °C	Boiling point, °C	Solubility, in grams per 100 cc		
								Cold water	Hot water	Other solvents
	Zinc									
z16	butyrate	$Zn(C_4H_7O_2)_2.2H_2O$	275.60	wh pr				10.7^{16}	d	
z17	caproate	$Zn(C_6H_{11}O_2)_2$	295.68					$1.03^{24.5}$		
z18	carbonate	Nat. smithsonite. $ZnCO_3$	125.39	col, trig, 1.818, 1.618	4.398	$-CO_2$, 300		0.001^{15}		s a, alk, NH_4 salts; i NH_3, acet, pyr
z19	chlorate	$Zn(ClO_3)_2.4H_2O$	304.33	col yelsh, cub, deliq	2.15	d 60	d	262^{20}	v s	167 al; s acet, eth, glyc
z20	chlorate, per-	$Zn(ClO_4)_2.6H_2O$	372.36	wh, rhomb, deliq, 1.508, 1.480	2.252 ± 0.01	105–107	d 200	s		s al
z21	chloride	$ZnCl_2$	136.28	wh, hex, deliq, 1.681, 1.713	2.91^{25}	283	732	432^{25}	615^{100}	$100^{12.5}$ al; v s eth; i NH_3
z22	chloroplatinate	$ZnPtCl_6.6H_2O$	581.27	yel, trig, hygr	2.717^{12}	d 160		v s	v s	v s al; d H_2SO_4
z23	chromate	$ZnCrO_4$	181.36	lem-yel pr	3.40			i	d	s a, liq NH_3; i acet
z24	chromate	$ZnCr_2O_4$	233.36	dk grn to black, cub	5.30^{15}					
z25	dichromate	$ZnCr_2O_7.3H_2O$	335.40	redsh-brn cr, or or-yel powd, hygr				v s	d	i al, eth; s a
z26	citrate	$Zn_3(C_6H_5O_7)_2.2H_2O$	610.35					sl s		
z27	cyanide	$Zn(CN)_2$	117.41	col, rhomb	1.852	d 800		0.0005^{20}		s alk, KCN, NH_3; i al
z28	ferrate (III)	Ferrite. $ZnFe_2O_4$	241.06	blk, oct	5.33^{20}	1590				s conc HCl; i dil a, alk
z29	ferrocyanide	$Zn_2Fe(CN)_6$	342.69	wh powd	1.85^{25}_{4}			i		s excess alk; i dil a
z30	ferrocyanide, trihydrate	$Zn_2Fe(CN)_6.3H_2O$	396.74	wh powd		d		i	i	i al, HCl; d NaOH; s NH_4OH; v sl s NH_3
z31	fluoride	ZnF_2	103.37	col, monocl or tricl	4.95^{25}_{4}	872	ca 1500	1.62^{20}	s	s hot a, NH_4OH; i al, NH_3
z32	fluoride, tetrahydrate	$ZnF_2.4H_2O$	175.43	col, rhomb	2.255	$-4H_2O$, 100	tr to ZnO, 3000	1.6^{18}	s	s a, alk, NH_4OH
z33	fluosilicate	$ZnSiF_6.6H_2O$	315.54	col, hex pr, 1.3824, 1.3956	2.104	d 100		v s		
z34	formaldehyde-sulfoxylate	$Zn(HSO_2.CH_2O)_2$	255.56	rhomb pr		d		v s	v s	d a; i al
z35	formaldehyde-sulfoxylate, basic	$Zn(OH)HSO_2.CH_2O$	177.47	rhomb pr		d		i	i	d a; i al
z36	formate	$Zn(CHO_2)_2$	155.41	col, cr	2.368	d		3.80	62^{100}	
z37	formate	$Zn(CHO)_2.2H_2O$	191.44	wh, monocl, 1.513, 1.526, 1.566	2.207^{20}	$-2H_2O$, 140	d	5.2^{20}	38^{100}	i al
z38	gallate	$ZnGa_2O_4$	268.81	wh fine cr, 1.74	6.15 calc	<800		i	i	i org solv; s dil a, NH_4OH
z39	glycerophosphate	$ZnC_3H_7O_6P$	235.43	wh amorph powd				s		i al, eth
z40	hydroxide(ε)	$Zn(OH)_2$	99.38	col, rhomb	3.053	d 125		v sl s		s a, alk
z41	iodate	$Zn(IO_3)_2$	415.18	wh, need	5.0632^{5}	d		0.87	1.31	s alk, HNO_3
z42	iodate, dihydrate	$Zn(IO_3)_2.2H_2O$	451.21	wh, cr powd	4.223^{25}_{4}	$-H_2O$, 200		0.877	1.32	s HNO_3, NH_4OH
z43	iodide	ZnI_2	319.18	col, hexag	4.7364^{25}_{4}	446	d 624	432^{18}	511^{100}	s a, al, eth, NH_3, $(NH_4)_2CO_3$
z44	d-lactate	$Zn(C_3H_5O_3)_2.2H_2O$	279.45					5.7^{15}	9^{33}	0.104 h 98 % al
z45	dl-lactate	$Zn(C_3H_5O_3)_2.3H_2O$	297.47	wh, rhomb cr				1.67^{105}	16.7^{100}	v sl s al
z46	laurate	$Zn(C_{12}H_{23}O_2)_2$	464.00	wh powd		128		0.01^{15}	0.019^{100}	0.010^{15} al
z47	permanganate	$Zn(MnO_4)_2.6H_2O$	411.33	vlt-br or bl, deliq	2.47	$-5H_2O$, 100		33.3	v s	d al, a
z48	nitrate, trihydrate	$Zn(NO_3)_2.3H_2O$	243.43	col, need		45.5		327.3^{40}		
z49	nitrate, hexahydrate	$Zn(NO_3)_2.6H_2O$	297.47	col, tetrag	2.065^{14}	36.4	$-6H_2O$, 105–131	184.3^{20}	∞	v s al
z50	nitride	Zn_3N_2	224.12	gray	6.22^{25}_{4}			d		s HCl
z51	oleate	$Zn(C_{18}H_{33}O_2)_2$	628.30	wax-like solid		70		i		s al, eth, bz, CS_2; sl s acet
z52	oxalate	$ZnC_2O_4.2H_2O$	189.42	wh powd	3.28^{25}_{4}	d 100		0.00079^{18}		s a, alk
z53	oxide	Nat. zincite. ZnO	81.37	wh, hex, 2.008, 2.029	5.606	1975		0.00016^{29}		s a, alk, NH_4Cl; i al, NH_3
z54	oxide, per-	$ZnO_2.\frac{1}{2}H_2O$	106.38	yelsh, powd	3.00 ± 0.08	$-O_2$, vac		sl d	d	d al, eth, acet
z55	1-phenol-4-sulfonate(p)	$Zn(C_6H_4SO_4)_2.8H_2O$	555.83	col cr or fine wh powd, effl		$-8H_2O$, 125		62.5	250^{100}	55.6^{25} al
z56	orthophosphate	$Zn_3(PO_4)_2$	386.05	col, rhomb	3.998^{15}	900		i	i	s a, NH_4OH; i al
z57	orthophosphate, dihydrogen	$Zn(H_2PO_4)_2.2H_2O$	295.38	tricl		d 100		d		
z58	orthophosphate, octahydrate	$Zn_3(PO_4)_2.8H_2O$	530.18	rhomb pl	3.109^{15}			i		s alk

No.	Name	Synonyms and Formulae	Mol. wt.	Crystalline form, properties and index of refraction	Density or spec. gravity	Melting point, °C	Boiling point, °C	Solubility, in grams per 100 cc		
								Cold water	Hot water	Other solvents
	Zinc									
z59	*ortho*phosphate, tetrahydrate	α—Hopeite. $Zn_3(PO_4)_2.4H_2O$	458.11	col, rhomb, 1.572, 1.591, 1.59	3.04	tr >105	....	i	i	v s a, NH_4OH, NH_4 salts
z60	*ortho*phosphate, tetrahydrate	β—Hopeite. $Zn_3(PO_4)_2.4H_2O$	458.11	col, rhomb, 1.574, 1.582, 1.582	3.03	tr >140	....	i	i	v s a, NH_4OH, NH_4 salts
z61	*ortho*phosphate, tetrahydrate	Parahopeite. $Zn_3(PO_4)_2.4H_2O$	458.11	col, tricl, 1.614, 1.625, 1.665	3.75	tr >163	....	i	i	v s a, NH_4OH, NH_4 salts
z62	pyrophosphate.......	$Zn_2P_2O_7$	304.68	wh powd.......	3.75^{22}			i	i	s a, alk, NH_4OH
z63	phosphide...........	Zn_3P_2	258.06	dk gray, tetrag, pois	4.55^{13}	>420	1100; subl in H_2	d		d H_2SO_4 ev H_2P s HNO_3; s (viol) dil a; i al
z64	hypophosphite......	$Zn(H_2PO_2)_2.H_2O$	213.36	col, cr powd, hygr				s		s alk
z65	picrate............	$Zn(C_6H_2N_3O_7)_2.8H_2O$	665.69	yel cr powd, expl		expl		s		
z66	salicylate.........	$Zn(C_7H_5O_3)_2.3H_2O$	393.65	need				5^{30}		s al
z67	selenate...........	$ZnSeO_4.5H_2O$	298.40	wh, tricl.......	2.591^{30}_4	d >50		s		
z68	selenide...........	$ZnSe$	144.33	yelsh to redsh, cub, 2.89	5.42^{15}_4	>1100		i		s a; d HNO_3
z69	silicate...........	Nat. hemimorphite. $2ZnO.SiO_2.H_2O$	240.84	rhomb, or trigon 1.614, 1.617, 1.636	3.45			i	i	
z70	*meta*silicate......	$ZnSiO_3$	141.45	col, rhomb.......	3.42	1437		i		i a
z71	*ortho*silicate.....	Nat. willemite. Zn_2SiO_4	222.82	trig, 1.694, 1.723.	4.103	1509		i		s acet a
z72	stearate..........	$Zn(C_{18}H_{35}O_2)_2$	632.33	light powd.......		130		i		i al, eth
z73	sulfate............	Nat. sinkosite. $ZnSO_4$.	161.43	col, rhomb, 1.658, 1.669, 1.670	3.54^{25}_4	d 600		s	s	sl s al; s MeOH, glyc
z74	sulfate, heptahydrate	Nat. goslarite. $ZnSO_4.7H_2O$	287.54	col, rhomb, effl. 1.457, 1.480, 1.484	1.957^{25}_4	100	$-7H_2O$, 280	96.5^{20}	663.6^{100}	sl s al, glyc
z75	sulfate, hexahydrate.	$ZnSO_4.6H_2O$	269.52	col, monocl or tetrag	2.072^{15}	$-5H_2O$, 70		s	117.5^{40}	
z76	sulfide,(α)........	Nat. wurtsite. ZnS.....	97.43	col, hex, 2.356, 2.378	3.98	$1700 \pm 20^{50\ atm}$	1185	0.00069^{18}	....	v s a; i ac a
z77	sulfide,(β)........	Nat. sphalerite. ZnS...	97.43	col, cub, 2.368.	4.102^{25}	tr 1020		0.000065^{18}		v s a
z78	sulfide, monohydrate.	$ZnS.H_2O$	115.45	yelsh-wh powd...	3.98	1049		i		s a
z79	sulfite............	$ZnSO_3.2H_2O$	181.46	wh, cr powd.......		$-2H_2O$, 100	d 200	0.16	d	i al; s H_2SO_3
z80	tartrate...........	$ZnC_4H_4O_6.H_2O$ (or $2H_2O$)	231.46	wh powd.......				0.055^{30}		s KOH, NaOH
z81	tellurate..........	Zn_3TeO_6	419.71	wh, gran ppt.......				i	i	s a
z82	telluride..........	$ZnTe$	192.97	red, cub, 3.56..	6.34^{15}	1238.5		d		s d a
z83	thiocyanate........	$Zn(SCN)_2$	181.53	wh powd, deliq				s		s al, NH_4OH
z84	valerate...........	$Zn(C_5H_9O_2)_2.2H_2O$	303.65	wh glist sc or powd				2.6^{24-25}	s	ca 2.5 al; v sl s eth
	Zinc complexes									
z85	diamminezinc chloride	$[Zn(NH_3)_2]Cl_2$ ...	170.34	col, rhomb, 1.625, 1.590	2.10	210.8	d 271	d		
z86	tetrammine perrhenate	$[Zn(NH_3)_4](ReO_4)_2$.....	633.89	wh, cub cr.......	3.608^{25}_4					0.1852 conc NH_4OH
z87	tetrapyridine fluosilicate	$[Zn(C_5H_5N)_4]SiF_6$	523.86	wh, rhomb.......	2.197					
z88	**Zirconium**...........	Zr	91.22	silver gray, met..	6.49	1852 ± 2	4377	i	i	s HF, aq reg; sl s a
z89	boride, di-........	ZrB_2	112.84	blk powd, ign in air		d >350		d ev H_2		
z90	bromide, di-.......	$ZrBr_2$	251.04	hex...........	6.085	ca 3000				
z93	bromide, tetra-....	$ZrBr_4$	410.86	wh cr powd, deliq		$450 \pm 1^{15\ atm}$	357 subl	i d		s liq NH_3, acetone; i bz, CCl_4
z94	bromide, tri-......	$ZrBr_3$	330.95	bl-blk powd.......		d 350		d ev H_2		
z95	carbide...........	ZrC	103.23	gray met, cub...	6.73	3540	5100	i		al s conc H_2SO_4
z96	carbonate, basic...	$3ZrO_2.CO_2.H_2O$	431.68	wh, amorph powd				i		s a
z97	chloride, di-......	$ZrCl_2$	162.13	blk...........	3.6^{18}	d 350		d ev H_2		
z98	chloride, tetra-...	$ZrCl_4$	233.03	wh cr.......	2.803^{15}	$437^{25\ atm}$	subl 331	s	d	s al, eth, conc HCl
z99	chloride, tri-.....	$ZrCl_3$	197.58	br cr.......	3.00^{15}	d 350		d ev H_2		s $-H_2$ conc al; i org cpd
z100	fluoride..........	ZrF_4	167.21	wh hex, 1.59..	4.43	subl ~600		1.388^{25}	d	sl s HF
z101	hydride...........	ZrH_2	93.24	gray-blk powd..						s dif HF, conc a
z102	hydroxide..........	$Zr(OH)_4$	159.25	wh amorp powd..	3.25	$-2H_2O$, 500		0.02	i	s min a
z103	iodide............	ZrI_4	598.84	wh need, hygr..		499 ± 2 6.3^{atm}	d ~600	s d	s	d al; s eth; v sl s CS_2, bz; i liq NH_3
z104	nitrate...........	$Zr(NO_3)_4.5H_2O$	429.32	col cr, deliq, 1.60, 1.61				v s		s al

No.	Name	Synonyms and Formulae	Mol. wt.	Crystalline form, properties and index of refraction	Density or spec. gravity	Melting point, °C	Boiling point, °C	Solubility, in grams per 100 cc		
								Cold water	Hot water	Other solvents
	Zirconium									
z105	nitride	ZrN	105.23	yel-brn cr	7.09	2980 ± 50	....	i	i	sl s inorg ac; s conc H_2SO_4, HF, aq reg
z106	oxide	Nat. baddeleyite. ZrO_2	123.22	col-yel-brn, monocl, 2.13, 2.19, 2.20	5.89	ca 2700	ca 5000	i	i	s H_2SO_4, HF
z107	oxide	Zirconia. ZrO_2 $HfO_2 < 2\%$	123.22	wh, monocl below 1000°, cub, above	5.6	2715	....	i	i	s H_2SO_4, HF
z108	oxide	Zirconium hydroxide, zirconic acid. $ZrO_2.xH_2O$	....	gel or wh amorph powd	3.25	$-2H_2O$, 550		0.02		s acids; i al, alk
z109	phosphide	ZrP_2	153.17	gray, brittle	4.77_4^{25}			i	....	v s conc hot H_2SO_4
z110	selenate	$Zr(SeO_4)_2.4H_2O$	449.20	hex trsp cr				s		sl s al, conc a
z111	selenite	$Zr(SeO_3)_2$	345.14	wh sm cr	4.3	$d \sim 400$		i	i	sl s H_2SO_4
z112	*ortho*silicate	Zircon, hyacinth. $ZrSiO_4$	183.30	tetr, var colors, 1.92–96; 1.97–2.02	4.56	2550	....	i	i	i a, aq reg, alk
z113	silicide	$ZrSi_2$	147.39	steel gray rhomb, lust met	4.88^{22}			i	i	s HF; i inorg a, aq reg
z114	sulfate	$Zr(SO_4)_2$	283.35	microcr powd, hygr	3.22^{16}	410 d	....	s	v s	....
z115	sulfate	$Zr(SO_4)_2.4H_2O$	355.41	wh cr powd, rhomb	3.22^{16}	$-3H_2O$, 135–150	....	v s		i al
z116	sulfide	ZrS_2	155.35	steelgray cr, hexag	3.87	~ 1550		i	i	i a
z117	**Zirconyl bromide**	$ZrOBr_2.xH_2O$		brill need, deliq		$-H_2O$, 120		s		s hot conc HBr
z118	chloride	$ZrOCl_2.8H_2O$	322.25	wh, need, tetr, effl, 1.552, 1.563	....	$-6H_2O$, 150	$-8H_2O$, 210	s	d	s al, eth; sl s HCl
z119	iodide	$ZrOI_2.8H_2O$	505.15	col, need, hygr		d	....	v s	v s	s al; v s eth
z120	sulfide	Zirconium sulfoxide. ZrOS	139.28	yel powd	4.87	ign in air		i	i	....

GRAVIMETRIC FACTORS AND THEIR LOGARITHMS
Rudolf Loebel

Compiled from International atomic weights of 1964. To facilitate use of this table the group of substances weighed under each element as well as the substance sought under each substance weighed are arranged in alphabetical order of their formulas.

Weighed	Sought	Factor	Log of Factor +10	Reciprocal of Factor	Log of Reciprocal of Factor +10
Aluminum					
Al	Al_2O_3	1.88946	10.27634	0.52925	9.72366
	$AlPO_4$	4.51987	10.65513	0.22125	9.34488
Al_4C_3	Al_2O_3	1.41653	10.15122	0.70595	9.84877
$Al(C_9H_6ON)_3$	Al	0.05873	8.76886	17.02811	11.23114
	Al_2O_3	0.11096	9.04516	9.01226	10.95483
$AlCl_3$	Al_2O_3	0.38233	9.58244	2.61554	10.41756
AlF_3	CaF_2	1.39464	10.14446	0.71703	9.85554
Al_2O_3	Al	0.52925	9.72366	1.88946	10.27634
	Al_4C_3	0.70595	9.84877	1.41653	10.15122
	$AlCl_3$	2.61552	10.41756	0.38233	9.58244
	$AlPO_4$	2.39214	10.37879	0.41804	9.62122
	$Al_2(SO_4)_3$	3.35567	10.52578	0.29800	9.47422
	$Al_2(SO_4)_3.18H_2O$	6.53605	10.81531	0.15300	9.18469
	$K_2SO_4.Al_2(SO_4)_3.24H_2O$	9.30532	10.96873	0.10747	9.03129
	$(NH_4)_2SO_4.Al_2(SO_4)_3.24H_2O$	8.89216	10.94901	0.11246	9.05100
$AlPO_4$	Al	0.22125	9.34488	4.51977	10.65512
	Al_2O_3	0.41804	9.62122	2.39211	10.37878
	P_2O_5	0.58196	9.76489	1.71833	10.23511
$Al_2(SO_4)_3$	Al_2O_3	0.29800	9.47422	3.35570	10.52578
$Al_2(SO_4)_3.18H_2O$	Al_2O_3	0.15300	9.18469	6.53595	10.81531
CaF_2	AlF_3	0.71703	9.85554	1.39464	10.14446
$K_2SO_4.Al_2(SO_4)_3.24H_2O$	Al_2O_3	0.10747	9.03129	9.30492	10.96872
$(NH_4)_2SO_4.Al_2(SO_4)_3.$ $24H_2O$	Al_2O_3	0.11246	9.05100	8.89205	10.94900
P_2O_5	$AlPO_4$	1.71831	10.23510	0.58196	9.76489
Ammonium					
Ag	NH_4Br	0.90802	9.95810	1.10130	10.04191
	NH_4Cl	0.49589	9.69538	2.01657	10.30462
	NH_4I	1.34366	10.12829	0.74424	9.87171
$AgBr$	NH_4Br	0.52161	9.71735	1.91714	10.28265
	NH_4Cl	0.37323	9.57198	2.67931	10.42802
AgI	NH_4I	0.61737	9.79055	1.61977	10.20945
$BaSO_4$	$(NH_4)_2SO_4$	0.56615	9.75293	1.76632	10.24707
Br	NH_4Br	1.22574	10.08840	0.81583	9.91160
Cl	NH_3	0.50880	9.70655	1.96541	10.29345
	NH_4Cl	1.50881	10.17864	0.66277	9.82136
HCl	NH_4Cl	1.46710	10.16646	0.68162	9.83354
I	NH_4I	1.14214	10.05772	0.87555	9.94229
$MgNH_4PO_4.6H_2O$	NH_3	0.06941	8.84142	14.40714	11.15857
	NH_4	0.07352	8.86641	13.60174	11.13360
	$(NH_4)_2O$	0.10613	9.02584	9.42241	10.97416
N	NH_2	1.21589	10.08489	0.82244	9.91510
	NH_4	1.28785	10.10987	0.77649	9.89014
	NH_4Cl	3.81903	10.58195	0.26184	9.41804
	NH_4NO_3	5.71466	10.75699	0.17499	9.24302
	$(NH_4)_2O$	1.85899	10.26928	0.53793	9.73072
	$(NH_4)_2SO_4$	4.71699	10.67367	0.21200	9.32634
NH_3	$MgNH_4PO_4.6H_2O$	14.40648	11.15855	0.06941	8.84142
	N	0.82244	9.91510	1.21589	10.08489
	NH_4	1.05919	10.02498	0.94412	9.97503
	NH_4Cl	3.14093	10.49706	0.31837	9.50293
	$(NH_4)_2CO_3$	2.82099	10.45040	0.35448	9.54959
	NH_4HCO_3	4.64199	10.66671	0.21542	9.33329
	NH_4NO_3	4.69998	10.67210	0.21277	9.32791
	$(NH_4)_2O$	1.52891	10.18438	0.65406	9.81562
	NH_4OH	2.05783	10.31341	0.48595	9.68659
	$(NH_4)_2PtCl_6$	13.03213	11.11501	0.07673	8.88497
	$(NH_4)_2SO_4$	3.87945	10.58877	0.25777	9.41123
	N_2O_5	3.17106	10.50121	0.31535	9.49879
	Pt	5.72763	10.75797	0.17459	9.24202
	SO_3	2.35053	10.37117	0.42544	9.62884
NH_4	Cl	1.96540	10.29345	0.50880	9.70655
	$MgNH_4PO_4.6H_2O$	13.60144	11.13359	0.07352	8.86641
	N	0.77648	9.89013	1.28786	10.10986
	NH_3	0.94412	9.97503	1.05919	10.02498

Weighed	Sought	Factor	Log of Factor +10	Reciprocal of Factor	Log of Reciprocal of Factor +10
Ammonium (contd.)					
NH_3	NH_4Cl	2.96542	10.47208	0.33722	9.52792
	$(NH_4)_2PtCl_6$	12.30389	11.09005	0.08128	8.90998
	Pt	5.40757	10.73301	0.18493	9.26701
NH_4Br	Ag	1.10130	10.04191	0.90802	9.95810
	AgBr	1.91713	10.28265	0.52161	9.71735
	Br	0.81583	9.91160	1.22575	10.08840
NH_4Cl	Ag	2.01656	10.30461	0.49589	9.69538
	AgCl	2.67934	10.42802	0.37323	9.57198
	Cl	0.66277	9.82136	1.50882	10.17864
	HCl	0.68162	9.83354	1.46709	10.16646
	N	0.26185	9.41805	3.81898	10.58194
	NH_3	0.31838	9.50294	3.14090	10.49706
	NH_4	0.33722	9.52791	2.96542	10.47208
	$(NH_4)_2O$	0.48677	9.68732	2.05436	10.31268
	NH_4OH	0.65516	9.81635	1.52634	10.18365
	$(NH_4)_2PtCl_6$	4.14913	10.61795	0.24101	9.38204
	Pt	1.82354	10.26091	0.54838	9.73908
$(NH_4)_2CO_3$	NH_3	0.35448	9.54959	2.82103	10.45040
NH_4HCO_3	NH_3	0.21542	9.33329	4.64209	10.66672
NH_4I	Ag	0.74422	9.87170	1.34369	10.12830
	AgI	1.61977	10.20946	0.61737	9.79055
	I	0.87555	9.94228	1.14214	10.05772
NH_4NO_3	NH_3	0.21277	9.32791	4.69991	10.67209
	$(NH_4)_2PtCl_6$	2.77280	10.44292	0.36064	9.55709
	N_2O_5	0.67470	9.82911	1.48214	10.17089
	Pt	1.21865	10.08588	0.82058	9.91412
$(NH_4)_2O$	$MgNH_4PO_4.6H_2O$	9.42281	10.97418	0.10613	9.02584
	N	0.53733	9.73069	1.86105	10.26931
	NH_3	0.65407	9.81562	1.52889	10.18438
	NH_4Cl	2.05437	10.31268	0.48677	9.68732
	$(NH_4)_2PtCl_6$	8.52378	10.93063	0.11732	9.06937
	N_2O_5	2.07406	10.31682	0.48215	9.68319
	Pt	3.74621	10.57359	0.26694	9.42641
NH_4OH	N	0.39967	9.60170	2.50206	10.39830
	NH_3	0.48595	9.68660	2.05782	10.31341
	NH_4	0.51471	9.71156	1.94284	10.28843
	NH_4Cl	1.52633	10.18365	0.65517	9.81635
	$(NH_4)_2PtCl_6$	6.33297	10.80158	0.15790	9.19841
	Pt	2.78334	10.44456	0.35928	9.55544
$(NH_4)_2PtCl_6$	NH_3	0.07674	8.88502	13.03101	11.11497
	NH_4	0.08128	8.90998	12.30315	11.09002
	NH_4Cl	0.24102	9.38206	4.14903	10.61794
	NH_4NO_3	0.36065	9.55709	2.77277	10.44291
	$(NH_4)_2O$	0.11732	9.06937	8.52370	10.93063
	NH_4OH	0.15791	9.19841	6.33272	10.80159
	$(NH_4)_2SO_4$	0.29768	9.47375	3.35931	10.52625
$(NH_4)_2SO_4$	$BaSO_4$	1.76632	10.24709	0.56615	9.75291
	H_2SO_4	0.74223	9.87054	1.34729	10.12947
	N	0.21200	9.32634	4.71698	10.67367
	NH_3	0.25777	9.41123	3.87943	10.58877
	$(NH_4)_2PtCl_6$	3.35927	10.52625	0.29768	9.47375
	$(NH_4)_2SO_4$	1.47640	10.16921	0.67732	9.83079
	SO_3	0.60589	9.78239	1.65046	10.21761
N_2O_5	NH_3	0.31535	9.49879	3.17108	10.50121
	NH_4NO_3	1.48214	10.17089	0.67470	9.82911
	$(NH_4)_2O$	0.48214	9.68318	2.07409	10.31682
Pt	NH_3	0.17459	9.24202	5.72770	10.75798
	NH_4	0.18493	9.26701	5.40745	10.73300
	NH_4Cl	0.54838	9.73908	1.82355	10.26092
	NH_4NO_3	0.82058	9.91412	1.21865	10.08588
	$(NH_4)_2O$	0.26694	9.42641	3.74616	10.57364
	NH_4OH	0.35928	9.55544	2.78334	10.44456
	$(NH_4)_2SO_4$	0.67732	9.83079	1.47641	10.16921
SO_3	NH_3	0.42543	9.62883	2.35056	10.37118
	$(NH_4)_2SO_4$	1.65046	10.21760	0.60589	9.78239
Antimony					
$K(SbO)C_4H_4O_6.\frac{1}{2}H_2O$	Sb	0.36460	9.56182	2.74273	10.43819
	Sb_2O_3	0.43647	9.63995	2.29111	10.36005

Weighed	Sought	Factor	Log of Factor +10	Reciprocal of Factor	Log of Reciprocal of Factor +10
Antimony (contd.)					
$K(SbO)C_4H_4O_6.\frac{1}{2}H_2O$	Sb_2O_4	0.46043	9.66317	2.17188	10.33684
	Sb_2S_3	0.50862	9.70640	1.96610	10.29360
Sb	$K(SbO)C_4H_4O_6.\frac{1}{2}H_2O$	2.74275	10.43819	0.36460	9.56182
	Sb_2O_3	1.19713	10.07814	0.83533	9.92186
	Sb_2O_4	1.26283	10.10137	0.79187	9.89866
	Sb_2O_5	1.32854	10.12340	0.75271	9.87659
	Sb_2S_3	1.39503	10.14458	0.71683	9.85540
	Sb_2S_5	1.65840	10.21969	0.60299	9.78031
Sb_2O_3	$K(SbO)C_4H_4O_6.\frac{1}{2}H_2O$	2.29111	10.36005	0.43647	9.63995
	Sb	0.83533	9.92186	1.19713	10.07814
	Sb_2O_4	1.05489	10.02320	0.94797	9.97680
	Sb_2O_5	1.10978	10.04523	0.90108	9.95476
	Sb_2S_3	1.16532	10.06645	0.85813	9.93356
	Sb_2S_5	1.38532	10.14155	0.72185	9.85845
Sb_2O_4	$K(SbO)C_4H_4O_6.\frac{1}{2}H_2O$	2.17190	10.33684	0.46043	9.66317
	Sb	0.79187	9.89866	1.26283	10.10137
	Sb_2O_3	0.94797	9.97680	1.05489	10.02300
	Sb_2O_5	1.05203	10.02203	0.95054	9.97797
	Sb_2S_3	1.10468	10.04324	0.90523	9.95671
	Sb_2S_5	1.31324	10.11834	0.76148	9.88166
Sb_2O_5	Sb	0.75270	9.87663	1.32853	10.12337
	Sb_2O_3	0.90108	9.95477	1.10977	10.04523
	Sb_2O_4	0.95054	9.97798	1.05202	10.02202
	Sb_2S_5	1.24828	10.09632	0.80109	9.90368
Sb_2S_3	$K(SbO)C_4H_4O_6.\frac{1}{2}H_2O)$	1.96603	10.29360	0.50863	9.70640
	Sb	0.71681	9.85542	1.39503	10.14458
	Sb_2O_3	0.85814	9.93356	1.16532	10.06645
	Sb_2O_4	0.90524	9.95676	1.10469	10.04332
	Sb_2O_5	0.95234	9.97879	1.05006	10.02121
Sb_2S_5	Sb	0.60299	9.78031	1.65840	10.21969
	Sb_2O_3	0.72186	9.85834	1.38570	10.14167
	Sb_2O_4	0.76148	9.88166	1.31323	10.11834
	Sb_2O_5	0.80110	9.90369	1.24828	10.09631
Arsenic					
As	As_2O_3	1.32032	10.12068	0.75739	9.87932
	As_2O_5	1.53387	10.18579	0.65195	9.81422
	As_2S_3	1.64194	10.21535	0.60904	9.78465
	As_2S_5	2.06991	10.31597	0.48311	9.68405
	$BaSO_4$	4.67291	10.66959	0.21400	9.33041
	$Mg_2As_2O_7$	2.07191	10.31637	0.48265	9.68364
	$MgNH_4AsO_4.\frac{1}{2}H_2O$	2.53968	10.40478	0.39375	9.59523
AsO_3	$BaSO_4$	2.84821	10.45457	0.35110	9.54543
	$Mg_2As_2O_7$	1.26286	10.10135	0.79185	9.89865
	$MgNH_4AsO_4.\frac{1}{2}H_2O$	1.54797	10.18976	0.64601	9.81024
AsO_4	$BaSO_4$	2.52018	10.40143	0.39680	9.59857
	$Mg_2As_2O_7$	1.11742	10.04821	0.89492	9.95178
	$MgNH_4AsO_4.\frac{1}{2}H_2O$	1.36969	10.13662	0.73009	9.86337
As_2O_3	As	0.75739	9.87932	1.32032	10.12068
	As_2O_5	1.16173	10.06511	0.86079	9.93490
	As_2S_3	1.24359	10.09468	0.80412	9.90532
	As_2S_5	1.56773	10.19527	0.63781	9.80472
	$BaSO_4$	3.53922	10.54891	0.28255	9.45110
	$Mg_2As_2O_7$	1.56925	10.19569	0.63725	9.80431
	$MgNH_4AsO_4.\frac{1}{2}H_2O$	1.92353	10.28410	0.51988	9.71590
As_2O_5	As	0.65195	9.81422	1.53380	10.18579
	As_2O_3	0.86077	9.93489	1.16175	10.06511
	As_2S_3	1.07046	10.02957	0.93418	9.97043
	As_2S_5	1.34947	10.13016	0.74103	9.86984
	$BaSO_4$	3.04648	10.48380	0.32825	9.51621
	$Mg_2As_2O_7$	1.35077	10.13058	0.74032	9.86942
	$MgNH_4AsO_4.\frac{1}{2}H_2O$	1.65573	10.21899	0.60396	9.78101
As_2S_3	As	0.60903	9.78464	1.64196	10.21536
	As_2O_3	0.80412	9.90532	1.24360	10.09468
	As_2O_5	0.93418	9.97043	1.07046	10.02957
	As_2S_5	1.26065	10.10060	0.79324	9.89939
	$Mg_2As_2O_7$	1.26187	10.10102	0.79247	9.89898
As_2S_5	As	0.48311	9.68405	2.06992	10.31595
	As_2O_3	0.63786	9.80472	1.56774	10.19527

Weighed	Sought	Factor	Log of Factor +10	Reciprocal of Factor	Log of Reciprocal of Factor +10
Arsenic (contd.)					
As_2S_5	As_2O_5	0.74103	9.86984	1.34947	10.13016
	As_2S_3	0.79324	9.89940	1.26065	10.10060
$BaSO_4$	As	0.21399	9.33039	4.67312	10.66961
	AsO_3	0.35110	9.54543	2.84819	10.45457
	AsO_4	0.39679	9.59856	2.52022	10.40143
	As_2O_3	0.28255	9.45110	3.53920	10.54890
	As_2O_5	0.32825	9.51621	3.04646	10.48379
$Ca_2As_2O_7$	As	0.43814	9.64161	2.28238	10.35839
	As_2O_3	0.57849	9.76230	1.72864	10.23770
$Mg_2As_2O_7$	As	0.48264	9.68363	2.07194	10.31638
	AsO_3	0.79184	9.89864	1.26288	10.10136
	AsO_4	0.89491	9.95178	1.11743	10.04822
	As_2O_3	0.63725	9.80431	1.56924	10.19569
	As_2O_5	0.74031	9.86942	1.35079	10.13059
	As_2S_3	0.79248	9.89899	1.26186	10.10102
$MgNH_4AsO_4.\frac{1}{2}H_2O$	As	0.39375	9.59523	2.53968	10.40478
	AsO_3	0.64600	9.81023	1.54799	10.18977
	AsO_4	0.73009	9.86337	1.36969	10.13662
	As_2O_3	0.51988	9.71590	1.92352	10.28410
	As_2O_5	0.60396	9.78101	1.65574	10.21899
Barium					
Ba	$BaCO_3$	1.43694	10.15744	0.69592	9.84256
	$BaCrO_4$	1.84455	10.26589	0.54214	9.73411
	$BaSiF_6$	2.03444	10.30844	0.49154	9.69156
	$BaSO_4$	1.69943	10.23030	0.58843	9.76969
$BaCl_2$	$BaCO_3$	0.94766	9.97665	1.05523	10.02334
	$BaCrO_4$	1.21647	10.08510	0.82205	9.91490
	$BaSO_4$	1.12077	10.04952	0.89224	9.95048
$BaCl_2.2H_2O$	$BaSO_4$	0.95546	9.98021	1.04662	10.01979
$BaCO_3$	Ba	0.69592	9.84256	1.43695	10.15747
	$BaCl_2$	1.05523	10.02334	0.94766	9.97665
	$BaCrO_4$	1.28366	10.10845	0.77902	9.89155
	$Ba(HCO_3)_2$	1.31426	10.11869	0.76088	9.88132
	BaO	0.77700	9.89042	1.28700	10.10958
	$BaSO_4$	1.18267	10.07286	0.84554	9.92713
	CO_2	0.22300	9.34830	4.48430	10.65170
$BaCrO_4$	Ba	0.54214	9.73411	1.84455	10.26589
	$BaCl_2$	0.82205	9.91490	1.21647	10.08510
	$BaCO_3$	0.77902	9.89155	1.28366	10.10846
	BaO	0.60530	9.78197	1.65207	10.21803
BaF_2	$BaSiF_6$	1.59359	10.20238	0.62751	9.79762
$Ba(HCO_3)_2$	$BaCO_3$	0.76088	9.88132	1.31427	10.11869
$Ba(NO_3)_2$	$BaSO_4$	0.89306	9.95088	1.11975	10.04912
BaO	$BaCO_3$	1.28701	10.10958	0.77699	9.89042
	$BaCrO_4$	1.65208	10.21803	0.60530	9.78197
	$BaSiF_6$	1.82233	10.26061	0.54878	9.73934
	$BaSO_4$	1.52211	10.18244	0.65698	9.81756
	CO_2	0.28701	9.45790	3.48420	10.54210
BaO_2	$BaSO_4$	1.37829	10.13934	0.72554	9.86066
BaS	$BaSO_4$	1.37780	10.13919	0.72579	9.86081
$BaSiF_6$	Ba	0.49152	9.69154	2.03451	10.30846
	BaF_2	0.62751	9.79762	1.59360	10.20238
	BaO	0.54878	9.73939	1.82222	10.26060
$BaSO_4$	Ba	0.58843	9.76969	1.69944	10.23030
	$BaCl_2$	0.89225	9.95049	1.12076	10.04952
	$BaCl_2.2H_2O$	1.04662	10.01979	0.95546	9.98021
	$BaCO_3$	0.84554	9.92713	1.18268	10.07286
	$Ba(NO_3)_2$	1.11975	10.04912	0.89306	9.95088
	BaO	0.65698	9.81756	1.52212	10.18244
	BaO_2	0.72554	9.86066	1.37828	10.13934
	BaS	0.72579	9.86081	1.37781	10.13911
CO_2	$BaCO_3$	4.48421	10.65169	0.22300	9.34830
	BaO	3.48421	10.54211	0.28701	9.45790
Beryllium					
Be	BeO	2.77530	10.44331	0.36032	9.55668
$BeCl_2$	BeO	0.31297	9.49551	3.19519	10.50450
BeO	Be	0.36032	9.55668	2.77531	10.44331
	$BeCl_2$	3.19525	10.50451	0.31296	9.49549

Weighed	Sought	Factor	Log of Factor +10	Reciprocal of Factor	Log of Reciprocal of Factor +10
Beryllium (contd.)					
BeO	$BeSO_4.4H_2O$	7.08211	10.85017	0.14120	9.14983
$Be_2P_2O_7$	Be	0.09389	8.97262	10.65076	11.02738
$BeSO_4.4H_2O$	BeO	0.14120	9.14983	7.08215	10.85017
Bismuth					
Bi	$BiAsO_4$	1.66475	10.22135	0.60069	9.77865
	Bi_2O_3	1.11484	10.04721	0.89699	9.95279
	BiOCl	1.24620	10.09559	0.80244	9.90441
	Bi_2S_3	1.23014	10.08996	0.81292	9.91005
$BiAsO_4$	Bi	0.60069	9.77865	1.66475	10.22135
	Bi_2O_3	0.66968	9.82587	1.49325	10.17413
$Bi(NO_3)_3.5H_2O$	Bi_2O_3	0.48030	9.68151	2.08203	10.31849
	BiOCl	0.53689	9.72988	1.86258	10.27011
Bi_2O_3	Bi	0.89699	9 95279	1.11484	10.04722
	$BiAsO_4$	1.49326	10.17414	0.66968	9.82587
	$Bi(NO_3)_3.5H_2O$	2.08204	10.31849	0.48030	9.68151
	BiOCl	1.11783	10.04837	0.89459	9.95163
	$BiONO_3$	1.23180	10.09054	0.81182	9.90946
	Bi_2S_3	1.10343	10.04275	0.90627	9.95726
BiOCl	Bi	0.80244	9.90441	1.24619	10.09559
	$Bi(NO_3)_3.5H_2O$	1.86256	10.27011	0.53690	9.72989
	Bi_2O_3	0.89458	9.95162	1.11784	10.04838
	$BiONO_3$	1.10195	10.04215	0.90748	9.95784
$BiONO_3$	Bi_2O_3	0.81182	9.90946	1.23180	10.09054
	BiOCl	0.90748	9.95784	1.10195	10.04216
$BiPO_4$	Bi	0.68754	9.83730	1.45446	10.16270
	Bi_2O_3	0.76651	9.88452	1.30461	10.11548
Bi_2S_3	Bi	0.81291	9.91005	1.23015	10.08996
	Bi_2O_3	0.90627	9.95726	1.10342	10.04274
Boron					
B	B_2O_3	3.21987	10.50784	0.31057	9.49216
	KBF_4	11.64619	11.06618	0.08586	8.93379
BO_2	B_2O_3	0.81314	9.91016	1.22981	10.08984
BO_3	B_2O_3	0.59192	9.77226	1.68942	10.22774
B_2O_3	B	0.31057	9.49216	3.21990	10.50785
	BO_2	1.22982	10.08985	0.81313	9.91016
	BO_3	1.68943	10.22774	0.59192	9.77226
	B_4O_7	1.11491	10.04724	0.89693	9.95276
	H_3BO_3	1.77630	10.24952	0.56297	9.75049
	KBF_4	3.61678	10.55832	0.27647	9.44165
	$Na_2B_4O_7.10H_2O$	2.73896	10.43758	0.36510	9.56241
B_4O_7	B_2O_3	0.89693	9.95276	1.11491	10.04724
$C_{20}H_{16}N_4.HBF_4$	B	0.02702	8.43169	37.00962	11.56832
	B_2O_3	0.08698	8.93942	11.49690	11.06058
H_3BO_3	B_2O_3	0.56297	9.75049	1.77629	10.24951
	KBF_4	2.03624	10.30883	0.49110	9.69117
KBF_4	B	0.08587	8.93384	11.64551	11.06616
	B_2O_3	0.27648	9.44167	3.61690	10.55834
	H_3BO_3	0.49110	9.69117	2.03625	10.30885
	$Na_2B_4O_7.10H_2O$	0.75725	9.87924	1.32057	10.12076
$Na_2B_4O_7.10H_2O$	B_2O_3	0.36510	9.56241	2.73898	10.43759
	KBF_4	1.32056	10.12075	0.75725	9.87924
Bromine					
Ag	Br	0.74079	9.86969	1.34991	10 13030
	BrO_3	1 18575	10.07399	0 84335	9.92601
	HBr	0.75013	9.87514	1.33310	10.12487
AgBr	Br	0.42555	9.62895	2.34990	10.37105
	BrO_3	0.68116	9.83325	1.46808	10.16675
	HBr	0.43092	9.63440	2.32062	10.36561
AgCl	Br	0.55754	9.74627	1.79359	10.25372
Br	Ag	1.34991	10.13030	0.74079	9.86969
	AgBr	2.34991	10.37105	0.42555	9.62895
	AgCl	1.79358	10.25372	0.55754	9.74627
	O	0.10011	9.00047	9.98901	10.99952
BrO_3	Ag	0.84335	9.92601	1.18575	10.07399
	AgBr	1.46809	10.16676	0.68116	9.83325
O	Br	9.98899	10.99952	0.10011	9.00047
HBr	Ag	1.33309	10.12486	0.75014	9.87514
	AgBr	2.32064	10.36561	0.43092	9.63440

Weighed	Sought	Factor	Log of Factor +10	Reciprocal of Factor	Log of Reciprocal of Factor +10
Cadmium					
Cd	$CdCl_2$	1.63087	10.21242	0.61317	9.78758
	$Cd(NO_3)_2$	2.10329	10.32290	0.47545	9.67711
	CdO	1.14235	10.05780	0.87539	9.94221
	CdS	1.28523	10.10898	0.77807	9.89102
	$CdSO_4$	1.85463	10.26825	0.53919	9.73174
$Cd(C_{13}H_8O_2N)_2$	Cd	0.21095	9.32418	4.74046	10.67582
	CdO	0.24098	9.38198	4.14972	10.61802
$CdCl_2$	Cd	0.61317	9.78758	1.63087	10.21242
	CdO	0.70045	9.84538	1.42765	10.15462
	CdS	0.78807	9.89657	1.26892	10.10343
	$CdSO_4$	1.13720	10.05584	0.87935	9.94417
$Cd(C_9H_6NO)_2$	Cd	0.28050	9.44793	3.56506	10.55207
	CdO	0.32043	9.50573	3.12081	10.49426
$CdMoO4$	Cd	0.41272	9.61566	2.42295	10.38434
	CdO	0.47147	9.67345	2.12103	10.32655
$Cd(NO_3)_2$	Cd	0.47545	9.67711	2.10327	10.32290
	CdO	0.54312	9.73490	1.84121	10.26510
	CdS	0.61106	9.78608	1.63650	10.21392
	$CdSO_4$	0.88177	9.94536	1.13408	10.05464
CdO	Cd	0.87539	9.94221	1.14235	10.05781
	$CdCl_2$	1.42765	10.15462	0.70045	9.85438
	$Cd(NO_3)_2$	1.84120	10.26510	0.54312	9.73490
	CdS	1.12508	10.05118	0.88883	9.94882
	$CdSO_4$	1.62352	10.21046	0.61595	9.78955
CdS	Cd	0.77807	9.89102	1.28523	10.10898
	$CdCl_2$	1.26893	10.10343	0.78807	9.89657
	$Cd(NO_3)_2$	1.63651	10.21392	0.61106	9.78608
	CdO	0.88883	9.94882	1.12507	10.05118
	$CdSO_4$	1.44303	10.15928	0.69299	9.84072
$CdSO_4$	Cd	0.53919	9.73174	1.85463	10.26825
	$CdCl_2$	0.87935	9.94417	1.13720	10.05584
	$Cd(NO_3)_2$	1.13408	10.05464	0.88177	9.94536
	CdO	0.61595	9.78955	1.62351	10.21046
	CdS	0.69299	9.84072	1.44302	10.15928
Calcium					
$BaSO_4$	CaS	0.30908	9.49007	3.23541	10.50993
	$CaSO_4$	0.58329	9.76588	1.71441	10.23411
	$CaSO_4.2H_2O$	0.73766	9.86786	1.35564	10.13214
Ca	$CaCl_2$	2.76921	10.44235	0.36111	9.55764
	$CaCO_3$	2.49726	10.39746	0.40044	9.60253
	CaF_2	1.94810	10.28961	0.51332	9.71039
	CaO	1.39920	10.14588	0.71469	9.85411
	$CaSO_4$	3.39671	10.53106	0.29440	9.46894
	Cl	1.76911	10.24776	0.56526	9.75225
$Ca_3(AsO_4)_2$	$Mg_2As_2O_7$	0.77990	9.89204	1.28222	10.10798
$Ca_2As_2O_7$	Ca	0.23439	9.36994	4.26639	10.63006
	CaO	0.32795	9.51581	3.04925	10.48420
$CaC_2O_4.H_2O$	Ca	0.27430	9.43823	3.64564	10.56178
	CaO	0.38379	9.58410	2.60550	10.41589
$CaCl_2$	Ca	0.36111	9.55764	2.76924	10.44236
	$CaCO_3$	0.90179	9.95511	1.10891	10.04489
	CaO	0.50527	9.70352	1.97914	10.29648
	$CaSO_4$	1.22660	10.08870	0.81526	9.91130
	Cl	0.63885	9.80540	1.56531	10.19460
$CaCO_3$	Ca	0.40044	9.60253	2.49725	10.39751
	$CaCl_2$	1.10890	10.04489	0.90179	9.95511
	$Ca(HCO_3)_2$	1.61964	10.20942	0.61742	9.79058
	CaO	0.56030	9.74842	1.78476	10.25158
	$CaSO_4$	1.36018	10.13360	0.73520	9.86641
	$CaSO_4.2H_2O$	1.72015	10.23557	0.58134	9.76442
	CO_2	0.43970	9.64316	2.27428	10.35684
	HCl	0.72854	9.86245	1.37261	10.13755
CaF_2	Ca	0.51332	9.71039	1.94810	10.28961
	$CaSO_4$	1.74360	10.24145	0.57353	9.75855
$Ca(HCO_3)$	$CaCO_3$	0.61742	9.79058	1.61964	10.20942
	CaO	0.34594	9.53900	2.89067	10.46100
$Ca(IO_3)_2$	Ca	0.10280	9.01199	9.72763	10.98801
	CaO	0.14384	9.15788	6.95217	10.84212

Weighed	Sought	Factor	Log of Factor +10	Reciprocal of Factor	Log of Reciprocal of Factor +10
Calcium (contd.)					
$Ca(NO_3)_2$	N_2O_5	0.65824	9.81838	1.51920	10.18162
CaO	Ca	0.71470	9.85412	1.39919	10.14588
	$CaCl_2$	1.97914	10.29648	0.50527	9.70352
	$CaCO_3$	1.78477	10.25158	0.56030	9.74842
	CaF_2	1.39230	10.14373	0.71824	9.85627
	$Ca(HCO_3)_2$	2.89069	10.46100	0.34594	9.53900
	$Ca_3(PO_4)_2$	1.84368	10.26569	0.54239	9.73431
	$CaSO_4$	2.42760	10.38518	0.41193	9.61482
	$CaSO_4.2H_2O$	3.07008	10.48715	0.32572	9.51285
	Cl	1.26437	10.10187	0.79091	9.89813
	CO_2	0.78477	9.89474	1.27426	10.10527
	MgO	0.71879	9.85660	1.39123	10.14340
	SO_3	1.42760	10.15461	0.70048	9.84540
$Ca_3(PO_4)_2$	CaO	0.54239	9.73431	1.84369	10.26569
	$CaSO_4$	1.31672	10.11950	0.75946	9.88051
	$Mg_2P_2O_7$	0.71755	9.85585	1.39363	10.14415
	$(NH_4)_3PO_4.12MoO_3$	12.09843	11.08273	0.08266	8.91730
	P_2O_5	0.45761	9.66050	2.18527	10.33950
CaS	$BaSO_4$	3.23538	10.50992	0.30908	9.49007
$CaSO_4$	$BaSO_4$	1.71441	10.23411	0.58329	9.76581
	Ca	0.29440	9.46894	3.39674	10.53107
	$CaCl_2$	0.81526	9.91130	1.22660	10.08870
	$CaCO_3$	0.73520	9.86641	1.36017	10.13360
	CaF_2	0.57353	9.75855	1.74359	10.24145
	CaO	0.41193	9.61482	2.42760	10.38518
	$Ca_3(PO_4)_2$	0.75946	9.88051	1.31673	10.11950
	SO_3	0.58809	9.76944	1.70042	10.23056
$CaSO_4.2H_2O$	$BaSO_4$	1.35564	10.13213	0.73766	9.86786
	$CaCO_3$	0.58134	9.76443	1.72016	10.23557
	CaO	0.32572	9.51285	3.07012	10.48716
	SO_3	0.46502	9.66747	2.15045	10.33252
$CaWO_4$	WO_3	0.80523	9.90592	1.24188	10.09408
Cl	Ca	0.56526	9.75225	1.76910	10.24775
	$CaCl_2$	1.56531	10.19460	0.63885	9.80540
	CaO	0.79091	9.89813	1.26437	10.10188
CO_2	$CaCO_3$	2.27428	10.35684	0.43970	9.64316
	CaO	1.27427	10.10526	0.78476	9.89474
HCl	$CaCO_3$	1.37256	10.13753	0.72857	9.86247
$Mg_2As_2O_7$	$Ca_3(AsO_4)_2$	1.28221	10.10796	0.77990	9.89204
MgO	CaO	1.39118	10.14339	0.71881	9.85661
$Mg_2P_2O_7$	$Ca_3(PO_4)_2$	1.39365	10.14415	0.71754	9.85585
$(NH_4)_3PO_4.12MoO_3$	$Ca_3(PO_4)_2$	0.08265	8.91725	12.09892	11.08275
N_2O_5	$Ca(NO_3)_2$	1.51920	10.18162	0.65824	9.81838
P_2O_5	$Ca_3(PO_4)_2$	2.18521	10.33949	0.45762	9.66051
SO_3	CaO	0.70046	9.84539	1.42763	10.15462
	$CaSO_4$	1.70043	10.23056	0.58809	9.76944
	$CaSO_4.2H_2O$	2.15046	10.33253	0.46502	9.66747
WO_3	$CaWO_4$	1.24188	10.09408	0.80523	9.90592
Carbon					
Ag	CN	0.24120	9.38238	4.14594	10.61762
	HCN	0.25054	9.39888	3.99138	10.60112
	KCN	0.60369	9.78081	1.65648	10.21918
$AgCN$	CN	0.19433	9.28854	5.14589	10.71146
	HCN	0.20185	9.30503	4.95417	10.69497
	KCN	0.48638	9.68698	2.05601	10.31302
$AgCNS$	CNS	0.34999	9.54406	2.85722	10.45594
$Ag_4Fe(CN)_6$	C	0.11200	9.04922	8.92857	10.95078
$AgOCN$	OCN	0.28033	9.44767	3.56722	10.55233
$BaCO_3$	C	0.06086	8.78433	16.43115	11.21567
	CO_2	0.22300	9.34830	4.48431	10.65170
	CO_3	0.30408	9.48299	3.28861	10.51701
BaO	CO_2	0.28701	9.45790	3.48420	10.54210
	CO_2 (bicarbonate)	0.57402	9.75893	1.74210	10.24107
$BaSO_4$	CNS	0.24885	9.39594	4.01849	10.60406
C	$BaCO_3$	16.4305	11.21565	0.06086	8.78433
	CO_2	3.66409	10.56397	0.27292	9.43604
$CaCO_3$	CO_2	0.43970	9.64316	2.27428	10.35684
$Ca(HCO_3)_2$	CO_2	0.54295	9.73476	1.84179	10.26524

Weighed	Sought	Factor	Log of Factor +10	Reciprocal of Factor	Log of Reciprocal of Factor +10
Carbon (contd.)					
CaO	CO_2	0.78477	9.89474	1.27426	10.10526
	CO_2 (bicarbonate)	1.56954	10.19577	0.63713	9.80423
CN	Ag	4.14599	10.61762	0.24120	9.38238
	AgCN	5.14599	10.71147	0.19433	9.28854
CNS	AgCNS	2.85720	10.45594	0.34999	9.54406
	$BaSO_4$	4.01846	10.60406	0.24885	9.39594
	CuCNS	2.09394	10.32097	0.47757	9.67904
CO_2	$BaCO_3$	4.48420	10.65169	0.22301	9.34832
	$Ba(HCO_3)_2$	2.94672	10.46934	0.33963	9.53066
	BaO	3.48421	10.54211	0.28701	9.45790
	C	0.27292	9.43603	3.66408	10.56397
	$CaCO_3$	2.27426	10.35684	0.43970	9.64316
	$Ca(HCO_3)_2$	1.84174	10.26523	0.54296	9.73477
	CaO	1.27426	10.10526	0.78477	9.89474
	CO_3	1.36354	10.13467	0.73339	9.86534
	Cs_2CO_3	7.40329	10.86943	0.13508	9.13059
	$CsHCO_3$	4.40632	10.64407	0.22695	9.35593
	$FeCO_3$	2.63249	10.42037	0.37987	9.57964
	$Fe(HCO_3)_2$	2.02092	10.30555	0.49482	9.69445
	K_2CO_3	3.14049	10.49700	0.31842	9.50300
	$KHCO_3$	2.27491	10.35696	0.43958	9.64304
	K_2O	2.14049	10.33050	0.46718	9.66948
	Li_2CO_3	1.67887	10.22502	0.59564	9.77498
	$LiHCO_3$	1.54410	10.18868	0.64763	9.81133
	Li_2O	0.67887	9.83179	1.47304	10.16821
	$MgCO_3$	1.91595	10.28239	0.52193	9.71761
	$Mg(HCO_3)_2$	1.66265	10.22080	0.60145	9.77920
	MgO	0.91595	9.96188	1.09176	10.03812
	$MnCO_3$	2.61185	10.41695	0.38287	9.58305
	$Mn(HCO_3)_2$	2.01059	10.30332	0.49737	9.69668
	MnO	1.61185	10.20733	0.62041	9.79268
	Na_2CO_3	2.40829	10.38171	0.41523	9.61829
	$NaHCO_3$	1.90882	10.28077	0.52388	9.71923
	Na_2O	1.40829	10.14869	0.71008	9.85131
	$(NH_4)_2CO_3$	2.18329	10.33911	0.45802	9.66088
	NH_4HCO_3	1.79632	10.25439	0.55669	9.74561
	$PbCO_3$	6.07135	10.78328	0.16471	9.21672
	Rb_2CO_3	5.24767	10.71996	0.19056	9.28003
	$RbHCO_3$	3.32856	10.52225	0.30043	9.47774
	Rb_2O	4.24767	10.62815	0.23542	9.37184
	$SrCO_3$	3.35446	10.52562	0.29811	9.47438
	$Sr(HCO_3)_2$	2.3818	10.37690	0.41985	9.62309
	SrO	2.35446	10.37189	0.42473	9.62811
CO_3	$BaCO_3$	3.2886	10.51701	0.30408	9.48299
	CO_2	0.73339	9.86533	1.36353	10.13466
Cs_2CO_3	CO_2	0.13507	9.13056	7.40357	10.86944
$CsHCO_3$	CO_2	0.22695	9.35593	4.40626	10.64407
CuCNS	CNS	0.47757	9.67904	2.09393	10.32097
$FeCO_3$	CO_2	0.37987	9.57964	2.63248	10.42037
$Fe(HCO_3)_2$	CO_2	0.49482	9.69445	2.02094	10.30556
HCN	Ag	3.99137	10.60112	0.25054	9.39888
	AgCN	4.95408	10.69497	0.20185	9.30503
KCN	Ag	1.65648	10.21918	0.60369	9.78081
	AgCN	2.05602	10.31302	0.48638	9.68698
K_2CO_3	CO_2	0.31842	9.50300	3.14051	10.49700
$KHCO_3$	CO_2	0.43958	9.64304	2.27490	10.35696
K_2O	CO_2	0.46718	9.66948	2.14050	10.33052
Li_2CO_3	CO_2	0.59564	9.77498	1.67887	10.22502
Li_2O	CO_2	1.47304	10.16821	0.67887	9.83179
$MgCO_3$	CO_2	0.52193	9.71761	1.91597	10.28239
$Mg(HCO_3)_2$	CO_2	0.60145	9.77920	1.66265	10.22080
MgO	CO_2	1.09176	10.03812	0.91595	9.96188
$MnCO_3$	CO_2	0.38287	9.58305	2.61185	10.41695
MnO	CO_2	0.62041	9.79268	1.61184	10.20733
Na_2CO_3	CO_2	0.41523	9.61829	2.40830	10.38171
$NaHCO_3$	CO_2	0.52388	9.71923	1.90883	10.28077
Na_2O	CO_2	0.71008	9.85131	1.40829	10.14869
$(NH_4)_2CO_3$	CO_2	0.45802	9.66088	2.18331	10.33911

Weighed	Sought	Factor	Log of Factor +10	Reciprocal of Factor	Log of Reciprocal of Factor +10
Carbon (contd.)					
NH_4HCO_3	CO_2	0.55669	9.74561	1.79633	10.25439
$PbCO_3$	CO_2	0.16471	9.21672	6.07128	10.78328
Rb_2CO_3	CO_2	0.19056	9.28003	5.24769	10.71996
$RbHCO_3$	CO_2	0.30043	9.47774	3.32856	10.52225
Rb_2O	CO_2	0.23542	9.37184	4.24773	10.62815
$SrCO_3$	CO_2	0.29811	9.47438	3.35447	10.52562
$Sr(HCO_3)_2$	CO_2	0.41984	9.62308	2.38186	10.37691
SrO	CO_2	0.42472	9.62810	2.35449	10.37190
Cerium					
Ce	$Ce_2(C_2O_4)_3.3H_2O$	2.13513	10.32943	0.46836	9.67058
	$Ce(NO_3)_4$	2.77005	10.44249	0.36100	9.55751
	$Ce(NO_3)_4(NH_4NO_3)_2.H_2O$	4.04111	10.60650	0.24746	9.39351
	CeO_2	1.22838	10.08933	0.81408	9.91067
	Ce_2O_3	1.17128	10.06866	0.85377	9.93134
	$Ce_2(SO_4)_3$	2.02833	10.30714	0.49302	9.69286
$Ce_2(C_2O_4)_3.3H_2O$	Ce	0.46835	9.67057	2.13516	10.32943
	$Ce_2(SO_4)_3$	0.95000	9.97772	1.05263	10.02228
$Ce(NO_3)_4$	Ce	0.36100	9.55751	2.77008	10.44249
	CeO_2	0.44345	9.64684	2.25505	10.35316
	Ce_2O_3	0.42284	9.62618	2.36496	10.37382
$Ce(NO_3)_4(NH_4NO_3)_2.$					
H_2O	Ce	0.24745	9.39349	4 04122	10.60651
	CeO_2	0.30396	9.48282	3.28991	10.51719
	Ce_2O_3	0.28984	9.46216	3.45018	10.53784
CeO_2	Ce	0.81408	9.91067	1.22838	10.08933
	$Ce(NO_3)_4$	2.25505	10.35316	0.44345	9.64685
	$Ce(NO_3)_4(NH_4NO_3)_2.H_2O$	3.28986	10.51718	0.30396	9.48281
	Ce_2O_3	0.95352	9.97933	1.04875	10.02068
Ce_2O_3	Ce	0.85377	9.93134	1.17128	10.06866
	$Ce(NO_3)_4$	2.36498	10.37383	0.42284	9.62618
	$Ce(NO_3)_4(NH_4NO_3)_2.H_2O$	3.45016	10.53784	0.28984	9.46216
	CeO_2	1.04874	10.02067	0.95353	9.97933
	$Ce_2(SO_4)_3$	1.73172	10.23848	0.57746	9.76152
$Ce_2(SO_4)_3$	Ce	0.49302	9.69286	2.02832	10.30714
	$Ce_2(C_2O_4)_3.3H_2O$	1.05265	10.02220	0.94998	9.97771
	Ce_2O_3	0.57746	9.76152	1.73172	10.23848
Cesium					
$AgCl$	$CsCl$	1.17468	10.06992	0.85130	9.93008
Cl	Cs	3.74877	10.57389	0.26675	9.42610
	$CsCl$	4.74877	10.67658	0.21058	9.32342
Cs	Cl	0.26675	9.42610	3.74883	10.57390
	$CsCl$	1.26675	10.10269	0.78942	9.89731
	Cs_2O_3	1.22576	10.08840	0.81582	9.91159
	Cs_2O	1.06019	10.02539	0.94323	9.97462
	Cs_2PtCl_6	2.53422	10.40385	0.39460	9.59616
	Cs_2SO_4	1.36139	10.13398	0.73454	9.86602
$CsB(C_6H_5)_4$	Cs	0.29394	9.46826	3.40205	10.53174
	Cs_2O	0.31164	9.49365	3.20883	10.50635
$CsCl$	$AgCl$	0.85130	9.93008	1.17467	10.06993
	Cl	0.21058	9.32342	4.74879	10.67658
	Cs	0.78942	9.89731	1.26675	10.10269
	Cs_2O	0.83693	9.92269	1.19484	10.07731
	Cs_2PtCl_6	2.00055	10.30114	0.49986	9.69885
	Cs_2SO_4	1.07470	10.03120	0.03049	9.96871
Cs_2CO_3	Cs	0.81582	0 01159	1.22576	10.08841
	Cs_9PtCl_6	2.06746	10.31544	0.48369	9.68457
	Cs_2SO_4	1.11065	10.04557	0.90037	9.95442
$CsClO_4$	Cs	0.57199	9.75739	1.74828	10.24261
	$CsCl$	0.72457	9.86008	1.38013	10.13992
	Cs_2O_3	0.70110	9.84578	1.42631	10.15421
	Cs_2O	0.60642	9.78277	1.64902	10.21723
	Cs_2SO_4	0.77870	9.89137	1.28419	10.10863
Cs_2O	Cs	0.94323	9.97462	1.06019	10.02539
	$CsCl$	1.19483	10.07731	0.83694	9.92269
	Cs_2PtCl_6	2.39034	10.37846	0.41835	9.62154
	Cs_2SO_4	1.28410	10.10860	0.77870	9.89140
	SO_3	0.28410	9.45347	3.51989	10.54653
Cs_2PtCl_6	Cs	0.39460	9.59616	2.53421	10.40385
	$CsCl$	0.49986	9.69885	2.00056	10.30115

Weighed	Sought	Factor	Log of Factor +10	Reciprocal of Factor	Log of Reciprocal of Factor +10
Cesium (contd.)					
Cs_2PtCl_6	Cs_2CO_3	0.48368	9.68456	2.06748	10.31544
	Cs_2O	0.41835	9.62154	2.39034	10.37846
Cs_2SO_4	Cs	0.73454	9.86602	1.36140	10.13399
	$CsCl$	0.93048	9.96871	1.07471	10.03129
	Cs_2CO_3	0.90037	9.95442	1.11065	10.04557
	Cs_2O	0.77876	9.89140	1.28409	10.10860
SO_3	Cs_2O	3.51987	10.54652	0.28410	9.45347
	Cs_2SO_4	4.51988	10.65513	0.22124	9.34486
Chlorine					
Ag	Cl	0.32866	9.51675	3.04266	10.48325
	HCl	0.33801	9.52893	2.95850	10.47107
$AgCl$	Cl	0.24736	9.39333	4.04269	10.60667
	ClO_3	0.58226	9.76512	1.71745	10.23488
	ClO_4	0.69389	9.84129	1.44115	10.15871
	HCl	0.25440	9.40552	3.93082	10.59448
$BaCrO_4$	Cl	0.27990	9.44700	3.57270	10.55299
Ca	Cl	1.76911	10.24776	0.56526	9.75225
Cl	Ag	3.04262	10.48325	0.32866	9.51675
	$AgCl$	4.04262	10.60666	0.24736	9.39333
	$BaCrO_4$	3.57276	10.55300	0.27990	9.44700
	Ca	0.56526	9.75225	1.76910	10.24775
	HCl	1.02843	10.01217	0.97236	9.98783
	K	1.10292	10.04255	0.90668	9.95745
	KCl	2.10292	10.32282	0.47553	9.67718
	Li	0.19572	9.29164	5.10934	10.70837
	Mg	0.34288	9.53514	2.91647	10.46486
	$MgCl_2$	1.34288	10.12804	0.74467	9.87196
	MnO_2	1.22609	10.08852	0.81560	9.91148
	Na	0.64846	9.81188	1.54212	10.18811
	$NaCl$	1.64846	10.21708	0.60663	9.21708
Cl	NH_4	0.50880	9.70655	1.96541	10.29346
	$PbCrO_4$	4.55787	10.65876	0.21940	9.34124
ClO_3	$AgCl$	1.71745	10.23488	0.58226	9.76512
	KCl	0.89340	9.95105	1.11932	10.04895
	$NaCl$	0.70032	9.84530	1.42792	10.15471
ClO_4	$AgCl$	1.44114	10.15870	0.69390	9.84130
	KCl	0.74967	9.87487	1.33392	10.12513
	$NaCl$	0.58765	9.76912	1.70169	10.23088
HCl	Ag	2.95850	10.47107	0.33801	9.52893
	$AgCl$	3.93086	10.59448	0.25440	9.40552
	NH_4Cl	1.46710	10.16646	0.68162	9.83354
	$(NH_4)_2SO_4$	1.81206	10.25817	0.55186	9.74183
K	Cl	0.90668	9.95745	1.10292	10.04255
KCl	Cl	0.47553	9.67718	2.10292	10.32282
	ClO_3	1.11932	10.04895	0.89340	9.95105
	ClO_4	1.33393	10.12513	0.74966	9.87486
Li	Cl	5.10924	10.70836	0.19572	9.29164
Mg	Cl	2.91650	10.46487	0.34288	9.53514
$MgCl_2$	Cl	0.74467	9.87196	1.34288	10.12804
MnO_2	Cl	0.81560	9.91148	1.22610	10.08853
Na	Cl	1.54212	10.18811	0.64896	9.81188
$NaCl$	Cl	0.60663	9.78293	1.64845	10.21708
	ClO_3	1.42791	10.15470	0.70032	9.84530
	ClO_4	1.70168	10.23088	0.58765	9.76912
NH_4	Cl	1.96539	10.29345	0.50880	9.70655
NH_4Cl	HCl	0.68162	9.83354	1.46709	10.16646
$(NH_4)_2SO_4$	HCl	0.55186	9.74184	1.81205	10.25817
$PbCrO_4$	Cl	0.21940	9.34124	4.55789	10.65876
Chromium					
Ag_2CrO_4	Cr	0.15674	9.19518	6.37999	10.80482
	Cr_2O_3	0.22895	9.35974	4.36777	10.64026
	CrO_3	0.30143	9.47919	3.31752	10.52082
	CrO_4	0.34966	9.54365	2.85992	10.45635
$BaCrO_4$	Cr	0.20525	9.31228	4.87211	10.68772
	CrO_3	0.39472	9.59629	2.53344	10.40371
	CrO_4	0.45788	9.66075	2.18398	10.33924
	Cr_2O_3	0.29998	9.47709	3.33356	10.52291
	$Cr_2(SO_4)_3.18H_2O$	1.41404	10.15046	0.70719	9.84954

Weighed	Sought	Factor	Log of Factor +10	Reciprocal of Factor	Log of Reciprocal of Factor +10
Chromium (contd.)					
$BaCrO_4$	$PbCrO_4$	1.27573	10.10576	0.78386	9.89424
Cr	$BaCrO_4$	4.87210	10.68772	0.20525	9.31228
	Cr_2O_3	1.46155	10.16482	0.68421	9.83519
	$PbCrO_4$	6.21547	10.79347	0.16089	9.20653
$Cr(C_9H_6NO)_3$	Cr	0.10733	9.03072	9.31706	10.96928
	Cr_2O_3	0.15677	9.19526	6.37877	10.80473
CrO_3	$BaCrO_4$	2.53345	10.40372	0.39472	9.59629
	Cr	0.51999	9.71600	1.92311	10.28401
	Cr_2O_3	0.75999	9.88081	1.31581	10.11920
	K_2CrO_4	1.94210	10.28827	0.51491	9.71173
	$K_2Cr_2O_7$	1.47105	10.16762	0.67979	9.83237
	$PbCrO_4$	3.23199	10.50947	0.30941	9.49053
CrO_4	$BaCrO_4$	2.18399	10.33925	0.45788	9.66075
	$PbCrO_4$	2.78618	10.44501	0.35891	9.55499
Cr_2O_3	$BaCrO_4$	3.33351	10.52291	0.29998	9.47709
	Cr	0.68420	9.83518	1.46156	10.16482
	CrO_3	1.31580	10.11919	0.75999	9.88081
	CrO_4	1.52634	10.18364	0.65516	9.81635
	$PbCrO_4$	4.25265	10.62866	0.23515	9.37135
$Cr_2(SO_4)_3.18H_2O$	$BaCrO_4$	0.70718	9.84953	1.41407	10.15047
	$PbCrO_4$	0.90217	9.95529	1.10844	10.04471
K_2CrO_4	CrO_3	0.51491	9.71173	1.94209	10.28827
	$PbCrO_4$	1.66418	10.22120	0.60090	9.77880
$K_2Cr_2O_7$	CrO_3	0.67979	9.83237	1.47104	10.16762
	$PbCrO_4$	2.19707	10.34184	0.45515	9.65815
$PbCrO_4$	Cr	0.16089	9.20652	6.21543	10.79347
	CrO_3	0.30941	9.49053	3.23196	10.50946
	CrO_4	0.35891	9.55499	2.78621	10.44501
	Cr_2O_3	0.23514	9.37133	4.25279	10.62868
	$Cr_2(SO_4)_3.18H_2O$	1.10843	10.04471	0.90218	9.95529
	K_2CrO_4	0.60090	9.77880	1.66417	10.22119
	$K_2Cr_2O_7$	0.45514	9.65815	2.19713	10.34186
Cobalt					
Co	$Co(NO_3)_2.6H_2O$	4.93731	10.69349	0.20254	9.30651
	$Co(NO_2)_3.(KNO_2)_3$	7.67433	10.88504	0.13030	9.11494
	CoO	1.27148	10.10431	0.78649	9.89569
	Co_3O_4	1.36197	10.13417	0.73423	9.86583
	$CoSO_4$	2.63001	10.41996	0.38023	9.58005
	$CoSO_4.7H_2O$	4.76984	10.67851	0.20965	9.32149
$Co(C_{10}H_6O_2N).2H_2O$	$(CoSO_4)_2.(K_2SO_4)_3$	7.06550	10.84914	0.14153	9.15085
	Co	0.09638	8.98399	10.37560	11.01602
	CoO	0.12255	9.08831	8.15993	10.91169
$(Co[C_5H_5N]_4).(SCN)_2$	Co	0.11990	9.07882	8.34028	10.92118
	CoO	0.15246	9.18316	6.55910	10.81684
$Co(C_9H_6ON)_2$	Co	0.16972	9.22973	5.89206	10.77027
	Co_2O_3	0.23883	9.37809	4.18708	10.62191
$Co(NO_3)_2.6H_2O$	Co	0.20254	9.30651	4.93730	10.69349
$Co(NO_2)_3.(KNO_2)_3$	Co	0.13030	9.11494	7.67460	10.88506
	CoO	0.16568	9.21927	6.03573	10.78073
CoO	Co	0.78648	9.89569	1.27149	10.10432
	$Co(NO_2)_3.(KNO_2)_3$	6.03571	10.78073	0.16568	9.21927
	Co_3O_4	1.07117	10.02986	0.93356	9.97014
	$CoSO_4$	2.06845	10.31564	0.48345	9.68435
	$(CoSO_4)_2.(K_2SO_4)_3$	5.55690	10.74483	0.17996	9.25518
Co_3O_4	Co	0.73423	9.86583	1.36197	10.13417
	CoO	0.93356	9.97014	1.07117	10.02986
$Co_2P_2O_7$	Co	0.40392	9.60630	2.47574	10.39371
	CoO	0.51357	9.71060	1.94715	10.28940
	Co_3O_4	0.55012	9.74046	1.81779	10.25953
	$CoSO_4$	1.06230	10.02624	0.94135	9.97375
	$CoSO_4.7H_2O$	1.92661	10.28479	0.51905	9.71521
$CoSO_4$	Co	0.38023	9.58005	2.62999	10.41996
	CoO	0.48345	9.68435	2.06847	10.31565
$CoSO_4.7H_2O$	Co	0.20965	9.32150	4.76985	10.67851
	CoO	0.26657	9.42581	3.75136	10.57419
$(CoSO_4)_2.(K_2SO_4)_3$	Co	0.14153	9.15085	7.06553	10.84914
	CoO	0.17996	9.25518	5.55679	10.74482
Columbium	See Niobium				

Weighed	Sought	Factor	Log of Factor +10	Reciprocal of Factor	Log of Reciprocal of Factor +10
Copper					
Cu	$Cu_2C_2H_3O_2.(AsO_2)_3$	3.98875	10.60084	0.25071	9.39917
	CuCNS	1.91407	10.28196	0.52245	9.71804
	CuO	1.25181	10.09754	0.79884	9.90246
	Cu_2O	1.12590	10.05150	0.88818	9.94850
	Cu_2S	1.25228	10.09770	0.79854	9.90230
	$CuSO_4.5H_2O$	3.92949	10.59433	0.25449	9.40567
$Cu_2C_2H_3O_2.(AsO_2)_3$	Cu	0.25071	9.39917	3.98867	10.60083
CuCNS	Cu	0.52245	9.71804	1.91406	10.28195
	CuO	0.65400	9.81558	1.52905	10.18443
$(Cu[C_5H_5N]_2.(SCN)_2$	Cu	0.18804	9.27425	5.31802	10.72575
	CuO	0.23539	9.37179	4.24827	10.62821
$Cu(C_7H_6NO_2)_2$	Cu	0.18922	9.27697	5.28485	10.72303
	CuO	0.23687	9.37451	4.22172	10.62549
$Cu(C_9H_6NO)_2$	Cu	0.18059	9.25669	5.53741	10.74330
	CuO	0.22606	9.35422	4.42360	10.64578
$Cu(C_{12}H_{10}ONS)_2$	Cu	0.12795	9.10704	7.81555	10.89296
	CuO	0.16017	9.20458	6.24337	10.79542
$Cu(NH_2C_6H_4CO_2)_2$	Cu	0.18922	9.27697	5.28485	10.72303
	CuO	0.23687	9.37451	4.22172	10.62549
CuO	Cu	0.79884	9.90246	1.25182	10.09754
	CuCNS	1.52904	10.18442	0.65401	9.81558
	Cu_2S	1.00038	10.00016	0.99962	9.99983
	$CuSO_4.5H_2O$	3.13905	10.49680	0.31857	9.50320
Cu_2O	Cu	0.88817	9.94850	1.12591	10.05150
	CuO	1.11183	10.04603	0.89942	9.95396
	Cu_2S	1.11224	10.04620	0.89909	9.95380
Cu_2S	Cu	0.79854	9.90230	1.25229	10.09770
	CuO	0.99962	9.99983	1.00004	10.00002
	Cu_2O	0.89908	9.95380	1.11225	10.04620
	$CuSO_4.5H_2O$	3.13787	10.49663	0.31869	9.50337
$CuSO_4.5H_2O$	Cu	0.25449	9.40567	3.92943	10.59433
	CuO	0.31857	9.50320	3.13903	10.49679
	Cu_2S	0.31869	9.50337	3.13785	10.49663
$Mg_2As_2O_7$	$Cu_2C_2H_3O_2.(AsO_2)_3$	1.08844	10.03681	0.91875	9.96320
Dysprosium					
Dy_2O_3	Dy	0.87131	9.94017	1.14770	10.05983
Erbium					
Er	Er_2O_3	1.14349	10.05824	0.87452	9.94177
Er_2O_3	Er	0.87452	9.94177	1.14349	10.05824
Europium					
Eu_2O_3	Eu	0.86361	9.93632	1.15793	10.06368
Fluorine					
BaF_2	$BaSiF_6$	1.59359	10.20238	0.62751	9.79762
$BaSiF_6$	BaF_2	0.62751	9.79762	1.59360	10.20238
	F	0.40795	9.61061	2.45128	10.38939
	HF	0.42960	9.63306	2.32775	10.36694
	H_2SiF_6	0.51568	9.71238	1.93919	10.28762
	SiF_4	0.37248	9.57110	2.68471	10.42889
	SiF_6	0.50847	9.70627	1.96668	10.29373
CaF_2	F	0.48664	9.68721	2.05491	10.31279
	6HF	0.51248	9.70968	1.95130	10.29033
	H_2SiF_6	0.61517	9.78900	1.62557	10.21100
	SiF_6	0.60657	9.78288	1.64861	10.21712
$CaSO_4$	F	0.27910	9.44576	3.58295	10.55424
	HF	0.29391	9.46821	3.40240	10.53178
F	$BaSiF_6$	2.45125	10.38939	0.40796	9.61062
	CaF_2	2.05491	10.31279	0.48664	9.68721
	$CaSO_4$	3.58293	10.55433	0.27910	9.44576
	H_2SiF_6	1.26407	10.10177	0.79110	9.89823
	K_2SiF_6	1.93244	10.28611	0.51748	9.71389
2HF	H_2SiF_6	3.60115	10.55644	0.27769	9.44356
6HF	H_2SiF_6	1.20038	10.07932	0.83307	9.92068
H_2SiF_6	$BaSiF_6$	1.93917	10.28762	0.51568	9.71237
	CaF_2	1.62555	10.21100	0.61518	9.78900
	F	0.79109	9.89823	1.26408	10.10178
	2HF	0.27769	9.44356	3.60114	10.55644
	6HF	0.83307	9.92068	1.20038	10.07932
	K_2SiF_6	1.52875	10.18434	0.65413	9.81566

Weighed	Sought	Factor	Log of Factor +10	Reciprocal of Factor	Log of Reciprocal of Factor +10
Fluorine (contd.)					
H_2SiF_6	SiF_4	0.72232	9.85873	1.38443	10.14129
	SiF_6	0.98601	9.99388	1.01419	10.00612
2KF	K_2SiF_6	1.89568	10.27777	0.52752	9.72224
K_2SiF_6	F	0.51748	9.71389	1.93244	10.28611
	6HF	0.54493	9.73634	1.83510	10.26366
	H_2SiF_6	0.65413	9.81566	1.52875	10.18434
	KF	0.52751	9.72223	1.89570	10.27777
	SiF_6	0.64498	9.80955	1.55044	10.19045
Na_2SiF_6	F	0.60615	9.78258	1.64976	10.21742
	6HF	0.63831	9.80503	1.56664	10.19498
	H_2SiF_6	0.76622	9.88435	1.30511	10.11565
	2NaF	0.44655	9.64987	2.23939	10.35013
	SiF_4	0.55344	9.74307	1.80688	10.25693
	SiF_6	0.75550	9.87823	1.32363	10.12177
PbClF	F	0.07261	8.86100	13.77221	11.13900
SiF_4	$BaSiF_6$	2.68467	10.42889	0.37249	9.57111
	H_2SiF_6	1.38444	10.14128	0.72231	9.85872
SiF_6	$BaSiF_6$	1.96666	10.29373	0.50848	9.70627
	CaF_2	1.64862	10.21712	0.60657	9.78288
	H_2SiF_6	1.01419	10.00612	0.98601	9.99388
	K_2SiF_6	1.55043	10.19045	0.64498	9.80955
Gallium					
Ga	Ga_2O_3	1.34423	10.12847	0.74392	9.87153
$Ga(C_9H_4NOBr_2)_3$	Ga	0.07146	8.85406	13.99384	11.14594
	Ga_2O_3	0.09606	8.98254	10.41016	11.01746
Ga_2O_3	Ga	0.74392	9.87153	1.34423	10.12847
Ga_2S_3	Ga	0.59178	9.77216	1.68982	10.22785
Germanium					
Ge	GeO_2	1.44083	10.15861	0.69404	9.84138
$(C_9H_6NOH)_4.$					
$(GeO_2.12MoO_3)$	Ge	0.03009	8.47842	33.23363	11.52158
	GeO_2	0.04335	8.63699	23.06805	11.36301
GeO_2	Ge	0.69404	9.84139	1.44084	10.15861
K_2GeF_6	Ge	0.27415	9.43799	3.64764	10.56201
Mg_2GeO_4	Ge	0.39193	9.59321	2.55148	10.40679
	GeO_2	0.56471	9.75183	1.77082	10.24817
Gold					
Au	$AuCl_3$	1.53998	10.18749	0.64936	9.81249
	$HAuCl_4.4H_2O$	2.09095	10.32034	0.47825	9.67966
	$KAu(CN)_4.H_2O$	1.81836	10.25968	0.54995	9.74032
$AuCl_3$	Au	0.64938	9.81250	1.53993	10.18750
C_6H_5SAu	Au	0.64339	9.80847	1.55427	10.19153
$HAuCl_4.4H_2O$	Au	0.47825	9.67966	2.09096	10.32034
$KAu(CN)_4.H_2O$	Au	0.54995	9.74032	1.81835	10.25967
Hafnium					
HfO_2	Hf	0.84797	9.92838	1.17929	10.07162
$Hf(C_6H_5CHOHCO_2)_4$	Hf	0.22794	9.35782	4.38712	10.64218
	HfO_2	0.26880	9.42943	3.72024	10.57057
Holmium					
Ho_2O_3	Ho	0.87297	9.94100	1.14551	10.05900
Hydrogen					
AgCNS	HCNS	0.35606	9.55152	2.80852	10.44848
$BaSO_4$	HCNS	0.25317	9.40341	3.94992	10.59659
CuCNS	HCNS	0.48586	9.68651	2.05821	10.31349
H	H_2O	8.93644	10.95116	0.11190	9.04883
	O	7.93644	10.89963	0.12600	9.10037
HCNS	AgCNS	2.80846	10.44847	0.35607	9.55154
	$BaSO_4$	3.94991	10.59659	0.25317	9.40341
	CuCNS	2.05822	10.31350	0.48586	9.68651
H_2O	H	0.11190	9.04883	8.93655	10.95117
O	H	0.12600	9.10037	7.93651	10.89963
Indium					
In	In_2O_3	1.20902	10.08244	0.92712	9.91757
	In_2S_3	1.41888	10.15194	0.70478	9.84805
$In(C_9H_6ON)_3$	In	0.20980	9.32181	4.76644	10.67819
	In_2O_3	0.25365	9.40423	3.94244	10.59577
In_2O_3	In	0.82711	9.91756	1.20903	10.08244
In_2S_3	In	0.70478	9.84805	1.41888	10.15194

Weighed	Sought	Factor	Log of Factor +10	Reciprocal of Factor	Log of Reciprocal of Factor +10
Iodine					
Ag	HI	1.18580	10.07401	0.84331	9.92599
	I	1.17646	10.07058	0.85001	9.92942
AgCl	I	0.88544	9.94716	1.12938	10.05284
AgI	HI	0.54483	9.73626	1.83543	10.26374
	I	0.54054	9.73283	1.85000	10.26717
	IO_3	0.74498	9.87214	1.34232	10.12786
	IO_4	0.81313	9.91016	1.22982	10.08985
	I_2O_5	0.71091	9.85181	1.40665	10.14819
	I_2O_7	0.77906	9.89157	1.28360	10.10843
HI	Ag	0.84331	9.92599	1.18580	10.07401
	AgI	1.83542	10.26374	0.54483	9.73626
	Pd	0.41590	9.61899	2.40442	10.38101
	PdI_2	1.40799	10.14860	0.71023	9.85140
	TlI	2.58981	10.41327	0.38613	9.58673
I	Ag	0.85000	9.92942	1.17647	10.07058
	AgCl	1.12937	10.05283	0.88545	9.94716
	AgI	1.85000	10.26717	0.54054	9.73283
	Pd	0.41921	9.62243	2.38544	10.37757
	PdI_2	1.41917	10.15203	0.70464	9.84797
	TlI	2.61039	10.41671	0.38308	9.58329
IO_3	AgI	1.34231	10.12785	0.74498	9.87214
	PdI_2	1.02971	10.01272	0.97115	9.98729
	TlI	1.89402	10.27738	0.52798	9.72262
IO_4	AgI	1.22981	10.08984	0.81313	9.91016
	PdI_2	0.94341	9.97470	1.05998	10.02530
	TlI	1.73528	10.23937	0.57628	9.76063
I_2O_5	AgI	1.40665	10.14819	0.71091	9.95181
	PdI_2	1.07907	10.03305	0.92672	9.96695
	TlI	1.98481	10.29772	0.50383	9.70228
I_2O_7	AgI	1.28360	10.10843	0.77906	9.89157
	PdI_2	0.98467	9.99329	1.01557	10.00671
	TlI	1.81120	10.25797	0.55212	9.74203
Pd	HI	2.40437	10.38100	0.41591	9.61900
	I	2.38542	10.37757	0.41921	9.62243
PdI_2	HI	0.71023	9.85140	1.40799	10.14860
	I	0.70463	9.70463	1.41918	10.15204
	IO_3	0.97114	9.98728	1.02972	10.01272
	IO_4	1.05998	10.02530	0.94341	9.97470
	I_2O_5	0.92672	9.96695	1.07907	10.03305
	I_2O_7	1.01556	10.00671	0.98468	9.99330
TlI	HI	0.38613	9.58673	2.58980	10.41327
	I	0.38308	9.58329	2.61042	10.41671
	IO_3	0.52798	9.72262	1.89401	10.27738
	IO_4	0.57627	9.76063	1.73530	10.23937
	I_2O_5	0.50382	9.70228	1.98484	10.29772
	I_2O_7	0.55212	9.74203	1.81120	10.25797
Iron					
Ag	$Fe_7(CN)_{18}$ (Prussian blue)	0.44253	9.64594	2.25973	10.35406
CN	$Fe_7(CN)_{18}$	1.83474	10.26358	0.54504	9.73643
CO_2	$FeCO_3$	2.63249	10.42037	0.37987	9.57964
	$Fe(HCO_3)_2$	2.02092	10.30555	0.49482	9.69445
	FeO	1.63249	10.21287	0.61256	9.78715
Fe	$Fe(HCO_3)_2$	3.18517	10.50313	0.31395	9.49686
	FeO	1.28648	10.10940	0.77731	9.89059
	Fe_2O_3	1.42973	10.15526	0.69943	9.84474
	$FePO_4$	2.70056	10.43145	0.37029	9.56854
	FeS	1.57414	10.19704	0.63527	9.80296
	$FeSO_4$	2.72009	10.43458	0.36763	9.56541
	$FeSO_4.7H_2O$	4.97817	10.69707	0.20088	9.30294
	$FeSO_4.(NH_4)_2SO_4.6H_2O$	7.02054	10.84637	0.14244	9.15363
$FeAsO_4$	$Mg_2As_2O_7$	0.79702	9.90147	1.25467	10.09853
$Fe(C_6H_5N[NO]O)_3$	Fe	0.11953	9.07748	8.36610	10.92252
	Fe_2O_3	0.17090	9.23274	5.85138	10.76726
$Fe(C_9H_6NO)_3$	Fe	0.11437	9.05821	8.74355	10.94169
	Fe_2O_3	0.16351	9.21354	6.11583	10.78646
$FeCl_3$	Fe_2O_3	0.49225	9.69219	2.03149	10.30781
$Fe_7(CN)_{18}$	Ag	2.25971	10.35405	0.44253	9.64594
	CN	0.54503	9.73642	1.83476	10.26358

Weighed	Sought	Factor	Log of Factor +10	Reciprocal of Factor	Log of Reciprocal of Factor +10
Iron (contd.)					
$FeCO_3$	CO_2	0.37986	9.57962	2.63255	10.42038
	FeO	0.62013	9.79248	1.61257	10.20752
	Fe_2O_3	0.68918	9.83833	1.45100	10.16167
$Fe(HCO_3)_2$	CO_2	0.49482	9.69445	2.02094	10.30555
	Fe	0.31396	9.49687	3.18512	10.50313
	FeO	0.40390	9.60627	2.47586	10.39373
	Fe_2O_3	0.44887	9.65212	2.22782	10.34788
FeO	CO_2	0.61256	9.78715	1.63249	10.21285
	Fe	0.77732	9.89060	1.28647	10.10940
	$FeCO_3$	1.61256	10.20751	0.62013	9.79248
	$Fe(HCO_3)_2$	2.47588	10.39373	0.40390	9.60627
	Fe_2O_3	1.11134	10.04584	0.89981	9.95415
	$FePO_4$	2.09918	10.32205	0.47638	9.67795
	FeS	1.22360	10.08764	0.81726	9.91236
	SO_3	1.11436	10.04703	0.89738	9.95298
Fe_2O_3	Fe	0.69943	9.84474	1.42974	10.15524
	$FeCl_3$	2.03149	10.30781	0.49225	9.69219
	$FeCO_3$	1.45099	10.16167	0.68918	9.83833
	$Fe(HCO_3)_2$	2.22781	10.34788	0.44887	9.65212
	$Fe(HCO_3)_3$	2.99200	10.47596	0.33422	9.52403
	FeO	0.89981	9.95415	1.11135	10.04584
	Fe_3O_4	0.96660	9.98525	1.03455	10.01475
	$FePO_4$	1.88886	10.27620	0.52942	9.72380
	FeS	1.10101	10.04113	0.90826	9.95821
	$FeSO_4$	1.90252	10.27933	0.52562	9.72067
	$FeSO_4.7H_2O$	3.48190	10.54182	0.28720	9.45818
	$Fe_2(SO_4)_3$	2.50406	10.39864	0.39935	9.60135
	$FeSO_4.(NH_4)_2SO_4.6H_2O$	4.91040	10.69112	0.20365	9.30888
Fe_3O_4	Fe_2O_3	1.03455	10.01475	0.96660	9.98525
$FePO_4$	Fe	0.37029	9.56854	2.70059	10.43145
	FeO	0.47638	9.67795	2.09916	10.32204
	Fe_2O_3	0.52942	9.72380	1.88886	10.27620
FeS	Fe	0.63527	9.80296	1.57413	10.19704
	FeO	0.81726	9.91236	1.22360	10.08764
	Fe_2O_3	0.90826	9.95821	1.10101	10.04179
$FeSO_4$	Fe	0.36763	9.56541	2.72013	10.43459
	Fe_2O_3	0.52562	9.72067	1.90252	10.27933
	SO_3	0.52704	9.72184	1.89739	10.27817
$FeSO_4.7H_2O$	Fe	0.20088	9.30294	4.97810	10.69706
	Fe_2O_3	0.28720	9.45818	3.48189	10.54182
$FeSO_4.(NH_4)_2SO_4.6H_2O$	Fe	0.14244	9.15363	7.02050	10.84637
	Fe_2O_3	0.20365	9.30888	4.91039	10.69112
$Fe_2(SO_4)_3$	Fe_2O_3	0.39935	9.60135	2.50407	10.39864
$Mg_2As_2O_7$	$FeAsO_4$	1.25468	10.09853	0.79702	9.90147
SO_3	FeO	0.89738	9.95298	1.11436	10.04703
	$FeSO_4$	1.89739	10.27816	0.52704	9.72184
Lanthanum					
La	La_2O_3	1.17277	10.06921	0.85268	9.93079
La_2O_3	La	0.85268	9.93079	1.17277	10.06921
Lead					
$BaSO_4$	$PbSO_4$	1.29927	10.11370	0.76966	9.88630
Pb	$PbCl_2$	1.34225	10.12783	0.74502	9.87217
	$PbCO_3$	1.28958	10.11044	0.77545	9.88955
	$(PbCO_3)_2.Pb(OH)_2$	1.24781	10.09615	0.80140	9.90385
	$PbCrO_4$	1.55982	10.19307	0.64110	9.80693
	PbO	1.07722	10.03231	0.92832	9.96770
	PbO_2	1.15445	10.06238	0.86621	9.93762
	$Pb(OH)_2$	1.16415	10.06601	0.85900	9.93399
	PbS	1.15474	10.06248	0.86600	9.93752
	$PbSO_4$	1.46363	10.16543	0.68323	9.83457
$Pb(C_2H_3O_2)_2.3H_2O$	$PbCrO_4$	0.85198	9.93043	1.17374	10.06957
	$PbSO_4$	0.79944	9.90279	1.25088	10.09722
$Pb(C_7H_5NO_2)_2$	Pb	0.43396	9.63746	2.30436	10.36255
	PbO	0.46747	9.66975	2.13971	10.33024
$PbCl_2$	Pb	0.74502	9.87218	1.34225	10.12783
	PbO	0.80255	9.90448	1.24603	10.09553
$PbCO_3$	Pb	0.77541	9.88954	1.28964	10.11047
	PbO	0.83529	9.92184	1.19719	10.07816

Weighed	Sought	Factor	Log of Factor +10	Reciprocal of Factor	Log of Reciprocal of Factor +10
Lead (contd.)					
$PbCO_3$	$PbSO_4$	1.13492	10.05497	0.88112	9.94504
$(PbCO_3)_2.Pb(OH)_2$	Pb	0.80141	9.90386	1.24780	10.09614
	$PbCrO_4$	1.25007	10.09693	0.79996	9.90307
	$PbSO_4$	1.17298	10.06929	0.85253	9.93017
$PbCrO_4$	Pb	0.64110	9.80692	1.55982	10.19307
	$Pb(C_2H_3O_2)_2.3H_2O$	1.17371	10.06956	0.85200	9.93044
	$(PbCO_3)_2.Pb(OH)_2$	0.79996	9.90307	1.25006	10.09693
	PbO	0.69061	9.83922	1.44800	10.16077
	Pb_3O_4	0.70710	9.84947	1.41423	10.15052
	$PbSO_4$	0.93833	9.97235	1.06572	10.02765
$Pb(NO_3)_2$	PbO	0.67388	9.82859	1.48394	10.17141
	PbO_2	0.72219	9.85865	1.38468	10.14135
	$PbSO_4$	0.91561	9.96171	1.09217	10.03829
PbO	Pb	0.92831	9.96770	1.07723	10.03231
	$PbCl_2$	1.24602	10.09553	0.80256	9.90448
	$PbCO_3$	1.19718	10.07816	0.83530	9.92184
	$PbCrO_4$	1.44800	10.16077	0.69061	9.83923
	$Pb(NO_3)_2$	1.48393	10.17141	0.67389	9.82859
	PbO_2	1.07169	10.03007	0.93311	9.96993
	PbS	1.07196	10.03018	0.93287	9.96982
	$PbSO_4$	1.35871	10.13313	0.73599	9.86687
PbO_2	Pb	0.86622	9.93763	1.15444	10.06237
	$Pb(NO_3)_2$	1.38467	10.14135	0.72219	9.85865
	PbO	0.93311	9.96993	1.07169	10.03007
	$PbSO_4$	1.26782	10.10306	0.78876	9.89694
Pb_3O_4	$PbCrO_4$	1.41423	10.15052	0.70710	9.84948
	$PbSO_4$	1.32702	10.12288	0.75357	9.87712
$Pb(OH)_2$	Pb	0.85900	9.93399	1.16414	10.06601
$Pb_2P_2O_7$	Pb	0.70434	9.84778	1.41977	10.15222
	PbO	0.75874	9.88009	1.31797	10.11991
PbS	Pb	0.86600	9.93752	1.15473	10.06249
	PbO	0.93287	9.96982	1.07196	10.03017
	$PbSO_4$	1.26750	10.10296	0.78895	9.89705
$PbSO_4$	$BaSO_4$	0.76966	9.88630	1.29928	10.11370
	Pb	0.68323	9.83457	1.46364	10.16543
	$Pb(C_2H_3O_2)_2.3H_2O$	1.25088	10.09722	0.79944	9.90279
	$PbCO_3$	0.88112	9.94504	1.13492	10.05497
	$(PbCO_3)_2.Pb(OH)_2$	0.85253	9.93071	1.17298	10.06929
	$PbCrO_4$	1.06572	10.02765	0.93833	9.97236
	$Pb(NO_3)_2$	1.09216	10.03828	0.91562	9.96172
	PbO	0.73599	9.86687	1.35871	10.13313
	PbO_2	0.78876	9.89694	1.26781	10.10305
	Pb_3O_4	0.75357	9.87712	1.32702	10.12288
	PbS	0.78895	9.89705	1.26751	10.10295
Lithium					
CO_2	Li_2CO_3	1.67887	10.22504	0.59564	9.77498
	$LiHCO_3$	1.54410	10.18868	0.64763	9.81133
	Li_2O	0.67887	9.83179	1.47304	10.16821
Li	LiCl	6.10924	10.78599	0.16369	9.21402
	Li_2CO_3	5.32404	10.72624	0.18783	9.27377
	Li_2O	2.15283	10.33201	0.46450	9.66699
	Li_3PO_4	5.56218	10.74524	0.17979	9.25477
	Li_2SO_4	7.92189	10.89883	0.12623	9.10115
LiCl	Li	0.16369	9.21402	6.10911	10.78598
	Li_2CO_3	0.87147	9.94025	1.14749	10.05975
	Li_2O	0.35239	9.54702	2.83776	10.45297
	Li_3PO_4	0.91045	9.95926	1.09836	10.04074
	Li_2SO_4	1.29670	10.11284	0.77119	9.88716
Li_2CO_3	CO_2	0.59564	9.77498	1.67887	10.22502
	Li	0.18782	9.27374	5.32425	10.72626
	LiCl	1.14747	10.05974	0.87148	9.94026
	$LiHCO_3$	1.83963	10.26473	0.54359	9.73527
	Li_2O	0.40436	9.60677	2.47304	10.39323
	Li_3PO_4	1.04473	10.01901	0.95719	9.98100
$LiHCO_3$	CO_2	0.64762	9.81132	1.54412	10.18868
	Li_2CO_3	0.54363	9.73530	1.83949	10.26470
	Li_2O	0.21982	9.34207	4.54918	10.65794
	Li_3PO_4	0.56795	9.75431	1.76072	10.24569

GRAVIMETRIC FACTORS AND THEIR LOGARITHMS (Continued)

Weighed	Sought	Factor	Log of Factor +10	Reciprocal of Factor	Log of Reciprocal of Factor +10
Lithium (contd.) Li₂O	CO₂	1.47304	10.16821	0.67887	9.83179
	Li	0.46449	9.66698	2.15290	10.33303
	LiCl	2.83767	10.45296	0.35240	9.54704
	Li₂CO₃	2.47304	10.39323	0.40436	9.60677
	LiHCO₃	4.54890	10.65791	0.21983	9.34209
	Li₃PO₄	2.58364	10.41223	0.38705	9.58777
	Li₂SO₄	3.67975	10.56582	0.27175	9.43417
	SO₃	2.67872	10.42809	0.37317	9.57191
Li₃PO₄	Li	0.17979	9.25477	5.56204	10.74523
	LiCl	1.09835	10.04074	0.91046	9.95926
	Li₂CO₃	0.95718	9.98099	1.04474	10.01901
	LiHCO₃	1.76070	10.24569	0.56796	9.75432
	Li₂O	0.38705	9.58777	2.58365	10.41223
	Li₂.SO₄.H₂O	1.65761	10.21949	0.60328	9.78052
Li₂SO₄	Li	0.12623	9.10116	7.92205	10.89883
	LiCl	0.77118	9.88716	1.29671	10.11284
	Li₂O	0.27175	9.43417	3.67975	10.56582
	Li₃PO₄	0.70213	9.84642	1.42424	10.15358
	SO₃	0.72823	9.86227	1.37319	10.13773
Li₂SO₄.II₂O	Li₃PO₄	0.60328	9.78052	1.65761	10.22948
SO₃	Li₂O	0.37317	9.57191	2.67974	10.42809
	Li₂SO₄	1.37318	10.13773	0.72824	9.86227
Lutetium Lu₂O₃	Lu	0.87938	9.94418	1.13716	10.05582
Magnesium BaSO₄	MgSO₄	0.51574	9.71243	1.93896	10.28757
	MgSO₄.7H₂O	1.05605	10.02368	0.94692	9.97631
Br	Mg	0.15212	9.18219	6.57376	10.81781
	MgBr₂	1.15212	10.06150	0.86797	9.93850
	MgBr₂.6H₂O	1.82807	10.26200	0.54703	9.73801
Cl	Mg	0.34288	9.53514	2.91647	10.46486
	MgCl₂	1.34288	10.12804	0.74467	9.87196
	MgCl₂.6H₂O	2.86643	10.45734	0.34887	9.54266
CO₂	MgCO₃	1.91595	10.28239	0.52193	9.71761
	MgO	0.91595	9.96187	1.09176	10.03812
I	Mg	0.09579	8.98132	10.43950	11.01868
	MgI₂	1.09578	10.03972	0.91259	9.96028
Mg	Br	6.57262	10.81780	0.15212	9.18219
	Cl	2.91650	10.46487	0.34288	9.53514
	I	10.43965	11.01869	0.09579	8.98132
	MgCO₃	3.46829	10.54011	0.28833	9.45989
	MgO	1.65807	10.21960	0.60311	9.78040
	Mg₂P₂O₇	4.57731	10.66061	0.21847	9.33939
	MgSO₄	4.95122	10.69471	0.20197	9.30529
MgBr₂	Br	0.86796	9.93850	1.15213	10.06150
MgBr.6H₂O	Br	0.54702	9.73800	1.82809	10.26200
MgC₂O₄	Mg	0.21643	9.33532	4.62043	10.66468
	MgO	0.35886	9.55493	2.78660	10.44508
Mg(C₉H₆NO)₂	Mg	0.07777	8.89081	12.85843	11.10919
	MgBr₂	0.58898	9.77010	1.69785	10.22990
	MgBr₂.6H₂O	0.93455	9.97060	1.07003	10.02939
	MgCO₃	0.26972	9.43091	3.70755	10.56909
	MgCl₂	0.30458	9.48370	3.28321	10.51630
	MgCl₂.6H₂O	0.65014	9.81301	1.53813	10.18699
	Mg(HCO₃)₂	0.46813	9.67037	2.13616	10.32963
	MgO	0.12895	9.11042	7.75494	10.88958
	MgSO₄	0.38505	9.58552	2.59707	10.41448
	MgSO₄.7H₂O	0.78842	9.89676	1.26834	10.10324
MgCl₂	Cl	0.74467	9.87196	1.34288	10.12804
	Mg₂P₂O₇	1.16872	10.06771	0.85564	9.93229
MgCl₂.6H₂O	Cl	0.34887	9.54266	2.86640	10.45723
	Mg₂P₂O₇	0.54753	9.73841	1.82638	10.26159
MgCl₂.KCl.6H₂O	Mg₂P₂O₇	0.40059	9.60270	2.49632	10.39730
MgCO₃	CO₂	0.52193	9.71761	1.91597	10.28239
	Mg	0.28833	9.45989	3.46825	10.54011
	Mg(HCO₃)₂	1.73559	10.23945	0.57617	9.76055
	MgO	0.47807	9.67949	2.09174	10.32051
	Mg₂P₂O₇	1.31977	10.12049	0.75771	9.87950

Weighed	Sought	Factor	Log of Factor +10	Reciprocal of Factor	Log of Reciprocal of Factor +10
Magnesium (contd.)					
$Mg(HCO_3)_2$	$MgCO_3$	0.57617	9.76055	1.73560	10.23945
	MgO	0.27545	9.44004	3.63042	10.55996
	$Mg_2P_2O_7$	0.76041	9.88105	1.31508	10.11895
MgI_2	I	0.91258	9.96027	1.09579	10.03973
MgO	CO_2	1.09176	10.03812	0.91595	9.96187
	Mg	0.60311	9.78040	1.65807	10.21960
	$MgCO_3$	2.09176	10.32051	0.47807	9.67949
	$Mg(HCO_3)_2$	3.63045	10.55996	0.27545	9.44004
	$Mg_2P_2O_7$	2.76064	10.44101	0.36223	9.55898
	$MgSO_4$	2.98613	10.47511	0.33488	9.52489
	SO_3	1.98611	10.29800	0.50350	9.70200
$Mg_2P_2O_7$	Mg	0.21847	9.33939	4.57729	10.66061
	$MgCl_2$	0.85563	9.93229	1.16873	10.06771
	$MgCl_2.6H_2O$	1.82638	10.26159	0.54753	9.73841
	$MgCl_2.KCl.6H_2O$	2.49633	10.39730	0.40059	9.60270
	$MgCO_3$	0.75771	9.87950	1.31977	10.12049
	$Mg(HCO_3)_2$	1.31508	10.11896	0.76041	9.88105
	MgO	0.36224	9.55900	2.76060	10.44101
	$MgSO_4$	1.08168	10.03410	0.92449	9.96590
	$MgSO_4.7H_2O$	2.21488	10.34535	0.45149	9.65465
$MgSO_4$	$BaSO_4$	1.93896	10.28757	0.51574	9.71243
	Mg	0.20197	9.30529	4.85123	10.69471
	MgO	0.33488	9.52489	2.98614	10.47511
	$Mg_2P_2O_7$	0.92449	9.96590	1.08168	10.03410
	SO_3	0.66511	9.82289	1.50351	10.17711
$MgSO_4.7H_2O$	$BaSO_4$	0.94693	9.97632	1.05604	10.02368
	$Mg_2P_2O_7$	0.45149	9.65465	2.21489	10.34535
	SO_3	0.32482	9.51164	3.07863	10.48836
SO_3	MgO	0.50350	9.70200	1.98610	10.29800
	$MgSO_4$	1.50351	10.17711	0.66511	9.82289
	$MgSO_4.7H_2O$	3.07863	10.48836	0.32482	9.51164
Manganese					
$BaSO_4$	$MnSO_4$	0.64696	9.81088	1.54569	10.18912
CO_2	$MnCO_3$	2.61184	10.41694	0.38287	9.58305
	MnO	1.61184	10.20733	0.62041	9.79268
Mn	$MnCO_3$	2.09230	10.32062	0.47794	9.67937
	MnO	1.29122	10.11100	0.77446	9.88900
	MnO_2	1.58246	10.19933	0.63193	9.80067
	Mn_2O_3	1.43684	10.15741	0.69597	9.84259
	Mn_3O_4	1.38830	10.14248	0.72031	9.85752
	$Mn_2P_2O_7$	2.58308	10.41213	0.38713	9.58786
MnC_2O_4	Mn	0.38429	9.58466	2.60220	10.41534
	Mn_3O_4	0.53352	9.72715	1.87434	10.27285
$Mn(C_9H_6NO)_2$	Mn	0.16005	9.20426	6.24805	10.79574
	Mn_3O_4	0.22220	9.34674	4.50045	10.65326
$MnCO_3$	CO_2	0.38287	9.58305	2.61185	10.41695
	Mn	0.47794	9.67937	2.09231	10.32063
	$Mn(HCO_3)_2$	1.53961	10.18741	0.64952	9.81259
	MnO	0.61713	9.79038	1.62040	10.20962
	Mn_3O_4	0.66353	9.82186	1.50709	10.17814
	$Mn_2P_2O_7$	1.23456	10.09152	0.81001	9.90849
	MnS	0.75689	9.87903	1.32120	10.12097
	$MnSO_4$	1.31365	10.11848	0.76124	9.88152
$Mn(HCO_3)_2$	$MnCO_3$	0.64952	9.81259	1.53960	10.18741
	MnO	0.40084	9.60297	2.49476	10.39703
	Mn_3O_4	0.43098	9.63446	2.32029	10.36555
MnO	CO_2	0.62041	9.79268	1.61184	10.20733
	Mn	0.77446	9.88900	1.29122	10.11099
	$MnCO_3$	1.62041	10.20963	0.61713	9.79038
	$Mn(HCO_3)_2$	2.49479	10.39703	0.40084	9.60297
	Mn_2O_3	1.11277	10.04641	0.89866	9.95360
	Mn_3O_4	1.07518	10.03148	0.93008	9.96852
	$Mn_2P_2O_7$	2.00049	10.30114	0.49988	9.69887
	MnS	1.22647	10.08865	0.81535	9.91134
	$MnSO_4$	2.12865	10.32811	0.46978	9.67189
	SO_3	1.12864	10.05255	0.88602	9.94744
MnO_2	Mn	0.63193	9.80067	1.58245	10.19933
	Mn_3O_4	0.87731	9.94315	1.13985	10.05684

Weighed	Sought	Factor	Log of Factor +10	Reciprocal of Factor	Log of Reciprocal of Factor +10
Manganese (contd.)					
MnO_2	$Mn_2P_2O_7$	1.63233	10.21281	0.61262	9.78719
Mn_2O_3	Mn	0.69597	9.84259	1.43684	10.15741
	MnO	0.89865	9.95359	1.11278	10.04641
	Mn_3O_4	0.96622	9.98508	1.03496	10.01492
Mn_3O_4	Mn	0.72030	9.85751	1.38831	10.14249
	$MnCO_3$	1.50709	10.17814	0.66353	9.82186
	$Mn(HCO_3)_2$	2.32032	10.36555	0.43098	9.63446
	MnO	0.93007	9.96852	1.07519	10.03149
	MnO_2	1.13984	10.05684	0.87732	9.94316
	Mn_2O_3	1.03496	10.01492	0.96622	9.98508
	$MnSO_4$	1.97978	10.29662	0.50511	9.70339
$Mn_2P_2O_7$	Mn	0.38713	9.58786	2.58311	10.41214
	$MnCO_3$	0.81000	9.90849	1.23457	10.09152
	MnO	0.49987	9.69886	2.00052	10.30114
	MnO_2	0.61262	9.78719	1.63233	10.21281
	$MnSO_4$	1.06405	10.02696	0.93981	9.97304
MnS	Mn	0.63146	9.80035	1.58363	10.19966
	$MnCO_3$	1.32120	10.12097	0.75689	9.87903
	MnO	0.81535	9.91134	1.22647	10.08865
	$MnSO_4$	1.73559	10.23945	0.57617	9.76055
$MnSO_4$	$BaSO_4$	1.54570	10.18913	0.64696	9.81088
	Mn	0.36383	9.56090	2.74854	10.43910
	MnO	0.46978	9.67189	2.12866	10.32811
	Mn_3O_4	0.50510	9.70338	1.97981	10.29663
	$Mn_2P_2O_7$	0.93980	9.97304	1.06406	10.02696
	MnS	0.57617	9.76055	1.73560	10.23945
	SO_3	0.53021	9.72445	1.88605	10.27555
SO_3	MnO	0.88603	9.94745	1.12863	10.05255
	$MnSO_4$	1.88604	10.27555	0.53021	9.72445
Mercury					
Hg	HgCl	1.17673	10.07068	0.84981	9.92932
	$HgCl_2$	1.35351	10.13146	0.73882	9.86854
	HgO	1.07976	10.03332	0.92613	9.96667
	HgS	1.15983	10.06440	0.86220	9.93561
$Hg_3(AsO_4)_2$	Hg	0.68413	9.83514	1.46171	10.16486
$Hg(C_{12}H_{10}ONS)_2$	Hg	0.31681	9.50080	3.15647	10.49920
HgCl	Hg	0.84981	9.92932	1.17673	10.07068
	$HgCl_2$	1.15023	10.06079	0.86939	9.93921
	$HgNO_3$	1.11248	10.04629	0.89889	9.95371
	HgO	0.91760	9.96265	1.08980	10.03735
	Hg_2O	0.88369	9.94630	1.13162	10.05370
	HgS	0.98564	9.99372	1.01457	10.00629
$HgCl_2$	Hg	0.73882	9.86854	1.35351	10.13146
	HgCl	0.86939	9.93921	1.15023	10.06079
	HgS	0.85691	9.93294	1.16698	10.06706
$Hg(CN)_2$	HgS	0.92091	9.96422	1.08588	10.03578
Hg_2CrO_4	Hg	0.77572	9.88971	1.28912	10.11029
$HgNO_3$	HgCl	0.89889	9.95371	1.11248	10.04629
	HgS	0.88598	9.94742	1.12869	10.05257
$Hg(NO_3)_2$	HgS	0.71673	9.85536	1.39523	10.14464
$Hg(NO_3)_2.H_2O$	HgS	0.67903	9.83189	1.47269	10.16812
HgO	Hg	0.92613	9.96667	1.07977	10.03333
	HgCl	1.08980	10.03735	0.91760	9.96265
	HgS	1.07415	10.03106	0.93007	9.96894
Hg_2O	HgCl	1.13100	10.05369	0.88370	9.94630
	HgS	1.11535	10.04741	0.89658	9.95259
HgS	Hg	0.86220	9.93561	1.15982	10.06440
	HgCl	1.01457	10.00629	0.98564	9.99372
	$HgCl_2$	1.16698	10.06706	0.85691	9.93294
	$Hg(CN)_2$	1.08588	10.03578	0.92091	9.96422
	$HgNO_3$	1.12869	10.05257	0.88598	9.94743
	$Hg(NO_3)_2$	1.39522	10.14464	0.71673	9.85536
	$Hg(NO_3)_2.H_2O$	1.47268	10.16811	0.67903	9.83189
	HgO	0.93097	9.96894	1.07415	10.03106
	Hg_2O	0.89656	9.95258	1.11537	10.04741
	$HgSO_4$	1.27509	10.10554	0.78426	9.89446
$HgSO_4$	HgS	0.78426	9.89446	1.27509	10.10554
Molybdenum					
Mo	MoO_3	1.50031	10.17618	0.66653	9.82382

Weighed	Sought	Factor	Log of Factor +10	Reciprocal of Factor	Log of Reciprocal of Factor +10
Molybdenum					
Mo	MoC	1.12518	10.05122	0.88875	9.94878
	MoS$_3$	2.00261	10.30159	0.49935	9.69841
	PbMoO$_4$	3.82666	10.58282	0.26132	9.41717
MoC	C	0.11127	9.04638	8.89715	10.95362
	Mo	0.88874	9.94877	1.12519	10.05122
MoO$_2$(C$_9$H$_6$NO)$_2$	Mo	0.23049	9.36265	4.33858	10.63735
	MoO$_3$	0.34580	9.53883	2.89184	10.46118
MoO$_3$	Mo	0.66653	9.82382	1.50031	10.17617
	MoS$_3$	1.33479	10.12541	0.74918	9.87459
	(NH$_4$)$_2$MoO$_4$	1.36175	10.13410	0.73435	9.86590
	(NH$_4$)$_3$PO$_4$.12MoO$_3$	1.08630	10.03595	0.92056	9.96405
	PbMoO$_4$	2.55058	10.40664	0.39207	9.59336
MoS$_3$	Mo	0.49935	9.69841	2.00260	10.30159
	MoO$_3$	0.74918	9.87459	1.33479	10.12541
	(NH$_4$)$_2$MoO$_4$	1.02019	10.00868	0.98021	9.99132
MoSi	Mo	0.77352	9.88847	1.29279	10.11152
	Si	0.22645	9.35497	4.41599	10.64503
(NH$_4$)$_2$MoO$_4$	MoO$_3$	0.73435	9.86590	1.36175	10.13410
	MoS$_3$	0.98021	9.99132	1.02019	10.00868
	(NH$_4$)$_3$PO$_4$.12MoO$_3$	0.79771	9.90185	1.25359	10.09816
	PbMoO$_4$	1.87302	10.27254	0.53390	9.72746
(NH$_4$)$_3$PO$_4$.12MoO$_3$	MoO$_3$	0.92054	9.96404	1.08632	10.03596
	(NH$_4$)$_2$MoO$_4$	1.25359	10.09816	0.79771	9.90185
PbMoO$_4$	Mo	0.26132	9.41717	3.82673	10.58283
	MoO$_3$	0.39207	9.59336	2.55058	10.40664
	(NH$_4$)$_2$MoO$_4$	0.53390	9.72746	1.87301	10.27254
Neodymium					
Nd	Nd$_2$O$_3$	1.16639	10.06684	0.85735	9.93315
Nd$_2$O$_3$	Nd	0.85735	9.93316	1.16638	10.06684
Nickel					
Ni	Ni(C$_4$H$_7$N$_2$O$_2$)$_2$	4.92148	10.69209	0.20319	9.30790
	Ni(NO$_3$)$_2$.6H$_2$O	4.95231	10.69481	0.20193	9.30520
	NiO	1.27254	10.10467	0.78584	9.89533
	NiSO$_4$	2.63618	10.42099	0.37934	9.57903
Ni	NiSO$_4$.7H$_2$O	4.78419	10.67981	0.20902	9.32019
Ni(C$_4$H$_7$N$_2$O$_2$)$_2$	Ni	0.20319	9.30790	4.92150	10.69210
	NiO	0.25857	9.41258	3.86742	10.58742
(Ni[C$_5$H$_5$N]$_4$)(SCN)$_2$	Ni	0.11950	9.07737	8.36820	10.92263
	NiO	0.15207	9.18204	6.57592	10.81776
Ni(C$_7$H$_6$O$_2$N)$_2$	Ni	0.17736	9.24886	5.63825	10.75114
	NiO	0.22573	9.35359	4.43007	10.64641
Ni(C$_9$H$_6$NO)$_2$	Ni	0.16918	9.22835	5.91086	10.77165
	NiO	0.21529	9.33303	4.64490	10.66698
Ni(NO$_3$)$_2$.6H$_2$O	Ni	0.20193	9.30520	4.95221	10.69480
	NiO	0.25696	9.40987	3.89166	10.59013
	NiSO$_4$	0.53231	9.72616	1.87860	10.27383
NiO	Ni	0.78584	9.89533	1.27252	10.10467
	Ni(C$_4$H$_7$N$_2$O$_2$)$_2$	3.86749	10.58743	0.25857	9.41258
	Ni(NO$_3$)$_2$.6H$_2$O	3.89171	10.59014	0.25696	9.40987
	NiSO$_4$	2.07161	10.31631	0.48272	9.68370
	NiSO$_4$.7H$_2$O	3.75960	10.57514	0.26599	9.42487
NiSO$_4$	Ni	0.37934	9.57903	2.63616	10.42098
	Ni(NO$_3$)$_2$.6H$_2$O	1.87859	10.27384	0.53231	9.72616
	NiO	0.48272	9.68370	2.07159	10.31630
	NiSO$_4$.7H$_2$O	1.81482	10.25884	0.55102	9.74117
NiSO$_4$.7H$_2$O	Ni	0.20902	9.32019	4.78423	10.67981
	NiO	0.26599	9.42487	3.75954	10.57514
	NiSO$_4$	0.55102	9.74117	1.81482	10.25884
Niobium					
C	Nb	7.73497	10.88846	0.12928	9.11153
	NbC	8.73493	10.94126	0.11448	9.05873
	½Nb$_2$O$_5$	11.06508	11.04396	0.09038	8.95607
Nb	C	0.12928	9.11153	7.73515	10.88848
	Nb$_2$O$_5$	1.43053	10.15550	0.69904	9.84450
NbC	C	0.11448	9.05873	8.73515	10.94127
	Nb	0.88552	9.94720	1.12928	10.05280
Nb$_2$O$_5$	Nb	0.69904	9.84450	1.43053	10.15550
Nitrogen					
AgNO$_2$	HNO$_2$	0.30552	9.48504	3.27311	10.51496

Weighed	Sought	Factor	Log of Factor +10	Reciprocal of Factor	Log of Reciprocal of Factor +10
Nitrogen (contd.)					
$AgNO_2$	N_2O_3	0.24698	9.39266	4.04891	10.60733
$C_{20}H_{16}N_4 \cdot HNO_3$	N	0.37312	9.57185	2.68010	10.42815
	NO_3	0.16517	9.21793	6.05437	10.78207
HNO_2	$AgNO_2$	3.27310	10.51496	0.30552	9.48504
HNO_3	N	0.22228	9.34690	4.49883	10.65310
	NH_3	0.27027	9.43180	3.70000	10.56820
	NH_4Cl	0.84889	9.92885	1.17801	10.07115
	$(NH_4)_2PtCl_6$	3.52221	10.54682	0.28391	9.45318
	NO	0.47619	9.67778	2.10000	10.32222
	Pt	1.54801	10.18977	0.64599	9.81023
	SO_3	0.63528	9.80297	1.57411	10.19703
	N_2O_5	0.53413	9.72765	1.87220	10.27235
N	HNO_3	4.49877	10.65310	0.22229	9.34692
	$NaNO_3$	6.06816	10.78306	0.16479	9.21693
	NH_3	1.21589	10 08489	0.82244	9.91510
	NH_4Cl	3.81902	10.58195	0.26185	9.41805
	$(NH_4)_2PtCl_6$	15.84563	11.19991	0.06311	8.80010
	$(NH_4)_2SO_4$	4.71699	10.67367	0.21200	9.32634
	NO_2	3.28454	10.51648	0.30446	9.48353
	NO_3	4.42680	10.64609	0.22590	9.35392
	N_2O_3	2.71341	10.43352	0.36854	9.56648
	N_2O_5	3.85566	10.58610	0.25936	9.41390
	Pt	6.96416	10.84287	0.14359	9.15712
	SO_3	2.85798	10.45606	0.34990	9.54394
$NaNO_3$	N	0.16479	9.21693	6.06833	10.78307
	N_2O_5	0.63539	9.80304	1.57384	10.19696
NH_3	HNO_3	3.69998	10.56820	0.27027	9.43180
	N	0.82244	9.91510	1.21589	10.08489
	NO_3	3.64079	10.56119	0.27467	9.43881
	N_2O_5	3.17107	10.50121	0.31535	9.49879
$NH_4B(C_6H_5)_4$	N	0.04153	8.61836	24.07898	11.38164
	NH_3	0.05049	8.70320	19.80590	11.29679
	NH_4	0.05348	8.72819	18.69858	11.27181
NH_4Cl	HNO_3	1.17799	10.07115	0.84890	9.92886
	N	0.26185	9.41805	3.81898	10.58195
	NO_3	1.15914	10.06413	0.86271	9.93586
	N_2O_5	1.00959	10.00415	0.99050	9.99585
$(NH_4)_2PtCl_6$	HNO_3	0.28392	9.45320	3.52212	10 54680
	N	0.06311	8.80010	15.84535	11.19990
	NO_3	0.27938	9.44620	3.57935	10.55380
	N_2O_5	0.24333	9.38620	4.10965	10.61380
$(NH_4)_2SO_4$	N	0.21200	9.32634	4.71698	10.67367
	N_2O_5	0.81740	9.91243	1.22339	10.08757
NO	HNO_3	2.10000	10.32222	0.47619	9.67778
	NO_2	1.53320	10.18560	0.65223	9.81440
	NO_3	2.06641	10.31522	0.48393	9.68478
	N_2O_3	1.26660	10.10264	0.78952	9.89736
	N_2O_5	1.79980	10.25522	0.55562	9.74478
NO_2	N	0.30446	9.48353	3.28450	10.51647
	NO	0.65223	9.81440	1.53320	10.18560
NO_3	N	0.22590	9.35392	4.42674	10.64608
	NH_3	0.27467	9.43881	3.64073	10.56119
	NH_4Cl	0.86270	9.93586	1.15915	10.06413
	NO	0.48393	9.68478	2.06641	10.31522
	Pt	1.57318	10.19678	0.63566	9 80322
N_2O_3	$AgNO_2$	4.04875	10.60702	0.24699	9.39268
	N	0.36854	9.56648	2.71341	10.43352
	NO	0.78951	9.89736	1.26661	10.10264
N_2O_5	KNO_3	1.87217	10.27235	0.53414	9.72766
	N	0.25936	9.41390	3.85564	10.58610
	$NaNO_3$	1.57382	10.19695	0.63540	9.80305
	NH_3	0.31535	9.49879	3.17108	10.50121
	NH_4Cl	0.99049	9.99585	1.00960	10.00415
	$(NH_4)_2PtCl_6$	4.10965	10.61380	0.24333	9.38620
	$(NH_4)_2SO_4$	1.22339	10.08757	0.81740	9.91243
	NO	0.55562	9.74478	1.79980	10.25522
	Pt	1.80621	10.25677	0.55365	9 74324
	SO_3	0.74124	9.86996	1.34909	10.13004

Weighed	Sought	Factor	Log of Factor +10	Reciprocal of Factor	Log of Reciprocal of Factor +10
Nitrogen (contd.)					
Pt	HNO_3	0.64595	9.81020	1.54811	10.18980
	N	0.14358	9.15709	6.96476	10.84291
	NO_3	0.63562	9.80320	1.57327	10.19680
	N_2O_5	0.55364	9.74323	1.80623	10.25678
SO_3	HNO_3	1.57410	10.19703	0.63528	9.80297
	N	0.34990	9.54394	2.85796	10.45605
	N_2O_5	1.34908	10.13004	0.74125	9.86996
Osmium					
Os	OsO_4	1.33649	10.12597	0.74823	9.87404
OsO_4	Os	0.74823	9.87404	1.33649	10.12597
Palladium					
K_2PdCl_6	Pd	0.26781	9.42783	3.73399	10.57217
	$PdCl_2.2H_2O$	0.53687	9.72987	1.86265	10.27013
Pd	K_2PdCl_6	3.73402	10.57217	0.26781	9.42783
	$PdCl_2.2H_2O$	2.00460	10.30205	0.49883	9.69795
	PdI_2	3.38534	10.52960	0.29539	9.47040
	$Pd(NO_3)_2$	2.16541	10.33554	0.46181	9.66446
$Pd(C_4H_7N_2O_2)_2$	Pd	0.31610	9.49982	3.16356	10.50018
$PdCl_2.2H_2O$	K_2PdCl_6	1.86263	10.27012	0.53688	9.72988
	Pd	0.49883	9.69795	2.00469	10.30204
$PdCl_2.C_{12}H_8N_2$	Pd	0.29762	9.47366	3.35999	10.52634
PdI_2	Pd	0.29539	9.47040	3.38536	10.52960
$Pd(NO_3)_2$	Pd	0.46181	9.66446	2.16539	10.33554
Phosphorus					
Ag_3PO_4	P	0.07400	8.86923	13.51351	11.13077
	PO_4	0.22689	9.35582	4.40742	10.64418
	P_2O_5	0.16954	9.22927	5.89831	10.77072
$Ag_4P_2O_7$	P	0.10232	9.00996	9.77326	10.99004
	PO_4	0.31374	9.49657	3.18735	10.50343
	P_2O_5	0.23446	9.37007	4.26512	10.62993
Al_2O_3	P_2O_5	1.39214	10.14368	0.71832	9.85632
$AlPO_4$	PO_4	0.77875	9.89140	1.28411	10.10860
	P_2O_5	0.58196	9.76489	1.71833	10.23511
$Ca_3(PO_4)_2$	P_2O_5	0.45762	9.66051	2.18522	10.33949
$FePO_4$	PO_4	0.62971	9.79914	1.58803	10.20086
	P_2O_5	0.47058	9.67263	2.12504	10.32737
$Mg_2P_2O_7$	H_3PO_4	0.88059	9.94471	1.13560	10.05523
	Na_2HPO_4	1.27565	10.10573	0.78391	9.89427
	$Na_2HPO_4.12H_2O$	3.21828	10.50763	0.31073	9.49238
	$NaNH_4.HPO_4.4H_2O$	1.87870	10.27386	0.53228	9.72614
	P	0.27833	9.44456	3.59286	10.55544
	PO_4	0.85341	9.93116	1.17177	10.06884
	P_2O_5	0.63776	9.80466	1.56799	10.19535
Na_2HPO_4	$Mg_2P_2O_7$	0.78392	9.89427	1.27564	10.10573
	P_2O_5	0.49995	9.69893	2.00020	10.30105
$Na_2HPO_4.12H_2O$	$Mg_2P_2O_7$	0.31072	9.49237	3.21833	10.50763
	P_2O_5	0.19816	9.29702	5.04643	10.70299
$NaNH_4HPO_4.4H_2O$	$Mg_2P_2O_7$	0.53228	9.72614	1.87871	10.27386
	P_2O_5	0.33946	9.53079	2.94586	10.46921
$(NH_4)_3PO_4.12MoO_3$	P	0.01651	8.21775	60.56935	11.78223
	PO_4	0.05061	8.70424	19.75894	11.29577
	P_2O_5	0.03782	8.57772	26.44104	11.42227
P	Ag_3PO_4	13.51403	11.13078	0.07400	8.86923
	$Ag_4P_2O_7$	9.77314	10.99004	0.10232	9.00996
	$Mg_2P_2O_7$	3.59282	10.55544	0.27833	9.44456
	$(NH_4)_3PO_4.12MoO_3$	60.5786	11.78234	0.01651	8.21775
	P_2O_5	2.29136	10.36009	0.43642	9.63990
	$P_2O_5.24MoO_3$	58.0564	11.76385	0.01723	8.23616
	$U_2P_2O_{11}$	11.52587	11.06167	0.08676	8.93832
PO_4	Ag_3PO_4	4.40744	10.64418	0.22689	9.35582
	$Ag_4P_2O_7$	3.18739	10.50343	0.31374	9.49657
	$AlPO_4$	1.28410	10.10860	0.77876	9.89140
	$FePO_4$	1.58803	10.20086	0.62971	9.79914
	$Mg_2P_2O_7$	1.17175	10.06884	0.85342	9.93116
	$(NH_4)_3PO_4.12MoO_3$	19.7570	11.29572	0.05062	8.70432
	$P_2O_5.24MoO_3$	18.9344	11.27725	0.05281	8.72272
	$U_2P_2O_{11}$	3.75902	10.57507	0.26603	9.42493
P_2O_5	Ag_3PO_4	5.89780	10.77069	0.16955	9.22930

Weighed	Sought	Factor	Log of Factor +10	Reciprocal of Factor	Log of Reciprocal of Factor +10
Phosphorus (contd.)					
P_2O_5	$Ag_4P_2O_7$	4.26520	10.62994	0.23446	9.37007
	Al_2O_3	0.71831	9.85631	1.39216	10.14369
	$AlPO_4$	1.71831	10.23510	0.58197	9.76440
	$Ca_3(PO_4)_2$	2.18521	10.33949	0.45762	9.66051
	$FePO_4$	2.12502	10.32736	0.47058	9.67263
	$Mg_2P_2O_7$	1.56798	10.19534	0.63776	9.80466
	Na_2HPO_4	2.00020	10.30107	0.49995	9.69893
	$Na_2HPO_4.12H_2O$	5.04623	10.70297	0.19817	9.29704
	$NaNH_4HPO_4.4H_2O$	2.94578	10.46920	0.33947	9.53080
	$(NH_4)_3PO_4.12MoO_3$	26.4377	11.42222	0.03783	8.57784
	P	0.43642	9.63990	2.29137	10.36010
	$P_2O_5.24MoO_3$	25.3370	11.40376	0.03947	8.59622
	$U_2P_2O_{11}$	5.03013	10.70158	0.19880	9.29842
$P_2O_5.24MoO_3$	P	0.01722	8.23603	58.07201	11.76397
	PO_4	0.05281	8.72272	18.93581	11.27728
	P_2O_5	0.03947	8.59627	25.33570	11.40373
$U_2P_2O_{11}$	P	0.08676	8.93832	11.52605	11.06176
	PO_4	0.26603	9.42493	3.75897	10.57507
	P_2O_5	0.19880	9.29842	5.03018	10.70158
Platinum					
$H_2PtCl_6.6H_2O$	K_2PtCl_6	0.93852	9.97244	1.06551	10.02756
	Pt	0.37673	9.57603	2.65442	10.42397
K_2PtCl_6	$H_2PtCl_6.6H_2O$	1.06551	10.02756	0.93852	9.97244
	Pt	0.40141	9.60359	2.49122	10.39541
	$PtCl_4$	0.69320	9.84086	1.44259	10.15915
	$PtCl_4.5H_2O$	0.87854	9.94376	1.13825	10.05624
$(NH_4)_2PtCl_6$	Pt	0.43950	9.64296	2.27531	10.35704
	$PtCl_4$	0.75897	9.88022	1.31758	10.11978
	$PtCl_6$	0.91854	9.96310	1.08868	10.03690
Pt	$H_2PtCl_6.6H_2O$	2.65442	10.42397	0.37673	9.57603
	K_2O	0.48287	9.68383	2.07095	10.31617
	K_2PtCl_6	2.49121	10.39641	0.40141	9.60359
	$(NH_4)_2PtCl_6$	2.27531	10.35704	0.43950	9.64296
	$PtCl_4$	1.72690	10.23727	0.57907	9.76273
	$PtCl_4.5H_2O$	2.18863	10.34017	0.45691	9.65983
$PtCl_4$	K_2PtCl_6	1.44259	10.15915	0.69320	9.84086
	$(NH_4)_2PtCl_6$	1.31757	10.11978	0.75897	9.88022
	Pt	0.57907	9.76273	1.72691	10.23727
$PtCl_4.5H_2O$	K_2PtCl_6	1.13825	10.05624	0.87854	9.94376
	Pt	0.45691	9.65983	2.18861	10.34017
$PtCl_6$	K_2PtCl_6	1.19199	10.07628	0.83893	9.92373
	$(NH_4)_2PtCl_6$	1.08869	10.03691	0.91854	9.96310
Potassium					
Ag	KBr	1.10328	10.04269	0.90639	9.95732
	KCl	0.69116	9.83958	1.44684	10.16042
	$KClO_3$	1.13612	10.05543	0.88019	9.94458
	$KClO_4$	1.28444	10.10872	0.77855	9.89129
	KCN	0.60369	9.78081	1.65648	10.21919
	KI	1.53895	10.18723	0.64979	9.81277
$AgBr$	KBr	0.63378	9.80194	1.57783	10.19806
$AgCl$	$KBrO_3$	0.88939	9.94909	1.12437	10.05091
	KCl	0.52019	9.71616	1.92237	10.28384
	$KClO_3$	0.85508	9.93201	1.16948	10.06799
	$KClO_4$	0.96673	9.98530	1.03443	10.01470
$AgCN$	KCN	0.48638	9.68698	2.05601	10.31302
AgI	KI	0.70709	9.84947	1.41425	10.15053
	KIO_3	0.91154	9.95978	1.09704	10.04022
$BaCrO_4$	K_2CrO_4	0.76658	9.88456	1.30450	10.11544
	$K_2Cr_2O_7$	0.58064	9.76391	1.72224	10.23609
$BaSO_4$	$KHSO_4$	0.58343	9.76599	1.71400	10.23401
	K_2S	0.47244	9.67435	2.11667	10.32565
	K_2SO_4	0.74664	9.87311	1.33933	10.12689
Br	K	0.48933	9.68960	2.04361	10.31040
	KBr	1.48933	10.17299	0.67144	9.82701
CaF_2	$KF.2H_2O$	2.41114	10.38223	0.41474	9.61778
$CaSO_4$	$KF.2H_2O$	1.38286	10.14078	0.72314	9.85922
Cl	K	1.10292	10.04255	0.90668	9.95745
	KCl	2.10292	10.32282	0.47553	9.67718

Weighed	Sought	Factor	Log of Factor +10	Reciprocal of Factor	Log of Reciprocal of Factor +10
Potassium (contd.)					
Cl	$KClO_3$	3.45677	10.53867	0.28929	9.46133
	$KClO_4$	3.90808	10.59196	0.25588	9.40804
	K_2O	1.32856	10.12338	0.75269	9.87662
CO_2	$KHCO_3$	2.27491	10.35696	0.43958	9.64304
	K_2CO_3	3.14049	10.49700	0.31842	9.50300
	K_2O	2.14049	10.33051	0.46718	9.66948
I	KI	1.30811	10.11665	0.76446	9.88335
	KIO_3	1.68634	10.22695	0.59300	9.77306
K	Br	2.04360	10.31040	0.48933	9.68960
	Cl	0.90668	9.95745	1.10292	10.04256
	KBr	3.04360	10.48339	0.32856	9.51661
	KCl	1.90668	10.28028	0.52447	9.71972
	$KClO_3$	3.13419	10.49614	0.31906	9.50387
	$KClO_4$	3.54337	10.54941	0.28222	9.45059
	KI	4.24546	10.62793	0.23555	9.37208
	KNO_3	2.58572	10.41259	0.38674	9.58742
	K_2O	1.20458	10.08084	0.83016	9.91916
	K_2PtCl_6	6.21467	10.79342	0.16091	9.20658
	K_2SO_4	2.22835	10.34799	0.44876	9.65201
	Pt	2.49463	10.39701	0.40086	9.60299
K_3AsO_4	$Mg_2As_2O_7$	0.60584	9.78236	1.65060	10.21764
$K(B[C_6H_5]_4)$	K	0.10912	9.03790	9.16422	10.96210
	K_2O	0.13144	9.11873	7.60803	10.88127
KBr	Ag	0.90639	9.95732	1.10328	10.04269
	$AgBr$	1.57783	10.19806	0.63378	9.80194
	Br	0.67144	9.82701	1.48934	10.17299
	K	0.32856	9.51662	3.04358	10.48338
	K_2O	0.39580	9.59748	2.52653	10.40253
$KBrO_3$	$AgBr$	1.12436	10.05091	0.88939	9.94909
$KC_{12}H_4O_{12}N_7$	K	0.08192	8.91339	12.20703	11.08661
	K_2O	0.09868	8.99423	10.13377	11.00577
KCl	Ag	1.44685	10.16043	0.69116	9.83958
	$AgCl$	1.92238	10.28384	0.52019	9.71616
	Cl	0.47553	9.67718	2.10292	10.32283
	K	0.52447	9.71972	1.90669	10.28028
	$KClO_3$	1.64379	10.21585	0.60835	9.78415
	$KClO_4$	1.85840	10.26914	0.53810	9.73086
	K_2CO_3	0.92692	9.96704	1.07884	10.03296
	$K_2Cr_2O_7$	1.97299	10.29512	0.50684	9.70487
	$KHCO_3$	1.34289	10.12804	0.74466	9.87196
	KNO_3	1.35614	10.13230	0.73739	9.86770
	K_2O	0.63180	9.80058	1.58278	10.19942
	K_2PtCl_6	3.25941	10.51314	0.30680	9.48686
	K_2SO_4	1.16871	10.06770	0.85564	9.93229
	Pt	1.30836	10.11673	0.76432	9.88328
$KClO_3$	Ag	0.88019	9.94458	1.13612	10.05543
	$AgCl$	1.16948	10.06799	0.85508	9.93201
	Cl	0.28929	9.46133	3.45674	10.53867
	KCl	0.60835	9.78415	1.64379	10.21584
$KClO_4$	Ag	0.77855	9.89129	1.28444	10.10872
	$AgCl$	1.03443	10.01470	0.96672	9.98530
	Cl	0.25588	9.40804	3.90808	10.59196
	K	0.28222	9.45059	3.54333	10.54941
	KCl	0.53810	9.73086	1.85839	10.26914
	K_2O	0.33995	9.53142	2.94161	10.46858
KCN	Ag	1.65648	10.21918	0.60369	9.78081
	$AgCN$	2.05602	10.31302	0.48638	9.68698
K_2CO_3	CO_2	0.31842	9.50300	3.14051	10.49700
	KCl	1.07883	10.03295	0.92693	9.96705
	K_2O	0.68158	9.83352	1.46718	10.16648
	KOH	0.81191	9.90951	1.23166	10.09049
	K_2PtCl_6	3.51638	10.54610	0.28438	9.45390
	K_2SO_4	1.26085	10.10067	0.79312	9.89934
K_2CrO_4	$BaCrO_4$	1.30449	10.11544	0.76658	9.88456
$K_2Cr_2O_7$	$BaCrO_4$	1.72220	10.23608	0.58065	9.76391
	KCl	0.50685	9.70488	1.97297	10.29512
	K_2O	0.32021	9.50543	3.12295	10.49456
$KF.2H_2O$	CaF_2	0.41474	9.61778	2.41115	10.38222

Weighed	Sought	Factor	Log of Factor +10	Reciprocal of Factor	Log of Reciprocal of Factor +10
Potassium (contd.)					
$KF.2H_2O$	$CaSO_4$	0.72314	9.85922	1.38286	10.14078
K_2HAsO_4	$Mg_2As_2O_7$	0.71165	9.85227	1.40519	10.14774
$KHCO_3$	KCl	0.74466	9.87196	1.34289	10.12804
	K_2O	0.47046	9.67252	2.12558	10.32748
	K_2PtCl_6	2.42716	10.38510	0.41200	9.61490
	K_2SO_4	0.87029	9.93966	1.14904	10.06034
$KHSO_4$	$BaSO_4$	1.71401	10.23401	0.58343	9.76599
	K_2SO_4	0.63988	9.80610	1.56279	10.19389
KI	Ag	0.64980	9.81278	1.53894	10.18722
	AgI	1.41425	10.15053	0.70709	9.84947
	I	0.76446	9.88335	1.30811	10.11665
	K	0.23555	9.37208	4.24538	10.62792
	K_2O	0.28374	9.45292	3.52435	10.54708
KIO_3	AgI	1.09705	10.04023	0.91154	9.95978
	I	0.59300	9.77305	1.68634	10.22695
$KMnO_4$	Mn_2O_3	0.49948	9.69852	2.00208	10.30148
	MnS	0.55051	9.74007	1.81650	10.25924
K_2MnO_4	Mn_2O_3	0.40041	9.60250	2.49744	10.39749
	MnS	0.44132	9.64475	2.26593	10.35525
KNO_2	K_2SO_4	1.02380	10.01022	0.97675	9.98978
	N_2O_3	0.44656	9.64988	2.23934	10.35012
KNO_3	K	0.38674	9.58742	2.58572	10.41260
	KCl	0.73739	9.86770	1.35613	10.13230
	K_2O	0.46586	9.66826	2.14657	10.33174
	K_2PtCl_6	2.40344	10.38083	0.41607	9.61917
	K_2SO_4	0.86179	9.93540	1.16038	10.06460
	N	0.13853	9.14154	7.21865	10.85846
	NH_3	0.16844	9.22645	5.93683	10.77356
	NO	0.29678	9.47243	3.36950	10.52757
	N_2O_5	0.53414	9.72766	1.87217	10.27235
K_2O	Cl	0.75269	9.87662	1.32857	10.12338
	CO_2	0.46718	9.66948	2.14050	10.33052
	K	0.83016	9.91916	1.20459	10.08085
	KBr	2.52667	10.40255	0.39578	9.59745
	KCl	1.58284	10.19944	0.63178	9.80057
	$KClO_3$	2.60186	10.41529	0.38434	9.58472
	$KClO_4$	2.94155	10.46858	0.33996	9.53143
	K_2CO_3	1.46718	10.16648	0.68158	9.83352
	$K_2Cr_2O_7$	3.12294	10.49456	0.32021	9.50543
	$KHCO_3$	2.12558	10.32748	0.47046	9.67252
	KI	3.52439	10.54709	0.28374	9.45292
	KNO_3	2.14655	10.33174	0.46586	9.66826
	KOH	1.19122	10.07599	0.83948	9.92401
	K_2PtCl_6	5.15918	10.71258	0.19383	9.28742
	K_2SO_4	1.84990	10.26715	0.54057	9.73285
	N_2O_5	1.14657	10.05940	0.87217	9.94060
KOH	K_2CO_3	1.23164	10.09048	0.81193	9.90952
	K_2O	0.83946	9.92400	1.19124	10.07600
K_2PtCl_6	K	0.16091	9.20658	6.21465	10.79342
	KCl	0.30680	9.48686	3.25948	10.51315
	K_2CO_3	0.28438	9.45390	3.51642	10.54610
	$KHCO_3$	0.41200	9.61490	2.42718	10.38510
	KNO_3	0.41606	9.61916	2.40350	10.38084
	K_2O	0.19383	9.28742	5.15916	10.71258
	K_2SO_4	0.35856	9 55456	2.78893	10.44544
	$K_2SO_4.Al_2(SO_4)_3.24H_2O$	1.95218	10.29052	0.51225	9.70948
	$K_2SO_4.Cr_2(SO_4)_3.24H_2O$	2.05512	10.31283	0.48659	9.68716
K_2S	$BaSO_4$	2.11666	10.32565	0.47244	9.67435
	K_2SO_4	1.58039	10.19877	0.63276	9.80124
K_2SiO_3	SiO_2	0.38943	9.59043	2.56786	10.40958
K_2SO_4	$BaSO_4$	1.33933	10.12689	0.74664	9.87311
	K	0.44876	9.65201	2.22836	10.34799
	KCl	0.85565	9.93230	1.16870	10.06770
	K_2CO_3	0.79312	9.89934	1.26084	10.10066
	$KHCO_3$	1.14904	10.06034	0.87029	9.93966
	$KHSO_4$	1.56281	10.19390	0.63987	9.80609
	KNO_2	0.97676	9 98979	1.02379	10.01021
	KNO_3	1.16038	10.06460	0.86179	9.93540

Weighed	Sought	Factor	Log of Factor +10	Reciprocal of Factor	Log of Reciprocal of Factor +10
Potassium (contd.)					
K_2SO_4	K_2O	0.54057	9.73285	1.84990	10.26715
	K_2PtCl_6	2.78889	10.44543	0.35857	9.55457
	K_2S	0.63276	9.80124	1.58038	10.19876
	SO_3	0.45942	9.66221	2.17666	10.33779
$K_2SO_4.Al_2(SO_4)_3.24H_2O$	K_2PtCl_6	0.51224	9.70947	1.95221	10.29053
$K_2SO_4.Cr_2(SO_4)_3.24H_2O$	K_2PtCl_6	0.48658	9.68715	2.05516	10.31284
$Mg_2As_2O_7$	K_3AsO_4	1.65059	10.21764	0.60584	9.78236
	K_2HAsO_4	1.40519	10.14774	0.71165	9.85227
Mn_2O_3	$KMnO_4$	2.00207	10.30148	0.49948	9.69852
	K_2MnO_4	2.49731	10.39747	0.40043	9.60253
MnS	$KMnO_4$	1.81649	10.25923	0.55051	9.74077
	K_2MnO_4	2.26592	10.35524	0.44132	9.64475
N	KNO_3	7.21847	10.85845	0.13853	9.14154
NH_3	KNO_3	5.93678	10.77355	0.16844	9.22645
NO	KNO_3	3.36954	10.52757	0.29678	9.47243
N_2O_3	KNO_2	2.23934	10.35012	0.44656	9.64988
N_2O_5	KNO_3	1.87217	10.27235	0.53414	9.72765
	K_2O	0.87217	9.94060	1.14657	10.05940
Pt	K	0.40086	9.60299	2.49464	10.39701
	KCl	0.76431	9.88327	1.30837	10.11673
SiO_2	K_2SiO_3	2.56783	10.40957	0.38943	9.59043
SO_3	K_2SO_4	2.17664	10.33779	0.45942	9.66221
Praseodymium					
Pr	Pr_2O_3	1.17032	10.06832	0.85447	9.93169
Pr_2O_3	Pr	0.85447	9.93169	1.17032	10.06831
Pr_6O_{11}	Pr	0.82770	9.91787	1.20817	10.08213
Rhenium					
$C_{20}H_{16}N_4.HReO_4$	Re	0.33038	9.51901	3.02682	10.48098
$(C_6H_5)_4AsReO_4$	Re	0.29392	9.46823	3.40229	10.53177
Rhodium					
Na_3RhCl_6	Rh	0.26757	9.42744	3.73734	10.57256
Rh	Na_3RhCl_6	3.73735	10.57256	0.26757	9.42744
$RhCl_3$	Rh	0.49175	9.69174	2.03355	10.30826
Rubidium					
$AgCl$	Rb	0.59635	9.77550	1.67687	10.22450
	$RbCl$	0.84368	9.92618	1.18528	10.07382
Cl	Rb	2.41080	10.38216	0.41480	9.61784
	$RbCl$	3.41071	10.53284	0.29319	9.46715
Rb	$AgCl$	1.67688	10.22450	0.59635	9.77550
	Cl	0.41480	9.61784	2.41080	10.38216
	$RbCl$	1.41477	10.15069	0.70683	9.84932
	Rb_2CO_3	1.35106	10.13068	0.74016	9.86933
	Rb_2O	1.09360	10.03886	0.91441	9.96114
	Rb_2PtCl_6	3.38569	10.52965	0.29536	9.47035
	Rb_2SO_4	1.56195	10.19367	0.64023	9.80634
$RbB(C_6H_5)_4$	Rb	0.21119	9.32467	4.73507	10.67533
	Rb_2O	0.23096	9.36354	4.32975	10.63647
$RbCl$	$AgCl$	1.18527	10.07382	0.84369	9.92618
	Cl	0.29319	9.46715	3.41076	10.53285
	Rb	0.70683	9.84932	1.41477	10.15069
	Rb_2CO_3	0.95493	9.97997	1.04720	10.02003
	Rb_2O	0.77296	9.08816	1.29373	10.11184
	Rb_2PtCl_6	2.39301	10.37896	0.41788	9.62105
	Rb_2SO_4	1.10399	10.04297	0.90581	9.95704
Rb_2CO_3	Rb	0.74019	9.86934	1.35100	10.12066
	$RbCl$	1.04720	10.02003	0.45493	9.97997
	$RbHCO_3$	1.26864	10.10335	0.78825	9.89666
	Rb_2PtCl_6	2.50595	10.39897	0.39905	9.60103
	Rb_2SO_4	1.15609	10.06299	0.86498	9.93701
$RbClO_4$	Rb	0.46220	9.66483	2.16357	10.33517
	Rb_2CO_3	0.62446	9.79550	1.60138	10.20449
	$RbCl$	0.65390	9.81551	1.52929	10.18448
	$RbHCO_3$	0.79218	9.89883	1.26234	10.10118
	Rb_2O	0.50546	9.70369	1.97840	10.29632
	Rb_2SO_4	0.72193	9.85850	1.38518	10.14151
$RbHCO_3$	Rb_2CO_3	0.78831	9.89670	1.26854	10.10330
	Rb_2PtCl_6	1.97546	10.29567	0.50621	9.70433
	Rb_2SO_4	0.91136	9.95969	1.09726	10.04031

Weighed	Sought	Factor	Log of Factor +10	Reciprocal of Factor	Log of Reciprocal of Factor +10
Rubidium (contd.)					
Rb_2O	Rb	0.91441	9.96114	1.09360	10.03887
	RbCl	1.29368	10.11182	0.77299	9.88817
	Rb_2PtCl_6	3.09591	10.49079	0.32301	9.50922
Rb_2PtCl_6	Rb_2SO_4	1.42827	10.15481	0.70015	9.84519
	Rb	0.29537	9.47037	3.38558	10.52963
	RbCl	0.41787	9.62103	2.39309	10.37896
	Rb_2CO_3	0.39905	9.60103	2.50595	10.39898
	$RbHCO_3$	0.50624	9.70436	1.97535	10.29565
Rb_2SO_4	Rb_2O	0.32301	9.50922	3.09588	10.49079
	Rb	0.64022	9.80633	1.56196	10.19367
	RbCl	0.90577	9.95701	1.10403	10.04298
	Rb_2CO_3	0.86498	9.93701	1.15610	10.06300
	$RbHCO_3$	1.09730	10.04033	0.91133	9.95968
	Rb_2O	0.70015	9.84520	1.42827	10.15481
Samarium					
Sm_2O_3	Sm	0.86235	9.93568	1.15962	10.06431
Scandium					
Sc_2O_3	Sc	0.65196	9.81422	1.53384	10.18578
$Sc(C_9H_6NO)_3.$					
(C_9H_6NOH)	Sc	0.07221	8.85860	13.84850	11.14140
	Sc_2O_3	0.11076	9.04438	9.02853	10.95562
Selenium					
H_2SeO_3	Se	0.61224	9.78692	1.63335	10.21308
H_2SeO_4	Se	0.54466	9.73613	1.83601	10.26389
$PbSeO_4$	Se	0.22550	9.35315	4.43459	10.64685
	SeO_2	0.31689	9.50091	3.15567	10.49909
Se	H_2SeO_3	1.63336	10.21308	0.61223	9.78691
	H_2SeO_4	1.83599	10.26387	0.54467	9.73613
	SeO_2	1.40527	10.14776	0.71161	9.85224
	SeO_3	1.60790	10.20626	0.62193	9.79374
SeO_2	Se	0.71161	9.85224	1.40526	10.14776
SeO_3	Se	0.62193	9.79374	1.60790	10.20626
Silicon					
$BaSiF_6$	SiF_4	0.37249	9.57111	2.68464	10.42888
	SiO_2	0.21503	9.33250	4.65051	10.66750
H_2SiO_3	SiO_2	0.76933	9.88611	1.29983	10.11388
K_2SiF_6	SiF_4	0.47249	9.67439	2.11645	10.32561
	SiO_2	0.27277	9.43580	3.66609	10.56420
Si	SiO_2	2.13932	10.33027	0.46744	9.66973
SiC	C	0.29955	9.47647	3.33834	10.52353
	Si	0.70045	9.84538	1.42765	10.15462
SiF_4	$BaSiF_6$	0.26847	9.42890	3.72481	10.57110
	K_2SiF_6	2.11645	10.32561	0.47249	9.67439
SiF_4	SiO_2	0.57730	9.76140	1.73220	10.23860
SiO_2	$BaSiF_6$	4.65041	10.66749	0.21503	9.33250
	H_2SiO_3	1.29983	10.11388	0.76933	9.88611
	K_2SiF_6	3.66614	10.56421	0.27277	9.43580
	Si	0.46744	9.66973	2.13931	10.33027
	SiF_4	1.73221	10.23861	0.57730	9.76140
	SiO_3	1.26627	10.10252	0.78972	9.89747
	SiO_4	1.53256	10.18542	0.65250	9.81458
	Si_2O	0.60058	9.77857	1.66506	10.22182
	$Si(OH)_4$	1.59965	10.20403	0.02514	9.79597
$SiO_2.12MoO_3$	Si	0.01571	8.19618	63.65372	11.80382
	SiO_2	0.03362	8.52660	29.74420	11.47340
SiO_3	SiO_2	0.78972	9.89747	1.26627	10.10252
SiO_4	SiO_2	0.65250	9.81458	1.53257	10.18542
Si_2O	SiO_2	1.66505	10.22142	0.60058	9.77857
$Si(OH)_4$	SiO_2	0.62514	9.79598	1.59964	10.20402
Silver					
Ag	AgBr	1.74079	10.24075	0.57445	9.75925
	AgCl	1.32866	10.12341	0.75264	9.87659
	AgCN	1.24120	10.09384	0.80567	9.90616
	AgI	2.17645	10.33775	0.45946	9.66225
	$AgNO_3$	1.57481	10.19723	0.63500	9.80277
	Ag_2O	1.07416	10.03107	0.93090	9.96893
	Ag_3PO_4	1.29347	10.11176	0.77311	9.88824

Weighed	Sought	Factor	Log of Factor +10	Reciprocal of Factor	Log of Reciprocal of Factor +10
Silver (contd.)					
Ag	$Ag_4P_2O_7$	1.40313	10.14710	0.71269	9.85290
	Br	0.74079	9.86970	1.34991	10.13030
	Cl	0.32866	9.51675	3.04266	10.48325
	I	1.17646	10.07058	0.85001	9.92942
AgBr	Ag	0.57445	9.75925	1.74080	10.24075
	Br	0.42555	9.62895	2.34990	10.37105
AgCl	Ag	0.75264	9.87659	1.32866	10.12342
	$AgNO_3$	1.18526	10.07382	0.84370	9.92619
	Ag_2O	0.80845	9.90765	1.23693	10.09235
	Br	0.55754	9.74628	1.79359	10.25372
	Cl	0.24736	9.39333	4.04269	10.60667
AgCN	Ag	0.80567	9.90616	1.24120	10.09384
Ag_2CrO_4	Ag	0.65034	9.81314	1.53766	10.18686
AgI	Ag	0.45946	9.66225	2.17647	10.33775
	I	0.54054	9.73283	1.85000	10.26717
$AgNO_3$	Ag	0.63499	9.80277	1.57483	10.19723
	AgCl	0.84370	9.92619	1.18526	10.07381
Ag_2O	Ag	0.93096	9.96893	1.07416	10.03107
	AgCl	1.23693	10.09235	0.80845	9.90765
Ag_3PO_4	Ag	0.77311	9.88824	1.29348	10.11176
$Ag_4P_2O_7$	Ag	0.71269	9.85290	1.40313	10.14710
Br	Ag	1.34991	10.13030	0.74079	9.86970
	AgBr	2.34991	10.37105	0.42555	9.62895
	AgCl	1.79358	10.25372	0.55754	9.74628
Cl	Ag	3.04261	10.48325	0.32867	9.51676
	AgCl	4.04262	10.60666	0.24736	9.39333
I	Ag	0.85000	9.92942	1.17647	10.07058
	AgI	1.85000	10.26717	0.54054	9.73283
Sodium					
Ag	NaBr	0.95392	9.97951	1.04831	10.02049
	NaCl	0.54179	9.73383	1.84573	10.26617
	NaI	1.38958	10.14288	0.71964	9.85712
AgBr	NaBr	0.54798	9.73876	1.82488	10.26123
AgCl	NaCl	0.40777	9.61042	2.45236	10.38959
	$NaClO_3$	0.74267	9.87080	1.34649	10.21921
	$NaClO_4$	0.85429	9.93161	1.17056	10.06839
AgI	NaI	0.63846	9.80513	1.56627	10.19487
$BaSO_4$	$NaHSO_4$	0.51439	9.71129	1.94405	10.28871
	$NaHSO_4.H_2O$	0.59157	9.77201	1.69042	10.22799
	Na_2S	0.33438	9.52424	2.99061	10.47577
	Na_2SO_3	0.54002	9.73241	1.85178	10.26759
	$Na_2SO_3.7H_2O$	1.08032	10.03355	0.92565	9.96645
	Na_2SO_4	0.60857	9.78431	1.64320	10.21569
	$Na_2SO_4.10H_2O$	1.38043	10.14001	0.72441	9.85998
B_2O_3	$Na_2B_4O_7$	1.44511	10.15990	0.69199	9.84010
	$Na_2B_4O_7.10H_2O$	2.73895	10.43758	0.36510	9.56241
Br	Na	0.28770	9.45894	3.47584	10.54106
	NaBr	1.28770	10.10981	0.77658	9.89019
	Na_2O	0.38781	9.58862	2.57858	10.41138
$CaCl_2$	NaCl	1.05321	10.02252	0.94948	9.97749
$CaCO_3$	Na_2CO_3	1.05894	10.02488	0.94434	9.97513
CaF_2	NaF	1.07551	10.03161	0.92979	9.96838
CaO	Na_2CO_3	1.88996	10.27645	0.52911	9.72355
$CaSO_4$	Na_2CO_3	0.77853	9.89128	1.28447	10.10873
Cl	Na	0.64846	9.81188	1.54212	10.18812
	NaCl	1.64846	10.21708	0.60663	9.78292
	Na_2O	0.87410	9.94156	1.14403	10.05844
CO_2	Na_2CO_3	2.40829	10.38171	0.41523	9.61829
	Na_2O	1.40829	10.14869	0.71008	9.85131
H_3BO_3	$Na_2B_4O_7$	0.81356	9.91039	1.22917	10.08961
	$Na_2B_4O_7.10H_2O$	1.54195	10.18807	0.64853	9.81193
I	Na	0.18116	9.25806	5.51998	10.74194
	NaI	1.18115	10.07231	0.84663	9.92769
	Na_2O	0.24419	9.38773	4.09517	10.61227
KBF_4	$Na_2B_4O_7$	0.39954	9.60156	2.50288	10.39844
	$Na_2B_4O_7.10H_2O$	0.75725	9.87924	1.32057	10.12076
$Mg_2As_2O_7$	Na_2HAsO_3	1.09454	10.03923	0.91363	9.96077
	Na_2HAsO_4	1.19761	10.07832	0.83500	9.92169

Weighed	Sought	Factor	Log of Factor +10	Reciprocal of Factor	Log of Reciprocal of Factor +10
Sodium (contd.)					
MgCl$_2$	NaCl	1.22756	10.08904	0.81462	9.91096
Mg$_2$P$_2$O$_7$	Na$_2$HPO$_4$	1.27565	10.10573	0.78391	9.89427
	Na$_2$HPO$_4$.12H$_2$O	3.21828	10.50763	0.31072	9.49237
	NaNH$_4$HPO$_4$.4H$_2$O	1.87870	10.27386	0.53228	9.72614
	Na$_3$PO$_4$	1.47318	10.16825	0.67880	9.83174
	Na$_4$P$_2$O$_7$.10H$_2$O	2.00414	10.30193	0.49897	9.69807
N	NaNO$_3$	6.06815	10.78306	0.16479	9.21693
Na	Br	3.47585	10.54106	0.28770	9.45894
	Cl	1.54212	10.18811	0.64846	9.81188
	I	5.52003	10.74194	0.18116	9.25806
	NaBr	4.47585	10.65088	0.22342	9.34912
	NaCl	2.54213	10.40520	0.39337	9.59480
	Na$_2$CO$_3$	2.30513	10.36269	0.43382	9.63731
	NaHCO$_3$	3.65410	10.56278	0.27367	9.43723
	NaI	6.52003	10.81425	0.15337	9.18574
	Na$_2$O	1.34797	10.12968	0.74186	9.87032
	Na$_2$SO$_4$	3.08921	10.48985	0.32371	9.51016
Na$_2$B$_4$O$_7$	B$_2$O$_3$	0.69198	9.84009	1.44513	10.15991
	H$_3$BO$_3$	1.22916	10.08961	0.81356	9.91039
	KBF$_4$	2.50287	10.39844	0.39954	9.60156
Na$_2$B$_4$O$_7$.10H$_2$O	B$_2$O$_3$	0.36510	9.56241	2.73898	10.43759
	H$_3$BO$_3$	0.64853	9.81193	1.54195	10.18807
	KBF$_4$	1.32057	10.12076	0.75725	9.87924
NaBr	Ag	1.04831	10.02048	0.95392	9.97951
	AgBr	1.82489	10.26123	0.54798	9.73876
	Br	0.77658	9.89019	1.28770	10.10981
	Na	0.22342	9.34912	4.47588	10.65088
	Na$_2$O	0.30116	9.47880	3.32049	10.52120
NaC$_2$H$_3$O$_2$.Mg(C$_2$H$_3$O$_2$)$_2$.					
3UO$_2$(C$_2$H$_3$O$_2$)$_2$.6½H$_2$O	Na	0.01527	8.18375	65.50075	11.81625
	NaBr	0.06833	8.83464	14.63400	11.16536
	Na$_2$CO$_3$	0.03519	8.54646	28.41474	11.45354
	NaCl	0.03881	8.58895	25.76589	11.41104
	NaF	0.02788	8.44536	35.86286	11.55465
	NaHCO$_3$	0.05579	8.74654	17.92500	11.25346
	NaI	0.09954	8.99801	10.04590	11.00199
	NaNO$_3$	0.05644	8.75162	17.71667	11.24837
	Na$_2$O	0.02058	8.31345	48.59086	11.68655
	NaOH	0.02656	8.42426	37.64746	11.57574
	Na$_2$SO$_4$	0.04716	8.67361	21.20261	11.32638
NaC$_2$H$_3$O$_2$.Zn(C$_2$H$_3$O$_2$)$_2$.					
3UO$_2$(C$_2$H$_3$O$_2$)$_2$.6½H$_2$O	Na	0.01495	8.17461	66.89410	11.85239
	NaBr	0.06691	8.82549	14.94545	11.17450
	Na$_2$CO$_3$	0.03446	8.53730	29.01999	11.46270
	NaCl	0.03800	8.57981	26.31440	11.42019
	NaF	0.02733	8.43621	36.62601	11.56379
	NaHCO$_3$	0.05466	8.73739	18.30663	11.26261
	NaI	0.09747	8.98886	10.25977	11.01114
	NaNO$_3$	0.05527	8.74247	18.09398	11.25753
	NaOH	0.02601	8.41511	38.44970	11.58489
	Na$_2$O	0.02015	8.30430	49.62532	11.69570
	Na$_2$SO$_4$	0.04618	8.66446	21.65392	11.33554
Na$_2$CO$_3$	CaCO$_3$	0.94434	9.97513	1.05894	10.02488
	CaO	0.52911	9.72355	1.88997	10.27645
	CaSO$_4$	1.28447	10.10873	0.77853	9.89128
	CO$_2$	0.41523	9.61829	2.40830	10.38171
	Na	0.43381	9.63730	2.30516	10.36270
	NaCl	1.10281	10.04250	0.90677	9.95750
	NaHCO$_3$	1.58520	10.20008	0.63084	9.79992
	NaOH	0.75474	9.87780	1.32496	10.12220
	Na$_2$O	0.58477	9.76699	1.71007	10.23301
	Na$_2$SO$_4$	1.34015	10.12715	0.74619	9.87285
Na$_2$CO$_3$.10H$_2$O	Na$_2$SO$_4$	0.49639	9.69582	2.01455	10.30417
NaCl	Ag	1.84573	10.26617	0.54179	9.73383
	AgCl	2.45236	10.38958	0.40777	9.61042
	Cl	0.60663	9.78292	1.64845	10.21707
	Na	0.39337	9.59480	2.54214	10.40520
	NaClO$_3$	1.82129	10.26038	0.54906	9.73962

Weighed	Sought	Factor	Log of Factor +10	Reciprocal of Factor	Log of Reciprocal of Factor +10
Sodium (contd.)	$NaClO_4$	2.09503	10.32118	0.47732	9.67881
	Na_2CO_3	0.90677	9.95750	1.10282	10.04251
	$NaHCO_3$	1.43742	10.15759	0.69569	9.84242
	Na_2HPO_4	1.21451	10.08440	0.82338	9.91560
	Na_2O	0.53025	9.72448	1.88590	10.27552
$NaCl$	Na_2SO_4	1.21521	10.08465	0.82290	9.91535
$NaClO_3$	$AgCl$	1.34650	10.12921	0.74267	9.87080
	$NaCl$	0.54906	9.73961	1.82129	10.26038
$NaClO_4$	$AgCl$	1.17055	10.06839	0.85430	9.93161
	$NaCl$	0.47732	9.67881	2.09503	10.32119
NaF	CaF_2	0.92979	9.96838	1.07551	10.03161
Na_2HAsO_3	$Mg_2As_2O_7$	0.91362	9.96077	1.09455	10.03923
Na_2HAsO_4	$Mg_2As_2O_7$	0.83499	9.92168	1.19762	10.07832
$NaHCO_3$	Na	0.27366	9.43721	3.65417	10.56279
	$NaCl$	0.69569	9.84242	1.43742	10.15759
	Na_2CO_3	0.63083	9.79991	1.58521	10.20009
	Na_2O	0.36889	9.56690	2.71084	10.43310
Na_2HPO_4	$Mg_2P_2O_7$	0.78392	9.89427	1.27564	10.10573
	$NaCl$	0.82338	9.91560	1.21451	10.08440
	Na_2O	0.43660	9.64008	2.29043	10.35992
	$Na_4P_2O_7$	0.93654	9.97153	1.06776	10.02847
	P_2O_5	0.49994	9.69892	2.00024	10.30108
$Na_2HPO_4.12H_2O$	$Mg_2P_2O_7$	0.31072	9.49237	3.21833	10.50763
	$Na_4P_2O_7$	0.37122	9.56963	2.69382	10.43037
	P_2O_5	0.19816	9.29702	5.04643	10.70298
$NaHSO_3$	SO_2	0.61564	9.78933	1.62433	10.21076
$NaHSO_4$	$BaSO_4$	1.94404	10.28871	0.51439	9.71129
$NaHSO_4.H_2O$	$BaSO_4$	1.69039	10.22799	0.59158	9.77201
NaI	Ag	0.71964	9.85712	1.38958	10.14288
	AgI	1.56626	10.19486	0.63846	9.80513
	I	0.84662	9.92769	1.18117	10.07231
	Na	0.15337	9.18574	6.52018	10.81426
	Na_2O	0.20674	9.31542	4.83699	10.68458
$NaNH_4HPO_4.4H_2O$	$Mg_2P_2O_7$	0.53228	9.72614	1.87871	10.27386
	NH_3	0.08146	8.91094	12.27596	11.08905
	P_2O_5	0.33946	9.53079	2.94586	10.46921
$NaNO_3$	N	0.16479	9.21693	6.06833	10.78307
	Na_2O	0.36461	9.56183	2.74266	10.43818
	NH_3	0.20037	9.30183	4.99077	10.69817
	NO	0.35303	9.54781	2.83262	10.45219
	N_2O_5	0.63539	9.80304	1.57384	10.19696
Na_2O	Br	2.57854	10.41137	0.38782	9.58863
	Cl	1.14401	10.05843	0.87412	9.94157
	CO_2	0.71008	9.85131	1.40829	10.14869
	I	4.09501	10.61225	0.24420	9.38775
	Na	0.74185	9.87032	1.34798	10.12968
	$NaBr$	3.32039	10.52119	0.30117	9.47881
	$NaCl$	1.88587	10.27551	0.53026	9.72449
	Na_2CO_3	1.71008	10.23302	0.58477	9.76699
	$NaHCO_3$	2.71078	10.43310	0.36890	9.56691
	Na_2HPO_4	2.29044	10.35992	0.43660	9.64008
	NaI	4.83686	10.68457	0.20675	9.31545
	$NaNO_3$	2.74265	10.43817	0.36461	9.56183
	$NaOH$	1.29065	10.11081	0.77480	9.88919
	Na_2SO_4	2.29176	10.36017	0.43635	9.63984
	N_2O_5	1.74269	10.24122	0.57383	9.75878
	SO_3	1.29176	10.11118	0.77414	9.88882
$NaOH$	Na_2CO_3	1.32495	10.12220	0.75475	9.87780
	Na_2O	0.77479	9.88918	1.29067	10.11082
$Na_4P_2O_7$	Na_2HPO_4	1.06775	10.02847	0.93655	9.97153
	$Na_2HPO_4.12H_2O$	0.26938	9.43037	3.71223	10.56963
$Na_4P_2O_7.10H_2O$	$Mg_2P_2O_7$	0.49897	9.69807	2.00413	10.30193
Na_2S	$BaSO_4$	2.99062	10.47576	0.33438	9.52424
Na_2SO_3	$BaSO_4$	1.85176	10.26758	0.54003	9.73242
	SO_2	0.50827	9.70609	1.96746	10.29391
$Na_2SO_3.7H_2O$	$BaSO_4$	0.92564	9.96644	1.08033	10.03356
	SO_2	0.25407	9.40495	3.93592	10.59505
Na_2SO_4	$BaSO_4$	1.64319	10.21569	0.60857	9.78431
	Na	0.32370	9.51014	3.08928	10.48986

Weighed	Sought	Factor	Log of Factor +10	Reciprocal of Factor	Log of Reciprocal of Factor +10
Sodium (contd.)					
	NaCl	0.82289	9.91534	1.21523	10.08466
	Na_2CO_3	0.74619	9.87285	1.34014	10.21715
	$Na_2CO_3.10H_2O$	2.01451	10.30417	0.49640	9.69583
	Na_2O	0.43635	9.63984	2.29174	10.36016
	SO_3	0.56365	9.75101	1.77415	10.24899
$Na_2SO_4.10H_2O$	$BaSO_4$	0.72441	9.85998	1.38043	10.14001
$Na_2U_2O_7.2ZnU_2O_7$	Na	0.02369	8.37457	42.21190	11.62544
	Na_2O	0.03193	8.50420	31.31851	11.49579
NH_3	$NaNH_4HPO_4.4H_2O$	12.27607	11.08906	0.08146	8.91094
	$NaNO_3$	4.99070	10.69816	0.20037	9.30183
NO	$NaNO_3$	2.83258	10.45218	0.35304	9.54782
N_2O_5	$NaNO_3$	1.57382	10.19695	0.63540	9.80305
	Na_2O	0.57382	9.75878	1.74271	10.24123
P_2O_5	Na_2HPO_4	2.00020	10.30107	0.49995	9.69893
	$Na_2HPO_4.12H_2O$	5.04623	10.70297	0.19817	9.29704
	$NaNH_4HPO_4.4H_2O$	2.94578	10.46920	0.33947	9.53080
SO_2	$NaHSO_3$	1.62442	10.21070	0.61560	9.78930
	Na_2SO_3	1.96756	10.29393	0.50824	9.70607
SO_3	Na_2O	0.77414	9.88882	1.29176	10.11118
	Na_2SO_4	1.77414	10.24899	0.56365	9.75101
Strontium					
CO_2	$SrCO_3$	3.35446	10.52562	0.29811	9.47438
SO_3	SrO	1.29424	10.11202	0.77265	9.88798
	$SrSO_4$	2.29422	10.36063	0.43588	9.63937
Sr	$SrCO_3$	1.68489	10.22657	0.59351	9.77343
	$Sr(NO_3)_2$	2.41532	10.38298	0.41402	9.61702
	SrO	1.18261	10.07284	0.84559	9.92716
	$SrSO_4$	2.09633	10.32146	0.47702	9.67854
$SrCl_2$	$SrCO_3$	0.93124	9.96906	1.07384	10.03094
	SrO	0.65363	9.81533	1.52992	10.18467
	$SrSO_4$	1.15865	10.06395	0.86307	9.93605
$SrCO_3$	CO_2	0.29811	9.47438	3.35447	10.52562
	Sr	0.59351	9.77343	1.68489	10.22657
	$SrCl_2$	1.07383	10.03095	0.93125	9.96907
	$Sr(HCO_3)_2$	1.42010	10.15232	0.70418	9.84768
	$Sr(NO_3)_2$	1.43352	10.15640	0.69758	9.84359
	SrO	0.70189	9.84627	1.42472	10.15373
	$SrSO_4$	1.24419	10.09489	0.80374	9.90511
SrC_2O_4	Sr	0.49886	9.69798	2.00457	10.30202
	SrO	0.58996	9.77082	1.69503	10.22918
$Sr(HCO_3)_2$	$SrCO_3$	0.70417	9.84768	1.42011	10.15232
	SrO	0.49425	9.69395	2.02327	10.30602
$Sr(IO_3)_2$	Sr	0.20031	9.30170	4.99226	10.69829
	SrO	0.23688	9.37453	4.22155	10.69829
$Sr(NO_3)_2$	Sr	0.41402	9.61702	2.41434	10.38298
	$SrCO_3$	0.69759	9.84360	1.43351	10.15640
	SrO	0.48963	9.68987	2.04236	10.31014
	$SrSO_4$	0.86793	9.93849	1.15217	10.06151
SrO	SO_3	0.77265	9.88798	1.29425	10.11202
	Sr	0.84559	9.92716	1.18261	10.07284
	$SrCl_2$	1.52992	10.18467	0.65363	9.81533
	$SrCO_3$	1.42472	10.15373	0.70189	9.84627
	$Sr(HCO_3)_2$	2.02326	10.30605	0.49425	9.69395
	$Sr(NO_3)_2$	2.04237	10.31014	0.48963	9.68987
	$SrSO_4$	1.77263	10.24862	0.56413	9.75138
$SrSO_4$	SO_3	0.43588	9.63937	2.29421	10.36063
	Sr	0.47703	9.67855	2.09630	10.32145
	$SrCl_2$	0.86308	9.93605	1.15864	10.06395
	$SrCO_3$	0.80373	9.90511	1.24420	10.09489
	$Sr(NO_3)_2$	1.15217	10.06151	0.86793	9.93848
	SrO	0.56413	9.75138	1.77264	10.24862
Sulfur					
As_2S_3	H_2S	0.41555	9.61862	2.40645	10.38138
	S	0.39097	9.59214	2.55774	10.40786
$BaSO_4$	FeS_2	0.25702	9.40997	3.89077	10.59003
	H_2S	0.14602	9.16441	6.84838	10.83559
	H_2SO_3	0.35166	9.54612	2.84366	10.45388
	H_2SO_4	0.42021	9.62347	2.37976	10.37653

Weighed	Sought	Factor	Log of Factor +10	Reciprocal of Factor	Log of Reciprocal of Factor +10
Sulfur (contd.)					
	S	0.13738	9.13792	7.27908	10.86208
	SO_2	0.27448	9.43851	3.64325	10.56149
	SO_3	0.34302	9.53532	2.91528	10.46468
	SO_4	0.41158	9.61445	2.42966	10.38555
$C_{12}H_{12}N_2.H_2SO_4$	S	0.11357	9.05526	8.80514	10.94474
	SO_4	0.34026	9.53181	2.93893	10.46819
CdS	H_2S	0.23591	9.37275	4.23890	10.62725
	S	0.22196	9.34627	4.50532	10.65372
FeS_2	$BaSO_4$	3.89081	10.59004	0.25702	9.40997
H_2S	As_2S_3	2.40646	10.38138	0.41555	9.61862
	$BaSO_4$	6.84859	10.83560	0.14602	9.16441
	CdS	4.23885	10.62725	0.23591	9.37275
	SO_3	2.34924	10.37093	0.42567	9.62907
H_2SO_3	$BaSO_4$	2.84363	10.45287	0.35166	9.54612
H_2SO_4	$BaSO_4$	2.37974	10.37653	0.42021	9.62347
	$(NH_4)_2SO_4$	1.34728	10.12946	0.74224	9.87054
	SO_3	0.81631	9.91186	1.22502	10.08814
$(NH_4)_2SO_4$	H_2SO_4	0.74223	9.87054	1.34729	10.12946
	SO_3	0.60589	9.78239	1.65046	10.21760
S	As_2S_3	2.55775	10.40786	0.39097	9.59214
	$BaSO_4$	7.27919	10.86208	0.13738	9.13792
	CdS	4.50536	10.65373	0.22196	9.34627
SO_2	$BaSO_4$	3.64329	10.56149	0.27448	9.43851
SO_2	$BaSO_4$	2.91524	10.46468	0.34302	9.53532
	H_2S	0.42567	9.62907	2.34924	10.37093
	$(NH_4)_2SO_4$	1.65047	10.21761	0.60589	9.78239
SO_4	$BaSO_4$	2.42968	10.38555	0.41158	9.61445
Tantalum					
Ta	$TaCl_5$	1.97965	10.29659	0.50514	9.70341
	Ta_2O_5	1.22105	10.08674	0.81897	9.91327
TaC	C	0.06225	8.79413	16.06451	11.20587
	Ta	0.93775	9.97209	1.06638	10.02791
$TaCl_5$	Ta	0.50514	9.70341	1.97965	10.29659
	Ta_2O_5	0.61680	9.79041	1.62127	10.20985
Ta_2O_4	Ta_2O_5	1.03757	10.01602	0.96379	9.98398
Ta_2O_5	Ta	0.81897	9.91327	1.22105	10.08673
	$TaCl_5$	1.62126	10.20985	0.61680	9.79014
	Ta_2O_4	0.96379	9.98398	1.03757	10.01602
Tellurium					
H_2TeO_4	Te	0.65906	9.81893	1.51731	10.18108
$H_2TeO_4.2H_2O$	Te	0.55565	9.74480	1.79969	10.25520
Te	H_2TeO_4	1.51732	10.18108	0.65906	9.81893
	$H_2TeO_4.2H_2O$	1.79969	10.25520	0.55565	9.74480
	TeO_2	1.25078	10.09718	0.79950	9.90282
	TeO_3	1.37618	10.13868	0.72665	9.86133
	$(TeO_2)_2SO_3$	1.56450	10.19438	0.63918	9.80562
TeO_2	Te	0.79950	9.90282	1.25078	10.09718
TeO_3	Te	0.72665	9.86133	1.37618	10.13868
$(TeO_2)_2SO_3$	Te	0.63918	9.80562	1.56450	10.19438
Terbium					
Tb_4O_7	Tb	0.85021	9.92953	1.17618	10.07048
Thallium					
$(C_6H_5)_4AsTlCl_4$	Tl	0.28014	9.44738	3.56964	10.55263
Tl	TlCl	1.17346	10.06947	0.85218	9.93053
	Tl_2CO_3	1.14682	10.05949	0.87198	9.94051
	Tl_2CrO_4	1.28377	10.10849	0.77896	9.89151
	$TlHSO_4$	1.47497	10.16878	0.67798	9.83122
	TlI	1.62093	10.20976	0.61693	9.79024
	$TlNO_3$	1.30337	10.11507	0.76724	9.88493
	Tl_2O	1.03914	10.01668	0.96233	9.98332
	Tl_2PtCl_6	1.99772	10.30055	0.50057	9.69946
	Tl_2SO_4	1.23501	10.09167	0.80971	9.90833
TlCl	Tl	0.85218	9.93053	1.17346	10.06947
	Tl_2PtCl_6	1.70240	10.23106	0.58741	9.76894
Tl_2CO_3	Tl	0.87198	9.94051	1.14682	10.05951
	Tl_2PtCl_6	1.74197	10.24104	0.57406	9.75896
Tl_2CrO_4	Tl	0.77895	9.89151	1.28378	10.10850
$TlHSO_4$	Tl	0.67798	9.83122	1.47497	10.16878

Weighed	Sought	Factor	Log of Factor +10	Reciprocal of Factor	Log of Reciprocal of Factor +10
Thallium (contd.)					
TlI	Tl	0.61693	9.79024	1.62093	10.20976
	Tl₂PtCl₆	1.23244	10.09076	0.81140	9.90924
TlNO₃	Tl	0.76724	9.88493	1.30338	10.11507
	Tl₂PtCl₆	1.53272	10.18546	0.65243	9.81453
Tl₂O	Tl	0.96223	9.98332	1.03914	10.01668
	Tl₂PtCl₆	1.92247	10.28386	0.52016	9.71614
Tl₂PtCl₆	Tl	0.50057	9.69946	1.99772	10.30054
	TlCl	0.58741	9.76894	1.70239	10.23106
	Tl₂CO₃	0.57406	9.75896	1.74198	10.24105
	TlI	0.81140	9.90924	1.23244	10.09076
	TlNO₃	0.65244	9.81454	1.53271	10.18546
	Tl₂O	0.52016	9.71614	1.92249	10.28386
	Tl₂SO₄	0.61821	9.79114	1.61757	10.20886
Tl₂SO₄	Tl	0.80971	9.90833	1.23501	10.09167
	Tl₂PtCl₆	1.61757	10.20886	0.61821	9.79114
Thorium					
Th	ThO₂	1.13790	10.05610	0.87881	9.94390
Th(C₉H₆NO)₄.(C₉H₆NOH)	Th	0.24327	9.38609	4.11066	10.61391
	ThO₂	0.27682	9.44220	3.61246	10.55781
ThCl₄	ThO₂	0.70626	9.84896	1.41590	10.15103
Th(NO₃)₄.6H₂O	ThO₂	0.44898	9.65223	2.22727	10.34777
ThO₂	Th	0.87881	9.94390	1.13790	10.05610
	ThCl₄	1.41590	10.15103	0.70626	9.84896
	Th(NO₃)₄.6H₂O	2.22729	10.34778	0.44898	9.65223
Thulium					
Tm₂O₃	Tm	0.87561	9.94231	1.14206	10.05769
Tin					
Sn	SnCl₂	1.59744	10.20342	0.62600	9.79657
	SnCl₂.2H₂O	1.90100	10.27898	0.52604	9.72102
	SnCl₄	2.19479	10.34140	0.45562	9.65860
	SnCl₄.(NH₄Cl)₂	3.09622	10.49083	0.32297	9.50916
	SnO	1.13480	10.05492	0.88121	9.94508
	SnO₂	1.26961	10.10367	0.78764	9.89633
SnCl₂	Sn	0.62600	9.79657	1.59744	10.20342
	SnO₂	0.79478	9.90025	1.25821	10.09975
SnCl₂.2H₂O	Sn	0.52604	9.72102	1.90100	10.27898
	SnO₂	0.66786	9.82469	1.49732	10.17531
SnCl₄	Sn	0.45562	9.65860	2.19481	10.34139
	SnO₂	0.57846	9.76227	1.72873	10.23772
SnCl₄.(NH₄Cl)₂	Sn	0.32297	9.50916	3.09626	10.49084
	SnO₂	0.41005	9.61284	2.43873	10.38716
SnO	Sn	0.88121	9.94508	1.13480	10.05491
	SnO₂	1.11879	10.04875	0.89382	9.95125
SnO₂	Sn	0.78764	9.89633	1.26962	10.10367
	SnCl₂	1.25821	10.09976	0.79474	9.90023
	SnCl₂.2H₂O	1.49731	10.17531	0.66786	9.82469
	SnCl₄	1.72871	10.23772	0.57847	9.76228
	SnCl₄.(NH₄Cl)₂	2.43872	10.38716	0.41005	9.61284
	SnO	0.89382	9.95125	1.11879	10.04875
Titanium					
K₂TiF₆	F	0.47472	9.67644	2.10650	10.32356
	K	0.32573	9.51286	3.07003	10.48714
	Ti	0.19951	9.29996	5.01228	10.70004
	TiO₂	0.33279	9.52217	3.00490	10.47783
Ti	K₂TiF₆	5.01232	10.70004	0.19951	9.29996
	TiC	1.25073	10.09717	0.79953	9.90283
	TiO₂	1.66806	10.22222	0.59950	9.77779
TiC	C	0.20049	9.30210	4.98778	10.69791
	Ti	0.79953	9.90283	1.25073	10.09717
TiO(C₉H₄NOCl₂)₂	Ti	0.09776	8.99016	10.22913	11.00984
	TiO₂	0.16306	9.21235	6.13271	10.78765
TiO(C₉H₆ON)₂	Ti	0.13600	9.13354	7.35294	10.86646
	TiO₂	0.22685	9.35574	4.40820	10.64426
TiO₂	K₂TiF₆	3.00488	10.47782	0.33279	9.52217
	Ti	0.59950	9.77779	1.66806	10.22221
	TiC	0.74969	9.87488	1.33388	10.12512

Weighed	Sought	Factor	Log of Factor +10	Reciprocal of Factor	Log of Reciprocal of Factor +10
Tungsten					
$FeWO_4$	W	0.60539	9.78203	1.65183	10.21797
	WO_3	0.76344	9.88277	1.30986	10.11722
$MgWO_4$	W	0.67552	9.82964	1.48034	10.17036
	WO_3	0.85189	9.93038	1.17386	10.06962
$MnWO_4$	W	0.60719	9.78332	1.64693	10.21668
	WO_3	0.76571	9.88406	1.30598	10.11593
$PbWO_4$	W	0.40403	9.60641	2.47506	10.39359
	WO_3	0.50952	9.70716	1.96263	10.29284
W	W_2C	1.03266	10.01396	0.96837	9.98604
	WC	1.06532	10.02748	0.93869	9.97252
	WO_2	1.17405	10.06969	0.85175	9.93031
	WO_3	1.26108	10.10075	0.79297	9.89925
W_2C	C	0.03163	8.50010	31.61555	11.49990
	W	0.96837	9.98604	1.03266	10.01396
WC	C	0.06133	8.78767	16.30523	11.21233
	W	0.93868	9.97252	1.06533	10.02749
WO_2	W	0.85175	9.93031	1.17405	10.06969
$WO_2(C_9H_6ON)_2$	W	0.36467	9.56190	2.74221	10.43810
	WO_3	0.45987	9.66264	2.17453	10.33736
WO_3	W	0.79297	9.89926	1.26108	10.10074
Uranium					
U	UO_2	1.13444	10.05478	0.88149	9.94522
	U_3O_8	1.17925	10.07160	0.84800	9.92840
	$U_2P_2O_{11}$	1.49981	10.17604	0.66675	9.82396
UO_2	U	0.88149	9.94522	1.13444	10.05478
	U_3O_8	1.03950	10.01682	0.96200	9.98318
	$U_2P_2O_{11}$	1.32268	10.12145	0.75604	9.87854
$UO_2(C_9H_6ON)_2.$					
(C_9H_7ON)	U	0.33835	9.52937	2.95552	10.47063
	UO_2	0.38384	9.58415	2.60525	10.41585
U_3O_8	U	0.84799	9.92839	1.17926	10.07161
	UO_2	0.96199	9.98317	1.03951	10.01683
	$UO_2(NO_3)_2.6H_2O$	1.78864	10.25252	0.55908	9.74747
$UO_2(NO_3)_2.6H_2O$	U_3O_8	0.55909	9.74748	1.78862	10.25252
$U_2P_2O_{11}$	U	0.66675	9.82396	1.49981	10.17603
	UO_2	0.75639	9.87875	1.32207	10.12125
Vanadium					
V	VC	1.23578	10.09194	0.80921	9.90806
	V_2O_5	1.78518	10.25168	0.56017	9.74832
VC	C	0.19080	9.28058	5.24109	10.71942
	V	0.80921	9.90806	1.23577	10.09194
VO_4	V_2O_5	0.79120	9.89829	1.26390	10.10171
V_2O_5	V	0.56017	9.74832	1.78517	10.25168
	VC	0.69225	9.84026	1.44456	10.15974
	VO_4	1.26390	10.10171	0.79120	9.89829
Ytterbium					
Yb	YbO_3	1.13870	10.05641	0.87819	9.94359
Yb_2O_3	Yb	0.87820	9.94359	1.13869	10.05640
Yttrium					
Y	Y_2O_3	1.26994	10.10378	0.78744	9.89622
Y_2O_3	Y	0.78744	9.89622	1.26994	10.10378
Zinc					
$BaSO_4$	ZnS	0.41744	9.62059	2.39555	10.37941
	$ZnSO_4.7H_2O$	1.23196	10.09059	0.81171	9.90940
Zn	$ZnNH_4PO_4$	2.72877	10.43596	0.36647	9.56404
	ZnO	1.24476	10.09508	0.80337	9.90492
	$Zn_2P_2O_7$	2.33043	10.36744	0.42911	9.63257
	ZnS	1.49044	10.17332	0.67094	9.82668
$Zn(C_9H_6NO)_2$	Zn	0.18483	9.26677	5.41038	10.73323
	ZnO	0.23007	9.36186	4.34650	10.63814
$ZnCl_2$	ZnO	0.59708	9.77603	1.67482	10.22397
$ZnCO_3$	ZnO	0.64899	9.81224	1.54086	10.18777
$(Zn[C_5H_5N]_2).(SCN)_2$	Zn	0.19241	9.28423	5.19724	10.71577
	ZnO	0.23951	9.37932	4.17519	10.62068
$ZnNH_4PO_4$	Zn	0.36646	9.56403	2.72881	10.43597
	ZnO	0.45616	9.65912	2.19221	10.34089
ZnO	Zn	0.80337	9.90492	1.24476	10.09509
	$ZnCl_2$	1.67482	10.22397	0.59708	9.77603

Weighed	Sought	Factor	Log of Factor +10	Reciprocal of Factor	Log of Reciprocal of Factor +10
Zinc (contd.)					
	$ZnCO_3$	1.54086	10.18776	0.64899	9.81224
	$ZnNH_4PO_4$	2.19221	10.34088	0.45616	9.65912
	$Zn_2P_2O_7$	1.87219	10.27235	0.53413	9.72765
	ZnS	1.19737	10.07823	0.83516	9.92177
	$ZnSO_4.7H_2O$	3.53373	10.54823	0.28299	9.45177
$Zn_2P_2O_7$	Zn	0.42911	9.63257	2.33040	10.36743
	ZnO	0.53413	9.72765	1.87220	10.27235
ZnS	$BaSO_4$	2.39556	10.37941	0.41744	9.62059
	Zn	0.67094	9.82668	1.49045	10.17332
	ZnO	0.83516	9.92177	1.19738	10.07822
	$ZnSO_4.7H_2O$	2.95125	10.47001	0.33884	9.52999
$ZnSO_4.7H_2O$	$BaSO_4$	0.81171	9.90940	1.23197	10.09060
	ZnO	0.28299	9.45177	3.53369	10.54823
	ZnS	0.33884	9.52999	2.95125	10.47001
Zirconium					
K_2ZrF_6	Zr	0.32187	9.50768	3.10684	10.49232
	ZrF_4	0.58999	9.77084	1.69494	10.22915
	ZrF_6	0.72407	9.85978	1.38108	10.14022
	ZrO_2	0.43478	9.63827	2.30001	10.36173
Zr	ZrO_2	1.35080	10.13059	0.74030	9.86941
	ZrC	1.13166	10.05372	0.88366	9.94629
$Zr(BrC_8H_6O_3)_4$	Zr	0.09020	8.95521	11.08647	11.04479
	ZrO_2	0.12184	9.08579	8.20749	10.91421
$Zr(C_8H_7O_3)_4$	Zr	0.13110	9.11760	7.62777	10.88240
	ZrO_2	0.17709	9.24819	5.64685	10.75181
ZrC	C	0.11635	9.06577	8.59476	10.93424
	Zr	0.88366	9.94629	1.13166	10.05372
ZrO_2	Zr	0.74030	9.86941	1.35080	10.13059
	ZrC	0.83777	9.92312	1.19365	10.07687
$Zr_2P_2O_7$	Zr	0.34402	9.53658	2.90681	10.46342
	ZrO_2	0.46470	9.66717	2.15193	10.33283

PHYSICAL CONSTANTS OF MINERALS

Compiled by Ralph Kretz

The following table presents data for many of the more common minerals.

In order to avoid duplication and save space, very few cross references are given in the body of the table. If the name sought is not found in the table, consult the **synonym index** given below.

Specific gravities are given at normal atmospheric temperatures, a more precise statement being valueless considering the large variations in natural minerals.

Hardness is given in terms of Mohs' scale. (See under Hardness.)

Indices of refraction for the sodium line, $\lambda = 5893$ Å, unless otherwise indicated. Li, $\lambda = 6708$ Å. Indices will invariably be given in the order ω, ϵ or α, β, γ. Uniaxial crystals are considered positive if $\epsilon > \omega$, negative if $\omega > \epsilon$. Biaxial crystals are considered positive if β is nearer α in value than it is γ and negative if β is nearer γ than α.

ABBREVIATIONS

Abbreviation	Meaning of abbreviation	Abbreviation	Meaning of abbreviation	Abbreviation	Meaning of abbreviation
bl	blue	grn	green	rhbdr	rhombohedral
blk	black	grnsh	greenish	rhomb	rhombic
blksh	blackish	hex	hexagonal	somet	sometimes
blsh	bluish	iridesc	iridescent	tarn	tarnishes
br	brown	monocl	monoclinic	tetr	tetragonal
brnsh	brownish	oft	often	tricl	triclinic
col	colorless	pa	pale	vlt	violet
cub	cubic	purp	purple	wh	white
dk	dark	(R)	radioactive	yel	yellow
Fe	Fe, ferrous iron	redsh	redish	yelsh	yellowish
Fe^{+3}	Fe, ferric iron				

SYNONYM INDEX

Compound sought	Listed	Compound sought	Listed
Acmite	Aegirine	Lead sulfate	Anglesite
Agate	Quartz (impure)	Lead sulfide	Galena
Aluminum hydroxide	Boehmite, Diaspore, Gibbsite	Limonite	Goethite (impure)
Amphibole	Actinolite, Anthophyllite, Cummingtonite, Glaucophane, Hornblende, Riebeckite, Tremolite	Lithiophyllite	Triphylite
		Lithium mica	Lepidolite
		Lodestone	Magnetite
Antimony oxide	Senarmontite, Valentinite	Magnesium carbonate	Magnesite
Antimony sulfide	Stibnite	Magnesium hydroxide	Brucite
Arsenic oxide	Arsenolite, Claudetite	Magnesium oxide	Periclase
Arsenic sulfide	Orpiment, Realgar	Magnesium sulfate	Kieserite
Barium carbonate	Witherite	Manganese carbonate	Rhodochrosite
Barium sulfate	Barite	Manganese hydroxide	Pyrochroite
Barytes	Barite	Manganese oxide	Hausmannite, Manganosite, Pyrolusite
Bauxite	Gibbsite, Boehmite, Diaspore	Manganese sulfide	Alabandite
Brimstone	Sulfur	Meerschaum	Serpentine
Bronzite	Orthopyroxene	Mica	Muscovite, Paragonite, Phlogopite, Biotite, Lepidolite
Cadmium sulfide	Greenockite		
Calamine	Hemimorphite	Native copper	Copper
Calcium carbonate	Aragonite, Calcite, Vaterite	Native gold	Gold
Calcium sulfate	Anhydrite, Gypsum	Nickel oxide	Bunsenite
Calcium sulfide	Oldhamite	Nickel sulfide	Millerite
Carborundum	Moissanite	Orthite	Allanite
Chalcedony	Quartz (impure, fibrous)	Penninite	Chlorite
Chinaclay	Kaolinite	Peridote	Olivine
Chloanthite	Skutterodite	Pistacite	Epidote
Chromespinel	Chromite	Pitchblende	Uraninite
Chrysolite	Serpentine	Plagioclase	Albite, Oligoclase, Andesine, Anorthite
Clinoptolite	Heulandite		
Clayminerals	Illite, Kaolinite, Montmorillonite	Potassium chloride	Sylvite
Clinochlore	Chlorite	Potassium sulfate	Arcanite
Cobaltbloom	Erythrite	Pyroxene	Diopsite, Angite, Aegirine, Jadeite, Pigeonite, Eustatite, Orthopyroxene
Copper chloride	Nantokite		
Copper oxide	Cuprite		
Copper sulfide	Chalcocite, Covellite, Digenite	Rocksalt	Halite
Emerald	Beryl	Ruby	Corundum
Emery	Mixture of Corundum, Magnetite and other minerals	Sapphire	Corundum
		Silica	Christobalite, Quartz, Tridymite
Epsom salt	Epsomite	Silver chloride	Cerargyrite
Feldspar	Orthoclase, Microcline, Anorthoclase, Albite, Oligoclase, Andesine, Anorthite	Silver iodide	Jodyrite, Miersite
		Silver sulfide	Acanthite, Argentite
		Smalltite	Skutterotite
Fibrolite	Sillimanite	Soapstone	Mixture of Talc and other minerals
Flint	Quartz (impure)	Sodium chloride	Halite
Fluorapatite	Apatite	Sodium sulfate	Thenardite
Fluorspar	Fluorite	Strontium carbonate	Strontianite
Garnet	Almandine, Pyrope, Spessartite, Andradite, Grossularite, Uvarovite, Hydrogrossularite	Strontium sulfate	Celestite
		Thorium oxide	Thorianite
		Tin oxide	Cassiterite
Garnierite	Serpentine (Ni-bearing)	Titanite	Sphene
Glauber salt	Mirabilite	Titanium oxide	Anatase, Brookite, Rutile
Hyacinth	Zircon	Uranium oxide	Uraninite
Iceland spar	Calcite	Zeolite	Natrolite, Mesolite, Scolecite, Thomasonite, Harmatome, Eddingtonite, Heulandite, Stilbite, Phillipsite, Chabazite, Gmelinite, Levyn, Laumontite, Mordenite
Idocrase	Vesuvianite		
Iron carbonate	Siderite		
Iron hydroxide	Goethite, Lepidocrocite		
Iron oxide	Hematite, Magnetite		
Iron spinel	Hercynite		
Iron sulfide	Marcasite, Pyrite, Pyrrhotite	Zincblende	Sphalerite
Lapis lazuli	Lazurite	Zinc carbonate	Smithsonite
Lead carbonate	Cerussite	Zinc oxide	Zincite
Lead chloride	Cotunnite	Zinc spinel	Gahnite
Lead chromate	Crocoite	Zinc sulfide	Sphalerite, Wurtzite
Lead oxide	Litharge, Minium	Zirconium oxide	Baddeleyite

Name	Formula	Sp. gr.	Hardness	Crystalline form and color	Index of refraction (Na) η; ω ϵ α β γ
Acanthite	AgS.	7.2–7.3	2–2.5	rhomb.(?), iron-blk.	
Actinolite	Ca₂((Mg,Fe)₅Si₈O₂₂(OH,F)₂	3.02–3.44	5–6	monocl., pa. to dk. grn.	1.599–1.688, 1.612–1.697, 1.622–1.705
Aegirine	NaFe⁺³Si₂O₆.	3.55–3.60	6	monocl., dk. grn. to grnsh. blk.	1.750–1.776, 1.780–1.820, 1.800–1.836
Åkermanite	Ca₂MgSi₂O₇.	2.944	5–6	tetr., col., gray-grn., br.	1.632, 1.640
Alabandite	MnS	4.050	3.5–4	cub., iron-blk., tarn., br.	
Albite	NaAlSi₃O₈.	2.63	6–6.5	tricl., col., wh., somet. yel., pink, grn.	1.527, 1.531, 1.538
Allanite	(Ca,Mn,Ce,La,Y,Th)₂(Fe,Fe⁺³,Ti)(Al,Fe⁺³)₂ Si₃O₁₂(OH)	3.4–4.2	5–6.5	monocl., pa. br. to blk.	1.690–1.791, 1.700–1.815, 1.706–1.828
Allemontite	AsSb.	5.8–6.2	3–4	hex., tin-wh. to redsh., gray, tarn. gray–brnsh. blk.	
Almandine	Fe₃Al₂Si₃O₁₂.	4.318	6.5–7.5	cub., red, dk. red, blk.	1.830
Altaite	PbTe.	8.15	3	cub., tin-wh., yelsh., tarn. bronze-yel.	
Aluminite	Al₂(SO₄)(OH).7H₂O	1.66–1.82	1–2	monocl.(?), wh.	1.459, 1.464, 1.470
Alunite	(K,Na)Al₃(SO₄)₂(OH)₆.	2.6–2.9	3.5–4	rhbdr., col., wh., yel., redsh., br.	1.572, 1.592
Alunogen	Al₂(SO₄)₃.18H₂O	1.77	1.5–2	tricl., col., wh., yelsh. wh., redsh. wh.	1.459–1.475, 1.461–1.478, 1.470–1.485
Amblygonite	(Li,Na)Al(PO₄)(F,OH)	3.0–3.1	5.5–6	tricl., wh., yelsh. wh., grnsh. wh., blsh. wh., gray	1.591, 1.604, 1.613
Analcite	NaAlSi₂O₆.H₂O	2.24–2.29	5.5	cub., wh., pink, gray	1.479–1.493
Anatase	TiO₂.	3.90	5.5–6	tetr., br., yelsh. br., redsh. br., bl., blk., grn., gray	2.5612, 2.4880
Andalusite	Al₂OSiO₄.	3.13–3.16	6.5–7.5	rhomb., pink, wh., red	1.629–1.640, 1.633–1.644, 1.638–1.650
Andesine	([NaSi]₀.₇–₀.₅[CaAl]₀.₃–₀.₅)AlSi₂O₈.	2.65–2.68	6–6.5	tricl., wh., gray, grn.	1.544–1.555, 1.548–1.558, 1.551–1.563
Andorite	PbAgSb₃S₆.	5.33–5.37	3–3.5	rhomb., dk. steel gray, somet. tarn. yel. or iridesc.	
Andradite	Ca₃Fe₂⁺³Si₃O₁₂.	3.859	6–7.5	cub., brnsh. red, blk., somet. yel., grn.	1.887
Anglesite	PbSO₄.	6.37–6.39	2.5–3	rho.nb., col., wh., somet. gray, yelsh., grn. tinge	1.8771, 1.8826, 1.8937
Anhydrite	CaSO₄.	2.98	3.5	rhomb., col., blsh. wh., vlt.	1.5698, 1.5754, 1.6136
Ankerite	Ca(Fe,Mg,Mn)(CO₃)₂.	2.8–3.1	3.5–4	rhbdr., br., yelsh. br., grnsh. br., pink	1.690–1.750, 1.510–1.548
Anorthite	CaAl₂Si₂O₈.	2.76	6–6.5	tricl., wh., yel., grn., blk.	1.577, 1.585, 1.590
Anorthoclase	(Na,K)AlSi₃O₈.	2.56–2.60	6	tricl., col., wh.	1.523, 1.528, 1.529
Anthophyllite	(Mg,Fe)₇Si₈O₂₂(OH,F)₂.	2.85–3.57	5.5–6	rhomb., wh., gray, grn., br., yelsh. br., dk. br.	1.596–1.694, 1.605–1.710, 1.615–1.722
Antimony	Sb.	6.61–6.72	3–3.5	hex., tin-wh.	
Apatite	Ca₅(PO₄)₃(OH,F,Cl)	3.1–3.35	5	hex., grn., wh., yel., br. red, bl.	1.629–1.667, 1.624–1.666
Apophyllite	KFCa₄Si₈O₂₀.8H₂O.	2.33–2.37	4.5–5	tetr., col., wh., pink, pa. yel., pa. grn.	1.534–1.535, 1.535–1.537
Aragonite	CaCO₃.	2.94 2.95	3.5–4	rhomb., col., wh.	1.530–1.531, 1.680–1.681, 1.685–1.686
Arcanite	K₂SO₄.	2.663	....	rhom., col., wh.	1.4935, 1.4947, 1.4973
Argentite	Ag₂S.	7.2–7.4	2–2.5	cub., blksh. lead gray	
Arsenic	As.	5.63–5.78	3.5	hex., tin-wh., tarn. dk. gray	
Arsenolite	As₂O₃.	3.86–3.88	1.5	cub., wh., somet. blsh., yelsh., redsh. tinge	1.755
Arsenopyrite	FeAsS.	5.9–6.2	5.5–6	monocl., silver-wh., to steel gray	
Atacamite	Cu₂(OH)₃Cl.	3.74–3.78	3–3.5	rhomb., grn., dk. grn., blksh. grn.	1.831, 1.861, 1.880
Augelite	Al₂(PO₄)(OH)₃.	2.696	4.5–5	monocl., col., wh., yelsh. wh., rose	1.5736, 1.5759, 1.5877
Augite	(Ca,Mg,Fe,Fe⁺³,Ti,Al)₂(Si,Al)₂O₆.	3.23–3.52	5.5–6	monocl., pa. br., br., purp. br., grn., blk.	1.671–1.735, 1.672–1.741, 1.703–1.761
Autunite	Ca(UO₂)₂(PO₄)₂.10–12H₂O.	3.1–3.2	2–2.5	tetr., yel., somet. grnsh. yel. to pa. grn.	1.577, 1.553
Axinite	(Ca,Mn,Fe)₃Al₂BO₃Si₄O₁₂(OH)	3.26–3.36	6.5–7	tricl., br., yelsh.	1.674–1.693, 1.681–1.701, 1.684–1.704
Azurite	Cu₃(OH)₂(CO₃)₂.	3.77	3.5–4	monocl., azure bl., dk. bl., pa. bl.	1.730, 1.758, 1.838
Baddeleyite	ZrO₂.	5.4–6.02	6.5	monocl., col., yel., grn., redsh. br., br., blk.	2.13, 2.19, 2.20
Barite	BaSO₄.	4.50	3–3.5	rhomb., col., wh., somet. br., dk. br., gray	1.6362, 1.6373, 1.6482
Benitoite	BaTi(SiO₃)₃.	3.65	6–6.5	rhbdr., bl., purp., col.	1.757, 1.804
Bertrandite	Be₄Si₂O₇(OH)₂.	2.6	6	rhomb., col.	1.589, 1.602, 1.613
Beryl	Be₃Al₂Si₆O₁₈.	2.66–2.83	7.5–8	hex., col., wh., blsh. grn., grnsh. yel., yel., bl.	1.565–1.590, 1.567–1.508
Beryllonite	NaBe(PO)₄.	2.81	5.5–6	monocl., col., wh., pa. yel.	1.5520, 1.5579, 1.561
Biotite	K(Mg,Fe)₃AlSi₃O₁₀(OH,F)₂.	2.7–3.3	2.5–3	monocl., blk., dk. br., redsh. br.	1.565–1.625–1.605–1.696, 1.605–1.696
Bismuth	Bi.	9.70–9.83	2–2.5	rhbdr., silver-wh. to redsh wh.	
Bismuthinite	Bi₂S₃.	6.75–6.81	2	rhomb., lead gray to tin-wh., tarn. yel. or iridesc.	
Bixbyite	(Mn,Fe)₂O₃.	4.945	6–6.5	cub., blk.	
Bloedite	Na₂Mg(SO₄)₂.4N₂O.	2.22–2.28	2.5–3	monocl., col., somet. blsh.-grn. or redsh.	1.483, 1.486, 1.487
Boehmite	AlO(OH).	3.01–3.06	3.5–4	rhomb., wh.	1.64–1.65, 1.65–1.66, 1.65–1.67
Boracite	Mg₃B₇O₁₃Cl.	2.91–2.97	7–7.5	rhomb., col., wh., gray, yel., blsh.-grn., grn.	1.66, 1.66, 1.67
Borax	Na₂B₄O₇.10H₂O.	1.715	2–2.5	monocl., col., wh., gray, blsh. or grnsh-wh.	1.4466, 1.4687, 1.4717
Bornite	Cu₅FeS₄.	5.06–5.08	3	cub., copper red to pinchbeck br., tarn. purp., iridesc.	
Boulangerite	Pb₅Sb₄S₁₁.	6.0–6.2	2.5–3	monocl., blsh. lead gray, oft, with yel. spots	
Bournonite	PbCuSbS₃.	5.80–5.86	2.5–3	rhomb., steel gray to blk.	
Braggite	PtS.	10.0	....	tetr., steel gray	
Braunite	(Mn,Si)₂O₃.	4.72–4.83	6–6.5	tetr., brns. blk. to steel gray	
Bravoite	(Ni,Fe)S₂.	4.62	5.5–6	cub., steel gray	
Breithauptite	NiSb.	8.23	5.5	hex., pa. copper red to vlt., tarn.	
Brochantite	Cu₄(SO₄)(OH)₆.	3.79	3.5–4	monocl., emerald-grn. to blksh. grn., pa. grn.	1.728, 1.771, 1.800
Bromyrite	AgBr.	6.47	2.5	cub., col., gray, yelsh., grnsh.-br.	2.253
Brookite	TiO₂.	4.08–4.20	5.5–6	rhomb., yelsh. br., redsh. br., blk.	2.5831, 2.5843, 2.7004
Brucite	Mg(OH)₂.	2.38–3.40	2.5	hex., wh., pa. grn., gray, bl., yel., br.	1.560–1.590, 1.580–1.600
Bunsenite	NiO.	6.898	5.5	cub., dk. pistachio-grn.	(Li) 2.37
Cacoxenite	Fe₄(PO₄)₃(OH)₃.12H₂O.	2.2–2.4	3–4	hex., yel. to brnsh.-yel., redsh yel., somet. grnsh	1.575–1.585, 1.635–1.656
Calcite	CaCO₃.	2.715–2.04	3	rhbdr., col., wh., somet. gray, yel., pink, bl.	1.658–1.740, 1.486–1.550
Caledonite	Cu₂Pb₅(SO₄)₃(CO₃)(OH)₆.	5.75–5.77	2.5–3	rhomb., dk. grn., blsh. grn.	1.815–1.821, 1.863–1.869, 1.906–1.912
Calomel	HgCl.	7.15	1.5	tetr., col., wh., gray, yelsh. wh., br.	1.973, 2.656
Cancrinite	(Na,Ca)₇₋₈AlSi₆O₂₄(CO₃SO₄Cl)₁.₅₋₂.1–5H₂O.	2.51–2.42	5–6	hex., col., wh., pa. bl., pa. grn., yel., redsh.	1.528–1.507, 1.503–1.495
Carnallite	KMgCl₃.6H₂O.	1.602	2.5	rhomb., col., wh., oft. redsh., somet. yel., bl.	1.466, 1.475, 1.494
Carnotite	K₂(UO₂)₂(VO₄)₂.3H₂O.	....	1–2	rhomb. or monocl., bright yel., yel., grnsh. yel., bl.	1.75, 1.92, 1.95
Cassiterite	SnO₂.	6.99	6–7	tetr., yelsh. or redsh. br., brnsh.-blk.	2.006, 2.0972
Celestite	SrSO₄.	3.96	3–3.5	rhomb., col., wh., pa. bl., redsh., grnsh., brnsh	1.621–1.622, 1.623–1.624, 1.630–1.631
Celsian	BaAl₂Si₂O₈.	3.10–3.39	6–6.5	monocl., col., wh., yel.	1.579–1.587, 1.583–1.593, 1.588–1.600
Cervantite	Sb₂O₄(?).	6.64	4–5	rhomb.(?), yel., wh., somet. redsh.-wh.	
Cerargyrite	AgCl.	5.55	2.5	cub., col., gray, grnsh.-br., tarn. purp., yelsh.	2.071
Cerussite	PbCO₃.	6.53–6.57	3–3.5	rhomb., col., wh., gray, somet. bl., blk., grn.	1.8036, 2.0765, 2.0786
Chabazite	(Ca,Na₂)Al₂Si₄O₁₂.6H₂O.	2.05–2.10	4.5	rhbdr., redsh.-wh., wh., yelsh., grnsh.	1.470–1.494
Chalcocite	Cu₂S.	5.5–5.8	2.5–3	rhomb., blksh., lead gray	
Chalcanthite	CuSO₄.5H₂O.	2.28	2.5	tricl., dk. bl. to sky bl., somet. grnsh.	1.514, 1.537, 1.543
Chalcopyrite	CuFeS₂.	4.1–4.3	3.5–4	tetr., brass-yel., tarn., iridisc.	
Chiolite	Na₅Al₃F₁₄.	3 00	3.5–4	tetr., wh. to col.	1.349, 1.342
Chlorite	(Mg,Al,Fe)₁₂(Si,Al)₈O₂₀(OH)₁₆.	2.6–3.3	2–3	monocl., grn., wh., yel., pink, br., red	1.57–1.66, 1.57–1.67, 1.57–1.67
Chloritoid	(Fe,Mg,Mn)₂(AlFe⁺³)Al₃O₂SiO₄(OH)₄.	3.51–3.80	6.5	monocl., tricl., dk. grn.	1.713–1.730, 1.719–1.734, 1.723–1.740

Name	Formula	Sp. gr.	Hardness	Crystalline form and color	Index of refraction (Na) $\eta; \omega \epsilon$ / $\alpha \beta \gamma$
Chondrodite	$Mg(OH,F)_2.2Mg_2SiO_4$	3.16–3.26	6.5	monocl., yel., br., red	1.592–1.615, 1.602–1.627, 1.621–1.646
Chromite	$FeCr_2O_4$	4.5–5.1	5.5	cub., blk.	2.16
Chrysoberyl	$BeAl_2O_4$	3.65–3.85	8.5	rhomb., grn., yel.	1.746, 1.748, 1.756
Chrysocolla	$CuSiO_3.2H_2O$	~2.4	2	rhomb., (?), grn., bl., br., blk.	1.575, 1.597, 1.598
Cinnabar	HgS	8.090	2–2.5	hex., red, brnsh. red, gray	(Li) 2.814, 3.143
Claudetite	As_2O_3	4.15	2.5	monocl., col. to wh.	1.87, 1.92, 2.01
Clinozoisite	$Ca_2Al_3Si_3O_{12}(OH)$	3.21–3.38	6.5	monocl., col., pa. yel., gray, grn.	1.670–1.715, 1.674–1.725, 1.690–1.734
Cobaltite	$CoAsS$	6.33	5.5	cub., silver wh., redsh., steel gray, blk.	....
Colemanite	$Ca_2B_6O_{11}.5H_2O$	2.42–2.43	4.5	monocl., col., wh., yelsh. wh., gray	1.586, 1.592, 1.614
Columbite	$(Fe,Mn)(Cb,Ta)_2O_6$	5.15–5.25	6	rhomb., iron blk. to br. blk.	....
Connellite	$Cu_{19}(SO_4)Cl_4(OH)_{32}.3H_2O(?)$	3.36	3	hex., azure bl.	1.724–1.738, 1.746–1.758
Copiapite	$(Fe,Mg)Fe_4^{+3}(SO_4)_6(OH)_2.20H_2O$	2.08–2.17	2.5–3	tricl., yel., grnsh. yel.	1.51–1.53, 1.53–1.55, 1.58–1.60
Copper	Cu	8.95	2.5–3	cub., red	....
Coquimbite	$Fe_2(SO_4)_3.9H_2O$	2.10–2.12	2.5	hex., pa. vlt. to dk. amethystine, yelsh., grnsh.	1.53–1.55, 1.55–1.57
Cordierite	$Al_3(Mg,Fe)_2Si_5AlO_{18}$	2.53–2.78	7	rhomb., gray-bl., bl., dk. bl.	1.522–1.558, 1.524–1.574, 1.527–1.578
Corundum	Al_2O_3	4.022	9	hex., col., bl., yel., purp., grn., pink, red	1.767–1.772, 1.759–1.763
Cotunnite	$PbCl_2$	5.80	2.5	rhomb., col. to wh., somet. yelsh., grnsh.	2.199, 2.217, 2.260
Covellite	CuS	4.6–4.76	1.5–2	hex., indigo bl., dk. bl., iridesc. brass yel. to red	....
Cristobalite	SiO_2	2.33	6–7	tetr.(?), col., wh., yel.	1.487, 1.484
Crocoite	$PbCrO_4$	5.96–6.02	2.5–3	monocl., red, orange red, orange yel.	2.29, 2.36, 2.66
Cryolite	Na_3AlF_6	2.96–2.98	2.5	monocl., col. to wh., brnsh., redsh., blk.	1.338, 1.338, 1.339
Cryolithionite	$Na_3Li_3Al_2F_{12}$	2.77	2.5–3	cub., col. to wh.	1.3395
Cubanite	$CuFe_2S_3$	4.03–4.18	3.5	rhomb., brass to bronze yel.	....
Cummingtonite	$(Mg,Fe)_7Si_8O_{22}(OH)_2$	3.2–3.5	5–6	monocl., dk. grn., br.	1.635–1.665, 1.644–1.675, 1.655–1.698
Cuprite	Cu_2O	6.14	3.5–4	cub., red, somet. blk.	....
Danburite	$CaSi_2B_2O_8$	3.0	7	rhomb., pa. yel., col., dk. yel., yelsh. br.	1.63, 1.63–1.64, 1.63–1.64
Datolite	$CaBSiO_4(OH)$	2.96–3.00	5–5.5	monocl., col., wh., yelsh., grnsh., pinksh.	1.622–1.626, 1.649–1.654, 1.666–1.670
Daubreelite	Cr_2FeS_4	3.80–3.82	?	cub., blk.	....
Derbylite	$Fe_6Ti_6Sb_2O_{23}(?)$	4.53	5	rhomb., pitch blk.	2.45, 2.45, 2.51
Diamond	C	3.50–3.53	10	cub., col., pa. yel. to dk. yel., pa. br. to dk. br., wh., blsh. wh.	2.4175
Diaspore	$AlO(OH)$	3.3–3.5	6.5–7	rhomb., wh., graysh. wh., col.	1.682–1.706, 1.705–1.725, 1.730–1.752
Digenite	Cu_2xS	5.546	2.5–3	cub., bl. to blk.	....
Diopside	$CaMgSi_2O_6$	3.22–3.38	5.5–6.5	monocl., wh., pa. grn., dk. grn.	1.664–1.695, 1.672–1.701, 1.695–1.721
Dioptase	$CuSi_6O_{18}.6H_2O$	3.5	5	rhbdr., emerald grn.	1.64–1.66, 1.70–1.71
Dolomite	$CaMg(CO_3)_2$	2.86	3.5–4	rhbdr., wh., oft. yel. or br. tinge, col.	1.679, 1.500
Douglasite	$K_2FeCl_4.2H_2O(?)$	2.16		pa. grn., tarn. brnsh. red	1.485–1.491, 1.497–1.503
Dyscrasite	Ag_3Sb	9.67–9.81	3.5–4	rhomb., silver wh., tarn. gray, yelsh. or blksh.	....
Eddingtonite	$BaAl_2Si_3O_{10}.4H_2O$	2.7–2.8		rhomb. or monocl., col., pink, br. wh.	1.541, 1.553, 1.557
Eglestonite	Hg_4OCl_2	8.4	2.5	cub., yel., orange-yel. to dk. brnsh., tarn. bl.	2.47–2.51
Emplectite	$CuBiS_2$	6.38	2	rhomb., gray to tin wh.	....
Empressite	$AgTe$	7.510	3–3.5	pa. bronze	....
Enargite	Cu_3AsS_4	4.4–4.5	3	rhomb., gray-blk. to iron-blk.	....
Enstatite	$MgSiO_3$	3.209	5–6	rhomb., col., gray, grn., yel., brn.	1.650–1.662, 1.653–1.671, 1.658–1.680
Epidote	$Ca_2Fe^{+3}Al_2Si_3O_{12}(OH)$	3.38–3.49	6	monocl., grn., yel., gray	1.715–1.751, 1.725–1.784, 1.734–1.797
Epsomite	$MgSO_4.7H_2O$	1.675–1.679	2–2.5	rhomb., col., wh. pink, grn.	1.4325, 1.4554, 1.4609
Erythrite	$(Co,Ni)_3(AsO_4)_2.8H_2O$	3.06	1.5–2.5	monocl., crimson-red, red, pa. pink	1.626, 1.661, 1.699
Eucairite	$CuAgSe$	7.6–7.8	2.5	silver wh. to lead gray	....
Euclasite	$BeAlSiO_4(OH)$	3.0–3.1	7.5	monocl., col., pa. grn., bl.	1.651, 1.655, 1.671
Eudialite	$(Na,Ca,Fe)_6ZrSi_6O_{18}(OH,Cl)(?)$	2.8–3.1	5.5	hex., pa. pink, red, br.	1.59–1.61, 1.59–1.61
Eulytite	$Bi_4Si_3O_{12}$	6.6	4.5	cub., br., yel., gray	2.05
Euxenite	$(Y,Ca,Ce,U,Th)(Cb,Ta,Ti)_2O_6$	5.0–5.9	5.5–6.5	rhomb., blk., grnsh. or brnsh. tint.	~2.2
Fayalite	Fe_2SiO_4	4.392	6.5	rhomb., grnsh., yelsh.	(Li) 2.37–2.43
Ferberite	$FeWO_4$	7.51	4–4.5	monocl., br. to blk.	2.1
Fergussonite	$(Y,Er,Ce,Fe)(Cb,Ta,Ti)O_4$	5.6–5.8	5.5–6.5	tetr., gray, yel., br., dk. br.	....
Fluorite	CaF_2	3.18	4	cub., bl., purp., wh., col., yel., grn.	1.433–1.435
Forsterite	Mg_2SiO_4	3.222	7	rhomb., wh., grnsh., yelsh.	1.635, 1.651, 1.670
Franklinite	$ZnFe_2^{+3}O_4$	5.07–5.34	5.5–6.5	Cub., blk. to br.-blk.	(Li) ~2.36
Gahnite	$ZnAl_2O_4$	4.62	7.5–8	cub., dk. bl.-grn., somet. yelsh. or brnsh.	1.79–1.81
Galena	PbS	7.57–7.59	2.5–2.75	cub. lead gray	....
Galenabismuthite	$PbBi_2S_4$	7.04	2.5–3.5	rhomb., pa. gray to tin-wh., lead gray, somet. tarn., yel. or irid.	....
Ganomalite	$(Ca,Pb)_{10}(OH,Cl)_2(Si_2O_7)_3$	5.4–5.7	3–4	hex., col., gray	1.910, 1.945
Gaylussite	$Na_2Ca(CO_3)_2.5H_2O$	1.991	2.5–3	monocl., col. to yelsh. wh., graysh. wh., wh.	1.4435, 1.5156, 1.5233
Gehlenite	$Ca_2Al_2SiO_7$	3.038	5–6	tetr., col., gray-grn., br.	1.669, 1.658
Geikielite	$MgTiO_3$	4.05	5–6	rhbdr., brnsh blk., blsh.	2.31, 1.95
Gibbsite	$Al(OH)_3$	2.38–2.42	2.5–3.5	monocl., wh., graysh., grnsh. or redsh.-wh.	1.56–1.58, 1.56–1.58, 1.58–1.60
Glauberite	$Na_2Ca(SO_4)_2$	2.75–2.85	2.5–3	monocl., gray, yelsh., somet. col., redsh.	1.515, 1.535, 1.536
Glauconite	$(K,Na,Ca)_{1.2-2}(Fe^{+3},Al,Fe,Mg)_4Si_{7-7.6}Al_{1-0.4}O_{20}(OH)_4.nH_2O$	2.4–2.95	2	monocl., col., ye.lsh. grn., grn., blsh. gray	1.592–1.610, 1.614–1.641, 1.614–1.641
Glaucophane	$Na_2MgAl_2Si_8O_{22}(OH)_2$	3.08–3.30	6	monocl., gray, lavender bl.	1.606–1.661, 1.622–1.667, 1.627–1.670
Gmelinite	$(Ca,Na_2)Al_2Si_4O_{12}.6H_2O$	~2.1	4.5	rhbdr., wh., redsh.-wh., yelsh., grnsh.	1.476–1.494, 1.474–1.480
Goethite	$FeO(OH)$	3.3–4.3	5–5.5	rhomb., blksh.-br., yelsh. or redsh.-br., yel.	2.260–2.275, 2.393–2.409, 2.398–2.515
Gold	Au	19.3	2.5–3	cub., yel.	....
Goslarite	$ZnSO_4.7H_2O$	1.978	2–2.5	rhomb., col., wh., somet. br., grn., bl.	1.4568, 1.4801, 1.4844
Graphite	C	2.09–2.23	1–2	hex., iron-blk. to steel gray	....
Greenockite	CdS	4.9	3–3.5	hex., yel. to orange	2.506, 2.529
Grossularite	$Ca_3Al_2Si_3O_{12}$	3.594	6–7.5	cub., wh., yel., grn., br., red	1.734
Gummite (R)	$UO_3.H_2O$	3.9–6.4	2.5–5	yel., orange, redsh.-yel., red, br. blk.	....
Gypsum	$CaSO_4.2H_2O$	2.30–2.37	2	monocl., wh., col., somet. gray, red, yel., br.	1.519–1.521, 1.523–1.526, 1.529–1.531
Halite	$NaCl$	2.16–2.17	2.5	cub., col. to wh., orange, red	1.544
Hambergite	$Be_2(OH)(BO_3)$	2.36	7.5	rhomb., col. to gray, wh., yel.	1.56, 1.59, 1.63
Hanksite	$Na_{22}K(SO_4)_9(CO_3)_2Cl$	2.562	3–3.5	hex., col., somet. pa.-yelsh. or gray	1.481, 1.461
Harmotome	$BaAl_2Si_6O_{16}.6H_2O$	2.41–2.47	4.5	monocl., or rhomb., col., wh., pink, gray, yel.	1.503–1.508, 1.505–1.509, 1.508–1.514
Hausmannite	Mn_3O_4	4.83–4.85	5.5	tetr., brnsh.-blk.	(Li) 2.46, 2.15
Haüyne	$(Na,Ca)_{4-8}Al_6Si_6O_{24}(SO_4,S)_{1-2}$	2.44–2.50	5.5–6	cub., wh., gray, grn., bl.	1.496–1.505
Hedenbergite	$CaFeSi_2O_6$	3.50–3.56	6	monocl., brnsh.-grn., dk. grn., blk.	1.716–1.726, 1.723–1.730, 1.741–1.751
Helvite	$Mn_4Be_3Si_3O_{12}S$	3.20–3.44	6	cub., yel., br., redsh.-brn.	1.728–1.749
Hematite	Fe_2O_3	5.26	5–6	rhbdr., steel gray, dull red to bright red	3.22, 2.94
Hemimorphite	$Zn_4Si_2O_7(OH)_2.H_2O$	3.45	5	rhomb., col., wh., pa. bl., pa. grn., br.	1.614, 1.617, 1.636
Hercynite	$FeAl_2O_4$	4.40	7.5–8	cub., blk.	1.835
Herderite	$CaBe(PO_4)(Fe,OH)$	2.95–3.01	5–5.5	monocl., col. to pa. yel. or grnsh.-wh.	1.592, 1.612, 1.621
Hessite	Ag_2Te	8.24–8.45	2–3	monocl., (<149.5°), cub. (>149.5°), gray	....
Heulandite	$(Ca,Na_2)Al_2Si_7O_{18}.6H_2O$	2.1–2.2	3.5–4	pseudo-monocl., col., wh., yel., pink, red, gray, br.	1.491–1.505, 1.493–1.503, 1.500–1.512

Name	Formula	Sp. gr.	Hardness	Crystalline form and color	Index of refraction (Na) $\eta; \ \omega \ \epsilon$ $\omega \ \beta \ \gamma$
Hopeite	$Zn_3(PO_4)_2.4H_2O$	3.0–3.1	3.25	rhomb., col. to grayish-wh., pa. yel.	1.57–1.59, 1.58–1.60, 1.58–1.60
Hornblende	$(Ca,Na,K)_{2-3}(Mg,Fe,Fe^{+3}Al)_5Si_6(Si,Al)_2$ $O_{22}(OH,F)_2$	3.02–3.45	5–6	monocl., grn., dk. grn., blk.	1.615–1.705, 1.618–1.714, 1.632–1.730
Huebnerite	$MnWO_4$	7.12	4–4.5	monocl., yel.-br. to red br., somet. br., blk.	2.17, 2.22, 2.32
Humite	$Mg(OH,F)_2.3Mg_2SiO_4$	3.2–3.32	6	rhomb., yel., orange	1.607–1.643, 1.619–1.653, 1.639–1.675
Huntite	$Mg_3Ca(CO_3)_4$	2.696		rhomb.(?)., wh.	
Hydrogrossularite	$Ca_3Al_2Si_2O_8(SiO_4)_{1-m}(OH)_{4m}$	3.594–3.13	6–7.5	cub., wh., buff, pa. grn., gray, pink	1.734–1.675
Hydromagnesite	$Mg(OH)_2(CO_3.3H_2O$	2.236	3.5	monocl., col. to wh.	1.520–1.526, 1.524–1.530, 1.544–1.546
Illite	$K_{1-1.5}Al_4Si_{7-6.5}Al_{1-1.5}O_{20}(OH)_4.$	2.6–2.9	1–2	monocl., wh.	
Ilmenite	$FeTiO_3$	4.68–4.76	5–6	rhbdr., iron-blk.	1.54–1.57, 1.57–1.61, 1.57–1.61
Iodyrite	AgI	5.69	1.5	hex., col. on exposure to light, yel., br.	2.21, 2.22
Jadeite	$NaAlSi_2O_6$	3.24–3.43	6	monocl., col., wh., grn., grnsh. bl.	1.640–1.658, 1.645–1.663, 1.652–1.673
Jamesonite	$Pb_4FeSb_6S_{14}$	5.63	2.5	monocl., gray-blk., somet. tarn. iridesc.	
Jarosite	$KFe_3(SO_4)_2(OH)_6$	2.91–3.26	2.5–3.5	rhbdr., ocherous, amber yel. to dk. br.	1.820, 1.715
Kainite	$KMg(SO_4)Cl.3H_2O$	2.15	2.5–3	monocl., col., gray bl., vlt., yelsh., redsh.	1.494, 1.505, 1.516
Kaliophyllite	$KAlSiO_4$	2.61	6	hex., col.	1.532, 1.537
Kaolinite	$Al_4Si_4O_{10}(OH)_8$	2.61–2.68	2–2.5	tricl. or monocl., wh., redsh.-wh., grnsh.-wh.	1.533–1.565, 1.559–1.569, 1.560–1.570
Kernite	$Na_2B_4O_7.4H_2O$	1.908	2.5	monocl., col., wh.	1.454, 1.472, 1.488
Kieserite	$MgSO_4.H_2O$	2.571	3.5	monocl., gray, wh., yelsh.	1.520, 1.533, 1.584
Kyanite	Al_2OSiO_4	3.53–3.65	5.5–7	tricl., bl., wh., gray, grn., yel., pink	1.712–1.718, 1.721–1.723, 1.727–1.734
Lanarkite	$Pb_2(SO_4)O$	6.92	2–2.5	monocl., gray to grnsh. wh., pa. yel.	1.925–1.931, 2.004–2.010, 2.033–2.039
Lanthanite	$(La,Ce)_2(CO_3)_3.8H_2O$	2.69–2.74	2.5–3	rhomb., col. to wh., pink, yelsh.	1.51–1.53, 1.584–1.500, 1.610–1.616
Laumontite	$CaAl_2Si_4O_{12}.4-3.5H_2O$	2.2–2.3	3–3.5	monocl., col., wh., red, yel., brn.	1.502–1.514, 1.512–1.522, 1.514–1.525
Laurionite	$Pb(OH)Cl$	6.24	3–3.5	rhomb., col. to wh.	2.08, 2.12, 2.16
Lawsonite	$CaAl_2(OH)_2Si_2O_7.II_2O$	3.05–3.10	6	rhomb., col., wh.	1.655, 1.674–1.675, 1.684–1.686
Lazulite	$(Mg,Fe)Al_2(PO_4)_2(OH)_2$	3.08–3.38	5.5–6	monocl., bl., blsh. wh., dk. bl., blsh. grn.	1.604–1.626, 1.626–1.654, 1.637–1.663
Lazurite	$Na_8Si_3Al_3O_{12}$	2.38–2.45	5–5.5	cub., berlin bl., azure bl., grnsh. bl., vlt.	1.500
Leadhillite	$Pb_4(SO_4)(CO_3)_2(OH)_2$	6.55	2.5–3	monocl., col. to wh., gray, pa. grn., pa. bl., yelsh.	1.87, 2.00, 2.01
Lepidocrocite	$FeO(OH)$	4.05–4.31	5	rhomb., ruby-red to red-br.	1.94, 2.20, 2.51
Lepidolite	$K_2(Li,Al)_{5-6}Si_{6-7}Al_{2-1}O_{20}(OH,F)_4.$	2.80–2.90	2.5–4	monocl., col., pa. pink, pa. purp.	1.525–1.548, 1.551–1.585, 1.554–1.587
Leucite	$KAlSi_2O_6$	2.47–2.50	5.5–6	tetr. (pseudo-cub.), wh., gray	1.508–1.511
Levyne	$(Ca,Na_2)Al_2Si_4O_{12}.6H_2O$	~2.1	4.5	rhbdr., wh., redsh. wh., yelsh., grnsh.	1–496–1.505, 1.491–1.500
Litharge	PbO	9.14	2	tetr., red	(Li) 2.665, 2.535
Loellingite	$FeAs_2$	7.39–7.41	5–5.5	rhomb., silver wh. to steel-gray	
Magnesite	$MgCO_3$	2.98–3.44	3.5–4.5	rhbdr., wh., col., somet. yel., br.	1.700–1.782, 1.509–1.563
Magnetite	Fe_3O_4	5.175	5.5–6.5	cub., blk. to br.-blk.	2.42
Malachite	$Cu_2(OH)_2(CO_3)$	4.03–4.07	3.5–4	monocl., bright grn. to dk. grn., blksh. grn.	1.652–1.658, 1.872–1.878, 1.906–1.912
Manganite	$MnO(OH)$	4.32–4.43	4	monocl., dk. steel-gray to iron-blk.	(Li) 2.25, 2.25, 2.53
Manganosite	MnO	5.364	5.5	cub., emerald grn., tarn. bl.	
Marcasite	FeS_2	4.887	6–6.5	rhomb., pa. bronze-yel., tin-wh.	
Marialite	$Na_4Al_3Si_9O_{24}Cl.$	2.50–2.62	5–6	tetr., col., wh., pa. grnsh. grn., gray, br.	1.546–1.550, 1.540–1.541
Marshite	CuI	5.68	2.5	cub., col. to pa. yel., on exposure to light, red	2.346
Mascagnite	$(NH_4)_2SO_4$	1.768	2–2.5	rhomb., col., gray, wh.	1.5202, 1.5230, 1.5330
Matlockite	$PbFCl$	7.12	2.5–3	tetr., col. or yel. to pa. amber, grnsh.	2.145, 2.006
Meionite	$Ca_4Al_6Si_6O_{24}CO_3$	2.78	5–6	tetr., col., wh., pa. grnsh. yel., gray, br.	1.590–1.600, 1.556–1.562
Melanterite	$FeSO_4.7H_2O$	1.898	2	monocl., grn., grnsh. bl., grnsh. wh.	1.47, 1.48, 1.49
Melilite	$(Ca,Na,K)_2(Mg,Fe,Fe^{+3},Al,Si)_3O_7$	2.95–3.05	5–6	tetr., yelsh., br., grn.-br.	1.624–1.666, 1.616–1.661
Mellite	$Al_2C_{12}O_{12}.18H_2O$	1.64	2–2.5	tetr., col., redsh., brnsh., somet. wh.	1.5393, 1.5110
Mendipite	$Pb_3O_2Cl_2$	7.24	2.5	rhomb., col. to wh., gray, oft. yel., red, bl. tinge	2.22–2.26, 2.25–2.29, 2.29–2.33
Mesolite	$Na_2Ca_2(Al_2Si_3O_{10}).8H_2O$	~2.26	5	monocl., col., wh., gray, yel., pink, red	$\beta = 1.504$–1.508
Metacinnabar	HgS	7.65	3	cub., graysh-blk.	
Microcline	$KAlSi_3O_8$	2.56–2.63	6–6.5	tricl., col., wh., pink, red, yel., grn.	1.514–1.529, 1.518–1.533, 1.521–1.539
Microlite	$(Na,Ca)_2Ta_2O_6(O,OH,F)$	4.2–6.4	5–5.5	cub., pa. col. to br., somet. red, grn.	~2.0
Miersite	AgI	5.64–5.68	2.5	cub., canary-yel.	2.18–2.22
Millerite	NiS	5.3–5.7	3–3.5	hex., pa. brass-yel. to bronze-yel., gray, tarn. iridesc.	
Mimetite	$Pb_5(AsO_4,PO_4)_3Cl$	7.24	3.5–4	hex. pa. yel. to yelsh. br., orange-yel., wh.	2.147, 2.128
Minium	Pb_3O_4	8.9–9.2	2.5	scarlet red, bl. red, somet. yel. tint.	(Li) 2.40–2.44
Mirabilite	$Na_2SO_4.10H_2O$	1.490	1.5–2	monocl., col. to wh.	1.391–1.397, 1.393–1.399, 1.395–1.401
Moissanite	SiC	3.218	9.5	hex., grn. to blk., somet. blsh., red	2.647–2.649, 2.689–2.693
Molybdenite	MoS_2	4.62–4.73	1–1.5	hex., lead-gray	
Monazite	$(Ce,La,Th)PO_4$	5.0–5.3	5	monocl., yel., br., redsh. br.	1.774–1.800, 1.777–1.801, 1.828–1.851
Monetite	$CaH(PO_4)$	2.929	3.5	tricl., wh., pa. yelsh.-wh.	1.587, ~1.615, 1.640
Monticellite	$CaMgSiO_4$	3.08–3.27	5.5	rhomb., col.	1.639–1.654, 1.646–1.664, 1.653–1.674
Montmorillonite	$(0.5Ca,Na)_{0.7}(Al,Mh,Fe)_4(Si,Al)_8O_{20}(OH)_4.$ nH_2O	2–3	1–2	monocl., wh., yel., grn.	1.48–1.61, 1.50–1.64, 1.50–1.64
Montroydite	HgO	11.23	2.5	rhomb., dk. red to brnsh. red, br.	(Li) 2.37, 2.5, 2.65
Mordenite	$(Na_2,K_2Ca)Al_2Si_{10}O_{24}.7H_2O$	2.12–2.15	3–4	rhomb., col., wh., red, yel., br.	1.472–1.483, 1.475–1.485, 1.477–1.487
Muscovite	$KAl_2Si_3AlO_{10}(OH,F)_2$	2.77–2.88	2.5–3	monocl., col., pa. grn., pa. red, pa. br.	1.552–1.574, 1.582–1.610, 1.587–1.616
Nantokite	$CuCl$	4.136	2.5	cub., col. to wh., grayish, grn.	1.925–1.935
Natrolite	$Na_2Al_2Si_3O_{10}.2H_2O$	2.20–2.26	5	rhomb., col., wh., gray, yel., pink, red	1.473–1.483, 1.476–1.486, 1.485–1.496
Nepheline	$Na_3KAl_4Si_4O_{16}$	2.56–2.665	5.5–6	hex., col., wh., gray	1.529–1.546, 1.526–1.540
Newberyite	$MgH(PO_4).3H_2O$	2.10	3.0–3.5	rhomb., col.	
Niccolite	$NiAs$	7.784	5.5	hex., pa. copper-red., tarn. gray to blk.	1.511–1.517, 1.514–1.520, 1.530–1.536
Nosean	$Na_8Al_6Si_6O_{24}SO_4$	2.40–2.40	5.5	cub., pa. chestnut-br.	1.495
Oldhamite	CaS	2.58	4	cub., pa. chestnut-br.	2.137
Oligoclase	$([NaSi]_{0.9-0.7}[CaAl]_{0.1-0.3})AlSi_2O_8.$	2.63–2.65	6–6.5	tricl., col., wh., gray, grnsh., pink	1.533–1.544, 1.537–1.548, 1.543–1.552
Olivenite	$Cu_2(AsO_4)(OH)$	3.9–4.5	3	rhomb., olive grn., grnsh.-br., br., gray	1.75–1.78, 1.79–1.82, 1.83–1.87
Olivine	$(Mg,Fe)_2SiO_4$	3.22–4.39	6.5–7	rhomb., grayish grn. to yelsh. br.	1.63–1.83, 1.65–1.87, 1.67–1.88
Opal	$SiO_2.nH_2O$	1.73–2.16	~6	col., wh., yel., br., red, grn., bl., blk., amorp.	1.41–1.46
Orpiment	As_2S_3	3.49	1.5–2	monocl., yel., brnsh. yel.	(Li) 2.4, 2.81, 3.02
Orthoclase	$KAlSi_3O_8$	2.55–2.63	6–6.5	monocl., col., wh., pink, red, yel., grn.	1.518–1.529, 1.522–1.533, 1.522–1.539
Orthopyroxene	$(Mg,Fe)SiO_3$	3.209–3.96	5–6	rhomb., col., gray, grn., yel., dk. brn.	1.650–1.768, 1.653–1.770, 1.658–1.788
Paragonite	$NaAl_2Si_3AlO_{10}(OH)_2$	2.85	2.5	monocl., col., pa. yel.	1.564–1.580, 1.594–1.609, 1.600–1.609
Parisite	$(Ce,La,Na)FCO_3.CaCO_3$	4.42	4.5	hex., brnsh., yel.	1.672, 1.771
Pectolite	$Ca_2NaH(SiO_3)_3$	2.86–2.90	4.5–5	tricl., col., wh	1.595–1.610, 1.605–1.615, 1.632–1.645
Penfieldite	$Pb_2Cl_3(OH)_2.$	6.6		hex., wh.	2.13, 2.21
Pentlandite	$(Fe,Ni)_9S_8.$	4.6–5.0	3.5–4	cub., pa. bronze-yel.	
Percylite	$PbCuCl_2(OH)_2(?)$	?	2.5	cub(?), sky bl.	2.04–2.06
Periclase	MgO	3.55–3.60	5.5	cub., col. to gray-wh., yel., brnsh. yel., grn., bl.	1.7350
Perovskite	$CaTiO_3$	3.97–4.26	5.5	pseudo cub., blk., gray-blk., brnsh. bl., redsh. br., br., yel.	2.30–2.38
Petalite	$LiAlSi_4O_{10}$	2.412–2.422	6.5	monocl., wh., gray, somet. pink, grn.	1.504–1.507, 1.510–1.513, 1.516–1.523

Name	Formula	Sp. gr.	Hardness	Crystalline form and color	Index of refraction (Na) η; ω ϵ / α β γ
Pharmacosiderite...	$Fe_3(AsO_4)_2(OH)_3.5H_2O$...	2.797	2.5	cub., olive-grn. to yel., br., redsh.	1.676–1.704
Phenakite.........	Be_2SiO_4...	2.98	7.5	rhbder., col., rose, yel., br.	1.654, 1.670
Phillipsite.......	$(0.5Ca,Na,K)_3Al_5Si_5O_{16}.6H_2O$...	2.2	4–4.5	monocl. or rhomb., col., wh., pink, gray, yel.	1.483–1.504, 1.484–1.509, 1.496–1.514
Phlogopite.......	$KMg_3AlSi_3O_{10}(OH,F)_2$.	2.76–2.90	2–2.5	monocl., col., yelsh.-br., grn., redsh.-br., br.	1.530–1.590, 1.557–1.637, 1.558–1.637
Phosgenite.	$Pb_2(CO_3)Cl_2$.	6.133	2–3	tetr., yelsh. wh. to yelsh. br., br., somet. wh., rose, gray	2.1181, 2.1446
Piemontite......	$Ca_2(Mn,Fe^{+3},Al)_3Si_3O_{12}(OH)$.	3.45–3.52	6	monocl., redsh. brn., blk.	1.732–1.794, 1.750–1.807, 1.762–1.829
Pigeonite.......	$(Mg,Fe,Ca)(Mg,Fe)Si_2O_6$.	3.30–3.46	6	monocl., br., grnsh. br., blk.	1.682–1.722, 1.684–1.722, 1.705–1.751
Platinum........	Pt...	14–19	4–4.5	cub., whitish, steel gray to dk. gray	
Pollucite.......	$CsAlSi_2O_6$...	2.9	6.5	tetr., (pseudo-cub.) col.	1.507–1.527
Polybasite......	$(Ag,Cu)_{16}Sb_2S_{11}$.	6.0–6.2	2–3	monocl., iron-blk.	
Powellite.......	$Ca(Mo,W)O_4$.	4.21–4.25	3.5–4	tetr., straw-yel., br., grnsh., somet. gray, bl., blk.	1.959–1.982, 1.967–1.993
Prehnite........	$Ca_2Al_2Si_3O_{10}(OH)_2$.	2.90–2.95	6–6.5	rhomb., pa. grn., yel., gray, wh.	1.611–1.632, 1.615–1.642, 1.632–1.665
Proustite.......	Ag_3AsS_3...	5.57	2–2.5	rhbdr., scarlet-vermillion	3.0877, 2.7924
Pseudobrookite...	Fe_2TiO_5...	4.33–4.39	6	rhomb., dk. red-br. to brnsh. blk. and blk.	(Li) 2.38, 2.39, 2.42
Psilomelane.....	$BaMn^{+2}Mn_8^{+4}O_{16}(OH)_4$..	4.71	5–6	rhomb., iron-blk. to steel-gray	
Pumpellyite.....	$Ca_4(Mg,Fe,Mn)(Al,Fe^{+3},Ti)_5(OH)_3Si_6O_{23}.2H_2O$	3.18–3.23	6	monocl., grn., blsh. grn., br.	1.674–1.702, 1.675–1.715, 1.688–1.722
Pyrargyrite......	Ag_3SbS_3..	5.85	2.5	rhbdr., deep red	(Li) 3.084, 2.881
Pyrite..........	FeS_2...	5.018	6–6.5	cub., pa. brass-yel., tarn. iridesc.	
Pyrochlore......	$NaCaCb_2O_6F$.	4.2–6.4	5–5.5	cub., br. to blk., yelsh., redsh. or blksh. br.	
Pyrochroite.....	$Mn(OH)_2$..	3.23–3.27	2.5	hex., col. to pa. grn. or bl., tarn. br. to blk.	1.72, 1.68
Pyrolusite......	MnO_2...	5.04–5.08	6–6.5	tetr., pa. steel-gray, iron-gray, blk., blsh.	
Pyromorphite....	$Pb_5(PO_4,AsO_4)_3Cl$.	7.00–7.08	3.5–4	hex., grn., yel., br., orange, brnsh. red., gray	2.058, 2.048
Pyrope.........	$Mg_3Al_2Si_3O_{12}$.	3.582	6–7.5	cub., red, pink	1.714
Pyrophyllite....	$Al_2Si_4O_{10}(OH)_2$.	2.65–2.90	1–2	monocl., wh., yel., pa. bl., gray-grn., brnsh.-grn.	1.534–1.556, 1.568–1.589, 1.596–1.601
Pyrrhotite......	$Fe_{1-0.9}S$.	4.58–4.65	3.5–4.5	hex., bronze-yel. to br., tarn., somet. iridesc.	
Quartz.........	SiO_2..	2.65	7	rhbdr., col., wh., blk., purp., grn., bl., rose	1.544, 1.553
Rammelsbergite..	$NiAs_2$..	7.0–7.2	5.5–6	tin. wh., redsh. tinge	
Raspite........	$PbWO_4$..	8.46	2.5–3	monocl., yelsh. br., pa. yel., gray	1.25–1.29, 1.25–1.29, 1.28–1.32
Realgar........	AsS...	3.56	1.5–2	monocl., aurora-red to orange-yel.	2.538, 2.684, 2.704
Riebeckite......	$Na_2Fe_3Fe_2^{+3}Si_8O_{22}(OH,F)_2$.	3.02–3.42	5	monocl., dk. bl., bl.	1.654–1.701, 1.662–1.711, 1.668–1.717
Rhodochrosite...	$MnCO_3$..	3.70	3.5–4	rhbdr., pink, red, br., brnsh.-yel.	1.816, 1.597
Rhodonite......	$(Mn,Fe,Ca)SiO_3$.	3.57–3.76	5.5–6.5	tricl., pink to brnsh. red	1.711–1.738, 1.716–1.741, 1.724–1.751
Rutile.........	TiO_2...	4.23–5.5	6–6.5	tetr., redsh. brn. to red, somet. yelsh., blsh.	2.605–2.613, 2.899–2.901
Safflorite......	$(Co,Fe)As_2$..	7.0–7.5	4.5–5	rhomb., tin-wh., tarn. dk. gray	
Samarskite.....	$(Y,Er,Ce,U,Ca,Fe,Pb,Th)(Cb,Ta,Ti,Sn)_2O_6$	5.69	5–6	rhomb., velvet blk., somet. brnsh. tint	~2.20
Sapphirine.....	$(Mg,Fe)_2Al_4O_6SiO_4$.	3.40–3.58	7.5	monocl., pa. bl., pa. grn.	1.701–1.717, 1.703–1.720, 1.705–1.724
Scapolite......	$(Na,Ca)_4Al_3(Al,Si)_3Si_6O_{24}(Cl,F,OH,CO_3,SO_4)$	2.50–2.78	5–6	tetr., col., wh., pa. grnsh. yel., gray, bl.	1.546–1.600, 1.540–1.562
Scheelite......	$CaWO_4$..	6.08–6.12	4.5–5	tetr., yelsh. wh., pa. yel., brnsh., col., wh., gray	1.920, 1.936
Scolecite......	$CaAl_2Si_3O_{10}.3H_2O$.	2.25–2.29	5	monocl., col., wh., gray, yel., pink, red	1.507–1.513, 1.516–1.520, 1.517–1.521
Scorodite......	$Fe^{+3}(AsO_4).2H_2O$.	3.28	3.5–4	rhomb., pa. grn., gray grn., br. somet. col., blsh., yel.	1.784, 1.795, 1.814
Sellaite.......	MgF_2...	3.15	5	tetr., col. to wh.	1.378, 1.390
Senarmontite...	Sb_2O_3..	5.50	2–2.5	pseudo-cub., col., gray-wh.	2.087
Serpentine.....	$Mg_3Si_2O_5(OH)_4$.	~2.55	2.5–3.5	monocl., wh., gray, grn., blsh. grn.	1.53–1.57, 1.56, 1.54–1.57
Siderite.......	$FeCO_3$...	3.96	4–4.5	rhbdr., yelsh. br., br., dk. br.	1.875, 1.635
Sillimanite....	Al_2OSiO_4.	3.23–3.27	6.5–7.5	rhomb., col., wh., yelsh., br., grnsh.	1.654–1.661, 1.658–1.662, 1.637–1.683
Silver.........	Ag...	10.1–11.1	2.5–3	cub., wh., tarn. gray or blk.	
Skutterudite...	$(Co,Ni)As_3$.	6.1–6.9	5.5–6	cub., between tin-wh. and silver-gray, tarn. gray or iridesc.	
Smithsonite....	$ZnCO_3$..	4.42–4.44	4–4.5	rhbdr., grayish wh. to dk. gray, grnsh., brnsh. wh.	1.848, 1.621
Sodalite.......	$Na_8Al_6Si_6O_{24}Cl_2$.	2.27–2.33	5.5–6	cub., bl., grn., yel., gray, pink	1.483–1.487
Sperrylite.....	$PtAs_2$...	10.58	6–7	cub., tin-wh.	
Spessartite....	$Mn_3Al_2Si_3O_{12}$.	4.190	6–7.5	cub., blk., dk. red, brnsh. red., bl., yelsh. orange	1.800
Sphalerite.....	ZnS...	3.9–4.1	3.5–4	cub., br., blk., yel., red, wh.	2.369
Sphene........	$CaTiSiO_4(O,OH,F)$.	3.45–3.55	5	monocl., col., yel., br., br., blk.	1.843–1.950, 1.870–2.034, 1.943–2.110
Spinel........	$MgAl_2O_4$..	3.55	7.5–8	cub., grn., red, bl., br. to col.	1.719
Spodumene.....	$LiAlSi_2O_6$.	3.03–3.22	6.5–7	monocl., col., gray-wh., pa. bl., pa. grn., yelsh.	1.648–1.663, 1.655–1.669, 1.662–1.679
Stannite......	Cu_2FeSnS_4.	4.3–4.5	4	tetr., steel gray to iron blk.	
Staurolite.....	$(Fe,Mg)_2(AlFe^{+3})_9O_6SiO_4(O,OH)_2$.	3.74–3.83	7.5	monocl., brn., yelsh.	1.739–1.747, 1.745–1.753, 1.752–1.761
Stercorite.....	$Na(NH_4)H(PO_4).4H_2O$.	1.615	2	tricl., wh., yelsh., brnsh.	1.439, 1.442, 1.469
Stibiotantalite.	$Sb(Ta,Cb)O_4$.	5.7–7.5	5.5	rhomb., dk. br. to pa. yel.-br., red-br., grnsh.-yel.	2.38, 2.41, 2.46
Stibnite......	Sb_2S_3...	4.61–4.65	2	rhomb., lead-gray to steel-gray	
Stilbite.......	$(Ca,Na_2K_2)Al_2Si_7O_{18}.7H_2O$.	2.1–2.2	3.5–4	monocl., col., wh., yel., pink, red, gray, br.	1.484–1.500, 1.492–1.507, 1.494–1.513
Stilpnomelane...	$(K,Na,Ca)_{0-1.4}(Fe^{+3}Fe,Mg,Al)_{6-8}Si_8O_{20}(OH)_4(O,OH,H_2O)_{4-8}$	2.59–2.96	3–4	monocl., dk. br., redsh. br., blk., dk. grn.	1.543–1.634, 1.576–1.745, 1.576–1.745
Stolzite.......	$PbWO_4$..	7.9–8.4	2.5–3	tetr., redsh. br., yelsh. gray, straw-yel., grnsh.	2.26–2.28, 2.18–2.20
Strengite......	$Fe^{+3}(PO_4).2H_2O$.	2.90	3.5–4.5	rhomb., red, carmine, vlt., near col.	1.707, 1.719, 1.741
Strontianite...	$SrCO_3$...	3.72	3.5	rhomb., col., wh., yel., grnsh., brnsh.	1.516–1.520, 1.664–1.667, 1.666–1.669
Struvite.......	$Mg(NH_4)(PO_4).6H_2O$.	1.71	2	rhomb., col., somet. yelsh., brnsh.	1.495, 1.496, 1.504
Sulfur.........	S...	2.07	1.5–2.5	rhomb., yel., brnsh., grnsh., redsh., gray	1.9579, 2.0377, 2.2452
Sylvanite......	$(Ag,Au)Te_2$.	8.161	1.5–2	monocl., steel-gray to silver-wh.	
Sylvite........	KCl...	1.99	2	cub., col., wh., somet. grayish, blsh., yelsh., red	1.49031
Talc..........	$Mg_3Si_4O_{10}(OH)_2$.	2.58–2.83	1	monocl., col., wh., pa. grn., dk. grn., br.	1.539–1.550, 1.589–1.594, 1.589–1.600
Tantalite......	$(Fe,Mn)(Ta,Cb)_2O_6$.	7.90–8.00	6.5	rhomb., iron-bl. to br.-blk.	2.26, 2.32, 2.43
Tapiolite......	$FeTa_2O_6$..	7.9	6–6.5	tetr., blk.	(Li) 2.27, 2.42
Tellurobismuthite..	Bi_2Te_3...	7.800–7.830	1.5–2	rhbdr., pa. lead-gray	
Terlinguaite....	Hg_2OCl..	8.725	2.5	monocl., yel. to grnsh.-yel., somet. br.	(Li) 2.33–2.37, 2.62–2.66, 2.64–2.68
Tetrahedrite...	$(Cu,Fe)_{12}Sb_4S_{13}$.	4.6–5.1	3–4.5	cub., flint-gray to iron-blk. to dull-blk.	
Thenardite.....	Na_2SO_4..	2.664	2.5–3	rhomb., col., grayish-wh., yelsh., brnsh. br., redsh.	1.464–1.471, 1.473–1.477, 1.481–1.485
Thermonatrite..	$Na_2CO_3.H_2O$.	2.255	1–1.5	rhomb., col. to wh., grayish, yelsh.	1.420, 1.506, 1.524
Thomsenolite...	$NaCaAlF_6.H_2O$.	2.981	2	monocl., col. to wh., somet. brnsh., redsh.	1.4072, 1.4136, 1.4150
Thomsonite....	$NaCa_2([Al,Si]_5O_{10})_2.6H_2O$	2.10–2.39	5–5.5	rhomb., col., wh., pink, br.	1.497–1.530, 1.513–1.533, 1.518–1.544
Thorianite (R)..	ThO_2...	9.7	6.5	cub., dk. gray to brnsh.-blk., blk.	~2.20
Thorite (R)....	$ThSiO_4$..	5.2–5.4	4.5–5	tetr., orange-yel., brnsh. to blk.	~1.8
Topaz.........	$Al_2SiO_4(OH,F)_2$.	3.49–3.57	8	rhomb., col., wh., yel., gray, grn., red, bl.	1.606–1.629, 1.609–1.631, 1.616–1.638

Name	Formula	Sp. gr.	Hardness	Crystalline form and color	Index of refraction (Na) η; ω ϵ ω β γ
Torbernite (R)	$Cu(UO_2)_2(PO_4)_2.8-12H_2O$	3.22	2–2.5	tetr., various shades of grn.	1.592, 1.582
Tourmaline	$Na(Mg,Fe,Mn,Li,Al)_3Al_6Si_6O_{18}(BO_3)_3(OH,F)_4$	3.03–3.25	7	rhbdr., blk., bl., grn., yel., red, col., br,	1.635–1.675, 1.610–1.650
Tremolite	$Ca_2Mg_5Si_8O_{22}(OH,F)_2$	3.0	5–6	monocl., col., gray, wh.	1.599, 1.612, 1.622
Tridymite	SiO_2	2.27	7	rhomb., col., wh.	1.471–1.479, 1.472–1.480, 1.474–1.483
Triphyllite-Lithiophyllite	$Li(Fe,Mn)PO_4$	3.34–3.58	4–5	rhomb., blsh. or grnsh. gray to yelsh. br., br.	1.66–1.70, 1.67–1.70, 1.68–1.71
Troegerite (R)	$(UO_2)_3(AsO_4)_2.12H_2O$		2–3	tetr., lemon-yel.	1.58–1.59, 1.625–1.635
Trona	$Na_3H(CO_3)_2.2H_2O$	2.14	2.5–3	monocl., gray or yelsh. wh., col.	1.412, 1.492, 1.540
Turquois	$Cu(Al,Fe^{+3})_6(PO_4)_4(OH)_8.4H_2O$	2.6–3.2	4.5–6	tricl., bl., grn., grnsh.-gray	1.61–1.78, 1.62–1.84, 1.65–1.84
Ullmannite	$NiSbS$	6.61–6.69	5–5.5	cub., steel-gray to silver-wh.	
Uraninite (R)	UO_2	8.0–11	5–6	cub., steel-blk., brnsh.-blk., grayish, grn.	
Uvarovite	$Ca_3Cr_2Si_3O_{12}$	3.90	6–7.5	cub., emerald-grn.	1.86
Valentinite	Sb_2O_3	5.76	2.5–3	rhomb., col. to wh., somet. yelsh., redsh., gray, br.	2.18, 2.35, 2.35
Vanadinite	$Pb_5(VO_4)_3Cl$	6.5–7.1	2.75–3	hex., orange-red, red, brnsh.-red, br., brnsh.- yel., yel.	2.416, 2.350
Variscite-Strengite	$(AlFe^{+3})(PO_4).2H_2O$	2.57–2.87	3.5–4.5	rhomb., pa. grn., grn., blsh.-grn., red, vlt., col.	1.563–1.707, 1.588–1.719, 1.594–1.741
Vaterite	$CaCO_3$	2.645		hex., col.	1.550, 1.640–1.650
Vermiculite	$(Mg,Ca)_{0.7}(Mg,Fe^{+3}Al)_6(Al,Si)_8O_{20}(OH)_4.8H_2O$	~2.3	~1.5	monocl., col., yel., grn., br.	1.525–1.564, 1.545–1.583, 1.545–1.583
Vesuvianite	$Ca_{10}(Mg,Fe)_2Al_4(Si_2O_7)_2(SiO_4)_5(OH,F)_4$	3.33–3.43	6–7	tetr., yel., grn., br.	1.700–1.746, 1.703–1.752
Villiaumite	NaF	2.79	2–2.5	cub., carmine, (nat.), col. (artif.)	1.327
Vivianite	$Fe_3(PO_4)_2.8H_2O$	2.67–2.69	1.5–2	monocl., col., tarn. pa. bl., grnsh. bl., dk. bl., blsh. blk.	1.579–1.616, 1.602–1.656, 1.629–1.675
Wagnerite	$Mg_2(PO_4)F$	3.15	5–5.5	monocl., yel., gray, somet. red, grn.	1.568, 1.572, 1.582
Wavellite	$Al_3(OH)_3(PO_4)_2.5H_2O$	2 36	3.25–4	rhomb., grnsh. wh., grn. to yel., somet. br., bl., wh.	1.520–1.535, 1.526–1.543, 1.545–1.561
Whewellite	$Ca(C_2O_4).H_2O$	2.23	2.5–3	monocl., col., somet. yelsh., brnsh.	1.491, 1.554, 1.650
Willemite	Zn_2SiO_4	3.9–4.1	5.5	rhbdr., wh., yel., grn., red, gray, br.	1.691, 1.719
Witherite	$BaCO_3$	4.29–4.30	3.5	rhomb., col., wh., gray, yelsh. br.	1.529, 1.676, 1.677
Wolframite	$(Fe,Mn)WO_4$	7.12–7.51	4–4.5	monocl., dk. gray, brnsh. blk. to iron blk.	(Li) ~2.26, 2.32, 2.42
Wollastonite	$CaSiO_3$	2.87–3.09	4.5–5	tricl., wh., col., gray, pa. grn.	1.616–1.640, 1.628–1.650, 1.631–1 653
Wulfenite	$PbMoO_4$	6.5–7.0	2.75–3	tetr., orange-yel. to yel., gray, grn., br., red	2.403, 2 283
Wurtzite	ZnS	3.98	3.5–4	hex., brnsh. blk.	2.356, 2.378
Xenotime	$Y(PO_4)$	4.4–5.1	4–5	tetr., yelsh. br. to redsh. br., somet. gray, wh., pa. yel., grnsh.	1.721, 1.816
Zeunerite (R)	$Cu(UO_2)_2(AsO_4)_2.10-16H_2O$			tetr.	1.602–1.610
Zincite	ZnO	5.64–5.68	4	hex., orange-yel. to dk. red, somet. yel.	2.013, 2.029
Zircon	$ZrSiO_4$	4.6–4.7	7.5	tetr., redsh. br., yel., gray, grn., col.	1.923–1.960, 1.968–2.015
Zoisite	$Ca_2Al_3Si_3O_{12}(OH)$	3.15–3.365	6	rhomb., gray, grnsh., brnsh.	1.685–1.705, 1.688–1.710, 1.697–1.725

X-Ray Crystallographic Data, Molar Volumes, and Densities of Minerals and Related Substances

From U.S. Geological Survey Bulletin 1248 by
Richard A. Robie, Philip M. Bethke and Keith M. Beardsley

An extensive list of references and the bases for the calculations and the selection of data are given in the above referenced Bulletin. Bulletin 1248 may be obtained from the Superintendent of Documents, U.S. Government Printing Office, Washington, D.C., 20402.

X-Ray Crystallographic Data of Minerals

Name and formula	Crystal system	Space group	Structure type	Z	a_o	b_o
Elements						
1 Silver Ag	cubic	Fm3m(225)	face-centered cubic	4	4.0862 ±.0002	
2 Arsenic As	hex-R	R$\bar{3}$m(166)	arsenic	6	3.760 ±.001	
3 Gold Au	cubic	Fm3m(225)	face-centered cubic	4	4.0786 ±.0002	
4 Bismuth Bi	hex-R	R$\bar{3}$m(166)	arsenic	6	4.5459 ±.0010	
5 Diamond C*	cubic	Fd3m(227)	diamond	8	3.5670 ±.0001	
6 Graphite C*	hex.	C6/mmc(194)	graphite	4	2.4612 ±.0001	
7 Copper Cu	cubic	Fm3m(225)	face-centered cubic	4	3.6150 ±.0005	
8 α-Iron Fe	cubic	Im3m(229)	body-centered cubic	2	2.8664 .0005	
9 Nickel Ni	cubic	Fm3m(225)	face-centered cubic	4	3.5238 ±.0005	
10 Lead Pb	cubic	Fm3m(225)	face-centered cubic	4	4.9505 ±.0005	
11 Platinum Pt	cubic	Fm3m(225)	face-centered cubic	4	3.9231 ±.0005	
12 orthorhombic Sulfur S	orth.	Fddd(70)	S_8 ring molecules	128	10.4646 ±.0020	12.8660 ±.0020
13 monoclinic Sulfur S	mon.	P2$_1$/c(14)	S_8 ring molecules	48	11.04 ±.03	10.98 ±.03
14 rhombohedral Sulfur S	hex-R	R$\bar{3}$(148)	S_6 ring molecules	18	10.818 ±.002	
15 Antimony Sb	hex-R	R$\bar{3}$m(166)	arsenic	6	4.310 ±.001	
16 Selenium Se	hex.	P3$_1$21(152) P3$_2$21(154)		3	4.3642 ±.0008	
17 Silicon Si	cubic	Fd3m(227)	diamond	8	5.4305 ±.0003	
18 β-Tin (white) Sn	tet.	14$_1$/amd(141)		4	5.8315 ±.0008	
19 Tellurium Te	hex.	P3$_1$21(152) P3$_2$21(154)		3	4.4570 ±.0008	
20 Zinc Zn	hex.	P6$_3$/mmc(194)	hexagonal close packed	2	2.665 ±.001	
Sulfides, arsenides, tellurides, selenides, and sulfosalts						
21 Shandite β-Ni$_3$Pb$_2$S$_2$*	hex-R	R$\bar{3}$m(166)		3	5.576 ±.010	
22 High-Argentite Ag$_2$S I	cubic			4	6.269 ±.020	

X-Ray Crystallographic Data of Minerals

Z;   The number of gram formula weights per unit cell.

r;   Indicates the data were obtained at an unspecified room temperature and may be taken as $25° + 5°C$.

*;   Indicates the measurements were made on a natural specimen which may have deviated slightly from the listed formula. Densities for these minerals were calculated using the formula weight for the stoichiometric phase.

hex-R;   Rhombohedral symmetry. To distinguish from true hexagonal symmetry.

X-Ray Crystallographic Data of Minerals

c_o	a_o	β_o	γ_o	Cell volume 10^{-24} cm³	Molar volume cm³	cal bar^{-1}	X-Ray density grams cm^{-3}	Temp. °C	
				Elements					
				68.227 ± .010	10.272 ± .002	.24556 ± .00008	10.501 ± .002	25	1
10.555 ± .003				129.23 ± .08	12.972 ± .002	.31007 ± .00023	5.776 ± .004	26	2
				67.847 ± .010	10.215 ± .002	.24420 ± .00008	19.282 ± .003	25	3
11.8622 ± .0030				212.29 ± .11	21.309 ± .011	.50934 ± .00030	9.8071 ± .0050	26	4
				45.385 ± .004	3.4166 ± .0003	.08170 ± .00005	3.5155 ± .0003	25	5
6.7079 ± .0010				35.189 ± .006	5.2982 ± .0009	.12668 ± .00007	2.2670 ± .0004	15	6
				47.242 ± .020	7.1128 ± .0030	.17005 ± .00012	8.9331 ± .0037	25	7
				23.551 ± .012	7.0918 ± .0037	.16954 ± .00013	7.8748 ± .0041	25	8
				43.756 ± .019	6.5880 ± .0028	.15750 ± .00011	8.9117 ± .0038	25	9
				121.32 ± .04	18.267 ± .006	.43663 ± .00018	11.342 ± .003	25	10
				60.379 ± .023	9.0909 ± .0035	.21732 ± .00013	21.460 ± .008	25	11
24.4860 ± .0040				3296.73 ± .97	15.511 ± .005	.37078 ± .00015	2.0671 ± .0006	25	12
10.92 ± .03		96.73 ± .50		1314.6 ± 6.4	16.49 ± .08	.3943 ± .0020	1.944 ± .009	103	13
4.280 ± .001				433.78 ± .19	14.514 ± .006	.34693 ± .00020	2.2092 ± .0010	r	14
11.279 ± .003				181.45 ± .09	18.213 ± .010	.43535 ± .00028	6.685 ± .004	26	15
4.9588 ± .0008				81.793 ± .033	16.420 ± .007	.39249 ± .00020	4.8088 ± .0019	26	16
				160.15 ± .03	12.056 ± .002	.28819 ± .00009	2.3296 ± .0004	25	17
3.1813 ± .0006				108.18 ± .04	10.289 ± .005	.38935 ± .00017	7.2867 ± .0024	26	18
5.9290 ± .0010				102.00 ± .04	20.476 ± .008	.48944 ± .00024	6.2316 ± .0025	25	19
4.947 ± .001				30.428 ± .024	9.162 ± .007	.2190 ± .0002	7.134 ± .006	25	20
				Sulfides, arsenides, tellurides, selenides, and sulfosalts					
13.058 ± .010				367.76 ± 1.35	73.83 ± .27	1.765 ± .007	8.867 ± .033	r	21
				246.4 ± 2.4	37.09 ± .36	.8866 ± .0085	6.680 ± .064	600	22

	Name and formula	Crystal system	Space group	Structure type	Z	a_o	b_o
	Sulfides, arsenides, tellurides, selenides, and sulfosalts—Continued						
23	Argentite Ag_2S II	cubic			2	4.870 ±.008	
24	Acanthite Ag_2S III	mon.	$P2_1/c(14)$		4	4.228 ±.002	6.928 ±.005
25	High-Naumanite Ag_2Se	cubic			2	4.993 ±.016	
26	Ag_2Te I	cubic			2	5.29 ±.01	
27	Ag_2Te II	cubic			4	6.585 ±.010	
28	Hessite Ag_2 Te III	mon.	$P2_1/c(14)$		4	8.09 ±.02	4.48 ±.01
29	$Ag_{1.55}Cu_{.45}S$ I	cubic			4	6.110 ±.010	
30	$Ag_{1.55}Cu_{.45}S$ II	cubic			2	4.825 ±.005	
31	Jalpaite $Ag_{1.55}Cu_{.45}S$ III	tet.			16	8.673 ±.004	
32	$Ag_{.93}Cu_{1.07}S$ I	cubic			4	5.961 ±.009	
33	$Ag_{.93}Cu_{1.07}S$ II	hex.			2	4.138 ±.004	
34	Stromeyerite $Ag_{.93}Cu_{1.07}S$ III	orth.	Cmcm(63)		4	4.066 ±.002	6.628 ±.003
35	Eucairite $AgCuSe$	orth.	pseudo P4/nmm(129)		10	4.105 ±.010	20.35 ±.02
36	Petzite Ag_3AuTe_2*	cubic	$14_132(214)$		8	10.38 ±.02	
37	Maldonite Au_2Bi	cubic	Fd3m(227)	Cu_2Mg	8	7.958 ±.002	
38	High-Digenite Cu_2S I	cubic			4	5.725 ±.010	
39	High-Chalcocite Cu_2S II	hex.			2	3.961 ±.004	
40	Chalcocite Cu_2S III	orth.	Ab2m(39)		96	11.881 ±.004	27.323 ±.010
41	Digenite $Cu_{1.79}S$ (Cu rich side)	cubic		deformed fluorite	4	5.5695 ±.0010	
42	Digenite $Cu_{1.77}S$ (S rich side)	cubic		deformed fluorite	4	5.5542 ±.0010	
43	Berzelianite Cu_2Se	cubic			4	5.85 ±.01	
44	High-Bornite Cu_5FeS_4*	cubic			1	5.50 ±.01	
45	Metastable Bornite Cu_5FeS_4	cubic			8	10.94 ±.02	
46	Low-Bornite Cu_5FeS_4*	tet.	$P\bar{4}2_1c(144)$		16	10.94 ±.02	
47	Umangite Cu_3Se_2	tet.	P4/mmm(123)		2	6.402 ±.010	
48	Heazelwoodite Ni_3S_2	hex-R	R32(155)		3	5.746 ±.001	
49	Maucherite $Ni_{11}As_8$	tet.	$P4_12_12(92)$		4	6.870 ±.001	

c_o	a_o	β_o	γ_o	Cell volume 10^{-24} cm³	Molar volume cm³	cal bar⁻¹	X-Ray density grams cm⁻³	Temp. °C	

Sulfides, arsenides, tellurides, selenides, and sulfosalts—Continued

c_o	a_o	β_o	γ_o	Cell volume 10^{-24} cm³	Molar volume cm³	cal bar⁻¹	X-Ray density grams cm⁻³	Temp. °C	
				115.5 ± .6	34.78 ± .17	.8313 ±.0041	7.125 ±.035	189	23
7.862 ±.003		99.58 ±.30		227.08 ± .29	34.19 ± .04	.8172 ±.0011	7.248 ±.009	25	24
				124.48 ± 1.20	37.48 ± .36	.8959 ±.0087	7.862 ±.076	170	25
				148.0 ± .8	44.58 ± .26	1.065 ±.006	7.702 ±.044	825	26
				285.54 ± 1.30	42.99 ± .20	1.028 ±.005	7.986 ±.036	250	27
8.96 ±.02		123.33 ±.30		271.33 ± 1.43	40.85 ± .22	.9764 ±.0052	8.405 ±.044	r	28
				228.10 ± 1.12	34.34 ± .17	.8209 ±.0041	6.635 ±.033	300	29
				112.33 ± .35	33.83 ± .11	.8085 ±.0026	6.736 ±.021	116	30
11.756 ±.006				884.30 ± .93	33.286 ± .035	.79559 ±.00088	6.8455 ±.0072	r	31
				211.82 ± .96	31.89 ± .14	.7623 ±.0035	6.283 ±.029	196	32
7.105 ±.007				105.36 ± .23	31.73 ± .07	.7583 ±.0017	6.316 ±.014	100	33
7.972 ±.004				214.84 ± .18	32.35 ± .03	.7732 ±.0007	6.194 ±.005	r	34
6.31 ±.01				527.12 ± 1.62	31.75 ± .10	.7588 ±.0024	7.887 ±.024	r	35
				1118.4 ± 6.5	84.19 ± .49	2.012 ±.012	9.214 ±.053	r	36
				503.98 ± .38	37.94 ± .03	.9068 ±.0007	15.891 ±.012	r	37
				187.64 ± .98	28.25 ± .15	.6753 ±.0036	5.633 ±.030	465	38
6.722 ±.007				91.34 ± .21	27.50 ± .06	.6574 ±.0015	5.786 ±.013	152	39
13.491 ±.004				4379.5 ± 2.5	27.475 ± .016	.65671 ±.00043	5.7924 ±.0034	r	40
				172.76 ± .09	26.012 ± .014	.6217 ±.0004	5.605 ±.003	25	41
				171.34 ± .09	25.798 ± .014	.6166 ±.0004	5.602 ±.003	25	42
				200.2 ± 1.0	30.14 ± .15	.7205 ±.0037	6.835 ±.035	170	43
				166.4 ± .0	100.2 ± .5	2.395 ±.013	5.008 ±.027	140	44
				1309.34 ± 7.18	98.57 ± .54	2.356 ±.013	5.091 ±.028	r	45
21.88 ±.04				2618.7 ±10.7	98.57 ± .40	2.356 ±.010	5.091 ±.021	r	46
4.276 ±.010				175.25 ± .68	52.77 ± .21	1.261 ±.005	6.604 ±.026	r	47
7.134 ±.002				203.98 ± .09	40.95 ± .02	.9788 ±.0005	5.867 ±.003	r	48
21.81 ±.01				1029.36 ± .56	154.98 ± .08	3.7043 ±.0021	8.0343 ±.0044	r	49

	Name and formula	Crystal system	Space group	Structure type	Z	a_o	b_o
	Sulfides, arsenides, tellurides, selenides, and sulfosalts—Continued						
50	Pentlandite $Fe_{5.25}Ni_{3.75}S_8$	cubic	Fm3m(225)		4	10.196 ±.010	
51	Pentlandite $Fe_{4.75}Ni_{5.25}S_8$	cubic	Fm3m(225)		4	10.095 ±.010	
52	Sternbergite $AgFe_2S_3$*	orth.	Ccmm(63)		8	11.60 ±.02	12.675 ±.020
53	Argentopyrite $AgFe_2S_3$*	orth.	Pmmm(47)		4	6.64 ±.01	11.47 ±.02
54	Realgar AsS*	mon.	$P2_1/m(11)$		16	9.29 ±.05	13.53 ±.05
55	Oldhamite CaS	cubic	Fm3m(225)	rock salt	4	5.689 ±.006	
56	Greenockite CdS	hex.	$P6_3mc(186)$	zincite	2	4.1354 ±.0010	
57	Hawleyite CdS	cubic	$F\bar{4}3m(216)$	sphalerite	4	5.833 ±.002	
58	(hypothetical) CdS	cubic	Fm3m(225)	rock salt	4	5.516 ±.002	
59	Cadmoselite $CdSe$	hex.	$P6_3mc(186)$	zincite	2	4.2977 ±.0010	
60	$CdTe$	cubic	$F\bar{4}3m(216)$	sphalerite	4	6.4805 ±.0006	
61	(hypothetical) CoS	cubic	$F\bar{4}3m(216)$	sphalerite	4	5.339 ±.001	
62	Chalcopyrite $(CuFeS_2)$ $CuFeS_{1.90}$	tet.	I42d(122)		4	5.2988 ±.0010	
63	Cubanite $CuFe_2S_3$*	orth.	Pcmn(62)		4	6.46 ±.01	11.12 ±.01
64	Covellite CuS	hex.	$P6_3/mmc(194)$		6	3.792 ±.001	
65	Klockmannite $CuSe$	hex.		deformed covellite	78	14.206 ±.010	
66	Troilite FeS	hex.	$P6_3/mmc(194)$	niccolite	2	3.446 ±.003	
67	Pyrrhotite $Fe_{.980}S$	hex.	$P6_3/mmc(194)$	defect niccolite	2	3.446 ±.001	
68	Pyrrhotite $Fe_{.885}S$	hex.	$P6_3/mmc(194)$	defect niccolite	2	3.440 ±.001	
69	(hypothetical) FeS	cubic	$F\bar{4}3m(216)$	sphalerite	4	5.455 ±.001	
70	(hypothetical) FeS	hex.	$P6_3mc(186)$	zincite	2	3.872 ±.001	
71	Cinnabar HgS	hex.	$P3_121(152)$ $P3_21(154)$	cinnabar	3	4.149 ±.001	
72	Metacinnabar HgS	cubic	$F\bar{4}3m(216)$	sphalerite	4	5.8517 ±.0010	
73	Tiemannite $HgSe$	cubic	$F\bar{4}3m(216)$	sphalerite	4	6.0853 ±.0050	
74	Coloradoite $HgTe$	cubic	$F\bar{4}3m(216)$	sphalerite	4	6.4600 ±.0006	
75	Alabandite MnS	cubic	Fm3m(225)	rock salt	4	5.2234 ±.0005	
76	(hypothetical) MnS	cubic	$F\bar{4}3m(216)$	sphalerite	4	5.611 ±.002	

X-Ray Crystallographic Data of Minerals

c_o	a_o	β_o	γ_o	Cell volume 10^{-24} cm³	Molar volume cm³	cal bar^{-1}	X-Ray density grams cm^{-3}	Temp. °C	
				Sulfides, arsenides, tellurides, selenides, and sulfosalts—Continued					
				1059.96 ± 3.12	159.59 ± .47	3.8144 ±.0113	4.823 ±.014	r	50
				1028.77 ± 3.06	154.89 ± .46	3.702 ±.011	4.998 ±.015	r	51
6.63 ±.01				974.81 ± 2.71	73.39 ± .20	1.754 ±.005	4.303 ±.012	r	52
6.45 ±.02				491.2 ± 1.9	73.96 ± .29	1.768 ±.007	4.269 ±.017	r	53
6.57 ±.03		106.55 ±.30		791.6 ± 6.4	29.80 ± .24	.7122 ±.0058	3.591 ±.029	r	54
				184.12 ± .58	27.722 ± .088	.6626 ±.0021	2.602 ±.008	r	55
6.7120 ±.0010				99.407 ± .050	29.934 ± .015	.71549 ±.00041	4.8261 ±.0024	r	56
				198.46 ± .20	29.88 ± .03	.7142 ±.0008	4.835 ±.005	r	57
				167.83 ± .18	25.27 ± .03	.6040 ±.0007	5.717 ±.006	r	58
7.0021 ±.0010				112.00 ± .05	33.727 ± .016	.80614 ±.00044	5.6738 ±.0028	r	59
				272.16 ± .08	40.977 ± .012	.97943 ±.00032	5.8569 ±.0016	25	60
				152.19 ± .09	22.91 ± .02	.5477 ±.0004	3.971 ±.002	r	61
10.434 ±.005				292.96 ± .18	44.109 ± .027	1.0543 ±.0007	4.0878 ±.0025	r	62
6.23 ±.01				447.53 ± 1.08	67.38 ± .16	1.611 ±.004	4.026 ±.010	r	63
16.34 ±.01				203.48 ± .16	20.42 ± .02	.4882 ±.0005	4.682 ±.001	r	64
17.25 ±.05				3014.8 ± 9.7	23.28 ± .08	.5564 ±.0018	6.122 ±.020	r	65
5.877 ±.001				60.439 ± .106	18.20 ± .03	.4350 ±.0008	4.830 ±.009	28	66
5.848 ±.002				60.14 ± .04	18.11 ± .01	.4329 ±.0003	4.793 ±.003	28	67
5.709 ±.003				58.507 ± .046	17.62 ± .02	.4211 ±.0004	4.625 ±.004	28	68
				162.32 ± .09	24.44 ± .01	.5842 ±.0004	3.597 ±.002	r	69
6.345 ±.002				82.38 ± .05	24.81 ± .02	.5930 ±.0004	3.544 ±.002	r	70
9.495 ±.002				141.55 ± .07	28.410 ± .015	.6792 ±.0004	8.187 ±.004	r	71
				200.38 ± .10	30.169 ± .016	.7211 ±.0004	7.712 ±.004	r	72
				225.34 ± .56	33.928 ± .084	.8110 ±.0020	8.239 ±.020	r	73
				269.59 ± .08	40.590 ± .011	.97016 ±.00032	8.0855 ±.0023	r	74
				142.51 + .04	21.457 ± .006	.51289 ±.00019	4.0546 ±.0012	r	75
				176.65 ± .19	26.60 ± .03	.6357 ±.0007	3.271 ±.004	r	76

X-Ray Crystallographic Data of Minerals

	Name and formula	Crystal system	Space group	Structure type	Z	a_o	b_o
	Sulfides, arsenides, tellurides, selenides, and sulfosalts—Continued						
77	(hypothetical) MnS	hex.	P6₃mc(186)	zincite	2	3.986 ±.001	
78	Niccolite NiAs	hex.	P6₃/mmc(194)	niccolite	2	3.618 ±.001	
79	Millerite NiS	hex-R	R3m(160)		9	9.616 ±.001	
80	Breithauptite NiSb	hex.	P6₃/mmc(194)	niccolite	2	3.942 ±.001	
81	Galena PbS	cubic	Fm3m(225)	rock salt	4	5.9360 ±.0005	
82	Clausthalite PbSe	cubic	Fm3m(225)	rock salt	4	6.1255 ±.0005	
83	Teallite PbSnS₂	orth.	Pbnm(62)	GeS	2	4.266 ±.003	11.419 ±.007
84	Altaite PbTe	cubic	Fm3m(225)	rock salt	4	6.4606 ±.0005	
85	Cooperite PtS	tet.	P4₂/mmc(131)		2	3.4699 ±.0006	
86	Herzenbergite SnS	orth.	Pbnm(62)	GeS	4	4.328 ±.002	11.190 ±.004
87	Sphalerite ZnS	cubic	F43m(216)	sphalerite	4	5.4093 ±.0005	
88	Wurtzite ZnS	hex.	P6₃mc(186)	zincite	2	3.8230 ±.0010	
89	Stilleite ZnSe	cubic	F43m(216)	sphalerite	4	5.6685 ±.0005	
90	ZnTe	cubic	F43m(216)	sphalerite	4	6.1020 ±.0006	
91	Orpiment As₂S₃*	mon.	P2₁/n(14)		4	11.49 ±.02	9.59 ±.02
92	Bismuthinite Bi₂S₃	orth.	Pbnm(62)	stibnite	4	11.150 ±.004	11.300 ±.004
93	Tellurobismuthite Bi₂Te₃	hex-R	R3m(166)	Bi₂Te₂S	3	4.3835 ±.0020	
94	Stibnite Sb₂S₃	orth.	Pbnm(62)	stibnite	4	11.229 ±.004	11.310 ±.004
95	Linnaeite Co₃S₄	cubic	Fd3m(227)	spinel	8	9.401 ±.001	
96	Greigite Fe₃S₄	cubic	Fd3m(227)	spinel	8	9.876 ±.002	
97	Daubreeite FeCr₂S₄	cubic	Fd3m(227)	spinel	8	9.966 ±.005	
98	Violarite FeNi₂S₄	cubic	Fd3m(227)	spinel	8	9.464 ±.005	
99	Polymidite Ni₃S₄	cubic	Fd3m(227)	spinel	8	9.480 ±.001	
100	Co-Safflorite CoAs₂	mon.		deformed marcasite	2	5.049 ±.002	5.872 ±.002
101	Safflorite (CO.₅Fe.₅)As₂	orth.	Pnnm(58)	marcasite	2	5.231 ±.002	5.953 ±.002
102	Cobaltite CoAsS*	cubic	P2₁3(198)	NiSbS	4	5.60 ±.05	
103	Glaucodot (Co,Fe)AsS*	orth.	Cmmm(65)		24	6.64 ±.05	28.39 ±.10

X-Ray Crystallographic Data of Minerals

c_o	a_o	β_o	γ_o	Cell volume 10^{-24} cm³	Molar volume cm³	cal bar⁻¹	X-Ray density grams cm⁻³	Temp. °C	

Sulfides, arsenides, tellurides, selenides, and sulfosalts—Continued

c_o	a_o	β_o	γ_o	Cell volume	Molar volume	cal bar⁻¹	X-Ray density	Temp.	
6.465 ±.002				88.96 ± .05	26.79 ± .02	.6403 ±.0004	3.248 ±.002	r	77
5.034 ±.001				57.07 ± .03	17.18 ± .01	.4108 ±.0003	7.776 ±.005	r	78
3.152 ±.001				252.41 ± .10	16.891 ± .006	.40374 ±.00020	5.3743 ±.0020	r	79
5.155 ±.001				69.37 ± .04	20.89 ± .01	.4994 ±.0004	8.639 ±.005	r	80
				209.16 ± .05	31.492 ± .008	.75272 ±.00024	7.5973 ±.0019	26	81
				229.84 ± .06	34.605 ± .009	.82713 ±.00025	8.2690 ±.0020	r	82
4.090 ±.002				109.24 ± .21	59.996 ± .063	1.4340 ±.0016	6.501 ±.007	r	83
				269.66 ± .06	40.601 ± .009	.97043 ±.00027	8.2459 ±.0019	r	84
6.1098 ±.0010				73.563 ± .028	22.152 ± .008	.5295 ±.0003	10.254 ±.004	r	85
3.978 ±.001				192.66 ± .12	29.01 ± .02	.6933 ±.0005	5.197 ±.003	r	86
				158.28 ± .04	23.831 ± .007	.56962 ±.00020	4.0885 ±.0011	r	87
6.2565 ±.0010				79.190 ± .043	23.846 ± .013	.56998 ±.00036	4.0859 ±.0022	r	88
				182.14 ± .05	27.424 ± .007	.65548 ±.00022	5.2630 ±.0014	r	89
				227.20 ± .07	34.209 ± .010	.81765 ±.00029	5.6410 ±.0017	r	90
4.25 ±.01		90.45 ±.30		468.3 ± 1.7	70.51 ± .25	1.685 ±.006	3.490 ±.013	r	91
3.981 ±.001				501.59 ± .28	75.520 ± .043	1.8050 ±.0011	6.8081 ±.0038	26	92
30.487 ±.003				507.33 ± .47	101.85 ± .09	2.4342 ±.0023	7.862 ±.007	25	93
3.8389 ±.0010				487.54 ± .28	73.406 ± .042	1.7545 ±.0010	4.6276 ±.0026	25	94
				830.85 ± .27	62.548 ± .020	1.4950 ±.0005	4.8772 ±.0016	r	95
				963.26 ± .59	72.52 ± .04	1.733 ±.001	4.079 ±.003	r	96
				989.83 ± 1.49	74.52 ± .11	1.781 ±.003	3.866 ±.006	r	97
				847.66 ± 1.34	63.81 ± .10	1.525 ±.002	4.725 ±.008	r	98
				851.97 ± .27	64.138 ± .020	1.5330 ±.0005	4.7458 ±.0015	r	99
3.127 ±.001		90.45 ±.20		92.706 ± .057	27.92 ± .02	.6672 ±.0005	7.479 ±.005	26	100
2.962 ±.002				92.237 ± .078	27.775 ± .024	.6639 ±.0006	7.461 ±.006	26	101
				175.62 ± 4.70	26.44 ± 71	.6320 ±.0170	6.275 ±.168	r	102
5.64 ±.05				1063.2 ±12.9	26.68 + .32	.6377 ±.0078	6.161 ±.075	r	103

	Name and formula	Crystal system	Space group	Structure type	Z	a_o	b_o
	Sulfides, arsenides, tellurides, selenides, and sulfosalts—Continued						
104	Cattierite CoS_2	cubic	Pa3(205)	pyrite	4	5.5345 ±.0005	
105	Trogtalite $CoSe_2$	cubic	Pa3(205)	pyrite	4	5.8588 ±.0010	
106	Loellingite $FeAs_2$	orth.	Pnnm(58)	marcasite	2	5.300 ±.002	5.981 ±.002
107	Arsenopyrite $FeAsS*$	tri.	P$\bar{1}$(2)		4	5.760 ±.010	5.690 ±.005
108	Gudmundite $FeSbS*$	mon.	B2_1/d(14)		8	10.00 ±.05	5.93 ±.03
109	Pyrite FeS_2	cubic	Pa3(205)	pyrite	4	5.4175 ±.0005	
110	Marcasite FeS_2*	orth.	Pnnm(58)	marcasite	2	4.443 ±.002	5.423 ±.002
111	Ferroselite $FeSe_2$	orth.	Pnnm(58)	marcasite	2	4.801 ±.005	5.778 ±.005
112	Frohbergite $FeTe_2$	orth.	Pnnm(58)	marcasite	2	5.265 ±.005	6.265 ±.005
113	Hauerite MnS_2	cubic	Pa3(205)	pyrite	4	6.1014 ±.0006	
114	Molybdenite MoS_2	hex.	P6_3/mmc(194)	molybdenite	2	3.1604 ±.0010	
115	Rammelsbergite $NiAs_2$	orth.	Pnnm(58)	marcasite	2	4.757 ±.002	5.797 ±.004
116	Pararammelsbergite $NiAs_2$	orth.	Pbca(61)		8	5.75 ±.01	5.82 ±.01
117	Gersdorfite $NiAsS$	cubic	P$2_1$3(198)		4	5.693 ±.001	
118	Vaesite NiS_2	cubic	Pa3(205)	pyrite	4	5.6873 ±.0005	
119	$NiSe_2$	cubic	Pa3(205)	pyrite	4	5.9604 ±.0010	
120	Melonite $NiTe_2$	hex.	P$\bar{3}$m1(164)	cadmium iodide	1	3.869 ±.010	
121	Sperrylite $PtAs_2$	cubic	Pa3(205)	pyrite	4	5.968 ±.005	
122	Laurite RuS_2	cubic	Pa3(205)	pyrite	4	5.60 ±.02	
123	Tungstenite WS_2	hex.	P6_3/mmc(194)	molybdenite	2	3.154 ±.001	
124	Co-Skutterudite $CoAs_{3-x}$ $CoAs_{2.95}$	cubic	Im3(204)		8	8.2060 ±.0010	
125	Fe-Skutterudite $FeAs_{3-x}$ $FeAs_{2.95}$	cubic	Im3(204)		8	8.1814 ±.0010	
126	Ni-Skutterudite $NiAs_{3-x}$ $NiAs_{2.95}$	cubic	Im3(204)		8	8.3300 ±.0010	
127	Tennantite $Cu_{12}As_4S_{13}$	cubic	I$\bar{4}$3m(217)	tetrahedrite	2 2	10.190 ±.004	
128	Tetrahedrite $Cu_{12}Sb_4S_{13}$	cubic	I$\bar{4}$3m(217)	tetrahedrite	2 2	10.327 ±.004	
129	Enargite Cu_3AsS_4	orth.	Pnn2(34)		2	6.426 ±.005	7.422 ±.005
130	Luzonite Cu_3AsS_4*	tet.	I$\bar{4}$2m(121)		2	5.289 ±.005	

c_o	a_o	β_o	γ_o	Cell volume 10^{-24} cm³	Molar volume cm³	cal bar^{-1}	X-Ray density grams cm^{-3}	Temp. °C	

Sulfides, arsenides, tellurides, selenides, and sulfosalts—Continued

c_o	a_o	β_o	γ_o	Cell volume 10^{-24} cm³	Molar volume cm³	cal bar^{-1}	X-Ray density grams cm^{-3}	Temp.	
				169.53 ± .05	25.524 ± .007	.61009 ±.00021	4.8213 ±.0013	r	104
				201.11 ± .10	30.279 ± .016	.72374 ±.00042	7.1618 ±.0037	r	105
2.882 ±.001				91.357 ± .056	27.51 ± .02	.6576 ±.0005	7.477 ±.005	26	106
5.785 ±.005	90.00 ±.20	112.23 ±.20	90.00 ±.20	175.51 ± .44	26.42 ± .07	.6316 ±.0016	6.162 ±.015	r	107
6.73 ± .03		90.00 ± .50		399.09 ± 3.35	30.04 ± .25	.7181 ±.0061	6.978 ±.059	r	108
				159.00 ± .04	23.940 ± .007	.57221 ±.00020	5.0116 ±.0014	r	109
3.3876 ±.0015				81.622 ± .060	24.579 ± .018	.58749 ±.00047	4.8813 ±.0036	25	110
3.587 ±.004				99.50 ± .17	29.96 ± .05	.7162 ±.0013	7.134 ±.013	r	111
3.869 ±.002				127.62 ± .17	38.43 ± .05	.9185 ±.0013	8.094 ±.011	r	112
				227.14 ± .07	34.198 ± .010	.81741 ±.00029	3.4816 ±.0010	28	113
12.295 ±.002				106.35 ± .07	32.025 ± .021	.76547 ±.00055	4.9982 ±.0033	26	114
3.542 ±.002				97.645 ± .096	29.41 ± .03	.7030 ±.0007	7.091 ±.007	26	115
11.428 ±.02				382.42 ± 1.15	28.79 ± .09	.6882 ±.0021	7.244 ±.022	r	116
				184.51 ± .10	27.78 ± .01	.6640 ±.0004	5.964 ±.003	26	117
				183.96 ± .05	27.697 ± 007	.66203 ⊥.00022	4.4350 ±.0012	r	118
				211.75 ± .11	31.882 ± .016	.76204 ±.00043	6.7948 ±.0034	20	119
5.308 ±.010				68.81 ± .38	41.44 ± .23	.9905 ±.0055	7.575 ±.042	84	120
				212.56 ± .53	32.00 ± .08	.7650 ±.0020	10.778 ±.027	r	121
				175.6 ± 1.9	26.44 ± .28	.6320 ±.0068	6.248 ±.067	r	122
12.362 ±.004				106.50 ± .08	32.069 ± .023	.76652 ±.00059	7.7325 ±.0055	26	123
				552.58 ± .20	41.599 ± .015	.99428 ±.00041	6.7298 ±.0025	r	124
				547.62 ± .20	41.226 ± .015	.98537 ±.00041	6.7158 ±.0025	r	125
				578.01 ± .21	43.513 ± .016	1.0400 ±.0004	6.4286 ±.0023	r	126
				1058.09 ± 1.25	318.62 ± .38	7.1652 ±.0090	4.642 ±.006	r	127
				1101.3 ± 1.3	331.64 ± .39	7.9266 ±.0094	5.024 ±.006	r	128
6.144 ±.005				293.03 ± .38	88.24 ± .12	2.109 ±.003	4.463 ±.006	26	129
10.440 ±.008				292.04 ± .60	87.94 ± .18	2.1019 ±.0043	4.478 ±.009	26	130

	Name and formula	Crystal system	Space group	Structure type	Z	a_o	b_o
	Sulfides, arsenides, tellurides, selenides, and sulfosalts—Continued						
131	Famatimite Cu_3SbS_4*	tet.	I$\bar{4}$m(121)		2	5.384 ±.005	
132	Proustite Ag_3AsS_3	hex-R	R3c(161)		6	10.816 ±.001	
133	Pyrargyrite Ag_3SbS_3	hex-R	R3c(161)		6	11.052 ±.002	
134	Miargyrite $AgSbS_2$*	mon.	Cc(9)		8	12.862 ±.013	4.111 ±.004
	Oxides and hydroxides						
135	Corundum Al_2O_3	hex-R	R$\bar{3}$c(167)	corundum	6	4.7591 ±.0004	
136	Boehmite $AlO(OH)$*	orth.	Cmcm(63)	lepidocrocite	4	2.868 ±.003	12.227 ±.003
137	Diaspore $AlO(OH)$*	orth.	Pbnm(62)		4	4.401 ±.005	9.421 ±.005
138	Gibbsite $Al(OH)_3$	mon.	P2$_1$/n(14)		8	9.719 ±.002	5.0705 ±.0010
139	Arsenolite As_2O_3	cubic	Fd3m(227)	diamond	16	11.074 ±.005	
140	Claudetite As_2O_3	mon.	P2$_1$/n(14)		4	5.339 ±.002	12.984 ±.005
141	Bromellite BeO	hex.	P6$_3$mc(186)	zincite	2	2.6979 ±.0005	
142	Bismite α-Bi_2O_3	mon.	P2$_1$/c(14)	pseudo orthorhombic	8	8.166 ±.005	13.827 ±.010
143	Lime CaO	cubic	Fm3m(225)	rock salt	4	4.8108 ±.0005	
144	Portlandite $Ca(OH)_2$	hex.	P$\bar{3}$ml(164)	CdI_2	1	3.5933 ±.0005	
145	Monteponite CdO	cubic	Fm3m(225)	rock salt	4	4.6953 ±.0010	
146	Cerianite CeO_2	cubic	Fm3m(225)	fluorite	4	5.4110 ±.0020	
147	CoO	cubic	Fm3m(225)	rock salt	4	4.260 ±.002	
148	Eskolaite Cr_2O_3	hex-R	R$\bar{3}$c(167)	corundum	6	4.9607 ±.0020	
149	Tenorite CuO	mon.	C2/c(15)		4	4.684 ±.005	3.425 ±.005
150	Cuprite Cu_2O	cubic	Pn3m(224)		2	4.2696 ±.0010	
151	Wustite $Fe_{.953}O$	cubic	Fm3m(225)	defect rock salt	4	4.3088 ±.0003	
152	Hematite Fe_2O_3	hex-R	R$\bar{3}$c(167)	corundum	6	5.0329 ±.0010	
153	Magnetite Fe_3O_4	cubic	Fd3m(227)	spinel	8	8.3940 ±.0005	
154	Goethite α-$FeO(OH)$*	orth.	Pbnm(62)		4	4.596 ±.005	9.957 ±.010
155	Lepidocrocite γ-$FeO(OH)$*	orth.	Amam(63)		4	3.868 ±.010	12.525 ±.010
156	α-Ga_2O_3	hex-R	R$\bar{3}$c(167)	corundum	6	4.9793 ±.0010	

c_o	a_o	β_o	γ_o	Cell volume 10^{-24} cm³	Molar volume cm³	cal bar^{-1}	X-Ray density grams cm^{-3}	Temp. °C	

c_o	a_o	β_o	γ_o	Cell volume 10^{-24} cm³	Molar volume cm³	cal bar^{-1}	X-Ray density grams cm^{-3}	Temp. °C	
Sulfides, arsenides, tellurides, selenides, and sulfosalts—Continued									
10.770 ±.008				312.19 ± .62	94.01 ± .19	2.2469 ±.0045	4.687 ±.009	26	131
8.6948 ±.0013				880.89 ± .21	88.420 ± .021	2.1133 ±.0006	5.595 ±.001	26	132
8.7177 ±.0020				922.18 ± .40	92.564 ± .040	2.2124 ±.0010	5.8506 ±.0025	26	133
13.220 ±.010		98.63 ±.15		691.10 ± 1.14	52.027 ± .086	1.244 ±.002	5.646 ±.009	r	134
Oxides and hydroxides									
12.9894 ±.0030				254.78 ± .07	25.575 ± .007	.61128 ±.00022	3.9869 ±.0011	25	135
3.700 ±.003				129.75 ± .17	19.535 ± .026	.46695 ±.00067	3.071 ±.004	26	136
2.845 ±.002				117.96 ± .17	17.760 ± .026	.4245 ±.0007	3.378 ±.005	r	137
8.6412 ±.0010		94.57 ±.25		424.49 ± .20	31.956 ± .015	.7638 ±.0004	2.441 ±.001	r	138
				1358.0 ± 1.8	51.118 ± .069	1.2218 ±.0017	3.870 ±.005	25	139
4.5405 ±.0010		94.27 ±.10		313.88 ± .19	47.259 ± .028	1.1296 ±.0007	4.1863 ±.0025	25	140
4.3772 ±.0005				27.592 ± .011	8.3086 ± .0032	.19862 ±.00012	3.0104 ±.0012	26	141
5.850 ±.004		90.00 ±.20		660.53 ± .77	49.73 ± .06	1.1885 ±.0014	9.371 ±.011	25	142
				111.34 ± .03	16.764 ± .005	.40071 ±.00017	3.3453 ±.0010	26	143
4.9086 ±.0020				54.888 ± .027	33.056 ± .016	.79011 ±.00043	2.2415 ±.0011	26	144
				103.51 ± .07	15.585 ± .010	.37254 ±.00028	8.2386 ±.0053	27	145
				158.43 ± .18	23.853 ± .026	.57016 ±.00068	7.216 ±.008	26	146
				77.31 ± .11	11.64 ± .02	.2782 ±.0004	6.438 ±.009	26	147
13.599 ±.010				289.82 ± .32	29.090 ± .032	.6953 ±.0008	5.225 ±.006	r	148
5.129 ±.005		99.47 ±.17		81.16 ± .17	12.22 ± .03	.2921 ±.0007	6.509 ±.014	26	149
				77.833 ± .055	23.437 ± .016	.56021 ±.00044	6.1047 + .0043	26	150
				70.000 ± .017	12.044 ± .003	.28791 ±.00011	5.7471 ±.0012	17	151
		13.7492 ±.0010		301.61 ± .12	30.274 ± .012	.72361 ±.00034	5.2749 ±.0021	25	152
				591.43 ± .11	44.524 ± .008	1.0642 ±.0002	5.2003 ±.0009	22	153
3.021 ±.003				138.2 ± .2	20.82 ± .04	.4975 ±.0009	4.269 ±.008	r	154
3.066 ±.003				148.54 ± .43	22.364 ± .064	.5346 ±.0016	3.973 ±.011	r	155
13.429 ±.003				288.34 ± .13	28.943 ± .013	.69179 ±.00036	6.4762 ±.0030	24	156

X-Ray Crystallographic Data of Minerals

Oxides and hydroxides—Continued

	Name and formula	Crystal system	Space group	Structure type	Z	a_o	b_o
157	Low-germania GeO_2	tet.	$P4/mnm(136)$	rutile	2	4.3963 ±.0010	
158	High-germania GeO_2	hex.	$P3_121(152)$ $P3_221(154)$	α-quartz	3	4.987 ±.002	
159	Ice H_2O	hex.	$P6_3/mmc(194)$		4	4.5212 ±.0010	
160	Hafnia HfO_2	mon.	$P2_1/c(14)$	baddeleyite	4	5.1156 ±.0010	5.1722 ±.0010
161	Montroydite HgO	orth.	$Pnma(62)$		4	6.608 ±.003	5.518 ±.003
162	Periclase MgO	cubic	$Fm3m(225)$	rock salt	4	4.2117 ±.0005	
163	Brucite $Mg(OH)_2$	hex.	$P\bar{3}ml(164)$	CdI_2	1	3.147 ±.004	
164	Manganosite MnO	cubic	$Fm3m(225)$	rock salt	4	4.4448 ±.0005	
165	Pyrolusite MnO_2	tet.	$P4/mnm(136)$	rutile	2	4.388 ±.003	
166	Bixbyite Mn_2O_3	cubic	$Ia3(206)$	Tl_2O_3	16	9.411 ±.005	
167	Hausmanite Mn_3O_4	tet.	$I4_1/amd(141)$		8	8.136 ±.005	
168	Molybdite MoO_3	orth.	$Pbnm(62)$		4	3.962 ±.002	13.858 ±.005
169	Bunsenite NiO	cubic	$Fm3m(225)$	rock salt	4	4.177 ±.002	
170	Litharge PbO red	tet.	$P4/nmm(129)$		2	3.9759 ±.0040	
171	Massicot PbO yellow	orth.	$Pb2a(32)$		4	5.489 ±.003	4.755 ±.004
172	Minium Pb_3O_4	tet.	$P4_2/mbc(135)$		4	8.815 ±.005	
173	Senarmontite Sb_2O_3	cubic	$Fm3m(225)$	arsenic trioxide	16	11.152 ±.003	
174	Valentinite Sb_2O_3	orth.	$Pccn(56)$	antimony trioxide	4	4.914 ±.002	12.468 ±.005
175	Cervantite Sb_2O_4	cubic	$Fd3m(227)$		8	10.305 ±.005	
176	Selenolite SeO_2	tet.	$P4_2/mbc(135)$ $P4_2bc(106)$		8	8.35 ±.01	
177	α-Quartz SiO_2*	hex.	$P3_121(152)$ $P3_221(154)$		3	4.9136 ±.0001	
178	β-Quartz SiO_2*	hex.	$P6_422(181)$ $P6_222(180)$		3	4.999 ±.001	
179	α-Cristobalite SiO_2	tet.	$P4_12_12(92)$ $P4_32_12(96)$		4	4.971 ±.003	
180	β-Cristobalite SiO_2	cubic	$Fd3m(227)$		8	7.1382 ±.0010	
181	Keatite SiO_2	tet.	$P4_12_12(92)$ $P4_32_12(96)$		12	7.456 ±.003	
182	β-Tridymite SiO_2	hex.	$P\bar{6}2c(172)$ $P6_3/mmc(194)$		4	5.0463 ±.0020	
183	Coesite SiO_2*	mon.	$B2/b(15)$		16	7.152 ±.001	12.379 ±.002

c_o	a_o	β_o	γ_o	Cell volume $10^{-24}\,cm^3$	Molar volume cm^3	Molar volume $cal\,bar^{-1}$	X-Ray density $grams\,cm^{-3}$	Temp. °C	
				Oxides and hydroxides—Continued					
2.8626 $\pm$ 0010				55.327 $\pm$ .032	16.660 $\pm$ .010	.39824 $\pm$ .00027	6.2777 $\pm$ .0036	25	157
5.652 $\pm$ .002				121.73 $\pm$ .11	24.438 $\pm$ .021	.58413 $\pm$ .00056	4.2797 $\pm$ .0038	26	158
7.3666 $\pm$ .0010				130.41 $\pm$ .06	19.635 $\pm$ .009	.46932 $\pm$ .00026	.9175 $\pm$ .0004	0	159
5.2948 $\pm$ .0010		99.18 $\pm$ .08		138.30 $\pm$ .06	20.823 $\pm$ .008	.49772 $\pm$ .00025	10.108 $\pm$ .004	r	160
3.519 $\pm$ .003				128.3 $\pm$ .1	19.32 $\pm$ .02	.4618 $\pm$ .0006	11.21 $\pm$ .01	25	161
				74.709 $\pm$ .027	11.248 $\pm$ .004	.26889 $\pm$ .00014	3.5837 $\pm$ .0013	25	162
4.769 $\pm$ .004				40.00 $\pm$ .11	24.63 $\pm$ .07	.5888 $\pm$ .0016	2.368 $\pm$ .006	26	163
				87.813 $\pm$ .030	13.221 $\pm$ .004	.31604 $\pm$ .00015	5.3653 $\pm$ .0018	26	164
2.865 $\pm$ .002				55.16 $\pm$ .08	16.61 $\pm$ .02	.3971 $\pm$ .0007	5.234 $\pm$ .008	r	165
				833.5 $\pm$ 1.3	31.37 $\pm$ .05	.7499 $\pm$ .0012	5.032 $\pm$ .008	25	166
9.422 $\pm$ .005				623.68 $\pm$ .84	46.95 $\pm$ .06	1.1222 $\pm$ .0016	4.873 $\pm$ .007	20	167
3.697 $\pm$ .004				202.98 $\pm$ .25	30.56 $\pm$ .04	.7305 $\pm$ .0010	4.710 $\pm$ .006	26	168
				72.88 $\pm$ .10	10.97 $\pm$ .02	.2623 $\pm$ .0004	6.809 $\pm$ .010	26	169
5.023 $\pm$ .004				79.40 $\pm$ .17	23.91 $\pm$ .05	.5715 $\pm$ .0013	9.334 $\pm$ .020	27	170
5.891 $\pm$ .004				153.8 $\pm$ .2	23.15 $\pm$ .03	.5533 $\pm$ .0007	9.641 $\pm$ .012	27	171
6.565 $\pm$ .003				510.13 $\pm$ .62	76.81 $\pm$ .09	1.836 $\pm$ .002	8.926 $\pm$ .009	25	172
				1386.9 $\pm$ 1.1	52.206 $\pm$ .042	1.2478 $\pm$ .0011	5.5837 $\pm$ 0045	26	173
5.421 $\pm$ .004				332.13 $\pm$ .31	50.007 $\pm$ .047	1.1952 $\pm$ .0012	5.8292 $\pm$ .0054	25	174
				1094.3 $\pm$ 1.6	82.38 $\pm$ .12	1.9690 $\pm$ .0029	3.733 $\pm$ .005	26	175
5.08 $\pm$ .01				354.2 $\pm$ 1.1	26.66 $\pm$ .08	.6373 $\pm$ .0020	4.161 $\pm$ .013	26	176
5.4051 $\pm$ .0001				113.01 $\pm$ .01	22.688 $\pm$ .001	.54229 $\pm$ .00007	2.6483 $\pm$ .0001	25	177
5.4592 $\pm$ .0020				118.15 $\pm$ .06	23.718 $\pm$ .013	.5669 $\pm$ .0004	2.639 $\pm$ .002	575	178
6.018 $\pm$ .003				170.95 $\pm$ .22	25.739 $\pm$ .033	.61521 $\pm$ .00083	2.3344 $\pm$ .0030	25	179
				363.72 $\pm$ .15	27.381 $\pm$ .012	.65447 $\pm$ .00032	2.1944 $\pm$ .0009	405	180
8.604 $\pm$ .005				478.3 $\pm$ .5	24.01 $\pm$ .02	.5738 $\pm$ .0006	2.503 $\pm$ .003	r	181
8.2563 $\pm$ .0030				182.08 $\pm$ .16	27.414 $\pm$ .024	.65527 $\pm$ .00002	2.1917 $\pm$ .0019	405	182
7.152 $\pm$ .001		120.00 $\pm$ .17		548.37 $\pm$ .95	20.641 $\pm$ .036	.49338 $\pm$ .00090	2.9110 $\pm$ .0050	25	183

X-Ray Crystallographic Data of Minerals

	Name and formula	Crystal system	Space group	Structure type	Z	a_o	b_o
				Oxides and hydroxides—Continued			
184	Stishovite SiO₂*	tet.	P4/mnm(136)	rutile	2	4.1790 ±.0010	
185	Melanophlogite SiO₂*	cubic	Pm3n(223)	clathrate type	46	13.402 ±.004	
186	Cassiterite SnO₂	tet.	P4/mnm(136)	rutile	2	4.738 ±.003	
187	Tellurite TeO₂*	orth.	Pbca(61)	tellurite	8	5.607 ±.003	12.034 ±.005
188	Paratellurite TeO₂	tet.	P4₁2₁2(92) P4₃2₁2(96)		4	4.810 ±.002	
189	Thorianite ThO₂	cubic	Fm3m(225)	fluorite	4	5.5952 ±.0005	
190	Rutile TiO₂	tet.	P4/mnm(136)		2	4.5937 ±.0005	
191	Anatase TiO₂	tet.	I4₁/amd(141)		4	3.785 ±.002	
192	Brookite TiO₂*	orth.	Pcab(61)		8	5.456 ±.002	9.182 ±.005
193	Titanium sesquioxide Ti₂O₃	hex-R	R3̄c(167)	corundum	6	5.149 ±.002	
194	Uraninite UO₂	cubic	Fm3m(225)	fluorite	4	5.4682 ±.0010	
195	Karelianite V₂O₃	hex-R	R3̄c(167)	corundum	6	4.952 ±.002	
196	Zincite ZnO	hex.	P6₃mc(186)	zincite	2	3.2495 ±.0005	
197	Baddeleyite ZrO₂	mon.	P2₁/c(14)	baddeleyite	4	5.1454 ±.0010	5.2075 ±.0010
				Multiple oxides			
198	Spinel MgAl₂O₄	cubic	Fd3m(227)	spinel	8	8.080 ±.002	
199	Hercynite FeAl₂O₄	cubic	Fd3m(227)	spinel	8	8.150 ±.004	
200	Galaxite MnAl₂O₄	cubic	Fd3m(227)	spinel	8	8.258 ±.002	
201	Gahnite ZnAl₂O₄	cubic	Fd3m(227)	spinel	8	8.0848 ±.0020	
202	Magnetite FeFe₂O₄	cubic	Fd3m(227)	spinel	8	8.3940 ±.0005	
203	Jacobsite MnFe₂O₄	cubic	Fd3m(227)	spinel	8	8.499 ±.002	
204	Trevorite NiFe₂O₄	cubic	Fd3m(227)	spinel	8	8.339 ±.003	
205	Picrochromite MgCr₂O₄	cubic	Fd3m(227)	spinel	8	8.333 ±.003	
206	Ilmenite FeTiO₃	hex-R	R3̄(148)	ilmenite	6	5.093 ±.005	
207	Geikielite MgTiO₃	hex-R	R3̄(148)	ilmenite	6	5.054 ±.005	
208	Pyrophanite MnTiO₃	hex-R	R3̄(148)	ilmenite	6	5.155 ±.005	
209	Cobalt Titanate CoTiO₃	hex-R	R3̄(148)	ilmenite	6	5.066 ±.001	

X-Ray Crystallographic Data of Minerals

c_o	a_o	β_o	γ_o	Cell volume 10^{-24} cm³	Molar volume cm³	cal bar^{-1}	X-Ray density grams cm^{-3}	Temp. °C	
				Oxides and hydroxides—Continued					
2.6649 ±.0010				46.540 ± .028	14.014 ± .009	.33500 ±.00025	4.2874 ±.0026	r	184
				2407.2 ± 2.2	31.516 ± .028	.75325 ±.00072	1.9065 ±.0017	r	185
3.188 ±.003				71.57 ± .11	21.55 ± .03	.5151 ±.0009	6.992 ±.011	26	186
5.463 ±.003				368.61 ± .32	27.750 ± .024	.66328 ±.00062	5.7514 ±.0050	25	187
7.613 ±.002				176.14 ± .15	26.52 ± .02	.6339 ±.0006	6.018 ±.005	25	188
				175.16 ± .05	26.373 ± .007	.63038 ±.00021	10.012 ±.003	25	189
2.9618 ±.0010				62.500 ± .025	18.820 ± .008	.44986 ±.00023	4.2453 ±.0017	25	190
9.514 ±.006				136.30 ± .17	20.522 ± .025	.4905 ±.0007	3.893 ±.005	r	191
5.143 ±.003				257.6 ± .2	19.40 ± .02	.4636 ±.0005	4.119 ±.004	r	192
13.642 ±.010				313.2 ± .3	31.44 ⊥ .03	.7515 ±.0009	4.574 ±.005	r	193
				163.51 ± .09	24.618 ± .014	.58843 ±.00037	10.969 ±.006	26	194
14.002 ±.010				297.36 ± .32	29.848 ± .032	.71342 ±.00081	5.0216 ±.0054	r	195
5.2069 ±.0005				47.615 ± .015	14.338 ± .005	.34273 ±.00016	5.6750 ±.0018	25	196
5.3107 ±.0010		99.23 ±.08		140.46 ± .06	21.148 ± .009	.50548 ±.00025	5.8267 ±.0023	r	197
				Multiple oxides					
				527.5 ± .4	39.71 ± .03	.9492 ±.0008	3.583 ±.003	26	198
				541.3 ± .6	40.75 ± .05	.9740 ±.0011	4.265 ±.005	25	199
				563.2 ± .4	42.39 ± .03	1.013 ±.001	4.078 ±.003	25	200
				528.45 ± .39	39.783 ± .030	.95088 ±.00075	4.6083 ±.0034	26	201
				591.43 ± .11	44.524 ± .008	1.0642 ±.0002	5.2003 ±.0009	22	202
				613.9 ± .4	46.22 ± .03	1.105 ±.001	4.990 ±.004	25	203
				579.9 +- .6	43.65 ⊥ .05	1.043 ±.001	5.370 ±.006	25	204
				578.6 ± .6	43.56 ± .05	1.041 ±.001	4.415 ±.005	26	205
14.055 ±.020				315.73 ± .75	31.69 ± .08	.7574 ±.0019	4.788 ±.012	r	206
13.898 ±.010				307.44 ± .65	30.86 ± .07	.7376 ±.0016	3.896 + .008	26	207
14.18 ±.01				326.3 ± .7	32.76 ± .07	.7829 ±.0017	4.605 ±.010	r	208
13.918 ±.005				309.34 ± .17	31.05 ± .02	.7422 ±.0004	4.986 ±.003	r	209

X-Ray Crystallographic Data of Minerals

	Name and formula	Crystal system	Space group	Structure type	Z	a_o	b_o
	Multiple oxides—Continued						
210	Perovskite CaTiO₃	orth.	Pcmn(62)	perovskite	4	5.3670 ±.0010	7.6438 ±.0010
211	Chrysoberyl BeAl₂O₄	orth.	Pmnb(62)	olivine	4	5.4756 ±.0020	9.4041 ±.0030
	Halides						
212	Halite NaCl	cubic	Fm3m(225)	rock salt	4	5.6402 ±.0002	
213	Sylvite KCl	cubic	Fm3m(225)	rock salt	4	6.2931 ±.0002	
214	Villiaumite NaF	cubic	Fm3m(225)	rock salt	4	4.6342 ±.0005	
215	Chlorargyrite AgCl	cubic	Fm3m(225)	rock salt	4	5.5491 ±.0005	
216	Bromargyrite AgBr	cubic	Fm3m(225)	rock salt	4	5.7745 ±.0005	
217	Nantockite CuCl	cubic	F43m(216)	sphalerite	4	5.416 ±.003	
218	Marshite CuI	cubic	F43m(216)	sphalerite	4	6.0507 ±.0010	
219	Miersite AgI	cubic	F43m(216)	sphalerite	4	6.4963 ±.0010	
220	Iodargyrite AgI	hex.	P6₃mc(186)	zincite	2	4.5955 ±.0010	
221	Calomel HgCl	tet.	14/mm(139)		4	4.478 ±.005	
222	Fluorite CaF₂	cubic	Fm3m(225)	fluorite	4	5.4638 ±.0004	
223	Sellaite MgF₂	tet.	P4₂/mnm(136)	rutile	2	4.621 ±.001	
224	Chloromagnesite MgCl₂	hex-R	R3m(166)		3	3.632 ±.004	
225	Lawrencite FeCl₂	hex-R	R3m(166)		3	3.593 ±.003	
226	Scacchite MnCl₂	hex-R	R3m(166)		3	3.711 ±.002	
227	Cotunnite PbCl₂	orth.	Pnmb(62)		4	4.535 ±.005	7.62 ±.01
228	Matlockite PbFCl	tet.	P4/nmm(129)		2	4.106 ±.005	
229	Cryolite Na₃AlF₆*	mon.	P2₁/n(14)		2	5.40 ±.01	5.60 ±.01
230	Neighborite NaMgF₃	orth.	Pcmn(62)	perovskite	4	5.363 ±.001	7.676 ±.001
	Carbonates and nitrates						
231	Calcite CaCO₃	hex-R	R3c(167)	calcite	6	4.9899 ±.0010	
232	Otavite CdCO₃	hex-R	R3c(167)	calcite	6	4.9204 ±.0010	
233	Cobalticalcite CoCO₃	hex-R	R3c(167)	calcite	6	4.6581 ±.0010	
234	Siderite FeCO₃	hex-R	R3c(167)	calcite	6	4.6887 ±.0010	

X-Ray Crystallographic Data of Minerals

c_o	a_o	β_o	γ_o	Cell volume 10^{-24} cm^3	Molar volume cm^3	cal bar^{-1}	X-Ray density grams cm^{-3}	Temp. °C	
				Multiple oxides—Continued					
5.4439 ±.0010				223.33 ± .07	33.626 ± .010	.80371 ± .00028	4.0439 ±.0012	r	210
4.4267 ±.0020				227.94 ± .15	34.320 ± .023	.82031 ±.00059	3.6997 ±.0025	25	211
				Halides					
				179.43 ± .02	27.015 ± .003	.64571 ±.00011	2.1634 ±.0002	26	212
				249.23 ± .02	37.524 ± .004	.89690 ±.00013	1.9868 ±.0002	25	213
				99.523 ± .032	14.984 ± .005	.35818 ±.00016	2.8021 ±.0009	25	214
				170.87 ± .05	25.727 ± .007	.01493 ±.00021	5.5710 ±.0015	26	215
				192.55 ± .05	28.991 ± .008	.69294 ±.00022	6.4772 ±.0017	26	216
				158.87 ± .26	23.92 ± .04	.5717 ±.0010	4.139 ±.007	25	217
				221.52 ± .11	33.353 ± .017	.7972 ±.0004	5.710 ±.003	26	218
				274.16 ± .10	41.278 ± .020	.9866 ±.0004	5.688 ±.003	r	219
7.5005 ±.0033				137.18 ± .10	41.308 ± .030	.9873 ±.0009	5.683 ±.004	25	220
10.910 ±.005				218.77 ± .50	32.939 ± .075	.7873 ±.0018	7.166 ±.016	26	221
				163.11 ± .04	24.558 ± .005	.58701 ±.00017	3.1792 ±.0007	25	222
3.050 ±.001				65.13 ± .04	19.61 ± .01	.4688 ±.0003	3.177 ±.002	18	223
17.795 ±.016				203.29 ± .48	40.81 ± .10	.9754 ±.0024	2.333 ±.006	r	224
17.58 ±.09				196.55 ± 1.06	39.46 ± .21	.9431 ±.0051	3.212 ±.017	r	225
17.59 ±.07				209.79 ± .86	42.11 ± .17	1.007 ±.004	2.988 ±.012	r	226
9.05 ±.01				312.74 ± .64	47.09 ± .10	1.1254 ±.0023	5.906 ±.012	26	227
7.23 ±.01				121.89 ± .34	36.70 ± .10	.8773 ±.0025	9.853 ±.028	26	228
7.776 ±.010		90.18 ±.25		235.1 ± .7	70.81 ± .20	1.692 ±.005	2.965 ±.009	r	229
5.503 ±.001				226.54 ± .07	34.11 ± .01	.8152 ⊥.0003	3.058 ±.001	18	230
				Carbonates and nitrates					
17.064 ±.002				367.96 ± .15	36.934 ± .015	.88278 ±.00041	2.7100 ±.0011	26	231
16.298 ±.003				341.72 ± .15	34.300 ± .015	.81983 ±.00041	5.0265 ±.0022	26	232
14.958 ±.003				281.07 ± .13	28.213 ± .013	.67435 ±.00036	4.2159 ±.0020	26	233
15.373 ±.003				292.68 ± .14	29.378 ± .014	.70219 ±.00037	3.9436 ±.0018	26	234

X-Ray Crystallographic Data of Minerals

	Name and formula	Crystal system	Space group	Structure type	Z	a_o	b_o
	Carbonates and nitrates—Continued						
235	Magnesite $MgCO_3$	hex-R	$R\bar{3}c(167)$	calcite	6	4.6330 ±.0010	
236	Rhodochrosite $MnCO_3$	hex-R	$R\bar{3}c(167)$	calcite	6	4.7771 ±.0010	
237	Nickelous Carbonate $NiCO_3$	hex-R	$R\bar{3}c(167)$	calcite	6	4.5975 ±.0010	
238	Smithsonite $ZnCO_3$	hex-R	$R\bar{3}(167)$	calcite	6	4.6528 ±.0010	
239	Dolomite $CaMg(CO_3)_2$*	hex-R	$R\bar{3}(148)$	calcite	3	4.8079 ±.0010	
240	Huntite $Mg_3Ca(CO_3)_4$*	hex-R	$R32(155)$	calcite	3	9.498 ±.003	
241	Norsethite $BaMg(CO_3)_2$*	hex-R	$R32(155)$	calcite	3	5.020 ±.005	
242	Vaterite $CaCO_3$	hex.			6	7.135 ±.005	
243	Witherite $BaCO_3$	orth.	$Pnam(62)$	aragonite	4	6.430 ±.005	8.904 ±.005
244	Aragonite $CaCO_3$	orth.	$Pnam(62)$	aragonite	4	5.741 ±.005	7.968 ±.005
245	Cerussite $PbCO_3$	orth.	$Pnam(62)$	aragonite	4	6.152 ±.005	8.436 ±.005
246	Strontianite $SrCO_3$	orth.	$Pnam(62)$	aragonite	4	6.029 ±.005	8.414 ±.005
247	Shortite $Na_2Ca_2(CO_3)_3$	orth.	$Amm2(38)$		2	4.961 ±.005	11.03 ±.02
248	Malachite $Cu_2(OH)_2CO_3$	mon.	$P2_1/a(14)$		4	9.502 ±.007	11.974 ±.007
249	Azurite $Cu_3(OH)_2(CO_3)_2$	mon.	$P2_1/a(14)$		2	5.008 ±.005	5.844 ±.005
250	Niter KNO_3	orth.	$Pnam(62)$	aragonite	4	6.431 ±.005	9.164 ±.005
251	Soda Niter $NaNO_3$	hex-R	$R\bar{3}c(167)$	calcite	6	5.0696 ±.0010	
252	Gerhardite $Cu_2(NO_3)(OH)_3$	orth.	$P2_12_12_1(19)$		4	6.075 ±.004	13.812 ±.008
	Sulfates and borates						
253	Barite $BaSO_4$	orth.	$Pnma(62)$	barite	4	8.878 ±.005	5.450 ±.005
254	Anhydrite $CaSO_4$	orth.	$Amma(63)$ $Ccmm(63)$	anhydrite	4	6.991 ±.005	6.996 ±.005
255	Anglesite $PbSO_4$	orth.	$Pnma(62)$	barite	4	8.480 ±.005	5.398 ±.005
256	Celestite $SrSO_4$	orth.	$Pnma(62)$	barite	4	8.359 ±.005	5.352 ±.005
257	Zinkosite $ZnSO_4$	orth.	$Pnma(62)$	barite	4	8.588 ±.008	6.740 ±.006
258	Arcanite KS_2SO_4	orth.	$Pnma(62)$	arcanite	4	5.772 ±.005	10.072 ±.005
259	Mascagnite $(NH_4)_2SO_4$	orth.	$Pnma(62)$	arcanite	4	7.782 ±.005	5.993 ±.005
260	Thenardite Na_2SO_4	orth.	$Fddd(70)$	thenardite	8	5.863 ±.005	12.304 ±.005

X-Ray Crystallographic Data of Minerals

c_o	a_o	β_o	γ_o	Cell volume 10^{-24} cm³	Molar volume cm³	cal bar^{-1}	X-Ray density grams cm^{-3}	Temp. °C	
Carbonates and nitrates—Continued									
15.016				279.13	28.018	.66969	3.0095	26	235
±.003				± .13	± .013	±.00036	±.0014		
15.664				309.57	31.073	.74272	3.6992	26	236
±.003				± .14	± .014	±.00039	±.0017		
14.723				269.51	27.052	.64660	4.3886	26	237
±.002				± .12	± .012	±.00034	±.0020		
15.025				281.69	28.275	.67583	4.4343	26	238
±.003				± .13	± .013	±.00037	±.0021		
16.010				320.50	64.341	1.5378	2.8661	26	239
±.003				± .15	± .029	±.0008	±.0013		
7.816				610.63	122.58	2.9299	2.880	26	240
±.004				± .50	± .10	±.0024	±.002		
16.75				365.6	73.39	1.754	3.838	r	241
±.02				± .8	± .17	±.004	±.009		
8.524				375.80	37.72	.9016	2.653	r	242
±.007				± .61	± .06	±.0015	±.004		
5.314				304.24	45.81	1.095	4.308	26	243
±.005				± .41	± .06	±.002	±.006		
4.959				226.85	34.15	.8164	2.930	26	244
±.005				± .33	± .05	±.0012	±.004		
5.195				269.61	40.59	.9702	6.582	26	245
±.005				± .38	± .06	±.0014	±.009		
5.107				259.07	39.01	.9323	3.785	26	246
±.005				± .37	± .06	±.0014	±.005		
7.12				389.6	117.3	2.804	2.610	r	247
±.01				± 1.0	± .3	±.007	±.007		
3.240		98.75		364.35	54.86	1.311	4.030	25	248
±.003		±.25		± .54	± .08	±.002	±.006		
10.336		92.45		302.22	91.01	2.1752	3.787	25	249
±.005		±.25		± .43	± .13	±.0031	±.005		
5.414				319.07	48.04	1.148	2.105	26	250
±.005				± .42	± .06	±.002	±.003		
16.829				374.57	37.598	.89866	2.2606	25	251
±.005				± .19	± .019	±.00049	±.0011		
5.592				469.21	70.65	1.689	3.399	r	252
±.004				± .53	± .08	±.002	±.004		
Sulfates and borates									
7.152				346.05	52.10	1.245	4.480	26	253
±.003				± .40	± .06	±.002	±.005		
6.238				305.09	45.94	1.098	2.964	26	254
±.005				± .39	± .06	±.002	±.004		
6.958				318.50	47.95	1.146	6.324	25	255
±.003				± .38	± .06	±.002	±.008		
6.866				307.17	46.25	1.105	3.972	26	256
±.005				± .41	± .06	±.002	±.005		
4.770				276.10	41.57	.9936	3.883	25	257
±.005				± .46	± .07	±.0017	±.006		
7.483				435.03	65.50	1.566	2.661	25	258
±.004				± .49	± .07	±.002	±.003		
10.636				496.04	74.68	1.7851	1.7693	25	259
±.005				± .57	± .09	±.0021	±.0020		
9.821				708.17	53.33	1.275	2.663	25	260
±.005				± .76	± .06	±.002	⊥.003		

X-Ray Crystallographic Data of Minerals

	Name and formula	Crystal system	Space group	Structure type	Z	a_o	b_o
	Sulfates and borates—Continued						
261	Gypsum $CaSO_4.2H_2O$*	mon.	C2/c(15)		4	5.68 ±.01	15.18 ±.01
262	Epsomite $MgSO_4.7H_2O$	orth.	$P2_12_12_1$(19)		4	11.86 ±.01	11.99 ±.01
263	Goslarite $ZnSO_4.7H_2O$	orth.	$P2_12_12_1$(19)	epsomite	4	11.779 ±.005	12.050 ±.005
264	Mirabilite $Na_2SO_4.10H_2O$	mon.	$P2_1/c$(14)		4	11.51 ±.01	10.38 ±.01
265	Chalcanthite $CuSO_4.5H_2O$	tri.	$P\bar{1}$(2)		2	6.1045 ±.0050	10.72 ±.01
266	Brochantite $Cu_4SO_4(OH)_6$*	mon.	$P2_1/c$(14)		4	13.066 ±.010	9.85 ±.01
267	Syngenite $K_2Ca(SO_4)_2.H_2O$	mon.	$P2_1/m$(11)		2	9.775 ±.005	7.156 ±.005
268	Alunite $KAl_3(SO_4)_2(OH)_6$	hex-R	R3m(160)		3	6.982 ±.005	
269	Natroalunite $NaAl_3(SO_4)_2(OH)_6$	hex-R	R3m(160)		3	6.974 ±.005	
270	Hexahydrite $MgSO_4.6H_2O$	mon.	C2/c(15)		8	10.110 ±.005	7.212 ±.004
271	Leonhardtite $MgSO_4.4H_2O$	mon.	$P2_1/n$(14)		4	5.922 ±.006	13.604 ±.004
272	Melanterite $FeSO_4.7H_2O$	mon.	$P2_1/c$(14)		4	14.072 ±.010	6.503 ±.007
273	Vanthoffite $MgSO_4.3Na_2SO_4$	mon.	$P2_1/c$(14)		2	9.797 ±.003	9.217 ±.003
274	Dolerophanite $Cu_2O(SO_4)$	mon.	C2/m(15)		4	9.355 ±.010	6.312 ±.005
275	Retgersite $NiSO_4.4H_2O$	tet.	$P4_12_12$(92) $P4_32_1$(96)		4	6.782 ±.004	
276	Colemanite $CaB_3O_4(OH)_3.H_2O$*	mon.	$P2_1/a$(14)		4	8.743 ±.004	11.264 ±.002
277	Borax $Na_2B_4O_7.10H_2O$	mon.	C2/c(15)		4	11.858 ±.005	10.674 ±.005
278	Kernite $Na_2B_4O_7.4H_2O$	mon.	$P2_1/c$(14)		4	7.022 ±.003	9.151 ±.004
279	Hambergite $Be_2BO_3.(OH,F)$*	orth.	Pbca(61)		8	9.755 ±.001	12.201 ±.001
	Phosphates, molybdates, and tungstates						
280	Berlinite $AlPO_4$	hex.	$P3_121$(152) $P3_221$(154)	a-quartz	3	4.942 ±.005	
281	Xenotime YPO_4	tet.	$14_1/amd$(141)	zircon	4	6.885 ±.005	
282	Hydroxylapatite $Ca_5(PO_4)_3OH$	hex.	$P6_3/m$(176)	apatite	2	9.418 ±.003	
283	Fluorapatite $Ca_5(PO_4)_3F$	hex.	$P6_3/m$(176)	apatite	2	9.3684 ±.0030	
284	Chlorapatite $Ca_5(PO_4)_3Cl$	hex.	$P6_3m$(176)	apatite	2	9.629 ±.005	
285	Carbonate-apatite $Ca_{10}(PO_4)_6CO_3H_2O$	hex.	$P6_3/m$(176)	apatite	1	9.436 ±.010	
286	Turquois $CuAl_6(PO_4)_4(OH)_8.4H_2O$*	tri.	$P\bar{1}$(2)		1	7.424 ±.008	7.629 ±.008

X-Ray Crystallographic Data of Minerals

c_o	a_o	β_o	γ_o	Cell volume 10^{-24} cm³	Molar volume cm³	cal bar⁻¹	X-Ray density grams cm⁻³	Temp. °C	

Sulfates and borates—Continued

c_o	a_o	β_o	γ_o	Cell volume 10^{-24} cm³	Molar volume cm³	cal bar⁻¹	X-Ray density grams cm⁻³	Temp. °C	
6.29 ±.01		113.83 ±.22		496.1 ± 1.5	74.69 ± .22	1.785 ±.005	2.305 ±.007	r	261
6.858 ±.007				975.22 ± 1.53	146.83 ± .23	3.5094 ±.0055	1.679 ±.003	25	262
6.822 ±.003				968.29 ± .72	145.79 ± .11	3.4845 ±.0026	1.9723 ±.0015	25	263
12.83 ±.01		107.75 ±.17		1459.9 ± 2.6	219.8 ± .4	5.253 ±.009	1.466 ±.003	24	264
5.949 ±.007	97.57 ±.17	107.28 ±.17	77.43 ±.17	361.88 ± .72	108.97 ± .22	2.6045 ±.0052	2.2912 ±.0046	r	265
6.022 ±.010		103.27 ±.25		754.3 ± 1.8	113.6 ± .2	2.715 ±.006	3.982 ±.009	r	266
6.251 + 005		104.00 ±.25		424.27 ± .68	127.76 ± .20	3.0535 ±.0049	2.5707 ±.0041	r	267
17.32 ±.01				731.2 ± 1.1	146.8 ± .2	3.508 ±.005	2.822 ±.004	r	268
16.69 ±.01				702.99 ± 1.09	141.1 ± .2	3.373 ±.005	2.821 ±.004	r	269
24.41 ±.01		98.30 + 10		1761.2 ± 1.6	132.58 ± .12	3.1680 ±.0029	1.7232 ±.0015	r	270
7.905 ±.005		90.85 ±.20		636.78 ± .78	95.88 ± .12	2.2915 ±.0029	2.0071 ±.0025	r	271
11.041 ±.010		105.57 ±.15		973.29 ± 1.69	146.54 ± .25	3.5025 ±.0061	1.8972 ±.0033	r	272
8.199 ±.003		113.50 ±.10		678.96 ± .65	204.45 ± .20	4.8866 ±.0047	2.6730 ±.0025	r	273
7.628 ±.005		122.29 ±.10		380.77 ± .70	57.33 ± .11	1.3703 ±.0026	4.171 ±.008	r	274
18.28 ±.01				840.80 ± 1.09	126.59 ± .16	3.0257 ±.0040	2.076 ±.003	25	275
6.102 ⊥.003		110.12 ±.08		564.26 ± .49	84.957 ± .073	2.0306 ±.0018	2.4194 ±.0021	r	276
12.197 ±.005		106.68 ±.03		1478.8 ± 1.1	222.66 ± .17	5.3217 ±.0041	1.7128 ±.0013	r	277
15.676 ±.008		108.83 ±.25		953.40 ± 1.61	143.55 ± .24	3.4309 ±.0058	1.9038 ±.0032	r	278
4.426 ±.001				526.79 ± .14	39.658 ± .011	.9479 ±.0003	2.3663 ±.0006	r	279

Phosphates, molybdates, and tungstates

c_o	a_o	β_o	γ_o	Cell volume 10^{-24} cm³	Molar volume cm³	cal bar⁻¹	X-Ray density grams cm⁻³	Temp. °C	
10.97 ±.007				232.03 ± .50	46.58 ± .10	1.113 ±.002	2.618 ±.006	25	280
5.982 ±.005				283.57 ± 48	42.69 ⊥ .07	1.020 ±.002	4.307 ±.008	26	281
6.883 ±.003				528.7 ± .5	159.2 ± .2	3.805 ±.004	3.155 ±.004	r	282
6.8841 ±.0030				523.25 ± .41	157.56 ± .12	3.7659 ±.0030	3.2007 ±.0025	25	283
6.777 ±.003				544.16 ± .61	163.86 ± .19	3.916 + .004	3.178 ±.004	r	284
6.883 ±.010				530.74 ± 1.36	319.6 ± .8	7.640 + 020	3.281 ⊥.008	r	285
9.910 ±.010	68 61 ±.20	60.71 ±.20	65.08 ±.20	461.40 ± 1.12	277.9 ± .7	6.6416 ±.0162	2.927 ±.007	r	286

	Name and formula	Crystal system	Space group	Structure type	Z	a_o	b_o
	Phosphates, molybdates, and tungstates—Continued						
287	Powellite $CaMoO_4$	tet.	$I4_1/a(100)$	scheelite	4	5.226 $\pm.005$	
288	Wulfenite $PbMoO_4$	tet.	$I4_1/a(100)$	scheelite	4	5.435 $\pm.005$	
289	Scheelite $CaWO_4$	tet.	$I4_1/a(100)$	scheelite	4	5.242 $\pm.005$	
290	Stolzite $PbWO_4$	tet.	$I4_1/a(100)$	scheelite	4	5.4616 $\pm.0030$	
291	Ferberite $FeWO_4$	mon.	$P2/c(13)$	wolframite	2	4.732 $\pm.004$	5.708 $\pm.003$
292	Huebnerite $MnWO_4$	mon.	$P2/c(13)$	wolframite	2	4.834 $\pm.004$	5.758 $\pm.005$
293	Wolframite $Fe_{.5}Mn_{.5}WO_4$	mon.	$P2/c(13)$	wolframite	2	4.782 $\pm.004$	5.731 $\pm.004$
294	Sanmartinite $ZnWO_4$	mon.	$P2/c(13)$	wolframite	2	4.691 $\pm.003$	5.720 $\pm.003$
	Ortho and ring structure silicates						
295	Forsterite Mg_2SiO_4	orth.	$Pbnm(62)$	olivine	4	4.758 $\pm.002$	10.214 $\pm.003$
296	Fayalite Fe_2SiO_4	orth.	$Pbnm(62)$	olivine	4	4.817 $\pm.005$	10.477 $\pm.005$
297	Tephroite Mn_2SiO_4*	orth.	$Pbnm(62)$	olivine	4	4.871 $\pm.005$	10.636 $\pm.005$
298	Lime Olivine γCa_2SiO_4	orth.	$Pbnm(62)$	olivine	4	5.091 $\pm.010$	11.371 $\pm.020$
299	Nickel Olivine Ni_2SiO_4	orth.	$Pbnm(62)$	olivine	4	4.727 $\pm.002$	10.121 $\pm.005$
300	Cobalt Olivine Co_2SiO_4	orth.	$Pbnm(62)$	olivine	4	4.782 $\pm.002$	10.301 $\pm.005$
301	Monticellite $CaMgSiO_4$	orth.	$Pbnm(62)$	olivine	4	4.827 $\pm.005$	11.084 $\pm.005$
302	Kerschsteinite $CaFeSiO_4$	orth.	$Pbnm(62)$	olivine	4	4.886 $\pm.005$	11.146 $\pm.005$
303	Knebelite $MnFeSiO_4$*	orth.	$Pbnm(62)$	olivine	4	4.854 $\pm.010$	10.602 $\pm.010$
304	Glauchroite $CaMnSiO_4$	orth.	$Pbnm(62)$	olivine	4	4.944 $\pm.004$	11.19 $\pm.01$
305	Fluor-Norbergite $Mg_2SiO_4.MgF_2$	orth.	$Pnmb(62)$		4	8.727 $\pm.005$	10.271 $\pm.010$
306	Chondrodite $2Mg_2SiO_4.MgF_2$*	mon.	$P2_1/c(14)$		2	7.89 $\pm.03$	4.743 $\pm.020$
307	Fluor-Humite $3Mg_2SiO_4.MgF_2$	orth.	$Pnma(62)$		4	10.243 $\pm.005$	20.72 $\pm.02$
308	Clinohumite $4Mg_2SiO_4.MgF_2$*	mon.	$P2_1/c(14)$		2	13.68 $\pm.04$	4.75 $\pm.02$
309	Grossularite $Ca_3Al_2Si_3O_{12}$	cubic	$Ia3d(230)$	garnet	8	11.851 $\pm.001$	
310	Uvarovite $Ca_3Cr_2Si_3O_{12}$	cubic	$Ia3d(230)$	garnet	8	11.999 $\pm.002$	
311	Andradite $Ca_3Fe_2Si_3O_{12}$	cubic	$Ia3d(230)$	garnet	8	12.048 $\pm.001$	
312	Goldmanite $Ca_3V_2Si_3O_{12}$	cubic	$Ia3d(230)$	garnet	8	12.070 $\pm.005$	

c_o	a_o	β_o	γ_o	Cell volume 10^{-24} cm³	Molar volume cm³	cal bar⁻¹	X-Ray density grams cm⁻³	Temp. °C	
Phosphates, molybdates, and tungstates—Continued									
11.43 ±.007				312.17 ± .63	47.00 ± .09	1.1234 ±.0023	4.256 ±.009	25	287
12.110 ±.007				357.72 ± .69	53.859 ± .104	1.2873 ±.0025	6.816 ±.013	25	288
11.372 ±.005				312.49 ± .61	47.049 ± .092	1.1245 ±.0023	6.120 ±.012	25	289
12.046 ±.005				359.32 ± .42	54.100 ± .064	1.2931 ±.0016	8.4110 ±.0099	25	290
4.965 ±.004		90.00 ±.05		134.11 ± .17	40.38 ± .05	.9652 ±.0013	7.520 ±.010	r	291
4.999 ±.004		91.18 ±.10		139.11 ± .20	41.89 ± .06	1.001 ±.002	7.228 ±.010	r	292
4.982 ±.004		90.57 ±.10		136.53 ± .18	41.11 ± .06	.9826 ±.0014	7.376 ±.010	r	293
4.925 ±.003		89.36 ±.20		132.14 ± .14	39.79 ± .04	.9511 ±.0010	7.872 ±.008	25	294
Ortho and ring structure silicates									
5.984 ±.002				290.81 ± .18	43.786 ± .027	1.0465 ±.0007	3.2136 ±.0020	25	295
6.105 ±.010				308.11 ± .62	46.389 ± .093	1.1088 ±.0023	4.3928 ±.0088	r	296
6.232 ±.005				322.87 ± .45	48.612 ± .067	1.1619 ±.0017	4.1545 ±.0058	r	297
6.782 ±.010				392.61 ± 1.19	59.11 ± .18	1.4129 ±.0043	2.914 ±.009	r	298
5.915 ±.002				282.98 ± .21	42.61 ± .03	1.0184 ±.0008	4.917 ±.004	r	299
6.003 ±.002				295.70 ± .21	44.52 ± .03	1.0642 ±.0008	4.716 ±.003	r	300
6.376 ±.005				341.13 ± .47	51.362 ± .071	1.2276 ±.0017	3.046 ±.004	r	301
6.434 ±.010				350.39 ± .67	52.756 ± .101	1.2609 ±.0025	3.564 ±.007	r	302
6.162 ±.010				317.11 ± .88	47.74 ± .13	1.1412 ±.0032	4.249 ±.012	r	303
6.529 ±.005				361.2 ± .9	54.38 ± .14	1.2997 ±.0032	3.441 ±.009	r	304
4.709 ±.002				422.09 ± .51	63.551 ± .077	1.5190 ±.0019	3.194 ±.004	25	305
10.29 ±.03		109.03 ±.30		364.0 ± 2.4	109.6 ± .7	2.620 ±.017	3.136 ±.021	r	306
4.735 ±.002				1004.9 ± 1.2	151.31 ± .18	3.0103 ±.0042	3.2017 ±.0037	25	307
10.27 ±.02		100.83 ±.50		655.5 ± 3.8	197.4 ± 1.1	4.717 ±.027	3.167 ±.018	r	308
				1664.43 ± .42	125.30 ± .03	2.9948 ±.0008	3.595 ±.001	25	309
				1727.57 ± .86	130.05 ± .07	3.1084 ±.0016	3.848 ±.002	26	310
				1748.82 ± .44	131.65 ± .03	3.1466 ±.0008	3.860 ±.001	25	311
				1758.42 2.19	132.38 ± .16	3.1639 ±.0040	3.765 ±.005	r	312

	Name and formula	Crystal system	Space group	Structure type	Z	a_o	b_o
	Ortho and ring structure silicates—Continued						
313	Almandite $Fe_3Al_2Si_3O_{12}$	cubic	Ia3d(230)	garnet	8	11.526 ±.001	
314	Pyrope $Mg_3Al_2Si_3O_{12}$	cubic	Ia3d(230)	garnet	8	11.459 ±.001	
315	Spessartite $Mn_3Al_2Si_3O_{12}$	cubic	Ia3d(230)	garnet	8	11.621 ±.001	
316	Zircon $ZrSiO_4$*	tet.	I4/amd(141)	zircon	4	6.604 ±.005	
317	Thorite $ThSiO_4$	tet.	I4/amd(141)	zircon	4	7.143 ±.004	
318	Coffinite $USiO_4$	tet.	I4/amd(141)	zircon	4	6.995 ±.004	
319	Kyanite Al_2SiO_5*	tri.	P$\bar{1}$(2)		4	7.123 ±.001	7.848 ±.002
320	Andalusite Al_2SiO_5*	orth.	Pnnm(58)		4	7.7959 ±.0050	7.8983 ±.0020
321	Sillimanite Al_2SiO_5*	orth.	Pbnm(62) Pnma(62)		4	7.4843 ±.0030	7.6730 ±.0030
322	3.2 Mullite $3Al_2O_3.2SiO_2$	orth.			3/4	7.557 ±.002	7.6876 ±.0020
323	2.1 Mullite $2Al_2O_3.SiO_2$	orth.	Pbam(55)		6/5	7.5788 ±.0020	7.6909 ±.0020
324	Staurolite $Fe_2Al_9Si_4O_{22}(OH)_2$*	mon.	C2/m(15)		2	7.90 ±.10	16.65 ±.15
325	Topaz $Al_2(SiO_4)(OH)$*	orth.	Pmnb(62)		4	8.394 ±.005	8.792 ±.007
326	Phenacite Be_2SiO_4*	hex-R	R$\bar{3}$(148)	phenacite	18	12.472 ±.005	
327	Willemite Zn_2SiO_4	hex-R	R$\bar{3}$(148)	phenacite	18	13.94 ±.01	
328	Dioptase CuH_2SiO_4*	hex-R	R$\bar{3}$(148)	phenacite	18	14.61 ±.02	
329	Larnite β-Ca_2SiO_4*	mon.	P2_1/n(14)		4	5.48 ±.02	6.76 ±.02
330	Akermanite $Ca_2MgSi_2O_7$	tet.	P$\bar{4}2_1$m(113)	melilite	2	7.8435 ±.0030	
331	Gehlenite $Ca_2Al_2SiO_7$	tet.	P$\bar{4}2_1$m(113)	melilite	2	7.690 ±.003	
332	Fe-Gehlenite $Ca_2Fe_2SiO_7$	tet.	P$\bar{4}2_1$m(113)	melilite	2	7.54 ±.01	
333	Hardystonite $Ca_2ZnSi_2O_7$*	tet.	P$\bar{4}2_1$m(113)	melilite	2	7.87 ±.03	
334	Sodium Melilite $NaCaAlSi_2O_7$	tet.	P$\bar{4}2_1$m(113)	melilite	2	8.511 ±.005	
335	Beryl $Be_3Al_2(Si_6O_{18})$*	hex.	P6/mmc(192)	beryl	2	9.215 ±.005	
336	Indialite high Cordierite $Mg_2Al_3(AlSi_5O_{18})$	hex.	P6/mmc(192)	beryl	2	9.7698 ±.0030	
337	Low Cordierite $Mg_2Al_3(AlSi_5O_{18})$	orth.	Cccm(66)		4	9.721 ±.003	17.062 ±.006
338	Fe-Indialite $Fe_2Al_3(AlSi_5O_{18})$	hex.	P6/mmc(192)	beryl	2	9.860 ±.010	
339	Fe-Cordierite $Fe_2Al_3(AlSi_5O_{18})$	orth.	Cccm(66)	cordierite	4	9.726 ±.010	17.065 ±.010

X-Ray Crystallographic Data of Minerals

c_o	a_o	β_o	γ_o	Cell volume 10^{-24} cm³	Molar volume cm³	cal bar⁻¹	X-Ray density grams cm⁻³	Temp. °C	
				Ortho and ring structure silicates—Continued					
				1531.21 ± .40	115.27 ± .04	2.7551 ±.0008	4.318 ±.001	25	313
				1504.67 ± .39	113.27 ± .03	2.7074 ±.0008	3.559 ±.001	25	314
				1569.39 ± .41	118.15 ± .03	2.8238 ±.0008	4.190 ±.001	25	315
5.979 ±.005				260.76 ± .45	39.261 ± .068	.9384 ±.0017	4.669 ±.008	25	316
6.327 ±.003				322.82 ± .39	48.60 ± .06	1.1617 ±.0015	6.668 ±.008	r	317
6.263 ±.005				306.45 ± .43	46.140 ± .064	1.103 ±.002	7.155 ±.010	r	318
5.564 ±.008	89.92 ±.15	101.25 ±.08	105.97 ±.08	292.83 ± .45	44.09 ± .07	1.054 ±.002	3.675 ±.006	25	319
5.5583 ±.0020				342.25 ± .27	51.530 ± .040	1.2316 ±.0010	3.145 ±.002	25	320
5.7711 ±.0040				331.42 ± .30	49.899 ± .044	1.1927 ±.0011	3.248 ±.003	25	321
2.8842 ±.0010				167.56 ± .09	134.55 ± .07	3.2159 ±.0016	3.166 ±.002	r	322
2.8883 ±.0010				168.35 ± .09	84.492 ± .043	2.0195 ±.0011	3.125 ±.002	r	323
5.63 ±.10		90.00 ±.25		740.5 ±17.5	223.0 ± 5.3	5.330 ±.126	3.825 ±.090	r	324
4.649 ±.003				343.10 ± .41	51.66 ± .06	1.2347 ±.0015	3.563 ±.005	26	325
8.252 ±.005				1111.6 ± 1.1	37.194 ± .037	.8890 ±.0009	2.960 ±.003	25	326
9.309 ±.003				1566.6 ± 2.3	52.42 ± .08	1.253 ±.002	4.251 ±.006	25	327
7.80 ±.01				1441.9 ± 4.4	48.24 ± .15	1.153 ±.004	3.247 ±.010	r	328
9.28 ±.02		94.55 ±.33		342.7 ± 1.8	51.60 ± .27	1.233 ±.006	3.338 ±.017	r	329
5.010 ±.003				308.22 ± .30	92.812 ± .090	2.2183 ±.0022	2.9375 ±.0029	r	330
5.0675 ±.0030				299.67 ± .29	90.239 ± .088	2.1568 ±.0022	3.0387 ±.0030	r	331
4.855 ±.005				276.01 ± .79	83.12 ± .24	1.9865 ±.0057	3.994 ±.011	r	332
5.01 ±.02				310.3 ± 2.7	93.44 ± .80	2.233 ±.019	3.357 ±.029	r	333
4.809 ±.003				348.35 ± .46	104.90 ± .14	2.507 ±.008	2.462 ±.003	r	334
9.102 ±.005				675.98 ± .82	203.55 ± .25	4.8651 ±.0060	2.641 ±.003	25	335
9.3517 ±.0030				773.02 ± .54	232.78 ± .16	5.5636 ±.0039	2.513 ±.002	25	336
9.339 ±.003				1548.96 ± .88	233.22 ± .13	5.5741 ±.0032	2.508 ±.001	25	337
9.285 ±.010				781.75 ± 1.80	235.40 ± .54	5.6264 ±.0130	2.753 ±.006	r	338
9.287 ±.010				1541.40 ± 2.47	232.08 ± .37	5.5468 ±.0089	2.792 ±.005	r	339

X-Ray Crystallographic Data of Minerals

	Name and formula	Crystal system	Space group	Structure type	Z	a_o	b_o
	Ortho and ring structure silicates—Continued						
340	Mn-Indialite $Mn_2Al_3(AlSi_5O_{18})$	hex.	P6/mmc(192)	beryl	2	9.925 ±.010	
341	Sapphirine $Mg_2Al_4O_6SiO_4$*	mon.	P2$_1$/c(14)		8	11.26 ±.03	14.46 ±.03
342	Elbaite $NaLiAl_{7.67}B_3Si_6O_{27}(OH)_4$*	hex-R	R3m(160)	tourmaline	3	15.842 ±.010	
343	Schorl $NaFe_3Al_6B_3Si_6O_{27}(OH)_4$*	hex-R	R3m(160)	tourmaline	3	16.032 ±.010	
344	Dravite $NaMg_3Al_6B_3Si_6O_{27}(OH)_4$	hex-R	R3m(160)	tourmaline	3	15.942 ±.010	
345	Uvite $CaMg_4Al_5B_3Si_6O_{27}(OH)_4$	hex-R	R3m(160)	tourmaline	3	15.86 ±.01	
346	Sphene $CaTiSiO_5$*	mon.	A2/a(15)		4	7.07 ±.01	8.72 ±.01
347	Datolite $CaBSiO_4(OH)$*	mon.	P2$_1$/c(14)		4	9.62 ±.03	7.60 ±.03
348	Euclase $AlBeSiO_4(OH)$*	mon.	P2$_1$/a(14)		4	4.763 ±.005	14.29 ±.02
349	Chloritoid $H_2FeAl_2SiO_7$*	mon.	C2/c(15)		8	9.48 ±.01	5.48 ±.01
350	Hemimorphite $Zn_4(OH)_2Si_2O_7.H_2O$*	orth.	Imm2(35)		2	8.370 ±.005	10.719 ±.005
351	Zoisite $Ca_2Al_3(SiO_4)_3OH$	orth.	Pnma(62)		4	16.15 ±.01	5.581 ±.005
352	Clinozoisite $Ca_2Al_3(SiO_4)_3OH$	mon.	P2$_1$/m(11)		2	8.887 ±.007	5.581 ±.005
353	Epidote $Ca_2Al_{1.5}Fe_{1.5}(SiO_4)_3OH$*	mon.	P2$_1$/m(11)		2	8.89 ±.02	5.63 ±.01
354	Piemontite $Ca_2Al_{1.5}Mn_{1.5}(SiO_4)_3OH$*	mon.	P2$_1$/m(11)		2	8.95 ±.02	5.70 ±.01
355	Lawsonite $CaAl_2Si_2O_7(OH)_2.H_2O$	orth.	Cccm(63)		4	8.787 ±.005	5.836 ±.005
	Chain and band structure silicates						
356	Enstatite $MgSiO_3$*	orth.	Pcab(61)		16	8.829 ±.010	18.22 ±.01
357	Clinoenstatite $MgSiO_3$	mon.	P2$_1$/c(15)		8	9.620 ±.005	8.825 ±.005
358	Protoenstatite $MgSiO_3$	orth.	Pbcn(60)		8	9.25 ±.01	8.74 ±.01
359	High Clinoenstatite $MgSiO_3$	tri.			8	10.000 ±.005	8.934 ±.004
360	Clinoferrosilite $FeSiO_3$	mon.	P2$_1$/c(14)		8	9.7085 ±.0010	9.0872 ±.0011
361	Orthoferrosilite $FeSiO_3$	orth.	Pcab(61)	enstatite	16	9.080 ±.002	18.431 ±.004
362	Diopside $CaMg(SiO_3)_2$	mon.	C2/c(15)	diopside	4	9.743 ±.005	8.923 ±.005
363	Hedenbergite $CaFe(SiO_3)_2$*	mon.	C2/c(15)	diopside	4	9.854 ±.010	9.024 ±.010
364	Johannsenite $CaMn(SiO_3)_2$*	mon.	C2/c(15)	diopside	4	9.83 ±.03	9.04 ±.03
365	Ureyite $NaCr(SiO_3)_2$	mon.	C2/c(15)	diopside	4	9.550 ±.016	8.712 ±.007

c_o	a_o	β_o	γ_o	Cell volume 10^{-24} cm³	Molar volume cm³	cal bar^{-1}	X-Ray density grams cm^{-3}	Temp. °C	
Ortho and ring structure silicates—Continued									
9.297 ±.010				793.11 ± .81	238.8 ± .5	5.708 ±.013	2.706 ±.006	r	340
9.95 ±.02		125.33 ±.50		1321.7 ± 9.7	99.50 ± .73	2.378 ±.017	3.464 ±.025	r	341
7.009 ±.010				1523.4 ± 2.9	305.82 ± .58	7.3093 ±.0140	3.271 ±.006	r	342
7.149 ±.010				1591.3 ± 3.0	319.45 ± .60	7.635 ±.014	3.297 ±.006	r	343
7.224 ±.010				1589.99 ± 2.97	319.19 ± .60	7.629 ±.014	3.004 ±.006	r	344
7.19 ±.01				1566.3 ± 2.9	314.4 ± .6	7.515 ±.014	3.095 ±.006	r	345
6.56 ±.01		113.95 ±.25		369.61 ± 1.13	55.65 ± .17	1.330 ±.004	3.523 ±.011	r	346
4.84 ±.02		90.15 ±.25		353.9 ± 2.3	53.28 ± .35	1.273 ±.008	3.003 ±.020	r	347
4.618 ±.005		100.25 ±.10		309.30 ± .64	46.57 ± .10	1.113 ±.002	3.116 ±.007	r	348
18.18 ±.01		101.77 ±.25		924.6 ± 2.2	69.61 ± .16	1.664 ±.004	3.619 ±.008	r	349
5.120 ±.005				459.36 ± .57	138.32 ± .17	3.306 ±.004	3.482 ±.004	25	350
10.06 ±.01				906.74 ± 1.34	136.52 ± .20	3.263 ±.005	3.328 ±.005	r	351
10.14 ±.01		115.93 ±.33		452.30 ± 1.45	136.20 ± .44	3.255 ±.010	3.336 ±.011	r	352
10.19 ±.02		115.40 ±.30		460.72 ± 1.97	138.7 ± .6	3.316 ±.014	3.587 ±.015	r	353
9.41 ±.02		115.70 ±.50		432.56 ± 2.38	130.3 ± .7	3.113 ±.017	3.810 ±.021	r	354
13.123 ±.008				672.96 ± .80	101.32 ± .12	2.4217 ±.0029	3.101 ±.004	r	355
Chain and band structure silicates									
5.192 ±.005				835.21 ± 1.32	31.44 ± .05	.7514 ±.0012	3.194 ±.005	r	356
5.188 ±.005		108.33 ±.17		418.10 ± .66	31.47 ± .05	.7523 ±.0012	3.190 ±.005	r	357
5.32 ±.01				430.10 ± 1.05	32.38 ± .08	.7739 ±.0019	3.101 ±.008	r	358
5.170 ±.003	88.27 ±.05	70.03 ±.04	91.01 ±.04	433.72 ± .40	32.65 ± .03	.7804 ±.0008	3.075 ±.003		359
5.2284 ⊥.004		108.43 + 05		437.60 ⊥ .15	32.943 ± .011	.7871 ±.0003	4.005 ±.002	r	360
5.238 ±.001				876.6 ± .54	33.00 ± .02	.7887 ±.0008	3.998 ±.004	r	361
5.251 ±.003		105.93 ±.25		438.97 ± .69	66.09 ± .10	1.580 ±.003	3.277 ±.005	r	362
5.263 ±.010		104.23 ±.33		453.64 ± 1.28	68.30 ± .19	1.632 ±.005	3.632 ⊥.010	r	363
5.27 ±.02		105.00 ±.50		452.35 ± 2.87	68.11 + .43	1.628 ±.010	3.629 ±.023	r	364
5.273 ±.008		107.44 ±.16		418.6 ± 1.1	63.02 ± .16	1.506 ±.004	3.605 ±.009	r	365

	Name and formula	Crystal system	Space group	Structure type	Z	a_o	b_o
	Chain and band structure silicates—Continued						
366	Jadeite $NaAl(SiO_3)_2$*	mon.	C2/c(15)	diopside	4	9.409 ±.005	8.564 ±.005
367	Acmite (Aegirine) $NaFe(SiO_3)_2$	mon.	C2/c(15)	diopside	4	9.658 ±.005	8.795 ±.005
368	Ca Tschermak Molecule $CaAl_2SiO_6$	mon.	C2/c(15)	diopside	4	9.615 ±.005	8.661 ±.005
369	Spodumene $LiAl(SiO_3)_2$	mon.	C2/c(15)	diopside	4	9.451 ±.002	8.387 ±.002
370	β-Spodumene $LiAl(SiO_3)_2$	tet.	P4₃2₁2(96) P4₁2₁2(92)		4	7.5332 ±.0008	
371	Pectolite $Ca_2NaH(SiO_3)_3$*	tri.	P1̄(2)		2	7.99 ±.01	7.04 ±.01
372	Wollastonite $CaSiO_3$*	tri.	P1̄(2)		6	7.94 ±.01	7.32 ±.01
373	Parawollastonite $CaSiO_3$*	mon.	P2₁(4)		12	15.417 ±.004	7.321 ±.002
374	Pseudowollastonite $CaSiO_3$*	tri.			24	6.90 ±.02	11.78 ±.02
375	Rhodonite $MnSiO_3$*	tri.	P1̄(2)		10	7.682 ±.002	11.818 ±.003
376	Bustamite $CaMn(SiO_3)_2$*	tri.	A1̄(2)		6	7.736 ±.003	7.157 ±.003
377	Pyroxmangite $MnFe(SiO_3)_2$*	tri.	P1̄(2)		7	7.56 ±.02	17.45 ±.05
378	Tremolite $Ca_2Mg_5[Si_8O_{22}](OH)_2$*	mon.	C2/m(12)	tremolite	2	9.840 ±.010	18.052 ±.020
379	Fluor-tremolite $Ca_2Mg_5[Si_8O_{22}]F_2$	mon.	C2/m(12)	tremolite	2	9.781 ±.007	18.01 ±.01
380	Ferrotremolite $Ca_2Fe_5[Si_8O_{22}](OH)_2$	mon.	C2/m(12)	tremolite	2	9.97 ±.01	18.34 ±.02
381	Grunerite $Fe_7[Si_8O_{22}](OH)_2$	mon.	C2/m(12)	tremolite	2	9.572 ±.005	18.44 ±.01
382	Cummingtonite (hypo.) $Mg_7[Si_8O_{22}](OH)_2$	mon.	C2/m(12)	tremolite	2	9.476 ±.010	17.935 ±.010
383	Riebeckite $Na_2Fe_3Fe_2[Si_8O_{22}](OH)_2$	mon.	C2/m(12)	tremolite	2	9.729 ±.020	18.065 ±.020
384	Magnesioriebeckite $Na_2Mg_3Fe_2[Si_8O_{22}](OH)_2$	mon.	C2/m(12)	tremolite	2	9.733 ±.010	17.946 ±.020
385	Gaucophane I $Na_2Mg_3Al_2[Si_8O_{22}](OH)_2$	mon.	C2/m(12)	tremolite	2	9.748 ±.010	17.915 ±.020
386	Glaucophane II $Na_2Mg_3Al_2[Si_8O_{22}](OH)_2$	mon.	C2/m(12)	tremolite	2	9.663 ±.010	17.696 ±.020
387	Fluor-edenite $NaCa_2Mg_5[AlSi_7O_{22}]F_2$	mon.	C2/m(12)	tremolite	2	9.847 ±.005	18.00 ±.01
388	Fluor-richterite $Na_2CaMg_5[Si_8O_{22}]F_2$	mon.	C2/m(12)	tremolite	2	9.823 ±.005	17.96 ±.01
389	Anthophyllite $Mg_7[Si_8O_{22}](OH)_2$	orth.	Pnma(62)		4	18.61 ±.02	18.01 ±.06
	Framework structure silicates						
390	Microcline $KAlSi_3O_8$	tri.	C1̄(2)		4	8.582 ±.002	12.964 ±.005
391	High Sanidine $KAlSi_3O_8$	mon.	C2/m(12)		4	8.615 ±.002	13.031 ±.003

c_o	a_o	β_o	γ_o	Cell volume 10^{-24} cm³	Molar volume cm³	cal bar^{-1}	X-Ray density grams cm^{-3}	Temp. °C	
				Chain and band structure silicates—Continued					
5.220		107.50		401.15	60.40	1.444	3.347	r	366
±.005		±.20		± .67	± .10	±.002	±.006		
5.294		107.42		429.06	64.60	1.544	4.411	r	367
±.005		±.20		± .70	± .11	±.003	±.007		
5.272		106.12		421.77	63.50	1.518	3.435	r	368
±.003		±.20		± .59	± .09	±.002	±.005		
5.208		110.07		387.7	58.37	1.395	3.188	r	369
±.001		±.03		± .1	± .02	±.001	±.001		
9.1540				519.48	78.215	1.8694	2.379	r	370
±.0008				± .12	± .018	±.0005	±.001		
7.02	90.05	95.27	102.47	383.84	115.58	2.763	2.876	r	371
±.01	±.25	±.25	±.25	± .99	± .30	±.007	±.007		
7.07	90.03	95.37	103.43	397.82	39.93	.9544	2.909	r	372
±.01	±.25	±.25	±.25	± 1.03	± .10	±.0025	±.008		
7.066		95.40		793.98	39.85	.9524	2.915	r	373
±.003		±.10		± .47	± .02	±.0006	±.002		
19.65	90.00	90.80	90.00	1597.0	40.08	.9579	2.899	r	374
±.02	±.30	±.30	±.30	± 5.6	± .14	±.0034	±.010		
6.707	92.36	93.95	105.66	583.77	35.158	.8403	3.727	r	375
±.002	±.05	±.05	±.05	± .31	± .019	±.0005	±.002		
13.824	90.52	94.58	103.87	740.38	74.32	1.776	3.326	r	376
±.010	±.25	±.25	±.25	± 1.08	± .11	±.003	±.005		
6.67	84.00	94.30	113.70	800.77	68.90	1.647	3.817	r	377
±.02	±.30	±.30	±.30	± 4.29	± .36	±.009	±.020		
5.275		104.70		906.34	272.92	6.523	2.977	r	378
±.010		±.25		± 2.43	± .73	±.018	±.008		
5.267		104.52		898.18	270.46	6.464	3.018	20	379
±.005		±.25		± 1.56	± .47	±.011	±.005		
5.30		104.50		938.24	282.53	6.753	3.434	r	380
±.01		±.10		± 2.92	± .69	±.017	±.008		
5.342		101.77		923.08	277.96	6.644	3.603	r	381
±.007		±.25		± 1.63	± .49	±.012	±.006		
5.292		102.23		878.97	264.68	6.326	2.950	r	382
±.005		±.25		± 1.58	± .47	±.011	±.005		
5.334		103.31		912.29	274.71	6.566	3.407	r	383
±.010		±.25		± 2.89	± .87	±.021	±.011		
5.299		103.30		900.74	271.24	6.483	3.102	r	384
±.010		±.25		± 2.37	± .71	±.017	±.008		
5.273		102.78		898.04	270.42	6.463	2.898	r	385
±.010		±.25		± 2.35	± .71	±.017	±.008		
5.277		103.67		876.79	264.02	6.310	2.968	r	386
±.010		±.10		± 2.17	± .65	±.016	±.007		
5.282		104.83		905.03	272.53	6.514	3.076	r	387
±.005		±.25		± 1.51	± .46	±.011	±.005		
5.268		104.33		900.47	271.15	6.481	3.033	r	388
±.005		±.25		± 1.48	± .45	±.011	±.005		
5.24				1756.3	264.4	6.320	2.953	r	389
±.01				± 7.0	± 1.1	±.025	±.012		
				Framework structure silicates					
7.222	90.62	115.92	87.68	722.06	108.72	2.5984	2.560	r	390
±.002	±.10	±.10	±.10	± .67	± .10	±.0025	±.002		
7.177		115.98		724.28	109.05	2.6064	2.552	r	391
±.002		±.10		± .69	± .10	±.0025	±.002		

X-Ray Crystallographic Data of Minerals

	Name and formula	Crystal system	Space group	Structure type	Z	a_o	b_o

Framework structure silicates—Continued

	Name and formula	Crystal system	Space group	Structure type	Z	a_o	b_o
392	Orthoclase $KAlSi_3O_8$*	mon.	C2/m(12)		4	8.562 ±.003	12.996 ±.004
393	Fe-Sanidine $KFeSi_3O_8$	mon.	C2/m(12)		4	8.689 ±.008	13.12 ±.01
394	Fe-Microcline $KFeSi_3O_8$	tri.	C$\bar{1}$(2)		4	8.68 ±.01	13.10 ±.01
395	Low Albite $NaAlSi_3O_8$	tri.	C$\bar{1}$(2)		4	8.139 ±.002	12.788 ±.003
396	High Albite (Analbite) $NaAlSi_3O_8$	tri.	C$\bar{1}$(2)		4	8.160 ±.002	12.870 ±.003
397	Anorthite $CaAl_2Si_2O_8$	tri.	P$\bar{1}$(2)	primitive cell	8	8.177 ±.002	12.877 ±.003
398	Synthetic $CaAl_2Si_2O_8$	hex.	P6$_3$/mcm(193)		2	5.10 ±.02	
399	Synthetic $CaAl_2Si_2O_8$	orth.	P2$_1$2$_1$2(18)		2	8.22 ±.02	8.60 ±.02
400	Celsian $BaAl_2Si_2O_8$*	mon.	I2$_1$/c(15)		8	8.627 ±.010	13.045 ±.010
401	Paracelsian $BaAl_2Si_2O_8$*	mon.	P2$_1$/a(14)		4	8.58 ±.02	9.583 ±.020
402	Banalsite $BaNa_2Al_4Si_4O_{16}$*	orth.			4	8.50 ±.02	9.97 ±.02
403	Danburite $CaB_2Si_2O_8$*	orth.	Pnam(62)		4	8.04 ±.02	8.77 ±.02
404	Low Nepheline $NaAlSiO_4$	hex.	C6$_3$(178)		8	9.986 ±.005	
405	High Carnegeite $NaAlSiO_4$	cubic			4	7.325 ±.004	
406	Kaliophilite natural $KAlSiO_4$*	hex.	P6$_3$22(182)		54	26.930 ±.010	
407	Kaliophilite synthetic $KAlSiO_4$	hex.	P6$_3$(173) P6$_3$22(182)		2	5.180 ±.002	
408	Kalsilite $KAlSiO_4$	hex.	P6$_3$(173)		2	5.1597 ±.0020	
409	Leucite $KAlSi_2O_6$	tet.	I4$_1$/a(100)		16	13.074 ±.003	
410	High Leucite $KAlSi_2O_6$*	cubic	Ia3d(230)		16	13.43 ±.05	
411	Fe-Leucite $KFeSi_2O_6$	tet.	I4$_1$/a(100)		16	13.205 ±.002	
412	Petalite $LiAlSi_4O_{10}$*	mon.	P2$_1$/n(14)		2	11.32 ±.03	5.14 ±.01
413	Marialite $Na_4Al_3Si_9O_{24}Cl$	tet.	I4/m(87) P4/m(83)		2	12.064 ±.008	
414	Meionite $Ca_4Al_6Si_6O_{24}CO_3$	tet.	I4/m(87) P4/m(83)		2	12.174 ±.008	

Sheet structure silicates

	Name and formula	Crystal system	Space group	Structure type	Z	a_o	b_o
415	Muscovite $KAl_2[AlSi_3O_{10}](OH)_2$*	mon.	C2/c(15)	2M$_2$ mica	4	5.203 ±.005	8.995 ±.005
416	Paragonite $NaAl_2[AlSi_3O_{10}](OH)_2$*	mon.	C2/c(15)	2M$_1$ mica	4	5.13 ±.03	8.89 ±.05
417	Lepidolite $K_2Al_3Li_2[AlSi_7O_{20}](OH)_4$*	mon.	C2/c(15)	2M$_2$ mica	2	9.2 ±.1	5.3 ±.1

c_o	a_o	β_o	γ_o	Cell volume 10^{-24} cm³	Molar volume cm³	cal bar⁻¹	X-Ray density grams cm⁻³	Temp. °C	
Framework structure silicates—Continued									
7.193 ±.003		116.02 ±.15		719.25 ± 1.02	108.29 ± .15	2.5883 ±.0037	2.570 ±.004	r	392
7.319 ±.007		116.10 ±.30		749.28 ± 2.24	112.81 ± .34	2.6964 ±.0081	2.723 ±.008	r	393
7.340 ±.007	90.75 ±.25	116.05 ±.25	86.23 ±.25	748.09 ± 1.92	112.63 ± .29	2.692 ±.007	2.727 ±.007	r	394
7.160 ±.002	94.27 ±.10	116.57 ±.10	87.68 ±.10	664.65 ± .60	100.07 ± .09	2.3918 ±.0022	2.620 ±.002	26	395
7.106 ±.002	93.54 ±.10	116.36 ±.10	90.19 ±.10	667.00 ± .60	100.43 ± .09	2.4003 ±.0022	2.611 ±.002	r	396
14.169 ±.003	93.17 ±.02	115.85 ±.02	91.22 ±.02	1338.9 ± .6	100.79 ± .04	2.4090 ±.0011	2.760 ±.001	r	397
14.72 ±.02				331.57 ± 2.64	99.85 ± .79	2.386 ±.019	2.786 ±.022	r	398
4.83 ±.01				341.44 ± 1.35	102.82 ± .41	2.457 ±.010	2.706 ±.011	r	399
14.408 ±.020		115.20 ±.25		1467.1 ± 4.2	110.45 ± .31	2.640 ±.008	3.400 ±.010	r	400
9.08 ±.02		90.00 ±.50		746.6 ± 2.9	112.4 ± .4	2.087 ±.010	3.340 ±.013	r	401
16.72 ±.03				1416.9 ± 5.1	213.3 ± .8	5.099 ±.018	3.092 ±.011	r	402
7.74 ±.02				545.8 ± 2.3	82.17 ± .35	1.964 ±.008	2.992 ±.013	r	403
8.330 ±.004				719.38 ± .80	54.16 ± .06	1.294 ±.002	2.623 ±.003	r	404
				393.03 ± .64	59.18 ± .10	1.414 ±.002	2.401 ±.004	750	405
8.522 ±.004				5352.4 ± 4.7	59.69 ± .05	1.427 ±.001	2.650 ±.002	r	406
8.559 ±.004				198.89 ± .18	59.89 ± .05	1.431 ±.001	2.641 ±.002	r	407
8.7032 ±.0030				200.66 ± .17	60.424 ± .051	1.4442 ±.0031	2.618 ±.002	r	408
13.738 ±.003				2348.23 ± 1.19	88.389 ± .045	2.1126 ±.0011	2.469 ±.001	25	409
				2422.3 ±27.1	91.18 ± 1.02	2.179 ±.024	2.394 ±.027	625	410
13.970 ±.003				2435.98 ± .91	91.692 ± .034	2.1915 ±.0009	2.695 ±.001	25	411
7.62 ±.01		105.90 ±.20		426.41 ± 1.57	128.4 ± .5	3.069 ±.011	2.385 ±.009	r	412
7.514 ±.004				1093.6 + 1.6	329.3 ± .5	7.871 ±.011	2.566 ±.004	r	413
7.052 ±.015				1134.07 ± 2.68	341.5 ± .8	8.162 ±.019	2.737 ±.007	r	414
Sheet structure silicates									
20.030 ±.010		91.47 ±.33		934.57 ± 1.21	140.71 ± .18	3.363 ±.004	2.831 ±.004	r	415
19.32 ±.10		95.17 ±.50		877.52 ± 8.47	132.1 ± 1.3	3.158 ±.031	2.893 ±.028	r	416
20.0 ±.2		98.00 ±.50		965.7 ±23.2	290.8 ± 7.0	6.950 ±.167	2.698 ±.065	r	417

X-Ray Crystallographic Data of Minerals

	Name and formula	Crystal system	Space group	Structure type	Z	a_o	b_o
	Sheet structure silicates—Continued						
418	Phlogopite $KMg_3[AlSi_3O_{10}](OH)_2$	mon.	Cm(8)	1M mica	2	5.326 ±.010	9.210 ±.010
419	Fluor-phlogopite $KMg_3[AlSi_3O_{10}]F_2$	mon.	Cm(8)	1M mica	2	5.299 ±.005	9.188 ±.005
420	Annite $KFe_3[AlSi_3O_{10}](OH)_2$	mon.	Cm(8)	1M mica	2	5.391 ±.010	9.350 ±.005
421	Ferriannite $KFe_3[FeSi_3O_{10}](OH)_2$	mon.	C2/m(12)		2	5.430 ±.002	9.404 ±.003
422	Margarite $CaAl_2[Al_2Si_2O_{10}](OH)_2*$	mon.	C2/c(15)	2M mica	4	5.13 ±.02	8.92 ±.03
423	Talc $Mg_3Si_4O_{10}(OH)_2*$	mon.	C2/c(15)	$2M_1$	4	5.287 ±.007	9.158 ±.010
424	Pyrophyllite $Al_2Si_4O_{10}(OH)_2*$	mon.	C2/c(15)	$2M_1$	4	5.14 ±.02	8.90 ±.02
425	Minnesotaite $Fe_3Si_4O_{10}(OH)_2*$	mon.	C2/c(15)		4	5.4 ±.1	9.42 ±.04
426	Dickite $Al_2Si_2O_5(OH)_4*$	mon.	Cc(9)		4	5.150 ±.002	8.940 ±.003
427	Kaolinite $Al_2Si_2O_5(OH)_4*$	tri.	P1(1)		2	5.155 ±.007	8.959 ±.010
428	Nacrite $Al_2Si_2O_5(OH)_4*$	mon.	Cc(9)		4	8.909 ±.010	5.146 ±.010
	Zeolites						
429	Analcite $NaAlSi_2O_6.H_2O$	cubic	Ia3d(230)		16	13.733 ±.005	
430	Natrolite $Na_2Al_2Si_3O_{10}.2H_2O*$	orth.	Fdd2(43)		8	18.30 ±.02	18.63 ±.02

X-Ray Crystallographic Data of Minerals

c_o	a_o	β_o	γ_o	Cell volume 10^{-24} cm³	Molar volume cm³	cal bar⁻¹	X-Ray density grams cm⁻³	Temp. °C	

Sheet structure silicates—Continued

c_o	a_o	β_o	γ_o	Cell volume 10^{-24} cm³	Molar volume cm³	cal bar⁻¹	X-Ray density grams cm⁻³		Temp. °C
10.311 ±.010		100.17 ±.10		497.83 ± 1.19	149.91 ± .36	3.5830 ±.0086	2.784 ±.007	r	418
10.135 ±.005		99.92 ±.10		486.07 ± .60	146.37 ± .18	3.498 ±.004	2.878 ±.004	r	419
10.313 ±.020		99.70 ±.25		512.40 ± 1.45	154.30 ± .44	3.688 ±.010	3.318 ±.009	r	420
10.341 ±.006		100.07 ±.20		519.92 ± .51	156.56 ± .15	3.7419 ±.0037	3.454 ±.003	r	421
19.50 ±.05		95.00 ±.50		888.9 ± 5.2	133.8 ± .8	3.199 ±.019	2.975 ±.017	r	422
18.95 ±.01		99.50 ±.20		904.94 ± 1.71	136.25 ± .26	3.2565 ±.0062	2.784 ±.005	r	423
18.55 ±.03		99.92 ±.20		835.9 ± 4.0	125.9 ± .6	3.008 ±.015	2.863 ±.014	r	424
19.4 ±.1		100.00 ±.50		971.8 ±19.2	146.3 ± 2.9	3.497 ±.069	3.239 ±.064	r	425
14.736 ±.005		103.58 ±.10		659.49 ± .49	99.30 ± .07	2.3733 ±.0018	2.600 ±.002	r	426
7.407 ±.008	91.68 ±.35	104.87 ±.35	89.93 ±.35	330.48 ± .86	99.52 ± .26	2.3785 ±.0062	2.594 ±.007	r	427
15.697 ±.020		113.70 ±.25		658.9 ± 2.1	99.21 ± .32	2.3713 ±.0076	2.602 ±.008	r	428

Zeolites

c_o	a_o	β_o	γ_o	Cell volume 10^{-24} cm³	Molar volume cm³	cal bar⁻¹	X-Ray density grams cm⁻³		Temp. °C
				2589.98 ± 2.83	97.49 ± .11	2.3301 ±.0026	2.258 ±.003	r	429
6.60 ±.01				2250.1 ± 4.8	169.39 ± .37	4.049 ±.009	2.245 ±.005	r	430

HEAT CAPACITY OF ROCK FORMING MINERALS

The units of heat capacity at constant pressure, C_p, in this table are cal kg⁻¹ deg⁻¹. Values of these units are given for several temperatures with the temperatures being in degrees C.

Heat capacity at other temperatures may be calculated by use of the equation $C_p = a + bT - cT^{-2}$. The units of these constants are cal kg⁻¹ deg⁻¹.

Mineral	Heat capacity at various temperatures						Constants for heat capacity equation		
	-200	0	200	400	800	1200	a	10³b	10⁵c
Albite	—	0.1695	0.236	0.26	0.286	—	1.018	0.187	0.268
Amphibole	—	0.177	0.246	0.27	0.296	—	1.067	1.183	0.281
Apatite	—	0.24	—	—	—	—	—	—	—
Arsenopyrite	—	0.103 at 55°C	—	—	—	—	—	—	—
Asbestos	—	0.195	—	—	—	—	—	—	—
Barite	0.047	0.1076	0.12	0.1315	0.1555	—	0.383	0.253	0
Cassiterite	—	0.0814	0.103	0.115	0.132	—	0.387	0.157	0.007
Chalcopyrite	—	0.129 at 50°C							
Diamond	—	0.104	0.253	0.328	0.445	—	0.754	1.067	0.454
Dolomite	—	0.222 at 60°C	—	—	—	—	—	—	—
Fluorite	0.0525	0.203	0.213	0.222	0.24	0.263	0.798	0.204	0
Galena	0.034	0.0496	0.0528	0.0562	—	—	0.188	0.007	0
Garnet	—	0.177 at 58°C							
β-Graphite	—	0.152	0.282	0.348	0.45	—	0.932	0.913	0.4077
Hematite	—	0.146	0.189	0.215	0.258	—	0.640	0.420	0.111
Ice	0.156	0.492	—	—	—	—	—	—	—
Kaolinite	—	0.222	0.244	—	—	—	0.806	0.463	0.0
Labradorite	—	0.196 at 60°C							
Magnesite	0.0383	0.207	—	—	—	—	—	—	—
Magnetite	—	0.1435	0.1985	0.222	—	—	0.744	0.340	0.177
Mica (mono-crystal)	—	0.208							
Microcline	—	0.163	0.227	0.248	0.342	—	0.988	0.166	0.263
Oligoclase	—	0.2035 at 60°C							
Olivine	—	0.189 at 36°C							
Orthoclase	—	0.146	0.226	0.251	0.347	—	0.043	0.124	0.351
Pyrite	0.0179	0.1195	0.142	0.165	—	—	0.373	0.466	0
Pyroxene	—	0.18	0.246	0.275	—	—	0.973	0.336	0.233
α-Quartz	0.0414	0.167	0.232	0.2695	—	—	0.7574	0.607	0.168
β-Quartz	—	—	—	—	0.28	0.3165	0.763	0.383	0
Serpentine	—	0.227							
Siderite	0.056	0.163							
Talc	—	0.208 at 59°C							
Zircon	—	0.146 at 60°C							

SOLUBILITY PRODUCT

The solubility product (or ion product constant) is the product of the concentrations of the ions in the saturated solution of a difficultly soluble salt. The concentrations are expressed as moles per liter of solution. The number of cations (or anions) resulting from the dissociation of one molecule of the salt, appears in the formula for calculations of the solubility product as the exponent of the concentration of the cation (or anion).

If two solutions, each containing one of the ions of a difficultly soluble salt, are mixed, no precipitation takes place unless the product of the ion concentrations in the mixture is greater than the solubility product.

In a solution containing two salts which yield a common ion the ratio of solubilities of the two salts is the ratio of the solubility products.

Substance	Solubility product at temperature noted	Substance	Solubility product at temperature noted
Aluminum hydroxide	4×10^{-13} (15°)	Lead iodide	7.47×10^{-9} (15°)
Aluminum hydroxide	1.1×10^{-15} (18°)	Lead iodide	1.39×10^{-8} (25°)
Aluminum hydroxide	3.7×10^{-15} (25°)	Lead oxalate	2.74×10^{-11} (18°)
Barium carbonate	7×10^{-9} (16°)	Lead sulfate	1.06×10^{-8} (18°)
Barium carbonate	8.1×10^{-9} (25°)	Lead sulfide	3.4×10^{-28} (18°)
Barium chromate	1.6×10^{-10} (18°)	Lithium carbonate	1.7×10^{-3} (25°)
Barium chromate	2.4×10^{-10} (28°)	Magnesium ammonium phosphate	2.5×10^{-13} (25°)
Barium fluoride	1.6×10^{-6} (9.5°)	Magnesium carbonate	2.6×10^{-5} (12°)
Barium fluoride	1.7×10^{-6} (18°)	Magnesium fluoride	7.1×10^{-9} (18°)
Barium fluoride	1.73×10^{-6} (25.8°)	Magnesium fluoride	6.4×10^{-9} (27°)
Barium iodate, $Ba(IO_3)_2.2H_2O$	8.4×10^{-11} (10°)	Magnesium hydroxide	1.2×10^{-11} (18°)
Barium iodate, $Ba(IO_3)_2.2H_2O$	6.5×10^{-10} (25°)	Magnesium oxalate	8.57×10^{-5} (18°)
Barium oxalate, $BaC_2O_4.3\frac{1}{2}H_2O$	1.62×10^{-7} (18°)	Manganese hydroxide	4×10^{-14} (18°)
Barium oxalate, $BaC_2O_4.2H_2O$	1.2×10^{-7} (18°)	Manganese sulfide	1.4×10^{-15} (18°)
Barium oxalate, $BaC_2O_4.\frac{1}{2}H_2O$	2.18×10^{-7} (18°)	Mercuric sulfide	4×10^{-53} to
Barium sulfate	0.87×10^{-10} (18°)		2×10^{-49} (18°)
Barium sulfate	1.08×10^{-10} (25°)	Mercurous bromide	1.3×10^{-21} (25°)
Barium sulfate	1.98×10^{-10} (50°)	Mercurous chloride	2×10^{-18} (25°)
Cadmium oxalate $CdC_2O_4.3H_2O$	1.53×10^{-8} (18°)	Mercurous iodide	1.2×10^{-28} (25°)
Cadmium sulfide	3.6×10^{-29} (18°)	Nickel sulfide	1.4×10^{-24} (18°)
Calcium carbonate (calcite)	0.99×10^{-8} (15°)	Potassium acid tartrate $[K^+]$ $[HC_4H_4O_6^-]$	3.8×10^{-4} (18°)
Calcium carbonate (calcite)	0.87×10^{-8} (25°)	Silver bromate	3.97×10^{-5} (20°)
Calcium fluoride	3.4×10^{-11} (18°)	Silver bromate	5.77×10^{-5} (25°)
Calcium fluoride	3.95×10^{-11} (26°)	Silver bromide	4.1×10^{-13} (18°)
Calcium iodate, $Ca(IO_3)_2. 6H_2O$	22.2×10^{-8} (10°)	Silver bromide	7.7×10^{-13} (25°)
Calcium iodate, $Ca(IO_3)_2.6H_2O$	64.4×10^{-8} (18°)	Silver carbonate	6.15×10^{-12} (25°)
Calcium oxalate, $CaC_2O_4.H_2O$	1.78×10^{-9} (18°)	Silver chloride	0.21×10^{-10} (4.7°)
Calcium oxalate, $CaC_2O_4.H_2O$	2.57×10^{-9} (25°)	Silver chloride	0.37×10^{-10} (9.7°)
Calcium sulfate	2.45×10^{-5} (25°C)	Silver chloride	1.56×10^{-10} (25°)
Calcium tartrate, $CaC_4H_4O_6.2H_2O$	0.77×10^{-6} (18°)	Silver chloride	13.2×10^{-10} (50°)
Cobalt sulfide	3×10^{-26} (18°)	Silver chloride	215×10^{-10} (100°)
Cupric iodate	1.4×10^{-7} (25°)	Silver chromate	1.2×10^{-12} (14.8°)
Cupric oxalate	2.87×10^{-8} (25°)	Silver chromate	9×10^{-12} (25°)
Cupric sulfide	8.5×10^{-45} (18°)	Silver cyanide $[Ag^+][Ag(CN)_2^-]$	2.2×10^{-12} (20°)
Cuprous bromide	4.15×10^{-8} (18–20°)	Silver dichromate	2×10^{-7} (25°)
Cuprous chloride	1.02×10^{-6} (18–20°)	Silver hydroxide	1.52×10^{-8} (20°)
Cuprous iodide	5.06×10^{-12} (18–20°)	Silver iodate	0.92×10^{-8} (9.4°)
Cuprous sulfide	2×10^{-47} (16–18°)	Silver iodide	0.32×10^{-16} (13°)
Cuprous thiocyanate	1.6×10^{-11} (18°)	Silver iodide	1.5×10^{-16} (25°)
Ferric hydroxide	1.1×10^{-36} (18°)	Silver sulfide	1.6×10^{-49} (18°)
Ferrous hydroxide	1.64×10^{-14} (18°)	Silver thiocyanate	0.49×10^{-12} (18°)
Ferrous oxalate	2.1×10^{-7} (25°)	Silver thiocyanate	1.16×10^{-12} (25°)
Ferrous sulfide	3.7×10^{-19} (18°)	Strontium carbonate	1.6×10^{-9} (25°)
Lead carbonate	3.3×10^{-14} (18°)	Strontium fluoride	2.8×10^{-9} (18°)
Lead chromate	1.77×10^{-14} (18°)	Strontium oxalate	5.61×10^{-8} (18°)
Lead fluoride	2.7×10^{-8} (9°)	Strontium sulfate	2.77×10^{-7} (2.9°)
Lead fluoride	3.2×10^{-8} (18°)	Strontium sulfate	3.81×10^{-7} (17.4°)
Lead fluoride	3.7×10^{-8} (26.6°)	Zinc hydroxide	1.8×10^{-14} (18–20°)
Lead iodate	5.3×10^{-14} (9.2°)	Zinc oxalate, $ZnC_2O_4.2H_2O$	1.35×10^{-9} (18°)
Lead iodate	1.2×10^{-13} (18°)	Zinc sulfide	1.2×10^{-23} (18°)
Lead iodate	2.6×10^{-13} (25.8°)		

PROPERTIES OF RARE EARTH METALS

F. H. Spedding

Symbol	M. P. °C [1]	B. P. °C	Heat of Vaporization $\Delta H_{,0}$ Kcal/g atm [2]	Density	Atomic Vol. (cm³/mole)	Metallic Radius Å	Electrical Resistivity Polycrystalline Wire 298°K (ohm-cm x 10⁻⁶)[3]	Residual Resistivity Wire 4.2°K (ohm-cm x 10⁻⁶)[3]	Compressibility cm²/kg x 10⁻⁶ **
Sc	1541	2831	89.9	2.989	15.041	1.640	52	3	2.26
Y	1522	3338	101.3	4.469	19.894	1.801	59	2	2.68
La	921	3457	103.1	6.145	22.603	1.879	61-80*	SC	4.04
Ce	799	3426	101.1	γ=6.767 β=6.657	20.400 / 21.049	1.820	70-80	10	4.10
Pr	931	3512	85.3	6.773	20.805	1.828	68	1	3.21
Nd	1021	3068	78.5	7.007	20.585	1.821	55	7	3.0
Pm	1168	2700 est.							
Sm	1077	1791	49.2	7.520	20.001	1.804	91	7	3.34
Eu	822	1597	41.9	5.243	28.981	1.984	91	1	8.29
			$\Delta H°298$						
Gd	1313	3266	95.3	7.900	19.904	1.801	127	1	2.56
Tb	1356	3123	93.4	8.229	19.312	1.783	114	4	2.45
Dy	1412	2562	70.0	8.550	19.006	1.774	100	5	2.55
Ho	1474	2695	72.3	8.795	18.753	1.766	88	3	2.47
Er	1529	2863	76.1	9.066	18.450	1.757	71	3	2.39
Tm	1545	1947	55.8	9.321	18.124	1.746	74	3	2.47
Yb	819	1194	36.5	6.965	24.843	1.939	28	2	7.39
Lu	1663	3395	102.2	9.840	17.781	1.735	60	2	2.38

Crystal usually mixture of α hcp and fcc lattice. SC - Superconductor

* Best values in author's opinion. Many numbers are taken from P. W. Bridgman's publication.

** Corrected for new temperature scale. Best values Ames Laboratory 2/1/72.

[1] Corrected for new temperature scale. Best values Ames Laboratory 2/1/72.

[2] Values from Thermodynamic Properties of Metals and Alloys (Review) R. Hultgren, R. Orr and K. Kelley. Supplements 1967.

[3] Weighted average of original papers 1/1/72.

PROPERTIES OF RARE EARTH METALS

F. H. Spedding

Symbol	Crystal Structure at Room Temperature 25°C		Allotropic Forms Transition Temperatures Expressed in °C	
Sc	Hex. (to 1335°)	a=3.3088Å, c=5.2680Å	bcc(above 1335°)	
Y	Hex. (to 1478°)	a=3.6482Å, c=5.7318Å	bcc(above 1478°)	a=4.08Å
La	Hex. (to 310°) (usually contains fcc also)	a=3.7740Å, c=12.171Å	fcc(310°-865°) bcc(above 865°)	a=4.26Å
Ce	fcc(~ 0° to 726°)	a=5.160Å	fcc(below-157° on cooling) (up to -94° on heating) Hex. (below-23° on cooling) (up to 168° on heating)	a=4.85Å a=3.68Å c=11.92Å
Pr	Hex. (to 795°)	a=3.6721Å, c=11.832Å	bcc(above 795°)	a=4.12Å
Nd	Hex. (to 863°)	a=3.6583Å, c=11.7966Å	bcc(above 863°)	a=4.13Å
Sm	*Rhom (to 926°)	a=8.9834Å, α=23° 49.5'	bcc(above 926°)	a=4.07Å
Eu	bcc	a=4.5827Å		
Gd	Hex. (to 1235°)	a=3.6336Å, c=5.7810Å	bcc(above 1235°)	a=4.05Å†
Tb	Hex. (to 1289°)	a=3.6055Å, c=5.6966Å	bcc(above 1289°)	a=4.02Å†
Dy	Hex. (to 1381°)	a=3.5915Å, c=5.6501Å	bcc(above 1381°)	a=3.98Å†
Ho	Hex.	a=3.5778Å, c=5.6178Å	Not present pure metals	
Er	Hex.	a=3.5592Å, c=5.5850Å	Not present pure metals	
Tm	Hex.	a=3.5375Å, c=5.5540Å	Not present pure metals	
Yb	Hex. (to 795°)	a=5.4848Å,	bcc(above 795°)	a=4.44Å
Lu	Hex.	a=3.5052Å, c=5.5494Å	Not present pure metals	

† Extrapolated from magnesium alloy studies. Hex. refers to close packed hexagonal. La, Ce, Pr, and Nd have a stacking order ABAC, the other rare earths ABAB. fcc refers to close packed face centered cubic with a stacking order ABC, ABC, bcc refers to body centered cubic. These high temperature forms are very soft and deform very easily.

* The rhombic Sm cell can be expressed as hexagonal with a=3.6290Å, c=26.207 and possess a stacking order ABABCBCAC

DENSITY OF LIQUID ELEMENTS

Gernot Lang

Data in this table consist of those published in various places in the literature. Generally, there has been excellent agreement among values obtained by different methods of measurement. Temperatures are in degrees C and densities in grams per cubic centimeter. Grams per cc × 62.427961 = pounds per cu ft.

Element:	Purity:	ρ_{mn}	ρ_{t_1}		ρ_{t_2}		ρ_{t_3}		Atm.:	Method:	Ref.
			t	ρ	t	ρ	t	ρ			
Ag	—	9.32	1100	9.17	1200	9.07	—	—	—	IBF	74
Ag	—	9.33	1100	9.20	1200	9.10	1300	9.00	—	DBF	33
Ag	99.9	—	1100	9.170	1200	9.070	1300	8.980	—	IBF	Q
Ag	—	9.285	1100	9.15	1200	9.07	1300	8.97	—	IBF	24
Ag	—	9.345	1100	9.20	—	—	—	—	H_2	Bubble pressure	46
Ag	—	9.33±0.01	1100	9.18	1200	9.08	1300	8.97	Ar	Bubble pressure	47
Ag	—	9.346	1100	9.22	1200	9.13	1300	9.04	—	DBF	39
Al	99.4	2.41	—	—	—	—	—	—	—	BF	62
Al	99.4	2.38₄	—	—	—	—	—	—	—	Pycnometer	15
Al	99.996	2.368	700	2.357	800	2.332	900	2.304	—	BF	25
Al	99.99	2.39	—	—	—	—	—	—	—	Pycnometer	60
Al	99.997	2.39	677	2.380	807	2.334	912	2.292	Ar	Bubble pressure	11
Au	99.96	17.28	1100	17.24	1200	17.12	1300	16.99	H_2	IBF	24
Au	—	17.361	1100	17.221	1200	17.099	1300	16.950	—	IBF	P
B	99.8	2.08±0.03	—	—	—	—	—	—	vac.	Weighing and vol. determin.	80
Ba	—	3.325	$\rho_t = 3.476 - (2.14 \cdot 10^{-4})t$ (t°C)						Ar	DBF	1
Ba	—	3.320	$\rho_t = 3.847 - 5.26 \cdot 10^{-4}T$ (T°K)						—	calculated	K
Be	—	—	1500	1.42±0.04	—	—	—	—	—	calculated	22
Bi	—	10.07	300	10.03	400	9.91	500	9.78	—	Manometer pressure	31
Bi	—	10.02	400	9.87	600	9.62	800	9.40	—	Dilatometer	7
Bi	—	10.07	400	9.90	500	9.78	600	9.66	—	Dilatometer	53
Bi	—	10.04	400	9.91	600	9.67	800	9.44	—	DBF	34
Bi	—	—	400	9.86	600	9.62	700	9.49	N_2	Bubble pressure	78
Bi	99.94	10.03	400	9.88	600	9.62	700	9.51	—	DBF	66
Bi	99.90	—	800	9.43	900	9.28	1000	9.15	H_2	Bubble pressure	57
Bi	—	10.02	300	9.98	400	9.85	500	9.73	—	Dilatometer	30
Bi	99.98	10.07	500	9.78	700	9.53	900	9.30	Ar	Bubble pressure	49
Bi	—	10.057	700	9.51±0.03	—	—	—	—	—	—	L
Ca	—	1.365	$\rho_t = 1.613 - 2.21 \cdot 10^{-4}T$ (T°K)						—	calculated	K
Cd	—	8.02	$\rho_t = 8.02 - 0.00110(t-320)$ (t°C)						—	Manometer pressure	31
Cd	99.97	—	340	8.009	400	7.942	500	7.821	N_2	Bubble pressure	28
Cd	—	—	385	7.94	479	7.83	560	7.74	Ar	Bubble pressure	76
Co	—	—	1600	8.08–8.13	—	—	—	—	—	Drop volume	59
Co	—	—	1500	ca. 8.05	—	—	—	—	—	BF	26
Co	99.99	7.67	1500	7.66	1600	7.54	1700	7.42	Ar	Bubble pressure	50
Co	—	—	1500	7.70	—	—	—	—	—	—	81
Co	99.53	7.76	$\rho_t = 9.51 - 9.88 \cdot 10^{-4}T$ (T°K)						vac.	Sessile drop (mp – 2200)	U
Cr	—	—	1950	6.00±0.13	—	—	—	—	vac.	Sessile drop	18
Cr	—	6.46	—	—	—	—	—	—	—	calculated	3
Cs	—	1.843	110	1.800	310	1.691	510	1.575	—	Pycnometer	H
Cs	—	1.851	$\rho_t = 1.853 - 5.71 \cdot 10^{-4}t$ (t°C)						—	Pycnometer (100–750°C)	F
Cu	—	7.99	1100	7.97	1200	7.81	1300	7.66	—	IBF	6
Cu	—	7.96₂	1100	7.94	1200	7.77	1300	7.62	—	Dilatometer	85
Cu	—	7.92₄	1100	7.91	1300	7.76	1500	7.61	—	DBF	84
Cu	99.99	7.940	1100	7.924	1200	7.846	1300	7.764	—	IBF	Q
Cu	—	—	1100	8.10	—	—	—	—	—	Drop volume	43
Cu	—	7.87₅	1100	7.86	1300	7.70	1500	7.55	—	DBF	45
Cu	—	—	1100	7.90	—	—	—	—	—	Pycnometer	52
Cu	—	7.99₇	1100	7.98	1300	7.81	1500	7.66	Ar	DBF	8
Cu	—	—	1100	8.07	—	—	—	—	—	Bubble pressure	Beer in 49
Cu	—	8.090	$\rho_t = 9.370 - 9.442 \cdot 10^{-4}T$ (T°K)						—	Drop volume	Mehairy in 49
Cu	—	8.03	1100	8.02	1300	7.86	1500	7.70	Ar	Bubble pressure	49
Fe	—	7.13	—	—	—	—	—	—	—	DBF	75
Fe	—	7.24	—	—	—	—	—	—	vac.	Drop volume	35
Fe	—	—	1550	7.01	—	—	—	—	air	Casting	79
Fe	—	7.15	—	—	—	—	—	—	—	DBF	42
Fe	—	6.99	$\rho_t = 8.523 - 8.358 \cdot 10^{-4}T$ (T°K)						Ar	DBF	38
Fe	Carbonyl	—	1550	7.189	—	—	—	—	—	—	27
Fe	—	7.015	$\rho_t = 8.618 - 8.83 \cdot 10^{-4}T$ (T°K)						Ar	DBF	C
Fe	—	—	1555	6.98	—	—	—	—	—	Bubble pressure	Beer in 49
Fe	99.96	7.03₅	1550	7.01	1600	6.94	1700	6.80	Ar	Bubble pressure	49
Fe	—	—	1550	7.13	—	—	—	—	—	—	70
Fe	99.9	7.02	$\rho_t = 8.50 - 8.17 \cdot 10^{-4}T$ (T°K)						vac.	Sessile drop	U

Element:	Purity:	ρ_{mp}	ρ_{t_1}		ρ_{t_2}		ρ_{t_3}		Atm.:	Method:	Ref.
			t	ρ	t	ρ	t	ρ			
Ga	—	6.20 ± 0.01	—	—	—	—	—	—	—	—	E
Ge	—	5.52	1000	5.50	1100	5.44	1200	5.39	—	Volumetric measurement	58
Ge	—	5.57_5	1000	5.56	1100	5.51	1200	5.45	N_2	Pycnometer	40
Ge	99.990	5.49	1000	5.46	1200	5.36	1500	5.21	Ar	Bubble pressure	49
Hf	—	12.0	—						—	calculated	3
		—	0	13.5951	20	13.5457	100	13.3514	—		—
In	—	—	231	6.99	302	6.93	421	6.84	Ar	Bubble pressure	76
Ir	—	20.0	—						—	Calculated	3
K	—	0.826		$\rho_t = 0.826 - 0.000222\,(t - 62.4)$ (t°C)					—		72
K	—	0.819		$\rho_t = 0.819 - 0.238 \cdot 10^{-3}\,(t - 64)$ (t°C)					—	Pycnometer (64–1400°C)	D
K	—	0.828	110	0.817	310	0.772	510	0.724	—	Pycnometer	H
Li	—	0.515		$\rho_t = 0.515 - 0.101 \cdot 10^{-3}\,(t - 200)$ (t°C)					—	Pycnometer (200–1600°C)	D
Li	—	0.518		$\rho_t = 0.5368 - 1.021 \cdot 10^{-4}\,t$ (t°C)					—	Pycnometer (400–1125°C)	F
Mg	—	—	700	1.575	800	1.555	—	—	—	DBF	67
Mg	99.5	1.585	700	1.570	800	1.550	900	1.525	—	IBF	N
Mg	—	1.57	—						—	Estimated	17
Mg	—	1.590		$\rho_t = 1.834 - 2.67 \cdot 10^{-4}\,T$ (T°K)					Ar	DBF	B
Mn	—	—	1440	$5.84 \pm 2\%$	—	—	—	—	He	Volumetric method	M
Mn	—	6.43	—						—		71
Mo	99.7	9.33	—	—	—	—	—	—	vac.	Drop volume	64
Mo	—	9.35	—						—	calculated	3
Na	—	0.938_5		$\rho_t = 0.938_5 - 0.000260\,(t - 96.5)$ (t°C)					—		72
Na	—	—		$\rho_t = 0.938 - 1.9 \cdot 10^{-4}\,T$ (T°K)					—	Bubble pressure	82
Na	—	0.927		$\rho_t = 0.927 - 0.238 \cdot 10^{-3}\,(t - 100)$ (t°C)					—	Pycnometer	D
Na	—	0.928	410	0.854	610	0.806	810	0.754	—	Pycnometer	H
Nb, Cb	—	7.83	—						—	calculated	3
Ni	—	—	1500	ca. 8.04	—	—	—	—	—	BF	26
Ni	—	7.905		$\rho_t = 9.908 - 11.598 \cdot 10^{-4}\,T$ (T°K)					Ar	DBF	C
Ni	99.85	7.77	1500	7.71_5	1600	7.59_5	1700	7.48	Ar	Bubble pressure	49
Ni	99.99	7.78		$\rho_t = 7.78 - 0.006\,(t - 1453)$ (t°C)					vac.	Sessile drop	21
Ni	—	—	1500	7.78					—		81
Ni	99.95	7.91		$\rho_t = 9.51 - 10.00 \cdot 10^{-4}\,T$ (T°K)					vac.	Sessile drop	U
Os	—	20.1	—						—	calculated	3
Pb	—	10.71		$\rho_t = 10.71 - 0.00139\,(t - 327)$ (t°C)					—	Manometer pressure	31
Pb	99.98	—	340	10.57	400	10.49	440	10.43	N_2	Bubble pressure	28
Pb	—	—	568	10.380	640	10.294	720	10.201	—	DBF	O
Pb	—	—	400	10.56	500	10.43	700	10.17	N_2	Bubble pressure	78
Pb	—	—	437	10.52	623	10.28	705	10.16	Ar	Bubble pressure	76
Pb	99.9923	10.678		$\rho_t = 10.678 - 13.174 \cdot 10^{-4}\,T$ (T°K)					Ar	DBF	A
Pd	—	10.7	—	—	—	—	—	—	—	calculated	20
Pd	—	10.7	—	—	—	—	—	—	—	calculated	3
Pd	99.95	—	1600	10.43	1700	10.31	1800	10.18_5	Ar	Bubble pressure	49
Pt	99.84	19.7 ± 0.25	—	—	—	—	—	—	vac.	Drop volume	19
Pt	99.999	—	1800	18.82 ± 0.02	—	—	—	—	Ar	Sessile drop	44
Pt	—	18.91	—	—	—	—	—	—	Ar	Bubble pressure	48
Pt	—	—	1800	18.82	1850	18.67_5	1875	18.60_5	Ar	Bubble pressure	49
Pu	—	—		$\rho_t = 17.57 - 1.45 \cdot 10^{-3}\,t$ (t°C) ± 0.21					—	(655–P60°C)	T
Pu	99.95	16.623	699	16.548	824	16.370	950	16.185	—	Pycnometer	32
Rb	—	1.48	—	—	—	—	—	—	—	estimated	56
Rb	—	1.463		$\rho_t = 1.481 - 4.51 \cdot 10^{-4}\,t$ (t°C)					—	Pycnometer	F
Rb	—	—	45.5	1.4505	47.4	1.4498	49.3	1.4469	vac.	Pycnometer	G
Re	99.4	18.9	—	—	—	—	—	—	vac.	Drop volume	64
Re	—	18.7	—	—	—	—	—	—	—	calculated	3
Rh	—	10.65	—	—	—	—	—	—	—	calculated	20
Rh	—	11.1	—	—	—	—	—	—	—	calculated	3
Ru	—	10.9	—	—	—	—	—	—	—	calculated	3
S	—	1.819		120–160°C: $\rho_t = 1.901 - 8.00 \cdot 10^{-4}\,t$ (t°C)					N_2	Bubble pressure	61
Sb	—	6.49	700	6.45	800	6.39	1000	6.27	—	IBF	7
Sb	99.52	—	650	6.530	700	6.509	800	6.424	N_2	Bubble pressure	28
Sb	—	—	700	6.41	800	6.38	900	6.35	H_2	Bubble pressure	78

Element:	Purity:	ρ_{mp}	ρ_{t_1}		ρ_{t_2}		ρ_{t_3}		Atm.:	Method:	Ref.
			t	ρ	t	ρ	t	ρ			
Sb	—	—	650	6.52	700	6.50	—	—	H_2	Bubble pressure	23
Sb	—	—	728	6.44	827	6.38	917	6.32	Ar	Bubble pressure	76
Sb	99.9	6.50	650	6.49	700	6.45	—		—	DBF	66
Sb	99.992	6.483	$\rho_t = 6.596 + 2.022 \cdot 10^{-4} T - 3.629 \cdot 10^{-7} T^2$ (T°K)							DBF, Bubble pressure	37
Sb	99.6	6.46_5	700	6.42	900	6.30	1200	6.13	Ar	Bubble pressure	49
Se	—	3.987	$\rho_t = 3.987 - 16 \cdot 10^{-4} (T - 493)$ (T°K)							—		13
Se	—	3.985	$\rho_t = 3.985 - 15.5 \cdot 10^{-4} (T - 490)$ (T°K)							—	Pycnometer	10
Se	—	4.06	$\rho_t = 4.06 - 5 \cdot 10^{-4} (T - 491)$ (T°K)							—	—	4
Se	—	3.984	—		—		—		—	—	I
Se	—	4.01	250	3.97	300	3.91	400	3.79	—	BF	51
Si	—	—	1550	2.54	—		—		—		14
Si	99.9	2.52_5	1450	2.51	1500	2.49	1600	2.46	Ar	Bubble pressure	49
Sn	—	6.988	300	6.94	500	6.81	800	6.64	—	DBF	12
Sn	—	6.98	—		—		—		—	DBF	63
Sn	—	7.01	$\rho_t = 7.01 - 0.00074 (t - 232)$ (t°C)							—	Manometer pressure	31
Sn	—	6.97	300	6.92	500	6.78	800	6.57	—	IBF	74
Sn	—	6.896	300	6.93	500	6.78	600	6.71	—	Dilatometer	53
Sn	—	6.966	300	6.92	600	6.72	1200	6.34	—	DBF	84
Sn	—	6.983	300	6.93	400	6.86	500	6.79	—	Pycnometer	73
Sn	—	7.00	300	6.95	500	6.80	600	6.74	N_2	Bubble pressure	65
Sn	—	—	625	6.67	—		—		N_2	Bubble pressure	78
Sn	—	6.99	300	6.94	400	6.87	—		H_2	Bubble pressure	23
Sn	—	6.993	$\rho_t = 6.98 - 0.00074 (t - 250)$ (t°C)							—	Manometer pressure	69
Sn	—	6.968 ± 0.005	300	6.93	400	6.87	500	6.79	—	Dilatometer	30
Sn	—	6.968	300	6.96	400	6.84	500	6.77	Ar	Bubble pressure	83
Sn	—	6.978 ± 0.022	300	6.93	600	6.70	1200	6.29	Ar	Bubble pressure	49
Ta	—	15.0	—		—		—		—	calculated	3
Te	—	5.75	460	5.75	500	5.74	600	5.70	—	Pycnometer	40
Te	—	—	460	5.58	600	5.53	—		N_2	Bubble pressure	77
Te	99.9999	5.797	460	5.79	600	5.72	700	5.66	Ar	Bubble pressure	49
Ti	98.7	4.11 ± 0.08	—		—		—		—	Capillary method	16
Ti	—	4.15	—		—		—		—	calculated	3
Tl	—	11.29	412	11.13	504	11.01	651	10.77	Ar	Bubble pressure	76
U	—	17.907	$\rho_t = 19.356 - 10.328 \cdot 10^{-4} T$ (T°K)							Ar	DBF	29
V	—	5.55	—		—		—		—	calculated	3
W	—	17.6	—		—		—		—	estimated	9
W	99.8	17.7	—		—		—		vac.	Drop volume	64
W	—	17.5	—		—		—		—	calculated	3
Zn	—	6.59	$\rho_t = 6.59 - 0.00097 (t - 419)$ (t°C)							—	Manometer pressure	31
Zn	—	—	600	6.35	—		—		—	IBF	7
Zn	—	6.56_2	500	6.47	600	6.37	700	6.29	—	Dilatometer	53
Zn	—	6.55_1	500	6.47	600	6.38	700	6.29	—	Pycnometer	73
Zn	—	6.64_5	500	6.56	600	6.45	800	6.25	—	DBF	67
Zn	—	6.64_4	500	6.58	600	6.49	800	6.22	—	DBF	68
Zn	—	6.64	500	6.57	600	6.50	700	6.43	N_2	Bubble pressure	65
Zn	—	—	500	6.55	—		—		H_2	Bubble pressure	78
Zn	—	6.64_5	—		—		—		—	Pycnometer	41
Zn	99.995	6.562	500	6.417	600	6.370	700	6.259	—	IBF	25
Zn	—	6.57_5	500	6.49	600	6.37	700	6.26	Ar	Bubble pressure	83
Zn	99.999	$6.57_7 \pm 0.012$	500	6.48	600	6.37	700	6.27	Ar	Bubble pressure	49
Zr	—	5.80	—		—		—		—	calculated	3

References

1. Addison and Pulham, J. Chem. Soc., 3873 (1962).
2. Allen, Trans. AIME, **227**, 1175 (1963).
3. Allen, Trans. AIME, **230**, 1537 (1964).
4. Astachov, Penin and Dobkina, Zh. Fiz. Chim., **20**, 403 (1946).
5. Beer (in Lucas), Mém. Sci. Rev. Mét., **61**, 1, 97 (1964).
6. Bornemann and Sauerwald, Z. Metallkunde, **14**, 145 (1922).
7. Bornemann and Sauerwald, Z. Metallkunde, **14**, 254 (1922).
8. Cahill and Kirshenbaum, J. Phys. Chem., **66**, 1080 (1962).
9. Calverley, Proc. Phys. Soc., **70**, 1040 (1957).
10. Campbell and Epstein, J. Amer. Chem. Soc., **64**, 2679 (1942).
11. Coy and Mateer, Trans. ASM, **58**, 99 (1965).
12. Day, Sosman and Hostetter, Am. J. Sci., **187**, 1 (1914).
13. Dobinsky and Weselowsky, Bull. Int. Acad. Polon., **A**, 446 (1936).

References (Continued)

14. Dshemilev, Popel and Zarevski, Fiz. Met. i Met., **18**, 83 (1964).
15. Edwards and Moorman, Chem & Met. Eng., **24**, 61 (1921).
16. Eljutin and Maurach, Izv. A. N., OTN, **4**, 129 (1956).
17. Eremenko, Ukr. Chim. Zh., **28**, 427 (1962).
18. Eremenko and Naidich, Izv. A. N., OTN, **2**, 111 (1959).
19. Eremenko and Naidich, Izv. A. N., OTN, **6**, 129 (1959).
20. Eremenko and Naidich, Izv. A. N., OTN, **6**, 100 (1961).
21. Eremenko and Nishenko, Ukr. Chim. Zh., **30**, 125 (1964).
22. Eremenko, Nishenko and Taj-Shou-Wej, Izv. A. N., OTN, **3**, 116 (1960).
23. Fisher and Phillips, J. Metals, **6**, 1060 (1954).
24. Gebhardt and Becker, Z. Metallkunde, **42**, 111 (1951).
25. Gebhardt, Becker and Dorner, Aluminium, **31**, 315 (1955).
26. Geld and Vertman, Fiz. Met i Met., **10**, 793 (1960).
27. Gogiberidse and Kekelidse, Izv. A. N., **3**, 125 (1963).
28. Greenaway, J. Inst. Met., **74**, 133 (1947).
29. Grosse, Cahill and Kirshenbaum, J. Amer. Chem. Soc., **83**, 4665 (1961).
30. Herczynska, Naturwiss., **47**, 200 (1960).
31. Hogness, J. Amer. Chem. Soc., **43**, 1621 (1921).
32. Jones, Ofte, Rohr and Wittenberg, Trans. ASM, **55**, 819 (1962).
33. Jouniaux, Bull. Soc. Chim. France, **47**, 524 (1930).
34. Jouniaux, Bull. Soc. Chim. France, **51**, 677 (1932).
35. Kingery and Humenik, J. Phys. Chem., **57**, 359 (1953).
36. Kirshenbaum and Cahill, Trans. ASM, **55**, 844 (1962).
37. Kirshenbaum and Cahill, Trans. ASM, **55**, 849 (1962).
38. Kirshenbaum and Cahill, Trans. AME, **224**, 816 (1962).
39. Kirshenbaum, Cahill and Grosse, J. Inorg. Nucl. Chem., **24**, 333 (1962).
40. Klemm et al., Monatsh. Chem., **83**, 629 (1952).
41. Knappwost and Restle, Z. Elektrochemie, **58**, 112 (1954).
42. Königer and Nagel, GieBerei TWB, **13**, 57 (1960).
43. Kozakevitch, Châtel, Urbain and Sage, Rev. de Mét., **52**, 139 (1955).
44. Kozakevitch and Urbain, C. R., Paris, **253**, 2229 (1961).
45. Lang, WADC-Techn. Rep., 57–488 (1957).
46. Lauermann and Metzger, Z. Phys. Chem., **216**, 37 (1961).
47. Lucas, C. R., Paris, **250**, 1850 (1960).
48. Lucas, C. R., Paris, **253**, 2526 (1961).
49. Lucas, Mém. Sci. Rev. Mét., **61**, 1 (1964).
50. Lucas, Mém. Sci. Rev. Mét., **61**, 97 (1964).
51. Lucas and Urbain, C. R., Paris, **258**, 6403 (1964).
52. Malmberg, J. Inst. Met., **89**, 137 (1960).
53. Matuyama, Sci. Rep. RITU, **18**, 19 (1929).
54. Mehairy and Wood (in Lucas), Mém. Sci. Rev. Mét., **61**, 1 (1964).
55. Metals Handbook: Properties and Selection of Metals, 8th edit., **1**, (1961).
56. Metals Reference Book, C. J. Smithells, 4th edit., **1**, 688 (1967).
57. Metzger, Z. Phys. Chem., **211**, 1 (1959).
58. Mokrovski and Regel, J. Phys. Techn., **22**, 1281 (1952).
59. Monma and Suto, J. Jap. Inst. Met., **1**, 69 (1960).
60. Naidich and Eremenko, Fiz. Met. i Met., **6**, 62 (1961).
61. Ono and Matsushima, Sci. Rep. RITU, **9**, 309 (1957).
62. Pascal and Jouniaux, C. R., Paris, **158**, 414 (1914).
63. Pascal and Jouniaux, Z. Elektrochemie, **22**, 72 (1916).
64. Pekarev, Izv. Vyss. Utch. Saved., Tsvetn. Met., **6**, 111 (1963).
65. Pelzel, Berg-u. Hütt. Mon. Hefte, Leoben, **93**, 248 (1948).
66. Pelzel, Z. Metallkunde, **50**, 392 (1959).
67. Pelzel and Sauerwald, Z. Metallkunde, **33**, 229 (1941).
68. Pelzel and Schneider, Z. Metallkunde, **35**, 121 (1943).
69. Pokrovski and Saidov, Zh. Fiz. Chim., **29**, 1601 (1955).
70. Popel, Smirnov, Zarevski, Dshemilev and Pastuchov, Izv. A. N., **1**, 62 (1965).
71. Popel, Zarevski and Dshemilev, Fiz. Met. i Met., **18**, 468 (1964).
72. Rink, C. R., Paris, **189**, 39 (1929).
73. Saeger and Ash, J. Res. Nat. Bur. Stand., **8**, 37 (1932).
74. Sauerwald, Z. Metallkunde, **14**, 457 (1922).
75. Sauerwald and Widawski, Z. anorg. allg. Chem., **155**. 1 (1926).
76. Schneider and Heymer, Z. anorg. allg. Chem., **286**, 118 (1956).
77. Smith and Spitzer, J. Phys. Chem., **66**, 946 (1962).
78. Stauffer, Thesis Göttingen (1953).
79. Stott and Rendall, J. Iron & Steel Inst., **175**, 374 (1953).
80. Tavadse, Bairamashvili, Chantadse and Zagareishvili, Doklady A. N., **150**, 544 (1963).

References (Continued)

81. Tavadse, Bairamashvili and Chantadse, Doklady A. N., **162,** 67 (1965).
82. Taylor, J. Inst. Met., **83,** 143 (1954).
83. Übelacker and Lucas, C. R., Paris, **254,** 1622 (1962).
84. Widawski and Sauerwald, Z. anorg. allg. Chem., **192,** 145 (1930).
85. Zimmermann and Esser, Arch. f. Eisenh., **2,** 867 (1929).
A) Kirshenbaum, Cahill and Grosse, J. Inorg. Nucl. Chem., **22,** 33 (1961).
B) McGonigal, Kirshenbaum and Grosse, J. Phys. Chem., **66,** 737 (1962).
C) Grosse and Kirshenbaum, J. Inorg. Nucl. Chem., **25,** 331 (1963).
D) Golchova, Teplofiz. Vysok. Temp., **4,** 360 (1966).
E) Bosio, C. R., Paris, **259,** 4545 (1964).
F) Spilrajn and Jakimovich, Teplofiz. Vysok. Temp., **5,** 239 (1967).
G) Jakimovich and Saars, Teplofiz. Vysok. Temp., **5,** 532 (1967).
H) Stone, Ewing, Spann, Steinkuller, Williams and Miller, J. Chem. Engng. Data, **11,** 320 (1966).
I) Shirai, Hamada and Kobayashi, J. Chem. Soc. Japan, **84,** 968 (1963).
K) Grosse and McGonigal, J. Phys. Chem., **68,** 414 (1964).
L) Cubicciotti, J. Phys. Chem., **68,** 537 (1964).
M) Watolin and Esin, Fiz. Met. i Met., **16,** 936 (1963).
N) Gebhardt, Becker and Trägner, Z. Metallkunde, **46,** 90 (1955).
O) Kubaschewski and Hörnle, Z. Metallkunde, **42,** 129 (1951).
P) Gebhardt and Dorner, Z. Metallkunde, **42,** 353 (1951).
Q) Gebhardt and Wörwag, Z. Metallkunde, **42,** 358 (1951).
R) Been, Edwards, Teeter and Chalkins, NEPA-1585, US-AEC (1950).
S) da C. Andrade and Dobbs, Proc. Roy. Soc., **211,** 12 (1952).
T) Wilkinson: Extractive and Physical Metallurgy of Plutonium and its Alloys, New York-London, 1960.
U) Saito and Sakuma, J. Jap. Inst. Met., **31,** 1140 (1967).

DENSITY OF LIQUID ELEMENTS

SUPPLEMENTARY TABLE

Gernot Lang

Element	Purity	ρ_{mp}	ρt_1 t°C	ρt_1 ρ	ρt_2 t°C	ρt_2 ρ	ρt_3 t°C	ρt_3 ρ	Atm.	Method	Ref.
Ag		9.36				$\rho_t = 9.36 - 0.00114\,(t-t_{mp})$		(t°C)		Bubble pressure	110
Ag	99.95					$\rho_t = 9.318 - 1.08 \cdot 10^{-3}\,(t-1000) \pm 0.006$ (1000−1200°C)			H_2	Bubble pressure	81
Ag	99.999	9.31				$\rho_t = 10.31 - 1.05 \cdot 10^{-3} \cdot t\,(t°C)$ (960−1150)			Ar	Sessile drop	88
Al	99.99	2.39				$\rho_t = 2.60 - 3.2 \cdot 10^{-4}\,t\,(t°C)$ (900−1750°C)			He	Drop volume	87
Al	99.999	2.365				$\rho_t = 2.576 - 3.2 \cdot 10^{-4}\,t\,(t°C)$			He	Sessile drop	108
Al	99.998	2.375				$\rho_t = 2.375 - 5.4 \cdot 10^{-4}\,(t-660)$		(t°C)	Ar	Sessile drop	97
Ba	99.5	3.32				$\rho_t = 3.59 - 2.74 \cdot 10^{-4}\,T$		(T°K)	N_2	Bubble pressure	90
Bi	99.9999	10.05				$\rho_t = 10.05 - 1.41 \cdot 10^{-3}\,(t-t_{mp})$		(t°C)	N_2	Volume determin.	96
Bi	99.98	10.04				$\rho_t = 10.04 - 1.44 \cdot 10^{-3}\,(t-t_{mp})$		(t°C)	N_2	Volume determin.	96
Bi	99.999	10.114				$\rho_t = 10.406 - 1.078 \cdot 10^{-3}\,t$ (271−414)		(t°C)	N_2	DBF	89
Bi	–	10.031				$\rho_t = 10.336 - 12.367 \cdot 10^{-4}\,t$		(t°C)	vac.	Pycnometer	92
Ca	–	1.365				$\rho_t = 1.613 - 2.21 \cdot 10^{-4}\,T$		(T°K)		Bubble pressure	90
Cd	99.999	7.996				$\rho_t = 8.388 - 12.205 \cdot 10^{-4}\,t$		(t°C)	Ar	Pycnometer	91
Co	99.53	7.78				$\rho_t = 9.5_7 - 10.1_7 \cdot 10^{-4}\,T$ (1780−2200)		(T°K)	Ar	Drop volume	103
Co	99.67	7.75				$\rho_t = 9.7_1 - 1.1_1 \cdot 10^{-3}\,T$		(T°K)	Ar	Bubble pressure	109
Cs	–	1.86				$\rho_t = 1.84/1 + 1.1755 \cdot 10^{-4}\,(t-82.4) + 7.656 \cdot 10^{-8}\,(t-82.4)^2$ (t°F, 29−704°C)			Ar	Pycnometer	86
Cs	–		40	1.840	271	1.711	376	1.655	Ar	Dilatometer	106
Fe	–	7.06				$\rho_t = 7.05 - 7.3 \cdot 10^{-4}\,(t-1550)$		(t°C)	H_2, He	Sessile drop	101
Fe	99.9	7.03				$\rho_t = 8.5_7 - 8.5_3 \cdot 10^{-4}\,T$ (1800−2150)		(T°K)	Ar	Drop volume	103
Fe	99.98	7.05				$\rho_t = 8.7_8 - 0.95_8 \cdot 10^{-3}\,T$		(T°K)	Ar	Bubble pressure	109
Fr	–		100	2.29						calculated	100
Ga	–	6.1136				$\rho_t = 6.11564 - 7.37437 \cdot 10^{-4}\,t + 1.37767 \cdot 10^{-7}\,t^2$ (t°C) (50−600°C)				Pycnometer	98

DENSITY OF LIQUID ELEMENTS

DENSITY OF LIQUID ELEMENTS (Continued)

Element	Purity	ρ_{mp}	ρ_{t_1}		ρ_{t_2}		ρ_{t_3}		Atm.	Method	Ref.
			t°C	ρ	t°C	ρ	t°C	ρ			
Hg	–	–	0	13.5951	20	13.5457	100	13.3514		–	105
In	99.999	7.032		$\rho_t = 7.153-0759 \cdot 10^{-3}t$				(t°C)	N_2	D B F (160–532)	89
In	99.999	7.016		$\rho_t = 7.146-8.362 \cdot 10^{-4}t$				(t°C)	Ar	Pycnometer	91
Mg	99.5		959	1.52	1053	1.47	–			Bubble pressure	90
Mo	–	9.1							vac.	Pendant drop and drop weight	95
Nb, Cb	–	7.6							vac.	Pendant drop and drop weight	95
Ni	–	7.82		$\rho_t = 7.81-8.7 \cdot 10^{-4}(t-1460)$				(t°C)	H_2, He	Sessile drop	U
Ni	–	7.65							vac.	Pendant drop and drop weight	95
Ni	99.95	7.95		$\rho_t = 9.8_1-10.8_0 \cdot 10^{-4}T$ (1890–2150)				(T°K)	Ar	Drop volume	103
Pb	99.999	10.330		$\rho_t = 10.650-9.8 \cdot 10^{-4}t$ (1000–1600)				(t°C)	He	Sessile drop	108
Pb	99.997	10.660		$\rho_t = 11.060-12.220 \cdot 10^{-4}t$				(t°C)	He	Pycnometer	107
Pd	99.998	10.379		$\rho_t = 12.193-11.69 \cdot 10^{-4}t$ (MP–1700)				(t°C)	He	Sessile drop	108
Rb	99.4	1.385		$\rho_t = 1.55643-2.6511 \cdot 10^{-4}t-6.26779/t$				(t°F, 66–1076°C)	Ar	Dilatometer	106
Rb	–	1.484		$\rho_t = 1.472/1+1.3309 \cdot 10^{-4}(t-102) + 5.2106 \cdot 10^{-8}(t-102)^2$				(t°F, 39–730°C)	Ar	Pycnometer	86
Sb	99.999	6.452		$\rho_t = 6.818-5.8 \cdot 10^{-4}t$ (1000–1600°C)				(t°C)	He	Sessile drop	108
Sb	99.999	6.535		$\rho_t = 6.962-0.673 \cdot 10^{-3}t$ (635–745°C)				(t°C)	N_2	D B F	89
Sb	–	5.493		$\rho_t = 6.902-6.486 \cdot 10^{-4}t$ (MP–746°C)				(t°C)	Ar	Pycnometer	93
Si	99.9999		1500	2.46					Ar	Pycnometer	94
Sn	99.999		246	6.964	336	6.900	400	6.854	vac.	Pycnometer	111
Sn	99.999	7.01		$\rho_t = 7.16-6.3 \cdot 10^{-4}t$				(t°C)	N_2	Bubble pressure	104
Sn	99.999	6.981		$\rho_t = 7.135-0.663 \cdot 10^{-3}t$ (MP–438°C)				(t°C)		D B F	89
Sn	99.999	6.973		$\rho_t = 7.139-7.125 \cdot 10^{-4}t$				(t°C)		Pycnometer	107
Sr	99.5	2.375		$\rho_t = 2.648-2.62 \cdot 10^{-4}T$				(T°K)		Bubble pressure	90

DENSITY OF LIQUID ELEMENTS (*Continued*)

Element	Purity	ρ_{mp}	ρ_{t_1} t°C	ρ	ρ_{t_2} t°C	ρ	ρ_{t_3} ρ	Atm.	Method	Ref.
Te	—	5.71			$\rho_t = 5.71 - 3.6 \cdot 10^{-4}(t - t_{mp})$		(t°C)		Bubble pressure	110
Te	99.7	5.86			$\rho_t = 5.86 - 0.73 \cdot 10^{-3}(t - t_{mp})$		(t°C)	N_2	Volume determin.	96
Ti	—	4.10						vac.	Pendant drop and drop weight	95
U	—	17.27			$\rho_t = 19.520 - 16.01 \cdot 10^{-4} \, T$		(T°K)	vac.	Pycnometer	102
V	—	5.3						vac.	Pendant drop and drop weight	95
Zr	—	5.60						vac.	Pendant drop and drop weight	95

REFERENCES

86. Achener, HTLMHTTM, Vol. I, Oak Ridge, p. 5, November 1964.
87. Ayushina, Lewin and Geld, Zh. Fiz. Chim., **42**, 2799 (1968).
88. Bernard and Lupis, Met. Trans., **2**, 555 (1971).
89. Berthou and Tougas, Met. Trans., **1**, 2978 (1970).
90. Bohdansky and Schins, J. Inorg. Nucl. Chem., **30**, 2331 (1968).
91. Crawley, Trans. AIME, **242**, 2237 (1968).
92. Crawley and Kiff, Met. Trans., **2**, 609 (1971).
93. Crawley and Kiff, Met. Trans., **3**, 158 (1972).
94. Eljutin, Kostikow and Lewin, Izv. Vys. Uch. Sav., Tsvetn. Met., **2**, 131 (1970).
95. Eljutin, Kostikow and Penkow, Poroshk. Met., **9**, 46 (1970).
96. Keskar and Hruska, Met. Trans., **1**, 2357 (1970).
97. Körber and Lohberg, Gießereiforschung, **23**, 173 (1971).
98. Koster, Hensel and Franck, Ber. Bunsenges., **74**, 43 (1970).
99. Nagamori, Trans. AIME, **245**, 1897 (1969).
100. Osminin, Zh. Fiz. Chim., **43**, 2610 (1969).
101. Popel, Shergin and Zarewski, Zh. Fiz. Chim., **43**, 2365 (1969).
102. Rohr and Wittenberg, J. Phys. Chem., **74**, 1151 (1970).
103. Saito and Sakuma, Sci. Rep. RITU, **22**, 57 (1970).
104. Schwaneke and Folke, Us-Bur. Min., Invest. Rep. No. **7372** (1970).
105. Stoffhütte. Taschenbuch der Werkstoffkunde, 4th ed. p. 1059, 1967.
106. Tepper, Murchison, Zelenak and Roehlich, HTLMHTTM, Vol. I, Oak Ridge, p. 26, November 1964.
107. Thresh, Crawley and White, Trans. AIME, **242**, 819 (1968).
108. Watolin, Esin, Uchow and Dubinin, Trudy Inst. Met. Sverdlovsk, **18**, 73 (1969).
109. Watanabe, Trans. Jap. Inst. Met., **12**, 17 (1971).
110. Wobst and Rentzsch, Z. Phys. Chem., **240**, 36 (1969).
111. Crawley, Trans. AIME, **245**, 1655 (1969).

HEAT OF FUSION OF SOME INORGANIC COMPOUNDS

RUDOLF LOEBEL

Values in parentheses are of uncertain reliability

Compound	Formula	M.P.,°C	H_f cal/g mole	H_f cal/g	Compound	Formula	M.P.,°C	H_f cal/g mole	H_f cal/g
Actinium[227]	Ac	1050 ± 50	(3400)	(11.0)	Bismuth trichloride	$BiCl_3$	223.8	2600	8.2
Aluminum	Al	658.5	2550	94.5	Bismuth trifluoride	BiF_3	726.0	(6200)	(23.3)
Aluminum bromide	Al_2Br_6	87.4	5420	10.1	Bismuth trioxide	Bi_2O_3	815.8	6800	14.6
Aluminum chloride	Al_2Cl_6	192.4	19600	63.6	Boron	B	2300	(5300)	(490)
Aluminum iodide	Al_2I_6	190.9	7960	9.8	Boron tribromide	BBr_3	−48.8	(700)	(2.9)
Aluminum oxide	Al_2O_3	2045.0	(26000)	(256.0)	Boron trichloride	BCl_3	−107.8	(500)	(4.3)
Antimony	Sb	630	4770	39.1	Boron trifluoride	BF_3	−128.0	480	7.0
Antimony tribromide	$SbBr_3$	96.8	3510	9.7	Boron triiodide	BI_3	31.8	(1000)	(2.5)
Antimony trichloride	$SbCl_3$	73.3	3030	13.3	Boron trioxide	B_2O_3	448.8	5500	78.9
Antimony pentachloride	$SbCl_5$	4.0	2400	8.0	Bromine	Br_2	−7.2	2580	16.1
Antimony trioxide	Sb_4O_6	655.0	(26990)	(46.3)	Bromine pentafluoride	BrF_5	−61.4	1355	7.07
Antimony trisulfide	Sb_4S_6	546.0	11200	33.0	Cadmium	Cd	320.8	1460	12.9
Argon	Ar	−190.2	290	7.25	Cadmium bromide	$CdBr_2$	567.8	(5000)	(18.4)
Arsenic	As	816.8	(6620)	(22.0)	Cadmium chloride	$CdCl_2$	567.8	5300	28.8
Arsenic pentafluoride	AsF_4	−80.8	2800	16.5	Cadmium fluoride	CdF_2	1110	(5400)	(35.9)
Arsenic tribromide	$AsBr_3$	30.0	2810	8.9	Cadmium iodide	CdI_2	386.8	3660	10.0
Arsenic trichloride	$AsCl_3$	−16.0	2420	13.3	Cadmium sulfate	$CdSO_4$	1000	4790	22.9
Arsenic trifluoride	AsF_3	−6.0	2486	18.9	Calcium	Ca	851	2230	55.7
Arsenic trioxide	As_4O_6	312.8	8000	22.2	Calcium bromide	$CaBr_2$	729.8	4180	20.9
Barium	Ba	725	1830	13.3	Calcium carbonate	$CaCO_3$	1282	(12700)	(126)
Barium bromide	$BaBr_2$	846.8	6000	21.9	Calcium chloride	$CaCl_2$	782	6100	55
Barium chloride	$BaCl_2$	959.8	5370	25.9	Calcium fluoride	CaF_2	1382	4100	52.5
Barium fluoride	BaF_2	1286.8	3000	17.1	Calcium nitrate	$Ca(NO_3)_2$	560.8	5120	31.2
Barium iodide	BaI_2	710.8	(6800)	(17.3)	Calcium oxide	CaO	2707	(12240)	(218.1)
Barium nitrate	$Ba(NO_3)_2$	594.8	(5900)	(22.6)	Calcium metasilicate	$CaSiO_3$	1512	13400	115.4
Barium oxide	BaO	1922.8	13800	93.2	Calcium sulfate	$CaSO_4$	1297	6700	49.2
Barium phosphate	$Ba_3(PO_4)_2$	1727	18600	30.9	Carbon dioxide	CO_2	−57.6	1900	43.2
Barium sulfate	$BaSO_4$	1350	9700	41.6	Carbon monoxide	CO	−205	199.7	7.13
Beryllium	Be	1278	—	260.0	Cyanogen	C_2N_2	−27.2	2060	39.6
Beryllium bromide	$BeBr_2$	487.8	(4500)	(26.6)	Cyanogen chloride	CNCl	−5.2	2240	36.4
Beryllium chloride	$BeCl_2$	404.8	(3000)	(30)	Cerium	Ce	775	2120	15.1
Beryllium fluoride	BeF_2	796.8	(6000)	(127.6)	Cerium (III) chloride	$CeCl_3$	820.8	(8000)	(32.4)
Beryllium iodide	BeI_2	479.8	(4500)	(17.1)	Cerium (IV) fluoride	CeF_4	976	(10000)	(46.3)
Beryllium oxide	BeO	2550.0	17000	679.7					
Bismuth	Bi	271	2505	12.0					
Bismuth tribromide	$BiBr_3$	216.8	(4000)	(8.9)					

Compound	Formula	M.P.,°C	H_f cal/g mole	H_f cal/g	Compound	Formula	M.P.,°C	H_f cal/g mole	H_f cal/g
Cesium	Cs	28.3	500	3.7	Hydrogen fluoride	HF	−83.11	1094	54.7
Cesium chloride	CsCl	641.8	3600	21.4	Hydrogen iodide	HI	−50.91	686.3	5.4
Cesium fluoride	CsF	704.8	(2450)	(16.1)	Hydrogen nitrate	HNO_3	−47.2	601	9.5
Cesium nitrate	$CsNO_3$	406.8	3250	16.6	Hydrogen oxide (water)	H_2O	0	1436	79.72
Chlorine	Cl_2	−103±5	1531	22.8	Deuterium oxide	D_2O	3.78	1516	75.8
Chromium	Cr	1890	3660	62.1	Hydrogen peroxide	H_2O_2	−0.7	2920	8.58
Chromium (II) chloride	$CrCl_2$	814	7700	65.9	Hydrogen selenate	H_2SeO_4	57.8	3450	23.8
Chromium (III) sequioxide	Cr_2O_3	2279	4200	27.6	Hydrogen sulfate	H_2SO_4	10.4	2360	24.0
Chromium trioxide	CrO_3	197	3770	37.7	Hydrogen sulfide	H_2S	−85.6	5683	16.8
Cobalt	Co	1490	3640	62.1	Hydrogen sulfide (di-)	H_2S_2	−89.7	1805	27.3
Cobalt (II) chloride	$CoCl_2$	727	7390	56.9	Hydrogen telluride	H_2Te	−49.0	1670	12.9
Cobalt (II) fluoride	CoF_2	1201	(9000)	(92.9)	Indium	In	156.3	781	6.8
Copper	Cu	1083	3110	49.0	Iodine	I_2	112.9	3650	14.3
Copper (I) bromide	CuBr	487	(2300)	(16.03)	Iodine chloride (α)	ICl	17.1	2660	16.4
Copper (II) chloride	$CuCl_2$	430	4890	24.7	Iodine chloride (β)	ICl	13.8	2270	13.3
Copper (I) chloride	CuCl	429	2620	26.4	Iron	Fe	1530.0	3560	63.7
Copper (I) cyanide	$Cu_2(CN)_2$	473	(5400)	(30.1)	Iron carbide	Fe_3C	1226.8	12330	68.6
Copper (I) iodide	CuI	587	(2600)	(13.6)	Iron (III) chloride	Fe_2Cl_6	303.8	20500	63.2
Copper (II) oxide	CuO	1446	2820	35.4	Iron (II) chloride	$FeCl_2$	677	7800	61.5
Copper (I) oxide	Cu_2O	1230	(13400)	(93.6)	Iron (II) oxide	FeO	1380	(7700)	(107.2)
Copper (I) sulfide	Cu_2S	1129	5500	34.6	Iron oxide	Fe_3O_4	1596	33000	142.5
Dysprosium	Dy	1407	4100	25.2	Iron penta-carbonyl	$Fe(CO)_5$	−21.2	3250	16.5
Dysprosium chloride	$DyCl_3$	646	(7000)	(26.0)	Iron (II) sulfide	FeS	1195	5000	56.9
Erbium	Er	1496	4100	24.5	Lanthanum	La	920	2400	17.4
Erbium trichloride	$ErCl_3$	775	(7000)	(26.0)	Lanthanum chloride	$LaCl_3$	861	(9000)	(36.6)
Europium	Eu	826	2500	16.4	Lead	Pb	327.3	1224	5.9
Europium trichloride	$EuCl_3$	622	(8000)	(20.9)	Lead bromide	$PbBr_2$	487.8	4290	11.7
Fluorine	F_2	−219.6	244.0	6.4	Lead chloride	$PbCl_2$	497.8	5650	20.3
Gadolinium	Gd	1312	3700	23.8	Lead fluoride	PbF_2	823	1860	7.6
Gadolinium trichloride	$GdCl_3$	608	(7000)	(26.6)	Lead iodide	PbI_2	412	5970	17.9
Gallium	Ga	29	1336	19.1	Lead molybdate	$PbMoO_4$	1065	(25800)	70.8
Germanium	Ge	959	(8300)	(114.3)	Lead oxide	PbO	890	2820	12.6
Gold	Au	1063	3030	15.3	Lead sulfide	PbS	1114	4150	17.3
Hafnium	Hf	2214	(6000)	(34.1)	Lead sulfate	$PbSO_4$	1087	9600	31.6
Holmium	Ho	1461	4100	24.8	Lead tungstate	$PbWO_4$	1123	(15200)	(33.4)
Holmium trichloride	$HoCl_3$	717	(8000)	(29.5)	Lithium	Li	178.8	1100	158.5
Hydrogen	H_2	−259.25	28	13.8	Lithium borate, meta-	$LibO_2$	845	(5570)	(111.9)
Hydrogen bromide	HBr	−86.96	575.1	7.1	Lithium bromide	LiBr	552	2900	33.4
Hydrogen chloride	HCl	−114.3	476.0	13.0	Lithium chloride	LiCl	614	3200	75.5

Compound	Formula	M.P.,°C	H_f cal/g mole	H_f cal/g	Compound	Formula	M.P.,°C	H_f cal/g mole	H_f cal/g
Lithium fluoride	LiF	896	(2360)	(91.1)	Neodymium trichloride	NdCl$_3$	758	(8000)	(31.9)
Lithium hydroxide	LiOH	462	2480	103.3	Neon	Ne	−248.6	77.4	3.83
Lithium iodide	LiI	440	(1420)	(10.6)	Nickel	Ni	1452	4200	71.5
Lithium metasilicate	Li$_2$SiO$_3$	1177	7210	80.2	Nickel chloride	NiCl$_2$	1030	18470	142.5
Lithium molybdate	Li$_2$MoO$_4$	705	4200	24.1	Nickel subsulfide	Ni$_3$S$_2$	790	5800	25.8
Lithium nitrate	LiNO$_3$	250	6060	87.8	Niobium	Nb	2496	(6500)	(68.9)
Lithium orthosilicate	Li$_4$SiO$_4$	1249	7430	60.5	Niobium pentachloride	NbCl$_5$	211	8400	30.8
Lithium sulfate	Li$_2$SO$_4$	857	3040	27.6	Niobium pentoxide	Nb$_2$O$_5$	1511	24200	91.0
Lithium tungstate	Li$_2$WO$_4$	742	(6700)	(25.6)	Nitrogen	N$_2$	−210	172.3	6.15
Lutetium	Lu	1651	4600	26.3	Nitrogen oxide (ic)	NO	−163.7	549.5	18.3
Lutetium chloride	LuCl$_3$	904	(9000)	(32)	Nitrogen oxide (ous)	N$_2$O	−90.9	1563	35.5
Magnesium	Mg	650	2160	88.9	Nitrogen tetroxide	N$_2$O$_4$	−13.2	5540	60.2
Magnesium bromide	MgBr$_2$	711	8300	45.0	Osmium	Os	2700	(7000)	(36.7)
Magnesium chloride	MgCl$_2$	712	8100	82.9	Osmium tetroxide (white)	OsO$_4$	41.8	2340	9.2
Magnesium fluoride	MgF$_2$	1221	5900	94.7	Osmium tetroxide (yellow)	OsO$_4$	55.8	4060	15.5
Magnesium oxide	MgO	2642	18500	459.0	Oxygen	O$_2$	−218.8	106.3	3.3
Magnesium phosphate	Mg$_3$(PO$_4$)$_2$	1184	(11300)	(42.9)	Palladium	Pd	1555	4120	38.6
Magnesium silicate	MgSiO$_3$	1524	14700	146.4	Phosphoric acid	H$_3$PO$_4$	42.3	2520	25.8
Magnesium sulfate	MgSO$_4$	1327	3500	28.9	Phosphoric acid, hypo-	H$_4$P$_2$O$_6$	54.8	8300	51.2
Manganese	Mn	1220	3450	62.7	Phosphorous acid, hypo-	H$_3$PO$_2$	17.3	2310	35.0
Manganese dichloride	MnCl$_2$	650	7340	58.4	Phosphorous acid, ortho-	H$_3$PO$_3$	73.8	3070	37.4
Manganese metasilicate	MnSiO$_3$	1274	(8200)	(62.6)	Phosphorus, yellow	P$_4$	44.1	600	4.8
Manganese (II) oxide	MnO	1784	13000	183.3	Phosphorus oxychloride	POCl$_3$	1.0	3110	20.3
Manganese oxide	Mn$_3$O$_4$	1590	(39000)	(170.4)	Phosphorus pentoxide	P$_4$O$_{10}$	569.0	17080	60.1
Mercury	Hg	−39	557.2	2.7	Phosphorus trioxide	P$_4$O$_6$	23.7	3360	15.3
Mercury bromide	HgBr$_2$	241	3960	10.9	Platinum	Pt	1770	4700	24.1
Mercury chloride	HgCl$_2$	276.8	4150	15.3	Potassium	K	63.4	574	14.6
Mercury iodide	HgI$_2$	250	4500	9.9	Potassium borate, meta-	KBO$_2$	947	(5660)	(69.1)
Mercury sulfate	HgSO$_4$	850	(1440)	(4.8)	Potassium bromide	KBr	742	5000	42.0
Molybdenum	Mo	2622	(6600)	(68.4)	Potassium carbonate	K$_2$CO$_3$	897	7800	56.4
Molybdenum dichloride	MoCl$_2$	726.8	6000	3.58	Potassium chloride	KCl	770	6410	85.9
Molybdenum hexafluoride	MoF$_6$	17	2500	11.9	Potassium chromate	K$_2$CrO$_4$	984	6920	35.6
Molybdenum trioxide	MoO$_3$	795	(2500)	(17.3)	Potassium cyanide	KCN	623	(3500)	(53.7)
Neodymium	Nd	1020	1700	11.8	Potassium dichromate	K$_2$Cr$_2$O$_7$	398	8770	29.8
					Potassium fluoride	KF	875	6500	111.9

Compound	Formula	M.P.,°C	H_f cal/g mole	H_f cal/g	Compound	Formula	M.P.,°C	H_f cal/g mole	H_f cal/g
Potassium hydroxide	KOH	360	(1980)	(35.3)	Silver cyanide	AgCN	350	2750	20.5
Potassium iodide	KI	682	4100	24.7	Silver iodide	AgI	557	2250	9.5
Potassium nitrate	KNO_3	338	2840	28.1	Silver nitrate	$AgNO_3$	209	2755	16.2
Potassium peroxide	K_2O_2	490	6100	55.3	Silver sulfide	Ag_2S	841	3360	13.5
Potassium phosphate	K_3PO_4	1340	8900	41.9	Silver sulfate	Ag_2SO_4	657	(4280)	(13.7)
Potassium pyro-phosphate	$K_4P_2O_7$	1092	14000	42.4	Sodium	Na	97.8	630	27.4
					Sodium borate, meta-	$NaBO_2$	966	8660	134.6
Potassium sulfate	K_2SO_4	1074	8100	46.4	Sodium bromide	NaBr	747	6140	59.7
Potassium sulfocyanide	KCNS	179	2250	23.1	Sodium carbonate	Na_2CO_3	854	7000	66.0
Potassium tungstate	K_2WO_4	929	(4400)	(13.6)	Sodium chloride	NaCl	800	7220	123.5
Praseodymium	Pr	931	2700	19.0	Sodium chlorate	$NaClO_3$	255	5290	49.7
Praseodymium chloride	$PrCl_3$	786	(8000)	(32.3)	Sodium cyanide	NaCN	562	(4360)	(88.9)
Promethium	Pm	(1027)	(3000)	(21)	Sodium fluoride	NaF	992	7000	166.7
Rhenium	Re	3167 ± 60	(7900)	(42.4)	Sodium hydroxide	NaOH	322	2000	50.0
Rhenium heptoxide	Re_2O_7	296	15340	30.1	Sodium iodide	NaI	662	5340	35.1
Rhenium hexafluoride	ReF_6	19.0	5000	16.6	Sodium molybdate	Na_2MoO_4	687	3600	17.5
Rubidium	Rb	38.9	525	6.1	Sodium nitrate	$NaNO_3$	310	3760	44.2
Rubidium bromide	RbBr	677	3700	22.4	Sodium phosphate, meta-	$NaPO_3$	988	(4960)	(48.6)
Rubidium chloride	RbCl	717	4400	36.4					
Rubidium fluoride	RbF	833	4130	39.5	Sodium peroxide	Na_2O_2	460	5860	75.1
Rubidium iodide	RbI	638	2990	14.0	Sodium pyro-phosphate	$Na_4P_2O_7$	970	(13700)	(51.5)
Rubidium nitrate	$RbNO_3$	305	1340	9.1	Sodium silicate, meta-	Na_2SiO_3	1087	10300	84.4
Samarium	Sm	1072	2600	17.3	Sodium silicate, di-	$Na_2Si_2O_5$	884	8460	46.4
Samarium chloride	$SmCl_2$	562	(6000)	(27.1)	Sodium silicate, aluminum-	$NaAlSi_3O_8$	1107	13150	50.1
Scandium	Sc	1538	3800	84.4					
Scandium trichloride	$ScCl_3$	940	(19000)	(125.4)	Sodium sulfide	Na_2S	920	(1200)	15.4
Selenium	Se	217	1220	15.4	Sodium sulfate	Na_2SO_4	884	5830	41.0
Selenium oxychloride	$SeOCL_3$	9.8	1010	6.1	Sodium thiocyanate	NaCNS	323	4450	54.8
Silicon	Si	1427	9470	337.0	Sodium tungstate	Na_2WO_4	702	5800	19.6
Silicondioxide (Cristobalite)	SiO_2	2100	2100	35.0	Strontium	Sr	757	2190	25.0
Silicondioxide (Quartz)	SiO_2	1470	3400	56.7	Strontium bromide	$SrBr_2$	643	4780	19.3
Disilane, hexafluoro-	Si_2F_6	−28.6	3900	22.9	Strontium chloride	$SrCl_2$	872	4100	26.5
Silicon tetrachloride	$SiCl_4$	−67.7	1845	10.8	Strontium fluoride	SrF_2	1400	4260	34.0
Silver	Ag	961	2700	25.0					
Silver bromide	AgBr	430	2180	11.6					
Silver chloride	AgCl	455	3155	22.0					

HEAT OF FUSION OF SOME INORGANIC COMPOUNDS (Continued)

Compound	Formula	M.P.,°C	H_f cal/g mole	cal/g	Compound	Formula	M.P.,°C	H_f cal/g mole	cal/g
Strontium oxide	SrO	2430	16700	161.2	Tin chloride, ous-	$SnCl_2$	247	3050	16.0
Sulfur (monatomic)	S	119	295	9.2	Tin iodide, ic-	SnI_4	143.4	(4330)	(6.9)
Sulfur dioxide	SO_2	−73.2	2060	32.2	Tin oxide	SnO	1042	(6400)	(46.8)
Sulfur trioxide (α)	SO_3	16.8	2060	25.8	Titanium	Ti	1800	(5000)	(104.4)
Sulfur trioxide (β)	SO_3	32.3	2890	36.1	Titanium bromide, tetra-	$TiBr_4$	38	(2060)	(5.6)
Sulfur trioxide (γ)	SO_3	62.1	6310	79.0	Titanium chloride, tetra-	$TiCl_4$	−23.2	2240	11.9
Tantalum	Ta	2996 ± 50	(7500)	34.6 to 41.5	Titanium dioxide	TiO_2	1825	(11400)	(142.7)
Tantalum pentachloride	$TaCl_5$	206.8	9000	25.1	Titanium oxide	TiO	991	14000	219
Tantalum pentoxide	Ta_2O_5	1877	48000	108.6	Tungsten	W	3387	(8420)	(45.8)
Tellurium	Te	453	3230	25.3	Tungsten dioxide	WO_2	1270	13940	60.1
Terbium	Tb	1356	3900	24.6	Tungsten hexafluoride	WF_6	−0.5	1800	6.0
Thallium	Tl	302.4	1030	5.0	Tungsten tetrachloride	WCl_4	327	6000	18.4
Thallium bromide, mono-	TlBr	460	5990	21.0	Tungsten trioxide	WO_3	1470	13940	60.1
Thallium carbonate	Tl_2CO_3	273	4400	9.5	Uranium[235]	U	∼1133	3700	20
Thallium chloride, mono-	TlCl	427	4260	17.7	Uranium tetrachloride	UCl_4	590	10300	27.1
Thallium iodide, mono-	TlI	440	3125	9.4	Vanadium	V	1917	(4200)	(70)
Thallium nitrate	$TlNO_3$	207	2290	8.6	Vanadium dichloride	VCl_2	1027	8000	65.6
Thallium sulfide	Tl_2S	449	3000	6.8	Vanadium oxide	VO	2077	15000	224.0
Thallium sulfate	Tl_2SO_4	632	5500	10.9	Vanadium pentoxide	V_2O_5	670	15560	85.5
Thorium	Th	1845	(<4600)	(<19.8)	Xenon	Xe	−111.6	740	5.6
Thorium dioxide	ThO_2	2952	291100	1102.0	Ytterbium	Yb	823	2200	12.7
Thorium chloride	$ThCl_4$	765	22500	61.6	Yttrium	Y	1504	4100	46.1
Thulium	Tm	1545	4400	26.0	Yttrium oxide	Y_2O_3	2227	25000	110.7
Thulium chloride	$TmCl_3$	821	(9000)	(32.6)	Yttrium trichloride	YCl_3	709	(9000)	(46)
Tin	Sn	231.7	1720	14.4	Zinc	Zn	419.4	1595	24.4
Tin bromide, ic-	$SnBr_4$	29.8	3000	6.8	Zinc chloride	$ZnCl_2$	283	(5540)	(40.6)
Tin bromide, ous-	$SnBr_2$	231.8	(1720)	(6.1)	Zinc oxide	ZnO	1975	4470	54.9
Tin chloride, ic-	$SnCl_4$	−33.3	2190	8.4	Zinc sulfide	ZnS	1700 ± 20	(9100)	(93.3)
					Zirconium	Zr	1857	(5500)	(60)
					Zirconium dichloride	$ZrCl_2$	727	7300	45.0
					Zirconium oxide	ZrO_2	2715	20800	168.8

Table of the Isotopes

Compiled by
Russell L. Heath
National Reactor Testing Station
Idaho Nuclear Corporation
Idaho Falls, Idaho

The following describes the information contained in each column of this table:

Column 1. This column lists the isotopes with the atomic number as a subscript and the atomic weight as a superscript. Isomers are indicated by the addition of the letter m to the superscript. Although they are not isotopes, the elements and their corresponding atomic numbers are also included in this column.

Column 2. % Natural Abundance. This column lists isotopic abundance in percent.

Column 3. Atomic Mass. This column lists atomic mass of isotopes in the physical scale. The atomic masses are all relative to the mass of the Carbon 12 isotope which has arbitrarily been assigned 12.00000 atomic mass units as recommended by the International Union of Pure and Applied Chemistry and the International Commission of Atomic Weights.

Column 4. Lifetime. This column lists the half-life of the radioactive isotopes. The notation used is: μs = microseconds, ms = milliseconds, s = seconds, m = minutes, d = days, and y = years.

Column 5. This column lists the observed modes of decay for all radioactive isotopes. Symbols used are: β^- = negative beta emission, β^+ = positron emission, α = alpha particle decay, E.C. = orbital electron capture, I.T. = isomeric transition from upper to lower isomeric state, n = neutron emission, and S.F. = spontaneous fission.

Column 6. Decay Energy. This lists the currently adopted values for the total disintegration energies (Q) in MeV. Where more than one mode of decay exists separate values are given.

Column 7. Particle Energies. This column lists the end-point energies of beta particle transitions or discrete energies of alpha particles in MeV.

Column 8. Particle Intensities. This column lists the intensities of groups or alpha particle transitions in MeV.

Column 9. Thermal Neutron Capture Cross Section. This column lists cross sections for thermal-neutron capture in barns (10^{-24} cm^2) or in millibarns (mb). Where neutron capture for a given nucleus may produce two isomers, the separate cross sections are listed if known. Fission cross sections are listed for the heavy elements and are designated by the symbol σ_f.

Column 10. I. This table lists the Nuclear Spin or Angular Momentum in units of $h/2\pi$.

Column 11. μ. This column lists values of the Nuclear Magnetic Moments of the isotope in nuclear magnetons, with diamagnetic correction.

TABLE OF THE ISOTOPES (*Continued*)

Isotope	% nat. abundance	Atomic mass	Lifetime	Modes of decay	Decay energy (MeV)	Particle energies (MeV)	Particle intensities	Thermal neutron capture cross-section	I	μ
n^1		1.008665	12m	β^-	0.7825	0.7825	100%		1/2	−1.9131
H		1.00797						$0.332 \pm 2mb$		
$_1H$	99.985	1.007825							1/2	+2.79278
$_1H^2$	0.015	2.0140						$0.51 \pm 0.01mb$	1	+0.85742
$_1H^3$		3.01605	12.26y	β^-	0.01861	0.01861	100%	$<6\mu b$	1/2	
He		4.0026						$\geq 7mb$		
$_2He^3$	0.00013	3.01603						$<0.1mb$	1/2	−2.1275
$_2He^4$	100	4.00260						≈ 0	0	
$_2He^5$		5.0123								
$_2He^6$		6.01888	0.81s	β^-	3.5098	3.5098	100%		0	<0.16
$_2He^8$		8.0375	0.1225s	β^- η	13	13	88% 12%			
Li		6.939								
$_3Li^5$		5.0125								
$_3Li^6$	7.42	6.01512						$45 \pm 10mb$	1	+0.82202
$_3Li^7$	92.58	7.01600						$37 \pm 4mb$	3/2	+3.2564
$_3Li^8$			0.855s	β^-, α	13	13			(2)	+1.6532
$_3Li^9$			0.175s	β^-, η	13.5	13.5 11	75% 25%			
Be		9.0122						$9.2 \pm 0.5mb$		
$_4Be^6$		6.0197								
$_4Be^7$		7.0169	53.37d	EC	0.861					
$_4Be^8$		8.0053	$2 \times 10^{-16}s$	α						
$_4Be^9$	100%	9.01218						$9.2 \pm 0.5mb$	3/2	−1.1776
$_4Be^{10}$		10.0135	$2.5 \times 10^6 y$	β^-	0.55	0.55	100%	$\leq 1mb$		
$_4Be^{11}$		11.0216	13.6s	β^-	11.5	11.5 9.3 4.7 3.6	61% 29% 6% 4%			
B		10.811								
$_5B^8$		8.0246	0.77s	β^+	18	13.7				
$_5B^9$		9.0133	$8 \times 10^{-19}s$	P						
$_5B^{10}$	19.78	10.0129						$(\sigma[\eta, \alpha]\ 3836b)$ $0.5 \pm 0.2b$	3	+1.8007
$_5B^{11}$	80.22	11.00931						$5 \pm 3mb$	3/2	+2.6885
$_5B^{12}$		12.0143	0.02s	β^-, α	13.4	13.4 9.0	~100% 1.3%		(1)	+1.003
$_5B^{13}$		13.0178	0.019s	β^-	13.4	13.4	93%			

Isotope	% nat. abundance	Atomic mass	Lifetime	Modes of decay	Decay energy (MeV)	Particle energies (MeV)	Particle intensities	Thermal neutron capture cross-section	I	μ
C		12.01115						3.4 ± 0.2mb		
$_6C^{10}$			19.45s	β^+	3.61	1.87				
$_6C^{11}$			20.3min	β^+, EC	1.98	0.98			3/2	± 1.03
$_6C^{12}$	98.89	12.0000						3.4 ± 0.3mb	0	
$_6C^{13}$	1.11	13.00335						0.9 ± 0.2mb	1/2	$+0.7024$
$_6C^{14}$			5730y	β^-	0.156	0.156		$<10^{-6}$b	0	
$_6C^{15}$			2.4s	β^-	9.8	9.82 / 4.51	32% / 68%			
$_6C^{16}$			0.74s	β^-, η						
N		14.0067								
$_7N^{12}$			0.011s	β^+	16.4	16.38				
$_7N^{13}$										
$_7N^{13}$	10.0m		9.97m	β^+	1.19	1.19			1/2	± 0.3221
$_7N^{14}$	99.63	14.00307						75 ± 7.5mb	1	$+0.4036$
$_7N^{15}$	0.37	15.00011						$24 \pm 8\mu$b	1/2	-0.2831
$_7N^{16}$			7.2s	β^-	10.44	10.44 / 4.27	26% / 68%			
$_7N^{17}$			4.16s	$\beta^-, (\eta)$	8.68	8.7 / 7.8 / 4.12 / 3.3 / 2.7	1.6% / 2.6% / 45% / 45% / 5%			
$_7N^{18}$			0.63s	β^-	13.9	9.4	100%			
O		15.9994								
$_8O^{13}$			0.0087s	β^+, (P)	17.8	6.40 (proton) / 6.79 (proton)	100† / 24			
$_8O^{14}$			71.0s	β^+	5.14	1.813 / 4.09	99.35% / 0.65%			
$_8O^{15}$			124s	β^+	2.76	1.70	100%		1/2	± 0.7189
$_8O^{16}$	99.759	15.99491						0.178 ± 0.025mb	0	
$_8O^{17}$	0.037							235 ± 10mb	5/2	-1.8937
$_8O^{18}$	0.204							0.21 ± 0.04mb	0	
$_8O^{19}$			29s	β^-	4.819	4.60 / 3.25	42% / 58%		5/2	
$_8O^{20}$			14s	β^-	3.81	2.7				
F		18.9984						9.8 ± 0.7mb		
$_9F^{17}$			66s	β^+	2.76	1.73	100%		(5/2)	± 4.722
$_9F^{18}$			109.7m	β^+, EC	1.65	0.635 / EC	97% / 3%			
$_9F^{19}$	100%	18.99840						9.8 ± 0.7mb	1/2	$+2.6288$

Isotope	% nat. abundance	Atomic mass	Lifetime	Modes of decay	Decay energy (MeV)	Particle energies (MeV)	Particle intensities	Thermal neutron capture cross-section	I	μ
$_9F^{20}$			11.4s	β^-					(2)	+2.094
$_9F^{21}$			4.4s	β^-	5.68	5.4 4.0				
$_9F^{22}$			4.0s	β^-	12	11				
Ne		20.183						38 ± 10mb		
$_{10}Ne^{17}$			0.10s	β^+, (P)						
$_{10}Ne^{18}$			1.5s	β^+	4.45	3.42 2.38	93% 7%			
$_{10}Ne^{19}$			17.5s	β^+	3.24	2.24			1/2	−1.887
$_{10}Ne^{20}$	90.92%	19.99244						38 ± 10mb	0	
$_{10}Ne^{21}$	0.257%	20.99395							3/2	−0.6618
$_{10}Ne^{22}$	8.82%	21.99138						36 ± 10mb	0	
$_{10}Ne^{23}$			37.6s	β^-	4.38	4.38 3.95 2.4	67% 32% 1.0%			
$_{10}Ne^{24}$			3.38m	β^-	2.47	1.98 1.10	92% 8%			
Na		22.9898						534 ± 5mb		
$_{11}Na^{20}$			0.39s	$\beta^+(\alpha)$	14					
$_{11}Na^{21}$			23s	β^+	3.54	2.51	98%		3/2	+2.386
$_{11}Na^{22}$			2.602y	β^*, EC				$40,000 \pm 5000$b	3	+1.746
$_{11}Na^{23}$	100%	22.9898						400 ± 30mb	3/2	+2.2175
$_{11}Na^{24}$			15.0h	β^-	5.51	4.17 1.389	0.003% 99+%		4	+1.690
$_{11}Na^{25}$			60s	β^-	3.83	4.0 3.1 2.6	65% 25% 7%			
$_{11}Na^{26}$			1.0s	β^-	8.5	6.7	>80%			
Mg		24.312						64 ± 2mb		
$_{12}Mg^{20}$			0.6s	β^+	9					
$_{12}Mg^{21}$			0.12s	$\beta^+(P)$						
$_{12}Mg^{23}$			12.1s	β^+	4.06	3.10				
$_{12}Mg^{24}$	78.70%	23.98504						52 ± 15mb	0	
$_{12}Mg^{25}$	10.13%	24.98584						0.18 ± 0.05b	5/2	−0.8553
$_{12}Mg^{26}$	11.17%	25.98259						0.03 ± 0.005b	0	
$_{12}Mg^{27}$			9.5min	β^-	2.61	1.75 1.59	58% 42%			

Isotope	% nat. abundance	Atomic mass	Lifetime	Modes of decay	Decay energy (MeV)	Particle energies (MeV)	Particle intensities	Thermal neutron capture cross-section	I	μ
$_{12}Mg^{28}$			21h	β^-	1.84	0.46				
Al		26.98153						$232 \pm 3mb$		
$_{13}Al^{24}$			2.1s	$\beta^+(\alpha)$	14	8.5				
$_{13}Al^{25}$			7.2s	β^+	4.26	3.24	100%			
$_{13}Al^{26m}$			6.4s	β^+		3.21				
$_{13}Al^{26}$			7.4×10^5y	β^+, EC	4.003	1.16				
$_{13}Al^{27}$	100%	26.98153						$232 \pm 3mb$	5/2	+3.6414
$_{13}Al^{28}$			2.31m	β^-	4.635	2.82	100%			
$_{13}Al^{29}$			6.6min	β^-	3.68	2.5 1.4	70% 30%			
$_{13}Al^{30}$			3.3s	β^-	7.3	5.0				
Si		28.086						$160 \pm 20mb$		
$_{14}Si^{25}$			0.23s	$\beta^+(P)$						
$_{14}Si^{26}$			2.1s	β^+	5.08	3.83 3.00	66† 34			
$_{14}Si^{27}$			4.2s	β^+	4.810	3.85				
$_{14}Si^{28}$	92.21%	27.97693						$160 \pm 40mb$	0	
$_{14}Si^{29}$	4.70%	28.97649						$280 \pm 90mb$	1/2	−0.5553
$_{14}Si^{30}$	3.09%	29.97376						$100 \pm 10mb$	0	
$_{14}Si^{31}$			2.62h	β^-	1.48	1.49	99+%			
$_{14}Si^{32}$			~650y	β^-	0.21	0.21				
P		30.9738						$190 \pm 10mb$		
$_{15}P^{28}$			0.28s	β^+	13.8	10.6	50%			
$_{15}P^{29}$			4.4s	β^+	4.95	3.96				
$_{15}P^{30}$			2.50m	β^+	4.24	3.27				
$_{15}P^{31}$	100%	**30.97376**						$190 \pm 10mb$	1/2	+1.1317
$_{15}P^{32}$			14.3d	β^-	1.710	1.710	100%		1	−0.2523
$_{15}P^{33}$			25d	β^-	0.248	0.249	100%			
$_{15}P^{34}$			12.4s	β^-	5.1	5.1 3.2	75% 25%			
S		32.064								
$_{16}S^{29}$			0.19s	$\beta^+(P)$						
$_{16}S^{30}$			1.4s	β^+	6.11	5.09 4.42	20† 80			
$_{16}S^{31}$			2.7s	β^+	5.44	4.39				

Isotope	% nat. abundance	Atomic mass	Lifetime	Modes of decay	Decay energy (MeV)	Particle energies (MeV)	Particle intensities	Thermal neutron capture cross-section	I	μ
$_{16}S^{32}$	95.0%	31.97207							0	
$_{16}S^{33}$	0.76%	32.97146						15 ± 10mb	3/2	+0.6433
$_{16}S^{34}$	4.22%	33.96786						200 ± 100mb	0	
$_{16}S^{35}$			88d	β^-	0.1674	0.1674	100%		3/2	± 1.0
$_{16}S^{36}$	0.014%	35.96709						140 ± 40mb	0	
$_{16}S^{37}$			5.06m	β^-	4.8	4.3 1.6	10% 90%			
$_{16}S^{38}$			2.87h	β^-	3.0	3.0 1.1	5% 95%			
Cl		35.453								
$_{17}Cl^{32}$			0.31s	$\beta^+(\alpha)$	13.2	9.5	~50%			
$_{17}Cl^{33}$			2.5s	β^+	5.57	4.51				
$_{17}Cl^{34m}$			32.0m	β^+, IT		2.5 1.3 4.5	26† 26 47			
$_{17}Cl^{34}$			1.56s	β^+	5.482	4.50				
$_{17}Cl^{35}$	75.53%	34.96885						44 ± 2b	3/2	+0.82183
$_{17}Cl^{36}$			3.1×10^5y	β^- β^+, EC	0.712 1.14	0.714 (β^-)	98.1% 1.9%	100 ± 30b	2	+1.285
$_{17}Cl^{37}$	24.47%							430 ± 100mb	3/2	+0.68411
$_{17}Cl^{38m}$			0.74s	IT						
$_{17}Cl^{38}$			37.3m	β^-	4.91	4.81 2.77 1.11	53% 16% 31%			
$_{17}Cl^{39}$			55.5m	β^-	3.44	3.45 2.18 1.91	7% 8% 85%			
$_{17}Cl^{40}$			1.4m	β^-	7.5	~7.5 ~3.2				
Ar		39.948								
$_{18}Ar^{35}$			1.83s	β^+	5.96	4.93	93%		(3/2)	+0.632
$_{18}Ar^{36}$	0.337%	35.96755						6 ± 2b	0	
$_{18}Ar^{37}$			35d	EC	0.814	EC	100%		3/2	+0.95
$_{18}Ar^{38}$	0.063%	37.96272						$0.8 + 0.2$b	0	
$_{18}Ar^{39}$			265y	β^-	3.44	0.565	100%	500 ± 200b	7/2	−1.3
$_{18}Ar^{40}$	99.60%							650 ± 30mb	0	
$_{18}Ar^{41}$			1.83h	β^-	2.491	1.198 2.49	99% 0.78%	0.5 ± 0.1b		
$_{18}Ar^{42}$			33y	β^-	0.60					
K	39.102									
$_{19}K^{37}$			1.23s	β^+	6.16	~5.1	98%			

Isotope	% nat. abundance	Atomic mass	Lifetime	Modes of decay	Decay energy (MeV)	Particle energies (MeV)	Particle intensities	Thermal neutron capture cross-section	I	μ
$_{19}K^{38m}$			0.95s	β^+		5.0	100%			
$_{19}K^{38}$			7.71m	β^+, EC	5.93	2.68			3	+1.374
$_{19}K^{39}$	93.1%	38.96371						2.2 ± 0.2b	3/2	0.3914
$_{19}K^{40}$	0.00118%	39.974	1.28×10^9y	β^-, β^+, EC	1.35 1.505	β^- β^+	1.35% 0.49%	70 ± 20b	4	−1.298
$_{19}K^{41}$	6.88%							1.3 ± 0.2b	3/2	+0.2149
$_{19}K^{42}$			12.4h	β^-	0.60	3.52 1.97	82% 18%		2	−1.140
$_{19}K^{43}$			22.4h	β^-	1.82	1.81 1.24 0.84 0.46	1.3% 3.5% 87% 8%		3/2	±0.163
$_{19}K^{44}$			22.0m	β^-	5.2	5.3 4.0 2.6	∼35% 9% 38%			
$_{19}K^{45}$			16m	β^-	4.2	4.0 2.1 1.1	15† 60 25		3/2	±0.173
Ca		40.08						0.44 ± 0.02b		
$_{20}Ca^{37}$			0.173s	β^+(P)	11.5					
$_{20}Ca^{38}$			0.66s	β^+						
$_{20}Ca^{39}$			0.87s	β^+	6.50	5.49				
$_{20}Ca^{40}$	96.947%	39.96259						430 ± 40mb	0	
$_{20}Ca^{41}$			8×10^4y	EC	0.427				7/2	−1.595
$_{20}Ca^{42}$	0.646%	41.95863						700 ± 160mb		
$_{20}Ca^{43}$	0.135%	42.95878						6.2 ± 1.1b	7/2	−1.317
$_{20}Ca^{44}$	2.083%	43.95549						1.1 ± 0.3b		
$_{20}Ca^{45}$			165d	β^-	0.252	0.258	100%			
$_{20}Ca^{46}$	0.186%	45.9537						250 ± 100mb		
$_{20}Ca^{47}$			4.53d	β^-	1.979	1.979 1.48 0.67	16% 2% 82%			
$_{20}Ca^{48}$	0.18%	47.9524						1.1 ± 0.1b		
$_{20}Ca^{49}$			8.8m	β^-	5.26	1.95 0.9	88† 12			
$_{20}Ca^{50}$			9s	β^-	3.9					
Sc		44.95592						25 ± 2b		
$_{21}Sc^{40}$			0.179s	β^+	14.5	9.1				
$_{21}Sc^{41}$			0.60s	β^+	6.50	5.6	100%			
$_{21}Sc^{42m}$			61s	β^+		2.82				

Isotope	% nat. abundance	Atomic mass	Lifetime	Modes of decay	Decay energy (MeV)	Particle energies (MeV)	Particle intensities	Thermal neutron capture cross-section	I	μ
$_{21}Sc^{42}$			0.68s	β^+	6.431	5.3	100%			
$_{21}Sc^{43}$			3.92h	β^+, EC	2.2	1.20 / 0.82 / 0.50	79† / 17 / 4		7/2	+4.62
$_{21}Sc^{44m}$			2.44d	IT / EC		98.6% / 1.4%			6	+3.88
$_{21}Sc^{44}$			3.92h	β^+	3.647	1.471	99%		2	+2.56
$_{21}Sc^{45}$	100%	44.95592						$25 \pm 2b$ / $11 \pm 4b$ (Sc^{46m})	7/2	+4.7564
$_{21}Sc^{46m}$			20s	IT	0.142					
$_{21}Sc^{46}$			83.80d	β^-	2.367	1.48 / 0.357	0.004% / 100%	$8.0 \pm 1b$	4	+3.03
$_{21}Sc^{47}$			3.43d	β^-	0.60	0.600 / 0.439	40% / 60%		7/2	+5.34
$_{21}Sc^{48}$			1.83d	β^-	3.98	0.65 / 0.47	94% / 6%		6	
$_{21}Sc^{49}$			57.5m	β^-	2.008	2.01	100%			
$_{21}Sc^{50m}$			0.35s	IT	0.258					
$_{21}Sc^{50}$			1.72m	β^-	6.5	3.6				
Ti		47.90						$6.1 \pm 0.2b$		
$_{22}Ti^{43}$			0.56s	β^+	6.8	5.5	100%			
$_{22}Ti^{44}$			48y	EC	0.16					
$_{22}Ti^{45}$			3.09h	β^+, EC	2.059	1.02	99+%		7/2	±0.095
$_{22}Ti^{46}$	7.93%	45.95263						$0.6 \pm 0.2b$		
$_{22}Ti^{47}$	7.28%	46.9518						$1.7 \pm 0.3b$	5/2	−0.7883
$_{22}Ti^{48}$	73.94%							$8.3 \pm 0.6b$		
$_{22}Ti^{49}$	5.51%	48.94787						$1.9 \pm 0.5b$	7/2	−1.1039
$_{22}Ti^{50}$	5.34%	49.9448						$140 \pm 30mb$		
$_{22}Ti^{51}$			5.8m	β^-	2.46	2.13 / 1.50	94% / 6%			
V		50.942						$5.06 \pm 0.06b$		
$_{23}V^{46}$			0.426s	β^+	7.054	6.0	100%			
$_{23}V^{47}$			33m	β^+, EC	2.92	1.89				
$_{23}V^{48}$			16.0d	β^+, EC	4.013	0.698				
$_{23}V^{49}$			330d	EC	0.601					
$_{23}V^{50}$	0.24%	49.9472	6×10^{15}y	EC				$100 \pm 60b$	6	+3.3470
$_{23}V^{51}$	99.76%	50.9440						$4.8 \pm 0.2b$	7/2	+5.149

Isotope	% nat. abundance	Atomic mass	Lifetime	Modes of decay	Decay energy (MeV)	Particle energies (MeV)	Particle intensities	Thermal neutron capture cross-section	I	μ
$_{23}V^{52}$			3.76m	β^-	3.97	2.47				
$_{23}V^{53}$			2.0m	β^-	3.5	2.50	100%			
$_{23}V^{54}$			55s	β^-	7.3	3.3	100%			
Cr		51.996						3.1 ± 0.2b		
$_{24}Cr^{48}$			23h	EC	1.4					
$_{24}Cr^{49}$			41.9m	β^-	5.26	1.54 1.39 0.73	50† 35 15		5/2	± 0.48
$_{24}Cr^{50}$	4.31%	49.9461						16.0 ± 0.5b		
$_{24}Cr^{51}$			27.8d	EC	0.752				7/2	± 0.94
$_{24}Cr^{52}$	83.76%	51.9405						0.76 ± 0.06b		
$_{24}Cr^{53}$	9.55%	52.9407						18.2 ± 1.5b	3/2	-0.4744
$_{24}Cr^{54}$	2.38%	53.9389						380 ± 40mb		
$_{24}Cr^{55}$			3.5m	β^-	2.59	2.50	100%			
$_{24}Cr^{56}$			5.9m	β^-	1.6	1.5				
Mn								13.3 ± 0.1b		
$_{25}Mn^{50m}$			2m	β^+, EC						
$_{25}Mn^{50}$			0.286s	β^+	7.631	6.6	100%			
$_{25}Mn^{51}$			45m	β^+, EC	3.19	2.17	97%		5/2	± 3.60
$_{25}Mn^{52m}$			21m	IT, β^+, EC	0.383	2% 98%			2	± 0.0077
$_{25}Mn^{52}$			5.7d	β^+, EC	4.708	0.575			6	± 3.075
$_{25}Mn^{53}$			2×10^6y	EC	0.598		100%	~170b	7/2	± 5.05
$_{25}Mn^{54}$			303d	EC	1.379			<10b	3	± 3.30
$_{25}Mn^{55}$	100%	54.9381						13.3 ± 0.1b	5/2	± 3.444
$_{25}Mn^{56}$			2.576h	β^-	3.702	2.84 1.03 0.72 0.30	47% 34% 18% 1%		3	$+3.218$
$_{25}Mn^{57}$			1.7m	β^-	2.7	2.55 1.10	82% 18%			
$_{25}Mn^{58}$			1.1m	β^-	6.5					
Fe		55.847						2.56 ± 0.05b		
$_{26}Fe^{52}$			8.2h	β^+, EC	2.37	0.80				
$_{26}Fe^{53}$			8.5m	β^+, EC	3.98	2.8 2.4 1.6	50† 38 12			
$_{26}Fe^{54}$	5.82%	53.9396						2.8 ± 0.4b		

Isotope	% nat. abundance	Atomic mass	Lifetime	Modes of decay	Decay energy (MeV)	Particle energies (MeV)	Particle intensities	Thermal neutron capture cross-section	I	μ
$_{26}Fe^{55}$			2.6y	EC	0.232					
$_{26}Fe^{56}$	91.66%	55.9349						2.5 ± 0.3b		
$_{26}Fe^{57}$	2.19%	56.9354						2.5 ± 0.2b	1/2	+0.0902
$_{26}Fe^{58}$	0.33%	57.9333						1.23 ± 0.05b		
$_{26}Fe^{59}$			45.1 ± 0.5d	β^-		1.573 0.475 0.273	0.3% 51% 48%		3/2	
$_{26}Fe^{60}$			3×10^5y	β^-	0.14					
$_{26}Fe^{61}$			6.0m	β^-	3.8	2.8				
Co		58.9332						37.5 ± 0.2b		
$_{27}Co^{54m}$			1.5m	β^+		4.3	100%			
$_{27}Co^{54}$			0.1945	β^+	8.252	>7.4				
$_{27}Co^{55}$			18.2h	β^+, EC	3.46	1.51 1.04 0.79	45† 33 2		(7/2)	±4.3
$_{27}Co^{56}$			77d	β^+, EC	4.57	1.50 0.44	96† 4		4	±3.85
$_{27}Co^{57}$			270d	EC	0.837				7/2	±4.65
$_{27}Co^{58m}$			9.0h	IT	0.025			1.4×10^5 $\pm 1 \times 10^4$b		
$_{27}Co^{58}$			71.3d	β^+, EC	2.309	1.3 0.474	0.0006% 83% EC 15% β^+	1700 ± 200b	2	±4.06
$_{27}Co^{59}$	100%	58.9332						19.9 ± 0.91b (Co^{60m}) 17 ± 2b (Co^{60})	7/2	~ +4.649
$_{27}Co^{60m}$			10.5m	IT β^-	0.05860	1.56	99% 1%	58 ± 8b		
$_{27}Co^{60}$			5.26 ± 0.01y		2.819	0.315 0.663 1.488	99.87% 0.008% 0.12%	2.0 ± 0.2b	5	+3.81
$_{27}Co^{61}$			1.650h ± 0.05	β^-	1.29	1.22 ± 0.04	100%			
$_{27}Co^{62m}$			1.6m	β^-						
$_{27}Co^{62}$			13.9m	β^-	5.22	2.88 0.88	75% 25%			
$_{27}Co^{63}$			52s	β^-	3.6	3.6	100%			
Ni		58.71						4.54 ± 0.1b		
$_{28}Ni^{56}$			6.10d	EC	2.11					
$_{28}Ni^{57}$			36.0h	β^+, EC	3.24	0.85 0.72 0.35	87† 11 2			
$_{28}Ni^{58}$	68.274%	57.9353						4.4 ± 0.4b		

Isotope	% nat. abundance	Atomic mass	Lifetime	Modes of decay	Decay energy (MeV)	Particle energies (MeV)	Particle intensities	Thermal neutron capture cross-section	I	μ
$_{28}Ni^{59}$			$8 \times 10^4 y$	EC	1.072		100%			
$_{28}Ni^{60}$	26.095%	58.9332						$2.6 \pm 0.2b$		
$_{28}Ni^{61}$	1.134%	60.9310						$2.5 \pm 0.9b$	3/2	-0.7487
$_{28}Ni^{62}$	3.593%	61.9283						$15 \pm 2b$		
$_{28}Ni^{63}$			92y	β^-	0.067	0.067	100%			
$_{28}Ni^{64}$	0.904%	63.9280						$1.52 \pm 0.24b$		
$_{28}Ni^{65}$			2.521h ± 0.005	β^-	2.139	0.412 0.513 0.655 1.022 2.139	0.7% 1.2% 30.2% 9.9% 58%	$20 \pm 2b$		
$_{28}Ni^{66}$			54.6h ± 0.9	β^-	0.20	0.20	100%			
$_{28}Ni^{67}$			50s	β^-	4.1	~2 2.3 3.2 4.1	22% 24% 4% 50%			
Cu		63.54						$3.8 \pm 0.1b$		
$_{29}Cu^{58}$			3.20s	β^+	8.569	8.2				
$_{29}Cu^{59}$			82.0s ± 0.4	β^+, EC	4.8	2.10 2.48 2.90 3.32 3.44 3.75	1.4% 10.9% 7.8% 4.1% 3.6% 70.8%			
$_{29}Cu^{60}$			23.0m ± 0.3	β^+, EC	6.12	0.52 0.55 0.61 0.77 1.02 1.08 1.71 1.83 1.91 2.00 2.48 3.00 3.92	0.1% 0.2% 0.2% 0.3% 1.0% 1.0% 0.8% 2.4% 11.8% 47.0% 4.2% 14.4% 8.4%		2	
$_{29}Cu^{61}$			3.41h	β^+, EC	2.242	0.307 0.560 0.933 1.148 1.216	0.03% 2.5% 6.3% 2.4% 52%		3/2	$+2.13$
$_{29}Cu^{62}$			9.8m	β^+, EC	3.939	0.87 1.75 2.923	1.5% 1.8% 93.9%		1	
$_{29}Cu^{63}$	69.09%	62.9298						$4.5 \pm 0.2b$	3/2	$+2.226$
$_{29}Cu^{64}$			12.9h	β^- β^+, EC	0.573 1.677	0.573 0.654	39.6% 19.3%	$<6000b$	1	-0.216

Isotope	% nat. abundance	Atomic mass	Lifetime	Modes of decay	Decay energy (MeV)	Particle energies (MeV)	Particle intensities	Thermal neutron capture cross-section	I	μ
$_{29}Cu^{65}$	30.91%	64.9278						2.3 ± 0.3b	3/2	+2.385
$_{29}Cu^{66}$			5.10m ±0.02	β^-	2.633	0.760 1.64 2.63	0.25% 9% 91%	130 ± 30b	1	±0.283
$_{29}Cu^{67}$			61.88h ±0.14	β^-	0.576	0.183 0.395 0.484 0.577	0.9% 51% 28% 20%			
$_{29}Cu^{68}$			30s	β^-	4.6	3.5 2.7 2.3	75% 22% 3%			
Zn		65.37						1.10 ± 0.04b		
$_{30}Zn^{60}$			2.1m	β^+, EC	4.16					
$_{30}Zn^{61}$			88 ± 1s	β^+, EC	5.91	4.27 4.94 5.44 5.91	7.8% 1.1% 10.8% 79.6%			
$_{30}Zn^{62}$			9.15 ± 0.03h	β^+, EC	1.679	0.66	15.2%			
$_{30}Zn^{63}$			38.40 ± 0.04m	β^+, EC	3.365	0.26 0.79 0.932 1.40 1.69 2.34	0.002% 0.08% 0.3% 6.9% 9.7% 76%		3/2	−0.282
$_{30}Zn^{64}$	48.89%	63.9291						0.82 ± 0.01b	0	
$_{30}Zn^{65}$			243.6d ±0.1	β^+, EC	1.353	0.325	1.54%		5/2	+0.769
$_{30}Zn^{66}$	27.81%	65.9260							0	
$_{30}Zn^{67}$	4.11%	65.9271							5/2	+0.8755
$_{30}Zn^{68}$	18.57	67.9249						0.09 ± 0.01b (Zn^{69m}) 1.0 ± 0.1b (Zn^{69})	0	
$_{30}Zn^{69m}$			13.9h	IT	0.4387					
$_{30}Zn^{69}$			58 ± 2m	β^-	0.925	0.925	100%			
$_{30}Zn^{70}$	0.62%	69.9253						9 ± 1mb (Zn^{71m}) 90 ± 10mb (Zn^{71})		
$_{30}Zn^{71m}$			4.0h	β^-		1.45				
$_{30}Zn^{71}$			2.4m	β^-	2.61	2.61 2.1	82% 14%			
$_{30}Zn^{72}$			46.5h	β^-	0.45	0.30 0.25	90% 10%			

Isotope	% nat. abundance	Atomic mass	Lifetime	Modes of decay	Decay energy (MeV)	Particle energies (MeV)	Particle intensities	Thermal neutron capture cross-section	I	μ
Ga	69.72							$3.1 \pm 0.3b$		
$_{31}Ga^{63}$			31s	β^+, EC	5.5	5.5	100%			
$_{31}Ga^{64}$			2.6m	β^+, EC	7.08	0.85 1.31 1.60 2.27 2.64 2.69 2.80 2.87	0.05% 0.04% 1.6% 5.3% 6.9% 31% 2.5% 31%			
$_{31}Ga^{65}$			15.2m	β^+, EC	3.26	0.266 0.769 0.895 1.190 1.327 1.370 1.468 2.030 2.122 2.183 2.237	0.003% 0.64% 0.8% 2.1% 0.4% 6.3% 1.5% 10.3% 53.1% 6.9% 7.2%			
$_{31}Ga^{66}$			9.4h	β^+, EC	5.175	0.367 0.720 0.770 0.935 1.373 1.781 4.153	1.1% 0.16% 0.8% 3.8% 0.1% 0.56% 48.6%		0	
$_{31}Ga^{67}$			78.1h	EC	1.0003				3/2	+1.850
$_{31}Ga^{68}$			68.3m	β^+, EC	2.919	0.82 1.895	1.2% 88%		1	±0.0117
$_{31}Ga^{69}$	60.4%	68.9257						$1.8 \pm 0.4b$	3/2	+2.016
$_{31}Ga^{70}$			21.1m	β^-	1.66	1.65 0.61 0.44	99+% 0.3% 0.5%		1	
$_{31}Ga^{71}$	39.6%	70.9249						$0.15 \pm 0.05b$	3/2	+2.562
$_{31}Ga^{72}$			14.10h	β^-	4.00	1.51 1.97 2.52 3.15	6% 4% 8% 8%		3	−0.1322
$_{31}Ga^{73}$			4.9h	β^-	1.55	0.4 1.19	5% 95%			
$_{31}Ga^{74}$			7.9m	β^-	5.60	2.6 4.0?				
$_{31}Ga^{75}$			2m	β^-	3.3	5.4	96%			
$_{31}Ga^{76}$			32s	β^-	~6					
Ge		72.59						2.3 ± 0.26		

Isotope	% nat. abundance	Atomic mass	Lifetime	Modes of decay	Decay energy (MeV)	Particle energies (MeV)	Particle intensities	Thermal neutron capture cross-section	I	μ
$_{32}Ge^{65}$			1.5m	β^+, EC	~6.5	3.8 4.8 5.5	2% 3% 94%			
$_{32}Ge^{66}$			9.4h	β^+, EC	3.0	1.2 1.44 1.60 1.69 1.74 1.87 1.93	2.7% 12.6% 43.1% 1.1% 4.0% 3.8% 16.5%			
$_{32}Ge^{67}$			19m	β^+, EC	4.43	0.68 1.24 1.60 1.96 2.33 2.58 3.08 3.24	0.08% 4.6% 11.4% 2.6% 7.7% 2.7% 13% 50.8%			
$_{32}Ge^{68}$			287d	EC	~0.7					
$_{32}Ge^{69}$			39h	β^+, EC	2.227	0.333 0.631 1.213	0.2% 2.3% 32.5%			
$_{32}Ge^{70}$	20.52%	69.9243						0.28 ± 0.07b	0	
$_{32}Ge^{71m}$			20ms	IT	0.198					
$_{32}Ge^{71}$			11.4d	EC	0.235		100%		1/2	+0.546
$_{32}Ge^{72}$	27.43%	71.9217						0.98 ± 0.09b	0	
$_{32}Ge^{73m}$			0.53s	IT	0.067		100%			
$_{32}Ge^{73}$	7.76%	72.9234						14 ± 1b	9/2	−0.8792
$_{32}Ge^{74}$	36.54%	73.9219						0.14 ± 0.3b	0	
$_{32}Ge^{75m}$			? 48.9s	IT	0.139		100%			
$_{32}Ge^{75}$			82.78m ±0.04	β^-	1.20	0.58 0.72 0.92 0.98 1.19	0.4% 0.3% 11% 1.4% 87%			
$_{32}Ge^{76}$	7.76%	75.9214						0.09 ± 0.02b	0	
$_{32}Ge^{77m}$			54s	IT β^-	0.159 2.75	2.7 2.9	1† 10			
$_{32}Ge^{77}$			11.3 ± 0.01h	β^-	2.75	0.71 1.38 2.20	23% 35% 42%			
$_{32}Ge^{78}$			1.47h	β^-	0.99	0.69 0.71	6% 94%			
As		74.9216						4.30 ± 0.10b		
$_{33}As^{69}$			15m	β^+, EC	3.9	2.9				

Isotope	% nat. abundance	Atomic mass	Lifetime	Modes of decay	Decay energy (MeV)	Particle energies (MeV)	Particle intensities	Thermal neutron capture cross-section	I	μ
$_{33}As^{70}$			53.0m ±0.6	β^+, EC	6.222	1.44 2.14 2.89	10† 75 6			
$_{33}As^{71}$			62h	β^+, EC	2.01	0.25 0.81	30%			
$_{33}As^{72}$			26h	β^+, EC	4.36	0.62 1.027 1.33 1.45 1.84 2.50 3.34	4% 3% 3% 5% 2% 56% 17%			
$_{33}As^{73}$			80.3d	EC	0.37					
$_{33}As^{74m}$			8.0s	IT	0.283					
$_{33}As^{74}$			17.9d	β^-	1.36	0.72 1.35	14% 18%			
				β^+, EC		0.91 1.51	26% 3.5%			
$_{33}As^{75}$	100%	74.9216						4.30 ± 0.10b	3/2	+1.439
$_{33}As^{76}$			26.5h	β^-	2.97	0.35 1.20 1.75 2.40 2.96	3% 6% 6% 32% 53%		2	−0.905
$_{33}As^{77}$			38.83h ±0.05	β^-	0.686	0.165 0.437 0.477 0.684	0.68% 0.6% 1.6% 97%			
$_{33}As^{78}$			91m	β^-	4.3	1.4 4.1	30% 70%			
$_{33}As^{79}$			9.0m	β^-	2.2	1.25 1.43 1.70 1.80 2.15	1.5% 0.5% 2% 1.5% 95%			
$_{33}As^{80}$			15.3s	β^-	6.0	3.0 3.5 3.7 4.1 4.2 4.5 5.3 6.0	0.4% 0.5% 4.3% 3.6% 1.7% 1.4% 32% 56%			
$_{33}As^{81}$			33s	β^-	3.8	3.8				
Se		78.96						12.2 ± 0.6b		
$_{34}Se^{70}$			44m	β^+, EC						
$_{34}Se^{71}$			5m	β^+, EC	4.4	3.4				
$_{34}Se^{72}$			8.4d	EC	0.6		100%			

Isotope	% nat. abundance	Atomic mass	Lifetime	Modes of decay	Decay energy (MeV)	Particle energies (MeV)	Particle intensities	Thermal neutron capture cross-section	I	μ
$_{34}Se^{73}$			7.1h	β^+, EC	2.75	0.25 0.75 1.32 1.68	1† 10 88 1			
$_{34}Se^{73}$			42m	β^+, EC	1.8					
$_{34}Se^{74}$	0.87%	73.9225						55 ± 5b	0	
$_{34}Se^{75}$			120.4d	β^-	0.865	0.293 0.465 0.625 0.601	0.1% 94% <2% 3%		5/2	
$_{34}Se^{76}$	9.02%	75.9192						21 ± 2b	0	
$_{34}Se^{77m}$			17.5s	IT	0.161		100%			
$_{34}Se^{77}$	7.58%	76.9199						42 ± 4b	1/2	+0.534
$_{34}Se^{78}$	23.52%	77.9173						0.33 ± 0.04b (Se^{79m}) 0.20 ± 0.106 (Se^{79})	0	
$_{34}Se^{79}$			6.5×10^4y	β^-	0.154	0.154	100%		7/2	−1.02
$_{34}Se^{80}$	49.82%	79.9165						0.08 ± 0.01b	0	
$_{34}Se^{81m}$			57m	IT	0.103		100%			
$_{34}Se^{81}$			18.6m	β^-	1.576	0.74 1.01 1.51	2% 2% ~93%			
$_{34}Se^{82}$	9.19%	81.9167						40 ± 10mb (Se^{83m}) 6 ± 1mb (Se^{83})	0	
$_{34}Se^{83m}$			70s	β^-		1.5 2.4 3.5	25% 25% 50%			
$_{34}Se^{83}$			23m	β^-	3.6	0.83 0.87 0.91 0.96 1.55 2.52 3.25	1% 13% 29% 37% 5% 10% 5%			
$_{34}Se^{84}$			3.3m	β^-						
$_{34}Se^{85}$			39s	β^-						
Br		79.909						6.8 ± 0.1b		
$_{35}Br^{74}$			36m	β^+, EC	~0.8	4 ?				
$_{35}Br^{75}$			1.7h	β^+, EC	2.72	0.3 0.6 0.8 1.70	19† 15 20 46			
$_{35}Br^{76}$			16.1h	4.6	β^+, EC		1.2 1.7 2.4 3.1 3.6	~3% 9% 12% 33% ~8%		1	±0.548

Isotope	% nat. abundance	Atomic mass	Lifetime	Modes of decay	Decay energy (MeV)	Particle energies (MeV)	Particle intensities	Thermal neutron capture cross-section	I	μ
$_{35}Br^{77}$			57h	β^+, EC	1.365	0.361	0.9%		3/2	
$_{35}Br^{78}$			6.4m	β^+, EC	3.573	1.937 2.52	11% 82%			
$_{35}Br^{79}$	50.54%	78.9183						2.6 ± 0.2b	3/2	+2.106
$_{35}Br^{80m}$			4.4h	IT	0.085				5	+1.317
$_{35}Br^{80}$			17.6m	β^- β^+, EC	1.871 2.01	β^+ 0.866 β^- 0.70 0.76 1.38 2.05	7.2% 0.23% 1.1% 0.2% 0.004% 0.08%		1	±0.514
$_{35}Br^{81}$	49.46%	80.9163						3.0 ± 0.2b (Br^{82m}) ^{c} 0.26b (Br^{82})	3/2	+2.270
$_{35}Br^{82m}$			? 6.1m	IT β^-	0.046	1.659 2.357	0.04% 0.2%			
$_{35}Br^{82}$			35.5h	β^-	3.092	0.257 0.440	~2% ~98%		5	±1.626
$_{35}Br^{83}$			2.41h	β^-	0.97	0.395 0.925	1.4% 98.6%			
$_{35}Br^{84}$			31.8m	β^-	4.8	0.89 1.45 2.9 3.9 4.8	19% 14% 15% 14% 32%			
$_{35}Br^{85}$			3.0m	β^-	2.8	2.8	100%			
$_{35}Br^{86}$			54s	β^-	7.1					
$_{35}Br^{87}$			55s	β^-, η	6.1	8.0 2.6	30† 70			
$_{35}Br^{88}$			16s	β^-, η						
$_{35}Br^{89}$			45s	β^-, η						
$_{35}Br^{90}$			1.6s	β^-, η						
Kr		83.80						24.5 ± 1.0b		
$_{36}Kr^{74}$			20m	β^+, EC	4.1	3.1				
$_{36}Kr^{75}$			5m	β^+, EC	~5.1					
$_{36}Kr^{76}$			14.8h	EC	~1.2					
$_{36}Kr^{77}$			1.19h	β^+, EC	2.99	1.64 1.68 1.85 1.86	2.3% 34.4% 40.7% 4.2%			
$_{36}Kr^{78}$	0.35%	77.9204						2.0 ± 0.5b		
$_{36}Kr^{79}$			34.9h	β^+, EC	1.628	0.209 0.299 0.325 0.604	0.03% 0.01% 0.2% 7.3%			

Isotope	% nat. abundance	Atomic mass	Lifetime	Modes of decay	Decay energy (MeV)	Particle energies (MeV)	Particle intensities	Thermal neutron capture cross-section	I	μ
$_{36}Kr^{80}$	2.27%	79.9164						$14 \pm 2b$		
$_{36}Kr^{81}$			$2.1 \times 10^5 y$	EC	0.29		100%			
$_{36}Kr^{82}$	11.56%	81.9135						$3 \pm 1b$ (Kr^{83m}) $32 \pm 15b$ (Kr^{83})	0	
$_{36}Kr^{83m}$			1.86h	IT						
$_{36}Kr^{83}$	11.55%							$180 \pm 40b$	9/2	−0.970
$_{36}Kr^{84}$	56.90%							$0.10 \pm 0.03b$	0	
$_{36}Kr^{85m}$			4.39hr	IT β^-	0.305	0.82				
$_{36}Kr^{85}$			10.76y	β^-	0.67				9/2	±1.005
$_{36}Kr^{86}$	17.37%							$0.06 \pm 0.02b$	0	
$_{36}Kr^{87}$			76m	β^-	3.89	3.8 3.3 1.3	~70% ~5% 25%			
$_{36}Kr^{88}$			2.80h	β^-	2.8	0.52 0.90 2.8	68% 12% 20%			
$_{36}Kr^{89}$			3.2m	β^-, η	4.6	4.0				
$_{36}Kr^{90}$			33s	β^-, η		~1 2.0 2.80	105 120 236			
$_{36}Kr^{91}$			10s	β^-		~3.6				
$_{36}Kr^{92}$			3.0s	β^-						
$_{36}Kr^{93}$			2.0s	β^-						
$_{36}Kr^{94}$			1.4s	β^-						
Rb		85.47						$0.5 \pm 0.1b$		
$_{37}Rb^{79}$			21m	β^+, EC	~3.6					
$_{37}Rb^{80}$			34s	β^+, EC	5.1	3.5 4.1	40% 60%			
$_{37}Rb^{81m}$			32m	IT	0.085				9/2	
$_{37}Rb^{81}$			4.7h	β^+, EC	2.26	0.575 1.05 1.4	23% 30% ~50%		3/2	+2.05
$_{37}Rb^{82m}$			6.4h	β^+		0.80	100%		5	+1.5
$_{37}Rb^{83}$			83d	EC	0.83				5/2	+1.4
$_{37}Rb^{84m}$			20m	EC, IT						
$_{37}Rb^{84}$			33.0d	β^+, EC	2.68	0.78 1.657	53† 47		2	−1.32

Isotope	% nat. abundance	Atomic mass	Lifetime	Modes of decay	Decay energy (MeV)	Particle energies (MeV)	Particle intensities	Thermal neutron capture cross-section	I	μ
$_{37}Rb^{85}$	72.15%	84.9117						55 ± 5mb (Rb^{86m}) 0.45 ± 0.04b (Rb^{86})	5/2	$+1.352$
$_{37}Rb^{86m}$			1.04m	IT	0.56		100%			
$_{37}Rb^{86}$			18.66d	β^-	1.78	0.71 1.78	8.8% 91.2%		2	-1.691
$_{37}Rb^{87}$	27.85%		5×10^{11}y	β^-	0.274	0.274	100%	0.12 ± 0.03b	3/2	$+2.750$
$_{37}Rb^{88}$			17.8m	β^-	5.2	2.5 3.6 5.3	9% 13% 78%	1.0 ± 0.2b	2	± 0.51
$_{37}Rb^{89}$			15.4m	β^-	3.92	0.67 1.61 2.8 3.92	28% 53% 5% 7%			
$_{37}Rb^{90}$			2.9m	β^-	6.6	1.3 2.0 2.2 2.5 4.4 5.8 6.6	10% 5% 17% 23% 15% 10%			
$_{37}Rb^{91}$			1.2m	β^-	~ 5.5	4.6				
$_{37}Rb^{92}$			5.3s	β^-	~ 7.6					
$_{37}Rb^{93}$			5.6s	β^-						
$_{37}Rb^{94}$			2.9s	β^-						
$_{37}Rb^{95}$			< 2.5s	β^-						
Sr		87.62						1.21 ± 0.06b		
$_{38}Sr^{80}$			1.7h	EC	2.0					
$_{38}Sr^{81}$			29m	β^+, EC	~ 3.8					
$_{38}Sr^{82}$			25d	EC	~ 0.4					
$_{38}Sr^{83}$			33h	β^+	2.21	0.44 0.81 1.15	1.3% 7.4% 11%			
$_{38}Sr^{84}$	0.56%	83.9134						0.57 ± 0.5 (Sr^{85m}) 0.31 ± 0.03 (Sr^{85})		
$_{38}Sr^{85m}$			70m	IT, EC	0.238					
$_{38}Sr^{85}$			64d	EC	1.11					
$_{38}Sr^{86}$	9.86%	85.9094						0.8 ± 0.1b (Sr^{87m})	0	
$_{38}Sr^{87m}$			2.83h	IT, EC			$\sim 100\%$			
$_{38}Sr^{87}$	7.02%	86.9089							9/2	-1.093
$_{38}Sr^{88}$	82.56%	87.9056						5 ± 1mb	0	
$_{38}Sr^{89}$			52d	β^-	1.463	1.463 0.55	$>99\%$ $<0.01\%$	0.5 ± 0.1b		

Isotope	% nat. abundance	Atomic mass	Lifetime	Modes of decay	Decay energy (MeV)	Particle energies (MeV)	Particle intensities	Thermal neutron capture cross-section	I	μ
$_{38}Sr^{90}$			28.1y	β^-	0.546	0.546	100%	$0.9 \pm 0.5b$		
$_{38}Sr^{91}$			9.67h	β^-	2.67	0.62 1.09 1.36 2.03 2.67	7% 33% 29% 4% 26%			
$_{38}Sr^{92}$			2.71h	β^-	1.9	0.55 1.5	90% 10%			
$_{38}Sr^{93}$			8m	β^-	4.8	2.2 2.6 2.8	10% 25% 65%			
$_{38}Sr^{94}$						2.1				
$_{38}Sr^{95}$			0.8m	β^-						
Y		88.905						$1.3 \pm 0.1b$		
$_{39}Y^{82}$			12m	β^+, EC	~7.5					
$_{39}Y^{83}$			7.5m	β^+, EC						
$_{39}Y^{84}$			41m	β^+, EC	6.3	2.9 3.5				
$_{39}Y^{85m}$			2.7h	β^+, EC		1.54	50%			
$_{39}Y^{85}$			5.0h	β^+, EC	3.26	1.1 2.1 2.24	4% 10% 55%			
$_{39}Y^{86m}$			48m	IT						
$_{39}Y^{86}$			14.6h	β^+, EC	5.27	1.04 1.25 1.60 2.02 2.34 3.15	4% 11% 5% 4% 1.1% 0.5%			
$_{39}Y^{87m}$			2.83h	IT	0.388					
$_{39}Y^{87}$			80h	β^+, EC .	1.7	0.7	~0.3%			
$_{39}Y^{88}$			106.6d ± 0.1	β^+, EC	3.621	0.76				
$_{39}Y^{89m}$			16s	IT	0.909					
$_{39}Y^{89}$	100%	88.9054						$1.3 \pm 0.1b$ (Y^{90}) $1.0 \pm 0.2mb$ (Y^{90m})	1/2	−0.1373
$_{39}Y^{90m}$			3.1h	IT β^-	0.685 2.95					
$_{39}Y^{90}$			64h	β^-	2.27	2.273	~100%		2	−1.63
$_{39}Y^{91m}$			50m	IT	0.555					
$_{39}Y^{91}$			58.8d	β^-	1.545	1.545 0.33	99.7% 0.3%	$1.4 \pm 0.3b$	1/2	± 0.164

Isotope	% nat. abundance	Atomic mass	Lifetime	Modes of decay	Decay energy (MeV)	Particle energies (MeV)	Particle intensities	Thermal neutron capture cross-section	I	μ
$_{39}Y^{92}$			3.53h	β^-	3.63	1.80 2.14 2.25 2.70 3.63	0.8% 1.5% 2.3% 3.1% 86%			
$_{39}Y^{93}$			10.2h	β^-	2.89	0.71 1.47 1.95 2.62 2.89	1.8% 0.9% 3.0% 4% 90%			
$_{39}Y^{94}$			20.3m	β^-	5.0	5.0				
$_{39}Y^{95}$			10.9m	β^-	~4.2					
$_{39}Y^{96}$			2.3m	β^-	~6.9	3.5				
Zr		91.22						0.182 ± 0.005b		
$_{40}Zr^{81}$			~10m	β^+, EC						
$_{40}Zr^{82}$			10m	β^+, EC						
$_{40}Zr^{83}$			~7m	β^+, EC						
$_{40}Zr^{84}$			16m	β^+, EC						
$_{40}Zr^{85}$			1.4h	β^+, EC						
$_{40}Zr^{86}$			16.5h	β^+, EC	1.2					
$_{40}Zr^{87}$			1.6h	β^+, EC	3.50	2.10				
$_{40}Zr^{88}$			85d	EC	~0.5					
$_{40}Zr^{89m}$			4.18m	IT, β^+		2.4				
$_{40}Zr^{89}$			78.4h	β^+, EC	2.834					
$_{40}Zr^{90m}$			0.81s	IT	2318.7					
$_{40}Zr^{90}$	51.46%	89.9043						0.10 ± 0.07b		
$_{40}Zr^{91}$	11.23%	90.9053						1.58 ± 0.12b	5/2	−1.303
$_{40}Zr^{92}$	17.11%	91.9046						0.25 ± 0.12b		
$_{40}Zr^{93}$			1.5×10^6y	β^-	0.090	0.060	≥95%	<4b		
$_{40}Zr^{94}$	17.40%	93.9061						75 ± 8mb		
$_{40}Zr^{95}$			65d	β^-	1.121	0.360 0.396 0.890 1.130	43% 55% 2% 0.4%			
$_{40}Zr^{96}$	2.80%	95.9082	$>3.6 \times 10^{17}$y					0.05 ± 0.01b		
$_{40}Zr^{97}$			17h	β^-	2.67	0.46 1.91				
$_{40}Zr^{98}$			1m	β^-	~1.5					
Nb		92.906						1.15 ± 0.05b		

Isotope	% nat. abundance	Atomic mass	Lifetime	Modes of decay	Decay energy (MeV)	Particle energies (MeV)	Particle intensities	Thermal neutron capture cross-section	I	μ
$_{41}Nb^{88}$			14m	β^+, EC	~7.2	3.2				
$_{41}Nb^{89m}$			42m	β^+, EC		3.1				
$_{41}Nb^{89}$			1.9h	β^+, EC	3.9	2.9				
$_{41}Nb^{90m}$			24s	IT						
$_{41}Nb^{90}$			14.6h	β^+, EC	6.11	0.55 0.86 1.50	4† 9 87			
$_{41}Nb^{91m}$			62d	EC IT						
$_{41}Nb^{91}$				EC	1.1					
$_{41}Nb^{92m}$			10.14 ± 0.03d	β^+, EC						
$_{41}Nb^{92}$			>350y	γ						
$_{41}Nb^{93}$	100%	92.9060						0.15 ± 0.1b (Nb^{94m}) 1.15 ± 0.05b (Nb^{94})	9/2	+6.167
$_{41}Nb^{94m}$			6.26 ± 0.01m	IT β^-	0.0415 2.1	1.15				
$_{41}Nb^{94}$			2.0 × 10⁴y	β^-	2.06	0.60	100%	11 ± 2b		
$_{41}Nb^{95m}$				IT	0.2357		100%			
$_{41}Nb^{95}$			35.15 ± 0.03d	β^-	0.925	0.1597 0.924	~100% ≤0.07%	<7b		
$_{41}Nb^{96}$			23.4h	β^-	3.15	0.71 0.70 0.80	27% 68% 5%			
$_{41}Nb^{97m}$			1.0m	IT	0.743					
$_{41}Nb^{97}$			72m	β^-	1.93	0.97 1.27	2% 98%			
$_{41}Nb^{98m}$			<2m	β^-						
$_{41}Nb^{98}$			51m	β^-	4.6	3.1				
$_{41}Nb^{99}$			10s	β^-						
$_{41}Nb^{99}$			2.4 m	β^-	3.2					
$_{41}Nb^{100}$			3.0m	β^-	~6.1					
$_{41}Nb^{100}$			11m	β^-	~6.1	3.1 3.5 42	~45% ~45% ~10%			
$_{41}Nb^{101}$			1.0m	β^-						
Mo		95.94						2.65 ± 0.05b		

Isotope	% nat. abundance	Atomic mass	Lifetime	Modes of decay	Decay energy (MeV)	Particle energies (MeV)	Particle intensities	Thermal neutron capture cross-section	I	μ
$_{42}Mo^{88}$			27m	β^+, EC						
$_{42}Mo^{89}$			7m	β^+, EC		4.0 4.9				
$_{42}Mo^{90}$			5.7h	β^+, EC	1.465	1.085	25%			
$_{42}Mo^{91m}$			66s	IT β^+, EC	0.658 6.1					
$_{42}Mo^{91}$			15.49m	IT, β^+	4.46	3.44				
$_{42}Mo^{92}$	15.84%	91.9063						<0.006b (Mo^{93m}) <0.3b (Mo^{93})	0	
$_{42}Mo^{93m}$			6.9h	IT	2.428					
$_{42}Mo^{93}$			>100y	EC						
$_{42}Mo^{94}$	9.04%	93.9047							0	
$_{42}Mo^{95}$	15.72%	94.90584						14.4 ± 0.5b	5/2	−0.9133
$_{42}Mo^{96}$	16.53%	95.9046						1.2 ± 0.6b	0	
$_{42}Mo^{97}$	9.46%	96.9058						2.2 ± 0.7b	5/2	−0.9325
$_{42}Mo^{98}$	23.78%	97.9055						0.14 ± 0.02b	0	
$_{42}Mo^{99}$			66.69 ± 0.06h	β^-	1.37	0.26 0.45 0.86 1.19	0.3% 17% 1% 82%			
$_{42}Mo^{100}$	9.63%	99.9076						0.20 ± 0.05b	0	
$_{42}Mo^{101}$			14.6m	β^-	2.82	0.84 1.23 1.61 2.23	38% 13% 25% 10%			
$_{42}Mo^{102}$			11m	β^-	1.2	1.2				
$_{42}Mo^{103}$			62s	β^-						
$_{42}Mo^{104}$			1.3m	β^-		2.2 4.8				
$_{42}Mo^{105}$			40s	β^-						
Tc										
$_{43}Tc^{92}$			4.4m	β^+, EC	7.9	4.1	92%			
$_{43}Tc^{93m}$			43m	IT EC	0.39 ~3.6					
$_{43}Tc^{93}$			2.7h	β^+, EC	3.19	0.64 0.80	32% 11%			
$_{43}Tc^{94m}$			53m	β^+, EC	~4.3	2.47				
$_{43}Tc^{94}$			293m	β^+, EC	4.26	0.816	11%			
$_{43}Tc^{95m}$			61d	IT β^+, EC	0.0389 ~1.7	0.49 0.71	10† 25			

Isotope	% nat. abundance	Atomic mass	Lifetime	Modes of decay	Decay energy (MeV)	Particle energies (MeV)	Particle intensities	Thermal neutron capture cross-section	I	μ
$_{43}Tc^{95}$			20.0h	EC	1.66					
$_{43}Tc^{96m}$			52m	IT	0.0344					
$_{43}Tc^{96}$					2.9					
$_{43}Tc^{97m}$			90d	IT	0.0965					
$_{43}Tc^{97}$			2.6×10^6y	EC	~0.3					
$_{43}Tc^{98}$			1.5×10^6y	β^-	1.7	0.3				
$_{43}Tc^{99m}$			6.0h	IT	0.1427					
$_{43}Tc^{99}$			2.12×10^5y	β^-	0.292	0.292		22 ± 3b	9/2	+ 5.68
$_{43}Tc^{100}$			17s	β^-		2.2 2.88 3.38				
$_{43}Tc^{101}$			14m	β^-	1.63	1.07 1.32				
$_{43}Tc^{102}$			4.5m	β^-	4.4	~2				
$_{43}Tc^{102}$			5s	β^-	4.4	4.4				
$_{43}Tc^{103}$			50s	β^-	2.4	2.0 2.2				
$_{43}Tc^{104}$			18m	β^-	5.8	2.4 3.3 4.6 > 5.3				
$_{43}Tc^{105}$			8m	β^-	3.4					
$_{43}Tc^{106}$			37s	β^-						
$_{43}Tc^{107}$			29 s	β^-						
Ru		101.07						3.0 ± 0.8b		
$_{44}Ru^{93}$			50s	β^+						
$_{44}Ru^{94}$			57m	EC						
$_{44}Ru^{95}$			1.7h	β^+, EC	2.03	0.7 1.01 1.33	1.3† 12 4			
$_{44}Ru^{96}$	5.51%	95.9076						0.21 ± 0.02b		
$_{44}Ru^{97}$			2.9d	EC	~1.2					
$_{44}Ru^{98}$	1.87%	97.9055						<8b		
$_{44}Ru^{99}$	12.72%	98.9061						10.6 ± 0.6b	5/2	− 0.63
$_{44}Ru^{100}$	12.62%	99.9030						10.4 ± 0.7b		
$_{44}Ru^{101}$	17.07%							3.1 ± 0.9b	5/2	− 0.69
$_{44}Ru^{102}$	31.61%	101.9037								
$_{44}Ru^{103}$			39.6d	β^-	0.74	0.90 0.203 0.382 0.445	7% 89% 1% 1%			

Isotope	% nat. abundance	Atomic mass	Lifetime	Modes of decay	Decay energy (MeV)	Particle energies (MeV)	Particle intensities	Thermal neutron capture cross-section	I	μ
						0.700	3%			
$_{44}Ru^{104}$	18.58%	103.9055						0.47 ± 0.2b		
$_{44}Ru^{105}$			4.44h	β^-	1.871	0.49 1.06 1.08 1.15 1.52 1.75 1.87	5% 14% 13% 44% ~2% ≤10% 11%	0.2 ± 0.02b		
$_{44}Ru^{106}$			367d	β^-	0.0394	0.0392	100%	146 ± 45mb		
$_{44}Ru^{107}$			4.2m	β^-	3.2	2.1 3.2				
$_{44}Ru^{108}$			4.5m	β^-	1.3	1.1 1.3	28% 72%			
Rh		102.905						150 ± 5b		
$_{45}Rh^{97}$			32m	β^+, EC	3.49	1.8 2.06 2.47				
$_{45}Rh^{98}$			8.7m	β^+, EC	4.2	2.5				
$_{45}Rh^{99m}$			4.7h	β^+, EC	~2.05	0.74				
$_{45}Rh^{99}$			16d	β^+, EC	~2.05	0.44 0.59 0.71 1.03				
$_{45}Rh^{100}$			20h	β^+, EC	3.64	0.20 0.58 0.8 1.30 1.6 2.12 2.68	 ~2% 3%			
$_{45}Rh^{101m}$			4.5d	IT EC	0.157 ~0.7		10%			
$_{45}Rh^{101}$			3.1y	EC	0.56					
$_{45}Rh^{102}$			2.9y	EC	2.3					
$_{45}Rh^{102}$			206d	β^+, EC β^-	2.32 1.15	β^- 0.59 1.15 β^+0.20 0.36 0.83 1.30	2% 20% 7% 3% 37% 29%			
$_{45}Rh^{103}$	100%	102.9048						11 ± 1b (Rh^{104m}) 139 ± 5b (Rh^{104})	1/2	−0.0883
$_{45}Rh^{104m}$			4.4m	IT β^-	0.129 ~2.5			800 ± 100b	5	

Isotope	% nat. abundance	Atomic mass	Lifetime	Modes of decay	Decay energy (MeV)	Particle energies (MeV)	Particle intensities	Thermal neutron capture cross-section	I	μ
$_{45}Rh^{104}$			43s	EC β^-	1.15 2.47	0.7 1.9 2.5	0.08% 1.4% 98.5%	40 ± 30b		
$_{45}Rh^{105m}$			45s	IT	0.129					
$_{45}Rh^{105}$			35.9h	β^-	0.565	0.249 0.262 0.568	20% 5% 75%	5700 ± 1200b (Rh^{106m}) 13,000 ± 2000b (Rh^{106})		
$_{45}Rh^{106}$			30s	β^-	3.54	2.0 2.4 3.1 3.53	3% 12% 11% 68%			
$_{45}Rh^{106}$			130m	β^-	~3.63	0.79 0.95 1.18 1.62	40% 38% 11% 10%			
$_{45}Rh^{107}$			22m	β^-	1.51	0.84 0.94 1.14 1.20				
$_{45}Rh^{108}$			17s	β^-	~4.5	3.5 4.0 4.5	22% 17% 51%			
$_{45}Rh^{109}$			<1h	β^-	~2.5					
$_{45}Rh^{110}$			5s	β^-	5.5	5.5				
Pd		106.4						6.0 ± 1.0b		
$_{46}Pd^{98}$			17m	EC β^+						
$_{46}Pd^{99}$			22m	β^+, EC	3.8	2.0				
$_{46}Pd^{100}$			4.0d	EC	~0.6					
$_{46}Pd^{101}$			8.4h	β^+, EC	1.99	0.49 0.78	17† 83			
$_{46}Pd^{102}$	0.96%	101.9049						4.8 ± 1.5b		
$_{46}Pd^{103}$			17d	EC	0.56					
$_{46}Pd^{104}$	10.97%	103.9036								
$_{46}Pd^{105}$	22.23%	104.9046							5/2	−0.642
$_{46}Pd^{106}$	27.33%	105.9032						13 ± 2mb (Pd^{107m}) 279 ± 29mb (Pd^{107})		
$_{46}Pd^{107m}$			22s	IT	0.21					
$_{46}Pd^{107}$			~7 × 10⁶y	β	0.035	0.035				
$_{46}Pd^{108}$	26.71%	107.90389						0.20 ± 0.04b (Pd^{109m}) 12 ± 2b (Pd^{109})	0	
$_{46}Pd^{109m}$			4.7m	IT	0.188					
$_{46}Pd^{109}$			13.47h	β^-	1.113	0.248 0.255 0.278	0.023% 0.002% 0.002%			

Isotope	% nat. abundance	Atomic mass	Lifetime	Modes of decay	Decay energy (MeV)	Particle energies (MeV)	Particle intensities	Thermal neutron capture cross-section	I	μ
						0.383	0.037%			
						0.394	0.022%			
						0.416	0.005%			
						0.703	0.010%			
						0.806	0.027%			
						1.030	99.87%			
$_{46}$Pd^{110}	11.81%							20 ± 15mb (Pd^{111m}) 0.4 ± 0.1b (Pd^{111})		
$_{46}$Pd^{111m}			5.5h	IT β^-	0.17		75% 25%			
$_{46}$Pd^{111}			22m	β^-	2.2	0.6 0.7 1.1 1.2 2.2				
$_{46}$Pd^{112}			21h	β^-	0.30	0.30	100%			
$_{46}$Pd^{113}			1.4m	β^-						
$_{46}$Pd^{114}			2.4m	β^-						
$_{46}$Pd^{115}			45s	β^-						
Ag		107.870						63.8 ± 0.6b		
$_{47}$Ag^{102}			15m	β^+, EC	~5.3					
$_{47}$Ag^{103m}			5.7s	IT	0.138					
$_{47}$Ag^{103}			66m	β^+,EC	2.6	1.3 1.6			7/2	
$_{47}$Ag^{104m}			30m	IT β^+, EC	0.02	2.7			2	+3.7
									5	+4.0
$_{47}$Ag^{104}			67m	β^+, EC	4.27					
$_{47}$Ag^{105}			40d	EC					1/2	±1.01
$_{47}$Ag^{106m}			8.4d	EC					6	
$_{47}$Ag^{106}			24m	β^+, EC	2.96	1.45 1.96	11† 89		1	
$_{47}$Ag^{107m}			44.3s	IT	0.093					
$_{47}$Ag^{107}	51.82%	106.90509						35 ± 5b	1/2	−0.1135
$_{47}$Ag^{108m}			>5y	IT EC	0.110		10% 90%			
$_{47}$Ag^{108}			2.42m	β^+, EC β^-	1.92 1.64	β^- 1.8 1.2 0.47 β^+ 0.88	96% 1.8% ~0.02%		1	+2.8
$_{47}$Ag^{109m}			40s	IT	0.0877				7/2	±4.3
$_{47}$Ag^{109}	48.18%	108.9047						4.2 ± 0.7b (Ag^{110m}) 89 ± 4b (Ag^{110})	1/2	−0.1305
$_{47}$Ag^{110m}			253d	β^- IT	~2.9 0.12	.0.087 0.529 1.5	61% 36% 0.6%	82 ± 11b	6	+3.604

Isotope	% nat. abundance	Atomic mass	Lifetime	Modes of decay	Decay energy (MeV)	Particle energies (MeV)	Particle intensities	Thermal neutron capture cross-section	I	μ
$_{47}Ag^{110}$			24.4s	β^-	~ 2.9	1.40 2.14 2.87	0.05% 12% 88%			
$_{47}Ag^{111m}$			74s	IT	0.07					
$_{47}Ag^{111}$			7.5d	β^-	1.05	0.69 0.79 1.04	6% 1% 93%		1/2	-0.146
$_{47}Ag^{112}$			3.2h	β^-	4.01	1.96 3.35 3.94	10% 22% 54%		2	± 0.054
$_{47}Ag^{113m}$			1.2m	β^-						
$_{47}Ag^{113}$			5.3h	β^-	2.00	2.0			1/2	± 0.159
$_{47}Ag^{114}$			4.5s	β^-	4.6	4.6				
$_{47}Ag^{114}$			2m	β^-	4.6					
$_{47}Ag^{115}$			20s	β^-						
$_{47}Ag^{115}$			20m	β^-	3.3	1.0 2.1 2.7 3.0 3.2				
$_{47}Ag^{116}$			2.5m	β^-	~ 6.1					
$_{47}Ag^{117}$			1.1m	β^-						
Cd		112.40						$2450 \pm 20b$		
$_{48}Cd^{103}$			10m	β^+, EC						
$_{48}Cd^{104}$			57m	EC	~ 1.2					
$_{48}Cd^{105}$			55m	β^+, EC	~ 2.8	0.8 1.69				
$_{48}Cd^{106}$	1.22%	105.907						$1.0 \pm 0.5b$		
$_{48}Cd^{107}$			6.5h	β^+, EC	1.417	0.302			5/2	-0.6144
$_{48}Cd^{108}$	0.88%	107.9040						$1.5 \pm 0.5b$	0	
$_{48}Cd^{109}$			$450 \pm 5d$	EC	0.16			$700 \pm 100b$	5/2	-0.8270
$_{48}Cd^{110}$	12.39%	109.9030						$0.10 \pm 0.03b$ (Cd^{111m})	0	
$_{48}Cd^{111m}$			48.6m	IT						
$_{48}Cd^{111}$	12.75%	110.9042							1/2	-0.5943
$_{48}Cd^{112}$	24.07%	111.9028						$0.06 \pm 0.02b$ (Cd^{113m})	0	
$_{48}Cd^{113m}$			14y	β^-	0.58	0.58	99+%		11/2	-1.087
$_{48}Cd^{113}$	12.26%	112.9046						$20,000 \pm 300b$	1/2	-0.6217
$_{48}Cd^{114}$	28.86%	113.9036						$0.36 \pm 0.007b$ (Cd^{115m}) $0.30 \pm 0.015b$ (Cd^{113})	0	

Isotope	% nat. abundance	Atomic mass	Lifetime	Modes of decay	Decay energy (MeV)	Particle energies (MeV)	Particle intensities	Thermal neutron capture cross-section	I	μ
$_{48}Cd^{115m}$			43d	IT	0.18	0.34 0.68	1.6%		11/2	−1.042
				$β^-$	1.62	1.62	97%			
$_{48}Cd^{115}$			53.5h	$β^-$	1.45	0.58⎱ 0.86⎰ 1.11	42% 58%		1/2	−0.648
$_{48}Cd^{116}$	7.58%	115.9050						27 ± 5mb (Cd^{117m}) 50 ± 8mb (Cd^{117})	0	
$_{48}Cd^{117m}$			3.4h	$β^-$	2.65	0.41 0.70				
$_{48}Cd^{117}$			2.4h	$β^-$	2.52	0.65 1.79 2.23				
$_{48}Cd^{118}$			49m	$β^-$	∼0.8					
$_{48}Cd^{119}$			2.7m	$β^-$	3.5	∼3.5				
$_{48}Cd^{119}$			10m	$β^-$	3.5	∼3.5				
In		114.82						194 ± 2b		
$_{49}In^{106}$			5.3m	$β^+$, EC	6.5	3 ? 4.85				
$_{49}In^{107}$			32m	$β^+$, EC	3.5	2.2				
$_{49}In^{108}$			39m	$β^+$, EC		2.28 2.66 3.50				
$_{49}In^{108}$			56m	$β^+$, EC		1.29				
$_{49}In^{109}$			4.3h	$β^+$, EC	2.02				9/2	+5.53
$_{49}In^{110m}$			4.9h	EC $β^+$					7	±10.5
$_{49}In^{110}$			67m	$β^+$, EC	3.93	2.25			2	
$_{49}In^{111}$			2.81d						9/2	+5.53
$_{49}In^{112m}$			20.7m	IT	0.156					
$_{49}In^{112}$			14m	$β^-$ $β^+$, EC	0.66	$β^-$ 0.66 $β^+$ 1.0 1.52	44% 6% 28%			
$_{49}In^{113m}$			100m	IT	0.3916				1/2	−0.210
$_{49}In^{113}$	4.28%	112.9043						3.2 ± 0.7b (In^{114m_2}) 4.5 ± 0.7b (In^{114m_1}) 3 ± 1b (In^{114})	9/2	+5.523
$_{49}In^{114m_2}$			0.0425	IT	0.502					

Isotope	% nat. abundance	Atomic mass	Lifetime	Modes of decay	Decay energy (MeV)	Particle energies (MeV)	Particle intensities	Thermal neutron capture cross-section	I	μ
$_{49}In^{114m_1}$			50.0d	IT EC	0.191		96.5% 3.5%		5	+4.7
$_{49}In^{114}$			72s	β^+, EC β^-	1.44 1.986	β^- 1.989 β^+ 0.40	98+% 0.039%			+1.7
$_{49}In^{115m}$			4.50h	IT β^-	0.335 0.82		95% 5%		1/2	−0.244
$_{49}In^{115}$	95.72%	114.9041						85 ± 10b (In^{116m_2}) 72 ± 4b (In^{116m_1}) 42 ± 4b (In^{116})	9/2	+5.534
$_{49}In^{116m_2}$			2.16s	IT	0.22					
$_{49}In^{116m_1}$			54m	β^-	3.39	0.60 0.87 1.00	21% 28% 51%		5	+4.3
$_{49}In^{116}$			14s	β^-	3.33	3.3	99%			
$_{49}In^{117m}$			1.93h	IT β^-	0.314 ~1.77	1.62 1.77	47% 16% 37%		1/2	±0.25
$_{49}In^{117}$			44m	β^-	1.47	0.74			9/2	
$_{49}In^{118}$			5s	β^-	4.2	4.2				
$_{49}In^{118}$			4.4m	β^-	4.3	1.3 2.0				
$_{49}In^{119m}$			18m	IT β^-	0.30 2.8	2.7	5%			
$_{49}In^{119}$			2.1m	β^-	2.5	1.6				
$_{49}In^{120}$			3.2s	β^-	~5.6	4.4 5.6	15% 85%			
$_{49}In^{120}$			46s	β^-	~5.3	2.2 3.1	~40% ~27%			
$_{49}In^{121}$			3.1m	β^-	~3.6	3.7				
$_{49}In^{121}$			30s	β^-						
$_{49}In^{122}$			8s	β^-	~6.7					
$_{49}In^{123}$			36s	β^-	~4.5					
$_{49}In^{123}$			10s	β^-						
$_{49}In^{124}$			4s	β^-	7.4	5				
Sn		118.69						0.63 ± 0.01b		
$_{50}Sn^{108}$			9m	EC						
$_{50}Sn^{109}$			18.1m	β^+, EC		~1.6				
$_{50}Sn^{110}$			4.0h	EC						
$_{50}Sn^{111}$			35m	β^+, EC	2.52	1.51	35.3%			
$_{50}Sn^{112}$	0.96%	111.9040						0.35 ± 0.08b (Sn^{113m}) 0.8 ± 0.2 (Sn^{113})		

Isotope	% nat. abundance	Atomic mass	Lifetime	Modes of decay	Decay energy (MeV)	Particle energies (MeV)	Particle intensities	Thermal neutron capture cross-section	I	μ
$_{50}\mathrm{Sn}^{113m}$			20m	IT EC	0.079 1.1		91% 9%			
$_{50}\mathrm{Sn}^{113}$			115d	EC	1.02					
$_{50}\mathrm{Sn}^{114}$	0.66%	113.9030								
$_{50}\mathrm{Sn}^{115}$	0.35%	114.9035							1/2	−0.918
$_{50}\mathrm{Sn}^{116}$	14.30%	115.9021						6 ± 2mb (Sn^{117m})	0	
$_{50}\mathrm{Sn}^{117m}$			14d	IT	0.317					
$_{50}\mathrm{Sn}^{117}$	7.61%	116.9031							1/2	−1.000
$_{50}\mathrm{Sn}^{118}$	24.03%	117.9018						10 ± 6mb (Sn^{119m})	0	
$_{50}\mathrm{Sn}^{119m}$			250d	IT	0.089				(3/2)	+0.67
$_{50}\mathrm{Sn}^{119}$	8.58%	118.9034							1/2	−1.046
$_{50}\mathrm{Sn}^{120}$								1 ± 1mb (Sn^{121m}) 140 ± 30mb (Sn^{121})	0	
$_{50}\mathrm{Sn}^{121m}$			76y	β^-	0.45	0.35	100%			
$_{50}\mathrm{Sn}^{121}$			27h	β^-	0.383	0.42	100%		3/2	±0.70
$_{50}\mathrm{Sn}^{122}$	4.72%	121.9034						1.0 ± 0.5 mb (Sn^{123m}) 0.15 ± 0.02b (Sn^{123})		
$_{50}\mathrm{Sn}^{123m}$			125d	β^-	1.42	1.42	100%			
$_{50}\mathrm{Sn}^{123}$			42m	β^-	1.46	1.46				
$_{50}\mathrm{Sn}^{124}$	5.94%	123.9052						0.14 ± 0.02b (Sn^{125m}) 4 ± 2mb (Sn^{125})		
$_{50}\mathrm{Sn}^{125m}$			9.7m	β^-	2.39	0.281 0.447 0.480 0.658 0.694 0.910 1.045 1.473 1.751 2.062	0.002% 0.2% 0.03% 0.9% 0.1% 0.3% <0.02% 0.2% <0.1% 98.3%			
$_{50}\mathrm{Sn}^{125}$			9.4d	β^-	2.34	0.34 0.46 0.95 1.3 2.37	1.9% 1.9% <0.25% ~0.8% 95%			
$_{50}\mathrm{Sn}^{126}$			~10^5y	β^-	~0.3					
$_{50}\mathrm{Sn}^{127}$			2.1h	β^-	1.5					
$_{50}\mathrm{Sn}^{127}$			4m	β^-	~3.1	2.7				

Isotope	% nat. abundance	Atomic mass	Lifetime	Modes of decay	Decay energy (MeV)	Particle energies (MeV)	Particle intensities	Thermal neutron capture cross-section	I	μ
$_{50}Sn^{128}$			59m	β^-	1.3	0.8				
Sb		121.75						$5 \pm 1b$		
$_{51}Sb^{112}$			0.9m	β^+, EC						
$_{51}Sb^{113}$			6.7m	β^+, EC	4.47	1.85 2.42				
$_{51}Sb^{114}$			3.3m	β^+, EC	6.3	2.7				
$_{51}Sb^{115}$			31m	β^+, EC	3.03	1.51				
$_{51}Sb^{116m}$			60m	β^+, EC		1.16				
$_{51}Sb^{116}$			15m	β^+, EC	4.6	1.5 2.4				
$_{51}Sb^{117}$			2.8h	β^+, EC	1.82	0.57			5/2	+2.67
$_{51}Sb^{118m_2}$			0.87s	IT						
$_{51}Sb^{118m_1}$			5.1h	β^+, EC	3.9					
$_{51}Sb^{118}$			3.5m	β^+, EC	3.7	1.5 2.7			1	±2.4
$_{51}Sb^{119}$			38hr	EC			100%		5/2	+3.45
$_{51}Sb^{120}$			15.9m	β^+, EC	2.69	1.70			1	+2.3
$_{51}Sb^{121}$	57.25%	120.9038						$55 \pm 10mb$ (Sb^{122m}) $6.2 \pm 0.3b$ (Sb^{122})	5/2	+3.359
$_{51}Sb^{122m}$			4.2m	IT	0.162					
$_{51}Sb^{122}$			2.8d	β^- β^+, EC	1.972 1.62	β^+ 0.56 β^- 0.74 1.40 1.97	4% 63% 30%		2	−1.90
$_{51}Sb^{123}$	42.75%	122.9041						$15 \pm 4mb$ (Sb^{124m_2}) $30 \pm 8mb$ (Sb^{124m_1}) $3.4 \pm 0.8b$ (Sb^{124})	7/2	+2.547
$_{51}Sb^{124m_2}$			21m	IT	0.035					
$_{51}Sb^{124m_1}$			93s	IT β^-	0.010					
$_{51}Sb^{124}$			60.3 ±0.2d	β^-	2.916	0.06 0.23 0.621 0.950 1.01 1.59 1.67 2.317	2% 11% 50% 5% 1.5% 5% 3% 22%	$6.5 \pm 1.5b$	3	

Isotope	% nat. abundance	Atomic mass	Lifetime	Modes of decay	Decay energy (MeV)	Particle energies (MeV)	Particle intensities	Thermal neutron capture cross-section	I	μ
$_{51}Sb^{125}$			2.7y	β^-	0.764	0.1 0.619 0.45 0.299 0.240 0.125	2% 13% 6% 43% 1% 28%			
$_{51}Sb^{126m}$			19m	IT β^-		1.9				
$_{51}Sb^{126}$			12.5d	β^-	3.7	1.9				
$_{51}Sb^{127}$			93h	β^-	1.60	0.86 1.11 1.57	50% 20% 30%			
$_{51}Sb^{128}$			11m	β^-	4.3	2.5				
$_{51}Sb^{129}$			4.3h	β^-	2.5	1.87				
$_{51}Sb^{130}$			2.6m	β^-						
$_{51}Sb^{131}$			25m	β^-						
$_{51}Sb^{132}$			2.1m	β^-						
$_{51}Sb^{133}$			4.2m	β^-						
Te		127.60						$4.7 \pm 0.1b$		
$_{52}Te^{115}$			6.0m	β^+, EC	4.5	2.8				
$_{52}Te^{116}$			2.50h	β^+, EC	1.6	0.44			0	
$_{52}Te^{117}$			61m	β^+, EC	3.50	1.7			1/2	
$_{52}Te^{118}$			6.00d	EC	~0.3					
$_{52}Te^{119m}$			4.7d	EC	~2.6				11/2	
$_{52}Te^{119}$			15.9h	β^+, EC	2.294	0.627	5%		1/2	± 0.25
$_{52}Te^{120}$	0.089%	119.9045						$0.34 \pm 0.06b$ (Te^{121m}) $2.0 \pm 0.3b$ (Te^{121})		
$_{52}Te^{121m}$			154d	IT EC, β^+	0.293 ~1.6		90%			
$_{52}Te^{121}$			17d	EC	1.29					
$_{52}Te^{122}$	2.46%	121.9030						$1.1 \pm 0.5b$ (Te^{123m}) $1.7 \pm 0.8b$ (Te^{123})		
$_{52}Te^{123m}$			117d	IT	0.247					
$_{52}Te^{123}$	0.87%	122.9042	1.2×10^{13}y	EC	~0.06			$410 \pm 30b$	1/2	-0.7359
$_{52}Te^{124}$	4.61%	123.9028						$40 \pm 25mb$ (Te^{125m}) $6.8 \pm 1.3b$ (Te^{125})		
$_{52}Te^{125m}$			58d	IT					3/2	$\sim +0.7$
$_{52}Te^{125}$	6.99%	124.9044						$1.56 \pm 0.16b$	1/2	-0.8871

Isotope	% nat. abundance	Atomic mass	Lifetime	Modes of decay	Decay energy (MeV)	Particle energies (MeV)	Particle intensities	Thermal neutron capture cross-section	I	μ
$_{52}$Te^{126}	18.71%	125.9032						125 ± 23mb (Te^{127m}) 0.90 ± 0.15b (Te^{127})	0	
$_{52}$Te^{127m}			109d	IT β^-	0.0887 0.77		99.2%			
$_{52}$Te^{127}			9.4h	β^-	0.69	0.28 0.50 0.70	0.32% 0.005% 99.7%			
$_{52}$Te^{128}	31.79%	127.9047						14 ± 4mb (Te^{129m}) 155 ± 40mb (Te^{129})	0	
$_{52}$Te^{129m}			34d	β^- IT	1.48 0.105	0.91 1.60				
$_{52}$Te^{129}			69m	β^-	1.48	0.39 0.67 1.00 1.45				
$_{52}$Te^{130}	34.48%	129.9067						0.02 ± 0.01b (Te^{131m}) 0.2 ± 0.1b (Te^{131})	0	
$_{52}$Te^{131m}			30h	β^- IT	2.46 0.1817 (18%)	0.45 0.48 0.50 0.53 0.56 0.63 0.84 2.46	10% 11% 12% 3% 13% 7% 16% 5%			
$_{52}$Te^{131}			25m	β^-		0.80 0.86 0.88 1.32 1.80 2.14	1.4% 1.6% 1.5% 1.0% 20% 62%			
$_{52}$Te^{132}			78h	β^-	0.50	0.22	100%			
$_{52}$Te^{133m}			50m	IT β^-	0.334		13%			
$_{52}$Te^{133}			12.5m	β^-	2.7	2.4 1.3	~30% ~70%			
$_{52}$Te^{134}			42m	β^-						
$_{52}$Te^{135}			<2m	β^-						
I		126.9044						6.2 ± 0.2b		
$_{53}$I^{117}			7m	β^+, EC						
$_{53}$I^{118}			14m	β^+, EC	7	5.5				
$_{53}$I^{119}			19m	β^+, EC						
$_{53}$I^{120}			1.3h	β^+, EC	5.6	2.1 4.0				

Isotope	% nat. abundance	Atomic mass	Lifetime	Modes of decay	Decay energy (MeV)	Particle energies (MeV)	Particle intensities	Thermal neutron capture cross-section	I	μ
$_{53}I^{121}$			2.1h	β^+, EC	2.36	1.2				
$_{53}I^{122}$			3.5m	β^+, EC	4.14	1.8 2.6 3.1				
$_{53}I^{123}$			13.3h	EC	~1.4				5/2	
$_{53}I^{124}$			4.2d	β^+, EC	3.17	0.79 1.53 2.13	8† 46 46		2	
$_{53}I^{125}$			60d	EC	0.149			900 ± 90b	5/2	+3.0
$_{53}I^{126}$			13d	β^+, EC β^-	2.150 1.251	β^+ 1.129 β^- 0.385 0.865 1.25	6† 29 12		2	
$_{53}I^{127}$	100%	126.9004						6.2 ± 0.2b	5/2	+2.808
$_{53}I^{128}$			25.08 ±0.05m	β^+, EC β^-	1.27 2.14	β^- 1.13 1.67 2.12	1.6% 13% 79%		1	
$_{53}I^{129}$			1.7×10^7y	β^-	0.189	0.189	100%	19 ± 2b (I^{130m}) 9 ± 1b (I^{130})	7/2	+2.617
$_{53}I^{130m}$			8.82 ± 0.04m	IT						
$_{53}I^{130}$			12.3 ± 0.1h	β^-	2.99	0.62 1.04 1.7	52% 48% 0.4%	18 ± 3b	5	
$_{53}I^{131}$			8.070 ± 0.009d	β^-	0.970	0.257 0.333 0.487 0.606 0.806	1.6% 6.9% 0.5% 90.4% 0.6%	~0.7b	7/2	+2.74
$_{53}I^{132}$			2.3h	β^-	3.56	0.72 0.80 0.91 0.98 1.16 1.60 1.75 2.12	16% 8% 5% 18% 20% 9% 6% 18%		4	±3.08
$_{53}I^{133}$			20.9 ± 0.1h	β^-	1.80	0.7 0.94 1.27			7/2	+2.84
$_{53}I^{134}$			52m	β^-	4.2	1.10 1.32 1.56 1.72 1.86 2.28 2.46	1.0% 23% 15% <4% 9% 12% 25%			
$_{53}I^{135}$			6.7h	β^-	~2.8	0.5 1.0 1.4	35% 40% 25%		7/2	
$_{53}I^{136}$			83s	β^-	7.0	2.7 4.3 5.6	9% 23% 16%			

Isotope	% nat. abundance	Atomic mass	Lifetime'	Modes of decay	Decay energy (MeV)	Particle energies (MeV)	Particle intensities	Thermal neutron capture cross-section	I	μ
						7.0	~6%			
$_{53}I^{137}$			23s	β^-, η						
$_{53}I^{138}$			5.9s	β^-, η						
$_{53}I^{139}$			2s	β^-, η						
Xe		131.30						24.5 ± 1b		
$_{54}Xe^{118}$			6m	β^+, EC						
$_{54}Xe^{119}$			6m	β^+, EC						
$_{54}Xe^{120}$			40m	β^+, EC						
$_{54}Xe^{121}$			39m	β^+, EC	3.0	2.8				
$_{54}Xe^{122}$			20h	EC	~0.5					
$_{54}Xe^{123}$			2.1h	β^+, EC	2.8	1.6				
$_{54}Xe^{124}$	0.096%	123.9061						100 ± 20b		
$_{54}Xe^{125m}$			55s	IT						
$_{54}Xe^{125}$			17h	EC						
$_{54}Xe^{126}$	0.090%	125.9042						1.5 ± 1.0b		
$_{54}Xe^{127m}$			75s	IT						
$_{54}Xe^{127}$			36.4d	EC	0.44					
$_{54}Xe^{128}$	1.92%	127.9035						0.43 ± 0.1b (Xe^{129m}) <8b (Xe^{129})		
$_{54}Xe^{129m}$			8.0d	IT	0.236					
$_{54}Xe^{129}$	26.44%	128.9048						21 ± 7b	1/2	−0.7768
$_{54}Xe^{130}$	4.08%	129.9035						0.34 ± 0.08b (Xe^{131m}) <26b (Xe^{131})		
$_{54}Xe^{131m}$			11.8d	IT	0.163				3/2	+0.6908
$_{54}Xe^{131}$	21.18%	130.9051						110 ± 20b		
$_{54}Xe^{132}$	26.89%	131.9042						0.53 ± 0.10b (Xe^{133m}) 50 ± 20mb (Xe^{133})	0	
$_{54}Xe^{133m}$			2.26d	IT	0.233					
$_{54}Xe^{133}$			5.27d	β^-	0.427	0.267 0.347	0.7% 99.3%			
$_{54}Xe^{134}$	10.44%	133.9054						0.23 ± 0.02b	0	
$_{54}Xe^{135m}$			15.6m		0.526					

Isotope	% nat. abundance	Atomic mass	Lifetime	Modes of decay	Decay energy (MeV)	Particle energies (MeV)	Particle intensities	Thermal neutron capture cross-section	I	μ
$_{54}Xe^{135}$			9.2h	β^-	1.16	0.55 0.92	3% 97%	2.64×10^6b $\pm\,0.1 \times 10^6$		
$_{54}Xe^{136}$	8.87%	135.9072						280 ± 28mb	0	
$_{54}Xe^{137}$			3.9m	β^-	4.0	3.6 4.1	33% 67%			
$_{54}Xe^{138}$			17m	β^-	2.8					
$_{54}Xe^{139}$			42s	β^-						
$_{54}Xe^{140}$			16s	β^-						
$_{54}Xe^{141}$			2s	β^-						
$_{54}Xe^{142}$			$\sim$1.5s	β^-						
Cs		132.905						30.0 ± 1.5b		
$_{55}Cs^{123}$			8m	β^+, EC						
$_{55}Cs^{125}$			45m	β^+, EC		2.05			1/2	+1.41
$_{55}Cs^{126}$			1.6m	β^+, EC		3.8				
$_{55}Cs^{127}$			6.2h	β^+, EC	2.1	1.02 0.677	2.5† 3		1/2	+1.46
$_{55}Cs^{128}$			3.8m	β^+, EC	3.93	1.30 1.90 2.44 2.88	8† 16 39 100			
$_{55}Cs^{129}$			32h	EC	$\sim$1.1				1/2	+1.479
$_{55}Cs^{130}$			30m	β^+, EC β^-	2.99 0.442	1.97 0.442	2%		1	$\pm$1.4
$_{55}Cs^{131}$			9.70d	EC	0.35				5/2	+3.54
$_{55}Cs^{132}$			6.5d	β^+, EC	2.09				2	+2.22
$_{55}Cs^{133}$	100%	133.9051						2.6 ± 0.2b (Cs^{134m}) 27.4 ± 1.5b (Cs^{134})	7/2	+2.579
$_{55}Cs^{134m}$			2.90 $\pm$0.01h	IT	0.138				8	+1.096
$_{55}Cs^{134}$			2.05y	β^-	2.062	0.089 0.410 0.662	28% 1% 71%	134 ± 12b	4	+2.990
$_{55}Cs^{135}$			3×10^6y	β^-	0.210	0.210	100%	8.7 ± 0.5b	7/2	+2.729
$_{55}Cs^{136}$			13d	β^-	2.54	0.341 0.56 0.657	93% 2% 7%		5	$\pm$3.70
$_{55}Cs^{137}$			30.23 $\pm$0.16y	β^-	1.176	0.511 1.176	94% 6%	110 ± 33 mb	7/2	+2.838

Isotope	% nat. abundance	Atomic mass	Lifetime	Modes of decay	Decay energy (MeV)	Particle energies (MeV)	Particle intensities	Thermal neutron capture cross-section	I	μ
$_{55}Cs^{138}$			32.2m	β^-	4.83	1.49 2.20 2.39 2.53 2.62 2.94 3.4	0.5% 10% 36% 5% 16% 12% 21%		3	± 0.5
$_{55}Cs^{139}$			9.5m	β^-	4.0					
$_{55}Cs^{140}$			66s	β^-	6.1					
$_{55}Cs^{141}$			24s	β^-						
$_{55}Cs^{142}$			2.3s	β^-						
$_{55}Cs^{143}$			2.0s	β^-						
$_{55}Cs^{144}$				β^-						
Ba		137.34						$1.2 \pm 0.1b$		
$_{56}Ba^{123}$			2m	β^+, EC						
$_{56}Ba^{125}$			6m	β^+, EC						
$_{56}Ba^{126}$			97m	EC	~ 1.3					
$_{56}Ba^{127}$			10m	β^+, EC	~ 3.6					
$_{56}Ba^{128}$			2.4d	EC	~ 0.7					
$_{56}Ba^{+129m}^{129}$			$\sim 2.5h$	β^+, EC	2.45	1.0 1.24 1.43	6† 24 78			
$_{56}Ba^{130}$	0.101%	129.9062						$2.5 \pm 0.3b$ (Ba^{131m}) $11 \pm 3b$ (Ba^{131})		
$_{56}Ba^{131m}$			15m	IT	0.18					
$_{56}Ba^{131}$			12d	EC	1.16					
$_{56}Ba^{132}$	0.097%	131.9057						$8.5 \pm 1.0b$		
$_{56}Ba^{133m}$			38.9h	IT	0.288					
$_{56}Ba^{133}$				EC	0.488					
$_{56}Ba^{134}$	2.42%	133.9043						$0.16 \pm 0.02b$ (Ba^{135m}) $2 \pm 2b$ (Ba^{135})	0	
$_{56}Ba^{135m}$			28.7h	IT	0.268					
$_{56}Ba^{135}$	6.59%	134.9056						$5.8 \pm 0.9b$	3/2	$+0.8365$
$_{56}Ba^{136m}$			0.32s	IT	2.04					
$_{56}Ba^{136}$	7.81%	135.9044						$10 \pm 1mb$ (Ba^{137m}) $0.4 \pm 0.4b$ (Ba^{137})	0*	
$_{56}Ba^{137m}$			2.55m	IT	0.6616					
$_{56}Ba^{137}$	11.32%							$5.1 \pm 0.4b$	3/2	$+0.9357$

Isotope	% nat. abundance	Atomic mass	Lifetime	Modes of decay	Decay energy (MeV)	Particle energies (MeV)	Particle intensities	Thermal neutron capture cross-section	I	μ
$_{56}Ba^{138}$	71.66%	137.9050						0.35 ± 0.15b	0	
$_{56}Ba^{139}$			82.9m	β^-	2.34	0.95 2.23 2.38	<1% 27% 72%	4 ± 1b		
$_{56}Ba^{140}$			12.8d	β^-	1.05	0.47 0.58 0.89 1.01 1.02	34% 11% ~3% 33% 19%	1.6 ± 0.3b		
$_{56}Ba^{141}$			18m	β^-	3.0	2.0 2.4 2.6 2.8 3.0				
$_{56}Ba^{142}$			11m	β^-	2.2	1.0 ~1.7				
$_{56}Ba^{143}$			12s	β^-						
La		138.91						8.9 ± 0.2b		
$_{57}La^{126}$			1.0m	β^+, EC						
$_{57}La^{127}$			3.5m	β^+, EC						
$_{57}La^{128}$			4.4m	β^+, EC						
$_{57}La^{129}$			10m	β^+, EC	~4.0					
$_{57}La^{130}$			8.7m	β^+, EC	~5					
$_{57}La^{131}$			59m	β^+, EC	2.96	0.70 1.42 1.94	17† 56 27			
$_{57}La^{132}$			4.5h	β^+, EC	5.3	3.8				
$_{57}La^{133}$			4.0h	β^+, EC	2.2	~1.2				
$_{57}La^{134}$			6.7m	β^+, EC	3.77	2.7				
$_{57}La^{135}$			19.5h	EC	~1.2	0.81				
$_{57}La^{136}$			9.5m	β^+, EC	2.9	1.8				
$_{57}La^{137}$			6×10^4y	EC	~0.5					
$_{57}La^{138}$	0.089%	137.9068							5	+3.707
$_{57}La^{139}$	99.911%	138.9061						8.8 ± 0.7b	7/2	
$_{57}La^{140}$			40.22 ± 0.1h	β^-	3.769	1.25 1.36 1.42 1.69 2.17	15% 35% 4% 18% 27%	2.8 ± 0.3b	3	
$_{57}La^{141}$			3.9h	β^-	2.43	0.9 2.43	~5% ~95%			
$_{57}La^{142}$			92m	β^-	4.51	0.86 1.06	12% 16%			

Isotope	% nat. abundance	Atomic mass	Lifetime	Modes of decay	Decay energy (MeV)	Particle energies (MeV)	Particle intensities	Thermal neutron capture cross-section	I	μ
						1.20	5%			
						1.79	11%			
						1.98	19%			
						2.11	24%			
						2.31	6%			
						2.33	1%			
						2.98	1.7%			
						3.85	2.4%			
						4.52	12%			
$_{57}La^{143}$			14m	β^-	3.3	3.3				
$_{57}La^{144}$			40s	β^-	5.6					
Ce		140.12						$0.73 \pm 0.08b$		
$_{58}Ce^{132}$			4.2h	EC	~1.2					
$_{58}Ce^{133}$			6.3h	β^+, EC	~2.8	1.3				
$_{58}Ce^{134}$			72h	EC	~0.16					
$_{58}Ce^{135}$			17.2h	β^+, EC	~2.1	0.81				
$_{58}Ce^{136}$	0.193%							$0.95 \pm 0.25b$ (Ce^{137m}) $6.3 \pm 1.5b$ (Ce^{137})		
$_{58}Ce^{137m}$			34.4h	IT EC	0.255				(11/2)	±0.89
$_{58}Ce^{137}$			9.0h	β^+, EC						
$_{58}Ce^{138}$	0.250%	137.9057						$15 \pm 5mb$ (Ce^{139m}) $1.1 \pm 0.3b$ (Ce^{139})		
$_{58}Ce^{139m}$			55s	IT	0.746					
$_{58}Ce^{139}$			140d	EC	0.27				(3/2)	±0.9
$_{58}Ce^{140}$	88.48%	139.9053						$0.58 \pm 0.06b$		
$_{58}Ce^{141}$			33d	β^-	0.581	0.444 0.582	60% 40%	$29 \pm 3b$	7/2	±0.97
$_{58}Ce^{142}$	11.07%	141.9090						$0.95 \pm 0.05b$		
$_{58}Ce^{143}$			33h	β^-	1.44	0.28 0.50 0.72 1.09 1.38	1% 3% 16% 42% 38%	$6.0 \pm 0.7b$	3/2	
$_{58}Ce^{144}$			284.9 ± 0.8d	β^-		0.175 0.24 0.309	24% 4.5% 76%	$1.0 \pm 0.1b$		
$_{58}Ce^{145}$			3.0m	β^-	~2.6	~2.0				
$_{58}Ce^{146}$			14m	β^-	~1.0	0.7				
$_{58}Ce^{147}$			65s	β^-						
$_{58}Ce^{148}$			43s	β^-						
Pr		140.907						$11.5 \pm 1.0b$		
$_{59}Pr^{134}$			17m	β^+, EC						

Isotope	% nat. abundance	Atomic mass	Lifetime	Modes of decay	Decay energy (MeV)	Particle energies (MeV)	Particle intensities	Thermal neutron capture cross-section	I	μ
$_{59}Pr^{135}$			22m	β^+, EC		2.5				
$_{59}Pr^{136}$			1.1h	β^+, EC		~2.0				
$_{59}Pr^{137}$			1.5h	β^+, EC	2.7	1.7				
$_{59}Pr^{138}$			2.1h	β^+, EC	4.79	1.65				
$_{59}Pr^{139}$			4.5h	β^+, EC	2.11	1.09				
$_{59}Pr^{140}$			3.39m	β^+, EC	3.34	2.32				
$_{59}Pr^{141}$	100%	140.9074						$3.9 \pm 0.5b$	5/2	+4.3
$_{59}Pr^{142}$			19.2h	β^-	2.16	0.64 2.15	4% 96%	$18 \pm 3b$	2	±0.26
$_{59}Pr^{143}$			13.7d	β^-	0.933	0.933	100%	$89 \pm 10b$	7/2	
$_{59}Pr^{144}$			17.3m	β^-	2.989	2.99 0.80 2.29	98% 1% 1.2%			
$_{59}Pr^{145}$			5.98h	β^-	1.80	1.80	95%			
$_{59}Pr^{146}$			24m	β^-	4.2	3.7 2.3	56% 44%			
$_{59}Pr^{147}$			12.0m	β^-	2.7	1.0 1.4 2.1 2.7	≤15% 30% 50% ≤5%			
$_{59}Pr^{148}$			2.0m	β^-	4.5					
Nd		144.24						$49 \pm 2b$		
$_{60}Nd^{138}$			22m	β^+	3.4	~2.4				
$_{60}Nd^{139m}$			5.5h	IT β^+	0.232					
$_{60}Nd^{139}$			5.2h	EC β^+	4.1	1.0 3.3	8† 100			
$_{60}Nd^{140}$			3.3d	EC						
$_{60}Nd^{141}$			2.5h	EC β^+	1.80	EC β^+ 0.78	95% 5%			
$_{60}Nd^{141m}$			64s	IT	0.755				3/2	
$_{60}Nd^{142}$	27.11%	141.9075						$18.8 \pm 0.7b$		
$_{60}Nd^{143}$	12.17%	142.9096						$330 \pm 10b$ $20 \pm 2mb$ (η, α)	7/2	−1.08
$_{60}Nd^{144}$	23.85%	143.9099	$\approx 5 \times 10^{15}y$	α		1.8		$4.0 \pm 0.5b$		
$_{60}Nd^{145}$	8.30%	144.9122						$50 \pm 4b$	7/2	−0.66
$_{69}Nd^{146}$	17.62%	145.9127						$1.4 \pm 0.2b$		
$_{60}Nd^{147}$			11.1d	β^-	0.91	0.82 0.38	77% 17%		5/2	±0.59

Isotope	% nat. abundance	Atomic mass	Lifetime	Modes of decay	Decay energy (MeV)	Particle energies (MeV)		Particle intensities	Thermal neutron capture cross-section	I	μ
$_{60}$Nd^{148}	5.73%	147.9165							2.5 ± 0.2b		
$_{60}$Nd^{149}			1.73h	β^-	1.66	1.55	1.01	17%		5/2	
						1.45	1.12	18%			
						1.40	1.40	18%			
						1.12	1.45	25%			
						1.01	1.55	11%			
$_{60}$Nd^{150}	5.62%	149.9207							1.3 ± 0.3b		
$_{60}$Nd^{151}			10m	β^-	2.31	2.14		17%			
						2.06		40%			
						1.99		9%			
						1.78		11%			
						1.47		16%			
Pm											
$_{61}$Pm^{141}			22m	β^+	3.6	2.6					
$_{61}$Pm^{142}			34s	β^+	4.82	β^+, 3.8		69%			
				EC		EC		31%			
$_{61}$Pm^{143}			265d	EC	1.1	EC					
$_{61}$Pm^{144}			≈400d	EC		EC					
$_{61}$Pm^{145}			17.7y	EC	0.14	EC					
$_{61}$Pm^{146}			≈710d	EC	1.72	EC			8400 ± 1680b		
				β^-	1.53	β^-, 0.78		35%			
$_{61}$Pm^{147}			2.5y	β^-	0.225	0.225		100%	90 ± 30b (Pm^{148m}) 100 ± 30b (Pm^{148})	7/2	±2.7
$_{61}$Pm^{148m}			42d	IT	2.59	β^- 0.5		37%	25,000 ± 4000b		
				β^-		0.6		19%			
						0.68		8%			
						0.8		24%			
						IT		6%			
$_{61}$Pm^{148}			5.39d	β^-	2.46	1.1		41%		1	+2.0
						2.0		14%			
						2.6		45%			
$_{61}$Pm^{149}			53.1h	β^-	1.06	0.19		0.6%	1350 ± 400b	7/2	
						0.47		0.3%			
						0.78		10%			
						1.06		89%			
$_{61}$Pm^{150}			2.7h	β^-	3.43	1.5					
						1.8					
						2.3					
						2.8					
						3.2					
$_{61}$Pm^{151}			28h	β^-	1.19	0.35		11%	<700b	5/2	±1.8
						0.50		6%			
						0.73		10%			
						0.84		43%			
						0.98		3%			
						1.05		11%			
						1.13		6%			
						1.19		10%			
$_{61}$Pm^{152}			6m	β^-		2.2					
$_{61}$Pm^{154}			2.5m	β^-		2.5					
3$_{10}$		150.35							5820 ± 100b		

Isotope	% nat. abundance	Atomic mass	Lifetime	Modes of decay	Decay energy (MeV)	Particle energies (MeV)	Particle intensities	Thermal neutron capture cross-section	I	μ
$_{62}Sm^{142}$			72m	EC β^+		EC β^+ 1.03	90% 10%			
$_{62}Sm^{143m}$			64s	IT	0.748					
$_{62}Sm^{143}$			8.9m	EC β^+	3.3	EC 2.5	50% 50%			
$_{62}Sm^{144}$	3.09	143.9117						$\approx 0.7b$		
$_{62}Sm^{145}$			340d	EC	0.65			$\approx 110b$		
$_{62}Sm^{146}$		146.9129	7×10^7y	α		2.55				
$_{62}Sm^{147}$	14.97	146.9146	1.06×10^{11}y	α	2.314	2.314		$75 \pm 11b$	7/2	-0.813
$_{62}Sm^{148}$	11.24	147.9146	1.2×10^{13}y	α	2.001	2.04		$2.4 \pm 0.3b$		
$_{62}Sm^{149}$	13.83	148.9169	$\sim 4 \times 10^{14}$y	α	1.90	1.84		$41,000 \pm 2000b$ $50 \pm 10mb$ (η, α)	7/2	-0.66
$_{62}Sm^{150}$	7.44	149.9170						$102 \pm 5b$		
$_{62}Sm^{151}$			93 ± 8y	β^-	0.076	0.055 0.076	1.7% 98.3%	$15,000 \pm 1800b$		
$_{62}Sm^{152}$	26.72%	151.9195						$210 \pm 10b$		
$_{62}Sm^{153}$			46.8 ± 0.1h	β^-	0.801	0.679 0.698 0.801	32% 48% 20%		3/2	-0.03
$_{62}Sm^{154}$	22.71%	153.9220						$5.5 \pm 1.1b$		
$_{62}Sm^{155}$			22m	β^-	1.65	1.65 1.50	93% 7%		3/2	
$_{62}Sm^{156}$			9.4h	β^-	0.72	0.43 0.70	44% 51%			
$_{62}Sm^{157}$			0.5m	β^-						
Eu		151.96						$4100 \pm 100b$		
$_{63}Eu^{144}$			10s	β^+, EC	6.32					
$_{63}Eu^{145}$			5.9d	β^+, EC						
$_{63}Eu^{146}$			4.6d	β^+, EC	3.86	0.80 1.47 2.1	0.4% 3.3% 0.14%			
$_{63}Eu^{147}$			22d	β^+, EC	1.8					
$_{63}Eu^{148}$			54d	β^+, EC	3.11	0.92	0.13%			
$_{63}Eu^{149}$			106d	EC	0.80	0.25 0.52 0.78 0.80	5% 4% 5% 85%			
$_{63}Eu^{150m}$			12.8h	β^+, EC β^-	2.25 1.01	β^- 1.01 β^+ 1.24				
$_{63}Eu^{150}$			5y	EC	2.25					

Isotope	% nat. abundance	Atomic mass	Lifetime	Modes of decay	Decay energy (MeV)	Particle energies (MeV)	Particle intensities	Thermal neutron capture cross-section	I	μ
$_{63}$Eu^{151m}			58μs	IT	0.196				7/2	+2.57
$_{63}$Eu^{151}	47.82%	150.9196						3.8 $\pm$ 1.9b (Eu^{152m_2}) 3000 $\pm$ 200b (Eu^{152m_1}) 5000 $\pm$ 300b (Eu^{152})	5/2	+3.464
$_{63}$Eu^{152m_2}			96m	IT	0.147					
$_{63}$Eu^{152m_1}			9.2h	β^- β^+, EC	1.82 1.857	β^- 0.55 1.88 β^+ 0.77 0.895	10† 0.004% 0.007%			
$_{63}$Eu^{152}			13y	β^+, EC β^-	1.86 1.82	β^- 0.22 0.36 0.68 1.05 1.46 β^+ 0.47 0.713	9† 13 51 6 21 0.005% 0.014%		3	$\pm$1.924
$_{63}$Eu^{153}	52.18%	152.9209						450 $\pm$ 100b	5/2	+1.530
$_{63}$Eu^{154}			16y	β^-	1.97	β^- 0.27 0.59 0.89 1.86	20% 45% 23% 12%	1500 $\pm$ 400b	3	$\pm$2.000
$_{63}$Eu^{155}			1.81y	β^-	0.248	0.10 0.15 0.19 0.25	34% 40% 10% 16%	14,000 $\pm$ 4000b		
$_{63}$Eu^{156}			15d	β^-	2.45	0.25 0.26 0.27 0.43 0.49 1.08 1.21 1.28 2.45	8% 9% 2.2% 8% 33% 2.3% 1.3% 6% 31%			
$_{63}$Eu^{157}			15.2h	β^-	1.34	0.55 0.65 0.86 0.90 1.28 1.35	2% 10% 35% 15% 30% 3%			
$_{63}$Eu^{158}			46m	β^-	3.5	1.11 1.9 2.5				
$_{63}$Eu^{159}			18m	β^-	2.57	1.0 1.5 1.75 1.90 2.35 2.57	10% 11% 11% 21% 21% 25%			
$_{63}$Eu^{160}			$\approx$2.5m	β^-	3.6					
Gd	157.25							49,000 $\pm$ 2000b		

Isotope	% nat. abundance	Atomic mass	Lifetime	Modes of decay	Decay energy (MeV)	Particle energies (MeV)	Particle intensities	Thermal neutron capture cross-section	I	μ
$_{64}Gd^{145}$			25m	EC β^+	5.2	EC β^+ 2.4	55% 45%			
$_{64}Gd^{146}$			4.6d	EC	~1.1					
$_{64}Gd^{147}$			35h	β^+, EC	~2.2					
$_{64}Gd^{148}$		147.9177	≈130y	α	3.27	3.18				
$_{64}Gd^{149}$		148.9189	9d	EC, α	3.17	α 3.01	0.0005%			
$_{64}Gd^{150}$		149.9185	2.1×10^6y	α	2.80	2.73	100%			
$_{64}Gd^{151}$			120d	EC, α	~0.4 2.61	2.60	~8 × 10^{-7}%			
$_{64}Gd^{152}$	0.200	151.9195	1.1×10^{14}y	α	2.24	2.15	100%	<125b		
$_{64}Gd^{153}$			242d	EC	0.243					
$_{64}Gd^{154}$	2.15	153.9207						102 ± 7b		
$_{64}Gd^{155}$	14.73	154.9226						61,000 ± 1000b	3/2	−0.27
$_{64}Gd^{156}$	20.47	155.9221								
$_{64}Gd^{157}$	15.68	156.9339						254,000 ± 2000b	3/2	−0.36
$_{64}Gd^{158}$	24.87	157.9241						3.5 ± 1.0b		
$_{64}Gd^{159}$			18h	β^-	0.95	0.59 0.89 0.95	13% 24% 63%		3/2	
$_{64}Gd^{160}$	21.90	159.9271						0.77 ± 0.01b		
$_{64}Gd^{161}$			3.7m	β^-	2.02	1.5 1.6		$(9.6 \pm 5) \times 10^4$b		
Tb		158.924						30 ± 10b		
$_{65}Tb^{147}$			24m	β^+, EC						
$_{65}Tb^{148}$			70m	β^+, EC	5.6	2.6 4.6				
$_{65}Tb^{149m}$			4.3m	EC α		3.99	0.025%			
$_{65}Tb^{149}$			4.1h	EC α	4.06	EC α 3.95	84% 16%			
$_{65}Tb^{150}$			3.1h	β^+, EC	4.79	1.5 2.8 3.6	5† 5 10			
$_{63}Tb^{151}$		150.9230	18h	EC α	~2.7 3.49	EC α 3.44	99+% 0.0005%			
$_{65}Tb^{152m}$			4m	β^+, EC α		α	0.002%			
$_{65}Tb^{152}$			18h	β^+, EC	4.2	0.42 0.85 1.30 1.93 2.82	1† 4 14 45 100			
$_{65}Tb^{153}$			55h	EC	~1.6					
$_{65}Tb^{154}$			8.5h	EC						

Isotope	% nat. abundance	Atomic mass	Lifetime	Modes of decay	Decay energy (MeV)	Particle energies (MeV)	Particle intensities	Thermal neutron capture cross-section	I	μ
$_{65}Tb^{154}$			21h	β^+, EC		EC	99+%			
$_{65}Tb^{155}$			5.6d	EC	0.9					
$_{65}Tb^{156m}$			5.5h	IT EC						
$_{65}Tb^{156}$			5.4d	EC					(3)	±1.4
$_{65}Tb^{157}$			150y	EC	0.06		100%			
$_{65}Tb^{158m}$			11s	IT	0.111					
$_{65}Tb^{158}$			1.2×10^3y	EC β^-	1.20 0.95	0.64 0.86	1% 13%		3	±1.74
$_{65}Tb^{159}$	100	159.9250						30 ± 10b	3/2	+1.95
$_{65}Tb^{160}$			73d	β^-	1.72	0.32 0.36 0.43 0.46 0.68 0.95 1.55 1.74	5% 10% 4% 44% 7% 29% 0.12% 0.34%	525 ± 100b	3	
$_{65}Tb^{161}$			6.9d	β^-	0.58	0.04 0.17 0.21 0.45 0.57 0.58	0.07% 0.02% 0.11% 26% 64% 10%		3/2	
$_{65}Tb^{162}$			7.5m	β^-	~2.8					
$_{65}Tb^{163m}$			7m	β^-						
$_{65}Tb^{163}$			6.5h	β^-	1.68	1.1 1.4 1.5 1.65	15% 40% 15% 30%			
$_{65}Tb^{164}$			23h	β^-	~3.8					
Dy		162.50						930 ± 20b		
$_{66}Dy^{149}$			≈15m	EC						
$_{66}Dy^{150}$			7.2m	α β^+, EC		α 4.2	18% 82%			
$_{66}Dy^{151}$			18m	β^+, EC α	~2.9 4.1	4.06	6%			
$_{66}Dy^{152}$		151.9244	2.5h	β^+, EC α	0.4 3.75	α 3.7	0.05%			
$_{66}Dy^{153}$		152.9254	6.4h	β^+, EC α	~2.1 3.57	α 3.48				
$_{66}Dy^{154m}$			13h	α		3.37				
$_{66}Dy^{154}$		153.9248	≈10^6y	α	2.93	2.85				
$_{66}Dy^{155}$			10.2h	β^+, EC β^+, EC		0.85 1.08	2% 0.14%			
$_{66}Dy^{156}$	0.052%	155.9238								
$_{66}Dy^{157}$			8.1h	EC						

Isotope	% nat. abundance	Atomic mass	Lifetime	Modes of decay	Decay energy (MeV)	Particle energies (MeV)	Particle intensities	Thermal neutron capture cross-section	I	μ
$_{66}Dy^{158}$	0.090%	157.9240						96 ± 20b		
$_{66}Dy^{159}$			144d	EC	0.38				3/2	
$_{66}Dy^{160}$	2.29%	159.9248						55 ± 9b		
$_{66}Dy^{161}$	18.88%	160.9266						585 ± 50b	5/2	−0.46
$_{66}Dy^{162}$	25.53%	161.9265						200 ± 50b		
$_{66}Dy^{163}$	24.97%	162.9284						140 ± 30b	5/2	+0.64
$_{66}Dy^{164}$	28.18%	163.9288						2100 ± 400b (Dy^{165m},4) 2600 ± 200b (Dy^{165m} + Dy^{165},4)		
$_{66}Dy^{165m}$			75s	IT β^-	0.108 1.30	β^- 0.89 1.0	87† 13			
$_{66}Dy^{165}$			2.3h	β^-	1.30	0.22 0.24 0.3 1.25 1.30	0.1% 0.03% 1.3% 15% 83%		7/2	
$_{66}Dy^{166}$			81.5h	β^-	0.482	0.05 0.40 0.482	1% 94% 5%			
$_{66}Dy^{167}$			4.4m	β^-						
Ho		164.930						65 ± 2b		
$_{67}Ho^{151}$			42s	α β^+, EC		4.60	30%			
$_{67}Ho^{151}$			36s	α β^+, EC		4.51	20%			
$_{67}Ho^{152}$			2.4m	α β^+, EC	4.50 6.4	4.38	30%			
$_{67}Ho^{152}$			52s	α β^+, EC	4.57	4.45	19%			
$_{67}Ho^{153}$			9m	α	4.02	3.92	0.3%			
$_{67}Ho^{154}$			7m	β^+, EC	~5.5					
$_{67}Ho^{155}$			50m	β^+, EC		2.1				
$_{67}Ho^{156}$			55m	β^+, EC	≈5	1.3 1.80 2.9	4† 14 1			
$_{67}Ho^{157}$			14m	β^+, EC						
$_{67}Ho^{158m}$			29m	IT β^+, EC	0.0673 4.1	1.32				
$_{67}Ho^{158}$			11m	β^+, EC	4.04					
$_{67}Ho^{159m}$			6.9s	IT	~2.0					
$_{67}Ho^{159}$			33m	EC	~1.8					
$_{67}Ho^{160m}$			5.0h	IT	3.36		66%			

TABLE OF THE ISOTOPES (Continued)

Isotope	% nat. abundance	Atomic mass	Lifetime	Modes of decay	Decay energy (MeV)	Particle energies (MeV)	Particle intensities	Thermal neutron capture cross-section	I	μ
				β^+, EC		0.31 0.57 1.01	0.01% 0.2% 0.08%			
$_{67}\text{Ho}^{160}$			23m	β^+, EC	3.30	1.9	0.02%			
$_{67}\text{Ho}^{161m}$			6s	IT	0.211					
$_{67}\text{Ho}^{161}$			2.5h	EC	~0.8				7/2	
$_{67}\text{Ho}^{162m}$			68m	IT EC	~2.26		63%			
$_{67}\text{Ho}^{162}$			15m	β^+, EC	2.16	~1.06 ~1.14	~56% ~44%			
$_{67}\text{Ho}^{163m}$			1.1s	IT	0.305					
$_{67}\text{Ho}^{163}$			>10³y	EC	~0.01					
$_{67}\text{Ho}^{164}$			37m	β^- EC	1.03 1.11	0.99	53% 47%			
$_{67}\text{Ho}^{165}$	100%	164.9303						3.45 ± 0.35b (Ho¹⁶⁶ᵐ) 61.2 ± 2.0b (Ho¹⁶⁶)	7/2	+4.08
$_{67}\text{Ho}^{166}$			26.9h	β^-	1.847	0.18 0.38 1.76 1.84	0.3% 1% 47% 52%		0*	
$_{67}\text{Ho}^{166m}$			1.2 × 10³y	β^-	1.847	≤0.067				
$_{67}\text{Ho}^{167}$			3.1h	β^-	1.0	0.28 0.96	50% 50%			
$_{67}\text{Ho}^{168}$			3.3m	β^-	3.3	≈2.2				
$_{67}\text{Ho}^{169}$			4.8m	β^-	2.1	1.20 1.95	75% 25%			
$_{67}\text{Ho}^{170}$			45s	β^-	4.2	≈3.1				
Er		167.26						160 ± 30b		
$_{68}\text{Er}^{158}$			2.5h	β^+, EC		0.8				
$_{68}\text{Er}^{159}$			36m	β^+, EC						
$_{68}\text{Er}^{160}$			29h	EC	~0.8					
$_{68}\text{Er}^{161}$			3.1h	β^+, EC	2.4	1.2				
$_{68}\text{Er}^{162}$	0.136%	161.9288						160 ± 30b		
$_{68}\text{Er}^{163}$			75m	β^+, EC	1.21	0.19	0.004%			
$_{68}\text{Er}^{164}$	1.56%	163.9293						13 ± 5b		
$_{68}\text{Er}^{165}$			10.3h	EC	0.37				5/2	±0.65
$_{68}\text{Er}^{166}$	33.41%	165.9304						10 ± 5b (Er¹⁶⁷ᵐ) 30 ± 5b (Er¹⁶⁷ᵐ + Er¹⁶⁷)		
$_{68}\text{Er}^{167m}$			2.3s	IT	0.208					

Isotope	% nat. abundance	Atomic mass	Lifetime	Modes of decay	Decay energy (MeV)	Particle energies (MeV)	Particle intensities	Thermal neutron capture cross-section	I	μ
$_{68}Er^{167}$	22.94%	166.9320						$700 \pm 50b$	7/2	−0.564
$_{68}Er^{168}$	27.07%	167.9324						$1.9 \pm 0.2b$		
$_{68}Er^{169}$			9.4d	β^-	0.34	0.332 0.340	42% 58%		1/2	+0.513
$_{68}Er^{170}$	14.88	169.9355						$6 \pm 1b$		
$_{68}Er^{171}$			7.52h	β^-	1.490	0.50 0.54 0.59 0.77 0.83 1.065 1.49	0.4% 0.5% 3.6% 0.4% 0.2% 91% 2.3%		5/2	±0.70
$_{68}Er^{172}$			49h	β^-	0.91	0.30 0.38 0.43 0.91	42% 44% 12% <10%			
Tm		168.934						$115 \pm 15b$		
$_{69}Tm^{161}$			30m	EC	3.5					
$_{69}Tm^{162}$			77m	β^+, EC	4.89					
$_{69}Tm^{162}$			22m	β^+, EC	4.89	0.9 2.3 3.82	3† 12 10			
$_{69}Tm^{163}$			1.8h	β^+, EC	2.27	0.40 1.1	7† 100		1/2	
$_{69}Tm^{164}$			1.9m	β^+, EC	~3.8	1.3 2.94	4† 100			
$_{69}Tm^{165}$			30.1h	β^+, EC	1.57	0.1	~0.004%			
$_{69}Tm^{166}$			7.7h	β^+, EC	3.04	1.10 1.94	0.3% 1.5%		2	±0.05 ·
$_{69}Tm^{167}$			9.6d	EC	1.16				1/2	
$_{69}Tm^{168}$			87d	EC	1.72					
$_{69}Tm^{169}$	100%	168.9344						$115 \pm 15b$	1/2	−0.230
$_{69}Tm^{170}$			$128.6 \pm 0.3d$	β^-	0.967	0.886 0.97	23% 77%	$92 \pm 4b$	1	±0.25
$_{69}Tm^{171}$			1.92y	β^-	0.098	0.097 0.030	98% 2%	$4.5 \pm 0.2b$	1/2	±0.23
$_{69}Tm^{172}$			63.6h	β^-	1.88	0.13 0.22 0.28 0.33 0.41 0.71 1.62 1.80 1.88	~0.05% 1% 10% 4% 14% 8% 1% 39% 23%			
$_{69}Tm^{173}$			8.2h	β^-	1.32	0.80 0.84 1.26	23% 75% 2%			

Isotope	% nat. abundance	Atomic mass	Lifetime	Modes of decay	Decay energy (MeV)	Particle energies (MeV)	Particle intensities	Thermal neutron capture cross-section	I	μ
$_{69}Tm^{174m}$			5.2m	β^-	3.0	0.7 1.2	~20% ~80%			
$_{69}Tm^{174}$			5.5m	β^-	2.5	2.5	100%			
$_{69}Tm^{175}$			20m	β^-	2.5	2.0				
$_{69}Tm^{176}$			1.5m	β^-	4.2	4.2				
Yb		173.04						$37 \pm 3b$		
$_{70}Yb^{164}$			76m	EC						
$_{70}Yb^{165}$			10m	β^+, EC	~2.7					
$_{70}Yb^{166}$			57.5h	EC	0.3					
$_{70}Yb^{167}$			18m	β^+, EC	1.96	0.65	0.4%			
$_{70}Yb^{168}$	0.135%	167.9339						$3200 \pm 400b$		
$_{70}Yb^{169}$			32d	EC	~1.2					
$_{70}Yb^{170}$	3.03%	169.9349						$9.4 \pm 0.9b$		
$_{70}Yb^{171}$	14.31%	170.9365						$50 \pm 5b$	1/2	+0.4919
$_{70}Yb^{172}$	21.82%	171.9366						$0.4 \pm 0.1b$		
$_{70}Yb^{173}$	16.13%	172.9383						$19 \pm 2b$	5/2	−0.6776
$_{70}Yb^{174}$	31.84%	173.9390						$46 \pm 4b$ (Yb^{175m}) $65 \pm 5b$ ($Yb^{175m} + Yb^{175}$)		
$_{70}Yb^{175m}$			0.067s	IT	0.513					
$_{70}Yb^{175}$			101h	β^-	0.467	0.073 0.22 0.35 0.466	11% <0.1% 2.1% 87%		(7/2)	±0.13
$_{70}Yb^{176}$	12.73%	175.9427						$5.5 \pm 1.0b$		
$_{70}Yb^{177m}$			6.5s	IT	0.33					
$_{70}Yb^{177}$			1.9h	β^-	1.40	0.17 0.18 0.25 1.1 1.25 1.3 1.40	3% 6% 1% 2% 17% 9% 60%			
Lu		174.97						$75 \pm 2b$		
$_{71}Lu^{167}$			54m	β^+, EC	3.0	1.1 1.5	1† 1			
$_{71}Lu^{168}$			7.1m	β^+, EC	~4.6	1.20				
$_{71}Lu^{169m}$			2.7m	IT	0.02%					
$_{71}Lu^{169}$			34h	β^+, EC	2.26	0.4 1.2	17† 100			
$_{71}Lu^{170m}$			0.7s	IT	0.093					

Isotope	% nat. abundance	Atomic mass	Lifetime	Modes of decay	Decay energy (MeV)	Particle energies (MeV)	Particle intensities	Thermal neutron capture cross-section	I	μ
$_{71}Lu^{170}$			2.0d	β^+, EC	3.41	2.39	0.19%			
$_{71}Lu^{171m}$			76s	IT	0.071					
$_{71}Lu^{171}$			8.3d	β^+, EC	~1.6					
$_{71}Lu^{172m}$			3.7m	IT	0.041	γ Energies 41.86				
$_{71}Lu^{172}$			6.70d	EC	~2.7					
$_{71}Lu^{173}$			≈1.37y	EC	0.69					
$_{71}Lu^{174m}$			140d	IT EC	0.171 ~1.7					
$_{71}Lu^{174}$			3.6y	EC	1.5					
$_{71}Lu^{175}$	97.41%	174.9409						21 ± 3b	7/2	+2.23
$_{71}Lu^{176m}$			3.7h	β^-	1.3	1.22 1.31	~65% ~35%		1	+0.318
$_{71}Lu^{176}$	2.59%		3×10^{10}y	β^-	1.02	0.42	100%	7 ± 2b (Lu^{177m}) 2050 ± 50b (Lu^{177})	7	+3.18
$_{71}Lu^{177m}$			155d	IT β^-	0.97		22% 78%	gamma rays in equilibrium with Lu^{177} (* with IT)		
$_{71}Lu^{177}$			6.7d	β^-	0.497	0.17 0.38 0.497	6.7% 7% 86%		7/2	+2.24
$_{71}Lu^{178}$			20m	β^-		1.5				
$_{71}Lu^{178}$			30m	β^-	2.25	2.25				
$_{71}Lu^{179}$			4.6h	β^-	1.34	1.1 1.35	13% 87%			
$_{71}Lu^{180}$			2.5m	β^-	3.3	3.3				
Hf		178.49						103 ± 3b		
$_{72}Hf^{168}$			22m	β^+, EC		EC β^+ 1.7				
$_{72}Hf^{169}$			1.5h	β^+, EC		~1.3				
$_{72}Hf^{170}$			12.2h	β^+, EC						
$_{72}Hf^{171}$			11h	EC						
$_{72}Hf^{172}$			≈5y	EC	~1					
$_{72}Hf^{173}$			23.6h	EC	>2					
$_{72}Hf^{174}$	0.18%	173.9403	2.0×10^{15}y	α	2.55	≈2.55		390 ± 55b		
$_{72}Hf^{175}$			70d	EC	0.59					
$_{72}Hf^{176}$	5.20%	175.94165						15 ± 15b		
$_{72}Hf^{177}$	18.50%	176.9435						1.1 ± 0.1b (Hf^{178m})	7/2	+0.61

Isotope	% nat. abundance	Atomic mass	Lifetime	Modes of decay	Decay energy (MeV)	Particle energies (MeV)	Particle intensities	Thermal neutron capture cross-section	I	μ
								380 ± 30b (Hf^{178})		
$_{72}Hf^{178m_2}$			>10y	IT	2.5					
$_{72}Hf^{178m_1}$			5s	IT	1.148					
$_{72}Hf^{178}$	27.14%	177.9439						52 ± 6b (Hf^{179m}) 75 ± 10b ($Hf^{179m} + Hf^{179}$)	0	
$_{72}Hf^{179m}$			18.6s	IT	0.375					
$_{72}Hf^{179}$	13.75%	178.9460						$0.34 + 0.03$b (Hf^{180m}) $65 + 15$b (Hf^{180})	9/2	−0.47
$_{72}Hf^{180m}$			5.5h	IT	1.143					
$_{72}Hf^{180}$	35.24%	179.9468						12.6 ± 0.7b	0	
$_{72}Hf^{181}$			42.4 ± 0.2d	β^-	1.023	0.4 0.408	7% 93%	$40 \, {}^{+\,40}_{-\,20}$b		
$_{72}Hf^{182}$			9×10^6y	β^-	~0.5	~0.5				
$_{72}Hf^{183}$			1.1h	β^-	2.2	0.7 1.2 1.6	25% 50% 25%			
Ta		180.948						22 ± 1b		
$_{73}Ta^{172}$			44m	β^+, EC	~5					
$_{73}Ta^{173}$			3.7h	β^+, EC						
$_{73}Ta^{174}$			1.3h	β^+, EC						
$_{73}Ta^{175}$			10.5h	EC	~2.3					
$_{73}Ta^{176}$			8.0h	EC	~3					
$_{73}Ta^{177}$			56.6h	EC	1.17					
$_{73}Ta^{178}$			9.4m	β^+, EC	1.9	0.80 0.89	7† 10			
$_{73}Ta^{178}$			2.1h	β^+, EC	1.9	1				
$_{73}Ta^{179}$			~600y	EC	0.115					
$_{73}Ta^{180m}$			8.1h	EC β^-	0.7 0.50	0.61 0.71	3% 10%			
$_{73}Ta^{180}$	0.0123%	179.9415	$>10^{13}$y	EC, β^-						
$_{73}Ta^{181m}$			$6.8\mu s$	IT	0.0063					
$_{73}Ta^{181}$	99.988%	180.9480						10 ± 2mb (Ta^{182m}) 22 ± 1b (Ta^{182})	7/2	+2.36

Isotope	% nat. abundance	Atomic mass	Lifetime	Modes of decay	Decay energy (MeV)	Particle energies (MeV)	Particle intensities	Thermal neutron capture cross-section	I	μ
$_{73}Ta^{182m}$			16.5m	IT	0.503					
$_{73}Ta^{182}$			115d	β^-	1.811	0.17 0.23 0.35 0.37 0.43 0.50 1.48 1.71	29% 3% 2.2% ~2% 42% 0.9% 0.24% 0.05%	$8200 \pm 600b$		
$_{73}Ta^{183}$			5.1d	β^-	1.068	0.48 0.62 0.66 0.76 0.78	0.7% 84% 6% 7% ~3%		7/2	
$_{73}Ta^{184}$			8.7h	β^-	2.75	1.19 1.45 1.76 2.22 2.64	93% 6% 0.9% 0.1% 0.15%			
$_{73}Ta^{185}$			50m	β^-	2.0	0.15 1.7	~30% ~70%			
$_{73}Ta^{186}$			10.5m	β^-	3.7	2.2				
W		183.85						$18.5 \pm 0.5b$		
$_{74}W^{173}$			16m	EC						
$_{74}W^{174}$			31m	EC						
$_{74}W^{175}$			34m	EC						
$_{74}W^{176}$			2.5h	β^+, EC	≈ 1.5	~2				
$_{74}W^{177}$			135m	EC	≈ 2					
$_{74}W^{178}$			21.5d	EC	≈ 0.3					
$_{74}W^{179m}$			5.2m	IT	0.222					
$_{74}W^{179}$			38m	EC	≈ 1.2					
$_{74}W^{180m}$			0.005s	IT						
$_{74}W^{180}$	0.14%	179.9470						$10 \pm 10b$		
$_{74}W^{181m}$			14μs	IT						
$_{74}W^{181}$			140d	EC	0.19					
$_{74}W^{182}$	26.41	181.9483						$20.7 \pm 0.5b$	0	
$_{74}W^{183m}$			5.3s	IT	0.309					
$_{74}W^{183}$	14.40%	182.9503						$10.2 \pm 0.3b$	1/2	+0.1172
$_{74}W^{184}$	30.64%	183.9510						$2.4 \pm 0.4mb$ (W^{185m}) $1.8 \pm 0.2b$ (W^{185})	0	
$_{74}W^{185m}$			1.62m	IT	0.368					
$_{74}W^{185}$			75.8d	β^-	0.432	0.432	100%		3/2	
$_{74}W^{186}$	28.41%	185.9543						$37 \pm 2b$	0	

Isotope	% nat. abundance	Atomic mass	Lifetime	Modes of decay	Decay energy (MeV)	Particle energies (MeV)	Particle intensities	Thermal neutron capture cross-section	I	μ
$_{74}W^{187}$			24h	β^-	1.315	0.43 0.47 0.55 0.63 ~0.71 1.316	0.5% ~1% 4.3% 59% 8% 19%	90 ± 40b	 3/2	
$_{74}W^{188}$			69d	β^-	0.349	0.059 0.285 0.349	0.9% 0.6% 98.6%			
$_{74}W^{189}$			11.5m	β^-	2.5	2.0 2.5				
Re		186.2						85 ± 5b		
$_{75}Re^{177}$			17m	β^+, EC	≈3	>0.4				
$_{75}Re^{178}$			15m	β^+, EC	≥4.1	3.1				
$_{75}Re^{179}$			20m	EC	≈2.5					
$_{75}Re^{180}$			2.4m	β^+, EC		1.1				
$_{73}Re^{180}$			20h	β^+, EC	2.9	≈1.9				
$_{75}Re^{181}$			18h	EC	≈1.7					
$_{75}Re^{182}$			12.7h	β^+, EC	2.86	0.55 1.74	0.06% 0.2%			
$_{75}Re^{182}$			64h	EC						
$_{75}Re^{183}$			71d	EC	~0.9					
$_{75}Re^{184m}$			169d	IT	0.188					
$_{75}Re^{184}$			3.8d	EC	~1.6					
$_{75}Re^{185}$	37.500%	184.9530						110 ± 5b	5/2	+3.172
$_{75}Re^{186}$			90h	β^-	1.071	0.30 0.933 1.071	0.1% 21% 74%		1	+1.73
$_{75}Re^{187}$	62.500%	186.9560	7×10^{10}y	β^-	<0.01	≤0.008		2.0 ± 0.5b (Re^{184m}) 75 ± 4b (Re^{184})	5/2	+3.204
$_{75}Re^{188m}$			18.7m	IT	0.172					
$_{75}Re^{188}$			16.7h	β^-	2.116	0.21 0.23 0.30 0.37 0.41 0.56 0.71 0.715 0.77 1.09 1.54 1.96 2.116	0.05% 0.06% 0.02% 0.026% 0.14% 0.012% 0.35% 0.026% 0.025% 0.5% 1.2% 18% 80%	<2b	1	+1.78
$_{75}Re^{189}$			24h	β^-	1.00	0.72 0.80 1.02				

Isotope	% nat. abundance	Atomic mass	Lifetime	Modes of decay	Decay energy (MeV)	Particle energies (MeV)	Particle intensities	Thermal neutron capture cross-section	I	μ
$_{75}Re^{190}$			2.8m	β^-	3.1	1.7				
$_{75}Re^{190m}$			2.8h	IT						
$_{75}Re^{191}$			9.8m	β^-	1.8	1.8				
$_{75}Re^{192}$			6s	β^-		2.5				
Os		190.2						15.3 ± 0.7b		
$_{76}Os^{181}$			23m	EC	≈ 2.8					
$_{76}Os^{182}$			22h	EC	≈ 1.1					
$_{76}Os^{183m}$			9.9h	IT EC	0.171 ≈ 2.2	IT EC	46% 54%			
$_{76}Os^{183}$			12h	EC	≈ 2.0					
$_{76}Os^{184}$	0.018%	183.9526						< 200b		
$_{76}Os^{185}$			94d	EC	0.982					
$_{76}Os^{186}$	1.59%	185.9539								
$_{76}Os^{187}$	1.64%	186.9560							1/2	+0.0643
$_{76}Os^{188}$	13.3%	187.9560								
$_{76}Os^{189m}$			5.7h	IT	0.03					
$_{76}Os^{189}$	16.1%	188.9586						0.26 ± 0.03mb (Os^{190m})	3/2	+0.6566
$_{76}Os^{190m}$			9.9m	IT	1.706					
$_{76}Os^{190}$	26.4%	189.9586						12 ± 6b (Os^{191m}) 4 ± 2b (Os^{191})		
$_{76}Os^{191m}$			13h	IT	0.074					
$_{76}Os^{191}$			15d	β^-	0.310	0.13				
$_{76}Os^{192}$	39.952%									
$_{76}Os^{193}$			31h	β^-	1.132	0.57 0.67 0.85 0.99 1.059	4% 7% 1% 9% 6%			
$_{76}Os^{194}$			6.0y	β^-	0.097	0.009 0.054 0.097	2% 98% < 2%			
$_{76}Os^{195}$			6.5m	β^-	2.0	~ 2				
Ir		192.2						425 ± 15b		
$_{77}Ir^{182}$			15m	β^+, EC	≈ 5.5					

Isotope	% nat. abundance	Atomic mass	Lifetime	Modes of decay	Decay energy (MeV)	Particle energies (MeV)	Particle intensities	Thermal neutron capture cross-section	I	μ
$_{77}Ir^{183}$			0.9h	EC						
$_{77}Ir^{184}$			3.2h	β^+, EC	>4.3					
$_{77}Ir^{185}$			14h	EC	≈ 2.5					
$_{77}Ir^{186}$			16h	β^+, EC	3.83	1.06 1.37 1.94	0.5% 1.9%			
$_{77}Ir^{186}$			1.7h	β^+, EC		0.8 1.30 1.93 2.6 3.4	22† 12 44 20 1			
$_{77}Ir^{187}$			10.5h	EC	≈ 1.6					
$_{77}Ir^{188}$			41h	β^+, EC		1.21 1.66				
$_{77}Ir^{189}$			13.3d	EC	≈ 0.6					
$_{77}Ir^{190m_2}$			3.2h	IT β^+, EC	0.175 ~ 2.3		6% 94%			
$_{77}Ir^{190m_1}$			1.2h	IT	0.026					
$_{77}Ir^{190}$			11d	EC	2.1					
$_{77}Ir^{191m}$			4.9s	IT	0.042				11/2	± 6
$_{77}Ir^{191}$	37.4%	190.9609						$0.4 \pm 0.2b$ (Ir^{192m_2}) $610 \pm 60b$ (Ir^{192m_1}) $300 \pm 30b$ (Ir^{192})	3/2	$+0.18$
$_{77}Ir^{192m_2}$			>5y	IT	0.161					
$_{77}Ir^{192m_1}$			1.4m	IT β^-	0.058 1.50	0.9 1.2 1.5	0.0025% 0.008% 0.007%			
$_{77}Ir^{192}$			74d	β^- β^+, EC	1.453 1.2	β^-, 0.24 0.536 0.672 β^+, 0.24	8% 41% 46% 1.5×10^{-5}%	$1100 \pm 400b$ (Ir^{193m})	4	
$_{77}Ir^{193m}$			12d	IT	0.08			$0.05 \pm 0.02b$ (Ir^{194m_2})	[1/2?]	<2
$_{77}Ir^{193}$	62.6%	192.9633						$110 \pm 15b$	3/2	$+0.18$
$_{77}Ir^{194}$			17.4h	β^-	2.24	0.98 1.62	2.0% 1.2%		1	
$_{77}Ir^{195}$			4.2h	β^-	1.0	0.6 1.0	$\approx 25\%$ $\approx 75\%$			
$_{77}Ir^{196m}$			84m	β^-	3.40	0.24 0.39 0.66 1.08	10% 4.7% 5.4% 80%			
$_{77}Ir^{196}$			52s	β^-	3.22	0.3 0.4	$\sim 1\%$ $\sim 1\%$			

Isotope	% nat. abundance	Atomic mass	Lifetime	Modes of decay	Decay energy (MeV)	Particle energies (MeV)	Particle intensities	Thermal neutron capture cross-section	I	μ
						0.82	~1%			
						1.09	16%			
						3.22	80%			
$_{77}Ir^{197}$			7m	β^-	2.0	1.5	~50%			
						2.0	~50%			
$_{77}Ir^{198}$			50s	β^-	4.4	~3.6				
Pt		195.09						9 ± 1b		
$_{78}Pt^{173}$			short	α	6.34	α 6.19				
$_{78}Pt^{174}$			0.7s	β^+, EC	6.17		20%			
				α		6.03	80%			
$_{78}Pt^{175}$			2.1s	α	6.09	5.95				
$_{18}Pt^{176}$			6s	α	5.87	5.74	1%			
				β^+, EC			99%			
$_{78}Pt^{177}$			6.6s	α	5.64	5.51	0.3%			
				β^+, EC			99 + %			
$_{78}Pt^{178}$			21s	α	5.56	5.28	0.07%			
				β^+, EC		5.44	1.3%			
$_{78}Pt^{179}$			33s	α	5.27	5.15	0.1%			
				β^+, EC						
$_{78}Pt^{180}$			50s	α	5.26	5.14	0.3%			
				β^+, EC						
$_{78}Pt^{181}$			51s	α	5.13	5.02	0.0006%			
				β^+, EC						
$_{78}Pt^{182}$			3.0m	α	4.95		≈0.02%			
				β^+, EC	≈3					
$_{78}Pt^{183}$			7m	β^+, EC	4.84	4.74				
				α						
$_{78}Pt^{184}$			20m	α	4.60	4.50				
				β^+, EC						
$_{78}Pt^{185}$			1.2h	EC						
$_{78}Pt^{186}$			3h	α	4.32	4.23				
				EC						
$_{78}Pt^{187}$			2h	EC						
$_{78}Pt^{188}$			10.2d	EC	0.51					
$_{78}Pt^{189}$			10.9h	EC						
$_{78}Pt^{190}$	0.0127%	189.960	6×10^{11}y	α		3.18				
$_{78}Pt^{191}$			3.0d	EC	~2.0					
$_{78}Pt^{192}$	0.78%	191.9614	~10^{15}y	α		2.6		2 ± 1b (Pt^{193m})		
$_{78}Pt^{193m}$			4.3d	IT	0.148					
$_{78}Pt^{193}$			<500y	EC	0.045					
$_{78}Pt^{194}$	32.9%	193.9628						87 ± 13mb		

Isotope	% nat. abundance	Atomic mass	Lifetime	Modes of decay	Decay energy (MeV)	Particle energies (MeV)	Particle intensities	Thermal neutron capture cross-section	I	μ
								(Pt^{195m}) 1.2 ± 0.9b (Pt^{195})	0	
$_{78}$Pt^{195m}			4.1d	IT	0.2593					
$_{78}$Pt^{195}	33.8%	194.9648						27 ± 2b	1/2	+0.6060
$_{78}$Pt^{196}	25.3%	195.9650						0.06 + 0.02b (Pt^{197m}) 0.9 ± 0.1b (Pt^{197})	0	
$_{78}$Pt^{197m}			80m	IT β$^-$	0.399 1.15		97%			
$_{78}$Pt^{197}			18h	β$^-$	0.75	0.48 0.67	10% 90%			
$_{78}$Pt^{198}	7.21%	197.9675						4.0 ± 0.5b		
$_{78}$Pt^{199m}			14.1s	IT	0.425					
$_{78}$Pt^{199}			30m	β$^-$	1.68	0.72 0.89 0.94 1.14 1.38 1.69	1% 10% 8% 14% 4% 63%	15 ± 10b		
$_{78}$Pt^{200}			11.5h	β$^-$	≈0.7					
Au		196.967						98.8 ± 0.3b		
$_{79}$Au^{185}			7m	α	5.18	5.07				
$_{79}$Au^{186}			12m	EC						
$_{79}$Au^{187}			8m	EC						
$_{79}$Au^{188}			8m	β$^+$, EC	5.2					
$_{79}$Au^{189}			30m	EC						
$_{79}$Au^{190}			39m	β$^+$, EC	≈4.4				1	±0.066
$_{79}$Au^{191}			3.2h	EC	≈2.0				3/2	±0.137
$_{79}$Au^{192}			4.1h	β$^+$, EC	3.24	2.22	1%		1	±0.00785
$_{79}$Au^{193m}			3.9s	IT EC	0.290	I.T	99%			
$_{79}$Au^{193}			16h	EC	≈1.1				3/2	±0.139
$_{79}$Au^{194}			39.5h	β$^+$, EC	2.51	1.21 1.55	1.3† 1.7		1	±0.074
$_{79}$Au^{195m}			31s	IT	0.318					
$_{79}$Au^{195}			183d	EC	0.227				3/2	±0.147
$_{79}$Au^{196}			6.18d	β$^+$, EC β$^-$	1.48 0.684	β$^-$, 0.259			2	±0.6
$_{79}$Au^{197m}			7.2s	IT	0.409				[1/2]†	+0.37†

Isotope	% nat. abundance	Atomic mass	Lifetime	Modes of decay	Decay energy (MeV)	Particle energies (MeV)	Particle intensities	Thermal neutron capture cross-section	I	μ
$_{79}Au^{197}$	100%	196.9666						$98.8 \pm 0.3b$	3/2	+0.14486
$_{79}Au^{198}$			2.693 $\pm 0.005d$	β^-	1.374	0.28 0.961 1.374	1.1% 98.9% 0.025%	$25,800 \pm 1200b$	2	+0.590
$_{79}Au^{199}$			3.15d	β^-	0.46	0.250 0.296 0.462	22.4% 71.6% 6.0%	$30 \pm 15b$	3/2	+0.270
$_{79}Au^{200}$			48.4m	β^-	2.21	0.61 1.84 2.21	24% 6% 70%			
$_{79}Au^{201}$			26m	β^-	1.5	1.0 1.5	5% 95%			
$_{79}Au^{203}$			5.5s	β^-	≈ 2.1	1.9				
Hg		200.59						$375 \pm 5b$		
$_{80}Hg^{185}$			50s	EC						
$_{80}Hg^{186}$			1.5m	EC						
$_{80}Hg^{187}$			3m	EC α		5.14?				
$_{80}Hg^{188}$			3.7m	EC						
$_{80}Hg^{189}$			10m	β^+, EC						
$_{80}Hg^{190}$			20m	EC						
$_{80}Hg^{191}$			55m	β^+, EC						
$_{80}Hg^{192}$			4.8h	EC	≈ 1.4					
$_{80}Hg^{193m}$			10h	IT β^+, EC	0.141	1.17	16%		13/2	−1.063
$_{80}Hg^{193}$			~6h	EC	2.34				3/2	−0.62
$_{80}Hg^{194}$			1.9y?	EC	≈ 0.4					
$_{80}Hg^{195m}$			40h	IT EC	0.176 ~1.7				13/2	−1.049
$_{80}Hg^{195}$			9.5h	EC	~1.5				1/2	+0.538
$_{80}Hg^{196}$	0.146%	195.9658						$120 \pm 15b$ (Hg^{197m}) $3000 \pm 100b$ (Hg^{197})		
$_{80}Hg^{197m}$			24h	IT EC	0.72 0.42	IT EC	94% 6%		13/2	−1.032
$_{80}Hg^{197}$			65h	EC	0.42				1/2	+0.5241
$_{80}Hg^{198}$	10.02%	197.9668						$0.02 \pm 0.01b$ (Hg^{199m})	0	
$_{80}Hg^{199m}$			43m	IT	0.533					
$_{80}Hg^{199}$	16.84%	198.9683						$2000 \pm 1000b$	1/2	+0.5027
$_{80}Hg^{200}$	23.13%	199.9683						$<60b$	0	
$_{80}Hg^{201}$	13.22%	200.9703						$<60b$	3/2	−0.5567

Isotope	% nat. abundance	Atomic mass	Lifetime	Modes of decay	Decay energy (MeV)	Particle energies (MeV)	Particle intensities	Thermal neutron capture cross-section	I	μ
$_{80}Hg^{202}$	29.80%	201.9706						4.9 ± 0.2b	0	
$_{80}Hg^{203}$			46.57 ±0.03d	β^-	0.492	0.210 0.49	100% <0.004%		5/2	+0.84
$_{80}Hg^{204}$	6.85%	203.9735						0.43 ± 0.10b	0	
$_{80}Hg^{205}$			5.5m	β^-	1.6	~1.4 ~1.6				
$_{80}Hg^{206}$			7.5m	β^-	1.31					
Tl		204.37						3.4 ± 0.5b		
$_{81}Tl^{191}$			10m	β^+, EC						
$_{81}Tl^{192}$			11m	β^+, EC						
$_{81}Tl^{193m}$			2.1m	IT						
$_{81}Tl^{193}$			23m	EC						
$_{81}Tl^{194m}$			32.8m	EC						
$_{81}Tl^{194}$			33m	EC	≈5.4					
$_{81}Tl^{195m}$			3.5s	IT	0.482					
$_{81}Tl^{195}$			1.2h	β^+, EC		1.8			1/2	
$_{81}Tl^{196m}$			1.41h	IT EC	0.395	IT EC	4% 96%			
$_{81}Tl^{196}$			1.84h	EC	4.6					
$_{81}Tl^{197m}$			0.54s	IT	0.609					
$_{81}Tl^{197}$			2.8h	EC	2.2				1/2	
$_{81}Tl^{198m}$			1.87h	IT EC	0.543 ~4.0		55% 45%		7	
$_{81}Tl^{198}$			5.3h	β^+, EC	3.5	0.7 1.4 2.1 2.4	4† 10 12 14		2	± <0.002
$_{81}Tl^{199}$			7.4h	EC	1.1				1/2	+1.59
$_{81}Tl^{200}$			26.1h	β^+, EC	2.454	1.07 1.44	5.6† 1.0		2	± ≤0.15
$_{81}Tl^{201m}$			2.1ms	IT	0.93					
$_{81}Tl^{201}$			73h	EC	≈0.41				1/2	+1.60
$_{81}Tl^{202}$			12.0d	EC	1.1				2	± ≤0.15
$_{81}Tl^{203}$	29.50%	202.9723						10 ± 1b	1/2	+1.6115
$_{81}Tl^{204}$			3.8y	β^- EC	0.763 0.34	0.7635 ± 0.0002 EC	97.9% 2%		2	±0.089
$_{81}Tl^{205}$	70.50%	204.9745						0.5 ± 0.2b	1/2	+1.6274
$_{81}Tl^{206}$			4.19m	β^-	1.524	1.524	100%		0*	
$_{81}Tl^{207m}$			1.3s	IT	1.34					

Isotope	% nat. abundance	Atomic mass	Lifetime	Modes of decay	Decay energy (MeV)	Particle energies (MeV)	Particle intensities	Thermal neutron capture cross-section	I	μ
$_{81}Tl^{207}$			4.78m	β^-	1.44	0.53 1.44	0.16% 99+%			
$_{81}Tl^{208}$			3.10m	β^-	4.994	1.04 1.29 1.52 1.792 2.38	4% 24% 23% 49% 0.03%			
$_{81}Tl^{209}$			2.2m	β^-	3.98	1.99	100%			
$_{81}Tl^{210}$			1.3m	β^-	5.50	1.3 1.9 2.3	25% 56% 19%			
Pb		203.973						180 ± 10mb		
$_{82}Pb^{194}$			11m	EC						
$_{82}Pb^{195}$			17m	EC						
$_{82}Pb^{196}$			37m	EC	≈2.8					
$_{82}Pb^{197m}$			42m	IT EC	0.319 ≈4.5	IT EC	20% 80%			
$_{82}Pb^{197}$				EC	≈4.1					
$_{82}Pb^{198}$			2.4h	EC	≈1.8					
$_{82}Pb^{199m}$			12.2m	IT	0.424					
$_{82}Pb^{199}$			1.5h	β^+, EC	≈3.2	2.8	17%			
$_{82}Pb^{200}$			21.5h	EC	≈0.9					
$_{82}Pb^{201m}$			61s	IT	0.629					
$_{82}Pb^{201}$			9.4h	β^+, EC	≈2.0	0.55				
$_{82}Pb^{202m}$			3.62h	IT EC	2.17 2.17	IT EC	90% 10%			
$_{82}Pb^{202}$			∼3 × 10⁵y	EC	0.05					
$_{82}Pb^{203m}$			6.1s	IT	0.825					
$_{82}Pb^{203}$			52.1h	EC	0.96					
$_{82}Pb^{204m}$			66.9m	IT	2.186					
$_{82}Pb^{204}$	1.48%	203.973						0.66 ± 0.07b		
$_{82}Pb^{205m}$			4ms	IT	1.01					
$_{82}Pb^{205}$			3 × 10⁷y	EC	≈0.035					
$_{82}Pb^{206}$	23.6%	205.9745						30 ± 1mb	0	
$_{82}Pb^{207m}$			0.8s	IT	1.633					
$_{82}Pb^{207}$	22.6%	206.9759						0.71 ± 0.01b	1/2	+0.5895
$_{82}Pb^{208}$	52.3%	207.9766						0.02 ± 0.01b	0	
$_{82}Pb^{209}$			3.30h	β^-	0.635	0.635	100%			

Isotope	% nat. abundance	Atomic mass	Lifetime	Modes of decay	Decay energy (MeV)	Particle energies (MeV)	Particle intensities	Thermal neutron capture cross-section	I	μ
$_{82}Pb^{210}$			21y	β^- α	0.061 3.72	β^- 0.015 0.061 α 3.72	81% 19% 1.7×10^{-6}%			
$_{82}Pb^{211}$			36.1m	β^-	1.37	0.10 0.26 0.34 0.53 0.59 0.96 1.36	0.01% 0.7% 0.1% 6% 0.4% 1% 92%			
$_{82}Pb^{212}$			10.64h	β^-	0.58	0.17 0.35 0.589	5% 81% 14%			
$_{82}Pb^{213}$			10m	β^-	≈ 1.8					
$_{82}Pb^{214}$			26.8m	β^-	1.04	0.59 0.65 1.03	6%			
Bi		208.980						34 ± 2mb		
$_{83}Bi^{199}$			24m	EC α		 5.47	99+% 0.01%		9/2	
$_{83}Bi^{200}$			35m	EC	≈ 6.5				7	
$_{83}Bi^{201m}$			52m	EC α	≈ 4.2 ≈ 4.7	5.28				
$_{83}Bi^{201}$			1.8h	EC	≈ 4.2				9/2	
$_{83}Bi^{202}$			95m	EC	≈ 5.5				5	
$_{83}Bi^{203}$			11.8h	β^+, EC α	≈ 4.4 4.3	β^+ 0.74 1.35 α 4.85	33† 67		9/2	+4.59
$_{83}Bi^{204}$			11.2h	EC	≈ 4.4				6	+4.25
$_{83}Bi^{205}$			15.3d	β^+, EC	2.70	0.98	0.06%		9/2	+5.5
$_{83}Bi^{206}$			6.24d	β^+, EC	3.65	0.98	8×10^{-4}%		6	+4.56
$_{83}Bi^{207}$			30y	EC	2.40					
$_{83}Bi^{208}$			3.7×10^5y	EC	2.87					
$_{83}Bi^{209}$	100%	208.9804						19 ± 2mb	9/2	+4.080
$_{83}Bi^{210m}$			3×10^6y	α		4.43 4.57 4.92 4.96	0.4% 6% 36% 38%			
$_{83}Bi^{210}$			5.01d	β^- α	1.16 5.044	β^- 1.160 α 4.654 4.691 }	99+% 1.3×10^{-4}%	54 ± 5mb	1	± 0.0442
$_{83}Bi^{211}$		210.9873	2.15m	α β^-	6.750 0.60	α 5.946 6.278 6.622 β^- 0.060	0.0037% 15.9% 84.1% 0.28%			
$_{83}Bi^{212}$			60.6m	β^- α	2.25 6.206	β^- 0.08 0.45 0.67	0.7% 0.1% 2.2%			

Isotope	% nat. abundance	Atomic mass	Lifetime	Modes of decay	Decay energy (MeV)	Particle energies (MeV)	Particle intensities	Thermal neutron capture cross-section	I	μ
						0.93	1.4%			
						1.55	5%			
						2.27	54%			
						α 5.178	5×10^{-5} †			
							$\alpha_T = 36\%$			
						5.291	1.3×10^{-4}			
						5.334	1×10^{-3}			
						5.473	0.014			
						5.547	1.1			
						5.617	1.7			
						6.051	69.9			
						6.090	27.2			
$_{83}Bi^{213}$			47m	β^-	1.42	β^- 0.96⎱ 1.39⎰	97.8%			
				α	5.98	α 5.55⎱ 5.87⎰	2.2%			
$_{83}Bi^{214}$			19.7m	β^-	3.28	β^- 0.82	2%			
				α	5.616	1.06	8%			
						1.14	5%			
						1.41	8%			
						1.50	19%			
						1.51	19%			
						1.88	10%			
						1.98	2%			
						2.65	5%			
						3.26	19%			
						α 4.941	0.25†			
						5.023	0.21			
						5.184	0.6			
						5.268	5.8			
						5.448	53.9			
						5.512	39.2			
$_{83}Bi^{215}$			7m	β^-	2.2					
Po										
$_{84}Po^{192}$										
$_{84}Po^{193}$			Short	α	7.1	7.0				
$_{84}Po^{194}$			0.5s	α	6.97	6.85				
$_{84}Po^{195m}$			1.4s	α		6.72				
$_{84}Po^{195}$			3s	α	6.77	6.63				
$_{84}Po^{196}$			6s	α	6.67	6.53				
$_{84}Po^{197m}$			25s	α		6.39				
$_{84}Po^{197}$			54s	α	6.43	6.30				
$_{84}Po^{198}$			1.7m	α	6.29	6.16				
$_{84}Po^{199m}$			4.2m	EC α		EC α 6.047	74% 26%			
$_{84}Po^{199}$			5.0m	EC α	6.06	EC α 5.942	97% 3%			
$_{84}Po^{200}$			11m	EC α	≈ 3.6 est. 5.97	EC α 5.850	88% 12%			
$_{84}Po^{201m}$			9m	EC α		EC α 5.776	97% 3%			

Isotope	% nat. abundance	Atomic mass	Lifetime	Modes of decay	Decay energy (MeV)	Particle energies (MeV)	Particle intensities	Thermal neutron capture cross-section	I	μ
$_{84}Po^{201}$			15.1m	EC α	≈ 5.3 est. 5.79	EC α 5.677	99% 1.1%		3/2	
$_{84}Po^{202}$			45m	EC α	≈ 3.0 est. 5.69	EC α 5.581	98% 2%		0	
$_{84}Po^{203}$			42m	EC α	≈ 4.4 est. 5.59	EC α 5.49	99% 0.02%		5/2	
$_{84}Po^{204}$			3.6h	EC α	≈ 2.5 est. 5.48	EC α 5.376	99% 0.6%		0	
$_{84}Po^{205}$			1.8h	EC α	≈ 3.6 est. 5.34	EC α 5.25	99+% 0.07%		5/2	+0.26
$_{84}Po^{206}$		205.9805	8.8d	EC α	1.80 calc. 5.33	EC α 5.224	95% 5%		0	
$_{84}Po^{207m}$			2.8s	IT						
$_{84}Po^{207}$		206.9816	5.7h	EC β^+ α	2.91 5.33	EC β^+, 1.14, 0.89 α 5.11	99+% 0.5% $\approx 0.01\%$		5/2	≈ 0.27
$_{84}Po^{208}$		207.9813	2.93y	α EC	5.21 1.41 calc.	5.114 EC	99+% 0.006%			
$_{84}Po^{209}$		208.9825	103y	α EC	4.98 1.89 calc.	4.882 EC	99+% 0.5%		1/2	
$_{84}Po^{210}$		209.9829	138.4d	α	5.408	5.305		<0.5mb (25s Po^{211}) <30 mb (0.5s Po^{211})	0	
$_{84}Po^{211m}$			25s	α		8.88 8.31 8.00 7.28	7% 0.25 1.66 91%			
$_{84}Po^{211}$		210.9866	0.52s	α	7.592	7.448 6.891 6.551	99% 0.50 0.53			
$_{84}Po^{212m}$			45s	α		11.65 14.27 14.85	97% 1.00% 2.0%			
$_{84}Po^{212}$		211.9889	3.04×10^{-7}s	α		8.785 + long range α's				
$_{84}Po^{213}$		212.9928	4.2×10^{-6}s	α	8.54	8.377 7.61	99+% 0.003			
$_{84}Po^{214}$		213.9952	1.64×10^{-4}s	α	7.835	7.687 6.905 + long range α's	99+% 0.01			
$_{84}Po^{215}$		214.9995	1.78×10^{-3}s	α	7.524	7.384 6.954 6.948	100% 0.034 0.022			

Isotope	% nat. abundance	Atomic mass	Lifetime	Modes of decay	Decay energy (MeV)	Particle energies (MeV)	Particle intensities	Thermal neutron capture cross-section	I	μ
$_{84}Po^{216}$		216.0019	0.15s	α	6.906	6.777 5.984	100% 2.1×10^{-3}			
$_{84}Po^{217}$			< 10s	α β⁻	6.67 ≈ 1.3 est.	6.55 β⁻	80% < 20%			
$_{84}Po^{218}$		218.0089	3.05m	α β⁻	6.111 0.278	α 6.002 5.181 β⁻	99.98% 99.9 + 0.0011 0.019%			
At										
$_{85}At^{200}$			0.9m	EC α	6.55	6.47 6.42				
$_{85}At^{201}$			1.5m	EC α	6.48	6.35				
$_{85}At^{202}$			3.0m	EC α	≈ 8.1 est. 6.359	EC α 6.234 6.120	88% 12% 36† 64			
$_{85}At^{203}$			7.4m	EC α	≈ 5.8 est. 6.211	EC α 6.092	86% 14%			
$_{85}At^{204}$			9.3m	EC α	7.1 est. 6.071	EC α 5.955	95.5% 4.52%			
$_{85}At^{205}$			26m	EC α	≈ 4.9 est. 6.018	EC α 5.902	82% 18%			
$_{85}At^{206}$			32m	EC α	≈ 6.0 est. 5.88	EC α 5.70	≈ 12% ≈ 88%			
$_{85}At^{207}$			1.79h	EC α	3.73 calc. 5.87	EC α 5.76	≈ 90% ≈ 10%			
$_{85}At^{208}$			1.6h	EC α	≈ 5.0 est. 5.77	EC α 5.65	99 + % 0.5%			
$_{85}At^{209}$			5.5h	EC α	3.49 calc. 5.758	EC α 5.648	95% ≈ 5%			
$_{85}At^{210}$			8.3h	EC α	3.87 calc. 5.631	EC α 5.525 5.443 5.361	99 + % 0.17% 32† 31 37			
$_{85}At^{211}$		210.9875	7.21h	EC α	0.79 calc. 5.981	EC . α 5.868	59.1% 40.9%		9/2	
$_{85}At^{212m}$			0.12s	α		7.899 7.837	34% 66			
$_{85}At^{212}$			0.30s	α	7.81	7.678 7.616	80% 20			
$_{85}At^{213}$		212.993090	Short	α	9.4	9.06				

Isotope	% nat. abundance	Atomic mass	Lifetime	Modes of decay	Decay energy (MeV)	Particle energies (MeV)	Particle intensities	Thermal neutron capture cross-section	I	μ
$_{85}At^{214}$		213.9963	Short	α	8.94	8.78 8.44 8.23	100% <0.2 <0.1			
$_{85}At^{215}$		214.9987	$\approx 10^{-4}$s	α	8.16	8.01 7.60	100% 0.05			
$_{85}At^{216}$		216.0024	$\approx 3 \times 10^{-4}$s	α	7.95	7.81 7.71 7.60⎱ 7.58⎰ 7.49 7.40 7.33 7.25	97% 2.1 0.2 0.5 0.23 0.09 0.06			
$_{85}At^{217}$		217.0046	0.032s	α	7.199	7.066 6.820 6.623 6.486	100% 0.025 0.003 0.040			
$_{85}At^{218}$		218.0086	≈ 2s	α β^-	6.816 2.83 calc.	6.697 6.653	94% ≈ 6 0.1%			
$_{85}At^{219}$		219.0114	0.9m	α β^-	6.39 1.7 calc.	α 6.28	97% ≈ 3%			
Rn										
$_{86}Rn^{204}$			75s	α	6.545	6.416				
$_{86}Rn^{205}$			1.8m	α	6.387	6.262				
$_{86}Rn^{206}$			6.5 m	α EC	6.382 ≈ 3.5 est.	α 6.258 EC	65% 35%			
$_{86}Rn^{207}$			11m	EC α	≈ 4.8 est. 6.23	EC α 6.15	96% 4%			
$_{86}Rn^{208}$			23m	EC α	≈ 3.0 est. 6.268	EC α 6.148	≈ 80% ≈ 20%			
$_{86}Rn^{209}$			30m	EC α	≈ 4.0 est. 6.161	EC α 6.044	83% 17%			
$_{86}Rn^{210}$		209.9897	2.42h	α EC	6.160 2.33 calc.	α EC 6.044	≈ 96% ≈ 4%			
$_{86}Rn^{211}$		210.9906	15h	EC α	2.89 calc. 5.966	EC α 5.853 5.785 5.619	74% 26% 33.5† 64.5 2.0			
$_{86}Rn^{212}$		211.9907	25m	α	6.39	6.271				
$_{86}Rn^{213}$			19ms	α	8.296	8.14				
$_{86}Rn^{215}$		214.9987	Short	α	8.78	8.6				
$_{86}Rn^{216}$		216.0002	$45\mu s$	α	8.201	8.05				
$_{86}Rn^{217}$		217.0039	$540\mu s$	α	7.888	7.742				
$_{86}Rn^{218}$		218.0056	0.035s	α	7.26	7.14 6.54	99.8% 0.16			

Isotope	% nat. abundance	Atomic mass	Lifetime	Modes of decay	Decay energy (MeV)	Particle energies (MeV)	Particle intensities	Thermal neutron capture cross-section	I	μ
$_{86}Rn^{219}$		219.0095	4.0s	α	6.944	6.817 6.551 6.527 6.423 6.310 6.222 6.157 6.146 6.101 5.999 5.946 5.785	81% 11.5 0.12 7.5 0.054 0.0026 0.017 0.0026 0.003 0.0044 0.0037 ≈ 0.001			
$_{86}Rn^{220}$		220.0114	55s	α	6.405	6.287 5.747	100% 0.07	$< 0.2b$		
$_{86}Rn^{221}$			25m	β^- α	≈ 1.0 est. 6.1	β^- 6.0 est.	$\approx 80\%$ $\approx 20\%$			
$_{86}Rn^{222}$		222.0175	3.823d	α	5.587	5.486 4.984 4.824	100% 8×10^{-2} 5×10^{-4}	$0.72 \pm 0.07b$		
$_{86}Rn^{223}$			43m	β^-						
$_{86}Rn^{224}$			1.9h	β^-						
Fr										
$_{87}Fr^{204}$			2.0s	α	7.17	7.03				
$_{87}Fr^{205}$			3.7s	α	7.05	6.92				
$_{87}Fr^{206}$			15.8s	α	6.93	6.80				
$_{87}Fr^{207}$			19s	α	6.91	6.78				
$_{87}Fr^{208}$			37s	α	6.79	6.66				
$_{87}Fr^{209}$			55s	α	6.79	6.66				
$_{87}Fr^{210}$			2.6m	α	6.68	6.56				
$_{87}Fr^{211}$			3.1m	α	6.68	6.56				
$_{87}Fr^{212}$		211.996	19m	EC α	≈ 5.2 est. 6.530	EC α 6.407 6.383 6.338 6.261 6.179 6.127 6.077 5.983 5.83	56% 44% 21† 23 12 40 2.1 1.0 0.4 0.1 0.05			
$_{87}Fr^{213}$			34s	α EC	6.91 2.10 calc.	6.78 EC	99.48% 0.52%			
$_{87}Fr^{214m}$			3.35ms	α	8.59	8.549 8.477	51% 49			
$_{87}Fr^{214}$			5.0ms	α	8.70	8.426 8.353	94.5% 5.5			
$_{87}Fr^{215}$			$\ll 1$ms	α	9.59	9.4				
$_{87}Fr^{217}$		217.0048	Short	α	8.5	8.31				
$_{87}Fr^{218}$		218.0095	Short	α	8.00	7.85 7.70	93% <0.5			

Isotope	% nat. abundance	Atomic mass	Lifetime	Modes of decay	Decay energy (MeV)	Particle energies (MeV)	Particle intensities	Thermal neutron capture cross-section	I	μ
						7.55	5			
						7.52	1			
						7.36	<0.5			
$_{87}Fr^{219}$		219.0092	20ms	α	7.44	7.30	98.4%			
						7.14	0.3			
						6.95	0.8			
						6.72	0.2			
						6.68	0.3			
$_{87}Fr^{220}$		220.0123	27.5s	α	6.80	6.68	85%			
						6.64	13			
						6.58	1			
						6.53	0.5			
						6.48	<0.1			
						6.40	<0.1			
$_{87}Fr^{221}$		221.0142	4.8m	α	6.457	6.340	83.4%			
						6.242	1.34			
						6.126	15.1			
						6.075	0.15			
						6.036	0.003			
						5.979	0.49			
						5.965	0.08			
						5.938	0.17			
						5.925	0.03			
						5.813	0.004			
						5.782	0.005			
						5.775	0.06			
						5.696?	~0.001			
						5.688	0.002			
$_{87}Fr^{222}$			14.8m	β^- α	2.03 calc. 5.87 calc.	β^- α	99+% 0.01–0.1%			
$_{87}Fr^{223}$		223.0198	22m	β^- α	1.15 ≈5.44 calc.	1.15 5.34	99.994% 0.006%			
$_{87}Fr^{224}$			≈2m	β^-	≈2.9 est.					
Ra										
$_{88}Ra^{213}$			2.7m	α	6.89	6.74 6.61	50% 50			
$_{88}Ra^{214}$			2.6s	α	7.31	7.17				
$_{88}Ra^{215}$			1·6ms	α	8.90	8.73				
$_{88}Ra^{216}$			<1ms	α	9.48	9.3				
$_{88}Ra^{217}$			Short	α	9.18	9.0				
$_{88}Ra^{219}$		219.0100	Short	α	8.16	8.0				
$_{88}Ra^{220}$		220.0110	23ms	α	7.59	7.45 6.90	≈99% ≈1			
$_{88}Ra^{221}$		221.0139	30s	α	6.883	6.758	31%			
						6.665	21			
						6.610	35			
						6.588	8			
						6.578	3			
						6.46?	0.4			
						6.40?	0.3			
						6.25	0.7			
						6.16?	0.3			
$_{88}Ra^{222}$		222.0154	38s	α	6.68	6.56	96%			
						(6.23)	4			
						(5.36)	7×10^{-3}			
						(4.31)	6×10^{-3}			

Isotope	% nat. abundance	Atomic mass	Lifetime	Modes of decay	Decay energy (MeV)	Particle energies (MeV)	Particle intensities	Thermal neutron capture cross-section	I	μ
$_{88}Ra^{223}$		223.0186	11.43d	α	5.977	5.870	0.87%	σ_f		
						5.865?	<0.02	$1.0 \pm 0.5b$		
						5.856	0.32	$\sigma(\eta, \gamma)$		
						5.833?		$130 \pm 20b$		
						5.745	9.1			
						5.714	53.7			
						5.605	26			
						5.538	9.1			
						5.500	0.8			
						5.479	≈0.008			
						5.432	2.3			
						5.364	0.11			
						5.337	0.10			
						5.285	0.13			
						5.281	0.10			
						5.257	0.043			
						5.234	0.042			
						5.210	0.0054			
						5.171	0.026			
						5.150	0.021			
						5.133	≈0.0017			
						5.110	$≈6 \times 10^{-4}$			
						5.084	$≈6 \times 10^{-4}$			
						5.054	$≈2 \times 10^{-4}$			
						5.034	$≈4 \times 10^{-4}$			
						5.023	$≈6 \times 10^{-4}$			
						5.012	$≈4 \times 10^{-4}$			
$_{88}Ra^{224}$		224.0202	3.64d	α	5.787	5.684	94.5%	$12.0 \pm 0.5b$		
						5.447	5.5			
						5.159	0.007			
						5.049	0.007			
						5.032	0.003			
$_{88}Ra^{225}$			14.8d	β^-	0.39 calc.	0.32				
$_{88}Ra^{226}$		226.0254	1600y	α		4.781	94.5%	$20 \pm 3b$		
						4.598	5.5			
						4.340	6×10^{-3}			
						4.194	9×10^{-4}			
						4.160	2.7×10^{-4}			
$_{88}Ra^{227}$			41.2m	β^-	1.31	1.31				
$_{88}Ra^{228}$			$5.77 \pm 0.02y$	β^-	0.055	0.024	30%	$36 \pm 5b$		
						0.048	70			
$_{88}Ra^{230}$			1h	β^-	0.9 est.	1.2				
Ac										
$_{89}Ac^{221}$		221.0157	Short	α	7.75	7.63				
$_{89}Ac^{222}$		222.0178	5s	α	7.13	7.00	93†			
						6.96	6			
$_{89}Ac^{223}$		223.0191	2.2m	α	6.781	6.659	37.6%			
						6.648	42.1			
						6.56	13.3			
						6.52	3.8			
						6.47	3.2			
				EC	0.56	EC	1%			
$_{89}Ac^{224}$		224.0217	2.9h	EC	1.38	EC	90%			
				α	6.32	α	≈10%			
						6.210	20.4†			
						6.203	11.9			
						6.155	1.03			
						6.138	25.6			
						6.056	21.9			
						6.014	1.4			
						6.000	6.7			

Isotope	% nat. abundance	Atomic mass	Lifetime	Modes of decay	Decay energy (MeV)	Particle energies (MeV)	Particle intensities	Thermal neutron capture cross-section	I	μ
						5.968	0.2			
						5.958	~0.04			
						5.942	4.4			
						5.916	0.94			
						5.909	0.15			
						5.902	0.15			
						5.877	1.7			
						5.867	0.1			
						5.860	0.75			
						5.854	0.25			
						5.851	~0.07			
						5.841	0.55			
						5.837	0.26			
						5.803	~0.02			
						5.776	0.06			
						5.768	0.24			
						5.739	~0.05			
						5.718	0.12			
						5.709	0.12			
						5.641	0.06			
$_{89}Ac^{225}$		225.0231	10.0d	α	5.931	5.829	52%			
						5.793	29			
						5.732	9.5			
						5.724	2.6			
						5.683	1.0			
						5.638	4.0			
						5.610	0.8			
						5.58	0.8			
						5.55	0.07			
						5.49	≈0.02			
						5.45	0.1			
						5.40	≈0.01			
						5.37	≈0.01			
						5.33	0.07			
						5.30	0.1			
						5.23	≈0.02			
$_{89}Ac^{226}$			29h	β^-	1.12	β^-	77%			
						1.1	41†			
						0.89	59			
				EC	0.77	EC	23%			
				α	5.54	5.44	Weak			
$_{89}Ac^{227}$		227.0278	21.6y	β^-	0.043	β^- 0.044	98.6%	$810 \pm 20b$	3/2	+1.1
				α	5.040	α	1.4%			
						4.950	47†			
						4.938	38			
						4.897	0.11			
						4.870	6.5			
						4.853	4.0			
						4.819	0.07			
						4.793	0.9			
						4.782	0.08			
						4.766	1.6			
						4.735	0.09			
						4.712	0.31			
						4.591	0.02			
						4.586	0.01			
						4.578	≈0.003			
						4.509	≈0.003			
						4.456	≈0.005			
						4.442	0.05			
						4.420	0.006			
						4.360	≈0.003			
$_{89}Ac^{228}$			6.13h	β^-	2.14	0.45	13%			
						0.62	6			
						1.18	53			
						1.70	6.7			

Isotope	% nat. abundance	Atomic mass	Lifetime	Modes of decay	Decay energy (MeV)	Particle energies (MeV)	Particle intensities	Thermal neutron capture cross-section	I	μ
						1.76	20			
						2.10	13			
$_{89}Ac^{229}$			66m	β^-	1.1	≈1.0				
$_{89}Ac^{230}$			<1m	β^-	≈2.9	≈2.2				
$_{89}Ac^{231}$			15m	β^-	2.1	2.1				
Th								7.4 ± 0.1b		
$_{90}Th^{223}$		223.0209	0.9s	α	7.7	7.55				
$_{90}Th^{224}$		224.0214	1.05s	α	7.30	7.17	79%			
						6.99	19			
						6.77	1.2			
						6.70	0.4			
$_{90}Th^{225}$		225.0237	8.0m	α	6.92	α	≥95%			
						6.797	9†			
						6.743	7			
						6.699	2			
						6.649	3			
						6.626	3			
						6.500	14			
						6.477	43			
						6.440	15			
						6.344	2			
						6.311	2			
				EC	0.68	EC	≤5%			
$_{90}Th^{226}$		226.0249	30.9m	α	6.45	6.33	79%			
						6.22	19			
						6.10	1.7			
						6.03	0.6			
$_{90}Th^{227}$		227.0278	18.5d	α	6.145	6.037	24.5%	$\sigma_f = 1500 \pm 1000b$		
						6.007	2.9			
						5.988	0.002			
						5.976	23.4			
						5.958	3.0			
						5.914	0.8			
						5.908	0.17			
						5.865	2.4			
						5.806	1.3			
						5.794	0.31			
						5.761	0.23			
						5.755	20.3			
						5.726	0.034			
						5.712	4.89			
						5.707	8.20			
						5.669	3.63			
						5.691	1.50			
						5.673	0.057			
						5.666	2.06			
						5.639	0.018			
						5.620	0.0070			
						5.612	0.22			
						5.599	0.17			
						5.584	0.18			
						5.531	0.021			
						5.508	0.0166			
						5.479	0.0012			
						5.457	0.0027			
						5.407	0.0004			
						5.363	0.00066			
						5.334	0.0002			
						5.320	0.0002			
						5.263	0.0026			
						5.247	0.0032			
						5.227	0.0098			
						5.208	0.0070			

Isotope	% nat. abundance	Atomic mass	Lifetime	Modes of decay	Decay energy (MeV)	Particle energies (MeV)	Particle intensities	Thermal neutron capture cross-section	I	μ
						5.192	0.0038			
						5.179	0.0012			
						5.169	0.0017			
						5.145	0.004			
						5.127	0.00062			
						5.109	0.00028			
						5.082	0.00015			
						5.054	0.00023			
						5.032	0.00031			
$_{90}Th^{228}$		228.0287	1.913y	α	5.521	5.424	71%	$120 \pm 15b$ $\sigma_f = <0.3b$		
						5.342	28			
						5.211	0.4			
						5.176	0.2			
						5.140	0.03			
$_{90}Th^{229}$		229.0316	7340y	α	5.167	5.054	6.7	$\sigma_f = 32 \pm 3b$	5/2	+0.38
						5.034	≈0.2			
						5.009	≈0.1			
						4.977	3.4			
						4.967	6.0			
						4.930	0.25			
						4.899	10.7			
						4.842	58.2			
						4.811	11.4			
						4.793	1.0			
						4.756	1.5			
						4.683	0.4			
$_{90}Th^{230}$		230.0331	$8.0 \times 10^4 y$	α	4.767	4.684	76%	$33 \pm 10b$		
						4.617	24			
						4.474	0.12			
						4.431	0.03			
$_{90}Th^{231}$			25.5h	β⁻	0.381	0.299	39%			
						0.218	33			
						0.134	20			
						0.090	8			
$_{90}Th^{232}$		232.0382	$1.41 \times 10^{10}y$	α	4.08	3.994	77%	$7.4 \pm 0.1b$		
						3.935	23			
						3.809	0.2			
$_{90}Th^{233}$			22.2m	β⁻	1.246	1.245	<87%	$1500 \pm 100b$ $\sigma_f = 15 \pm 2b$		
						1.158				
						1.073				
						0.88				
						0.79				
						0.58				
$_{90}Th^{234}$		234.0436	24.1d	β⁻	0.263	0.191	65%	$1.8 \pm 0.5b$		
						0.100	35			
Pa										
$_{91}Pa^{225}$			2.0s	α	≈7.5est.	7.25				
$_{91}Pa^{226}$		226.0278	1.8m	α	6.99	α	74%			
						6.86	52†			
						6.82	46			
						6.73	1			
				EC	2.78	EC	26%			
$_{91}Pa^{227}$		227.0289	38.3m	α	6.581	α	≈85%			
						6.465	50.7			
						6.423	11.8			
						6.415	15.2			
						6.401	9.6			
						6.376	2.6			
						6.356	8.0			
						6.336	0.7			

Isotope	% nat. abundance	Atomic mass	Lifetime	Modes of decay	Decay energy (MeV)	Particle energies (MeV)	Particle intensities	Thermal neutron capture cross-section	I	μ
						6.326	0.4			
						6.299	0.8			
				EC	1.00	EC	15%			
$_{91}$Pa^{228}		228.0310	26h	EC	2.10	EC	≈ 98%			
				α	6.227	α	≈ 2			
						6.118	10.5†			
						6.105	12.0			
						6.091	2.3			
						6.078	20.7			
						6.066	1.0			
						6.041	2.3			
						6.028	9.0			
						6.011	0.8			
						5.998	0.3			
						5.989	1.1			
						5.982	2.8			
						5.975	2.7			
						5.947	0.6			
						5.941	0.5			
						5.922	0.8			
						5.907	1.1			
						5.874	1.4			
						5.858	0.3			
						5.843	0.4			
						5.805	7.3			
						5.799	11.3			
						5.779	1.4			
						5.765	2.0			
						5.760	1.4			
						5.756	2.5			
						5.711	1.0			
$_{91}$Pa^{229}			1.5d	EC	0.22	EC	99 + %			
				α	5.837	α	0.25			
						5.74	0.5†			
						5.70	1.5			
						5.671	18.5			
						5.631	9.7			
						5.616	13.3			
						5.592	4.6			
						5.581	36.5			
						5.566	3.9			
						5.537	8.8			
						5.518	0.6			
						5.502	0.7			
						5.480	1.7			
						5.423	0.07			
						5.414	0.15			
						5.321	0.05			
$_{91}$Pa^{230}								$\sigma_f = 1500 \pm 250$b		
			17.7d	EC	1.30	EC	89.6%			
				β^-	0.56	β^- 0.41	10.4%			
				α	5.438	α	0.0032%			
						5.343	23†			
						5.338	15			
						5.325	18			
						5.310	13			
						5.299	17			
						5.286	3			
						5.274	3			
						5.267	3.5			
						5.215	0.5			
						5.181	0.5			
						5.151	0.4			
						5.117	0.6			
						5.082	0.7			
						5.058	0.4			
						4.971	0.7			
						4.932	0.4			
						4.796	≈ 0.03			
						4.764	0.2			

Isotope	% nat. abundance	Atomic mass	Lifetime	Modes of decay	Decay energy (MeV)	Particle energies (MeV)	Particle intensities	Thermal neutron capture cross-section	I	μ
$_{91}Pa^{231}$		231.0359	3.25×10^4y	α	5.148	5.051 5.024 5.022 5.017 5.005 4.977 4.967 4.943 4.926 4.892 4.845 4.787 4.729 4.705 4.673 4.635 4.624 4.591 4.558 4.500 4.14	11.0% $? \approx 2.5$ 22 ? 25.4 1.4 0.4 22.8 3.0 0.002 1.4 0.04 8.4 ≈ 1.0 1.5 0.1 0.1 0.015 0.008 0.003	200 ± 10b $\sigma_f = 10 \pm 5$mb	3/2	± 1.98
$_{91}Pa^{232}$			1.31d	β^-	1.34	0.32 1.19 1.30	98% 0.8 0.7	760 ± 100b $\sigma_f = 700 \pm 100$b		
$_{91}Pa^{233}$			27.0d	β^-	0.571	0.58 0.254 0.154	12% 56 32	22 ± 4b (Pa^{234m}) 21 ± 3b (Pa^{234})	3/2	$+3.4$
$_{91}Pa^{234m}$			1.17m	β^- IT		2.29 1.53 1.25	$98+$% 0.13%			
$_{91}Pa^{234}$		234.043	6.75h	β^-	2.23	0.23 0.51 0.73 1.02 1.35	14% 66 11 7 ≤ 2			
$_{91}Pa^{235}$			23.7m	β^-	1.4	1.4				
$_{91}Pa^{236}$			12m	β^-	≈ 2.9	3.3				
$_{91}Pa^{237}$			39m	β^-	2.30	β^- 2.30 1.3 0.8	60% 30 10			
U								σ(abs) = 7.595 ± 0.07b $\sigma_f = 4.172$ ± 0.015b		
$_{92}U^{227}$		227.0309	1.3m	α	7.1	6.8				
$_{92}U^{228}$		228.0313	9.3m	α EC	6.80 0.36	α 6.68 6.59 6.44 6.40 EC	≥ 95% 70† 29 0.7 0.6 ≤ 5%			
$_{92}U^{229}$		229.0332	58m	EC α	1.32 6.473	EC α 6.362 6.334 6.299 6.262 6.225 6.187	≈ 80% ≈ 20% 64† 20 11 1 3 1			

Isotope	% nat. abundance	Atomic mass	Lifetime	Modes of decay	Decay energy (MeV)	Particle energies (MeV)	Particle intensities	Thermal neutron capture cross-section	I	μ
$_{92}U^{230}$		230.0339	20.8d	α	5.991	5.887 5.816 5.666 5.661 5.585 5.542 5.532	67.5% 31.9 0.038 0.26 0.012 0.0005 0.0001	$\sigma_f = 25 \pm 10b$		
$_{92}U^{231}$			4.3	EC α	0.36 5.55	EC α 5.46	99+% 0.0055%	$\sigma_f = 400 \pm 300b$		
$_{92}U^{232}$		232.0372	73.6y	α SF	5.414	5.320 5.263 5.137 4.997 4.946 4.929 4.51	68.6% 31.2 0.28 2.9×10^{-3} 1.7×10^{-4} 2.1×10^{-4} 2.4×10^{-5}	$75 \pm 10b$ $\sigma_f = 75 \pm 10b$ $\sigma(abs.) = 150 \pm 10b$		
$_{92}U^{233}$		233.0395	$1.62 \times 10^5 y$	α	4.909	4.824 4.804 4.796 4.783 4.758 4.754 4.751 4.729 4.701 4.687 4.681 4.664 4.656 4.641 4.634 4.626 4.615 4.611 4.590 4.572 4.565 4.538 4.513 4.507 4.503 4.483 4.465 4.457 4.411 4.404 4.309	84.4% 0.051 0.28 13.23 0.016 0.163 0.01 1.61 0.06 0.0028 0.01 0.042 0.005 0.003 0.01 ≤ 0.004 0.004 0.006 0.007 0.0023 0.0028 0.004 0.018 0.012 0.001 0.0014 0.003 0.0028 0.0004 0.0003 0.0009		5/2	+0.54
$_{92}U^{234}$		234.0409	$2.47 \times 10^5 y$	α	4.856	4.773 4.722 4.599 4.265 4.139	72% 28 0.35 4.5×10^{-5} 3×10^{-5}	$\sigma_{(abs)} = 95 \pm 7b$ $\sigma_f \leq 0.65b$		
$_{92}U^{235}$		235.0439	$7.1 \times 10^8 y$	α SF	4.681	4.597 4.556 4.502 4.445? 4.415 4.396 4.366 4.344? 4.323 4.266 4.216 4.157	4.6% 3.7 1.2 0.6 4 57 18 1.5 3 0.6 5.7 ≈ 0.5	$100.5 \pm 1.4b$ $\sigma_f = 579.5 \pm 2.0b$ $\sigma_{(abs)} = 679.9 \pm 2.3b$	7/2	−0.35
$_{92}U^{235m}$			26.1m	IT	<0.001					

Isotope	% nat. abundance	Atomic mass	Lifetime	Modes of decay	Decay energy (MeV)	Particle energies (MeV)	Particle intensities	Thermal neutron capture cross-section	I	μ
$_{92}U^{236}$		236.0457	$2.39 \times 10^{-7}y$	α SF	4.573	4.493 4.443 4.330	74% 26 0.3	$6.0 \pm 0.5b$ $\sigma_f = 0$		
$_{92}U^{237}$			6.75d	β^-	0.517	0.248 ≈ 0.09	>80% ≈ 12	$480 \pm 160b$ $\sigma_f = 2b$		
$_{92}U^{238}$		238.0508	4.51×10^9y	α SF	4.268	4.195 4.147 4.135	77% 23 0.23	$2.720 \pm 0.025b$		
$_{92}U^{239}$			23.5m	β^-	1.28	1.29 1.21	20% 80	$22 \pm 5b$ $\sigma_f = 14 \pm 3b$		
$_{92}U^{240}$			14.1h	β^-	0.5	0.36 0.32	75% 25			
Np										
$_{93}Np^{229}$			4.0m	α		6.89				
$_{93}Np^{230}$			4.6m	α		6.66				
$_{93}Np^{231}$		231.0383	~50m	α	6.40	6.29				
$_{93}Np^{232}$			$\approx 13m$	EC	≈ 2.6					
$_{93}Np^{233}$		233.0406	35m	EC α	≈ 1.0 5.7	EC α 5.54	99+% 0.001%			
$_{93}Np^{234}$			4.40d	EC β^+	1.80	EC 0.8	99+% $\approx 0.05\%$	$\sigma_f = 900 \pm 300b$		
$_{93}Np^{235}$			410d	EC α	1.23 5.187	EC α 5.10 5.02 4.93 4.87	99+% 0.0016 3.8† 84 12 1			
$_{93}Np^{236m}$			> 5000y	EC, β^-				$\sigma_f = 2800 \pm 800b$		
$_{93}Np^{236}$		236.0466	22h	β^- EC	0.52 0.91	0.51 0.36 EC	$\approx 40\%$ ≈ 10 $\approx 50\%$			
$_{93}Np^{237}$		237.0480	2.14×10^6y	α	4.956	4.872 4.870 4.862 4.816 4.802 4.787 4.770 4.765 4.740 4.711 4.707 4.698? 4.693 4.663 4.638 4.638 4.598 4.594 4.580 4.573 4.514 4.385	0.4% 0.9 0.2 1.5 1.6 51 19 17 0.02 0.13 0.29 0.07 0.18 1.6 0.17 4.6 0.06 0.08 0.02 0.05 0.01 0.02	$170 \pm 5b$ $\sigma_f = 19 \pm 3mb$	5/2	+5
$_{93}Np^{238}$			2.1d	β^-	1.29	1.24 1.13?	38% 3	$\sigma(\eta, \gamma)$ 0 $\sigma_f = 2000 \pm 300b$	2	

Isotope	% nat. abundance	Atomic mass	Lifetime	Modes of decay	Decay energy (MeV)	Particle energies (MeV)	Particle intensities	Thermal neutron capture cross-section	I	μ
						0.28	20			
						0.25	31			
						0.20?	8			
$_{93}Np^{239}$			2.35d	β^-	0.723	0.713	7%	$35 \pm 10b$	5/2	
						0.654	4	(Np^{240m})		
						0.437	48	$25 \pm 15b$		
						0.393	13	(Np^{240})		
						0.332	28	$\sigma_f = <1b$		
$_{93}Np^{240m}$			7.3m	β^-	2.18	0.7	7%			
						1.30	10			
						1.60	31			
						2.18	52			
$_{93}Np^{240}$			63m	β^-	2.0	0.89				
$_{93}Np^{241}$			16m	β^-	1.4	1.4				
Pu										
$_{94}Pu^{232}$		232.0411	36m	EC α	1.0 6.70	EC α 6.70	$\leq 98\%$ $\geq 2\%$			
$_{94}Pu^{233}$			20m	EC α	≈ 2.0 6.42	EC 6.31	$99+\%$ 0.1%			
$_{94}Pu^{234}$		234.0433	9.0h	EC α	0.4 6.30	EC α 6.203 6.152 6.032	94% 6% 68† 32 0.4			
$_{94}Pu^{235}$			26m	EC α	1.1 5.96	EC α 5.86	$99+\%$ 0.003%			
$_{94}Pu^{236}$		236.0461	2.85y	α SF	5.868	5.769 5.722 5.616 5.21 5.08	69% 31 0.18 2.7×10^{-4} 6×10^{-4}	$\sigma_f = 170 \pm 35b$		
$_{94}Pu^{237m}$			0.18s	IT SF	0.145					
$_{94}Pu^{237}$		237.0483	45.6d	EC α SF	0.22 5.74	EC α 5.66 5.37	$99+\%$ $3.3 \times 10^{-3}\%$ 21† 79	$\sigma_f = 2500 \pm 500b$		
$_{94}Pu^{238}$		238.0495	86	α SF	5.592	5.499 5.456 5.358 5.214 4.70	72% 28 0.09 0.005 1.1×10^{-4}	$560 \pm 25b$ $\sigma_f = 16.5 \pm 1.0b$		
$_{94}Pu^{239}$		239.0522	24,400y	α SF	5.243	5.157 5.145 5.112? 5.107 5.078 5.066 5.056 5.031 5.010 5.001 4.988 4.963 4.957 4.937 4.914	73.3% 15.1 ≤ 0.03 11.5 0.032 0.0009 0.021 0.005 0.008 0.0006 0.005 0.003 0.0005 0.003 0.0008	$265.7 \pm 3.7b$ $\sigma_f = 742.4 \pm 3.5b$ $\sigma_{(abs)} = 1008.1 \pm 4.9b$	1/2	+0.200

Isotope	% nat. abundance	Atomic mass	Lifetime	Modes of decay	Decay energy (MeV)	Particle energies (MeV)	Particle intensities	Thermal neutron capture cross-section	I	μ
						4.873	0.0007			
						4.863	0.0008			
						4.830	0.0015			
						4.801	0.0006			
						4.775	0.0006			
						4.754?	0.0004			
						4.743⎫ 4.739⎭	0.0026			
						4.695	0.0004			
						4.636	0.0002			
$_{94}Pu^{240}$		240.0540	6580y	α SF	5.255	5.168 5.123 5.020 4.856 4.49	76% 24 0.09 3×10^{-3} 2.1×10^{-5}	$290 \pm 15b$		
$_{94}Pu^{241}$			13.2y	β^- α	0.0208 5.144	0.0208 α 5.051 5.041 4.998? 4.995 4.971 4.968? 4.896 4.853 4.798 4.73	99 + % 0.0023% 0.35† 1.0 0.36 1.1 83 12 1.2 0.03	$360 \pm 15b$ $\sigma_f = 1011 \pm 9b$ $\sigma_{(abs)} = 1371 \pm 18b$	5/2	-0.73
$_{94}Pu^{242}$		242.0587	$3.79 \times 10^5 y$	α	4.98	4.903 4.863	76% 24	$20 \pm 3b$		
$_{94}Pu^{243}$			4.98h	β^-	0.59	0.579 0.490	62% 38	$75 \pm 50b$ $\sigma_f = 196 \pm 16b.$		
$_{94}Pu^{244}$			$8 \times 10^7 y$	α SF	4.66	α		$1.8 \pm 0.3b$		
$_{94}Pu^{245}$			10h	β^-	≈ 1.2			$260 \pm 150b$		
$_{94}Pu^{246}$			10.9d	β^-	0.37	0.15 0.33	$\approx 73\%$ ≈ 27			
Am										
$_{95}Am^{237}$			$\approx 1.3h$	EC α	≈ 1.5 ≈ 6.2	EC 6.02	99 + % 0.005%			
$_{95}Am^{238}$			1.9h	EC	≈ 2.3					
$_{95}Am^{239}$			12.1h	EC α	0.81 5.93	EC 5.78	99 + % 0.005%			
$_{95}Am^{240}$			51h	EC	≈ 1.3					
$_{95}Am^{241}$		241.0567	458y	α	5.640	5.545 5.313 5.486 5.469? 5.443 5.417 5.389 5.322 5.279 5.244 5.223 5.194 5.182 5.178 5.156 5.114	0.25% 0.12 86 <0.04 12.7 ≈ 0.01 1.3 0.015 0.0005 0.0024 0.0013 0.0006 0.0009 0.0003 0.0007 0.0004	$70 \pm 5b$ (Am^{242m}) $670 \pm 60b$ (Am^{242}) $\sigma_f = 3.15 \pm 0.1b$	5/2	$+1.59$

Isotope	% nat. abundance	Atomic mass	Lifetime	Modes of decay	Decay energy (MeV)	Particle energies (MeV)	Particle intensities	Thermal neutron capture cross-section	I	μ
						5.096	0.0004			
						5.089	0.0004			
						5.068	0.00014			
						5.004	0.001			
						4.834	0.0007			
						4.800	0.00009			
$_{95}Am^{242m}$			152y	IT	0.048	IT	99.52%	$2400 \pm 500b$		
				α	5.588	α	0.48	$\sigma_f = 7200 \pm 300b$		
						5.411	1.2†			
						5.367	1.5			
						5.315	0.8			
						5.207	89			
						5.142	6.1			
						5.088	0.3			
						5.067	0.2			
$_{95}Am^{242}$			16.0h	β^-	0.66	0.667	$\approx 33\%$	$<200b$	1	± 0.382
						0.625	≈ 49	$\sigma_f = 2100 \pm 200b$		
				EC	0.73	EC	≈ 18			
$_{95}Am^{243}$		243.0614						$180 \pm 20b$	5/2	+1.4
			7.37×10^3y	α	5.439	5.350	0.16%			
						5.321	0.12			
						5.276	87.9			
						5.234	10.6			
						5.181	1.1			
						5.113	5.4×10^{-3}			
						5.088	4×10^{-3}			
						5.035 }	2.2×10^{-3}			
						5.029				
						5.008	1.6×10^{-3}			
						4.946	3.4×10^{-4}			
						4.930	1.8×10^{-4}			
						4.919	8×10^{-5}			
						4.695	6×10^{-4}			
$_{95}Am^{244m}$			26m	β^-		1.50	$99+\%$			
				EC		EC	0.039%			
$_{95}Am^{244}$			10.1h	β^-	1.429	0.387	100%	$2300 \pm 300b$		
$_{95}Am^{245}$			2.1h	β^-	0.905	0.905	78%			
						(0.709)	≈ 5			
						(0.653)	≈ 17			
$_{95}Am^{246}$			25.0m	β^-	2.29	1.31	79%			
						1.60	14			
						2.10	7			
$_{95}Am^{247}$			20m	β^-		227				
						285				
Cm										
$_{96}Cm^{238}$		238.0530	2.5h	EC	≈ 1.0	EC	$<90\%$			
				α	6.63	6.51	>10			
$_{96}Cm^{239}$			2.9h	EC	≈ 1.7	EC	100%			
$_{96}Cm^{240}$		240.0555	26.8d	α	6.441	6.292	71.1%			
						6.249	28.9			
						6.150	0.052			
				SF		5.992	0.014			
$_{96}Cm^{241}$			35d	EC	0.77	EC	$\approx 99\%$			
				α	6.184	α	1%			
						6.083	0.64%			
						6.039	0.10			
						5.941	71.5			
						5.929	16.3			
						5.887	11.5			
						5.831	2			

Isotope	% nat. abundance	Atomic mass	Lifetime	Modes of decay	Decay energy (MeV)	Particle energies (MeV)	Particle intensities	Thermal neutron capture cross-section	I	μ
						5.824	1.4			
						5.810	1.2			
						5.789	1.8			
						5.784	0.6			
						5.781	3.0			
						5.732	0.9			
$_{96}Cm^{242}$		242.0588	163d	α		6.115	74.2%	$20 \pm 10b$		
						6.071	25.8	$\sigma_f = <5b$	0	
						5.974	0.036			
						5.819	4.6×10^{-3}			
						5.611	2×10^{-5}			
						5.516	2.5×10^{-4}			
						5.191	2.5×10^{-5}			
				SF		5.148	$\leq 5 \times 10^{-6}$			
$_{96}Cm^{243}$		243.0614	32y	α	6.168	α	99.7%	$250 \pm 50b$		
						6.067	1.5	$\sigma_f = 700 \pm 50b$		
						6.057	4.7			
						6.010	1.1			
						5.993	5.6			
						5.907	0.1			
						5.876	0.7			
						5.786	73.5			
						5.742	10.6			
						5.686	1.6			
						5.682	0.2			
						5.646	0.03			
						5.639	0.14			
						5.622	0.06			
						5.612	≈ 0.04			
						5.609 ⎫ 5.607? ⎬	0.01			
						5.593	0.01			
						5.587	≈ 0.02			
						5.582	≈ 0.009			
						5.575	0.007			
						5.568	0.007			
						5.537	0.002			
						5.532	0.006			
						5.523	0.002			
						5.332	0.003			
						5.323	0.003			
						5.316	0.001			
						5.267	0.0015			
				EC	0.006	EC	0.3%			
$_{96}Cm^{244}$		244.0629	17.6y	α	5.902	5.806	76.4%	$13 \pm 5b$		
						5.765	23.6	$\sigma_f = 1.0 \pm 0.5b$		
						6.664	0.02			
						5.513	3.4×10^{-3}			
						5.313	$\sim 4 \times 10^{-5}$			
						5.215	$\sim 1 \times 10^{-4}$			
				SF		4.960	3×10^{-4}			
						4.920	1.3×10^{-4}			
$_{96}Cm^{245}$		245.0653	$9.3 \times 10^3 y$	α	5.624	5.533	0.5%	$250 \pm 50b$		
						5.492		$\sigma_f = 2000 \pm 80b$		
						5.468	2.7			
						5.464	2.0			
						5.359	87.6			
						5.305	4.5			
						5.255	0.3			
						5.245	0.7			
						5.240	0.5			
						5.231	0.6			
						5.199	0.35			
						5.175	0.25			
						5.158	0.3			
$_{96}Cm^{246}$		246.0674	$5.5 \times 10^3 y$	α SF	5.476	5.385	79%	$8.4 \pm 2.0b$		
						5.342	21			

Isotope	% nat. abundance	Atomic mass	Lifetime	Modes of decay	Decay energy (MeV)	Particle energies (MeV)	Particle intensities	Thermal neutron capture cross-section	I	μ
$_{96}Cm^{247}$			1.6×10^7y	α	≈ 5.3			180b $\sigma_f = 108 \pm 5b$		
$_{96}Cm^{248}$			4.7×10^5y	α SF	5.161	α 5.080 5.036 SF	89% 82† 18 11%	6 ± 2b		
$_{96}Cm^{249}$		249.0758	64m	β^-	0.9	0.9		1.6 ± 1.0b		
$_{96}Cm^{250}$			1.7×10^4y	SF		SF	100%			
Bk										
$_{97}Bk^{243}$			4.6h	EC α	1.51 6.871	EC α 6.758 6.718 6.666 6.605 6.574 6.542 6.502 6.446 6.394 6.210 6.182	99 + % 0.15% 15† 12 1.2 0.7 26 19 7 0.7 0 3 14 3.9			
$_{97}Bk^{244}$			4.4h	EC α	≈ 2.2 6.79	EC α 6.666 6.624	99 + % 0.006% ≈ 50† ≈ 50			
$_{97}Bk^{245}$			4.98d	EC α	0.82 6.464	EC α 6.358 6.317 6.265 6.200 6.153 6.124 6.087 6.038 5.985 5.889 5.858	99 + % 0.11% 16† 15 1.4 1.4 19 15 5.6 0.6 0.2 22 4.0			
$_{97}Bk^{246}$			1.8d	EC	≈ 1.5	EC	100%			
$_{97}Bk^{247}$		247.0702	1.4×10^3y	α	5.86	5.68 5.52 5.31	37% 58 5			
$_{97}Bk^{248}$			16h	β^- EC	0.65 0.5	0.65 EC	70% 30%			
$_{97}Bk^{249}$			314d	β^- α SF	0.125 5.520	β^- 0.125 α 5.431 5.412 5.384 5.345 5.109 5.046	99 + % 0.0022% 6.7† 69 18 2.6 2.7 0.12	1000 ± 500b		
$_{97}Bk^{250}$			3.22h	β^-	1.76	0.73 1.72 1.76	89% 6 5	$\sigma_f = 960 \pm 150b$		
Cf										
$_{98}Cf^{242}$			3.7m	α	7.49	7.37				

Isotope	% nat. abundance	Atomic mass	Lifetime	Modes of decay	Decay energy (MeV)	Particle energies (MeV)	Particle intensities	Thermal neutron capture cross-section	I	μ
$_{98}Cf^{244}$		244.0659	25m	α	7.59	7.18				
$_{98}Cf^{245}$			44m	EC α	1.52 7.23	EC 7.12	70% 30%			
$_{98}Cf^{246}$		246.0688	36h	α SF	6.87	6.760 6.718 6.63 6.47	78% 22 0.18			
$_{98}Cf^{247}$			2.5h	EC	≈0.8					
$_{98}Cf^{248}$		248.0724	360d	α SF	6.37	6.27 5.84	82% 18			
$_{98}Cf^{249}$		249.0748	360y	α SF	6.295	6.201 6.146 6.079 5.997? 5.948 5.905 5.848 5.812 5.784? 5.755 5.693	1.9% 1.1 0.4 0.08 3.3 3.0 1.2 84 0.5 4.4 0.4	300 ± 200b $\sigma_f = 1735 \pm 70b$		
$_{98}Cf^{250}$		250.0766	13y	α SF	6.128	6.031 5.987 5.889	83% 17 0.32	1500 ± 500b $\sigma_f = <350b$		
$_{98}Cf^{251}$			≈800y	α	5.94	6.072 6.012 5.937 5.849 5.813 5.797 5.762 5.726 5.672 5.645 5.630 5.600 5.564 5.501	2.7% 12.3 0.5 27.8 4.1 2.8 3.9 1.1 34.7 2.8 4.8 0.5 1.8 0.3	2100 ± 1000b $\sigma_f = 4000$ ± 1000b		
$_{98}Cf^{252}$			2.65y	α SF	6.217	α 6.119 6.076 5.975 SF	97% 84.3† 15.5 0.28 3%	10 ± 5b		
$_{98}Cf^{253}$		253.0850	17.6d	β⁻ α	0.27 6.2	0.27 } 0.17?} α 5.979 5.921	99+% 0.31% 94.7† 5.3	≈165b		
$_{98}Cf^{254}$			60.5d	α SF	5.929	α 5.834 5.792 SF	≈0.2% 83† 17 99+%	<2b		
Es										
$_{99}Es^{246}$			7.3m	EC α	≈3.6 7.48	EC α 7.33	90% 10%			
$_{99}Es^{247}$			5.0m	EC α	≈2.2 ≈7.3	EC 7.33	≈93% ≈7%			

Isotope	% nat. abundance	Atomic mass	Lifetime	Modes of decay	Decay energy (MeV)	Particle energies (MeV)	Particle intensities	Thermal neutron capture cross-section	I	μ
$_{99}Es^{248}$			25m	EC α	≈2.8 6.99	EC 6.88	99+% ≈0.3%			
$_{99}Es^{249}$			2h	EC α	1.40 6.88	EC 6.77	99+% 0.13%			
$_{99}Es^{250}$			8h	EC	2.1	EC	100%			
$_{99}Es^{251}$			1.5d	EC α	≈0.4 6.59	EC α 6.48	99+% 0.53%			
$_{99}Es^{252}$		252.0829	≈140d	α	6.75	6.639 6.58 6.493 6.26 6.23 6.09 6.07? 6.02 5.99 5.94?	82† 13 2.3 0.8 0.33 0.6 0.11 1.1 0.07 0.09			
$_{99}Es^{253}$		253.0847	20.47d	α SF	6.747	6.640 6.631 6.601 6.597 6.559 6.547 6.504 6.486 6.436 6.256 6.216 6.165 6.03 5.93–6.04 5.91 5.73	90% 0.8 0.7 6.6 0.75 0.85 0.26 0.08 0.1 0.04 0.04 0.015 2×10^{-4} 1×10^{-4} 3×10^{-5} 8×10^{-5}	150 ± 5db		
$_{99}Es^{254m}$			39.3h	β^- EC SF		β^- 1.127 0.48 EC	99+% 25† 75 0.08%	$\sigma_f = 1840 \pm 80b$		
$_{99}Es^{254}$		254.0881	276d	α	6.623	6.486 6.437 6.424 6.392 6.367 6.355 6.331 6.284 6.276 6.20 6.19 6.113 6.056	0.27% 93 1.7 0.13 2.9 0.74 0.05 0.16 0.22 0.05 0.05 0.33 0.16	<40b $\sigma_f = 3060 \pm 180b$		
$_{99}Es^{255}$			38.3d	β^- α	≈0.5 ≈6.8	 6.307	91.5% 8.5%	≈40b		
$_{99}Es^{256}$			Short	β^-						
Fm										
$_{100}Fm^{248}$		248.0772	0.6m	α						
$_{100}Fm^{249}$			≈2.5m	α	8.0	7.9				

Isotope	% nat. abundance	Atomic mass	Lifetime	Modes of decay	Decay energy (MeV)	Particle energies (MeV)	Particle intensities	Thermal neutron capture cross-section	I	μ
$_{100}Fm^{250}$		250.0795	30m	α	7.56	7.44	100%			
$_{100}Fm^{251}$			7h	EC α	≈1.6 ≈7.4	EC 6.90	≈99% ≈1%			
$_{100}Fm^{252}$		252.0827	23h	α	7.17	7.05	100%			
$_{100}Fm^{253}$			3d	EC α	0.4 7.3	EC α 6.96 6.91	89% 11% 4† 1			
$_{100}Fm^{254}$		254.0870	3.24h	α SF	7.310	7.200 7.158 7.061 SF	85% 14 0.9 0.055%			
$_{100}Fm^{255}$			20.1h	α	7.244	7.130 7.106 7.084 7.027 6.985 6.968 6.956 6.923 6.896 6.895 6 880 6.842 6.811 6.710 6.59 6.54 6.49 6.41	0.09% 0.10 0.43 93.4 0.11 5.3 0.024 0.017 0.01 0.60 0.013 0.002 0.12 0.03 0.020 0.015 0.0035 0.0003	26 ± 3b		
$_{100}Fm^{256}$			2.7h	SF α	6 96	SF 6.86	97% 3%			
$_{100}Fm^{257}$			80d	α	6.871	6.76? 6.703 6.526 6.450 6.36?	0.4% 3.2 94 2.2 0.5			
Md										
$_{101}Md^{255}$		255.0906	0.6h	EC α	≈0.6 7.46	EC 7.35	90% 10%			
$_{101}Md^{256}$			1.5h	EC α	1.4 7.28	EC 7.18	97% 3%			
$_{101}Md^{257}$			3h	EC α	7.18?	EC α 7.25? 7.08	≈92% ≈8%			
No										
$_{102}No^{251}$			1s	α	8.8	8.68? 8.58	≈20% ≈80			
$_{102}No^{252}$			2.1s	α SF	8.55	8.41 SF	≈70% 30%			
$_{102}No^{253}$			95s	α	8.2	8.01				
$_{102}No^{254}$			55s	α	8.23	8.10				
$_{102}No^{255}$			3m	α	8.24	8.11				

Isotope	% nat. abundance	Atomic mass	Lifetime	Modes of decay	Decay energy (MeV)	Particle energies (MeV)	Particle intensities	Thermal neutron capture cross-section	I	μ
$_{102}No^{256}$			2.7s	α SF	8.56	8.43 SF	99 + % 0.5%			
$_{102}No^{257}$			20s	α	8.4	8.27 8.23	$\approx 50\%$ ≈ 50			
Lr										
$_{103}Lr^{256}$			8s	α		8.6				
$_{103}Lr^{257}$										
Ku										
$_{104}Ku^{260}$			0.3s	SF						
$_{105}?^{260}$				α		9.4				
$_{105}?^{261}$			1.8s	α		8.93				
$_{105}?^{262}$			40s	α		8.45				

Gamma Energies and Intensities of Radionuclides

Compiled by
Russell L. Heath

National Reactor Testing Station
Idaho Nuclear Corporation
Idaho Falls, Idaho

The following table lists the Gamma Energies and Intensities of Radionuclides for a large number of the radioactive isotopes. The values of the gamma-ray energies are given in keV. The abbreviation Ann. Rad. refers to 511.006 keV photon associated with the annihilation of positrons in matter. The values for the gamma-ray intensities are given in percent of decays for a given gamma-ray transition and not the percent of transitions between two given energy levels in the daughter nucleus. Relative intensities for gamma rays are indicated by the symbol †.

Gamma energies (KeV)	Gamma intensities
$_2\text{He}^8$	
99	88%
$_4\text{Be}^7$	
477.575 ± 0.02	
$_4\text{Be}^{11}$	
2120	32%
4640	2.1%
5860	2.4%
6790	4.4%
7970	1.7%
$_5\text{B}^{12}$	
3230	0.0005%
4430	1.3%
$_5\text{B}^{13}$	
3670	7%
$_6\text{C}^{10}$	
717	100%
1030	1.7%
$_6\text{C}^{15}$	
5299	68%
$_7\text{N}^{12}$	
4430	2.4%
$_7\text{N}^{13}$	
Ann. Rad.	
$_7\text{N}^{16}$	
6128.9 ± 0.4	100†
7117.0 ± 0.5	7
$_7\text{N}^{17}$	
870	7†
2190	1
$_7\text{N}^{18}$	
820	60†
1650	63
1980	100
2470	43
$_8\text{O}^{14}$	
2311	99%
Ann. Rad.	
$_8\text{O}^{15}$	
Ann. Rad.	
$_8\text{O}^{19}$	
112	2.7†
200	97

Gamma energies (KeV)	Gamma intensities
1370	59
1440	2.7
$_8\text{O}^{20}$	
1070	
$_9\text{F}^{17}$	
Ann. Rad.	
$_9\text{F}^{18}$	
Ann. Rad.	
$_9\text{F}^{21}$	
345	100†
1380	13
$_9\text{F}^{22}$	
1274.52 ± 0.07	15†
2060	10
$_{10}\text{Ne}^{17}$	
Ann. Rad.	
$_{10}\text{Ne}^{18}$	
Ann. Rad.	
1041	7%
$_{10}\text{Ne}^{19}$	
Ann. Rad.	
$_{10}\text{Ne}^{23}$	
440	1000†
1630	28
1960	0.4
2070	3.0
2270	0.2
2550	0.8
2870	0.1
2990	0.9
$_{10}\text{Ne}^{24}$	
472	100†
880	8
$_{11}\text{Na}^{20}$	
Ann. Rad.	
$_{11}\text{Na}^{21}$	
Ann. Rad.	
347	2.3%
$_{11}\text{Na}^{22}$	
Ann. Rad.	
1274.52 ± 0.07	
$_{11}\text{Na}^{24}$	
1368.650 ± 0.050	100%

Gamma energies (KeV)	Gamma intensities
2754.10 ± 0.07	100%
3850	0.09%
4230	0.0015%
$_{11}\text{Na}^{25}$	
400	10†
580	9
980	10
1610	3
$_{11}\text{Na}^{26}$	
1820	
$_{12}\text{Mg}^{20}$	
Ann. Rad.	
$_{12}\text{Mg}^{21}$	
Ann. Rad.	
$_{12}\text{Mg}^{23}$	
Ann. Rad.	
440	9.1%
$_{12}\text{Mg}^{27}$	
80	0.7%
840	70%
1013	30%
$_{12}\text{Mg}^{28}$	
32	96†
391	31
950	29
350	70
$_{13}\text{Al}^{24}$	
Ann. Rad.	
1368	40†
2754	32
4200	15
5400	6
7100	7
$_{13}\text{Al}^{25}$	
Ann. Rad.	
$_{13}\text{Al}^{26m}$	
Ann. Rad.	
$_{13}\text{Al}^{26}$	
Ann. Rad.	
1830	99.7%
1120	3.7%
2960	0.3%
$_{13}\text{Al}^{27}$	
1780	100%
$_{13}\text{Al}^{28}$	
1280	85%
2430	15%

Gamma energies (KeV)	Gamma intensities
$_{13}Al^{30}$	
2240	10†
3520	6
$_{14}Si^{26}$	
Ann. Rad.	
820	
$_{14}Si^{27}$	
Ann. Rad.	
$_{14}Si^{31}$	
1260	<1%
$_{15}P^{28}$	
1790	75%
2600	
4440	10%
4900	
6100	
6700	
7000	
7600	5%
$_{15}P^{29}$	
1280	0.8%
2430	0.2%
$_{15}P^{30}$	
2160	0.5%
$_{15}P^{34}$	
2100	
4000	0.2%
$_{16}S^{29}$	
Ann. Rad.	
$_{16}S^{30}$	
Ann. Rad.	
687	80%
$_{16}S^{31}$	
Ann. Rad.	
1270	1.1%
$_{16}S^{37}$	
3090	90%
$_{16}S^{38}$	
1880	95%
$_{17}Cl^{32}$	
Ann. Rad.	

Gamma energies (KeV)	Gamma intensities
2210	70%
2770	
4270	7%
4770	14%
$_{17}Cl^{33}$	
2900	0.3%
$_{17}Cl^{34m}$	
Ann. Rad.	
640	
770	
1176.9 ± 1.0	32%†
2128.2 ± 1.0	100%
3303.9 ± 1.0	32%
4100	1%
146.5 ± 0.3	IT (50%)
$_{17}Cl^{34}$	
Ann. Rad.	
$_{17}Cl^{38m}$	
660	
$_{17}Cl^{38}$	
1600	85%†
2167.6 ± 0.7	100
3760	0.05
$_{17}Cl^{39}$	
246	90%†
1270	100
1520	85
$_{17}Cl^{40}$	
1460	
2830	
3100	
5800	
$_{18}Ar^{35}$	
Ann. Rad.	
1190	5%
1730	2%
$_{18}Ar^{37}$	
Cl X-ray	
$_{18}Ar^{41}$	
1293	99.2%
1660	0.05%
$_{19}K^{37}$	
Ann. Rad.	
2790	2%
$_{19}K^{38m}$	
Ann. Rad.	
$_{19}K^{38}$	
Ann. Rad.	
1650	weak
2167.6 ± 0.7	99+%

Gamma energies (KeV)	Gamma intensities
$_{19}K^{40}$	
Ann. Rad.	
1460	11%
$_{19}K^{42}$	
310	1.1†
600	0.1
900	0.1
1020	0.1
1524	100
1924	0.3
2440	0.2
$_{19}K^{43}$	
220.4 ± 0.8	3%
372.6 ± 1.0	85%
396.9 ± 0.8	11%
593.6 ± 1.0	13%
617.5 ± 1.0	81%
990.2 ± 2.0 }	~2%
1021.9 ± 2.0 }	
$_{19}K^{44}$	
480	
630	
740	
900	1†
1060	1
1157.02 ± 0.1	100
1499.63 ± 0.25	
1740	13†
2080	
2170	
2550	12
3400	
3660	6
4400	
4600	
5000	0.6
$_{19}K^{45}$	
175	
500	
900	
1230	
1710	
1900	
2100	
2350	
2600	
3100	
$_{20}Ca^{37}$	
Ann. Rad.	
$_{20}Ca^{38}$	
Ann. Rad.	
3.5	
$_{20}Ca^{39}$	
Ann. Rad.	
$_{20}Ca^{45}$	
12.5	

Gamma energies (KeV)	Gamma intensities
$_{20}Ca^{49}$	
490	5%
520	0.05%
760	0.05%
810	5%
1290	71%
$_{20}Ca^{49}$	
3100	88%
4050	10%
4680	0.8%
$_{20}Ca^{50}$	
72	
258	
$_{21}Sc^{40}$	
Ann. Rad.	
3750	
$_{21}Sc^{41}$	
Ann. Rad.	
$_{21}Sc^{42m}$	
Ann. Rad.	
438	100†
1230	
1520	100
$_{21}Sc^{42}$	
Ann. Rad.	
$_{21}Sc^{43}$	
220	
370	
620	
960	
$_{21}Sc^{44m}$	
271.19 ± 0.8 (IT)	98.6%
1001.99 ± 0.1	
1126.16 + 0.15	
1157.02 ± 0.1	
$_{21}Sc^{44}$	
Ann. Rad.	
1126.16 ± 0.15	
1157.02 ± 0.1	
1499.63 ± 0.25	
$_{21}Sc^{46m}$	
142	
$_{21}Sc^{46}$	
889.25 ± 0.07	100%
1120.50 ± 0.07	100%

Gamma energies (KeV)	Gamma intensities
$_{21}Sc^{47}$	
159.38 ± 0.08	40%
$_{21}Sc^{48}$	
175.4 ± 0.2	6%
983.46 ± 0.15	100%
1037.5 ± 0.2	100%
1311.9 ± 0.2	100%
$_{21}Sc^{49}$	
1780	0.03%
$_{21}Sc^{50m}$	
258	
$_{21}Sc^{50}$	
520	85†
1120	100
1570	100
$_{22}Ti^{44}$	
67.85 ± 0.07	10†
78.40 ± 0.10	14
$_{22}Ti^{45}$	
718	
1238	
1408	
1665	
$_{22}Ti^{51}$	
320.07 ± 0.05	100†
605	1.5
928	4.4
$_{23}V^{46}$	
Ann. Rad.	
$_{23}V^{47}$	
1500	
1800	0.8%
2160	0.2%
$_{23}V^{48}$	
Ann. Rad.	
290.1 ± 0.4	
928.3 ± 0.3	
944.1 ± 0.2	10†
983.46 ± 0.15	100
1311.9 ± 0.2	98
1437.6 ± 0.4	
2240.1 ± 0.2	2.7
$_{23}V^{52}$	
935	0.14%
1331	0.9%
1433	100%
1531	0.16%

Gamma energies (KeV)	Gamma intensities
$_{23}V^{53}$	
1000	100%
$_{23}V^{54}$	
834.795 ± 0.04	100%
990	100%
2210	100%
$_{24}Cr^{48}$	
116	95
310	100%
$_{24}Cr^{49}$	
62.31 ± 0.1	15†
90.7 ± 0.1	30
152.85 ± 0.1	14
610	
$_{24}Cr^{51}$	
320.080 ± 0.013	9%
$_{24}Cr^{56}$	
26	
83	
$_{25}Mn^{50m}$	
Ann. Rad.	
660	<1†
790	3
1110	3
1280	<1
1450	1
$_{25}Mn^{50}$	
Ann. Rad.	
$_{25}Mn^{51}$	
1560	
2030	
$_{25}Mn^{52m}$	
3.83	2%
Ann. Rad.	
$_{25}Mn^{52}$	
Ann. Rad.	
345.7	1%
630	
744	100%
846.8	100%
938.1	84%
1070	
1214	
1246	
1332	6%
1434	100%
1463	ω
2620	0.08%

Gamma energies (KeV)	Gamma intensities
$_{25}Mn^{54}$	
834.795 ± 0.04	100%
$_{25}Mn^{56}$	
846.78 ± 0.06	100†
1810.96 ± 0.2	30
2113.2 ± 0.2	15.3
2522.6 ± 0.3	1.2
2657.24 ± 0.2	0.7
2959.8 ± 0.2	0.4
3367 ± 1.0	0.21
$_{25}Mn^{57}$	
117	
134	
220	
350	
690	
$_{25}Mn^{58}$	
360	
410	
520	
570	
820	
1000	
1250	
1400	
1600	
2200	
2800	
$_{26}Fe^{52}$	
165	
Ann. Rad.	
383	
$_{26}Fe^{53}$	
Ann. Rad.	38%
377.5 ± 0.5	
$_{26}Fe^{55}$	
Mn X-rays	
$_{26}Fe^{59}$	
142.45 ± 0.08	0.8%
192.23 ± 0.08	2.5%
334.81 ± 0.10	0.3%
1099.27 ± 0.08	56%
1291.58 ± 0.10	44%
$_{26}Fe^{61}$	
130	11†
180	3
230	0.3
300	48
1030	98
1200	100
1650	1.4
1980	0.7

Gamma energies (KeV)	Gamma intensities
$_{27}Co^{54m}$	
Ann. Rad.	
410	1†
1140	1
1410	1
$_{27}Co^{54}$	
Ann. Rad.	
$_{27}Co^{55}$	
Ann. Rad.	
95	0.5%
245	<0.06%
390	
415	
480	12%
650	0.5%
750	0.2%
805	2.5%
892	2.4%
930	80%
985	0.9%
1060	0.4%
1210	1.0%
1320	6%
1370	4.2%
1410	13%
1580	0.09%
1800	0.06%
2190	0.11%
2310	
$_{27}Co^{56}$	
Ann. Rad.	
263	
788.0 ± 0.2	0.36%
846.78 ± 0.06	100%
977.4 ± 0.1	1.5%
1037.85 ± 0.06	14%
1175.08 ± 0.07	1.6%
1140.18 ± 0.1	
1175.1 ± 0.1	
1238.29 ± 0.04	64%
1360.219 ± 0.04	4%
1771.33 ± 0.06	14%
1810.46 ± 0.07	
1963.64 ± 0.1	0.68%
2015.33 ± 0.07	2.6%
2034.90 ± 0.07	6.6%
2112.95 ± 0.1	0.56%
2212.8 ± 0.1	0.60%
2598.52 ± 0.1	14%
3009.56 ± 0.1	0.6%
3202.18 ± 0.1	2.9%
3253.61 ± 0.1	7.2%
3273.16 ± 0.1	1.6%
3451.68 ± 0.1	0.72%
3547.5 ± 0.2	0.2%
$_{27}Co^{57}$	
Fe X-rays	
14.41 ± 0.020	8.4%
122.060 ± 0.010	85%
136.471 ± 0.010	11%
231	0.0005%

Gamma energies (KeV)	Gamma intensities
339.7	0.0048%
352.4	0.0037%
366.7	0.0007%
570.3	0.014%
692.1	0.16%
706.8	0.0067%
$_{27}Co^{58}$	
810.81 ± 0.12	100†
864.02 ± 0.17	1.38
1674.94 ± 0.2	0.61
$_{27}Co^{60m}$	
58.60 ± 0.010	
830	0.008%
1332.483 ± 0.040	0.25%
2160	0.0008%
$_{27}Co^{60}$	
1173.226 ± 0.040	99.88%
1332.483 ± 0.046	100%
2158	0.001%
$_{27}Co^{61}$	
67.4 ± 0.4	100%
$_{27}Co^{62}$	
1172	100†
1470	11
1740	11
2030	4
$_{28}Ni^{56}$	
163	99%
276	35%
472	35%
748	48%
812	87%
1560	14%
$_{28}Ni^{57}$	
Ann. Rad.	
129.3 ± 1.0	14%
1377.6 ± 1.0	86%
1757.8 ± 1.0	6%
1783.0 ± 1.5	1%
1882.4 ± 1.0	8%
$_{28}Ni^{59}$	
Co X-rays	
$_{28}Ni^{65}$	
344	
366	4.8%
507	0.35%
610	0.15%
771	0.07%
855	0.07%
1115.51 ± 0.07	15.2%
1480	
1624	0.76%
1725	0.53%

Gamma energies (KeV)	Gamma intensities	Gamma energies (KeV)	Gamma intensities	Gamma energies (KeV)	Gamma intensities
$_{28}Ni^{67}$		1611.1	0.025%	$_{30}Zn^{65}$	
		1662.9	0.04%		
890	24%	1730.4	0.04%	1115.51 ± 0.07	50.6%
900	50%	1997	0.004%	344	0.003%
1260	22%	2122.4	0.04	771	0.003%
$_{29}Cu^{58}$		$_{29}Cu^{62}$		$_{30}Zn^{69m}$	
Ann. Rad.		Ann. Rad.		438.7 ± 0.2	100%
		875.4	1%		
$_{29}Cu^{59}$		1170	3%	$_{30}Zn^{71m}$	
Ann. Rad.		$_{29}Cu^{64}$		130	10†
340	3.6%			210	
425	1.4%	Ann. Rad.		385	100
465	4.1%	1348	0.6%	495	73
878	9.4%			609	68
1301	9.9%	$_{29}Cu^{66}$		760	6
1680	1.5%	833.6	0.25%	880	
		1039.0 ± 1	9%	920	3
$_{29}Cu^{60}$				990	8
Ann. Rad.		$_{29}Cu^{67}$		1120	4
467	2.8%	91.26 ± 0.02	6.2%	1310	1
826	19.2%	93.31 ± 0.02	35%	1370	0.7
910	3.4%	184.6	45%	1490	1.0
1037	3.3%	209.0	0.09%	1640	0.11
1292	1.5%	300.2	0.6%	1740	0.27
1332.483 ± 0.04	87.3%	393.6	0.2%	1850	0.08
1792	44.9%			1960	0.06
1863	4.7%	$_{29}Cu^{68}$		2400	0.08
1920	0.6%	810	18†		
1938	1.7%	1080	100	$_{30}Zn^{71}$	
2061 ± 3	0.9%	1240	3	120	7†
2158 ± 2	3.5%	188	5	385	10
2693	0.5%			510	100
2747	0.9%	$_{30}Zn^{60}$		680	2
2268	0.09%	Ann. Rad.		920	24
2399	0.7%			1120	10
2428	0.6%	$_{30}Zn^{61}$		1630	1.1
3124	5.1%	Ann. Rad.			
3164 ± 2	0.7%	470	10.9%	$_{30}Zn^{72}$	
3195 ± 2	1.9%	690	1.8%	18	
3222	0.2%	966	2.9%	46	
3252	0.3%	1640	6%	145	90%
3271 ± 3	0.9%			190	10%
4022 ± 3	1.0%	$_{30}Zn^{62}$			
4080	0.1%	Ann. Rad.		$_{31}Ga^{63}$	
4332	0.09%	40.88		Ann. Rad.	
4503	0.09%	243.47 ± 0.2	1.6%		
4550	0.06%	246.99 ± 0.2	1.0%	$_{31}Ga^{64}$	
4584	0.02%	305.2 ± 0.3	0.2%	Ann. Rad.	
		349.7 ± 0.3	0.3%	427.1	0.9%
$_{29}Cu^{61}$		393.94 ± 0.25	1.4%	756.7	1.6%
Ann. Rad.		507.35 ± 0.18	12.8%	808.8	14%
23.2 ± 0.3		548.38 ± 0.2	12.6%	991.6	46%
44.8 ± 0.5		596.76 ± 0.2	20.3%	918.9	8.3%
55.4 ± 0.5				1276.4	6.9%
67.6 ± 0.2	4.9%			1386.9	14%
283.0 ± 0.2	13%			1455.2	1.9%
373.6 ± 0.3	1.9%	$_{30}Zn^{63}$		1566.6	4.3%
405.2 ± 0.3		Ann. Rad.		1617.2	1.7%
529.3 ± 0.3	0.3%	669.8 ± 0.4	11.2%	1626.2	1.4%
588.6 ± 0.3	1.2%	961.2 ± 0.4	8.4%	1799.3	4.6%
656.01 ± 0.2	9.6%	1411.3 ± 0.4	0.9%	1995.2	2.9%
1074.5	0.03%	1555	0.2%	2195.2	11%
1185.0 ± 0.3	3.6%			2270.5	2.3%
1446.7	0.04%			2374.8	7.8%
1543.6	0.03%				

Gamma energies (KeV)	Gamma intensities
2433.5	0.6%
2550	0.9%
2804.3	0.7%
3262.9	0.3%
3366.1	1.7%
3425.1	5.1%
4215	0.1%
4454.7	0.9%
4749.0	0.05%
$_{31}Ga^{65}$	
Ann. Rad.	
53.9 ± 0.4	31%
61.2 ± 0.4	15%
90.1 ± 1	1%
115.2 ± 0.4	·55%
153.2 ± 0.4	8.5%
207.1 ± 0.4	1.8%
751.3 ± 0.4	7.3%
769	1.2%
932.4 ± 0.4	1.7%
1047	1.1%
1227	0.8%
1342	0.3%
1353	0.8%
1414	0.27%
1480	0.7%
1764	0.1%
1855	0.15%
1970	0.04%
$_{31}Ga^{66}$	
Ann. Rad.	
833.6	6%
1039.0	39%
1232.6	0.63%
1332	1.3%
1356.9	0.67%
1419.0	0.63%
1508.5	0.59%
1918.7	2.4%
2190.3	5.9%
2215.4	0.16%
2394	0.24%
2423.0	2.0%
2752.1	25%
2780.5	0.13%
2932	0.34%
3229.5	1.5%
3257	0.13%
3381.2	1.6%
3423.0	0.94%
3433.0	0.29%
3766	0.12%
3791.3	1.0%
4087.5	1.1%
4295.5	3.6%
4462.0	0.71%
4806.0	1.6%
$_{31}Ga^{67}$	
91.26	2.9%
93.31	70%
184.46 ± 0.2	20.7%
200.96 ± 0.2	2.3%
300.17 ± 0.2	15%

Gamma energies (KeV)	Gamma intensities
353.0 ± 0.4	
393.43 ± 0.2	4.1%
494.4 ± 0.3	0.08%
595.9 ± 0.4	
703.6	0.012%
794.7	0.05%
887.9 ± 0.4	0.12%
$_{31}Ga^{68}$	
Ann. Rad.	
578.3	0.04%
805.8	0.09%
1077.1 ± 1	3.2%
1261.3	0.1%
1764.5	0.01%
1884.5 ± 1	0.13%
2338	0.001%
$_{31}Ga^{70}$	
173	0.15%
1042	0.5%
1215	
$_{31}Ga^{72}$	
601	8†
630	24
690	
786	4
812	4
834	100
894	11
1050	7
1231	1.4
1263	1.3
1278	1.8
1377	0.4
1400	0.3
1465	5
1602	6
1685	1.0
1718	0.5
1866	7
2114	1.1
2201	35
2460	0.7
2491	11
2508	19
2620	0.2
2849	0.4
3050	
3050	0.01
3100	0.01
3340	0.007
3680	0.0007
$_{31}Ga^{73}$	
13.5	
53.39 ± 0.2	9†
68.66 ± 0.3	1
285.0 ± 0.3	3
297.37 ± 0.2	97
325.74 ± 0.2	10
379.28 ± 0.4	
739.37 ± 0.25	
767.87 ± 0.3	
833.3 ± 0.3	

Gamma energies (KeV)	Gamma intensities
$_{31}Ga^{74}$	
53.92 ± 0.4	
380	2†
500	11
595.6 ± 0.2	87
600	13
720	2
870	5
980	4
1110	5
1200	6
1330	5
1460	6
1560	2
1700	3
1760	3
1930	6
2350	45
2550	3
2730	3
2970	2
3230	3
3410	2
$_{31}Ga^{75}$	
360?	1%
580	3%
$_{31}Ga^{76}$	
560	
960	
1120	
$_{32}Ge^{65}$	
655	
1670	
$_{32}Ge^{66}$	
Ann. Rad.	
43.83	43.8%
65.11	7.8%
90.9	0.5%
108.93	16.5%
120.05	0.4%
147.87	1.0%
154.85	0.6%
181.96	7.5%
190.17	7.5%
245.75	6.1%
272.90	11.9%
302.51	2.4%
338.01	9.9%
381.85	29%
427.51	0.3%
492.76	0.4%
536.58	6.1%
706.04	3.8%
$_{32}Ge^{67}$	
Ann. Rad.	
166	89.7%
166.5	24.2%
360	5.3%
558	0.09%
661	0.26%

Gamma energies (KeV)	Gamma intensities
720	0.14%
728	3.9%
828	5.0%
915	9.8%
981	2.4%
1082	2.3%
1162	1.7%
1283	0.35%
1450	0.9%
1477	8.5%
1644	2.1%
1810	1.7%
1837	0.4%
2004	0.8%
2170	0.09%
2559	0.13%
2726	0.1%
2991	0.1%
3065	0.1%
3157	0.1%
3398	
$_{32}Ge^{69}$	
Ann. Rad.	
234.8 ± 0.3	0.29%
318.7 ± 0.3	1.33%
532.8 ± 0.3	0.2%
553.3 ± 0.4	0.61%
574.0 ± 0.3	11.8%
587.8 ± 0.4	0.27%
762.0 ± 0.4	0.18%
788.0 ± 0.4	0.32%
872.0 ± 0.3	9.6%
1001.7 ± 0.4	
1051.8 ± 0.4	0.32%
1106.5 ± 0.3	26%
1206.3 ± 0.4	0.26%
1336.2 ± 0.3	2.94%
1349.5 ± 0.4	0.27%
1487.8 ± 1	0.06%
1525.6 ± 1	0.15%
1572.3 ± 1	0.13%
1891.8 ± 0.4	0.27%
1924.0 ± 0.5	0.08%
2023.9 ± 0.5	0.34%
$_{32}Ge^{71m}$	
23.0	
175.0	
$_{32}Ge^{73m}$	
13.5	
54	
$_{32}Ge^{75m}$	
139	~100%
$_{32}Ge^{75}$	
66	2.5†
200	13
264	100
427	2.6

Gamma energies (KeV)	Gamma intensities
477	2.6
628	1.3
$_{32}Ge^{77m}$	
159 (IT)	55†
215	100
$_{32}Ge^{77}$	
156.3 ± 0.3	16.3 ± 2.2†
177.4 ± 0.4	1.0 ± 0.4
194.9 ± 0.2	48.5 ± 4.3
211.03 ± 0.04	998.0 ± 90.0
215.51 ± 0.04	871.0 ± 78.0
255.0 ± 0.25	2.6 ± 2.1
264.45 ± 0.025	1700.0 ± 116.0
338.5 ± 0.15	30.8 ± 2.8
367.49 ± 0.04	485.0 ± 32.0
416.35 ± 0.04	815.0 ± 51.0
439.5 ± 0.23	10.3 ± 5.1
461.4 ± 0.22	41.9 ± 3.7
475.5 ± 0.15	35.9 ± 3.3
557.7 ± 0.08	569.0 ± 28.0
582.5 ± 0.18	25.5 ± 3.9
613.6 ± 0.4	23.9 ± 5.8
624.6 ± 0.4	2.0 ± 0.6
632.3 ± 0.23	314.0 ± 16.0
673.1 ± 0.25	21.9 ± 1.9
698.8 ± 0.35	8.35 ± 0.69
714.1 ± 0.09	269.0 ± 14.0
743.2 ± 0.40	4.8 ± 1.4
745.6 ± 0.28	35.2 ± 4.9
749.9 ± 0.28	32.6 ± 4.6
766.8 ± 0.25	26.0 ± 2.6
781.3 ± 0.25	33.5 ± 4.0
784.8 ± 0.25	40.9 ± 4.9
794.7 ± 0.35	4.9 ± 1.4
810.6 ± 0.20	78.1 ± 5.8
823.6 ± 0.26	20.9 ± 3.6
843.7 ± 0.30	7.9 ± 2.1
875.3 ± 0.30	26.0 ± 10.0
907.2 ± 0.35	22.3 ± 4.1
914.2 ± 0.5	4.2 ± 1.0
922.9 ± 0.35	16.8 ± 2.5
925.5 ± 0.30	26.2 ± 3.9
929.1 ± 0.30	29.2 ± 4.4
939.6 ± 0.35	6.5 ± 1.6
946.9 ± 1.0	0.4 ± 0.25
959.1 ± 0.8	2.6 ± 0.7
968.1 ± 0.8	2.4 ± 0.6
986.3 ± 0.8	2.3 ± 0.6
997.1 ± 0.5	2.3 ± 0.5
1062.1 ± 1.5	1.4 ± 0.5
1085.0 ± 0.15	216.0 ± 14.0
1115.4 ± 0.4	3.1 ± 0.6
1125.7 ± 0.4	3.0 ± 0.6
1151.8 ± 0.4	6.2 ± 1.4
1193.3 ± 0.2	86.2 ± 4.3
1202.7 ± 0.6	2.0 ± 1.0
1216.0 ± 0.4	3.5 ± 1.3
1242.4 ± 0.3	10.4 ± 2.8
1264.2 ± 0.3	26.7 ± 3.2
1280.8 ± 0.4	3.4 ± 0.9
1296.3 ± 0.4	2.9 ± 0.7
1309.5 ± 0.5	16.1 ± 2.9
1313.1 ± 0.5	9.2 ± 1.7
1319.8 ± 0.5	13.5 ± 2.2
1368.5 ± 0.5	90.5 ± 9.1
1452.6 ± 0.7	5.9 ± 1.4
1464.8 ± 0.8	5.5 ± 1.3

Gamma energies (KeV)	Gamma intensities
1477.1 ± 0.6	11.1 ± 1.9
1479.9 ± 0.6	8.3 ± 1.4
1495.1 ± 0.5	18.6 ± 3.0
1529.0 ± 0.5	2.1 ± 0.6
1539.4 ± 0.5	4.9 ± 1.4
1573.3 ± 0.25	22.7 ± 1.4
1709.6 ± 0.6	10.4 ± 2.5
1719.7 ± 0.6	14.7 ± 2.9
1726.9 ± 0.9	4.2 ± 1.3
1830.9 ± 0.8	1.5 ± 0.5
1846.5 ± 0.5	5.4 ± 1.6
1879.9 ± 0.8	1.0 ± 0.4
1928.8 ± 0.8	0.7 ± 0.3
2000.1 ± 0.3	19.2 ± 3.7
2038.5 ± 0.5	1.2 ± 0.3
2077.4 ± 0.5	8.0 ± 2.3
2089.7 ± 0.5	7.3 ± 2.2
2126.5 ± 0.4	4.8 ± 1.5
2248.0 ± 1.0	0.7 ± 0.3
2329.4 ± 1.0	0.8 ± 0.2
2341.5 ± 0.4	16.4 ± 3.2
$_{32}Ge^{78}$	
277	94%
294	6%
$_{33}As^{69}$	
Ann. Rad.	
86.8 ± 1.0	
146.0 ± 0.5	
232.8 ± 0.4	
$_{33}As^{70}$	
Ann. Rad.	1.98†
0.176 ± 0.2	3.2
0.2405	0.26
0.2523	3.6
0.2942	0.23
0.2988	0.47
0.4480 ± 0.0010	0.20
0.4509 ± 0.0010	0.13
0.4922	1.2
0.4970	3.1
0.5952	20.0
0.6076	4.8
0.6530	0.73
0.6684	25.9
0.7448	25.5
0.7602	0.30 ± 0.15
0.8281	0.43
0.8893	3.8
0.8931	2.4
0.9019	1.7
0.9057	14.9
0.9421	1.7
0.9538	0.58
1.0400	100
1.0993	5.4
1.1143	25.9
1.1181	3.9
1.2183	0.22
1.2961	0.21 ± 0.10
1.3322	0.75
1.3360	0.75
1.3394	10.9
1.3518	0.72

Gamma energies (KeV)	Gamma intensities
1.4125	10.5
1.4183	0.61 ± 0.20
1.4961	1.9
1.5071	0.48 ± 0.30
1.5121	0.34 ± 0.20
1.5233	6.2
1.5666	0.34 ± 0.20
1.5879	0.54
1.7079	21.9
1.7813	4.8
1.8831	0.63
1.9450	0.10
1.9490	0.20
2.0077	3.6
2.0200	20.4
2.0647 ± 0.0030	$\leqq 0.15$
2.0955 ± 0.0030	0.22 ± 0.18
2.1576	0.45
2.2193	0.13 ± 0.07
2.2561	0.16 ± 0.08
2.3266	0.14 ± 0.07
2.3334	0.10 ± 0.07
2.4212	0.10
2.4250	0.10
2.4493	0.43
2.5195 ± 0.0030	0.09
2.6372	0.37
2.7804 ± 0.0030	0.09
2.8523 ± 0.0030	0.05
2.9649 ± 0.0030	0.09
3.1256	0.08
4.0906 ± 0.0030	0.02
4.3279 ± 0.0030	0.02
4.4345 ± 0.0030	0.01

$_{33}As^{71}$

Gamma energies (KeV)	Gamma intensities
Ann. Rad.	
23.0	
174.70 ± 0.2	
247.14 ± 0.5	
279.22 ± 0.5	
326.53 ± 0.3	
349.87 ± 0.4	
373.57 ± 0.5	
391.22 ± 0.3	
465.00 ± 0.6	
499.85 ± 0.17	
526.57 ± 0.2	
572.15 ± 0.3	
615.26 ± 0.3	
622.72 ± 0.5	
679.71 ± 0.5	
685.41 ± 0.8	
707.0 ± 0.3	
712.5 ± 0.3	
747.0 ± 0.3	
851.2 ± 0.3	
920.6 ± 0.2	
1026.7 ± 0.2	
1033.54 ± 0.2	
1037.87 ± 1.0	
1095.48 ± 0.15	
1139.3 ± 0.2	
1231.28 ± 0.4	
1298.43 ± 0.2	
1331.5 ± 1.5	

$_{33}As^{72}$

Gamma energies (KeV)	Gamma intensities
Ann. Rad.	
595.79 ± 0.2	
600.84 ± 0.17	
629.88 ± 0.15	10†
634.6 ± 0.4	
756.7 ± 0.3	
765.7 ± 0.3	
786.42 ± 0.17	
834.03 ± 0.13	100
894.17 ± 0.15	2
1050.65 ± 0.16	3
1212.6 ± 0.5	
1215.3 ± 0.5	
1379.2 ± 0.4	
1390.3 ± 0.3	
1464.08 ± 0.18	
1475.8 ± 0.2	
1710.7 ± 0.3	
1917.8 ± 0.3	1
1991.1 ± 0.4	
2071.7 ± 0.4	
2090.6 ± 0.5	
2105.2 ± 0.5	
2109.6 ± 0.5	
2201.57 ± 0.1	4
2248.3 ± 0.3	0.9
2507.7 ± 0.16	
2523.4 ± 0.4	
2528.8 ± 0.4	
2620.9 ± 0.4	
2780.0 ± 0.5	0.6
3111.2 ± 1.0	
3481.3 ± 1.0	
3994.3 ± 1.0	

$_{33}As^{73}$

Gamma energies (KeV)	Gamma intensities
13.3 ± 0.2	0.44†
53.415 ± 0.035	100

$_{33}As^{74m}$

Gamma energies (KeV)	Gamma intensities
283	100%

$_{33}As^{74}$

Gamma energies (KeV)	Gamma intensities
Ann. Rad.	
595.86 ± 0.14	100†
608.4 ± 0.2	0.2
634.73 ± 0.15	25.6
887.2 ± 0.7	0.048
993.6 ± 0.8	0.021
1204.0 ± 0.3	0.47
1604.0 ± 1.0	0.013
2198.8 ± 1.0	0.019

$_{33}As^{76}$

Gamma energies (KeV)	Gamma intensities
510	0.5†
559.1	100
562.8	1.0
657.04	15
665.4	
708	0.3
740	0.5
775	0.4
858	0.3
869	0.24
1213.3	

Gamma energies (KeV)	Gamma intensities
1216.25	10
1220	2
1228.63	2.3
1439.4	1.2
1453	0.54
1550	0.2
1789.8	0.77
1880	0.2
2096.6	1.3
2111.1	0.73
2434	0.05
2656	0.08

$_{33}As^{77}$

Gamma energies (KeV)	Gamma intensities
87.86 ± 0.12	0.26%
161.86 ± 0.12	0.34%
238.96 ± 0.12	1.65%
270.74 ± 0.15	0.008%
281.63 ± 0.12	0.06%
520.63 ± 0.15	0.61%

$_{33}As^{78}$

Gamma energies (KeV)	Gamma intensities
620	42†
700	15
830	8
990	2.5
1110	2.9
1210	4.2
1310	11
1490	2.1
1700	1.7
1820	1.4
1940	1.5
2050	1.0
2240	1.0
2650	1.4

$_{33}As^{79}$

Gamma energies (KeV)	Gamma intensities
96	100%
360	2%
430	2%
540	0.5%
730	0.5%
890	1%

$_{33}As^{80}$

Gamma energies (KeV)	Gamma intensities
666	42%
785 }	
812 }	1.4%
1220	3.6%
1640	4%
1770	1.7%
1840	0.5%
2300	0.3%
2350	0.4%

$_{34}Se^{70}$

Ann. Rad.

$_{34}Se^{71}$

Ann. Rad.
160

Gamma energies (KeV)	Gamma intensities
$_{34}Se^{72}$	
46.0	
$_{34}Se^{73}$	
Ann. Rad.	
67.5 ± 0.5	
360.7 ± 0.5	
427.9 ± 0.5	
$_{34}Se^{73}$	
Ann. Rad.	
88	
251	
580	
1080	
$_{34}Se^{75}$	
24.3	
66.65	1.6†
96.731 ± 0.007	5.6
121.113 ± 0.010	28
135.998 ± 0.010	96
198.600 ± 0.020	2.4
264.648 ± 0.015	100
279.522 ± 0.012	42
303.892 ± 0.020	2.3
400.641 ± 0.015	20
$_{34}Se^{77m}$	
161	
$_{34}Se^{81m}$	
103	
$_{34}Se^{81}$	
270	0.3%
276	2.0%
290	1.3%
561	0.3%
565	1%
836	1%
$_{34}Se^{83m}$	
356	15%
676	13%
989	14%
1031	13%
1063	4%
1664	2%
2054	10%
2147	0.2%
$_{34}Se^{83}$	
226	31%
356	73%
357	3.5%
512	45%
554	3%
676	13%
720	22%
801	15%

Gamma energies (KeV)	Gamma intensities
837	14%
866	9%
1065	6%
1082	2%
1192	4%
1299	9%
1319	4%
1344	6%
1355	3%
1421	0.7%
1558	3%
1784	4%
1830	1.3%
1855	3%
1897	9%
2291	12%
2338	4%
2421	1%
$_{35}Br^{74}$	
Ann. Rad.	
640	
$_{35}Br^{75}$	
Ann. Rad.	
112.51 ± 0.5	
141.50 ± 0.25	
236.0 ± 0.2	
286.70 ± 0.18	
293.1 ± 0.2	
316.0 ± 0.4	
377.6 ± 0.3	
428.2 ± 0.3	
431.8 ± 0.3	
566.1 ± 0.3	
598.5 ± 0.4	
608.8 ± 0.3	
657.0 ± 0.4	
771.0 ± 0.6	
796.4 ± 0.8	
860.0 ± 1.0	
897.6 ± 1.0	
912.1 ± 0.6	
949.9 ± 1.5	
952.8 ± 1.0	
962.1 ± 1.0	
$_{35}Br^{76}$	
Ann. Rad.	
358.4 ± 0.5	
399.31 ± 0.5	
472.7 ± 0.3	
490.1 ± 0.5	
558.99 ± 0.25 ⎫	
562.4 ± 0.5 ⎬	95†
598.8 ± 0.4	
604.2 ± 0.5	
657.2 ± 0.25	28
665.3 ± 0.5	
681.6 ± 0.5	
696.0 ± 0.5	
727.1 ± 0.5	
730.7 ± 0.5	
789.2 ± 0.5	
803.5 ± 0.5	
836.6 ± 0.5	
867.7 ± 0.5	

Gamma energies (KeV)	Gamma intensities
882.2 ± 0.5	
886.6 ± 0.5	
901.0 ± 0.5	
942.7 ± 0.5	
981.2 ± 0.5	
1029.7 ± 0.5	
1032.2 ± 0.5	
1129.9 ± 0.4	
1212.9 ± 0.5	
1216.2 ± 0.3	
1228.7 ± 0.5	
1369.0 ± 0.4	
1380.4 ± 0.4	
1428.8 ± 0.6	
1439.2 ± 0.6	
1453.7 ± 0.5	
1470.9 ± 0.5	
1488.5 ± 0.4	
1560.1 ± 0.6	
1568.2 ± 0.5	
1578.7 ± 0.6	
1787.6 ± 0.5	
1853.1 ± 0.25	
2096.2 ± 0.4	
2110.8 ± 0.4	
2135.0 ± 0.4	
2281.2 ± 0.4	
2329.2 ± 0.5	
2334.0 ± 0.7	
2348.7 ± 0.5	
2390.50 ± 0.3	
2439.0 ± 0.6	
2510.2 ± 0.5	
2600.7 ± 0.6	
2617.6 ± 0.7	
2792.15 ± 0.25	8
2900.3 ± 0.5	
2950.0 ± 0.25	12
2996.8 ± 0.3	
3023.4 ± 0.7	
3092.3 ± 0.7	
3603.5 ± 0.5	3
3929.5 ± 0.7	0.1
4436.7 ± 1.0	0.07
$_{35}Br^{77}$	
87.86 ± 0.12	1.6%
161.86 ± 0.12	1.9%
180.74 ± 0.15	
187.34 ± 0.2	
200.4 ± 0.12	0.7%
231.3 ± 0.2	
238.96 ± 0.12	27%
243.3 ± 0.2	
249.77 ± 0.12	2.5%
270.74 ± 0.15	1%
281.63 ± 0.12	3%
297.15 ± 0.13	8%
303.76 ± 0.15	
384.98 ± 0.18	0.6%
439.37 ± 0.15	1.6%
484.52 ± 0.18	3%
510.8 ± 0.2	
Ann. Rad.	
520.63 ± 0.15	23%
565.82 ± 0.25	
567.94 ± 0.2	
574.64 ± 0.2	
578.85 ± 0.18	7%

GAMMA ENERGIES AND INTENSITIES OF RADIONUCLIDES (*Continued*)

Gamma energies (KeV)	Gamma intensities	Gamma energies (KeV)	Gamma intensities	Gamma energies (KcV)	Gamma intensities
585.39 ± 0.18		₃₅Br⁸⁴		24	4%
662.5 ± 0.5				107.6	9%
757.3 ± 0.25	2%	270	1†	131	84%
817.8 ± 0.25	3%	350	3	148	40%
1005.2 ± 0.3	2%	430	5	279	3%
		470	2	313	3%
		520	6	607	
₃₅Br⁷⁸		610	5	734	
		740	7		
Ann. Rad.	13%	810	18		
614.1		880	100	₃₆Kr⁷⁹	
		1010	20		
		1210	8	44	
₃₅Br⁸⁰ᵐ		1470	4	136.0	0.7%
		1570	2	181	0.08%
85		1740	4	208.5	0.7%
37		1900	36	217.3	2%
		2050	4	261.3	11.5%
		2170	4	299.7	1.3%
₃₅Br⁸⁰		2470	16	306.7	2.5%
		2820	4	308	
	616†	3030	8	345	0.1%
2.8%	639	3280	6	389.1	1.6%
	666	3930	25	397.4	10.1%
0.2%	704			523	0.3%
0.3%	812			526	0.2%
6.8%	1257	₃₅Br⁸⁵		616	0.1%
83.6%				726	0.05%
		305.0	23%	810	0.14%
		(Kr⁸⁵ᵐ)		833	1.7%
₃₅Br⁸²ᵐ				860	0.08%
				935	0.1%
46(IT)		₃₅Br⁸⁷		1026	0.13%
698.4				1072	0.09%
776.8		1440	100†	1115	0.4%
1474.8		1850	18	1165	0.09%
		2480	18	1332	0.5%
		2640	16		
₃₅Br⁸²		2980	25		
		3180	16	₃₆Kr⁸¹	
92.3 ± 0.1	0.4%	3800	11		
100.9 ± 0.1		4000	7	Br X-rays	
137.1 ± 0.1		4190	21		
221.28 ± 0.05	2.3%	4800	17	₃₆Kr⁸³ᵐ	
273.22 ± 0.05	1.2%	5000	17		
295.5 ± 0.1		5200	12	32	
452.9 ± 0.1				93	
554.24 ± 0.05	73%				
606.23 ± 0.1		₃₅Br⁸⁸		₃₆Kr⁸⁵ᵐ	
619.02 ± 0.05	43%				
698.30 ± 0.05	27%	760		151.2	
776.45 ± 0.05	83%			305.0	
827.80 ± 0.05	24%	₃₆Kr⁷⁴			
1007.55 ± 0.1				₃₆Kr⁸⁵	
1044.02 ± 0.05	29%	Ann. Rad.			
1084	0.4%			514	
1317.52 ± 0.07	28%	₃₆Kr⁷⁶			
1474.93 ± 0.1	17%			₃₆Kr⁸⁷	
1650.5 ± 0.2	0.8%	39			
1777.6 ± 0.5	0.12%	77		402.4 ± 0.2	100†
1871	0.05%	104		850	19
1959	0.05%	135		2050	~6
2056	0.02%	197		2570	42
		267			
		316			
₃₅Br⁸³		360		₃₆Kr⁸⁸	
		407			
32	100%	452		28	
93	100%			166	20†
521	1.4%	₃₆Kr⁷⁷		196.1 ± 0.2	100

Gamma energies (KeV)	Gamma intensities	Gamma energies (KeV)	Gamma intensities	Gamma energies (KeV)	Gamma intensities
360	14	$_{37}$Rb^{81m}		3240	1.4
850	65			3520	1.1
1369.6 ± 0.2		85		3680	0.4
1550	40			4780	1.4
2391.6 ± 0.3	100	$_{37}$Rb^{81}			
				$_{37}$Rb^{89}	
$_{36}$Kr^{89}		190	100 %		
		370	1.1 %	272.69 ± 0.1	2.3†
230	85†	450	29 %	287.97 ± 0.1	1.0
360	28	560	2.9 %	657.76 ± 0.05	16.9
430	29	820	1.1 %	947.72 ± 0.05	16.4
510	42	1040	0.9 %	1031.89 ± 0.05	100
600	100			1248.07 ± 0.05	75.4
740	32	$_{37}$Rb^{82m}		1538.41 ± 0.1	3.2
880	65			2008.21 ± 0.1	3.4
1120	45	554.3	70 %	2196.13 ± 0.1	25.4
1290	31	619.1	41 %	2569.96 ± 0.1	16.6
1510	88	698.4	27 %	2706.76 ± 0.2	2.1
1710	34	776.8	83 %	3508.43 ± 0.5	2.3
1930	10	827.6	26 %		
2040	16	1044.1	31 %	$_{37}$Rb^{90}	
2230	10	1317.2	30 %		
2420	22	1474.8	17 %	530	4 %
2570	10			720	4 %
2840	25			830	56 %
		$_{37}$Rb^{83}		860	6 %
$_{36}$Kr^{90}				1030	5 %
		93		1110	7 %
105	15†	520.43 ± 0.2	46 %	1240	2 %
120	65	529.65 ± 0.2	16 %	1400	5 %
236	16	552.63 ± 0.2	16 %	1700	3 %
495	12	651	0.09 %	1820	3 %
536	48	682	0.03 %	2200	2 %
640	7	790.1 ± 0.2	0.7 %	2510	2 %
670	4	801	0.3 %	2710	1 %
720	4			2840	2 %
770	3	$_{37}$Rb^{84m}		3070	5 %
890	2			3340	15 %
970	4	215.6 ± 0.3		3540	5 %
1110	48	248.3 ± 0.4		4130	11 %
1230	3	445.5		4340	13 %
1340	4	463.6 ± 0.4		4370	4 %
1400	5			4600	5 %
1540	17			5100	2 %
1630	4	$_{37}$Rb^{84}		5200	4 %
1700	5				
1790	11	Ann. Rad.		$_{38}$Sr^{80}	
1940	2	882.9 ± 0.2	100†		
2030	1	1016	0.53	580	
2120	2	1892	1.1		
2480	4			$_{38}$Sr^{81}	
2580	2	$_{37}$Rb^{86m}			
2700	2			Ann. Rad.	
2940	3	560	~100 %		
3080	2			$_{38}$Sr^{82}	
3170	1	$_{37}$Rb^{86}			
3600	1			Rb X-rays	
		1078	8.8 %		
$_{37}$Rb^{79}				$_{38}$Sr^{83}	
		$_{37}$Rb^{88}			
Ann. Rad.				41.9 ± 0.5	
		898.0 ± 0.2	63†	94.1 ± 0.2	
$_{37}$Rb^{80}		1390	6	159.7 ± 0.25	
		1835.9 ± 0.2	100	289.9 ± 0.25	
Ann. Rad.		2110	4.5	381.56 ± 0.15	
616		2680	11	389.4 ± 0.2	
704?		3010	1.4	418.4 ± 0.2	
				423.5 ± 0.2	
				438.2 ± 0.2	

Gamma energies (KeV)	Gamma intensities
Ann. Rad.	
658.8 ± .0.5	
736.9 ± 1.0	
762.51 ± 0.15	
778.35 ± 0.2	
804.9 ± 1.0	
818.92 ± 0.3	
831.3 ± 2.0	
818.3 ± 2.0	
853.9 ± 1.5	
890.1 ± 2.0	
908.0 ± 1.0	
944.6 ± 1.5	
994.1 ± 0.5	
1043.6 ± 0.4	
1054.8 ± 0.3	
1098.1 ± 2.0	
1147.09 ± 0.2	
1159.81 ± 0.2	
1214.8 ± 1.5	
1237.6 ± 2.0	
1324.7 + 3.0	
1562.63 ± 0.2	
1951.81 ± 0.3	
2089.84 ± 1.0	
2146.9 ± 1.0	

$_{38}Sr^{85m}$

Gamma energies (KeV)	Gamma intensities
7 ± 0.1	
151.28 ± 0.1	14% (EC)
231.69 ± 0.1	85% (IT)
238.65 ± 0.15	~4% (IT)

$_{38}Sr^{85}$

Gamma energies (KeV)	Gamma intensities
360	0.002%
513.998 ± 0.02	~100%
880	0.017%

$_{38}Sr^{87m}$

Gamma energies (KeV)	Gamma intensities
388.40 ± 0.08	~100%

$_{38}Sr^{89}$

Gamma energies (KeV)	Gamma intensities
910	<0.01%

$_{38}Sr^{91}$

Gamma energies (KeV)	Gamma intensities
118.31 ± 0.1	0.21†
261.00 ± 0.1	1.25
272.30 ± 0.1	0.20
274.29 ± 0.05	3.0
555.57 ± 0.05	94.7
620.13 ± 0.1	5.1
631.29 ± 0.1	1.75
652.91 ± 0.05	36.9
749.84 ± 0.05	69.7
761.29 ± 0.1	2.08
925.83 ± 0.05	12.2
1024.29 ± 0.05	100
1054.70 ± 0.2	0.5
1281.09 ± 0.1	2.75
1413.58 ± 0.1	3.39

Gamma energies (KeV)	Gamma intensities
1473.83 ± 0.2	0.47
1546.53 ± 0.3	0.13
1723.63 ± 0.3	0.40

$_{38}Sr^{92}$

Gamma energies (KeV)	Gamma intensities
241.53 ± 0.1	3.36†
430.45 ± 0.1	4.64
953.32 ± 0.1	4.30
1384.00 ± 0.05	100

$_{38}Sr^{93}$

Gamma energies (KeV)	Gamma intensities
178	17†
210	6
255	13
360	7
400	5
450	9
530	7
600	100
710	35
880	73
1080	9
1180	19
1260	19
1660	16
1860	4
2190	4
2450	6
2580	5
3000	

$_{38}Sr^{94}$

Gamma energies (KeV)	Gamma intensities
1420	

$_{39}Y^{82}$

Gamma energies (KeV)	Gamma intensities
Ann. Rad.	

$_{39}Y^{83}$

Gamma energies (KeV)	Gamma intensities
Ann. Rad.	

$_{39}Y^{84}$

Gamma energies (KeV)	Gamma intensities
200	
453	
590	15†
795	100
982	90
1041	50
1270	9
1470	6

$_{39}Y^{85m}$

Gamma energies (KeV)	Gamma intensities
503	
700	
770	
920	

$_{39}Y^{85}$

Gamma energies (KeV)	Gamma intensities
Ann. Rad.	
230.86 ± 0.2	

Gamma energies (KeV)	Gamma intensities
627.4 ± 0.2	
699.06 ± 0.2	
768.0 ± 0.2	
1030.1 ± 0.2	
1101.9 ± 0.2	
1122.8 ± 0.2	
1151.6 ± 0.2	
1220.8 ± 0.2	
1403.8 ± 0.7	
1584.1 ± 0.7	
1889.7 ± 0.7	
2123.5 ± 1.0	
2172.4 ± 1.0	
2351.2 ± 1.0	
2750	

$_{39}Y^{86m}$

Gamma energies (KeV)	Gamma intensities
10.2	
208.0	
152.2 ± 0.5	
188.8 ± 0.5	
191.8 ± 0.5	
252.0 ± 0.3	
265.2 ± 0.3	
307.3 ± 0.3	
331.4 ± 0.3	
370.7 ± 0.3	
443.2 ± 0.25	
514 ± 2	
580.6 ± 0.3	
608.1 ± 0.6	
627.7 ± 0.15	
645.6 ± 0.18	
703.3 ± 0.2	
709.7 ± 0.3	
767.7 ± 0.4	
777.3 ± 0.2	
826.2 ± 0.5	
833.5 ± 1.0	
896.6 ± 2	
1024.0 ± 0.25	
1076.8 ± 0.2	
1153.1 ± 0.3	
1253.6 ± 0.8	
1349.5 ± 0.5	
1407	
1854.1 ± 0.3	
1920.4 ± 0.3	
2567.2 ± 0.6	
2610.7 ± 1.0	
2830	
3060	
3340	
3660	
3860	

$_{39}Y^{87m}$

Gamma energies (KeV)	Gamma intensities
381.1 ± 0.5	99%

$_{39}Y^{87}$

Gamma energies (KeV)	Gamma intensities
388.4 ± 0.08	~100%
484.8 ± 0.5	~100%
Ann. Rad.	

$_{39}Y^{88}$

Gamma energies (KeV)	Gamma intensities
898.00 ± 0.03	92%
1836.075 ± 0.05	~100%
2734.07 ± 0.08	<1%
$_{39}Y^{89m}$	
909.07 ± 0.1	100%
$_{39}Y^{90m}$	
202.4	100†
482	95.7
2320	0.4
$_{39}Y^{90}$	
1.734	0.4%
$_{39}Y^{91m}$	
555.59 ± 0.07	~100%
$_{39}Y^{91}$	
1.21	0.3%
$_{39}Y^{92}$	
447.99 ± 0.05	18.2†
492.17 ± 0.1	3.6
560.81 ± 0.05	18.5
844.12 ± 0.1	9.1
912.66 ± 0.1	4.8
934.44 ± 0.05	100
972.35 ± 0.2	0.6
1132.29 ± 0.1	1.5
1405.44 ± 0.05	32.3
1848.07 ± 0.2	2.1
1885.9 ± 0.5	0.2
2066	
$_{39}Y^{93}$	
266.75 ± 0.05	100†
428.31 ± 0.1	0.1
478.15 ± 0.1	0.2
658.21 ± 0.1	1.8
680.27 ± 0.05	9.7
714.42 ± 0.1	0.3
743.51 ± 0.1	1.9
947.12 ± 0.05	29.6
1158.73 ± 0.1	0.4
1182.5 ± 0.1	0.5
1203.28 ± 0.1	1.8
1425.39 ± 0.1	3.6
1470.04 ± 0.2	1.0
1827.15 ± 0.1	1.4
1917.71 ± 0.07	22.3
2184.2 ± 0.2	1.4
2190.8 ± 0.2	2.6
2472.5 ± 0.3	0.2
$_{39}Y^{94}$	

Gamma energies (KeV)	Gamma intensities
560	6%
920	43%
1130	5%
1420	
1650	2.4%
1900	1.6%
2130	2.4%
2570	1.5%
2840	0.7%
3060	1.3%
3530	1.1%
$_{39}Y^{96}$	
700	
1000	
1500	
$_{40}Zr^{81}$	
Ann. Rad.	
$_{40}Zr^{82}$	
Ann. Rad.	
$_{40}Zr^{83}$	
Ann. Rad.	
$_{40}Zr^{84}$	
Ann. Rad.	
$_{40}Zr^{85}$	
Ann. Rad.	
$_{40}Zr^{86}$	
Ann. Rad.	
28	21†
243	100
612	5.4
$_{40}Zr^{87}$	
1200	
2200	
Ann. Rad.	
$_{40}Zr^{88}$	
392.6 ± 0.3	100%
$_{40}Zr^{89m}$	
588	94%
1506	6%
$_{40}Zr^{89}$	
Ann. Rad.	
909.07 ± 0.1	
1621.4 ± 0.6	
1713.3 ± 0.4	

Gamma energies (KeV)	Gamma intensities
$_{40}Zr^{90m}$	
132.5 ± 0.4	
2186.1 ± 2.0	
2318.7 ± 2.0	
$_{40}Zr^{95}$	
235.7 ± 0.2	
724.24 ± 0.06	
756.87 ± 0.07	
$_{40}Zr^{97}$	
254.1 ± 0.2	
355.6 ± 0.1	
602.5 ± 0.1	
703.8 ± 0.1	
743.2 ± 0.2	
971.5 ± 0.4	
1147.9 ± 0.2	
1276.1 ± 0.2	
1362.7 ± 0.2	
1712.6 ± 0.4	
1750.6 ± 0.3	
1852.0 ± 0.3	
$_{41}Nb^{88}$	
76	
141	
272	
399	
671	
1058	
1083	
$_{41}Nb^{89m}$	
588	
(Zr^{89m})	
1506	
$_{41}Nb^{89}$	
1510	
1626	
1713	
1832	
1911	
2220	
2572	
2574	
2961	
3018	
3093	
3282	
3333	
3513	
3577	
3838	
3908	
$_{41}Nb^{90m}$	
3	
122.4	

Gamma energies (KeV)	Gamma intensities		Gamma energies (KeV)	Gamma intensities		Gamma energies (KeV)	Gamma intensities
$_{41}Nb^{90}$			**$_{41}Nb^{97}$**			1271	0.002
						1387	0.001
132.5 ± 0.3	5†		658.0 ± 0.2	98 %		1455	0.0008
141.5 ± 0.3	75		743.2 ± 0.2	2 %		1463	0.0004
371.5 ± 1.0	3		1021.66 ± 0.2			1482	0.0004
Ann. Rad.			1148.0 ± 0.2				
890.0 ± 1.0						**$_{42}Mo^{91m}$**	
1128.7 ± 1.5	97		**$_{41}Nb^{98}$**				
1269.5 ± 2.0						658	57 %
2186.27 ± 1.0	14		330	9†		Ann. Rad.	
2318.7 ± 1.0	82		720	75		1210	16 %
			780	100		1530	22 %
$_{41}Nb^{91m}$			1160	30			
			1440	10		**$_{42}Mo^{91}$**	
104.5			1520	4			
1210			1680	10		Ann. Rad.	
			1880	4			
$_{41}Nb^{92m}$			1930	8		**$_{42}Mo^{93m}$**	
			2240				
Ann. Rad.			2440			264	100 %
912.66 ± 0.1	1.8 %		2700			685	100 %
934.44 ± 0.05	99 %					1479	100 %
1848.07 ± 0.2	0.8 %		**$_{41}Nb^{99}$**				
						$_{42}Mo^{93}$	
$_{41}Nb^{94m}$			100	1†			
			260	1		30.4	85 %
41.5							
703	0.002 %		**$_{41}Nb^{100}$**			**$_{42}Mo^{99}$**	
872	0.2 %						
			140	10†		40.6	1†
$_{41}Nb^{94}$			360	55		140.3 ± 0.2	
			450	40		180.9 ± 0.2	7
702.59 ± 0.15	100 %		530	100		366.3 ± 0.2	1.8
871.16 ± 0.15	100 %		650			410	0.15
			2200			739.3 ± 0.2	15
$_{41}Nb^{95m}$			2300			777.6 ± 0.2	4
			2650			940	0.14
235.7 ± 0.2	100 %		2850				
						$_{42}Mo^{101}$	
$_{41}Nb^{95}$			**$_{41}Nb^{100}$**			80	3 %
						191	25 %
765.87 ± 0.09	~100 %		530	100†		193	2 %
			620	60		300	7 %
$_{41}Nb^{96}$			1040	10		400	2 %
			1150	10		510	15 %
219.13 ± 0.3			1470	5		590	21 %
241.46 ± 0.1						700	1 %
350.13 ± 0.2			**$_{42}Mo^{88}$**			704	11 %
372.20 ± 0.1						840	1 %
460.16 ± 0.15			Ann. Rad.			890	15 %
480.43 ± 0.15						950	2 %
568.69 ± 0.08			**$_{42}Mo^{89}$**			1020	25 %
719.38 ± 0.08						1140	1 %
778.18 ± 0.15			Ann. Rad.			1180	11 %
810.53 ± 0.15						1280	3 %
849.96 ± 0.15			**$_{42}Mo^{90}$**			1380	9 %
1091.45 ± 0.15						1460	1 %
1199.97 ± 0.15			42.70	6†		1560	11 %
1497.6 ± 0.2			122.4	36		1660	3 %
			162.9	0.43		2080	16 %
$_{41}Nb^{97m}$			203.1	0.26			
			257.34	14.2		**$_{42}Mo^{104}$**	
743.20 ± 0.15	100 %		323.2	0.08			
			421.0	0.001		70	
			445.4	0.036			
			472.2	0.005		**$_{43}Tc^{92}$**	
			489.8	0.003			
			941.5	0.004			
			990	0.001			

Gamma energies (KeV)	Gamma intensities
90	~20†
140	67
240	30
330	90
790	95
1540	100

$_{43}Tc^{93m}$

Gamma energies (KeV)	Gamma intensities
390	63%
2660	18%

$_{43}Tc^{93}$

Gamma energies (KeV)	Gamma intensities
860	3%
1350	65%
1490	33%
2030	0.4%
2440	0.4%

$_{43}Tc^{94m}$

Gamma energies (KeV)	Gamma intensities
871.01 ± 0.08	100 ± 5
875.45 ± 0.12	1.6 ± 0.1
993.01 ± 0.10	2.3 ± 0.8
1195.8 ± 0.4	0.9 ± 0.2
1521.52 ± 0.17	5.6 ± 1.1
1868.50 ± 0.25	6.2 ± 0.4
2393 ± 1	0.5 ± 0.2
2739.7 ± 0.3	4.5 ± 0.5
3128.2 ± 0.4	2.7 ± 0.7

$_{43}Tc^{94}$

Gamma energies (KeV)	Gamma intensities
449.07 ± 0.06	2.6 ± 1.0†
532.13 ± 0.10	2.6 ± 1.0
702.60 ± 0.08	99.8 ± 6
742.2 ± 0.3	1.2 ± 0.6
849.65 ± 0.08	97.7 ± 6
871.01 ± 0.08	100 ± 5
916.12 ± 0.10	7.4 ± 1.5
1362.7 ± 0.6	0.9 ± 0.4
1508.6 ± 0.7	0.66 ± 0.3
1591.7 ± 0.3	2.4 ± 1.0

$_{43}Tc^{95m}$

Gamma energies (KeV)	Gamma intensities
Ann. Rad.	
38.9	
204.2	100†
584	55
763	1
784	2
788	15
823	12
837	39
1040	6
1630	0.1

$_{43}Tc^{95}$

Gamma energies (KeV)	Gamma intensities
204	1%
680	2%
768	82%
840	11%
930	1.7%
1060	4%

$_{43}Tc^{96m}$

Gamma energies (KeV)	Gamma intensities
34.4	

$_{43}Tc^{96}$

Gamma energies (KeV)	Gamma intensities
312	0.5†
778.18 ± 0.15	100
810.53 ± 0.15	82
849.96 ± 0.15	100
1119	17

$_{43}Tc^{97m}$

Gamma energies (KeV)	Gamma intensities
96.5	100%

$_{43}Tc^{97}$

Gamma energies (KeV)	Gamma intensities
Mo X-rays	

$_{43}Tc^{98}$

Gamma energies (KeV)	Gamma intensities
669	100†
770	100

$_{43}Tc^{99m}$

Gamma energies (KeV)	Gamma intensities
142.7	100%

$_{43}Tc^{100}$

Gamma energies (KeV)	Gamma intensities
542	
600	
710	
810	
890	
1010	
1310	
1490	
1800	

$_{43}Tc^{101}$

Gamma energies (KeV)	Gamma intensities
127	0.8†
130	2.6
183	0.4
186	2.3
235	0.8
307	100
380	1.8
410	0.4
545	8
640	1.0
720	1.2
850	0.36
940	0.24

$_{43}Tc^{102}$

Gamma energies (KeV)	Gamma intensities
470	

$_{43}Tc^{103}$

Gamma energies (KeV)	Gamma intensities
135	17†
210	10
350	

$_{43}Tc^{104}$

Gamma energies (KeV)	Gamma intensities
360	
530	

Gamma energies (KeV)	Gamma intensities
630	
890	
1150	
1250	
1370	
1580	
1630	
1900	
2200	
2500	
2700	
3200	
3400	
3700	
4000	
4400	
4700	

$_{43}Tc^{105}$

Gamma energies (KeV)	Gamma intensities
110	

$_{44}Ru^{95}$

Gamma energies (KeV)	Gamma intensities
Ann. Rad.	
254.6 ± 0.4	
290.3 ± 0.3	
301.0 ± 0.3	
336.5 ± 0.2	
367.2 ± 0.3	
511.006	
551.6 ± 0.3	
591.1 ± 0.3	
627.0 ± 0.3	
653.0 ± 0.5	
749.4 ± 0.5	
807.6 ± 0.3	
843.2 ± 0.5	
1051.7 ± 0.5	
1097.5 ± 0.2	
1159.5 ± 0.3	
1179.6 ± 0.3	
1218.8 ± 0.5	
1230.2 ± 0.4	
1267.5 ± 0.5	
1303.1 ± 0.3	
1353.9 ± 0.5	
1410.8 ± 0.4	
1434.0 ± 0.5	
1459.5 ± 0.4	
2323.8 ± 0.5	

$_{44}Ru^{97}$

Gamma energies (KeV)	Gamma intensities
96.5	0.04†
215.4	100
324.4	9
565	<1

$_{44}Ru^{103}$

Gamma energies (KeV)	Gamma intensities
39.8 ± 0.1	0.072 ± 0.008
53.3 ± 0.1	0.30 ± 0.03
65	<0.01
295.2 ± 0.1	0.21 ± 0.02
358	<0.03
443.0 ± 0.1	0.31 ± 0.03
497.1 ± 0.1	100 ± 10
557.1 ± 0.1	0.76 ± 0.07
610.3 ± 0.1	4.8 ± 0.4

Gamma energies (KeV)	Gamma intensities	Gamma energies (KeV)	Gamma intensities	Gamma energies (KeV)	Gamma intensities
$_{44}Ru^{105}$		921.0 ± 0.7		233.22 ± 0.2	
		938.0 ± 0.6		237.60 ± 0.2	
129.53	27%	1261.27 ± 0.2		306.52 ± 0.2	
149.04	2%			545.15 + 0.2	
150	2%			595.73 ± 0.3	
188	2%	$_{45}Rh^{99}$			
210	2%				
262.84	9%	Ann. Rad.		$_{45}Rh^{101}$	
315.50	10%	89.7 ± 0.3†	100 ± 4†		
326.1	3%	120.3 ± 0.2	0.22 ± 0.05	127.23 ± 0.04	117†
330.9		175.45 ± 0.05	6.58 ± 0.3	157.44 ± 0.08 IT	
393.36	3%	232.75 ± 0.05	1.64 ± 0.25	179.64 ± 0.06	
413.51	2%	279.00 ± 0.15	0.78 ± 0.08	184.09 ± 0.08	
469.38	19%	295.76 ± 0.08	4.04 ± 0.25	198.02 ± 0.04	100
499.28	3%	322.32 ± 0.05	20.4 ± 0.9	233.72 ± 0.08	
575.19	1%	353.06 ± 0.05	115 ± 9	238.20 ± 0.15	
656.15	2%	442.59 ± 0.05	6.42 ± 0.4	306.87 ± 0.03	1
676.32	6%	486.28 ± 0.08	1.44 ± 0.08	325.24 ± 0.06	15
724.2	44%	528.53 ± 0.05	132 ± 10	545.00 ± 0.10	
875.8	2%	575.6 ± 0.3	0.65 ± 0.1		
969.4	1.0%	618.08 ± 0.05	14.4 ± 0.8		
1350	0.1%	733.93 ± 0.06	0.93 ± 0.15	$_{45}Rh^{102}$	
1380	<0.1%	764.90 ± 0.07	1.25 ± 0.09		
1580	<0.1%	807.07 ± 0.05	4.1 ± 0.3	345.89 ± 0.12	0.87 ± 0.10†
1730	<0.1%	896.65 ± 0.15	2.7 ± 0.3	415.25 ± 0.15	2.1 ± 0.3
		940.38 ± 0.12	4.9 ± 0.8	418.52 ± 0.18	9.4 ± 0.1
$_{44}Ru^{107}$		998.51 ± 0.10	2.8 ± 0.2	420.4 ± 0.2	3.2 ± 0.3
		1009.6 ± 0.2	0.19 ± 0.05	475.06 ± 0.04	95 + 4
195	14%	1060.6 ± 0.2	0.86 ± 0.08	628.05 ± 0.05	8.3 ± 0.4
370		1088.88 ± 0.15	1.0 ± 0.2	631.29 ± 0.05	56 ± 2
480		1209.1 ± 0.4	0.80 ± 0.08	692.4 ± 0.2	1.6 ± 0.2
860	7%	1293.34 ± 0.15	0.95 ± 0.05	695.6 ± 0.3	2.9 ± 0.4
930	4%	1325.2 ± 0.4	0.60 ± 0.06	697.49 ± 0.08	44 ± 2
1030	4%	1482.8 ± 0.3	0.42 ± 0.05	766.84 ± 0.06	34 ± 2
1290	4%	1531.5 ± 0.4	1.62 ± 0.12	1046.59 ± 0.07	34 ± 2
		1571.9 ± 0.6	0.74 ± 0.07	1103.16 ± 0.06	4.6 ± 0.3
$_{44}Ru^{108}$		1616.5 ± 0.8	0.77 ± 0.07	1112.84 ± 0.07	19 ± 1
		1660.9 ± 0.4	0.20 ± 0.05	1323.6 ± 0.5	0.46 ± 0.08
165	28%	1970.2 ± 0.7	0.34 ± 0.03		
				$_{45}Rh^{102}$	
$_{45}Rh^{97}$		$_{45}Rh^{100}$			
				Ann. Rad.	
Ann. Rad.		Ann. Rad.	†	415.25 ± 0.15	0.03 ± 0.02†
190		302.2 ± 0.3		418.52 ± 0.18	0.12 ± 0.02
260		340.9 ± 0.4		456.42 ± 0.15	0.08 ± 0.02
430		370.7 ± 1.5		468.58 ± 0.04	2.9 ± 0.2
860		446.1 ± 0.4		475.06 ± 0.04	46 ± 3
1180		539.5 ± 0.3		556.60 ± 0.04	2.0 ± 0.2
1570		588.3 ± 0.4		628.05 ± 0.05	4.5 ± 0.4
1760		591.0 ± 1.0		631.29 ± 0.05	0.10 ± 0.03
1960		686.6 ± 0.6		636.81 ± 0.10	0.23 ± 0.03
2160		822.5 ± 0.4		680.66 ± 0.05	0.58 ± 0.04
2540		1033.7 ± 0.6		733.93 ± 0.08	0.10 ± 0.02
		1107.6 ± 0.4		739.58 ± 0.07	0.53 ± 0.08
$_{45}Rh^{98}$		1341.4 ± 0.4		930.5 ± 0.3	0.03 ± 0.02
		1362.2 ± 0.3		1046.59 ± 0.07	0.43 ± 0.03
Ann. Rad.		1553.7 ± 0.3		1103.16 ± 0.06	2.9 ± 0.1
650		1865.5 ± 0.5		1105.7 ± 0.3	0.39 ± 0.03
		1930.2 ± 0.4		1158.10 ± 0.06	0.58 ± 0.04
$_{45}Rh^{99m}$		2376.2 ± 0.3		1362.08 ± 0.20	0.39 ± 0.03
		2530.3 ± 0.5		1562.2 ± 0.4	0.11 ± 0.03
Ann. Rad.				1568.7 ± 0.6	0.01 ± 0.01
89.3 ± 0.6				1580.5 ± 0.3	0.05 ± 0.01
250.6 ± 0.5		$_{45}Rh^{101m}$		1786.4 ± 0.4	0.01 ± 0.01
276.6 ± 0.5				2037.0 ± 0.3	0.03 ± 0.02
321.7 ± 0.4		127.23 ± 0.2		2261.3 ± 0.4	0.02 ± 0.02
340.3 ± 0.25		157.35 ± 0.2	IT		
446.0 ± 0.3		179.40 ± 0.2			
558.2 ± 0.4		183.91 ± 0.2			
575.7 ± 0.4		197.80 ± 0.2		$_{45}Rh^{104m}$	

Gamma energies (KeV)	Gamma intensities
31.86 ⎫	
51.43 ⎬ IT	
77.55 ⎪	
97.11 ⎭	
560	
760	0.1 %
770	0.1 %
930	0.03 %
1340	0.02 %
1530	0.03 %
1700	< 0.03 %

$_{45}Rh^{104}$

Gamma energies (KeV)	Gamma intensities
555.5	2 %
1240	0.12 %
1800	< 0.002 %

$_{45}Rh^{105m}$

Gamma energies (KeV)	Gamma intensities
129.4	100 %

$_{45}Rh^{105}$

Gamma energies (KeV)	Gamma intensities
38.8	
215.8	
280.54	0.17 %
306.31	5 %
319.24	19 %
442.3	
497.0	

$_{45}Rh^{106}$

Gamma energies (KeV)	Gamma intensities
511.9 ± 0.2	100†
616.30 ± 0.2	45
622.1 ± 0.2	6
710	0.2
873.8	1.8
1050.4 ± 0.2	6.8
1130	2.3
1490	0.16
1550	0.64
1770	0.19
1950	0.08
2090	0.13
2360	0.17
2640	0.03

$_{45}Rh^{106}$

Gamma energies (KeV)	Gamma intensities
220	20†
407	20
450	35
511.9 ± 0.2	100
620	33
735	47
820	40
1050.4 ± 0.2	29
1140	14
1220	19
1560	2.1
1740	2.0
1860	2.0
2120	1.0
2280	0.5

$_{45}Rh^{107}$

Gamma energies (KeV)	Gamma intensities
115	0.5 %
285	3 %
307	73 %
570	1.8 %
680	2.7 %

$_{45}Rh^{108}$

Gamma energies (KeV)	Gamma intensities
433.99 ± 0.2	43 %
614.29 ± 0.2	22 %
510	40 %
1520	5 %

$_{45}Rh^{110}$

Gamma energies (KeV)	Gamma intensities
375	

$_{46}Pd^{98}$

Gamma energies (KeV)	Gamma intensities
132	
Ann. Rad.	

$_{46}Pd^{99}$

Gamma energies (KeV)	Gamma intensities
Ann. Rad.	
140	
275	
420	
670	

$_{46}Pd^{100}$

Gamma energies (KeV)	Gamma intensities
32.7	
42.1	51†
55.8	3
74.8	70
84.0	100
126.1	33
139.7	1.2
151.7	2.5
158.8	8

$_{46}Pd^{101}$

Gamma energies (KeV)	Gamma intensities
24	†
269.6 ± 0.2	27
296.1 ± 0.2	100
320.6 ± 0.2	3.6
355.2 ± 0.3	
428.2 ± 0.4	
453.5 ± 0.25	4.0
556.0 ± 0.2	2.2
590.54 ± 0.15	80
611.7 ± 0.4	
723.8 ± 0.4	16
748.6 ± 0.4	3.9
854.0 ± 1.0	
881.0 ± 1.0	
992.8 ± 0.4	5.5
1177.7 ± 0.4	1.6
1201.8 ± 0.4	7
1218.3 ± 0.4	2.5
1288.7 ± 0.4	10
1311.4 ± 0.6	1.5
1638.0 ± 2.5	

$_{46}Pd^{103}$

Gamma energies (KeV)	Gamma intensities
53	†
65	0.001
298	0.009
324	0.003
362	0.06
498	0.013

$_{46}Pd^{107m}$

Gamma energies (KeV)	Gamma intensities
210	

$_{46}Pd^{109m}$

Gamma energies (KeV)	Gamma intensities
188	

$_{46}Pd^{109}$

Gamma energies (KeV)	Gamma intensities
44.8 ± 0.6†	3.6
88.036 ± 0.008	8900 ± 800
103.6 ± 0.7	2.2
134.7 ± 0.7	3.2
145.9 ± 0.7	2.7
311.5 ± 0.5	(100)
390.9 ± 0.8	2.5 ± 0.5
413.5 ± 1	49 ⎰ 26ᵇ⁾
415.2 ± 0.6	⎱ 23
424.7 ± 0.8	1.8 ± 0.4
448.2 ± 0.8	2.6 ± 0.6
551.3 ± 0.8	1.5 ± 0.5
557.8 ± 0.5	6.2 ± 0.8
602.4 ± 0.5	21.5 ± 2
636.1 ± 0.5	27 ± 3
647.3 ± 0.6	65 ± 5
701.8 ± 0.8	9.2 ± 1
707.3 ± 0.8	4.5 ± 0.5
736.7 ± 0.7	5.0 ± 0.6
781.8 ± 0.7	33 ± 3
(863)	< 0.5

$_{46}Pd^{111m}$

Gamma energies (KeV)	Gamma intensities
170	
others (see below)*	

$_{46}Pd^{111}$

Gamma energies (KeV)	Gamma intensities
50	
70	
160	620†
280 ⎫	71
290 ⎬	
380 ⎫	177
400 ⎭	
450	36
500	32
560	68
630	100
750	39
830	10
900	9
960	11
*1080	18
1130	17
*1250	16
1380	9
1440	5
*1640	23
*1690	11
*1900	9

Gamma energies (KeV)	Gamma intensities	Gamma energies (KeV)	Gamma intensities	Gamma energies (KeV)	Gamma intensities
$_{46}Pd^{112}$		401.7 ± 0.4		433.99 ± 0.13	10†
		415.0 ± 0.4		$614.29 + 0.15$	10
18.5	20%	421.1 ± 0.4		722.81 ± 0.18	10
		437.4 ± 0.4			
$_{47}Ag^{102}$		443.5 ± 0.2	18	$_{47}Ag^{108}$	
		527.4			
Ann. Rad.		560.9 ± 0.4		433.8	0.45%
		618.1 ± 0.4		510	
$_{47}Ag^{103m}$		644.8 ± 0.3	16	614.29 ± 0.15	0.26%
		650.9 ± 0.4		633.2	1.7%
138		673.3 ± 0.4		841	0.02%
		681.4 ± 0.5		1010	
$_{47}Ag^{103}$		727.6 ± 0.4			
		743.4 ± 0.4		$_{47}Ag^{109m}$	
Ann. Rad		807.6 ± 0.4			
120	26†	962.8 ± 0.5		88.036 ± 0.008	
150	23	1088.2 ± 0.3	4.2		
240	10			$_{47}Ag^{110m}$	
270	34	$_{47}Ag^{106m}$			
380				116.41 (IT)	
760		194.9		446.2	
920		221.5		620.10	
1010	12	228.5		657.6	100†
1160	9	328.3		677.5	10
1280	13	309.9		686.8	7
		406.0		706.6	10
$_{47}Ag^{104m}$		429.5		744.2	
		450.8		763.8	24
Ann. Rad.		474.2		817.9	8
555		511.8		884.5	74
		600.9		937.3	33
$_{47}Ag^{104}$		616.0		1384.3	22
		680		1475.9	4
Ann. Rad.		703.3		1505.2	11
167		716.2		1562.5	1.2
262		717.1			
355		748.2		$_{47}Ag^{110}$	
443		792.8			
478		803.9		657.6	12%
556	100†	807.5		817.9	
750	20	824.5		1475.9	0.02%
767	57	847.5			
854	15	1045.7		$_{47}Ag^{111m}$	
938	35	1127.8			
1260	4	1199		70	100%
1340	10	1223			
1530	8			$_{47}Ag^{111}$	
1620	9	$_{47}Ag^{106}$			
1810	8			95	
		Ann. Rad.		247	1%
$_{47}Ag^{105}$		295		342	6%
		450		610	
64.0 ± 0.1	18†	616.2 ± 0.6			
74.1		621.4 ± 0.6		$_{47}Ag^{112}$	
89.9 ± 0.2		870.3 ± 0.6			
112.7 ± 0.2	0.013	1045.9 ± 0.6		606.2 ± 0.5	41%
155.7 ± 0.3	0.9	1124.6 ± 0.6		617.0 ± 0.4	
183.0 ± 0.3	0.7	1520		694.1 ± 0.5	
280.4 ± 0.3	62	1730		716.8 ± 0.8	
284.8 ± 0.4	0.003	1880		775.8 ± 1.0	1%
289.4 ± 0.4		2170		850.8 ± 0.6	2%
306.3 ± 0.3	1.6			1103.4 ± 1.0	1%
311.8 ± 0.4		$_{47}Ag^{107m}$		1252.2 ± 1.0	0.5%
319.4 ± 0.3	0.11			1311.5 ± 1.0	1%
325.8 ± 0.4		93.1	100%	1386.7 ± 0.5	4%
329.0 ± 0.4				1539.0 ± 1.0	1%
331.8 ± 0.3		$_{47}Ag^{108m}$		1612.9 ± 0.7	2%
344.7 ± 0.3	69			2055.8 ± 0.8	
360.8 ± 0.3		30.2			
370.3 ± 0.3		79.49 ± 0.18			
392.8 ± 0.3					

Gamma energies (KeV)	Gamma intensities
2105.7 ± 0.6	2%
2211.0 ± 1.5	
2359.8 ± 2.5	0.5%
2506.4 ± 1.0	
2685.0 ± 1.0	0.6%
2827.2 ± 1.0	0.7%
2749.5 ± 2.0	0.6%
$_{47}Ag^{113}$	
97.2 ± 0.3	
258.8 ± 0.3	20
298.6 ± 0.2	100†
316.2 ± 0.3	10
333.1 ± 0.3	5
339.3 ± 0.3	5
364.6 ± 0.3	1
382.0 ± 0.3	1
583.7 ± 0.3	5
672.4 ± 0.3	9
680.9 ± 0.3	9
884.0 ± 0.3	4
988.7 ± 0.3	5
1194.8 ± 0.3	4
$_{47}Ag^{114}$	
570	
$_{47}Ag^{115}$	
110	1%
140	9%
170	2%
220	44%
240	7%
280	13%
360	10%
420	7%
450	1%
470	10%
620	1%
640	3%
1040	2%
1080	2%
1480	11%
1660	8%
1760	2%
1860	3%
1900	7%
2030	2%
2120	13%
2500	1%
$_{48}Cd^{103}$	
Ann. Rad.	
220	
630	
850	
$_{48}Cd^{104}$	
66.7	

Gamma energies (KeV)	Gamma intensities
83.6	
123.6	
134.2	
$_{48}Cd^{105}$	
Ann. Rad.	
25.5	
27.7	
263	
292.5	
308	
312	
317	
321	
325	
336	
341	
347	
433	
607	
1901	
1960	
2000	
2050	
2280	
2320	
$_{48}Cd^{107}$	
Ann. Rad.	
32.6	
93.1(IT)	
300.7	
324.6	
422.6	
526.4	
596.8	
624.5	
719.8	
786.7	
796.0	
799.0	
818	
828.9	
897	
949.0	
1049	
1130	
1222.4	
$_{48}Cd^{109}$	
88.036 ± 0.008	
$_{48}Cd^{111m}$	
149.6	30†
246	94
$_{48}Cd^{113m}$	
265	~0.1%

Gamma energies (KeV)	Gamma intensities
$_{48}Cd^{115m}$	
130	0.07†
162	1.3
210	0.15
292	0.2
485	16
935	100
1130	5
1240	45
1420	2
$_{48}Cd^{115}$	
35	0.5†
230	0.6
262	2.0
485	10
530	26
$_{48}Cd^{117m}$	
89	
161	
222	
273	
293	
314	
345	
366	6†
434	
462	
565	
631	2
702	3
715	5
748	3
762	
832	
862	3
880	
931	2
1029	4
1052	
1065	11
1117	5
1165	
1233	8
1248	3
1260	2
1338	9
1371	
1408	9
1433	12
1562	7
1652	
1659	
1682	3
1723	9
1939	
1998	17
2095	2
2311	
2319	4
2394	
2407	
$_{48}Cd^{117}$	

Gamma energies (KeV)	Gamma intensities		Gamma energies (KeV)	Gamma intensities		Gamma energies (KeV)	Gamma intensities
89			330			745	
161			383			761	
222			391			816	
273			411			844	
293			570			884	
314			633			937	
345			731			995	
434			753			1118	
462			781			1500	
565			842				
832	11†		872				
880			924			₄₉In¹¹⁰	
947	8		1013				
964	3		1033			658	100†
1009	0.7		1054			817	
1052						1180	3
1142						1520	2
1274	1		₄₉In¹⁰⁹			1780	1.3
1303	54					2200	2
1381	2					2800	0.6
1397	6†		Ann. Rad.			3000	
1577	46		60			3460	
1708	6		89			3650	
1835			94				
			205				
			228			₄₉In¹¹¹	
₄₉In¹⁰⁶			262				
			289			172.5	93†
Ann. Rad.			301			247	100
530	17†		326				
630	10		329				
1650			340			₄₉In¹¹²ᵐ	
1850			349				
			410			156	
			422				
₄₉In¹⁰⁷			428				
			446			₄₉In¹¹²	
Ann. Rad.			456				
220	46%		519			Ann. Rad.	
320			533			621	6%
730			546			860	0.4%
840			578			1240	0.5%
940			615			1480	0.3%
1050			623				
1250			627				
1520			651			₄₉In¹¹³ᵐ	
1720			678				
1940			725			391.689 ± 0.010	100%
2260			821				
			825				
			862			₄₉In¹¹⁴ᵐ²	
₄₉In¹⁰⁸			920				
			947			311	
Ann. Rad.			1050			191.6	
383			1190				
633			1550				
842			1610			₄₉In¹¹⁴ᵐ¹	
			1680				
						191.6	
₄₉In¹⁰⁸						358	
			₄₉In¹¹⁰ᵐ			724	
75			121				
120			399			₄₉In¹¹⁴	
150			411				
175			463			Ann. Rad.	
243			562			1299	
264			584				
325			642				
			658				
			707				

Gamma energies (KeV)	Gamma intensities
₄₉In¹¹⁵ᵐ	
335	
₄₉In¹¹⁶ᵐ²	
164	
₄₉In¹¹⁶ᵐ¹	
138.3	3%
385	1%
417.0	36%
818.7	17%
1097.2	53%
1293.3	80%
1508	11%
1753	<0.4%
1770	1.5%
2111	20%
₄₉In¹¹⁶	
434	0.12%
950	0.1%
1293	1.2%
2200	0.01%
₄₉In¹¹⁷ᵐ	
158.63 ± 0.15	16%
315.33 ± 0.18	
₄₉In¹¹⁷	
158.63 ± 0.15	
552.49 ± 0.15	
₄₉In¹¹⁸	
1220	
₄₉In¹¹⁸	
210	3†
440	7
640	10
690	42
810	7
1050	83
1230	100
1250	6
1490	1.4
1540	1.0
2040	3
₄₉In¹¹⁹ᵐ	
24	
311 ± 0.2	
762.91 ± 0.4	
₄₉In¹¹⁹	

Gamma energies (KeV)	Gamma intensities
730	5†
820	100
₄₉In¹²⁰	
1171	
₄₉In¹²⁰	
90	12†
198	9
260	1
710	12
860	34
940	12
1020	61
1170	100
1190	7
1280	14
1470	6
1870	7
2010	6
2220	3
2630	2
₄₉In¹²¹	
940	
₄₉In¹²⁴	
990	3†
1130	10
3210	3
₅₀Sn¹⁰⁹	
Ann. Rad.	
335	
521	
890	
1120	
₅₀Sn¹¹⁰	
283	
₅₀Sn¹¹¹	
Ann. Rad.	
372.9 ± 0.8	16.5 ± 2†
458.0 ± 0.6	11.8 ± 1
536.2 ± 0.6	6.5 ± 1
563.6 ± 0.8	10.5 ± 1.5
616 ± 1	≦ 4
635 ± 1	≦ 4
762.0 ± 0.6	46 ± 3
953.6 ± 0.8	18 ± 1.5
1026.1 ± 0.8	10 ± 1.5
1101.2 ± 0.8	28 ± 3
1153.0 ± 0.6	(100)
1542.5 ± 0.8	27 ± 3
1610.3 ± 0.8	40 ± 3
1915.1 ± 0.8	56 ± 4
2106.6 ± 1	12 ± 1
2178.2 ± 1	9 ± 1
2212.9 ± 1	5.8 ± 0.7
2324.8 ± 1	9 ± 1

Gamma energies (KeV)	Gamma intensities
₅₀Sn¹¹³	
391.689 ± 0.010	98.2%
255	1.8%
₅₀Sn¹¹⁷ᵐ	
158	
159	
₅₀Sn¹¹⁹ᵐ	
23.83	~20%
65	100%
₅₀Sn¹²¹ᵐ	
37.15	
₅₀Sn¹²³	
159.7 ± 0.5	100†
381 ± 1	0.04 ± 0.004
542 ± 1	0.02 ± 0.004
552 ± 1	0.007 ± 0.002
₅₀Sn¹²⁵ᵐ	
331.7	100†
386.1	0.082
589.6	0.20
643.0	0.15
662 ± 1	0.046
776 ± 1	0.018
840.8	0.075
1017.5	0.093
1093 ± 1	0.050
1152 ± 1	0.015
1294 ± 1	0.013
1305 ± 1	0.012
1349 ± 1	0.016
1368.5	0.10
1404.1	0.71
1484.2	0.22
1582 ± 1	0.0058
1615.3	0.13
1634 ± 1	0.024
1735.5	0.033
1913.7	0.020
1947 ± 1	0.013
2113 ± 1	0.0016
₅₀Sn¹²⁵	
342	10†
470	14
810	30
910	30
1070	100
1160	3.3
1410	3.3
1990	14
2230	1.1
₅₀Sn¹²⁶	

Gamma energies (KeV)	Gamma intensities		Gamma energies (KeV)	Gamma intensities		Gamma energies (KeV)	Gamma intensities
			$_{51}Sb^{116m}$			$_{51}Sb^{124m_2}$	
60							
67			Ann. Rad.			25	
92			99	30%			
			140	30%		$_{51}Sb^{124m_1}$	
$_{50}Sn^{127}$			406	36%			
			545	68%		505	100†
270			960	75%		602.70 ± 0.18	100
440			1060	27%		645.76 ± 0.18	100
490			1290	100%			
580							
820						$_{51}Sb^{124}$	
990			$_{51}Sb^{116}$				
1100						443.86 ± 0.3	
1480			Ann. Rad.			602.70 ± 0.18	100†
1600			99			645.76 ± 0.18	7.5
2000			930	26†		709.3 ± 0.2	
2140			1290	85		713.8 ± 0.2	4·
2320			2230	14		722.72 ± 0.18	
2580						735.2 ± 0.5	
2680						790.7 ± 0.25	
2820			$_{51}Sb^{117}$			968.2 ± 0.2	2.5
						1045.2 ± 0.2	2.4
			Ann. Rad.			1325.6 ± 0.2	2
$_{50}Sn^{127}$			158	100%		1355.4 ± 0.5	
						1368.5 ± 0.2	
495			$_{51}Sb^{118m_2}$			1489.08 ± 0.3	2.1
						1526.4 ± 0.3	1.1
$_{50}Sn^{128}$			140	4†		1580.1 ± 0.2	0.6
			300	10		1691.0 ± 0.07	51
44	7†		380	10		2091.1 ± 0.2	7
72	19					2183.3 ± 0.5	
500	61		$_{51}Sb^{118m_1}$			2293.6 ± 0.4	0.6
570	22						
			Ann. Rad.				
$_{51}Sb^{112}$			40.7	29%		$_{51}Sb^{125}$	
			253.5	93%			
Ann. Rad.			1049	100%		35.6 ⎱	
1257			1090			109.5 ⎰ (Te^{125m})	1†
			1229	100%		117.1	
$_{51}Sb^{113}$						172.8	~1.5
			$_{51}Sb^{118}$			176.43	20
						204.2	<1
79 (Sn^{113m})			Ann. Rad.			208.2	<1
320			830			227.9	2.6
640			1229			321.1	5
700			1250			380.4	4
760						407.8	100
810			$_{51}Sb^{119}$			427.9	
950						443.6	
1030			23.83			463.4	33
1200						600.6	62
1520			$_{51}Sb^{120}$			606.7	17
						635.9	36
$_{51}Sb^{114}$			Ann. Rad.			671.4	6
			1171				
Ann. Rad.						$_{51}Sb^{126m}$	
900			$_{51}Sb^{122m}$				
1299						410	
			26			670	
			61				
$_{51}Sb^{115}$			75			$_{51}Sb^{126}$	
			$_{51}Sb^{122}$			290	
Ann. Rad.						410	
499	100†		Ann. Rad.			580	
980	5		563.9	70%		690	
1240	5		686	3.5%		850	
2220	1		1137	0.7%		990	
			1258	0.7%			

$_{51}Sb^{127}$

Gamma energies (KeV)	Gamma intensities
62	
252.7	
290.6	
392.1	
412.0	
445.2	
473.2	
543.2	
603.8	
684.9	
697.9	
721.4	
782.6	

$_{51}Sb^{128}$

Gamma energies (KeV)	Gamma intensities
320	
743	
750	
1070	

$_{51}Sb^{129}$

Gamma energies (KeV)	Gamma intensities
73	
340	
460	
540	
660	
810	
910	
1024	
1240	
1740	

$_{51}Sb^{130}$

Gamma energies (KeV)	Gamma intensities
190	
330	
820	
940	

$_{51}Sb^{131}$

Gamma energies (KeV)	Gamma intensities
640	37%
950	~48%

$_{52}Te^{115}$

Gamma energies (KeV)	Gamma intensities
Ann. Rad.	
720	34†
960	6
1080	24
1280	32
1380	32
1580	6
2200	2

$_{52}Te^{116}$

Gamma energies (KeV)	Gamma intensities
	93.9

$_{52}Te^{117}$

Gamma energies (KeV)	Gamma intensities
	720

$_{52}Te^{118}$

Gamma energies (KeV)	Gamma intensities
Sb X-rays	

$_{52}Te^{119m}$

Gamma energies (KeV)	Gamma intensities
153.0	94†
164	6
207.6	38
400	
760	
917	6
946	10
984	12
1008	
1050	8
1099	7
1140	10
1221	100
1370	2.2
2090	7

$_{52}Te^{119}$

Gamma energies (KeV)	Gamma intensities
645	100†
700	13
1760	4.2

$_{52}Te^{121m}$

Gamma energies (KeV)	Gamma intensities
81.78 ⎱ IT	
212.21 ⎰	
37.15	
103	0.02†
910	0.2
1000	0.2
1100	3.4

$_{52}Te^{121}$

Gamma energies (KeV)	Gamma intensities
37.15	
65.58	0.4
470.4	1.4
507.5	18
573.1	80†

$_{52}Te^{123m}$

Gamma energies (KeV)	Gamma intensities
88.46	100%
159.0	100%

$_{52}Te^{125m}$

Gamma energies (KeV)	Gamma intensities
35.3	
109.6	

$_{52}Te^{127m}$

Gamma energies (KeV)	Gamma intensities
88.7 (IT)	
57.6	0.19†
591	0.0006
657	0.0043

$_{52}Te^{127}$

Gamma energies (KeV)	Gamma intensities
57.6	
145	0.0016†

Gamma energies (KeV)	Gamma intensities
203	0.017
214	0.012
360	0.046
417	0.31

$_{52}Te^{129m}$

Gamma energies (KeV)	Gamma intensities
105.7 (IT)	2.3% (equilib.)
158.91	0.15%
208.9	0.3%
250.57 ± 0.2	0.46%
278.4	0.7%
281.15	0.22%
342.90	0.05%
459.4 ± 0.3	0.90%
487.4	1.7%
556.7	0.22%
624.4	0.1%
671.9	0.05%
696.0	5%
729.7	1.36%
741.1	0.09%
802.2	0.24%
817.2	0.17%
833.5	0.05%
844.9	0.07%
982.2	0.03%
1022.6	0.04%
1084.0	0.71%
1111.8	0.27%

$_{52}Te^{129}$

Gamma energies (KeV)	Gamma intensities
27	
208.95	2.9†
250.6	5
278.4	9
281.1	1
342.9	0.3
345	0.1
459.6	100
487.4	19
532	2.3
556.7	2.1
573	0.6
624.4	1.0
671.9	0.5
696.0	73
729.7	16
741.1	0.8
802.2	2.8
817.2	1.8
833.5	0.7
844.9	0.8
982.2	0.3
1022.6	0.5
1050	0.5
1084.0	10
1112	3.5
1233	0.3
1262	0.7
1400	0.3

$_{52}Te^{131m}$

Gamma energies (KeV)	Gamma intensities
181.7 (IT)	68% (equilibrium)

Gamma energies (KeV)	Gamma intensities	Gamma energies (KeV)	Gamma intensities	Gamma energies (KeV)	Gamma intensities
102.2	7.5%	(IT) 334.14 ± 0.07	15	$_{53}I^{117}$	
149.8	24%	344.5 ± 0.2	1.5		
182.4	2.1%	347.22 ± 0.09	1.3	Ann. Rad.	
200.7	7.6%	355.57 ± 0.14	0.6	160	
240.9	8.4%	362.81 ± 0.15	1.1	340	
334.3	11%	376.83 ± 0.14	0.6		
452.4	6.5%	396.96 ± 0.09	1.7		
665.1	5%	429.02 ± 0.11	3.6	$_{53}I^{118}$	
773.7	46%	444.90 ± 0.09	4.4		
782.5	7.6%	462.11 ± 0.16	3.4	Ann. Rad.	
793.8	16%	471.85 ± 0.09	2.3	550	1†
822.8	6.7%	478.59 ± 0.10	1.8	600	4
852.3	26%	519.6 ± 0.2	0.5	1150	
1125.5	15%	534.85 ± 0.11	2.0		
1206.6	12%	574.04 ± 0.10	3.6		
1645.8	1.5%	622.03 ± 0.16	1.6	$_{53}I^{119}$	
1887.7	1.7%	647.40 ± 0.08	34		
2001.0	2.7%	702.75 ± 0.12	4.3	Ann. Rad.	
2240	0.7%	731.69 ± 0.15	1.7	260	
2330	0.3%	733.89 ± 0.10	3.3	780	
		779.75 ± 0.10	3.9		
		795.7 ± 0.4	1.5		
$_{52}Te^{131}$		800.51 ± 0.12	2.2	$_{53}I^{120}$	
		863.91 ± 0.13	29		
149.8	100†	882.83 ± 0.12	4.8	Ann. Rad.	
279	1.0	897.7 ± 0.4	0.5	560	5†
343	1.1	912.58 ± 0.10	100	620	1
384	1.1	914.72 ± 0.13	19	1520	
452.4	24.0	934.4 ± 0.3	1.5		
493	7.0	978.19 ± 0.09	9.3		
544	0.4	980.4 ± 0.2	2.7	$_{53}I^{121}$	
603	5.9	982.9 ± 0.2	1.3		
654	1.8	1029.8 ± 0.2	1.8	Ann. Rad.	
695	0.5	1061.83 ± 0.11	3.1	213	100†
727	0.4	1348.9 ± 0.2	2.9	270	3
842	0.2	1459.1 ± 0.2	2.5	320	7
898	0.3	1516.1 ± 0.3	1.1	600	
933	1.2	1531.6 ± 0.4	1.0	740	
948	3.0	1587.4 ± 0.2	2.2		
952	0.6	1683.3 ± 0.2	6.7		
997	5.1	1704.4 ± 0.3	1.1	$_{53}I^{122}$	
		1855.7 ± 0.3	1.3		
		2004.9 ± 0.3	5.4	Ann. Rad.	
$_{52}Te^{132}$		2027.7 ± 0.4	1.4	560	100†
		2049.2 ± 0.4	1.7	690	7
49.3 ± 0.3				780	5
111.81 ± 0.2				1250	1
116.48 ± 0.2				1420	1
228.3 ± 0.2		$_{52}Te^{133}$		1750	2
				2180	1
		311.99 ± 0.08	70%	2540	0.2
$_{52}Te^{133m}$		407.63 ± 0.07	31%	2740	
		474.72 ± 0.13	1.1%	2920	
74.1 ± 0.2	0.8†	719.65 ± 0.10	8.3%	3170	
81.5 ± 0.2	0.8	786.77 ± 0.10	7.2%	3450	
88.0 ± 0.2	3.0	844.39 ± 0.07	4.6%		
94.9 ± 0.2	6.0	930.67 ± 0.10	5.4%		
164.34 ± 0.09	1.6	1000.77 ± 0.11	0.8%	$_{53}I^{123}$	
168.87 ± 0.09	12	1021.07 ± 0.15	3.4%		
177.1 ± 0.2	1.5	1252.2 ± 0.2	1.4%	159.1 ± 0.1	100
178.2 ± 0.2	1.0	1333.23 ± 0.12	11%	183.7 ± 1.0	0.03 ± 0.02
184.45 ± 0.10	0.4	1405.7 ± 0.2	0.8%	192.7 ± 1.0	0.03 ± 0.02
193.22 ± 0.10	1.2	1717.65 ± 0.15	3.2%	248.3 ± 0.5	0.08 ± 0.01
198.2 ± 0.2	0.6	1881.5 ± 0.4	1.3%	281.0 ± 0.5	0.08 ± 0.01
213.36 ± 0.08	4.2			346.6 ± 0.5	0.12 ± 0.02
220.94 ± 0.13	0.5			440.4 ± 0.5	0.42 ± 0.02
224.03 ± 0.13	0.4	$_{52}Te^{134}$		505.6 ± 0.6	0.31 ± 0.05
244.28 ± 0.10	0.7			529.0 ± 0.4	1.27 ± 0.11
251.49 ± 0.10	0.6	80	13%	538.5 ± 0.5	0.32 ± 0.02
257.64 ± 0.09	1.0	170	16%	624.9 ± 0.5	0.08 ± 0.01
261.55 ± 0.07	14	204	21%	687.7 ± 0.6	0.03 ± 0.01
		262	19%	736.1 ± 0.06	0.04 ± 0.01
				784.4 ± 0.6	0.05 ± 0.01

Gamma energies (KeV)	Gamma intensities

$_{53}I^{124}$

Gamma energies (KeV)	Gamma intensities
Ann. Rad.	
602.7 ± 0.18	100†
645.76 ± 0.18	18
722.72 ± 0.18	21
890	0.4
968.2 ± 0.2	0.8
1045.2 ± 0.2	0.8
1325.6 ± 0.2	1.5
1368.5 ± 0.2	5
1450	1.1
1500	6
1691.0 ± 0.07	21
1900	0.8
2091.1 ± 0.2	3
2293.6 ± 0.4	2.3
2740	0.9

$_{53}I^{125}$

Gamma energies (KeV)	Gamma intensities
35.48	

$_{53}I^{126}$

Gamma energies (KeV)	Gamma intensities
Ann. Rad.	
388.7 ± 0.2	
491.3 ± 0.2	
666.2 ± 0.2	
753.8 ± 0.2	
879.9 ± 0.2	
1420.0 ± 0.2	

$_{53}I^{128}$

Gamma energies (KeV)	Gamma intensities
442.9 ± 0.2	17%
526.6 ± 0.2	1.8%
743.3 ± 0.15	0.3%
969.5 ± 0.2	0.3%

$_{53}I^{129}$

Gamma energies (KeV)	Gamma intensities
39.58	

$_{53}I^{130}$

Gamma energies (KeV)	Gamma intensities
419	36†
538	100
669	100
743	87
1150	12

$_{53}I^{131}$

Gamma energies (KeV)	Gamma intensities
80.164 ± 0.009	2.6%
177.19 ± 0.08	0.3%
272.45 ± 0.2	0.07%
284.31 ± 0.08	5.9%
318.14 ± 0.15	0.09%
325.80 ± 0.15	0.24%
364.49 ± 0.08	79%
503.13 ± 0.15	0.35%
637.01 ± 0.15	6.7%
642.80 ± 0.17	0.2%
722.92 ± 0.15	1.8%

$_{53}I^{132}$

$_{53}I^{132}$ (continued)

Gamma energies (KeV)	Gamma intensities
147.10 ± 0.3	5.0†
254.9	2.0
262.75 ± 0.3	8.42
505.80 ± 0.3	7.87
522.48 ± 0.3	24.55
546.95 ± 0.4	1.70
620.95 ± 0.3	2.49
630.16 ± 0.3	15.44
650.51 ± 0.3	2.80
727.04 ± 0.3	4.96
729.08 ± 0.25	1.44
772.49 ± 0.25	59.77
780.24 ± 0.25	1.0
784.92 ± 0.4	0.35
809.77 ± 0.2	2.04
812.30 ± 0.3	4.19
863.26 ± 0.4	0.40
876.96 ± 0.4	0.63
910.44 ± 0.3	0.57
927.82 ± 0.4	0.37
954.66 ± 0.25	9.72
984.38 ± 0.4	0.40
1035.29 ± 0.4	0.29
1136.11 ± 0.3	1.29
1143.64 ± 0.4	0.62
1173.22 ± 0.4	0.48
1290.74 ± 0.4	0.39
1295.34 ± 0.5	0.54
1298.0 ± 0.4	0.25
1372.0 ± 0.3	0.70
1398.71 ± 0.4	2.21
1442.46 ± 0.3	0.43
1920.84 ± 0.4	0.24
2002.08 ± 0.4	0.21
2088.5 ± 0.5	0.07
2175.0 ± 1	0.02
2226.0 ± 1	0.03
2395.0 ± 1	0.01

$_{53}I^{133}$

Gamma energies (KeV)	Gamma intensities
151.1 ± 0.3	0.029
234.3 ± 0.4	†
245.9 ± 0.3	0.081
262.7 ± 0.3	0.38
267.3 ± 0.4	0.10
386.4 ± 0.3	0.088
417.1 ± 0.3	0.18
422.9 ± 0.3	0.43
427.7 ± 0.4	0.099
438.9 ± 0.4	0.083
510.5 ± 0.3	2.08
529.90 ± 0.15	89% 100
600.4 ± 0.3	0.046
608.1 ± 0.3	0.086
618.0 ± 0.25	0.64
680.3 ± 0.2	0.79
706.65 ± 0.2	1.77
768.46 ± 0.25	0.51
789.5 ± 0.3	0.058
820.63 ± 0.3	0.187
835.3 ± 0.35	
856.37 ± 0.25	1.39
875.40 ± 0.25	5.26
910.1 ± 0.3	0.26
1052.3 ± 0.3	0.64
1060.3 ± 0.4	0.20
1236.56 ± 0.2	1.78
1293.9 ± 0.3	0.30
1298.32 ± 0.2	2.72

Gamma energies (KeV)	Gamma intensities
1350.6 ± 0.3	0.18
1460.9 ± 0.3	0.18
1592.5 ± 0.3	0.08

$_{53}I^{134}$

Gamma energies (KeV)	Gamma intensities
135.4 ± 0.3	3.51†
152.2 ± 0.4	0.12
162.6 ± 0.3	0.26
188.5 ± 0.3	
216.9 ± 0.4	0.29
235.43 ± 0.3	1.85
319.68 ± 0.3	0.44
356.88 ± 0.3	
405.35 ± 0.15	6.84
433.24 ± 0.17	4.13
458.88 ± 0.25	1.04
488.90 ± 0.25	1.63
514.48 ± 0.2	2.30
540.81 ± 0.15	7.66
565.0 ± 0.4	
595.29 ± 0.15	11.24
621.77 ± 0.17	9.93
628.12 ± 0.25	2.60
667.58 ± 0.25	0.74
677.26 ± 0.17	7.70
730.77 ± 0.2	1.79
766.67 ± 0.18	3.98
772.2 ± 0.4	0.60
816.7 ± 0.3	
847.04 ± 0.08	96% 100
857.29 ± 0.15	7.51
875.3 ± 0.3	0.35
884.18 ± 0.1	67.81
947.69 ± 0.15	4.19
967.4 ± 0.25	0.6
974.72 ± 0.17	4.90
1040.1 ± 0.2	1.52
	0.5
1072.52 ± 0.17	15.91
1100.3 ± 0.3	0.75
1103.5 ± 0.3	0.66
1136.15 ± 0.18	10.68
1353.5 ± 0.3	0.33
1455.2 ± 0.3	2.48
1469.5 ± 0.5	0.81
1613.54 ± 0.3	4.61
1741.4 ± 0.35	2.41
1806.7 ± 0.35	5.62
2311.9 ± 1.0	0.4
2467.1 ± 1.0	0.21

$_{53}I^{135}$

Gamma energies (KeV)	Gamma intensities
135.4 ± 0.5	
197.0 ± 0.4	
220.45 ± 0.08	5.37†
229.64 ± 0.18	0.64
249.56 ± 0.08	6.24
264.16 ± 0.08	
288.26 ± 0.08	9.03
289.6 ± 0.4	1.24
305.3 ± 0.2	0.43
361.6 ± 0.2	
403.0 ± 0.3	
415.0 ± 0.2	1.44
417.54 ± 0.1	10.79
429.9 ± 0.2	0.97

Gamma energies (KeV)	Gamma intensities
433.69 ± 0.15	1.93
451.7 ± 0.2	0.83
510.60 ± 0.17	0.94
526.43 ± 0.10	21.16
(Xe^{135m})	
546.54 ± 0.10	22.75
559.0 ± 0.5	
648.8 ± 0.3	
650.2 ± 0.3	2.56
667.8 ± 0.3	1.25
707.9 ± 0.6	2.92
836.84 ± 0.12	20.10
884.1 ± 0.3	4.07
972.42 ± 0.18	7.41
1038.74 ± 0.15	29.86
1101.5 ± 0.4	5.79
1123.8 ± 0.2	13.18
1131.56 ± 0.18	79.73
1168.9 ± 0.4	3.02
1260.45 ± 0.15	100 34.9 %
1281.8 ± 0.4	
1298.3 ± 0.4	
1367.5 ± 0.3	
1398.0 ± 0.6	
1457.65 ± 0.15	31.36
1470.0 ± 0.6	
1503.0 ± 0.5	3.92
1566.6 ± 0.4	3.70
1678.20 ± 0.17	30.10
1706.6 ± 0.2	13.03
1791.36 ± 0.2	25.16
1830.7 ± 0.4	1.89
1927.1 ± 0.5	
2046.1 ± 0.5	2.76
2256.6 ± 0.8	
2268.6 ± 1	
2408.6 ± 1	2.78
2465.9 ± 1.5	

$_{53}$I^{136}

Gamma energies (KeV)	Gamma intensities
200	12%
270	18%
390	19%
460	~2%
530	~2%
710	3%
1000	6%
1320	70%
1325	25%
1550	4%
1720	2%
1910	5%
2200	7%
2400	12%
2630	10%
2800	8%
3200	5%

$_{54}$Xe^{118}

Ann. Rad.	

$_{54}$Xe^{119}

Ann. Rad.	
100	

$_{54}$Xe^{120}

Gamma energies (KeV)	Gamma intensities
Ann. Rad.	
55	
73	
176	
760	

$_{54}$Xe^{121}

Ann. Rad.	
80	
95.5	
132.5	
437	

$_{54}$Xe^{122}

90.3	
148.2	
239	

$_{54}$Xe^{123}

Ann. Rad.	
148.6	
177.6	
328.6	
680	
900	
1100	

$_{54}$Xe^{125m}

75	
111	

$_{54}$Xe^{125}

54.7	
74.6	
113.1	
187.6	
242.2	
460	

$_{54}$Xe^{127m}

125	
175	

$_{54}$Xe^{127}

Gamma energies (KeV)	Gamma intensities
57.60	
145.22	3.9%
172.10	24%
202.84	67%
374.96	20%

$_{54}$Xe^{129m}

39.58	
196.56	

$_{54}$Xe^{131m}

163.98 ± 0.10	

$_{54}$Xe^{133m}

Gamma energies (KeV)	Gamma intensities
232.8	

$_{54}$Xe^{133}

79.55	0.25%
80.97	35%
161	0.03%
220	
302	0.003%
382	0.001%

$_{54}$Xe^{135m}

526.43 ± 0.10	

$_{54}$Xe^{135}

249.56 ± 0.1	9.2%
360	0.009%
610	0.3%

$_{54}$Xe^{137}

455	33%

$_{54}$Xe^{138}

160	33†
260	100
420	63
1730	44
1990	30

$_{54}$Xe^{139}

180	4†
220	100
300	57
1150	23

$_{54}$Xe^{140}

130	

$_{55}$Cs^{123}

Ann. Rad.	

$_{55}$Cs^{125}

Ann. Rad.	
112	

$_{55}$Cs^{126}

Ann. Rad.	
385	38%

$_{55}$Cs^{127}

Ann. Rad.	
125	13†
286	
406	100

$_{55}$Cs^{128}

Gamma energies (KeV)	Gamma intensities	Gamma energies (KeV)	Gamma intensities	Gamma energies (KeV)	Gamma intensities
Ann. Rad.		86.4	5.6%	Ann. Rad.	
441	50†	153.38 ± 0.2	8.2%	$_{56}Ba^{125}$	
528		164.0 ± 0.2	4.5%	Ann. Rad.	
576		176.7 ± 0.2	13%		
940	1.5	273.8 ± 0.2	12%	$_{56}Ba^{126}$	
1200	2.1	340.6 ± 0.15	44%	230	100†
1660	0.4	818.5 ± 0.2	100%	700	33
2180	0.4	1048.1 ± 0.2	80%		
2420	0.2	1235.4 ± 0.2	20%	$_{56}Ba^{128}$	
				134	
$_{55}Cs^{129}$				278	
94	1.3†	$_{55}Cs^{137}$			
174	1.0	661.630 ± 0.03	84.8 ± 0.5%	$_{56}Ba^{+129m}$	
270	0.8				
278	6			Ann. Rad.	
321	8	$_{55}Cs^{138}$		53.2	
375	100			73.2	
416	52	66.7 ± 0.3		129	
550	9	75.41 ± 0.4	0.08†	135.7	
591	1.7	107.6 ± 0.3	0.06	176.9	
900	0.5	112.27 ± 0.25	0.16	182.3	
950	0.18	137.89 ± 0.15	1.58	202.3	
		165.75 ± 0.2	3.17	214.2	
		191.83 ± 0.3	0.5	220.6	
$_{55}Cs^{130}$		212.04 ± 0.3		237.4	
		227.60 ± 0.18	1.56	263.6	
Ann. Rad.		324.53 ± 0.2	0.43	286.0	
		364.1 ± 0.3		293.5	
$_{55}Cs^{132}$		408.67 ± 0.2	5.3	328.2	
		421.39 ± 0.3	0.43	475	
Ann. Rad.		462.51 ± 0.18	35.49	481	
464.58 ± 0.4		516.53 ± 0.2	0.65	501	
505.55 ± 0.4		546.71 ± 0.15	12.69	534	
510.58 ± 0.4		871.61 ± 0.18	6.07	543	
566.91 ± 0.3		1009.65 ± 0.18	37.86	547	
630.12 ± 0.3		1146.88 ± 0.2	1.49	554	
667.60 ± 0.2		1283.4 ± 0.8		557	
772.53 ± 0.3		1343.33 ± 0.3	1.64	561	
796.09 ± 0.3		1435.74 ± 0.18	73% 100	597	
1031.87 ± 0.3		1444.59 ± 0.25	1.32	679	
1136.00 ± 0.3		2217.75 ± 0.2	18.52	690	
1298.11 ± 0.4		2316.5 ± 1.5		700	
1317.90 ± 0.4		2345.0 ± 0.5	0.81	713	
1461.09 ± 0.5		2582.6 ± 0.4		738	
1985.68 ± 0.4		2639.4 ± 0.3	9.97	748	
		3340	0.5	759	
$_{55}Cs^{134m}$				768	
		$_{55}Cs^{139}$		779	
~10				802	
127.6		500		820	
137.4		630		829	
		800		833	
$_{55}Cs^{134}$		1280		872	
		1900		892	
475.34 ± 0.1	1.8%	2080		933	
563.20	8%			957	
569.33	14%			963	
604.7	98%	$_{55}Cs^{140}$		1000	
795.8	88%			1035	
801.9	9%	590		1045	
1038.6	1.1%	880		1122	
1167.9	1.9%	1140		1163	
1365.1	3.4%	1620		1179	
1400.5	0.08%	1850		1208	
		2060		1221	
		2320		1252	
$_{55}Cs^{136}$		2720		1458	
		3150		1624	
66.9 ± 0.2	13.7%	$_{56}Ba^{123}$			

Gamma energies (KeV)	Gamma intensities
$_{56}Ba^{131m}$	
78	2†
110	100
$_{56}Ba^{131}$	
54.84	
78.69	
82.24	
92.25	
123.73	
133.54	
137.3	
157.0	
216.0	
239.6	
246.8	
249.4	
294.5	
351.2	
373.2	
404.3	
427.7	
451.7	
461.3	
462.9	
480.6	
486.6	
496.3	
573	
585	
620.2	
674	
696	
832	
914	
924.4	
969.1	
1048.2	
$_{56}Ba^{133m}$	
275.7	
12.29	
$_{56}Ba^{133}$	
	†
53.17 ± 0.04	3.68 ± 0.09
79.60 ± 0.05	4.9 ± 0.59
80.997 ± 0.006	55.3 ± 4.2
160.66 ± 0.06	1.01 ± 0.05
223.43 ± 0.26	0.75 ± 0.04
276.43 ± 0.26	11.6 ± 0.17
303.09 ± 0.21	29.9 ± 0.29
356.26 ± 0.15	≡ 100
384.09 ± 0.20	14.9 ± 0.26
$_{56}Ba^{135m}$	
268	100 %
$_{56}Ba^{136m}$	
163.7	
818	
1050	

Gamma energies (KeV)	Gamma intensities
$_{56}Ba^{137m}$	
661.630 ± 0.030	
$_{56}Ba^{139}$	
165.85 ± 0.010	27 %
1270	
1430	
$_{56}Ba^{140}$	
13.85	
29.97	30 %
132.7	1.7 %
162.7	8 %
304.9	7 %
423.8	3 %
437.6	5 %
537.3	29 %
$_{56}Ba^{141}$	
113.08 ± 0.05	2†
180.70 ± 0.09	0.7
190.33 ± 0.05	100
276.94 ± 0.04	52
304.18 ± 0.04	57
343.66 ± 0.04	31
389.66 ± 0.07	3.1
457.52 ± 0.05	12
462.13 ± 0.06	10
467.26 ± 0.06	13
625.21 ± 0.04	7
647.78 ± 0.04	13
739.02 ± 0.1	10
831.70 ± 0.04	4.1
876.01 ± 0.14	8
929.28 ± 0.08	1.5
981.40 ± 0.15	1.7
1160.55 ± 0.1	3
1197.3 ± 0.2	13
1273.4 ± 0.2	1.3
1310.7 ± 0.2	2.1
1436.64 ± 0.1	2.0
1501.28 ± 0.18	0.7
1551.0 ± 0.3	0.9
1740.8 ± 0.2	7
$_{56}Ba^{142}$	
77 ± 1	41†
231.57 ± 0.09	59
255.33 ± 0.07	100
286.13 ± 0.16	7
309.5 ± 0.3	11
364.03 ± 0.07	28
379.42 ± 0.16	3
425.05 ± 0.07	30
432.42 ± 0.16	5.6
589.95 ± 0.2	3.5
599.61 ± 0.1	13
769.71 ± 0.17	4.2
840.07 ± 0.12	19
894.86 ± 0.1	82
944.02 ± 0.07	47
1000.90 ± 0.1	53
1078.52 ± 0.07	56
1093.95 ± 0.09	17

Gamma energies (KeV)	Gamma intensities
1126.1 ± 0.1	10
1203.81 ± 0.1	97
1380.3 ± 0.2	14
$_{57}La^{126}$	
Ann. Rad.	
$_{57}La^{127}$	
Ann. Rad.	
$_{57}La^{128}$	
Ann. Rad.	
$_{57}La^{129}$	
Ann. Rad.	
$_{57}La^{130}$	
Ann. Rad.	
356	
450	
550	
720	
810	
910	
1010	
1190	
1450	
1550	
$_{57}La^{131}$	
Ann. Rad.	
115	23†
169	5
214	8
254	8
285	17
364	20
417	20
450	8
600	7
878	1
$_{57}La^{132}$	
Ann. Rad.	
470	
560	
660	
900	
1030	
1220	
1450	
1580	
1920	
$_{57}La^{133}$	
Ann. Rad.	
260	
$_{57}La^{134}$	
Ann. Rad.	
560	

Gamma energies (KeV)	Gamma intensities
604.6	
760	
820	
900	
980	
1170	
1300	
1470	
1550	
1760	
1980	
2150	
2240	
2590	

$_{57}La^{135}$

Gamma energies (KeV)	Gamma intensities
52.4	
87.4	
117.0	
118	
132	
205	
265	
300	
379	
515	
544	
549	
569	
571	
602	
661	
679	
777	
821	
865	
901	

$_{57}La^{136}$

Gamma energies (KeV)	Gamma intensities
Ann. Rad.	
830	

$_{57}La^{140}$

Gamma energies (KeV)	Gamma intensities
109.6 ± 0.2	0.22%
131.15 ± 0.2	0.45%
241.9	0.55%
266.5	0.5%
328.7	21%
432.5	3%
487.0	46%
510.9	0.35%
751.7	0.45%
815.8	24%
867.9	5.7%
919.6	2.5%
925.2	6.7%
951.0	0.6%
1085.3	1%
1596.2	97%
2010.4	0.4%
2348.2	0.8%
2521.8	3.2%
2547.7	0.09%

$_{57}La^{141}$

Gamma energies (KeV)	Gamma intensities
1370	2%

$_{57}La^{142}$

Gamma energies (KeV)	Gamma intensities
106.47 ± 0.1	0.25
178.32 ± 0.1	0.23
418.2 ± 0.3	0.1
430.3 ± 0.3	0.1
510.11 ± 0.1	0.4
578.25 ± 0.08	2.8
641.27 ± 0.05	100 (50%)
861.68 ± 0.1	3.5
894.94 ± 0.05	18 4
1011.42 ± 0.07	7.8
1043.89 ± 0.07	4.6
1160.40 ± 0.1	2.4
1233.07 ± 0.1	3.6
1363.55 ± 0.2	3.4
1545.93 ± 0.2	6.5
1723.23 ± 0.3	2.4
1756.60 ± 0.1	5.4
1901.56 ± 0.1	11.3
2004.87 ± 0.3	2.0
2055.6 ± 0.2	3.5
2187.49 ± 0.1	8.8
2397.95 ± 0.1	24.4
2543.1 ± 0.3	15.7
2666.5 ± 0.3	2.0
2971.8 ± 0.3	6.5
3314.1 ± 0.3	0.9
3460.1 ± 0.3	0.6
3611 ± 1	1.2
3632.6 ± 0.4	1.8
3719.7 ± 0.5	0.3
3850.1 ± 0.5	0.3

$_{57}La^{143}$

Gamma energies (KeV)	Gamma intensities
200	8†
440	13
620	100
800	44
920	8
1070	26
1170	57
1580	28
1700	19
1980	35
2220	6
2460	13
2560	27
2850	15

$_{58}Ce^{132}$

Gamma energies (KeV)	Gamma intensities
180	

$_{58}Ce^{133}$

Gamma energies (KeV)	Gamma intensities
1800	

$_{58}Ce^{135}$

Gamma energies (KeV)	Gamma intensities
52.4	
87.4	
117.0	
118.0	
132	
205	
265	
300	
379	
515	
544	

Gamma energies (KeV)	Gamma intensities
549	
569	
571	
602	
661	
679	
777	
821	
865	
901	

$_{58}Ce^{137m}$

Gamma energies (KeV)	Gamma intensities
254.5 (IT)	99.4%
168	45†
762	16
825	38
836	8.5
994	0.15
1004	2.1
1160	0.2

$_{58}Ce^{137}$

Gamma energies (KeV)	Gamma intensities
Ann. Rad.	
10	†
433	5
436	31
446	204
479	1.7
481	~4.0
492	1.0
698	3.5
771	0.9
781	0.4
916	6.7
926	3.4

$_{58}Ce^{139m}$

Gamma energies (KeV)	Gamma intensities
746	

$_{58}Ce^{139}$

Gamma energies (KeV)	Gamma intensities
165.854 ± 0.010	100%

$_{58}Ce^{141}$

Gamma energies (KeV)	Gamma intensities
145.443 ± 0.006	49%

$_{58}Ce^{143}$

Gamma energies (KeV)	Gamma intensities
57.37	11.5%
142	0.4%
231.60	2%
293.22	43%
350.6 ± 0.1	3%
374	0.4%
490.42	2%
587.38	0.5%
664.59 ± 0.1	5.5%
721.96 ± 0.1	6%
880.4 ± 0.2	1%
940	0.2%
1040	0.2%
1110	0.4%

$_{58}Ce^{144}$

Gamma energies (KeV)	Gamma intensities
33.57	
40.93	
53.41	
59.03	
80.12	
99.95	
133.53	11%
$_{58}$Ce^{146}	
50	
110	20†
142	42
220	50
270	12
320	100
$_{59}$Pr^{134}	
Ann. Rad.	
220	
300	
410	
640	
960	
$_{59}$Pr^{135}	
Ann. Rad.	
80	
220	
300	
$_{59}$Pr^{136}	
Ann. Rad.	
170	
~800	
~1100	
$_{59}$Pr^{137}	
Ann. Rad.	
$_{59}$Pr^{138}	
Ann. Rad.	
298	77†
400	9
550	~5
790	100
1040	98
1200	1
1830	0.4
$_{59}$Pr^{139}	
Ann. Rad.	
270	12†
1350	27
1610	16
$_{59}$Pr^{140}	
Ann. Rad.	
306	
1596	
1902	

Gamma energies (KeV)	Gamma intensities
$_{59}$Pr^{142}	
1575.43 ± 0.3	4%
$_{59}$Pr^{143}	
no γ	
$_{59}$Pr^{144}	
696.48 ± 0.09	1.5%
1489.14 ± 0.07	0.35%
2185.32 ± 0.05	0.9%
$_{59}$Pr^{145}	
72	
680	
750	
920	
980	
1050	
1160	
$_{59}$Pr^{146}	
455	77%
597	10%
750	16%
780	15%
920	6%
1020	5%
1370	6%
1510	27%
1720	4%
1970	2%
2230	4%
2390	3%
2730	1.7%
$_{59}$Pr^{147}	
78	17%
105	
127	
310	
340	25%
560	39%
610	10%
650	24%
1260	11%
$_{59}$Pr^{148}	
300	
$_{60}$Nd^{138}	
Ann. Rad.	
$_{60}$Nd^{139m}	
232	
$_{60}$Nd^{139}	
Ann. Rad.	
36.5	

Gamma energies (KeV)	Gamma intensities
114	
132.7	
200	
210	
217	
708	100
737	42
773	68†
821	
822	
828	
900	25
983	70
1030	30
1100	30
1240	20
1340	20
1480	10
1580	8
1720	4
1850	3
2050	10
$_{60}$Nd^{141}	
Ann. Rad.	
145.443 ± 0.0006	
1126.8 ± 0.3	
1147.5 ± 0.3	
1292.6 ± 0.3	
1298.6 ± 0.3	
$_{60}$Nd^{141m}	
0.755	100%
$_{60}$Nd^{147}	
91.0 ± 0.2	27%
120.5	0.5%
196.6	0.4%
275.4	0.8%
319.4	2.0%
398.1	1.6%
410.4	0.7%
439.8	1.2%
489.3	0.2%
531.0	13%
594.7	0.25%
685.8	0.8%
$_{60}$Nd^{149}	
30.00 ± 0.10	
58.90 ± 0.03	1.3%
65.37 ± 0.05	0.041%
74.3 ± 0.2	
74.7 ± 0.2	
71.33 ± 0.2	
91.12 ± 0.05	0.063%
97.00 ± 0.03	1.3%
107.76 ± 0.10	
114.31 ± 0.03	16.1%
117.0 ± 0.2	
122.41 ± 0.05	0.20%
126.62 ± 0.05	0.10%
137.02 ± 0.08	0.040%
139.21 ± 0.05	0.41%
155.87 ± 0.03	5.2%

Gamma energies (KeV)	Gamma intensities	Gamma energies (KeV)	Gamma intensities	Gamma energies (KeV)	Gamma intensities
177.82 ± 0.05	0.14%	768.17 ± 0.10	0.059%	58.62 ± 0.10	0.35%
185.50 ± 0.08	0.079%	781.42 ± 0.20	0.006%	69.19 ± 0.05	1.27%
188.64 ± 0.03	1.7%	786.74 ± 0.10	0.011%	81.85 ± 0.25	0.49%
192.03 ± 0.05	0.51%	793.43 ± 0.10	0.022%	85.18 ± 0.06	1.98%
198.93 ± 0.03	1.25%	795.84 ± 0.20	0.006%	90.04 ± 0.05	1.60%
208.15 ± 0.05	2.5%	808.80 ± 0.10	0.146%	102.89 ± 0.13	0.48%
211.32 ± 0.03	23.4%	809.8 ± 0.5	0.025%	109.07 ± 0.55	<0.001%
214.02 ± 0.07		813.2 ± 0.5	0.008%	116.79 ± 0.04	32.56%
226.85 ± 0.05	0.14%	829.4 ± 0.4	0.006%	138.88 ± 0.04	6.31%
229.57 ± 0.05	0.43%	832.20 ± 0.10	0.019%	149.49 ± 0.07	0.33%
240.23 ± 0.03	3.4%	837.41 ± 0.10	0.030%	158.74 ± 0.20	0.50%
245.71 ± 0.05	0.89%	842.86 ± 0.10	0.048%	170.75 ± 0.04	3.39%
250.84 ± 0.10	0.032%	849.93 ± 0.10	0.022%	175.07 ± 0.05	6.12%
254.20 ± 0.07	0.075%	859.43 ± 0.20	0.013%	183.14 ± 0.08	0.36%
258.07 ± 0.05	0.33%	861.54 ± 0.10	0.019%	197.23 ± 0.13	0.27%
267.70 ± 0.03	5.2%	865.03 ± 0.15	0.018%	199.73 ± 0.12	0.30%
270.18 ± 0.03	9.2%	871.40 ± 0.10	0.032%	208.10 ± 0.14	0.31%
273.28 ± 0.08	0.20%	873.8 ± 0.2	0.0052%	239.29 ± 0.30	0.83%
275.46 ± 0.05	0.51%	886.59 ± 0.3	0.0073%	249.27 ± 0.30	0.16%
276.96 ± 0.10	0.28%	907.70 ± 0.2	0.0063%	255.69 ± 0.04	13.3%
282.47 ± 0.05	0.52%	915.3 ± 0.3	0.0045%	263.56 ± 0.07	0.67%
288.21 ± 0.05	0.59%	923.88 ± 0.08	0.099%	300.58 ± 0.08	1.58%
294.82 ± 0.05	0.50%	929.44 ± 0.15	0.012%	312.49 ± 0.35	0.25%
301.14 ± 0.05	0.33%	935.94 ± 0.2	0.0056%	320.13 ± 0.11	0.63%
310.99 ± 0.05	0.44%	938.77 ± 0.2	0.0060%	324.56 ± 0.35	0.48%
326.57 ± 0.03	4.0%	945.82 ± 0.10	0.021%	332.76 ± 0.11	0.63%
342.85 ± 0.10	0.029%	951.96 ± 0.15	0.0086%	347.11 ± 0.11	0.39%
347.8 ± 0.2		964.00 ± 0.15	0.018%	356.91 ± 0.11	0.38%
349.23 ± 0.03	1.29%	967.44 ± 0.15	0.0094%	402.33 ± 0.06	1.41%
352.75 ± 0.10	0.056%	971.7 ± 0.3	0.0033%	407.53 ± 0.10	0.45%
357.05 ± 0.05	0.047%	979.03 ± 0.08	0.096%	414.49 ± 0.35	0.24%
360.05 ± 0.05	0.14%	986.7 ± 0.3	0.0033%	423.54 ± 0.03	5.31%
366.64 ± 0.05	0.57%	992.9 ± 0.2	0.013%	426.60 ± 0.30	0.50%
380.94 ± 0.10	0.058%	1022.79 ± 0.08	0.105%	439.37 ± 0.20	0.35%
384.69 ± 0.05	0.29%	1027.19 ± 0.10	0.0098%	460.58 ± 0.08	0.74%
396.77 ± 0.10	0.085%	1031.8 ± 0.2	0.0041%	524.35 ± 0.11	0.42%
423.54 ± 0.03	8.2%	1041.97 ± 0.10	0.023%	531.99 ± 0.15	0.16%
425.7 ± 0.3		1051.9 ± 0.3	0.0037%	542.19 ± 0.35	0.45%
443.53 ± 0.03	1.29%	1076.05 ± 0.15	0.021%	549.99 ± 0.11	0.70%
480.21 ± 0.15	0.051%	1078.78 ± 0.10	0.058%	562.72 ± 0.17	0.21%
483.53 ± 0.15	0.073%	1100.78 ± 0.10	0.052%	577.41 ± 0.11	0.26%
493.86 ± 0.15	0.044%	1123.6 ± 0.4	0.014%	585.20 ± 0.16	1.09%
497.81 ± 0.15	0.047%	1125.41 ± 0.15	0.025%	589.61 ± 0.10	0.30%
510.29 ± 0.15	0.051%	1128.5 ± 0.3	0.0034%	596.93 ± 0.09	0.60%
515.45 ± 0.20		1135.9 ± 0.2	0.0021%	619.02 ± 0.12	0.35%
533.17 ± 0.15	0.074%	1141.8 ± 0.2	0.0034%	629.78 ± 0.31	0.14%
538.00 ± 0.20		1150.1 ± 0.2	0.0030%	658.58 ± 0.20	0.66%
540.49 ± 0.03	6.6%	1172.1 ± 0.3	0.0044%	670.50 ± 0.18	0.22%
556.40 ± 0.10	1.00%	1175.7 ± 0.2	0.0044%	677.95 ± 0.06	2.22%
579.25 ± 0.07	0.077%	1190.4 ± 0.2	0.0029%	724.17 ± 0.18	0.28%
583.07 ± 0.07	0.072%	1197.8 ± 0.2	0.0066%	736.21 ± 0.06	5.92%
594.48 ± 0.10	0.028%	1202.3 ± 0.2	0.0019%	739.17 ± 0.12	1.71%
598.06 ± 0.15	0.033%	1225.7 ± 0.3	0.0014%	755.56 ± 0.11	1.08%
630.24 ± 0.07	0.19%	1234.11 ± 0.10	0.0250%	765.46 ± 0.70	0.16%
635.47 ± 0.07	0.096%	1239.0 ± 0.6	0.0014%	768.09 ± 0.70	0.22%
654.82 ± 0.03	8.4%	1259.6 ± 0.2	0.0033%	773.60 ± 0.18	0.28%
661.8 ± 0.3	0.016%	1264.0 ± 0.2	0.0060%	797.48 ± 0.06	4.65%
671.6 ± 1.0	0.012%	1280.3 ± 0.3	0.0010%	829.05 ± 0.18	0.22%
673.6 ± 0.5	0.014%	1284.3 ± 0.3	0.0007%	841.05 ± 0.11	0.96%
675.8 ± 0.2	0.028%	1290.10 ± 0.15	0.0039%	852.98 ± 0.14	0.42%
681.29 ± 0.2	0.011%	1298.4 ± 0.3	0.0015%	866.44 ± 0.26	0.32%
686.96 ± 0.07	0.092%	1312.13 ± 0.15	0.0068%	870.65 ± 0.24	0.32%
696.29 ± 0.05	0.17%	1357.2 ± 0.40	0.0021%	876.33 ± 0.14	0.48%
712.62 ± 0.07	0.072%	1381.5 ± 0.3	0.0021%	897.72 ± 0.24	0.41%
718.40 ± 0.10	0.026%	1448.1 ± 0.5	0.0004%	904.69 ± 0.16	0.35%
727.90 ± 0.15	0.019%	1454.3 ± 0.4	0.0011%	914.15 ± 0.11	1.21%
740.61 ± 0.10	0.017%	1473.9 ± 0.5	0.0003%	925.53 ± 0.22	0.16%
749.68 ± 0.15	0.012%	1495.8 ± 0.3	0.0008%	943.11 ± 0.22	0.37%
754.33 ± 0.10	0.030%	1568.4 ± 0.4	0.0005%	958.09 ± 0.11	0.46%
758.6 ± 0.3	0.014%			1016.30 ± 0.10	2.80%
761.45 ± 0.15	0.020%			1020.21 ± 0.50	0.19%

$_{60}$Nd^{151}

Gamma energies (KeV)	Gamma intensities
1032.47 ± 0.18	0.11%
1035.98 ± 0.14	0.19%
1041.76 ± 0.11	0.35%
1048.05 ± 0.09	0.67%
1066.60 ± 0.14	0.17%
1073.00 ± 0.22	0.085%
1077.49 ± 0.37	0.15%
1080.09 ± 0.21	0.30%
1100.11 ± 0.20	0.093%
1107.20 ± 0.11	0.44%
1122.59 ± 0.06	4.46%
1126.56 ± 0.25	0.28%
1132.53 ± 0.18	0.18%
1136.54 ± 0.15	0.23%
1145.84 ± 0.17	0.25%
1157.02 ± 0.13	0.21%
1180.90 ± 0.06	14.65%
1189.33 ± 0.10	0.31%
1201.15 ± 0.13	0.20%
1213.34 ± 0.14	0.093%
1217.44 ± 0.25	0.046%
1224.39 ± 0.27	0.051%
1232.79 ± 0.14	0.11%
1238.30 ± 0.18	0.065%
1250.84 ± 1.12	0.051%
1254.53 ± 1.12	0.051%
1270.64 ± 0.21	0.19%
1286.17 ± 0.12	0.26%
1293.94 ± 0.33	0.11%
1297.75 ± 0.21	0.19%
1314.61 ± 0.12	0.31%
1328.36 ± 0.12	0.31%
1333.33 ± 0.14	0.12%
1341.61 ± 0.23	0.11%
1346.45 ± 0.2	0.033%
1360.20 ± ?	0.15%
1362.87 ± 0.20	0.31%
1379.25 ± 0.17	0.16%
1363.48 ± 0.21	0.078%
1395.41 ± 1.09	0.13%
1425.30 ± 0.27	0.068%
1444.41 ± 0.60	0.055%
1446.97 ± 0.90	0.035%
1465.62 ± 0.24	0.077%
1476.06 ± 0.19	0.11%
1485.66 ± 0.14	0.28%
1498.74 ± 1.14	0.029%
1501.58 ± 1.14	0.029%
1507.58 ± 0.41	0.032%
1533.61 ± 0.28	0.049%
1550.03 ± 0.14	0.36%
1554.05 ± 0.25	0.072%
1566.73 ± 0.24	0.085%
1572.02 ± 0.25	0.10%
1578.63 ± 0.18	0.21%
1592.75 ± 0.25	0.044%
1598.20 ± 0.26	0.12%
1618.17 ± 0.16	0.41%
1636.75 ± 0.24	0.12%
1640.44 ± 0.37	0.032%
1647.45 ± 0.30	0.051%
1686.86 ± 0.26	0.015%
1717.27 ± 0.20	0.091%
1732.31 ± 0.27	0.048%
1753.48 ± 0.25	0.045%
1757.10 ± 0.31	0.053%
1762.06 ± 0.29	0.025%
1775.61 ± 0.19	0.25%
1782.81 ± 0.31	0.051%
1786.86 ± 0.26	0.078%
1794.20 ± 0.26	0.056%

Gamma energies (KeV)	Gamma intensities
1807.24 ± 0.35	0.068%
1811.34 ± 0.37	0.074%
1819.23 ± 0.24	0.062%
1830.21 ± 0.50	0.012%
1836.12 ± 0.43	0.014%
1849.02 ± 0.31	0.023%
1855.24 ± 0.63	0.011%
1863.59 ± 0.23	0.043%
1873.68 ± 1.19	0.0074%
1877.58 ± 0.36	0.011%
1892.45 ± 0.19	0.018%
1903.89 ± 0.44	0.021%
1909.40 ± 0.35	0.037%
1912.38 ± 1.21	0.0040%
1926.15 ± 0.28	0.042%
1932.83 ± 0.30	0.024%
2019.32 ± 0.29	0.037%
2105.83 ± 0.57	0.0058%
2254.82 ± 0.42	0.0065%

$_{61}Pm^{141}$

Gamma energies (KeV)	Gamma intensities
Ann. Rad.	

$_{61}Pm^{142}$

Gamma energies (KeV)	Gamma intensities
1570	0.2%

$_{61}Pm^{143}$

Gamma energies (KeV)	Gamma intensities
742	47%

$_{61}Pm^{144}$

Gamma energies (KeV)	Gamma intensities
476	45%
616	100%
696.48 ± 0.09	100%

$_{61}Pm^{145}$

Gamma energies (KeV)	Gamma intensities
67	12%
725	8%

$_{61}Pm^{146}$

Gamma energies (KeV)	Gamma intensities
453	65%
742	30%
749	35%

$_{61}Pm^{148m}$

Gamma energies (KeV)	Gamma intensities
61.5 ± 0.2 (IT)	
75.6 ± 0.2 (IT)	
98.5 ± 0.2	3.3%
189.5 ± 0.3	
288.0 ± 0.2	13%
311.7 ± 0.3	2.8%
414.1 ± 0.3	17%
432.7 ± 0.3	6%
443.1 ± 0.4	
501.1 ± 0.4	7%
550.1 ± 0.2	95%
592.4 ± 0.4	
599.5 ± 0.3	8%
611.1 ± 0.3	6%
629.9 ± 0.2	87%
725.6 ± 0.2	36%
896.2 ± 0.3	

$_{61}Pm^{148}$

Gamma energies (KeV)	Gamma intensities
914.9 ± 0.2	21%
1013.7 + 0.3	20%
1465.1 ± 0.2	27%

Gamma energies (KeV)	Gamma intensities
550.1 ± 0.2	50%
914.9 ± 0.2	16%
1465.1 ± 0.2	24%

$_{61}Pm^{149}$

Gamma energies (KeV)	Gamma intensities
K X-ray 22.5	2 ± 0.7
208.1 ± 1	0.008 ± 0.006
242.4 ± 1	0.009 ± 0.006
254.4 ± 0.5	0.045 ± 0.02
263.3 ± 0.4	0.091 ± 0.04
276.9 ± 0.4	0.27 ± 0.10
285.90 ± 0.05	31.0 ± 2
304.9 ± 0.4	0.022 ± 0.01
327.4 ± 0.4	0.034 ± 0.01
350.6 ± 0.4 (doublet)	0.023 ± 0.01
359.4 ± 0.4	0.022 ± 0.01
531 ± 1	0.012 ± 0.01
535.8 ± 0.4	0.13 ± 0.03
545 ± 1	0.025 ± 0.01
548 ± 1	0.019 ± 0.01
558.4 ± 0.4	0.14 ± 0.03
568.5 ± 0.4	0.18 ± 0.03
590.9 ± 0.3	0.68 ± 0.08
613.9 ± 0.4	0.13 ± 0.02
636.6 ± 0.4	0.062 ± 0.02
807.8 ± 0.5	0.15 ± 0.02
830.5 ± 0.5	0.30 ± 0.04
833.2 ± 0.5	0.30 ± 0.04
859.4 ± 0.5	1.02 ± 0.15
881.9 ± 0.5	0.23 ± 0.03

$_{61}Pm^{150}$

Gamma energies (KeV)	Gamma intensities
334	100†
410	10
590	5
720	11
840	25
880	17
1170	32
1230	6
1330	31
1750	14
1960	3.5
2060	1.7
2530	1.3
2750	0.4
2910	0.5
3080	0.16

$_{61}Pm^{151}$

Gamma energies (KeV)	Gamma intensities
100.00	2.7%
101.80	1.6%
104.80	3.8%
139.30	0.5%
156.20	0.2%
163.37	2.5%
167.84	9.9%
177.05	4.8%

Gamma energies (KeV)	Gamma intensities
186.60	0.2%
201.94	0.1%
208.97	2.0%
227.21	0.3%
232.36	1.2%
236.73	1.0%
240.00	3.9%
254.07	0.2%
270.41	0.1%
275.10	7.4%
280.11	0.2%
290.63	0.8%
306.60	0.2%
323.79	1.5%
329.60	0.25%
339.93	24%
344.80	2.2%
349.60	0.1%
353.10	0.1%
379.67	1.0%
406.80	0.2%
440.66	1.6%
445.51	4.3%
451.24	0.3%
490.10	0.1%
516.00	0.2%
564.90	0.4%
636.20	1.5%
654.30	0.3%
669.10	0.8%
671.40	1.0%
704.40	0.3%
717.85	4.4%
736.30	4.8%
753.00	1.4%
773.00	0.8%
808.10	0.6%
817.90	0.3%
848.90	0.3%
948.90	0.4%
953.90	0.1%

$_{61}Pm^{152}$

120	
240	
1000	

$_{62}Sm^{142}$

Ann. Rad.	

$_{62}Sm^{143m}$

748	

$_{62}Sm^{143}$

Ann. Rad.	
1050	

$_{62}Sm^{145}$

61.3	92%(78%)
485	0.003%

$_{62}Sm^{151}$

21.6	1.7%

$_{62}Sm^{153}$

Gamma energies (KeV)	Gamma intensities
54.19	0.006†
68.23	0.004
69.68	17
75.43	0.61
83.4	0.75
89.5	0.58
103.23	100
151.6	0.03
172.9	0.31
411	0.01
424	0.013
438	0.01
450	0.01
463	0.05
521	0.025
531	0.23
533	0.12
539	0.06
578	0.01
603	0.014
609	0.04
636	0.018

$_{62}Sm^{155}$

75	0.3†
104.35	73
140	1.7
246	4
450	0.18
510	0.3
650	0.2
920	0.03
990	0.04
1180	0.06
1270	0.13

$_{62}Sm^{156}$

22.6	
25.3	
38.1	
65.0	
87.6	40%
103	
166	
204	
219	
244	
269	
291	

$_{62}Sm^{157}$

570	

$_{63}Eu^{144}$

Ann. Rad.	

$_{63}Eu^{145}$

Ann. Rad.	
110.94 ± 0.15	2.4†
191.25 ± 0.15	0.9
542.51 ± 0.15	7.5
653.46 ± 0.15	24

Gamma energies (KeV)	Gamma intensities
713.7 ± 0.3	0.5
764.65 ± 0.15	3.1
893.57 ± 0.20	75
974.90 ± 0.15	3.8
1658.38 ± 0.15	1.9
1803.90 ± 0.15	1.9
1876.84 ± 0.15	2.0
1996.61 ± 0.15	12.3

$_{63}Eu^{146}$

Ann. Rad.	†
27.18	
146.3 ± 0.2	
267.6 ± 0.2	
271.78 ± 0.20	
397.32 ± 0.20	
410.80 ± 0.20	
430.29 ± 0.20	
621.68 ± 0.20	
628.7 ± 0.2	
633.6 ± 0.20	
665.31 ± 0.20	
667.84 ± 0.20	12†
743.1 ± 0.2	
747.1 ± 0.2	100
791.14 ± 0.20	
865.0 ± 0.20	
888.60 ± 0.20	
893.61 ± 0.20	
900.23 ± 0.20	
909.33 ± 0.20	
913.93 ± 0.20	
702.50 ± 0.20	
704.77 ± 0.20	
1058.28 ± 0.20	7
1133.02 ± 0.20	
1150.53 ± 0.20	
1176.26 ± 0.20	
1296.88 ± 0.20	6
1378.26 ± 0.20	
1407.55 ± 0.20	
1414.89 ± 0.20	5
1516.96 ± 0.20	
1522.67 ± 0.20	
1533.55 ± 0.20	8
1685.95 ± 0.20	2.4
1690.94 ± 0.20	
1756.02 ± 0.20	3
1880	1.1
1930	2
2080	3
2160	1.8
2300	1.3
2410	1.4
2510	0.7

$_{63}Eu^{147}$

Ann. Rad.	
76.4	1.1†
121.23 ± 0.20	10.9
160.87 ± 0.20	0.04
166.3 ± 0.20	0.04
197.23 ± 0.20	21.4
327.92 ± 0.20	0.1
601.49 ± 0.20	5.6
677.54 ± 0.20	9.3
798.78 ± 0.20	4.8

Gamma energies (KeV)	Gamma intensities
857.02 ± 0.20	2.8
879.5 ± 0.20	0.14
933.2 ± 0.20	3.6
943.2 ± 0.20	0.4
955.97 ± 0.20	3.6
1064.0 ± 0.20	0.7
1077.11 ± 0.20	6.0
1119.87 ± 0.20	0.46
1179.95 ± 0.20	0.1
1197.0 ± 0.20	0.1
1255.90 ± 0.20	0.82
1318.0 ± 0.20	0.18
1331.50 ± 0.20	0.34
1349.93 ± 0.20	0.16
1448.74 ± 0.20	0.18
1459.92 ± 0.20	0.22

$_{63}Eu^{148}$

Gamma energies (KeV)	% β decays
Ann. Rad.	
22.41 ± 0.10	
67.63 ± 0.10	
98.40 ± 0.10	0.09 ± 0.03
116.3 ± 0.2	0.10 ± 0.03
121.18 ± 0.12	0.006 ± 0.003
166.2 ± 0.3	0.05 ± 0.02
182.8 ± 0.2	0.11 ± 0.3
189.6 ± 0.2	0.10 ± 0.3
215.9 ± 0.2	
241.5 ± 0.1	1.04 ± 0.10
243.6 ± 0.2	0.23 ± 0.05
252.3 ± 0.3	0.05 ± 0.02
279.1 ± 0.5	0.06 ± 0.02
287.9 ± 0.2	0.22 ± 0.05
296.0 ± 0.3	
310.0 ± 0.3	0.22 ± 0.05
311.4 ± 0.1	1.14 ± 0.10
319.1 ± 0.3	0.05 ± 0.02
377.5 ± 0.5	
413.9 } ± 0.1 413.9 }	{ 18.6 ± 0.5
432.6 ± 0.1	2.79 ± 0.20
437.2 ± 0.3	
468.4 ± 0.3	0.49 ± 0.08
481.2 ± 0.5	0.16 ± 0.05
495.2 ± 0.3	0.25 ± 0.06
501.3 ± 0.1	0.75 ± 0.13
505.2 ± 0.5	0.28 ± 0.07
516.7 ± 0.3	0.40 ± 0.10
528.5 ± 0.3	0.19 ± 0.05
550.20 ± 0.5	99.00 ± 0
553.2 ± 0.1	17.1 ± 0.5
571.90 ± 0.05	9.1 ± 0.3
587.6 ± 0.5	0.08 ± 0.03
590.1 ± 0.2	0.32 ± 0.08
595.2 ± 0.3	0.20 ± 0.06
599.5 ± 0.2	0.31 ± 0.10
602.6 ± 0.3	0.23 ± 0.16
611.26 ± 0.05	19.3 ± 0.5
620.0 ± 0.1	1.0 ± 0.1
629.90 ± 0.05	70.9 ± 3.0
654.3 ± 0.1	1.31 ± 0.15
657.0 ± 0.5	0.17 ± 0.06
667.7 ± 0.5	0.13 ± 0.05
669.9 ± 0.2	0.34 ± 0.06
675.4 ± 0.5	0.08 ± 0.03
683.2 ± 0.1	1.06 ± 0.10
690.7 ± 0.5	0.08 ± 0.03
714.8 ± 0.1	1.54 ± 0.12

Gamma energies (KeV)	Gamma intensities
719.6 ± 0.3	0.11 ± 0.03
725.7 ± 0.1	12.2 ± 1.0
734.8 ± 1.0	0.06 ± 0.03
756.6 ± 0.5	0.19 ± 0.05
770.4 ± 0.2	0.38 ± 0.07
780.2 ± 0.5	0.08 ± 0.03
799.2 ± 0.2	0.34 ± 0.07
870 ± 0.1	4.9 ± 0.5
895.8 ± 0.1	0.55 ± 0.10
903.9 ± 0.2	0.34 ± 0.07
906.9 ± 0.3	0.15 ± 0.04
915.3 ± 0.1	2.4 ± 0.2
924.9 ± 0.2	0.27 ± 0.06
930.5 ± 0.1	2.4 ± 0.2
938.2 ± 1.0	0.11 ± 0.04
949.7 ± 0.2	0.21 ± 0.06
964.2 ± 0.4	0.20 ± 0.07
967.3 ± 0.1	2.9 ± 0.3
980.0 ± 0.5	0.13 ± 0.04
989.7 ± 0.2	0.39 ± 0.08
1013.9 ± 0.2	0.41 ± 0.08
1034.1 ± 0.1	7.9 ± 0.7
1043.9 ± 1.0	0.04 ± 0.02
1047.5 ± 0.3	0.20 ± 0.07
1066.8 ± 0.2	0.29 ± 0.08
1069.2 ± 0.4	0.22 ± 0.08
1082.2 ± 0.5	0.17 ± 0.07
1089.3 ± 0.5	0.20 ± 0.07
1097.5 ± 0.7	0.10 ± 0.04
1104.3 ± 0.2	0.45 ± 0.09
1107.9 ± 0.3	0.10 ± 0.03
1113.8 ± 0.3	0.13 ± 0.04
1126.9 ± 0.5	0.10 ± 0.03
1146.9 ± 0.1	1.9 ± 0.2
1151.7 ± 0.5	0.08 ± 0.03
1156.4 ± 0.5	0.04 ± 0.02
1165.3 ± 0.5	0.08 ± 0.03
1180.5 ± 0.5	0.30 ± 0.08
1183.3 ± 0.1	1.7 ± 0.2
1194.1 ± 0.5	0.13 ± 0.04
1207.4 ± 0.2	0.59 ± 0.12
1219.7 ± 0.5	0.08 ± 0.03
1222.0 ± 0.5	0.09 ± 0.03
1230.0 ± 0.5	0.03 ± 0.02
1236.6 ± 0.2	0.39 ± 0.09
1267.1 ± 0.5	0.09 ± 0.03
1276.5 ± 0.5	0.07 ± 0.03
1309.8 ± 0.2	0.46 ± 0.09
1328.5 ± 0.2	1.22 ± 0.15
1344.6 ± 0.1	3.3 ± 0.3
1353.6 ± 0.2	0.47 ± 0.09
1362.6 ± 0.2	0.55 ± 0.10
1409.0 ± 0.6	0.10 ± 0.03
1454.3 ± 0.3	0.25 ± 0.07
1460.5 ± 0.2	1.12 ± 0.12
1493.2 ± 0.6	0.07 ± 0.03
1503.0 ± 0.3	0.13 ± 0.04
1512.0 ± 0.3	0.04 ± 0.02
1521.9 ± 0.3	0.11 ± 0.03
1536.1 ± 0.3	0.08 ± 0.03
1543.1 ± 0.2	0.71 ± 0.13
1547.3 ± 0.4	0.08 ± 0.03
1551.7 ± 0.5	0.02 ± 0.01
1560.7 ± 0.2	0.87 ± 0.10
1565.0 ± 0.6	0.03 ± 0.02
1621.1 ± 0.1	4.6 ± 0.5
1635.3 ± 0.3	0.18 ± 0.04
1650.4 ± 0.1	3.7 ± 0.5
1664.5 ± 0.5	0.08 ± 0.03
1677.8 ± 0.1	0.42 ± 0.08
1748.1 ± 0.5	0.02 ± 0.01

Gamma energies (KeV)	Gamma intensities
1776.9 ± 0.3	0.04 ± 0.02
1940.0 ± 0.5	0.05 ± 0.03
1974.2 ± 0.5	0.03 ± 0.02
2173.2 ± 0.3	0.22 ± 0.06

$_{63}Eu^{149}$

Gamma energies (KeV)	Gamma intensities
22.5	760 ± 40†
72.9	0.08 ± 0.04
178.4 ± 0.4	0.17 ± 0.08
207.9 ± 0.4	0.06 ± 0.03
251.0 ± 1	0.14 ± 0.07
254.5 ± 0.3	5.9 ± 0.6
277.0 ± 0.3	33 ± 2
281.1 ± 0.5	0.19 ± 0.07
327.5 ± 0.3	39 ± 2
350.0 ± 0.3	3.4 ± 0.3
505.9 ± 0.3	5.5 ± 0.5
528.5 ± 0.3	5.3 ± 0.5
535.9 ± 0.3	0.46 ± 0.1
558.4 ± 0.3	0.62 ± 0.1

$_{63}Eu^{150m}$

Gamma energies (KeV)	Gamma intensities
209.27 ± 0.35	0.55 ± 0.08†
285.23 ± 0.35	
334.04 ± 0.20	100 ± 8.0
372.96 ± 0.35	
406.47 ± 0.20	70.9 ± 5.7
424.96 ± 0.35	0.2 ± 0.04
438.67 ± 0.30	
446.22 ± 0.35	
620.48 ± 0.35	0.80 ± 0.12
632.57 ± 0.25	
712.13 ± 0.25	3.34 ± 0.30
747.12 ± 0.30	
831.77 ± 0.30	5.0 ± 0.4
860.2 ± 0.6	0.23 ± 0.06
893.6 ± 0.4	
921.22 ± 0.30	5.6 ± 0.4
1046.2 ± 0.8	0.21 ± 0.05
1057.3 ± 0.8	
1165.63 ± 0.30	6.45 ± 0.58
1193.89 ± 0.7	0.46 ± 0.1
1223.0 ± 0.3	5.0 · ± 0.4
1268.9 ± 0.5	
1452.0 ± 0.5	0.37 ± 0.13
1462.9 ± 0.4	
1533.3 ± 1.0	
1592.5 ± 1.0	
1629.8 ± 0.7	1.45 ± 0.19
1963.90 ± 0.30	2.91 ± 0.30
1998.3 ± 0.7	

$_{63}Eu^{150}$

Gamma energies (KeV)	Gamma intensities
61.278 ± 0.02	
78.830 ± 0.02	
205.101 ± 0.09	
284.760 ± 0.13	
298.031 ± 0.03	
305.438 ± 0.15	
310.826 ± 0.23	
315.132 ± 0.11	
333.965 ± 0.02	
340.369 ± 0.04	
345.968 ± 0.13	
382.063 ± 0.05	

Gamma energies (KeV)	Gamma intensities
402.252 ± 0.07	
439.402 ± 0.01	
448.744 ± 0.03	
461.788 ± 0.02	
464.497 ± 0.08	
474.544 ± 0.14	
496.298 ± 0.23	
505.480 ± 0.02	
510.078 ± 0.10	
515.776 ± 0.03	
520.042 ± 0.02	
542.989 ± 0.10	
571.244 ± 0.02	
584.253 ± 0.07	
591.026 ± 0.19	
596.334 ± 0.09	
607.237 ± 0.12	
612.446 ± 0.10	
614.908 ± 0.09	
667.031 ± 0.06	
675.804 ± 0.03	
712.139 ± 0.02	
731.212 ± 0.03	
737.405 ± 0.02	
741.475 ± 0.02	
748.062 ± 0.02	
750.890 ± 0.03	
756.473 ± 0.11	
759.336 ± 0.13	
828.486 ± 0.04	
830.860 ± 0.05	
836.574 ± 0.09	
859.885 ± 0.04	
869.250 ± 0.03	
899.079 ± 0.02	
910.989 ± 0.16	
923.371 ± 0.06	
1045.975 ± 0.06	
1049.065 ± 0.02	
1071.251 ± 0.10	
1083.081 ± 0.10	
1122.762 ± 0.05	
1165.546 ± 0.17	
1170.605 ± 0.02	
1193.801 ± 0.02	
1197.125 ± 0.02	
1212.956 ± 0.12	
1246.984 ± 0.01	
1251.077 ± 0.11	
1261.831 ± 0.04	
1274.1 ± 0.4	
1308.755 ± 0.03	
1322.037 ± 0.07	
1334.064 ± 0.04	
1343.877 ± 0.02	
1350.386 ± 0.08	
1379.064 ± 0.20	
1383.431 ± 0.30	
1390.0 ± 0.4	
1401.509 ± 0.31	
1413.507 ± 0.39	
1460.913 ± 0.15	
1465.365 ± 0.81	
1476.686 ± 0.59	
1485.557 ± 0.03	
1592.893 ± 0.20	
1636.623 ± 0.07	
1677.832 ± 0.35	
1690.696 ± 0.10	
1783.269 ± 0.10	

Gamma energies (KeV)	Gamma intensities
$_{63}Eu^{151m}$	
196	
$_{63}Eu^{152m_2}$	
18.3	
39.7	
89.8	
$_{63}Eu^{152m_1}$	
Ann. Rad.	
73.2 ± 0.3	†
76.8 ± 0.3	
85.15 ± 0.10	0.13
90.14 ± 0.10	0.23
121.92 ± 0.10	5.0
244.3 ± 0.3	
270.97 ± 0.15	0.07
344.08 ± 0.15	1.7
562.66 ± 0.15	0.3
688.9 ± 0.15	
841.39 ± 0.15	11.1
869.72 ± 0.15	0.09
963.10 ± 0.15	9.3
970.03 ± 0.15	0.5
995.03 ± 0.15	0.07
1314.33 ± 0.15	0.8
1388.79 ± 0.15	0.6
1411.26 ± 0.15	0.04
$_{63}Eu^{152}$	
Ann. Rad.	
121.83 ± 0.10	0.3†
147.79 ± 0.10	0.2
161.41 ± 0.10	
166.89 ± 0.15	0.1
167.9 ± 0.3	0.2
244.54 ± 0.15	7.6
251.40 ± 0.15	0.14
271.01 ± 0.15	0.09
275.07 ± 0.15	0.04
284.42 ± 0.15	0.08
295.84 ± 0.15	0.44
315.37 ± 0.15	0.05
324.81 ± 0.15	0.07
329.23 ± 0.15	0.13
344.19 ± 0.15	28.5
366.25 ± 0.15	0.22
367.71 ± 0.15	1.0
385.91 ± 0.15	0.31
411.06 ± 0.15	2.8
415.94 ± 0.15	0.13
443.96 ± 0.15	3.6
488.71 ± 0.15	0.44
493.51 ± 0.15	0.05
503.41 ± 0.15	0.13
563.96 ± 0.15	0.47
566.25 ± 0.15	0.15
586.17 ± 0.15	0.41
674.78 ± 0.15	0.14
678.62 ± 0.15	0.61
688.88 ± 0.15	0.90
719.11 ± 0.15	0.40
779.08 ± 0.15	14.5
810.54 ± 0.15	0.32
841.44 ± 0.15	0.20
867.53 ± 0.15	4.4

Gamma energies (KeV)	Gamma intensities
919.40 ± 0.15	0.57
926.98 ± 0.15	0.49
964.21 ± 0.15	16.2
1005.15 ± 0.15	1.0
1086.00 ± 0.15	11.8
1089.91 ± 0.15	1.9
1112.20 ± 0.15	15.4
1213.02 ± 0.15	1.7
1234.0 ± 0.3	0.25
1249.95 ± 0.15	0.3
1292.62 ± 0.15	0.2
1299.18 ± 0.15	1.9
1408.11 ± 0.15	22.9
1447.93 ± 0.15	0.14
1457.76 ± 0.15	0.6
1528.94 ± 0.15	0.7
$_{63}Eu^{154}$	
59.75 ± 0.10	4.0%
122.91 ± 0.10	40.0%
145.60 ± 0.10	0.2%
188.04 ± 0.15	0.3%
238.34 ± 0.15	0.1%
247.73 ± 0.15	6.7%
444.22 ± 0.15	0.7%
478.23 ± 0.15	0.3%
581.91 ± 0.15	1.0%
591.70 ± 0.15	5.4%
692.38 ± 0.15	1.9%
723.29 ± 0.15	21%
756.78 ± 0.15	4.6%
765.74 ± 0.15	1.0%
815.71 ± 0.15	0.6%
845.57 ± 0.15	0.5%
873.24 ± 0.15	12.3%
904.21 ± 0.15	1.0%
996.36 ± 0.15	11.3%
1004.84 ± 0.15	20%
1274.53 ± 0.15	37%
1396.00 ± 0.15	1.9%
1460.97 ± 0.15	1.2%
1494.14 ± 0.15	0.6%
1593.07 ± 0.15	0.6%
1596.61 ± 0.15	1.9%
$_{63}Eu^{155}$	
43.37 ± 0.05	†
58.12 ± 0.10	0.06
60.07 ± 0.05	2.8
86.60 ± 0.05	72.4
105.36 ± 0.05	48.2
$_{63}Eu^{156}$	
88.97 ± 0.05	45%
190.37 ± 0.10	0.5%
199.27 ± 0.07	0.6%
434.33 ± 0.08	0.23%
472.57 ± 0.08	0.17%
490.35 ± 0.08	0.17%
599.43 ± 0.07	2.1%
646.23 ± 0.07	6.3%
709.85 ± 0.07	0.9%
723.44 ± 0.07	5.4%
768.27 ± 0.20	0.09%
797.67 ± 0.10	0.09%
811.73 ± 0.07	9.7%

Gamma energies (KeV)	Gamma intensities
820.32 ± 0.07	0.16%
836.37 ± 0.07	0.11%
841.10 ± 0.31	0.22%
858.19 ± 0.13	0.27%
866.98 ± 0.07	1.5%
944.06 ± 0.07	2.4%
960.41 ± 0.07	1.6%
969.81 ± 0.07	0.38%
1111.81 ± 0.10	0.55%
1027.53 ± 0.07	0.38%
1040.36 ± 0.10	0.54%
1065.08 ± 0.07	5.3%
1075.92 ± 0.07	2.4%
1079.19 ± 0.07	4.7%
1129.31 ± 0.18	0.17%
1140.51 ± 0.07	0.31%
1153.72 ± 0.07	12.6%
1168.94 ± 0.15	0.31%
1230.66 ± 0.07	8.7%
1242.47 ± 0.07	7.1%
1258.30 ± 0.6	0.21%
1277.50 ± 0.07	3.2%
1366.44 ± 0.07	1.8%
1455.02 ± 0.20	0.14%
1587.06 ± 0.20	0.20%
1675.92 ± 0.50	0.17%
1681.13 ± 0.10	0.42%
1857.24 ± 0.10	0.32%
1876.91 ± 0.10	1.5%
1937.66 ± 0.10	2.0%
1945.92 ± 0.10	0.12%
1965.91 ± 0.10	4.4%
2026.68 ± 0.10	3.8%
2031.57 ± 0.10	0.44%
2097.77 ± 0.10	5.3%
2110.64 ± 0.30	0.16%
2116.46 ± 0.15	0.17%
2181.05 ± 0.10	4.1%
2186.82 ± 0.10	6.1%
2205.57 ± 0.10	1.7%
2211.85 ± 0.10	0.20%
2269.85 ± 0.10	2.4%

$_{63}$Eu^{157}

Gamma energies (KeV)	Gamma intensities
40.6	
51.8	
54.5	
64.0	85†
77.0	
131.4	
276.6	
320.5	
330.7	10
361.8	
372.8	
413.1	100
477.3	20
527.0	
623.3	20
687.5	10
729.4	5

$_{63}$Eu^{158}

Gamma energies (KeV)	Gamma intensities
80	100†
180	
520	25
610	8

Gamma energies (KeV)	Gamma intensities
750	8
900	26
950	49
980	20
1110	11
1190	16
1260	5
1330	4
1960	3
2180	2

$_{63}$Eu^{159}

Gamma energies (KeV)	Gamma intensities
54	
75	
90	90†
130	
145	68
165	16
220	26
670	100
740	50
880	64
970	10
1050	25
1100	25
1270	8
1350	8
1370	25
1440	25
1500	
1600	

$_{64}$Gd^{145}

Gamma energies (KeV)	Gamma intensities
80	9†
1030	10
1750	100

$_{64}$Gd^{146}

Gamma energies (KeV)	Gamma intensities
22.9	
77.7	30†
114.7	
115.5	
154.8	48
198.8	
329	

$_{64}$Gd^{147}

Gamma energies (KeV)	Gamma intensities
106.6	
111	
166.3	
194.0	
214.8	
229.4	150†
240.5	
260.8	
297.5	
310.0	
328.6	
370.0	
396.1	
485	
559	
609	
617	

Gamma energies (KeV)	Gamma intensities
625	
632	75†
780	60
940	80
1350	6

$_{64}$Gd^{149}

Gamma energies (KeV)	Gamma intensities
149.4 ± 0.5	100†
214.2 ± 0.7	
252.2 ± 0.7	
260.6 ± 0.6	
272.2 ± 0.6	
299.3 ± 0.5	69
346.6 ± 0.5	42
404.2 ± 0.7	
459.8 ± 0.7	<4
478.7 ± 0.7	
496.3 ± 0.6	4
516.5 ± 0.6	10
534.3 ± 0.6	9
645.2 ± 0.6	4
663.3 ± 0.8	
666.2 ± 0.6	
748.4 ± 0.5	19
762.9 ± 0.7	
780.8 ± 0.7	
788.8 ± 0.5	16
812.6 ± 0.6	
876.0 ± 0.6	1.3
933.0 ± 0.6	2.1
938.5 ± 0.5	6
947.8 ± 0.5	

$_{64}$Gd^{151}

Gamma energies (KeV)	Gamma intensities
21.6	4.4†
153.7	6
175	2.7
244	4.5
308	0.8
350	0.3

$_{64}$Gd^{153}

Gamma energies (KeV)	Gamma intensities
68.23	0.5†
69.68	11
75.43	0.4
83.37	1.0
89.48	0.3
97.430 ± 0.005	132
103.178 ± 0.003	100
172.85	

$_{64}$Gd^{159}

Gamma energies (KeV)	Gamma intensities
58	1.9†
80	0.43
225	1.9
290	0.35
306	0.8
334	0.42
348	2.4
363	100
536	
558	0.21
579	0.6
617	0.17

Gamma energies (KeV)	Gamma intensities	Gamma energies (KeV)	Gamma intensities	Gamma energies (KeV)	Gamma intensities
$_{64}Gd^{161}$		732		2370	
56.6	†	794		2400	
77.6	0.3	799		2530	
102.4	17	805		2580	
105.5	1.0	906		2600	
133.7		939		2670	
165.3	7	979		2710	
180.6	3.5	1010		2800	
258.8	3	1025		2920	
273	2	1053			
283.8	12	1090		$_{65}Tb^{153}$	
315.3	37	1097			
361.0	100	1171		19.4	
482	3.2	1250		41.6	
531	2.6	1308		51.8	
		1312		68.2	≈20
$_{65}Tb^{147}$				82.8	190
Ann. Rad.		$_{65}Tb^{152m}$		87.6	50
305		Ann. Rad.		88.4	45
		140	25†	102.3	190
$_{65}Tb^{148}$		230	30	109.7	180
Ann. Rad.				129.2	≈13
780		$_{65}Tb^{152}$		139.8	<10
1120		271.2	13†	141.9	35
		344.4	100	170.5	220
$_{65}Tb^{149m}$		351.5		174.4	<50
Ann. Rad.		411.2		183.5	25
		432.5		185.9	<5
$_{65}Tb^{149}$		496.7		193.6	≈4
165.5		527.1		195.2	28
187.3		586.7		208.1	<50
352		615.6		212.1	1000
388		623.1		249.6	72
464		676		262	15
652		679		266	<2
818		704	2.5	271	<2
856		753		275	7
1206		766		278	<2
		779		299	<2
$_{65}Tb^{150}$		929		303	28
637	100†	931		315	30
930	35	975		320	≈7
		991		327	≈5
$_{63}Tb^{151}$		1048		333	<2
108.2		1110		340	5
180.1	50†	1138		349	<1
192.0		1187		355	5
251.8	100	1206		362	4
287.2	100	1263		393	≈3
318.5		1300		400	≈4
380.1		1303		407	≈3
384.6		1319		419	≈3
395.2		1328		436	25
416.0		1348		442	6
426.4		1352		448	4
443.8		1361		455	13
479.2	80†	1412		467	15
499.8		1519		496	10
512		1588		507	16
588		1598		526	6
604	100†	1670		531	7
704		1783		549	6
		1791		566	<2
		1910		571	<2
		1940		599	<2
		2040		629	10
		2100		636	<2
		2190		653	5
		2260		665	10
				689	8
				740	7

Gamma energies (KeV)	Gamma intensities
762	<2
816	7
836	29
847	6
853	<5
858	<5
904	35
918	<5
946	32
974	10
993	37
1102	13
1203	2.4
1276	1.9
1364	0.9

$_{65}Tb^{154}$

Gamma energies (KeV)	Gamma intensities
123.07 ± 0.2	
225.7 ± 0.3	
231.7 ± 0.3	
247.7 ± 0.2	
346.6 ± 0.2	
381.9 ± 0.4	
415.9 ± 0.3	
444.6 ± 0.4	
517.9 ± 0.3	
540.10 ± 0.25	
557.2 ± 0.2	
598.0 ± 0.4	
642.4 ± 0.6	
649.5 ± 0.3	
676.4 ± 0.4	
692.3 ± 0.3	
704.6 ± 0.5	
714.5 ± 0.5	
722.1 ± 0.5	
756.9 ± 0.3	
815.5 ± 1.0	
873.2 ± 0.2	
892.7 ± 0.3	
925.3 ± 1.0	
996.4 ± 0.2	
1004.8 ± 0.2	
1060.0 ± 1.0	
1148.9 ± 1.0	
1152.4 ± 1.0	
1258.4 ± 1.5	
1274.9 ± 1.0	
1289.0 ± 1.5	
1292.0 ± 1.5	
1410.0 ± 2.0	
1491.0 ± 3.0	
1967.0 ± 2.0	
2186.0 ± 1.5	

$_{65}Tb^{154}$

Gamma energies (KeV)	Gamma intensities
123.1	
141.4	
225.7	
247.7	
265.9	
346.6	
426.9	
444.6	
557.2	
602.6	

Gamma energies (KeV)	Gamma intensities
680.8	
692.3	
815.5	
873.2	
996.4	
1124	
1274.9	
1292.0	
1460	
1994	
2062	
2116	
2186	

$_{65}Tb^{155}$

Gamma energies (KeV)	Gamma intensities
45.35 ± 0.10	
58.03 ± 0.10	
60.03 ± 0.10	7†
72.83 ± 0.10	
74.99 ± 0.10	
86.53 ± 0.07	100
99.02 ± 0.10	
101.14 ± 0.10	
105.29 ± 0.07	69
120.53 ± 0.10	
148.63 ± 0.08	8
161.26 ± 0.08 }	23
163.28 ± 0.07 }	
175.20 ± 0.10	
203.05 ± 0.10	
216.04 ± 0.10	
220.69 ± 0.10	
226.94 ± 0.10	
239.53 ± 0.10	
262.30 ± 0.10	
268.56 ± 0.10	
281.03 ± 0.10	
286.93 ± 0.10	
321.74 ± 0.10	
367.32 ± 0.10	10
370.70 ± 0.10	
402.05 ± 0.10	
559.09 ± 0.10	
180.06 ± 0.10	
181.59 ± 0.10	
206.60 ± 0.10	
208.22 ± 0.10	
200.48 ± 0.10	

$_{65}Tb^{156m}$

Gamma energies (KeV)	Gamma intensities
88.4 (IT)	

$_{65}Tb^{156}$

Gamma energies (KeV)	Gamma intensities
88.97 ± 0.05	
111.9	
115.6	
155.2	
170.8	
199.27 ± 0.07	
262.5	
266.9	
296.3	
356.4	
374.0	
381.4	

Gamma energies (KeV)	Gamma intensities
422.4	
535.2	
687.5	
782	
844	
867	
927	
944.06 ± 0.07	
951	
963	
1012	
1040.36 ± 0.1	
1043	
1068	
1070	
1157	
1162	
1225	
1338	
1425	
1649	
1849	
1951	
2014	
2090	
2105	
2141	
2268	
2281	
2310	

$_{65}Tb^{158m}$

Gamma energies (KeV)	Gamma intensities
0.111	100%

$_{65}Tb^{158}$

Gamma energies (KeV)	Gamma intensities
79.5	12%
99	4%
182	10%
218	1%
782	10%
928	0.2%
946	47%
964	22%
1110	2.2%
1190	1.8%

$_{65}Tb^{160}$

Gamma energies (KeV)	Gamma intensities
86.788 ± 0.002	
93.919 ± 0.006	
176.490 ± 0.030	
197.035 ± 0.008	5.1
215.646 ± 0.008	3.97
230.628 ± 0.013	0.09
237.638 ± 0.086	
246.489 ± 0.016	0.03
298.582 ± 0.010	26.3
309.557 ± 0.018	0.87
337.324 ± 0.030	0.34
349.935 ± 0.110	
379.449 ± 0.090	
392.514 ± 0.026	
486.075 ± 0.080	5.1
682.349 ± 0.110	3.97
765.194 ± 0.110	0.09

Gamma energies (KeV)	Gamma intensities
871.9 ± 1.5	0.45
879.333 ± 0.070	31.8
962.085 ± 0.220	12.6
966.099 ± 0.120	27.6
1003.26 ± 0.30	1.14
1068.9 ± 1.5	0.13
1103.22 ± 0.25	0.7
1115.29 ± 0.19	1.70
1178.12 ± 0.19	16.6
1200.21 ± 0.37	2.67
1251.3 ± 0.5	0.11
1271.87 ± 0.25	8.28
1311.90 ± 0.30	3.16
1358.6 ± 0.2	0.02
1460.9 ± 0.2	0.05
1592.7 ± 0.2	0.02
$_{65}$Tb^{161}	
25.55 ± 0.2	
43.8	
57.38 ± 0.18	16† 21%
74.68 ± 0.15	100
77.41 ± 0.15	0.5
86.81 ± 0.15	2.0
103.06 ± 0.10	0.12
105.92 ± 0.10	0.9
131.61 ± 0.10	<1
298.55 ± 0.10	
340	
410	
470	
540	
$_{65}$Tb^{162}	
40	17†
80.82 ± 0.3	8
185.18 ± 0.25	26
260.01 ± 0.15	100
795.80 ± 0.5	0.8
807.53 ± 0.2	44
882.27 ± 0.25	18
888.16 ± 0.2	36
$_{65}$Tb^{163m}	
180	
$_{65}$Tb^{163}	
25	80†
120	
160	5
235	30
330	100
360	1
440	1
510	35
$_{66}$Dy^{150}	
390	
Ann. Rad.	

Gamma energies (KeV)	Gamma intensities
$_{66}$Dy^{151}	
145	
$_{66}$Dy^{152}	
Ann. Rad.	
275.2	
$_{66}$Dy^{153}	
80.8	
82.5	
93	
99.7	
147.8	
149.0	
174.1	
218.9	
240.7	
244.5	
254.5	
274.4	
303.8	
389.8	
415.7	
512.4	
544.7	
$_{66}$Dy^{155}	
Ann. Rad.	
65.43	
90.38	2.3†
115.4	
155.8	
161.4	
181	
184.6	
205.7	
227	100
271.4	
389	
433	
451	
461	
484	
498	
508	
550	
587	
642	
654	
664	
723	
745	
761	
813	
837	
844	
892	
905	
929	
1000	9†
1091	8
1155	
1164	
1250	6
1390	5
1450	6

Gamma energies (KeV)	Gamma intensities
1660	4
$_{66}$Dy^{157}	
60.8	
83.01	0.5†
143.8	0.0016
182.2	2
265.3	
326.2	100
554	
577	
597	
636	
743	
769	
775	
985	
992	
$_{66}$Dy^{159}	
58.0	4%
80.0	
138	
211	4×10^{-5}%
290	1.2×10^{-4}%
348	9×10^{-4}%
$_{66}$Dy^{165m}	
108.16	100†
152	9
361.7	17
514	55
650	1
750	0.5
$_{66}$Dy^{165}	
94.70	370†
279.6	57
361.5	100
479	3
501	0.6
514	2.9
545	17
566	14
575	8
621	10
633	64
695	2
716	64†
995	6
1056	3
1080	10
$_{66}$Dy^{166}	
28.23	†
54.23	
82.45	100
288	0.7
344	2
371.6	8
425.8	10

Gamma energies (KeV)	Gamma intensities	Gamma energies (KeV)	Gamma intensities	Gamma energies (KeV)	Gamma intensities
$_{67}$Ho^{151}		851		1155.4 ± 1.0	
Ann. Rad.		946		1198.9 ± 1.0	
		948		1271.7 ± 1.0	
$_{67}$Ho^{151}		1450		1285.3 ± 1.0	
		1600		1522.6 ± 1.0	
Ann. Rad.		1800		1594.7 ± 1.0	
		2060		1613.2 ± 1.0	
$_{67}$Ho^{152}		2200		1654.5 ± 1.0	
		2620		1719	
Ann. Rad.				1784	
		$_{67}$Ho^{158}		1807	
$_{67}$Ho^{152}				1872	
		Ann. Rad.		1927	
Ann. Rad.		see Ho^{158m}		1959	
				2008	
$_{67}$Ho^{153}		$_{67}$Ho^{159m}		2069	
				2190	
Ann. Rad.		206		2550	
355				2619	
		$_{67}$Ho^{159}		2638	
				2675	
$_{67}$Ho^{155}		69.51 ± 0.30		2728	
		79.79 ± 0.30		2763	
Ann. Rad.		100.55 ± 0.30			
92		120.94 ± 0.30			
117		131.86 ± 0.30		$_{67}$Ho^{161m}	
138		152.23 ± 0.40			
209		155.88 ± 0.40		211.1	
243		159.43 ± 0.40			
326		173.02 ± 0.40		$_{67}$Ho^{161}	
		177.51 ± 0.40			
		186.09 ± 0.40		25.7	100†
$_{67}$Ho^{156}		252.96 ± 0.30		60.03 ± 0.30	4
		258.74 ± 0.40		75.03 ± 0.40	
138	100†	265.91 ± 0.40		77.79 ± 0.20	10
266.4	99	296.59 ± 0.40		98.1 ± 0.7	1.8
366.7	23	309.51 ± 0.30		103.00 ± 0.20	1.2
685.2		538.20 ± 0.40		137.9 ± 1.0	
890		706.54 ± 0.40		156.90 ± 0.30	1.7
1200		807.05 ± 0.40		175.08 ± 0.30	1.6
1410		838.36 ± 0.40		210.8	0.6
				234.5	
$_{67}$Ho^{157}				339.7	
		$_{67}$Ho^{160m}		416.0	
Ann. Rad.				760	0.3
87		Ann. Rad.			
152		60.1 (IT)	Equilibrium		
190		86.91 ± 0.30	with	$_{67}$Ho^{162m}	
277		107.7 ± 0.7	Ho^{160}		
710		196.76 ± 0.20		38.63	(IT)
860		297.79 ± 0.20		58.88 ± 0.40	
900				81.15 ± 0.20	
1200				90.28 ± 0.40	
		$_{67}$Ho^{160}		95.46 ± 0.40	
				184.70 ± 0.20	
$_{67}$Ho^{158m}		405.5 ± 1.0		275.2 ± 0.7	
		645.20 ± 0.20		282.48 ± 0.20	
Ann. Rad.		728.00 ± 0.20		302.8 ± 0.7	
67.3 (IT)		753.0 ± 0.7		333.8 ± 0.7	
98.9		765.2 ± 0.7		392.6 ± 1.0	
193.7		826.1 ± 1.0		424.3 ± 1.0	
218.3		871.88 ± 0.40		936.72 ± 0.20	
309		879.28 ± 0.20		1220.0 ± 0.40	
320		962.32 ± 0.25		1319.9 ± 0.8	
356		966.24 ± 0.25		1374.4 ± 0.8	
463		1004.4 ± 0.7			
471		1068.8 ± 0.7		$_{67}$Ho^{162}	
647		1131.3 ± 1.0			
848				Ann. Rad.	~50%
				81.15 ± 0.2	

GAMMA ENERGIES AND INTENSITIES OF RADIONUCLIDES (*Continued*)

Gamma energies (KeV)	Gamma intensities
$_{67}Ho^{163m}$	
305	~80%
$_{67}Ho^{164}$	
37.3	3.6†
73.4 ± 0.2	3.3
91.4 ± 0.2	3.5
$_{67}Ho^{166}$	
80.573 ± 0.015	%
184.407 ± 0.015	0.002 ± 0.0005
674.991 ± 0.040	0.020 ± 0.002
705.342 ± 0.040	0.015 ± 0.002
785.949 ± 0.040	0.013 ± 0.002
1379.432 ± 0.065	0.93 ± 0.05
1581.89 ± 0.08	0.181 ± 0.009
1662.44 ± 0.08	0.116 ± 0.006
1749.94 ± 0.10	0.025 ± 0.002
1830.57 ± 0.15	0.008 ± 0.001
$_{67}Ho^{166m}$	
80.573 ± 0.015	12.5 ± 0.6%
94.653 ± 0.030	0.14 ± 0.01%
119.038 ± 0.030	0.18 ± 0.02%
121.161 ± 0.030	0.26 ± 0.03%
135.238 ± 0.035	0.10 ± 0.01%
140.618 ± 0.040	0.04 ± 0.01%
160.064 ± 0.045	0.10 ± 0.01%
161.748 ± 0.045	0.11 ± 0.01%
184.407 ± 0.015	73.2 ± 3.7%
190.711 ± 0.025	0.22 ± 0.02%
214.763 ± 0.045	0.55 ± 0.07%
215.875 ± 0.030	2.6 ± 0.2%
231.282 ± 0.040	0.24 ± 0.02%
233.28 ± 0.09	0.16 ± 0.02%
239.99 ± 0.08	0.05 ± 0.01%
259.716 ± 0.020	1.10 ± 0.06%
280.456 ± 0.020	29.8 ± 1.5%
300.744 ± 0.020	3.75 ± 0.19%
329.12 ± 0.08	0.16 ± 0.02%
339.78 ± 0.08	0.17 ± 0.02%
365.739 ± 0.025	2.52 ± 0.13%
410.941 ± 0.025	11.6 ± 0.6%
451.524 ± 0.025	3.06 ± 0.15%
464.825 ± 0.040	1.52 ± 0.08%
529.813 ± 0.030	10.2 ± 0.5%
570.992 ± 0.030	5.75 ± 0.29%
594.481 ± 0.040	0.70 ± 0.04%
611.522 ± 0.065	1.39 ± 0.08%
639.770 ± 0.060	
644.45 ± 0.10	0.18 ± 0.02%
670.509 ± 0.040	5.77 ± 0.29%
691.211 ± 0.050	1.53 ± 0.08%
711.693 ± 0.040	58.7 ± 2.9%
736.67 ± 0.08	0.40 ± 0.03%
752.265 ± 0.040	13.1 ± 0.7%
778.817 ± 0.040	3.30 ± 0.17%
810.309 ± 0.040	62.7 ± 3.1%
830.560 ± 0.040	10.6 ± 0.6%
875.64 ± 0.05	0.79 ± 0.06%
1010.25 ± 0.10	0.10 ± 0.01%
1120.31 ± 0.07	0.23 ± 0.02%
1146.82 ± 0.07	0.22 ± 0.02%

Gamma energies (KeV)	Gamma intensities
1241.44 ± 0.06	1.00 ± 0.05%
1282.12 ± 0.07	0.23 ± 0.02%
1400.72 ± 0.08	0.55 ± 0.03%
1427.05 ± 0.08	0.59 ± 0.03%
$_{67}Ho^{167}$	
57.1	
73.7	
79.3	
83.4	
133.4	
136.9	
150.4	
207.78 ± 0.08	
237.7	
241.1	
260.1	
266.5	
271.7	
304.3	
320.7	
322.8	
331.0	
347.7	
386.6	
403.4	
459.3	
531.58 ± 0.1	
$_{67}Ho^{168}$	
79.80 ± 0.2	
184.2 ± 0.2	2†
556.9 ± 0.5	2
741.3 ± 0.2	100
821.1 ± 0.3	92
$_{67}Ho^{169}$	
80	
150	12†
680	10
760	30
840	15
920	5
$_{67}Ho^{170}$	
430	
$_{68}Er^{158}$	
Ann. Rad.	
67.2	
71.9	
315	
250	
387	
875	
906	
978	
$_{68}Er^{159}$	
205.9 (IT)	
370	

Gamma energies (KeV)	Gamma intensities
627	
840	
1200	
1400	
1800	
2600	
$_{68}Er^{161}$	
Ann. Rad.	
45.6	
59.5	
84.5	
94.3	
106.1	
112.6	
122.6	
138.7	
144.0	
146.7	
156.5	
172.0	
172.6	
190.6	
207.0	
215.9	
218.2	
244.5	
250.2	
252.5	
265.3	
283.3	
354.0	
372.7	
$_{68}Er^{163}$	
Ann. Rad.	
300	0.01%
430	0.06%
1100	0.04%
$_{68}Er^{167m}$	
207.8	50%
$_{68}Er^{169}$	
8.42	0.1%
$_{68}Er^{171}$	
5.1	
12.4	
86	
111.63	25%
116.69	3%
124	
166.4	0.6%
210.4	0.6%
236	0.5%
277.0	0.65%
295.6	28%
308.2	63%
371.2	0.4%
404	0.03%
418.9	0.09%
544	0.04%

Gamma energies (KeV)	Gamma intensities
557	0.08 %
573	0.07 %
606	0.1 %
619	0.13 %
670	0.3 %
675	0.4 %
732	0.2 %
783	0.31 %
796	0.80 %
842	0.04 %
869	0.06 %
882	0.07 %
906	0.9 %
911	0.2 %
962	0.11 %

$_{68}Er^{172}$

Gamma energies (KeV)	Gamma intensities
29.2	
59.6	
67.9	
128	
164	0.9 %
203	0.9 %
346	0.6 %
384	2.4 %
407	40 %
446	2.5 %
476	1.0 %
535	0.3 %
610	40 %

$_{69}Tm^{161}$

Gamma energies (KeV)	Gamma intensities
45.6	
59.5	
84.5	
94.3	
106.1	
112.6	
122.6	
138.7	
144	
146.7	
156.7	
172.0	
172.6	
190.6	
207.0	
215.9	
218.2	
244.5	
250.2	
252.5	
265.3	
283.3	
354.0	
327.7	

$_{69}Tm^{162}$

Gamma energies (KeV)	Gamma intensities
Ann. Rad.	
102	20†
236	10

$_{69}Tm^{162}$

Gamma energies (KeV)	Gamma intensities
Ann. Rad.	
102	

$_{69}Tm^{163}$

Gamma energies (KeV)	Gamma intensities
Ann. Rad.	
22.2	
60.2	
69.2	
80.5	
83.9	
85.1	
104.3	
145.3	
164.4	
165.4	
190.1	
239.7	
241.5	
249.2	
275.3	
299.9	
335.4	
345.6	
393.5	
404.2	
471.2	
505.1	
531.0	
549.9	
579.9	
613.0	
655.5	
671.1	

$_{69}Tm^{164}$

Gamma energies (KeV)	Gamma intensities
Ann. Rad.	
91	
211	
356	
361	
391	
773	
862	
907	
930	

$_{69}Tm^{165}$

Gamma energies (KeV)	Gamma intensities
15.45	
27.75	
30.05	
35.2	
47.15	
53.2	
54.45	
59.15	
60.4	
70.55	
77.2	
82.25	
86.9	
88.2	
113.6	
141.4	
150.8	
156.0	
165.5	
175.7	†
181.5	
195.6	
197.2	
205.2	
209.9	
218.2 ± 0.2	100 ± 5
221.5	
223.9	
229	
233.2	
234.6	
242.4 ± 0.2	1040 ± 30
248.9	
249.7	
264.4	17 ± 2
275.6	
279.9 ± 0.3	20 ± 2
286.1	
292.3	
295.9	
296.9 ± 0.3	
306.9	4.8 ± 1.5
312.2	14 ± 2
321	
330.5	3.6 ± 1.8
336	
345.7 ± 0.3	
346.6	89 ± 4
356.3 ± 0.3	81 ± 3
363	
365.3	16 ± 3
377	w
384.1	
389.2 ± 0.3	80 ± 4
400.2	5.8 ± 1.7
414	w
420.7	10 ± 3
426.9	w
429.9	w
436	w
442.4	24 ± 3
448.1	57 ± 4
456.0	47 ± 16
459.9 ± 0.3	110 ± 9
471.8	9 ± 2
477.7	12 ± 2
487.0	31 ± 3
502	w
507	w
513	w
513.5	10 ± 3
526.8	32 ± 5
530.9	c
542.2	46 ± 4
558.3	19 ± 5
563.7	67 ± 5
570	w
573.8	14 ± 3
577.3	7 ± 4
589.4	57 ± 5
605.6	
608.1	
622.8	9 ± 3
630	w
663	w
664.6	12 ± 3
677.3	≈6
680.5	≈4
698.6	41 ± 3
734	w
747.4	8 ± 3
791.0	18 ± 4
806.4 ± 0.1	343 ± 12
821.2	w

Gamma energies (KeV)	Gamma intensities
826.9	
837.7	13 ± 2
855	3.9 ± 0.5
892.8	
907.8	
932.4	
952.8	
991	
1042	
1045.7	
1067	
1096	
1131.0	48 ± 2
1184.5	74 ± 4
1232	0.9 ± 0.3
1246.4	
1262	0.3 ± 0.1
1289	3.2 ± 0.5
1333	0.2 ± 0.1
1339	0.4 ± 0.1
1344	0.3 ± 0.1
1365	1.8 ± 0.4
1379.5	8.5 ± 1.0
1426.9	19.5 ± 1.6

$_{69}Tm^{166}$

Gamma energies (KeV)	Gamma intensities
Ann. Rad.	
80.573 ± 0.015	
184.39 ± 0.05	12.6
214.76 ± 0.04	4.4
594.48 ± 0.04	4.5
598.8 ± 0.3	2.9
654.50 ± 0.10	0.4
672.28 ± 0.08	7.6
674.91 ± 0.08	2.7
691.28 ± 0.08	8.4
705.83 ± 0.15	12.8
712.83 ± 0.15	0.6
727.98 ± 0.15	0.5
757.84 ± 0.10	2.9
778.83 ± 0.08	23.4
785.91 ± 0.08	12.7
810.33 ± 0.08	1.34
875.63 ± 0.08	4.9
1030.37 ± 0.03	7.9
1078.86 ± 0.15	0.6
1084.78 ± 0.20	0.3
1119.15 ± 0.13	0.2
1152.32 ± 0.05	2.4
1161.91 ± 0.07	1.1
1176.68 ± 0.04	12.4
1216.08 ± 0.09	0.9
1235.41 ± 0.04	2.4
1248.80 ± 0.12	0.2
1263.44 ± 0.07	1.3
1273.53 ± 0.04	19.2
1300.74 ± 0.06	1.8
1313.31 ± 0.28	0.3
1347.12 ± 0.05	1.3
1374.21 ± 0.04	7.4
1432.18 ± 0.12	1.3
1447.84 ± 0.09	0.8
1505.04 ± 0.08	1.1
1622.48 ± 0.20	0.7
1652.80 ± 0.07	1.4
1868.0 ± 0.1	5.3
1907.63 ± 0.16	0.7
2008.41 ± 0.26	0.4
2052.2 ± 0.2	23.2
2079.5 ± 0.2	8.3

Gamma energies (KeV)	Gamma intensities
2092.11 ± 0.06	2.1
2192.29 ± 0.13	0.2

$_{69}Tm^{167}$

Gamma energies (KeV)	Gamma intensities
57.1	
207.78 ± 0.08	100†
266.5	
322.8	
531.58 ± 0.1	4.18 ± 0.3

$_{69}Tm^{168}$

Gamma energies (KeV)	Gamma intensities
79.80 ± 0.2	9.19
99.0 ± 0.2	0.6
99.3 ± 0.2	3.3
173.5 ± 0.3	0.054
184.2 ± 0.2	17.2
198.2 ± 0.2	52.1
272.9 ± 0.4	0.103
348.5 ± 0.3	0.33
422.2 ± 0.4	0.32
447.4 ± 0.2	24.5
546.7 ± 0.3	2.84
556.9 ± 0.5	0.206
631.6 ± 0.5	8.98
645.7 ± 0.5	1.52
673.4 ± 0.3	0.223
720.3 ± 0.2	12.2
730.6 ± 0.2	5.14
741.3 ± 0.2	12.6
748.2 ± 0.3	0.451
815.9 ± 0.2	50.0
821.1 ± 0.3	11.7
829.9 ± 0.2	6.95
853.5 ± 0.7	0.05
914.9 ± 0.3	3.0
928.9 ± 0.5	0.05
1014.1 ± 0.5	0.06
1167.5 ± 0.5	0.085
1277.3 ± 0.3	1.70
1322.6 ± 0.7	0.03
1351.2 ± 0.7	0.10
1358.0 ± 1.0	0.01
1461.3 ± 0.4	0.42
1592.5 ± 0.4	

$_{69}Tm^{170}$

Gamma energies (KeV)	Gamma intensities
84.262 ± 0.005	3.4 %

$_{69}Tm^{171}$

Gamma energies (KeV)	Gamma intensities
66.7	~2 %

$_{69}Tm^{172}$

Gamma energies (KeV)	Gamma intensities
78.70 ± 0.08	58.0 ± 4
90.6 ± 0.1	0.32 ± 0.06
112.8 ± 0.2[b]	~0.1
131.8 ± 0.2[a]	~0.1
133.6 ± 0.2[a]	~0.1
142.50 ± 0.10	1.8 ± 0.2
145.0 ± 0.2	~0.2
181.55 ± 0.08	44.0 ± 4
203.6 ± 0.3	~0.1
238.5 ± 0.2[a]	~0.2

Gamma energies (KeV)	Gamma intensities
351.8 ± 0.2[a]	~0.2
374.1 ± 0.3	~0.1
399.63 ± 0.08	2.5 ± 0.5
423.0 ± 0.2	~0.5
429.0 ± 1.0	~0.1
436.07 ± 0.08	4.2 ± 0.4
490.31 ± 0.08	6.7 ± 0.6
528.23 ± 0.10	2.0 ± 0.3
542.0 ± 0.4[b]	~0.1
565.5 ± 0.15	0.7 ± 0.2
858.7 ± 0.3	2.0 ± 0.6
912.10 ± 0.08	25.0 ± 3
964.20 ± 0.10	5.3 ± 0.6
1003.0 ± 0.3	~1.0
1040.1 ± 0.3	2.6 ± 0.6
1076.3 ± 0.1[a]	13.0 ± 2
1093.68 ± 0.08	≡104.0
1116.0 ± 0.3	~1
1119.2 ± 0.3	3.8 ± 1.0
1154.9 ± 0.2[a]	3.3 ± 1.0
1184.0 ± 0.5	~1
1205.7 ± 0.2	3.4 ± 0.8
1289.0 ± 0.15	8.4 ± 1.0
1348.4 ± 0.15	2.6 ± 0.6
1387.27 ± 0.08	95.0 ± 6
1398.17 ± 0.08	11.0 ± 2
1402.6 ± 0.15	2.5 ± 0.6
1440.8 ± 0.4	~0.5
1461.0 ± 0.1[a]	4.9 ± 0.5
1466.07 ± 0.08	76.0 ± 6
1470.47 ± 0.08	27.0 ± 3
1476.8 ± 0.10	4.5 ± 0.6
1491.0 ± 1.0	~0.5
1529.87 ± 0.08	84.0 ± 6
1545.0 ± 1.00	~0.5
1584.2 ± 0.10	10.0 ± 1.5
1592.7 ± 0.10[a]	1.5 ± 0.3
1608.62 ± 0.08	69.0 ± 5
1622.1 ± 0.10	1.0 ± 0.2

$_{69}Tm^{173}$

Gamma energies (KeV)	Gamma intensities
66	1.1†
399	89
465	7.6

$_{69}Tm^{174m}$

Gamma energies (KeV)	Gamma intensities
76	9†
176	75
273	95
366	104
500	17
630	5
990	100
1270	8

$_{69}Tm^{175}$

Gamma energies (KeV)	Gamma intensities
513	

$_{70}Yb^{165}$

Gamma energies (KeV)	Gamma intensities
Ann. Rad.	

$_{70}Yb^{166}$

Gamma energies (KeV)	Gamma intensities
820	

Gamma energies (KeV)	Gamma intensities
$_{70}Yb^{167}$	
Ann. Rad.	
25.6	
37.1	
63.0	
106	4†
113.3	10
116.5	
131.8	
150.3	
168.9	
176.1	2.3
920	
1040	
1250	
1440	
1520	
$_{70}Yb^{169}$	
8.42	
20.74	†
63.12	164
93.6	6.6
109.77	51
118.17	4.8
130.51	32
177.18	58
197.97	100
261.05	4.6
307.68	31.0
336.0	0.02
$_{70}Yb^{175m}$	
513	
$_{70}Yb^{175}$	
113.81	31†
137.65	2.2
144.85	5.9
251.3	3.8
282.6	62
396.1	100
$_{70}Yb^{177m}$	
104	
228	
$_{70}Yb^{177}$	
121.6	0.23†
138.4	~1
147.4	
150.8	
161.16	
790	0.2
940	1.1
1079	5
1120	0.7
1239	5†
$_{71}Lu^{167}$	
Ann. Rad.	

Gamma energies (KeV)	Gamma intensities
29.6	
56.2	
78.6	
100.1	
102.5	
123.1	
129.1	
151.8	
178.7	
181.9	
188.5	
198.9	
213.0	
222.5	
229.5	
235.6	
239.0	
258.2	
261.5	
278.1	
307.8	
317.2	
361.4	
371.8	
401.2	
601	
$_{71}Lu^{168}$	
Ann. Rad.	
87	7†
900	10
990	13
1440	
1810	
2100	
$_{71}Lu^{169m}$	
29.0	
$_{71}Lu^{169}$	
Ann. Rad.	
24.2	
62.8	
70.9	
75.0	
87.4	
92.0	
104.4	
110.9	
133.5	
144.6	
157	
165.2	
191.4	
198.4	
238.7	
291.6	
369.6	
379.2	
404.6	
456.8	
470.8	
484.0	
489.7	
549.1	
577.1	

Gamma energies (KeV)	Gamma intensities
647.5	
881	
891	
962	
1062	
1076	
1173	
1187	
1207	
1273	
1380	
1394	
$_{71}Lu^{170m}$	
44.6	
48.4	
$_{71}Lu^{170}$	
Ann. Rad.	
84.262 ± 0.005 (IT)	
152.8	
193.5	
221.2	
222.7	
223.8	
228.5	
236.1	
241.7	
251.3	
283.4	
286.8	
301.9	
323.9	
366.4	
369.9	
372.2	
382.8	
384.8	
389.1	
396.2	
410.6	
419.8	
443.6	
455.7	
479.0	
492.3	
497.1	
540.4	
544.6	
572.2	
579.6	
689.1	
841	
857	
940	
955	
987	
989	
1001	
1005	
1030	
1056	
1063	
1103	
1136	
1141	
1148	
1225	

Gamma energies (KeV)	Gamma intensities	Gamma energies (KeV)	Gamma intensities	Gamma energies (KeV)	Gamma intensities
1228		714		927.0 ± 1.0	
1231		741		929.1 ± 0.1	3.10
1260		768		967.5 ± 1.5	0.18
1266		782		999.5 ± 1.0	< 0.2
1283		827		1002.8 ± 0.13	5.59
1298		842		1013.7 ± 1.0	
1310		854		1020.2 ± 1.0	0.16
1325				1022.4 ± 0.5	1.4
1344				1039.7 ± 1.0	~0.1
1368			$_{71}Lu^{172}$	1041.2 ± 0.2	0.40
1398				1080.8 ± 0.2	0.93
1408		78.73 ± 0.12	9.6	1093.7 ± 0.1	64.75
1431		90.60 ± 0.15	4.5	1113.2 ± 0.2	1.7
1453		112.7 ± 0.2	1.20	1115.7 ± 1.0	0.4
1458		119.1 ± 1.17	0.050	1126.6 ± 1.0	< 0.1
1483		134.4 ± 0.3	0.058	1184.4 ± 0.2	0.3
1515		145.8 ± 1.3	0.10	1212.0 ± 1.0	< 0.1
1517		151.7 ± 1.0	0.034	1283.8 ± 0.7	< 0.1
1553		163.4 ± 1.6	0.093	1288.3 ± 0.7	0.22
1569		174.7 ± 1.0	0.12	1322.8 ± 1.0	< 0.1
1577		181.4 ± 0.1	19.3	1370.3 ± 0.2	0.70
1688		196.2 ± 0.4	0.090	1387.2 ± 0.1	0.88
1816		203.2 ± 0.1	4.60	1397.1 ± 0.4	0.23
1861		210.2 ± 0.5	0.10	1399.1 ± 1.5	0.13
1939		228.9 ± 0.6	0.35	1402.7 ± 0.2	0.58
1956		247.0 ± 0.4	0.62	1440.4 ± 0.2	0.64
2039		264.6 ± 0.2	0.65	1466.2 ± 0.2	0.60
2124		269.9 ± 0.1	1.63	1470.3 ± 1.0	0.70
2359		279.5 ± 0.1	0.98	1477.0 ± 1.0	~0.5
2488		318.8 ± 0.8	0.12	1490.0 ± 1.0	1.10
2512		323.8 ± 0.1	1.30	1532.5 ± 1.0	0.09
2655		330.3 ± 0.7	0.52	1543.0 ± 0.2	0.90
2684		337.4 ± 1.5	~0.03	1579.3 ± 1.0	0.14
2700		352.4 ± 1.5	< 0.03	1584.2 ± 0.1	2.47
2740		358.2 ± 1.5	~0.10	1602.8 ± 0.2	0.26
2775		366.5 ± 0.6	0.30	1608.8 ± 0.8	0.095
2836		372.4 ± 0.3	2.50	1622.0 ± 0.1	2.06
2872		373.3 ± 1.0	< 0.4	1666.7 ± 0.3	0.24
2930		377.4 ± 0.1	3.37	1670.6 ± 0.2	0.51
2955		399.6 ± 0.2	0.55	1724.5 ± 0.2	0.55
3023		410.2 ± 0.1	2.08	1813.0 ± 0.3	0.20
		415.9 ± 1.5	0.11	1914.7 ± 0.4	0.63
		422.4 ± 1.5	0.10	1920.2 ± 1.5	0.03
	$_{71}Lu^{171m}$	427.0 ± 1.5	< 0.1	1931.9 ± 1.5	0.03
		432.5 ± 0.3	1.65	1955.3 ± 1.5	< 0.03
71.2		437.1 ± 1.5	~0.25	1994.4 ± 0.4	0.16
		442.6 ± 1.5	~0.18	2025.2 ± 0.9	0.059
	$_{71}Lu^{171}$	482.3 ± 0.5	0.49	2083.5 ± 0.3	0.29
		486.1 ± 0.5	0.60	2096.1 ± 0.5	0.11
		490.4 ± 0.1	1.83		
Ann. Rad.		512.8 ± 1.5	0.16		
19.3		524.0 ± 1.5	0.21		$_{71}Lu^{173}$
27.0		528.2 ± 0.1	3.80		
46.5		536.2 ± 1.2	0.56	78.70	12.5%
55.7		540.2 ± 0.2	1.44	100.63	6.1%
66.7		551.2 ± 1.5	0.38	171.36	3.2%
72.3		566.3 ± 1.5	0.10	179.33	1.9%
75.9		577.0 ± 1.5	0.27	272.05	26%
85.5		584.8 ± 0.8	0.32	285.40	0.8%
91.3		594.5 ± 0.7	0.43	351.0	1.0%
109.2		607.2 ± 0.7	0.50	457	0.3%
122.2		623.1 ± 1.5	0.22	558	0.8%
132.2		631.4 ± 1.5	0.39	637	0.05%
141.3		681.8 ± 0.6	0.67		
154.6		697.3 ± 0.2	6.20		
163.8		709.1 ± 0.6	0.79		$_{71}Lu^{174m}$
170.6		723.2 ± 1.1	0.40		
195.0		810.1 ± 0.1	16.5	44.6 (IT)	
518		816.2 ± 1.4	1.02	59.1 (IT)	
627		900.8 ± 0.1	29.4	67.1 (IT)	8%
668		910 ± 1.0	~0.68	76.50	
690		912.1 ± 0.1	15.0		

Gamma energies (KeV)	Gamma intensities
176.66	0.5%
272.87	0.7%
449.6	0.07%
992.1	0.08%

$_{71}Lu^{174}$

76.5	8.1%
1241.76 ± 0.2	9%
1318.24 ± 0.3	0.12%

$_{71}Lu^{176m}$

88.36	0.0004%
1050	0.0009%
1140	

$_{71}Lu^{176}$

88.36	16†
203	89
306	100

$_{71}Lu^{177m}$

71.64	6.8†
105.36	100
112.97	179
*115.83	5.0
117.2	1.8
*121.6	52
128.5	127
136.7	12
145.8	7
*147.1	29
153.3	133
159.7	5.4
*171.8	37
174.4	96
177.0	26
182.0	0.8
*195.5	7
204.1	114
208.36	485
214.4	48
*218.1	27
228.4	287
233.8	45
249.7	47
*268.8	25
281.8	108
283.4	5
291.4	8
292.5	8
296.5	38
299.0	12
305.5	14
313.7	9
*319.0	78
321.4	9
327.7	136
341.6	13
*367.4	23
378.5	222
385.0	24
*413.6	131
418.5	161

Gamma energies (KeV)	Gamma intensities
426.3	3.4
466.0	19

$_{71}Lu^{177}$

71.64	2.4†
112.97	100
136.7	0.74
208.36	171
249.7	3.3
321.4	3.4

$_{71}Lu^{178}$

93.179	
215	
325	
425	

$_{71}Lu^{178}$

93.179	
215	
325	
425	

$_{71}Lu^{179}$

90	
213	

$_{72}Hf^{168}$

Ann. Rad.	
129	
170	

$_{72}Hf^{169}$

Ann. Rad.	
115	

$_{72}Hf^{170}$

Ann. Rad.	
44.6	
48.4	
120.2	
164.7	
990	
1280	
1650	
2030	
2360	
2520	
2940	

$_{72}Hf^{171}$

70.1	
122	
188	
290	
340	

Gamma energies (KeV)	Gamma intensities
470	
660	
860	
1070	

$_{72}Hf^{172}$

23.99	
41.86	
44.08	
81.8	
114	
125.8	

$_{72}Hf^{173}$

4.65	
17.8	
123.6	
134.9	
139.6	
161.8	
171.3	
297	
306	
311	18†
357	
422	
539	
549	
555	
567	
577	
617	
624	
717	
759	
764	
853	
857	
874	
878	
898	
1032	
1037	
1069	
1204	
1209	
1213	
1351	
1485	
1551	
1781	

$_{72}Hf^{175}$

89.36	40†
113.81	3.6
161.3	0.3
229.6	7.3
318.9	
343.4	1000
433.0	16

$_{72}Hf^{178m2}$

88.878 ± 0.015	67
93.181 ± 0.015	18

Gamma energies (KeV)	Gamma intensities
213.444 ± 0.015	86
216.673 ± 0.015	71
237.40 ± 0.03	10
238.66 ± 0.1[b]	2.5
257.62 ± 0.02	18
277.35 ± 0.05	1.6
296.80 ± 0.04	10
325.562 ± 0.015	100
426.371 ± 0.015	105
454.05 ± 0.04	19
495.01 ± 0.03	82
535.02 ± 0.04	11
574.21 ± 0.03	101

$_{72}Hf^{178m_1}$

Gamma energies (KeV)	Gamma intensities
88.878 ± 0.015	67%
93.181 ± 0.015	18%
213.44 ± 0.015	86%
325.562 ± 0.015	96%
426.371 ± 0.015	100%

$_{72}Hf^{179m}$

Gamma energies (KeV)	Gamma intensities
161	5%
217	99.5%
325	0.5%

$_{72}Hf^{180m}$

Gamma energies (KeV)	Gamma intensities
57.54	29†
93.33	10
215.3	50
332.5	57
444	49
501	8

$_{72}Hf^{181}$

Gamma energies (KeV)	Gamma intensities
3.9	
6.3	
133.02	40†
136.25	6
136.86	1.7
345.9	13
476.0	~1.7
482.0	81
615.5	0.2

$_{72}Hf^{182}$

Gamma energies (KeV)	Gamma intensities
97.89 ± 0.1	0.08%
114.33 ± 0.02	2.6%
156.09 ± 0.02	7.0%
172.54 ± 0.1	0.2%
270.405 ± 0.01	80%

$_{72}Hf^{183}$

Gamma energies (KeV)	Gamma intensities
140	2†
170	0.9
210	2
280	3

Gamma energies (KeV)	Gamma intensities
320	4
400	5
460	58
610	2†
720	6
820	100
900	6

$_{73}Ta^{172}$

Gamma energies (KeV)	Gamma intensities
Ann. Rad.	
92	
115	
155	
208	
270	
1100	
1300	

$_{73}Ta^{173}$

Gamma energies (KeV)	Gamma intensities
Ann. Rad.	
37.4	
58.0	
69.8	
81.5	
90.2	
115.0	
160.4	
172.1	
180.6	

$_{73}Ta^{174}$

Gamma energies (KeV)	Gamma intensities
Ann. Rad.	
90.9	
125	
160	
205	
280	
350	

$_{73}Ta^{175}$

Gamma energies (KeV)	Gamma intensities
35.8	
50.5	
70.5	
77.3	
81.5	
100.8	
104.3	
125.9	
126.6	
132.0	
142.0	
162.0	
162.5	
179.1	
185.8	
192.7	
196.4	
207.4	
213.4	
230.8	
266.9	
280.5	
288.9	
294.0	

Gamma energies (KeV)	Gamma intensities
308.9	
348.5	
361.4	
365.7	
386.0	
393.2	
404	
433	
436	
443	
450	
462	
475	
525	
533	
540	
602	
622	
694	
732	
751	
762	
810	
815	
852	
854	
860	
867	
878	
902	
964	
1000	
1013	
1038	
1121	
1146	
1252	
1376	
1383	
1470	
1639	

$_{73}Ta^{176}$

Gamma energies (KeV)	Gamma intensities
88.35	
91.3	
99.6	
103.4	
125.6	
131.1	
146.7	
156.8	
158.2	
175.6	
190.4	
201.9	
240.0	
366	
415	
639	
646	
678	
686	
711	
723	
741	
938	
1025	
1140	
1162	

Gamma energies (KeV)	Gamma intensities
1192	
1203	
1225	
1255	
1272	
1296	
1343	
1359	
1489	
1504	
1557	
1586	
1618	
1633	
1672	
1681	
1699	
1707	
1723	
1778	
1825	
1864	
1908	
1958	
2045	
2137	
2219	
2247	
2312	
2460	
2467	
2519	
2602	
2622	
2760	
2831	
2925	

$_{73}Ta^{177}$

Gamma energies (KeV)	Gamma intensities
51.1	
71.6	0.003 %
96.2	
112.97	6 %
136.7	
208.38	1.0 %
249.7	0.02 %
257.3	
298.1	
321.3	0.024 %
357.3	0.002 %
396.0	
420.9	0.0018 %
424.7	0.13 %
452.9	
492.5	0.0015 %
509	0.0024 %
526.9	
549.4	
598.5	0.009 %
633.1	0.039 %
735.2	0.04 %
737.0	0.016 %
746.0	0.22 %
848.2	
945.4	0.055 %
1058.4	0.30 %

$_{73}Ta^{178}$

$_{73}Ta^{178}$

Gamma energies (KeV)	Gamma intensities
Ann. Rad.	
93	
203	
214	
970	
1100	
1170	
1180	
1200	
1260	
1330	
1340	
1390	
1430	
1440	
1460	
1480	

$_{73}Ta^{178}$

Gamma energies (KeV)	Gamma intensities
88.8	
93.1	
213.6	10†
325.7	11
331.7	3
426.8	10

$_{73}Ta^{179}$

No γ

$_{73}Ta^{180m}$

Gamma energies (KeV)	Gamma intensities
93.4 ± 0.2	27 %
103.6 ± 0.2	3 %
200	

$_{73}Ta^{180}$

Gamma energies (KeV)	Gamma intensities
400	

$_{73}Ta^{181m}$

Gamma energies (KeV)	Gamma intensities
6.3	

$_{73}Ta^{182m}$

Gamma energies (KeV)	Gamma intensities
146.785 ± 0.01	75†
171.586 ± 0.01	≡ 100
184.951 ± 0.01	51
318.401 ± 0.04	14
356.468 ± 0.07	0.6

$_{73}Ta^{182}$

Gamma energies (KeV)	Gamma intensities
31.74	
42.71	
65.72	
67.75	8 %
84.68	3.34 %
100.10	41 %
113.67	1.8 %
116.41	0.4 %
152.441 ± 0.003	57 %
156.386 ± 0.003	72 %

Gamma energies (KeV)	Gamma intensities
179.394 ± 0.004	33 %
222.114 ± 0.004	97 %
229.335 ± 0.017	3.6 %
264.079 ± 0.009	24 %
927.903 ± 0.07	0.6 %
1001.654 ± 0.041	2.8 %
1113.050 ± 0.08	0.6 %
1121.218 ± 0.016	35.6 %
1157.357 ± 0.060	1.04 %
1188.978 ± 0.019	16.5 %
1221.354 ± 0.019	27.9 %
1230.982 ± 0.021	11.4 %
1257.401 ± 0.036	1.56 %
1273.657 ± 0.050	0.67 %
1289.126 ± 0.032	1.44 %
1342.743 ± 0.010	0.27 %
1373.638 ± 0.015	0.24 %
1387.2 ± 0.2	0.08 %
1410.0 ± 0.2	0.05 %
1453.0 ± 0.2	0.03 %

$_{73}Ta^{183}$

Gamma energies (KeV)	Gamma intensities
40.98	1.8†
46.48	22
52.59	22
82.92	1.4
84.71	5.1
99.08	27
101.93	1.2
102.48	0.51
103.15	0.35
107.93	44
109.73	2.4
120.73	0.23
142.27	1.4
144.12	9.5
160.53	11
161.34	35†
162.32	19
192.64	1.35
203.28	1.5
205.08	3.4
208.81	2.3
209.86	17
244.26	32
245.24	1.2
246.06	100
291.72	14.1
313.00 / 313.28	27
353.99	43
365.64	2.0
406.61	1.9

$_{73}Ta^{184}$

Gamma energies (KeV)	Gamma intensities
111	
160	
250	
300	
410	
530	38†
660	7
790	34
900	100
950	30
1060	9

Gamma energies (KeV)	Gamma intensities	Gamma energies (KeV)	Gamma intensities	Gamma energies (KeV)	Gamma intensities
1100	1.3	450.8		57.2	†
1160	25	502.0		71.95 ± 0.03	37.3
1270	10†	528.0		106.57 ± 0.08	0.09
1320	1.8	562.0		113.72 ± 0.06	0.33
1440	5	568		134.24 ± 0.03	29.4
		615		206.20 ± 0.04	0.53
$_{73}Ta^{185}$		630		239.10 ± 0.10	0.28
		639		246.35 ± 0.07	0.38
75	8†	673		479.51 ± 0.03	80.47
100	16	712		511.70 ± 0.06	2.53
110	1	722		551.51 ± 0.10	18.98
135	5	760		588.90 ± 0.12	0.65
175	100	787		618.24 ± 0.04	23.25
245	8	797		625.42 ± 0.07	3.93
		827		685.72 ± 0.04	100
$_{73}Ta^{186}$		858		745.33 ± 0.10	1.00
		877		772.85 ± 0.07	14.75
122	25†	1016		864.53 ± 0.10	1.25
200	100	1036		879.0 ± 0.5	0.47
300	25	1067			
410	20	1174		$_{74}W^{188}$	
510	45	1269			
608	45	1295		63.58	0.9%
730	65			227	0.3%
940	15	$_{74}W^{179m}$		290.5	0.6%
$_{74}W^{175}$		221.8		$_{74}W^{189}$	
260		$_{74}W^{179}$		94	2†
800				130	12
1300		30.7		178	13
1600				220	3
		$_{74}W^{180m}$		258	100
				360	10
$_{74}W^{176}$				417	96
		0.102		550	28
Ann. Rad.		0.35		860	20
33.58		0.5		960	17
50.55		0.22			
61.29				$_{75}Re^{177}$	
84.14		$_{74}W^{181m}$			
94.9				Ann. Rad	
100.2		0.37			
				$_{75}Re^{178}$	
$_{74}W^{177}$		$_{74}W^{181}$			
				Ann. Rad	
		63	35%		
30.5		136.3	0.11%	$_{75}Re^{179}$	
70.45		152.5	0.2%		
101.8				221.8	
115.7		$_{74}W^{183m}$		280	
142.6					
143.9		46	†	$_{75}Re^{180}$	
156.0		52			
186.4		105	19	Ann. Rad.	
203.0		160	3.5	110	
223.3				880	
259.2		$_{74}W^{185m}$			
271.1				$_{75}Re^{180}$	
290.0		60			
308.1		131		Ann. Rad.	
317.5		175			
367.6				$_{75}Re^{181}$	
377.1		$_{74}W^{187}$			
381.5				19.7	
388.9		36.3		31.1	
417.1		49.2		38.1	
427.2					

Gamma energies (KeV)	Gamma intensities	Gamma energies (KeV)	Gamma intensities	Gamma energies (KeV)	Gamma intensities
43.5		$_{75}Re^{182}$		217.48 ± 0.15	
65.0				226.16 ± 0.15	
71.7				247.44 ± 0.15	
72.7		31.7		256.44 ± 0.15	
93.7		42.0		264.07 ± 0.15	
102.7		42.7		276.30 ± 0.15	
103.1		65.8		281.45 ± 0.15	
109.9		67.8		286.53 ± 0.15	
110.3		84.7		295.70 ± 0.15	
113.3		100.1		300.15 ± 0.15	
137.2		113.7		323.36 ± 0.15	
144.3		116.4		339.06 ± 0.15	
154.4		152.5		341.93 ± 0.15	
163.9		156.4		346.13 ± 0.15	
164.6		179.4		351.07 ± 0.15	
165.8		198.4		357.11 ± 0.15	
175.2		222.0		1157.40 ± 0.20	
177.4		229.3		1181.09 ± 0.20	
186.2		264.0		1188.78 ± 0.20	
195.0		470.0		1221.10 ± 0.15	
197.0		514.3		1230.76 ± 0.15	
252.0		536.1		1257.18 ± 0.30	
262.6		598.5		1288.67 ± 0.30	
276.2		649.5		1293.66 ± 0.30	
295.9		734.5		1342.33 ± 0.30	
318.6		786.6		1426.88 ± 0.15	
331.9		810		1438	
353.6		836			
356.1		895			
360.7		901		$_{75}Re^{183}$	
365.5		928			
382.3		960		46.73 ± 0.15	78%
389.0		1002		52.77 ± 0.15	25%
408.7		1045		67.29 ± 0.15	
441.8		1122		69.22 ± 0.15	
475.6		1158		82.99 ± 0.15	3.1%
487.2		1189		84.79 ± 0.15	12%
489.0		1222		99.11 ± 0.15	25%
515.7		1231		107.94 ± 0.15	11%
522.2		1257		109.74 ± 0.15	11%
557.7		1274		115.90 ± 0.15	
587.6		1289		117.19 ± 0.15	
639.0		1374		118.58 ± 0.15	
651.2		1387		126.49 ± 0.15	
661.8		1438		125.18 ± 0.15	
668.2		1955		144.06 ± 0.15	0.3%
693.9		2014		169.01 ± 0.15	
738.1		2023		192.54 ± 0.15	0.5%
769.6		2054		215.18 ± 0.15	
781.4				220.15 ± 0.15	
804				221.59 ± 0.15	
805		$_{75}Re^{182}$		229.29 ± 0.15	
823				244.36 ± 0.15	0.8%
840		47.05 ± 0.15		245.94 ± 0.15	1.8%
854		53.04 ± 0.15		313.11 ± 0.15	0.6%
880		87.31 ± 0.15		318.09 ± 0.15	
883		100.07 ± 0.15		354.71 ± 0.15	0.7%
908		113.62 ± 0.15			
954		116.45 ± 0.15			
989		130.75 ± 0.15		$_{75}Re^{184m}$	
994		133.72 ± 0.15			
1000		145.39 ± 0.15			
1009		149.00 ± 0.15		83.4	70%
1076		152.37 ± 0.15		104.7	70%
1087		156.34 ± 0.15		111.43 ± 0.1	61%
1103		172.83 ± 0.15		161.27 ± 0.15	10%
1384		187.47 ± 0.15		216.53 ± 0.15	15%
1441		189.62 ± 0.15		252.82 ± 0.15	10%
1469		191.33 ± 0.15		384.21 ± 0.15	~2%
1538		198.29 ± 0.15		641.9 ± 0.15	1.5%
		214.24 ± 0.15		792.83 ± 0.10	28%
		215.83 ± 0.15			

Gamma energies (KeV)	Gamma intensities
894.68 ± 0.10	23%
903.20 ± 0.10	36%

75Re184

Gamma energies (KeV)	Gamma intensities
71.11 ± 0.15	
87.50 ± 0.2	
91.42 ± 0.2	
104.80 ± 0.1	
111.43 ± 0.10	59%
117.43 ± 0.10	
118.67 ± 0.20	
124.47 ± 0.20	
126.52 ± 0.20	
161.27 ± 0.15	
169.21 ± 0.20	
170.57 ± 0.20	
178.27 ± 0.20	
180.0 ± 0.3	
216.53 ± 0.15	0.5%
226.72 ± 0.15	
252.82 ± 0.15	4.7%
317.97 ± 0.15	1%
363.97 ± 0.25	
384.21 ± 0.15	
536.61 ± 0.15	
539.24 ± 0.20	0.3%
641.90 ± 0.15	2.3%
769.75 ± 0.15	5%
792.83 ± 0.10	36%
850.78 ± 0.15	
859.19 ± 0.15	
894.68 ± 0.10	19%
903.20 ± 0.10	41%
920.88 ± 0.15	~4%
953.64 ± 0.20	
962.02 ± 0.15	
970.77 ± 0.20	
1005.88 ± 0.20	
1010.11 ± 0.20	
1022.49 ± 0.15	
1109.86 ± 0.15	
1173.72 ± 0.15	
1274.96 ± 0.25	
1384	

75Re186

Gamma energies (KeV)	Gamma intensities
176	2.1
191	1.2
230	0.6

75Re188m

Gamma energies (KeV)	Gamma intensities
2.4	
15.9	
63.58	
92.45	
105.96	

75Re188

Gamma energies (KeV)	Gamma intensities
155.03	1550† 3%
297	1.7
321	1.6
452	7
478	100 0.27%
485	8

Gamma energies (KeV)	Gamma intensities
633	141
641	1.2
672	10
824	4
829	40
846	0.6
881	1.6
932	58
963	1.3
967	1.8†
977	0.7
1019	1.6
1132	9
1150	3.6
1171	1.1
1176	2.1
1191	1.2
1230	0.6
1307	7
1322	1.3
1368	1.1
1457	1.8
1610	11
1732	3.5
1786	2.6
1803	4.1
1866	0.6
1957	1.6

75Re189

Gamma energies (KeV)	Gamma intensities
30.8	
36.2	
69.5	
95.2	
147.2	
150.1	
185.9	
188.6	
206.4	
211.0	
216.8	
219.4	
245.0	

75Re190

Gamma energies (KeV)	Gamma intensities
187	10†
392	10
570	10
830	3

75Re192

Gamma energies (KeV)	Gamma intensities
200	
290	
370	
480	
570	

76Os181

Gamma energies (KeV)	Gamma intensities
93	
101	

76Os182

Gamma energies (KeV)	Gamma intensities
27.6	†
55.5	
180.2	7
263.2	1.4
509.9	10

76Os183m

Gamma energies (KeV)	Gamma intensities
67.3	6%
147	
170.7	46%
1.036	6%
1.103	26%
1.1095	22%

76Os183

Gamma energies (KeV)	Gamma intensities
114.4	
145.4	
151.0	
167.9	
236.2	
259.8	
355.5	
381.8	
477.2	
496.1	
737	
808	
851	
887	
889	
1163	
1440	

76Os185

Gamma energies (KeV)	Gamma intensities
71.6	1.5%
125.3	2.4%
162.6	1.1%
233.4	1.4%
592.0	1.2%
645.8	81%
718	4.2%
872	6.5%
879	6.5%

76Os189m

Gamma energies (KeV)	Gamma intensities
30.81	

76Os190m

Gamma energies (KeV)	Gamma intensities
38.9	<1%
186.7	100%
361.2	100%
502.5	100%
616.5	100%

76Os191m

Gamma energies (KeV)	Gamma intensities
74.2	

76Os191

Gamma energies (KeV)	Gamma intensities
49.5	
82.33	

Gamma energies (KeV)	Gamma intensities	Gamma energies (KeV)	Gamma intensities	Gamma energies (KeV)	Gamma intensities
96.45		24.2		342.5	
129.4		30.4		351.7	
178.9		33.8		364.9	
186.7		37.4		387.9	
		60.0		403.3	
₇₆Os¹⁹³		90.4		406.6	
		94.5		412	
73	1.45†	97.4		420.7	
98	0.04	100.7		542.2	
99	0.02	119.6		551.4	
107	0.37	124.9		558.0	
139	2.93	126.9		565.4	
153	0.02	127.9		570.3	
180	0.09	129.4		584.4	
181	0.18	153.6		592	
219	0.16	158.3		600	
234	0.033	160.7		622.1	
252	0.134	185.0		630.3	
280	1.00	220.4		636.2	
289	0.19	222.3		650.0	
298	0.16	223.8		662	
321	0.76	254.4		679.5	
361	0.21	266.5		684.8	
378	0.08	300.4		693.6	
387	0.75	307.1		706	
419	0.133	314.4		712.6	
441	0.065	321.5		729.5	
460	2.32	339.2		745	
485	0.113	352.4		760.0	
517	0.02	377.7		767.3	
532	0.05	406.8		773.1	
558	1.10	419.1		780.8	
573	0.01	431.4		794	
660	0.002	507.0		805.5	
712	0.011	513.7		841.3	
848	0.003	539.4		885	
875	0.0135	745.7		933.2	
				943.6	
₇₆Os¹⁹⁴		₇₇Ir¹⁸⁶		960	
				1011.0	
43.0	10%	Ann. Rad.		1026.5	
78	0.03%	70.9		1057.1	
		87.19		1107	
₇₇Ir¹⁸²		102.1		1172	
		119.4		1187.9	
Ann. Rad.		137.15		1314	
133		143.0		1324	
278		160.0		1440	
↓		167·1		1467	
4000		220.0		1508	
		224.1		1597	
		234.5		1647	
₇₇Ir¹⁸³		252.5		1701	
		269.0		1738	
240		272.8		1743	
		276.5		1752	
₇₇Ir¹⁸⁴		284.3		1789	
		288.8		1801	
Ann Rad.		293.0		1805	
125	100†	296.7		1815	
267	200	299.4		1869	
392	90	302.9		1906	
830		305.6		1939	
960		309.6		1953	
1090		311.8		1975	
↓		321.2		2000	
4300		322.6		2260	
		326.6		2312	
₇₇Ir¹⁸⁵		330.2		2340	
		334.0		2360	
				2383	

Gamma energies (KeV)	Gamma intensities	Gamma energies (KeV)	Gamma intensities	Gamma energies (KeV)	Gamma intensities
2389		322.9	12	1653	10
2397		332.4		1689	2
2413		346.7		1705	7
2429		350.0	1.6	1717	25
2498		351.7		1721	
2513		352.7		1728	
2564		371.4		1732	
2578		379.6		1737	
2617		385.3	1.4	1760	
2678		399.0		1775	
2733		424.5		1784	
2748		447.7		1789	
2826		452.9		1805	
2854		478.0		1812	1
2994		478.6	100	1904	
3043		514.8	3.2	1931	
		522.7		1945	18
		566.7	3	1968	
₇₇Ir¹⁸⁶		586.2		2013	3
		594.0		2052	22
Ann. Rad.		599.0		2061	30
137.15		620.6	6	2098	45
295		633.1 }	180	2100	
630		634.8 }		2196	10
770		641.5	3.4	2217	80†
990		652.4		2294	1.5
		672.3	9	2344	
		736.8		2350	
₇₇Ir¹⁸⁷		747.6		2494	
		757.2	2.0	2525	
65.1		777.5	†	2623	
73.7		781.9		2700	
85.0		810.5			
125.5		821.2			
137.9		824.8		₇₇Ir¹⁸⁹	
162.6		828.6			
177.5		829.5		25.7	
187.1		886.0		30.8	
313.8		905.9		33.3	
399.2		940.0		36.2	
400.9		943.6		56.5	
426.9		947.4		59.1	
491.1		983.8		59.3	
501.5		987.7	13	69.6	
576.5		1013		95.2	
610.6		1018	6	97.8	
799.4		1053		138.3	
912.6		1097	8	147.1	
976.7		1143	2	149.9	
987.0		1150	4	164.0	
1103		1175	6	180.5	
1112		1193	†	185.9	
		1206	42	188.6	
		1210	1.5	197.4	
₇₇Ir¹⁸⁸		1296	4	206.3	
		1304		216.7	
Ann. Rad.		1307		219.3	
85.0		1323	10	233.5	
95.6		1329	4	245.0	
115.7		1333	4	275.8	
123.1		1337			
150.5		1430			
155.0	209	1436	9	₇₇Ir¹⁹⁰ᵐ²	
157.0		1446			
158.0		1453	4	38.9	
162.2		1458	7	116.7	
175.4		1463 }	7	148.7 (IT)	
189.3		1466 }		186.7	75†
222.3		1560	4	206.6	
268.3		1575	12	361.2	100
279.6		1620	4	502.5	115
312.0				616.5	103

Gamma energies (KeV)	Gamma intensities	Gamma energies (KeV)	Gamma intensities	Gamma energies (KeV)	Gamma intensities
$_{77}\text{Ir}^{190m_1}$		1437		1048.7	0.07
		1464		1104.1	0.06
26.3		1473		1151.3	1.6
		1482		1175.5	0.17
$_{77}\text{Ir}^{190}$		1517		1184.1	0.79
		1525		1219.0	0.34
97.8		1534		1294	0.26
100.0		1543		1342.4	0.11
137.8		1584		1431	0.02
182.1		1606		1469.4	0.93
186.7		1677		1480	< 0.05
190.5		1685		1488	0.9
196.8		1700		1512	0.13
198.0		1711		1623	0.24
199.3				1671	0.033
207.8		$_{77}\text{Ir}^{191m}$		1784	0.025
223.8				1798	0.06
235.3		41.8		1805	0.06
251.4		47		1808	0.09
282.9		82.3		1832	0.009
288.2		129.4		1926	0.012
294.6				2044	0.022
361.2				2115	0.009
371.1		$_{77}\text{Ir}^{192m_2}$			
380.1				$_{77}\text{Ir}^{195}$	
394.8		161			
397.3				98.5	100†
402.4		$_{77}\text{Ir}^{192m_1}$		129.9	50
407.2				330	60
447.5		58(IT)		370	40
462.5		317		430	30
485.3		612		660	20
490.8					
502.5		$_{77}\text{Ir}^{192}$		$_{77}\text{Ir}^{196m}$	
518.4					
557.8		136.34	2.7†		
569.3		201.28	5.6	103.3 ± 0.2	17 ± 2
605.3		205.79	38	340.7 ± 0.4	1.6 ± 0.2
655.9		283.4	4	355.9 ± 0.2	98 ± 3
690.0		295.9	360	393.5 ± 0.2	101 ± 2
726.4		308.43	370	420.9 ± 0.3	2.6 ± 0.1
750.7		316.5	1000–85 %	447.1 ± 0.2	98 ± 2
768.5		374.6	6	521.4 ± 0.2	100
801		416.6	≤ 3	553.0 ± 0.3	0.66 ± 0.04
829.0		468.05	600	566.4 ± 0.4	0.3 ± 0.1
833		484.6	40	615.9 ± 0.4	0.44 ± 0.05
836		489.1	4	633.5 ± 0.3	1.15 ± 0.05
839		588.6	49	647.3 ± 0.2	95 ± 3
915		604.38	105	673.9 ± 0.2	0.18 ± 0.04
933		612.43	70	693.9 ± 0.2	4.4 ± 0.3
953		884.6	5	722.0 ± 0.4	0.67 ± 0.07
1036		1062	0.5	727.3 ± 0.2	2.7 ± 0.1
1079				760.6 ± 0.3	0.78 ± 0.05
1110				835.6 ± 0.2	6.6 ± 0.2
1116		$_{77}\text{Ir}^{193m}$		849.4 ± 0.3	0.53 ± 0.05
1131				868.1 ± 0.3	0.48 ± 0.04
1134		80.2		887.0 ± 0.5	0.11 ± 0.02
1184				893.0 ± 0.5	0.20 ± 0.02
1200				904.6 ± 0.5	0.10 ± 0.02
1234		$_{77}\text{Ir}^{194}$		914.6 ± 0.3	0.30 ± 0.05
1314				926.0 ± 0.5	0.07 ± 0.02
1324		29.362	6.5†	1024.6 ± 0.3	0.26 ± 0.03
1329		300.7	0.9	1068 ± 2	0.074 ± 0.018
1339		328.54	33	1080.5 ± 0.5	0.12 ± 0.02
1355		622.1	0.8	1116.7 ± 0.8	0.073 ± 0.022
1386		645.3	2.7	1281.6 ± 0.5	0.061 ± 0.024
1391		890.1	0.10	1341.5 ± 0.5	0.29 ± 0.03
1397		925.3	0.09	1355.8 ± 0.5	0.06 ± 0.01
1403		938.9	1.5	1394.0 ± 0.5	0.074 ± 0.015
1414		1000.2	0.08	1482.5 ± 0.4	2.4 ± 0.2

GAMMA ENERGIES AND INTENSITIES OF RADIONUCLIDES (*Continued*)

Gamma energies (KeV)	Gamma intensities
$_{77}Ir^{196}$	
KX	40 ± 30
332.8 ± 0.3	23 ± 1
355.4 ± 0.3	100
446.6 ± 0.3	24 ± 2
779.4 ± 0.3	55 ± 2
1047.0 ± 0.7	5 ± 1
1228.6 ± 1.2	1.8 ± 0.4
1468.4 ± 0.8	4.4 ± 0.7
1564.2 ± 0.8	4.7 ± 1.0
$_{77}Ir^{197}$	
510	~50%
$_{77}Ir^{198}$	
780	
$_{78}Pt^{174}$	
Ann. Rad.	
$_{78}Pt^{177}$	
Ann. Rad.	
$_{78}Pt^{178}$	
Ann. Rad.	
160	
$_{78}Pt^{180}$	
Ann. Rad.	
$_{78}Pt^{181}$	
Ann. Rad.	
$_{78}Pt^{182}$	
Ann. Rad.	
$_{78}Pt^{183}$	
Ann. Rad.	
$_{78}Pt^{185}$	
35	
63	
1560	
$_{78}Pt^{186}$	
140	
190	
680	
1400	

Gamma energies (KeV)	Gamma intensities
$_{78}Pt^{187}$	
110	
184	
2010	
$_{78}Pt^{188}$	
Ir KX	100†
41.9	0.4
54.8	0.3
96.7	0.2
98.4	0.4
132.8	0.30
140.3	2.2
187.6	19.2
195.1	18.4
280.4	0.22
283.0	0.11
290.6	0.11
381.6	7.0
423.6	4.4
478.3	1.9
$_{78}Pt^{189}$	
71.6	
82.1	
94.2	
113.8	
141.1	
176.3	
181.3	
186.7	
190.8	
203.7	
223.3	
225.6	
243.4	
252.0	
258.2	
300.4	
317.6	
403.8	
542	
544.8	
568.8	
607	
626.9	
644	
720.9	
735	
792	
798	
$_{78}Pt^{191}$	
82.33	
96.45	
129.39	
172.2	10.2%
178.9	3.2%
186.8	
187.8	
219.7	
221.8	
227.4	
268.8	

Gamma energies (KeV)	Gamma intensities
351.2	9.9%
360.0	16.6%
409.3	28.8%
456.5	9.6%
501.4	
539.0	40.5%
569.1	
575.6	
587.9	
624.1	
632.6	
$_{78}Pt^{193m}$	
12.58	
135.5	
$_{78}Pt^{195m}$	
30.8	
98.5	12%
129.4	2.8%
129.9	
$_{78}Pt^{197m}$	
52.9 (IT)	†
130.2	21
279.3	21
346 (IT)	100
$_{78}Pt^{197}$	
77.35	20%†
191.4	5.7%
268	0.006%
279	<0.0001%
$_{78}Pt^{199m}$	
32	~5†
393	100
$_{78}Pt^{199}$	
75	†
179	38
220	w
245	16
315	11
320	22
475 D	45
540	100
715	14
790	10
960	8
$_{79}Au^{186}$	
160	
220	
330	
400	

Gamma energies (KeV)	Gamma intensities	Gamma energies (KeV)	Gamma intensities	Gamma energies (KeV)	Gamma intensities
$_{79}Au^{188}$		620.3		163.94	
		674.2		202.9	
Ann. Rad.		702.0		216.15	
250		732.5		226.9	
330				236.3	
630		$_{79}Au^{192}$		285.34	
				293.62	
		Ann. Rad.		300.71	
$_{79}Au^{189}$		45.1		328.54	
		96.8		365.0	
39.44		104.7		482.8	
45.7		137		528.9	
88.6		157		544.7	
166.6		167		589.4	
215.9		205		593.7	
440		283		607.6	
446		295		622.1	
		308		645.3	
		316		668.6	
$_{79}Au^{190}$		415		672	
		437		676.1	
Ann. Rad.		466		703.6	
295.7		588		736.5	
301.6		612		818.7	
319		783		843.9	
598		1158		847.4	
623				856.1	
1400				860	
1400				890.1	
1760		$_{79}Au^{193m}$		894.4	
2080				925.3	
2400		31.9		938.9	
2700		220		948.4	
2940		290.6 (IT)		1002.2	
3250				1007.5	
3460				1030.9	
		$_{79}Au^{193}$		1038.8	
				1048.7	
		12.7		1081.6	
		37.4		1104.1	
$_{79}Au^{191}$		44.3		1119.7	
		73.7		1141.0	
48.3		99.8		1150.9	
91.03		112.4		1156.6	
132.90		114.0		1175.5	
136.10		117.9		1183.6	
158.8		119.4		1187.1	
166.5		155.7	0.35%	1195.1	
194.1		173.5	2.0%	1208.5	
206.4		186.1	9%	1219.0	
210.0		187.5		1267.4	
244.4		221.3		1292	
253.9		231.8	0.5%	1293.9	
279.9		255.6	4.6%	1302.6	
280.5		258.4		1308.6	
284.0		268.2	4.4%	1342.4	
312.7		290.0	0.2%	1421.8	
336.3		303.6		1432.3	
368.7		317.7	1.3%	1442.0	
386.9		334.8		1450.5	
390.4		377.6	1.3%	1463.7	
399.6		425	0.25%	1469.4	
408.3		440	3.1%	1479.8	
413.8		477	0.5%	1487.9	
421.5		490	0.6%	1492.7	
451.3				1513	
478.8				1519	
487.5				1547.9	
495.9		$_{79}Au^{194}$		1563.4	
525.9				1592.9	
586.4		107.2		1596.2	

Gamma energies (KeV)	Gamma intensities
1602.0	
1618	
1622.6	
1633.5	
1671	
1675.9	
1690.2	
1735.8	
1758	
1786.3	
1798.0	
1803	
1806	
1813	
1830.1	
1835.9	
1886.8	
1893.1	
1911.1	
1924.6	
1960	
1970.1	
1983.9	
2044.1	
2085.8	
2114.0	
2164.1	
2216	
2299	
2313	
2357	
2366	
2371	
2399	
2414	

$_{79}Au^{195m}$

Gamma energies (KeV)	Gamma intensities
318	

$_{79}Au^{195}$

Gamma energies (KeV)	Gamma intensities
30.8	
98.82 ± 0.15	
129.12 ± 0.15	

$_{79}Au^{196}$

Gamma energies (KeV)	Gamma intensities
107.13 ± 0.1	1.7†
332.9 ± 0.25	280
355.7 ± 0.3	1000
425.8 ± 0.3	5
520.9 ± 0.5	0.5
758.5 ± 0.4	0.4
960	0.06
1091.3 ± 0.3	2.4

$_{79}Au^{197m}$

Gamma energies (KeV)	Gamma intensities
130.2	
279	

$_{79}Au^{198}$

Gamma energies (KeV)	Gamma intensities
411.795 ± 0.009	99%
675.883 ± 0.018	1%
1087.678 ± 0.027	0.2%

$_{79}Au^{199}$

Gamma energies (KeV)	Gamma intensities
49.828 ± 0.004	
158.372 ± 0.004	76%
208.200 ± 0.006	16.6%

$_{79}Au^{200}$

Gamma energies (KeV)	Gamma intensities
367.97	30%
1225	8.4%
1594	15.6%

$_{79}Au^{201}$

Gamma energies (KeV)	Gamma intensities
530	5%

$_{79}Au^{203}$

Gamma energies (KeV)	Gamma intensities
690	

$_{80}Hg^{186}$

Gamma energies (KeV)	Gamma intensities
125	
270	
350	
440	

$_{80}Hg^{187}$

Gamma energies (KeV)	Gamma intensities
175	
255	
400	

$_{80}Hg^{188}$

Gamma energies (KeV)	Gamma intensities
140	

$_{80}Hg^{189}$

Gamma energies (KeV)	Gamma intensities
Ann. Rad.	
165	
240	
320	

$_{80}Hg^{190}$

Gamma energies (KeV)	Gamma intensities
28.8	
100.8	†
129.8	
142.7	10
155.0	
165.4	
171.5	
220	1

$_{80}Hg^{191}$

Gamma energies (KeV)	Gamma intensities
252.6	
274.1	

$_{80}Hg^{192}$

Gamma energies (KeV)	Gamma intensities
31.5	
40.9	
47.7	

Gamma energies (KeV)	Gamma intensities
99.4	
104.5	
105.3	
114.5	
120.1	
135.9	
142.5	
146.0	
157.2	
204.6	
245.4	
262.7	
274.8	
279.2	
306.5	
436.7	

$_{80}Hg^{193m}$

Gamma energies (KeV)	Gamma intensities
32.2	
38.2	
39.5 (IT)	
101.2 (IT)	
165.9	
218	
220	
257	
281	
291	
299	
342	
345	
361	
364	
382	
383	
408	
462	
488	
500	
510	
535	
537	
574	
601	
624	
675	
701 D	
712	
861	
871	
879	
914	
933	
997	
1113	
1175	
1233	
1243	
1328	
1343	
1489	
1646	

$_{80}Hg^{193}$

Gamma energies (KeV)	Gamma intensities
38.2	
186.8	
574	
762	

Gamma energies (KeV)	Gamma intensities		Gamma energies (KeV)	Gamma intensities		Gamma energies (KeV)	Gamma intensities
855			$_{80}Hg^{205}$			$_{81}Tl^{197}$	
1040							
1078			203			18.18	
						133.9	
$_{80}Hg^{195m}$			$_{80}Hg^{206}$			152.2	
						156.3	
16.2 (IT)			310			173.8	
37.2 (IT)						269.6	
53.3 (IT)			$_{81}Tl^{191}$			277.5	
56.7						308.5	
61.4			Ann. Rad.			426.0	
123.0 (IT)						433.1	
172.6			$_{81}Tl^{192}$			444	
200.5						451.8	
261.5			Ann. Rad.			578.3	
318.5			424			585	
368						791	
386.0			$_{81}Tl^{193m}$			857	
387.6						890	
452			365			980	
467						1010	
526			$_{81}Tl^{193}$				
560						$_{81}Tl^{198m}$	
575			241				
680			261			23.1 (IT)	
963			270			48.7	
1242			291			259.6 (IT)	
			309			260.9 (IT)	
$_{80}Hg^{195}$			321			282.4 (IT)	
			330			411	13
61.4						586	10
180.2			$_{81}Tl^{194m}$			635	10
200.5							
207.1			97.2			$_{81}Tl^{198}$	
261.5							
600			$_{81}Tl^{194}$			194	
780						227	
821			427			284.5	
842						400.4	
930			$_{81}Tl^{195m}$			411.8	100†
1020						586.5	
1110			99.1			637	
1172			383			675.7	
						1089	3†
$_{80}Hg^{197m}$			$_{81}Tl^{195}$			1202	24
						1440	27
130.2	†		37.2			2010	17
134.0 (IT)	1		225.8			2450	6
165.3 (IT)	0.01		242.1			2780	2
202	0.23		247.3				
279.3	16		279			$_{81}Tl^{199}$	
			562				
$_{80}Hg^{197}$			883			36.83	
						49.82	4†
77.34 ± 0.005	34		$_{81}Tl^{196m}$			51.9	
191.5	1.0†		33.7			158.36	54
269	0.06		84.4			195.1	9
			120.1			208.18	119
			425.8			247.2	93
$_{80}Hg^{199m}$						284.0	13
			$_{81}Tl^{196}$			333.9	16
158						403.5	4
368			426			455.1	136
						492	10
$_{80}Hg^{203}$			$_{81}Tl^{197m}$				
						$_{81}Tl^{200}$	
279.190 ± 0.007			222				
			385			Ann. Rad.	

Gamma energies (KeV)	Gamma intensities
116.5	
134	
181	
227	
251	
276	
289	
309	
368	1000†
388	
545	
555	
579	120†
629	8
661	12
690	
712	8
786	15
829	87
887	5
898	9
939	
1029	
1207	330
1227	58
1265	†
1275	
1341	10
1364	45
1410	18
1479	
1517	42
1569	
1593	
1604	6
1718	7
1745	
1900	
1920	
1966	
1991	
2012	

$_{81}Tl^{201m}$

Gamma energies (KeV)	Gamma intensities
230	
331.2	
361.3	
600	

$_{81}Tl^{201}$

Gamma energies (KeV)	Gamma intensities
30.60	
32.19	
135.34	7%
165.9	0.3%
167.4	26%

$_{81}Tl^{202}$

Gamma energies (KeV)	Gamma intensities
439.4 ± 0.2	100†
509.4 ± 0.3	
520.3 ± 0.3	4
959.7 ± 0.4	0.07

$_{81}Tl^{207m}$

Gamma energies (KeV)	Gamma intensities
351	
1000	

$_{81}Tl^{207}$

Gamma energies (KeV)	Gamma intensities
897.3	0.16%

$_{81}Tl^{208}$

Gamma energies (KeV)	Gamma intensities
233	
252	†
277.33	7
486	0.1
510.72	23
583.169 ± 0.013	86
763.2	2
860	12
1094	0.6
2614.611 ± 0.060	100

$_{81}Tl^{209}$

Gamma energies (KeV)	Gamma intensities
120	100%
450	100%
1560	100%

$_{81}Tl^{210}$

Gamma energies (KeV)	Gamma intensities
97	4%
296	80%
360	4%
380	3%
795	100%
910	3%
1060	12%
1110	7%
1210	17%
1310	21%
2010	7%
2090	5%
2280	3%
2360	8%
2430	9%

$_{82}Pb^{194}$

Gamma energies (KeV)	Gamma intensities
0.204	

$_{82}Pb^{195}$

Gamma energies (KeV)	Gamma intensities
99.1	
383	
393	

$_{82}Pb^{196}$

Gamma energies (KeV)	Gamma intensities
191.8	
240.3	
253.2	
367	
494	
503	

$_{82}Pb^{197m}$

Gamma energies (KeV)	Gamma intensities
84.9 (IT)	
222.4	
234.4 (IT)	
387	

$_{82}Pb^{197}$

Gamma energies (KeV)	Gamma intensities
385	
387	

$_{82}Pb^{198}$

Gamma energies (KeV)	Gamma intensities
30.8	
116.9	10†
122.6	
173.4	100
259.5	24
290.3	50
365.4	
382.0	
389.5	
397.7	
575.0	
649.0	
743	8
865.3	20

$_{82}Pb^{199m}$

Gamma energies (KeV)	Gamma intensities
424	

$_{82}Pb^{199}$

Gamma energies (KeV)	Gamma intensities
352.8	19%
367.0	90%
721.0	10%
Ann. Rad.	

$_{82}Pb^{200}$

Gamma energies (KeV)	Gamma intensities
32.74	
109.54	
142.30	
147.61	
161.4	
235.61	
257.15	
268.42	
289.1	
289.9	
302.85	
315.30	
450.5	
457.6	
605.3	

$_{82}Pb^{201m}$

Gamma energies (KeV)	Gamma intensities
629	

$_{82}Pb^{201}$

Gamma energies (KeV)	Gamma intensities
Ann. Rad.	
58.9	
129.8	
285.0	
309.2	
331.2	
345.3	
361.3	
381.4	
395.1	
406.0	
545.9	

Gamma energies (KeV)	Gamma intensities
584.6	
692.5	
708.6	
753.2	
767.3	
803.5	
820.3	
826.0	
907.4	
945.8	
1069.8	
1098.4	
1115	
1149	
1239	
1309	

$_{82}Pb^{202m}$

Gamma energies (KeV)	Gamma intensities
129.3 (IT)	
148.9	
240.3 (IT)	
241.1	
335.6	
389.9	
422.1 (IT)	90%
459.8	10%
490.4	10%
547.2 (IT)	
657.6 (IT)	
787.2 (IT)	
961.4 (IT)	90%

$_{82}Pb^{203m}$

Gamma energies (KeV)	Gamma intensities
825.2	

$_{82}Pb^{203}$

Gamma energies (KeV)	Gamma intensities
279.190 ± 0.007	99+%
401.28 ± 0.3	4.6%
680.67 ± 0.3	0.8%

$_{82}Pb^{204m}$

Gamma energies (KeV)	Gamma intensities
373.4 ± 0.6	
899.10 ± 0.2	
911.66 ± 0.2	

$_{82}Pb^{205m}$

Gamma energies (KeV)	Gamma intensities
26.22 ± 0.11	†
284.12 ± 0.10	4.8
310.37 ± 0.07	0.26
703.40 ± 0.03	100
1014.22 ± 0.06	3.3

$_{82}Pb^{207m}$

Gamma energies (KeV)	Gamma intensities
569.684 ± 0.014	100%
1063.614 ± 0.04	100%

$_{82}Pb^{210}$

Gamma energies (KeV)	Gamma intensities
46.52	4.1%

$_{82}Pb^{211}$

Gamma energies (KeV)	Gamma intensities
65.5	2†
84	1
310	0.7
340	1
404.84	100
426.99	53
612	3
702	13
766.3	19
831.8	100
860	0.1
1020	0.5
1076	0.5
1104	3.8
1188	0.4
1265	0.2

$_{82}Pb^{212}$

Gamma energies (KeV)	Gamma intensities
115.1	0.7%
176.7	0.2%
238.60 ± 0.007	47%
300.1	3.2%
415.2	0.16%

$_{82}Pb^{214}$

Gamma energies (KeV)	Gamma intensities
53.24	
196	
206	
241.92	3.7†
259	
272	
275	
279	
295	†
352.0	36
481	
534	
549	
777	

$_{83}Bi^{200}$

Gamma energies (KeV)	Gamma intensities
462	
1027	

$_{83}Bi^{201}$

Gamma energies (KeV)	Gamma intensities
629	

$_{83}Bi^{202}$

Gamma energies (KeV)	Gamma intensities
422	
961	

$_{83}Bi^{203}$

Gamma energies (KeV)	Gamma intensities
Ann. Rad.	
59.99	
126.4	

Gamma energies (KeV)	Gamma intensities
186.5	
263.9	
381.4	
626	
722	
758	0.2†
820.1	240
825.2	100
847.4	
932	
1034	
1184	
1256	
1510	
1523	
1537	
1846 }	180
1896 }	

$_{83}Bi^{204}$

Gamma energies (KeV)	Gamma intensities
78.5	
80.2	
90.9	
92.2	
100.2	
140.9	
170.2	
175.9	
213.4	
216.0	
219.1	
221.9	
227.5	
240.5	
249.0	
252.9	
289.3	
292.2	
330.5	
368.0	
374.7	
405.0	
412.2	
421.5	
438.5	
473.4	
502	
522	
532	
542	
622	
661	
663	
671	
692	
709	
710	
719	
724	
791	
899	
912	
918	
984	
1203	
1211	

$_{83}Bi^{205}$

Gamma energies (KeV)	Gamma intensities
Ann. Rad.	

Gamma energies (KeV)	Gamma intensities
26.22 $\pm$ 0.11	
45.43 $\pm$ 0.075	
90.03 $\pm$ 0.024	
115.409 $\pm$ 0.181	0.2332 $\pm$ 0.022
122.466 $\pm$ 0.083	0.0465 $\pm$ 0.007
129.742 $\pm$ 0.127	0.0314 $\pm$ 0.006
147.315 $\pm$ 0.068	0.0755 $\pm$ 0.001
149.505 $\pm$ 0.236	0.0216 $\pm$ 0.006
157.269 $\pm$ 0.219	0.0352 $\pm$ 0.010
165.113 $\pm$ 0.143	0.0466 $\pm$ 0.013
185.293 $\pm$ 0.115	0.2806 $\pm$ 0.037
205.841 $\pm$ 0.273	0.0987 $\pm$ 0.017
221.024 $\pm$ 0.135	0.0926 $\pm$ 0.012
235.997 $\pm$ 0.046	0.1664 $\pm$ 0.043
260.511 $\pm$ 0.052	3.1038 $\pm$ 0.338
262.815 $\pm$ 0.067	1.1908 $\pm$ 0.172
282.261 $\pm$ 0.103	1.1461 $\pm$ 0.030
284.124 $\pm$ 0.103	4.8029 $\pm$ 0.545
310.369 $\pm$ 0.069	0.2648 $\pm$ 0.044
313.052 $\pm$ 0.092	0.1771 $\pm$ 0.019
349.550 $\pm$ 0.045	1.4781 $\pm$ 0.083
354.598 $\pm$ 0.053	0.0767 $\pm$ 0.002
361.601 $\pm$ 0.105	0.1787 $\pm$ 0.033
488.349 $\pm$ 0.183	0.1895 $\pm$ 0.055
493.701 $\pm$ 0.033	0.9765 $\pm$ 0.103
498.840 $\pm$ 0.152	0.5467 $\pm$ 0.115
511.429 $\pm$ 0.062	3.2392 $\pm$ 0.091
549.855 $\pm$ 0.014	8.8773 $\pm$ 0.236
553.723 $\pm$ 0.276	0.3873 $\pm$ 0.104
561.264 $\pm$ 0.203	0.1970 $\pm$ 0.057
570.581 $\pm$ 0.030	13.2248 $\pm$ 0.723
573.867 $\pm$ 0.037	1.7325 $\pm$ 0.321
576.213 $\pm$ 0.144	1.0763 $\pm$ 0.073
579.781 $\pm$ 0.020	16.7838 $\pm$ 0.422
609.782 $\pm$ 0.198	0.3556 $\pm$ 0.080
626.720 $\pm$ 0.024	1.7814 $\pm$ 0.062
646.065 $\pm$ 0.060	0.1963 $\pm$ 0.029
688.595 $\pm$ 0.102	0.6343 $\pm$ 0.058
703.401 $\pm$ 0.028	100.0000 $\pm$ 0.000
717.352 $\pm$ 0.104	0.7737 $\pm$ 0.154
720.752 $\pm$ 0.232	0.3716 $\pm$ 0.093
723.673 $\pm$ 0.118	0.5270 $\pm$ 0.093
729.676 $\pm$ 0.225	0.2556 $\pm$ 0.164
744.881 $\pm$ 0.075	2.3298 $\pm$ 0.150
759.120 $\pm$ 0.049	3.7326 $\pm$ 0.203
761.470 $\pm$ 0.099	2.1655 $\pm$ 0.225
772.096 $\pm$ 0.319	0.1131 $\pm$ 0.024
780.837 $\pm$ 0.081	1.5576 $\pm$ 0.270
787.764 $\pm$ 0.130	0.3587 $\pm$ 0.051
795.692 $\pm$ 0.075	0.4267 $\pm$ 0.128
800.918 $\pm$ 0.141	0.4230 $\pm$ 0.064
806.431 $\pm$ 0.036	0.5268 $\pm$ 0.153
813.813 $\pm$ 0.046	1.4921 $\pm$ 0.196
828.213 $\pm$ 0.126	0.9586 $\pm$ 0.107
852.779 $\pm$ 0.255	0.2291 $\pm$ 0.043
860.103 $\pm$ 0.089	1.4043 $\pm$ 0.274
871.861 $\pm$ 0.089	1.3232 $\pm$ 0.132
890.087 $\pm$ 0.021	2.0553 $\pm$ 0.129
894.649 $\pm$ 0.027	2.6969 $\pm$ 0.215
901.776 $\pm$ 0.144	0.4171 $\pm$ 0.067
910.843 $\pm$ 0.037	5.2527 $\pm$ 0.202
922.027 $\pm$ 0.162	0.2010 $\pm$ 0.031
931.249 $\pm$ 0.686	0.1803 $\pm$ 0.004
950.763 $\pm$ 0.067	1.2799 $\pm$ 0.076
971.488 $\pm$ 0.147	0.9149 $\pm$ 0.169
978.513 $\pm$ 0.350	0.1241 $\pm$ 0.027
987.557 $\pm$ 0.300	53.3456 $\pm$ 1.175
1001.896 $\pm$ 0.039	1.7873 $\pm$ 0.191
1014.218 $\pm$ 0.059	3.2914 $\pm$ 0.181
1031.720 $\pm$ 0.276	0.1260 $\pm$ 0.024
1043.661 $\pm$ 0.041	23.8732 $\pm$ 1.309

Gamma energies (KeV)	Gamma intensities
1051.613 $\pm$ 0.751	0.1545 $\pm$ 0.015
1065.952 $\pm$ 0.105	0.3447 $\pm$ 0.033
1072.212 $\pm$ 0.084	0.9954 $\pm$ 0.117
1107.539 $\pm$ 0.107	0.3714 $\pm$ 0.081
1189.943 $\pm$ 0.027	7.3423 $\pm$ 0.348
1199.814 $\pm$ 0.210	0.6296 $\pm$ 0.160
1208.569 $\pm$ 0.075	1.6523 $\pm$ 0.121
1216.294 $\pm$ 0.272	0.2327 $\pm$ 0.044
1264.422 $\pm$ 0.310	0.8413 $\pm$ 0.102
1351.471 $\pm$ 0.099	3.5151 $\pm$ 0.375
1438.606 $\pm$ 0.236	0.3400 $\pm$ 0.060
1500.944 $\pm$ 0.609	0.9486 $\pm$ 0.333
1522.121 $\pm$ 1.091	0.6432 $\pm$ 0.147
1550.807 $\pm$ 0.232	2.5417 $\pm$ 0.654
1563.112 $\pm$ 0.130	0.7286 $\pm$ 0.145
1577.395 $\pm$ 0.273	0.5087 $\pm$ 0.180
1594.466 $\pm$ 2.001	0.3268 $\pm$ 0.152
1614.343 $\pm$ 0.045	6.3607 $\pm$ 0.417
1619.059 $\pm$ 0.207	0.7599 $\pm$ 0.067
1764.274 $\pm$ 0.063	93.0470 $\pm$ 3.98
1775.795 $\pm$ 0.038	11.0945 $\pm$ 0.691
1818.270 $\pm$ 0.399	0.1727 $\pm$ 0.034
1844.759 $\pm$ 0.400	0.0663 $\pm$ 0.004
1861.691 $\pm$ 0.019	17.4466 $\pm$ 0.871
1903.346 $\pm$ 0.056	6.7117 $\pm$ 0.332
1965.948 $\pm$ 0.558	0.0484 $\pm$ 0.020
2565.467 $\pm$ 0.844	0.1624 $\pm$ 0.058
2606.776 $\pm$ 0.412	0.0681 $\pm$ 0.019

$_{83}Bi^{206}$

Gamma energies (KeV)	Gamma intensities
107.2	
123.6	
184.0	21†
202.7	
234.4	
262.8	2.9
313.7	3.0
343.5	26
386.1	
398.1	10
497.1	18
516.3	46
537.6	34
620.7	4.0
632.4	4.5
657.3	5.3
740	3.6
754	2.7
803.1	100
816	
842	
880.8	73
895.0	19
1018.9	8
1099	13
1405	
1596	8
1720	36
1845	
1880	
1903	

$_{83}Bi^{207}$

Gamma energies (KeV)	Gamma intensities
569.684 $\pm$ 0.014	100†
897.3	0.16
1063.610 $\pm$ 0.04	76
1430	0.16
1769.7	8

$_{83}Bi^{208}$

Gamma energies (KeV)	Gamma intensities
2614.611 $\pm$ 0.06	100%

$_{83}Bi^{210m}$

Gamma energies (KeV)	Gamma intensities
262	10†
300	30
340	
610	

$_{83}Bi^{211}$

Gamma energies (KeV)	Gamma intensities
350.7	15.9%

$_{83}Bi^{212}$

Gamma energies (KeV)	Gamma intensities
39.85	
144.9	
288.2	0.28%
328.0	0.11%
434	
453	
473	
493	
616	
727	7.1%
785	1.1%
893	0.42%
953	0.1%
1074 } 1079	0.6%
1513	0.31%
1620	1.8%
1800 } 1809	0.1%

$_{83}Bi^{213}$

Gamma energies (KeV)	Gamma intensities
320	
437	

$_{83}Bi^{214}$

Gamma energies (KeV)	Gamma intensities
63	
191	
450	1%
609.3	47%
666	2%
703	0.8%
721	0.7%
768.7	5.3%
787	1.2%
806	1.5%
821	
825	
874	0.4%
934.8	3.3%
960	0.5%
1050	0.5%
1120	16%
1155	1.8%
1207	0.6%
1238	6.0%
1281	1.7%
1379	4.8%
1390–1400 complex	4%
1416	
1509	2.4%

Gamma energies (KeV)	Gamma intensities	Gamma energies (KeV)	Gamma intensities	Gamma energies (KeV)	Gamma intensities
1541	0.8 %	222.0			
1583	0.9 %	222.7		$_{84}Po^{212m}$	
1600	0.6 %	224.0		570	≈ 2 %
1661	1.2 %	249.6		2610	2.6
1681	0.2 %	288.0			
1728	3.2 %	297.1?		$_{84}Po^{214}$	
1764	17 %	307.5			
1836	0.3 %	330.2		800	0.014 %
1848	2.3 %	345.2			
1877	0.2 %	369.3		$_{84}Po^{215}$	
1897	0.3 %	380.1?			
2017	0.07 %	390.1?		≈ 443	
2090		402.4			
2117	1.3 %	405.7		$_{85}At^{206}$	
2162		468.5?			
2204	6 %	503.3		68	
2435	2.0 %	531.7			
2700	0.04 %	629.9		$_{85}At^{208}$	
2770	0.04 %	669.5			
2890	0.04 %	688		180	20†
2990	0.04 %	698?		250	
3070	0.04 %	742.7		660	80
		771		120	
		892			
$_{84}Po^{206}$		911.8		$_{85}At^{209}$	
59.9		948			
82.9		955		90.8	
107?		992.6		195.0	24†
117.6		1020		545	66
140.6		1149		780	100
146?		1212			
170.8		1280		$_{85}At^{210}$	
171.5		1318			
181?		1361		46.5	
282.1		1373		116.5	0.68†
286.5	35†	1586		202.0	0.17
311.5		1663		245.3	79
338.4	41†	1747		298.9	0.13
354.8		1763		316.9	0.14
369?		1797		402.4	0.78
381?		1847		499.1	0.13
453?		2061		506.9	0.63
463.5		2600?		518.7	0.13
469.1				527.6	1.1
511.4 ⎫				544.8	0.09
522.4 ⎭	100†	$_{84}Po^{208}$		584.0	0.32
538?		285	≈ 0.003 %	602?	
555		600	≈ 0.006 %	615.1	0.31
580				623.1	0.52
646		$_{84}Po^{209}$		630.9	0.30
669				639.5	0.23
678		260.5 ⎫		643.7	0.46
807.6	57†	262.8 ⎭	≈ 0.4 %	701.1	0.43
818?		910	≈ 0.5	726	?
862				817.8	1.7
981		$_{84}Po^{210}$		853.1	1.4
1008				882	0.25
1033	84†	803	1.2 × 10⁻³ %		?
1320				930.6	0.96
		$_{84}Po^{211m}$		956.7	1.8
$_{84}Po^{207}$				977	0.63
		0.90	1.7 %	1088	0.28
100		560	≈ 80	1180	100
139.7?		106.0	≈ 80	1204	?
149.6				1289	0.46
156.1		$_{84}Po^{211}$		1324	0.36
158.0				1436	29
177.7		880		1483	48
205.2		561		1552	0.16
214.4?				1599	14

Gamma energies (KeV)	Gamma intensities	Gamma energies (KeV)	Gamma intensities	Gamma energies (KeV)	Gamma intensities
1648	0.09	606	≈ 0.0026	329.8	0.10
1719	0.11	673	≈ 0.01	334.3	0.05
1955	0.38	833	≈ 0.001	338.7	0.2
2002	0.11	888	≈ 0.001	342.5	0.09
2052	0.05	1053	≈ 0.0003	369.0	0.32
2226	0.05			723	0.15
2239	?	**₈₆Rn²²⁰**		746.5	0.07
2254	1.4			756	0.04
2273	0.33	542	≈ 0.07 %	767	0.08
2285	?			776.7	1.23
2306	0.029	**₈₆Rn²²²**		784	0.07
2353	0.13			793	0.03
		510	0.07 %	798	0.03
₈₅At²¹¹				804	0.17
		₈₇Fr²¹²		813	0.06
670	Weak			822	0.03
		39		826	0.14
₈₅At²¹²ᵐ		62		835	0.02
		66		841	0.02
63		70		847	0.14
		123		860	0.01
₈₅At²¹²				864	0.01
		₈₇Fr²¹⁹		876.5	0.13
63				892	0.01
		163		898	0.05
₈₅At²¹⁵		189		908	0.04
		352			
≈ 400		493		**₈₈Ra²²⁰**	
		530			
₈₅At²¹⁷				465	1 %
		₈₇Fr²²¹			
268				**₈₈Ra²²¹**	
455		63	9.1 %		
595		68	0.4	89	3.5 %
		91?		152	13
₈₆Rn²¹¹		98	0.05	176	2
		99.5	0.12	219	0.1
γ with EC		118.0	0.04	293	0.6
32		150.0	0.08	320	0.7
113.9		171.3	0.08	415	0.5
168.6		218.0	12.5		
232		268?	<0.04	**₈₈Ra²²²**	
264		282.8	~0.01		
296		303	~0.03	324.6	3.9 %
333		324.1	0.02	325	8 × 10⁻³
445	39†	359.1	0.04	473	7 × 10⁻³
680	100	381.8	0.04	526	3 × 10⁻³
865	24	409.1	0.15	795	3 × 10⁻³
946	29			846	4 × 10⁻³
1130	31	**₈₇Fr²²³**			
1370	52			**₈₈Ra²²³**	
1800	0.8	49.8	40†		
γ with α		50.2	100	31.2	
68.7	100†	61.5	<0.8	≈ 68?	≈ 0.4 %
169	6.5	79.8	25	122.2	2
234	6.5	100.3	≈ 3	131	≈ 3
		134.4	1.6	143.1?	
₈₆Rn²¹⁸		173.5	0.4	144.2	4.1
		184.8	0.9	148	
609.4	0.2 %	205.0	3.2	154.1	5.5
		234.8	10	158.6	1.7
₈₆Rn²¹⁹		246	0.13	179.6	0.5
		250.2	0.13	269.6	10
130		256.2	0.13	288	≈ 0.2
271	9 %	286.1	0.05	324	2.3
371	≈ 0.002	289.7	≈ 0.9	330	≈ 5.1
380	≈ 0.0005	300.0	0.17	338	2.8
401	6.5	304.5	0.07	362	≈ 0.07
517	≈ 0.04	307	0.09	371	0.45
536	≈ 0.0003	312.7	0.08	441	0.2
562	≈ 0.002	318	≈ 1.7		

Gamma energies (KeV)	Gamma intensities		Gamma energies (KeV)	Gamma intensities		Gamma energies (KeV)	Gamma intensities
446	0.4		351	0.06		783	1.4
580	≤0.1		362	0.1		796	4
			373	Weak		836	2.5
$_{88}$Ra^{224}			384	0.06		831	8
240.98	3.7%		453	0.3		912.2	23
290	9×10^{-3}		482	0.1		922	
410	4×10^{-3}		517	0.04		966	20
650	6×10^{-3}		529	0.06		1035	
						1095	
$_{88}$Ra^{225}			**$_{89}$Ac^{226}**			1464	1.1
40	33%					1503	2.5
			γ with β$^-$			1593	4.5
$_{88}$Ra^{226}			72.13			1642	2.4
185.7	100†		158.5	100†			
260	0.29		230.4	151		**$_{89}$Ac^{231}**	
420	0.021		γ with EC			185	
450	0.009		67.8			280	
610	0.033		185	100†		390	
			255	132		710	
$_{88}$Ra^{227}							
27.3			**$_{89}$Ac^{227}**			**$_{90}$Th^{224}**	
291	4%					177	9%
498	0.6		γ with β$^-$			235	0.4
			9.3			297	0.3
$_{88}$Ra^{228}			15.2			410	0.8
10.3			24.5				
26.3			γ with α			**$_{90}$Th^{225}**	
			12.7			151	1†
$_{89}$Ac^{223}			70.2	12†		246	5
82	0.23%		83 }			322	30
96	0.2		87 }	≈27		362	5
120	?<0.05		99.5	20		450	1
≈170	?≤0.8		107	1		490	1
			121.5	4			
$_{89}$Ac^{224}			134	2		**$_{90}$Th^{226}**	
132	100†		147	6		111.1	4.8%
216	224		160	14		131.3	0.34
			172	4		190.6	0.15
$_{89}$Ac^{225}			190?	<0.5		206.5	0.26
36.6						197	0.4
38.4			**$_{89}$Ac^{228}**			242.4	1.2
62.8	0.5%						
75	1.2		57.5			**$_{90}$Th^{227}**	
85.5	3		78.1			29.9	
87.5	≤2		99			31.6	
90	≤0.5		113?			44.5	1.4%
96	≤1		129.1	5†		45.1	
100	~3		155?			48.3	
109	0.6		178.2			50.2	10.5
123	0.3		184	1.7		56.1	<0.2
134	~0.1		209	4.3		61.5	0.8
146	0.2		232			68.8	≈0.1
150	1		270	4.1		79.8	≈2.6
158	0.8		282	0.3		94.0	≈3
187	0.8		321			100.3	<0.3
196	0.3		327.5	3.3		113.1	≈2
216	1		338	15		141.6	0.13
241	0.03		410	2.5		154.2	0.1
254	0.3		443			173.5	≲0.1
324	Weak		463	3.6		184.8	≲0.1
340			473			205.0	0.32
			484			206.2	0.5
			510			210.7	1.0
			555			212.0	
			573				
			619				
			752				
			769				

Gamma energies (KeV)	Gamma intensities
218.8	0.08
234.8	
236.0	12.0
247.7	1.4
250.2	0.7
250.4	
256.26	6.4
273.0	0.46
279.8	≤ 0.05
281.5	0.30
286.1	1.8
289.7	< 0.3
296.6	0.40
300.0	2.5
304.5	1.2
312.7	0.83
318	0.2
323	≤ 0.1
329.8	2.8
334.3	1.2
342.5	0.46
351?	≤ 0.2
371	0.03
384	0.06
404?	≤ 0.04
671	0.002
760	0.002
776	0.0015

$_{90}Th^{228}$

Gamma energies (KeV)	Gamma intensities
84.5	1.6 %
132	0.19
167	0.12
205	0.03
216	0.29
234?	7×10^{-5}

$_{90}Th^{229}$

Gamma energies (KeV)	Gamma intensities
17.3	
23.7	
25.3	
32	
42.7	
56.7	
68.9	
75.1	
86.3	
107.2	
124.4	
131.9	
137.0	
143.0	
154.2	
156.5	
179.9	
193.4	
210.7	
217.0	
242.2	
269?	

$_{90}Th^{230}$

Gamma energies (KeV)	Gamma intensities
67.8	0.59 %
110	1×10^{-4} %
ˈ42	0.07 %

Gamma energies (KeV)	Gamma intensities
184	1.4×10^{-2} %
206	$\approx 5 \times 10^{-6}$ %
235	$\approx 5 \times 10^{-6}$ %
253	1.7×10^{-2} %
257	$\approx 8 \times 10^{-4}$ %

$_{90}Th^{231}$

Gamma energies (KeV)	Gamma intensities
17.21	
18.07	
25.6	
42.8	0.7
58.54	6
63.79	
68.50	
72.7	3.4
76.04	
81.22	13
82.07	7
84.20	100
89.94	15
99.27	2.1
102.2	7
106.8	0.34
112.6	0.29
115.4?	0.03
116.8	0.38
124.9	1.0
134.0	0.42
135.66	1.3
145.90	0.5
163.10	2.4
164.7	0.13
174.1	0.29
183.4	0.5
188.7	0.05
218.0	0.6
236.1	0.13
249.8	0.017
267.8	0.02

$_{90}Th^{232}$

Gamma energies (KeV)	Gamma intensities
59	

$_{90}Th^{233}$

Gamma energies (KeV)	Gamma intensities
29.35	690⁺
57.15	23
74.7	22
86.00	1150
131.1	24
148.2	6
151.5	4
153.6	28
162.5	96
169.1	190
179.0	16
186.8	14
190.54	55
195.0	70
201.6	13
210.1	15
211.3	8
216.6	6.3
226.1	9.6
250.5	2
252.9	5
257.3	29
278.7	3.3

Gamma energies (KeV)	Gamma intensities
285.5	9
346.6	5
359.9	50
361.4	16
368.0	2
377.2	16
399.0	6
408.8	1.6
412.5	5.7
418.4	5
431.0	9.8
433.0	6
441.0	103
447.7	62
459.2	600
467.5	7.8
473.9	1.5
490.8	74
497.1	9
499.0	91
505.5	2.1
513.6	8.6
517.0	2.9
526.5	27
531.8	1.8
552.1	10
554.9	1.5
562.7	30
573.5	18
595.2	69
599.1	20
609.9	36
642.3	12
663.4	1
669.7	290
677.8	37
681.2	8
698.4	5
703.6	4.5
707.8	5
716.8	24
724.9	37
740.9	13
744.9	2.9
751.6	1
757.6	18
764.3	49
774.0	5.9
782.7	2.6
784.2	2.1
804.8	13
806.4	5.7
811.4	3.3
815.9	12
817.0	6.7
846.8	0.6
849.3	2
871.0	0.9
873.8	3.5
880.7	3.3
890.6	61
898.4	1.4
935.9	21
942.0	3.3
948.0	3.2
960.8	2.9
962.8	0.6
969.1	4.9
978.1	3.2
984.8	6.2
995	0.4

Gamma energies (KeV)	Gamma intensities	Gamma energies (KeV)	Gamma intensities	Gamma energies (KeV)	Gamma intensities
1001	0.5	739.6		464	
1008	1.2	745.6		508	420
1012	1.7	756.2	230	520	
1146	1.2	773.4	375	572	100
		782.6		624	
$_{90}$Th^{234}		792.2	≈70	634	
		796	≤600	730	210
29.9		817.4		783	160
63.2 }		831.4	375	901 }	1600
63.6 }	85†	835.8		920 }	
69.8		836.4	730	954	3500
93.1 }		841.0	170	1012	
93.5 }	100	853.8		1027	240
		871.0	520	γ with β⁻	
$_{91}$Pa^{227}		889.0		51.7	
		905.2	310		
50	<20†	912.2	3100		
65	62	923	930	$_{91}$Pa^{231}	
67	12	966.0	2200		
110	20	970.0	1680	18.9	
		976.8	620	25.3	
$_{91}$Pa^{228}		1034.1		27.3	
		1095		29.9	
γ with α		1123		38.1	
130	27†	1168		44.0?	
150	34	1253	130	52.6	
170	11	1293	83	57.1	
200	14	1423		63.5	
220	10	1464	155	74.0	
240	55	1489		77.2	
280	49	1503		96.7	
310	100	1563	15	100.7	
345	21	1593	620	102.6	
γ with EC		1624		244	
57.5		1678		257	
77.7		1708		259.8	
99	13†	1744	230	274	
129.1		1758		283.1	
137.8		1838		299.4	
156		1888	415	302.0	
178.0				313	
184		$_{91}$Pa^{232}		329.2	
191.3?	55			342	
209	320	γ with EC		356.3	
224	122	42.37		409	
270	320	γ with α		437	
278	71	26?		439	
282	310	40		488	
327.5	950	51		513	
338	740	52		517	
341.1	250	64			
397		65			
410	1350	71		$_{91}$Pa^{232}	
445.4					
462	320	$_{91}$Pa^{230}		47.6	
463	2900			80.2	0.1%
469.2		γ with Ec		81.2?	0.02
617		53		105.4	2.1
622		122		109.0	3.0
641		230		132.5	0.02
662		280		139.2	0.7
666		320		150.1	12
670		340		174.9	0.025
680		379		178	0.020
694		380		183.9	1.6
704		398	135†	290	0.03
713	135	401	100	388.0	
732		444		422.0	
		456	500	454.2	
				472.8	4
				516	3
				564	

Gamma energies (KeV)	Gamma intensities	Gamma energies (KeV)	Gamma intensities	Gamma energies (KeV)	Gamma intensities
584	6	822 ⎫		₉₂U²³³	
645		873			
676		875		29.0	60†
687		878 ⎬	70	42.4	310
693		920		54.6	68
712		922		66.0	3.9
757		941		71.8	12
820		976 ⎭		97.1	100
865		1020	≈ 8	117.1	13
868		1130	23	118.9	16
895		1340	?2	120.7	11
971		1410	?6	124.0	2.7
		1620	?3	135.3	10
		1850	?1	144.8	9
₉₁Pa²³³				146.4	26
		₉₁Pa²³⁵		164.5	27
17.26				187.9	8
28.54		No γ		208.1	9
40.35	0.015%			217.0	16
41.65		₉₁Pa²³⁷		245.4	14
57.9				248.4	6
75.28	0.8	90	50†	260	1.2
86.59	1.7	145	45	261.5	1.4
95.8		205	55	268.1	1.0
103.86	0.7	275	20	274.5	2.0
145.4	0.44	330	40	277.9	6
271.6	0.29	405	30	288.0	4.9
300.2	6.3	460	100	291.2	23
303.1		550	30	316.8	32
311.9	34	590	25	320.2	11
320		750	50	323.1	3.2
340.5	3.9	800	45	328.2	0.1
375.4	0.56	870	100	336.4	2.3
398.6	1.1	920	100	353.9	0.23
415.9	1.5	1040	35	365.5	3.2
		1320	10	383.0	0.4
		1420	15	393.3	0.07
₉₁Pa²³⁴ᵐ					
		₉₂U²²⁸		₉₂U²³⁴	
43.5					
236		152	20†	53.3	100†
255	0.05%	187	30	120.9	34
746	Weak	246	40	460	
765	0.36			510	
790	Weak	₉₂U²³⁰		580	
811					
1001	0.59	72.13	0.54%	₉₂U²³⁵	
		154.4	0.21		
		158.8	0.13	110	2.5%
₉₁Pa²³⁴		230.6	0.18	143	11
				163	5
43.3		₉₂U²³¹		180	0.5
99.8				185	54
126.3	≈ 24†	18.05		201	0.8
153.0	9	25.64	12%	204	5
186.0	≈ 3	58.54			
196.7	4	68.5		₉₂U²³⁵ᵐ	
208	? ≤ 16	81.3			
223.9	≈ 2	82.1		0.075	
226.7?		84.18	7		
227.3	12	108.2		₉₂U²³⁶	
287	≈ 10	220	1		
294.3?				≈ 50	
323	? ≈ 3				
355	? ≈ 6	₉₂U²³²		₉₂U²³⁷	
370.1	5.3				
565	15	57.6	0.21%	13.81	
694		129.0	0.082	26.35	2.4%
727		270.5	3.8 ×10⁻³	33.20	
791	≤ 5	327.8	3.4 ×10⁻³	38.54	
804		500	2.2 ×10⁻⁵	43.42	

Gamma energies (KeV)	Gamma intensities
51.01	0.2
59.54	36
64.83	1.3
114.09	
164.61	2.0
208.00	23
221.80	0.022
234.40	0.021
267.54	0.76
292.7	0.003
332.36	1.3
335.38	0.10
337.7	0.008
368.59	0.050
370.94	0.12

$_{92}U^{238}$

48	

$_{92}U^{239}$

Gamma energies (KeV)	Gamma intensities
43.520 ± 0.042	104.553%
74.660 ± 0.022	1106.989%
83.822 ± 0.307	3.094%
86.716 ± 0.065	1.392%
110.973 ± 0.222	0.442%
117.658 ± 0.030	3.204%
174.009 ± 0.028	0.398%
186.149 ± 0.020	0.729%
187.396 ± 0.036	0.148%
190.345 ± 0.067	0.067%
191.973 ± 0.060	0.062%
196.850 ± 0.100	0.049%
201.186 ± 0.065	0.045%
210.960 ± 0.091	0.072%
220.531 ± 0.017	0.575%
228.141 ± 0.016	
231.70 ± 0.10	0.069%
255.27 ± 0.123	0.063%
258.438 ± 0.046	0.058%
260.792 ± 0.112	0.051%
296.963 ± 0.070	0.035%
301.862 ± 0.074	0.036%
304.123 ± 0.117	0.033%
306.836 ± 0.042	0.103%
312.049 ± 0.026	0.090%
317.182 ± 0.107	0.076%
321.901 ± 0.132	0.027%
326.227 ± 0.036	0.080%
334.255 ± 0.018*	
345.060 ± 0.038	0.045%
357.858 ± 0.036	0.106%
361.814 ± 0.063	0.072%
363.064 ± 0.217	0.020%
373.524 ± 0.016	0.426%
378.055 ± 0.028	0.189%
395.353 ± 0.127	0.022%
399.3 ± 0.2	0.011%
407.645 ± 0.031	0.057%
434.751 ± 0.045	0.075%
445.732 ± 0.085	0.039%
448.141 ± 0.024	0.177%
452.054 ± 0.089	0.039%
462.435 ± 0.124	0.036%
474.487 ± 0.109	0.067%
486.865 ± 0.016	1.18%
492.594 ± 0.045	0.086%
499.091 ± 0.177	0.033%
504.707 ± 0.053	0.089%
506.462 ± 0.109	0.039%
517.851 ± 0.084	0.065%
522.080 ± 0.076	0.053%
532.887 ± 0.116	0.040%
541.221 ± 0.078	0.054%
544.608 ± 0.059	0.089%
548.099 ± 0.126	0.044%
560.511 ± 0.047	0.131%
575.295 ± 0.026	0.269%
577.640 ± 0.222	0.028%
587.726 ± 0.038	0.486%
589.709 ± 0.116	0.137%
602.659 ± 0.076	0.101%
624.016 ± 0.045	0.168%
631.080 ± 0.017	1.518%
662.238 ± 0.016	3.956%
664.178 ± 0.093	0.203%
691.091 ± 0.044	0.127%
695.246 ± 0.083	0.084%
697.394 ± 0.232	0.031%
700.748 ± 0.079	0.062%
703.239 ± 0.077	0.065%
707.379 ± 0.084	0.072%
710.171 ± 0.208	0.029%
714.155 ± 0.073	0.092%
722.865 ± 0.025	0.623%
727.345 ± 0.155	0.051%
730.972 ± 0.026	0.254%
748.108 ± 0.016	2.234%
767.643 ± 0.100	0.097%
772.809 ± 0.175	0.075%
774.742 ± 0.034	0.372%
779.78 ± 0.200	0.010%
788.187 ± 0.056	0.105%
791.322 ± 0.031	0.204%
793.576 ± 0.084	0.058%
812.933 ± 0.017	1.732%
819.232 ± 0.018	3.176%
831.834 ± 0.075	0.079%
840.806 ± 0.250	0.080%
844.091 ± 0.015	3.515%
846.466 ± 0.060	0.880%
866.89 ± 0.300	0.040%
868.06 ± 0.300	0.040%
869.88 ± 0.300	0.040%
874.215 ± 0.070	0.093%
876.029 ± 0.140	0.048%
881.353 ± 0.169	0.027%
884.497 ± 0.031	0.264%
889.506 ± 0.036	0.525%
895.412 ± 0.130	0.035%
913.569 ± 0.076	0.057%
917.30 ± 0.30	0.070%
918.80 ± 0.40	0.080%
920.70 ± 0.40	0.070%
921.80 ± 0.40	0.050%
922.80 ± 0.50	0.030%
928.154 ± 0.043	0.126%
933.057 ± 0.037	0.791%
939.241 ± 0.284	0.014%
943.145 ± 0.180	0.034%
948.713 ± 0.173	0.027%
953.677 ± 0.190	0.030%
959.322 ± 0.305	0.167%
961.235 ± 0.167	0.403%
964.351 ± 0.037	2.156%
974.609 ± 0.079	0.082%
992.169 ± 0.066	0.076%
1000.996 ± 0.300	0.035%
1002.392 ± 0.200	0.035%
1009.744 ± 0.114	0.044%
1012.659 ± 0.117	0.040%
1032.238 ± 0.084	0.076%
1040.567 ± 0.199	0.021%
1065.70 ± 0.300	0.010%
1097.070 ± 0.102	0.052%
1122.40 ± 0.300	0.015%
1144.80 ± 0.300	0.015%

$_{92}U^{240}$

440	

$_{93}Np^{234}$

43.49	
99.7	
233.6	
234.6	
238.6?	
247.9	
266?	
298?	
450	
483?	
485?	
516	
526	
557	
744	
752	
768	
788	
793	
810	
812	
854	
1003	
1105	
1196	
1240	
1395	
1439	
1531	
1562	
1575	
1606	

$_{93}Np^{235}$

26	15†
84	9

$_{93}Np^{236}$

γ with EC	
45.32	
643	
688	
γ with β⁻	
44.6	

$_{93}Np^{237}$

20?	
29.6	14†
55.0?	
56.8	
84.5?	
85.9	14
105.0	
108.4	
133.5	
144.5	0.8

Gamma energies (KeV)	Gamma intensities
160?	
207	
240	

$_{93}Np^{238}$

Gamma energies (KeV)	Gamma intensities
44.1	
101.7	
119.8	
221.0	
292.6?	
871	
885	
925	
940	
943	
986	83†
989	
1027⎫	
1030⎬	100
1034	
1095?	

$_{93}Np^{239}$

Gamma energies (KeV)	Gamma intensities
44.65	
49.41	
57.26	
61.48	
67.86	
88.06	
106.13	22.8†
106.47	
166.4	
181.7	0.077
209.726 ± 0.02	3.4
226.4	
228.2 ± 0.1	11.8
254.2	0.12
272.809 ± 0.09	0.089
277.56 ± 0.015	14.1
285.37 ± 0.04	0.82
315.83 ± 0.04	1.5
334.25 ± 0.02	2.1
392.4	0.0016
429.5	0.0037
434.7	0.012
447.6	2.6×10^{-4}
454.2	8.0×10^{-4}
461.9	0.0016
469.8	0.0011
484.3	0.0010
492.3	0.0060
497.8	0.0031
498.7	
504.2	7.7×10^{-4}

$_{93}Np^{240m}$

Gamma energies (KeV)	Gamma intensities
42.9	
260	1.9%
304	0.9
557	21
599	13
760	1.3
792?	
816	1.6
820	0.3
844?	
860	
863	

Gamma energies (KeV)	Gamma intensities
898	1.2
940	0.3
945	1.9
1092?	
1490	1.5
1530	1.9
1620	0.7

$_{93}Np^{240}$

Gamma energies (KeV)	Gamma intensities
85	
160	
245	
440	
560	
600	
920	
1000	
1160	

$_{94}Pu^{234}$

Gamma energies (KeV)	Gamma intensities
0.047	

$_{94}Pu^{236}$

Gamma energies (KeV)	Gamma intensities
47	0.031%
110	0.012
165	6.6×10^{-4}
452	1.7×10^{-4}
570	1.0×10^{-4}
640	2.4×10^{-4}

$_{94}Pu^{237m}$

Gamma energies (KeV)	Gamma intensities
145	100%

$_{94}Pu^{237}$

Gamma energies (KeV)	Gamma intensities
33.2	
43.5	
55.6?	
59.6	
76.4?	
96.0?	

$_{94}Pu^{238}$

Gamma energies (KeV)	Gamma intensities
43.49	0.038%
99.8	8×10^{-3}
153.1	1×10^{-3}
203	4×10^{-6}
743	9×10^{-6}
767	3.5×10^{-5}
786	6×10^{-6}
810	$<1 \times 10^{-6}$

$_{94}Pu^{239}$

Gamma energies (KeV)	Gamma intensities
38.70 ± 0.03	$(1.63 \pm 0.16)^b$
41.99 ± 0.10	$(2.8 \pm 0.4)^d$
46.19 ± 0.07	$(2.35 \pm 0.30)^c$
51.61 ± 0.03	$(1.35 \pm 0.14)^a$
54.01 ± 0.05	$(1.13 \pm 0.20)^c$
56.82 ± 0.04	$(7.3 \pm 0.8)^f$
59.57	^{241}Am
65.73 ± 0.08	$(2.7 \pm 0.5)^d$
67.70 ± 0.05	$(1.4 \pm 0.3)^f$
68.72 ± 0.06	$(4.2 \pm 0.6)^f$
72.79	Pb $K_{\alpha 2}$
74.96	Pb $K_{\alpha 1}$
77.60 ± 0.05	$(4.1 \pm 0.6)^d$

Gamma energies (KeV)	Gamma intensities
78.48 ± 0.05	$(1.7 \pm 0.2)^c$
84.30	Pb $K_{\beta 3}$
84.82	Pb $K_{\beta 1}$
87.34	Pb $K_{\beta 2}$
89.94 ± 0.06	$(1.1 \pm 0.2)^d$
94.64	U $K_{\alpha 2}$
98.46	U $K_{\alpha 1}$
99.46	Pu $K_{\alpha 2}$
102.93 ± 0.08	$(2.6 \pm 0.4)^f$
103.64	Pu $K_{\alpha 1}$
110.38	U $K_{\beta 3}$
111.29	U $K_{\beta 1}$
114.55	U $K_{\beta 2}$
115.32 ± 0.05	$(7.4 \pm 0.9)^f$
116.18 ± 0.05	$(7.1 \pm 0.8)^f$
117.15	Pu $K_{\beta 1}$
119.89 ± 0.08	$(2.8 \pm 0.4)^d$
120.59	Pu $K_{\beta 2}$
122.35 ± 0.12	$(3.0 \pm 1.5)^e$
123.73 ± 0.08	$(1.9 \pm 0.3)^d$
124.41 ± 0.12	$(4.8 \pm 0.8)^d$
125.00 ± 0.12	$(4.8 \pm 0.8)^d$
129.27 ± 0.03	$(5.6 \pm 0.7)^b$
141.66 ± 0.06	$(9.8 \pm 0.9)^d$
144.18 ± 0.08	$(2.7 \pm 0.4)^d$
146.07 ± 0.08	$(9.8 \pm 1.0)^d$
159.6 ± 0.2	$(2.0 \pm 1.0)^c$
160.07 ± 0.13	$(5.0 \pm 2.0)^e$
161.47 ± 0.05	$(1.0 \pm 0.2)^f$
167.95 ± 0.18	$(2.0 \pm 0.1)^c$
171.37 ± 0.08	$(9.8 \pm 0.9)^d$
173.61 ± 0.10	$(2.9 \pm 0.4)^e$
179.20 ± 0.08	$(2.9 \pm 0.3)^d$
184.53 ± 0.15	$(2.0 \pm 0.1)^e$
188.13 ± 0.10	$(4.2 \pm 0.6)^e$
189.34 ± 0.07	$(7.4 \pm 0.9)^d$
193.13 ± 0.12	$(5.9 \pm 0.8)^c$
195.68 ± 0.07	$(8.9 \pm 1.0)^d$
203.55 ± 0.04	$(4.8 \pm 0.4)^f$
209.34 ± 0.08	$(1.1 \pm 0.3)^d$
225.46 ± 0.08	$(1.1 \pm 0.2)^d$
237.6 ± 0.2	
238.2 ± 0.2	$(1.4 \pm 0.2)^c$
242.08 ± 0.08	$(9.3 \pm 0.9)^e$
243.38 ± 0.07	$(2.0 \pm 0.5)^c$
244.90 ± 0.09	$(4.9 \pm 0.8)^c$
248.82 ± 0.08	$(7.5 \pm 0.9)^e$
255.38 ± 0.07	$(6.6 \pm 0.8)^d$
258.20 ± 0.10	$(3.8 \pm 0.6)^e$
263.92 ± 0.07	$(1.9 \pm 0.3)^d$
265.68 ± 0.12	$(3.0 \pm 0.9)^c$
297.48 ± 0.07	$(4.1 \pm 0.6)^d$
302.84 ± 0.10	$(7.2 \pm 0.9)^c$
307.71 ± 0.10	$(3.9 \pm 0.8)^f$
311.74 ± 0.06	$(2.0 \pm 0.2)^d$
316.44 ± 0.08	$(9.9 \pm 1.2)^f$
320.83 ± 0.06	$(4.6 \pm 0.5)^d$
323.81 ± 0.06	$(4.4 \pm 0.5)^c$
332.84 ± 0.04	$(4.3 \pm 0.4)^f$
336.14 ± 0.05	$(9.4 \pm 1.1)^d$
341.51 ± 0.06	$(6.0 \pm 0.8)^d$
345.02 ± 0.03	$(5.0 \pm 0.5)^f$
353.60 ± 0.10	$(2.7 \pm 0.6)^c$
361.90 ± 0.08	$(1.1 \pm 0.2)^d$
367.08 ± 0.08	$(8.2 \pm 0.9)^d$
368.57 ± 0.08	$(8.1 \pm 0.9)^d$
371.67 ± 0.10	$(3.9 \pm 0.6)^c$
375.04 ± 0.03	$(1.5 \pm 0.1)^b$
380.19 ± 0.05	$(3.0 \pm 0.3)^f$
382.77 ± 0.05	$(2.5 \pm 0.3)^f$
392.7 ± 0.2	$(2.7 \pm 0.5)^f$

$a = \times 10^{-2}, b = \times 10^{-3}, c = \times 10^{-4}, d = \times 10^{-5}, e = \times 10^{-6}$

Gamma energies (KeV)	Gamma intensities
393.1 ± 0.2	(2.7 ± 0.5)^c
399.54 ± 0.09	(9.0 ± 1.5)^e
410.92 ± 0.06	(1.4 ± 0.3)^d
413.71 ± 0.03	(1.5 ± 0.1)^b
422.62 ± 0.05	(1.2 ± 0.2)^c
426.79 ± 0.08	(3.3 ± 0.5)^d
430.12 ± 0.12	(4.8 ± 0.8)^e
445.78 ± 0.12	(7.5 ± 1.1)^e
451.49 ± 0.05	(1.8 ± 0.2)^c
457.57 ± 0.10	(1.2 ± 0.4)^e
461.09 ± 0.10	(3.0 ± 0.6)^e
481.58 ± 0.10	(5.1 ± 1.0)^e
558.31 ± 0.12	(2.4 ± 0.5)^e
617.45 ± 0.10	(2.1 ± 0.4)^e
618.6 ± 0.2	(2.1 ± 0.4)^e
633.3 ± 0.2	(1.2 ± 0.3)^e
640.05 ± 0.08	(5.7 ± 0.9)^e
645.80 ± 0.06	(1.3 ± 0.3)^d
651.98 ± 0.10	(5.1 ± 1.0)^e
655.20 ± 0.20	(1.5 ± 0.3)^e
658.82 ± 0.10	(9.6 ± 1.2)^e
703.52 ± 0.10	(4.8 ± 0.9)^e
717.59 ± 0.15	(1.8 ± 0.4)^e
756.10 ± 0.20	(3.9 ± 0.7)^e
769.12 ± 0.15	(9.6 ± 1.2)^e

$_{94}Pu^{240}$

Gamma energies (KeV)	Gamma intensities
45.28	
103.6	
160	
642.3	1.4 × 10^-5 %
687.8	4 × 10^-6

$_{94}Pu^{241}$

Gamma energies (KeV)	Gamma intensities
76.8	0.7 %
103.5	4.4
148.5	9.0
160.0	0.3

$_{94}Pu^{243}$

Gamma energies (KeV)	Gamma intensities
12.2?	
29.7?	
36.7	
42.2	1 %
54	
84	21
96	
134?	
381	0.7

$_{94}Pu^{246}$

Gamma energies (KeV)	Gamma intensities
27	13 %
44	≈ 30
80	3
100?	
180.4	10
224.0	25

$_{95}Am^{238}$

Gamma energies (KeV)	Gamma intensities
360	
580	30†
950	
980	80
1350	

$_{95}Am^{239}$

γ with α
48	

γ with EC
Gamma energies (KeV)	Gamma intensities
44.70	Weak
49.47	
57.31	
67.91	
181.8	
209.9	
226.5	
228.3	
277.6	

$_{95}Am^{240}$

Gamma energies (KeV)	Gamma intensities
42.87	
98.9	
900	23 %
1000	77
1400	< 10

$_{95}Am^{241}$

Gamma energies (KeV)	Gamma intensities
26.36	2.5 %
33.21	0.17
43.44	0.07
55.56	
59.57	36
67.5	
99.00	0.024
102.97	0.019
106?	< 0.001
114.2	4.3 × 10^-4
118.2	4 × 10^-4
123.2	1.8 × 10^-3
125.3	4.5 × 10^-3
146.6	1.6 × 10^-4
150.1	3.5 × 10^-5
154.4	8 × 10^-6
156.4	1.2 × 10^-5
158.3	9 × 10^-6
161.7	9 × 10^-6
164.6	2.5 × 10^-5
166.2	5 × 10^-6
169.6	8.5 × 10^-5
173.1	5 × 10^-6
175.0	7 × 10^-6
191.9	3 × 10^-5
197.0	1.3 × 10^-5
208.00	5.6 × 10^-4
221.4	3 × 10^-5
242.4	3 × 10^-5
245.0	3 × 10^-5
248.0	5.5 × 10^-5
267.4	3.5 × 10^-5
292.8	2 × 10^-5
294.9	5.5 × 10^-5
310.3	1.5 × 10^-5
312.1	8 × 10^-5
322.5	1.9 × 10^-4
332.4	1.4 × 10^-4
335.4	5.7 × 10^-4
343.3?	1.1 × 10^-4
351.8	9 × 10^-5
368.6	2.8 × 10^-4
371.0	6 × 10^-5
376.8	1.4 × 10^-4
383.6	5.5 × 10^-5
391.0	4 × 10^-5
419.4	6 × 10^-5

Gamma energies (KeV)	Gamma intensities
426.8	3 × 10^-5
445.1	4.5 × 10^-5
454?	< 1.7 × 10^-5
462	1.4 × 10^-5
511.6	8.5 × 10^-5
525.7	8 × 10^-5
570	1.0 × 10^-5
591.5?	7 × 10^-5
597	1.0 × 10^-5
609.8	2.3 × 10^-4
619.6	8 × 10^-5
641	1.0 × 10^-5
653.1	9 × 10^-5
663.0	5.3 × 10^-4
676?	< 2 × 10^-6
680	6 × 10^-6
688.7	4 × 10^-5
695	1.0 × 10^-5
710	9 × 10^-6
723.2	4.8 × 10^-4
737	1.2 × 10^-5
757.3	1.0 × 10^-4
767.0	8 × 10^-6
770.7	1 × 10^-5

$_{95}Am^{242m}$

γ with IT
48.6	

γ with α
Gamma energies (KeV)	Gamma intensities
42	
49.3	41
66.8	4.6
67.9	1.6
69	
73.3?	1.3
86.7	8
92.5	0.9
109.6	5.3
111.1	0.6
121.8	1.3
135.5	2.3
136.1	2.1
152.9	0.3
153.9	1.0
163.4	5.2
194.9	
206.4	

$_{95}Am^{242}$

γ with β−
42.12	

γ with EC
44.50	

$_{95}Am^{243}$

Gamma energies (KeV)	Gamma intensities
31.42	0.03 %
43.53	5.3
50.6	0.0027
55.4	0.0094
74.673	61
86.7	0.37
117.8	0.75
142.0	0.13
169	0.0012
195	0.00085
500?	
570?	

$a = \times 10^{-2}, b = \times 10^{-3}, c = \times 10^{-4}, d = \times 10^{-5}, e = \times 10^{-6}.$

Gamma energies (KeV)	Gamma intensities
620	0.0003
650	0.0010
$_{95}Am^{244m}$	
42.9	
980?	<1%
1050	<1
$_{95}Am^{244}$	
42.9	
99.4	5%
154	19
206	
540	≈0.4
746	66
900	25
$_{95}Am^{245}$	
36	
56?	
78?	
140	
153	
240	1.2%
252.3	20
296	0.55
$_{95}Am^{246}$	
171	
228	
238	0.3%
244.6	1.5
245.4	1.5
256	0.2
262	0.14
270.3	1.0
288	0.1
402	0.3
734	1.2
752	1
759	0.8
799.0	28.6
834	2.2
987	1.1
1037	14.4
1063	19.3
1079	31.5
1086	1.7
$_{96}Cm^{239}$	
188	
$_{96}Cm^{241}$	
γ with α	
145	
γ with EC	
470	
600	
$_{96}Cm^{242}$	
44.11	0.039%
101.9	0.0035
157.7	0.0023
210	≈2 ×10⁻⁵
562	1.8 ×10⁻⁴

Gamma energies (KeV)	Gamma intensities
605	1.4×10^{-4}
≈900	2×10^{-5}
941	3×10^{-5}
$_{96}Cm^{243}$	
106	
210	~5%
228	~6.5
227	11
$_{96}Cm^{244}$	
42.88	0.021%
100	1.5×10^{-3}
150	1.3×10^{-3}
264	1.2×10^{-4}
~570 }	2.5×10^{-4}
~610 }	
~830	7×10^{-5}
$_{96}Cm^{245}$	
≈130	5%
173	14
$_{97}Bk^{243}$	
γ with EC	
755	10†
840	30
946	8
γ with α	
42	4†
146.4	8
187.1	41
558	13
$_{97}Bk^{244}$	
γ with EC	
144.5	7†
154.0	3.6
177.0	5.0
187.6	16
217.6	100
233.8	2.9
333.5	10
490	14
745	6
870	5
892	88
922	17
988	4.0
1153	7
1178	4.0
1233	2.8
1252	2.2
1333	0.9
1505	2.0
$_{97}Bk^{245}$	
γ with EC	
252.7	31%
380.5	3.5
384.6	1.5
γ with α	
165.5	
207.4	
474	

Gamma energies (KeV)	Gamma intensities
$_{97}Bk^{246}$	
734	4.6†
800	100
834	8
986	0.5
1037	2.8
1063	5
1079	5
1082	10
1124	8
$_{97}Bk^{247}$	
84	40%
≈270	30
$_{97}Bk^{248}$	
No γ	
$_{97}Bk^{249}$	
307	2.2†
327.2	12
$_{97}Bk^{250}$	
42.2	
98.2	
990	47%
1032	39
$_{98}Cf^{246}$	
42	0.014%
96	0.012
146	0.0035
$_{98}Cf^{247}$	
295	20†
417	13
460	9
$_{98}Cf^{249}$	
43.0	0.03%
55.0	0.20
66.7	0.04
92.6	0.4
241.0	0.3
252.8	3.0
266.7	0.7
295.9	0.17
333.4	16
388.4	72
$_{98}Cf^{250}$	
42.9	17%
$_{98}Cf^{251}$	
177	
224	
$_{98}Cf^{252}$	
43.3	0.014%
100.2	0.01
≈160	0.002

Gamma energies (KeV)	Gamma intensities	Gamma energies (KeV)	Gamma intensities
$_{99}Es^{252}$		316	0.15
74	0.3 %	342	0.009
154	0.07	348	0.007
198	0.08	377	0.015
228	0.23	385	0.05
278	0.21		
~400	1.1	$_{100}Fm^{254}$	
~520	0.15	41	0.2 %
~570	0.14	98	0.028
		151	0.001
$_{99}Es^{253}$			
8.80		$_{100}Fm^{255}$	
30.83		58.6	0.9 %
41.79		60.0	0.19
42.98		72.9	0.034
51.96		80.5 }	1.34
55.11		81.2 }	
62.09		85.7	0.009
66.85		98.5	0.007
73.43		~120	0.03
73.82		178	0.007
78.6		~340	0.003
93.75		~370	0.005
98.09		~440	0.003
114.06		~490	0.003
121.98			
135.5			
145.4		$_{100}Fm^{257}$	
368.8	0.7†		
381.2	10.4	62	
386.1		78	
387.2	36	103	1 %
389.18	55	180	8
428.94	11	242	10
433.2	5		
442.2			
448.2	1.5		
475.0			
500.2			
≈750			
≈900			
$_{99}Es^{254m}$			
44			
104	0.6†		
544	3		
583.3	9		
648.1	100		
688.2	~40		
693.1	~80		
~990	2.0		
$_{99}Es^{254}$			
34.4			
35.5			
42.6			
63	2.0 %		
69.7			
70.4			
80.8			
85.1			
150	0.02		
233?	0.008		
249	0.025		
264	0.05		
278	0.03		
285	0.01		
304	0.07		

PERMISSIBLE QUARTERLY INTAKES OF RADIONUCLIDES

Karl Z. Morgan

The following table lists the permissible quarterly intakes (oral and inhalation) or radionuclides and critical body organs recommended by NCPR for occupational exposure.

PERMISSIBLE QUARTERLY INTAKES (ORAL AND INHALATION) OF RADIONUCLIDES AND CRITICAL BODY ORGANS RECOMMENDED BY NCRP FOR OCCUPATIONAL EXPOSURE (1)

Radionuclide	Radioactive half-life days	Solubility state	Oral intake		Intake by inhalation	
			Critical organ	Permissible quarterly intake microcuries	Critical organ	Permissible quarterly intake microcuries
3-H	4.50E 03	Sol.	Body tissue	6.4E 03(2)	Body tissue	3.1E 03(2)
7-BE	5.36E 01	Sol.	GI LLI	3.6E 03	Tot. body	3.5E 03
		Insol.	GI LLI	3.6E 03	Lungs	7.5E 02
14-C	2.00E 06	Sol.	Fat	1.6E 03	Fat	2.2E 03
18-F	7.80E-02	Sol.	GI SI	1.7E 03	GI SI	3.3E 03
		Insol.	GI ULI	1.0E 03	GI ULI	1.6E 03
22-NA	9.50E 02	Sol.	Tot. body	8.0E 01	Tot. body	1.1E 02
		Insol.	GI LLI	6.0E 01	Lungs	5.3E 00
24-NA	6.30E-01	Sol.	GI SI	3.8E 02	GI SI	7.6E 02
		Insol.	GI LLI	5.6E 01	GI LLI	8.9E 01
31-SI	1.10E-01	Sol.	GI S	1.8E 03	GI S	3.5E 03
		Insol.	GI ULI	3.8E 02	GI ULI	6.2E 02
32-P	1.43E 01	Sol.	Bone	3.8E 01	Bone	4.4E 01
		Insol.	GI LLI	4.6E 01	Lungs	4.9E 01
35-S	8.71E 01	Sol.	Testes	1.3E 02	Testes	1.7E 02
		Insol	GI LLI	5.4E 02	Lungs	1.6E 02
36-CL	1.20E 08	Sol.	Tot. body	1.6E 02	Tot. body	2.2E 02
		Insol.	GI LLI	1.2E 02	Lungs	1.4E 01
38-CL	2.60E-02	Sol.	GI S	8.0E 02	GI S	1.6E 03
		Insol.	GI S	8.0E 02	GI S	1.3E 03
42-K	5.20E-01	Sol.	GI S	6.2E 02	GI-S	1.2E 03
		Insol.	GI LLI	4.0E 01	GI LLI	6.7E 01
45-CA	1.64E 02	Sol.	Bone	1.8E 01	Bone	2.0E 01
		Insol.	GI LLI	3.6E 01	Lungs	7.5E 01
47-CA	4.90E 00	Sol.	Bone	1.0E 02	Bone	1.1E 02
		Insol.	GI LLI	6.6E 01	GI LLI	1.1E 02
					Lungs	1.2E 02
46-SC	8.50E 01	Sol.	GI LLI	7.6E 01	Liver	1.5E 02
					GI LLI	1.5E 02
		Insol.	GI LLI	7.6E 01	Lungs	1.4E 01
47-SC	3.43E 00	Sol.	GI LLI	1.8E 02	GI LLI	3.6E 02
		Insol.	GI LLI	1.8E 02	GI LLI	2.9E 02
48-SC	1.83E 00	Sol.	GI LLI	5.4E 01	GI LLI	1.1E 02
		Insol.	GI LLI	5.4E 01	GI LLI	8.7E 01
48-V	1.61E 01	Sol.	GI LLI	5.8E 01	GI LLI	1.2E 02
		Insol.	GI LLI	5.8E 01	Lungs	3.5E 01
51-CR	2.78E 01	Sol.	GI LLI	3.2E 03	GI LLI	6.4E 03
					Tot. body	6.7E 03
		Insol.	GI LLI	3.0E 03	Lungs	1.4E 03
52-MN	5.55E 00	Sol.	GI LLI	6.6E 01	GI LLI	1.3E 02
		Insol.	GI LLI	6.0E 01	Lungs	8.7E 01
					GI LLI	9.5E 01
54-MN	3.00E 02	Sol.	GI LLI	2.6E 02	Liver	2.4E 02
		Insol.	GI LLI	2.4E 02	Lungs	2.2E 01
56-MN	1.10E-01	Sol.	GI LLI	2.4E 02	GI LLI	4.7E 02
		Insol.	GI LLI	2.0E 02	GI LLI	3.3E 02
55-FE	1.10E 03	Sol.	Spleen	1.6E 03	Spleen	5.3E 02
		Insol.	GI LLI	4.6E 03	Lungs	6.4E 02
59-FE	4.51E 01	Sol.	GI LLI	1.2E 02	Spleen	9.3E 01
		Insol.	GI LLI	1.1E 02	Lungs	3.3E 01
57-CO	2.70E 02	Sol.	GI LLI	1.1E 03	GI LLI	2.2E 03
		Insol.	GI LLI	7.6E 02	Lungs	1.0E 02
58M-CO	3.80E-01	Sol.	GI LLI	5.6E 03	GI LLI	1.1E 04
		Insol.	GI LLI	4.0E 03	Lungs	5.5E 03
58-CO	7.20E 01	Sol	GI LLI	2.6E 02	GI LLI	5.3E 02
					Tot. body	6.0E 02
		Insol	GI LLI	1.8E 02	Lungs	3.5E 01

Radionuclide	Radioactive half-life days	Solubility state	Oral intake		Intake by inhalation	
			Critical organ	Permissible quarterly intake microcuries	Critical organ	Permissible quarterly intake microcuries
60-CO	1.90E 03	Sol	GI LLI	9.8E 01	GI LLI	2.0E 02
					Tot. body	2.2E 02
		Insol.	GI LLI	7.0E 01	Lungs	5.5E 00
59-NI	2.90E 07	Sol.	Bone	4.0E 02	Bone	2.9E 02
		Insol.	GI LLI	4.0E 03	Lungs	4.7E 02
63-NI	2.90E 04	Sol	Bone	5.4E 01	Bone	4.0E 01
		Insol	GI LLI	1.4E 03	Lungs	1.7E 02
65-NI	1.10E-01	Sol.	GI ULI	2.8E 02	GI ULI	5.6E 02
		Insol.	GI ULI	2.0E 02	GI ULI	3.3E 02
64-CU	5.30E-01	Sol.	GI LLI	6.6E 02	GI LLI	1.3E 03
		Insol.	GI LLI	4.2E 02	GI LLI	6.6E 02
65-ZN	2.45E 02	Sol.	Tot. body	2.0E 02	Tot. body	6.6E 01
			Prostate	2.4E 02	Prostate	8.0E 01
			Liver	2.6E 02		
		Insol.	GI LLI	3.6E 02	Lungs	3.6E 01
69M-ZN	5.80E-01	Sol.	GI LLI	1.4E 02	Prostate	2.4E 02
		Insol.	GI LLI	1.2E 02	GI LLI	2.0E 02
69-ZN	3.60E-02	Sol.	GI S	3.6E 03	Prostate	4.4E 03
		Insol.	GI S	3.6E 03	GI S	5.8E 03
72-GA	5.90E-01	Sol.	GI LLI	7.4E 01	GI LLI	1.5E 02
		Insol.	GI LLI	7.4E 01	GI LLI	1.2E 02
71-GE	1.20E 01	Sol.	GI LLI	3.2E 03	GI LLI	6.4E 03
		Insol.	GI LLI	3.2E 03	Lungs	4.0E 03
73-AS	7.60E 01	Sol.	GI LLI	9.6E 02	Tot. body	1.3E 03
		Insol.	GI LLI	9.2E 02	Lungs	2.4E 02
74-AS	1.75E 01	Sol.	GI LLI	1.1E 02	GI LLI	2.2E 02
		Insol.	GI LLI	1.0E 02	Lungs	7.8E 01
76-AS	1.10E 00	Sol.	GI LLI	4.0E 01	GI LLI	8.0E 01
		Insol.	GI LLI	3.8E 01	GI LLI	6.2E 01
77-AS	1.60E 00	Sol.	GI LLI	1.6E 02	GI LLI	3.3E 02
		Insol.	GI LLI	1.6E 02	GI LLI	2.5E 02
75-SE	1.27E 02	Sol.	Kidneys	6.0E 02	Kidneys	7.8E 02
			Tot. body	6.8E 02		
		Insol.	GI LLI	5.4E 02	Lungs	7.6E 01
82-BR	1.50E 00	Sol.	Tot. body	5.2E 02	Tot. body	7.1E 02
			GI SI	5.6E 02		
		Insol.	GI LLI	7.4E 01	GI LLI	1.2E 02
86-RB	1.86E 01	Sol.	Tot. body	1.3E 02	Tot. body	1.8E 02
			Pancreas	1.3E 02	Pancreas	1.8E 02
					Liver	2.5E 02
		Insol.	GI LLI	4.8E 01	Lungs	4.2E 01
87-RB	1.80E 13	Sol.	Pancreas	2.2E 02	Pancreas	3.1E 02
					Tot. body	4.0E 02
					Liver	4.2E 02
		Insol.	GI LLI	3.4E 02	Lungs	4.0E 01
85M-SR	4.90E-02	Sol.	GI SI	1.3E 04	GI SI	2.5E 04
		Insol.	GI SI	1.3E 04	GI SI	2.2E 04
85-SR	6.50E 01	Sol.	Tot. body	1.9E 02	Tot. body	1.4E 02
		Insol.	GI LLI	3.4E 02	Lungs	6.6E 01
89-SR	5.05E 01	Sol.	Bone	2.4E 01	Bone	1.7E 01
		Insol.	GI LLI	5.6E 01	Lungs	2.2E 01
90-SR	1.00E 04	Sol.	Bone	8.0E-01	Bone	7.3E-01
		Insol.	GI LLI	7.0E 01	Lungs	3.5E 00
91-SR	4.00E-01	Sol.	GI LLI	1.4E 02	GI LLI	2.7E 02
		Insol.	GI LLI	9.8E 01	GI LLI	1.6E 02
92-SR	1.10E-01	Sol.	GI ULI	1.4E 02	GI ULI	2.7E 02
		Insol.	GI ULI	1.2E 02	GI ULI	1.8E 02
90-Y	2.68E 00	Sol.	GI LLI	4.0E 01	GI LLI	8.0E 01
		Insol.	GI LLI	4.0E 01	GI LLI	6.4E 01
91M-Y	3.50E-02	Sol.	GI SI	6.8E 03	GI SI	1.4E 04
		Insol.	GI SI	6.8E 03	GI SI	1.1E 04
91-Y	5.80E 01	Sol.	GI LLI	5.2E 01	Bone	2.2E 01
		Insol.	GI LLI	5.2E 01	Lungs	2.0E 01

Radionuclide	Radioactive half-life days	Solubility state	Oral intake		Intake by inhalation	
			Critical organ	Permissible quarterly intake microcuries	Critical organ	Permissible quarterly intake microcuries
92-Y	1.50E-01	Sol.	GI ULI	1.2E 02	GI ULI	2.4E 02
		Insol.	GI ULI	1.2E 02	GI ULI	1.8E 02
93-Y	4.20E-01	Sol.	GI LLI	5.4E 01	GI LLI	1.1E 02
		Insol.	GI LLI	5.4E 01	GI LLI	8.6E 01
93-ZR	4.00E 08	Sol.	GI LLI	1.6E 03	Bone	8.0E 01
		Insol.	GI LLI	1.6E 03	Lungs	2.0E 02
95-ZR	6.33E 01	Sol.	GI LLI	1.3E 02	Tot. body	8.0E 01
		Insol.	GI LLI	1.3E 02	Lungs	2.0E 01
97-ZR	7.10E-01	Sol.	GI LLI	3.6E 01	GI LLI	7.3E 01
		Insol.	GI LLI	3.6E 01	GI LLI	5.6E 01
93M-NB	3.70E 03	Sol.	GI LLI	8.0E 02	Bone	7.6E 01
		Insol.	GI LLI	8.0E 02	Lungs	1.0E 02
95-NB	3.50E 01	Sol.	GI LLI	1.9E 02	Tot. body	2.9E 02
					GI LLI	3.8E 02
		Insol.	GI LLI	1.9E 02	Lungs	6.2E 01
97-NB	5.10E-02	Sol.	GI ULI	1.9E 03	GI ULI	3.8E 03
		Insol.	GI ULI	1.9E 03	GI ULI	2.9E 03
99-MO	2.79E 00	Sol.	Kidneys	3.6E 02	Kidneys	4.5E 02
			GI LLI	4.8E 02		
		Insol.	GI LLI	7.8E 01	GI LLI	1.3E 02
96M-TC	3.60E-02	Sol.	GI LLI	2.4E 04	GI LLI	4.7E 04
		Insol.	GI LLI	2.0E 04	Lungs	1.8E 04
96-TC	4.30E 00	Sol.	GI LLI	2.0E 02	GI LLI	4.0E 02
		Insol.	GI LLI	9.4E 01	GI LLI	1.5E 02
97M-TC	9.20E 01	Sol.	GI LLI	7.2E 02	GI LLI	1.4E 03
		Insol.	GI LLI	3.4E 02	Lungs	9.5E 01
97-TC	3.70E 06	Sol.	GI LLI	3.4E 03	GI LLI	6.7E 03
					Kidneys	8.0E 03
		Insol.	GI LLI	1.6E 03	Lungs	1.8E 02
99M-TC	2.50E-01	Sol.	GI ULI	1.1E 04	GI ULI	2.4E 04
		Insol.	GI ULI	5.6E 03	GI ULI	8.7E 03
99-TC	7.70E 07	Sol.	GI LLI	6.6E 02	GI LLI	1.3E 03
		Insol.	GI LLI	3.2E 02	Lungs	3.8E 01
97-RU	2.80E 00	Sol.	GI LLI	7.2E 02	GI LLI	1.4E 03
		Insol.	GI LLI	7.0E 02	GI LLI	1.1E 03
103-RU	4.10E 01	Sol.	GI LLI	1.6E 02	GI LLI	3.3E 02
		Insol.	GI LLI	1.6E 02	Lungs	5.3E 01
105-RU	1.90E-01	Sol.	GI ULI	2.2E 02	GI ULI	4.4E 02
		Insol.	GI ULI	2.0E 02	GI ULI	3.3E 02
106-RU	3.65E 02	Sol.	GI LLI	2.4E 01	GI LLI	4.7E 01
		Insol.	GI LLI	2.4E 01	Lungs	3.5E 00
103M-RH	3.80E-02	Sol.	GI S	2.4E 04	GI S	4.7E 04
		Insol.	GI S	2.4E 04	GI S	3.8E 04
105-RH	1.52E 00	Sol.	GI LLI	2.6E 02	GI LLI	5.3E 02
		Insol.	GI LLI	2.0E 02	GI LLI	3.3E 02
103-PD	1.70E 01	Sol.	GI LLI	6.8E 02	Kidneys	8.4E 02
		Insol.	GI LLI	5.4E 02	Lungs	4.7E 02
109-PD	5.70E-01	Sol.	GI LLI	1.8E 02	GI LLI	3.5E 02
		Insol.	GI LLI	1.4E 02	GI LLI	2.2E 02
105-AG	4.00E 01	Sol.	GI LLI	1.9E 02	GI LLI	3.8E 02
		Insol.	GI LLI	1.9E 02	Lungs	5.1E 01
110M-AG	2.70E 02	Sol.	GI LLI	6.0E 01	GI LLI	1.2E 02
		Insol.	GI LLI	6.0E 01	Lungs	6.4E 00
111-AG	7.50E 00	Sol.	GI LLI	8.8E 01	GI LLI	1.8E 02
		Insol.	GI LLI	8.6E 01	GI LLI	1.4E 02
109-CD	4.75E 02	Sol.	GI LLI	3.4E 02	Liver	3.3E 01
					Kidneys	3.5E 01
		Insol.	GI LLI	3.4E 02	Lungs	4.5E 01
115M-CD	4.30E 01	Sol.	GI LLI	5.0E 01	Liver	2.2E 01
		Insol.	GI LLI	5.0E 01	Lungs	2.2E 01
115-CD	2.20E 00	Sol.	GI LLI	6.8E 01	GI LLI	1.4E 02
		Insol.	GI LLI	7.2E 01	GI LLI	1.1E 02

Radionuclide	Radioactive half-life days	Solubility state	Oral intake		Intake by inhalation	
			Critical organ	Permissible quarterly intake microcuries	Critical organ	Permissible quarterly intake microcuries
113M-IN	7.30E-02	Sol.	GI ULI	2.6E 03	GI ULI	5.3E 03
		Insol.	GI ULI	2.6E 03	GI ULI	4.2E 03
114M-IN	4.90E 01	Sol.	GI LLI	3.4E 01	Kidneys	6.4E 01
					GI LLI	6.7E 01
					Spleen	7.1E 01
		Insol.	GI LLI	3.4E 01	Lungs	1.3E 01
115M-IN	1.90E-01	Sol.	GI ULI	7.4E 02	GI ULI	1.5E 03
		Insol.	GI ULI	7.4E 02	GI ULI	1.2E 03
115-IN	2.20E 17	Sol.	GI LLI	1.8E 02	Kidneys	1.5E 02
		Insol.	GI LLI	1.8E 02	Lungs	2.2E 02
113-SN	1.12E 02	Sol.	GI LLI	1.7E 02	Bone	2.2E 02
		Insol.	GI LLI	1.6E 02	Lungs	3.3E 01
125-SN	9.50E 00	Sol.	GI LLI	3.6E 01	GI LLI	7.3E 01
		Insol.	GI LLI	3.4E 01	Lungs	5.3E 01
					GI LLI	5.5E 01
122-SB	2.80E 00	Sol.	GI LLI	5.8E 01	GI LLI	1.2E 02
		Insol.	GI LLI	5.8E 01	GI LLI	9.1E 01
124-SB	6.00E 01	Sol.	GI LLI	4.6E 01	GI LLI	9.3E 01
		Insol.	GI LLI	4.6E 01	Lungs	1.2E 01
125-SB	8.77E 02	Sol.	GI LLI	2.0E 02	Lungs	3.3E 02
					Tot. body	3.6E 02
					GI LLI	4.0E 02
					Bone	4.5E 02
		Insol.	GI LLI	2.0E 02	Lungs	1.7E 01
125M-TE	5.80E 01	Sol.	Kidneys	3.2E 02	Kidneys	2.2E 02
			GI LLI	3.6E 02		
			Testes	4.4E 02		
		Insol.	GI LLI	2.4E 02	Lungs	8.0E 01
127M-TE	1.05E 02	Sol.	Kidneys	1.2E 02	Kidneys	8.2E 01
					Testes	8.7E 01
		Insol.	GI LLI	1.1E 02	Lungs	2.5E 01
127-TE	3.90E-01	Sol.	GI LLI	5.2E 02	GI LLI	1.0E 03
		Insol.	GI LLI	3.4E 02	GI LLI	5.3E 02
129M-TE	3.30E 01	Sol.	GI LLI	6.6E 01	Kidneys	4.9E 01
					Testes	5.6E 01
		Insol.	GI LLI	4.0E 01	Lungs	2.0E 01
129-TE	5.10E-02	Sol.	GI S	1.6E 03	GI S	3.3E 03
		Insol.	GI ULI	1.6E 03	GI ULI	2.5E 03
131M-TE	1.25E 00	Sol.	GI LLI	1.2E 02	GI LLI	2.4E 02
		Insol.	GI LLI	7.4E 01	GI LLI	1.2E 02
132-TE	3.20E 00	Sol.	GI LLI	6.4E 01	GI LLI	1.3E 02
		Insol.	GI LLI	4.2E 01	GI LLI	6.6E 01
126-I	1.33E 01	Sol.	Thyroid	3.4E 00	Thyroid	4.5E 00
		Insol.	GI LLI	1.8E 02	Lungs	2.0E 02
129-I	6.30E 09	Sol.	Thyroid	7.6E-01	Thyroid	1.0E 00
		Insol.	GI LLI	4.2E 02	Lungs	4.5E 01
131-I	8.00E 00	Sol.	Thyroid	4.0E 00	Thyroid	5.3E 00
		Insol.	GI LLI	1.3E 02	GI LLI	2.0E 02
					Lungs	2.0E 02
132-I	9.70E-02	Sol.	Thyroid	1.1E 02	Thyroid	1.5E 02
		Insol.	GI ULI	3.6E 02	GI ULI	5.8E 02
133-I	8.70E-01	Sol.	Thyroid	1.5E 01	Thyroid	2.0E 01
		Insol.	GI LLI	8.2E 01	GI LLI	1.3E 02
134-I	3.60E-02	Sol.	Thyroid	2.4E 02	Thyroid	3.1E 02
		Insol.	GI S	1.2E 03	GI S	2.0E 03
135-I	2.80E-01	Sol.	Thyroid	4.8E 01	Thyroid	6.4E 01
		Insol.	GI LLI	1.4E 02	GI LLI	2.2E 02
131-CS	1.00E 01	Sol.	Tot. body	4.8E 03	Tot. body	6.6E 03
					Liver	8.0E 03
		Insol.	GI LLI	1.9E 03	Lungs	2.0E 03
134M-CS	1.30E-01	Sol.	GI S	1.1E 04	GI S	2.2E 04
		Insol.	GI ULI	2.2E 03	GI ULI	3.6E 03

Radionuclide	Radioactive half-life days	Solubility state	Oral intake		Intake by inhalation	
			Critical organ	Permissible quarterly intake microcuries	Critical organ	Permissible quarterly intake microcuries
134-CS	8.40E 02	Sol.	Tot. body	1.7E 01	Tot. body	2.4E 01
		Insol.	GI LLI	8.0E 01	Lungs	8.0E 00
135-CS	1.10E 09	Sol.	Liver	2.2E 02	Liver	2.9E 02
			Spleen	2.4E 02	Spleen	3.3E 02
			Tot. body	2.6E 02	Tot. body	3.6E 02
		Insol.	GI LLI	4.6E 02	Lungs	5.6E 01
136-CS	1.30E 01	Sol.	Tot. body	1.7E 02	Tot. body	2.4E 02
		Insol.	GI LLI	1.3E 02	Lungs	1.1E 02
137-CS	1.10E 04	Sol.	Tot. body	3.0E 01	Tot. body	4.0E 01
			Liver	3.6E 01		
			Spleen	4.4E 01		
			Muscle	4.8E 01		
		Insol.	GI LLI	8.8E 01	Lungs	9.1E 00
131-BA	1.16E 01	Sol.	GI LLI	3.6E 02	GI LLI	7.3E 02
		Insol.	GI LLI	3.4E 02	Lungs	2.2E 02
140-BA	1.28E 01	Sol.	GI LLI	5.2E 01	Bone	8.0E 01
		Insol.	GI LLI	5.0E 01	Lungs	2.7E 01
140-LA	1.68E 00	Sol.	GI LLI	4.8E 01	GI LLI	9.6E 01
		Insol.	GI LLI	4.8E 01	GI LLI	7.6E 01
141-CE	3.20E 01	Sol.	GI LLI	1.8E 02	Liver	2.7E 02
					GI LLI	3.6E 02
					Bone	3.6E 02
		Insol.	GI LLI	1.8E 02	Lungs	9.8E 01
143-CE	1.33E 00	Sol.	GI LLI	8.0E 01	GI LLI	1.6E 02
		Insol.	GI LLI	8.0E 01	GI LLI	1.3E 02
144-CE	2.90E 02	Sol.	GI LLI	2.4E 01	Bone	6.0E 00
		Insol.	GI LLI	2.4E 01	Lungs	4.0E 00
142-PR	8.00E-01	Sol.	GI LLI	6.0E 01	GI LLI	1.2E 02
		Insol.	GI LLI	6.0E 01	GI LLI	9.8E 01
143-PR	1.37E 01	Sol.	GI LLI	9.8E 01	GI LLI	2.0E 02
		Insol.	GI LLI	9.8E 01	Lungs	1.1E 02
144-ND	7.30E 17	Sol.	Bone	1.3E 02	Bone	5.1E-02
		Insol.	GI LLI	1.6E 02	Lungs	1.8E-01
147-ND	1.13E 01	Sol.	GI LLI	1.2E 02	Liver	2.2E 02
					GI LLI	2.4E 02
		Insol.	GI LLI	1.2E 02	Lungs	1.4E 02
149-ND	8.30E-02	Sol.	GI LLI	5.6E 02	GI LLI	1.1E 03
		Insol.	GI ULI	5.6E 02	GI ULI	9.1E 02
147-PM	9.20E 02	Sol.	GI LLI	4.4E 02	Bone	4.0E 01
		Insol.	GI LLI	4.4E 02	Lungs	6.0E 01
149-PM	2.20E 00	Sol.	GI LLI	8.8E 01	GI LLI	1.8E 02
		Insol.	GI LLI	8.8E 01	GI LLI	1.4E 02
147-SM	4.80E 13	Sol.	Bone	1.1E 02	Bone	4.4E-02
		Insol.	GI LLI	1.4E 02	Lungs	1.6E-01
151-SM	3.70E 04	Sol.	GI LLI	7.4E 02	Bone	4.0E 01
		Insol.	GI LLI	7.4E 02	Lungs	8.7E 01
153-SM	1.96E 00	Sol.	GI LLI	1.5E 02	GI LLI	3.1E 02
		Insol.	GI LLI	1.5E 02	GI LLI	2.5E 02
152M-EU	3.80E-01	Sol.	GI LLI	1.3E 02	GI LLI	2.5E 02
		Insol.	GI LLI	1.3E 02	GI LLI	2.0E 02
152-EU	4.70E 03	Sol.	GI LLI	1.5E 02	Kidneys	7.6E 00
		Insol.	GI LLI	1.5E 02	Lungs	1.1E 01
154-EU	5.80E 03	Sol.	GI LLI	4.4E 01	Kidneys	2.4E 00
					Bone	2.4E 00
		Insol.	GI LLI	4.4E 01	Lungs	4.4E 00
155-EU	6.21E 02	Sol.	GI LLI	4.0E 02	Kidneys	5.8E 01
					Bone	6.2E 01
		Insol.	GI LLI	4.0E 02	Lungs	4.5E 01
153-GD	2.36E 02	Sol.	GI LLI	4.2E 02	Bone	1.4E 02
		Insol.	GI LLI	4.2E 02	Lungs	5.6E 01
159-GD	7.50E-01	Sol.	GI LLI	1.6E 02	GI LLI	3.1E 02
		Insol.	GI LLI	1.6E 02	GI LLI	2.5E 02

Radionuclide	Radioactive half-life days	Solubility state	Oral intake		Intake by inhalation	
			Critical organ	Permissible quarterly intake microcuries	Critical organ	Permissible quarterly intake microcuries
160-TB	7.30E 01	Sol.	GI LLI	8.8E 01	Bone	6.2E 01
		Insol.	GI LLI	9.0E 01	Lungs	2.0E 01
165-DY	9.70E-02	Sol.	GI ULI	8.0E 02	GI ULI	1.6E 03
		Insol.	GI ULI	8.0E 02	GI ULI	1.3E 03
166-DY	3.40E 00	Sol.	GI LLI	7.6E 01	GI LLI	1.5E 02
		Insol.	GI LLI	7.6E 01	GI LLI	1.2E 02
166-HO	1.10E 00	Sol.	GI LLI	6.2E 01	GI LLI	1.2E 02
		Insol.	GI LLI	6.2E 01	GI LLI	1.0E 02
169-ER	9.40E 00	Sol.	GI LLI	1.9E 02	GI LLI	3.8E 02
		Insol.	GI LLI	1.9E 02	Lungs	2.4E 02
171-ER	3.10E-01	Sol.	GI ULI	2.2E 02	GI ULI	4.4E 02
		Insol.	GI ULI	2.2E 02	GI ULI	3.6E 02
170-TM	1.27E 02	Sol.	GI LLI	9.2E 01	Bone	2.2E 01
		Insol.	GI LLI	9.2E 01	Lungs	2.2E 01
171-TM	6.94E 02	Sol.	GI LLI	1.0E 03	Bone	6.9E 01
		Insol.	GI LLI	1.0E 03	Lungs	1.4E 02
175-YB	4.10E 00	Sol.	GI LLI	2.2E 02	GI LLI	4.4E 02
		Insol.	GI LLI	2.2E 02	GI LLI	3.6E 02
177-LU	6.80E 00	Sol.	GI LLI	2.0E 02	GI LLI	4.0E 02
		Insol.	GI LLI	2.0E 02	GI LLI	3.3E 02
					Lungs	4.4E 02
181-HF	4.60E 01	Sol.	GI LLI	1.4E 02	Spleen	2.4E 01
		Insol.	GI LLI	1.4E 02	Lungs	4.5E 01
182-TA	1.12E 02	Sol.	GI LLI	8.0E 01	Liver	2.4E 01
		Insol.	GI LLI	8.0E 01	Lungs	1.4E 01
181-W	1.40E 02	Sol.	GI LLI	7.2E 02	GI LLI	1.4E 03
		Insol.	GI LLI	6.4E 02	Lungs	7.8E 01
185-W	7.40E 01	Sol.	GI LLI	2.4E 02	GI LLI	4.7E 02
		Insol.	GI LLI	2.2E 02	Lungs	6.9E 01
187-W	1.00E 00	Sol.	GI LLI	1.4E 02	GI LLI	2.7E 02
		Insol.	GI LLI	1.2E 02	GI LLI	2.0E 02
183-RE	7.30E 01	Sol.	GI LLI	1.1E 03	Tot. body	1.6E 03
		Insol.	GI LLI	5.6E 02	Lungs	9.8E 01
186-RE	3.79E 00	Sol.	GI LLI	1.9E 02	GI LLI	3.8E 02
		Insol.	GI LLI	9.4E 01	GI LLI	1.5E 02
187-RE	1.80E 13	Sol.	GI LLI	5.0E 03	Skin	5.6E 03
			Skin	5.6E 03		
		Insol.	GI LLI	5.0E 03	Lungs	3.1E 02
188-RE	7.10E-01	Sol.	GI LLI	1.3E 02	GI LLI	2.5E 02
		Insol.	GI LLI	6.2E 01	GI LLI	1.0E 02
185-OS	9.50E 01	Sol.	GI LLI	1.5E 02	GI LLI	2.9E 02
		Insol.	GI LLI	1.3E 02	Lungs	2.9E 01
191M-OS	5.80E-01	Sol.	GI LLI	5.0E 03	GI LLI	1.0E 04
		Insol.	GI LLI	4.8E 03	Lungs	5.8E 03
191-OS	1.60E 01	Sol.	GI LLI	3.4E 02	GI LLI	6.7E 02
		Insol.	GI LLI	3.2E 02	Lungs	2.5E 02
193-OS	1.30E 00	Sol.	GI LLI	1.2E 02	GI LLI	2.4E 02
		Insol.	GI LLI	1.1E 02	GI LLI	1.7E 02
190-IR	1.20E 01	Sol.	GI LLI	4.0E 02	GI LLI	8.0E 02
		Insol.	GI LLI	3.6E 02	Lungs	2.5E 02
192-IR	7.45E 01	Sol.	GI LLI	8.0E 01	Kidneys	7.8E 01
		Insol.	GI LLI	7.2E 01	Lungs	1.6E 01
194-IR	7.90E-01	Sol.	GI LLI	6.8E 01	GI LLI	1.4E 02
		Insol.	GI LLI	6.0E 01	GI LLI	9.6E 01
191-PT	3.00E 00	Sol.	GI LLI	2.4E 02	GI LLI	4.7E 02
		Insol.	GI LLI	2.2E 02	GI LLI	3.5E 02
193M-PT	3.40E 00	Sol.	GI LLI	2.2E 03	GI LLI	4.4E 03
		Insol.	GI LLI	2.0E 03	GI LLI	3.3E 03
					Lungs	4.0E 03
193-PT	1.80E 05	Sol.	Kidneys	1.9E 03	Kidneys	6.4E 02
		Insol.	GI LLI	3.0E 03	Lungs	2.0E 02

Radionuclide	Radioactive half-life days	Solubility state	Oral intake Critical organ	Oral intake Permissible quarterly intake microcuries	Intake by inhalation Critical organ	Intake by inhalation Permissible quarterly intake microcuries
197M-PT	5.60E-02	Sol.	GI ULI	2.0E 03	GI ULI	4.0E 03
		Insol.	GI ULI	1.9E 03	GI ULI	2.9E 03
197-PT	7.50E-01	Sol.	GI LLI	2.4E 02	GI LLI	4.7E 02
		Insol.	GI LLI	2.2E 02	GI LLI	3.5E 02
196-AU	5.60E 00	Sol.	GI LLI	3.2E 02	GI LLI	6.4E 02
		Insol.	GI LLI	3.0E 02	Lungs	3.8E 02
198-AU	2.70E 00	Sol.	GI LLI	1.0E 02	GI LLI	2.0E 02
		Insol.	GI LLI	9.2E 01	GI LLI	1.5E 02
199-AU	3.15E 00	Sol.	GI LLI	3.4E 02	GI LLI	6.7E 02
		Insol.	GI LLI	3.2E 02	GI LLI	5.1E 02
197M-HG	1.00E 00	Sol.	Kidneys	3.8E 02	Kidneys	4.5E 02
		Insol.	GI LLI	3.4E 02	GI LLI	5.3E 02
197-HG	2.70E 00	Sol.	Kidneys	6.0E 02	Kidneys	7.3E 02
		Insol.	GI LLI	9.8E 02	GI LLI	1.5E 03
203-HG	4.58E 01	Sol.	Kidneys	3.6E 01	Kidneys	4.4E 01
		Insol.	GI LLI	2.2E 02	Lungs	7.8E 01
200-TL	1.13E 00	Sol.	GI LLI	8.8E 02	GI LLI	1.6E 03
		Insol.	GI LLI	4.4E 02	GI LLI	7.1E 02
201-TL	3.00E 00	Sol.	GI LLI	6.2E 02	GI LLI	1.2E 03
		Insol.	GI LLI	3.4E 02	GI LLI	5.5E 02
202-TL	1.20E 01	Sol.	GI LLI	2.4E 02	GI LLI	4.7E 02
		Insol.	GI LLI	1.4E 02	Lungs	1.5E 02
204-TL	1.10E 03	Sol.	GI LLI	2.2E 02	Kidneys	3.8E 02
					GI LLI	4.4E 02
		Insol.	GI LLI	1.2E 02	Lungs	1.6E 01
203-PB	2.17E 00	Sol.	GI LLI	7.8E 02	GI LLI	1.6E 03
		Insol.	GI LLI	7.0E 02	GI LLI	1.1E 03
210-PB	7.10E 03	Sol.	Tot. body	2.4E-01	Kidneys	7.8E-02
			Kidneys	2.8E-01		
		Insol.	GI LLI	3.6E 02	Lungs	1.5E-01
212-PB	4.40E-01	Sol.	GI LLI	3.8E 01	Kidneys	1.1E 01
			Kidneys	4.0E 01		
		Insol.	GI LLI	3.4E 01	Lungs	1.2E 01
206-BI	6.40E 00	Sol.	GI LLI	7.6E 01	Kidneys	1.2E 02
		Insol.	GI LLI	7.6E 01	Lungs	9.1E 01
207-BI	2.90E 03	Sol.	GI LLI	1.3E 02	Kidneys	1.1E 02
		Insol.	GI LLI	1.3E 02	Lungs	8.6E 00
210-BI	5.00E 00	Sol.	GI LLI	8.2E 01	Kidneys	4.0E 00
		Insol.	GI LLI	8.2E 01	Lungs	3.6E 00
212-BI	4.20E-02	Sol.	GI S	7.0E 02	Kidneys	6.0E 01
		Insol.	GI S	7.0E 02	Lungs	1.3E 02
210-PO	1.38E 02	Sol.	Spleen	1.4E 00	Spleen	3.1E-01
					Kidneys	3.1E-01
		Insol.	GI LLI	5.8E 01	Lungs	1.3E-01
211-AT	3.00E-01	Sol.	Thyroid	3.4E 00	Thyroid	4.4E 00
			Ovaries	3.4E 00		
		Insol.	GI ULI	1.5E 02	Lungs	2.2E 01
220-RN[3]	6.40E-04				Lungs	1.8E 02
222-RN[3]	3.82E 00				Lungs	1.8E 01
223-RA	1.17E 01	Sol.	Bone	1.4E 00	Bone	1.1E 00
		Insol.	GI LLI	8.4E 00	Lungs	1.5E-01
224-RA	3.64E 00	Sol.	Bone	4.6E 00	Bone	3.5E 00
		Insol.	GI LLI	1.1E 01	Lungs	4.5E-01
226-RA	5.90E 05	Sol.	Bone	2.4E-02	Bone	1.8E-02
		Insol.	GI LLI	6.4E 01	Lungs	3.3E-02
228-RA	2.40E 03	Sol.	Bone	5.6E-02	Bone	4.2E-02
		Insol.	GI LLI	5.0E 01	Lungs	2.4E-02
227-AC	8.00E 03	Sol.	Bone	3.8E 00	Bone	1.5E-03
		Insol.	GI LLI	6.0E 01	Lungs	1.6E-02
228-AC	2.60E-01	Sol.	GI ULI	1.7E 02	Liver	4.7E 01
					Bone	5.3E 01
		Insol.	GI ULI	1.7E 02	Lungs	1.1E 01

Radionuclide	Radioactive half-life days	Solubility state	Oral intake		Intake by inhalation	
			Critical organ	Permissible quarterly intake microcuries	Critical organ	Permissible quarterly intake microcuries
227-TH	1.84E 01	Sol.	GI LLI	3.6E 01	Bone	2.2E-01
		Insol.	GI LLI	3.6E 01	Lungs	1.1E-01
228-TH	7.00E 02	Sol.	Bone	1.5E 01	Bone	5.6E-03
		Insol.	GI LLI	2.6E 01	Lungs	3.8E 03
230-TH	2.90E 07	Sol.	Bone	3.4E 00	Bone	1.4E-03
		Insol.	GI LLI	6.4E 01	Lungs	6.4E-03
231-TH	1.07E 00	Sol.	GI LLI	4.6E 02	GI LLI	9.3E 02
		Insol.	GI LLI	4.6E 02	GI LLI	7.5E 02
232-TH	5.10E 12	Sol.	Bone	3.0E 00	Bone	1.2E-03[4]
		Insol.	GI LLI	7.6E 01	Lungs	7.3E-03
234-TH	2.41E 01	Sol.	GI LLI	3.4E 01	Bone	3.6E 01
		Insol.	GI LLI	3.4E 01	Lungs	2.0E 01
NAT-TH[5]		Sol.	Bone	2.6E 00	Bone	1.0E-03[4]
		Insol.	GI LLI	1.9E 01	Lungs	2.5E-03
230-PA	1.77E 01	Sol.	GI LLI	4.8E 02	Bone	1.1E 00
		Insol.	GI LLI	5.0E 02	Lungs	4.9E-01
231-PA	1.30E 07	Sol.	Bone	1.7E 00	Bone	7.1E-04
		Insol.	GI LLI	5.4E 01	Lungs	6.7E-02
233-PA	2.74E 01	Sol.	GI LLI	2.4E 02	Kidneys	3.8E 02
		Insol.	GI LLI	2.4E 02	Lungs	1.1E 02
230-U	2.08E 01	Sol.	Kidneys	4.8E 00	Kidneys	1.8E-01
		Insol.	GI LLI	9.2E 00	Lungs	7.1E-02
232-U	2.70E 04	Sol.	Bone	1.7E 00	Bone	6.4E-02
		Insol.	GI LLI	5.8E 01	Lungs	1.7E-02
233-U	5.90E 07	Sol.	Bone	8.4E 00	Bone	3.3E-01
		Insol.	GI LLI	6.4E 01	Lungs	7.5E-02
234-U	9.10E 07	Sol.	Bone	8.6E 00	Bone	3.5E-01
		Insol.	GI LLI	6.4E 01	Lungs	7.5E-02
235-U[5]	2.60E 11	Sol.	Kidneys	7.4E 00	Kidneys	2.9E-01
					Bone	3.6E-01
		Insol.	GI LLI	5.6E 01	Lungs	8.0E-02
236-U[5]	8.70E 09	Sol.	Bone	9.0E 00	Bone	3.6E-01
		Insol.	GI LLI	6.8E 01	Lungs	7.8E-02
238-U[5]	1.60E 12	Sol.	Kidneys	1.2E 00	Kidneys	4.5E-02
		Insol.	GI LLI	7.0E 01	Lungs	8.6E-02
240-U	5.88E-01	Sol.	GI LLI	6.8E 01	GI LLI	1.4E 02
		Insol.	GI LLI	6.8E 01	GI LLI	1.1E 02
NAT-U[5]		Sol.	Kidneys	1.2E 00	Kidneys	4.5E-02
		Insol.	GI LLI	3.2E 01	Lungs	4.0E-02
237-NP	8.00E 08	Sol.	Bone	6.2E 00	Bone	2.5E-03
		Insol.	GI LLI	7.0E 01	Lungs	7.5E-02
239-NP	2.33E 00	Sol.	GI LLI	2.6E 02	GI LLI	5.3E 02
		Insol.	GI LLI	2.6E 02	GI LLI	4.2E 02
238-PU	3.30E 04	Sol.	Bone	1.0E 01	Bone	1.2E-03
		Insol.	GI LLI	5.6E 01	Lungs	2.2E-02
239-PU	8.90E 06	Sol.	Bone	9.0E 00	Bone	1.1E-03
		Insol.	GI LLI	5.8E 01	Lungs	2.4E-02
240-PU	2.40E 06	Sol.	Bone	9.0E 00	Bone	1.1E-03
		Insol.	GI LLI	5.8E 01	Lungs	2.4E-02
241-PU	4.80E 03	Sol.	Bone	4.6E 02	Bone	5.6E-02
		Insol.	GI LLI	2.6E 03	Lungs	2.4E 01
242-PU	1.40E 08	Sol.	Bone	9.4E 00	Bone	1.1E-03
		Insol.	GI LLI	6.2E 01	Lungs	2.4E-02
243-PU	2.08E 01	Sol.	GI LLI	6.8E 02	GI ULI	1.1E 03
		Insol.	GI ULI	6.8E 02	GI ULI	1.4E 03
244-PU	2.80E 10	Sol.	Bone	8.6E 00	Bone	1.0E-03
		Insol.	GI LLI	2.2E 01	Lungs	2.0E-02
241-AM	1.70E 05	Sol.	Kidneys	7.6E 00	Bone	3.6E-03
					Kidneys	3.8E-03
		Insol.	GI LLI	5.4E 01	Lungs	6.4E-02
242M-AM	5.60E 04	Sol.	Bone	8.8E 00	Bone	3.5E-03

Radionuclide	Radioactive half-life days	Solubility state	Oral intake		Intake by inhalation	
			Critical organ	Permissible quarterly intake microcuries	Critical organ	Permissible quarterly intake microcuries
		Insol.	GI LLI	1.8E 02	Lungs	1.6E-01
242-AM	6.77E-01	Sol.	GI LLI	2.6E 02	Liver	2.4E 01
		Insol.	GI LLI	2.6E 02	Lungs	2.9E 01
243-AM	2.90E 06	Sol.	Bone	8.8E 00	Bone	3.5E-03
					Kidneys	3.8E-03
		Insol.	GI LLI	5.6E 01	Lungs	6.7E-02
244-AM	1.81E-02	Sol.	GI SI	9.6E 03	Bone	2.5E 03
					Kidneys	2.7E 03
		Insol.	GI SI	9.6E 03	Lungs	1.5E 04
					GI(SI)	1.5E 04
242-CM	1.62E 02	Sol.	GI LLI	4.8E 01	Liver	7.5E-02
		Insol.	GI LLI	5.0E 01	Lungs	1.0E-01
243-CM	1.30E 04	Sol.	Bone	1.0E 01	Bone	4.0E-03
		Insol.	GI LLI	5.0E 01	Lungs	6.2E-02
244-CM	6.70E 03	Sol.	Bone	1.4E 01	Bone	5.6E-03
		Insol.	GI LLI	5.2E 01	Lungs	6.2E-02
245-CM	7.30E 06	Sol.	Bone	7.0E 00	Bone	2.9E-03
		Insol.	GI LLI	5.6E 01	Lungs	6.7E-02
246-CM	2.40E 06	Sol.	Bone	7.2E 00	Bone	2.9E-03
		Insol.	GI LLI	5.6E 01	Lungs	6.6E-02
247-CM	3.30E 10	Sol.	Bone	7.2E 00	Bone	2.9E-03
		Insol.	GI LLI	4.4E 01	Lungs	6.7E-02
248-CM	1.70E 08	Sol.	Bone	8.8E-01	Bone	3.6E-04
		Insol.	GI LLI	2.6E 00	Lungs	8.2E-03
249-CM	4.40E-02	Sol.	GI S	4.4E 03	Bone	7.8E 03
		Insol.	GI S	4.4E 03	GI S	7.1E 03
249-BK	2.90E 02	Sol.	GI LLI	1.2E 03	Bone	5.8E-01
		Insol.	GI LLI	1.2E 03	Lungs	7.5E 01
250-BK	1.34E-01	Sol.	GI ULI	4.4E 02	Bone	9.1E 01
		Insol.	GI ULI	4.4E 02	GI ULI	7.1E 02
249-CF	1.70E 05	Sol.	Bone	8.2E 00	Bone	9.8E-04
		Insol.	GI LLI	4.8E 01	Lungs	6.2E-02
250-CF	3.70E 03	Sol.	Bone	2.6E 01	Bone	3.1E-03
		Insol.	GI LLI	5.0E 01	Lungs	6.2E-02
251-CF	2.90E 05	Sol.	Bone	8.6E 00	Bone	1.0E-03
		Insol.	GI LLI	5.2E 01	Lungs	6.2E-02
252-CF	8.03E 02	Sol.	GI LLI	1.5E 01	Bone	4.0E-03
		Insol.	GI LLI	1.5E 01	Lungs	2.0E-02
253-CF	1.80E 01	Sol.	GI LLI	2.8E 02	Bone	5.3E-01
		Insol.	GI LLI	2.8E 02	Lungs	4.7E-01
254-CF	5.60E 01	Sol.	GI LLI	2.4E-01	Bone	3.3E-03
		Insol.	GI LLI	2.4E-01	Lungs	3.1E-03
253-ES	2.00E 01	Sol.	GI LLI	4.6E 01	Bone	4.7E-01
		Insol.	GI LLI	4.6E 01	Lungs	3.8E-01
254M-ES	1.60E 00	Sol.	GI LLI	3.8E 01	Bone	3.3E 00
		Insol.	GI LLI	3.8E 01	Lungs	3.6E 00
254-ES	4.80E 02	Sol.	GI LLI	2.8E 01	Bone	1.2E-02
		Insol.	GI LLI	2.8E 01	Lungs	6.7E-02
255-ES	3.00E 01	Sol.	GI LLI	5.6E 01	Bone	3.1E-01
		Insol.	GI LLI	5.6E 01	Lungs	2.5E-01
254-FM	1.35E-01	Sol.	GI ULI	2.4E 02	Bone	4.0E 01
		Insol.	GI ULI	2.4E 02	Lungs	4.4E 01
255-FM	8.96E-01	Sol.	GI LLI	6.6E 01	Bone	1.0E 01
		Insol.	GI LLI	6.6E 01	Lungs	6.7E 00
256-FM	1.11E-01	Sol.	GI ULI	1.8E 00	Bone	1.7E 00
		Insol.	GI ULI	1.8E 00	Lungs	1.1E 00

[1] These quarterly intakes are calculated from values of (MPC)$_a$ and (MPC)$_w$ recommended by the NCRP for occupational exposure (see NBS Handbook 69 and NCRP Report No. 32)* except for uranium, ^{90}Sr, and certain transuranic isotopes given by the ICRP (see ICRP Publications 2 and 6).** Specifically, except where indicated in the footnotes, the quarterly intakes are calculated to two-digit accuracy as $91 \times 2 \times 10^7 \times$ (MPC)$_a$ and $91 \times 2200 \times$ (MPC)$_w$ where $91 \sim$ days/quarter, $2 \times 10^7 \sim$ cc of air breathed/day, 2200 $\sim$ cc of water intake/day, and (MPC)$_a$, (MPC)$_w$ are μCi/cc of air and water recommended as limits for occupational exposure for the 168-hour week. These quarterly intakes are calculated for standard adult man and would be expected to deliver a total dose (= dose commitment) to the critical organ of 1/4 the maximum permissible annual dose (MPD) recommended as limiting by the NCRP for

occupational exposure. These limiting MPD are the following: Bone, skin, thyroid—MPD = 30 rem; blood-forming organs, lenses of the eyes, gonads—MPD = 5 rem/yr; other organs—MPD = 15 rem/yr. These limits are not appropriate for exposure of the population or, specifically, for persons below the age of 18 years. For more detailed information on appropriate exposure limits recommended by the NCRP, see NBS Handbook 69 and NCRP Report No. 32.*

The abbreviations GI, S, SI, ULI, and LLI refer to gastrointestinal tract, stomach, small intestine, upper large intestine, and lower large intestine, respectively.

With few exceptions, the above intakes do not take account of chemical toxicity which should be considered separately.

[2] This intake includes absorption through the skin (see ICRP Publication 2, p. 22).**

[3] The daughter isotopes of ^{220}Rn and ^{222}Rn are assumed present to the extent they occur in unfiltered air (see NBS Handbook 69, p. 12).* For all other isotopes, the daughter elements are not considered as part of the intake and if present must be considered on the basis of the rules for mixtures.

[4] These are provisional values for ^{232}Th and nat-Th (see footnote, p. 83, NBS Handbook 69).*

[5] A curie of natural uranium is here considered to correspond to 2.94 g and a curie of natural thorium to 9.0 g of these materials (see NBS Handbook 69, p. 14).* For soluble nat-U, ^{238}U, ^{236}U, and ^{235}U these limits are based on considerations of chemical toxicity (see ICRP Publication 6, p. 13).**

* NBS Handbook 69, *Maximum Permissible Body Burdens and Maximum Permissible Concentrations of Radionuclides in Air and Water for Occupational Exposure*, 1959 (available from the Superintendent of Documents, U.S. Government Printing Office, Washington, D.C. 20402). NCRP Report No. 32, *Radiation Protection in Educational Institutions*, 1966 (NCRP Publications, P.O. Box 4867, Washington, D.C. 20008).

** *Recommendations of the International Commission on Radiological Protection*, ICRP Publication 2 (Pergamon Press, London, 1959) or with the bibliography, *Healthy Phys.* 3, 1–380 (June 1960); ICRP Publication 6 (A Pergamon Press Book, 1964, distributed by The Macmillan Co., New York).

CRYOGENIC PROPERTIES OF GASES

Property and Conditions		He	Ne	Ar	Kr	Xe	H_2	CH_4	NH_3	N_2	O_2	F_2
Density	32F, 1 atm, lb/ft³	0.01114	0.0562	0.1113	0.234	0.368	0.00561	0.0448	0.0481	0.0781	0.0892	0.106
	0C, 1 atm, Kg/m³	0.1784	0.9002	1.783	3.748	5.895	0.0899	0.718	0.770	1.251	1.429	1.698
Boiling Point	°F, 1 atm	-452.08	-410.89	-302.3	-242.1	-160.8	-423.2	-263.2	-28.03	-320.4	-297.35	-306.7
	°C, 1 atm	-268.934	-246.048	-185.7	-152.90	-107.1	-252.87	-164.0	-33.35	-195.8	-182.97	-188.14
Melting Point	°F, 1 atm	-458.0*	-415.6	-308.6	-249.9	-169.4	-434.5	-296.46	-107.9	-345.87	-361.1	-363.3
	°C, 1 atm	-272.2*	-248.67	-189.2	-156.6	-111.9	-259.14	-182.48	-77.7	-209.86	-218.4	-219.62
Vapor Density at Boiling Point	lb/ft³	0.999	0.593	0.368	0.518	0.606	0.0830	0.1124	0.0556	0.288	0.296	
	Kg/m³	16.002	9.499	5.895	8.289	9.707	1.329	1.8004	0.8906	4.613	4.4756	
Liquid Density at Boiling Point	lb/ft³	7.803	74.91	86.77	149.8	193.5	4.37	26.47	42.58	50.19	71.23	94.4
	Kg/m³	125.	1200.	1390	2400	3100.	70.0	424.	682.1	804.0	1142.0	1512.
Vapor Pressure of Solid at M.P.	lb/in.²		6.25	9.98	10.6	11.8	1.04	1.35	0.87	1.86	0.038	0.002
	Torrs		323	516	549	612	54	70	45.2	96.4	2.0	0.12
Heat of Vaporization at Boiling Point	BTU/lb	10.3	37.4	70.0	46.4	41.4	194.4	248.4	588.6	85.7	91.588	73.7
	Kcal/Kg	5.72	20.8	38.9	25.8	23.0	108.	138.	327.	47.6	50.88	40.9
Heat of Fusion at Melting Point	BTU/lb	1.8	7.2	12.1	7.0	5.9	25.2	26.1	152.1	11.0	5.9	5.8
	Kcal/Kg	1.0	4.0	6.7	3.9	3.3	14.0	14.5	84.0	6.1	3.27	3.2
C_p	59F, 1 atm, BTU/lb-°F or 15C, 1 atm, Kcal/Kg-°C	1.25**	0.25***	0.125	0.06***	0.04***	3.39	0.528	0.523	0.248	0.220	0.180
C_p/C_v	15-20C, 1 atm	1.66**	1.64***	1.67	1.68***	1.66***	1.41	1.31	1.31	1.40	1.40	
Critical Temperature	°F	-450.2	-379.7	-188.5	-82.7	61.9	-399.8	-116.5	270.3	-232.8	-181.3	-200.2
	°C	-267.9	-228.7	-122.5	-63.7	16.6	-239.9	-82.5	132.4	-147.1	-118.57	-129.0
Critical Pressure	lb/in.² (absolute)	33.2	394.6	705.2	798.0	855.0	188.1	672.	1639	492.3	731.4	808.3
	Kg/cm²	2.33	27.7	49.6	56.1	60.1	13.2	47.2	115.5	34.6	51.4	56.8

*at 26 atmospheres
**at -292F or -180C
***Approximate

VISCOSITY AND THERMAL CONDUCTIVITY OF NITROGEN AT CRYOGENIC TEMPERATURES

The viscosity and thermal conductivity of nitrogen gas for the temperature range 5 K–135 K have been computed from the second Chapman-Enskog approximation. Quantum effects, which become appreciable at the lower temperatures, are included by utilizing collision integrals based on quantum theory. A Lennard-Jones (12-6) potential was assumed. The computations yield viscosities about 20% lower than those predicted for the high end of this temperature range by the method of corresponding states, but the agreement is excellent when the computed values are compared with existing experimental data.

$T, °K$	η, micropoise	$\lambda, \dfrac{\mu cal}{cm\ sec\ °K}$
4.575	4.16639	1.10990
5.49	4.85525	1.29307
6.405	5.54773	1.47715
7.320	6.24722	1.63156
8.235	6.95025	1.85020
9.15	7.65067	2.03666
13.725	10.95231	2.91729
18.3	13.85738	3.69313
22.875	16.55204	4.41068
27.45	19.21670	5.11847
32.025	21.9423	5.84208
36.60	24.7606	6.59077
41.175	27.67445	7.36545
45.75	30.67422	8.16348
54.9	36.8747	9.81383
64.05	43.2469	11.51005
82.35	56.14634	14.94298
91.5	62.54767	16.64610
137.25	92.96598	24.74580

From Pearson, W. E., NASA Technical Note D-7565, National Aeronautics and Space Administration, 1974 (available from Superintendent of Documents, U.S. Government Printing Office, Washington, D.C.).

DEFINITIVE RULES FOR NOMENCLATURE OF ORGANIC CHEMISTRY

IUPAC 1957 Rules.

Section A. Hydrocarbons

Section B. Fundamental Heterocyclic Systems

These rules are taken from 'Definitive Rules for the Nomenclature of Organic Chemistry' which were adopted unanimously by the Commission on Nomenclature and by The Council of the International Union of Pure and Applied Chemistry at Paris 1957, and subsequently published by Butterworths Scientific Publications on behalf of the Union. The extracts are printed here by permission of the Union and of Butterworths Scientific Publications. Future 'tentative' rules will be published in the Bulletin of the Union, and when made 'definitive' in its Journal 'Pure and Applied Chemistry.'

RULES

A. HYDROCARBONS

Acyclic Hydrocarbons

A-1

1.1.—The first four saturated unbranched acyclic hydrocarbons are called methane, ethane, propane and butane. Names of the higher members of this series consist of a numerical prefix and the termination "-ane." Examples of these numerical prefixes are shown in the table below. The generic name of saturated acyclic hydrocarbons (branched or unbranched) is "alkane."

Examples:

n		n		n		n	
1	Methane	12	Dodecane	22	Docosane	32	Dotriacontane
2	Ethane	13	Tridecane	23	Tricosane	33	Tritriacontane
3	Propane	14	Tetradecane	24	Tetracosane	40	Tetracontane
4	Butane	15	Pentadecane	25	Pentacosane	50	Pentacontane
5	Pentane	16	Hexadecane	26	Hexacosane	60	Hexacontane
6	Hexane	17	Heptadecane	27	Heptacosane	70	Heptacontane
7	Heptane	18	Octadecane	28	Octacosane	80	Octacontane
8	Octane	19	Nonadecane	29	Nonacosane	90	Nonacontane
9	Nonane	20	Eicosane	30	Triacontane	100	Hectane
10	Decane	21	Heneicosane	31	Hentriacontane	132	Dotriacontahectane
11	Undecane						

1.2.—Univalent radicals derived from saturated unbranched acyclic hydrocarbons by removal of hydrogen from a terminal carbon atom are named by replacing the ending "-ane" of the name of the hydrocarbon by "-yl." The carbon atom with the free valence is numbered as 1. As a class, these radicals are called normal, or unbranched-chain, alkyls.

Examples:

Pentyl $\overset{5}{C}H_3-\overset{4}{C}H_2-\overset{3}{C}H_2-\overset{2}{C}H_2-\overset{1}{C}H_2-$

Undecyl $\overset{11}{C}H_3-[\overset{10-2}{C}H_2]_9-\overset{1}{C}H_2-$

A-2

2.1.—A saturated branched acyclic hydrocarbon is named by prefixing the designations of the side chains to the name of the longest chain present in the formula.

Example:

$$\overset{5}{C}H_3-\overset{4}{C}H_2-\overset{3}{C}H-\overset{2}{C}H_2-\overset{1}{C}H_3$$
$$|$$
$$CH_3$$

3-Methylpentane

DEFINITIVE RULES FOR NOMENCLATURE OF ORGANIC CHEMISTRY

These names are retained for unsubstituted hydrocarbons only

Isobutane	$(CH_3)_2CH—CH_3$
Isopentane	$(CH_3)_2CH—CH_2—CH_3$
Neopentane	$(CH_3)_4C$
Isohexane	$(CH_3)_2CH—CH_2—CH_2—CH_3$

Chemical Abstracts index names for the above compounds are 2-methylpropane, 2-methylbutane, 2,2-dimethylpropane, and 2-methylpentane.

2.2. The longest chain is numbered from one end to the other by arabic numerals, the direction being so chosen as to give the lowest numbers possible to the side chains. When series of locants containing the same number of terms are compared term by term, that series is "lowest" which contains the lowest number on the occasion of the first difference. This principle is applied irrespective of the nature of the substituents.

Examples:

$$\overset{5}{C}H_3—\overset{4}{C}H_2—\overset{3}{C}H—\overset{2}{C}H_2—\overset{1}{C}H_3$$
$$| $$
$$CH_3$$

3-Methylpentane

$$\overset{6}{C}H_3—\overset{5}{C}H—\overset{4}{C}H_2—\overset{3}{C}H—\overset{2}{C}H—\overset{1}{C}H_3$$
$$\qquad |\qquad\qquad |\quad\;\; |$$
$$\qquad CH_3\qquad\; CH_3\; CH_3$$

2,3,5-Trimethylhexane (not 2,4,5-Trimethylhexane)

$$\overset{10}{C}H_3—\overset{9}{C}H_2—\overset{8}{C}H—\overset{7}{C}H—\overset{6}{C}H_2—\overset{5}{C}H_2—\overset{4}{C}H_2—\overset{3}{C}H_2—\overset{2}{C}H—\overset{1}{C}H_3$$
$$\qquad\qquad |\qquad |\qquad\qquad\qquad\qquad\qquad\quad |$$
$$\qquad\qquad CH_3\;\; CH_3\qquad\qquad\qquad\qquad\quad\; CH_3$$

2,7,8-Trimethyldecane (not 3,4,9-Trimethyldecane)

$$\overset{9}{C}H_3—\overset{8}{C}H_2—\overset{7}{C}H_2—\overset{6}{C}H_2\;\;\overset{5}{C}H\;\;\overset{4}{C}H\;\;\overset{3}{C}H_2—\overset{2}{C}H_2—\overset{1}{C}H_3$$
$$\qquad\qquad\qquad\qquad\qquad |\qquad |$$
$$\qquad\qquad\qquad\qquad\; CH_3\;\; CH_2—CH_2—CH_3$$

5-Methyl-4-propylnonane (not 5-Methyl-6-propylnonane since 4,5 is lower than 5,6)

2.25.—Univalent branched radicals derived from alkanes are named by prefixing the designation of the side chains to the name of the unbranched alkyl radical possessing the longest possible chain starting from the carbon atom with the free valence, the starting atom being numbered as 1.

Examples:

1-Methylpentyl	$\overset{5}{C}H_3\overset{4}{C}H_2\overset{3}{C}H_2\overset{2}{C}H_2\overset{1}{C}H(CH_3)—$
2-Methylpentyl	$CH_3CH_2CH_2CH(CH_3)CH_2—$
5-Methylhexyl	$(CH_3)_2CHCH_2CH_2CH_2CH_2—$

These names are retained for the unsubstituted radicals only

Isopropyl	$(CH_3)_2CH—$
Isobutyl	$(CH_3)_2CHCH_2—$
sec-Butyl	$CH_3CH_2CH—$
	$\qquad\qquad\quad |$
	$\qquad\qquad\; CH_3$
tert-Butyl	$(CH_3)_3C—$
Isopentyl	$(CH_3)_2CHCH_2CH_2—$
Neopentyl	$(CH_3)_3CCH_2—$
	$\qquad\qquad\; CH_3$
	$\qquad\qquad\quad |$
tert-Pentyl	$CH_3CH_2C—$
	$\qquad\qquad\quad |$
	$\qquad\qquad\; CH_3$
Isohexyl	$(CH_3)_2CHCH_2CH_2CH_2—$

2.3. If two or more side chains of different nature are present, they may be cited (a) in order of increasing complexity or (b) in alphabetical order.

(a) The side chains are arranged in order of increasing complexity by applying the following criteria in series until a decision is reached:

(i) The less complex is that containing the smaller total number of carbon atoms.

Examples:

$$CH_3$$
$$|$$
$$CH_3—C—\quad\text{ less complex than}$$
$$|$$
$$CH_3$$

$$\overset{5}{C}H_3\;\;\overset{4}{C}H_2\;\;\overset{3}{C}H_2\;\;\overset{2}{C}H_2—\overset{1}{C}H_2—$$

(ii) The less complex is that containing the longer straight chain.

Example:

$$\overset{4}{C}H_3-\overset{3}{C}H_2-\overset{2}{C}H-\overset{1}{C}H_2-\ \ (CH_3)\quad \text{less complex than}\quad \overset{3}{C}H_3-\overset{2}{C}-\overset{1}{C}H_2-\ \ (CH_3,\ CH_3)$$

(iii) The less complex is that whose longest substituent has the lower locant.

Example:

$$\overset{5}{C}H_3-\overset{4}{C}H_2-\overset{3}{C}H-\overset{2}{C}H-\overset{1}{C}H_2-\ \ (CH_3,\ CH_3\ CH_2)\quad \text{less complex than}\quad \overset{5}{C}H_3-\overset{4}{C}H_2-\overset{3}{C}H-\overset{2}{C}H-\overset{1}{C}H_2-\ \ (CH_3,\ CH_2\ CH_3)$$

(iv) The less complex is that whose next longest substituent has the lower locant.

Example:

$$\overset{5}{C}H_3-\overset{4}{C}H_2-\overset{3}{C}H-\overset{2}{C}H-\overset{1}{C}H_2-\ \ (CH_3,\ CH_2\ CH_3)\quad \text{less complex than}\quad \overset{5}{C}H_3-\overset{4}{C}H-\overset{3}{C}H-\overset{2}{C}H_2-\overset{1}{C}H_2-\ \ (CH_3,\ CH_3\ CH_2)$$

(v) The less complex is that which is the more saturated.

Example:

$$\overset{3}{C}H_3-\overset{2}{C}H_2-\overset{1}{C}H_2-\quad \text{less complex than}\quad \overset{3}{C}H_3-\overset{2}{C}H=\overset{1}{C}H-$$

(vi) The less complex is that whose multiple linkage has the lower locant.

Example:

$$\overset{3}{C}H_3-\overset{2}{C}H=\overset{1}{C}H-\quad \text{less complex than}\quad \overset{3}{C}H_2=\overset{2}{C}H-\overset{1}{C}H_2-$$

(b) The alphabetical order is decided as follows:

(i) The names of simple radicals are first alphabetized and the multiplying prefixes are then inserted.

Example:

$$\overset{7}{C}H_3-\overset{6}{C}H_2-\overset{5}{C}H_2-\overset{4}{C}H-\overset{3}{C}-\overset{2}{C}H_2-\overset{1}{C}H_3$$

ethyl is cited before methyl, thus 4-Ethyl-3,3-dimethylheptane

(ii) The name of a complex radical is considered to begin with the first letter of its complete name.

Example:

$$\overset{13}{C}H_3-\overset{12-8}{[CH_2]_5}-\overset{7}{C}H-\overset{6}{C}H_2-\overset{5}{C}H-\overset{4}{C}H_2-\overset{3}{C}H_2-\overset{2}{C}H_2-\overset{1}{C}H_3$$

dimethylpentyl (as a complete single substituent) is alphabetized under "d," thus
7-(1,2-Dimethylpentyl)-5-ethyltridecane

(iii) In cases where complex radicals are composed of identical words, priority for citation is given to that radical which contains the lowest locant at the first cited point of difference in the radical.

Example:

$$\overset{13}{C}H_3-\overset{12-9}{[CH_2]_4}-\overset{8}{C}H-\overset{7}{C}H_2-\overset{6}{C}H-\overset{5}{C}H_2-\overset{4}{C}H_2-\overset{3}{C}H_2-\overset{2}{C}H_2-\overset{1}{C}H_3$$

6-(1-Methylbutyl)-8-(2-methylbutyl)tridecane

Chemical Abstracts has long been a proponent of the alphabetical order for prefixes. The alphabetical order as given in **A-2.3(b)** is the order used by *Chemical Abstracts*.

2.4.—If two or more side chains are in equivalent positions, the one to be assigned the lower number is that cited first in the name, whether the order of citation is based on complexity or on the alphabetical order.

Examples:

(a) Order based on complexity

$$\overset{8}{C}H_3-\overset{7}{C}H_2-\overset{6}{C}H_2-\overset{5}{C}H-\overset{4}{C}H-\overset{3}{C}H_2-\overset{2}{C}H_2-\overset{1}{C}H_3$$
$$\qquad\qquad\qquad CH_3-CH_2\ \ CH_3$$

4-Methyl-5 ethyloctane

(b) Alphabetical order

$$\overset{8}{C}H_3-\overset{7}{C}H_2-\overset{6}{C}H_2-\overset{5}{C}H-\overset{4}{C}H-\overset{3}{C}H_2-\overset{2}{C}H_2-\overset{1}{C}H_3$$
$$\qquad\qquad\qquad CH_3\ \ CH_2-CH_3$$

4 Ethyl-5-methyloctane

$$\overset{8}{C}H_3-\overset{7}{C}H_2-\overset{6}{C}H_2-\overset{5}{C}H-\overset{4}{C}H-\overset{3}{C}H_2-\overset{2}{C}H_2-\overset{1}{C}H_3$$
$$\qquad\qquad\qquad CH_3-CH\ \ CH_2$$
$$\qquad\qquad\qquad\qquad CH_3\ \ CH_2-CH_3$$

4-Propyl-5-isopropyloctane

$$\overset{8}{C}H_3-\overset{7}{C}H_2-\overset{6}{C}H_2-\overset{5}{C}H-\overset{4}{C}H-\overset{3}{C}H_2-\overset{2}{C}H_2-\overset{1}{C}H_3$$
$$\qquad\qquad\qquad CH_2\ \ CH-CH_3$$
$$\qquad\qquad\qquad CH_3-CH_2\ \ CH_3$$

4-Isopropyl-5-propyloctane

2.5.—The presence of identical unsubstituted radicals is indicated by the appropriate multiplying prefix di-, tri-, tetra-, penta-, hexa-, hepta-, octa-, nona-, deca-, undeca-, *etc*.

Example:

$$\qquad\qquad CH_3$$
$$\overset{5}{C}H_3-\overset{4}{C}H_2-\overset{3}{C}-\overset{2}{C}H_2-\overset{1}{C}H_3$$
$$\qquad\qquad CH_3$$

3,3-Dimethylpentane

The presence of identical radicals each substituted in the same way may be indicated by the appropriate multiplying prefix bis-, tris-, tetrakis-, pentakis-, *etc*. The complete expression denoting a side chain may be enclosed in parentheses or the carbon atoms in side chains may be indicated by primed numbers.

Example:

$$\qquad\qquad\qquad\qquad\qquad CH_3$$
$$\qquad\qquad\qquad\overset{3*}{C}H_3-\overset{2*}{C}H_2-\overset{1*}{C}-CH_3$$
$$\overset{10}{C}H_3-\overset{9}{C}H_2-\overset{8}{C}H_2-\overset{7}{C}H_2-\overset{6}{C}H_2-\overset{5}{C}-\overset{4}{C}H_2-\overset{3}{C}H_2-\overset{2}{C}H-\overset{1}{C}H_3$$
$$\qquad\qquad\qquad\qquad\qquad CH_3-CH_2-C-CH_3\qquad\ \ CH_3$$
$$\qquad\qquad\qquad\qquad\qquad\qquad\qquad CH_3$$

(a) Use of primes and order of complexity, * indicates primed numbers: 2-Methyl-5,5-bis-1′,1′-dimethylpropyldecane.
(b) Use of parentheses and alphabetical order, * indicates unprimed numbers: 5,5-Bis(1,1-dimethylpropyl)-2-methyldecane.
(c) Use of primes and alphabetical order, * indicates unprimed numbers: 5,5-Bis-1′,1-dimethylpropyl-2-methyldecane.

Chemical Abstracts uses parentheses and the alphabetical order without primes (A-2.5(b)). *Chemical Abstracts* would name the example in (b) 2-Methyl-5,5-di-*tert*-pentyldecane.

$$\qquad\qquad\qquad\qquad\qquad CH_3$$
$$\qquad\qquad\overset{4*}{C}H_3-\overset{3*}{C}H_2-\overset{2*}{C}H_2-\overset{1*}{C}-CH_3$$
$$\overset{13}{C}H_3-[\overset{12-10}{C}H_2]_3-\overset{9}{C}H_2-\overset{8}{C}H_2-\overset{7}{C}-\overset{6}{C}H_2-\overset{5}{C}H_2-\overset{4}{C}H_2-\overset{3}{C}H_2-\overset{2}{C}H_2-\overset{1}{C}H_3$$
$$\overset{5**}{C}H_3-\overset{4**}{C}H_2-\overset{3**}{C}H_2-\overset{2**}{C}H_2-\overset{1**}{C}-CH_3$$
$$\qquad\qquad\qquad\qquad\qquad CH_3$$

(a) Use of primes and order of complexity, * indicates primed numbers, ** indicates doubly primed numbers: 7-1′,1′-Tri methylbutyl-7-1″,1″-dimethylpentyltridecane.
(b) Use of parentheses and alphabetical order, * and ** indicate unprimed numbers: 7-(1,1-Dimethylbutyl)-7-(1,1-dimethylpentyl)-tridecane

2.6.—If chains of equal length are competing for selection as main chain in a saturated branched acyclic hydrocarbon, then the choice goes in series to:

(a) The chain which has the greatest number of side chains.

Example:

$$\overset{7}{C}H_3-\overset{6}{C}H_2-\overset{5}{C}H-\overset{4}{C}H-\overset{3}{C}H-\overset{2}{C}H-\overset{1}{C}H_3$$
$$\qquad\qquad\quad CH_3\ \ CH_2\ \ CH_3\ \ CH_3$$
$$\qquad\qquad\qquad\qquad CH_2-CH_3$$

2,3,5-Trimethyl-4-propylheptane

(b) The chain whose side chains have the lowest-numbered locants.

Example:

$$\overset{7}{C}H_3-\overset{6}{C}H_2-\overset{5}{C}H-\overset{4}{C}H-\overset{3}{C}H_2-\overset{2}{C}H-\overset{1}{C}H_3$$

with substituents:
- at C5: CH_3
- at C4: CH_2 — $CH-CH_3$ — CH_3
- at C2: CH_3

4-Isobutyl-2,5-dimethylheptane

(c) The chain having the greatest number of carbon atoms in the smaller side chains.

$$CH_3CH_2\overset{}{C}H-\overset{}{C}H-\overset{}{C}H-CH_2-\overset{7}{C}...$$

13 12 11 10 9 8 7 6 5 4 3 2 1

7,7-Bis(2,4-dimethylhexyl)-3-ethyl-5,9,11-trimethyltridecane

(d) The chain having the least branched side chains.

(1) Here the choice lies between two possible main chains of equal length, each containing six side chains in the same positions. Listing in increasing order, the number of carbon atoms in the several side chains of the first choice as shown and of the alternate second choice results as follows:

first choice   1, 1, 1, 2, 8, 8
second choice   1, 1, 1, 1, 8, 9

The expression, "the greatest number of carbon atoms in the smaller side chains," is taken to mean the largest side chain at the first point of difference when the size of the side chains is examined step by step. Thus, the selection in this case is made at the fourth step where 2 is greater than 1.

6-(1-Ethylpropyl)-7-(1-pentylhexyl)tetradecane

A-3

3.1.—Unsaturated unbranched acyclic hydrocarbons having one double bond are named by replacing the ending "-ane" of the name of the corresponding saturated hydrocarbon with the ending "-ene." If there are two or more double bonds, the ending will be "-adiene," "-atriene," *etc*. The generic names of these hydrocarbons (branched or unbranched) are "alkene," "alkadiene," "alkatriene," *etc*. The chain is so numbered as to give the lowest possible numbers to the double bonds.

Examples:

2-Hexene $\overset{6}{C}H_3-\overset{5}{C}H_2-\overset{4}{C}H_2-\overset{3}{C}H=\overset{2}{C}H-\overset{1}{C}H_3$

1,4-Hexadiene $\overset{6}{C}H_3-\overset{5}{C}H=\overset{4}{C}H-\overset{3}{C}H_2-\overset{2}{C}H=\overset{1}{C}H_2$

These non-systematic names are retained

Ethylene $CH_2=CH_2$ Allene $CH_2=C=CH_2$

Chemical Abstracts retains allene for the unsubstituted hydrocarbon only.

3.2.—Unsaturated unbranched acyclic hydrocarbons having one triple bond are named by replacing the ending "-ane" of the name of the corresponding saturated hydrocarbon with the ending "-yne." If there are two or more triple bonds, the ending will be "-adiyne," "-atriyne," *etc*. The generic names of these hydrocarbons (branched or unbranched) are "alkyne," "alkadiyne," "alkatriyne," *etc*. The chain is so numbered as to give the lowest possible numbers to the triple bonds.

The name "acetylene" for $HC \equiv CH$ is retained.

3.3.—Unsaturated unbranched acyclic hydrocarbons having both double and triple bonds are named by replacing the ending "-ane" of the name of the corresponding saturated hydrocarbon with the ending "-enyne," "-adienyne," "-atrienyne," "-enediyne," *etc*. Numbers as low as possible are given to double and triple bonds even though this may at times give "-yne" a lower number than "-ene." When there is a choice in numbering the double bonds are given the lowest numbers.

Examples:

1,3-Hexadien-5-yne $\overset{6}{H}C\equiv\overset{5}{C}-\overset{4}{C}H=\overset{3}{C}H-\overset{2}{C}H=\overset{1}{C}H_2$

3-Penten-1-yne $\overset{5}{C}H_3-\overset{4}{C}H=\overset{3}{C}H-\overset{2}{C}\equiv\overset{1}{C}H$

1-Penten-4-yne $\overset{5}{H}C\equiv\overset{4}{C}-\overset{3}{C}H_2-\overset{2}{C}H=\overset{1}{C}H_2$

3.4.—Unsaturated branched acyclic hydrocarbons are named as derivatives of the unbranched hydrocarbons which contain the maximum number of double and triple bonds. If there are two or more chains competing for selection as the chain with the maximum number of unsaturated bonds, then the choice goes to (1) that one with the greatest number of carbon atoms; (2) the number of carbon atoms being equal, the one containing the maximum number of double bonds. In other respects, the same principles apply as for naming saturated branched acyclic hydrocarbons. The chain is so numbered as to give the lowest possible numbers to double and triple bonds in accordance with Rule **A-3.3.**

Examples:

3,4-Dipropyl-1,3-hexadien-5-yne

$$CH_2-CH_2-CH_3$$
$$CH\equiv\overset{6}{C}-\overset{5}{C}-\overset{3}{\overset{|}{C}}=\overset{2}{C}H=\overset{1}{C}H_2$$
$$\underset{4}{|}$$
$$CH_2-CH_2-CH_3$$

5-Ethynyl-1,3,6-heptatriene

$$\overset{7}{C}H_2=\overset{6}{C}H-\overset{5}{C}H-\overset{4}{C}H=\overset{3}{C}H-\overset{2}{C}H=CH_2$$
$$\underset{|}{}$$
$$C\equiv CH$$

5,5-Dimethyl-1-hexene

$$CH_3$$
$$\overset{6}{C}H_3-\overset{5}{\overset{|}{C}}-\overset{4}{C}H_2-\overset{3}{C}H_2-\overset{2}{C}H=\overset{1}{C}H_2$$
$$\underset{|}{}$$
$$CH_3$$

4-Vinyl-1-hepten-5-yne

$$\overset{7}{C}H_3-\overset{6}{C}\equiv\overset{5}{C}-\overset{4}{C}H-\overset{3}{C}H_2-\overset{2}{C}H=\overset{1}{C}H_2$$
$$\underset{|}{}$$
$$CH=CH_2$$

The name "isoprene" is retained for the unsubstituted compound only

$$CH_3$$
$$CH_2=CH-\overset{|}{C}=CH_2$$

3.5.—The names of univalent radicals derived from unsaturated acyclic hydrocarbons have the endings "-enyl," "-ynyl," "-dienyl," etc., the positions of the double and triple bonds being indicated where necessary. The carbon atom with the free valence is numbered as 1.

Examples:

Ethynyl	$CH\equiv C-$
2-Propynyl	$CH\equiv C-CH_2-$
1-Propenyl	$CH_3-CH=CH-$
2-Butenyl	$CH_2-CH=CH-CH_2-$
1,3-Butadienyl	$CH_2=CH-CH=CH-$
2-Pentenyl	$CH_3-CH_2-CH=CH-CH_2-$
2-Penten-4-ynyl	$CH\equiv C-CH=CH-CH_2-$

Exceptions: These names are retained

Vinyl (for ethenyl) $CH_2=CH-$
Allyl (for 2-propenyl) $CH_2=CH-CH_2-$
Isopropenyl $CH_2=C-$ (for unsubstituted radical only)
(for 1-methylvinyl) $\underset{|}{}$
               CH_3

3.6.—When there is a choice for the fundamental chain of a radical, that chain is selected which contains (1) the maximum number of double and triple bonds; (2) the largest number of carbon atoms, and (3) the largest number of double bonds.

Examples:

$$\overset{10}{C}H_3-\overset{9}{C}H=\overset{8}{C}H-\overset{7}{C}H=\overset{6}{C}H-\overset{5}{C}H-\overset{4}{C}H=\overset{3}{C}H-\overset{2}{C}\equiv\overset{1}{C}-$$
$$\underset{|}{}$$
$$CH_2-CH_2-CH=CH-CH_3$$

5-(3-Pentenyl)-3,6,8-decatrien-1-ynyl

$$\overset{12}{C}H_3—\overset{11}{C}H_2—\overset{10}{C}\equiv\overset{9}{C}—\overset{8}{C}H=\overset{7}{C}H—\overset{6}{C}H—\overset{5}{C}H=\overset{4}{C}H—\overset{3}{C}H=\overset{2}{C}H—\overset{1}{C}H_2—$$
$$\overset{}{|}$$
$$CH=CH—CH=CH—CH_3$$

6-(1,3-Pentadienyl)-2,4 7-dodecatrien-9-ynyl

$$\overset{11}{C}H_3—\overset{10}{C}H=\overset{9}{C}H—\overset{8}{C}H=\overset{7}{C}H—\overset{6}{C}H—\overset{5}{C}H=\overset{4}{C}H—\overset{3}{C}H=\overset{2}{C}H—\overset{1}{C}H_2$$
$$|$$
$$CH=CH—C\equiv C—CH_3$$

6-(1-Penten-3-ynyl)-2,4,7,9-undecatetraenyl

$$\overset{4}{C}H_3—\overset{3}{C}H=\overset{2}{C}—\overset{1}{C}H_2—$$
$$|$$
$$CH_2—CH_2—CH_2—CH_2—CH_2—CH_2—CH_2—CH_2—CH_3$$

2-Nonyl-2-butenyl

A-4

4.1.—Bivalent and trivalent radicals derived from univalent acyclic hydrocarbon radicals whose authorized names end in "-yl" by removal of one or two hydrogen atoms from the carbon atom with the free valences are named by adding "-idene" or "-idyne," respectively, to the name of the corresponding univalent radical. The carbon atom with the free valence is numbered as 1.

The name "methylene" is retained for the radical $CH_2=$.

Examples:

Methylidyne[1]	$CH\equiv$
Ethylidene	$CH_3—CH=$
Ethylidyne	$CH_3—C\equiv$
Vinylidene	$CH_2=C=$
Isopropylidene[2]	$(CH_3)_2C=$

4.2.—The names of bivalent radicals derived from normal alkanes by removal of a hydrogen atom from each of the two terminal carbon atoms of the chain are ethylene, trimethylene, tetramethylene, *etc*.

Examples:

Pentamethylene	$—CH_2—CH_2—CH_2—CH_2—CH_2—$
Hexamethylene	$—CH_2—CH_2—CH_2—CH_2—CH_2—CH_2—$

Names of the substituted bivalent radicals are derived in accordance with Rules **A-2.2** and **A-2.25**.

Example:

$$\text{Ethylethylene}\qquad —\overset{2}{C}H_2—\overset{1}{C}H—$$
$$|$$
$$CH_2—CH_3$$

The name "propylene" is retained

$$CH_3—CH—CH_2—$$
$$|$$

4.3.—Bivalent radicals similarly derived from unbranched alkenes, alkadienes, alkynes, *etc*., by removing a hydrogen atom from each of the terminals carbon atoms are named by replacing the endings "-ene," "-diene," "-yne," *etc*., of the hydrocarbon name by "-enylene," "-dienylene," "-ynylene," *etc*., the positions of the double and triple bonds being indicated where necessary.

Example:

$$\text{Propylene}\qquad —\overset{3}{C}H_2—\overset{2}{C}H=\overset{1}{C}H—$$

The name "vinylene" is retained (for ethenylene)

$$—CH=CH—$$

Names of the substituted bivalent radicals are derived in accordance with Rule **A-3.4**.

Examples:

$$\text{4 Propyl-2-pentenylene}\qquad —\overset{5}{C}H_2—\overset{4}{C}H—\overset{3}{C}H=\overset{2}{C}H—\overset{1}{C}H_2—$$
$$|$$
$$CH_2—CH_2—CH_3$$

4.4.—Trivalent, quadrivalent and higher valent acyclic hydrocarbon radicals of two or more carbon atoms with the free valences at each end of a chain are named by adding to the hydrocarbon name the

(1) The group $=CH—$ may be referred to as the "methine" group.
(2) For unsubstituted radical only.

terminations "-yl" for a single free valence, "-ylidene" for a double and "-ylidyne" for a triple free valence on the same atom (the final "e" in the name of the hydrocarbon is elided when followed by a suffix beginning with "-yl"). If different types are present in the same radical, they are cited and numbered in the order of "-yl" "-ylidene," "-ylidyne."

Examples:

Butanediylidene	$=\overset{4}{C}H-\overset{3}{C}H_2-\overset{2}{C}H_2-\overset{1}{C}H=$
Butanediylidyne	$=\overset{4}{C}-\overset{3}{C}H_2-\overset{2}{C}H_2-\overset{1}{C}=$
1-Propanyl-3-ylidene	$=\overset{3}{C}H-\overset{2}{C}H_2-\overset{1}{C}H_2-$
Propadienediylidene	$=\overset{3}{C}=\overset{2}{C}=\overset{1}{C}=$
2-Pentenediylidyne	$\equiv\overset{5}{C}-\overset{4}{C}H_2-\overset{3}{C}H=\overset{2}{C}H-\overset{1}{C}\equiv$
1-Butanyliden-4-ylidyne	$\equiv\overset{4}{C}-\overset{3}{C}H_2-\overset{2}{C}H_2-\overset{1}{C}H=$

4.5.—Multivalent radicals containing three or more carbon atoms with free valences at each end of a chain and additional free valences at intermediate carbon atoms are named by adding the ending "-triyl," "-tetrayl," "-diylidene," "diylylidene," *etc.*, to the hydrocarbon name.

Examples:

$$-\overset{3}{C}H_2-\overset{2}{C}H-\overset{1}{C}H_2- \qquad\qquad -\overset{3}{C}H_2-\overset{2}{C}-\overset{1}{C}H_2-$$

1,2,3-Propanetriyl   1,3-Propanediyl-2-ylidene

Monocyclic Hydrocarbons
A-11

11.1.—The names of saturated monocyclic hydrocarbons (with no side chains) are formed by attaching the prefix "cyclo" to the name of the acyclic saturated unbranched hydrocarbon with the same number of carbon atoms. The generic name of saturated monocyclic hydrocarbons (with or without side chains) is "cycloalkane."

Examples:

Cyclopropane   Cyclohexane

11.2.—Univalent radicals derived from cycloalkanes (with no side chains) are named by replacing the ending "-ane" of the hydrocarbon name by "-yl," the carbon atom with the free valence being numbered as 1. The generic name of these radicals is "cycloalkyl."

Examples:

Cyclopropyl   Cyclohexyl

11.3.—The names of unsaturated monocyclic hydrocarbons (with no side chains) are formed by substituting "-ene," "-adiene," "-atriene," "-yne," "-adiyne," *etc.*, for "-ane" in the name of the corresponding cycloalkane. The double and triple bonds are given numbers as low as possible as in Rule A-3.3.

Examples:

Cyclohexene   1,3-Cyclohexadiene   1-Cyclodecen-4-yne

The names "fulvene" (for methylenecyclopentadiene) and "benzene" are retained.

11.4.—The names of univalent radicals derived from unsaturated monocyclic hydrocarbons have the endings "-enyl," "-ynyl," "-dienyl," *etc.*, the positions of the double and triple bonds being indicated according to the principles of Rule **A-3.3.** The carbon atom with the free valence is numbered as 1, except as stated in the rules for terpenes(see Rules **A-72** to **A-75**).

Examples:

2-Cyclopenten-1-yl   2,4-Cyclopentadien-1-yl

The radical name "phenyl" is retained.

The point of attachment is numbered 1 and the double and triple bonds are given numbers as low as possible. The number 1 for the point of attachment is given in the radical name to emphasize the fact that the point of attachment takes precedence over the double and triple bonds (except with terpenes which have fixed numberings).

11.5.—Names of bivalent radicals derived from saturated or unsaturated monocyclic hydrocarbons by removal of two atoms of hydrogen from the same carbon atom of the ring are obtained by replacing the endings "-ane," "-ene," "-yne," by "-ylidene," "-enylidene" and "-ynylidene," respectively. The carbon atom with the free valences is numbered as 1, except as stated in the rules for terpenes.

Examples:

Cyclopentylidene   2,4-Cyclohexadien-1-ylidene

11.6.—Bivalent radicals derived from saturated or unsaturated monocyclic hydrocarbons by removing a hydrogen atom from each of two different carbon atoms of the ring are named by replacing the endings "-ane," "-ene," "-diene," "-yne," *etc.*, of the hydrocarbon name by "-ylene," "-enylene," "-dienylene," "-ynylene," *etc.*, the positions of the double and triple bonds and of the points of attachment being indicated. Preference in lowest numbers is given to the carbon atoms having the free valences.

Examples:

1,3-Cyclopentylene   3-Cyclohexen-1,2-ylene   2,5-Cyclohexadien-1,4-ylene

The name "phenylene" is retained

Phenylene (*p*-shown)

A-12

12.1.—These names for substituted monocyclic aromatic hydrocarbons are retained

CH_3—CH—CH_3

Cumene   Cymene (*p*-shown)   Mesitylene

HC=CH_2

Styrene   Toluene   Xylene (*o*-shown)

12.2.—Other substituted monocyclic aromatic hydrocarbons are named as derivatives of benzene or of one of the compounds listed in Part 1 of this rule. However, if the substituent introduced into such a compound, is identical with one already present in that compound, then the substituted compound is named as a derivative of benzene (see Rule **61.4**).

Chemical Abstracts makes certain exceptions to the last part of this rule in order to favor a larger parent, although still treating like groups alike, *e.g.*, an *ar*-methyl derivative of cymene is indexed at Cumene, dimethyl-, not at Benzene, isopropyldimethyl-.

12.3.—The position of substituents is indicated by numbers except that *o*- (*ortho*-), *m*- (*meta*-) and *p*- (*para*-) may be used in place of 1,2-, 1,3-, and 1,4-, respectively, when only two substituents are present. The lowest numbers possible are given to substituents, choice between alternatives being governed by Rule **A-2** so far as applicable, except that when names are based on those of compounds listed in Part 1 of this rule the first priority for lowest numbers is given to the substituent(s) already present in those compounds.

Examples:

1-Ethyl-4-pentylbenzene or
p-Ethylpentylbenzene

1,4-Diethyl-
benzene or *p*-
Diethyl-
benzene

4-Ethylsty-
rene or *p*-
Ethylstyrene

Chemical Abstracts limits the use of *o*-, *m*- and *p*- to like substituents when both are expressed as prefixes, *e.g.*, *p*-diethyl-benzene, 1-ethyl-4-pentylbenzene. However, when one substituent is expressed in the name, *m*-, *o*- or *p*- is used to indicate the position of the second and different substituent, *e.g.*, *o*-ethylcumene.

1,4-Divinylben-
zene or *p*-Divinyl-
benzene, not *p*-
Vinylstyrene

1,2,3-Trimethyl-
benzene, not
Methylxylene
nor Dimethyl-
toluene

1,2-Dimethyl-3-
propylbenzene
or 3-Propyl-
o-xylene

1-Ethyl-2-propyl-3-butylbenzene (Order of complexity)
or 1-Butyl-3-ethyl-2-propylbenzene (Alphabetical order)

12.4.—The generic name of monocyclic and polycyclic aromatic hydrocarbons is "arene."

A-13

13.1.—Univalent radicals derived from monocyclic aromatic hydrocarbons and having the free valence at a ring atom are given the names listed below. Such radicals not listed below are named as substituted phenyl radicals. The carbon atom having the free valence is numbered as 1.

Phenyl C_6H_5—

Cumenyl (*m*-shown)

Mesityl

Tolyl (*o*-shown)

Xylyl (2,3-shown)

13.2.—Since the name phenylene (*o*-, *m*-, or *p*-) is retained for the radical —C_6H_4— (exception to Rule **A-11.6**) bivalent radicals formed from substituted benzene derivatives and having the free valences at ring atoms are named as substituted phenylene radicals. The carbon atoms having the free valences are numbered 1,2-, 1,3-, or 1,4- as appropriate.

13.3.—These trivial names for radicals having a single free valence in the side chain are retained:

Benzyl	C_6H_5—$\overset{\alpha}{C}H_2$—
Cinnamyl	C_6H_5—$\overset{\gamma}{C}H$=$\overset{\beta}{C}H$—$\overset{\alpha}{C}H_2$—
Phenethyl	C_6H_5—$\overset{\beta}{C}H_2$—$\overset{\alpha}{C}H_2$—
Styryl	C_6H_5—$\overset{\beta}{C}H$=$\overset{\alpha}{C}H$—
Trityl	$(C_6H_5)_3C$—

Chemical Abstracts limits trityl to the unsubstituted radical.

13.4.—Multivalent radicals of aromatic hydrocarbons with free valences in the side chain are named in accordance with Rule **A-4**.

Examples:		
	Benzylidyne	C_6H_5—C=
	Cinnamylidene	C_6H_5—$\overset{\gamma}{C}H$=$\overset{\beta}{C}H$—$\overset{\alpha}{C}H$=

A-14

14.1.—The generic names of univalent and bivalent aromatic hydrocarbon radicals are "aryl" and "arylene," respectively.

Fused Polycyclic Hydrocarbons
A-21

21.1.—The names of polycyclic hydrocarbons with maximum number of non-cumulative[1] double bonds end in "-ene." The names listed on pp. 11 and 12 are retained.

21.2.—The names of hydrocarbons containing five or more fused benzene rings in a straight linear arrangement are formed from a numerical prefix as specified in Rule **A-1.1** followed by "-acene."

Examples:

Pentacene   Hexacene

The following list contains the names of polycyclic hydrocarbons which are retained (see Rule **A-21.1**).

(1) Pentalene   (2) Indene   (7) *as*-Indacene   (8) *s*-Indacene

(3) Naphthalene   (4) Azulene   (9) Acenaphthylene   (10) Fluorene

(5) Heptalene   (6) Biphenylene

(1) Cumulative double bonds are those present in a chain in which at least three contiguous carbon atoms are joined by double bonds; non-cumulative double bonds comprise every other arrangement of two or more double bonds in a single structure. The generic name "cumulene" is given to compounds containing three or more cumulative double bonds.

$$CH_2=C=C=C=CH_2$$
Cumulative
$$CH_3—CH=CH—CH=CH—CH=CH_2$$
or

Non-cumulative

(11) Phenalene (12) Phenanthrene[1] (27) Hexaphene (28) Hexacene[2]

(13) Anthracene[1] (14) Fluoranthene

(15) Acephenanthrylene (16) Aceanthrylene (29) Rubicene (30) Coronene

(17) Triphenylene (18) Pyrene (31) Trinaphthylene[3] (32) Heptaphene

(19) Chrysene (20) Naphthacene

(21) Pleiadene (22) Picene (33) Heptacene[2]

(23) Perylene (24) Pentaphene (34) Pyranthrene

(25) Pentacene[2] (26) Tetraphenylene[3] (35) Ovalene

Beginning with Volume 51 Subject Index *Chemical Abstracts* uses biphenylene in place of cyclobutadibenzene and phenalene in place of benzonaphthene. The polycyclic hydrocarbons which have the trivial names listed above may be used as the base components in naming orthofused or ortho- and peri-fused polycyclic systems for which there are no acceptable trivial names.

(1) Denotes exception to systematic numbering. See Rule A-22.5.

(2) See Rule A-21.2.

(3) For isomer shown only.

21.3.—"Ortho-fused"[4] or "ortho- and peri-fused"[5] polycyclic hydrocarbons with maximum number of noncumulative double bonds which contain at least two rings of five or more members and which have no accepted trivial name such as those of **21.1** of this Rule, are named by prefixing to the name of a component ring or ring system (the base component) designations of the other components. The base component should contain as many rings as possible (provided it has a trivial name), and should occur as far as possible from the beginning of the list of Rule **A-21.1.** The attached components should be as simple as possible.

Example:

(not Naphthophenanthrene; benzo is "simpler" than naphtho, even though there are two benzo rings and only one naphtho)

Dibenzophenanthrene

(4) Polycyclic compounds in which two rings have two, and only two, atoms in common are said to be "ortho-fused." Such compounds have n common faces and $2n$ common atoms (Example I).

(5) Polycyclic compounds in which one ring contains two, and only two, atoms in common with each of two or more rings of a contiguous series of rings are said to be "ortho- and peri-fused." Such compounds have n common faces and fewer than $2n$ common atoms (Examples II and III).

Examples:

I

II

CH₂

III

3 common faces
6 common atoms
"Ortho-fused" system

7 common faces
8 common atoms

5 common faces
6 common atoms

"Ortho- and peri-fused" systems

21.4.—The prefixes designating attached components are formed by changing the ending "-ene" of the name of the component hydrocarbon into "-eno," *e.g.*, "pyreno" (from pyrene). When more than one prefix is present, they are arranged in alphabetical order. These common abbreviated prefixes are recognized (see list in **21.1** of this Rule)

Acenaphtho	from	Acenaphthylene
Anthra	from	Anthracene
Benzo	from	Benzene
Naphtho	from	Naphthalene
Perylo	from	Perylene
Phenanthro	from	Phenanthrene

For monocyclic prefixes other than "benzo-," the following names are recognized, each to represent the form with the maximum number of non-cumulative double bonds: cyclopenta, cyclohepta, cycloocta, cyclonona, *etc.* When the base component is a monocyclic system, the ending "-ene" signifies the maximum number of noncumulative double bonds, and does not denote one double bond only.

Examples:

H₂C

1H-Cyclopentacycloöctene

Benzocycloöctene

In forming names of polycyclic systems from the above carbocyclic prefixes the final "o" or "a" of the prefix is elided before another vowel, except in the case of anthra, phenanthro and prefixes ending in -eno from which the "a" and "o" are never elided. Examples: benz[a]anthracene, cyclopent[a]acenaphthylene, anthra[1,2 − a]anthracene, fluoreno[4,3,2-de]anthracene.

The ending "-ene" to signify the maximum number of noncumulative double bonds in all fused carbocyclic systems means that the endings -diene, triene, tetraene, *etc.*, are unnecessary when the base component is a monocyclic ring of seven or more carbon atoms. Higher stages of hydrogenation are indicated by the use of the prefixes dihydro-, tetrahydro-, *etc.* (*cf.* Rule **A-23.1**). *Chemical Abstracts* follows Rules **A-21.4** and **A-23.1** instead of Alternate Rule **A-23.5.**

21.5.—Isomers are distinguished by lettering the peripheral sides of the base component *a, b, c, etc.,* beginning with "*a*" for the side "1,2," "*b*" for "2,3" (or in certain cases "2,2a") and lettering every side around the periphery. To the letter as early in the alphabet as possible, denoting the side where fusion occurs, are prefixed, if necessary, the numbers of the positions of attachment of the other component. These numbers are chosen to be as low as is consistent with the numbering of the component, and their order conforms to the direction of lettering of the base component (see Examples II and IV). When two or more prefixes refer to equivalent positions so that there is a choice of letters, the prefixes are cited in alphabetical order according to Rule **A-21.4** and the location of the first cited prefix is indicated by a letter as early as possible in the alphabet (see Example V). The numbers and letters are enclosed in brackets and placed immediately after the designation of the attached component. This expression merely defines the manner of fusion of the components.

Examples:

Benz[a]anthracene

6H-Naphtho[2,1,8,7-defg]-
naphthacene

Dibenz[a,j]anthracene
(not Naphtho[2,1-b]phenanthrene)

Indeno[1,2-a]indene

1H-Benzo[a]cyclopent[j]anthracene

The completed system consisting of the base component and the other components is then renumbered according to Rule **A-22,** the numbering of the component parts being ignored.

Naphthalene   +   Perylene   →   Naphtho[8,1,2-bcd]-
perylene

21.6.—When a name applies equally to two or more isomeric condensed parent ring systems with the maximum number of non-cumulative double bonds and when the name can be made specific by indicating the position of one or more hydrogen atoms in the structure, this is accomplished by modifying the name with a locant, followed by italic capital H for each of these hydrogen atoms. Such symbols ordinarily precede the name. The said atom or atoms are called "indicated hydrogen." The same principle is applied to radicals and compounds derived from these systems.

Examples:

3H-Fluorene

2H-Indene

A-22

22.1.—For the purposes of numbering, the individual rings of a polycyclic "ortho fused" or "ortho- and peri-fused" hydrocarbon system usually are drawn as follows:

◁ or ▷   □   ⬠ or ⬠

⬡   ⬡ or ⬡   ⬡

and the polycyclic system is oriented so that (a) the greatest number of rings are in a horizontal row and (b) a maximum number of rings are above and to the right of the horizontal row (upper right quadrant).

If two or more orientations meet these requirements, the one is chosen which has as few rings as possible in the lower left quadrant.

Correct orientation   Incorrect orientation   Incorrect orientation

The system thus oriented is numbered in a clockwise direction commencing with the carbon atom not engaged in ring-fusion in the most counterclockwise position of the uppermost ring, or if there is a choice, of the uppermost ring farthest to the right, and omitting atoms common to two or more rings.

Correct   Incorrect

22.2.—Atoms common to two or more rings are designated by adding roman letters "a," "b," "c," *etc.*, to the number of the position immediately preceding. Interior atoms follow the highest number, taking a clockwise sequence wherever there is a choice.

Examples: [*cf.* **Note** below]

Correct   Incorrect

22.3.—When there is a choice, carbon atoms common to two or more rings follow the lowest possible numbers.

Examples:

Correct   Incorrect   Correct   Incorrect

Note: I.   4, 4, 8, 9 is lower than 4, 5, 9, 9.
      II.   2, 5, 8 is lower than 3, 5, 8.
     III.   2, 3, 6, 8 is lower than 3, 4, 6, 8 or 2, 4, 7, 8.

22.4.—When there is a choice, the carbon atoms which carry an indicated hydrogen atom are numbered as low as possible.

Examples:

Correct   Incorrect

22.5.—The following are recommended exceptions to the above rules on numbering

Anthracene   Phenanthrene

Cyclopenta[a]phenanthrene
(15H- shown)
See also rules on steroids

A-23

23.1.—The names of "ortho-fused" or "ortho- and peri-fused" polycyclic hydrocarbons with less than maximum number of non-cumulative double bonds are formed from a prefix "dihydro-," "tetrahydro-," etc., followed by the name of the corresponding unreduced hydrocarbon. The prefix "perhydro-" signifies full hydrogenation. When there is a choice for H used for indicated hydrogen it is assigned the lowest available number.

Examples: Exceptions: These names are retained

1,4-Dihydro-   Perhydroanthracene   Indan   Acenaphthene   Cholanthrene
naphthalene

6,7-Dihydro-5H-benzo-   4,5,6,7,8,9-Hexahydro-   Aceanthrene   Acephenanthrene
cycloheptene   1H-cyclopentacycloöctene

16,17-Dihydro-15H-cyclopenta[a]   Violanthrene   Isoviolanthrene
phenanthrene

Chemical Abstracts follows this Rule instead of the alternate Rule 23.5.

23.2.—When there is a choice, the carbon atoms to which hydrogen atoms are added are numbered as low as possible.

Example:

Correct   Incorrect

23.3.—Substituted polycyclic hydrocarbons are named according to the same principles as substituted monocyclic hydrocarbons (see Rules **A-12** and **A-61**).

23.5 (Alternate to part of Rule **A-23.1**).—The names of "ortho-fused" polycyclic hydrocarbons which have (a) less than the maximum number of non-cumulative double bonds, (b) at least one terminal unit which is most conveniently named as an unsaturated cycloalkane derivative, and (c) a double bond at the positions where rings are fused together, may be derived by joining the name of the terminal unit to that of the other component by means of a letter "o" with elision of a terminal "e". The abbreviations for fused aromatic systems laid down in Rule **A-21.4** are used, and the exceptions of Rule **A-23.1** apply.

Examples:

1,2-Benzo-
1,3-cycloheptadiene

1,2-Cyclopenta-
1′,3′-dienocycloöctene

1,2-Cyclopentenophenanthrene

Chemical Abstracts follows Rules **A-21.4** and **A-23.1** instead of this alternate rule.

A-24

24.1.—For radicals derived from polycyclic hydrocarbons, the numbering of the hydrocarbon is retained. The point or points of attachment are given numbers as low as is consistent with the fixed numbering of the hydrocarbon.

24.2.—Univalent radicals derived from "ortho-fused" or "ortho- and peri-fused" polycyclic hydrocarbons with names ending in "-ene" by removal of a hydrogen atom from an aromatic or alicyclic ring are named in principle by changing the ending "-ene" of the names of the hydrocarbons to "-enyl."

Examples:

2-Indenyl   1-Pyrenyl   1-Acenaphthenyl

Exceptions:

Naphthyl
(2-shown)

Anthryl
(2-shown)

Phenanthryl
(2-shown)

5,6,7,8-Tetrahydro-
2-naphthyl

The above exceptions are limited to the simple rings as shown. Radicals from names of fused derivatives of these rings are formed according to the Rule, *e.g.*, benz[*a*]anthracenyl.

24.3.—Bivalent radicals derived from univalent polycyclic hydrocarbon radicals whose names end in "-yl", by removal of one hydrogen atom from the carbon atom with the free valence are named by adding "-idene" to the name of the corresponding univalent radical.

Example:

1-Acenaphthenylidene

24.4.—Bivalent radicals derived from "ortho-fused" or "ortho- and peri-fused" polycyclic hydrocarbons by removing of a hydrogen atom from each of two different carbon atoms of the ring are named by changing the ending "-yl" of the univalent radical name to "-ylene."

Examples:

2,7-Phenanthrylene   3,8-Acenaphthenylene

Chemical Abstracts names multivalent radicals with three or more free valences derived from polycyclic hydrocarbons by an extension of Rule **B-5.13** to carbocyclic systems. Example: 1,4,5-anthracenetriyl.

A-28

28.1.—Radicals formed from hydrocarbons consisting of polycyclic systems and side chains are named according to the principles of the preceding rules.

Bridged Hydrocarbons

A-31. von Baeyer System

31.1.—Saturated alicyclic hydrocarbon systems consisting of two rings only, having two or more atoms in common, take the name of an open chain hydrocarbon containing the same total number of carbon atoms preceded by the prefix "bicyclo-." The number of carbon atoms in each of the three bridges[1] connecting the two tertiary carbon atoms is indicated in brackets in descending order.

Examples:

Bicyclo [1.1.0]-butane   Bicyclo [3.2.1]-octane   Bicyclo [5.2.0]nonane

31.2.—The system is numbered commencing with one of the bridge-heads, numbering proceeding by the longest possible path to the second bridge-head; numbering is then continued from this atom by the longer unnumbered path back to the first bridge-head and is completed by the shortest path.

Examples:

Bicyclo [3.2.1]octane   Bicyclo [4.3.2]undecane

Note: Longest path 1, 2, 3, 4, 5
Next longest path 5, 6, 7, 1
Shortest path 1, 8, 5

(1) A bridge is a valence bond or an atom or an unbranched chain of atoms connecting two different parts of a molecule. The two tertiary carbon atoms connected through the bridge are termed "bridge-heads."

31.3.—Unsaturated hydrocarbons are named in accordance with the principles set forth in Rule **A-11.3.** When there is a choice in numbering unsaturation is given the lowest numbers.

$$CH_2—CH—CH$$

$$^7CH_2$$

$$CH_2—CH—CH$$

Bicyclo [2.2.1]hept-2-ene

Chemical Abstracts names the above ring system 2-norbornene by Rule **A-74.2**, but follows the above Rule for hydrocarbons which do not have terpene names.

31.4.—Radicals derived from these hydrocarbons are named in accordance with the principles set forth in Rule **A-11.4.** The numbering of the hydrocarbon is retained and the point or points of attachment are given numbers as low as is consistent with the fixed numbering of the hydrocarbon.

Example:

$$CH—CH—CH—$$

$$^7CH_2$$

$$CH—CH—CH_2$$

Bicyclo[2.2.1]hept-5-en-2-yl

Chemical Abstracts names the above radical 5-norbornen-2-yl by Rule **A-75.2**, but follows the above Rule for radicals derived from hydrocarbons which do not have terpene names. Radicals derived from the saturated hydrocarbons (except terpenes) are named by replacing the ending "-ane" of the hydrocarbon name by ,"-yl." The point of attachment is given a number as low as is consistent with the fixed numbering of the hydrocarbon.

A-32

32.11.—Cyclic hydrocarbon systems consisting of three or more rings may be named in accordance with the principles stated in Rule **A-31.** The appropriate prefix "tricyclo-," "tetracyclo-," *etc.*, is substituted for "bicyclo-" before the name of the open-chain hydrocarbon containing the same total number of carbon atoms.

32.12.—A polycyclic system is regarded as containing a number of rings equal to the number of scissions required to convert the system into an open-chain compound.

32.13.—The word "cyclo" is followed by brackets containing, in decreasing order, numbers indicating the number of carbon atoms in: the two branches of the main ring, the main bridge, the secondary bridges.

Examples:

$$HC\quad CH$$

$$^7CH_2$$

$$H_2C\quad CH_2$$

Tricyclo[2.2.1.0^1]heptane

$$H_2C——CH—CH—CH_2$$

$$H_2C^9\quad ^{11}CH_2\quad ^{12}CH_2\quad ^4CH_2$$

$$H_2C——CH—CH—CH_2$$

Tricyclo[5.3.1.1^1]dodecane

(1) For location and numbering of the secondary bridge see Rules **A-32.22. A32.23, A-32.31.**

32.21.—The main ring and the main bridge form a bicyclic system whose numbering is made in compliance with Rule **A-31.**

32.22.—The location of the other or so-called secondary bridges is shown by superscripts following the number indicating the number of carbon atoms in the said bridges.

32.23.—For the purpose of numbering, the secondary bridges are considered in decreasing order. The numbering of any bridge follows from the part already numbered, proceeding from the highest-numbered bridge-head.

Numbering of the secondary bridges by proceeding from the highest-numbered bridge-head of each bridge is an improvement over the former practice of "following the shortest path from the highest previous number."

32.31.—When there is a choice, the following criteria are considered in turn until a decision is made:

(a) The main ring shall contain as many carbon atoms as possible, two of which must serve as bridgeheads for the main bridge.

Tricyclo[5.4.0.0^{2,9}]undecane
Correct numbering

Tricyclo[4.2.1.2^{7,9}]undecane
Incorrect numbering

Tricyclo[5.3.2.0^{4,9}]dodecane
Correct numbering

Tricyclo[5.2.3.0^{4,11}]dodecane
Incorrect numbering

(b) The main bridge shall be as large as possible.

Tetracyclo[5.2.2.0^{3,8}.0^{4,11}]-
undecane
Correct numbering

Tetracyclo[5.2.1.1^{4,10}.0^{2,6}]-
undecane
Incorrect numbering

(c) The main ring shall be divided as symmetrically as possible by the main bridge.

Tricyclo[4.4.1.1^{1,5}]dodecane:
Correct numbering

Tricyclo[5.3.1.1^{1,6}]dodecane:
Incorrect numbering

(d) The superscripts locating the other bridges shall be as small as possible (in the sense indicated in Rule **A-2.2**)

Tricyclo[5.5.1.0^{3,11}]tridecane
Correct numbering

Tricyclo[5.5.1.0^{5,9}]tridecane
Incorrect numbering

A-34 (Alternate to Rule A-35)

34.1.—Polycyclic hydrocarbon systems which can be regarded as "ortho-fused" or "ortho- and peri-fused" systems according to Rule **A-21** and which, at the same time, have other bridges,[1] are first named as "ortho-fused" or "ortho- and peri-fused" systems. The other bridges are then indicated by prefixes derived from the corresponding hydrocarbon by replacing the final "-ane," "-ene," *etc.*, by "-ano," "-eno," *etc.*, and their positions are indicated by the points of attachment in the parent compound. If bridges of different types are present, they are cited in alphabetical order.

Examples of bridge names

Butano	—CH_2—CH_2—CH_2—CH_2—		Etheno	—CH=CH—
Benzeno (*o-, m-, p-*)	—C_6H_4—		Methano	—CH_2—
Ethano	—CH_2—CH_2—		Propano	—CH_2—CH_2—CH_2—

1,4-Dihydro-1,4-
methanopentalene

9,10-Dihydro-9,10-(2-buteno)-
anthracene

7,14-Dihydro-7,14-ethano-
dibenz[*a,h*]anthracene

(1) The term "bridge," when used in connection with an "ortho-fused" or "ortho- and peri-fused" polycyclic system as defined in note to Rule **A-31.1**, also includes "bivalent cyclic systems."

34.2.—The parent "ortho-fused" "or ortho- and peri-fused" system is numbered as prescribed in Rule **A-22.** Where there is a choice, the position numbers of the bridge-heads should be as low as possible. The remaining bridges are then numbered in turn starting each time with the bridge atom next to the bridge-head possessing the highest number.

Example:

$$\begin{array}{cccccc}
H_2C & H_2C & HC & & & \\
8 & 9 & 1 & & & \\
H_2C^7 & CH & CH\,^{12}CH_2\,^2CH_2 & & & \\
H_2C_6 & CH & CH\,_{11}CH_2\,_3CH_2 & & & \\
5 & 10 & 4 & & & \\
CH_2 & CH_2 & CH & & &
\end{array}$$

Perhydro-1,4-ethanoanthracene

not

$$\begin{array}{ccc}
H_2C & H_2C & HC \\
8 & 9 & 1 \\
H_2C^7 & CH & CH\,_{11}CH_2\,^2CH_2 \\
H_2C_6 & CH & CH\,_{12}CH_2\,_3CH_2 \\
5 & 10 & 4 \\
CH_2 & CH_2 & CH
\end{array}$$

or

$$\begin{array}{ccc}
HC & H_2C & H_2C \\
8 & 9 & 1 \\
H_2C^7\,^{11}CH_2CH & CH & ^2CH_2 \\
H_2C_6\,_{12}CH_2CH & CH & _3CH_2 \\
5 & 10 & 4 \\
CH & CH_2 & CH_2
\end{array}$$

34.3.—When there is a choice of position numbers for the points of attachment for several individual bridges, the lowest numbers are assigned to the bridge-heads in the order of citation of the bridges and the bridge atoms are numbered according to the preceding rule.

Example:

$$\begin{array}{ccc}
CH & CH_2 & CH \\
8 & 9 & 1 \\
H_2C^7 & CH & CH\,^{13}CH_2\,^2CH_2 \\
^{11}CH_2 & & \\
H_2C_6 & CH & CH\,_{12}CH_2\,_3CH_2 \\
5 & 10 & 4 \\
CH & CH_2 & CH
\end{array}$$

Perhydro-1,4-ethano-5,8-methanoanthracene

34.4.—When the bridge is formed from a bivalent cyclic hydrocarbon radical, low numbers are given to the carbon atoms constituting the shorter bridge and numbering proceeds around the ring.

10,11-Dihydro-5,10-*o*-benzeno-5*H*-benzo[*b*]fluorene

Chemical Abstracts follows this rule instead of the Alternate Rule **A-35**.

A-35 (Alternate to Rule A-34)

35.1.—Polycyclic hydrocarbons which can be regarded as "ortho-fused" or "ortho- and peri-fused" according to Rule **A-21** and which have also other bridges may be named as "ortho-fused" or "ortho- and peri-fused" systems into which bivalent radicals are substituted.

35.2.—Compounds which are named in accordance with **35.1** of this rule are numbered as prescribed in Rule **A-34**. The bridge is numbered independently. Numbering of the bridge is started at the lower-numbered bridge head. Numbers assigned to the bridge atoms are primed.

Examples:

9,10-Dihydro-9,10-(2'-butylene)anthracene

7,14-Dihydro-7,14-ethylene-dibenz[a,h]anthracene

Chemical Abstracts follows Rule A-34 instead of this Alternate Rule.

Spiro Hydrocarbons

A "spiro union" is one formed by a single atom which is the only common member of two rings. A "free spiro union" is one constituting the only union direct or indirect between two rings.[1] The common atom is designated as the "spiro atom." According to the number of spiro atoms present, the compounds are distinguished as monospiro, dispiro, trispiro compounds, *etc.* The following rules apply to the naming of compounds containing free spiro unions.

(1) An example of a compound where the spiro union is *not* free is:

A-41 (Alternate to Rule A-42)

41.1.—Monospiro compounds consisting of only two alicyclic rings as components are named by placing "spiro" before the name of the normal acyclic hydrocarbon of the same total number of carbon atoms. The number of carbon atoms linked to the spiro atom in each ring is indicated in ascending order in brackets placed between the spiro prefix and the hydrocarbon name.

Examples:

Spiro[3.4]octane   Spiro[3.3]heptane

41.2.—The carbon atoms in monospiro hydrocarbons are numbered consecutively starting with a ring atom next to the spiro atom, first through the smaller ring (if such be present) and then through the spiro atom and around the second ring.

Example:

Spiro[4.5]decane

41.3.—When unsaturation is present, the same numbering pattern is maintained, but in such a direction around the rings that the double and triple bonds receive numbers as low as possible in accordance with Rule A-11.

Example:

$$H_2C-CH_2 \quad HC=CH$$

Spiro[4.5]deca-1,6-diene

41.4.—If one or both components of the monospiro compound are fused polycyclic systems, "spiro" is placed before the names of the components arranged in alphabetical order and enclosed in brackets. Established numbering of the individual components is retained. The lowest possible number is given to the spiro atom, and the numbers of the second component are marked with primes. The position of the spiro atom is indicated by placing the appropriate numbers between the names of the two components.

Example:

Spiro[cyclopentane-1,1'-indene]

41.5.—Monospiro compounds containing two similar polycyclic components are named by placing the prefix "spirobi" before the name of the component ring system. Established numbering of the polycyclic system is maintained and the numbers of one component are distinguished by primes. The position of the spiro atom is indicated in the name of the spiro compound by placing the appropriate locants before the name.

Example:

1,1'-Spirobiindene

41.6.—Polyspiro compounds consisting of three or more alicyclic systems are named by placing "dispiro-," "trispiro-," "tetraspiro-," etc., before the name of the normal acyclic hydrocarbon of the same total number of carbon atoms. The numbers of carbon atoms linked to the spiro atoms in each ring are indicated in brackets in the same order as the numbering proceeds about the ring. Numbering starts with a ring atom next to a terminal spiro atom and proceeds in such a way as to give the spiro atoms as low numbers as possible.

Example:

Dispiro[5.1.7.2]heptadecane

41.7.—Polycyclic compounds containing more than one spiro atom and at least one fused polycyclic component are named in accordance with **41.4** of this rule by replacing "spiro" with "dispiro," "trispiro," etc., and choosing the end components by alphabetical order.

Example:

Dispiro[fluorene-9,1'-cyclohexane-4',1''-indene]

This represents the method of naming spiro compounds which is followed by *Chemical Abstracts* instead of the Alternate Rule **A-42.**

A-42

42.1 (Alternate to **A-41.1** and **A-41.2**).—When two dissimilar cyclic components are united by a spiro union the name of the larger component is followed by the affix "spiro" which, in turn, is followed by the name of the smaller component. Between the affix "spiro" and the name of each component system is inserted the number denoting the spiro-position in the appropriate ring system, these numbers being as low as permitted by any fixed numbering of the component. The components retain their respective numberings but numbers for the component mentioned second are primed. Numbers 1 may be omitted when a free choice is available for a component.

Examples:

Cyclopentanespiro-
cyclobutane

Cyclohexanespirocyclo-
pentane

2*H*-Indene-2-spiro-1'-cyclopentane

42.2 (Alternate to **A-41.3**).—Rule **A-41.3** applies also with appropriate different numbering where nomenclature is according to Rule **A-42.1**, but the spiro-junction has priority for lowest numbers over unsaturation.

Example:

2-Cyclohexenespiro-(2'-cyclopentene)

42.3 (Alternate to **A-41.5**).—The nomenclature of Rule **A-41.5** is applied also to monocyclic components with identical saturation, the spiro-union being numbered 1.

Examples:

Spirobicyclohexane   but   2-Cyclohexenespiro-
(3'-cyclohexene)

42.4 (Alternate to **A-41.6** and **A-41.7**).—Polycyclic compounds containing more than one spiro atom are named in accordance with Rule **A-42.1** starting from the senior[1] end-component irrespective of whether the components are simple or fused rings.

Examples:

Cyclooctanespirocyclopentane-3'-spirocyclohexane   Fluorene-9-spiro-1'-cyclohexane-4'-spiro-1''-indene

(1) "Seniority" in respect to spiro compounds is based on the principles: (i) an aggregate is senior to a monocycle; (ii) of aggregates, the senior is that containing the largest number of individual rings; (iii) of aggregates containing the same number of individual rings, the senior is that containing the largest ring; (iv) if aggregates consist of equal number of equal rings the senior is the first occurring in the alphabetical list of names.

Chemical Abstracts follows Rule **A-41** instead of this alternate Rule.

Hydrocarbon Ring Assemblies

A-51

51.1.—Two or more cyclic systems (single rings or fused systems) which are directly joined to each other by double or single bonds are named "ring assemblies" when the number of such direct ring junctions is one less than the number of cyclic systems involved.

Examples:

Ring assemblies

Fused polycyclic system

A-52

52.1.—Assemblies of two identical cyclic hydrocarbon systems are named in either of two ways: (a) by placing the prefix "bi-" before the name of the corresponding radical, or (b) for systems joined by a single bond by placing the prefix "bi-" before the name of the corresponding hydrocarbon. In each case, the numbering of the assembly is that of the corresponding radical or hydrocarbon, one system being assigned unprimed numbers and the other primed numbers. The points of attachment are indicated by placing the appropriate locants before the name.

Examples:

1,1'-Bicyclopropyl
or 1,1'-Bicyclopropane

1,1'-Bicyclopentadienylidene

52.2.—If there is a choice in numbering, unprimed numbers are assigned to the system which has the lower-numbered point of attachment.

Example:

1,2'-Binaphthyl
or 1,2'-Binaphthalene

52.3.—If two identical hydrocarbon systems have the same point of attachment and contain substituents at different positions, the locants of these substituents are assigned according to Rule **A-2.2**; for this purpose an unprimed number is considered lower than the same number when primed. Assemblies of primed and unprimed numbers are arranged in ascending numerical order.

Examples:

2,3,3',4',5'-
Pentamethylbiphenyl
(not 2',3,3',4,5-
Pentamethylbiphenyl)

2-Ethyl-2'-
propylbiphenyl

52.4.—The name "biphenyl" is used for the assembly consisting of two benzene rings:

Biphenyl

A-53

53.1.—Other hydrocarbon ring assemblies are named by selecting one ring system as the base component and considering the other system as substituents of the base component. Such substituents are arranged in alphabetical order. The base component is assigned unprimed numbers and the substituents are assigned numbers with primes.

53.2.—The base component is chosen by considering these characteristics in turn until a decision is reached:

(a) The system containing the larger number of rings.

Examples:

2-Phenylnaphthalene

4-Cyclooctyl-4'-cyclopentylbiphenyl

(b) The system containing the larger ring.

Examples:

2-(2'-Naphthyl)azulene

1,4-Dicyclopropylbenzene
or p-Dicyclopropylbenzene

(c) The system in the lowest state of hydrogenation (see also **53.3** of this rule).

Example:

Cyclohexylbenzene

(d) The order of ring systems as set forth in the list of Rule **A-21.1.**

53.3.—Compounds covered by **53.2**(c) of this rule may also be named as hydrogenation products according to Rule **A-23.**

Example:

1,2,3,3',4,4'-Hexahydro-1,1'-binaphthyl

The name of the second example in (a) which contains as a base component the ring assembly "biphenyl" indicates that the word system as used here includes ring assemblies as base components.

Chemical Abstracts does not use primed numbers with the groups which may be considered as substituent groups expressed as prefixes and attached to the name of the base component, Examples: 2-(2,4-dichlorophenyl)naphthalene; 2(2-naphthyl)-azulene.

A-54

54.1.—Unbranched assemblies consisting of three or more identical hydrocarbon ring systems are named by placing an appropriate numerical prefix before the name of the hydrocarbon corresponding to the repetitive unit. These numerical prefixes are used:

3. ter-	5. quinque-	7. septi-	9. novi-
4. quater-	6. sexi-	8. octi-	10. deci-

Example:

Tercyclopropane

54.2.—Unprimed numbers are assigned to one of the terminal systems, the other systems being primed serially. Points of attachment are assigned the lowest numbers possible.

Examples:

2,1′:5′,2″:6″,2‴-Quaternaphthalene

1,1′:3′,1″-Tercyclohexane

54.3.—As exceptions, unbranched assemblies consisting of benzene rings are named by using the appropriate prefix with the radical name "phenyl."

Examples:

p-Terphenyl
or 1,1′:4′,1″-Terphenyl

m-Terphenyl
or 1,1′:3′,1″-Terphenyl

Cyclic Hydrocarbons with Side Chains

(Note: *cf.* Rules **A-12** and **A-13**)

A-61

61.1.—Hydrocarbons more complex than those envisioned in Rule **A-12**, composed of cyclic nuclei and aliphatic chains, are named according to one of the methods given below. Choice is made so as to provide the name which is the simplest permissible or the most appropriate for the chemical intent.

61.2.—When there is no generally recognized trivial name for the hydrocarbon, then (1) the radical name denoting the aliphatic chain is prefixed to the name of the cyclic hydrocarbon, or (2) the radical name for the cyclic hydrocarbon is prefixed to the name of the aliphatic compound. Choice between these methods is made according to the more appropriate of the following principles: (a) the maximum number of substitutions into a single unit of structure; (b) treatment of a smaller unit of structure as a substituent into a larger.

61.3.—In accordance with the principle (a) of **61.2** of this rule, hydrocarbons containing several chains attached to one cyclic nucleus generally are named as derivatives of the cyclic compound; and compounds containing several side chains and/or cyclic radicals attached to one chain are named as derivatives of the acyclic compound.

Examples:

2-Ethyl-1-methylnaphthalene   Diphenylmethane

1,5-Diphenylpentane

$CH_3CH_2CH_2-CH-C=CH-$

2,3-Dimethyl-1-phenyl-1-hexene

61.4.—In accordance with principle (b) of **61.2** of this rule, a hydrocarbon containing a small cyclic nucleus attached to a long chain is generally named as a derivative of the acyclic hydrocarbon; and a hydrocarbon containing a small group attached to a large cyclic nucleus is generally named as a derivative of the cyclic hydrocarbon.

Examples: $CH_3[CH_2]_{10}CH_2CH_2CH_2CH_2CH_2-$

1-Phenylhexadecane

$CH_3[CH_2]_{10}CH_2CH_2CH_2CH=CH-$

1-Phenyl-1-hexadecene

9-(1,2-Dimethylpentyl)-   7-(3-Phenylpropyl)-
anthracene   benz[a]anthracene

61.5.—Recognized trivial names for composite radicals are used if they lead to simplifications in naming.

Examples:

1-Benzylnaphthalene   1,2,4-Tris(3-p-tolylropyl)benzene

Terpene Hydrocarbons

Owing to long-established custom, terpenes are given exceptional treatment in these rules.

A-71. Acyclic Terpenes[1]

71.1.—The acyclic terpene hydrocarbons are named in a manner similar to that used for other unsaturated acyclic hydrocarbons when pure compounds are involved.

Example:

7-Methyl-3-methylene-1,6-octadiene

A-72. Cyclic Terpenes

72.1.—The following structural types with their special names and special systems of numbering are used as the basis for the specialized nomenclature of monocyclic and bicyclic terpene hydrocarbons. The name "bornane" replaces camphane and bornylane; "norbornane" replaces norcamphane and norbornylane.

(1) For a more complete discussion of terpene nomenclature see "Nomenclature for Terpene Hydrocarbons," Advances in Chemistry Series No. 14 (American Chemical Society).

Fundamental terpene types:

I
Menthane (*p*-form)

II
Thujane

III
Carane

IV
Pinane

V
Bornane

Nor-structures:

VI
Norcarane

VII
Norpinane

VIII
Norbornane

A-73. Monocyclic Terpenes

73.1.—Menthane Type: Monocyclic terpene hydrocarbons of this type (ortho, meta, and para isomers) are named menthane, menthene, menthadiene, *etc.*, are given the fixed numbering of menthane (Formula I). Such compounds substituted by additional alkyl groups are named in accordance with Rule **A-11.**

Examples:

m-Menthane   1-*p*-Menthene   1,4(8)-*p*-Menthadiene

73.2.—Tetramethylcyclohexane Type: Monocyclic terpene hydrocarbons of this type are named systematically as derivatives of cyclohexane, cyclohexene, and cyclohexadiene (see Rule **A-11**).

Examples:

1,1,2,3-
Tetramethyl-
cyclohexane

1,2,3,3-
Tetramethyl-
cyclohexene

1,5,5,6-
Tetramethyl-
1,3-cyclohexadiene

A-74. Bicyclic Terpenes

74.1.—Bicyclic terpene hydrocarbons having the skeleton of Formula II or this skeleton and additional side chains except methyl or isopropyl (or methylene if one methylene group is already present) are named as thujane, thujene, thujadiene, *etc.*, and are given the fixed numbering shown for thujane (Formula II). Other hydrocarbons containing the thujane ring-skeleton are named from bicyclo[3.1.0]hexane and are given systematic bicyclo numbering (*cf.* Rule **A-31**).

Example:

4(10)-Thujene

1-Isopropyl-2,4-
dimethylenebicyclo-
[3.1.0]hexane

5-Isopropyl-
bicyclo[3.1.0]hex-
2-ene

74.2.—Bicyclic terpene hydrocarbons having the skeleton of Formula III, IV, or V and additional side chains except methyl (or methylene if one methylene group is already present) are named, respectively, as carane, carene, caradiene, *etc.*; pinane, pinene, pinadiene, *etc.*; bornane, bornene, bornadiene, *etc.* They are given, respectively, the fixed numbering shown for carane (Formula III), pinane (Formula IV), and bornane (Formula V). Other hydrocarbons containing the ring-skeleton of carane, pinane, or bornane are named, respectively, from norcarane (Formula VI), norpinane (Formula VII), or norbornane (Formula VIII). These names are preferred to those from bicyclo [4.1.0]heptane, bicyclo[3.1.1]heptane, or bicyclo [2.2.1]heptane. The nor-names are given systematic bicyclo numbering (*cf.* Rule **A-31**).

Examples:

2-Carene

7,7-Dimethyl-
2,4-norcaradiene

2(10),3-Pinadiene

4-Methylenepinane

2,4,7,7-Tetra-
methylnorcarane

6,6-Dimethyl-2-
vinyl-2-norpinene

2-Bornene   2,2-Dimethylnorbornane   2,7,7-Trimethyl-2-norbornene

74.3.—The name "camphene" is retained for the unsubstituted compound 2,2-dimethyl-3-methylene-norbornane.

Camphene

A-75. Terpene Radicals

75.1.—Simple acyclic hydrocarbon terpene radicals are named and numbered according to Rule **A-3.5.** The trivial names geranyl, neryl, linalyl and phytyl are retained for the unsubstituted radicals.

75.2.—Radicals derived from menthane, pinane, thujane, carane, bornane, norcarane, norpinane, and norbornane are named in accordance with the principles set forth in Rules **A-1.2** and **A-11.4** except that the saturated radicals of pinane are named pinanyl, pinanylene, and pinanylidene. The numbering of the hydrocarbon is retained and the point or points of attachment, whether in the ring or side chain, are given numbers as low as is consistent with the fixed numbering of the hydrocarbon.

Examples:

1-*p*-Menthen-8-yl   3-Pinanyl   4(10)-Thujen-10-yl

2-Pinen-10-ylidene   5-Norbornen-2-yl

75.3.—Radicals not named in Rules **A-75.1** and **A-75.2** are named as described in Rules **A-11** and **A-31.4.**

DEFINITIVE RULES FOR NOMENCLATURE OF ORGANIC CHEMISTRY

B. FUNDAMENTAL HETEROCYCLIC SYSTEMS

B-1. Extension of Hantzsch-Widman System

1.1.—Monocyclic compounds containing one or more hetero atoms in a three- to ten-membered ring are named by combining the appropriate prefix or prefixes from Table I (eliding "a" where necessary) with a stem from Table II. The state of hydrogenation is indicated either in the stem, as shown in Table II, or by the prefixes "dihydro-," "tetrahydro-," *etc.*, according to Rule **B-1.2.**

TABLE I

Element	Valence	Prefix
Oxygen	II	Oxa
Sulfur	II	Thia
Selenium	II	Selena
Tellurium	II	Tellura
Nitrogen	III	Aza
Phosphorus	III	Phospha[a]
Arsenic	III	Arsa[a]
Antimony	III	Stiba[a]
Bismuth	III	Bisma
Silicon	IV	Sila
Germanium	IV	Germa
Tin	IV	Stanna
Lead	IV	Plumba
Mercury	II	Mercura

[a] When immediately followed by "in-" or "-ine," "phospha-" should be replaced by "phosphor-," "arsa-" should be replaced by "arsen-" and "stiba" should be replaced by "antimon-".

"Bora" for boron is used frequently. *Chemical Abstracts* has placed boron with the valence of III between lead and mercury in Table I. This table shows the valence of tin and lead as IV instead of II (a correction of a typographical error).

TABLE II

No. of members in the ring	Rings containing nitrogen		Rings containing no nitrogen	
	Unsaturation[a]	Saturation	Unsaturation[a]	Saturation
3	-irine	-iridine	-irene	irane[e]
4	-ete	-etidine	-ete	-etane
5	-ole	-olidine	-ole	-olane
6	-ine[b]	[c]	-ine[b]	-ane[d]
7	-epine	[c]	-epine	-epane
8	-ocine	[c]	-ocin	-ocane
9	-onine	[c]	-onin	-onane
10	-ecine	[c]	-ecin	-ecane

[a] Corresponding to the maximum number of non-cumulative double bonds, the hetero elements having the normal valences shown in Table I. [b] For phosphorus, arsenic, antimony, see the special provisions of Table I. [c] Expressed by prefixing "perhydro-" to the name of the corresponding unsaturated compound. [d] Not applicable to silicon, germanium, tin and lead. In this case, "perhydro-" is prefixed to the name of the corresponding unsaturated compound. [e] The syllables denoting the size of rings containing 3, 4 or 7–10 members are derived as follows: "ir" from *tri-*, "et" from *tetra*, "ep" from *hepta*, "oc" from *octa*, "on" from *nona*, and "ec" from *deca*.

Examples:

Oxirane   Aziridine   2*H*-Azepine

1.2.—Heterocyclic systems whose unsaturation is less than the one corresponding to the maximum number of noncumulative double bonds are named by using the prefixes "dihydro-," "tetrahydro-," etc.

In the case of 4- and 5-membered rings, a special termination is used for the structures containing one double bond, when there can be more than one noncumulative double bond.

No. of members of the partly saturated rings	Rings containing nitrogen	Rings containing no nitrogen
4	-etine	-etene
5	-oline	-olene

Examples:

1,2-Azarset-3-ine   3-Silolene

1.3.—Multiplicity of the same hetero atom is indicated by a prefix "di," "tri-," etc., placed before the appropriate "a" term (Table I).

Example:

1,3,5-Triazine (or s-Triazine)

1.4.—If two or more kinds of "a" terms occur in the same name, their order of citation is by descending group number of the Periodic Table and increasing atomic number in the group as illustrated by the sequence in Table I.

Examples:

1,2-Oxathiolane   Thiazole

1.51.—The position of a single hetero atom determines the numbering in a monocyclic compound.

Example:

Azocine

1.52.—When the same hetero atom occurs more than once in a ring, the numbering is chosen to give the lowest locants to the hetero atoms.

Example:

1,2,4-Triazine (or as-Triazine)

1.53.—When hetero atoms of different kinds are present, the locant 1 is given to a hetero atom which is as high as possible in Table I. The numbering is then chosen to give the lowest locants to the hetero atoms.

Examples:

6H-1,2,5-Thiadiazine
(not 2,1,4-Thiadiazine)
(not 1,3,6-Thiadiazine)

2H,6H-1,5,2-Dithiazine
(not 1,3,4-Dithiazine)
(not 1,3,6-Dithiazine)
(not 1,5,4-Dithiazine)

The numbering must begin with the sulfur atom. This condition eliminates 2,1,4-thiadiazine. Then the nitrogen atoms receive the lowest possible locant, which eliminates 1,3,6-thiadiazine.

The numbering must begin with a sulfur atom. The choice of this atom is determined by the set of locants which can be attributed to the remaining hetero atoms of any kind. As the set 1,2,5 is lower than 1,3,4 or 1,3,6 or 1,5,4 in the usual sense, the name is 1,5,2-dithiazine.

B-2. Trivial and Semi-trivial Names

2.11.—The following trivial and semi-trivial names constitute a partial list of such names which are retained for the compound and as a basis of fusion names. They are arranged in the inverse order of the precedence prescribed in Rule **B-3**. The names of the radicals shown are formed according to Rule **B-5**.

Parent Compound	Radical Name	Parent Compound	Radical Name
(1) Thiophene	Thienyl (2-shown)	(12) Pyrrole	Pyrrolyl (3- shown)
(2) Benzo[b]thiophene (replacing thianaphthene)	Benzo[b]thienyl (2-shown)	(13) Imidazole	Imidazolyl (2- shown)
(3) Naphtho[2,3-b]thiophene (replacing thiophanthrene)	Naphtho[2,3-b]thienyl (2-shown)	(14) Pyrazole	Pyrazolyl (1- shown)
(4) Thianthrene	Thianthrenyl (2-shown)	(15) Pyridine	Pyridyl (3- shown)
(5) Furan	Furyl (3-shown)	(16) Pyrazine	Pyrazinyl
(6) Pyran (2H-shown)	Pyranyl (2H-Pyran-3-yl shown)	(17) Pyrimidine	Pyrimidinyl (2-shown)
(7) Isobenzofuran	Isobenzofuranyl (1-shown)	(18) Pyridazine	Pyridazinyl (3- shown)
(8) Chromene (2H- shown)	Chromenyl (2H-Chromen-3-yl shown)	(19) Indolizine	Indolizinyl (2-shown)
(9) Xanthene[1]	Xanthenyl[1] (2- shown)	(20) Isoindole	Isoindolyl (2- shown)
(10) Phenoxathiin	Phenoxathiinyl (2- shown)	(21) 3H-Indole	3H-Indolyl (3H-Indol-2-yl shown)
(11) 2H-Pyrrole	2H-Pyrrolyl (2H-Pyrrol-3-yl shown)		

(1) Denotes exceptions to systematic numbering.

Parent Compound	Radical Name	Parent Compound	Radical Name

(22) Indole — Indolyl (1- shown)

(23) 1H-Indazole — Indazolyl (1H-Indazol-3-yl shown)

(24) Purine[1] — Purinyl[1] (8- shown)

(25) 4H-Quinolizine — 4H-Quinolizinyl (4H-Quinolizin-2-yl shown)

(26) Isoquinoline — Isoquinolyl (3- shown)

(27) Quinoline — Quinolyl (2- shown)

(28) Phthalazine — Phthalazinyl (1- shown)

(29) Naphthyridine (1,8- shown) — Naphthyridinyl (1,8-Naphthyridin-2-yl shown)

(30) Quinoxaline — Quinoxalinyl (2- shown)

(31) Quinazoline — Quinazolinyl (2- shown)

(32) Cinnoline — Cinnolinyl (3- shown)

(33) Pteridine — Pteridinyl (2- shown)

(34) 4aH-Carbazole[1] — 4aH-Carbazolyl[1] (4aH-Carbazol-2-yl shown)

(35) Carbazole[1] — Carbazolyl[1] (2- shown)

(36) β-Carboline — β-Carbolinyl (β-Carbolin-3-yl shown)

(37) Phenanthridine — Phenanthridinyl (3- shown)

(38) Acridine[1] — Acridinyl[1] (2- shown)

(39) Perimidine — Perimidinyl (2- shown)

(40) Phenanthroline (1,7- shown) — Phenanthrolinyl (1,7-Phenanthrolin-3-yl shown)

Parent Compound	Radical Name	Parent Compound	Radical Name

(41) Phenazine — Phenazinyl (1- shown)

(44) Phenothiazine — Phenothiazinyl (2- shown)

(42) Phenarsazine — Phenarsazinyl (2- shown)

(45) Isoxazole — Isoxazolyl (3- shown)

(46) Furazan — Furazanyl (3- shown)

(43) Isothiazole — Isothiazolyl (3- shown)

(47) Phenoxazine — Phenoxazinyl (2- shown)

Chemical Abstracts uses 2*H*-1-benzopyran instead of chromene, and 9*H*-pyrido[3,4-*b*]indole instead of *β*-carboline.

B-2.12.—The following trivial and semi-trivial names are retained but are not recommended for use in fusion names. The names of the radicals shown are formed according to Rule **B-5.**

Parent Compound	Radical Name	Parent Compound	Radical Name

(1) Isochroman — Isochromanyl (3- shown)

(5) Imidazolidine — Imidazolidinyl (2- shown)

(2) Chroman — Chromanyl (7- shown)

(6) Imidazoline (2- shown[1]) — Imidazolinyl (2-Imidazolin-4-yl[1] shown)

(3) Pyrrolidine — Pyrrolidinyl (2- shown)

(7) Pyrazolidine — Pyrazolidinyl (1- shown)

(4) Pyrroline (2- shown[1]) — Pyrrolinyl (2-Pyrrolin-3-yl[1] shown)

(8) Pyrazoline (3- shown[2]) — Pyrazolinyl (3-Pyrazolin-2-yl[2] shown)

(1) The "2-" denotes the position of the double bond.
(2) The "3-" denotes the position of the double bond.
(3) For 1-piperidyl use piperidino.

Parent Compound	Radical Name		Parent Compound	Radical Name
(9) Piperidine	Piperidyl[3] (2- shown)	(12)	Isoindoline	Isoindolinyl (1- shown)
(10) Piperazine	Piperazinyl (1- shown)	(13)	Quinuclidine	Quinuclidinyl (2- shown)
(11) Indoline	Indolinyl (1- shown)	(14)	Morpholine	Morpholinyl[1] (3- shown)

B-3. Fused Heterocyclic Systems

3.1.—"Ortho-fused" and "ortho- and peri-fused" ring compounds containing hetero atoms are named according to the fusion principle described in Rule **A-21** for hydrocarbons. The components are named according to Rules **A-21**, **B-1** and **B-2**. The base component should be a heterocycle. If there is a choice, the base component should be, by order of preference:

(a) A nitrogen-containing component.

Example:

Benzo[*h*]isoquinoline
not Pyrido[3,4-*a*]naphthalene

(b) A component containing a hetero atom (other than nitrogen) as high as possible in Table I.

Example:

Thieno[2,3-*b*]furan
not Furo[2,3-*b*]thiophene

(c) A component containing the greatest number of rings.

Example:

7*H*-Pyrazino[2,3-*c*]carbazole
not 7*H*-Indolo[3,2-*f*]quinoxaline

(d) A component containing the largest possible individual ring.

Example:

2*H*-Furo[3,2-*b*]pyran
not 2*H*-Pyrano[3,2-*b*]furan

(1) For 4-morpholinyl use morpholino.

(e) A component containing the greatest number of hetero atoms of any kind.

Example:

5H-Pyrido[2,3-d][1,2]oxazine
not [1,2]Oxazino[4,5-b]pyridine

(f) A component containing the greatest variety of hetero atoms.

Examples:

1H-Pyrazolo[4,3-d]oxazole
not 1H-Oxazolo[5,4-c]-
pyrazole

4H-Imidazo[4,5-d]thiazole
not 4H-Thiazolo[4,5-d]-
imidazole

(g) A component containing the greatest number of hetero atoms first listed in Table I.

Example:

Selenazolo[5,4-f]benzothiazole[1]
not Thiazolo[5,4-f]benzoselenazole

(1) In this example the hetero atom first listed in Table I is sulfur and the greatest number of sulfur atoms in a ring is one.

(h) If there is a choice between components of the same size containing the same number and kind of hetero atoms choose as the base component that one with the lower numbers for the hetero atoms before fusion.

Example:

Pyrazino[2,3-d]pyridazine

3.2.—If a position of fusion is occupied by a hetero atom, the names of the component rings to be fused are so chosen as both to contain the hetero atom.

Example:

Imidazo[2,1-b]thiazole

3.3.—These contracted fusion prefixes may be used: furo, imidazo, isoquino, pyrido, pyrimido, quino and thieno.

Examples:

Furo[3,4-c]cinnoline   4H-Pyrido[2,3-c]carbazole

3.4.—In peripheral numbering of the complete fused systems, the ring system is oriented and numbered according to the principles of Rule **A-22**. When there is a choice of orientations, it is made in the following sequence in order to:

(a) Give low numbers to hetero atoms.

Examples:

Benzo[b]furan   Cyclopenta[b]pyran   4H-[1,3]Oxathiolo-
[5,4-b]pyrrole (N.B.
1,3,4 lower than 1,3,6)

(b) Give low numbers to hetero atoms in order of Table I.

Example:

Thieno[2,3-b]furan

(c) Allow carbon atoms common to two or more rings to follow the lowest possible numbers (see Rules **A-22.2** and **A-22.3**). [A hetero atom common to the two rings is numbered according to Rule **B-3.4**(e).]

Examples:

not   or

Imidazo[1,2-b][1,2,4]triazine
(or Imidazo[1,2-b]-as-triazine)

In a compound name for a fusion prefix (*i.e.*, when more than one pair of brackets is required), the points of fusion in the compound prefix are indicated by the use of unprimed and primed numbers, the unprimed numbers being assigned to the ring attached directly to the base component, thus

Pyrido[1′,2′:1,2]imidazo-
[4,5-b]quinoxaline

not

or

or

(d) Give hydrogen atoms lowest numbers possible.

4H-1,3-Dioxolo[4,5-d]imidazole

(e) The ring is numbered as for hydrocarbons but numbers are given to all hetero atoms even when common to two or more rings. Interior hetero atoms are numbered last following the shortest path from the highest previous number.

B-4. "a" Nomenclature

4.1.—Names of heterocyclic compounds also may be formed by prefixing "a" terms (see Table I of Rule **B-1.1**) to the name of the corresponding homocyclic compound. The letter "a" should not be elided. There are two methods of applying this principle:

4.1(a). Stelzner Method.—In this method, the "a" term name relates to that of the hydrocarbon with the same distribution of bonds in the rings. Thus, I is not so related to benzene but to 1,4-cyclohexadiene, and II is not so related to naphthalene but to 1,4-dihydronaphthalene.

I   II

4.1(b). Chemical Abstracts Method.—If the corresponding homocyclic compound is partially or completely hydrogenated and if this state of hydrogenation is denoted in its name without the use of hydro prefixes, as indan and cyclohexane, the procedure is the same as in (a). In other cases, positions in the skeleton of the corresponding homocyclic compound which are occupied by hetero atoms are denoted by the "a" terms, and the parent heterocyclic compound is considered to be that which contains the maximum number of conjugated or isolated[1] double bonds; hydrogen is added, as necessary, as hydro prefixes and/or *H* to the "a" name thus obtained.

Examples:

Structure	Stelzner Method	Chemical Abstracts Method
	Sila-2,4-cyclo-pentadiene	Sila-2,4-cyclo-pentadiene
	Sila-1,3-cyclo-pentadiene	Sila-1,3-cyclo-pentadiene
	Silabenzene	Silabenzene
	7-Azabicyclo-[2.2.1]heptane	7-Azabicyclo-[2.2.1]heptane
	1,3-Dithia-1,2,3,4-tetrahydro-naphthalene	4*H*-1,3-Dithia-naphthalene
	1,4-Dithia-1,4-di-hydronaph-thalene	1,4-Dithianaph-thalene

(1) Isolated double bonds are those which are neither conjugated nor cumulative as in

or the B ring of

Structure	Stelzner Method	Chemical Abstracts Method
	2,4,6-Trithia-3a,7a-diazaper-hydroindene	2,4,6-Trithia-3a,7a-diazain-dene
	2-Oxa-1,2-dihydro-pyrene	1*H*-2-Oxapyrene
	2,7,9-Triazaphen-anthrene	2,7,9-Triazaphe-nanthrene

4.2.—In fusion names, the "a" terms precede the completed name of the parent hydrocarbon. If two or more kinds of "a" terms occur in the same name, the procedure described in Rule **B-1.4** applies. Prefixes denoting ordinary substitution procede the "a" terms.

Example:

3,4-Dimethyl-5-azabenz[*a*]anthracene

Chemical Abstracts follows Rule **B-4.1** (b). Since "a" names for heterocyclic systems are based on the name of the carbocyclic system, the numbering of the "a" name must agree with the numbering of the carbocyclic parent. When there is a choice in direction of numbering the ring is numbered so as to give (1) lowest numbers to the hetero atoms, (2) lowest numbers to hetero atoms as high as possible in Table 1 (Rule **B-1.1**).

B-5. Radicals

5.11.—Univalent radicals derived from heterocyclic compounds by removal of hydrogen from a ring are in principle named by adding "yl" to the names of the parent compounds (with elision of final "e" if present).

Examples:
Indolyl from indole
Pyrrolinyl from pyrroline
Triazolyl from triazole
Triazinyl from triazine

(For further examples see Rule **B-2.11**).

These exceptions are retained: furyl, pyridyl, piperidyl, quinolyl, isoquinolyl and thienyl (from thiophene) (see also Rule **B-2.12**).

As exceptions, the names "piperidino" and "morpholino" are preferred to "1-piperidyl" and "4-morpholinyl."

5.12.—Bivalent radicals derived from univalent heterocyclic radicals whose names end in "-yl" by removal of one hydrogen atom from the atom with the free valence are named by adding "-idene" to to the name of the corresponding univalent radical.

Example:

2-Pyranylidene

5.13.—Multivalent radicals derived from heterocyclic compounds by removal of two or more hydrogen atoms from different atoms in the ring are named by adding "-diyl," "-triyl," *etc.*, to the name of the ring system.

Example:

2,4-Quinolinediyl

5.21.—The use of "a" terms (Rule **B-4**) does not affect the formation of radical names. Such names are strictly analogous to those of the hydrocarbon analogs except that the "a" terms establish numbering in whole or in part.

Examples:

1,3-Dioxa-4-cyclohexyl   1,10-Diaza-4-anthryl

B-6. Cationic Hetero Atoms

6.1.—According to the "a" nomenclature, heterocyclic compounds containing cationic hetero atoms are named in conformity with the preceding rules by replacing "oxa-," "thia-," "aza-," *etc.*, by "oxonia-," "thionia-," "azonia-," *etc.*, the anion being designated in the usual way.

Examples:

1-Oxoniaanthracene chloride

4a-Azoniaanthracene chloride

1-Thioniabicyclo[2.2.1]heptane chloride

1-Methyl-1-oxoniacyclohexane chloride

HETEROCYCLIC SPIRO COMPOUNDS

B-10 (Alternate to B-11)

10.1.—Heterocyclic spiro compounds containing single-ring units only may be named by prefixing "a" terms (see Table I, Rule **B-1.1**) to the names of the spiro hydrocarbons formed according to Rules **A-41.1, A-41.2, A-41.3** and **A-41.6.** The numbering of the spiro hydrocarbon is retained and the hetero atoms in the order of Table I are given as low numbers as are consistent with the fixed numbering of the ring. When there is a choice, hetero atoms are given lower numbers than double bonds.

Examples:

1-Oxaspiro[4.5]decane   6,8-Diazoniadispiro[5.1.6.2]hexadecane dichloride

10.2.—If at least one component of a mono- or polyspiro compound is a fused polycyclic system, the spiro compound is named according to Rule **A-41.4** or **A-41.7,** giving the spiro atom as low a number as possible consistent with the fixed numberings of the component systems.

Examples:

3,3′-Spirobi[3*H*-indole]   Spiro[piperidine-4,9′-xanthene]

Chemical Abstracts names heterocyclic spiro compounds according to Rules **B-10.1** and **B-10.2.**

B-11 (Alternate to B-10)

11.1.—Heterocyclic spiro compounds are named according to Rule **A-42,** the following criteria being applied where necessary: (a) spiro atoms have numbers as low as consistent with the numbering of the individual component systems; (b) heterocyclic components have priority over homocyclic components of the same size; (c) priority of heterocyclic components is decided according to Rule **B-3.** Parentheses are used where necessary for clarity in complex expressions.

Examples:

Cyclohexanespiro-2'-(tetrahydrofuran)

Tetrahydropyran-2-
spirocyclohexane

3,3'-Spirobi(3H-indole)

1,2,3,4-Tetrahydro-
quinoline-4-spiro-4'-
piperidine

Hexahydroazepinium-1-spiro-1'-imid-
azolidine-3'-spiro-1''-piperidinium
dibromide

Chemical Abstract follows Rule **B-10.**

BRIDGED HETEROCYCLIC COMPOUNDS

Bridged heterocyclic bicyclo and polycyclo compounds are named by *Chemical Abstracts* by application of the "a" nomenclature to the names of bicyclo and polycyclo hydrocarbon systems which have been named according to Rules **A-31** and **A-32.**

Bridged heterocyclic compounds which can be regarded as ortho-fused or ortho- and peri-fused systems with additional bridges are named by extending Rule **A-34** to heterocyclic systems. Bridge names such as epoxy (—O—), epithio (—S—), epoxymethano (—O—CH₂—) are used.

INDEX

DEFINITIVE RULES FOR NOMENCLATURE OF ORGANIC CHEMISTRY

This list is taken, by permission, from the Introduction to the Subject Index
of *Chemical Abstracts*, Volumes 39 and 41.

acenaphthenyl $C_{12}H_9$—
  (*from acenaphthene*)
acetamido CH_3CONH—
acetenyl = ethynyl
acetimido $CH_3C(:NH)$—
acetonyl CH_3COCH_2—
acetonylidene CH_3COCH=
acetoxy CH_3COO—
acetyl CH_3CO—
acetylene =CHCH=
acridyl $C_{13}H_8N$— (*from acridine*)
acrylyl $CH_2:CHCO$—
adipyl —$OC(CH_2)_4CO$—
alanyl CH_3CHNH_2CO—
alkoxy RO— (*R = any alkyl radical*)
allyl $CH_2:CHCH_2$—
β-allyl = isopropenyl
amino H_2N—(*properly, in acid groups only; by some used synonymously with amino*)
amidoxalyl = oxamyl
amino H_2N—
amoxy $CH_3(CH_2)_4O$—
amyl $CH_3(CH_2)_4$—

tert-amyl

$$CH_3CH_2 \atop (CH_3)_2 \big\rangle C—$$

amylidene $CH_3(CH_2)_3CH$=
anilino C_6H_5NH—
anisal = anisylidene
anisoyl p-$CH_3OC_6H_4CO$—
anisyl = methoxyphenyl or methoxybenzyl
anisylidene p-$CH_3OC_6H_4CH$=
anthranoyl o-$H_2NC_6H_4CO$—
anthraquinonyl $C_{14}H_7O_2$— (*from anthraquinone, 2 isomers*)
anthryl $C_{14}H_9$— (*from anthracene, 3 isomers*)
anthrylene —$C_{14}H_8$— (*from anthracene, 14 isomers*)
antimono —Sb:Sb—
antipyroyl (*from antipyric acid*)

$$OC.N(C_6H_5).N(CH_3)C(CH_3):CCO—$$

antipyryl (*from antipyrine*)

$$OC.N(C_6H_5).N(CH_3)C(CH_3):C—$$

arseno —As:As—
arsenoso O:As—
arsinico (*from arsinic acid*)
  $(HO)OAs$=

arsino H_2As—
arso O_2As—
arsono (*from arsonic acid*)
  $(HO)_2OAs$—
arsylene HAs=
asaryl $2,4,5$-$(CH_3O)_3C_6H_2$—
asparagyl
  $H_2NCOCH_2CHNH_2CO$—
aspartyl —$COCH_2CHNH_2CO$—
auro Au—
azido N_3—
azino =NN=.
azo —N:N— (*as connective*)
azoxy —N(O)N—
benzal = benzylidene
benzamido C_6H_5CONH—
benzenyl = benzylidyne
benzidino $H_2NC_6H_4C_6H_4NH$—
  (*from benzidine*)
benziloyl $(C_6H_5)_2C(OH)CO$—
benzimidazolyl $C_7H_5N_2$— (*from benzimidazole*)
benzimido $C_6H_5C(:NH)$—
benzofuryl C_8H_5O— (*from benzofuran*)
benzhydryl $(C_6H_5)_2CH$—
benzhydrylidene $(C_6H_5)_2C$=
benzopyranyl C_9H_7O— (2-α-, etc.) (*from benzopyran*)
benzoxazolyl C_7H_4NO— (*from benzoxazole*)
benzoxy C_6H_5COO—
benzoyl C_6H_5CO—
benzoylene —C_6H_4CO—
benzyl $C_6H_5CH_2$—
benzylidene C_6H_5CH—
benzylidyne C_6H_5C≡
biphenylene —$C_6H_4C_6H_4$—
biphenylenebisazo
  —N:NC_6H_4C_6H_4N:N—
biphenylyl (2-, 3- or 4-)
  $C_6H_5C_6H_4$— (*from biphenyl*)
biphenylycarbonyl
  $C_6H_5C_6H_4CO$—
biphenylyloxy $C_6H_5C_6H_4O$—
bornyl (*from borneol*)

$$\overset{7}{C}(CH_3)_2 \atop CH_2.CH.CH_2.CH_2.C(CH_3).CH— \atop 3\ 4\ 5\ 6\ 1\ 2$$

boryl O:B—
bromo Br—
1-butenyl $CH_3CH_2CH:CH$—
2-butenyl $CH_3CH:CHCH_2$—
3-butenyl $CH_2:CH(CH_2)_2$—

butoxy $CH_3(CH_2)_3O$—
butyl $CH_3(CH_2)_3$—

sec-butyl

$$CH_3CH_2 \atop CH_3 \big\rangle CH—$$

tert-butyl $(CH_3)_3C$—
butylene (1,4) = tetramethylene
butylidene $CH_3(CH_2)_2CH$=
butyryl $CH_3(CH_2)_2CO$—
camphanyl $C_{10}H_{17}$— (*from camphane, 3 isomers*)
camphoroyl $C_{10}H_{14}O_2$= (*from camphoric acid*)
camphoryl $C_{10}H_{19}O$— (*from camphor*)
camphorylidene $C_{10}H_{14}O$= (*from camphor*)
caproyl $CH_3(CH_2)_4CO$—
capryl $CH_3(CH_2)_8CO$—
caprylyl $CH_3(CH_2)_6CO$—
carbamido = ureido
carbamyl H_2NCO—
carbanilino = phenylcarbamyl
carbazolyl $C_{12}H_8N$— (*from carbazole, 5 isomers*)
carbethoxy C_2H_5OOC—
carbomethoxy CH_3OOC—
carbonyl OC=
carbonyldioxy —OCOO—
carboxy HOOC—
carbyl —C—

carvacryl

$$\overset{4}{(CH_3)_2CH} \atop C_6H_3—^2 \atop ^1CH_3$$

cetyl = hexadecyl
chaulmoogroyl
  $C_5H_7(CH_2)_{12}CO$— (*from chaulmoogric acid*)
chaulmoogryl
  $C_5H_7(CH_2)_{12}CH_2$— (*from chaulmoogryl alcohol*)
chloro Cl—
chloromercuri ClHg—
chrysenyl $C_{18}H_{11}$— (*from chrysene*)
cinnamal = cinnamylidene
cinnamenyl = styryl
cinnamoyl $C_6H_5CH:CHCO$—
cinnamyl $C_6H_5CH:CHCH_2$—
cinnamylidene
  $C_6H_5CH:CHCH$=

cresotyl 2,3-HO(CH$_3$)C$_6$H$_3$CO—
(*from cresotic acid*) (*2,3-shown*)
cresoxy = toloxy
cresyl = *ar*-hydroxytolyl = tolyl
cresylene = tolylene
crotonyl CH$_3$CH:CHCO—
crotyl = 2-butenyl
cumal = *p*-cuminylidene
cumidino (CH$_3$)$_2$CHC$_6$H$_4$NH—
cuminal = *p*-cuminylidene
cuminyl *p*-(CH$_3$)$_2$CHC$_6$H$_4$CH$_2$—
cuminylidene
    p-(CH$_3$)$_2$CHC$_6$H$_4$CH=
cumoyl (*from cumic acid*)
    p-(CH$_3$)$_2$CHC$_6$H$_4$CO
cumyl (CH$_3$)$_2$CHC$_6$H$_4$—
cyanato NCO—
cyano NC—
cyclobutyl (*from cyclobutane*)
    C$_4$H$_7$—
cyclohexadienyl (2,4- shown)

$$\underset{6\quad5\quad4\quad3\quad2\quad1}{CH_2.CH:CH.CH:CH.CH—}$$

cyclohexadienylidene (2,4- *or*
    2,5-; 2,5- *shown*)

$$CH:CH.CH_2CH:CH.C=$$

cyclohexenyl C$_6$H$_9$— (*from*
    cyclohexene. 3 isomers)
cyclohexenylidene (2-shown)

$$CH_2.CH_2.CH_2.CH:CH.C=$$

cyclohexyl C$_6$H$_{11}$— (*from cyclo-*
    hexane)
cyclohexylidene

$$CH_2.CH_2.CH_2.CH_2.CH_2.C=$$

cyclopentenyl C$_5$H$_7$— (*from*
    cyclopentene)
cyclopentyl C$_5$H$_9$— (*from*
    cyclopentane)
cyclopropyl C$_3$H$_5$— (*from*
    cyclopropane)
cymyl C$_{10}$H$_{13}$— (*from cymene*)
2-*p*-cymyl = carvacryl
3-*p*-cymyl = thymyl
decyl CH$_3$(CH$_2$)$_9$—
desyl C$_6$H$_5$COCH(C$_6$H$_5$)—
diazo —N:N— or N:N=
diazoamino —N:NNH—
disilanoxy H$_3$SiSiH$_2$O—
disilanyl H$_3$SiSiH$_2$—
disilanylamino H$_3$SiSiH$_2$NH—
disilanylene —SiH$_2$SiH$_2$—
disilazanoxy H$_3$SiNHSiH$_2$O—
disilazanyl H$_3$SiNHSiH$_2$—
disilazanylamino
    H$_3$SiNHSiH$_2$NH—
disiloxanoxy H$_3$SiOSiH$_2$O—
disiloxanyl H$_3$SiOSiH$_2$—
disiloxanylamino
    H$_3$SiOSiH$_2$NH—
dodecyl CH$_3$(CH$_2$)$_{10}$CH$_2$—
duryl 2,3,5,6-(CH$_3$)$_4$C$_6$H—

durylene

enanthyl CH$_3$(CH$_2$)$_5$CO—
epoxy —O— (*to different atoms*
    already united in some other way)
ethene = ethylene
ethenyl = ethylidyne = vinyl
ethinyl = ethynyl
ethoxalyl C$_2$H$_5$OOCCO—
ethoxy C$_2$H$_5$O—
ethyl CH$_3$CH$_2$—
ethylene —CH$_2$CH$_2$—
ethylenedioxy —O(CH$_2$)$_2$O—
ethylidene CH$_3$CH=
ethylidyne CH$_3$C≡
ethynyl CH:C—
ethynylene —C:C—
fenchyl C$_{10}$H$_{17}$— (*from fenchane*)
fluorenyl C$_{13}$H$_9$— (*from fluorene,*
    5 isomers)
fluorenylidene C$_{13}$H$_8$= (*from*
    fluorene)
fluoro F—
formamido HCONH—
formazyl

formyl OCH—
furfural = furfurylidene

furfuryl O.CH:CH.CH:CCH$_2$—

furfurylidene

O.CH:CH.CH:CCH=

2-furoyl O.CH:CH.CH:CCO—

3-furoyl CH:CH.O.CH:CCO—
furyl (2 *isomers*, 2- *shown*)

O.CH:CH.CH:C—

furylidene

geranyl C$_{10}$H$_{17}$— (*from geraniol*)
glutamyl—
    —OCCHNH$_2$(CH$_2$)$_2$CO—
glutaryl OC(CH$_2$)$_3$CO—
glyceroyl CH$_2$OHCHOHCO—

glyceryl —CH$_2$CHCH$_2$—
glycolyl HOCH$_2$CO—
glycyl H$_2$NCH$_2$CO—
glyoxylyl OCHCO—
guaiacyl = *o*-methoxyphenyl
guanidino H$_2$NC(:NH)NH—

guanyl H$_2$NC(:NH)—
hendecyl CH$_3$(CH$_2$)$_{10}$—
heptyl CH$_3$(CH$_2$)$_6$—
hexadecyl CH$_3$(CH$_2$)$_{14}$CH$_2$—
hexyl CH$_3$(CH$_2$)$_5$—
hippuryl C$_6$H$_5$CONHCH$_2$CO—
homopiperonyl
    3,4-(CH$_2$O$_2$)C$_6$H$_3$CH$_2$CH$_2$—
hydnocarpoyl C$_5$H$_7$(CH$_2$)$_{10}$CO—
    (*from hydnocarpic acid*)
hydnocarpyl C$_5$H$_7$(CH$_2$)$_{10}$CH$_2$—
    (*from hydnocarpyl alcohol*)
hydrazi

hydrazino H$_2$NNH—
hydrazo —HNNH— (*to*
    different atoms)
hydrazono H$_2$NN=
hydrocinnamoyl
    C$_6$H$_5$CH$_2$CH$_2$CO—
hydroxamino HONH—
hydroximino = isonitroso
hydroxy (hydroxyl) HO—
-idene *added to any radical usu-*
    ally means a double bond at
    point of attachment
imidazolidyl C$_3$H$_7$N$_2$— (*from*
    imidazolidine)
imidazolyl C$_3$H$_3$N$_2$— (*from*
    imidazole, 4 isomers)
imido NH= (*properly, in acid*
    groups only); *by some used*
    synonymously with imino)
imino NH=
indanyl C$_9$H$_9$— (*from indan,*
    4 isomers)
indenyl C$_9$H$_7$— (*from indene,*
    7 isomers)
indolyl C$_8$H$_6$N— (*from indole,*
    7 isomers)
indolylidene

indyl = indolyl
iodo I—
iodoso OI—
iodoxy O$_2$I—
isoallyl = propenyl
isoamoxy
    (CH$_3$)$_2$CHCH$_2$CH$_2$O—
isoamyl (CH$_3$)$_2$CHCH$_2$CH$_2$—
isoamylidene
    (CH$_3$)$_2$CHCH$_2$CH=
isobutenyl = 2-methylpropenyl
isobutoxy (CH$_3$)$_2$CHCH$_2$O—
isobutyl (CH$_3$)$_2$CHCH$_2$—
isobutyryl (CH$_3$)$_2$CHCO—
isocyanato OCN—
isocyano C:N—
isohexyl (CH$_3$)$_2$CH(CH$_2$)$_3$—

isoindolyl C_8H_6N— (*from isoindole*, 4 *isomers*)

isoleucyl
$CH_3CH_2CH(CH_3)$-$CHNH_2CO$—

isonitro HOON$=$

isonitroso HON$=$

1-isopentenyl = 3-methyl-1-butenyl

isophthalal = isophthalylidene

isophthaloyl —OCC_6H_4CO— (*m*)

isophthalylidene
$=HCC_6H_4CH=$ (*m*)

isopropenyl $CH_2:C(CH_3)$—

isopropoxy $(CH_3)_2CHO$—

isopropyl $(CH_3)_2CH$—

isopropylidene $(CH_3)_2C=$

isoquinolyl C_9H_6N— (*from isoquinoline*, 7 *isomers*)

isothiocyano $S:C:N$—

isovaleryl $(CH_3)_2CHCH_2CO$—

isoxazolyl C_3H_2NO— (*from isoxazole*, 5 *isomers*)

keto = oxo

lauroyl (*from lauric acid*)
$CH_3(CH_2)_{10}CO$—

leucyl (*from leucine*)
$(CH_3)_2CHCH_2CHNH_2CO$—

malonyl —$OCCH_2CO$—

menthyl

$CH_3CH.(CH_2)_2.CH[CH(CH_3)_2].CH_2CH$—
1   4   3 2

(*from menthane*; 2-*p*- *shown*)

mercapto HS—

mercuri —Hg—

mesityl $2,4,6-(CH_3)_3C_6H_2$—

α-mesityl $3,5-(CH_3)_2C_6H_3CH_2$—

mesyl = methylsulfonyl

methene = methylene

methenyl = methylidyne

methionyl $CH_2(SO_2)_{22}=$

methoxy CH_3O—

methyl CH_3—

methylene $CH_2=$

methylenedioxy —OCH_2O—

methylidyne $CH\equiv$

methylol = (hydroxymethyl)

morpholinyl (*from morpholine*)
= C_4H_8NO—

myristoyl (*from myristic acid*)
$CH_3(CH_2)_{12}CO$—

naphthal = naphthylmethylene

naphthalimido (*from naphthalimide*) $C_{10}H_6(CO)_2N$—

naphthmyl = naphthyl methylidyne

naphthoxy $C_{10}H_7O$—

naphthoyl $C_{10}H_7CO$—

naphthyl (1- or 2-) $C_{10}H_7$—

naphthylene $C_{10}H_6=$

naphthylidene

1(4)-, etc.

nitramino O_2NNH—

nitrilo $N\equiv$

nitro O_2N—

aci-nitro = isonitro

nitroso ON—

nonyl $CH_3(CH_2)_8$—

norcamphanyl C_7H—$_{11}$ (*from norcamphane*)

octyl $CH_3(CH_2)_7$—

oleoyl (*from oleic acid*)
$C_{17}H_{33}CO$—

oxalyl —OCCO—

oxamido $H_2NCOCONH$—

oxamyl H_2NCOCO—

oxazolyl C_3H_2NO— (*from oxazole*)

oximido = isonitroso

oxo $O=$ (*to same atom*)

oxy —O— (*used as a connective;* cf. *epoxy and oxo*)

palmitoyl $CH_3(CH_2)_{14}CO$— (*from palmitic acid*)

pelargonyl $CH_3(CH_2)_7CO$— (*from pelargonic acid*)

pentamethylene
—$CH_2(CH_2)_3CH_2$—

pentazolyl $N=N—N=N—N$—

pentenyl (*like butenyl*) C_5H_9—

pentyl = amyl

perimidyl $C_{11}H_7N_2$— (*from perimidine*, 8 *isomers*)

perseleno $Se:Se=$

perthio (*replacing 0 only*) $S=S=$

phenacyl $C_6H_5COCH_2$—

phenacylidene $C_6H_5COCH=$

phenanthryl $C_{14}H_9$— (*from phenanthrene*, 5 *isomers*)

phenanthrylene —$C_{14}H_8$— (*several isomers*)

phenenyl $C_6H_3\equiv$ (*s-, as-, v-*)

phenethyl $C_6H_5CH_2CH_2$—

phenetidino $C_2H_5OC_6H_4NH$—

phenetyl (*o*, *m*, or *p*)
$C_2H_5OC_6H_4$—

phenoxy C_6H_5O—

phenyl C_6H_5—

phenylacetyl $C_6H_5CH_2CO$—

phenylazo $C_6H_5N:N$—

phenylcarbamido = phenylureido

phenylene $C_6H_4=$ (*o*, *m* or *p*)

phenylenebisazo
—$N \cdot NC_6H_4N:N$— (*o, m, p*)

phenylidene = cyclohexadienylidene

phenylsulfamyl $C_6H_5NHSO_2$—

phenylsulfonamido $C_6H_5SO_2NH$

phenylureido $C_6H_5NHCONH$—

phospharseno —P:As—

phosphazo —P:N—

phosphinico HOOP= (*from phosphinic acid*)

phosphino H_2P—

phospho O_2P—

phosphono $(HO)_2OP$—

phosphoro —P:P—

phosphoroso OP—

phthalal = phthalylidene

phthalidyl $C_6H_4CO.O.CH$—
(*from phthalide*)

phthalidylidene $C_6H_4CO.O.C=$
(*from phthalide*)

phthalimido $C_6H_4(CO)_2N$— (*o*)

phthaloyl —OCC_6H_4CO— (*o*)

phthalylidene $=HCC_6H_4CH=$ (*o*)

phytyl

$(CH_3)_2CH(CH_2)_3CH(CH_3)(CH_2)_3$-$—CH(CH_3)(CH_2)_3C(CH_3):CHCCH_2$—

picryl $2,4,6-(NO_2)_3C_6H_2$—

piperidyl $C_5H_{10}N$— (*from piperidine*, 4 *isomers*)

piperonyl
$3,4-(CH_2O_2)C_6H_3CH_2$—

piperonylidene
$3,4-(CH_2O_2)C_6H_3CH=$

pivalyl $(CH_3)_3CCO$— (*from pivalic acid*)

prolyl (*from proline*)

$NH.CH_2.CH_2.CH_2.CH.CO$—

propargyl = 2-propynyl

propenyl $CH_3CH:CH$—

propenylidene $CH_3CH:C=$

propiolyl $HC:CCO$—

propionyl CH_3CH_2CO—

propoxy $CH_3CH_2CH_2O$—

propyl $CH_3CH_2CH_2$—

propylene —$CH(CH_3)CH_2$—

propylidene $CH_3CH_2CH=$

1-propynyl $CH_3C:C$—

2-propynyl $CH:CCH_2$—

pseudoallyl = isopropenyl

as-pseudocumyl
$2,3,5-(CH_3)_3C_6H_2$—

s-pseudocumyl
$2,4,5-(CH_3)C_6H_2$—

v-pseudocumyl
$2,3,6-(CH_3)_3C_6H_2$—

pseudoindolyl C_8H_6N— (*from pseudoindole*, 7 *isomers*)

pyranyl C_5H_5O— (2-α, 2-γ, 3-α-, etc.)

pyrazinyl $C_4H_3N_2$— (*from pyrazine*)

pyrazolidyl $C_3H_7N_2$— (*from pyrazolidine*)

pyrazolyl $C_3H_3N_2$— (*from pyrazole*, 4 *isomers*)

pyrenyl $C_{16}H_9$— (*from pyrene*)

pyridyl C_5H_4N— (*from pyridine*, 3 *isomers*)

pyridylidene

4(1), etc.

pyrimidyl $C_4H_3N_2$— (from pyrimidine)

pyromucyl = 2-furoyl

pyrrolidyl C_4H_8N— (from pyrrolidine, 3 isomers)

pyrroyl

CH:CH.CH:CH.N.CO—

pyrryl C_4H_4N— (from pyrrole, 3 isomers)

quinazolyl $C_8H_5N_2$— (from quinazoline)

quinolyl C_9H_6N— (from quinoline, 7 isomers)

quinonyl $C_6H_3O_2$— (from quinone)

quinoxalyl $C_8H_5N_2$— (from quinoxaline)

salicyl = o-hydroxyphenyl = o-hydroxybenzyl

salicylidene HOC_6H_4CH= (o)

salicyloyl HOC_6H_4CO— (o)

selenino $(HO)OSe$—

seleninyl OSe=

seleno Se=

selenocyano $NCSe$—

selenono HO_3Se—

selenonyl $—SeO_2$—

selenyl HSe—

semicarbazido $NH_2CONHNH$—

senecioyl $(CH_3)_2C:CHCO$— (from senecioic acid)

siloxy H_3SiO—

silyl H_3S—

silylamino H_3SiNH—

1-silyldisilanyl $(H_3Si)_2SiH$—

silylene H_2Si=

silylidene HSi≡

stannyl H_3Sn—

stearoyl $CH_3(CH_2)_{16}CO$—

stibarseno $—Sb:As$—

stibinico $HOOSb$=

stibino H_2Sb—

stibo O_2Sb—

stibono $(HO)_2OSb$—

stiboso $O:Sb$—

stibyl = stibino

stibylene HSb=

styrene $—CH(C_6H_5)CH_2$—

styrolene = styrene

styryl $C_6H_5CH:CH$—

succinamyl
$H_2NCOCH_2CH_2CO$—

succinimido $(CH_2CO)_2N$—

succinyl $—OCCH_2CH_2CO$—

sulfamino HO_3SNH—

sulfamyl H_2NO_2S—

sulfanilamido
$p-H_2NC_6H_4SO_2NH$— (from sulfanilamide)

sulfanilyl $p-H_2NC_6H_4SO_2$— (from sulfanilic acid)

sulfyhydryl = mercapto

sulfino HO_2S—

sulfinyl OS=

sulfo HO_3S—

sulfonamido $—SO_2NH$—

sulfonyl $—SO_2$—

sulfuryl = sulfonyl

tauryl $H_2NCH_2CH_2SO_2$—

telluro Te=

terephthalal = terephthalylidene

terephthaloyl $—OCC_6H_4CO$— (p)

terephthalylidene
$=HCC_6H_4CH$= (p)

tetramethylene
$—CH_2CH_2CH_2CH_2$—

tetrazolyl CHN_4— (from tetrazole, 2 isomers)

thenoyl C_4H_3SCO— (from thiophenecarboxylic acid, 2 isomers)

thenyl (2 isomers) $C_4H_3SCH_2$—

thenylidene (2 isomers)
C_4H_3SCH=

thiazolidyl C_3H_6NS— (from thiazolidine)

thiazolyl C_3H_2NS— (from thiazole, 3 isomers)

thienyl C_4H_3S— (from thiophene, 2 isomers)

thio $—S$—

thiocarbamyl H_2NCS—

thiocarbonyl SC=

thiocyano NCS—

thiohydroxy = mercapto

thiol (S replacing O in OH)
Used in place of "thio" when required for distinction

thiono (S replacing O in CO)
Used in place of "thio" when required for distinction

thionyl = sulfinyl

thioxo (S replacing 2H in $> CH_2$)

thiuram = thiocarbamyl

thujyl $C_{10}H_{17}$— (from sabinane, attached at 2-position)

thymyl (from thymol)

HC:C(CH₃).CH:CH.C[CH(CH₃)₂].C—

toloxy (o, m, or p) $CH_3C_6H_4O$—

toluidino (o, m or p)
$CH_3C_6H_4ONH$—

toluyl (o, m or p)
$CH_3C_6H_4CO$—

α-toluyl = phenylacetyl

tolyl (o, m or p) $CH_3C_6H_4$—

α-tolyl = benzyl

tolylene (6 isomers) $CH_3C_6H_3$=

α-tolylene = benzylidene

tosyl = tolylsufonyl

triazeno $NH_2N:N$—

triazinyl $C_3H_2N_3$— (from triazine)

triazo = azido

triazolyl $C_2H_2N_3$— (from triazole)

trimethylene $—CH_2CH_2CH_2$—

trisilanyl $H_3SiSiH_2SiH_2$—

trisilanylene $—SiH_2SiH_2SiH_2$—

trityl = triphenylmethyl

tryptophyl $C_{11}H_{11}B_2O$— (from tryptophan)

tyrosyl
$p-HOC_6H_4CH_2CHNH_2CO$— (from tyrosine)

undecyl = hendecyl (in sense $C_{11}H_{23}$—)

uramino = ureido

ureido H_2NCONH—
(by some used synonymously with ureylene)

ureylene $—HNCONH$—

valeryl $CH_3(CH_2)_3CO$—

valyl $(CH_3)_2CHCHNH_2CO$— (from valine)

vanillal = vanillylidene

vanilloyl
$3,4-(CH_3O)(HO)C_6H_3CO$—

vanillyl
$3,4-(CH_3O)(HO)C_6H_3CH_2$—

vanillylidene
$3,4-(CH_3O)(HO)C_6H_3CH$=

veratral = veratrylidene

veratroyl $3,4-(CH_3O)_2C_6H_3CO$—

veratryl $3,4-(CH_3O)_2C_6H_3CH_2$—

veratrylidene
$3,4-(CH_3O)_2C_6H_3CH$=

vinyl $H_2C:CH$—

vinylene $—CH:CH$—

vinylidene $H_2C:C$=

xanthyl $C_{13}H_9O$— (from xanthene, 6 isomers)

xenyl = biphenylyl

xyloyl $(CH_3)_2C_6H_3CO$— (from xylic acid, 7 isomers)

xylyl $(CH_3)_2C_6H_3$—

xylylene $—H_2CC_6H_4CH_2$—

ORGANIC RING COMPOUNDS

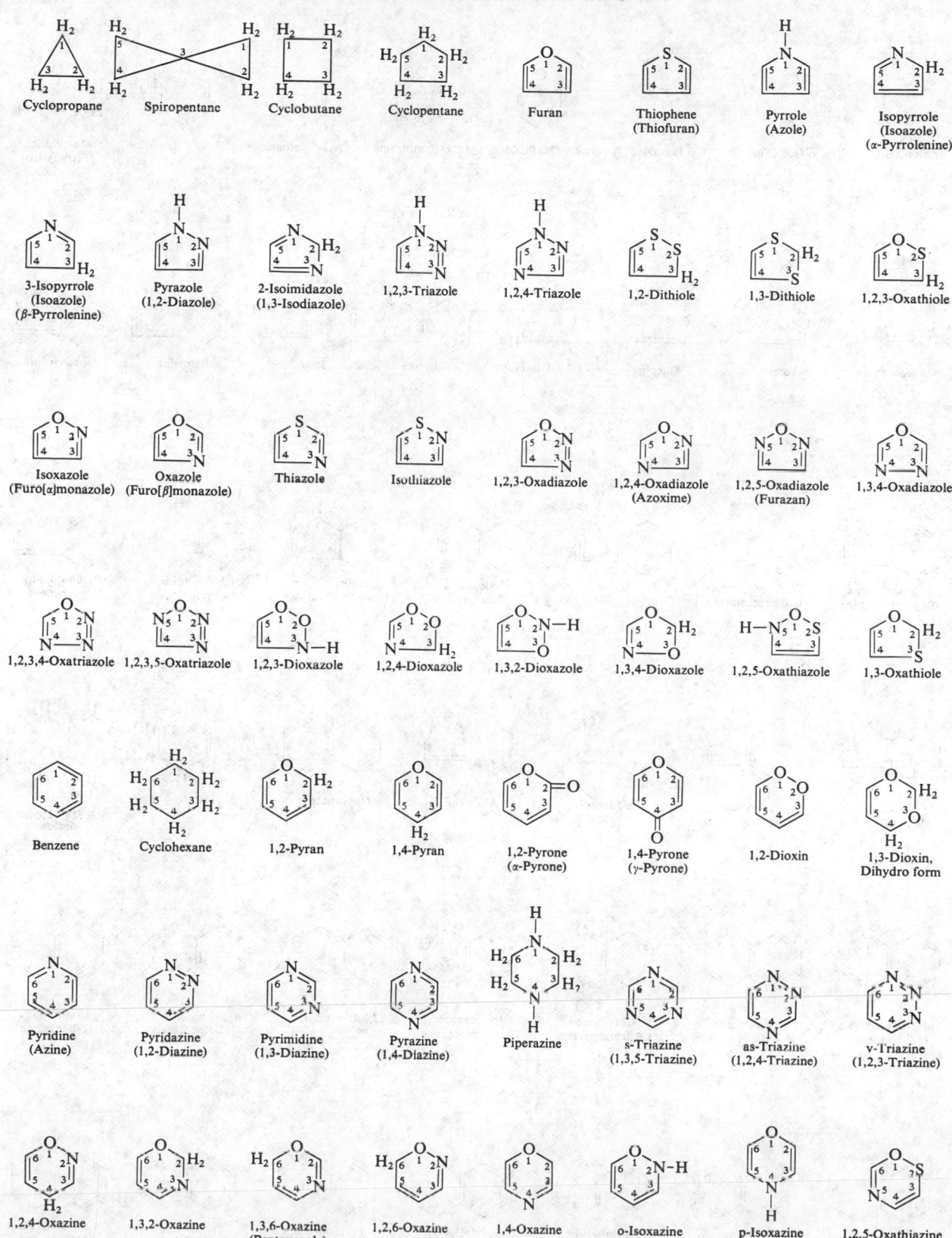

Cyclopropane   Spiropentane   Cyclobutane   Cyclopentane   Furan   Thiophene (Thiofuran)   Pyrrole (Azole)   Isopyrrole (Isoazole) (α-Pyrrolenine)

3-Isopyrrole (Isoazole) (β-Pyrrolenine)   Pyrazole (1,2-Diazole)   2-Isoimidazole (1,3-Isodiazole)   1,2,3-Triazole   1,2,4-Triazole   1,2-Dithiole   1,3-Dithiole   1,2,3-Oxathiole

Isoxazole (Furo[α]monazole)   Oxazole (Furo[β]monazole)   Thiazole   Isothiazole   1,2,3-Oxadiazole   1,2,4-Oxadiazole (Azoxime)   1,2,5-Oxadiazole (Furazan)   1,3,4-Oxadiazole

1,2,3,4-Oxatriazole   1,2,3,5-Oxatriazole   1,2,3-Dioxazole   1,2,4-Dioxazole   1,3,2-Dioxazole   1,3,4-Dioxazole   1,2,5-Oxathiazole   1,3-Oxathiole

Benzene   Cyclohexane   1,2-Pyran   1,4-Pyran   1,2-Pyrone (α-Pyrone)   1,4-Pyrone (γ-Pyrone)   1,2-Dioxin   1,3-Dioxin, Dihydro form

Pyridine (Azine)   Pyridazine (1,2-Diazine)   Pyrimidine (1,3-Diazine)   Pyrazine (1,4-Diazine)   Piperazine   s-Triazine (1,3,5-Triazine)   as-Triazine (1,2,4-Triazine)   v-Triazine (1,2,3-Triazine)

1,2,4-Oxazine   1,3,2-Oxazine   1,3,6-Oxazine (Pentoxazole)   1,2,6-Oxazine   1,4-Oxazine   o-Isoxazine   p-Isoxazine   1,2,5-Oxathiazine

C-50

ORGANIC RING COMPOUNDS (Continued)

1,4-Oxazine

o-Isoxazine

p-Isoxazine

1,2,5-Oxathiazine

1,2,6-Oxathiazine

1,4,2-Oxadiazine

1,3,5,2-Oxadiazine

Morpholine
(Tetrahydro-
p-isoxazine)

Azepine

Oxepin

Thiepin

1,2,4-Diazepine

Indene

Isoindene

Benzofuran
(Coumarone)

Isobenzofuran

Thionaphthene
(Benzothiofuran)

Isothionaphthene
(Isobenzothiofuran)

Indole

Indolenine
(3-Pseudoindole)

2-Isobenzazole
(Pseudoisoindole)

1,5-Pyrindine
(4-Pyrindine)

Pyrano[3,4-b]-
pyrrole

Isoindazole
(Benzpyrazole)

Indoxazine
(Benzisoxazole)

Benzoxazole

Anthranil

Naphthalene

Tetralin

Decalin
(Bicyclo[4,4,0]-
decane)

1,2-Benzopyran
(1,2-Chromene)

Coumarin
(1,2-Benzopyrone)

Chromone
(1,4-Benzopyrone)

Isocoumarin
(2,1-Benzopyrone)

2,3-Benzopyrone

Quinoline
(1-Benzazine)

Isoquinoline
(2-Benzazine)

Cinnoline
(1,2-Benzodiazine)

Quinazoline
(1,3-Benzodiazine)

Naphthyridine

Pyrido[3,4-b]-
pyridine

Pyrido[3,2-b]-
pyridine

Pyrido[4,3-b]-
pyridine

1,3,2-Benzoxazine

ORGANIC RING COMPOUNDS (Continued)

1,4,2-Benzoxazine

2,3,1-Benzoxazine

3,1,4-Benzoxazine

1,2-Benzisoxazine

1,4-Benzisoxazine

Anthracene

Phenanthrene

Benzonaphthene
(Phenalene)

Fluorene

Carbazole

Xanthene

Acridine

Norpinane

Purine

Steroid ring system

R; nearly always methyl
R'; usually methyl
R"; various groups

A more extensive listing of ring compounds and systems may be found in the following:

Chemical Abstracts, annual subject index.

The Ring Index, Patterson and Capell, Reinhold Publishing Company, 1940.

Lexikon der Kohlenstoffverbindungen, Richter, Leopold Voss, 1910.

The numbering system for the compounds listed above is that used in The Ring Index.

TABLE OF PHYSICAL PROPERTIES OF ORGANIC COMPOUNDS
EXPLANATION OF TABLE

The section of this book dealing with Physical Constants of Organic Compounds was prepared by Saul Patai, Ph.D. and J. Zabicky, Ph.D. Enlarged and revised by Zvi Rappoport, Ph.D., 1969

KEY TO THE EXPLANATION
(numbers refer to paragraphs)

TABLE OF PHYSICAL PROPERTIES OF ORGANIC COMPOUNDS

1. The table of Physical Constants of Organic Compounds is a compilation of data on some 13600 organic compounds that include those of wide application in teaching, industry, medicine and research.

CONTENTS OF TABLE

2. **Number of entry.** Each entry has a number preceded by a letter corresponding to the first letter of the name of the parent compound (see paragraphs 17–26, 31, 32). Cross references are left unnumbered. The number of entry is used in the formula, melting point and boiling point indexes (see paragraphs 13–15).

3. **Name of compound.** See rules for naming of compounds (paragraphs 16 ff.).

4. **Synonyms and formula.**

a) *Synonyms.* For the sake of brevity, the number of synonyms in an entry is limited. Additional synonyms may readily be formed by derivation from the names given to simpler or less substituted compounds; *e.g.*: **Benzoic acid, 4-nitro,** ethyl ester is given no synonyms but they may be derived from those appearing under **Benzoic acid,** for example ethyl *p*-nitrobenzene-carboxylate.

b) *Formula.* Each entry has either a structural or an empirical formula. For compounds having complex structural formula both are given.

i) Structural formulas—simple ones are given in this column, complex ones at the end of the Table.

ii) Empirical formulas are given if the compound is cyclic and appears among a series of compounds derived from the same cyclic parent compound; e.g.:

u134 **Uric acid, 7-methyl-** $C_6H_6N_4O_3$. *See* u131 means that in entry u131 appears the numbered skeleton of **Uric acid,** and the structural formula of u134 may be derived from that of u131.

Structural formulas in the Table give generally no configurational details, and when they do, they seldom give absolute configurations. These details are to be looked for either in the original literature or in specialized textbooks.

5. **Molecular weight.** Computed according to International Atomic Weight values of 1961.

6. **Color, crystalline form, specific rotation and max(log ε).**

a) *Color*: Solid compounds are to be considered as crystalline if not otherwise stated. Data on solvents used and solvents of crystallization are given in brackets. Some examples will explain the usage of the Table (see also list of abbreviations):

ABBREVIATION	MEANING
pl	plates
pl(al)	plates obtained from alcohol as the solvent
pl(al + 1½)	plates obtained from alcohol crystallizing with 1½ molecules of the **same solvent** per molecule of compound
pl(al + ?)	as above but the amount of solvent of crystallization per molecule of compound is undefined
pl(aq ace + 2w)	here the solvent of crystallization is one of the components of the solvent, *i.e.*, two molecules of water
(al)	compound crystallizes from alcohol but crystalline form is not reported.

If no melting point is given in the Table the compound is a liquid at room temperature, unless otherwise stated.

b) *Crystalline form*: No special remark is made if the compound is colorless or no data on its color are available; otherwise an abbreviation appears before the crystalline form. (See table of abbreviations).

c) *Specific rotation* appears according to the common usage, *e.g.*:

$$[a]_D^{25} - 25.8(w, c = 4)$$

d) $\lambda_{max}(\log \varepsilon)$: The main maxima in the ultraviolet spectra, in the solvent shown in the superscript (see list of abbreviations) are given with the logarithm of the molar absorption coefficient ε. Solvent is missing when it was not given in the original reference, log ε is missing when it was not determined. Mostly the long wave absorption maxima is only given, but for important compounds (especially aromatic ones) some of the lower wavelength maxima are also given.

Bracketed abbreviations indicate solvent and concentration, *i.e.*, in the above example, solvent water and concentration 4%.

7. **Melting point.** Remarks on this physical property appear as abbreviations after the m.p. Melting points of questionable accuracy are given in brackets.

8. **Boiling point.** The pressure at which this physical property was determined appears as a superscript. If no superscript is given, pressure is about one atmosphere. Remarks on this physical property appear as abbreviations. Boiling points of questionable accuracy are given in brackets.

9. **Density** is relative to water, otherwise it has the dimensions g/ml. A superscript indicates the temperature of the liquid and a subscript indicates the temperature of water to which the density is referred.

10. **Refractive index** is reported for the D line of the spectrum of sodium (n_D). The temperature of determination of this physical property appears as a superscript.

11. **Solubility.** Data are given for the most common solvents. As numerical data on this property scarcely appear in the literature, and when they appear their degree of approximation is not great, it was preferred to rely on the intuitive meaning that the following scale has for the chemist (corresponding abbreviations in brackets): insoluble (i), slightly soluble (δ), soluble (s), very soluble (v), miscible (∞), decomposes (d). If no special remark is made about the temperature, the reference is to room temperature; otherwise, a superscript appears.

12. **Literature references** are given to general sources of data such as *Beilstein's Handbook, Elsevier's Encyclopaedia*, etc. The superscript after the boldtype number indicates the number of the supplement (Ergenzungswerk) of *Beilstein's Handbook*; e.g.: **B7¹**, 12 means page 12 of the first supplement to volume 7 of *Beilstein*.

INDEXES

Three indexes are found at the end of the Table:

13. **Empirical formula index** is arranged according to increasing C, H, and remaining elements in alphabetical order. Hydrates are entered under the formula of the *anhydrous* compound. Salts, complexes, etc., are found under their total formulae.

14. **Melting point index** is arranged according to increasing melting or freezing points. Only the lower temperature of the melting range is given. Remarks to the melting point in the main table, such as decomposition, sublimation, etc., are omitted. Melting points are rounded off to the nearest unit.

15. **Boiling point index** is arranged according to increasing boiling point of compounds of which the boiling point is given at a pressure near to 1 atm. (*i.e.*, 700–780 mm. Hg). Only the lower temperature of the boiling range is given. No special entries are made for remarks on the boiling point contained in the main table. Boiling points are rounded off to the nearest unit.

RULES FOR THE NAMING OF COMPOUNDS*

16. Naming of compounds is based mainly on *International Union of Chemistry* (*IUC*) and *Chemical Abstracts* usages, with variations adapted to the scope and range of the Table, in order to enable the user to find compounds even when their trivial names are not known.

17. A suitable systematic nomenclature is used in order to bring as near as possible compounds that are isomeric derivatives of the same parent compound, *e.g.*, physical properties appear under the entries **Benzene, 1,2-dihydroxy-, Benzene, 1,3-dihydroxy-,** and **Benzene, 1,4-dihydroxy-;** under **Hydroquinone, Pyrocatechol** and **Resorcinol** a cross reference directs the user towards the systematic names. No special entry or cross-reference is made for *e.g.*, **Bromoresorcinol;** this will be found under **Benzene, bromo(dihydroxy)-,** with the appropriate numbering before the names of the substituents. Another example: **4-Chloroquinaldine;** the trivial name of the parent compound is **Quinaldine,** it appears as: **Quinaldine** *see* **Quinoline, 2-methyl-;** accordingly the properties of **4-Chloroquinaldine** will appear under **Quinoline, 4-chloro-2-methyl-.**

18. Physical constants of a compound having widely used trivial and systematic names will appear under one of them only. The remaining names will appear with a cross-reference to the assigned name, *e.g.*:

Resorcinol *see* **Benzene, 1,3-dihydroxy-**

Propanoic acid, 2-amino- *see* **Alanine**

Very complicated compounds such as some natural products, dyes, etc. appear almost exclusively under their trivial names.

---

* The rules for nomenclature followed by the Table were adapted to the present, relatively limited scope of some thousands of compounds. For other use the IUPAC 1957 rules, which appear in this Handbook, may be consulted.

19. Rules adopted by the Table for the naming of compounds according to their functional groups appear in paragraphs 27 ff.

20. The naming of a compound has three phases:
a) Determination of the parent compound.
b) Determination and numbering of the substituents in the skeleton of the parent compound.
c) Determination of the derivatives of the principal functions of the compound.

e.g.:

CO_2H benzene ring with CH_3	Phase a) **Benzoic acid**
	Phase b) **3-methyl-**

Accordingly it appears as **Benzoic acid, 3-methyl-**

$CO_2C_2H_5$ benzene ring with CH_3	Phase a) **Benzoic acid**
	Phase b) **3-methyl-**
	Phase c) ethyl ester

therefore it appears as **Benzoic acid, 3-methyl-**, ethyl ester.

21. The parent compound has at most one kind of principal function, (*e.g.:* acid) but this function may be multiple, (*e.g.:* diacid, triacid, etc.); examples:

$CH_3COCH_2CH_2CO_2H$ appears as **Pentanoic acid, 4-oxo-**
                                     not as: **Pentanon-4-on-1-oic acid**

$HO_2CCH_2CH(CH_3)COCH_2CO_2H$ appears as **Hexanedioic acid, 3-methyl-4-oxo-**

Unsaturation is not considered as a function and, when possible, it is included in the name of the parent compound; *e.g.:*

$CH_2:CHCH_2CO_2H$ appears as **3-Butenoic acid.**

Exceptions to this rule are some cyclic ketones that may be designated as ring systems (see paragraph 83) and some natural products, such as **Pregnenolone** (the functions alcohol and ketone appear in the parent compound).

22. Entries in the Table are made first according to alphabetical order of parent compounds (paragraph 20, phase a), and then according to alphabetical order of the substituents in the skeleton of the parent compound (paragraph 20, phase b). It should be emphasized that numbers or single letters that are used in the designation of the compound are not considered for the alphabetisation. If the designation of a compound includes phase c of paragraph 20 this compound appears immediately after the compound that is designated without phase c and has the same substituents bearing the same numbers; *e.g.:*

> **Benzoic acid**
> **Benzoic acid, 2-chloro-**
> **Benzoic acid, 2-chloro-**, ethyl ester
> **Benzoic acid, 3-chloro-**
> **Benzoic acid, 3-chloro-**, allyl ester

23. Prefixes indicating multiplicity of substituents as **di-, tri-, bis-, tris,** etc. and the prefix **iso-,** as in **dimethyl-, tripropyl-, bis(nitrophenyl)-, tris(aminomethyl)-, isopropyl-,** etc., are indexed under **d, t, b, t, i** respectively. The prefixes *sec-* and *tert-* are regarded as numbers, and therefore, they are not considered for the alphabetization.

24. If the designation of a compound is difficult, the use of the empirical formula index is suggested (paragraph 13).

25. When a compound is designated by the name of its principal functional group that alone is not a compound, as is the case with some amines, ketones, azo-compounds, etc., after the name of the functions the skeleton is designated by alphabetical order, and then the substituents on each of the groups attached to the principal function; *e.g.:*

**Amine, benzyl 2-naphthyl phenyl,
4,5'-dihydroxy-4''-nitro-**

It is to be noted that substituents of benzyl (the first radical in the name) are unprimed; substituents of naphthyl (the second radical in the name) are primed; substituents of phenyl (the third radical in the name) are doubly primed.

26. The principal function of the parent compound has a number as low as possible.

HYDROCARBONS*

27. **Aliphatic hydrocarbons.** IUC rules 4–10 are followed, but some remarks are added:

a) For C_{11} hendecane (and not undecane) is used (see IUC rule 5).

b) From the possibilities in IUC rule 7 the alphabetical order is used always (see paragraph 22).

c) Regarding IUC rules 8 and 9: numbers before the name of the hydrocarbon or the particle indicating unsaturation indicate the carbon with the lower number of the two connected by the unsaturated link, e.g.:

$CH_3CH_2CH_2CH:CH_2$	**1-Pentene**
$CH_2:C:CHCH_3$	**1,2-Butadiene**
$CH_3C:CCH:CHCH:CHCH_3$	**2,4-Octadien-6-yne**

d) Regarding IUC rule 10: in an unsaturated hydrocarbon the longest chain containing the maximum number of double and triple bonds will be considered; e.g.:

$$CH_2:C\!-\!CH:CH_2$$
$$\mid$$
$$CH_2CH_3$$

appears as   **1-3-Butadiene, 2-ethyl-**
not as   **1-Pentene, 3-methylene-**
not as   **1-Butene, 2-ethenyl-**

Preference is given to the double bond over the triple bond in the fundamental chain; e.g.:

$$CH_2:CHCHCH:CH_2$$
$$\mid$$
$$C:CH$$

Appears as   **1,4-Pentadiene, 3-ethenyl-**
not as   **1-Penten-4-yne, 3-ethenyl-**

28. **Cyclic hydrocarbons:**

a) *Saturated monocyclic* hydrocarbons follow IUC rule 11.

b) *Unsaturated cyclic* hydrocarbons follow IUC rule 12 with the following comments: the names **tetralin** for 1,2,3, 4-tetrahydronaphthalene, **decalin** for decahydronaphthalene, **indan** for 2,3-dihydroindene, and special names for steroidal skeletons are retained.

c) *Aromatic parent hydrocarbons.* The names **benzene, naphthalene, anthracene** are used. For linear arrangements of four or more fused benzene rings names are formed by a numeric prefix denoting the number of fused benzene rings and the suffix -cene: **tetracene, pentacene,** etc. The usual trivial names are given to other arrangements: **phenanthrene, chrysene, indene, fluorene, benzanthrene, dibenzophenanthrene,** etc.

d) *Bridged hydrocarbon ring systems* appear under the headings: **bicyclo-** or **tricyclo-** according to Baeyer's system; e.g.:

Bicyclo[3.1.0]hexane

However in most cases compounds having such structures appear only under their trivial names.

e) *Spiro, dispiro, etc.* compounds appear under these headings; e.g.:

Spiro[4,5]decane

f) *Cyclic hydrocarbons with side chains.* IUC rules 49aI and 49aII are followed with some variations: the *Chemical Abstracts* usage is followed in conjunction with IUC rule 49aI: the parent compound is (when possible) the one containing the higher number of carbon atoms; e.g.: **Benzene, pentyl-**, *not* Pentane, 1-phenyl-; **Docosane, 1(1-naphthyl)-**, *not* Naphthalene, 1-docosyl-. The form **Hexane, phenyl-** is preferred. When the side chain is unsaturated and the cyclic compound is benzene or a benzene derivative, preference is given to the unsaturated aliphatic hydrocarbon; e.g.: $C_6H_5CH_2CH_2CH:CH_2$ is **1-Butene, 4-phenyl-**; $C_6H_5C:CCH_2CH_3$ is **1-Butyne, 1-phenyl-**.

The following are exceptions:

$C_6H_5C:CH$	**Benzene, ethynyl-**
$C_6H_5CH_2CH:CH_2$	**Benzene, allyl-**
$C_6H_5CH:CHCH_3$	**Benzene, propenyl-**
$C_6H_5CH:CH_2$	**Styrene**
$C_6H_5CH:CHC_6H_5$	**Stilbene**

* In order to avoid unnecessary repetition, the 1930 Liége rules for nomenclature of the International Union of Chemistry are referred to only by number, e.g. IUC rule 1. These rules may be found in *J. Am. Chem. Soc.* **55**, 3905-25 (1933); the IUPAC 1957 rules appeared after preparation of this table.

For alkyl derivatives of benzene the only trivial name retained is **toluene** for $C_6H_5CH_3$. Toluene derivatives appear under the heading **Toluene** if no other carbon atom is attached either to the methyl group or to the ring; otherwise the name will appear under **Benzene** or elsewhere as suitable; *e.g.*:

H_2N—⟨ ⟩—CH_3 **Toluene, 4-amino-**

$(CH_3)_2CH$—⟨ ⟩—CH_3 **Benzene, 1-isopropyl-4-methyl-**

⟨ ⟩—⟨ ⟩—CH_3 **Biphenyl, 4-methyl-**

Substitution in the methyl group of toluene will be labelled a and the word benzyl will not appear as a parent compound (only as a substituent); *e.g.*:

Cl—⟨ ⟩—CH_2Br **Toluene, a-bromo-4-chloro-**

⟨ ⟩—CH_2OH **Toluene, a-hydroxy-**
                         (cross-reference under **Benzyl alcohol**).

Regarding IUC rule 49aII the trivial name **Stilbene** is used instead of **Ethene, 1,2-diphenyl-**.

29. **Heterocyclic systems.** Trivial names are used, or when these are lacking systematic names are formed by using the homocyclic system name and the particles **oxa-, aza-, thia-,** etc.

The following trivial names are used for simple heterocyclic compounds: **furan, pyran, pyrrole, pyrazole, imidazole, piperidine, pyridine, pyrazine, pyrimidine, pyrazidine, thiophene,** etc. Fused heterocyclic systems follow the same rule; trivial names such as acridine, indole, quinoline, isoquinoline, quinazoline, quinoxaline, xanthene, etc., or juxtaposed names such as **1,2-benzopyran,** etc. are used. All names of fused ring systems beginning with **benzo-, dibenzo-,** etc. appear under **b, d,** etc. respectively.

30. **Radicals.** Normal alkyl radicals are named according to the Geneva designation. The following radical names are also used: **phenyl, benzyl, tolyl, styryl, allyl, isopropyl, isobutyl,** *sec*-**butyl,** *tert*-**butyl, ethenyl, ethynyl.** Larger non-normal alkyl radicals are designated by forming the longest chain containing the radical linkage and numbering the carbon on which the radical links itself to other groups according to the nearest end of the longest chain; *e.g.*:

$$\overset{8}{C}H_3\overset{7}{C}H_2\overset{6}{C}H\overset{5}{C}H_2\overset{4}{C}H\overset{3}{C}H_2\overset{2}{C}H\overset{1}{C}H_3$$
$$\qquad\quad | \qquad\quad\quad |$$
$$\qquad\; CH_3 \qquad\;\; CH_3$$
         (2,6-dimethyl-4-octyl)-

The following IUC rules are also used: 54–62, 64, 65, 67.

31. **Substituted Hydrocarbons.** The following substituents never appear in a parent compound: **arsono-** (—AsO), **arso-** (—AsO$_2$), **boryl-** (—BO), **bromo-** (—Br), **chloro-** (—Cl), **fluoro-** (—F), **iodo-** (—I), **iodoso-** (—IO), **iodoxy-** (—IO$_2$), **nitro-** (—NO$_2$), **nitroso-** (—NO), **phospho-** (—PO$_2$), **phosphoroso-** (—PO), **stibo-** (—SbO$_2$), **triazo-** (—N$_3$). These are always treated as substituents (paragraph 20, phase b).

COMPOUNDS CONTAINING FUNCTIONAL GROUPS

32. **Order of precedence of functions.** When a compound bears one or more functions the parent compound is designated according to the following order of precedence: onium compound, acid (and derivatives of the acidic function), aldehyde, ketone, alcohol, amine, ether, sulfide, sulfone, sulfoxide, etc.

ONIUM COMPOUNDS

33. Onium compounds appear mainly under their trivial names.

34. **Ammonium compounds.** When four organic radicals are attached to the N atom, the compound appears under **Ammonium,** otherwise it appears as the corresponding salt of an amine; *e.g.*:

$C_6H_5\overset{+}{N}(CH_3)_3I^-$ **Ammonium, phenyl trimethyl,** iodide

$(C_2H_5)_3\overset{+}{N}H\ Cl^-$ **Amine, triethyl,** hydrochloride

$Cl^-\overset{+}{N}H_3CH_2CO_2H$ **Glycine,** hydrochloride

35. **Betaines.** The word betaine appears after the name of the corresponding acid ("betaine" alone is the name of a compound); *e.g.*:

$C_6H_5(CH_3)_2\overset{+}{N}CH_2COO^-$ **Glycine,** N,N-**dimethyl-**N-**phenyl-,** betaine

ACIDS AND ACID DERIVATIVES

36. Aliphatic monocarboxylic acids. The longest chain containing the carboxylic group is taken as the parent compound. The carbon of the carboxyl group is numbered 1. The Geneva nomenclature is followed. (IUC rule 29); *e.g.*:

$$\overset{6}{C}H_3\overset{5}{C}H_2\overset{4}{C}H_2\overset{3}{C}H\overset{2}{C}H_2\overset{1}{C}O_2H$$
$$\underset{\displaystyle CH:CH_2}{|}$$

Hexanoic acid, 3-ethenyl-

$$\overset{5}{C}H_3\overset{4}{C}H_2\overset{3}{C}H:\overset{2}{C}\overset{1}{C}O_2H$$
$$\underset{\displaystyle CH_3}{|}$$

2-Pentenoic acid, 2-methyl-

In exception to this rule, the following trivial names are retained:

HCO_2H **Formic acid**
CH_3CO_2H **Acetic acid**
$C_6H_5CH:CHCO_2H$ **Cinnamic acid**

37. Cyclic acids. After the name of the ring the suffix **-carboxylic acid** is attached. The atom to which the carboxyl is attached is numbered 1 unless the ring system has a fixed numbering, in which case the carboxylic group takes a number as low as possible; *e.g.*:

—CO_2H **2-Cyclopentenecarboxylic acid**

—CO_2H **2-Phenanthrenecarboxylic acid**

CO_2H / CO_2H **1,3-Benzenedicarboxylic acid**
(cross reference under **Isophthalic acid**)

HO_2C——CO_2H **1,4-Benzenedicarboxylic acid**
(cross reference under **Terephthalic acid**)

Linear acids are given preference over cyclic acids; *e.g.*:

CO_2H / —CH_2CO_2H **Acetic acid, (2-carboxyphenyl)-**
(cross reference under **Homophthalic acid**)

Exceptions: **benzoic acid, 1-naphthoic acid, 2-naphthoic acid, phthalic acid.**

38. Aliphatic, dicarboxylic acids are found under the Geneva name of the chain containing both carboxylic groups; *e.g.*:

$$HO_2\overset{5}{C}\overset{4}{C}H_2\overset{3}{C}:\overset{2}{C}H\overset{1}{C}O_2H$$
$$\underset{\displaystyle CH_2(CH_2)_6CH_3}{|}$$

2-Pentenedioic acid, 3-octyl-

Trivial names are used for the following acids: **oxalic, malonic, succinic, maleic, fumaric, tartaric, citric.**

39. Aliphatic polycarboxylic acids are designated using the **-carboxylic acid** suffix; *e.g.*:

$$HO_2CCH_2CH_2CHCH_2CO_2H$$
$$\underset{\displaystyle CO_2H}{|}$$

1,2,4-Butanetricarboxylic acid

40. Thioacids. After the name of the acid one of the following particles will appear: **thio-, dithio-, thiolo-, thiono-.** The last two appear only when it is certain that the ketonic or the hydroxylic oxygen is substituted by a sulfur atom.

41. **Imidic, hydroxamic, nitrolic and nitrosolic acids.** Only simple compounds of this type appear in the Table. The various cases arising are exemplified as follows:

$CH_3CH_2CH_2C(:NH)OH$ **Butanimidic acid**

$C_6H_5C(:NH)OH$ **Benzimidic acid**

—$C(:NH)OH$ **2-Pyrrolecarboxymidic acid**

$CH_3CH_2C(:NOH)OH$ **Propanehydroxamic acid**

$C_6H_5C(:NOH)OH$ **Benzohydroxamic acid**

—$C(:NOH)OH$ **2-Furancarbohydroxamic acid**

$CH_3C(:NOH)NO_2$ **Acetonitrolic acid**

$CH_3C(:NOH)NO$ **Acetonitrosolic acid**

42. **Sulfonic and sulfinic acids.** According to IUC rule 47, with the following comment: onium and carboxylic acids are functions that precede the sulfonic and sulfinic acids, and so when the former functions are present in the compound the particles **sulfo-** and **sulfino-** will be used; *e.g.:*

HO_3S——CO_2H **Benzoic acid, 4-sulfo-**

43. **Sulfenic acids** are found under the corresponding hydrocarbon structure followed by the suffix **sulfenic acid;** *e.g.:*

C_6H_5—S—OC_2H_5 **Benzenesulfenic acid, ethyl ester.**

44. **Aldehydic and ketonic acids.** When the carbonyl group is present in the principal chain the particle **oxo-** is used; *e.g.:*

$CH_3\overset{O}{\overset{\|}{C}}CH_2COOH$ **Butanoic acid, 3-oxo-**
(cross reference under **Acetoacetic acid**)

$CH_3\underset{CHO}{\overset{|}{C}H}CH_2CH_2CO_2H$ **Pentanoic acid, 4-methyl-5-oxo-**

If the aldehyde group is not in the principal chain the particles **formyl-** or **oxo-** are used; *e.g.:*

Benzoic acid, 3-formyl-

$CH_3CH_2COCH_2\underset{CH_3(CH_2)_3CH_2}{\overset{|}{C}H}CO_2H$ **Dodecanoic acid, 2(2-oxobutyl)-**

See however paragraphs 83, 84.

45. **Hydroxyacids.** The hydroxy group is considered as a substituent; *e.g.:*

$CH_3CHOHCO_2H$ **Propanoic acid, 2-hydroxy-**
(cross reference under **Lactic acid**).

Exceptions: **tartaric, citric,** and acids derived from carbohydrates such as gluconic, mannonic, etc.

46. **Aminoacids.** Most of them appear under their trivial names with cross references under their systematic names.

47. **Orthoacids** appear under the heading **Ortho-;** *e.g.:*

$CH_3C(OCH_3)_3$ **Orthoacetic acid, trimethyl ester.**

$C_6H_5C(OC_2H_5)_3$ **Orthobenzoic acid, triethyl ester.**

48. **Acids attached by a non-carbon link.** The following examples explain the usage of the Table where the same acid appears attached twice to a non-carbon atom:

$NH(CH_2CO_2H)_2$ **Acetic acid, iminodi-**

     Benzoic acid, 2,3′-oxydi-

     Benzenesulfonic acid, 2,3′-azodi-

If the acids are different the name of the compound may appear under one of them or under the name of the linking functions.

49. After the name of the parent acid the particle **per-** is used; *e.g.:*

CH_3CO_3H **Acetic acid, per-**

50. **Organic acids other than carboxylic, sulfonic, sulfinic and sulfenic.** See IUC rule 34.

51. **Inorganic acids.** Their derivatives may appear either under the name of the acid or under the name of the organic base; *e.g.:*

$SO_2(OCH_3)_2$ **Sulfuric acid,** dimethyl ester
$C_6H_5NH_2.HNO_3$ **Aniline** nitrate.

52. **Isocyanides.** The prefix **isocyano-** is used for the substituent —NC; *e.g.:*

C_6H_5—NC   **Benzene, isocyano-**

53. **Anhydrides.**

a) *Symmetrical anhydrides of monobasic acids.* After the name of the acid comes the word anhydride; *e.g.:*

$(CH_3CHBrCO)_2O$ **Propanoic acid, 2-bromo-,** anhydride.

b) *Mixed anhydrides:* Both possible names appear (one of them as a cross-reference); *e.g.:*

$CH_3CHClCOOCOCH_2CH_2Cl$ **Propanoic acid, 2-chloro-,** anhydride with 3-chloropropanoic acid; and also:
     Propanoic acid, 3-chloro-, anhydride with 2-chloropropanoic acid.

c) *Cyclic anhydrides of polyacids* are named by placing the word anhydride after the name of the acid; *e.g.:*

     1,4,5,8-Naphthalenetetracarboxylic acid, 1:8,4:5-dianhydride

     Phthalic acid, 3-sulfo-, anhydride.

54. **Acid halides and azides.** The name of the substituent of the hydroxyl group appears after the name of the corresponding acid; *e.g.:*

$CH_3CHClCOCl$ **Propanoic acid, 2-chloro-,** chloride

     Benzoic acid, azide

55. **Amides.**

a) *Primary amides* appear under the name of the corresponding acid followed by the word amide; *e.g.:*

CH_3CONH_2 **Acetic acid,** amide
     (cross reference under **Acetamide**)

CH₃

—SO₂NH₂

2-Toluenesulfonic acid, amide

CONH₂

4-Quinolinecarboxylic acid, amide

Nevertheless, when in forming the name of the corresponding acid the particle **carboxy-** is used, and this group turns to an amide group, the prefix **carbamyl-** is used; *e.g.:*

CONH₂

—CH₂CH₂CO₂H

Propanoic acid, 3(2-carbamylphenyl)- (see paragraph 37),

CONH₂

—CH₂CH₂CONH₂

Propanoic acid, 3(2-carbamylphenyl)-, amide

b) *N-Alkyl, N-Aryl and other N-derivatives of amides.* Substituents in the N atom appear in alphabetical order after the word amide; *e.g.:*

Br

CH₃CON

C₆H₅

Acetic acid, amide, *N*-bromo-*N*-phenyl-

Compounds with heterocyclic radicals attached to the *N*-atom of formamide, acetamide and benzamide are named with the heterocycle as parent compound using the particles **formamido-, acetamido-** and **benzamido;** *e.g.:*

—NHCOCH₃

Pyridine, 2-acetamido-

HCONH—

Benzothiazole, 5-formamido-

Derivatives of other amides follow the general rule stated above, *e.g.:*

CH₃CH₂CONH—

Propanoic acid, amide, *N*(2-pyridyl)-

Amides in which the amide nitrogen is part of a heterocyclic system are named as acyl derivatives of that heterocycle:

NO₂

O   N—C—

O

NO₂

Morpholine, 4(3,5-dinitrobenzoyl)-

c) *Secondary and tertiary amides* are named according to the largest carboxylic acid from which it can be derived; *e.g.:*

CH₃CONHCOCH₃   **Acetic acid,** amide, *N*-acetyl-
                        (cross reference under **Diacetamide**)

C₆H₅CONHCOCH₃   **Benzoic acid,** amide, *N*-acetyl-

(C₆H₅CO)₃N   **Benzoic acid,** amide, *N,N*-dibenzoyl-
                        (cross reference under **Tribenzamide**)

A mixed amide of a carboxylic and a sulfonic acid is named as a derivative of the amide of the carboxylic acid *e.g.:*

CH₃CH₂CONHSO₂—   —NH₂   **Propanoic acid,** amide, *N*(4-aminobenzenesulfonyl)-

d) *Amides of hydroxamic acids.* As in paragraph 52a.

56. **Polypeptides.** A small number of polypeptides appear in the Table. They are found under their trivial name, or under the name of the amino acid that retains its carboxylic group and shares its amino group; *e.g.:*

CH₃CH(NH₂)CONHCH₂CONHCH₂CO₂H

Glycine, *N*(*N*-alanylglycyl)-

C–63

57.   **Hydrazides of acids.** See paragraph 110.

58.   **Esters.** After the name of the corresponding acid comes the radical and the word ester; *e.g.:*

$C_6H_5COOC_6H_5$ **Benzoic acid,** phenyl ester

$HOSO_2OCH_3$ **Sulfuric acid,** monomethyl ester

Nevertheless, esters of complicated and polyvalent alcohols may appear under the name of the alcohol; *e.g.:*

$CH_2O_2C(CH_2)_{15}CH_3$
$CHO_2C(CH_2)_{15}CH_3$ **Glycerol,** triheptadecenoate
$CH_2O_2C(CH_2)_{15}CH_3$

Menthol, acetate

Aspirin, *see* **Benzoic acid, 2-hydroxy-,** acetate

59.   **Orthoesters.** See paragraph 47.

60.   **Amidoximes** are treated as amides of hydroxamic acid (see paragraphs 41, 55).

61.   **Amidines.** After the name of the corresponding acid the word **amidine** appears; *e.g.:*

$CH_3(CH_2)_6C(:NH)NH_2$ **Octanoic acid,** amidine

The nitrogen atom of the $-NH_2$ group is designated N and that of the $=NH$ group N'. If a nitrogen atom of the amidine function is a part of a ring the compound is named according to the heterocyclic system.

62.   **Betaines.** See paragraph 35.

63.   **Lactams and lactones.** If there is no name for the ring system of the compound, the word lactam or lactone appears after the name of the corresponding aminoacid or hydroxyacid; *e.g.:*

Hexanoic acid, 5-amino-, lactam,
        see **2-Piperidone, 6-methyl-**

64.   **Nitriles.** After the name of the corresponding acid the word nitrile appears; *e.g.:*

$CH_3CH(NH_2)CN$ **Alanine,** nitrile

2-Naphthoic acid, nitrile

$CH_3(CH_2)_5CN$ **Heptanoic acid,** nitrile

$NCCH_2CO_2H$ **Malonic acid,** mononitrile
                                       (cross-reference under **Cyanoacetic acid**)

If the group $-CN$ comes instead of a $-CO_2H$ group that is designated as **carboxy-,** the particle **cyano-** is used; *e.g.:*

Propanoic acid, 3(2-cyanophenyl)-

65. **Imides.** The word imide appears after the name of the corresponding dicarboxylic acid:

Phthalic acid, imide
(cross-reference under **Phthalimide**)

Succinic acid, 2-methyl-, imide, *N*-bromo-

For imides of monobasic acids see paragraph 55c.

66. **Cyanates, isocyanates, thiocyanates and isothiocyanates,** appear under the headings **Cyanic acid, Ioscyanic acid, Thiocyanic acid** and **Isothiocyanic acid** respectively, or, when the radical attached to these groups is complicated, the compound appears under the name of the corresponding alcohol (these rules are identical to those given for esters, amides, etc. in paragraphs 58, ff.).

ALDEHYDES

67. Geneva names for saturated and unsaturated aliphatic mono- and di-aldehydes are formed by dropping the final **e** of the name of the hydrocarbon and adding -al or (without dropping the **e**) **-dial.** The largest chain having the aldehydic group (or groups) as terminals is chosen.

Examples:

$CH_3(CH_2)_9CHO$ **Hendecanal**

$\overset{5}{C}H_3\overset{4}{C}H_2\overset{3}{C}H{:}\overset{2}{C}H\overset{1}{C}HO$ **2-Pentenal**

$OCHCH_2CH{:}CHCH{:}CHCH_2CHO$ **3,5-Octadienedial**

Some trivial names are used whenever the trivial name of the corresponding acid is used, *e.g.*: **formaldehyde, acetaldehyde, benzaldehyde, 1- and 2-naphthaldehyde, cinnamaldehyde,** etc.

When the **-carboxylic acid** nomenclature is used for the corresponding acid (see paragraphs 37, 39), the name of the aldehyde is formed by the use of the suffix **-carboxaldehyde;** *e.g.*:

—CHO   **1-Cyclohexenecarboxaldehyde**

OCH——CHO   **1,4-Benzenedicarboxaldehyde**

$OCH(CH_2)_4CH(CHO)_2$ **1,1,5-Pentanetricarboxaldehyde**

When a function of higher rank (see paragraph 32) appears in the molecule the —CHO group is designated as **oxo-** or as **formyl-** as the case demands; *e.g.*:

OCH——CO$_2$H   **Benzoic acid, 4-formyl-**

$OCHCH_2CH_2CO_2H$ **Butanoic acid, 4-oxo-**

$CH_3CH_2CH_2CHCH_2CO_2H$
$\;\;\;\;\;\;\;\;\;\;\;\;\;\;\; |$
$\;\;\;\;\;\;\;\;\;\;\;\;\;\;\; CHO$ **Hexanoic acid, 3-formyl-**

68. **Acetals, hemiacetals and hydrates of aldehydes or ketones** appear in the Table immediately after the corresponding aldehyde or ketone. The following examples illustrate the nomenclature:

$CH_3CH_2CH(OC_2H_5)$ **Propanal,** diethyl acetal

$CH_3CH_2CH(OCH_3)OH$ **Propanal,** methyl hemiacetal

$Cl_3CCH(OH)_2$ **Acetaldehyde, trichloro-,** hydrate

69.   **Thioaldehydes** are named by using the particles **-thial, -carbothialdehyde, thioformyl-** or **thioxo-** corresponding to the oxygen analogs (see paragraph 67). If the corresponding aldehydes appear under trivial names, the particle **thio-** is used; *e.g.:*

CH_3CHS	**Acetaldehyde, thio-**
CH_3CH_2CHS	**Propanethial**

3-Pyridinecarbothialdehyde

Benzoic acid, 2-thioformyl-

$SCHCH_2CO_2H$	**Propanoic acid, 3-thioxo-**

70.   **Azines.** See paragraph 109.

71.   **Imines.** See paragraph 99.

72.   **Oximes.** The word oxime appears after the name of the corresponding aldehyde (or ketone).

KETONES

73.   Ketones with no ring attached directly to the carbonyl group are named according to IUC rule 27.

74.   Ketones with one aromatic ring attached to the carbonyl group are named according to IUC rule 27; *e.g.:*

2-Buten-1-one, 1(2,4-dimethylphenyl)-3-methyl-

$CH_3CH_2COC_6H_5$	**1-Propanone, 1-phenyl-** (cross-reference under **Propiophenone**)

The following are exceptions:

$C_6H_5COCH_3$	**Acetophenone**
$C_6H_5CH:CHCOC_6H_5$	**Chalcone**
$C_6H_5COC_6H_5$	**Benzophenone.**

75.   Monoketones with two rings attached to both sides of the carbonyl group appear under the heading **Ketone,** followed by the two rings in alphabetical order and then followed by the substituents in the rings (see paragraph 25); *e.g.:*

Ketone, 1,2'-dinaphthyl, 4'-chloro-4,6,6'-trimethyl-

Ketone, cyclohexyl 2-pyrryl, 3,5'-dimethyl-5-fluoro-

Exception:

$C_6H_5COC_6H_5$	**Benzophenone**

76. Acetyl derivatives of cyclic compounds other than acetophenone are named according to the name of the cyclic compound:

   Furan, 2-acetyl-

Cyclopropane, acetyl-

77. **Acetals, hemiacetals and hydrates of ketones.** See paragraph 68.

78. **Thiones (thioketones)** follow the Geneva system and IUC rule 27. When the corresponding ketone was given a trivial name the thione has the same name followed by the particle **thio-**; *e.g.:*

$C_6H_5CSCH_3$ Acetophenone, thio-

The particle **thioacetyl-** is used to designate the group CH_3CS— and its use is similar to that of the particle **acetyl-** (see paragraph 76). The heading corresponding to **Ketone** is **Thione**; and it is used as described in paragraph 75; *e.g.:*

Thione, cyclohexyl 3-pyridyl

The particle corresponding to **oxo-** is **thioxo-**; *e.g.:*

Cyclohexanecarboxylic acid, 5-methyl-2-thioxo-, amide, *N*-methyl-

79. **Ketenes.** According to IUC rule 28.

80. **Azines.** See paragraph 109.

81. **Imines.** See paragraph 99.

82. **Oximes.** See paragraph 72.

83. **Cyclic ketones and thiones.** When a cyclic system whose leading function is ketone or thione originally had two hydrogens in the site where O= or S= are attached, the compound gets the name of the parent compound with the ending **-one** or **-thione** *e.g.:*

Tetralin

2-Tetralone

Pyran

4-Pyrone

The ring system so obtained (including oxo- or thioxo- functions) may be used as a new ring system for the naming of compounds containing higher order functions (see paragraph 21); *e.g.:*

   4-Pyrone-3-carboxylic acid

If the compound originally had only one hydrogen at the site of the ketonic function, the particles **oxo-** or **thioxo-** together with **dihydro-**, **tetrahydro-**, etc. are used; *e.g.*:

Quinoline

Quinoline, 1,2-dihydro-2-oxo-

84. Quinones. IUC rule 46 is followed. The quinone ring system may be used as a basis for the naming of compounds containing higher order functions.

1,4-Benzoquinone-2-carboxylic acid

ALCOHOLS

85. Aliphatic alcohols appear under their Geneva names (IUC rule 20).

86. Monocyclic aliphatic alcohols appear under their Geneva names (IUC rule 20); *e.g.*:

Cyclohexanol, 2-methyl-

3-Cyclopenten-1-ol

87. Heterocyclic and aromatic alcohols (phenols). The name **Phenol** is used for C_6H_5OH and ring substituted derivatives with **no carbon** attached to the ring and no other hydroxyl group or higher order of precedence functions; *e.g.*:

Phenol, 3-amino-

Phenol, 4-methoxy-

Otherwise the compound appears under benzene, toluene or elsewhere; *e.g.*:

Toluene, 3-hydroxy-

Benzene, 1-hydroxy-3-isopropyl-

Benzene, 1,3-dihydroxy-
(cross-reference under **Resorcinol**)

Toluene, *a*,2-dihydroxy-

Benzene, 1-amino-, 3,5-dihydroxy-

Alcohols precede phenols in order; *e.g.:*

Methanol, (4-hydroxyphenyl)phenyl-

2-Propanol, 1(2-hydroxyphenyl)-

Exception: **Toluene, *a*-hydroxy-,** *not* **Methanol, phenyl-**
Other aromatic and heterocyclic phenols or alcohols will be named considering the hydroxyl group as an ordinary substituent; *e.g.:*

Naphthalene, 1,2-dihydroxy-

Piperidine, 3-hydroxy-

88.   **Polyalcohols** such as **glycerol, erythrol,** etc. appear under their trivial names. Exception: **1,2-ethanediol.**

89.   **Sugars** appear under their trivial names.

90.   **Esters of complicated alcohols.** See paragraph 58.

91.   **Hemiacetals and hydrates of aldehydes and ketones.** See paragraph 68.

92.   The **carbinol** nomenclature for alcohols **is not used.**

93.   **Thiols.** Aliphatic thiols follows IUC rule 22. Aromatic and heterocyclic thiols and molecules containing higher order functions together with the SH group will be named using the particle **mercapto.** Thiol is lower than alcohol but higher than amine in the order of precedence; *e.g.:*

CH_3CH_2SH **Ethanethiol**

HS—————CO_2H **Benzoic acid, 4-mercapto-**

$HSCH_2CH_2OH$ **Ethanol, 2-mercapto-**

94.   **Hydroperoxides.** See paragraph 112.

AMINES AND IMINES

95.   The amine function is generally considered as an ordinary substituent (like **chloro-, nitro-,** etc.) *e.g.:*

$CH_3CH_2NH_2$ **Ethane, amino-**

——NH_2 **Pyridine, 3-amino-**

96. The name **aniline** is used for the compound $C_6H_5NH_2$ and as a parent compound for its derivatives unless a carbon atom is attached to the benzene ring or a function of rank higher than amino is present in the molecule; *e.g.*:

$O_2N-\langle\bigcirc\rangle-NH_2$ **Aniline, 4-nitro-**

$H_2N-\langle\bigcirc\rangle-OH$ **Phenol, 4-amino-**

$C_2H_5-\langle\bigcirc\rangle-N(CH_2CH:CH_2)_2$ **Benzene, 1-diallylamino-4-ethyl-**

$CH_3CONH-\langle\bigcirc\rangle$ **Acetic acid,** amide, *N*-phenyl-
(cross reference under **Acetanilide**)

Biphenyl, 4(ethylmethylamino)-

97. A list of names beginning with the word *Amine* appears in the Table; sometimes a cross-reference is given to the preferred name based on the largest radical present. If the choice is between a saturated and an unsaturated radical of the same number of carbon atoms, the unsaturated one is preferred. Regarding this nomenclature see paragraph 25.

$NH(CH_2C_6H_5)_2$ **Amine, dibenzyl-**

$C_2H_5-N-CH_3$
   C_6H_5 **Amine, ethyl methyl phenyl,**
           see **Aniline,** *N*-ethyl-*N*-methyl-

$-NHC_6H_5$ **Naphthalene, 2(phenylamino)-,**
           see **Amine, 2-naphthyl phenyl**

$-NH-\langle\bigcirc\rangle-Cl$ **Amine, 2-naphthyl phenyl, 1,4′-dichloro-**
           (see paragraph 25)

98. **Hydroxylamine derivatives.** See paragraph 111.

99. **Imines.** The particle **imino-** is used for the group $NH=$ when it is attached to a single carbon atom; *e.g.*:

$CH_3CH=NH$ **Ethane, imino-**

In some instances when the *imine* group comes in place of the oxygen of a keto-group the word imine appears after the name of the ketone; *e.g.*:

1,4-Benzoquinone, 2-chloro, 4-imine

(This is similar to the usage in the case of oximes, see paragraph 72.)

ETHERS

100. Simple and complex monoethers are found under the name **Ether** followed by the two radicals (without substituents) attached to the oxygen in alphabetical order and finally followed by the substituents in the skeleton of the ether (see paragraph 25); *e.g.*:

CH_3OCH_3 **Ether, dimethyl**

$BrCH_2OCH_2Br$ **Ether, dimethyl, 1,1′-dibromo-**

$(C_6H_5)_2CHOCH_3$ **Ether, (diphenylmethyl) methyl**

$C_6H_5CH_2OC_6H_5$ **Ether, benzyl phenyl**

$HC:COC_6H_5$ **Ether, ethynyl phenyl**

101. Alkoxy derivatives of benzene (linear, saturated and with less than 6 carbons) and alkoxy derivatives of polycyclic or heterocyclic hydrocarbons appear under the cyclic hydrocarbon as a parent compound; *e.g.:*

Benzene, methoxy
(cross-reference under **Anisole**)

Isoquinoline, 3-ethoxy-

102. **Epoxy compounds.** Follow IUC rule 24, but cyclic ethers such as **furan, dioxan, dioxolan,** etc. are designated by their heterocyclic system name.

103. **Polyethers.** Some appear under their trivial names. Ethers of polyalcohols sometimes appear after the name of the corresponding alcohol.

104. **Peroxides.** See paragraph 112.

105. **Thioethers.** See paragraph 114.

106. **Orthoesters.** See paragraph 47.

MISCELLANEOUS FUNCTIONS

107. **Azo and azoxy compounds. Azo** and **Azoxy** are the headings for these compounds. After the word **azo** or **azoxy** comes the names of the hydrocarbon (if symmetrical) or hydrocarbons (if unsymmetrical) attached to the azo or azoxy group in alphabetical order; places of substitution are given with unprimed numbers for the first hydrocarbon and primed numbers for the second hydrocarbon (see paragraph 25); *e.g.:*

Azo, benzene 1-naphthalene, 2-bromo$_2$, 4'-hydroxy-

Azobenzene, 2-bromo-4,4'-dinitro-

1,2'-Azoxynaphthalene, 4'-methoxy-2-methyl-

In the case of **azoxy** no attempt is made to distinguish between the nitrogen atoms.
Some of the azo compounds are cross-referred to other parent compounds (see paragraph 48).
Some multiple azo compounds are named by derivation from the most highly substituted nucleus; *e.g.:*

$C_6H_5N:N-$$-N:NC_6H_5$ **Biphenyl, 4,4'-bis(phenylazo)-**

108. **Azides.** Azides of acids according to paragraph 54.
For other azides the particle **triazo-** is used (see paragraph 31); *e.g.:*

$CH_3CH_2N_3$ **Ethane, triazo-**

109. **Azines.** Appear under the name of the corresponding aldehyde or ketone if they are symmetrical; if not, under two headings with cross references; *e.g.:*

2-Butanone, azine

CH₃
 \
  C:NN:CHCH₃
 /
CH₃

2-Propanone, azine with acetaldehyde

see **Acetaldehyde,** azine with 2-propanone

110. **Hydrazine derivatives.** Monoacyl derivatives of hydrazine are entered under the name of the acid followed by the word hydrazide; *e.g.:*

$CH_3CONHNH_2$ **Acetic acid,** hydrazine

Diacyl hydrazines appear under **Hydrazine,** *e.g.:*

$CH_3CONHNHCOC_6H_5$
      1   2
                Hydrazine, 1-acetyl-2-benzoyl-

When a function of higher order of precedence (amino or higher) is also present, it may be convenient to use the particle **hydrazino-;** *e.g.:*

$NH_2NHCH_2CH_2CN$ **Propanoic acid, 3-hydrazino,** nitrile

$NH_2NHCONH_2$
  1   2   3   4
          is **Semicarbazide,** with derivatives under this name, but semicarbazones appear under the corresponding ketone or aldehyde.

$NH_2CONHNHCONH_2$
  1   2   3   4   5   6
          is **Biurea,** with all its derivatives appearing under this name.

111. **Hydroxylamine derivatives. Hydroxylamino-** is used for HONH—, and **aminooxy** for NH₂O—. Names of *N*-acyl derivatives of hydroxylamine are derived from that of the corresponding amide; *e.g.:*

$CH_3CONHOH$ **Acetic acid, amide,** *N*-hydroxy-

Oximes are explained in paragraph 72.

112. **Peroxides and hydroperoxides.** Peroxides are listed under **Peroxide** and hydroperoxides are listed under **Hydroperoxide;** *e.g.:*

C_2H_5OOH **Hydroperoxide, ethyl**

$C_6H_5CH_2OOCH_2C_6H_5$ **Peroxide, dibenzyl**

$C_6H_5OOCH_3$ **Peroxide, methyl phenyl**

113. **Miscellaneous Phosphorus, Arsenic and Antimony Compounds.** IUC rule 34 is followed.

114. **Sulfides, disulfides, trisulfides sulfoxides and sulfones** follow rules identical to those of **ethers** see (paragraphs 100, 101), using an appropriate word or particle, as in the following examples:

CH_3OCH_3	**Ether, dimethyl**
CH_3SCH_3	**Sulfide, ,,**
CH_3SSCH_3	**Disulfide, ,,**
CH_3SSSCH_3	**Trisulfide, ,,**
$CH_3S(O)CH_3$	**Sulfoxide, ,,**
$CH_3S(O_2)CH_3$	**Sulfone, ,,**
$CH_3OC_2H_5$	**Ether, ethyl methyl**
$CH_3SC_2H_5$	**Sulfide, ,, ,,**
$CH_3SSC_2H_5$	**Disulfide, ,, ,,**
$CH_3SSSC_2H_5$	**Trisulfide, ,, ,,**
$CH_3S(O)C_2H_5$	**Sulfoxide, ,, ,,**
$CH_3S(O_2)C_2H_5$	**Sulfone, ,, ,,**
$C_6H_5OCH_3$	**Benzene, methoxy-**

$C_6H_5SCH_3$ **Benzene, methylthio-**

$C_6H_5SSCH_3$,,   **methyldithio**

$C_6H_5SSSCH_3$,,   **methyltrithio-**

$C_6H_5S(O)CH_3$,,   **methylsulfinyl-**

$C_6H_5S(O_2)CH_3$,,   **methylsulfonyl-**

115. Urea derivatives. According to IUC rule 36.

Cyclic urea derivatives are named according to their ring system or trivial names:

Barbituric acid

Quinazoline, 2,4-dioxo-1,2,3,4-tetrahydro-

The ureido function follows in order of precedence after the onium and the acid functions. The particle **ureido-** is used for the group NH_2CONH- and **thioureido-** for NH_2CSNH-; *e.g.:*

NH_2CONH-⟨ ⟩$-CO_2H$ **Benzoic acid, 4-ureido-**

SYMBOLS AND ABBREVIATIONS

$[\alpha]$	specific rotation	fl	flakes	par	partial
δ	slightly	flr	fluorescent	peth	petroleum ether
$>$	above, more than	fr	freezes	pk	pink[3]
$<$	below, less than	fr. p.	freezing point	Ph	phenyl
∞	soluble in all proportions	fum	fuming	pl	plates
*	name approved by the International Union of Chemists (I.U.C.)[1]	gel	gelatinous	pr	prisms
		gl	glacial	Pr	propyl
		gold	golden	**Prak**	J. Prak. Chem.
Ω	IR, or UV, or NMR spectra referenced	gr	green[3]	purp	purple[3]
		gran	granular	pw	powder
?	unknown	gy	gray[3]	Py	pyrimidene
aa	acetic acid	h	hot	pym	pyramids
abs	absolute	**H**	Helv. Chim. Acta	rac	racemic
ac	acid	hex	hexagonal	rect	rectangular
Ac	acetyl	hp	heptane	red	red
ace	acetone	htng	heating	res	resinous
al	alcohol[2]	hx	hexane	rh	rhombic
alk	alkali	hyd	hydrate	rhd	rhombohedral
Am	J. Am. Chem. Soc.	hyg	hygroscopic	s	soluble
Am	amyl (pentyl)	i	insoluble	s	secondary[7]
amor	amorphous	i-	iso-	sc	scales
anh	anhydrous	ign	ignites	sec	secondary[7]
aqu	aqueous	in	inactive	sf	softens
as	asymmetric	inflam	inflammable	sh	shoulder
atm	atmospheres	infus	infusible	silv	silvery
b	boiling	irid	iridescent	sl	slightly (δ)
B	Beilstein	iso	isooctane	so	solid
Ber	Chem. Ber.	**J**	J. Chem. Soc.	sol	solution
bipym	bipyramidal	JOC	J. Org. Chem.	solv	solvent
bk	black[3]	L, l	levo[4]	sph	sphenoidal
bl	blue[3]	la	large	st	stable
br	brown[3]	lf	leaf	sub	sublimes
bt	bright	lig	ligroin	suc	supercooled
Bu	butyl	liq	liquid	sulf	sulfuric acid
bz	Benzene	lo	long	sym	symmetrical
C	Chem. Abs.	lt	light	syr	syrup
c	percentage concentration	m	melting	t	tertiary[7]
ca	about (circa)	m-	meta-	ta	tablets
chl	chloroform	**M**	molar (concentration)	tcl	triclinic
co	columns	**M**	Merck Index, 7th Edition	tert	tertiary[7]
col	colorless	mcl	monoclinic	Tct	Tetrahedron
con	concentrated	Me	methyl	tetr	tetragonal
cor	corrected	met	metallic	THF	tetrahydrofuran
cr	crystals	micr	microscopic	to	toluene
cy	cyclohexane	min	mineral	tr	transparent
d	decomposes	mod	modification	trg	trigonal
D	line in the spectrum of sodium (subscript)	mut	mutarotatory	undil	undiluted
		n	normal chain, refractive index	uns	unsymmetrical
D, d	dextro[4]			unst	unstable
δd	slight decomposition	N	normal (concentration)	v	very
dil	diluted	N	nitrogen[6]	vac	vacuum
diox	dioxane	nd	needles	var	variable
distb	distillable	o-	ortho-	vap	vapor
dk	dark	oct	octahedral	vic	vicinal
Dl, dl	racemic[4]	og	orange[3]	visc	viscous
dlq	deliquescent	oos	ordinary organic solvents	volat	volatile or volatilises
DMF	dimethyl formamide	or	or	vt	violet[3]
E	Elsevier's	ord	ordinary	w	water
eff	efflorescent	org	organic	wh	white[3]
Et	ethyl	orh	orthorhombic	wr	warm
eth	ether[5]	os	organic solvents	wx	waxy
exp	explodes	p-	para	ye	yellow[3]
extrap	extrapolated	pa	pale	xyl	xylene

1 For I.U.C. rules of nomenclature see General Index.
2 Generally means ethyl alcohol.
3 The abbreviation of a color ending in "sh" is to be read as ending with the suffix "-ish," *e.g.*, grsh means greenish.
4 D, L generally mean configuration and d, l generally mean optical rotation, but there are many examples in the chemical literature for which the meaning of these symbols is ambiguous and/or interchangeable.
5 Generally means diethyl ether.
6 N indicates a position in the molecule.
7 s and sec, or t and tert, are used as convenient.

No.	Name	Synonyms and Formula	Mol. wt.	Color, crystalline form, specific rotation and λ_{max} (log ε)	m.p. °C	b.p. °C	Density	n_D	w	al	eth	ace	bz	other solvents	Ref.

Abietic acid

No.	Name	Synonyms and Formula	Mol. wt.	Color, crystalline form, specific rotation and λ_{max} (log ε)	m.p. °C	b.p. °C	Density	n_D	w	al	eth	ace	bz	other solvents	Ref.
Ω a1	**Abietic acid**	Sylvic acid. $C_{20}H_{30}O_2$.	302.46	mcl pl (al-w) $[\alpha]_D^{25}-116$ (al, c = 1) λ^{al} 234 (2.50), 241 (4.37)	173–4	250^9	....	....	i	s	v	s	v	CS_2 s MeOH s	B9², 424
Ω a2	—,methyl ester	$C_{21}H_{32}O_2$. *See* a1	316.49	....		$225–6^{16}$	1.049_4^{20}	1.5344	i	s	...	...	...	aa s	B9², 430
—	**Acacetin**	*see* **Flavone,** 5,7-dihydroxy-4'-methoxy-													
a3	**Acenaphth-** **anthracene**	Naphtho-2',3':4,5-acenaphthene.	254.34	pa ye lf (lig) λ^{al} 227 (4.86), 289.5 (3.80), 321 (3.19)	192.5–3.5	....	....	....	i	...	...	...	s	con sulf s aa s lig s^h	E14s, 565
Ω a4	**Acenaphthene**	Naphthyleneethylene.	154.21	nd (al) λ^{al} 227.5 (4.86), 289 (3.80), 300 (3.60), 321 (3.19)	96.2	279^{760}	1.02442_4^{99} 1.225_4^0	1.6048^{95}	i	δ s^h	...	...	v	aa s	B5², 495
a5	—,1-amino-	$C_{12}H_{11}N$. *See* a4.	169.23	cr (peth)	135	sub	....	....	δ	v	...	s	...	os s	B12², 764
a6	—,3-amino-	$C_{12}H_{11}N$. *See* a4.	169.23	pl (al), nd (peth) pk in air	81.5		....	....		s	...	...	...	chl s (red sol)	E13, 148
a7	—,4-amino-	$C_{12}H_{11}N$. *See* a4.	169.23	nd (al, w)	87		....	....	s^h	...	...	s	...	os v lig s^h	B12², 764
a8	—,5-amino-	$C_{12}H_{11}N$. *See* a4.	169.23	nd (lig) red in air	108		....	....		s	...	...	...		E13, 149
Ω a9	—,5-bromo-	$C_{12}H_9Br$. *See* a4	233.12	pl (al) λ^{al} 250 (3.3), 290 (4.1), 300 (4.2), 313 (4.0)	52	335^{760}	1.4392_5^{52}	1.6565^{54}	i	δ s^h	...	...	...		B5¹, 276
a10	—,5-chloro-	$C_{12}H_9Cl$. *See* a4.	188.66	pl or nd (al)	70.5	319.2^{770} 163^{13}	1.1954_4^{70}	1.6288^7	i	δ s^h	...	...	...		B5¹, 276
a11	—,5-iodo-	$C_{12}H_9I$. *See* a4	280.11	nd (al)	65		1.6738_6^{62}	1.6909^{65}	i	s	...	...	s	aa s sulf s	E13, 145
a12	—,3-nitro-	$C_{12}H_9NO_2$. *See* a4	199.21	gr-ye nd (aa)	151.5		....	....	i	...	...	...	...	sulf s (gy-bl → red) con alk s (red) aa s^h	E13, 147
—	—,1-oxo-	*See* **1-Acenaphthenone**													
a13	**5-Acenaphthene-** **carboxylic acid**	5-Acenaphthoic acid.	198.22	nd (bz or lig) λ^{al} 236.5 (4.45), 311 (3.9)	220–1		....	....					δ s^h	lig s^h	B9¹, 280
Ω a14	**Acenaphthene-** **quinone**	Acenaphthaquinone.	182.18	ye nd (aa) λ^{al} 225 (4.45), 327 (3.86), 338 (3.86)	261		....	....	i	δ	...	...	δ s^h	lig s^h aa δ, s^h	E13, 169
a15	**3-Acenaphthene** **sulfonic acid**	....	234.28	hyg nd (bz)	87–9		....	....	s						E13, 181
a16	**1-Acenaphthenone**	1-Oxoacenaphthene.	168.21	nd (al)	121		....	....	s^h	s^h	...	...	v	chl s sulf s (ye-gr) NaOH s (vt)	E13, 164
Ω a17	**Acenaphthylene**....	....	152.21	pr (eth), pl (al) λ^{cy} 276 (3.48), 311 (3.88), 323 (3.98), 335 (3.66), 340 (3.67)	92–3	265–75 par d 156–60²⁸	0.8988_2^{16}	....	i	v	v	...	v		B5², 530
Ω a18	**Acetaldehyde**......	Acetic aldehyde. Ethanal*. CH_3CHO	44.05	λ^{cy} 290 (1.23), λ^{gas} 178 (3.48), 181 (3.60), 181.5 (4.05)	−121	20.8^{760}	0.7834_4^{18}	1.3316^{20}	∞^h	∞	∞	...	∞		B1³, 2617
a19	—,bis(2-chloro-ethyl) acetal	1,1-Bis(2-chloroethoxy)-ethane*. $CH_3CH(OCH_2CH_2Cl)_2$	187.07	....		194–6d $106–7^{14}$	1.1737_4^{20}	1.45266^{20}	d^h	δ	δ	...	...		B1³, 2644
a20	—,diacetate.......	Ethylidene diacetate. $CH_3CH(O_2CCH_3)_2$	146.14	....	18.9	169^{760} $65–7^{10}$	1.3985^{25}	1.070^{25}		...	s	s	...		B2², 167
Ω a21	—,diethyl acetal ...	Acetal. 1,1-Diethoxyethane*. Ethylidene diethyl ether. $CH_3CH(OC_2H_5)_2$	118.18	volat λ^w 270 (0.9)	....	103.2^{760} 21^{22}	0.8314_4^{20}	1.3834^{20}	s	∞	∞	v	...	chl s	B1³, 2641
Ω a22	—,dimethyl acetal .	1,1-Dimethoxyethane*. Ethylidene dimethyl ether. $CH_3CH(OCH_3)_2$	90.12	....	−113.2	64.5	0.85015_4^{20}	1.3668^{20}	s	s	s	v	...	chl s	B1², 671
Ω a23	—,2,4-dinitro-phenylhydrazone (stable form)	....	224.19	ye sc (al) λ^{al} 355 (4.3)	168.5 (164)		....	....	i	s^h	s	s	v	chl v	B15¹, 490
a24	—,—(unstable form)	$C_8H_8N_4O_4$. *See* a23	224.19	og-red	146 (157)		....	....	i						B15¹, 490
Ω a25	—,oxime	Acetaldoxime. CH_3CH:NOH	59.07	nd λ^{al} <220	47	115^{760}	0.9656_4^{20}	1.42567^{20}	s^h	∞	∞	...	...		B1³, 675
a26	—,phenylhydra-zone	*N*-Ethylidene-*N*'-phenyl-hydrazine. CH_3CH:$NNHC_6H_5$	134.18	(i) nd or ta (ii) nd λ^{al} 268 (4.25)	(i) 98–101 (ii) 57	$133–6^{21}$	....	....		s	...	...	...	lig δ^h	B15², 54

For explanations, symbols and abbreviations see beginning of table. For structural formulas see end of table.

No.	Name	Synonyms and Formula	Mol. wt.	Color, crystalline form, specific rotation and λ_{max} (log ε)	m.p. °C	b.p. °C	Density	n_D	w	al	eth	ace	bz	other solvents	Ref.
	Acetaldehyde														
a27	—,semicarbazone..	$CH_3CH:NNHCONH_2$	101.11	nd (w or al) λ^{al} 262 (2.38), 266 (2.25)	163	......	1.0300^0_1	....	δ s^h	s					**B3**[3], 48
a28	—,**amino**-, diethyl acetal	Acetalylamine. Aminoacetal. β,β-Diethoxyethylamine. $H_2NCH_2CH(OC_2H_5)_2$	133.19	....		163	0.9159^{25}	1.4170^{20}	v	v	v			chl v	**B4**[2], 758
—	—,**ammonia**......	see **Ethanol, 1-amino-**													
a29	—,**bromo**-, diethyl acetal	2-Bromoacetal. $BrCH_2CH(OC_2H_5)_2$	197.08	....		180^{760} (170) d 66^{18}	1.280^{20}_4	1.4376^{20}	...	s^h	s				**B1**[2], 682
a30	—,**chloro**-.......	Chloroethanal. $ClCH_2CHO$	78.50	λ^{cy} 279.5 (1.54)		85–5.5[748]					s				**B1**[2], 675
Ω a31	—,—,diethyl acetal	Chloroacetal. $ClCH_2CH(OC_2H_5)_2$	152.62	....		157.4^{760} $71–2^{35}$	1.0180^{20}_4	1.4170^{20}	δ^h	∞	∞			dil sulf d	**B1**[2], 676
Ω a32	—,—,dimethyl acetal	$ClCH_2CH(OCH_3)_2$	124.57	....		$127–8^{760}$	1.068^{20}_4	1.4150^{20}		s	s	s	s		**B1**[3], 2660
Ω a33	—,**dichloro**-......	Cl_2CHCHO	112.94	λ^{cy} 301.5 (1.59)		$90–1^{760}$					s				**B1**[2], 676
a35	—,—,diethyl acetal	Dichloroacetal. $Cl_2CHCH(OC_2H_5)_2$	187.07	....		183–4 $67–71^{12}$	1.1383^{14}				s				**B1**[2], 677
a36	—,—,ethyl hemiacetal	$Cl_2CHCH(OH)OC_2H_5$	159.02			109.5–111 63–5[56]	1.314^{26}	1.4360^{20}	δ	∞	∞		∞	lig δ	**B1**[2], 677
a37	—,—,hydrate.....	$Cl_2CHCH(OH)_2$	130.96	cr (bz), ta	56–7 (43)	97 (118)			v	s	v			CS_2 s	**B1**[1], 614
a38	—,**dimethyl-amino**-, diethyl acetal	Dimethylaminoacetal. $(CH_3)_2NCH_2CH(OC_2H_5)_2$	161.25	ye		170–1 (165)	0.885^7	1.4129^{20}	v	s	s	s		os s	**B4**, 308
Ω a39	—,**diphenyl**-......	2,2-Diphenylethanal*. $(C_6H_5)_2CHCHO$	196.25	λ^{al} 255 (3.34), 300 sh (2.41)		315 δd 157.5^7	1.1061^{21}_4	1.5920^{21}	i	v	v		v		**B7**[2], 370
a40	—,**ethoxy**-.......	$C_2H_5OCH_2CHO$.........	28.12	....		71–3	0.942^{20}_4	1.3956^{20}	s	s		s			**B1**, 818
a41	—,**ethylmethyl-amino**-, diethyl acetal	$CH_3(C_2H_5)NCH_2CH(OC_2H_5)_2$	175.27	....		179–80			i	s	s	s		os v	**B4**, 309
a42	—,**hydroxy**-.......	Glycolaldehyde. Glycolic aldehyde. $HOCH_2CHO$	60.05	pl	97	....	1.366^{100}	1.4772^{19}	v	v	δ				**B1**[2], 863
a43	—,—,diethyl acetal	2,2-Diethoxyethanol*. $HOCH_2CH(OC_2H_5)_2$	134.18	....		167 57–8[8]	0.888^{24}_4	1.4073^{20}							**B1**[2], 864
a44	—,**methoxy**-......	CH_3OCH_2CHO	74.08	....		92.3^{770}	1.005^{25}_4	1.3950^{20}	s	s	s	s			**B1**[3], 3180
a45	—,**2-oxo-2-phenyl**-, hydrate	Benzoyl formaldehyde hydrate. Phenyl glyoxal hydrate. $C_6H_5COCH(OH)_2$	152.15	nd (w, chl, al-lig, eth-lig)		93–4			δ	s	s			chl, CS_2 s	**B1**[2], 864
a46	—,—,dioxime.....	Phenyl glyoxime. $C_6H_5C(:NOH)CH:NOH$	164.18	nd (chl) λ^{al} 231 (4.15)	180	....			v^h	s	s			chl δ	**B7**[2], 602
a47	—,—,1-oxime	Isonitrosoacetophenone. $C_6H_5COCH:NOH$	149.15	mcl pr or lf (chl, w)	129	....			δ s^h		s			chl s^h	**B7**[2], 600
Ω a48	—,**phenyl**-.......	α-Tolualdehyde. α-Toluic aldehyde. $C_6H_5CH_2CHO$	120.16	(w) λ^{al} 252 (291), 288 sh (2.0), 291 sh (2.33)	33–4	195 88^{18}	1.0272^{20}_4	1.5255^{20}	δ	∞	∞		v		**B7**[1], 292
a49	—,**tribromo**-......	Bromal. Br_3CCHO	280.76	....		174^{760} 61^9	2.6650^{25}_4	1.5939^{20}	d	s	s	s			**B1**[2], 683
a50	—,—,ethyl hemiacetal	Bromal monoethyl acetal. $Br_3CCH(OH)OC_2H_5$	326.83	nd	44	d			δ	v	s				**B1**[2], 684
a51	—,—,hydrate.....	$Br_3CCH(OH)_2$............	298.77	mcl pr (w+1)	53.5	d	2.5662^{20}_4		s	s	s	s		chl s	**B1**[2], 683
Ω a52	—,**trichloro**-......	Chloral. Cl_3CCHO	147.39	λ^{cy} 290 (1.58)	−57.5	97.75^{760}	1.5121^{20}_4	1.45572^{20}	v^h	s^h	s^h				**B1**[2], 677
a53	—,—,butyl hemiacetal	Chloral n-butyl alcoholate. $Cl_3CCH(OH)OC_4H_9^n$	221.51	nd	49–50	$129–30^{743}$			...	v^h	s				**B1**[3], 267
a54	—,—,diethyl acetal	Trichloroacetal. $Cl_3CCH(OC_2H_5)_2$	221.51	....		205^{760} $84–5^{10}$	1.266^{25}	1.4586^{25}	δ	∞	∞			glycerol ∞	**B1**, 621
a55	—,—,ethyl hemiacetal	Chloral alcoholate. $Cl_3CCH(OH)OC_2H_5$	193.46	nd (al)	56–7 (50)	$115–6^{760}$	1.143^{40}		s^h	s^h	s^h				**B1**[2], 681
a56	—,—,hydrate.....	Trichloroethylidene glycol. $Cl_3CCH(OH)_2$	165.40	mcl pl (w)	57	96.3^{764} d	1.9081^{20}_4		v	v	v	v	v	chl, Py, to v	**B1**[2], 680
a57	—,—,β,β,β-trichloro-*tert*-butyl hemiacetal	Chloralacetone chloroform. $Cl_3CCH(OH)OC(CCl_3)(CH_3)_2$	324.86	nd (bz)	65	sub			δ s^h	s	s		s^h		**B1**, 622
—	**Acetaldoxime**.....	see **Acetaldehyde**, oxime													
—	**Acetamide**.......	see **Acetic acid**, amide													
—	—,α-**cyano**-......	see **Malonic acid**, monoamide mononitrile													
—	—,**diisobutyl**-.....	see **Pentanoic acid**, 2-isobutyl-4-methyl-, amide													
—	**Acetamidine**......	see **Acetic acid**, amidine													
—	**Acetanilide**.......	see **Acetic acid**, amide, N-phenyl-													
—	—,**thio**-.........	see **Acetic acid**, thiono-, amide, N-phenyl													
Ω a58	**Acetic acid**........	Ethanoic acid*. CH_3CO_2H	60.05	rh (hyg) λ^{al} 208 (1.5)	16.604	117.9^{760} 17^{10}	1.0492^{20}_4	1.3716^{20}	∞	∞	∞	∞	∞	os s CS_2 s	**B2**[2], 91 **B5**[2], 761
Ω a59	—,**allyl ester**......	Allyl acetate. $CH_3CO_2CH_2CH:CH_2$	100.13	....		103.5^{760}	0.9276^{20}_4	1.4049^{20}	δ	∞	∞	s			**B2**[2], 150

For explanations, symbols and abbreviations see beginning of table. For structural formulas see end of table.

No.	Name	Synonyms and Formula	Mol. wt.	Color, crystalline form, specific rotation and λ_{max} (log ε)	m.p. °C	b.p. °C	Density	n_D	w	al	eth	ace	bz	other solvents	Ref.
	Acetic acid														
Ω a60	—,amide	Acetamide. Ethanamide*. CH₃CONH₂	59.07	trg mcl (al-eth) λ^{MeOH} 205 (2.21)	82.3	221.2⁷⁶⁰ 120²⁰	0.9986⁸⁵₄ 1.1590²⁰₂₀	1.4278⁷⁸	s	v	i	...	δ sʰ	chl s Py s	B2², 177
a61	—,—(labile form)	CH₃CONH₂	59.07	rh	48.5	221.2⁷⁶⁰ 99⁷	....	1.4158¹¹⁰	v	v					B2, 175
Ω a62	—,—,N-acetyl-	N-Acetylacetamide. Diacetamide. (CH₃CO)₂NH	101.11	nd (eth) λ^{eth} 260 (1.95)	79	223.5⁷⁶⁰ 113¹³	....		s	s	s	...		lig s	B2², 180
a63	—,—,N-acetyl-N-(4-chlorophenyl)-	p-Chlorodiacetanilide.	211.65	cr (al, eth) λ^{al} 251 (4.23)	66–7					v	v		v		B12, 612
a64	—,—,N-acetyl-N(4-ethoxyphenyl)-	p-Ethoxydiacetanilide.	221.26	nd (lig)	53.5–4	182¹²			δ	v	δ	...	δ	aa v lig δʰ	B13, 468
a65	—,—,N-acetyl-N-ethyl-	Diacetylethylamine. (CH₃CO)₂NC₂H₅	129.16	....		195–9⁷⁶⁰	1.0092²⁰	1.4513²⁰	i	v					B4¹, 352
a66	—,—,N-acetyl-N-methyl-	Diacetylmethylamine. (CH₃CO)₂NCH₃	115.13	....	−25	194.5⁷⁴¹ 114.5⁶¹	1.0663²⁵₄	1.4502²⁵	∞		i				B4¹, 329
a67	—,—,N-acetyl-N-phenyl-	Diacetanilide. (CH₃CO)₂NC₆H₅	177.21	ta (lig) λ^{chl} 242 (3.01)	37–8	200¹⁰⁰ 142⁴¹			δ	s			s	to s	B12², 145
a68	—,—,N(4-acetylphenyl)-	p-Acetylacetanilide. 4-Acetylaminoacetophenone.	177.21	nd (w) λ^{al} 283 (4.53)	166–7				δ vʰ	v	δ	...	δ	lig s to s	B14², 33
Ω a69	—,—,N(2-aminoethyl)-	N-Acetylethylenediamine. CH₃CONHCH₂CH₂NH₂	102.14	wh (bz)	51 (cor)	128³			s	s	i	...	sʰ		Am 63, 852
a70	—,—,N(2-aminophenyl)-	o-Aminoacetanilide.	150.18	pl (bz) λ^{al} 266 (3.45)	132				s	s	δ	...	sʰ		B13², 15
a71	—,—,N(3-aminophenyl)-	m-Aminoacetanilide.	150.18	nd or pl (bz) λ^{al} 271 (3.32)	87–9				v	v	δ	v	δ		B13², 27
Ω a72	—,—,—,hydrochloride	C₈H₁₀N₂O.HCl. See a71	186.64	redsh pl (al)	248–51				v	s	i	...	i		B13², 27
Ω a73	—,—,N(4-aminophenyl)-	p-Aminoacetanilide.	150.18	nd (w) λ^{al} 260 (4.26), 312 sh (3.15)	165–8 (162)	267⁷⁶⁰			s vʰ	v	v				B13², 50
a74	—,—,N-benzyl-	N-Acetylbenzylamine. CH₃CONHCH₂C₆H₅	149.19	lf (eth) λ^{al} 258 (2.34)	61	>300⁷⁶⁰ 157²				v	v				B12², 588
a75	—,—,N-bromo-, hydrate	Acetobromamide. CH₃CONHBr.H₂O	155.99	bt ye pl (w+1)	70–80 (hyd) 108–9 (anh)	39–40¹³			sʰ	s	s	...		chl δ	B2, 181
a76	—,—,N-bromo-N-phenyl-	N-Bromoacetanilide. CH₃CONBrC₆H₅	214.08	ye pl (peth)	88									chl v lig δ	B12², 296
a77	—,—,N(2-bromophenyl)-	o-Bromoacetanilide.	214.08	nd (al) λ^{al} 234 (3.88)	99				i	s	s				B12², 342
a78	—,—,N(3-bromophenyl)-	m-Bromoacetanilide.	214.08	nd (aq al) λ^{al} 246 (4.15), 278 (3.04), 286 (2.93)	87.5					v	v				B12, 634
Ω a79	—,—,N(4-bromophenyl)-	p-Bromoacetanilide.	214.08	nd (60 % al) mcl pr λ^{al} 252 (4.27)	168		1.717		iʰ δʰ	s	δ	...	δ	chl s	B12², 348
Ω a80	—,—,N-butyl-	CH₃CONH(CH₂)₃CH₃	115.18	....		229		1.4388²⁵							B4², 634
Ω a81	—,—,N-butyl-N-phenyl-	N-Butylacetanilide. CH₃CON(C₆H₅)(CH₂)₃CH₃	191.28	$\lambda^{95 \% al}$ <220	24.5	281⁷⁶⁰ 141¹⁰	0.9912²⁰₂₀	1.5146²⁰							B12, 247
a82	—,—,N(4-butylphenyl)-	p-Butylacetanilide.	191.28	wh pl (al)	105				i						B12², 634
a83	—,—,N(2-chloro-4-nitrophenyl)-	2-Chloro-4-nitroacetanilide.	214.62	pr (al)	139–40				i	δ					B12, 733
a84	—,—,N(2-chloro-5-nitrophenyl)-	2-Chloro-5-nitroacetanilide.	214.62	nd (al)	156				i	δ					B12, 732
Ω a85	—,—,N(3-chloro-4-nitrophenyl)-	3-Chloro-4-nitroacetanilide.	214.62	pa ye nd (al)	145				i	δ			δ		B12², 399
a86	—,—,N(4-chloro-2-nitrophenyl)-	4-Chloro-2-nitroacetanilide.	214.62	ye nd (al)	104				i	δ					B12², 397
Ω a87	—,—,N(4-chloro-3-nitrophenyl)-	4-Chloro-3-nitroacetanilide.	214.62	ye nd (al)	150				i	sʰ					B12², 732
a88	—,—,N-chloro-N-phenyl-	N-Chloroacetanilide. CH₃CON(Cl)C₆H₅	169.61	nd (dil aa), pl (peth-chl)	91				δ						B12², 295
Ω a89	—,—,N(2-chlorophenyl)-	o-Chloroacetanilide.	169.61	nd (dil aa) λ^{al} 240 (4.02)	87–8 (sub 50–60)				i	s	v	s vʰ			B12², 317
Ω a90	—,—,N(3-chlorophenyl)-	m-Chloroacetanilide.	169.61	nd (50 % aa) λ^{al} 278 (3.04), 286 (2.95)	79				δ	v	v		v	CS₂ v	B12², 321
a91	—,—,N(4-chlorophenyl)-	p-Chloroacetanilide.	169.61	nd (aq aa), ta (al, ace), cr (w) λ^{al} 249 (4.25)	179		1.385²²₄		i sʰ	s vʰ	v			CCl₄ δ	B12², 327
a92	—,—,N(2-chloro-3-tolyl)-	3-Acetamino-2-chlorotoluene.	183.64	nd (al)	133–4				i	δ		s		lig δ	B12, 871
a93	—,—,N(3-chloro-2-tolyl	2-Acetamino-6-chlorotoluene.	183.64	nd (dil al)	157–9 (136)				δʰ	s			s		B12, 836

For explanations, symbols and abbreviations see beginning of table. For structural formulas see end of table.

No.	Name	Synonyms and Formula	Mol. wt.	Color, crystalline form, specific rotation and λ_{max} (log ε)	m.p. °C	b.p. °C	Density	n_D	w	al	eth	ace	bz	other solvents	Ref.
	Acetic acid														
a94	—,—,N(3-chloro-4-tolyl)-	4-Acetamino-2-chlorotoluene.	183.64	tcl cr	105				i	s					B12, 989
a95	—,—,N(4-chloro-2-tolyl)-	2-Acetamino-5-chlorotoluene.	183.64	lf (al)	140				i	s[h]					B12, 836
a96	—,—,N(4-chloro-3-tolyl)-	5-Acetamino-2-chlorotoluene.	183.64	lf (al)	91.2–.7				i	s		s			B12, 871
a97	—,—,N(5-chloro-2-tolyl)-	2-Acetamino-4-chlorotoluene.	183.64	nd (w)	139–40				s[h]	s	s				B12[1], 389
a98	—,—,N(5-chloro-3-tolyl)-	5-Acetamino-3-chlorotoluene.	183.64	nd (al)	151					s					B12, 871
a99	—,—,N(4-cyclohexylphenyl)-	4-Cyclohexylacetanilide.	217.31	nd (peth)	129				δ[h]	v	v			chl v	B12[2], 667
a100	—,—,N,N-diacetyl-	Triacetamide. (CH₃CO)₃N	143.14	nd (eth)	79						s				B2[1], 82
a101	—,—,N,N-diethyl-.	CH₃CON(C₂H₅)₂	115.18	λ^w ca. 200 (3.96)		185–6 91[30]	0.9130[17.4]	1.4374[17.4]	s	s	∞	∞	∞		B4[2], 602
a102	—,—,N,N-dimethyl-	CH₃CON(CH₃)₂	87.12	λ^{hp} 218 (3.00)	–20	165[758] 84[32]	0.9366[25]	1.4380[20]	∞	∞	∞	∞	∞	chl ∞	B4[2], 564
a103	—,—,N(2,4-dimethyl-6 nitrophenyl)-	4-Acetamino-5-nitro-m-xylene.	208.22	yesh nd (w)	172–3				s[h]	s			s		B12[2], 612
a104	—,—,N(2,4-dimethylphenyl)-	2,4-Acetoxylide.	163.22	nd (al)	128–9	170[10]			δ	v					B12[2], 608
Ω a105	—,—,N(2,3-dinitrophenyl)-	2,3-Dinitroacetanilide.	225.16	nd (al)	187					δ	δ		δ	chl δ	B12[2], 405
Ω a106	—,—,N(2,4-dinitrophenyl)-	2,4-Dinitroacetanilide.	225.16	ye nd (al or bz)	125–6 (121)				i	v[h]	s	s[h]			B12[2], 410
a107	—,—,N(2,5-dinitrophenyl)-	2,5-Dinitroacetanilide.	225.16	nd (al)	121				i	s v[h]					B12, 758
a108	—,—,N(2,6-dinitrophenyl)-	2,6-Dinitroacetanilide.	225.16	nd (aa)	197				i	s			aa s		B12, 758
a109	—,—,N(3,4-dinitrophenyl)-	3,4-Dinitroacetanilide.	225.16	ye cr (al), nd (w)	144–5				s[h]	v[h]					B12[2], 414
a110	—,—,N(3,5-dinitrophenyl)-	3,5-Dinitroacetanilide.	225.16	ye nd (dil aa, w)	191				δ	v[h]	i		aa v[h]		B12, 759
a111	—,—,N,N-diphenyl-	N-Acetyldiphenylamine. N-Phenylacetanilide. CH₃CON(C₆H₅)₂	211.27	rh or nd (w or lig) λ^{al} 237 (4.29)	103	sub			δ	s	δ				B12, 247
a112	—,—,N,N-dipropyl-	CH₃CON(CH₂CH₂CH₃)₂	143.23			209–210 101[16]	0.8992[17.4]	1.4419[17.4]							B4, 142
a113	—,—,N(2-ethoxy-4-nitrophenyl)-	2-Acetamino-5-nitrophenetole.	224.22	nd (al)	202				i						B13[2], 194
a114	—,—,N(2-ethoxy-5-nitrophenyl)-	2-Acetamino-4-nitrophenetole.	224.22	ye nd (al)	199					v[h]		v	chl v		B13[2], 193
a115	—,—,N(4-ethoxy-2-nitrophenyl)-	4-Acetamino-3-nitrophenetole.	224.22	ye nd (w)	104					v	v	v	chl v		B13[2], 287
a116	—,—,N(4-ethoxy-3-nitrophenyl)-	4-Acetamino-2-nitrophenetole.	224.22	nd (dil al)	123				i	v	δ	v	chl v lig δ aa s		B13[2], 285
a117	—,—,N(5-ethoxy-2-nitrophenyl)-	3-Acetamino-4-nitrophenetole.	224.22	nd (al)	95				i	v	v	v	chl v lig s[h]		B13[1], 136
a118	—,—,N(2-ethoxyphenyl)-	o-Acetophenetidide.	179.22	lf (dil al)	79	> 250			i	s	s		os s		B13[2], 172
a119	—,—,N(3-ethoxyphenyl)-	m-Acetophenetidide.	179.22	gy pl (w)	97–9				δ	s	s				B13[1], 133
a120	—,—,N(4-ethoxyphenyl)-	p-Acetophenetidide. Phenacetin.	179.22	mcl pr	137–8	d		1.571	δ	s	δ	s	δ	Py v chl s	B13[2], 244
Ω a121	—,—,N-ethyl-.	CH₃CONHC₂H₅	87.12			205 104–5[18]	0.9424[4.5]		∞	∞				aa s	B4, 109
a122	—,—,N-ethyl-N(3-nitrophenyl)-	N-Ethyl-3-nitroacetanilide.	208.22	pa ye nd (dil al)	88–9						v				B12, 704
a123	—,—,N-ethyl-N-(4-nitrophenyl)-	N-Ethyl-4-nitroacetanilide.	208.22	lf or pr (dil al)	118 9				δ	v	δ		v	lig, CS₂ i	B12, 720
Ω a124	—,—,N-ethyl-N-phenyl-	N-Ethylacetanilide. CH₃CON(C₂H₅)C₆H₅	163.22	(w), rh (eth) λ^{hp} 239 (3.74)	55	258[731]			s		s				B12[2], 143
—	—,—,N(formyl-phenyl)-	see **Benzaldehyde, acetamido-**													
a125	—,—,N(2-hydroxyethyl)-	N-Acetylethanolamine. CH₃CONHCH₂CH₂OH	103.12	nd (ace)	63–5	166–7[8]	1.1079[25]	1.4674[20]	∞			s[h]	δ	lig δ	B4[1], 430
a126	—,—,N(2-hydroxy-1-naphthyl)-	1-Acetamino-2-naphthol.	201.23	lf (w, dil al, MeOH)	235 d	sub				s	s	s	s	NaOH v CS₂ s	B13[2], 414
a127	—,—,N(4-hydroxy-3-nitrophenyl)-N-methyl-	(al)	210.19		161–2										B13[1], 186
Ω a128	—,—,N(2-hydroxyphenyl)-	2-Acetaminophenol. o-Hydroxyacetanilide.	151.17	pl (dil al)	209				δ v[h]	v	v		v	alk v	B13[2], 171
Ω a129	—,—,N(3-hydroxyphenyl)-	3-Acetaminophenol. m-Hydroxyacetanilide.	151.17	nd (w)	148–9				v	v	δ		δ	chl δ	B13[3], 213
Ω a130	—,—,N(4-hydroxyphenyl)-	4-Acetaminophenol. p-Hydroxyacetanilide.	151.17	mcl pr (w, al)	169–71		1.293[21]		i s[h]	v					B13[2], 243
a131	—,—,N(2-hydroxyphenyl)-N-methyl-	2-(Acetylmethylamino)-phenol.	165.19	nd (bz-peth)	151				δ	v	v		v	peth i	B13[2], 173

For explanations, symbols and abbreviations see beginning of table. For structural formulas see end of table.

Acetic acid

No.	Name	Synonyms and Formula	Mol. wt.	Color, crystalline form, specific rotation and λ_{max} (log ε)	m.p. °C	b.p. °C	Density	n_D	w	al	eth	ace	bz	other solvents	Ref.
a132	—,—,N(4-hydroxy-phenyl)-N-methyl-	4-(Acetylmethylamino)-phenol.	165.19	sc (w)	245	....			δ	v	s	...	...	....	B13[1], 162
a133	—,—,N(4-iodo-phenyl)-	p-Iodoacetanilide.........	261.07	ta (w), pr (w, al) λ^{al} 254 (4.36)	184.5	....			δ v^h	v	v	...	v	....	B12[2], 362
a134	—.—.N-isopropyl-N-phenyl-	N-Isopropylacetanilide $CH_3CON(C_6H_5)CH(CH_3)_2$	177.22	lf (lig)	39	262–3[712]								lig s[h]	B12, 246
a135	—,—,N(2-methoxy-3-nitrophenyl)-	3-Nitro-o-acetanisidide.....	210.19	pa ye pr (dil aa, MeOH)	103–4	....					s			MeOH s[h] aa s[h]	B13[2], 195
a136	—,—,N(2-methoxy-4-nitrophenyl)-	4-Nitro-o-acetanisidide.....	210.19	pa ye cr (AcOEt)	153–4	....					s		s[h]	lig i AcOEt s[h]	B13[2], 194
a137	—,—,N(2-methoxy-5-nitrophenyl)-	5-Nitro-o-acetanisidide.....	210.19	nd (w)	178	....			δ s[h]				δ	....	B13[2], 193
a138	—,—,N(2-methoxy-6-nitrophenyl)-	6-Nitro-o-acetanisidide.....	210.19	pa ye nd (dil al)	158–9	....				s[h]			s	....	B13[2], 192
a139	—,—,N(3-methoxy-2-nitrophenyl)-	2-Nitro-m-acetanisidide....	210.19	br amor (al)	265 sub	....			δ	s			s	lig i	B13[1], 136
a140	—,—,N(3-methoxy-4-nitrophenyl)-	4-Nitro-m-acetanisidide....	210.19	ye nd (w)	165	....			δ	v				aa v lig i	B13[1], 137
a141	—,—,N(3-methoxy-5-nitrophenyl)-	5-Nitro-m-acetanisidide....	210.19	nd (aa)	201	....			i	s	δ	...	s	aa s AcOEt s chl, lig δ	B13[2], 216
Ω a142	—,—,N(4-methoxy-2-nitrophenyl)-	2-Nitro-p-acetanisidide....	210.19	ye nd (al)	116.5–7	....			s[h]	s	s	...	s	aa s	B13[2], 287
a143	—,—,N(4-methoxy-3-nitrophenyl)-	3-Nitro-p-acetanisidide....	210.19	og-ye nd (w or dil al)	153	....			s	s[h]			δ	lig δ	B13[1], 186
a144	—,—,N(5-methoxy-2-nitrophenyl)-	6-Nitro-m-acetanisidide....	210.19	wh nd (al)	125	....			δ	s[h]				lig δ	B13[1], 136
Ω a145	—,—,N(2-methoxy-phenyl)-	o-Acetanisidide.	165.19	nd (w) λ^{al} 244 (4.02), 280 (3.66)	87–8	303–5			v^h	v	s	s	...	os s aa s	B13[2], 172
a146	—,—,N(3-methoxy-phenyl)-	m-Acetanisidide.........	165.19	nd or pl (w) λ^{al} 245 (4.07), 280 (3.49)	81	....			v^h	v	s	s	...	os s	B13[1], 133
Ω a147	—,—,N(4-methoxy-phenyl)-	p-Acetanisidide. Methacetin.	165.19	pl (w) λ^{al} 249 (4.17), 280 sh (3.34)	130–2	....			δ	s	δ	s	...	chl s	B13[2], 243
Ω a148	—,—,N-methyl-...	$CH_3CONHCH_3$.........	73.10	nd λ^w < 210	28	204–6[760] 95[14]	0.9571[25/4]	1.4301[20]	v	v	v	v	v	chl v lig i	B4[2], 563
Ω a150	—,—,N-methyl-N-(1-naphthyl)-	$CH_3CON(CH_3)C_{10}H_7^\alpha$......	199.26	nd (lig)	95–7	....			δ	s	s	s	...	lig δ	B12[2], 741
a151	—,—,N-methyl-N-(4-nitrophenyl)-	....	194.19	pl (w) λ^{al} 288 (4.04)	153	....			δ s[h]	s	s	...	s	....	B12[1], 352
Ω a152	—,—,N-methyl-N-phenyl-	Exalgin. $CH_3CON(CH_3)C_6H_5$	149.19	nd (eth), pr (al), lf (lig), λ^{al} 226 (3.75)	102–4	253[712]	1.0036[105/4]	1.576	s	s	s[h]	...	...	lig s[h]	B12[2], 142
a153	—,—,N-methyl-N-(2-tolyl)-	N-Methyl-o-acetotoluidide..	163.22	λ^{al} 263 (2.5), 270 (2.5)	55–6	260					s				B12, 793
a154	—,—,N-methyl-N(3-tolyl)-	N-Methyl-m-acetotoluidide .	163.22	cr	66	....					s				B12, 861
a155	—,—,N-methyl-N(4-tolyl)-	N-Methyl-p-acetotoluidide..	163.22	lf (eth-al)	83	283[760]					s	s	...	lig s	B12[2], 502
Ω a156	—,—,N(1-naph-thyl)-	Aceto-1-naphthalide. $CH_3CONHC_{10}H_7^\alpha$	185.23	cr (al)	160	....			s[h]	s[h]	δ	...	...	....	B12, 1230
Ω a157	—,—,N(2-naph-thyl)-	Aceto-2-naphthalide. $CH_3CONHC_{10}H_7^\beta$	185.23	lf (al, w)	134	....			s[h]	s[h]				....	B12, 1284
a158	—,—,N(1-nitro-2-naphthyl)-	....	230.23	ye nd (al) λ^{cy} 340 (3.63)	126 (123.5)	....			δ	s	s	...	s	aa s lig i	B12, 1313
Ω a159	—,—,N(2-nitro-phenyl)-	o-Nitroacetanilide.	180.18	ye pr (lig), lf (dil al) λ^{al} 233 (4.23), 270 (3.62), 340 (3.40)	94	100[0.1]	1.419[15]		s[h]	s	v	...	s v^h	chl s lig s[h]	B12[2], 371
Ω a160	—,—,N(3-nitro-phenyl)-	m-Nitroacetanilide........	180.18	wh lf (al) λ^{al} 242 (4.35), 270 sh (3.75), 326 (3.18)	154–6	100[0.0074]			s[h]	s	i	...	...	alk s chl s Ph NO_2 s	B12[2], 380
Ω a161	—,—,N(4-nitro-phenyl)-	p-Nitroacetanilide.	180.18	ye pr (w) λ^{al} 222 (4.12), 316 (4.06)	216 (207)	100[0.0084]			δ v^h	s	δ	...	...	aa δ chl, lig δ alk s (og)	B12[2], 389
Ω a162	—,—,N(2-nitro-4-tolyl)-	2-Nitro-p-acetotoluidide....	194.19	dk ye nd (peth) (metast) λ^{cy} 368 (3.62)	96 (metast 93.5)	....			δ	δ				peth δ	B12[2], 536
a163	—,—,N(4-octyl-phenyl)-	p-Octylacetanilide	247.39	lf or pl (al)	94	....			i	v^h	v				B12, 1185
Ω a164	—,—,N-phenyl-...	Acetanilide. Antifebrin. $CH_3CONHC_6H_5$	135.17	rh or pl (w) λ^{al} 242 (4.16)	114.3 (115–6)	304[760]	1.2190[15]		δ s[h]	v	s	v	s	chl, MeOH v to s, v^h	B12[2], 137
a165	—.—.N-phenyl-N-propyl-	$CH_3CON(C_6H_5)CH_2CH_2CH_3$	177.25	mcl lf (eth, lig)	49 (56)	266[712]			i	v	v				B12, 246

For explanations, symbols and abbreviations see beginning of table. For structural formulas see end of table.

No.	Name	Synonyms and Formula	Mol. wt.	Color. crystalline form. specific rotation and λ_{max} (log ε)	m.p. °C	b.p. °C	Density	n_D	w	al	eth	ace	bz	other solvents	Ref.
	Acetic acid														
Ω a166	—,—,N(2-tolyl)-...	o-Acetotoluidide	149.19	nd (al) λ^{al} 230 (3.80), 280 sh (2.32)	110	296	1.168^{15}	....	δ	s v^h	s	s v^h	δ s^h	chl s aa, MeOH s	B12², 439
Ω a167	—,—,N(3-tolyl)-...	m-Acetotoluidide..........	149.19	nd (w) λ^{al} 245 (4.15), 282 sh (2.81)	65.5	303 182–3¹⁴	1.141^{15}	....	δ	v	v	...	...		B12², 468
Ω a168	—,—,N(4-tolyl)-...	p-Acetotoluidide..........	149.19	mcl cr or nd (dil al) λ^{al} 245 (4.20), 286 sh (2.79)	148.5 (153)	307 sub	1.212^{15}	....	δ s^h	s	s	...	δ	aa, chl, MeOH s lig δ	B12², 501
a169	—,amidine	Acetamidine. Ethanamidine.* $CH_3C(:NH)NH_2$	58.08	$\lambda^{w, pH = 13}$ 219 (3.04)	−35	....	....	....	d^h δ				ac s		B2², 183
Ω a170	—,—,hydrochloride	$CH_3C(:NH)NH_2 \cdot HCl$	94.55	nd or pr (al)	177–8 (167)	....	....	....	s				i		B2², 184
a171	—,—,N,N'-diphenyl-	$CH_3C(:NC_6H_5)NHC_6H_5$...	210.28	nd (al)	131–2	....	....	....	δ v^h		v			ac s	B12², 144
Ω a172	—,anhydride......	Acetic anhydride. Ethanoic anhydride*. $(CH_3CO)_2O$	102.09	λ^{iso} 224.5 (1.68)	−73.1	139.55 44¹⁵	1.0820^{20}_4	1.39006^{20}	v	s	∞	s		chl s	B2², 170
Ω a173	—,benzyl ester....	$CH_3CO_2CH_2C_6H_5$	150.18	....	−51.5	215.5⁷⁶⁰ 93–4¹⁰	1.0550^{20}_4	1.5232^{20}	δ	∞	s	s	...		B6², 415
Ω a174	—,bromide.......	Acetyl bromide. Ethanoyl bromide*. CH_3COBr	122.96	ye in air	−96	76⁷⁶⁰ (81)	1.6625^{16}_4	1.45376^{16}	d	d	∞	s	∞	chl ∞	B2², 176
a175	—,2-bromoethyl ester	$CH_3CO_2CH_2CH_2Br$	167.01		−13.8	162–3	1.514^{20}_4	1.457^{23}	v	s	s	...	...	chl v	B2¹, 57
a176	—,bromomethyl ester	$CH_3CO_2CH_2Br$	152.98			130–3⁷⁵⁰	1.6350^{20}_4	1.4520^{20}	i	s	v	...	...	chl v	B2², 166
a177	—,2-buten-1-yl ester	Crotonyl acetate. Crotyl acetate. $CH_3CO_2CH_2CH:CHCH_3$	114.15			132⁷⁶¹	0.9192^{20}_4	1.4181^{20}	δ	s	s	s	...		B2³, 283
Ω a178	—,butyl ester	$CH_3CO_2(CH_2)_3CH_3$	116.16		−77.9	126.5 (125)	0.8825^{20}_4	1.3941^{20}	δ	∞	∞	s	...		B2², 140
a179	—,sec-butyl ester (d)	$CH_3CO_2CH(CH_3)CH_2CH_3$.	116.16	$[\alpha]^{20}_D$ +25.43	....	112⁷⁶⁰	0.8758^{16}_4	1.3877^{20}	i	s	s	s	...		B2¹, 59
Ω a180	—,—(dl)	$CH_3CO_2CH(CH_3)CH_2CH_3$.	116.16		....	112.2⁷⁶⁰	0.8716^{20}_4	1.3888^{20}	i	s	s	s	...		B2², 141
a181	—,—(l)	$CH_3CO_2CH(CH_3)CH_2CH_3$.	116.16	$[\alpha]^{19}_{546}$ −20.2 (c = 5)	....	116–7⁷⁶⁰	0.8730^{19}_4	1.3899^{18}	i	s	s	s	...		B2³, 241
Ω a182	—,tert-butyl ester..	$CH_3CO_2C(CH_3)_3$	116.16			97–8⁷⁶⁰	0.8665^{20}_4	1.3853^{20}	...	s	s	...	...	aa s	B2², 142
Ω a183	—,chloride	Acetyl chloride. Ethanoyl chloride*. CH_3COCl	78.50	fum λ^{peth} 220 (2.01)	−112	50.9⁷⁶⁰	1.1051^{20}_4	1.38976^{20}	d	d	∞	∞	∞	chl ∞	B2², 175
a184	—,1-chloroethyl ester	$CH_3CO_2CHClCH_3$	122.55			121.5⁷⁴⁶ δd	1.110^{20}	1.409^{20}	d						B2¹, 71
Ω a185	—,2-chloroethyl ester	$CH_3CO_2CH_2CH_2Cl$	122.55			145 50¹⁸	1.178^{20}_4	1.4234^{20}	i	∞	∞	s	...		B2², 136
a186	—,2-chloroiso-propyl ester	$CH_3CO_2CH(CH_3)CH_2Cl$...	136.58			149–50	1.0788^{20}	1.4223^{20}	i	s	s	...	...		B2, 130
a187	—,chloromethyl ester	$CH_3CO_2CH_2Cl$	108.53			115–6⁷⁵⁷	1.194^{20}	1.409^{20}	i	s	s	...	...	con sulf s	B2², 166
Ω a188	—,3-chloropropyl ester	$CH_3CO_2CH_2CH_2CH_2Cl$	136.58			163–5⁷⁴⁷ 62–3¹⁰	1.250^{19}	1.431^{20}	i	s	s	s	...		B2², 139
Ω a189	—,cyclohexyl ester.	....	142.20			173 63¹²	0.9698^{20}_4	1.4401^{20}	i	∞	∞	...	...		B6², 10
Ω a190	—,decyl ester	$CH_3CO_2(CH_2)_9CH_3$	220.33		−15.05	244 125.8¹⁵·⁵	0.8671^{20}_4	1.4273^{20}	i	s	s	...	s	aa s	B2, 135
a191	—,1,3-dichloroiso-propyl ester	$CH_3CO_2CH(CH_2Cl)_2$	171.03			202–8 81¹⁵	1.281^{20}	1.4542^{20}	i	s	s	...	...	chl s	B2², 140
a193	—,1,1-dimethyl-butyl ester	$CH_3CO_2C(CH_3)_2CH_2CH_2CH_3$	144.22			152–3⁷⁵⁵ 34.5¹⁰	0.8798^{18}	1.4068^{18}	i	s	s	...	...		B2², 145
—	—,1,1-dimethyl-propyl ester	See **Acetic acid**, 2-methyl-2-butyl ester													
a195	—,2,4-dinitrophenyl ester	....	226.15	cr (MeOH)	72–3	....	....	....	i						B6¹, 127
a196	—,3,5-dinitrophenyl ester	....	226.15	cr (bz-peth)	126–7	....	....	....	i				v	aa v^h	B6, 258
Ω a197	—,ethenyl ester....	Vinyl acetate. $CH_3CO_2CH:CH_2$	86.09	wh (unst), bl-gr (st) λ^{hn} 258 sh (−0.3)	−93.2	72.2–2.3⁷⁶⁰	0.9317^{20}_4	1.3959^{20}	i v^h	∞	s	s	s	os s chl s CCl_4 s	B2², 147
Ω a198	—,2-ethoxyethyl ester	Cellosolve acetate. $CH_3CO_2CH_2CH_2OCH_3$	132.16	....	−61.7	156.4 49¹²	0.9749^{20}_4	1.4058^{20}	v	∞	∞	s	...	os v	B2², 155
Ω a199	—,ethyl ester......	Ethyl acetate. $CH_3CO_2CH_2CH_3$	88.12	λ^{MeOH} 209 (1.86)	−83.578	77.06⁷⁶⁰	0.9003^{20}_4	1.3723^{20}	s	∞	∞	v	v	chl ∞, os v	B2², 129
Ω a200	—,2-ethylbutyl ester	$CH_3CO_2CH_2CH(C_2H_5)_2$...	144.22		< −100	162–3⁷⁶⁰ 63²⁰	0.8790^{20}_4	1.4109^{20}	i	s	s	...	...		B2³, 257
Ω a201	—,2-ethylhexyl ester	$CH_3CO_2CH_2CH(C_2H_5)C_4H_9^n$	172.27		−93	199 95²⁵	0.8734^{20}_{20}	1.4204^{20}	i	s	s	...	...		B2³, 261
a202	—,3-ethyl-3-pentyl ester	$CH_3CO_2C(C_2H_5)_3$	158.24			160–3	....	....	i	s	s				B2, 134
Ω a203	—,fluoride.......	Acetyl fluoride. Ethanoyl fluoride*. CH_3COF	62.04	fum	< −60	20.8⁷⁶⁰	1.002^{15}_4	....	d	∞^d	∞	...	s	CS_2 δ chl s	B2², 175
Ω a204	—,furfuryl ester ...	....	140.15	....	....	177	1.1175^{20}_4	1.4627^{20}	i	s	s	...	...		B17², 115

For explanations, symbols and abbreviations see beginning of table. For structural formulas see end of table.

No.	Name	Synonyms and Formula	Mol. wt.	Color, crystalline form, specific rotation and λ_{max} (log ε)	m.p. °C	b.p. °C	Density	n_D	w	al	eth	ace	bz	other solvents	Ref.
	Acetic acid														
Ω a205	—,heptyl ester	$CH_3CO_2(CH_2)_6CH_3$	158.24		−50.2	192.4^{760} 96^{28}	0.8750^{15}_4	1.4150^{20}	i	s	s	...	...		**B2**, 134
a206	—,4-heptyl ester	$CH_3CO_2CH(C_3H_7)_2$	158.24			$170–2^{760}$ $69–70^{17}$	0.8742^0_0	1.4105^{19}	i		s	...	...		**B2**, 134
Ω a207	—,hexadecyl ester	Cetyl acetate. $CH_3CO_2(CH_2)_{15}CH_3$	284.49	α: nd, β: wax α:18.5 β:24.2	$220–5^{205}$ $180–1^6$		0.8574^{25}_4	1.4438^{20}	i	δ	...	...	...		**B2²**, 146
Ω a208	—,hexyl ester	$CH_3CO_2(CH_2)_5CH_3$	144.22		−80.9	171.5^{760} 61.5^{12}	0.8779^{15}_4	1.4092^{20}	i	v	v	...	...		**B2²**, 145
a209	—,2-hexyl ester (d)	$CH_3CO_2CH(CH_3)C_4H_9^a$	144.22			158^{760} 57^{20}	0.8658^{18}_4	1.4014^{25}	i	v	v	...	...		**B2²**, 145
a210	—,—(dl)	$CH_3CO_2CH(CH_3)C_4H_9^a$	144.22			$157–8^{760}$	0.865^{15}_{15}	1.4014^{25}	i	v	v	...	...		**B2³**, 256
a211	—,3-hexyl ester (d)	$CH_3CO_2CH(C_2H_5)CH_2CH_2CH_3$	144.22	$[\alpha]_D^{20}+0.55$		149–51	0.8672^{20}_4	1.4037^{20}	i	v	v	...	...		**B2¹**, 61
Ω a212	—,2-hydroxyethyl ester	Glycol monoacetate. $CH_3CO_2CH_2CH_2OH$	104.12			187–9	1.108^{15}		∞	∞	∞	...	...		**B2²**, 154
Ω a213	—,3-hydroxyphenyl ester	Resorcinol monoacetate. Euresol.	152.16	ye		283d			i	s		...	...		**B6²**, 817
a214	—,iodide	Acetyl iodide. Ethanoyl iodide*. CH_3COI	169.95	turn br (separate I_2) fum		108 36^{50}	2.0674^{20}_2	1.5491^{20}	d	d	s	...	...		**B2²**, 177
Ω a215	—,isobutyl ester	$CH_3CO_2CH_2CH(CH_3)_2$	116.16		−98.58	117.2^{760}	0.8712^{20}_4	1.3902^{20}	δ	∞	∞	s	...		**B2²**, 142
Ω a216	—,isopropenyl ester	$CH_3CO_2C(CH_3):CH_2$	100.12		−92.9	$92–4^{732}$	0.9090^{20}	1.4033^{20}	δ	s	v	s	...		**B2³**, 278
Ω a217	—,isopropyl ester	$CH_3CO_2CH(CH_3)_2$	102.13		−73.4	90^{760}	0.8718^{20}_0	1.3773^{20}	s	s	∞	s	...		**B2²**, 139
Ω a218	—,menthyl ester (l)		198.31	$[\alpha]_D^{20}-79.42$		109^{10}	0.9185^{20}_0	1.4469^{20}							**B6²**, 42, 50
Ω a219	—,2-methoxyethyl ester	Methyl cellosolve acetate. $CH_3CO_2CH_2CH_2OCH_3$	118.13			$144.5–5^{19}_9$ $40–1^{12}$	1.0090^{19}_9	1.4002^{20}	s	s	s	...	...		**B2²**, 154
a220	—,2-methoxyphenyl ester		166.18	λ^{al} 207 (3.3), 277 (3.3)	31–2	$134–5^{18}$			i	s	s	...	...		**B6¹**, 416
Ω a221	—,methyl ester	Methyl acetate. $CH_3CO_2CH_3$	74.08		−98.1	57	0.9330^{20}_4	1.3593^{20}	v	∞	∞	v	s	chl v	**B2²**, 125
a222	—,2-methyl-2-butyl ester	tert-Amyl acetate. $CH_3CO_2C(CH_3)_2CH_2CH_3$	130.19			124–4.5	0.8740^{20}	1.4010^{20}	δ	s	s	s	...	diox s aa s	**B2³**, 143
Ω a223	—,3-methylbutyl ester	Isoamyl acetate. $CH_3CO_2CH_2CH_2CH(CH_3)_2$	130.19		−78.5	142	0.8670^{20}_4	1.4003^{20}	δ	∞	∞	s	...	AmOH s	**B2²**, 144
a224	—,methylene diester	Methanediol diacetate. $(CH_3CO_2)_2CH_2$	132.13		−23	164–5	1.136^{20}_4	1.4025^{24}	δ	∞	∞	...	...	os v	**B2²**, 163
a225	—,2-methyl-3-heptyl ester	$CH_3CO_2CH(C_4H_9^a)CH(CH_3)_2$	172.27			172	0.875^{20}	1.4166^{20}	i	s	...	...	...		**B2**, 134
a226	—,3-methyl-2-heptyl ester	$CH_3CO_2CH(CH_3)CH(CH_3)C_4H_9^a$	172.27			185	0.8545^{21}_4	1.418^{21}	i	s	...	...	...		**B2²**, 146
a227	—,6-methyl-2-heptyl ester	$CH_3CO_2CH(CH_3)(CH_2)_3CH(CH_3)_2$	172.27			$187–8^{768}$	0.8494^{20}	1.4137^{20}	i	s	...	...	...		**B2**, 135
a228	—,6-methyl-3-heptyl ester	$CH_3CO_2CH(C_2H_5)(CH_2)_2CH(CH_3)_2$	172.27			184–5	0.8554^{20}	1.41602^{20}	i	s	...	...	...		**B2**, 146
a229	—,2-methyl-1-naphthyl ester	1-Acetoxy-2-methyl-naphthalene.	200.24	nd (eth-peth)	81–2				i		s	...	...		**B6³**, 3027
a230	—,4-methyl-1-naphthyl ester	1-Acetoxy-4-methyl-naphthalene.	200.24	nd (eth-peth)	86–8				i			...	...		**C64**, 19519
a231	—,6-methyl-1-naphthyl ester	5-Acetoxy-2-methyl-naphthalene.	200.24			124^2			i			...	...		**B6³**, 3028
a232	—,7-methyl-1-naphthyl ester	1-Acetoxy-7-methyl-naphthalene.	200.24		39–41	188^{15}			i			...	...		**C25**, 1515
a233	—,2-methyl-3-pentyl ester	$CH_3CO_2CH(C_3H_7^i)C_2H_5$	144.22			148.5^{747}	0.8688^{20}		i	s	s	...	...		**B2**, 133
a234	—,3-methyl-3-pentyl ester	$CH_3CO_2C(C_2H_5)_2CH_3$	144.22			148	0.8834^{20}_{20}	1.4109^{18}	i	s	s	...	...		**B2²**, 145
a237	—,4-methyl-2-pentyl ester	$CH_3CO_2CH(C_4H_9^i)CH_3$	144.22			147–8	0.8805^0	1.3980^{20}	i	s	s	...	...		**B2**, 133
a238	—,2-methylpentyl ester	$CH_3CO_2CH_2CH(CH_3)(CH_2)_2CH_3$	144.22			162.2^{746}	0.8717^{25}_{25}		i	s	s	...	...		**B2**, 133
a239	—,1-naphthyl ester	α-Naphthyl acetate	186.21	nd or pl (al) $\lambda^{95\%al}$ 232 (4.5), 282 (3.65)	49				i	s	s	...	...		**B6²**, 580
Ω a240	—,2-naphthyl ester	β-Naphthyl acetate	186.21	nd (al) $\lambda^{95\%al}$ 228 (4.8), 277 (3.7)	70				i	s	s	...	...	chl s	**B6²**, 600
Ω a241	—,nitrile	Acetonitrile. Cyanomethane. Ethanenitrile*. Methyl cyanide. CH_3CN	41.05	λ^{undil} 274 (−2.7)	−45.72	81.6	0.7857^{20}	1.34423^{20}	∞	∞	∞	∞	∞	CCl_4 ∞	**B2²**, 181
Ω a242	—,nitrilotri-	Triglycolamic acid. Trimethylamine-α,α',α''-tricarboxylic acid. $N(CH_2CO_2H)_3$	191.14	pr	242 d (258–9)				δ	s^h		...	...		**B4²**, 801
a243	—,2-nitrophenyl ester		181.15	nd or pr (lig) $\lambda^{95\%al}$ 256 (3.75)	40–1	253 d			s	v	v	v	v	lig δ, s^h	**B6²**, 210
a244	—,3-nitrophenyl ester		181.15	nd (peth) $\lambda^{95\%al}$ 257 (3.9)	55–6				s	s	s	...	...	lig s	**B6²**, 214
Ω a245	—,4-nitrophenyl ester		181.15	lf (dil al) λ^{al} 270 (4.00)	81–2				v^h	s	...	...	v	os s lig s	**B6²**, 223

For explanations, symbols and abbreviations see beginning of table. For structural formulas see end of table.

No.	Name	Synonyms and Formula	Mol. wt.	Color, crystalline form, specific rotation and λ_{max} (log ε)	m.p. °C	b.p. °C	Density	n_D	w	al	eth	acc	bz	other solvents	Ref.
	Acetic acid														
a246	—,octadecyl ester	$CH_3CO_2(CH_2)_{17}CH_3$	312.54	....	34.5	$222-3^{15}$			i	s	....				$B2^2$, 147
Ω a247	—,octyl ester	$CH_3CO_2(CH_2)_7CH_3$	172.27	....	−38.5	$166-8^1$ 210 $112-3^{30}$	0.8705_4^{20}	1.4190^{20}	i	s	s	...	...	os s	$B2^2$, 146
a248	—,2-octyl ester (d)	$CH_3CO_2CH(CH_3)(CH_2)_5CH_3$	172.27	$[\alpha]_D^{20} + 7.04$ $[\alpha]_D^{17} + 5.64$ (undil)	....	196^{760} 84^{15}	0.8606_4^{19}	1.4141^{20}	i	s	s	...	s	CS_2, Py s	$B2^2$, 146
a249	—,—(dl)	$CH_3CO_2CH(CH_3)(CH_2)_5CH_3$	172.27	....	....	194.5^{744}	0.8626_4^{14}	1.4146^{20}	i	s	s				$B2^2$, 146
a250	—,—(l)	$CH_3CO_2CH(CH_3)(CH_2)_5CH_3$	172.27	$[\alpha]_D^{14.5} - 6.0$	....	196^{760} $89-90^{17}$	0.8570_4^{20}	1.4140^{20}	i	s	s				$B2^2$, 146
a251	—,3-octyl ester (l)	$CH_3CO_2CH(C_2H_5)(CH_2)_4CH_3$	172.27	$[\alpha]_D^{20} - 4.30$	....	$191-1.5^{760}$ 56.5^3	0.8641_4^{20}	1.4152^{20}	i	s	s			CS_2 s	$B2^1$, 62
a252	—,2-oxopropyl ester	Acetonyl acetate. Acetoxy-acetone. $CH_3CO_2CH_2COCH_3$	116.13	....	....	$170-1^{755}$ 65^{11}	1.0757_4^{20}	1.4141^{20}	v	v	v				$B2^2$, 168
Ω a253	—,pentyl ester	Amyl acetate. $CH_3CO_2(CH_2)_4CH_3$	130.19	....	−70.8	149.25^{760}	0.8756_4^{20}	1.4023^{20}	δ	∞	∞				$B2^2$, 143
a253¹	—,2-pentyl ester (d)	d-2-Amyl acetate. $CH_3CO_2CH(CH_3)CH_2CH_2CH_3$	130.19	$[\alpha]_D^{20} + 17.16$ (undil) $[\alpha]_D^{20} + 15.41$ (al)	....	$130-1$	0.8692_4^{18}	1.3960^{20}	i	s	s	s			$B2^1$, 60
a253²	—,—(dl)	$CH_3CO_2CH(CH_3)CH_2CH_2CH_3$	130.19	....	....	134	0.8692_4^{18}	1.3960^{20}	i	s	s	s			$B2^2$, 143
a253³	—,—(l)	$CH_3CO_2CH(CH_3)CH_2CH_2CH_3$	130.19	$[\alpha]_D^{20} + 3.30$	....	142	0.8803^{13}	1.4012^{20}	i	s	s				$B2$, 131
a254	—,3-pentyl ester	$CH_3CO_2CH(C_2H_5)_2$	130.19	....	....	132^{741}	0.8712_4^{20}	1.4005^{20}	i	s	s				$B2^2$, 143
Ω a255	—,phenacyl ester	ω-Acetoxyacetophenone. $CH_3CO_2CH_2COC_6H_5$	178.19	rh pl	49 9.5	270	1.1169_4^{55}	1.5036^{65}	i	v	v	...	δ	chl v lig δ	$B8^2$, 89
Ω a256	—,phenyl ester	O-Acetylphenol. $CH_3CO_2C_6H_5$	136.16	$\lambda^{al} 265 (2.7)$	....	195.7 $75-6^8$	1.0780_4^{20}	1.5033^{20}	δ	∞	∞			chl ∞	$B6^2$, 153
a257	—,2-phenylethyl ester	β-Phenethyl acetate. $CH_3CO_2CH_2CH_2C_6H_5$	164.21	....	−31.1	232.6^{760} 153^{76}	1.0883_4^{20}	1.5171^{20}	i	s	s				$B6^2$, 451
a258	—,piperazinium salt	$2CH_3CO_2H.C_4H_{10}N_2$	206.24	cr (n-BuOH)	208.5-9	....			s	s	i				Am 56, 1759
Ω a259	—,propyl ester	$CH_3CO_2CH_2CH_2CH_3$	102.13	....	−95	101.6^{760}	0.8878_4^{20}	1.3842^{20}	δ	∞	∞				$B2^2$, 137
Ω a260	—,tetrahydro-furfuryl ester	....	144.17	....	....	$204-7^{756}$	1.0624_4^{25}	1.4350^{25}	∞	∞	∞			chl ∞	$B17^2$, 107
a261	—,2-tolyl ester	o-Cresyl acetate	150.18	....	....	208 89^{10}	1.0533^{15}	1.5002^{20}	δ	v	v				$B6^2$, 330
Ω a262	—,3-tolyl ester	m-Cresyl acetate	150.18	....	12	212	1.043_4^{26}	1.4978^{26}	i	∞	∞	...	∞	chl ∞ lig ∞	$B6^2$, 352
Ω a263	—,4-tolyl ester	p-Cresyl acetate	150.18	....	....	212.5 $107-9^5$	1.0512_4^{17}	1.5163^{23}	δ	s	s			chl s	$B6^2$, 378
a264	—,1,2,2-trimethyl-propyl ester (d)	$CH_3CO_2CH(CH_3)C(CH_3)_2CH_3$	144.22	$[\eta]_D^{25} + 16.2$	....	141^{756}	0.856_4^{25}	1.4001^{25}	i		s				$B2^3$, 258
a265	—,—(dl)	$CH_3CO_2CH(CH_3)C(CH_3)_2CH_3$	144.22	....	....	143^{757}		1.402^{23}	i		s				$B2$, 133
—	—,vinyl ester	See **Acetic acid**, ethenyl ester													
a266	—,4-acetylamino-phenyoxy-, amide	....	208.22	nd (w)	208	....			δ v^h	v	i	...	i	....	B13, 465
—	—,amino-	See **Glycine**													
a267	—,—,phenyl-(dl)-	α-Amino-α-toluic acid. Phenyl glycine. $C_6H_5CH(NH_2)CO_2H$	151.17	rh lf	290 (258)	sub slowly			i	δ		...		os δ	$B14^2$, 282
a268	—,—,—,nitrile (dl)	α-Cyanobenzylamine. $C_6H_5CH(NH_2)CN$	132.18	hyg lf (lig)	55	....								lig δ	$B14^2$, 285
a269	—,2-amino-phenyl, nitrile	2-Aminobenzyl cyanide	132.18	lf (dil al) $\lambda^{al} 240 (4.0),$ $288 (3.4)$	72	....			i	s	δ		v		$B14^2$, 279
a270	—,4-amino-phenyl-	p-Amino-α-toluic acid	151.17	pl (w)	199–200d	....			i s^h	δ					$B14^2$, 280
a271	—,—,nitrile	....	132.18	lf (w) $\lambda^{al} 295 (2.21)$	46	312 177^{11}			$δ^h$	s				CS_2 $δ^h$ ∞ ∞	$B14^2$, 281
—	—,(?-amino-phenyl) oxo	see **Isatic acid**													
a272	—,arsono-	$H_2O_3AsCH_2CO_2H$	183.98	pl (w or aa)	152d		2.425_4^{20}		v	i	i		i	AcOEt i	$B4^2$, 999
—	—,benzoyl-	see **Propanoic acid**, 3-oxo-3-phenyl-													
a273	—,bis(2,4-dinitro-phenyl)-, ethyl ester	....	420.30	lf (al), nd (bz or aa)	154				i	i	δ	...	δ	chl, CS_2 δ	B9, 675
a274	—,—,methyl ester	....	406.27	lf (chl-MeOH)	159				i					MeOH i chl v	B9, 675
Ω a275	—,bromo-	$BrCH_2CO_2H$	138.95	hex or rh	50	208^{760} $127.2-7.6^{30}$	1.9335_5^{50}	1.4804^{50}	∞	∞	∞	s	s	....	$B2^2$, 201
a276	—,—,amide	$BrCH_2CONH_2$	137.97	nd (al or bz)	91	....			v	δ	i	...	v^h		$B2^1$, 97
Ω a277	—,—,bromide	$BrCH_2COBr$	201.86	....		150	2.317_{22}^{22}	1.5449^{20}	d	d	...	s			$B2^2$, 215

For explanations, symbols and abbreviations see beginning of table. For structural formulas see end of table.

No.	Name	Synonyms and Formula	Mol. wt.	Color, crystalline form, specific rotation and λ_{max} (log ε)	m.p. °C	b.p. °C	Density	n_D	Solubility						Ref.
									w	al	eth	ace	bz	other solvents	
	Acetic acid														
a278	—,—,tert-butyl ester	$BrCH_2CO_2C(CH_3)_3$	195.06	....		$73-4^{25}$ 50^{14}		1.4430^{30}	i	s	s	...	...	os v	B2[1], 96
Ω a279	—,—,ethyl ester ...	$BrCH_2CO_2CH_2CH_3$	167.01			$168-9$ $58-9^{15}$	1.5059^{20}_{20}	1.4489^{20}	i	∞	∞	s	...	os v	B2[2], 202
a280	—,—,isobutyl ester	$BrCH_2CO_2CH_2CH(CH_3)_2$	195.06			188^{752} 74.5^{10}	1.3269^{20}_{4}		i	v	v	s	...	os v	B2[1], 96
Ω a281	—,—,methyl ester	$BrCH_2CO_2CH_3$	152.98			$144d$ 64^{33}			i	s	s	s	...	os v	B2[2], 202
a282	—,—,nitrile......	$BrCH_2CN$...........	119.95	pa ye		$150-1^{752}$ 46^{13}				δ	s	s	s		B2, 216
a283	—,—,phenyl ester..	$BrCH_2CO_2C_6H_5$	215.05	pl (al)	32	140^{20}	1.4099^{20}_{4}	1.4518^{20}		s	v			os s	B6[1], 87
a284	—,—,propyl ester..	$BrCH_2CO_2CH_2CH_2CH_3$	181.04		38 (32)	$215\,\delta\,d$ $103-4^{11}$	1.9848^{31}	1.5014^{31}	v	v	s	v		os s	B2, 215
a285	—,bromochloro-	$BrClCHCO_2H$	173.40	....		$174d$	1.5890^{22}_{4}	1.4659^{24}		s	s				B2[2], 204
a286	—,—,ethyl ester ...	$BrClCHCO_2CH_2CH_3$	201.45			$145-60$ 87^{82}			v	s				chl s[h]	B2, 217
a287	—,bromodifluoro-..	F_2BrCCO_2H	174.94	lf (chl)	40									to v[h], chl s MeOH δ	B9[2], 471
a288	—,bromo-(diphenyl)-	$(C_6H_5)_2CBrCO_2H$	291.15	(chl-peth)	$133-4$	....									
a289	—,—,bromide	$(C_6H_5)_2CBrCOBr$	354.05	nd (lig)	$65-6$	....			d	v d[h]	v		v	chl v	B9[1], 283
a290	—,bromofluoro- ...	$BrFCHCO_2H$	156.95		48	183 103^{20}			s	v				chl v	B2, 216
a291	—,—,amide	$BrFCHCONH_2$	155.96	nd (CCl_4)	44				v	v	v			CCl_4 s[h]	B2, 217
a292	—,(2-bromo-phenoxy)-	....	231.05	nd (dil al), cr (w) $\lambda^{0.1\,N\,NaOH}$ 273.5 (3.31)	142.5				v	v	v			chl v AcOEt v	B6, 198
a293	—,(4-bromo-phenoxy)-	....	231.05	pr (al), cr (w) $\lambda^{0.1\,N\,NaOH}$ 279 (3.14)	$161.4-1.8$				δ	v	v			CS_2 δ	B6, 200
a294	—,bromo-(phenyl)-, nitrile	$C_6H_5CHBrCN$	196.05	yesh cr (dil al) λ^{hx} 235 (3.8)	29	$242d$ $132-4^{12}$	1.539^{29}_{4}		i	v	v	v	v	chl v	B9[2], 311
a295	—,(2-bromo-phenyl)-	o-Bromotoluic acid	215.05	cr (aa)	$105-6$					v	v			CS_2 v aa v[h] lig δ, v[h]	B9, 450
a296	—,—,nitrile......	2-Bromobenzyl cyanide.	196.05	λ^{al} <235	1	$145-7^{14}$			i	v					B9[1], 181
a297	—,(3-bromo-phenyl)-	m-Bromotoluic acid.	215.05	nd (w)	$100-1$				δ v[h]						B9[1], 181
a298	—,(4-bromo-phenyl)-	....	215.05	nd (w)	116	sub			δ s[h]	v	v			CS_2 v	B9[2], 309
a299	—,—,nitrile......	4-Bromobenzyl cyanide.	196.05	pa ye cr (al) λ^{al} 266 (2.37)	47	....			i	s	...	...	v	CS_2 v	B9[1], 181
a300	—,(4-bromo-phenyl)-α-hydroxy-(dl)	p-Bromomandelic acid.	231.05	nd (bz) λ^{al} 259 (2.40), 265 (2.42)	$118-20$				v	v	v			chl v[h]	B10[2], 125
a301	—,(2-carboxy-phenoxy)-	o-(Carboxymethoxy) benzoic acid. Salicylacetic acid.	196.17	nd (w)	$190-2$ (151)				δ s[h]	s	s	s	s[h]	aa s chl δ lig δ	B10[1], 31
a302	—,(3-carboxy-phenoxy)-	m-(Carboxymethoxy) benzoic acid.	196.17	cr	$206-7$										B10[1], 65
a303	—,(4-carboxy-phenoxy)-	p-(Carboxymethoxy) benzoic acid.	196.17	nd (ace or w)	$280-2$				δ	v	v	v	s	chl v	B10[2], 94
a304	—,(2-carboxy-phenyl)-	o-Carboxy-α-toluic acid. Homophthalic acid.	180.17	cr (w, eth)	$185-7$				s[h]	s	δ	...	i	chl i	B9[2], 617
a305	—,—,nitrile......	o-Carboxyphenylacetonitrile.	161.16	cr (aa), nd (w or bz)	116d (126)				δ s[h]	v	v		v	CCl_4 v	B9[2], 618
a306	—,(3-carboxy-phenyl)-	m-Carboxy-α-toluic acid. Homoisophthalic acid.	180.17	nd or pl (w)	$184-5$				δ s[h]	s	s		δ	chl δ	B9, 860
a307	—,(4-carboxy-phenyl)-	p-Carboxy-α-toluic acid. Homoterephthalic acid.	180.17	cr (dil al)	$239-41$				δ	s	s		s		B9, 861
a308	—,(2-carboxy-phenyl)-2-oxo-	o-Carboxyphenylglyoxylic acid. Phthalonic acid.	194.15	cr (w + 2)	146(anh)					s	s	s	δ	chl δ	B10[2], 604
Ω a309	—,chloro-(α)	$ClCH_2CO_2H$	94.50	mcl pr λ^{al} 218 sh(1.7)	63	187.85 104^{20}	1.4043^{40}_{4}	1.4351^{55}	v	s	s		s	chl, CS_2 s	B2[2], 187
a310	—,—,(β)...........	$ClCH_2CO_2H$	94.50	mcl pr	56.2	187.85 104^{20}	1.4043^{40}_{4}	1.4351^{55}	v	s	s		s	chl, CS_2 s	B2[2], 187
a311	—,—,(γ)...........	$ClCH_2CO_2H$	94.50	mcl	52.5	187.85 104^{20}	1.3978^{65} 1.4043^{40}	1.4351^{55}	v	s	s		s	chl, CS_2 s	B2[2], 187
Ω a312	—,—,amide	$ClCH_2CONH_2$	93.51	mcl pr λ^{MeOH} 442 sh(2.1)	121 (118)	$224-5^{743}$			s	v	δ		s	chl, CS_2 s	B2, 199
a313	—,—,—,N-allyl-N-phenyl-	$ClCH_2CON(CH_2CH:CH_2)C_6H_5$	217.74	....		$119^{0.5}$		1.5079^{25}							Am 78, 2556
a314	—,—,—,N,N-bis(2-chloroallyl)-	$ClCH_2CON(CH_2CCl:CH_2)_2$	242.53			$161-3^{12}$ $130^{2.1}$		1.5220^{25}							Am 78, 2556
a315	—,—,—,N,N-bis(3-chloroallyl)-	$ClCH_2CON(CH_2CH:CHCl)_2$	242.53			$140-5^{1}$		1.5220^{25}							Am 78, 2556
a316	—,—,—,N,N-bis(2-chloropropyl)-	$ClCH_2CON(CH_2CHClCH_3)_2$	246.57			$134^{0.7}$		1.5018^{25}							Am 78, 2556
a318	—,—,—,N,N-bis(2-ethylhexyl)-	$ClCH_2CON[CH_2CH(C_2H_5)C_4H_9]_2$	317.95			$154^{0.8}$		1.4622^{25}							Am 78, 2556

For explanations, symbols and abbreviations see beginning of table. For structural formulas see end of table.

No.	Name	Synonyms and Formula	Mol. wt.	Color, crystalline form, specific rotation and λ_{max} (log ε)	m.p. °C	b.p. °C	Density	n_D	w	al	eth	ace	bz	other solvents	Ref.
	Acetic acid														
a319	—,—,—,N,N-bis(2-methylallyl)-	ClCH₂CON(CH₂C(CH₃):CH₂)₂	201.70			133–5[20] 110[7?]		1.4882[2]							Am 78, 2556
a320	—,—,—,N,N-bis(3-methylbutyl)-	ClCH₂CON[CH₂CH₂CH(CH₃)₂]₂	233.79			109[0.6]		1.4625[25]							Am 78, 2556
a321	—,—,—,N-butyl-..	ClCH₂CONHC₄H₉ⁿ	149.62			110[7]		1.4665[25]							Am 78, 2556
a322	—,—,—,N-sec-butyl-	ClCH₂CONHC₄H₉ˢ........	149.62	cr (peth)	45–5.5	68[0.7]								peth sʰ	Am 78, 2556
a323	—,—,—,N-tert-butyl-	ClCH₂CONHC₄H₉ᵗ........	149.62	cr (peth)	84									peth sʰ	Am 78, 2556
a324	—,—,—,N-butyl-N-ethyl-	ClCH₂CON(C₄H₉ⁿ)C₂H₅	177.68			90[1.5] (115[1])		1.4665[25]							Am 78, 2556
a325	—,—,—,N-butyl-N-isopropyl-	ClCH₂CON(C₄H₉ⁿ)C₃H₇ⁱ	191.70			82[0.5]		1.4655[25]							Am 78, 2556
a326	—,—,—,N(2-chloroallyl)-	ClCH₂CONHCH₂CCl:CH₂	168.02			101[1.4]		1.5078[25]							Am 78, 2556
a327	—,—,—,N(3-chloroallyl)-	ClCH₂CONHCH₂CH:CHCl	168.02	cr (peth)	52–3.5	112[0.5]								peth sʰ	Am 78, 2556
a328	—,—,—,N(2-chloroallyl)-N-phenyl-	ClCH₂CON(CH:CClCH₂)C₆H₅	243.12			138[0.7]		1.5602[25]							Am 78, 2556
a329	—,—,—,N(4-chloro-4-nitrophenyl)-	....	263.08	cr (peth)	118–9										Am 78, 2556
a330	—,—,—,N(4-chlorophenyl)-N-ethyl-	....	323.11	cr (peth)	70–1									peth s	Am 78, 2556
a331	—,—,—,N(2-chloropropyl)-	ClCH₂CONHCH₂CHClCH₃	170.04			88[1.5]		1.4942[25]							Am 78, 2556
a332	—,—,—,N(3-chloropropyl)-	ClCH₂CONHCH₂CH₂CH₂Cl	170.04		36–7										Am 78, 2556
a333	—,—,—,N,N-diallyl-	ClCH₂CON(CH₂CH:CH₂)₂.	173.64			92[0.7]		1.4932[25]							Am 78, 2556
a334	—,—,—,N,N-dibenzyl-	ClCH₂CON(CH₂C₆H₅)₂.	273.77			190[1.8]		1.5837[25]							Am 78, 2556
a335	—,—,—,N,N-di-sec-butyl-	ClCH₂CON(C₄H₉ˢ)₂	205.73			92[0.7]		1.4681[25]							Am 78, 2556
a336	—,—,—,N(2,3-dichloroallyl)	ClCH₂CONHCH₂CCl:CHCl	202.47			126–31[1.8]		1.5311[25]							Am 78, 2556
a337	—,—,—,N(2,4-dichlorobenzyl)-	....	252.54	cr (bz)	96.5–7.5								sʰ		Am 78, 2556
a338	—,—,—,N(3,4-dichlorobenzyl)-	....	252.54	cr (dil al)	105–6					s					Am 78, 2556
a339	—,—,—,N(2,4-dichlorophenyl)-	....	238.50	cr (dil al)	101–2					s				peth sʰ	Am 78, 2556
a340	—,—,—,N(2,5-dichlorophenyl)-	....	238.50	cr (dil al)	116–7					s				peth sʰ	Am 78, 2556
a342	—,—,—,N(2,3-dichloropropyl)-	ClCH₂CONHCH₂CHClCH₂Cl	204.50	cr (peth)	65–6									peth sʰ	Am 78, 2556
a343	—,—,—,N,N-diethyl-	ClCH₂CON(C₂H₅)₂	149.62			190–5[25]			v						B4[2], 602
a344	—,—,—,N,N-dihexyl-	ClCH₂CON[(CH₂)₅CH₃]₂ .	261.84	cr (peth)	114.5–5.5										Am 78, 2556
a345	—,—,—,N,N-diisobutyl-	ClCH₂CON(C₄H₉ⁱ)₂	205.73			99[2]		1.4642[25]							Am 78, 2556
a346	—,—,—,N,N-diisopropyl-	ClCH₂CON(C₃H₇ⁱ)₂	177.68	cr (peth)	48.5–9.5	86[2.7]		1.4619[25]							Am 78, 2556
a347	—,—,—,N(2,4-dinitrophenyl)-	....	259.61	nd (al)	114–4.5										B9[2], 315
a348	—,—,—,N,N-dipentyl-	ClCH₂CON(C₅H₁₁ⁿ)₂.......	233.79			126[1]		1.4651[25]							Am 78, 2556
a349	—,—,—,N,N-dipropyl-	ClCH₂CON(C₃H₇ⁿ)₂	177.68			120[8] 90–2[0.8]		1.4670[20]							Am 78, 2556
a350	—,—,—,N-ethyl-N-hexyl-	ClCH₂CON[(CH₂)₅CH₃]C₂H₅	205.73			120[1.1]		1.4978[25]							Am 78, 2556
a351	—,—,—,N-furfuryl-	....	173.61	cr (peth)	58–8.5	......								peth εʰ	Am 78, 2556
a352	—,—,—,N-hexyl-..	ClCH₂CONH(CH₂)₅CH₃.	177.68	cr (peth)	108.5–9.5	95–105[0.2]								peth sʰ	Am 78, 2556
a353	—,—,—,N-hexyl-N-methyl-	ClCH₂CON[(CH₂)₅CH₃]CH₃	191.70			134[3.8]		1.5005[25]							Am 78, 2556
a354	—,—,—,N(3-isopropoxypropyl)-	ClCH₂CONHCH₂CH₂CH₂OCH(CH₃)₂	193.68	....		92[0.5]		1.4625[25]							Am 78, 2556
a355	—,—,—,N-isopropyl-	ClCH₂CONHCH(CH₃)₂ ...	136.60	cr (peth)	62–2.5									peth sʰ	Am 78, 2556
a356	—,—,—,N(3-methoxypropyl)-	ClCH₂CONHCH₂CH₂CH₂OCH₃	165.62		30	88[0.5]		1.4712[25]							Am 78, 2556
a357	—,—,—,N(2-methylallyl)-	ClCH₂CONHCH₂C(CH₃):CH₂	147.61			96[1]		1.4860[25]							Am 78, 2556
a358	—,—,—,N(3-methylbutyl)-	ClCH₂CONHCH₂CH₂CH(CH₃)₂	163.65	....	−15	134.5[13]									B4[2], 647

For explanations, symbols and abbreviations see beginning of table. For structural formulas see end of table.

No.	Name	Synonyms and Formula	Mol. wt.	Color, crystalline form, specific rotation and λ_{max} (log ε)	m.p. °C	b.p. °C	Density	n_D	w	al	eth	ace	bz	other solvents	Ref.
	Acetic acid														
a359	—,—,—,N-pentyl-	ClCH$_2$CONH(CH$_2$)$_4$CH$_3$	163.65	....		82[0.5]		1.4665[25]	...	....	...	...	...		Am 78, 2556
a360	—,—,—,N-propyl-	ClCH$_2$CONHCH$_2$CH$_2$CH$_3$	135.59		62–2.5	105–6[10.5]			s	s	s	s	...	chl s peth s[h]	B4[1], 365
a361	—,—,—,N-tetradecyl-	ClCH$_2$CONH(CH$_2$)$_{13}$CH$_3$	289.89	cr (peth)	64–5										Am 78, 2556
a362	—,—,—,N-tetrahydrofurfuryl-		177.63	cr (peth)	62.5–3.5									peth s[h]	Am 78, 2556
a363	—,—,anhydride	(ClCH$_2$CO)$_2$O	170.98	pr (bz)	46	203[760]	1.5497[20]		d	d[h]	δ			chl δ	B2[2], 193
a364	—,—,benzyl ester	ClCH$_2$CO$_2$CH$_2$C$_6$H$_5$	184.62			147.5[9] 84–6[0.4]	1.2223[4]	1.5426[18]		s	s			chl s	B6, 435
Ω a365	—,—,butyl ester	ClCH$_2$CO$_2$(CH$_2$)$_3$CH$_3$	150.61			183 94[38]	1.0704[20]	1.4297[20]	i	s	s				B2[2], 192
a366	—,—,sec-butyl ester	ClCH$_2$CO$_2$CH(CH$_3$)CH$_2$CH$_3$	150.61			163–4[760]	1.0622[20]	1.4251[19]	i	s	s				B2[3], 443
Ω a367	—,—,chloride	Chloroacetyl chloride. ClCH$_2$COCl	112.94			107[760] (108–10)	1.4202[20]	1.4541[20]	d	d	∞	s			B2[2], 193
a368	—,—,2-chloroethyl ester	ClCH$_2$CO$_2$CH$_2$CH$_2$Cl	157.00			202[760] 89[10]	1.3600[25]	1.4619[25]	d[h]						B2, 198
Ω a369	—,—,ethyl ester	ClCH$_2$CO$_2$CH$_2$CH$_3$	122.55		−26	144[760] 52[20]	1.1585[20]	1.4215[20]	i	∞	∞	∞	s		B2[2], 191
a370	—,—,2-hydroxyethyl ester	ClCH$_2$CO$_2$CH$_2$CH$_2$OH	138.55			240d 86[1.6]	1.3300[20]	1.4609[20]	∞	∞					C27, 4216
a371	—,—,isobutyl ester	ClCH$_2$CO$_2$CH$_2$CH(CH$_3$)$_2$	150.61			170	1.0612[20]	1.4255[20]	s		s	s		os s	B2[1], 89
a372	—,—,isopropyl ester	ClCH$_2$CO$_2$CH(CH$_3$)$_2$	136.58			150.4–1.6[760]	1.0888[20]	1.4192[20]	i	s	s				B2[2], 192
a373	—,—,2-methoxyethyl ester	Methyl cellosolve chloroacetate. ClCH$_2$CO$_2$CH$_2$CH$_2$OCH$_3$	152.58			85–6[9] 60[1.3]	1.2015[20]	1.4382[20]	d	v					C27, 4216
Ω a374	—,—,methyl ester	ClCH$_2$CO$_2$CH$_3$	108.53	....	−32.12	129.8[760] 29[10]	1.2337[20]	1.4218[20]	δ	∞	∞	∞	∞		B2[2], 191
Ω a375	—,—,nitrile	Chloromethyl cyanide. ClCH$_2$CN	75.50			126–7 30–2[15]	1.1930[20]	1.4202[25]	d		s				B2[2], 194
a376	—,—,phenyl ester	ClCH$_2$CO$_2$C$_6$H$_5$	170.60	nd or pl (al)	44–5	230–5 114[8]	1.2202[44]	1.5146[44]	i	v	v				B6[2], 154
a377	—,—,4-phenylphenacyl ester		288.73	cr	116				i						C24, 503
a378	—,—,piperazinium salt	2ClCH$_2$CO$_2$H · C$_4$H$_{10}$N$_2$	275.13	cr (al)	145–6				s	s[h]	i				Am 56, 1759
a379	—,—,propyl ester	ClCH$_2$CO$_2$CH$_2$CH$_2$CH$_3$	136.58			161[764]	1.1033[20]	1.4261[20]	i		s			os s	B2[1], 89
a380	—,—,4-tolyl ester		184.62	pl	32	162[45]			i	s	s	s	s	os s	B6[2], 378
a381	—,chloro-(diphenyl)-	(C$_6$H$_5$)$_2$CClCO$_2$H	246.70	pl (bz-lig)	118–9d					s	s	s		aa v[h] lig v[h]	B9[2], 471
a382	—,—,amide	(C$_6$H$_5$)$_2$CClCONH$_2$	245.71	cr (to)	115					s	s	s	s	chl v	B9[1], 283
a383	—,—,chloride	(C$_6$H$_5$)$_2$CClCOCl	265.14	cr (lig)	50–1	180[14]			d	d	δ				B9[2], 471
a384	—,—,ethyl ester	(C$_6$H$_5$)$_2$CClCO$_2$C$_2$H$_5$	274.75	pl (chl), cr (al)	43–4	185[14] 108[0.005]				s	s			chl s[h]	B9[1], 282
a385	—,(4-chloro-2-methylphenoxy)-		200.62	pl (bz or to)	120				δ[h]	v	v		s	CCl$_4$ s	B6[3], 1265
a386	—,(6-chloro-2-methyl-5-pyrimidyl)-, ethyl ester		214.65	....	35–6	108–12[11]			i		s	s	s		Am 59, 1714
Ω a387	—,(2-chlorophenoxy)-		186.60	nd (w or al) $\lambda^{w.0.1\,N\,HCl}$ 272 (3.20), 279 (3.15)	148–9				s[h]	s[h]					B6[2], 172
Ω a388	—,(3-chlorophenoxy)-		186.60	cr (w) $\lambda^{w.0.1\,N\,HCl}$ 272 (3.18), 279.5 (3.14)	109.7–10.2				i		s	s			B6[3], 683
Ω a389	—,(4-chlorophenoxy)-		186.60	pr or nd (w) $\lambda^{w.0.1\,N\,HCl}$ 278 (3.11), 284 sh(3.01)	156–7				δ						B6[2], 177
a390	—,chloro-(phenyl)-(d)	d-α-Chloro-α-toluic acid. C$_6$H$_5$CHClCO$_2$H	170.60	cr (peth), [α]$_D^{20}$ +191.9(bz)	60–1				δ	s	v		s	lig s[h] chl s	B9[2], 306
Ω a391	—,—,(dl)	C$_6$H$_5$CHClCO$_2$H	170.60	lf (peth)	78				δ	v	v			lig δ, s[h]	B9[2], 307
a392	—,—,(l)	C$_6$H$_5$CHClCO$_2$H	170.60	nd (peth), [α]$_D^{18}$ −191.3 (bz)	61				δ	v	v		v	chl v lig s[h]	B9[2], 307
a393	—,(2-chlorophenyl)-	o-Chloro-α-toluic acid.	170.60	nd (w)	96				δ	v[h]					B9[1], 178
a394	—,—,nitrile	2-Chlorobenzyl cyanide.	151.60	grsh-ye nd λ^{al} 266 (2.33), 273 (2.22)	24	251[760] 170[120]	1.1737[4]	1.15341[18]							B9, 448
Ω a395	—,(3-chlorophenyl)-	m-Chloro-α-toluic acid.	170.60	nd (hp), pl (aq al)	77.5–8.5 (74)				δ	δ	∞		δ		B9[2], 306
a396	—,(4-chlorophenyl)-	p-Chloro-α-toluic acid.	170.60	nd (w)	105–6				s	s	s		s		B9[2], 306
a397	—,(4-chlorophenyl)hydroxy-	p-Chloromandelic acid.	186.60	nd (bz)	119–20				s	v				s[h]	B10[1], 92
	—,—,cyano-	see **Malonic acid**, mononitrile													

For explanations, symbols and abbreviations see beginning of table. For structural formulas see end of table.

No.	Name	Synonyms and Formula	Mol. wt.	Color, crystalline form, specific rotation and λ_{max} (log ε)	m.p. °C	b.p. °C	Density	n_D	Solubility w	al	eth	ace	bz	other solvents	Ref.
	Acetic acid														
a398	—,(3-cyano-phenyl)-, nitrile	3-Cyanobenzyl cyanide. Homoisophthalonitrile.	142.16	nd (w)	84	....	....	....	s[h]	s	s	....	s	chl s	B9, 860
a399	—,1-cyclohexenyl, nitrile	....	121.18	λ^{al} 217 (4.14)	....	144[90] 105[22]	0.9473[21 4]	1.4787[21]	i	s	s				B9[2], 32
a400	—,cyclohexyl-.....	....	142.20	nd (HCO₂H)	33	244–6 135[13]	1.0423[18 4]	1.4775[20]	δ	...	s	s		os s	B9[2], 9
a401	—,cyclohexyl-idene, nitrile	....	121.18	....	....	107–8[22] 90[10]	0.9483[15 4]	1.4832[25]		s	s				B9[2], 34
Ω a402	—,diazo, ethyl ester	Diazoacetic ester. Ethyl diazoacetate. N₂CHCO₂CH₂CH₃	114.10	ye rh λ^{al} 247 (4.13)	−22	140–1[720]δd 44.5–6.5[13]	1.0852[18 4]	1.4605[20]	δ	∞	∞	....	∞	lig ∞	B3[2], 390
Ω a403	—,dibromo-.......	Br₂CHCO₂H	217.86	dlq cr	48	232–4d 195[250]	....	....	v	v	s				B2[2], 205
a404	—,—,amide,N,N-dimethyl-	Br₂CHCON(CH₃)₂	244.93	pr (w or eth)	79–80	128[16]	....	....			δ				B4, 59
a405	—,—,ethyl ester ...	Br₂CHCO₂CH₂CH₃	245.91	....	....	194[760] 121[74]	1.9025[20 20]	1.5017[13]	i	∞	∞				B2[1], 97
a406	—,—,methyl ester	Br₂CHCO₂CH₃	231.88	....	....	181.5–3.5	....	....		s	s				B2, 219
Ω a407	—,dichloro-....	Cl₂CHCO₂H	128.94	....	13.5	194[760] 91–2[12]	1.5634[20 0]	1.4658[20]	∞	∞	∞	s			B2[2], 194
Ω a408	—,—,amide	Cl₂CHCONH₂	127.96	mcl pr (w)	99.4	233–4[745] sub	....	....	s[h]	∞	∞				B2[2], 196
a409	—,—,anhydride ...	(Cl₂CHCO)₂O	239.87	....	....	214–6d 100–2[16]	1.574[24]	....	d	d					B2, 204
a410	—,—,butyl ester	Cl₂CHCO₂(CH₂)₃CH₃	185.05	....	....	193.4–4.6 102[37]	1.1820[20]	1.4420[20]	i	s	s			os s	B2, 204
Ω a411	—,—,chloride....	Cl₂CHCOCl	147.39	....	....	108–10[760]	1.5315[16 4]	1.4591[20]	d	d	∞				B2[2], 193
Ω a412	—,—,ethyl ester ...	Cl₂CHCO₂CH₂CH₃	157.00	....	....	155.5[764] (158) 56[10]	1.2827[20 4]	1.4386[20]	δ	∞	∞	s			B2[2], 196
a413	—,—,(2-hydroxy-ethyl) ester	Cl₂CHCO₂CH₂CH₂OH	173.00	....	81–2[0.5]		1.4384[20 4]	1.4735[20]	δ	s					B2[3], 460
a414	—,—,isopropyl ester	Cl₂CHCO₂CH(CH₃)₂	171.03	....	....	163.8–4.8	1.2053[20 4]	1.4328[20]		s	s				B2[3], 459
Ω a415	—,—,methyl ester .	Cl₂CHCO₂CH₃	142.97	....	−51.91	142.8[760] 38[10]	1.3774[20 4]	1.4429[20]	i	s					B2[2], 196
a416	—,—,nitrile......	Cl₂CHCN	109.94	....	....	112–3	1.369[20]	1.4391[25]		s	s			MeOH s	B2[1], 92
a417	—,—,propyl ester..	Cl₂CHCO₂CH₂CH₂CH₃	171.03	....	....	176[760]	1.2240[20]	1.4398[20]	i	s	s				B2[2], 196
Ω a418	—,(2,4-dichloro-phenoxy)-	....	221.04	cr (bz) $\lambda^{w,0.1 N HCl}$ 282 (3.26), 289 sh(3.20)	140–1	160[0.4]	....	....	i	s	s		δ		Am 63, 1768
a419	—,diethoxy-, ethyl ester	(C₂H₅O)₂CHCO₂CH₂CH₃	176.22	....	....	199 83–5[13]	0.994[18]	1.4089[25]	...	v	v				B3[2], 389
Ω a420	—,difluoro-	F₂CHCO₂H	96.03	....	−0.35	134.2[766] 67–70[20]	1.5255[20]	1.3420[20]	∞	∞	∞	∞		∞	B2[2], 185
Ω a421	—,(2,5-dihydroxy-phenyl)-	Homogentisic acid.	168.16	pr (w + l), lf (al-chl) λ^w 290 (3.58)	152–4		....	....	v	v	v		i	chl i	B10[2], 267
a422	—,diiodo-	I₂CHCO₂H.	311.85	lt ye cr or wh nd (bz)	110 (96)		....	....	s	s[h]	s[h]		s[h]		B2[1], 99
Ω a423	—,(3,4-dimeth-oxyphenyl)-	Homoveratric acid.	196.21	nd (w + l), cr (bz-peth) λ 279 (3.45)	80–2 (hyd), 98–9 (anh)		....	....	s	v	v				B10[2], 268
a424	—,—,amide	....	195.22	cr (w)	145–7 (142)		....	....		s	s				B10[1], 198
a425	—,(2,4-dimethyl-phenyl) hydroxy-	2,4-Dimethylmandelic acid..	180.21	rh (w), lf (to or peth-chl), nd (bz)	119 (115)		....	....	v[h]	v	v		s[h]	chl v	B10, 275
a426	—,(2,5-dimethyl-phenyl) hydroxy-	2,5-Dimethylmandelic acid..	180.21	nd or pr (bz)	116.5–7		....	....	δ	v	v			chl v	B10[2], 168
a427	—,(3,4-dimethyl-phenyl) hydroxy-	3,4-Dimethylmandelic acid..	180.21	lf (bz)	135		....	....	s	s[h]			v[h]		B10[2], 167
a428	—,(2,4-dinitro-phenoxy)-	....	242.15	pa ye pr (w)	147–8		....	....	δ	s	s		i	alk s	B6[2], 244
a429	—,(3,5-dinitro-phenoxy)-	....	242.15	pa br cr pw	207		....	....	δ	s	s			alk s	B6, 259
Ω a430	—,(2,4-dinitro-phenyl)-	....	226.15	nd (w)	179–80d	d	....	....	δ[h]	s	s				B9[2], 315
a431	—,—,chloride....	....	244.59	ye lf (CS₂)	77	....	....	....	d	...	v	v	chl v		B9[1], 185
a432	—,—,ethyl ester ...	....	254.20	nd (w)	37	....	....	....	δ	...	v	v	chl v		B9, 459
a433	—,(2,6-dinitro-phenyl)-	....	226.15	ye lf (aa)	201–2d	....	....	....	δ	s[h]			os v	aa δ	B9[1], 185
Ω a434	—,diphenyl-......	(C₆H₅)₂CHCO₂H	212.25	nd (w), lf (al) λ^{al} 260 (2.6)	148	195[25] (sub)	1.258[15 15]	....	δ v[h]	v[h]	s			chl s, v[h]	B9[2], 466
Ω a435	—,—,amide	(C₆H₅)₂CHCONH₂	211.25	pl (al)	167.5–8.5	....	....	....		s[h]	s			chl v, v[h]	B9[2], 468
a436	—,—,anhydride ...	[(C₆H₅)₂CHCO]₂O	406.49	nd (eth)	98	220–5[15]	....	....	d[h]	d[h]	δ		v	chl v lig δ	B9[1], 281
Ω a437	—,—,chloride.....	(C₆H₅)₂CHCOCl	230.70	pl (lig)	56–7	178[15]	....	....	d	d				lig s[h]	B9[1], 281

For explanations, symbols and abbreviations see beginning of table. For structural formulas see end of table.

No.	Name	Synonyms and Formula	Mol. wt.	Color. crystalline form. specific rotation and λ_{max} (log ε)	m.p. °C	b.p. °C	Density	n_D	Solubility						Ref.
									w	al	eth	ace	bz	other solvents	
	Acetic acid														
a438	—,—,ethyl ester . . .	$(C_6H_5)_2CHCO_2CH_2CH_3$	240.31	nd (al), rh (AcOEt)	59	195^{25}			i	v	v	. . .	. . .	CS_2 v	B9[1], 281
a439	—,—,methyl ester .	$(C_6H_5)_2CHCO_2CH_3$	226.28	mcl pl (AcOEt), lf (dil al)	60				i	s	s	. . .	. . .	AcOEt s[h]	B9[2], 467
Ω a440	—,—,nitrile	$(C_6H_5)_2CHCN$	193.25	pr (eth, peth)	72–3 (75–6)	$181–4^{12}$			. . .	s[h]	v	. . .	. . .	lig δ, s[h]	B9[2], 469
Ω a441	—,diphenyl-(hydroxy)-	Benzilic acid. $(C_6H_5)_2C(OH)CO_2H$	228.25	mcl nd (w)	151	d 180			δ v[h]	v	v	. . .	. . .	con sulf s (red)	B10[2], 223
a442	—,—,ethyl ester	Ethyl benzilate. $(C_6H_5)_2C(OH)CO_2CH_2CH_3$	256.31	pr or nd	34	201^{21}		1.5620^{20}	i	s	s	. . .	. . .	con sulf s	B10[2], 225
a443	—,—,methyl ester .	Methyl benzilate. $(C_6H_5)_2C(OH)CO_2CH_3$	242.28	mcl or tcl cr (al)	75	187^{13}			i	s[h]	s	. . .	. . .	con sulf s aa s	B10[2], 225
—	—,diureido-	see **Allantoic acid**													
Ω a444	—,ethoxy-	Glycolic acid ethyl ether. $C_2H_5OCH_2CO_2H$	104.12			$206–7^{760}$ 111^{25}	1.1021^{20}_4	1.4194^{20}	v[h]	v[h]	v[h]	. . .	. . .		B3[2], 170
a445	—,—,chloride.	$C_2H_5OCH_2COCl$	122.55			$123–4$ $49–50^{37}$	1.1170^{20}_4	1.4204^{20}	d	d	s	s	. . .		B3[2], 173
Ω a446	—,—,ethyl ester . . .	$C_2H_5OCH_2CO_2CH_2CH_3$	132.16	λ^{al} 214 (1.92)		158^{760} (152^{760}) 52^{12}	0.9701^{20}_4 0.9945^{50}	1.4029^{20}	. . .	s	s	s	. . .		B3[2], 172
a447	—,—,l-menthyl ester		242.36	$[\alpha]^{20}_D -66.35$		155^{20}	0.9545^{20}_4		δ	s	s	. . .	. . .	chl s	B6[2], 47
a448	—,—,methyl ester .	$C_2H_5OCH_2CO_2CH_3$	118.13			$147–8^{734}$	1.0112^{15}		. . .	s	s	s	. . .		B3[1], 91
a449	—,—,piperazinum salt	$2C_2H_5OCH_2CO_2H.C_4H_{10}N_2$	294.35		120–1 (cor)				s	s	δ	. . .	. . .		Am 70, 2759
a450	—,(2-ethoxyphenyl)-		180.21	nd (lig), cr (w)	103–4				. . .	δ	δ	. . .	. . .	lig s[h]	B10[1], 82
Ω a451	—,(ethylthio)-	$C_2H_5SCH_2CO_2H$	120.18		–8.5	164^{83} 109^5	1.1497^{20}_4		v	v	v	. . .	. . .		B3[1], 95
a452	—,9-fluorenyl-		224.26	mcl nd (al)	138–9	$218–20^{11}$			. . .	s	s	. . .	. . .		E13, 95
Ω a453	—,fluoro-	FCH_2CO_2H	78.04	nd	35.2	165^{760}	1.3693^{36}		s[h]	s[h]	. . .	. . .	. . .		B2[2], 185
Ω a456	—,2-furyl-	2-Furanacetic acid.	126.11	lf (bz, peth)	68–9	$102–4^{0.4}$			s	. . .	. . .	. . .	s[h]	MeOH s peth s[h]	Am 62, 1512
a457	—,—,nitrile.	Furfuryl cyanide.	107.11			$78–80^{20}$	1.0854^{25}_4	1.4693^{20}	δ	v	v	. . .	. . .		C49, 1695
—	—,guanidino-	see **Glycocyamine**													
Ω a458	—,hydroxy-	Glycolic acid. $HOCH_2CO_2H$	76.05	rh, nd (w), lf (eth)	80	d			s	s	s	. . .	. . .		B3[2], 167
a459	—,—,acetate.	Acetoxyacetic acid. $CH_3CO_2CH_2CO_2H$	118.09	nd (bz)	67–8	$144–5^{12}$ $113–4^{4.6}$			v	v	v	v	i	chl v	B3[2], 171
a460	—,—,—,ethyl ester	Ethyl acetoxyacetate. Ethyl acetylglycolate. $CH_3CO_2CH_2CO_2CH_2CH_3$	146.14			179	1.0880^{20}_4	1.4112^{20}	δ	s	s	. . .	. . .	aa s	B3[2], 172
a461	—,—,amide.	Glycolamide. Glycolic amide. $HOCH_2CONH_2$	75.07	lf (al), rh (AcOEt)	120		1.415^{13}		v	δ	δ	. . .	. . .		B3[2], 173
a462	—,—,anhydride . . .	Glycolic anhydride. $(HOCH_2CO)_2O$	134.09	pw	128–30	d			i	i	i	. . .	. . .		B3[1], 92
a463	—,—,ethyl ester . . .	Ethyl glycolate. $HOCH_2CO_2CH_2CH_3$	104.11			160 69^{25}	1.0826^{23}_4	1.4180^{20}	s	∞	∞	. . .	. . .		B3[2], 171
Ω a464	—,—,methyl ester	Methyl glycolate. $HOCH_2CO_2CH_3$	90.08			151.1	1.1677^{18}_4		s	∞	∞	. . .	. . .		B3[2], 171
Ω a465	—,—,nitrile.	Formaldehyde cyanohydrin. Glycolonitrile. $HOCH_2CN$	57.05		< –72	183 δd 119^{24}		1.4117^{19}	v	v	v	. . .	i	chl i	B3[2], 174
a466	—,hydroxy(4-iodophenyl)-,(dl)	p-Iodomandelic acid.	278.05		135				v	v	v	. . .	. . .	lig δ	B10, 210
a467	—,hydroxy-(4-isopropylphenyl)-, (d)	d-p-Isopropylmandelic acid	194.23	lf (w), $[\alpha]^7_D +134.9$ (abs al, c = 4.06)	153–4				δ s[h]	s	v	. . .	. . .		B10, 279
a468	—,—(dl)	$C_{11}H_{14}O_3$. See a467	194.23	nd (w)	159.2–60				δ	s	v	. . .	. . .		B10[1], 120
a469	—,—(l)	$C_{11}H_{14}O_3$. See a467	194.23	ta (20 % al), $[\alpha]^7_D -135$ (abs al, c = 4.09)	153–4				δ s[h]	v	v	. . .	. . .		B10, 279
a470	—,hydroxy-(phenyl)-, (D, –)	l-Mandelic acid. l-Phenylglycolic acid. $C_6H_5CH(OH)CO_2H$	152.16	ta, $[\alpha]^{20}_D -158.0$ (w, c = 2.5) –187.44 (aa)	133–5		1.341		s	s	v	. . .	. . .	aa s chl s	B10[2], 114
Ω a471	—,—(DL)	dl-Mandelic acid. dl-Phenylglycolic acid. $C_6H_5CH(OH)CO_2H$	152.16	pl (w), rh (bz) λ^{al} 252 (3.1), 258 (2.0), 265 (1.9)	121–3 (119)	d	1.300^{20}_4		s	v	v	. . .	. . .		B10[2], 118
a472	—,—,—,(solvate). .	$C_6H_5CH(OH)CO_2H$	152.16	mcl (bz +1)	32.6–.7				. . .	. . .	. . .	. . .	. . .		B10[2], 118
a473	—,—(L, +).	d-Mandelic acid. d-Phenylglycolic acid. $C_6H_5CH(OH)CO_2H$	152.16	pl (w), $[\alpha]^{20}_D +156.6$ (w, c = 2.9)	134–5				s v[h]	s	v	. . .	. . .	chl s	B10[2], 114
a474	—,—,acetate (D) . .	l-O-Acetylmandelic acid. $C_6H_5CH(O_2CCH_3)CO_2H$	194.19	nd (w +1), $[\alpha]^{20}_D -156.4$ (ace)	96.5–8 (anh)				δ s[h]	v	v	v	s	chl v CCl_4 δ lig δ	B10[1], 85

For explanations, symbols and abbreviations see beginning of table. For structural formulas see end of table.

Acetic acid

No.	Name	Synonyms and Formula	Mol. wt.	Color, crystalline form, specific rotation and λ_{max} (log ε)	m.p. °C	b.p. °C	Density	n_D	w	al	eth	acc	bz	other solvents	Ref.
Ω a475	—,—,—(DL)	$C_6H_5CH(O_2CCH_3)CO_2H$ . . .	194.19	cr (bz), amor (chl–peth), cr (w+1), nd (w+½)	38–9 (+1 w), 79–80 (anh)	. . . .			δ s^h	v	v	. . . .	v	chl v	B10², 120
Ω a476	—,—,acetate chloride (dl)	dl-O-Acetylmandelyl chloride. $C_6H_5CH(O_2CCH_3)COCl$	212.64	. . . .	. . . .	150–5³³ 129¹⁰					v	v	v	chl v lig v	B10¹, 89
a477	—,—,amide (dl) . . .	α-Hydroxy-α-toluamide. dl-Mandelamide. $C_6H_5CH(OH)CONH_2$	151.17	pl (bz or al)	134–5				δ	v^h	δ		s^h	. . . .	B10², 122
a478	—,—,—,N-ethyl-(D)	l-N-Ethylmandelamide. $C_6H_5CH(OH)CONHC_2H_5$	179.22	pl (chl–peth), $[\alpha]_D^{16}$ −34.4 (al, c = 3.7) $[\alpha]_D^{18}$ −103.6 (ace)	65.5–6.5				v	s	s	s	s	chl s	B10², 117
a479	—,—,—,—(DL) . . .	$C_6H_5CH(OH)CONHC_2H_5$	179.22	pl (chl–peth), [α]²⁰	53–4				s	s	s	s	s	peth δ	B10¹, 89
a480	—,—,ethyl ester (D, −)	l-Ethyl mandelate. $C_6H_5CH(OH)CO_2CH_2CH_3$	180.21	(peth), $[\alpha]_D^{20}$ −128.4 (chl, c = 6.67), $[\alpha]_D^{14}$ −200.2 (CS_2, c = 2)	35	150²¹	1.1270²⁰₄			s	s	. . . .		CS_2 s lig s^h	B10², 116
Ω a481	—,—,—(DL)	$C_6H_5CH(OH)CO_2CH_2CH_3$	180.21	nd (peth)	37	253–5 141¹⁵				s	s			CS_2 s lig s	B10², 121
a482	—,—,—(L, +)	$C_6H_5CH(OH)CO_2CH_2CH_3$	180.21	(peth), $[\alpha]_D^{20}$ +205.1 (CS_2, c = 0.7)	33		1.1270²⁰							CS_2 s lig s^h	B10², 114
a483	—,—,methyl-ester (D, −)	l-Methyl mandelate. $C_6H_5CH(OH)CO_2CH_3$	166.18	cr (peth) $[\alpha]_D^{20}$ −131.5 (w) $[\alpha]_D^{18}$ −214 (CS_2)	55	160³² 135¹²	1.1756²⁰		s	s	s	s	s	chl s peth s^h	B10², 115
Ω a484	—,—,—(DL)	$C_6H_5CH(OH)CO_2CH_3$	166.18	pl (bz–lig)	58	250 δd 144²⁰	1.1756²⁰		δ	s	s	. . .	s^h	chl s peth s^h	B10², 120
a485	—,—,—(L, +)	$C_6H_5CH(OH)CO_2CH_3$	166.18	cr (peth) $[\alpha]_D^{20}$ +133.6 (w) $[\alpha]_D^{20}$ +252 (CS_2)	55.5	160³²	1.1756²⁰		s	s	s	s	s	chl s peth s^h	B10², 114
a486	—,—,nitrile (D, +)	D(+)-Benzaldehyde cyanohydrin. D(+)-Mandelonitrile. $C_6H_5CH(OH)CN$	133.15	nd, $(\alpha)^{25}_{5461}$ +46.9 (bz)	28.5–9.5				i	s	s				B10², 117
a487	—,—,—(DL)	$C_6H_5CH(OH)CN$	133.15	ye pr $\lambda^{3:1\,hx-eth}$	22	170d	1.1165²⁰₄	1.5201²⁰	i	s	s				B10², 123
a488	—,—,—(L, −)	$C_6H_5CH(OH)CN$	133.15	250 (2.05), 255 (2.12), 263 (2.10)					i	s	s				B10¹, 86
a489	—,(3-hydroxy-4-methoxy-phenyl)-	Homoisovanillic acid.	182.17	. . . .	130–1				s	s	s		s^h		B10², 268
a490	—,(2-hydroxy-5-nitrophenyl)-		197.15	nd	160–2				v	s	s		δ	chl δ	B10, 189
a491	—,—,ethyl ester . . .		225.20	pr or pl(al)	154–5					s^h	δ		s	chl s lig δ	B10, 189
Ω a492	—,(3-hydroxy-phenoxy)-	Resorcinol-O-acetic acid	168.16	nd or pr (w, to)	158–9				s^h	s				to s^h	B6, 817
a493	—,—,ethyl ester		196.21	pr (w, bz)	55	274 δd 170–3¹¹			i s^h				s^h	lig δ	B6, 817
a494	—,(4-hydroxy-phenoxy)-	Hydroquinone-O-acetic acid	168.16	nd (to), pr (w+½)	154 (hyd)				s^h					to s^h	B6, 847
Ω a495	—,(2-hydroxy-phenyl)-	o-Hydroxy-α-toluic acid	152.16	nd (eth), pr (chl) $\lambda^{0.1N\,HCl}$ 271 (3.3), $\lambda^{0.1N\,NaOH}$ 293 (3.6)	147–9	240–3d			δ	. . .	s			chl δ	B10², 112
a496	—,—,amide		151.17	lf (al–chl)	118					s^h			. . . .	chl ρ^h	D10, 188
a497	—,—,hydrazide	. . . .	166.18	lf (chl or ba), nd (al)	151	. . . .				s^h		s		chl s^h	B10², 112
a498	—,—,nitrile	o-Hydroxybenzyl cyanide . . .	133.15	nd (bz–lig)	117–9				s^h	s	s	s	s	os v lig i	B10, 188
Ω a499	—,(3-hydroxy-phenyl)-	m-Hydroxy-α-toluic acid	152.16	nd (bz–lig)	131–4	190¹¹			v	v	v	.	s	lig δ	B10², 112
a500	—,—,nitrile	m-Hydroxybenzyl cyanide . .	133.15	pl (w) λ^{alk} 245 (4.01), 294 (3.46)	52–3				s v^h						B10, 189
a501	—,(4-hydroxy-phenyl)-	p-Hydroxy-α-toluic acid	152.16	nd (w) λ^{al} 225 (3.9), 278 (3.2)	149–51	sub			δ v^h	v	v				B10², 112
a502	—,—,nitrile	p-Hydroxybenzyl cyanide . . .	133.15	pl (w), mcl pr	69–70	330.5⁷⁵⁶ 210¹⁰			δ	v	v				B10², 113
Ω a503	—,iminodi-	Diglycolamidic acid. $HN(CH_2CO_2H)_2$	133.11	rh pr	247.5 (225d)				δ	i	i			. . . .	B4², 800

For explanations, symbols and abbreviations see beginning of table. For structural formulas see end of table.

No.	Name	Synonyms and Formula	Mol. wt.	Color. crystalline form. specific rotation and λ_{max} (log ε)	m.p. °C	b.p. °C	Density	n_D	Solubility						Ref.
									w	al	eth	ace	bz	other solvents	
	Acetic acid														
Ω a504	—,—,dinitrile	α,α′-Dicyanodimethylamine. Iminodiacetonitrile. HN(CH₂CN)₂	95.11	lf(al), cr(w)	78	......			s	s^h	δ	...	δ	chl δ	B4[1], 481
a505	—,(3-indolyl)-	Heteroauxin. λ^w 282 (3.70)	175.19	lf(bz), pl(chl)	165–6				i	v	s	s	s^h	chl δ, s^h	B22[2], 50
Ω a506	—,iodo-	ICH₂CO₂H. λ^{al} 224 (2.71), 273 (2.66)	185.95	pl (w, peth)	83	d			s^h	s^h	δ	...	...	peth s^h	B2[2], 206
Ω a507	—,—,amide	ICH₂CONH₂.	184.97	cr (w)	95	178–80[760]			s^h		s	s			B2[1], 99
Ω a508	—,—,ethyl ester ...	ICH₂CO₂CH₂CH₃.	214.00	oil		73[16]	1.8173$_4^{13}$	1.5079[13]		s	s				B2[2], 206
Ω a509	—,(2-isopropyl-5-methylphenoxy)-	Thymoxyacetic acid.	208.24	nd (dil al), cr (bz)	149–50				δ s^h	v	v		s^h		B6[2], 499
a510	—,(4-isopropyl-phenyl)-, amide	....	177.25	pl (bz)	170				i	s	δ		s^h		B9, 561
a512	—,Isothiocyanato-ethyl ester	Carbethoxymethyl isothio-cyanate. SCNCH₂CO₂CH₂CH₃	145.18	red in air	......	215 δd 110[10]	1.1649$_4^{18}$					s			B4[1], 480
Ω a513	—,menthoxy-(l) ...	cr (eth), $[\alpha]_D^{20}$ −92.93 (MeOH)	214.31		53–5	171[11]					v	s	v	os v	B6[1], 25
a514	—,—,chloride(l) ...	$[\alpha]_D^{13}$ −84.8 (chl)	232.75			128–31[11]			d^h	d^h	s				B6[1], 25
Ω a515	—,mercapto-	Thioglycolic acid. HSCH₂CO₂H $\lambda^{w, pH=10}$ 240 (3.26)	92.12		−16.5	120[20] 96[5]	1.3253[20]	1.5030[20]	∞	∞	∞				B3[2], 175
a516	—,—,acetate.	Acetylthioglycolic acid. CH₃COSCH₂CO₂H λ^{MeOH} 231 (3.53)	134.16	ye		158–9[17] 115–8[2.5]			s		s	s		os v	B3[1], 96
Ω a516[1]	—,—,amide,N(2-naphthyl)-	Thionalide. C₁₀H₇NHCOCH₂SH	217.29	nd	111–2				i					os v	C29, 3330
Ω a517	—,—,—,N-phenyl-	Thioglycolic acid anilide. HSCH₂CONHC₆H₅	167.23	nd (w or al)	110.5–11				s^h	v	v	...	δ	lig δ	B12[1], 265
Ω a518	—,—,ethyl ester ...	HSCH₂CO₂CH₂CH₃.	120.18			156–8 55[17]	1.0964[15]	1.4582[20]	δ	s	s		s	lig δ	B3[2], 180
a519	—,(2-mercapto-phenyl)-	....	168.23	pl (w, bz-lig)	96–7				δ s^h	v	v		s	lig δ	B10[1], 82
Ω a520	—,methoxy-	Methylglycolic acid. CH₃OCH₂CO₂H	90.08	hyg	......	203–4 96[13]	1.1768$_4^{20}$	1.4168[20]	s	s	s				B3[2], 170
a521	—,—,amide,N(4-ethoxyphenyl)-	p-Phenetitide methoxyacetic acid.	209.25	nd (dil al)	99–100				δ^h	v	v				B13, 489
Ω a522	—,—,chloride.	CH₃OCH₂COCl	108.53			99 46–9[62]	1.1871$_4^{20}$	1.4196[20]	d	d	s	s	...	chl v	C55, 18727
Ω a523	—,—,ethyl ester ...	CH₃OCH₂CO₂CH₂CH₃.	118.13			142[758] 44–5.5[9]	1.0118[15]	1.4050[20]	δ	v	v			os s	B3[2], 172
Ω a524	—,—,methyl ester	CH₃OCH₂CO₂CH₃.	104.12			131[763] 57[50]	1.0511$_4^{20}$	1.3962[20]	δ	v	v	s		os s	B3[2], 171
Ω a525	—,—,nitrile	CH₃OCH₂CN.	71.08			118.1	0.9492$_4^{20}$	1.3831[20]	δ	s	s	s		ac, alk, os s	B3[2], 174
a526	—,—,piperazinium salt	2CH₃OCH₂CO₂H.C₄H₁₀N₂	266.30	cr (al)	155.7–6 (cor)				s	s	i				Am 70, 2759
a527	—,methoxy-(phenyl)-(D, −)	C₆H₅CH(OCH₃)CO₂H	166.18	nd (peth),$[\alpha]_D^{13}$ −150.0 (al), −168.5 (w)[2]	63–4				s	s	s		s	lig s^h	B10[1], 85
a528	—,—,(dl)	C₆H₅CH(OCH₃)CO₂H	166.18	pl (lig)	71–2				δ	v	v			lig δ, s^h	B10[1], 87
a529	—,(4-methoxy-2-nitrophenyl)-	....	211.18	ye nd (50 % al)	157–8 d						s			aa s^h	B10[2], 113
a530	—,(2-methoxy-phenoxy)-	Pyrocatechol methyl ether O-acetic acid.	182.18	nd (w)	123–5 (129)				v^h	v	v	...	s	aa s lig i	B6[2], 784
a531	—,(3-methoxy-phenoxy)-	Resorcinol methyl ether O-acetic acid.	182.18	nd (w)	118				δ v^h						B6, 817
a532	—,(2-methoxy-phenyl)-	o-Methoxy-α-toluic acid.	166.18	nd (w)	123	100–1[2]			s^h	v	v	v	v	to v^h chl v aa v lig δ	B10, 188
a533	—,—,nitrile.......	o-Methoxybenzyl cyanide. o-Methoxy-α-tolunitrile.	147.18	pr(bz-lig)	68.5	141–3[11] 114[3]							s^h	lig δ	B10[2], 112
Ω a534	—,(4-methoxy-phenyl)-	Homoanisic acid. p-Methoxy-α-toluic acid.	166.18	pl (w)	86–8.5	138–40[2–3]			i s^h		s		s^h	lig δ	B10[2], 113
Ω a535	—,—,nitrile.	p-Methoxybenzyl cyanide. p-Methoxy-α-tolunitrile.	147.18			286–7 152[16]	1.0845$_4^{20}$	1.5309[20]	...	s	s				B10[2], 113
—	—,methylguanido-	see Creatine													
a537	—,(2-methyl-3-indolyl)-	....	189.22	(ace)	195–200 (196–7d)				δ^h	s^h	s	s^h		chl δ^h	B22, 69
Ω a538	—,(1-naphthoxy)-	C₁₀H₇OCH₂CO₂H	202.21	pr		190			δ	v	v			aa s	B6[2], 580
Ω a539	—,(2-naphthoxy)-	C₁₀H₇OCH₂CO₂H	202.21	pr (w) λ^{chl} 272 (3.69), 311 (3.14), 325.5 (3.25)	156				s^h	s	s			aa s	B6[2], 602
Ω a540	—,(1-naphthyl)- ...	α-Naphthaleneacetic acid. C₁₀H₇CH₂CO₂H	186.21	wh nd (w)	133	d			δ s^h	δ s^h	v	v	s	chl v aa s	B9[2], 456

For explanations, symbols and abbreviations see beginning of table. For structural formulas see end of table.

No.	Name	Synonyms and Formula	Mol. wt.	Color, crystalline form, specific rotation and λ_{max} (log ε)	m.p. °C	b.p. °C	Density	n_D	w	al	eth	ace	bz	other solvents	Ref.
	Acetic acid														
a541	—,—,amide	$C_{10}H_7^{\beta}CH_2CONH_2$	185.23	nd (w, al)	180–1 sub				i s^h	...	s	...	s	CS_2 s aa s	E12B, 3267
Ω a542	—,—,nitrile	$C_{10}H_7^{\beta}CH_2CN$	167.21	wx so	32–3	$162–4^{12}$		1.6192^{20}		s					E12B, 3268
a543	—,(2-naphthyl)-, amide	$C_{10}H_6^{\beta}CH_2CONH_2$	185.23	lf (w)	202–4.6d				δ^h	s	s				E12B, 3275
a544	—,—,nitrile	$C_{10}H_7^{\beta}CH_2CN$	167.21	nd or lf (dil al or tetralin)	85.6–6.2	$145–50^2$ $202–5^{28}$			δ^h	δ	v		v	chl v, CS_2, AcOEt v peth i	E12B, 3275
a545	—,nitro-	$O_2NCH_2CO_2H$	105.05	nd (chl)	92–3d (89)				d	v	v	...	v^h	chl v^h peth i	$B2^2$, 207
a546	—,—,ethyl ester	$NO_2CH_2CO_2CH_2CH_3$	133.11	λ^{MeOH} 270 (2.2)		$105–7^{25}$ 83^6	1.1953_4^{20}	1.4250^{20}	δ	∞	v			dil alk s	$B2^2$, 207
a547	—,(2-nitro- phenoxy)-		197.15	pr (w)	158.2–8.5				δ	s	s				$B6^2$, 211
a548	—,nitro(phenyl)-, nitrile	α-Nitrobenzyl cyanide. $C_6H_5CH(NO_2)CN$	162.15		39–40										$B9^2$, 313
Ω a549	—,(2-nitro- phenyl)-		181.15	nd (w), pl (dil al) λ^{al} 259 (3.75)	141–2				s^h	s					$B9^2$, 311
a550	—,—,nitrile	o-Nitrobenzyl cyanide	162.15	nd (al-w), pr (aa or al)	84	178^{12} $137–9^1$			s^h	s	s	s	s	chl s alk s aa s^h	$B9^2$, 311
a551	,(3-nitro- phenyl)-		181.15	nd (w)	122				s^h	s					$B9^2$, 311
a552	—,—,nitrile	m-Nitrobenzyl cyanide	162.15	(eth-lig)	63	$180^{1.5}$			v	s	v		v	chl v lig δ	$B9^2$, 312
Ω a553	—,(4-nitro- phenyl)-		181.15	pa ye nd (w) λ^{al} 272 (3.98)	153–5				δ s^h	s					$B9^2$, 312
Ω a554	—,—,nitrile	p-Nitrobenzyl cyanide.	162.15	pl λ^{al} 262 (4.81)	116–7	$195–7^{12}$			δ	s	s		s	chl s	$B9^2$, 313
a555	—,—,piperazinium salt	$2(C_8H_7NO_4).C_4H_{10}N_2$. See a553	448.44	cr (al)	205.5–9.5 (cor)				s^h	s^h	i				Am 70, 2759
a556	—,(2-nitro- phenyl)oxo-	o-Nitrobenzoylformic acid. o-Nitrophenylglyoxylic acid.	195.13	pr (w + 1)	123 (156–7d) (anh) 76–7 (hyd)				$∞^h$	s	δ	v	δ	aa v lig δ to δ	$B10^1$, 315
a557	—,oxo-,	Glyoxylic acid. Aldehydo- formic acid. $OHCCO_2H$	74.04	rh pr (w + $\frac{1}{2}$) $\lambda^{w, pH=7.1}$ 565 (0.1), 576 (0.9), 580 (1.0), 584 (0.9)	70 5 (+ $\frac{1}{2}$w) 98 (anh)				v	δ	δ		δ		$B3^2$, 385
Ω a558	—,oxo(phenyl)-	Benzoylformic acid. Phenyl- glyoxylic acid. $C_6H_5COCO_2H$	150.14	pr (CCl_4)	66	$147–51^{12}$			v	s	s			CS_2 i	$B10^2$, 454
Ω a559	—,—,methyl ester	Methyl benzoylformate. $C_6H_5COCO_2CH_3$	164.16	ye		$246–8$ 137^{14}		1.5268^{20}							$B10^2$, 455
Ω a560	—,—,nitrile	Benzoyl cyanide. C_6H_5COCN	131.14	ta	32–3	$206–8$ 99^{19}			i	v	v				$B10^2$, 457
a561	—,—,nitrile oxime	Phenylglyoxylonitrile oxime. $C_6H_5C(:NOH)CN$	146.15	lf(w), nd	127–8				s^h	v	s		v		$B10^2$, 457
a562	—,oxo(2-thienyl)-	2-Thienylglyoxylic acid.	156.16	vlt cr (w + 1)	91.5 (anh) 58–9 (hyd)				v	v					B18, 407
a563	—,oxydi-	Diglycolic acid. Oxydietha- noic acid. $O(CH_2CO_2H)_2.H_2O$	152.11	mcl pr (w + 1)	148	d			s	s	s				$B3^1$, 90
a564	—,—,dichloride	Diglycolyl dichloride. $O(CH_2COCl)_2$	170.99			116^{15}			d	d				chl s	B3, 240
a566	—,per-	Acetyl hydroperoxide. Peracetic acid. CH_3CO_2OH	76.05	λ^w <240 (> 1.4)	0.1	105 (exp 110)	1.226_4^{15}	1.3974^{20}	v	s	v			sulf v	$B2^3$, 379
Ω a567	—,phenoxy-	Glycolic acid phenyl ether. $C_6H_5OCH_2CO_2H$	152.16	nd or pl (w) λ^{hx} 270 (3.10), 276 (3.06)	98–9	285 d			s	v	v		v	CS_2 v aa v	$B6^2$, 157
a568	—,—,amide	$C_6H_5OCH_2CONH_2$	151.17	nd (w, al)	101.5				i δ^h	v^h					B6, 162
a569	—,—,anhydride	$(C_6H_5OCH_2CO)_2O$	286.29	lf (cth)	67–9				i	δ	δ		v	lig δ	B6, 162
Ω a570	—,—,chloride	$C_6H_5OCH_2COCl$.	170.60			$225–6$ 111^{13}			d	d	s			lig δ	$B6^2$, 158
a571	—,—,ethyl ester	$C_6H_5OCH_2CO_2CH_2CH_3$	180.21			$250–1$ 136^{19}	1.104^{18}		i	s	s				$B6^2$, 157
a572	—,—,methyl ester	$C_6H_5OCH_2CO_2CH_3$	166.18		245	130^{14}	1.1493_4^{20}	1.5155^{20}	i	∞	∞			CS_2 ∞	B6, 162
a573	—,—,nitrile	$C_6H_5OCH_2CN$.	133.15			$239–40^{760}$ 128^{17}	1.0991_4^{20}	1.5246^{20}		s	s		v		$B6^2$, 158

For explanations, symbols and abbreviations see beginning of table. For structural formulas see end of table.

Acetic Acid

No.	Name	Synonyms and Formula	Mol. wt.	Color, crystalline form, specific rotation and λ_{max} (log ε)	m.p. °C	b.p. °C	Density	n_D	w	al	eth	ace	bz	other solvents	Ref.
Ω a574	—,phenyl-	Phenylethanoic acid*. α-Toluic acid. $C_6H_5CH_2CO_2H$	136.16	lf, pl (peth) λ^{al} 247.5 (2.05), 258.5 (2.26), 267.5 sh (1.85)	77	265.5 144.5[12]	1.091[77] 1.228[4]	....	δ	v	v	s	...	CS_2 v lig i	B9[2], 294
Ω a575	—,—,amide	α-Toluamide. $C_6H_5CH_2CONH_2$	135.17	pl or lf (w) λ 242 (2.04), 258 (2.33), 264 (2.29), 268 (2.12)	157	....	....	....	δ s[h]	s	δ	...	δ s[h]	....	B9[1], 175
a576	—,—,—,N-methyl-	$C_6H_5CH_2CONHCH_3$	149.19	cr (bz) λ^{MeOH} 258 (2.3)	58	....	....	....	δ	v	v	...	δ	chl v	B9[2], 300
a577	—,—,—,N-phenyl-	α-Phenylacetanilide. $C_6H_5CH_2CONHC_6H_5$	211.27	pr (al) λ^{al} 244 (4.26)	117–8	....	....	....	i	s	v				B12, 275
a578	—,—,anhydride	α-Toluic anhydride. $(C_6H_5CH_2CO)_2O$	254.29	pr or nd (eth)	71–2	195–8[12]	....	....		s[h]	s			chl s	B9[2], 299
Ω a579	—,—,chloride	Phenacetyl chloride. α-Toluyl chloride. $C_6H_5CH_2COCl$	154.60	....		170[250] 104–5[24]	1.16817[20/4]	1.5325[20]	d	d	v				B9[2], 300
Ω a580	—,—,ethyl ester	$C_6H_5CH_2CO_2CH_2CH_3$	164.21	λ^{al} 220 (3.26)	....	227[760] 120–1[20]	1.0333[20]	1.4980[20]	i	∞	∞				B9[2], 297
Ω a581	—,—,isobutyl ester	Eglantine. $C_6H_5CH_2CO_2CH_2CH(CH_3)_2$	192.24	....	247 123–5[14]		0.999[18]		i	s	s				B9[2], 298
Ω a582	—,—,methyl ester	$C_6H_5CH_2CO_2CH_3$	150.18		....	218[760] 131–2[50]	1.0633[16/16]	1.5075[20]	i	∞	∞	s			B9[2], 297
Ω a583	—,—,nitrile	Benzyl cyanide. α-Tolunitrile. $C_6H_5CH_2CN$	117.15	λ^{al} 258 (2.25), 264 (2.15)	–23.8	234 107[12]	1.01572[20]	1.5230[20]	i	∞	∞	s			B9[2], 302
Ω a584	—,—,2-phenylethyl ester	$C_6H_5CH_2CO_2CH_2CH_2C_6H_5$	240.31		26.5	177–8[4–5]	1.080[25/25]		i	s					B9[2], 299
a585	—,—,piperazinium salt	$2C_6H_5CH_2CO_2H \cdot C_4H_{10}N_2$	358.44	nd (al)	146.5–7.5	....	....	....	s[h]	s[h]	i				Am 56, 150
a586	—,3-pyrenyl-		260.30	nd or pl (PhCl)	220d	....	....	....						dil alk s con sulf s PhCl s	E14s, 441
a587	—,sulfo-	Sulfoethanoic acid*. $HO_3SCH_2CO_2H$	140.12	hyg ta (w + 1)	84–6	245[760]d	....	....	s	s	i	s		chl i	B4[2], 531
a588	—,2-thienyl-	2-Thiopheneacetic acid.	142.18	cr (w)	76 (62)	....	....	....	s[h]	s	s				B18, 293
Ω a589	—,thiolo-	Ethanethioic acid. Thioacetic acid. CH_3COSH	76.12	ye λ^{MeOH} 240 sh (2.10)	< –17	87[760] 26–7[35]	1.064[20]	1.4648[20]	s v[h]	v	∞	v			B2[2], 208
Ω a591	—,—,ethyl ester	$CH_3COSCH_2CH_3$	104.18	....		116.4[760] 66[85]	0.97922[20/4]	1.4583[21]	i	v	v				B2[2], 209
a592	—,thiolo-thiono-	Dithioacetic acid. Methyl carbithionic acid. CH_3CS_2H	92.18	ye-red oil		66[85] 37[15]	1.24[20]		s	v	v	v	v	chl v aa v	B2[2], 212
Ω a593	—,thiono-,amide	Thioacetamide. CH_3CSNH_2	75.13	cr (al), pl (eth) λ^{al} 210 (3.66), 260 (4.08)	115–6	....	....	....	v	v	δ		δ	lig δ	B2[2], 210
a594	—,—,—,N-phenyl-	Thioacetanilide. $CH_3CSNHC_6H_5$	151.23	nd (w)	74.5–6	d	....	....	i		i			alk s	B12[2], 142
a595	—,2-tolyl-	o-Methyl-α-toluic acid.	150.18	nd (w)	88–90	....	....	....	s[h]	s	s	s			B9[1], 207
Ω a597	—,—,nitrile	o-Methyl benzyl cyanide. o-Methyl-α-tolunitrile.	131.18	λ^{al} 262 (2.43)		244[760]	1.0156[22]	1.5252[20]	i	s	s	s	s		B9[2], 349
a598	—,3-tolyl-	m-Methyl-α-toluic acid.	150.18	nd (w)	62	120–3[26] 245–7[745]	1.0022[22]	1.5233[20]							B9[1], 208
a599	—,—,nitrile	m-Methyl benzyl cyanide. m-Methyl-α-tolunitrile.	131.18			δd (241) 133[15]			i	s	s	s	s		B9[2], 349
Ω a600	—,4-tolyl-	p-Methyl-α-toluic acid.	150.18	nd or pl (al or w)	91–3	265–7 (sub)	....	....	δ v[h]	s	s	s		chl s	B9[2], 349
Ω a601	—,—,nitrile	p-Methyl benzyl cyanide. p-Methyl-α-tolunitrile.	131.18	λ^{al} 267 (2.49)	18	242–3[760] 122[13]	0.9922[22]	1.5167[20]	i	s	s	s	s		B9[2], 349
Ω a602	—,2-tolyloxy-	o-Cresoxyacetic acid.	166.18	lf (w) λ^{al} 270 (3.17), 278 (3.11)	156.8–7.4	....	....	....	s[h]	s	s		δ	os δ con sulf s	B6[2], 331
Ω a603	—,3-tolyloxy-	m-Cresoxyacetic acid.	166.18	nd (w)	103–4	....	....	....	s[h]	s	s		s		B6[2], 353
a604	—,4-tolyloxy-	p-Cresoxyacetic acid.	166.18	nd (w)	136	....	....	....	s[h]	s	s		s	alk s	B6[2], 380
a605	—,tribromo-	Br_3CCO_2H	296.76	mcl	135 (133)	245[760]	....	....	s	s	s				B2[2], 205
a606	—,—,amide	Br_3CCONH_2	295.77	mcl pr (al)	121–2	sub	....	....	v	v[h]	v		δ	chl δ	B2[2], 206
a607	—,—,bromide	Br_3CCOBr	359.66			210–5 86[11]	....	....	d	d	s		s	chl s	B2[2], 206
Ω a608	—,—,ethyl ester	$Br_3CCO_2CH_2CH_3$	324.81			225 148[73]	2.2300[20/20]	1.5438[13]		s	s				B2[2], 205
a609	—,(2,4,6-tribromophenoxy)-		388.85	nd (dil al)	200	....	....	....	i	v	v			CS_2 i lig i	B6, 205
Ω a610	—,trichloro-	Cl_3CCO_2H	163.39	dlq cr	α 58 β49.6	197.55[760] 141–2[25]	1.62[25] 1.6218[64/1] 1.6237[70/70]	1.4603[61]	v	s	v				B2[2], 196
a611	—,—,amide	Cl_3CCONH_2	162.40	mcl pr (w)	142	238–9[746]	....	....	δ	v	v				B2[1], 94
a612	—,—,—,N,N-diethyl-	$Cl_3CCON(C_2H_5)_2$	218.52	pr	27	109[9]	....	1.4900[24]	δ						B4, 110
a613	—,—,—,N,N-dimethyl-	$Cl_3CCON(CH_3)_2$	190.46		12	230–3 δ d 84[4]	1.390[20]	1.5017[25]	δ				s	chl s	B4, 59

For explanations, symbols and abbreviations see beginning of table. For structural formulas see end of table.

No.	Name	Synonyms and Formula	Mol. wt.	Color, crystalline form, specific rotation and λ_{max} (log ε)	m.p. °C	b.p. °C	Density	n_D	w	al	eth	ace	bz	other solvents	Ref.
	Acetic acid														
a614	—,—,—,N-phenyl-	α-Trichloroacetanilide. Cl$_3$CCONHC$_6$H$_5$	238.50	lf (dil al)	95–7	168–70[760]	....	....	i δ[h]	s					B12[2], 142
a615	—,—,anhydride	(Cl$_3$CCO)$_2$O	308.76	....		222–4d 98–100[11]	1.6908[20]	....	d	d	s		aa s		B2[2], 200
a616	—,—,bromide	Cl$_3$CCOBr	226.29		143		1.900[15/15]	....							B2, 211
a617	—,—,butyl ester	Cl$_3$CCO$_2$(CH$_2$)$_3$CH$_3$	219.50			203–5 97–9[19]	1.2778[20/4]	1.4525[25]	d i	d s	s s	s	s s		B2[3], 471
a618	—,—,sec-butyl ester	Cl$_3$CCO$_2$CH(CH$_3$)CH$_2$CH$_3$	219.50			93–4[24]	1.2636[20/4]	1.4483[20]	i	s	s		s		B2[3], 472
a619	—,—,tert-butyl ester	Cl$_3$CCO$_2$C(CH$_3$)$_3$	219.50	cr (pentane, MeOH)	25.5	54–5[7] 37[1]	1.2363[25]	1.4398[25]	i	v	s		MeOH v		B2[3], 473
a620	—,—,chloride	Cl$_3$CCOCl	181.83	....		118	1.6202[20/4]	1.4695[20]	d	d	∞				B2[2], 200
a621	—,—,2-chloroethyl ester	Cl$_3$CCO$_2$CH$_2$CH$_2$Cl	225.89			217[766] 100[14]	1.5357[20/4]	1.4813[20]	d	d[h]					B2, 209
a622	—,—,2-hydroxy-ethyl ester	Cl$_3$CCO$_2$CH$_2$CH$_2$OH	207.44			130–4[12]	1.5322[20]	1.4775[20]	δ	v	....		CCl$_4$ v		B2[3], 474
Ω a623	—,—,ethyl ester	Cl$_3$CCO$_2$CH$_2$CH$_3$	191.44			167.5–8 62[12]	1.3836[20]	1.4505[20]	i	s	s		s		B2[2], 200
a624	—,—,isobutyl ester	Cl$_3$CCO$_2$CH$_2$CH(CH$_3$)$_2$	219.50			187–9[760] 93–4[20]	1.2636[20/4]	1.4483[20]	i	s	s		s		B2, 209
Ω a625	—,—,isopropyl ester	Cl$_3$CCO$_2$CH(CH$_3$)$_2$	205.47			173.5[747] 65.5–7[15]	1.3034[20/4]	1.4428[20]	i	s	s		s		B2[3], 471
a626	—,—,2-methoxy-ethyl ester	Cl$_3$CCO$_2$CH$_2$CH$_2$OCH$_3$	221.47		14.6–4.8	98.0–9.5[17]	1.3826[20]	1.4563[20]	i	s	s		s		B2[3], 474
a627	—,—,methyl ester	Cl$_3$CCO$_2$CH$_3$	177.42		−17.5	153.8 44.5[12]	1.4874[20/4]	1.4572[20]	i	v	v				B2[2], 199
a628	—,—,2(2-methyl-butyl) ester	Cl$_3$CCO$_2$C(CH$_3$)$_2$CH$_2$CH$_3$	233.52			191[756] 105[30]	1.2505[20/20]	....	i	s	s		s		B2[3], 473
a629	—,—,3-methylbutyl ester	Cl$_3$CCO$_2$CH$_2$CH$_2$CH(CH$_3$)$_2$	233.52			217[760] 92–5[11]	1.2314[20/4]	1.4521[20]	i	s	s		s		B2[2], 200
a630	—,—,nitrile	Cl$_3$CCN	144.39		−42	84.6[741]	1.4403[25]	1.4409[20]	i						B2, 212
a631	—,—,pentyl ester	Cl$_3$CCO$_2$(CH$_2$)$_4$CH$_3$	233.52			220.3–2.3 118[30]	1.2475[20/20]	....	i	s	s		s		B2[3], 473
a632	—,—,piperazinium salt	2Cl$_3$CCO$_2$H·C$_4$H$_{10}$N$_2$	412.91	cr (al)	121–1.5	....	....	....	s	s[h]	i				Am 56, 1759
a633	—,—,propyl ester	Cl$_3$CCO$_2$CH$_2$CH$_2$CH$_3$	205.47			187 69[10]	1.3221[20]	1.4501[20]	i	s	s				B2[3], 471
a634	—,—,trichloro-methyl ester	Cl$_3$CCO$_2$CCl$_3$	280.75		34	191–2 73–4[10]	1.6733[15]	....			s		s	chl s lig s	B3, 17
Ω a635	—,(2,4,5-trichloro-phenoxy)-		255.49	cr (bz) $\lambda^{0.1N\,HCl}$ 287.5 (3.35), 295 (3.32)	157–8 (153)	....	....	....	i				v[h]	lig s	Am 63, 1768
Ω a636	—,(2,4,6-trichloro-phenoxy)-		255.49	cr (al) $\lambda^{0.1N\,HCl}$ 278.5 (2.82), 286 (2.82)	177	....	....	....	δ[h]	s[h]			δ	lig δ	B6, 192
a637	,trifluoro-	F$_3$CCO$_2$H	114.02	....	−15.25	72.4	1.5351[0]	....	s	s	s	s			B2[2], 186
a638	—,—,amide,N-phenyl-	Trifluoroacetanilide. F$_3$CCONHC$_6$H$_5$	189.14	(60 %al) λ^{al} 245 (4.04)	87.6	....	....	....	s	v	s				B12[2], 141
a639	—,—,anhydride	(F$_3$CCO)$_2$O	210.03	....			....	....							
Ω a640	—,—,nitrile	F$_3$CCN	95.03		−65	39.5–40.1 −63.9[760]	1.490[25]	1.269[25]	d	d	s		aa s		B2[2], 186
a641	—,triiodo-	I$_3$CCO$_2$H	437.74	ye lf	150d		....	....	s	s	s				B2[3], 428
a642	—,trinitro-,nitrile	(NO$_2$)$_3$CCN	176.05	wx	41.5		....	....	s	s	s				B2, 225
Ω a643	—,triphenyl-	(C$_6$H$_5$)$_3$CCO$_2$H	288.35	mcl pr (al), lf (aa)	271 (267–71)	220 exp	....	....	d i	d s	s δ		δ	MeOH s, aa, lig s CS$_2$ chl δ	B9[2], 500
—	—,ureido-	see **Hydantoic acid**													
—	**Acetic anhydride**	see **Acetic acid, anhydride**													
—	**Acetoacetic acid**	see **Butanoic acid, 3-oxo-***													
—	**Acetoin**	see **2-Butanone, 3-hydroxy-***													
—	**Acetol**	see **2-Propanone, 1-hydroxy-***													
—	**Acetonaphthone**	see **Naphthalene, acetyl-**													
—	**Acetone**	see **2-Propanone***													
—	**Acetonedicar-boxylic acid**	see **Pentanedioic acid, 3-oxo-***													
—	**Acetonic acid**	see **Propanoic acid, 2-hydroxy-2-methyl-***													
—	**Acetonitrile**	see **Acetic acid, nitrile**													
a644	**Acetonitrolic acid**	Ethylnitrolic acid. CH$_3$C(:NOH)NO$_2$	104.07	ye rh (w, al, eth)	87–8d	....	....	....	s	s	s	s	...	oos s	B2[2], 185
—	**Acetonylacetone, dioxime***	see **2,5-Hexanedione, dioxime***													
Ω a645	**Acetophenone**	Acetylbenzene. Methyl phenyl ketone	120.16	mcl pr or pl λ^{al} 243 (4.12)	20.5	202.0[760] 79[10]	1.0281[20/4]	1.53718[20]	i	s	s	s	δ	chl δ con sulf s (og)	D7[7], 208
Ω a646	—,oxime	C$_6$H$_5$C(:NOH)CH$_3$	135.17	nd (w) λ^{al} 246 (4.0)	60	245 119[20]	....	....	δ s[h]	v	v	v	v	chl v lig v	B7[2], 216

For explanations, symbols and abbreviations see beginning of table. For structural formulas see end of table.

No.	Name	Synonyms and Formula	Mol. wt.	Color, crystalline form, specific rotation and λ_{max} (log ε)	m.p. °C	b.p. °C	Density	n_D	w	al	eth	ace	bz	other solvents	Ref.
	Acetophenone														
—	—,4-acetylamino-	see **Acetic acid**, amide, N(4–acetylphenyl)-													
Ω a647	—,2-amino-	o-Acetaniline C8H9NO. See a645	135.17	ye cr λ^{al} 226 (4.32), 254 (3.75), 359 (3.64)	20	250–2 δd 135[17]	....	1.6160[20]	i	...	s	...	...		B14[2], 28
Ω a648	—,3-amino-	m-Acetylaniline. C8H9NO. See a645	135.17	pa ye pl (al), lf (eth) λ^{al} 231 (4.36), 255 sh (3.85), 338 (3.28)	98–9	289–90	....		δ	s[h]					B14[2], 30
Ω a649	—,4-amino-	p-Acetylaniline. C8H9NO. See a645	135.17	ye mcl pr (al) λ^{al} 316 (4.30)	106	293–5 195–200[15]	....		δ s[h]	s	s	...	δ	chl δ lig δ	B14[2], 30
Ω a650	—,4-amino-α-chloro-	p-Aminophenacyl chloride. C8H8ClNO. See a645	169.62	ye pl	148	....									B14[1], 367
a651	—,4-amino-3-chloro-	C8H8ClNO. See a645.	169.62	pr (chl-peth)	92	....									B14, 49
Ω a652	—,3-amino-4-methoxy-	C9H11NO2. See a645	165.19	pr (al)	102	....				s	s		v		B14[2], 141
—	—,benzal-	see **Chalcone**													
—	—,benzylidene-	see **Chalcone**													
Ω a653	—,α-bromo-	Phenacyl bromide. C6H5COCH2Br	199.05	nd (al), rh pr (dil al), pl (peth) λ^{al} 251	50–1	135[18]	1.647[20]₄	....	i	s v[h]	v		v	chl v peth s[h]	B7[2], 220
Ω a654	—,2-bromo-	C8H7BrO. See a645	199.05	ye λ^{al} 236 (3.69), 282 (2.89)	....	131–5[20] 112[10]		1.5678[20]							B7[2], 220
Ω a655	—,4-bromo-	C8H7BrO. See a645	199.05	lf (al) λ^{al} 253 (4.20)	50–1	255.5[736] 130[11]	1.647	....	i	s	s	s	s	CS2, aa, lig s	B7[2], 220
a656	—,α-bromo-3-chloro-	m-Chlorophenacyl bromide. C8H6BrClO. See a645	233.50	nd	39.5–40	....				v					Am 83, 4277
Ω a657	—,α-bromo-4-chloro-	p-Chlorophenacyl bromide. C8H6BrClO. See a645	233.50	nd	96–7	....									B7, 285
a658	—,4-bromo-α-chloro-	p-Bromophenacyl chloride. C8H6BrClO. See a645	233.50	nd (al)	116–7	....					v[h]				B7, 285
a659	—,α-bromo-4-methyl-	p-Methylphenacyl bromide. C9H9BrO. See a645	213.08	nd or lf (al)	51	155–9[14]			d	s	s				B7[2], 239
a660	—,4-tert-butyl-2,6-dimethyl-3,5-dinitro-	Musk ketone. C14H18N2O5. See a645	294.31	ye	134.5–6.5	....			i	δ					C52, 8988
Ω a661	—,α-chloro-	Phenacyl chloride. Chloromethyl phenyl ketone. C6H5COCH2Cl	154.60	pl (dil al), rh, lf (peth), λ^{hx} 246 (3.92), 280 (3.00), 291 (2.86), 329 (1.83)	56–5	247[760] 139–41[14]	1.324[15]₄	....	i	v	v	s	v	CS2 v peth s[h]	B7[2], 219
a662	—,2-chloro-	o-Chlorophenyl methyl ketone. C8H7ClO. See a645	154.60	λ^{al} 238 (3.74), 281 (2.88)	....	227–8[738] 113[18]	1.2016[17]₄	1.685[25]	δ		s				B7[2], 218
a663	—,3-chloro-	m-Chlorophenyl methyl ketone. C8H7ClO. See a645	154.60	λ^{al} 240 (4.00), 286 (3.02)	....	241–5[744] (227–9) 127–31[30]	1.2130[0]₄	1.5494[20]		s	s	s			B7[2], 218
Ω a664	—,4-chloro-	p-Chlorophenyl methyl ketone. C8H7ClO. See a645	154.60	λ^{al} 249 (4.23), 272 (2.95), 284 (2.70)	20	273[760] 106[10]	1.1922[20]₄	1.5550[20]	i	∞	∞				B7[2], 219
a665	—,α-chloro-2,4-dimethyl-	2,4-Dimethylphenacyl chloride. C10H11ClO. See a645	182.65	nd	62	....				v	v		v		B7[2], 249
a666	—,α-chloro-α-isonitroso-	Benzoylformyl chloridoxime. C6H5COCCl(:NOH)	183.60	lf (bz), pr (chl)	133	....			i	v	v		v	chl v CCl4 δ	B10[2], 460
a667	—,α-chloro-4-methyl-	p-Methylphenacyl chloride. C9H9ClO. See a645	168.63	nd (al)	57–8	260–3 δd 113[4]			d	v	s				B7[1], 165
Ω a668	—,α,4-dibromo-	p-Bromophenacyl bromide. C8H6Br2O. See a645	277.96	nd (al)	110–2	....			i	s[h]	s				B7[2], 222
Ω a669	—,α,α-dichloro-	Phenacylidene chloride. C6H5COCHCl2	189.04	amor	20–1.5	249 143[25]	1.340[16]	1.5686[20]		s			s		B7[2], 220
a670	—,α,4-dichloro-	p-Chlorophenacyl chloride. C8H6Cl2O. See a645	189.04	nd (al)	101–2	270				s v[h]			s	MeOH s	B7[1], 152
Ω a671	—,2,4-dichloro-	C8H6Cl2O. See a645.	189.04	$\lambda^{dil\ MeOH}$ 252 (3.95), 290 sh (3.04)	33–4	245–7 140–50[15]		1.5640[20]	i						B7[2], 219
Ω a672	—,3,4-dichloro-	C8H6Cl2O. See a645.	189.04	nd (peth) $\lambda^{dil\ MeOH}$ 254 (4.16), 290 sh (3.18)	76	135[12]	....		i					lig s[h]	B7[2], 219

For explanations, symbols and abbreviations see beginning of table. For structural formulas see end of table.

No.	Name	Synonyms and Formula	Mol. wt.	Color, crystalline form, specific rotation and λ_{max} (log ε)	m.p. °C	b.p. °C	Density	n_D	Solubility						Ref.
									w	al	eth	ace	bz	other solvents	
	Acetophenone														
a673	—,2,3-dihydroxy-..	3-Acetylcatechol. $C_8H_8O_3$. See a645	152.16	ye pr (bz-lig)	97–8	....	....	....	...	s	...	...	...	alk s	B8[1], 613
Ω a674	—,2,4-dihydroxy-..	Resacetophenone. $C_8H_8O_3$. See a645	152.16	nd or lf λ^{iso} 232 (3.84), 270 (4.17), 316 (3.84)	147	....	1.1800[141]	....	i	s^h	δ	...	δ	chl i, Py s aa s	B8[2], 294
Ω a675	—,2,5-dihydroxy-..	2-Acetylhydroquinone. Quinacetophenone. $C_8H_8O_3$	152.16	ye-gr nd (dil al or w) λ^{al} 230 (4.48), 257 (4.04), 370 (3.95)	204–5	....	....	....	δ s^h	s	δ	...	δ		B8[2], 297
a676	—,3,4-dihydroxy-..	Acetylpyrocatechol. $C_8H_8O_3$. See a645	152.16	nd (w or chl) λ^{al} 230 (4.30), 276 (4.00), 307 (3.90)	115–6	....	....	....	s^h					chl s^h	B8[2], 298
a677	—,3,5-dihydroxy-..	$C_8H_8O_3$. See a645	152.16	cr (w) λ^{al} 218 (4.30), 265 (3.90), 321 (3.60)	147–8	....	....	....	s v^h	v	v	v	δ		B8[2], 301
—	—,3,4-dihydroxy-β-methylamino-	see **Adrenalone**													
a677[1]	—,3,4-dimethoxy-..	Acetoveratrone. $C_{10}H_{12}O_3$. See a645	180.21	pr (dil al) λ^{al} 228 (4.21), 272.5 (4.02), 303.5 (3.88)	51	286–8[760] 160– 2[10–15]	....	....	s^h	s^h	s^h	...	s^h	chl s^h	B8[2], 298
a677[2]	—,3,5-dimethoxy-4-hydroxy-	Acetosyringone. $C_{10}H_{12}O_4$. See a645	196.21	nd (w), pr (peth) λ^{al} 302 (4.04)	122–3	....	....	....	s^h	s	s	...		aa s lig i	B8[2], 244
Ω a678	—,2,4-dimethyl-..	$C_{10}H_{12}O$. See a645	148.21	λ^{al} 251 (4.15), 282 (3.73), 291 (3.11)		228[760] 110[13]	1.0121[15]	1.5340[20]	i	s	...	...	...		B7[2], 248
a679	—,2,5-dimethyl-..	$C_{10}H_{12}O$. See a645	148.21			232–3[760] 107[13]	0.9963[19]	1.5291[20]	i	v	v	...	v	CS_2 v	B7[2], 248
a680	—,3,4-dimethyl-..	$C_{10}H_{12}O$. See a645	148.21	λ^{hp} 249 (4.18), 282 (3.11), 294 (2.90)		246–7 213[310]	1.0090[14]	1.5413[15]	i	v	v	...	v	chl v aa v	B7[2], 248
a681	—,3-dimethyl-amino-	$C_{10}H_{13}NO$. See a645	163.22	λ^{al} 242 (4.60), 360.5 (3.54)	43	148[13]	....	....			v				B14, 45
a682	—,4-dimethyl-amino-	$C_{10}H_{13}NO$. See a645	163.22	nd (w, peth) λ^{al} 239 (3.82), 334 (4.43)	105.5	172–5[11]	....	....	v^h		v	...		lig v^h	B14[2], 32
a683	—,2-ethoxy-......	o-Acetylphenetole. $C_{10}H_{12}O_2$. See a645	164.21	pr (dil al), pl (lig)	43	243–4	1.0036[78]	....	δ	v	v	...		lig s^h	B8, 85
a684	—,4-ethoxy-......	p-Acetylphenetole. $C_{10}H_{12}O_2$. See a645	164.21	pl (eth) λ^{al} 270 (4.26), 279 (4.23)	39	....	....	....		v	v^h	...			B8[2], 85
Ω a685	—,α-hydroxy-..	Benzoyl carbinol. Phenacyl alcohol. $C_6H_5COCH_2OH$	136.16	hex pl (al or eth), pl (w or dil al, +w), pr (lig)	89.5–90.5 (anh) 73–4 (hyd)	124–6[12] (sub 56[1])	1.0963[09]	....	s^h	v	v	...		chl s lig δ	B8[2], 88
a686	—,—,acetate......	Phenacyl acetate. $C_6H_5COCH_2O_2CCH_3$	178.19	rh pl (eth, lig or peth)	49–9.5	270 150 2[10]	1.1169[65]	....	i	v	v	...	s	chl v lig s	B8[2], 89
Ω a687	—,2-hydroxy-.....	o-Acetylphenol. $C_8H_8O_2$. See a645	136.16	λ^{iso} 253 (4.00), 325 (3.70)	4–6	218[760] 106[17]	1.1307[20]	1.5584[20]	δ	∞	∞	...		aa ∞	B8[2], 81
Ω a688	—,3-hydroxy-.....	m-Acetylphenol. $C_8H_8O_2$. See a645	136.16	nd or lf λ^{al} 218 (4.30), 252.5 (3.95), 311 (3.60)	96	296[756] 153[5]	1.0992[109]	1.5348[109]	δ v^h	v	v	...	v	chl v lig i	B8[2], 84
Ω a689	—,4-hydroxy-.....	p-Acetylphenol. $C_8H_8O_2$. See a645	136.16	nd (eth, dil al) λ^{al} 279 (4.15), 315 sh (2.2)	109–10	147–8[3]	1.1090[109]	1.5577[109]	δ s^h	v	v	...		chl s	B8[2], 84
a690	—,α-hydroxy-4-methoxy-	Anisoyl carbinol. $C_9H_{10}O_3$. See a645	166.18	pl (dil al)	104	....	....	....			s	...	s		B8[1], 618
a691	—,2-hydroxy-3-methoxy-	o-Acetovanillon. $C_9H_{10}O_3$. See a645	166.18	pa ye nd (peth or eth-peth)	53–4	....	....	....			s	...	s		B8[2], 293
Ω a692	—,2-hydroxy-4-methoxy-	Peonol. $C_9H_{10}O_3$. See a645	166.18	nd (w) λ^{al} 230 (4.0), 273.5 (4.20), 314 (3.90)	52–3	158[20]	1.3102[81]	1.5432[61]	δ	s		...	s	chl s CS_2 s	B8[2], 294
Ω a693	—,2-hydroxy-5-methoxy-	$C_9H_{10}O_3$. See a645	166.18	pa ye pr (dil al) λ^{al} 227.5 (4.60), 255.5 (3.95), 357.5 (3.78)	52	....	....	....	s^h			...	s		B8, 271
a694	—,3-hydroxy-4-methoxy-	Isoacetovanillon. $C_9H_{10}O_3$. See a645	166.18	cr (eth-lig) or cr (w +1) λ^{al} 231 (4.60), 274 (4.20), 310 (4.04)	67–8 (+1w) 91 (anh)	....	....	....	s^h		s^h	...			B8[2], 298

For explanations, symbols and abbreviations see beginning of table. For structural formulas see end of table.

No.	Name	Synonyms and Formula	Mol. wt.	Color, crystalline form, specific rotation and λ_{max} (log ε)	m.p. °C	b.p. °C	Density	n_D	Solubility						Ref.
									w	al	eth	ace	bz	other solvents	
	Acetophenone														
a695	—,4-hydroxy-α-methoxy-	$C_9H_{10}O_3$. See a645	166.18	nd (bz), pr (w + $\frac{1}{2}$)	130–1	....			s^h	v	s	v	s^h	lig δ	B8[2], 302
a696	—,4-hydroxy-2-methoxy-	Isopeonol. Resacetophenone 2-methyl ether. $C_9H_{10}O_3$. See a645	166.18	nd (w) λ^{al} 230.5 (4.00), 278 (4.3), 309 (4.0)	138	....			s^h	...	...	...	s	lig s	B8[1], 618
Ω a697	—,4-hydroxy-3-methoxy-	Acetovanillon. Apocynin. $C_9H_{10}O_3$. See a645	166.18	pr (w) λ^{al} 229 (4.6) 275 (4.30), 308 (4.00)	115	295–300 233–5[15–20]			δ v^h	s	v	s	s	chl v lig δ	B8[2], 298
a698	—,5-isopropyl-2-methyl-	2-Acetyl-p-cymene. Carvacryl methyl ketone. $C_{12}H_{16}O$. See a645	176.25	....	< −20	249–50 (244) 124–5[12]	0.956_4^{20}	1.5181^{20}							B7[2], 262
Ω a699	—,2-methoxy-	o-Acetylanisole. $C_9H_{10}O_2$. See a645	150.17	ye λ^{al} 211 (4.32), 247 (3.92), 306 (3.58)	....	245	1.0897_4^{20}	1.5393^{20}	δ	s		s			B3, 232
Ω a700	—,3-methoxy-	m-Acetylanisole. $C_9H_{10}O_2$. See a645	150.17	λ^{al} 217 (4.35), 249 (3.94), 306 (3.39)	95–6	240 125–6[12]	1.0343^{19}	1.5410^{20}	s	s		s			B8[1], 535
Ω a701	—,4-methoxy-	p-Acetylanisole. $C_9H_{10}O_2$. See a645	150.17	pl (eth) λ^{al} 217 (4.07), 271.5 (4.22)	38–9	258 138–9[15]	1.0818_4^{41}	1.53349^{20} 1.547^{41}	δ	s	s	s			B8[2], 84
Ω a702	—,4-methoxy-3-nitro-	4-Acetyl-2-nitroanisole $C_9H_9NO_4$. See a645	195.17	nd (al)	99.5	....				s^h	s	s	s		B8[1], 538
Ω a703	—,2-methyl-	o-Acetyltoluene. $C_9H_{10}O$. See a645	134.17	λ^{al} 242 (3.92)	....	214[761] 89–92[10]	1.026_4^{20}	1.5276^{20}		s	s	s			B7[2], 237
Ω a704	—,3-methyl-	m-Acetyltoluene. $C_9H_{10}O$. See a645	134.17	λ^{al} 244.5 (4.05), 285 (3.11), 291 sh (3.08)	....	220[760] 109[12]	1.0070_4^{20}	1.5270^{20}		s	s	s			B7[2], 237
Ω a705	—,4-methyl-	p-Acetyltoluene. $C_9H_{10}O$. See a645	134.17	nd λ^{al} 252 (4.18)	28	226[760] 113[11]	1.0051_4^{20}	1.5335^{20}	i	s	s		s	chl s	B7[1], 238
Ω a706	—,2-nitro-	$C_8H_7NO_3$. See a645	165.15	(al) λ^{al} 257 (3.78)	28–9	158[16]		1.5468^{20}	i	v	v			chl v	B7[2], 222
Ω a707	—,3-nitro-	$C_8H_7NO_3$. See a645	165.15	nd (al) λ^{al} 226 (4.35), 260 sh (3.81), 300 sh (2.90)	81	202 167[18]			v^h	δ	v				B7[2], 223
Ω a708	—,4-nitro-	$C_8H_7NO_3$. See a645	165.15	yesh pr (al) λ^{al} 261 (4.15), 298 sh (3.34), 312 sh (3.08)	80–2	....				s	v				B7[2], 223
a709	—,α,α,α-trichloro-	$C_6H_5COCCl_3$	223.50	....		256–7 145[25]	1.425^{16}		i	s	v				B7[1], 152
Ω a710	—,2,3,4-trihydroxy-	4-Acetylpyrogallol. Gallacetophenone. $C_8H_8O_4$. See a645	168.15	pa ye nd or lf (w) λ^{MeOH} 237 (3.93), 296 (4.10)	173	....			s^h	v	s	v	δ	chl δ aa v lig v	B8[2], 493
Ω a711	—,2,4,6-trihydroxy-	2-Acetylphloroglucinol. Phloroacetophenone. $C_8H_8O_4$. See a645	168.15	ye (in alk) nd (w + 1)	222–4 (anh)	....			δ s^h	v	v	$δ^h$	chl δ aa v	B8[2], 442
Ω a712	—,2,4,5-trimethyl-	5-Acetylpseudocumene. $C_{11}H_{14}O$. See a645	162.22	....	10–1	246–7 137–8[20]	1.0039_4^{15}	1.541^{15}	i	v	v		v	CS_2 v aa v	B7[2], 256
Ω a713	—,2,4,6-trimethyl-	Acetylmesitylene. $C_{11}H_{14}O$. See a645	162.22	λ^{al} 245 sh (3.40)	....	240.5[735] 120[12]	0.9754_4^{20}	1.5175^{20}	i	s	s	s	s	....	B7[2], 257
a714	—,α,α,α-triphenyl-(α form)	α-Benzopinacolone. $C_6H_5COC(C_6H_5)_3$	348.45	nd	206–7	....				i			s	chl, CS_2 s aa i	C55, 22234
a715	—,(β form)	β-Benzopinacolone. $C_6H_5COC(C_6H_5)_3$	348.45	nd (al)	182	....			i	δ s^h	s			s	chl, CS_2 s aa s^h	B7[2], 513
—	Acetopyruvic acid	see Pentanoic acid, 2,4-dioxo-*													
—	Acetosyringone	see Acetophenone, 3,5-dimethoxy-4-hydroxy-													
—	Acetovanillon	see Acetophenone, 4-hydroxy-3-methoxy-													
—	Acetoveratrone	see Acetophenone, 3,4-dimethoxy-													
—	Acetoxime	see 2-Propanone, oxime*													
—	Aceturic acid	see Glycine, N-acetyl-													
—	Acetylacetone	see 2,4-Pentanedione*													
—	Acetylbenzoyl	see 1,2-Propanedione, 1-phenyl-*													
—	Acetyl bromide	see Acetic acid, bromide													
—	Acetyl chloride	see Acetic acid, chloride													
—	Acetylene	see Ethyne*													
—	Acetylenedicarboxylic acid	see 2-Butynedioic acid*													
—	Acetyl fluoride	see Acetic acid, fluoride													
—	Acetyl iodide	see Acetic acid, iodide													

For explanations, symbols and abbreviations see beginning of table. For structural formulas see end of table.

No.	Name	Synonyms and Formula	Mol. wt.	Color, crystalline form, specific rotation and λ_{max} (log ε)	m.p. °C	b.p. °C	Density	n_D	w	al	eth	ace	bz	other solvents	Ref.

Achroodextrin

a718	Achroodextrin.....	$C_{36}H_{62}O_{31}$	990.88	amor	....				s	i	...	...	...		C25,
a719	Aconic acid		128.08	lf (eth), rh (w, al) λ^{al} 216.5 (4.6), 270 sh (2.1)	164	d			v	s	...	...	...	MeOH s	3018 B18, 395
a720	Aconine	$C_{25}H_{41}NO_9$.	499.61	amor,[α] +23 λ^{1NHCl} <220	132				s	s	δ	...	...	chl s lig δ	C19, 291
—	Aconitic acid	see 1,2,3-Propanetricarboxylic acid*													
Ω a721	Aconitine	$C_{34}H_{47}NO_{11}$.	645.76	rh lf, $[α]_D^{20}$ +19 (chl, c=0.95) λ^{chl} 230 (4.15), 273 (3.03), 280 (2.95)	204				i	s	δ	...	s	chl s peth i	C51, 446
a723	—,hydrobromide ..	$C_{34}H_{47}NO_{11}$.HBr. 1½ H_2O. See a721	753.71	yesh pr (w), $[α]_D$ −31 (w, c=2.3)	209–10				s^h	s	s	...	...		C51, 446
a724	—,hydrochloride(l)	$C_{34}H_{47}NO_{11}$. HCl. 3½ H_2O. See a721	745.27	(w +3½) $[α]_D$ −30.5(w)	170–2				s	s	s	...	...		M, 15
a725	—,nitrate(l).......	$C_{34}H_{47}NO_{11}$. HNO_3. See a721	708.77	$[α]_D^{20}$ −35(2 % aq sol)	ca. 200d				s	s		...	...		M,15
Ω a727	Acridine..........	2,3,5,6-Dibenzopyridine.	179.22	rh nd or pr (al), mcl, orh (2 forms) λ^{al} 240 (5.2), 340 (3.8)	111 (sub 100)	345–6 (>360)	1.005_4^{20}		$δ^h$	v	v	...	v	CS_2 v	B20², 300
a728	—,2-amino-.......	$C_{13}H_{10}N_2$. See a727.	194.24	ye nd (w or al +1) λ^{al} 240 (4.7), 260 (4.9), 358 (4.0)	213–4				s^h	v	s	...	...	dil ac s	B22, 462
a729	—,3-amino-.......	$C_{13}H_{10}N_2$. See a727.	194.24	ye-og nd (dil al or bz-lig) $\lambda^{2:1\,al-eth}$ 240 (4.5), 280 (1.8), 355 (4.1), 440 (5.0), 460 (4.9)	224 (cor)				s	...	v	s	s	dil ac v	B22², 376
a730	—,4-amino-.......	$C_{13}H_{10}N_2$. See a727.	194.24	red-br pr (peth), og nd (MeOH) λ^{al-eth} 212 (4.4), 243 (4.6), 287 (4.6), 350 (3.1), 460 (3.5)	108	183–4			...	v	s	s	s	MeOH s^h con sulf s dil HCl s lig δ	B22², 376
a731	—,—hydrochloride	$C_{13}H_{10}N_2$. HCl. See a727 ...	230.70	ye nd (dil al)	234d	....			v	s	...	...	...		B22², 376
Ω a732	—,9-amino-.......	$C_{13}H_{10}N_2$. See a727.	194.24	ye nd (ace or al) λ^{al} 260 (5.4), 410 (3.9)	241 (cor) (237)				s^h	s	...	s^h	...	dil HCl v	B21², 280
a733	—,2-amino-5(4-aminophenyl)-	Chrysaniline. $C_{19}H_{15}N_3$. 2H_2O. See a727	321.38	ye nd (95 % al +2w)	260–7				i	δ	...	...	...		B22², 403
a734	—,9-chloro-.......	$C_{13}H_8ClN$. See a727	213.68	nd (al)	122	sub			δ	v	...	...	...		B20², 301
a735	—,3,6-diamino-....	$C_{13}H_{11}N_3$. See a727.......	209.25	ye nd (al or w) λ^{al} 265 (4.8), 290 sh (4.4), 460 (4.7)	284–6				s^h	v	δ	...	δ	con sulf s	B22², 397
a736	—,6,9-diamino-2-ethoxy-	Rivanol. $C_{15}H_{15}N_3O$. See a727	253.31	ye nd	123–4d	....			...	...	...	...	...		B22², 458
Ω a737	—,9,10-dihydro-..	Acridan. Carbazine. ms-Dihydroacridine. $C_{13}H_{11}N$. See a727	181.24	pl or pr (al) λ^{al} 250 sh, 290 (4.14)	169–71	d300 sub			i	v^h	0	s	...		B20², 291
Ω a738	—,9,10-dihydro-9-oxo-	ms-Acridone. $C_{13}H_9NO$. See a727	195.22	ye lf (al) λ^{al} 379 (3.90), 398 (3.95)	354	>354 (no d)			i	δ v^h	i	...	i	alk, aa s^h con sulf s chl i	B21², 280
a739	—,2-methyl-.....	$C_{14}H_{11}N$. See a727........	193.25	ye nd (dil al)	134				δ	s	s	...	s	con sulf s lig δ	B20¹, 173
a740	—,9-phenyl-......	$C_{19}H_{13}N$. See a727.......	255.32	lf, ye nd (al) λ^{chl} 260 (4.49), 360 (4.01)	184	403–4 sub			i	δ	s	...	v	con sulf v	B20², 332
—	ms-Acridone	see Acridine, 9, 10-dihydro-9-oxo-													
—	Acrolein..........	see Propenal*													
—	β-Acrose	see Sorbose (L)													
—	Acrylamide	see Propenoic acid, amide*													

For explanations, symbols and abbreviations see beginning of table. For structural formulas see end of table.

No.	Name	Synonyms and Formula	Mol. wt.	Color, crystalline form, specific rotation and λ_{max} (log ε)	m.p. °C	b.p. °C	Density	n_D	Solubility						Ref.
									w	al	eth	ace	bz	other solvents	
	Acrylic acid														
—	**Acrylic acid**	*see* **Propenoic acid***													
—	**Acrylyl chloride**	*see* **Propenoic acid, chloride**													
a741	**Actidione** (*l*)	Cycloheximide.	281.36	pl (AmOH, 30% MeOH) $[\alpha]_D^{25}-33$ (chl, c=1)	144–5	. . . .	. . . . .	. . . .	δ	v	δ	. . . .	. .	os v lig i	**Am 70,** 1223
—	**Adabine**	*see* **Urea, 1(2-bromo-2-ethylbutanoyl)-**													
Ω a742	**Adamantane**	Tricyclo [3,3,1,1^{3,7}] decane.	136.24	nd (sub)	268 (sealed tube)	sub	1.07	1.568					s	. . . .	**E13,** 1058
—	**Adenine**	*see* **Purine, 6-amino-**													
Ω a743	**Adenosine**	Adenine-9-*d*-ribofuranoside. 6-Amino-g-ribofuranoside purine.	267.25	nd (w + 1½) $[\alpha]_D^{20}-60.0$ (w, c=1), -43.5 (10% HCl, c=2) λ^{al} 260 (4.23)	235–6 (anh)				s v^h	i					**B31,** 27
Ω a744	**5-Adenylic acid**	Adenosine-5-phosphate. Muscle adenylic acid. Synadenylic acid. $C_{10}H_{14}N_5O_7P$.	347.23	pw, nd (w, dil al) cr (+w, w–ace) $[\alpha]_D^{50}-41.78$ (w) $\lambda^{w,pH=1.1}$ 255 (4.16)	195d 208d (sealed tube)				v^h	s				10% HCl s	**B31,** 27
—	**Adipamic acid**	*see* **Hexanedioic acid, monoamide***													
—	**Adipic acid**	*see* **Hexanedioic acid***													
—	**Adipoin**	*see* **Cyclohexanone, 2-hydroxy-**													
Ω a745	**Adonitol**	Adonite. Ribitol.	152.15	pr (w), nd (al)	104	. . . .	. . . .	. . . .	s	s^h	i	. . . .	. .	lig i	**B1²,** 604
a746	**Adrenaline** (*d*)	*d*-Epinephrine. *d*-1-[3,4-Dihydroxyphenyl]-2-methylaminoethanol.	183.21	$[\alpha]_D^{20}+50.5$ (HCl) λ^w 290 (2.90)	215d	. . . .	. . . .	. . . .	δ	i				aa s	**B13²,** 525
a747	—(*l*)	$C_9H_{13}NO_3$. *See* a746	183.21	br (in air), pw $[\alpha]_D^{20}-53$ (aq HCl)	211–2 (215 rapid htng)	. . . .	. . . .	. . . .	δ	i				aa s min ac s	**B13²,** 523
a748	**Adrenalone**		181.19	nd λ^{al} 232 (4.08), 279 (3.93), 312 (3.86)	235–6d	. . . .	. . . .	. . . .	δ	δ	δ	. . . .	. .	. . . .	**B14²,** 157
a749	**Adrenochrome** (*dl*) . .	. . . .	179.18	red-br rods (MeOH-HCO₂H, +½w) $[\alpha]_D^{18}-106$ $\lambda^{w,pH=6.5}$ 485 (3.3)	125d (anh)				v	v	i	. . .	i	lig i	**C31,** 5397
a750	**Adrenosterone**	Δ^4-Androstene-3,11,17-trione. $C_{19}H_{24}O_3$.	300.40	nd (al), lf (eth) $[\alpha]_D^{20}+262$ (abs al, c=1) $[\alpha]_D^{25}+281$ (ace) λ 235	222 (cor)	sub (vac)	. . . .	. . . .	δ	s	s	s	. .	chl s	**E14s,** 2979
—	**Adurol**	*see* **Benzene, 2-bromo-1,4-dihydroxy-***													
—	**Agaric acid**	*see* **1,2,3-Nonadecanetricarboxylic acid, 2-hydroxy-***													
a751	**Ajmalicine**	Py-tetrahydroserpentine. δ-Yohimbine. $C_{21}H_{24}N_2O_3$.	352.44	pr (MeOH) $[\alpha]_D^{24}-60$ (chl, c=0.5) λ^{al} 225 (4.68), 280 (3.91)	258d 261–3(vac)	. . . .	. . . .	. . . .	i					MeOH s	**Am 76,** 1332
Ω a752	**Ajmaline**	$C_{20}H_{26}N_2O_2$	326.44	pl (+3.5 w, aq AcOEt) $[\alpha]_D^{20}+144$ (chl) λ^{al} 249 (3.9), 290 (3.4)	158–60 (hyd) 250–7 (anh)	. . . .	. . . .	. . . .	i	s	δ	. . .	δ	chl s AcOEt s	**J1954,** 1242
a753	**α-Alanine** (D)	*l*-α-Aminopropionic acid. $CH_3CH(NH_2)CO_2H$	89.10	nd (w, al) $[\alpha]_D^{25}-13.6$ (6N HCl, c=1)	314d (297d)	sub	. . . .	. . . .	s v^h	δ	i	. . . .	. .	. . . .	**B4²,** 812
Ω a754	—(*DL*)	$CH_3CH(NH_2)CO_2H$	89.10	orh pr or nd (w) $\lambda^{w,pH=10}$ 205 (0.7)	295–6d (289d)	sub 258	1.424	. . . .	s v^h	δ	i	i	. .	Py δ	**B4²,** 814
a755	—(*L*)	$CH_3CH(NH_2)CO_2H$	89.10	rh (w), $[\alpha]_D^{25}+2.8$ (w, c=6), $+9.55$ (HCl)	314d (297d)	sub 160–5	1.432²³	. . . .	v	δ	i	i	. .	. . . .	**B4²,** 809
Ω a756	—,ethyl ester hydrochloride (*dl*)	$CH_3CH(NH_2)CO_2CH_2CH_3$. HCl	153.61	pr or hyg nd (al)	87–8 (129)	d	. . . .	. . . .	v	v	v	. . . .	. .	. . . .	**B4²,** 819

For explanations, symbols and abbreviations see beginning of table. For structural formulas see end of table.

No.	Name	Synonyms and Formula	Mol. wt.	Color, crystalline form, specific rotation and λ_{max} (log ε)	m.p. °C	b.p. °C	Density	n_D	Solubility						Ref.
									w	al	eth	ace	bz	other solvents	
	β-Alanine														
Ω a756[1]	**β-Alanine**	β-Aminopropionic acid. $H_2NCH_2CH_2CO_2H$	89.10	nd, rh pr (al)	207d (199d)	....	1.437[19]	....	s	δ	i	i	...	...	B4[2], 827
a757	**α-Alanine,** N-alanyl-(l)	$H_2NCH(CH_3)CONHCH(CH_3)CO_2H$	160.17	lf, $[\alpha]_D^{20}$ −21.6 (w) $\lambda^{w,pH=1}$ 270 sh (3.1)	298	....	....	....	v	δ	i	...	...	...	B4[2], 813
—	—,3-anthraniloyl-(l)	see Kynurenine (l)													
a758	—,N-benzoyl-(d) ...	$CH_3CH(NHCOC_6H_5)CO_2H$	193.21	pl (w), $[\alpha]_D^{20}$ −2.4 (w, c = 1), +37.3 (alk)	152–4	....	....	....	s	s	δ	...	...	...	B9[2], 179
Ω a759	—,—(dl)	$CH_3CH(NHCOC_6H_5)CO_2H$	193.21	pl or pr, lf (eth) $\lambda^{w,pH=7}$ 248 (4.1), 287 (3.1)	165–6 d	....	....	....	s	s	δ	...	...	...	B9[2], 179
a760	—,—(l)	$CH_3CH(NHCOC_6H_5)CO_2H$	193.21	$[\alpha]_D^{20}$ +2.4 (w, c = 1) −37.3 (alk)	151	....	....	....	δ	...	...	...	...	...	B9[2], 179
a761	—,N(carboxy-methyl)-(dl)	$HO_2CCH_2NHCH(CH_3)CO_2H$	147.13	cr (dil al or w)	222–3	....	....	....	s	i	i	...	...	...	B4[1], 497
a762	—,N(4 chloro-phenyl)-, nitrile	....	180.64	lf (eth-peth)	114.5	....	....	....	...	s	s	...	v^h	chl v lig i	B12, 617
a763	—,N,N-diethyl-, nitrile	$(C_2H_5)_2NCH(CH_3)CN$	126.20	....	....	81[27] 55[11]	0.857[16]	....	s	s	s	...	...	...	C35, 1404
Ω a764	—,3(3,4-dihy-droxyphenyl)-(L)	l-Dopa	197.19	pl (dil al), pr or nd (w + SO_2) $[\alpha]_D^{15}$ −39.5 (w, p = 1.3) −12.7(4 % HCl, c = 1)	285.5d	....	....	....	s	i	i	i	i	MeOH s alk s aa i	B14[2], 399
a765	—,N-fumaryl-(DL)	Fumaroalanide. $HO_2CCH:CHCONHCH(CH_3)CO_2H$	187.15	nd	229d	....	....	....	δ s^h	s	δ	...	...	$NaHCO_3$ s lig i	C37, 2030
a766	—,N-methyl-(dl) ...	$CH_3CH(NHCH_3)CO_2H$ ...	103.12	rh pr (abs al)	sinters 280	sub 292	....	....	δ	i s^h	...	...	...	...	B4[2], 821
a767	**β-Alanine,** N-methyl-	$CH_3NHCH_2CH_2CO_2H$	103.12	pl (al, +1w)	99–100 (+1w) 146 (anh)	....	....	....	v	v^h	...	δ	...	chl δ	B4[2], 828
a768	—,—,ethyl ester ...	$CH_3NHCH_2CH_2CO_2CH_2CH_3$	131.18	....	....	80[21]	1.0082[20,20]	1.4443[20]	...	s	s	...	...	dil HCl s	B4[2], 828
a769	—,—,nitrile	β-Methylaminopropio-nitrile*. $CH_3NHCH_2CH_2CN$	84.13	....	....	101–4[49] 74[16]	0.8992[20,4]	1.4320[20]	s	...	...	s	s	MeOH, chl s	B4[3], 1264
—	**α-Alanine,3-phenyl-**	see Phenylalanine													
a770	—,N-phenyl-, nitrile	α-Cyanoethyl aniline. $C_6H_5NHCH(CH_3)CN$	146.19	nd (bz or dil al), lf (dil al, bz, eth)	92	....	....	....	i δ^h	v	v	...	v	chl v	B12[1], 266
—	**Alantolactone**	see Helenin													
—	**Aldehydin**	see Pyridine, 5-ethyl-2-methyl-													
—	**Aldol**	see Butanal, 3-hydroxy-*													
Ω a772	**Aldrin**	Octalene.	364.93	....	104–4.5	....	....	....	i	s	s	s	s	oos s	C44, 2690
—	**Aleuritic acid**	see Hexadecanoic acid, 9,10,16-trihydroxy-*													
—	**Alizarin**	see 9,10-Anthraquinone, 1,2-dihydroxy-*													
—	**Alizarin cyanine R**	see 9,10-Anthraquinone, 1,2,4,5,8-pentahydroxy-*													
—	**Alkanin** (d)	see Shikonine													
Ω a773	—(l)	$C_{16}H_{16}O_5$	288.30	red br pr (bz, sub), nd (eth-al) $[\alpha]_{Cd}^{20}$ −157 (bz)	149	sub 140[0.001]	....	....	i	δ	δ	...	...	alk s chl δ aa s	C30, 1050
a774	**Allantoic acid**	Dicarbamidoacetic acid. Diureidoacetic acid. $(H_2NCONH)_2CHCO_2H$	176.14	nd, lf (MeOH)	173d	....	....	....	δ	0	...	...	...	os δ dil ac δ	B3[3], 388
Ω a775	**Allantoin**	Glyoxyldiureide. 5-Ureidohydantoin.	158.12	mcl pl or pr (w)	238–40	....	....	....	δ s^h	s^h	i	...	...	MeOH i NaOH s	B25[2], 379
a776	**Allanturic acid**	Glyoxalylurea. 5-Hydroxy-2,4-imidazoledione.	116.08	amor hyg pw	turns br at 180	....	....	....	δ	i	...	...	...	hot alk d os i	B25[2], 388
—	**Allene**	see Propadiene*													
a777	**Allicin**	S-Oxodiallyl disulfide.	162.27	....	d	1.112[20]	1.561[20]		δ	∞	∞	...	∞	...	Am 66, 1950
a778	**Allitol**(D)	D-Allodulcitol.	182.18	....	150–1	....	....	....	s	i	i	...	i	....	Am 68, 1443
—	**Allocholesterol**	see Coprostenol													
—	**Allocinnamic acid**	see Cinnamic acid (cis)													

For explanations, symbols and abbreviations see beginning of table. For structural formulas see end of table.

No.	Name	Synonyms and Formula	Mol. wt.	Color, crystalline form, specific rotation and λ_{max} (log ε)	m.p. °C	b.p. °C	Density	n_D	w	al	eth	ace	bz	other solvents	Ref.
	Alloisoleucine														
Ω a779	Alloisoleucine(*l*)	$CH_3CH_2CH(CH_3)CH(NH_2)CO_2H$ 131.18		lf (w), $[\alpha]_D^{20}$ −14.2 (w, c = 2)	280–1d				s	δ					B4, 457
a780	Allomucic acid.....	Tetrahydroxyadipic acid. $HO_2C(CHOH)_4CO_2H$	210.14	nd or pr	198–200 (176d)				s^h	δ					B3², 376
a781	Allonic acid, γ-lactone(*D*)	....	178.14	pr(al) $[\alpha]_D^{20}$ −6.8(w, c = 11)	120				s	δ s^h					B18¹, 406
—	Alloocimene A.....	see 2,4,6-octatriene, 2,6-dimethyl-*													
—	Allophanamide	see Biuret													
—	Allophanic acid	see 1-Ureacarboxylic acid ...													
a782	Allose (*D*)	....	180.16	cr (w) $[\alpha]_D$ +0.58 → +14.41 (w, c = 5) (mut)	128–8.5				s	i					B31, 82
a783	—(*L*)	$C_6H_{12}O_6$. See a782........	180.16	pr (dil al) $[\alpha]_D^{20}$ −0.58(al), −1.90 → −13.88 (w, c = 5) (mut)	128–9				s	δ					Am 55, 2167
a784	Alloxan	Mesoxalylurea. Pyrimidinetetrone.	142.07	wh tcl, rh pr (w +4), orh cr (aa, ace, sub) $\lambda^{w,pH=4}$ 265 sh (1.9), $\lambda^{w,pH=6.8}$ 243 (3.40)	256d (anh) (turn pk at 230)	sub (vac)			v	s		s	s	aa s	B24², 301
a785	Alloxanic acid.....	....	160.09	tcl pr (eth)	162–3d				s	s	δ				B25², 266
a786	Alloxantin........	....	286.16	rh pr (w +2) $\lambda^{0.03NHCl}$ 270 (3.57)	253–5d (ye at 225)				δ s^h	δ	δ				B26², 335
—	Allylacetic acid	see 4-Pentenoic acid*													
—	Allyl alcohol	see 2-Propenol*													
—	Allyl amine	see Propene, 3-amino-*													
—	Allyl bromide	see Propene, 3-bromo-*													
—	Allyl cellosolve	see Ethanol, 2-allyloxy-													
—	Allyl chloride	see Propene, 3-chloro-*													
—	Allyl cyanide	see 3-Butenoic acid, nitrile													
—	Allyl fluoride	see Propene, 3-fluoro-*													
—	Allyl iodide	see Propene, 3-iodo-*													
—	Allyl mustard oil ...	see Isothiocyanic acid, allyl ester													
—	Aloe-emodine	see 9,10-Anthraquinone, 1,8-dihydroxy-3-hydroxy-methyl-													
a787	Aloetic acid	....	450.24	og-ye nd (aa), ye cr (w +1)	285d (>285 exp)				δ s^h					NH_4OH v alk s (red) acs^h	E13, 575
Ω a788	Aloin	Barbaloin. $C_{21}H_{22}O_9$	386.36	ye nd (al) $[\alpha]_D$ −8.3 (dil al), −10.4 (AcOEt)	148.5 (150)				s	s	δ	s	δ	KOH s chl i	J1956, 3141
—	Alphol	see Benzoic acid, 2-hydroxy-, 1-naphthyl ester													
a789	Alstonine	$C_{21}H_{20}N_2O_3$	348.41	ye nd (ace) λ^{al} 250 (4.5), 308 (4.3), 375 (3.7)	205–10d (>300d)										B27², 824
a790	Altrose(*d*)	....	180.16	pr (MeOH-al) $[\alpha]_D^{20}$ +11.7 → 33.1 (w, c = 7.6) (mut)	103–5				s	i				MeOH s^h	B31, 83
a791	—(*l,β*)	$C_6H_{12}O_6$. See a790	180.16	pr (al, aa) −28.55 → −32.30 (w) (mut)	107–9.5				s	i s^h					Am 56, 1153
a792	Amalic acid	Tetramethylalloxantin. $C_{12}H_{14}N_4O_8$.	324.25	cr (w)	245d				δ^h	i				KOH s	B26², 336
a793	Amarine.........	$C_{21}H_{18}N_2$	298.39	pr (eth, bz-lig)	136	d198			i	s	s			s	lig i	B23², 274
a794	—,hydrate.....	$C_{21}H_{18}N_2 \cdot \frac{1}{2}H_2O$	307.40	pr (aq al + ½w)	106				i	s					B23², 274
Ω a795	Amaron	Benzoin imide. Ditolan azotide. Tetraphenyl-pyrazine.	384.49	tcl nd or pr (ace, al), nd (aa)	246	sub			i	δ^h	δ	s^h	s^h	chl, CS_2 s aa s^h con sulf s (red)	B23², 304
a796	Amine, allyl methyl	$CH_2{:}CHCH_2NHCH_3$	71.12	....		65		1.4065²⁰	∞	∞	v	v			B4, 206

For explanations, symbols and abbreviations see beginning of table. For structural formulas see end of table.

Amine

No.	Name	Synonyms and Formula	Mol. wt.	Color, crystalline form, specific rotation and λ_{max} (log ε)	m.p. °C	b.p. °C	Density	n_D	w	al	eth	ace	bz	other solvents	Ref.
a797	—,benzyl diphenyl	$C_6H_5CH_2N(C_6H_5)_2$	259.36	nd (al)	95	....	....	....	δ	δ v[h]	v	v	v	aa δ lig v	B12[2], 551
Ω a798	—,benzyl ethyl phenyl	N-Benzyl-N-ethylaniline. $C_6H_5CH_2N(C_2H_5)C_6H_5$	211.31	pa ye	34–6	285–6[710] δd 186[22]	1.034[19]4	1.5930[20]	i	s	s	...	...		B12[2], 550
a799	—,benzyl ethyl 2-tolyl	N-Benzyl-N-ethyl-o-toluidine	225.34	ye	....	230[20–5]	....	....	i						B12, 1033
a800	—,benzyl methyl 2-tolyl	N-Benzyl-N-methyl-o-toluidine.	211.31	ye	....	167[13]	....	....	i	s				os s	B12, 1033
a801	—,benzyl N-nitroso phenyl	$C_6H_5CH_2N(NO)C_6H_5$	212.25	ye nd (al)	58	....	....	....	i	s	s			chl s	B12[2], 572
Ω a802	—,benzyl phenyl	N-Benzylaniline. $C_6H_5CH_2NHC_6H_5$	183.26	pr (MeOH) λ^{al} 250 (4.1), 294 (3.3)	37–8	306–7 (321[775]) 171.5[10]	1.0698[15]15 1.0298[65]65	1.6118[25]	i	s	v			lig s MeOH s[h]	B12[2], 548
a803	—,benzyl 2-tolyl ...	N-Benzyl-o-toluidine	197.28	cr (al, eth)	60	300–5[760] 176[10]	1.0142[65]65	1.5861[65]	i	s				os s chl s	B12[2], 551
a804	—,benzyl 3-tolyl- ...	N-Benzyl-m-toluidine	197.28	pa ye oil	....	312[760] 180[10]	1.0083[65]65	1.5845[65]	i	δ	v		v	chl v	B12[2], 552
a805	—,benzyl 4-tolyl ...	N-Benzyl-p-toluidine	197.28	ye lf	19–20	319[765] 181[10]	1.0064[65]65	1.5832[65]	i	v	v	...	v	chl v	B12[2], 553
a806	—,benzylidene ethyl	$C_6H_5CH\!\cdot\!NC_2H_5$	133.20	λ^{al} 245 (4.14), 278 (3.1), 290 sh (2.9)	....	195[749] 117[12]	0.9370[20]4	1.5365[26]	i	s	s	s			B7[2], 163
a807	—,benzylidene methyl	$C_6H_5CH\!:\!NCH_3$	119.17	λ^{al} 245 (4.18)	....	185[760] 90–1[30]	0.9672[14]2	1.5526[20]	...	s	s	s			B7[2], 162
a808	—,bis(dimethyl-phosphino)	Amino-bis(dimethyl phosphine). $(CH_3)_2PNHP(CH_3)_2$	137.10		39.5	d 33.5[5.4] sub	....	....	d	d				os ∞	Am 75, 3869
—	—,tert-butyl	see Propane, 2-amino-2-methyl-*													
a809	—,butyl diethyl, 2'2''-dihydroxy-	Bis(2-hydroxyethyl)butyl-amine. $CH_3(CH_2)_3N(CH_2CH_2OH)_2$	161.25		....	273–5[741] 176–80[35]	0.9692[20]4	1.4625[20]	∞	∞	∞	s	∞	lig i	B4, 285
a810	—,butyl dimethyl ...	$CH_3(CH_2)_3N(CH_3)_2$ ...	101.19		....	95[761]	0.7206[20]4	1.3970[20]	∞	∞	∞	∞	∞		B4[2], 632
a811	—,butyl ethyl ...	$CH_3(CH_2)_3NHCH_2CH_3$ ...	101.19		....	108–9	0.7398[20]4	1.4040[20]	∞	∞	∞	∞	∞	.....	B4, 157
a812	—,sec-butyl ethyl(d)	$CH_3CH_2CH(CH_3)NHCH_2CH_3$	101.19	$[α]^{15}_D$ +18	....	98	0.7396[15]15	1.4043[15]	∞	∞	∞	∞	∞	os s	B4[3], 307
a813	—,—(dl)	$CH_3CH_2CH(CH_3)NHCH_2CH_3$	101.19		−104.5	97 8[741]	0.7358[20]4	....	∞	∞	∞	∞	∞	os s	B4[2], 636
a814	—,butyl ethyl, 2,2'-dihydroxy-	$HOCH_2CH_2NHCH_2CH(OH)CH_2CH_3$	133.19	yesh	....	137[9]	1.0310[20]4	1.4690[20]	s	s	...	s		lig i	C44, 7853
a815	—,—,3,2'-dihydroxy-	$HOCH_2CH_2NHCH_2CH_2CH(OH)CH_3$	133.19	yesh	....	107–9[1]	1.0331[20]2	1.4718[20]	s			s		lig i	C59, 6392
—	—,cyano diphenyl	see Cyanamide, diphenyl-													
—	—,cyclohexyl phenyl	see Aniline, N-cyclohexyl-													
Ω a816	—,diallyl	$NH(CH_2CH\!:\!CH_2)_2$	97.16	λ^{aa}–HNO₃ salt 296 (0.91)	....	111[760]	....	1.4387[20]		s	s				B4[2], 663
Ω a817	—,dibenzyl	$NH(CH_2C_6H_5)_2$	197.28	λ^{aa}–HNO₃ salt 296 (0.94)	−26	300d 270[250]	1.0256[22]2	1.5731[20]	i	v	v				B12[2], 553
a818	—,dibenzyl ethyl	$CH_3CH_2N(CH_2C_6H_5)_2$	225.34		....	306 131[<1]	....	....	i	v	v			ac s	B12[2], 553
Ω a819	—,dibenzyl phenyl	$C_6H_5N(CH_2C_6H_5)_2$	273.38	nd or pr (al)	71–2	>300d 226[10]	1.0444[80]4	1.6065[80]	i	δ s[h]	s		s	aa δ, v[h]	B12[2], 554
Ω a820	—,dibutyl	$NH(CH_2CH_2CH_2CH_3)_2$	129.25	λ^{al}–HNO₃ salt 301 (0.83)	−60 to −59	159[761] 48[13]	0.7670[20]2	1.4177[20]	s	v	v				B4[2], 633
Ω a821	—,di-sec-butyl...	$[CH_3CH_2CH(CH_3)]_2NH$	129.25		−55	135[765]	0.7534[20]2	1.4162[20]	v	s				os s	B4[2], 636
a822	—,—,3,3'-di-hydroxy-	$[CH_3CH(OH)CH(CH_3)]_2NH$	161.25	yesh	....	112–5[3]	0.9775[20]2	1.4162[20]	v	v	δ	v		lig δ	C49, 11689
a823	—,dibutyl,3,3'-dimethyl	Diisoamyl amine. $[(CH_3)_2CHCH_2CH_2]_2NH$	157.30		−44	188	0.7672[21]1	1.4235[20]	i	s	∞				B4[2], 646
Ω a825	—,dicyclohexyl....		181.33		−0.10	255.8[760] δd 113.5[9]	0.9123[20]4	1.4842[20]	δ[h]	s	s		s		B12[2], 7
a826	—,didodecyl	$[CH_3(CH_2)_{10}CH_2]_2NH$	353.68	α 55–6	....	....	....	....		v	δ	v		chl v diox s	Am 77, 485
Ω a827	—,diethyl........	$(CH_3CH_2)_2NH$	73.14	λ^{gas} 194.2 (3.47), 222 sh (2.47)	−48 fp −50	56.3[760]	0.7056[20]2	1.3864[20]	v	∞	s				B4[2], 590
Ω a828	—,—,hydrochloride	$(CH_3CH_2)_2NH\!\cdot\!HCl$	109.60	lf (al-eth)	227 30	320–30	1.0477[21]52	....	v	v	δ	δ		chl s	B4[2], 592
a829	—,—,2-amino-2'-hydroxy-	N-(2-Hydroxyethyl)ethylene-diamine. $H_2NCH_2CH_2NHCH_2CH_2OH$	104.15		....	238–40 123[10]	1.0254[25]5	1.4863[20]	∞	∞	δ	s	δ	lig δ	B4, 286
—	—,—,2,2'-diamino-	see Diethylenetriamine													
Ω a830	—,—,2,2'-dihydroxy-	Diethanolamine. Diethylol-amine. $NH(CH_2CH_2OH)_2$	105.14	pr	28	271[760] 154–5[10]	1.0966[20]4	1.4776[20]	v	v	δ		δ		B4[2], 729
Ω a831	—,—,1,1'-diphenyl-	$NH[CH(CH_3)C_6H_5]_2$	225.34	ye	....	295–8 190[10]	1.018[13]	1.573	δ						B12[2], 589

For explanations, symbols and abbreviations see beginning of table. For structural formulas see end of table.

No.	Name	Synonyms and Formula	Mol. wt.	Color, crystalline form, specific rotation and λ_{max} (log ε)	m.p. °C	b.p. °C	Density	n_D	w	al	eth	ace	bz	other solvents	Ref.
	Amine														
Ω a832	—,—,2,2'-diphenyl-	NH(CH$_2$CH$_2$C$_6$H$_5$)$_2$	225.34	. . . .	28–30	335–7[603] 190[15]		1.5550[25]	i	v	v	. . .	. . .	ac s	B12[2], 593
a833	—,diethyl methyl . . .	(CH$_3$CH$_2$)$_2$NCH$_3$	87.17			66[760]	0.7032$_4^{23}$	1.3879[25]	v	v	v				B4[2], 593
a834	—,—,2,2'-dichloro-, hydrochloride	(ClCH$_2$CH$_2$)$_2$NCH$_3$.HCl . . .	192.52	hyg nd	111–2				v	s					Am 81, 5167
—	—,—,2,2-diethoxy-	*see* Acetaldehyde, ethyl-methylamino-, diethyl acetal													
a835	—,—,2,2'-dihydroxy-	(HOCH$_2$CH$_2$)$_2$NCH$_3$	119.17	. . . .		246–8[747] 123–5[4]	1.0377[20]	1.4642[20]	∞	∞	δ				B4[2], 729
Ω a836	—,—,1'''-methoxy-	CH$_3$OCH$_2$N(CH$_2$CH$_3$)$_2$	117.19			116.5–7[763] 53[68]			s	s	s			HCl s	B4[2], 598
a837	—,diethyl N-nitro . .	(CH$_3$CH$_2$)$_2$NNO$_2$	118.14			206.5[757] 93[16]	1.057[15]		δ	∞	∞				B4, 130
a838	—,diethyl N-nitroso	(CH$_3$CH$_2$)$_2$NNO	102.14	ye λ^{al} 233 (3.7), 350 (1.95)		176.9[760]	0.9422$_4^{20}$	1.4386[20]	s	s	s				B4[2], 617
a839	—,diethyl phenyl, 2,2'-dihydroxy-	N-Phenyldiethanolamine. (HOCH$_2$CH$_2$)$_2$NC$_6$H$_5$	181.24	pl (al)	58	228[15]			δ	v	v	v	v		B12[2], 109
a840	—,difurfuryl		177.21			135–42[15] 102–3[1]	1.1045$_4^2$	1.5168[20]	i		s				B18[2], 418
Ω a841	—,diheptyl	[CH$_3$(CH$_2$)$_6$]$_2$NH	213.41	nd	30	271[750] 134–6[9]			δ	s	v				B4[2], 652
Ω a843	—,dihexyl	[CH$_3$(CH$_2$)$_5$]$_2$NH	185.36			192–5[9] 112–4[12]		1.4339[20]		s	s				B4[2], 650
a844	—,di-2-hydrindyl,1,1'-dihydroxy-(d)		281.36	nd (al) $[\alpha]_D^{18}$ +83.2 (dil HCl, c = 0.3)	223	. . . .				s^h				os δ	B13[1], 265
a845	—,—(dl)	C$_{18}$H$_{19}$NO$_2$. See a844	281.36	nd or pl (dil al)	205	. . . .			δ	v	v		v		B13[1], 267
a846	—,—(l)	C$_{18}$H$_{19}$NO$_2$. See a844	281.36	nd (al), $[\alpha]_D^{18}$ −83.3 (dil HCl, c = 0.3)	223	. . . .			δ	s^h	v			os δ	B13[1], 266
Ω a847	—,diisobutyl	[(CH$_3$)$_2$CHCH$_2$]$_2$NH . . .	129.25		−73.5 (−77)	139–40[760]		1.4090[20]	δ	s	s	s	s		B4[2], 638
a848	—,diisopropyl	[(CH$_3$)$_2$CH]$_2$NH	101.19	λ^{al} 301 (0.82)	−61	84[760]	0.7169$_4^{20}$	1.3924[20]	δ	s	s	s	s		B4, 630
a849	—,diisopropyl N-nitroso	Nitrous diisopropylamide. [(CH$_3$)$_2$CH]$_2$NNO	130.19	cr (eth, w)	48	194.5 76–81[14]	0.9422$_4^{20}$		δ s^h	s	s				B4, 156
Ω a850	—,dimethyl	(CH$_3$)$_2$NH	45.09	λ^{gas} 190.5 (3.51), 222 (2.0)	−93	7.4	0.6804$_4^0$	1.350[17]	v	s	s				B4[2], 550
Ω a851	—,—,hydrochloride	Dimethylammonium chloride. (CH$_3$)$_2$NH.HCl	81.56	rh, nd (al)	171	. . . .			v	s	i			chl v	B4[2], 552
a852	—,—,hexafluoro-	Bis(trifluoromethyl)amine. (CF$_3$)$_2$NH	153.03		−130	−6.7[760]	1.561$_4^{-14.4}$		d						C35, 434
a853	—,—,perfluoro-	(CF$_3$)$_2$NF	171.02			−37			i						J1949, 3080
a854	—,dimethyl isobutyl	(CH$_3$)$_2$CHCH$_2$N(CH$_3$)$_2$ . .	101.19			80–1[760]	0.7097$_4^{20}$	1.3907[20]	s					ac v	B4[2], 638
a855	—,dimethyl N-nitro	Dimethylnitramine. Nitric dimethylamide. (CH$_3$)$_2$NNO$_2$	90.08	nd (eth)	58	187[759]	1.1090$_4^{72}$	1.4462[72]	s	s	s	s	s		B4[1], 342
Ω a856	—,dimethyl N-nitroso	Dimethylnitrosamine. Nitrous dimethylamide. (CH$_3$)$_2$NNO	74.08	ye λ^{al} 231 (3.85), 346 (2.00)	. . . .	154[760]	1.0059$_4^{20}$	1.4358[20]	s	s	s				B4[2], 585
a857	—,dimethyl pentyl	CH$_3$(CH$_2$)$_4$N(CH$_3$)$_2$	115.22			123	0.743[20]	1.4083[20]	δ^h		∞				B4[2], 642
a858	—,di-2-naphthyl . .	(C$_{10}$H$_7$)$_2$NH	269.35	lf (bz)	172.2	471			i	δ^h	s		δ s^h	aa s^h	B12[2], 717
a859	—,dioctadecyl	[CH$_3$(CH$_2$)$_{16}$CH$_2$]$_2$NH	522.01		73–4				i	i	δ	i	δ	chl v	C35, 3963
Ω a860	—,dioctyl	[CH$_3$(CH$_2$)$_6$CH$_2$]$_2$NH	241.47	nd	35.6	297–8 175[14]	0.7968$_4^{26}$	1.4415[26]	i	v	v				B4[2], 655
a860[1]	—,di-2-octyl	[CH$_3$(CH$_2$)$_4$CH(CH$_3$)]$_2$NH	241.47			281.5[739]	0.7948$_4^{20}$		i	v	v				B4, 197
Ω a861	—,dipentyl	[CH$_3$(CH$_2$)$_4$]$_2$NH	157.30			202–3[760] 91–3[14]	0.7771$_4^{20}$	1.4272[20]	δ	v	∞	s			B4[2], 642
a862	—,—,2,2'-dihydroxy-2,2'-dimethyl-	[CH$_3$CH$_2$CH$_2$C(CH$_3$)(OH)CH$_2$]$_2$NH	217.36			165–70[15]	0.9264$_4^{20}$	1.4584[20]	v	v	v			lig i	C53, 16829
Ω a863	—,diphenyl	N-Phenylaniline	169.23	mcl lf (dil al) λ^{al} 208 (4.33), 286 (4.29)	54–5	302 179[22]	1.160$_{20}^{22}$		i	v	v	v	v	Py, CCl$_4$ v AcOEt v aa s lig s	B12[2], 101
a864	—,—,hydrobromide	(C$_6$H$_5$)$_2$NH.HBr	250.15	pl (dil al)	230d	. . . .			s	δ	i		i		B12, 180
Ω a865	—,—,2-amino-	N-Phenyl-o-phenylenediamine. C$_{12}$H$_{12}$N$_2$. See a863	184.24	nd (w) $\lambda^{95\%al}$ 237 (3.95), 280 (3.85)	80–1	312.5[744]			δ		s		s	chl s lig δ	B13[2], 13

For explanations, symbols and abbreviations see beginning of table. For structural formulas see end of table.

No.	Name	Synonyms and Formula	Mol. wt.	Color, crystalline form, specific rotation and λ_{max} (log ε)	m.p. °C	b.p. °C	Density	n_D	Solubility						Ref.
									w	al	eth	ace	bz	other solvents	
	Amine														
a866	—,—,4-amino-	N-Phenyl-p-phenylene-diamine. black base P. $C_{12}H_{12}N_2$. See a863	184.24	nd (al), cr (lig) $\lambda^{95\%al}$ 281 (4.18)	66 (al), 75 (lig)	354 $155^{0.026}$			δ	v^h	s	...	...	lig s^h	B13, 76
a867	—,—,4,4'-bis(di-methylamino)-	Leuco base of Bindschedler green. $C_{16}H_{21}N_3$. See a863	255.37	tetr pl (CS_2)	119 (116)	....			δ s^h	δ	s	...	...	lig δ $CS_2 s^h$	B13², 56
a868	—,—,4,4'-di-amino-	p,p'-Iminodianiline. $C_{12}H_{13}N_3$. See a863	199.26	lf (w)	158	d			δ s^h	s	s	...	...		B13², 55
a869	—,—,2,2'-dinitro-	$C_{12}H_9N_3O_4$. See a863	259.22	lf (al, ace MeOH), ye cr (al, aa) λ^{al} 255 (4.18), 264(4.22), 420 (3.97)	169	....				v^h		s	...	MeOH s^h aa v^h	B12¹, 341
Ω a870	—,—,2,4-dinitro-	$C_{12}H_9N_3O_4$. See a863	259.22	ye red nd (al) λ^{al} 231.5 (4.11), 350.5 (4.23)	157	....			i	s^h	δ	s	δ s^h	chl s Py s	B12², 407
Ω a871	—,—,2,4'-dinitro-	$C_{12}H_9N_3O_4$. See a863	259.22	red nd (aa)	222–3 (219)	....			i	δ	...	δ	s^h	to s chl s	B12², 387
a872	—,—,2,6-dinitro-	$C_{12}H_9N_3O_4$. See a863	259.22	og lf (al, aa)	107–8	....			i	s^h	...	...	...	aa s^h	B12², 413
a873	—,—,3,4'-dinitro-	$C_{12}H_9N_3O_4$. See a863	259.22	pa ye (chl, aq Py)	217 (softens 205)	....				δ	...	v	...	chl s^h con ac s	B12², 387
a874	—,—,4,4'-dinitro-	$C_{12}H_9N_3O_4$. See a863	259.22	ye nd (al) λ^{al} 232 (4.06), 402 (4.58)	216–6.5	....			i	δ s^h	...	s	δ	to i aa s	B12², 387
a875	—,—,2,4-dinitro-4'-hydroxy-	$C_{12}H_9N_3O_5$. See a863	275.22	red lf	195–6									alk s	B13¹, 150
a876	—,—,2,4-dinitro-5-hydroxy-	$C_{12}H_9N_3O_5$. See a863	275.22	dk ye nd (al)	139						s^h				B13¹, 138
a877	—,—,2,6-dinitro-2'-hydroxy-	$C_{12}H_9N_3O_5$. See a863	275.22	red vt nd (al)	191						s^h	v^h		v^h	aa v^h	B13, 365
a878	—,—,2,6-dinitro-3-hydroxy-	$C_{12}H_9N_3O_5$. See a863	275.22	ye br nd (MeOH)	124–5						s^h				MeOH s^h	B13², 216
Ω a880	—,—,2,2',4,4',6,6'-hexanitro-	Dipicrylamine. $C_{12}H_5N_7O_{12}$. See a863	439.21	pa ye pr (aa), cr (93% HNO_3) λ^{eth} 250 (4.10), 372 (4.18)	244d	....			i	i	δ	δ	i	aq alk s Py v to CCl_4 i	B12², 422 B12², 422
a881	—,—,2-hydroxy-	2-Anilinophenol. $C_{12}H_{11}NO$. See a863	185.23	pr (w) λ^{al} 274 (4.2), 298 (4.0)	69–70	$180–9^{20}$			δ^h	s	s	...	δ	aa s	B13, 365
Ω a882	—,—,3-hydroxy-	3-Anilinophenol. $C_{12}H_{11}NO$. See a863	185.23	lf (w)	81.5–2	340			δ s^h	v	v	v	s	dil ac s lig δ	B13², 213
a883	—,—,4-hydroxy-	4-Anilinophenol. $C_{12}H_{11}NO$. See a863	185.23	lf (w) λ^{al} 288 (4.1)	73	330 $215–6^{12}$			δ	v	v	...	v^h	chl v lig δ ac, alk s	B13², 231
Ω a884	—,—,2-nitro-	$C_{12}H_{10}N_2O_2$. See a863	214.23	og pl (dil al), rh bipym λ^{al} 220 (4.13), 259 (4.15), 428 (3.82)	75.5	....			i	s				....	B12², 369
a885	—,—,3-nitro-	$C_{12}H_{10}N_2O_2$. See a863	214.23	red nd or pl (dil al) λ^{al} 265 (4.26), 282 (4.21), 367 (3.17)	114					v	v	...	v	lig δ	B12², 377
Ω a886	—,—,4-nitro-	$C_{12}H_{10}N_2O_2$. See a863	214.23	ye nd, tab (CCl_4) λ^{al} 228 (3.82), 258 (3.98), 391 (4.29)	133.5–4.5	211^{30}			i	v				aa v con sulf s (vt)	B12², 386
Ω a887	—,—,4-nitroso-	$C_{12}H_{10}N_2O$. See a863	198.23	blsh bk (al), ye pw, pl (bz) λ^{al-HCl} 259 (3.62), 406 (4.31)	143	....			δ	v^h	v	...	v	chl v lig δ	B12², 122
—	—,—,4-sulfo-	see Benzenesulfonic acid, 4-phenylamino-[1]													
a888	—,—,2,2',4,4'-tetrabromo-	$C_{12}H_7Br_4N$. See a863	484.83	nd (chl or bz)	187.5 (182)	....			i	δ^h	...	...	s^h	chl s^h	B12², 356
a889	—,—,2,2',4,4'-tetranitro-	$C_{12}H_7N_5O_8$. See a863	349.22	ye nd or cr (aa), red-br pl (al) λ^{al} 219.5 (4.35), 358 (4.24), 401.5 (4.36)	201–1.5	....			i^h	δ^h	...	δ s^h	δ^h	chl, AcOEt δ^h aa s^h Py s	B12², 409
a890	—,diphenyl ethyl	$(C_6H_5)_2NCH_2CH_3$	197.28	....	....	295.5–6.5⁷⁶⁰ 148^{11}	1.0396^{20}_{20}	1.6095^{20}	i	s	s	...	...	....	B12², 105
a891	—,diphenyl methyl	$(C_6H_5)_2NCH_3$	183.26	λ^{al} 245 (3.9), 290 (4.0)	−7.55	293–4 145^{10}	1.0476^{20}_{4}	1.6193^{20}	i	δ	...	...	...	MeOH δ	B12², 105

For explanations, symbols and abbreviations see beginning of table. For structural formulas see end of table.

No.	Name	Synonyms and Formula	Mol. wt.	Color, crystalline form, specific rotation and λ_{max} (log ε)	m.p. °C	b.p. °C	Density	n_D	w	al	eth	ace	bz	other solvents	Ref.

Amine

No.	Name	Synonyms and Formula	Mol. wt.	Color...	m.p. °C	b.p. °C	Density	n_D	w	al	eth	ace	bz	other	Ref.
Ω a892	—,diphenyl N-nitroso	Nitrous diphenylamide. $(C_6H_5)_2NNO$	198.23	ye pl (lig) λ^{al} 290 (3.88)	66.5	....			δ v^h		....		s^h		B12[2], 310
—	—,dipicryl	see Amine, diphenyl, 2,2', 4,4',6,6'-hexanitro-													
Ω a893	—,dipropyl	$(CH_3CH_2CH_2)_2NH$	101.19	....	−39.6 (−63)	109.4–10.4	0.7400_4^{20}	1.4050^{20}	s	s	∞	v	v	....	B4[2], 622
a894	—,—,3,3'-diallyloxy-2,2'-dihydroxy-	$[CH_2:CHCH_2OCH_2CH(OH)CH_2]_2NH$	245.32	....	73	180–5[2–3]			s	s		s		lig i	C52, 15129
a895	—,—,2,2'-dihydroxy-	Diisopropanolamine. $[CH_3CH(OH)CH_2]_2NH$	133.19	cr	44.5–5.5	249–50[745] 151[23]	0.9892^{20}		s	s	δ				B4[2], 737
a896	—,dipropyl ethyl, 2,2',2''-trihydroxy-	$[CH_3CH(OH)CH_2]_2NCH_2CH_2OH$	177.25	....		155–6[1]	1.0458_4^{20}	1.4708^{20}	v	v		v		lig δ	C48, 7628
a897	—,dipropyl isobutyl, perfluoro-	$(CF_3)_2CFCF_2N(CF_2CF_2CF_3)_2$	571.08	....		146–8[760]	1.84_4^{25}	1.283^{25}	...	s	s			....	J1951, 102
a898	—,dipropyl methyl, 3,3'-dihydroxy-	$(HOCH_2CH_2CH_2)_2NCH_3$	147.22	hyg		164–5[13]			∞	∞	δ		v	....	B4[2], 735
a899	—,dipropyl N-nitroso	Dipropyl nitrosamine. Nitrous dipropylamide. $(CH_3CH_2CH_2)_2NNO$	130.19	golden λ^{al} 233 (3.85), 350 (1.95)		206[760] 89[13]	0.9163_4^{20}	1.4437^{20}	δ	∞	δ		v	....	B4[2], 628
a900	—,di-2-tolyl		197.28	bl flr, wh cr $\lambda^{95\%al}$ 240 (3.84)	52–3	312[727] 192[23]			δ					....	B12[2], 437
a901	—,di-3-tolyl		197.28	pa ye (peth) $\lambda^{95\%al}$ 259 (3.90)	53	319–20			δ	s	s			peth s^h	B12[2], 467
a902	—,di-4-tolyl		197.28	nd (peth)	79	330.5[760]			δ		s			peth s^h	B12[2], 494
a903	—,3,4-ditolyl, hydrochloride		233.74	cr $\lambda^{95\%al}$ 255 (4.12)	202–3				s	v	i	v	v	chl v lig i	B12[1], 414
a904	—,ethyl methyl ...	$CH_3NHCH_2CH_3$	59.11	....		36–7			v	v	s	s		os s	B4[2], 589
a905	—,—,hydrochloride	$CH_3NHCH_2CH_3 \cdot HCl$	95.57	pl (al-eth)	126–30				v	v	i			chl s	B4[2], 589
a906	—,ethyl N-nitrosophenyl	N-Ethylphenylnitrosamine. $C_6H_5N(NO)CH_2CH_3$	150.18	yesh λ^{al} 271.5 (3.83)		119.5–20[15]	1.0874_4^{20}		i					aa s	B12[2], 310
Ω a907	—,ethyl propyl, 2,2'-dihydroxy-	$HOCH_2CH_2NHCH_2CH(OH)CH_3$	119.17	yesh		120–3[1]	1.0455_4^{20}	1.4695^{20}	s	s		s		....	C40, 4732
a908	—,ethyl 2-tolyl, 2-hydroxy-		151.21			285–6 149[4]	1.0794_4^{20}	1.5675^{20}						chl s	B12[2], 437
a909	—,ethyl 4-tolyl, 2-hydroxy-		151.21	pl (eth-lig)	42–3	286–8 153–5[4]			δ d^h	v	v		v	chl v ac v	B12[2], 495
a910	—,methyl propyl ...	$CH_3NHCH_2CH_2CH_3$	73.14	....		61–2.5[760]	0.7204^{17}	1.3858^{25}	s	s	s	s		....	B4[2], 621
Ω a911	—,1-naphthyl phenyl	$C_{10}H_7^\beta NHC_6H_5$	219.29	lf (lig), pr or nd (al) λ^{MeOH} 217 (4.78), 252.5 (4.25), 339 (3.94)	62	335[528] 226[8]			δ	s	s		s	chl s aa s	B12[2], 682
Ω a912	—,2-naphthyl phenyl	$C_{10}H_7^\beta NHC_6H_5$	219.29	nd (MeOH) λ^{al} 220 (4.7), 275 (4.4), 312 (4.3)	108	395–9.5 237[13]			i	s	s		s	aa s (bl flr)	B12, 1275
a913	—,1-naphthyl propyl	$C_{10}H_7^\beta NHCH_2CH_2CH_3$	185.27	ye		316–8[771]			i	δ	δ		δ	aa δ	B12, 1224
a914	—,1-naphthyl 2-tolyl		233.32	nd (lig)	94–5	198–202[9]			i	s	s		s	lig s^h	B12, 1255
a915	—,1-naphthyl 4-tolyl		233.32	pr (al)	79	360[528] 236[15]			δ s^h	δ	s		s	con sulf s peth s^h	B12, 1278
a916	—,2-naphthyl 2-tolyl	Yellow OB	233.32	lf (lig)	95–6 (105)	400–5 235–7[14]					s	s	s	chl v lig v	B12, 1277
a917	—,2-naphthyl 4-tolyl		233.32	red lf (al)	103–3.5	....				δ s^h	s		s	PrOH s lig δ	B12, 1277
Ω a918	—,triallyl	$(CH_2:CHCH_2)_3N$	137.23	....		155–6 (cor)	0.8094^{20}	1.4502^{20}		s	s	s	s	ac s	B4, 208
Ω a919	—,tribenzyl	$(C_6H_5CH_2)_3N$	287.41	pl (eth), mcl (al) λ^{al} 247.5 sh (2.9), 252.5 (2.9)	91–2	380–90 230[13]	0.9912_4^{95}		δ	δ s^h	s		s	....	B12[2], 555
Ω a920	—,tributyl	$(CH_3CH_2CH_2CH_2)_3N$	185.36	hyg λ^{chl} 242 (3.0)		213[760] 91–2[9]	0.7771_0^{20}	1.4297^{20}	δ	v	v	s	s	....	B4[2], 633
Ω a921	—,—,perfluoro-	$(CF_3CF_2CF_2CF_2)_3N$	671.10	....		179[760]	1.873_4^{25}	1.291^{25}	...				s	....	J1951, 102
a922	—,—,2,2',2''-trimethyl-	Tri-active-amylamine. $[CH_3CH_2CH(CH_3)CH_2]_3N$	227.44	....		230–7 94[4]	0.7964^{13}	1.43305^{20}	i	s	v		v	chl v	B4[2], 642
Ω a923	—,—,3,3',3''-trimethyl-	Triisoamylamine. $[(CH_3)_2CHCH_2CH_2]_3N$	227.44	....		235[760] 94[4]	0.7848_4^{20}	1.4331^{20}	i	v	∞		∞	CCl_4 ∞	B4[2], 646
a924	—,tridodecyl	$[CH_3(CH_2)_{10}CH_2]_3N$	522.01	....	fr 15.7	220–8[0.03]		1.4567^{25}	δ	δ	∞	δ	∞	chl ∞	Am 74, 4287

For explanations, symbols and abbreviations see beginning of table. For structural formulas see end of table.

No.	Name	Synonyms and Formula	Mol. wt.	Color, crystalline form, specific rotation and λ_{max} (log ε)	m.p. °C	b.p. °C	Density	n_D	w	al	eth	ace	bz	other solvents	Ref.
Ω a925	**Amine** —,triethyl	$(CH_3CH_2)_3N$	101.19	λ^{hp} 196 (3.70)	−114.7	89.3[760]	0.7275[20]	1.4010[20]	s δ[h]	s	s	v	v	chl v	B4[2], 593
Ω a926	—,—,hydrochloride	$(CH_3CH_2)_3N.HCl$	137.65	hex (al)	260d	sub 245	1.0689[21]		v	s	i		δ	chl v	B4[1], 348
a927	—,—,hydroiodide	$(CH_3CH_2)_3N.HI$	229.11	pr (95 % al)	181		1.924		v	s	i		δ	chl s	B4, 101
Ω a928	—,—,2-bromo-, hydrobromide	$BrCH_2CH_2N(CH_2CH_3)_2.HBr$	261.01	nd (al-eth)	209				v	δ v[h]					B4[2], 619
Ω a929	—,—,2,2-di-ethoxy-	Diethylaminoacetal. $(CH_3CH_2)_2NCH_2CH(OCH_2CH_3)_2$	189.30			194–5	0.863[16]	1.4189[20]	s	s	s			os s	B4, 309
a930	—,—,2,2′-dihy-droxy-	2,2′-Ethyliminodiethanol. $(HOCH_2CH_2)_2NC_2H_5$	133.19	ye		246–8[760] 118[3]	1.0135[20]	1.4663[20]	v	v	δ				B4, 284
Ω a931	—,—,perfluoro-	$(CF_3CF_2)_3N$	371.05			70.3[760]	1.736[25]	1.262[25]							J1951, 102
a932	—,—,2,2′,2″-tri-chloro-	Nitrogen mustard gas. $(ClCH_2CH_2)_3N$	204.53	pa ye	−4	143–4[15]			δ	∞	∞		∞	HCl s	J1935, 1217
a933	—,—,2,2′,2″-tri-hydroxy-	Triethanolamine. $(HOCH_2CH_2)_3N$	149.19	hyg cr	21.2	277[150] 206–7[15]	1.1242[20]	1.4852[20]	∞	∞	δ		δ	chl s lig δ	B4[2], 729
a934	—,—,—,hydro-chloride	$(HOCH_2CH_2)_3N. HCl$	185.65	cr (al)	179–80				δ	δ s[h]					B4, 285
a935	—,trifurfuryl		257.29		fr in liq air	136 8[1]			i		s				B18[2], 418
a936	—,triheptyl	$[CH_3(CH_2)_6]_3N$	311.60			330[762] 151–4[1]			i	v	v			ac s	B4, 193
a937	—,trihexyl	$[CH_3(CH_2)_5]_3N$	269.52			263–4 119[15]			i	v	v			ac s	B4[2], 650
a938	—,triisobutyl	$[(CH_3)_2CHCH_2]_3N$	185.36		−21.8	191.5[760] 84[15]	0.7684[20]	1.4252[17]	i	v	∞				B4[2], 639
Ω a939	—,trimethyl	$(CH_3)_3N$	59.11	λ^{gas} 161 (3.4), 190.5 (3.59), 227 (2.95)	−117.2	2.87[760]	0.6709[0] 0.6356[20]	1.3631[0]	v	s	s	s	s	chl, to v	B4[2], 553
Ω a940	—,—hydrochloride	$(CH_3)_3N.HCl$	95.57	mcl dlq nd (al)	277–8d	sub at 200			s	s	i			chl s	B4[2], 555
a941	—,—,oxide	$(CH_3)_3NO$	75.11	hyg nd (w + 2)	255–7 (hyd) 96 (anh)				s	s	i		i	chl s[h]	B4[2], 556
a942	—,—,oxide hydrochloride	$(CH_3)_3NO.HCl$	111.57	nd (al)	218–20d				v	s[h]				MeOH s[h]	B4[2], 556
a943	—,—,oxide hydroiodide	$(CH_3)_3NO. HI$	203.02	pr (al)	130d				v	v	i				B4, 50
a944	—,—,perfluoro-	$(CF_3)_3N$	221.03			−7 to −6									J1951, 102
—	—,—,1,1′,1″-tricarboxy-	*see* Acetic acid, nitrilotri-													
a945	—,trioctadecyl	$[CH_3(CH_2)_{16}CH_2]_3N$	774.50		54.6					i	v		v	chl s	C34, 6221
Ω a946	—,tripentyl	$[CH_3(CH_2)_4]_3N$	227.44			240–5 130[14]	0.7907[20]	1.43665[20]	i	s	s			ac s	B4[2], 642
Ω a947	—,triphenyl	$(C_6H_5)_3N$	245.33	mcl (MeOH, AcOEt, bz) λ^{al} 297 (4.30)	127	365	0.774[0]	1.353[16]	i	δ s[h]	s		s	MeOH s[h]	B12[2], 106
Ω a948	—,tripropyl	$(CH_3CH_2CH_2)_3N$	143.28		−93.5	156[760]	0.7558[20]	1.4181[20]	δ	∞	∞				B4[2], 623
Ω a949	—,—,perfluoro-	$(CF_3CF_2CF_2)_3N$	521.07			130[760]	1.822[4]	1.279[25]							J1951, 102
a950	—,—,2,2′,2″-trihydroxy-	Triisopropanolamine. $[CH_3CH(OH)CH_2]_3N$	227.31		45	170–80[10]	1.02[20]		s	s					Am 73, 3635
a951	—,3,3′,4″-tritolyl		287.41	nd (al)	89–90				i	s				os v	B12[1], 415
a952	—,tri(4-tolyl)		287.41	cr (aa)	117					δ	s	s	v	con sulf s chl v sulf s lig δ	B12[2], 494
—	Aminometh-anamidine	*see* Guanidine													
—	Aminonaphtho-sulfonic acid	*see* 1-Naphthalenesulfonic acid, 4-amino-5-hydroxy-*													
Ω a953	Ammelide	6-Amino-s-triazine-2,4-diol* Cyanuromonoamide.	128.09	mcl pr (w) $\lambda^{w,pH}$ 222 (4.15), $\lambda^{w,pH=12}$ 226 (3.99)	d				δ[h]	i			i	dil sulf δ ac, alk s aa δ oos i	B26[2], 132
Ω a954	Ammeline	4,6-Diamino-s-triazin-2-ol* Cyanurodiamide.	127.11	nd aq (Na_2CO_3) $\lambda^{w,pH=7}$ 230 (3.88)	d				i	i	i		i	ac s alk s aa i	B26[2], 132
Ω a955	Ammonium, benzyl trimethyl, bromide	$C_6H_5CH_2N(CH_3)_3Br$	230.16	pl (al-lig), (w)	235				s[h]	s[h]					B12[2], 546
Ω a956	—,—,chloride	$C_6H_5CH_2N(CH_3)_3Cl$	185.70	(ace)	243				v			s[h]			B12[1], 448
Ω a957	—,—,iodide	$C_6H_5CH_2N(CH_3)_3I$	277.15	(al)	180					s					B12[1], 448
a958	—,—,nitrate	$C_6H_5CH_2N(CH_3)_3NO_3$	212.25		151–60				s	s					B12[2], 546
a959	—,dodecyl tri-methyl, chloride	$CH_3(CH_2)_{11}N(CH_3)_3Cl$	263.90		246d				v	v	i	v	i	MeOH v chl v	C55, 1442

For explanations, symbols and abbreviations see beginning of table. For structural formulas see end of table.

No.	Name	Synonyms and Formula	Mol. wt.	Color, crystalline form, specific rotation and λ_{max} (log ε)	m.p. °C	b.p. °C	Density	n_D	w	al	eth	ace	bz	other solvents	Ref.
	Ammonium														
Ω a960	—,phenyl trimethyl, bromide	$C_6H_5N(CH_3)_3Br$	216.13	hyg pr (al or al-eth)	213–4				v	s^h	i			aa s^h	B12², 88
a961	—,—,chloride	$C_6H_5N(CH_3)_3Cl$	171.67	hyg nd (al-eth) λ^{al} 255 (2.3)	d				s	v				chl δ	B12², 88
a962	—,—,iodide	$C_6H_5N(CH_3)_3I$	263.12	lf (al)	224 (216)				v	s		δ		chl i, $δ^h$ aa s	B12², 89
a963	—,propyl trimethyl, 2-acetoxy-chloride (D)	O-Acetyl-β-methylcholine chloride. $CH_3CH(O_2CCH_3)CH_2N(CH_3)_3Cl$	195.69	hyg, $[\alpha]_D$ +41.9	172–3	d			s	s	i				C30, 4541
a964	—,—,—,—(L)	$CH_3CH(O_2CCH_3)CH_2N(CH_3)_3Cl$	195.69	$[\alpha]_D$ −41.3	172–3	d			s						C32, 5583
a965	—,—,2-hydroxy-,chloride	β-Methylcholine chloride. $CH_3CH(OH)CH_2N(CH_3)_3Cl$	153.65	pr (BuOH)	165	d			s	s	i				C41, 989
—	—,purpurate	see **Murexide**													B4, 157
Ω a966	—,tetrabutyl, iodide	$[CH_3(CH_2)_3]_4NI$	369.38	lf (w or bz)	148				δ s^h	v				os s MeOH v	B4, 157
Ω a967	—,tetraethyl, bromide	$(CH_3CH_2)_4NBr$	210.17	dlq (al)			1.3970_4^{20}		v	v				chl v MeOH v	B4², 597
a968	—,—,hydroxide tetrahydrate	$(CH_3CH_2)_4NOH.4H_2O$	219.32	nd (w +4)	49–50	d (vac)			v	s					B4², 596
Ω a969	—,tetramethyl, bromide	$(CH_3)_4NBr$	154.06	dlq ditetr bipym	230d	(360 sub in vac)	1.56		v	δ	i		i	chl i MeOH s	B4², 558
Ω a970	—,—,chloride	$(CH_3)_4NCl$	109.60	dlq ditetr bipym (dil al)	420 (sealed tube) (d > 320)		1.169_4^{20}		s	δ	i		i	chl i MeOH v	B4², 557
a972	—,—,hydroxide, monohydrate	$(CH_3)_4NOH.H_2O$	109.17		130–5d without melting				s		i		i		B4, 50
a973	—,—,hydroxide, trihydrate	$(CH_3)_4NOH.3H_2O$	145.20		60				s		i		i		B4, 50
a974	—,—,hydroxide, pentahydrate	$(CH_3)_4NOH.5H_2O$	181.23	hyg nd	62–3	d			v ∞^h	v	i				B4², 557
Ω a975	—,—,iodide	$(CH_3)_4NI$	201.05	pr (w)	>230d (>355)		1.829		δ	δ	i	δ		chl i alk δ liq SO_2 s MeOH δ	B4², 558
a976	—,tetrapropyl, bromide	$(CH_3CH_2CH_2)_4NBr$	266.27		252 (cor)				s					chl s	J1929, 1291
Ω a977	—,—,iodide	$(CH_3CH_2CH_2)_4NI$	313.27	rh bipym	280d		1.3138_4^{25}		v	s	δ			chl v aa s MeOH v	B4², 624
a978	**Amphetamine** (d)	Dexedrine. β-Phenyl isopropylamine. $C_6H_5CH_2CH(NH_2)CH_3$	135.21	$[\alpha]_D^{15}$ +37.6 (bz, c = 8)		203–4 80¹⁰	0.949_4^{15}	1.4704^{20}	δ	s	s				B12², 621
a979	—(dl)	Benzedrine. $C_6H_5CH_2CH(NH_2)CH_3$	135.21			203⁷⁶⁰ 97²⁰	0.9306_4^{25}	1.518^{26}	δ	s				chl s	C49, 1537
a980	—,sulfate (d)	Dexedrine sulfate. $2(C_6H_5CH_2CH(NH_2)CH_3).H_2SO_4$	368.50	$[\alpha]_D^{20}$ +22 (w, c = 8)	d > 300		1.15_4^{25}		v	δ	i				C50, 4210
a981	—,—(dl)	Benzedrine sulfate. $2(C_6H_5CH_2CH(NH_2)CH_3).H_2SO_4$	368.50		280–1 (d >300)		1.15_4^{25}		v	δ	i				C49, 1537
Ω a982	**Amygdalin**	Amigdaloside. Mandelonitrile β-gentiobioside. $C_{20}H_{27}NO_{11}$.	457.44	$[\alpha]_D^{20}$ −42 (w, c = 1)	223–6 (216)				v^h s^h	δ	i			chl i	B31, 401
a983	—,trihydrate	$C_{20}H_{27}NO_{11}.3H_2O$. See a982	511.48	rh (w +3), $[\alpha]_D^{20}$ −40 (w, c = 1)	200 (remelts 125–30)				s ∞^h	δ s^h	i			chl i	B31, 400
—	**Amylamine**	see **Pentane, 1-amino-***													
—	**Amyl bromide**	see **Pentane, 1-bromo-***													
—	**Amyl chloride**	see **Pentane, 1-chloro-***													
—	**Amyl iodide**	see **Pentane, 1-iodo-***													
a984	**α-Amyrin**	α-Amyrenol. $C_{30}H_{50}O$.	426.74	nd (al), $[\alpha]_D^{17}$ +91.6 (bz, c = 1.3) +83.5 (chl) λ^{al} 207 (3.82)	186	243⁰·⁷				s^h	s		s	chl, aa s peth δ	E14s, 1067
a985	**β-Amyrin**	β-Amyrenol. $C_{30}H_{50}O$.	426.74	nd (lig or al), $[\alpha]_D^{19}$ +99.8 (bz, c = 1.3), +88.4 (chl) λ^{al} 207 (3.82)	197–7.5	260⁰·⁸			i	δ	s		s	chl s aa s lig δ	E14s, 946
—	**Amytal**	see **Barbituric acid, 5-ethyl-5-(3-methylbutyl)-**													
a986	**Anabasine** (l)	Neonicotine. l-2(3-Pyridyl)-piperidine. $C_{10}H_{14}N_2$.	162.24	darkens in air, $[\alpha]_D^{20}$ −83.1 λ^{al} 261 (3.46)	9	276⁷⁶⁰ 105²	1.0455_{20}^{20}	1.5430^{20}	∞	s	s		s		B23², 113
a988	**Anagyrine**	Monolupine. Rhombinine. $C_{15}H_{20}N_2O$.	244.34	pa ye glass, $[\alpha]_D^{25}$ −168 (al, c = 4.8)		260–70¹² 210–5⁴			s $δ^h$	v	s			chl v dil HCl v lig i	B24², 84
a989	**Analgen**	5-Benzamido-8-ethoxyquinoline. Benzanalgen. Chinalgen. Labordin. Quinolagen.	292.34	ye nd (al)	206				δ	δ s^h	δ			ac s	B22, 503

For explanations, symbols and abbreviations see beginning of table. For structural formulas see end of table.

No.	Name	Synonyms and Formula	Mol. wt.	Color, crystalline form, specific rotation and λ_{max} (log ε)	m.p. °C	b.p. °C	Density	n_D	w	al	eth	ace	bz	other solvents	Ref.
	Anatabine														
a990	Anatabine (l)	2(3-Pyridyl)-1,2,3,6-tetrahydropyridine. $C_{10}H_{12}N_2$	160.22	$[\alpha]_D^{17} -177.8$ $\lambda^{al} 262 (3.53)$		$145-6^{10}$	1.0911^{19}	1.5676^{20}	∞	s	s	...	s		C31, 3055
a991	Androstane	Etioallocholane.	260.47	lf(ace-MeOH or chl-ace) $[\alpha]_D^{16} +2$(chl, c = 1.2)	50–2	$75-80^{0.01}$ (sub $60^{0.003}$)			i	s	s	s	...	MeOH s chl s lig s	E14s, 1396
Ω a992	Androsterone	3α-Hydroxy-17-ketoandrostane. $C_{19}H_{30}O_2$	290.45	lf or nd (al, ace) $[\alpha]_D^{20} +94.6$ (abs al, c = 0.7) $\lambda^{con sulf}$ 305 (3.70), 412 (3.91), 485 (3.10)	185–5.5 (cor)				δ	s	s	s	s	os s	C46, 8136
a993	Anemonin	Anemone camphor. $C_{10}H_8O_4$	192.18	rh pl (chl), nd (al or bz)	158				δ s^h	δ s^h	i			chl s alk s lig δ	B19², 182
—	Anethole	see Benzene,1-methoxy-4-propenyl-*													
—	Angelic acid	see 2-Butenoic acid, 2-methyl-(cis)*													
a994	Anhalamine	$C_{11}H_{15}NO_3$	209.25	nd (al)	187–8				s^h	v^h i	δ	v	δ	chl δ^h peth δ	B21², 157
a995	Anhalonidine	$C_{12}H_{17}NO_3$	223.28	oct (bz, eth)	160–1				s	s	δ	...	s^h	chl s peth δ	B21², 157
a996	Anhalonine (d)	$C_{12}H_{15}NO_3$	221.26	$[\alpha]_D^{25} +56.7$ (chl)	84.5–5.5	$140^{0.02}$			s	s	v			chl s peth s	B27², 542
a997	—(dl)	$C_{12}H_{15}NO_3$. See a996	221.26	rh nd (peth)	85–5.5				s	s	v		v	chl v peth s	B27², 542
a998	—(l)	$C_{12}H_{15}NO_3$. See a996	221.26	nd (peth) $[\alpha]_D^{25} -56.3$ (chl, c = 4)	86	$140^{0.02}$			s	s	v			chl s peth s	B27², 542
a999	—,hydrochloride (l)	$C_{12}H_{15}NO_3 \cdot HCl$. See a996.	257.72	rh pr, $[\alpha]_D^{25} -40.5$(al)	254–5d				δ v^h	s	δ	...		chl δ	B27², 542
a1000	Anhydroecgonine (dl)	Ecgonidine. $C_9H_{13}NO_2$.	167.20	cr (MeOH, MeOH-eth), cr (w + 1)	226–30d				v	δ	δ		δ	chl δ lig δ	B22², 26
a1001	—,hydrochloride	Ecgonidine hydrochloride. $C_9H_{13}NO_2 \cdot HCl$. See a1000	203.66	rh nd (al + lw), ta (w) $[\alpha]_D^{15} -62.7$(w)	240–1				s^h	s	s				B22, 31
Ω a1002	Aniline	Aminobenzene. Phenylamine.	93.13	$\lambda^{al} 234.5 (3.90),$ 284.5 (3.23)	–6.3	184.13^{760} 68.3^{10}	1.02173^{20}_4	1.5863^{20}	s ∞^h	∞	∞	∞	∞	CCl_4 s lig s	B12², 44
Ω a1003	—,benzenesulfonate	$C_6H_5NH_2 \cdot C_6H_5SO_3H$	251.31	nd	240 δd (218)				v	v	i		i	CS_2 i	B12², 75
Ω a1004	—,hydrochloride	$C_6H_5NH_2 \cdot HCl$	129.60	lf or nd λ^{HCl} 243 (2.0), 248 (2.1), 254 (2.18), 260 (2.08)	198	245^{760}	1.2215^4		v	v	i		...	chl i	B12², 65
a1005	—,nitrate	$C_6H_5NH_2 \cdot HNO_3$	156.15	rh	d 190		1.356^4		v	v					B12², 66
a1006	—,oxalate (acid)	$C_6H_5NH_2 \cdot H_2C_2O_4$	183.17	ta (aq al)	150–1				v	v	v		v		B12², 73
a1007	—, (neutral)	$2(C_6H_5NH_2) \cdot H_2C_2O_4$	276.30	tcl pr (w)	174–5d				v	δ	i	δ			B12², 73
Ω a1008	—,phosphate	$C_6H_5NH_2 \cdot H_3PO_4$	191.13	nd (al), lf (w-al)	180				v	v	i				B12, 117
a1009	—,picrate		322.24	ye or red mcl pr (w), dk gr	181		1.558		δ	s			i		B12², 72
a1010	—,sulphate(acid)	$C_6H_5NH_2 \cdot H_2SO_4 \cdot \frac{1}{2}H_2O$	200.21	lf(w + $\frac{1}{2}$) $\lambda^{1N H_2SO_4}$ 244 (2.08), 256 (2.12), 259 (2.02)	162										B12², 66
Ω a1011	—,—(neutral)	$2(C_6H_5NH_2) \cdot H_2SO_4$	284.34	lf(al)	d		1.377^4		s	δ	i				B12², 66
a1012	—,3-acetamido-	N-Acetyl-m-phenylene-diamine. $C_8H_{10}N_2O$. See a1002	150.18	lf(ace-bz), nd or pl (bz)	87–9	d at 100			v	v	s	v	i		B13², 27
a1013	—,4-acetamido-, sulfate	N-Acetyl-p-phenylenediamine sulfate. $C_8H_{10}N_2O \cdot H_2SO_4$.	248.26	nd (oth al)	283d				v	v	i				B13, 95
Ω a1014	—,N-allyl-	$CH_2:CHCH_2NHC_6H_5$	133.20	ye		$217-9^{736}$ $105-8^{12}$	0.9822^5_4	1.5630^{20}	δ	s	∞	s			B12², 96
—	—,N-benzyl-	see Amine, benzyl phenyl													
Ω a1015	—,N-benzylidene-	Benzalaniline. $C_6H_5CH:NC_6H_5$	181.24	pa ye nd (CS₂), pl (dil al) $\lambda^{al} 238 (3.98),$ 262 (4.24), 306 sh (3.95)	54 (51–2)	310	1.038^{55}_4	1.600^{99}	i	s	s			liq SO_2, NH_3 s	B12², 113
Ω a1016	—,2-bromo-	C_6H_6BrN. See a1002	172.03	$\lambda^{cy} 235 (3.93),$ 289 (3.48)	32 (fr 28.7)	229^{760} 110.5^{19}	1.578^{20}_4	1.6113^{20}_4	i	s	s				B12², 341
Ω a1017	—,3-bromo-	C_6H_6BrN. See a1002	172.03	$\lambda^{cy} 237.5 (3.89),$ 290 (3.38)	18.5 (fr 16.7)	251^{760} 130^{12}	$1.5793^{20.4}$	$1.6260^{20.4}$	δ	s	s				B12², 342

For explanations, symbols and abbreviations see beginning of table. For structural formulas see end of table.

No.	Name	Synonyms and Formula	Mol. wt.	Color. crystalline form. specific rotation and λ_{max} (log ε)	m.p. °C	b.p. °C	Density	n_D	w	al	eth	ace	bz	other solvents	Ref.

Aniline

No.	Name	Synonyms and Formula	Mol. wt.	Color etc.	m.p.	b.p.	Density	n_D	w	al	eth	ace	bz	other	Ref.
Ω a1018	—,4-bromo-	C_6H_6BrN. See a1002	172.03	rh bipym, nd (60 % al) λ^{al} 245 (4.12), 296.5 (3.20)	66.4	d	1.4970_4^{100}		i	s	s				B12², 344
a1019	—,2-bromo-4,6-dichloro-	$C_6H_4BrCl_2N$. See a1002	240.92	nd (al)	83.5	273⁷⁶⁰				v			v	chl v	B12², 355
a1020	—,4-bromo-2,3-dichloro-	$C_6H_4BrCl_2N$. See a1002	240.92	nd	77.5					v	v		v		B12, 653
a1021	—,4-bromo-2,5-dichloro-	$C_6H_4BrCl_2N$. See a1002	240.92	nd	91					v	v				B12, 654
Ω a1022	—,4-bromo-3,5-dichloro-	$C_6H_4BrCl_2N$. See a1002	240.92	nd (w + al)	129				s^h	v			v	chl v	B12, 654
a1023	—,3-bromo-N,N-diethyl-	$C_{10}H_{14}BrN$. See a1002	228.14			142¹⁰				s		s			B12¹, 315
Ω a1024	—,4-bromo-N,N-diethyl-	$C_{10}H_{14}BrN$. See a1002	228.14	nd or pr	33	270			i	v	v				B12², 347
Ω a1025	—,2-bromo-N,N-dimethyl-	$C_8H_{10}BrN$. See a1002	200.09	λ^{hp} 188 (4.6), 216 (4.2), 255 (3.7)		107–8¹⁴	1.3880_{25}^{25}	1.5748^{25}		v					B12¹, 313
a1026	—,3-bromo-N,N-dimethyl-	$C_8H_{10}BrN$. See a1002	200.09	λ^{cy} 254 (4.11), 303 (3.43)	11	259 (cor) 126¹⁴				v				aa v con ac s	B12², 343
Ω a1027	—,4-bromo-N,N-dimethyl-	$C_8H_{10}BrN$. See a1002	200.09	lf (al) λ^{cy} 260 (4.29), 310 (3.34)	55 (58)	264⁷⁶⁰			i	s	v			os s	B12², 345
a1028	—,2-bromo-3,5-dinitro-	$C_6H_4BrN_3O_4$. See a1002	262.03	ye lf (al)	181				δ v^h					HNO₃ s	B12, 762
a1029	—,2-bromo-4,5-dinitro-	$C_6H_4BrN_3O_4$. See a1002	262.03	pa ye (al)	186				v^h						B12, 762
Ω a1030	—,2-bromo-4,6-dinitro-	$C_6H_4BrN_3O_4$. See a1002	262.03	ye nd (aa or al)	153–4	sub				v^h		v^h		aa s^h	B12², 418
a1030ˢ	—,4-bromo-2,5-dinitro-	$C_6H_4BrN_3O_4$. See a1002	262.03	ye cr (al)	186				v^h						B12, 761
a1031	—,4-bromo-2,6-dinitro-	$C_6H_4BrN_3O_4$. See a1002	262.03	og-red pl (abs al)	163 (cor) (160)				v^h						B12², 418
a1032	—,5-bromo-2,4-dinitro-	$C_6H_4BrN_3O_4$. See a1002	262.03	pa ye nd (dil al)	178.4					v	v		v	chl v	B12², 417
a1033	—,6-bromo-2,3-dinitro-	$C_6H_4BrN_3O_4$. See a1002	262.03	dk red cr (al)	158				v^h						B12, 760
Ω a1034	—,2-bromo-4-nitro-	$C_6H_5BrN_2O_2$. See a1002	217.03	ye nd (al)	104.5					s				aa v	B12², 403
Ω a1035	—,2-bromo-5-nitro-	$C_6H_5BrN_2O_2$. See a1002	217.03	pa ye nd (al)	141					s	v		v	chl v lig δ	B12², 402
a1036	—,3-bromo-4-nitro-	$C_6H_5BrN_2O_2$. See a1002	217.03	ye nd (al)	175–6					v			i	chl, lig i	B12², 403
a1037	—,4-bromo-2-nitro-	$C_6H_5BrN_2O_2$. See a1002	217.03	og-ye nd (w)	111.5	sub			δ s^h	v					B12², 401
a1038	—,4-bromo-3-nitro-	$C_6H_5BrN_2O_2$. See a1002	217.03	nd (al)	132					s	s			chl, aa s	B12², 402
a1039	—,5-bromo-2-nitro-	$C_6H_5BrN_2O_2$. See a1002	217.03	red-ye nd (dil al)	151–2					v				aa v	B12², 402
a1040	—,6-bromo-2-nitro-	$C_6H_5BrN_2O_2$. See a1002	217.03	og or ye nd (dil al)	74–5		1.988								B12², 402
Ω a1041	—,N-butyl-	N-Phenylbutylamine. $C_6H_5NHCH_2CH_2CH_2CH_3$	149.24	λ^{iso} 245 (4.16), 295 (3.36)	−14.4	241.6⁷⁶⁰ 118–20¹⁵	0.93226_4^{20}	1.53412^{20}	δ	v	s				B12², 95
Ω a1042	—,N-sec-butyl-	$C_6H_5NHCH(CH_3)CH_2CH_3$	149.24			225⁷⁵⁹ 112–4²²		1.5333^{20}						os s	B12², 96
a1043	—,2-chloro-(α)	C_6H_6ClN. See a1002	127.57	λ^{al} 237 (3.8), 291 (3.3)	−14	208.84	1.21253_4^{20}	1.58951^{20}	i	∞	s	s		os s	B12², 314
a1044	—,(β)	C_6H_6ClN. See a1002	127.57	λ^{al} 236 (3.8), 291 (3.3)	−1.9	208.84⁷⁶⁰ 84.6¹⁰	1.21266_4^{20}	1.5889^{20}	i	∞	s	s	∞	CCl_4 ∞ os s	B12², 314
a1045	—,—,hydrochloride	$C_6H_6ClN·HCl$. See a1002	164.04	pl (w, aq al)	235		1.505^{18}		s	δ					B12², 315
Ω a1046	—,3-chloro-	C_6H_6ClN. See a1002	127.57	λ^{al} 240 (3.8), 292 (3.3)	−10.3	229.92⁷⁶⁰ 101.2¹⁰	1.21606_4^{20}	1.59414^{20}	i	∞	∞	∞	∞	CCl_4 ∞ os s	B12², 319
Ω a1047	—,—,hydrochloride	$C_6H_6ClN·HCl$. See a1002	164.04	pl	221.5–2.5				v	v					B12², 320
Ω a1048	—,4-chloro-	C_6H_6ClN. See a1002	127.57	rh pr λ^{al} 242 (3.9), 295 (3.2)	72.5	232⁷⁶⁰	1.429_4^{19}	1.5546^{87}	s^h	s	s	s		os s	B12², 322
Ω a1049	—,4-chloro-N,N-diethyl-	$C_{10}H_{14}ClN$. See a1002	183.68	nd (al)	45.5–6.5	251–3 95–6¹·⁵				s^h					B12², 324
a1050	—,4-chloro-N,N-dimethyl-	$C_8H_{10}ClN$. See a1002	155.63	nd (al) λ^{cy} 257 (4.17), 308 (3.30)	35.5	231 (233–6)				s^h					B12¹, 304
a1051	—,4-chloro-N,N-dimethyl-3-nitro-	$C_8H_9ClN_2O_2$. See a1002	200.63	ye nd (dil al)	81.5–2.5					s				lig s	B12, 732
a1052	—,3-chloro-2,6-dinitro-	$C_6H_4ClN_3O_4$. See a1002	217.57	og-ye nd (al)	112					s^h					B12², 416
Ω a1053	—,4-chloro-2,6-dinitro-	$C_6H_4ClN_3O_4$. See a1002	217.57	og-ye nd (al)	147 (cor)					s^h					B12², 416

For explanations, symbols and abbreviations see beginning of table. For structural formulas see end of table.

No.	Name	Synonyms and Formula	Mol. wt.	Color, crystalline form, specific rotation and λ_{max} (log ε)	m.p. °C	b.p. °C	Density	n_D	w	al	eth	ace	bz	other solvents	Ref.
	Aniline														
a1054	—,5-chloro-2-ethoxy-	5-Chloro-o-phenetidine. $C_8H_{10}ClNO$. See a1002	171.63	nd (dil al)	42	....			δ	ε	...	...	s	chl s	B13, 383
a1055	—,2-chloro-N-ethyl-	$C_8H_{10}ClN$. See a1002	155.63			219^{726}	1.104^{25}_4								B12², 316
a1056	—,4-chloro-2-methoxy-	4-Chloro-o-anisidine. C_7H_8ClNO. See a1002	157.61	nd or pr (dil al)	52	260^{760}				s	s		s	....	B13², 184
Ω a1057	—,5-chloro-2-methoxy-	5-Chloro-o-anisidine. C_7H_8ClNO. See a1002	157.61	nd (dil al)	84					s				lig δ	B13², 183
Ω a1058	—,2-chloro-4-nitro-	$C_6H_5ClN_2O_2$. See a1002	172.57	ye nd (lig-CS_2, w, 20 % aa)	108	....			δ	v	v			CS_2 v lig i	B12², 398
a1059	—,3-chloro-4-nitro-	$C_6H_5ClN_2O_2$. See a1002	172.57	ye lf (bz) λ^{al} 233 (3.79), 374 (4.13)	156–7					s	s			aa s lig, CS_2 i	B12², 398
Ω a1060	—,4-chloro-2-nitro-	$C_6H_5ClN_2O_2$. See a1002	172.57	dk og-ye pr (dil al), nd (lig, w) λ^{aa} 410 (3.7)	116–7					v	v			aa v lig δ	B12², 396
Ω a1061	—,4-chloro-3-nitro-	$C_6H_5ClN_2O_2$. See a1002	172.57	ye nd or pr (w), nd (peth)	103				s^h	v				chl s lig δ	B12², 397
a1062	—,5-chloro-2-nitro-	$C_6H_5ClN_2O_2$. See a1002	172.57	gold-ye nd (CS_2), ye lf (al, bz)	126.5	sub				s	s			lig CS, δ dil aa s	B12², 397
a1063	—,5-chloro-3-nitro-	$C_6H_5ClN_2O_2$. See a1002	172.57	og-ye nd (al)	133–4	....			s^h	s				aa s	B12, 732
a1064	—,6-chloro-2-nitro-	$C_6H_5ClN_2O_2$. See a1002	172.57	ye nd (dil al) λ^{cy} 231.5 (4.22), 275 (3.74), 382 (3.76)	76						s			50 % al s	B12², 397
a1065	—,6-chloro-3-nitro-	$C_6H_5ClN_2O_2$. See a1002	172.57	ye nd (lig)	121					s	s	s		aa v CS_2, lig δ	B12², 398
a1066	—,N-cyclohexyl-	Cyclohexylphenylamine.	175.28	mcl pr	16	279^{764} $134–5^6$	1.0155^{20}_4	1.5610^{20}	i	s	s		s	....	B12², 98
a1067	—,2,3-dibromo-	$C_6H_5Br_2N$. See a1002	250.93	pl (dil al)	43				δ	s	s		...	aa v AcOEt s	B12, 655
Ω a1068	—,2,4-dibromo-	$C_6H_5Br_2N$. See a1002	250.93	rh bipym (chl), nd or lf (dil al)	79.5–80.5	156^{24}	2.260^{20}			s	s			aa s chl s^h	B12², 356
Ω a1069	—,2,5-dibromo-	$C_6H_5Br_2N$. See a1002	250.93	pr (al)	53–5					v	s				B12², 357
Ω a1070	—,2,6-dibromo-	$C_6H_5Br_2N$. See a1002	250.93	nd (al) λ^w 293 (3.45)	87–8 (83–4)	262–4				v	v	...	v	chl v	B12², 357
a1071	—,3,4-dibromo-	$C_6H_5Br_2N$. See a1002	250.93	lf (dil al)	81	100 sub				s^h					B12¹, 329
a1072	—,3,5-dibromo-	$C_6H_5Br_2N$. See a1002	250.93	nd (dil al) λ^{al} 212 (4.5), 250 (4.0), 305 (3.5)	57					v	v		v		B12², 357
a1073	—,2,4-dibromo-6-nitro-	$C_6H_4Br_2N_2O_2$. See a1002	295.93	ye cr	128	....									B12², 403
Ω a1074	—,2,6-dibromo-4-nitro-	$C_6H_4Br_2N_2O_2$. See a1002	295.93	ye nd (al or aa)	207				δ					aa s	B12², 404
Ω a1075	—,N,N-dibutyl- ...	$C_6H_5N(CH_2CH_2CH_2CH_3)_2$	205.34	λ^{iso} 259 (4.25), 304 (3.41)	−32.20	274.8^{760} 138.8^{10}	0.9037^{20}_4	1.5186^{20}	i	∞	∞	v	v	ac s	B12², 95
Ω a1076	—,2,3-dichloro-	$C_6H_5Cl_2N$. See a1002	162.02	nd (lig)	24	252				s	v	s	δ	lig δ	B12, 621
a1077	—,2,4-dichloro-	$C_6H_5Cl_2N$. See a1002	162.02	pr (ace), nd (dil al), (lig)	63–4	245^{759}	1.567^{20}		δ	s	s				B12², 333
Ω a1078	—,2,5-dichloro-	$C_6H_5Cl_2N$. See a1002	162.02	nd (lig) λ^w 293 (2.45)	50	251			δ	s	s		s	CS_2 s	B12², 336
Ω a1079	—,3,4-dichloro-	$C_6H_5Cl_2N$. See a1002	162.02	nd (lig)	72	272 145^{15}				s	s		δ		B12², 337
Ω a1080	—,3,5-dichloro-	$C_6H_5Cl_2N$. See a1002	162.02	nd (lig, dil al)	51–3	260^{741}			i	s	s			lig s^h	B12², 337
a1081	—,2,6-dichloro-4-ethoxy-	4-Amino-3,5-dichloro-phenetole. $C_8H_9Cl_2NO$. See a1002	206.07	nd (dil al)	46	275			δ	v	v	v		chl v	B13², 276
a1082	—,3,5-dichloro-4-ethoxy-	4-Amino-2,6-dichloro-phenetole. $C_8H_9Cl_2NO$. See a1002	206.07	nd (peth)	105–7					v	v		v	aa δ	B13², 275
a1083	—,N-dichloromethylene-	Phenyliminophosgene. Phenylisocyanide dichloride. $C_6H_5N:CCl_2$	174.04	oil	19,5	210^{760} 96^{19}	1.205^{15}								B12², 245
Ω a1084	—,2,6-dichloro-4-nitro-	Dichloran. $C_6H_4Cl_2N_2O_2$. See a1002	207.02	ye nd (al, aa) λ^{bp} 240 (3.90), 322 (4.16)	191						s			ac s	B12², 400
Ω a1085	—,N,N-diethyl-	Diethylphenylamine. $C_6H_5N(C_2H_5)_2$	149.24	ye oil λ^{iso} 259 (4.22), 303 (3.38)	−38.8	216.27 92^{10}	0.93507^{20}_4	1.5409^{20}	δ	s	v	s		chl v	B12², 92
a1086	—,N,N-diethyl-2-ethoxy-	N,N-Diethyl-o-phenetidine. $C_{12}H_{19}NO$. See a1002	193.29	....		231–3			i	∞	∞	...	∞	chl, CS_2 ∞	B13, 365
a1087	—,N,N-diethyl-3-ethoxy-	N,N-Diethyl-m-phenetidine. $C_{12}H_{19}NO$. See a1002	193.29	λ^{al} 236 (3.97), 400 (4.33)	....	268–70 (288) 145^{14}		1.5325^{25}	...	s			s	aa s	B13¹, 131

For explanations, symbols and abbreviations see beginning of table. For structural formulas see end of table.

No.	Name	Synonyms and Formula	Mol. wt.	Color, crystalline form, specific rotation and λ_{max} (log ε)	m.p. °C	b.p. °C	Density	n_D	Solubility						Ref.
									w	al	eth	ace	bz	other solvents	
	Aniline														
a1088	—,N,N-diethyl-3-nitro-	$C_{10}H_{14}N_2O_2$. See a1002	194.24	ye	....	288–90			i	...	...	...	...		**B12**[1], 346
a1089	—,N,N-diethyl-4-nitro-	$C_{10}H_{14}N_2O_2$. See a1002	194.24	ye nd (lig), pl (al) λ^{al} 236 (3.93), 316 (3.26), 393.5 (4.34)	77–8	....	1.225		...	s^h	...	...	...	lig δ	**B12**[1], 351
Ω a1090	—,N,N-diethyl-4-nitroso-	$C_{10}H_{14}N_2O$. See a1002	178.24	gr mcl pr (eth), gr lf (ace) λ^{al} 236.5 (3.50), 275 (3.73), 425 (4.51)	87–8	....	1.24_4^{15}		δ	s	s	s^h	...	....	**B12**[2], 365
a1091	—,2,4-diiodo-	$C_6H_5I_2N$. See a1002.......	344.92	br nd or rh cr (al)	95–6		2.748		δ s^h	s v^h	v	v	s	chl, CS_2 v lig s	**B12**, 675
a1092	—,2,5-diiodo-	$C_6H_5I_2N$. See a1002.......	344.92	nd (al)	88–9	....				s	v	s	...	os s	**B12**, 675
a1093	—,2,6-diiodo-	$C_6H_5I_2N$. See a1002.......	344.92	nd (al)	122					s	s	s	s	os s	**B12**, 675
a1094	—,3,4-diiodo-	$C_6H_5I_2N$. See a1002.......	344.92	pa ye lf or pr (bz-peth)	74.5					s	s	...	s	peth δ	**B12**, 675
a1095	—,3,5-diiodo-	$C_6H_5I_2N$. See a1002.......	344.92	nd (al)	110 (107)					s	s	...	...	chl s	**B12**[1], 377
a1096	—,2,4-diiodo-3-nitro-	$C_6H_4I_2N_2O_2$. See a1002	389.92	pa ye mcl pl	125					v	...	...	...	os v lig δ	**B12**, 747
a1097	—,2,6-diiodo-3-nitro-	$C_6H_4I_2N_2O_2$. See a1002	389.92	ye nd (dil al)	145.5 (149)					v	...	...	...	os s AcOEt δ	**B12**, 747
Ω a1098	—,2,6-diiodo-4-nitro-	$C_6H_4I_2N_2O_2$. See a1002	389.92	pa ye lf or nd (bz)	245 (248)					δ^h	...	s^h	...	....	**B12**[2], 405
a1099	—,4,6-diiodo-2-nitro-	$C_6H_4I_2N_2O_2$. See a1002	389.92	ye nd (ace)	154	....			δ	δ	s	s^h	...	chl s, aa s	**B12**[1], 361
a1100	—,4,6-diiodo-3-nitro-	$C_6H_4I_2N_2O_2$. See a1002	389.92	pa ye nd (eth-al)	149					δ^h	s	...	...	....	**B12**, 747
a1101	—,2,3-dimethoxy-	3-Aminoveratrole. $C_8H_{11}NO_2$. See a1002	153.18		....	137^{15}			s	...	...	...	...	:	**B13**[2], 464
Ω a1102	—,2,4-dimethoxy-	4-Aminoresorcinol dimethyl ether. $C_8H_{11}NO_2$. See a1002	153.18	pl (lig)	33.5 (cor) (39–40)				δ	s	s	...	s	lig s^h	**B13**[2], 470
a1103	—,2,6-dimethoxy-	2-Aminoresorcinol dimethyl ether. $C_8H_{11}NO_2$. See a1002	153.18	pl (al), lf (peth)	75	146^{23}			δ	v	v	...	v	aa v lig s	**B13**[2], 468
Ω a1104	—,3,4-dimethoxy-	4-Aminoveratrole. $C_8H_{11}NO_2$. See a1002	153.18	lf (eth)	87–8 (90)					...	s^h	...	...	....	**B13**[2], 465
Ω a1105	—,N,N-dimethyl-	$C_6H_5N(CH_3)_2$	121.18	pa ye λ^{al} 235 (4.1), 251 (4.11), 293 (3.2)	2.45 (fp 1.96)	194.15^{760} 77^{13}	0.9557_4^{20}	1.5582^{20}	δ	s	s	s	s	chl v os s	**B12**[2], 82
a1106	—,—,hydrochloride	$C_6H_5N(CH_3)_2 \cdot HCl$.	157.65	hyg pl (w), (bz)	85–95		1.1156_4^{19}		s	s	i	...	δ	chl s	**B12**[2], 86
a1107	—,—,N,N-dimethyl-,N-oxide	$C_6H_5N(:O)(CH_3)_2$.........	137.18	pr λ^{al} 248 (2.4), 282 sh (0.8)	152–3				v	v	v	...	...	chl v	**B12**[2], 88
a1108	—,N,N-dimethyl-2-nitro-	$C_8H_{10}N_2O_2$. See a1002	166.18	ye-og λ^{al} 246 (4.1), 273 sh (3.4), 429 (3.3)	fp-20	146^{20}	1.1794_4^{20}	1.6102^{20}	s	v^h	s	...	...	chl v	**B12**[2], 369
Ω a1109	—,N,N-dimethyl-3-nitro-	$C_8H_{10}N_2O_2$. See a1002	166.18	og-ye or red mcl pr (eth or eth-al) λ^{al} 249 (4.3), 405 (3.2)	60–1	$280–5^{760}$	1.313^{17}	....	i	s	s	...	...	....	**B12**[2], 377
Ω a1110	—,N,N-dimethyl-4-nitro-	$C_8H_{10}N_2O_2$. See a1002	166.18	ye nd (al) λ^{al} 232 (3.96), 314 (3.27), 392 (4.30)	164.5				i	s^h	s	...	...	aa s^h	**B12**[2], 386
Ω a1111	—,N,N-dimethyl-4-nitroso-	Accelerene. $C_8H_{10}N_2O$. See a1002	150.18	gr pl (eth) λ^{al} 234 (3.67), 273 (3.82), 305 (3.18), 314 (3.14)	92.5–3.5		1.145^{20}	....	δ	s	s	...	...	$HCONH_2$ s	**B12**[2], 364
a1112	—,4-dimethyl-amino-N(2,4,6-trinitrobenzylidene)-	....	359.30	bk gr lf ($PhCO_2Et$), nd($PhNO_2$ +1)	268 exp				i	...	...	δ	δ	chl, AcOEt, aa δ	**B13**, 85
Ω a1113	—,2,4-dinitro-	$C_6H_5N_3O_4$. See a1002	183.12	ye nd (dil ace), gr-ye ta (al) λ^{aa} 257 (3.79), 335 (2.94)	180 (188)		1.615^{14}	....	i δ^h	δ	s	...	...	HCl s^h	**B12**[2], 405
Ω a1114	—,2,6-dinitro-	$C_6H_5N_3O_4$. See a1002	183.12	gold lf (50 % aa), ye nd (al) λ^{cy} 223 (4.43), 249 (4.15), 307 (2.98), 408 (3.99)	141–2				i	δ	s	...	s^h	lig i	**B12**[2], 413
Ω a1115	—,N,N-dipropyl-	$C_6H_5N(CH_2CH_2CH_3)_2$.....	177.29	lt ye	....	245^{760} 127^{10}	0.9104^{20}	1.5271^{20}	i	s	s	s	s	....	**B12**[2], 95
Ω a1116	—,2-ethoxy-	o-Aminophenetole. o-Phenetidine. $C_8H_{11}NO$. See a1002	137.18	....	< −21	232.5^{760} $127–8^{14}$		1.5560^{20}	δ	s	s	...	...	....	**B13**[2], 166

For explanations, symbols and abbreviations see beginning of table. For structural formulas see end of table.

No.	Name	Synonyms and Formula	Mol. wt.	Color, crystalline form, specific rotation and λ_{max} (log ε)	m.p. °C	b.p. °C	Density	n_D	w	al	eth	ace	bz	other solvents	Ref.
	Aniline														
a1117	—,3-ethoxy-	m-Aminophenetole. m-Phenetidine. $C_8H_{11}NO$. *See* a1002	137.18	....		248[760] 127–8[11]			δ	s	s			....	B13[2], 211
Ω a1118	—,4-ethoxy-	p-Aminophenetole. p-Phenetidine. $C_8H_{11}NO$. *See* a1002	137.18	....	2.4	254[760] 125[12]	1.0652[16]4	1.5528[20]	δ	s	s			....	B13[2], 224
a1119	—,4-ethoxy-N-(2-hydroxy-benzylidene)-	N-Salicylidene-p-phenetidine. Malakin.	241.29	pa ye or grsh pl or nd (al)	94 (92)	....			i	s[h]	s		s	....	B13[2], 241
a1120	—,2-ethoxy-4-nitro-	4-Nitro-o-phenetidine. $C_8H_{10}N_2O_3$. *See* a1002	182.18	ye nd (dil al)	91				δ	s	s	s		lig δ	B13, 390
a1121	—,2-ethoxy-5-nitro-	5-Nitro-o-phenetidine. $C_8H_{10}N_2O_3$. *See* a1002	182.18	ye nd (dil al)	96–7	205–6[14]			δ	s	s	s		....	B13[2], 192
a1122	—,2-ethoxy-6-nitro-	6-Nitro-o-phenetidine. $C_8H_{10}N_2O_3$. *See* a1002	182.18	ye or og cr (w)	60				s[h]					....	B13, 388
a1123	—,3-ethoxy-4-nitro-	4-Nitro-m-phenetidine. $C_8H_{10}N_2O_3$. *See* a1002	182.18	nd (dil al)	122–3				δ	s	s	s	s	os s lig i	B13[1], 137
a1124	—,4-ethoxy-2-nitro-	2-Nitro-p-phenetidine. $C_8H_{10}N_2O_3$. *See* a1002	182.18	red pr (al)	113					δ g[h]	v			chl v	B13[2], 286
a1125	—,4-ethoxy-3-nitro-	3-Nitro-p-phenetidine. $C_8H_{10}N_2O_3$. *See* a1002	182.18	og ye nd (bz, to-lig, dil al)	41				δ^h			s	s	os v lig i	B13[2], 284
a1126	—,5-ethoxy-2-nitro-	6-Nitro-m-phenetidine. $C_8H_{10}N_2O_3$. *See* a1002	182.18	ye nd (dil al)	105–6				i	s[h]		s	s	os s	B13[1], 136
a1127	—,5-ethoxy-3-nitro-	5-Nitro-m-phenetidine. $C_8H_{10}N_2O_3$. *See* a1002	182.18	ye, og-red nd (al)	115				δ	v		s	s	os s	B13, 422
Ω a1128	—,N-ethyl-	Ethyl phenylamine. $C_6H_5NHC_2H_5$	121.18	λ^{iso} 245 (4.12), 294 (3.35)	−63.5	204.72[760] 97.5–8[18]	0.9625[20]4	1.5559[20]	i v[h]	∞	∞	v	v	os s	B12[2], 90
Ω a1129	—,—,hydrochloride	$C_6H_5NHC_2H_5 \cdot HCl$	157.65	nd	178.5 (176)	....	1.0085[182]4		s	s	i		chl s	B12[2], 91
a1130	—,N-ethyl-N-methyl-	$C_6H_5N(CH_3)C_2H_5$	135.21	....		203–5[760] 93–5[12]	0.9193[55]		i	∞	∞			....	B12[2], 91
a1131	—,N-ethyl-N-nitroso-	$C_6H_5N(NO)C_2H_5$	150.18	yesh λ^{al} 272 (3.80)		130[20]	1.0874[20]4	1.55977[20]	i					aa s	B12, 580
Ω a1132	—,2-fluoro-	C_6H_6FN. *See* a1002	111.12	pa ye λ^{cy} 234 (4.00), 283 (3.26)	−28.5	174.5–6[757] 58[11]	1.1513[21]	1.5421[20]	i	s	s			....	B12[2], 314
Ω a1133	—,3-fluoro-	C_6H_6FN. *See* a1002	111.12	pa ye		187–9[760] 82.3[18]	1.1561[19]	1.5436[20]	δ	s	s			....	B12[2], 314
Ω a1134	—,4-fluoro-	C_6H_6FN. *See* a1002	111.12	pa ye λ^{cy} 230 (3.85), 293 (3.34), 296 (3.34), 300 sh (3.32)	−0.8	180.5– 2.5[757] 85[19]	1.1725[20]4	1.5195[20]4	δ	s	s			....	B12[2], 314
Ω a1135	—,N-formyl-N-methyl-	N-Methylformanilide. $C_6H_5N(CHO)CH_3$	135.17	λ^{hp} 240 (4.00)	14–5	243[760] 131[22]	1.0948[20]4	1.5589[20]	i	s	s	s	s	....	B12[2], 136
—	—,N(2-hydroxy-ethyl)-N-methyl)-	*see* Ethanol, 2[methyl (phenyl)amino]-*													
—	—,p,p′-iminodi-	*see* Amine, diphenyl, diamino-													
Ω a1136	—,2-iodo-	C_6H_6IN. *See* a1002	219.03	nd (dil al) λ^{cy} 237 (3.92), 292 (3.51)	60–1	....			δ	v	v	s		os s	B12[2], 360
Ω a1137	—,3-iodo-	C_6H_6IN. *See* a1002	219.03	lf or nd λ^{cy} 232 sh (4.02), 239 (3.94), 292 (3.43), 299 (3.34)	33	280 145–6[15]		1.6811[20]	i	s				chl s	B12[2], 360
Ω a1138	—,4-iodo-	C_6H_6IN. *See* a1002	219.03	nd (w) λ^{al} 250 (4.27)	67–8	....			δ	s	s			os s peth δ	B12[2], 361
a1139	—,N-isobutyl-	$C_6H_5NHCH_2CH(CH_3)_2$	149.24	$\lambda^{dil\ al-HCl}$ 248 (2.29), 254 (2.34), 260 (2.20)		231–2[760] (225–7) 109– 10[13]	0.9400[18]4	1.5328[20]	i		v	v		....	B12[2], 96
Ω a1140	—,N-isopropyl-	$C_6H_5NHCH(CH_3)_2$	135.21	$\lambda^{dil\ al-HCl}$ 248 (2.19), 254 (2.27), 260 (2.13)		203–4[760] 72–5[14]		1.5380[20]		s	s	s	s	....	B12[2], 95
Ω a1141	—,2-mercapto-	2-Aminothiophenol. C_6H_7NS. *See* a1002	125.19	nd	26	234 125–7[6]		1.4606[20]		s				....	B13[2], 198
a1142	—,3-mercapto-	3-Aminothiophenol. C_6H_7NS. *See* a1002	125.19	....		180–90[16]				v	i			aa s peth i	B13[1], 140
a1143	—,—,hydrochloride	$C_6H_7NS \cdot HCl$. *See* a1002	161.66		232	sub			v	v				....	B13, 425
a1144	—,4-mercapto-	4-Aminothiophenol. C_6H_7NS. *See* a1002	125.19	cr	46	140–5[15]			s	s				....	B13[2], 296
a1145	—,2-methoxy-	o-Anisidine. C_7H_9NO. *See* a1002	123.16	λ^{al} 236 (3.87), 286 (3.47)	6.22	224[760] 90[4]	1.0923[20]	1.5713[20]	δ	s	s	s	s	....	B13[2], 165
a1146	—,3-methoxy-	m-Anisidine. C_7H_9NO. *See* a1002	123.16	λ^{al} 236 (3.89), 286 (3.40)	−1–1	251 (cor)	1.096[20]2	1.5794[20]	δ	s	s	s		....	B13[2], 211

For explanations, symbols and abbreviations see beginning of table. For structural formulas see end of table.

Aniline

No.	Name	Synonyms and Formula	Mol. wt.	Color, crystalline form, specific rotation and λ_{max} (log ε)	m.p. °C	b.p. °C	Density	n_D	w	al	eth	ace	bz	other solvents	Ref.
a1147	—,4-methoxy-	p-Anisidine. C_7H_9NO. See a1002	123.16	ta (w), rh pl λ^{al} 235 (3.97), 300 (3.35)	57.2	243 (cor) 115[13]	1.071^{37}_4	1.5559^{67}	s	v	v	s	s	....	B13[2], 223
a1148	—,—,hydrochloride	$C_7H_9NO \cdot HCl$. See a1002	159.62	lf, nd	236	....	....	....	s	s	s	...	...	....	B13[2], 223
a1149	—,2-methoxy-4-nitro-	4-Nitro-o-anisidine. $C_7H_8N_2O_3$. See a1002	168.16	pa ye nd (dil al)	139–40	....	1.2112^{156}	....	...	v	...	v	...	....	B13[2], 194
a1150	—,2-methoxy-5-nitro-	5-Nitro-o-anisidine. $C_7H_8N_2O_3$. See a1002	168.16	og-red nd (al, eth, w) $\lambda^{w,pH=7}$ 219 (3.90), 257 (3.78), 310 sh (3.38), 400 (4.09)	118	....	1.2068^{156}	....	s^h	v	s^h	v	v^h	AcOEt, aa v lig δ	B13[2], 192
a1151	—,2-methoxy-6-nitro-	6-Nitro-o-anisidine. $C_7H_8N_2O_3$. See a1002	168.16	ye, pa red nd (al) λ^{cy} 236 (4.15), 284 (3.70), 393 (3.66)	76	....	....	....	s^h	...	s	...	...	....	B13[2], 191
a1152	—,3-methoxy-2-nitro-	2-Nitro-m-anisidine. $C_7H_8N_2O_3$. See a1002	168.16	ye nd (bz) λ^{cy} 233 (4.02), 290 (3.37), 355.5 (3.37)	124–4.5 (143)	....	....	....	...	s	...	s	...	....	B13[1], 136
a1153	—,3-methoxy-4-nitro-	4-Nitro-m-anisidine. $C_7H_8N_2O_3$. See a1002	168.16	ye nd (al)	169	sub	....	....	...	s	...	...	...	aa s	B13[1], 136
a1154	—,3-methoxy-5-nitro-	5-Nitro-m-anisidine. $C_7H_8N_2O_3$. See a1002	168.16	og cr (w)	120	....	1.2034^{156}	....	s^h	s	...	s	s	lig i	B13[2], 216
a1155	—,4-methoxy-2-nitro-	2-Nitro-p-anisidine. $C_7H_8N_2O_3$. See a1002	168.16	dk red pr (w or al)	129	....	....	....	s	s	s	...	δ	....	B13[2], 286
a1156	—,4-methoxy-3-nitro-	3-Nitro-p-anisidine. $C_7H_8N_2O_3$. See a1002	168.16	red (eth), og pr or pl (eth-lig) $\lambda^{w,pH=11}$ 230.5 (4.30), 259 sh (3.76), 285 (3.72), 448 (3.67)	57–7.5	....	....	....	s^h	s	s	s	s	to δ	B13[2], 284
Ω a1157	—,N-methyl-	Methyl phenylamine. $C_6H_5NHCH_3$	107.16	λ^{al} 240 (4.0), 294 (3.18)	−57	196.25^{760} 86^{15}	0.98912^{20}_4	1.5684^{20}	i	s	s	...	...	chl s	B12[2], 79
Ω a1158	—,—,hydrochloride	$C_6H_5NHCH_3 \cdot HCl$	143.62	nd(chl-eth)	122.5–3 (cor)	....	1.0660^{131}_4	....	v	s	i	...	i	chl v	B12[2], 81
a1159	—,N-3-methylbutyl-	N-Isoamylaniline. $C_6H_5NHCH_2CH_2CH(CH_3)_2$	163.26	....	....	254.5^{760} $126–7^{14}$	0.8912^{55}_4	1.5305^{20}	i	∞	∞	...	...	....	B12[2], 96
a1160	—,N-methyl-2-nitro-	$C_7H_8N_2O_2$. See a1002	152.16	red or og nd (peth) λ^{al} 279 (3.5), 429 (3.7)	38	d	....	....	$δ^h$	s	s	s	s	os, con ac s lig δ	B12[2], 369
a1161	—,N-methyl-3-nitro-	$C_7H_8N_2O_2$. See a1002	152.16	red-ye nd or pr (al), cr (lig)	68	....	....	....	s^h	s	s	...	s	lig s^h	B12[2], 377
Ω a1162	—,N-methyl-4-nitro-	$C_7H_8N_2O_2$. See a1002	152.16	br-ye pr (al), cr (eth) λ^{al} 315 (3.2), 387 (4.28)	152	d	1.201^{155}_4	....	i	s	δ	...	s	lig δ	B12[2], 385
a1163	—,N-methyl-N-nitroso-	Methylnitroso phenylamine. $C_6H_5N(NO)CH_3$	136.17	ye	14.7	225 d 121[13]	1.1240^{20}_4	1.57688^{20}	i	s	s	...	...	....	B12[2], 309
Ω a1164	—,N-methyl-4-nitroso-	$C_7H_8N_2O$. See a1002	136.17	bl pl (bz)	118	....	....	....	δ	s	s	...	δ	chl s s^h lig δ	B7[2], 575
Ω a1165	—,N-methyl-N,2,4,6-tetranitro-	Tetryl.	287.15	ye pr (al) λ^{al} 225 (4.4), 300 (3.4)	131–2	exp 187	1.57^{19}	....	i	δ s^h	δ	s	s	Py s chl δ CS_2 i	B12, 770
Ω a1166	—,4-methylthio-	4-Aminothioanisole. C_7H_9NS. See a1002	139.22	λ^{al} 240 (3.91), 264 (4.14), 295 (3.21)	....	272–3 140[15]	1.1379^{20}_4	1.6395^{20}	...	s	s	s	s	solvento	B13[2], 297
a1167	—,N-nitro-	Diazobenzolic acid. Nitranilide. Phenylnitramine. $C_6H_5NHNO_2$	138.13	lf (peth)	46–7	exp on htng	....	....	v	s	s	s	s	peth δ	B16[2], 343
Ω a1168	—,2-nitro-	$C_6H_6N_2O_2$. See a1002	138.13	gold-ye pl or nd (w) λ^{al} 231 (4.23), 276 (3.70), 402 (3.74)	71.5 (cor) (74–6)	284 165–6[28]	1.442^{15}	....	δ s^h	s	v v^h	v	v	chl v	B12[2], 367
Ω a1169	—,3-nitro-	$C_6H_6N_2O_2$. See a1002	138.13	ye nd, rh bipym (w) λ^{al} 236 (4.21), 275 sh (3.64), 374 (3.17)	114	305–7d $100^{0.16}$	1.1747^{160}_4 1.430_4	....	δ s^h	s	s v^h	s s^h	δ	MeOH v chl s	B12[2], 374
Ω a1170	—,4-nitro-	$C_6H_6N_2O_2$. See a1002	138.13	pa ye mcl nd (w) λ^{al} 227 sh (3.86), 375 (4.19)	148.5–9.5	331.73 $106^{0.03}$	1.424^{20}_4	....	i δ	s	s v^h	s	δ	MeOH v to, chl s	B12[2], 383
a1171	—,5-nitro-2-propoxy-	$C_9H_{12}N_2O_3$. See a1002	196.21	og (PrOH-peth)	49–9.5	....	....	....	i	s	...	...	...	lig i	C45, 7544

For explanations, symbols and abbreviations see beginning of table. For structural formulas see end of table.

No.	Name	Synonyms and Formula	Mol. wt.	Color, crystalline form, specific rotation and λ_{max} (log ε)	m.p. °C	b.p. °C	Density	n_D	Solubility						Ref.
									w	al	eth	ace	bz	other solvents	
	Aniline														
a1172	—,4-nitroso-	p-Benzoquinoneimine oxime. $C_6H_6N_2O$. See a1002	122.13	bl nd (bz) λ^{MeOH} 270 (3.6), 415 (4.5)	173–4	d on htng	....	....	s	s	...	...	δ	....	B7[2], 575
a1173	—,2,3,4,5,6-penta-bromo-	$C_6H_2Br_5N$. See a1002	487.66	nd (al-to)	265–6	....	....	....		s	...	...	δ	to δ	B12, 669
a1174	—,2,3,4,5,6-penta-chloro-	$C_6H_2Cl_5N$. See a1002	265.35	nd (al)	232	....	....	....		s	s	...	...	lig s	B12[2], 341
Ω a1175	—,2-phenoxy-	2-Aminodiphenyl ether. $C_{12}H_{11}NO$. See a1002	185.23	cr (lig) λ^{al} 233 sh (4.0), 270 (3.44), 277 (3.47), 289 (3.43)	44–5	307–8[728] 172–3[14]	....	....		s	s	s	s	os v	B13[2], 167
Ω a1176	—,3-phenoxy-	3-Aminodiphenyl ether. $C_{12}H_{11}NO$. See a1002	185.23	pr (lig) λ^{al} 220 sh (4.30), 272 (3.32), 278 (3.37), 288 (3.40)	37	315 190–1[14]	....	....		s	s	s	s	os s lig δ	B13, 404
Ω a1177	—,4-phenoxy-	4-Aminodiphenyl ether. $C_{12}H_{11}NO$. See a1002	185.23	nd (w), cr (dil al) λ^{al} 241.5 (4.11), 270 sh (3.42), 278 (3.33), 298 (3.27)	85–6	315–20[30] 187–9[14]	....	....	s[h]	v	v	...	...	lig δ	B13[2], 227
—	—,N-phenyl-	see Amine, diphenyl													
a1178	—,N-propyl-	Phenylpropylamine. $C_6H_5NHCH_2CH_2CH_3$	135.21	....	....	222 (cor) 100[11]	0.9443$_4^{20}$	1.5428[20]	i	v	s	...	...	lig s	B12[2], 94
a1179	—,2,3,4,5-tetra-chloro-	$C_6H_3Cl_4N$. See a1002	230.91	nd (al)	118–20	....	....	....		s	v	...	v	aa v	B12[2], 340
a1180	—,2,3,5,6-tetra-chloro-	$C_6H_3Cl_4N$. See a1002	230.91	nd (lig, al)	108	....	....	....	i	s	v	...	...	CS_2, lig v	B12[2], 340
a1181	—,2,4,5-tribromo-	$C_6H_4Br_3N$. See a1002 λ^{al} 268 (2.2), 274 (2.3), 284 (2.05)	329.83	nd (al)	80–1 (85)	....	....	....		v	v	...	v	dil ac s	B12, 662
Ω a1182	—,2,4,6-tribromo-	$C_6H_4Br_3N$. See a1002 λ^{al} 249 (4.1), 315 (3.4)	329.83	nd (al, bz)	122	300	2.35$_{20}^{20}$	....	i	δ s[h]	s	...	...	chl s	B12[2], 358
a1183	—,—,hydro-bromide	$C_6H_4Br_3N \cdot HBr$. See a1002	410.75	nd	195–6d	sub	....	....	d	i	i	...	i	lig i	B12[1], 330
a1184	—,3,4,5-tribromo-	$C_6H_4Br_3N$. See a1002	329.83	nd (al)	123	....	....	....	i	s	s	...	...	....	B12, 668
a1185	—,2,3,4-trichloro-	$C_6H_4Cl_3N$. See a1002	196.46	nd (lig)	73 (68)	292[774]	....	....		v	...	...	...	lig s	B12, 626
Ω a1186	—,2,4,5-trichloro-	$C_6H_4Cl_3N$. See a1002	196.46	nd (lig or 50 % al) λ^{al} 248 (4.15), 313 (4.06)	96.5	ca. 270	....	....		s	s	...	...	CS_2 v lig δ	B12[2], 338
a1187	—,2,4,6-trichloro-	sym-Trichloroaniline. $C_6H_4Cl_3N$. See a1002 λ^{al} 244 (3.9), 310 (3.4)	196.46	cr (al), nd (lig or peth)	78.5	262[746]	....	....	i	s	s	...	...	CS_2 v lig s	B12[2], 339
a1188	—,2,3,5-triiodo-	$C_6H_4I_3N$. See a1002	470.82	nd	116	....	....	....		s	δ	...	s	aa s lig δ	B12, 676
a1189	—,2,3,6-triiodo-	$C_6H_4I_3N$. See a1002	470.82	nd (al or al-eth)	116.8	....	....	....	s[h]	i		...		....	B12, 676
a1190	—,2,4,6-triiodo-	$C_6H_4I_3N$. See a1002	470.82	ye nd or pl (al), pr (aa) λ^{MeOH} 229 (4.50), 255 sh (4.03), 315 (3.63)	185.5	....	....	....		δ s[h]		...		AcOEt v CS_2, aa s	B12[2], 364
a1191	—,3,4,5-triiodo-	$C_6H_4I_3N$. See a1002	470.82	nd (al-ace)	174.5 d	....	....	....		s	s	v	s	chl, pcth	B12, 676
a1192	—,2,4,6-trinitro-	Picramide. TNA. $C_6H_4N_4O_6$. See a1002 λ^{aa} 324 (4.0), 408 (3.9)	228.12	dk ye pr (aa)	192–5	exp	1.762[14]	....	i	δ	δ	s	s	AcOEt s aa δ[h] chl δ v	B12[2], 421
—	Anisaldehyde	see Benzaldehyde, 4-methoxy-													
—	Anisic acid	see Benzoic acid, 4-methoxy-													
—	Anisidine	see Aniline, methoxy-													
—	Anisoin	see Benzoin, 4,4′-di-methoxy-													
—	Anisole	see Benzene, methoxy-*													
—	Anol	see Benzene, 1-hydroxy-4(1-propenyl)-*													

For explanations, symbols and abbreviations see beginning of table. For structural formulas see end of table.

No.	Name	Synonyms and Formula	Mol. wt.	Color, crystalline form, specific rotation and λ_{max} (log ε)	m.p. °C	b.p. °C	Density	n_D	w	al	eth	ace	bz	other solvents	Ref.
	Anthracene														
Ω a1193	**Anthracene**		178.24	ta or mcl pr (al) λ^{al} 218 (4.04), 252 (3.23), 295 (2.78), 310 (3.11), 324 (3.45), 340 (3.73), 357 (3.89), 376 (3.87)	216.2–.4	340 (cor) 226.5⁵³ sub	1.283₄²⁵	....	i	δʰ	δ	δ sʰ	δ sʰ	to δ, sʰ chl, CCl₄, CS₂ δ	B5², 569
a1194	—,1-acetyl-	$C_{16}H_{12}O$. See a1193	220.27	pa ye (al) λ^{al} 240 (4.7), 251 (4.7), 375 (3.7)	107.5–9.0	....				sʰ				....	B7², 450
a1195	—,2-acetyl-	$C_{16}H_{12}O$. See a1193	220.27	ye (al), cr (AcOEt-peth) λ^{al} 240 (4.4), 260 (4.8), 350 (3.7)	190–2 (186)					sʰ				....	B7², 450
a1196	—,9-acetyl-	$C_{16}H_{12}O$. See a1193	220.27	pa ye (al) λ^{cy} 255 (5.2), 347 (3.7), 364 (3.9), 382 (3.9)	76					sʰ				aa s	B7², 450
a1197	—,1-amino-	1-Anthrylamine. $C_{14}H_{11}N$. See a1193	193.25	gold-ye nd (al) λ^{al} 240 (4.9), 259 (4.8), 369 (3.6)	130 (119)				i	v				con HCl i	B12², 785
a1198	—,2-amino-	2-Anthrylamine. $C_{14}H_{11}N$. See a1193	193.25	ye lf (al) λ^{eth} 244 (4.3), 263 (4.6), 408 (3.6)	238–41	sub			i	s				os δ con sulf i	B12², 785
a1199	—,9-amino-	9-Anthrylamine. $C_{14}H_{11}N$. See a1193	193.25	ye lf (dil al), br (bz) λ^{chl} 290 (5.0), 390 (3.8), 410 (3.8)	145–50					s	s		s	chl s	B7², 416
a1200	—,9-benzoyl-	9-Anthrophenone. $C_{21}H_{14}O$. See a1193	282.35	ye nd (bz, aa, AcOEt)	148							s	sʰ	CCl₄, CS₂, Ac₂O s aa sʰ	B13, 321
a1201	—,1-chloro-	$C_{14}H_9Cl$. See a1193	212.68	lf (aa) λ^{chl} 257 (4.02), 365 (3.80), 384 (3.76)	83.5	....	1.1707₄¹⁰⁰	1.6959¹⁰⁰	i	s	s		s	CCl₄ s	E13, 235
a1202	—,2-chloro-	$C_{14}H_9Cl$. See a1193	212.68	nd or lf λ^{chl} 255.5 (5.18), 342 (3.57), 380 (3.69)	215 (223)				i					CCl₄ s	E13, 236
a1203	—,9-chloro-	$C_{14}H_9Cl$. See a1193	212.68	gold-ye nd (al) λ^{al} 255 (5.5), 340 (3.4), 392 (3.9)	106				i	sʰ	s		s	CCl₄, CS₂, con sulf s (gr)	E13, 236
a1204	—,10-chloro-9,10-dihydro-9-nitro-	$C_{14}H_{11}ClNO_2$. See a1193	259.70	nd (bz)	163					δ			sʰ	chl δ	B5², 549
a1207	—,9,10-diamino-	$C_{14}H_{12}N_2$. See a1193	208.27	red cr	196	....			i						C35, 3998
Ω a1208	—,9,10-dibromo- ..	$C_{14}H_8Br_2$. See a1193	336.05	ye nd (to or xyl) λ^{hx} 250 (5.32), 265 (5.32)	226	sub			i	δ	δ		δ sʰ	chl s to sʰ	B5², 577
a1209	—,9,10-dichloro-	$C_{14}H_8Cl_2$. See a1193	247.14	ye nd (MeCOEt or CCl₄) λ^{al} 252 (5.0), 259 (5.3), 325 (3.1), 341 (3.5), 379 (4.0), 401 (4.1)	212–2.5					δ	δ		s		B5², 575
Ω a1210	—,9,10-dihydro- ...	$C_{14}H_{12}$. See a1193	180.25	ta or pr λ^{al} 260 (4.0), 270 (4.0)	111	305 165–70¹³ sub	0.8976₁¹¹	....	i	s	s		s	....	B5², 545
a1211	—,9,10-dihydro-9-ethyl-	$C_{16}H_{16}$. See a1193	208.31	....	....	320–3 δd (cor)	1.049₁₈¹⁸		i	∞	∞		∞	aa s	B5, 649
a1212	—,9,10-dihydro-9-hydroxy-	Hydroanthrol. $C_{14}H_{12}O$. See a1193	196.25	nd (peth)	76	....			sʰ	s	s		s	CS₂, lig s	B6², 660
a1213	—,9,10-dihydro-10-nitro-9-oxo-	10-Nitroanthrone. $C_{14}H_9NO_3$. See a1193	239.23	cr (bz-lig), nd (CS₂)	140 (148d)					s			vʰ	alk s CS₂ sʰ	B7², 240
Ω a1214	—,9,10-dihydro-9-oxo-	Anthrone. $C_{14}H_{10}O$. See a1193	194.24	nd (bz-lig, aa) λ^{al} 253 (4.35)	155 (165–70)							s	sʰ	con sulf s dil alk sʰ	B7², 414

For explanations, symbols and abbreviations see beginning of table. For structural formulas see end of table.

No.	Name	Synonyms and Formula	Mol. wt.	Color, crystalline form, specific rotation and λ_{max} (log ε)	m.p. °C	b.p. °C	Density	n_D	Solubility						Ref.
									w	al	eth	ace	bz	other solvents	
	Anthracene														
a1215	—,1,2-dihydroxy-..	1,2-Anthradiol. $C_{14}H_{10}O_2$. See a1193	210.24	pa gr lf	160–2					v	v	...	...	aa v alk s (dk)	B6², 998
a1216	—,1,5-dihydroxy-..	1,5-Anthradiol. Rufol. $C_{14}H_{10}O_2$. See a1193	210.24	ye nd	265d	....				s	s	...	s	alk, aa s	B6, 1032
a1217	—,1,8-dihydroxy-..	1,8-Anthradiol. Chrysazol. $C_{14}H_{10}O_2$. See a1193	210.24	ye nd (dil al), lf (al–aa)	225d				i	s	s	...	s	alk, AcOEt s	B6, 1033
a1218	—,2,6-dihydroxy-..	2,6-Anthradiol. Flavol. $C_{14}H_{10}O_2$. See a1193	210.24	pa ye lf (al)	295–300d (dk at 270)	....			i	v	v	...	...	aa s	B6², 999
a1219	—,9,10-dihydroxy-	9,10-Anthradiol. Anthraquinol. $C_{14}H_{10}O_2$. See a1193	210.24	br or ye nd	180					s	s	...	δ	chl δ	B8², 214
Ω a1220	—,1,3-dimethyl-...	$C_{16}H_{14}$. See a1193	206.29	pa bl flr lf (eth), cr (al)	83	140–5²			i	v	v	...	...		B5², 592
Ω a1221	—,2,3-dimethyl-..	$C_{16}H_{14}$. See a1193	206.29	bl gr flr lf (bz)	252	....			i	s	s	...	v		B5², 592
a1222	—,9-ethyl-.......	$C_{16}H_{14}$. See a1193	206.29	bl flr lf (al or MeOH)	59	....	1.0413²⁹	1.6762⁹⁹	i	s	s	...	...		B5², 591
a1223	—,1,2,3,4,5,6-hexahydro-	$C_{14}H_{16}$. See a1193	184.28	lf (MeOH), cr (al)	67 (70)	160¹⁵				δ		...	v		B5², 472
Ω a1224	—,1-hydroxy-..	1-Anthrol. $C_{14}H_{10}O$. See a1193	194.24	cr (bz), br nd or lf (al or aa) λ^{DMF} 395 (3.60)	158 (150–3)	224¹³			i	v	v	...	...	NaOH, os s	B6², 669
a1225	—,2-hydroxy-.....	2-Anthrol. $C_{14}H_{10}O$. See a1193	194.24	yc (bz), br lf or nd (dil al)	255 (200d)	....			i	v	v	v	s^h	KOH s	B6², 669
a1226	—,9-hydroxy-.....	9-Anthrol. Anthranol. $C_{14}H_{10}O$. See a1193	194.24	ye red lf (dil al), pa ye nd (aa)	160–4 (120 rapid htng)	....			i	s		...	s^h	os v aq alk s	B7², 414
a1227	—,1-hydroxy-9,10-dihydro-	$C_{14}H_{12}O$. See a1193	196.25	sl grsh flr lf or nd (bz, peth)	94					s	s	...	...	aa s	B6², 660
a1228	—,2-hydroxy-9,10-dihydro-	$C_{14}H_{12}O$. See a1193	196.25	(bz–peth), lf (dil al)	129	....			δ			...	...	os v	B6², 660
a1229	—,1-methyl-.....	$C_{15}H_{12}$. See a1193	192.26	bl nd (MeOH), lf (al) λ^{iso} 253 (5.22), 343 (3.74), 359 (3.93), 377 (3.92)	85–6	199–200	1.0471²⁹	1.6802⁹⁹	i	s	s	...	s	chl, sulf s al (bl flr)	B5², 585
Ω a1230	—,2-methyl-.....	$C_{15}H_{12}$. See a1193	192.26	gr-bl flr lf (sub)	209–9.5	sub	1.81⁰₄	....	i	δ	δ	i	s	chl, CS_2 s MeOH, aa δ	B5², 586
Ω a1231	—,9-methyl-.....	$C_{15}H_{12}$. See a1193	192.26	yesh nd (dil al), pr (bz, al, MeOH) λ^{al} 252 (5.18), 256 (5.33), 318 (3.04), 331 (3.44), 348 (3.76), 366 (3.96), 386 (3.95)	81.5	196–7¹²	1.065⁹⁹₄	1.6959⁹⁹	...	s	s	s	s	os v	B5², 587
Ω a1232	—,9-nitro-.......	$C_{14}H_9NO_2$. See a1193	223.23	ye nd (al), pr (aa or xyl) λ^{al} 331 (3.42), 347 (3.61), 363 (3.66), 382 (3.58)	146	>360 ca. 275¹⁷			i	δ s^h		...	v	CS_2 v aa δ, s^h	B6², 1245
Ω a1233	—,1,2,3,4,5,6,7,8-octahydro-	Octhracene, $C_{14}H_{18}$. See a1193	186.30	pl (al) λ^{al} 270 (3.0), 280 (3.2), 285 (3.29)	78 (74)	293–5⁷⁶⁰ 167¹²	1.131⁰₄ 0.9703⁸⁰₄	1.5372⁸⁰	i	s v^h		...	v	aa s, v^h	B5², 422
a1234	—,9-phenyl-.....	$C_{20}H_{14}$. See a1193	254.34	bl flr in sol, lf (al), (aa or al) λ^{al} 255.5 (5.16), 346.5 (3.90), 384 (4.08)	156	417			i	s^h	s^h	...	s^h	CS_2, chl s^h	B5², 639
a1235	—,1,2,9-trihydroxy-	$C_{14}H_{10}O_3$. See a1193	226.24	og ye lf	149–51	....						...	...	con sulf, alk s	B8², 371
a1236	—,1,2,10-trihydroxy-	$C_{14}H_{10}O_3$. See a1193	226.24	ye lf, nd (al–w)	208	....			δ	v	v	v	s	aa v	B8², 372
a1237	—,1,4,9-trihydroxy-	$C_{14}H_{10}O_3$. See a1193	226.24	og–red nd (al)	156	....				s^h		...	...		B8, 330
a1238	—,1,5,9-trihydroxy-	$C_{14}H_{10}O_3$. See a1193	226.24	gold lf (al)	200d without melting	....			...	s^h		...	...		B8, 330
a1239	—,1,8,9-trihydroxy-	Anthralin. Cignolin. $C_{14}H_{10}O_3$. See a1193	226.24	ye pl or nd (lig)	178–80	....			i	s	δ	s	s	chl, Py v dil NaOH s(ye) lig s^h	E13, 372

For explanations, symbols and abbreviations see beginning of table. For structural formulas see end of table.

No.	Name	Synonyms and Formula	Mol. wt.	Color, crystalline form, specific rotation and λ_{max} (log ε)	m.p. °C	b.p. °C	Density	n_D	Solubility						Ref.
									w	al	eth	ace	bz	other solvents	
	Anthracene														
a1240	—,1,9,10-trihy-droxy-(enol form)	$C_{14}H_{10}O_3$. See a1193	226.24	gr nd (eth)	204–6	....	....	....		s	s		...		B8², 372
a1241	—,1,9,10-trihy-droxy-(keto form)	....	226.24	ye nd (lig)	135–7	δ				s			...	os δ	B8², 372
a1242	—,2,3,9-trihy-droxy-	$C_{14}H_{10}O_3$. See a1193	226.24	ye br nd (al)	288–9	....	....	....		s	s	s	...	aa s	B8², 372
a1243	9-Anthracenecar-boxaldehyde	9-Anthraldehyde.	206.25	og nd (dil aa) λ^{al} 234 (4.5), 262 (4.7), 372 (3.8), 404 (3.9)	104–5	....	....	....	i			...	s	aa s	E13, 320
a1244	1-Anthracenecar-boxylic acid	1-Anthroic acid.	222.25	ye nd (aa), ye pr (al or AcOEt), bt ye nd (sub) λ^{al} 250 (5.0), 355 (3.7), 375 (3.7)	251–2	sub	....	....	i	s^h	s	...	δ	alk s aa s^h chl δ	B9², 493
a1245	2-Anthracenecar-boxylic acid	2-Anthroic acid.	222.25	ye lf (al), nd, lf (sub)	281	sub	....	....	i	s^h	δ	...	δ	aa s alk s (bl flr) chl δ	B9², 494
Ω a1246	9-Anthracenecar-boxylic acid	9-Anthroic acid.	222.25	pa ye nd (bz, al) λ^{al} 254 (5.17), 344 (3.73), 362 (3.89), 381 (3.83)	217d	sub	....	....	i δ^h	s		...	...	....	B9², 494
—	Anthrachrysone	see 9,10-Anthraquinone, 1,3,5,7-tetrahydroxy-*													
—	Anthraflavin	see 9,10-Anthraquinone, 2,6-dihydroxy-*													
—	Anthragallol	see 9,10-Anthraquinone, 1,2,3-trihydroxy-*													
—	Anthralin	see Anthracene, 1,8,9-trihydroxy-*													
a1247	Anthranil	3,4-Benzoisoxazol.	119.12	λ 304 (3.5)	< −18	215⁷⁶⁰ δd 99¹³	1.8127₄²⁰	1.5845²⁰	δ^h	s	...	s	...	os, ac s	B27², 17
—	Anthranilaldehyde	see Benzaldehyde, 2-amino-													
—	Anthranilic acid	see Benzoic acid, 2-amino-													
—	Anthranol	see Anthracene, hydroxy-*													
—	Anthrapurpurin	see 9,10-Anthraquinone, 1,2,7-trihydroxy-*													
Ω a1248	9,10-Anthra-quinone*	....	208.23	ye rh nd (al, bz) λ^{al} 252 (4.7), 278 (4.1), 330 (3.7)	286 (sub)	379.8⁷⁶⁰	1.438⁴	....	i	δ	i	...	δ s^h	con sulf s chl, CCl_4 δ to δ, s, s^h	B7², 709
Ω a1249	—,1-amino-*	$C_{14}H_9NO_2$. See a1248	223.23	red nd (al), (gl aa) λ^{al} 234 (4.53), 306 (3.82), 497 (2.83)	253–4	sub	....	....	i	δ	s	s	s	con HCl s chl aa s $phNO_2$ s^h	B22², 618
Ω a1250	—,2-amino-*	$C_{14}H_9NO_2$. See a1248	223.23	red nd (al, aa, sub) λ^{MeOH} 242 (4.49), 298 (4.37), 327 (3.95), 440 (3.65)	303–6	sub	....	....	i	δ	i	s	s	chl s	B14², 107
a1251	—,1-amino-2-benzoyl-	$C_{21}H_{13}NO_3$. See a1248	327.34	red nd (aa)	190	....	....	....		δ		...	...	aa s^h	B14¹, 482
a1252	—,2-amino-3-benzoyl-	$C_{21}H_{13}NO_3$. See a1248	327.34	ye pl (Py)	331	....	....	....		δ		...	δ	Py v aa δ	B14¹, 482
a1253	—,1-amino-2-bromo-*	$C_{14}H_8BrNO_2$. See a1248	302.15	ye-red nd (aa), nd (xyl) λ^{al} 308 (3.64), 469 (3.88)	182	....	....	....	i	δ	δ	δ	δ	Py v aa, to s lig δ	B14¹, 446
a1254	—,1-amino-3-bromo-*	$C_{14}H_8BrNO_2$. See a1248	302.15	red nd (to) λ^{al} 305 sh (3.87), 471 (3.84)	243	....	....	....	i	i	i	i	δ	Py, $PhNO_2$ s to δ	B14¹, 446
a1255	—,3-amino-1,2-dihydroxy-*	3-Aminoalizarin. $C_{14}H_9NO_4$. See a1248	255.23	dk red pr (aa)	>300	sub δd	....	....		δ		...	.	aq NH_3 s aq HCl δ	E13, 565
a1256	—,4-amino-1,2-dihydroxy-*	4-Aminoalizarin. $C_{14}H_9NO_4$. See a1248	255.23	gr-bl nd (al)	d	....	....	....		s^h		...	.	alk s (crimson) $PhNO_2$ s^h	E13, 565
a1257	—,2-amino-1-hydroxy-*	2-Aminoerythroxyanthraqui-none. $C_{14}H_9NO_3$. See a1248	239.23	red br nd (al)	226–7	sub	....	....	i	s	s		s	Py v con sulf s aq NH_3 δ	B14², 167

For explanations, symbols and abbreviations see beginning of table. For structural formulas see end of table.

No.	Name	Synonyms and Formula	Mol. wt.	Color, crystalline form, specific rotation and λ_{max} (log ε)	m.p. °C	b.p. °C	Density	n_D	Solubility						Ref.
									w	al	eth	ace	bz	other solvents	
	Anthraquinone														
a1258	—,1-bromo-*	$C_{14}H_7BrO_2$. See a1248	287.12	ye nd (bz), cr (xy, phNO$_2$)	188	sub			i	s			s	PhNO$_2$, con sulf s	B7^2, 717
a1259	—,2-bromo-*	$C_{14}H_7BrO_2$. See a1248	287.12	ye nd (to), (gl aa)	204.5	sub			i	δ			s^h	AmOH s to, aa s^h	B7^2, 717
a1260	—,3-bromo-1,2-dihydroxy-*	3-Bromoalizarin. $C_{14}H_7BrO_4$. See a1248	319.12	br-red nd (to)	260–1	sub			s	δ			δ	Py, dil alk s (bl-vt) con alk s (red) con sulf s (red) aa δ	E13, 555
Ω a1261	—,1-bromo-4-methylamino-*	$C_{15}H_{10}BrNO_2$. See a1248	316.16	br-red nd (Py)	194				i	δ				Py, ac s	B14^1, 447
a1262	—,2-bromo-1-methylamino-*	$C_{15}H_{10}BrNO_2$. See a1248	316.16	br nd (aa)	170–2				i	δ			s^h	Py, aa s^h	B14^1, 446
Ω a1263	—,1-chloro-*	$C_{14}H_7ClO_2$. See a1248	242.66	ye nd (to or al) λ^{MeOH} 253 (4.63), 266 (4.15), 333 (3.70), 415 (2.00)	162	sub			i	δ^h	∞		s^h	PhNO$_2$ aa s AmOH s^h	B7^2, 714
Ω a1264	—,2-chloro-*	$C_{14}H_7ClO_2$. See a1248	242.66	pa ye nd (aa or al) λ^{MeOH} 256 (4.69), 265 (4.36), 274 (4.23), 325 (3.59)	211	sub			i	δ	i		δ s^h	to v^h PhNO$_2$, con sulf s	B7^2, 714
a1265	—,1,2-diamino-*	$C_{14}H_{10}N_2O_2$. See a1248	238.25	vt nd (PhNO$_2$) λ^{sulf} 262 (4.72), 360 (3.82)	303 4						δ	δ		Py, con sulf s con HCl i dil HCl, chl, xy δ	B14^2, 112
a1266	—,1,3-diamino-*	$C_{14}H_{10}N_2O_2$. See a1248	238.25	red (PhNO$_2$)	290						δ	i		Py v con sulf s (gr) PhNO$_2$ δ, s^h	B14^2, 112
Ω a1267	—,1,4-diamino-*	$C_{14}H_{10}N_2O_2$. See a1248	238.25	dk vt nd (Py), vt cr (al) λ^{al} 249 (4.45), 288 (4.09), 300 (4.08), 522 (2.83), 551 (3.04), 592 (3.04)	268				δ v^h	s			s	PhNO$_2$, Py v aa s	B14^2, 113
Ω a1268	—,1,5-diamino-*	$C_{14}H_{10}N_2O_2$. See a1248	238.25	dk red nd (al, aa) $\lambda^{oClC_6H_4OH}$ 500 (4.08)	319 (cor)	sub			i	δ	δ	δ	δ	con sulf s PhNO$_2$ s^h chl δ	B14^2, 116
a1269	—,1,6-diamino-*	$C_{14}H_{10}N_2O_2$. See a1248	238.25	red nd (aa), lf (MeOPh)	297				i	δ			s	PhNO$_2$, aa s^h	B14^2, 119
a1270	—,1,7-diamino-*	$C_{14}H_{10}N_2O_2$. See a1248	238.25	red nd (PhNO$_2$)	290				i	δ	δ		s	PhNO$_2$ s^h, os δ	B14^1, 470
a1271	—,1,8-diamino-*	$C_{14}H_{10}N_2O_2$. See a1248	238.25	red (al or aa, Py, PhNO$_2$) λ^{diox} 250 (4.4), 435 (4.0), 458 (4.1), 490 (4.0)	265				i	s	δ			Py, PhNO$_2$ s aa δ	B14^2, 119
a1272	—,2,3-diamino-*	$C_{14}H_{10}N_2O_2$. See a1248	238.25	red (PhNO$_2$)	353							δ		sulf, Py, PhNO$_2$ s chl, xyl δ	B14^2, 120
Ω a1273	—,2,6-diamino-*	$C_{14}H_{10}N_2O_2$. See a1248	238.25	red-br pr (aq Py) λ^{diox} 281 (4.0), 333 (4.1), 384 (3.7)	>325 (320d)				δ^h	s^h			s	con sulf, chl, xy δ Py s^h	B14^2, 120
a1274	—,2,7-diamino-*	$C_{14}H_{10}N_2O_2$. See a1248	238.25	og-ye nd (al or PhNO$_2$), dk red nd (sub)	>330	sub			i	δ	δ			dil sulf, con ac s	B14^1, 473
a1275	—,2,3-dibromo-*	$C_{14}H_6Br_2O_2$. See a1248	366.02	ye nd (to)	283	sub				δ			s	chl, con sulf s	B7^2, 718
a1276	—,2,7-dibromo-*	$C_{14}H_6Br_2O_2$. See a1248	366.02	lt ye lf (MeOPh) ye pl (sub)	248	sub			i	δ^h			s	con sulf s aa s^h	B7^2, 718
a1277	—,1,3-dichloro-*	$C_{14}H_6Cl_2O_2$. See a1248	277.11	ye nd (aa)	209–10				i	δ^h	δ^h	δ^h		PhNO$_2$ s aa s^h	B7^1, 411
a1278	—,1,4-dichloro-*	$C_{14}H_6Cl_2O_2$. See a1248	277.11	og-ye nd (aa) λ^{cy} 213 (4.45), 256 (4.6), 357 (4.6)	187.5–8				i	δ	δ		δ s^h	PhNO$_2$, Py v aa s^h	B7^2, 715

For explanations, symbols and abbreviations see beginning of table. For structural formulas see end of table.

No.	Name	Synonyms and Formula	Mol. wt.	Color, crystalline form, specific rotation and λ_{max} (log ε)	m.p. °C	b.p. °C	Density	n_D	w	al	eth	ace	bz	other solvents	Ref.
	Anthraquinone														
Ω a1279	—,1,5-dichloro-*	$C_{14}H_6Cl_2O_2$. See a1248	277.11	yesh (to), ye nd (aa) λ^{al} 254 (5.24), 344 (4.43)	252	....			i	δ	...	δ	δ	PhNO₂, con sulf s aa s^h	B7², 715
a1280	—,1,6-dichloro-*	$C_{14}H_6Cl_2O_2$. See a1248	277.11	pa ye nd (aa)	203–4				i	δ	δ	v	...	PhNO₂, to, anisole v	B7², 715
a1281	—,1,7-dichloro-*	$C_{14}H_6Cl_2O_2$. See a1248	277.11	ye nd (aa) λ^{cy} 213 (4.42), 263 (4.7), 270 (4.3), 282 (4.3)	213–4				i	δ	...	...	...	PhNO₂, aa s^h	B7², 716
Ω a1282	—,1,8-dichloro-*	$C_{14}H_6Cl_2O_2$. See a1248	277.11	ye nd (aa)	202–3				i	δ	...	s^h	to, phNO₂ s^h	B7², 716
a1283	—,2,3-dichloro-*	$C_{14}H_6Cl_2O_2$. See a1248	277.11	ye nd (aa)	271				i	δ	...	s^h	aa δ, s^h	B7², 716
a1284	—,2,6-dichloro-*	$C_{14}H_6Cl_2O_2$. See a1248	277.11	ye nd (aa or al), pa ye lf (PhCl)	291–1.5				i	s^h	...	...	v^h	aa s^h con sulf s	B7², 716
a1285	—,2,7-dichloro-*	$C_{14}H_6Cl_2O_2$. See a1248	277.11	yesh nd (MeOPh)	212 (231)				i	...	s	...	...	MeOPh s^h	B7², 717
a1286	—,1,2-dihydroxy-*	Alizarin. $C_{14}H_8O_4$. See a1248	240.23	og or red tcl nd or pr. (al, sub) λ^{al} 248 (4.4), 435 (3.8)	289–90 (cor)	430 sub			δ	s	s	s	s	Py ∞ CS₂ s MeOH s^h chl i	B8², 487
a1287	—,1,3-dihydroxy-*	Purpuroxanthin. Xanthopurpurin. $C_{14}H_8O_4$. See a1248	240.23	ye-red nd (sub), pr (aa +2) λ^{al} 246 (4.43), 284 (4.36), 415 (3.79)	268–70				i	s	s	v	s	PhNO₂ s alk s(red) aa s^h	E13, 526
Ω a1288	—,1,4-dihydroxy-*	Quinizarin. $C_{14}H_8O_4$. See a1248	240.23	ye red lf(eth), dk red nd (al), red cr (to, aa) λ^{DMF} 330 sh (3.5), 470 (3.9), 520 sh (3.7)	200–2 (aa) 194 (to)	....			s^h	s^h	s^h	...	s^h	KOH, sulf s	B9², 889
a1289	—,1,5-dihydroxy-*	Anthrarufin. $C_{14}H_8O_4$. See a1248	240.23	pa ye pl (gl aa, sub) λ^{al} 225 (4.57), 253 (4.24), 287 (3.98), 418 (3.98), 437 (3.98)	280	sub			i	δ	δ	δ	s	con sulf,s CS₂ δ	B8², 496
a1290	—,1,6-dihydroxy-*	$C_{14}H_8O_4$. See a1248	240.23	og-ye nd (gl aa)	276	....				δ s^h	...	s	δ s^h	dil alk, PhNO₂ s	B8¹, 721
a1291	—,1,7-dihydroxy-*	$C_{14}H_8O_4$. See a1248	240.23	ye nd (sub)	292–3	sub			i	s	s	...	s	chl, CS₂, aa s	B8¹, 721
Ω a1292	—,1,8-dihydroxy-*	Chrysazin. Istizin. $C_{14}H_8O_4$. See a1248	240.23	red or redsh-ye nd or lf (al) λ^{al} 222 (4.6), 253 (4.4), 284 (4.1), 430 (4.1)	193	sub			i	s	s	s	...	alk, aa, chl s PhNO₂ δ	B8², 500
a1293	—,2,3-dihydroxy-*	Hystazarin. Hystazin $C_{14}H_8O_4$. See a1248	240.23	ye-br nd (aa), ye nd (sub)	>330	sub			i	δ	δ	δ	i	sulf, NH₃, NaOH s	B8², 504
Ω a1294	—,2,6-dihydroxy-*	Anthraflavin. Anthraflavic acid. $C_{14}H_8O_4$. See a1248	240.23	ye nd (al) λ^{al} 274 (4.53), 301.5 (4.28), 349 (3.90)	360d	....			δ	δ	i	...	i	con sulf, alk s chl i	B8², 504
Ω a1295	—,2,7-dihydroxy-*	Isoanthraflavin. Isoanthra-flavic acid. $C_{14}H_8O_4$. See a1248	240.23	ye nd (+1w, dil al), nd (sub)	350–5	sub			i	s	δ	...	δ	aa s chl δ	B9², 890
a1296	—,1,8-dihydroxy-3-hydroxy-methyl-*	Aloe-emodin. Rhabarberone. $C_{15}H_{10}O_5$. See a1248	270.25	og-ye nd (to, al) λ^{MeOH} 220 (3.7), 255 (3.3), 283 (3.0), 430 (3.0)	223–4	sub				v^h	s	...	s	NH₄OH, sulf, Na₂CO₃ s (red)	E13, 571
—	—,1,8-dihydroxy-3-hydroxy-methyl-2,4,5,7-tetranitro-*	see **Aloetic acid**													
a1296¹	—,1,2-dihydroxy-3-iodo-*	β-Iodoalizarin. $C_{14}H_7IO_4$. See a1248	366.11	og-red nd (xyl)	228.6–9.7	....			s	...	...	...	...	sulf s(og-red)	E13, 555
a1297	—,1,2-dihydroxy-3-methyl-*	β-Methylalizarin. $C_{15}H_{10}O_4$. See a1248	254.25	og nd	245	sub				s	s	s	s		B8², 510
Ω a1298	—,1,8-dihydroxy-3-methyl-*	Chrysophanic acid, Chrysophanol. $C_{15}H_{10}O_4$. See a1248	254.25	ye hex or mcl nd (sub)	196	sub	0.92		δ	δ s^h	δ	s	s^h	chl. aa s lig δ	B8², 510
a1299	—,1,2-dihydroxy-3-nitro-*	Alizarin orange. β-Nitroalizarin. $C_{14}H_7NO_6$. See a1248	285.22	og-ye nd (bz), ye pl (gl aa, al)	244d	sub d			δ s^h	s	...	...	s	sulf, chl, aa s	B8², 491

For explanations, symbols and abbreviations see beginning of table. For structural formulas see end of table.

No.	Name	Synonyms and Formula	Mol. wt.	Color, crystalline form, specific rotation and λ_{max} (log ε)	m.p. °C	b.p. °C	Density	n_D	w	al	eth	ace	bz	other solvents	Ref.
	Anthraquinone														
a1300	—,1,2-dihydroxy-4-nitro-*	4-Nitroalizarin. $C_{14}H_7NO_6$. See a1248	285.22	gold-ye nd (aa or al)	289d	sub d			δ	s			s	sulf, chl, aa s	B8², 491
a1301	—,1,8-dihydroxy-2,4,5,7-tetrabromo-*	2,4,5,7-Tetrabromochrysazin. $C_{14}H_4Br_4O_4$. See a1248	555.82	og-ye nd (bz)	312	. . . . . .							δ	dil KOH s aa δ	B8¹, 722
a1302	—,1,4-dihydroxy-5,6,7,8-tetrachloro-*	5,6,7,8-Tetrachloro-quinizarine. $C_{14}H_4Cl_4O_4$. See a1248	378.00	red pl (aa)	270	. . . . . .				δ	δ		s	NaOH s aa s^h	B8¹, 716
a1303	—,1,8-dihydroxy-2,4,5,7-tetranitro-*	Chrysammic acid. Chrysamminic acid. $C_{14}H_4N_4O_{12}$. See a1248	420.21	ye pl or lf	exp	d			δ	s	s			ac s	B8¹, 723
a1304	—,1,2-dimethyl-*	$C_{16}H_{12}O_2$. See a1248	236.27	nd (ace or aa)	156	. . . . . .			i	s	s	s^h	s	aa s^h	B7², 743
a1305	—,1,3-dimethyl-*	$C_{16}H_{12}O_2$. See a1248	236.27	nd (aa)	162	. . . . . .			i	δ			δ	aa s^h	B7², 743
a1306	—,1,4-dimethyl-*	$C_{16}H_{12}O_2$. See a1248	236.27	ye nd (al, sub)	140–1	sub			i	δ s^h			s	xyl, aa s	B7², 743
Ω a1307	—,2,3-dimethyl-*	$C_{16}H_{12}O_2$. See a1248	236.27	ye nd (al, to or xyl), cr (aa)	210	sub				s^h			s^h	xyl s². aa s^h	B7², 744
a1308	—,2,6-dimethyl-*	$C_{16}H_{12}O_2$. See a1248	236.27	ye nd (aa or al)	242	sub				δ^h				to, PhNO₂ s aa s^h	B7², 744
a1309	—,2,7-dimethyl-*	$C_{16}H_{12}O_2$. See a1248	236.27	yesh nd (al)	170	. . . . . .			i	s^h					B7², 744
a1310	—,1,3-dinitro-*	$C_{14}H_6N_2O_6$. See a1248	298.21	ye nd (HNO₃)	246–50 (240)	. . . . . .			i					HNO₃ s	E13, 436
a1311	—,1,5-dinitro-*	$C_{14}H_6N_2O_6$. See a1248	298.21	pa ye nd (xyl or PhNO₂), ye cr (sub) λ^{diox} 258 (4.6), 322 (3.7), 400 sh (2.2)	422 (385)	sub			i	δ^h	δ^h		δ^h	PhNO₂ v con sulf δ, aa δ	B7², 721
a1312	—,2-ethyl-1-nitro-*	$C_{16}H_{11}NO_4$. See a1248	281.27	yesh br (aa)	226	. . . . . .							. . .	aa δ	B7², 743
a1313	—,1,2,3,5,6,7-hexahydroxy-*	Rufigallol. Rufigallic acid. $C_{14}H_8O_8$. See a1248	304.23	red rh, red-ye nd (sub) λ^{al} 222 (4.18), 258 (3.85), 295 (4.64), 349 (3.92), 438 (3.92)	. . . .	sub d			i	δ s^h	δ s^h	s		alk s	E13, 613
Ω a1314	—,1-hydroxy-*	Erythroxyanthraquinone. $C_{14}H_8O_3$. See a1248	224.23	red-og nd (al, sub) λ^{MeOH} 252 (4.46), 266 (4.15), 327 (3.52), 402 (3.74)	194–5	sub			i	s	s	. . .	s	liq NH₃ δ	B8², 388
Ω a1315	—,2-hydroxy-*	$C_{14}H_8O_3$. See a1248	224.23	ye pl or nd (al or aa), ye lf (sub) λ^{al} 250 (4.4), 277 (4.3), 340 (3.5), 406 (3.7)	306	sub			i	s	s			aq NH₃, KOH s	B8², 393
Ω a1316	—,2-methyl-*	$C_{15}H_{10}O_2$. See a1248	222.25	yesh nd (al, aa or sub)	182–3 (177–9)	sub			i	v	δ	. . .	s	con sulf v aa s	B7², 733
Ω a1317	—,1-methyl-amino-*	$C_{15}H_{11}NO_2$. See a1248	237.26	ye-red nd	170	. . . . . .					s			chl, aa s	B14², 100
a1318	—,2-methyl amino-*	$C_{15}H_{11}NO_2$. See a1248	237.26	red nd (aa)	226–7	. . . . . .					s	δ		aa, to v chl s	B14², 108
a1319	—,2-methyl-1-nitro-*	$C_{15}H_9NO_4$. See a1248	267.24	pa ye nd (aa)	270–1	. . . . . .			i	i^h	δ^h		δ^h	PhNO₂ s chl δ aa δ^h	E13, 433
a1320	—,6-methyl-1,2,5-trihydroxy-*	Morindone. $C_{15}H_{10}O_5$. See a1248	270.25	og-red nd (to)	282				i	v	v		v	Py v sulf s (bl-vt)	E13, 588
a1321	—,6-methyl-1,3,8-trihydroxy-*	Emodin. Frangula-emodine. $C_{15}H_{10}O_5$. See a1248	270.25	og-red mcl nd (aa), cr (dil aa + 1w) og nd (dil Py) λ^{MeOH} 220 (4.5), 245 (4.2), 290 (4.3), 440 (3.95)	256–7	sub			i	s	δ		i	alk s aa δ chl, CCl₄, CS₂ i	B8², 563
a1322	—,1-nitro-*	$C_{14}H_7NO_4$. See a1248	253.22	yesh pr (ace), nd (aa) λ^{MeOH} 255 (4.57), 325 (3.63)	232.5–3.5	270–1⁷			i	δ	δ	s	s	chl, aa s	B7², 719
a1323	—,2-nitro-*	$C_{14}H_7NO_4$. See a1248	253.22	ye nd (aa or al) λ^{MeOH} 258 (4.60), 323 (3.72), 420 (1.30)	184.5–5	sub			i	δ	δ	s	. . .	sulf, chl s aa s^h lig δ	B7², 720
a1324	—,1,2,4,5,8-pentahydroxy-*	Alizarin cyanine R. Alizarin pentacyanine. $C_{14}H_8O_7$. See a1248	288.24	br lf (PhNO₂)	d	sub								alk, sulf s (bl with red flr)	E13, 613

For explanations, symbols and abbreviations see beginning of table. For structural formulas see end of table.

No.	Name	Synonyms and Formula	Mol. wt.	Color, crystalline form, specific rotation and λ_{max} (log ε)	m.p. °C	b.p. °C	Density	n_D	w	al	eth	ace	bz	other solvents	Ref.
	Anthraquinone														
a1325	—,1,2,4,6-tetra-hydroxy-*	Hydroxyflavopurpurin. $C_{14}H_8O_6$. See a1248	272.23	dk red nd (sub)	....					v			...	Py v aa δ	B8², 582
a1326	—,1,2,4,7-tetra-hydroxy-*	4-Hydroxyanthrapurpurin. $C_{14}H_8O_6$. See a1248	272.23	red-ye (al, Py or aa)	....					s				con sulf, NH₃ s	B8², 582
a1327	—,1,2,5,6-tetra-hydroxy-*	Rufiopin. $C_{14}H_8O_6$. See a1248	272.23	og-red nd (Py)	340	sub			s^h	s	δ	...	δ	aa s chl δ	B8², 583
a1328	—,1,2,5,8-tetra-hydroxy-*	Quinalizarin. $C_{14}H_8O_6$. See a1248	272.23	red nd (PhNO₂)	>275	sub			i	δ	δ	δ	δ	alk, os, aa δ	B8², 584
a1329	—,1,2,6,7-tetra-hydroxy-*	$C_{14}H_8O_6$. See a1248	272.23	og nd (PhNO₂)	>330					δ			δ^h	xyl δ^h PhNO₂ δ, s^h	B8², 584
a1330	—,1,2,7,8-tetra-hydroxy-*	$C_{14}H_8O_6$. See a1248	272.23	red nd or pr (aa)	318d					δ			δ^h	sulf, Py, NaOH s, PhNO₂, aa δ	B8², 585
a1331	—,1,3,5,7-tetra-hydroxy-*	Anthrachrysone. $C_{14}H_8O_6$. See a1248	272.23	yesh nd (al + 2w)	150–60d (+2w) >360 (anh)	sub			i	s	δ	s	s	CS₂ i chl, lig δ aa s	B8², 585
a1332	—,1,4,5,8-tetra-hydroxy-*	$C_{14}H_8O_6$. See a1248	272.23	gr nd (aa), br nd (bz-lig) λ^{peth} 488 (4.1), 523 (4.4), 548 (4.4), 562 (4.5)	>300	sub			i	s	...		...	alk s Ac₂O δ	B8², 586
Ω a1333	—,1,2,3-tri-hydroxy-*	Anthragallic acid. Anthragallol. $C_{14}H_8O_5$. See a1248	256.23	ye nd (dil al), br (aa), og nd (sub) λ^{al} 245 (4.30), 287 (4.49), 414 (3.81)	313	sub at 290				δ	s	s	...	CS₂, aa s sulf, alk δ	B8², 549
a1334	—,1,2,4-tri-hydroxy-*	Purpurin. $C_{14}H_8O_5$. See a1248	256.23	og-red, dk red or og-ye nd (al)	259	sub			δ^h	v^h	s	...	v^h	aa v^h	B8, 509
a1335	—,1,2,5-tri-hydroxy-*	2-Hydroxyanthrarufin. $C_{14}H_8O_5$. See a1248	256.23	red nd (gl aa, sub)	278 (274)				i		s				B8², 554
Ω a1336	—,1,2,6-tri-hydroxy-*	Flavopurpurin. $C_{14}H_8O_5$. See a1248	256.23	ye nd (al)	>330 (sub >160)	459 par d			s^h	s	δ	...	s	alk (vt)	B8², 555
Ω a1337	—,1,2,7-tri-hydroxy-*	Anthrapurpurin. $C_{14}H_8O_5$. See a1248	256.23	og nd (al)	374 (sub 170)	462⁷⁶⁰ par d			δ^h	s^h	δ	...	i	chl, aa s^h	B8², 555
a1338	—,1,2,8-tri-hydroxy-*	2-Hydroxychrysazin. $C_{14}H_8O_5$. See a1248	256.23	red nd (aa, sub)	239–40	sub			i	δ					B8², 557
a1339	—,1,3,8-tri-hydroxy-*	$C_{14}H_8O_5$. See a1248	256.23	bt red-br nd (bz), gold-ye pl (AcOEt) λ^{al} 256 (4.2), 292 (4.1), 450 (3.9)	287–8				δ				...	con sulf (red-og) con alk s (red)	B8², 557
a1340	—,1,4,5-tri-hydroxy-*	5-Hydroxyquinizarin. $C_{14}H_8O_5$. See a1248	256.23	red-br nd or lf (PhNO₂), dk red nd (Py) λ^{cy} 480 (4.08), 495 (4.13), 516 (4.04), 529 (4.04)	271	....			δ	δ			...	aa s^h	B8², 557
a1341	—,1,4,6-tri-hydroxy-*	6-Hydroxyquinizarin. $C_{14}H_8O_5$. See a1248	256.23	bt red nd (al), br pw	>300 (256)	....			δ	s			...	alk, Py s chl δ	B8², 558
Ω a1342	**9,10-Anthra-quinone-2-carboxylic acid**		252.23	ye nd (aa)	290–2	sub			...	δ	i	s	i	aa δ	B10², 581
a1342¹	—,1,3-dihydroxy-	Munjistin. $C_{15}H_8O_6$. See a1342	284.24	ye nd (al-w + 1w), lf (aa)	230–1	sub			δ s^h	v^h	s	...	s	chl, sulf, alk s aa s	B10², 761
a1343	—,1,4-dihydroxy-	$C_{15}H_8O_6$. See a1342	284.24	ye br or red nd (PhNO₂)	249–50	....				δ	δ	s	δ	to, alk s aa s^h	B10¹, 509
a1344	—,4,5-dihydroxy-	Cassic acid. Rhein. $C_{15}H_8O_6$. See a1342	284.24	ye or og nd (MeOH, Py) $\lambda^{95 \% al}$ 230 (4.62), 255 (4.32), 440 (4.04)	321–1.5	sub			δ^h	δ	δ	δ	δ	Py v, sulf, alk s chl δ	B10¹, 510
a1345	—,4,5-dihydroxy-7-methoxy-	Emodic acid monomethyl ether. Parietinic acid. $C_{16}H_{10}O_7$. See a1342	314.26	red-br or ye nd (sub)	300	sub							...	os δ	B10², 767
a1346	—,1-nitro-	$C_{15}H_7NO_6$. See a1342	297.23	nd (al or aa)	288d				...	s^h	i	s^h	...	aa s^h lig i	B10², 586
a1347	—,—,chloride.	$C_{15}H_6ClNO_5$. See a1342	315.67	....	243–4				d^h	d^h				....	E13, 665
a1348	—,5-nitro-	$C_{15}H_7NO_6$. See a1342	297.23	yesh nd (aa)	....								...	sulf, aa s	E13, 665

For explanations, symbols and abbreviations see beginning of table. For structural formulas see end of table.

9,10-Anthraquinone

No.	Name	Synonyms and Formula	Mol. wt.	Color, crystalline form, specific rotation and λ_{max} (log ε)	m.p. °C	b.p. °C	Density	n_D	w	al	eth	ace	bz	other solvents	Ref.
a1349	9,10-Anthra-quinone-1,5-disulfonic acid	. . . .	368.35	ye nd (HCl +4w), pl (dil aa +4w) $\lambda^{NH_3 salt}$ 255 (4.5)	310–1d	. . . .			v	s		δ	δ	sulf, aa s chl δ	B11[2], 195
a1350	9,10-Anthra-quinone-1,6-disulfonic acid	. . . .	368.35	ye nd (HCl + 5w), gold pr (dil aa + 5w)	215–7d	. . . .			v					aa s	B11[2], 196
a1351	9,10-Anthra-quinone-1,7-disulfonic acid	. . . .	368.35	ye hyg pw (dil aa +4w)	d at 120	. . . .			v	v		. . .		aa s	B11[2], 197
a1352	9,10-Anthra-quinone-1,8-disulfonic acid	. . . .	368.35	ye nd(+5w)	293–4d	. . . .			v	s				aa s	B11[2], 197
Ω a1353	9,10-Anthra-quinone-1-sulfonic acid	α-Sulfoanthraquinone	288.29	lf (aa), ye lf (con HCl +3w) λ^w 257 (4.61), 328 (3.63)	214 (cor) (anh) 218 (hyd)	. . . .			v	s				aa v^h	B11[2], 192
Ω a1354	9,10-Anthra-quinone-2-sulfonic acid	β-Sulfoanthraquinone	288.29	ye lf (+3w)		. . . .			v	s	i				B11[2], 193
a1355	—,amide	$C_{14}H_9NO_4S$. See a1354	287.30	ye nd (aa)	261	. . . .				δ				CS_2, to, chl δ	B11, 339
a1356	9,10-Anthra-quinone-1-sulfonic acid, 5-chloro-	$C_{14}H_7ClO_5S$. See a1353	322.73	ye rh pr (HCl or aa +4w)	236–7	. . . .			v					sulf s (ye)	E13, 707
a1357	9,10-Anthra-quinone-2-sulfonic acid, 5-nitro-	$C_{14}H_7NO_7S$. See a1354	333.28	yesh pl (dil HNO_3)	255d	. . . .			δ v^h					dil HNO_3 s^h	B11[2], 195
—	Anthrarufin	see 9,10-Anthraquinone, 1,5-dihydroxy-*													
—	Anthroic acid	see Anthracenecarboxylic acid													
—	9-Anthrone	see Anthracene,9,10-dihydro-9-oxo-													
a1358	Antimalarine	Plasmocid.	287.41	. . . .		$182^{1.0}$	1.0569_4^{24}	1.5855^{24}			δ			dil HCl s	C40, 3563
a1359	Antipyrine (α-form)	Analgesine. 2,3-Dimethyl-1-phenyl-5-pyrazolone. Phenazone.	188.23	mcl lf or sc (w, bz or eth) λ^{al} 223 (3.91), 247 (3.97), 273 (3.98)	114	319^{741} $211–2^{10}$	1.0747_4^{130}	1.5697	v	v	δ		s	chl v Py s lig, liq SO_2 δ	B24[2], 11
a1360	—(β-form)	$C_{11}H_{12}N_2O$. See a1359	188.23	cr (unst)	109 (β → α at 18)	. . . .					δ			. . . .	B24[2], 11
a1361	—,2-hydroxy-benzoate	Salazolon. Salipyrazolone. Salipyrine. $C_{11}H_{12}N_2O.C_7H_6O_3$. See a1359	326.35	pw	92	. . . .			δ s^h	v^h	δ			chl v^h	B24[1], 197
a1362	—,m-amino-	$C_{11}H_{13}N_3O$. See a1359	203.25	redsh in air (bz)	148	. . . .			s	s	i			chl s	B24[1], 210
a1363	—,o-amino-	$C_{11}H_{13}N_3O$. See a1359	203.25	nd (AcOEt-eth)	165	. . . .			s	s				chl s	B24[1], 210
a1364	—,p-bromo-	$C_{11}H_{11}BrN_2O$. See a1359 . . .	267.13	nd (w)	122	300^9			s s^h	v	s^h			chl, to v	B24, 33
a1365	—,p-dimethyl-amino-	$C_{13}H_{17}N_3O$. See a1359	231.30	pr or pl (lig or AcOEt) λ^{al} 255 (4.04)	134–5	. . . .			s	s	δ		s	lig δ	B24, 46
—	Antipyrine chloral	see Hypnal													
a1366	Aphanin	$C_{40}H_{54}O$	550.88	bl-bk lf (bz-MeOH) λ^{chl} 474, 504	178	. . . .			i	δ	δ		δ	CS_2, chl v	C32, 3454
a1367	Aphylline	$C_{15}H_{24}N_2O$	248.37	$[α]_D^{20} +10.3$ (MeOH, c = 20)	52–7	200^4			s	s	s		s	dil HCl v	C26, 2742
—	Apigenin	see Flavone,4',5,7-tri-hydroxy-													
a1368	Apiol	2,5-Dimethoxysafrole. Parsley camphor.	222.24	nd	29.5	294 179^{33}	1.015_4^{20}	1.5360^{20}	i	s	s	s	s	chl, lig s	B19[2], 98
a1369	Apoatropine	Atropamine. $C_{17}H_{21}NO_2$ . .	271.36	pr (chl)	62	. . . .			δ	v	v	v	v	chl, CS_2 v lig δ	B21[2], 18
Ω a1370	—,hydrochloride . .	$C_{17}H_{21}NO_2.HCl$. See a1369 .	307.82	lf (w)	239	. . . .			δ s^h	δ	i	δ			B21[1], 197
a1371	Apocinchonidine . . .	$C_{19}H_{22}N_2O$. See a1372	294.40	lf (al), $[α]_D^{20}$ −139.3 (chl-al, c = 2)	252	. . . .			i	v	δ			chl v lig δ	B23[1], 131
a1372	Apocinchonine	Allocinchonine. $C_{19}H_{22}N_2O$.	294.40	pr (al), $[α]_D^{20}$ +167.4 (abs al, c = 3)	219	. . . .			i	s v^h			δ	chl δ, lig δ	B23[1], 131

For explanations, symbols and abbreviations see beginning of table. For structural formulas see end of table.

No.	Name	Synonyms and Formula	Mol. wt.	Color, crystalline form, specific rotation and λ_{max} (log ε)	m.p. °C	b.p. °C	Density	n_D	w	al	eth	ace	bz	other solvents	Ref.
	Apocinchonine														
a1373	—,hydrochloride	$C_{19}H_{22}N_2O.HCl.2H_2O.$ See a1372	366.89	nd (+2w) $[\alpha]_D^{16}+139$ (w, c = 0.006)	....				s	...	i	...	i	....	B23, 419
a1374	**Apocodeine**	Apomorphine 3-methyl ether. Pseudoapocodeine. $C_{18}H_{19}NO_2$.	281.36	pr (MeOH) $[\alpha]_D^{23}-90$ (abs al, c = 0.449) λ 280 (4.05), 313 (3.50)	122.5–4.5 (anh)				...	δ	s	s	s	lig s	B21, 188
a1375	—,(ethanol solvate)	$C_{18}H_{19}NO_2.C_2H_5OH$ See a1374	327.43	lf(al +1)	104.5–6.5					s^h				....	B21, 188
a1376	—,(methanol solvate)	$C_{18}H_{19}NO_2.CH_3OH$ See a1374	313.40	nd(MeOH +1)	85									MeOH s^h	B21, 188
—	**Apocupreine**	see **Apoquinine**													
a1377	**Apocyclene**		122.21	cr (al)	42.5–43	$138–9^{764}$	0.8710_4^{40}	1.4514^{40}	i	s	s	...	s	aa s	E13, 1042
—	**Apocynin**	see **Acetophenone,4-hydroxy-3-methoxy-**													
—	**Apofencho-camphoric acid**	see **1,3-Cyclopentane dicarboxylic acid, 4,4-dimethyl-***													
a1378	**Apomorphine**	$C_{17}H_{17}NO_2$	267.33	hex pl (chl-peth), rods (eth +1), gr in air $\lambda^{ey}280$ (384), 288 (3.81)	195d				δ	s	s	s	s	chl, alk s HCl, lig δ	B21², 142
Ω a1379	—,hydrochloride	$C_{17}H_{17}NO_2.HCl.\frac{1}{2}H_2O$ See a1378	312.80	gr in air, mcl pr $[\alpha]_D^{25}-48$ (w, c = 1.2) $\lambda^w 274$ (4.22), 306 sh (3.52)	200–10d				δ s^h	δ	δ	...	...	chl δ	B21², 143
—	**Aponal**	see **Carbamic acid, 2-methyl-2-butyl ester.**													
a1380	**Apoquinine** (α-form)	Apocupreine. $C_{19}H_{22}N_2O_2$.	310.40	pr (eth), $[\alpha]_D^{20}$ -214.8 (al)	184d				i s^h	s	δ	δ	s	KOH s chl δ	B23², 412
a1381	—(β-form)	$C_{19}H_{22}N_2O_2.2H_2O$. See a1380	346.43	$[\alpha]_D^{20}-194$ (al)	190d				i	s	...	δ	...	......	B23², 412
a1382	**Aposafranone**	Benzeneindone. 10-Phenyl-2-phenazinone.	272.31	br, gr (red in sol), nd (al)	248–9				δ^h	s			s	dil ac s	B23², 364
a1383	**Arabinose** (D) (α-form)		150.13	cr (MeOH), $[\alpha]_D^{20}+105$ (cor)	155.5–6.5		1.585		v	δ	i	i		MeOH i	B31, 32
a1384	—(D) (β-form)	$C_5H_{10}O_5$. See a1383	150.13	(aq MeOH) $[\alpha]_D^{20}-175 \rightarrow -108$ (mut)	155.5–6.5		1.625		v	δ	i	i	...	MeOH i	B31, 32
a1385	—(DL)	Pectinose. $C_5H_{10}O_5$. See a1383	150.13	pr, nd (al)	164.5 (cor)		1.585_4^{20}		v	δ	i	...	i		B31, 46
a1386	—(L) (α-form)		150.13	orh cr (pr), cr (dil al)	159–60		1.585_4^{20}		v	δ	i				B31, 34
a1387	—(L) (β-form)	$C_5H_{10}O_5$. See a1386	150.13	orh, $[\alpha]_D^{20}$ $+190.6$ $\rightarrow +104.5$ (c = 3) (mut)	159–60		1.625_4^{20}		v	δ	i				B31, 34
a1388	—, diphenyl-hydrazone (D)		316.36	orh pr (dil al)	207				δ	δ			i		B31, 33
a1389	—,—(DL)	$C_{17}H_{20}N_2O_4$. See a1388	316.36	nd (aq Py)	206				i δ^h	i δ^h	i			Py v CS_2 i	B31, 47
a1390	—,—(L)		316.36	orh pr, nd (dil al), $[\alpha]_D^{20}$ $+18.5$ (Py)	204–5				δ	s^h	i				B31, 44
Ω a1391	**Arabitol** (D)	Arabite. D-Lyxitol. 1,2,3,4,5-Pentanepentol	152.15	pr (dil al) $[\alpha]_D^{20}+11.8$ (borax sol, c = 9.5)	103–4				v	δ	i				B1, 531
a1392	—(DL)	$C_5H_{12}O_5$. See a1391	152.15	pr (90 % al), cr (al-ace)	106				v	δ	i				B1, 531
Ω a1393	—(L)	$C_5H_{12}O_5$. See a1391	152.15	$[\alpha]_D -5.4$ (borax sol)	102–3				v	δ	i				B1², 604
a1394	**Arabonic acid** (D)		166.13	(dil aa), $[\alpha]_D^{25}$ $+10.5$ (c = 6.0)	114–16				v	s	i			aa δ	B3², 303
a1395	—(DL)	$C_5H_{10}O_6$. See a1394	166.13						s		i		i		B2², 982
a1396	—(L)	$C_5H_{10}O_6$. See a1394	166.13	cr (al or MeOH) $[\alpha]_D^{20}-9.6$ $\rightarrow -41.7$ (21 days) (w, c = 2.5) (mut)	118–9				v		i		i		B3², 303
—	**Arachidic acid**	see **Eicosanoic acid***													
	Arachidonic acid	see **6,10,14,18-Eicosatetrae-noic acid***													

For explanations, symbols and abbreviations see beginning of table. For structural formulas see end of table.

No.	Name	Synonyms and Formula	Mol. wt.	Color, crystalline form, specific rotation and λ_{max} (log ε)	m.p. °C	b.p. °C	Density	n_D	w	al	eth	ace	bz	other solvents	Ref.
	Aramite														
a1397	Aramite	Niagaramite. $C_{15}H_{23}ClO_4S$	334.87	....	−37.1	195^2 $175^{00.1}$	1.145^{20}_{20}	1.5100^{20}	i	s	v	v	v	os v	M, 97
Ω a1398	Arbutin	Hydroquinone β-d-gluco-pyranoside. Uvasol. $C_{12}H_{16}O_7$.	272.24	nd (w +1) $[\alpha]^{25}_D - 64$ (w, c − 3) λ^{al} 290 (1.55)	199.5– 200(st) (anh) 165 (unst)	....	....	....	v	s	δ	...	i	chl, CS, i	B31, 210
a1399	—, hydrate	$C_{12}H_{16}O_7 . H_2O$. See a1398	290.27	$[\alpha]^{17}_D - 60.3$ (w, p = 5)	142	....	....	....		s		...	i	....	B31, 210
a1400	Arecaidine	Arecaine. N-Methylguvacine. 1-Methyl-1,2,5,6-tetrahydro-nicotinic acid. $C_7H_{11}NO_2$.	141.16	pl (dil al), ta (dil al +1 w)	232(anh)	....	....	....	v	i	i	...	i	dil al v chl i	B22[2], 12
a1401	Arecoline	Arecaidine methyl ester. Methyl 1-methyl-1,2,5,6-tetrahydro nicotinate. $C_8H_{13}NO_2$.	155.20	$\lambda^{al}214(4.03)$	....	209(220) 94^{17}	1.0504^{20}_{20}	1.4860^{20}	∞	∞	∞	...		chl s	B22[2], 12
Ω a1402	—, hydrobromide	$C_8H_{13}NO_2 . HBr$. See a1401	236.12	mcl pr (al)	172(177.4 −7.9)	....	....	....	v	s v^h	δ	...		chl δ	B22[2], 12
Ω a1403	—, hydrochloride	$C_8H_{13}NO_2 . HCl$. See a1401	191.66	nd (al)	157–8	....	....	....	s	s	δ	...		chl δ	B22[1], 490
Ω a1404	Arginine (DL)	DL-2-Amino-5-guanido-pentanoic acid*. $H_2NC(:NH)NH(CH_2)_3CH(NH_2)CO_2H$	174.20	$\lambda^w 205$ (3.28)	217–8	....	....	....	i	i	i	...	i	.,...	B4[2], 850
Ω a1405	—(L)	$H_2NC(:NH)NH(CH_2)_3CH(NH_2)CO_2H$	174.20	pr (+2w), anh mcl pl (60 % al), $[\alpha]^{20}_D + 12.5$ (w, c = 3.5) $\lambda^w 205$ (3.28)	244d (223d) (anh) 105d (hyd)	....	....	....	s	δ	i	...			B4[2], 845
a1406	—, diflavianate (l)	$C_6H_{14}N_4O_2 . (C_{10}H_6N_2O_8S)_2$. See a1405	802.67	ye nd	202d	....	....	....	d	d	...	...		ac i	B4[2], 848
a1407	—, dipicrate (dl)	$C_6H_{14}N_4O_2 . 2C_6H_3N_3O_7$. See a1404	632.42		196d	....	....	....				...			B4[2], 850
a1408	—, —(l)	$C_6H_{14}N_4O_2 . 2C_6H_3N_3O_7$. See a1405	632.42		200d	....	....	....		i		...			B4[2], 848
a1409	—, flavianate (l)	$C_6H_{14}N_4O_2 . C_{10}H_6N_2O_8S$. See a1405	488.44	ye-og lf	258–60d	....	....	....	i	i	i	...			B4[2], 847
a1410	—, picrate (d)	$C_6H_{14}N_4O_2 . C_6H_3N_3O_7 . 2H_2O$. See a1404	439.34	nd (w)	217–8d	....	....	....	δ			...			B6, 287
a1411	—, —(dl)	$C_6H_{14}N_4O_2 . C_6H_3N_3O_7$. See a1404	403.31	pr (w)	200(223d)	....	....	....	i	i	i	...			B4[2], 851
a1412	—, —(l)	$C_6H_{14}N_4O_2 . C_6H_3N_3O_7 . 2H_2O$. See a1405	439.34	ye nd (w)	217–8d	....	....	....	δ	i	i	...			B4[2], 848
a1413	—, benzylidene (l)	$C_{13}H_{18}N_4O_2$. See a1405	262.32	lf(w)	204–5	....	....	....	s^h			...		MeOH, ac s alk i	B4[2], 848
—	Arsanilic acid	see Benzenearsonic acid, 4-amino-*													
a1414	Arsenic acid, triethyl ester*	Ethyl arsenate*. $(C_2H_5O)_3AsO$	226.11	....	....	235–8 118– $20^{15.5}$	1.3023^{20}_0	1.4343^{20}	d						B1[2], 332
a1415	Arsenous acid, triethyl ester*.	Ethyl arsenite.* $(C_2H_5O)_3As$	210.11	....	....	165–6 66.5– 7^{12}	1.2239^{20}_4	1.4369^{13}	d						B1[2], 332
a1416	Arsine, bis(penta-fluoroethyl)-iodo-*	$(CF_3CF_2)_2AsI$	439.86	....	....	120^{760}	....	....							C49, 14635
a1416[1]	—, bis(trifluoro-methyl)-*	$(CF_3)_2AsH$	213.94	....	....	19^{760} $−25^{108}$	....	....							J1953, 1552
a1417	—, bis(trifluoro-methyl)bromo-*	$(CF_3)_2AsBr$	292.84		....	59.5^{745}	....	1.398^{20}	i						J1953, 1552
a1418	—, bis(trifluoro-methyl) chloro*	$(CF_3)_2AsCl$	248.39		....	46^{760}	....	1.351^{19}							J1953, 1552
a1419	—, bis(trifluoro-methyl) fluoro-*	$(CF_3)_2AsF$	231.93		....	25^{760}	....	....							J1953, 1552
a1420	—, bis(trifluoro-methyl)iodo-*	$(CF_3)_2AsI$	339.84	ye oil $\lambda^{eth} 287$ (3.08)	....	92^{760}	....	1.425^{25}	i $δ^h$d		s				J1953, 1552
a1421	—, bis(trifluoro-methyl)methyl-*	$(CF_3)_2AsCH_3$	227.97		....	52^{760}	....	....							J1953, 1552
a1422	—, chloro-(diphenyl)-*	$(C_6H_5)_2AsCl$	264.59	rh pl (peth)	44	333^{760} 193^{20}	1.48204^{16}_4	1.6332^{56}	i	v	s	s	s		B16[1], 437
a1423	—, dibromo(tri-fluoromethyl)-*'	CF_3AsBr_2	303.75		....	118^{745}	....	1.528^{20}							J1953, 1552
a1424	—, dichloro-(methyl)-*	CH_3AsCl_2	160.86		−42.5	133 37^{25}	1.8358^{20}	1.5677^{15}	δ	v	s			os s	B4[2], 979
a1425	—, dichloro-(phenyl)-*	$C_6H_5AsCl_2$	222.93		....	254.4–7.6 131^{14}	1.6516^{19}_4	1.6386^{15}	i	v	s	s	s		B16[2], 411
a1426	—, dichloro(tri-fluoromethyl)-*	CF_3AsCl_2	214.83		....	71	....	1.431^{20}	i	s		s			J1953, 1552
a1427	—, diethyl-*	$(C_2H_5)_2AsH$	134.05		....	105(97)	1.1338^{24}	1.4709	δ	s	v	s	v		B4[2], 980
a1428	—, (difluoro)-ethenyl, 2-chloro-*	$ClCH:CHAsF_2$	174.41		....	>140d 43.5^{15}	....	....	d						B4[3], 1809

For explanations, symbols and abbreviations see beginning of table. For structural formulas see end of table.

C-122

No.	Name	Synonyms and Formula	Mol. wt.	Color, crystalline form, specific rotation and λ_{max} (log ε)	m.p. °C	b.p. °C	Density	n_D	Solubility						Ref.
									w	al	eth	ace	bz	other solvents	
	Arsine														
a1429	—, difluoro-(ethyl)-*	$C_2H_5AsF_2$	141.98	fum in air	−38.7	94.3 74[100]	1.708[17]	....	d	...	...	...	...		B4[3], 1799
a1430	—, difluoro-(methyl)-*	CH_3AsF_2	127.95	fum in air	−29.7	76.5	1.924[18]	....	d	...	...	...	...		B4[3], 1796
a1431	—, difluoro-(phenyl)-*	$C_6H_5AsF_2$	190.03	wax	42	110[48]			d						J1946, 1123
a1432	—, diiodo(tri-fluoromethyl)-*	CF_3AsI_2	397.74	λ^{eth} 230 (3.74), 267 (3.60)		183 δd 100[48]			d						J1953, 1552
a1433	—, dimethyl-*	Cacodyl hydride. $(CH_3)_2AsH$.	106.00	ign in air	....	36[760]	1.213$^{29}_{29}$		δ	∞	∞	∞	∞	chl, CS_2, aa ∞	B4[2], 978
a1434	—, dimethyl(tri-fluoromethyl)-*	$(CH_3)_2AsCF_3$	174.00	....		58									J1953, 1552
a1435	—, diphenyl-*	$(C_6H_5)_2AsH$	230.14	oil	....	174[25]	1.30$^{25}_{25}$		i	s	s				B16[2], 406
a1436	—, ethyl-*	$C_2H_5AsH_2$	106.00		....	36[760]	1.217$^{22}_{22}$		i	s	s				B4[2], 980
a1437	—, methyl-*	CH_3AsH_2	91.97		−143	2[760]			δ	∞	∞			CS_2 ∞	B4[2], 978
a1438	—, triethyl-*	$(C_2H_5)_3As$	162.11			138–9[760]	1.150$^{20}_x$	1.467[20]	i	∞	∞				B4[2], 980
a1439	—, (trifluoro-methyl)-*	CF_3AsH_2	145.94			−11.6[781]									J1953, 1552
a1440	—, trimethyl-*	$(CH_3)_3As$	120.03		−87.3	52[760]	1.144[15]		δ	s	s		s		B4[2], 978
a1441	—, triphenyl-*	$(C_6H_5)_3As$	306.24	tcl pr (bz, eth-peth) λ^{al} 248 (4.12)	60.5–1.5	360 (under CO_2)	1.2634$^{48}_4$	1.6888[21]	i	δ	v		v		B16[2], 407
a1442	—, tris(penta-fluoroethyl)-*	$(CF_3CF_2)_3As$	431.96			96–3									C49, 14635
a1443	—, tris(trifluoro-methyl)-*	$(CF_3)_3As$	281.94			33.3			i	...	s				J1952, 2198
a1444	Arsine oxide, 4-methoxy-phenyl-		198.05	cr (chl-eth or bz-peth)	114–6 (anh)								s	chl s	B16[2], 448
a1445	—, methyl-*	Methylarsinic acid anhydride. CH_3AsO	105.96	pr (CS_2), (al)	95	275d			i	s	δ	...	s	chl s	B4[2], 992
a1446	—, phenyl-	C_6H_5AsO	168.03	cr (bz-eth or chl-eth) λ^{al} 216 (3.97), 234 (3.72)	144–6 (127–30)				i	δ v[h]	i		v[h]	chl v	B16[2], 443
a1447	—, 2-tolyl-		182.06	pw	145–6				v[h]	...	i			alk δ	B16, 861
a1448	—, 4-tolyl-		182.06	pw	156				v[h]	...	i			alk δ	B16, 861
a1449	Arsinic acid, bis(trifluoro-methyl)-*	Perfluorocacodylic acid, $(CF_3)_2AsO_2H$	245.94	nd (sub), rh(w)	150d	10^{-3} sub			s					chl δ^h	J1953, 1552
a1450	—, diphenyl-*	$(C_6H_5)_2AsO_2H$	262.14	nd, pr $\lambda^{0.1\,NHCl}$ 220 (4.26), 263 (3.14)	178				δ s[h]	s	δ		δ	chl s	B16[2], 443
a1451	Arsonium, tetra-phenyl-, bromide	$(C_6H_5)_4AsBr$	463.26		281–4				δ	s		δ		MeOH s	J1940, 1192
a1452	—, —, chloride	$(C_6H_5)_4AsCl$	418.80	λ^{diox} 259 (3.44), 265 (3.48), 272 (3.45)	264–5				v	s		δ		MeOH s	Am 55, 3056
a1453	Artemisic acid	$C_{15}H_{16}O_3$	244.29	nd (dil aa) $[\alpha]_D^{18.5}$ +70.4 (al)	135–6					v	v			aa, lig v	E12B, 3469
—	Arterenol (l)	see Noradrenalin (l)													
—	Artificial musk	see Benzene,1-tert-butyl-3-methyl-2,4,6-trinitro-*													
—	Asaron	see Benzene,1-propenyl-2,4,5-trimethoxy-*													
—	Asaronic acid	see Benzoic acid, 2,4,5-tri-methoxy-*													
Ω a1454	Ascaridole	$C_{10}H_{16}O_2$	168.24	unst, $[\alpha]_D$ −4.14 λ^{al} 238 (3.56), 241 (3.56)	3.3	exp[760] 115[15] 39–40[0.2]	1.0103$^{20}_4$	1.4769[20]	i d[h]	s	...	s	s	os, to, peth s	B19[2], 18
a1455	Ascorbic acid (D)	$C_6H_8O_6$	176.14	pl or mcl nd $[\alpha]_D^{18}$ −48 (MeOH, c = 1) $[\alpha]_D^{20}$ −23.8 (w, c = 3) λ^{al} 254 (3.9)	192d (189d)				v	s	i	...	i	chl i	C54, 3229
a1456	—(DL)	$C_6H_8O_6$. See a1455	176.14	λ^{al} 245 (3.9)	168–9				v	s	i	...	i	chl i	Am 74, 5162
Ω a1457	—(L)	Antiscorbutin. Vitamin C. $C_6H_8O_6$. See a1455	176.14	pl or mcl nd $[\alpha]_D^{20}$ +24 (w, c = 1) $[\alpha]_D^{20}$ +48 (MeOH, c = 1) λ^w 244 (3.98)	192d (189d)		1.65		v	s	i	...	i	chl, peth i	Am 74, 5162
a1458	—, 6-desoxy-(L)		160.14	pr (AcOEt) $[\alpha]_D^{22}$ +36.7 (0.1N HCl, c = 1)	168	sub 160[0.001]			v	s	i	s	i	AcOEt δ	H21, 273

For explanations, symbols and abbreviations see beginning of table. For structural formulas see end of table.

No.	Name	Synonyms and Formula	Mol. wt.	Color, crystalline form, specific rotation and λ_{max} (log ε)	m.p. °C	b.p. °C	Density	n_D	Solubility						Ref.
									w	al	eth	ace	bz	other solvents	
	β-Asparagine														
Ω a1459	β-Asparagine (D) ..	$H_2NCOCH_2CH(NH_2)CO_2H.H_2O$ 150.14		$[\alpha]_D^{20} +5.41$ (w, c = 1.3)	234.5 (anh) 215 (hyd)		1.543_4^{15}	....	δ s^h	i	i	...	i	MeOH i	B4[1], 531
a1460	—(DL)	$C_4H_8N_2O_3.H_2O$. See a1459..	150.14	tcl cr (w + 1), pr(w-al) λ^w 220 sh (2.0)	182–3	213–5d	1.4540_4^{15}	....	δ s^h	i	i	...	i	MeOH i	B4[2], 900
Ω a1461	—(L)	$C_4H_8N_2O_3$. See a1459	132.13	rh (w + 1) $[\alpha]_D^{20} -5.42$ (w, c = 1.3) $\lambda^{w, pH = 10.6}$ 217sh (2.5)	236 (anh)		1.543_4^{15}	....	s v^h	i	i	...	i	MeOH i	B4[2], 896
Ω a1462	**Aspartic acid** (D) ...	Aminosuccinic acid. Asparaginic acid. $HO_2CCH_2CH(NH_2)CO_2H$	133.11	$[\alpha]_D^{20} -25.5$ (HCl)	269–71		1.6613_{13}^{13}	....	s^h	i	i	...	i	dil HCl s	B4[1], 531
Ω a1463	—(DL)	Asparacemic acid. $C_4H_7NO_4$. See a1462.	133.11	mcl pr (w)	338–9 (275 sealed tube)		1.6632_{13}^{13}	....	δ s^h	i	i	...	i	Py i	B4[2], 900
a1464	—(L)	$C_4H_7NO_4$. See a1462..	133.11	rh lf (w) $[\alpha]_D^{20} +4.36$ (w) $[\alpha]_D^{24} +24.6$ (6N HCl, c = 2)	324d (rapid htng) 270–1 (sealed tube)		1.6613_{13}^{13}	....	δ s^h	i	i	...	i	dil HCl s Py i	B4[2], 892 B14[2], 653
Ω a1465	—, N-benzoyl-(L) ..	$HO_2CCH_2CH(NHCOC_6H_5)CO_2H$ 237.21		nd or lf $[\alpha]_D^{20} +37$ (0.76 N NaOH)	171–3			....	δ^h	δ	i	...	..	chl i	B9[2], 185
a1466	**Aspidospermine** ...	Vallesine. $C_{22}H_{30}N_2O_2$	354.50	nd or pr(al), nd(peth) $[\alpha]_D^{15} -100.2$ (al) λ^{MeOH} 220 (4.52), 256 (4.04)	212 sub 180	220[2]			δ	s	δ	...	s	chl s	J1940, 1051
—	**Aspirin**	see **Benzoic acid, 2-hydroxy-, acetate**													
—	**Atabrin**	see **Quinacrine, dihydrochloride** (dl)													
a1467	**Atisine**	Anthorine. $C_{22}H_{33}NO_2$	343.51	rh bipym	57–60				δ	s	s	...	..	chl MeOH-KOH s	Am 78, 4139
a1468	—, hydrochloride ..	$C_{22}H_{33}NO_2$. HCl. See a1467	377.96	nd (dil al) $[\alpha]_D +28$ (w, c = 1.1) λ^{al} < 220	340 (311)				v	v	i	...	..		C36, 4826
—	**Atophan**	see **4-Quinolinecarboxylic acid, 2-phenyl-**													
—	**Atoquinol**	see **4-Quinolinecarboxylic acid, 2-phenyl-, allyl ester**													
—	**Atranol**	see **Benzaldehyde, 2,6-dihydroxy-4-methyl-**													
—	**Atrolactic acid**	see **Propanoic acid, 2-hydroxy-2-phenyl-***													
—	**Atropamine**	see **Apoatropine**													
—	**Atropic acid**	see **Propenoic acid, 2-phenyl-***													
Ω a1469	**Atropine**	dl-Daturine. dl-Hyoscyamine. Troyl tropate. $C_{17}H_{23}NO_3$.	289.36	rh nd (dil al), orh pr (ace) λ^{MeOH} 252 (2.22), 258 (2.29), 262 (2.21)	118–9	sub (vac) 93–110			δ^h	v	s	...	s	chl v dil ac s lig i	B21[2], 19
a1470	—, hydrochloride ..	$C_{17}H_{23}NO_3$. See a1469	325.84	nd (al)	165				3	s	...	...	...		B21, 20
a1471	—, pentanoate	$C_{17}H_{23}NO_3$. $C_5H_{10}O_2 \cdot \frac{1}{2}H_2O$ See a1469	400.52	or	42				∞	∞	δ	...	...		M, 111
a1472	—, sulfate	$2(C_{17}H_{23}NO_3)$. H_2SO_4. H_2O. See a1469.	694.82	nd (al-eth or al-ace) λ^w 252 (2.5), 259 (2.6), 264 (2.4)	194 (anh)	sub			v	v	i	...	..	chl δ	B21[2], 20
—	**Auligen**	see **Xantogen, diethyl-**													
a1473	**Auramine** (base) ...	Bis (p-dimethylaminophenyl) methyleneimine. Apyonin.	267.38	yc or col pl (al) λ^{aa} 270 (3.48), 372 (3.54), 440.5 (3.74)	136				i	s	δ	...	...		B14[2], 58

For explanations, symbols and abbreviations see beginning of table. For structural formulas see end of table.

Auramine

No.	Name	Synonyms and Formula	Mol. wt.	Color. crystalline form. specific rotation and λ_{max} (log ε)	m.p. °C	b.p. °C	Density	n_D	w	al	eth	ace	bz	other solvents	Ref.
a1474	—(dye).........	Auramine hydrochloride. Auramine O. $C_{17}H_{21}N_3 \cdot HCl \cdot H_2O$. See a1473	321.85	ye nd (w) λ^{al} 365 (4.30), 425 (4.79)	267	....	....		δ	s	δ	...	...	chl v	B14[2], 58
a1475	—, N-methyl-	$C_{18}H_{23}N_3$. See a1473......	281.41	ye cr (al)	133				i	s	...	s	δ	aa s	B14, 93
a1476	Aureomycin......	Biomycine. Chlorotetra-cycline. CTC. Duomycine. $C_{22}H_{23}ClN_2O_8$.	478.89	gold ye, ye flr $[\alpha]_D^{23} - 275$ (MeOH) λ^{al} 380 (4.0)	168–9				i	δ	i	δ	δ	Cellosolve, diox s peth i	C47, 7169
Ω a1477	—,hydrochloride ..	$C_{22}H_{23}ClN_2O_8 \cdot HCl$. See a1476	515.35	ye orh $[\alpha]_D^{20} - 106.5$ (dil HCl) $\lambda^{0.01\,NHCl}$ 230 (4.2), 270 (4.2), 345 sh (4.9), 370 (4.0)	216d				δ	...	...	...	...	....	C50, 9696
Ω a1478	Aurin............	Corallin. Pararosolic acid. Rosolic acid.	290.32	dk red lf or rh $\lambda^{10\,\%\,Na_2CO_3}$ 279 (4.2), 525 (4.85)	d 308–10	......			i	s	δ	...	i	alk, aa s chl δ	B8[2],417
a1479	Auxin A.........	Auxenetriolic acid. $C_{18}H_{32}O_5$.	328.45	hex (al-lig) $[\alpha]_D^{20} - 3.19$ (al)	196	....	1.292_4^{19}	....	δ	s	δ	...	i	MeOH, AcOEt s peth i	C45, 2416
a1480	Auxin B.........	Auxenolonic acid. $C_{18}H_{30}O_4$.	310.44	cr (al-lig) $[\alpha]_D^{20} - 2.8$ (al)	183		1.269_4^{20}			s	s				C45, 2416
a1481	1-Azacyclo-octane, 2-methyl-	α-Methyl heptamethylene-imine	127.23	nd (ace)	156–7	$162–3^{746}$	0.853^{20}	1.4620^{21}							B20[1],30
—	Azelaic acid.......	see Nonanedioic acid*													
a1482	Azetidine.........	Trimethyleneimine.	57.09	....	63^{748}		0.8436^{20}	1.4287^{25}	∞	∞	v	v	v		B20, 2
—	Azibenzyl........	see Ketone, benzyl phenyl, α-diazo-													
a1483	Aziridine	Azirane. Dihydroazirine. Ethyleneimine.	43.07	....	56^{756}		0.8321_4^{20}		∞	∞	v	v	v	os ∞	B20[2], 3
a1484	Azo, benzene ethane	Ethylphenyl diimide. $C_6H_5N{:}NC_2H_5$	134.18	bt ye oil	....	$175–85^{760}$ $82.5–3^{20}$	0.9628_4^{20}	α: 1.5313 β: 1.5579	i	s	s	...	s	dil ac δ	B16[2], 3
a1485	—,benzene methane	Methylphenyl diimide. $C_6H_5N{:}NCH_3$	120.17	ye oil λ^{al}287 (3.9), 396 (2.2)		150^{760}d 60^{15}				s	s				B16, 7
a1485[1]	—,benzene 1-naphthalene	....	231.30	dk red lf (al) λ^{al} 219 (4.58), 266 (4.03), 273 (4.03), 290 (3.94), 372 (4.10)	70					s	s	...	s	lig s	B16, 78
a1485[2]	—,benzene 2-naphthalene	....	231.30	ye (al) λ^{al} 219 (4.48), 265 (4.13), 277 (4.13), 287 (4.13), 328 (4.28)	131					s	s	...	s	lig s	B16[1], 231
a1486	—,benzene 1-naphthalene, 2'-amino-	Yellow AB. $C_{16}H_{13}N_3$. See a1485[1]	247.30	red pl (al) λ^{al} 340 (3.9), 450 (4.2)	102–4				i	v			...	aa v con sulf s (bl)	B16[2], 193 B25[2], 545
a1487	—,—,4'-amino-....	Naphthyl red. $C_{16}H_{13}N_3$. See a1485[1]	247.30	red lf (dil al), nd (dil al) λ^{al} 285 (4.2), 330 (3.4), 350 (3.5), 455 (4.3)	125–5.5					s	s		s		B16[2], 186
a1488	—,—,—,hydro-chloride	$C_{16}H_{13}N_3 \cdot HCl$. See a1485[1]	283.76	gr nd, pr (al or aa)	205–6				δ	s[h]			...	aa s[h]	B16[1], 324
a1489	—,—,2,3-di-methyl-2'-hydroxy-	$C_{18}H_{16}N_2O$. See a1485[1]	276.34	pa ye amor (al-bz)	125–30 (189)				i	s[h]			δ s[h]	to, CCl_4 s	B16[2], 71
a1490	—,—,2,4-di-methyl-2'-hydroxy-	$C_{18}H_{16}N_2O$. See a1485[1]	276.34	red nd (al)	166				i	s	s				B16[2], 72
a1491	—,—,2,5-di-methyl-2'-hydroxy-	$C_{18}H_{16}N_2O$. See a1485[1]	276.34	nd (al)	153				i	δ s[h]			δ		B16, 168
a1492	—,—,3,4-di-methyl-2'-hydroxy-	$C_{18}H_{16}N_2O$. See a1485[1]	276.34	red nd (al)	146				i	δ s[h]	δ ..		v	chl v	B16[1], 260
a1493	—,benzene 2-naphthalene, 2,4-dimethyl-1'-hydroxy-	$C_{18}H_{16}N_2O$. See a1485[2]	276.34	gold-red lf or nd (al-chl)	186					δ[h]			s	chl, CS_2 s lig, alk i	B16[1], 249

For explanations, symbols and abbreviations see beginning of table. For structural formulas see end of table.

No.	Name	Synonyms and Formula	Mol. wt.	Color, crystalline form, specific rotation and λ_{max} (log ε)	m.p. °C	b.p. °C	Density	n_D	Solubility						Ref.
									w	al	eth	ace	bz	other solvents	
	Azo														
a1494	—,—,4-dimethyl-amino-	$C_{18}H_{17}N_3$. See 1485[2]	275.36	ye-br (bz-lig) $\lambda^{50\,\%al-1.2N\,HCl}$ 325 (4.15), 545 (4.54)	174									s^h	B16, 321
a1495	—,benzene 1-naphthalene 4,4'-dinitro-2-hydroxy-	$C_{16}H_{10}N_4O_5$. See a1485[1]	338.28	cr (gl aa) purp bl sol in al-NaOH	231									aa s^h os δ aq alk i	B16[1], 268
a1496	—,—,4,8'-dinitro-4'-hydroxy-	$C_{16}H_{10}N_4O_5$. See a1485[1]	338.28	red ($PhNO_2$)	252–60d							i		alk s $PnNO_2 s^h$ to lig i	B16, 161
a1497	—,benzene 2-naphthalene, 4,4'-dinitro-1'-hydroxy-	$C_{16}H_{10}N_4O_5$. See a1485[2]	338.28	red nd ($PhNO_2$-aa)	255d						δ		δ	$PhNO_2$ s aa δ	B16[2], 67
a1498	—,—,4,5'-dinitro-1'-hydroxy-	$C_{16}H_{10}N_4O_5$. See a1485[2]	338.28	cr (bz)	210	235d				s	s		s^h	$PhNO_2$ y chl s	B16, 154
a1499	—,benzene 1-naphthalene, 2'-hydroxy-	Sudan Yellow. $C_{16}H_{12}N_2O$. See a1485[1]	248.29	red-gold lf or nd (al) λ^{al} 315 (3.9), 422 (4.1), 480 (4.3)	133–4						s^h	s		s	lig, CS_2, con HCl s	B16[2], 70
a1500	—,—,4'-hydroxy-	$C_{16}H_{12}N_2O$. See a1485[1]	248.29	vt-br lf (bz) λ^{al} 410 (4.2), 470 (4.0)	205–6d					i	s^h			s^h	dil NaOH con sulf v aa s^h	B16[2], 67
a1501	—,benzene 2-naphthalene, 1'-hydroxy-	$C_{16}H_{12}N_2O$. See a1485[2]	248.29	red nd (al) λ^{al} 294 (4.12), 356 (3.92), 490 (4.12)	138	sub			i	v^h				aa s con alk i	B16[1], 248
a1502	—,benzene 1-naphthalene 2'-hydroxy-2-nitro-	$C_{16}H_{11}N_3O_3$. See a1485[1]	293.29	og-red nd (gl aa) λ^{chl} 410 (3.9), 480 (4.3), 500 (4.4)	294						δ				al-NaOH, aa s^h	B16[2], 70
a1503	—,—,2'-hydroxy-4-nitro-	Para red. Paranitraniline red. $C_{16}H_{11}N_3O_3$. See a1485[1]	293.29	br-og pl(to or bz)	257 (>300)				i	s		s			B16[2], 70
a1504	—,—,2'-hydroxy-4'-nitro-	$C_{16}H_{11}N_3O_3$. See a1485[1]	293.29	dk brsh-red nd (bz)	206–7					i			s^h	dil NaOH i	B16[1], 267
a1506	—,—,4'-hydroxy-2'-nitro-	$C_{16}H_{11}N_3O_3$. See a1485[1]	293.29	og-red nd (bz) λ^{al} 467	164						s			s^h	aa s dil KOH s^h	E12B, 1915
a1507	—,—,4'-hydroxy-3-nitro-	$C_{16}H_{11}N_3O_3$. See a1485[1]	293.29	dk red nd (al) λ^{al} 447	242–3d						s				NaOH s	E12B, 1762
a1508	—,—,4'-hydroxy-4-nitro-	$C_{16}H_{11}N_3O_3$. See a1485[1]	293.29	red nd	277–9d				i	s	δ		s	aa, chl s $PhNO_2 s^h$	B16[1], 237
a1509	—,benzene 2-naphthalene, 1'-hydroxy-4'-nitro-	$C_{16}H_{11}N_3O_3$. See a1485[2]	293.29	dk red nd (gl aa)	182–2					δ^h			s^h	aa s^h	E12B, 1914
a1510	—,1-naphthalene 2-pyridine, 2-hydroxy-		249.28	og-red nd (al)	137				i	s	s			dil ac s, dil alk s^h	B22[1], 694
a1511	—,—,4-hydroxy-		249.28	gr-red nd					i					dil ac, dil alk, con sulf s	B22[1], 694
a1512	**Azobenzene** (cis)	Azobenzide. Benzene-azobenzene. Diphenyldiimide.	182.23	og-red pl (peth) λ^{al} 243 (4.02), 281 (3.72), 433 (3.18)	71				δ	s	s		s	aa, lig s	B16[2], 4
a1513	—(trans)		182.23	og red mcl lf (al) λ^{al} 226 (3.99), 320 (4.28), 350 (2.63)	68.5	293[760]	1.203_4^{20}	1.6266^{78}	δ	s	s		s	Py v MeOH, chl, aa s lig δ	B16[2], 4
a1514	—,4-acetamido-	$C_{14}H_{13}N_3O$. See a1513	239.28	gold-ye nd (al) λ^{chl} 347 (4.37)	144 6				δ	s	δ		δ		B16[1], 155
a1515	—,2-acetamido-4',5-dimethyl-	$C_{16}H_{17}N_3O$. See a1513	267.33	ye nd (al-aa)	157				i	s	s			chl s	B16[2], 182
a1516	—,4-acetamido-2',3-dimethyl-	$C_{16}H_{17}N_3O$. See a1513	267.33	red nd (al)	186–7				i	δ	s			chl s	B16[2], 179
a1517	—,4-acetoxy-2'-methyl-	$C_{15}H_{14}N_2O_2$. See a1513	254.29	red-ye lf (al)	68				i	s^h					B16, 105
a1518	—,4-acetoxy-3-methyl-	$C_{15}H_{14}N_2O_2$. See a1513	254.29	ye pl (dil al)	81–2					s	s		s	chl s	B16, 130
a1519	—,4-acetoxy-4'-methyl-	$C_{15}H_{14}N_2O_2$. See a1513	254.29	og nd (al, bz)	98					s^h					B16[7], 42

For explanations, symbols and abbreviations see beginning of table. For structural formulas see end of table.

No.	Name	Synonyms and Formula	Mol. wt.	Color, crystalline form, specific rotation and λ_{max} (log ε)	m.p. °C	b.p. °C	Density	n_D	Solubility						Ref.
									w	al	eth	ace	bz	other solvents	

Azobenzene

No.	Name	Synonyms and Formula	Mol. wt.	Color, cryst. form, λ_{max}	m.p.	b.p.	Density	n_D	w	al	eth	ace	bz	other	Ref.
a1520	—,2-amino-	2-Benzeneazoaniline. $C_{12}H_{11}N_3$. See a1513	197.24	red nd or pr (al) λ^{al} 222 (4.17), 258 sh (3.95), 313 (4.17), 424 (3.91)	59	....			i	δ	v	v	v	os v	B16², 147
a1521	—,3-amino-	3-Benzeneazoaniline. $C_{12}H_{11}N_3$. See a1513	197.24	(i) og-ye nd (peth) (ii) br-red cr λ^{al} 301 (4.2), 461 sh (3.3)	(i) 69–70 (ii) 90–1	....			i	s	s	s	s	chl s	B16, 304
a1522	—,4-amino-	4-Benzeneazoaniline. $C_{12}H_{11}N_3$. See a1513	197.24	og mcl nd (al) λ^{al} 251 (4.0), 384 (4.4)	127	>360			δ^h	s^h	s	...	s^h	chl s lig δ	B16², 149
a1523	—,—,hydrobromide	$C_{12}H_{11}N_3 \cdot$ HBr. See a1513 ..	278.04	bk-vt nd (dil al)	206–7	....				δ	δ				B16, 307
a1524	—,—,hydrochloride	$C_{12}H_{11}N_3 \cdot$ HCl. See a1513 .	233.70	bl-vt or pa red nd or pw (w or HCl)	240	....			s^h	s^h				HCl s^h	B16², 149
a1525	—,4-amino-2,2'-dimethyl-	o-Tolueneazo-m-toluidine... $C_{14}H_{15}N_3$. See a1513	225.30	ye nd (lig)	116–7	....			δ	s				lig v^h	B16², 180
a1526	—,4-amino-2,3'-dimethyl-	m-Tolueneazo-m-toluidine .. $C_{14}H_{15}N_3$. See a1513	225.30	ye-gold nd (al), ye-br nd (lig)	80	....			δ	s		.		lig s^h	B16², 181
a1527	—,4-amino-2',3-dimethyl-	o-Tolueneazo-o-toluidine ... $C_{14}H_{15}N_3$. See a1513	225.30	ye lf (al)	101.5–3	....			i	s				chl s	B16², 178
a1528	—,4-amino-2,4'-dimethyl-	p-Tolueneazo-m-toluidine... $C_{14}H_{15}N_3$. See a1513	225.30	ye pl (al), gold-ye (lig)	127	....				s^h				lig s^h	B16, 348
a1529	—,4-amino-3,3'-dimethyl-	m-Tolueneazo-o-toluidine... $C_{14}H_{15}N_3$. See a1513	225.30	ye br lf or nd (lig)	124	....				s^h				lig s^h	B16, 345
a1530	—,4-amino-3,4'-dimethyl-	p-Tolueneazo-o-toluidine... $C_{14}H_{15}N_3$. See a 1513	225.30	og-ye nd (lig), ye pl (al)	128	....			i	δ s^h				lig δ, s^h	B16¹, 322
a1531	—,4-benzoxy-4'-methyl-	4-p-Tolueneazophenol benzyl ether. $C_{20}H_{18}N_2O$... See a1513	302.38	pa ye lf (lig)	128	....				s	v		v	lig s^h	B16, 107
a1532	—,3,3'-bis(dimethylamino)-	3,3'-Azo-bis(N,N-dimethylaniline). $C_{16}H_{20}N_4$. See a1513	268.37	red nd (al)	118	....			i	s			s	lig δ	B16, 305
a1533	—,4,4'-bis(dimethylamino)-	4,4'-Azo-bis(N,N-dimethylaniline). $C_{16}H_{20}N_4$. See a1513	268.37	og nd (bz) $\lambda^{95\% \, sulf - al}$ 405 (4.52), 485 sh (3.80)	273 (266)	sub				δ	s	...	v	chl v	B16², 174
a1534	—,4-bromo-	$C_{12}H_9BrN_2$. See a1513......	261.13	og nd (lig) $\lambda^{15\% \, sulf}$ 328 (4.3)	90–1	sub			i	s	s	...	s	lig s	B16², 14
a1535	—,4-diacetamido-2,3'-dimethyl-	$C_{18}H_{19}N_3O_2$. See a1513.....	309.37	(i) red nd (lig), (ii) cr	(i) 65 (ii) 75	....				s	s	s	s	os v	B16¹, 322
a1536	—,2,2'-diamino-	o,o'-Azodianiline. $C_{12}H_{12}N_4$. See a1513	212.26	red pl (al or bz)	134	....			δ	δ	s	s	δ	....	B16², 148
a1537	—,2,4-diamino-	Chrysoidine. $C_{12}H_{12}N_4$. See a1513	212.26	pa ye nd (w)	117.5	....			δ^h	s	s	...	s	chl s	B16², 203
a1538	—,4,4'-diamino-	p,p'-Azodianiline. $C_{12}H_{12}N_4$. See a1513	212.26	gold-ye nd (al), og-ye pr (al or bz) λ^{al} 305 sh (3.7), 399 (4.5), 430 sh (4.4)	250–1	....			δ	s	s	...	v	chl v lig δ	B16², 174
a1539	—,2,2'-diethoxy-	o-Azophenetole. $C_{16}H_{18}N_2O_2$. See a1513	270.34	red pr (al) λ^{bz} 317 (4.0), 370 (4.1)	131	240d			i	s	s	...	s	HCl s	B16, 92
a1540	—,4,4'-diethoxy-	p-Azophenetole. $C_{16}H_{18}N_2O_2$. See a1513	270.34	ye-lf (al) λ^{bz} 362 (4.4), 428 sh (3.3)	162 (159)	d			i	δ v^h	s	...	s	chl s aa v^h	B16², 44
a1541	—,2,2'-dihydroxy-	o-Azophenol. $C_{12}H_{10}N_2O_2$. See a1513	214.23	gold-ye lf (bz), nd (al) λ^{al} 259 (3.80)	172	sub			i	δ s^h	v	...	δ s^h	con alk s	B16², 33
a1541¹	—,2,4-dihydroxy-	Benzeneazoresorcinol. Sudan G. $C_{12}H_{10}N_2O_2$. See a1513	214.23	dk red nd (dil al)	161 ($\frac{1}{3}$w) 170 (anh)	....			i	v	v	...	v	chl, aa v	B16², 80
a1542	—,3,3'-dihydroxy-	m-Azophenol. $C_{12}H_{10}N_2O_2$. See a1513	214.23	ye lf (dil al)	207	....			δ	s^h	v	v	δ	alk s lig δ	B16², 37
a1543	—,4,4'-dihydroxy-	p-Azophenol. $C_{12}H_{10}N_2O_2 \cdot H_2O$. See a1513	232.24	og-ye pl (dil al + 1w), gr (st), red (metast), ta (eth) λ^{al} 355 (4.3)	216–6.5 (anh)	....			δ	s	s	s	δ	aa, lig δ	B16², 43
a1544	—,2,4-dihydroxy-4'-nitro-	4-(p-Nitrobenzeneazo)-resorcinol. $C_{12}H_9N_3O_4$. See a1513	259.22	red pw (al or MeOH)	200	....			i	δ^h			δ	aa, to δ	B16², 81
a1545	—,2,2'-dimethyl-	o-Azotoluene. $C_{14}H_{14}N_2$. See a1513	210.28	dk red mcl pr (eth) λ^{al} 235 (3.98), 332 (4.24)	55–6	....	1.0215$_4^{55}$	1.6180^{65}	i	s	v	...	v	CS_2, chl s	B16², 19

For explanations, symbols and abbreviations see beginning of table. For structural formulas see end of table.

No.	Name	Synonyms and Formula	Mol. wt.	Color, crystalline form, specific rotation and λ_{max} (log ε)	m.p. °C	b.p. °C	Density	n_D	w	al	eth	ace	bz	other solvents	Ref.
	Azobenzene														
a1546	—,3,3′-dimethyl- (cis)	m-Azotoluene. $C_{14}H_{14}N_2$. See a1512	210.28	red (peth) λ^{chl} 329 (3.84), 424 (3.24)	46	....	....							....	**J1953** 2143
a1547	—,—(trans).......	$C_{14}H_{14}N_2$. See a1513	210.28	og-red orh λ^{chl} 331 (4.18), 447 (2.79)	54–4.5	....	1.0123^{66}	1.6152^{66}		v	v	...	v	....	**B16[7]**, 20
a1548	—,4,4′-dimethyl- (cis)	p-Azotoluene. $C_{14}H_{14}N_2$. See a1512	210.28	dk red λ^{al} 247.5 (4.04), 296 (3.80), 438 (3.31)	104	....	....		i				s	lig s^h	**C48**, 2475
a1549	—,—(trans).......	$C_{14}H_{14}N_2$. See a1513	210.28	og-ye nd (al) λ^{al} 233 (4.19), 336 (4.41), 438 (2.87)	144	....	....		i	δ	s	...	s	lig s dil ac i	**B16[2]**, 21
a1549[1]	—,4-dimethyl-amino-	Butter yellow. Methyl yellow. $C_{14}H_{15}N_3$. See a1513	225.30	ye lf (al) λ^{al} 410 (4.44)	117	d			i	v	s			Py v ac s lig δ^h	**B16[2]**, 151
a1550	—,2,2′-dimethyl-4-ethoxy-	$C_{16}H_{18}N_2O$. See a1513	254.34	dk red nd (al)	64					s	s	s	s	lig s	**B16**, 134
a1551	—,2,3′-dimethyl-4-ethoxy-	$C_{16}H_{18}N_2O$. See a1513	254.34	red pr (al)	73					v	s	s	s	os v	**B16**, 135
a1552	—,2′,3-dimethyl-4-ethoxy-	$C_{16}H_{18}N_2O$. See a1513	254.34	red cr (lig)	35–7					s	δ		s	lig s^h	**B16**, 131
a1553	—,2,4′-dimethyl-4-ethoxy-	$C_{16}H_{18}N_2O$. See a1513	254.34	og-red pl (al)	64					v	v		v	lig v	**B16**, 135
a1554	—,3,3′-dimethyl-4-ethoxy-	$C_{16}H_{18}N_2O$. See a1513	254.34	red-ye pl (al)	46–7					s	s	s	s	lig s	**B16**, 131
a1555	—,3,4′-dimethyl-4-ethoxy-	$C_{16}H_{18}N_2O$. See a1513	254.34	og-ye nd (al)	73–4	251^{42}				s	s	s	s	os v	**B16**, 131
a1556	—,4′,5-dimethyl-2-ethoxy-	$C_{16}H_{18}N_2O$. See a1513	254.34	pa red nd (abs al)	43	$253–5^{63}$			s^h	s		...			**B16**, 141
a1557	—,2,2′-dimethyl-4-hydroxy-	4-o-Tolueneazo-m-cresol. $C_{14}H_{14}N_2O$. See a1513	226.28	og-red pl (bz), red cr (w+1)	113(anh) 83(hyd)					v	v		v		**B16[2]**, 61
a1558	—,2,3-dimethyl-4-hydroxy-	4-Benzeneazo-o-3-xylenol. $C_{14}H_{14}N_2O$. See a1513	226.28	red pr (al, lig)	132				i	s	s	s	s	oos s lig s^h	**B16[2]**, 60
a1559	—,2,3′-dimethyl-4-hydroxy-	4-m-Tolueneazo-m-cresol. $C_{14}H_{14}N_2O$. See a1513	226.28	og-ye pl (bz)	106–7				δ	v	s		v	lig v	**B16[2]**, 61
a1560	—,2,4-dimethyl-5-hydroxy-	5-Benzeneazo-2,4-xylenol. $C_{14}H_{14}N_2O$. See a1513	226.28	og-ye nd (lig-peth)	114					v	s	v	v	MeOH, aa peth v	**B16**, 146
a1561	—,2,4′-dimethyl-4-hydroxy-	4-p-Tolueneazo-m-cresol. $C_{14}H_{14}N_2O$. See a1513	226.28	og-ye pr (bz)	135					v	v		v	lig δ	**B16[2]**, 62
a1562	—,3,3′-dimethyl-4-hydroxy-	4-m-Tolueneazo-o-cresol. $C_{14}H_{14}N_2O$. See a1513	226.28	gold-ye nd (bz)	115					v	v		v	os v	**B16[2]**, 60
a1563	—,3,4′-dimethyl-4-hydroxy-	4-p-Tolueneazo-o-cresol. $C_{14}H_{14}N_2O$. See a1513	226.28	og nd (bz)	163					s	s		s	os v	**B16[2]**, 60
a1564	—,3,5-dimethyl-2-hydroxy-	6-Benzeneazo-m-4-xylenol. $C_{14}H_{14}N_2O$. See a1513	226.28	dk red nd (al, lig) λ^{al} 332 (4.38), 395 (3.93)	90					v	v		v	aa, lig v	**B16**, 145
a1565	—,3,5-dimethyl-4-hydroxy-	4-Benzeneazo-2,6-xylenol. $C_{14}H_{14}N_2O$. See a1513	226.28	ye nd, pr (lig) λ^{al} 351 (4.45)	95–6					s	s		s	os v aa s lig s^h	**B16**, 145
a1566	—,4,4′-dimethyl-2-hydroxy-	6-p-Tolueneazo-m-cresol. $C_{14}H_{14}N_2O$. See a1513	226.28	og-red cr (lig)	150–1					s	s		s	lig v^h alk δ	**B16[2]**, 61
a1567	—,4′,5-dimethyl-2-hydroxy-	2-p-Tolueneazo-p-cresol. $C_{14}H_{14}N_2O$. See a1513	226.28	red cr, ye pl (to)	112–3				δ v^h	v		v	chl v to s	**B16[2]**, 63
a1569	—′,2-ethoxy-	o-Benzeneazophenetole. $C_{14}H_{14}N_2O$. See a1513	226.28	red pl or mcl pr (peth)	44				v	v	v		v	os v peth v^h	**B16**, 91
a1570	—,3-ethoxy-	m-Benzeneazophenetole. $C_{14}H_{14}N_2O$. See a1513	226.28	pl (peth)	63.5–4	200^{22}				v	v		v	os v	**B16**, 95
a1571	—,4-ethoxy-	p-Benzeneazophenetole. $C_{14}H_{14}N_2O$. See a1513	226.28	og nd (60–70 % al) $\lambda^{15 \% al}$ 225 sh (4.2), 348 (4.3), 415 sh (2.9)	85	339–40	1.0400_4^{100}	1.6419_{5875}^{100}	...	v	v	s	v	os v	**B16[2]**, 40
a1572	—,4-ethoxy-2-methyl-	$C_{15}H_{16}N_2O$. See a1513	240.31	og-red nd (dil al)	51.5–2.0				δ	v	v	...	...	lig v	**B16**, 134
a1573	—,4-ethoxy-2′-methyl-	$C_{15}H_{16}N_2O$. See a1513	240.31	og pl (al)	53				δ	s	s	...	s	chl s	**B16**, 105
a1574	—,4-ethoxy-3-methyl-	$C_{15}H_{16}N_2O$. See a1513	240.31	og nd or mcl pr (al)	60				s	s		s	lig s	**B16**, 130
a1575	—,4-ethoxy-3′-methyl-	$C_{15}H_{16}N_2O$. See a1513	240.31	og-red pr (al)	65					s	v		v		**B16**, 106
a1576	—,4-ethoxy-4′-methyl-	$C_{15}H_{16}N_2O$. See a1513	240.31	red lf (al)	121–2	251^{47}				s v^h			s	chl v	**B16**, 107
a1577	—,2-hydroxy-	o-Benzeneazophenol. $C_{12}H_{10}N_2O$. See a1513	198.23	og-red nd (eth) λ^{al} 323 (4.26)	82.5–3				δ	s	s	s	s	os, dil alk s (og-red)	**B16[2]**, 32
a1578	—,—,benzoate	$C_{19}H_{14}N_2O_2$. See a1513	302.34	og-red nd (lig) λ^{eth} 260 (>3.0), 380 (1.8)	93				s^h		...		s^h	lig s^h	**B16**, 91

For explanations, symbols and abbreviations see beginning of table. For structural formulas see end of table.

No.	Name	Synonyms and Formula	Mol. wt.	Color, crystalline form, specific rotation and λ_{max} (log ε)	m.p. °C	b.p. °C	Density	n_D	w	al	eth	ace	bz	other solvents	Ref.
	Azobenzene														
a1579	—, 3-hydroxy-	m-Benzeneazophenol. $C_{12}H_{10}N_2O$. See a1513	198.23	ye nd (w, lig), pr (bz) λ^{eth} 248 (2.8), 380 (1.8)	116.5–7				i	s	s	s	s	dil alk s lig δ	B16, 94
a1580	—, —, acetate	$C_{14}H_{12}N_2O_2$. See a1513	240.27	og pl (peth)	67.5									peth s[h]	B16, 95
a1581	—, —, benzoate	$C_{19}H_{14}N_2O_2$. See a1513	302.34	og-red pl (peth)	92									peth s[h]	B16, 95
a1582	—, 4-hydroxy-	p-Benzeneazophenol. $C_{12}H_{10}N_2O$. See a1513	198.23	ye lf (bz), og pr (al) λ^{al} 236.5 (4.0)	155–7	220–30[20] δd			i	v	v		s	con sulf, dil alk s (ye)	B16[2], 38
a1583	—, —, acetate	$C_{14}H_{12}N_2O_2$. See a1513	240.27	og lf (al), nd (al, lig) λ^{al} 325 (4.34), 440 (2.80)	89	>360d				s[h]				lig s[h]	B16[1], 236
a1584	—, —, benzoate	$C_{19}H_{14}N_2O_2$. See a1513	302.34	og-ye nd (al, lig), ye-red pr (eth, al), ye lf (al)	138					δ s[h]	δ s[h]			to v lig s[h]	B16[2], 41
a1585	—, 4-hydroxy-2'-methoxy-2-methyl-	$C_{14}H_{14}N_2O_2$. See a1513	242.28	og	161				δ	v	s				B16, 135
a1586	—, 4-hydroxy-2'-methoxy-3-methyl-	$C_{14}H_{14}N_2O_2$. See a1513	242.28	og red pl (dil al)	68					v	v		v		B16, 131
a1587	—, 2-hydroxy-4-methyl-	6-Benzeneazo-m-cresol. $C_{13}H_{12}N_2O$. See a1513	212.25	red pl (lig)	122					s		s	s	chl, lig s alk δ	B16[1], 241
a1588	—, —, benzoate	$C_{20}H_{16}N_2O_2$. See a1513	316.36	og-ye nd (lig)	98					δ		v		MeOH δ	B16[1], 241
a1589	—, 2-hydroxy-5-methyl-	2-Benzeneazo-p-cresol. $C_{13}H_{12}N_2O$. See a1513	212.25	og-ye lf (bz, bz-lig), gold lf (w-al), λ^{bz} 330 (4.49), 410 (4.28)	108–9	sub				s	s		s	chl s	B16[2], 62
a1590	—, 4-hydroxy-2-methyl-	4-Benzeneazo-m-cresol. $C_{13}H_{12}N_2O$. See a1513	212.25	ye nd (lig) λ^{al} 352 (4.2)	109					s	s			chl s	B16[2], 61
a1591	—, 4-hydroxy-2'-methyl-	o-Tolueneazo-p-phenol. $C_{13}H_{12}N_2O$. See a1513	212.25	red pl or lf (bz-lig), og-ye nd (bz)	107–8					s	s		v	chl s lig δ	B16[2], 41
a1592	—, 4-hydroxy-3-methyl-	4-Benzeneazo-o-cresol. $C_{13}H_{12}N_2O$. See a1513	212.25	gold-ye lf or nd (al) $\lambda^{DMF-alk}$ 489 (4.62)	128–30				i δ[h]	s	s		s	chl, lig s	B16[2], 59
a1593	—, —, benzoate	$C_{20}H_{16}N_2O_2$. See a1513	316.36	ye nd (al)	110–1					δ v[h]	v	v		chl v	B16[2], 130
a1594	—, 4-hydroxy-3'-methyl-	m-Tolueneazo-p-phenol. $C_{13}H_{12}N_2O$. See a1513	212.25	ye pl (al), dk ye pr (bz-lig)	144–5					s[h]			s	lig δ	B16[2], 41
a1595	—, 4-hydroxy-4'-methyl-	p-Tolueneazo-p-phenol. $C_{13}H_{12}N_2O$. See a1513	212.25	og-red mcl, ye (Na_2CO_3 sol or bz-lig), og-ye (bz-lig) $\lambda^{10\%Sulf}$ 240 (4.8), 360 (4.32), 470 (4.04)	152				δ s[h]	v	v		v	alk s	B16[2], 42
a1596	—, —, benzoate	$C_{20}H_{16}N_2O_2$. See a1513	316.36	og-red pr (bz), redsh-ye nd (lig)	178						v	v	s[h]	lig s[h]	B16[1], 237
a1597	—, 2-methoxy-	o-Benzeneazoanisole. $C_{13}H_{12}N_2O$. See a1513	212.25	og-red nd (dil al) λ^{al} 317 (4.2), 353 (4.2), 430 (3.0)	41	195–7[14]	1.0728_4^{100}		i	s[h]		s		os v	B16[2], 33
a1598	—, 3-methoxy-	m-Benzeneazoanisole. $C_{13}H_{12}N_2O$. See a1513	212.25	og-red pl (MeOH) λ 312.5 (4.34), 444.5 (2.75)	32.5–3.5	193–3.5[15]			i	s[h]		s		os v MeOH s[h]	B16, 95
Ω a1599	—, 4-methoxy-	p-Benzeneazoanisole. $C_{13}H_{12}N_2O$. See a1513	212.25	og-red pl, lf (al), (peth) λ^{al} 342 (4.3), 432 (3.2)	56(64)	340	1.12^{75}		i	s[h]	s	s		os v	B16[2], 40
a1600	—, 4-methoxy-4'-methyl-	$C_{14}H_{14}N_2O$. See a1513	226.28	og-ye pr (al)	110–1					s[h]	s	s	s	os s	B16[1], 236
Ω a1601	—, 4-nitro-	$C_{12}H_9N_3O_2$. See a1513	227.23	lf, nd (al, lig) λ^{al} 333 (4.4), 446 (3.0)	135(155)					s[h]		s	s	chl, aa, lig s	B16[2], 17
a1602	—, 4-phenyl-amino-	4-Anilineazobenzene. $C_{18}H_{15}N_3$. See a1513	273.34	ye pl or pr λ^{al} 260 (4.10), 380 (4.19), 450 sh (4.80)	82				i	v	v			lig v	B16, 315
a1603	—, 2,4,3'-triamino-	Bismark's brown. $C_{12}H_{13}N_5$. See a1513	227.27	og lf (w), red (bz)	143–5				i	v	v				B16, 386
a1604	2-Azobenzene-carboxylic acid	o-Benzeneazobenzoic acid.	226.24	og-red nd or pl (al)	97–8(95)					v	v	s	v	aa v	B16[2], 97

For explanations, symbols and abbreviations see beginning of table. For structural formulas see end of table.

No.	Name	Synonyms and Formula	Mol. wt.	Color, crystalline form, specific rotation and λ_{max} (log ε)	m.p. °C	b.p. °C	Density	n_D	w	al	eth	ace	bz	other solvents	Ref.
	3-Azobenzenecarboxylic acid														
a1605	3-Azobenzene-carboxylic acid	m-Benzeneazobenzoic acid.	226.24	og-red pl (w), red lf (al)	170–1				δ^h	s	v	...	v	chl, AcOEt s	B16, 229
a1606	4-Azobenzene-carboxylic acid	p-Benzeneazobenzoic acid...	226.24	red pl or lf (al) λ^{PrOH} 323 (4.42)	248.5–9.5 (241)					s^h	s	s	s	chl s aa s^h lig, $CS_2 \delta$	B16[2], 98
—	2-Azobenzene-carboxylic acid, 4'-dimethyl-amino-	see **Methyl red**													
a1607	3-Azobenzene-carboxylic acid, 4-hydroxy-	5-Benzeneazosalicylic acid. $C_{13}H_{10}N_2O_3$. See a1605	242.24	nd (bz) λ^{al} 350 (4.4)	220d					s	s	s	δ	chl δ $CS_2 \delta^h$	B16[2], 100
a1608	—,4-hydroxy-2'-nitro-	5-o-Nitrobenzeneazosalicylic acid. $C_{13}H_9N_3O_5$. See a1605	287.23	br-red cr (al)	215–7				δ	s^h				aa s^h chl δ	B16[2], 101
a1609	—,4-hydroxy-3'-nitro-	5-m-Nitrobenzeneazosalicylic acid. $C_{13}H_9N_3O_5$. See a1605	287.23	red-br nd (al)	237				i	v	v	v	v	chl, aa v	B16[2], 101
a1610	—,4-hydroxy-4'-nitro-	5-p-Nitrobenzeneazosalicylic acid. $C_{13}H_9N_3O_5$. See a1605	287.23	og-br nd (dil aa)	257				i	s				aa s to s^h	B16[2], 101
a1611	—,3'-sulfo-	$C_{13}H_{10}N_2O_5S$. See a1605	306.30	ye lf (al)	d				v	v	i				B16, 268
a1612	2,2'-Azobenzene-dicarboxylic acid	o-Azobenzoic acid.	270.25	dk ye nd (al)	245–5.5 (cor)				δ^h	s^h	v		i		B16[1], 287
a1613	3,3'-Azobenzene-dicarboxylic acid	m-Azobenzoic acid.	270.25	ye nd (aa)	340d				i	δ^h	i				B16, 233
a1614	4,4'-Azobenzene-dicarboxylic acid	p-Azobenzoic acid.	270.25	dk ye nd (al), red nd (aa) $\lambda^{0.1 N NaOH}$ 225 (4.08), 331 (4.41), 430 (3.11)	d330				i	i	i			aa δ^h os i	B16, 236
a1614[1]	3,3'-Azobenzene-disulfonic acid		342.35	ye lf (w + 5)					s	s	s				B16[2], 114
a1615	—,diamide	$C_{12}H_{12}N_4O_4S_2$. See a1614[1]	340.38	ye nd (al)	305					s^h				os δ	B16, 268
a1616	—,dichloride	$C_{12}H_8Cl_2N_2O_4S_2$. See a1614[1]	379.25	red nd (eth)	166–7				d	d^h	s^h		δ		B16, 268
a1617	—,diethyl ester	$C_{16}H_{18}N_2O_6S_2$. See a1614[1]	398.46	gold-ye nd (eth)	100				δ	s	s				B16, 268
a1617[1]	3,4'-Azobenzene-disulfonic acid		342.35	syr											B16, 279
a1618	—,diamide	$C_{12}H_{12}N_4O_4S_2$. See a1617[1]	340.38	ye nd (al)	17258 (288)				δ	s^h					B16, 279
a1619	—,dichloride	$C_{12}H_8Cl_2N_2O_4S_2$. See a1617[1]	379.25	red nd (eth, CS_2)	123–5				d^h	d^h	s^h			$CS_2 s^h$	B16, 279
a1619[1]	4,4'-Azobenzene-disulfonic acid		342.35	red nd (w + 2,3 or 5)	169d (anh)				s						B16[2], 119
a1620	—,diamide	$C_{12}H_{12}N_4O_4S_2$. See a1619[1]	340.38	og nd (al) $\lambda^{50\% al}$ 232 (4.0), 337 (4.3)	>250d				δ	δ^h	i		i		B16, 280
a1621	—,dichloride	$C_{12}H_8Cl_2N_2O_4S_2$. See a1619[1]	379.25	br-red nd (eth, bz)	222				d^h	d^h	δ s^h	...	v	chl v	B16, 280
a1622	3,3'-Azobenzene-disulfonic acid, 4,4'-dimethyl-, dichloride	$C_{14}H_{12}Cl_2N_2O_4S_2$. See a1614[1]	407.30	dk red (bz)	194				d^h	d^h	δ		s^h		B16, 283
a1623	—,6,6'-dimethyl-, dichloride	$C_{14}H_{12}Cl_2N_2O_4S_2$. See a1614[1]	407.30	red pr (bz + 2)	220				d^h	d^h	δ		s^h		B16, 285
a1624	4,4'-Azobenzene-disulfonic acid, 2,2'-dimethyl-, diamide	$C_{14}H_{16}N_4O_4S_2$. See a1619[1]	368.44	pl (NH_3)	>250				δ					NH_3 v	B16, 284
a1625	—,—,dichloride	$C_{14}H_{12}Cl_2N_2O_4S_2$. See a1619[1]	407.30	dk red nd (bz)	218				d^h	d^h	s		v^h		B16, 284
a1626	3,3'-Azobenzene-disulfonic acid, 2,2',4,4',6,6'-hexabromo-, dichloride	$C_{12}H_2Br_6Cl_2N_2O_4S_2$ See a1614[1]	852.65	vt pl (bz)	222–4				d		δ		δ s^h		B16, 269
a1627	—,4,4',6,6'-tetrabromo-, dichloride	$C_{12}H_4Br_4Cl_2N_2O_4S_2$. See a1614[1]	694.85	red nd (bz)	232–3				d	d^h	δ		s^h		B16, 269
a1628	4,4'-Azobenzene-disulfonic acid, 2,2',6,6'-tetrabromo-,	$C_{12}H_6Br_4N_2O_6S_2$. See a1619[1]	657.96	ye-br lf (bz)	258–62				d^h	d^h	δ		v		B16, 281
a1629	4-Azobenzene-sulfonic acid	4-Phenylazobenzenesulfonic acid*.	262.29	og-red lf (w + 3) λ^{al} 232 (4.07), 320 (4.32), 439 (2.90)	127(hyd)				δ v^h	δ	δ		...		B16[2], 115
a1630	—,chloride	$C_{12}H_9ClN_2O_3S$. See a1629	280.74	og-red nd or pl (bz) λ^{hp} 230, 320	82				i	s			s^h		B16, 272

For explanations, symbols and abbreviations see beginning of table. For structural formulas see end of table.

No.	Name	Synonyms and Formula	Mol. wt.	Color, crystalline form, specific rotation and λ_{max} (log ε)	m.p. °C	b.p. °C	Density	n_D	Solubility						Ref.
									w	al	eth	ace	bz	other solvents	
	4-Azobenzenesulfonic acid														
a1631	—,4'-chloro-	$C_{12}H_9ClN_2O_3S$. See a1629	296.74	br nd (w) λ^{al} 295 (4.4), 415 (3.1)	148				v	v					**B16**, 271
a1632	—,—,amide	$C_{12}H_{10}ClN_3O_2S$. See a1629	295.75	ye-br pr (al)	211					δ s^h	δ				**B16**, 272
a1633	—,—,chloride	$C_{12}H_8Cl_2N_2O_2S$. See a1629	315.19	red pr (eth)	130				d^h	s	s				**B16**, 272
—	2-Azobenzene-sulfonic acid, 4'-dimethylamino-, sodium salt	see **Methyl orange**													
a1634	3-Azobenzene-sulfonic acid, 4'-formyl-3'-hydroxy-		306.30	red lf	>270				v	v	i			HCl δ	**B16**, 267
a1635	4-Azobenzene-sulfonic acid, 4'-hydroxy-	$C_{12}H_{10}N_2O_4S$. See a1629	278.29	ye red pr (dil al), amor (w) $\lambda^{w, pH = 2.9}$ 347 (4.36)	200d				s	v^h	δ				**B16²**, 115
a1636	3-Azobenzene-sulfonic acid, 4'-hydroxy-3'-nitro-		323.29	gold-ye pr (dil (HCl + w)	116(+ w), 235d (anh)				v	v					**B16**, 267
a1637	4-Azobenzene-sulfonic acid, 4'-methyl-, chloride	$C_{13}H_{11}ClN_2O_2S$. See a1629	294.76	red pr (bz)	130–2				d^h	d^h	v		s^h	chl v	**B16**, 272
—	Azobenzoic acid	see **Azobenzenedicarboxylic acid**													
a1638	p,p'-Azobiphenyl	Di-p-xenyldiimide.	334.42	og-red pl (bz) λ 334.5 (4.48), 450.5 (2.95)	256(250)				i	i	s			con sulf s aa i	**B16²**, 27
a1639	Azodicarboxylic acid, diamide	Azobisformamide. Azodicarbonamide. $H_2NCON:NCONH_2$	116.08	og nd (w)	225 (180–4)				s^h	i	δ			os i	**B3²**, 99
a1640	—,diethyl ester	$C_2H_5O_2CN:NCO_2C_2H_5$	174.16	og-ye		106^{13}	1.1104$_4^{19.2}$	1.4199^{19}					os s	**B3²**, 98
a1641	**Azomethane** (trans)	Dimethyldiazene. Dimethyldiimide. $CH_3N:NCH_3$	58.08	col or pa ye gas λ^w 345(1.3)	−78	1.5	0.744$_{15}^0$					C_7H_{16}, CCl_4 s	**B4³**, 1747
å1642	—,hexafluoro-	$F_3CN:NCF_3$	166.03	pa grsh gas	−133	−31.6			δ						**C35**, 433
Ω a1643	1,1'-Azo-naphthalene	Di-α-naphthyldiimide.	282.35	red nd (gl aa) λ^{al} 214 (4.87), 266 (4.26), 400 (4.21)	190	sub			i	δ		s	v	con sulf, AmOH s aa s^h	**B16²**, 26
a1644	1,2'-Azo-naphthalene	α,β-Naphthyldiimide.	282.35	red nd, br lf (aa) λ^{al} 216 (4.76), 264 (4.35), 310 (402), 381 (4.24)	136 (144–5)				i	s			s	aa, con sulf s (vt)	**E12B**, 936
Ω a1645	2,2'-Azo-naphthalene	Di-β-naphthyldiimide.	282.35	red lf (bz), og-ye nd (chl, al) λ^{al} 214 (4.57), 262 (4.39), 290 (4.18), 335 (4.35)	208	sub			i	δ	δ			con sulf s (red) chl s^h	**E12B**, 936
a1646	1,1'-Azo-naphthalene, 4-amino-	$C_{20}H_{15}N_3$. See a1643	297.36	red-br nd $\lambda^{al - 0.1NHCl}$ 355, 530	183(cor)				i	δ	δ		δ		**B16¹**, 325
—	Azophenol	see **Azobenzene, dihydroxy-**													
—	Azotoluene	see **Azobenzene, dimethyl-**													
a1647	**Azoxybenzene** (cis)		198.23	nd λ^{al} 231 (3.92), 260 (3.85), 323 (4.16)	87		1.1662$_4^{20}$	1.633^{20}							**B16**, 624
a1648	—,(trans)		198.23	bt ye nd λ^{al} 322 (4.19)	36	d	1.1590$_4^{26}$	1.652^{20}	i	s	s			lig v	**B16²**, 313
a1649	—,4-bromo-	$C_{12}H_7BrN_2O$. See a1648	277.13	dk ye pl $\lambda^{dil sulf}$ 250 (3.87), 355 (4.40)	93.5–4.5		1.4138$_4^{100}$		i	s			s^h	MeOH s^h	**B16²**, 315
a1650	—,2,2'-dimethoxy-	o-Azoxyanisole. $C_{14}H_{14}N_2O_3$. See a1648	258.28	ye-og cr (al), og pr (MeOH) λ^{al} 227 (3.59), 304 (3.41), 330 (3.37), 342 (3.37)	81				i	s	s	s	s	MeOH s^h, chl v	**B16**, 635
a1651	—,3,3'-dimethoxy-	m-Azoxyanisole. $C_{14}H_{14}N_2O_3$. See a1648	258.28	ye cr (al) $\lambda^{50\%al}$ 235 (4.0), 267 (3.8), 324 (4.1)	51–2					s^h	s^h				**B16²**, 325

For explanations, symbols and abbreviations see beginning of table. For structural formulas see end of table.

No.	Name	Synonyms and Formula	Mol. wt.	Color, crystalline form, specific rotation and λ_{max} (log ε)	m.p. °C	b.p. °C	Density	n_D	Solubility						Ref.
									w	al	eth	ace	bz	other solvents	
	Azoxybenzene														
Ω a1652	—,4,4′-dimethoxy-	p-Azoxyanisole. $C_{14}H_{14}N_2O_3$. See a1648	258.28	ye mcl nd (al) λ^{al} 242 (4.06), 336 (4.41)	119–21		1.171_4^{115}				s^h		s	s		B16[2], 326
a1653	2,2′-Azoxyben-zenedicarboxylic acid	o-Azoxybenzoic acid.	286.25	ye pl or pr (al)	254.5	....			δ	s^h	δ	s	δ	Py v aa s chl, lig i	B16[2], 335
a1654	3,3′-Azoxyben-zenedicarboxylic acid	m-Azoxybenzoic acid.	286.25	pa ye nd or lf (gl aa)	320d	....			i	...	δ			....	B16[1], 388
Ω a1655	4,4′-Azoxyben-zenedicarboxylic acid	p-Azoxybenzoic acid.	286.25	ye amor pw $\lambda^{1N\ NaOH}$ 262 (4.06), 335 (4.24)	360d (398, 242)	....			i	i	i			Py s oos i	B16[2], 336
—	**Azoxybenzoic acid**	see **Azoxybenzenedi-carboxylic acid**													
a1656	1,1′-Azoxy-naphthalene	$C_{10}H_7^a N:NC_{10}H_7^a$ .... ↓ O	298.35	ye or red orh pl (al) λ^{al} 218 (4.93), 262 (4.11), 288 (3.91), 364 (4.06)	127				i	s^h	δ			con sulf s (vt)	E12B, 1038
a1657	2,2′-Azoxy-naphthalene	$C_{10}H_7^\beta N:NC_{10}H_7^\beta$ .... ↓ O	298.35	ye or red nd (al, eth, gl aa) λ^{al} 216 (4.7l), 263 (4.41), 289 (4.24), 346 (4.41)	167–8				i	δ	δ		s	chl s aa s^h MeOH δ	E12B, 1039
Ω a1658	Azulene		128.19	bl or grsh-bk lf (al) λ^{hx} 274 (4.79), 340 (3.67), 579 (2.51), 632 (2.51), 659 (2.18), 665 sh (2.15)	99–100.5	270d $115-35^{10}$			i	s^h	s	s		ac, oos s	E12A, 421
a1659	—,1,3,5-trinitro-, benzene addition compound	$C_{16}H_{11}N_3O_6$. See a1658 ...	341.28	br nd	166.5–7.5	....				s^h				....	H20, 224
a1660	—,1,4-dimethyl-7-isopropyl-	Guaiazulene. $C_{15}H_{18}$. See a1658	198.31	bl-vt pl (al) λ^{al} 254 (4.4), 287 (4.7), 350 (3.7), 370 (3.6), 610 (2.6), 625 (2.6), 665 (2.5)	31.5	$167-8^{12}$	0.973_0^{20}			s^h	s			AcOEt s	E12A, 424
a1661	—,1,5-dimethyl-8-isopropyl-	Chamazulene. $C_{15}H_{18}$. See a1658	198.31	bl liq λ^{118} 286 (4.59), 305 sh (3.98), 350 (3.63), 368 (3.50)	....	161^{12}	0.9883_4^{20}	....	i	s	s			AcOEt, peth s	B5[2], 474
a1662	—,4,8-dimethyl-2-isopropyl-	Elemazulene. Vetivazulene. $C_{15}H_{18}$. See a1658	198.31	red-vt nd (al) $\lambda^{50\%sulf}$ 228 (4.31), 272 (4.44), 374 (4.25)	31.5–2.0	$140-60^2$				s^h	s				E12A, 427
a1663	—,Δ^4-octahydro-(trans)	trans-Bicyclo-[5,3,0]-Δ^2 decene. $C_{10}H_{16}$. See a1658	136.24	....	....	$68-9^{12}$	0.8996_4^{21}	1.4419^{20}	i	s				aa s	E12A, 421

For explanations, symbols and abbreviations see beginning of table. For structural formulas see end of table.

No.	Name	Synonyms and Formula	Mol. wt.	Color, crystalline form, specific rotation and λ_{max} (log ε)	m.p. °C	b.p. °C	Density	n_D	w	al	eth	ace	bz	other solvents	Ref.
	Baeyer's acid														
—	Baeyer's acid	see 2-Naphthalenesulfonic acid, 7-amino-													
—	Baicalin	see Flavone, 5, 6, 7-tri-hydroxy-													
—	B.A.L.	see 1-Propanol, 2,3-dimercapto-													
b1	Bandrowski's base	1,4-Benzoquinonebis(2,5-diaminoanil)	318.38	dk red or br lf	238				δ					os δ dil HCl s	B13², 146
—	Banthine bromide	see Methantheline bromide													
—	Barbital	see Barbituric acid, 5,5-diethyl-													
Ω b2	Barbituric acid	Pyrimidinetrione.	128.09	rh pr (w+2) λ^{al} 269 (3.74), 311 (4.23)	248	260d			s^h δ	δ	s				B24², 267
b3	—,5-allyl-5-butyl-	$C_{11}H_{16}N_2O_3$. See b2	224.26	(w, dil al)	128				s^h	s^h					B24², 292
b4	—,5-allyl-5(2-cyclopenten-1-yl)-	Cyclopal.	234.26	(w, dil al)	139–40				δ s^h	v					C24, 5308
b5	—,5-allyl-5-isobutyl-	Sandoptal. $C_{11}H_{16}N_2O_3$. See b2	224.26	(w, dil al)	138				δ v^{wr}	s	s	s		chl s lig i	B24², 292
b6	—,5-allyl-5-isopropyl-1-methyl-	Narconumal. $C_{11}H_{16}N_2O_3$ See b2	224.26	(w, dil al)	56–7	176–8¹²				s	s	s	s		C32, 1052
b7	—,5-allyl-5-phenyl-	Alphenal. Prophenal. $C_{13}H_{12}N_2O_3$. See b2	244.25		156–7.5				δ	v	v		δ	lig i chl s	C26, 4828
Ω b8	—,5-amino-	Uramil. $C_4H_5N_3O_3$. See b2	143.10	nd or pl (w)	>400				s^h i		i		i	chl, con sulf s	B25¹, 704
Ω b9	—,5-benzylidene-		216.21	pr (aa) λ^{al} 331	256				i	i	i	s^h			B24², 299
b10	—,5(2-bromoallyl)-5-isopropyl-	Propallylonal. Nostal. $C_{10}H_{13}BrN_2O_3$. See b2	289.14	(dil aa, dil al)	181				δ	v	δ	v	δ	chl δ aa v	B24², 291
Ω b11	—,5(1-cyclo-hexenyl)-5-ethyl-	Cyclobarbital. Cyclobarbitone.	236.27	lf (w)	172–4				i s^h	v	s			dil alk s aa δ	B24², 294
b12	—,5,5-diallyl-	Allobarbitone. Curral. Dial. $C_{10}H_{12}N_2O_3$. See b2	208.22	pl (w or 50 % al)	174				δ	s	s		s		B24², 293
b13	—,5,5-dibromo-	Dibromin. $C_4H_2Br_2N_2O_3$. See b2	285.89	pl (MeOH-bz), lf (dil HNO₃)	235	d			δ s^h	v	s			sulf s	B24², 272
Ω b14	—,5,5-diethyl-	Barbital. Barbitone. Veronal. $C_8H_{12}N_2O_3$. See b2	184.20	(i) trig (w) (ii) mcl pr (iii) mcl nd (iv) tcl $\lambda^{w, pH=1}$ 239 (3.0)	(i) 190 (ii) 183 (iii) 181 (iv) 176		1.220		δ s^h	s^h	s			chl, lig, peth, aa s	B24², 279
b15	—,5,5-diethyl-1-methyl-	Metharbital. $C_9H_{14}N_2O_3$. See b2	198.22	nd $\lambda^{w, p0=1-6}$ 222.5 (3.90) $\lambda^{w, pH=11-14}$ 245 (3.94)	150–1				s^h						B24², 281
b16	—,5,5-dipropyl-	Proponal. Propytal. $C_{10}H_{16}N_2O_3$. See b2	212.25	pl (w)	146 (166)				i δ^h	v	v		v	dil alk s chl v	B24², 286
b17	—,5-ethyl-5-hexyl-	$C_{12}H_{20}N_2O_3$. See b2	240.31	nd (w)	112–3				δ	s	s		s		B24², 288
b18	—,5-ethyl-5-isopropyl-	Ipral. Probarbital. $C_9H_{14}N_2O_3$. See b2	198.22	nd (w)	203				δ	i	s				B24², 284
b19	—,5-ethyl-5(2-methylallyl)-2-thio-		226.28		160–1				i					dil alk s	C33, 5599
b20	—,5-ethyl-5(3-methylbutyl)-	Amobarbital. Amytal. $C_{11}H_{18}N_2O_3$. See b2	226.28	lf (w, dil al) $\lambda^{w, pH=10.5}$ 242	156–8				δ	v	v	∞		chl s peth i	B24², 287
Ω b21	—,5-ethyl-1-methyl-5-phenyl-	Mephobarbital. Prominal. $C_{13}H_{14}N_2O_3$. See b2	246.27	wh cr (w)	176				δ s^h	v	δ			chl s	C28, 781
b22	—,5-ethyl-5-pentyl-	$C_{11}H_{18}N_2O_3$. See b2	226.28	cr (dil al)	135–6				δ s^h	v	v			chl s	B24², 286
b23	—,5-ethyl-5(2-pentyl)-	Nembutal. Pentobarbital. $C_{11}H_{18}N_2O_3$. See b2	226.28	nd (w) $\lambda^{w, pH=9.65}$ 240 (4.11) $\lambda^{w, pH=14}$ 256 (3.88)	130				δ	s	s				B24², 287
b24	—,5-ethyl-5-phenyl-	Luminal. Phenobarbital. $C_{12}H_{12}N_2O_3$. See b2	232.24	pl (w) $\lambda^{w, pH=7.3}$ 240 (3.6) $\lambda^{w, pH=13}$ 255 (3.9)	(i) 174 (st) (ii) 156–7 (unst) (iii) 166–7 (unst)				i s^h	s	s		i		B24², 297
Ω b25	—,5-ethyl-5(1-piperidyl)-	Eldoral.	239.28	wh cr (dil al)	215				δ s^h	s	s	s	i	chl, alk, ac s	C36, 3160
Ω b26	—,5(2-furfuryl-idene)-2-thio-		222.22	ye pl	>280d				i	i			i	aa i py s	B27, 607
b27	—,5-hydroxy-	Dialuric acid. $C_4H_4N_2O_4$. See b2	144.09	pr or pl nd (+1w, w) $\lambda^{w, pH=7.4}$ 275 (4.22)	224 (anh) 214–5 (+w)				δ v^h	s		s	i	aa, py s	B25², 61

For explanations, symbols and abbreviations see beginning of table. For structural formulas see end of table.

No.	Name	Synonyms and Formula	Mol. wt.	Color, crystalline form, specific rotation and λ_{max} (log ε)	m.p. °C	b.p. °C	Density	n_D	w	al	eth	ace	bz	other solvents	Ref.
	Barbituric acid														
b28	—,5-methyl-5-phenyl-	Rutonal. $C_{11}H_{10}N_2O_3$. *See* b2	218.21	cr	220	......			i	s	s	...	...	alk s	**B24²**, 296
b29	—,5-nitro-	Dilituric acid. $C_4H_3N_3O_5$. *See* b2	173.09	pr, lf(w + 3) λ^w 314 (4.0) $\lambda^{w,pH=13}$ 334 (4.1)	180–1 176 (anh)	......			s^h	s	i	...	...		**B24²**, 273
b30	—,5(2-phenylethyl)-	$C_{12}H_{12}N_2O_3$. *See* b2	232.24	cr	212–3	......			δ	v	s	...	...		**B24²**, 296
Ω b31	—,2-thio-	.... λ^{al} 235 (3.74), 285 (4.26)	144.15	pl (w)	235 d	......			δ s^h	s	s	...	...	dil alk, dil HCl s	**B24²**, 275
—	**Batyl alcohol**	*see* Glycerol, 1-octadecyl ether													
b32	**Bebeerine**(d)	Chondrodendrin. $C_{36}H_{38}N_2O_6$	594.72	cr (bz, eth, chl-MeOH), $[\alpha]_D^{25}$ +297 (al). $[\alpha]_D^{20}$ +332 (Py) λ^{MeOH} 282 (3.96)	221–1.5, 161 (+bz)	......				s	s	v		chl v MeOH s	**B27²**, 896
b33	—(l)	Curine. $C_{36}H_{38}N_2O_6$.	594.72	pr, nd (chl-MeOH), $[\alpha]_D^{20}$ −328 (Py) $[\alpha]_D^{28}$ −298(al)	221, 165–7 (+bz), 159–63 (+al)	......			δ s^h	δ	δ	s	s	chl, Py, ac s	**B27²**, 894
—	**Behenic acid**	*see* Docosanoic acid													
—	**Behenolic acid**	*see* 13-Docosynoic acid													
Ω b35	**Benzaldehyde**	Benzenecarbonal*. Benzenecarboxaldehyde.	106.13	λ^{cy} 241 (4.15), 247 sh (4.06), 277.5 (3.08), 287 sh (3.00)	−26 (fr −56.9 55.6)	178.1⁷⁶⁰ 62¹⁰	1.0415¹⁵	1.5463²⁰	δ	∞	∞	v	v	liq NH_3 s lig v	**B7²**, 145
Ω b36	—,azine	Dibenzalhydrazine. $C_6H_5CH:NN:CHC_6H_5$ λ^{cy} 300 (4.6)	208.27	ye pr (al)	93	......			i	s^h	s	s	s	chl s	**B7²**, 171
b37	—,diacetate	Benzylidene diacetate. $C_6H_5CH(O_2CCH_3)_2$	208.22	pl (eth)	46	220⁷⁶⁰ 154²⁰	1.11²⁰	......	i	v	v	...	s		**B7²**, 161
b38	—,hydrazone	$C_6H_5CH:NNH_2$.	120.15	lf λ^{al} 267 (4.2)	16	140¹⁴	......	......	d	s	s	...	...		**B7²**, 171
b39	—,imine, N-ethyl-	N-Benzethylamine. $C_6H_5CH:NC_2H_5$	133.20	λ^{al} 246 (4.2), 278 sh (3.1), 289 (2.9)	......	195⁷⁴⁹	0.937²⁰₄	1.5378²⁵	i	s	s	...	...		**Am 80**, 4320
b40	—,—, N-methyl-	N-Benzalmethylimine. $C_6H_5CH:NCH_3$	119.17	λ^{al} 245 (4.18)	......	185⁷⁶⁰ 90–1³⁰	0.9672¹⁵₄	1.5540²⁰	δ						**B7²**, 162
b41	—,—, N(4-tolyl)-	N-Benzal-p-toluidine. $C_6H_5CH:NCH_3$	195.27	ye cr	35	318⁷⁵⁵ 178¹¹			i	s	s	...	s		**B12²**, 496
b42	—,oxime(anti)	anti-Benzaldoxime. $C_6H_5CH:NOH$	121.14	nd (eth) λ^{al} 247 (4.2), 288 sh (2.8)	130	......	1.145²⁰₄		s^h	v	v	...	s		**B7²**, 169
Ω b43	—,—(syn)	syn-Benzaldoxime. $C_6H_5CH:NOH$	121.14	pr λ^{al} 255 (4.2), 282 sh (3.2), 292 (3.0)	36–7	200 118–9¹⁰	1.1111²⁰₄	1.5908²⁰	δ	s	v	...	v		**B7²**, 167
Ω b44	—,phenylhydrazone	$C_6H_5CH:NNHC_6H_5$ λ^{al} 237 (4.17), 302 (4.06), 345 (4.39)	196.26	nd (lig). pr	156	......			δ s^h	δ	δ	s^h	s^h	liq NH_3 s	**B15²**, 57
b45	—,2-acetamido-	$C_9H_9NO_2$. *See* b35 λ^{MeOH} 292 (3.4)	163.18	nd (w)	70–1				s^h	...	s	s	...	os s	**B14**, 26
b46	—,3-acetamido-	$C_9H_9NO_2$. *See* b35	163.18	pl (bz)	84				δ	v	s	...	s^h		**B14**, 29
b47	—,4-acetamido-	$C_9H_9NO_2$. *See* b35	163.18	pr (w)	156				s	δ	...	...	s		**B14**, 38
Ω b48	—,2-amino-	Anthranilaldehyde. C_7H_7NO. *See* b35	121.14	silv lf λ^{hx} 255 (3.75), 262 sh (3.54), 352 (3.66)	39–40	......			δ	v	v	...	s	chl s lig i	**B14**, 21
b49	—,—,oxime		136.17	nd (bz)	135–6	......			δ	v	v	...	δ	CS_2 v aa s lig δ	**B14**, 24
Ω b50	—,3-amino-	C_7H_7NO. *See* b35 λ^{hx} 245 (3.95), 256 (3.87)	121.14	nd (AcOEt)	28–30	......					s	...	...	ac s	**B14²**, 21
b51	—,—,oxime		136.17	nd (bz)	88 (195)					v	v	...	s	lig δ	**B14**, 28
b52	—,4-amino-	C_7H_7NO. *See* b35 λ^{hx} 291 (4.21), 296 (4.21)	121.14	pl (w)	71–2	......			s	s	s	...	...	ac s	**B14²**, 22
b53	—,—,oxime	$C_7H_8N_2O$. *See* b42	136.17	ye cr (w)	124					v	v	...	...	ac s	**B14**, 31
Ω b54	—,2-bromo-	C_7H_5BrO. *See* b35 λ^{hx} 245.5 (4.10) 252 (4.00), 292 (3.32), 301 (3.24)	185.03		21–2	230 118¹²		1.5928²⁰	i	v	v	...	v		**B7²**, 181
b55	—,—,diacetate		287.12		84–6						s^h	s	...		**B7²**, 181
Ω b56	—,3-bromo-	C_7H_5BrO. *See* b35 λ^{hx} 242 (4.06)	185.03		......	233–6⁷⁶⁰		1.5935²⁰	i	v	v	...	...		**B7²**, 182
Ω b57	—,4-bromo-	C_7H_5BrO. *See* b35 λ^{hx} 257.5 (4.27)	185.03	lf (dil al)	67	66–8²			i	v	...	...	v		**B7²**, 182

For explanations, symbols and abbreviations see beginning of table. For structural formulas see end of table.

Benzaldehyde

No.	Name	Synonyms and Formula	Mol. wt.	Color, crystalline form, specific rotation and λ_{max} (log ε)	m.p. °C	b.p. °C	Density	n_D	w	al	eth	ace	bz	other solvents	Ref.
b58	—,—,diacetate....		287.12	ye	94–5					s^h	s					B7², 182
b59	—,2-bromo-4-hydroxy-	C₇H₅BrO₂. See b35	201.03	pa ye nd (w)	159.5				δ s^h						B8², 74
b60	—,2-bromo-5-hydroxy-	C₇H₅BrO₂. See b35	201.03	nd (w)	135				i	v	v	s	v	chl s	B8², 57
b61	—,3-bromo-2-hydroxy-	C₇H₅BrO₂. See b35	201.03	nd (dil al)	49				δ	s	s	s	s	alk, os s	B8, 54
b62	—,3-bromo-4-hydroxy-	C₇H₅BrO₂. See b35	201.03	lf (w)	124				δ	v	v	v		chl, aa s lig δ	B8, 82
b63	—,4-bromo-2-hydroxy-	C₇H₅BrO₂. See b35	201.03	nd (dil al)	52				δ	s	v	s	s	os s	B8, 54
b64	—,4-bromo-3-hydroxy-	C₇H₅BrO₂. See b35	201.03		131.5								s	chl v	B8², 56
Ω b65	—,5-bromo-2-hydroxy-	C₇H₅BrO₂. See b35	201.03	nd (al), lf (eth) λ^{al} 240 (3.7), 278 (2.0), 337 (3.5)	105–6				i	s	s				B8², 45
b66	—,5-bromo-4-hydroxy-3-methoxy-	5-Bromovanillin. C₈H₇BrO₃. See b35	231.05	pl (aa), nd, pl (al) λ^{al} 213.5 (4.36), 234 (4.29), 291 (4.10)	164–6				i	s^h	δ		δ		B8², 286
Ω b67	—,2-chloro-	C₇H₅ClO. See b35	140.57	nd λ^{hx} 246 (4.04), 252 (3.93), 292 (3.24), 300 (3.15), 302 (3.15)	12.39	211.9⁷⁶⁰ 84.3¹⁰	1.2483²⁰₄	1.5662²⁰	δ	s	s	s	s		B7², 177
Ω b68	—,3-chloro-	C₇H₅ClO. See b35	140.57	pr λ^{hx} 241.5 (4.06), 248 (4.00), 288 (3.15), 298 (3.08)	17–8	213–4⁷⁶⁰ 55¹	1.2410²⁰₄	1.5650²⁰	δ	s	s	s	s		B7², 178
Ω b69	—,4-chloro-	C₇H₅ClO. See b35	140.57	pl λ^{hx} 253 (4.26), 259 (4.19), 276 (3.18), 286 (3.00)	47.5	213–4⁷⁶⁰ 72–5³	1.196⁶¹₄	1.5552⁶¹	s	v	v	s	v	CS₂, aa s	B7², 178
b70	—,2-chloro-3-hydroxy-	C₇H₅ClO₂. See b35	156.57	cr (aq aa)	139.5					v				aa v chl δ	B8², 54
b71	—,2-chloro-4-hydroxy-	C₇H₅ClO₂. See b35	156.57	nd (w or aa)	147–8				s^h	s	s			aa v^h	B8, 81
b72	—,2-chloro-5-hydroxy-	C₇H₅ClO₂. See b35	156.57	nd (w or aa)	110.5–11.5					s				aa v	B8¹, 526
b73	—,3-chloro-2-hydroxy-	C₇H₅ClO₂. See b35	156.57	nd (MeOH)	55					s	s	s	s	os v	B8¹, 523
b74	—,3-chloro-4-hydroxy-	C₇H₅ClO₂. See b35	156.57	nd (w)	139	149–50¹⁴			δ s^h	v	v			chl δ	B8, 81
b75	—,4-chloro-2-hydroxy-	C₇H₅ClO₂. See b35	156.57	nd (al or aq aa)	52.5				s		s	s	s	os v	J1927, 1740
b76	—,4-chloro-3-hydroxy-	C₇H₅ClO₂. See b35	156.57	nd (al)	121					s	s	s	s	os s	B8²; 55
b77	—,5-chloro-2-hydroxy-	C₇H₅ClO₂. See b35	156.57	pl (al) λ^{al} 338 (3.57)	99–100	105¹²			i	v	s			alk s	B8², 45
b78	—,—.oxime	C₇H₆ClNO₂. See b42	171.58	nd (w)	128					s^h					B8, 53
b79	—,5-chloro-4-hydroxy-3-methoxy-	5-Chlorovanillin. C₈H₇ClO₃. See b35	186.60	tetr λ^{diox} 280 (4.1), 305 sh (3.8)	165				i	s^h				aa s^h	B8², 286
b80	—,2,3-dichloro-....	C₇H₄Cl₂O. See b35	175.02	cr (dil al)	65–7					v	v				Am 68, 861
Ω b81	—,2,4-dichloro-....	C₇H₄Cl₂O. See b35	175.02	pr $\lambda^{aq\ MeOH}$ 218 (4.23), 263 (4.14), 300 sh (3.30)	72				i	s	s		s	aa s	B7², 180
b82	—,2,5-dichloro-....	C₇H₄Cl₂O. See b35	175.02	nd (al)	58	231–3			i	v	v		v	chl v CS₂ s	B7, 237
b83	—,2,6-dichloro-....	C₇H₄Cl₂O. See b35	175.02	nd (lig)	71				i	s^h	s^h			lig s^h	B7, 237
Ω b84	—,3,4-dichloro-....	C₇H₄Cl₂O. See b35	175.02		44	247–8			i	s	s			lig s^h	B7, 238
b85	—,3,5-dichloro-....	C₇H₄Cl₂O. See b35	175.02	nd or lf (dil al)	65	235–40⁷⁴⁸			δ^h	s	s	v	v	os v	C28, 754
b86	—,2,4-dichloro-3-hydroxy-	C₇H₄Cl₂O₂. See b35	191.02	cr (aa)	141									lig δ, v^h	B8², 55
b87	—,2,6-dichloro-3-hydroxy-	C₇H₄Cl₂O₂. See b35	191.02	cr (w)	142				δ^h					aa s	B8², 56
b88	—,3,5-dichloro-2-hydroxy-	C₇H₄Cl₂O₂. See b35	191.02	ye rh (aa)	95				i						B8, 54
b89	—,—.oxime	C₇H₅Cl₂NO₂. See b42	206.03	nd (dil al)	195–6				i	v	v	v			B8, 54
b90	—,3,5-dichloro-4-hydroxy-	C₇H₄Cl₂O₂. See b35	191.02	nd (chl, dil al)	158–9					v	v		δ	aa s chl, lig δ	B8, 81
b91	—,4,6-dichloro-3-hydroxy-	C₇H₄Cl₂O₂. See b35	191.02	nd	130				v^h	s	s		v	lig i	B8¹, 526
b92	—,2,3-diethoxy-....	C₁₁H₁₄O₃. See b35	194.23			169³⁷				s	s				B8², 268

For explanations, symbols and abbreviations see beginning of table. For structural formulas see end of table.

No.	Name	Synonyms and Formula	Mol. wt.	Color, crystalline form, specific rotation and λ_{max} (log ε)	m.p. °C	b.p. °C	Density	n_D	w	al	eth	ace	bz	other solvents	Ref.
	Benzaldehyde														
b93	—,3,4-diethoxy-	Protocatechualdehyde diethyl ether. $C_{11}H_{14}O_3$. See b35	194.23			278–80				s					B8, 256
Ω b94	—,4-diethyl-amino-	$C_{11}H_{15}NO$. See b35	177.25	ye nd (w) λ^{al} 243 (3.78), 348 (4.52)	41	174[7]			v	s	s		s		B14[2], 25
Ω b95	—,2,4-dihydroxy-	β-Resorcylaldehyde. $C_7H_6O_3$. See b35	138.12	nd (eth-lig) λ^{eth} 232 (3.93), 280 (4.14), 310 (3.82)	201–2	220–8[22]			s	v	v		δ	chl v aa s	B8[2], 272
b96	—,—,oxime	$C_7H_7NO_3$. See b42	153.14		192				s	v	v			chl v	B8[2], 274
Ω b97	—,2,5-dihydroxy-	Gentisic aldehyde. $C_7H_6O_3$. See b35	138.12	ye nd (bz)	99				v	v	v		s[h]	chl v lig δ	B8[2], 276
Ω b98	—,3,4-dihydroxy-	Protocatechualdehyde. $C_7H_6O_3$. See b35	138.12	lf (w, to) λ^{al} 250 (2.55), 300 (2.05)	153–4				s v[h]	v	v				B8[2], 277
b99	—,—,oxime	$C_7H_7NO_3$. See b42	153.14	nd (w)	157d				v	v	δ	δ	chl δ		B8[2], 285
b100	—,2,6-dihydroxy-4-methyl-	Atranol. $C_8H_8O_3$. See b35	152.16	ye nd (w)	124 118–9 ($+\frac{1}{2}$w)				v[h]	v	v		s[h]	chl v alk s lig s[h]	B8[2], 304
b101	—,3,5-diiodo-4-hydroxy-	$C_7H_4I_2O_2$. See b35	373.91	nd (al)	206.5				δ	s[h]		s		aa s	B8[2], 48
Ω b102	—,2,4-dimethoxy-	$C_9H_{10}O_3$. See b35	166.18	nd (al or lig)	72	165[10]			i	s	s		s	lig s	B8[2], 273
Ω b103	—,3,4-dimethoxy-	Veratraldehyde. $C_9H_{10}O_3$. See b35	166.18	nd (eth, lig, tol) λ^w 230 (4.19), 278 (4.05), 308 (3.97)	44 (58)	258 172–5[18]			δ	v	v				B8[2], 282
b104	—,2,4-dimethoxy-6-hydroxy-	$C_9H_{10}O_4$. See b35	182.18	nd, pl (dil al) λ^{al} 215 (4.2), 294 (4.31), 330 sh (3.58)	71	190–5[25] 165[10]			i	v	v		v	chl, aa v	B8[2], 436
b105	—,2,6-dimethoxy-4-hydroxy-	$C_9H_{10}O_4$. See b35	182.18	nd or pl (MeOH), pr (bz)	70–1										B8[2], 436
b106	—,3,4-dimethoxy-5-hydroxy-	$C_9H_{10}O_4$. See b35	182.18		62–3	177–80[12]					v		v	aa v lig v[h]	B8[2], 437
b106[1]	—,3,5-dimethoxy-4-hydroxy-	Syringaldehyde. $C_9H_{10}O_4$. See b35	182.18	br nd (lig) λ^{al} 215 (4.31), 231 (4.25), 308.5 (4.18)	113	192–3[14]			δ	v	v		v[h]	chl, aa v lig δ	B8[2], 437
b107	—,2,4-dimethyl-	$C_9H_{10}O$. See b35	134.18		−9– −8	218–99[10] 99[10]				s	s	s	s		B7[2], 240
b108	—,2,5-dimethyl-	$C_9H_{10}O$. See b35	134.18			220[738] 100[10]				v	s	s	s	os s	B7[1], 166
b109	—,3,4-dimethyl-	$C_9H_{10}O$. See b35	134.18			223–5[760]				s	s	s	s		B7[2], 240
b110	—,3,5-dimethyl-	$C_9H_{10}O$. See b35	134.18		9	220 2				s	s	s	s		B7[2], 240
Ω b111	—,4-dimethyl-amino-	$C_9H_{11}NO$. See b35	149.19	lf (w) λ^{al} 240 (3.7), 340 (4.5)	74	176 7[17]			δ	s	s	s	s	os s	B14[2], 23
b112	—,2,4-dinitro-	$C_7H_4N_2O_5$. See b35	196.12	pa ye pr (al), pl (bz) λ^{cy} 230 (1.00), 300 (0.07)	72	190– 210[10–20]			δ	s	s		s	lig δ	B7[2], 205
b113	—,2,6-dinitro-	$C_7H_4N_2O_5$. See b35	196.12	lf (dil aa)	123				s[h]	s	s		s	chl, aa s CS_2 δ	B7[2], 206
b114	—,2-ethoxy-	$C_9H_{10}O_2$. See b35	150.18		20–2	247–9 143–7[25]				∞	∞				B8, 43
b115	—,3-ethoxy-	$C_9H_{10}O_2$. See b35	150.18			245.5[760]	1.0768[20]4	1.5408[20]		s	s		s		B8, 60
b116	—,4-ethoxy-	$C_9H_{10}O_2$. See b35	150.18		13–4	249 140[20]	1.08[21]21			v	v		v		B8, 73
b117	—,3-ethoxy-2-hydroxy-	$C_9H_{10}O_3$. See b35	166.18		64–5	263–4[740]			δ					os s	B8[2], 267
Ω b118	—,3-ethoxy-4-hydroxy-	Bourbonal. Ethylvanillin. $C_9H_{10}O_3$. See b35	166.18	pl or sc (w)	77–8				δ	s[h]	s			chl s	B8[2], 282
b119	—,4-ethoxy-2-hydroxy-	$C_9H_{10}O_3$. See b35	166.18	nd (dil al)	35					v					B8, 242
b120	—,5-ethoxy-2-hydroxy-	$C_9H_{10}O_3$. See b35	166.18	ye pr	51.5	230			δ	v	v			chl v	B8, 245
Ω b121	—,4-ethoxy-3-methoxy-	$C_{10}H_{12}O_3$. See b35	180.21	mcl pr	64–5 (73–4)	sub			δ[h]	s	s		s	chl, aa s	B8[2], 283
Ω b122	—,2-hydroxy-	Salicylaldehyde. $C_7H_6O_2$. See b35	122.13	λ^{hx} 257 (4.07), 324 (3.56)	−7	197[760] 93[25]	1.1674[20]4	1.5740[20]	δ	∞	∞	v	v		B8, 31
Ω b123	—,—,azine	Salazine. $C_{14}H_{12}N_2O_2$. See b36	240.27	ye nd or lf (al) λ^{al} 295 (4.48)	214				i	s			v	chl s alk v	B8[2], 43
Ω b124	—,—,oxime	Salicylaldoxime. $C_7H_7NO_2$. See b42	137.14	pr (bz-peth) λ^{al} 265 (3.8), 305 (3.6)	63				δ	v	v		v	lig i	B8[2], 42
Ω b125	—,3-hydroxy-	$C_7H_6O_2$. See b35	122.13	nd (w) λ^{hx} 250 (3 98), 302 (3.46), 307 (3.45)	108	240[760] 161[20]			δ	s	s	s	s	lig i	B8[2], 52

For explanations, symbols and abbreviations see beginning of table. For structural formulas see end of table.

Benzaldehyde

No.	Name	Synonyms and Formula	Mol. wt.	Color, crystalline form, specific rotation and λ_{max} (log ε)	m.p. °C	b.p. °C	Density	n_D	w	al	eth	ace	bz	other solvents	Ref.
b126	—,—,azine	$C_{14}H_{12}N_2O_2$. See b36	240.27	ye pl (al) λ^{al} 306 (4.45), 330 (4.33)	162	....	....		i	δ	...	...	δ	chl δ	B8[1], 526
b127	—,—,oxime	$C_7H_7NO_2$. See b42	137.14	(bz)	90				v	v	v	...	i	chl δ lig i	B8[1], 525
Ω b128	—,4-hydroxy-	$C_7H_6O_2$. See b35	122.13	nd (w) λ^{hx} 281 (4.08), 288 (3.78)	117		1.129_4^{130}	1.5705_a^{130}	δ s[h]	v	v	v	s	....	B8[2], 63
b129	—,—,azine	$C_{14}H_{12}N_2O_2$. See b36	240.27	ye (al) λ^{al} 335 (4.64)	239–40 (268d) 273 (+w)	....			δ[h]	v	...	...	v	CCl4, lig δ	B8[1], 531
b131	—,4-hydroxy-2-iodo-3-methoxy-	2-Iodovanillin. $C_8H_7IO_3$. See b35	278.05	....	155–6				i	s	δ				Am 57, 2500
b132	—,4-hydroxy-5-iodo-3-methoxy-	5-Iodovanillin. $C_8H_7IO_3$. See b35	278.05	pa ye	180				i	δ	δ				B8[2], 289
Ω b133	—,2-hydroxy-3-methoxy-	o-Vanillin. $C_8H_8O_3$. See b35	152.16	lt ye-lt gr nd (w, lig) λ^{diox} 265 (4.0), 340 (3.5)	44–5	$265\text{-}6^{760}$ 128^{10}			δ	v	v		v	CCl4 v lig s	B8[2], 267
b134	—,2-hydroxy-4-methoxy-	4-Methoxysalicylaldehyde. $C_8H_8O_3$. See b35	152.16	nd (w), cr (al)	40–2				δ s[h]	s v[h]	v	...	v	lig v	B8[2], 272
b135	—,2-hydroxy-5-methoxy-	5-Methoxysalicylaldehyde. $C_8H_8O_3$. See b35	152.16	ye (w)	4	$247\text{-}8^{760}$			δ	v	v				B8[2], 276
Ω b136	—,3-hydroxy-4-methoxy-	Isovanillin. $C_8H_8O_3$. See b35	152.16	pl (w) $\lambda^{0.01N\,NaOH}$ 292 (3.92) 360 (3.78)	116–7	179^{15}	1.196		δ s[h]	s	s	...	s[h]	chl v aa s	B8[2], 282
b137	—,3-hydroxy-5-methoxy-	$C_8H_8O_3$. See b35	152.16	....	130–1	110–20 sub				v			v	aa v lig δ	B8[2], 291
b138	—,4-hydroxy-2-methoxy-	$C_8H_8O_3$. See b35	152.16	lf (bz), nd (w)	153	....			δ	s[h]	s	...	δ	chl s lig δ	B8[2], 272
Ω b139	—,4-hydroxy-3-methoxy-	Vanillin. $C_8H_8O_3$. See b35	152.16	(i) nd (w, lig) (ii) tetr (w, lig) λ^{al} 279 (4.01), 309 (4.02)	(i) 77–9 (ii) 81–2	285 170^{15}	1.056		δ v[h]	v	v	v	s[h]	CS2, chl v lig s[h]	B8[2], 278
b140	—,—,acetate	Vanillin acetate.	194.19	nd (eth) λ^{al} 257 (4.05), 305 (3.63)	102–3 (78–9)	....			δ	v	v				B8[2], 283
b141	—,2-hydroxy-3-nitro-	3-Nitrosalicylaldehyde. $C_7H_5NO_4$. See b35	167.12	nd (aa)	109–10						s		s		B8[2], 48
b142	—,2-hydroxy-5-nitro-	5-Nitrosalicylaldehyde. $C_7H_5NO_4$. See b35	167.12	(dil aa)	126						s	s	s		B8[2], 48
b143	—,—,oxime	$C_7H_6N_2O_4$. See b42	182.14		225								s		B8[2], 48
b144	—,3-hydroxy-2-nitro-	$C_7H_5NO_4$. See b35	167.12	nd or pl (bz, lig)	152						s		s[h]	lig δ	B8[2], 58
b145	—,—,oxime	$C_7H_6N_2O_4$. See b42	182.14	pa ye nd	172.5						s	s			B8[2], 58
b146	—,3-hydroxy-4-nitro-	$C_7H_5NO_4$. See b35	167.12	ye lf	128				δ	v	v		v	chl s lig δ	B8[2], 58
b147	—,—,oxime	$C_7H_6N_2O_4$. See b42	182.14	ye nd (chl)	164					v			δ	chl s	B8[2], 58
b148	—,4-hydroxy-2-nitro-	$C_7H_5NO_4$. See b35	167.12	ye nd	67				δ	v	v	v	v		B8, 83
b149	—,4-hydroxy-3-nitro-	$C_7H_5NO_4$. See b35	167.12	dk ye nd (al, w)	144.5				s[h] v[h]	s		...		chl δ	B8[2], 77
b150	—,—,oxime	$C_7H_6N_2O_4$. See b42	182.14	pr or nd (al-chl)	169					s	s		δ	aa s chl, lig δ	B8[2], 77
Ω b151	—,4-isopropyl-	Cumaldehyde. Cuminal. $C_{10}H_{12}O$. See b35	148.21	λ^{iso} 251.5 (4.24), 277.5 (3.19)	....	235–6 $103\text{-}4^{10}$	0.9755_4^{20}	1.5301^{20}	i	s	s				B7[2], 247
Ω b152	—,2-methoxy-	o-Anisaldehyde. $C_8H_8O_2$. See b35	136.16	pr λ^{hx} 253 (3.93), 306 (3.66), 314 (3.62)	37–8	$243\text{-}4^{760}$ $124\text{-}5^{18}$	1.13262_4^{20}	1.5600^{20}	i	s	v		s	chl v	B8[2], 40
b153	—,3-methoxy-	m-Anisaldehyde. $C_8H_8O_2$. See b35	136.16	λ^{hx} 251 (3.81), 304 (3.48), 313 (3.43)	....	230 62^1	1.1187^{20}	1.5530^{20}	i	s	v	s	v	chl v	B8[2], 53
Ω b154	—,4-methoxy-	p-Anisaldehyde. $C_8H_8O_2$. See b35	136.16	λ^{hx} 272 (4.20), 278 (4.10), 286 (3.74)	0	249.5^{760} 83^2	1.1191^{15}	1.5730^{20}	i	∞	∞	v	s	chl v	B8[2], 64
b155	—,—,oxime	$C_8H_9NO_2$. See b42	151.17	nd(bz) λ^{al} 265 (4.24)	64–5 (anti) 133 (syn)								δ		B8[2], 69
b156	—,2-methoxy-3-nitro-	$C_8H_7NO_4$. See b35	181.15	ye pr (dil al), nd (bz)	89–90	....			i	s	s				B8, 56
Ω b157	—,2-methyl-	o-Tolualdehyde. C_8H_8O. See b35	120.16	λ^{hx} 251 (4.11), 291 (3.23)	....	200 94^{10}	1.0386^{19}	1.5481^{20}	δ[h]	s	s	v	s	chl s	B7, 295
b158	—,3-methyl-	m-Tolualdehyde. C_8H_8O. See b35	120.16	λ^{hx} 251 (4.08), 280 (4.08), 290 (2.90)	....	199 $93\text{-}4^{17}$	1.0189^{21}	1.5413^{21}	δ	∞	∞	v	s	chl s	B7, 296
Ω b159	—,4-methyl-	p-Tolualdehyde. C_8H_8O. See b35	120.16	λ^{hx} 251 (4.18), 257 (4.10), 279 (3.08), 284 (3.00)	....	$204\text{-}5^{760}$ 106^{10}	1.0194_4^{17}	1.5454^{20}	δ	∞	∞	∞		chl v	B7, 297

For explanations, symbols and abbreviations see beginning of table. For structural formulas see end of table.

No.	Name	Synonyms and Formula	Mol. wt.	Color, crystalline form, specific rotation and λ_{max} (log ε)	m.p. °C	b.p. °C	Density	n_D	Solubility w	al	eth	ace	bz	other solvents	Ref.
	Benzaldehyde														
Ω b160	—,3,4-methylene-dioxy-	Piperonal.	150.14	wh-ye (w) λ^{al} 275 (3.8), 315 (4.0)	37	263[760] 140[15]			δ s^h	v	∞	s			B19[2], 141
b161	—,—,oxime		165.15	(MeOH) λ^{al} 265 (4.1), 310 (3.9)	146						s				B19[2], 147
Ω b162	—,2-nitro-	$C_7H_5NO_3$. See b35	151.12	ye nd (w) λ^{hx} 222 (4.18), 270 (3.56), 285 (3.23)	43.5–4	153[23]	1.2844[50]4		δ	v	v	v	v	os v	B7[2], 185
b163	—,—,diacetate		253.21	pr (lig)	90				s^h	s	s	s	s	os s	B7[2], 187
b164	—,—,dimethyl acetal		197.19	gr-ye		274–6[762] 138–9[11]							s		B7[1], 137
Ω b165	—,3-nitro-	$C_7H_5NO_3$. See b35	151.12	lt ye nd (w) λ^{hx} 225 (4.41), 258 (2.85), 287 (3.00)	58	164[23]	1.2792[20]4		δ	s	s	v	v	os s	B7[2], 190
b166	—,—,diacetate		253.21	pr or nd (al)	72		1.393			s	s	s	s	os, aa s	B7[2], 192
b167	—,—,dimethyl acetal		197.19			162–4[19]	1.209[15]						s		B7, 253
Ω b168	—,4-nitro-	$C_7H_5NO_3$. See b35	151.12	lf, pr (w) λ^{al} 259 (4.14), 284 (3.53), 295 (3.32), 305 (3.08)	106	sub	1.496		δ	v	δ		s	aa s lig δ	B7[2], 196
b169	—,—,diacetate		253.21	pr (al)	127					s	s	s	s	os s	B7[2], 198
b170	—,—,dimethyl acetal		197.19		23–5	294–6[774]							s		B7[2], 198
b171	—,pentachloro-	C_7HCl_5O. See b35	278.35	nd (bz, al) λ^{iso} 262 (3.8), 290 (2.9)	202.5				δ	v	v	v	CS₂ v		B7[1], 134
b172	—,2,3,4,5-tetra-chloro-	$C_7H_2Cl_4O$. See b35	243.91		106										B7[2], 181
b173	—,2,3,4-trichloro-	$C_7H_3Cl_3O$. See b35	209.46	nd (al)	91				δ v^h						B7, 238
b174	—,2,3,5-trichloro-	$C_7H_3Cl_3O$. See b35	209.46	nd (al)	56					v	v	v	v	os s	B7[2], 180
b175	—,2,3,6-trichloro-	$C_7H_3Cl_3O$. See b35	209.46	nd (lig)	86–7						v	v	v	lig δ, v^h	B7, 238
b176	—,2,4,5-trichloro-	$C_7H_3Cl_3O$. See b35	209.46	nd (al)	112–3				δ	v	v	v	v	chl, CS₂ v	B7, 238
b177	—,2,4,6-trichloro-	$C_7H_3Cl_3O$. See b35	209.46	λ^{al} 260 (3.7), 304 (2.8), 346 (1.5)	58–9						v			lig δ, v^h	B7, 238
b178	—,3,4,5-trichloro-	$C_7H_3Cl_3O$. See b35	209.46	nd (al)	90–1				δ^h	v^h	v	v	v	chl v peth s	B7[2], 180
b179	—,2,4,6-tri-methyl-	Mesitylaldehyde. $C_{10}H_{12}O$. See b35	148.21	λ^{hx} 264 (4.16), 300 (3.32)	14	237–40 192[50]			i	s	s	s	s		B7[2], 250
b180	—,2,4,6-trinitro-	$C_7H_3N_3O_7$. See b35	241.12	dk gr pl (bz)	119				i	s	s	s	s	chl, aa s	B7[2], 207
—	Benzaldoxime	see **Benzaldehyde**, oxime													
—	Benzamarone	see **1,5-Pentanedione, 1,2,3,4,5-pentaphenyl-**													
—	Benzamide	see **Benzoic acid**, amide													
—	Benzamidine	see **Benzoic acid**, amidine													
—	Benzanilide	see **Benzoic acid**, amide, N-phenyl-													
Ω b181	1,2-Benzanthra-cene	2,3-Benzophenanthrene. Naphthanthracene. Tetraphene. $C_{18}H_{12}$	228.30	ye br flr pl or lf (al-aa) λ^{bz} 281 (4.85), 292 (4.98), 301 (4.04), 317 (3.64), 331 (3.79), 344 (3.84), 376 (2.80), 386 (2.96)	162 (167)	435[760] sub			i	δ^h	s	s	v	os s aa δ	E14, 329
—	2,3-Benzanthra-cene	see **Naphthacene**													
b182	1,2-Benzanthra-cene, 9,10-di-hydro-	$C_{18}H_{14}$. See b181	230.31	lf (bz, al, aa)	112				i	δ			δ	aa δ	E14, 330
b183	—,9,10-dimethyl-	$C_{20}H_{16}$. See b181	256.35	pa ye pl (al, aa) λ^{al} 296.5 (4.90), 345 (3.83), 364 (3.54), 384 (3.83)	122–3				i	δ		s	v	CS₂, to s	E14s, 139
b184	—,4'-hydroxy-	$C_{18}H_{12}O$. See b181	244.30	pa ye or og nd (bz) λ^{al} 278 (4.7), 288 (4.7), 315 (4.3)	225								s	Py, to s aa v	E14s, 171

For explanations, symbols and abbreviations see beginning of table. For structural formulas see end of table.

No.	Name	Synonyms and Formula	Mol. wt.	Color, crystalline form, specific rotation and λ_{max} (log ε)	m.p. °C	b.p. °C	Density	n_D	Solubility						Ref.
									w	al	eth	ace	bz	other solvents	

1,2-Benzanthracene

No.	Name	Synonyms and Formula	Mol. wt.	Color...	m.p.	b.p.	Density	n_D	w	al	eth	ace	bz	other solvents	Ref.
Ω b185	—,3-methyl-	$C_{19}H_{14}$. See b181	242.32	pl (bz-al), nd (bz-lig) λ^{al} 270.5 (4.68), 291 (4.96), 340.5 (3.86), 377 (2.76)	156–7	$160^{0.1}$ sub			i	s	...	s	s	xyl, aa, Py, peth s	E14s, 116
Ω b186	—,4-methyl-	$C_{19}H_{14}$. See b181	242.32	nd (al) λ^{hx} 252 (4.51), 257 (4.51), 280 (4.85), 288 (4.91), 300 (4.27)	126.2–7.2				i	s	s	...	...	xyl s	E14s, 117
Ω b187	—,5-methyl-	$C_{19}H_{14}$. See b181	242.32	ye mcl pl (bz-al) λ^{al} 261 (4.47), 269 (4.66), 278 (4.85), 285 (4.81), 315 (3.70), 328 (3.80)	160–0.6				i	s	s	...	s	xyl s	E14s, 118
Ω b188	—,6-methyl-	$C_{19}H_{14}$. See b181	242.32	pl (al) λ^{al} 257 (4.58), 269.5 (4.61), 279 (4.85), 289 (4.92), 330 (3.83), 360 (3.60), 385 (2.48)	150.5–1.5				i	s^h	s	...	...	chl s xyl, CS_2 s^h	E14s, 119
b189	—,7-methyl-	$C_{19}H_{14}$. See b181	242.32	ye pl (al) λ^{hx} 258 (4.55), 272 (4.58), 282 (4.87), 293 (4.98), 304 (4.10)	183–3.6				i	s^h	...	...	...	aa s^h	E14s, 119
Ω b190	—,8-methyl-	$C_{19}H_{14}$. See b181	242.32	pl or nd (al, aa)	118				i	s	...	...	...	aa s	E14s, 120
Ω b191	—,9-methyl-	$C_{19}H_{14}$. See b181	242.32	pa ye nd or pl (aa, MeOH) λ^{al} 223 (4.5), 260 (4.6), 270 (4.6), 280 (4.8), 290 (4.9), 353 (3.8), 370 (3.7), 390 (3.0)	138				i	s	...	...	...	CS_2, aa s	E14s, 121
Ω b192	—,10-methyl-	$C_{19}H_{14}$. See b181	242.32	λ^{al} 232 (4.5), 258 (4.6), 280 (4.9), 298 (5.0), 353 (3.9), 370 (3.8), 388 (2.9)	141				i	s	s	s	...	CS_2, CCl_4 aa s	E14s, 122
b193	1,2-Benzanthra-cene-10-carbox-aldehyde		256.31	ye pr or nd λ^{al} 292 (4.61), 302 (4.65), 383 (3.91)	148					s	s	s	s	MeOH s	E14s, 186
b194	1,2-Benz-3,4-anthraquinone	2,3-Benzo-9,10-phenanthra-quinone. Tetraphene-5,6-quinone.	258.28	red nd (to) λ^{al} 234 (4.40), 256 (4.56), 400 (3.78)	262–3d					δ			δ	sulf s to, aa δ	B7², 759
b195	1,2-Benz-9,10-anthraquinone		258.28	ye pr (aa) λ^{al} 224 (4.4), 255 (4.5), 266 (4.7), 277 (4.7), 288 (4.9), 300 (4.0), 325 (3.7), 340 (3.7), 372 (2.7), 384 (2.8)	169	sub				δ	δ	s	v	chl v aa, sulf s lig δ	B7², 760
b196	Benzanthrene		216.29	lf (al) λ^{al} 227 (4.67), 247 (4.35), 329 (4.26), 344 (4.17)	84					s	...	...	...	sulf s (red) aa, xyl s	E14s, 343
Ω b197	1,9-Benzanthr-10-one		230.27	ye nd (xyl or al) λ^{al} 394 (4.00)	170					i	...	...	...	sulf s^h → og-red	B7², 468
b198	—,bz-1-bromo-	$C_{17}H_9BrO$. See b197	309.17	ye nd (aa)	178 (170)					s	...	...	...	MeOH, sulf s	E14s, 355
b199	—,bz-1-chloro-	$C_{17}H_9ClO$. See b197	264.71	ye nd (aa)	182–3					s	...	...	δ	PhCl, aa δ	E14s, 354

For explanations, symbols and abbreviations see beginning of table. For structural formulas see end of table.

1,9-Benzanthr-10-one

No.	Name	Synonyms and Formula	Mol. wt.	Color, crystalline form, specific rotation and λ_{max} (log ε)	m.p. °C	b.p. °C	Density	n_D	w	al	eth	ace	bz	other solvents	Ref.
b200	—,bz-2-hydroxy-	$C_{17}H_{10}O_2$. See b197	246.27	ye nd (PhCH$_2$OH)	294							:		sulf, alk s os δ	E14s, 373
b201	—,4-hydroxy-	$C_{17}H_{10}O_2$. See b197	246.27	ye nd (aa)	178–9						s		v^h	sulf s	E14s, 371
—	Benzaurine	see Methanol, bis (4-hydroxyphenyl)-phenyl-													
—	Benzedrine	see Amphetamine (dl)													
Ω b202	Benzene*	Benzol. Phene*	78.12	rh pr λ 243 (2.2), 249 (2.3), 256 (2.4), 261 (2.2)	5.5 (3.3)	80.1^{760}	0.87865^{20}_4	1.5011^{20}	δ	∞	∞	∞		chl, aa ∞	B5^2, 119
—	—,acetyl-	see Acetophenone													
Ω b203	—,allyl-	3-Phenylpropene*. C_9H_{10}. See b202	118.18	λ^{al} 210 (3.9), 260 (2.3), 270 (2.3)	−40	156^{760} 47^{13}	0.8920^{20}_4	1.5131^{20}	i				s	chl, CCl$_4$ s	B5^2, 373
b204	—,1-allyl-4-bromo-	C_9H_9Br. See b202	197.08			222–3^{730} 96^{12}	1.324^{15}_4	1.559^{15}	i				s	chl s	B5^2, 373
b205	—,2-allyl-4-chloro-1-hydroxy-	C_9H_9ClO. See b202	168.63	pr (lig)	48	130–2^{15}	1.171^{15}			s			s	chl, alk s	B6^1, 282
Ω b206	—,1-allyl-3,4-dimethoxy-	$C_{11}H_{14}O_2$. See b202	178.23	cr (hx) λ^{al} 230 (3.8), 280 (3.4)	−4	254.7^{760} 104^2	1.0396^{20}_4	1.5340^{20}	i	s	s				B6^3, 5024
b207	—,1-allyl-2-hydroxy-	$C_9H_{10}O$. See b202	134.18	λ^{al} 260 sh (3.1), 275 (3.4)	−6	220^{760} 93–4^8	1.0255^{15}_{15}	1.5181^{20}				v			B6, 282
b208	—,1-allyl-4-hydroxy-	Chavicol. $C_9H_{10}O$. See b202	134.18		16	235–6^{760} 120^{12}	1.033^{18}_4	1.5448^{20}	s^h	∞	∞			chl, peth ∞	B6^2, 529
Ω b209	—,5-allyl-1-hydroxy-2-methoxy-	Betel phenol. Chavibetol. $C_{10}H_{12}O_2$. See b202	164.21		8.5	253–4^{760} 111^6	1.0613^{21}_4	1.5413^{20}		s	s				B6^2, 923
—	—,amino-*	see Aniline													
b210	—,1-amino-2-butyl-*	o-Butylaniline. $C_{10}H_{15}N$. See b202	149.24	ye oil		122–5^{12}	0.953^{20}_4					s	s	os, ac s	B12^2, 633
b211	—,1-amino-4-butyl-*	p-Butylaniline. $C_{10}H_{15}N$. See b202	149.24	pa ye		261^{760} 133–4^{14}	0.945^{20}_4		i	s		s	s	os. ac s	B12^2. 633
b212	—,1-amino-4-sec-butyl-(dl)	$C_{10}H_{15}N$. See b202	149.24			238^{762} 118^{15}	0.949^{15}	1.5360^{20}			v		v		B12^2, 635
b213	—,1-amino-2-tert-butyl-	$C_{10}H_{15}N$. See b202	149.24	λ^{iso} 237 (3.89), 286 (3.35)		233–5	0.977^{15}	1.5453^{20}			v	v	v	ac s	B12^2, 636
b214	—,1-amino-3-tert-butyl-	$C_{10}H_{15}N$. See b202	149.24			229^{708}					v	v	v		B12^2, 637
Ω b215	—,1-amino-4-tert-butyl-	$C_{10}H_{15}N$. See b202	149.24	ye-red (peth) λ^{iso} 237 (4.03), 292 (3.25)	17	240^{740} (228^{762})	0.9525^{15}	1.5380^{20}	δ	∞	∞		v		B12^3, 637
b216	—,1-amino-4-cyclohexyl-*		175.28	pl (lig)	55					s			s		B12^2, 667
b217	—,2-amino-3,5-dibromo-1-ethoxy-*	$C_8H_9Br_2NO$. See b202	294.99	pr (dil al)	52					s				lig s^h	B13, 387
b218	—,5-amino-1,3-dibromo-2-methoxy-*	$C_7H_7Br_2NO$. See b202	280.96	pl (lig) λ^w 302.5 (3.69)	66					s	s	s	s	chl, aa s	B13, 517
b219	—,1-amino-2-diethylamino-*	$C_{10}H_{16}N_2$. See b202	164.25	oil		312^{744} 127^{25}			δ	s		s	s	os s	B13^1, 16
b220	—,1-amino-3-diethylamino-*	$C_{10}H_{16}N_2$. See b202	164.25			276–8^{760} 117^4			δ	s					B13^2, 26
b221	—,1-amino-4-diethylamino-*	$C_{10}H_{16}N_2$. See b202	164.25	ye oil		260–2 139–40^{10}							s		B13^2, 40
b222	—,1-amino-3,5-dihydroxy-*	Phloramin. $C_6H_7NO_2$. See b202	125.13	nd	146–52				δ	s	i				B13, 787
b223	—,4-amino-1,2-dihydroxy-*	$C_6H_7NO_2$. See b202	125.13	br-vt nd (al-bz)	124–5d				s	s	v	δ	δ		B13^2, 464
Ω b224	—,1-amino-2,3-dimethyl-*	2,3-Xylidine. $C_8H_{11}N$. See b202	121.18	λ^{iso} 236 (3.88), 286 (3.29)	< −15	221–2^{760} 106^{15}	0.9931^{20}	1.5684^{20}	δ	v	v				B12^2, 601
Ω b225	—,1-amino-2,4-dimethyl-*	2,4-Xylidine. $C_8H_{11}N$. See b202	121.18	λ^{al} 290 (3.2)	16	214^{760} 91^{10}	0.9723^{20}_4	1.5569^{20}	δ	s			s		B12^2, 602
Ω b226	—,1-amino-3,5-dimethyl-*	3,5-Xylidine. $C_8H_{11}N$. See b202	121.18	λ^{iso} 239 (3.85), 289 (3.24)	9.8	220–1 99–100^{20}	0.9706^{11}_4	1.5581^{11}	δ	s					B12^3, 613
Ω b227	—,2-amino-1,3-dimethyl-*	2,6-Xylidine. $C_8H_{11}N$. See b202	121.18	λ^{iso} 233 (3.92), 284 (3.37)	11.2	214^{739}	0.9842^{20}	1.5610^{20}	i	s	s				B12^2, 604
Ω b228	—,2-amino-1,4-dimethyl-*	2,5-Xylidine. $C_8H_{11}N$. See b202	121.18	ye lf (lig) λ^{iso} 236 (3.88), 288 (3.39)	15.5	214^{760} 97–101^{10}	0.9790^{21}_4	1.5591^{21}	δ	s					B12^2, 614
Ω b229	—,4-amino-1,2-dimethyl-*	3,4-Xylidine. $C_8H_{11}N$. See b202	121.18	pl or pr (lig) λ^{al} 240 (3.97)	51	226^{760}	1.076^{18}		δ	s				lig v	B12^2, 602
b230	—,1-amino-2-dimethylamino-	$C_8H_{12}N_2$. See b202	136.20	oil λ^{al} 240 sh (3.81), 293 (3.45)		218^{751} 117^{25}	0.995^{25}		δ	v	v	v	v	os v	B13, 15
b231	—,1-amino-3-dimethylamino-	$C_8H_{12}N_2$. See b202	136.20	λ^{al} 245 sh (3.9), 298 (3.4)	< −20	268–70^{740} 138^{10}	0.995^{25}		δ	v	v				B13, 38

For explanations, symbols and abbreviations see beginning of table. For structural formulas see end of table.

No.	Name	Synonyms and Formula	Mol. wt.	Color, crystalline form, specific rotation and λ_{max} (log ε)	m.p. °C	b.p. °C	Density	n_D	w	al	eth	ace	bz	other solvents	Ref.
	Benzene														
b232	—,1-amino-4-dimethylamino-	$C_8H_{12}N_2$. See b202	136.20	nd (bz) λ^{eth} 284 (4.24), 328 (3.46)	53 (40.5)	262 158[11]	1.036_4^{20}		s	v	v		v	chl s lig δ	B13, 72
b233	—,1-amino-2,3-dimethyl-4-nitro-*	$C_8H_{10}N_2O_2$. See b202	166.18	ye pr (al) λ^{al} 382 (3.99)	114					v^h					B12, 1103
b234	—,1-amino-2,3-dimethyl-5-nitro-*	$C_8H_{10}N_2O_2$. See b202	166.18	pa ye nd (al)	111–2					v^h					B12[1], 479
b235	—,1-amino-2,4-dimethyl-3-nitro-*	$C_8H_{10}N_2O_2$. See b202	166.18	ye nd	81–2 (78)				s^h	s				lig s	B12[2], 612
Ω b236	—,1-amino-2,4-dimethyl-5-nitro-*	$C_8H_{10}N_2O_2$. See b202	166.18	og ye nd (al)	123					v^h					B12[2], 612
b237	—,1-amino-3,4-dimethyl-2-nitro-*	$C_8H_{10}N_2O_2$. See b202	166.18	red pr (al)	65–6				i	v^h					B12[1], 481
b238	—,1-amino-3,5-dimethyl-2-nitro-*	$C_8H_{10}N_2O_2$. See b202	166.18	ye nd (lig)	56										B12[2], 613
b239	—,1-amino-4,5-dimethyl-2-nitro-*	$C_8H_{10}N_2O_2$. See b202	166.18	red-br pr (al)	140						δ	s	s	os v lig i	B12, 1106
b240	—,2-amino-1,3-dimethyl-4-nitro-*	$C_8H_{10}N_2O_2$. See b202	166.18	ye nd (dil al) λ^{al} 380 (4.16)	81–2						s				B12[2], 605
b241	—,2-amino-1,3-dimethyl-5-nitro-*	$C_8H_{10}N_2O_2$. See b202	166.18	og-ye nd	158						s				B12[2], 606
b242	—,2-amino-1,5-dimethyl-3-nitro-*	$C_8H_{10}N_2O_2$. See b202	166.18	og-red nd or pl (lig)	76						s				B12[2], 612
b243	—,2-amino-3,4-dimethyl-1-nitro-*	$C_8H_{10}N_2O_2$. See b202	166.18	red pl (al)	118–9					v^h				con HCl v	B12, 1102
b244	—,5-amino-1,2-dimethyl-3-nitro-*	$C_8H_{10}N_2O_2$. See b202	166.18	og lf (al)	74–5					v^h					B12, 1106
b245	—,5-amino-1,3-dimethyl-2-nitro-*	$C_8H_{10}N_2O_2$. See b202	166.18	og pr (bz), lf (lig) λ^{al} 240 (3.87), 301 (3.48), 385 (3.68)	133				s^h	v			s	lig δ	B12[2], 613
b245[1]	—,(1-amino-ethyl)-(d)*	$C_6H_5CH(CH_3)NH_2$	121.18	$[\alpha]_D^{25}$ +39.2 (MeOH)		187[760]	0.9651^{15}		s	v	v				B12[2], 586
Ω b245[2]	—,—(dl)*	$C_6H_5CH(CH_3)NH_2$	121.18			187[760] 87[24]	0.9395^{15}	1.5238^{25}	s	∞	∞				B12[2], 586
b245[3]	—,—(l)*	$C_6H_5CH(CH_3)NH_2$	121.18	$[\alpha]_D^{18}$ −38 (MeOH)		184–6 77[16]	0.9520^{20}_4		s	v	v				B12[2], 586
Ω b246	—,1-amino-2-ethyl-*	o-Ethylaniline. $C_8H_{11}N$. See b202	121.18	λ^{iso} 234 (3.90), 286 (3.37)	−43	209–10[760]	0.983_4^{22}	1.5584^{22}	δ	v	v				B12[2], 584
b247	—,1-amino-3-ethyl-*	m-Ethylaniline. $C_8H_{11}N$. See b202	121.18		−64	214–5[764] 93–5[6]	0.9896^0		s^h	v	v				B12[1], 468
Ω b248	—,1-amino-4-ethyl-*	p-Ethylaniline. $C_8H_{11}N$. See b202	121.18		−4.87	217.8[760] 92.3[10]	0.9679^{20}_4	1.5554^{20}	δ	v	v				B12[2], 584
Ω b248[1]	—,(2-amino-ethyl)-*	β-Phenethylamine. $C_6H_5CH_2CH_2NH_2$	121.18			197–8	0.9580^{24}	1.5290^{25}	s	v	v				B12[12], 591
b249	—,—,hydro-chloride*	$C_6H_5CH_2CH_2NH_2.HCl$	157.65	pl or lf (al)	218–9				v	v	i				B12[2], 592
b250	—,4(2-amino-ethyl)-1,3-dihydroxy-, hydrochloride*	$C_8H_{11}NO_2.HCl$. See b202	189.64	nd (w)	237d				v	v	δ				B13[2], 486
b251	—,1(2-amino-ethyl)-2-hydroxy-*	$C_8H_{11}NO$. See b202	137.18	rh (al-eth)	152–3										B13, 624
b252	—,1(2-amino-ethyl)-3-hydroxy-, hydrochloride*	$C_8H_{11}NO.HCl$. See b202	173.65	cr (al-eth)	145										B13[1], 233
—	—,1(2-amino-ethyl)-4-hydroxy-*	see **Tyramine**													
b253	—,5-amino-2-hydroxy-4-isopropyl-1-methyl-	4-Aminocarvacrol. $C_{10}H_{15}NO$. See b202	165.24	cr (MeOH)	134									MeOH s^h	B13[2], 392
b254	—,6-amino-3-hydroxy-4-isopropyl-1-methyl-	4-Aminothymol. $C_{10}H_{15}NO$. See b202	165.24	nd, sc (bz)	178–9					s	δ		v	os s	B13[2], 393

For explanations, symbols and abbreviations see beginning of table. For structural formulas see end of table.

No.	Name	Synonyms and Formula	Mol. wt.	Color, crystalline form, specific rotation and λ_{max} (log ε)	m.p. °C	b.p. °C	Density	n_D	Solubility						Ref.
									w	al	eth	ace	bz	other solvents	
	Benzene														
b255	—,1-amino-4-isobutyl-(dl)	$C_{10}H_{15}N$. See b202	149.24	pa ye	....	238^{762} 112^{11}	0.949_4^{15}		i	∞		∞	v	os m	B12², 635
Ω b256	—,1-amino-2-isopropyl-	$C_9H_{13}N$. See b202	135.21	λ^{iso} 234 (3.89), 286 (3.36)	....	$220-1^{745}$ 95^{13}	0.9760_4^{12}		i		s		s		B12², 624
b257	—,1-amino-4-isopropyl-	Cumidine. $C_9H_{13}N$. See b202	135.21	λ^{al} 234.8 (3.99), 288.2 (3.23)	−63	225^{760}	0.9532_4^{20}	1.5415^{20}	i v^h	s^h	s				B12², 625
b258	—,2-amino-1-isopropyl-4-methyl-	Thymylamine. $C_{10}H_{15}N$. See b202	149.24	oil λ^{al} 238 (3.81), 286.5 (3.27)	....	$238-42^{760}$			δ	∞	∞				B12², 642
b259	—,2-amino-4-isopropyl-1-methyl-	Carvacrylamine. $C_{10}H_{15}N$. See b202	149.24	....	−16	241^{760} 118^{12}	0.9942_4^{20}	1.5387^{20}	δ	s	s				B12², 638
Ω b260	—,1-amino-2-mercapto-*	o-Aminothiophenol. C_6H_7NS. See b202	125.19	nd λ 360 (3.5)	26	234 $125-7^6$					s				B13, 397
b261	—,1-amino-3-mercapto-*	m-Aminothiophenol. C_6H_7NS. See b202	125.19	pa ye oil	....	$180-90^{16}$			i	s	s			aa s peth i	B13, 425
Ω b262	—,1-amino-4-mercapto-*	p-Aminothiophenol. C_6H_7NS. See b202	125.19	wh gran	46	$140-5^{16}$			s		s				B13, 533
b263	—,1-amino-2-methoxy-3-nitro-	$C_7H_8N_2O_3$. See b202	168.16	pa ye nd (lig)	67	....					s			lig s^h	B13², 195
b264	—,2-amino-4-methoxy-1-nitro-*	$C_7H_8N_2O_3$. See b202	168.16	br nd	131	sub					s				B13², 215
b265	—,1-amino-4-methylamino-*	$C_7H_{10}N_2$. See b202	122.17	lf (eth-peth) λ^{eth} 253 (4.16), 329 (3.48)	36	$257-9.5$ 152^{20}			v	v	v	v	v	os s	B13, 71
b266	—,1(aminomethyl)-4-isopropyl-*	Cuminylamine. $C_{10}H_{15}N$. See b202	149.24	oil	....	$225-7^{724}$ $111-2^{11}$			i		s				B12, 1172
b267	—,1(aminomethyl)-2,4,5-trimethyl-	$C_{10}H_{15}N$. See b202	149.24	nd (dil al)	65	....			i $δ^h$	s^h				chl s	B12, 1177
b268	—,5(aminomethyl)-1,2,3-trimethyl-	$C_{10}H_{15}N$. See b202	149.24	lf (w)	123	....				s^h					B12, 1176
b269	—,1-amino-4-octyl-*	1(4-Aminophenyl)octane*. $C_{14}H_{23}N$. See b202	205.35	....	20	$310-1^{760}$ $170-2^{17}$			i	∞					B12, 1185
b270	—,1-amino-2,3,4,5,6-pentamethyl-	$C_{11}H_{17}N$. See b202	163.26	mcl pr (al)	152–3	$277-8$			i	s	s				B12², 646
b271	—,1-amino-2-propyl-*	o-Propylaniline. $C_9H_{13}N$. See b202	135.21	λ^{oy} 287.5 (3.34)	....	226^{758} 116^{15}	0.9602_4^{30}	1.5427^{30}	i	s	s				B12², 620
b272	—,1-amino-4-propyl-*	p-Propylaniline. $C_9H_{13}N$. See b202	135.21	....	....	$224-6^{760}$			δ						B12, 1143
b273	—,1(2-aminopropyl)-4-hydroxy-(l)*	L-Paredrine. $C_9H_{13}NO$. See b202	151.21	$[\alpha]_D^{17}$ − 52 (al)	111	....				s^h	s			chl s	H34, 2202
b274	—,1-amino-2,3,4,5-tetramethyl-*	Prehnidine. $C_{10}H_{15}N$. See b202	149.24	lf (w)	70	$259-60$			s^h	v	v			lig v	B12, 1175
b275	—,1-amino-2,3,4,6-tetramethyl-*	Isoduridine. $C_{10}H_{15}N$. See b202	149.24	....	23–4	255	0.978^{24}			s					B12¹, 506
Ω b276	—,1-amino-2,4,5-trimethyl-*	Pseudocumidine. $C_9H_{13}N$. See b202	135.21	nd (w)	68	$234-5$	0.957		v	s					B12², 629
Ω b277	—,2-amino-1,3,5-trimethyl-*	Mesidine. $C_9H_{13}N$. See b202	135.21	λ^{iso} 237 (3.94), 289 (3.39)	−5	$232-3$	0.9633	1.5495^{20}	δ	s	s			chl s	B12², 631
—	—,azido.........	see **Benzene, triazo-***													
Ω b278	—,1-benzyl-4-ethyl-	p-Ethyldiphenylmethane. $C_{15}H_{16}$. See b202	196.30	λ^{iso} 260 (2.77), 263 (2.75), 266 (2.80), 269 (2.75), 274 (2.69)	−24	297^{760} $85^{0.2}$	0.9777^{20}	1.5616^{20}	δ	s	s			chl s	B5, 614
b279	—,1-benzyl-2-hydroxy-	2-Benzylphenol. $C_{13}H_{12}O$. See b202	184.24	cr (peth)	(i) 21 (metast) (ii) 51,5–3 (nt)	312 $159-62^{12}$									B6, 675
b280	—,1-benzyl-4-hydroxy-	4-Benzylphenol. $C_{13}H_{12}O$. See b202	184.24	nd (al)	84	$320-2$ $198-200^{10}$			s^h	s	s		s	chl, aa s	B6, 678
Ω b281	—,1,2-bis(bromomethyl)-*	o-Xylylene bromide. $C_8H_8Br_2$. See b202	263.98	rh (chl)	95	$128-30^{4.5}$	1.988^0		i	s	s			chl, lig, peth s	B5², 285
Ω b282	—,1,3-bis(bromomethyl)-*	m-Xylylene bromide. $C_8H_8Br_2$. See b202	263.98	nd (chl), pr (ace)	77	$135-40^{20}$	1.959^0		i	s	s			chl, lig s	B5², 294
Ω b283	—,1,4-bis(bromomethyl)-*	p-Xylylene bromide. $C_8H_8Br_2$. See b202	263.98	mcl pr (al), cr (chl, bz)	145–7	245 $155-8^{14}$	2.012^0		i	v	δ		s	chl v	B5, 385
b284	—,1,3-bis(bromomethyl)-5-methyl-*	$C_9H_{10}Br_2$. See b202	278.00	pr	66	....			i	$δ$ v^h	s		s	lig s	B5², 315
b285	—,1,3-bis(carboxymethoxy)-*	$C_{10}H_{10}O_6$. See b202	226.19	nd (aa, w)	195	....			s^h					aa s^h	B6², 817

For explanations, symbols and abbreviations see beginning of table. For structural formulas see end of table.

No.	Name	Synonyms and Formula	Mol. wt.	Color, crystalline form. specific rotation and λ_{max} (log ε)	m.p. °C	b.p. °C	Density	n_D	w	al	eth	ace	bz	other solvents	Ref.
b286	—.—.diethyl ester*	$C_{14}H_{18}O_6$. See b202.	282.30	nd (eth)	42	228^{32}			i					lig δ	B6, 818
Ω b287	—,1,2-bis(chloro-methyl)-*	o-Xylylene chloride. $C_8H_8Cl_2$. See b202	175.07	mcl (lig)	55	239–41 130–5[19]	1.393^0		i	v	v			chl, lig v	B5[2], 283
Ω b288	—,1,3-bis(chloro-methyl)-*	m-Xylylene chloride. $C_8H_8Cl_2$. See b202	175.07		34.2	250–5	1.302^{20}		i	v	v				B5[2], 291
Ω b289	—,1,4-bis(chloro-methyl)-*	p-Xylylene chloride. $C_8H_8Cl_2$. See b202	175.07	pl (al) λ^{al} 268 (2.30)	100	240–5d 135[16]	1.417^0		i	v^h	v	v		chl v aa δ	B5[2], 300
b290	—,1,2-bis(cyano-methyl)-*	o-Xylylene dicyanide. $C_{10}H_8N_2$. See b202	156.20	(i) nd or pr (MeOH) (ii) pr(al)	(i) 18 (unst) (ii) 60 (st)				i	s^h	s			lig i	B9[2], 623
b291	—,1,3-bis(cyano-methyl)-*	m-Xylylene dicyanide. $C_{10}H_8N_2$. See b202	156.20	nd (w), pr (eth)	30	$305–10^{300}$ $170^{20–30}$			i	s^h	s		s	chl s lig i	B9[2], 624
b292	—,1,4-bis(cyano-methyl)-*	p-Xylylene dicyanide. $C_{10}H_8N_2$. See b202	156.20	pr (al), nd (w)	98				i s^h	s^h	s			chl s	B9[2], 624
Ω b293	—,1,2-bis(di-bromomethyl)-*	$C_8H_6Br_4$. See b202.	421.77	mcl	116–7				δ s^h					chl v lig i	B5, 367
b294	—,1,3-bis(di-bromomethyl)-*	$C_8H_6Br_4$. See b202.	421.77	nd (al), pl (chl)	107				i	s^h			v	chl v lig, aa s	B5, 375
b295	—,1,4-bis(di-bromomethyl)-*	$C_8H_6Br_4$. See b202.	421.77	mcl pr (chl)	172				δ^h	δ	δ		v	chl δ, s^h	B5, 386
b296	—,1,2-bis(diethyl-amino)-*	$C_{14}H_{24}N_2$. See b202.	220.36			119^{10}	0.9267_4^{13}	1.5213^{13}		s	s				B13[2], 12
b297	—,1,3-bis(diethyl-amino)-*	$C_{14}H_{24}N_2$. See b202.	220.36			148^9	0.9522_4^{12}	1.5537^{12}		s	s				B13[2], 26
b298	—,1,4-bis(diethyl-amino)-*	$C_{14}H_{24}N_2$. See b202.	220.36	mcl pr, pl (al-w)	52	280				v	v		v	chl, lig v	B13[2], 40
b299	—,1,4-bis-(dimethyl-amino)-*	$C_{10}H_{16}N_2$. See b202.	164.25	lf (dil al or lig) λ^{gy} 228 sh (3.67), 264 (4.21), 304 sh (3.27)	51	260			δ s^h	v	v		v	chl v lig s	B13[2], 40
b301	—,1,3-bis(1,1-dimethyl-propyl)-2-hydroxy-5-methyl-	$C_{17}H_{28}O$. See b202.	248.41			283^{760} 165^{20}	0.931_4^{25}	1.4950^{20}			c			alk i	C38, 4170
b302	—,1,2-bis(hy-droxymethyl)-*	Phthalyl alcohol. o-Xylylene glycol. $C_8H_{10}O_2$. See b202	138.17	pl (eth, peth) λ^{al} 261 (2.3), 267 (2.3)	65–6.5				s	s	v		δ		B6, 910
b303	—,1,3-bis(hy-droxymethyl)-*	Isophthalyl alcohol m-Xylylene glycol. $C_8H_{10}O_2$. See b202	138.17	nd (bz)	57 (46–7)	$154–9^{13}$	1.1359^{53}		v	s	s			AcOEt v	B6[1], 446
b304	—,1,4-bis(hy-droxymethyl)-*	Terephthalyl alcohol p-Xylylene glycol. $C_8H_{10}O_2$. See b202	138.17	nd (w)	115–6				v	v	v	s			B6[2], 891
b304[1]	—,1,2-bis(meth-ylamino)-4-chloro-*	$C_8H_{11}ClN_2$. See b202	170.64	pr (lig)	61				s						B13, 25
b305	—,1,3-bis(3-methylbutoxy)-*	Resorcinol diisoamyl ether. $C_{16}H_{26}O_2$. See b202	250.39		47				i						B6, 815
b306	—,1,3-bis(phen-ylazo)-2,4-di-hydroxy-*	$C_{18}H_{14}N_4O_2$. See b202	318.34	red nd (chl-al)	222						δ			con ac, con alk s, chl v^h	B16, 185
b307	—,1,5-bis(phen-ylazo)-2,4-di-hydroxy-*	$C_{18}H_{14}N_4O_2$. See b202	318.34	br-red nd	217				i	δ	δ			sulf, chl s	B16, 186
b308	—,1,3-bis(4-tolyl-amino)-*	$C_{20}H_{20}N_2$. See b202.	288.40	nd (al)	138–9				i	δ	δ				B13, 42
Ω b309	—,bromo-*	Phenyl bromide. C_6H_5Br. See b202	157.02	λ^{al} 213.5 (3.86)	− 30.82	156^{760} 43^{18}	1.4950_4^{20}	1.5597^{20}	i	v	v		v	CCl_4 s	B5[2], 158
Ω b310	—,(4-bromo-butoxy)-*	$C_{10}H_{13}BrO$. See b202.	229.12	cr (al)	41	$153–6^{18}$				δ s^h					B6[2], 146
Ω b311	—,1-bromo-4-tert-butyl-	$C_{10}H_{13}Br$. See b202.	213.13		19	$231–2^{760}$ 103^{10}	1.2286_4^{20}	1.5436^{20}	i		s	s	s	chl s	B5[2], 320
Ω b312	—,1-bromo-2-chloro-*	C_6H_4BrCl. See b202.	191.46		− 12.3	204^{765}	1.6382_4^{25}	1.5809^{20}	i				v		B5[2], 161
Ω b313	—,1-bromo-3-chloro-*	C_6H_4BrCl. See b202.	191.46		− 21.5	196	1.6302_4^{20}	1.5771^{20}	i	v	v				B5[2], 161
Ω b314	—,1-bromo-4-chloro-*	C_6H_4BrCl. See b202.	191.46	nd or pl (al, eth)	68	196^{756}	1.576_4^{71}	1.5531^{70}	i	δ s^h	s		s	chl s	B5[2], 162
b315	—,1-bromo-4-cyclohexyl-*	$C_{12}H_{15}Br$. See b202.	239.16			160^{23}	1.2833_4^{25}	1.5584^{20}					s	chl s	B5[2], 396
b316	—,1-bromo-2,3-dichloro-*	$C_6H_3BrCl_2$. See b202.	225.91	pl or lf (al)	60	243^{705}			i	δ v^h	s		v		B5, 209
b318	—,1-bromo-3,5-dichloro-*	$C_6H_3BrCl_2$. See b202.	225.91	pr (al)	82–4	232^{757}			i	s^h	s		v	chl s	B5, 210
b319	—,2-bromo-1,3-dichloro-*	$C_6H_3BrCl_2$. See b202.	225.91	pl (al)	65	242^{765}			i		v		v	chl v	B5, 210
b320	—,2-bromo-1,4-dichloro-*	$C_6H_3BrCl_2$. See b202.	225.91	pr or nd (al)	35	235^{731} 119^{26}			i	s v^h	v		v	chl, lig v	B5, 210

For explanations, symbols and abbreviations see beginning of table. For structural formulas see end of table.

No.	Name	Synonyms and Formula	Mol. wt.	Color, crystalline form, specific rotation and λ_{max} (log ε)	m.p. °C	b.p. °C	Density	n_D	w	al	eth	ace	bz	other solvents	Ref.
	Benzene														
b321	—,4-bromo-1,2-dichloro-*	$C_6H_3BrCl_2$. See b202	225.91	pr	25	237[757] 124[33]			i	δ v^h	v	...	v	chl v	B5, 210
b322	—,1-bromo-2,4-dihydroxy-*	$C_6H_5BrO_2$. See b202	189.02		103	138–41[12]			v	δ	v		δ	CS_2, chl δ	B6[2], 819
b323	—,1-bromo-3,5-dihydroxy-*	$C_6H_5BrO_2$. See b202	189.02	nd (bz), pr(w+1)	79(+w), 87				v^h		s		v^h s		B6[2], 820
b324	—,2-bromo-1,3-dihydroxy-*	$C_6H_5BrO_2$. See b202	189.02	nd (chl), cr (peth)	102–3				s	s	s			chl s	B6[2], 819
Ω b325	—,2-bromo-1,4-dihydroxy-*	Adurol. $C_6H_5BrO_2$. See b202	189.02	lf (lig) cr (chl)	110–1	sub			v	v	v		v	chl. lig δ aa s	B6[2], 846
b326	—,4-bromo-1,2-dihydroxy-*	4-Bromocatechol. $C_6H_5BrO_2$. See b202	189.02	pr or nd (chl)	87				v	v	v		v^h	chl, peth δ	B6[2], 781
b327	—,1-bromo-2,3-dimethyl-*	C_8H_9Br. See b202	185.07			214 83[11]	1.365[20]4		i	...	v	s	s		B5[1], 180
b328	—,1-bromo-2,4-dimethyl-*	C_8H_9Br. See b202	185.07	λ^{hx} 359 (2.83), 367 (2.84), 379 (2.76)	0	205 84[13]		1.5501[20]	i	v	v		s		B5[2], 293
Ω b329	—,2-bromo-1,4-dimethyl-*	C_8H_9Br. See b202	185.07	lf or pl λ^{hx} 359.5 (2.88), 369 (2.83), 377.5 (2.72)	9	199–200 88–9[13]	1.3582[18]	1.5514[18]	i	v	v		s		B5[3], 301
Ω b330	—,4-bromo-1,2-dimethyl-*	C_8H_9Br. See b202	185.07	λ^{hx} 359 (2.75), 370 (2.78), 379.5 (2.63)	−0.2	214.5	1.3708[20]4	1.5530[20]	i	v	v				B5[2], 285
b331	—,1-bromo-2,3-dinitro-*	$C_6H_3BrN_2O_4$. See b202	247.01	pa ye pl (al)	101–2	320			i	v^h	δ				B5[1], 138
b332	—,1-bromo-2,4-dinitro-*	$C_6H_3BrN_2O_4$. See b202	247.01	ye nd (al) $\lambda^{w,pH=7.4}$ 265 (4.01)	75				d^h	v^h					B5[1], 138
b333	—,2-bromo-1,3-dinitro-*	$C_6H_3BrN_2O_4$. See b202	247.01	ye pr (al)	107				d^h	δ v^h					B5[1], 138
b334	—,2-bromo-1,4-dinitro-*	$C_6H_3BrN_2O_4$. See b202	247.01	nd (al), pr (al-eth)	70				...	δ v^h	v				B5[1], 139
b335	—,4-bromo-1,2-dinitro-*	$C_6H_3BrN_2O_4$. See b202	247.01	nd (al), pl (al-eth)	34–5 (unst), 59–60 (st)				...	δ v^h	v			MeOH δ peth i	B5[1], 138
b336	—,1-bromo-2-ethoxy-*	C_8H_9BrO. See b202	201.07			222–6			i	v	v				B6, 197
b337	—,1-bromo-3-ethoxy-*	C_8H_9BrO. See b202	201.07			222 (228–31)			i	v	v				B6[2], 184
Ω b338	—,1-bromo-4-ethoxy-*	C_8H_9BrO. See b202	201.07		4	230–2 109[17]	1.4071[25]4	1.5517[20]	i	v	v				B6[2], 185
b338[1]	—,(1-bromoethyl)-(d)*	C_8H_9Br. See b202	185.07	$[\alpha]_D^{14}$ +1.5		203 86–8[15]	1.3108[23]	1.5612[20]	i	s	s				B5[2], 278
Ω b339	—,—,(dl)*	C_8H_9Br. See b202	185.07			202–3[760] 85[13]	1.3605[20]4	1.5612[20]	d^h	s	s		s		B5[2], 278
Ω b340	—,(2-bromoethyl)-*	C_8H_9Br. See b202	185.07			217–8[734] 92[11]	1.3587[20]4	1.5572[20]	i	v	s		s		B5[2], 278
Ω b341	—,1-bromo-4-fluoro-*	C_6H_4BrF. See b202	175.01	λ^{cy} 215 (3.85), 265 (2.90), 271 (3.02), 278 (2.95)	−8 (fr −17.4)	152[764]	1.4946[20]4	1.5604[20]	i	s	v				B5[2], 161
Ω b342	—,1-bromo-2-iodo-*	C_6H_4BrI. See b202	282.91		9–10	257[754] 120–1[15]	2.2571[25]4	1.6618[25]	i	δ	...	s		aa δ	B5[2], 167
b343	—,1-bromo-3-iodo-*	C_6H_4BrI. See b202	282.91	λ^{peth} 235 (4.06)	−9.3	252[754] 120[18]			i	δ	s			aa δ	B5[2], 168
Ω b344	—,1-bromo-4-iodo-*	C_6H_4BrI. See b202	282.91	pr or pl (eth-al) λ^{al} 237.5 (4.24)	92	252[754]			i	δ	s		s		B5[2], 168
Ω b345	—,1-bromo-4-isopropyl-	$C_9H_{11}Br$. See b202	199.10		−22.54 (−17.3)	218.7[760] 97–8[5]	1.3145[20]	1.5569[20]	i				s	chl s	B5[2], 307
b346	—,(β-bromoisopropyl)-	$C_9H_{11}Br$. See b202	199.10	$[\alpha]_D^{20}$(d) +15.6, (l) −15.6		188–9 106–8[18]	1.3155[20]	1.5548[28]	i				s	chl s	B5[1], 191
b347	—,2-bromo-4-isopropyl-1-methyl-	$C_{10}H_{13}Br$. See b202	213.13			234.3[760] 99[9]	1.2689[14]4	1.5360[20]	i	v	s			chl s	B5[1], 205
Ω b348	—,1-bromo-4-mercapto-*	C_6H_5BrS. See b202	189.08	lf (al)	75	230–1			δ^h	δ v^h	v			sulf, CCl_4, chl v	B6[2], 300
b349	—,1-bromo-2-methoxy-*	C_7H_7BrO. See b202	187.04	λ^{cy} 218 sh (3.92), 266 sh (3.26), 273.5 (3.44), 280.5 (3.45)	2.5	216 (223) 94[10]	1.5018[20]4	1.5727[20]	i	v	v				B6[2], 183
b350	—,1-bromo-3-methoxy-*	C_7H_7BrO. See b202	187.04	λ^{cy} 218 sh (3.93), 267 sh (3.16), 272.5 (3.37), 279.5 (3.36)		210–1[752] 105[16]		1.5635[20]	i	s	s		s	CS_2 s	B6[2], 184

For explanations, symbols and abbreviations see beginning of table. For structural formulas see end of table.

No.	Name	Synonyms and Formula	Mol. wt.	Color, crystalline form, specific rotation and λ_{max} (log ε)	m.p. °C	b.p. °C	Density	n_D	w	al	eth	ace	bz	other solvents	Ref.
	Benzene														
Ω b351	—,1-bromo-4-methoxy-*	C_7H_7BrO. See b202	187.04	λ^{cy} 226 (4.10), 274 sh (3.13), 279 (3.24), 287 (3.19)	13–4	215 100[16]	1.4564[20/4]	1.5642[20]	δ	v	v	...	...	chl v	B6[2], 185
b352	—,1(bromomethyl)-3,5-dimethyl-*	Mesityl bromide. $C_9H_{11}Br$. See b202	199.10	nd (eth)	40	229–31[740] δd 118[22]	....	....	...	v	v	...	s	chl v	B5[1], 200
Ω b353	—,1(bromomethyl)-2-methyl-*	o-Xylyl bromide. C_8H_9Br. See b202	185.07	pr	21	216–7[742] 108[16]	1.3811[23]	1.5730[20]	i	s	s	s	s	os s	B5[2], 285
Ω b354	—,1(bromomethyl)-3-methyl-*	m-Xylyl bromide. C_8H_9Br. See b202	185.07	....	...	212–3 δd 105[13]	1.3711[23]	1.5660[20]	i	v	v	...	...	os s	B5[2], 293
Ω b355	—,1(bromomethyl)-4-methyl-*	p-Xylyl bromide. C_8H_9Br. See b202	185.07	nd (al) λ^{hx} 236 (3.7)	35	218–20[740]	1.324	....	i	s	v^h	...	...	chl v^h	B5[2], 301
Ω b356	—,1-bromo-2-nitro-*	$C_6H_4BrNO_2$. See b202	202.01	pa ye (al) λ^{hx} 293 (3.12)	43	258[756]	1.6245[80/4]	....	i	v	s	s	s	....	B5[2], 188
Ω b357	—,1-bromo-3-nitro-*	$C_6H_4BrNO_2$. See b202	202.01	rh λ^{hx} 255 (3.85), 293 (3.11), 302 (3.12)	17 (unst) 56 (st)	265[760]	1.7036[20/4]	1.5979[20]	δ	s	s	...	s	....	B5[2], 188
Ω b358	—,1-bromo-4-nitro-*	$C_6H_4BrNO_2$. See b202	202.01	rh or mcl pr (al) λ^{hx} 269.2 (4.6)	127	256[760]	1.948	....	i	s	s	...	s	....	B5[2], 189
b359	—,1-bromo-2-nitroso-*	C_6H_4BrNO. See b202	186.01	nd	98	....	....	....	...	...	...	...	s	chl s	B5, 232
b360	—,1-bromo-4-nitroso*	C_6H_4BrNO. See b202	186.01	nd (al) λ^{al} 227 (3.80), 293 (4.00), 315 (4.08), 750 (1.62)	95	....	....	....	...	s^h	...	...	s	chl v lig s^h	B5[2], 171
b361	—,(3-bromo-1-propenyl)-*	Cinnamyl bromide. C_9H_9Br. See b202	197.08	nd (al, eth)	34	130[10]	1.3428[30]	1.610–1.613[20]	i	s^h	...	...	...	hx s	B5[2], 372
b362	—,(3-bromopropoxy)-*	γ-Phenoxypropyl bromide. $C_9H_{11}BrO$. See b202	215.10	....	7–8	127[18]	1.365[16/16]	....	...	...	v	...	...	....	B6[2], 145
b363	—,(1-bromopropyl)-(dl)*	$C_9H_{11}Br$. See b202	199.10	d[α]D +5.9 (al, c = 1) l[α]D[20] −5.7 (eth, c = 10)	....	105[17]	1.3098[19/4]	1.5517[19]	i d^h	...	v	...	s	....	B5[2], 305
b364	—,(2-bromopropyl)-*	$C_9H_{11}Br$. See b202	199.10	....	....	107–9[16]	1.2908[16]	1.5450[20]	i d^h	...	v	...	...	chl s	B5[1], 190
b365	—,(3-bromopropyl)-*	$C_9H_{11}Br$. See b202	199.10	λ^{al} 242.5 (2.13), 248 (2.23), 253.5 (2.33), 259 (2.38), 264.5 (2.27), 268 (2.24)	....	110[12]	1.3106[25/4]	1.5440[25]	i	...	v	...	...	....	B5[2], 305
b366	—,1-bromo-4-triazo-*	$C_6H_4BrN_3$. See b202	198.03	pl λ^{al} 253 (4.0), 291 (3.2)	20	105[10]	....	....	i	δ	v	...	v	....	B5[2], 208
b367	—,1-bromo-2,3,5-trimethyl-*	$C_9H_{11}Br$. See b202	199.10	....	< −15	238[760] (223) 117[17]	....	1.5516[26]	i	...	...	...	s	sulf s	B5[1], 196
Ω b368	—,1-bromo-2,4,5-trimethyl-*	$C_9H_{11}Br$. See b202	199.10	nd (al)	73	233–5	....	....	i	v^h	...	...	...	....	B5[1], 196
b369	—,2-bromo-1,3,5-trimethyl-*	Bromomesitylene. $C_9H_{11}Br$. See b202	199.10	λ^{al} 269 (2.36)	−1	225 117[25]	1.3191[10]	1.5510[20]	i	...	v	...	s	....	B5[2], 315
Ω b370	—,butoxy-*	Butyl phenyl ether. $C_{10}H_{14}O$. See b202	150.22	....	−19.4	210[760] 95[17]	0.9351[20/4]	1.4969[20]	...	...	s	s	s	....	B6[2], 145
b371	—,sec-butoxy-	sec-Butyl phenyl ether. $C_{10}H_{14}O$. See b202	150.22	....	....	194.5[760] 70–2[5]	0.9415[20/4]	1.4926[25]	i	...	s	...	...	....	B6[2], 146
Ω b372	—,butyl-*	$C_{10}H_{14}$. See b202	134.22	λ^{iso} 248 (2.1), 253 (2.2), 259 (2.3), 262 (2.3), 265 (2.2), 268 (2.2)	−88	183[760] 62.2[10]	0.8601[20/4]	1.4898[20]	i	∞	∞	∞	∞	peth, CCl_4 ∞	B5[2], 317
b373	—,sec-butyl-(d)	$C_{10}H_{14}$. See b202	134.22	[α]D[20] +27.3 (undil)	−75	173[760] 63[15]	0.8621[20/4]	1.4895[20]	i	∞	∞	∞	∞	peth, CCl_4 ∞	B5[2], 319
Ω b374	—,—(dl)	$C_{10}H_{14}$. See b202	134.22	λ^{iso} 248 (2.0), 253 (2.2), 258 (2.3), 261 (2.3), 264 (2.2), 267 (2.2)	−75.47	173[760] 53.6[10]	0.8621[20/4]	1.4902[20]	i	∞	∞	∞	∞	peth, CCl_4 ∞	B5[2], 319
b375	—,—(l)	$C_{10}H_{14}$. See b202	134.22	[α]D[23] −17.9 (al, c = 5)	....	61[18]	0.868[24/4]	1.4891[20]	i	∞	∞	∞	∞	peth, CCl_4 ∞	B5[3], 931

For explanations, symbols and abbreviations see beginning of table. For structural formulas see end of table.

No.	Name	Synonyms and Formula	Mol. wt.	Color, crystalline form, specific rotation and λ_{max} (log ε)	m.p. °C	b.p. °C	Density	n_D	w	al	eth	ace	bz	other solvents	Ref.
	Benzene														
Ω b376	—,tert-butyl-	$C_{10}H_{14}$. See b202	134.22	λ^{hx} 253 (2.2), 257 (2.3), 264 sh (2.2), 267 (2.1)	−57.85	169^{760} 50.7^{10}	0.8665_4^{20}	1.4927^{20}	i	v	v	∞	∞	peth, CCl_4 ∞	$B5^2$, 320
b377	—,1-butyl-2,4-dihydroxy-*	$C_{10}H_{14}O_2$. See b202	166.22	....	47–8	$164–6^{6–7}$			i	δ	...	...	δ	chl δ	$B6^3$, 898
b378	—,1-tert-butyl-2,3-dimethyl-4-hydroxy-	$C_{12}H_{18}O$. See b202	178.28	....		259^{760} 145^{20}									$B6^3$, 2019
b379	—,1-tert-butyl-2,5-dimethyl-4-hydroxy-	$C_{12}H_{18}O$. See b202	178.28	....	71.2	264^{760} 136^{10}	0.939_4^{80} 1.001_4^{27}	1.5311^{20}	...	...	...	...	...	alk s	$B6^3$, 2019
b380	—,1-tert-butyl-3,5-dimethyl-2-hydroxy-	$C_{12}H_{18}O$. See b202	178.28	....	22.3	249^{760} 115^{10}	0.917_4^{80}	1.5183^{20}	...	...	...	...	...	alk i	$B6^3$, 2020
b381	—,1-tert-butyl-4,5-dimethyl-2-hydroxy-	$C_{12}H_{18}O$. See b202	178.28	....	46.0	145^{20} 127^{10}	0.920_4^{80} 0.973_4^{27}	1.5222^{20}	...	...	...	...	...	alk i	$B6^3$, 2019
b382	—,5-tert-butyl-1,3-dimethyl-2-hydroxy-	$C_{12}H_{18}O$. See b202	178.28	pr (peth)	82.4	248^{760} 119^{10}	0.916_4^{80} 0.959_4^{27}		...	...	...	...	...	alk s	$B6^3$, 2019
b383	—,1-tert-butyl-3,5-dimethyl-2,4,6-trinitro-	Musk xylene. $C_{12}H_{15}N_3O_6$, See b202	297.27	pl, nd (al) λ^{al} < 220	110 (unst) (114)	....	....		i	δ v^h	s	...	...		$B5^2$, 340
b384	—,2-tert-butyl-3,5-dinitro-1-iso-propyl-4-methyl-	Moskene. $C_{14}H_{20}N_2O_4$. See b202	280.33	pa ye cr	132–3				i	δ	...	...	...		C49, 3044
Ω b385	—,5-tert-butyl-1,3-dinitro-4-methoxy-2-methyl-	Musk ambrette. $C_{12}H_{16}N_2O_5$. See b202	268.25	pa ye lf (al)	84–6	185^{16}			i	δ	s	...	...		$B6^3$, 1984
b386	—,2-tert-butyl-1,3-dinitro-4,5,6-trimethyl-	Musk tebetene. $C_{13}H_{18}N_2O_4$. See b202	266.30	pa ye pr (al)	135–6.5				i	δ	s	...	...		$B5^3$, 1055
b387	—,2-tert-butyl-4-ethyl-1-hydroxy-	$C_{12}H_{18}O$. See b202	178.28	....	23	250^{760} 123^{10}			...	...	s	...	...	alk i	$B6^2$, 2012
b388	—,4-tert-butyl-2-ethyl-1-hydroxy-	$C_{12}H_{18}O$. See b202	178.28	....		257^{760} 141^{20}			...	...	...	...	...		$B6^3$, 2012
Ω b389	—,1-butyl-2-hydroxy-*	o-Butylphenol. $C_{10}H_{14}O$. See b202	150.22	....		235^{760} 106.5^{10}	0.975_4^{20}	$1.5180^{25.5}$	i	s	s	...	...	alk s	$B6^3$, 1843
Ω b390	—,1-butyl-3-hydroxy-*	m-Butylphenol. $C_{10}H_{14}O$. See b202	150.22	....		248^{760} 123^{10}	0.974_4^{20}		i	s	s	...	...	alk s	$B6^2$, 485
Ω b391	—,1-butyl-4-hydroxy-*	p-Butylphenol. $C_{10}H_{14}O$. See b202	150.22	....	22	248^{760} $138–9^{18}$	0.978_4^{20}	$1.5165^{25.5}$	i	s	s	...	...	alk s	$B6^2$, 485
Ω b392	—,1-sec-butyl-4-hydroxy-	p-sec-Butylphenol. $C_{10}H_{14}O$. See b202	150.22	nd, $[\alpha]_D^{20}$ + 13.3 (m-xyl)	61–2	$240–2^{760}$	0.9883_{20}^{20}	1.5182^{21}	i	s	v	...	...	alk s	$B6^2$, 487
Ω b393	—,1-tert-butyl-2-hydroxy-	o-t-Butylphenol. $C_{10}H_{14}O$. See b202	150.22	λ^{al} 216 (3.71), 271 (3.36), 277 (3.31)	....	221^{760} 99^{10}	0.9783_4^{20}	1.5160^{20}	...	s	v	...	...	alk s	$B6^2$, 489
Ω b394	—,1-tert-butyl-3-hydroxy-	m-t-Butylphenol. $C_{10}H_{14}O$. See b202	150.22	nd (peth)	41–2	240^{760} 132.5^{20}			...	s	v	...	...	alk s	$B6^3$, 1862
Ω b395	—,1-tert-butyl-4-hydroxy-	p-t-Butylphenol. $C_{10}H_{14}O$. See b202	150.22	nd (lig) λ^{al} 225 (3.9), 278 (3.4), 285 sh (3.2)	101	239.5^{760} 114^{10}	0.908_4^{80}	1.4787^{114}	s^h	s	s	...	...	alk s	$B6^2$, 489
Ω b396	—,1-tert-butyl-2-hydroxy-4-methyl-	$C_{11}H_{16}O$. See b202	164.25	....	46–7 37 (+ ½w)	224^{760} 127^{11}	0.922_4^{80}	1.5250^{20}	i	s	s	s	...	os s	$B6^2$, 507
Ω b397	—,2-tert-butyl-1-hydroxy-4-methyl-	$C_{11}H_{16}O$. See b202	164.25	nd (peth) λ^{al} 281 (3.22)	55 (44)	237^{760} 111^{10}	0.9247_4^{75}	1.4969^{75}	i	...	s	s	s	os s	$B6^3$, 1978
Ω b398	—,4-tert-butyl-1-hydroxy-2-methyl-	$C_{11}H_{16}O$. See b202	164.25	yesh	27–8	$235–7^{740}$ 132^{20}	0.965_4^{20}	1.5230^{20}	i	...	s	s	s	os s	$B6^2$, 507
b399	—,1-butyl-2-methyl-*	$C_{11}H_{16}$. See b202	148.25	....		208^{760} 81^{10}	0.8710_4^{20}	1.4960^{20}	i	δ	s	s	v	....	B5, 437
b400	—,1-butyl-3-methyl-*	$C_{11}H_{16}$. See b202	148.25	....		205^{760} 79^{10}	0.8590_4^{20}	1.4910^{20}	i	δ	s	s	v	....	B5, 437
b401	—,1-butyl-4-methyl-*	$C_{11}H_{16}$. See b202	148.25	....	−85	207^{760} 80.6^{10}	0.8586_4^{20}	1.4916^{20}	i	δ	s	s	s	....	B5, 437
b402	—,1-sec-butyl-4-methyl-	$C_{11}H_{16}$. See b202	148.25	....		197^{760} 73^{10}	0.8640^{19}	1.493^{20}	i	...	v	...	s	chl v	$B5^2$, 333
Ω b403	—,1-tert-butyl-4-methyl-	$C_{11}H_{16}$. See b202	148.25	....	−52	193^{760} 70^{10}	0.8612_4^{20}	1.4918^{20}	i	δ	v	s	s	chl v	$B5^1$, 210
b404	—,1-tert-butyl-3-methyl-2,4,6-trinitro-	Artificial musk. $C_{11}H_{13}N_3O_6$. See b202	283.24	ye nd (al)	96–7	....			i	v	v	...	s	chl s	B5, 438
b405	—,2-tert-butyl-4-methyl-1,3,5-trinitro-	Musk baur. $C_{11}H_{13}N_3O_6$. See b202	283.24	ye nd (al)	97	....			i	s	s	...	s	chl, peth s	B5, 438

For explanations, symbols and abbreviations see beginning of table. For structural formulas see end of table.

Benzene

No.	Name	Synonyms and Formula	Mol. wt.	Color, crystalline form, specific rotation and λ_{max} (log ε)	m.p. °C	b.p. °C	Density	n_D	w	al	eth	ace	bz	other solvents	Ref.
—	—,(1-butynyl)-*	see **Butyne, phenyl-**													
Ω b407	—,chloro-*	Phenyl chloride C_6H_5Cl. See b202	112.56	λ^{al} 245 (1.95), 251 (2.34), 258 (2.13), 264 (2.45), 272 (2.32)	−45.6	132[760] 22[10]	1.1058[20]₄	1.5241[20]	i	∞	∞	...	v	chl, CCl_4, CS_2 v	B5[2], 148
b408	—,2-chloro-1,4-diacetamido-*	$C_{10}H_{11}ClN_2O_2$. See b202	226.67	nd	196–7	....	....	....		s			δ	....	B13, 118
b409	—,1-chloro-2,4-diamino-*	$C_6H_7ClN_2$. See b202	142.59	pl or nd	91	....	....	....	δ	s				lig i	B13[2], 29
b410	—,1-chloro-3,5-diamino-*	$C_6H_7ClN_2$. See b202	142.59	rh pr (al), nd (to-al)	105–6	....	....	....	s[h]	s	s	s	δ	chl s lig i	B13[2], 29
b411	—,2-chloro-1,3-diamino-*	$C_6H_7ClN_2$. See b202	142.59	....	85–6	....	....	....			s				B13[1], 15
b412	—,2-chloro-1,4-diamino-*	$C_6H_7ClN_2$. See b202	142.59	nd (bz-lig)	64	....	....	....	s				s[h]	lig s[h]	B13[2], 58
Ω b413	—,4-chloro-1,2-diamino-*	$C_6H_7ClN_2$. See b202	142.59	pl (bz-lig), lf (w)	76	....	....	....	δ	v	v		s	lig s	B13, 25
b414	—,1-chloro-2,3-dihydroxy-*	$C_6H_5ClO_2$. See b202	144.56	cr (lig)	46–8	110–1[11]	....	....						lig v	B6[1], 388
Ω b415	—,1-chloro-2,4-dihydroxy-*	$C_6H_5ClO_2$. See b202	144.56	(i) cr (al) (ii) cr (bz) λ^w 215 sh (3.78), 282.5 (3.45)	(i) 89 (ii) 105	259 147[18]	....	....	v	v	v	v	v	CS_2 v	B6[2], 818
b416	—,1-chloro-3,5-dihydroxy-*	$C_6H_5ClO_2$. See b202	144.56	hyg nd (sub) λ^{al} 222 sh (3.9), 280 (3.3), 285 (3.3)	117	sub	....	....	s		s	s	...	os s peth i	B6[2], 819
Ω b417	—,2-chloro-1,3-dihydroxy-*	$C_6H_5ClO_2$. See b202	144.56	....	97–8	....	....	....							C40, 565
Ω b418	—,2-chloro-1,4-dihydroxy-*	$C_6H_5ClO_2$. See b202	144.56	red lf (chl), nd (bz)	108	263	....	....	v	s	s	v[h]		chl s[h]	B6[2], 844
b419	—,4-chloro-1,2-dihydroxy-*	$C_6H_5ClO_2$. See b202	144.56	lf (bz-peth)	90–1	139[10.5]	....	....	v	v	v			aa v lig δ	B6[2], 787
b420	—,1-chloro-2,4-dimethyl-*	C_8H_9Cl. See b202	140.61	λ^{hx} 358 (2.94), 369.5 (2.92), 374.5 (2.87)	....	187–8[760] 89[24]	1.0598[20]₂₀	1.5230[25]	i	...	...	s	v		B5[2], 291
b421	—,1-chloro-3,5-dimethyl-*	C_8H_9Cl. See b202	140.61	λ^{hx} 364.5 (2.41), 374.5 (2.48), 386 (2.40)	....	187–8[760] 66[12]	....	....	i	...	...	s	v		B5, 373
Ω b422	—,2-chloro-1,4-dimethyl-*	C_8H_9Cl. See b202	140.61	....	1.6	187 (192)	1.0589[15]₁₅	....	i	...	...	s	v		B5[1], 186
Ω b423	—,4-chloro-1,2-dimethyl-*	C_8H_9Cl. See b202	140.61	λ^{hx} 359 (2.67), 370 (2.70), 378.5 (2.57)	−6	194[755]	1.0692[15]₁₅	....	i	...	...	s	v		B5, 363
b424	—,1-chloro-2,3-dimethyl-4-hydroxy-*	C_8H_9ClO. See b202	156.61	nd (peth)	85	....	....	....		s	s	s	...	os s peth δ	B6, 454
b425	—,1-chloro-2,3-dimethyl-5-hydroxy-*	C_8H_9ClO. See b202	156.61	nd (peth)	98	....	....	....		s		s	...	chl v peth δ	B6[2], 456
b426	—,1-chloro-2,4-dimethyl-5-hydroxy-*	C_8H_9ClO. See b202	156.61	nd (lig or w)	90–1	....	....	....	s[h]	s	s	s	...	os s	B6[1], 242
b427	—,1-chloro-2,5-dimethyl-4-hydroxy-*	C_8H_9ClO. See b202	156.61	silv-gy nd (lig)	74–5	....	....	....	v	s			s	CS_2 v MeOH, aa, peth s lig δ	B6[2], 467
b428	—,1-chloro-3,4-dimethyl-2-hydroxy-*	C_8H_9ClO. See b202	156.61	....	....	221–3[760] 100[17]	....	....	s	s	s	s	s	os s	B6[1], 241
b429	—,1-chloro-4,5-dimethyl-2-hydroxy-*	C_8H_9ClO. See b202	156.61	nd (peth)	72	....	....	....	v	s			s	peth, CS_2 v aa s	B6[2], 456
b430	—,2-chloro-1,3-dimethyl-5-hydroxy-*	C_8H_9ClO. See b202	156.61	λ^w 260 (3.12), 286.5 (3.14)	115–6	246	....	....	δ	s	s		δ	peth δ	B6[2], 463
b431	—,2-chloro-1,5-dimethyl-3-hydroxy-*	C_8H_9ClO. See b202	156.61	nd	49–50	....	....	....			s				B6[2], 464
b432	—,2-chloro-3,4-dimethyl-1-hydroxy-*	C_8H_9ClO. See b202	156.61	cr (peth)	27	187–9	....	1.5538[20] (1.5300[20])		...	...			peth s[h]	B6[2], 456
b433	—,5-chloro-1,3-dimethyl-2-hydroxy-*	C_8H_9ClO. See b202	156.61	nd (w)	83	....	....	....	δ	s	...		s	aa s peth δ	B6[3], 1738
b434	—,1-chloro-2,3-dinitro-*	$C_6H_3ClN_2O_4$. See b202	202.56	pr (al), cr (MeOH)	78	....	....	....	i	δ	s	...	...		B5[2], 196

For explanations, symbols and abbreviations see beginning of table. For structural formulas see end of table.

No.	Name	Synonyms and Formula	Mol. wt.	Color, crystalline form, specific rotation and λ_{max} (log ε)	m.p. °C	b.p. °C	Density	n_D	Solubility						Ref.
									w	al	eth	ace	bz	other solvents	
	Benzene														
Ω b435	—,1-chloro-2,4-dinitro-*	$C_6H_3ClN_2O_4$. See b202	202.56	α: ye rh (eth) β: ye rh (eth), nd (al)	α: 53 (st) β: 43 (unst) γ: 27 (unst)	315[762] 158–60[1]	1.4982[75]4 α: 1.697[22] β 1.6867[16]	1.5857[60]	i δ[h]	δ s[h]	s	...	s	CS_2 s	B5[2], 196
b436	—,1-chloro-3,5-dinitro-*	$C_6H_3ClN_2O_4$. See b202	202.56	nd (al, MeOH, peth)	59	....			i	s	v	...			B5, 264
Ω b437	—,2-chloro-1,3-dinitro-*	$C_6H_3ClN_2O_4$. See b202	202.56	ye nd (al, aa)	88	315	1.6867[16]	....	i	s	s	...		to s	B5[1], 137
b438	—,4-chloro-1,2-dinitro-*	$C_6H_3ClN_2O_4$. See b202	202.56	α: cr (al) β: pr (lig) γ: mcl or rh nd (eth or lig)	α: 36 β: 37 γ: 40–1	315d 160[4]	1.6867[20]4	....	i	δ s[h]	v	...	v	CS_2 s	B5[2], 196
Ω b439	—,1-chloro-2-ethoxy-*	C_8H_9ClO. See b202	156.61			210 97–8[15]	1.1288[25]4	1.5284[25]	i	s	s	...		chl s	B6[2], 171
b440	—,1-chloro-3-ethoxy-*	C_8H_9ClO. See b202	156.61			204 5[717]	1.1712[20]4		i	v	v	...	v	aa v	B6, 185
Ω b441	—,1-chloro-4-ethoxy-*	C_8H_9ClO. See b202	156.61		21	212–4 98[17]	1.1254[20]4	1.5252[20]		s	s	...	v	aa s	B6[2], 176
Ω b442	—,(2-chloro-ethoxy)-*	C_8H_9ClO. See b202	156.61	pr	28	217–20[760] 100–2[12]			i	v	v	v	v	lig v	B6[2], 144
b443	—,(1-chloro-ethyl)-(d)*	d-α-Phenethyl chloride. C_8H_9Cl. See b202	140.61	$[\alpha]_D^{20} + 50.6$ (undil)	....	85[20]	1.0631[20]4	1.5250[25]	d[h]	s		...	s		B5[2], 277
b444	—,—(dl)*	α-Phenethyl chloride. C_8H_9Cl. See b202	140.61	λ[cy] 218 (3.73), 260 (2.3)	....	81–2[17]	1.0620[20]4	1.5276[20]	d[h]	s	s	...	s		B5[2], 277
b445	—,—(l)*	l-α-Phenethyl chloride. C_8H_9Cl. See b202	140.61	$[\alpha]_D^{20} -30.1$ (undil)	....	85[20]	1.0632[20]4		d[h]	s	s	...	s		B5[1], 177
Ω b446	—,(2-chloro-ethyl)-*	β-Phenethyl chloride. C_8H_9Cl. See b202	140.61	λ[al] 209 (3.87)	....	197–8[760] 92[20]	1.069[25]	1.5276[20]	i	s	s	...	v	CS_2, lig s	B5[2], 277
b447	—,1-chloro-4-ethyl-*	C_8H_9Cl. See b202	140.61		−62.6	184.4[760] 63.5[10]	1.0455[20]4	1.5175[20]	i	∞	s	∞	v	peth, CCl_4 ∞ aa s	B5[1], 177
b448	—,(2-chloro-ethylthio)-*	C_8H_9ClS. See b202	172.68			117–8[11]	1.1769[25]4	1.5828[20]				...		chl s	B6[2], 287
Ω b449	—,1-chloro-2-fluoro-*	C_6H_4ClF. See b202	130.55	λ[hx] 210 (4.00), 214 (4.00), 260 (3.00), 266 (3.15), 272 (3.18)	−43	137.6[760]	1.2233[20]4	1.4968[30]	i			s	s		B5[2], 153
Ω b450	—,1-chloro-4-fluoro-*	C_6H_4ClF. See b202	130.55	λ[hx] 209 (3.74), 215 (3.74), 263 (2.89), 271 (3.04), 277 (3.06)	−26.85	130[757]	1.226[20]4	1.4990[15]	i	s	s	...	s		B5[2], 153
Ω b451	—,1-chloro-4-hydroxy-5-isopropyl-2-methyl-*	6-Chlorothymol. $C_{10}H_{13}ClO$. See b202	184.67	nd or pl (lig)	59–61	259–63			v	s	s	...	s	alk, peth s	B6[3], 499
b452	—,1-chloro-3-hydroxylamino-*	C_6H_6ClNO. See b202	143.57	pl (bz)	49	....			s			...	s	pcth s	B15[2], 8
b453	—,1-chloro-4-hydroxylamino-*	C_6H_6ClNO. See b202	143.57	lf (dil al)	87–8	....			δ s[h]	s	s	...	v	chl v peth δ	B15[2], 9
Ω b454	—,1-chloro-2-iodo-*	C_6H_4ClI. See b202	238.46	λ[cy] 231 (4.01), 238 (4.01)	....	234–5[760] 110[16]	1.9515[25]	1.6331[25]	i			s			B5[1], 119
b455	—,1-chloro-3-iodo-*	C_6H_4ClI. See b202	238.46	λ[cy] 231 (4.01), 238 (4.01)		230			i			...			B5[2], 167
Ω b456	—,1-chloro-4-iodo-*	C_6H_4ClI. See b202	238.46	lf (ace), (al) λ[cy] 236.3 (4.20)	57	227 108[13]	1.886[57]		i		s	...		$PhNO_2$ s	B5[2], 167
b457	—,1-chloro-4-isopropyl-*	$C_9H_{11}Cl$. See b202	154.64		−12.27	198.3[760] 74[10]	1.0208[20]4	1.5117[20]	i	∞	∞	∞	v	peth, CCl_4 ∞	B5[2], 307
Ω b458	—,1-chloro-2-mercapto-*	o-Chlorobenzenethiol. C_6H_5ClS. See b202	144.62			205–6 117[11]	1.2752[20]		δ	δ		...			B6[3], 1032
Ω b459	—,1-chloro-3-mercapto-*	m-Chlorobenzenethiol. C_6H_5ClS. See b202	144.62			205–7	1.2637[13]		i	s	s	...		peth, chl s	B6[3], 1034
Ω b460	—,1-chloro-4-mercapto-*	p-Chlorobenzenethiol. C_6H_5ClS. See b202	144.62	pr or pl (al)	61 (54)	205–7			i	v[h]	v	...	v		B6[2], 297
Ω b461	—,1-chloro-2-methoxy-*	C_7H_7ClO. See b202	142.59	λ[cy] 222 (3.87), 267 sh (3.20), 272.5 (3.38), 280 (3.39)	−26.6	198.5–9.5[760] 90–1[16]	1.1911[20]	1.5480[20]	i	s	s	...			B6[2], 171
b462	—,1-chloro-3-methoxy-*	C_7H_7ClO. See b202	142.59	λ[cy] 219 (3.86), 272 (3.33), 279 (3.33)		193–4 70[9]	1.1759[12]4	1.5365[20]	i	s	s	...			B6[1], 100
Ω b463	—,1-chloro-4-methoxy-*	C_7H_7ClO. See b202	142.59	λ[cy] 227 (4.07), 279 (3.28), 287 (3.27)	< −18	197.5[760] 73[10]	1.201[20]4	1.5390[20]	i	v	v	...		chl v	B6[2], 175
b464	—,1-chloro-3-methoxy-2-nitro-*	$C_7H_6ClNO_3$. See b202	187.58		56	....				s[h]	s	...	s	chl s	B6[2], 226

For explanations, symbols and abbreviations see beginning of table. For structural formulas see end of table.

No.	Name	Synonyms and Formula	Mol. wt.	Color, crystalline form, specific rotation and λ_{max} (log ε)	m.p. °C	b.p. °C	Density	n_D	w	al	eth	ace	bz	other solvents	Ref.
	Benzene														
Ω b465	—,4-chloro-1-methoxy-2-nitro-*	$C_7H_6ClNO_3$. See b202	187.58	ye nd or pr (al) $\lambda^{aq\ MeOH}$ 220.5 (4.28), 265 (3.59), 349 (3.43)	98				...	s[h]	δ	...	...	MeOH s lig δ	B6[2], 226
b466	—,1(chloromethyl)-2,4-dimethyl-*	$C_9H_{11}Cl$. See b202	154.64			215–6 86–7[12]			i d[h]	v	v	...	v		B5[2], 313
b467	—,1(chloromethyl)-4-ethyl-*	$C_9H_{11}Cl$. See b202	154.64			95–6[15]		1.5290[25]	d[h]	s	...	...	s	chl s	B5[2], 310
b468	—,1(chloromethyl)-2-methyl-*	o-Xylyl chloride. C_8H_9Cl. See b202	140.61			197–9 80[12]		1.5410[20]	i	s	∞	∞	...		B5[2], 283
b469	—,1(chloromethyl)-3-methyl-*	m-Xylyl chloride. C_8H_9Cl. See b202	140.61			195–6 101–2[30]	1.064[20]	1.5345[20]	i	s	∞	...			B5[2], 291
Ω b470	—,1(chloromethyl)-4-methyl-*	p-Xylyl chloride. C_8H_9Cl. See b202	140.61			200–2 81[15]	1.05122[20]	1.5380	i	s	∞	...			B5[2], 299
b471	—,(chloro-tert-butyl)-	$C_{10}H_{13}Cl$. See b202	168.67			222[741] 104–5[18]	1.04724[20]	1.52474[20]	i	∞	∞	∞	∞	CCl_4, lig ∞	B5[2], 320
Ω b472	—,1-chloro-2-nitro-*	$C_6H_4ClNO_2$. See b202	157.56	mcl nd λ^{MeOH} 252 (3.51)	33.5–35	246[760] 119[8]	1.368[242]		i	s	s	v	s	to, Py v CCl_4 s MeOH s	B5[2], 180
Ω b473	—,1-chloro-3-nitro-*	$C_6H_4ClNO_2$. See b202	157.56	pa ye rh pr (al) λ^{MeOH} 257.5 (3.89)	24 (unst) 46 (st)	235–6[760]	1.3434[50]	1.5374[80a]	i	s v[h]	s	...	s	CS_2, chl, aa s	B5[2], 182
Ω b474	—,1-chloro-4-nitro-*	$C_6H_4ClNO_2$. See b202	157.56	mcl pr λ^{MeOH} 270.5 (4.03)	83.6	242[760] 113[8]	1.2979[90.5]	1.5376[100a]	i	δ v[h]	s	...	...	CS_2 s	B5[2], 183
b475	—,1-chloro-2-nitroso-*	C_6H_4ClNO. See b202	141.56	nd (al)	65.5–6.5				...	v	v	...	v	chl v peth v[h]	B5[2], 171
b476	—,1-chloro-3-nitroso-*	C_6H_4ClNO. See b202	141.56	nd (bz)	72 (77)				...	v	v	v	v	chl v	B5[2], 171
b477	—,1-chloro-4-nitroso-*	C_6H_4ClNO. See b202	141.56	(aa or al) λ^{al} 226 (3.87), 288 (4.03), 313 (4.08), 750 (1.66)	92–3				...	s	...	...	...	chl v aa s[h]	B5[2], 171
b478	—,(3-chloropropoxy)-*	$C_9H_{11}ClO$. See b202	170.64		12	245–55 139[25]	1.1167[20]	1.5235[25]	...	...	v	s	...		B6, 142
b479	—,(3-chloropropylthio)-*	$C_9H_{11}ClS$. See b202	186.71			116–7[4]	1.1536[20]	1.5752[20]	...	...	...	s	...	Py s	B6[2], 288
b480	—,1-chloro-4-triazo-*	$C_6H_4ClN_3$. See b202	153.57	λ^{al} 267 (3.82), 279 (3.85)	20	96[20]			i	...	s	...	...		B5[3], 648
b481	—,2-chloro-1,3,5-trimethyl-*	$C_9H_{11}Cl$. See b202	154.64	λ^{al} 268 (2.35)	< −20	204–6 104[25]	1.0337[30]	1.5212[30]	i	v	v	...	...		B5[2], 315
b482	—,1-chloro-2,4,5-trinitro-*	$C_6H_2ClN_3O_6$. See b202	247.55	ye lf (al)	116				i	v[h]	...	...	s	aa s	B5[2], 205
Ω b483	—,2-chloro-1,3,5-trinitro-*	Picryl chloride. $C_6H_2ClN_3O_6$. See b202	247.55	wh nd or pl (chl, al-lig) λ^{al} 340 (2.8)	83		1.797[20]		i	s[h]	δ	v	s v[h]	to, Py v chl v[h] peth δ	B5[2], 205
Ω b484	—,cyclohexyl-*	Phenylcyclohexane*. $C_{12}H_{16}$. See b202	160.26	pl λ^{iso} 254.5 (2.23), 259 (2.33), 264 (2.21), 267.5 (2.25)	7–8	235–6 127–8[30]	0.95024[20]	1.5329[20]	i	v	s	...	...		B5, 503
Ω b485	—,4-cyclohexyl-1,3-dihydroxy-*	$C_{12}H_{16}O_2$. See b202	192.24	nd (bz, chl), cr (bz-peth)	127–8				δ	δ	...	...	...		B6[2], 929
Ω b486	—,1-cyclohexyl-2-hydroxy-*	$C_{12}H_{16}O$. See b202	176.24	nd (lig)	56–7	283[760] 147[17]			i	s	...	...	...	aa s lig s[h]	B6[2], 548
Ω b487	—,1-cyclohexyl-4-hydroxy-*	$C_{12}H_{16}O$. See b202	176.24	nd (bz)	133	293.5–5.5[752] 132–5[4]			i	v	v	...	s	CCl_4 v[h] lig δ	B6[2], 548
b488	—,cyclopentyl-*	Phenylcyclopentane*. $C_{11}H_{14}$. See b202	146.24			219[760] 102[18]	0.9462[20]	1.5280[20]	i	...	s	...	...		B5[2], 393
b489	—,1,2-diacetamido-*	$C_{10}H_{12}N_2O_2$. See b202	192.22	nd (w) λ^{al} 278 sh (3.0)	185–6				s[h]	s	δ	s	δ	chl, aa s	B13, 20
Ω b490	—,1,4-diacetyl-*	$C_{10}H_{10}O_2$. See b202	162.19	pr (al, eth)	114	sub			...	v[h]	...	...	...		B7[2], 624
b491	—,1,5-diacetyl-2,4-dihydroxy-	Resodiacetophenone. $C_{10}H_{10}O_4$. See b202	194.19	nd (al) λ^{al} 252 (4.66), 275 (4.04), 318 (3.91)	185				i	s[h]	s	s	s[h]	os s[h]	B8[2], 456
Ω b492	—,1,2-diamino-*	o-Phenylenediamine. $C_6H_8N_2$. See b202	108.15	brsh ye lf (w), pl (chl) λ^{cy} 235.5 (3.82), 289 (3.54)	102–3	256–8[760]			s[h]	v	s	...	s	chl s	B13, 6

For explanations, symbols and abbreviations see beginning of table. For structural formulas see end of table.

No.	Name	Synonyms and Formula	Mol. wt.	Color, crystalline form, specific rotation and λ_{max} (log ε)	m.p. °C	b.p. °C	Density	n_D	w	al	eth	ace	bz	other solvents	Ref.
	Benzene														
Ω b493	—,1,3-diamino-*	m-Phenylenediamine. $C_6H_8N_2$. See b202	108.15	rh (al) λ^{cy} 240 sh (3.85), 293 (3.42)	63–4	282–4[760]	1.0696[58] 1.1421[10/10]	1.6339[58]	v	s	s	...	s v[h]	....	B13[1], 10
Ω b494	—,1,4-diamino-*	p-Phenylenediamine. $C_6H_8N_2$. See b202	108.15	wh pl (bz, eth) λ^{cy} 246 (3.93), 315 (3.30)	140	267			s[h] δ	s[h]	s	...	s[h]	chl s	B13, 61
b495	—,1,2-diamino-3,5-dichloro-*	$C_6H_6Cl_2N_2$. See b202	177.03	nd (al)	60.5					s[h]					B13, 27
b496	—,1,3-diamino-2,5-dichloro-*	$C_6H_6Cl_2N_2$. See b202	177.03	nd (w)	100				v[h]	s			v		B13[2], 29
b497	—,1,2-diamino-2,5-dichloro-*-	$C_6H_6Cl_2N_2$. See b202	177.03	pr (w)	170				δ	δ					B13, 118
b498	—,1,5-diamino-2,4-dichloro-*	$C_6H_6Cl_2N_2$. See b202	177.03	nd (dil al)	136–7					s					B13, 54
b499	—,2,3-diamino-1,4-dichloro-*	$C_6H_6Cl_2N_2$. See b202	177.03	nd (50 % al)	100				s	s	s	v	os v peth δ		B13[2], 20
b500	—,2,5-diamino-1,3-dichloro-*	$C_6H_6Cl_2N_2$. See b202	177.03	nd, pr (dil al)	124–5.5				s	s	s	s	s	os s	B13[1], 37
b501	—,1,2-diamino-4,5-dimethoxy-*	$C_8H_{12}N_2O_2$. See b202	168.20	bl pr	131–2				s	s	i			to δ	B13, 782
b502	—,1,2-diamino-4-methoxy-*	$C_7H_{10}N_2O$. See b202	138.17	gr pl	50–2 (130–1.5)	167–70[11]				∞					Am 69, 586
Ω b503	—,2,4-diamino-1-methoxy-*	$C_7H_{10}N_2O$. See b202	138.17	nd (eth)	67–8					s	s[h]				B13[2], 308
b504	—,1,4-diamino-2-methoxy-5-methyl-*	$C_8H_{12}N_2O$. See b202	152.20	....	166				δ	s	s				B13[2], 349
b505	—,2,3-diamino-1-methoxy-4-methyl-*	$C_8H_{12}N_2O$. See b202	152.20	pr (eth-bz)	75–6				δ	v	v		δ		B13[2], 349
b506	—,1,2-diamino-4-methyl-*	$C_7H_{10}N_2$. See b202	122.17	pl (lig)	89–90	265 92[1]			s						B13, 148
Ω b507	—,1,2-diamino-3-nitro-*	$C_6H_7N_3O_2$. See b202	153.14	dk red nd (dil al)	158–9				δ				ac s		B13[1], 10
Ω b508	—,1,2-diamino-4-nitro-*	$C_6H_7N_3O_2$. See b202	153.14	dk red nd $\lambda^{20\%sulf}$ 380 (4.08)	199–200								ac s		B13, 29
b509	—,1,4-diamino-2,3,5,6-tetra-methyl-*	Diaminodurene. $C_{10}H_{16}N_2$. See b202	164.25	nd (w) λ^{cy} 288 sh (3.67), 264 (4.21), 304 sh (3.27)	149				s[h]	v	s	...	chl v		B13[2], 76
b510	—,1,2-dibenzoxy-*	Pyrocatechol dibenzyl ether. $C_{20}H_{18}O_2$. See b202	290.37	yesh nd or pr (al)	63–4				i	s[h]	s	...	peth s		B6, 772
b511	—,1,4-dibenzoxy-*	Hydroquinone dibenzyl ether. $C_{20}H_{18}O_2$. See b202	290.37	pl (al)	130				i	s[h]	s	...	aa s		B6, 845
Ω b512	—,1,2-dibromo-*	$C_6H_4Br_2$. See b202	235.92	λ^{hx} 257 (2.40), 263 (2.40), 270 (2.46), 278 (2.39)	7.1	225[760] 92[10]	1.9843[20/4]	1.6155[20]	i	s	∞	∞	∞	peth, CCl_4 ∞	B5[2], 162
Ω b513	—,1,3-dibromo-*	$C_6H_4Br_2$. See b202	235.92	λ^{hx} 257 (2.33), 264 (2.62), 270 (2.77), 278 (2.63)	−7	218[760] 66[5]	1.9523[20/4]	1.6083[17]	i	s	∞				B5[2], 162
Ω b514	—,1,4-dibromo-*	$C_6H_4Br_2$. See b202	235.92	pl λ^{al} 228 (4.19), 265.5 (2.46), 273 (2.48), 282 (2.29)	87.33	218–9	1.8322[100] 2.261[17]	1.5742	i	s v[h]	v	v	s v[h]	CS_2 v to s, v[h]	B5[2], 163
b515	—,1,5-dibromo-2,4-dimethyl-*	$C_8H_8Br_2$. See b202	263.98	pl (al)	68	255–6			i	s[h]					B5[2], 294
b516	—,1,2-dibromo-3-nitro-*	$C_6H_3Br_2NO_2$. See b202	280.91	mcl pr	85				i		s	v	chl v aa s[h]		B5[2], 190
b517	—,1,2-dibromo-4-nitro-*	$C_6H_3Br_2NO_2$. See b202	280.91	nd (al, aa), mcl pr	58–9	296 180[20]	2.354[8]	1.9835[111]	i	s		s	aa s		B5, 249
b518	—,1,3-dibromo-2-nitro-*	$C_6H_3Br_2NO_2$. See b202	280.91	nd (al), mcl pr (al)	84	sub	1.9211[111] 2.211[8]		i	s[h]	s	s			B5, 250
b519	—,1,3-dibromo-5-nitro-*	$C_6H_3Br_2NO_2$. See b202	280.91	pl or pr (eth), lf or nd (al)	106		1.9341[111] 2.363[8]		i	s[h]	s[h]	s			B5, 250
Ω b520	—,1,4-dibromo-2-nitro-*	$C_6H_3Br_2NO_2$. See b202	280.91	yesh pl (ace) λ^{al} 233.5 (4.24), 309 (3.18)	85–6		1.9416[111] 2.368[8]		i			s[h]	s		B5, 250
b521	—,2,4-dibromo-1-nitro-*	$C_6H_3Br_2NO_2$. See b202	280.91	ye pl or pr (al)	62		1.9581[111] 2.356[8]		i	s[h]	...	s	s	chl s	B5, 250
b522	—,2,3-dibromo-1,4,5-trimethyl-*	$C_9H_{10}Br_2$. See b202	278.00	nd (al)	63–4	293–4			i	v	v		v	chl v	B5, 403
Ω b523	—,2,4-dibromo-1,3,5-trimethyl-*	$C_9H_{10}Br_2$. See b202	278.00	nd (al)	65.5	285 (278–9)			i	δ v[h]			s		B5, 408
b524	—,1,2-dibutoxy-*	Pyrocatechol dibutyl ether. $C_{14}H_{22}O_2$. See b202	222.33	ye		241[766] 135–8[12]									C24, 3500

For explanations, symbols and abbreviations see beginning of table. For structural formulas see end of table.

No.	Name	Synonyms and Formula	Mol. wt.	Color, crystalline form, specific rotation and λ_{max} (log ε)	m.p. °C	b.p. °C	Density	n_D	Solubility						Ref.
									w	al	eth	ace	bz	other solvents	

Benzene

No.	Name	Synonyms and Formula	Mol. wt.	Color, crystalline form	m.p. °C	b.p. °C	Density	n_D	w	al	eth	ace	bz	other solvents	Ref.
Ω b525	—,1,4-di-*tert*-butyl-	$C_{14}H_{22}$. See b202	190.33	nd (MeOH) λ^{iso} 217 (4.0), 250 (2.2), 256 (2.4), 263 (2.5), 270 (2.5)	80–1	237[743] 109[15]			i	s	s	. . .	. . .		B5[2], 344
b526	—,1,3-di-*tert*-butyl-5-ethyl-2-hydroxy-	$C_{16}H_{26}O$. See b202	234.39	λ^{iso} 277.5 (3.34), 283 (3.34), 307 (1.55)	44	272[760] 140[10]								alk i	Am 67, 304
Ω b527	—,1,4-di-*tert*-butyl-2,5-dihydroxy-	$C_{14}H_{22}O_2$. See b202	222.33	cr (aq aa) λ^{diox} 229 (3.5), 294 (3.5)	213–4	. . . . . .									Am 64, 937
Ω b529	—,1,3-di-*tert*-butyl-2-hydroxy-	$C_{14}H_{22}O$. See b202	206.33	pr (al) λ^{al} 268 (3.19), 274 (3.18)	39	133[20]		1.5001[25]	. . .	s[h]			. . .	alk i	Am 73, 3179
Ω b530	—,2,4-di-*tert*-butyl-1-hydroxy-	$C_{14}H_{22}O$. See b202	206.33	λ^{iso} 226 (3.7), 268 (3.2), 274 (3.3), 276 (3.3), 283 (3.3)	56.5	263.5[760] 146[20]		1.5080[20]	. . .				. . .	alk i	Am 60, 2496
b531	—,1,3-di-*tert*-butyl-2-hydroxy-5-methyl-	Ionol. $C_{15}H_{24}O$. See b202	220.36	λ^{iso} 227 (3.75), 277 (3.34), 283 (3.34)	71	265[760] 136[10]	0.8937[25]	1.4859[75]	i	s	. . .	s	s	peth s alk i	Am 69, 1624
b532	—,1,5-di-*tert*-butyl-2-hydroxy-3-methyl-	$C_{15}H_{24}O$. See b202	220.36	λ^{cy} 275 (3.41), 280 sh (3.38)	51 (52.5)	269[760] 138.5[10]	0.891[80]	. . . . . .						alk i	Am 67, 305
b533	—,1,5-di-*tert*-butyl-2-hydroxy-4-methyl-	$C_{15}H_{24}O$. See b202	220.36	. . . .	62.1	282[760] 167[20]	0.912[80]		i	s	s	s	s	CCl_4 s alk i	C38, 4170
b534	—,1,3-di-*tert*-butyl-2-hydroxy-5(2-methyl-2-butyl)-	$C_{19}H_{32}O$. See b202	276.47	. . . .	47	135–8[6]									Am 67, 304
Ω b535	—,1,2-dichloro-*	$C_6H_4Cl_2$. See b202	147.01	λ^{al} 250 (1.98), 256 (2.13), 263 (2.36), 270 (2.44), 277 (2.37)	−17.0	180.5[760] 86[18]	1.3048[20]	1.5515[20]	i	s	s	∞	∞	lig, CCl_4 ∞	B5[2], 153
Ω b536	—,1,3-dichloro-*	$C_6H_4Cl_2$. See b202	147.01	λ^{al} 250 (1.90), 256 (2.15), 263 (2.40), 270 (2.52), 278 (2.43)	−24.7	173[760] 53[10]	1.2884[20]	1.5459[20]	i	s	s	∞	s	lig, CCl_4 ∞	B5[2], 154
Ω b537	—,1,4-dichloro-*	$C_6H_4Cl_2$. See b202	147.01	mcl pr. lf (ace) λ^{al} 258 (2.24), 266 (2.46), 273 (2.60), 280 (2.51)	53.1	174[760] 55[10]	1.2475[20]	1.5285[20]	i	∞	s	∞	s	CS_2, chl s	B5[2], 154
b538	—,1,2-dichloro-4,5-dihydroxy-*	$C_6H_4Cl_2O_2$. See b202	179.00	pr (chl-CS_2), nd (bz-peth) $\lambda^{w, pH=1}$ 258 (3.45), 316 (4.15), 325 (4.14)	116–7	. . . . . .			v	v	. . .		v		B6[1], 389
b539	—,1,3-dichloro-2,5-dihydroxy-*	$C_6H_4Cl_2O_2$. See b202	179.00	nd or lf (w, bz)	164	. . . . . .			s[h]	s	. . .	v	s[h]		B6[2], 845
b540	—,1,4-dichloro-2,5-dihydroxy-*	$C_6H_4Cl_2O_2$. See b202	179.00	nd or pr (w, ace, bz) λ^{al} 305 (3.7)	172.5	. . . . . .			s	v	v	v	. . .		B6[2], 845
b541	—,1,5-dichloro-2,3-dihydroxy-*	$C_6H_4Cl_2O_2$. See b202	179.00	pr	83–4	. . . . . .			δ v[h]	s	. . .	v	. . .		B6, 783
Ω b542	—,1,5-dichloro-2,4-dihydroxy-*	$C_6H_4Cl_2O_2$. See b202	179.00	cr (sub) nd	113	254 sub			v	v	v	v	. . .	lig δ	B6[2], 819
b543	—,2,3-dichloro-1,4-dihydroxy-*	$C_6H_4Cl_2O_2$. See b202	179.00	cr (sub) nd (w + 2)	146–8 (anh)	. . . . . .					v		. . .	lig i	B6[2], 845
b544	—,1,2-dichloro-4,5-dimethyl-3-hydroxy-*	$C_8H_8Cl_2O$. See b202	191.07	cr (peth)	90	. . . . . .						v	v	s	chl v peth δ	B6[2], 454
b545	—,1,3-dichloro-4,5-dimethyl-2-hydroxy-*	$C_8H_8Cl_2O$. See b202	191.07	cr (peth)	52	. . . . . .						s	. . .		peth δ	B6[2], 456
b546	—,1,4-dichloro-2,3-dimethyl-5-hydroxy-*	$C_8H_8Cl_2O$. See b202	191.07	nd (peth)	84	. . . . . .						s	. . .		peth δ, s[h]	B6[2], 456
b547	—,2,4-dichloro-1,3-dimethyl-5-hydroxy-*	$C_8H_8Cl_2O$. See b202	191.07	. . . .	83	. . . . . .						s	. . .		lig δ, s[h]	B6[2], 464
b548	—,2,4-dichloro-1,5-dimethyl-3-hydroxy-*	$C_8H_8Cl_2O$. See b202	191.07	cr (peth)	87–8	105–10[1]						s	. . .		chl v	Am 75, 6311

For explanations, symbols and abbreviations see beginning of table. For structural formulas see end of table.

No.	Name	Synonyms and Formula	Mol. wt.	Color, crystalline form, specific rotation and λ_{max} (log ε)	m.p. °C	b.p. °C	Density	n_D	Solubility						Ref.
									w	al	eth	ace	bz	other solvents	
	Benzene														
b549	—,3,4-dichloro-1,2-dimethyl-5-hydroxy-*	$C_8H_8Cl_2O$. See b202	191.07	nd (peth)	102.5	. . . .	. . . .	. . . .			s	s	s	os s	B6[2], 456
b550	—,2,4-dichloro-1-ethoxy-*	$C_8H_8Cl_2O$. See b202	191.07	. . . .		237	. . . .	. . . .	i	s	s	. . .	s	. . . .	B6, 189
b551	—,(1,2-dichloroethyl)-*	Styrene dichloride. $C_8H_8Cl_2$. See b202	175.07	. . . .		233–4[759] 115[15]	1.2405[15]	1.5544[15]	i	s	s	s	s	. . . .	B5[2], 278
b552	—,1,4-dichloro-2-iodo-*	$C_6H_3Cl_2I$. See b202	272.90	pl (al)	21	255–6 134[12]	. . . .	. . . .	i	s	s	. . .	s	chl s	B5, 221
b553	—,2,4-dichloro-1-methoxy-*	$C_7H_6Cl_2O$. See b202	177.03	pr	28–9	233[740] 125[10]	. . . .	. . . .	i	s	s	. . .	s	. . . .	B6[1], 103
Ω b554	—,1,2-dichloro-3-nitro-*	$C_6H_3Cl_2NO_2$. See b202	192.00	mcl nd (peth, aa) $\lambda^{aq\ MeOH}$ 211 (4.15), 276 (3.56), 320 sh (3.30)	61–2	257–8	1.721[14]	. . . .	i	s	s	s	s	peth, aa s os v	B5[2], 185
Ω b555	—,1,2-dichloro-4-nitro-*	$C_6H_3Cl_2NO_2$. See b202	192.00	(i) nd (al, CCl_4) (ii) liq	43	255 6 189[100]	1.45587[5]	. . . .	i	s[h]	s				B5[2], 186
b556	—,1,3-dichloro-2-nitro-*	$C_6H_3Cl_2NO_2$. See b202	192.00	nd or pr (al, CS_2)	72.5	130[8]	1.603[17] 1.4094[80]	. . . .	i	s[h]	s				B5[2], 186
b557	—,1,3-dichloro-5-nitro-*	$C_6H_3Cl_2NO_2$. See b202	192.00	mcl pr or lf (aa, al) λ^{hx} 257 (3.79), 307 (3.08)	65.4	. . . .	1.692[14] 1.4000[100]	. . . .	i	s[h]	s				B5[2], 186
Ω b558	—,1,4-dichloro-2-nitro-*	$C_6H_3Cl_2NO_2$. See b202	192.00	pl or pr (al), pl (AcOEt) $\lambda^{aq\ MeOH}$ 220 (4.28), 258 (3.52), 314 (3.18)	56	267	1.669[22] 1.4390[25]	. . . .	i	s[h]	s	. . .	s	chl, CS_2 s	B5, 245
Ω b559	—,2,4-dichloro-1-nitro-*	$C_6H_3Cl_2NO_2$. See b202	192.00	nd (al)	34	258.5 100–1[4]	1.4390[80]	1.5512[78]$_\alpha$	i	s	s	. . .	s	. . . .	B5[2], 185
b560	—,1-dichlorophosphino-4-isopropyl-*	$C_9H_{11}Cl_2P$. See b202	221.07	. . . .		268–70 129–30[10]	1.1917[25]	1.5677[25]	d[h]	d	. . .	s			B16, 773
b561	—,2,4-dichloro-1-triazo-*	$C_6H_3Cl_2N_3$. See b202	188.02	ye nd (al), pr (ace or bz)	54	. . . .	. . . .	. . . .	i	s	s	. . .	s	peth, chl s	B5[2], 208
Ω b562	—,1,2-diethoxy-*	Catechol diethyl ether. $C_{10}H_{14}O_2$. See b202	166.22	pr (peth, dil al) λ^{al} 224.5 (3.82), 275 (3.28)	43–5	219–9.5	1.00752[5]	1.5083[25]	. . .	v	s				B6[2], 780
b563	—,1,3-diethoxy-*	Resorcinol diethyl ether. $C_{10}H_{14}O_2$. See b202	166.22	pr λ^{hx} 269 (3.35), 274 (3.45), 280 (3.41)	12.4	235[756]	. . . .	. . . .	i	s	s				B6[2], 814
Ω b564	—,1,4-diethoxy-*	Hydroquinone diethyl ether. $C_{10}H_{14}O_2$. See b202	166.22	pl (dil al) λ^{hx} 292 (3.48)	72	246	. . . .	. . . .		v	s	. . .	s	chl s	B6[2], 840
Ω b565	—,1,2-diethyl-*	$C_{10}H_{14}$. See b202	134.22	λ^{iso} 257 (2.28), 264 (2.38), 272 (2.32)	−31.2	183.4[760] 63[10]	0.8800[20]	1.5035[20]	i	∞	∞	∞	∞	CCl_4, lig ∞	B5[2], 327
Ω b566	—,1,3-diethyl-*	$C_{10}H_{14}$. See b202	134.22	λ^{iso} 258 (2.28), 264 (2.39), 268 (2.26), 272 (2.32)	−83.89	181[760] 60[10]	0.86024[20]	1.4955[20]	i	∞	∞	∞	∞	CCl_4, lig ∞	B5[2], 327
Ω b567	—,1,4-diethyl-*	$C_{10}H_{14}$. See b202	134.22	λ^{iso} 259 (2.47), 265 (2.60), 267 (2.58), 273 (2.62)	−42.85	183.8[760] 63[10]	0.86204[20]	1.4967[20]	i	∞	∞	∞	∞	CCl_4, lig ∞	B5[2], 327
Ω b568	—,1,3-diethyl-5-methyl-*	$C_{11}H_{16}$. See b202	148.25	. . . .	−74.12	205[760] 79[10]	0.87484[20]	1.5027[20]	i	∞	∞	∞	∞	CCl_4, lig ∞	B5, 441
Ω b569	—,1,2-dihydroxy-*	Catechol. Pyrocatechol. $C_6H_6O_2$. See b202	110.11	cr λ^{cy} 214 (3.83), 270 sh (3.34), 274 (3.40), 280 (3.35)	105	245[750]	1.1493[21]	1.604	s	s	s	v	s[h] δ	alk. chl, CCl_4 s	B6[3], 4187
b570	—,—,carbonate . . .		136.11	pr (ace or al)	120	225–30	. . . .	. . . .		s[h]	. . .	. . .	s[h]		B19[1], 660
Ω b571	—,—,diacetate	$C_{10}H_{10}O_4$. See b202	194.19	nd (al)	64–5	142–3[9]	. . . . . .	. . . .	i	v	v	. . .		chl v peth s	B6[2], 784
b572	—,—,dibenzoate . .	$C_{20}H_{14}O_4$. See b202	318.33	lf (eth-al)	86	189–91[102]	. . . .	. . . .	i	s	s	. . .	s	. . . .	B9[2], 112
b573	—,—,monoacetate .	$C_8H_8O_3$. See b202	152.16	pl	57–8	189–91[102] 148[25]	. . . .	. . . .	v	v	. . .	v	s[h]	peth s	B6[2], 783
—	—,—,monobenzoate	see **Benzoic acid,** 2-hydroxyphenyl ester													
Ω b574	—,1,3-dihydroxy-*	Resorcinol. $C_6H_6O_2$. See b202	110.11	nd (bz) pl (w) λ^{al} 220 (3.79), 276 (3.33)	(i) 111 (st) (ii) 108.5 (unst)	276.5[760] 178[16]	1.2717		s	s	s	. . .	δ	CCl_4 ∞ aa v chl δ, s[h]	B6[2], 802
Ω b575	—,—,diacetate	$C_{10}H_{10}O_4$. See b202	194.19	. . . .		278 153–4[12]	. . . .	. . . .	i	v	v	. . .		. . . .	B6[2], 817
Ω b576	—,—,dibenzoate . .	$C_{20}H_{14}O_4$. See b202	318.33	pl (dil al)	117	. . . .	. . . .	. . . .	. . .	s	s	. . .	s	. . . .	B9[3], 113

For explanations, symbols and abbreviations see beginning of table. For structural formulas see end of table.

No.	Name	Synonyms and Formula	Mol. wt.	Color, crystalline form, specific rotation and λ_{max} (log ε)	m.p. °C	b.p. °C	Density	n_D	w	al	eth	ace	bz	other solvents	Ref.
	Benzene														
Ω b577	—,1,4-dihydroxy-*	Hydroquinone. Quinol. $C_6H_6O_2$. See b202	110.11	mcl pr (sub), nd (w), pr (MeOH) λ^w 288 (3.36)	173–4	285^{730}	1.328^{15}	....	s v^h	v	s	v	i	$CCl_4 \infty$	B6², 832
Ω b578	—,—,diacetate	$C_{10}H_{10}O_4$. See b202	194.19	pl (w, al) λ^{al} 265 (2.7), 270 sh (2.6)	123–4		0.8731^{25}_4	....	s^h	v^h	v	....	....	lig, chl v aa v^h	B6², 843
b579	—,—,dibenzoate ..	$C_{20}H_{14}O_4$. See b202	318.33	mcl nd (al or to)	204				i	s^h	i	....	....	to s^h	B9², 114
b580	—,1,2-dihydroxy-3,5-dimethyl-*	$C_8H_{10}O_2$. See b202	138.17	pr (w), nd (peth-bz) λ^{al} 282 (3.30)	73–4				v	v	v	....	....		B6, 911
b581	—,1,2-dihydroxy-4,5-dimethyl-*	$C_8H_{10}O_2$. See b202	138.17	mcl pr or nd (peth) λ^{al} 286.5 (3.50)	87–8	sub			v	v	v	....	δ	sulf s peth δ^h	B6¹, 444
b582	—,1,3-dihydroxy-2,4-dimethyl-*	$C_8H_{10}O_2$. See b202	138.17	nd (peth) λ^{al} 279 (3.19)	149–50	sub			v	v	v	....			B6³, 4588
b583	—,1,3-dihydroxy-2,5-dimethyl-*	$C_8H_{10}O_2$. See b202	138.17	nd (bz), pr (w) λ^{MeOH} 272 (3.88), 281 (3.85)	163	277–80			s^h	s	s	....			B6², 891
b584	—,1,4-dihydroxy-2,3-dimethyl-*	$C_8H_{10}O_2$. See b202	138.17	cr (w), pr (MeCN) λ^{diox} 225 (3.8), 300 (3.6)	224–5 δd				s	s	s	....			B6, 908
b585	—,1,4-dihydroxy-2,5-dimethyl-*	$C_8H_{10}O_2$. See b202	138.17	lf (w, al, MeOH, bz)	217 sub				s^h	s	s	....	δ	CS_2 δ chl s	B6, 915
b586	—,1,5-dihydroxy-2,4-dimethyl-*	$C_8H_{10}O_2$. See b202	138.17	mcl pr, (w + 1), nd (sub) λ^{al} 286 (3.53)	125	276–9 sub			s	s	s	....			B6², 889
b587	—,1,5-dihydroxy-3,4-dimethyl-*	$C_8H_{10}O_2$. See b202	138.17	nd (bz), pr (w + 1) λ^{al} 282 (3.35)	136–7 115–7 (+1w)	sub			s	v	s	....	δ	aa s, peth, CS_2, chl δ	B6, 908
b588	—,2,5-dihydroxy-1,3-dimethyl-*	$C_8H_{10}O_2$. See b202	138.17	nd (xyl), cr(w)	153–4				s	s	s	....			B6³, 4588
b589	—,1,3-dihydroxy-2,4-dinitro-*	$C_6H_4N_2O_6$. See b202	200.11	ye lf(al) λ^{al} 400 (4.30)	147–8				δ	δ	....				B6², 823
b590	—,1,3-dihydroxy-2,4-dinitroso-*	$C_6H_4N_2O_4$. See b202	168.11	ye rh pl (50 % al) lf (+1w, aq MeOH) λ^{al} 253 (4.01), 292.5 (3.96)	168				s	s					B7², 851
b591	—,1,3-dihydroxy-2,4-di(2-tolylazo)-	$C_{20}H_{18}N_4O_2$. See b202	346.39	red nd (chl-al)	212					δ	....		s	chl s	B16, 186
b592	—,1,3-dihydroxy-2,4-di(4-tolylazo)-	$C_{20}H_{18}N_4O_2$. See b202	346.39	nd (chl-al)	230.5				δ					os s	B16, 186
b593	—,2,4-dihydroxy-1,5-di(4-tolylazo)-	$C_{20}H_{18}N_4O_2$. See b202	346.39	ye nd (chl-al)	255–6				s	δ				chl v^h	B16, 187
Ω b594	—,2,4-dihydroxy-1-ethyl-*	$C_8H_{10}O_2$. See b202	138.17	pr (chl or bz) λ^{al} 281 (3.46)	98–9	131^{15}			δ	δ	δ	....			B6², 885
Ω b595	—,2,4-dihydroxy-1-hexyl-*	$C_{12}H_{18}O_2$. See b202	194.28	pa ye nd (lig) λ^w 280 (3.42)	68–9	333 178^8			i	s	s	s	s	chl s lig δ	B6², 904
b596	—,1,2-dihydroxy-4-iodo-*	$C_6H_5IO_2$. See b202	236.01	lf (CCl₄)	92	sub			δ	s	s	s	s	chl, peth δ	B6³, 4262
b597	—,1,3-dihydroxy-5-iodo-*	$C_6H_5IO_2$. See b202	236.01	nd (+1w, bz), nd (sub)	92.3 (105–13)	sub			i	v				peth i	B6², 821
b598	—,1,4-dihydroxy-2-iodo-*	$C_6H_5IO_2$. See b202	236.01		115–6										B6³, 4440
b599	—,2,4-dihydroxy-1-iodo-*	$C_6H_5IO_2$. See b202	236.01	pr, nd (+1w, w)	67				δ	s	s	s		chl s	B6², 821
b600	—,2,4-dihydroxy-1-isobutyl-	$C_{10}H_{14}O_2$. See b202	166.22		62–3.5	$166–8^{6–7}$			δ	s	s				B6², 899
Ω b601	—,1,2-dihydroxy-4-isopropyl-	$C_9H_{12}O_2$. See b202	152.20	lf (lig)	78	270–2 168^{26}								peth s^h	B6, 929
b602	—,1,4-dihydroxy-2-isopropyl-	$C_9H_{12}O_2$. See b202	152.20	lf (w) λ^{sulf} 289 (3.53)	130–1									lig s^h	B6, 929
b603	—,2,4-dihydroxy-1-isopropyl-	$C_9H_{12}O_2$. See b202	152.20	cr (aq aa)	105	265–81 $114^{0.2}$			δ	s	s				B6², 896
b604	—,1,4-dihydroxy-2-isopropyl-5-methyl-	Thymohydroquinone. $C_{10}H_{14}O_2$. See b202	166.22	pr (dil al) λ^{al} 293 (3.59)	143	290 sub			δ s^h	s	s	....	i	peth i	B6², 901
Ω b605	—,2,3-dihydroxy-1-isopropyl-4-methyl-	$C_{10}H_{14}O_2$. See b202	166.22		48	270			δ		s	s		os s peth i	B6², 900
Ω b606	—,1,2-dihydroxy-3-methoxy-*	$C_7H_8O_3$. See b202	140.15	nd	43–4	129^{10}									B6², 1065
b607	—,1,3-dihydroxy-2-methoxy-*	$C_7H_8O_3$. See b202	140.15	cr (bz)	85–7	$154–5^{24}$								s^h δ	B6, 1081

For explanations, symbols and abbreviations see beginning of table. For structural formulas see end of table.

No.	Name	Synonyms and Formula	Mol. wt.	Color, crystalline form, specific rotation and λ_{max} (log ε)	m.p. °C	b.p. °C	Density	n_D	w	al	eth	ace	bz	other solvents	Ref.
	Benzene														
b608	—,1,3-dihydroxy-5-methoxy-*	$C_7H_8O_3$. See b202	140.15	pl (bz) λ^{al} <215 (>4.15), 265 (2.88)	78–81	213[16]	....		δ	v	v	...	δ	....	B6, 1101
Ω b609	—,1,2-dihydroxy-3-methyl-*	$C_7H_8O_2$. See b202	124.15	lf (bz)	68 (47)	241 127[12]			s	s	...	...	s	chl s	B6[2], 858
Ω b610	—,1,3-dihydroxy-2-methyl-*	$C_7H_8O_2$. See b202	124.15	pr (bz) λ^{cy} 274 (3.02)	119–21	264 168[16]			s	s	s	...	s		B6, 878
b611	—,2,4-dihydroxy-1(3-methyl-butyl)-*	$C_{11}H_{16}O_2$. See b202	180.25		68–70	177–8[6]	....		δ	s	s	...	s		B6[2], 903
b612	—,2,4-dihydroxy-1(4-methyl-pentyl)-*	$C_{12}H_{18}O_2$. See b202	194.28	lf (peth)	71	190[12]		1.5292[25]	δ	s	s	...	s		B6, 905
Ω b613	—,1,3-dihydroxy-2-nitro-*	$C_6H_5NO_4$. See b202	155.11	og-red pr (al) λ^w 345 (4.15)	87–8 (85)	....			v^w	s^h		...			B6[2], 822
b614	—,1,4-dihydroxy-2-nitro-*	$C_6H_5NO_4$. See b202	155.11	og-red rh (w) $\lambda^{IN\,HCl}$ 280 (3.74), 395 (3.45), $\lambda^{IN\,NaOH}$ 238 (4.10), 540 (3.59)	133–4	....			s^h	v	v	...	s	lig δ	B6[3], 4442
b615	—,2,4-dihydroxy-1-nitroso-*	2-Hydroxy-1,4-benzoquinone oxime. $C_6H_5NO_3$. See b202	139.11	ye nd (+w), br nd (chl)	150d	....			s	v	s	v	i	chl s CS_2 i	B8, 235
b616	—,1,3-dihydroxy-4-pentyl-*	$C_{11}H_{16}O_2$. See b202	180.25		72–3 (43–4)	168–70[6-7]			i	s	s	...	s		B6[2], 902
b617	—,1,3-dihydroxy-5-pentyl-*	Olivetol. $C_{11}H_{16}O_2$. See b202	180.25	nd (+w), pr(bz-lig)	49 (anh) 41 (+w)	164[5]			v	s	s	s	s		J1945, 311
b618	—,1,2-dihydroxy-4-propyl-*	$C_9H_{12}O_2$. See b202	152.20	pr (w, bz)	60	152[13] 111–2[0.2]	1.100[18]	1.4440[18]	δ	s	s	s	s^h		B6[2], 892
b619	—,1,3-dihydroxy-5-propyl-*	Divarinol. $C_9H_{12}O_2$. See b202	152.20	lf (+1w, w) lf (bz)	83–4 (anh) 51 (hyd)	148–9[3]			s^h δ	s	s	s	aa s		B6[2], 893
Ω b620	—,2,4-dihydroxy-1-propyl-*	$C_9H_{12}O_2$. See b202	152.20	pr (bz), nd (peth)	82–3	172[14]			s	s	s	...	s		B6[3], 4611
Ω b621	—,1,2-dihydroxy-3,4,5,6-tetra-bromo-*	$C_6H_2Br_4O_2$. See b202	425.72	nd (bz, al) lf (bz-peth)	192–3	....				s	...	δ	s		B6[2], 788
b622	—,1,4-dihydroxy-2,3,5,6-tetra-bromo-*	$C_6H_2Br_4O_2$. See b202	425.72	mcl pr (al-eth)	244	....	3.023[21]		i	v	v	...	aa s		B6[2], 848
b623	—,1,2-dihydroxy-3,4,5,6-tetra-chloro-*	$C_6H_2Cl_4O_2$. See b202	247.89	cr (dil al, bz), cr (+1w, aq aa), cr (+3w, aq aa) λ^{iso} 287 (3.28)	110 (anh) 194–5 (+1w) 94 (+3w)	....							δ		B6[2], 787
b625	—,1,3-dihydroxy-2,4,5,6-tetra-chloro-*	$C_6H_2Cl_4O_2$. See b202	247.89	nd (w)	141	....			v^h s	v	v	...	v	aa v	B6[2], 819
Ω b626	—,1,4-dihydroxy-2,3,5,6-tetra-chloro-*	$C_6H_2Cl_4O_2$. See b202	247.89	nd (aa) λ^{chl} 305 (3.7)	232	sub			i	v	v	...	i	aa δ CS CCl_4 i	B6[2], 846
b627	—,1,4-dihydroxy-2,3,5,6-tetra-iodo-*	$C_6H_2I_4O_2$. See b202	613.70	(aa)	258	....				δ	s	δ	chl s alk s^h aa δ		B6[1], 417
b628	—,1,4-dihydroxy-2,3,5,6-tetra-methyl-*	Durohydroquinone. $C_{10}H_{14}O_2$. See b202	166.22	nd (al) λ^w 283 (3.33)	233	....				s^h	δ	...			Am 48, 1422
b629	—,1,3-dihydroxy-2,4,6-tribromo-*	$C_6H_3Br_3O_2$. See b202	346.82	nd (w)	112	....			δ	s	s	...			B6, 822
b630	—,1,4-dihydroxy-2,3,5-tribromo-*	$C_6H_3Br_3O_2$. See b202	346.82	nd (chl)	136–7	....			v^h	v	v	...	v	aa v lig s	B6[2], 848
b631	—,1,2-dihydroxy-3,4,5-trichloro-*	$C_6H_3Cl_3O_2$. See b202	213.46	(i) pr (+1w, aa) (ii) pr (+½w, bz)	(i) 115 (ii) 134–5	....			i	s	s	...	aa s		B6[1], 389
b632	—,2,4-dihydroxy-1,3,5-trichloro-*	$C_6H_3Cl_3O_2$. See b202	213.46	nd (w)	83	....			δ	v	v	...			B6, 820
b633	—,1,3-dihydroxy-2,4,5-trimethyl-*	$C_9H_{12}O_2$. See b202	152.20	cr	156	....									B6, 931
b634	—,1,3-dihydroxy-4,5,6-trimethyl-*	$C_9H_{12}O_2$. See b202	152.20	nd or lf	163–4	....			δ	v	v	v	s	chl s peth i	B6, 930
b635	—,1,4-dihydroxy-2,3,5-trimethyl-*	$C_9H_{12}O_2$. See b202	152.20	nd (w)	168–70d	....			v^h δ	v	v	...	v		B6, 930
b636	—,2,4-dihydroxy-1,3,5-trimethyl-*	Mesorcinol. $C_9H_{12}O_2$. See b202	152.20	pl (al), lf	149–50	275			δ	v	v	...	s		B6, 939

For explanations, symbols and abbreviations see beginning of table. For structural formulas see end of table.

Benzene

No.	Name	Synonyms and Formula	Mol. wt.	Color, crystalline form, specific rotation and λ_{max} (log ε)	m.p. °C	b.p. °C	Density	n_D	w	al	eth	ace	bz	other solvents	Ref.
Ω b637	—,2,4-dihydroxy-1,3,5-trinitro-*	Styphnic acid. $C_6H_3N_3O_8$	245.11	hex (al), ye cr (aa) λ^{al} 400 (4.20)	179–80	sub	....		δ	s	s	...	...	....	B6², 825
b638	—,1,2-diiodo-*	$C_6H_4I_2$. See b202	329.91	pl or pr (lig)	27	286⁷⁵⁰ 109³	2.54²⁰	1.7179²⁰	δ	δ	v	...	...	....	B5², 168
b639	—,1,3-diiodo-*	$C_6H_4I_2$. See b202	329.91	rh pl or pr (eth-al)	40.4 (36.5)	285⁷⁶⁰	2.47²⁵	....	i	s	s	...	...	chl s	B5², 168
Ω b640	—,1,4-diiodo-* ...	$C_6H_4I_2$. See b202	329.91	rh lf (al) λ^{al} 241.6 (4.27)	131–2	285 sub	....		i	s	v	...	...	....	B5², 168
b641	—,1,2-diisopropyl-	$C_{12}H_{18}$. See b202	162.28	λ^{iso} 257 (2.28), 263 (2.39), 267.5 (2.25), 271 (2.29)	−56.7	204⁷⁶⁰ 115.4⁵⁰	0.8701²⁰₄	1.4960²⁰	i	∞	∞	∞	∞	CCl_4 ∞	B5, 447
Ω b642	—,1,3-diisopropyl-	$C_{12}H_{18}$. See b202	162.28	λ^{iso} 257 (2.26), 263 (2.37), 267 (2.23), 270 (2.28)	−63.1	203.2⁷⁶⁰ 75⁹	0.8559²⁰₄	1.4883²⁰	i	∞	∞	∞	∞	CCl_4 ∞	B5, 447
Ω b643	—,1,4-diisopropyl-	$C_{12}H_{18}$. See b202	162.28	λ^{iso} 259 (2.36), 264 (2.54), 272 (2.58)	−17.1	210.3⁷⁶⁰ 120⁵⁰	0.8568²⁰₄	1.4898²⁰	i	∞	∞	∞	∞	CCl_4 ∞	B5², 339
b644	—,1,2-di-mercapto-*	Dithiocatechol. $C_6H_6S_2$. See b202	142.25	λ 230 (4.3), 285 sh (3.2)	28–9	238–9 120¹⁷	....			v	v	...	v	AcOEt s	B6², 799
b645	—,1,3-di-mercapto-*	Dithioresorcinol. $C_6H_6S_2$. See b202	142.25	lf (dil al)	27	245 123¹⁷	....		δ	v	v	v	v	os, alk v	B6², 829
b646	—,1,4-di-mercapto-*	Dithioquinol. $C_6H_6S_2$. See b202	142.25	lf (al)	98	....					v	...	v	aa v lig δ	B6², 854
Ω b647	—,1,2-di-methoxy-*	Veratrole. $C_8H_{10}O_2$. See b202	138.17	cr (lig) λ^{cy} 225 (3.85), 271 (3.39), 275 (3.41), 280 (3.28)	22.5	206⁷⁵⁹ 90¹⁰	1.0842²⁵₂₅	1.5827²¹ₐ	δ	s	s	...	...	....	B6², 779
Ω b648	—,1,3-di-methoxy-*	Resorcinol dimethyl ether. $C_8H_{10}O_2$. See b202	138.17	λ^{cy} 220 (3.86), 267 sh (3.23), 271.5 (3.34), 277.5 (3.33)	−52	217–8	1.0552²⁵₂₅ 1.0705⁴₄	1.5231²⁰	δ	s	s	...	s	sulf s	B6², 813
Ω b649	—,1,4-di-methoxy-*	Hydroquinone dimethyl ether. $C_8H_{10}O_2$. See b202	138.17	lf (w) λ^{cy} 226 (3.99), 280 sh (3.40), 287 (3.51), 290 (3.51), 297 (3.41)	58–60	212.6 109²⁰	1.0526⁵⁵₅₅		δ	s	v	...	v	....	B6², 839
b650	—,1,2-dimethoxy-4,5-dinitro-*	$C_8H_8N_2O_6$. See b202	228.17	ye nd (al)	130–2	....	1.3164¹⁴⁰₄		i	δ	...	...	...	MeOH δ	B6², 794
b651	—,1,2-dimethoxy-4-iodo-*	$C_8H_9IO_2$. See b202	264.06	nd (dil MeOH)	35	163–4²⁶ 90⁰·²	....			s	...	...	s	MeOH sʰ	B6¹, 390
b652	—,1,4-dimethoxy-2-isopropyl-	$C_{11}H_{16}O_2$. See b202	180.25	....		114–6¹⁵	1.0129¹⁷	1.5105¹⁷			s	...	s	....	B6, 929
b653	—,1,2-dimethoxy-3-nitro-*	$C_8H_9NO_4$. See b202	183.17	nd (al)	64–5	....	1.1404¹³³₄		i	v	v	...	v	aa s lig i	B6², 790
Ω b654	—,1,2-dimethoxy-4-nitro-*	$C_8H_9NO_4$. See b202	183.17	ye nd (al-w) λ^{al} 322.5 (3.90)	98	230¹⁵⁻²⁰	1.1888¹³³		i	v	v	...		chl s lig δ	B6², 790
b655	—,1,3-dimethoxy-2-nitro-*	$C_8H_9NO_4$. See b202	183.17	ye nd (al or aa)	131	....			i	sʰ	δ	...	s	chl s aa sʰ lig i	B6¹, 404
b656	—,1,3-dimethoxy-5-nitro-*	$C_8H_9NO_4$. See b202	183.17	pa ye nd (AcOEt)	89	....	1.1693¹³²₄		i	s	δ	...	s	os s lig i	B6², 822
Ω b657	—,1,4-dimethoxy-2-nitro-*	$C_8H_9NO_4$. See b202	183.17	gold-ye nd (dil al) $\lambda^{aq\ MeOH}$ 273 (3.52), 372 (3.42)	72–3	169¹³ sub	1.1666¹³²₄		i	sʰ	...	...	bz	chl, sulf s	B6², 849
Ω b658	—,2,4-dimethoxy-1-nitro-*	$C_8H_9NO_4$. See b202	183.17	nd (al) λ^{al} 322.5 (3.90)	76–7	....	1.1876¹³²₄		i	s	...	...	...	os s lig i	B6², 822
b659	—,1,2-dimethoxy-4-propenyl-(cis)*	Isoeugenol methyl ether. 4-Propenylveratrol. $C_{11}H_{14}O_2$. See b202	178.23	λ^{al} 256 (4.16), 289 (3.58)	....	270.5⁷⁶⁰ 138–40¹²	1.0521²⁰	1.5616²⁰	i	...	...	s	s	....	B6, 956
Ω b660	—,1,2-dimethyl-* ..	o-Xylene. C_8H_{10}. See b202 ..	106.17	λ^{cy} 265 (2.3), 271 (2.2)	−25.18	144.4⁷⁶⁰ 32¹⁰	0.8802²⁰₄	1.5055²⁰	i	∞	∞	∞	∞	peth, CCl_4 ∞	B5², 281
Ω b661	—,1,3-dimethyl-* ..	m-Xylene. C_8H_{10}. See b202..	106.17	λ^{cy} 269 (2.3), 274 (2.3)	−47.87	139.1⁷⁶⁰ 28.1¹⁰	0.8642²⁰₄	1.4972²⁰	i	∞	∞	∞	∞	os, peth ∞	B5², 287
Ω b662	—,1,4-dimethyl-* ..	p-Xylene. C_8H_{10}. See b202 ..	106.17	mcl pr (al) λ^{al} 267 (2.7), 275 (2.7)	13.26	138.35⁷⁶⁰ 27.2¹⁰	0.8611²⁰₄	1.4958²⁰	i	∞	∞	∞	∞	os, peth ∞	B5², 296
b663	—,1,2-dimethyl-3,4-dinitro-*	3,4-Dinitro-o-xylene. $C_8H_8N_2O_4$. See b202	196.17	nd (al)	82	....				δ sʰ	s	...	s	CS_2, CCl_4 os sʰ	B5², 287
b664	—,1,2-dimethyl-3,5-dinitro-*	3,5-Dinitro-o-xylene. $C_8H_8N_2O_4$. See b202	196.17	ye nd (al or peth)	77	....				s	...	s	s	chl s	B5¹, 181

For explanations, symbols and abbreviations see beginning of table. For structural formulas see end of table.

Benzene

No.	Name	Synonyms and Formula	Mol. wt.	Color, crystalline form, specific rotation and λ_{max} (log ε)	m.p. °C	b.p. °C	Density	n_D	w	al	eth	ace	bz	other solvents	Ref.
b665	—,1,2-dimethyl-4,5-dinitro-*	4,5-Dinitro-o-xylene. $C_8H_8N_2O_4$. See b202	196.17	nd (al, bz or aa)	118	....			δ^h	s^h	s	s	s	chl CS_2 s peth δ os δ	B5[1], 181
b666	—,1,3-dimethyl-2,5-dinitro-*	2,5-Dinitro-m-xylene. $C_8H_8N_2O_4$. See b202	196.17	ye (al)	101	....			...	s	s	s	s	chl, CS_2 s	B5[2], 295
b667	—,1,4-dimethyl-2,3-dinitro-*	2,3-Dinitro-p-xylene. $C_8H_8N_2O_4$. See b202 λ^{hx} 295 (3.16)	196.17	mcl pr (al)	93	....			i	v^h	s	s	s	chl s	B5[2], 302
b668	—,1,4-dimethyl-2,5-dinitro-*	2,5-Dinitro-p-xylene. $C_8H_8N_2O_4$. See b202	196.17	ye nd (al)	147–8 (142)	....			i	s^h	δ	s	s	chl s	B5[1], 188
b669	—,2,3-dimethyl-1,4-dinitro-*	3,6-Dinitro-o-xylene. $C_8H_8N_2O_4$. See b202	196.17	nd (al)	89–90	....			i	s	s	s	s	peth, chl s	B5[1], 181
b670	—,2,5-dimethyl-1,3-dinitro-*	2,6-Dinitro-p-xylene. $C_8N_8N_2O_4$. See b202 λ^{hx} 295 (3.18)	196.17	nd (al)	123–4	....			i	s	s^h	s	s	chl s	B5[2], 302
b671	—,1,2-dimethyl-4-ethyl-*	$C_{10}H_{14}$. See b202	134.22	λ^{iso} 266 (2.6), 275 (2.7)	−67.0	189.75^{760} 67.8^{10}	0.8745_4^{20}	1.5031^{20}	i	∞	∞	∞	∞	peth, CCl_4 s	B5[2], 328
b672	—,1,3-dimethyl-5-ethyl-*	$C_{10}H_{14}$. See b202	134.22	λ^{hx} 200 (4.02)	−84.33	183.75^{760} 63.0^{10}	0.8648_4^{20}	1.4981^{20}	i	∞	∞	∞	∞	peth, CCl_4 s	B5[2], 328
b673	—,1,4-dimethyl-2-ethyl-*	$C_{10}H_{14}$. See b202	134.22	λ^{iso} 267 (2.67), 276 (2.70)	−53.68	186.91^{760} 64.9^{10}	0.8772_4^{20}	1.5043^{20}	i	∞	∞	∞	∞	peth, CCl_4 s	B5[2], 328
b674	—,2,4-dimethyl-1-ethyl-*	$C_{10}H_{14}$. See b202	134.22	λ^{iso} 267 (2.7), 276 (2.7)	−62.9	188.4^{760} 66.5^{10}	0.8763_4^{20}	1.5038^{20}	i	∞	∞	∞	∞	peth, CCl_4 s	B5[2], 328
Ω b675	—,1,2-dimethyl-3-hydroxy-*	2,3-Dimethylphenol. o-3-Xylenol. $C_8H_{10}O$. See b202	122.17	nd (w or dil al) λ^{hx} 273 (3.15), 278 (3.19)	75	218^{760} 95.4^{10}		1.5420^{20}	δ	s	s	....	....		B6[2], 453
Ω b676	—,1,2-dimethyl-4-hydroxy-*	3,4-Dimethylphenol. $C_8H_{10}O$. See b202	122.17	nd (w) λ^{hx} 277.5 (3.28), 284 (3.24)	66–8	225^{760} 106.8^{10}	0.9830_4^{20}	....	δ	s	∞	....	....		B6[2], 455
b677	—,—,acetate......	$C_{10}H_{12}O_2$. See b202.	164.21	....	22	235 140^{80}			i	s	s	....	s		B6[2], 455
Ω b678	—,1,3-dimethyl-2-hydroxy-*	2,6-Dimethylphenol. $C_8H_{10}O$. See b202	122.17	lf or nd (al) λ^{al} 271 (3.19), 275.5 (3.16)	49.0	212^{760} 91.2^{10}			s	∞	∞	....	....		B6[2], 457
Ω b679	—,1,3-dimethyl-5-hydroxy-*	3,5-Dimethylphenol. $C_8H_{10}O$. See b202	122.17	nd (w or peth) λ^{cy} 281.5 (3.21)	68	219.5 sub 102.3^{10}	0.9680_4^{20}	....	s	∞	∞	....	....		B6[2], 462
Ω b680	—,1,4-dimethyl-2-hydroxy-*	2,5-Dimethylphenol. $C_8H_{10}O$. See b202	122.17	nd (w), pr (al-eth) λ^{cy} 276 (3.28)	75	211.5^{762}			δ	s	s	....	....		B6[2], 466
b681	—,—,acetate......	$C_{10}H_{12}O_2$. See b202.	164.21	....	< −20	237^{768}	1.0624^{15}		i	s	s	....	....		B6, 495
Ω b682	—,2,4-dimethyl-1-hydroxy-*	2,4-Dimethylphenol. $C_8H_{10}O$. See b202	122.17	nd (w) λ^{cy} 280 (3.31)	27–8	210^{760} 89.3^{10}	0.9650_4^{20}	1.5420^{14}	δ	∞	∞	....	....		B6[3], 458
b683	—,—,acetate......	$C_{10}H_{12}O_2$. See b202.	164.21	....		226 108^{13}	$1.0298_4^{15.5}$	1.4990^{15}	i	s	s	....	....		B6, 487
b684	—,1,5-dimethyl-2-hydroxy-3-(hydroxymethyl)-*	$C_9H_{12}O_2$. See b202	152.20	nd (bz-peth)	57–8	....				s	s	....	s^h	peth s^h	B6, 939
b685	—,1,2-dimethyl-3-hydroxy-5-nitro-*	$C_8H_9NO_3$. See b202	167.17	og-ye nd (bz or w)	109 (120–1)	....			s^h	v	....	v	s^h	aa v chl s^h peth i	B6[2], 455
b686	—,1,2-dimethyl-4-hydroxy-5-nitro-*	$C_8H_9NO_3$. See b202	167.17	ye rh (al) λ^{hx} 283 (3.97), 357 (3.66)	86.8–7.5	....			....	v	v	....	v	chl v peth δ	B6, 484
b687	—,1,3-dimethyl-2-hydroxy-4-nitro-*	$C_8H_9NO_3$. See b202	167.17	lf pr (bz), nd (lig)	99–100	....			....	v	....	....	s^h	chl v lig s^h	B6, 485
Ω b688	—,1,3-dimethyl-2-hydroxy-5-nitro-*	$C_8H_9NO_3$. See b202	167.17	pr (MeOH) λ^{al} 322.5 (4.05)	171	....			....	s	s	s	δ	chl v MeOH s^h lig δ	B6, 486
b689	—,1,4-dimethyl-2-hydroxy-3-nitro-*	$C_8H_9NO_3$. See b202	167.17	nd (peth) λ^{hx} 285 (3.77), 358 (3.38)	34–5	236d 150^{15}			....	v	s	s	s	os v	B6[1], 246
b690	—,1,4-dimethyl-2-hydroxy-5-nitro-*	$C_8H_9NO_3$. See b202	167.17	pa ye nd (dil al) λ^{hx} 234 (3.77), 310 (3.83)	122–3	....			s^h	s	s	s	s		B6[1], 246
b691	—,1,5-dimethyl-2-hydroxy-3-nitro-*	$C_8H_9NO_3$. See b202	167.17	ye nd (al) λ^{hx} 202.5 (3.92), 366 (3.58)	73	....			s^h						B6[2], 461
Ω b692	—,1,5-dimethyl-3-hydroxy-2-nitro-*	$C_8H_9NO_3$. See b202	167.17	ye nd (lig or dil MeOH) λ^{hx} 287 (3.96), 352 (3.57)	66–6.5	....			....	v	s	s	s	os s lig s^h peth i	B6[1], 244
b693	—,2,5-dimethyl-1-hydroxy-3-nitro-*	$C_8H_9NO_3$. See b202.	167.17	ye lf (peth)	91	....			δ	v	v	....	....	peth s^h	B6, 497
b694	—,1,2-dimethyl-4-hydroxy-3,5,6-tribromo-*	$C_8H_7Br_3O$. See b202	358.87	nd (al)	173–4	....			i	s	....	....	....		B6[1], 240
b695	—,1,3-dimethyl-5-hydroxy-2,4,6-tribromo-*	$C_8H_7Br_3O$. See b202	358.87	nd (al)	166	....			s	s	....	....	....		B6[2], 465

For explanations, symbols and abbreviations see beginning of table. For structural formulas see end of table.

Benzene

No.	Name	Synonyms and Formula	Mol. wt.	Color, crystalline form, specific rotation and λ_{max} (log ε)	m.p. °C	b.p. °C	Density	n_D	w	al	eth	ace	bz	other solvents	Ref.
b696	—,1,2-dimethyl-3-hydroxy-4,5,6-trichloro-*	$C_8H_7Cl_3O$. See b202	225.50	nd (dil al or peth)	180–1					v				aa s[h] peth δ	B6[2], 454
b697	—,1,2-dimethyl-4-hydroxy-3,5,6-trichloro-*	$C_8H_7Cl_3O$. See b202	225.50	nd (peth)	182.5					v				peth v[h] aa s[h]	B6[2], 456
b698	—,1,3-dimethyl-4-hydroxy-2,5,6-trichloro-*	$C_8H_7Cl_3O$. See b202	225.50	pa ye nd	174							s			B6[2], 460
Ω b699	—,1,3-dimethyl-5-hydroxy-2,4,6-trichloro-*	$C_8H_7Cl_3O$. See b202	225.50	ye nd (peth) λ^{ey} 290 (3.2)	117–8									peth v[h]	B6[3], 1761
b700	—,1,4-dimethyl-2-hydroxy-3,5,6-trichloro-*	$C_8H_7Cl_3O$. See b202	225.50	pa gr nd (al, aq MeOH)	175–6				i	s	v		v	chl v	B6[2], 467
b701	—,1,2-dimethyl-3-iodo-*	C_8H_9I. See b202	232.07			228–230.6 125–6[15]	1.6395_4^{20}	1.6074^{20}				s			B5[2], 286
b702	—,1,2-dimethyl-4-iodo-*	C_8H_9I. See b202	232.07			231–2.4 111[11]	1.6334_4^{18}	1.6049^{18}				s			B5[2], 286
b703	—,1,3-dimethyl-2-iodo-*	C_8H_9I. See b202	232.07	oil	11.2	229.8–30.8 102.3[14]	1.6158_4^{20}	1.6035^{20}	i			s	s		B5, 375
b704	—,1,3-dimethyl-5-iodo-*	C_8H_9I. See b202	232.07	oil		230.2–31.8 117[27]	$1.6085_4^{18.5}$	$1.5967^{18.5}$	i			s		os s	B5[2], 294
b705	—,1,4-dimethyl-2-iodo-*	C_8H_9I. See b202	232.07			227–8δd 106–8[13]	1.6168_4^{17}	1.5992^{17}	i			s	s		B5[2], 302
Ω b706	—,2,4-dimethyl-1-iodo-*	C_8H_9I. See b202	232.07			230.7–31.7δd 111[14]	1.6282_4^{16}	1.6008^{16}	i			s	s		B5[2], 294
Ω b707	—,1,2-dimethyl-3-methoxy-*	$C_9H_{12}O$. See b202	136.20	λ^{ey} 270.5 (3.1), 274 (3.2), 278.5 (3.2)	29	199 85[18]	0.9596^{40}	1.5120^{40}	i	v	v		v		B6[2], 453
Ω b708	—,1,2-dimethyl-4-methoxy-*	$C_9H_{12}O$. See b202	136.20	λ^{ey} 278.5 (3.3), 284.7 (3.3)		204–5 96–7[17]	0.9744_4^{14}	1.5198^{14}	i	s	s		s		B6[2], 455
Ω b709	—,1,3-dimethyl-2-methoxy-*	$C_9H_{12}O$. See b202	136.20	λ^{al} 262 (2.50), 266 (2.49), 270 (2.42)		182–3	0.9619_4^{14}	1.5053^{14}	i	s	s				B6[2], 457
Ω b710	—,1,3-dimethyl-5-methoxy-*	$C_9H_{12}O$. See b202	136.20	λ^{ey} 220 (3.86), 264 sh (2.95), 271 (3.16), 278 (3.23)		194.5 89[15]	0.9627_4^{15}	1.5110^{20}	i	s	s		s	CS_2, aa s	B6[2], 462
Ω b711	—,1,4-dimethyl-2-methoxy-*	$C_9H_{12}O$. See b202	136.20	λ^{ey} 219 (3.86), 270 sh (3.28), 273 (3.32), 278.5 (3.33)		194[772]	0.9693_4^{13}	1.5182^{13}	i	s	s		s	CS_2, peth s	B6[2], 466
Ω b712	—,2,4-dimethyl-1-methoxy-*	$C_9H_{12}O$. See b202	136.20			192 83–4[15]	0.9740_4^{16}	1.5190^{16}	i	s	s		s	CS_2 s	B6[2], 459
Ω b713	—,1,2-dimethyl-3-nitro-*	$C_8H_9NO_2$. See b202	151.17	nd (al) λ^{iso} 251 (3.62)	15	240[760] 131[20]	1.1402^{20}	1.5441^{20}	i	s					B5[2], 286
Ω b714	—,1,2-dimethyl-4-nitro-	$C_8H_9NO_2$. See b202	151.17	ye pr (al) λ^{al} 278 (3.96)	30–1	254[750] (231[760]) 143[21]			i	∞[h]					B5[2], 286
Ω b715	—,1,3-dimethyl-2-nitro-*	$C_8H_9NO_2$. See b202	151.17		13	222[760] 84.6[0.05]	1.112^{15}	1.5202^{20}	i	v					B5[2], 294
b716	—,1,3-dimethyl-5-nitro-*	$C_8H_9NO_2$. See b202	151.17	nd (al) λ^{al} 271 (3.87)	75	273[739]			i	v	v				B5[2], 295
Ω b717	—,1,4-dimethyl-2-nitro-*	$C_8H_9NO_2$. See b202	151.17	pa ye		239.5–41[760] 64–5[0.35]	1.132^{15}	1.5415^{20}	i	s					B5[2], 302
Ω b718	—,2,4-dimethyl-1-nitro-*	$C_8H_9NO_2$. See b202	151.17		9	245[744] 122[18]	$1.126^{17.5}$		i	s	s				B5[2], 294
b721	—,1,2-dimethyl-3,4,5,6-tetrabromo-*	$C_8H_6Br_4$. See b202	421.77	nd (bz)	262	374–5			i	δ[h]			s[h]	peth s	B5[2], 285
b722	—,1,3-dimethyl-2,4,5,6-tetrabromo-*	$C_8H_6Br_4$. See b202	421.77	nd (xyl or al)	248 (252)				i	i			v	xyl s[h]	B5[2], 294
b723	—,1,3-dimethyl-2,4,6-trinitro-*	$C_8H_7N_3O_6$. See b202	241.16	pa ye pr or lf (al-bz) λ^{Py} 413 (4.22), 600 (4.00)	184		1.604^{19}		i	δ s[h]	δ	s[h]	v	Py v, chl v[h] AcOEt s HNO_3 δ[h]	B5[2], 295
b724	—,1,4-dimethyl-2,3,5-trinitro-*	$C_8H_7N_3O_6$. See b202	241.16	mcl nd (al), lf (al-bz)	139–40	410 exp	1.59^{19}		i	s					B5[2], 303
Ω b725	—,1,2-dinitro-*	$C_6H_4N_2O_4$. See b202	168.11	nd (bz), pl (al)	118.5	319[773] 194[30]	1.3119_4^{120} 1.565^{17}		i	s v[h]			s	chl, MeOH, AcOEt, to s	B5[2], 193

For explanations, symbols and abbreviations see beginning of table. For structural formulas see end of table.

No.	Name	Synonyms and Formula	Mol. wt.	Color, crystalline form, specific rotation and λ_{max} (log ε)	m.p. °C	b.p. °C	Density	n_D	w	al	eth	ace	bz	other solvents	Ref.
	Benzene														
Ω b726	—,1,3-dinitro-*	$C_6H_4N_2O_4$. See b202	168.11	rh pl (al) λ^{al} 242 (4.21), 305 (3.04)	90.02	291[756] 167[14]	1.575$^{18}_4$		δ^h	v^h	s	v	v^h	Py v to, chl, MeOII s	B5[2], 193
Ω b727	—,1,4-dinitro-*	$C_6H_4N_2O_4$. See b202	168.11	nd (al) λ^{al} 266 (4.16)	174	299[777] 183[34] sub	1.625$^{18}_4$		i	δ	...	s	s	aa. to, AcOEt s chl δ	B5[2], 195
b728	—,1,3-dinitro-2-ethoxy-*	$C_8H_8N_2O_5$. See b202	212.17	nd (eth)	59.5–60.5	137–9[3]			i	δ	s				B6[1], 127
b729	—,1,3-dinitro-5-ethoxy-*	$C_8H_8N_2O_5$. See b202	212.17	nd (al)	97.5				δ	δ	s				B6, 258
b730	—,1,4-dinitro-2-ethoxy-*	$C_8H_8N_2O_5$. See b202	212.17	lf (al)	96–8 (85)				i	δ	δ				B6[2], 245
Ω b731	—,2,4-dinitro-1-ethoxy-*	$C_8H_8N_2O_5$. See b202	212.17	nd or lf (al) λ^{ey} 283	86–7				i	δ s^h	...	s	δ		B6[3], 858
Ω b732	—,2,4-dinitro-1-fluoro-*	$C_6H_3FN_2O_4$. See b202	186.10	pa ye (al) λ^{iso} 260 (3.8), 295 sh (2.9)	25.8	296 178[25]	1.4718[84]		...	s^h					B5[3], 634
b733	—,1,3-dinitro-5-isopropyl-4-hydroxy-6-methyl-	2,6-Dinitrothymol. $C_{10}H_{12}N_2O_5$. See b202	240.22	pr (peth)	55.5				i	s	s	s	δ	lig s^h	C37, 6254
b734	—,1,2-dinitro-3-methoxy-*	$C_7H_6N_2O_5$. See b202	198.14	nd (al), pl (to)	119		1.2290[137] 1.524[20]		i	s^h	s			lig s^h	B6[2], 239
b735	—,1,2-dinitro-4-methoxy-*	$C_7H_6N_2O_5$. See b202	198.14	ye nd (dil al)	71		1.3332[110]			s				CS_2, MeOH s	B6[1], 127
b736	—,1,3-dinitro-2-methoxy-*	$C_7H_6N_2O_5$. See b202	198.14	nd (al, MeOII)	118		1.3000[128] 1.319[20]			δ				CS_2, MeOH s	B6[2], 245
b737	—,1,3-dinitro-5-methoxy-*	$C_7H_6N_2O_5$. See b202	198.14	nd (al) λ^w 254 (4.12), 340 (3.45)	105.5		1.558[12]		δ^h	δ		s	s	CS_2, MeOH s	B6[3], 869
b738	—,1,4-dinitro-2-methoxy-*	$C_7H_6N_2O_5$. See b202	198.14	nd (bz-lig) $\lambda^{90\%al}$ 220 (4.1), 310 (4.02)	97	>360 136–8[2]	1.476[18]		δ	s^h	s		s	CS_2, MeOH s lig δ^h	B6[1], 127
Ω b739	—,2,4-dinitro-1-methoxy-*	$C_7H_6N_2O_5$. See b202	198.14	nd (al or w)	(i) 94.5–5.5 (st) (ii) 87–8 (unst)	206–7[12] sub	1.3364[131] 1.546[15]		δ^h	s^h	s	s	s	to, Py v CS_2 s	B6[2], 241
Ω b740	—,1,4-dinitro-2,3,5,6-tetra-methyl-*	Dinitrodurene. $C_{10}H_{12}N_2O_4$. See b202	224.22	pr (al)	211–2	sub			i	δ^h	v	...	s		B5[2], 330
b741	—,2,4-dinitro-1,3,5-trimethyl-*	$C_9H_{10}N_2O_4$. See b202	210.19	rh (al) λ^{ey} 238 sh (3.59)	86	418 exp			i	s^h					B5[2], 316
—	—,diphenyl-*	see Terphenyl													
Ω b742	—,1,2-dipropoxy-*	Catechol dipropyl ether. $C_{12}H_{18}O_2$. See b202	194.28			234–7 117–20[12]	0.9554$^{33}_4$	1.4950[27]							C45, 1974
b743	—,1,3-dipropoxy-*	Resorcinol dipropyl ether. $C_{12}H_{18}O_2$. See b202	194.28			251 127–8[12]	1.035$^{20}_{21}$	1.5138[83]							B6[2], 815
Ω b744	—,1,3-dipropyl-2-hydroxy-*	$C_{12}H_{18}O$. See b202	178.28		28	256 114–6[5]			s		s				B6[2], 511
Ω b745	—,(1,2-epoxy-ethyl)-*	Styrene oxide. C_8H_8O. See b202	120.16	λ^{al} 250 sh (2.2), 254 (2.24), 260 (2.28), 265 sh (2.10)		194.1 84–5[15]	1.0523$^{16}_4$	1.5342[20]	i	s	s		s		B17, 49
—	—,ethenyl-*	see Styrene													
Ω b746	—,ethoxy-*	Phenetole. $C_8H_{10}O$. See b202	122.17	λ^{hx} 271 (3.29)	−29.5	170[760] 60[9]	0.9666$^{20}_4$	1.5076[20]	i	s	s		s		B6, 140
b747	—,1-ethoxy-4-ethyl-*	$C_{10}H_{14}O$. See b202	150.22			211 92–3[12]	0.9385$^{17}_4$		i	s	s	s	s		B6[1], 234
Ω b748	—,1-ethoxy-2-fluoro-*	C_8H_9FO. See b202	140.16		−16.7	171.4 64[11]	1.0874[17]	1.4932[17]	i	s	s				B6[2], 169
b749	—,1-ethoxy-3-fluoro-*	C_8H_9FO. See b202	140.16		−27.5	171.4[755] 65.2[13]	1.0716$^{16}_4$	1.4847[17]	i				s		B6[2], 170
Ω b750	—,1-ethoxy-4-fluoro-*	C_8H_9FO. See b202	140.16		−8.5	173[766] 54[7]	1.0715[18]	1.4826[18]	i				s	chl s	B6[2], 170
b751	—,1-ethoxy-2-iodo-*	C_8H_9IO. See b202	248.07			245[716] 121–31[18]			i	s	s	s	s	o3 s	B6, 207
b752	—,1-ethoxy-4-iodo-*	C_8H_9IO. See b202	248.07	cr (dil MeOH)	29	249–50[729]			i	s	v		s	chl v	B6, 208
b753	—,1-ethoxy-3-mercapto-*	$C_8H_{10}OS$. See b202	154.23			238–9				s	s	s	s	CS_2, alk s	B6, 833
b754	—,1-ethoxy-4-mercapto-*	$C_8H_{10}OS$. See b202	154.23		1.6	238				s	s		s	CS_2 s	B6[2], 852
b755	—,1-ethoxy-2-nitro-*	$C_8H_9NO_3$. See b202	167.17	br ye	2.1	267 149[16]	1.1903[15]	1.5425[20]	i	v	v		s		B6[2], 210
b756	—,1-ethoxy-3-nitro-*	$C_8H_9NO_3$. See b202	167.17	br ye	36	284 (264δd), 169[70]d			i	s	s		s		B6[2], 214
Ω b757	—,1-ethoxy-4-nitro-*	$C_8H_9NO_3$. See b202	167.17	pr (al-w or eth) λ^{hx} 295 (4.12)	60 (57–8)	283 168[15]	1.1176$^{100}_4$		δ	v^a δ	v	∞	∞	peth s^h	B6[1], 221

For explanations, symbols and abbreviations see beginning of table. For structural formulas see end of table.

Benzene

No.	Name	Synonyms and Formula	Mol. wt.	Color. crystalline form. specific rotation and λ_{max} (log ε)	m.p. °C	b.p. °C	Density	n_D	w	al	eth	ace	bz	other solvents	Ref.
Ω b758	—,ethyl-*	C_8H_{10}. See b202	106.17	λ^{al} 206 (4.5), 259 (2.2)	−94.97	136.2[760] 25.8[10]	0.8670[20]	1.4959[20]	i	∞	∞	...	...		B5[2], 274
Ω b759	—,1-ethyl-2-hydroxy-*	2-Ethylphenol. Phlorol. $C_8H_{10}O$. See b202	122.17	λ^{cy} 270 (3.30), 276 (3.28)	< −18	207[760] 84.1[10]	1.0371[0]	1.5367[20]	δ	∞	∞	s	s		B6, 442
Ω b760	—,1-ethyl-3-hydroxy-*	3-Ethylphenol. $C_8H_{10}O$. See b202	122.17	λ^{cy} 273 (3.25)	−4	214[760] 99.3[10]	1.0283[20]	...	δ	v	v	...	s		B6, 471
Ω b761	—,1-ethyl-4-hydroxy-*	4-Ethylphenol. $C_8H_{10}O$. See b202	122.17	nd λ^{cy} 273 (3.26), 276 (3.34), 282 (3.30)	47–8	219[760] 99.5[10]	...	1.5239[25]	δ	v	v	s	v	CS_2 v	B6, 472
b762	—,1-ethyl-2-iodo-*	C_8H_9I. See b202	232.07	...		226	1.6189[16]	1.5941[22]	i	...	...	s	s	os s	B5[1], 177
b763	—,1-ethyl-4-iodo-*	C_8H_9I. See b202	232.07	...	−17	209	1.6095[16]	1.5909[22]	i	...	...	s	s	os s	B5[1], 178
b764	—,1-ethyl-4-isobutyl-	$C_{12}H_{18}$. See b202	162.28	...		211	...	...	i	...	s	s	...		C46, 11144
b765	—,1-ethyl-3-isopropyl-	$C_{11}H_{16}$. See b202	148.25	...	< −20	192.0[760] 69.2[10]	0.8592[4]	1.4921[20]	i	s	s	...	v		B5, 440
b766	—,1-ethyl-4-isopropyl-	$C_{11}H_{16}$. See b202	148.25	...	< −20	136.6[760] 73[10]	0.8585[20]	1.4923[20]	i	...	s	...	v		B5[2], 334
b767	—,1-ethyl-2-methoxy-*	$C_9H_{12}O$. See b202	136.20	...		186–8[755] 80[14]	0.9636[19]	1.5142[20]	i	...	v	...	s		B6, 471
Ω b768	—,1-ethyl-3-methoxy-*	$C_9H_{12}O$. See b202	136.20	...		196–7[758] 74[10]	0.9575[18]	1.5102	i	...	v	...	s		B6, 472
b769	—,1-ethyl-4-methoxy-*	$C_9H_{12}O$. See b202	136.20	...		195–6 83–4[10]	0.9624[15]	1.5120[20]	i	...	v	...	s		B6, 472
Ω b770	—,1-ethyl-2-methyl-*	C_9H_{12}. See b202	120.20	λ^{iso} 263.5 (2.40), 271 (2.32)	−80.83	165.2[760] 62.3[20]	0.8807[20]	1.5046[20]	i	∞	∞	∞	∞	peth, CCl_4 ∞	B5, 396
b771	—,1-ethyl-3-methyl-*	C_9H_{12}. See b202	120.20	λ^{iso} 268.5 (2.31), 272 (2.40)	−95.55	161.3[760] 45.6[10]	0.8645[20]	1.4966[20]	i	v	v	∞	∞	peth, CCl_4 ∞	B5[2], 309
b772	—,1-ethyl-4-methyl-*	C_9H_{12}. See b202	120.20	λ^{iso} 264 (2.53), 268 (2.66), 272 (2.33)	−62.35	162[760] 45.6[10]	0.8614[20]	1.4959[20]	i	v	v	∞	∞	peth, CCl_4 ∞	B5[2], 310
Ω b773	—,1-ethyl-2-nitro-*	$C_8H_9NO_2$. See b202	151.17	λ^{iso} 250 (3.72)	−23	228 116[22]	1.1139[20]	1.5354[20]	i	v	v	s	...		B5[2], 279
b774	—,1-ethyl-3-nitro-*	$C_8H_9NO_2$. See b202	151.17	...		242–3	1.1345[0]	...	i	v	v	s	...		B5, 358
Ω b775	—,1-ethyl-4-nitro-*	$C_8H_9NO_2$. See b202	151.17	λ^{snv} 251 (3.97)	−12.3 (−32)	245–6 134–6[23]	1.1192[20]	1.5455[20]	i	v	v	s	...		B5[2], 279
b776	—,1-ethyl-4-propyl-*	$C_{11}H_{16}$. See b202	148.25	...		205[760]	0.8594[20]	1.4921[20]	i	v	s	...	∞		B5, 439
b777	—,(ethylthio-)*	Ethyl phenyl sulfide. $C_8H_{10}S$. See b202	138.23	λ^{hx} 257 (3.89)		205[760] 84[10]	1.0211[20]	1.5670[20]	i	...	...	...	...		B6[2], 287
Ω b778	—,ethynyl-*	Phenylacetylene. C_8H_6. See b202	102.14	λ^{al} 235 (4.18), 244 (4.13)	−44.8	142–4 44[18]	0.9281[20]	1.5485[20]	i	∞	∞	s	s		B5[2], 406
Ω b779	—,fluoro-*	C_6H_5F. See b202	96.11	λ^{al} 254 (3.00), 259 (3.11), 266 (3.08)	−41.2 fr −39.2	85.1[760]	1.0225[20]	1.4684[40]	i	∞	∞	∞	∞	CCl_4, lig ∞	B5[2], 147
Ω b780	—,1-fluoro-4-iodo-*	C_6H_4FI. See b202	222.00	λ^{cy} 266 (3.27), 271 sh (3.20), 280 sh (3.00)	(i) −27.2 (ii) −18	182–4 67–9[11]	1.9523[15]	1.5270[22]	i	s	s	s	v		B5[2], 167
Ω b781	—,1-fluoro-2-methoxy-*	C_7H_7FO. See b202	126.13	λ^{cy} 268 (3.23), 293 (3.16)	−39	154–5 59.2[12]	1.5489[17]	1.4969[17.5]	i	s	s	s	v		B6[2], 169
Ω b782	—,1-fluoro-4-methoxy-*	C_7H_7FO. See b202	126.13	λ^{cy} 275 (3.44), 278.5 (3.51), 284.5 (3.44)	−45	154[760]	1.178[18]	1.4886[18]	i	s	s	s	v		B6[1], 98
Ω b783	—,1-fluoro-2-nitro-*	$C_6H_4FNO_2$. See b202	141.10	ye	−5.9	214.6d 86–7[11]	1.3285[18]	1.5489[17]	i	s	s	s	s		B5[2], 180
Ω b784	—,1-fluoro-3-nitro-*	$C_6H_4FNO_2$. See b202	141.10	ye λ^{al} 254 (3.8), 290 sh (3.3)	(i) 41 (st) (ii) 3.1 (unst) (iii) 3.6 (unst)	198– 200[760] 86[19]	1.3254[19]	1.5262[15]	i	s	s	s	s		B5[2], 180
Ω b785	—,1-fluoro-4-nitro-*	$C_6H_4FNO_2$. See b202	141.10	ye nd λ^{al} 212 (4.0), 263 (3.9)	(i) 27 (st) (ii) 21.5 (unst)	206–7 87[14]	1.3300[20]	1.5316[20]	i	s	s	s	s		B5[2], 180
b786	—,hexabromo-*	C_6Br_6. See b202	551.52	mcl nd (bz)	327 (306)	...	...	...	i	s	δ	...	s[h]	chl, peth s aa s[h]	B5[2], 164
Ω b787	—,hexachloro-*	C_6Cl_6. See b202	284.79	nd (bz-al) λ^{iso} 291 (2.32), 301 (2.25)	230	322 sub	1.5691[23.6]	...	i	δ	s	...	v[h]	chl s	B5[2], 157
Ω b788	—,hexaethyl-*	$C_{18}H_{30}$. See b202	246.44	mcl pr (al or bz) λ^{iso} 272.5 (2.36), 276 sh (2.33), 281 (2.25)	129	298	0.8305[130]	1.4736[130]	i	s[h]	v	...	v	sulf s	B5[2], 358
Ω b789	—,hexahydroxy-*	Hexaphenol-. $C_6H_6O_6$. See b202	174.11	nd (w)	>300	...	...	...	δ	δ	δ	...	δ		B5[2], 116
b790	—,hexaiodo-*	C_6I_6. See b202	833.49	red-br nd or mcl pr (bz)	350d	...	...	...	i	i	i	...	...	$PhNO_2$ s[h]	B5[2], 169

For explanations, symbols and abbreviations see beginning of table. For structural formulas see end of table.

No.	Name	Synonyms and Formula	Mol. wt.	Color. crystalline form. specific rotation and λ_{max} (log ε)	m.p. °C	b.p. °C	Density	n_D	Solubility						Ref.
									w	al	eth	ace	bz	other solvents	
	Benzene														
Ω b791	—,hexamethyl-*	Mellitene. $C_{12}H_{18}$. See b202 .	162.28	rh pr or nd (al) λ^{al} 275 (2.26)	166–7	265	1.0630^{25}	....	i	v^h s	s	s	v^h s	aa s	B5[2], 34
—	—,hydroxy-*......	*see* **Phenol***													
b792	—,1-hydroxy-2-hydroxymethyl-4-methyl-*	Homosaligenine. $C_8H_{10}O_2$. See b202	138.17	lf (w or chl), pr (al), lf (w)	106–7	....	....	....	v^h s	v	v	....	s		B6[2], 889
b793	—,1-hydroxy-4-isobutyl-	$C_{10}H_{14}O$. See b202	150.22	....	51–2	235–9 125–6[11]	0.9796^{20}_{20}	1.5319^{25}	δ	s	s	....	s		B6[3], 1859
Ω b794	—,1-hydroxy-2-isopropyl-	o-Cumenol. $C_9H_{12}O$. See b202	136.20	λ^{al} 271 (3.55), 276 sh (3.30)	15–6	213–4[760]	1.012^{20}_4	1.5315^{20}	δ	s	s	s	s		B6, 504
b795	—,1-hydroxy-3-isopropyl-	$C_9H_{12}O$. See b202	136.20	....	26	228	....	1.5261^{20}	δ	...	s	....	s		B6, 505
Ω b796	—,1-hydroxy-4-isopropyl-	$C_9H_{12}O$. See b202	136.20	nd (peth) λ^{cy} 272 sh (3.23), 275 (3.32), 281 (3.28)	62–3	228–30[745] 109–10[10]	0.990^{20}	1.5228^{20}	δ	...	s	....	s		B6, 505
Ω b797	—,2-hydroxy-1-isopropyl-4-methyl-	Thymol. $C_{10}H_{14}O$. See b202	150.22	pl (aa or ace) λ^{cy} 276 (3.34), 282 (3.34)	52	233 92[2-8]	0.925^{50}_4	1.5227^{20}	i	v	v	....	....	AcOEt, chl, aa v	B6[2], 494
b798	—,—,acetate......	$C_{12}H_{16}O_2$. See b202	192.24	....	....	245 131[21]	1.009^0	....	i	∞	∞	....	∞	chl ∞	B6[2], 499
b799	—,—,carbonate ...	Thymotal. Tyratol. $C_{21}H_{26}O_3$. See b202	326.44	nd or pr	49	....	....	....	i	v^h	....	....	....	chl s	B6[2], 499
Ω b800	—,2-hydroxy-4-isopropyl-1-methyl-	Carvacrol. $C_{10}H_{14}O$. See b202	150.22	nd λ^{al} 277.5 (3.26)	1	237.7 101–2.5[10]	0.9772^{20}_4	1.5230^{20}	δ	v	v	s	v	alk s	B6[2], 492
b801	—,—,acetate......	$C_{12}H_{16}O_2$. See b202	192.24	....	....	245–8	0.9896^{25}	1.4913^{28}	i	v	s	....	s		B6[2], 494
b802	—,1-hydroxy-2-isopropyl-5-methyl-4-nitroso-	$C_{10}H_{13}NO_2$. See b202	179.22	yesh red	175	....	....	....	i	v	v	....	....	chl v	B7[2], 596
b803	—,1-hydroxy-5-isopropyl-2-methyl-3-nitroso-	$C_{10}H_{13}NO_2$. See b202	179.22	yesh pr (bz), nd (dil al)	153	....	....	....	i	v	v	....	v	chl v	B7[2], 596
b804	—,hydroxyl-amino-*	Phenylhydroxylamine. C_6H_7NO. See b202	109.13	nd (w, bz or peth) λ^{al} 236 (3.8), 279 (3.0)	83–4	....	....	....	s^h	v	v	....	v^h	chl v lig i	B15[2], 4
b805	—,—,N-nitroso-...	$C_6H_6N_2O_2$. See b202	138.13	nd (lig)	59	....	....	....	i	v	v	....	....	os v	B16[2], 344
b806	—,1-hydroxy-2-methoxy-4-propenyl-(cis)*	Isoeugenol (cis). $C_{10}H_{12}O_2$. See b202	164.21	λ^{al} 258 (4.14), 292 (3.58)	....	134–5[13] 80–1[0.5]	1.0837^{20}_4	1.5726^{20}	δ	s	s	....	....		B6, 955
b807	—,—,acetate......	$C_{12}H_{14}O_3$. See b202	206.24	....	....	160–2[13]	1.0947^{19}	1.5418^{20}	i	....	s	....	....		B6[3], 5007
Ω b808	—,—(trans)*	Isoeugenol (trans). $C_{10}H_{12}O_2$. See b202	164.21	λ^{al} 260 (4.22), 267 (4.18), 300 sh (3.70)	33–4	141–2[13]	1.0852^{20}_4	1.5784^{20}	δ	s	s	....	....		B6, 955
b809	—,—,acetate	$C_{12}H_{14}O_3$. See b202	206.24	nd (al or bz-lig)	80–1	282–3	1.0251^{100}	1.5052^{100}_4	i	....	s	....	....		B6[2], 919
b809[1]	—,1-hydroxy-4(2-methyl-2-butyl)-*	4-tert-Amylphenol. $C_{11}H_{16}O$. See b202	164.25	nd	94–6	262.5[760] (265–7) 138[15]	....	....	i	....	....	....	....		B6, 548
b810	—,1-hydroxy-2-methyl-4(3-methyl-3-pentyl)-*	$C_{13}H_{20}O$. See b202	192.31		35	145–6[13]	....	1.5200^{25}	i	....	....	s	....	os s	C48, 1328
b811	—,1-hydroxy-4(3-methyl-1-butyl)-*	$C_{11}H_{16}O$. See b202	164.25	nd (w)	93	255 126[14]	0.9579^{23}_{20}	1.5050^{27}	i	v	v	....	....		B6[3], 1960
b812	—,1-hydroxy-methyl-4-isopropyl-	Cumic alcohol. $C_{10}H_{14}O$. See b202	150.22	....	28	249	0.9818^{18}_4	1.5210^{20}	δ	∞	∞	....	....		B6, 543
b813	—,1-hydroxy-2-methyl-3,4,5-trichloro-*	$C_7H_5Cl_3O$. See b202	211.48	nd (lig)	77	....	....	....	δ	....	....	s	....	os v alk s lig s^h	B6[1], 175
b814	—,1-hydroxy-4-methyl-2,3,5-trichloro-*	$C_7H_5Cl_3O$. See b202	211.48	nd (aa or lig)	66–7	....	....	....	δ	....	....	s	....	os v alk s	B6, 404
b815	—,2-hydroxy-4-methyl-1,3,5-trichloro-*	$C_7H_5Cl_3O$. See b202	211.48	nd (w), pl (peth)	47	265 162–3[28]	....	....	s^h δ	s	s	....	δ	chl s aa s^h peth δ	B6[2], 356
Ω b816	—,hydroxy-(pentamethyl)-*	$C_{11}H_{16}O$. See b202	164.25	nd (al, peth or ace) λ^{al} 280.5 (3.20)	128	267	....	....	i	....	....	....	....		B6[1], 270
b817	—,1-hydroxy-4-pentyl-*	$C_{11}H_{16}O$. See b202	164.25		23	250.5[760] 119–20[3]	0.960^{20}_4	1.5272^{25}	i	s	s	....	....	peth δ	B6[3], 1950
b818	—,1-hydroxy-4(1-propenyl)-*	Anol. $C_9H_{10}O$. See b202	134.18	pl (w), lf λ^{al} 259 (4.27), 289 (3.45)	93–4	250d 140–5[15]	....	....	$δ^h$	s	s	....	....	os s	B6, 566
b819	—,1-hydroxy-2-propyl-*	$C_9H_{12}O$. See b202	136.20	....	....	220[760] 106.7[10]	1.015^{20}_4	....	δ	s	s	....	....		B6[2], 469

For explanations, symbols and abbreviations see beginning of table. For structural formulas see end of table.

No.	Name	Synonyms and Formula	Mol. wt.	Color, crystalline form, specific rotation and λ_{max} (log ε)	m.p. °C	b.p. °C	Density	n_D	w	al	eth	ace	bz	other solvents	Ref.
	Benzene														
Ω b820	—,1-hydroxy-3-propyl-*	$C_9H_{12}O$. See b202	136.20		26	228^{760} 111.2^{10}	0.987^{20}	1.5223^{20}	δ	s	s				B6, 499
b821	—,1-hydroxy-4-propyl-*	$C_9H_{12}O$. See b202	136.20		22	232.6^{760} 111.7^{10}	1.009_4^{20}	1.5379^{25}	δ	s	s				B6², 469
b822	—,1-hydroxy-2,3,4,6-tetra-methyl-*	Isodurenol. $C_{10}H_{14}O$. See b202	150.22	cr (peth) λ^{al} 280.2 (3.23)	80–1	230–50					s				B6, 546
Ω b823	—,1-hydroxy-2,3,5,6-tetra-methyl-*	Durenol. $C_{10}H_{14}O$. See b202.	150.22	nd (lig), pr (al) λ^{al} 276 (3.08)	118–9	247^{760}								peth, aa s	B6³, 1919
Ω b824	—,2-hydroxy-1,3,5-tri-tert-butyl-	$C_{18}H_{30}O$. See b202.	262.44	cr (al, peth) λ^{al} 273 (3.3), 281 sh (3.2)	131	278^{760} 130^{15}	0.864_4^{27}		i	s^h		s		os s alk i	B6³, 2094
Ω b825	—,1-hydroxy-2,4,5-trimethyl-*	Pseudocumenol. $C_9H_{12}O$. See b202	136.20	nd (lig)	72	232^{760}			i	v	v				B6, 509
b826	—,—,acetate	$C_{11}H_{14}O_2$. See b202.	178.23	nd (peth)	34–4.5	245–6				s	s			peth s^h	B6², 482
Ω b827	—,2-hydroxy-1,3,5-trimethyl-*	Mesitol. $C_9H_{12}O$. See b202.	136.20	nd (peth or MeOH) λ^{cy} 284.5 (3.28)	72	221 sub			δ	v	v			alk s	B6², 483
Ω b828	—,iodo-*	Phenyl iodide. C_6H_5I. See b202	204.01	λ^{al} 227.5 (4.08)	−31.27	188.3^{760} 75^{10}	1.8308_4^{20}	1.6200^{20}	i	s	∞	∞	∞	CCl_4, lig ∞ chl s	B5², 165
b829	—,(2-iodoetho-xy)-*	C_8H_9IO. See b202	248.07	cr (dil al)	31–2									os s	B6¹, 81
Ω b830	—,1-iodo-2-methoxy-*	C_7H_7IO. See b202	234.04	λ^{cy} 269 (3.38), 275.5 (3.53), 283 (3.51)		$239–40^{730}$ $91–2^2$	1.8^{20}				v	v	v	chl, lig v	B6², 198
Ω b831	—,1-iodo-3-methoxy-*	C_7H_7IO. See b202	234.04	λ^{cy} 274.5 (3.43), 282 (3.41)		$244–5$ 123^{14}					v	v			B6¹, 109
Ω b832	—,1-iodo-4-methoxy-*	C_7H_7IO. See b202	234.04	lf (al), nd (MeOH) λ^{cy} 279 (3.20), 288 (3.08)	53	237^{726} 139^{25}				s^h	s				B6³, 774
b833	—,1-iodomethyl-2-methyl-*	C_8H_9I. See b202	232.07	nd (eth), (peth)	33–4							s^h		peth s^h	B5², 286
b834	—,1-iodomethyl-4-methyl-*	C_8H_9I. See b202	232.07	nd (eth), (peth)	46–7				i			s^h	s	peth s^h	B5², 302
Ω b835	—,1-iodo-2-nitro-*	$C_6H_4INO_2$. See b202.	249.01	ye rh nd (al) λ^{al} 260 sh (3.5), 310 (3.1)	54	$288–9^{729}$ 162^{18}	1.9186^{75}		i	s	s				B5², 190
Ω b836	—,1-iodo-3-nitro-*	$C_6H_4INO_2$. See b202.	249.01	mcl pr λ^{al} 262 (3.81), 308 (3.00)	(i) 38.5 (st) (ii) 9.9 (unst)	280 153^{14}	1.9477_4^{50}		i	s	s			aa s	B5², 191
Ω b837	—,1-iodo-4-nitro-*	$C_6H_4INO_2$. See b202.	249.01	ye nd (al) λ^{al} 223 (3.9), 294 (4.0)	174	289^{772}			i	s				aa s	B5², 191
Ω b838	—,iodoso-*	C_6H_5IO. See b202	220.01	ye pw	210 exp				s^h	s^h	i	i	i	peth i	B5², 166
b839	—,1-iodo-2-triazo-*	$C_6H_4IN_3$. See b202	245.03	ye		$90–10^{0.9}$	1.8893_4^{25}	1.6631^{25}		s				os s	B5¹, 142
Ω b840	—,iodoxy-*	$C_6H_5IO_2$. See b202	236.01	nd (w)	236–7 exp				s^h	i		i	i	aa s^h chl i	B5², 167
b841	—,isobutoxy-*	Isobutyl phenyl ether. $C_{10}H_{14}O$. See b202	150.22			196	0.9240_{15}^{24}	1.4932^{24}				s	s	peth δ	B6², 146
b842	—,1-isobutoxy-2-nitro-*	$C_{10}H_{13}NO_3$. See b202.	195.22	ye oil		275–80	1.1361^{20}				s				B6, 218
Ω b843	—,isobutyl-*	$C_{10}H_{14}$. See b202	134.22	λ^{iso} 248 (2.1), 259 (2.3), 265 (2.2), 268 (2.2)	−51.5	172.8^{760} 53.1^{10}	0.8532_4^{20}	1.4866^{20}	i	∞	∞	∞	∞	peth, CCl_4 ∞	B5, 319
Ω b844	—,isocyano-	Phenyl isocyanate. C_7H_5NO. See b202	119.12	λ^{hx} 226 (4.04), 256 (2.59), 270 (2.76), 277 (2.67)		$162–3^{751}$ 55^{13}	$1.0956_4^{19.6}$	$1.5368_4^{19.6}$	d	d	s				J1934, 2011
b845	—,isopropenyl-*	C_9H_{10}. See b202	118.18	λ^{peth} 242.5 (4.04), 277 (2.44)	−23.21	165.4^{760} 48.5^{10}	0.9106_4^{20}	1.5386^{20}	i	s	s	∞	∞	peth, CCl_4 ∞	B5², 374
Ω b846	—,isopropoxy-*	$C_9H_{12}O$. See b202	136.20	λ^{hx} 273 (3.28)	−33.05	176.8^{760}	0.9408_4^{20}	1.4975^{20}	s	s	s	s	s		B6², 145
Ω b847	—,isopropyl-	Cumene. C_9H_{12}. See b202.	120.20	λ^{hx} 254 (2.3), 251 (2.4), 267 (2.3)	−96	152.4^{760} 38.2^{10}	0.8618_4^{20}	1.4915^{20}	i	∞	∞	∞	∞	CCl_4, peth ∞	B5², 306
b848	—,1-isopropyl-2-methyl-	o-Cymene. $C_{10}H_{14}$. See b202	134.22	λ^{iso} 257 (2.2), 263 (2.4), 267 (2.2), 270 (2.3)	−71.54	178.15^{760} 57.3^{10}	0.8766_4^{20}	1.5006^{20}	i	∞	∞	∞	∞	peth, CCl_4 ∞	B5¹, 322
b849	—,1-isopropyl-3-methyl-	m-Cymene. $C_{10}H_{14}$. See b202	134.22	λ^{iso} 257 (2.2), 264 (2.4), 268 (2.2), 271 (2.3)	−63.75	175.14^{760} 55.0^{10}	0.8610_4^{20}	1.4930^{20}	i	∞	∞	∞	∞	CCl_4, peth ∞ chl s	B5², 322

For explanations, symbols and abbreviations see beginning of table. For structural formulas see end of table.

No.	Name	Synonyms and Formula	Mol. wt.	Color, crystalline form, specific rotation and λ_{max} (log ε)	m.p. °C	b.p. °C	Density	n_D	w	al	eth	ace	bz	other solvents	Ref.
	Benzene														
Ω b850	—,1-isopropyl-4-methyl-	p-Cymene. $C_{10}H_{14}$. See b202	134.22	λ^{hx} 261 (2.4), 267 (2.6), 274 (2.6)	−67.94	177.1[760] 56.3[10]	0.8573$_4^{20}$	1.4909[20]	i	∞	∞	∞	∞	CCl_4, peth ∞ chl s	B5[2], 322
b851	—,4-isopropyl-1-methyl-2-nitro-	$C_{10}H_{13}NO_2$. See b202	179.22	....	....	126[10]	1.0744$_4^{20}$	1.5301[20]	i	v	v	...	...	....	B5[2], 326
b852	—,1-isopropyl-2-nitro-	2-Nitrocumene. $C_9H_{11}NO_2$. See b202	165.19	pa ye λ^{iso} 247 (3.62)	....	103[9]	1.101[12]	1.5259[20]	i	...	...	s	s	aa s	B5[2], 307
b853	—,1-isopropyl-4-nitro-	$C_9H_{11}NO_2$. See b202	165.19	pa ye oil λ^{gas} 251.3 (3.96)	....	122[9]	1.0830$_4^{20}$	1.5367[20]	i	...	...	s	s	lig s	B5[2], 308
Ω b854	—,mercapto-*	Thiophenol. Benzenethiol. C_6H_6S See b202	110.18	λ^{al} 237 (3.85)	−14.8	168.7[760] 46.4[10]	1.0766$_4^{20}$	1.5893[20]	i	s	s	...	s	....	B6[2], 284
Ω b855	—,1-mercapto-4-methoxy-*	4-Mercaptoanisole. C_7H_8OS. See b202	140.22			227–9 89–90[5]	1.1313$_4^{25}$	1.5801[25]		s	s	s	s	....	B6[2], 852
b856	—,1-mercapto-2-nitro-*	$C_6H_5NO_2S$. See b202	155.18	ye nd (peth or CCl_4) λ^{al} 270.5 (3.76), 354 (3.57)	58.5 (61)	....				s	s	s	s	alk s	B6[2], 303
b857	—,1-mercapto-4-nitro-*	$C_6H_5NO_2S$. See b202	155.18	(eth, chl, ace) λ^{al} 317.5 (4.38)	79	....			s[h]	s	v	v	...	alk s lig, aa δ	B6[2], 309
b858	—,2-mercapto-1,3,5-trinitro-*	Thiopicric acid. $C_6H_3N_3O_6S$. See b202	245.17	ye nd	114				v d[h]	v d[h]	v	v	v	chl v peth i	B6[2], 316
Ω b859	—,methoxy-*	Anisole. C_7H_8O. See b202	108.15		−37.5	155	0.9961$_4^{20}$	1.5179[20]	i	s	∞	v	s	....	B6[2], 139
b860	—,1-methoxy-4-(3-methylbutyl)-*	p-Isopentylanisole. $C_{12}H_{13}O$. See b202	178.28			121[14]			i				s	....	B6[1], 296
Ω b861	—,1-methoxy-2-nitro-*	$C_7H_7NO_3$. See b202	153.14	λ^{cy} 249 (3.53), 304 (3.40)	10.45	276.8[757] 144[4]	1.2540$_4^{20}$	1.5161[20]	i	∞	∞	...	...	....	B6[2], 209
Ω b862	—,1-methoxy-3-nitro-*	$C_7H_7NO_3$. See b202	153.14	nd (al), pl (bz-lig) λ^{cy} 260 (3.79), 313 (3.38)	38–9	258	1.373[18]		i	s	v	...	...	....	B6[2], 214
Ω b863	—,1-methoxy-4-nitro-*	$C_7H_7NO_3$. See b202	153.14	pr (al), nd (dil al) λ^{al} 306 (4.04)	54	274 (258–60)	1.2192$_4^{60}$	1.5070[60]	i	v	v	...	...	peth δ	B6[2], 220
Ω b864	—,1-methoxy-4-propenyl-* (trans)	Anethole. $C_{10}H_{12}O$. See b202	148.21	lf (al) λ^{iso} 258 (4.25)	21.35	234.5[763] 115[12]	0.9882$_4^{20}$	1.5615[20]	δ	∞	∞	s	v	os ∞	B6[2], 523
b865	—,1-methoxy-2,3,4,6-tetrabromo-*	$C_7H_4Br_4O$. See b202	423.75	nd (dil al or aa)	113–4 (104)	340			i	s	...	...	v	....	B6[2], 196
b866	—,1-methoxy-2,3,4,5-tetrachloro-*	$C_7H_4Cl_4O$. See b202	245.92	cr (MeOH)	83	....			i	v	...	...	v	MeOH v	B6[2], 182
b867	—,1-methoxy-2,3,5,6-tetrachloro-*	$C_7H_4Cl_4O$. See b202	245.92	nd (al)	89–90	....			i	s	v	...	v	MeOH s[h]	B6[2], 182
b868	—,2-methoxy-1,3,4,5-tetrachloro-*	$C_7H_4Cl_4O$. See b202	245.92	nd (MeOH), pr (al)	64–5	....			i	s[h]	v	...	v[h]	MeOH s[h]	B6[2], 182
b869	—,1-methoxy-2,3,4-tribromo-*	$C_7H_5Br_3O$. See b202	344.84	nd (al)	106	....			i	s	...	v	v	os v chl s	B6[2], 192
b870	—,1-methoxy-2,3,5-tribromo-*	$C_7H_5Br_3O$. See b202	344.84	pr (dil al)	82	305–12			i	v	...	v	v	os v	B6[2], 192
b871	—,1-methoxy-2,4,5-tribromo-*	$C_7H_5Br_3O$. See b202	344.84	nd (al)	105	306–9[775]			i	s	...	s	s	os s	B6[2], 192
Ω b872	—,2-methoxy-1,3,5-tribromo-*	$C_7H_5Br_3O$. See b202	344.84	nd (al) λ^{al} 282 (3.00), 289.5 (3.00)	88	297–9	2.491		δ	δ	...	v	v	os s	B6[2], 193
b873	—,5-methoxy-1,2,3-tribromo-*	$C_7H_5Br_3O$. See b202	344.84	cr (al)	91–4	300–10			i	s	...	v	v	os s	B6[2], 195
b874	—,1-methoxy-2,3,5-trichloro-*	$C_7H_5Cl_3O$. See b202	211.48	nd (al)	84	....			i	s	...	v	...	os s	B6[2], 180
b875	—,1-methoxy-2,4,5-trichloro-*	$C_7H_5Cl_3O$. See b202	211.48	nd (dil al)	77.5	252–5[747]			i	v	...	v	...	os s	B6[2], 180
b876	—,2-methoxy-1,3,4-trichloro-*	$C_7H_5Cl_3O$. See b202	211.48	pr (al)	45	227–9[756]			i	s	...	...	s	os s	B6[2], 180
Ω b877	—,2-methoxy-1,3,5-trichloro-*	$C_7H_5Cl_3O$. See b202	211.48	mcl nd (al) λ^{al} 280.5 (2.94), 287.5 (2.94)	61–2 (65)	240[738]	1.640		i	s	...	v	v	os s	B6[2], 181
b878	—,2-methoxy-1,3,5-triiodo-*	$C_7H_5I_3O$. See b202	485.83	lf (bz), nd (eth or al) λ^{al} 277 sh (2.99)	98–9	....			i	v	...	...	v	os s	B6[2], 204
b879	—,1-methoxy-2,3,4-trinitro-*	$C_7H_5N_3O_7$. See b202	243.13	pa ye lf (al)	155	exp			i	s[h] δ	...	...	v	δ aa v lig i	B6[1], 129
b880	—,1-methoxy-2,3,5-trinitro-*	$C_7H_5N_3O_7$. See b202	243.13	ye nd (al)	106.8	....	1.618[15]		s[h]	v	...	...	s	v	B6[2], 253

For explanations, symbols and abbreviations see beginning of table. For structural formulas see end of table.

No.	Name	Synonyms and Formula	Mol. wt.	Color, crystalline form, specific rotation and λ_{max} (log ε)	m.p. °C	b.p. °C	Density	n_D	w	al	eth	ace	bz	other solvents	Ref.
	Benzene														
b881	—,1-methoxy-2,4,5-trinitro-*	$C_7H_5N_3O_7$. See b202	243.13	ye (al)	106–7	....	....	....	v^h	...	s	...	s	chl, aa s lig i	$B6^2$, 253
Ω b882	—,2-methoxy-1,3,5-trinitro-*	$C_7H_5N_3O_7$. See b202	243.13	(i) nd (dil MeOH) (ii) 56–7 (MeOH) $\lambda^{al-KOEt}$ 410 (4.4), 490 (4.2)	(i) 68.5–9.0 (ii) 56–7		1.4947^{80}	....	i	v^h	s	...	v	chl v	$B6^2$, 280
—	—,methyl-*......	see **Toluene**													
b883	—,(3-methyl-butoxy)-*	$C_{11}H_{16}O$. See b202	164.25			225^{760} (216^{718})	0.9198^{22}	1.4872^{20}	s						$B6^2$, 146
Ω b884	—,(2-methyl-2-butyl)-	$C_{11}H_{16}$. See b202	148.25			192.4^{760} $71–2^{12}$	0.8587^{20}_4	1.4934^{20}	i	∞	∞				$B5^2$, 333
b885	—,(3-methyl-butyl)-*	$C_{11}H_{16}$. See b202	148.25			199^{760}	0.8558^{20}_4	1.4853^{20}	i	s	s		v		$B5^2$, 332
b886	—,(4-methyl-pentyl)-*	$C_{12}H_{18}$. See b202	162.28			$214–5^{740}$	0.8568^{16}		i	s	s		v		**B5**, 444
b887	—,1-methyl-2-propyl-*	$C_{10}H_{14}$. See b202	134.22	λ^{iso} 263 (2.2), 271 (2.1)	−60.2	185^{760} 63.5^{10}	0.8744^{20}	1.4998^{20}							$B5^2$, 321
b888	—,1-methyl-3-propyl-*	$C_{10}H_{14}$. See b202	134.22	λ^{iso} 259 (2.3), 265 (2.4), 268 (2.3), 272 (2.4)		182^{760} 61.4^{10}	0.8610^{20}	1.4936^{20}							$B5^2$, 321
b889	—,1-methyl-4-propyl-*	$C_{10}H_{14}$. See b202	134.22	λ^{iso} 259 (2.5), 268 (2.7), 274 (2.7)	−63.6	183^{760} 61.9^{10}	0.8584^{20}	1.4919^{20}	i	s	s		v		$B5^2$, 321
b890	—,methylthio-*....	Thioanisole. Methyl phenyl sulfide. C_7H_8S. See b202	124.22	λ^{al} 254 (3.98)	....	193^{760} 74^{10}	1.0579^{20}_4	1.5868^{20}	i	s		v		os s	$B6^2$, 287
Ω b891	—,nitro-*........	$C_6H_5NO_2$. See b202	123.11	λ^{al} 260 (3.91)	5.7	210.8^{760}	1.2037^{20}_4	1.5562^{20}	δ	v	v	v	v		$B5^2$, 171
b892	—,(α-nitro-isopropyl)-	$C_9H_{11}NO_2$. See b202	165.19			224d $125–7^{15}$	1.1025^{20}_0	1.5209^{20}	i			s	s		$B5^2$, 308
Ω b893	—,nitro(penta-chloro)-*	Brassicol. Tritisan. $C_6Cl_5NO_2$. See b202	295.34	cr (al)	144		1.718^{25}_4		i	δ		...	s	chl s	C50, 3196
Ω b894	—,nitroso-*	C_6H_5NO. See b202	107.11	rh or mcl (al-eth) λ^{chl} 750 (1.65)	68–9	$57–9^{18}$			i	s	s	s	s	lig v	$B5^2$, 169
Ω b895	—,1-nitro-2,3,5,6-tetrachloro-*	$C_6HCl_4NO_2$. See b202	260.89	cr (al)	99–100		1.744^{25}_4		i	s		...	s	chl s	C29, 6884
Ω b896	—,1-nitro-2-triazo-*	$C_6H_4N_4O_2$. See b202	164.12	ye nd (bz-al) pr (al) λ^{al} 241 (4.2), 264 (3.8), 322 (3.5)	53–5						v		v	aa v chl s	**B5**, 278
Ω b897	—,1-nitro-3-triazo-*	$C_6H_4N_4O_2$. See b202	164.12	wh nd (dil al or peth) λ^{al} 245 (4.3), 318 (3.3)	56				i	v	v	...	v	CS_2 v	**B5**, 278
Ω b898	—,1-nitro-4-triazo-*	$C_6H_4N_4O_2$. See b202	164.12	wh pl (dil al) λ^{al} 306 (4.02), 400 (2.4)	75				i	v^h	v^h	...	v^h	CS_2, aa v^h	**B5**, 278
b899	—,1-nitro-2,3,4-tribromo-*	$C_6H_2Br_3NO_2$. See b202	359.82	cr (al)	85.4				i	s	v	...	v	AcOEt v	**B5**, 251
b900	—,1-nitro-2,3,5-tribromo-*	$C_6H_2Br_3NO_2$. See b202	359.82	nd	119.5 (81)				i		v		v		**B5**, 251
b901	—,1-nitro-2,4,5-tribromo-*	$C_6H_2Br_3NO_2$. See b202	359.82	nd (al)	95–5.5	sub			i	v^h	v	...	v	CS_2 v	**B5**, 251
b902	—,2-nitro-1,3,4-tribromo-*	$C_6H_2Br_3NO_2$. See b202	359.82	pl or pr (eth-al)	185 sub				i	s^h	v	...	v		**B5**, 251
b903	—,2-nitro-1,3,5-tribromo-*	$C_6H_2Br_3NO_2$. See b202	359.82	mcl pr (chl)	125	177^{11}			i	$δ^h$	s			chl v aa s^h	$B5^2$, 190
b904	—,5-nitro-1,2,3-tribromo-*	$C_6H_2Br_3NO_2$. See b202	359.82	tcl (eth-al)	112	sub	2.645		i		v	...	v		$B5^1$, 133
Ω b905	—,1-nitro-2,3,4-trichloro-*	$C_6H_2Cl_3NO_2$. See b202	226.45	nd (al)	55.5				i	δ		...		CS_2 s	$B5^2$, 186
Ω b906	—,1-nitro-2,4,5-trichloro-*	$C_6H_2Cl_3NO_2$. See b202	226.45	pr (al or CS_2), nd (al)	57–8	288	1.790^{22}		i	s^h δ	s	...	s	CS_2 s	$B5^2$, 187
b907	—,2-nitro-1,3,4-trichloro-*	$C_6H_2Cl_3NO_2$. See b202	226.45	nd (al)	89				i	s		...		lig δ	$B5^2$, 187
b908	—,2-nitro-1,3,5-trichloro-*	$C_6H_2Cl_3NO_2$. See b202	226.45	nd (al) λ^{al} 345 (2.3)	71				i	s^h δ	s			CS_2, lig v	$B5^2$, 187
b909	—,5-nitro-1,2,3-trichloro-*	$C_6H_2Cl_3NO_2$. See b202	226.45	pa ye tcl (al)	72.5		1.807		i	s^h		...			$B5^2$, 187
b910	—,1-nitro-2,3,5-triiodo-*	$C_6H_2I_3NO_2$. See b202	500.80	ye pr	124				i	s^h	s	...		os s	**B5**, 256
b911	—,1-nitro-2,4,5-triiodo-*	$C_6H_2I_3NO_2$. See b202	500.80	pa ye nd (CS_2)	178				i	δ	δ	δ		CS_2 s^h chl δ	**B5**, 256
b912	—,2-nitro-1,3,4-triiodo-*	$C_6H_2I_3NO_2$. See b202	500.80	nd (aa), pr (CS_2)	137				i			...		CS_2, aa s^h	**B5**, 256

For explanations, symbols and abbreviations see beginning of table. For structural formulas see end of table.

Benzene

No.	Name	Synonyms and Formula	Mol. wt.	Color, crystalline form, specific rotation and λ_{max} (log ε)	m.p. °C	b.p. °C	Density	n_D	w	al	eth	ace	bz	other solvents	Ref.
b913	—,5-nitro-1,2,3-triiodo-*	$C_6H_2I_3NO_2$. See b202	500.80	ye pr (chl), nd (al)	167	....	3.256	....	i	δ	v	...	v	aa v^h chl s	B5[2], 192
b914	—,1-nitro-2,3,5-trimethyl-*	$C_9H_{11}NO_2$. See b202	165.19	pr (al)	20	139–40[7]				s					B5, 404
b915	—,1-nitro-2,4,5-trimethyl-*	$C_9H_{11}NO_2$. See b202	165.19	ye nd (al)	71	265				s				peth s	B5[2], 313
Ω b916	—,2-nitro-1,3,5-trimethyl-*	$C_9H_{11}NO_2$. See b202	165.19	rh nd (al) λ^{iso} 250 (3.34)	44	255[760]	1.51			v^h					B5[2], 316
b917	—,pentaamino-*	$C_6H_{11}N_5$. See b202	153.19	dk br nd	228d	....			s	i	i			os i	B13[2], 155
b918	—,pentabromo-*	C_6HBr_5. See b202	472.62	wh nd (aa or al)	160–1	sub				δ s^h	δ		s	chl s lig, aa δ	B5[1], 117
b919	—,pentachloro-*	C_6HCl_5. See b202	250.34	nd (al) λ^{al} 288 (2.56), 298 (2.54)	86	277	1.8342[16.5]		i	s^h i	δ		δ	CS_2, chl δ	B5[2], 157
b920	—,pentaethyl-*	$C_{16}H_{26}$. See b202	218.39		< −20	277	0.8995[19/19]	1.5127[20]	i	v	v		v		B5[2], 358
b921	—,pentaiodo-*	C_6HI_5. See b202	707.60	nd (al)	172	sub			i	δ	δ		s	chl, aa s	B5, 229
Ω b922	—,pentamethyl-*	$C_{11}H_{16}$. See b202	148.25	pr (al) λ^{hx} 270 (1.3)	54.3	232[760] 100[10]	0.917[20]	1.527[20]	i	v			v		B5[2], 336
b923	—,pentoxy-*	$C_{11}H_{16}O$. See b202	164.25			230[756] 111[17]	0.9270[20/20]	1.4947[20]	i	s		s			B6[1], 82
Ω b924	—,pentyl-*	$C_{11}H_{16}$. See b202	148.25		−75	205.4[760] 80.6[10]	0.8585[20/4]	1.4878[20]	i	∞	∞	∞	∞	CCl_4, peth ∞	B5[2], 331
b924[1]	—,(2-pentyl)-*	$C_{11}H_{16}$. See b202	148.25	λ^{al} 247.5 (2.06), 255 (2.20), 258 (2.31), 264 (2.20), 267.5 (2.21)	....	198–9[757]	0.8594[21/4]	1.4875[21]	i	s	s				B5, 434
Ω b925	—,propenyl-(cis)*	C_9H_{10}. See b202	118.18		−60.5	69[28]	0.9088[20]	1.5420[20]	i	∞	∞	∞	∞	peth, CCl_4 ∞	B5[2], 371
b925[1]	—,—(trans)*	C_9H_{10}. See b202	118.18	λ^{al} 249.5 (4.22)	−27.1	175–6	0.9019[25]	1.5508[20]	i	∞	∞	∞	∞		B5[2], 371
Ω b926	—,1-propenyl-2,4,5-trimethoxy-*(α-form)	α-Asaron. $C_{12}H_{16}O_3$. See b202	208.24	mcl nd (w)	67 (62)	296[760] 167–8[12]	1.165[20]	1.5683[20]	s^h	s	s			peth, chl, CCl_4 s	B6[2], 1092
Ω b927	—,propoxy-*	Phenyl propyl ether. $C_9H_{12}O$. See b202	136.20		−27.09	189.9[760]	0.9474[20/4]	1.5014[20]		s	s				B6[2], 145
Ω b928	—,propyl-*	C_9H_{12}. See b202	120.20	λ^{iso} 249 (2.07), 261.5 (2.31), 264.5 (2.19), 268 (2.20)	−99.5	159.2[760] 43.3[10]	0.8620[20/4]	1.4920[20]	i	∞	∞	∞	∞	peth, CCl_4 ∞	B5[2], 303
b929	—,1,2,3,5-tetrabromo-*	$C_6H_2Br_4$. See b202	393.72	nd (al)	99–100	329			i	s^h	s		s	CS_2 s	B5[1], 117
b930	—,1,2,4,5-tetrabromo-*	$C_6H_2Br_4$. See b202	393.72	mcl pr (CS_2)	182		3.072[20]		i	δ	v				B5[2], 164
Ω b931	—,1,2,3,4-tetrachloro-*	$C_6H_2Cl_4$. See b202	215.90	nd (al) λ^{al} 274 (2.42), 280 (2.52), 291 (2.46)	47.5	254[760]			i	s^h δ	v			CS_2, aa, lig v	B5[2], 156
b932	—,1,2,3,5-tetrachloro-*	$C_6H_2Cl_4$. See b202	215.90	nd (al) λ^{al} 274 (2.32), 281 (2.50), 291 (2.44)	54.5	246			s^h	δ	s		s	CS_2, lig v	B5[2], 157
Ω b933	—,1,2,4,5-tetrachloro-*	$C_6H_2Cl_4$. See b202	215.90	nd, mcl pr (eth, al or bz) λ^{al} 276 (2.81), 285 (3.02), 294 (3.02)	139.5–40.5	243–6 (240)	1.858[22]		i	δ^h	v		s	chl, CS_2 s	B5[2], 157
b934	—,1,2,3,4-tetraethyl-*	$C_{14}H_{22}$. See b202	190.33		11.6	251[734] 121.7[14]	0.8875[20/4]	1.5125[20]	i	v	s				B5[2], 344
b935	—,1,2,4,5-tetraethyl-*	$C_{14}H_{22}$. See b202	190.33		10	250	0.8788[20/4]	1.5054[20]	i	v	v				B5, 455
b936	—,1,2,3,5-tetrahydroxy-*	$C_6H_6O_4$. See b202	142.11	nd (w), lf (eth AcOEt)	−165–7				v	v		v	i	AcOEt s chl, aa i	B6[1], 570
b937	—,1,2,4,5-tetrahydroxy-*	$C_6H_6O_4$. See b202	142.11	lf (w or aa)	232–3				v	v	v			aa δ	B6[2], 1120
b938	—,1,2,3,4-tetraiodo-*	$C_6H_2I_4$. See b202	581.70	pr (CS_2 or eth-aa)	136 (114)	sub			i	v	v			chl v	B5, 229
b939	—,1,2,3,5-tetraiodo-*	$C_6H_2I_4$. See b202	581.70	pr (eth or aa)	148	sub			i	δ	δ			aa v^h chl δ	B5, 229
b940	—,1,2,4,5-tetraiodo-*	$C_6H_2I_4$. See b202	581.70	pr (bz), nd (eth)	254 (165)	sub (vac)			i	δ	δ			CS_2 v aa s	B5, 229
Ω b941	—,1,2,3,4-tetramethyl-*	Prehnitene. $C_{10}H_{14}$. See b202	134.22	cr (peth) λ^{al} 268 (2.50), 272.5 (2.41), 276.5 (2.39)	−6.25	205[760] 79.4[10]	0.9052[20/4]	1.5203[20]	i	∞	∞	∞	∞	CCl_4, peth ∞	B5[2], 329
Ω b942	—,1,2,3,5-tetramethyl-*	Isodurene. $C_{10}H_{14}$. See b202	134.22	λ^{al} 269 (2.7), 275 (2.7), 278 (2.3)	−23.68	198[760] 74.4[10]	0.8903[20/4]	1.5130[20]	i	∞	∞	∞	∞	CCl_4, peth ∞	B5[3], 976

For explanations, symbols and abbreviations see beginning of table. For structural formulas see end of table.

No.	Name	Synonyms and Formula	Mol. wt.	Color, crystalline form, specific rotation and λ_{max} (log ε)	m.p. °C	b.p. °C	Density	n_D	Solubility						Ref.
									w	al	eth	ace	bz	other solvents	
	Benzene														
Ω b943	—,1,2,4,5-tetra-methyl-*	Durene. $C_{10}H_{14}$. See b202...	134.22	λ^{al} 268 (2.8), 272 (2.8), 278 (2.84)	79.24	196.8[760] 73.5[10]	0.8380_4^{81} 0.8875_4^{20}	1.4790^{81} 1.5116^{20}	i	∞	∞	∞	∞	CCl_4, peth ∞	B5², 329
Ω b944	—,1,3,5-triacetyl-	$C_{12}H_{12}O_3$. See b202.......	204.23	nd (w, aa or al) λ^{al} 226 (4.6), 294 (2.7)	163	....	....	....	s^h	s^h	δ	...	...	aa v	B7², 831
b945	—,1,2,3-triamino-*.	$C_6H_9N_3$. See b202	123.16	cr (dil HCl)	103	336	....	....	v	v	v	...	...		B13², 145
b946	—,1,2,4-triamino-*.	$C_6H_9N_3$. See b202	123.16	pl or lf (chl)	95–8 (99)	340	....	....	v	v	δ	...	...	chl s	B13², 146
b947	—,triazo-*.......	Azidobenzene. Phenyl azide. $C_6H_5N_3$. See b202	119.13	pa ye oil λ^{cy} 248 (3.9), 256 (3.1), 278 (3.3)	−27.5	70[11]	1.0880_{20}^{20}	1.5589^{25}	i	δ	δ	...	...		B5², 207
b948	—,1,2,3-tri-bromo-*	$C_6H_3Br_3$. See b202	314.82	pl (al)	87.8	....	2.658	....	i	δ^h	v	...	...		B5¹, 117
b949	—,1,2,4-tri-bromo-*	$C_6H_3Br_3$. See b202	314.82	nd (al or eth)	44–5	275	....	....	i	s	v	v	δ	CCl_4, CS_2 v	B5², 164
Ω b950	—,1,3,5-tri-bromo-*	$C_6H_3Br_3$. See b202	314.82	nd or pr (al) λ^{al} 267 (2.3), 277 (2.4), 289 (2.1)	121.5–2.5 (124, sub)	271[765]	....	....	i	δ^h	s	...	s	chl s	B5², 164
b951	—,2,4,6-tri-bromo-1,3,5-trimethyl-*	$C_9H_9Br_3$. See b202	356.90	tcl nd (al or bz)	227–8	....	....	....	i	i	s	...	s		B5², 315
Ω b952	—,1,2,3-tri-chloro-*	$C_6H_3Cl_3$. See b202	181.45	pl (al) λ^{al} 265 (2.10), 273 (2.20), 280 (2.10)	53–4	218–9	....	....	i	δ	v	...	v	CS_2 v	B5², 156
Ω b953	—,1,2,4-tri-chloro-*	$C_6H_3Cl_3$. See b202	181.45	rh λ^{al} 270 (2.54), 278 (2.75), 287 (2.72)	16.95	213.5[760] 84.8[10]	1.4542_4^{20}	1.5717^{20}	i	δ	v	...	v		B5², 156
Ω b954	—,1,3,5-tri-chloro-*	$C_6H_3Cl_3$. See b202	181.45	nd λ^{al} 266 (2.26), 273 (2.37), 281 (2.23)	63–4	208[763]	....	....	i	δ	v	...	v	CS_2, lig v	B5², 156
b955	—,1,2,3-trichloro-4,5,6-trihydroxy-*	$C_6H_3Cl_3O_3$. See b202	229.45	nd (al or bz) nd (+3w, w)	185	....	....	....	v^h	v	v	...	δ	chl, CCl_4, CS_2 δ	B6, 1084
b956	—,1,2,4-trichloro-3,5,6-trihydroxy-*	$C_6H_3Cl_3O_3$. See b202	229.45	nd (bz or aa)	160	....	....	....	δ	v	v	...	...	peth δ	B6², 1072
b957	—,1,3,5-trichloro-2,4,6-trihydroxy-*	$C_6H_3Cl_3O_3$. See b202	229.45	cr (al)	136	sub	....	....	i	s	v	...	i		B6, 1104
b958	—,1,3,5-triethoxy-*	Phloroglucinol triethyl ether. $C_{12}H_{18}O_3$. See b202	210.28	cr (al, dil, al)	43.5	175[24]	....	....	i	v	v	...	...		B6², 1079
b959	—,1,2,4-triethyl-*	$C_{12}H_{18}$. See b202	162.28			217.5[755] 99[15]	0.8738_4^{20}	1.5024^{20}	i	s	s	...	...		B5², 340
Ω b960	—,1,3,5-triethyl-*..	$C_{12}H_{18}$. See b202	162.28	λ^{iso} 217.5 (3.94), 258 (2.18), 264 (2.31), 271 (2.23)	−66.5	216[760]	0.8631_4^{20}	1.4969^{20}	i	v	v	...	...		B5², 340
Ω b961	—,1,2,3-tri-hydroxy-*	Pyrogallol. $C_6H_6O_3$. See b202	126.11	lf or nd (bz) λ^{al} 266 (2.92)	133–4	309[760] 171[12]	1.453_4^4	1.561^{134}	v	v	v	...	i	NH_3 v	B6², 1059
b962	—,—,triacetate....	$C_{12}H_{12}O_6$. See b202..	252.23	pr (al)	165	....	....	....	i	s		...	...		B6², 1066
b963	—,1,2,4-tri-hydroxy-*	Hydroxyquinol. $C_6H_6O_3$. See b202	126.11	pl (eth), lf or pl (w) $\lambda^{w,pH=5.4}$ 288 (3.44)	140.5–1.0	....	....	....	v	v	v	...	i	CS_2, chl i	B6², 1071
b964	—,—,triacetate....	$C_{12}H_{12}O_6$. See b202........	252.23	nd (MeOH)	97–8	>300	....	....	w	s^h	v	...	...	MeOH s^h	B6², 1072
Ω b965	—,1,3,5-tri-hydroxy-*	Phloroglucinol. $C_6H_6O_3$. See b202	126.11	lf or nd (w +2) λ^{al} 269 (2.70)	117 (hyd) 218–9 (anh)	sub	1.46	....	δ	v	v	...	v	Py v	B6, 1075
b966	—,—,diacetate....	$C_{10}H_{10}O_5$. See b202...	210.19	pl (w)	104	....	....	....	s^h	s	s	s	...	lig δ	B6¹, 547
b967	—,—,triacetate....	$C_{12}H_{12}O_6$. See b202...	252.23	pr (w), nd (dil al) λ^{MeOH} 261.5 (2.56)	105–6	....	....	....	i	s^h		...	...		B6², 1079
b968	—,1,2,3-triiodo-*	$C_6H_3I_3$. See b202	455.80	nd (al), pr (bz)	116	sub	....	....	i	s	s	...	...	chl s	B5¹, 122
b969	—,1,2,4-triiodo-*	$C_6H_3I_3$. See b202	455.80	nd (al)	91.5	sub	....	....	i	s^h	s	...	...	chl s	B5¹, 122
b970	—,1,3,5-triiodo-*	$C_6H_3I_3$. See b202	455.80	nd (aa) λ^{MeOH} 232 (4.56)	184.2	sub	....	....	i	δ	δ	...	δ	aa s^h chl δ	B5¹, 122
Ω b971	—,1,2,3-tri-methoxy-*	Pyrogallol trimethyl ether. $C_9H_{12}O_3$. See b202	168.20	rh nd (al) λ^{MeOH} 267 (2.82)	48–9	235[760] 140[12]	1.1118_{45}^{45}	....	i	∞	∞	∞	∞	CCl_4, peth ∞	B6², 1066
Ω b972	—,1,3,5-tri-methoxy-*	Phloroglucinol trimethyl ether. $C_9H_{12}O_3$. See b202	168.20	pr (al), lf (peth) λ^{MeOH} 265 (2.68)	54–5	255.5[760]	....	....							B6², 1078
b973	—,1,2,3-tri-methyl-*	Hemimellitene. C_9H_{12}. See b202	120.20	λ^{iso} 195 (4.74), 204–220 (4.00)	−25.37	176.1[760] 56.7[10]	0.8944_4^{20}	1.5139^{20}	i	∞	∞	∞	∞	CCl_4, peth ∞	B5², 311

For explanations, symbols and abbreviations see beginning of table. For structural formulas see end of table.

No.	Name	Synonyms and Formula	Mol. wt.	Color, crystalline form, specific rotation and λ_{max} (log ε)	m.p. °C	b.p. °C	Density	n_D	w	al	eth	ace	bz	other solvents	Ref.
	Benzene														
Ω b974	—,1,2,4-tri-methyl-*	Pseudocumene. C_9H_{12}. See b202	120.20	λ^{iso} 196 (4.71), 204–220 (3.91)	−43.8	169.35[760] 51.6[10]	0.8758[20]	1.5048[20]	i	∞	∞	∞	∞	CCl_4, peth ∞	B5[2], 312
Ω b975	—,1,3,5-tri-methyl-*	Mesitylene. C_9H_{12}. See b202.	120.20	λ^{al} 258 (2.2), 263 (2.2), 267 (2.2), 273 (2.3)	−44.7	164.7[760] 48.7[10]	0.8652[20]	1.4994[20]	i	∞	∞	∞	∞	CCl_4, peth ∞	B5[2], 313
b976	—,1,2,3-trimethyl-4,5,6-trinitro-*	$C_9H_9N_3O_6$. See b202	255.19	pr (al)	209				i	s	...	s	s[h]		B5, 400
b977	—,1,2,4-trimethyl-3,5,6-trinitro-*	$C_9H_9N_3O_6$. See b202	255.19	rh pr (al)	185				i	δ	...	...	v[h]	to v[h]	B5[2], 316
b978	—,1,3,5-trimethyl-2,4,6-trinitro-*	Trinitromesitylene. $C_9H_9N_3O_6$. See b202	255.19	tcl nd (al), pr (ace) λ^{al} <220	238.2	415 exp			i	δ[h]	δ[h]	s	s		B5[3], 923
b979	—,1,2,3-trinitro-*	$C_6H_3N_3O_6$. See b202	213.11	ye nd or pr (MeOH)	127.5				i	s[h]	...	...			B5[2], 203
b980	—,1,2,4-trinitro-*	$C_6H_3N_3O_6$. See b202	213.11	lf (eth), pa ye pr (al) $\lambda^{5\%al}$ 235 (4.19)	61–2				δ[h]	s	s	s	v	chl v MeOH s	B5[2], 203
Ω b981	—,1,3,5-trinitro-*	$C_6H_3N_3O_6$. See b202	213.11	rh pl (bz), lf (w) λ^{al} 222 (4.5) 330 (2.5)	(i) 121–2 (ii) 61	315[760] 175[2]	1.4775[152]		δ[h]	δ	δ	v	s	chl, Py s to v[h], CS_2 δ	B5[2], 203
Ω b982	—,1,3,5-tri-phenyl-*	$C_{24}H_{18}$. See b202	306.41	rh nd (al or aa) λ^{hx} 253 (4.76)	176 (cor)	459[717]	1.199[30.3]		i	s	s	...	v	CS_2 s aa s	B5[2], 670
b983	—,1,3,5-tris-(phenylamino)-*	sym-Trianilinobenzene. $C_{24}H_{21}N_3$. See b202.	351.46	nd (al)	193				i	δ	v	...	δ	sulf s (vt-red)	B13[2], 147
b984	—,1,3,5-tris-(4-tolylamino)-	$C_{27}H_{27}N_3$. See b202.	393.54	nd (al)	186–7					δ				sulf s (bl-gr)	B13, 299
Ω b985	**Benzenearsonic acid***	Phenylarsonic acid.	202.02	cr (w) λ^{al} 256 (4.0), 262 (4.1), 270 (4.1)	158–62d				s	v					B16[7], 457
Ω b986	—,2-amino-*	$C_6H_8AsNO_3$. See b985	217.07	nd (al-eth)	153–4				v	v	δ	...	...	alk, aa s	B16[2], 483
b987	—,3-amino-*	$C_6H_8AsNO_3$. See b985	217.07	pr (w)	215				s[h]	δ	δ	...	δ	alk s os δ	B16[2], 489
Ω b988	—,4-amino-*	Arsanilic acid. $C_6H_8AsNO_3$. See b985	217.07	mcl nd (w or al)	232		1.9571[20]		s[h]	s[h] δ	s	i	i	aa δ chl i	B16[2], 491
b989	—,3-amino-4-hydroxy-*	$C_6H_8AsNO_4$. See b985	233.07	pr (w + ½)	290d (darkens 170)				i	δ				os δ	B16[2], 521
b990	—,2-bromo-*	$C_6H_6AsBrO_3$. See b985	280.94	lf (w), pr (dil al)	201d 173–5 (+1w)				s[h]	v					B16[2], 458
b991	—,2-chloro-*	$C_6H_6AsClO_3$. See b985	236.49	nd (w or dil al)	186–7				s[h]	s	i	...	i	MeOH s chl i	B16[2], 457
Ω b992	—,3-chloro-*	$C_6H_6AsClO_3$. See b985	236.49	cr (w)	175				s	s	s[h]	...	v	MeOH s	B16[2], 457
Ω b993	—,4-chloro-*	$C_6H_6AsClO_3$. See b985	236.49	wh nd (al)	383–5d				s	s	s[h]	...	v	alk v	B16[2], 457
b994	—,2-hydroxy-*	$C_6H_7AsO_4$. See b985	218.04	nd (w)	190–1				v[h]	v	i	v[h]	...	aa v[h] chl δ	B16[2], 464
b995	—,3-hydroxy-*	$C_6H_7AsO_4$. See b985	218.04	cr (w)	162–73d				v	v	...	δ[h]	i	aa v[h] chl i	B16[1], 454
Ω b996	—,4-hydroxy-*	$C_6H_7AsO_4$. See b985	218.04	nd (ace)	170–4				v	v	δ	...	...	aa δ	B16[2], 466
b997	—,2-hydroxy-3-nitro-*	$C_6H_6AsNO_6$. See b985	263.04	pr (w) cr (w)	252–4				s[h]	s[h]					B16[2], 465
b998	—,2-hydroxy-5-nitro-*	$C_6H_6AsNO_6$. See b985	263.04	pa ye (w)	250d				v[h]	v[h]	i	s	...		B16[2], 465
b999	—,3-hydroxy-2-nitro-*	$C_6H_6AsNO_6$. See b985	263.04	ye pl (al)	208d					s[h]					B16[2], 466
b1000	—,4-hydroxy-2-nitro-*	$C_6H_6AsNO_6$. See b985	263.04	ye nd (w)	228				v[h]						B16[2], 469
—	—,methyl-*	see **Toluenearsonic acid**													
Ω b1001	—,2-nitro-*	$C_6H_6AsNO_5$. See b985	246.03	lt ye nd (w) λ^{al} 262 (3.76)	235d				δ s[h]	δ s[h]	δ	...	...	aa s	B16[1], 449
b1002	—,3-nitro-*	$C_6H_6AsNO_5$. See b985	246.03	lt yc lf (w) λ^{al} 252.5 (3.89)	200 (182)				δ	δ	i	...	δ	chl δ	B16[2], 458
Ω b1003	—,4-nitro-*	$C_6H_6AsNO_5$. See b985	246.03	lf or nd (w)	>310 (298–300)				δ s[h]	δ s[h]					B16[1], 450
b1004	—,4-nitroso-*	$C_6H_6AsNO_4$. See b985	230.03	ye nd	180d				δ s[h]	δ	i	...	...	aa v chl i	B16[1], 449
Ω b1005	—,4-ureido	Carbarsone $C_7H_9AsNO_4$. See b985	260.08	nd (w)	174				δ v[h]	δ	i	...	...	alk s chl i	B16[2], 497
Ω b1006	**Benzeneboronic acid***	Phenylboric acid.	121.93	nd (w) λ^{hp} 225 sh (3.95), 235 (3.81), 267.5 (2.88), 272.5 (2.89), 280 (2.78)	218–20				δ v[h]	s	sh	s		to s	B16[2], 638
Ω b1007	—,4-bromo-*	$C_6H_6BBrO_2$. See b1006	200.83	cr (w)	266–72				δ		s	...	...	chl s	B16[2], 638
b1008	—,2-chloro-*	$C_6H_6BClO_2$. See b1006	156.38	cr (w)	149				δ	s	s	...	s	lig s	Am 56, 975

For explanations, symbols and abbreviations see beginning of table. For structural formulas see end of table.

No.	Name	Synonyms and Formula	Mol. wt.	Color, crystalline form, specific rotation and λ_{max} (log ε)	m.p. °C	b.p. °C	Density	n_D	w	al	eth	ace	bz	other solvents	Ref.
	Benzeneboronic acid														
b1009	—,4-chloro-*	$C_6H_6BClO_2$. See b1006	156.38	nd (w)	306–7 (270–5)				δ		s				B16[2], 638
—	Benzenecarboxylic acid*	see Benzoic acid													
b1010	Benzene-diazonium chloride*	Diazobenzene chloride. $C_6H_5N(:N)Cl$	140.57	nd (al) λ^w 263 (4,05)	exp				s	s	δ	s	i	aa v chl i	B16[1], 352
b1011	Benzene-diazonium cyanide*	$C_6H_5N(:N)CN$	131.14	ye pr (w)	69				δ						B16, 432
b1012	Benzene-diazonium nitrate*	$C_6H_5N(:N)NO_3$	167.13	nd (al-eth)	90 exp				s	δ	i		i	chl i	B16[2], 268
b1013	Benzene-diazonium tribromide*	$C_6H_5N(:N)Br_3$	344.85	pl (al)	63.5				i	δ	i				B16, 431
—	1,2-Benzenedi-carboxaldehyde	see Phthalaldehyde													
Ω b1014	1,3-Benzenedi-carboxaldehyde	Isophthalaldehyde.	134.14	nd (dil al) λ^{MeOH} 225 (4.15), 240 (4.11), 290 (3.18), 330 (2.36)	89–90	245–8[771]			δ	v	δ	s	s	os s lig δ	B7[2], 606
Ω b1015	1,4-Benzenedi-carboxaldehyde	Terephthalaldehyde.	134.14	nd (w)	116	247[771]			δ s[h]	v	s			alk s	B7, 675
—	1,2-Benzenedi-carboxylic acid*	see Phthalic acid													
Ω b1016	1,3-Benzenedi-carboxylic acid*	Isophthalic acid.	166.14	nd (w or al) λ^{al} 208 (4.60), 225 (4.07), 280 (2.93), 288 (2.92)	348	sub			δ	s	i		i	aa s lig i	B9[2], 608
b1016[1]	—,diamide		164.18	pl (w)	280				δ^h	δ^h			i	os i	B9, 834
b1017	—,—.N,N,N',N'-tetraethyl-	$C_{16}H_{24}N_2O_2$. See b1016[1]	276.38	cr (eth-bz)	85	242[12]			i	v	δ	v	v	lig i	B9[2], 609
Ω b1018	—,dichloride	$C_8H_4Cl_2O_2$. See b1016	203.03	pr (eth)	43–4	276 136[11]	1.3880[17 4]	1.570[47]	δ	δ	s				B9[2], 609
Ω b1019	—,diethyl ester*	$C_{12}H_{14}O_4$. See b1016	222.24	λ^{al} 280, 289	11.5	302[760] 170[2.4]	1.1239[17 4]	1.508[18]	i						B9[1], 372
Ω b1020	—,dimethyl ester*	$C_{10}H_{10}O_4$. See b1016	194.19	nd (dil al) λ^{al} 222 sh (3.11)	67.8–8.3 (cor)	282[760] 124[12]	1.194[20 4]	1.5168[20]	δ						B9[2], 609
Ω b1021	—,dinitrile	1,3-Dicyanobenzene	128.14	nd (al) λ^{MeOH} 342 (2.68), 355 (2.65)	162				δ^h	v[h]	s		s	chl s peth i	B9, 836
b1022	—,mononitrile	3-Cyanobenzoic acid.	147.13	nd (w)	217	sub δd			v[h]	v	v				B9[2], 609
b1023	—,piperazinium salt	$C_8H_6O_4 \cdot C_4H_{10}N_2$. See b1016	252.27		252d				s[h]	s[h]	s[h]				Am 70, 2758
Ω b1024	1,4-Benzenedi-carboxylic acid*	Terephthalic acid.	166.14	nd (sub) λ^{diox} 242 (4.21), 286 (3.23)	>300 sub sub without melting	sub			i	i s[h]	i			chl, aa i	B9, 841
b1025	—,diamide		164.18	nd (w), pl (aa)	>250				δ^h	i	i		i	chl i	B9[1], 376
b1026	—,—.N,N,N',N'-tetraethyl-	$C_{16}H_{24}N_2O_2$. See b1025	276.38	cr (eth-al)	127				i	v	δ		s	lig i	B9[2], 613
Ω b1027	—,dichloride		203.03	nd or pl (lig)	83–4	125–7[9]			d	d	s				B9, 844
Ω b1028	—,diethyl ester*	$C_{12}H_{14}O_4$. See b1024	222.24	mcl pr (al, peth) λ^{al} 227 (3.9), 275 (3.1)	44	302[760] 142[2]	1.1098[45 45]		i	v	s				B9, 844
Ω b1029	—,dimethyl ester*	$C_{10}H_{10}O_4$. See b1024	194.19	nd (eth) λ^{al} 241.6 (3.32)	141.0–1.8 (cor)	sub			δ^h	δ v[h]	s			MeOH δ	B9, 843
b1030	—,dinitrile	1,4-Dicyanobenzene.	128.14	nd (w, MeOH) λ^{MeOH} 348 (3.25), 360 (3.21), 405 (4.35), 425 (4.30)	222	sub			i	δ s[h]	δ^h		s[h]	aa v[h]	B9[2], 613
b1031	—,monoamide	Terephthalamic acid.	165.15		>300	sub 250			i	i	i		i	chl, os i	B9, 845
Ω b1032	—,mononitrile	4-Cyanobenzoic acid.	147.14	pl or lf (w)	219				s[h]	s	s			aa s[h]	B9[2], 613
b1033	—,piperazinium salt	$C_8H_6O_4 \cdot C_4H_{10}N_2$. See b1024	252.27		>350d				δ^h	s[h]	δ^h				Am 70, 2758
b1034	1,3-Benzenedicar-boxylic acid, 2-amino-*	$C_8H_7NO_4$. See b1016	181.15	pl (al), nd (aa)	>260	sub 267–9			δ	s	s				B14[2], 337
b1035	—,—.dimethyl ester*	$C_{10}H_{11}NO_4$. See b1016	209.20	nd (al)	103–4					δ					B14[2], 337
b1036	—,4-amino-*	$C_8H_7NO_4$. See b1016	181.15	nd (w)	336–7				δ	v[h]	s	s		aa v[h]	B14[1], 633

For explanations, symbols and abbreviations see beginning of table. For structural formulas see end of table.

1,3-Benzenedicarboxylic acid

No.	Name	Synonyms and Formula	Mol. wt.	Color, crystalline form, specific rotation and λ_{max} (log ε)	m.p. °C	b.p. °C	Density	n_D	w	al	eth	ace	bz	other solvents	Ref.
b1037	—,—,dimethyl ester*	$C_{10}H_{11}NO_4$. See b1016	209.20	nd (al)	131.5				δ	δ	...			MeOH δ	**B14**[2], 337
Ω b1038	—.5-amino-*	$C_8H_7NO_4$. See b1016	181.15	pr (al), pl (w)	>360	sub			i	δ					**B14**[1], 636
Ω b1039	—,—,dimethyl ester*	$C_{10}H_{11}NO_4$. See b1016	209.20	lf or pl (MeOH)	176				i		s				**B14**, 556
b1040	1,4-Benzenedicarboxylic acid, 2-amino-*	$C_8H_7NO_4$. See b1024	181.15	ye cr (w)	324–5d (cor)				δ	δ	δ	i	i	peth. chl aa i	**B14**[1], 637
b1041	—,—,dimethyl ester*	$C_{10}H_{11}NO_4$. See b1024	209.20	nd (bz), cr (al)	134				...	s[h]	s[h]	s		chl s	**B14**, 559
b1042	—,2-benzoyl-	Benzophenone-2,5-dicarboxylic acid. $C_{15}H_{10}O_5$. See b1024	270.25	nd	291–2				i	s	s		i	to i	**B10**, 881
Ω b1043	1,3-Benzenedicarboxylic acid, 4-bromo-*	$C_8H_5BrO_4$. See b1016	245.04	nd (al)	287 (283)				i	v[h]			i		**B9**, 838
Ω b1044	1,4-Benzenedicarboxylic acid, 2-bromo-*	$C_8H_5BrO_4$. See b1024	245.04	nd (w or al)	299				δ v[h]	v	i		i		**B9**[2], 614
b1045	1,3-Benzenedicarboxylic acid, 4-chloro-*	$C_8H_5ClO_4$. See b1016	200.58	nd (w)	295				δ s[h]	v	δ		i	chl i	**B9**[1], 372
b1046	—,5-chloro-*	$C_8H_5ClO_4$. See b1016	200.58	nd (w + ½)	278 (anh)				δ v[h]	s			i	chl i	**B9**, 838
Ω b1047	1,4-Benzenedicarboxylic acid, 2-chloro-*	$C_8H_5ClO_4$. See b1024	200.58	cr (w)	320				δ[h]	v	v				**B9**, 847
b1048	1,3-Benzenedicarboxylic acid, 4,6-dichloro-*	$C_8H_4Cl_2O_4$. See b1016	235.03	nd (w or dil al)	280				i	v	v			chl v	**B9**, 838
Ω b1049	1,4-Benzenedicarboxylic acid, 2,5-dichloro-*	$C_8H_4Cl_2O_4$. See b1024	235.03	nd (w)	306	sub			s[h] δ	s	v				**B9**, 847
b1050	—,2,5-dihydroxy-*	$C_8H_6O_6$. See b1024	198.13	ye cr (al, w)	d				s[h]	s[h]	s[h]				**B10**, 554
b1051	1,3-Benzenedicarboxylic acid, 4,5-dimethoxy-*	Isohemipinic acid. $C_{10}H_{10}O_6$. See b1016	226.19	nd (w)	245–6				s[h] δ	s	s				**B10**, 553
b1052	—,4,6-dimethyl-*	α-Cumidic acid. $C_{10}H_{10}O_4$. See b1016	194.19	nd (w), pr (al-bz), lf (sub)	266	sub			i δ[h]	s					**B9**[2], 627
b1053	—,2-hydroxy-*	$C_8H_6O_5$. See b1016	182.13	nd (w + 1) λ^{a1} 213 (4.51), 319 (3.70)	244.5 (239) (hyd) 250 (anh)				δ[h]	v	v			chl s	**B10**[2], 352
Ω b1054	—,4-hydroxy-*	$C_8H_6O_5$. See b1016	182.13	nd (w), lf (dil al) λ^{a1} 218 (4.45), 255 (4.05), 301 (3.50)	310				i δ[h]	v	v			aa s[h] chl i	**B10**[2], 352
b1055	—,5-hydroxy-*	$C_8H_6O_5$. See b1016	182.13	nd (w + 2), cr (aq al)	293	sub			i v[h]	v	v		s		**B10**[1], 257
Ω b1056	—,5-methyl-*	Uvitic acid. $C_9H_8O_4$. See b1016	180.17	nd (w)	298				δ[h] i	s	s	s		chl, peth δ	**B9**[1], 380
b1057	—,2-nitro-, dimethyl ester*	$C_{10}H_9NO_6$. See b1016	239.19	nd (w or al)	135				δ	s	s			MeOH δ peth i	**B9**[1], 373
Ω b1058	—,5-nitro-*	$C_8H_5NO_6$. See b1016	211.13	gr lf (+ 1½w)	260–1 (anh)	sub			i v[h]	v	v				**B9**[1], 373
b1059	—,—,diethyl ester*	$C_{12}H_{13}NO_6$. See b1016	267.24	nd (al)	83.5				δ	δ v[h]					**B9**, 840
Ω b1060	—,—,dimethyl ester*	$C_{10}H_9NO_6$. See b1016	239.19	nd (dil al)	123				i	s	s				**B9**[2], 611
Ω b1061	1,4-Benzenedicarboxylic acid, 2-nitro-*	$C_8H_5NO_6$. See b1024	211.13	nd (w)	270–5				s[h]	v[h]					**B9**, 851
b1062	1,3-Benzenedicarboxylic acid, tetrabromo-*	$C_8H_2Br_4O_4$. See b1016	481.74	nd (w)	288–92				s[h]				i		**B9**, 839
b1063	1,4-Benzenedicarboxylic acid, tetrabromo-*	$C_8H_2Br_4O_4$. See b1024	481.74	nd (w)	266→ an-hydride				i s[h]	δ	δ		δ	aa δ	**B9**, 850
b1064	1,3-Benzene-disulfonic acid, 4-amino-*		253.25	nd (w + 2)	120d				s	s	i			alk s	**B14**[2], 470
b1065	—,4-hydroxy-*		254.24	nd (w)	>100d				v	v	i				**B11**[2], 139
Ω b1066	Benzenehexacarboxylic acid*	Mellitic acid.	342.18	nd (al) λ^w 236 sh (4.3), 296 (3.1)	286–8d				v	s				sulf s[h]	**B9**[2], 741
Ω b1067	Benzenepenta-carboxylic acid*		298.17	nd (w + 5) λ^w 393 (3.2)	228–30 (+5w) 238 (anh)				v[h]	s	δ		i	AcOEt δ peth i	**B9**[2], 737

For explanations, symbols and abbreviations see beginning of table. For structural formulas see end of table.

No.	Name	Synonyms and Formula	Mol. wt.	Color, crystalline form, specific rotation and λ_{max} (log ε)	m.p. °C	b.p. °C	Density	n_D	Solubility						Ref.
									w	al	eth	ace	bz	other solvents	
	Benzenephosphinic acid														
Ω b1068	**Benzenephosphinic acid***	$C_6H_5P(OH)_2$	142.10	pl (aq MeOH) λ^{al} 216 (3.85), 264.5 (2.79)	82–3	....	....	....	s v^h	v	δ	...	...	......	**B16**, 791
b1069	—,diethyl ester* ...	$C_6H_5P(OC_2H_5)_2$ ...	198.20		......	235	1.032^{16}	....	i	s	s	...	i	......	**B16**, 791
b1070	**Benzenephosphonic acid***	$C_6H_5PO_3H_2$	158.10	lf (w) λ^{al} 258 (2.59), 263.5 (2.72), 270 (2.64)	160	....	....	....	v	s	s	...	i	......	**B16²**, 390
b1071	—,dichloride......	$C_6H_5POCl_2$	194.99		......	258 $137–8^{15}$	1.197^{25}	1.5581^{25}	d						**B16**, 804
b1072	—,tetrachloride	$C_6H_5PCl_4$	249.89		73				d	d^h					**B16**, 804
b1073	**Benzenephosphothionic acid, ethyl 4-nitrophenyl ester***	EPN.	323.31		36		1.272^{25}	1.5978^{30}	i	s	s	...	s	......	**C46**, 2742
b1074	**Benzeneseleninic acid***	$C_6H_5SeO_2H$	189.07	pl (w) λ^{al} 220 (4.04), 260 (3.12)	124–5	....	1.6652^{123}	....	δ			...	i	alk v	**B11²**, 241
b1075	**Benzeneselenonic acid***	$C_6H_5SeO_3H$	205.07	nd	142	d	....	....	v	v	i	...	i	......	**B11¹**, 111
b1076	**Benzenesiliconic acid***	$C_6H_5SiO_2H$	138.20	glassy so (eth)	92				i	s	s				**B16**, 911
b1077	**Benzenestibonic acid***	$C_6H_5SbO_3H_2$ ...	248.87	nd (aa)	139	....	....	....	i	δ	...	δ	...	C_2Cl_4 s	**B16²**, 584
b1078	**Benzenesulfenic acid, chloride**	Benzenesulfenyl chloride.	144.62	red liq	......	$73–5^9$ 58^3							s		**B6²**, 295
Ω b1079	—,2,4-dinitro-, chloride	$C_6H_3ClN_2O_4S$. See b1078 ...	234.62	ye pr (bz-peth or CCl_4) $\lambda^{CH_2ClCH_2Cl}$ 260 (3.60)	99 (95–6)								v	chl, aa v peth δ	**B6²**, 316
Ω b1080	—,2-nitro-, chloride	$C_6H_4ClNO_2S$. See b1078....	189.62	ye nd (bz)	75							v	v	chl v	**B6²**, 308
b1081	—,4-nitro-, chloride	$C_6H_4ClNO_2S$. See b1078....	189.62	ye lf (peth)	52	$125^{0.1}$			d	d			v	aa d	**B6¹**, 160
b1082	**Benzenesulfinic acid**	....	142.18	pr (w) λ^{al} 218 (3.99), 245 (3.40)	84	d at 100			s^h δ	s	s	...	s	peth i	**B11²**, 3
Ω b1083	—,chloride	C_6H_5SOCl	160.62	pl (peth)	38	$71–2^{1.5}$	1.3469^{25}	1.3470^{25}	d	d	s	...	chl s^h		**B11²**, 4
b1084	—,ethyl ester* ...	$C_6H_5SO_2C_2H_5$ ...	170.23	liq	......	d			i	∞	∞	...	∞		**B11**, 6
Ω b1085	—,3-acetamido- ...	$C_8H_9NO_3S$. See b1082.	199.23	cr (w)	145				s^h						**B14²**, 427
Ω b1086	—,4-acetamido- ...	$C_8H_9NO_3S$. See b1082.	199.23	cr (w)	160 (153)				s^h						**B14²**, 427
b1087	—,4-bromo-*	$C_6H_5BrO_2S$ See b1082	221.08	nd (w)	114				d^h	v	v				**B11²**, 5
b1088	—,4-chloro-*	$C_6H_5ClO_2S$. See b1082	176.62	lf or nd (w)	99 (93)				s^h	v	v				**B11²**, 4
—	—,methyl-*	see **Toluenesulfinic acid**													
b1089	—,3-nitro-*	$C_6H_5NO_4S$. See b1082.	187.18	nd	98				s	s	s	s	i		**B11²**, 5
b1090	—,4-nitro-*	$C_6H_5NO_4S$. See b1082.	187.18	pr or nd (w) λ^w 264 (4.05)	159				δ	v	s	...	aa v		**B11²**, 5
Ω b1091	**Benzenesulfonic acid***	....	158.18	nd (bz). λ^{al} 213 (3.89), 253 (2.27), 259 (2.41), 263 (2.46), 270 (2.38)	65–6 (anh)				v	v	i	...	δ	aa s CS_2 i	**B11²**, 18
Ω b1092	—,hydrate*	$C_6H_5SO_3H \cdot 1.5H_2O$	176.20	pl (w)	45–6				s	s	i	...	δ	CS_2 i	**B11²**, 18
Ω b1093	—,amide	Benzenesulfonamide.	157.19	lf, nd (w) λ^{al} 219 (3.95), 259 (2.50), 264 (2.70), 271 (2.50)	156				δ	s^h	s	...	v		**B11²**, 24
Ω b1094	—,—,N,N-dichloro-	Dichloramine B. $C_6H_5SO_2NCl_2$	226.08	ye mcl or pl	76					s					**B11²**, 28
Ω b1095	—,—,N-hydroxy-.	$C_6H_5SO_2NHOH$	173.19	pl (w), rh	126d				v^h	v	v	v	δ	aa v chl δ	**B11¹**, 14
b1096	—,—,N-phenyl-	Benzenesulfonanilide. $C_6H_5SO_2NHC_6H_5$	233.29	tetr pr (al)	110				δ	v	v				**B12²**, 298
Ω b1097	—,chloride	$C_6H_5SO_2Cl$	176.62	λ^{al} 210 (4.08), 270 (3.10)	14.5	$251–2d$ 120^{10}	1.3842^{15}_{15}		i				chl v		**B11²**, 23
Ω b1098	—,ethyl ester* ...	$C_6H_5SO_2C_2H_5$	186.23		......	156^{15}	1.2167^{20}_4	1.5081^{20}	δ d^h	s	v	...	chl v		**B11²**, 20
Ω b1099	—,fluoride	$C_6H_5SO_2F$	160.17	λ^{peth} 267 (3.1), 273 (2.9)	......	$203–4$ $90–1^4$	1.3286^{20}_4	1.4932^{18}	...	s	s				**B11²**, 23
b1100	—,isopropyl ester..	$C_6H_5SO_3C_3H_7^i$	200.26		......			1.5003^{20}	δ	v	v				**B11²**, 20
Ω b1101	—,methyl ester* ..	$C_6H_5SO_3CH_3$	172.21	λ^{al} 213 (3.90), 320 (2.6)	......	154^{20}	1.2730^{17}	1.5151^{20}	δ	v	v	...	chl v		**B11²**, 20
b1102	—,propyl ester* ..	$C_6H_5SO_3C_3H_7^n$	200.26	λ^{al} 217.5 (3.93), 259 (2.83), 265 (3.00), 272 (2.93)	......	100d $162–3^{15}$	1.1804^{17}_4	1.5035^{25}	δ	s	v	...	chl v		**B11²**, 20
Ω b1103	—,sodium salt*	$C_6H_5SO_3Na$	180.16	nd or lf (w + 1) λ 257 (2.5), 263 (2.6), 269 (2.5)	450d				s v^h	δ^h					**B11²**, 18

For explanations, symbols and abbreviations see beginning of table. For structural formulas see end of table.

No.	Name	Synonyms and Formula	Mol. wt.	Color, crystalline form, specific rotation and λ_{max} (log ε)	m.p. °C	b.p. °C	Density	n_D	Solubility						Ref.
									w	al	eth	ace	bz	other solvents	

Benzenesulfonic acid

No.	Name	Synonyms and Formula	Mol. wt.	Color...	m.p.	b.p.	Density	n_D	w	al	eth	ace	bz	other	Ref.
b1104	—,3-acetamido-, amide	$C_8H_{10}N_2O_2S$. See b1093	214.25	(aa) $\lambda^{95\%al}$ 243 (4.1), 280 (3.1)	216–9							s		aa s	**B14**, 718
b1105	—,—,chloride	$C_8H_8ClNO_3S$. See b1091	233.69	nd (bz-peth)	88				d	s	s		δ	aa s	**B14²**, 435
b1106	—,4-acetamido-, amide	$C_8H_{10}N_2O_3S$. See b1093	214.25	nd (aa) $\lambda^{95\%al}$ 255 (4.3)	219–20				s^h	s^h		s^h			**B14**, 702
b1107	—,—,chloride	$C_8H_8ClNO_3S$. See b1091	233.69	nd (bz), pr (bz-chl)	149				d	v	v		s^h	chl s^h	**B14**, 439
Ω b1108	—,2-amino-*	Orthanilic acid $C_6H_7NO_3S$. See b1091	173.19	pr (+½w) λ^w 235 (3.8), 294 (3.2)	>320d				δ	i s^h	i				**B14²**, 429
b1109	—,—,amide	$C_6H_8N_2O_2S$. See b1093	172.22	mcl pl, nd or pr (w) λ^{al} 206 (4.42), 245.5 (3.93), 306 (3.54)	152.5–3.5				δ v^h	v		v	i	aa s	**B14²**, 429
Ω b1110	—,3-amino-*	Metanilic acid. $C_6H_7NO_3S$. See b1091	173.19	nd, pr (w+½) λ^w 237 (3.2), 262 (2.5), 269 (2.6), 289 (2.6)	d				δ	δ	i				**B14²**, 434
b1111	—,—,amide	$C_6H_8N_2O_2S$. See b1093	172.22	lf or nd (w) λ^w 209.5 (4.48), 238.5 (3.86), 297 (3.36)	142				δ s^h	v					**B14**, 690
Ω b1112	—,4-amino-*	Sulfanilic acid $C_6H_7NO_3S$. See b1091	173.19	rh pl or mcl (w+2) λ^{al} 250 (4.22)	288		1.485^{25}_4		s^h δ	i	i				**B14²**, 436
Ω b1113	—,—,amide	Sulfanilamide. $C_6H_8N_2O_2S$. See b1093	172.22	lf (aq al) λ^{al} 258.5 (4.28)	165–6		1.08		s^h	s	s	s		MeOH s chl, peth δ	**B14**, 698
b1114	—,—,—,N-acetyl-	$C_8H_{10}N_2O_3S$. See b1093	214.25	pr (w) λ^{al} 257 (4.35)	182–4				δ	s	i	v		alk v	**C50**, 15543
—,—,—,N(4,6-dimethyl-2-pyrimidyl)-		see **Sulfamethazine**													
—,—,—,N-guanido-		see **Sulfaguanidine**													
—,—,—,N(4-methyl-2-pyrimidyl)-		see **Sulfamerazine**													
—,—,—,N(2-pyridyl)-		see **Sulfapyridine**													
—,—,—,N(2-quinoxalinyl)-		see **Sulfaquinoxaline**													
—,—,—,N(2-thiazolyl)-		see **Sulfathiazole**													
b1115	—,2-amino-4-chloro-*	$C_6H_6ClNO_3S$. See b1091	207.64	nd or pl (w)	310–30d				δ s^h	δ				aa δ	**B14²**, 430
b1116	—,2-amino-5-chloro-*	$C_6H_6ClNO_3S$. See b1091	207.64	nd (w)	280d				δ s^h						**B14²**, 430
b1117	—,2-amino-3,4-dimethyl-*	$C_8H_{11}NO_3S$. See b1091	201.25	pr (w+1)	300d				δ						**B14¹**, 731
b1118	—,2-amino-3,5-dimethyl-*	$C_8H_{11}NO_3S$. See b1091	201.25	pr or pl (w)	d				i	i	i		i		**B14²**, 452
b1119	—,2-amino-3,6-dimethyl-*	$C_8H_{11}NO_3S$. See b1091	201.25	amor	260				δ	i		i			**B14¹**, 732
b1120	—,2-amino-4,5-dimethyl-*	$C_8H_{11}NO_3S$. See b1091	201.25	pl	>300				δ^h						**B14¹**, 731
b1121	—,3-amino-2,5-dimethyl-*	$C_8H_{11}NO_3S$. See b1091	201.25	nd (w+1)					δ						**B14¹**, 732
b1122	—,3-amino-4,5-dimethyl-*	$C_8H_{11}NO_3S$. See b1091	201.25	red nd (w+1)	315				δ						**B14¹**, 731
b1123	—,4-amino-2,3-dimethyl-*	$C_8H_{11}NO_3S$. See b1091	201.25	nd	305				δ						**B14¹**, 731
b1124	—,4-amino-2,5-dimethyl-*	$C_8H_{11}NO_3S$. See b1091	201.25	pl or nd	>300										**B14¹**, 732
b1125	—,5-amino-2,3-dimethyl-*	$C_8H_{11}NO_3S$. See b1091	201.25	pl (w+2)	294d				s	δ			δ		**B14¹**, 731
b1126	—,5-amino-2,4-dimethyl-*	$C_8H_{11}NO_3S$. See b1091	201.25	pr or nd	290d				δ	i		i	chl i		**B14**, 734
b1127	—,3-amino-4-hydroxy-*	$C_6H_7NO_4S$. See b1091	189.19	rh (w+½)	>300 (155–6)				δ	i	i				**B14**, 814
b1128	—,3-amino-4-hydroxy-5-nitro-*	$C_6H_6N_2O_6S$. See b1091	234.19	pr (w)					s^n	δ					**B14¹**, 748
b1129	—,4(2-amino-1-naphthylazo)-*		327.37	dk gr nd (w)					s^h δ	v^h	i				**B16²**, 199
b1130	—,4(4-amino-1-naphthylazo)-*		327.37	dk gr cr (w)					δ v^h	δ					**B16²**, 191

For explanations, symbols and abbreviations see beginning of table. For structural formulas see end of table.

No.	Name	Synonyms and Formula	Mol. wt.	Color, crystalline form, specific rotation and λ_{max} (log ε)	m.p. °C	b.p. °C	Density	n_D	w	al	eth	ace	bz	other solvents	Ref.
	Benzenesulfonic acid														
b1131	—,4(4-amino-phenylsulfon-amido)-,amide	....	327.38	$\lambda^{w,pH=2}$ 247.5 (4.14), $\lambda^{w,pH=11}$ 270.5 (4.36)	137	....			δ s^h	s	s	s	...	chl i peth i	C51, 2780
b1132	—,2-bromo-*	$C_6H_5BrO_3S$. See b1091	237.08	nd	....	....			v	v					B11, 56
b1133	—,—,amide	$C_6H_6BrNO_3S$. See b1093....	236.09	nd (w), pr (al)	186	....			δ	δ					B11, 56
b1134	—,—,chloride....	$C_6H_6BrClO_2S$. See b1091	255.52	pr (eth)	51	....			d^h	d^h	δ				B11, 56
b1135	—,3-bromo-,amide	$C_6H_6BrNO_2S$. See b1093....	236.09	nd or lf (w), pr (al)	154	....			δ s^h	δ s^h					B11, 57
b1136	—,4-bromo-*	$C_6H_5BrO_3S$. See b1091	237.08	nd (al)	102–3	155^{25}			v	s					B11, 57
b1137	—,—,amide	$C_6H_6BrNO_2S$. See b1093....	236.09	nd (w or dil al)	166	....			δ s^h	v					B11, 57
b1138	—,—,bromide	$C_6H_4Br_2O_2S$. See b1091	299.98	cr (eth or bz)	77	....			d^h	d^h			s		B11[1], 16
Ω b1139	—,—,chloride....	$C_6H_4BrClO_2S$. See b1091	255.52	tcl or mcl pr (eth)	76	153^{15}			i	d	v				B11, 57
b1140	—,2-chloro-,amide	$C_6H_6ClNO_2S$. See b1093....	191.64	lf (al)	188	....				s					B11, 54
b1141	—,3-chloro-,amide	$C_6H_6ClNO_2S$. See b1093....	191.64	lf (dil al)	148	....			v^h	v	v				B11, 54
b1142	—,4-chloro-*	$C_6H_5ClO_3S$. See b1091	192.62	nd (w + 1)	67	147–8^{25}			s	s	i		i		B11, 54
Ω b1143	—,—,amide....	$C_6H_6ClNO_2S$. See b1093....	191.64	nd (w)	145–6.5	....			v^h	v^h	v^h				B11, 55
Ω b1144	—,—,chloride....	$C_6H_4Cl_2O_2S$. See b1091	211.07	pr or pl (eth)	55	141^{15}			d^h	d^h	v		v		B11, 55
Ω b1145	—,4-chloro-phenyl ester*	Chlorfenson. Ovotran. $C_{12}H_8Cl_2O_3S$. See b1091	303.18	λ^{al} 230 (4.27), 266 (3.05), 269 (3.04), 277 (2.91)	86.5	....			i	δ		s			C51, 1264
b1146	—,3,4-diamino-* .	$C_6H_8N_2O_3S$. See b1091	188.22	nd	d	....			v^h				i		B14, 717
b1147	—,3,5-diamino-* .	$C_6H_8N_2O_3S$. See b1091	188.22	....	d	....			δ v^h	δ	i				B14[2], 446
b1148	—,2,5-dichloro-,dihydrate*	$C_6H_4Cl_2SO_3.2H_2O$. See b1091	263.11	nd (w + 2)	<100	....			v	s	δ				B11[2], 30
b1149	—,—,chloride....	$C_6H_3Cl_3SO_2$. See b1091	245.51	mcl pr (bz)	38	....			d^h	d^h					B11[2], 30
b1150	—,3,4-dichloro-,dihydrate*	$C_6H_4Cl_2SO_3.2H_2O$. See b1091	263.11	nd	71–2	....			v	v	v				B11, 55
b1151	—,—,chloride....	$C_6H_3Cl_3SO_2$. See b1091	245.51	mcl pr	fp 22.4	....			d^h	d^h					B11[1], 16
b1152	—,3,5-diiodo-4-hydroxy-,trihydrate*	Sozoiodolic acid. $C_6H_4I_2SO_4.3H_2O$. See b1091	480.02	nd (eth), pr (w + 3)	120 (hyd) 190d (anh)	....			v	v	v				B11[2], 137
b1153	—,2,3-dimethyl-,chloride	$C_8H_9ClO_2S$. See b1091	204.68	pr (peth)	47	....			d	d^h				peth v^h	B11, 120
b1154	—,3,4-dimethyl-* ..	$C_8H_{10}O_3S$. See b1091	186.23	pl or pr (chl + 2w)	63–4	....			v						B11[2], 78
b1155	—,—,chloride....	$C_8H_9ClO_2S$. See b1091	204.68	pr (eth)	51–2	....			d	d^h	v				B11, 121
b1156	—,3,5-dimethyl-,chloride	$C_8H_9ClO_2S$. See b1091	204.68	nd (peth or bz)	94	....			d	d^h	v				B11, 126
Ω b1157	—,2,4-dinitro-*	$C_6H_4N_2O_7S$. See b1091	248.17	nd (w + 3)	130 (anh) 108 (hyd)	....			v	v	δ		i	peth i	B11[2], 36
b1158	—,3,5-dinitro-*	$C_6H_4N_2O_7S$. See b1091	248.17	ye red (dil al)	235	....			i s^h	s^h	δ		δ	aa δ lig δ	B11, 79
b1159	—,3-ethylamino-* ..	$C_8H_{11}NO_3S$. See b1091	201.25	nd (w)	294d	....			δ						B14[2], 435
b1160	—,4-ethylamino-* ..	$C_8H_{11}NO_3S$. See b1091	201.25	pl (w)	258d	....			v						B14[1], 721
b1161	—,4-fluoro-,amide ..	$C_6H_6FNO_2S$. See b1093	175.18	pl or nd (w, al)	126	....			δ	v	v	v	δ		B11, 54
Ω b1162	—,—,chloride....	$C_6H_4ClFO_2S$. See b1091	194.61	pl or nd	36	95–$6^{2.2}$			d^h	d^h	v		v	chl v	B11, 53
Ω b1163	—,2-formyl-,chloride	2-Benzaldehyde sulfonyl chloride. $C_7H_5ClO_3S$. See b1091	204.55	cr (bz)	114	....			d	d	s				B11[2], 78
Ω b1164	—,4-hydrazino-* ..	Phenylhydrazine-4-sulfonic acid. $C_6H_8N_2O_3S$. See b1091	188.22	nd or lf (w)	286	....			δ	δ					B15[2], 305
b1165	—,2-hydroxy-*	o-Phenolsulfonic acid. $C_6H_6O_4S$. See b1091	174.18	cr (w + ¾)	50d; 145d (+w)	....			v	v					B11[2], 131
b1166	—,4-hydroxy-*	p-Phenolsulfonic acid. $C_6H_6O_4S$. See b1091	174.18	nd	....	....			s	s					B11[2], 134
b1167	—,—,amide	$C_6H_7NO_3S$. See b1093......	173.19	cr (al or w)	176–7	....			s^h	s^h					B11, 243
b1168	—,4-hydroxy-5-isopropyl-2-methyl-	α-Thymolsulfonic acid. $C_{10}H_{14}O_4S$. See b1091	230.29	pl (+1w)	91–2	....			v						B11[2], 151
b1169	—,4-hydroxy-3-nitro-*	$C_6H_5NO_6S$. See b1091......	219.17	ye pl (AcOEt-bz) nd (w + 3)	141–2 (anh) 51.5 (hyd)	....			s	v				AcOEt v chl v^h	B11, 245
b1170	—,2-isopropyl-5-methyl-	$C_{10}H_{14}O_3S$. See b1091	214.29		130–1	....			v	s	i				B11[2], 84
b1171	—,4-isopropyl-2-methyl-	$C_{10}H_{14}O_3S$. See b1091	214.29	pl or pr	88–90	....			v	δ	δ		δ	chl δ	B11, 139
b1172	—,5-isopropyl-2-methyl-	$C_{10}H_{14}O_3S$. See b1091	214.29	pl (+2w), mcl pr	220, 78–9 (+2w)	....			v						B11[2], 83

For explanations, symbols and abbreviations see beginning of table. For structural formulas see end of table.

Benzenesulfonic acid

No.	Name	Synonyms and Formula	Mol. wt.	Color, crystalline form, specific rotation and λ_{max} (log ε)	m.p. °C	b.p. °C	Density	n_D	w	al	eth	ace	bz	other solvents	Ref.
b1173	—,2-methoxy-, chloride	$C_7H_7ClO_3S$. See b1091	206.65	nd (peth)	56	126–9[0.3]			d	d	s			peth s[h]	B11, 235
Ω b1174	—,4-methoxy-, chloride-*	$C_7H_7ClO_3S$. See b1091	206.65	nd or pr (bz)	42–3				d	s d[h]	s		s[h]		B11[2], 136
—	—,methyl-*	see Toluenesulfonic acid													
b1175	—,2-nitro-*	$C_6H_5NO_5S$. See b1091	203.17		85 (70)				v	s	i				B11[2], 31
b1176	—,—,chloride	$C_6H_4ClNO_4S$. See b1091	221.62	pr (lig, eth-peth) $\lambda^{95\%\,al}$ 280 sh (3.2)	68.5–9.5				d[h]	d[h]	s			peth δ	B11[2], 32
Ω b1177	—,3-nitro-*	$C_6H_5NO_5S$. See b1091	203.17	pl	48				v[h]	s	i		i		B11, 68
Ω b1178	—,—,chloride	$C_6H_4ClNO_4S$. See b1091	221.62	mcl pr (eth), nd (lig) $\lambda^{95\%\,al}$ 231–41 sh (4.0)	64				i d[h]	d[h]	s				B11[2], 33
Ω b1179	—,4-nitro-*	$C_6H_5NO_5S$. See b1091	203.17	(+2w) λ^w 271 (4.01)	95 (109–11)				v						B11[2], 33
Ω b1180	—,—,chloride	$C_6H_4ClNO_4S$. See b1091	221.62	mcl nd (peth, lig)	79.5–80.5				d[h]	d[h]	s			peth s[h]	B11[1], 21
b1180[1]	—,4-phenyl-amino-	4-Sulfodiphenylamine. $C_{12}H_{11}NO_3S$. See b1091	249.29	pl (al-eth)	206.5				v	v	i				B14[1], 721
b1181	—,4-ureido, amide	$C_7H_9N_3O_3S$. See b1091	215.23	nd (al)	206–7				s[h]	s[h]					C51, 6692
Ω b1182	1,2,3,4-Benzene-tetracarboxylic acid*	Prehnitic acid	254.16	pr (+6w) λ^w 257 sh (3.7), 294 (3.2)	241d				s			s			B9[2], 730
Ω b1183	—,tetramethyl ester*	$C_{14}H_{14}O_8$. See b1182	310.26	nd (MeOH or w) λ^{al} 240 sh (3.91), 288 (3.11)	133–5				i δ[h]	v	δ		v	MeOH δ	B9[2], 730
Ω b1184	1,2,3,5-Benzene-tetracarboxylic acid, tetramethyl ester*	Tetramethyl mellophanate.	310.26	nd (MeOH, al)	111				i	s[h]					B9[1], 435
Ω b1185	1,2,4,5-Benzene-tetracarboxylic acid*	Pyromellitic acid	254.16	tcl pl (w +2) λ^w 252 sh (3.9), 297 (3.4)	276 (281–4.5) (anh) 242 (+2w)				δ	s					B9, 998
b1186	—,tetraethyl ester*	$C_{18}H_{22}O_8$. See b1185	366.37	nd (al)	54	sub			i	s[h]					B9, 998
Ω b1187	—,tetramethyl ester*	$C_{14}H_{14}O_8$. See b1185	310.26	lf (al, MeOH) λ^{al} 240 sh (3.96), 291 (3.37)	143–4				i	δ[h]					B9, 998
—	Benzenethiol*	see Benzene, mercapto-*													
Ω b1188	1,2,3-Benzenetri-carboxylic acid*	Hemimellitic acid	210.15	tcl pl (+2w), nd (w) λ^w 284 (2.9)	197d (anh) 223–4 (hyd)		1.546[20]		v[h]		δ			con HCl i	B9[3], 712
b1190	1,2,4-Benzenetri-carboxylic acid*	Trimellitic acid	210.15	nd (w), cr(aa or al) λ^w 248 (3.9), 296 (3.2)	238d				v	v	v	δ	i	CCl_4 i chl i CS_2 i aa s[h]	B9[2], 712
Ω b1191	1,3,5-Benzenetri-carboxylic acid*	Trimesic acid	210.15	pr or nd (w +1) λ^w 288 (2.8), 297 sh (2.6)	380 (anh)				δ	v	s				B9[2], 712
b1192	—,triethyl ester*	$C_{15}H_{18}O_6$. See b1191	294.31	pr or nd (al)	133.5–4.5				i	s[h]	v		s	CS_2 v aa s	B9[2], 712
Ω b1193	—,trimethyl ester*	$C_{12}H_{12}O_6$. See b1191	252.23	nd (dil al) λ^{al} 216 (4.61)	144				i	s					B9[1], 430
b1194	—,2-chloro-*	$C_9H_5ClO_6$. See b1191	244.59	nd or pl (w +1)	285 (anh) 278 (hyd)	sub			s[h]	v	v			chl i	B9, 980
b1195	1,2,4-Benzenetri-carboxylic acid, 6-hydroxy-*	$C_9H_6O_7$. See b1190	226.14	pr (w +2)	278–81d				s	s					B10, 580
b1196	1,3,5-Benzenetri-carboxylic acid, 2-hydroxy-*	$C_9H_6O_7$. See b1191	226.14	pr (w +1), nd (w +2)	306 (anh)				s[h]	v[h]	δ		i	chl i lig i	B10, 580
b1197	1,3,5-Benzenetri-sulfonic acid*		318.30	cr (w +3)	d >100				s	s	i		i		B11[2], 128
—	Benzestrol	see Hexane,2,4-bis(4-hydroxyphenyl)-3-ethyl-*													
—	Benzhydrol	see Methanol, diphenyl-*													
—	Benzidine	see Biphenyl, 4,4'-diamino-													
—	Benzidinesulfone	see Dibenzothiophene, 2,7-diamino-, 9,9-dioxide													
Ω b1198	Benzil	Dibenzoyl. 1,2-Diphenyl-1,2-ethandione. Diphenyl-glyoxal.* $C_6H_5COCOC_6H_5$	210.23	ye pr (al) λ^{al} 260 (4.3), 330 sh (2.4), 385 (1.9)	95–6	346–8d 188[12]	1.084[102]		i	v	v	s	v		B7[2], 764

For explanations, symbols and abbreviations see beginning of table. For structural formulas see end of table.

Benzil

No.	Name	Synonyms and Formula	Mol. wt.	Color, crystalline form, specific rotation and λ_{max} (log ε)	m.p. °C	b.p. °C	Density	n_D	w	al	eth	ace	bz	other solvents	Ref.
Ω b1199	—,dioxime(*anti*)...	α-Benzil dioxime. Diphenylglyoxime.	240.27	lf (al or ace) λ^{al} 226 (4.20), 240 (4.20)	238d	....			i	i	i	....	....	alk s aa i	B7[2], 680
b1200	—,—(*syn*).......	β-Benzil dioxime..........	240.27	nd (al) λ^{al} 252 (4.41)	207d	....			δ^h	s	s	....	....	NH$_3$ s alk s aa s	B7[2], 681
b1201	—,—(*amphi*)......	γ-Benzil dioxime...........	240.27	nd (al + 1), (aa)	164–6 100 (+al)	....			i	s	...	s	s	peth δ, lig i alk s CCl$_4$ δ	B7[2], 681
b1202	—,monooxime(α)..	....	225.25	lf (dil al, bz, MeOH) λ^{al} 250 sh (4.01)	137–8	200d			δ	v	v	...	δ	chl s aa v lig δ	B7[2], 678
b1203	—,—(β).........	....	225.25	pr or nd (bz + ½) λ^{al} 250 sh (4.01)	70 (+½bz) 113–4				δ	v	v	s	s	lig δ, chl s	B7[2], 679
b1204	—,osazone(*anti*)...	....	390.49	ye nd (al) λ^{al} 239 (4.6), 295 (4.3), 342 (4.6)	230–2				i	δ	...	δ	v^h	chl v^h	B15[2], 72
b1205	—,—(*syn*)........	....	390.49	ye nd (bz-al)	210				δ	s	...	δ	s	aa δ	B15[2], 72
—	**Benzilic acid**......	*see* **Acetic acid, diphenyl (hydroxy)-**													
Ω b1206	**Benzimidazole**.....	Benzoglyoxaline. 1,3-Benzodiazole.	118.14	rh bipym pl (w) λ^w 245 (3.72), 271 (3.79), 278 (3.78)	170.5 (173)	>360[760]			δ v^h	v	δ	...	i	dil alk s dil HCl v lig i	B23[2], 151
b1207	—,2-amino-	C$_7$H$_7$N$_3$. *See* b1206	133.15	pl (w) λ^{al} 244 (3.83), 283 (3.89)	224	....			s	s	δ	s	δ	....	B24[1], 240
b1208	—,2-hydroxy-.....	*o*-Phenylene urea. C$_7$H$_6$N$_2$O. *See* b1206	134.14	lf (w or al) λ^{al} 225.5 (3.86), 280 (3.88)	318d	....			δ	v	δ	s	δ	alk δ con HCl s	B24[2], 62
Ω b1209	—,5,6-dimethyl-...	C$_9$H$_{10}$N$_2$. *See* b1206.......	146.19	(eth) $\lambda^{w,pH=8}$ 246 (3.59), 279 (3.66), 286 (3.67)	205–6	140[3] sub			s	s	s	...		chl s	C50, 1087
b1210	—,2-mercapto-.....	C$_7$H$_6$N$_2$S. *See* b1206	150.20	pl (dil al, aq NH$_3$)	298 (304)	....			δ	v					B24[2], 65
b1211	—,1-methyl-......	C$_8$H$_8$N$_2$. *See* b1206.......	132.18	nd (peth), pl (al) λ^{al} 254 (3.78), 274 (3.70), 281 (3.70)	66	286[756]	1.1254$_4^{20}$	1.6013[7]	...	s^h		...		peth s^h	B23[2], 152
Ω b1212	—,2-methyl-......	C$_8$H$_8$N$_2$. *See* b1206.......	132.18	pr or nd (w) λ^{al} 274 (3.81), 288 (3.86)	176–7				s	δ	δ	...	i	....	B23[2], 160
b1213	—,4-methyl-......	C$_8$H$_8$N$_2$. *See* b1206.......	132.18	pl (w), nd (bz) λ^{al} 247 (3.85), 271 (3.60), 279 (3.63)	145				s^h	s	δ	...		....	B23[1], 38
Ω b1214	—,5-methyl-......	C$_8$H$_8$N$_2$. *See* b1206.......	132.18	(w) λ^{al} 245 (3.74), 277 (3.71), 283 (3.69)	114				s^h					....	B23[1], 38
b1215	—,2-methyl-1(2-naphthyl)-5-nitro-	C$_{18}$H$_{13}$N$_3$O$_2$. *See* b1206	303.32	nd (al)	162	....			s	s	s	...	v	aa s	B23, 150
b1216	—,2-methyl-5-nitro-1-phenyl-	C$_{14}$H$_{11}$N$_3$O$_2$. *See* b1206	253.26	nd (al)	170–1	....			i	s^h				....	B23[2], 161
Ω b1217	—,6-nitro-........	C$_7$H$_5$N$_3$O$_2$. *See* b1206.....	163.14	nd (w) λ^{al} 235 (4.30), 302 (3.97)	209–10 (205)				i	v	i	...	i	chl i, ac s	B23[2], 154
Ω b1218	—,2-phenyl-......	C$_{13}$H$_{10}$N$_2$. *See* b1206......	194.24	pl (aa, al-w), nd (bz, w) λ^{al} 240 (4.7), 301 (4.35)	293 (300)				δ	s	...	...	δ	chl δ aa s	B23[2], 238
b1219	**4,5-Benzindane**....	1,2-Cyclopentanonaphthalene.	168.24	oil λ 226 (4.89), 279 (3.78), 320 (3.17)	....	294–5[757] 170[5]	1.066$_4^{20}$	1.6290[20]	i			...		aa s	E13, 13
b1220	**1,2-Benzisothiazole, 5-hydroxy-3-phenyl-**	....	227.29	nd (dil al or aa)	159–60	....			...	v		v	δ	alk v aa v lig i	B27[2], 87
b1221	**Benzisoxazole, 3-methyl-**	....	133.15	....	....	108–10[16]			i	...	s	...	...	lig δ	C45, 2472

For explanations, symbols and abbreviations see beginning of table. For structural formulas see end of table.

No.	Name	Synonyms and Formula	Mol. wt.	Color, crystalline form, specific rotation and λ_{max} (log ε)	m.p. °C	b.p. °C	Density	n_D	Solubility						Ref.
									w	al	eth	ace	bz	other solvents	

1,2-Benzocarbazole

No.	Name	Synonyms and Formula	Mol. wt.	Color etc.	m.p.	b.p.	Density	n_D	w	al	eth	ace	bz	other	Ref.
b1222	1,2-Benzo-carbazole,3,4-dihydro-	. . . .	219.29	(lig or MeOH) λ^{al} 249 (4.36), 320 (4.25), 329 (4.36)	163–4	. . . . . .	. . . . . .	. . . . . .					. . .	MeOH s^h lig s^h	B20², 315
b1223	1,2-Benzo-1-cyclooctene-3-one	. . . .	174.25	λ^{al} 249.6 (3.85)		87–8[0.001]		1.5577[25]		. . .	. . .	. . .	. . .		Am 76, 5462
—	1,2-Benzodiazole	see **Indazole**													
b1224	5,6-Benzoflavone	β-Naphthoflavone	272.31	nd (al) λ 274, 315	167–8					δ^h	s		v^h	con sulf s (bl)	B17², 414
Ω b1225	7,8-Benzoflavone	α-Naphthoflavone	272.31	ye pl (al), lf or nd (dil al) λ^{al} 280 (4.48), 348 (3.74)	157–9 (167)					δ			. . .	sulf s (ye)	B17², 414
b1226	3,4-Benzofluor-anthene	. . . .	252.32	nd (bz) λ^{al} 256 (4.54), 301 (4.54), 338 (3.96), 369 (3.84)	168				i				δ		E14s, 569
b1227	10,11-Benzo-fluoranthene	. . . .	252.32	ye pl (al), nd (aa) λ^{al} 242 (4.60), 318 (4.48), 332 (4.04), 383 (4.00)	166				i	δ			. . .	aa δ	E14s, 570
b1228	11,12-Benzofluor-anthene	. . . .	252.32	pa ye nd (bz) λ^{al} 240 (4.75), 308 (4.75), 400 (4.16)	217	480[760]			i	s			s	aa s	E14s, 573
Ω b1229	1,2-Benzofluorene	Chrysofluorene	216.29	pl (ace or aa) λ^{al} 263 (4.86), 296 (4.20), 316 (4.14)	189–90	413[760] (398[758])				δ	s	s^h	chl s		E14, 299
b1230	—,9-phenyl-	$C_{23}H_{16}$. See b1229	292.39	nd (aa)	195.5	. . . . . .			. . .	δ^h	v		v	sulf s	E14, 299
Ω b1231	Benzofuran	Coumaron.	118.14	λ^{al} 245 (4.0), 278 (3.3), 285 (3.3)	< −18	174[760] 62–3[15]	1.0913[23]	1.5611[17]	i	s	s		. . .		B17², 57
b1232	—,2(chloro-methyl)-2,3-dihydro-	C_9H_9ClO. See b1231	168.63	. . . .	41–2	118–9[11]	1.2196[7.5]{16}	1.5620[7.5]	i		s	s			C40, 3755
—	—,2,3-dihydro-	see **Coumaran**													
Ω b1233	—,2-methyl-	C_9H_8O. See b1231	132.17	λ^{al} 250 (4.1), 275 (3.7), 285 (3.7), 310 (2.5)	. . . . . .	197.3–.8[760] 93–4[20]	1.0540[20]{4}	1.5495[22]	i	s	s		. . .		B17², 59
Ω b1234	—,3-methyl-	C_9H_8O. See b1231	132.17	λ^{al} 248 (3.97), 276 (3.40), 283 (3.40)	. . . . . .	196 7[742] 86[20]	1.0540[23]{4}	1.5536[16]	i	s	s		. . .		B17¹, 26
Ω b1235	—,5-methyl-	C_9H_8O. See b1231	132.17	λ^{al} 245 (4.01), 288 (3.47)	. . . . . .	197–9 83.5[17]	1.0603[19]	1.5570[19]	i	s	s		. . .	sulf s	B17¹, 27
Ω b1236	—,7-methyl-	C_9H_8O. See b1231	132.17	λ^{al} 244 (4.03), 282 (3.25)	. . . . . .	190–1	1.0490[19]	1.5525[17]	i	s	s		. . .	sulf s	B17, 61
Ω b1237	Benzohydroxamic acid	. . . .	137.14	rh ta, lf (eth) λ^{al} 270 (3.6)	131–2	exp			s^h	s	δ		δ		B9², 213
—	—,amide	see **Benzoic acid**, amidoxime.													
b1238	—,2-hydroxy-	Salicylhydroxamic acid. $C_7H_7NO_3$. See b1237	153.14	nd (aa)	168				δ	v	v			aa s^h	B10², 60
Ω b1239	Benzoic acid	Benzenecarboxylic acid.	122.13	mcl lf or nd λ^{al} 227 (4.06)	122.4	249[760] 133[10] (100 sub)	1.2659[15]{15} 1.0749[130]	1.504[132]	δ s^h	v	s	v	v^h s	CCl₄ s lig δ to, chl, MeOH s	B9², 72
b1240	—,4-acetamido-phenyl ester	p-Benzoyloxyacetanilide. $C_{15}H_{13}NO_3$. See b1239	255.28	nd (al)	171				δ^h	v			v	aa v lig i	Am 70, 2705
b1241	—,2-acetylphenyl ester	o-Benzoyloxyacetophenone, $C_{15}H_{12}O_3$. See b1239	240.26	nd (al)	88				i	v	v			aa v	B9², 133
b1242	—,4-acetylphenyl ester	p-Benzoyloxyacetophenone. $C_{15}H_{12}O_3$. See b1239	240.26	nd (al, aq MeOH)	135–6				i	s^h	s			aa v	B9², 133
Ω b1243	—,allyl ester	$C_6H_5CO_2CH_2CH:CH_2$	162.19	ye	. . . . . .	242 (228)	1.0578[15]{15}	1.5178[20]	i	s	s	s		MeOH s	B9², 93
Ω b1244	—,amide	Benzamide	121.14	mcl pr or pl (w) λ^{al} 225 (4.0), 270 sh (2.8)	132.5–3.5	290	1.0792[130]{4} 1.341[4]		δ v^h	v	δ		δ	CCl₄ v CS₂ v	B9², 163
b1245	—,—,N(3-chloro-2-methylphenyl)-	$C_{14}H_{12}ClNO$. See b1244	245.71	nd (al)	173				i	s	s	v	δ	aa δ	B12², 455
b1246	—,—,N,N-diphenyl-	N-Benzoyldiphenylamine. $C_6H_5CON(C_6H_5)_2$	273.34	rh pr (al), nd	180				δ	δ s^h	δ				B12², 155
Ω b1247	—,—,N(1-naph-thyl)-	$C_6H_5CONHC_{10}H_7$	247.30	nd (al or aa)	161–2	. . . . . .	. . . . . .		. . .	δ	. . .		s	aa s	B12², 525

For explanations, symbols and abbreviations see beginning of table. For structural formulas see end of table.

No.	Name	Synonyms and Formula	Mol. wt.	Color, crystalline form, specific rotation and λ_{max} (log ε)	m.p. °C	b.p. °C	Density	n_D	w	al	eth	ace	bz	other solvents	Ref.
	Benzoic acid														
b1248	—,—,N(2-nitrophenyl)-	$C_{13}H_{10}N_2O_3$. See b1244	242.24	gold-ye nd (al) λ^{al} 246 (4.3), 354 (3.5)	98	....			δ	s	v	....	....	....	B12[1], 342
•b1249	—,—,N(3-nitrophenyl)-	$C_{13}H_{10}N_2O_3$. See b1244	242.24	pl $(C_5H_{11}OH)$ λ^{al} 262 (4.3), 319 sh (3.2)	157	....			i	δ	v	....	....	chl v	B12[2], 380
b1250	—,—,N(4-nitrophenyl)-	$C_{13}H_{10}N_2O_3$. See b1244	242.24	ye nd (AcOEt) λ^{al} 321 (4.3)	199	....			i	δ[h] i	....	....	....	chl i	B12[2], 391
Ω b1251	—,—,N-phenyl- ...	Benzanilide. $C_6H_5CONHC_6H_5$	197.24	lf (al) λ^{al} 222 (4.19), 267 (4.20)	163	117–9[10] sub	1.315		i	δ v[h]	δ	....	aa δ		B12[2], 152
b1252	—,—,N(2-tolyl)-...	$C_{14}H_{13}NO$. See b1244	211.27	rh nd (AcOEt-ace)	145–6	....	1.205[15]		δ[h]	s	s	....	....		B12[2], 441
b1253	—,—,N(3-tolyl)-...	$C_{14}H_{13}NO$. See b1244	211.27	mcl pr (dil al)	125	....	1.170[15]			s		....	....		B12[1], 400
b1254	—,—,N(4-tolyl)-...	$C_{14}H_{13}NO$. See b1244	211.27	rh nd (al)	158	232	1.202[15]		i	s	s	....	....		B12[2], 505
b1255	—,amidine	Benzamidine. $C_6H_5C(:NH)NH_2$	120.17	lf (al) λ^w 229 (3.96), 268 (2.91)	80	....			s	v	δ	....	....		B9[2], 199
Ω b1256	—,—,hydrochloride	$C_6H_5C(:NH)NH_2.HCl$	156.62	rh pr (w +2)	169, 72 (+2w)				s[h]	s[h]		....	....		B9[2], 199
b1257	—,—,N,N-diphenyl-	$C_6H_5C(:NH)N(C_6H_5)_2$	272.35	rh pl (eth) $\lambda^{al, 1N HCl}$225 (4.24), 270 (3.8)	112	....				s	s	s	....		B12[2], 155
b1258	—,—,—,hydrochloride	$C_6H_5C(:NH)N(C_6H_5)_2.HCl.$	308.82	mcl pr or nd (al) λ^{al} 225 (4.24), 270 (3.8)	223d	....			v	v		....	....		B12, 270
b1259	—,—.N,N-diphenyl-	$C_6H_5C(:NC_6H_5)NHC_6H_5$.	272.35	nd (bz or al) pr (al) $\lambda^{al, 1N HCl}$ 273 (4.11)	146–7	....			δ	v	v	....	....		B12[2], 157
b1260	—,—,N(1-naphthyl)-	$C_6H_5C(:NH)NHC_{10}H_7^a$.....	246.32	pl (al)	141	....			i	s	s	....	....		B12, 1233
b1261	—,amidoxime.....	Benzamidoxime. $C_6H_5C(NH_2):NOH$	136.17	mcl pr (w) λ^w 250 (3.73)	80	....			δ	s	v	....	s	chl s lig i	B9[2], 214
Ω b1262	—,anhydride.....	Benzoic anhydride. $(C_6H_5CO)_2O$	226.24	pr (eth) λ^{peth} 238 (4.52), 277 (3.41)	42–3	360[760]	1.1989$^{15}_4$	1.5767[15]	i	s	s	....	s	lig i	B9[2], 147
b1263	—,azide.........	Benzoyl azide. $C_6H_5CON_3$.	147.14	pl (ace)	32	exp			i	s	s	....	....		B9[2], 219
b1264	—,benzoylmethyl ester	ω-Benzoyloxyacetophenone. $C_6H_5CO_2CH_2COC_6H_5$	240.26	pl (dil al)	118.5	....				s[h]	v	....	v	chl v	B9[2], 133
Ω b1265	—,benzyl ester	$C_6H_5CO_2CH_2C_6H_5$	212.25	nd or lf λ^{al} 229 (4.2), 267 (3.0), 272 (3.0), 280 (2.9)	21	323–4[760] (cor) 170–1[11]	1.1121$^{25}_4$	1.5680[20]	i	s	s	s	s	MeOH s chl s peth s	B9[2], 100
b1266	—,bromide	Benzoyl bromide. C_6H_5COBr	185.03	....	−24	218–9 48–50[0.05]	1.570[15]	1.5868[25]	d	d	∞	....	....		B9[2], 162
Ω b1267	—,butyl ester	$C_6H_5CO_2C_4H_9^n$.........	178.23	....	−22.4	250.3[760]	1.000[20]	1.4940[25]	i	∞	∞	s	....		B9[2], 90
Ω b1268	—,chloride	Benzoyl chloride. C_6H_5COCl	140.57	....	0	197.2[760] 71[9]	1.2120[20]	1.5537[20]	d	d	∞	....	s	CS_2 s	B9[2], 159
b1269	—,1-chloroethyl ester	$C_6H_5CO_2CHClCH_3$	184.62	....		134[30]	1.172[20]	....	i	s	s	....	....		B9[2], 127
b1270	—,2-chloroethyl ester	$C_6H_5CO_2CH_2CH_2Cl$......	184.62	....		254[729] 118–20[2]			i	v	v	....	....		B9[2], 90
b1271	—,cyclohexyl ester	$C_{13}H_{16}O_2$. See b1239......	204.27	....	< −10	285	1.0429[20]	1.5200[25]	i	s	s	....	....		B9[1], 65
b1272	—,2-ethoxyethyl ester	Ethyl cellosolve benzoate. $C_6H_5CO_2(CH_2)_2OC_2H_5$	194.23	λ^{cy} 228 (4.08), 273 (2.94), 280 (2.86)		260–1[739]	1.0585$^{25}_{25}$	1.4969[25]	i	v	v	v	v	os v	Am 54, 4370
Ω b1273	—,ethyl ester.....	$C_6H_5CO_2C_2H_5$	150.18	....	−34.6	213[760] 87[10]	1.0468$^{20}_4$	1.5007[20]	i	s	∞	s	s	chl s peth s	B9[2], 88
Ω b1274	—,fluoride.......	Benzoyl fluoride. C_6H_5COF .	124.12	....		154–5	>1	....	d[h]	v	v	....	....		B9[1], 94
b1275	—,hexyl ester	$C_6H_5CO_2(CH_2)_5CH_3$	206.29	λ^{al} 228 (4.05), 273 (2.94), 280 (2.85)		272[760] 139–40[8]			i	s	s	....	....		B9[2], 93
Ω b1276	—,hydrazide......	Benzoyl hydrazine. $C_6H_5CONHNH_2$	136.17	pl (w) $\lambda^{0.1N NaOH}$ 265 (3.72), 280 (2.16)	113–7	267d			s	s	δ	δ	....	chl δ	B9[2], 214
b1277	—,2-hydroxyethyl ester	1,2-Ethanediol monobenzoate. $C_6H_5CO_2CH_2CH_2OH$	166.18	....	45	150–1[10]			i	s		....	....		B9[2], 108
Ω b1278	—,2-hydroxyphenyl ester	Pyrocatechol monobenzoate. $C_{13}H_{10}O_3$. See b1239 .	214.22	nd (w)	130–1	....			s[h]	s		....	....		B9, 130
Ω b1279	—,3-hydroxyphenyl ester	Resorcinol monobenzoate. $C_{13}H_{10}O_3$. See b1239 .	214.22	pr (dil al) λ^{Pr^iOH} 320 (1.38)	135–6	....				i	s	....	....	chl v aa v	B9[2], 113

For explanations, symbols and abbreviations see beginning of table. For structural formulas see end of table.

Benzoic acid

No.	Name	Synonyms and Formula	Mol. wt.	Color, crystalline form, specific rotation and λ_{max} (log ε)	m.p. °C	b.p. °C	Density	n_D	w	al	eth	ace	bz	other solvents	Ref.
b1280	—,4-hydroxyphenyl ester	Hydroquinone monobenzoate. $C_{13}H_{10}O_3$. See b1239	214.22	nd (al)	163–4d				i	s	v	...	v	chl v	B9[2], 113
b1281	—,iodide	Benzoyl iodide. C_6H_5COI	232.02	nd	3	128[20]	1.748[18/18]	1.137[20]	d	s	∞				B9[2], 162
Ω b1282	—,isobutyl ester	$C_6H_5CO_2C_4H_9^i$	178.23			242[760]	0.9990[20/4]		i	∞	∞	s			B9[2], 91
Ω b1283	—,isopropyl ester	$C_6H_5CO_2C_3H_7^i$	164.21	λ^{al} 228 (4.01), 273 (2.89), 280 (2.80)		218[760]	1.0172[15/15]	1.4890[25]	i	s	s	s			B9[2], 90
b1284	—,2-methoxyethyl ester	$C_6H_5CO_2(CH_2)_2OCH_3$	180.21			254–6[760]	1.0891[25/23]	1.5040[25]	δ	s	s	s	s		B9, 129
b1285	—,2-methoxyphenyl ester	Guaiacyl benzoate. $C_{14}H_{12}O_3$. See b1239	228.25	(al) λ^{al} 224 (4.2), 271 (3.6),	58				δ[h]	v[h]	v	s	...	chl v aa δ	B9[2], 112
Ω b1286	—,methyl ester	$C_6H_5CO_2CH_3$	136.16	λ^{al} 227 (4.09)	−12.3	199.6[760] 96–8[24]	1.0888[20]	1.5164[20]	i	s	∞			MeOH s	B9[2], 87
Ω b1287	—,3-methylbutyl ester	Isoamyl benzoate. $C_6H_5CO_2(CH_2)_2CH(CH_3)_2$	192.24	λ^{al} 228 (4.09), 273 (2.96), 280 (2.88)		262.3[760] 133[14]	1.0040[20]	1.4950[20]	i	s	∞				B9[2], 92
b1288	—,methylene diester	Methanediol dibenzoate. $(C_6H_5CO_2)_2CH_2$	256.26	nd or pr (eth)	99	225d	1.275[22]		i	δ	s	s	s	MeOH v[h] CCl₄ v peth δ	B9[2], 127
b1289	—,1-naphthyl ester	$C_6H_5CO_2C_{10}H_7^a$	248.29	pl or pr (al-eth)	56				i	s[h]	v				B9, 125
Ω b1290	—,2-naphthyl ester	$C_6H_5CO_2C_{10}H_7^b$	248.29	nd or pr (al)	107				i	s[h]	δ			aa δ v[h]	B9, 125
Ω b1291	—,nitrile	Phenyl cyanide. Benzonitrile.	103.13	λ^{al} 222 (4.11), 230 (4.04)	−13	190.7 69[10]	1.0102[15/15]	1.5289[20]	δ[h]	∞	∞	v	v		B9[2], 196
b1292	—,2-nitrobenzyl ester	$C_{14}H_{11}NO_4$. See b1239	257.25	nd (dil al)	101–2				i	s[h]	s		s	aa s lig δ	B9, 121
b1293	—,3-nitrobenzyl ester	$C_{14}H_{11}NO_4$. See b1239	257.25		71–2				i	s	s				C25, 92
b1294	—,4-nitrobenzyl ester	$C_{14}H_{11}NO_4$. See b1239	257.25		94–5				i	s	s				B9[1], 68
Ω b1295	—,phenyl ester	$C_6H_5CO_2C_6H_5$	198.22	mcl pr (eth-al) λ^{al} 265 sh (3.3)	71	314[760] (299)	1.235[20]		i	s[h]	s[h]				B9[2], 96
b1296	—,1-phenylethyl ester	$C_6H_5CO_2CH(CH_3)C_6H_5$	226.28			189[21] 123.6[2]	1.1108[18]	1.5588[21]	i	s	s				B9, 121
b1297	—,2-phenyl-hydrazide	1-Benzoyl-2-phenylhydrazine. $C_6H_5CONHNHC_6H_5$	212.25	pr (al), nd (w), lf (dil al) λ^{al} 279 (3.5)	168	314			δ	s[h]	δ		s	chl s	B15[2], 97
Ω b1298	—,4-phenyl-phenacyl ester		316.34		167										C24, 5031
Ω b1299	—,propyl ester	$C_6H_5CO_2C_3H_7^n$	164.21		−51.6	231[760]	1.0230[20]	1.5000[20]	i	∞	∞				B9[2], 90
b1300	—,tetrahydro-furfuryl ester		206.24			300–2[750] 138–40[2]	1.1370[20]	1.1372[0]	i	∞	∞			chl ∞	B17[2], 107
b1301	—,2-tolyl ester	$C_{14}H_{12}O_2$. See b1239	212.25	λ 273 (3.3)		307–8[728] 154–6[8.5]	1.114[19]		i	s	v				B9[2], 98
b1302	—,3-tolyl ester	$C_{14}H_{12}O_2$. See b1239	212.25	λ 276 sh (3.2)	55–6	314 168–70[8]			i	s	s			CS₂ s	B9[2], 99
Ω b1303	—,4-tolyl ester	$C_{14}H_{12}O_2$. See b1239	212.25	pl (eth-al) λ 275 sh (3.4)	71.5	316			i	s	s			CS₂ s	B9[2], 99
b1304	—,2-acetamido-	$C_9H_9NO_3$. See b1239	179.18	nd (aa) λ^{al} 221 (4.41), 252 (4.13), 305 (3.67)	185				δ v[h]	s[h]	v	v	v	aa v[h]	B14[2], 219
b1305	—,3-acetamido-	$C_9H_9NO_3$. See b1239	179.18	nd (al) λ^{al} 297 (3.2)	248–50				i δ[h]	v[h]	δ				B14[2], 241
Ω b1306	—,4-acetamido-	$C_9H_9NO_3$. See b1239	179.18	nd (aa) λ^{al} 268 (4.3)	256.5 (250d)				i	s	δ				B14[2], 264
b1307	—,2-acetamido-4-ethoxy-	$C_{11}H_{13}NO_4$. See b1239	223.23	nd (al or MeOH)	199d				δ[h]	v[h]	δ[h]		δ[h]	chl δ[h] MeOH v[h]	B14[1], 657
b1308	—,5-acetamido-2-ethoxy-	$C_{11}H_{13}NO_4$. See b1239	223.23	nd (w)	190				δ[h]	s					B14, 583
b1309	—,2-acetyl-	$C_9H_8O_3$. See b1239	164.17	nd (w), pr (bz) λ^{al} 228 (3.9)	114–5	110–2[2]			s[h]	∞					B10[2], 479
b1310	—,4-acetyl-	$C_9H_8O_3$. See b1239	164.17	nd (w)	210	sub			s[h]	δ	δ			chl δ lig i	B10[2], 480
b1311	—,—,methyl ester	$C_{10}H_{10}O_3$. See b1239	178.19	nd (w)	95	160 5[4] sub			s[h]						B10, 695
b1312	—,5-allyl-2-hydroxy-3-methoxy-	Eugenic acid. $C_{11}H_{12}O_4$. See b1239	208.22	pl (w+1)	85–8 (+1w) 127 (anh)				i s[h]	s	s				B10[1], 215
Ω b1314	—,2-amino-	Anthranilic acid. $C_7H_7NO_2$. See b1239	137.14	lf (al) λ^{al} 247 (3.83), 332 (3.65)	146–7	sub	1.412[20]		s v[h]	s v[h]	s		δ s[h]	chl v[h] Py v	B14[2], 205
Ω b1315	—,—,amide	$C_7H_8N_2O$. See b1244	136.17	lf (chl or w) λ^{al} 250 (3.8), 335 (3.6)	110–11.5	300			s[h]	s	δ		δ	AcOEt v	B14[2], 210
Ω b1316	—,—,butyl ester	$C_{11}H_{15}NO_2$. See b1239	193.25		<0	182[760]			i	s	s				B14[2], 209
Ω b1317	—,—,ethyl ester	$C_9H_{11}NO_2$. See b1239	165.19	λ^{al} 225 (4.3), 250 (3.85), 338 (3.7)	13	268[760] 145–7[15]	1.1174[20/4]	1.5646[20]	i	s	s				B14[2], 209

For explanations, symbols and abbreviations see beginning of table. For structural formulas see end of table.

Benzoic acid

No.	Name	Synonyms and Formula	Mol. wt.	Color, crystalline form, specific rotation and λ_{max} (log ε)	m.p. °C	b.p. °C	Density	n_D	w	al	eth	ace	bz	other solvents	Ref.
Ω b1318	—,—,isobutyl ester	$C_{11}H_{15}NO_2$. See b1239	193.25	....	24–5	156–7[13.5]									B14[2], 209
Ω b1319	—,—,methyl ester	$C_8H_9NO_2$. See b1239	151.17	λ^{al} 248 (3.7), 341 (3.7)	24–5	256[760] 135.5[15]	1.1682[19]_4	1.5810[25]	δ	v	v				B14[2], 208
b1320	—,—,nitrile	o-Cyanoaniline. $C_7H_6N_2$. See b1291	118.14	ye pr (CS_2), nd (peth) λ^{al} 245 (3.8), 325 (3.7)	51	263[751]			δ	v	v	v	v	Py v chl v peth i CS_2 v	B14[2], 210
b1321	—,—,phenyl ester	$C_{13}H_{11}NO_2$. See b1239	213.24	nd (al)	70	....			δ	v	v				B14[2], 210
b1322	—,—,propyl ester	$C_{10}H_{13}NO_2$. See b1239	179.22			270[760]									B14[2], 209
Ω b1323	—,3-amino-	$C_7H_7NO_2$. See b1239	137.14	ye nd (w) λ^{al} 241 sh (3.85), 319 (3.32)	174 (180)	sub δd	1.5105[4]		δ s^h	δ s^h	s	v	i	chl δ, v^h MeOH v	B14[2], 237
b1324	—,—,amide	$C_7H_8N_2O$. See b1244	136.17	ye mcl nd (+1w), nd (bz) λ^{al} 240 sh (3.8), 310 (3.3)	79–80 (hyd) 113–14 (anh)				s	s	s		δ	chl δ	B14[1], 559
Ω b1326	—,—,ethyl ester	$C_9H_{11}NO_2$. See b1239	165.19			294 160–1[5]	1.1248[22]_4	1.5600[22]	δ	v	v				B14[2], 239
b1327	—,—,methyl ester	$C_8H_9NO_2$. See b1239	151.17	lf λ^{al} 250 sh (3.7), 323 (3.3)	39 (53–4)	152–3[11]	1.232[20]			v	v		v	chl v lig s peth δ	B14[2], 238
b1328	—,—,nitrile	m-Cyanoaniline. $C_7H_6N_2$. See b1291	118.14	nd (dil al or CCl_4) λ^{al} 250 (3.8), 320 (3.4)	53–4	288–90[760]			δ s^h	v	v	v		CS_2 s^h chl v	B14[2], 240
Ω b1329	—,4-amino-	$C_7H_7NO_2$. See b1239	137.14	mcl pr (w) λ^{al} 220 (3.95), 289 (4.27)	188–9		1.374[25]_4		s^h	s v^h	s		i	chl i, v^h	B14[2], 246
b1330	—,—,amide	$C_7H_8N_2O$. See b1244	136.17	ye cr (+¼w) λ^{al} 285 (4.3)	183	....			δ	s	s				B14, 425
b1331	—,—,—,N(2-diethylamino-ethyl)-, hydro-chloride	Procaine amide hydro-chloride. $C_{13}H_{21}N_3O\cdot HCl$. See b1244	271.79	cr λ^w 278	165–9 (177–9)				v	s	i		i	chl δ	C54, 428
b1332	—,—,—,N-phenyl-	$C_{13}H_{12}N_2O$. See b1244	212.25	λ^{al} 295 (4.1)	135–6	....				s					B14, 425
Ω b1333	—,—,butyl ester	Butesin. $C_{11}H_{15}NO_2$. See b1239	193.25	(al or bz)	58	173–4[8]			i	s	s	s	s	chl s	B14[2], 249
b1334	—,—,—,picrate	$C_{28}H_{33}N_5O_{11}$. See b1239	615.60	ye pw	109–10				δ	s	s	s	s	chl s	B14[2], 249
Ω b1335	—,2-diethyl-aminoethyl ester	Novocaine. Procaine. $C_{13}H_{20}N_2O_2$. See b1239	236.32	nd (w+2), pl (lig or eth) λ^w 221 (3.90), 290 (4.23)	51 (+2w) 61				δ	s	s	s	s	chl s	C54, 428
Ω b1336	—,—,—,hydro-chloride	Novocaine hydrochloride Procaine hydrochloride. $C_{13}H_{20}N_2O_2\cdot HCl$. See b1239	272.78	nd (al), mcl or tcl pl (w)	156		0.707[17]		v	s	i			chl δ	B14[2], 251
Ω b1337	—,—,ethyl ester	Benzocaine. $C_9H_{11}NO_2$. See b1239	165.19	nd (w), rh (eth) λ^{al} 292 (4.4)	92	310			i	v	v			chl s ac s	B14[2], 248
Ω b1338	—,—,methyl ester	$C_8H_9NO_2$. See b1239	151.17	lf or nd (aq MeOH) λ^{al} 294 (4.3)	114	....									B14[2], 247
b1339	—,—,nitrile	$C_7H_6N_2$. See b1291	118.14	pr or pl (w) λ^{al} 275 (4.3)	86				δ v^h	v	v	v	v	chl v, aa v lig δ CS_2 δ CCl_4 δ	B14[1], 570
b1340	—,—,phenyl ester	$C_{13}H_{11}NO_2$. See b1239	213.24	nd (al)	173					v	v				B14[1], 568
b1341	—,—,propyl ester	Propaesin. $C_{10}H_{13}NO_2$. See b1239	179.22	pr	75				δ	v	v			chl v	B14[2], 248
b1342	—,—,2,2,2-trichloro-ethyl ester	$C_9H_8Cl_3NO_2$. See b1239	268.54	nd (peth)	87				i		v				Am 77, 1575
b1343	—,2-amino-3,4-dichloro-	$C_7H_5Cl_2NO_2$. See b1239	206.03	nd (aa)	237–8 (242)				δ	v	v		δ	chl s aa δ, s^n	B14, 367
Ω b1344	—,2-amino-3,5-dichloro-	$C_7H_5Cl_2NO_2$. See b1239	206.03	nd or lf (al)	231–2d				i	v	v	s	s	os v	B14[1], 549
b1345	—,2-amino-3,6-dichloro-	$C_7H_5Cl_2NO_2$. See b1239	206.03	nd (w or aa)	155	sub			v^h	v	v	v	v^h	aa s^h	B14, 367
b1346	—,2-amino-4,5-dichloro-	$C_7H_5Cl_2NO_2$. See b1239	206.03	nd (aa)	213–4				δ	s	s			aa s	B14[1], 549
b1347	—,4-amino-3,5-dichloro-	$C_7H_5Cl_2NO_2$. See b1239	206.03	(al) $\lambda^{w,pH=1}$ 220 (4.34), 280 (4.17)	291				i	δ s^h	δ		δ	chl δ aa δ peth δ	B14[2], 271
b1348	—,6-amino-2,3-dichloro-	$C_7H_5Cl_2NO_2$. See b1239	206.03	nd (MeOH)	176–7d				s^h	v	v			MeOH v aa v	B14, 368
Ω b1349	—,2-amino-3,5-diiodo-	$C_7H_5I_2NO_2$. See b1239	388.93	pr (al)	232–3				i^h	δ	v		δ	....	B14[2], 233
b1350	—,—,ethyl ester	$C_9H_9I_2NO_2$. See b1239	416.99	pr (al)	101					δ s^h					B14[1], 555
b1351	—,2-amino-4,5-diiodo-	$C_7H_5I_2NO_2$. See b1239	388.93	cr (dil NH_3)	210–20d				i^h	s	s		s^h	....	B14[1], 555
b1352	—,—,ethyl ester	$C_9H_9I_2NO_2$. See b1239	416.99	pr (al)	137				$δ^h$	s^h	s		s	....	B14[1], 555

For explanations, symbols and abbreviations see beginning of table. For structural formulas see end of table.

No.	Name	Synonyms and Formula	Mol. wt.	Color, crystalline form, specific rotation and λ_{max} (log ε)	m.p. °C	b.p. °C	Density	n_D	Solubility						Ref.
									w	al	eth	ace	bz	other solvents	
	Benzoic acid														
Ω b1353	—,4-amino-3,5-diiodo-	$C_7H_5I_2NO_2$. See b1239	388.93	nd (aa-NH_3)	>350				i	i				$PhNO_2\ \delta$ AcOEt δ aa i	B14, 439
b1354	—,—,ethyl ester	$C_9H_9I_2NO_2$. See b1239	406.99	nd (al)	148					δ					B14, 439
Ω b1355	—,2-amino-3-hydroxy-	$C_7H_7NO_3$. See b1239	153.14	lf (w) $\lambda^{0.5N\ NaOH}$ 230 (4.27), 331 (3.63)	164				s^h δ	s	s			chl s	B14², 355
b1356	—,2-amino-4-hydroxy-	$C_7H_7NO_3$. See b1239	153.14	nd (w) λ^{al} 261 (4.04), 320 (3.78)	148d				s v^h	s	s	s	δ	chl, to δ	B14², 359
b1357	—,2-amino-5-hydroxy-	$C_7H_7NO_3$. See b1239	153.14	vt pr (w) λ^{al} 250 sh (3.7), 360 (3.5)	252d (darkens 235)				s^h	s	s	s	s	os s	B14², 357
b1358	—,3-amino-2-hydroxy-	$C_7H_7NO_3$. See b1239	153.14		235d				i	i	i				B14², 350
Ω b1359	—,3-amino-4-hydroxy-	$C_7H_7NO_3$. See b1239	153.14	pr (w+1) λ^w 253 (3.84), 297 (3.54)	210 (anh)				s^h	δ^h	i		i	chl i aa s^h	B14, 593
Ω b1360	—,—,methyl ester	$C_8H_9NO_3$. See b1239	167.17	(i) nd (bz or aa) (st) (ii) nd (chl) (unst)	(i) 143 (ii) 111				i s^h	v	ε		δ	ac s alk s	B14², 360
Ω b1361	—,4-amino-2-hydroxy-	$C_7H_7NO_3$. See b1239	153.14	nd, pl (al-eth) λ^{al} 237 (3.89), 279 (4.09), 305 (4.12)	150–1d (240)				s	s	s	s	i	peth, chl i	B14, 579
b1362	—,4-amino-3-hydroxy-	$C_7H_7NO_3$. See b1239	153.14	pl (dil al)	216				δ	v	v				B14², 356
b1363	—,—,methyl ester	Orthoform. $C_8H_9NO_3$. See b1239	167.17	pl (bz, w)	120–1 (142)				δ	v	v	s		aa v lig i	B14¹, 356
Ω b1364	—,5-amino-2-hydroxy-	$C_7H_7NO_3$. See b1239	153.14	nd (w)	283				δ^h	i					B14², 352
b1365	—,2-amino-4-iodo-	$C_7H_6INO_2$. See b1239	263.04	pr (dil al)	208d				δ	v	v		δ		B14¹, 554
Ω b1366	—,2-amino-5-iodo-	$C_7H_6INO_2$. See b1239	263.04	nd or pr (dil al)	210.5d				δ	v	v	s		os v peth δ	B14², 233
Ω b1367	—,2-amino-3-methyl-	$C_8H_9NO_2$. See b1239	151.17	nd (al), pr (w)	172				δ	v	v				B14², 290
b1368	—,2-amino-4-methyl-, nitrile	$C_8H_8N_2$. See b1291	132.18	lf (dil al)	94				i	s		s	s	chl s	B14², 291
b1369	—,2-amino-5-methyl-	$C_8H_9NO_2$. See b1239	151.17	lf (al), nd (w)	175				δ	s	v				B14², 291
b1370	—,—,nitrile	$C_8H_8N_2$. See b1291	132.18	cr (dil al)	63				s^h	s	s	s	s	os s lig δ	B14, 482
b1371	—,2-amino-6-methyl-	$C_8H_9NO_2$. See b1239	151.17	nd (MeOH)	125–6d									MeOH s^h	B14², 290
b1372	—,—,nitrile	$C_8H_8N_2$. See b1291	132.18	ye pr (bz), (w)	128				δ s^h				δ		B14², 290
b1373	—,3-amino-2-methyl-, nitrile	$C_8H_8N_2$. See b1291	132.18	nd (w)	95.5				δ						B14, 477
b1374	—,3-amino-4-methyl-	$C_8H_9NO_2$. See b1239	151.17	nd (al)	164–6				s	s					B14, 487
b1375	—,—,nitrile	$C_8H_8N_2$. See b1291	132.18	pr (al)	81–2				δ	s	s	v	v	os v	B14, 487
b1376	—,3-amino-5-methyl-, nitrile	$C_8H_8N_2$. See b1291	132.18	nd (lig)	75					s				lig δ	B14¹, 600
b1377	—,4-amino-2-methyl-	$C_8H_9NO_2$. See b1239	151.17	nd (a) $\lambda^{w, pH=3.6}$ 223 (3.98), 288 (4.08)	165d (153)	sub			s^h						B14, 477
b1378	—,—,nitrile	$C_8H_8N_2$. See b1291	132.18	rh cr (al)	90					s^h					B14¹, 598
Ω b1379	—,4-amino-3-methyl-	$C_8H_9NO_2$. See b1239	151.17	nd (w)	170				v^h						B14², 290
b1380	—,—,nitrile	$C_8H_8N_2$. See b1291	132.18	nd (w) λ^w 240 (3.89), 320 (3.58)	95				s^h						B14¹, 600
b1381	—,5-amino-2-methyl-	$C_8H_9NO_2$. See b1239	151.17	pr (w)	196				s^h	v^h					B14², 290
b1382	—,—,nitrile	$C_8H_8N_2$. See b1291	132.18	nd (peth)	88	$100-10^{22}$			δ^h	s				peth δ^h	B14², 290
b1383	—,4-amino-methyl-, nitrile, hydrochloride	$C_8H_8N_2 \cdot HCl$. See b1291	168.63	pl (al)	274					δ					B14, 488
b1384	—,2-amino-3-nitro-	$C_7H_6N_2O_4$. See b1239	182.14	ye nd (w)	208–9		1.558^{15}			i	v	v		δ	chl δ	B14², 233
Ω b1385	—,2-amino-4-nitro-	$C_7H_6N_2O_4$. See b1239	182.14	og pr (dil al)	269				i δ^h	v	v	v		xyl s	B14², 234
b1386	—,2-amino-5-nitro-	$C_7H_6N_2O_4$. See b1239	182.14	lf (al), ye nd (w, dil al)	268–70 (280)				i s^h	s	s		i	chl i, xyl i	B14², 234
b1387	—,2-amino-6-nitro-	$C_7H_6N_2O_4$. See b1239	182.14	ye nd or lf (w)	184				v^h	v	v	v	δ	chl δ aa v	B14¹, 557
b1388	—,3-amino-2-nitro-	$C_7H_6N_2O_4$. See b1239	182.14	ye nd (w, dil al)	156–7				δ s^h	s	s	v	δ	aa s^h lig i	B14, 414

For explanations, symbols and abbreviations see beginning of table. For structural formulas see end of table.

No.	Name	Synonyms and Formula	Mol. wt.	Color, crystalline form, specific rotation and λ_{max} (log ε)	m.p. °C	b.p. °C	Density	n_D	w	al	eth	ace	bz	other solvents	Ref.
	Benzoic acid														
b1389	—,3-amino-4-nitro-	$C_7H_6N_2O_4$. See b1239	182.14	red pl or nd (al)	298d				δ	s	s	v	...	aa s^h	B14, 415
Ω b1390	—,3-amino-5-nitro-	$C_7H_6N_2O_4$. See b1239	182.14	ye pr (w)	209–10				δ	s^h	δ	...	δ	CS_2 δ aa v^h	B14, 415
b1391	—,4-amino-2-nitro-	$C_7H_6N_2O_4$. See b1239	182.14	red nd (w), pr (dil aa)	239.5d				s^h δ	s	δ	...	δ	aa s	B14[1], 583
b1392	—,4-amino-3-nitro-	$C_7H_6N_2O_4$. See b1239	182.14	red-ye nd (al)	284d				i	δ^h	δ	v	...	aa s	B14[1], 583
b1393	—,5-amino-2-nitro-	$C_7H_6N_2O_4$. See b1239	182.14	ye nd or pr (w)	235d				δ^h	s	δ	v	...	aa s	B14[2], 245·
Ω b1394	—,3-amino-2,4,6-tribromo-	$C_7H_4Br_3NO_2$. See b1239	373.84	nd (w)	171.5–3				s^h δ	v					B14, 413
b1395	—,2-benzamido-	$C_{14}H_{11}NO_3$. See b1239	241.25	nd (al or bz)	181				i	v	v				B14[2], 221
b1396	—,3-benzamido-	$C_{14}H_{11}NO_3$. See b1239	241.25	red pr (al)	252–3		1.5105[4]		δ	s	δ				B14[1], 562
b1397	—,4-benzamido-	$C_{14}H_{11}NO_3$. See b1239	241.25	nd (al)	278				δ^h	s	s			aa s	B14[1], 577
Ω b1398	—,2-benzoyl-	2-Benzophenonecarboxylic acid. $C_{14}H_{10}O_3$. See b1239	226.24	tcl nd (w + 1) $\lambda^{H_3PO_4-P_2O_5}$ 234 (4.05), 278 (4.08)	127–9 (anh) 93.4 (+w)					v	v		s^h		B10[2], 517
b1399	—,—,amide	$C_{14}H_{11}NO_2$. See b1244	225.25	nd (to)	165 (cor)				i	v	v	v	v	to s^h	B10, 749
Ω b1400	—,—,ethyl ester	$C_{16}H_{14}O_3$. See b1239	254.29	rh pl (dil al)	58		1.2215[4][64]	1.560[64]	i	v	v			sulf s	B10[2], 517
Ω b1401	—,—,methyl ester	$C_{15}H_{12}O_3$. See b1239	240.26	pl or mcl pr (dil al) λ^{MeOH} 247 (4.22)	52	350–2[760]	1.1903[19][4]	1.591[20]	i	v	v			sulf s	B10[2], 517
b1402	—,3-benzoyl-	3-Benzophenonecarboxylic acid. $C_{14}H_{10}O_3$. See b1239	226.24	nd (w), fl (dil al)	161–2	sub			δ s^h	s	s		δ	to δ	B10[2], 521
Ω b1403	—,4-benzoyl-	4-Benzophenonecarboxylic acid. $C_{14}H_{10}O_3$. See b1239	226.24	nd (dil aa), pl (al), mcl lf (w)	198–200 (226–7)	sub			δ	s	s		δ	chl δ aa s	B10[2], 521
b1404	—,2-benzoyl-4-chloro-	$C_{14}H_9ClO_3$. See b1239	260.68	cr (xyl)	180.5					s	s			chl s lig, CS_2 δ	B10[1], 356
b1405	—,2-benzoyl-3,4,5,6-tetrachloro-, methyl ester	$C_{15}H_8Cl_4O_3$. See b1239	378.05	nd (MeOH)	92				i	s^h				MeOH s^h	B10, 750
Ω b1406	—,2-benzyl-	$C_{14}H_{12}O_2$. See b1239	212.25	nd (dil al)	118	sub			δ	s	s			chl s	B9[2], 471
b1407	—,3-benzyl-	$C_{14}H_{12}O_2$. See b1239	212.25	nd (w), lf (dil al)	108	sub			δ	v	v			chl v	B9, 676
b1408	—,4-benzyl-	$C_{14}H_{12}O_2$. See b1239	212.25	nd (w), lf (dil al)	157–8	sub			δ	s	s			chl s	B9[1], 284
Ω b1409	—,4-(benzylsulfonamido)-	Caronamide.	291.33		229–30				δ	s			δ	chl δ aa s	C45, 3418
Ω b1410	—,2-bromo-	$C_7H_5BrO_2$. See b1239	201.03	mcl pr (w), nd λ^{al} 225 sh (3.92), 280 (2.92)	150	sub	1.929[25][4]		δ s^h	s	s	s		chl s	B9[2], 230
Ω b1411	—,—,amide	C_7H_6BrNO. See b1244	200.04	nd (w)	160.5–1.5	sub			δ	s	δ				B9, 348
Ω b1412	—,—,chloride	C_7H_4BrClO. See b1239	219.47	nd	11	245[760] 118[10]		1.5965[20]	d	d^h					B9[2], 231
b1413	—,—,ethyl ester	$C_9H_9BrO_2$. See b1239	229.08			254–5 135[15]	1.4438[15][4]	1.5455[15]	δ	s	s	s	s	os s	B9, 348
b1414	—,—,methyl ester	$C_8H_7BrO_2$. See b1239	215.05			244[760] 122[17]			i	s					B9, 348
Ω b1415	—,—,nitrile	C_7H_4BrN. See b1291	182.03	nd (w)	55.5	251–3[754]			s^h	s^h	v				B9[2], 232
b1416	—,—,piperazinium salt	$C_{18}H_{20}Br_2N_2O_4$. See b1239	488.19		227–30d (cor)				δ^h	s^h	i				Am 70, 2758
Ω b1417	—,3-bromo-	$C_7H_5BrO_2$. See b1239	201.03	mcl nd (dil al) λ^{al} 224 sh (3.80), 262 (2.75), 282 (2.88)	155	>280	1.845[20]		i	s	s				B9[2], 232
b1418	—,—,amide	C_7H_6BrNO. See b1244	200.04	lf (w or al)	155.3	sub			δ s^h	v					B9[2], 232
Ω b1419	—,—,ethyl ester	$C_9H_9BrO_2$. See b1239	229.08			261[760] (255) 133[15]	1.4308[19][4]	1.5430[19]	...	s	s	v	s	os s	B9[2], 232
b1420	—,—,methyl ester	$C_8H_7BrO_2$. See b1239	215.05	pl	32	122.5[15]			δ	s	s				B9[1], 143
Ω b1421	—,—,nitrile	C_7H_4BrN. See b1291	182.03	(al) λ^{al} 229 (3.98), 288 (2.97)	39–40	225[760] 112–4[14]			δ	v	v				B9[2], 233
b1422	—,—,piperazinium salt	$C_{18}H_{20}Br_2N_2O_4$. See b1239	488.19		169–71				δ^h	s^h	i				Am 70, 2758
Ω b1423	—,4-bromo-	$C_7H_5BrO_2$. See b1239	201.03	nd (eth), lf (w), mcl pr λ^{al} 240 (4.10)	254.5		1.894[20]		δ s^h	s	s				B9[2], 233
Ω b1424	—,—,amide	C_7H_6BrNO. See b1244	200.04	nd or pl (w)	192–2.5				s^h	v	δ		i	CS_2 i lig i chl, aa s	B9, 353
Ω b1425	—,—,chloride	C_7H_4BrClO. See b1239	219.47	nd (peth) λ^{cy} 264 (4.33)	42	245–7[760] δd 123–6[15]			d	v	v		v	lig v	B9[2], 235
b1426	—,—,ethyl ester	$C_9H_9BrO_2$. See b1239	229.08	λ^{al} 244 (4.24)		262[737] 129[15]	1.4332[17][4]	1.5438[17]	δ	s	s	s	s	os s	B9[2], 234

For explanations, symbols and abbreviations see beginning of table. For structural formulas see end of table.

Benzoic acid

No.	Name	Synonyms and Formula	Mol. wt.	Color, crystalline form, specific rotation and λ_{max} (log ε)	m.p. °C	b.p. °C	Density	n_D	Solubility						Ref.
									w	al	eth	ace	bz	other solvents	
b1427	—,—,methyl ester	$C_8H_7BrO_2$. See b1239	215.05	lf (dil al), nd (eth) λ^{al} 245 (4.26)	81	....	1.689	....		s	s	s	v	chl v peth s	B9², 234
Ω b1428	—,—,nitrile	C_7H_4BrN. See b1291	182.03	nd (w or al) λ^{al} 241 (4.30), 263 (2.87), 282 (2.68)	114–4.5	235–7⁷⁶⁰			s^h	s	s	....	....		B9², 236
b1429	—,—,piperazinium salt	$C_{18}H_{20}Br_2N_2O_4$. See b1239	488.19	....	224–6				δ^h	s^h	i				Am 70, 2758
b1430	—,2-bromo-3-chloro-	$C_7H_4BrClO_2$. See b1239	235.47	cr (bz)	143–4				i				v^h		B9, 355
b1431	—,2-bromo-5-chloro-	$C_7H_4BrClO_2$. See b1239	235.47	cr (bz)	153				i	s			v^h		B9, 355
b1432	—,3-bromo-2-chloro-	$C_7H_4BrClO_2$. See b1239	235.47	cr (al)	165				i	v^h s					B9, 356
b1433	—,3-bromo-4-chloro-	$C_7H_4BrClO_2$. See b1239	235.47	pl (dil aa), cr (al)	215–6				i	s			aa v		B9², 236
b1434	—,4-bromo-3-chloro-	$C_7H_4BrClO_2$. See b1239	235.47	pl (dil aa), cr (al)	218				δ	v			aa v^h		B9², 236
b1435	—,5-bromo-2-chloro-	$C_7H_4BrClO_2$. See b1239	235.47	nd (w), cr (aa)	155–6				δ	v			aa δ, v^h		B9, 356
b1436	—,3-bromo-2,4-dihydroxy-	$C_7H_5BrO_4$. See b1239	233.03	br or ye nd (w)	202				s^h				aa s		B10², 254
b1437	—,5-bromo-2,3-dihydroxy-	$C_7H_5BrO_4$. See b1239	233.03	pr (w + 1), nd (w)	187 (pr), 215 (nd)				δ s^h	v	v	δ	aa v	B10¹, 175
b1438	—,5-bromo-2,4-dihydroxy-	$C_7H_5BrO_4$. See b1239	233.03	micr pr (w + 1)	212				δ s^h	v	v				B10², 254
b1439	—,5-bromo-3,4-dihydroxy-	$C_7H_5BrO_4$. See b1239	233.03	nd (w, aa, dil al)	230				s^h				aa s^h		B10¹, 192
b1440	—,2-bromo-3,5-dinitro-	$C_7H_3BrN_2O_6$. See b1239	291.02	ye nd (w)	213				δ	v			s	aa v lig s	B9², 284
b1441	—,2-bromo-3-hydroxy-	$C_7H_5BrO_3$. See b1239	217.03	nd (w)	160–1				δ v^h		s				B10², 83
b1442	—,2-bromo-4-hydroxy-	$C_7H_5BrO_3$. See b1239	217.03	nd (w)	151				δ v^h		s				B10², 103
b1443	—,2-bromo-5-hydroxy-	$C_7H_5BrO_3$. See b1239	217.03	(w)	185d				δ s^h		s				B10², 84
b1444	—,3-bromo-2-hydroxy-	$C_7H_5BrO_3$. See b1239	217.03	nd (dil al)	184.5				δ^h	v	v	v	δ	MeOH v, chl δ	B10², 63
b1445	—,3-bromo-4-hydroxy-	$C_7H_5BrO_3$. See b1239	217.03	nd or pr (+w) (w)	177				δ v^h	v	v		aa v	B10², 103
b1446	—,4-bromo-2-hydroxy-	$C_7H_5BrO_3$. See b1239	217.03	pl, nd (w)	214 (165)				δ v^h	v					B10², 63
b1447	—,4-bromo-3-hydroxy-	$C_7H_5BrO_3$. See b1239	217.03	nd (w)	227				δ s^h						B10², 63
Ω b1448	—,5-bromo-2-hydroxy-	$C_7H_5BrO_3$. See b1239	217.03	nd (w or dil al) λ^w 232 sh (3.92), 308 (3.52)	168–9	sub >100			v^h δ	v	v				B10², 63
b1449	—,2-bromo-3-nitro-	$C_7H_4BrNO_4$. See b1239	246.02	(dil al)	191				δ s^h	v					B9², 277
b1450	—,2-bromo-4-nitro-	$C_7H_4BrNO_4$. See b1239	246.02	nd (w or dil al)	166–7	sub >155			δ s^h	v	v				B9², 277
b1451	—,2-bromo-5-nitro-	$C_7H_4BrNO_4$. See b1239	246.02	nd (w)	180–1	sub			δ s^h	v	v		chl v		B9², 277
b1452	—,3-bromo-2-nitro-	$C_7H_4BrNO_4$. See b1239	246.02	(eth)	250				δ		v^h	v^h			B9², 276
b1453	—,3-bromo-4-nitro-	$C_7H_4BrNO_4$. See b1239	246.02	nd (dil al)	197				δ	v	v		chl v		B9, 408
b1454	—,3-bromo-5-nitro-	$C_7H_4BrNO_4$. See b1239	246.02	nd (w. bz or eth), pl (al)	159–60				δ s^h	v	v		s	CS_2 s aa v chl s	B9², 277
b1455	—,4-bromo-2-nitro-	$C_7H_4BrNO_4$. See b1239	246.02	nd (w)	163				s^h	v	v		v	chl v	B9², 276
b1456	—,4-bromo-3-nitro-	$C_7H_4BrNO_4$. See b1239	246.02	nd (dil aa)	203–4	sub			i s^h	v					B9², 277
b1457	—,5-bromo-2-nitro-	$C_7H_4BrNO_4$. See b1239	246.02	cr (w, al, bz, to)	140		1.920¹⁸		δ^h	s			v^h		B9, 406
b1458	—,2-tert-butyl-	$C_{11}H_{14}O_2$. See b1239	178.23	pl (dil al)	80.3–.8				i	v					B9², 365
b1459	—,3-tert-butyl-	$C_{11}H_{14}O_2$. See b1239	178.23	nd (peth)	127–7.5					v			peth v	B9, 560
Ω b1460	—,4-tert-butyl-	$C_{11}H_{14}O_2$. See b1239	178.23	nd (dil al) $\lambda^{al-0.01\,N\,HCl}$ 237.5 (4.21)	164.5–5.5				i	v		v	peth v^h		B9², 365
b1461	—,4-butylamino-(2-dimethylamino-ethyl) ester, hydrochloride	Tetracaine hydrochloride. $C_{15}H_{25}ClN_2O_2$. See b1239	300.83	....	147–50				v	s	i	...	i	....	C54, 429
—	—,(carboxy-methoxy)-	see Acetic acid, (carboxyphenoxy)-													
b1462	—,4-(4-carboxy-benzoyl)-	p,p'-Benzophenonedi-carboxylic acid. $C_{15}H_{10}O_5$. See b1239	270.25	nd (al)	> 360	sub			i	δ	δ	δ	δ	aa s	B10², 618

For explanations, symbols and abbreviations see beginning of table. For structural formulas see end of table.

Benzoic acid

No.	Name	Synonyms and Formula	Mol. wt.	Color, crystalline form, specific rotation and λ_{max} (log ε)	m.p. °C	b.p. °C	Density	n_D	w	al	eth	ace	bz	other solvents	Ref.
Ω b1465	—,2-chloro-......	$C_7H_5ClO_2$. See b1239	156.57	mcl pr (w) λ^{al} 229 sh (3.71), 278 (2.88)	142	sub	1.544^{20}	....	s^h	v	v	v	s	CS_2, lig δ peth s^h AcOEt v	$B9^2$, 221
Ω b1466	—,—,amide	C_7H_6ClNO. See b1244...	155.59	rh nd (w)	142.4	....	....	....	s^h	s	s	...	...		B9, 336
b1467	—,—,anhydride	$C_{14}H_8Cl_2O_3$. See b1239...	295.14	nd (al)	79.6	....	....	....		v			v	chl v lig δ	$B9^2$, 223
Ω b1468	—,—,chloride.....	$C_7H_4Cl_2O$. See b1239...	175.02	λ^{cy} 242 (3.95)	−4	238^{760} 110^{15}	....	1.5726^{20}	d	d					$B9^2$, 223
b1469	—,—,ethyl ester ...	$C_9H_9ClO_2$. See b1239...	184.62	....	....	243^{760} $122–5^{15}$	1.1942^{15}_4	1.5247^{15}	i	s	v				B9, 336
b1470	—,—,methyl ester ..	$C_8H_7ClO_2$. See b1239...	170.62	....	....	$234–5^{762}$	....	....		s					$B9^2$, 222
Ω b1471	—,—,nitrile.......	C_7H_4ClN. See b1291...	137.57	nd λ^{cy} 230 (4.00), 272 (2.89), 288 (3.17)	43–6	232	....	....	$δ^h$	s	s	...	...		$B9^2$, 223
b1472	—,—,piperazinium salt	$C_{18}H_{20}Cl_2N_2O_4$. See b1239	399.28	....	217–8d	....	....	....	s	s	s	...	...		Am 70, 2758
Ω b1473	—,3-chloro-.......	$C_7H_5ClO_2$. See b1239...	156.57	pr (w) λ^{al} 230 (3.92), 284 (2.98)	158 (155)	sub	1.496^{25}_4	....	v^h	s	v	...	δ s^h	CS_2 δ lig δ CCl_4 δ	$B9^2$, 223
b1474	—,—,amide	C_7H_6ClNO. See b1244...	155.59	nd $\lambda^{60\% \, sulf}$ 248 (3.98)	135.5–7.0	....	....	....	δ s^h	s	s	...	...		B9, 338
b1475	—,—,anhydride	$C_{14}H_8Cl_2O_3$. See b1239...	295.14	nd (al or peth), lf (bz)	95.5	....	....	....			v		v	peth s^h chl v lig δ	$B9^2$, 224
Ω b1476	—,—,chloride.....	$C_7H_4Cl_2O$. See b1239...	175.02	λ^{cy} 244 (4.08), 254 (4.06)	....	225 $103–4^{14}$	....	1.5677^{20}	d	d					$B9^2$, 224
Ω b1477	—,—,ethyl ester ...	$C_9H_9ClO_2$. See b1239...	184.62	....	....	245 121^{20}	1.1859^{15}_4	1.5223^{15}	i	s	s				$B9^1$, 139
b1478	—,—,methyl ester ..	$C_8H_7ClO_2$. See b1239...	170.60	....	21	231^{763} 114^{18}	....	....	i	s	s				B9, 338
b1479	—,—,nitrile.......	C_7H_4ClN. See b1291...	137.57	nd λ^{cy} 228 (4.02), 271 (2.80), 287 (3.06)	40–2	$99–100^{15}$	....	....	i	s	s				$B9^2$, 225
Ω b1480	—,4-chloro-.......	$C_7H_5ClO_2$. See b1239...	156.57	tcl pr (al-eth) λ^{al} 234 (4.18)	243	....	....	....	i s^h	v	δ	δ	i	lig i CCl_4, CS_2 i	$B9^2$, 225
Ω b1481	—,—,amide	C_7H_6ClNO. See b1244...	155.59	nd (eth)	179–80	....	....	....	s^h	v	v	...	...		$B9^2$, 227
b1482	—,—,anhydride	$C_{14}H_8Cl_2O_3$. See b1239...	295.14	nd or lf (bz)	193–4	....	....	....		δ	i	...	δ	CS_2 i chl δ peth i	$B9^2$, 227
Ω b1483	—,—,chloride.....	$C_7H_4Cl_2O$. See b1239...	175.02	....	16	222^{760} 111^{18}	1.3770^{20}_4	1.5756^{20}							$B9^2$, 227
Ω b1484	—,—,ethyl ester ...	$C_9H_9ClO_2$. See b1239...	184.62	....	....	$237–8$ 122^{15}	....	....		s					$B9^1$, 140
b1485	—,—,methyl ester ..	$C_8H_7ClO_2$. See b1239...	170.60	nd or mcl pr	44	....	1.382^{20}	....		s					$B9^2$, 226
Ω b1486	—,—,nitrile.......	C_7H_4ClN. See b1291...	137.57	nd (al) λ^{cy} 243 (4.22), 270 (2.66), 281 sh (2.18)	94–6	223^{750} 95^5	....	....	$δ^h$	s	s	s	s	chl s lig δ	$B9^2$, 288
b1487	—,—,piperazinium salt	$C_{18}H_{20}Cl_2N_2O_4$. See b1239	399.28	....	219–20d	....	....	....	s	s	δ	...	...		Am 70, 2758
Ω b1488	—,2(4-chloro-benzoyl)-	$C_{14}H_9ClO_3$. See b1239...	260.68	cr (bz, aa) λ^{MeOH} 254.5 (4.25)	150 (148)	....	....	....	$δ^h$	s	s	...	s^h		$B10^2$, 518
b1489	—,2-chloro-3-hydroxy-	$C_7H_5ClO_3$. See b1239...	172.57	lf (w or bz)	157.5–8.5	....	....	....	δ v^h			...	v^h		B10, 142
b1490	—,2-chloro-4-hydroxy-	$C_7H_5ClO_3$. See b1239...	172.57	nd (w)	159	....	....	....	δ v^h			s			$B10^2$, 102
b1491	—,2-chloro-5-hydroxy-	$C_7H_5ClO_3$. See b1239...	172.57	(w)	178–9	....	....	....	δ	v^h		s			B10, 143
b1492	—,2-chloro-6-hydroxy-	$C_7H_5ClO_3$. See b1239...	172.57	nd (w)	166	....	....	....	s	s	s	...	...	os s	B10, 104
b1493	—,3-chloro-2-hydroxy-	$C_7H_5ClO_3$. See b1239...	172.57	nd (w)	180 (182)	....	....	....	δ	s		...	...	chl. aa s	$B10^2$, 61
b1494	—,—,ethyl ester ...	$C_9H_9ClO_3$. See b1239...	200.62	nd	21	$269–70$ 147^{12}	....	....		s					B10, 101
b1495	—,—,methyl ester .	$C_8H_7ClO_3$. See b1239...	186.60	nd (MeOH or al)	38	260 δd	....	....		s					B10, 101
Ω b1496	—,3-chloro-4-hydroxy-	$C_7H_5ClO_3$. See b1239...	172.57	nd (w)	170–2	sub	....	....	δ v^h	v	v	v	δ	chl δ lig δ	B10, 175
b1497	—,4-chloro-2-hydroxy-	$C_7H_5ClO_3$. See b1239...	172.57	nd (w)	207	sub δd	....	....	δ	s		...	s	chl s	$B10^2$, 61
b1498	—,4-chloro-3-hydroxy-	$C_7H_5ClO_3$. See b1239...	172.57	nd (w)	219.5–20.5	....	....	....	δ v^h			...	...		$B10^2$, 83
Ω b1499	—,5-chloro-2-hydroxy-	$C_7H_5ClO_3$. See b1239...	172.57	nd (w or al) λ^w 230 (3.90), 314 (3.53)	173–4 (168)	....	....	....	s	v	s	...	v	chl v, aa s	$B10^2$, 62
b1500	—,—,ethyl ester ...	$C_9H_9ClO_3$. See b1239...	200.62	nd (al)	25	....	....	....		s^h					B10, 103
b1501	—,—,methyl ester ..	$C_8H_7ClO_3$. See b1239...	186.60	nd (al)	50	249d	....	....		v					B10, 103

For explanations, symbols and abbreviations see beginning of table. For structural formulas see end of table.

No.	Name	Synonyms and Formula	Mol. wt.	Color, crystalline form, specific rotation and λ_{max} (log ε)	m.p. °C	b.p. °C	Density	n_D	w	al	eth	ace	bz	other solvents	Ref.
	Benzoic acid														
b1502	—.5-chloro-2-methoxy-	$C_8H_7ClO_3$. See b1239	186.60	nd (w)	81–2				v	v	...	v	...		B10, 103
b1503	—.2-chloro-4-methyl-	$C_8H_7ClO_2$. See b1239	170.60	nd (al)	155–6				δ v^h	v	v	...	v^h	chl v	B9, 497
b1504	—.2-chloro-5-methyl-	$C_8H_7ClO_2$. See b1239	170.60	nd (w or al)	167				v^h	v^h					B9, 479
b1505	—.2-chloro-6-methyl-	$C_8H_7ClO_2$. See b1239	170.60	nd (w)	102				δ^h						B9², 320
b1506	—.3-chloro-2-methyl-	$C_8H_7ClO_2$. See b1239	170.60	nd (al)	159 (154)				...	v	s				B9, 467
b1507	—.3-chloro-4-methyl-	$C_8H_7ClO_2$. See b1239	170.60	nd or lf (dil al)	200–2				δ^h	v					B9, 498
b1508	—.3-chloro-5-methyl-	$C_8H_7ClO_2$. See b1239	170.60	nd (dil al)	178				δ	v					B9, 479
b1509	—.4-chloro-2-methyl-	$C_8H_7ClO_2$. See b1239	170.60	nd (w, al, dil aa, bz)	173				v^h	v^h		...	δ v^h	aa v	B9, 468
b1510	—.4-chloro-3-methyl-	$C_8H_7ClO_2$. See b1239	170.60	nd (w)	209–10				i δ^h						B9, 478
b1511	—.5-chloro-2-methyl-	$C_8H_7ClO_2$. See b1239	170.60	nd (al)	168.5–9.5				v	v^h					B9², 320
b1512	—.3-chloro-methyl-, nitrile	C_8H_6ClN. See b1291	151.60	pr (al)	67	258–60⁷⁶⁰									B9, 479
b1513	—.4-chloro-methyl-, nitrile	C_8H_6ClN. See b1291	151.60	pr (al)	79.5	263⁷⁵⁶									B9, 498
Ω b1514	—.2-chloro-4-nitro-	$C_7H_4ClNO_4$. See b1239	201.57	nd (w)	140–2				s^h	s	s	...	s^h		B9², 276
Ω b1515	—.2-chloro-5-nitro-	$C_7H_4ClNO_4$. See b1239	201.57	nd or pr (w)	165 (168)		1.608¹⁸		δ	s	s		s		B9², 275
b1516	—.3-chloro-2-nitro-	$C_7H_4ClNO_4$. See b1239	201.57	nd or pl (w)	237–9		1.566¹⁸		δ^h	s	s		i		B9, 400
b1517	—.3-chloro-5-nitro-	$C_7H_4ClNO_4$. See b1239	201.57	nd (w)	147				δ	s	s		aa s		B9, 403
Ω b1518	—.4-chloro-2-nitro-	$C_7H_4ClNO_4$. See b1239	201.57	pl (bz-lig), pr (bz), nd (w)	142–3				s^h	s	s		s^h		B9², 274
Ω b1519	—.—.nitrile	$C_7H_3ClN_2O_2$. See b1291	182.57	nd (w)	100–1				v^h	s	s				B9², 275
Ω b1520	—.4-chloro-3-nitro-	$C_7H_4ClNO_4$. See b1239	201.57	nd or pl (w)	181–2		1.645¹⁸		i s^h	δ					B9², 275
Ω b1521	—.—.ethyl ester	$C_9H_8ClNO_4$. See b1239	229.63	ye nd (al)	59					v	v		aa s		B9, 402
b1522	—.—.methyl ester	$C_8H_6ClNO_4$. See b1239	215.59	nd (MeOH)	83		1.522¹⁸			v	v		aa s		B9, 402
b1523	—.5-chloro-2-nitro-, methyl ester	$C_8H_6ClNO_4$. See b1239	215.59	pl (MeOH)	48.5		1.453¹⁸							MeOH v	B9, 401
b1524	—.2,3-diamino-	$C_7H_8N_2O_2$. See b1239	152.16	nd (dil al)	190–1d	d			δ	v			aa v		B14¹, 585
b1525	—.2,4-diamino-	$C_7H_8N_2O_2$. See b1239	152.16	nd	140	>200d			s^h	v			aa v		B14, 448
b1526	—.2,5-diamino-	$C_7H_8N_2O_2$. See b1239	152.16	br pr (w)	darkens 200				δ	δ	δ				B14, 448
Ω b1527	—.3,4-diamino-	$C_7H_8N_2O_2$. See b1239	152.16	lf (w)	215–8d				δ s^h	v					B14¹, 586
Ω b1528	—.3,5-diamino-	$C_7H_8N_2O_2$. See b1239	152.16	nd (+1w)	240 (rapid htng)				δ s^h	s	v				B14, 453
b1529	—.3-diazo-2-hydroxy-	$C_7H_4N_2O_3$. See b1239	164.12	ye nd (ace)	155d							s			B16, 553
b1530	—.2,3-dibromo-	$C_7H_4Br_2O_2$. See b1239	279.93	nd (w)	149–50				δ^h					lig δ s^h	B9¹, 146
b1531	—.2,4-dibromo-	$C_7H_4Br_2O_2$. See b1239	279.93	lf (w)	174	sub			δ	s	s				B9², 237
b1532	—.2,5-dibromo-	$C_7H_4Br_2O_2$. See b1239	279.93	nd (al or w)	157				s^h	s	s		chl s aa s		B9², 237
b1533	—.2,6-dibromo-	$C_7H_4Br_2O_2$. See b1239	279.93	nd (w), (lig) λ^{al} 262 (2.97), 272 (2.94)	150–1	ca 335δd 209–10¹⁶			s^h	v	v	s	peth δ chl v		B9², 237
Ω b1534	—.3,4-dibromo-	$C_7H_4Br_2O_2$. See b1239	279.93	nd (w), pl (al)	234–5				s^h	s	s		MeOH s		B9², 237
b1535	—.3,5-dibromo-2,4-dihydroxy-6-methyl-, ethyl ester	$C_{10}H_{10}Br_2O_4$. See b1239	354.01	pr (al)	144				...	δ v^h	s				B10², 275
b1536	—.2,6-dibromo-3,4,5-trihydroxy-	Gallobromol. $C_7H_4Br_2O_5$. See b1239	327.93	nd, pr or lf (w + 1)	139d (hyd)				v	v	v		chl i		B10², 347
b1537	—.2,3-dichloro-	$C_7H_4Cl_2O_2$. See b1239	191.02	nd (w)	168.3 (164)				s	s	s				B9², 228
Ω b1538	—.2,4-dichloro-	$C_7H_4Cl_2O_2$. See b1239	191.02	nd (w or bz) λ^{MeOH} 282 (2.76)	164.2	sub			s^h	s	s		s	chl s	B9², 228
Ω b1539	—.—.chloride	$C_7H_3Cl_3O$. See b1239	209.47	liq	15–8	150³⁴ 111⁷·⁵		1.5895²⁰	d^h	d^h					B9², 229
Ω b1540	—.2,5-dichloro-	$C_7H_4Cl_2O_2$. See b1239	191.02	nd (w)	154.4	301⁷⁶⁰			δ s^h	s	s				B9², 229
Ω b1541	—.2,6-dichloro-	$C_7H_4Cl_2O_2$. See b1239	191.02	nd (al), pr (w) λ^{MeOH} 273 (2.56)	144 (139)	sub			s^h	s	s		s		B9², 229
Ω b1542	—.3,4-dichloro-	$C_7H_4Cl_2O_2$. See b1239	191.02	nd (w, al, bz) λ^{MeOH} 282 (2.93), 291 (2.96)	208–9				s^h	v	s		...		B9¹, 141

For explanations, symbols and abbreviations see beginning of table. For structural formulas see end of table.

No.	Name	Synonyms and Formula	Mol. wt.	Color, crystalline form, specific rotation and λ_{max} (log ε)	m.p. °C	b.p. °C	Density	n_D	w	al	eth	ace	bz	other solvents	Ref.
	Benzoic acid														
Ω b1543	—,—.chloride.....	$C_7H_3Cl_3O$. See b1239	209.47	liq	24–6	242[760] 160[42]			d^h	d^h	..	..	..		B9, 344
b1544	—.3,5-dichloro-...	$C_7H_4Cl_2O_2$. See b1239	191.02	nd (al or w)	188	sub			δ	s	s	..	..	lig δ	B9[2], 229
b1545	—.3,5-dichloro-2-hydroxy-	$C_7H_4Cl_2O_3$. See b1239	207.01	nd (dil al). rh pr	220–1 (223)	sub δd			δ^h	v	s	..	..		B10[1], 48
Ω b1546	—.3,5-dichloro-4-hydroxy-	$C_7H_4Cl_2O_3$. See b1239	207.01	nd (dil al or dil aa)	269	sub δd			δ s^h	v	v	..	..		B10[1], 78
b1547	—.2(N,N-dichloro-sulfamyl)-	....	270.09	yesh gr pl (chl)	146–8 exp				δ^h	..	..	..	..	chl δ^h	B11, 377
b1548	—.4(N,N-dichloro-sulfamyl)-	Halazone.	270.09	pr (aa)	213	....			δ^h	..	..	..	..	chl δ^h aa v^h peth i	B11[2], 220
b1549	—.2,3-dihydroxy-...	o-Pyrocatechuic acid. $C_7H_6O_4$. See b1239	154.12	pr or nd (w + 1)	204 (anh)	....	1.5422[20]	....	s	s	s	..	..		B10[2], 248
Ω b1550	—.2,4-dihydroxy-...	β-Resorcylic acid. $C_7H_6O_4$. See b1239	154.12	cr +w(w) λ^w 248 (4.05), 292 (3.72), 227 (2.19)	....	....			s^h	s	s	..	s	CS_2 i	B10[2], 251
Ω b1551	—.2,5-dihydroxy-..	Gentisic acid. $C_7H_6O_4$. See b1239	154.12	nd or pr (w) λ^w 320 (3.63)	205				v	v	v	..	i	chl i CS_2 i	B10[2], 257
Ω b1552	—.2,6-dihydroxy-..	γ-Resorcylic acid. $C_7H_6O_4$. See b1239	154.12	nd (+w) λ^{al} 250 (3.80), 277 (3.29), 311 (3.54)	167d (150–70)				s^h	s	s	..	i	chl i	B10[2], 259
Ω b1553	—.3,4-dihydroxy-..	Protocatechuic acid. $C_7H_6O_4$. See b1239	154.12	mcl nd (w + 1) $\lambda^{1N HCl}$ 259 (3.94), 293 (3.64)	200–2d		1.524[4]		v^h δ	v	s	..	i		B10, 389
Ω b1554	—.3,5-dihydroxy-..	α-Resorcylic acid. $C_7H_6O_4$. See b1239	154.12	pr or nd (+1½w) λ^w 208 (4.49), 248 (4.03), 292 (3.69)	238–40, 232–3 (+w)				δ v^h	v	v	..	..		B10[2], 266
Ω b1555	—.2,4-dihydroxy-6-methyl-	o-Orsellinic acid. $C_8H_8O_4$. See b1239	168.16	nd (dil aa +lw) λ^{al} 260 (4.1), 300 (3.6)	176d				..	s	s	..	..		B10[2], 272
b1556	—,—.ethyl ester ...	$C_{10}H_{12}O_4$. See b1239	196.21	lf (aa), pr (al)	132	sub			δ^h	v	v	..	δ	chl δ lig δ	B10[2], 274
b1557	—.2,4-dihydroxy-6-pentyl-	Olivetol carboxylic acid. $C_{12}H_{16}O_4$. See b1239	224.24	wh nd	147	....			..	..	..	..	..		C36, 7068
b1558	—.2-[(2,4-di-hydroxyphenyl)-phenylmethyl]-	....	320.35	aa, eth, w	186.9–7.4				s^h	s	s	..	..	aa s^h	B10, 455
Ω b1559	—.3,5-diiodo-2-hydroxy-	$C_7H_4I_2O_3$. See b1239	389.92	nd (al or aa)	235–6				δ	v	v	..	i	chl i	B10[2], 65
b1560	—,—.ethyl ester ...	$C_9H_8I_2O_3$. See b1239	417.98	lf (al)	133				i	s	s	..	s	chl s	B10, 114
b1561	—.3,5-diiodo-4-hydroxy-	$C_7H_4I_2O_3$. See b1239	389.92	nd (dil al)	237	d260			i	v	v	..	δ	chl δ lig δ	B10[2],105
b1562	—,—.ethyl ester ...	$C_9H_8I_2O_3$. See b1239	417.98	nd (dil al)	123				i	s	..	..	..	os s	B10[2], 105
b1563	—.2,4-di-methoxy-, nitrile	$C_9H_9NO_2$. See b1291	163.18	cr (al, lig)	96				..	..	..	..	δ	to δ aa v PhNO$_2$ s^h	B10[2], 253
b1564	—.2,5-di-methoxy-, amide	$C_9H_{11}NO_3$. See 1244	181.19	lf (bz-peth), nd (w)	141–2				δ v^h	v	v^h	v	v	chl v	B10[1], 184
b1565	—,—.nitrile.......	$C_9H_9NO_2$. See b1291	163.18	nd (al)	82				..	..	s^h	..	v	chl v lig δ	B10[2], 258
Ω b1566	—.2,6-di-methoxy-, nitrile	$C_9H_9NO_2$. See b1291	163.18	nd or pl	118–20	310[760]			δ	v^h	δ	s	v	CS_2 δ lig δ chl v	B10[2], 260
Ω b1567	—.3,4-dimethoxy-..	Veratric acid. $C_9H_{10}O_4$. See b1239	182.18	nd (w or aa), rh (sub) λ^{al} 258 (4.1), 291 (3.7)	181–2 (anh)	sub			δ^h i	v	v	..	..		B10[2], 259
Ω b1568	—,—.amide	Veratramide. $C_9H_{11}NO_3$. See b1244	181.19	cr (w)	164				v^h	..	s	..	s		B10[2], 264
Ω b1569	—,—.nitrile.......	Veratronitrile. $C_9H_9NO_2$. See b1291	163.18	nd (w)	67–8				s^h	s^h	..	..	s		B10[2], 264
b1570	—.3,5-di-methoxy-, amide	$C_9H_{11}NO_3$. See b1244	181.19	nd (bz) λ^{MeOH} 247 (3.68), 299 (3.37)	148–9				s^h	v	v	v^h	..	lig v^h	B10[2], 267
b1571	—.2,3-dimeth-oxy-4-hydroxy-	$C_9H_{10}O_5$. See b1239	198.18	pl or lf (w or al)	154–5				δ s^h	s	..	v	..	chl v lig i MeOH v	B10[2], 332
b1572	—.2,3-dimeth-oxy-5-hydroxy-	$C_9H_{10}O_5$. See b1239	198.18	pl or lf (w)	186–8				s^h	s^h	..	..	..		B10[2], 333
b1573	—.2,4-dimeth-oxy-6-hydroxy-	$C_9H_{10}O_5$. See b1239	198.18	nd (eth-bz)	152–4d				s^h	s	s	v	..		B10[2], 334
b1574	—.2,6-dimeth-oxy-4-hydroxy-	$C_9H_{10}O_5$. See b1239	198.18	pl (w)	175				s^h	δ	δ	v	..	Py v	B10[1], 235
b1575	—.3,4-dimeth-oxy-2-hydroxy-	$C_9H_{10}O_5$. See b1239	198.18	nd (w)	169–72				s^h	..	..	..	..	chl s	B10, 465
b1576	—.3,4-dimeth-oxy-5-hydroxy-	$C_9H_{10}O_5$. See b1239	198.18	nd (aa or w)	197–8				s	s	s	..	..	aa s	B10[2], 340

For explanations, symbols and abbreviations see beginning of table. For structural formulas see end of table.

No.	Name	Synonyms and Formula	Mol. wt.	Color, crystalline form. specific rotation and λ_{max} (log ε)	m.p. °C	b.p. °C	Density	n_D	w	al	eth	ace	bz	other solvents	Ref.
	Benzoic acid														
Ω b1577	—,3,5-dimethoxy-4-hydroxy-	Syringic acid. $C_9H_{10}O_5$. See b1239	198.18	nd (w) λ^{al} 228 (4.0), 275 (4.0)	204–5	......			δ	s	v	v	...	chl v	B10, 480
b1578	—,4,5-dimethoxy-2-hydroxy-	$C_9H_{10}O_5$. See b1239	198.18	nd (w) λ^{al} 222 (4.30), 257 (4.03), 318 (3.87)	202d	......			δ s^h	s					B10[1], 234
b1579	—,—,methyl ester	$C_{10}H_{12}O_5$. See b1239	212.21	nd (w)	95	......			δ						B10[1], 234
b1580	—,2,3-dimethyl-	Hemellitic acid. 2.3-Xylylic acid. $C_9H_{10}O_2$. See b1239	150.18	pr (al)	144	......			δ^h i	s^h	s				B9[1], 209
b1581	—,2,4-dimethyl-	2.4-Xylylic acid. $C_9H_{10}O_2$. See b1239	150.18	mcl or tcl nd (w) λ^{al} 243 (4.1), 282 (3.1), 290 sh (2.8)	127 (anh) 90 (hyd)	267[727] sub			δ^h	s^h	...	s	s	chl. to s aa s^h	B9[2], 350
b1582	—,2,5-dimethyl-	Isoxylylic acid. 2,5-Xylylic acid. $C_9H_{10}O_2$. See b1239	150.18	nd (al) λ^{al} 232 (2.61), 269 (2.81), 286 (2.91)	132	268[760] sub	1.069^{21}_4	......	i	s	s	s	s		B9[1], 210
b1583	—,2,6-dimethyl-	2,6-Xylylic acid. $C_9H_{10}O_2$. See b1239	150.18	nd (lig) λ^{al} 270 (2.86)	116	274.5			δ	s	s			lig δ. s^h	B9[2], 350
Ω b1584	—,3,4-dimethyl-	Paraxylylic acid. 3,4-Xylylic acid. $C_9H_{10}O_2$. See b1239	150.18	pr (al) $\lambda^{w,pH=3.6}$ 242 (3.95)	166	sub			i δ^h	s	s				B9[2], 353
Ω b1585	—,3,5-dimethyl-	Mesitylenic acid. 3,5-Xylylic acid. $C_9H_{10}O_2$. See b1239	150.18	nd (w or al)	170–1	sub			δ^h	v	v				B9[2], 354
b1586	—,2(dimethylamino)-	N,N-Dimethylanthranilic acid. $C_9H_{11}NO_2$. See b1239	165.19	pr. nd (eth)	72	sub δd			v	v	s^h				B14[2], 213
Ω b1587	—,3(dimethylamino)-	$C_9H_{11}NO_2$. See b1239	165.19	nd (w) λ^{al} 263 (4.0), 338 (3.3)	151				v^h δ	s	s				D14, 392
b1588	—,4(dimethylamino)-	$C_9H_{11}NO_2$. See b1239	165.19	nd (al) λ^{al} 227 (3.87), 308 (4.41)	242.5–3.5 (244–6d)				...	s	δ				B14[2], 259
Ω b1589	—,2,4-dinitro-	$C_7H_4N_2O_6$. See b1239	212.12	nd (w)	183	......			δ s^h	δ s^h			δ v^h		B9[2], 279
Ω b1590	—,2,5-dinitro-	$C_7H_4N_2O_6$. See b1239	212.12	pr (w) λ^{aqNH_3} 515 (0.95)	177				δ s^h	s	s		δ		B9[2], 279
b1591	—,2,6-dinitro-	$C_7H_4N_2O_6$. See b1239	212.12	nd (w)	202–3				δ s^h	s	s				B9[2], 279
Ω b1592	—,3,4-dinitro-	$C_7H_4N_2O_6$. See b1239	212.12	nd (w) λ^{al} 570 (0.90)	165				δ s^h	v	v				B9[1], 167
Ω b1593	—,3,5-dinitro-	$C_7H_4N_2O_6$. See b1239	212.12	mcl pr (al)	205				δ s^h	s	δ	...	i	aa s	B9[2], 279
Ω b1594	—,—,benzyl ester	$C_{14}H_{10}N_7O_6$. See b1239	302.25	nd (lig)	112										J1959, 3183
Ω b1595	—,—,butyl ester	$C_{11}H_{12}N_2O_6$. See b1239	268.23	mcl nd (al)	62.5		1.488		...	s^h					B9[2], 280
Ω b1596	—,—,chloride	$C_7H_3ClN_2O_5$. See b1239	230.57	ye nd (bz)	74	196[12]			d	d	s				B9[2], 283
Ω b1597	—,—,ethyl ester	$C_9H_8N_2O_6$. See b1239	240.18	nd (al)	92.9		1.295^{111}	1.560		s^h					B9, 414
Ω b1598	—,—,furfuryl ester		292.22	(bz-Py)	78–81										B17[2], 115
Ω b1599	—,—,isobutyl ester	$C_{11}H_{12}N_2O_6$. See b1239	268.23	mcl pl or nd (al)	87–8					s^h	s^h				B9[2], 281
Ω b1600	—,—,isopropyl ester	$C_{10}H_{10}N_2O_6$. See b1239	254.20	nd (al)	122					s^h					B9[2], 280
Ω b1601	—,—,methyl ester	$C_8H_6N_2O_6$. See b1239	226.15	nd (w)	112				s^h	s^h					B9, 414
Ω b1602	—,—,pentyl ester	$C_{12}H_{14}N_2O_6$. See b1239	282.26	......	46.4				s^h	s^h					B9[2], 281
b1603	—,—,phenyl ester	$C_{13}H_8N_2O_6$. See b1239	288.23	rods (al)	145–6				i	s^h	δ		v		B9, 119
Ω b1604	—,—,propyl ester	$C_{10}H_{10}N_2O_6$. See b1239	254.20	mcl pl (al)	73				i	s^h					B9[2], 280
Ω b1605	—,—,tetrahydrofurfuryl ester		296.24	nd (al)	83–4				i	s^h					Am 62, 3516
b1606	—,2,4-dinitro-3-hydroxy-	$C_7H_4N_2O_7$. See b1239	228.12	(w)	204				δ v^h	s	s				B10[2], 85
Ω b1607	—,3,5-dinitro-2-hydroxy-	$C_7H_4N_2O_7$. See b1239	228.12	ye nd or pl (+1w) $\lambda > 450$	182 (anh) 174 (hyd)				s	s	s	s			B10, 122
b1608	—,3,5-dinitro-4-hydroxy-	$C_7H_4N_2O_7$. See b1239	228.12	ye lf (al)	248 9	......			λ s^h	v^h	v				B10[1], 100
b1609	—,2-ethoxy-	$C_9H_{10}O_3$. See b1239	166.18	......	20.7	211–2[35]			δ s^h	δ					B10[2], 40
Ω b1610	—,—,amide	$C_9H_{11}NO_2$. See b1244	165.19	nd (w, al or AcOEt-peth)	132–4				δ s^h	v^h	v^h				B10[2], 58
b1611	—,—,ethyl ester	$C_{11}H_{14}O_3$. See b1239	194.23	......		251[760] 180–5[113]	1.005^{20}	......	δ	v	s				B10, 74
b1612	—,—,nitrile	C_9H_9NO. See b1291	147.18	......	5	260.7 153[15]				v	v			lig v	B10, 97
b1613	—,3-ethoxy-	$C_9H_{10}O_3$. See b1239	166.18	nd (w or sub)	137	sub			s	s	s		s		B10[1], 64
b1614	—,—,amide	$C_9H_{11}NO_2$. See b1244	165.19	nd (w)	139–9.5					v	s	v	...	peth δ chl v lig δ	B10, 141
b1615	—,—,ethyl ester	$C_{11}H_{14}O_3$. See b1239	194.23	......		264 172–3[50]	1.0725^{18}_{18}	......	i δ^h	v	v				B10, 139

For explanations, symbols and abbreviations see beginning of table. For structural formulas see end of table.

No.	Name	Synonyms and Formula	Mol. wt.	Color, crystalline form, specific rotation and λ_{max} (log ε)	m.p. °C	b.p. °C	Density	n_D	w	al	eth	ace	bz	other solvents	Ref.
	Benzoic acid														
Ω b1616	—.4-ethoxy-	$C_9H_{10}O_3$. See b1239	166.18	nd (w)	198.5				δ^h	s	s	...	s		B10[2], 92
b1617	—,—.amide	$C_9H_{11}NO_2$. See b1244	165.19	pr (dil al)	206				δ	v					B10[2], 101
Ω b1618	—,—.ethyl ester	$C_{11}H_{14}O_3$. See b1239	194.23			275 148–9[14]	1.076[12]		i	v	v				B10[2], 98
b1619	—,—.nitrile	C_9H_9NO. See b1291	147.18	nd (lig)	61–2	258			δ	v	v			lig v[h]	B10[2], 101
b1620	—,—.piperazinium salt	$C_{22}H_{30}N_2O_6$. See b1239	418.50		176–7d				δ	s[h]	i				Am 70, 2758
b1621	—.4-ethoxy-2-hydroxy-	$C_9H_{10}O_4$. See b1239	182.18	nd (w or bz)	154				δ s[h]	v	v		v		B10, 379
b1622	—.2-ethyl-	$C_9H_{10}O_2$. See b1239	150.18	nd (w)	68	259[760]	1.0413_4^{100}	1.5099^{100}	δ	v				lig δ	B9[2], 349
b1623	—.3-ethyl-	$C_9H_{10}O_2$. See b1239	150.18	nd (w or dil al)	47		1.042^{100}	1.5345^{100}	i	s	v				B9[1], 208
b1624	—.4-ethyl-	$C_9H_{10}O_2$. See b1239	150.18	pr (al), pl or lf (w)	113.5				δ v[h]	s			s	chl s	B9[2], 349
b1625	—.2(ethylamino)-	$C_9H_{11}NO_2$. See b1239	165.19	pr or nd (dil al)	154					s	s	s			B14[2], 213
b1626	—.3(ethylamino)-	$C_9H_{11}NO_2$. See b1239	165.19	nd or pr (dil al)	112	sub			δ^h	v	v	s			B14, 393
b1627	—.4(ethylamino)-	$C_9H_{11}NO_2$. See b1239	165.19	cr (bz)	177–8					s	s	s	s	os s	B14[1], 572
Ω b1628	—.2-fluoro-	$C_7H_5FO_2$. See b1239	140.12	nd (w) λ^{a1} 223 (4.98), 273 (3.21), 280 (3.11)	126.5		1.460_4^{25}		δ v[h]	v	v		i	chl s CS_2 i	B9[2], 220
Ω b1629	—.3-fluoro-	$C_7H_5FO_2$. See b1239	140.12	lf (w) λ^{a1} 225 (4.0), 274 (3.23), 281 (3.15)	124		1.474_4^{25}		δ						B9[2], 220
Ω b1630	—.4-fluoro-	$C_7H_5FO_2$. See b1239	140.12	pr (w) λ^{a1} 228 (4.04), 262 (2.70), 268 (2.48)	185		1.479_4^{25}		δ s[h]	s	s				B9[2], 220
Ω b1631	—,—.nitrile	C_7H_4FN. See b1291	121.12	nd (peth) λ^{iso} 228 (4.0), 258 (2.4), 272 (2.4)	34.8	188.8[750]	1.1070^{55}	1.4925^{55}						peth s[h]	B9[2], 221
b1632	—.2-formamido-	$C_8H_7NO_3$. See b1291	165.15	nd (w + ½)	169				δ	s	v		δ		B14[2], 219
Ω b1633	—.2-formyl-	Phthalaldehydic acid. $C_8H_6O_3$. See b1239	150.14	lf (+ w) λ^{hx} 224 (3.90), 276 (2.93), 286 (2.60)	98–9 (hyd) 240–50 (anh)		1.404		s	v	v				B10, 666
b1634	—.3-formyl-	Isophthalaldehydic acid. $C_8H_6O_3$. See b1239	150.14	nd (w)	175				s[h]	v	v				B10[2], 465
b1635	—,—.nitrile	3-Cyanobenzaldehyde. C_8H_5NO. See b1291	131.14	nd (eth)	79–81	210			v[h]	v	v			chl v	B10, 671
Ω b1636	—.4-formyl-	Terephthalaldehydic acid. $C_8H_6O_3$. See b1239	150.14	nd (w) λ^{hx} 249 (4.24), 279 (3.22), 298 (3.20)	256	sub			δ^h	s	s			chl s	B10, 671
Ω b1637	—,—.nitrile	4-Cyanobenzaldehyde. C_8H_5NO. See b1291	131.14	nd (w), pr (eth or dil al)	101–2	133[12]			s[h]	v	v			chl v	B10[2], 465
b1638	—.3-formyl-2-hydroxy-	$C_8H_6O_4$. See b1239	166.14	nd (w + 1)	179				δ s[h]	s					B10[2], 675
b1639	—.3-formyl-4-hydroxy-	$C_8H_6O_4$. See b1239	166.14	pr (w)	244	sub			δ s[h]	s	s			chl δ alk s	B10[2], 675
b1640	—.4-formyl-3-hydroxy-	$C_8H_6O_4$. See b1239	166.14	nd (w)	234	sub			δ^h	s	s			alk s	B10, 954
b1641	—.5-formyl-2-hydroxy-	$C_8H_6O_4$. See b1239	166.14	nd (w)	250d				δ^h	s[h]	s			chl i	B10[2], 675
Ω b1642	—.2-hydrazino-	$C_7H_8N_2O_2$. See b1239	152.16	nd (w) λ^{a1} 280 (3.8), 343 (3.6)	250–1				s[h]	δ s[h]	δ				B15[2], 295
b1643	—,—.hydrochloride	$C_7H_8N_2O_2$.HCl. See b1239	188.62	nd (w)	194–5d				v[h]				i		B15[2], 295
b1644	—.3-hydrazino-	$C_7H_8N_2O_2$. See b1239	152.16	pa ye lf (w) λ^{a1} 276 (4.1), 330 (3.2)	186d				δ^h	δ	i				B15[1], 205
Ω b1645	—.4-hydrazino-	$C_7H_8N_2O_2$. See b1239	152.16	ye nd or pl (w) λ^{a1} 322 (4.2)	114 (220–5d)				δ s[h]		i				B15[2], 297
b1646	—.2,2'-hydrazodi-		272.26	pl or pr (al)	205				i	s[h]				lig δ	B15[2], 296
b1647	—.3,3'-hydrazodi-		272.26	nd (al)	206d					s	s	s	s	os s	B15, 629
b1648	—.4,4'-hydrazodi-		272.26	nd (al), cr (aa + 1)	286d				i	δ^h				aa s[n]	B15, 632
Ω b1649	—.2-hydroxy-	Salicylic acid. $C_7H_6O_3$. See b1239	138.12	nd (w), mcl pr (al) λ^{a1} 207 (4.46), 236 (3.85), 303 (3.57)	159	211[20] sub	1.443_4^{20}	1.565	δ v[h]	v	v	v	δ s[h]	chl, CCl_4, to δ MeOH v	B10[2], 25
b1650	—,—.4-acetamido-phenyl ester	Salophene. $C_{15}H_{13}NO_4$. See b1239	271.28	pl (w), lf (al)	187–8				i δ^h				s	peth i	B13[2], 247
Ω b1651	—,—.acetate	Aspirin. $C_9H_8O_4$. See b1239	180.17	nd (w), mcl ta (w) λ^{eth} 275 (3.11)	135 (rapid htng)				s[h] d[h]	v	s		δ	chl s	B10[2], 41
Ω b1652	—,—.amide	$C_7H_7NO_2$. See b1244. Salicylanilide.	137.14	ye lf (dil al) λ^{a1} 302 (3.62)	142	181.5[14]	1.175_4^{140}		δ	s	δ				B10, 87

For explanations, symbols and abbreviations see beginning of table. For structural formulas see end of table.

No.	Name	Synonyms and Formula	Mol. wt.	Color, crystalline form, specific rotation and λ_{max} (log ε)	m.p. °C	b.p. °C	Density	n_D	w	al	eth	ace	bz	other solvents	Ref.
	Benzoic acid														
b1653	—,—,—,N-phenyl-	$C_{13}H_{11}NO_2$. See b1244. Salicylanilide.	213.24	pr (w or al), lf (w) λ^{chl} 265 sh (4.13), 295 (2.16)	136–7	....			s^h	δ	δ	...	δ	chl δ	B12, 500
b1654	—,—,—,N(2-tolyl)-	$C_{14}H_{13}NO_2$. See b1244	227.27	nd (al)	144					s^h					B12², 450
b1655	—,—,anhydride	$C_{14}H_{10}O_5$. See b1239	258.23	amor	255d				i	v	v				C37, 3073
Ω b1656	—,—,benzyl ester	$C_{14}H_{12}O_3$. See b1239	228.25	λ^{al} 240 (4.1), 308 (3.7)	....	170^5 320^{760}	1.1799^{20}_4	1.5805^{20}	δ	s	s				B10², 51
b1657	—,—,—,acetate	$C_{16}H_{14}O_4$. See b1239	270.29		26	$197–200^7$	Density		...	v	v	v	v	os v lig δ peth δ	B10², 52
Ω b1658	—,—,butyl ester	$C_{11}H_{14}O_3$. See b1239	194.23		−5.9	270–2 (260) $136–8^{10}$	1.0728^{20}_4	1.5115^{20}	δ	s	s				B10², 49
b1659	—,—,(2-carboxy-phenyl) ether	Disalicylic acid. $C_{14}H_{10}O_5$. See b1239	258.23	cr $(Cl_2CHCHCl_2)$	230d				i	v^h	s		i	aa, MeOH s chl i	B10², 54
b1660	—,—,chloride	$C_7H_5ClO_2$. See b1239	156.57		19–9.5	92^{15}	1.3112^{20}	1.5812^{20}	d	δ	v				B10¹, 43
b1661	—,—,2.4-dinitro-benzyl ester	$C_{14}H_{10}N_2O_7$. See b1239	318.25	ye pl (aa)	168				i	δ	i	...	i	AcOEt v^h aa v^h	B10², 52
Ω b1662	—,—,ethyl ester	$C_9H_{10}O_3$. See b1239	166.18		2–3	234 132.8^{37}	1.1326^{20}_2	1.5296^{20}	i	∞	v				B10², 47
b1663	—,—,—,acetate	Ethyl aspirin. $C_{11}H_{12}O_4$. See b1239	208.22			272^{760} 148–50^{15}	1.1566^{15}		i	s	v	v	v	os s	B10², 48
Ω b1664	—,—,hydrazide	$C_7H_8N_2O_2$. See b1239	152.16	pl (al). pr (w) λ^{al} 295 (3.7)	147	....			i^h s^h	v	δ		s		B10², 61
Ω b1665	—,—,2-hydroxy-ethyl ester	$C_9H_{10}O_4$. See b1239	182.18		37	173^{15}	1.2537^{15}_{15}		δ	v	v		v	chl v	B10², 53
Ω b1666	—,—,isobutyl ester	$C_{11}H_{14}O_3$. See b1239	194.23		5.9	260–2 $136–8^{10}$	1.0639^{20}_4	1.5087^{20}	i	s	s				B10, 76
b1667	—,—,isopropyl ester	$C_{10}H_{12}O_3$. See b1239	180.21			240–2 118^{17}	1.0729^{20}	1.5065^{20}	i	∞	∞				C50, 15531
Ω b1668	—,—,menthyl ester	$C_{17}H_{24}O_3$. See b1239	276.38	λ^{al} 318 (2.0)		190^{15} $143^{0.6}$	1.0467^{20}	1.5198^{26}	i	∞	∞		∞	os v	B10², 50
b1669	—,—,methoxy-methyl ester	Mesotan. $C_9H_{10}O_4$. See b1239	182.18			162^{42}	1.2^{15}		δ	∞	∞	∞	∞	chl ∞	B10², 54
b1670	—,—,2-methoxy-phenyl ester	$C_{14}H_{12}O_4$. See b1239	244.25		70	....			i	s	s			chl s	B10, 81
Ω b1671	—,—,methyl ester	$C_8H_8O_3$. See b1239	152.16	λ^{al} 238 (3.97), 306 (3.64)	−8 to −7	223.3^{760}	1.1738^{20}_4	1.5369^{20}	δ	v	v				B10², 44
b1672	—,—,—,benzoate	$C_{15}H_{12}O_4$. See b1239	256.26	pr (al or eth) λ 277 (3.31)	92	385d 270–80^{120}			i δ^h	s	s		s	chl s	B10², 47
Ω b1673	—,—,3-methyl-butyl ester	Isoamyl salicylate. $C_{12}H_{16}O_3$. See b1239	208.24	λ^{al} 310 (3.6)		$276–7^{743}$ $151–2^{15}$	1.0535^{20}_4	1.5080^{20}	i	v	v			chl s	B10², 49
b1674	—,—,1-naphthyl ester	Alphol. $C_{17}H_{12}O_3$. See b1239	264.28		83	....				δ	s				E12B, 1183
b1675	—,—,2-naphthyl ester	Betol. $C_{17}H_{12}O_3$. See b1239	264.28	cr (al)	95.5	....	1.11^{116}		i	δ s^h	s		s		B10², 53
b1676	—,—,nitrile	2-Cyanophenol. C_7H_5NO. See b1291	119.12	pr (bz) λ^w 231 (3.95), 294 (3.61)	98	149^{14}	1.1052^{100}_4	1.5372^{100}	δ	v	v		v	chl v	B10², 60
b1677	—,—,4-nitrobenzyl ester	$C_{14}H_{11}NO_5$. See b1239	273.25	cr (dil al)	97–8	....			δ	v	v		v		B10², 52
b1678	—,—,pentyl ester	$C_{12}H_{16}O_3$. See b1239	208.24	λ^{al} 300 (3.9)		148–54^{760}	1.065^{15}_{15}	1.506^{20}	δ	∞	∞				B10², 49
Ω b1679	—,—,phenyl ester	Salol. $C_{13}H_{10}O_3$. See b1239	214.22	pl (MeOH) λ^{al} 300 (3.7)	43	173^{12}	1.2614^{30}_4		i	v	v	v	v	aa, to s CCl_4. Py v	B10, 76
b1680	—,—,propyl ester	$C_{10}H_{12}O_3$. See b1239	180.21		96–8	239^{760} (250)	1.0979^{20}_4	1.5161^{20}	δ	∞	∞				B10, 75
Ω b1681	—,3-hydroxy-	$C_7H_6O_3$. See b1239	138.12	nd (w), pl or pr (al) λ^{al} 234 (3.78), 301 (3.36)	201.5–3	....			δ v^h	s^h	s	s	i	MeOH s	B10², 79
Ω b1682	, amide	$C_7H_7NO_2$. See b1244	137.14	pl (w) λ^{al} 250 sh (3.7), 323 (3.3)	170.5				δ s^h	s	s		l	chl l CS_2 l	B10², 82
Ω b1683	—,—,—;N-phenyl-	$C_{13}H_{11}NO_2$. See b1244	213.24	nd or pl (w, dil al)	156				δ	s	δ		δ	chl i	B12¹, 269
b1684	—,—,chloride	$C_7H_5ClO_2$. See b1239	156.57		< 15	110 $3^{0.5}$			d	d				chl s	B10¹, 66
Ω b1685	—,—,ethyl ester	$C_9H_{10}O_3$. See b1239	166.18	pl (bz)	73.8	295 211^{65}			δ	s	s				B10², 81
Ω b1686	—,—,methyl ester	$C_8H_8O_3$. See b1239	152.16	nd (bz-peth)	71.5 (70)	280^{709} 178^{17}				s			s^h	peth s^h	B10², 81
Ω b1687	—,—,nitrile	3-Cyanophenol. C_7H_5NO. See b1291	119.12	pr (al or eth). lf (w)	83–4				v^h	v	v		v	chl v	B10, 141
Ω b1688	—,4-hydroxy-	$C_7H_6O_3$. See b1239	138.12	pr or pl (w, al, xyl-al), cr (dil al or ace-MeOH, +1w) λ^{al} 293.5 (4.18)	214.5–5.5 (anh)	....			δ v^h	v^h	s	s	δ	CS_2 i	B10², 88

For explanations, symbols and abbreviations see beginning of table. For structural formulas see end of table.

No.	Name	Synonyms and Formula	Mol. wt.	Color, crystalline form, specific rotation and λ_{max} (log ε)	m.p. °C	b.p. °C	Density	n_D	w	al	eth	ace	bz	other solvents	Ref.
	Benzoic acid														
b1689	—,—,amide	$C_7H_7NO_2$. See b1244	137.14	nd (w + 1) λ^{al} 220 (3.92), 288 (4.24)	162 (hyd)	....	....		δ s^h	s	s	....	....	CS_2, chl	**B10²**, 100
b1690	—,—,—,N-phenyl-	$C_{13}H_{11}NO_2$. See b1244	213.24	pl or nd (w)	201–2 (198)	....	....		δ	v	δ	...	i	chl, CS_2 δ	**B12²**, 257
Ω b1691	—,—,butyl ester	$C_{11}H_{14}O_3$. See b1239	194.23	....	68–9				δ	s					**C51**, 9129
Ω b1692	—,—,ethyl ester	$C_9H_{10}O_3$. See b1239	166.18	cr (dil al)	116–8	297–8	....		δ	v	v	...		CS_2 i lig δ chl, peth δ	**B10²**, 96
Ω b1693	—,—,methyl ester	$C_8H_8O_3$. See b1239	152.16	nd (dil al) λ^{al} 258 (4.22)	131	270–80d	....		δ	v	v	v			**B10²**, 95
Ω b1694	—,—,nitrile	4-Cyanophenol. C_7H_5NO. See b1291	119.12	lf (w) λ^{al} 247 (4.3)	113	....	....		δ s^h	v	v			chl v	**B10²**, 101
Ω b1695	—,—,propyl ester	$C_{10}H_{12}O_3$. See b1239	180.21	pr (eth) λ^{al} 257 (3.21)	96.2–98		1.0630_4^{102}	1.5050^{102}	i s^h	s^h					**B10²**, 97
b1696	—,4(α-hydroxy-benzyl)-	$C_{14}H_{12}O_3$. See b1239	228.25	nd (w)	164–5				s^h	v	v			chl δ to δ	**B10**, 346
b1697	—,2-hydroxy-5-bromo-, acetate	$C_9H_7BrO_4$. See b1239	259.06	nd (al)	60				i	v	s				**B10²**, 64
b1699	—,2-hydroxy-(dithio)-	Dithiosalicylic acid. o-Hydroxydithiobenzoic acid.	170.25	og-ye nd (peth)	48–50				s	s	s		s	MeOH s	**B10²**, 78
b1700	—,2-hydroxy-3-iodo-	$C_7H_5IO_3$. See b1239	264.02	nd (w)	199		....		δ s^h	v	v	...	i	chl i	**B10²**, 64
b1701	—,2-hydroxy-4-iodo-	$C_7H_5IO_3$. See b1239	264.02	pl or nd (al)	230d		....		δ	s v^h	s			chl i	**B10²**, 65
b1702	—,2-hydroxy-5-iodo-	$C_7H_5IO_3$. See b1239	264.02	nd (w)	197		....		δ s^h	v	s	...	i	chl i	**B10²**, 65
b1703	—,3-hydroxy-2-iodo-	$C_7H_5IO_3$. See b1239	264.02	nd (chl)	158–9		....		δ s^h	s	s			chl s^h	**B10²**, 84
b1704	—,3-hydroxy-4-iodo	$C_7H_5IO_3$. See b1239	264.02	nd (w)	226–8d		....		δ s^h	s	s				**B10²**, 84
b1705	—,4-hydroxy-2-iodo-	$C_7H_5IO_3$. See b1239	264.02	nd (w)	215d		....		s^h	s	s	δ			**B10²**, 104
b1706	—,4-hydroxy-3-iodo-	$C_7H_5IO_3$. See b1239	264.02	nd (w + ½)	173.5–4.5	sub	....		s^h	v	v	δ^h		chl δ aa s lig i	**B10²**, 104
b1707	—,5-hydroxy-2-iodo-	$C_7H_5IO_3$. See b1239	264.02	nd (w)	198	sub 160	....		s^h	v	v	...	i		**B10²**, 84
b1708	—,2-hydroxy-3-isopropyl-6-methyl-	o-Thymotinic acid. $C_{11}H_{14}O_3$. See b1239	194.23	nd (w, bz, lig)	127	sub	....		i δ^h	s	s	...	s	lig s^h chl, aa s	**B10²**, 170
b1709	—,2-hydroxy-5-isopropyl-3-methyl-	$C_{11}H_{14}O_3$. See b1239	194.23	nd (w)	147		....		i	v					**B10**, 282
b1710	—,2-hydroxy-5-isopropyl-4-methyl-	$C_{11}H_{14}O_3$. See b1239	194.23	nd (bz)	189–90		....								**B10²**, 171
b1711	—,2-hydroxy-6-isopropyl-3-methyl-	o-Carvacrotinic acid. $C_{11}H_{14}O_3$. See b1239	194.23	nd (w)	136	sub	....		δ	v	v				**B10**, 282
b1712	—,4-hydroxy-5-isopropyl-2-methyl-	p-Thymotinic acid. $C_{11}H_{14}O_3$. See b1239	194.23	pl (dil al)	157	....	....		δ^h	v	v	...	v	chl v	**B10²**, 171
b1713	—,3-hydroxy-4-methoxy-	Isovanillic acid. $C_8H_8O_4$. See b1239	168.16	nd, pr, pl (w) λ^{al} 256 (4.00), 293.5 (4.71)	255–7	sub	....		δ s^h	v	v				**B10²**, 261
Ω b1714	—,4-hydroxy-3-methoxy-	Vanillic acid. $C_8H_8O_4$. See b1239	168.16	nd (w) λ^{al} 263 (4.00), 292 (3.72)	213–5	sub	....		δ	s	v				**B10²**, 261
Ω b1715	—,—,ethyl ester	$C_{10}H_{12}O_4$. See b1239	196.21	nd (dil al) λ^{diox} 259 (4.05), 290 (3.72)	44	291–3	....		i	v	v				**B10**, 397
Ω b1716	—,—,methyl ester	$C_9H_{10}O_4$. See b1239	182.18	nd (dil al)	64	285–7 118²	....			s^h				peth s^h	**B10¹**, 189
b1717	—,2-hydroxy-4-methoxy-6-methyl-	Everninic acid. $C_9H_{10}O_4$. See b1239	182.18	nd (peth or w)	171–2 (157)	....	....		δ s^h	v	δ	v	δ	aa v lig δ AcOEt s	**B10²**, 273
b1718	—,—,methyl ester	Sparassol. $C_{10}H_{12}O_4$. See b1239	196.21	pr (w), lf (MeOH)	67–8	....	....		δ^h	s	v	v	...	MeOH s peth s chl v	**B10²**, 273
Ω b1719	—,2-hydroxy-3-methyl-	2,3-Cresotic acid. $C_8H_8O_3$. See b1239	152.16	nd (w or dil al)	169–70		....		δ s^h	s	s	...	s^h	chl s	**B10²**, 131
b1720	—,—,chloride	$C_8H_7ClO_2$. See b1239	170.60	....	27–8	87–9¹⁶	....		d	d^h					**B10²**, 132
Ω b1721	—,2-hydroxy-4-methyl-	2,4-Cresotic acid. $C_8H_8O_3$. See b1239	152.16	nd (w), pr (al), pl (chl) λ^{MeOH} 238 (3.99), 297 (3.64)	177.8	sub	....		δ s^h	s	v	...	s^h	chl s	**B10²**, 137

For explanations, symbols and abbreviations see beginning of table. For structural formulas see end of table.

No.	Name	Synonyms and Formula	Mol. wt.	Color, crystalline form, specific rotation and λ_{max} (log ε)	m.p. °C	b.p. °C	Density	n_D	Solubility						Ref.
									w	al	eth	ace	bz	other solvents	
	Benzoic acid														
b1722	—,2-hydroxy-5-methyl-	2,5-Cresotic acid. $C_8H_8O_3$. See b1239	152.16	nd (w or peth)	153	....			δ s^h	s	s	...	s	chl s, peth s^h CS$_4$ i	B10[2], 134
b1723	—,2-hydroxy-6-methyl-	2,6-Cresotic acid. $C_8H_8O_3$. See b1239	152.16	nd (chl) λ^{MeOH} 240 (3.75), 307 (3.52)	173 (184)				δ s^h	v	v	...		chl s	B10[2], 128
b1724	—,3-hydroxy-2-methyl-	2,3-Cresotic acid. $C_8H_8O_3$. See b1239	152.16	nd (w or dil al)	145–6	....			δ s^h	v	v				B10, 214
b1725	—,3-hydroxy-4-methyl-	3,4-Cresotic acid. $C_8H_8O_3$. See b1239	152.16	nd or pr (w) λ^{al} 206 (4.67), 244 (4.08), 298 (3.65)	208.5	sub			δ s^h	s	s	...	δ	peth δ chl i	B10[2], 140
b1726	—,3-hydroxy-5-methyl-	3,5-Cresotic acid. $C_8H_8O_3$. See b1239	152.16	nd (w)	210	sub			s^h	v	v	...		chl δ	B10, 227
b1727	—,4-hydroxy-2-methyl-	4,2-Cresotic acid. $C_8H_8O_3$. See b1239	152.16	nd (w + ½) λ^w 242 (3.91), 275 sh (3.5)	177–8	236–7 sub			δ s^h	s	s			chl i	B10[2], 127
b1728	—,4-hydroxy-3-methyl-	4,3-Cresotic acid. $C_8H_8O_3$. See b1239	152.16	nd (w + ½) λ^w 250 (4.10), 280 sh (3.6)	174–5 (anh)				s^h δ					chl δ^h	B10[2], 133
b1729	—,5-hydroxy-2-methyl-	3,6-Cresotic acid. $C_8H_8O_3$. See b1239	152.16	nd or pr (w)	185	....			δ s^h	v	v			chl δ	B10, 215
b1730	—,2-(hydroxymethyl)-	2-Carboxybenzyl alcohol. $C_8H_8O_3$. See b1239	152.16	nd (w)	128 (120)				s	v	v				B10, 218
—	—,—,lactone	see **Phthalide**													
b1731	—,2-hydroxy-3-nitro-	$C_7H_5NO_5$. See b1239.......	183.12	yesh nd (aa, w + 1) $\lambda^{w, pH=3.7}$ 357 (3.64)	148–9 (anh) 128–9 (↓w)				δ	v	v	s	s	chl s	B10[2], 66
b1732	—,2-hydroxy-4-nitro-	$C_7H_5NO_5$. See b1239 ...	183.12	ye nd (w or dil al)	235	....			δ s^h	v	...	s	δ	chl s aa s lig i	B10[2], 66
b1733	—,2-hydroxy-5-nitro-	$C_7H_5NO_5$. See b1239 ...	183.12	nd (w)	229–30	....	1.650[20]		δ s^h	v	v	v	v	os v	B10[2], 67
b1734	—,2-hydroxy-6-nitro-	$C_7H_5NO_5$. See b1239 ...	183.12	pa ye nd					v	v					J1950, 2049
b1736	—,3-hydroxy-2-nitro-	$C_7H_5NO_5$. See b1239 ...	183.12	pl or pr (w + 1)	180.5–1.5 (178)				s	v	v				B10[2], 84
Ω b1737	—,3-hydroxy-4-nitro-	$C_7H_5NO_5$. See b1239 ...	183.12	ye lf (w)	235				δ	s	s				B10[2], 85
b1738	—,3-hydroxy-5-nitro-	$C_7H_5NO_5$. See b1239 ...	183.12	ye lf or pl (25 % HCl)	167				s^h	v	v				B10[2], 85
Ω b1739	—,4-hydroxy-3-nitro-	$C_7H_5NO_5$. See b1239 ...	183.12	nd or lf (w)	186–7				s^h	v	v				B10[2], 106
b1740	—,5-hydroxy-2-nitro-	$C_7H_5NO_5$. See b1239 ...	183.12	ye nd or pr (w + 1)	172 (165)				v	v	v				B10[2], 85
b1741	—,2-hydroxy-3-sulfo-	$C_7H_6O_6S$. See b1239	218.19	pr (w + 2)	120				v	v	s			aa s	B11[2], 231
b1742	—,2-hydroxy-5-sulfo-	$C_7H_6O_6S$. See b1239 ...	218.19	hyg nd (w + 2)	120 (anh) 198–9d (+2w)				∞	∞	v				B11[2], 232
b1743	—,3-hydroxy-4-sulfo-	$C_7H_6O_6S$. See b1239 ...	218.19	ye-gr nd (w + 2½)	208 (213)				v	v	i				B11, 413
b1744	—,3-hydroxy-5-sulfo-	$C_7H_6O_6S$. See b1239 ...	218.19	nd (w + 1)	120d				s	v	v				B11, 413
b1745	—,4-hydroxy-3-sulfo-	$C_7H_6O_6S$. See b1239 ...	218.19	nd or lf (w)	d				v	s	i				B11[2], 235
Ω b1746	—,2-iodo-	$C_7H_5IO_2$. See b1239 ...	248.02	nd (w) λ^{al} 233 sh (3.85), 285 (3.16)	163	233 exp	2.249[25]/4	....	δ	al	δ				B9[2], 239
Ω b1747	—,—,methyl ester .	$C_8H_7IO_2$. See b1239	262.05	....		277–8[729] 146[16]	1.6052[20]		...	s^h					B9, 364
Ω b1748	—,3-iodo-	$C_7H_5IO_2$. See b1239	248.02	mcl pr (ace) λ^{al} 217 (4.42), 284 (2.98), 290 sh (2.95)	187–8	sub			δ	v	δ				B9[2], 240
Ω b1749	—,—,methyl ester .	$C_8H_7IO_2$. See b1239	262.05	nd (dil al)	54–5	276–7[739] 149– 50[18]			i	s	v	v		os v^h lig i	B9, 365
Ω b1750	—,4-iodo-	$C_7H_5IO_2$. See b1239 ...	248.02	mcl pr (dil al), lf (sub) λ^{al} 252 (4.26), 282 sh (3.23)	(i) 270 (st) (ii) 228–9 (unst)	sub	2.184[20]		δ s^h	δ	δ				B9[2], 240
Ω b1751	—,—,methyl ester .	$C_8H_7IO_2$. See b1239	262.05	nd (eth-al)	114	sub				s^h	s^h				B9, 367
b1752	—,2-iodo-3-nitro- ..	$C_7H_4INO_4$. See b1239.......	293.02	pr (w)	206				s^h	s	s				B9[2], 278
b1753	—,2-iodo-4-nitro- ..	$C_7H_4INO_4$. See b1239.......	293.02	pa ye pr (w)	146–7 (143)	....			δ s^h	s	s		δ	CCl$_4$ δ lig δ	B9[1], 166
b1754	—,4-iodo-2-nitro- ..	$C_7H_4INO_4$. See b1239.......	293.02	ye lf or pr (dil al)	192–3	....			δ^h	v	v	s^h			B9[2], 278

For explanations, symbols and abbreviations see beginning of table. For structural formulas see end of table.

No.	Name	Synonyms and Formula	Mol. wt.	Color, crystalline form, specific rotation and λ_{max} (log ε)	m.p. °C	b.p. °C	Density	n_D	w	al	eth	ace	bz	other solvents	Ref.

Benzoic acid

No.	Name	Synonyms and Formula	Mol. wt.	Color, crystalline form	m.p. °C	b.p. °C	Density	n_D	w	al	eth	ace	bz	other solvents	Ref.
b1755	—,4-iodo-3-nitro-	$C_7H_4INO_4$. See b1239	293.02	ye pr (al)	213	....			δ	s	...	...	...		B9[2], 278
b1756	—,5-iodo-3-nitro-	$C_7H_4INO_4$. See b1239	293.02	nd (al), pr (peth)	167	....			s^h	v	...	...	...		B9[2], 278
Ω b1757	—,2-iodoso-	$C_7H_5IO_3$. See b1239	264.02	lf (w)	223–5d	....			δ s^h	δ s^h	δ	...	...		B9[2], 239
b1758	—,3-iodoso-	$C_7H_5IO_3$. See b1239	264.02	ye amor	175–80	....			d^h	δ	δ	...	i	chl i	B9, 365
b1759	—,4-iodoso-	$C_7H_5IO_3$. See b1239	264.02	amor	212d	....			d^h	i	...	...	i	chl i	B9, 366
b1760	—,2-isopropyl-	o-Cuminic acid. $C_{10}H_{12}O_2$. See b1239	164.21	pr (w or peth)	64	160–1[25]			δ s^h	v	v	...	s	peth s	B9, 546
Ω b1761	—,4-isopropyl-	Cumic acid. p-Cuminic acid. $C_{10}H_{12}O_2$. See b1239	164.21	tcl pl (al)	117–8	sub	1.162[4]		δ s^h	v	v	...	v	peth s	B9, 546
Ω b1762	—,2-mercapto-	Thiosalicylic acid. $C_7H_6O_2S$. See b1239	154.19	lf or nd (al, w, aa) λ[al] 220 (4.18), 239 sh (3.81)	168–9 (165)	sub			s^h	s	s	...		aa s lig δ	B10[2], 70
Ω b1763	—,2-methoxy-	o-Anisic acid. $C_8H_8O_3$. See b1239	152.16	pl (w), fl (al) λ[al] 226 (3.82), 280 (3.40)	101	200			δ v^h	v	v	...	s	chl v CCl_4 s	B10[2], 39
Ω b1764	—,—,amide	$C_8H_9NO_2$. See b1244	151.17	nd (bz), pr (eth), pl (w)	129	....			δ	v	...	v^h		sulf s (ye)	B10[2], 58
Ω b1765	—,—,chloride	$C_8H_7ClO_2$. See b1239	170.60			254[760] 128[11]			d	d^h	...	...	...		B10[2], 55
b1766	—,—,ethyl ester	$C_{10}H_{12}O_3$. See b1239	180.21			261[760] 135–6[12]	1.1124[20/4]	1.5224[20]	i	s	s	...	...		B10[2], 48
b1767	—,—,methyl ester	$C_9H_{10}O_3$. See b1239	166.18	λ[al] 234 (3.82), 294 (3.54)		245[760] 127[11]	1.1571[19]	1.534[19.5]	i	s	...	...	...		B10[2], 46
b1768	—,—,nitrile	C_8H_7NO. See b1291	133.15	λ[al] 232 (3.95), 294 (3.65)	24.5	255–6 146[20]	1.1063[20.5/4]			s	v	...	...		B10[2], 60
b1769	—,—,piperazinium salt	$C_{20}H_{26}N_2O_6$. See b1239	390.45		190.4–1.4	....			s	s	i	...	...		Am 70, 2758
Ω b1770	—,3-methoxy-	m-Anisic acid. $C_8H_8O_3$. See b1239	152.16	nd (w)	110	170–2[10]			δ s^h	s	s	...	s	CCl_4 δ chl v	B10[2], 80
b1771	—,—,chloride	$C_8H_7ClO_2$. See b1239	170.60	λ[al] 230 (3.83), 293 (3.39)		243–4[760] 123–5[15]			d	d^h	s	s	v^h		B10, 140
b1772	—,—,ethyl ester	$C_{10}H_{12}O_3$. See b1239	180.21			260–1[760] 110[5]	1.0993[20/4]	1.5161[20]	i	s	s	...	...		B10[2], 81
b1773	—,—,methyl ester	$C_9H_{10}O_3$. See b1239	166.18			252(238) 121–4[10]	1.1310[20/4]	1.5224[20]	i	s	s	...	...		B10[2], 81
b1774	—,—,piperazinium salt	$C_{20}H_{26}N_2O_6$. See b1239	390.45		137–8.5d	....			s^h	s	$δ^h$	...	...		Am 70, 2758
Ω b1775	—,4-methoxy-	Anisic acid. $C_8H_8O_3$. See b1239	152.16	pr or nd (w) λ[al] 249 (4.14)	185	275–80			i s^h	v	v	...		chl s MeOH v	B10[2], 91
b1776	—,—,amide	$C_8H_9NO_2$. See b1244	151.17	nd or ta (w)	166.5–7.5	295[760]			s	v	δ	...	...		B10[2], 100
b1777	—,—,butyl ester	$C_{12}H_{16}O_3$. See b1239	208.24			183[40]	1.054[16.5]	1.5141[18.5]	i	s	s	...	...		B10[2], 97
Ω b1778	—,—,chloride	$C_8H_7ClO_2$. See b1239	170.60	nd	24–5	262–3 91[1]	1.261[20]	1.580[20]	d	d^h	s	s	v^h		B10, 77
Ω b1779	—,—,ethyl ester	$C_{10}H_{12}O_3$. See b1239	180.21	λ[al] 254 (4.3)	7–8	269–70[760] 136–7[13]	1.1038[20/4]	1.5254[20]	i	s	s	...	...		B10[2], 96
Ω b1780	—,—,methyl ester	$C_9H_{10}O_3$. See b1239	166.18	fl (al or eth)	49	256[760] 160[20]			i	s	s	...	...		B10[2], 95
Ω b1781	—,—,nitrile	C_8H_7NO. See b1291	133.15	nd (w), lf (al) λ[al] 248 (4.29), 273 (3.33), 283 (2.92)	61–2	256–7 (240) 106–8[6]			i s^h	v^h	v	...	s		B10[2], 101
b1782	—,—,piperazinium salt	$C_{20}H_{26}N_2O_6$. See b1239	390.45		172–4	....			δ	s^h	i	...	...		Am 56, 150
b1783	—,5-methoxy-2(4-methoxy-phenoxy)-	$C_{15}H_{14}O_5$. See b1239	274.28	cr (bz-lig)	95	....							bz		B10[1], 181
b1784	—,3-methoxy-2(methyl-amino)-, methyl ester	Damascenine. $C_{10}H_{13}NO_3$. See b1239	195.22	pr (al)	27–9	270[750] δd 147–8[10]			i $δ^h$	v	v	...	s	CS_2 v lig v chl v	B14[1], 654
Ω b1785	—,2-methyl-	o-Toluic acid. $C_8H_8O_2$. See b1239	136.16	pr or nd (w) λ[cy] 231.5 (4.02)	107–8	258–9[751]	1.062[115]	1.512[115]	i s^h	v	v	...		chl s	B9, 462
Ω b1786	—,—,amide	C_8H_9NO. See b1244	135.17	pl (w) or nd (w) λ[95 % al] 270 (2.85)	147 (143)	....			δ v^h	v	δ	...	δ		B9, 465
b1786[1]	—,—,anhydride	$C_{18}H_{14}O_3$. See b1239	254.29		38–9	>325[760] 11[220]			d	d	v	...	...		B9[2], 319
b1787	—,—,chloride	C_8H_7ClO. See b1239	154.60			213–14[760] 88–90[12]		1.5549[20]	d	d^h	v	...	...		B9[2], 319
b1788	—,—,ethyl ester	$C_{10}H_{12}O_2$. See b1239	164.21	λ 279 (3.02)	< −10	227 102.5[13]	1.0325[21/4]	1.507[22]	i	∞	∞	...	...		B9, 463
b1789	—,—,methyl ester	$C_9H_{10}O_2$. See b1239	150.18	....	< −50	215[760] 97[15]	1.068[20/4]		i	∞	∞	...	...		B9, 463

For explanations, symbols and abbreviations see beginning of table. For structural formulas see end of table.

No.	Name	Synonyms and Formula	Mol. wt.	Color, crystalline form, specific rotation and λ_{max} (log ε)	m.p. °C	b.p. °C	Density	n_D	Solubility						Ref.
									w	al	eth	ace	bz	other solvents	

Benzoic acid

No.	Name	Synonyms and Formula	Mol. wt.	Color etc.	m.p.	b.p.	Density	n_D	w	al	eth	ace	bz	other	Ref.
Ω b1790	—,—,nitrile	C_8H_7N. See b1291	117.15	λ^{al} 228 (4.02), 276 (3.15), 284 (3.15)	−14 to −13	205^{760} 90^{15}	0.9955^{20}_4	1.5279^{20}	i	∞	∞	...	...	...	B9², 319
b1791	—,—,4-phenyl-phenacyl ester		330.39	cr (dil al)	94.5	...									Am 52, 3715
Ω b1792	—,3-methyl-	m-Toluic acid. $C_8H_8O_2$. See b1239	136.16	pr (w or al) λ^{cy} 232.5 (4.03)	111–3	263 sub	1.054^{112}	1.509	δ	v	v				B9, 475
Ω b1793	—,—,amide	C_8H_9NO. See b1244	135.17	nd (eth) $\lambda^{95\%al}$ 230 sh (4.05), 276 (2.95)	97	...			δ	s	δ		δ		B9, 477
b1794	—,—,anhydride	$C_{16}H_{14}O_3$. See b1239	254.29	cr (peth)	71	230^{17}				s	v	s	v	chl v	B9², 324
b1795	—,—,chloride	C_8H_7ClO. See b1239	154.60		−23	$219-20^{766}$ 105^{20}	1.173^{20}_4	1.5485^{20}	d	d^h	s				B9², 324
b1796	—,—,ethyl ester	$C_{10}H_{12}O_2$. See b1239	164.21			234 (227) $103-5^{10}$	1.0265^{21}_4	1.505^{22}	i	∞	∞				B9, 476
Ω b1797	—,—,methyl ester	$C_9H_{10}O_2$. See b1239	150.18	λ 348 (3.04), 360 (3.06)	...	221^{758} (215)	1.061^{20}_4		l	s					B9³, 324
Ω b1798	—,—,nitrile	C_8H_7N. See b1291	117.15	λ^{al} 228 (4.03), 276 (3.08), 284 (3.09)	−23	213^{759} 84.5^{10}	1.0316^{20}_4	1.5252^{20}	i δ^h	∞	∞				B9², 325
b1799	—,—,4-phenyl-phenacyl ester		303.39	cr (dil al)	136.5	...									Am 52, 3715
Ω b1800	—,4-methyl-	p-Toluic acid. $C_8H_8O_2$. See b1239	136.16	nd (w) λ^{cy} 239 (4.18)	182	275 (cor) sub			i δ^h	v	v			MeOH v	B9, 483
Ω b1801	—,—,amide	C_8H_9NO. See b1244	135.17	nd or pl (w) $\lambda^{95\%al}$ 269 (4.3)	160 (158)	...			δ v^h	v	v		δ	chl δ	B9, 486
b1802	—,—,anhydride	$C_{16}H_{14}O_3$. See b1239	254.29	pl (MeOH), nd (al) λ^{peth} 242 (4.59)	95 (98)	...					s	s	v	chl s	B9², 329
Ω b1803	—,—,chloride	C_8H_7ClO. See b1239	154.60		−2 (−4)	$225-7^{760}$ 102^{15}	1.1686^{20}_4	1.5547^{20}	d	d^h	s				B9², 329
Ω b1804	—,—,ethyl ester	$C_{10}H_{12}O_2$. See b1239	164.21	λ^w 240 (4.08)	...	235.7^{760} 110^{12}	1.0269^{18}_4	1.5089^{18}	i	∞	∞				B9, 484
Ω b1805	—,—,methyl ester	$C_9H_{10}O_2$. See b1239	150.18	cr (aq MeOH or peth) λ^{undil} 354 (2.75)	33.2	222.5^{760}			i	v	v				B9, 484
Ω b1806	—,—,nitrile	C_8H_7N. See b1291	117.15	nd (al) λ^{al} 232 (4.20), 267 (2.82), 279 (2.66)	29.5	217.6^{760} 91^{11}	0.9805^{30}_{30}		i	v	v				B9², 330
b1807	—,—,4-phenyl-phenacyl ester		330.39	...	165	...									Am 52, 3715
b1808	—,—,piperazinium salt	$C_{20}H_{26}N_2O_4$. See b1239	358.44		203.0–.3				δ	s	δ^h				Am 70, 2758
b1809	—,2(methyl-amino)-	$C_8H_9NO_2$. See b1239	151.17	pl (al or lig)	179	$80^{0.01}$			δ	v	v		v	chl v lig s	B14², 212
b1810	—,—,ethyl ester	$C_{10}H_{13}NO_2$. See b1239	179.22		39	266^{760} $141-3^{15}$			i	v	v				B14², 213
b1811	—,—,methyl ester	$C_9H_{11}NO_2$. See b1239	165.09	cr (peth)	18.5–9.5	255^{760} $130-1^{13}$	1.120^{15}	1.5839^{12}	i	s	s				B14², 212
b1812	—,3(methyl-amino)-	$C_8H_9NO_2$. See b1239	151.16	pl (peth)	127	...			i δ^h	v	i	v	chl v lig i	B14, 391
b1813	—,—,methyl ester	$C_9H_{11}NO_2$. See b1239	165.19	cr (al)	72	...			i	v	v				B14, 392
Ω b1814	—,4(methyl-amino)-	$C_8H_9NO_2$. See b1239	151.16	nd (bz, w or dil al)	168 (159)	...			s^h	v	v		s^h	AcOEt s	B14², 259
b1815	—,—,methyl ester	$C_9H_{11}NO_2$. See b1239	165.19	pl (dil al or lig)	95.5	...			i	s	s				B14¹, 571
b1816	—,3(3-methyl-butoxy)-	m-Isoamyloxybenzoic acid. $C_{12}H_{16}O_3$. See b1239	208.24	cr (al)	74–5					δ s^h					B10¹, 64
Ω b1817	—,4(3-methyl-butoxy)-	p-Isoamyloxybenzoic acid. $C_{12}H_{16}O_3$. See b1239	208.24	nd	141–2										B10¹, 70
b1818	—,—,chloride	$C_{12}H_{15}ClO_2$. See b1239	226.71	...		$180 \ 2^{12}$			d	d^h					B10¹, 77
Ω b1819	—,3,4-methyl-enedioxy-	Piperonylic acid. $C_8H_6O_4$. See b1239	166.14	nd (al), pr (sub)	229–31	sub			i	δ	δ			chl i	B19², 292
b1820	—,—,chloride	$C_8H_5ClO_3$. See b1239	184.58	cr	80	155^{25}								peth v	B19, 270
b1821	—,—,ethyl ester	$C_{10}H_{10}O_4$. See b1239	194.19	pr	18.5	$285.5-6.5$ $164-5^{11}$			i	v	v			peth v	B19², 293
b1822	—,—,methyl ester	$C_9H_8O_4$. See b1239	180.17	nd or lf (peth)	53	$273-4^{760}$ δd				v	v			peth v, MeOH s CCl_4 v	B19², 293
b1823	—,2-methyl-4-nitro-, nitrile (colorless)	$C_8H_6N_2O_2$. See b1291	162.15	lf (sub)	100 (105)	sub			δ^h	δ		v	v	chl v	B9¹, 188
b1824	—,—,—,(yellow)	$C_8H_6N_2O_2$. See b1291	162.15	ye nd (al)	113–5				δ^h	δ		v	v	chl v	B9¹, 188
b1825	—,2-methyl-5-nitro-, nitrile	$C_8H_6N_2O_2$. See b1291	162.15	nd (95% al)	105	$174-5^{10}$			s^h	v^h	v	v	v	chl v	B9², 323

For explanations, symbols and abbreviations see beginning of table. For structural formulas see end of table.

No.	Name	Synonyms and Formula	Mol. wt.	Color, crystalline form, specific rotation and λ_{max} (log ε)	m.p. °C	b.p. °C	Density	n_D	w	al	eth	ace	bz	other solvents	Ref.
	Benzoic acid														
b1826	—,2-methyl-6-nitro-, nitrile	$C_8H_6N_2O_2$. See b1291	162.15	pl (bz)	109–10	....				s	...	s	s	os s	B9[2], 323
b1827	—,3-methyl-2-nitro-, nitrile	$C_8H_6N_2O_2$. See b1291	162.15	nd (al)	84	....				s[h]	...	s	s	chl s	B9[1], 191
b1828	—,3-methyl-4-nitro-, nitrile	$C_8H_6N_2O_2$. See b1291	162.15	pr (al), nd λ^w 225 (4.08), 280 (3.83)	80	....			i	s[h]	...	...	...		B9[1], 192
b1829	—,3-methyl-5-nitro-, nitrile	$C_8H_6N_2O_2$. See b1291	162.15	nd (lig)	104–5	....				s	...	...	...	lig s[h]	B9[1], 192
b1830	—,4-methyl-2-nitro-, nitrile	$C_8H_6N_2O_2$. See b1291	162.15	nd (w)	101	....			s[h]	v	...	...	v	chl v lig δ	B9[2], 334
b1831	—,4-methyl-3-nitro-, nitrile	$C_8H_6N_2O_2$. See b1291	162.15	pa ye nd (w)	107–8	171[12]			s	s	v	v	v	chl v	B9[2], 334
b1832	—,5-methyl-2-nitro-, nitrile	$C_8H_6N_2O_2$. See b1291	162.15	nd (al)	93–4	....			v[h]	...	...	...	v	aa v	B9[1], 192
b1834	—,2(1-naphthoyl)-	$C_{18}H_{12}O_3$. See b1239	276.30	pr (al-w)	176.4	....			δ[h] i	...	v	v	v	chl s sulf s	E12B, 3614
b1835	—,2(2-naphthoyl)-	$C_{18}H_{12}O_3$. See b1239	276.30	nd (to)	168	....			δ	v	v	v	s	os v aa v	E12B, 3621
Ω b1836	—,2-nitro-	$C_7H_5NO_4$. See b1239	167.12	tcl nd (w) λ^{al} 250 sh (3.54)	147–8	....	1.575^{20}_4		s[h]	v	s v[h]	v	δ	chl δ, s[h] lig δ MeOH v	B9[2], 242
b1837	—,—,amide	$C_7H_6N_2O_3$. See b1244	166.14	nd (dil al) λ^{al} 250 (3.7),	176.6	317			s[h]	s	s	...	...		B9[2], 246
b1838	—,—,—,N-phenyl-	$C_{13}H_{10}N_2O_3$. See b1244	242.24	nd (al or bz) λ^{al} 246 (4.3), 354 (3.5)	155	....			i	v	δ	...	s	chl s lig δ	B12[2], 153
b1839	—,—,azide	$C_7H_4N_4O_3$. See b1239	192.14	ye pr (eth)	37.5	....				...	v	...	v	chl v	B9, 376
Ω b1840	—,—,ethyl ester	$C_9H_9NO_4$. See b1239	195.18	tcl (dil al)	30	275 173[18]			i	s	s	...	...		B9[2], 245
Ω b1841	—,—,hydrazide	$C_7H_7N_3O_3$. See b1239	181.15	ye-br pr (w) λ^{al} 245 sh (3.6), 350 sh (2.3)	123	....			s	s	i	i	i	chl i	B9[2], 246
Ω b1842	—,—,methyl ester	$C_8H_7NO_4$. See b1239	181.15	....	−13	275 176[21]	1.2855^{20}		i	s	s	s	s	MeOH s chl s lig i	B9[2], 244
Ω b1843	—,—,nitrile	$C_7H_4N_2O_2$. See b1291	148.12	nd (w or aa) λ^{al} 279 (3.78), 296 sh (3.35)	111	sub			δ s[h]	s	s	v	s	CCl_4, aa s CS_2, peth δ chl v	B9[2], 246
Ω b1844	—,3-nitro-	$C_7H_5NO_4$. See b1239	167.12	mcl pr (w) λ^{al} 215 (4.35), 255 (3.85)	140–2	....	1.494^{20}_4		δ	v	v	v	δ	chl s MeOH v peth δ	B9[2], 247
b1845	—,—,amide	$C_7H_6N_2O_3$. See b1244	166.14	ye mcl nd (w) λ^{al} 260 (3.8)	142.7	310–5			s[h]	s	s	...	...		B9[2], 252
b1846	—,—,—,N-phenyl-	$C_{13}H_{10}N_2O_3$. See b1244	242.24	lf (w or al) λ^{al} 262 (4.3) 319 sh (3.2)	153–4	sub			i	s	s	...	s		B12[2], 153
b1847	—,—,azide	$C_7H_4N_4O_3$. See b1239	192.14	pl (dil al) λ^{al} 230 (4.3). 262 sh (3.9). 330 sh (2.4)	68	....			i	v	v	...	v	aa v	B9, 338
Ω b1848	—,—,chloride	$C_7H_4ClNO_3$. See b1239	185.57	ye cr λ^{cy} 232 (4.40)	35	275–8[760] 154–5[18]			d	d	v	...	...		B9[2], 252
Ω b1849	—,—,ethyl ester	$C_9H_9NO_4$. See b1239	195.18	mcl pr	47	296–8 156[10]			i	v	v	...	...		B9[2], 248
Ω b1850	—,—,hydrazide	$C_7H_7N_3O_3$. See b1239	181.15	nd (w) λ^{al} 255 (4.0). 350 sh (2.2)	153–4	....			δ v[h]	δ v[h]	i	...	i	chl i	B9[2], 256
Ω b1851	—,—,methyl ester	$C_8H_7NO_4$. See b1239	181.15	nd λ^{al} 219 (4.37) 251 (3.86), 284 sh (3.10)	78	....			i	δ	δ	...	...	MeOH δ	B9[2], 248
Ω b1852	—,—,nitrile	$C_7H_4N_2O_2$. See b1291	148.12	nd (w) λ^{al} 255 (3.8), 335 sh(2.1)	118	sub			s[h]	s	v	v	s[h]	peth i aa v	B9[2], 254
Ω b1853	—,4-nitro-	$C_7H_5NO_4$. See b1244	167.12	mcl lf (w) λ^{al} 258 (4.08), 294 sh (3.40)	242	sub	1.610^{20}		i s[h]	s	s	δ s[h]	δ	chl s lig i CS_2 δ MeOH v	B9[2], 256
Ω b1854	—,—,amide	$C_7H_6N_2O_3$. See b1244	166.14	nd (w) λ^w 265 (4.06)	201.4	....			i	s	s	...	...		B9[2], 271
b1855	—,—,—,N-phenyl-	$C_{13}H_{10}N_2O_3$. See b1244	242.24	lf (eth) λ^{al} 321 (4.3)	211	....			i	s	s	...	s		B12[2], 153
b1856	—,—,butyl ester	$C_{11}H_{13}NO_4$. See b1239	223.23	nd	35.3	160[8]			...	s[h]	v	...	v		B9[2], 259
Ω b1857	—,—,chloride	$C_7H_4ClNO_3$. See b1239	185.57	ye nd (lig)	75	202–5[105] 150–2[15]			d	d	s	...	...		B9[2], 270
Ω b1858	—,—,ethyl ester	$C_9H_9NO_4$. See b1239	195.18	tcl lf (al) λ^{al} 259 (4.00)	57	186.3[760]			i	s	s	...	...		B9[2], 258

For explanations, symbols and abbreviations see beginning of table. For structural formulas see end of table.

Benzoic acid

No.	Name	Synonyms and Formula	Mol. wt.	Color, crystalline form, specific rotation and λ_{max} (log ε)	m.p. °C	b.p. °C	Density	n_D	w	al	eth	ace	bz	other solvents	Ref.
Ω b1859	—,—,hydrazide	$C_7H_7N_3O_3$. See b1239	181.15	yesh nd (w) λ^{al} 260 (4.0), 375 (2.5)	214				δ^h	δ^h	i		i	chl i	B9[2], 274
Ω b1860	—,—,methyl ester	$C_8H_7NO_4$. See b1239	181.15	ye mcl lf λ^{al} 259 (4.12)	96				i	s	s			chl s	B9[2], 258
Ω b1861	—,—,nitrile	$C_7H_4N_2O_2$. See b1291	148.12	lf (al), nd (bz) λ^{al} 258 (4.07), 303 (3.00)	149	sub			δ s^h	δ s^h	δ			chl s aa s	B9[2], 273
b1862	—,—,2,2,2-tri-chloroethyl ester	$C_9H_7Cl_3O_2$. See b1239	253.51	pr (al)	71	106–7[1]	1.352_4^{25}	1.5343^{26}							Am 70, 3370
b1863	—,2-nitroso-	$C_7H_5NO_3$. See b1239	151.12	cr (al or aa)	210d (214d)					s^h δ	δ		δ	aa, δ, s^h	B9[2], 241
b1864	—,3-nitroso-	$C_7H_5NO_3$. See b1239	151.12	cr	230d					s	δ		δ		B9, 369
b1865	—,4-nitroso-	$C_7N_5NO_3$. See b1239	151.12	ye pw	>350					s^h	δ		δ	aa δ	B9[2], 242
b1866	—,4-octyl-	$C_{15}H_{22}O_2$. See b1239	234.34	lf (al)	139 (100)					s^h					B9, 571
Ω b1867	—,pentachloro-	$C_7HCl_5O_2$. See b1239	294.35	nd or pl (bz or dil aa)	208	sub (vac) δd				v				to v aa v	B9[1], 142
b1868	—,—,chloride	C_7Cl_6O. See b1239	312.80	pl (al)	87					v^h				MeOH v^h	C24, 108
b1869	—,pentamethyl-	$C_{12}H_{16}O_2$. See b1239	192.24	nd (w), lf or nd (dil al) λ^{sulf} 286 (4.6), 344 (3.7)	210.5	sub			i	v^h					B9, 569
b1870	—,per-	Perbenzoic acid. C_6H_5COOOH	138.12	mcl pl (peth)	41–3	97–110[13-5] sub			i δ^h	v	v	s	s	chl s peth δ	B9[2], 157
Ω b1871	—,2-phenoxy-	$C_{13}H_{10}O_3$. See b1239	214.22	lf (dil al) $\lambda^{diox-cy}$ 222 (4.14), 285 (3.49)	113–4	355d[760]			i δ^h	v	v			chl s	B10[2], 40
—	—,phenyl-	See **Biphenylcarboxylic acid**													
b1872	—,2(phenyl-amino)-	$C_{13}H_{11}NO_2$. See b1239	213.24	lf, nd or pr (al)	184d				i δ^h	v^h	δ		δ^h		B14[2], 213
b1873	—,2-phosphono-	$C_7H_7O_5P$. See b1239	202.11	nd (w or al)	>300				v	δ					B16, 820
b1874	—,2-propyl-	$C_{10}H_{12}O_2$. See b1239	164.21	lf (dil al)	58	272[739] 164–5[20]			s	v	v				B9[1], 213
Ω b1875	—,4-propyl-	$C_{10}H_{12}O_2$. See b1239	164.21	pr or lf (w)	141				v^h	v	v		v	CS_2 v lig s chl v	B9, 545
b1876	—,3(1-semicarb-azido)-, amide	Cryogenine. $C_8H_{10}N_4O_2$. See b1244	194.20	cr	172				i	s	s		s	chl s	B15[2], 297
—	—,x-sulfamido-	see **Benzoic acid, x-sulfo-,** x-amide (x = 2, 3, 4)													
b1877	—,2-sulfo-	o-Carboxybenzenesulfonic acid. $C_7H_6O_5S$. See b1239	202.19	nd (w +3)	141 (anh) 70 (+3w)				v	v	i				B11[2], 215
b1878	—,—,1-amide	$C_7H_7NO_4S$. See b1244	201.20	pr (w +1)	193–4 (anh)				v	v					B11[2], 215
Ω b1879	—,—,2-amide	o-Sulfamylbenzoic acid. $C_7H_7NO_4S$. See b1239	201.20	pl or nd (w)	165–7 (rapid htng) 153–5 (slow htng)				v	v	v				B11[2], 216
b1880	—,—,anhydride (endo)		184.17	pl or pr (bz)	129.5	184–6[18]			i s^h		s		s	chl s	B19[2], 137
—	—,—,imide	see **Saccharine**													
b1881	—,—,nitrile	$C_7H_5NO_3S$. See b1291	183.19	nd (w)	279.5				s^h	s	δ			chl δ	B11[2], 372
Ω b1882	—,3-sulfo-	m-Carboxybenzenesulfonic acid. $C_7H_6O_5S$. See b1239	202.19	cr (w +2)	141 (anh) 98 (hyd)				v	v	v		i	chl. peth i	B11[2], 217
b1883	—,—,3-amide	m-Sulfamylbenzoic acid. $C_7H_7NO_4S$. See b1239	201.20	pl (w)	246 (238)				s^h δ	s					B11[2], 218
b1884	—,—,3-chloride	$C_7H_5ClO_4S$. See b1239	220.63	pr (bz)	133–4				d^h	d^h	s		s^h		B11[2], 218
b1885	—,—,dichloride	$C_7H_4Cl_2O_3S$. See b1239	239.08		20.4	153–4[7]									B11, 386
b1886	—,4-sulfo-	p-Carboxybenzene sulfonic acid. $C_7H_6O_5S$. See b1239	202.19	nd (w +3)	259–60 (anh) 94 (hyd)				v	v					B11[2], 218
Ω b1887	—,—,4-amide	p-Sulfamylbenzoic acid. $C_7H_7NO_4S$. See b1239	201.20	pr or fl (w)	290–2d				i δ^h	v	δ		i		B11[2], 219
b1888	—,—,4-chloride	$C_7H_5ClO_4S$. See b1239	220.63	nd (ace)	237–8d				d^h	d^h		s		to s	B11[2], 219
Ω b1889	—,2,3,4,5-tetra-chloro-	$C_7H_2Cl_4O_2$. See b1239	259.91	nd (al), cr (ace-w)	194–5				δ	v	v				B9, 346
b1890	—,2,3,4,5-tetra-hydroxy-	$C_7H_6O_6$. See b1239	186.12	pr	84–5				v						C50, 14644
—	—,2(3,4,5,6-tetra-hydroxyxanthyl)-	see **Gallin**													
b1891	—,thiolo-	$C_6H_5C(:O)SH$	138.19	yc pl (aa)	24	85–7[10]		1.6040_4^{20}	i	v	v	s	s	CS_2 v os s	B9[2], 286
b1892	—,thiono-, amide, N-phenyl-	$C_6H_5CSNHC_6H_5$	213.30	ye pl or pr (al)	102	d			i	v	s		s^h	chl s lig δ	B12[2], 154

For explanations, symbols and abbreviations see beginning of table. For structural formulas see end of table.

No.	Name	Synonyms and Formula	Mol. wt.	Color, crystalline form, specific rotation and λ_{max} (log ε)	m.p. °C	b.p. °C	Density	n_D	w	al	eth	ace	bz	other solvents	Ref.
	Benzoic acid														
b1893	—,2(2-toluyl)	$C_{15}H_{12}O_3$. See b1239.......	240.26	nd (w + 1), cr (bz)	130–2 (anh) 84(+w)				s	s^h	s	...	...	MeOH s	B10², 524
b1894	—,2(3-toluyl)-	$C_{15}H_{12}O_3$. See b1239.......	240.26	nd (w + 1), nd (bz)	162.2–2.4				s^h	...	v	v			B10², 524
b1895	—,2(4-toluyl)-	$C_{15}H_{12}O_3$. See b1239.......	240.26	pr (+ 1w, al–to) nd (al)	146				$δ^h$	v	v	v	v	to v^h	B10², 525
b1896	—,—.methyl ester .	$C_{16}H_{14}O_3$. See b1239.......	254.29	pl (MeOH)	66 (61)				$δ^h$	v	...	...	v		B10, 759
b1897	—.4(2-toluyl)-	$C_{15}H_{12}O_3$. See b1239.......	240.26		177									xyl s^h	B10², 527
b1898	—.4(4-toluyl)-	$C_{15}H_{12}O_3$. See b1239.......	240.26	nd (MeOH or ace	228				$δ^h$	v	...	v	δ	chl δ	B10², 528
b1899	—,2,3,5-triamino-	$C_7H_9N_3O_2$. See b1239.......	167.13	cr (w)	d				v^h	$δ^h$	i				B14, 455
b1900	—,3,4,5-triamino-	$C_7H_9N_3O_2$. See b1239.......	167.13	nd (w + ½)	d				s^h δ	i	i				B14, 455
b1901	—,2,3,4-tribromo-	$C_7H_3Br_3O_2$. See b1239.......	358.83	nd (bz)	197–8				i	s	s	...	s^h		B9¹, 147
b1902	—,2,3,5-tribromo-	$C_7H_3Br_3O_2$. See b1239.......	358.83	nd (al)	193–4				i	v^h	v	v	δ	lig i, peth δ	B9¹, 147
b1903	—,2,4,5-tribromo-	$C_7H_3Br_3O_2$. See b1239.......	358.83	nd (al or bz)	195–6				i	s^h	s	...		lig s^h	B9¹, 147
b1904	—,2,4,6-tribromo-	$C_7H_3Br_3O_2$. See b1239.......	358.83	pr (w)	198				δ	s	s	...			B9², 238
b1905	—,3,4,5-tribromo-	$C_7H_3Br_3O_2$. See b1239.......	358.83	nd (bz or al)	240				i	s	s	...		aa s^h	B9¹, 148
Ω b1906	—,2,3,4-trichloro-	$C_7H_3Cl_3O_2$. See b1239.......	225.46	nd (w) $λ^{MeOH}$ 289 (2.79)	187–8										B9, 345
Ω b1907	—,2,3,5-trichloro-	$C_7H_3Cl_3O_2$. See b1239.......	225.46	nd (w) $λ^{MeOH}$ 295 (3.01)	163				i	s	s	s	s	os s	B9, 345
b1908	—,2,3,6-trichloro-	$C_7H_3Cl_3O_2$. See b1239.......	225.46	$λ^{MeOH}$ 283 (2.74)	124–5				δ v^h						B9, 345
Ω b1909	—,2,4,5-trichloro-	$C_7H_3Cl_3O_2$. See b1239.......	225.46	nd (w or sub) $λ^{MeOH}$ 292 (2.97)	168	sub			s^h i	s	s	...			B9¹, 141
b1910	—,2,4,6-trichloro-	$C_7H_3Cl_3O_2$. See b1239.......	225.46	nd (w) $λ^{MeOH}$ 274 (2.43)	164				$δ^h$	v^h	v	...		chl v	B9, 345
b1911	—,3,4,5-trichloro-	$C_7H_3Cl_3O_2$. See b1239.......	225.46	nd (dil al) $λ^{MeOH}$ 288 (2.86), 274 (2.43)	210				$δ^h$	s	s	s	s	CS_2 δ	B9², 230
Ω b1912	—,2,3,4-trihydroxy-	$C_7H_6O_5$. See b1239	170.12	nd (+w)	207–8 d (215–20)	sub			δ	s	s	s	i	CS_2 i AcOEt s	B10², 331
b1913	—,—,ethyl ester ...	$C_9H_{10}O_5$. See b1239	198.18	cr (w + 1)	102 (anh) 86(+w)				s^h i	v	v				B10, 467
b1914	—,—.methyl ester .	$C_8H_8O_5$. See b1239.......	184.16	nd (w + 2½)	151–2				s^h	s					B10, 466
b1915	—,2,4,5-trihydroxy-	$C_7H_6O_5$. See b1239	170.12	nd (w + ½)	217–8d				v^h	v					B10², 334
Ω b1916	—,2,4,6-trihydroxy-	$C_7H_6O_5$. See b1239	170.12	(w + 1) $λ^{MeOH}$ 262.5 (4.12), 297.5 (3.44)	100d				s^h δ	s	s	i			B10², 334
b1917	—,—,ethyl ester ...	$C_9H_{10}O_5$. See b1239	198.18	pr or nd (w + 1), pr (lig)	129				s^h	v	v	v^h		lig δ	B10¹, 236
b1918	—,—.methyl ester .	$C_8H_8O_5$. See b1239	184.16	cr (dil al)	174–6				δ	v	v	...	δ	CCl_4 δ	B10, 469
b1919	—,3,4,5-trihydroxy-	Gallic acid. $C_7H_6O_5$. See b1239	170.12	pr (w + 1) $λ^{al}$ 272.5 (4.06)	253d		1.694⁶₄		v^h δ	v	δ	s	i	chl i	B10², 335
b1920	—,—,amide	Gallamide. $C_7H_7NO_4$. See b1244	169.14	lf (w + 1½)	244–5d				s^h δ	s		...		chl s aa s	B10², 346
b1921	—,—,—,N-phenyl-	Gallanilide. $C_{13}H_{11}NO_4$. See b1244	245.24	lf (+ 2w, dil al)	207				v^h i	s	...			chl i aa s	B12², 263
Ω b1922	—,—,ethyl ester ...	$C_9H_{10}O_5$. See b1239.......	198.18	mcl pr (w + 2½), nd (chl) $λ^{MeOH}$ 275 (4.00)	160–2 (anh) 158 (hyd)				s^h δ	s	s	...		chl $δ^h$ AcOEt s	B10², 343
Ω b1923	—,—,isopropyl ester	$C_{10}H_{12}O_5$. See b1239.......	212.21		123–4.5				s	s	s	...	i	chl s^h	B10², 343
Ω b1924	—,—,methyl ester .	Gallicin. $C_8H_8O_5$. See b1239	184.16	mcl pr (MeOH) $λ^{al}$ 217 (4.72), 275 (4.32)	202				δ	v		...		MeOH v^h	B10², 342
Ω b1925	—,—,propyl ester..	$C_{10}H_{12}O_5$. See b1239.......	212.21	nd (w) $λ^{al}$ 275	150				δ s^h						B10², 343
Ω b1926	—,2,3,5-triiodo-	$C_7H_3I_3O_2$. See b1239.......	499.81	pr (al)	224–6				i	v^h	v	...	$δ^h$		B9¹, 150
b1927	—,2,4,5-triiodo-	$C_7H_3I_3O_2$. See b1239.......	499.81	nd (al)	248				i	s^h	s	...	i		B9¹, 150
Ω b1928	—,3,4,5-triiodo-	$C_7H_3I_3O_2$. See b1239.......	499.81	pr (al)	292–3				i	v					B9, 367
b1930	—,2,3,4-trimethoxy-	$C_{10}H_{12}O_5$. See b1239.......	212.21	cr (w or peth)	100				s	s	s				B10², 332
b1931	—,2,4,5-trimethoxy-	Asaronic acid. $C_{10}H_{12}O_5$. See b1239	212.21	nd (al or bz-peth)	144	300⁷⁶⁰			s^h i	s		...		peth s	B10², 334
Ω b1932	—,3,4,5-trimethoxy-	$C_{10}H_{12}O_5$. See b1239.......	212.21	mcl nd (w) $λ^{al}$ 215 (4.2), 260 (3.7), 300 sh (3.2)	171–2	225–7¹⁰			δ	v	v	...		chl v	B10², 340
b1933	—,2,3,4-trimethyl-	Prehnitylic acid. $C_{10}H_{12}O_2$. See b1239	164.21	pr (al) $λ^{al}$ 237 (3.78), 287 (3.01)	167.5				s^h	s^h	s^h				B9, 552
b1934	—,2,3,5-trimethyl-	γ-Isodurylic acid. $C_{10}H_{12}O_2$. See b1239	164.21	pl (lig) $λ^{al}$ 239 (3.69), 288 (3.15)	127					s					B9, 552
b1935	—,2,3,6-trimethyl-	$C_{10}H_{12}O_2$. See b1239.......	164.21	nd (w or peth) $λ^{al}$ 223 (3.99), 279 (2.90)	110–1				s	s	s				B9, 552

For explanations, symbols and abbreviations see beginning of table. For structural formulas see end of table.

No.	Name	Synonyms and Formula	Mol. wt.	Color, crystalline form, specific rotation and λ_{max} (log ε)	m.p. °C	b.p. °C	Density	n_D	Solubility						Ref.
									w	al	eth	ace	bz	other solvents	
	Benzoic acid														
b1936	—,2,4,5-trimethyl-	Durylic acid. $C_{10}H_{12}O_2$. *See* b1239	164.21	nd (bz) λ^{al} 237 (3.87), 286 (3.21)	152–3				δ^h i	v	v	...	δ	....	B9[2], 361
Ω b1937	—,2,4,6-tri-methyl-	β-Isodurylic acid. Mesitoic acid. $C_{10}H_{12}O_2$. *See* b1239	164.21	pr (lig) λ^{al} 235 sh (3.51), 270 sh (2.62)	155				δ	s	s	s	...	chl s	B9, 553
b1938	—,—,chloride	Mesitoyl chloride. $C_{10}H_{11}ClO$. *See* b1239	182.65	....		143–6[60]			d			s		....	B9[1], 360
b1939	—,3,4,5-tri-methyl-	α-Isodurylic acid. $C_{10}H_{12}O_2$. *See* b1239	164.21	nd (w) λ^{al} 238.5 (4.01)	215–6				δ^h i	s	s				B9, 554
b1940	—,2,3,6-trinitro-	$C_7H_3N_3O_8$. *See* b1239	257.12	wh nd (w + 2)	160d, 55 (+2w)				δ^h	s					B9[1], 168
b1941	—,2,4,5-trinitro-	$C_7H_3N_3O_8$. *See* b1239	257.12	ye lf or pl (w)	194.5d				s^h	v	v		s	peth δ	B9[1], 168
Ω b1942	—,2,4,6-trinitro-	$C_7H_3N_3O_8$. *See* b1239	257.12	rh (w) λ^{Et_2NH} 475 (2.90)	228.7d				δ	v	s	s	δ	MeOH v	B9[2], 285
b1943	—,3,4,5-trinitro-	$C_7H_3N_3O_8$. *See* b1239	257.12	ye nd (eth +1)	168d				d^h		s			MeOH v	B9[1], 168
b1944	**Benzoin** (d)	Benzoylphenylcarbinol. α-Hydroxybenzyl phenyl ketone.	212.25	nd, $[\alpha]_D^{15}$ +92.8 (Py. c = 1)	133–4				v^h		v			MeOH v[h] Py s	B8[2], 193
Ω b1945	—(dl)	$C_{14}H_{12}O_2$. *See* b1944	212.25	pr (al) λ^{al} 248 (4.1)	137	344[768] 194[12]	1.310$_4^{20}$		δ^h	s^h	δ			aa v chl s	B8[2], 193
b1946	—(l)	$C_{14}H_{12}O_2$. *See* b1944	212.25	nd (MeOH), $[\alpha]_D^{13}$ −117.5 (ace, c = 1.25)	133–4					v^h		v		MeOH s[h]	B8, 167
Ω b1947	—,acetate (dl)	$C_6H_5CH(OCOCH_3)COC_6H_5$	254.29	pr or pl (eth)	83	....				v	v				B8[2], 196
b1948	—,ethyl ether (dl)	$C_6H_5CH(OC_2H_5)COC_6H_5$	240.31	nd (lig)	62	194–5[20]	1.1016^{17}	1.5727^{17}	...	v	v		v	lig s[h]	B8[2], 195
b1949	—,hydrazone (dl)	$C_6H_5CH(OH)C(:NNH_2)C_6H_5$	226.28	pr (al)	75				i	v^h					B8, 176
b1950	—,methyl ether (dl)	$C_6H_5CH(OCH_3)COC_6H_5$	226.28	nd (lig)	49–50	188–9[15]	1.1278$_4^{14}$			v	v		v	lig v[h]	B8[2], 194
b1951	—,oxime (l)	$C_6H_5CH(OH)C(:NOH)C_6H_5$	227.27	amor or pr (bz), $[\alpha]_D^{24}$ −3.2 (chl. c = 0.85)	163.5–4.5				i	s	s	s	δ^h		B8, 167
Ω b1952	—,—,(dl, anti)	$C_{14}H_{13}NO_2$. *See* b1951	227.27	pr (bz) λ^{al} 290 (3.0), 301 (2.0), 311 (1.0)	151–2				i	s	s	s			B8[2], 196
b1953	—,—,(dl, syn)	$C_{14}H_{13}NO_2$. *See* b1951	227.27	pr (eth)	99				i	s	s	s			B8[2], 196
b1954	—,succinate	$[C_6H_5CH(COC_6H_5)O_2CCH_2-]_2$	506.56	lf (al)	129				i	s	s	s		CS_2 s	B8, 175
Ω b1955	—,4,4′-dimethoxy-	Anisoin. $C_{16}H_{16}O_4$. *See* b1944	272.30	pr (dil al) λ^{al} 220 (4.38), 277 (4.33)	113				δ^h δ	v^h	δ	s			B8[2], 470
—	**Benzonitrile**	*see* **Benzoic acid**, nitrile													
	1,2-Benzophe-nanthrene	*see* **Chrysene**													
Ω b1956	**3,4-Benzophe-nanthrene**	Benzo(c)phenanthrene	228.30	nd or pl (lig or al) λ^{al} 232 (4.5), 280 (4.9), 302 (4.0), 325 (3.6), 355 (2.5), 372 (2.4)	68	....			i	δ		...	...	lig δ	E14, 356
Ω b1957	**9,10-Benzophe-nanthrene**	Triphenylene.	228.30	nd (al, chl, bz) λ^{al} 248.5 (4.94), 257 (5.18), 273 (4.28), 284 (4.23)	199	425			i	s	s	...	v	chl v aa s	E14, 357
b1958	**1,2-Benzophen-azine**	Benzo[α]phenazine. *ang*-Naphthaphenazine.	230.26	pr (al), ye nd (bz) λ^{MeOH} 224 (4.63), 277.5 (4.72), 380 (4.06), 400 (4.08)	142.5	>360			i	s	s	s	δ	aa s	B23[2], 259
Ω b1959	**Benzophenone**	Diphenyl ketone. Benzoyl-benzene	182.21	(α) rh pr (al or eth); (β) mcl pr λ^{al} 253 (4.24); λ^{hx} 346 (2.1), 361 sh (2.0)	(α) 48.1 (β) 26	305.9[760]	(α) 1.146^{20} (β) 1.1076	(α) 1.6077^{19} (β) 1.6059^{23}	i	v	v	v	s	aa v MeOH s CS_2 v chl v	B7[2], 349
b1960	—,imine	$(C_6H_5)_2C:NH$	181.24	....		282 158[12]	1.0847$_4^{19}$	1.6191^{19}	d		s			peth s	B7[2], 355
Ω b1961	—,oxime	$(C_6H_5)_2C:NOH$	197.24	nd (al) λ^{al} 231 (4.14), 251 (4.03)	144	....			i	v^h	s	v		MeOH v[h] chl s	B7[2], 355
b1962	—,phenyl-hydrazone	$(C_6H_5)_2C:NNHC_6H_5$	272.35	pr or nd (al) λ^{al} 345 (4.26)	137				i	δ	s		s	aa s	B15[2], 63

For explanations, symbols and abbreviations see beginning of table. For structural formulas see end of table.

No.	Name	Synonyms and Formula	Mol. wt.	Color, crystalline form, specific rotation and λ_{max} (log ε)	m.p. °C	b.p. °C	Density	n_D	w	al	eth	ace	bz	other solvents	Ref.
	Benzophenone														
Ω b1963	—,2-amino-	$C_{13}H_{11}NO$. See b1959	197.24	pa ye lf or pr (al) λ^{al} 235 (4.3), 385 (3.8)	110–1 (105–6)				i	s^h	s				B14², 51
b1964	—,3-amino-	$C_{13}H_{11}NO$. See b1959	197.24	ye nd (w) λ^{al} 245 (4.3), 335 (3.3)	87				δ	s	s				B14¹, 388
Ω b1965	—,4-amino-	$C_{13}H_{11}NO$. See b1959	197.24	lf (dil al) λ^{al} 245 (4.2), 335 (4.3)	124				s^h δ	s	s			aa s	B14², 54
b1966	—,2-amino-4'-methyl-	$C_{14}H_{13}NO$. See b1959	211.27	ye pr or pl (al)	96					v	v		v		B14², 63
b1967	—,2-amino-5-methyl-	$C_{14}H_{13}NO$. See b1959	211.27	ye nd or pl (al)	66					v	v	v		chl v lig v aa v	B14, 106
b1968	—,3-amino-4-methyl	$C_{14}H_{13}NO$. See b1959	211.27	pa ye nd (MeOH)	109				δ^h	v	v	v	v	MeOH s^h CS₂ s^h chl v	B14², 63
b1969	—,3-amino-4'-methyl-	$C_{14}H_{13}NO$. See b1959	211.27	pr (al)	111					v	v				B14, 107
b1970	—,4-amino-3-methyl-	$C_{14}H_{13}NO$. See b1959	211.27	ye pr (w)	112				δ s^h	v	v				B14, 105
b1971	—,4-amino-4'-methyl-	$C_{14}H_{13}NO$. See b1959	211.27	nd (bz)	186–7					v	v		s^h	chl v lig δ CS₂ v	B14, 107
b1973	—,4,4'-bis-(diethylamino)-	$C_{21}H_{28}N_2O$. See b1959	324.47	lf (al)	95–6					δ v^h					B14², 59
Ω b1974	—,4,4'-bis(di-methylamino)-	Michler's ketone. $C_{17}H_{20}N_2O$. See b1959	268.36	lf (al), nd (bz) λ^{al} 370 (4.28), 390 sh (4.36)	179	>360d			i	δ	i		v^h	Py v	B14², 57
b1975	—,4,4'-bis(di-methylamino), thio-	$C_{17}H_{20}N_2S$. See b1959	284.43	pl	204				i	i	δ		s	chl s lig i aa s	B14², 60
b1976	—,2-bromo-	$C_{13}H_9BrO$. See b1959	261.13	pr (al), nd (lig)	42	345⁷⁵⁹	1.517¹⁴		i	s^h		s		lig s^h	B7², 360
b1977	—,3-bromo-	$C_{13}H_9BrO$. See b1959	261.13	nd (al)	81.5 (77)	185–7⁵			i	s^h					B7², 360
Ω b1978	—,4-bromo-	$C_{13}H_9BrO$. See b1959	261.13	lf (al)	82.5	350⁷⁵⁷			i	δ^h	δ		δ	peth δ	B7², 360
b1979	—,2-chloro-	$C_{13}H_9ClO$. See b1959	216.67	pl (chl-lig)	52–6	330 185–8¹³									B7¹, 227
b1980	—,3-chloro-	$C_{13}H_9ClO$. See b1959	216.67	nd	82–3					δ			v		B7¹, 227
Ω b1981	—,4-chloro-	$C_{13}H_9ClO$. See b1959	216.67	nd (al) λ^{al} 260 (4.32)	77–8	332⁷⁷¹				s^h	s^h	s			B7², 359
b1982	—,2-chloro-3,5-dinitro-	$C_{13}H_7ClN_2O_5$. See b1959	306.67	ye nd (aa)	149					δ				chl s aa s^h lig i	B7, 428
b1983	—,2,2'-diamino-	$C_{13}H_{12}N_2O$. See b1959	212.25	lf (dil al), pr (bz)	134–5				i	s	s				B14, 87
b1984	—,3,3'-diamino-	$C_{13}H_{12}N_2O$. See b1959	212.25	nd (al)	173–4	285¹¹			i s^h	s	s				B14¹, 390
b1985	—,4,4'-diamino-	$C_{13}H_{12}N_2O$. See b1959	212.25	nd (al)	244–5				d^h	s	s				B14², 56
b1986	—,4,4'-dibromo-	$C_{13}H_8Br_2O$. See b1959	340.04	pl (al)	177	395			i	s^h	δ	s	s	chl s CS₂ s	B7, 423
Ω b1987	—,2,4-dichloro-	$C_{13}H_8Cl_2O$. See b1959	251.13	pr (al) λ^{al} 262 (4.36)	67	214–5²²	1.393¹⁴			s^h					B7, 420
Ω b1988	—,4,4'-dichloro-	$C_{13}H_8Cl_2O$. See b1959	251.13	pl (al) λ^{al} 265 (4.39)	147–8	353⁷⁵⁷			i	s^h	v	s		chl v aa v	B7, 420
b1989	—,2,2'-dihydroxy-	$C_{13}H_{10}O_3$. See b1959	214.22	lf or pr (lig) λ^{al} 260 (4.07), 336 (4.76)	59.5	330–40			i	s	s			chl s	B8², 354
b1990	—,2,3'-dihydroxy-	$C_{13}H_{10}O_3$. See b1959	214.22	nd (w)	126				s^h	s	s				B8, 315
Ω b1991	—,2,4-dihydroxy-	$C_{13}H_{10}O_3$. See b1959	214.22	nd (w) λ^{MeOH} 242 (3.94), 290 (3.96), 338 (4.12)	144 (146)				i	s	v		δ	aa v	B8², 352
b1992	—,2,4'-dihydroxy-	$C_{13}H_{10}O_3$. See b1959	214.22	pl (w)	150–1				δ^h	s^h	s		s^h		B8², 354
b1993	—,2,5-dihydroxy-	$C_{13}H_{10}O_3$. See b1959	214.22	ye nd (dil al)	125–6				s^h	s	s		s		B8², 353
b1994	—,3,3'-dihydroxy-	$C_{13}H_{10}O_3$. See b1959	214.22	nd (w)	170				s^h	s	s				B8, 316
b1995	—,3,4-dihydroxy-	$C_{13}H_{10}O_3$. See b1959	214.22	nd (w)	206				s^h	s	s				B8, 316
b1996	—,4,4'-dihydroxy-	$C_{13}H_{10}O_3$. See b1959	214.22	nd (lig), cr (w) λ^{MeOH} 295 (4.28)	210		1.133¹³¹		δ s^h	s	s	s	i	CS₂, chl i, MeOH s	B8², 354
b1997	—,2,4-dihydroxy-6-methoxy-	Isocotoin. $C_{14}H_{12}O_4$. See b1959	244.25	ye nd (lig)	162				s			s		lig δ	B8², 467
b1998	—,2,6-dihydroxy-4-methoxy-	Cotoin. $C_{14}H_{12}O_4$. See b1959	244.25	yesh pr (chl) lf or nd (w)	130–1				δ^h	s	s	s	s^h	chl s CS₂ s	B8², 467
b1999	—,4,4'-diiodo-	$C_{13}H_8I_2O$. See b1959	434.03	pl (to) nd (bz)	238.5	281¹²			i	δ				to s^h	B7, 425
b2000	—,2,4-dimethoxy-	$C_{15}H_{14}O_3$. See b1959	242.28	pr (dil al) λ^{MeOH} 245 (4.18), 280 (3.86), 310 (3.78)	87–8	218¹⁰			i	v	δ			chl v lig δ	B8², 353
Ω b2001	—,2,4'-dimethoxy-	$C_{15}H_{14}O_3$. See b1959	242.28	nd (al)	100				i	v^h	v		v	aa v	B8¹, 640
b2002	—,2,5-dimethoxy-	$C_{15}H_{14}O_3$. See b1959	242.28	(lig)	51	225³⁸			i	δ	δ			lig δ	B8², 354
b2003	—,3,4-dimethoxy-	$C_{15}H_{14}O_3$. See b1959	242.28	nd or pl (al)	103–4				i	v					B8², 354
b2004	—,3,4'-dimethoxy-	$C_{15}H_{14}O_3$. See b1959	242.28	pr (al)	58–9				i	v^h s					B8², 354

For explanations, symbols and abbreviations see beginning of table. For structural formulas see end of table.

No.	Name	Synonyms and Formula	Mol. wt.	Color, crystalline form, specific rotation and λ_{max} (log ε)	m.p. °C	b.p. °C	Density	n_D	Solubility						Ref.
									w	al	eth	ace	bz	other solvents	
	Benzophenone														
Ω b2005	—,4,4'-dimethoxy-	$C_{15}H_{14}O_3$. See b1959	242.28	nd (al) λ^{al} 220 (4.25), 293 (4.37)	146 (144)	....			i	v^h	s	s	v	chl v	B8, 317
Ω b2006	—,4,4'-dimethyl-	$C_{15}H_{14}O$. See b1959	210.28	rh (al) λ^{al} 265 (4.32), 328 (2.5)	95	333^{725}			i	v^h	v	s	...	chl v CS_2 v	B7[2], 387
b2007	—,3(dimethyl- amino)-	$C_{15}H_{15}NO$. See b1959	225.29	pa ye pl (al) λ^{al} 260 (4.4), 370 (3.1)	47	216^{15}				s^h					B14[1], 388
b2008	—,4(dimethyl- amino)-	$C_{15}H_{15}NO$. See b1959	225.29	ye lf(al), nd (peth) λ^{al} 245 (4.2), 355 (4.4)	92–3	....			i	δ v^h	v	...	...	peth s^h chl s	B14[2], 54
b2009	—,2,2'-dinitro-	$C_{13}H_8N_2O_5$. See b1959	272.21	nd (to or aa)	188–9				i					to s^h aa s^h	B7, 427
Ω b2010	—,2-hydroxy-	$C_{13}H_{10}O_2$. See b1959	198.22	pl (dil al) λ^{al} 260 (4.1), 335 (3.7)	39	250^{560}			i	v	v	...	v	peth δ aa v	B8, 155
b2011	—,3-hydroxy-	$C_{13}H_{10}O_2$. See b1959	198.22	lf or pl (al)	116					v	v				B8, 157
Ω b2012	—,4-hydroxy-	$C_{13}H_{10}O_2$. See b1959	198.22	nd (al) pr (dil al) λ^{al} 290 (4.1), 345 (2.7)	135 (st), 122 (unst)				s^h δ	v	v			aa v	B8[2], 184
b2013	—,2-methoxy-	$C_{14}H_{12}O_2$. See b1959	212.25	λ^{cy} 245 (4.0), 285 (3.4), 315 (3.0), 360 (1.9)	41	$194–6^{18}$			i				s	aa s	B8[2], 182
b2014	—,3-methoxy-	$C_{14}H_{12}O_2$. See b1959	212.25	λ^{al} 255 (4.0), 315 (3.3)	44 (37)	$342–3^{730}$ 201^{17}			i	v			v	aa v	B8[1], 569
b2015	—,4-methoxy-	$C_{14}H_{12}O_2$. See b1959	212.25	pr (eth) λ^{al} 224 (4.07), 252 (3.96), 290 (4.21)	61–2	$354–5^{729}$ 168^{12}			i	v	v	s	s	chl s aa s	B8[1], 569
Ω b2016	—,2-methyl-	$C_{14}H_{12}O$. See b1959	196.25	λ^{al} 252 (4.2), 282 sh (3.6), 332 sh (2.2)	< –18	309.5^{762} 128^{12}			i					os s	B7[2], 371
Ω b2017	—,3-methyl-	$C_{14}H_{12}O$. See b1959	196.25	λ^{al} 256 (4.2), 297 (3.3), 330 sh (2.2)	oil	$314–5^{725}$ 170^8	$1.088^{17.5}$		i	s	s	...	s	chl s aa s	B7[2], 372
Ω b2018	—,4-methyl-	$C_{14}H_{12}O$. See b1959	196.25	mcl pr λ^{al} 260 (4.2), 335 (2.2)	59–60 (st) 55 (unst)	$327–8^{760}$			i	δ^h	s	...	s	lig δ chl s	B7[2], 372
b2019	—,—.imine	$C_{14}H_{13}N$. See b1959	195.27		37	147^5	1.0617^{20}_4	1.6097^{20}	i						B7[1], 235
b2020	—,—.diphenyl- acetal	$C_{26}H_{22}O_2$. See b1959	366.47	(dil al, eth — peth)	134	....			i	i				os s peth i	B7[2], 372
b2021	—,4-methyl-2- nitro-	$C_{14}H_{11}NO_3$. See b1959	241.25	nd or pl (al)	126–7	sub			i	s^h			s	chl s aa s^h	B7, 442
b2022	—,4-methyl-2'- nitro-	$C_{14}H_{11}NO_3$. See b1959	241.25	pr (aa or al)	155				i	δ^h	δ		s^h	chl s aa s^h lig δ	B7, 442
b2023	—,4-methyl-3- nitro-	$C_{14}H_{11}NO_3$. See b1959	241.25	pa ye pl (al or aa)	130–2				δ	s	s	v	v	CS_2 v aa v chl v	B7[2], 374
Ω b2024	—,4-methyl-3'- nitro-	$C_{14}H_{11}NO_3$. See b1959	241.25	lf (al)	111				i	δ	s		s	chl s	B7[2], 375
b2025	—,4-methyl-4'- nitro-	$C_{14}H_{11}NO_3$. See b1959	241.25	nd (al)	122–4	sub			i	s	s		s	chl s CS_2 s aa s	B7[2], 375
b2026	—,—.oxime	$C_{14}H_{12}N_2O_3$. See b1959	256.26	nd (eth-lig)	145					s	s		s	lig δ	B7, 443
b2027	—,2-nitro-	$C_{13}H_9NO_3$. See b1959	227.22	mcl (al) λ^{al} 258 (4.3)	105				i	s	s	...	...	....	B7[2], 362
b2028	—,3-nitro-	$C_{13}H_9NO_3$. See b1959	227.22	ye nd (al) λ^{al} 232 (4.32), 248 (4.28)	95	234^{18}			i	s^h					B7[2], 362
Ω b2029	—,4-nitro-	$C_{13}H_9NO_3$. See b1959	227.22	nd or lf (al) λ^{al} 266 (4.30)	138	....	1.406^0_4		δ	δ s^h	δ		s	CS_2 v lig δ	B7[2], 362
b2030	—,2,2',3,4-tetra- hydroxy-	$C_{13}H_{10}O_5$. See b1959	246.22	ye lf or pl (w +1)	149 102 (+w)				s^h δ	v	v	...	δ	aa v lig δ	B8[2], 539
Ω b2031	—,2,2',4,4'-tetra- hydroxy-	$C_{13}H_{10}O_5$. See b1959	246.22	ye nd (w +1½) λ^{MeOH} 287 (4.01), 348 (4.17)	196–8				s^h δ	v	v	v	s^h	chl s^h aa s MeOH v	B8[2], 540
b2032	—,2,2',4,6'-tetra- hydroxy-	Isoeuxanthonic acid. $C_{13}H_{10}O_5$. See b1959	246.22	(w +1)	200d				v^h δ	s	s				B8, 496
b2033	—,2,2',5,6'-tetra- hydroxy-	Euxanthoic acid. $C_{13}H_{10}O_5$ See b1959	246.22	ye nd (w)	200–2d				s v^h	s					B8[2], 541
b2034	—,2,3',4,4'-tetra- hydroxy-	$C_{13}H_{10}O_5$. See b1959	246.22	nd (w +2)	202 (anh)				s^h δ	v	v	v	δ	aa v lig i	B8[2], 541
b2035	—,2,3',4,6-tetra- hydroxy-	$C_{13}H_{10}O_5$. See b1959	246.22	pa ye lf (w)	246d				v^h	v	δ				B8[2], 540
b2036	—,2,4,4',6-tetra- hydroxy-	$C_{13}H_{10}O_5$. See b1959	246.22	pr or nd (w +2)	210				s^h	s	s				B8[2], 540

For explanations, symbols and abbreviations see beginning of table. For structural formulas see end of table.

No.	Name	Synonyms and Formula	Mol. wt.	Color, crystalline form, specific rotation and λ_{max} (log ε)	m.p. °C	b.p. °C	Density	n_D	Solubility						Ref.
									w	al	eth	ace	bz	other solvents	

Benzophenone

No.	Name	Synonyms and Formula	Mol. wt.	Color/form/λmax	m.p.	b.p.			w	al	eth	ace	bz	other solvents	Ref.
b2037	—,3,3′,4,4′-tetra-hydroxy-	$C_{13}H_{10}O_5$. See b1959	246.22	(w) λ^{al} 236 (4.22), 280 sh (4.00), 323 (4.19)	227–8				s^h	s			s	peth δ	B8^2, 541
b2038	—,2,2′,4,4′-tetra-methoxy-	$C_{17}H_{18}O_5$. See b1959	302.33	ye lf (dil al) λ^{MeOH} 278 (4.45), 312 (4.42)	130				δ	v					B8^2, 540
b2039	—,2,2′,5,5′-tetra-methoxy-	$C_{17}H_{18}O_5$. See b1959	302.33	ye (aa or al)	109					v^h s	s		v	chl v aa s, v^h	B8, 497
b2040	—,2,2′,6,6′-tetra-methoxy-	$C_{17}H_{18}O_5$. See b1959	302.33	pl (bz)	204					δ^h	δ		δ	chl v aa δ	B8^1, 735
b2041	—,2,3′,4,4′-tetra-methoxy-	$C_{17}H_{18}O_5$. See b1959	302.33	nd, lf or pr (al)	126 (107)					s				con sulf →ye	B8^1, 735
b2042	—,2,3′,4,5′-tetra-methoxy-	$C_{17}H_{18}O_5$. See b1959	302.33	nd (bz-peth)	73–4					v	v		v^h	chl v aa δ^h peth i	B8^1, 735
b2043	—,2,3′,4′,5-tetra-methoxy-	$C_{17}H_{18}O_5$. See b1959	302.33	pr (dil al)	101–2					s	s			con sulf →og	B8^2, 541
b2044	—,2,3,4,6-tetra-methoxy-	$C_{17}H_{18}O_5$. See b1959	302.33	nd (lig)	125–6				i	v		v	v	lig s^h	B8^1, 734
b2045	—,2,4,4′,5-tetra-methoxy-	$C_{17}H_{18}O_5$. See b1959	302.33	ye pw (al)	122–4					s		v	v	chl v	B8^1, 734
b2046	—,2,4,4′,6-tetra-methoxy-	$C_{17}H_{18}O_5$. See b1959	302.33	pr (al)	146					s	s				B8, 496
b2047	—,3,3′,4,4′-tetra-methoxy-	Veratrophenone. $C_{17}H_{18}O_5$. See b1959	302.33	pr (al) λ^{al} 234 (4.40), 283.5 (4.11), 316 (4.24)	145					v^h s			s	peth δ	B8^2, 541
b2048	—,3,3′,4,5′-tetra-methoxy-	$C_{17}H_{18}O_5$. See b1959	302.33	nd (bz)	114–5					v	v		v^h	chl v lig i aa δ	B8^1, 735
b2049	—,thio-	$C_6H_5CSC_6H_5$	198.29	bl nd (peth) λ^{al} 595 (2.22)	53–4	174^{14}			δ	δ		v	chl v peth δ os v	B7^2, 365
b2050	—,2,2′,6-tri-hydroxy-	$C_{13}H_{10}O_4$. See b1959	230.22	ye nd (dil al)	133–4				i s^h	s	s		s		B8^2, 468
b2051	—,2,3,4-tri-hydroxy	Callobenzophenone. $C_{13}H_{10}H_4$. See b1959	230.22	ye nd (dil al) λ^{MeOH} 227 (4.24), 272 (3.38)	140–1				s^h δ	s	s	s	δ	aa s	B8^2, 466
b2052	—,2,4,4′-tri-hydroxy-	$C_{13}H_{10}O_4$. See b1959	230.22	ye nd (w + 2)	200–1				s^h	s					B8^2, 468
b2053	—,2,4,6-tri-hydroxy-	$C_{13}H_{10}O_4$. See b1959	230.22	ye nd (w + 1, dil al)	165				v^h δ	v	v		δ	chl δ lig i	B8^2, 466
b2054	—,3,4,5-tri-hydroxy-	$C_{13}H_{10}O_4$. See b1959	230.22	ye pl (+ 1w), col (chl)	177–8 (anh)				v^h δ	v	v		δ	peth i	B8, 422
b2055	—,2,3,4-tri-methoxy-	$C_{16}H_{16}O_4$. See b1959	272.30	pr (dil al)	55					s	v				B8, 418
b2056	—,2,4,4′-tri-methoxy-	$C_{16}H_{16}O_4$. See b1959	272.30	nd (al)	73–4					s^h	v		v	aa v lig i	B8^1, 702
b2057	—,2,4,5-tri-methoxy-	$C_{16}H_{16}O_4$. See b1959	272.30	ye nd (w)	97				δ^h i	v	v	v	v		B8^1, 701
b2058	—,2,4,6-tri-methoxy-	$C_{16}H_{16}O_4$. See b1959	272.30	mcl pr or rh pl (al)	115				δ^h i	v^h	v			peth i aa δ, v^h chl v	B8, 420
b2059	—,3,3′,4-tri-methoxy-	$C_{16}H_{16}O_4$. See b1959	272.30	nd (MeOH)	83–4					s		v	v	MeOH s^h	B8^2, 468
b2060	—,3,4,4′-tri-methoxy-	$C_{16}H_{16}O_4$. See b1959	272.30	nd (al)	98–9				δ^h i	s^h	v	v			B8, 422
b2061	—,3,4′,5-tri-methoxy-	$C_{16}H_{16}O_4$. See b1959	272.30	nd (bz)	97–8					v	v		v	chl v lig i aa δ	B8^1, 702
—	Benzophenone-carboxylic acid	see Benzoic acid, benzoyl-													
—	Benzopinacol	see 1,2-Ethanediol, tetraphenyl-													
—	α-Benzopina-colone	see Acetophenone, α,α,α-triphenyl-													
—	1,4-Benzopyran, 2,3-dihydro-	see Chroman													
—	1,2-Benzopyrazole	see Indazole													
Ω b2062	3,4-Benzopyrene		252.32	pa ye mcl nd (bz-MeOH) λ^{al} 225 (4.44), 265.5 (4.66), 274 (4.50), 284 (4.66), 296.5 (4.76), 347 (4.10), 364 (4.36), 384.5 (4.44), 403 (3.60)	176.5–7.5				i					con sulf s → og-red	E14, 457
b2063	—,5-amino-	$C_{20}H_{13}N$. See b2062	267.33	ye pl (bz-lig)	239–41				δ	s	δ	v	v	MeOH δ chl v	E14s, 697

For explanations, symbols and abbreviations see beginning of table. For structural formulas see end of table.

3,4-Benzopyrene

No.	Name	Synonyms and Formula	Mol. wt.	Color, crystalline form, specific rotation and λ_{max} (log ε)	m.p. °C	b.p. °C	Density	n_D	w	al	eth	ace	bz	other solvents	Ref.
b2064	—,5-hydroxy-.....	C$_{20}$H$_{12}$O. See b2062.......	268.32	nd (eth-lig)	207–9	....				v	.....	.....	v	alk s[h] aa s	E14s, 701
b2065	—,8-hydroxy-.....	C$_{20}$H$_{12}$O. See b2062	268.32	ye nd (bz-peth)	226–7d					s	s	s	s		E14s, 704
—	1,2-Benzopyrone...	*see* **Isocoumarin**													
—	2,1-Benzopyrone...	*see* **Coumarin**													
—	1,4-Benzopyrone...	*see* **Chromone**													
—	Benzo[α]pyrrole....	*see* **Indole**													
Ω b2066	5,6-Benzo-quinoline	Benzo[f]quinoline. β-Naphthoquinoline	179.22	lf (peth or w) λ^{al} 316 (3.34), 323 (3.26), 330 (3.62), 338 (3.28), 346 (3.71)	94	350[721] 202–5[8]			δ[h]	v	v	s	v	....	B20[2], 302
Ω b2067	7,8-Benzo-quinoline	Benzo[h]quinoline. α-Naphthoquinoline	179.22	lf (eth), pl (peth) λ^{al} 316 (3.18), 323 (3.08), 330 (3.45), 346 (3.51)	52	338[719] 233[47]			δ	s	s	s	s	os s	B20[2], 302
b2068	—,2-methyl-......	C$_{14}$H$_{11}$N. See b2067........	193.25	....	....	324–6	1.1464$^{20}_{4}$	1.6738[20]	i	s					B20, 471
b2068[1]	1,2-Benzoquinone..	o-Quinone	108.10	red pl or pr λ^{eth} 385 (3.20), 580 (1.47)	60–70d				d	...	s	s	s	peth i	B7, 600
Ω b2069	1,4-Benzo-quinone*	p-Quinone	108.10	ye mcl pr (w) λ^{al} 242 (4.26), 285 sh (2.6), 434 (1.26), 454 (1.22)	115.7	sub	1.318$^{20}_{4}$		s[h] δ	s	s	.....	.....	peth δ lig s[h]	B7, 609
b2070	—,diimine........		106.13	ye nd	124								s[h]	chl s	B7[2], 574
Ω b2071	—,—,N,N-di-chloro-	C$_6$H$_4$Cl$_2$N$_2$. See b2070	175.02	nd (w)	126d				s[h] i	v[h]	v		v[h]		B7, 621
Ω b2072	—,dioxime......		138.13	pa ye nd (w)	240d				s[h]						B7, 627
b2073	—,monoimine, N-chloro-		141.56	ye nd (peth) λ^{al} 232 (4.29)	85				v	δ[h]	δ			chl δ[h]	B7, 619
—	—,monooxime....	*see* **Phenol, 4-nitroso-***													
b2074	—,2-bromo-6-methyl-*	C$_7$H$_5$BrO$_2$. See b2069	201.03	ye nd (al), pr (eth or lig)	95	sub			δ	v	v			chl v	B7[2], 591
b2075	—,5-bromo-2-methyl-*	C$_7$H$_5$BrO$_2$. See b2069	201.03	ye lf (lig)	106						v			lig δ, v[h]	B7[2], 591
b2076	1,2-Benzo-quinone, 3-chloro-*	C$_6$H$_3$ClO$_2$. See b2068[1]	142.54	pa ye-red pr (hx)	68d						s				B7[1], 338
b2077	—,4-chloro-*......	C$_6$H$_3$ClO$_2$. See b2068[1]	142.54	pa ye-red nd (hx)	78				d		s			lig s[h]	B7[1], 338
Ω b2078	1,4-Benzo-quinone, 2-chloro-*	C$_6$H$_3$ClO$_2$. See b2069	142.54	ye red rh (hx) λ^{al} 248 (4.1), 321 (2.8), 424 (1.6)	57				v	v	v			chl v	B7[2], 579
b2079	—,—,oxime	3-Chloro-4-nitrosophenol. C$_6$H$_4$NClO$_2$. See b2069....	157.56	gr-ye nd (bz-aa) λ^{eth} 291 (4.1), 403 (3.4)	184d				δ	s	s				B7[2], 579
b2080	—,2-chloro-3-methyl-*	C$_7$H$_5$ClO$_2$. See b2069	156.57	cr (lig)	55				δ	v				chl v lig v	B7[1], 353
b2081	—,2-chloro-5-methyl-*	C$_7$H$_5$ClO$_2$. See b2069	156.57	ye nd (w or al)	105				s[h]	v	v			chl v	B7[2], 590
b2082	—,2-chloro-6-methyl-*	C$_7$H$_5$ClO$_2$. See b2069	156.57	ye nd (w)	90				δ[h]	v	v			chl v	B7[1], 353
Ω b2083	—,2,6-dibromo-, 1-imine, N-chloro-	C$_6$H$_2$Br$_2$ClNO. See b2073...	299.36	ye pr (aa, al)	85–6				i						B7[2], 584
b2084	—,—,4-imine, N-chloro-	C$_6$H$_2$Br$_2$ClNO. See b2073...	299.36	ye pr (al or aa)	83					s[h]					B7[2], 584
b2085	—,3,5-dibromo-2,6-dimethyl-*	C$_8$H$_6$Br$_2$O$_2$. See b2069	293.95	ye lf (al)	176	sub			i	s					B7[2], 593
b2086	—,3,5-dibromo-2-methyl-*	C$_7$H$_4$Br$_2$O$_2$. See b2069	279.93	ye	117	....	....			v	v			chl v	B7[2], 591
Ω b2087	—,2,5-di-*tert*-butyl-	C$_{14}$H$_{20}$O$_2$. See b2069	220.32	ye (al) λ^{CCl_4} 254 (4.3), 310 (2.48), 460 (1.4)	152.5				i	s[h]			s	aa s	B7, 670
b2088	1,2-Benzo-quinone, 4,5-dichloro-*	C$_6$H$_2$Cl$_2$O$_2$. See b2068[1]	176.99	yesh red pr or pl	94d (unst)						s		s		B7[1], 338
b2089	1,4-Benzo-quinone, 2,3-dichloro-*	C$_6$H$_2$Cl$_2$O$_2$. See b2069	176.99	ye lf	100–1 (96)						s		s		B7[2], 580
Ω b2090	—,2,5-dichloro-*...	C$_6$H$_2$Cl$_2$O$_2$. See b2069	176.99	pa ye mcl pr (al) λ^{hx} 270 (4.34), 327 (2.45)	161–2	....			i	s[h] δ	s	....	....	chl s	B7[2], 580

For explanations, symbols and abbreviations see beginning of table. For structural formulas see end of table.

1,4-Benzoquinone

No.	Name	Synonyms and Formula	Mol. wt.	Color, crystalline form, specific rotation and λ_{max} (log ε)	m.p. °C	b.p. °C	Density	n_D	w	al	eth	ace	bz	other solvents	Ref.
Ω b2091	—,2,6-dichloro-*	$C_6H_2Cl_2O_2$. See b2069	176.99	ye rh (lig, bz) λ^{hx} 269 (4.30), 327 (2.79)	120–1				δ^h	δ				chl s	B7, 633
Ω b2092	—,—,1-imine, N-chloro-	$C_6H_2Cl_3NO$. See b2073	210.45	ye nd (al)	67–8				δ	s^h	v	δ	δ	chl v peth:	B7², 581
Ω b2093	—,2,5-dichloro-3,6-dihydroxy-*	Chloranilic acid. $C_6H_2Cl_2O_4$. See b2069	208.99	red lf (w + 2) $\lambda^{50\%\,al}$ 325 (4.1)	283–4				s^h						B8², 433
Ω b2094	—,2,5-di-hydroxy-*	$C_6H_4O_4$. See b2069	140.10	dk ye nd (AcOEt) λ^{al} 285 (4.3), 400 (2.6)	211	215 sub δd			δ	s^h	i	δ		AcOEt δ aa s	B8², 432
b2095	—,2,5-dihydroxy-3-undecyl-*	Embelin. $C_{17}H_{26}O_4$. See b2069	308.42	og-red pl (al-bz)	143	sub			i					os s^h lig δ	B8², 452
Ω b2096	—,2,5-dihydroxy-3-methoxy-6-methyl-*	Spinulosin. $C_8H_8O_5$. See b2069	184.16	red-bl	202–3	120¹ sub			δ s^h					alk s	C32, 5027
Ω b2097	—,2,6-di-methoxy-*	$C_8H_8O_4$. See b2069	168.16	ye mcl pr (aa) λ^{al} 287 (4.22), 375 (2.86)	256	sub			δ^h	δ	δ			alk v aa v^h	B8², 433
Ω b2098	—,2,3-dimethyl-*	o-Xyloquinone. $C_8H_8O_2$. See b2069	136.16	ye nd λ^{al} 248 (4.22), 254 sh (4.2), 334 (2.60), 432 (1.48)	55	sub			δ	s	s				B7², 593
Ω b2099	—,2,6-dimethyl-*	$C_8H_8O_2$. See b2069	136.16	ye nd λ^{al} 253 (4.29), 317 (2.54), 426 (1.32)	72–3	sub	1.0479_4^{78}								B7², 593
Ω b2100	—,2,5-diphenyl-*	$C_{18}H_{12}O_2$. See b2069	260.30	og-ye pl (bz or aa) λ^{diox} 240 (4.37), 388 (3.94)	214				i	δ			s^h	aa s^h	B7², 757
b2101	—,3-hydroxy-2-methoxy-5-methyl-	Fumigatin. $C_8H_8O_4$. See b2069	168.16	br nd or pl (peth)	116				δ	v	v	v	v	chl v peth δ	C38, 1218
b2102	1,2-Benzo-quinone, 5-iso-propyl-4-methyl-, 1-oxime	$C_{10}H_{13}NO_2$. See b2068¹	179.22	nd (bz-chl)	165–7d								s^h	chl s^h	B7², 595
b2103	1,4-Benzo-quinone, 2-iso-propyl-5-methyl-, dioxime	Thymoquinone dioxime. $C_{10}H_{14}N_2O_2$. See b2072	194.24	pr (al)	235d darkens at 200				s	v^h δ	s		δ	chl δ aa δ, v^h	B7, 665
b2104	1,2-Benzo-quinone, 3-methoxy-*	$C_7H_6O_3$. See b2068¹	138.12	br-red pl, pr, nd λ^{al} 375 (3.21)	115–20				s	s	s		v	chl v	B8², 264
b2105	—,4-methoxy-, 1-oxime	$C_7H_7NO_3$. See b2068¹	153.14	ye pr	158–9				δ	v			v	aa v	B8², 264
b2106	1,4-Benzo-quinone, 2-methoxy-*	$C_7H_6O_3$. See b2069	138.12	ye nd (w) λ^{hx} 248 (4.02), 343 (3.04)	145	sub 80–90			s^h	v				lig δ	B8², 265
b2107	—,2-methyl-6-propyl-, 4-oxime	$C_{10}H_{13}NO_2$. See b2069	179.22	br nd (lig)	93–4								v	aa v lig s^h	B7², 595
b2108	—,2-methyl-*	Toluquinone. $C_7H_6O_2$. See b2069	122.13	ye pl or nd λ^{al} 264 (4.14), 312 (2.77), 429 (1.28)	69	sub	$1.087_4^{15.5}$		δ s^h	s	s				B7², 588
b2109	—,2-methyl-3,5,6-tribromo-*	$C_7H_3Br_3O_2$. See b2069	358.83	ye pl (al)	235–6				i	δ	s	s			B7², 592
b2110	—,phenyl-*	$C_{12}H_8O_2$. See b2069	184.21	ye lf (peth, al) λ^{CCl_4} 250 (4.1), 280 sh (3.4), 369 (3.46), 460 sh (2.0)	114				δ^h	s^h			s	peth s^h chl v	B7, 740
Ω b2111	—,tetrachloro-*	Chloranil. $C_6Cl_4O_2$. See b2069	245.88	ye mcl pr (bz) ye lf (aa) λ^{sy} 290 (4.34)	290 sealed tube	sub			i	δ^h	s			CS_2 δ chl δ lig i	B7², 581
Ω b2112	—,tetrahydroxy-*	$C_6H_4O_6$. See b2069	172.10	bl-bk cr $\lambda^{ac-MeOH}$ 310 (4.44)					v^h δ	v	δ				B8², 572
Ω b2113	—,tetramethyl-*	Duroquinone. $C_{10}H_{12}O_2$. See b2069	164.21	ye nd (al or lig) λ^{al} 259 (4.25), 267 (4.26), 338 (2.38), 430 sh (1.44)	111–2				i	s	s	s	s	sulf s aa s lig δ, s^h	B7², 597
b2114	—,trichloro-*	$C_6HCl_3O_2$. See b2069	211.43	ye pl (al) λ^{al} 278 (4.1), 362 (2.6)	169–70				i	s^h	v				B7², 581

For explanations, symbols and abbreviations see beginning of table. For structural formulas see end of table.

No.	Name	Synonyms and Formula	Mol. wt.	Color, crystalline form specific rotation and λ_{max} (log ε)	m.p. °C	b.p. °C	Density	n_D	w	al	eth	ace	bz	other solvents	Ref.
	α-Benzosuberone														
b2115	α-Benzosuberone	1-Benzosuberanone.	160.22	λ^{al} 248 (3.92), 287 (3.24), 316 sh (2.27)	....	124–5[7] 108[1]	1.0780_4^{20}	1.5698^{20}	...	s	...	...	...	...	C50, 4850
—	Benzotetronic acid	see Coumarin, 4-hydroxy-	...												
Ω b2116	Benzothiazole	....	135.19	λ^{al} 250 (3.74), 284 (3.22), 296 (3.15)	2	231[760] (228) 131[34]	1.2460_4^{20}	1.6379^{20}	δ	v	v	s	...	CS_2 v	B27[2], 17
Ω b2117	—,2,-amino-	$C_7H_6N_2S$. See b2116	150.20	pl (w) λ^{al} 222 (4.52), 264 (4.09)	132				δ	s	s	...	...	chl s con HCl s	B27[2], 225
b2118	—,6-amino-	$C_7H_6N_2S$. See b2116	150.20	pr (w)	87				i	s	i	...	...		B27, 366
Ω b2119	—,2-amino-6-ethoxy-	$C_9H_{10}N_2OS$. See b2116	194.26	nd (al) 225 (4.5), 270 (4.1)	163–4				v	s^h		...	...	MeOH s^h	B27[2], 335
b2120	—,5-amino-2-mercapto-	$C_7H_6N_2S_2$. See b2116	182.27	nd (PhNH$_2$)	216									PhNH$_2$ s^h	B27[2], 475
b2121	—,6-amino-2-mercapto-	$C_7H_6N_2S_2$. See b2116	182.27	....	263										B27[2], 475
b2122	—,2-amino-4-methyl-	$C_8H_8N_2S$. See b2116	164.22	nd (w), pl (al)	145				δ	δ		...	...		B27[2], 237
b2123	—,2-amino-5-methyl-	$C_8H_8N_2S$. See b2116	164.24	pl (dil al)	171–2 (145)					s					B27[2], 240
Ω b2124	—,2-amino-6-methyl-	$C_8H_8N_2S$. See b2116	164.24	nd (w), pr (dil al)	142				δ^h s^h	s		...	...		B27[2], 241
Ω b2125	—,2-chloro-	C_7H_4ClNS. See b2116	169.63		24	248, 135–6[28]	1.3715_4^{19}	1.6338^{19}	...	s	s	s	...		B27[2], 18
b2126	—,5-chloro-2-methyl-	C_8H_6ClNS. See b2116	183.66	pl (eth)	69	70–90[0.5] sub			...	s		...	...	peth s	B27[2], 22
b2127	,6-dimethyl amino-2-mercapto-	$C_9H_{10}N_2S_2$. See b2116	210.32	ye nd (bz)	230d				...	δ	s	...	...		B27[2], 475
b2128	—,2(2,4-dinitro-phenylthio)-	$C_{13}H_7N_3O_4S_2$. See b2116	333.35	ye	162	....	1.24_4^{20}		i	δ s^h	δ	...	...		C48, 1443
b2129	—,2-hydroxy-	C_7H_5NOS. See b2116	151.19	pr (dil al), nd	138	360			i	v	v	...	...		B27[2], 225
b2130	—,6-hydroxy-2-phenyl-	$C_{13}H_9NOS$. See b2116	227.29	wh nd (dil al)	227–7.5 (cor)				i	s	i	s	s	aa s lig i	B27[2], 88
Ω b2131	—,2(2-hydroxy-phenyl)-	$C_{13}H_9NOS$. See b2116	227.29	nd or lf (al) λ^{al} 258 (3.85), 288 (4.12), 333 (4.20)	132–3	175–93[3]			v	s^h		...	...		B27[2], 91
Ω b2132	—,2-mercapto-	$C_7H_5NS_2$. See b2116	167.25	nd (al or dil MeOH) λ^{MeOH} 235 (4.12), 282 sh (3.34), 320 (4.43)	180.2–1.7		1.42_4^{20}		i	s^h	δ	...	δ	aa δ, s^h	B27[2], 233
b2133	, ,benzoate	$C_{14}H_9NOS_2$. See b2116	271.36	ye	132				i	s^h δ	δ	...	...		C51, 3491
b2134	—,2-mercapto-4-methyl-	$C_8H_7NS_2$. See b2116	181.28	nd (dil aa)	186									aa s^h	B27[2], 240
b2135	—,2-mercapto-5-methyl-	$C_8H_7NS_2$. See b2116	181.28	nd (to)	171–3				i	s		s	s^h	to s^h	B27[2], 241
b2136	—,2-mercapto-6-methyl-	$C_8H_7NS_2$. See b2116	181.28	....	181				i	s		s	s^h	to s^h	B27[2], 242
b2137	—,2-mercapto-7-methyl-	$C_8H_7NS_2$. See b2116	181.28		184							s	s^h	to s	B27[2], 242
b2138	—,2-mercapto-6-nitro-	$C_7H_4N_2O_2S_2$. See b2116	212.25	ye nd (aa)	255–7				i					aa s^h	B27[2], 234
Ω b2139	—,2-methyl-	C_8H_7NS. See b2116	149.22	λ^{al} 218 (4.32), 252 (3.85), 283 (3.40)	14	238 150–1[15]	1.1763_4^{19}	1.6092^{19}	i	s		...	...		B27[2], 21
Ω b2140	—,2(methylthio)-	$C_8H_7NS_2$. See b2116	181.28	pr (dil al) λ^{MeOH} 278 (4.1), 288 (4.0), 299 (3.9)	52					s^h		...	...		B27[2], 71
Ω b2141	—,2-phenyl-	$C_{13}H_9NS$. See b2116	211.29	nd (dil al) λ^{al} 225 (4.30), 297 (4.20)	114	>360			i	s^h	s	...	...	CS_2 s	B27[2], 37
b2142	—,2-phenylamino	$C_{13}H_{10}N_2S$. See b2116	226.30	nd (al) λ^{al} 222 (4.29), 302 (4.39)	161							...	δ	MeOH δ AcOEt s	B27[2], 226
b2143	Benzothiazoline, 3-methyl-2-imino-	....	164.24	pl (w), nd (al) λ^{al} 252 (3.94), 278 (3.77), 286 (3.84)	128				δ v^h	v	v	...	...	chl v	B27[2], 228
b2144	—,3-methyl-2-thioxo-	....	181.28	nd (al), pr (aa) λ^{MeOH} 241 (4.12), 324 (4.41)	90	335[757]			i	s^h δ	δ	...	v	CS_2 δ aa δ, s^h chl v	B27[2], 233

For explanations, symbols and abbreviations see beginning of table. For structural formulas see end of table.

Benzothiophene

No.	Name	Synonyms and Formula	Mol. wt.	Color, crystalline form, specific rotation and λ_{max} (log ε)	m.p. °C	b.p. °C	Density	n_D	w	al	eth	ace	bz	other solvents	Ref.
b2145	Benzothiophene....	Thionaphthene	134.20	lf λ^{al} 227 (4.45), 257 (3.74), 288 (3.31)	32	221[760] 103–5[20]	1.1484$_4^{32}$	1.6374[37]	i	v	s	s	s	os s	B17[2], 58
b2146	—,3-hydroxy-.....	C_8H_6OS. See b2145	150.20	nd (w)	71				δ s^h	v	v	v	v	alk s peth δ	B17[2], 128
b2147	—,4-hydroxy-.....	C_8H_6OS. See b2145	150.20	nd (sub), cr (peth)	78–9	sub			δ	s				alk s, peth s^h	B17, 121
b2148	2,3-Benzothio-phenequinone	Thioisatin.	164.18	gold-ye pr (al)	121	247[760]			i	s			s	aa s	B17, 467
Ω b2149	1,2,3-Benzo-triazole	Azimidobenzene.	119.13	nd (chl or bz)	100	204[15] 159[2]			δ	s	s		s	to, chl, DMF s	B26[2], 17
b2150	1,2,3-Benzoxadi-azole, 5,7-dinitro-	....	210.11	ye pl (al)	158					s^h				.....	B16[2], 287
Ω b2151	Benzoxazole......	....	119.12	pr (dil al) λ^{al} 231 (3.90), 270 (3.53), 276 (3.51)	31	182.5[760] 45[4]		1.5594[20]	i	s				sulf s	B27[2], 17
b2152	—,2-chloro-......	C_7H_4ClNO. See b2151....	153.57	....	7	201–2	1.3453$_4^{18}$	1.5678[20]	i					.....	B27[2], 17
b2153	—,2-hydroxy-.....	2(3)-Benzoxazolone. $C_7H_5NO_2$. See b2151	135.13	nd (bz or w +1)	141–2 (anh) 97–8 (+w)	230[30]			δ	s	s			.....	B27[2], 223
b2154	—,4-hydroxy-2-phenyl-	$C_{13}H_9NO_2$. See b2151.....	211.22	nd (bz)	138–9				δ	v	v		s^h	aa v lig δ	B27[2], 88
b2155	—,5-hydroxy-2-phenyl-	$C_{13}H_9NO_2$. See b2151.....	211.22	nd (lig or dil al)	175						v		v	chl v aa v	B27[2], 88
b2156	—,6-hydroxy-2-phenyl-	$C_{13}H_9NO_2$. See b2151.....	211.22	nd	216–7				δ	δ	δ	v	s^h δ	aa v	B27, 117
b2157	—,7-hydroxy-2-phenyl	$C_{13}H_9NO_2$. See b2151.....	211.22	nd (bz or dil al)	191–2						v	v	v^h	chl v lig v	B27[2], 91
b2158	—,2(2-hydroxy-phenyl)-	$C_{13}H_9NO_2$. See b2151.....	211.22	pink nd (al or aa) λ^{cy} 231 sh (4.06), 322 (4.24)	123–4	338			δ	s	s	s	s	os v	B27[2], 91
b2159	—,2-mercapto-....	C_7H_5NOS. See b2151	151.19	nd (w)	196				δ s^h	δ	v			aa v NH_3 s	B27[2], 224
Ω b2160	—,2-methyl-	C_8H_7NO. See b2151.....	133.16		8.5–10	200–1[760] 59–60[12]	1.1211$_4^{20}$	1.5497[20]	i	v	∞			.....	B27[2], 20
b2161	2,3-Benzoxazin-1-one	....	147.14	cr (bz)	120d									.....	B27[1], 278
—	2(3)-Benzoxazolone	see Benzoxazole, 2-hydroxy-													
—	Benzoyl chloride	see Benzoic acid, chloride													
—	Benzyl alcohol	see Toluene, α-hydroxy-													
—	Benzylamine	see Toluene, α-amino-													
—	Benzyl bromide	see Toluene, α-bromo-													
—	Benzyl chloride	see Toluene, α-chloro-													
—	Benzyl cyanide	see Acetic acid, phenyl-, nitrile													
—	Benzyl iodide	see Toluene, α-iodo-													
b2162	Berbamine........	$C_{37}H_{40}N_2O_6$	608.74	lf (+2w, al) cr (peth) $[\alpha]_D^{25}$ +109 (chl) λ^{al} 380 (1.9)	197–210 (anh) 156 (hyd)				δ	s	s			peth s chl s	B27[2], 891
b2163	Berberine........	$C_{20}H_{19}NO_5$	353.38	red ye nd (w +6), cr (chl +1) λ^w 262.5 (4.7), 347.5 (4.3), 425 (3.6)	145 (anh) 110 (+6w)	anh→ hyd→			i s	s δ	s δ		δ	chl δ	B27[2], 567
b2164	—,compound with chloroform	$C_{21}H_{18}Cl_3NO_4$	454.74	ye tcl ta (chl −al)	179 (145)				δ	δ				chl v	B27, 492
b2165	—,hydrochloride	$C_{20}H_{22}ClNO_6$	407.86	ye cr (w +2), nd (w +4), λ^{al} 270 (4.03), 350 (4.58)					δ v^h	i	i			chl i	B27[1], 514
b2166	—,nitrate........	$C_{20}H_{18}N_2O_7$	398.38	red ye nd (al)	155d				v^h	δ				chl i	B27, 500
b2167	—,sulfate (trihydrate)	$C_{40}H_{42}N_2O_{15}S$	822.88	red-ye nd					s	s				chl i	B27, 500
b2168	—,tetrahydro- (dl)	$C_{20}H_{21}NO_4$	339.40	mcl nd (al)	173–4				δ	s				CS_2 v chl v	B27[2], 557
—	Berberonic acid	see 2,4,5-Pyridinetri-carboxylic acid													
b2169	Berbine (dl)	....	235.33	nd (eth or MeOH)	89				i	v	s	s		os v lig, peth δ	B20[2], 311
Ω b2170	Betaine	Lycine. Oxyneurine. $(CH_3)_3NCH_2COO^-$	117.15	(w +1), pr or lf (al)	293d (anh) (310d)				v	s	δ			MeOH v	B4[2], 785

For explanations, symbols and abbreviations see beginning of table. For structural formulas see end of table.

Betol

No.	Name	Synonyms and Formula	Mol. wt.	Color, crystalline form, specific rotation and λ_{max} (log ε)	m.p. °C	b.p. °C	Density	n_D	w	al	eth	ace	bz	other solvents	Ref.
—	Betol	*see* Benzoic acid, 2-hydroxy-2-naphthyl ester													
b2172	Betonicine	$C_7H_{13}NO_3$	159.19	pr (dil al +1w) $[\alpha]_D^{21} -37$ (w,c = 4.8)	252d (anh)				δ	s	...	...	...	...	B22[1], 547
b2173	Betulin	Lupenediol. $C_{30}H_{50}O_2$	442.73	nd (al +1) $[\alpha]_D^{15} +20$(Py, c = 2)	251–2	170–80[0.08] δd			i	δ s[h]	s[h]	...	δ s[h]	chl δ, s[h] aa s[h] AcOEt s lig δ	E14, 568
b2174	Betulinic acid	Betulic acid. $C_{30}H_{48}O_3$	456.71	pl or nd (al +1) $[\alpha]_{546}^{22} +7.9$ (Py)	316–8				δ	δ	δ	δ	δ	chl δ Py s	B6[2], 939
b2175	Biacene	Biacenaphthene. Biacenaphthylidene.	304.39	red-ye pl or nd (bz) λ^{bz} 254 (3.54), 298 (3.54), 340 (3.99), 403 (4.77)	277								s	CS_2 s[h]	E13, 187
—	Biacetyl	*see* 2,3-Butanedione*													
—	Biacetylene	*see* Butadiyne*													
—	Bianiline	*see* Biphenyl, diamino-													
—	Bianisole	*see* Biphenyl, dimethoxy-													
b2176	10,10′-Bianthronyl	Bianthrone.	386.45	pl (ace)	256–8d				i	δ	i	...	...	chl v alk i	E13, 766
b2177	Biarsine, tetraethyl-	Ethyl cacodyl. $(C_2H_5)_2AsAs(C_2H_5)_2$	266.09			185–7	1.1388[24]	1.4709	i	s	s	...	...	...	B4, 616
b2178	—,tetrakis(trifluoromethyl)-	Perfluorocacodyl. $(CF_3)_2AsAs(CF_3)_2$	425.87			106–7[760]		1.372[19]	i						J1952, 2552
—	—,tetramethyl-	*see* Cacodyl													
—	2,2′-Bicamphane-2,2′-diol	*see* Camphor pinacol (*l*)													
b2179	3,3′-Bicoumarin		290.28	nd (aa)	>330				...	i	i	...	i	chl δ	B19, 183
—	Bicresol	*see* Biphenyl, dihydroxydimethyl-													
b2180	Bicyclo[2,2,1]-hepta-2,5-diene		92.15	λ^{al} 205 (3.31), 214 (3.14), 220 (2.74), 230 (2.30)	−19.1	89.5[760]	0.9064[20]	1.4702[20]	i	s	s	s	s	to ∞ lig ∞	C54, 12073
b2181	Bicyclo[2,2,1]-heptane	Norbornylane. Norbornane. Norcamphane.	96.17		87.5–7.8	sub			i	s	s	s	s	PrOH s	B5[2], 45
b2182	Bicyclo[4,1,0]-heptane, 7-aza-		97.16		20–2	48–51[22]			i	s	s	...	s	...	B7[1], 7
—	Bicyclo[2,2,1]-heptane, 1,7,7-trimethyl-	*see* Camphane													
Ω b2183	Bicyclo[2,2,1]-heptane-2,3-dicarboxylic acid	2,3-Norcamphanedicarboxylic acid	184.19		192–5				δ s[h]	δ	δ	...	...	...	E12A, 982
b2184	—,anhydride	$C_9H_{10}O_3$. *See* b2183	166.18		165–7				...	...	...	...	s[h]	...	E12A, 982
b2185	Bicyclo[2,2,1]-heptane-2-carboxaldehyde		122.17	cr (w)		70–2[22]	1.0227[19]	1.4760[25]	i	...	s	...	...	...	E12A, 705
b2186	Bicyclohexyl (*cis, cis*)	Dodecahydrobiphenyl	166.31		4	238	0.8914[20]	1.4766[20]	i	∞	∞	...	...	...	B5[3], 273
b2187	—(*trans, trans*)	$C_{12}H_{22}$. *See* b2186	166.31		4.2	217–9 95–6[9]	0.8592[20]	1.4663[20]	i	∞	∞	...	...	...	B5, 108
b2188	1,1′-Bicyclohexyldicarboxylic acid, dinitrile		216.33	lf (ace)	224.5–5.5				...	...	s	eth	...	...	B9[2], 571
b2189	Bicyclo[3,3,1]-nonane		124.23	cr (MeOH)	145–6	169–70 sub			i	s	...	...	...	MeOH s[h] aa s[h]	E12A, 1057
b2190	Bicyclo[2,2,2]-octane		110.20		169–71				i	...	...	...	...	...	E12A, 1060
b2191	Bicyclo[3,2,1]-octane		110.20		149.5–41				i	...	...	...	...	...	E12A, 1048
b2192	Bicyclo[3,3,0]-octane (*cis*)		110.20		< −80	137[765]	0.8638[25]	1.4595[25]	i	...	...	...	...	...	E12A, 80
b2193	—(*trans*)	C_8H_{14}. *See* b2192	110.20		−30	132[755]	0.8626[18]	1.4625[18]	i	...	...	...	...	...	E12A, 80
b2194	Bicyclo[3,3,0]-octane-2,6-dione		138.17		45	86–8[0.2]	1.1290[60]	1.4877[54]							E12A, 84
b2195	Bicyclo[2,2,2]-octane, 2-methyl-	C_9H_{16}. *See* b2190	124.23		33–4	158–8.5[749]	0.8664[40.5]	1.4608[40.5]	i	...	...	...	...	...	E12A, 1068
b2196	Bicyclo[3,3,0]-octan-2-one (*cis*)		124.19		72[12] 50[2.3]		1.0097[20]	1.4790[20]	δ	s	...	s	...	...	E12A, 82
Ω b2197	9,9′-Bifluorenyl-		330.43	nd (bz-al) λ^{al} 266 (4.33), 291.5 (3.99), 302.5 (4.09)	247				i	δ	δ	...	δ	Py s[h] aa s[h]	E13, 123

For explanations, symbols and abbreviations see beginning of table. For structural formulas see end of table.

No.	Name	Synonyms and Formula	Mol. wt.	Color, crystalline form, specific rotation and λ_{max} (log ε)	m.p. °C	b.p. °C	Density	n_D	w	al	eth	ace	bz	other solvents	Ref.
	9,9'-Bifluorenyl														
b2198	—,9,9'-diphenyl-	$C_{38}H_{26}$. See b2197	482.63	pl (bz)	256 (under CO_2)		1.266_4^0		i				δ	os δ	B5², 638
b2199	**Bifluorenylidene**		328.42	red nd (bz) λ^{diox} 244 (4.89), 272 (4.60), 308 (3.38), 340 (4.50), 458 (4.37)	194–5				i		s		s	chl s	E13, 123
—	**Bigitaligenin**	see **Gitoxigenin**													
—	**Bigitaline**	see **Gitoxine**													
b2200	**Biguanide**	$H_2NC(:NH)NHC(:NH)NH_2$ λ^w 231 (3.98)	101.11	pr or nd (al)	136	d at 142			v	s			i	chl i	B3², 76
b2201	—,1(2-tolyl)-	$C_9H_{13}N_5$. See b2200 $\lambda^{aq\,HCl}$ 236 (4.19)	191.24	nd or pl (w + ½)	144				δ v^h	v	i	v	i	chl i	B12, 803
b2202	**2,2'-Biindane, 1,1',3,3'-tetraoxo-**	Bisdiketohydrindene	290.28	vt nd ($PhNO_2$) red nd (bz)	297 (270)								s^h	$PhNO_2$ δ alk s	B7², 863
b2203	**Bikhaconitine**	$C_{36}H_{51}NO_{11}$	673.81	$[\alpha]_D$ +12(al)	118–23 (anh) 113–16 (+w)				i	s	s			chl s peth i	C19, 2104
b2204	**Bilifucsin**	$C_{16}H_{20}N_2O_4$	304.35	dk br pw	183				i	s	i			chl i aa s alk s	C30, 1936
Ω b2205	**Bilirubin**	Haematoidine. $C_{33}H_{36}N_4O_6$	584.68	red mcl pr or pl (chl) $\lambda^{w,\,pH=8}$ 437 (4.67)					i	δ	δ		s	CS_2 s chl s	C38, 1230
Ω b2206	**Biliverdin**	Dehydrobilirubin. Oöcyan. $C_{33}H_{34}N_4O_6$. See b2205 λ^{MeOH} 378 (4.61), 640–50 (4.11)	582.66	dk gr pl or pr (MeOH)	>300 (206–9)				i	s	δ		s	MeOH δ chl δ CS_2 δ alk s	J1961, 2264
—	**Binaphthol**	see **Binaphthyl, dihydroxy-**													
b2207	**1,1-Binaphthyl**	α,α'-Dinaphthyl	254.34	(i) pl (aa) (ii) rh (peth) λ^{al} 220 (5.0), 283 (4.1), 295 (4.1)	(i) 144.5–5.0 (ii) 160.5	>360 240–4¹²			i	δ s^h	s	s	s	CS_2 s	B5², 642
Ω b2208	**2,2-Binaphthyl**	β,β-Dinaphthyl.	254.34	bl fluor pl (al) λ^{al} 215 (4.6), 255 (5.0), 307 (4.3)	187–8	452⁷⁵³ sub			i	δ	s		s^h	aa δ CS_2 s	B5², 643
b2209	**1,1-Binaphthyl, 4,4'-diamino-3,3'-dimethyl-**	$C_{22}H_{20}N_2$. See b2207	312.42		213						s		v	peth s	B13², 140
Ω b2210	—,2,2'-dihydroxy-	1,1'-Bi-2-naphthol. β-Dinaphthol. $C_{20}H_{14}O_2$. See b2207	286.33	nd (al), cr (to)	220				i	s	s			chl δ alk s	B6², 1026
b2211	—,4,4'-dihydroxy-	4,4'-Bi-1-naphthol. α-Dinaphthol. $C_{20}H_{14}O_2$. See b2207	286.33	pl	300	sub			i	s	s		δ	chl s alk s	B6, 1053
Ω b2212	**Biotin**	Vitamin H. Coenzyme R. $C_{10}H_{16}N_2O_3S$.	244.32	nd (w) $[\alpha]_D^{22}$ +92 (0.1N NaOH, c = 1)	232.3 d				s	s	δ			chl δ	Am 67, 2096
b2213	—,methyl ester	$C_{11}H_{18}N_2O_3S$. See b2213	258.34	pl (MeOH-eth) $[\alpha]_D^{22}$ +57 (chl)	166.7	sub			δ	s	i	s	δ	chl s peth i	C43, 1810
—	**Bioxirane**	see **Butane, 1,2,3,4-diepoxy-**													
—	**Biphenol**	see **Biphenyl, dihydroxy-**													
Ω b2214	**Biphenyl**	Diphenyl. Phenylbenzene. λ^{al} 247 (4.24)	154.21	lf (dil al)	71	255.9⁷⁶⁰ 145²²	0.8660_4^0	1.588⁷⁷ 1.475²⁰	i	s	s		v	CCl_4, CS_2, MeOH v	B5², 479
b2215	—,2-acetamido-	$C_{14}H_{13}NO$. See b2214 λ^{al} 231 (4.1)	211.27	pr or nd (dil al or peth)	121	355⁷⁶⁰			i	v	v				B12², 747
b2216	—,3-acetamido-	$C_{14}H_{13}NO$. See b2214 λ^{al} 242 (4.4)	211.27	nd (al)	149				i	s^h	s		v^h		B12², 751
b2217	—,4-acetamido-	$C_{14}H_{13}NO$. See b2214 λ^{al} 237 (4.29)	211.27	cr (dil MeOH)	172				i	v		v		MeOH v	B12², 755
b2218	—,4-acetamido-3-nitro-	$C_{14}H_{12}N_2O_3$. See b2214	256.26	ye nd (al)	132				i	s^h	s			aa s^h	B12², 760
Ω b2219	—,4-acetyl-	4-Phenylacetophenone. $C_{14}H_{12}O$. See b2214 λ^{al} 284 (4.30)	196.25	pr (ace), cr (al)	121	325–7			i	v	v				B7², 337
b2220	—,2-amino-	$C_{12}H_{11}N$. See b2214 λ^{al} 300 (3.5)	169.23	lf (dil al)	51–3	299⁷⁶⁰ 170¹⁵			i	s	s		s	peth δ	B12², 747
b2221	—,3-amino-	$C_{12}H_{11}N$. See b2214 λ^{al} 234(4.37), 302 (3.39)	169.23	nd	30	254¹³⁵ 195¹⁵			δ	s	s	s	s		B12², 751
b2222	—,4-amino-	Xenylamine. $C_{12}H_{11}N$. See b2214 λ^{al} 278 (4.24)	169.23	lf (dil al)	53–4	302 191¹⁵			δ	s	s			chl s	B12², 753

For explanations, symbols and abbreviations see beginning of table. For structural formulas see end of table.

No.	Name	Synonyms and Formula	Mol. wt.	Color, crystalline form, specific rotation and λ_{max} (log ε)	m.p. °C	b.p. °C	Density	n_D	w	al	eth	ace	bz	other solvents	Ref.
	Biphenyl														
b2223	—,3-amino-4-hydroxy-	$C_{12}H_{11}NO$. See b2214	185.23	nd (chl)	208					v	v		v		B13[2], 419
b2224	—,4-amino-2'-hydroxy-	$C_{12}H_{11}NO$. See b2214	185.23	nd (to)	181–2				δ	s				to δ alk s aa s	B13[2], 419
Ω b2225	—,4-amino-4'-hydroxy-	$C_{12}H_{11}NO$. See b2214	185.23	pl (dil al) λ^{sulf} 285 (4.26)	273				i	δ	i	i	δ	aa δ	B13[2], 420
b2226	—,5-amino-2-hydroxy-	$C_{12}H_{11}NO$. See b2214	185.23	nd (al or bz)	201				i	s[h]	δ		s	chl δ lig i	B13[1], 280
b2227	—,2-amino-4'-nitro-	$C_{12}H_{10}N_2O_2$. See b2214	214.23	og-red nd (al)	159					s[h]					B12[2], 750
b2228	—,2-amino-5-nitro-	$C_{12}H_{10}N_2O_2$. See b2214	214.23	ye nd (al)	125					s[h]					B12[2], 750
b2229	—,3-amino-4-nitro-	$C_{12}H_{10}N_2O_2$. See b2214	214.23	og nd (dil al)	116										B12[2], 752
b2230	—,3-amino-4'-nitro-	$C_{12}H_{10}N_2O_2$. See b2214	214.23	og nd (al)	137					s[h]				aa s	B12[2], 753
b2231	—,4-amino-2'-nitro-	$C_{12}H_{10}N_2O_2$. See b2214	214.23	red mcl pr (al)	99				δ[h] i	v					B12[1], 547
b2232	—,4-amino-3-nitro-	$C_{12}H_{10}N_2O_2$. See b2214	214.23	red nd (al) λ^{al} 268 (4.4), 425 (3.6)	170–1					s[h]	s			chl s aa s	B12[1], 760
b2233	—,4-amino-4'-nitro-	$C_{12}H_{10}N_2O_2$. See b2214	214.23	red nd (al) λ^{al} 247.5 (4.10), 379 (4.19)	203–4				i[h]	s[h]				aa s[h]	B12[2], 761
b2234	—,2-benzyl-	o-Biphenylylphenylmethane. $C_{19}H_{16}$. See b2214	244.34	mcl nd (al)	54 6	283–7[110]			i	s	s		v		B5, 708
Ω b2235	—,4-benzyl-	$C_{19}H_{16}$. See b2214	244.34	lf	85	285–6[110]	1.171_4^0		i	s	v		s		B5[2], 618
b2236	—,4,4'-bis-(diethylamino)-	$C_{20}H_{28}N_2$. See b2214	296.46	nd (al)	85					s v[h]	s				B13[2], 98
b2237	—,2,4-bis(di-methylamino)-	$C_{16}H_{20}N_2$. See b2214	240.35	pl (al)	51–2	206–7[11]				s v[h]	s				B13[2], 88
b2238	—,4,4'-bis(di-methylamino)-	$C_{16}H_{20}N_2$. See b2214	240.35	nd (al or bz-lig)	198	>360				δ s[h]	δ		v[h]	chl v AcOEt s[h] lig δ[h]	B13[2], 97
b2239	—,4,4'-bis-(ethylamino)-	$C_{16}H_{20}N_2$. See b2214	240.35	nd or pl (al)	120.5 (116)					v[h]	v[h]		v	lig δ	B13, 222
b2240	—,4,4'-bis-(methylamino)-	$C_{14}H_{16}N_2$. See b2214	212.30	lf (al or w or lig) λ^{cy} 288 (4.8)	91–1.5				δ[h]	s[h]				lig s	B13[2], 97
b2241	—,4,4'-bis-(phenylamino)-	$C_{24}H_{20}N_2$. See b2214	336.44	lf (to) λ^{al} 334.5 (4.66)	244–5				i	δ	δ		δ	to v[h] aa v[h]	B13[2], 98
b2242	—,2-bromo-	$C_{12}H_9Br$. See b2214	233.12		fp 1.5–2.0	296–8 160[11]	1.2175^{26}	1.6248^{25}	i	s	s				B5[2], 485
Ω b2243	—,3-bromo-	$C_{12}H_9Br$. See b2214	233.12			299–301 169–73[17]		1.6411^{20}	i						B5[2], 485
Ω b2244	—,4-bromo-	$C_{12}H_9Br$. See b2214	233.12	pl (al) λ^{al} 256 (4.41)	91.2	310	0.9327_4^{25}		i	s	s		s	CS_2, aa s	B5[2], 485
b2245	—,4(bromo-acetyl)-	p-Phenylphenacyl bromide. $C_{14}H_{11}BrO$. See b2214	275.15	nd (95 % al)	127				i	δ s[h]				CCl_4 s peth s[h]	Am 52, 3715
b2246	—,3-bromo-4-hydroxy-	$C_{12}H_9BrO$. See b2214	249.11	nd (chl-peth)	96				δ	v				chl v[h] aa v	B6[2], 625
b2247	—,4-bromo-4'-hydroxy-	$C_{13}H_9BrO$. See b2214	249.11	pl (al)	164–6				δ	v	v	v	v	chl v	B6[2], 625
Ω b2248	—,2-chloro-	$C_{12}H_9Cl$. See b2214	188.66	mcl (dil al)	34	274 154[12]	$1.1499^{32.5}$		i	s	v			CCl_4 s lig v	B5[2], 483
b2249	—,3-chloro-	$C_{12}H_9Cl$. See b2214	188.66		16	284–5 150–60[6]	1.1579_4^{25}	1.6181^{25}	i	s	s	v			B5[2], 483
Ω b2250	—,4-chloro-	$C_{12}H_9Cl$. See b2214	188.66	lf (lig or al) λ^{al} 203 (4.61), 253 (4.32)	77.7	291 180– 95[20–30]			i	s	s			lig s	B5[2], 483
b2251	—,4-(chloro)-acetyl)-	p-Phenylphenacyl chloride. $C_{14}H_{11}ClO$. See b2214	230.70	pl (al)	125					s[h]					B7, 443
b2252	—,3-chloro-2-hydroxy	$C_{12}H_9ClO$. See b2214	204.66		6	317–8d	1.24_4^{25}	1.6237^{30}	i	s	s	s	s	os s	C29, 3688
b2253	—,4-chloro-4'-hydroxy-	$C_{12}H_9ClO$. See b2214	204.66	cr (dil al)	146–7				δ	s	s	s	s	peth δ	B6[2], 625
b2254	—,2,2'-diaceta-mido-	$C_{16}H_{16}N_2O_2$. See b2214	268.32	pr (al)	164.2–5.3				δ	v	δ		v	peth δ aa v	B13, 210
b2255	—,2,4-diaceta-mido-	$C_{16}H_{16}N_2O_2$. See b2214	268.32	nd (al)	202					s					B13, 212
b2256	—,4,4'-diaceta-mido-	$C_{16}H_{16}N_2O_2$. See b2214	268.32	nd (aa)	328.30				i	δ	δ				B13[2], 102
Ω b2257	—,2,2'-diamino-	o-Benzidine. o,o'-Bianiline. $C_{12}H_{12}N_2$. See b2214	184.24	mcl pr or nd (al) λ^{al} 295 (3.76)	81	162[4]			s v[h]	s			s		B13[2], 87
b2258	—,2,4'-diamino-	Diphenyline. $C_{12}H_{12}N_2$. See b2214	184.24	nd (dil al) λ^{al} 235 (4.2), 300 (3.9)	54.5	363[760]			s	s	s		s		B13[2], 88
b2259	—,3,3'-diamino-	m-Benzidine. $C_{12}H_{12}N_2$. See b2214	184.24	nd (w), pr (bz) λ^{al} 228 (4.56), 302 (3.68), 314 sh (3.55)	93.5–4	205 –15[0.001]			δ s[h]		v		s[h]		B13[2], 90

For explanations, symbols and abbreviations see beginning of table. For structural formulas see end of table.

No.	Name	Synonyms and Formula	Mol. wt.	Color, crystalline form, specific rotation and λ_{max} (log ε)	m.p. °C	b.p. °C	Density	n_D	w	al	eth	ace	bz	other solvents	Ref.
	Biphenyl														
b2260	—,3,4-diamino-	$C_{12}H_{12}N_2$. See b2214	184.24	lf (eth or al)	103					s v^h	s				B13[2], 89
Ω b2261	—,4,4′-diamino-	Benzidine. $C_{12}H_{12}N_2$. See b2214	184.24	nd (w) λ^{al} 287 (4.4)	(i) 125 (unst) (ii) 122 (unst) (iii) 128 (st)	400[740]			δ^h	s	δ				B13[2], 90
Ω b2262	—,4,4′-diamino-3,3′-dimethoxy-	o-Dianisidine. $C_{14}H_{16}N_2O_2$. See b2214	244.30	lf or nd (w)	137				i s^h	s	s	s	s	chl s	B13[2], 502
b2263	—,4,4′-diamino-2,2′-dimethyl-	Bitoluidine. m-Tolidine. $C_{14}H_{16}N_2$. See b2214	212.30	pr (w) λ^{al} 248 (4.2), 290 sh (3.6)	108–9				s^h	v	v				B13, 255
Ω b2264	—,4,4′-diamino-3,3′-dimethyl-	o-Tolidine. $C_{14}H_{16}N_2$. See b2214	212.30	lf (dil al) λ^{al} 284 (4.4)	131–2				δ	v	v				B13, 256
b2265	—,4,4′-diamino-3-ethoxy-	$C_{14}H_{16}N_2O$. See b2214	228.30	nd (w)	134				δ	v^h	δ		δ		B13[2], 419
Ω b2266	—,4,4′-dibromo-	$C_{12}H_8Br_2$. See b2214	312.03	mcl pr (MeOH) λ^{al} 262 (4.37)	164	355–60			i	δ^h			s		B5[2], 485
Ω b2267	—,4,4′-dichloro-	$C_{12}H_8Cl_2$. See b2214	223.11	pr or nd (al or to-peth) λ^{al} 201 (4.63), 259 (4.40), 283 sh (3.95)	148–9	315–9			i	δ^h			s		B5[2], 484
b2268	—,4,4′-dichloro-2,2′-dinitro-	$C_{12}H_6Cl_2N_2O_4$. See b2214	313.10	ye cr (al)	140				i	δ s^h			s	aa s^h lig δ	B5[2], 584
b2269	—,4,4′-diethoxy-3,3′-diethyl-	$C_{20}H_{26}O_2$. See b2214	298.43	lf (al)	120				i	δ					B6, 1015
b2270	—,2,2′-diethoxy-3,3′-dimethyl-	$C_{18}H_{22}O_2$. See b2214	270.38	lf (al)	85				i	δ					B6[2], 974
b2271	—,4,4′-diethoxy-3,3′-dimethyl-	$C_{18}H_{22}O_2$. See b2214	270.38	nd (al)	53				i	δ					B6[2], 974
b2272	—,4,4′-diethoxy-3,3′-dimethyl-	$C_{18}H_{22}O_2$. See b2214	270.38	pl (al)	156				i	δ	δ				B6, 1010
b2273	—,3,3′-diethyl-6,6′-dihydroxy-	$C_{16}H_{18}O_2$. See b2214	242.32	nd (dil al)	131				i	δ					B6[2], 981
Ω b2274	—,4,4′-difluoro-	$C_{12}H_8F_2$. See b2214	190.21	mcl pr (al) lf (w) λ^{al} 245 (4.18), 271.5 sh (3.60)	94–5	254–5 119[14]			i s^h	v	s	s	v^h	chl v aa v^h MeOH v^h	B5[2], 482
b2275	—,2,2′-dihydroxy-	o,o′-Biphenol. $C_{12}H_{10}O_2$. See b2214	186.21	lf (w+l), pr (to) λ^{hp} 270 (3.7), 280 (3.65)	110–2 (anh) 71–3 (hyd)	325–6[760]			s^h	s	s	s	s	peth δ aa s alk s	B6[2], 960
b2276	—,2,4′-dihydroxy-	o,p′-Biphenol. $C_{12}H_{10}O_2$. See b2214	186.21	mcl pr or nd (dil al)	162–3	342 206–10[11]			δ^h	s	s	s	s		B6[2], 961
b2277	—,2,5-dihydroxy-	Phenylhydroquinone. $C_{12}H_{10}O_2$. See b2214	186.21	nd (dil al)	97–8				i						B6, 989
b2278	—,3,3′-dihydroxy-	m,m′-Biphenol. $C_{12}H_{10}O_2$. See b2214	186.21	nd (w) λ^{al} 255 (4.08)	123–4	247[18]			s^h δ	s	s		s	chl s	B6[2], 961
b2279	—,3,4-dihydroxy-	4-Phenylpyrocatechol. $C_{12}H_{10}O_2$. See b2214	186.21		145	>360			δ^h	v	v	s	s	CS_2 δ chl v	B6[2], 961
Ω b2280	—,4,4′-dihydroxy-	p,p′-Biphenol. $C_{12}H_{10}O_2$. See b2214	186.21	nd or pl (al) λ^{al} 210 sh (4.3), 268 (4.3)	274–5	sub			ϱ	s	s		δ		B6[2], 962
b2281	—,4,4′-dihydroxy-3,3′-diethyl-5,5′-dimethyl-	$C_{18}H_{22}O_2$. See b2214	270.38	nd (aa)	148					v		v	v	peth δ aa v	B6[2], 984
b2282	—,2,2′-dihydroxy-3,3′-dimethyl-	$C_{14}H_{14}O_2$. See b2214	214.27	nd (peth)	113	sub				v		v	v	peth δ	B6[2], 974
b2283	—,2,2′-dihydroxy-5,5′-dimethyl-	$C_{14}H_{14}O_2$. See b2214	214.27	nd (bz or w) λ^{al} 293 (3.91)	153.5	sub			δ^h	s	v	s	s	os s	B6[2], 974
b2284	—,2,2′-dihydroxy-6,6′-dimethyl-	$C_{14}H_{14}O_2$. See b2214	214.27	pl (dil al)	164				i	v					C35, 2138
b2285	—,2,5-dihydroxy-2′,5-dimethyl-	$C_{14}H_{14}O_2$. See b2214	214.27		158				i	v	v	δ δ^h			B6[2], 973
b2286	—,4,4′-dihydroxy-3,3′-dimethyl-	$C_{14}H_{14}O_2$. See b2214	214.27	lf (w), nd λ^{al} 265 (4.3)	161				δ^h	s	v				B6[2], 974
b2287	—,—,diacetate	$C_{18}H_{18}O_4$. See b2214	298.34	wh nd (al or aa)	135.5				i	v	v				B6[1], 492
b2288	—,5,5′-dihydroxy-2,2′-dimethyl-	$C_{14}H_{14}O_2$. See b2214	214.27	pr (al)	229				i δ^h	v			δ^h	peth i	B6[2], 973
b2289	—,4,4′-dihydroxy-3,3′,5,5′-tetramethoxy-	Hydrocerulignone. $C_{16}H_{18}O_6$. See b2214	306.32	mcl pr (al)	190				δ	s	δ			CS_2 i	B6[1], 593
b2290	—,2,2′-dihydroxy-3,3′,5,5′-tetramethyl-	$C_{16}H_{18}O_2$. See b2214	242.32	nd or pl (eth or lig)	137.5–8.5	140–60[0.05]			i	v	v			peth δ^h lig v^h	B6[2], 981
b2291	—,4,4′-dihydroxy-3,3′,5,5′-tetramethyl-	$C_{16}H_{18}O_2$. See b2214	242.32	pa ye nd or pr (aa)	222–3	sub				s^h			δ^h	aa s^h	B6, 1015

For explanations, symbols and abbreviations see beginning of table. For structural formulas see end of table.

No.	Name	Synonyms and Formula	Mol. wt.	Color, crystalline form, specific rotation and λ_{max} (log ε)	m.p. °C	b.p. °C	Density	n_D	Solubility						Ref.
									w	al	eth	ace	bz	other solvents	
	Biphenyl														
b2292	—,4,4′-dihydroxy-3,3′,5,5′-tetra-nitro-	$C_{12}H_6N_4O_{10}$. See b2214	366.20	ye nd λ^{MeOH} 355 (3.8)	223				i						**B6**², 963
b2293	—,2,2′-dimethoxy-	o,o′-Bianisole. $C_{14}H_{14}O_2$. See b2214	214.27	rh bipyr pr (al) λ 278 (3.8)	155	307–8⁷⁶⁶	1.268		i	v^h	δ^h	...	v^h	CCl₄, chl, CS₂ v^h lig δ^h	**B6**², 960
Ω b2294	—,3,3′-dimethoxy-	m,m′-Bianisole. $C_{14}H_{14}O_2$. See b2214	214.27	nd (dil al) λ^{cy} 258 (4.08), 290 (3.81)	36	328 211–20¹⁵			i	v	v	s	v	CS₂ v aa v chl v	**B6**², 961
b2295	—,4,4′-dimethoxy-	p,p′-Bianisole. $C_{14}H_{14}O_2$. See b2214	214.27	lf (bz) λ^{hx} 263 (4.34)	173	sub			i	v^h	δ	...	v	peth i chl v	**B6**², 962
b2296	—,2,2′-dimethoxy-5,5′-dimethyl-	$C_{16}H_{18}O_2$. See b2214	242.32	nd (dil al)	71	188¹²			δ^h	s	s	s	s	os v	**B6**², 975
b2297	—,2,5′-dimethoxy-2′,5-dimethyl-	$C_{16}H_{18}O_2$. See b2214	242.32	pr (al)	86	168⁴			i	δ v^h	...	...	s	peth s	**B6**², 973
b2298	—,4,4′-dimethoxy-3,3′-dimethyl-	$C_{16}H_{18}O_2$. See b2214	242.32	pr (al)	145.5				i	δ s^h	δ	...			**B6**, 1009
Ω b2299	—,2,2′-dimethyl-	o,o′-Bitolyl. $C_{14}H_{14}$. See b2214	182.27	cr (al) λ^{peth} 228 sh (3.78), 256 sh (2.89), 266.5 sh (2.83)	19.5–20.2	256⁷⁶⁰	0.9906²⁰	1.5752²⁰	i	v	v	s	v		**B5**², 512
b2300	—,2,3′-dimethyl-	o,m′-Bitolyl. $C_{14}H_{14}$. See b2214	182.27	λ^{peth} 238 (3.98), 271 sh (3.04)		270⁷⁶⁰	0.9924²⁰	1.5810²⁰	i	v	v	s	v		**B5**², 512
b2301	—,2,4′-dimethyl-	o,p′-Bitolyl. $C_{14}H_{14}$. See b2214	182.27	λ^{peth} 239 (4.07), 275 (3.01)		273–6⁷⁶⁰ 137¹²·⁵	0.9924²⁰	1.5826²⁰	i	v	v	s	v		**B5**², 512
Ω b2302	—,3,3′-dimethyl-	m,m′-Bitolyl. $C_{14}H_{14}$. See b2214	182.27	λ^{peth} 208 (4.69), 250.5 (4.21)	9–9.5	280⁷⁶⁰ 150¹⁸	0.9993⁴²⁰	1.5946²⁰	i	v	v	s	v		**B5**, 513
Ω b2303	—,4,4′-dimethyl-	p,p′-Bitolyl. $C_{14}H_{14}$. See b2214	182.27	mcl pr (eth) λ^{peth} 203 (4.64), 254.5 (4.32), 274 sh (4.00)	125 (121.5)	295⁷⁶⁰	0.917¹²¹⁴		i	δ	s	s	s	CS₂ s	**B5**², 514
b2304	—,3,3′-dimethyl-4,4′-dipropoxy-	$C_{20}H_{26}O_2$. See b2214	298.43	lf	115				i	δ v^h					**B6**, 1010
Ω b2305	—,2,2′-dinitro-	$C_{12}H_8N_2O_4$. See b2214	244.22	ye mcl pr or nd (al) λ^{iso} 253 (4.1)	127–8		1.45 (so)		i	v^h	s	...	s^h	aa s^h lig δ	**B5**², 490
b2306	—,2,4′-dinitro-	$C_{12}H_8N_2O_4$. See b2214	244.22	mcl pr (al) λ^{iso} 265 (4.2)	93–4		1.474		i	v^h	s	...	s^h	aa s^h	**B5**², 491
b2307	—,3,3′-dinitro-	$C_{12}H_8N_2O_4$. See b2214	244.22	ye-og nd (al or aa) λ^{al} 244 (4.48), 300 sh (3.46)	200				i	δ	δ	...	s^h	aa s^h	**B5**², 491
Ω b2308	—,4,4′-dinitro-	$C_{12}H_8N_2O_4$. See b2214	244.22	nd (al) λ^{al} 306 (4.40)	240–3				i	δ s^h	...	...	s^h	aa s^h	**B5**², 491
—	—diphenyl-........	see **Quaterphenyl**													
—	—dodecahydro-	see **Bicyclohexyl**													
b2310	—,2-ethoxy-	$C_{14}H_{14}O$. See b2214	198.27	pr (peth)	34	276 132⁶				s	s	s	s	chl s	**B6**, 672
b2311	—,3-ethoxy-	$C_{14}H_{14}O$. See b2214	198.27	(peth)	35	305 158⁸				s	s	s	s	os s	**B6**, 674
Ω b2312	—,2-hydroxy-	o-Phenylphenol. $C_{12}H_{10}O$. See b2214	170.21	nd (peth) λ^{MeOH} 247 (4.1), 286 (3.7)	58–60 (67–5)	286⁷⁶⁰ (275) 145¹⁴	1.213²⁵		i	s	v	s	s	lig s Py v, ∞^{h}	**B6**², 623
Ω b2313	—,3-hydroxy-	m-Phenylphenol. $C_{12}H_{10}O$. See b2214	170.21	nd (w or peth) λ^{al} 250 (4.2) 285 (3.5)	78	>300			δ	v	v	...	v	peth s Py v	**B6**², 624
Ω b2314	—,4-hydroxy-	p-Phenylphenol. $C_{12}H_{10}O$. See b2214	170.21	nd or pl (dil al) λ^{al} 260 (4.24)	165–7	305–8 sub			δ	v	v	...	v	peth δ chl v Py v	**B6**², 624
b2315	—,2-hydroxy-2′-methoxy-5,5′-dimethyl-	$C_{15}H_{16}O_2$. See b2214	228.29		223	205¹²				v	v	...	v	chl v	**B6**², 974
b2316	—,2-iodo-	$C_{12}H_9I$. See b2214	280.11	λ^{hx} 226 (4.3)		189–92³⁶ 158⁶	1.6038²⁵₂₅	1.6620²⁰	i	s^h	s	...	s	aa s	**B5**², 486
b2317	—,4-iodo-	$C_{12}H_9I$. See b2214	280.11	nd (al or aa) λ^{al} 258.6 (4.41)	113–4	320 δd 183¹¹			i	s^h	s	...	s	aa s	**B5**², 486
Ω b2318	—,2-methoxy-	$C_{12}H_{12}O$. See b2214	184.24	pr (peth) λ^{al} 264 (4.11), 285 (3.74)	29	274 150¹³	1.0233⁹⁹	1.5641⁹⁹	i	s^h	...	...	...	peth s	**B6**², 623
b2319	—,4-methoxy-	$C_{13}H_{12}O$. See b2214	184.24	pl (al) λ^{al} 261 (4.32)	90	157¹⁰	1.0278¹⁰⁰₄	1.5744¹⁰⁰	i	s^h	s	...	...		**B6**², 625
Ω b2320	—,2-methyl-	$C_{13}H_{12}$. See b2214	168.24	λ^{al} 237 (4.00)	-0.2	255.3⁷⁶⁰ 130–6²⁷	1.010²²	1.5914²⁰	i	s	s	s	s		**B5**², 504
Ω b2321	—,3-methyl-	$C_{13}H_{12}$. See b2214	168.24	λ^{iso} 248 (4.2)	4.53	272.7⁷⁶⁰ 148–50²⁰	1.0182¹⁷	1.5972²⁰	i	s	s	s	s		**B5**³, 504
Ω b2322	—,4-methyl-	$C_{13}H_{12}$. See b2214	168.24	pl (lig or MeOH) λ^{iso} 250 (4.22)	49–50	267–8 134–6¹⁵	1.015²⁷		i	s	s	...	...	os v	**B5**², 504
Ω b2323	—,2-nitro-	$C_{12}H_9NO_2$. See b2214	199.21	pl (al or MeOH) λ^{iso} 231 (4.2)	37.2	320 201³⁰	1.44		i	δ^h	s	...	...		**B5**², 487

For explanations, symbols and abbreviations see beginning of table. For structural formulas see end of table.

No.	Name	Synonyms and Formula	Mol. wt.	Color, crystalline form, specific rotation and λ_{max} (log ε)	m.p. °C	b.p. °C	Density	n_D	w	al	eth	ace	bz	other solvents	Ref.
	Biphenyl														
Ω b2324	—,3-nitro-	$C_{12}H_9NO_2$. See b2214	199.21	ye pl or nd (dil al) λ^{iso} 245 (4.4), 303 (3.3)	62	225–30[35]			i	s	s	...	...	aa s lig s	B5[2], 487
Ω b2325	—,4-nitro-	$C_{12}H_9NO_2$. See b2214	199.21	ye nd (al) λ^{iso} 295 (4.2)	114–4.5	340[760] 224[30]			i	δ v[h]	s	...	s	chl s aa s	B5[2], 487
b2326	—,3,3′,5,5′-tetra-hydroxy-	Diresorcinol. $C_{12}H_{10}O_4$. See b2214	218.21	pl or nd (w+2)	310 (anh)				s[h]	s	s	i	i	aa i	B6[2], 1129
b2327	—,2,2′,4,4′-tetra-nitro-	$C_{12}H_6N_4O_8$. See b2214	334.20	ye pr (bz)	165–6				i	δ	δ	...	v	aa v	B5[2], 494
b2328	—,2,4,4′-triamino-	$C_{12}H_{13}N_3$. See b2214	199.26	nd	134										B13[2], 149
b2329	2-Biphenylcar-boxylic acid		198.22	lf (dil al) λ^{al} 245 (4.07)	113.5–4.5	343–4[760] 199[10]			i	v	...	...	v	aa v	B9[2], 463
b2330	—,nitrile		179.22	nd	41 (32)	170–2[15] 151[5]				s	v				B9[2], 463
Ω b2331	3-Biphenylcar-boxylic acid		198.22	lf (al) λ^{al} 231 (4.32), 250 sh (4.10)	165–6 (161)				δ	s	s	s	s	aa s lig s	B9[2], 464
Ω b2332	4-Biphenylcar-boxylic acid		198.22	nd (bz or al)	228	sub			δ[h] i	s	s	s			B9[2], 464
b2333	—,nitrile		179.22	cr (al or peth) λ^{al} 264.5 (4.42)	88				i	v	v	...			B9[2], 464
b2334	3-Biphenylcar-boxylic acid, 2-hydroxy-	$C_{13}H_{10}O_3$. See b2331	214.22	cr (bz)	186–7					s[h]					B10, 341
Ω b2335	2,2′-Biphenyldi-carboxylic acid	Diphenic acid.	242.23	mcl pr or lf (w), cr (aa) $\lambda^{w,pH=1.5}$ 284 (3.5), $\lambda^{w,pH=6}$ 275 (3.4)	233.5 (229)	sub			i δ[h]	s	s	...		os s	B9[2], 655
b2336	—,anhydride	$C_{14}H_8O_3$. See b2335	224.23	nd (aa or bz)	217	sub			i	...	δ	...		aa v	B17[2], 497
b2337	—,dichloride	$C_{14}H_8Cl_2O_2$. See b2335	279.14		94 (97)					v	s	...	v	aa v	B9[2], 657
b2338	—,diethyl ester	$C_{18}H_{18}O_4$. See b2335	298.34		42				i	v	s	...	s		B9[2], 656
Ω b2339	—,dimethyl ester	$C_{16}H_{14}O_4$. See b2335	270.29	mcl pr (MeOH)	74	204–6[14]			i	v	s	...	s		B9[2], 656
b2340	—,imide	$C_{14}H_9NO_2$. See b2335	223.23	nd (al)	219–20				δ[h] s[h]	δ	δ	...		chl v	B21[2], 392
b2341	2,3′-Biphenyldi-carboxylic acid	Isodiphenic acid	242.22	nd (w or dil aa)	216				δ[h]	v					B9[2], 663
b2342	2,4′-Biphenyldi-carboxylic acid		242.23	lf (al)	272–3				δ	v[h]		...	s	aa v	B9[2], 663
b2343	3,3′-Biphenyldi-carboxylic acid		242.23	lf (al)	356–7				δ[h]	δ s[h]		...	i	aa δ chl s lig i	B9[2], 664
b2344	—,dimethyl ester	$C_{16}H_{14}O_4$. See b2343	270.29	lf (MeOH)	104				i	v	v	...	v	lig δ	B9, 927
b2345	3,4′-Biphenyldi-carboxylic acid		242.23	nd (PhNO₂)	334–5				i	δ	...	δ	...	PhNO₂ s	B9, 927
b2346	—,dimethyl ester	$C_{16}H_{14}O_4$. See b2345	270.29	nd (MeOH or lig)	98.5–9.5				i	...	...	...	...	MeOH s lig s	B9, 927
b2347	3,5-Biphenyldi-carboxylic acid		242.23	lf (aa)	>310				i	v	v	v	v	aa s[h]	B9, 926
b2348	—,dimethyl ester	$C_{16}H_{14}O_4$. See b2347	270.29	lf (MeOH)	214				i	δ	...	δ			B9[2], 665
b2349	2,2′-Biphenyl-dicarboxylic acid, 3,3′-dimethyl-	$C_{16}H_{14}O_4$. See b2325	270.29		230					s	s	s	s		B9[1], 407
b2350	—,4-nitro-	$C_{14}H_9NO_6$. See b2335	287.23	lf, pr or wh nd (w)	217 (250)				i s[h]	v	v	...	δ	lig δ	B9[2], 659
b2351	—,5-nitro-	$C_{14}H_9NO_6$. See b2335	287.23	lf (w or dil al)	267				δ v[h]	v	v	...	s	MeOH v	B9[2], 659
b2352	—,6-nitro-(dl)	$C_{14}H_9NO_6$. See b2335	287.23	lf (w)	248–50 d				i v[h]	s	s	s	δ	chl δ lig δ aa v	B9[2], 659
Ω b2353	—,2,2′-Biphenyl-disulfonic acid, dichloride		351.24	pr (chl), cr (aa)	142–4				d[h]	d[h]	s	...	v	chl v	B11[2], 123
b2354	3,3-Biphenyl-disulfonic acid, diamide		312.37	nd (ace)	285						s		...	MeOH s	B11, 219
b2355	—,dichloride		351.24	nd (chl)	128				d[h]	d[h]	s	...	s	AcOEt s	B11, 219
b2356	4,4′-Biphenyl-disulfonic acid		314.34	pr	72.5	>200			s						B11, 219
b2357	—,diamide	$C_{12}H_{12}N_2O_4S_2$. See b2356	312.37	nd (w)	300				v[h]	δ	s	...	δ	CS₂ s	B11, 220
b2358	—,dichloride	$C_{12}H_8Cl_2O_4S_2$. See b2356	351.24	pr (aa)	205–7				d[h]	d[h]	s	...	s	CS₂ δ aa s	B11[2], 124
b2359	2,2′-Biphenyl-disulfonic acid, 4,4′-diamino-	$C_{12}H_{12}N_2O_6S_2$. See b2353	344.37	lf	175 d				δ	i	i				B14[1], 743
b2360	—,4,4′-diamino-5,5′-dimethyl-	$C_{14}H_{16}N_2O_6S_2$. See b2359	372.42	nd (w+1½)					s[h]	i	i			aa i	B14, 796
Ω b2361	2,2′-Bipyridyl		156.20	pr (peth) λ^{MeOH} 235 (4.01), 280 (3.85)	71–3	272–5[760]			δ	v	v	...	v	chl v lig v	B23[2], 211

For explanations, symbols and abbreviations see beginning of table. For structural formulas see end of table.

No.	Name	Synonyms and Formula	Mol. wt.	Color, crystalline form, specific rotation and λ_{max} (log ε)	m.p. °C	b.p. °C	Density	n_D	w	al	eth	ace	bz	other solvents	Ref.
	2,3'-Bipyridyl														
b2362	2,3'-Bipyridyl	Isonicoteine	156.20	λ^{al} 238 (4.15), 275 (4.07)	. . . .	295.5–6.5 122–5[1]	1.140_4^{20}	1.6223^{20}	i	v	v	. . .	v	peth δ chl v	B23[2], 212
Ω b2363	2,4'-Bipyridyl		156.20		61.5	280–2 148–50[1]			δ	v	v	. . .		chl v	B23, 200
b2364	3,3'-Bipyridyl		156.20	λ^{al} 225 (3.64), 274 (2.89)	68	291–2[760] 190–2[25]	1.1635_{20}^{20}		v	v	δ	. . .		peth δ	B23[2], 212
b2365	3,4'-Bipyridyl		156.20	lf (peth)	62	297			v	s	δ	. . .		peth s	B23[2], 212
b2366	4,4'-Bipyridyl		156.20	nd (w +2) λ^w 238 (4.2), 264 sh (3.9)	114 (171–2) (anh) 73(+2w)	305[760] sub			δ s^h	v	s	. . .	v	chl v lig v	B23[2], 212
b2367	2,2'-Biquinolyl		256.31	pl or lf (al) λ^{al} 258 (4.87), 302 (4.30), 327 (4.37)	196	. . . .			i	v^h	s	s	s	os s	B23[2], 267
b2368	2,3'-Biquinolyl		256.31	lf (al), ye pl or nd (bz)	176–7	>400			i	s^h	s	. . .	s^h	chl s^h	B23[2], 267
b2369	2,6'-Biquinolyl		256.31	pl (al)	144	. . . .			i	s	δ	s	s		B23, 294
b2370	2,7'-Biquinolyl (higher melting)		256.31	mcl pl (al)	160	. . . .			i	s^n	δ	. . .	δ		B23, 294
b2371	—, (lower melting)	$C_{18}II_{12}N_2$. See b2370	256.31	tcl	115	. . . .				v	s	. . .	v	peth δ	B23, 294
b2372	3,4'-Biquinolyl		256.31	pw (peth)	83–4	. . . .				s		. . .	s	peth δ	B23[2], 267
b2373	3,7'-Biquinolyl		256.31	lf or nd (al or bz)	190	. . . .			i	s^h	δ	. . .	s	chl s	B23[2], 268
b2374	4,4'-Biquinolyl		256.31	pr (peth)	171	. . . .			i	v	i	s	s	peth δ	B23[2], 268
b2375	4,6'-Biquinolyl		256.31	cr (bz)	122	. . . .			i	v	i	. . .	v	AcOEt v chl v	B23, 294
b2376	6,6'-Biquinolyl		256.31	lf (al)	181	. . . .			i	s^n	δ	. . .			B23, 295
b2377	6,8'-Biquinolyl		256.31	lf (al)	148	. . . .			i	s^h	δ	. . .	v^h		B23, 296
b2378	8,8'-Biquinolyl		256.31	lf or pl (al or aa) λ^{al} 230 (4.92), 293 (4.00), 305 (4.00), 318 sh (3.95)	205–7	. . . .			i	s^h	δ	s	s	chl v lig δ CCl_4 s	B23[2], 268
b2379	Biquinone, 3,3'-dihydroxy-5,5'-dimethyl-	Phenicin	274.23	yesh-br (al) λ^{chl} 268 (4.52), 406 (3.36)	230–1	. . . .			δ	v^h		. . .		chl v aa v	C54, 397
—	Bismark brown	see Azobenzene, 2,4,3'-triamino-													
b2380	Bistibine. tetramethyl-	$(CH_3)_2SbSb(CH_3)_2$	303.64	br-red nd	17.5	190[760]			i		s	. . .	s	. . . .	J1935, 366
—	Bistyryl	see 1,3-Butadiene, 1,4-diphenyl-*													
Ω b2381	2,2'-Bithiophene . . .	2,2'-Bithienyl	166.27	lf (al) λ^{al} 246 (3.78), 301 (4.11)	33	260[760] 103[3]			i	v	s	. . .		aa s	B19[2], 26
b2382	—, hexabromo-	$C_8Br_6S_2$. See b2381	639.67	nd (bz)	257–8	. . . .			i			. . .	s^h		B19, 33
—	Bitolyl	see Biphenyl, dimethyl-													
Ω b2383	Biuret	Allophanamide. Carbamoylurea. $H_2NCONHCONH_2$	103.08	pl (al), nd (w +1) $\lambda^{w, pH=13}$ 216 (3.75)	190d (193d)	. . . .			δ v^h	v	i	. . .			B3[2], 60
b2384	—, acetyl-	$CH_3CONHCONHCONH_2$	145.12	nd (w or al)	193–4	. . . .			s	s	δ	i	δ		B3[1], 33
b2385	—, 1,5-diamino-	$H_2NNHCONHCONHNH_2$	133.11	pr (dil al), nd (aa)	199–200d	. . . .			v	δ	δ	. . .		aa v^h	B3, 101
b2386	Bixin	$C_{25}H_{30}O_4$. $CH_3O_2CCH:-[CHC(CH_3):CHCH:]_4-CHCO_2H$	394.52	vt pr (ace) $\lambda^{95\%al}$ 448 (3.92), 480 (3.86)	198	. . . .			i	s^h	δ	s^h	δ	aa δ chl s	C54, 2406
b2387	Boric acid, tributyl ester	Tributoxyborine. $B(OC_4H_9^n)_3$	230.16	oil	. . . .	230–1 114–5[15]	0.8567_4^{20}	1.4106^{18}	d	s	v	. . .	s	MeOH v	B1[2], 398
b2388	—, triethyl ester	Triethoxyborine. $B(OC_2H_5)_3$	146.00		120[760]		0.8546_4^{28}	1.3749^{20}	d	∞	∞	. . .			B1[2], 333
b2389	—, triisopropyl ester	Triisopropoxyborine. $B(OC_3H_7^i)_3$	188.08		104[760] 52–3[17]		0.8251_4^{20}	1.3772^{20}	d	s	s	. . .	v	i-PrOH v	B1[2], 382
b2390	—, trimethyl ester . .	Trimethoxyborine. $B(OCH_3)_3$	103.92		–29.3	67–9	0.915^{20}	1.3568^{20}	d	v	∞	. . .	s	MeOH ∞	B1[3], 1210
b2391	—, tripropyl ester . .	Tripropylborine. $B(OC_3H_7^n)_3$	188.08		179–80[760] 64[9]		0.8576_4^{20}	1.3948^{20}	d	∞	∞	. . .		PrOH s	B1[2], 369
b2392	—, tris(3-methylbutyl) ester	Triisoamyl borate. $B[OCH_2CH_2CH(CH_3)_2]_3$	272.24		254–5 132–3[12]		0.8518_4^{20}	1.4156^{20}	d	∞	∞	. . .			B1[3], 1645
b2393	—, trithio-, trimethyl ester	Tris(methylthio)borine. $B(SCH_3)_3$	152.11		5	218.2[760]	1.126^{20}	1.5788^{20}	d	d	s	. . .		os ∞	C55, 9346
b2394	Borine, bis(dimethylamino)fluoro-	$[(CH_3)_2N]_2BF$	117.96		–44.3	106[760]			d	d	s	s		os ∞	Am 76, 3905
b2395	—, bis(methylthio)methyl-	$(CH_3S)_2BCH_3$	120.05		–59	100[147]			d	d	v	v		os ∞	Am 78, 1523
b2396	—, difluoro(dimethylamino)-	$(CH_3)_2NBF_2$	92.89	rh	165–8d	sub 132			d			. . .			Am 76, 3904

For explanations, symbols and abbreviations see beginning of table. For structural formulas see end of table.

Boric acid

No.	Name	Synonyms and Formula	Mol. wt.	Color, crystalline form, specific rotation and λ_{max} (log ε)	m.p. °C	b.p. °C	Density	n_D	w	al	eth	ace	bz	other solvents	Ref.
b2397	—,difluoro(phenyl)-	$C_6H_5BF_2$	125.92		−36.2	97–8^{747}	1.087^{25}	1.4441^{25}	d	...	s	...	s		B16[2], 638
b2398	—,difluoro(4-tolyl)-		139.94			127.8^{747}	1.055^{25}	1.4535^{25}	d	...	s	...	s		C18, 992
b2399	—,dimethylarsino-, (tetramer)	$[(CH_3)_2AsBH_2]_4$	471.28		150	185^{11}			i	s	v	v	...	os s	Am 76, 389
b2400	—,—,(trimer)	$[(CH_3)_2AsBH_2]_3$	353.46		50	146^{26}			i	s	v	v	...	os s	Am 76, 386
b2401	—,dimethyl(dimethylamino)-	$(CH_3)_2NB(CH_3)_2$	84.99		−92	65^{760}					v	v		os ∞	Am 78, 1521
b2402	—,dimethyl)(dimethylphosphino)-, (trimer)	$[(CH_3)_2PB(CH_3)_2]_3$	305.78		333	200^{10}			i	s					C54, 9767
b2403	—,dimethyl(methoxy)-	$CH_3OB(CH_3)_2$	71.92			21^{760}			d	d	v	v		os ∞	Am 75, 3872
b2404	—,dimethyl(methylthio)-	$CH_3SB(CH_3)_2$	87.98		−84	71^{760}			d	d	v	v		os ∞	Am 76, 3307
b2405	—,(dimethylphosphino)-, (tetramer)	$[(CH_3)_2PBH_2]_4$	295.48	nd	161	190^{29}			i	s	v	v		os s	C54, 4166
b2406	—,—,(trimer)	$[(CH_3)_2PBH_2]_3$	221.61	rh	86	90^4			i	s	v	v		os s	C53, 16062
b2407	—,methylthio-, (polymer)	$(CH_3SBH_2)_n$		d					d	d	v	v		os ∞	C55, 27015
b2408	—,triethyl-	$B(C_2H_5)_3$	98.00		−92.9	95–6^{760}	0.6961^{23}		δ	s	s				B4[2], 1022
b2409	—,triisobutyl-	$B(C_4H_9^i)_3$	182.16			188^{766} 86^{20}	0.7380$^{25}_4$	1.4188^{23}	δ	s	s	...	s		B4[2], 1022
b2410	—,trimethyl-	$B(CH_3)_3$	55.92	λ^{hx} 260 (3.78)	−161.5	20			δ	v	v				B4[2], 1022
b2411	—,triphenyl-	$B(C_6H_5)_3$	242.13	wh cr λ^{hp} 240 (4.04), 270 (3.35)	142	245–50^{15}			i	d	δ		s	lig s	B16[2], 636
b2412	—,tripropyl-	$B(C_3H_7^n)_3$	140.08		−56	159^{760} 43–4^{17}	0.7204^{25}	1.4135$^{22.5}$	δ	s	s				B4[2], 1022
b2413	—,tris(3-methylbutyl)-	$B[CH_2CH_2CH(CH_3)_2]_3$	224.24			119^{14}	0.7600$^{23}_4$	1.4321	v	s	s			os v	B4[2], 1023
—	—,tris(methylthio)-	*see* **Boric acid, trithio-, trimethyl ester**													
b2414	**Borneol** (d)	$C_{10}H_{18}O$	154.26	lf or hex pl (peth) [α]$^{20}_D$ +37.7 (al)	208	212^{760} sub	1.011$^{20}_4$		δ	s	s	...	v	lig s	B6[2], 82
Ω b2415	—(dl)	$C_{10}H_{18}O$. *See* b2414.	154.26	lf (lig)	210.5	sub	1.011^{20}		i	v	v	v			B6[2], 82
b2416	—(l)	$C_{10}H_{18}O$. *See* b2414.	154.26	hex pl [α]$^{20}_D$ −37.74 (al)	208.6	210^{779}	1.1011$^{20}_4$		i	v	v	v			B6[2], 82
b2417	—,acetate (d)	$C_{12}H_{20}O_2$. *See* b2414.	196.29	rh, [α]$^{20}_D$ +44.4 (al)	29	223–4^{760} 107^{15}	0.9920^{20}		δ	s	s				B6[2], 83
Ω b2418	—,—(dl)	$C_{12}H_{20}$. *See* b2414	196.29		< −17	223–4^{760}	0.9838$^{20}_4$	1.4630^{20}							B6[2], 86
b2419	—,—(l)	$C_{12}H_{20}O_2$. *See* b2414	196.29	[α]$^{20}_D$ −44.45 (undil)	29	223–4^{760} 107^{15}	0.9920^{20}	1.4634^{20}	δ	s	s				B6[2], 85
Ω b2420	—,formate(d)	$C_{11}H_{18}O_2$. *See* b2414	182.27	[α]$_D$ +48.75 (undil)		90^{10}	1.009^{22}	1.4708^{15}							B6[2], 85
b2421	**Bornyl amine**(d)		153.27	[α]$^{20}_D$ +47.2 (al)	163	200 sub			i	v	v	v	s	os v	B12[2], 39
b2422	**Bornyl chloride**(d)		172.70	nd [α]$_D$ +34.5 (eth), [α]^4_D +31 (to)	132	207–8 sub			i	s	s	...	s	peth s	B5[2], 62
b2423	**Bornylene**(d)	2-Bornene	136.24	cr (al) [α]$_D$ +30.5 (to)	109–10	146^{750} sub									B5[1], 80
b2424	—(l)	$C_{10}H_{16}$. *See* b2423	136.24	cr (al) [α]$^{19}_D$ −23.9 (bz)	113	146^{746}			i	s	s				B5[2], 105
—	**Bourbonal**	*see* **Benzaldehyde, 3-ethoxy-4-hydroxy-**													
—	**Brassidic acid**	*see* **13-Docosenoic acid (trans)***													
b2425	**Brazilein**		284.27	red-br nd or lf (w + 1)	250				s^h	s	δ		s	chl s aa s	B18[2], 194
—	**British antilewisite**	*see* **1-Propanol,2,3-dimercapto-***													
—	**Bromal**	*see* **Acetaldehyde, tribromo-**													
Ω b2426	**Bromocresol green**	3,3',5,5'-Tetrabromo-m-cresolsulfonphthalein	698.04	wh or red (+7w), ye (aa) $\lambda^{0.01N\ NaOH}$ 613 (4.66)	218–9				δ	v	v		s	AcOEt v aa s	B19[2], 108
—	**Bromoform**	*see* **Methane, tribromo-***													
Ω b2427	**Bromophenol blue**	3,3',5,5'-Tetrabromophenolsulfonphthalein	670.02	hex pr (aa−ace) $\lambda^{w,pH=5.2}$ 440 (3.48), 600 (4.82) $\lambda^{0.01N\ NaOH}$ 595 (4.82)	279d				δ	s			s	aa s	B19[2], 105
—	romopicrin	*see* **Methane, nitrotribromo-***													
—	**Bromoprene**	*see* **1,3-butadiene, 2-bromo-***													

For explanations, symbols and abbreviations see beginning of table. For structural formulas see end of table.

No.	Name	Synonyms and Formula	Mol. wt.	Color, crystalline form, specific rotation and λ_{max} (log ε)	m.p. °C	b.p. °C	Density	n_D	w	al	eth	ace	bz	other solvents	Ref.
	Bromural														
—	Bromural.......	see Urea, 1(2-bromo-3-methylbutanoyl)-													
Ω b2428	Brucine	$C_{23}H_{26}N_2O_4$...	394.44	mcl pr (w +4), $[\alpha]^{20}_{5461}$ −149.5 $[\alpha]^{20}_{5893}$ −120.5 (chl, c = 1) λ^{al} 264 (4.01), 301 (3.94)	178 (anh) 105 (hyd)	....			δ	v	δ	...	δ	chl v	**B27²**, 797
b2429	—,hydrochloride ..	$C_{23}H_{27}ClN_2O_4$. See b2428	430.94	pr	....				s	s					**B27²**, 797
b2430	—,nitrate, dihydrate	$C_{23}H_{31}N_3O_9$. See b2428	493.52	pr	230d	sub			s	s					**B27²**, 797
b2431	—,sulfate, heptahydrate	$C_{46}H_{68}N_4O_{19}S$. See b2428..	1013.1	nd, $[\alpha]_D$ −24.4 (w)					s v^h	δ			i	chl δ MeOH v	**B27²**, 797
b2432	**Bufotalin**	$C_{26}H_{36}O_6$.	444.58	cr(+ 1 al, al) $[\alpha]^{20}_D$ + 5.4 (chl, c = 0.5) λ^{al} 304 (3.78)	223d				i	s				chl s	**C53**, 2281
b2433	**Bulbocapnine** (d)...	$C_{19}H_{19}NO_4$.	325.37	pr(al) $[\alpha]_D$ +237.1 (chl, c = 4)	199–200				i	s				os s chl v	**B27²**, 554
b2434	—(l)	$C_{19}H_{19}NO_4$. See b2433	325.37		209–10										**B27¹**, 467
b2435	**1,2-Butadiene***	Methylallene. CH_2:C:CHCH₃	54.09	λ^{gas} 178 (4.3), 186 sh (3.6)	−136.19	10.85^{760}	0.676$^0_0$ 0.652^{20}	1.4205$^{1.3}$	i	∞	∞		v		**B1²**, 224
Ω b2436	**1,3-Butadiene*** ...	Bivinyl. CH_2:CHCH:CH₂...	54.09	λ^{al} 217 (4.32)	−108.91	−4.41	0.6211$^{20}_{20}$	1.4292^{-25}	i	s	s	v	s	os s	**B1³**, 929
b2437	**1,2-Butadiene, 4-bromo-***	CH_2:C:CHCH₂Br	133.00			109–11^{760}	1.4255$^{20}_4$	1.5248^{20}				s			**B1³**, 929
b2438	**1,3-Butadiene, 2-bromo-***	Bromoprene. CH_2:CBrCH:CH₂	133.00	grsh-ye oil	42–3^{165}		1.397$^{20}_4$	1.4988^{20}	i	s	s			os v	**B1³**, 955
b2439	**1,2-Butadiene, 4-chloro-***	CH_2:C:CHCH₂Cl	88.54			88	0.9891$^{20}_4$	1.4775^{20}	δ	s	s	v	s	os v	**B1³**, 928
b2440	**1,3-Butadiene, 1-chloro-***	CH_2:CHCH:CHCl	88.54			68	0.9606$^{20}_4$	1.4712^{20}		s	s			chl v	**B1³**, 949
b2441	—,2-chloro-*	Chloroprene. CH_2:CClCH:CH₂	88.54	λ^{hx} 223 (4.15)		59.4^{760} 6.4^{100}	0.9583$^{20}_4$	1.4583^{20}	δ		∞	∞	∞	os ∞	**B1³**, 949
b2442	—,1-chloro-2-methyl-*	CH_2:CHC(CH₃):CHCl....	102.57			107 50.4^{100}	0.9710$^{20}_4$	1.4792^{20}	i	v^h		s		chl s	**B1³**, 974
b2443	—,1-chloro-3-methyl-*	CH_2: C(CH₃)CH : CHCl	102.57			99–100	0.9543$^{20}_4$	1.4719^{20}	i	s	s	s		chl s	**B1³**, 975
Ω b2444	—,2-chloro-3-methyl-*	CH_2: C(CH₃)CCl : CH₂	102.57			93^{760}	0.9593$^{20}_4$	1.4686^{20}	i	s	v		v	chl v	**B1³**, 975
b2445	—,1,2-dichloro-* ...	CH_2: CHCCl : CHCl	122.98			60–5^{105} 35^{40}	1.1991$^{20}_4$	1.4960^{20}						CCl_4 v	**B1³**, 954
b2446	—,2,3-dichloro-* ...	CH_2: CClCCl : CH₂	122.98			98^{760} 41–3^{85}	1.1829$^{20}_4$	1.4890^{20}						chl v	**B1³**, 954
Ω b2447	—,2,3-dimethyl-* ..	Biisopropenyl. CH_2: C(CH₃)C(CH₃): CH₂	82.15	λ^{hx} 226 (4.33)	−76	68–78^{760}	0.7267$^{20}_4$	1.4394^{20}	i	s	s		v	chl v	**B1³**, 991
b2448	—,1,4-diphenyl-* (cis, cis)	cis, cis-Bistyryl. C_6H_5CH: CHCH: CHC₆H₅	206.29	lf or nd (MeOH or al) λ^{bz} 239 (4.23), 313 (4.48)	70.5	....	0.9697$^{100.0}$	1.6183$^{100.0}$	i	s^h δ	v		v	peth s chl v aa s^h	**B5²**, 550
Ω b2449	—,—(trans, trans)*.	trans, trans-Bistyryl. C_6H_5CH: CHCH: CHC₆H₅	206.29	lf (al or aa) λ^{bz} 334 (4.68), 352 (4.50)	152.5	350^{720}			i	s	δ		s	peth s chl s	**B5²**, 589
—	—,1,4-epoxy-*	see Furan													
b2450	—,1-ethoxy-*	CH_2: CHCH : CHOC₂H₅	98.15			109–12	0.8154$^{20}_4$	1.4529^{20}		s	v	v	s	chl s	**B1³**, 1975
b2451	—,2-ethoxy-*	CH_2: CHC(OC₂H₅): CH₂	98.15			94.5–5.5^{760}	0.8177$^{20}_4$	1.4400^{20}		v	v	v	s	os v	**B1³**, 1977
b2452	—,2-fluoro-*	Fluoroprene. CH_2: CHCF: CH₂	72.08			12^{760}	0.8434$^4_4$	1.400^4							**B1³**, 948
Ω b2453	—,hexachloro-* ...	CCl_2: CClCCl: CCl₂	260.76	λ^{hp} 253 (3.7)	−21	215^{760} 101^{20}	1.6820$^{20}_4$	1.5542^{20}	i	s	s				**B1³**, 955
b2454	—,hexafluoro-*, ...	CF_2: CFCF: CF₂	162.04		−132.4 to 132.1	6^{760}	1.553$^{-20}_4$	1.378^{-20}							**B1³**, 948
b2455	**1,2-Butadiene, 4-iodo-***	CH_2: C: CHCH₂I	179.99			130^{760}	1.7129$^{20}_4$	1.5709^{20}							**B1³**, 929
b2456	**1,3-Butadiene, 2-iodo-***	Iodoprene. CH_2: CHCI: CH₂	179.99			111–5^{700}	1.7278$^{20}_4$	1.5616							**B1³**, 956
b2457	**1,2-Butadiene, 4-methoxy-***	CH_2: C: CHCH₂OCH₃	84.13			87–9	0.8286$^{20}_4$	1.435^{20}			s				**B1³**, 1974
Ω b2458	**1,3-Butadiene, 1-methoxy-***	CH_2: CHCH : CHOCH₃	84.13			91–2^{760}	0.8296$^{20}_4$	1.4594^{20}	s	s	v				**B1³**, 1975
b2459	—,2-methoxy-*....	CH_2: CHC(OCH₃): CH₂ .	84.13			75^{760}	0.8272$^{20}_4$	1.4442^{20}		v	v	v	v	os v	**B1³**, 1976
b2460	**1,2-Butadiene, 3-methyl-***	asym-Dimethylallene. CH_2: C: (CH₃)₂	68.13		−120	40^{760}	0.6804$^{20}_4$	1.4166^{20}	i	∞	∞	∞	∞	peth, CCl_4 ∞	**B1³**, 976
Ω b2461	**1,3-Butadiene, 2-methyl-***	Isoprene. CH_2: CHC(CH₃): CH₂	68.13	λ^{iso} 217.5 (4.28), 223.5 (4.33), 230 (4.16)	−146	34^{760}	0.6810$^{20}_4$	1.4219^{20}	i	∞	∞	∞	∞		**B1³**, 966
b2462	—,pentafluoro 2-trifluoromethyl-*	Perfluoroisoprene. F_2C: C(CF₃)CF: CF₂	212.05			39^{760}	1.527$^0_0$	1.3000^0			s	s	s		**C49**, 2479

For explanations, symbols and abbreviations see beginning of table. For structural formulas see end of table.

No.	Name	Synonyms and Formula	Mol. wt.	Color, crystalline form, specific rotation and λ_{max} (log ε)	m.p. °C	b.p. °C	Density	n_D	w	al	eth	ace	bz	other solvents	Ref.
	1,3-Butadiene														
b2463	—,1-phenyl-, (trans)*	$CH_2:CHCH:CHC_6H_5$.....	130.19	λ^{iso} 233 (3.81), 280 (4.35), 306 (3.65)	4.5	76^{11}	0.9286^{20}_4	1.6089^{25}	i	s	s	s	s	os s	B5[2], 414
b2464	1,2,3,4-tetra-chloro-, (liquid)*	$ClCH:CClCCl:CHCl$.....	191.87		−4	188 67^{10}	1.516^{15}_{15}	1.5455^{20}	i	s	s	s	s	os s	B1[3], 954
b2465	—,—,(solid)*.....	$ClCH:CClCCl:CHCl$.....	191.87	λ^{hp} 248 (4.3)	52	....	1.4961^{20}	1.5438^{20}	i	s	s	s	s	chl v os s	B1[3], 954
b2466	—,1,2,3-trichloro-*	$CH_2:CClCCl:CHCl$....	157.44			$33-4^9$	1.4060^{20}_4	1.5262^{20}	....	....	s	....	....	chl s	B1[3], 954
b2467	2,3-Butadien-1-ol*	$CH_2:C:CHCH_2OH$.....	70.09			$126-8^{756}$ $69-9^{45}$	0.9164^{20}_4	1.4759^{20}	s	s	s	s	os v	B1[3], 1974
b2468	Butadiyne*......	Biacetylene. $CH:CC:CH$....	50.06	λ^{iso} 224 (2.35), 247 (2.26), 251.5 (1.74)	−36.4	10.3^{760}	0.7364^0_4	1.4189^5	v	s	v	v	....	chl s	B1[3], 1056
b2469	—,1,4-bis(1-hydroxycyclo-hexyl)-*	....	246.35	cr (bz) λ^{al} 232.5 (2.51), 243 (2.54), 257 (2.34)	174	....			i δ^h				δ^h	MeOH s chl δ^h	C31, 4283
b2470	—,1,4-dichloro-*	$ClC:CC:CCl$.....	118.95	nd	1–3	....			....	....	....	....	....	chl v	B1[2], 246
Ω b2471	Butanal*	Butyraldehyde. $CH_3CH_2CH_2CHO$	72.12	λ^v 225 (1.07), 282.5 (1.13)	−99	75.7^{760}	0.8170^{20}_4	1.3843^{20}	s	∞	∞	v	v		B1[2], 721
Ω b2472	—,oxime	$CH_3CH_2CH_2CH:NOH$	87.12	....	−29.5	152^{715}	0.923^{20}		v	∞	∞	v	v	bz	B1[2], 724
Ω b2473	—,phenylhydrazone	$CH_3CH_2CH_2CH:NNHC_6H_5$	162.24	....	93–5	$190-5^{80}$ 152^{14}			....	s	s	s	s	os s	B15[2], 55
b2474	—,2-benzylidene-	α-Ethylcinnamaldehyde. 2-Ethyl-3-phenylpropenal. $C_6H_5CH:C(C_2H_5)CHO$	160.22	ye λ^{al} 253.5 (4.09)		$157-8^5$	1.0201^{22}_2	1.578^{20}							C26, 4684
b2475	—,3-chloro-, diethyl acetal	$CH_3CHClCH_2CH(OC_2H_5)_2$	180.68	....		$70-1^{12}$	0.9709^{20}_4	1.4210^{20}	i	∞	∞	v	v	os ∞	B1[2], 724
b2476	—,4-chloro-*.....	$ClCH_2CH_2CH_2CHO$	106.55	....		$50-1^{13}$	$1.107^{8.5}_{15}$	$1.4466^{8.5}$	v	v	v	v			B1[3], 2767
b2477	—,2,3-dichloro-*.....	$CH_3CHClCHClCHO$	141.00			$58-60^{20}$	1.2666^{21}_4	1.4618^{21}	i	s	s	v	v	chl s	B1[2], 724
Ω b2478	—,2-ethyl-*	$(C_2H_5)_2CHCHO$	100.16			$117-9^{160}$	0.8110^{20}_4	1.4025^{20}	δ	∞	∞	v	v		B1[2], 749
Ω b2479	—,3-hydroxy-*	Aldol. $CH_3CHOHCH_2CHO$	88.12			83^{20} $d85$	1.103^{20}	1.4238^{20}	∞	∞	s	v	v		B1[2], 868
Ω b2480	—,2-methyl-(dl)* ..	$CH_3CH_2CH(CH_3)CHO$	86.14	λ^{al} 295 (1.32)		$92-3^{760}$ 54^{200}	0.8029^{20}_4	1.3869^{20}	i	s	s	v			B1, 682
Ω b2481	—,3-methyl-*	Isovaleraldehyde. $(CH_3)_2CHCH_2CHO$	86.14	λ^{vap} 190.1	−51	92.5^{760}	0.7977^{20}_4	1.3902^{20}	δ	s	s	v	v		B1[2], 742
b2482	—,—,oxime	$(CH_3)_2CHCH_2CH:NOH$	101.15		48.5	161.3^{759}	0.8934^{20}_4	1.4367^{20}	i	s	v	v	v		B1[2], 744
b2483	—,2,2,3-trichloro-*	n-Butyrchloral. $CH_3CHClCCl_2CHO$	175.44			$163-5^{760}$ 49^8	1.3956^{20}_4	1.4755^{20}	s	s	s	s	s		B1[2], 725
Ω b2484	—,—,hydrate	$CH_3CHClCCl_2CH(OH)_2$	192.46	rh pl or lf (w)	78	d	1.694^{20}_4		s^h	v	s	s	s		B1[2], 725
Ω b2485	Butane*	$CH_3CH_2CH_2CH_3$	58.13		−138.35	−0.5	0.6012^{20}_4 0.5788^{20}_4	1.3543^{-13} 1.3326^{20}	s	v	v	v		chl v	B1[2], 261
Ω b2486	—,1-amino-*	n-Butylamine. $CH_3CH_2CH_2CH_2NH_2$	73.14		−49.1	77.8^{760}	0.7414^{20}_4	1.4031^{20}	∞	s	s			chl s	B4[2], 631
b2487	—,2-amino-(d)* ...	sec-Butylamine. $CH_3CH_2CH(CH_3)NH_2$	73.14	$[\alpha]^{20}_D$ +7.4 (w)	−104.5	63^{760}	0.724^{20}	1.344^{20}	s	∞	∞	v		chl s	B4[1], 372
Ω b2488	—,—,(dl)*	$CH_3CH_2CH(CH_3)NH_2$	73.14		< −72	63.5^{764}	0.7246^{20}_4	1.3932^{20}	s	∞	∞	v		chl s	B4[2], 636
b2489	—,—,(l)*	$CH_3CH_2CH(CH_3)NH_2$	73.14	$[\alpha]^{20}_D$ −7.4 (w, c = 4.7)		63	0.7205^{20}_4		v	v	v	v		chl s	B4[2], 372
b2490	—,2-amino-2,3-dimethyl-*	$(CH_3)_2CHC(CH_3)_2NH_2$	101.19			$104-5^{760}$	0.7683^0_0	1.4096^{17}							B4, 193
b2491	—,3-amino-2,2-dimethyl-*	$(CH_3)_3CCH(CH_3)NH_2$	101.19		−20	102^{760}		1.4105^{25}	s^h	s	s	s	s		B4, 193
b2492	—,—,hydro-chloride*	$(CH_3)_3CCH(CH_3)NH_2.HCl$	137.65	nd (CH_2Cl_2-CS_2)	300–1 (cor)	sub 245			v						B4, 193
Ω b2493	—,1-amino-3-methyl-*	$(CH_3)_2CHCH_2CH_2NH_2$	87.17			$95-7^{761}$	0.7505^{20}_4	1.4083^{20}	∞	∞	s	s			B4[2], 644
b2494	—,2-amino-2-methyl-*	$CH_3CH_2C(CH_3)_2NH_2$	87.17		−105	77^{760}	0.7312^{25}	1.3954^{25}	∞	∞	v				B4[2], 644
b2495	—,2-amino-3-methyl-*	$(CH_3)_2CHCH(CH_3)NH_2$	87.17			$84-7^{760}$	0.7574^{19}	1.4096^{18}	v	s					B4[2], 644
b2496	1,4-bis(dicar-bethoxyamino)-	$C_2H_5O_2CNH(CH_2)_4NHCO_2C_2H_5$	232.28	nd (lig)	85–6	....			i	s	s		s	chl s lig s^h	B4[1], 421
b2496[1]	1,4-bis(di-methylamino)-	Tetramethylputrescine. $(CH_3)_2NCH_2CH_2CH_2CH_2N(CH_3)_2$	232.28	....		168^{740} $78-80^{28}$	0.7942^{15}	1.4621^{25}	s	s	s	s	s		B4[2], 702
b2497	—,2,2-bis(ethyl-sulfonyl)-*	Trional. $CH_3CH_2C(SO_2C_2H_5)_2CH_3$	144.27 / 242.36	pl (w)	76	d	1.199^{85}_4		δ	v	s	s	s	peth s lig s CCl_4 s	B1[2], 731
b2498	—,1,1-bis(4-hydroxyphenyl)-*	....	242.32	nd (to)	137	270^{12}			s	s	s	s	s^h	to s^h	B6[2], 980
b2499	—,2,2-bis(4-hydroxyphenyl)-*	....	242.32	nd or pr (w)	133–4 (128)	$250-3^{12}$			i	v	v	v	δ	MeOH v	B6[2], 980
Ω b2500	—,1-bromo-*	n-Butyl bromide. $CH_3CH_2CH_2CH_2Br$	137.03		−112.4	101.6^{760} 18.8^{30}	1.2758^{20}_8	1.4401^{20}	i	∞	∞	∞		chl s	B1[2], 290
Ω b2501	—,2-bromo-(dl)* ..	sec-Butyl bromide. $CH_3CH_2CH(CH_3)Br$	137.03		−111.9	91.2^{760}	1.2585^{20}_4	1.4366^{20}	i		∞	∞		chl s	B1[3], 293
b2502	—,—,(l)*	$CH_3CH_2CH(CH_3)Br$	137.03	$[\alpha]^{22}_D$ −23.13 (undil)		$90-1$	1.2536^{25}_4	$1.4359^{19.5}$	i	∞	∞	∞		chl s	B1[3], 293
Ω b2503	—,1-bromo-4-chloro-*	$ClCH_2CH_2CH_2CH_2Br$	171.48			$174-5^{756}$ $63-4^{10}$	1.488^{20}_4	1.4885^{20}	i	s	s			chl s	B1[3], 294

For explanations, symbols and abbreviations see beginning of table. For structural formulas see end of table.

No.	Name	Synonyms and Formula	Mol. wt.	Color, crystalline form, specific rotation and λ_{max} (log ε)	m.p. °C	b.p. °C	Density	n_D	Solubility w	al	eth	ace	bz	other solvents	Ref.
	Butane														
b2504	—,2-bromo-1-chloro-*	$CH_3CH_2CHBrCH_2Cl$	171.48	....	....	$146-7^{758}$	1.468_4^{20}	1.4880^{20}	i	s	s	...	s	chl s	B1[2], 83
b2505	—,1-bromo-3,3-dimethyl-*	$(CH_3)_3CCH_2CH_2Br$	165.08	....	....	138 54^{40}	1.1556_4^{20}	1.4440^{20}	i	s	s	...	...	chl v	B1[3], 409
b2506	—,2-bromo-2,3-dimethyl-*	$(CH_3)_2CHCBr(CH_3)_2$	165.08	....	24–5	$132-3^{742}$ 87^{180}	1.1772^{20}	1.4517	d[h]		s	...	...	chl v	B1[3], 414
b2507	—,1-bromo-4-fluoro-*	$FCH_2CH_2CH_2CH_2Br$	155.01	....	....	$134-5^{740}$		1.4370^{25}	i	v	v	...	...		C51, 7300
b2508	—,1-bromo-2-methyl-(d)*	act-Amyl bromide. $CH_3CH_2CH(CH_3)CH_2Br$.	151.05	$[\alpha]_D^{20} +3.68$	....	121.6^{760}	1.2234_4^{20}	1.4451^{20}	i	s	s	...	...	chl v	B1[3], 362
b2509	—,—(dl)*	$CH_3CH_2CH(CH_3)CH_2Br$...	151.05	....	....	120.5^{760} 12.3^{10}	1.2205_4^{20}	1.4452^{20}	i	s	s	...	...	chl v	B1[3], 363
Ω b2510	—,1-bromo-3-methyl-*	Isoamyl bromide. $(CH_3)_2CHCH_2CH_2Br$	151.05	....	−112	120.4^{760} 12.3^{10}	1.2071_4^{20}	1.4420^{20}	i	s	s	...	...	chl v	B1[3], 363
Ω b2511	—,1-chloro-*	n-Butyl chloride. $CH_3CH_2CH_2CH_2Cl$	92.57	....	−123.1	78.44^{760}	0.8862_4^{20}	1.4021^{20}	i	∞	∞	...	...	chl v	B1[3], 275
Ω b2512	—,2-chloro-(dl)* ...	sec-Butyl chloride. $CH_3CH_2CHClCH_3$	92.57	....	−131.3	68.25^{760}	0.8732_4^{20}	1.3971^{20}	i	∞	∞	...	v	chl v	B1[3], 278
b2513	—,—(l)*	$CH_3CH_2CHClCH_3$	92.57	$[\alpha]_D^{20} -8.48$	−140.5	68^{760}	0.8950_4^0		i	∞	∞	...	v	chl v	B1[2], 81
b2514	—,1-chloro-2,2-dimethyl-*	neo-Hexyl chloride. $CH_3CH_2C(CH_3)_2CH_2Cl$	120.62	....	....	116^{735}		1.4200^{20}	i	v	v	...	...	chl v	B1[3], 408
b2515	—,1-chloro-3,3-dimethyl-*	$(CH_3)_3CCH_2CH_2Cl$...	120.62	....	....	115^{760} 41^{50}	0.8670_4^{20}	1.4161^{20}	i	v	v	...	...	chl v	B1[3], 408
b2516	—,2-chloro-2,3-dimethyl-*	$(CH_3)_2CHCCl(CH_3)_2$	120.62	....	−10.4	112^{760}	0.8780_4^{20}	1.4191^{20}	d	s	...	s	...		B1[3], 414
b2517	—,3-chloro-2,2-dimethyl-*	Pinacolyl chloride. $CH_3CHClC(CH_3)_3$	120.62	....	−0.9	111^{760} 7^{10}	0.8767_4^{20}	1.4182^{20}	i		v	...	...		B1[3], 408
b2519	—,1-chloro-4-fluoro-*	$FCH_2CH_2CH_2CH_2Cl$	110.57	....	....	114.7^{760}	1.0627_4^{25}	1.4020^{25}	i	v	v	...	...		B1[3], 279
b2520	—,1-chloro-2-methyl-(d)*	act-Amyl chloride. $CH_3CH_2CH(CH_3)CH_2Cl$	106.60	$[\alpha]_{5892}^{20} +1.64$	....	100.5^{760} 43^{100}	0.8857_4^{20}	1.4126^{20}	i	s	s	...	...	chl v	B1[3], 356
b2521	—,—(dl)*	$CH_3CH_2CH(CH_3)CH_2Cl$...	106.60	....	....	99.9^{760} 52.2^{50}	0.8818_{15}^{15}	1.4102^{25}		s	s	...	...		B1[3], 357
Ω b2522	—,1-chloro-3-methyl-*	Isoamyl chloride. $(CH_3)_2CHCH_2CH_2Cl$	106.60	....	−104.4	98.8^{760}	0.8704_4^{20}	1.4084^{20}	δ	∞	∞	...	...	chl v	B1[3], 359
Ω b2523	—,2-chloro-2-methyl-*	tert-Amyl chloride. $CH_3CH_2CCl(CH_3)_2$	106.60	....	−73.5	85.6^{760}	0.8653_4^{20}	1.4055^{20}	δ	s	s	...	...		B1[3], 357
b2524	—,2-chloro-3-methyl-(dl)*	sec-Isoamyl chloride. $(CH_3)_2CHCHClCH_3$	106.60	....	....	92.8^{760} 25.7^{60}	0.8620_4^{20}	1.4020^{20}		s	v	...	...		B1[1], 46
b2525	—,2(chloromethyl)-1,3-dichloro-(dl)*	$CH_3CHClCH(CH_2Cl)_2$	175.49	....	....	$79-81^{15}$	1.2793_4^{15}		i	s	s	...	...	chl s	C31, 1003
b2526	—,2(chloromethyl)-1,2,3-trichloro-*	$CH_3CHClCCl(CH_2Cl)_2$	209.94	....	....	$102-3^{13}$	1.3977_4^{18}	1.5012_a^{18}	i		v	...	...	chl v	B1[3], 362
b2527	—,1-chloro-2,2,3,3-tetramethyl-*	$(CH_3)_3CC(CH_3)_2CH_2Cl$	148.68	....	52–3	80.1^{40}			i		v	...	...		B1[3], 502
b2528	—,2-chloro-2,3,3-trimethyl-*	$(CH_3)_2CClC(CH_3)_3$	134.65	....	136 (132)	sub			i		v	...	...	MeOH δ[h]	B1[1], 59
b2529	—,1,4-diamino-*	Putrescine. $H_2NCH_2CH_2CH_2CH_2NH_2$	88.15	lf	27–8	$158-9^{760}$	0.877_4^{25}	1.4569^{20}	s			...	...		B4, 264
b2530	—,—,dihydrochloride*	$H_2NCH_2CH_2CH_2CH_2NH_2 \cdot 2HCl$	161.08	nd or lf (al or w)	315d (290)	sub			v	v[h]	i	...	i	MeOH i	B4[2], 701
Ω b2533	—,1,2-dibromo-*	$CH_3CH_2CHBrCH_2Br$	215.94	λ 212 (3.1)	−65.4	166.3^{760} 53.8^{10}	1.7915_4^{20}	1.4025^{20} (1.5150^{20})	i		s	...	...	chl s	B1[3], 295
Ω b2534	—,1,3-dibromo-*	$CH_3CHBrCH_2CH_2Br$	215.94	....	....	174^{760} 72^{20}	1.800^{20}	1.507^{20}	i		s	...	...	chl s	B1[3], 295
Ω b2535	—,1,4-dibromo-*	Tetramethylene dibromide. $BrCH_2CH_2CH_2CH_2Br$	215.94	λ 212 (2.8)	−16.53	197^{760} 79^{10}	1.7890^{20}	1.5190^{20}	i		s	...	...	chl s	B1[3], 295
b2536	—,2,3-dibromo-*	$CH_3CHBrCHBrCH_3$	215.94	λ <225	< −80	161^{760}	1.7893_4^{22}	1.5133^{22}	i		s	...	...	chl s	B1[3], 296
b2537	—,1,1-dichloro-*	Butylidene dichloride. $CH_3CH_2CH_2CHCl_2$	127.03	....	....	113.8^{760}	1.0863_4^{20}	1.4355^{20}	i		s	...	...	chl s	B1[3], 280
Ω b2538	—,1,2-dichloro-*	$CH_3CH_2CHClCH_2Cl$	127.03	....	....	124^{760}	1.1116_4^{25}	1.4450^{20}	i		s	...	...	chl s	B1[3], 280
Ω b2539	—,1,3-dichloro-*	$CH_3CHClCH_2CH_2Cl$	127.03	....	....	134^{760}	1.1582^{20}	1.4445^{20}	i		s	...	...	chl s	B1[3], 281
Ω b2540	—,1,4-dichloro-*	Tetramethylene dichloride. $ClCH_2CH_2CH_2CH_2Cl$	127.03	....	−37.3	163.0^{760} 39.7^{10}	1.1408^{20}	1.4542^{20}	i		s	...	...	chl s	B1[3], 81
b2541	—,2,2-dichloro-*	$CH_3CH_2CCl_2CH_3$	127.03	....	−74	104		1.4295	i		s	...	...	chl s	B1[3], 282
Ω b2542	—,2,3-dichloro-*	$CH_3CHClCHClCH_3$	127.03	....	−80.0	116^{760} 49.5^{80}	1.1134_4^{20}	1.4420^{20}	i		s	...	...	chl s	B1[2], 282
b2543	—,2,2-dichloro-3,3-dimethyl-*	$(CH_3)_3CCCl_2CH_3$	155.07	....	151–2	....			i	v[h]	s[h]	...	...		B1[3], 409
b2544	—,2,3-dichloro-2,3-dimethyl-*	$(CH_3)_2CClCCl(CH_3)_2$	155.07	pr (dil al)	164	....			i	v	v	...	...		B1, 152
b2545	—,1,1-dichloro-3-methyl-(dl)*	$(CH_3)_2CHCH_2CHCl_2$	141.04	....	....	130 $48-9^{40}$	1.0473^{20}	1.4344^{20}	i		s	...	...	chl s	B1[1], 47
b2546	—,1,2-dichloro-2-methyl-(dl)*	$CH_3CH_2CCl(CH_3)CH_2Cl$	141.04	....	....	$133-5$ 71.5^{100}	1.0785_4^{20}	$1.4432^{23.5}$	d	s	s	...	...	chl s	B1[3], 360
b2547	—,1,3-dichloro-3-methyl-(d)*	$(CH_3)_2CClCH_2CH_2Cl$	141.04	....	....	$145-6$ 39^{10}	1.0654_4^{20}	1.4455^{20}	i	...	s	...	...	chl s	B1[3], 361

For explanations, symbols and abbreviations see beginning of table. For structural formulas see end of table.

No.	Name	Synonyms and Formula	Mol. wt.	Color, crystalline form, specific rotation and λ_{max} (log ε)	m.p. °C	b.p. °C	Density	n_D	w	al	eth	ace	bz	other solvents	Ref.
	Butane														
b2548	—,1,4-dichloro-2-methyl-*	ClCH₂CH₂CH(CH₃)CH₂Cl	141.04	....	....	168–9⁷⁶⁰ 50¹²	1.1003²⁵₄	1.4562²¹	i	...	...	...	...	chl s	B1², 101
b2549	—,2,3-dichloro-2-methyl-*	CH₃CHClCCl(CH₃)₂	141.04	....	....	138⁷⁶⁰ 37.5²⁰	1.0696¹⁵₄	1.4450¹⁸	i	s	s	...	...	...	B1³, 360
Ω b2550	—,1:2,3:4-diepoxy-(dl)*	Bioxirane. Butadiene dioxide.	86.09	....	4	144⁷⁶⁰	1.113²⁰	1.435²⁰	s	s	...	...	...	...	B19², 14
b2551	—,—(meso)*		86.09	....	−16	138⁷⁶⁷	1.1157²⁰₄	1.4330²⁰	∞	v	...	...	...	...	B19, 15
b2552	—,1(diethyl-amino-methoxy)-*	Butyl (diethylaminomethyl) ether. CH₃CH₂CH₂CH₂OCH₂N(C₂H₅)₂	159.27	....	....	172–4⁷⁵⁴				v	...	...	...	os s	B4², 598
b2553	—,1,4-difluoro-octachloro-*	FCCl₂CCl₂CCl₂CCl₂F	369.67	....	4–5	152.5²⁰	1.9272²⁰₄	1.5256²⁰							Am 62, 342
b2554	—,2,2-di(2-furyl)-		190.25	....	64–6¹		1.0330²⁰₄	1.4970²⁰	i	s	s	...	...	MeOH s	C52, 13702
Ω b2555	—,1,4-diiodo-*	Tetramethylene diiodide. ICH₂CH₂CH₂CH₂I	309.92	....	5.8	125–6¹⁵d	2.349²⁶₄	1.619²⁵	i	...	...	...	...	os s	B1³, 302
Ω b2556	—,2,2-dimethyl-* .	neo-Hexane. CH₃CH₂C(CH₃)₃	86.18	....	−99.87	49.74⁷⁶⁰	0.6485²⁰₄	1.3688²⁰	i	s	s	v	v	peth, CCl₄ v	B1³, 405
Ω b2557	—,2,3-dimethyl-* .	(CH₃)₂CHCH(CH₃)₂	86.18	....	−128.53	58⁷⁶⁰	0.6616²⁰₄	1.3750²⁰	i	s	s	v	v	peth, CCl₄ v	B1³, 410
b2558	—,1,4-dinitro-*	O₂NCH₂CH₂CH₂CH₂NO₂ .	148.13	pr (al or MeOH) λ^{a1} 277 (1.60)	33–4	176–8¹³			i	δ	s	...	s	MeOH sⁿ	B1³, 305
b2559	—,2,3-dinitro-(dl)*	CH₃CHNO₂CHNO₂CH₃ ..	148.13	pr (eth)	48–9					δ	s	...	...	MeOH δʰ lig δ	B1³, 305
b2560	—,—(meso)*	CH₃CHNO₂CHNO₂CH₃ ..	148.13	pr (eth)	....	76–7¹				δ	s	...	...	lig δ	B1³, 305
Ω b2561	—,1,2-epoxy-*	1,2-Butylene oxide.	72.12	....	....	63.3	0.8371⁷₄	1.3851²⁰	dʰ	v	∞	v	v	os v	B17², 17
—	—,1,4-epoxy-*	see Furan, tetrahydro-													
b2562	—,2,3-epoxy-(cis)* .	β-Butylene oxide	72.12	....	−80	59.7⁷⁴²	0.8226²⁵₄	1.3802²⁰	d	...	v	v	v	os v	B17², 17
b2563	—,—(trans)*		72.12	....	−85	56–7⁷⁶⁰	0.8010²⁵₄	1.3736²⁰	d	...	v	v	v	os v	B17², 17
b2564	—,1-fluoro-*	Butyl fluoride. CH₃CH₂CH₂CH₂F	76.12	....	−134	32.5⁷⁶⁰	0.7789²⁰₄	1.3396²⁰							B1³, 273
b2565	—,1,1,2,2,3,4,4-heptachloro-*	Cl₂CHCHClCCl₂CHCl₂ ..	299.24	....	....	137.5¹³·⁵ 97.5²	1.742²⁰₂₀	1.5407²⁰	i	...	...	s	...	CCl₄ v	B1³, 289
b2566	—,1,1,2,3,4,4-hexachloro-* (liquid)	Cl₂CHCHClCHClCHCl₂ ..	264.79	....	....	111¹⁰	1.6460²⁰₄	1.5258²⁰	i	...	...	s	...	CCl₄ s	B1³, 288
b2567	—,—(solid).......	Cl₂CHCHClCHClCHCl₂ ..	264.79	nd (al), pr (bz, aa)	109–10				i	...	...	s	...	CCl₄ s	B1³, 288
Ω b2568	—,1-iodo-*	Butyl iodide. CH₃CH₂CH₂CH₂I	184.02	λ^{MeOH} 254 (2.70)	−103	130.53⁷⁶⁰ 19.2¹⁰	1.6154²⁰₄	1.5001²⁰	i	∞	∞	...	...	chl v	B1³, 294
Ω b2569	—,2-iodo-(dl)*	sec-Butyl iodide. CH₃CH₂CHICH₃	184.02	λ^{MeOH} 258.5 (277)	−104.2	120⁷⁶⁰ 33⁴⁵	1.5920²⁰₄	1.4991²⁰	i	∞	∞	...	...	chl v	B1³, 301
b2570	—,—(l)*	CH₃CH₂CHICH₃	184.02	[α]_D −12.15 (al, c = 20)	....	117.5–8.5	1.585²⁰	1.4945¹⁹	i	∞	∞	...	...	chl v	B1³, 301
b2571	—,1-iodo-2-methyl-(d)*	act-Amyl iodide. CH₃CH₂CH(CH₃)CH₂I	198.05	[α]_D¹⁵ +5.78 (undil)	....	148⁷⁶⁰ 47.1²⁰	1.5253²⁰₄	1.4977²⁰	i	s	s	...	...	...	B1³, 366
b2572	—,—(dl)*	CH₃CH₂CH(CH₃)CH₂I ..	198.05	....	....	144–7		1.497²⁰	i	s	s	...	...	...	B1³, 366
Ω b2573	—,1-iodo-3-methyl-*	Isoamyl iodide. (CH₃)₂CHCH₂CH₂I	198.05	....	....	147⁷⁶⁰	1.5118²⁰₄	1.4939²⁰	δ	∞	∞	...	...	...	B1³, 367
b2574	—,2-iodo-2-methyl-*	tert-Amyl iodide. CH₃CH₂CI(CH₃)₂	198.05	....	....	124.5⁷⁶⁰	1.4937²⁰₄	1.4981²⁰	i	...	...	...	...	...	B1³, 366
b2575	—,2-iodo-3-methyl-*	(CH₃)₂CHCHICH₃	198.05	....	....	138–9⁷⁶⁰			i	v	s	s	...	os s	B1¹, 49
Ω b2577	—,1-isocyano-*	Butylcarbylamine. Butyl isocyanide. CH₃CH₂CH₂CH₂NC	83.13	....	....	118⁷⁶⁰		1.4061²⁰	i	∞	∞	...	...	...	B4³, 294
b2578	—,1-isocyano-3-methyl-*	Isoamylcarbylamine. (CH₃)₂CHCH₂CH₂NC	97.16	....	....	140⁷⁶⁰	0.806²⁰₄	1.406²⁰	i	∞	∞	...	...	...	B4, 184
Ω b2579	—,2-methyl-*	Isopentane. (CH₃)₂CHCH₂CH₃	72.15	....	−159.9	27.85⁷⁶⁰	0.6201²⁰₄	1.3537²⁰	i	s	s	...	...	...	B1³, 352
b2580	—,2-methyl-1,2,3-trichloro-*	CH₃CHClCCl(CH₃)CH₂Cl .	175.49	....	....	183–5⁷⁶² 65.5¹¹	1.2527²⁰₄		i	...	...	...	...	chl s	B1³, 361
b2581	—,2-methyl-2,3,3-trichloro-*	CH₃CCl₂CCl(CH₃)₂	175.49	....	....	182–3	1.215¹⁵	1.472²¹	i	...	...	s	...	chl s aa vʰ	B1³, 361
Ω b2582	—,1-nitro-*	CH₃CH₂CH₂CH₂NO₂ ...	103.12	λ^{a1} 272 (1.40)	....	153⁷⁶⁰	0.9710²⁰₄	1.4103²⁰	δ	∞	∞	...	...	alk s	B1³, 303
b2583	—,2-nitro-(dl)*	CH₃CH₂CHNO₂CH₃	103.12	λ^{a1} 279 (1.39)	−132	140⁷⁶⁰	0.9854¹⁷	1.4044²⁰	δ	∞	∞	...	...	...	B1³, 303
b2585	—,1,1,2,2,3,4,4-octachloro-*	Cl₂CHCCl₂CCl₂CHCl₂ ...	333.69	cr (al)	81				i	vʰ	s	s	s	os s	B1³, 289
b2586	—,1,1,2,3,4-penta-chloro-(liquid)*	ClCH₂CHClCHClCHCl₂ ..	230.35	....	....	95.5¹¹	1.561¹⁸	1.5140¹⁸	i	...	...	...	...	CCl₄ v	B1³, 288
b2587	—,—(solid)*	ClCH₂CHClCHClCHCl₂ ..	230.35	lf (al)	49	230 102¹¹	1.539⁵³	1.5065⁵³	i	vʰ	...	...	...	CCl₄ v	B1³, 287
b2588	—,1,2,2,3,4-penta-chloro-*	ClCH₂CHClCCl₂CH₂Cl. ..	230.35	....	....	85¹⁰	1.5543²⁰₄	1.5157²⁰	i	...	...	s	...	chl s	B1³, 288
b2589	—,1,1,4,4-tetra-bromo-*	Br₂CHCH₂CH₂CHBr₂ ...	373.73	....	....	138–45¹⁰	2.529²⁰₄	1.6077²⁰	i	δ	∞	...	∞	chl ∞	B1, 121

For explanations, symbols and abbreviations see beginning of table. For structural formulas see end of table.

No.	Name	Synonyms and Formula	Mol. wt.	Color, crystalline form, specific rotation and λ_{max} (log ε)	m.p. °C	b.p. °C	Density	n_D	w	al	eth	ace	bz	other solvents	Ref.
	Butane														
b2590	—,1,2,2,3-tetra-bromo-*	$CH_3CHBrCBr_2CH_2Br$	373.73	....	−2	$128-30^{14}$ 97.5^7	2.5100^{20}_4	1.6070^{20}	i	...	...	s	...		B1[3], 298
b2591	—,1,2,2,4-tetra-bromo-*	$BrCH_2CH_2CBr_2CH_2Br$.....	373.73	nd (lig)	72–3	....			i					lig s^h	B1[3], 298
Ω b2592	—,1,2,3,4-tetra-bromo-(dl)*	$BrCH_2CHBrCHBrCH_2Br$ ..	373.73	lf (peth)	40–1				i	v	v	s		lig s	B1[3], 298
b2593	—,—(meso)*	$BrCH_2CHBrCHBrCH_2Br$ ..	373.73	nd (al or lig)	118–9	$180-1^{60}$			i	s^h		s		chl s lig δ	B1[3], 298
b2594	—,2,2,3,3-tetra-bromo-*	$CH_3CBr_2CBr_2CH_3$	373.73	lf (lig), pr (eth-lig)	243				i	δ	s	s	s	chl v lig s	B1[3], 298
b2595	—,1,1,1,2-tetra-chloro-*	$CH_3CH_2CHClCCl_3$.....	195.91	....		$134-5^{742}$	1.3932^{20}_{20}	1.4920^{25}	i	...	...	s		chl s	B1[3], 280
b2596	—,1,2,2,3-tetra-chloro-*	$CH_3CHClCCl_2CH_2Cl$.....	195.91	....	−48 to −46	182 85^{10}	1.4276^{18}_8	1.491^{20}	i		s	s		chl s	B1[3], 286
b2597	—,1,2,3,3-tetra-chloro-*	$CH_3CCl_2CHClCH_2Cl$.....	195.91	....		90^{32} $55-7^{10}$	1.4204^{20}_4	1.4958^{20}	i		s	s		chl s	B1[3], 286
b2601	—,2,2,3,3-tetra-methyl-*	$(CH_3)_3C(CH_3)_2C(CH_3)_2CH_3$	114.23	lf (eth)	100.7	106.5^{760} 13.1^{10}	0.8242^{20} 0.6485^{110}	1.4695^{20}	i		s				B1[3], 501
b2602	—,1,1,2-tri-bromo-*	$CH_3CH_2CHBrCHBr_2$.....	294.83	....		216.2^{760} 98^{14}	2.1836^{20}_4	1.5626^{17}	i	s	s	s		chl s	B1[2], 84
b2603	—,1,2,2-tri-bromo-*	$CH_3CH_2CBr_2CH_2Br$.....	294.83	....		213.8^{760} 90.1^{14}	2.1692^{20}_4	1.5624^{16}	i	s	s	s		chl s	B1[2], 85
b2604	—,1,2,3-tri-bromo-*	$CH_3CHBrCHBrCH_2Br$	294.83	....	−19	220^{760} 97^{10}	2.1908^{20}_4	1.5680^{20}	i	s	s	s		chl s	B1[2], 85
b2605	—,1,2,4-tri-bromo-*	$BrCH_2CH_2CHBrCH_2Br$ ..	294.83	....	−18	215^{760} 93^{10}	2.170^{20}_4	1.5608^{20}	i	s	s	s		chl s	B1[2], 85
b2606	—,1,3,3-tri-bromo-*	$CH_3CBr_2CH_2CH_2Br$	294.83	....		$200-5^{760}$ 70^8	1.4464^{20}_4	1.5564^{20}	i	s	s	s		chl s	B1[3], 298
Ω b2607	—,2,2,3-tri-bromo-*	$CH_3CHBrCBr_2CH_3$.....	294.83		1.85	206^{760} 86^{10}	2.1724^{20}_4	1.5602^{20}	i	s	s	s		chl s	B1[2], 85
b2608	—,1,1,3-tri-chloro-*	$CH_3CHClCH_2CHCl_2$.....	161.46	....		152^{753}	1.317^{15}	1.4600^{15}	i	s	s			chl v	B1[3], 285
b2609	—,1,2,3-tri-chloro-*	$CH_3CHClCHClCH_2Cl$.....	161.46	....		$165-8^{725}$ 63^{28}	1.3164^{20}_4	1.4790^{20}	i	s	s			chl v	B1[3], 285
b2610	—,2,2,3-tri-chloro-*	$CH_3CHClCCl_2CH_3$.....	161.46	....		$143-5^{760}$	1.2699^{20}_4	1.4645^{20}	i					chl v	B1[3], 285
Ω b2611	—,2,2,3-tri-methyl-*	Triptan. $(CH_3)_2CHC(CH_3)_3$	100.21		−24.19	80.88^{760}	0.6901^{20}_4	1.3894^{20}	i	s	s	v	v	peth, CCl_4 v	B1[3], 454
Ω b2612	1-Butanearsonic acid*	n-Butylarsonic acid. $CH_3CH_2CH_2CH_2AsO_3H_2$	182.05		160				v	s	i			....	B4[2], 997
b2613	1-Butaneboronic acid, 3-methyl-*	Isoamylboric acid. $(CH_3)_2CHCH_2CH_2B(OH)_2$	115.97	pl (w)	169	....			v^h	s	s	s		os s	B4[2], 1023
—	Butanedial*	see Succinaldehyde													
—	1,1-Butanedi-carboxylic acid*	see Malonic acid, propyl-													
—	Butanedioic acid* ..	see Succinic acid													
—	—,2,3-dihydroxy-*	see Tartaric acid													
b2614	1,2-Butanediol (d)*	$CH_3CH_2CHOHCH_2OH$	90.12	$[\alpha]^{20}_D +14.5$ (al, c = 6)	....	192–4 $68^{0.4}$	$1.0059^{17.5}_{17.5}$	1.4375^{20}	v	∞	s	s			B1[2], 544
Ω b2615	—(dl)*	α-Butyleneglycol. $CH_3CH_2CHOHCH_2OH$	90.12			190.5^{760} 96.5^{10}	1.0024^{20}_4	1.4378^{20}	s	s	s	s			B1[2], 545
b2616	—(l)*	$CH_3CH_2CHOHCH_2OH$	90.12	$[\alpha]^{22}_D -7.4$ (al, c = 4)		$94-6^{12}$			s	s	s	s			B1[2], 544
b2617	1,3-Butanediol (d)*	β-Butyleneglycol. $CH_3CHOHCH_2CH_2OH$	90.12	$[\alpha]^{22}_D +18.5$ (al, c = 4)		204 $60-5^{0.8}$	1.0053^{20}_4	1.4418^{20}	s	s	i				B1[2], 545
Ω b2618	—(dl)*	$CH_3CHOHCH_2CH_2OH$	90.12			207.5^{760} $103-4^8$	1.0053^{20}_4	1.4410^{20}							B1[2], 545
b2619	—(l)*	$CH_3CHOHCH_2CH_2OH$	90.12	$[\alpha]^{25}_D -18.8$ (al, c = 4)		$107-10^{23}$	1.005^{20}_4								B1[3], 2167
Ω b2620	—,sulfite		135.16		5	185^{760} $76-7^{17}$	1.2352^{20}_4	1.4461^{20}	d^h	v	v	v	v	aa v	B1[3], 2171
Ω b2621	1,4-Butanediol*	Tetramethyleneglycol. $HOCH_2CH_2CH_2CH_2OH$	90.12		20.1	235 (230) 120^{10}	1.0171^{20}_{20}	1.4460^{20}	∞	s	δ				B1[2], 545
b2622	2,3-Butanediol (d)*	$CH_3CHOHCHOHCH_3$	90.12	$[\alpha]^5_D$ +12.5 (undil)	34 (25) (anh), 16.8 (+5w)	$180-2^{760}$	0.9872^{25}	1.4306^{25}	∞	∞	s	s			B1[2], 546
Ω b2623	—(dl)*	$CH_3CHOHCHOHCH_3$	90.12	cr (Pr^i_2O)	7.6	182.5^{760} 86^{16}	1.0033^{20}_4	1.4310^{25}	∞	∞	s	s			B1[2], 546
b2624	—(l)*	$CH_3CHOHCHOHCH_3$	90.12	$[\alpha]^{25}_D -13.0$ (undil)	19.7	$178-81^{760}$ 77.5^{10}	0.9869^{25}	1.4340^{18}	∞	∞	s	s			B1[2], 547
b2625	—(meso)*	$CH_3CHOHCHOHCH_3$	90.12	cr (Pr^i_2O)	34.4 (23.4)	181.7 83.5^{10}	1.0003^{20}_4	1.4367^{25}	v	s	s				B1[2], 546
Ω b2626	—,2,3-dimethyl-*	Pinacol. Tetramethylethylene glycol. $(CH_3)_2COHCOH(CH_3)_2$	118.17	nd (al or eth)	43 (38)	174.4^{760}			δ v^h	v	v			CS_2 δ	B1[2], 553
Ω b2627	—,—,—,hexa-hydrate*	Pinacol hydrate. $(CH_3)_2COHCOH(CH_3)_2.6H_2O$	226.27	pl (w + 6)	47	....	0.967^{15}		δ v^h	v	v			CS_2 δ	B1[2], 553
b2628	—,2,3-diphenyl-* ..	Acetophenonepinacol. $CH_3COH(C_6H_5)COH(C_6H_5)CH_3$	242.32	pr (dil al)	121–2				i	v	v			peth δ	B6[2], 979

For explanations, symbols and abbreviations see beginning of table. For structural formulas see end of table.

No.	Name	Synonyms and Formula	Mol. wt.	Color. crystalline form. specific rotation and λ_{max} (log ε)	m.p. °C	b.p. °C	Density	n_D	w	al	eth	ace	bz	other solvents	Ref.
	1,3-Butanediol														
b2629	**1,2-Butanediol, 3-methyl-***	α-Isoamylene glycol. $(CH_3)_2CHCHOHCH_2OH$	104.15	....		206 81–3[5]	0.9987_4^0	....		s	s				B1[2], 550
b2630	**1,3-Butanediol, 3-methyl-***	γ-Isoamylene glycol. $(CH_3)_2C(OH)CH_2CH_2OH$	104.15	....		202–3 108[16]	0.9448_4^{20}	1.4452^{20}	s	s					B1[1], 251
b2631	**2,3-Butanediol, 2-methyl-***	β-Isoamylene glycol. $CH_3CH(OH)COH(CH_3)_2$	104.15	....		175 68[5]	0.9920_{25}^{25}	1.4375^{20}	s	s	s				B1[2], 550
Ω b2632	**2,3-Butanedione***	Biacetyl. Dimethylglyoxal. $CH_3COCOCH_3$	86.09	λ^{hp} 510 (−3.22)	−2.4	88[760]	$0.9808_4^{18.5}$	1.3951^{20}	v	∞	∞	v	s		B1[2], 824
Ω b2633	—, dioxime	Dimethyl glyoxime. $CH_3C(:NOH)C(:NOH)CH_3$	116.13	nd (to or dil al) λ^{al} 227 (4.23)	245–6 (cor) (235)	sub 234–5			i	v	v		δ	to δ	B1[2], 826
Ω b2634	—, monooxime	Biacetyl monooxime. $CH_3COC(:NOH)CH_3$	101.11	pr (chl), lf (w) λ^{al} 229 (4.11)	77–8	185–6[760]			δ	v	v			chl v alk s	B1[2], 826
Ω b2635	**1,3-Butanedione, 1-phenyl-***	Benzoylacetone. $CH_3COCH_2COC_6H_5$	162.19	pr λ^{al} 310.5 (4.14)	56	261–2[760]	1.0599_4^{74}	1.5678^{78}	i	v	v		s		B7[2], 616
b2636	**1,4-Butane-dithiol-***	$HSCH_2CH_2CH_2CH_2SH$	122.25	....	−53.9	195–6[760] 110–2[50]	1.0621_4^0	1.5290^{20}	i	v					B1[3], 2177
b2637	**1-Butanephos-phonic acid***	Butylphosphonic acid. $CH_3CH_2CH_2CH_2PO_3H_2$	138.10	pl (bz)	106	d	....	....	v	v	v		δ v^h		Am 75, 3379
b2638	**2-Butanephos-phonic acid***	sec-Butylphosphonic acid. $CH_3CH_2CH(CH_3)PO_3H_2$	138.10	pl (bz-peth)	56	d	....	....	v	v	v		s	peth δ	Am 75, 3379
b2639	**1-Butanesulfonic acid, amide**	n-Butylsulfonamide. $CH_3CH_2CH_2CH_2SO_2NH_2$	137.12	lf (eth-lig)	48		....	....	v	v	v		v	lig i	B4, 8
b2640	—, chloride	$CH_3CH_2CH_2CH_2SO_2Cl$	156.63	....		75[10]		1.4559^{20}	d	d^h					B4, 8
b2641	**1,2,3,4-Butane-tetracarboxylic acid (dl)***	$HO_2CCH_2[CH(CO_2H)]_2CH_2CO_2H$	234.16	lf (w) cr (ace)	236–7 (slow htng)		....	....	v		δ		i	chl δ lig i	B2[1], 333
Ω b2642	— (meso)*	$HO_2CCH_2[CH(CO_2H)]_2CH_2CO_2H$	234.16	nd or pr (w)	192–3 d		....	....	v	s			i	lig i	B2[2], 702
Ω b2643	**1-Butanethiol***	n-Butyl mercaptan. $CH_3CH_2CH_2CH_2SH$	90.19	λ^{iso} 225–30 (2.20)	−115.67	98.46[760]	0.8337_4^{20}	1.4440^{20}	δ	v	v				B1[2], 398
Ω b2644	**2-Butanethiol (d)***	$CH_3CH_2CHSHCH_3$	90.19	$[\alpha]_D^{20}$ +15.7 λ^{iso} 225–30 (2.13)		85–95 37.4[134]	0.8299_4^{20}	1.43385^{25}		s	s		s	peth s	B1[3], 1549
Ω b2645	— (dl)*	sec-Butyl mercaptan. $CH_3CH_2CHSHCH_3$	90.19	....		85[760]	0.8295_4^{20}	1.4366^{20}		s	s		s	peth s	B1[3], 1548
b2646	— (l)*	$CH_3CH_2CHSHCH_3$	90.19	$[\alpha]_D^{17}$ −17.35		83–4	0.8300_4^{17}			s	s		s	peth s	B1[3], 1549
b2647	**1-Butanethiol, 2-methyl-(d)***	act-Amyl mercaptan. $CH_3CH_2CH(CH_3)CH_2SH$	104.22	$[\alpha]_D^{23}$ +3.21		118.2[760]	0.8420_4^{20}	1.4440^{20}							B1[2], 421
Ω b2648	—, 3-methyl-*	Isoamyl mercaptan. $(CH_3)_2CHCH_2CH_2SH$	104.22	λ^{iso} 225 sh (2.3)		118[760]	0.8350_4^{20}	1.4418^{20}	i	∞	∞				B1[2], 434
—	**1,2,3-Butanetri-carboxylic acid, 2,3-dimethyl-***	see **Camphoronic acid**													
Ω b2649	**1,2,3-Butanetriol***	1-Methylglycerol. $CH_3CH(OH)CH(OH)CH_2OH$	106.12	....		170[20] 140–2[1]		1.4462^{20}	v	v					B1[3], 2343
Ω b2650	**1,2,4-Butanetriol***	$HOCH_2CH(OH)CH_2CH_2OH$	106.12	....		172–4[12] 132–3[1]	1.018^{20}	1.4688^{20}	v	v					B1[3], 2344
Ω b2651	**Butanoic acid***	Butyric acid. $CH_3CH_2CH_2CO_2H$	88.12	λ^w 208 (1.8), 270 sh (−0.8)	−4.26 f.p. −19	163.53[760]	0.9577_4^{20}	1.3980^{20}	∞	∞	∞				B2[3], 576
Ω b2652	—, allyl ester	$CH_3CH_2CH_2CO_2CH_2CH:CH_2$	128.17	....		142–3[772] 44.5[15]	0.9017_4^{20}	1.4158^{20}	i	∞	∞				B2, 272
Ω b2653	—, amide	Butyramide. $CH_3CH_2CH_2CONH_2$	87.12	lf (bz) λ^{bz} 282 (2.68)	114.8	216	0.8850^{120}	1.4087^{130}		s	δ		i		B2[2], 251
b2654	—,—, N,N-diethyl-	$CH_3CH_2CH_2CON(C_2H_5)_2$	143.23	....		206 97[16]		1.4403^{25}	∞	s	v				B4[2], 604
b2655	—,—, N,N-dimethyl-	$CH_3CH_2CH_2CON(CH_3)_2$	115.18	....	−40	185–8 124–5[100]	0.9064_4^{25}	1.4391^{25}	s	s	∞	∞	∞	peth ∞ CS_2 ∞	B4[2], 564
Ω b2656	—,—, N-phenyl-	Butyranilide. $CH_3CH_2CH_2CONHC_6H_5$	163.22	mcl pr (al, bz, eth) λ^{al} 242 (4.17)	97	189[15]	1.134	....	i	v	v				B12[2], 146
Ω b2657	—, anhydride*	Butyric anhydride. $(CH_3CH_2CH_2CO)_2O$	158.20	λ^{bz} 282.5 (1.90)	−75	199.4 201.4[760] 85–6[8]	0.9668_4^{20}	1.4070^{20} (1.4124^{20})	d	d	s				B2[2], 251
Ω b2658	—, benzyl ester	$CH_3CH_2CH_2CO_2CH_2C_6H_5$	178.23	....		238–40 105[7]	1.0111^{20}	1.4920^{20}	i	v	v				B6[2], 417
b2659	—, bromide	Butyryl bromide. $CH_3CH_2CH_2COBr$	151.01	....		128[760]	1.4162_{17}^{17}	1.1596^{17}							B2[2], 251
Ω b2660	—, (4-bromo-phenacyl) ester	....	285.15	rod (dil al)	64		....								B8[2], 90
Ω b2661	—, butyl ester*	$CH_3CH_2CH_2CO_2(CH_2)_3CH_3$	144.22	....	−91.5	166.6[760] 55[13]	0.8709_4^{20}	1.4075^{20}	i	∞	∞				B2[2], 246
b2662	—, sec-butyl ester (d)	$CH_3CH_2CH_2CO_2CH(CH_3)CH_2CH_3$	144.22	$[\alpha]_D^{20}$ +22	−91.5	151.5[747] 54[18]	0.8737_4^{13}	1.4011^{20}		s	s		s	CS_2 s Py s	B2[2], 247
Ω b2663	—,— (dl)	$CH_3CH_2CH_2CO_2CH(CH_3)CH_3$	144.22	....		152.5[760] 52[16]	0.8609_4^{20}	1.4019^{20}							C33, 5806
b2664	—, tert-butyl ester	$CH_3CH_2CH_2CO_2C(CH_3)_3$	144.22	....		145–7	....	$1.4007^{17.5}$		s	s	s			B2[3], 601
Ω b2665	—, chloride	Butyryl chloride. $CH_3CH_2CH_2COCl$	106.55	....	−89	102[760]	1.0277_4^{20}	1.4121^{20}	d	d	∞				B2[2], 251
Ω b2666	—, cyclohexyl ester*	....	170.25	....		212[750]	0.9572_4^0	....	i	s				os s	B6[1], 6

For explanations, symbols and abbreviations see beginning of table. For structural formulas see end of table.

No.	Name	Synonyms and Formula	Mol. wt.	Color, crystalline form, specific rotation and λ_{max} (log ε)	m.p. °C	b.p. °C	Density	n_D	w	al	eth	ace	bz	other solvents	Ref.
	Butanoic acid														
b2667	—,2,2-dimethyl-propyl ester*	neo-Pentyl butyrate. $CH_3CH_2CH_2CO_2CH_2C(CH_3)_3$	158.24	....	....	$165-6^{760}$	0.8719^0	....							B2, 272
Ω b2668	—,ethyl ester*	$CH_3CH_2CH_2CO_2C_2H_5$	116.16	....	-100.8	$121-6^{760}$ 48.8^{50}	0.8785^{20}_4	1.4000^{20}	δ	s	s				B2[2], 244
b2669	—,furfuryl ester	....	168.20	....	....	$212-3^{764}$	1.0530^{20}	1.4231^{20}	δ	s	∞				B17[2], 115
b2670	—,heptyl ester*	$CH_3CH_2CH_2CO_2(CH_2)_6CH_3$	186.30	....	-57.5	225.87^{760} 105^{10}	0.8637^{20}	1.4231^{20}	i	s				oo s	B2, 272
Ω b2671	—,hexyl ester*	$CH_3CH_2CH_2CO_2(CH_2)_5CH_3$	172.27	....	-78	208	0.8652^{20}	1.4160^{15}	i	s				oo s	B2, 272
Ω b2672	—,isobutyl ester*	$CH_3CH_2CH_2CO_2CH_2CH(CH_3)_2$	144.22	....	....	157^{760}	0.8364^{18}_4	1.4032^{20}	δ	∞	∞				B2[2], 247
Ω b2673	—,isopropyl ester*	$CH_3CH_2CH_2CO_2CH(CH_3)_2$	130.19	....	....	$130-1^{760}$	0.8588^{20}	1.3936^{20}	i	v	v				B2, 271
Ω b2674	—,methyl ester*	$CH_3CH_2CH_2CO_2CH_3$	102.13	....	-84.8	102.3^{760}	0.8984^{20}	1.3878^{20}	δ	∞	∞				B2[2], 243
b2675	—,2-methylbutyl ester (d)*	$CH_3CH_2CH_2CO_2CH_2CH(CH_3)CH_2CH_3$	158.24	$[\alpha]^{20}_D +3.5$	....	179^{765}	0.8620^{20}	1.4135^{20}							B2[2], 247
b2676	—,—(dl)	$CH_3CH_2CH_2CO_2CH_2CH(CH_3)CH_2CH_3$	158.24	....	....	$166-6.7^{760}$	0.862^{20}_4	1.4100^{25}							C39, 4083
b2677	—,2-methyl-2-butyl ester	tert-Amyl butyrate. $CH_3CH_2CH_2CO_2C(CH_3)_2CH_2CH_3$	158.24	....	....	164	0.8646^{15}_0								B2, 271
Ω b2678	—,3-methylbutyl ester*	Isoamyl butyrate $CH_3CH_2CH_2CO_2CH_2CH_2CH(CH_3)_2$	158.24	....	....	178.5^{760} $65-8^{12}$	0.8651^{20}_4	1.4110^{20}	i	v	v				B2[2], 247
b2679	—,1-methylpentyl ester (d)	sec-Hexyl butyrate $CH_3(CH_2)_3CQCH(CH_3)CH_2$	172.27	$[\alpha]_D +10.16$	....	85^{20}	0.8744^{21}_4		i	s	s				B2[1], 120
Ω b2680	—,nitrile	Butyronitrile. Propyl cyanide. $CH_3CH_2CH_2CN$	69.11	....	-112	118^{760}	0.7936^{20}	1.3842^{20}	δ	∞	∞		s		B2[2], 252
b2681	—,octyl ester*	$CH_3CH_2CH_2CO_2(CH_2)_7CH_3$	200.33	....	-55.6	244.1^{760}	0.8629^{20}	1.4267^{15}_{He}	i	s				oo s	B2[2], 248
Ω b2682	—,pentyl ester*	Amyl butyrate. $CH_3CH_2CH_2CO_2(CH_2)_4CH_3$	158.24	....	-73.2	186.4 $78-80^{18}$	0.8713^{15}_4	1.4123^{20}	i	v	v				B2[2], 247
b2683	—,phenyl ester*	$CH_3CH_2CH_2CO_2C_6H_5$	164.21	$\lambda^{al} 259 (2.3), 266 (2.3)$	....	$227-8^{760}$ $(220-2)$ 85^8	1.0382^{15}_4	1.0267^{15}_{15}	i	s	s				B6[2], 155
Ω b2684	—,4-phenyl-phenacyl ester	....	282.34	cr (al)	97	....	....	....	i						Am 73, 5301
b2685	—,piperazinium salt	$2(CH_3CH_2CH_2CO_2H).C_4H_{10}N_2$	262.35	....	$121-2$	....	....	....	s	s	i				Am 56, 1759
Ω b2686	—,propyl ester*	$CH_3CH_2CH_2CO_2CH_2CH_2CH_3$	130.19	....	-97.2	143^{760} 39.2^{14}	0.8730^{20}	1.4001^{20}	δ	∞	∞				B2[2], 246
b2687	—,4(5-ace-naphthyl)-4-oxo-	....	254.29	nd (al or aa)	208d	....	....	....		s^h			s^h	xyl s^h	B10[2], 532
b2688	—,2-acetyl-3-oxo-, ethyl ester	Ethyl diacetoacetate. Ethyl α-acetylacetoacetate. $(CH_3CO)_2CHCO_2C_2H_5$	172.19	....	....	$209-11$ 104^{16}	1.1045^{20}_4	1.4690^{20}	δ	v	v		v		B3[2], 467
b2689	—,2-amino-(d)*	$CH_3CH_2CHNH_2CO_2H$	103.12	lf (dil al) $[\alpha]^{16}_D +8.4$ (w, c = 4)	292d (303 sealed tube)	....	....	....	v	δ	i		i		B4[2], 831
Ω b2690	—,—(dl)*	$CH_3CH_2CHNH_2CO_2H$	103.12	lf (w)	304d (307d sealed tube)	sub	....	....	v	δ	i		i		B4[2], 831
Ω b2691	—,—(l)*	$CH_3CH_2CHNH_2CO_2H$	103.12	lf (w-al), cr (al) $[\alpha]^{20}_D -14.9$ (w, c = 5) $[\alpha]^{20}_D +20.6$ (5N HCl)	292d (>300)	....	....	....	s	δ	δ		i	MeOH s	B4[2], 831
b2692	—,3-amino-(d)*	$CH_3CHNH_2CH_2CO_2H$	103.12	pr (MeOH) $[\alpha]^{20}_D +35.3$ w, p = 9.6)	d at 220	....	....	....	v	i	i		i		B4[1], 504
Ω b2693	—,—(dl)*	$CH_3CHNH_2CH_2CO_2H$	103.12	nd (al)	193-4	....	....	....	v	i	i		i		B4[2], 833
b2694	—,—(l)*	$CH_3CHNH_2CH_2CO_2H$	103.12	pr (MeOH) $[\alpha]^{20}_D -35.2$ (w, p = 10)	d at 220	....	....	....	v	i	i		i		B4[1], 504
Ω b2695	—,4-amino-*	Piperidinic acid. $H_2NCH_2CH_2CH_2CO_2H$	103.12	pr or nd (dil al), lf (MeOH-eth)	203d	....	....	....	v	δ	i	δ	i	MeOH δ^h	B4[2], 837
—	—,2-amino-3-hydroxy-*	see **Threonine**													
b2696	—,3-amino-2-hydroxy-*	3-Methylisoserine. $CH_3CHNH_2CH(OH)CO_2H$	119.12	pr (dil al)	200d	....	....	....	s	δ	i			MeOH δ	B4, 313
b2697	—,4-amino-2-hydroxy-*	$H_2NCH_2CH_2CH(OH)CO_2H$	119.12	pr (w or dil al)	214	....	....	....	v	δ^h	i				B4[1], 548
b2698	—,4-amino-3-hydroxy-(dl)*	$H_2NCH_2CH(OH)CH_2CO_2H$	119.12	pr (w), cr (dil al)	218	....	....	....	δ v^h	δ	δ	δ	δ	MeOH δ oos δ	B4[2], 937
—	—,2-amino-2-methyl-*	see **Isovaline**													
—	—,2-amino-3-methyl-*	see **Valine**													
b2699	—,3-amino-3-methyl-*	$(CH_3)_2CNH_2CH_2CO_2H$	117.15	pr (w + 1), cr (dil al), nd (eth-al)	217	....	....	....	v	δ	i				B4[3], 1364
—	—,2-amino-4(methylthio)-*	see **Methionine**													

For explanations, symbols and abbreviations see beginning of table. For structural formulas see end of table.

No.	Name	Synonyms and Formula	Mol. wt.	Color, crystalline form, specific rotation and λ_{max} (log ε)	m.p. °C	b.p. °C	Density	n_D	w	al	eth	ace	bz	other solvents	Ref.
	Butanoic acid														
b2700	—,2-benzoyl-, ethyl ester	Ethyl benzoyl ethyl acetate. $CH_3CH_2CH(COC_6H_5)CO_2C_2H_5$	220.27	. . . .	. . . . . .	152^7 $122^{1.5}$	1.0706_4^{15}	1.509^{15}	i	. . .	s				$B10^2$, 488
—	—,2-benzylidene-	see Cinnamic acid, α-ethyl-													
b2701	—,2-benzylidene-3-oxo-, ethyl ester	Ethyl α-acetylcinnamate. Ethyl α-benzalacetoacetate. $C_6H_5CH{:}C(COCH_3)CO_2C_2H_5$	218.26	rh pl or pyr (dil al)	60–1	$295-7^{760}$	. . . .		i	δ	δ	. . .	δ	chl v CS_2 δ	$B10^2$, 503
b2702	—,2-bromo-(d)*	$CH_3CH_2CHBrCO_2H$	167.01	$[α]_D^{20} +35.2$ (eth, c = 20), $+12.9$ (w, c = 4)	. . . .	$105-7^{15}$ $66-9^{0.04}$	1.568_4^{20}	1.4483^{15}	. . .	s					$B2^2$, 255
Ω b2703	—,—(dl)*	$CH_3CH_2CHBrCO_2H$	167.01		−4	217d 108^{13}	1.5669_{20}^{20}		s	s	s				$B2^2$, 255
b2704	—,—,amide	$CH_3CH_2CHBrCONH_2$. . .	166.03	lf (bz), nd (ace)	112–3				v	v	v	v^h	v^h		$B2^1$, 125
b2705	—,—,bromide	$CH_3CH_2CHBrCOBr$. . . .	229.91			$172-4$ $57-60^{10}$			d	d	s				$B2^2$, 255
Ω b2706	—,—,chloride	$CH_3CH_2CHBrCOCl$.	185.45			$150-2$ 43^{12}	1.5320^{20}		d^h	d^h	s				$B2^1$, 125
Ω b2707	—,—,ethyl ester*	$CH_3CH_2CHBrCO_2C_2H_5$	195.06			177.5^{765} $43-4^{5.5}$	1.3297_{20}^{20}	1.4475^{20}	i	∞	∞				$B2^2$, 255
b2708	—,—,methyl ester*	$CH_3CH_2CHBrCO_2CH_3$	181.04			$170-2$ $75-8^{18}$	1.4528^{20}	1.4029^{25}		s					$B2^1$, 125
b2708¹	—,4-bromo-*	$BrCH_2CH_2CH_2CO_2H$. . .	167.01		33	$124-7^7$									$B2^2$, 256
b2709	—,—,methyl ester*	$BrCH_2CH_2CH_2CO_2CH_3$	181.04			$186-7$ 86^{15}	1.371^{25}	1.4567^{25}	. . .	s					$B2^2$, 283
Ω b2710	—,—,nitrile	$BrCH_2CH_2CH_2CN$. . . .	148.01			$205-7^{760}$ 91^{12}	1.4967_4^{20}	1.4818^{20}	. . .	s	s				$B2^2$, 256
Ω b2711	—,2-bromo-2-ethyl-, amide	Neuronal. $(C_2H_5)_2CBrCONH_2$	194.08		67	. . . .			δ v^h	v	v		v	peth δ	$B2^2$, 293
b2712	—,2-bromo-2-ethyl-3-methyl-, amide	2-Bromo-2-isopropylbutyramide. Neodorme. $(CH_3)_2CHCBr(C_2H_5)CONH_2$	208.11	nd (sub)	50–1	sub			δ d^h	v	v	s	v	peth s os s	$B2^2$, 299
b2713	—,2-bromo-3-methyl-(d)*	$(CH_3)_2CHCHBrCO_2H$	181.04	pr (peth) $[α]_D^{20} +22.8$ (bz, p = 4), $+4.5$ (w, c = 1.6), $+7.5$ (eth, c = 7)	43.5–5.5	230^{760} $95-100^2$			δ	v	s	s	s	peth v^h	$B2^2$, 279
Ω b2714	—,—(dl)*	$(CH_3)_2CHCHBrCO_2H$	181.04	pr (eth or chl)	44	230^{760}δd $136-40^{25}$	1.459^{20}	. . . .	δ	v	s	s	s		$B2^2$, 279
b2715	—,—(l)*	$(CH_3)_2CHCHBrCO_2H$	181.04	cr (peth) $[α]_D^{20} -21.6$ (bz, p = 4)	43.5–5.5	150^{40} $119-20^{14}$			δ	v	s	s	s		$B2^2$, 279
b2716	—,—,amide (dl)	$(CH_3)_2CHCHBrCONH_2$	180.05	lf (bz)	133	. . . .			s^h					lig s^h	B2, 318
Ω b2717	—,—,ethyl ester (dl)*	$(CH_3)_2CHCHBrCO_2CO_2H_5$	209.09			186 $73-4^{12}$	1.2760_4^{20}	1.4496^{20}	. . .	v	v				$B2^2$, 279
b2718	—,—,methyl ester (dl)*	$(CH_3)_2CHCHBrCO_2CH_3$	195.06			$176.4-7.8^{760}$ $64-5^{11}$	1.353_{13}^{13}	1.4530^{20}	. . .	s	s				B2, 317
b2719	—,3-bromo-3-methyl-*	$(CH_3)_2CBrCH_2CO_2H$	181.04	nd (lig)	73.5	. . . .			δ	v	v		v	lig i	$B2^2$, 278
b2720	—,2-bromo-3-oxo-, amide, N-phenyl-	α-Bromoacetoacetanilide. $CH_3COCHBrCONHC_6H_5$	256.11	lf (al)	138d	. . . .			δ	s^h	δ	. . .	. . .	chl δ	$B12^1$, 276
b2721	—,—,ethyl ester*	Ethyl α-bromoacetoacetate. $CH_3COCHBrCO_2C_2H_5$	209.05			$210-5d$ $104-10^{15}$	1.4294_4^{14}	1.463^{14}	. . .	s	s				$B3^2$, 427
b2722	—,4-bromo-3-oxo, ethyl ester*	Ethyl γ-bromoacetoacetate. $BrCH_2COCH_2CO_2C_2H_5$	209.05			$114-7^{14}$ $56^{0.005}$	1.4840_4^{20}	1.5281^{20}	δ	v	v				$B3^2$, 427
Ω b2723	—,2-chloro-*	$CH_3CH_2CHClCO_2H$	122.55			189^{627} 101^{15}	1.1796_4^{20}	1.4411^{20}	δ v^h	v	v				$B2^2$, 253
b2724	—,—,chloride	$CH_3CH_2CHClCOCl$.	141.00			$130-1^{760}$ $51-2^{41}$	1.2360^{17}	1.4475^{20}	d	d	s				$B2^1$, 123
b2725	—,—,ethyl ester*	$CH_3CH_2CHClCO_2C_2H_5$	150.61			$163-4^{760}$ 63^{70}	1.0560^{20}	1.4248^{20}	. . .	s	s				B2, 277
b2726	—,—,methyl ester*	$CH_3CH_2CHClCO_2CH_3$	136.58			$145-6^{756}$	1.0979^{14}	1.4247^{20}	. . .	s	s			MeOH s	B2, 277
Ω b2727	—,3-chloro-(dl)*	$CH_3CHClCH_2CO_2H$ . . .	122.55	cr (eth)	16	116^{22}	1.1898_4^{20}	1.4421^{20}	. . .	s	v^h	. . .	. . .		$B2^2$, 253
b2728	—,—,chloride	$CH_3CHClCH_2COCl$	141.00			$40-1^{12}$	1.2163_4^{20}	1.4509^{20}	d	d		. . .	. . .	CS_2 s	$B2^2$, 253
b2729	—,—,ethyl ester*	$CH_3CHClCH_2CO_2C_2H_5$	150.61			109 65^{15}	1.0517_4^{20}	1.4246^{20}	i	s		. . .	. . .	CCl_4 s	$B2^2$, 253
b2730	—,—,methyl ester*	$CH_3CHClCH_2COCH_3$	136.58			$155-6^{760}$	1.0996_4^{20}	1.4258^{20}	i	. . .	v	. . .			B2, 277
b2731	—,4-chloro-*	$ClCH_2CH_2CH_2CO_2H$ . . .	122.55		16	196^{22} $68^{0.2}$	1.2236_4^{20}	1.4642^{20}	δ	. . .	v				$B2^2$, 253
Ω b2732	—,—,chloride	$ClCH_2CH_2CH_2COCl$	141.00			$173-4^{760}$ $60-1^{12}$	1.2581_4^{20}	1.4616^{20}	d	d	s				$B2^2$, 254
b2733	—,—,ethyl ester*	$ClCH_2CH_2CH_2CO_2C_2H_5$. .	150.61			186^{760} 77^{10}	1.0756_4^{20}	1.4311^{20}	. . .	s	s	s			$B2^2$, 254
Ω b2734	—,—,methyl ester*	$ClCH_2CH_2CH_2CO_2CH_3$	136.58			$175-6^{764}$ 55^4	1.1201_4^{20}	1.4321^{20}	i	v^h	v	s			B2, 278
Ω b2735	—,—,nitrile	$ClCH_2CH_2CH_2CN$	103.55			$189-91^{760}$ $(196-7)$ 75^{11}	1.0934^{15}	1.4413^{20}	i	s	s	. . .	. . .		$B2^2$, 254

For explanations, symbols and abbreviations see beginning of table. For structural formulas see end of table.

No.	Name	Synonyms and Formula	Mol. wt.	Color, crystalline form, specific rotation and λ_{max} (log ε)	m.p. °C	b.p. °C	Density	n_D	w	al	eth	ace	bz	other solvents	Ref.
	Butanoic acid														
b2736	—,2-chloro-2-methyl-*	$CH_3CH_2CCl(CH_3)CO_2H$	136.58			200^{5754} δd	1.1204_4^{20}	1.4445^{20}	i	s	s				B2, 306
b2737	—,—,chloride	$CH_3CH_2CCl(CH_3)COCl$	155.04			144^{750}	1.187^{14}		d		s				B2, 307
b2738	—,—,ethyl ester*	$CH_3CH_2CCl(CH_3)CO_2C_2H_5$	164.63			175^{747}	1.069^{14}	1.4368^{11}	i	s	s				B2, 306
b2739	—,2-chloro-3-methyl-*	2-Chloroisovaleric acid. $(CH_3)_2CHCHClCO_2H$	136.58		20–2	$210–2^{756}$ 126^{32}	1.135^{13}	1.4450^{11}	i	s	s				B2, 316
b2740	—,—,chloride	$(CH_3)_2CHCHClCOCl$	155.04			$148–9^{760}$	1.135^{13}		d	d	s				B2, 316
b2741	—,—,ethyl ester*	$(CH_3)_2CHCHClCO_2C_2H_5$	164.63			$178–9^{756}$	1.021^{13}		i	s	s				B2, 316
b2742	—,2-chloro-2-methyl-3-oxo-, ethyl ester*	Ethyl α-chloro-α-aceto-propionate. $CH_3COCCl(CH_3)CO_2C_2H_5$	178.62			$116–7^{75}$	1.157_4^{18}	1.4382^{18}		s					B3[1], 237
b2743	—,2-chloro-3-oxo-, amide, N-phenyl-	α-Chloroacetoacetanilide. $CH_3COCHClCONHC_6H_5$	211.65	nd (al)	137.5				i	v	v			chl v MeOH v	B12[2], 267
b2744	—,—,ethyl ester*	Ethyl α-chloroacetoacetate. $CH_3COCHClCO_2C_2H_5$	164.59			197^{748} δd $86–9^{12}$	1.19_{17}^{14}	1.4414^{20}	δ	v	v				B3[2], 426
b2745	—,4-chloro-3-oxo-, chloride	$ClCH_2COCH_2COCl$	154.99			$117–9^{17}$	1.4397_4^{20}	1.4860^{20}	d	d			s	CCl_4 s	Am 62, 1147
b2746	—,—,ethyl ester*	Ethyl γ-chloroacetoacetate. $ClCH_2COCH_2CO_2C_2H_5$	164.59		–8	220d 115^{14}	1.2157_4^{20}	1.4546^{17}	δ	s	s	s	s	chl s oos s	B3[2], 426
b2747	—,4(4-chlorophenyl)-3-hydroxy-3-oxo-2-phenyl-*		304.73	nd (eth-peth)	139–40				i	s^h	s	s	s	peth δ	B10[2], 710
b2748	—,2,3-dibromo-(high m.p.)*	Dibromocrotonic acid. $CH_3CHBrCHBrCO_2H$	245.91	nd (eth), mcl (CS_2)	87	$100–10^{20}$			δ d^h	v	v		v		B2[3], 634
b2749	—,— (low m.p.)*	Dibromoisocrotonic acid. $CH_3CHBrCHBrCO_2H$	245.91	nd (lig)	59–60				δ	s	s				B2[1], 125
Ω b2750	—,—,ethyl ester*	$CH_3CHBrCHBrCO_2C_2H_5$	273.96	nd	58–9	113^{30} $103–4^{17}$			δ	s	s				B2, 285
Ω b2751	—,2,4-dibromo-, ethyl ester*	$BrCH_2CH_2CHBrCO_2C_2H_5$	273.96			$149–50^{52}$	1.6990_0^{20}	1.4960^{20}	i	s	s				B2, 285
b2752	—,2,2-dibromo-3-oxo-, ethyl ester*	Ethyl α,α-dibromoaceto-acetate. $CH_3COCBr_2CO_2C_2H_5$	287.96			$120–4^{13}$			δ	s	s				B3[2], 427
b2753	—,2,3-dichloro-(high m.p.)*	Dichloroisocrotonic acid. $CH_3CHClCHClCO_2H$	157.00	pr (dil al)	78	131.5^{20}			δ	s	s			peth δ	B2, 279
b2754	—,— (low m.p.)*	Dichlorocrotonic acid. $CH_3CHClCHClCO_2H$	157.00	pr (dil al)	63	$124–5^{20}$			δ	s	s		s	CS_2 v lig δ chl s	B2, 279
b2755	—,2,2-dichloro-3-oxo-, ethyl ester	Ethyl α,α-dichloroacetoacetate. $CH_3COCCl_2CO_2C_2H_5$	199.04			$205–7^{756}$ 91^{11}	1.293_{17}^{16}	1.4492^{17}		s					B3[2], 427
b2756	—,2,2-diethyl-3-oxo-, ethyl ester*	$CH_3COC(C_2H_5)_2CO_2C_2H_5$	186.25			$215–6^{744}$ 64^3	0.9717_4^{18}	1.4326^{17}	i	∞	∞				B3[3], 1958
Ω b2757	—,2,4-dihydroxy-3,3-dimethyl-, amide, N-(3-hydroxypropyl)-	Panthothenyl alcohol. $HOCH_2C(CH_3)_2CHOHCONH(CH_2)_2CH_2OH$	205.26	$[\alpha]_D^{20}$ +29.7 (w, 3 %)		$118–20^{0.2}$		1.4935^{20}	v	v	δ				C41, 6199
Ω b2758	—,2,2-dimethyl-*	$CH_3CH_2C(CH_3)_2CO_2H$	116.16		–14	186^{760} 80^{11}	0.9276_4^{20}	1.4145^{20}	δ	s	s				B2[2], 293
b2759	—,—,chloride	$CH_3CH_2C(CH_3)_2COCl$	134.61			132^{760} 27^{11}	0.9801_4^{20}	1.4245^{20}	d	d	s				B2, 336
b2760	—,2,3-dimethyl-*	$(CH_3)_2CHCH(CH_3)CO_2H$	116.16		–1.5	191.7^{760} 90^{16}	0.9275_4^{20}	1.4146^{20}	s	s	s				B2[2], 294
b2761	—,—,amide	$(CH_3)_2CHCH(CH_3)CONH_2$	115.18	pl (ace-peth)	130.9				δ	s	s				B2, 338
b2762	—,—,chloride	$(CH_3)_2CHCH(CH_3)COCl$	134.61			$135–6^{751}$ $38–9^{18}$	0.9795_4^{20}		d^h	d^h	s				B2[3], 761
Ω b2763	—,3,3-dimethyl-*	tert-Butylacetic acid. $(CH_3)_3CCH_2CO_2H$	116.16		6–7	190^{760} 96^{26}	0.9124^{20}	1.4096^{20}	δ	s	s				B2, 337
Ω b2764	—,—,amide	$(CH_3)_3CCH_2CONH_2$	115.18	lf (w or ace-peth)	134						s				B2[3], 759
b2765	—,—,chloride	$(CH_3)_3CCH_2COCl$	134.61			$128–30^{745}$ 68^{100}	0.9696_4^{20}	1.4210^{20}	d	d	s				B2[3], 759
b2766	—,2,2-dimethyl-3-oxo-, ethyl ester	$CH_3COC(CH_3)_2CO_2C_2H_5$	158.20			184^{760} $40–1^3$	0.9773_{20}^{20}	1.4180^{20}	δ	s	s				B3[2], 439
b2767	—,3,3-dioxo-,2-phenylhydrazone	$CH_3COC·NNH(C_6H_5)CO_2H$	206.20	ye nd or lf (al-eth)	161				i	s^h	s^h				B15[2], 133
b2768	—,2,4-diphenyl-3-oxo-, nitrile	Benzyl α-cyanobenzyl ketone. $C_6H_5CH_2COCH(C_6H_5)CN$	235.29	nd (bz-peth)	86				i				s	aa s	B10, 762
b2769	—,2,4-diphenyl-4-oxo-, nitrile	$C_6H_5COCH_2CH(C_6H_5)CN$	235.29	pl (al) λ^{al} 244 (4.16), 268 sh (3.11), 281 (3.04)	127.5					v	v			chl v	B10[2], 528
b2770	—,3,4-epoxy-, nitrile	Epicyanohydrin.	83.09	pr	162				δ s^h	s					B18, 261
b2771	—,2,3-epoxy-3-phenyl-, ethyl ester*		206.24			$272–5$ $147–9^{12}$	1.0442^{20}	1.5182^{20}			s				B18[1], 442
Ω b2772	—,2-ethyl-*	Diethylacetic acid. $(C_2H_5)_2CHCO_2H$	116.16		–31.8	194^{760} 90^{13}	0.9239_4^{20}	1.4132^{20}	δ	∞	∞				B2[2], 291

For explanations, symbols and abbreviations see beginning of table. For structural formulas see end of table.

No.	Name	Synonyms and Formula	Mol. wt.	Color, crystalline form, specific rotation and λ_{max} (log ε)	m.p. °C	b.p. °C	Density	n_D	w	al	eth	ace	bz	other solvents	Ref.
	Butanoic acid														
b2773	—,—,amide,N,N-diethyl-	$(C_2H_5)_2CHCON(C_2H_5)_2$....	171.29	....		220–1 108[12]			δ	s	v	...	v	....	B4, 111
b2774	—,—,chloride....	$(C_2H_5)_2CHCOCl$........	134.61	....		140[760] 40[20]	0.9825_4^{20}	1.4234^{20}	d	d^h	v				B2[2], 292
b2775	—,—,nitrile.......	3-Cyanopentane. $(C_2H_5)_2CHCN$	97.16	....		145.1– 5.6[760] 37[11]		1.3891^{24}	...	∞	∞				B2[2], 292
b2776	—,2-ethyl-2-methyl-*	$(C_2H_5)_2C(CH_3)CO_2H$......	130.19	....	< −20	208.4– 8.6[760] 104[13]		1.4250^{20}	i	s					B2[2], 299
Ω b2777	—,2-ethyl-3-oxo-, ethyl ester*	Ethyl ethylacetoacetate. $CH_3COCH(C_2H_5)CO_2C_2H_5$	158.20	....		190[760] (195[743]) 58[3]	0.9847_4^{16}	1.4214^{25}		v	s				B3[2], 438
b2778	—,—,methyl ester*	$CH_3COCH(C_2H_5)CO_2CH_3$.	144.17	....		182[760] 79–80[14]	0.995^{14}			s	s	s			B3[2], 437
b2779	—,4-fluoro-*	$FCH_2CH_2CH_2CO_2H$	106.10	....		76–8[5]		1.3993^{25}	s	v	v				B2[3], 621
Ω b2780	—,2-hydroxy-(dl)* .	$CH_3CH_2CHOHCO_2H$	104.12	nd (CCl₄)	44–4.5	260d 140[14]	1.125^{20}		s	s	s				B3[2], 216
b2781	—,—,ethyl ester (d)*	$CH_3CH_2CHOHCO_2C_2H_5$ ..	132.16	$[\alpha]_D^{22} + 8.4$		165–70	0.978^{15}	1.4101		s					B3[2], 215
b2782	—,—,—(dl)*	$CH_3CH_2CHOHCO_2C_2H_5$ ..	132.16	....		167[760] 74.5[25]	1.0069_4^{20}	1.4179^{20}		s					B3[2], 217
Ω b2783	—,3-hydroxy-(dl)* .	$CH_3CHOHCH_2CO_2H$	104.12	....	48–50	130[12 − 14] 94–6[0.1]		1.4424^{20}	v	v	v		i		B3[2], 220
b2784	—,—(l)*	$CH_3CHOHCH_2CO_2H$	104.12	$[\alpha]_D^{25} - 24.5$ (w, c = 5)	49–50				v	v	v		i		B3[2], 219
Ω b2785	—,—,ethyl ester (dl)*	$CH_3CHOHCH_2CO_2C_2H_5$ ..	132.16	....		184–5[755] 76–7[15]	1.0172_4^{20}	1.4182^{20}	s	s					B3[2], 221
b2786	—,—,methyl ester (l)*	$CH_3CHOHCH_2CO_2CH_3$ ..	118.13	$[\alpha]_D^{20} - 21.09$		76–7[20]	1.0582_{20}^{20}		v	v	v		v	peth δ	B3[2], 219
b2787	—,4-hydroxy-*	$HOCH_2CH_2CH_2CO_2H$	104.12	....	< −17	d at 178–80									B3[2], 222
Ω b2788	—,—,lactone*	γ-Butyrolactone	86.09	λ^{MeOH} 209 (1.63)	−42	206[760] 89[12]	1.1286_0^{16}	1.4341^{20}	∞	v	v	v	v		B17[2], 286
b2789	—,2-hydroxy-2-isopropyl-3-methyl-, nitrile	Diisopropylketone cyanohydrin. $[(CH_3)_2CH]_2C(OH)CN$	141.22	rh (eth or peth)	59	111[18]			i	s	s	s	s	os s	B3[2], 239
b2790	—,2-hydroxy-3-methyl-(d)*	$(CH_3)_2CHCHOHCO_2H$	118.13	cr (eth-peth) $[\alpha]_D^{20} - 1.81$ (w, c = 12)	69.5	124–5[13]			s	s	s				B3, 328
Ω b2791	—,—(dl)*	$(CH_3)_2CHCHOHCO_2H$	118.13	rh bipyr	86				s	s	s				B3, 328
b2792	—,3-hydroxy-3-methyl-*	$(CH_3)_2COHCH_2CO_2H$	118.13	....	< −32	162[12]	0.9384_4^{20}	1.5081^{20}	s	s	s				B3, 327
b2793	—,4-hydroxy-2-methylene-, lactone*	....	98.10	$\lambda^{al} < 220$		85–6[10] 37[0.35]	1.1206^{20}	1.4650^{20}	s	v	s	s	s	os s	Am 68, 2332
—	—,4-hydroxy-3-oxo-, lactone*	see **Furan, 2,4-dioxo-, (tetrahydro)-**													
Ω b2794	—,4(3-indolyl)-	....	203.24	pl (bz-peth)	124								v^h	peth i	B22[2], 54
b2795	—,2-isopropyl-3-oxo-, ethyl ester*	$CH_3COCH(C_3H_7)CO_2C_2H_5$	172.23	....		201[758] 97–8[20]	0.9648_4^{18}	$1.4256_4^{18.5}$	i	∞	∞				B3[2], 441
b2795[1]	—,4-oxo-4-(4-methoxyphenyl)-	....	208.22	nd	150–1				s^h	s			s	chl s	B10[2], 681
b2796	—,2-methyl-(d)* ...	$CH_3CH_2CH(CH_3)CO_2H$ ..	102.13	$[\alpha]_D^{15} + 19.2$ (w)		176[760] 77[12]	0.9419_4^{20}	1.4058^{20}	δ	∞	∞				B2[2], 270
Ω b2797	—,—(dl)*	$CH_3CH_2CH(CH_3)CO_2H$ ..	102.13	λ 205 (4.1), 255 (2.2)	< −80	177 71.5[10.5]	0.9410_4^{20}	1.4051^{20}	δ	∞	∞				B2[2], 270
b2798	—,—(l)*	$CH_3CH_2CH(CH_3)CO_2H$ ..	102.13	$[\alpha]_D^{14} - 10.1$ (al) $[\alpha]_D^{20} - 24$ (w, c = 0.9)		176–7 71–2[12]	0.9340_4^{20}	1.4042^{25}	δ	∞	∞				B2[3], 685
b2799	—,—,chloride (dl) .	$CH_3CH_2CH(CH_3)COCl$..	120.58	....		116[760]	0.9917_4^{20}	1.4170^{20}	d^h	d^h	v				B2, 315
b2800	—,—,ethyl ester (d)*	$CH_3CH_2CH(CH_3)CO_2C_2H_5$	130.19	$[\alpha]_{5892}^{26} + 5.16$		131–3[730] 35[16]	0.8689_4^{25}	1.3964^{20}	i	s			s		B2, 306
b2801	—,—,nitrile (dl)	$CH_3CH_2CH(CH_3)CN$....	83.13	....		125[760]	0.7913_4^{15}	1.3933^{20}	s	s	s				B2, 306
Ω b2802	—,3-methyl-*	Isovaleric acid. $(CH_3)_2CHCH_2CO_2H$	102.13	....	−29.3 (−37)	176.7[760]	0.9286_4^{20}	14033^{20}	s	∞	∞			chl ∞	B2[2], 271
b2803	—,—,amide	$(CH_3)_2CHCH_2CONH_2$	101.15	mcl lf (al)	137	224–8[760]			s	s	s			peth v	B2[2], 277
b2804	—,—,anhydride*	$[(CH_3)_2CHCH_2CO]_2O$	186.25	....		215[762] 102–3[15]	0.9327_4^{20}	1.4043^{20}	d^h	d^h	s				B2[2], 277
b2805	—,—,bromide	Isovaleryl bromide. $(CH_3)_2CHCH_2COBr$	165.03	mcl pl (al)		143[760]			d	d^h	s				B2[2], 277
Ω b2806	—,—,chloride....	Isovaleryl chloride. $(CH_3)_2CHCH_2COCl$	120.58	....		114.5– 5.5[771]	0.9844_4^{20}	1.4149^{20}	d	d	s				B2[2], 277
Ωb2806[1]	—,—,ethyl ester	$(CH_3)_2CHCH_2CO_2C_2H_5$ ..	130.19	....	−99.3	134.7[760]	0.8656_4^{20}	1.3962^{20}	i	v	v				B2[2], 275
Ω b2807	—,—,isobutyl ester	$(CH_3)_2CHCH_2CO_2C_4H_9$ ..	158.24	....		171.4[760] 60–2[12]	0.8736_4^{20}	1.4057^{20}	i	∞	∞	v			B2[2], 276
b2808	—,—,isopropyl ester*	$(CH_3)_2CHCH_2CO_2C_3H_7$ ..	144.22	....		142[756] 68.5– 70[55]	0.8538^{17}	$1.3960^{20.5}$	i	s	s	v			B2[2], 275
Ω b2809	—,—,methyl ester*	$(CH_3)_2CHCH_2CO_2CH_3$	116.16	....		116.7[760]	0.8808_4^{20}	1.3927^{20}	i	v	v	v			B2[2], 274

For explanations, symbols and abbreviations see beginning of table. For structural formulas see end of table.

No.	Name	Synonyms and Formula	Mol. wt.	Color. crystalline form. specific rotation and λ_{max} (log ε)	m.p. °C	b.p. °C	Density	n_D	Solubility						Ref.
									w	al	eth	ace	bz	other solvents	
	Butanoic acid														
Ω b2810	, ,nitrile......	Isobutyl cyanide. Isovaleronitrile. $(CH_3)_2CHCH_2CN$	83.13	....	fp → −100.85	130.5 53[50]	0.7914[20]₄	1.3927[20]	δ	∞	∞	v	...	......	**B2**[2], 278
b2811	—,—,propyl ester*.	$(CH_3)_2CHCH_2CO_2C_3H_7^n$ ...	144.22	....		155.7[760] 49.5[13]	0.8617[20]₄	1.4031[20]	i	∞	∞				**B2**[2], 275
Ω b2812	—,2-methyl-3-oxo-, ethyl ester*	Ethyl methylacetoacetate. $CH_3COCH(CH_3)CO_2C_2H_5$	144.17	....		187[760] 44[2]	0.9941[20]	1.4185[20]	δ	s	s	v	...	......	**B3**[2], 432
Ω b2813	—,—,methyl ester*	$CH_3COCH(CH_3)CO_2CH_3$ ..	130.15	....		177.4[760] 80[20]	1.0247[25]₂₅	1.416[24]	...	s	s				**B3**[3], 1225
b2814	—,3-methyl-2-phenyl-*	$(CH_3)_2CHCH(C_6H_5)CO_2H$.	178.23	pr (lig)	63	159–60[14]	....			s	v		lig δ		**B9**[2], 364
b2815	—,—,amide......	$(CH_3)_2CHCH(C_6H_5)CONH_2$	177.25	nd (dil al)	111–2	180–2[14]	....		i	s	s		lig δ		**B9**[2], 364
b2816	—,—,nitrile......	$(CH_3)_2CHCH(C_6H_5)CN$,	159.23	....		245–9[765] 123–4[15]	0.967[15.5]	1.5038[25]	i	s	s	s			**B9**[2], 364
Ω b2817	—,2-oxo-*........	α-Ketobutyric acid. $CH_3CH_2COCO_2H$	102.09	pl	31–2	80–2[16]	1.200[17]₇	1.3972[20]	v	v	δ				**B3**[2], 411
b2818	—,—,oxime	$CH_3CH_2C(:NOH)CO_2H$	117.11	nd (w or ba) tcl (diox)	164	....			δ	v	δ				**B3**[2], 412
b2819	—,3-oxo-*	Acetoacetic acid. $CH_3COCH_2CO_2H$	102.09	syr	....	<100d	....		∞	∞	δ				**B3**[2], 412
b2820	—,—,allyl ester....	Allyl acetoacetate. $CH_3COCH_2CO_2CH_2CH:CH_2$	142.16	....	−85	194–5[737] 66.5[14]	1.0385[20]₂₀	1.4398[20]	s	∞			∞	lig s	**B3**[3], 1203
Ω b2821	—,—,—,amide,N(2-chlorophenyl)-	....	211.65	nd	105	....			d[h]	s	i		...	lig i	**B12**[2], 319
Ω b2822	—,—,—,N-phenyl-	Acetoacetanilide. $CH_3COCH_2CONHC_6H_5$	177.21	pl or nd (bz or lig) λ^{al} 244 (4.12)	86	....			δ	s	s	s[h]	chl s lig, ac, alk s		**B12**[2], 266
Ω b2823	—,—,—,N(2-tolyl)-	....	191.23	pr (AcOEt) λ^{al} 236 (3.48)	107–8	....			δ	s		s	lig δ		**B12**[2], 450
b2824	—,—,—,N(3-tolyl)-	....	191.23	pl (bz-peth)	57–8	....			δ	s		s	lig δ		**B12**[1], 404
Ω b2825	—,—,—,N(4-tolyl)-	....	191.23	pr (AcOEt) λ^{al} 248 (4.16)	95	....			δ	s		s	lig δ		**B12**[2], 521
b2826	—,—,butyl ester*..	$CH_3COCH_2CO_2C_4H_9^n$......	158.20	....	−35.6	127[50] 85[8]	0.9671[25]	1.4137[20]	δ	s	s		∞	lig ∞	**B3**[3], 1201
b2827	—,—,chloride.....	Acetoacetyl chloride. CH_3COCH_2COCl	120.54	....	−50 (−20d)	....			d	d	v				**B3**[3], 1204
Ω b2828	—,—,ethyl ester* ..	Ethyl acetoacetate. $CH_3COCH_2CO_2C_2H_5$	130.15	λ^{al} 248 (3.2)	< −80	180.4[760] 74[14]	1.0282[20]₄	1.4194[20]	v	∞	∞	...	s	chl s	**B3**[2], 415
b2829	—,—,—,(enol form)	$CH_3C(OH):CHCO_2C_2H_5$...	130.15	λ^{vap} 238.5 (4.21)			1.0119[10]	1.4432[20]							**B3**[2], 415
b2830	—,—,—,(keto form)	$CH_3COCH_2CO_2C_2H_5$...	130.15	λ^{vap} 263 (2.47)	−39		1.0368[10]₄	1.4171[20]							**B3**[2], 415
b2831	—,—,isopropyl ester*	$CH_3COCH_2CO_2CH(CH_3)_2$.	144.17	λ^{al} 244 (2.96)	−27.3	185–7 75–6[15]	0.9835[25]₄	1.4173[20]	s	∞	∞		lig ∞		**B3**, 659
Ω b2832	—,—,methyl ester*	Methyl acetoacetate. $CH_3COCH_2CO_2CH_3$	116.12	λ^{al} 240 (3.18)	27–8	171.7[760] 60[8]	1.0762[20]₄	1.4184[20]	v	∞	∞				**B3**[2], 414
Ω b2833	—,—,nitrile......	Acetoacetonitrile. Cyano-acetone. CH_3COCH_2CN	83.09	....		120–5				v	v				**B3**[2], 424
b2834	—,3-oxo-2-phenyl-, ethyl ester*	$CH_3COCH(C_6H_5)CO_2C_2H_5$	206.24	....		156[22] 110[0.8]	1.0855[20]₄	1.5176[20]							**B10**[2], 485
b2835	—,—,nitrile......	$CH_3COCH(C_6H_5)CN$....	159.19	pr (bz), cr (dil al or ace-peth)	90–1	....			δ[h]	v	v		v	chl v peth δ	**B10**[2], 485
Ω b2836	—,4-oxo-4-phenyl-*	β-Benzoylpropionic acid. $C_6H_5COCH_2CH_2CO_2H$	178.19	lf (dil al)	116	....			s[h]	s		s	s	chl s CS₂ s	**B10**, 696
b2838	—,3-oxo-2-propyl-, ethyl ester*	Ethyl α-acetovalerate. $CH_3COCH(C_3H_7^n)CO_2C_2H_5$	172.23	....		224[760] 85[5], s	0.9661[20]₄	1.4255[20]							**B3**[2], 441
Ω b2839	—,2-phenoxy-*....	$CH_3CH_2CH(OC_6H_5)CO_2H$.	180.21	nd (w), pl (lig) λ^{cy} 270 (3.18)	99 (82–3)	258	....		δ s[h]	s	s	s	s	lig s[h]	**B6**, 163
b2840	—,—,amide......	$CH_3CH_2CH(OC_6H_5)CONH_2$	179.22	nd (w or al)	123	....			d[h]	s[h]	v	v	s[h]	chl v	**B6**, 164
b2841	—,—,ethyl ester* ..	$CH_3CH_2CH(OC_6H_5)CO_2C_2H_5$	208.24	....		250–1[748] 87–90[5]	1.0388[21]		i	∞	∞	s		chl s	**B6**, 164
b2842	—,—,nitrile......	$CH_3CH_2CH(OC_6H_5)CN$	161.21	....		228– 30[748]d					s	s			**B6**, 164
b2843	—,4-phenoxy-*....	$C_6H_5OCH_2CH_2CH_2CO_2H$.	180.21	pl (lig), cr (w)	64–5	192–7[15]	....		i	v	v	s	s	CS₂ chl s lig s[h]	**B6**[1], 150
b2844	—,—,amide	$C_6H_5OCH_2CH_2CH_2CONH_2$	179.22	lf (dil al), nd (bz)	80	....				v[h]	s				**B6**, 164
b2845	—,—,ethyl ester* ..	$C_6H_5OCH_2CH_2CH_2CO_2C_2H_5$	208.24	....		170–3[25]	1.045[35]₂₅	1.491[33]		s	s				**B6**[2], 159
b2846	—,—,nitrile......	$C_6H_5OCH_2CH_2CH_2CN$	161.21	nd	45–6	287–9[765] 170.5[22]			δ[h]		s				**B6**[2], 159
Ω b2847	—,2-phenyl-*	$CH_3CH_2CH(C_6H_5)CO_2H$.	164.21	pl (eth) λ^{hp} 252 (2.15), 258 (2.30), 264 (2.18)	47.5	270–2[760] 148–50[14]			δ[h]	s	s	s	s		**B9**[2], 356
Ω b2848	—,—,amide	$CH_3CH_2CH(C_6H_5)CONH_2$	163.22	cr	86	185[10]	....			s			δ	......	**B9**[2], 356
b2849	—,—,methyl ester*	$CH_3CH_2CH(C_6H_5)CO_2CH_3$	178.23	nd (dil al)	77–8	228[760]	....		i	s	s				**B9**[2], 356

For explanations, symbols and abbreviations see beginning of table. For structural formulas see end of table.

Butanoic acid

No.	Name	Synonyms and Formula	Mol. wt.	Color, crystalline form, specific rotation and λ_{max} (log ε)	m.p. °C	b.p. °C	Density	n_D	w	al	eth	ace	bz	other solvents	Ref.
b2850	—,—,nitrile	$CH_3CH_2CH(C_6H_5)CN$	145.21			238–40[765] 141–3[8]	0.977[14]		i	s	s	…	s		B9[2], 356
b2851	—,3-phenyl-, amide	$CH_3CH(C_6H_5)CH_2CONH_2$	163.22	nd (dil al)	106–7					s		…	δ		B9[1], 212
Ω b2852	—,4-phenyl-*	$C_6H_5CH_2CH_2CH_2CO_2H$	164.21	lf (w) λ 242 (1.79), 258 (2.62), 267 (2.12)	52	290[760] 171[15]			s[h]	s	s				B9[2], 354
b2853	—,—,amide	$C_6H_5CH_2CH_2CH_2CONH_2$	163.22	pl (w) λ[al] 260 (2.2)	84.5				s[h]	v	v				B9[1], 211
Ω b2854	—,—,nitrile	$C_6H_5CH_2CH_2CH_2CN$	145.21			142–5[16]				v	v				B9[2], 354
b2855	—,4(3-pyrenyl)-	3-Pyrenebutyric acid	288.35	pl (aa)	190								s	aa s[h]	E14, 392
b2856	—,2,2,3,3-tetramethyl-, amide	$(CH_3)_3CC(CH_3)_2CONH_2$	143.23	nd (peth-al), cr (dil NH_3)	201–2				δ	s[h]				lig i	B2[2], 305
b2857	—,3-thioxo-, ethyl ester	$CH_3CSCH_2CO_2C_2H_5$	146.21	dk red		75[15]	1.0554[21]_4	1.4712[26]	…	s	s				B3[2], 427
b2858	—,2,2,3-trichloro-*	$CH_3CHClCCl_2CO_2H$	191.44	lf or nd (peth)	60	236–8			v		v			peth v[h]	B2[2], 255
b2859	—,—,ethyl ester*	$CH_3CHClCCl_2CO_2C_2H_5$	219.50			212 101.5[17]	1.3138[20]_20			v	v				B2, 281
b2860	—,2,2,4-trichloro-*	$ClCH_2CH_2CCl_2CO_2H$	191.44	cr (peth)	73–5				s	v	v				B2, 281
b2861	—,2,3,3-trichloro-*	$CH_3CCl_2CHClCO_2H$	191.44	pl (lig)	52				δ	v	v	v	v	chl v CS_2 v	B2, 281
b2862	—,4,4,4-trichloro-*	$Cl_3CCH_2CH_2CO_2H$	191.44	nd (w)	55				s[h]	v	v			chl s	B2[3], 629
—	—,2,3,4-trihydroxy-	see Threonic acid													
b2863	—,2,2,3-trimethyl-, chloride	$(CH_3)_2CHC(CH_3)_2COCl$	148.63			148–50			d		s				B2[3], 300
Ω b2864	1-Butanol*	$CH_3CH_2CH_2CH_2OH$	74.12		−89.53	117.25[760]	0.8098[20]	1.39931[20]	s	∞	∞	v	s		B1[2], 387
b2865	2-Butanol (d)	sec-Butyl alcohol. $CH_3CH_2CHOHCH_3$	74.12	[α][20]_D +13.9 (undil)		99.5[760]	0.8080[20]	1.3954[20]	v	∞	∞	s	s		B1[2], 404
Ω b2866	—(dl)*	$CH_3CH_2CHOHCH_3$	74.12	λ[hp] 170–8 (2.5), 208–14 sh (1.5)	−114.7	99.5[760] 45.5[60]	0.8063[20]	1.3978[20]	v	∞	∞	v	s		B1[2], 400
b2867	—(l)*	$CH_3CH_2CHOHCH_3$	74.12	[α][20]_D −13.9		99.5[760]	0.8070[20]	1.3975[20]	v	∞	∞	v	s		B1[2], 405
—	tert-Butanol	see 2-Propanol, 2-methyl-*													
b2868	1-Butanol, 2-amino-(d)*	$CH_3CH_2CHNH_2CH_2OH$	89.14	[α][20]_D +9.8 (w)		80[11]	0.947[20]	1.4518[20]	∞						B4[3], 771
Ω b2869	—,—(dl)*	$CH_3CH_2CHNH_2CH_2OH$	89.14		−2	178 (174)	0.9162[20]	1.4489[25]	∞	∞	∞				B4[1], 438
b2870	—,3-amino-*	$CH_3CHNH_2CH_2CH_2OH$	89.14			82–5[19]		1.4534[25]	s	s					B4[1], 438
Ω b2871	—,4-amino-*	$H_2NCH_2CH_2CH_2CH_2OH$	89.14			206[776] 100[15]	0.967[12]	1.4625[20]	s	s	i				B4[1], 439
Ω b2872	2-Butanol, 3-amino-(dl)*	$CH_3CHNH_2CHOHCH_3$	89.14		18–20 (44)	159–60[745] 70[20]	0.9299[25]_4	1.4502[20]	s	s		s		lig i	B4[3], 778
b2873	1-Butanol, 2-amino-1-phenyl-*	$CH_3CH_2CHNH_2CH(C_6H_5)OH$	165.24	pl (bz-eth)	79–80					v			s	chl s peth δ	B13[2], 390
b2874	2-Butanol, 3-bromo-(dl)*	$CH_3CHBrCHOHCH_3$	153.03			154[760] 46–50[8]	1.4550[20]_4	1.4780[20]		s	s				B1[3], 1542
b2875	1-Butanol, 2-chloro-*	$CH_3CH_2CHClCH_2OH$	108.57			83[72] 74–6[25]	1.062[25]_4	1.4438[20]	v	v					B1[3], 1516
Ω b2876	—,4-chloro-*	Tetramethylene chlorohydrin. $ClCH_2CH_2CH_2CH_2OH$	108.57			84–5[16]	1.0883[20]	1.4518[20]	v	v	v				B1[2], 398
Ω b2877	2-Butanol, 1-chloro-*	$CH_3CH_2CHOHCH_2Cl$	108.57			141[760] 52[15]	1.068[25]_4	1.4400[20]		v	v				B1[2], 402
b2878	—,3-chloro-*	$CH_3CHClCHOHCH_3$	108.57			138–40 52–4[30]	1.0669[20]_4	1.4432[20]		v	v				B1[2], 403
b2879	—,—(erythro, dl)*	$CH_3CHClCHOHCH_3$	108.57			135.4[748] 56.1[30]	1.0610[25]_4	1.4397[25]		v	v			chl v	B1[3], 1538
b2880	—,4-chloro-*	$ClCH_2CH_2CHOHCH_3$	108.57			67[20]		1.4408[26]		v	v				B1[1], 188
b2881	—,1-chloro-2-methyl-*	$CH_3CH_2COH(CH_3)CH_2Cl$	122.60			150–2	1.0161[20]	1.4469[20]		v	v				B1[2], 424
b2882	—,3-chloro-2-methyl-*	$CH_3CHClCOH(CH_3)_2$	122.60			141–2 55–6[30]	1.0295[20]	1.4436[20]	s	v	v				B1[2], 424
b2883	—,1,3-dichloro-*	$CH_3CHClCHOHCH_2Cl$	143.02			63–4[10]	1.2860[15]	1.4766[20]		v	v				B1, 373
Ω b2884	1-Butanol, 2,2-dimethyl-*	tert-Amyl carbinol. $CH_3CH_2C(CH_3)_2CH_2OH$	102.18		< −15	136.7[760]	0.8283[20]	1.4208[20]	δ	s	s				B1[3], 1675
b2885	—,2,3-dimethyl-(d)*	Isopropyl dimethyl carbinol. $(CH_3)_2CHCH(CH_3)CH_2OH$	102.18	[α][25]_D +1.9		142[760]	0.823[25]_4								B1[3], 1677
Ω b2886	—,—(dl)*	$(CH_3)_2CHCH(CH_3)CH_2OH$	102.18			144–5[761]	0.8297[20.5]	1.4195[20.5]		s	s	s			B1[3], 1677
Ω b2887	—,3,3-dimethyl-*	$(CH_3)_3CCH_2CH_2OH$	102.18		−60	143	0.844[15]_4	1.4323[15]	δ	s	s				B1[3], 1677
Ω b2888	2-Butanol, 2,3-dimethyl-*	$(CH_3)_2CHCOH(CH_3)_2$	102.18		−14	118.4[760]	0.8236[20]	1.4176[20]	s	∞	∞				B1[2], 441
Ω b2889	—,3,3-dimethyl-(dl)*	Pinacolyl alcohol. $(CH_3)_3CCHOHCH_3$	102.18		5.6	120.4[760]	0.8122[25]	1.4148[20]	δ	s	∞				B1[2], 441
Ω b2890	1-Butanol, 2-ethyl-*	$(C_2H_5)_2CHCH_2OH$	102.18		< −15	146.27[760]	0.8326[20]	1.4220[20]	δ	s	s				B1, 412

For explanations, symbols and abbreviations see beginning of table. For structural formulas see end of table.

No.	Name	Synonyms and Formula	Mol. wt.	Color, crystalline form, specific rotation and λ_{max} (log ε)	m.p. °C	b.p. °C	Density	n_D	Solubility						Ref.
									w	al	eth	ace	bz	other solvents	
	1-Butanol														
b2891	—,4-fluoro-*	Tetramethylene fluorohydrin. FCH$_2$CH$_2$CH$_2$CH$_2$OH	92.12			58[15]		1.3942[25]	s	v	v	v			B1[3], 1516
b2892	—,2-methyl-(d)*	act-Amyl alcohol. CH$_3$CH$_2$CH(CH$_3$)CH$_2$OH	88.15	[α]$_D^{20}$ −5.90 (undil)		128[760] 65.7[50]	0.8193$_4^{20}$	1.4102[20]	δ	∞	∞	v			B1[2], 421
Ω b2893	—,—(dl)*	CH$_3$CH$_2$CH(CH$_3$)CH$_2$OH.	88.15			127.5–8[760] 70[60]	0.8152[25]	1.4092[20]	δ	∞	∞	v			B1[2], 422
b2894	—,—(l)*	CH$_3$CH$_2$CH(CH$_3$)CH$_2$OH.	88.15	[α]$_D^{18}$ +3.75		129[760]	0.816$_8^{18}$	1.4098[20]	δ	∞	∞	v			B1[3], 1619
Ω b2895	—,3-methyl-*	Isopentyl alcohol. (CH$_3$)$_2$CHCH$_2$CH$_2$OH	88.15			128.5[750]	0.8092$_4^{20}$	1.4053$_4^{20}$	δ	∞	∞	v			B1[3], 1633
Ω b2896	2-Butanol, 2-methyl-*	tert-Amyl alcohol. CH$_3$CH$_2$COH(CH$_3$)$_2$	88.15	$\lambda^{con\ sulf}$ 300 (2.85)	−8.4	102[760] 50[60]	0.8059[25]	1.4052[20]	s	∞	∞	s	s	chl s	B1[2], 422
b2897	—,3-methyl-(d)*	(CH$_3$)$_2$CHCHOHCH$_3$	88.15	[α]$_D^{20}$ +5.34 (al)		112[734]	0.8225$_4^{16}$	1.4089[20]	δ	s	s	v	s	chl s	B1[1], 196
Ω b2898	—,—(dl)*	(CH$_3$)$_2$CHCHOHCH$_3$	88.15			112.9[760] 61[60]	0.8180$_4^{20}$	1.4089[20]	δ	∞	∞	v		CCl$_4$ s	B1[2], 425
b2899	1-Butanol, 2-methyl-1-phenyl-*	sec-Butyl phenyl carbinol. CH$_3$CH$_2$CH(CH$_3$)CH(C$_6$H$_5$)OH	164.25			120[13]			i	∞	∞	v	∞	os v	B6[2], 505
b2900	—,2-methyl-4-phenyl-(dl)*	C$_6$H$_5$CH$_2$CH$_2$CH(CH$_3$)CH$_2$OH	164.25			135[11]	0.9719$_4^{20}$	1.5173[16]	i	v	∞	v	v	os v	B6[1], 269
b2901	—,3-methyl-1-phenyl-*	(CH$_3$)$_2$CHCH$_2$CHOHC$_6$H$_5$	164.25			235–6[746] 122[9]	0.9537$_4^{19}$	1.5080[18]	i	v	v	v	v	os v	B6, 548
b2902	—,3-methyl-2-phenyl-*	(CH$_3$)$_2$CHCH(C$_6$H$_5$)CH$_2$OH	164.25			130[15]	0.9694[25]	1.5137[25]	i	v	v	v	v	os v	B6[2], 506
b2903	2-Butanol, 2-methyl-1-phenyl-(dl)*	CH$_3$CH$_2$COH(CH$_3$)CH$_2$C$_6$H$_5$	164.25			215–25[747] 103–5[11]	0.9754$_4^{20}$	1.5182[20]	i	s	s			lig s	B6[2], 505
b2904	—,2-methyl-3-phenyl-*	CH$_3$CH(C$_6$H$_5$)COH(CH$_3$)$_2$	164.25			196–8 118[24]	0.9794$_4^{20}$	1.5193[20]	i	s	s	s	s	os s	B6[1], 270
Ω b2905	—,2-methyl-4-phenyl-*	C$_6$H$_5$CH$_2$CH$_2$COH(CH$_3$)$_2$.	164.25	nd	24.5	121[13]	0.9626$_4^{21}$	1.5077[21]	i	v	v	v	v	os v	B6[2], 506
b2906	—,3-methyl-3-phenyl-*	(CH$_3$)$_2$CHCOH(C$_6$H$_5$)CH$_3$	164.25			196–8[760]	0.9653$_4^{13}$	1.5161[13]	i	s	s	s	s	os s	B6[1], 269
Ω b2907	1-Butanol-, 2-nitro-*	CH$_3$CH$_2$CHNO$_2$CH$_2$OH	119.12	λ^{al} 279 (1.47)	−47	105[10]	1.1332[25]	1.4390[20]	s	∞	∞	v		aa s	B1, 370
b2908	—,1-phenyl-(dl)*	α-Propylbenzyl alcohol. CH$_3$CH$_2$CH$_2$CHOHC$_6$H$_5$	150.22		16	232[760] 113–5[12]	0.9740$_4^{20}$	1.5139[20]	i	v	∞	v	v	os v	B6[2], 486
b2909	—,2,2,3-tri-chloro-*	CH$_3$CHClCCl$_2$CH$_2$OH	177.46	pr (dil al)	62	199–200[760] 97–8[18]			δ[h]	s	s	s			B1[2], 398
b2910	2-Butanol, 1,1,1-trichloro-*	CH$_3$CH$_2$CHOHCCl$_3$	177.46			169–71[738] 82–4[22]	1.3670$_{25}^{25}$	1.4800[20]	δ[h]	v	v	v	v	chl v CS$_2$ v	B1[2], 403
b2911	—,2,3,3-tri-methyl-*	(CH$_3$)$_3$CCOH(CH$_3$)$_2$	116.21	cr (dil al + ¼w)	83–4	131–2[760] 40–1[15]	0.8380$_4^{15}$	1.4233[22]	δ s[h]	∞	∞	v			B1[2], 447
Ω b2912	2-Butanone*	Ethyl methyl ketone. CH$_3$CH$_2$COCH$_3$	72.12	λ^{al} 273.5 (1.24)	−86.35	79.6[760] 30[119]	0.8054$_4^{20}$	1.3788[20]	v	∞	∞	∞	∞		B1[2], 726
Ω b2913	—,oxime	CH$_3$CH$_2$C(:NOH)CH$_3$	87.12		−29.5	152–3[760] 59–60[15]	0.9232$_4^{20}$	1.4410[20]	s	∞	∞	v			B1[2], 730
b2914	—,1-chloro-*	CH$_3$CH$_2$COCH$_2$Cl	106.55			137–8[760] 34–5[10]	1.0850$_4^{20}$	1.4372[20]	i					MeOH v[h]	B1[2], 731
b2915	—,3-chloro-*	CH$_3$CHClCOCH$_3$	106.55			115[760] (117–9) 40[30]	1.0554[0]	1.4219[20]	i	v	v				B1[2], 731
b2916	—,4-chloro-*	ClCH$_2$CH$_2$COCH$_3$	106.55			120–1[760]d 48[15]	1.0680[23]	1.4284[23]	i	v	v			MeOH v	B1[2], 731
b2917	—,3-chloro-3-methyl-*	(CH$_3$)$_2$CClCOCH$_3$	120.58			117.2[758]	1.0083$_4^{20}$	1.4204[20]	i	s	s				B1[3], 2818
Ω b2918	—,3,4-dibromo-4-phenyl-*	Benzalacetone dibromide. C$_6$H$_5$CHBrCHBrCOCH$_3$	306.01	nd (al)	124–5				i	δ s[h]	s	s	s	chl v	B7[2], 244
b2919	—,1,3-dichloro-*	CH$_3$CHClCOCH$_2$Cl	141.00			166–7[760] 55.5[10]	1.3116$_4^{20}$	1.4686[20]	i	s	s	s	s	os s	B1[1], 348
Ω b2920	—,4(diethyl-amino)-*	(C$_2$H$_5$)$_2$NCH$_2$CH$_2$COCH$_3$.	143.23			84[30] 53[4]	0.8630$_4^{20}$	1.4333[24]	δ	s	s	s			B4[1], 452
Ω b2921	—,3,3 dimethyl *	Pinacolone. (CH$_3$)$_3$CCOCH$_3$	100.16	λ^{al} 282 (2.62)	−49.8	106[760]	0.8012[25]	1.3952[20]	δ	s	s	s			B1[3], 354
Ω b2922	—,3,3-diphenyl-*	CH$_3$C(C$_6$H$_5$)$_2$COCH$_3$	224.31	pr (al) λ^{al} 260 (2.7), 300 (2.6)	41	310–1[760] 176[16]	1.069[20]	1.5748[20]	i	s v[h]	s			chl v aa v	B7[2], 393
b2923	—,1-hydroxy-*	CH$_3$CH$_2$COCH$_2$OH	88.12	λ^{al} 276 (1.28)		160[760] (153–4) 48[9]	1.0272$_4^{20}$	1.4189[20]	v	v	v				B1[2], 870
Ω b2924	—,3-hydroxy-(dl)*	Acetoin. CH$_3$CHOHCOCH$_3$	88.12	λ^{w} 272.5 (−0.5)	−72	143[760] 37[11]	1.0062$_{20}^{20}$	1.4171[20]	∞	δ	δ	s		lig i	B1[2], 870
b2925	—,1(1-hydroxy-2-naphthyl)-*		214.27	ye nd (eth)	85–6	145–52[1]			i	s	s				B8, 152
Ω b2926	—,3-methyl-*	Isopropyl methyl ketone. (CH$_3$)$_2$CHCOCH$_3$	86.14	λ^{al} 280 (1.32)	−92	94–4.5[760]	0.8051$_4^{20}$	1.38804[20]	δ	∞	∞	v			B1[2], 741
b2927	—,—,oxime	(CH$_3$)$_2$CHC(:NOH)CH$_3$.	101.15			157–0			δ	∞	∞				B1, 687
b2928	1-Butanone, 3-methyl-1-phenyl-*	Isovalerophenone. (CH$_3$)$_2$CHCH$_2$COC$_6$H$_5$	162.23	λ^{al} 243 (4.09)		236.5[764] 137–8[38]	0.9701$_4^{16.4}$	1.5139[15.3]	i	∞	∞	v			B7[2], 252

For explanations, symbols and abbreviations see beginning of table. For structural formulas see end of table.

No.	Name	Synonyms and Formula	Mol. wt.	Color, crystalline form, specific rotation and λ_{max} (log ε)	m.p. °C	b.p. °C	Density	n_D	w	al	eth	ace	bz	other solvents	Ref.
	1-Butanone														
Ω b2929	—,1-phenyl-*	Butyrophenone. $CH_3CH_2CH_2COC_6H_5$	148.21	λ^{al} 240 (4.06), 276 (3.00)	11.5–3.0	228–9[760]	0.9882[20]	1.5203[20]	i	∞	∞	v		peth δ	B7[2], 241
Ω b2930	2-Butanone, 1-phenyl-*	Ethyl benzyl ketone. $CH_3CH_2COCH_2C_6H_5$	148.21	λ^{al} 284 (2.11)		230[755]	1.002[0]		i	s	∞	v			B7[2], 243
Ω b2931	—,4-phenyl-*	Benzylacetone. $C_6H_5CH_2CH_2COCH_3$	148.21	λ^{cy} 281 (1.51)		233–4 115[13]	0.9849[22]	1.511[22]	i	s	s	v			B7[2], 243
Ω b2932	1-Butanone, 1(4-tolyl)-	p-Methylbutyrophenone.	162.24		12	251.5[758]	0.9745[20]	1.5232[20]	i	v	v				B7[2], 254
Ω b2933	2-Butenal (trans)*	Crotonaldehyde. $CH_3CH:CHCHO$	70.09	λ^{al} 218 (4.25)	−74	104–5 (102–3[765])	0.8495[25]	1.4366[20]	s	v	v	v	∞		B1[2], 787
Ω b2934	—,diethyl acetal	$CH_3CH:CHCH(OC_2H_5)_2$	144.22			147–8 49[17]	0.8473[18]	1.4097[20]	i	∞	∞	∞	∞	peth ∞	B1[2], 789
b2935	—,2-bromo-, diethyl acetal	$CH_3CH:CBrCH(OC_2H_5)_2$	223.12			86[15]	1.2255[21]	1.4565[21]							B1[1], 380
b2936	—,2-chloro-*	$CH_3CH:CClCHO$	104.54	λ < 210		147–8 53–4[20]	1.1404[23]	1.4780[23]	δ	s	s			CCl_4 s chl s	B1[2], 789
b2937	—,3-ethoxy-, diethyl acetal	1,1,3-Triethoxy-2-butene*. $CH_3C(OC_2H_5):CHCH(OC_2H_5)_2$	188.27			190–5 79–82[10]	0.908[21]	1.430[21]							B1[3], 3267
b2938	—,2-methyl-*	Tiglaldehyde. $CH_3CH:C(CH_3)CHO$	84.13			116.5–7.5[738] 63–5[119]	0.8710[20]	1.4475[20]	s	∞	∞				B1[2], 792
b2939	—,3-methyl-*	β,β-Dimethylacrolein. Senecio-aldehyde. $(CH_3)_2C:CHCHO$	84.13			133[730]	0.8722[20]	1.4526[20]	s	s	s				B1[3], 2990
Ω b2940	1-Butene-*	α-Butylene. $CH_3CH_2CH:CH_2$	56.12	λ^{gas} 162 sh (4.0), 175 (4.2), 187 (4.1)	−185.35	−6.3[760]	0.5951[20]	1.3962[20] (1.3465[20])	i	v	v		s		B1[3], 715
Ω b2941	2-Butene (cis)*	cis-β-Butylene. $CH_3CH:CHCH_3$	56.12	λ^{gas} 160 sh (4.1), 175 (4.3), 196 (3.00), 200 (2.7)	−138.91	3.7[760]	0.6213[20]	1.3931[−25]	i	v	v		s		B1[3], 728
Ω b2942	—(trans)*	trans-β-Butylene. $CH_3CH:CHCH_3$	56.12	λ^{gas} 163 (3.9), 177 (4.1), 187 (3.8), 202 (2.7)	−105.55	0.88[760]	0.6042[20]	1.3848[−25]	i	v	v		s		B1[3], 730
b2943	1-Butene, 4-bromo-*	$BrCH_2CH_2CH:CH_2$	135.01			98.5[758]	1.3230[20]	1.4622[20]	i	s	s	s			B1[3], 727
b2944	—,2-bromo-3-methyl-*	$(CH_3)_2CHCBr:CH_2$	149.04			105[757]	1.2328[20]	1.4504[20]	i		s		s	chl s	B1[3], 800
b2945	2-Butene, 1-bromo-3-methyl-*	$(CH_3)_2C:CHCH_2Br$	149.04			129–33d 50–1[40]	1.2819[20]	1.4930[15]	i d[h]	s	s	s	s	CS_2 s chl s	B1[3], 796
b2946	—,2-bromo-3-methyl-*	$(CH_3)_2C:CBrCH_3$	149.04			119–20[766]	1.2773[20]	1.4738[20]	i		s	s		chl s	B1[3], 796
b2947	1-Butene, 2-bromo-4-phenyl-*	$C_6H_5CH_2CH_2CBr:CH_2$	211.11			117–8[21] 90–1[5]	1.2901[20]	1.5450[20]	i			s			B5[2], 380
b2948	2-Butene, 1 bromo-4-phenyl-*	$C_6H_5CH_2CH:CHCH_2Br$	211.11			126– 30[10.5]	1.2660[20]	1.5678[20]	i			s			B5[2], 379
b2949	—,2-bromo-3-phenyl-*	$CH_3C(C_6H_5):CBrCH_3$	211.11			120–30[11]	1.3348[20]	1.5811[20]	i		s	s		chl s	B5, 488
b2950	1-Butene, 1-chloro-(cis)*	$CH_3CH_2CH:CHCl$	90.55			63.5[760]	0.9153[15]	1.4194[15]	i	∞	v	s		chl s	B1[3], 723
b2951	—,— (trans)*	$CH_3CH_2CH:CHCl$	90.55			68[760]	0.9205[15]	1.4225[15]	i	∞	v	s		chl s	B1[3], 723
b2952	—,2-chloro-*	$CH_3CH_2CCl:CH_2$	90.55			58.5[760]	0.9107[15]	1.4115[21]	i	∞	v	s		chl s	B1, 204
b2953	—,3-chloro-*	$CH_3CHClCH:CH_2$	90.55			64–5[766]	0.8978[20]	1.4149[20]			v	v		chl s	B1[3], 723
b2954	—,4-chloro-*	$ClCH_2CH_2CH:CH_2$	90.55			75[773]	0.9211[20]	1.4233[20]	i		v	v		chl v	B1[3], 724
b2955	2-Butene, 1-chloro-(cis)	$CH_3CH:CHCH_2Cl$	90.55			84.1[758]	0.9426[20]	1.4390[20]	i	s		s		chl s	B1[2], 176
b2956	—,— (trans)*	$CH_3CH:CHCH_2Cl$	90.55			84.8[752]	0.9295[20]	1.4350[20]	i			s		chl s	B1[2], 176
b2957	—,2-chloro-(cis)*	$CH_3CH:CClCH_3$	90.55		−117.3	70.6[760]	0.9239[20]	1.4240[20]	i	∞		s		chl s	B1[3], 740
b2958	—,— (trans)*	$CH_3CH:CClCH_3$	90.55		−105.8	62.8	0.9138[20]	1.4190[20]	i	∞		s		chl s	B1[3], 741
b2959	1-Butene, 3-chloro-2-chloro-methyl-*	$CH_3CHClC(CH_2Cl):CH_2$	139.04			155[760] 31–3[7]	1.1233[20]	1.4724[20]	i			s		chl s	B1[3], 787
b2960	2-Butene, 1-chloro-2,3-dimethyl-*	$(CH_3)_2C:C(CH_3)CH_2Cl$	118.61			111–2[756]	0.9355[20]	1.4605[20]			v	v		chl v	B1[3], 819
b2961	1-Butene, 1-chloro-2-methyl-*	$CH_3CH_2C(CH_3):CHCl$	104.58			96–7[760] (88–90.5[718])	0.9170[20]	1.4141[20]	i		v	v			B1[2], 187
b2962	—,1-chloro-3-methyl-*	$(CH_3)_2CHCH:CHCl$	104.58			86–8[756]		1.4229[20]	i		s	s		chl s	B1[3], 799
b2963	—,3-chloro-2-methyl-*	$CH_3CHClC(CH_3):CH_2$	104.58			94[760]	0.9088[20]	1.4304[20]	i		v	v		chl s	B1[3], 787
b2964	2-Butene, 1-chloro-2-methyl-*	$CH_3CH:C(CH_3)CH_2Cl$	104.58			110[760] 26.4[25]	0.9327[20]	1.4481[20]	d[h]	v	v	v		chl s	B1[2], 189
b2965	—,1-chloro-3-methyl-*	$(CH_3)_2C:CHCH_2Cl$	104.58			109[760] 54.3[95]	0.9273[20]	1.4485[20]	i	s	s	s		chl v	B1[2], 191

For explanations, symbols and abbreviations see beginning of table. For structural formulas see end of table.

2-Butene

No.	Name	Synonyms and Formula	Mol. wt.	Color, crystalline form, specific rotation and λ_{max} (log ε)	m.p. °C	b.p. °C	Density	n_D	w	al	eth	ace	bz	other solvents	Ref.
b2966	—,2-chloro-3-methyl-*	Trimethylvinyl chloride. $(CH_3)_2C{:}CClCH_3$	104.58	....		94^{760} (97–8)	0.9324^{20}_{4}	1.4320^{20}	i		s	v	s	...	chl s	B1[2], 189
b2967	1-Butene, 2(chloromethyl)-1,3-dichloro-*	$CH_3CHClC(CH_2Cl){:}CHCl$	174.47	....		$68–70^{8}$	1.2775^{17}_{4}		i						CCl_4 s	B1[3], 788
b2968	2-Butene, 1,4-dibromo-(trans)*	$BrCH_2CH{:}CHCH_2Br$	213.91	pl (peth)	53–4	205^{760} 85^{10}	....		δ	v		s			MeOH v peth v	B1[2], 206
b2969	1-Butene, 1,3-dichloro-*	$CH_3CHClCH{:}CHCl$	125.00			125^{760} $58–60^{25}$	1.1341^{24}_{4}	1.4647^{20}	i		s	s	s	...	chl s	B1[2], 724
b2970	—,2,3-dichloro-*	$CH_3CHClCCl{:}CH_2$	125.00			112	1.1340^{20}	1.4580^{20}	i			s	s		chl s	B1[3], 724
b2971	2-Butene, 1,1-dichloro-*	$CH_3CH{:}CHCHCl_2$	125.00			125–7	1.1310^{20}	1.466^{18}	i			s	v		chl s	B1[3], 741
b2972	—,1,2-dichloro-(high b.p.)*	$CH_3CH{:}CClCH_2Cl$	125.00			130.2-0.8^{760}	1.1601^{20}_{4}	1.4734^{20}	i			s	v		chl v	B1[3], 741
b2973	—,—(low b.p.)*	$CH_3CH{:}CClCH_2Cl$	125.00			$116–8^{765}$	1.1544^{20}	1.4642^{20}	i				v		CCl_4 v	B1[3], 741
b2974	—,1,3-dichloro-(cis)*	$CH_3CCl{:}CHCH_2Cl$	125.00			129.9^{745} 34^{20}	1.1605^{20}_{4}	1.4735^{20}	i	s	s	s	s	s	os s, chl s	B1[3], 742
b2975	—,—(trans)*	$CH_3CCl{:}CHCH_2Cl$	125.00			130^{745} 53^{50}	1.1585^{20}_{4}	1.4719^{20}	i	s	s	s	s	s	os s, chl s	B1[3], 742
b2976	—,1,4-dichloro-(cis)*	$ClCH_2CH{:}CHCH_2Cl$	125.00		−48	152.5^{758} 22.5^{3}	1.1882^{25}	1.4887^{25}	i	s	s	s	s	s	os s, chl s	B1[3], 743
b2977	—,—(trans)*	$ClCH_2CH{:}CHCH_2Cl$	125.00		1–3	155.5^{758} 55.5^{20}	1.1832^{25}	1.4871^{25}	i	s	s	s	s	s	os s, chl s	B1[3], 743
b2978	—,2,3-dichloro-(cis)*	$CH_3CCl{:}CClCH_3$	125.00			$125–6^{758}$	1.1618^{20}_{4}	1.4590^{20}	i	s	s	s	s	s	os s, chl s	B1[3], 743
b2979	—,—(trans)*	$CH_3CCl{:}CClCH_3$	125.00			101.3^{758}	1.1416^{20}_{4}	1.4582^{20}	i	s	s	s	s	s	os s, chl s	B1[3], 744
b2980	1-Butene, 3,3-dichloro-2-methyl-*	$CH_3CCl_2C(CH_3){:}CH_2$	139.04			$151–3^{760}$	1.1276^{19}_{4}	1.4737^{19}_{c}	i			s	s	...	chl s	B1[3], 787
b2981	2-Butene, 1,3-dichloro-2-methyl-*	$CH_3CCl{:}C(CH_3)CH_2Cl$	139.04			$151–3^{760}$	1.1293^{20}_{4}	....	i				v		chl s	B1[3], 795
b2982	—,1,4-dichloro-2-methyl-*	$ClCH_2CH{:}C(CH_3)CH_2Cl$	139.04			93^{50} 56^{10}	1.1526^{20}_{4}	1.4932^{20}	i				v		chl v	B1[3], 795
—	—,1,1-diethoxy-	see 2-Butenal, diethyl acetal*													
Ω b2983	1-Butene, 2,3-dimethyl-*	$(CH_3)_2CHC(CH_3){:}CH_2$	84.16	λ^{gas} 169 (3.9), 187 (4.0), 198 (3.6)	−157.3	55.67^{760}	0.6803^{20}_{4}	1.3995^{20}	i	s	s	s	s		CS_2 s	B1[3], 816
Ω b2984	—,3,3-dimethyl-*	$(CH_3)_3CCH{:}CH_2$	84.16	λ^{gas} 174 (4.1), 188 (3.6)	−115.2	41.2^{760}	0.6529^{20}_{4}	1.3763^{20}	i			s	s		chl s	B1[3], 814
b2985	2-Butene, 2,3-dimethyl-*	$(CH_3)_2C{:}C(CH_3)_2$	84.16	λ^{al} 198 (4.12)	−74.28	73.2^{760}	0.7080^{20}_{4}	1.4122^{20}	i			s	s		chl s	B1[3], 817
Ω b2986	1-Butene, 3,4-epoxy-*	Butadiene mono-oxide. Vinyloxirane.	70.09	λ^{al} <210		70^{760}	0.9006^{0}	1.4168^{20}	s		s	s	s		os s	B17[1], 13
Ω b2987	—,2-ethyl-*	3-Methylenepentane. $(C_2H_5)_2C{:}CH_2$	84.16	λ^{gas} 172 (3.7), 187 (3.9), 195 sh (3.8)	−131.53	64.7^{760}	0.6894^{20}_{4}	1.3969^{20}	i			s	s		chl s	B1[3], 814
b2988	—,2-ethyl-3-methyl-*	$(CH_3)_2CHC(C_2H_5){:}CH_2$	98.19	λ^{iso} <215		89	0.7150^{20}_{4}	1.410^{20}	i			s	s		chl s	B1[3], 833
b2989	2-Butene, 1,1,2,3,4,4-hexachloro-(liquid)*	$Cl_2CHCCl{:}CClCHCl_2$	262.78	....	−19	$97–8^{10}$	1.651^{15}_{15}	1.5331	i						chl s	B1[3], 744
b2990	—,—(solid)*	$Cl_2CHCCl{:}CClCHCl_2$	262.78	lf (al)	80 (78)		....			v^{h}	v			v	chl v CCl_4 v	B1[3], 744
Ω b2991	1-Butene, 2-methyl-*	$CH_3CH_2C(CH_3){:}CH_2$	70.14	λ^{gas} 200 (3.44)	−137.56	31.16^{760}	0.6504^{20}_{4}	1.3778^{20}	i	s	s	s	s		....	B1[3], 784
Ω b2992	—,3-methyl-*	$(CH_3)_2CHCH{:}CH_2$	70.14	λ^{gas} 195 (2.50)	−168.5	20^{760}	0.6272^{20}_{4}	1.3643^{20}	i	∞	∞		s		lig v	B1[2], 187
Ω b2993	2-Butene, 2-methyl-*	$(CH_3)_2C{:}CHCH_3$	70.14	λ^{gas} 205 (2.93)	−133.77	38.57^{760}	0.6623^{20}_{4}	1.3874^{20}	i	s	s		s		lig v	B1[2], 187
b2994	1-Butene, octafluoro-*	Perfluoro-α-butylene. $F_3CCF_2CF{:}CF_2$	200.03	....		4.8^{764}	1.5443^{0} 1.615^{-20}	....								B1[3], 722
Ω b2995	2-Butene, octafluoro-*	Perfluoro-β-butylene. $F_3CCF{:}CFCF_3$	200.03		−129 (−139)	$0–3^{760}$	1.5297^{0}									B1[3], 739
b2996	—,1,1,1,4,4-pentachloro-*	$Cl_2CHCH{:}CHCCl_3$	228.33			$78–80^{11}$	1.612^{21}_{21}	1.5538^{21}		s^{h}					chl s	B1[3], 744
b2997	1-Butene, 1,3,4,4-tetrachloro-*	$ClCH{:}CHCHClCHCl_2$	193.89			88^{20}	1.0711^{20}_{4}	1.4773^{20}	i				s		chl s	B1[3], 726
b2998	—,2,3,3,4-tetrachloro-*	$ClCH_2CCl_2CClCH_2$	193.89			$41–2^{7}$	1.4602^{20}_{4}	1.5133^{20}	i			s			chl s	B1[3], 726
b2999	—,2,3,4-trichloro-*	$ClCH_2CHClCCl{:}CH_2$	159.44			60^{20}	1.3430^{20}_{4}	1.4944^{20}	i			s	s		chl s	B1[3], 725
b3000	2-Butene, 1,2,4-trichloro-*	$ClCH_2CH{:}CClCH_2Cl$	159.44			$67–9^{10}$	1.3843^{20}_{4}	1.5175^{20}	i			s	s		chl s	B1[3], 744
—	—,1,1,3-triethoxy-*	see 2-Butenal, 3-ethoxy-, diethyl acetal													
b3001	1-Butene, 2,3,3-trimethyl-*	Triptene. $(CH_3)_3CC(CH_3){:}CH_2$	98.19		−109.9	77.87^{760}	0.7050^{20}_{4}	1.4029^{20}					s		MeOH s	B1[3], 834
—	3-Butene, 1,1-dicarboxylic acid*	see Malonic acid, allyl-													

For explanations, symbols and abbreviations see beginning of table. For structural formulas see end of table.

No.	Name	Synonyms and Formula	Mol. wt.	Color, crystalline form, specific rotation and λ_{max} (log ε)	m.p. °C	b.p. °C	Density	n_D	w	al	eth	ace	bz	other solvents	Ref.
	Butenedioic acid														
—	**Butenedioic acid** (cis)*	see **Maleic acid**													
—	—, (trans)*	see **Fumaric acid**													
b3002	**2-Butene-1,4-diol** (cis)*	$HOCH_2CH\!:\!CHCH_2OH$	88.12	....	4	235^{760} 132^{16}	1.0698_4^{20}	1.4782^{20}	s	v					B1[3], 2255
b3003	—, (trans)*	$HOCH_2CH\!:\!CHCH_2OH$....	88.12	....	25	131^{13}	1.0700_4^{20}	1.4755^{20}	v	v					B1[3], 2256
b3004	**3-Butene-1,2-diol***	Vinylethylene glycol. $CH_2\!:\!CHCHOHCH_2OH$	88.12	....		196.5 98^{16}	1.0470_4^{20}	1.4628^{21}	s	v					B1[3], 2252
b3005	**2-Butene-1-,4-dione, 1,4-diphenyl-**(cis)*	Dibenzoyl ethylene. $C_6H_5COCH\!:\!CHCOC_6H_5$	236.27	nd (al) λ^{al} 260 (4.26)	134 (130)	....			i	s[h]	s	s	s	chl s oos s	B7[2], 741
b3006	—, — (trans)*	$C_6H_5COCH\!:\!CHCOC_6H_5$..	236.27	ye nd (al or bz) λ^{al} 269(4.27)	111	....				δ			s	chl v aa s lig i	B7[2], 741
b3007	**2-Butenoic acid** (cis)*	Isocrotonic acid. $CH_3CH\!:\!CHCO_2H$	86.09	nd or pr (peth) λ^{al} 204 (4.06)	15.5	169.3^{760} 74^{15}	1.0267_4^{20}	1.4483^{14}	v		s	s			B2[2], 394
Ω b3009	—, (trans)*	Crotonic acid. $CH_3CH\!:\!CHCO_2H$	86.09	mcl nd or pr (w or lig) λ^{al} 205 (4.20)	71.5–1.7	185^{760} (189)	1.018_4^{15} 0.9604_4^{77}	1.4249^{77}	v	v	s	s		lig s[h]	B2[2], 390
Ω b3010	—, amide (trans)	Crotonamide. $CH_3CH\!:\!CHCONH_2$	85.11	nd (ace) λ^{al} <216	161.5 (cor)	sub at 140^{13}		1.4420^{165}	δ	s	δ		s		B2[2], 392
Ω b3011	—, anhydride (trans)*	Crotonic anhydride. $(CH_3CH\!:\!CHCO)_2O$	154.17	....		246–8 129^{19}	1.0397^{20}	1.4745^{20}	d	d					B2[3], 1265
Ω b3012	—, chloride (trans)	Crotonyl chloride. $CH_3CH\!:\!CHCOCl$	104.54	λ^{al} <210		124–5[760] 35^{18}	1.0905^{20}	1.460^{18}	d	d					B2[2], 392
b3012[1]	—, ethyl ester (cis)*	Ethyl isocrotonate. $CH_3CH\!:\!CHCO_2C_2H_5$	114.15	....		136^{760}	0.9182_4^{20}	1.4242^{20}	i					oss s	B2[2], 394
Ω b3013	—, — (trans)*	Ethyl crotonate. $CH_3CH\!:\!CHCO_2C_2H_5$	114.15	λ^{al} 210 (4.10)		136.5^{760} $58–9^{48}$	0.9175_4^{20}	1.4243^{20}	i	s	s				B2[2], 392
Ω b3014	—, methyl ester (trans)*	Methyl crotonate. $CH_3CH\!:\!CHCO_2CH_3$	100.13	λ^{al} 212 (4.16), 250 sh (2.3)	−42	121 (118.8– 9.3)	0.9444_4^{20}	1.4242^{20}	i	v	v				B2[2], 392
Ω b3015	—, nitrile (trans)	Crotononitrile. $CH_3CH\!:\!CHCN$	67.09	....	−51.5	$120–1^{762}$	0.8239_4^{20}	1.4225^{20}			s	s			B2[2], 393
Ω b3016	**3-Butenoic acid***	Vinylacetic acid. $CH_2\!:\!CHCH_2CO_2H$	86.09	....	−35	169^{764} (163) $69–70^{12}$	1.0091_4^{20}	1.4239^{20}	s	∞	∞				B2[2], 389
b3017	—, ethyl ester*	$CH_2\!:\!CHCH_2CO_2C_2H_5$	114.14	λ^{hx} 225 sh (2.0)	....	119	0.9122^{20}	1.4105^{20}		s					B2, 407
b3018	—, nitrile	Allyl cyanide. $CH_2\!:\!CHCH_2CN$	67.09	....	−84	119	0.8329^{20}	1.4060^{20}	δ	∞	∞				B2[2], 389
Ω b3019	**2-Butenoic acid, 3-amino-, ethyl ester** (trans)*	$CH_3C(NH_2)\!:\!CHCO_2C_2H_5$	129.16	mcl pr λ^{al} 275 (4.26) 20–1 (unst)	34 (st)	210–5d[760] 105^{15}	1.0219_4^{19}	1.4988^{22}	i	s	s		s	chl s CS_2 s lig s	B3[2], 423
b3020	—, 3-bromo- (trans)*	$CH_3CBr\!:\!CHCO_2H$	165.00	nd (lig), lf (w)	97	....			δ	s	s		s	CS_2 s aa s	B2, 419
b3021	—, 4-bromo-, ethyl ester (trans)*	$BrCH_2CH\!:\!CHCO_2C_2H_5$	193.05	....		$97–8^{15}$ $66–70^{0.3}$	1.402_4^{16}	1.4925^{20}		v					C50, 10804
b3022	—, 2-chloro- (cis)*	$CH_3CH\!:\!CClCO_2H$	120.54	nd (w) λ^{al} 228 (3.85)	67				s	v				CS_2 v lig δ v[h]	B2[2], 396
b3023	—, — (trans)*	$CH_3CH\!:\!CClCO_2H$	120.54	nd (w or peth) λ^{al} 222 (4.02)	100.5	212 $111–2^{14}$			δ	s	s		s		B2[2], 395
b3024	—, —, ethyl ester (cis)*	$CH_3CH\!:\!CClCO_2C_2H_5$	148.59	....		75^{30} 58^{12}	1.1021_4^{18}			s	s				B2[2], 396
b3025	—, —, — (trans)*	$CH_3CH\!:\!CClCO_2C_2H_5$	148.59	....		176–8 61^{10}	1.1133_4^{20}	1.4538^{20}		s	s				B2[2], 395
b3026	—, —, methyl ester (trans)*	$CH_3CH\!:\!CClCO_2CH_3$	134.57	....		161.5^{762} 59.5^{16}	1.160_4^{20}	1.4569^{23}		s	s				B2[2], 395
b3027	—, 3-chloro- (cis)*	$CH_3CCl\!:\!CHCO_2H$	120.54	cr (w) λ^{hx} 226 (4.64)	61	195 sub	1.1995^{66}	1.4704^{66}	δ	v	s		s	peth v[h] CS_2 v	B2[2], 396
b3028	—, — (trans)*	$CH_3CCl\!:\!CHCO_2H$	120.54	λ^{hx} 221 (4.30)	94–5	206–11 δd			δ	s	s		s	CS_2 v	B2[2], 396
b3029	—, —, ethyl ester (cis)*	$CH_3CCl\!:\!CHCO_2C_2H_5$	148.59	....		161.4 50^{10}	1.0860_4^{20}	1.4542_4^{19}	δ	s	s				B2[1], 190
b3030	—, —, — (trans)*	$CH_3CCl\!:\!CHCO_2C_2H_5$	148.59	....		184 66^{10}	1.1062_4^{20}	1.4592^{20}	δ	s	s				B2[2], 396
b3031	—, —, methyl ester (cis)*	$CH_3CCl\!:\!CHCO_2CH_3$	134.57	....		142.4 $42–3^{13}$	1.138_4^{20}	1.4573^{19}	δ	v				MeOH v	B2[2], 396
b3032	—, —, — (trans)*	$CH_3CCl\!:\!CHCO_2CH_3$	134.57	....		$64–7^{14}$	1.157_4^{20}	1.4630^{20}	δ	v					B2[2], 396
b3033	—, 4-chloro- (trans)*	$ClCH_2CH\!:\!CHCO_2H$......	120.54	cr (eth-peth)	83	$117–8^{13}$			δ[h]	v				peth δ aa v	B2, 418
b3034	—, 2,3-dibromo-4-oxo-*	Mucobromic acid. $O\!:\!CHCBr\!:\!CBrCO_2H$	257.88	pl (eth-lig), rh cr (w)	125	....			s v[h]	v	v		δ	chl δ CS_2 δ	B3[2], 460
Ω b3035	—, 2,3-dichloro-4-oxo-*	Mucochloric acid. $O\!:\!CHCCl\!:\!CClCO_2H$	168.97	mcl pr (eth-lig), pl (w) λ^{al} 227 (3.9)	127	....			δ s[h]	s	s	s	s		B3, 727
b3036	—, 2-ethyl- (trans)*	$CH_3CH\!:\!C(C_2H_5)CO_2H$....	114.15	mcl pr (peth)	45–6	209 109^{13}	0.9578_4^{50}	1.4475^{50}	δ	s	s				B2[2], 208
b3037	**3-Butenoic acid, 2-hydroxy-, ethyl ester***	$CH_2\!:\!CHCHOHCO_2C_2H_5$	130.14	....		173^{756}d 68^{15}	1.0470_4^{15}	1.436^{13}	v	∞	∞				B3, 271
b3038	—, 2-hydroxy-4-phenyl-*	Benzallactic acid. $C_6H_5CH\!:\!CHCHOHCO_2H$	178.19	nd (w)	137	....			δ v[h]		i		i	CS_2 δ lig δ	C51, 10449

For explanations, symbols and abbreviations see beginning of table. For structural formulas see end of table.

2-Butenoic acid

No.	Name	Synonyms and Formula	Mol. wt.	Color, crystalline form, specific rotation and λ_{max} (log ε)	m.p. °C	b.p. °C	Density	n_D	w	al	eth	ace	bz	other solvents	Ref.
b3039	2-Butenoic acid, 2-methyl- (cis)*	Angelic acid. $CH_3CH:C(CH_3)CO_2H$	100.13	mcl pr or nd λ^{al} 215.5 (3.97)	45–6	185 (cor) 88–9[10]	0.9834[49] 0.9539[76]	1.4434[47]	δ s^h	s	v	...	...	...	B2[2], 401
Ω b3040	—,—(trans)*.....	Tiglic acid. $CH_3CH:C(CH_3)CO_2H$	100.13	ta (w) λ^{al} 212.5 (4.09)	64.5–5.0	198.5[760] (cor)	0.9641[76]	1.4330[76]	δ s^h	s	s	...	...	...	B2[2], 401
b3041	—,—,chloride (trans)	Tiglyl chloride. $CH_3CH:C(CH_3)COCl$	118.56	....		146–8[760] 45[12]			d	d	s	...	...	...	B2, 431
b3042	—,—,ethyl ester* ..	$CH_3CH:C(CH_3)CO_2C_2H_5$ ..	128.17	....		156[760] 55.5[11]	0.9200[20]	1.4340[20]	...	s	s	...	...	...	B2[2], 401
b3042[1]	—,3(4-nitrophenyl)-*	....	207.19	pa ye nd (aa)	168–9	....								aa s^h	B9, 615
Ω b3043	—,4-oxo-4-phenyl-*	β-Benzoylacrylic acid. $C_6H_5COCH:CHCO_2H$	176.18	nd or pr (to) λ^{al} 238 (4.05), 260 sh (4.00), 360 (1.88)	99				δ s^h	s	s	...	...	to s^h lig δ	B10[2], 499
b3043[1]	—,—,hydrate*	$C_6H_5COCH:CHCO_2H.H_2O$	194.19	lf (w + 1)	65				s^h	s	v	...	...		B10, 726
b3044	3-Butenoic acid, 4-phenyl-*	Styrylacetic acid. $C_6H_5CH:CHCH_2CO_2H$ ...	162.19	nd (w), pr (CS_2) λ^{al} 250 (4.24), 283 (3.18), 292 (2.99)	87	302			i δ^h	v	v	...	...	CS_2 v^h	B9[2], 407
Ω b3045	2-Buten-1-ol (trans)*	Crotyl alcohol. $CH_3CH:CHCH_2OH$	72.12	....	< 30	121.2[760]	0.8521[20]	1.4288[20]	v	∞	∞	...	...		B1[2], 480
—	—,acetate	see Acetic acid, 2-buten-1-yl ester													
b3046	3-Buten-1-ol*	Allylcarbinol. $CH_2:CHCH_2CH_2OH$	72.12			113.5[760]	0.8424[20]	1.4224[20]	s	∞	∞	s	...		B1[2], 480
b3047	3-Buten-2-ol(d)*	$CH_3CHOHCH:CH_2$	72.12	$[\alpha]_D^{20}$ +33.9 (undil)		96.2–.5[745]	0.8362[15]	1.4120[20]							B1[2], 480
b3048	—(dl)*	$CH_3CHOHCH:CH_2$	72.12		< –100	97.3[760]	0.8318[20]	1.4137[20]	δ						B1[2], 479
b3049	2-Buten-1-ol, 2-chloro-*	$CH_3CH:CClCH_2OH$	106.55			159[760]	1.1180[20]	1.4682[20]	s	v					B1[2], 481
b3050	—,4-chloro-*	$ClCH_2CH:CHCH_2OH$	106.55			64–5[2]	1.0968[20]	1.4845[20]	d^h	v	v				B1[3], 1901
b3051	3-Buten-1-ol 2-chloro-*	$CH_2:CHCHClCH_2OH$	106.55			66.5–7[30]	1.1044[20]	1.4665[20]		v	v				B1[3], 1897
b3052	3-Buten-2-ol, 1-chloro-*	$CH_2:CHCHOHCH_2Cl$	106.55			144–7 63.3[30]	1.1112[20]	1.4643[20]						chl v	B1[3], 1893
b3053	—,3-chloro-*	$CH_3CHOHCCl:CH_2$	106.55			53–7[19]	1.1138[23]			v	v				B1[3], 1893
b3054	3-Butene-2-one*	Methyl vinyl ketone. $CH_3COCH:CH_2$	70.09	λ^{al} 210 (3.81)		81.4[760] 33–4[130]	0.8636[20]	1.4081[20]	s	s	v	v	s	MeOH s aa s	B1[2], 786
b3055	—,4-bromo-4-phenyl-*	(α-Bromobenzal)acetone. $CH_3COCH:CBrC_6H_5$	225.09			150–1[10] 128–31[1]									B7, 367
Ω b3056	2-Buten-1-one, 1,3-diphenyl-*	Dypnone. β-Methylchalcone. $CH_3C(C_6H_5):CHCOC_6H_5$	222.29	λ^{cy} 288.5 (4.24)		340–5 δd 225[22]	1.108[20]	1.6312[20]							B7[2], 433
Ω b3057	3-Buten-2-one, 4(2-furyl)-	Furfuralacetone.	138.16	nd λ^{al} 236 (3.28), 316 (4.36)	39–40	229d 112–5[10]	1.0496[27]	1.5788[45]	i	v	v			chl v peth s con sulf s (ye)	B17[2], 326
Ω b3058	—,4(4-hydroxy-3-methoxy-phenyl)-	Vanillalacetone. $C_{11}H_{12}O_3$. See b3065	192.22	nd (dil al)	129	....			δ	v	v		v		B8[2], 326
b3059	—,4(2-hydroxy-phenyl)-	Salicylideneacetone. $C_{10}H_{10}O_2$. See b3065	162.19	nd (al or lig), pr (bz) λ^{al} 285 (4.1), 335 (4.0)	140	....			δ	s^h	v	...	s^h		B8[2], 153
b3060	—,4(3-hydroxy-phenyl)-	$C_{10}H_{10}O_2$. See b3065	162.19	ye pr (bz)	97–8								s^h		B8[2], 155
b3061	—,4(4-hydroxy-phenyl)-	$C_{10}H_{10}O_2$. See b3065	162.19	nd (w) λ^{al} 234 (4.01), 323 (4.37)	114–5 (109)				δ s^h	v				aa v	B8[2], 155
Ω b3062	—,4(4-methoxy-phenyl)-	Anisylideneacetone. $C_{11}H_{12}O_2$. See b3065	176.22	lf (al, MeOH, eth or aa) λ^{al} 233.5 (3.92) 242 (4.27)	73				i	v	v		s	aa s sulf s (ye)	B8[2], 155
Ω b3063	—,3-methyl-	Isopropenyl methyl ketone. $CH_3COC(CH_3):CH_2$	84.13	λ^{al} 219.5 (3.80)	–54	98[760]	0.8527[20]	1.4220[20]	δ	∞					B1, 733
Ω b3064	—,4(3,4-methylenedioxy-phenyl)-(trans)	Piperonalacetone. $C_{11}H_{10}O_3$. See b3065	190.20	nd					i δ^h	s v^h	s		s	chl v peth s	B8[2], 157
Ω b3065	—,4-phenyl-(trans)*	Benzalacetone. Methyl styryl ketone.	146.19	pl λ^{al} 221 (4.00), 286.5 (4.32)	42	262[760] 140[16]	1.0097[45]	1.5836[46]	i	v	s	s	s	chl s peth δ	B7[2], 287
b3066	1-Buten-3-yne*	Vinylacetylene. $HC:CCH:CH_2$	52.08	λ^{iso} 219 (3.88), 227.5 (3.89)		5.1[760]	0.7095[0]	1.4161[1]	i				s		B1[3], 1032
b3067	—,4-chloro-*	$ClC:CCH:CH_2$	86.52			55–7[760]	1.0022[20]	1.4656[20]						chl s	B1[3], 1038
b3068	—,1-methoxy-*	$HC:CCH:CHOCH_3$	82.10			122–5[760] d 30–2[13]	0.906[20]	1.4818[20]	i					os v	C53, 21292
Ω b3069	—,2-methyl-*	Isopropylideneacetylene. Valylene. $CH:CC(CH_3):CH_2$	66.10			34[760]	0.6801[11]	1.4105[20]							B1[3], 1039

For explanations, symbols and abbreviations see beginning of table. For structural formulas see end of table.

No.	Name	Synonyms and Formula	Mol. wt.	Color, crystalline form, specific rotation and λ_{max} (log ε)	m.p. °C	b.p. °C	Density	n_D	Solubility						Ref.
									w	al	eth	ace	bz	other solvents	
	Butesin														
—	Butesin.	*see* **Benzoic acid, 4-amino-**, butyl ester													
—	*tert*-Butyl bromide	*see* **Propane, 2-bromo-2-methyl-***													
—	*tert*-Butyl chloride	*see* **Propane, 2-chloro-2-methyl-***													
—	Butylene	*see* **Butene***													
—	Butylene oxide.	*see* **Butane, epoxy-***													
b3070	1-Butyne*	$CH_3CH_2C{:}CH$	54.09	λ^{gas} 172 (3.65)	−125.72	8.1^{760}	0.6784_4^0 0.6502_4^{10}	1.3962^{20}	i	s	s	. . .	. . .		B1[2], 223
b3071	2-Butyne*	Dimethylacetylene. $CH_3C{:}CCH_3$	54.09	. . . .	−32.26	27^{760}	0.6910_4^{20}	1.3921^{20}	i	s	s	. . .	. . .		B1[3], 925
b3072	—,1-chloro-*	$CH_3CH_2C{:}CCl$	88.54			$104\text{–}6^{760}$	1.0152^{20}	1.4581^{20}	. . .	s	v	v	. . .		B1[3], 927
b3073	1-Butyne, 3-chloro-3-methyl-*	$(CH_3)_2CClC{:}CH$	102.57			$77\text{–}9$	0.9061^{20}								B1[3], 965
Ω b3074	2-Butyne, 1,4-dibromo-*	$BrCH_2C{:}CCH_2Br$	211.90	λ^{al} <217	. . . .	92^{15}	2.014^{18}	1.588^{18}	. . .	. . .	s^h	s	. . .	chl v	B1[3], 927
Ω b3075	—,1,4-dichloro-* . . .	$ClCH_2C{:}CCH_2Cl$	122.98			$165\text{–}6^{760}$ 73^{24}	1.258_4^{20}	1.5058^{20}	. . .	s	s	s	. . .	chl v	B1[3], 927
b3076	—,1,4-diiodo-* . . .	$ICH_2C{:}CCH_2I$	305.89	nd (al) λ 240 (4.00)	53	$70\text{–}2^{0.1}$			δ	s^h	s	s	. . .	chl v d in air	B1[3], 927
b3077	1-Butyne, 3,3-dimethyl-*	*tert*-Butylacetylene. $(CH_3)_3CC{:}CH$	82.15	. . . .	−81.2	$39\text{–}40^{760}$	0.6695_4^{20}	1.3738^{20}							B1[3], 991
Ω b3078	2-Butyne, hexa-fluoro-*	Perfluoro-2-butyne*. $CF_3C{:}CCF_3$	162.04		−117.4	$−24.6^{760}$			. . .	s	s	s	. . .	CCl_4 s aa s	B1[3], 926
b3079	1-Butyne, 3-methyl-*	Isopropylacetylene. $(CH_3)_2CHC{:}CH$	68.13	. . . .	−89.7	29.35^{760}	0.6660_4^{20}	1.3723^{20}	i	∞	∞	. . .	. . .		B1[3], 965
b3080	—,4-phenyl-*	$C_6H_5CH_2CH_2C{:}CH$	130.19			190^{760} 83^{15}	0.9258_4^{20}	1.5208^{20}	i						B5[2], 413
Ω b3081	2-Butynedioic acid*	Acetylenedicarboxylic acid. $HO_2CC{:}CCO_2H$	114.06	pl (eth), cr (+2w, aq eth)	179	. . . .			v	v	v	. . .	. . .		B2[2], 670
Ω b3082	—,diethyl ester* . . .	$C_2H_5O_2CC{:}CCO_2C_2H_5$	170.17		1–2	184^{200} 108^{13}	1.0675_4^{20}	1.4425^{20}	. . .	s	s	. . .	. . .	CCl_4 s	B2[2], 671
Ω b3083	—,dimethyl ester* . . .	$CH_3O_2CC{:}CCO_2CH_3$	142.11			$195\text{–}8^{760}$ $\delta d\ 98^{20}$	1.1564_4^{20}	1.4434^{20}	. . .	s	s	. . .	. . .	CCl_4 s	B2[2], 671
Ω b3084	2-Butyne-1,4-diol*	$HOCH_2C{:}CCH_2OH$	86.09	pl (bz, AcOEt), lf (aa)	58	238^{760} 145^{15}		1.4804^{20}	v	v	δ	v	i	chl δ peth i MeOH v	B1[1], 261
b3085	3-Butyne-1,2-diol* . .	$HC{:}CCHOHCH_2OH$	86.09		40	$64\text{–}6^{0.2}$			s	s	δ	. . .	. . .		B1[2], 569
b3086	2-Butynoic acid* . . .	Tetrolic acid. $CH_3C{:}CCO_2H$	84.08	pl (eth, peth or CS_2) λ^{al} 205.5 (3.80)	78	203^{760} $99\text{–}100^{18}$	0.9641_4^{20}		. . .	s	s	s	. . .	chl, CS_2 s	B2[2], 451
b3087	—,ethyl ester*	$CH_3C{:}CCO_2C_2H_5$	112.14			163^{760} 105^{190}	0.9641_4^{20}	1.4372^{20}							B2[1], 208
b3088	2-Butyn-1-ol*	$CH_3C{:}CCH_2OH$	70.09		−2.2	143^{760} $52\text{–}3^{14}$	0.9370_4^{20}	1.4530^{20}	. . .	s	∞	. . .	. . .		B1[3], 1973
Ω b3089	3-Butyn-1-ol*	$HOCH_2CH_2C{:}CH$.	70.09		−63.6	129^{760}	0.9257_4^{20}	1.4409^{20}	s	v	. . .	. . .	. . .	MeOH v	B1[3], 1972
b3090	3-Butyn-2-ol*	$CH{:}CCHOHCH_3$	70.09			107^{760}	0.8858^{20}	1.4265^{20}	s	v	s	. . .	. . .		B1[3], 1971
Ω b3091	—,2-methyl-*	$(CH_3)_2COHC{:}CH$	84.13		+3 (−3.5)	104^{760} 56^{97}	0.8618_4^{20}	1.4207^{20}	s	s	. . .	. . .	. . .		B1[2], 505
—	Butyraldehyde	*see* **Butanal***													
—	Butyramide	*see* **Butanoic acid**, amide													
—	Butyric acid	*see* **Butanoic acid***													
—	Butyroin	*see* **4-Octanone, 5-hydroxy-***													
—	Butyrolactone	*see* **Butanoic acid, 4-hydroxy-, lactone***													
—	Butyrophenone	*see* **1-Butanone, 1-phenyl-***													

For explanations, symbols and abbreviations see beginning of table. For structural formulas see end of table.

No.	Name	Synonyms and Formula	Mol. wt.	Color. crystalline form. specific rotation and λ_{max} (log ε)	m.p. °C	b.p. °C	Density	n_D	Solubility						Ref.
									w	al	eth	ace	bz	other solvents	

Cacodyl

c1	Cacodyl.........	Diarsenic tetramethyl Dimethylarsenic. Tetra-methylbiarsine. $(CH_3)_2AsAs(CH_3)_2$	209.98	pl	−6	165[760]	1.447[15]	....	δ	s	s	...	...		B4[2], 1002
c2	Cacodyl chloride...	Dimethylarsenic mono-chloride. Dimethyl-chlorarsine. $(CH_3)_2AsCl$	140.45	....	< −45	109	1.5046[12]	1.5203[12]	i	s	i	...	...		B4[2], 987
c3	Cacodyl oxide.....	Alkarsine. Bis-dimethyl-arsenous oxide. Dicacodyl oxide. $(CH_3)_2AsOAs(CH_3)_2$	225.98	....	−25	150[760]	1.4816[15]	1.5255[9]	δ	s	s	...	...		B4[2], 989
c4	—,perfluoro-......	Bis(trifluoromethyl) arsenous oxide. $(CF_3)_2AsOAs(CF_3)_2$	441.87			100[760]		1.3540[20]	...	...	...	...	...		J 1953, 1562
c5	Cacodyl sulfide....	Bis-dimethylarsine sulfide. Dicacodyl sulfide. $(CH_3)_2AsSAs(CH_3)_2$	242.05	....	< −40	211[760]			δ	s	s	...	...		B4, 608
c6	Cacodyl trichloride	Dimethylarsenic trichloride. Dimethylorthoarsenic acid trichloride. $(CH_3)_2AsCl_3$	211.35	cr (eth)	d at 50	....			d	d	d	...	...	CS_2 s	B4, 612
—	Cacodylic acid.....	see **Dimethylarsinic acid**													
—	Cadalene.........	see **Naphthalene, 1,6-di-methyl-4-isopropyl-**													
—	Cadaverine.......	see **Pentane, 1,5-diamino-***													
c7	β-Cadinene(l).....	3,9-Cadinadiene..........	204.36	$[\alpha]_D^{22}$ −15.9 (chl, c = 1) ($[\alpha]_D$ −251) λ^{hx} 250 (2.65), 323 (0.75)		274[760] 149[20]	0.9239[20]	1.5059[20]	i	δ	s	...	...	lig s chl s[h]	B5[2], 347
—	Caffeic acid.......	see **Cinnamic acid, 3,4-dihydroxy-**													
Ω c8	Caffeine.........	Theine. 1,3,7-Trimethyl-xanthine.	194.20	wh nd (w + 1), hex pr (sub) λ^{al} 227 (4.3), 235 (4.3), 274 (4.3)	238 (anh)	sub 178 sub 89[15]	1.23[19]	....	δ s[h]	δ	i	δ	δ	Py s chl s[h] aa δ CS_2, CCl_4 i	B26[2], 266
c9	—,benzoate.......	$C_8H_{10}N_4O_2 \cdot C_6H_5CO_2H$. *See* c8	316.32	wh so pw	....	....			s	s		...	...		B26[2], 268
c10	—,citrate........	$C_8H_{10}N_4O_2 \cdot C_6H_8O_7$. *See* c8	386.32	mcl cr	....	....			d	d		...	...		B26[2], 269
c11	—,hydrobromide..	$C_8H_{10}N_4O_2 \cdot HBr \cdot 2H_2O$. *See* c8.	311.14	ye	d 80–100	....			s	d	i	...	...	chl i	B26[1], 137
c12	—,hydrochloride..	$C_8H_{10}N_4O_2 \cdot HCl \cdot 2H_2O$. *See* c8.	266.69	mcl pr	d 80–100	....			d	d		...	...		B26[2], 268
c13	—,hydroiodide diiodide	Caffeine iodide. Diiodocaffeine hydroiodide. Caffeine triiodide. $C_8H_{10}N_4O_2 \cdot I_2 \cdot HI \cdot 1\frac{1}{2}H_2O$. *See* c8	603.01	gr pr	171d	....			i	v	i	...	...	chl δ	B26, 466
c14	—,2-hydroxy-benzoate	Caffeine salicylate. $C_8H_{10}N_4O_2 \cdot C_7H_6O_3$. *See* c8	332.32	wh nd (w)	137	....			δ	s		...	...		B26[2], 269
c16	—,3-methyl-butanoate	Caffeine isovalerate. $C_8H_{10}N_4O_2 \cdot C_5H_{10}O_2$. *See* c8	296.33	unst nd	....	....			s			...	...		B26, 467
c17	—,sulfate........	$C_8H_{10}N_4O_2 \cdot H_2SO_4$. *See* c8..	292.27	wh nd	....	....			d	d		...	...		B26, 466
c18	—,8-ethoxy-......	1,3,7-Trimethyl-2,6-dioxo-8-ethoxypurine. $C_{10}H_{14}N_4O_3$. *See* c8	238.25	wh or yesh nd (w)	143	....			δ	v[h]	δ	...	...		B26[2], 322
c19	—,8-methoxy-	$C_9H_{12}N_4O_3$. *See* c8.......	224.22	wh nd (al or w)	176	....	1.399[25]		s[h]	v		...	s		B26[2], 322
Ω c20	Calciferol.......	Irradiated ergosterol. Vitamin D2. $C_{28}H_{44}O$.	396.67	pr (ace) $[\alpha]_D^{20}$ +102.5 (al), +81 (ace) λ^{al} 265 (4.27)	115–8	sub at 0.0006 mm			i	s	s	ace s	...		E12A, 170
c21	Camphane.......	Bornane. Bornylane. Dihydrocamphene. 1,7,7-Trimethyl-bicyclo[2.2.1]heptane	138.25	hex pl (al), pr (MeOH)	158–9	sub 161			i	s[h]	s	...	...	AcOEt s MeOH s[h]	E12A, 570
—	—,2,3-dioxo-......	see **Camphorquinone**													
c22	3-Camphane-carboxylic acid		182.27	pl (dil aa) $[\alpha]_D^{20}$ +56 (al, p = 8)	90–1	153[13]						s	...	aa v	B9[2], 52
—	2,3-Cam-phanedione	see **Camphorquinone**													
c23	Camphene(d).....	....	136.24	nd, $[\alpha]_D^{17}$ +103.9 (eth, c = 4), +104.7 (al) λ^{al} 206 (3.74)	52	160–2[760] 52[17]	0.8450[50]	1.4570[25]	i	δ	s	...	...		B5[3], 380
Ω c24	—(dl)...........	$C_{10}H_{16}$. *See* c23	136.24	nd (sub)	51–2	158.5–9.5[760]	0.879[20]	1.4551[54]	i	v	v	...	...		B5[3], 380
Ω c25	—(l)...........	$C_{10}H_{16}$. *See* c23	136.24	$[\alpha]_D^{19}$ −106.1 (eth, c = 4)	52	158[760]	0.8446[60]	1.4564[54]							B5[3], 380

For explanations, symbols and abbreviations see beginning of table. For structural formulas see end of table.

No.	Name	Synonyms and Formula	Mol. wt.	Color, crystalline form, specific rotation and λ_{max} (log ε)	m.p. °C	b.p. °C	Density	n_D	w	al	eth	ace	bz	other solvents	Ref.
	Camphenilone														
c26	**Camphenilone** (d)	....	138.21	$[\alpha]_D^{20}$ +70.4 (al)	41	193^{751} 76^{12}	....		i	...	s			....	B7[1], 59
—	**Camphenol**	See **1-Epiborneol**													
—	**Camphol**	See **Isoborneol**													
c27	**Campholic acid**	....	170.25	pr, $[\alpha]_D^{20}$ +59.3 (bz) λ <220	106	255^{768} 146^{12}	....		δ s^h	s	s			....	B9[2], 17
c28	—(dl)	$C_{10}H_{18}O_2$. See c27	170.25	tcl pr	109	....	....		i	v	s			....	B9[2], 19
c29	—(l)	$C_{10}H_{18}O_2$. See c27	170.25	pr (dil al) $[\alpha]_D^{15}$ −49.1 (al)	106–7	250^{760}	....		i	s	s			....	B9, 36
c30	**Campholytic acid** (α,l)	....	154.21	$[\alpha]_D^{13}$ −60.4	....	240–3 140^{15}	1.0145^{18}	1.4712^{17}						lig v	B9[1], 33
c31	**Camphor** (d)	d-2-Camphanone. Formosa camphor. Laurel camphor. $C_{10}H_{16}O$.	152.24	pl, $[\alpha]_D^{20}$ +44.26 (al) λ^{al} 290 (1.48)	179.8	sub 204^{760}	0.990_4^{25}	1.5462	i	v	v	s	s	chl, CCl₄, MeOH, aa v	B7[2], 93
Ω c32	—(dl)	$C_{10}H_{16}O$. See c31	152.24	wh λ^{al} 290 (1.48)	178.8	sub	....		i	v	v	s	s	chl, aa v	B7[2], 104
c33	—(l)	$C_{10}H_{16}O$. See c31	152.24	$[\alpha]_D^{16}$ −44.2 (al, c =16.5) λ^{al} 290 (1.49)	178.6	204 sub	0.9853^{18}		i	v	v	s	s	chl, aa v	B7[2], 103
c34	—,oxime (d)	....	167.25	pr (lig-eth) $[\alpha]_D^{22}$ +42.5 (al)	115	....	....		i	v	s			....	B7[1], 80
c35	—,—(dl)	$C_{10}H_{17}NO$. See c34	167.25	cr (peth)	118	....	....		i	v	s			....	B7[2], 104
c36	—,—(l)	$C_{10}H_{17}NO$. See c34	167.25	mcl nd or pr (dil al) $[\alpha]_D^{20}$ −42.4 (al)	118	249–54d	1.014^{16}		i	v	s			....	B7[1], 84
c37	—,3-amino-(d)	3-Aminocamphor. 3-Camphorylamine. $C_{10}H_{17}NO$. See c31	167.25	wx	110 −15d	244	....		i	v	s			....	B14[2], 6
c38	—,3-bromo-(d,α)..	$C_{10}H_{15}BrO$. See c31	231.14	pr (al) $[\alpha]_D^{20}$ +129.3 (MeOH, c =4.6), +122.7 (bz) λ^{bz} 307.5 (1.98)	76	274 δd sub	1.449_4^{20}		i	s v^h	v		s	chl, CCl₄ s	B7[2], 100
Ω c39	—,—(dl,α).........	$C_{10}H_{15}BrO$. See c31	231.14		51	....	....		i	v	v		s	chl s	B7[2], 105
c40	—,—(l,α).........	$C_{10}H_{15}BrO$. See c31	231.14	mcl nd (al) $[\alpha]_D^{18}$ −138.8 (ace, c =6)	76	....	....		i	v	v		s	chl s	B7[2], 104
c41	—,—(d,α').......	$C_{10}H_{15}BrO$. See c31	231.14	nd (dil al) $[\alpha]_D^{20}$ +29.4 λ^{bz} 312 (1.95)	78	265d	1.484^{14}			v				chl, CS₂, aa v	B7[2], 101
Ω c42	—,8-bromo-(d)	π-Bromocamphor. $C_{10}H_{15}BrO$. See c31	231.14	tetr pr (lig) $[\alpha]_D^9$ +122.2 (chl) λ^{al} 289 (1.77)	93	sub	....			s	v^h	s	s	os s peth s^h	B7, 123
c43	—,—(dl)	$C_{10}H_{15}BrO$. See c31	231.14	pr (eth-peth), pym (eth)	92.7	sub	....			s	v^h	s	s	os s peth s^h	B7, 136
Ω c44	—,10-bromo-(d) ...	$C_{10}H_{15}BrO$. See c31	231.14	pr (peth) $[\alpha]_D^{20}$ +19.2 (abs al), +15.7 (bz) λ^{cy} 293 (1.39)	78	265d	....		i	v^h	v	s	v	chl, CS₂, aa v	B7[2], 101
c45	—,—(dl)	$C_{10}H_{15}BrO$. See c31	231.14	cr	77	....	....							....	B7[2], 105
c46	—,3-chloro-(d,α)...	$C_{10}H_{15}ClO$. See c31	186.68	lf, $[\alpha]_D^{20}$ +71.1 (bz, c = 9.2), +97 (al) λ^{cy} 305 (1.72)	94	244–7d	....		s^h	s^h	s	s	s	CS₂, chl s	B7[2], 100
c47	—,—(d,α').......	$C_{10}H_{15}ClO$. See c31	186.68	$[\alpha]_D^{20}$ +35 (al, c = 5) λ^{cy} 306 (1.75)	118	231d	....		δ	δ	s			CS₂, chl s	B7[2], 100
Ω c48	—,8-chloro-(d)	π-Chlorocamphor. $C_{10}H_{15}ClO$. See c31	186.68	pr, $[\alpha]_D$ +99.9 (chl)	139	....	....							....	B7, 119
c49	—,—(dl)	$C_{10}H_{15}ClO$. See c31	186.68	....	138	sub	....							os v	B7, 136
c50	—,10-chloro-(d) ...	$C_{10}H_{15}ClO$. See c31	186.68	pr (al) $[\alpha]_D^{14}$ +40.7 (al)	132–5	....	....			s	v		s	chl, peth, aa s	B7[2], 100
c51	—,3,3-dibromo-(d)	$C_{10}H_{14}Br_2O$. See c31	310.04	wh-ye rh pr (al, peth), $[\alpha]_D^{20}$ +40 (chl), +39.2 (al) λ^{al} 323 (1.88)	64	δ sub δ d	$1.854_4^{21.6}$		i	v	v		v	chl, peth v AcOEt s	B7[2], 101

For explanations, symbols and abbreviations see beginning of table. For structural formulas see end of table.

No.	Name	Synonyms and Formula	Mol. wt.	Color, crystalline form, specific rotation and λ_{max} (log ε)	m.p. °C	b.p. °C	Density	n_D	w	al	eth	ace	bz	other solvents	Ref.
	Camphor														
c52	—, 3-nitro-(l)	$C_{10}H_{15}NO_3$. See c31	197.24	mcl pr (bz), $[\alpha]_D^{13}$ $-26 \to -9$ (al) (mut) $[\alpha]_D^{15}$ $-124 \to -104$ (bz) (mut)	104				i	s	s	...	v	chl v lig s peth δ	B7[2], 103
—	**Camphoramic acid**	*See* **Camphoric acid,** monoamide													
c53	**3-Camphorcar-boxylic acid** (d)		196.25	pr (eth, 50 % al) $[\alpha]_D^{20} +34.9$ (bz)	128d				s	v	s	...	v	lig δ	B10[2], 442
c54	—(dl)	$C_{11}H_{16}O_3$. See c53	196.25	cr (bz)	136–7				s	v	s^h	...	v^h	AcOEt s	B10[1], 308
c55	—(l)	$C_{11}H_{16}O_3$. See c53	196.25	pr (eth), cr (bz) $[\alpha]_D^{20} -64$ (al), -57.4 (AcOEt)	127–8d				s	v	s^h	...	v^h	AcOEt s	B10[1], 308
c56	**Camphoric acid** (d)	1,2,2-Trimethylcyclopentane-1,3-dicarboxylic acid.	200.24	pr lf (w^h) $[\alpha]_D^{20} +47.7$ (al), $+50.8$ (ace)	188.2		1.186_4^{20}		δ s^h	v	v	s	i	MeOH v to, lig, chl l	B9[2], 534
Ω c57	—(dl)	$C_{10}H_{16}O_4$. See c56	200.24	pr (al, aa), mcl nd	208 (203)		1.228_4^{20}		v^h	s	v	...	s	chl δ	B9[1], 332
c58	—(l)	$C_{10}H_{16}O_4$. See c56	200.24	cr (w), $[\alpha]_D^{16}$ -48.1 (abs al, c = 8)	187.5		1.190		δ	s	s	s	...	MeOH s aa δ	B9[2], 539
Ω c59	—, anhydride (d)		182.22	rh (al), pr (bz)	223.5	>270d	1.194^{20}		δ	δ	δ	...	s	chl δ	B17[1], 238
Ω c60	—,—(dl)	$C_{10}H_{14}O_3$. See c59	182.22	rh (al)	221	270	1.194_4^{20}		δ	δ	δ	...	s	AcOEt, CS_2 s chl δ	B17, 459
c61	—,—(l)	$C_{10}H_{14}O_3$. See c59	182.22	$[\alpha]_D -77$ (bz)	221	>270	1.194_4^{20}		i	δ	δ	...	s	...	B17, 459
c62	—, diethyl ester (d)	$C_{14}H_{24}O_4$. See c56	256.35	$[\alpha]_D^{15} +7.5$ (al), $+9$ (bz)		286^{752} 164^{20}	1.0298_4^{20}	1.4535^{26}	i	s	s	...	s	CCl_4 s	B9[2], 536
c62[i]	—, dimethyl ester (d)	$C_{12}H_{20}O_4$. See c56	228.29	$[\alpha]_D +49.07$ (al)	< −16	264^{738} 155^{15}	1.0747_4^{20}	1.4627^{19}	i	v	s	...	s		B9[2], 535
c63	—, 1-monoamide (d)	β-Camphoramic acid.	199.25	pl, nd, $[\alpha]_D^{20} +74$ (al)	183				δ s^h	s	δ	s	δ	lig δ	B9[2], 536
c64	—, 3-monoamide (d)	α-Camphoramic acid.	199.25	nd or lf (w) $[\alpha]_D^{20} +25$ (al)	176–7				s^h	s^h	δ	s^h	δ^h	MeOH s^h chl δ	B9[2], 536
c65	—,—(dl)	$C_{10}H_{17}NO_3$. See c64	199.25	nd (w)	198				s^h	s^h	δ	s^h	δ^h	chl δ	B9, 761
c67	**Camphoronic acid** (d)	$(CH_3)_2C(CO_2H)C(CH_3)(CO_2H)CH_2CO_2H$	218.21	nd (w) $[\alpha]^{19} +27.05$ (w)	159d				v	v	v	s	i	chl v peth i	B2, 837
c68	—(dl)	$(CH_3)_2C(CO_2H)C(CH_3)(CO_2H)CH_2CO_2H$	218.21	nd or pr (w)	172d				δ	v	v	s	i	peth i	B2, 839
c69	—(l)	$(CH_3)_2C(CO_2H)C(CH_3)(CO_2H)CH_2CO_2H$	218.21	nd (w) $[\alpha]_D^{19} -26.9$ (w)	164–5d (rapid htng)				v	v	s	s	i	chl v peth i	B2[2], 690
c70	**Camphor pinacol** (l)	2,2′-Bicamphane-2,2′-diol.	306.49	rh, $[\alpha]_D -27.2$ (bz)	158				i	s	s	...	s		B6[3], 4767
Ω c71	**Camphorquinone** (l)	3-Ketocamphor. 2,3-Camphanedione.	166.22	ye nd (dil al, w), pr (eth) $[\alpha]_D^{20}$ -113.2 (bz), -105.4 (chl) $\lambda^{al} 269$ (1.4), 279 (1.4), 468 (1.5)	199	sub			s^h	v	v	...	s	chl s	B7, 581
c72	**3-Camphorsulfonic acid,** methyl ester (d)		246.33	cr (MeOH), nd (peth), $[\alpha]_D^{20}$ $+98.6$ (chl, c = 5) $\lambda^{al} 288$ (1.43)	77	201^{20}			i	v	s	...	v	MeOH v os s	B2, 179
c73	**10-Camphorsulfonic acid** (d)		232.30	pr (aa), $[\alpha]_D^{20}$ $+32.8$ (AcOEt, c = 3), $+24$ (w) $\lambda^w 283$ (1.54)	195d				v		i	...	...	aa δ	B2[2], 180
c74	—(dl)	$C_{10}H_{16}O_4S$. See c73	232.30	cr (aa)	202d				v		i	...	...	aa δ	B2[2], 182
c75	—(l)	$C_{10}H_{16}O_4S$. See c73	232.30	cr (aa), nd (AcOEt), $[\alpha]_D^{20}$ -20.75 (w)	194–5d				v		i	...	...	AcOEt, aa δ	B2[2], 182
c76	**α-Camphylamine**	4-(2-Aminoethyl)-1,5,5-tri-methylcyclopentene	153.27	$[\alpha]_D +6$		194–6 95^{12}	0.8688^{20}	1.4728^{18}							B12[2], 35
c77	**β-Camphylamine**	2-(2-Aminoethyl)-1,5,5-tri-methylcyclopentine.	153.27			206	0.8697_{20}^{20}								B12, 40

For explanations, symbols and abbreviations see beginning of table. For structural formulas see end of table.

No.	Name	Synonyms and Formula	Mol. wt.	Color, crystalline form, specific rotation and λ_{max} (log ε)	m.p. °C	b.p. °C	Density	n_D	w	al	eth	ace	bz	other solvents	Ref.
	Canadine														
c78	**Canadine** (d)	d-Tetrahydroberberine. $C_{20}H_{21}NO_4$.	339.40	ye nd (dil al) $[\alpha]_D^{29} +299$ (chl, c = 1) λ^{MeOH} 288 (3.83)	132 (140)	....			i	v	s	...	s	chl s lig δ^h	B27[2], 557
Ω c79	—(dl)	$C_{20}H_{21}NO_4$. See c78	339.40	mcl nd (al) λ^{MeOH} 288 (3.83)	174	....			δ	δ	..	...	...	chl, CS_2 v	B27[2], 557
c80	—(l)	$C_{20}H_{21}NO_4$. See c78	339.40	ye nd (al), $[\alpha]_D^{20}$ −299.2 (chl) λ^{MeOH} 288 (3.83)	134	....			i	v	s	...	s	chl s lig δ^h	B27[2], 557
c81	**Canaline**	$H_2NOCH_2CH_2CH(NH_2)CO_2H$	134.14	nd (al) $[\alpha]_D^{21} -8.31$ (w)	214d	....			v	s^h	i	..	i	....	B4[3], 1636
c82	**Canavanine** (L)	$NH:C(NH_2)NHOCH_2CH_2CH(NH_2)CO_2H$	176.18	cr (al), $[\alpha]_D^{20} +7.9$ (w, c = 2)	184	....			s	i	i	..	i	....	B4[3], 1636
—	**Canescine**	see **Deserpidine**													
c83	**Cannabidiol**		314.47	rods (peth) λ^{bz} 217 (3.1), 275 (2.0), 280 (2.0)	67	187–90[2]			i	s	s	.	. s	chl s	Am 63, 2209
c84	**Cannabinol**	$C_{21}H_{26}O_2$	310.44	pl, lf (peth) $[\alpha]^{20} -148$ (al) λ^{al} 220 (4.55), 285 (4.26)	77	185[0.05]			i	s	s	s	s	alk, peth s	B17[2], 151
Ω c85	**Cantharidin**	$C_{10}H_{12}O_4$	196.21	rh pl or sc	218	sub 84			i	δ	δ	δ	δ	aa, con sulf s chl δ	B19[2], 179
—	**Capraldehyde**	see **Decanal***													
—	**Capric acid**	see **Decanoic acid***													
—	**Caproaldehyde**	see **Hexanal***													
—	**Caproic acid**	see **Hexanoic acid***													
—	**ε-Caprolactam**	see **Hexanoic acid, 6-amino-, lactam***													
—	**Caprophenone**	see **1-Hexanone, 1-phenyl-***													
—	**Caprylaldehyde**	see **Octanal***													
—	**Caprylic acid**	see **Octanoic acid***													
c86	**Capsaicin**	$C_{18}H_{27}NO_3$	305.42	mcl pl or sc (petn) λ^{al} 227 (3.91), 281 (3.43)	65	210-20[0.01]			i	v	s	...	s	peth s con HCl δ	B13[2], 482
—	**Captan**	see **4-Cyclohexene-1,2-dicarboxylic acid, imide, N (trichloromethylthio)-**													
c87	**Carbamic acid,** benzyl ester	$H_2NCO_2CH_2C_6H_5$	151.17	pl (to), lf (w)	91 (86–7)	220d			δ^h	v	δ	...	...	to s	B6, 437
Ω c88	—,4-benzylphenyl ester		227.27	....	145				δ^h	v^h	...	..	v	NaOH s	B6[2], 630
Ω c89	—,butyl ester......	$H_2NCO_2C_4H_9^n$	117.15	pr	54	204 δd				v					B3[2], 25
c90	—,chloride	Carbamoyl chloride. H_2NCOCl	79.49		62[760]d				d	d					B3[1], 15
Ω c91	—,ethyl ester......	Urethane. $H_2NCO_2C_2H_5$ ...	89.10	pr (bz, to)	48.5–50	185[760]	0.9862_4^{21}	1.4144^{52}	v	v	v	..	v	chl, py, to v lig δ	B3[2], 19
c92	—,isobutyl ester ...	$H_2NCO_2C_4H_9^i$	117.15	lf	67	207		1.4098^{76}	i	s	s	..	..		B3[2], 26
Ω c93	—,isopropyl ester ..	$H_2NCO_2C_3H_7^i$	103.12	nd	92–4	181[711]	0.9995^{66}		v	v	v				B3[2], 25
Ω c94	—,methyl ester	Urethylan. $H_2NCO_2CH_3$	75.07	nd	54	177 82[14]	1.1361_4^{46}	1.4125^{56}	v	v	v	..	..		B3[2], 18
c95	—,2-methyl-2-butyl ester	tert-Amyl carbamate. Aponal. $H_2NCO_2C(CH_3)_2C_2H_5$	131.18	nd (dil al)	85–7	....			δ	δ	..	s	s	os v lig δ	B3[1], 14
c96	—,3-methylbutyl ester	$H_2NCO_2CH_2CH_2CH(CH_3)_2$	131.18	nd (w^h)	64 (59)	220[760] 114.5[16]	0.9438_4^{21}	1.4175^{71}	s^h	s	s	..	..		B3[2], 26
—	—,nitrile	see **Cyanamide**													
c97	—,propyl ester	$H_2NCO_2CH_2CH_2CH_3$	103.12	pr	60	196 92–2.5[12]			s	s	s	s	s		B3[2], 25
Ω c98	—,N-benzyl-, ethyl ester	$C_6H_5CH_2NHCO_2C_2H_5$	179.22	lf (lig)	49 (44)	230δd			δ	v	v	...	v	chl v lig s^h	B12[2], 563
c99	—,N-benzyl-N-nitro-, ethyl ester	$C_6H_5CH_2N(NO_2)CO_2C_2H_5$	224.22	ye	....	d	1.213^{20}	1.5203^{20}	..	∞	∞	..	..		C55, 24616
c100	—,N-butyl-, butyl ester	$C_4H_9^nNHCO_2C_4H_9^n$	173.26			88[3]	0.9238_{20}^{20}	1.4359^{20}	..	∞	∞	..	..		Am 73, 5043
c101	—,N-butyl-N-nitro-, butyl ester	$C_4H_9^nN(NO_2)CO_2C_4H_9^n$	218.26	λ^{al} 238 (3.83)	....	98[3]	1.048^{20}	1.448^{20}	...	∞	∞	..	..		Am 73, 5449
c102	—,N-tert-butyl-N-nitro-, ethyl ester	$C_4H_9^nN(NO_2)CO_2C_2H_5$	190.20	λ^{al} 239 (3.43)	....	56[2]d	1.051^{20}	1.4331^{20}	...	∞	∞	..	..		Am 83, 1191
c103	—,N-cyclohexyl-(N-ethyl)-dithio-, hexyl (ethyl)-, ammonium salt		330.60	ye	93	....			s^h	v	s	..	..		B12[2], 12

For explanations, symbols and abbreviations see beginning of table. For structural formulas see end of table.

No.	Name	Synonyms and Formula	Mol. wt.	Color, crystalline form. specific rotation and λ_{max} (log ε)	m.p. °C	b.p. °C	Density	n_D	Solubility						Ref.
									w	al	eth	ace	bz	other solvents	
	Carbamic acid														
c104	—,N-**dibenzyldi-thio**-, dibenzyl-ammonium salt	$(C_6H_5CH_2)_2NCS_2$ $NH_2(CH_2C_6H_5)_2$	470.71	ye (eth)	82	....			s	v					**B12**, 1058
c105	—,N,N-**diethyl**-	$(C_2H_5)_2NCO_2H$	117.15	nd (eth)	−15d	171	0.9276_4^{20}	1.4206^{20}	v	v	δ				**B4**², 611
Ω c106	—,N,N-**diethyl**-, chloride	N,N-Diethylchloroformamide. $(C_2H_5)_2NCOCl$	135.60	....	....	186 (190)			d^h	d^h					**B4**², 611
c107	—,N,N-**diethyldi-thio**-, benzylidene ester	$[(C_2H_5)_2NCS_2]_2CHC_6H_5$	386.67	ye (al)	110				i	s^h					**C29**, 8408
c108	—,—,diethylammonium salt	$(C_2H_5)_2NCS_2^- \overset{+}{N}H_2(C_2H_5)_2$	222.42	ye pl (eth-al)	88 (82)				v	v	δ				**B4**, 121
Ω c109	—,N,N-**diethyl-thio**-, chloride	$(C_2H_5)_2NCSCl$	151.66	pr	48–51	108^{10}									**B4**, 121
c110	—,N,N-**dimethyl-dithio**-, dimethyl-ammonium salt	$(CH_3)_2NCS_2^- \overset{+}{N}H_2(CH_3)_2 \cdot \tfrac{1}{2}C_6H_6$	205.37	ye pl (bz + ½) nd (al–eth, unsolv)	125 (+ ½bz), 134–6 (unsolv)				v	v	δ				**B4**², 577
Ω c111	—,—,2,4-dinitro-phenyl ester		287.32	ye	152–3	....	1.54^{20}		i	s^h		s	s		**C51**, 3481
c112	—,N,N-**dimethyl-thio**-, chloride	$(CH_3)_2NCSCl$	123.61	pr	42.5–3.5	98^{10}					v			peth, chl s	**B4**, 576
c113	—,N,N-**diphenyl**-, chloride	$(C_6H_5)_2NCOCl$	231.68	lf (al)	85										**B12**², 241
c114	—,—,ethyl ester	Diphenylurethan. $(C_6H_5)_2NCO_2C_2H_5$ λ^{al} 238 (7.13)	241.29	pr (lig)	72	360^{760}			s	δ	s		s	peth s	**B12**², 240
c115	—,**dithio**-	Aminodithioformic acid. Aminomethanethionothiolic acid*. H_2NCS_2H $\lambda^{al-NH_4 salt}$ 291 (4.30), 345 (2.60)	93.17	nd					d	v					**B3**², 155
c116	—,N-**ethyl**-, butyl ester	$C_2H_5NHCO_2C_4H_9^n$	145.20			66^3	0.9413_{20}^{20}	1.4301^{20}	s	∞	∞				**C55**, 2334
Ω c117	—,—,ethyl ester	Ethylurethan. $C_2H_5NHCO_2C_2H_5$	117.15			176^{760} 75^{14}	0.9813_4^{20}	1.4215^{20}	s	v	v				**B4**², 607
c118	—,N-**ethyl**-N-**nitro**-, butyl ester	$C_2H_5N(NO_2)CO_2C_4H_9^n$	190.20			79^3	1.091_{20}^{20}	1.4455^{20}	s	∞	∞				**Am73**, 5043
c119	—,—,ethyl ester	$C_2H_5N(NO_2)CO_2C_2H_5$	162.15	λ^{al} 237 (3.75)		107^{31}	1.163_{20}^{20}	1.4432^{20}	i	∞	∞				**Am73**, 5449
c119¹	—,methyl ester	$C_2H_5N(NO_2)CO_2CH_3$	148.13	λ^{al} 235 (3.75)		72^{11}	1.233_{20}^{20}	1.4483^{20}	i	∞	∞				**Am73**, 5449
Ω c120	—,N-**ethyl-idenedi**-, diethyl ester	Ethylidenediurethan. $CH_3CH(NHCO_2C_2H_5)_2$	204.23	nd (eth)	126	$170–8^{20}$			v	v	δ	v	δ	chl, MeOH s to, lig δ	**B3**¹, 11
c121	—,N-**isobutyl**-, ethyl ester	Isobutylurethan. $C_4H_9NHCO_2C_2H_5$	145.20		> −65	110^{30} 96^{17}	0.9432_4^{20}	1.4288^{20}	δ	v	v				**B4**², 640
c122	—,N-**isopropyl**, ethyl ester	Isopropylurethan. $C_3H_7^iNHCO_2C_2H_5$	131.18			79^{15}	0.9548_{20}^{20}	1.4229^{20}	δ	∞	∞				**B4**¹, 369
c123	—,N-**isopropyl**-N-**nitro**-, ethyl ester	$C_3H_7^iN(NO_2)CO_2C_2H_5$	176.17	λ^{al} 240 (3.7)		72^7	1.112_{20}^{20}	1.4381^{20}	i	∞	∞				**Am73**, 5449
c124	—,N-**methyl**-, ethyl ester	Methylurethan. $CH_3NHCO_2C_2H_5$	103.12			170^{760} 80^{15}	1.0115_4^{20}	1.4183^{20}	v	s	v				**B4**², 567
c125	—,N-**methyl**-N-**phenyl**-, chloride	$CH_3N(C_6H_5)COCl$	169.62	pl (al)	88–9	280			i	v	v			s^h	**B12**², 235
c126	—,N-**nitro**-, ethyl ester	$O_2NNHCO_2C_2H_5$ λ^{al} 215 (3.9), 260 sh (2.6), 290 sh (2.2)	134.09	pl (eth, lig)	64	140d	1.0074_4^{20}		v	v	v			lig δ	**B3**², 99
c127	—,N-**nitro**-N-**propyl**-, ethyl ester	$C_3H_7^nN(NO_2)CO_2C_2H_5$ λ^{al} 239 (3.80)	176.17			66^3	1.123_{20}^{20}	1.4431^{20}	i	∞	∞				**Am73**, 5449
c128	—,—,methyl ester	$C_3H_7^nN(NO_2)CO_2CH_3$	162.15					1.1585_{15}^{15}		v	∞	∞				**B4**, 146
c129	—,N-**phenyl**-, ethyl ester	Ethyl carbanilate. $C_6H_5NHCO_2C_2H_5$	165.19	wh nd (w), pl (dil al) λ^{al} 235.5 (4.23), 278 (2.93)	53	237^{760} δd 152^{14}	1.1064_4^{20}	1.5376^{10}	i s^h	v	v		s		**B12**², 184
c130	—,—,isobutyl ester	$C_6H_5NHCO_2C_4H_9^i$	193.25	nd (dil al)	86	216^{760}			δ	v	v		s		**B12**¹, 219
c131	—,—,isopropyl ester	$C_6H_5NHCO_2C_3H_7^i$	179.22	wh nd (al) λ^{al} 235.5 (4.23), 274 (2.92)	90 (76)		1.09^{20}	1.4989^{91}	i	s			s		**B12**, 321
c132	—,—,propyl ester	$C_6H_5NHCO_2C_3H_7^n$	179.22	wh nd (dil al)	57–9	192^{758}			δ	s	v		s		**B12**, 321
Ω c133	—,N-**propyl**-, ethyl ester	$C_3H_7^nNHCO_2C_2H_5$	131.18			192^{758} 92^{22}	0.9921^{15}		s						**B4**², 626
c134	—,**thiolo**-, ethyl ester	$H_2NCOSC_2H_5$	105.16	pl (w)	109	sub d			i s^h	s	v				**B3**¹, 64
c135	—,**thiono**-, ethyl ester	Thiourethan. Xanthogen-amide. $H_2NCSOC_2H_5$	105.16	mcl lf or pyr	41	d	1.069_4^{20}	1.520^{20}	δ	∞	∞			chl v	**B3**², 97
—	**Carbamyl chloride**	see **Carbamic acid**, chloride													

For explanations, symbols and abbreviations see beginning of table. For structural formulas see end of table.

No.	Name	Synonyms and Formula	Mol. wt.	Color, crystalline form, specific rotation and λ_{max} (log ε)	m.p. °C	b.p. °C	Density	n_D	w	al	eth	ace	bz	other solvents	Ref.
	Carbamyl guanidine														
—	Carbamyl guanidine	see Guanidine, 1-ureido-													
—	Carbanilic acid	see Carbamic acid, N-phenyl-													
—	Carbanilide	see Urea, 1,3-diphenyl-													
Ω c136	Carbazide	$H_2NNHCONHNH_2$	90.09	nd (dil al)	154	....	1.616^{20}	....	v	v					B3[2], 96
c137	—,1,5-diphenyl-	$CO(NHNHC_6H_5)_2$	242.28	cr (al + 1), cr (aa)	170	d	....	....	δ^h	s^h	δ	s^h	s	aa s	B15[2], 107
c138	—,1-phenyl-	$C_6H_5NHNHCONHNH_2$	166.18	nd (al)	151	....	....	....	s	s^h					B15[2], 107
c139	—,1,1,5,5-tetraphenyl-	$[(C_6H_5)_2NNH]_2CO$	394.48	(al), nd (aa)	242	....	....	....		v^h				aa v^h	B15[2], 115
c140	—,3-thio-	$H_2NNHCSNHNH_2$	106.15	nd, pl (w)	170d	....	....	....	v^h	δ^h	i			alk v	B3[2], 137
—	Carbazine	see Acridine, 9,10-dihydro-													
Ω c141	Carbazole	Dibenzopyrrole. Diphenylenimine.	167.21	pl or lf	247–8	355^{760} 200^{147}	....	....	i	s^h δ	δ	s v^h	s^h δ	Py δ, s^h chl, to, aa, CS_2 δ	B20[2], 279
Ω c142	—,9-acetyl-	$C_{14}H_{11}NO$. See c141	209.25	(eth), nd (w) λ^{al} 230 (4.61), 262.5 (4.23), 286 (4.05), 300 (3.79), 312 (3.82)	69	190^6	1.161^{100}_{24}	1.640^{100}	δ^h						B20[2], 283
c143	—,9-benzoyl-	$C_{19}H_{13}NO$. See c141	271.32	nd or pr (al)	98.5	....	....	....		v^h			v		B20[1], 165
c144	—,9-benzyl-	$C_{19}H_{15}N$. See c141	257.34	nd (al)	118–120 (114)	$267-8^{24}$	....	....	i	δ			v		B20[2], 283
c145	—,9-butyl-	$C_{16}H_{17}N$. See c141	223.32	nd (al)	58	$218-9^{19}$	....	....	i	δ	v				B20[1], 164
c146	—,9-ethenyl-	$C_{14}H_{11}N$. See c141	193.25	cr (al)	66	....	....	....	i	δ	v				B20[2], 282
Ω c147	—,9-ethyl-	$C_{14}H_{13}N$. See c141	195.27	nd (al) λ^{cy} 236 (4.7), 294 (4.35), 329 (3.6), 343 (3.75)	68	190^{10}	1.059^{80}_4	1.6394^{80}	i	v^h	v				B20[2], 282
c148	—,9-methyl-	$C_{13}H_{11}N$. See c141	181.24	nd, lf (al) λ^{al} 235(4.61), 293 (4.23), 329.5 (3.56), 343.5 (4.59)	88	195^{12}	....	....	i	δ	v				B20[2], 281
c149	—,1-nitro-	$C_{12}H_8N_2O_2$. See c141	212.22	ye nd (aa) λ^{al} 223.5 (4.54), 260 (3.97), 300.5 (4.16), 403 (3.88)	187	....	....	....	i					aa v CS_2 s peth δ	B20[2], 288
c150	—,3-nitro-	$C_{12}H_8N_2O_2$. See c141	212.22	ye λ^{al} 230.5 (4.45), 280 (4.40), 306 (4.16), 363 (4.01)	214 (205–7)	....	....	....	i		δ		δ	peth, chl, aa δ	B20[2], 288
c151	—,3-nitro-9-nitroso-	$C_{12}H_7N_3O_3$. See c141	241.21	ye nd (al) λ^{al} 255.5 (4.51), 307 (3.99), 332 (4.02)	169 (164)	....	....	....		s^h				chl s lig δ	B20[2], 289
c152	—,1-oxo-1,2,3,4-tetrahydro-	$C_{12}H_{11}NO$. See c141	185.23	nd (dil al) λ^{al} 237 (4.21), 308.5 (4.36)	170	....	....	....		s			s	aa s	B21[2], 275
Ω c153	—,9-phenyl-	$C_{18}H_{13}N$. See c141	243.31	nd or pl (al)	95	....	....	....		v^h	v		v	aa v	B20[2], 282
c154	—,9-propionyl-	$C_{15}H_{13}NO$. See c141	223.28	....	90	....	....	....		v	v			peth δ	B20[1], 165
c155	—,9-propyl-	$C_{15}H_{15}N$. See c141	209.29	nd (al)	50	....	....	....	i	δ	v				B20[1], 164
Ω c156	—,1,2,3,4-tetrahydro-	$C_{12}H_{13}N$. See c141	171.25	lf (dil al) λ^{al} 227 (4.72), 282 (3.97), 290 (3.92)	120	$325-30$ 190^{10}	....	....	i	s	v		v	MeOH v	B20[2], 257
c157	Carbazone, 1,5-diphenyl-	$C_6H_5N:NCONHNHC_6H_5$	240.27	og nd (bz), pr (al) λ^w ca. 470	157d	....	....	....	i	v			v	chl v	B16[2], 9
—	Carbinol	see Methanol*													
—	Carbitol	see Diethyleneglycol, mono-ethyl ether													
—	α-Carbocinchomeronic acid	see 2,3,4-Pyridinetri-carboxylic acid													
c158	Carbodiimide, diphenyl-	$C_6H_5N:C:NC_6H_5$	194.24	....	168–170	331^{760} 218^{31}	....	....	δ	δ	δ		s		B12[2], 246
—	Carbohydrazide	see Carbazide													
Ω c159	Carbon dioxide	CO_2	44.00	....	−56.6 (at 5.2 atm)	-78.5^{760} sub	0.00198 (gas at 0° 1 atm 1.0310^{−20} (liq)	....							B3, 4

For explanations, symbols and abbreviations see beginning of table. For structural formulas see end of table.

No.	Name	Synonyms and Formula	Mol. wt.	Color, crystalline form, specific rotation and λ_{max} (log ε)	m.p. °C	b.p. °C	Density	n_D	w	al	eth	ace	bz	other solvents	Ref.
	Carbon diselenide														
c160	Carbon diselenide	CSe_2	169.93	ye	−45.5	126[760] 46[60]	2.6824[20/4]	1.8454[20]	...	...	...	...	...		B3[3], 366
Ω c161	Carbon disulfide	CS_2	76.14	λ[cy] 314 (2.89), 319 (2.83)	−111.53	46.25[760] 0[128]	1.2632[20/4]	1.6319[20]	s	∞	∞	...	...	chl s	B3[2], 139
c162	Carbonic acid, bis-(2-chloroethyl) ester*	$OC(OCH_2CH_2Cl)_2$	187.03		8	241	1.3506[20]	1.461[20]	i	...	...	...	...		B3[2], 5
c163	—,bis(3-chloropropyl) ester*	$OC(OCH_2CH_2CH_2Cl)_2$	215.08			265−70[740]			...	...	...	...	...		B3[2], 5
c164	—,bis(2-ethoxyethyl) ester*	$OC(OCH_2CH_2OC_2H_5)_2$	206.24			245−6[758] 112−3[5]	1.0439[20/4]	1.4227[20]	...	v	v	v	...		B3[3], 17
Ω c165	—,bis(2-methoxyethyl) ester*	$OC(OCH_2CH_2OCH_3)_2$	178.19			230−2[760] 99−100[5]	1.0988[20/4]	1.4204[20]	...	s	s	s	...		B3[3], 17
c166	—,bis(2-methoxyphenyl) ester*	Duotal.	274.28	cr (al)	89				i	δ	s	...	...	chl v	B6[2], 784
c166[1]	—,bis(3-methylbutyl) ester*	$OC[OCH_2CH_2CH(CH_3)_2]_2$	202.30			232.5[751] 122[16]	0.9067[20/4]	1.4174[20]	i	...	...	...	...		B3[2], 7
c167	—,bis(trichloromethyl) ester*	$OC(OCCl_3)_2$	296.75	cr (eth, peth)	79	203[760] δd			...	...	δ[h]	...	...	peth δ[h]	B3[1], 8
Ω c168	—,dibutyl ester*	$OC(OC_4H_9^n)_2$	174.24			207[760] 96−7[16]	0.9251[20/4]	1.4117[20]	i	ε	s	...	...		B3[2], 6
c169	—,di-tert-butyl ester*	$OC(OC_4H_9^t)_2$	174.24	cr (al)	40 sub	158[767]			i	s[h]	...	...	...		B3[3], 11
—	—,dichloride*	see Phosgene													
Ω c170	—,diethyl ester*	$OC(OC_2H_5)_2$	118.13		−43	126	0.9752[20/4]	1.3845[20]	i	s	s	...	...		B3[3], 5
—	—,dihydrazide	see Carbazide													
c171	—,diisobutyl ester*	$OC(OC_4H_9^i)_2$	174.24			190[760] 85[16]	0.9138[20/0]	1.4072[20]	i	∞	∞	...	...		B3[2], 6
c172	—,diisopropyl ester*	$OC(OC_3H_7^i)_2$	146.19			147[760] 43[12]	0.9162[20/0]	1.3932[20]	i	s	s	...	...		B3[2], 6
Ω c173	—,dimethyl ester*	$OC(OCH_3)_2$	90.08	λ[undil] <180	2−4	90−1	1.0694[20/4]	1.3687[20]	i	s	s	...	...		B3[2], 3
Ω c175	—,diphenyl ester*	$OC(OC_6H_5)_2$	214.22	nd (al, bz)	83 (88)	306[760] 168[15]	1.1215[87/4]	s	i	s[h]	s	...		CCl_4 s aa s[h]	B6[2], 156
c176	—,dipropyl ester*	$CO(OC_3H_7^n)_2$	146.19			168[760] 59.5[11]	0.9435[20/0]	1.4008[20]	δ	∞	∞	...	...	aa s	B3[2], 5
Ω c177	—,di-2-tolyl ester		242.28	nd (al)	60 (57)	144−5[0.5]			i	s[h]	...	s	...	aa v	B6[2], 330
Ω c178	—,di-3-tolyl ester		242.28	cr (al)	50.5−1.0				i	s[h]	...	s	...	chl s	B6[2], 353
Ω c179	—,di-4-tolyl ester		242.28	nd (al)	115				δ	δ	...	δ	δ s[h]	chl s	B6[2], 380
—	—,ethylene ester	see 1,3-dioxolan-2-one													
c180	—,monoethyl mono 2-butoxyethyl ester	$C_2H_5OCOOCH_2CH_2OC_4H_9^n$	190.24			224−4.4[759]	0.9756[25]	1.4143[25]	i	s	s	s	...		B3[3], 14
c181	—,monoethyl monomethyl ester	$CH_3OCOOC_2H_5$	104.12		−14	107.2−.8[765]	1.0122[20]	1.3778[20]	i	∞	∞	...	...		B3[2], 4
c182	—,dithiolo-, diethyl ester	$OC(SC_2H_5)_2$	150.26	ye		197 85−7[19]	1.085[19]	1.5237[18]	i	s	s	...	...		B3[1], 84
c183	—,trithio-	$SC(SH)_2$	110.22	red	−30	57d	1.47[17]		d	s	...	...	...	chl, to s	B3[2], 161
Ω c184	Carbon monoxide	CO	28.01		−205.06	−191.47[760] 760	0.4220[−141] 0.7909[−19]	0.00125 at 0°/1 atm	δ	s	...	...	s	aa s	B1, 720
—	Carbon suboxide	see Propadiene, 1,3-dioxo-*													
—	Carbon tetrabromide	see Methane, tetrabromo-*													
—	Carbon tetrachloride	see Methane, tetrachloro-*													
—	Carbon tetrafluoride	see Methane, tetrafluoro-*													
—	Carbon tetraiodide	see Methane, tetraiodo-*													
c185	Carbonyl fluoride	COF_2	66.01		−114	−83[760] −128[39]	1.139[−114]		d	d	...	...	...		B3[2], 9
c186	Carbonyl sulfide	Carbon oxysulfide. COS	60.08		−138	−50[760]	0.0021 at 1 atm 1.24[−87] 1.028[17/4]		δ	s	...	...	...	al KOH v	B3[2], 104
—	Carbostyril	see Quinoline, 2-hydroxy-													
c187	Carbothialdine		162.28	cr (al) λ[iv] 243 (3.70), 288 (4.11)	120d				i	v[h]	i	...	...	ac s	B27[2], 687
—	Cardiazol	see Metrazol													
Ω c188	Δ[3]-Carene(dl)		136.24			167[732] 44−5[8]	0.8602[20/4]	1.4759[20]	i	s	s	s	s	aa s	B5[3], 362
c189	—(l)	Isodiprene. $C_{10}H_{16}$. See c188	136.24	[α][30/D] −5.72 λ[iso] 220 (2.3) 250 (0.92)		168−9[705] 123−4[200]	0.8586[30/30]	1.4684[30]	i	...	s	s	s	aa, peth s	E12A, 34
c190	Δ[4]-Carene(l)		136.24	[α][30/D] +62.2		167[707] 64[29]	0.8441[30/4]	1.4740[30]	i	...	s	s	s	aa, peth s	E12A, 34
—	Caricaxanthin	see Cryptoxanthin													

For explanations, symbols and abbreviations see beginning of table. For structural formulas see end of table.

C-234

Carminic acid

No.	Name	Synonyms and Formula	Mol. wt.	Color, crystalline form, specific rotation and λ_{max} (log ε)	m.p. °C	b.p. °C	Density	n_D	w	al	eth	ace	bz	other solvents	Ref.
Ω c191	Carminic acid	$C_{22}H_{20}O_{13}$	492.40	red mcl pr (aq MeOH) $[\alpha]_{6450}^{15} +51.6$ (w, p = 1)	d at 136	....			s^h	s	δ	...	i	chl i	B10², 776
c192	Carnaubyl alcohol..	$CH_3(CH_2)_{29}OH$	438.81	lf (al)	69				δ	s		s			B1², 472
—	Carnegine	see Isoquinoline, 6,7-di-methoxy-1,2-dimethyl-1,2,3,4-tetrahydro-													
c193	Carnosine(D, −)	Ignotine. β-Alanyl-D(−)-histidine	226.24	$[\alpha]_D^{18} -20.4$ (w, c = 1.5)	260				s	i					B25², 408
Ω c194	—,(L, +).........	$C_9H_{14}N_4O_3$. See c193	226.24	nd (w-al) $[\alpha]_D^{20} +24.1$ (w, c = 1.5)	246–50d (308)				v	i					B25², 408
c195	α-Carotene	α-Carotin. $C_{40}H_{56}$	536.90	red pl or pr (peth, bz–MeOH) $[\alpha]_{Cd} +385$ (bz, c = 0.08) λ^{bz} 277 (3.26), 340 (3.84), 436 (4.92), 458 (5.09), 488 (5.03)	187.5	....	1.00_{20}^{20}	....	i	δ	s	...	s	chl, CS_2 v peth δ	B30, 91
Ω c196	β-Carotene	β-Carotin. $C_{40}H_{56}$ · Provitamin A.	536.90	red br hex pr (bz–MeOH), red rh (peth) λ^{bz} 278 (4.30), 364 (4.62), 463 (5.10), 494 (4.77)	184	....	1.00_{20}^{20}	....	i	δ	s	s	s	peth s chl δ	B30, 87
c197	γ-Carotene........	γ-Carotin. $C_{40}H_{56}$	536.90	red pr (bz-MeOH), vt pr (bz-eth) λ^{peth} 410 sh, 435, 460, 490.5	178				i	i	δ		s	chl s peth δ	B30, 92
—	β-Carotene, dehydro-	see Isocarotene													
c199	Carpaine(d).......	$C_{28}H_{50}N_2O_4$	478.72	mcl pr (al or ace) $[\alpha]_D^{21} +24.7$ (al, c = 1.07)	121	sub $120^{0.05}$	....		δ	s	s	s	s	chl s peth i	B27³, 209
c200	—,hydrochloride(d)	$C_{28}H_{50}N_2O_4$ · HCl. See c199.	515.18	wh mcl nd or pl	225d	....	....		v	s	s				B27², 210
c201	Carpiline	Carpidine. Pilosine. $C_{16}H_{18}N_2O_3$.	286.33	pl (al), pr (dil al or w) $[\alpha]_D^{20} +35.9$ (al), +40.2 (chl)	187	....	....		δ s^h	v^h	δ	δ	δ	dil ac v chl, AcOEt δ	B27¹, 612
—	Carvacrol	see Benzene, 2-hydroxy-4-isopropyl-1-methyl-													
—	o-Carvacrotonic acid	see Benzoic acid, 2-hydroxy-6-isopropyl-3-methyl-													
—	Carvacrylamine ...	see Benzene, 2-amino-4-isopropyl-1-methyl-													
c202	Carvenone(dl).....		152.24	λ^{al} 312 (1.70)		235.5–6.0⁷⁶² 104¹⁰	0.9263_4^{20}	1.4826^{20}	i			s			B7², 79
c203	—(l)............	$C_{10}H_{16}O$. See c202.	152.24	$[\alpha]_D -2.08$		232–4⁷⁶⁰	0.9290_0^{20}	1.4805	i			s			B7¹, 66
c204	Carveol, dihydro-(d)		154.26	$[\alpha]_D^{16} +34.2$		225⁷⁶⁰ 107¹⁵	0.9274_4^{20}	1.4780^{20}	i		s				B6², 70
c205	—,—(l)...........	$C_{10}H_{16}O$. See c204.	154.26	$[\alpha]_D^{20} -33.3$		107¹⁴ 90⁴	0.9368^{15}	1.4836^{20}	i		s				B6¹, 43
c206	β-Carveol, dihydro-		154.26	$[\alpha]_D +7.64$		120²⁰	0.9266_4^{20}	1.4809^{20}							B6, 64
Ω c207	Carvomenthane(d) .		138.25	$[\alpha]_{5780} +118$		175–7⁷⁶⁰ 77²⁴	0.8246_4^{18}	1.4563^{18}	i	s	s		s	peth s	B5², 52
c208	Carvomenthol(d)...	Hexahydrocarvacrol	156.27	$[\alpha]_D^{21} +31.40$	222	102¹⁴	0.8995^{20}	1.4617^{20}		v	s				B6², 39
c209	—(l, neo)	$C_{10}H_{20}O$. See c208.	156.27	$[\alpha]_D^{21} -41.7$		217–8⁷⁶⁰ 102¹⁸	0.9012_0^{20}	1.4632^{20}		v	s				B.⁻¹, 19
c210	Carvomenthone(d)		154.26	$[\alpha]_D^{21} +17.15$ λ^{al} 283 (1.43)		218–20⁷⁴⁵ 95–9¹⁵	0.9075^{15}	1.4544^{20}			s			chl s	B7², 37
Ω c211	Carvone(d)	Carvol	150.22	$[\alpha]_D^{20} +69.1$ λ^{al} 235 (3.93), 318 (1.62)		231⁷⁶⁰ 104¹¹	0.9608_0^{20}	1.4999^{18}	δ^h	v	s			chl s	B7², 128
c212	—(dl)...........	$C_{10}H_{14}O$. See c211.	150.22	λ^{al} 235 (3.93), 318 (1.62)		231⁷⁶⁰ 85⁵	0.9645_{15}^{15}	1.5003^{20}	δ^h	v	s			chl s	B7², 130

For explanations, symbols and abbreviations see beginning of table. For structural formulas see end of table.

No.	Name	Synonyms and Formula	Mol. wt.	Color, crystalline form, specific rotation and λ_{max} (log ε)	m.p. °C	b.p. °C	Density	n_D	Solubility						Ref.
									w	al	eth	ace	bz	other solvents	
	Carvone														
Ω c213	—(l)	$C_{10}H_{14}O$. See c211	150.22	$[\alpha]_D^{20}$ −62.46 λ^{a1} 235 (3.93), 318 (1.62)	. . . .	231[760] 98[9]	0.9593_4^{20}	1.4988^{20}	δ^h	v	s	. . . .	. . . .	chl s	B7[2], 129
c214	—,oxime(α,d)	D-Carvoxime(α).	165.24	lf (al) $[\alpha]_D^{17}$ +39.71 (al, p = 8.45) λ^{a1} 234 (4.21)	72	. . . .				s	s	s	. . . .		B7[2], 129
c215	—,—(α,l)	L-Carvoxime(α). $C_{10}H_{15}NO$. See c214	165.24	mcl (dil al) $[\alpha]_D^{18}$ −39.43 (al, p = 4.33)	73.5	. . . .	1.0140^{73}			s	s	s	s		B7[2], 129
c216	—,—(β,d)	$C_{10}H_{15}NO$. See c214	165.24	nd (dil al) $[\alpha]_D$ +68.3 (bz)	57–8	. . . . . .				s	s	s	s	oos v	B7[1], 102
c217	—,—(β,l)	$C_{10}H_{15}NO$. See c214	165.24	nd (al)	56–7					s	s	s	s		B7[1], 102
c218	—,—(dl)	dl-Carvoxime. $C_{10}H_{15}NO$. See c214	165.24		93–4										B7[1], 103
c219	—,dihydro-(d)		152.24	$[\alpha]_D$ +17.5	. . . .	221–2	0.928^{19}	1.4724			s	s	s		B7[1], 69
c220	—,—(l)	$C_{10}H_{16}O$. See c219	152.24	$[\alpha]_D^{20}$ −19 $[\alpha]_D^{31}$ −46.63	. . . .	221–2 104[18]	0.9253_4^{20}	1.4717^{20}	i		s	s	s		B7[2], 81
—	—,tetrahydro-	see **Carvomenthone**													
c221	α-**Caryophyllene** . . .	$C_{15}H_{24}$	204.36	$[\alpha]_D^{20}$ +1.0 ±0.3 (chl, c = 9.26) λ 280 (2.1)	123[10]	. . . . .	0.8905_2^{20}	1.5038^{20}							Am72, 5350
c222	β-**Caryophyllene** . . .	$C_{15}H_{24}$	204.36	$[\alpha]_D^{20}$ −9.08	122[13.5]	. . . . .	0.9075_2^{20}	1.4988^{20}	i				s		B5[3], 1083
c223	γ-**Caryophyllene** . . .	Isocaryophyllene. $C_{15}H_{24}$.	204.36	$[\alpha]_D^{19}$ −26.2	130 −1[24]	. . . . .	0.8953_2^{20}	1.4967^{19}					s		B5[3], 1085
c224	**Caryophyllenic acid**(l, cis)	$C_9H_{14}O_4$. See c224	186.21	pr (w) $[\alpha]_{546}$ −7.4	77–8	. . . . .			s	s	s	s	s		B9[2], 531
c225	—(d,trans)	$C_9H_{14}O_4$. See c224	186.21	nd (cy) $[\alpha]_D^{20}$ +35.3 (bz)	81–2	. . . . .			v	s	s	s	s	lig δ	B9[2], 531
c226	**Caryophyllin**	Oleanolic acid. $C_{30}H_{48}O_3$	456.72	nd or pr (al) $[\alpha]_D^{20}$ +83.3 (chl, c = 0.9) λ^{a1} 207 (3.67)	310d	280–308 sub (vac)			i	δ	δ	δ	δ	Py v aa v[h] MeOH s CCl_4 δ	B10[2], 198
Ω c227	**Catechin**(cis'd)	3,5,7,3',4'-Flavanpentol, (one form). $C_{15}H_{14}O_6$.	290.28	nd (w + 4) $[\alpha]_D^{18}$ +18.4 (w, p = 0.9)	96 (hyd) 177 (anh)	240–5	1.344_4^4	. . . . . .	v^h	v	δ	v	i	aa v lig δ chl i	B17[2], 254
c228	—(cis,dl)	$C_{15}H_{14}O_6$. See c227	290.28	nd (w +3)	212–4d				δ	v	δ	v	i	chl i	B17[2], 256
c229	—(cis,l)	$C_{15}H_{14}O_6$. See c227	290.28	nd (+4, w) $[\alpha]_{5780}$ 16.8 (w-ace, p = 3)	96 (hyd) 177 (anh)				δ	v	δ	v	i	lig δ aa v chl i	B17[2], 255
—	**Catechol**	see **Benzene, 1,2-dihydroxy-***													
—	**Caulophylline**	see **Cytisine, N-methyl-**													
c230	**Cedrene**	$C_{15}H_{24}$	204.36	$[\alpha]_D^{20}$ −91.3	. . . .	262–3[760] .124–6[12]	0.9342^{20}	1.5034^{20}	i		. . . .	. . . .	s	lig s	B5[2], 350
Ω c231	**Cellobiose**(β)	Glucose-β-glucoside	342.30	cr (dil al) $[\alpha]_D^{20}$ +14.2 → +34.6 (w, c = 8, 15 hr) (mut)	d 225	. . . .			s v^h	i	i	i	i	. . . .	B31, 380
c232	—,octa-acetate(α) . .	Octaacetylcellobiose. $C_{28}H_{38}O_{19}$. See c231	678.61	nd (al) $[\alpha]_D^{20}$ +43.6 (chl, c = 6)	229.5	. . . .			i	i	i		. . . .	chl, aa v	B31, 382
c233	—,—(β)	$C_{28}H_{38}O_{19}$. See c231	678.61	nd (al) $[\alpha]_D^{20}$ −14.7 (chl, c = 5)	202 (192)	. . . .				s^h			δ	chl v	B31, 383
—	**Cellosolve, acetate** . .	see **Acetic acid, 2-ethoxyethyl ester**													
c234	**Cellulose**	Polycellobiose. $(C_6H_{10}O_5)_x$ . .	$(162.14)_x$	wh amor	260–70d	. . . .	1.27–1.61		i	i	eth i	i	i	$Cu(OH)_2$.$(NH_3)_4$ s oos i	
c235	—,hexanitrate	Chief constituent of gun-cotton. $(C_{12}H_{14}N_6O_{22})_x$	$(594.27)_x$	wh amor	160–70 ign	. . . .	1.66		i	i	i		i	$PhNO_2$ s	
c236	—,pentanitrate	$(C_{12}H_{15}N_5O_{20})_x$	$(549.28)_x$	wh amor	. . . .	. . . .	1.66		i	i	i		i	MeOH, eth-al s	
c237	—,tetranitrate	Constituent of collodion. $(C_{12}H_{16}N_4O_{18})_x$	$(504.26)_x$	wh amor	. . . .	. . . .	1.66		i	i	i		i	MeOH, eth-al s	
c238	—,triacetate	$(C_{12}H_{16}O_8)_x$	$(288.26)_x$	non inflam yesh fl $[\alpha]_D$ −22.5 (chl)	. . . . . .	. . . .			i	i	i	i	i	$ClCH_2CH_2Cl$, chl, $PhNO_2$, aa s	
c239	—,triethyl ether . . .	Ethyl cellulose. Triethyl cellulose. $(C_{12}H_{22}O_5)_x$.	$(246.31)_x$	wh nd (bz) $[\alpha]_D^{20}$ +26.1 (bz)	240–55	. . . .			i	δ	s^h				
c240	—,trinitrate	Constituent of collodion. $(C_{12}H_{17}N_3O_{16})_x$.	$(459.28)_x$	wh	. . . .	. . . .	1.66		i	i	. . . .		s	MeOH, AcOEt s aa s^h	
c241	**Cepharanthine**	$C_{37}H_{38}N_2O_6$	606.73	ye amor pw nd (+1¼ bz, ace-bz) $[\alpha]_D^{19}$ +277 (chl)	145–55 (anh) 103 (+ 1¼ bz)	. . . .			i		s	s	s	lig i	C49, 1745

For explanations, symbols and abbreviations see beginning of table. For structural formulas see end of table.

No.	Name	Synonyms and Formula	Mol. wt.	Color, crystalline form, specific rotation and λ_{max} (log ε)	m.p. °C	b.p. °C	Density	n_D	Solubility						Ref.
									w	al	eth	ace	bz	other solvents	
	Cerane														
c242	Cerane..........	Isohexacosane. $CH_3(CH_2)_{24}CH_3$	366.72	pl (eth), sc(w)	61	$207^{0.7}$	....		i δ^h	s	s	...	...	....	B1[2], 143
—	Cerotic acid.......	see Hexacosanoic acid*													
—	Ceryl alcohol......	see 1-Hexacosanol*													
c243	Cerulignone.......	....	304.30	bl gr					i	i	i	i	i	$PhNO_2$, sulf, PhOH s oos i	B8[2], 573
—	Cetene..........	see 1-Hexadecene*													
—	Cetyl amine......	see Hexadecane, 1-amino-*													
—	Cetyl bromide.....	see Hexadecane, 1-bromo-*													
—	Cevadine.........	see Veratrine													
c244	Cevagenine......	$C_{27}H_{43}NO_8$	509.65	nd (MeOH-eth) $[\alpha]_D^{20} -52$ (chl) $[\alpha]_D^{20} -47.5$ (al) $\lambda^{al} 280$ (1.7)	246–8 (242)										H35, 1270
Ω c245	Chalcone (trans)...	Benzalacetophenone. Benzylidene acetophenone. 1,3-Diphenyl-2-propen-l-one.	208.26	pa ye lf, pr, nd (peth) $\lambda^{al} 228$ (2.99) 358 (3.39)	(i) 59 (st) (ii) 57 (iii) 49 (unst) (iv) 48 (v) 30 (vi) 18	$345–8^{760}$ δd 208^{25}	1.0712_4^{62}		i	δ	s	s	s	chl, CS_2, sulf s lig i	B7[2], 423
c246	—,4,4′-dimethyl-..	$C_{17}H_{16}O$. See c245........	236.32	cr (MeOH)	127–9				i	s	s	...	...	MeOH s[h]	B7[2], 441
c247	—,3,3′-dinitro-....	$C_{15}H_{16}N_2O_5$. See c245.....	298.26	pa yen nd (aa) $\lambda^{al} 247$ (4.22), 314 (4.45)	210–1				i	i	i	...	s	Ac_2O s[h]	B7[2], 429
c248	—,2-methoxy-.....	o-Anisylideneacetophenone. $C_{16}H_{14}O_2$. See c245	238.29	yesh nd (peth or eth-lig) $\lambda^{al} 252$ (4.08), 344 (3.83)	64–5					v	v	...	v	chl v, con sulf s lig δ	B8[2], 218
c249	—,3-methoxy-.....	$C_{16}H_{14}O_2$. See c245	238.29	yesh pl or pr (MeOH)	65	247^{12}			i	s	s	s	s	oos s	B8[1], 579
Ω c250	—,4-methoxy-.....	$C_{16}H_{14}O_2$. See c245	238.29	ye nd (al) $\lambda^{al} 240$ (4.09), 344 (4.07)	79 (74)	$187.5–8^{19}$			i	v[h]	s	...	...	chl, aa, con sulf s MeOH v[h]	B8[2], 218
Ω c251	—,3,4-methyl-enedioxy-	Piperonylideneacetophenone. $C_{16}H_{12}O_3$. See c245	252.27	ye nd (al)	128 (122)				i	s[h]		...	...	con sulf s (og-ye) aa s	B19[2], 167
c252	—,2-nitro-........	$C_{15}H_{11}NO_3$. See c245	253.26	pa br nd (al) $\lambda^{al} 210$ (4.17), 276 (4.29)	125					s[h]	s	...	...	aa's	B7[2], 428
c253	—,2′-nitro-........	$C_{15}H_{11}NO_3$. See c245	253.26	nd (al) $\lambda^{al} 287$ (4.32)	128–9					s[h]	s	...	...	con sulf → pa ye	B7[2], 429
c254	—,3-nitro-........	$C_{15}H_{11}NO_3$. See c245	253.26	ye nd (al or bz) $\lambda^{al} 215$ (4.11), 290 (4.43)	145–6					s	i	...	...	chl, aa s peth i	B7[2], 429
c255	—,4-nitro-........	$C_{15}H_{11}NO_3$. See c245	253.26	pa ye nd (al), pl (bz) $\lambda^{al} 210$ (4.18), 315 (4.48)	164					s[h]	i	...	...	chl s lig i	B7[2], 429
c256	—,α-nitro-........	$C_6H_5CH:C(NO_2)COC_6H_5$..	253.26	ye pl (eth or bz-lig), cr (aa) $\lambda^{al} 257$ (4.21), 313 (4.14)	90				i	...	s	s	s	oos v	B7, 483
—	Chamazulene......	see Azulene, 1,5-dimethyl-8-isopropyl-													
c257	Chaulmoogric acid(d)	d-13(2-Cyclopentenyl)tridecanoic acid. Hydrocarpylacetic acid. $C_{18}H_{32}O_2$.	280.46	pl or lf (al, aa) $[\alpha]_D +62$ (chl)	68.5	$247–8^{20}$			i	δ	s	...	...	chl s	B9[2], 58
c258	—(dl)...........	$C_{18}H_{32}O_2$. See c257........	280.46	cr (peth)	68.5	$247–8^{20}$									B9[2], 61
—	Chavibetol.......	see Benzene, 4-allyl-1-hydroxy-2-methoxy-													
—	Chavieol	see Benzene, 1-allyl-4-hydroxy-													
c259	Chelerythrine	$C_{19}H_{21}NO_5$.	365.39	cr (chl-MeOH), cr (al + 1)	207				δ	δ	δ^h	s[h]	...	chl s AcOEt δ	B27[2], 563
Ω c260	Chelidonic acid	Jervasic acid. 4-Pyrone-2,6-dicarboxylic acid.	184.11	rose mcl nd (al-w +1w) $\lambda 270$ (4.0)	262				s[h]	δ		...	...		B18[2], 367
c261	—,diethyl ester	$C_{11}H_{12}O_6$. See c260	240.22	pr, nd $\lambda^{MeOH} 270$ (4.0)	69 (63)				δ^h	s[h]	s	...	...		B18[2], 367
c262	Chelidonine(d)	$C_{20}H_{19}NO_5$.	353.38	mcl pl (al +1w) $[\alpha]_D +151$ (al, 1 %) $\lambda^{MeOH} 239$ (3.92), 289 (3.87)	136–40d				i[h]	s v[h]	s v[h]	...	...	chl s	B27[2], 615
c263	—,hydrochloride(d)	$C_{20}H_{19}NO_5 \cdot HCl$. See c262..	389.84	wh (w)	....				i	δ^h	δ^h	...	...		B27, 557
—	Chenodeoxy-cholic acid	see Cholanic acid, $3\alpha,7\alpha$-dihydroxy-													

For explanations, symbols and abbreviations see beginning of table. For structural formulas see end of table.

No.	Name	Synonyms and Formula	Mol. wt.	Color, crystalline form, specific rotation and λ_{max} (log ε)	m.p. °C	b.p. °C	Density	n_D	w	al	eth	ace	bz	other solvents	Ref.
	Chimyl alcohol														
—	Chimyl alcohol	see **Glycerol, 1-hexadecyl ether**													
—	Chloral	see **Acetaldehyde, trichloro-**													
—	Chloralacetone-chloroform	see **Acetaldehyde, trichloro-**, β,β,β-trichloro-*tert*-butyl hemiacetal													
—	Chloral formamide	see **Formic acid, amide**, N(1-hydroxy-2,2,2-trichloro-ethyl)-													
—	Chloral hydrate	see **Acetaldehyde, trichloro-, hydrate**													
Ω c264	Chloralide	2,5-Bis(trichloromethyl)-1,3-dioxolan-4-one.	322.79	pr (al or eth)	116	272–3 147–8[12]	....		i	v[h] δ	v	....	....	aa v	B19[1], 656
—	Chloramphenicol...	see **Chlormycetin**													
—	Chloranil	see **1,4-Benzoquinone, tetrachloro-***													
—	Chloranilic acid...	see **1,4-Benzoquinone, 2,5-dichloro-3,6-dihydroxy-***													
—	Chloretone.......	see **2-Propanol, 2-methyl-1,1,1-trichloro-***													
—	Chloroform	see **Methane, trichloro-**													
—	Chloroform-*d*	see **Methane, deutero-trichloro-***													
c265	Chloromycetin	Chloramphenicol. Syntomycetin. $C_{11}H_{12}Cl_2N_2O_5$.	323.14	pa ye pl or nd (w), $[\alpha]_D^{25}$ +19 (al, c = 5), −25.5 (AcOEt) λ 278 (3.99)	150.5–1.5	sub vac	....		δ	v	δ	v	i	chl s	Am 71, 2458
c266	Chlorophyll a......	$C_{55}H_{72}MgN_4O_5$	893.53	bl bk hex pl λ^{hx} 440 (4.0), 660 (3.9)	150–3	....	....		i	v[h]	v[h]	....	....	lig s	M, 245
c267	Chlorophyll b......	$C_{55}H_{70}MgN_4O_6$	907.51	bl bk gr pw λ^{hx} 460 (4.2), 650 (3.6)	120–30	....			i[h]	v[h]	v[h]	....	....	Py v[h] MeOH, lig s	M, 245
—	Chloropicrin	see **Methane, nitrotri-chloro-***													
—	Chloroprene	see **1,3-Butadiene, 2-chloro-***													
—	Chlorosulfonic acid, ethyl ester	see **Sulfuric acid, mono-chloride monoethyl ester**													
c268	Chlorpromazine ...	Largactil. Thorazine. $C_{17}H_{19}ClN_2S$.	318.87	λ 250 (4.5), 320 (3.5)	....	200–5[0.8]			i	v	v	....	v	chl v dil HCl s	C50, 1931
c269	—,hydrochloride ...	$C_{17}H_{19}ClN_2S \cdot HCl$. See c268	355.33	λ 250 (4.5), 300 (3.5)	194–7d (180)	....			s	v	i	....	i	MeOH, PrOH, chl v	C50, 1931
—	Chlortetracyline ...	see **Aureomycin**													
c270	Cholanic acid......	Ursocholanic acid. $C_{24}H_{40}O_2$.	360.59	nd (al), cr (aa) $[\alpha]_D^{20}$ +21.7 (chl) $\lambda^{97\%\ sulf}$ 313 (3.88)	163–4	....	....			s		....	....	chl, aa s	E14, 170
c271	—,ethyl ester......	$C_{26}H_{44}O_2$. See c270	388.64	lf, nd (dil al) $[\alpha]_D^{19}$ +21 (chl)	93–4	273[12]						....	....	chl s	Am 77, 3308
c272	—,methyl ester	$C_{25}H_{42}O_2$. See c270	374.61	nd $[\alpha]_D$ +23 ±2 (diox)	87–8	....						....	....	diox s	Am 77, 3308
Ω c273	—,3α,6α-di-hydroxy-	Hyodeoxycholic acid. $C_{24}H_{40}O_4$. See c270	392.56	cr (AcOEt) $[\alpha]_D^{20}$ +37.2 (MeOH) $\lambda^{65\%\ sulf}$ 276 (3.51), 380 (4.18)	198–9	....	....		δ	s	δ	δ	δ	aa s AcOEt δ	C50, 5067
c274	—,3α,7α-di-hydroxy-	Chenodeoxycholic acid. $C_{24}H_{40}O_4$. See c270	392.59	nd (AcOEt-hp) $[\alpha]_D^{20}$ +11.1 (al, c = 2.1) $\lambda^{65\%\ sulf}$ 272 (3.58), 380 (4.35)	143 (119)	....			i	v	s	v	i	aa s peth i	C48, 3377
—	—,3,12-dihydroxy-	see **Desoxycholic acid**													
—	—,3,7,12-tri-hydroxy-	see **Cholic acid**													
—	—,3,7,12-trioxo-..	see **Dehydrocholic acid**													
c275	Cholanthrene......	Benz[*j*]aceanthrene.	254.34	pa ye lf (bz-al) λ^{al} 261.5 (4.60), 274 (4.60), 284.5 (4.80), 295 (4.90)	174.5–5.0d	sub 210[0.2]	....		i	s		....	s	aa, lig, to s	B5[3], 2469
c276	—,6,7-dihydro-20-methyl-	$C_{21}H_{18}$. See c275	270.37	lf (MeOH)	133	....						....	....	MeOH s[h]	B5[3], 2429

For explanations, symbols and abbreviations see beginning of table. For structural formulas see end of table.

No.	Name	Synonyms and Formula	Mol. wt.	Color, crystalline form, specific rotation and λ_{max} (log ε)	m.p. °C	b.p. °C	Density	n_D	Solubility						Ref.
									w	al	eth	ace	bz	other solvents	
	Cholanthrene														
c277	—,11,14-dihydro-20-methyl-	$C_{21}H_{18}$. See c275	270.37	nd (PrOH)	138–9	....	....				...	...	...	PrOH s^h	B5³, 2429
c278	—,20-methyl-	$C_{21}H_{16}$. See c275	268.38	yesh nd (bz) λ^{al} 327 (3.63), 343 (3.79), 359 (3.88)	180	....	....		i		...	...	...	....	B5³, 2484
c279	$\Delta^{2,4}$-Cholestadiene .	$C_{27}H_{44}$	368.65	cr (eth-ace) $[\alpha]_D^{23}$ +168.5 (eth, c = 1.5) λ^{al} 276 (4.04)	68.5	....	....		i	s	s	...	...	chl s	B5², 1428
c280	$\Delta^{3,5}$-Cholestadiene .	Cholesterilene. $C_{27}H_{44}$	368.65	wh nd (al) $[\alpha]_D^{20}$ −129.6 (chl, c = 3) λ^{cy} 193 (2.50), 228 (4.23), 235 (4.27), 244 (4.07)	80	260¹³	0.9254¹⁰⁰		i^h	s^h	∞	...	∞	chl ∞ lig v	B5³, 1429
c281	$\Delta^{5,7}$-Cholesta-dien-3β-ol	7-Dehydrocholesterol. Provitamin D₃. $C_{27}H_{44}O$.	384.65	pl (+1w, eth-MeOH) $[\alpha]_D^{25}$ −115 (chl, c = 2.5) λ^{eth} 262 (3.99)	150–1 (143)	....	....		i	δ	s	s	...	oos s	B6³, 2819
c282	$\Delta^{4,6}$-Cholestadien-3-one	$C_{27}H_{42}O$	382.64	ye pr $[\alpha]_D^{20}$ +31 (chl) λ^{al} 284 (4.36)	78	....	....		i	...	...	...	...	....	J1956, 627
c283	**Cholestane**.......	$C_{27}H_{48}$	372.69	sc or pl (eth-al, ace, AcOEt) $[\alpha]_D^{20}$ +30.2 (chl, c = 2) λ 175	80–80.5	250¹	0.9090⁴⁸⁸	1.4887⁸⁸	i	δ	v	...	v	chl v MeOH δ	B5³, 1133
—	—,3β-hydroxy-....	see **Cholestanol**													
c284	3β-Cholestane-carboxylic acid	$C_{28}H_{48}O_2$. See c283	416.70	nd, $[\alpha]_D^{25}$ +28.8 (chl, c = 1.7)	210–1	....	....				...	...	...	....	Am 75, 6234
c285	3,6-Cholestane-dione	$C_{27}H_{44}O_2$. See c283	400.65	nd, $[\alpha]_D^{20}$ +8.9 (c = 0.98) λ^{MeOH} 295 (1.75)	171–2	....	....				...	...	...	....	H37, 258
c286	3α-Cholestanol	Epicholestanol. Epidihydro-cholesterol. $C_{27}H_{48}O$. See c283	388.69	nd (al) $[\alpha]_D^{20}$ +34 (chl, c = 1.1)	188	....	....				...	...	...	....	B3², 2135
c287	3β-Cholestanol	Dihydrocholesterol. 3β-Hydroxycholestane. $C_{27}H_{48}O$. See c283	388.69	lf (al + 1 w) pr, pl (MeOH) $[\alpha]_D^{22}$ +24.2 (chl, c = 1.3)	141–3 (146)	....	....		i	v^h	v	...	...	chl v con sulf s MeOH δ	B6³, 2131
c288	3-Cholestanone	Zymostanone. $C_{27}H_{46}O$. See c283	386.67	nd or lf (al) $[\alpha]_D$ +42 (chl, c = 2.12) λ^{al} 280 (1.86)	128–30	....	....		i	s^h	...	...	...	....	Am 77, 190
c289	6-Cholestanone, 3β-hydroxy-	6-Ketocholestanol. $C_{27}H_{46}O_2$. See c283	402.67	nd (al) $[\alpha]_D$ −3.0 (chl)	150–1	....	....		i	s^h	...	...	...	....	Am 76, 532
c290	7-Cholestanone, 3β-hydroxy-	7-Oxocholestanol. 7-Keto-cholestanol. $C_{27}H_{46}O_2$. See c283	402.67	pl, $[\alpha]_D^{22}$ −34 (chl)	165–8	....	....		i	s^h	...	...	...	....	Am 76, 532
c291	2-Cholestene	Neocholestene. $C_{27}H_{46}$	370.67	nd (eth-ace or al) $[\alpha]_D$ +66 (c = 1.65) λ^{al} 205 (3.75)	75–6	....	....				...	...	...	....	B5³, 1520
c292	5-Cholestene	$C_{27}H_{46}$	370.67	wh pr or nd (al) $[\alpha]_D^{18}$ −56.3 (chl) λ^{cy} 193 (3.91) λ^{al} 206 (3.32)	93–4 (90)	....	....				...	...	...	....	B5³, 1323
c293	—,3β-bromo-	Cholesteryl bromide. $C_{27}H_{45}Br$. See c292	449.57	mcl lf (al) $[\alpha]_D^{20}$ −19 (bz, c = 0.4) λ^{al} 209 (3.72)	100–2 (99)	....	....		i	s^h	...	...	s	chl s	B5³, 1327
c294	—,3β-chloro-......	Cholesteryl chloride. $C_{27}H_{45}Cl$. See c292	405.12	nd (al or ace) $[\alpha]_D^{20}$ −26.4 (bz), −33.3 (chl) λ^{al} 207 (3.52)	96	....	....		i	s^h	...	s^h	s	CS₂ v aa v^h chl s	B5³, 1324
c295	—,3β-iodo-	Cholesteryl iodide. $C_{27}H_{45}I$. See c292	496.57	nd (ace or AcOEt) $[\alpha]_D^{20}$ −11.9 (chl, c = 1)	106–7	....	....		i	δ	...	δ	s	chl lig s EtOAc s^h	B5³, 1328
c296	5-Cholestene-3β, 7β-diol	7β-Hydroxycholesterol. $C_{27}H_{46}O_2$. See c292	402.67	wh nd (eth) $[\alpha]_D^{20}$ +7.2 (chl, c = 2)	177–8.5	sub 145⁰·⁰⁰⁵	....				...	...	...	....	B6³, 1328

For explanations, symbols and abbreviations see beginning of table. For structural formulas see end of table.

No.	Name	Synonyms and Formula	Mol. wt.	Color, crystalline form, specific rotation and λ_{max} (log ε)	m.p. °C	b.p. °C	Density	n_D	Solubility						Ref.
									w	al	eth	ace	bz	other solvents	

1-Cholesten-3-one

No.	Name	Synonyms and Formula	Mol. wt.	Color, crystalline form, specific rotation and λ_{max} (log ε)	m.p. °C	b.p. °C	Density	n_D	w	al	eth	ace	bz	other solvents	Ref.
c297	1-Cholesten-3-one	$C_{27}H_{44}O$	384.65	nd (dil ace or al) $[\alpha]_D^5 +88.2$ (chl) $\lambda^{al} 231$ (3.99)	99–101 (95)	....								s	....	Am 75, 3513
Ω c298	4-Cholesten-3-one	....	384.65	nd or pl (al) $[\alpha]_D^{20} +92$ (chl, c = 2.01) $\lambda^{hx} 241$ (4.26), 314 (1.65), 323.5 (1.69), 349 (1.53), 367 (1.15)	81–2	....			i	δ	s	...	s	peth, CS_2 s AcOEt δ	C50, 1568
c299	5-Cholesten-3-one	$C_{27}H_{44}O$. See c292	384.65	lf (al) $[\alpha]_D^{20} -4.3$ (chl) $\lambda^{al} 285$ (2.00)	127	....			i	s^h	s	...	...		C50, 1568
—	Cholesterilene	see 3,5-Cholestadiene													
Ω c300	Cholesterol	Δ^5-3β-Cholestenol. Cholesterin. $C_{27}H_{46}O$.	386.67	rh or tcl lf (al + 1w), nd (eth) $[\alpha]_D^{20} -31.5$ (eth, c = 2), −39.5 (chl, c = 2) $\lambda^{al} 206$ (3.53)	148.5 (anh) (150.1)	360δd 233$^{0.5}$	1.067$_4^{20}$	....	i	δ^h	v	δ^h	s	diox, chl v CS_2, aa s	B6³, 2607
Ω c301	—,acetate	Cholesteryl acetate. $C_{29}H_{48}O_2$. See c300	428.71	wh nd (ace or al), $[\alpha]_D^{20} -47.7$ (chl, c = 2) $\lambda^{al} 197$ (3.89)	115–6	....				δ	...	s	s	s chl s	B6³, 2630
c302	—,benzoate.......	Cholesteryl benzoate. $C_{34}H_{50}O_2$. See c300	490.78	wh nd, $[\alpha] -13.7$ (chl, c = 0.9) $\lambda^{al} 230$ (4.16)	152–3	....					i	...		chl s	E14, 53
c303	—,hexadecanoate..	Cholesteryl palmitate. $C_{43}H_{76}O_2$. See c300	625.09	wh nd (eth or al), $[\alpha]^{20} -25.4$ (chl, c = 2)	80	....			i^h	s^h	s^h	s^h	s	chl s	B6³, 2640
—	—,7β-hydroxy-	see 5-Cholestene-3β, 7β-diol													
—	—,7-dehydro-	see 5,7-Cholestadien-3β-ol													
—	Cholesteryl bromide	see 5-Cholestene, 3β-bromo-													
—	Cholesteryl chloride	see 5-Cholestene, 3β-chloro-													
c304	Cholestrophane	Dimethylparabanic acid. Oxalyldimethylurea.	142.12	lf or pl (w or al)	155.5	275–7 148–50^{13}			s v^h	δ	s	...	...		B24², 265
Ω c305	Cholic acid........	Cholanic acid. 3α, 7α, 12α-Trihydroxy-5β-cholanoic acid. $C_{24}H_{40}O_5$	408.59	rh (eth), tetr rh (w or dil al + 1w), cr (al + 1) $[\alpha]_D^{20} +37$ (al, c = 0.6) $\lambda^{65\% sulf} 318$ (4.16), 377.5 (2.71)	198 (anh)	....			δ	s	v	s	...	chl v alk, aa s	E14, 191
Ω c306	Choline	Trimethyl (2-hydroxyethyl) ammonium hydroxide. $(CH_3)_3\overset{+}{N}CH_2CH_2OH . OH^-$	121.18	syr	....	....			v	v	i	i	i	chl, CS_2, CCl_4 i	B4², 720
Ω c307	—,O-acetyl-, bromide	Acetylcholine bromide. Progmoline. $(CH_3)_3\overset{+}{N}CH_2CH_2O_2CCH_3 . Br^-$	226.12	hex pr (dil al)	143	d			v d^h	s	i	...	...	MeOH s	B4², 724
Ω c308	—,—,chloride.....	Acetylcholine chloride. $(CH_3)_3\overset{+}{N}CH_2CH_2O_2CCH_3 . Cl^-$	181.66	yesh nd	151	....			s d	s^h	i	...	...		B4³, 656
Ω c309	—,O-benzoyl-, chloride	$(CH_3)_3\overset{+}{N}CH_2CH_2O_2CC_6H_5 . Cl^-$	243.74	pr (ace-al)	200	....	....		s^h	...	s^h	...	...		D9¹, 90
Ω c310	—,carbamate, chloride	$(CH_3)_3\overset{+}{N}CH_2CH_2O_2CNH_2 . Cl^-$	182.65	hyg pr or pw	210–2 (205)	....			v	δ	i	...	...	MeOH v chl i	C38, 1800
—	Chondrodendrin ...	see Bebeerine(d)													
c311	Chroman	Dihydrobenzopyran	134.18	$\lambda^{hx} 276$ (3.33), 284 (3.43)	....	214–5^{742} 98–9^{18}	1.0610^{20}	1.5444^{20}	s^h					oos ∞	B17, 52
Ω c312	Chromone	α-Benzopyrone. 4-Oxo-1,4-chromene. $\lambda^{al} 274.5$ (4.20), 312.5 (3.91)	146.15	nd (peth or w)	59	sub			δ^h	s	s	...	s	chl s	B17¹, 170
—	—,2-phenyl-	see Flavone													
—	Chromotropic acid	see 2,7-Naphthalene disulfonic acid, 4,5-di-hydroxy-*													

For explanations, symbols and abbreviations see beginning of table. For structural formulas see end of table.

Chrysammic acid

No.	Name	Synonyms and Formula	Mol. wt.	Color, crystalline form, specific rotation and λ_{max} (log ε)	m.p. °C	b.p. °C	Density	n_D	Solubility						Ref.
									w	al	eth	ace	bz	other solvents	
—	Chrysammic acid	see 9,10-Anthraquinone, 1,8-dihydroxy-2,4,5,7-tetranitro-*													
—	Chrysaniline	see Acridine, 2-amino-5(4-aminophenyl)-													
—	Chrysanthemum-monocarboxylic acid	see Cyclopropanecarboxylic acid, 2,2-dimethyl-3(2-methylpropenyl)-*													
—	Chrysanthemumic acid	see Cyclopropanecarboxylic acid, 2,2-dimethyl-3(2-methylpropenyl)*													
—	Chrysazin	see 9,10-Anthraquinone, 1,8-dihydroxy-*													
—	Chrysazol	see Anthracene, 1,8-di-hydroxy-*													
Ω c313	Chrysene	1,2-Benzophenanthrene. Benzo[a]phenanthrene.	228.30	red bl flr rh pl (bz, aa) λ^{al} 222 (4.55), 258 (4.96), 268 (5.20), 295 (4.08), 320 (4.12), 344 (2.81), 353 (2.57), 361 (2.80)	255–6	448	1.274[20]	....	i	δ	δ	δ	δ s^h	to s^h CS₂, aa δ	B5³, 2380
c314	—,5,6-dimethyl-	$C_{20}H_{16}$. See c313	256.35	pl or nd (bz-al) λ^{al} 228 (4.3), 272 (5.0), 330 (4.1), 345 (2.8)	128–9	200^{0.5} (sub 140 vac)			i	s				CS₂, aa s	B5³, 2418
c315	—,1-methyl-	$C_{19}H_{14}$. See c313	242.32	lf (hx, bz, to) λ^{al} 259 (4.54), 281 (4.81), 292 (4.89), 302 (3.97), 337 (3.81), 352 (3.87), 390 (2.87)	256.5–7.0	sub 130–40 (vac)			i	s					B5³, 2395
c316	—,2-methyl-	$C_{19}H_{14}$. See c313	242.32	lf (bz-al)	229.5–30 (225)	....			i	s				aa s	B5³, 2395
c317	—,3-methyl-	$C_{19}H_{14}$. See c313	242.32	lf (bz-peth) λ^{cy} 268 (4.9), 275 (5.1), 297 (4.1), 324 (4.1), 355 (3.0)	172.5–3.5					s					B5³, 2395
—	Chrysin	see Flavone, 5,7-dihydroxy-													
—	Chrysoidine	see Azobenzene, 2,4-diamino-													
—	Chrysophanic acid	see 9,10-Anthraquinone, 1,8-dihydroxy-3-methyl-*													
c318	5,6-Chryso-quinone	....	258.28	red nd (bz or to), lf or pl (aa) λ^{diox} 250 (4.5), 385 (3.75)	239.5	sub	....	....	i	s^h	δ	....	s^h	sulf s aa δ to δ, s^h	B7², 760
c319	6,12-Chryso-quinone		258.28	red ye nd (aa)	288–90d	....			i	s^h				aa s^h	B7¹, 441
—	Cinchomeronic acid	see 3,4-Pyridinedicarboxylic acid													
c320	Cinchonamine	$C_{19}H_{24}N_2O$.	296.42	rh nd (al), orh pr (MeOH) $[\alpha]_D^{20}$ +123 (al, c = 0.66) λ^{al} 230 sh (4.2), 282 (4.0), 292 (4.0)	186 (194)				i	v^h	v^h		s	chl s	B23², 358
c321	Cinchonicine	Cinchotoxine. $C_{19}H_{22}N_2O$.	294.40	nd or pr (eth) $[\alpha]_D^{15}$ +48 (al, c = 1)	58–60	....			i	v	v	v	v	chl v	B24², 100
c322	Cinchonidine	Cinchovatine. α-Quinidine. $C_{19}H_{22}N_2O$.	294.40	orh pl or pr (al) $[\alpha]_D^{20}$ −109.20 (al, p = 1) $\lambda^{w, pH = 1}$ 305 sh (3.81), 315 (3.87)	210.5	sub			i	s	δ	....	i	Py, chl, MeOH s peth i	B23², 373
c323	—,bisulfate	$C_{19}H_{22}N_2O \cdot H_2SO_4 \cdot 5H_2O$. See c322	482.56	mcl pr $[\alpha]_D$ −110 (al)	....				v	v			i		B23, 441

For explanations, symbols and abbreviations see beginning of table. For structural formulas see end of table.

No.	Name	Synonyms and Formula	Mol. wt.	Color, crystalline form, specific rotation and λ_{max} (log ε)	m.p. °C	b.p. °C	Density	n_D	w	al	eth	ace	bz	other solvents	Ref.
	Cinchonidine														
c324	—,hydrochloride	$C_{19}H_{22}N_2O \cdot HCl \cdot H_2O$. See c322	348.88	wh pr (w) $[\alpha]_D^{20} -117.6$ (w, c = 1.2)	242d (anh)	....	....	....	s	v	δ	...	i	chl v	B23[2], 373
c325	—,sulfate	$(C_{19}H_{22}N_2O)_2 \cdot H_2SO_4 \cdot 6H_2O$. See c322	794.97	mcl eff nd (al + 2w) $[\alpha]_D^{18.5} -97.9$ (w, c = 1.2)	205 (anh)	....	....	....	δ	δ	i	...	i	chl δ	B23[2], 373
c326	β-Cinchonidine	$C_{19}H_{22}N_2O$	294.40	pr or lf (al or dil al) $[\alpha]_D^{25} -126.6$ (al, c = 0.5)	241	....	....	....	i	v	δ	...	...	chl v	B23[1], 131
Ω c327	**Cinchonine**	$C_{19}H_{22}N_2O$. See c322	294.40	nd or mcl cr (al) $[\alpha]_D^{17} +229$ (al) $\lambda^{w, pH=6}$ 285 (3.71), 300 (3.57), 313 (3.40)	255 (265)	sub >220	....	....	i	δ	δ	i	i	chl s MeOH, Py δ peth i	B23[2], 369
c328	—,bisulfate	$C_{19}H_{22}N_2O \cdot H_2SO_4 \cdot 4H_2O$. See c322	464.53	rh oct (w) $[\alpha]_D^8 +195$ (w, c = 2)		....	....	....	v	v	i	...	...		B23[2], 371
c329	—,dihydrochloride	$C_{19}H_{22}N_2O \cdot 2HCl$. See c322	367.32	pl, $[\alpha]_D^{21} +205.5$ (w, c = 3.6)		....	....	....	v	s	i	...	i	....	B23[1], 133
c330	—,hydrochloride	$C_{19}H_{22}N_2O \cdot HCl \cdot 2H_2O$. See c322	366.89	mcl $[\alpha]_D^{25} +133.6$ (chl, c = 1.4)	ca. 215 (anh)	....	1.234	....	s v^h	v	δ	...	i	chl s	B23[2], 370
c331	—,nitrate	$C_{19}H_{22}N_2O \cdot HNO_3 \cdot \frac{1}{2}H_2O$. See c322	366.42	mcl (w)		....	....	....	s	v	...	...	i	....	B23, 430
c332	—,sulfate	$(C_{19}H_{22}N_2O)_2 \cdot H_2SO_4 \cdot 2H_2O$. See c322	722.91	rh pr (w) $[\alpha]_D^5 +169$ (w, c = 1.4)	206–7 (198) (anh)	....	....	....	s^h v^h	ε	i	...	i	MeOH v chl δ	B23[2], 371
—	**Cinchoninic acid**	see **4-Quinolinecarboxylic acid**													
—	**Cinchopene**	see **4-Quinolinecarboxylic acid, 2-phenyl-**													
c333	**Cinchotine**	Hydrocinchonine. Pseudo-cinchonine. $C_{19}H_{24}N_2O$.	296.42	pr $[\alpha]_D^{21} +203.4$ $\lambda^{w, pH=1}$ 298 (3.67), 308 (3.85), 314 (3.87)	268–9	....	....	....	s^h	δ	i	...	...		B23[2], 356
Ω c334	**1,4-Cineole**	p-Cineole. 1,4-Epoxy-p-menthane.	154.26	 l	l	173–4	0.8997[20]	1.4562[20]	δ	∞	∞	...	s	lig s	B17[2], 32
c335	**1,8 Cineole**	Cajeputol. Eucalyptol.	154.26	 l	1.5	176.4 61[14]	0.9267[20]	1.4586[20]	i	s	s	...	...	chl s	B17[2], 32
c336	**Cineolic acid(d)**	Tetrahydro-2,6,6-trimethylpyran-2,5-dicarboxylic acid.	216.24	cr (w + l) $[\alpha]_D^{20} +18.6$ (w, p = 8.21)	79 (+w) 138–9	....	....	....	δ s^h	v	δ	...	δ	chl, AcOEt v lig δ	B18, 322
c337	—(dl)	$C_{10}H_{16}O_5$. See c336	216.24	(i) 197.5 (ii) 208		....	....	....	δ s^h	v^h	v	...	δ	chl δ	B18[2], 285
c338	—(l)	$C_{10}H_{16}O_5 \cdot H_2O$. See c336	234.25	rh (w + l) $[\alpha]_D^{20} -19.1$ (w)	79 (+w) 138.9 (anh)	....	....	....	δ s^h	$δ^h$	δ	...	δ	chl δ	B18, 322
Ω c339	**Cinnamaldehyde** (trans)	Cinnamic aldehyde. β-Phenylacrolein. 3-Phenylpropenal (trans)*	132.17	yesh λ^{al} 291 (4.40)	−7.5	253[760] δd 127[16]	1.0497[20]	1.6195[20]	δ	s	s	...	...	chl s lig i	B7[2], 273
Ω c340	—,oxime (syn)	$C_6H_5CH:CHCH:NOH$	147.18	nd λ^{al} 290 (4.3)	138.5	....	....	....	δ	δ	δ	...	s		B7[2], 278
c341	—,4-hydroxy-3-methoxy-	Coniferaldehyde. Ferulaldehyde. $C_{10}H_{10}O_3$. See c339	178.19	cr (bz)	84	157[2.5]	....	....	δ	s	s	...	s	chl v	B8, 288
c342	—,4-methyl-	$C_{10}H_{10}O$. See c339	146.19	ye lf (dil al)	41.5	154[25]	....	....	s^h						B7, 369
c343	—,α-methyl-	$C_6H_5CH:C(CH_3)CHO$	146.19	ye λ^{al} 280 (4.3)	....	150[100] 131–2[16]	1.0407[17]	1.6057[17] (1.3917[20])							B7[2], 291
c344	—,2-nitro-	$C_9H_7NO_3$. See c339	177.16	nd (eth or al) λ^{al} 250 (4.3), 280 sh (4.0)	127.0–7.5	....	....	....	v^h	s^h	s	...	...	chl v	B7[2], 281
c345	—,3-nitro-	$C_9H_7NO_3$. See c339	177.16	ye nd (w), pr (al), cr (aa)	116	....	....	....	$δ^h$	δ s^h	δ	...	v	aa v	B7[2], 282
c346	—,4-nitro-	$C_9H_7NO_3$. See c339	177.16	nd (w or al) λ^{al} 295 (4.3)	141–2	....	....	....	s^h	v	s	s	s	oos v	B7[2], 282
—	—,α-pentyl-	see **Heptanal, 2-benzylidene-***													
—	**Cinnamalmalonic acid**	see **Malonic acid, cinnamylidene** (trans)													
—	**Cinnamein**	see **Cinnamic acid**, benzyl ester													
c347	**Cinnamic acid** (cis) (1st form)	Isocinnamic acid. cis-β-Phenylacrylic acid.	148.17	mcl pr (w) λ^{al} 263–5 (4.0)	42	....	....	....	δ s^h					aa, lig v CCl₄ s	B9[2], 393
c348	—(cis) (2nd form)	$C_9H_8O_2$. See c347	148.17	lo mcl pr (lig) λ^{al} 267 (3.98)	58	265	....	....	δ s^h	s	v	v	v	chl, lig s	B9[2], 393

For explanations, symbols and abbreviations see beginning of table. For structural formulas see end of table.

Cinnamic acid

No.	Name	Synonyms and Formula	Mol. wt.	Color, crystalline form, specific rotation and λ_{max} (log ε)	m.p. °C	b.p. °C	Density	n_D	Solubility						Ref.
									w	al	eth	ace	bz	other solvents	
c349	—(cis) (3rd form) ..	Allocinnamic acid. Isocinnamic acid. $C_9H_8O_2$. See c347	148.17	mcl pr λ^{al} 266 (3.99)	68	....			δ s^h	v^h	v^h	...	...	lig s	B9², 393
Ω c350	—(trans)	trans-β-Phenylacrylic acid. trans-3-Phenylpropenoic acid.*	148.17	mcl pr (dil al) λ^{al} 210 (4.24), 215 (4.28), 221 (4.18), 268 (4.31)	135–6 (cor) (133)	300⁷⁶⁰ (cor)	1.2475⁴₄	....	i δ^h	v	s	s	s	chl, to, MeOH s lig, peth i	B9², 377
Ω c351	—,allyl ester	Allyl cinnamate $C_6H_5CH:CHCO_2CH_2CH:CH_2$	188.23	....		286d 163¹⁷	1.048²³	1.530²⁰	i	v	∞				B9², 387
Ω c352	—,amide(trans)	Cinnamamide. $C_6H_5CH:CHCONH_2$	147.18	nd (bz) λ 273 (4.4)	148.0–8.5 (cor)	....			δ^h	v	v			CS_2 v	B9², 391
c353	—,anhydride(trans)	nd (bz or al), pr (al) λ^{peth} 290 (4.69)	278.31		138 (136)	....			i	δ s^h		v^h			B9², 390
Ω c354	—,benzyl ester (trans)	Benzyl cinnamate. Cinnamein. $C_6H_5CH:CHCO_2CH_2C_6H_5$	238.29	pr	39 (34)	350d 244⁵	1.109¹⁵		i	s	s	s			B9², 388
Ω c355	—,chloride(trans)..	Cinnamoyl chloride. $C_6H_5CH:CHCOCl$	166.61	....	37–8	257.5⁷⁶⁰ 131¹¹	1.1617⁴⁵₄	1.614⁴²·⁵	i	s^h	s	v	s	CCl_4, lig s	B9², 390
Ω c356	—,ethyl ester(trans)	Ethyl cinnamate. $C_6H_5CH:CHCO_2C_2H_5$	176.22	λ^{al} 216.5 (4.14), 222 (4.09), 277 (4.30)	12 (6.5)	271.5⁷⁶⁰ 144¹⁵	1.0491²⁰₄	1.5598²⁰	i	s	s	s	s	oos v	B9², 385
Ω c357	—,isopropyl ester (trans)	$C_6H_5CH:CHCO_2CH(CH_3)_2$	190.25	....		268–70 153–5²⁰	1.0320²⁰	1.5455²⁰	i	s	s	s	s	chl s	B9², 387
c358	—,2-methoxy-phenyl ester(trans)	o-Anisyl cinnamate. Guaiacol cinnamate.	254.29	wh nd (al)	130	....			i			s	s	chl s	B9², 389
Ω c359	—,methyl ester (trans)	Methyl cinnamate. $C_6H_5CH:CHCO_2CH_3$	162.19	cr (peth or dil al) λ^{al} 217 (4.22), 223 (4.14), 278 (4.37)	36.5	261.9⁷⁶⁰ 127¹⁰	1.0911²⁰₄	1.5766²¹	i	v	v	s	s	oos v	B9², 384
c360	—,nitrile(cis)......	Allocinnamonitrile. cis-Cinnamonitrile. cis-Styryl cyanide. $C_6H_5CH:CHCN$	129.16	λ 273 (4.22)	−4.4	249 139³⁰	....	1.5843²⁰	i	s			v		Am 58, 2428
c361	—,—(trans)......	$C_6H_5CH:CHCN$	129.16	....	22	263.8 134–6¹²	1.0304²⁰₄	1.6013²⁰	i	s	s	s			B9², 392
c362	—,2-octyl ester (trans, d)	$C_6H_5CH:CHCO_2CH(CH_3)(CH_2)_5CH_3$ 260.38 $[[\alpha]_D^{17}+40.19$		....	218²⁸	0.9645²⁰	1.5145²⁰	i				s	chl s	B9¹, 229
c363	—,—(trans, dl)	$C_6H_5CH:CHCO_2CH(CH_3)(CH_2)_5CH_3$ 260.38		....	240⁶⁰ 213²⁸	0.9715¹⁷₄		i				s	chl s	B9¹, 230
c364	—,—(trans, l)	$C_6H_5CH:CHCO_2CH(CH_3)(CH_2)_5CH_8$ 260.38 $[[\alpha]_D^{17}-39.78$		....	211²⁸	0.9692¹⁷₄		i				s	chl s	B9¹, 229
c365	—,phenyl ester (trans)	$C_6H_5CH:CHCO_2C_6H_5$	224.26	....	72.5	205–7¹⁵				s		s		s	B9², 387
Ω c366	—,p-phenyl-phenacyl ester (trans)		342.40	....	182.5										Am 52, 3719
c367	—,propyl ester (trans)	$C_6H_5CH:CHCO_2CH_2CH_2CH_3$ 190.25		....		285⁷⁶⁰	1.0435⁰₀		i						B9², 387
c368	—,4-ureidophenyl ester (trans)		282.30	wh	204	....			i	s		s			C52, 10721
Ω c369	—,α-acetamido-(trans)	$C_6H_5CH:C(NHCOCH_3)CO_2H$ 205.22		cr (+2w) λ^{al} 273 (4.36)	185–6 (+2w) 193–4 (anh)				s						B10², 471
c370	—,2-amino-(trans) .	$C_9H_9NO_2$. See c350........	163.18	ye nd (w)	158–9d				s^h	s	s				B14², 316
c371	—,3-amino-(trans) .	$C_9H_9NO_2$. See c350........	163.18	pa ye nd (w or al)	185 (181)				s^h	v	v		ac, alk s		B14², 316
Ω c372	—,4-amino-(trans) .	$C_9H_9NO_2$. See c350........	163.18	ye nd (w or al)	175–6d				s^h	s	s				B14², 317
c373	—,2-benzamido-(trans)	$C_{16}H_{13}NO_3$. See c350	267.29	nd (al)	191–3					δ^h		s	aa s^h oos δ		B14¹, 617
c374	—,3-benzamido-(trans)	$C_{16}H_{13}NO_3$. See c350	267.29	nd (AcOEt)	229					s^h		s	δ	aa s	B14¹, 618
c375	—,4-benzamido-(trans)	$C_{16}H_{13}NO_3$. See c350	267.29	lf (aa), nd (ace)	274d					δ		v^h	s	aa v^h	B14¹, 619
c376	—,α-bromo-(cis) ...	α-Bromoallocinnamic acid. $C_6H_5CH:CBrCO_2H$	227.06	lf (w), pr (chl) λ^{al} 206 (4.03), 257 (4.16)	120–1				s^h				s	CS_2 s	B9², 399
c377	—,—(trans)........	$C_6H_5CH:CBrCO_2H$	227.06	nd (w) λ^{al} 206 (4.1), 217 (4.05), 273 (4.19)	131–2				v^h	∞	s		s		B9², 398
c378	—,β-bromo(cis)....	β-Bromoallocinnamic acid. $C_6H_5CBr:CHCO_2H$	227.06	nd (bz), pl (al) λ^{al} 205 (4.3), 230 sh (3.93), 267 (3.74)	159–60				δ^h	δ	s	...	δ s^h	chl s	B9², 398
c379	—,—(trans).......	$C_6H_5CBr:CHCO_2H$	227.06	pa ye nd or pl (w), pr (chl) λ^{al} 205 (4.2), 263 (4.07)	135				δ^h	s		s^h	s^h	CS_2 δ	B9², 397

For explanations, symbols and abbreviations see beginning of table. For structural formulas see end of table.

Cinnamic acid

No.	Name	Synonyms and Formula	Mol. wt.	Color, crystalline form, specific rotation and λ_{max} (log ε)	m.p. °C	b.p. °C	Density	n_D	w	al	eth	ace	bz	other solvents	Ref.
c380	—,2-carboxy- (trans)	β(2-Carboxyphenyl)acrylic acid. o,β-Styrenedicarboxylic acid. $C_{10}H_8O_4$. See c350	192.18	pr or nd (w) λ^{al} 220 (4.18), 272 (4.18)	208–9	....	....	....	δ^h	v	δ	...	i	$CS_2 \delta$ chl i	B9², 641
c381	—,3-carboxy- (trans)	$C_{10}H_8O_4$. See c350.........	192.18	nd (ace-lig)	275 (264)	....	....	....	i	δ	δ	...	i	aa v chl i	B9², 642
c382	—,4-carboxy- (trans)	$C_{10}H_8O_4$. See c350.........	192.18	pw	358d	sub >350	....	....	...	i	i	...	i	aa s^h oos i	B9², 642
c383	—,α,β-dibromo- (cis)	$C_6H_5CBr:CBrCO_2H$	305.97	ye pr or pl (chl or lig) λ^{al} 205 (4.3), 236 (4.06), 288 (3.47)	100	124⁰·⁵	....	....	i	s^h	s	...	...	chl, aa s lig s^h peth δ	B9², 401
c384	—,2,4-dihydroxy- (trans)	Umbellic acid. $C_9H_8O_4$. See c350	180.17	ye nd or pl λ^{MeOH} 217 (4.1), 286 (4.0), 324 (4.1)	d260 (darkens at 240)	....	....	....	s^h	s	i	...	i	lig i	B10², 293
c385	—,2,5-dihydroxy- (trans)	$C_9H_8O_4$. See c350	180.17	ye cr (w), cr (dil al + 1w) λ^{MeOH} 220 (4.1), 274 (4.2), 350 (3.8)	207d	....	....	....	...	s	...	...	...	....	B10, 435
Ω c386	—,3,4-dihydroxy- (trans)	Caffeic acid. $C_9H_8O_4$. See c350	180.17	ye pr or pl (w) λ^{al} 244 (4.05), 299 (4.18), 326 (4.27)	225d (200)	....	....	....	s^h	s	δ	...	...	....	B10², 294
c387	—,3,5-dihydroxy- (trans)	$C_9H_8O_4$. See c350	180.17	nd (w + ½)	245–6	....	....	....	v^h	v	v	...	i	....	B10², 297
c388	—,2,3-dimethoxy- (trans)	$C_{11}H_{12}O_4$. See c350.........	208.22	nd	180–1	....	....	....	δ	δ	...	...	...	oos δ	B10², 292
c389	—,2,4-dimethoxy- (cis)	$C_{11}H_{12}O_4$. See c347.........	208.22	nd (al) λ^{MeOH} 217 (3.9), 271 (3.9), 310 (3.9)	138	....	....	....	...	v	v	...	v	....	B10², 293
c390	—,— (trans)......	$C_{11}H_{12}O_4$. See c350.........	208.22	nd (w or dil al) λ^{MeOH} 217 (4.1), 244 (4.1), 286 (4.2), 322 (4.2)	187.5–9.0	....	....	....	δ	v	v	...	v	chl v lig i	B10², 293
c391	—,2,5-dimethoxy- (trans)	$C_{11}H_{12}O_4$. See c350........	208.22	pa ye or ye-gr nd (w) λ^{MeOH} 223 (4.1), 274 (4.2, 340 (3.8)	148–9	....	....	....	δ s^h	s	s	...	...	oos, alk v	B10², 294
Ω c392	—,3,4-dimethoxy- (trans)	$C_{11}H_{12}O_4$. See c350........	208.22	nd (w, dil al), pa ye pw (dil aa) λ^{al} 220, 258, 290, 318	183	....	....	....	s^h	v	v	...	...	aa s^h	B10², 294
c393	—,3,5-dimethoxy- (trans)	$C_{11}H_{12}O_4$. See c350........	208.22	nd (w)	175–6	....	....	....	v^h	v	v	...	v	....	B10², 297
Ω c394	—,3,5-dimethoxy-4-hydroxy-(trans)	5-Methoxyferulic acid. Sinapic acid. $C_{11}H_{12}O_5$. See c350	224.22	pa ye nd (al) λ^{al} 225 (4.0), 240 (4.0), 320 (4.2)	192	....	....	....	δ	s^h	δ	...	...	....	B10, 508
c395	—,α-ethyl-(cis)	α-Benzalbutyric acid. $C_6H_5CH:C(C_2H_5)CO_2H$	176.22	nd (w)	82	....	....	....	v^h	v	v	...	v	CS_2 v	B9, 623
c396	—,— (trans)......	$C_6H_5CH:C(C_2H_5)CO_2H$	176.22	nd (w)	106 (114)	....	....	....	i	v	s	...	...	lig δ, s^h	B9¹, 258
Ω c397	—,2-hydroxy- (trans)	trans-o-Coumaric acid. $C_9H_8O_3$. See c350	164.17	nd (w) λ^w 274 (4.26), 325 (4.00)	217d	....	....	....	δ	s	δ	...	...	chl, CS_2 i	B10², 174
Ω c398	—,3-hydroxy- (trans)	trans-m-Coumaric acid. $C_9H_8O_3$. See c350	164.17	pr (w) λ^{eth} 277 (4.29), 319 (3.70)	193	....	....	....	s^h	s	s	...	s	chl, CS_2 i	B10², 178
Ω c399	—,4-hydroxy- (trans)	trans-p-Coumaric acid. $C_9H_8O_3$. See c350	164.17	nd (w + 1), cr (w^h) λ^{al} 227 (4.09), 312 (4.36)	215d	....	....	....	δ	s^h	s	...	δ	lig i	B10², 178
Ω c400	—,4-hydroxy-3-methoxy-(trans)	Ferulic acid. $C_{10}H_{10}O_4$. See c350	194.19	pr or nd (w) λ^{al} 234 (4.10), 296 (4.09), 323 (4.22)	171	....	....	....	s^h	s	δ	...	δ	AcOEt v chl s lig δ	B10², 294
c401	—,4-isopropyl- (trans)	Cumylideneacetic acid. $C_{12}H_{14}O_2$. See c350	190.25	pr (bz)	165	....	....	....	δ^h	s	...	...	s^h	aa s^h	B9, 629
Ω c402	—,4-methoxy- (trans)	$C_{10}H_{10}O_3$. See c350........	178.19	wh nd (al)	172–5	....	....	....	δ	δ	...	...	δ	CCl_4, aa s	B10², 179

For explanations, symbols and abbreviations see beginning of table. For structural formulas see end of table.

No.	Name	Synonyms and Formula	Mol. wt.	Color, crystalline form, specific rotation and λ_{max} (log ε)	m.p. °C	b.p. °C	Density	n_D	Solubility						Ref.
									w	al	eth	ace	bz	other solvents	
	Cinnamic acid														
c403	—,α-methyl-(cis)...	α-Benzalpropionic acid. β-Phenylmethacrylic acid. $C_6H_5CH:C(CH_3)CO_2H$	162.19	nd (bz or CS_2) λ^{al} 205 (4.3), 257 (4.20)	74	288 190^{21}			δ	v	v	...	v	CS_2 v peth s	B9[2], 409
c404	—,—(trans)......	$C_6H_5CH:C(CH_3)CO_2H$....	162.19	pr (aa, eth or dil al) λ^{al} 206 (4.2), 261 (4.22)	81–2				δ	v	s	...	v	peth s	B9, 615
c405	—,2-methyl-4-nitro-(trans)	$C_{10}H_9NO_4$. See c350	207.19	nd (al)	256				δ^h	δ^h	i				B9[1], 256
c406	—,4-methyl-3-nitro-(trans)	$C_{10}H_9NO_4$. See c350	207.19	ye pl or nd (al)	173.5				v^h	s	v	...		lig i	B9[1], 257
c407	—,α-methyl-2-nitro-	$C_{10}H_9NO_4$. See c350	207.19	mcl pr (al)	164–5					v	v	δ		lig δ	B9[1], 256
c408	—,α-methyl-3-nitro-	$C_{10}H_9NO_4$. See c350	207.19	nd or pw λ^{al} 258 (4.35)	203.5 (198)					s^h	v	v		aa v lig δ	B9[1], 256
c409	—,α-methyl-4-nitro-	$C_{10}H_9NO_4$. See c350	207.19	ye rh (aa), tcl pym (aa, al-eth) λ^{al} 282 (3.98)	208					s^h	δ	δ		aa s^h oos δ	B9[1], 256
c411	—,2-nitro-(cis)....	$C_9H_7NO_4$. See c347......	193.16	yesh (bz or chl)	146–7					v			v^h	chl δ	B9[1], 246
c412	—,—(trans)......	$C_9H_7NO_4$. See c350......	193.16	nd (al) λ^{al} 248 (4.1), 290 sh (4.6)	242–3	sub			i	s^h	v	...	i		B9[2], 402
c413	—,—,ethyl ester (trans)	$C_{11}H_{11}NO_4$. See c350......	221.22	ye rh bipym (al)	44				v^h	v^h		v^h	$CS_2 v^h$		B9[2], 402
c414	—,—,methyl ester (trans)	$C_{10}H_9NO_4$. See c350	207.19	wh nd (w)	73	$187–9^{15}$			δ^h	v^h					B9[2], 402
c415	—,3-nitro-(cis)....	$C_9H_7NO_4$. See c347....	193.16	nd	158										B9[1], 247
c416	—,—(trans)......	$C_9H_7NO_4$. See c350......	193.16	nd (al) λ^{al} 263 (4.4), 305 sh (3.1)	204.5–5.5				δ	δ	δ		s^h		B9[2], 402
c417	—,—,ethyl ester (trans)	$C_{11}H_{11}NO_4$. See c350......	221.22	nd (al), pr (aa)	78–9				δ	δ	δ		v	chl v	B9[2], 403
c418	—,—,methyl ester (trans)	$C_{10}H_9NO_4$. See c350......	207.19	pa ye pr (MeOH)	123–4	d			i	δ	s	v		MeOH δ	B9[2], 403
Ω c419	—,4-nitro-(trans)..	$C_9H_7NO_4$. See c350......	193.16	yesh-wh pr (al) λ^{al} 295 (4.3)	286 (289)				δ^h	δ	δ			CS_2, lig i	B9[2], 404
c420	—,—,ethyl ester (trans)	$C_{11}H_{11}NO_4$. See c350......	221.22	pl (aa) λ^{al} 300 (4.34)	141–2				i	i	δ				B9[2], 404
c421	—,—,methyl ester (trans)	$C_{10}H_9NO_4$. See c350......	207.19	wh nd (al) λ^{al} 299.5 (4.32)	162	281–6				s^h	δ				B9[2], 404
c422	—,—,piperazinium salt(trans)	$2C_9H_7NO_4 \cdot C_4H_{10}N_2$. See c350	472.46	....		248d			δ^h	s	i				Am 70, 2758
	—,α-phenyl-......	see Propenoic acid, 2,3-diphenyl-*													
Ω c424	—,3,4,5-tri-methoxy-(trans)	$C_{12}H_{14}O_5$. See c350......	238.24	nd (w) $\lambda^{w, pH=10}$ 298 (4.28)	126–7	....			s^h					chl s	Am 77, 2241
	Cinnamic alcohol ..	see 2-Propen-1-ol, 3-phenyl-*													
	Cinnamylidene chloride	see Propene, 3,3-dichloro-1-phenyl-*													
	Citraconic acid	see Maleic acid, methyl-													
Ω c425	**Citral a**	Geranial	152.24	λ^{al} 237 (4.16)	......	229^{760} $118–9^{20}$	0.8888^{20}	1.4898^{20}	i	∞	∞	...			B1[3], 3056
c426	**Citral b**	Neral	152.24	λ^{al} 237 (4.16)	......	120^{20} 103^{12}	0.8869^{20}	1.4869^{20}	i	∞	∞	...			B1[3], 3056
	Citramalic acid	see Succinic acid, 2-hydroxy-2-methyl-													
c427	**β-Citraurin**	$C_{30}H_{40}O_2$	432.65	pl (bz-peth), cr (al) λ 467, 497	147				i	v	v	v	v	CS_2 v lig δ	H21, 448
Ω c428	**Citric acid**	2-Hydroxy-1,2,3-propanetri-carboxylic acid.* $HOC(CH_2CO_2H)_2CO_2H$	192.14	rh (w + 1)	153 (anh) (156–7)	d	1.542^{18}_{8} (hyd) 1.665^{18}_{4} (anh)		v	v	s		i	AcOEt s chl, to i	B3[2], 359
c429	—,piperazinium salt	$HOC(CH_2CO_2H)_2CO_2H \cdot C_4H_{10}N_2$ 278.27	278.27	....	141–2				s	s	i				Am 70, 2758
c430	—,triamide	Citramide. Citric triamide. $HOC(CH_2CONH_2)_2CONH_2$	189.17	(w)	210–5d				s^h	i	i				B3[1], 197
c431	—,tribenzyl ester ..	Benzyl citrate. $HOC(CH_2CO_2CH_2C_6H_5)_2CO_2CH_2C_6H_5$	462.51	nd (al)	51					s^h	v			oos s	B6[2], 421
Ω c432	—,triethyl ester....	Ethyl citrate. $HOC(CH_2CO_2C_2H_5)_2CO_2C_2H_5$	276.29	....	......	294^{760} 185^{17}	1.1369^{20}_{4}	1.4455^{20}	i	s	s				B3[2], 370
c433	—,trimethyl ester ..	Methyl citrate. $HOC(CH_2CO_2CH_3)_2CO_2CH_3$	234.21	tcl	78.5–79	$287d$ 176^{16}			δ	v	v				B3[2], 370
c434	—,triphenyl ester ..	Phenyl citrate. $HOC(CH_2CO_2C_6H_5)_2CO_2C_6H_5$	420.42	nd (al)	124.5				i	s^h	s				B6, 170
c435	—,tripropyl ester ..	Propyl citrate. $HOC(CH_2CO_2C_3H_7^n)_2CO_2C_3H_7^n$	318.37	....	......	198^{18}				s	s				B3, 568

For explanations, symbols and abbreviations see beginning of table. For structural formulas see end of table.

Citric acid

No.	Name	Synonyms and Formula	Mol. wt.	Color, crystalline form, specific rotation and λ_{max} (log ε)	m.p. °C	b.p. °C	Density	n_D	w	al	eth	ace	bz	other solvents	Ref.
c436	—,anhydro-methylene-	1,3-Dioxolan-4-one-5,5-diacetic acid.	204.15	(w)	298	....	....	....	v[h]	δ	δ	v	...	chl v alk s	B19[2], 324
c437	Citrinin	$C_{13}H_{14}O_5$	250.25	ye nd (MeOH) $[\alpha]_D^{11} -37$ λ^{al} 250 (3.97), 331 (4.02), 400 sh (4.2)	178–9d	....	....	....	i	δ	δ	s	s	alk, chl, diox s	J1963, 3777
c438	Citronellal(d)	d-Rhodinal. $(CH_3)_2C{:}CH(CH_2)_2CH(CH_3)CH_2CHO$	154.26	$[\alpha]_D^{18} +13.09$ λ^{al} 235 (1.93), 290 sh (1.08)	....	207.8^{760} 92^{14}	0.8573_4^{20}	1.4456^{20}	δ	s	s				B1[2], 803
Ω c439	—(dl)..........	$C_{10}H_{18}O$ See c438	154.26	λ^{al} 235 (1.93), 290 sh (1.08)	....	$207-8^{760}$ $79-81^{10}$	0.8535_4^{17}	1.4473^{20}							B1[2], 805
c440	—(l)..........	$C_{10}H_{18}O$. See c438	154.26	$[\alpha]_D^{20} -2.5$ λ^{al} 235 (1.93), 290 sh (1.08)	....	$205-6$ 87^{10}	0.8567_4^{17}	1.4479^{20}	δ	∞	∞				B1[2], 805
c441	Citronellol(d)	d-Rhodinol. $(CH_3)_2C{:}CH(CH_2)_2CH(CH_3)CH_2CH_2OH$	156.27	$[\alpha]_D^{17} +6.8$ λ^{al} 212 (2.98)	....	244.4^{760} (222) 118^{17}	0.8590^{20}	1.4565^{20}	δ[h]	∞	∞				B1[2], 495
Ω c442	—(dl)..........	Dihydrogeraniol. $C_{10}H_{20}O$. See c441	156.27	λ^{al} 212 (2.98)	....	99^{10}	0.8560_4^{20}	1.4543^{20}	δ[h]	∞	∞				B1[2], 495
c443	—(l)..........	l-Rhodinol. $C_{10}H_{20}O$. See c441	156.27	$[\alpha]_D^{18} -5.3$ λ^{al} 212 (2.98)	....	$108-9^{10}$	0.859_4^{18}	1.4576^{18}							B1[2], 496
Ω c444	Citrulline(L)	α-Amino-δ-ureidovaleric acid. N-δ-Carbamyl-ornithine. δ-Ureidonor-valine. $H_2NCONH(CH_2)_3CH(NH_2)CO_2H$	175.19	pr (aq MeOH) $[\alpha]_D^{20} +3.7$ (w, c = 2)	234–7 (222)	....	....	....	s	i				MeOH l	B4[3], 1347
—	Civetone	see 9-Cycloheptadecen-1-one*													
—	Cleve's acid	see 1-Naphthalenesulfonic acid, 3-amino-*													
—	Clupanodonic acid	see Docosapentaenoic acid*													
—	Cocaethyline......	see Ecgonine, benzoate, ethyl ester													
c445	Cocaine(d)	β-Cocaine. Benzoyl methyl ecgonine. $C_{17}H_{21}NO_4$.	303.36	mcl pr (eth) $[\alpha]_D^{20} +15.8$ (chl, p = 10) λ^{al} 229 (4.2), 274 (3.0), 281 (2.9)	98	....	....	....	i	v	v	s	s		B22[2], 150
c446	—(dl)..........	$C_{17}H_{21}NO_4$. See c445	303.36	rh bipym pr (peth) λ^{al} 229 (4.2), 274 (3.0), 281 (2.9)	79–80	....	....	....	i	v	s	v	chl, CCl_4, lig v		B22[2], 156
c447	—(l)..........	$C_{17}H_{21}NO_4$. See c445	303.36	mcl pr (al) $[\alpha]_D^{20} -16.3$ (chl, c = 4), $[\alpha]_D^{18} -35$ 50% al, c = 1) λ^{al} 229 (4.2), 274 (3.0), 281 (2.9)	98	$187-8^{0.1}$ (sub 75–90 (vac))		1.5022^{98}	δ[h]	v	v	s	v	chl, Py v CS_2 s	B22[2], 151
c448	—,chromate(l)	$C_{17}H_{21}NO_4 \cdot H_2CrO_4 \cdot H_2O$. See c445	439.40	og ye lf	127	....	....	....	δ						B22, 200
c449	—,hydro-chloride(dl)	$C_{17}H_{21}NO_4 \cdot HCl$. See c445	339.82	pl (al) λ^w 233 (4.09), 274 (3.03)	187 (cor)	....	....	....	v	v	i	s	i	chl s	B22[2], 156
c450	—,—,(l)..........	$C_{17}H_{21}NO_4 \cdot HCl$. See c445.	339.82	mcl pr (al), or (w + ?) $[\alpha]_D^{20} -71.95$ (w) λ^w 233 (4.09), 274 (3.03)	197	....	....	....	v	v	i	s	i	chl s	B22[2], 153
c451	"Cocaine cinnamate"(d)	O-Cinnamoyl-d-ecgonine methyl ester.	329.40	pr, $[\alpha]$ +2 (al)	68	....	....	....	i	s	s	s	s	chl, lig s	B22, 207
c452	—(l)..........	$C_{19}H_{23}NO_4$. See c451	329.40	mcl pr, nd (bz) $[\alpha]_D^{15} -4.7$ (chl, c = 10)	121	....	....	....	i	s	s	s	s	chl, lig s	B22[2], 154
c453	Coclaurine(l)......	$C_{17}H_{19}NO_3$.	285.35	pl (al) $[\alpha]_D^{20}$ 17.01	220–1	....	....	....	δ	δ v[h]	δ	δ v[h]	i	chl δ peth i	C47, 6430
c454	Codamine	$C_{20}H_{25}NO_4$.	343.43	pr (bz or eth)	127	....	....	....	ε[h]	v	s		...	chl v	B21[2], 184

For explanations, symbols and abbreviations see beginning of table. For structural formulas see end of table.

No.	Name	Synonyms and Formula	Mol. wt.	Color, crystalline form, specific rotation and λ_{max} (log ε)	m.p. °C	b.p. °C	Density	n_D	Solubility						Ref.
									w	al	eth	ace	bz	other solvents	
	Codeine														
c455	**Codeine**	Morphine 3-methyl ether. $C_{18}H_{21}NO_3$.	299.37	rh oct (+ 1w, w or dil al), cr (eth or CS_2) $[\alpha]_D^{15} - 137.8$ (al, p = 2) λ^{al} 212 (4.4), 236 sh (3.7), 286 (3.2)	157–8.5 (156)	250^{12} (sub 140–5$^{1.5}$)	1.32	....	s^h	v	s	...	s	chl, to, MeOH s peth i	B27², 137
c456	—,hydrate	$C_{18}H_{21}NO_3 . H_2O. See$ c455	317.39	rh oct (w, aq al) $[\alpha]_D^{15} - 136$ (al, c = 2.8)	....	....	1.31	....	δ	v	s	v	s	chl v	B27², 137
c457	—,hydrochloride	$C_{18}H_{21}NO_3 . HCl . 2H_2O.$ See c455	371.87	nd, $[\alpha]_D^{15} - 108.2$ (w) λ^w 238 sh (3.70), 285.5 (3.24)	287d	....	....	....	v	s					B27², 143
c458	—,phosphate	$C_{18}H_{21}NO_3 . H_3PO_4 . 1\frac{1}{2}H_2O.$ See c455	424.39	lf or pr (dil al) λ^w 212 (4.41), 284 (3.22)	220–35d	....	....	....	v	s^h	s	...		chl s	B27², 144
c459	—,sulfate	$(C_{18}H_{21}NO_3)_2 . H_2SO_4 . 5H_2O$ See c455	786.90	pr, $[\alpha]_D^{15} - 100.9$ (w, p = 3)	278 (anh)	....	....	....	s	δ	i			chl i	B27², 144
c460	**β-Codeine**	Neopine. $C_{18}H_{21}NO_3$	299.37	nd (peth) $[\alpha]_D^{23} - 28$ (chl, c = 7.5) λaq. HBr 210 (4.6), 232 sh (3.8), 284 (3.2)	127.5				s	s	s		s	MeOH, chl v lig δ	B27², 176
c461	**Codeine, dihydro-** (d)	Cohydrin. Dihydroneopine. Paracodin. $C_{18}H_{23}NO_3$.	301.39	cr (+ 1w, dil MeOH) $[\alpha]_D + 146.4$ (al, c = 2) λ^{al} 285.5 (3.23)	112–3	248^{15}									B27², 103
c462	**Colchiceine**	N-Acetyltrimethyl colchicinic acid. $C_{21}H_{23}NO_6$.	385.42	pa ye nd (diox) $[\alpha]_D^{14} - 252.5$ (chl, c = 1.2) λ^{al} 244 (4.47), 350 (4.22)	178–9		1.24		δ	v	i	...	i	chl v	B14², 190
Ω c463	**Colchicine**(l)	$C_{22}H_{25}NO_6$	399.45	ye pl (w + 1½), pa ye nd (AcOEt), ye cr (bz + 1) $[\alpha]_D^{17} - 121$ (chl, c = 0.9), −429 (w, c = 1.72) λ^{al} 244 (4.47), 351 (4.21)	155–7 (anh) 140 (+ 1 bz)				s	s	δ	...	δ	chl, MeOH s CCl_4 δ peth i	B14², 191
c464	**Colchicinic acid, trimethyl-**	$C_{19}H_{21}NO_5$	343.39	pa ye nd (al) $[\alpha]_D^{25} - 184.5$ (chl, c = 1)	155–7				s	s					Am 75, 5292
—	**α-Collidine**	see **Pyridine, 4-ethyl-2-methyl-**													
—	**β-Collidine**	see **Pyridine, 3-ethyl-4-methyl-**													
—	**γ-Collidine**	see **Pyridine, 2,4,6-tri-methyl-**													
—	**Comenic acid**	see **4-Pyrone-2-carboxylic acid, 5-hydroxy-**													
c465	**Conessine**	Neriine. Wrightine. $C_{24}H_{40}N_2$.	356.60	lf or pl (ace) $[\alpha]_D^{20} + 25.3$ (al, c = 0.7)	125–6	$165–7^{0.1}$			δ	...	...	...		aa s	C28, 5072
Ω c466	**Congo red**	$C_{32}H_{22}N_6Na_2O_6S_2$	696.68	pw λ^w 350 (4.5), 500 (4.7)	....	....			δ	s	i				B16², 223
c467	**Conhydrine**(d)	α-Hydroxyconiine. 2(1-Hydroxypropyl) piperidine. $C_8H_{17}NO$.	143.23	lf (eth) $[\alpha]_D + 10$ (w)	121	226^{760}			s	v	v			chl s Py δ	B21², 11
c467¹	—(dl) (lower m.p.)	$C_8H_{17}NO. See$ c467	143.23	nd (peth)	69–70	sub			v	v	v		v		B21², 12
c467²	—(dl) (higher m.p.)	$C_8H_{17}NO. See$ c467	143.23	nd (eth)	98–9	sub			v	v	v		v		B21², 11
c468	**α-Coniceine**(d)	2-Methylconidine	125.22	$[\alpha]_D^{15} + 18.4$ (al, c = 2)	− 16	158^{760}	$0.891_4^{15.5}$		δ						B20, 152
c469	—(dl)	$C_8H_{15}N. See$ c468	125.22			156–9	$0.890_4^{15.5}$		δ						B20, 153
c470	**β-Coniceine**(d)	2-Propenylpiperidine	125.22	nd, $[\alpha]_D^{45} + 49.9$	38.5–9.0	168–9	0.8716_4^{15}		δ	s	s				B20, 146
c471	—(dl)	$C_8H_{15}N. See$ c470	125.22	nd	8	$168.5–70^{753}$			δ	s	s				B20, 146
c472	—(l)	$C_8H_{15}N. See$ c470	125.22	nd, $[\alpha]_D^{45} - 50.5$	41	$168.5–9^{760}$	0.8520_4^{50}		δ	s	s				B20, 146
c473	**γ-Coniceine**	....	125.22			$173–4^{760}$ $64–5^{14}$	0.8720_4^{20}	1.4607^{18}	δ	s					B20, 144
—	**δ-Coniceine**	see **Piperolidine**													

For explanations, symbols and abbreviations see beginning of table. For structural formulas see end of table.

No.	Name	Synonyms and Formula	Mol. wt.	Color, crystalline form, specific rotation and λ_{max} (log ε)	m.p. °C	b.p. °C	Density	n_D	w	al	eth	ace	bz	other solvents	Ref.
	ε-Coniceine														
c474	ε-Coniceine(d)	d-2-Methylconidine. Stereoisomer of c468	125.22	$[\alpha]_D^{15} +67.4$	....	151.5 4.0	0.8856_4^{15}	....							B20, 151
c475	—(dl)	$C_8H_{15}N$. See c474	125.22			150–1	$0.8836_{}^{15}$								B20, 152
c476	—(l)	$C_8H_{15}N$. See c474	125.22	$[\alpha]_D^{15} -87.34$		151–3.5	0.8642_4^{15}								B20, 151
Ω c477	α-Conidendrin	Tsugalactone. Tsugaresinol. $C_{20}H_{20}O_6$.	356.38	cr (al) $[\alpha]_D^{20} -54.5$ (ace, c = 2.1) λ^{al} 230 sh (4.13), 284 (3.83)	255–6	....	....		i	s	s	s	s	peth i	Am 77, 432
—	Conidine, 2-methyl-	see α-Coniceine													
c478	—,3-methyl-(d)		125.22	$[\alpha]_D^8 +16$		158^{760}	0.8856_4^{15}		δ	s	s				B20, 153
c479	—,—(dl)	$C_8H_{15}N$. See c478	125.22			158^{760}	0.8946_4^{15}		δ	s	s				B20, 153
c480	—,—(l)	$C_8H_{15}N$. See c478	125.22	$[\alpha]_D^{17} -17.1$		158^{760}	0.8856_4^{15}		δ	s	s				B20, 153
—	Coniferaldehyde	see Cinnamaldehyde, 4-hydroxy-3-methoxy-													
c481	Coniferin	$C_{16}H_{22}O_8$	342.35	nd (w +2) $[\alpha]_D^{20} -68$ (w, c = 0.5) λ^w 260 (3.22)	186 (anh)				s^n	δ	i			Py, con sulf s	B31, 221
Ω c482	Coniferyl alcohol		180.21	pr (eth-lig) λ^{chl} 270 (4.2), 295 sh (3.7)	74	$163–5^3$			δ^h i	s	v			alk s	B6², 1093
Ω c483	Coniine(d)	Conicine. 2-Propylpiperidine.	127.23	$[\alpha]_D^{20} +15.6$	−2	$166–7^{760}$ 64^{18}	0.8440^{20}	$1.4512^{21.9}$	δ	∞	v		s	chl δ	B20², 61
c484	—(dl)	$C_8H_{17}N$. See c483	127.23			$166–7^{745}$ $59–63^{17}$	0.8447^{20}	1.4513^{23}	δ	∞	v		s	oos s	B20², 62
c485	—(l)	$C_8H_{17}N$. See c483	127.23	$[\alpha]_D^{15} -15.6$		166^{760} 64^{18}	0.845_4^{15}	1.4512^{22}	δ	∞	v		s	oos s	B20², 62
c486	—,hydrobromide (d)	$C_8H_{17}N$. HBr. See c483	208.15	pr	211 (207)				v	v	s			oos v chl s	B20, 112
c487	—,hydrochloride (d)	$C_8H_{17}N$. HCl. See c483	163.69	orh (w) $[\alpha]_D^{20} +10.1$ (liq NH_3, c = 8)	221				v	v	δ	δ		chl s	B20², 61
Ω c488	—,—(dl)	$C_8H_{17}N$. HCl. See c483	163.69	nd (al-eth)	216–7				v	s	δ				B20¹, 31
c489	—,—(l)	$C_8H_{17}N$. HCl. See c483	163.69	nd	220–1				v	v	i				B20, 118
c490	—,picrate(d)	$C_8H_{17}N . C_6H_3N_3O_7$. See c483	356.34	ye pr (w)	75				s^h	s	s				B20, 112
c491	—,—(l)	$C_8H_{17}N . C_6H_3N_3O_7$. See c483	356.34	ye pr (w)	74				s^h	s	s				B20², 62
c492	—,N-methyl-(d)	$C_9H_{19}N$. See c483	141.26	$[\alpha]_D^{24} +82.4$	....	$173–4^{757}$	0.8326_4^{23}	1.4538^{13}	δ	s		s		oos s	B20², 61
c493	Conquinamine	$C_{19}H_{24}N_2O_2$	312.42	ye tetr $[\alpha]_D^5 +200$ (116) (al, c = 0.5) λ^{al} 245 (4.0), 299 (3.4)	123				δ	s	s			chl s	B27², 667
—	Conyrine	see Pyridine, 2-propyl-													
c496	Copaene	$C_{15}H_{24}$	204.36	$[\alpha]_D -25.8$	....	$246–51$ $119–20^{10}$	0.8996_4^{20}	1.4894^{20}	i		s	s		aa, lig s	B5², 349
c497	Coproergostane	Pseudoergostane. $C_{28}H_{50}$	386.71	nd (ace) $[\alpha]_D^{19} +25.3$ (chl, c = 2)	64				i		s	s^h		chl s	B5³, 1143
c498	Coprostane	Pseudocholestane. $C_{27}H_{48}$	372.69	orh nd (al, ace or eth-al) $[\alpha]_D^{20} +25.1$ (chl, c = 2)	72		$0.9119_4^{87.7}$	1.4884_4^{88}	i	δ	v			chl, oos v	B5³, 1132
c499	3β-Coprostanol	Coprosterol. Strecorin. $C_{27}H_{48}O$. See c498	388.69	nd (MeOH) $[\alpha]_D^{18} +28$ (chl, c = 1.8)	102 (105)				i	v	v		v	chl v MeOH δ	B6³, 2128
c500	Coprostenol	Allocholesterol. 4-Cholesten-3β-ol. $C_{27}H_{46}O$.	386.67	nd (al + MeOH) 142 $[\alpha]_D +43.7$ (bz, c = 1) λ^{al} 207 (3.81)	142	....	....		i	s	v	v	v	chl, diox, Py v	B6³, 2604
Ω c501	Coprostenone	Δ^4-Cholesten-3-one. $C_{27}H_{44}O$.	384.65	pl (MeOH) $[\alpha]_D +88.6$ (chl) λ^{al} 242.5 (4.18)	81–2	....	....			δ	v		v	lig v AcOEt δ	E14, 120
—	Coprosterol	see Coprostanol													
Ω c502	Coronene	Hexabenzobenzene	300.36	ye nd (bz) λ^{al} 290 (5.04)	438–40 (cor)	525^{760}	1.377		i				δ^h	con sulf i	J1952, 2991
c503	Corticosterone	11,21-Dihydroprogesterone. $C_{21}H_{30}O_4$.	346.47	nd (+al, al), pl (ace) $[\alpha]_D^5 +223$ (al, c = 1.1) λ^w 248 (4.20)	180–2 (cor) (177–9)	sub $190^{0.01}$			i	s	s	s			Am 78, 1414

For explanations, symbols and abbreviations see beginning of table. For structural formulas see end of table.

C-248

No.	Name	Synonyms and Formula	Mol. wt.	Color, crystalline form, specific rotation and λ_{max} (log ε)	m.p. °C	b.p. °C	Density	n_D	Solubility						Ref.
									w	al	eth	ace	bz	other solvents	
	Corticosterone														
c504	—,11-dehydro-	$C_{21}H_{28}O_4$	344.46	pr (ace-w, al, ace or ace-eth), $[\alpha]_D^{25} +258$ (al), $+239$ (diox)	183–3.5	distb vac			i	s	...	s	s	.....	E14s, 2972
Ω c505	—,17-hydroxy-	Cortisol. Hydrocortisone. $C_{21}H_{30}O_5$. See c503	362.47	pl (al or i-PrOH) $[\alpha]_D^{22} +167$ (al) $\lambda^{al} 242$ (4.19)	220	....			δ^h	s^h	...	...	...	diox, aa s	E14s, 2868
—	**Cotisol**	see **Corticosterone, 17-hydroxy-**													
c506	**Cortisone**	17-hydroxy-11-dehydro-corticosterone. $C_{21}H_{28}O_5$. See c504	360.46	rhd nd (al), cr (ace) $[\alpha]_D^{25} +209$ (95% al, c = 1.2) $\lambda^{al} 238$ (4.18)	230–1 (224d)				i	v	δ	v	δ	MeOH v sulf s chl δ	Am 73, 4055
c507	—,21-acetate......	$C_{23}H_{30}O_6$. See c504	402.49	nd (ace), rods (chl) $[\alpha]_D^{25} +164$ (ace, c = 0.5) $\lambda^{al} 237$ (4.18)	239–4.1				i	δ	δ	s	...	chl v peth δ	J1954, 125
c508	**Corybulbine**(d)	Corydalis-G. $C_{21}H_{25}NO_4$ ...	355.44	nd (al) $[\alpha]_D^{20} +303$ (chl, c = 1.4) $\lambda^{MeOH} 286$ (3.76)	237–8 (244 sealed tube)				i	δ	δ	s	s^h	chl, HCl s AcOEt δ	B21², 200
c509	—(dl)...........	$C_{21}H_{25}NO_4$. See c508	355.44	cr (chl-al)	220–2				i	s	s	s	s^h	chl s	B21, 217
c510	**Corycavamine**.....	$C_{21}H_{21}NO_5$...........	367.41	pr (eth or al) $[\alpha]_D^{20} +166.6$ (chl, c = 2.2)	149					s			...	chl s	B27², 621
c511	**Corycavine**.......	$C_{21}H_{21}NO_5$ $\lambda^{MeOH} 288$ (3.99)	367.41	orh pl (al)	221–2				i	δ s^h				chl s alk i	B27², 621
c512	**Corydaldine**......	$C_{11}H_{13}NO_3$	207.23	mcl pr (w or al)	175				s	s	s		s	chl s peth i	B21², 442
c513	**Corydaline**(d)	Corydalis-A. $C_{22}H_{27}NO_4$	369.47	pr (al) $[\alpha]_D^{20} +311$ (al, c = 0.8) $\lambda^{MeOH} 282$ (3.76)	136				i	s^h	s		s	chl, CS_2 s	B21², 200
c514	—(dl)...........	$C_{22}H_{27}NO_4$. See c513	369.47	cr (al) $\lambda^{MeOH} 282$ (3.76)	135–6				δ	s^h	s				B21², 200
c515	—($meso$, d)	$C_{22}H_{27}NO_4$. See c513	369.47	pr (eth) $[\alpha]_D +180$ (chl, c = 3) $\lambda^{MeOH} 282$ (3.76)	155–6 (152)				δ	s^h	s				B21¹, 257
c516	—($meso$, dl)......	$C_{22}H_{27}NO_4$. See c513	369.47	cr (al) $\lambda^{Me}F^H$ 282 (3.76)	163–4 (158)				δ	s^h	s				B21², 200
c517	—($meso$, l)........	$C_{22}H_{27}NO_4$. See c513	369.47	pr (eth) $[\alpha]_D^{20} -181$ (chl, c = 3) $\lambda^{MeOH} 282$ (3.76)	155–6 (152)				δ	s^h	s				B21¹, 257
c518	**Corynantheine**(β) ..	$C_{22}H_{28}N_2O_3$	384.48	$[\alpha]_D^{18} +28.8$ (MeOH, c = 1.0) $\lambda^{al} 225$ (4.7), 272 (3.9), 282 (3.9), 291 (3.8)	165–6					s					H35, 851
—	**Corynine**........	see **Yohimbine**													
c519	**Cotarnine**	$C_{12}H_{15}NO_4$........... $\lambda^{al} 245$ (3.9), 279 (3.6), 326 (3.8)	237.26	nd (bz), cr (eth)	132–3d	....			δ	s	s	...	s	chl, Na_2CO_3, NH_4OH s NaOH i	B27², 543
c520	—,chloride	Stypticin. $C_{12}H_{14}ClNO_3 \cdot 2H_2O$. See c519	291.74	ye pw or nd (al-AcOEt) $\lambda^{al} 255$ (0.65) 338 (0.89)	197	....			s	s			...	.....	B27¹, 456
c521	—,O(hydrogen phthalate)	$C_{12}H_{14}NO_3 \cdot O_2CC_6H_4CO_2H$. See c519	385.38	ye	115d	....			δ						B27, 476
c522	—,O-phthalate....	Styptol. $(C_{12}H_{14}NO_3)_2 \cdot C_6H_4(CO_2)_2$. See c519	604.62	og cr or pw	103–5	....			s						B27, 476
—	**Cotoin**	see **Benzophenone, 2,6-di-hydroxy-4-methoxy-**													
Ω c523	**Coumalic acid**	α-Pyrone-5-carboxylic acid .. $\lambda^{MeOH} 240$ (3.9), 290 (3.6)	140.10	pr (MeOH)	205–10δd 207–9 (+1w)	218¹²⁰ partially sub			δ d^h	s	δ	δ	i	aa s AcOEt δ chl, lig i	B18², 326

For explanations, symbols and abbreviations see beginning of table. For structural formulas see end of table.

No.	Name	Synonyms and Formula	Mol. wt.	Color, crystalline form, specific rotation and λ_{max} (log ε)	m.p. °C	b.p. °C	Density	n_D	Solubility						Ref.
									w	al	eth	acc	bz	other solvents	

Coumaran

No.	Name	Synonyms and Formula	Mol. wt.	Color...	m.p.	b.p.	Density	n_D	w	al	eth	acc	bz	other	Ref.
c524	Coumaran	2,3-Dihydrobenzofuran. Dihydrocoumarone.	120.16	λ^{hx} 283 (3.49), 289 (3.49)	−21.5	188–9 76[14]	1.05762[24]	1.5426[20]	i	s	s			chl, CS$_2$ s	B17[1], 22
c525	3-Coumaranone		134.14	red nd (al)	102–3	152–4[16]			δ	s[h]			s	alk s lig δ	B17[2], 126
—	Coumaric acid	see Cinnamic acid, hydroxy-													
—	o-Coumaric acid, lactone	see Coumarin													
—	Coumarilic acid	see Coumarone-2-carboxylic acid													
Ω c526	Coumarin	1,2-Benzopyrone. o-Coumaric acid lactone. Coumarinic lactone.	146.15	rh pym (eth) λ^{al} 274.5 (4.20), 312.5 (3.91)	71	301.72[760]	0.9354[20]		s[h]	s	v			Py, chl v alk s	B17[2], 357
c527	—,6-chloro-	C$_9$H$_5$ClO$_2$. See c526	180.59	nd (al) λ^{al} 222 (4.38), 272 (4.02), 321 (3.65)	165				δ	v[h]	v[h]		s	CS$_2$ v	B17[2], 359
Ω c528	—,7-diethyl-amino-4-methyl-	C$_{14}$H$_{17}$NO$_2$. See c526	231.30	cr (al, bz-lig) λ^{al} 243 (4.19), 278 (2.28), 318 (3.60), 375 (4.41)	89 (al) 135 (bz-lig)				δ[h]	s	s	s		oos s	B18, 612
Ω c529	—,3,4-dihydro-	Hydrocoumarin. Melilotic lactone. Melilotol. C$_9$H$_8$O$_2$. See c526	148.17	lf λ^{al} 266 (2.85), 273 (2.86), 312 (1.02)	25	272 145[18]	1.169[18]	1.5563[20]	i	δ	δ			chl s	B17[2], 334
c530	—,6,7-dihydroxy-	Aesculetin. Esculetin. C$_9$H$_6$O$_4$. See c526	178.15	nd (w + 1), pr (aa), lf (sub) λ^{al} 261.5 (3.7), 303 (3.8), 354 (4.1)	276	sub			δ	s[h]	δ	s		alk, chl, AcOEt s	B18[2], 68
c531	—,7,8-dihydroxy-	Daphnetin. C$_9$H$_6$O$_4$. See c526	178.15	yesh (dil al) λ^{al} 258 (3.8), 335 (4.1)	261–3 (258)	sub			s[h]	s[h]	δ		δ	aa s[h] chl, CS$_2$ δ	B18[2], 69
Ω c532	—,5,7-dihydroxy-4-methyl-	C$_{10}$H$_8$O$_4$. See c526	192.18	nd (al), lf (aa) λ^{al} 250 (3.73), 320 (4.08)	282–4				δ	v[h]	δ		δ	alk v chl δ	B18[1], 351
Ω c533	—,6,7-dihydroxy-4-methyl-	4-Methylaesculetin. C$_{10}$H$_8$O$_4$. See c526	192.18	ye nd (dil al) λ^{al} 290 (3.73), 348 (4.09)	274–6				s[h]	s[h]				aa s[h]	B18[1], 351
Ω c534	—,7,8-dihydroxy-4-methyl-	4-Methyldaphnetin. C$_{10}$H$_8$O$_4$. See c526	192.18	nd (w), pr (al)	242–5 (235)				i	s					B18[1], 352
c534[1]	—,7,8-dihydroxy-6-methoxy-	Fraxetin. C$_{10}$H$_8$O$_3$. See c526	208.18	pl (dil al) λ^{al} 273 (3.5), 348 (4.0)	230–2				δ[h]	s	δ				B18[2], 152
Ω c535	—,5,7-dimethoxy-	Citropten. Limettin. C$_{11}$H$_{10}$O$_4$. See c526	206.20	pr or nd (al) λ^{al} 250 (3.8), 260 (3.8), 330 (4.2)	148–50	200δd			δ[h]	v[h]	i	v		chl v aa s lig i	B18[1], 348
Ω c536	—,7-ethoxy-4-methyl-	Maraniol. C$_{12}$H$_{12}$O$_3$. See c526	204.23	wh	114				i	s					C28, 578
Ω c537	—,4-hydroxy-	Benzotetronic acid. C$_9$H$_6$O$_3$. See c526	162.15	nd (w)	213–4 (232)				s[h]	s	s				B17[2], 469
c538	—,6-hydroxy-	C$_9$H$_6$O$_3$. See c526	162.15	nd (dil HCl)	250		1.25		δ	s				AcOEt s	B18[1], 306
Ω c539	—,7-hydroxy-	Umbelliferone. C$_9$H$_6$O$_3$. See c526	162.15	nd (w) λ^{MeOH} 217 (4.1), 240 sh (3.5), 325 (4.2)	230–1	sub			δ[h]	∞	δ			chl, aa ∞	B18[2], 16
c540	—,8-hydroxy-	C$_9$H$_6$O$_3$. See c526	162.15	nd (dil al) λ^{al} 255 (3.9), 295 (4.0)	160				s[h]	s	i		i	aa s chl i	C34, 3252
c541	—,7-hydroxy-6-methoxy-	Chrysatropic acid. Gelseminic acid. Scopoletin. C$_{10}$H$_8$O$_4$. See c526	192.18	nd or pr (al) λ^{al} 255 (3.8), 299 (3.8), 350 (4.1)	204				δ	δ	δ		i	chl s aa s CS$_2$ i	B18[2], 68
Ω c542	—,7-hydroxy-4-methyl-	4-Methylumbelliferone. C$_{10}$H$_8$O$_3$. See c526	176.18	nd (al) λ^{al} 325 (4.20)	185–7				δ[h]	s	δ			aa, alk s chl δ	B18[2], 19
c543	—,4-hydroxy-3(1-phenyl-3-oxo-butyl)-	Coumadin. Warfarin. C$_{19}$H$_{16}$O$_4$	308.34	cr (al) λ^{al} 271 (3.04), 287 (3.05), 306 (3.04)	161				i			s		diox s	Am 66, 900
c543[1]	—,7-methoxy-	Herniarin. C$_{10}$H$_8$O$_3$. See c526	176.18	lf (w or MeOH) λ^{al} 290 (3.85), 323 (4.17)	117–8				δ	s	s			con sulf, alk s	B18[2], 17
Ω c544	—,3-methyl-	C$_{10}$H$_8$O$_3$. See c526	160.18	rh bipym (al) λ^{al} 275 (4.02), 308 (3.80)	91	292.5			δ[h]	s				aq KOH i	B17[2], 362
Ω c545	—,4-methyl-	C$_{10}$H$_8$O$_2$. See c526	160.18	nd (w), pr (bz) λ^{al} 270 (4.00), 310 (3.78)	83–4					s			s	alk s[h]	B17[2], 362

For explanations, symbols and abbreviations see beginning of table. For structural formulas see end of table.

No.	Name	Synonyms and Formula	Mol. wt.	Color, crystalline form, specific rotation and λ_{max} (log ε)	m.p. °C	b.p. °C	Density	n_D	w	al	eth	ace	bz	other solvents	Ref.
	Coumarin														
c546	—,6,7,8-tri-methoxy-	Fraxetin dimethyl ether. $C_{12}H_{12}O_5$. See c526	236.23	rh bipym pl (dil al) λ^{al} 228 (4.2), 296 (4.0), 338 (3.8)	103–4	$90–100^{0.2}$				s	s				B18², 152
c547	3-Coumarin-carboxylic acid	....	190.16	nd (w or bz)	190d				s^h	s	i		i	alk s lig i	B18², 336
Ω c548	2-Coumarone-carboxylic acid	Coumarilic acid	162.15	nd (w) λ^{al} 266 (4.24), 292.5 (3.76)	192–3	310–5δd			s^h	s				CS_2, chl δ	B18², 276
c549	—,ethyl ester......	$C_{11}H_{10}O_3$. See c548	190.20	....	30–1	274^{720} 161^{15}	$1.1656^{28.5}$	$1.564^{27.6}$							B18¹, 442
Ω c550	—,3-methyl-	$C_{10}H_8O_3$. See c548	176.18	nd (dil al) λ^{al} 270 (4.25), 294 (3.86)	188–9					s^h					B18, 309
—	Coumaryl alcohol ..	see 2-Propen-1-ol, 3-hydroxyphenyl-													
c551	Coumestrol	$C_{15}H_8O_5$	268.24	gy micr rods λ^{MeOH} 247, 342	385d				i^h	δ	i	δ^h			Am 80, 3969
c552	—,diacetate.......	$C_{19}H_{12}O_7$. See c551	352.30	pl λ^{MeOH} 237 (4.4), 293 (4.1), 326 (4.4), 342 (4.3)	234				i^h	i	i	δ^h			Am 80, 4381
Ω c553	Creatine.........	(α-Methylguanido)acetic acid. $H_2NC(:NH)N(CH_3)CH_2CO_2H$	131.14	mcl pr (w + 1) $\lambda^{w,pH=8}$ 215 (3.1)	303		1.33		s	δ	i				B4², 796
Ω c554	Creatinine	1-Methylglycocyamidine....	113.12	rh pr (w + 2), lf (w) $\lambda^{w,pH=7}$ 235 (3.90)	ca. 300d (260)				s^h	δ	i	i		chl i	B24², 128
—	Cresol	see Toluene, hydroxy-													
—	Cresolol	see Toluene, 4-hydroxy-3-methoxy-													
—	Cresorcinol	see Toluene, 2,4-dihydroxy-													
—	Cresotic acid	see Benzoic acid, 2-hydroxy-3-methyl-													
—	Croceic acid......	see 1-Naphthalenesulfonic acid, 7-hydroxy-													
Ω c555	Crocetin(trans)	Gardenin. $C_{20}H_{24}O_4$	328.41	brick red rh (Ac_2O) λ^{al} 256 (2.92), 415 (3.5), 432 (3.7), 460 (3.65)	285–7 (cor)				δ	δ	i	H	i	oos i NaOH v Py s	B30, 106
—	Crocic acid	see Croconic acid													
c556	Croconic acid	Crocic acid	142.07	pa ye nd (+3w, al-diox) λ^{MeOH} 298 (4.2), 360 (3.9)	eff 100 sub d > 150, d ca. 120 (+3w)				v	s					B8², 532
—	Crotonaldehyde....	see 2-Butenal*													
—	Crotonic acid	see 2-Butenoic acid(trans)*													
—	Crotyl alcohol	see 2-Buten-1-ol*													
—	Cryogenine	see Benzoic acid, 3(1-semi-carbazido)-, amide													
c557	Cryptopine	Cryptocavine. $C_{21}H_{23}NO_5$..	369.42	pr or pl (bz), nd (chl-MeOH) $\lambda^{0.02N HCl}$ 234 (4.0), 285 (3.8)	223 (cor)		1.315_4^{20}		i	δ	δ		δ	chl, aa s	B27², 578
c558	Cryptoxanthin.....	Caricaxanthin. β-Caroten-3-ol. Cryptoxanthol. $C_{40}H_{56}O$.	552.90	garnet red pr (bz-MeOH) α: λ^{hx} 268 (4.41), 333 (3.86), 421 (4.99), 446 (5.16), 475 (5.12), β: λ^{hx} 274 (4.33), 346 (3.84), 452 (5.14), 479 (5.07)	169				i	δ			v	chl, Py v lig δ	B30, 93
c559	Cubebin.........	$C_{20}H_{20}O_6$	356.38	nd (al or bz) $[\alpha]_D^{25}$ −45.6 (chl, c = 5)	131–2				i	s	s			chl s con sulf s (red) peth δ	B19², 470

For explanations, symbols and abbreviations see beginning of table. For structural formulas see end of table.

Cumaldehyde

No.	Name	Synonyms and Formula	Mol. wt.	Color, crystalline form, specific rotation and λ_{max} (log ε)	m.p. °C	b.p. °C	Density	n_D	w	al	eth	ace	bz	other solvents	Ref.
—	Cumaldehyde	see Benzaldehyde, 4-isopropyl-													
—	Cumene	see Benzene, isopropyl-*													
—	Cumenol	see Benzene, hydroxy-(isopropyl)-*													
—	Cumic acid	see Benzoic acid, 4-isopropyl-													
—	Cumic alcohol	see Benzene, 1(hydroxymethyl)-4-isopropyl-*													
—	m-Cumidic acid	see 1,3-Benzenedicarboxylic acid, 4,6-dimethyl-*													
—	Cumidine	see Benzene, 1-amino-4-isopropyl-*													
—	Cuminic acid	see Benzoic acid, isopropyl-													
—	Cuminylamine	see Benzene, 1(aminomethyl)-4-isopropyl-*													
c563	Cupreine	Hydroxycinchonine. $C_{19}H_{22}N_2O_2$.	310.40	pr (eth) $[\alpha]_D^{17}$ 175.5 (al)	198 (anh)	....	....	....	i	s	δ	...	δ	NaOH s chl, peth δ	B23, 510
c564	c-Curarine-III, hydroxide	c-Fluorocuranine hydroxide. $C_{20}H_{24}N_2O_2$	328.46	cr (MeOH-eth)	212	....	....	....		s	s	i		....	H36, 102
c565	ar-Curcumene	$C_{15}H_{22}$	202.34	$[\alpha]_D^{18}$ +35.8 λ^{bz} 212 (3.8), 261 (2.6), 267 (2.7), 274 (2.7)	....	140^{19} $117-8^7$	0.8821_{20}^{20}	1.4989^{20}	i	...	...	...	s		B5², 402
Ω c566	Curcumin	$C_{21}H_{20}O_6$	368.39	or ye pr, rh pr (MeOH) λ^{diox} 265 (4.18), 420 (4.77)	183	....	....	....	i	s	δ	δ	δ	aa, alk s CS_2 δ lig i	B8, 554
—	Curine	see Bebeerine(l)													
c567	Cuscohygrine	α,α'-Bis(N-methyl-α-pyrrolidyl)acetone. Bellaradine. Cuskhygrine. $C_{13}H_{24}N_2O$.	224.35		185^{32} 152^{14}	....	0.9782_4^{16}	....	∞	s	s	s	s		B24, 78
c568	—,hydrate	$C_{13}H_{24}N_2O\cdot3\frac{1}{2}H_2O$. See c567	287.40	nd (w)	40–1	....	....	....		s	s		s		B24, 78
c569	Cusparine	$C_{19}H_{17}NO_3$	307.35	(i) wh nd (peth) (ii) ye nd (iii) pr	(i) 92 (ii) 92 (iii) 110–22	....	....	....	i	s	s	v	v	chl v lig δ	B27, 483
c570	Cyamelide	sym-Trioxanetriimine	129.08	amor pw	d	....	1.127_4^{15}	....	i	i	i	i	i	con sulf s d^h NH_4OH δ oos i	B3, 35
—	Cyanacetamide	see Malonic acid, monoamide mononitrile													
c571	Cyanamide	Carbamic acid nitrile. Carbamonitrile. Carbodiimide. H_2NCN	42.04	nd	42 (46)	140^{19}	1.0729_4^{18} 1.282_4^{20} (so)	1.4418^{48}	v	v	s	s	s	chl s CS_2 δ	B3, 74
c572	—,benzyl-	$C_6H_5CH_2NHCN$	132.18	pl (eth)	43	....	....	....	i	s	s		s		B12, 1051
Ω c573	—,diallyl-	$(CH_2{:}CHCH_2)_2NCN$	122.17			$140-5^{90}$ 95^9	....	....	i	s	s	s	s	oos s	B4², 666
c574	—,dibutyl-	$(C_4H_9)_2NCN$	154.26			$187-91^{190}$ $146-51^{35}$	....	....	i	s	s	s	s	oos s	B4², 635
Ω c575	—,diethyl-	N-Cyanodiethylamine. $(C_2H_5)_2NCN$	98.15			188^{760} 68^{10}	0.854_4^{20}	1.4126^{25}	i	s	s			HCl d	B4, 121
Ω c576	—,dimethyl-	N-Cyanodimethylamine. $(CH_3)_2NCN$	70.10			163.5^{760} 56^{15}	....	1.4089^{19}	v	s	s	s		....	B4², 574
c577	—,diphenyl-	N-cyanodiphenylamine. $(C_6H_5)_2NCN$	194.24	pr (al)	73–4	$235-40^{60}$	....	....	i	δ^h	...	...		lig s MeOH s^h	B4³, 145
c578	—,methyl)-(1-naphthyl)-	N-methyl-N-cyano-α-naphthylamine. $C_{10}H_7N(CH_3)CN$	182.23	yesh		$185-7^3$	....	....	i	s	s				B12², 697
c579	—,phenyl-	Carbanilonitrile. Cyananilide. N-Cyanoaniline. $C_6H_5NHCN\cdot\frac{1}{2}H_2O$	127.15	cr (w, eth), lf (aa, dil KOH) λ^{al} 252 (4.5), 276 (3.5), 303 (2.9), 330 sh (2.8)	47 (hyd)	....	....	....	δ	v	v			KOH s	B12, 368
c580	Cyanic acid	Carbonimid Isocyanic acid. HOCN	43.03	gas	$-81-79$	23.5^{760}	1.140_4^{20} (liq)	....		s	s		s	chl, aa s	B3, 31
c581	—,ethyl ester	C_2H_5OCN	71.08			$162d$ 30^{12}	0.894_4^{20}	1.3788^{25}	i	∞	m				Tet 1964, 2829

For explanations, symbols and abbreviations see beginning of table. For structural formulas see end of table.

No.	Name	Synonyms and Formula	Mol. wt.	Color. crystalline form. specific rotation and λ_{max} (log ε)	m.p. °C	b.p. °C	Density	n_D	Solubility						Ref.
									w	al	eth	ace	bz	other solvents	
	Cyanoacetanilide														
—	**Cyanoacetanilide**	see **Malonic acid**, monoamide mononitrile, *N*-phenyl-													
—	**Cyanoacetic acid**	see **Malonic acid**, mononitrile													
c581[1]	**Cyanogen**	Oxalic acid dinitrile. NCCN	52.04	gas λ^{gas} 219	−27.9	−21.17[760]	0.9537_4^{-21}		s	s		.	.		B2[2], 511
c582	**Cyanogen bromide**	Bromine cyanide. BrCN	105.93	nd	52	61.4[760]	2.015_4^{20}		s	s	s	.	.		B3, 39
c583	**Cyanogen chloride**	Chlorine cyanide. ClCN	61.47	gas	−6	12.66[760]	1.186_4^{20}		s	s	v	.	.		B3, 38
c584	**Cyanogen iodide**	Iodine cyanide. ICN	152.92	nd (al, or eth)	146–7	sub >45	2.84^{18}		δ	s	s	.	.		B3, 41
c585	**Cyanogen sulfide**	Cyanogen thiocyanate. $S(CN)_2$	84.10	rh pl	65	sub 30–40			s	s	s	.	.		B3, 180
Ω c586	**Cyanuric acid, dihydrate**	2,4,6-Triazinetriol*. Tricyanic acid. Trihydroxycyanidine.	165.11	mcl (w +2) $\lambda^{w, pH=8}$ 214 (4.01)	>360d	d	1.768^0 2.500_4^{20} (anh)		s	δ s^h	i	i	i	con sulf, Py s chl, aa i	B26[2], 131
—	—,triamide	see **Melamine**													
c587	—,tribenzyl ester	Benzyl cyanurate. $C_{24}H_{21}N_3O_3$. See c586	399.46	nd (al)	159	>320			i	s	δ	.	.		B26[1], 76
Ω c588	—,trichloride	Cyanuric chloride. Trichloro-*s*-triazine*. Trichlorocyanidine. Tricyanogen chloride.	184.41	cr (eth or bz) λ^{al} 241 (3.41)	154	190[720]			i	s		.	.		B26[2], 16
Ω c589	—,thio-	Thiocyanuric acid. Trithiocyanuric acid.	177.27	ye pr	200d				δ	i	δ	.	.		B26, 259
—	**Cyanurotriamide**	see **Melamine**													
—	**Cyclamen aldehyde**	see **Propanal**, 3(4-isopropylphenyl)-2-methyl-*													
—	**Cyclobarbital**	see **Barbituric acid**, 5(1-cyclohexenyl)-5-ethyl-													
Ω c590	**Cyclobutane***	Tetramethylene	56.12		−50	12[760]	0.720_4^5	1.4260^{20}	i	v	∞	v	s	peth s	B5, 17
c591	—,ethyl-*	C_6H_{12}. See c590	84.16		−142.9	70.7[760]	0.7284_4^{20}	1.4020^{20}	i	∞	∞	s	s	peth s	B5[1], 11
c592	—,methyl-*	C_5H_{10}. See c590	70.14		−36.3[760]		0.6884_4^{20}	1.3866^{20}	i	∞	∞	s	s	peth s	B5[1], 5
Ω c593	—,octafluoro-*	Perfluorocyclobutane. C_4F_8. See c590	200.03		−38.7	−4[764]	1.724^0_4						s		Am 70, 4090
Ω c594	**Cyclobutanecarboxylic acid***	Tetramethylenecarboxylic acid.	100.13		−2	190[754] 74–5[2]	1.0599_4^{20}	1.4400^{20}	δ	∞	∞	s	s		B9[2], 5
Ω c595	**1,1-Cyclobutanedicarboxylic acid***		144.14	pr (eth or w) (160)	156.6(cor)				v	s	s	.	s	lig δ	B9[2], 514
Ω c596	—,diethyl ester*	$C_{10}H_{16}O_4$. See c595	200.24			229[755] (224) 104[12]	1.0456_4^{20}	1.4344^{20}		v		.	.		B9[2], 514
Ω c597	**1,2-Cyclobutanedicarboxylic acid** (*cis, dl*)*	Ethylenesuccinic acid	144.14	pl (w), pr (bz)	138				v	v	v	.	δ	lig δ	B9[2], 515
c598	—(*trans, d*)*	$C_6H_8O_4$. See c597	144.14	$[\alpha]_D^{30}$ + 123.3 (w, c = 1.2)	105				s	s		.	.		B9[2], 515
Ω c599	—(*trans, dl*)*	$C_6H_8O_4$. See c597	144.14	rh nd (bz)	131				s	s		.	.	con HCl δ	B9[2], 515
Ω c600	—(*trans, l*)*	$C_6H_8O_4$. See c597	144.14	nd (HCl) $[\alpha]_D^{30}$ − 124.3 (w, c = 0.8)	105				s	s		.	.		B9[2], 515
c601	**1,3-Cyclobutanedicarboxylic acid** (*cis*)*		144.14	pr (w)	143.0–3.5	252			v	v	δ	.	.		B9, 726
c602	—(*trans*)*	$C_6H_8O_4$. See c601	144.14	pr (w), nd (sub)	171	sub			v^h	s	δ	.	.		B9, 726
c603	**Cyclobutene***	Cyclobutylene	54.09	λ^{gas} 175 (4.0)		2	0.733^0_0				v	s	s	peth s	B5[1], 29
c604	—,hexafluoro-*	Perfluorocyclobutene. C_4F_6. See c603	162.04		−60	3[760]	1.602_4^{-20}	1.298^{-20}				.	.		B5[3], 170
c605	**Cyclocamphane**	Epicyclene. Isocyclene. β-Pericyclocamphane.	136.24		117–8	150–1[743]	0.7948^{121}					.	.	aa s	B5[3], 393
c606	**1,6-Cyclodecanediol** (*trans*)*		172.27	cr (AcOEt, chl)	151–3							.	s	AcOEt, chl s^h	B6[3], 4105
c607	**1,6-Cyclodecanedione***		168.24	cr (eth) λ^{al} 287 (1.54)	100				i		s^h	.	s	aa s	B7[2], 540
Ω c608	**Cyclodecanol***		156.27		40–1	125[12]	0.9606_4^{20}	1.4926^{20}	i		s	.	s	chl s	B6[3], 120
c609	**Cyclodecanone***		154.26	amor pw λ^{al} 283 (1.18)	28	106.7[13]	0.9654_4^{20}	1.4806^{20}			s	.	s	chl s	B7[2], 36
c610	**9-Cycloheptadecen-1-one***	Civetone	250.43		32.5	342[742] 159[2]	0.9170_4^{33}	1.4830^{33}	δ	s	s	.	s		B7[2], 121
Ω c611	**Cycloheptane***	Heptamethylene. Suberane	98.19		−12	118.48[760]	0.8098_4^{20}	1.4436^{20}	i	v	v	.	s	lig, chl s	B5[2], 15
Ω c612	—,1-aza-*	Hexamethylenimine. Homopiperidine.	99.18			138.0–8.2[749]	0.8643_4^{22}	1.4631^{20}	s	v	v	.	v		B20, 94
Ω c613	—,bromo-*	Suberyl bromide. $C_7H_{13}Br$. See c611	177.09			101.5[40] 75[12]	1.2887_4^{22}	1.4996^{20}	i		v	.	v	chl v	B5[2], 15
c614	—,methyl-*	C_8H_{16}. See c611	112.22			134[760]	0.8001_4^{20}	1.4401^{20}	i	v	v	.	s	peth s	B5[2], 20

For explanations, symbols and abbreviations see beginning of table. For structural formulas see end of table.

No.	Name	Synonyms and Formula	Mol. wt.	Color, crystalline form, specific rotation and λ_{max} (log ε)	m.p. °C	b.p. °C	Density	n_D	Solubility						Ref.
									w	al	eth	ace	bz	other solvents	
1,2-Cycloheptanedione															
c615	**1,2-Cyclo-heptanedione***	$C_7H_{10}O_2$. See c611	126.16	yc λ^{hx} 280 (1.3), 375 (0.8), 405 (0.7), 420 (0.6)	−40	107–9[17]	1.0607$^{22}_{22}$	1.4689[22]	...	s	...	...	...	...	C50, 6327
Ω c616	**Cycloheptanol***	Suberol. Suberyl alcohol. $C_7H_{14}O$. See c611	114.19	....	2	185[760] 95[24]	0.9554[20]	1.4705[20]	δ	v	v	...	...	...	B6[2], 16
Ω c617	**Cycloheptanone***	Suberone. $C_7H_{12}O$. See c611.	112.17	λ^{al} 285 (1.30)	....	178.5– 9.5[760] 71[19]	0.9508$^{20}_4$	1.4608[20]	i	v	s	...	...	...	B7[2], 14
c618	**Cycloheptasil-oxane, tetradeca-methyl-***	....	519.09	....	−26	154[20]	0.9703[20]	1.4040[20]	...	...	...	...	...	...	Am 68, 667
c619	**1,3,5-Cyclo-heptatriene***	Tropilidene.	92.15	cubic (at −80) λ^{al} 261 (3.54)	−79.49	117[760] 60.5[122]	0.8875[19]	1.5343[20]	i	s	s	...	v	chl v	B5, 280
c620	**2,4,6-Cyclohepta-trien-1-one***	Tropone	106.13	λ^{MeOH} 225 (4.30), 232 (4.29), 303 (3.87)	−7––5	113[15] 84–5[6]	1.0952[22]	1.6172[22]	∞	...	δ	...	δ	hx s	Am 73, 876
c621	**—,2-amino-***	C_7H_7NO. See c620	121.14	ye pl (bz) λ^{al} 242 (4.4), 337 (4.1), 397 (4.0)	106–7	....	....	....	s^h	s	...	...	s	chl s	C46, 7559
c622	**—,3-bromo-2-hydroxy-***	$C_7H_5BrO_2$. See c620	201.03	ye pl or nd λ^{chl} 258 (4.58), 329 (3.87), 364 (3.84), 381.5 (3.86)	107–8	....	....	....	...	s	s	...	s	...	C49, 2405
c623	**—,2-hydroxy-***	Tropolone. $C_7H_6O_2$. See c620	122.13	nd λ^{al} 228 (4.36), 320 (3.83), 351 (3.76)	51–2	sub 40[4]	....	....	s	s	s	s	...	oos s	Am 74, 4456
Ω c624	**—,2-hydroxy-4-isopropyl-***	$C_{10}H_{12}O_2$. See c620	164.21	pa ye (peth) λ^{al} 344 (4.09), 393 (3.09)	50–1	....	....	....	δ	...	...	...	δ	lig δ	C45, 2884
c625	**—,2-hydroxy-4-methyl-***	$C_8H_8O_2$. See c620	136.16	nd (peth) λ^{cy} 235 (4.4), 320 (3.7), 352 (3.7), 372 (3.5)	75–6	....	....	....	...	...	s	...	...	chl s	C46, 5035
c626	**—,2-methoxy-***	$C_8H_8O_2$. See c620	136.16	pa ye nd (+½w) λ^{al} 235 (4.46), 319 (3.88), 350 (3.81), 363 sh (3.64)	41 (+½w)	128[5]	....	....	...	...	s	...	s	...	C46, 4521
Ω c627	**Cycloheptene***	Suberene. Suberylene.	96.17	....	−56	115[760]	0.8228$^{20}_4$	1.4552[20]	i	s	s	...	s	peth, chl s	B5[2], 42
c628	**1,3-Cyclo-hexadiene***	1,2-Dihydrobenzene	80.14	λ^{al} 259 (4.00)	−89	80.5[760]	0.8405$^{20}_4$	1.47548[20]	i	s	v	...	s	peth, chl s	B5[2], 79
c629	**1,4-Cyclo-hexadiene***	1,4-Dihydrobenzene	80.14	λ^{hx} 224 (1.5), 270 (−0.5)	−49.2	85.6[760]	0.8471$^{20}_4$	1.4725[20]	i	∞	∞	...	s	peth, chl s	B5[2], 80
c630	**1,3-Cyclo-hexadiene, 5-methyl-(dl)***	1,2-Dihydrotoluene. C_7H_{10}. See c628	94.16	λ^{al} 259 (3.69)	....	101.5[762]	0.8354[20]	1.4763[20]	i	v	s	...	s	lig s	B5[1], 62
c631	**—,octafluoro-***	C_6F_8. See c628	224.05	....	....	63–4	1.601[20]	1.3149[20]	...	...	...	...	...	...	J1954, 3780
c632	**1,4-Cyclo-hexadiene, octafluoro-***	C_6F_8. See c629	224.05	....	....	57–8	....	1.318[18]	...	...	...	...	...	...	J1954, 3780
c633	**1,4-Cyclohexa-diene-1,2-dicar-boxylic acid***	3,6-Dihydrophthalic acid	168.16	mcl pr (w)	153	....	....	....	δ s^h	s	...	...	...	...	B9, 781
c634	**2,4-Cyclohexa-diene-1,2-dicar-boxylic acid***	2,3-Dihydrophthalic acid	168.16	pr (w or al)	179–80	....	....	....	$δ^h$	s	δ	...	...	...	B9, 781
c635	**2,6-Cyclohexa-diene-1,2-dicar-boxylic acid***	4,5-Dihydrophthalic acid	168.16	tcl (w)	215	....	....	....	δ s^h	s	...	s	...	....	B9, 782
c636	**2,5-Cyclo-hexadien-1-one, hexachloro-***	Hexachlorophenol.	300.78	λ^{cy} 262 (4.20), 268 (4.20)	107	....	....	....	i	...	...	...	s	CCl_4 s	B7[1], 96
Ω c637	**Cyclohexane***	Hexahydrobenzene. Hexamethylene.	84.16	....	6.55	80.74[760]	0.77855$^{20}_4$	1.42662[20]	i	∞	∞	∞	∞	lig, CCl_4 ∞	B5, 21
c638	**—,acetyl-***	Cyclohexyl methyl ketone. Hexahydroacetophenone. $C_8H_{14}O$. See c637	126.20	....	....	180–1[760] 69[12]	0.9176$^{20.7}_0$	1.45652[16]	i	s	s	...	s	...	B7[2], 23
Ω c639	**—,allyl-**	3-Cyclohexylpropene.* C_9H_{16}. See c637	124.23	....	....	151.5[757]	0.8135[20]	1.4500[20]	...	v	s	s	s	chl, lig s	B5[2], 49
Ω c640	**—,amino-***	Cyclohexylamine. Hexa-hydroaniline. $C_6H_{13}N$. See c637	99.18	....	−17.7	134.5[760] 30.5[15]	0.8191$^{20}_4$	1.4316[20]	s	v	∞	∞	∞	oos ∞	B12[2], 4

For explanations, symbols and abbreviations see beginning of table. For structural formulas see end of table.

Cyclohexane

No.	Name	Synonyms and Formula	Mol. wt.	Color, crystalline form, specific rotation and λ_{max} (log ε)	m.p. °C	b.p. °C	Density	n_D	w	al	eth	ace	bz	other solvents	Ref.
c641	—,—,hydrochloride*	$C_6H_{13}N$. HCl. See c637	135.64	nd (w or al-eth)	206–7	......			v	v	s^h	...	i	....	$B12^2$, 4
Ω c642	—,bromo-*	Cyclohexyl bromide. $C_6H_{11}Br$. See c637	163.06		−56.5	166.2^{760} 45.5^{10}	1.3359^{20}	1.4957^{20}	i	∞	∞	∞	∞	lig, CCl_4 ∞	B5, 24
c643	—,1-bromo-1-methyl-*	$C_7H_{13}Br$. See c637	177.09			156–60 $65–9^{16}$	1.2510^{20}	1.4866^{20}	i	s	...	...	...	chl s	$B5^1$, 12
Ω c644	—,1-bromo-3-methyl-(dl)*	$C_7H_{13}Br$. See c637	177.09			181.0– 1.2 δd 60^{11}	1.275^{25}_4	1.4979^{20}	i		v	...	s		$B5^2$, 18
Ω c645	—,1-bromo-4-methyl-*	$C_7H_{13}Br$. See c637	177.09			130^{200} 55^{15}			i		s	...	s		$B5^2$, 18
c646	—,(bromomethyl)-*	$C_7H_{13}Br$. See c637	177.09			$76–7^{26}$	1.2763^{25}	1.4907^{20}	i		s		s	chl s	$B5^2$, 18
Ω c647	—,butyl-*	1-Cyclohexylbutane.* $C_{10}H_{20}$. See c637	140.27		−74.7	180.95^{760} 59^{10}	0.7992^{20}_4	1.4408^{20}	i						$B5^2$, 25
Ω c648	—,sec-butyl-	2-Cyclohexylbutane.* $C_{10}H_{20}$. See c637	140.27			179.34^{760}	0.8131^{20}_4	1.44673^{20}	i				s		$B5^2$, 26
Ω c649	—,tert-butyl-	$C_{10}H_{20}$. See c637	140.27		−41.17	171.5^{760}	0.81267^{20}	1.44694^{20}	i						$B5^2$, 26
Ω c650	—,(butylamino)-*	N-Butylcyclohexylamine. $C_{10}H_{21}N$. See c637	155.29			207			δ	v	v	...	s		$B12^2$, 7
Ω c651	—,chloro-*	Cyclohexyl chloride. $C_6H_{11}Cl$. See c637	118.61		−43.9	143^{760}	1.000^{20}	1.4626^{20}	i	∞	∞	∞	∞	chl v	B5, 21
Ω c652	—,cyclopentyl-*	.....	152.28			215.1^{760}	0.8758^{20}	1.4725^{20}	i						$B5^3$, 268
Ω c653	—,1,2-dibromo-(cis)*	$C_6H_{10}Br_2$. See c637	241.97		9.7	115^{14}	1.803^{25}_{25}	1.5514^{25}			s	s	s	chl, CCl_4, lig s	$B5^2$, 12
Ω c654	—,—(trans, dl)*	$C_6H_{10}Br_2$. See c637	241.97		−4 (−2)	$145–6^{100}$ 105^{20}	1.7759^{20}_4	1.5445^{19}	i	s	s	s	s	oos s	$B5^2$, 12
c655	—,1,3-dibromo-(cis)*	$C_6H_{10}Br_2$. See c637	241.97	rods (al)	112	......			δ	s^h			v	lig δ	$B5^3$, 13
c656	—,—(trans)*	$C_6H_{10}Br_2$. See c637	241.97		1	116^{16}		1.5480^{20}	i	s^h			v		$B5^2$, 13
Ω c657	—,1,4-dibromo-(cis)*	$C_6H_{10}Br_2$. See c637	241.97			$137–8^{25}$	1.7834^{20}	1.5531^{20}	i		s				$B5^2$, 13
Ω c658	—,—(trans)*	$C_6H_{10}Br_2$. See c637	241.97	cr (eth)	113	......			i		s^h				$B5^2$, 13
c659	—,1,2-dichloro-(cis)*	$C_6H_{10}Cl_2$. See c637	153.05		−1.5	$206–9^{763}$ 91^{20}	1.2021^{20}	1.4967^{20}					s	CCl_4 s	$B5^1$, 8
Ω c660	—,—(trans, dl)*	$C_6H_{10}Cl_2$. See c637	153.05		−6.3	189^{760} 78^{20}	1.1839^{20}_4	1.4902^{20}							$B5^1$, 8
c661	—,(diethyl-amino)-*	$C_{10}H_{21}N$. See c637	155.29			$192–3^{740}$ $85–6^{20}$	0.872^{20}_0				s				$B12^2$, 6
c662	—,(difluoro-amino)-deca-fluoro-*	Perfluorocyclohexylamine. $C_6F_{13}N$. See c637	333.05			$75–6^{760}$	1.787^{25}	1.286^{25}							J1950, 1966
Ω c663	—,1,1-dimethyl-*	C_8H_{16}. See c637	112.22		−33.50	119.54^{760} 10^{10}	0.7809^{20}_4	1.4290^{20}	i	s	s	s	s	CCl_4, lig ∞	$B5^2$, 20
Ω c664	—,1,2-dimethyl-(cis)*	C_8H_{16}. See c637	112.22		−50.1	129.73^{760} 18.3^{10}	0.7963^{20}_4	1.4360^{20}	i	s	∞	∞	∞	lig v CCl_4 s	$B5^2$, 21
Ω c665	—,—(trans)*	C_8H_{16}. See c637	112.22		−89.2	123.42^{760} 12.9^{10}	0.7760^{20}_4	1.4270^{20}	i	s	s	∞	∞	lig v CCl_4 s	$B5^2$, 21
Ω c666	—,1,3-dimethyl-(cis)*	C_8H_{16}. See c637	112.22		−75.57	120.1^{760} 11.1^{10}	0.7660^{20}_4	1.4229^{20}	i	s	s	∞	∞	CCl_4, lig ∞	B5, 36
c667	—,—(trans, d)*	C_8H_{16}. See c637	112.22	$[\alpha]_{549}$ +1.33	−90.10	124.45^{760} 15.0^{10}	0.7847^{20}_4	1.4309^{20}	i	s	s	∞	∞	CCl_4, lig ∞	C40, 6427
Ω c668	—,1,4-dimethyl-(cis)*	C_8H_{16}. See c637	112.22		−87.44	124.32^{760} 14.4^{10}	0.7829^{20}_4	1.4230^{20}	i	s	s	∞	∞	CCl_4, lig ∞	B5, 38
Ω c669	—,—(trans, dl)*	C_8H_{16}. See c637	112.22		−37.0	119.35^{760} 10.0^{10}	0.7626^{20}_0	1.4209^{20}	i	s	s	∞	∞	CCl_4, lig ∞	C30, 2180
c670	—,1,2-dimethyl-ene-*		108.19	λ^{al} 220 (3.88)		124^{740} $60–1^{90}$	0.8229^{25}	1.4718^{25}	i	s	s	v	s	chl s	Am 75, 4780
Ω c671	—,1,2-epoxy-*	Cyclohexene oxide. 7-Oxabicyclo[4,1,0] heptane. $C_6H_{10}O$. See c637	98.15		< −10	131.5^{760} $54–5^{10}$	0.9663^{20}	1.4519^{20}	i	v	v	v	v	chl s	$B17^2$, 29
c672	—,1,2-epoxy-4-(epoxyethyl)-*	4-Vinylcyclohexene dioxide. $C_8H_{12}O_2$. See c637	140.18		< −55	227^{760} 92^5	1.0986^{20}_{20}	1.4787^{20}	v						C46, 2574
c673	—,1,2-epoxy-4-ethenyl-	3-Vinyl-7-oxabicyclo[4,1,0]-heptane. $C_8H_{12}O$. See c637	124.19		< −100	169^{760} 20^2	0.9598^{20}_{20}	1.4700^{20}	δ						Am 81, 3350
Ω c674	—,ethyl-*	C_8H_{16}. See c637	112.22		−111.32	131.78^{760} 20.5^{10}	0.7880^{20}_4	1.4330^{20}	i	s	s	s	s	CCl_4 ∞ lig v	$B5^2$, 20
Ω c675	—,(ethylamino)-*	$C_8H_{17}N$. See c637	127.23			164^{760} $62–5^{15}$	0.868^{20}_0		δ	∞	∞				$B12^2$, 6
c676	—,fluoro-*	$C_6H_{11}F$. See c637	102.15		13	100.2 48^{100}	0.9279^{20}	1.4146^{20}	i					Py s	Am 77, 3099
c677	—,hendecafluoro-(trifluoro-methyl)-*	Perfluoromethylcyclohexane. C_7F_{14}. See c637	350.06		−44.72	76.14^{760}	1.7878^{25}_4	1.285^{17}				s	s^h	CCl_4, to, AcOEt s	J1955, 1749
c678	—,1,1,2,3,4,5,6-heptachloro-, (ε, dl)	$C_6H_5Cl_7$. See c637	325.28	rods	55.0–5.5	......			i	δ	δ		δ	....	C46, 441
c679	—,1,2,3,4,5,6-hexabromo-(β or cis)*	Benzene-β-hexabromide. $C_6H_6Br_6$. See c637	557.57	pr	253d	......			i	i	i	i	i		B5, 25

For explanations, symbols and abbreviations see beginning of table. For structural formulas see end of table.

No.	Name	Synonyms and Formula	Mol. wt.	Color, crystalline form, specific rotation and λ_{max} (log ε)	m.p. °C	b.p. °C	Density	n_D	w	al	eth	ace	bz	other solvents	Ref.
	Cyclohexane														
c680	—,—(α or trans) ...	$C_6H_6Br_6$. See c637	557.57	mcl pr (xyl)	212	....			i	δ	δ		δ		B5, 25
Ω c681	—,1,2,3,4,5,6-hexachloro-(α, dl)*	Benzene-trans-hexachloride. $C_6H_6Cl_6$. See c637	290.83	mcl pr (al or aa)	159.5–60	288	1.87^{20}	....	i	v^h			s	Ph NH_2 v chl s	B5², 11
Ω c682	—,—(β)*	Benzene-cis-hexachloride. $C_6H_6Cl_6$. See c637	290.83	cr (bz, al or xyl)	314–5 sub >314	$60^{0.58}$	1.89^{19}	....	i	δ			δ	chl, aa δ	B5², 11
Ω c683	—,—(γ)*	Benzene γ-hexachloride. Gammexane. Lindane. $C_6H_6Cl_6$. See c637	290.83	nd (al)	112.5–3	323.4^{760} 176.2^{10}			i	δ		s	v		B5, 8
Ω c684	—,—(δ)*	$C_6H_6Cl_6$. See c637	290.83	pl	141.5–2.0	$60^{0.34}$	....	....	i	δ					B5, 8
Ω c685	—,iodo-*	Cyclohexyl iodide. $C_6H_{11}I$. See c637	210.06	....		180 δd 81.5^{20}	1.6244^{20}	1.5477^{20}	i	s	s	s	s	oos v lig.	B5², 13
Ω c686	—,isobutyl-	$C_{10}H_{20}$. See c637	140.27		−94.85	171.3^{760}	0.7952^{20}_4	1.43861^{20}	i	s	v	s	v	chl s	B5², 26
Ω c687	—,isopropyl-*	Hexahydrocumene. Normenthane. C_9H_{18}. See c637	126.24		−89.8	154.5^{760} 38.3^{10}	0.8023^{20}_4	1.4410^{20}	i	v	v	∞	∞	lig, CCl_4 ∞	B5, 41
—	,isopropyl-(methyl)-*	see **Menthane**													
Ω c688	—,methyl-*	Hexahydrotoluene. C_7H_{14}. See c637	98.19		−126.59	100.9^{760} 16.3^{10}	0.7694^{20}_4	1.4231^{20}	i	s	s	∞	∞	lig, CCl_4 ∞	B5, 29
Ω c689	—,(methyl-amino)-	$C_7H_{15}N$. See c637	113.20			$145–7^{748}$ $(154–8)$ $76–7^{18}$	0.8660^{23}	1.4530^{23}	δ	v	∞				B12², 5
Ω c690	—,(3-methyl-butyl)-*	1-Cyclohexyl-3-methylbutane.* Isoamylcyclohexane. $C_{11}H_{22}$. See c637	154.30			196.5^{760}	0.8023^{20}_4	1.4420^{20}	i				s	lig s	B5², 32
Ω c691	—,methylene-*		96.17		−106.7	$102–3^{764}$	0.8074^{20}_4	1.4523^{20}	i		s		s	lig s	B5², 44
Ω c692	—,nitro-*	$C_6H_{11}NO_2$. See c637	129.16	λ 280 (1.4)	fr. −34	205.5^{768} 95^{22}	1.0610^{20}_4	1.4612^{19}	i	s			s	lig s	B5¹, 10
Ω c693	—,pentyl-*	$C_{11}H_{22}$. See c637	154.30		−57.5	202.8^{760} 75.3^{10}	0.8037^{20}_4	1.4437^{20}	i	v	s	s	s	....	B5², 32
—	—,phenyl-*	see **Benzene, cyclohexyl-***													
Ω c694	—,propyl-*	C_9H_{18}. See c637	126.24		−94.9	156.7^{760} 40.1^{10}	0.7936^{20}_4	1.43705^{20}	i	∞	s	∞	s	CCl_4 ∞ peth v aa s	B5², 23
—	—,(2-propyn-1-yl)*	see **Propyne, 3-cyclohexyl-***													
c695	—,1,3,5-tri-methyl-(cis)*	Hexahydromesitylene. C_9H_{18}.	126.24		−49.7	138.5^{760}	0.7708^{20}_4	1.4269^{20}	i		s		s	lig s	B5, 45
c696	—,—(trans)*	C_9H_{18}. See c637	126.24		−107.4	140.5^{760}	0.7794^{20}_4	1.4307^{20}	i		s		s	lig s	B5³, 122
c697	Cyclohexanecar-boxaldehyde	Formylcyclohexane. Hexahydrobenzaldehyde.	112.17	λ^{cy} <186		159.3^{760} 36^{10}	0.9035^{20}_4	1.4496^{20}	s		s			chl s	B7², 20
Ω c698	Cyclohexanecar-boxylic acid*	Hexahydrobenzoic acid.	128.17	mcl pr	31–2	$232–3$ $120–1^{13}$	1.0334^{22}_4	1.4599^{22} 1.4520^{38}	δ	v	....		v	chl v	B9, 7
Ω c699	—,chloride	$C_7H_{11}ClO$. See c698	146.62			180^{760} (184) $75–7^{15}$	1.0962^{15}_4	1.4711^{20}	d	d					B9, 9
Ω c700	—,ethyl ester* ...	$C_9H_{16}O_2$. See c698	156.23			196^{760} 83^{12}	0.9362^{20}_4	1.45012^{15}	i	v	s		s	AcOEt, chl v	B9, 8
c701	—,methyl ester*	$C_8H_{14}O_2$. See c698	142.20			183^{760} 73^{15}	0.9954^{15}_4	1.4433^{20}	i	s	s		s	chl s	B9¹, 5
c702	—,propyl ester*	$C_{10}H_{18}O_2$. See c698	170.25			215.5	0.9530^{15}_4	1.4486^{15}	i	s	s		s	chl s	B9, 8
c703	—,1,1-azobis-, dinitrile.	1,1-Bicyanoazocyclohexane.	244.34	cr (lig) λ^{MeOH} 350 (1.23)	ca. 100				i					lig s^h	B16², 97
Ω c704	—,epoxy-,nitrile*	C_7H_9NO. See c698	123.16		−33	244.5^{760} 110^{10}	1.0929^{20}_{20}	1.4763^{20}	s						C46, 3011
c705	—,1-hydroxy-, nitrile	Cyclohexanone cyanohydrin. $C_7H_{11}NO$. See c698	125.17		34–6	$109–13^9$		1.4643^{20}	s	i	s	i	i	oos i	Am 77, 4571
Ω c706	—,2-hydroxy-*	Hexahydrosalicylic acid. $C_7H_{12}O_3$. See c698	144.17	nd (AcOEt)	111				v	v	v		δ		B10, 5
Ω c706¹	—,1,3,4,5-tetra-hydroxy-(d)	d-Quinic acid. $C_7H_{12}O_6$. See c698	192.17	mcl pr (w) $[α]^{20}_D$ +44 (w, c = 10)	164	d	1.637	....	v^h	δ	i				B10, 538
c706²	—,(dl).	$C_7H_{12}O_6$. See c698	192.17	pr (w)	142	d			v^h	δ	i				B10, 538
c706³	—,(l).	$C_7H_{12}O_6$. See c698	192.17	pr (w), $[α]^{18}_D$ −44.1 (w, c = 12)	172	d	1.64	....	v^h	δ	δ			ac, alk s	B10², 377
c707	**1,2-Cyclohexane-dicarboxylic acid (cis)***	Hexahydrophthalic acid.	172.19	tcl nd (al)	192	d			δ	s	s		s	lig δ chl i	B9, 730
c708	—,(trans, d)*	$C_8H_{12}O_4$. See c707	172.19	pw (w) $[α]_D$ +18.2	179–83				v^h		δ		δ		B9, 732
c709	—,(trans, dl)*	$C_8H_{12}O_4$. See c707	172.19	lf or pr (w)	222				v^h		δ		δ	chl, peth i	B7, 731
c710	—,(trans, l)*	$C_8H_{12}O_4$. See c707	172.19	pw (w) $[α]_D$ −18.5	179–83										B9, 732
c711	—,diethyl ester (cis)*	$C_{12}H_{20}O_4$. See c707	228.29	....		133^{10}	1.0540^{20}_4	1.4551^{14}					s		B9², 521
c712	—,—,(trans, dl)* ..	$C_{12}H_{20}O_4$. See c707	228.29	....		135^{11}	1.040^{20}_4	$1.4522^{13.8}$					s		B9², 522
c713	**1,3-Cyclohexane-dicarboxylic acid (cis)***	cis-Hexahydroisophthalic acid.	172.19	nd (con HCl), cr (w)	167–7.8 (188)	....		....	v	v	s		v	lig δ	B9², 522

For explanations, symbols and abbreviations see beginning of table. For structural formulas see end of table.

No.	Name	Synonyms and Formula	Mol. wt.	Color, crystalline form, specific rotation and λ_{max} (log ε)	m.p. °C	b.p. °C	Density	n_D	w	al	eth	ace	bz	other solvents	Ref.
	1,3-Cyclohexanedicarboxylic acid														
c714	—(trans, d)*	$C_8H_{12}O_4$. See c713	172.19	cr (w), $[\alpha]_D^{22}$ + 23.8 (w, c=4)	134				s	s	s			peth δ	B9[2], 523
c715	—(trans, dl)*	$C_8H_{12}O_4$. See c713	172.19	nd (w)	150.5				v^h	s	s			peth δ	B9[2], 523
c716	—(trans, l)*	$C_8H_{12}O_4$. See c713	172.19	(w), $[\alpha]_D^{22}$ −23.2 (w, c=2)	134				v^h	s	s			peth δ	B9[2], 523
c717	—,diethyl ester (cis)*	$C_{12}H_{20}O_4$. See c713	228.29			288 142[11]	1.04502[20]	1.4521[20]							B9[2], 523
c718	—,——(trans, dl)*	$C_{12}H_{20}O_4$. See c713	228.29			286[756] 142[12]	1.04852[1]	1.4530[20]							B9[2], 523
c719	**1,4-Cyclohexanedicarboxylic acid (cis)***	cis-Hexahydroterephthalic acid.	178.19	lf (w)	170–1				s^h	v	v			chl v	B9[2], 523
Ω c720	—(trans)*	$C_8H_{12}O_4$. See c719	172.19	pr (w), pl (ace)	312–3	300 sub			$δ^h$	v	δ	s		chl i	B9[2], 524
c721	—,diethyl ester (cis)*	$C_{12}H_{20}O_4$. See c719	228.29			151[13]	1.05162[1]	1.4522[21]			s				B9[2], 524
c722	—,——(trans)*	$C_{12}H_{20}O_4$. See c719	228.29	nd	43–4		1.01102[0]	1.4337[64]			s				B9[2], 529
Ω c723	**1,2-Cyclohexanediol (cis)***		116.16	cr (eth), pl (bz)	99–101	120[15]	1.02974[101]			s	s	s	s		B6[2], 743
Ω c724	—(trans, dl)*	$C_6H_{12}O_2$. See c723	116.16	cr (AcOEt or ace)	105	117[13]	1.1472[4]		s	s	s	s			B6[2], 744
c725	**1,4-Cyclohexanediol (cis)***	cis-Quinitol.	116.16	pr (ace)	113–4				s	s	i	δ s^h		MeOH s chl δ	B6[2], 747
Ω c726	—(trans)*	$C_6H_{12}O_2$. See c725	116.16	mcl pl (ace)	143		1.182[20]		s	s	i	δ s^h		MeOH s	B6[2], 748
Ω c727	**1,2-Cyclohexanedione***	Dihydropyrocatechol.	112.14	cr (peth) λ^{al} 266 (3.42)	38–40	193–5[760] 96–7[25]		1.4995[20]	s	s	s	s			B7[2], 526
Ω c728	—,dioxime*	Nioxime. $C_6H_{10}N_2O_2$. See c727	142.16	nd (w or ace) $\lambda^{w, pH=6.5}$ 232.5 (4.12)	191–3				s^h	s		s^h			B7[2], 526
Ω c729	**1,3-Cyclohexanedione***	Dihydroresorcinol.	112.14	pr (bz or AcOEt) λ^{al} 253 (4.35), 282 (4.47)	105–6		1.0861[91]	1.4576[102]	s	s	δ	s	δ	chl s	B7[2], 526
c730	—,dioxime*	$C_6H_{10}N_2O_2$. See c729	142.16	cr (w)	156–7				v^h	v				aa v^h	B7, 555
Ω c731	**1,4-Cyclohexanedione***	Tetrahydroquinone.	112.14	mcl pl (w), nd (peth)	78	sub 100			s	s	s	s	s		B7[2], 526
c732	—,dioxime	$C_6H_{10}N_2O_2$. See c731	142.16	cr (w)	188				s						B7[2], 526
c733	**1,3-Cyclohexanedione, 2-bromo-***	$C_6H_7BrO_2$. See c729	191.03	micr nd	169–70				i	s^h					B7, 556
c734	**1,2-Cyclohexanedione, 3,5-dimethyl-***	$C_8H_{12}O_2$. See c727	140.19	cr (dil MeOH)	71–2				s					alk v MeOH s^h	B7[1], 314
Ω c735	**1,3-Cyclohexanedione, 5,5-dimethyl-***	Dimedone. Methone. $C_8H_{12}O_2$. See c729	140.19	yesh nd (w, aq ace), mcl pr (al-eth) λ^{al} 257 (4.22)	150				$δ^h$	v	δ	s		chl, aa v CCl_4 s peth δ	B7[2], 531
Ω c736	**1,2,3,4,5,6-Cyclohexanehexacarboxylic acid***	Hexahydromellitic acid.	348.22	syr	d				v	v	δ				B9, 1007
c736[1]	**Cyclohexanehexone, octa hydrate***	Cyclohexone hydrate.	312.19	mic nd (dil HNO_3)	100–1				s^h	δ	δ			alk s	B7[2], 882
c737	**1,2,3,4,5-Cyclohexanepentol (d)***	Protoquercitol. d-Quercite. d-Quercitol.	164.16	pr (w or dil (al), $[\alpha]_D^{15}$ +25 (240) (w, c=10)	235–7		1.5845[13]		v	i $δ^h$	i		i	MeOH δ	B6[2], 1151
c738	—(l)*	Viboquercitol. $C_6H_{12}O_5$. See c737	164.16	pr (w), nd (al), nd (w + 1) $[\alpha]_D^{20}$ −50 (w, c=4)	180–1 (anh) (cor)				v	δ	i		i	MeOH δ	B6, 1188
Ω c739	**Cyclohexanethiol***	Cyclohexyl mercaptan.	116.23	λ^{cy} 230 (2.14)		158[760] 41[12]	0.97822[4]	1.4921[20]	i	s	s	s	s	chl s	B6[2], 14
c740	**1,3,5-Cyclohexanetrione, trioxime***	Phloroglucinol trioxime.	171.16	pw (aa)	155 (exp) (darkens at 140)				δ	δ				chl, alk, ac s	B15, 34
c741	—,2,2-dimethyl-* (trioxoform)	Filicin. Filicinic acid. Filigic acid.	154.17	cubic or rhd (al)	213–5δd				$δ^h$	v^h	δ		δ	Na_2CO_3 v aa δ peth i	B7[1], 470
Ω c742	**Cyclohexanol***	Hexahydrophenol. Hexalin.	100.16	hyg nd	25.15	161.1[760]	0.96242[0]	1.4641[20]	s	s	s	s	∞	CS_2 ∞	B6[2], 5
c743	—,1-acetyl-	$C_8H_{14}O_2$. See c742	142.20			125–6[50] 91[11]	1.02482[5]	1.4670[25]		s	s				B8[2], 7
c744	—,2-allyl-(trans)	$C_9H_{16}O$. See c742	140.23			94–6[15]	0.9432[0]	1.4778[20]	i					MeOH, aa s	Am74, 399
c745	—,2-amino-(trans, dl)*	$C_6H_{13}NO$. See c742	115.18	hyg	68	105[10]								chl v ac s	B13[2], 157
Ω c746	—,2-butyl (trans)*	$C_{10}H_{20}O$. See c742	156.27			111–2[16] 75–6[3]	0.90202[0]	1.4641[20]	i					oos v	B6[3], 121
c747	—,2-chloro-(cis, dl)*	cis-Cyclohexene chlorohydrin. $C_6H_{11}ClO$. See c742	134.61	hyg (peth)	36–7	93–4[26]	1.1261[25]	1.4894[25]		s			s	chl s	B6[3], 39
c748	—,—(cis, l)*	$C_6H_{11}ClO$. See c742	134.61	hyg $[\alpha]_{546}$ 19.5		87[15]	1.137[15]	1.4894[25]	s	s			s	chl s	B6, 7

For explanations, symbols and abbreviations see beginning of table. For structural formulas see end of table.

No.	Name	Synonyms and Formula	Mol. wt.	Color, crystalline form, specific rotation and λ_{max} (log ε)	m.p. °C	b.p. °C	Density	n_D	w	al	eth	ace	bz	other solvents	Ref.
	Cyclohexanol														
Ω c749	—,—(trans)*	$C_nH_{11}ClO$. See c742.	134.61	pr (bz-lig)	29	93^{26}	1.146^{16}_{16}	1.4899^{20}	...	v	s	...	s	chl s	$B6^2$, 12
Ω c750	—,4-chloro-(trans)*	$C_6H_{11}ClO$. See c742.	134.61	pl (cy)	82–3	106^{14}	1.1435^{17}_4	1.4930^{17}	...	s	s	...	s	chl s	$B6^1$, 12
c751	—,3-(dimethyl-amino)-*	$C_8H_{17}NO$. See c742.	143.23		73	231^{740} $126-7^{22}$	0.9766^{25}_{25}	1.4852^{20}	...	s					$B13^2$, 159
Ω c752	—,1-ethyl-*	$C_8H_{16}O$. See c742.	128.22	pr λ^{sulf} 333 (3.40)	34.5–5.0	166 67^{16}	0.9227^{25}	1.4633^{20}	δ				s	peth s	$B6^2$, 26
c753	—,2-ethyl-(cis, dl)*	$C_8H_{16}O$. See c742.	128.22			$180-2^{760}$ 74^{12}	0.9274^{21}_4	1.4655^{21}	i		s	s	s	oos v peth s	$B6^2$, 26
c754	—,—(trans, dl)*	$C_8H_{16}O$. See c742.	128.22			79^{12}	0.9193^{21}_4	1.4640^{21}	i		s	s	s	oos v peth s	$B6^2$, 26
Ω c755	—,1-ethynyl-*	$C_8H_{12}O$. See c742.	124.19	cr (peth)	31–2	174^{760} 73^{12}	0.9873^{20}	1.4822^{20}	i	s			s	peth s	$B6^2$, 100
c757	—,2(1-hydroxy-ethyl)-*	$C_8H_{16}O_2$. See c742.	144.22			140^{12}	0.976^{20}	1.4900^{20}	i					oos v	C50, 3299
—	—,2-Isopropyl 5-methyl-*	see **Neoisomenthol**													
Ω c758	—,1-methyl-*	$C_7H_{14}O$. See c742.	114.19		25	155^{760} 70^{25}	$9 919^{20}_4$	1.4595^{20}	i	s			s	chl s	$B6^2$, 16
Ω c759	—,2-methyl-(cis, dl)*	$C_7H_{14}O$. See c742.	114.19		7 (−4)	165 60^{12}	0.9360^{20}_4	1.4640^{20}	δ	∞	s				$B6^2$, 20
c760	—,—(trans, d)*	$C_7H_{14}O$. See c742.	114.19	$[\alpha]^{20.1}_D$ +17.19 (undil)		166 78^{20}	0.9454^{20}	1.4610^{20}	δ	∞	s				$B6^2$, 18
Ω c761	—,—(trans, dl)*	$C_7H_{14}O$. See c742.	114.19		−4.3 to −3.7	$167.2-7.6$ 78^{20}	0.9247^{20}_4	1.4616^{20}	δ	∞	s				$B6^2$, 18
c762	—,—(trans, l)*	$C_7H_{14}O$. See c742.	114.19	$[\alpha]^{19}_D$ −35.5 (undil)		166^{760} 78^{20}	0.9454^{20}	1.4610^{20}	δ	∞	s				$B6^2$, 18
Ω c763	—,3-methyl-(cis, l)*	$C_7H_{14}O$. See c742.	114.19	$[\alpha]^{22}_D$ −4.75 (undil)	−4.7	$174-5^{760}$ 94^{12}	0.9155^{20}_4	1.4574^{20}	δ	∞	∞				$B6^2$, 20
Ω c764	—,—(trans, l)*	$C_7H_{14}O$. See c742.	114.19	$[\alpha]^{20}_D$ −7.3 (undil)	−1	$174-5^{762}$ 84^{13}	0.9214^{20}_4	1.4590^{20}	δ	∞	v				$B6^2$, 20
Ω c765	—,4-methyl-(cis)*	$C_7H_{14}O$. See c742.	114.19		−9.2	$173-4^{760}$ $78-9^{20}$	0.9170^{20}_4	1.4614^{20}	δ	∞	s				$B6^2$, 22
Ω c766	—,—(trans)*	$C_7H_{14}O$. See c742.	114.19			$173-4^{760}$ 54^3	0.9118^{21}_4	1.4561^{20}	δ	∞	s				$B6^2$, 22
Ω c767	—,2-phenyl-(cis, dl)*	$C_{12}H_{16}O$. See c742.	176.24		41–2 (56)	$140-1^{16}$	1.035^{16}	1.5415^{16}	...						$B6^2$, 548
Ω c768	—,—(trans, dl)*	$C_{12}H_{16}O$. See c742.	176.24	cr (peth)	56–7	$152-5^{16}$					s			chl s	$B6^2$, 548
Ω c769	—,2,2,6,6-tetra kis(hydroxy-methyl)-*	$C_{10}H_{20}O_5$. See c742.	220.27	pl (al)	131				v	v	i	i	i	MeOH v Py s	$B6^2$, 1151
c770	—,1,2,2-tri-methyl-(dl)*	$C_9H_{18}O$. See c742.	142.24	cr (+½w)	41 (hyd)	$81.4-1.8^{20}$	0.9230^{20}	1.4682^{20}	i		s		s	oos s	$B6^2$, 16
c771	—,1,2,6-tri-methyl-*	$C_9H_{18}O$. See c742.	142.24			78^{23}	0.9126^{15}_4	1.4598^{15}	i		s		s	oos s	$B6^1$, 17
c772	—,1,3,3-tri-methyl-*	$C_9H_{18}O$. See c742.	142.24	pr (dil al)	74				i	v	s	s	s	oos v	$B6^1$, 16
c773	—,1,3,5-tri-methyl-*	$C_9H_{18}O$. See c742.	142.24			181 $82-3^{19}$	0.8876^{17}_4	$1.454^{16.3}$	i	s	s		s	chl s	$B6^1$, 17
c774	—,1,4,4-tri-methyl-*	$C_9H_{18}O$. See c742.	142.24	hyg nd (dil al)	58	$79-80^{15}$			i	s	s		s	chl s	$B6^1$, 16
c775	—,2,2,3-tri-methyl-*	$C_9H_{18}O$. See c742.	142.24			$85-7^{15}$			i	s	s		s	chl s	$B6^1$, 16
c776	—,2,2,5-tri-methyl-*	Pulenol. $C_9H_{18}O$. See c742.	142.24			$187-9^{760}$ $90-2^{23}$	0.8955^{20}_4	1.4569^{20}	i	s	s		s	oos s	B6, 22
c777	—,2,2,6-tri-methyl-(liquid)*	$C_9H_{18}O$. See c742.	142.24			$186-7^{753}$	0.9128^{20}_4	1.4600^{20}	i	s	s		s	chl s	$B6^1$, 16
c778	—,—(solid)*	$C_9H_{18}O$. See c742.	142.24	cr (peth or al)	51	87^{28}			i	s	s		s	chl s	$B6^1$, 16
c779	—,2,3,3-tri-methyl-*	$C_9H_{18}O$. See c742.	142.24	nd	28	197 97^{19}			i	v	eth	v	s	oos v	$B6^1$, 16
c780	—,2,3,6-tri-methyl-*	$C_9H_{18}O$. See c742.	142.24			$193-5^{747}$	0.9117^{17}_4		i	s	s		s	chl s	B6, 22
c781	—,2,4,5-tri-methyl-(cis)*	$C_9H_{18}O$. See c742.	142.24	hyg		$191-3^{760}$ 84^{17}	0.9120^{20}_4	1.463^{20}	i	s	s		s	chl s	$B6^2$, 36
c782	—,—(trans)*	$C_9H_{18}O$. See c742.	142.24	hyg		196^{749} 112^{35}	0.9064^{20}_4	1.461^{20}	i	s	s		s	chl s	$B6^2$, 36
Ω c783	—,3,3,5-tri-methyl-(cis)*	cis-Dihydroisophorole. $C_9H_{18}O$. See c742	142.24		37.3	$201-3^{750}$ 92^{12}	0.9006^{16}_4	1.4550^{16}	i	s	s		s	chl s	$B6^1$, 16
Ω c784	—,—(trans)*	$C_9H_{18}O$. See c742.	142.24	cr (eth)	55.8	189.2^{760}	0.8643^{60}_{20}		i	s	s		s	chl s	$B6^1$, 16
Ω c785	**Cyclohexanone***	Ketohexamethylene. Pimelic ketone. $C_6H_{10}O$.	98.15	λ^{al} 284(1.26)	−16.4 (−45)	155.65^{760} 47^{15}	0.9478^{20}_4	1.4507^{20}	s	s	s	s	s	chl s	$B7^2$, 5
Ω c786	—oxime*	$C_6H_{11}NO$. See c785.	113.16	hex pr (lig)	90	$206-10$			s	s	s			MeOH s	$B7^2$, 10
c787	—,2-acetyl-*	$C_8H_{12}O_2$. See c785.	140.19	λ^{al} 290 (3.95)		$111-2^{18}$	1.0782^{20}	1.5138^{20}							$B7^2$, 530
c788	—,2-butyl-*	$C_{10}H_{18}O$. See c785.	154.26			70^2	0.905^{20}_4	1.4545^{20}	i				s	oos v	Am 78, 5339
Ω c789	—,2-butylidene-	$C_{10}H_{16}O$. See c785.	152.24			$98-100^{10}$ $(95-100^3)$	0.935^{20}_4	1.4800^{20}	i	s	v	v	v	oos v	C49, 1598
Ω c790	—,2-chloro-*	C_6H_9ClO. See c785.	132.59	λ^{al} 294(1.38)	23	82^{13}	1.161^{20}_{16}	1.4825^{20}			s		s	diox s	$B7^2$, 11
c791	—,3-chloro-*	C_6H_9ClO. See c785.	132.59			$91-2^{14}$					s				$B7$, 10
c792	—,4-chloro-*	C_6H_9ClO. See c785.	132.59			95^{17}		1.4867^{20}			s				$B7^2$, 11
c793	—,2,6-dibenzyl-idene-	$C_{20}H_{18}O$. See c785.	274.37	ye nd (al) λ^{al} 330 (4.40)	117–8	$185-95^{20}$				δ			s	aa s	$B7^2$, 465

For explanations, symbols and abbreviations see beginning of table. For structural formulas see end of table.

No.	Name	Synonyms and Formula	Mol. wt.	Color, crystalline form, specific rotation and λ_{max} (log ε)	m.p. °C	b.p. °C	Density	n_D	Solubility						Ref.
									w	al	eth	ace	bz	other solvents	
	Cyclohexanone														
c794	—,2,6-dibromo-(cis)*	$C_6H_8Br_2O$. See c785	255.96	cr (eth or aa)	106–7						s^h	s^h			B7[2], 12
c795	—,2,4-dimethyl-, oxime (cis)*	$C_8H_{15}NO$. See c785	141.21	nd (al)	98–9				i	s^h					B7[2], 26
c797	—,2,5-di-methyl-(d)*	$C_8H_{14}O$. See c785	126.20	$[\alpha]^{20}$ +11.6 (undil)		$172-4^{750}$ 51^{10}	0.8985_4^{20}	1.4445^{20}	i	s	s				B71, 19
c798	—,—(trans, dl)*	$C_8H_{14}O$. See c785	126.20			$171–3$ (176) $76–7^{27}$	0.9025^{20}	1.4446^{20}	i	s	s				B7[2], 27
c799	—,2(dimethyl-aminomethyl)-*	$C_9H_{17}NO$. See c785	155.24			$92^{10.5}$	0.9504_4^{20}	1.4672^{20}	δ	s	s				B14[2], 3
Ω c800	—,2-ethylidene-*	$C_8H_{12}O$. See c785	124.19	λ^{a1} 250 (3.60)		92^{20}	0.9622^{20}	1.4882^{20}	i					oos v	B7[2], 58
c801	—,2-hydroxy-*	Adipoin. $C_6H_{10}O_2$. See c785	114.15	nd (MeOH or al) λ^{a1} 279 (1.28)	113(92)			1.4785^{21}	v^h	v^h	i		i	peth i	B8[2], 3
c802	—,2-isopropyl-*	$C_9H_{16}O$. See c785	140.23	λ 230 (2.09), 293 (1.29)		$72–3^9$	0.922_4^{16}	1.4564^{15}	i	s	s	s	s	oos v	B7[2], 30
c803	—,2-methyl-(d)*	$C_7H_{12}O$. See c785	112.17	$[\alpha]_D^{25}$ +14.21 (chl)		$167–8^{735}$	0.9262_4^{18}	1.4440^{25}	i	s	s				B7[2], 15
Ω c804	—,—(dl)*	$C_7H_{12}O$. See c785	112.17	λ 284 (1.2)	–13.9	165^{757} 90^{20}	0.9250_4^{20}	1.4483^{20}	i	s	s				B7[2], 16
c805	—,—(l)*	$C_7H_{12}O$. See c785	112.17	$[\alpha]_D^{25}$ –15.22 (undil)		$59–60^{20}$	0.9230_4^{25}	1.4440^{25}	i	s	s				B7[2], 15
c806	—,3-methyl-(d)*	$C_7H_{12}O$. See c785	112.17	$[\alpha]_D^{20}$ +12.7 (undil)		169^{760}	0.9155_4^{20}	1.4493^{20}	i	s	s				B7[2], 17
Ω c807	—,—(dl)*	$C_7H_{12}O$. See c785	112.17		–73.5	$168–9^{738}$ 65^{15}	0.9136_4^{20}	1.44566^{20}	i	s	s				B7[2], 18
Ω c808	—,4-methyl-*	$C_7H_{12}O$. See c785	112.17	λ 281 (1.2)	–40.6	170^{761}	0.9138_4^{20}	1.4451^{20}	i	s	s				B7[2], 19
Ω c809	—,2-propyl-*	$C_9H_{16}O$. See c785	140.23			195^{760} 70^4	0.927_4^{20}	1.4538^{20}	i	s	v	s	v	oos v	B7[2], 30
c810	**Cyclohexa-siloxane, dodecamethyl-**		444.93		–3	245 128^{20}	0.9672	1.4015^{20}	i						Am 68, 667
Ω c811	**Cyclohexene***	3,4,5,6-Tetrahydrobenzene.	82.15	λ^{a1} 207 (2.65)	–103.50	82.98^{760}	0.8102_4^{20}	1.4465^{20}	i	∞	∞	∞	∞	CCl₄, lig ∞	B5[2], 37
c812	—,1-acetyl-	Tetrahydroacetophenone. $C_8H_{12}O$. See c811	124.19			$201–2^{760}$ $63–4^6$	0.9655_4^{20}	1.4881^{20}							B7[2], 58
c813	—,3-bromo-*	C_6H_9Br. See c811	161.05			$80–2^{40}$ $57.5-$ 58^{12}	1.3890_4^{20}	1.5230^{20}	i		s		s	chl s	B5[2], 40
Ω c814	—,decafluoro-*	Perfluorocyclohexene. C_6F_{10}. See c811	262.05			$52–3^{750}$		1.293^{20}							J 1952, 1251
c815	—,1-ethenyl-*	C_8H_{12}. See c811	108.19	λ^{a1} 230 (4.32)		145^{760} $50–2^{22}$	0.8623_4^{15}	1.4915^{20}	i		s		s	MeOH v	B5[1], 62
c816	—,4-ethenyl-*	C_8H_{12}. See c811	108.19			128.9^{760} $66–7^{100}$	0.8299_4^{20}	1.4639^{20}	i		s		s	peth s	B5[2], 81
—	—,1-isopropyl-4-methyl-	see **Menthene**													
Ω c817	—,1-methyl-*	C_7H_{12}. See c811	96.17	λ^{a1} 208 (3.15)	–121	110^{760} 24.6^{30}	0.8102_4^{20}	1.4503^{20}	i		s		s	CCl₄ s	B5[2], 42
c818	—,3-methyl-(d)*	C_7H_{12}. See c811	96.17	$[\alpha]_D^{20}$ +110		104^{760}	0.8010_4^{20}	1.4444^{20}	i		s		s	peth, chl s	B5[2], 43
c819	—,—(dl)*	C_7H_{12}. See c811	96.17		–115.5	104^{760} 0.46^{10}	0.7990_4^{20}	1.4414^{20}	i		s		s	peth, chl s	B5[2], 43
Ω c820	—,4-methyl-*	C_7H_{12}. See c811	96.17		–115.5	102.74^{760} 19^{30}	0.7991_4^{20}	1.4414^{20}	i	s	s		s		B5[2], 43
c821	—,1,3,4,5,6-penta-chloro-(γ)*	$C_6H_5Cl_5$. See c811	254.37		$115–6^4$			1.5630^{20}							Am 76, 1244
c822	—,—(δ)	$C_6H_5Cl_5$. See c811	254.37		68.2–8.6		1.80			al					Am 76, 1244
c823	—,1-phenyl-*	1,2,3,4-Tetrahydrobiphenyl. $C_{12}H_{14}$. See c811	158.25	λ^{iso} 250 (4.08)	–11	$251–3^{760}$ $125–6^{14}$	0.9939_4^{20}	1.5718^{20}	i		s	s		MeOH v	B5[2], 419
c824	—,1-Cyclohexene-1-carboxaldehyde	Δ^1-Tetrahydrobenzaldehyde.	110.16	λ^{a1} 231 (4.12)		72^{15}	0.9694_4^{20}	1.5005^{20}	i		s	s			J 1955, 320
Ω c825	3-Cyclohexene-1-carboxaldehyde	Δ^3-Tetrahydrobenzaldehyde.	110.16	fr –96.1		164^{760} 52^{13}	0.9709_4^{20}	1.4725^{19}	i			s		MeOH s	B7[2], 57
c826	1-Cyclohexene-1-carboxylic acid*	Δ^1-Tetrahydrobenzoic acid.	126.16	pl λ^{a1} 218 (4.01)	38	$240–2^{760}$ 138^{14}	1.109_4^{20}	1.4902_{He}^{20}	δ	s	s	s			B9[2], 30
Ω c827	3-Cyclohexene-1-carboxylic acid*	Δ^3-Tetrahydrobenzoic acid.	126.16		17	237^{748} $132.5-$ 3.0^{20}	1.0815_4^{20}	1.4812^{20}	v	s	s				B9[2], 30
Ω c828	2-Cyclohexene-1-carboxylic acid, 2,6-dimethyl-4-oxo-, ethyl ester*	3,5-Dimethyl-4-carboxy-2-cyclohexen-1-one.	196.25			$157–8^{18}$	1.0493_4^{20}	1.4773^{20}				s			B10[2], 436
c829	1-Cyclohexene-1,2-dicarboxylic acid*	Δ^1-Tetrahydrophthalic acid.	170.17	mcl pl (w)	126				v						B9[2], 556
Ω c830	—,anhydride*		152.16	pl (eth) λ^{CH_3CN} 255 (3.10)	74				d^h	s	v	s		chl s	B17[2], 457

For explanations, symbols and abbreviations see beginning of table. For structural formulas see end of table.

No.	Name	Synonyms and Formula	Mol. wt.	Color, crystalline form, specific rotation and λ_{max} (log ε)	m.p. °C	b.p. °C	Density	n_D	Solubility						Ref.
									w	al	eth	ace	bz	other solvents	
	2-Cyclohexene-1,2-dicarboxylic acid														
c831	2-Cyclohexene-1,2-dicarboxylic acid, anhydride*	Δ^2-Tetrahydrophthalic anhydride.	152.16	pr (eth)	78–9	.....	.....	.....	d^h	s	s	...	...	chl s	B17[2], 457
Ω c832	4-Cyclohexene-1,2-dicarboxylic acid, anhydride (cis)*	cis-Δ^4-Tetrahydrophthalic anhydride.	152.16	pl (eth or lig)	103–4	.....	.....	.....	d^h	s	s	s	...	chl, os s lig δ	B17[2], 457
c833	—,—(trans, d)*....	$C_8H_8O_3$. See c832.	152.16	lf, $[\alpha]_D^{25}$ +6.6 (al)	128	.....	.....	.....	d^h	v		v		.....	B17, 462
c834	—,—(trans, dl)*..	$C_8H_8O_3$. See c832.	152.16	cr (bz-lig)	141 (130)	.....	.....	.....	d^h	s		s		chl s	B17, 462
Ω c835	—,imide, N(tri-chloromethylthio)-	Captan.	300.60	cr (bz, CCl_4)	172	.....	1.74	.....				δ	δ	.....	C46, 11232
—	**Cyclohexene oxide**	see Cyclohexane, 1,2-epoxy-*													
c836	2-Cyclo-hexen-1-ol*	.....	98.15	.....		164–6[760] 63–5[12]	0.9923[15]	1.4790[25]	...	s		s			B6[2], 60
c837	—,5-methyl-(cis, d)*	$C_7H_{12}O$. See c836.	112.17	$[\alpha]_D^{30}$ +6.95	.....	83[25]	0.9391[25]	1.4727[25]			s			lig s	Am 77, 4042
c838	—,—(cis, l)*.....	$C_7H_{12}O$. See c836.	112.17	$[\alpha]_D^{25}$ −7		82[25]	0.9391[25]	1.4727[25]			s			lig s	Am 77, 4042
c839	—,—(trans, d)*....	$C_7H_{12}O$. See c836.	112.17	$[\alpha]_D^{27}$ +127 (ace, c = 19.4)		68–9[24]	0.9430[20]	1.4737[25]			s			lig s	Am 77, 4042
c840	—,—(trans, l)*...	$C_7H_{12}O$. See c836.	112.17	$[\alpha]_D^{27}$ −163.9		82–3[24]	0.9430[20]	1.4737[25]			s			lig s	Am 77, 4042
Ω c841	2-Cyclohexen-1-one*	.....	96.14	λ^{al} 225 (3.68)		169–71[760] 61–2[10]	0.9620[25]	1.4883[20]			v		s		B7[2], 55
c842	—,2,5-dimethyl-*	$C_8H_{12}O$. See c841.	124.19			189–90	0.938[22]	1.4753[22]			s	s			B7[1], 51
Ω c843	—,3,5-dimethyl-*	$C_8H_{12}O$. See c841.	124.19	λ^{al} 233(4.16) 310 (1.70)		208–9 94[17]	0.9400[20]	1.4812[20]			s	s			B7[2], 59
c844	—,3,6-dimethyl-*	$C_8H_{12}O$. See c841.	124.19	λ 236 (4.10)		75[19]	1.008[18][18]	1.4805[18]	i		s	s			B7[1], 51
c845	3-Cyclohexen-1-one,4,6-dimethyl-*		124.19			194	0.9539[0]	.....	i		s				B7, 61
—	2-Cyclohexen-1-one,3-hydroxy-*	see 1,3-Cyclohexanedione*													
c846	—,5-isopropyl-3-methyl-*	m-6-Menten-5-one. Hexeton. $C_{10}H_{16}O$. See c841	152.24	pa ye λ^{al} 234.5 (4.10)		244 124[15]	0.9340[21]	1.4865[21]	δ	v	v			oos ∞	B7[2], 74
c847	—,2-methyl-*	$C_7H_{10}O$. See c841.	110.16	λ^{al} 235 (3.98)		178–9[760] 56[9]	0.9667[20]	1.4833[20]					s		B7[2], 57
Ω c848	—,3-methyl-*....	$C_7H_{10}O$. See c841.	110.16	λ^{al} 235 (4.10)	−21	200–2[760] 78–9[12]	0.9693[20]	1.49475[20]	∞				s		B7[2], 56
—	—,3,5,5-tri-methyl-*	see Isophorone													
—	Cyclohexone, hydrate	see Cyclohexanchexone, octahydrate.*													
—	Cyclone.........	see Cyclopentadienone, tetraphenyl-													
—	Cyclonite........	see 1,3,5-Triazine, hexa-hydro-1,3,5-trinitro-													
c850	Cyclononanone*....		140.23	λ^{al} 280 (1.20)	34	148.5[24]	0.9560[20]	1.4729[20]			s				B7[2], 29
c851	Cyclonona-siloxane, octa-decamethyl-		667.40			188[20]		1.4070[20]	i				s	lig s	Am 68, 358
c852	Cyclononene (cis)*		124.23			167–9[760] 73–4[30]	0.8671[20]	1.4805[20]	i				s		Am 74, 3643
c853	—(trans)*.......	C_9H_{16}. See c852.	124.23			94–6[30]	0.8615[20]	1.4799[20]	i				s		Am 74, 3643
Ω c854	1,5-Cyclooctadiene (cis, cis)*		108.19		−70→ −69	150.8[757] 51–2[25]	0.8818[25]	1.4905[25]	i				s	CCl_4 s	B5, 116
Ω c855	Cyclooctane*	Octamethylene.	112.22		14.3	148.5–9.5[749] 63[45]	0.8349[20]	1.4586[20]	i				s	lig s	B5[2], 20
Ω c856	Cyclooctanol*....		128.22		25.1	99[16] 74[3]	0.9740[20]	1.4871[20]	...	s		s			B6[?], 25
Ω c857	Cyclooctanone....	Azelaone....	126.20	λ^{al} 282 (1.34)	28–30	194–8[761] (202[113]) 74[12]	0.9581[20]	1.4694[20]	i	s		s	s		B7[2], 22
c858	—,semicarbazone.	$C_9H_{17}N_3O$. See c857.......	183.26	lf (dil MeOH)	170–1									MeOH s[h]	B7[2], 22
c859	Cycloocta-siloxane, hexa-decamethyl-		593.25		31.5	290[760] 175[20]	1.177	1.4060[20]	i				s	lig s	Am 67, 667
Ω c860	Cycloocta-tetraene*		104.16	ye or wh λ^{al} 280 (2.64)	−4.68	140.56[760] 29.1[10]	0.9206[20]	1.5381[20]		s	s	s	s		B5[1], 228
Ω c861	Cyclooctene(cis)....		110.20		−12	138[760] 42[18]	0.8472[20]	1.4698[20]		s	s			CCl_4 s	B5[2], 45
Ω c862	—(trans).........		110.20		−59	143[760] 75[78]	0.8483[20]	1.4741[25]	...	s				chl s	B5[2], 45
Ω c863	Cyclopenta-decanone*	Exaltone.	224.39	λ^{al} 282 (1.32)	63	120[0.3]	0.8895	1.4637[66]	δ	s		s			B7[2], 50
c864	—,3-methyl-*	Muscone. Muskone. $C_{16}H_{30}O$. See c863	238.42	ye, $[\alpha]_D^{17}$ −13 (undil)		327–30[752] 130[0.5]	0.9221[17]	1.4802[17]	δ	∞	s	s			B7[?], 51

For explanations, symbols and abbreviations see beginning of table. For structural formulas see end of table.

No.	Name	Synonyms and Formula	Mol. wt.	Color, crystalline form, specific rotation and λ_{max} (log ε)	m.p. °C	b.p. °C	Density	n_D	w	al	eth	ace	bz	other solvents	Ref.
	1,3-Cyclopentadiene														
c865	1,3-Cyclopenta-diene*	Cyclopentadiene*.	66.10	λ^{al} 238 (3.62)	−97.2	40.0[760]	0.8021[20/4]	1.4440[20]	i	∞	∞	s	∞	....	B5[2], 77
c866	—,hexachloro-	Perchlorocyclopentadiene. C_5Cl_6	272.77	ye gr liq λ^{hp} 323 (3.2)	−9	239[753] 48–9[0.3]	1.7019[25/5]	1.5658[20]							Am 69, 1918
—	Cyclopentadiene-benzoquinone	see Naphthalene, 5,8-dioxo-1,4,5,8,9,10-hexahydro-1,4-methylene-*													
Ω c867	Cyclopenta-dienone, tetra-phenyl-*	Cyclone. Tetracyclone.	384.48	bk-vt lf, cr (aa or xyl) λ^{iso} 260 (4.45), 342 (3.82), 512 (3.11)	220–1						s			s	iso s xyl, aa s[h]	B7[2], 521
Ω c868	Cyclopentane*	Pentamethylene.	70.14	....	−93.879	49.262[760]	0.7457[20/4]	1.4065[20]	i	∞	∞	∞	∞	CCl_4, peth ∞	B5[2], 4
c869	—,acetyl-........	Cyclopentyl methyl ketone. $C_7H_{12}O$. See c868	112.17	λ^{al} 279 (1.37)		158–9.5 (163)	0.9182[20/20]	1.4409[25]			s				B7[2], 20
Ω c870	—,bromo-*	Cyclopentyl bromide. C_5H_9Br. See c868	149.04	....		136.7–7.7[760] 56[48]	1.3873[20/4]	1.4886[20]							B5[2], 4
c871	—,butyl-*	C_9H_{18}. See c868	126.23	....	−107.98	156.7[760] 41.6[10]	0.7846[20/4]	1.4316[20]	i	∞	∞	∞	∞	peth, CCl_4 ∞	B5[2], 25
Ω c872	—,chloro-*	Cyclopentyl chloride . C_5H_9Cl. See c868	104.58	....		113.5–4.5[752]	1.0051[20/4]	1.4510[20]	i	s	s	s	s	oos s	B5[2], 4
c873	—,1,2-diethyl-(trans)*	C_9H_{18}. See c868	124.24	....	−95.6	153.58[760]	0.7832[20/4]	1.4295[20]	i	∞	∞		s	peth s	B5[2], 126
Ω c874	—,ethyl-*	C_7H_{14}. See c868	98.19	....	−138.44	103.5[760] 19.36[30]	0.7665[20/4]	1.4198[20]	i	∞	∞		∞	CCl_4 ∞ to, peth s	B5[3], 78
c875	—,isopropyl-*	C_8H_{16}. See c868	112.22	....	−111.4	126.4[760] 16.3[10]	0.7765[20/4]	1.4258[20]	i	∞	∞		s	CCl_4 ∞ peth v	B5[2], 22
Ω c876	—,methyl-*	Methylpentamethylene. C_6H_{12}. See c868.	84.16	....	−142.4	71.8[760]	0.7486[20/4]	1.4097[20]	i	∞	∞		∞	lig, CCl_4 ∞	B5, 27
c877	—,1-methyl-2-propyl-(trans)*	C_9H_{18}. See c868	126.24	....	−104.9	152.58[760]	0.7921[20/4]	1.4321[20]							C45, 7026
c878	—,propyl-*	1-Cyclopentylpropane. C_8H_{16}. See c868	112.22	....	−117.3	130.95[760] 21.2[10]	0.7763[20/4]	1.4266[20]	i	∞	∞		s	peth, CCl_4 v	B5[2], 22
c879	Cyclopentanecar-boxaldehyde	....	98.15	....		133–4[760]	0.9371[20/4]	1.1432[20]	s	s	s				B7[2], 14
Ω c880	Cyclopentanecar-boxylic acid*	....	114.15	....	−7 (−4)	212.5–13.5[752] 104[11]	1.0527[20/4]	1.4532[20]	δ					MeOH s	B9[2], 6
c881	—,3-formyl-2,2,3-trimethyl-, methyl ester (d)	$C_{11}H_{18}O_3$. See c880	198.27	$[\alpha]_D$ + 51.4 (al)		130–2[8]	1.048[20/4]	1.4160[25]	δ	s				MeOH s	Am 64, 1416
Ω c882	—,2-oxo-, ethyl ester	$C_8H_{12}O_3$. See c880	156.19	λ^{al} 258 (2.5)		218[704] 110[16]	1.0781[20/4]	1.4519[20]			s		s		B10[2], 419
—	—,1,2,2,3-tetra-methyl-	See Campholic acid													
c883	1,2-Cyclopentane-dicarboxylic acid (cis)*	....	158.16	nd (w)	140	....			s						B9, 728
c884	—(trans, d)*	$C_7H_{10}O_4$. See c883	158.16	cr (w), $[\alpha]_D$ + 87.6 (w, c = 0.9)	181	....			s[h]	s	δ		δ	chl δ	B9[1], 316
c885	—(trans, dl)*	$C_7H_{10}O_4$. See c883	158.16	cr (w)	162–3	....			s[h]	v[h]	δ		δ	AcOEt s chl, peth δ	B9[2], 518
c886	—(trans, l)*	$C_7H_{10}O_4$. See c883	158.16	cr (w), $[\alpha]_D$ −85.9 (w, c = 1.2)	180–1	....			s[h]	s	δ		δ	chl δ	B9[1], 316
Ω c887	1,3-Cyclopentane-dicarboxylic acid (cis)*	Norcamphoric acid.	158.16	pr (w)	121	>300d			s[h]	s	s	s	s[h]	chl s peth i	B9[2], 518
c888	—(trans, d)*	$C_7H_{10}O_4$. See c887	158.16	cr (CCl_4) $[\alpha]_D$ + 5.9 (w, c = 5)	93.5	....			s					CCl_4 s[h]	B9[2], 519
c889	—(trans, dl)*	$C_7H_{10}O_4$. See c887	158.16	pr (CCl_4)	88	....			s					CCl_4 s[h]	B9[2], 519
c890	—(trans, l)*	$C_7H_{10}O_4$. See c887	158.16	cr (CCl_4) $[\alpha]_D$ −5.3 (w, c = 5)	93	....			s					CCl_4 s[h]	B9[2], 519
c891	—,4,4-dimethyl-(cis)*	Apofenchocamphoric acid. $C_9H_{14}C_4$. See c887	186.21	mcl	144–5				s[h]	v	v		δ		B9[2], 529
—	—,1,2,2-trimethyl-*	See Camphoric acid													
Ω c892	Cyclopentanol*	....	86.14	....	−19	140.85[760] 53[10]	0.9478[20/4]	1.4530[20]	δ	s	s	s			B6[3], 4
c893	—,2-acetyl-1,3,3,4,4-penta-methyl- (α)	Desoxymesityl oxide. $C_{12}H_{22}O_2$. See c892	198.31	cr (peth-eth)	45	....			i			s			B8[2], 11
Ω c894	Cyclopentanone*	Adipic ketone. Ketopentamethylene.	84.12	λ^{al} 290 (1.28)	−51.3	130.65[760]	0.94869[20]	1.4366[20]	i	s	∞	s		MeOH, hx s	B7[2], 3
c895	—,2-methyl-*	$C_6H_{10}O$. See c894	98.15	....	−75	139.5[760] 44[18]	0.9139[20]	1.4364[20]	s	v	v	v			B7[2], 13

For explanations, symbols and abbreviations see beginning of table. For structural formulas see end of table.

No.	Name	Synonyms and Formula	Mol. wt.	Color, crystalline form, specific rotation and λ_{max} (log ε)	m.p. °C	b.p. °C	Density	n_D	Solubility						Ref.
									w	al	eth	ace	bz	other solvents	
	Cyclopentanone														
c896	—,3-methyl- (d)*	$C_6H_{10}O$. See c894.	98.15	$[\alpha]_D^{25} + 143.7$ (undil) λ^{al} 288 (1.34)	−58.4	143.5^{742} 42.5– 44^{13}	0.9140_4^{19}	1.4340^{19}	v	v	v	v	...	aa v	B7², 13
Ω c897	—,—(dl)*	$C_6H_{10}O$. See c894.	98.15	λ^{al} 288 (1.34)	....	144 4.5^{760} 38^{11}	0.913^{22}	1.4329^{20}	s	v	v	v	...	aa v	B7², 14
c898	**Cyclopentasilox- ane, decamethyl-**	....	370.78	....	−38	210^{760} 101^{20}	0.9593^{20}	1.3982^{20}	i	...	...	...	...		Am 68, 358
Ω c899	**Cyclopentene***	λ^{gas} 182.8 (4.13)	68.13		−135.076	44.242^{760}	0.7720_4^{20}	1.4225^{20}	i	s	s	...	s	peth s	B5², 35
c900	—,3-chloro-*	C_5H_7Cl. See c899.	102.57		....	$25–31^{30}$	1.0577^{15}	1.4708^{26}	i	s	s	...	...	chl s	B5², 36
Ω c901	—,octachloro-*	Perchlorocyclopentene. C_5Cl_8. See c899	943.68	nd (al) λ^{hp} < 230 (4.0)	41	283^{760} 140^{10}	1.8200_5^{20}	1.5660^{50}	i	v^h				chl s	B5, 62
—	3-Cyclopentene- carboxylic acid, 2,2,3-trimethyl-*	see α-**Campholytic acid**													
c902	**3-Cyclopenten-1- one, 3,4-bis(4- methoxy- phenyl)-***	....	294.35	ye br	129	....			i	s	s	s	...	oos s	B8, 355
c903	**1,2-Cyclopenteno- phenanthrene**	....	218.30	nd (al), cr (peth) λ^{al} 215 (4.3), 257 (4.75), 300 (4.27), 345 (3.0), 352 (3.0)	135–6	....			i	s			...	peth s^h	E14, 15
c904	**2,3-Cyclopenteno- phenanthrene**		218.30	pl or pr (al), nd (MeOH)	84–5								...	MeOH s^h	E14s, 19
c905	**9,10-Cyclo- pentenophen- anthrene**		218.30	pl (xyl), nd (i-PrOH)	155–6				i	s			s		E14s, 25
c906	**1,2-Cyclopenteno- phenanthrene, 3-methyl-**	$C_{18}H_{16}$. See c903	232.33	cr (aa)	126–7				i				...	aa s^h	E14, 16
Ω c907	**Cyclopropane***	Trimethylene.	42.08	....	−127.6	-32.7^{760}	0.720_4^{-79} 0.6769_4^{-30}	$1.3799^{-42.5}$	s	v	v	...	s	peth s	B5², 3
Ω c908	—,acetyl-	Cyclopropyl methyl ketone. C_5H_8O. See c907	84.13	λ^{al} 206 (3.12), 270 (1.33)	fp − 68.4	114^{772}	0.8983_4^{20}	1.42514^{20}	s	v	v	...	s		B7², 5
Ω c909	—,1,1-dimethyl-*	C_5H_{10}. See c907.	70.14	....	−108.96	20.63^{760}	0.6589_4^{20}	1.3668^{20}	i	s	v	...	...	sulf v	B5, 20
c910	—,methoxy-*	Cyprome ether. C_4H_8O. See c907	72.12	....	−119	44.7^{760}	0.8100_4^{20}	1.3802^{20}	s	s	v	...	s	oos s	Am 69, 2451
c911	—,methyl-*	C_4H_8. See c907.	56.12	....	−177.2	4–5	0.6912_4^{-20}		δ	v	v	...	s	sulf s	B5², 3
Ω c912	**Cyclopropanecar- boxylic acid***	Ethyleneacetic acid.	86.09		18–9	182–4	1.0885_4^{20}	1.4390^{20}	s^h	s	s				B9², 3
Ω c913	—,nitrile-	Cyclopropanecarbonitrile*. Cyclopropyl cyanide.	67.09	λ^{al} 208 (0.82)		135^{760} $69–70^{88}$	0.8946_4^{20}	1.42293^{20}						hx s	B9², 4
c914	—,2,2-dimethyl- 3(2-methyl- propenyl)- (cis, d)*	d, cis-Chrysanthemumic acid. $C_{10}H_{16}O_2$. See c912.	168.24	pr, $[\alpha]_D^{22} + 83.3$ (chl, c = 1.6)	40–2	$95^{0.1}$					s		...	chl s	C47, 3247
c915	—,—(cis, dl)*	$C_{10}H_{16}O_2$. See c912.	168.24	pr (AcOEt), cr (peth)	115–6						s		...	oos s AcOEt s^h	B9², 47
c916	—,—(cis, l)*	$C_{10}H_{16}O_2$. See c912.	168.24	pr, $[\alpha]_D^{19} − 83.3$ (chl, c = 1.6)	41–3	$95^{0.1}$					s		...	chl s	C47, 3247
c917	—,—(trans, d)*	d, trans-Chrysanthemumic acid. $C_{10}H_{16}O_2$. See c912	168.24	pr, $[\alpha]_D^{20} + 25.8$ (chl, c = 2.5)	18–21	$245 \, \delta d$ 135^{12}			δ	v	v	...	oos v chl s	B9², 45
c918	—,—(trans, dl)*	$C_{10}H_{16}O_2$. See c912.	168.24	pr (AcOEt)	54	$145–6^{13}$					s		...	chl, AcOEt s	B9², 46
c919	—,—(trans, l)*	$C_{10}H_{16}O_2$. See c912.	168.24	$[\alpha]_D^{20} − 25.8$ (chl, 2.9 %)	17–21	$99–100^{0.2-0.8}$					s		...	AcOEt v chl s	C47, 3247
c920	**1,1-Cyclopropane- dicarboxylic acid***	Ethylenemalonic acid. Vinaconic acid.	130.10	pr or nd (chl), pr (w + l)	140–1	....			s		s		...	chl s	B9, 721
Ω c921	—,diethyl ester*	$C_9H_{14}O_4$. See c920.	186.21	....	.....	$214–6^{748}$ 99.100^{11}	1.0566_{25}^{25}	1.4345^{18}		v	v				B9², 512
Ω c922	**1,2-Cyclopropane- dicarboxylic acid (cis)***		130.10	pr (eth or w)	139				s	v	v		δ	conHCl v chl, peth δ	B9², 513
c923	—,(trans, d)*	$C_5H_6O_4$. See c922.	130.10	$[\alpha]_D^{27} + 84.87$(w)	175				v	v	v	...	δ	chl δ	B9, 724
Ω c924	—,(trans, dl)*	$C_5H_6O_4$. See c922.	130.10	nd (eth), pl (ace-bz)	175	210^{30}			v	v	v	...	δ	chl δ	B9², 514
c925	—,(trans, l)*	$C_5H_6O_4$. See c922.	130.10	$[\alpha]_D^{17}$ 84.40 (w)	175				s	v		...	δ	chl δ	B9, 724
c926	—,diethyl ester (cis)*	$C_9H_{14}O_4$. See c922.	186.21		106.5– 7.5		1.062_4^{12}	1.4450^{20}							B9², 513
c927	—,dimethyl ester (cis)*	$C_7H_{10}O_4$. See c922.	158.16			$219–20^{760}$ 110^3	1.1584_{16}^{16}	1.4472^{14}							B9¹, 315
c928	—,1-bromo-*	$C_5H_5BrO_4$. See c922.	209.00	pr (eth-chl), cr (ace-bz)	173	....					v	v	...	chl δ	B9², 514
c929	**1,2,3-Cyclopro- panetricarboxylic acid***		174.11	nd (w), cr (HCl)	220				s	s		...	...	chl δ	B9², 702

For explanations, symbols and abbreviations see beginning of table. For structural formulas see end of table.

Cyclotetrasiloxane

No.	Name	Synonyms and Formula	Mol. wt.	Color, crystalline form, specific rotation and λ_{max} (log ε)	m.p. °C	b.p. °C	Density	n_D	w	al	eth	ace	bz	other solvents	Ref.
Ω c930	Cyclotetrasiloxane, octamethyl-	....	296.62		17.5	175.8[760] 74[20]	0.9561[20]	1.3968[20]	i	..	..	..	..		Am 68, 358
c931	—, octaphenyl-	....	793.20	nd (bz-al or aa)	200–1	330–4[1]	....	....	i	δ	..	..	s	aa s[h]	Am 67, 2173
c932	—,1,3,5,7-tetra-methyl, 1,3,5,7-tetraphenyl-	....	544.91	cr (aa)	99	237[1.5]	1.1183[20]	1.5461[20]	i	..	..	∞	..	hp ∞	Am 70, 1115
c933	Cyclotrisiloxane, hexaphenyl-	....	594.90	pl (bz-al or aa)	190	290–300[1]	1.23[25]	....	i	δ	..	..	s	aa s	Am 69, 488
c934	—,1,3,5-triethyl-1,3,5-triphenyl-	....	450.77		177.5	166[0.025]	1.0952[25]	1.5402[25]	i	..	s	..	..		Am 70, 3758
c935	—,1,3,5-trimethyl-1,3,5-triphenyl- (cis)	....	408.68	pl (al)	99.5	165–85[1.5]	....	....	i	s[h]	..	..	..		Am 70, 1115
c936	—, (trans)	$C_{21}H_{24}O_3Si_3$. See c935	408.68	nd (al)	39.5	190[1.5]	1.1062[20]	1.5397[20]	i	s[h]	..	..	..		Am 70, 1115
c937	Cymarose	4,5-Dihydroxy-3-methoxy-hexanal*. 3-Methyldigi-toxose. $CH_3(CHOH)_2CH(OCH_3)CH_2CHO$	162.19	pr (eth-peth), nd (ace) $[\alpha]_D^{21} +53.4$ (w, c = 2.2) (mut)	100–2 (92–4)		....	....	v	v	δ	v	i	chl, peth δ	B31, 19
—	Cymene	see Benzene, isopropyl-(methyl)-*													
c938	Cysteic acid (d)	L-2-Amino-3-sulfopropanoic acid*. β-Sulfoalanine. $HO_2CCH(NH_2)CH_2SO_3H$	169.16	oct cr or nd (dil al), pr or nd (w + 1) $[\alpha]_D^{20} +8.66$ (w)	260d (anh)		....	....	s[h]	i	..	..	i		B4[3], 1713
c939	—(dl)*	$HO_2CCH(NH_2)CH_2SO_3H$..	169.16	pr (w)	272–4d		....	....	s[h]	i	..	..	i		B4[2], 951
Ω c940	Cysteine(L)	L-β-Mercaptoalanine. $HSCH_2CH(NH_2)CO_2H$	121.16	cr (w) $[\alpha]_D^{30} +9.8$ (w, c = 1.3) $\lambda^{w.pH = 9}$ 231 (3.49)	ca. 240d		....	....	v	v	i	i	i	aa v	B4[2], 920
Ω c941	Cystine(D)	D-Dicystine. $[HO_2CCH(NH_2)CH_2S-]_2$	240.30	cr (dil NH₃) $[\alpha]_D^{20} +224$ (1N HCl, c = 1.00)	247–9		....	....	δ s[h]	i	..	..	..	ac, alk s	B4[2], 919
Ω c942	—(DL)	$[HO_2CCH(NH_2)CH_2S-]_2$	240.30		260		....	....	δ s[h]	i	..	..	..		B4[2], 936
Ω c943	—(L)	$[HO_2CCH(NH_2)CH_2S-]_2$	240.30	hex pl or pr (w) $[\alpha]_D^{20} -223.4$ (1N HCl, c = 1.00) $\lambda^{0.01N HCl}$ 250 (2.5)	260–1d	1.677	....	....	δ s[h]	i	i	..	i	ac, alk s	B4[2], 925
Ω c944	—(meso)	$[HO_2CCH(NH_2)CH_2S-]_2$	240.30	$\lambda^{w.pH = 7}$ 250 sh (2.57)	200–218d		....	....	i	..	..	..	..		B4[2], 936
Ω c945	Cytidine	Cytosine-3β-D-ribo-furanoside. $C_9H_{13}N_3O_5$.	243.22	nd (dil al) $[\alpha]_D^{20.5} +35.3$ (w, c = 1) λ^w 271 (3.95)	230–1d		....	....	v	δ	..	..	..		B31, 24
c946	Cytidylic acid b	3'-Cytosylic acid. $C_9H_{14}N_3O_8P$.	323.20	orh nd $[\alpha]_D^{20} +49.4$ (w, c = 1) λ^w 271 (3.96)	233–4d		....	....	s[h]	s[h]	..	..	..		B31, 25
Ω c947	Cytisine (l)	Baptitoxine. Sophorine. Ulexine. $C_{11}H_{14}N_2O$.	190.25	orh pr (aa or ace), $[\alpha]_D^{17} -120$ (w) λ^{MeOH} 235 (3.9), 306 (4.0)	154.5 sub	218[2]	....	....	s	s	i	s	v	chl s peth i	B24[2], 70
c948	—, N-methyl-	Caulophylline. $C_{12}H_{16}N_2O$. See c947	204.28	cr (w + 2), nd (al, bz or lig), pr (al) $[\alpha]_D^{18.5} -230$ (w) λ^{MeOH} 234 (3.81), 309 (3.90)	137		....	....	s	v	..	v	v	chl v	B24[2], 70
—	Cytosylic acid	see Cytidylic acid													
Ω c949	Cytosine	4-Amino-1,2-dihydro-1,3-diazin-2-one*. 4-Amino-2-pyrimidone. 6-Amino-uracil.	111.10	mcl or tcl pl (w + 1) $\lambda^{w.pH = 7}$ 267 (3.79)	320–25d		....	....	s[h]	δ	i	..	..	ac s	B24, 314
Ω c950	—,5-methyl-	$C_5H_7N_3O$. See c949	125.13	pr (w + ½) $\lambda^{w.pH = 7}$ 278 (3.8) $\lambda^{w.pH = 14}$ 289.5 (3.91)	270d		....	....	s	δ	i	..	..	ac s	B24, 355
—	—,3β-D-ribo-furanoside	see Cytidine													

For explanations, symbols and abbreviations see beginning of table. For structural formulas see end of table.

Daidzein

No.	Name	Synonyms and Formula	Mol. wt.	Color, crystalline form, specific rotation and λ_{max} (log ε)	m.p. °C	b.p. °C	Density	n_D	w	al	eth	ace	bz	other solvents	Ref.
—	Daidzein	see Isoflavone, 4',7-dihydroxy-													
—	Damascenine......	see Benzoic acid, 3-methoxy-2-(methylamino)-, methyl ester													
—	Danilone	see 1,3-Indanedione, 2-phenyl-													
—	Daphnetin	see Coumarin, 7,8-dihydroxy-													
—	Datiscetin	see Flavone, 2',3,5,7-tetrahydroxy-													
—	D.D.D.	see Ethane, 1,1-bis(4-chlorophenyl)-2,2-dichloro-													
—	D.D.T.	see Ethane, 1,1-bis(4-chlorophenyl)-2,2,2-trichloro-													
d1	1,3-Decadiene*	$CH_3(CH_2)_5CH{:}CHCH{:}CH_2$	138.25			$168\text{-}70^{760}$	0.750^{20}		δ				s		$B1, 260$
d2	3,7-Decadiene-5-yne,4,7-dipropyl-*	$C_2H_5CH{:}C(C_3H_7)C{:}CCH{:}C(C_3H_7)C_2H_5$ 218.39				$125\text{-}7^{18}$	0.8131^{19}	1.4890^{20}	i				s		$B1^1, 129$
d4	4,6-Decadiyne*	Dipentyne. $CH_3CH_2CH_2C{:}CC{:}CCH_2CH_2CH_3$ 134.22				88^{12}	0.8695^{19}		i						$B1^2, 248$
Ωd5	4,6-Decadiyne-3,8-diol,3,8-dimethyl-*	$C_2H_5COH(CH_3)C{:}CC{:}CCOH(CH_3)C_2H_5$ 194.28			89–91				δ	s^h			δ s^h	CCl_4 δ MeOH s	C53, 18868
d6	Decalin(cis)	Bicyclo[4,4,0]decane. Decahydronaphthalene. Naphthane.	138.25	λ < 210	−43.01	195.65^{760} 69.4^{10}	0.8965^{20}	1.4810^{20}	i	∞	v	v	∞	chl v	$B5^2, 5657$
d7	—(trans)	$C_{10}H_{18}$. See d6	138.25	λ < 210	−30.4	187.25^{760} 63^{10}	0.8699^{20}	1.4695^{20}	i	v	v	v	∞	chl v MeOH δ	$B5^2, 243$
d8	—,1-amino-(cis)	cis-Decalylamine. $C_{10}H_{19}N$. See d6	153.27		(i) 8 (ii) −2	100^{12}								os, ac s	$B12^2, 35$
d9	—,—(trans)	$C_{10}H_{19}N$. See d6	153.27		(i) −18 (ii) −1	106^{16}								os, ac s	$B12^2, 35$
d10	—,1-chloro-	$C_{10}H_{17}Cl$. See d6	172.70			d^{760} $114\text{-}6^{20}$									Am 76, 4420
d11	—,2-methylene-(trans)	$C_{11}H_{18}$. See d6	150.27			$200\text{-}1^{756}$ $82\text{-}2.5^{10}$	0.8897^{20}	1.4841^{22}							E12B, 106
d12	1,3-Decalindione (cis)	1,3-Diketodecalin	166.22	nd (bz, ace, dil al) λ^{diox} 245 (4.11), 301 (1.98)	124–5					s		s	s^h	alk s	E12B, 2804
d13	—(trans)	$C_{10}H_{14}O_2$. See d12	166.22	nd (bz, dil al) λ^{diox} 244 (4.02), 295 (2.03)	152–3								s	alk s	E12B, 2805
d14	2,3-Decalindione (cis)	2,3-Diketodecalin	166.22	rh (al, ace, lig)	88–9				δ	s				alk s	E12B, 2812
d15	—(trans)	$C_{10}H_{14}O_2$. See d14	166.22	nd (w), lf (dil al) λ^{al} 269 (3.87)	100–1				δ					os s lig s^h	E12B, 2812
d17	2-Decalincarboxylic acid (cis)	Decahydro-2-naphthoic acid.	182.27	cr (hx)	81	150^{15}			s	s		s		chl s	E12B, 4086
Ωd18	Decanal*	Capraldehyde. n-Decylaldehyde. $CH_3(CH_2)_8CHO$	156.27	$\lambda^{C_{10}H_{22}}$ 222 (1.9), 293 (1.4)	ca. −5	$208\text{-}9$ 81^7	0.830^{15}	1.4287^{20}	i	s	s	s			$B1^2, 764$
d19	—,oxime	Capraldoxime. $CH_3(CH_2)_8CH{:}NOH$	171.29	lf (dil MeOH)	69				i	s	s				$B1, 711$
Ωd20	Decane*	$CH_3(CH_2)_8CH_3$	142.29		−29.7	174.1^{760} 57.6^{10}	0.7300^{20}	1.41023^{20}	i	∞	s				$B1^3, 519$
Ωd21	—,1-amino-*	n-Decylamine. $CH_3(CH_2)_9NH_2$	157.30		17 fr. 16.1	220.5^{760} 95.8^{10}	0.7936^{20}	1.4369^{20}	δ	∞	∞	∞	∞	chl ∞	$B4, 199$
Ωd22	—,1-bromo-*	n-Decyl bromide. $CH_3(CH_2)_9Br$	221.19		−29.2	240.6^{760} 110^{10}	1.0702^{20}	1.4557^{20}	i		v			chl v	$B1^3, 523$
Ωd23	—,2-bromo-(dl)*	$CH_3(CH_2)_7CHBrCH_3$	221.19			111^{11}	1.0512^{11}	1.4526^{af}	i		v			chl v	$B1^3, 523$
d24	—,1-bromo-10-fluoro-*	$F(CH_2)_{10}Br$	239.18			$131\text{-}2^{11}$	1.1522^{20}	1.4512^{25}	i	v	v				C51, 7300
Ωd25	—,1-chloro-*	n-Decyl chloride. $CH_3(CH_2)_9Cl$	176.73		−31.3	223.4^{760} 97^{10}	0.8705^{20}	1.4379^{20}	i	v	v			chl v	$B1^3, 522$
d26	—,1-chloro-10-fluoro-*	$F(CH_2)_{10}Cl$	194.72			115^9	0.9572^{10}	1.4333^{25}	i	v	v				C51, 7300
d27	—,1,10-diamino-*	Decamethylene diamine. $H_2N(CH_2)_{10}NH_2$	172.32		61.5	140^{12}									$B4^2, 712$
Ωd28	—,1,10-dibromo-*	Decamethylene dibromide. $Br(CH_2)_{10}Br$	300.09	pl (al)	28	160^{15}δd $127\text{-}30^4$	1.335^{30}	1.4905^{20}	i	δ v^h	s				$B1^2, 130$
d29	—,1-fluoro-*	n-Decyl fluoride $CH_3(CH_2)_9F$	160.28		−35	186.2^{760} 69^{10}	0.8194^{20}	1.4085							$B1^2, 129$
Ωd30	—,1-iodo-*	n-Decyl iodide. $CH_3(CH_2)_9I$	268.18		−16.3	132^{15}	1.2546^{20}	1.4838^{20}	i	δ	s				$B1^3, 523$
Ωd31	Decanedioic acid*	Sebacylic acid. Sebacic acid. $HO_2C(CH_2)_8CO_2H$	202.25	lf	134.5	295^{100} 232^{10}	1.2705^{20}	1.422^{133}	δ	s	s	s		i	$B2^2, 608$

For explanations, symbols and abbreviations see beginning of table. For structural formulas see end of table.

No.	Name	Synonyms and Formula	Mol. wt.	Color, crystalline form, specific rotation and λ_{max} (log ε)	m.p. °C	b.p. °C	Density	n_D	w	al	eth	ace	bz	other solvents	Ref.
	Decanedioic acid														
Ω d32	—,diamide	Decanediamide. Sebacamide*. $H_2NCO(CH_2)_8CONH_2$	200.28	pr or pl (aa)	210				i δ^h	i v^h.				aa v	B2, 720
Ω d33	—,dibutyl ester	Di-n-butyl sebacate. $C_4H_9^nO_2C(CH_2)_8CO_2C_4H_9^n$	314.47		−10 (1)	344–5 227[17]	0.9405[15]	1.4433[15]	i		s				B2, 719
Ω d34	—,dichloride	Sebacyl chloride. $ClCO(CH_2)_8COCl$	239.14		−2.5	220[75] 165[11]	1.1212[20]	1.4684[18]	d						B2[2], 610
Ω d35	—,diethyl ester*	Diethyl sebacate. $C_2H_5O_2C(CH_2)_8CO_2C_2H_5$	258.36		5 (1.25)	306[773] 188[19]	0.9646[20]	1.4366[20]	δ	s		s	i		B2[1], 293
d36	—,di(2-ethyl-butyl) ester*	$(C_2H_5)_2CHCH_2O_2C(CH_2)_8CO_2CH_2CH(C_2H_5)_2$ 370.58			−22	344–6[760]	0.920[25]		i	s	s	s	s		B2, 719
d37	—,di(2-ethylhexyl) ester*	$C_4H_9^nCH(C_2H_5)CH_2O_2C(CH_2)_8CO_2CH_2CH(C_2H_5)(C_4H_9^n)$ 426.69			−48	256[5]	0.912[25]	1.451[25]	i	s	s	s	s		B2[3], 1810
Ω d38	—,dimethyl ester*	Dimethyl sebacate. $CH_3O_2C(CH_2)_8CO_2CH_3$	230.31	lo pr	38	175[20] 144[5]	0.9882[28]	1.4355[28]	i	s	s	s	s		B2, 719
Ω d39	—,dinitrile	1,8-Dicyanooctane. Sebaconitrile. $NC(CH_2)_8CN$	164.25			204[16]	0.9313[20]	1.4474[20]	i						B2[2], 610
d39[1]	—,monomethyl ester, mononitrile	9-Carbomethoxynonanonitrile. $NC(CH_2)_8CO_2CH_3$	197.28		3–4	178[16]	0.934[20]	1.4398[25]	i	s	s				B2[3], 1816
Ω d40	**1,10-Decanediol***	Decamethyleneglycol. $HO(CH_2)_{10}OH$	174.29	nd (w)	72–5	175–6[14]			δ	v	δ v^h			lig i	B1[2], 560
Ω d41	**1-Decanethiol***	n-Decyl mercaptan. $CH_3(CH_2)_9SH$	174.35	λ^{MeOH} 231 (3.64)	−26	240.6[760] 125–7[19]	0.8443[20]	1.4569[20]	i	s	s				B1[3], 761
Ω d42	**Decanoic acid***	Capric acid. n-Decylic acid. $CH_3(CH_2)_8CO_2H$	172.27	nd	fr. 31.5	270[760] 148–50[11]	0.8858[40]	1.4288[40]	δ	∞^h	s	v	v	chl, peth v	B2[2], 309
d43	—,amide	Capramide. Decanamide*. $CH_3(CH_2)_8CONH_2$	171.29	lf (eth)	108 fr. 98		0.999[20]	1.4261[110]	i	s	s	s	δ	CCl_4 δ	B2, 356
Ω d44	—,anhydride*	Capric anhydride. $[CH_3(CH_2)_8CO]_2O$	326.53	lf	24.7		0.8865[25]	1.400[25]	i	s	s				B2[2], 311
Ω d45	—,chloride	Capryl chloride. $CH_3(CH_2)_8COCl$	190.72		−34.5	232[760] 114[15]	0.973[8]		d	d	s				B2, 356
d46	—,decyl ester*	n-Decyl caprate. $CH_3(CH_2)_8CO_2(CH_2)_9CH_3$	312.54		9.7	219[15]	0.8586[20]	1.4423[20]	i		s				B2, 356
Ω d47	—,ethyl ester*	Ethyl caprate. $CH_3(CH_2)_8CO_2C_2H_5$	200.33		−20	241.5[760] 122–4[13]	0.8650[20]	1.4256[20]	i	∞	∞			chl ∞	B2[3], 842
d48	—,isopropyl ester*	Isopropyl caprate. $CH_3(CH_2)_8CO_2CH(CH_3)_2$	214.35			121[10]	0.8543[20]	1.4221[25]							B2[3], 842
Ω d49	—,methyl ester*	Methyl caprate. $CH_3(CH_2)_8CO_2CH_3$	186.30		−18 (−10)	224[760] 114[15]	0.8730[20]	1.4259[20]	i	v	v			chl ∞	B2[3], 841
d50	—,nitrile	Caprinitrile. Nonyl cyanide. $CH_3(CH_2)_8CN$	153.27		fr. −17.9	243[760] 106[10]	0.8199[20]	1.4296[20]	i	∞	∞	∞		chl ∞	B2, 356
d51	—,piperazinium salt	$C_4H_{10}N_2 \cdot 2CH_3(CH_2)_8CO_2$	430.68		93				δ^h	s^h	i				Am 70, 2758
d52	—,propyl ester*	Propyl caprate. $CH_3(CH_2)_8CO_2C_3H_7^n$	214.35			128.5[10]	0.8623[20]	1.4280[20]							B2[3], 842
d53	—,2-bromo-*	$CH_3(CH_2)_7CHBrCO_2H$	251.17		4	140–1[2]	1.1912[24]	1.4595[24]			v				B2, 356
d54	—,10-fluoro-*	$F(CH_2)_9CO_2H$	190.26		49	135–8[10]			δ	v	v			lig s	B2[3], 846
d55	—,2-octyl-*	9-Heptadecanecarboxylic acid. $[CH_3(CH_2)_7]_2CHCO_2H$	284.49	nd or lf (al)	38.5	212–8[13]			i	s^h					B2[2], 368
d56	—,4-oxo-*	γ-Ketocapric acid. $CH_3(CH_2)_5COCH_2CH_2CO_2H$	186.25	(dil al)	70–1					s^h					B3[2], 449
Ω d57	**1-Decanol***	Decyl alcohol. $CH_3(CH_2)_9OH$	158.29		fr. 7	229[760] 107–8[7]	0.8297[20]	1.43719[20]	i	∞	∞	∞	∞	chl ∞	B1[2], 459
Ω d58	**2-Decanol(dl)***	$CH_3(CH_2)_7CHOHCH_3$	158.29		−2.4	211 110–11[10]	0.8250[20]	1.4326[25]	i	s	∞	s			B1[3], 1762
Ω d59	**4-Decanol***	$CH_3CH_2CH_2CHOH(CH_2)_5CH_3$ 158.29			−11.8 to −8.8	210–1 96[13]	0.8262[20]	1.4320[20]	i						B1, 426
d60	**1-Decanol, 10-chloro-***	$Cl(CH_2)_{10}OH$	192.73		12–3	185–9[15]	0.9630[25]	1.4578[20]	i	v	v				B1[3], 1761
d61	—,10-fluoro-*	$F(CH_2)_{10}OH$	176.28		ca. 22	136–7[15]	0.919[20]	1.4322[25]	i	v	v				C51, 7300
Ω d62	**2-Decanone***	Methyl n-octyl ketone. $CH_3CO(CH_2)_7CH_3$	156.27	nd	14 fr. 3.1	210–1[767] 95–7[12]	0.8248[20]	1.4255[20]	i	s	s				B1[2], 764
Ω d63	**3-Decanone***	Ethyl n-heptyl ketone. $CH_3CH_2CO(CH_2)_6CH_3$	156.27		1–3.8	203[754]	0.8251[20]	1.4252[20]		s	s				B1[1], 367
Ω d64	**4-Decanone***	n-Propyl n-hexyl ketone. $CH_3CH_2CH_2CO(CH_2)_5CH_3$	156.27	nd	−9	206–7 87–9[11]	0.824[20]	1.4240[21]	i	∞	∞				B1, 711
d65	**Decasiloxane, dicosamethyl-**	$CH_3[Si(CH_3)_2O]_9Si(CH_3)_3$	755.63			183[4]	0.925[20]	1.3988[20]	i	δ			s	lig s	C47, 4679
Ω d66	**1-Decene***	n-Decylene. $CH_3(CH_2)_7CH:CH_2$	140.27		fr. −66.3	170.56[760] 54.3[10]	0.7408[20]	1.4215[20]	i	∞	∞				B1[3], 858
d67	**5-Decene(cis)***	cis-1,2-Dibutylethylene. $CH_3(CH_2)_3CH:CH(CH_2)_3CH_3$	140.27		−112	170[739] 73[30]	0.74451[20]	1.4258[20]	i	∞	∞				B1[3], 859
Ω d68	—(trans)*	$CH_3(CH_2)_3CH:CH(CH_2)_3CH_3$ 140.27			−73	170.2[739]	0.74012[20]	1.4243[20]	i	∞	∞				B1[3], 859
d69	**1-Decene, 2-bromo-***	$CH_3(CH_2)_7CBr:CH_2$	219.17			115–6[22]	1.0844[20]	1.4629[20]							B1[3], 859
d70	**2-Decene, 1-bromo-***	$CH_3(CH_2)_6CH:CHCH_2Br$	219.17			121[17]	1.074[18]	1.4716[18]						lig s	B1[3], 859

For explanations, symbols and abbreviations see beginning of table. For structural formulas see end of table.

1-Decen-3-yne*

No.	Name	Synonyms and Formula	Mol. wt.	Color, crystalline form, specific rotation and λ_{max} (log ε)	m.p. °C	b.p. °C	Density	n_D	w	al	eth	ace	bz	other solvents	Ref.
d71	1-Decen-3-yne*	$CH_3(CH_2)_5C:CCH:CH_2$	136.24	....		76^{20} 45^4	0.7873^{20}	1.4620^{20}	...	...	...	...	...	...	**B1³**, 1049
d72	1-Decen-4-yne*	$CH_3(CH_2)_4C:CCH_2CH:CH_2$	136.24	....		$73-4^{22}$	0.7880^{20}	1.445^{20}	...	...	...	...	...	...	**B1³**, 1049
d73	2-Decen-4-yne*	$CH_3(CH_2)_4C:CCH:CHCH_3$	136.24	....		55^5	0.7850^{25}_5	1.4609^{25}	...	...	...	...	...	...	**B1³**, 1049
Ω d74	1-Decyne*	n-Octylacetylene. $CH_3(CH_2)_7C:CH$	138.25	....	-36	174^{760} 57^{10}	0.7655^{20}	1.4265^{20}	i	s	s	...	os s		**B1³**, 1016
d75	3-Decyne*	$CH_3CH_2C:C(CH_2)_5CH_3$	138.25	....		$175-6^{760}$	0.7652^{21}_4	1.433^{21}_4	...	...	...	...	...	...	**B1³**, 1017
d76	4-Decyne*	$CH_3(CH_2)_4C:C(CH_2)_2CH_3$	138.25	....		74.5^{19}	0.772^{17}_4	1.436^{17}	...	...	...	...	...	...	**B1³**, 1017
d77	5-Decyne*	Dibutylacetylene. $CH_3(CH_2)_3C:C(CH_2)_3CH_3$	138.25	....	-73	177^{751} 78.8^{25}	0.7690^{20}_4	1.4331^{20}	i	s	s	...	...	...	**B1³**, 1017
d78	4-Decyne, 3,3-dimethyl-*	$CH_3CH_2C(CH_3)_2C:C(CH_2)_4CH_3$	166.31			86^{20}	0.7731^{20}_4	1.4399^{20}	...	...	...	...	...	...	**B1³**, 1026
—	Dehydroacetic acid	see 4-Hexenoic acid, 2-acetyl-5-hydroxy-3-oxo-, lactone													
Ω d79	Dehydrocholic acid	3,7,12-Trioxocholanic acid.	402.54	(ace). $[\alpha]_D^{20} + 26$ (al, c = 1.4) λ^{al} 290 (2.95), $\lambda^{0.1N\,NaOH}$ 285 (3.04)	237	....			i	δ	i	s	δ	chl s AcOEt s	**E14**, 211
d80	Dehydro-ergosterol	$\Delta^{5:6,7:8,9:11.22:23}$-Ergostatetraen-3-ol. $C_{28}H_{42}O$.	394.65	lf(al +1w), pl (al), nd (eth) $[\alpha]_D^{15} + 149.2$ (chl, c = 1.9) λ^{al} 310 (3.95), 324 (4.00), 340 (3.82)	146	$230^{0.5}$			...	s^h	v	s	v	chl v AcOEt s MeOH δ	**J1957**, 93
—	Dehydromucic acid	see 2,5-Furandicarboxylic acid													
Ω d81	Delphinidine chloride	3,3',4',5,5',7'-Hexahydroxy-flavinium chloride. $C_{15}H_{11}ClO_7$.	338.70	br pr, nd or pl (HCl) λ^{al} 275 (4.20), 522 (4.54)	>350 (anh)	....			v	v	...	...	...	MeOH v AcOEt s	**B18²**, 247
d82	Delphinine	$C_{33}H_{45}NO_9$	599.73	orh (al) $[\alpha]_D^{25} + 25$ (al) λ^{al} 230 (4.15), 273 (2.96)	198–200d				i	s	s	s	...	chl s	**J1952**, 1750
d82¹	Demissine	$C_{50}H_{33}NO_{20}$	1050.22	nd (al) $[\alpha]-20(Py)$	276–9 (305–8d)				...	s^h	...	...	...	MeOH s^h, dil ac s	**C45**, 3855
d83	Derritol	$C_{21}H_{22}O_6$	370.41	ye nd (MeOH) $[\alpha]_D^{20} - 66.2$ (chl, c = 3)	164 (161)	$220-5^{0.06}$			i	...	...	...	...	alk v	**B18²**, 223
Ω d84	Deserpidine	Canescine. 11-Desmethoxy-reserpine. $C_{32}H_{38}N_2O_8$.	578.67	nd or pr $[\alpha]_D^{24.5} - 137$ (chl) λ^{al} 217 (4.81), 271 (4.30)	229–32				i	s^h	...	...	...	chl s	**Am 77**, 4335
—	Desmethyl-morphine	see Normorphine													
—	Desoxalic acid	see 1,1,2-Ethanetricarboxylic acid, 1,2-dihydroxy-*													
—	Desoxybenzoin	see Ketone, benzyl phenyl													
Ω d85	Desoxycholic acid	3,12-Dihydroxycholanic acid. $C_{24}H_{40}O_4$.	392.59	(al) $[\alpha]_D^{20} + 57$ (al) $\lambda^{65\%\,H_2SO_4}$ 310 (3.79), 380 (3.29)	176				i	v	δ	δ	i	chl δ aa δ	**C48**, 1147
d86	Desoxycorti-costerone	Δ^4-Pregnene-3,20-dion-21-ol. $C_{21}H_{30}O_3$.	330.47	pl (eth) $[\alpha]_D^{20} + 178$ (al, c = 1) λ^{al} 240 (4.2)	141–2				δ	v	eth	v	...	...	**E14**, 153
d87	Desthiobiotin	$C_{10}H_{18}N_2O_3$	214.27	lo nd (w) $[\alpha]_D^{21} + 10.7$ (w, c = 2)	156–8				s	...	...	...	...		**J1948**, 1552
d88	—, methyl ester	$C_{11}H_{20}N_2O_3$. See d87	228.29	cr (MeOH) $[\alpha]_D^{28} + 2.6$ (chl, c = 2)	69–70	$194-7^{0.03}$			...	s^h	...	...	...	MeOH s chl v	**C44**, 4934
—	Desyl chloride	see Ketone, benzyl phenyl, α-chloro-													
—	O-Deutero-methanol	see Methanol-d													
—	Deuteroxy(tri-deutero)methane	see Methan-d₃-ol-d													
—	Dexedrine	see Amphetamine													
Ω d89	Dextrin (starch)	Amylin. $(C_6H_{10}O_5)_n$	(162.14)ₙ	amor $[\alpha]_D > +200$	chars		1.0384^{20}_4		s	i	i	...	...	...	**J1925**, 636
—	Dextronic acid	see Gluconic acid(D)													
—	Dextrose	see Glucose(D)													
d90	Dextropimaric acid, methyl ester	$C_{21}H_{32}O_2$	316.49	$[\alpha]_D + 60.5$ (MeOH)	69	$149^{0.03}$	1.030^{19}_4	1.5208^{19}	...	v	v	...	...	...	**B9²**, 435

For explanations, symbols and abbreviations see beginning of table. For structural formulas see end of table.

No.	Name	Synonyms and Formula	Mol. wt.	Color, crystalline form, specific rotation and λ_{max} (log ε)	m.p. °C	b.p. °C	Density	n_D	w	al	eth	ace	bz	other solvents	Ref.
	Diacetamide														
—	**Diacetamide**	*see* **Acetic acid**, amide, *N*-acetyl-													
—	**Diacetanilide**	*see* **Acetic acid**, amide, *N*-acetyl-*N*-phenyl-													
—	**Diacetoacetic acid,** ethyl ester	*see* **Butanoic acid, 2-acetyl-3-oxo-,** ethyl ester													
—	**Diacetonamine**	*see* **2-Pentanone, 4-amino-4-methyl-***													
—	**Dialuric acid**	*see* **Barbituric acid, 5-hydroxy-**													
d91	**Diazoamino-benzene**	1,3-Diphenyltriazene	197.24	ye lf or pr (al) λ^{al} 275 (3.9), 355 (4.3)	98	....	....		i	v[h]	v	...	v	Py v	**B16²,** 351
d92	—(isomer)........	$C_{12}H_{11}N_3$. *See* d91	197.24	ye pr (bz)	80–1	....	....						s	lig s	**B16²,** 351
d93	—,2,2'-dimethyl-...	$C_{14}H_{15}N_3$. *See* d91	225.30	og (al)	51	....	....			s	s	...		lig s	**B16,** 703
d94	—,2,4'-dimethyl-...	$C_{14}H_{15}N_3$. *See* d91	225.30	ye nd (lig)	120	....	....							lig v	**B16,** 708
d95	—,2',3-dimethyl-...	$C_{14}H_{15}N_3$. *See* d91	225.30	ye cr (lig)	74	....	....					s	s	lig v	**B16,** 705
d96	—,3,3'-dimethyl-...	$C_{14}H_{15}N_3$. *See* d91	225.30	ye nd (peth)	52	....	....				s	s	s	os v	**B16¹,** 407
d97	—,3,4'-dimethyl-...	$C_{14}H_{15}N_3$. *See* d91	225.30	ye nd (lig)	97	....	....							os s lig s	**B16,** 708
d98	—,4,4'-dimethyl-...	$C_{14}H_{15}N_3$. *See* d91	225.30	red-ye nd (lig), pr (al) λ^{cy} 238 (4.23), 295 (4.00), 355 (4.34)	118	....	....			s[h]				sulf s lig s[h]	**B16²,** 355
d99	—,4,4'-dinitro-	$C_{12}H_9N_5O_4$. *See* d91	287.24	ye nd (al), lf (bz) λ^{al} 273 (3.75), 400 (4.6)	240d	....	....		i	δ[h]	s	δ	δ	chl δ	**B16²,** 354
d100	—,3-methyl-......	$C_{13}H_{13}N_3$. *See* d91	211.27	ye nd (lig)	86	....	....								**B16,** 714
d101	—,4-methyl-......	$C_{13}H_{13}N_3$. *See* d91	211.27	ye pl (lig)	86–7	....	....		i						**B16²,** 354
d102	**1,1'-Diazoamino-naphthalene**	....	297.36	ye lf (al)	exp >100	....	....								**B16,** 716
d103	**2,2'-Diazoamino-naphthalene**	....	297.36	red nd (xyl)	156	....	....							con sulf →vt	**Ber 19,** 1282
—	**Diazoamino-toluene**	*see* **Diazoaminobenzene, dimethyl-**													
—	**Diazomethane**	*see* **Methane, diazo-**													
d104	**1,2:3,4-Dibenz-anthracene**	Dibenz[a,c]anthracene. Naphtho-2',3':9,10-phen-anthrene.	278.36	nd (aa or al) λ^{al} 248 (4.62), 265 (4.73), 275 (5.01), 286 (5.13), 321 (3.89), 349 (3.45), 374 (2.63)	205 (200–2)	....	....						s	AcOH s[h] peth δ	**B5²,** 668
d105	**1,2:5,6-Dibenz-anthracene**	Dibenz[a,h]anthracene	278.36	pl (dil ace), silv lf (aa) λ^{bz} 290 (5.0), 300 (5.2), 373 (3.0), 385 (2.6), 395 (3.1)	269–70 (262)	....	....		i	δ	...	s	s	CS₂ s aa s	**E14s,** 604
d106	**1,2:6,7-Dibenz-anthracene**	1,2-Benzonaphthacene. Isopentaphene.	278.36	ye lf or nd (xyl) λ^{bz} 362 (3.16), 380 (3.50), 401 (3.80), 425 (3.97), 425.5 (4.00)	263–4	sub 275²⁻⁴	....							con sulf s	**B5²,** 667
d107	**1,2:7,8-Dibenz-anthracene**	Dibenz[a,j]anthracene. Dinaphthanthracene.	278.36	og lf or nd (bz) λ^{bz} 304 (5.2), 338 (4.3), 351 (3.7), 385 (2.5), 395 (2.4)	197–8	....	....		i	δ	δ	...	δ	aa i peth s	**B5²,** 668
d108	**1,2:5,6-Dibenz-anthracene, 4',4''-dihydroxy-**	$C_{22}H_{14}O_2$. *See* d105	310.36	og (bz) λ^{al} 238 (4.80), 298 (4.88), 324 (4.36), 338 (4.28), 354 (4.35), 365 (3.69), 384 (3.99), 403 (4.15)	415–8	sub 300²⁻³·¹⁰⁻⁴	....		i	δ[h]	i[h]	...	...	....	**E14s,** 620
d109	**Dibenzanthrone**	Violanthrone.	456.51	vt-bl or bk nd (PhNO₂ or quinoline) $\lambda^{con\ sulf}$ 380 (4.2), 570 (4.4), 755 (4.3), 850 (4.3)	490–5d	....	....			i		...	...	i	xyl, Py sulf s (vt) aa i	**E14s,** 907

For explanations, symbols and abbreviations see beginning of table. For structural formulas see end of table.

1,2:5,6-Dibenzofluorene

No.	Name	Synonyms and Formula	Mol. wt.	Color, crystalline form, specific rotation and λ_{max} (log ε)	m.p. °C	b.p. °C	Density	n_D	w	al	eth	ace	bz	other solvents	Ref.
d110	1,2:5,6-Dibenzo-fluorene	13H-Dibenzo[a,g]fluorene...	266.35	pl (bz-al or AcOEt) λ^{diox} 255 (4.9), 278 (4.2), 294 (4.2), 334 (4.4), 351 (4.4)	174–5	195–200$^{0.5}$	....		i	δ	δ	...	s	to, PhNO$_2$ s	E14s, 520
d111	1,2:7,8-Dibenzo-fluorene	13H-Dibenzo[b,h]fluorene...	266.35	lf (bz), pl (aa) λ^{al} 258 (4.4), 264 (4.8), 278 (5.0), 318 (3.8), 330 (4.0), 342 (4.2), 358 (3.9)	234	....			i	δ	δ	...	s	....	E14s, 518
d112	1,2:6,7-Dibenzo-9-fluorenone	....	280.33	og-ye pl or pr (xyl or aa)	214	sub 190–200$^{0.04}$								to s^h sulf s (red)	E14s, 514
Ω d113	— Dibenzolfulvene ... Dibenzofuran	see Fluorene, 9-methylene- Diphenylene oxide	168.21	lf or nd (al) λ^{al} 217 (4.5), 245 (4.0), 250 (4.3), 280 (4.2), 285 (4.2), 295 (4.0), 300 sh (4.2)	86–7	287^{760}	1.0886$^{29}_4$	1.6079$^{29}_4$	δ	s	v	s	s^h	aa v	B17^2, 67
d114	—,1-amino-.......	C$_{12}$H$_9$NO. See d113.......	183.21	br nd (dil MeOH)	85	....									Am 75, 4845
d115	—,2-amino-.......	C$_{12}$H$_9$NO. See d113.......	183.21	pl (dil al) λ^{al} 218 (4.46), 238 (4.13), 261 (4.11), 314 (4.22)	128	....			i	v^h	v				B18^2, 423
d116	—,3-amino-......	C$_{12}$H$_9$NO. See d113......	183.21	(dil al) λ^{al} 217 (4.44), 237 (4.13), 261 (4.11), 302 sh (4.15), 313 (4.22)	94 (99)										B18^1, 557
d117	—,4-amino-......	C$_{12}$H$_9$NO. See d113......	183.21	(al)	85	....									Am 61, 1365
d118	—,2-bromo-......	C$_{12}$H$_7$BrO. See d113	247.10	nd (al), lf (aa) λ^{al} 222 (4.58), 251 (4.19), 288 (4.25), 310 (3.67)	110	220^{40}				s		...		aa δ	B17^2, 68
d119	—,3-bromo-......	C$_{12}$H$_7$BrO. See d113	247.10	lf (al) λ^{al} 219 (4.55), 254 (4.31), 290 (4.31), 300 (4.22)	120	220^{40}			i	s^h	s	...			J1931, 529
d120	—,4-bromo-......	C$_{12}$H$_7$BrO. See d113	247.10	....	67	....									Am 76, 5783
d122	—,2,8-dibromo-	C$_{12}$H$_6$Br$_2$O. See d113.......	326.00	lf (al)	199–200					s	v	...	v	aa v	B17^2, 69
d123	—,3,6-dinitro-	C$_{12}$H$_6$N$_2$O$_5$. See d113.....	258.19	....	245										C49, 720
d124	—,3,8-dinitro-	C$_{12}$H$_6$N$_2$O$_5$. See d113.....	258.19	....	255–6					δ		s	i		xyl δ lig i	B17^2, 69
d125	—,1-nitro-	C$_{12}$H$_7$NO$_3$. See d113.....	213.20	lt ye nd (al) λ^{al} 210 (4.65), 244 (4.10), 336 (3.92)	120–1										Am 66, 1884
Ω d126	—,3-nitro-	C$_{12}$H$_7$NO$_3$. See d113	213.20	ye nd (aa) λ^{al} 322 (4.23)	181–2	180–5^3			i	δ^h	δ	...		aa s^h	B17^2, 69
d127	—,4-nitro-........	C$_{12}$H$_7$NO$_3$. See d113.....	213.20	ye nd	130–7 (126)	190–205^{13}	....	....	...						Am 75, 4844
d128	1-Dibenzofuran-carboxylic acid	....	212.22	nd (50 % al)	232–3										Chl, 12065
Ω d129	2-Dibenzofuran-carboxylic acid	....	212.22	nd (dil al) nd (aa)	246–7 (252–5)				δ	s^h	s				B18, 313
d130	4-Dibenzofuran-carboxylic acid	....	212.22	nd (al)	209–10										Am 56, 1416
d131	1,2:6,7-Dibenzo-phenanthrene	Naphtho-2',1':1,2-anthracene. Benzo[b]chrysene. 3,4-Benzotetraphene.	278.36	pa gr-ye lf (xyl) λ^{diox} 247 (4.56), 280 (4.90), 288 (5.13), 305 (4.68), 365 (3.93), 384 (3.78), 392 (3.60)	294				i				s	diox s	B5^2, 668

For explanations, symbols and abbreviations see beginning of table. For structural formulas see end of table.

1,2:7,8-Dibenzophenanthrene

No.	Name	Synonyms and Formula	Mol. wt.	Color, crystalline form, specific rotation and λ_{max} (log ε)	m.p. °C	b.p. °C	Density	n_D	w	al	eth	ace	bz	other solvents	Ref.
—	1,2:7,8-Dibenzophenanthrene	see Picene													
d132	2,3:6,7-Dibenzophenanthrene	Dibenzo[b,h]phenanthrene. Pentaphene.	278.36	ye-gr nd or lf (xyl) λ^{al} 245 (4.92), 257.5 (5.06), 314.5 (5.00), 345 (4.47), 356 (4.44), 399 (2.98), 412 (2.56), 423.5 (2.98)	257	....			i	δ	δ	...	s	xyl δ	B5³, 2552
—	Dibenzo-1,4-pyran	see Xanthene													
d133	1,2:4,5-Dibenzo-pyrene	Dibenzo[a,e]pyrene	302.38	pa ye nd (xyl) λ^{bz} 294.5 (4.72), 306.5 (4.83), 343 (4.06), 360 (4.24), 378 (4.30), 396 (3.24), 416 (2.84)	233–4					δ	...	δ	δ	to s^h con sulf s (ye-red) aa δ	E14s, 805
—	Dibenzopyrrole	see Carbazole													
Ω d134	Dibenzothiophene ..	Diphenylene sulfide	184.27	nd (dil al or lig) λ^{al} 234 (4.9), 256 (4.3), 262 (4.1), 286 (4.2), 303 (3.5), 325 (3.6)	99–100	332–3 152–4³	....		s v^h	v	...	...	v	MeOH s^h	B17², 70
d135	—,2-amino-	$C_{12}H_9NS$. See d134	199.28	lf (dil al) λ^{al} 237 (4.62), 262 sh (4.20), 289 (3.85), 296 (3.90), 346 (3.43)	122–3										B18², 423
Ω d136	—,3-amino-	$C_{12}H_9NS$. See d134	199.28	(dil al) λ^{al} 242 (4.70), 282 (4.17), 303 (4.11)	129–31										B18², 423
Ω d137	—,2-bromo-	$C_{12}H_7BrS$. See d134	263.16	nd (al)	125–6 (98–9)										B17², 70
d138	—,—,monoxide ...	3-Bromodiphenylene sulfonide.	279.16	....	171–2										B17², 71
d139	—,3-bromo-, dioxide	....	295.16	....	224–5										Am 75, 3843
d140	—,4-bromo-	$C_{12}H_7BrS$. See d134	263.16	(al)	84										Am 76, 5786
d141	—,2,8-diamino-	$C_{12}H_{10}N_2S$. See d134	214.29	nd (al)	194–6						v^h				B18², 427
d142	—,3,7-diamino-	$C_{12}H_{10}N_2S$. See d134	214.29	pa ye cr	169–70										Am 74, 1166
d143	—,—,dioxide	Benzidine sulfone	246.29	ye nd (al)	327–8					i^n	i^n	i		i^n		B18, 591
d147	—,2,8-dibromo-	$C_{12}H_6Br_2S$. See d134	342.06	(aa) λ^{al} 242 (4.68), 290 (4.33), 329 (4.01)	229										Am 69, 1920
d148	—,—,dioxide	....	374.06	(aa)	361–2										Am 76, 5786
d150	—,3,7-dinitro-, dioxide	....	306.26	(ace)	273–5										Am 74, 1165
Ω d151	—,2-nitro-	$C_{12}H_7NO_2S$. See d134	229.26	pa ye nd λ^{al} 227 (4.4), 241 (4.4), 253 (4.4), 273 (4.3), 305 (3.9), 338 (3.9)	186										B17², 71
d152	—,—,dioxide		261.26	(ace) λ^{al} 252 (4.50), 275 sh (3.97), 332 (3.20)	257–8										Am 74, 1165
Ω d153	—,3-nitro-	$C_{12}H_7NO_2S$. See d134	229.26	pa ye (dil al) λ^{al} 222 (4.5), 240 sh (4.2), 320 (4.2)	153–4										Am 74, 1165
d154	—,—,monoxide ...		245.26	(al)	210										Am 70, 1749
d155	2-Dibenzothio-phenecarboxylic acid	....	228.28	(al)	255										B18², 279

For explanations, symbols and abbreviations see beginning of table. For structural formulas see end of table.

4-Dibenzothiophenecarboxylic acid

No.	Name	Synonyms and Formula	Mol. wt.	Color, crystalline form, specific rotation and λ_{max} (log ε)	m.p. °C	b.p. °C	Density	n_D	w	al	eth	ace	bz	other solvents	Ref.
d156	4-Dibenzothio-phenecarboxylic acid	. . . .	228.28	(dil MeOH) λ^{al} 282 (3.85), 340 (3.51)	261–2	. . . .	. . . . . .	. . .							**Am 74,** 266
d157	—,dioxide.	. . . .	260.28	. . . .	337–8											**Am 75,** 278
—	Dibenzoxazine	*see* **Phenoxazine**													
—	Dibenzyl	*see* **Ethane, 1,2-diphenyl-**													
d158	Diborane, methylthio-	$CH_3SB_2H_5$	73.76	. . . .		–101.5	53^{760} (extrap.) $(–35^9)$	. . . . . .	. . .	d	d	. . .	s	s	os ∞	**Am 76,** 3307
—	Dichloramine B	*see* **Benzenesulfonic acid, amide, N,N-dichloro-**													
—	Dichloramine T	*see* **4-Toluenesulfonic acid, amide, N,N-dichloro-**													
—	Dichlorophene	*see* **Methane, bis(5-chloro-2-hydroxyphenyl)-**													
d159	Dicoumarin(*cis*) . . .		292.30	lf (aa)	262					i						**B19,** 181
d160	—(*trans*)		292.30	nd or pl (aa)	> 275										aa δ	**B19,** 181
d161	Dicoumarol	4,4′-Dihydroxy-3,3′-methyl-ene biscoumarin. Melitoxin. $C_{19}H_{12}O_6$	336.31	nd λ 280 (4.34)	288–92					i	i	i	i	δ	chl δ	**B19,** 197
d162	Dictamnine	2,3-(4-Methoxy-2,3-quinolino)-furan.	199.21	pr (al) λ^{al} 236 (4.78), 309 (3.95), 329 (3.88)	133–4					δ	v^h	s		. . .	chl, AcOEt con sulf s	**B27²,** 79
d163	Dicyclohexadiene	. . . .	160.26	. . . .	. . . . .	$229–30^{766}$ 104^{16}	0.9950^{20}_4	$1.5267^{20.5}$	i	δ	v	v	v	aa v	**E13,** 1038
Ω d164	α-Dicyclopenta-diene (*endo* form)	. . . .	132.21	λ^{iso} 217 (1.4)	32	$170\,δd$ $64–5^{14}$	0.9302^{15}_4	1.5050^{35}	. . .	s	v			CCl_4 v aa s peth s	**E13,** 1018
d165	—,3,4,5,6,7,8,8a-heptachloro-	Heptachlor.	373.32	wh, λ^{al} 236 (4.78), 309 (3.96), 328 (3.88)	95–6 (93)		$1.57–9^9$	. . .	i	s	s	s	s	lig s	**B5³,** 1286
Ω d166	—,tetrahydro- . . . . (*endo* form)	Tricyclodecane.	136.24	(al or aa)	77	193^{769} $86–7^{12}$	0.9128^{79}	1.4726^{79}	i	s	s			aa s	**B5³,** 390
Ω d167	Dieldrin	Octalox.	380.93	. . . .	175–6		1.75		i	δ	v	δ	s		**B5³,** 390
—	Diethanolamine	*see* **Amine, diethyl, 2,2′-dihydroxy-**													
Ω d168	Diethylene glycol . .	2,2′-Dihydroxydiethyl ether. 2,2′-Oxydiethanol. $HOCH_2CH_2OCH_2CH_2OH$	106.12	. . . .	–10.5	245^{760} 133^{14}	1.1197^{15}_4	1.4472^{20}	∞	∞	i	∞	i		**B1²,** 520
d169	—,diacetate.	$CH_3CO_2CH_2CH_2OCH_2CH_2O_2CCH_3$	190.20	. . . .		$245–51^{760}$ $110–35^{16}$	1.1078^{15}_{15}	1.4348^{20}	s	v		∞			**B2²,** 155
d170	—,diethyl ether. . . .	Diethyl carbitol. $C_2H_5OCH_2CH_2OCH_2CH_2OC_2H_5$	162.23	. . . .		189^{760}	0.9063^{20}_4	1.4115^{20}	v	v	v			os v	**B1³,** 2098
d171	—,dioctadecanoate	Diethylene glycol distearate. Glycosterin. $[CH_3(CH_2)_{16}CO_2CH_2]_2O$	611.02	wx	54–5	. . . . . .	0.9333^{20}_4			i	i				**C50,** 9692
d172	—,dioleate	$[CH_3(CH_2)_7CH:CH(CH_2)_7CO_2CH_2]_2O$	635.04	pa ye liq		. . . . . .	0.9310^{20}_4			∞	∞				**C47,** 4618
d173	—,monobutyl ether	Butyl carbitol. $CH_3(CH_2)_3OCH_2CH_2OCH_2CH_2OH$	162.23	. . . .	–68.1	231^{760} 118^{12}	0.9553^{20}_4	1.4321^{20}	∞	v	v	v	s		**B1²,** 521
d174	—,-,acetate.	$CH_3(CH_2)_3OCH_2CH_2OCH_2CH_2O_2CCH_3$	204.27	. . . .	–32	245^{760}	0.985^{20}_4	1.4262^{20}	s	∞	∞	∞		oos ∞	**B2³,** 308
d175	—,monododec-anoate	Diethylene glycol monolaurate. Glaurin. $CH_3(CH_2)_{10}CO_2CH_2CH_2OCH_2CH_2OH$	288.43	lt ye	17–8	$> 270^{760}$	0.96^{25}_{25}		∞	∞	∞	∞	s	to s	**C37,** 3202¹
Ω d176	—,monoethyl ether	Carbitol. Cellosolve. $CH_3CH_2OCH_2CH_2OCH_2CH_2OH$	134.18	hyg liq	. . . . . .	195^{760}	0.9881^{20}_4	1.4300^{20}	∞	∞	∞	∞		oos ∞	**B1²,** 520
d177	—,-,acetate.	Carbitol acetate. $CH_3CH_2OCH_2CH_2OCH_2CH_2O_2CCH_3$	176.22	hyg liq	–25	218^{760}	1.0096^{20}_4	1.4230^{20}	∞	∞	∞	∞		oos s	**B2²,** 155
d178	—,mono(2-hydroxypropyl) ether	$CH_3CHOHCH_2OCH_2CH_2OCH_2CH_2OH$	164.20	. . . .		277.9^{760}	1.0789^{20}_4	1.4498^{20}	∞	v			v	MeOH, CCl_4 v	**C52,** 17693
d179	—,monomethyl ether	Methyl carbitol. $CH_3OCH_2CH_2OCH_2CH_2OH$	120.15	. . . .		193^{760}	1.0270^{20}_4	1.4264^{20}	∞	v	v	∞			**C32,** 2217⁵
Ω d180	Diethylene-triamine	2,2′-Diaminodiethylamine. $(NH_2CH_2CH_2)_2NH$	103.17	ye hyg liq	–39	207^{760}	0.9586^{20}_{20}	1.4810^{25}	∞	∞	i			lig s	**B4²,** 695
d181	*m*-Digallic acid	Gallic acid 3-monogallate.	332.23	nd (dil al + 1w)	268–70d (280d)	. . . . . .			i s^h	s	δ	s		MeOH s aa δ	**B10²,** 344
—	Digine	*see* **Gitogenin**													
d182	Digitalose	3-Methyl *D*-fucose.	178.19	nd (AcOEt). $[\alpha]^{22}_D + 109 \rightarrow + 126$ (mut)	106 (fresh) 119 (after 4 months)					s					AcOEt s^h	**H32,** 163
d183	Digitogenin	5α,22α-Spirostan-2,3,15-triol.	448.65	nd (al) $[\alpha]^{19}_D – 18$ (chl. c = 1.4)	280–3					i	s^h δ				chl s	**E14,** 286

For explanations, symbols and abbreviations see beginning of table. For structural formulas see end of table.

No.	Name	Synonyms and Formula	Mol. wt.	Color. crystalline form. specific rotation and λ_{max} (log ε)	m.p. °C	b.p. °C	Density	n_D	Solubility						Ref.
									w	al	eth	ace	bz	other solvents	
	Digitoxigenin														
d184	Digitoxigenin	3 β,14-Dihydroxy-5β-card-20(22) enolide. $C_{23}H_{34}O_4$	374.53	(dil MeOH) $[\alpha]_D^{20}$ +19.1 (MeOH, c = 1.36) $\lambda^{50\%al}$ 220 (4.21)	253 (256)	. . . .	. . . .	. . . .	s					MeOH v	E14, 225
Ω d185	Digitoxin	$C_{41}H_{64}O_{13}$	764.96	wh (chl − eth), pl (dil al) $[\alpha]_D^{20}$ +4.8 (diox. c = 1.2) λ^{al} 220 (4.3)	255–6	. . . .	. . . .	. . . .	δ	v	s			chl. MeOH, Py s	E14, 230
—	Digitoxit	see 1,3,4,5-Hexanetetrol													
Ω d186	Digitoxose	2-Desoxy-D-altromethylose.	148.16	cr (MeOH − eth or AcOEt) $[\alpha]_D^{18}$ +27.9 to +43.3 (pyr, c = 1) (mut)	112	. . . .	. . . .	. . . .	v			v		Py s AcOEt s[h]	B31, 19
—	.3-methyl-	see Cymarose													
—	Diglycolic acid	see Acetic acid, oxydi-													
d187	Digoxigenin	3α,12.14β-Trihydroxy-5β-card-20(22)enolide. $C_{23}H_{34}O_5$	390.53	pr (AcOEt). $[\alpha]_D^{20}$ +23.1 (MeOH, c = 1.7) $\lambda^{50\%al}$ 220 (4.13)	222	. . . .	. . . .	. . . .	v					chl δ MeOH v	E14, 239
d190	Dihydrosamidin . . .	. . . .	388.42	$[\alpha]_D$ +19 (al)	117–9	. . . .	. . . .	. . . .	i	s	s				Am 79, 3534
d191	Diisoeugenol	. . . .	328.41	nd (bz, lig or al)	180–1	. . . .	. . . .	. . . .		s[h]	v		δ	chl v	B6², 917
d192	Dilactic acid	1.1′-Dicarboxydiethyl ether. Dilactylic acid. $HO_2CCH(CH_3)OCH(CH_3)CO_2H$	162.14	rh	112–3 (105–7)	. . . .	. . . .	. . . .	s	δ	s		δ		B3⁴, 205
—	α,γ-Dilaurin	see Glycerol, 1,3-dido-decanoate													
—	Dilirutic acid	see Barbituric acid, 5-nitro-													
—	Dimedone	see 1,3-Cyclohexanedione, 5,5-dimethyl-													
d193	Dimethisoquin, hydrochloride	Quotane	308.86	. . . .	146	. . . .	. . . .	. . . .	s	s				. . . . .	Am 71, 937
Ω d194	Dimethylarsinic acid	Alkargen. Cacodylic acid. $(CH_3)_2AsO_2H$	138.00	tcl	200	. . . .	. . . .	. . . .	v	v	i				B4², 993
d195	Dimethyl phosphinic acid, ethyl ester	$(CH_3)_2PO_2C_2H_5$	122.11	. . . .		89^{15}	1.0278_4^{25}	1.4261^{25}	δ	s	s				Am 73, 5466
—	Dimite	see Ethanol, 1,1-bis(4-chlorophenyl)-													
—	Dinicotinic acid	see 3,5-Pyridinedicarboxylic acid													
d197	1,3-Dioxane	m-Dioxane. Trimethylene glycol methylene ether.	88.12	λ^{vap} 180 (3.8)	−42	105^{755}	1.0342_4^{20}	1.4165_x^{20}	∞	∞	∞	∞	∞		B19², 4
Ω d198	1,4-Dioxane	Diethylene dioxide. p-Dioxane. Glycol ethylene ether.	88.12	λ^{vap} 180 (3.8)	11.8	101^{750}	1.0337_4^{20}	1.4224^{20}	∞	∞	∞	∞	∞	os ∞ aa ∞	B19², 4
Ω d199	—.2,3-dichloro-	$C_4H_6Cl_2O_2$. See d198	157.00	. . . .	30	$80–2^{10}$	1.4682_4^{20}	1.4928^{20}	i d[h]		v	v	v	chl, CCl_4, diox v lig v	Am 68, 2046
Ω d200	1,3-Dioxane, 2,4-dimethyl-	$C_6H_{12}O_2$. See b197	116.16	. . . .		115–8 (120)	0.9392_4^{20}	1.4136^{20}	δ					os v	B19², 10
d201	—.5-ethyl-4-propyl-	$C_9H_{18}O_2$. See d197	158.24	. . . .		196^{760}	0.9305_4^{20}	1.4370^{20}	i					os s	C52, 2795
d202	1,4-Dioxane, heptachloro-	$C_4HCl_7O_2$. See d198	329.22	. . . .	54–6	$123–8^8$	. . . .	. . . .	i		v	v	v	chl, CCl_4 v lig v	C54, 12468
d203	1,3-Dioxane, 5-hydroxy-2-methyl-	$C_5H_{10}O_3$. See d197	118.13	. . . .		176^{760}	1.0705_4^{17}	1.4375^{17}	∞						B19², 70
Ω d204	—.4-methyl-	$C_5H_{10}O_2$. See d197	102.13	. . . .		114^{760}	0.9758^{20}	1.4159^{20}	δ					os v	C52, 8145
Ω d205	—.4-methyl-4-phenyl-	$C_{11}H_{14}O_2$. See d197	178.23	. . . .	35–40	256^{760} 102^4	1.0864^{20}	1.5240^{20}	i					os s	C52, 8145
d206	—.2-phenyl-	$C_{10}H_{12}O_2$. See d197	164.21	nd (peth)	41	252–4 $98–9^4$	. . . .	. . . .	d[h]	v	v				B19², 22
d207	—.4-phenyl-	$C_{10}H_{12}O_2$. See d197	164.21	. . . .		245^{760} $128–30^{13}$	1.1038_4^{20}	1.5306^{18}	i					os s	B19¹, 616
	2,5-p-Dioxanedione	see Glycolide													
Ω d208	3-Dioxolane	Glycol methylene ether.	74.08	. . . .	−95	78^{765}	1.0600_2^{20}	1.3974_x^{20}	∞	s	s	s			B19², 3
d209	—.4-(hydroxymethyl)-2-methyl-	Glycerol ethylidene ether. $C_5H_{10}O_3$. See d208	118.13	. . . .		187^{760} $68–70^1$	1.1243_4^{17}	1.4413^{17}	δ	s					B19², 71
d210	—.2-methyl-	$C_4H_8O_2$. See d208	88.12	. . . .		$81–2^{760}$	0.9811_4^{20}	1.4035^{17}	v	∞	∞				B19², 8

For explanations, symbols and abbreviations see beginning of table. For structural formulas see end of table.

No.	Name	Synonyms and Formula	Mol. wt.	Color, crystalline form, specific rotation and λ_{max} (log ε)	m.p. °C	b.p. °C	Density	n_D	Solubility						Ref.
									w	al	eth	ace	bz	other solvents	

1,3-Dioxolan-4-carboxaldehyde

No.	Name	Synonyms and Formula	Mol. wt.	Color etc.	m.p.	b.p.	Density	n_D	w	al	eth	ace	bz	other	Ref.
d211	1,3-Dioxolan-4-carboxaldehyde, 2,2-dimethyl-	. . . . .	130.15	. . . . .		74^{50}		1.4189^{25}	s^h	. . .					B19[2], 136
Ω d212	1,3-Dioxolan-2-one	1,2-Ethanediol carbonate*. Ethylene carbonate. Glycol carbonate.	88.06	mcl pl (al)	39–40	248^{760}	1.3218^{39}_4	1.4158^{50}	∞	∞	∞	. . .	∞	chl ∞ AcOEt ∞ aa ∞	B19, 100
Ω d213	—,4-methyl-	Propylene carbonate. Isopropylene carbonate. $C_4H_6O_3$. See d212	102.09	. . . . .	−48.8	242^{760}	1.2069^{20}_{20}	1.4189^{20}	v	v	v	v	s	. . . . . .	C49, 12303
—	α,γ-Dipalmitin	see Glycerol, 1,3-dihexadecanoate													
—	Dipentene	see d,l-Limonene													
d214	Diphenadione	Diandin. Dipaxin. 2-Diphenylacetyl-1,3-indanedione.	340.38	pa ye mcl (al)	146–7	. . . . .	1.670_β		i	δ^h	. . .	s	δ	CH_3CN, aa, cy s	C49, 3264
—	Diphenic acid	see 2,2'-Biphenyldicarboxylic acid													
—	Diphenyleneimine	see Carbazole													
—	Diphenylene oxide	see Dibenzofuran													
—	Diphenylene sulfide	see Dibenzothiophen													
—	Diphenylmethane carboxylic acid	see Benzoic acid, benzyl-													
—	Diphosgene	see Formic acid, chloro-, trichloromethyl ester													
d215	Diphosphine, tetrakis (trifluoromethyl)-	$(F_3C)_2PP(CF_3)_2$	337.97	. . . . .		84^{760}	>1.0	. . . . .	i δd^h						J1953, 1565
—	Dipicolinic acid	see 2,6-Pyridinedicarboxylic acid													
d216	Diploicin	$C_{16}H_{10}Cl_4O_5$.	424.07	(bz)	232 (225d)	. . . . .			i	i	i	. . .	i	lig δ aa i	B19[2], 238
—	Dipropionamide	see Propanoic acid, amide, N-propionyl-													
d217	Dipropylene glycol	2,2'-Dihydroxydipropyl ether. $(CH_3CHOHCH_2)_2O$	134.18	. . . . .		229–32	1.0224^{20}_{20}		∞	s					B1[3], 2149
—	Disalicylic acid	see Benzoic acid, 2-hydroxy-, (2-carboxyphenyl) ester													
d218	Diselenide, diphenyl	$C_6H_5SeSeC_6H_5$	312.13	ye nd λ^{al} 240 (4.24), 265 (3.74), 329 (3.03)	63–4	. . . . .	1.5578^{80}_4 1.743^{20}_4			s^h	s		xyl s MeOH s^h	B6[2], 319
d219	Disiloxane, 1,3-diphenyl-1,1,3,3-tetramethyl-	$C_6H_5Si(CH_3)_2OSi(CH_3)_2C_6H_5$	286.53	λ^{al} 264 (3.01)	. . . . .	110^2	0.9763^{20}_4	1.5176^{20}							Am 79, 1437
d220	—,hexaethyl-	$[(C_2H_5)_3Si]_2O$	246.55	. . . . .		233^{756} 129^{30}	0.8590^0_0	1.4340^{20}							B4, 627
Ω d221	—,hexakis(2-ethylbutoxy)-	$([(C_2H_5)_2CHCH_2O]_3Si)_2O$	679.20	. . . . .	< −54	220^1	0.9219^{20}_{20}	1.4330^{20}	i	δ	s		s		C48, 3761
d222	—,hexakis(2-ethylhexoxy)-	$([CH_3(CH_2)_3CH(C_2H_5)CH_2O]_3Si)_2O$	847.52	. . . . .		$253^{0.9}$	0.9044^{20}_{20}	1.4402^{20}	i	δ	s		s		C48, 3761
—	α,γ-Distearin	see Glycerol, 1,3-dioctadecanoate													
d223	Distibine, tetrakis-(trifluoromethyl)-	Perfluoroantimony cacodyl. $(F_3C)_2SbSb(CF_3)_2$	519.53	pa ye or col, slow d	. . . . .	ca. 136^{760}	. . . . .		i					alk d	J1957, 3708

Disulfide

No.	Name	Synonyms and Formula	Mol. wt.	Color etc.	m.p.	b.p.	Density	n_D	w	al	eth	ace	bz	other	Ref.
Ω d225	—,bis(dibutyl-thiocarbamyl)	$[(C_4H_9)_2NCS]_2S_2$	408.76	red liq	. . . . .		1.03^{20}		i	δ	s				B4[3], 302
Ω d226	—,bis(diethyl-thiocarbamyl)	Antabuse. Antietil. $[(C_2H_5)_2NCS]_2S_2$	296.54	(al)	71–2		1.17^{17}		i	s^h	δ		chl v		B4[2], 613
Ω d227	—,bis(dimethyl-thiocarbamyl)	Arasan. $[(CH_3)_2NCS]_2S_2$.	240.43	wh or ye mcl (chl-al) λ^{chl} 243 (4.1), 282 (4.06)	155–6 (151)	129^{70}			i	δ s^h	δ		chl s		B4[2], 557
d228	—,bis(ethyl-methylthiocarbamyl)	$[CH_3N(C_2H_5)CS]_2S_2$	268.49	ye	72				i	δ	δ		chl s		C43, 6856
Ω d229	—,bis(1-piperidyl-thiocarbamyl)	Dicyclopentamethylenethiuram disulfide.	320.56		137–8 (129)				i	s^h	δ		chl s		Am 65, 1267
d230	—,diacetyl	$CH_3COSSCOCH_3$	150.22		20	$105–6^{18}$			i d^h	v	v		CS_2 v		B2[2], 210
Ω d231	—,2,2'-dibenzo-thiazyl	2,2'-Dithiobisbenzothiazole.	332.50	lt ye sc (bz) λ^{al} 271 (4.32)	180	d	1.50^{20}_4		i	i		v^h	chl δ		B27[1], 249

For explanations, symbols and abbreviations see beginning of table. For structural formulas see end of table.

No.	Name	Synonyms and Formula	Mol. wt.	Color, crystalline form, specific rotation and λ_{max} (log ε)	m.p. °C	b.p. °C	Density	n_D	w	al	eth	ace	bz	other solvents	Ref.
	Disulfide														
d232	—,dibenzoyl	$C_6H_5COSSCOC_6H_5$	274.36	pr (al), sc (chl-peth)	136	d			i	δ^h	δ^h	...	...	CS_2 s^h	B9², 289
d233	—,dibenzyl	$C_6H_5CH_2SSCH_2C_6H_5$	246.40	lf (MeOH or al), nd (aa) λ^{al} 265 (3.1), 285 sh (2.4)	(i) 71–2 (ii) 69				δ	s^h	s	...	s	MeOH s	B6², 437
d234	—,—,4,4′-dimeth-oxy-		306.45	lf or nd (al)	101				i	i	...	...	v	chl v	B6, 901
d235	—,dibutyl	$CH_3(CH_2)_3SS(CH_2)_3CH_3$	178.36	λ^{al} 204 (3.32), 251.5 (2.60)		226⁷⁶⁰ 85³	0.9383²⁰₄	1.4926²⁰	i	∞	∞				B1³, 1524
d236	—,—,3,3′-di-methyl-	Isoamyl sulfide. $(CH_3)_2CHCH_2CH_2SSCH_2CH_2CH(CH_3)_2$	206.42	λ^{al} 251 (2.59)		250	0.9192²⁰	1.4864²⁰	d						B1³, 1647
d237	—,diethoxy	Ethoxyl disulfide. $C_2H_5OSSOC_2H_5$	154.25			67–8¹⁶	1.0913²⁰₄	1.4766²⁰							B1³, 1314
d238	—,diethyl	$C_2H_5SSC_2H_5$	122.25	λ^{al} 202 (3.32), 251.5 (2.62)	−101.52	154⁷⁶⁰ 40¹⁰	0.9931²⁰₄	1.5073²⁰	δ	∞	∞				B1², 345
Ω d239	—,—,2,2′-diamino-	Dithiobisethylamine. Cysta-mine. $H_2NCH_2CH_2SSCH_2CH_2NH_2$	152.28			d			s		δ				B4², 731
d240	—,di(2-furfuryl)		226.32		10	112–3⁰·⁵				v				os v lig δ	B17², 116
d241	—,diisopropyl	$(CH_3)_2CHSSCH(CH_3)_2$	150.31	λ^{iso} 245 (2.36)		177.2⁷⁶⁰ 56.8¹⁰	0.9435²⁰₄	1.4916²⁰	i		s				B1³, 1480
d242	—,dimethyl	CH_3SSCH_3	94.20	λ^{iso} 256 (2.5)	−84.72	109.7⁷⁶⁰ 6.4¹⁰	1.0625²⁰₄	1.5259²⁰	i	∞	∞				B1², 278
d243	—,—,hexafluoro-	F_3CSSCF_3	202.14	λ^{gas} 235 (2.46)	34.6⁷⁶⁰	>1.26			i	s				CS_2 i peth s	J1952, 2198
d244	—,—,1,1,1′,1′-tetraphenyl-	$(C_6H_5)_2CHSSCH(C_6H_5)_2$	398.60	nd (al) λ^{al} 265 sh (3.5)	152–3					s^h	s		s	CS_2 v	B6², 636
d245	—,1,1′-dinaphthyl-	$(C_{10}H_7)^\alpha SS(C_{10}H_7)^\alpha$	318.46	pl (al), nd (lig) λ^{chl} 287 (4.2)	91		1.144²⁰		i	δ	v			lig i	B6², 588
d246	—,2,2′-dinaphthyl-	$(C_{10}H_7)^\beta SS(C_{10}H_7)^\beta$	318.46	nd λ^{chl} 255 (4.6), 288 (4.2), 322 sh (3.7), 335 sh (3.5)	139–40		0.8409²⁰₄	1.4555²⁰	i	v	v			lig i	B6¹, 317
d247	—,dipentyl	n-Amyl disulfide. $CH_3(CH_2)_4SS(CH_2)_4CH_3$	206.42			119⁷	0.9221²⁰	1.4889²⁰	i		s				B1³, 1608
d248	—,diphenyl		218.34	nd (al) or rh λ^{al} 240 (4.23), 270 sh (3.50), 300 sh (3.2)	61–2	310⁷⁶⁰ 192¹⁵	1.3532²⁰₄		i	s	s		s	CS_2 s	B6, 323
d249	—,—,2,2′-di-amino-	$C_{12}H_{12}N_2S_2$. See d248.	248.37	pa ye pl or nd (50 % al) λ^{al} 221 (4.41), 342 (3.78)	93				i	v^h	s				B13², 201
d250	—,—,3,3′-di-amino-	$C_{12}H_{12}N_2S_2$. See d248.	248.37	nd (dil al)	62				i	v	v		v	lig i	B13², 219
d251	—,—,4,4′-di-amino-	$C_{12}H_{12}N_2S_2$. See d248.	248.37	ye or col pr or nd (w, eth or dil al) λ^{al} 256 (4.23), 294 sh (4.11)	85 (77)				s^h	v	v		δ^h	chl v lig δ^h	B13², 300
Ω d252	—,—,4,4′-di-chloro-2,2′-dinitro-	$C_{12}H_6Cl_2N_2O_4S_2$. See d248.	377.23	ye (ace-al)	212–3					δ	...	δ	s	CCl_4 δ peth i lig δ	B6², 313
d253	—,—,5,5′-di-chloro-2,2′-dinitro-	$C_{12}H_6Cl_2N_2O_4S_2$. See d248.	377.23	ye nd (90 % aa)	171				i	δ			v	chl, CS_2 v lig i	B6², 314
d254	—,—,4,4′-diethoxy-	$C_{16}H_{18}O_2S_2$. See d248.	306.45	nd (al)	48–9				i	s^h					B6¹, 421
d255	—,—,2,2′-dimethoxy-	$C_{14}H_{14}O_2S_2$. See d248.	278.40	nd (al)	88–90				i	s^h					B6, 795
d257	—,—,2,2′-dimeth-oxy-5,5′-dimethyl-	$C_{16}H_{18}O_2S_2$. See d248.	306.45	pa ye pr (al), pl (al or eth)	74		1.160⁷⁷		i	s^h					B6², 874
Ω d258	—,—,2,2′-dinitro-	$C_{12}H_8N_2O_4S_2$. See d248.	308.35	ye nd (bz or aa), pl (aa) λ^{al} 240 (4.37)	198–9				i	δ	i	δ	δ	peth i aa δ	B6², 307
Ω d259	—,—,3,3′-dinitro-	Nitrophenide. $C_{12}H_8N_2O_4S_2$. See d248.	308.35	ye nd (al) or rh λ^{al} 242 (4.47), 320 sh (3.41)	84					δ	s				B6, 339
Ω d260	—,—,4,4′-dinitro-	$C_{12}H_8N_2O_4S_2$. See d248.	308.35	nd (aa), pl (al) λ^{al} 228 sh (4.10), 315 (4.30)	182					δ				aa δ	B6², 312
Ω d261	—,—,2,2′4,4′-tetranitro-	$C_{12}H_6N_4O_8S_2$. See d248.	398.35	ye nd (al) λ^{al} 248 (4.19)	303d				i					oos i $PhNO_2$, Py s	B6², 316
d262	—,dipropyl	$CH_3CH_2CH_2SSCH_2CH_2CH_3$	150.31	λ^{al} 250 (2.7)		193.5⁷⁵⁰	0.9599²⁰₄	1.4981²⁰							B1³, 1435

For explanations, symbols and abbreviations see beginning of table. For structural formulas see end of table.

No.	Name	Synonyms and Formula	Mol. wt.	Color, crystalline form, specific rotation and λ_{max} (log ε)	m.p. °C	b.p. °C	Density	n_D	Solubility						Ref.
									w	al	eth	ace	bz	other solvents	
	Disulfide														
d263	—,di-2-tolyl........	....	246.40	lf (al) λ^{al} 240 (4.21), 280 (3.45), 325 sh (2.95)	38–9	....	....	....	i	s	s	s	...	os s	B6², 342
d264	—,di-4-tolyl......	....	246.40	nd or lf (al) λ^{al} 242 (4.29), 270 (3.65), 315 sh (3.2)	47–8	210–15²⁰	1.114⁵¹	....	i	s	v	s	...	chl s	B6², 400
—	Ditaine...........	see **Echitamine**													
—	Ditan	see **Methane, diphenyl-**													
Ω d265	1,4-Dithiane	Diethylene disulfide........	120.25	mcl pr λ^{al} 225 sh (2.54), 292 (2.5)	111–2	199–200	....	....	δ^h	s^h	s	...	...	CS₂ s aa s^h	B19², 6
d266	1,3,5-Dithiazine, 4,5-dihydro-5-methyl-	Methylthioformaldine......	135.25	nd (eth)	65	ca. 185d				s	s	v		aa s	B27, 460
d267	1,4-Dithline 2,5-diphenyl-	....	268.40	ye pr (al) λ 260 (4.35), 308 (3.95)	118–9	....	....	....	i	s			v	con sulf s alk s	B19², 46
—	Dithioacetic acid ...	see **Acetic acid, thionothiolo-**													
d268	1,3-Dithiolane.....	Trimethylene 1,3-disulfide.	106.21	λ^{cy} 207 (3.13), 247 (2.56)	–51	175⁷⁶⁰	1.259¹⁷	1.5975¹⁵		s	s	...		xyl s	B19², 3
Ω d269	Dithizone.........	Diphenylthiocarbazone. Formazyl mercaptan. $C_6H_5N{:}NCSNHNHC_6H_5$	256.33	bl-bk (chl-al) λ^{ace} 445 (4.29), 610 (4.51)	165–9d	....	....	....	i	δ	δ	...		chl, alk s	B16, 26
d270	Diurea	Dicarbamide. p-Urazine.	116.08	pr (w)	270	....	....	....	δ^h	δ				aa δ	B26², 258
—	Divarinol........	see **Benzene, 1,3-dihydroxy-5-propyl-**													
Ω d271	Djenkolic acid.....	β,β'-Methylenedithiodialan- ine. $HO_2CCH(NH_2)CH_2SCH_2SCH_2CH(NH_2)CO_2H$ $[\alpha]_D^{25}$ –47.5 (1% HCl, c = 2)	254.33	nd (w, HCl)	300–50d	....	....	....	s^h					dil ac s dil alk s	B4³, 1591
Ω d272	Docosane*.......	$CH_3(CH_2)_{20}CH_3$	310.61	pl (to), cr (eth)	44.4	368.6⁷⁶⁰ 213¹⁰	0.7944₄²⁰	1.4455²⁰	i	s^h	v	...		chl s	B1³, 574
Ω d273	Docosanoic acid* ..	Behenic acid. Docosoic acid. $CH_3(CH_2)_{20}CO_2H$	340.60	nd	80	306⁶⁰	0.8223⁹⁰	1.4270¹⁰⁰	δ	δ	δ			chl s	B2³, 373
d274	—,ethyl ester	Ethyl behenate. $CH_3(CH_2)_{20}CO_2C_2H_5$	368.65	nd (al), cr (ace)	50	240–2¹⁰	0.8820⁵¹	....	i	s	s			chl s	B2², 374
d275	—,methyl ester	Methyl behenate. $CH_3(CH_2)_{20}CO_2CH_3$	354.62	nd (ace)	54	224–5¹⁵	....	1.4339⁶⁰	i	s	s			chl s	B2², 373
Ω d276	1-Docosanol*.....	Docosyl alcohol. $CH_3(CH_2)_{21}OH$	326.61	(ace, chl)	71 (87)	180⁰·²²	....	....	δ	v	δ v^h	...		chl s MeOH v peth v^h	B1³, 1846
d277	4,7,11-Docosatrien- 18-ynoic acid	Clupanodonic acid. $CH_3(CH_2)_2C{:}C(CH_2)_5CH{:}CH\ CH_2$ $HO_2CCH_2CH{:}CHCH_2CH{:}CHCH_2$	330.52	pa ye λ^{MeOH} 240 (4.28), 275 (4.2), 300 (4.2), 328 (4.2), 346 (3.7)	< –78	236⁵	0.9290²⁰	1.4868²⁰	i		s				C49, 1550
Ω d278	13-Docosenoic acid*(cis)	Erucic acid. $CH_3(CH_2)_7CH{:}CH(CH_2)_{11}CO_2H$	338.58	nd (al)	33–4	265¹⁵	0.860⁵⁵₄	1.4758²⁰	i	s	v	...		MeOH v	B2², 445
Ω d279	—(trans)*	Brassidic acid. Brassic acid. Isoerucic acid. $CH_3(CH_2)_7CH{:}CH(CH_2)_{11}CO_2H$	338.58	pl (al)	61.5	282³⁰	0.8585⁵⁷₄	1.4472⁶⁴	i	δ	δ			chl s	B2², 447
d280	—,anhydride (trans)*	Brassidic anhydride. $[CH_3(CH_2)_7CH{:}CH(CH_2)_{11}CO]_2O$	659.15	nd (al), pl (eth, ace, peth)	64	0.835²⁰₄	1.4366¹⁰⁰		i	δ	s	s		peth s	B2², 448
d281	—,13,14-diiodo-, ethyl ester*(trans)	Iodobrassid $CH_3(CH_2)_7CI{:}CI(CH_2)_{11}CO_2C_2H_5$	618.43	nd or sc	37 (40)	d			i	s v^h	v		v	chl v	B2², 448
d282	13-Docosynoic acid*	Behenolic acid. $CH_3(CH_2)_7C{:}C(CH_2)_{11}CO_2H$	336.57	mcl pr or nd (al)	59.5	....	....	....	i	v	v			chl s	B2², 462
Ω d282¹	Dodecanal*.......	Lauraldehyde. $CH_3(CH_2)_{10}CHO$	184.33	lf	44.5 (12)	185¹⁰⁰ 100³·⁵	0.8352¹⁵	1.435²²	i	s	v				B1³, 2911
d283	—,dimethyl acetal .	1,1-Dimethoxydodecane*. $CH_3(CH_2)_{10}CH(OCH_3)_2$	230.40	....		132–4⁶	....	1.4310²⁵		v	v			MeOH v	Am 80, 6613
Ω d284	Dodecane*.......	$CH_3(CH_2)_{10}CH_3$	170.34	....	–9.6	216.3⁷⁶⁰ 91.5¹⁰	0.7487₄²⁰	1.4216²⁰	i	v	v	v		chl, CCl₄ v	B1³, 539
Ω d285	—,1-amino-*......	Dodecylamine. Laurylamine. $CH_3(CH_2)_{11}NH_2$	185.36	....	28.3	259⁷⁶⁰ 126.5¹⁰	0.8015²⁰₄	1.4421²⁰	δ	(α)	∞		∞	chl, CCl₄ ∞	B4, 200
d286	—,—,acetate......	$CH_3(CH_2)_{11}NH_2.CH_3CO_2H$	245.41	....	fr. 69.5	....	....	....	v	v			δ		C48, 2525
d287	—,—,hydrochloride	$CH_3(CH_2)_{11}NH_2.HCl$	221.82	....	98				v	v	i		δ s^h		Am 74, 4287
Ω d288	—,1-bromo-*......	Dodecyl bromide. Lauryl- bromide. $CH_3(CH_2)_{11}Br$	249.24	....	–9.5	276⁷⁶⁰ 139¹⁰	1.0399²⁰₄	1.4583²⁰	i	s	s	s	∞		B1³, 542
d289	—,1-bromo-12-fluoro-*	$F(CH_2)_{12}Br$.............	267.23	....		85–6⁰·¹⁵	....	1.4524²⁵	i	v	v	s			C51, 7300
Ω d290	—,1-chloro-*......	Dodecyl chloride. Lauryl chloride. $CH_3(CH_2)_{11}Cl$	204.79	....	fr. –9.3	260⁷⁶⁰ 126.4¹⁰	0.8682²⁰₄	1.4433²⁰	i	v	...	∞	s	CCl₄ ∞ lig ∞	B1³, 541

For explanations, symbols and abbreviations see beginning of table. For structural formulas see end of table.

No.	Name	Synonyms and Formula	Mol. wt.	Color, crystalline form, specific rotation and λ_{max} (log ε)	m.p. °C	b.p. °C	Density	n_D	w	al	eth	ace	bz	other solvents	Ref.
	Dodecane*														
d291	—,1,12-dibromo-*	$BrCH_2(CH_2)_{10}CH_2Br$	328.14	nd (aa, al)	41	215^{15}		1.4840^{20}	i	v	s	....	...	chl v aa s	B1[2], 543
d292	—,1-iodo-*	$CH_3(CH_2)_{11}I$	296.24	....	0.3	298.2^{760} 153^{10}	1.1999^{20}_4	1.4840^{20}	i	s ∞^h	∞	∞	...	chl, CCl_4 ∞ MeOH s AcOEt s[h]	B1[1], 67
Ω d293	**Dodecanedioic acid**, dimethyl ester*	$CH_3O_2C(CH_2)_{10}CO_2CH_3$...	258.36	pr	31.3	$167–9^9$ 150^2			i	.	....	...	...		B2[3], 1844
Ω d294	**1-Dodecanethiol*** ..	Dodecyl mercaptan. Lauryl mercaptan. $CH_3(CH_2)_{11}SH$	202.41	....	....	$142–5^{15}$	0.8450^{20}_{20}	1.4589^{20}	i	s	s	..	..		B1[3], 1789
Ω d295	**Dodecanoic acid*** ..	Lauric acid. Undecane-1-carboxylic acid. $CH_3(CH_2)_{10}CO_2H$	200.33	nd (al)	44	131^1	0.8679^{50}_5	1.4304^{50}	i	v	v s	s	∞^h v	peth s MeOH v	B2[3], 868
d296	—,amide*	Lauramide. $CH_3(CH_2)_{10}CONH_2$	199.34	nd	110	199^{12}		1.4287^{110}	i	s	δ	s	δ	CCl_4 s[h]	B2[3], 894
d297	—,—,N-phenyl-...	Lauranilide. $CH_3(CH_2)_{10}CONHC_6H_5$	275.44	nd (dil al) λ^{cy} 241 (4.19)	78	....			i	s	s	s	s	CCl_4, chls	B12[2], 148
d298	—,anhydride*.....	Lauric anhydride. $[CH_3(CH_2)_{10}CO]_2O$	382.64	lf (al or eth)	41.8	166	0.8533^{70}	1.4292^{70}	d	s[h]	....	..	..		B2[2], 321
d299	—,benzyl ester* ..	Benzyl laurate. $CH_3(CH_2)_{10}CO_2CH_2C_6H_5$	290.45	....	8.5	$209–11^{12}$	0.9457^{25}_{25}	1.4812^{24}	i	s	v	...	v	chl v peth s	B6[2], 417
Ω d300	—,chloride	Lauryl chloride. $CH_3(CH_2)_{10}COCl$	218.77	....	−17	145^{18}		1.4458^{20}	d	d	s	..	..		B2[2], 321
Ω d301	—,ethyl ester* ..	Ethyl laurate. $CH_3(CH_2)_{10}CO_2C_2H_5$	228.38	....	fr. −1.8	273^{764} 154^{15}	0.8618^{20}	1.4311^{20}	i	v	∞	..	..		B2[3], 884
d302	—,isopropyl ester* .	Isopropyl laurate. $CH_3(CH_2)_{10}CO_2C_3H_7^i$	242.41	....	....	196^{60} 117.4^2	0.8536^{20}	1.4280^{25}							B2[3], 886
Ω d303	—,methyl ester* ..	Methyl laurate. $CH_3(CH_2)_{10}CO_2CH_3$	214.35	....	fr. 5.2	262^{766} 141^{15}	0.8702^{20}	1.4319^{20}	i	∞	∞	∞	∞	MeOH, chl, CCl_4, AcOEt s	B2[3], 883
Ω d304	—,nitrile	Lauronitrile. Undecyl cyanide. $CH_3(CH_2)_{10}CN$	181.33	....	fr. 4	277^{760} 131^{10}	0.8240^{20}_4	1.4361^{20}	i	∞	∞	∞	∞	chl ∞	B2[3], 895
d305	—,phenyl ester* ..	Phenyl laurate. $CH_3(CH_2)_{10}CO_2C_6H_5$	276.42	lf (al)	24.5	210^{15}			i	s	s	s	s		B6, 154
d306	—,4-phenyl-phenacyl ester.	....	394.56	....	86	....			i		....	...	...		C32, 4943
d307	—,piperazinium salt	$C_4H_{10}N_2 \cdot 2CH_3(CH_2)_{10}CO_2H$	486.79		92–2.5				s	s	i	..	..		Am 70, 2758
d308	—,propyl ester* ..	Propyl laurate. $CH_3(CH_2)_{10}CO_2CH_2CH_2CH_3$	242.31			205^{60} 124^2	0.8600^{20}	1.4335^{20}							B2[2], 885
d309	—,2-bromo-*	$CH_3(CH_2)_9CHBrCO_2H$ ..	279.23	pl	32	$157–9^2$	1.1474^{24}	1.4585^{24}	i	v	s	..	v	chl, ligs	B2, 363
d310	—,12-fluoro-*	$F(CH_2)_{11}CO_2H$	218.32		60–1	....			i	v	v	..	..	ligs[h]	C51, 7300
Ω d311	**1-Dodecanol***	Lauryl alcohol. $CH_3(CH_2)_{11}OH$	186.32	lf (dil al)	26 (22)	$255–9^{760}$ 150^{20}	0.8309^{24}		i	s	s	..	..		B1[2], 463
d312	**6-Dodecanol***	$CH_3(CH_2)_4CHOH(CH_2)_5CH_3$	186.34	(peth)	30	119^9			i	s	s	..	..		B1, 428
Ω d313	**2-Dodecanone***	n-Decyl methyl ketone. $CH_3CO(CH_2)_9CH_3$	184.33		21	$246–7^{760}$ 144^{11}	0.8198^{30}_4	1.4330^{20}	i	s	s	s	s	os s	B1[2], 769
Ω d314	**1-Dodecanone, 1-phenyl-***	Laurophenone. Lauroyl-benzene. n-Undecyl phenyl ketone. $CH_3(CH_2)_{10}COC_6H_5$	260.43	og cr	46–7	$222–3^{21}$ 187^5	0.8969^{52}_4	1.4850^{52}	i	s	s	s	s		B7[1], 186
—	**1,6,10-Dodeca-trien-3-ol, 3,7,11-trimethyl-***	see **Nerolidol**													
Ω d315	**1-Dodecene***	α-Dodecylene. $CH_3(CH_2)_9CH:CH_2$	168.33		−35.23	213.4^{760} 88.7^{10}	0.7584^{20}_4	1.4300^{20}	i	s	s	s	...	peth s	B1[3], 869
d316	**2-Dodecenedioic acid**(cis)*	Traumatic acid. $HO_2CCH:CH(CH_2)_8CO_2H$	228.29	(al, ace)	67–8	....			δ	s	s	...	s	chls	B2[3], 1978
d317	—(trans)*	$HO_2CCH:CH(CH_2)_8CO_2H$.	228.29	(al, ace)	165–6	....			δ	s	s	..	s	chls	B2[3], 1979
d318	**1-Dodecen-3-yne*** ...	$CH_2:CHC:C(CH_2)_7CH_3$.	164.29			78^4	0.7858^{25}_5	1.4510^{25}							B1[3], 1055
d319	**1-Dodecyne***	$CH:C(CH_2)_9CH_3$	166.31		−19	215^{760} 89^{10}	0.7788^{20}_4	1.4340^{20}	i	s	s	s	s		B1[3], 1024
d320	**2-Dodecyne***	$CH_3C:C(CH_2)_8CH_3$	166.31		−9	105^{15}	0.7917^{15}_5	1.4828^{20}	i	s	s	s	s		B1[3], 1025
d321	**3-Dodecyne***	$CH_3CH_2C:C(CH_2)_7CH_3$.	166.31			95^{12}	0.7871^{20}	1.4442^{20}	i	s	s	s	s		B1[3], 1025
d322	**6-Dodecyne***	Di n-amylacetylene. $CH_3(CH_2)_4C:C(CH_2)_4CH_3$	166.31			209^{745} 100^{14}	0.7871^{20}	1.4442^{20}	i	s	s	s	s		B1[3], 1025
Ω d323	**Dotriacontane***	Dicetyl. $CH_3(CH_2)_{30}CH_3$	450.89	pl (bz, chl, aa, eth)	69.7	467^{760} 292.7^{10} suc	0.8124^{20}	1.4550^{20}	i	δ	s[h]	..	v[h] δ	CCl_4, aa s[h] chl δ, CS_2 s	B1[3], 587
d324	**1-Dotriacontanol*** ..	$CH_3(CH_2)_{30}CH_2OH$	466.89	pl (bz)	89.4	sub $200–50^1$		.	i						B1[3], 1851
—	**Dulcitol**	see **Galactitol**													
—	**Durene**	see **Benzene, 1,2,4,5-tetra-methyl-**													
—	**Durenol**	see **Benzene, 1-hydroxy-2,3,5,6-tetramethyl-**													
—	**Durohydro-quinone**	see **Benzene, 1,4-dihydroxy-2,3,5,6-tetramethyl-**													

For explanations, symbols and abbreviations see beginning of table. For structural formulas see end of table.

No.	Name	Synonyms and Formula	Mol. wt.	Color, crystalline form, specific rotation and λ_{max} (log ε)	m.p. °C	b.p. °C	Density	n_D	Solubility						Ref.
									w	al	eth	ace	bz	other solvents	
	Duroquinone														
—	Duroquinone	*see* 1,4-Benzoquinone, tetramethyl-													
—	Durylic acid	*see* Benzoic acid, 2,4,5-trimethyl-													
—	Dypnone	*see* 2-Buten-1-one, 1,3-diphenyl-													

For explanations, symbols and abbreviations see beginning of table. For structural formulas see end of table.

Ecgonidine

No.	Name	Synonyms and Formula	Mol. wt.	Color, crystalline form, specific rotation and λ_{max} (log ε)	m.p. °C	b.p. °C	Density	n_D	w	al	eth	ace	bz	other solvents	Ref.
e1	Ecgonidine(l)	Anhydroecgonine(l)	167.21	cr (MeOH-eth) [α]$_D^{14}$ −84.6 (w, p = 1.7)	235d					s	δ				B22², 26
e2	Ecgonine(dl)		185.23	pl (w +3) λ^{al} 218 (3.8), 224 sh (3.7) 275 (3.3)	203 (212) (anh) 93–118 (+3w)				v^h	s	i	δ	δ	chl δ	B22², 156
e3	—(l)	Tropinecarboxylic acid. C$_9$H$_{15}$NO$_3$. See e2	185.23	mcl pr (al +1w) [α]$_D^{15}$ −45.5 (w, c = 5)	205 (anh) 198 (hyd)				v	s	i	δ	δ	MeOH s chl δ	B22², 150
e4	—,hydrate(l)	C$_9$H$_{15}$NO$_3$.H$_2$O. See e2	203.23	mcl pr (al), eff 120–30	198				v	δ	δ	δ	δ	MeOH s chl δ	B22, 196
e5	—,benzoate(l)	O-Benzoyl-l-ecgonine.	289.34	nd (w) [α]$_D^{14}$ −63.5 (w, p = 1.7)	195				δ s^h	s	i		v^h	dil ac, dil alk s	B22², 150
e6	—,—,ethyl ester(l)	Cocaethyline. Homococaine. C$_{18}$H$_{23}$NO$_4$. See e5	317.39	pr (eth)	109				δ	s	s				B22, 202
e7	—,—,tetra-hydrate(l)	C$_{16}$H$_{19}$NO$_4$.4H$_2$O. See e5	361.40	pr (w) [α]$_D^{15}$ −44.6 (abs al, c = 3)	92				δ s^h	s	i		v^h		B22, 197
e8	—,hydrochloride(l)	C$_9$H$_{15}$NO$_3$.HCl. See e2	221.69	rh (al), nd (i-AmOH) [α]$_D^{15}$ −59 (w, c = 10)	246				s	s				MeOH v i-AmOH δ	B22², 150
e8¹	Echinochrome A	C$_{12}$H$_{10}$O$_7$	266.21	dk red nd (to) λ^w 400 (3.7), 465 (3.7), 480 (3.8), 550 (3.5)	220d	Sub 120$^{10^{-4}}$			i	s	s	s		chl, peth δ	C55, 6710
e9	—,3,6,7-trimethyl ether	C$_{15}$H$_{16}$O$_7$. See e8¹	308.29	dk red lf (aq diox), nd λ^{chl} 323, 476 502, 537	133 vac (130)				i	s				MeOH, NaOH s (bl)	C55, 6710
e10	Echinopsine	N-Methyl-γ-quinolone.	159.19	α nd(bz), (w +1) β cr (al) λ^{al} 215 (4.2), 290 (3.6), 320 (4.2), 330 (4.2)	α152 β135				s v^h	v	δ		v^h	chl, MeOH v	B21², 259
e11	Echitamidine	C$_{20}$H$_{26}$N$_2$O$_3$	342.44	pl (eth) [α]$_D^{16}$ −515 (al)	244d				s	s				con HNO$_3$ (bl→ye)	J 1932, 2628
e12	Echitamine	Ditaine. C$_{22}$H$_{28}$N$_2$O$_4$.4H$_2$O.	456.54	pr (al +4w) eff 105 (−3w) [α]$_D^{20}$ −29 (al) λ^{al}236 (4.1), 296 (4.0), 331 (4.3)	206 (+1w)				s	s	s			chl, con sulf s (red) peth i	J 1925, 1640
e13	—,hydrochloride	C$_{22}$H$_{28}$N$_2$O$_4$.HCl	420.94	nd (w), [α]$_D^{5}$ −58 (w, c = 1) λ^{al} 235 (3.93), 295 (3.55)	295–300d				s	v	δ		δ		J 1925, 1640
e14	Echitin	C$_{32}$H$_{52}$O$_2$	468.77	lf [α]$_D$ +73 (eth)	170					s^h	s	s	s	peth s	M 397
e15	Egonol	C$_{19}$H$_{18}$O$_5$	326.35	pl (BuOH)	118	228–30$^{0.15}$								chl s	C33, 5394
Ω e16	Eicosane*	Didecyl.CH$_3$(CH$_2$)$_{18}$CH$_3$	282.56	lf (al)	36.8	343^{760} 195.7^{10}	0.7886$_4^{20}$	1.4425^{20}	i		s	v	s	peth s	B1³, 570
Ω e17	Eicosanedioic acid*	Octadecane-1,18-dicarboxylic acid. HO$_2$C(CH$_2$)$_{18}$CO$_2$H	342.53	cr (bz or al)	125–6.5 (124)	233–4²									B2³, 1880
Ω e18	Eicosanoic acid*	Arachidic acid. Eicosoic acid. CH$_3$(CH$_2$)$_{18}$CO$_2$H	312.54	pl (al)	77	328 δd 203–5¹	0.8240^{100}	1.425^{100}	i	δ s^h	v		s	chl s peth δ	B2², 369
Ω e19	—,ethyl ester*	CH$_3$(CH$_2$)$_{18}$CO$_2$C$_2$H$_5$	340.60		50(42)	295–7^{100} 186–7²			i	s	s		s	chl s	B2², 370
e20	—,methyl ester*	CH$_3$(CH$_2$)$_{18}$CO$_2$CH$_3$	326.57	lf (MeOH)	54.5 (47)	215–6^{10} 188²		1.4317^{60}	i	s	s		s	chl s	B2², 370
Ω e21	1-Eicosanol*	Arachidic alcohol. pri-n-Eicosyl alcohol. CH$_3$(CH$_2$)$_{18}$CH$_2$OH	298.56	wx (al), cr (chl)	72.5–3.0 (67)	369^{760} 220–5³	0.8405$_4^{20}$ suc	1.4550^{20} suc	i	δ		v	s^h	peth s^h	B1³, 1843
e22	2-Eicosanol*	2-Eicosyl alcohol CH$_3$(CH$_2$)$_{17}$CH(OH)CH$_3$	298.56	cr (MeOH)	63–4 (60)	357^{760}	0.8378$_4^{20}$ suc	1.4524^{20} suc 1.4312^{80}	i			v	s^h	peth s^h	B1³, 1843
e23	2-Eicosanone*	Methyl n-octadecyl ketone. CH$_3$(CH$_2$)$_{17}$COCH$_3$	296.54	lf (MeOH)	58					s	s	s	s		B1³, 2932
e24	3-Eicosanone*	Ethyl n-heptadecyl ketone. CH$_3$(CH$_2$)$_{16}$COC$_2$H$_5$	296.54	lf (al)	60–1					δ	s	s	s	chl, aa s	B1², 774
e25	—,oxime*	CH$_3$(CH$_2$)$_{16}$C(:NOH)C$_2$H$_5$	311.56	nd (al)	α 55.5–6.5 β 64–5					δ	s	s		peth δ	B1, 719
e26	7-Eicosanone*	Hexyl n-tridecyl ketone. CH$_3$(CH$_2$)$_{12}$CO(CH$_2$)$_5$CH$_3$	296.54	cr	52.7–3.4	210–1^{11}		1.4258^{80}			s	s			C49, 1546

For explanations, symbols and abbreviations see beginning of table. For structural formulas see end of table.

5,8,11,14-Eicosatetraenoic acid

No.	Name	Synonyms and Formula	Mol. wt.	Color, crystalline form, specific rotation and λ_{max} (log ε)	m.p. °C	b.p. °C	Density	n_D	w	al	eth	ace	bz	other solvents	Ref.
e27	5,8,11,14-Eico-satetraenoic acid*	Arachidonic acid. $CH_3(CH_2)_3(CH_2CH:CH)_4(CH_2)_3CO_2H$	304.48	λ 233 (4.24), 257 (4.09), 268 (4.21), 315 (3.82)	−49.5	d	....	1.4824^{20} 1.5563^{23}	i	s	s	s	...	os s	B2², 469
Ω e28	1-Eicosene*	$CH_3(CH_2)_{17}CH:CH_2$	280.54	....	28.5	341^{760} $151^{1.5}$	0.7882_4^{30}	1.4440^{30}	i	...	...	...	s	peth s	B1³, 881
e29	1-Eicosyne*	$CH_3(CH_2)_{17}C:CH$	278.53	....	36	340^{760} 191.8^{10}	0.8073_4^{20}	1.4501^{20}	i	...	...	...	s	peth s	B1, 262
—	Elaidic acid	see 9-Octadecenoic acid (trans)*													
—	Elaidyl alcohol	see 9-Octadecen-1-ol (trans)*													
e30	α-Elaterin	$C_{32}H_{44}O_8$	556.67	cr (chl-MeOH or al) λ 234 (4.0), 267 sh (3.87) $[\alpha]_D^{20}$ − 64.3 (chl, c = 1.6)	234	....			i	δ	s	...	s	chl s	J95, 1989
e31	β-Elaterin	$C_{20}H_{28}O_5$	348.45	nd (al) $[\alpha]_D^{25}$ + 13.9	195.5	....			i	i δ^h	δ	...	δ	chl s	J95, 1989
—	Eldoral	see Barbituric acid, 5-ethyl-5-piperidyl-													
e32	Elemane	Dihydroelemene. $C_{15}H_{30}$	210.41	....		$115–9^{10}$	0.8509_4^{20}	1.4640^{20}	i	...	...	...	s	peth s	B5², 117
e33	Elemenonic acid	Dihydro-β-elemonic acid. $C_{30}H_{48}O_3$.	456.72	nd (al or AcOEt), $[\alpha]_D$ + 43.7 (chl, c = 0.9)	249–50 (246)	....									J1963, 2762
e34	α-Elemol		222.38	cr (al) $[\alpha]_D$ − 5.8 (chl, c = 3.4)	52.5–3.5	$142–3^{12}$	0.9345_4^{18}	1.4980^{18}							B6³, 410
—	Eleostearic acid	see 9,11,13-Octadecatrienoic acid*													
e35	Ellagene	Indeno-2′,3′:2,3-fluorene.	254.34	pl (bz) λ^{chl} 309 (4.65), 324 (4.68)	216										E14s, 498
e36	Ellagic acid, dihydrate	$C_{14}H_6O_8.2H_2O$	338.23	pa ye nd (Py) $\lambda^{aq-diox}$ 248 (4.64), 305 (3.92), 360 (4.0)	450–80 d without m	....			δ	δ	i	δ	δ	alk s (ye) os δ	B19², 284
e37	Elliptic acid	$C_{20}H_{18}O_8$	386.36	nd (aq al)	190										J1942, 587
—	Embelin	see 1,4-Benzoquinone, 2,5-dihydroxy-3-dodecyl-													
e38	Emeraldine	$C_{48}H_{40}N_8$	726.90	indigo-bl pw							i		...	i	80 % aa s chl, gl aa i	B12¹, 147
e39	Emetine(l)	Cephaline-O-methyl ether $C_{29}H_{40}N_2O_4$.	480.66	amor pw (ye under light) λ^{al} 235 sh (4.2), 285 (3.8), 360 sh (2.2) $[\alpha]_D^{20}$ − 50 (chl, c = 2)	74 (cor)	....			i	s	s	s	δ	chl δ	B23², 449
Ω e40	—, hydrochloride(l)	$C_{29}H_{40}N_2O_4.2HCl.7H_2O$. See e39	679.69	nd (w) $[\alpha]_D$ + 11 (w, c=1) + 21 (w, c = 8) $\lambda^{dil\,HCl}$ 230 (1.6), 280 (0.65)	269–70d				v	s	i	...			B23², 451
e41	Emicymarin	$C_{30}H_{46}O_9$	550.70	nd or pr (+ MeOH) $[\alpha]_D^{20}$ + 12.8 (al, c = 2.5)	ca. 207				δ						J1963, 1461
—	Emodin	see 9,10-Anthracene-quinone, 6-methyl-1,3,8-trihydroxy-													
—	Enanthic acid	see Heptanoic acid*													
e42	Enneaphyllin	$C_{90}H_{154}$	1236.24	rods (bz)	98					s	δ	i	s	AcOEt, to s lig δ Py i	C32, 2686
e43	Eosin	2,4,5,7-Tetrabromofluorescein.	647.93	ye-red λ^w 520 (5.1)	295–6				i	s	i	...	δ	alk s chl, aa δ	B19², 254
e44	—, sodium salt decahydrate	Eosin dye. Sodium eosin. $C_{20}H_6Br_4Na_2O_5.10H_2O$. See e43	871.90	red nd (dil al) eff 150 λ 519 (4.91)					s	s	i				B19, 230
e45	Ephedrine(d)	$C_6H_5CH(OH)CH(CH_3)NHCH_3$	165.24	pl (w) $[\alpha]_D$ + 13.4 (4 % w)	40	225^{760}			s	s	s	s	s	chl s	Am 69, 128

For explanations, symbols and abbreviations see beginning of table. For structural formulas see end of table.

No.	Name	Synonyms and Formula	Mol. wt.	Color, crystalline form, specific rotation and λ_{max} (log ε)	m.p. °C	b.p. °C	Density	n_D	Solubility						Ref.
									w	al	eth	ace	bz	other solvents	

Ephedrine

No.	Name	Synonyms and Formula	Mol. wt.	Color...	m.p.	b.p.	Density	n_D	w	al	eth	ace	bz	other	Ref.
e46	—(dl)............	Racephedrine. $C_{10}H_{15}NO$. See e45	165.24	nd (eth or peth) λ^{al} 240 (1.78), 254 (2.26)	76–7	135–7[12]			s	s	s	...	s	chl s	B13[2], 376
e47	—(l)............	Natural ephedrine. $C_{10}H_{15}NO.H_2O$. See e45	183.25	pl (w + 1) $[\alpha]_D^{20}$ −6.3 (al) λ^{al} 252 (2.2), 258 (2.3), 266 (2.2)	40	225[760]			s	s	s	...	s	chl s	C34, 2852
Ω e48	—,hydrochloride(d)	$C_{10}H_{15}NO.HCl$. See e45....	201.70	pl (abs al) $[\alpha]_D^{20}$ +35.8 (w, c = 11.5) $\lambda^{dil\,HCl}$ 250 (2.2), 257 (2.3), 263 (2.2)	218				v	s	i				B13[2], 375
e49	—,—(dl)........	Ephetonin. $C_{10}H_{15}NO.HCl$. See e45	201.70	pl (al) $\lambda^{dil\,HCl}$ 250 (2.2), 257 (2.3), 263 (2.2)	189–90				v	s	i				B13[2], 376
e50	—,—(l).........	$C_{10}H_{15}NO.HCl$. See e45....	201.70	orh nd, $[\alpha]_D^{20}$ −36.6 (w, c = 5)	218–20				v	s	i				C51, 4304
Ω e51	—,sulfate(l)......	$(C_{10}H_{15}NO)_2.H_2SO_4$. See e45	428.54	hex pl or orh nd (w), $[\alpha]$ −31.5 (w, c = 5)	245–8d				v	δ					C21, 2169
e52	—,N-methyl(l)	$C_6H_5CH(OH)CH(CH_3)N(CH_3)_2$ 179.26		nd or pl (al or eth. $[\alpha]_D$ −29.5 (MeOH, c = 4.5)	87–8 (cor)	v volat			i	s	s[h]			MeOH s	B13[2], 378
e53	—,N-(4-nitro-benzoyl)-(dl)	....	314.35	pa ye pl (al)	162										Am 69, 128
e54	Epi-β-amyrin....	....	426.74	cr (MeOH) $[\alpha]_D$ +73.3 (chl)	225 (cor)										E14s, 948
e55	Epi-α-amyrin, acetate	....	468.77	nd (chl-MeOH) $[\alpha]_D$ +39 (chl)	135 (cor)										E14s, 1070
e56	Epiandrosterone...	Androstan-3β-ol-17-one. Isoandrosterone. $C_{19}H_{30}O_2$.	290.45	cr (bz-peth, ace) $[\alpha]_D^{20}$ +108 (MeOH) λ^{sulf} 405 (2.90)	177–9 (176)										E14, 144
e57	Epiborneol(l)......	3-Camphanol............	154.26	nd (C_5H_{12}) $[\alpha]_D^{17}$ +11.1 (al)	181–2	213[742]								peth s	B6[2], 91
e58	—,acetate		196.29	$[\alpha]_D^{16}$ +15.63	< −15	101[11]	0.9872[14]	1.4651[14]							B6[2], 92
e59	Epibreinonol......	Breinonol A. Breienonol A.	440.72	pl (MeOH), nd (chl), $[\alpha]_D^{17}$ +37 (chl)	204										E14s, 1083
—	Epibromohydrin	see Propane, 3-bromo-1,2-epoxy-*													
e60	Epicamphor(d)	3-Bornanone. $C_{10}H_{16}$.	152.24	$[\alpha]_D^{17}$ +45.4 (bz)	182				δ	s	s			peth v	B7[1], 86
e61	—(dl)...........	See e60	152.24	cr (peth)	175–7				δ	v	v			peth v	B7[2], 104
e62	—(l)............	β-Camphor. $C_{10}H_{16}O$. See e60.	152.24	$[\alpha]_D^{19}$ −58.21 (bz, c = 13)	184 (cor) (186–7)	213			δ	v	v			peth v	B7[2], 105
e63	—,oxime(d).......		167.25	nd (MeOH) $[\alpha]_D$ −98.9	103						s	s			B7[1], 86
e64	—,—(dl)........	$C_{10}H_{17}NO$. See e63	167.25	nd (dil al)	98–100						s	s			B7[1], 87
e65	—,—(l)..........	$C_{10}H_{17}NO$. See e63	167.25	nd (dil MeOH) $[\alpha]_D$ +100.5 (bz, c = 6.3)	103–4				i	s[h]	s	s		os s	B7[1], 86
e66	—,semicarbazone (d)		209.29	nd (al)	237–8				i	s[h]					B7[1], 86
e67	—,—(l)..........	$C_{11}H_{19}N_3O$. See e66	209.29	nd (al), $[\alpha]_D^{20}$ +145 (MeOH, c = 0.73)	237–8d				i	s[h]					B7[1], 86
e68	—,bromo-(l)		231.14	nd or pr (peth) $[\alpha]_D$ −86.6 (AcOEt, c = 3.6)	133–4					δ			v	chl v lig s	B7[1], 86
e70	α-Epicamphyl-amine	....	153.27	$[\alpha]_D$ +17.6 (bz, c = 6.5)		127–8[100]			v						B12[2], 35
e71	Epicatechin(dl)	Epicatechol. $C_{15}H_{14}O_6$	290.28	nd (w + 1), pr (w + 4) λ^{al} 279 (3.56)	224–6d anh (cor)				δ	s	δ	s			B17[2], 258
e72	—(l)............	$C_{15}H_{14}O_6$. See e71	290.28	cr (w + 4) $[\alpha]_D^{25}$ −69 (al) $[\alpha]_D$ −60 (1:1 ace −w, c = 2) λ^{al} 279 (3.56)	245d (cor) (242)				δ	s	δ	s			B17[2], 257

For explanations, symbols and abbreviations see beginning of table. For structural formulas see end of table.

β-Epichlorohydrin

No.	Name	Synonyms and Formula	Mol. wt.	Color, crystalline form, specific rotation and λ_{max} (log ε)	m.p. °C	b.p. °C	Density	n_D	w	al	eth	ace	bz	other solvents	Ref.
—	β-Epichloro-hydrin	see **Propane, 2-chloro-1,3-epoxy***													
—	Epicholestanol	see **3α-Cholestanol**													
e74	Epicholestan-4-ol	4α-Hydroxycholestane. $C_{27}H_{48}O$.	388.69	lf (al, MeOH – ace) $[\alpha]_D^{21} + 29.0$ (chl)	187–8				i		s			chl s	E14, 65
e75	Epicholestanol	ε-Cholestanol. 3α-Hydroxy-cholestane. $C_{27}H_{48}O$.	388.69	nd (al, MeOH) $[\alpha]_D^{20} + 34$ (chl, c = 1.7)	185–6				i	δ s^h	s			chl s MeOH δ	E14, 59
e76	Epicholesterol	5-Cholesten-3α-ol. $C_{27}H_{46}O$.	386.67	cr (al, chl-MeOH) $[\alpha]_D^{30} - 37.5$ (al) $\lambda^{hx} 192 (3.95)$	141.5					δ s^h					E14, 56
e77	Epicoprostanol	3-α-Coprostanol. Epicopro-sterol. $C_{27}H_{48}O$.	388.69	cr (al, ace) $[\alpha]_D^{20} + 31.6$ (chl)	117–8				i	s	s		v	chl s	E14, 60
e78	Epicoprostenol	4-Cholesten-3α-ol. Epiallocholesterol. $C_{27}H_{46}O$	386.67	nd (ace) $[\alpha]_D^{24} + 120.8$ (bz)	84 (82)					s	v	δ s^h	v	chl v	E14, 37
—	Epicyclene	see **Cyclocamphane**													
e79	Epidicentrin(dl)	dl-Domesticine methyl ether. $C_{20}H_{21}NO_4$	339.40	pr (MeOH)	142					v^h	s			chl v^h	B27², 553
e80	—(l)	$C_{20}H_{21}NO_4$. See e79	339.40	pr (MeOH) $[\alpha]_D^{18} - 101.3$ (chl, c = 0.5)	138–9					v^h	s			chl v^h	B27², 553
e81	Epiergosterol(D)	$\Delta^{7,9(11),22}$-Ergostatrien-3α-ol. $C_{28}H_{44}O$.	396.67	nd (eth-MeOH) $[\alpha]_D^{19} + 36.2$ (chl)	203–4										E14s, 1752
e82	Epifucitol(d)	$C_6H_{14}O_3$	166.18	cr (eth, w) $[\alpha]_D^{21} + 2.2$ (w, c = 1)	105–7				s		s				Am 74, 4373
e83	—(l)	$C_6H_{14}O_5$. See e83	166.18	cr (w), $[\alpha]_D^{20} - 2.3$ (w, c = 1)	105–7				s		s				C24, 2431
e84	Epifucose(l)	6-Deoxy-D-glucose. α-D-Glucomethylose. l-Talomethylose.	164.16	cr (AcOEt) $[\alpha]_D - 36.9$ (w, c = 6)	135–45				s		i	i		abs al s	B31, 65
	Epiiodohydrin	see **Propane, 1,2-epoxy-3-iodo-***													
e85	Epiisofenchol	4,6,6-Trimethyl-2-norbor-nanol.	154.26	nd (sub) $[\alpha]_D^{20} - 7.35$	71–2 (67)										E12A, 645
e86	Epiisofenchone(d)	4,6,6-Trimethyl-2-norbor-nanone	152.24	$[\alpha]_D + 13.6$		195	0.9342^{20}	1.459^{20}			s	s			F12A, 732
e87	—(dl)	$C_{10}H_{16}O$. See e86	152.24			195–8 90–3²¹		1.4625^{25}			s	s			E12A, 732
e88	Epilupinine	d-Isolupinine	169.27	nd (peth) $[\alpha]_D^{17} + 32$ (al, c = 1.5)	76–8				s		s	s	s	os s peth δ	B21², 30
—	Epimethylin	see **Ether, methyl propyl, 2′,3′-epoxy-**													
—	Epinephrine	see **Adrenaline**													
e89	Epinine		167.21	nd (al)	188–9 (cor)				δ s^h	δ $δ^h$			δ	os δ	B13², 487
e90	Epiquinidine	$C_{20}H_{24}N_2O_2$.	324.43	cr (AcOEt), lf (eth) $[\alpha]_D^{20} + 103.7$ (al, c = 0.86) $\lambda^{w, pH=1} 315$ (3.62), 350 (3.62)	113					v	s				C31, 1816
e91	Epirhodanhydrin	2,3-Epoxypropylrhodanine. CH_2CHCH_2SCN (with O)	115.16	dk red liq, garlic smell	d				i	s				chl s	B17, 106
e92	Episarsapogenin	$C_{27}H_{44}O_3$	416.65	nd (ace) $[\alpha]_D - 71$ $\lambda^{al} 215 (3.78)$	204–6 (198)										E14, 284
e93	Epitruxillic acid	2,4-cis-Diphenylcyclobutane 1,3-trans-dicarboxylic acid*.	296.33	cr (dil al or bz-aa)	285–7						δ		δ		B9², 691
e94	Equilenin(d)	$C_{18}H_{18}O_2$	266.34	nd (dil al) $[\alpha]_D^6 + 87$ (diox) $\lambda^{MeOH} 235, 281, 340$	258–9 (251)	170 80^{0.01} sub				δ s^h		δ		chl δ	F14, 134
e95	—(dl)	$C_{18}H_{18}O_2$. See e94	266.34	cr (bz) λ^{MeOH} 235, 281, 340	276–8										Am 67, 2274
e96	—(l)	$C_{18}H_{18}O_2$. See e94	266.34	$[\alpha]_D^{30} - 85$ (diox) $\lambda^{MeOH} 235, 281, 340$	258–9 (cor)	170–80¹ sub				s^h					Am 67, 2274

For explanations, symbols and abbreviations see beginning of table. For structural formulas see end of table.

No.	Name	Synonyms and Formula	Mol. wt.	Color, crystalline form, specific rotation and λ_{max} (log ε)	m.p. °C	b.p. °C	Density	n_D	Solubility						Ref.
									w	al	eth	ace	bz	other solvents	
	Equilin														
Ω e97	**Equilin**	$C_{18}H_{20}O_2$	268.36	orh sph pl (AcOEt) $[\alpha]_D +308$ (diox, c = 2) $\lambda^{97\%sulf}$ 232 (4.00), 353 (4.38), 459 (3.62)	238–40	170–200 sub vac	....	....	δ	s	...	s	...	diox, AcOEt s	E14, 135
e98	**—, α-dihydro-**	$\Delta^{1,3,5(10),7}$-Estratetraene-3, 17β-diol. $C_{18}H_{22}O_2$.	270.38	cr (ace) $[\alpha]_D +220$ (diox, c = 1) λ^{MeOH} 225, 260, 305	174.6	....	....	....	δ	s	...	s	...	sulf, diox s	E14s, 1962
e99	**Equisetrin**	Kaempferol-7-diglucoside. $C_{27}H_{30}O_{16}$.	610.53	ye nd (+2w)	195–6	....	....	....						sulf s	C34, 7910
e100	**Equol**	4′,7-Isoflavandiol. $C_{15}H_{14}O_3$.	242.28	cr (aq al) $[\alpha]_{5461} -21.5$	189–90.5	....	....	....							C52, 20511
e101	**Eremophilol**	$C_{15}H_{24}O$.	220.36	visc oil $[\alpha]_{5461} -55.6$ (MeOH)	....	164.5^{13}	....	1.5202^{20}							E12B, 1432
e102	**Eremophilone**	$C_{15}H_{22}O$	218.34	nd (MeOH) $[\alpha]_{5461} -207$ (MeOH) λ^{al} 241 (3.99), 318 (1.92)	42–3	171^{15}	0.9994^{25}_{25}	1.5182^{25}							E12B, 2597
e103	**—,8,9-epoxy-**	$C_{15}H_{22}O_2$	234.34	nd (peth) λ^{al} 295 (1.7)	63–4	....	....	....	i	s	s	s	v	oos v	E12B, 2600
e104	**Ergine**	Ergonovine. Lysergamide. $C_{16}H_{17}N_3O$.	283.33	cr (MeOH +1), pr (aq ace +2w) $[\alpha]^{20}_{5461}$ +598 (chl), $[\alpha]_D +479$ (Py) λ^{MeOH} 241 (4.30), 311 (3.95)	135d resolidify 140, remelt 190	....	....	....	δ		δ	...		os δ	H32, 506
—	**Ergobasine**........	*see* **Ergometrine**													
—	**Ergobasinine**......	*see* **Ergometrinine**													
e107	**Ergocornine**.......	$C_{31}H_{39}N_5O_5$	561.70	cr (MeOH) $[\alpha]^{20}_D -188$ (chl), c = 1), −105 (Py)	182–4d	....	....	....	i	s	...	s	s^h	chl, AcOEt s	H34, 1544
e108	**Ergocorninine**	$C_{31}H_{39}N_5O_5$. *See* e107	561.70	lo pr (al) $[\alpha]^{20}_D +409$ (chl, c = 1)	228d	....	....	....	i	s	...	v	s^h	chl v AcOEt s	B27², 860
Ω e109	**Ergocristine**......	$C_{35}H_{39}N_5O_5$	609.63	rh (bz +2) $[\alpha]^{20}_D -183$ (chl, c = 1) $[\alpha]_D -93$ (Py) λ^{MeOH} 240 (4.30), 311 (3.95)	175d (170–90)d	....	....	....	i	s	...	s	...	chl s	H34, 1544
Ω e110	**Ergocristinine**	$C_{35}H_{39}N_5O_5$. *See* e109	609.63	pr (al, AcOEt) $[\alpha]^{20}_D +366$ (chl, c = 0.68), +460 (Py) λ^{MeOH} 241 (4.33), 312 (3.96)	237–8d (226d)	....	....	....	i	$δ^h$	...	δ	...	chl δ	B27², 860
e111	**Ergocryptine**......	$C_{32}H_{41}N_5O_5$	575.72	pr (al, MeOH) $[\alpha]^{20}_D -187$ (chl, c = 1), −112 (Py) λ^{MeOH} 240 (4.31), 312 (3.97)	212–4d	....	....	....	i	s	...	...	...	chl s	H34, 1544
e112	**Ergocryptinine**	$C_{32}H_{41}N_5O_5$. *See* e111	575.72	lo pr (al) $[\alpha]^{20}_D +408$ (chl, c = 1), +479 (Py) λ^{MeOH} 240 (4.31), 313 (3.96)	245d	....	....	....	δ	s^h	...	v	...	chl v	B27², 860
e113	**Ergometrine**(*l*)	Ergobasine. *l*-Lysergic-*l*(β-hydroxyisopropylamide. $C_{19}H_{23}N_3O_2$.	325.42	nd (bz) $[\alpha]^{20}_D -89$ (w)	159–62d (cor)	....	....	....	δ	s	...	s	...	chl δ	Am 69, 1701
Ω e114	**Ergometrinine**(*d*) ..	Ergobasinine. *d*-Isolysergic-*d*-(β-hydroxyisopropyl-amide. $C_{19}H_{23}N_3O_2$.	325.42	pr (ace) $[\alpha]^{20}_D +416$ (chl, c = 0.26), +413 (MeOH)	195–7d	....	....	....	i	δ	...	δ	...	Py, chl s	Am 60, 1701

For explanations, symbols and abbreviations see beginning of table. For structural formulas see end of table.

Ergometrinine

No.	Name	Synonyms and Formula	Mol. wt.	Color, crystalline form, specific rotation and λ_{max} (log ε)	m.p. °C	b.p. °C	Density	n_D	w	al	eth	ace	bz	other solvents	Ref.
e115	—(l)............	$C_{19}H_{23}N_3O_2$. See e114	325.42	pr (ace) $[\alpha]_D^{20}$ −415 (chl, c = 0.26)	196d (cor)	....			i	δ	...	δ		Py, chl s	**Am 60,** 1701
e116	Ergopinacol II....	Bisergostadienol. $C_{56}H_{36}O_2$.	791.31	nd (bz-al) $[\alpha]_D$ −155 (Py, c = 0.8)	205										**E14,** 74
e117	Ergosine........	$C_{30}H_{37}N_5O_5$............	547.66	pr (MeOH, AcOEt) $[\alpha]_D^{20}$ + 16 (ace), −161 (chl, c = 1) λ^{MeOH} 240 (4.33), 312 (3.99)	228d							s	...	chl s MeOH δ	**H34,** 1544
e118	Ergosinine.......	$C_{30}H_{37}N_5O_5$. See e117......	547.66	pr (al, aq ace, bz), nd (MeOH + ½) $[\alpha]_D^{20}$ + 420 (chl, c = 1) λ^{MeOH} 241 (4.32), 312 (3.96)	220d (228d)				i	δ	...	s	...	chl s	**J1937,** 396
e119	$\Delta^{5:6,7:8}$-Ergostadien-3β-ol	22,23-Dihydroergosterol. Provitamin D₄. $C_{28}H_{46}O$.	398.68	nd (MeOH-AcOEt) $[\alpha]_D^{19}$ −109 (chl)	152–3										**E14s,** 1754
e120	$\Delta^{14,22}$-Ergostadien-3β-ol	$C_{28}H_{46}O$............	398.68	cr (MeOH) $[\alpha]_D^{20}$ −9 (chl)	116										**E14s,** 1762
e121	α-Ergostadienone	lf (al) $[\alpha]_D^{19}$ +2 (chl)	396.67	lf (al) $[\alpha]_D^{19}$ +2 (chl)	182–3										**E14,** 125
e122	Ergostane.......	24-Methyl-5α-cholestane. $C_{28}H_{50}$.	386.71	lf or pl (eth − MeOH or ace) $[\alpha]_D^{23}$ +21 (chl, c = 2)	85				i	δ	v	v	...	chl v	**E14,** 23
e123	Ergostanol.......	Brassicastanol. Ergostan-3β-ol. $C_{28}H_{50}O$.	402.71	nd (MeOH-eth) $[\alpha]_D$ +15.94 (chl, c = 1.8) $\lambda^{97\% sulf}$ 321 (3.82), 410 sh (3.07), 480 sh (2.75)	144–5				i		s	...		chl s	**E14s,** 1767
e124	$\Delta^{3,5,7,22}$-Ergo-statetraene	$C_{28}H_{42}$.................	378.65	pl (Ac₂O or al) $[\alpha]_D^{20}$ −40.5 (chl) λ 301.5 (4.20), 316 (4.28), 331.5 (4.15)	104										**E14s,** 1434
e125	$\Delta^{4,6,22}$-Ergo-statrienone	Isoergosterone. $C_{28}H_{42}O$....	394.65	nd (ace-eth) λ^{al} 284 (4.42)	110										**E14,** 124
e126	α-Ergostenol......	$\Delta^{8:14}$-Ergosten-3β-ol. α-Tetrahydroergosterol. $C_{28}H_{46}O$.	400.70	lf or nd (MeOH) nd (gl aa) $[\alpha]_D^{16}$ +11 (MeOH, c = 0.9) λ^{hx} 208 (4.05)	131 (134–5)					δ	s	...	s	chl s	**E14s,** 1765
e127	β-Ergostenol......	$\Delta^{14:15}$-Ergosten-3β-ol. β-Tetrahydroergosterol. $C_{28}H_{46}O$.	400.70	pl or ta (al) $[\alpha]_D^{20}$ +21.2 (chl, c = 0.9) λ^{hx} 196 (3.93)	141–2										**E14s,** 1767
e128	γ-Ergostenol......	$\Delta^{7:8}$-Ergosten-3β-ol. β-Tetrahydroergosterol. $C_{28}H_{46}O$.	400.70	nd (MeOH), cr (Pr'OH), lf (w) $[\alpha]_D^{19}$ 0 λ^{al} 195.5 (3.92)	148(152)						s				**E14s,** 1763
e129	δ-$\Delta^{8,9}$-Ergostenol ..	$C_{28}H_{46}O$............	400.70	$[\alpha]_D$ +39	155									chl s	**J1949,** 214
Ω e130	Ergosterol........	$\Delta^{5,7,22}$-Ergostatrien-3β-ol. Ergosterin. $C_{28}H_{44}O$.	396.67	pl (+ w, al), nd (eth), $[\alpha]_D^{20}$ −135 (chl, c = 1.2) λ^{al} 271 (3.80), 281 (3.82), 293 (3.57)	168 (+ 1, w)	250^{0.01}			i	δ s^h	δ s^h		s	chl s aa, peth δ	**E14s,** 1735
e131	Ergosterol D	$\Delta^{7,9,11,22}$-Ergostatrien-3β-ol. $C_{28}H_{44}O$.	396.67	nd (al) $[\alpha]_D^{17}$ +24.6	167					δ s^h	...	...	s	chl s	**E14s,** 1752

For explanations, symbols and abbreviations see beginning of table. For structural formulas see end of table.

No.	Name	Synonyms and Formula	Mol. wt.	Color, crystalline form, specific rotation and λ_{max} (log ε)	m.p. °C	b.p. °C	Density	n_D	Solubility						Ref.
									w	al	eth	ace	bz	other solvents	
	Ergosterol														
e133	Ergosterol,5,6-dihydro-	α-Dihydroergosterol. $C_{28}H_{46}O$.	398.68	lf (ace), pl (chl-MeOH, AcOEt-MeOH) $[\alpha]_D^{20} -19$ (chl) $\lambda^{97\%sulf}$ 238 (3.57), 319 (3.95), 419 (3.51), 469 sh (3.28)	176–7	....			...	...	...	...	...		E14s, 1758
e134	Ergosterone.......	$\Delta^{4,7,22}$-Ergostatrienone. $C_{28}H_{42}O$.	394.65	nd (ace-MeOH) $[\alpha]_D^{20} -0.52$ (chl) λ^{al} 242 (4.15)	132–2.5	....									E14, 124
e135	Ergotamine.......	$C_{33}H_{35}N_5O_5$.............	581.68	nd (al), pr (bz) pl (aq ace) $[\alpha]_D^{20} -160$ (chl, c = 1) λ^{al} 318 (3.86)	213–4d	....			i	δ	s	δ	s	PhNO₂ v chl, Py s peth i	B27², 860
Ω e136	Ergotaminine.....	$C_{33}H_{35}N_5O_5$.............	581.68	rh pl (MeOH), pl (al) $[\alpha]_D^{20} +369$ (chl, c =0.5) λ^{MeOH} 241 (4.28), 309 (393)	252d	....			i	δ		δ	δ	Py v chl s peth i	B27², 860
e137	Ergothioneine.....	Thiasine. Thioneine. $C_9H_{15}N_3O_2S$.	229.30	pl (w +2), nd or lf (dil al) $[\alpha]_D +115$ (w, c =1) $\lambda^{w, pH =2-10}$ 258 (2.16)	290d	....			v^h	δ^h	i	δ	i	MeOH δ^h chl i	B25², 413
—	Eriodictol	see Flavanone,3′,4′,5,7-tetrahydroxy-													
—	Erucic acid.......	see 13-Docosenoic acid(cis)													
e138	Erysocine........	$C_{18}H_{21}NO_3$.............	299.37	nd (eth) $[\alpha]_D +238.1$	162	....			i	s	s	...	...	chl s	Am 62, 1677
e139	Erysodine	$C_{18}H_{21}NO_3$.............	299.37	nd (al) $[\alpha]_D^{27} +248$ (al) λ^{ac} 235 (4.4), 285 (3.5)	204–5	....			i	s	s	...	...	chl s	Am 73, 589
e140	Erysonine	$C_{17}H_{19}NO_3$.............	285.35	cr (al), $[\alpha]_D^{25} +285-8$ (aq HCl), +272 (morpholine)	236–7d	....			...	δ	...	δ	δ	os δ	Am 36, 1544
e141	Erysopine	$C_{17}H_{19}NO_3$.............	285.35	cr (al) $[\alpha]_D^{25} +265.2$ (al-glycerol)	241–2	....			δ	δ	...	...	...	chl δ	Am 73, 589
e142	Erysothiopine	$C_{19}H_{21}NO_7S$	407.45	cr (al-w +w) $[\alpha]_D^{25} +194$ (al)	168–9	....									Am 66, 1083
e143	Erysovine........	$C_{18}H_{21}NO_3$.............	299.37	pr (eth) $[\alpha]_D +252$ (al)	178–9	....				s	s	...	...	chl s	Am 73, 589
e144	Erythraline	$C_{18}H_{19}NO_3$.............	297.34	cr (al) $[\alpha]_D^{27} +211.8$ (al) λ^{ac} 238 (4.4), 290 (3.6); λ^{alk} 230 (4.2), 290 (3.6)	106–7	....				s	...	...	...	chl s	Am 73, 589
e145	Erythramine	Dihydroerythraline. $C_{18}H_{21}NO_3$.	299.37	cr (eth-peth) $[\alpha]_D^{30} +228$ (al, c =0.19) λ^{ac} 240 (3.6), 290 (3.6)	103–4	$125^{3.9 \cdot 10^{-4}}$				s	s	s	s	lig i	Am 73, 589
e146	Erythratine	$C_{18}H_{19}NO_4$.............	315.37	cr (eth-peth +½w) $[\alpha]_D^{28} +145.5$ (al) λ^{al} 293 (0.68)	170	....									Am 73, 589
e147	Erythritol(d)	d-Erythryte. L-Threite.	122.12	pr (w), nd (al) $[\alpha]_D +11.1$ (al, c =5), -4.4 (w, c =5-10)	88–9	....			s		i	...	i	....	B1³, 2360
Ω e148	—(l)............	l-Erythryte. D-Threite.	122.12	pr (w), nd (al) $[\alpha]_D -11.1$ (al, c =5), -4.33 (w, c =6)	90–1	....			s		i	...	i	....	B1³, 2360

For explanations, symbols and abbreviations see beginning of table. For structural formulas see end of table.

No.	Name	Synonyms and Formula	Mol. wt.	Color, crystalline form, specific rotation and λ_{max} (log ε)	m.p. °C	b.p. °C	Density	n_D	Solubility						Ref.
									w	al	eth	ace	bz	other solvents	
	Erythritol														
e148[1]	—(meso)	. . . .	122.12	bipym tetr pr	121.5	329–31 294– 6[200]	1.451$_4^{20}$	. . . .	v	δ s[h]	i			Py v	B1[3], 2356
e148[2]	—,tetranitrate . . . . (meso)	pl or lf (al)	302.11	pl or lf (al)	6[1]	. . . .	. . . .	. . . .	i	s	s	. . . . .		glycerol s	B1[3], 2358
e149	β-Erythroidine	$C_{16}H_{19}NO_3$	273.34	cr (abs al) $[\alpha]_D^{25}+88.8$ (w) λ^{al-HCl} 238 (4.40)	99.5–100	. . . .	. . . .	. . . .	s	v	s	. . .	v	chl s	Am 80, 3905
e150	Erythronic acid, γ-lactone (D)	. . . .	118.09	pr $[\alpha]_D^{20}-73.2$ (w, c=4)	104–5	. . . .	. . . .	. . . .		s[h]					B18[2], 54
e151	—,—,(L).	$C_4H_6O_4$. See e150.	118.09	nd (AcOEt) $[\alpha]_D^{20}+73$ (w, c=4)	105 (cor)	. . . .	. . . .	. . . .		s[h]					B18[2], 54
Ω e152	Erythrose (D).	$C_4H_8O_4$. See e152.	120.12	syr $[\alpha]_D^{20}+1 \to$ -14.8 (w, c=11, 3 days) (mut)			. . . .	. . . .	s	v					B31, 12
e153	—(L)	$C_4H_8O_4$. See e152.	120.12	syr $[\alpha]_D^{24}+11.5 \to$ $+30.5$ (w, c=3, 3 days) (mut)					s	v					B31, 12
Ω e154	Erythrosin	2,4,5,7-Tetraiodofluorescein.	835.91	og-ye (eth) λ^w 530 (5.12)			. . . .	. . . .	δ	s	s	. . .	i	aq ace s lig i	B19[2], 258
Ω e155	—(dye)	Disodium salt of erythrosin. Iodeosin B. $C_{20}H_6I_4Na_2O_5$.	879.87	red-br pw λ^{alk} 522.5 (4.86)					v	s			i		M, 415
e156	Erythrulose (L)	$HOCH_2CH(OH)COCH_2OH$.	120.12	syr $[\alpha]_D^{30}+11.31$ (w, at equilibrium) (mut)		d			s	s	i				B31, 14
c157	Escholerine	$C_{41}H_{61}NO_{12}$	775.95	pl (ace-w) $[\alpha]_D^{25}-30$ (Py, c=1)	235d				i		s				Am 76, 1152
—	Esculetin	see Coumarin, 6,7-dihydroxy-													
Ω e158	Esculin.	Aesculin. $C_{15}H_{16}O_9$.	340.29	pr (w +2) $[\alpha]_D^{18}-14.6$ (MeOH) $[\alpha]_D^{22}-38$ (Py, c=1.5) λ^{al} 227 (4.2), 251 sh (3.7), 298 (3.8), 338 (4.1)	205d	230d	. . . .	. . . .	δ s[h]	δ s[h]	δ	. . .	. . .	alk, aa, Py, AcOEt s chl s[h]	B31, 246
Ω e159	α-Estradiol	$C_{18}H_{24}O_2$	272.39	nd (+½w, 80 % al) $[\alpha]_D^{20}+56$ (diox, c=0.9)	220–3				i	s		s	δ^h	peth s	E14, 98
e159[1]	β-Estradiol	$C_{18}H_{24}O_2$. See e159	272.39	pr (80 % al) $[\alpha]_D^{25}+76-83$ (diox) λ^{al} 280 (3.33)	178–9				i	s	. . .	s	. . .	diox s	E14, 99
—	Estragole	see Benzene, 1-allyl-4-methoxy-													
Ω e160	Estriol	$C_{18}H_{24}O_3$	288.39	lf (al), mcl (dil al) $[\alpha]_D+61$ (al), $+30$ (Py) λ^{al} 281 (3.34)	288d (cor)	. . . .	1.27	. . . .	. . .	s	δ	. . .	δ	Py v os δ	E14s, 2152
Ω e161	Estrone	$C_{18}H_{22}O_2$	270.38	α mcl (al) β, γ orh (al) $[\alpha]_D^{25}+158$ to $+168$ (diox) λ^{al} 280 (3.37)	260 d	. . . .	β 1.236 γ 1.228		i	δ^h	δ	δ^h	δ	diox, Py s chl δ^h	E14, 135
—	Ethanal*	see Acetaldehyde													
Ω e162	Ethane*	CH_3CH_3	30.07	gas, hex cr	−183.3	−88.63	0.572^{-108} 0.509$_7^{-60}$	1.03769 at 0°/546 mm.	i	δ	. . .	δ	s	. . . .	B1[3], 120
e163	—,amino-*	Ethylamine. $C_2H_5NH_2$ . . .	45.09	λ^{gas} 177 (3.20), 213 (2.90)	−81	16.6[760]	0.6829$_4^{20}$	1.3663[20]	∞	∞	∞	. . .	. . .		B4[2], 586

For explanations, symbols and abbreviations see beginning of table. For structural formulas see end of table.

No.	Name	Synonyms and Formula	Mol. wt.	Color, crystalline form, specific rotation and λ_{max} (log ε)	m.p. °C	b.p. °C	Density	n_D	w	al	eth	ace	bz	other solvents	Ref.
	Ethane														
e164	—,—,hydro-bromide*	$C_2H_5NH_2$.HBr	126.01	mcl nd or pl (al)	159.5				s	v			i	chl δ	B4², 588
Ω e165	—,—,hydro-chloride*	$C_2H_5NH_2$.HCl	81.56	mcl pl (al)	109–10	d315			v	v	i	i	i	chl i	B4², 588
e166	—,—,hydroiodide*	$C_2H_5NH_2$.HI	173.01	mcl nd (w)	188.5		2.100		v	δ	i		i		B4², 588
e167	—,1-amino-2-bromo-, hydro chloride*	$BrCH_2CH_2NH_2$.HCl	160.45	lf (al-AcOEt)	174–5d (cor)				v	v	i		s		B4², 618
Ω e168	—,1-amino-2-chloro-, hydro-chloride*	$ClCH_2CH_2NH_2$.HCl	115.99	hyg cr (AmOH or al-eth)	144(148)				v	v	i	s		os v	B4, 133
—	—,2-amino-1,1-diethoxy-*	see **Acetaldehyde, 2-amino-,** diethyl acetal													
Ω e169	—,1-amino-2-diethylamino-*	N′,N-diethylethylenediamine	116.21			144⁷⁶⁰ 38–40¹⁵	0.8280²⁰	1.4340²⁰	∞	s	s			to s	B4², 690
Ω e170	—,1-amino-2-ethoxy-*	2-Aminodiethyl ether. $C_2H_5OCH_2CH_2NH_2$	89.14			108⁷⁵⁸ (cor)	0.8512²⁰	1.4101²⁰	∞	∞	∞	s	s		B4², 718
Ω e171	—,1-amino 2-methoxy-*	$CH_3OCH_2CH_2NH_2$	75.11			95⁷⁵⁶			v	v					B4², 718
e176	—,aminoxy-*	Ethoxylamine. α-Ethyl-hydroxylamine. $C_2H_5ONH_2$	61.05			68	0.8827⁸		∞	∞	∞			os ∞	B1², 333
Ω e177	—,1,2-bis(4-aminophenyl)-*	α,α′-Bi-p-toluidine. 4,4′-Diaminobenzyl.	212.30	pl (w)	135–6 sub	sub			i sʰ	v					B13¹, 75
e178	—,1,2-bis-(benzoyl-amino)-*	N,N′-Dibenzoyl-ethylenediamine. $C_6H_5CONHCH_2CH_2NHCOC_6H_5$	268.32	pr or nd (al)	247				i	i				aa vʰ	B9², 187
e179	—,1,2-bis(2-bromophenyl)-*	2,2′-Dibromobibenzyl	340.07	pl (al)	84.5	138–48⁰·⁰¹³				sʰ					B5², 507
e180	—,1,2-bis(4-bromophenyl)-*	4,4′-Dibromobibenzyl.	340.07	pr (al)	115	ca. 198¹⁰					i δʰ		δ		B5², 507
Ω e181	—,1,2-bis(2-chloroethoxy)-*	Triglycol dichloride ether. $ClCH_2CH_2OCH_2CH_2OCH_2CH_2Cl$	187.07			230⁷⁶⁰ 118¹⁰	1.197²⁰₂₀	1.4592²⁵							C52, 18219
e182	—,1,1-bis(4-chlorophenyl)-2,2-dichloro-*	DDD. Rothane	320.05	λ^{al} 233 (4.3)	109–10										Am 79, 5979
Ω e183	—,2,2-bis(4-chlorophenyl)-1,1,1-trichloro-	DDT. Dichlorodiphenyl-trichloroethane.	354.49	nd (al) λ^{al} 240 (4.3), 270 (2.8)	108.5–9	260			i	δ sʰ	v	v	v	Py v chl, peth s	Am 75, 4853
Ω e184	—,1,2-bis(ethyl-thio)-*	$C_2H_5SCH_2CH_2SC_2H_5$	150.31			217 95.5¹³	0.9815²⁰	1.5118²⁰		s	s				B1³, 2131
Ω e185	—,2,2-bis(4-methoxyphenyl)-1,1,1-trichloro-*	Methoxychlor	345.66	cr (dil al) λ^{bz} 230 (4.3), 238 (4.2), 270 (3.9), 275 (3.8)	94				i	s	v		v	os v	H27, 892
e186	—,1,2-bis(2-methoxy-phenoxy)-*	Guaiacol ethylene ether	274.32	nd (al)	139–40				i	v	v				B6, 772
Ω e187	—,1,2-bis(methyl-amino)-*	N,N′-Dimethylethylene-diamine. $CH_3NHCH_2CH_2NHCH_3$	88.15			120	0.828¹⁵₄			s	s	s		dil HCl s	B4², 689
e189	—,1,2-bis(methyl-thio)-*	$CH_3SCH_2CH_2SCH_3$	122.25			182.5⁷⁵⁰ 78–80¹¹	1.0371²⁰	1.5292²⁰	s	s	s	s		chl s	B1³, 2130
Ω e190	—,1,2-bis(2-nitro-phenyl)-*	2,2′-Dinitrobibenzyl	272.26	pr (aa)	127(122)					δ sʰ	v		v	aa sʰ	B5, 603
e191	—,1,2-bis(4-nitro-phenyl)-*	4,4′-Dinitrobibenzyl	272.26	yesh nd (al or bz)	180.5 (cor)					i δʰ	δ		δ sʰ	chl δ aa aʰ	B5³, 1821
e192	—,1,2-bis(phenyl-amino)-*	N,N′-Diphenyl-ethylenediamine. $C_6H_5NHCH_2CH_2NHC_6H_5$	212.30	lf (dil al) λ 250 (4.44), 294 (3.70)	74 68–9 (+1 w)	178–82²			i	s	s		s		B12², 287
e193	—,1,2-bis(phenyl-sulfonyl)-*	$C_6H_5SO_2CH_2CH_2SO_2C_6H_5$	310.39	nd or lf (al)	180				δʰ	sʰ			s	aa sʰ	B6³, 997
e194	—,1,2-bis(phenyl-thio)-*	$C_6H_5SCH_2CH_2SC_6H_5$	246.40	ta (al) λ^{al} 256 (4.00)	70				i			s			B6³, 994
Ω e195	—,bromo-*	Ethyl bromide. C_2H_5Br	108.97		−118.6	38.40⁷⁶⁰	1.4604²⁰₀	1.4239²⁰	δ	∞	∞			chl ∞	B1³, 171
Ω e196	—,1-bromo-2-chloro-*	Ethylene chlorobromide. $BrCH_2CH_2Cl$	143.42		−16.7	107⁷⁶⁰	1.7392²⁰	1.4908²⁰	δ	s	s				B1³, 179
e197	—,1-bromo-2-fluoro-*	$BrCH_2CH_2F$	126.96			71.5–1.8⁷⁶⁰	1.7044²⁵₄	1.4236²⁰	i	v	v				B1³, 178
Ω e199	—,chloro-*	Ethyl chloride. C_2H_5Cl	64.52		−136.4	12.27⁷⁶⁰	0.8978²⁰	1.3676²⁰	δ	v	∞				B1³, 133
e200	—,1-chloro-2-diethylamino-, hydrochloride*	β-Chlorotriethylammonium chloride. $ClCH_2CH_2N(C_2H_5)_2$.HCl	172.10	nd (al-eth)	210–1 (cor)				s	s	i				B4², 618
e201	—,1-chloro-1,2-dinitro-1,2,2-trifluoro-*	$F_2C(NO_2)CClFNO_2$	208.48			98.5–100⁷⁶⁰									J1953, 2081
e202	—,1-chloro-2-fluoro-*	$ClCH_2CH_2F$	82.51			57⁷⁵⁰	1.1747²⁰₀	1.3775²⁰	i	v	v				B1³, 138
Ω e203	—,1-chloro-1-nitro-*	$CH_3CHClNO_2$	109.51	$\lambda^{50 \%al-alk}$ 237 (4.00)		124–5⁷⁶⁰ (127.5)	1.2860²⁰₂₀	1.4224²⁰	i					alk s	B1, 101

For explanations, symbols and abbreviations see beginning of table. For structural formulas see end of table.

Ethane

No.	Name	Synonyms and Formula	Mol. wt.	Color, crystalline form, specific rotation and λ_{max} (log ε)	m.p. °C	b.p. °C	Density	n_D	w	al	eth	ace	bz	other solvents	Ref.
Ω e204	—,chloropenta-fluoro-*	$ClCF_2CF_3$	154.47	gas	−106	−38[760]	....	....	i	s	s	...	...		B1[3], 139
e205	—,1(2-chloro-ethoxy)-2-phenoxy-*	β-chloro-β′-phenoxy diethyl ether. $C_6H_5OCH_2CH_2OCH_2CH_2Cl$	200.67			149[10] 127[4]	1.149[15][15]								B6[2], 150
e206	—,2(2-chloro-phenyl)-2(4-chlorophenyl)-1,1,1-trichloro-*	o,p′-DDT.	354.49	cr (MeOH) λ[80% al] 235 (4.2), 275 (2.8), 280 (2.7)	....	74–4.5 (cor)									Am 67, 1498
Ω e207	—,1,2-diamino-* ...	Ethylenediamine. 1,2-Ethanediamine. $H_2NCH_2CH_2NH_2$	60.11	....	8.5	116.5[760]	0.8995[20][20]	1.4568[20]	v	∞	i		i		B4[2], 676
e208	—,—,hydrate*	$H_2NCH_2CH_2NH_2.H_2O$	78.12		10	118[760]	0.9642[20.5]	1.4500[20.5]	∞						B4[2], 677
Ω e209	—,—,hydro-chloride*	$H_2NCH_2CH_2NH_2.2HCl$ ...	133.02	mcl pr (w)	300–330 sub	sub		1.633	s	i					B4[2], 677
e210	—,2-diazo-1,1,1-trifluoro-*	Trifluorodiazoethane. N_2CHCF_3	110.04	ye	13[752]				s		s				Am 65, 1460
e211	—,1,1-dibromo-*	Ethylidene bromide. CH_3CHBr_2	187.87		−63	108[760] 9.0[10]	2.0555[20][4]	1.5128[20]	i	s	v	s	s		B1[3], 181
Ω e212	—,1,2-dibromo-*	Ethylene bromide. $BrCH_2CH_2Br$	187.87		9.79	131.36[760] 29.1[10]	2.1792[20][4]	1.5387[20]	δ	v	∞	s	s		B1[3], 182
e213	—,1,2-dibromo-1,1-dichloro-*	$BrCH_2CBrCl_2$	256.76		−66.85	178.3[760] 58.8[10]	2.2622[20][4]	1.5567[20]	i	s	s			os s	B1[2], 64
e214	—,1,2-dibromo-1,2-dichloro-*	$BrCHClCHBrCl$	256.76		−26	195[760] 84[45]	2.135[20][4]	1.5662[20]	i	s	s			os s	B1[3], 190
Ω e215	—,1,1-dichloro-*	Ethylidene chloride. CH_3CHCl_2	98.96		−96.98	57.28[760]	1.1757[20][4]	1.4164[20]	δ	v	v	s	s	....	B1[3], 139
Ω e216	—,1,2-dichloro-*	Ethylene chloride. $ClCH_2CH_2Cl$	98.96		−35.36	83.47[760]	1.2351[20]	1.4448[20]	δ	v	∞	s	s	oos, chl s	B1[3], 141
e217	—,1,1-dichloro-2,2-difluoro-1,2-dinitro-*	$O_2NCF_2CCl_2NO_2$	224.94			142[760]d 81–2[108]			i						J1953, 2081
e218	—,1,1-dichloro-1,2,2,2-tetra-fluoro-*	Cl_2CFCF_3	170.92		−94	3.6[760] (cor)	1.455[25][4]	1.3092[0]	i	s	s	...	s	chl s	B1[3], 152
—	—,1,2-diethoxy-*	See 1,2-Ethanediol, diethyl ether													
—	—,2,2-diethoxy-1,1,1-trichloro-*	see Acetaldehyde, trichloro-, diethyl acetal													
Ω e221	—,1,1-difluoro-*	Ethylidene fluoride. CH_3CHF_2	66.05	gas	−117	−24.7	0.95[20] (at sat pressure)	1.3011[−72] 1.26[20] (liq)							B1[3], 130
e222	—,1,2-difluoro-*	Ethylene fluoride. FCH_2CH_2F	66.05			30.7[760]	....	....			s		s	chl s	B1, 82
e223	—,1,1-difluoro-1,2,2,2-tetra-chloro-*	$F_2CClCCl_3$	203.83		40.6	91.5[760] (cor)	....	....	i	s	s	...		chl s	B1[3], 164
Ω e224	—,1,2-difluoro-1,1,2,2-tetra-chloro-*	$Cl_2CFCFCl_2$.	203.83		25	93[760] −37.5[1]	1.6447[25][4]	1.4130[25]	i	s	s	...	s	chl s	B1[3], 165
e225	—,(difluoro-amino)penta-fluoro-*	Perfluoroethylamine. $F_3CCF_2NF_2$	171.02			−35[760]			i						Am 81, 3599
e227	—,1,1-diiodo-*	Ethylidene iodide. CH_3CHI_2	281.86			179–80[760] 60–1[12]	2.84[0]	1.673[20]	i	v	v	...	s	chl s	B1[3], 198
Ω e228	—,1,2-diiodo-*	Ethylene iodide. ICH_2CH_2I.	281.86	ye mcl pr or rh (eth), d in lt	83	200[760] 74[10]	3.325[20][4]	1.871[20]	δ	s	s	s	...	chl s	B1[2], 69
—	—,1,2-di-methoxy-*	see 1,2-Ethanediol, dimethyl ether													
e230	—,1,2-di-N-morpholyl-	....	200.28	wh-yesh (eth or lig)	75 (71)	160–3[25] (153–4[9])			v	v		s	s	MeOH s	B27, 7
e231	—,1,1-dinitro-*	$CH_3CH(NO_2)_2$	120.07	ye mcl (bz or MeOH) λ[hx] 280 (1.76)	185–6 (cor) 72[12]		1.3503[24][81]		δ	s	s		....		B1[2], 70
e232	—,1,2-dinitro-1,2-diphenyl-(dl)*	α,α′-Dinitrobibenzyl. $C_6H_5CH(NO_2)CH(NO_2)C_6H_5$	272.26	(al), pr (aa)	154–5					v	v	v	v	os, aa, chl v lig s	B5[2], 508
e233	—,—,(meso).	$C_6H_5CH(NO_2)CH(NO_2)C_6H_5$	272.26	nd (aa)	235–6 (226d)					δ	δ	v	...	aa δ, s[h]	B5[2], 508
e234	—,1,2-dinitro-1,1,2,2-tetra-fluoro-*	$O_2NCF_2CF_2NO_2$	192.03		−41.5	58–9[760]	1.6024[25][4]	1.3265[25]	i				s		B1[3], 203
Ω e235	—,1,2-diphen-oxy-*	Ethylene glycol diphenyl ether. $C_6H_5OCH_2CH_2OC_6H_5$	214.27	lf (al)	98	180–5[12]	....	....	i	δ s[h]	s		s	chl s	B6[2], 150
Ω e236	—,1,1-diphenyl-*	α-Methyldtan. $CH_3CH(C_6H_5)_2$	182.27	λ[97% suf] 430 (4.35)	−21.5	286[760] (270) 148[15]	0.9997[20][4]	1.5756[20]	i	∞	∞	...	s		B5[2], 653

For explanations, symbols and abbreviations see beginning of table. For structural formulas see end of table.

No.	Name	Synonyms and Formula	Mol. wt.	Color. crystalline form. specific rotation and λ_{max} (log ε)	m.p. °C	b.p. °C	Density	n_D	Solubility						Ref.
									w	al	eth	ace	bz	other solvents	

Ethane

Ω e237	—,1,2-diphenyl-*	Bibenzyl. Dibenzyl. $C_6H_5CH_2CH_2C_6H_5$	182.27	nd (al) λ^{diox} 265 (2.9), 290 sh(2.6)	52.2	285^{760} $95-6^1$	0.9583_4^{60}	1.5476^{60}	i	s v^h	s	...	...	CS_2 liq SO_2 s liq NH_3 i	B5², 506
Ω e238	—,2,2-diphenyl-1,1,1-trichloro-*	$(C_6H_5)_2CHCCl_3$	285.60	lf (al or MeOH) λ^{cy} 260 (2.6), 268 (2.5)	65	...	...	...	...	s v^h	...	...	...	...	B5², 510
e239	—,1,1-di-4-tolyl-		210.32	...	< −20	$298-9$ $153-6^{11}$	0.974_4^{20}	...	i	...	...	s	aa s		B5², 502
Ω e240	—,1,2-di-4-tolyl-		210.32	lf (MeOH, or dil al), pl (lig) λ^{cy} 221 (4.2), 254 (2.6), 267 (2.9), 275 (2.9), 343 (0.8)	$82-3$ (85)	$296-8^{730}$ 178^{18}			i	δ		s	peth s		B5², 521
e240¹	—,2,2-di-4-tolyl-1,1,1-trichloro-		313.66	mcl pr (al or eth-al) $\lambda^{80\%al}$ 235 (4.1), 277 (2.7)	92				i	s v^h	v	s			B5², 522
Ω e241	—,1,2-epoxy-*	Ethylene oxide. Oxirane.	44.05	λ^{gas} 169 (3.58), 171 (3.57)	−111	13.5^{746}	0.8824_{10}^{10}	1.3597^7	s	s	s	s	s		B17², 9
e242	—,1,2-epoxy-1-phenyl-*	Styrene oxide.	120.16	λ^{al} 254 (2.24), 260 (2.28), 265 sh (2.1)	−35.6	194.1^{760} $20^{0.3}$	1.0469_4^{25}	1.5342^{20}	δ	s	∞	...	∞		B17², 49
e243	—,1-ethoxy-2-methoxy-*	$C_2H_5OCH_2CH_2OCH_3$	104.15	...		102^{760}	0.8529_4^{20}	1.3868^{20}	∞	∞	∞	s	s	chl s	B1³, 2078
e244	—,1-ethoxy-2-methylamino-*	Ethyl β-methylaminoethyl ether. $CH_3NHCH_2CH_2OC_2H_5$	103.17	...		$114-5^{744}$ (cor)	0.8363_4^{20}	1.4147^{20}	∞	∞	∞	s	s	chl s	B4, 276
e245	—,fluoro-*	Ethyl fluoride. C_2H_5F	48.06	gas	−143.2	-37.7^{760}	0.00220 at $ca.0°$ 0.7182_4^{20} (liq)	1.2656^{20}	s	v	v				B1³, 130
e246	—,fluoropenta-chloro-*	$FCCl_2CCl_3$	220.29	...	101.3 (97)	$134-6^{760}$			i	s	s				B1³, 168
e247	—,hexabromo-*	Perbromoethane. Br_3CCBr_3	503.48	rh pr (bz)	d 200–10	d	2.823_4^{20}	1.863	i	δ^h	δ	...	...	CS_2 s	B1³, 193
Ω e248	—,hexachloro-*	Perchloroethane. Cl_3CCCl_3	236.74	rh (al-eth)	$186.8-7.4$ (sealed tube)	186^{777}	2.091_4^{20}		i	v	v	...	s	liq HF δ	B1³, 168
Ω e249	—,hexafluoro-*	Perfluoroethane. F_3CCF_3	138.01	gas	−94	−79	1.590^{-78}		i	δ	δ				B1³, 132
e250	—,hexaphenyl-*	$(C_6H_5)_3CC(C_6H_5)_3$	486.67	cr (ace)	145–7d	d				s^h	s	s	δ	chl, CS_2, MeOH v CCl_4, lig δ lig i	B5², 626
e251	—,N-hydroxyl-amino-*	β-Ethylhydroxylamine. C_2H_5NHOH	61.09	nd (lig)	59–60d	...	0.9079_4^{20}	1.4152^{20} 1.4152^{64}	v	v	δ	...	δ	lig δ	B4², 953
e252	—,2-imino-1,1,1-trichloro-*	Chloralimide. 2,2,2-Trichloroethylideneimide. $Cl_3CCH:NH$	146.40		150–5				δ	v	v				M, 233
Ω e253	—,iodo-*	Ethyl iodide. CH_3CH_2I	155.97	...	−108 (−111)	72.3^{760}	1.9358_4^{20}	1.5133^{20}	δ^d	∞	∞	s	...	os ∞	B1³, 193
Ω e254	—,isocyano-	Ethylcarbylamine. Ethyliso-cyanide. C_2H_5NC	55.08	...	< −66	79^{775}	0.7402_4^{20}	1.3622^{20}	v	∞	∞	s			B4², 600
e254¹	—,1(4-methoxy-phenyl)-1-phenyl-*	1-p-Anisyl-1-phenylethane.	212.30	...		$180-2^{19}$ $130^{0.5}$	1.0473_4^{20}	1.5725^{20}	i	...	...	...	...	os s	B6², 639
Ω e255	—,nitro-*	$CH_3CH_2NO_2$	75.07	λ^{al} 260 (1.63)	−50	115^{760}	1.0448_4^{25}	1.3917^{20}	δ	∞	∞	...	...	dil alk s	B1³, 199
e256	—,nitropenta-fluoro-*	$F_3CCF_2NO_2$	165.02	λ^{vap} 281(1.45)		0^{760}					s				J1956, 3416
e257	—,1-nitro-2,2,2-trifluoro-*	$F_3CCH_2NO_2$	129.04			96^{760}	1.3914_4^{20}	1.3394^{20}							Am 72, 3579
e258	—,1(2-nitrophenyl)-2(4-nitrophenyl)-*	2,4'-Dinitrobibenzyl.	272.26	nd (dil al)	74–5				i	v					B5, 603
e259	—,nitrosopenta-fluoro-*	F_3CCF_2NO	149.02	bl λ^{vap} 692 (1.37), 708 (1.37)		-42^{760}									J1956, 3416
Ω e260	—,pentabromo-*	Br_3CCHBr_2	424.58	mcl pr (dil al)	56–7	210^{300}d	3.312_4^{20}		i	s	v				B1³, 193
Ω e261	—,pentachloro-*	Pentalin. Cl_3CCHCl_2	202.30	...	−29	162^{760}	1.6796_4^{20}	1.5025^{20}	i	∞	∞	...	s	aa s	B1³, 165
e262	—,pentaiodo-*	I_3CCHI_2	659.55	mcl pr (aa)	182–4				i	s	s	s	s	aa s	B1¹, 31
e264	—,1,1,1,2-tetra-bromo-	Br_3CCH_2Br	345.67	...	0.0	112^{18}d	2.8748_4^{20}	1.6277^{20}	i	s	s	s	s	chl s	B1³, 191
Ω e265	—,1,1,2,2-tetra-bromo-*	Acetylene tetrabromide. $Br_2CHCHBr_2$	345.67	yesh	0	243.5^{760} 114.8^{10}	2.9656_4^{20}	1.6353^{20}	i	∞	∞	s	s	chl, $PhNH_2$, aa ∞	B1³, 192
e266	—,1,1,1,2-tetra-chloro-*	Cl_3CCH_2Cl	167.85	yesh red	−70.2	130.5^{760} 22.1^{10}	1.54064_4^{20}	1.4821^{20}	δ	∞	∞	...	s	chl s	B1³, 158
Ω e267	—,1,1,2,2-tetra-chloro-*	Acetylene tetrachloride. $Cl_2CHCHCl_2$	167.85	...	−36 (fp −43.8)	146.2^{760} 33.9^{10}	1.5953_4^{20}	1.4940^{20}	δ	∞	∞	...	s	chl s	B1³, 159
e268	—,1,1,1,2-tetra-fluoro-*	F_3CCH_2F	102.03	...		-26.5^{736}			i	...	s				Am 82, 543
e269	—,1,1,1,2-tetra-phenyl-*	$(C_6H_5)_3CCH_2C_6H_5$	334.47	mcl (eth-peth)	143–4	$277-80^{21}$			i	δ	...	δ	s		B5², 674

For explanations, symbols and abbreviations see beginning of table. For structural formulas see end of table.

No.	Name	Synonyms and Formula	Mol. wt.	Color. crystalline form. specific rotation and λ_{max} (log ε)	m.p. °C	b.p. °C	Density	n_D	Solubility						Ref.
									w	al	eth	ace	bz	other solvents	
	Ethane														
e270	—,1,1,2,2-tetra-phenyl-*	$(C_6H_5)_2CHCH(C_6H_3)_2$	334.47	cr (bz + l), rh nd (chl) λ^{al} 263 (3.05), 270.5 (2.91)	214–5	358–62 260[16]				δ^h			s^h	aa s	B5[2], 673
e271	—,triazo-*	Azidoethane. Ethyl azide. $CH_3CH_2N_3$	71.08	. . . .		49[760]								peth s	B1[2], 71
Ω e272	—,1,1,2-tribromo-*	Br_2CHCH_2Br	266.77	. . . .	−29.3	188.93[760] 73.1[10]	2.6211[20]	1.5933[20]	i	s	s		s	chl s	B1[3], 191
Ω e273	—,1,1,1-trichloro-*	Methylchloroform. CH_3CCl_3	133.41	. . . .	−30.41	74.1[760]	1.3390[20]	1.4379[20]	i	∞	∞			chl s	B1[2], 55
Ω e274	—,1,1,2-trichloro-*	Cl_2CHCH_2Cl	133.41	. . . .	−36.5	113.77[760] 9.48[10]	1.4397[20]	1.4714[20]	δ	s	∞			chl s	B1[3], 154
e275	—,1,1,1-trichloro-2,2,2-trifluoro-*	Cl_3CCF_3	187.38	. . . .	14.2	45.8[760] (cor)	1.5790[20]	1.3610[25]	i	s	s			chl s	B1[3], 157
Ω e276	—,1,1,2-trichloro-1,2,2-trifluoro-*	$Cl_2CFCClF_2$	187.38	. . . .	−36.4	47.7[760] (cor)	1.5635[25]	1.3557[25]	i	s	∞		∞	chl s	B1[3], 157
e277	—,1,1,1-trifluoro-*	CH_3CF_3	84.04	gas	−111.3	−47.3[760]	0.00378				s			chl s	B1[3], 131
e278	—,1,1,1-triiodo-*	Methyliodoform. CH_3CI_3	407.76	ye oct (al)	95 (93)					δ	v		v	CS_2 v lig δ	B1[3], 199
e279	—,1,1,1-triphenyl-*	α-Methyltritan. $(C_6H_5)_3CCH_3$	258.37	nd (al, eth) λ^{al} 262 (2.9)	95	205–10[18]			i	δ s^h	s		s	aa δ	B5[1], 350
e280	—,1,1,2-triphenyl-*	$(C_6H_5)_2CHCH_2C_6H_5$	258.37	mcl lf (dil al), nd (al) λ^{al} 208 (4.4), 261 (2.8), 270 (2.7)	57	348–9[751] (cor) (396–400)			i	v	v		v	MeOH δ	B5[2], 620
e281	**Ethanearsonic acid***	Ethylarsonic acid. $C_2H_5AsO_3H_2$	154.00	nd (al), rh nd (w)	99.5	209–11[12]			v	v				alk v	B4[3], 1823
e282	**Ethaneboronic acid***	Ethylboric acid. $C_2H_5B(OH)_2$	73.89	volat pl (eth)	40 sub	d			v	v					B4, 642
—	**Ethanedial***	*see* **Glyoxal**													
—	**Ethanedionic acid***	*see* **Oxalic acid**													
—	**1,1-Ethanediol, diacetate**	*see* **Acetaldehyde**, diacetate													
Ω e283	**1,2-Ethanediol***	Dihydroxyethane*. Ethylene glycol. Glycol. $HOCH_2CH_2OH$	62.07	. . . .	−11.5	198[760] (cor) 93[13]	1.1088[20]	1.4318[20]	∞	∞	s	∞	δ	aa ∞ chl s	B1[3], 2053
e284	—,bis(chloro-acetate)	$ClCH_2CO_2(CH_2)_2O_2CCH_2Cl$	215.03	pr (eth-peth)	45–6	142–4[2]			i	d^h	v				B2[3], 448
—	—,carbonate	*see* **1,3-Dioxolan-2-one**													
Ω e285	—,diacetate	Ethylene acetate. $CH_3CO_2CH_2CH_2O_2CCH_3$	146.14	. . . .	−31	190[760]	1.1063[20]	1.4159[20]	v	∞	∞	∞	∞	CS_2, CCl_4, aa ∞	B2[3], 309
e286	—,dibenzoate	Ethylene benzoate. $C_6H_5CO_2CH_2CH_2O_2CC_6H_5$	270.29	rh pr (eth)	73–4	> 360d			i		s				B9[2], 109
e287	—,dibutanoate*	Ethylene butyrate. $C_3H_7CO_2CH_2CH_2O_2CC_3H_7$	202.25	. . . .		240 118–21[11]	1.0005[20]	1.42619[20]	i	v	s				B2[2], 272
e288	—,didodecanoate*	Ethylene laurate. $CH_3(CH_2)_{10}CO_2CH_2CH_2O_2C(CH_2)_{10}CH_3$	426.69	pl (al)	56.6	188[20]			i	v	v				B2[2], 320
Ω e289	—,diethyl ether	1,2-Diethoxyethane*. $C_2H_5OCH_2CH_2OC_2H_5$	118.18	. . . .		123.5[760]	0.8484[20]	1.3860[20]		s	s	s	s	os v	B1[2], 519
Ω e290	—,diformate	$HCO_2CH_2CH_2O_2CH$	118.09	. . . .		174	1.193[0]	1.3580	δ	s	s				B2, 23
e291	—,dihexadecylate*	Ethylene palmitate. $CH_3(CH_2)_{14}CO_2CH_2CH_2O_2C(CH_2)_{14}CH_3$	538.91	lf or nd (al-chl)	72 (69)	226 (vac)	0.8594[78]		i		s^h	v		oos v	B2[2], 338
Ω e292	—,dimethyl ether	1,2-Dimethoxyethane*. $CH_3OCH_2CH_2OCH_3$	90.12	. . . .	−58	83–4[760]	0.86285[20]	1.3796[20]	s	s	s	s	s	chl s	B1[3], 2073
e293	—,dinitrate*	Ethylene nitrate. $O_2NOCH_2CH_2ONO_2$	152.06	ye	−22.3	197–200[760]	1.4918[20]		i	s	s			alk d	B1[3], 2112
e294	—,dinitrite*	Ethylene nitrite. $ONOCH_2CH_2ONO$	120.07	. . . .	< −15	98	1.2156[0]		i	s	s			glycerol s	B1, 469
e295	—,dioctadecylate*	Ethylene stearate. $CH_3(CH_2)_{16}CO_2CH_2CH_2O_2C(CH_2)_{16}CH_3$	595.02	lf	79 (77)	241[20]	0.8581[78]		i	i	v				B2[2], 354
e296	—,dipropanoate*	Ethylene propionate. $C_2H_5CO_2CH_2CH_2O_2CC_2H_5$	174.20	. . . .		211	1.020[15]		δ	∞	∞				B2, 242
e297	—,ditetradecylate*	Ethylene myristate. $CH_3(CH_2)_{12}CO_2CH_2CH_2O_2C(CH_2)_{12}CH_3$	482.80	cr (eth or ace)	65	. . . .			i	i	s	v	v	CCl_4 v	B2[2], 327
e298	—,dithiocyanate	$NCSCH_2CH_2SCN$	144.22	rh pl or nl (w), ta (al or eth)	90	d			δ s^h	s	v	δ			B3[2], 123
e301	—,1,2-bis(4-methoxyphenyl)-* (lower m.p. form)	p,p'-Dimethoxyhydro-benzoin. Isohydroanisoin.	274.32	cr (eth), nd (bz)	125–6										B6[2], 1130
e302	—,—,(higher m.p. form)	Hydroanisoin. $C_{16}H_{18}O_4$. See e301.	274.32	rh ta or lf (al)	173–4				i δ^h	δ s^h	i δ^h				B6[2], 1129
e304	—,1,2-dicyclo-hexyl-(dl)*	Cyclohexanonepinacol. Dodecahydrobenzoin.	226.36	nd	129–30								v	peth s	Am 71, 829

For explanations, symbols and abbreviations see beginning of table. For structural formulas see end of table.

No.	Name	Synonyms and Formula	Mol. wt.	Color, crystalline form, specific rotation and λ_{max} (log ε)	m.p. °C	b.p. °C	Density	n_D	w	al	eth	ace	bz	other solvents	Ref.
	1,2-Ethanediol														
e305	—,1,2-diphenyl-(d)*	d-Hydrobenzoin. d-Isohydrobenzoin.	214.27	nd (w), lf or pr (abs al) [α]$_D$ +92 (abs al, c=1.2), +128 (bz, c=0.3) λ^{al} 253 (2.51), 258 (2.60), 263 sh (2.5)	148.5–9.5d (cor)	....			δ^h	s	...	...	δ^h	MeOH, AcOEt s	B6[2], 970
Ω e306	—,—(dl)*	$C_{14}H_{14}O_2$. See e305	214.27	nd (w or al), ta (eth) λ^{al} 253 (2.51), 258 (2.60), 263 sh (2.5)	122–3 (anh)	>300[760] 133[0.023]	....		i δ^h	v	v	...	...	chl v lig i	B6[2], 969
e307	—,—(l)*	$C_{14}H_{14}O_2$. See e305	214.27	lf (eth, abs al or bz), pr (bz or abs al) [α]$_D$ −92 (abs al, c=1.2) λ^{al} 253 (2.51), 258 (2.60), 263 sh (2.5)	148.5–9.5d (cor)	....				v	s^h	v	s^h	MeOH, AcOEt v chl s^h	B6[2], 970
e308	—,—(meso)*	Tolylene glycol. $C_{14}H_{14}O_2$. See e305	214.27	nd or lf (w or bz-peth), mcl lf (al, w) λ^{al} 253 (2.51), 258 (2.60), 263 sh (2.5)	139–40	>300[760] 139[0.023]			i δ^h	v	...	...	...	chl v lig i	B6[2], 967
Ω e309	—,phenyl-(dl)*	Phenyl ethylene glycol. $C_6H_5CH(OH)CH_2OH$	138.17	nd (lig) λ^{al} 252 (2.21), 228 (2.26)	69–70	272–4[755]			v	v	v	...	v	lig δ, v^h	B6[2], 887
Ω e309[1]	—,tetraphenyl-*	Benzopinacol. $(C_6H_5)_2C(OH)COH(C_6H_5)_2$	366.47	pr (bz +1), cr (ace +2)	182–3 (slow htng) 193–5 (rapid htng)	....			i	δ^h	s	s^h	s^h	chl, CS_2 s lig, liq NH_3 i	B6[2], 1034
—	**1,1-Ethanediol, 2,2,2-tribromo-***	see Acetaldehyde, tribromo-, hydrate													
Ω e310	**1,2-Ethanedione, 1,2-di(2-furyl)-**	Bipyromucyl. Furil.	190.16	ye nd (al), cr (bz) λ^w 227.5 (3.97), 302.5 (4.24)	165–6 (cor)	....			δ	s	s	...	s^h	chl s	B19[2], 183
—	—,1,2-diphenyl-*	see Benzil													
e311	**1,2-Ethanedisulfonic acid***	Ethylenedisulfonic acid. $HO_3SCH_2CH_2SO_3H$	190.19	hyg nd (gl aa or aa-Ac$_2$O)	111–2 (+2w) 174 (anh)	....			v	v	i	...	...	diox s	B4[3], 36
Ω e312	**1,2-Ethanedithiol***	Dithioglycol. Ethylene mercaptan. $HSCH_2CH_2SH$	94.20	....	−41.2	146[760] 46–7[6]	1.1243$^{20}_4$	1.5590^{20}	i	s	s	s	s	alk v	B1[2], 529
e313	**Ethanedithiolic acid, diethyl ester***	Diethyl dithioloxalate. $C_2H_5SCOCOSC_2H_5$	178.28	ye nd (eth)	27	235 80–2[32]	1.0565$^{21}_4$	....			s^h				B2[2], 515
e314	**Ethanephosphonic acid***	Ethylphosphonic acid. $C_2H_5PO_3H_2$	110.05	pl or nd (w)	61–2 (44)	....			v	v	v	...	i	lig i	B4[3], 1779
e315	—,diethyl ester*	$C_2H_5PO(OC_2H_5)_2$	166.16	....		198[760] 83[13]	1.0259$^{20}_4$	1.4163^{20}	δ	s	s	...	...		B4[2], 975
e316	—,dimethyl ester*	$C_2H_5PO(OCH_3)_2$	138.10	....		82[18]	1.1029$^{30}_4$	1.4128^{30}	s	s	...	...	s		J1954, 3222
e317	**Ethanesulfinic acid***	Ethylsulfinic acid. $C_2H_5SO_2H$	94.13	syr	....									alk s	B4[2], 524
e318	**Ethanesulfonic acid***	Ethylsulfonic acid. $C_2H_5SO_3H$	110.13	hyg	−17	123[1]	1.3341^{25}	1.4335^{20}	s	s	...	...	i	alk s	B4[2], 525
e319	—,chloride*	$C_2H_5SO_2Cl$	128.58	pa ye	....	171[760] 65[13]	1.357$^{22.5}$	1.4531^{20}	d	d	v	...	...		B4[2], 526
—	—,2-amino-*	see Taurine													
e320	—,2-bromo-, chloride	$BrCH_2CH_2SO_2Cl$	207.48	pa ye	....	102[13]	1.921^{20}	1.5242^{20}	d	d	...	...	...		B4[2], 526
e321	—,1-chloro-, chloride*	$CH_3CHClSO_2Cl$	163.02	....		80–1[22] 50–3[3]		1.4782^{20}	δ						B1[3], 2656
e322	—,2-chloro-* chloride	$ClCH_2CH_2SO_2Cl$	163.02	....		200–3[760] 93–7[17]	1.555$^{20}_4$	1.4920^{20}	d	d	...	...	...		B4[2], 526
Ω e323	—,2-hydroxy-, dihydrate*	Isethionic acid. $HOCH_2CH_2SO_3H.2H_2O$	152.17	hyg cr (aa-Ac$_2$O)	111–2	....			v	s	i	i	i	CCl_4 i	B4[2], 529
e324	**1,1,2,2-Ethanetetracarboxylic acid, 1,2-diethyl ester***	$C_2H_5O_2CCH(CO_2H)CH(CO_2H)CO_2C_2H_5$	262.22	hyg lf (+½w)	132–3d	....			s	v	v	...	...	chl, CS_2 δ	B2, 858
e325	—,tetraamide	Dimalonamide. Ethane-1,1,2,2-tetracarbonamide*. $(H_2NCO)_2CHCH(CONH_2)_2$	202.17	....	230d				δ^h	δ^h	i	i	i	os i	B2, 859

For explanations, symbols and abbreviations see beginning of table. For structural formulas see end of table.

1,1,2,2-Ethanetetracarboxylic acid

No.	Name	Synonyms and Formula	Mol. wt.	Color, crystalline form, specific rotation and λ_{max} (log ε)	m.p. °C	b.p. °C	Density	n_D	w	al	eth	ace	bz	other solvents	Ref.
Ω e326	—,tetraethyl ester*.	Ethyl dimalonate. $(C_2H_5O_2C)_2CHCH(CO_2C_2H_5)_2$	318.33	tetr pr (al-peth)	77	305d	1.064^{80}	1.4105^{80}		s					B2[2], 699
e327	—,tetramethyl ester*	Methyl dimalonate. $(CH_3O_2C)_2CHCH(CO_2CH_3)_2$	262.22	cr (eth, al, bz)	138					v^h	δ		s^h	lig i	B2[2], 699
Ω e328	Ethanethiol* .	Ethyl hydrosulfide. Ethyl mercaptan. Ethyl thioalcohol. C_2H_5SH	62.13	λ^{al} 195 (3.15), 225 sh (2.2)	−144.4	35^{760}	0.8391^{20}_4	1.43105^{20}	δ	s	s	s		dil alk s	B1[2], 341
e329	—,sodium salt.....	Sodium thioethylate. C_2H_5SNa	84.12	wh cr λ^{al} 195 (3.15), 225 sh (2.2)	d					v	s			i	B1, 341
Ω e330	—,2-amino-*......	Cysteamine. $H_2NCH_2CH_2SH$	77.15	cr (sub)	99–100	d^{760} sub (vac)				v	s			dil HCl v	B4[1], 431
e331	—,2-chloro-*.....	$ClCH_2CH_2SH$	96.58			113^{760}	$1.1826^{20}_{?}$	1.4929^{20}	s	v	v			diox v	B1[3], 1381
Ω e332	—,1-phenyl-(l)* ...	$CH_3CH(C_6H_5)SH$	138.23	$[\alpha]^{20}_D$ −89 (al, c=6)		$199–200$ 83^{10}	1.0222^{20}	1.5593^{20}		s	s	s	s		B6[2], 445
e333	1,1,1-Ethanetricarboxylic acid*	$CH_3C(CO_2H)_3$	162.10	pr	159d					s	s	s			B2[3], 2026
e334	1,1,2-Ethanetricarboxylic acid*	Carboxysuccinic acid. $HO_2CCH_2CH(CO_2H)_2$	162.10	pr (w)	178d					v	v	v		$δ^h$	B2[2], 681
e335	—,1,2-dihydroxy-*.	Desoxalic acid. $HO_2CC(OH)COH(CO_2H)_2$	194.10	hyg (+1w)	45d					v d^h						B3, 586
—	Ethanoic acid*...	see Acetic acid													
Ω e336	Ethanol*	Alcohol. Ethyl alcohol. Methyl carbinol. C_2H_5OH	46.07	λ^{gas} 181 (2.51)	−117.3 (−112.3)	78.5 4^{16}	0.7893^{20}	1.3611^{20}	∞	∞	∞	∞	s	chl, aa ∞	B1[3], 1223
e337	—(o–d) .	o-Deuteroethanol. Deuteroxyethane. C_2H_5OD	47.08			78.8^{760}	$0.801^{25}_{?}$	1.3610^{20}						aa ∞ CCl₄ s	B1[3], 1287
Ω e338	—,2-allyloxy-*	Allyl cellosolve. Glycol monoallyl ether. $CH_2:CHCH_2OCH_2CH_2OH$	102.13			159^{755} 64^{15}	0.9580^{20}	1.4358^{20}	∞	v			s	MeOH, CCl₄ s	B1, 468
Ω e339	—,1-amino-*......	Acetaldehyde-ammonia. $CH_3CH(OH)NH_2$	61.09	rh (eth-al)	97	110 δd			s		δ				C52, 10081
Ω e340	—,2-amino-*......	Colamine. Ethanolamine. $H_2NCH_2CH_2OH$	61.09		10.3	170^{760} 58^5	1.0180^{20}_4	1.4541^{20}	∞	∞	δ		δ	glycerol ∞ chl s lig δ	B4[2], 717
—	—,2-amino-1(3,4-dihydroxyphenyl)-(l)*	see Noradrenaline (l)													
Ω e341	—,2-amino-1-phenyl-*	$H_2NCH_2CH(OH)C_6H_5$	137.18	nd (al-eth-peth)	56–7 (40)	160^{17}			v	s					B13[2], 361
e342	—,1-amino-2,2,2-trichloro-*	Chloral-ammonia. $Cl_3CCH(OH)NH_2$	164.42	nd (al)	72–4	100d			δ	s	v		v		B1[2], 681
Ω e343	—,2(2-aminoethylamino)-*	$H_2NCH_2CH_2NHCH_2CH_2OH$	104.15	hyg liq		$238–40^{732}$ (cor) 91.2^5	0.9556^{25}_4	1.4860^{20}	v	v	δ				B4, 286
e344	—,2(2-aminophenyl)-*		137.18	ye in air		$152–3^6$		1.5849^{19}	s						B13[2], 362
e345	—,2(4-aminophenyl)-*		137.18	nd (al)	108					δ s^h					B13[2], 362
e346	—,2-benzyloxy-	Glycol monobenzyl ether. $C_6H_5CH_2OCH_2CH_2OH$	152.20		< −75	256^{760} 138^{15}	1.0640^{20}_4	1.5233^{20}	s	s	s				B6[2], 413
e346[1]	—,1,1-bis(4-chlorophenyl)-*	4,4'-Dichloro-α-methyl-benzhydrol. Dimite.	267.16	cr (al-w) λ^{sulf} 240 (3.8), 325 (4.2), 370 sh (3.5), 450 (4.9), 500 sh (3.01)	69–70				i	i	s				Am 73, 1856
Ω e347	—,2-bromo-*......	Ethylene bromohydrin. $BrCH_2CH_2OH$	124.97			$149–50^{750}$ 51^4	1.7629^{20}_4	1.4915^{20}	∞	∞	∞			oos v lig δ	B1[2], 337
Ω e348	—,2-butoxy-*	Glycol monobutyl ether. $C_4H_9OCH_2CH_2OH$	118.18			171^{760} 50^4	0.9015^{20}_4	1.4198^{20}	∞	∞	∞				B1[2], 519
Ω e349	—,2-butylamino-*.	$C_4H_9NHCH_2CH_2OH$	117.19			199 200^{760} $91–2^{11}$	$0.9007^{20}_{?}$	1.4437^{20}	v	v	v				B4, 283
Ω e350	—,2-chloro-*......	Ethylene chlorohydrin. $ClCH_2CH_2OH$	80.52		−67.5	128^{760} 44^{20}	1.20027^{20}_4	1.44189^{20}	∞	∞	δ			os ∞	B1[2], 333
e351	—,2-chloro-1-phenyl-*	Styrene chlorohydrin. $C_6H_5CH(OH)CH_2Cl$	156.61			128^{17} $91.5^{1.5}$	1.1926^{20}	1.5523^{20}		s	v				B6[2], 446
Ω e352	—,2(2-chloroethoxy)-*	β-Chloroethyl cellosolve. $ClCH_2CH_2OCH_2CH_2OH$	124.57			$180–85$ $91–2^{13}$		1.4505^{19}	v	∞	v				B1[2], 519
Ω e353	—,1-cyclohexyl-*	Methylcyclohexylcarbinol.	128.22	λ^{al} 255 (3.8)		189 $81–2^{15}$	0.9250^{20}	1.4677^{20}			s				B6[2], 27
Ω e354	—,2-cyclohexyl-* .		128.22			$207–9^{757}$ $97–9^{15}$	0.9229^{20}	1.4641^{20}		s	s		s		B6[2], 27
Ω e355	—,2-cyclopentyl-*		114.19			$183–4^{770}$ $96–7^{24}$	$0.9180^{20}_{?}$	1.4577^{20}	i		s				B6[2], 25
Ω e356	—,2,2-dichloro-*	Cl_2CHCH_2OH	114.96			146^{760} $37–8^6$	$1.4040^{25}_{?}$	1.4626^{25}	δ	s	s				B1, 338
—	—,2,2-diethoxy-* .	see Acetaldehyde, 2-hydroxy-, diethyl acetal													

For explanations, symbols and abbreviations see beginning of table. For structural formulas see end of table.

No.	Name	Synonyms and Formula	Mol. wt.	Color, crystalline form, specific rotation and λ_{max} (log ε)	m.p. °C	b.p. °C	Density	n_D	w	al	eth	ace	bz	other solvents	Ref.
	Ethanol														
Ω e358	—,2-diethyl-amino-*	β-Hydroxytriethylamine. $(C_2H_5)_2NCH_2CH_2OH$	117.19	hyg	....	163^{760} $56-7^{15}$	0.8921^{20}_4	1.4412^{20}	∞	s	s	s	s	peth s	B4[2], 727
Ω e359	—,2-dimethyl-amino-*	$(CH_3)_2NCH_2CH_2OH$	89.14		....	134^{760} (cor)	0.8866^{20}_4	1.4300^{20}	∞	∞	∞				B4[2], 719
e360	—,1,2-diphenyl-(d)*	Benzyl phenyl carbinol. $C_6H_5CH_2CH(OH)C_6H_5$	198.27	nd (eth-peth or dil al) $[\alpha]^{25}_D +53$ (al)	67–8	$167-70^{10}$	1.0358^{20}_4	....	i	v	v				B6[2], 637
e361	—,—(dl)*	$C_6H_5CH_2CH(OH)C_6H_5$	198.27	nd (bz-peth)	69	177^{15} $125-30^2$	....	....	i	v	v				B6[2], 638
e362	—,—(l)*	$C_6H_5CH_2CH(OH)C_6H_5$	198.27	nd (eth-peth) $[\alpha]^{20}_D -9.4$ (w, c = 10)	67	....	1.0358^{20}_4	....	i	v	v				B6[2], 637
Ω e363	—,2-ethoxy-*	Ethyl cellosolve. Glycol monoethyl ether. $C_2H_5OCH_2CH_2OH$	90.12		....	135^{760} 35^{10}	0.9297^{20}_4	1.4080^{20}	∞	∞	∞	∞			B1[2], 518
Ω e364	—,2-ethylamino-* ..	$C_2H_5NHCH_2CH_2OH$	89.14		....	$169-70^{760}$ $78-80^{27}$	0.914^{20}_2	1.444^{20}	v	v	v				B4[2], 727
Ω e365	—,2-(ethylthio)-* ..	$C_2H_5SCH_2CH_2OH$	106.19		ca. −100	184 $35^{0.12}$	1.0166^{20}_2	1.4867^{20}	δ	s	...	v			B1[3], 2120
Ω e366	—,2-fluoro-*	Ethylene fluorohydrin. FCH_2CH_2OH	64.06		−26.45	103.5	1.1040^{20}_2	1.3647^{18}	∞	∞	∞				B1[2], 333
Ω e367	—,2-hexyloxy-* ...	Hexyl cellosolve. $CH_3(CH_2)_5OCH_2CH_2OH$	146.23	....	−45.1	208^{760}_{20} 96^{13}	0.8894^{20}_{20}	1.4291^{20}	δ	v	v				B1[3], 2086
e368	—,2-iodo-*	Ethylene iodohydrin. ICH_2CH_2OH	171.97			$176-7\delta d$ $85-8^{25}$	2.1968^{20}_2 2.2289^0_4	1.5713^{20}	s	v	v				B1[3], 1363
e368[1]	—,isobutoxy-	Isobutyl cellosolve. $C_4H_9^bOCH_2CH_2OH$	118.18			159^{745}	0.8900^{20}_2	1.4143^{20}	v	v	v				B1[3], 2084
Ω e369	—,2-isobutyl-amino-*	$C_4H_9NHCH_2CH_2OH$	117.19			$199-200$ (cor) 90^{16}	0.8818^{20}_4	1.4402^{20}	v	v	v				B4, 283
e370	—,2-isopropoxy-* ..	Isopropyl cellosolve. $C_3H_7^iOCH_2CH_2OH$	104.15			144^{743}	0.9030^{20}_2	1.4095^{20}	∞	∞	∞	s			B1[3], 2080
e371	—,2-isopropyl-amino-*	$C_3H_7^iNHCH_2CH_2OH$	103.17			$172-4^{760}$ $76-7^{15}$	0.8970^{20}_4	1.4395^{20}	∞	∞	∞				B4, 282
Ω e372	—,2-mercapto-* ...	Monothioethylene glycol. Thioglycol. $HSCH_2CH_2OH$	78.13			$157-8^{742}\delta d$ 55^{13}	1.1143^{20}_2	1.4996^{20}	s	s	s		s		B1[2], 523
Ω e373	—,2-methoxy-*	Methyl cellosolve. $CH_3OCH_2CH_2OH$	76.11		−85.1	125^{768}	0.9647^{20}_4	1.4024^{20}	∞	v	∞	s	∞		B1[3], 2069
e374	—,1(2-methoxy-phenyl)-*	o-Anisylmethylcarbinol.	152.20			128^{17}	1.0862^{15}_4	1.5312^{25}	i	s					B6[2], 886
e375	—,1(3-methoxy-phenyl)-*	m-Anisylmethylcarbinol.	152.20			133^{15}	1.0781^{19}_4	1.5325^{20}	i	v	v				B6[2], 886
e376	—,1(4-methoxy-phenyl)-*	p-Anisylmethylcarbinol.	152.20			ca. 310^{760} δd $140-1^{17}$	1.0794^{20}_4	1.5310^{25}	i		s	s		con sulf s	B6[2], 886
Ω e377	—,2-methyl-amino-*	$CH_3NHCH_2CH_2OH$	75.11			158^{760} (cor) 52^6	0.937^{20}	1.4385^{20}	∞	∞	∞				B4[2], 718
—	—,2-methylamino-1-phenyl-(l)*	see Halostachine													
e378	—,2(methyl-phenyl)amino-*	$C_6H_5N(CH_3)CH_2CH_2OH$ ..	151.21	yesh $\lambda^{95\%\,al}$ 256	....	150^{14}	0.9995^{15}_0	....	s^h	v	v	v	v		B12[2], 107
e380	—,2(methylthio)-* ..	$CH_3SCH_2CH_2OH$	92.17			$68-70^{20}$	1.0640^{20}_{20}	1.4867^{30}	s	v	v				B1[2], 524
—	—,morpholinyl-	see Morpholine, 4(2-hydroxy-ethyl)-													
e381	—,1(1-naphthyl)-(dl)*	$C_{10}H_7^aCH(OH)CH_3$	172.23	nd(peth)	66	178^{15} $119-25^1$	1.1190^{14}_4	1.6188^{25}	i	s	...	s	s	chl s	B6[2], 619
e382	—,—(l)*	$C_{10}H_7^aCH(OH)CH_3$	172.23	nd, $[\alpha]^{20}_D -78.9$ (al, c = 5)	47	166^{11}	1.1190^{14}_4	1.6180^{25}	i	s	...	s	s	chl s	B6[2], 619
e383	—,2(2-naphthyl-amino)-*	$C_{10}H_7^\beta NHCH_2CH_2OH$	187.24	lf (eth or al)	52	$197-8^3$	....	....		v					B12[2], 717
e384	—,2-nitro-*	$O_2NCH_2CH_2OH$	91.07	λ^{al} 270 (1.45)	−80	194^{765} 102^{10}	1.270^{15}_4	1.4438^{19}	∞	∞	∞	∞	i		B1[3], 1364
Ω e385	—,2-phenoxy-* ...	Phenoxytol. $C_6H_5OCH_2CH_2OH$	138.17	....	....	237 $134-5^{18}$	1.1020^{22}_2	1.5340^{20}	i	s	s			alk s	B6[3], 567
e386	—,1-phenyl-(d)* ...	$C_6H_5CH(OH)CH_3$	122.17	$[\alpha]^{19}_D +42.9$ (undil) λ^{sulf} 435 (4.0)		203^{760} 100^{18}	1.0129^{20}_2	1.5272^{20}		v			s	chl s	B6[2], 444
Ω e387	—,—(dl)*	$C_6H_5CH(OH)CH_3$	122.17	glassy λ^{sulf} 435 (4.0)	20	203.4^{760} 87.25^{10}	1.0135^{20}_4	1.5275^{20}_4	i	v			s	chl s	B6[2], 444
e388	—,—(l)*	$C_6H_5CH(OH)CH_3$	122.17	$[\alpha]^{23}_D -45.5$ (MeOH, c = 5) λ^{sulf} 435 (4.0)		$202-4^{760}$ 93^{14}	1.0129^{20}_2	1.5272^{20}	δ	v			s		B6[2], 444
Ω e389	—,2-phenyl-*	Benzylcarbinol. Phenethyl-alcohol. $C_6H_5CH_2CH_2OH$	122.17	glass λ^{hx} 271 (3.29)	fr −27	218.2^{760} 97.4^{10}	1.0202^{20}_2	1.5325^{20}	δ	∞	∞				B6[2], 448
Ω e390	—,2-phenyl-amino-*	2-Anilinoethanol. $C_6H_5NHCH_2CH_2OH$	137.18	$\lambda^{95\%\,al}$ 248	....	286^{760} 167^{17}	1.0945^{20}_2	1.5760^{20}	δ	v	v			chl v	B12[2], 106
—	—,piperidyl-	see Piperidine, hydroxy-ethyl-													
Ω e391	—,2-propoxy-*	Propyl cellosolve. $C_3H_7^nOCH_2CH_2OH$	104.15	....		150^{743}	0.9112^{20}_2	1.4133^{20}	s	v	v				B1[3], 2079

For explanations, symbols and abbreviations see beginning of table. For structural formulas see end of table.

No.	Name	Synonyms and Formula	Mol. wt.	Color, crystalline form, specific rotation and λ_{max} (log ε)	m.p. °C	b.p. °C	Density	n_D	w	al	eth	ace	bz	other solvents	Ref.
	Ethanol														
e393	—,1(3-tolyl)-.....	....	136.20	....		112[12]	0.9974[15]	1.5240[20]	i	v	v	...	...	....	B6[2], 478
e394	—,1(4-tolyl)-.....	....	136.20	....		219[756] 120[19]	0.9944[20]	1.5246[20]	i	v	v	...	...	....	B6[2], 479
—	—,tolylamino-.....	*see* **Amine, ethyl tolyl, hydroxy-**													
e395	—,2(4-tolylthio)-...	....	168.26	....		282–3d 174[30]				s	s	...	s	aa s chl δ lig i	B6[2], 396
e396	—,2-triazo-*	$N_3CH_2CH_2OH$	87.08	....		75[40] 60[8]	1.149[24/24]	1.4578[25]	∞						B1[1], 171
Ω e397	—,2,2,2-tri-bromo-*	Avertin. Bromethol. Ethobrom. Renarcol. Br_3CCH_2OH	282.77	nd or pr (peth)	81–1.5	92–3[10]			δ	v	v	...	s	peth s[h]	B1[2], 338
e398	—,2,2,2-tri-chloro-*	Cl_3CCH_2OH	149.41	hyg rh ta or pl	19	151[737] 52[11]		1.4861[20]	δ	∞	∞	...		alk s	B1[3], 1358
Ω e399	—,1,1,2-tri-phenyl-*	Benzyldiphenylcarbinol. $(C_6H_5)_2C(OH)CH_2C_6H_5$	274.37	nd (bz-lig), pr (peth)	89–90	222[11]			i	v	δ	...		peth, lig δ	B6[2], 696
e400	—,2,2,2-tri-phenyl-*	Tritylcarbinol. $(C_6H_5)_3CCH_2OH$	274.37	cr (al, eth, lig)	110.5d	....			i	s	s	...	s	lig s	B6[2], 696
Ω e401	Ethene*	Ethylene. $CH_2:CH_2$	28.05	gas, mcl pr λ^{gas} 161.5 (3.94), 166 (3.8), 174 (3.7)	−169.15 fr −181	−103.71[760] 0.00126 (at 0° 760 mm) 0.384[−10]		1.363[100]	i	δ	s	δ	δ	....	B1[1], 75
e402	—,amino-*	Ethenylamine. Vinylamine. $CH_2:CHNH_2$	43.07	....		55–6[756]	0.8321[21]		∞	s	∞				B4, 203
e403	—,bromo-*	Vinyl bromide. $CH_2:CHBr$..	106.96	....	−139.54	15.80[760] (liq)	1.4933[20]	1.4410[20]	i	s	v	...		chl s	B1[2], 162
Ω e404	—,1-bromo-1,2,2-triphenyl-*	$(C_6H_5)_2C:CBrC_6H_5$	335.25	nd (aa) λ^{al} 230 (4.3), 290 (3.9)	116–7	....			i					aa s[h]	B5[1], 355
Ω e405	—,chloro-*	Vinyl chloride. $CH_2:CHCl$..	62.50	gas	−153.8	−13.37[760]	0.9106[20]	1.3700[20]	δ	s	v	...		chl s	B1[2], 157
e406	—,1-chloro-2-dichloroarsino-(*trans*)*	Lewisite. $ClCH:CHAsCl_2$	207.32	....	0.1	196[760]d 93[26]	1.888[20/4]		i	s	s	...		os s alk d	B4[3], 1810
e407	—,1-chloro-1,2,2-triphenyl-*	$(C_6H_5)_2C:CClC_6H_5$	290.80	λ^{al} cr (al) 228 (4.3), 288 (4.0)	117	....			i	s	s	...	s	chl v peth s	B5[1], 355
e408	—,1,2-dibromo-(*cis*)*	*Sym*-Dibromoethylene. $BrCH:CHBr$.	185.86	....	−53	112.5[760]	2.2464[20]	1.5428[20]	i	v	v	...	s	chl s	B1[3], 672
Ω e409	—,—(*trans*)* ...	$BrCH:CHBr$	185.86	....	−6.5	108[760]	2.2308[20]	1.5505[18]	i	v	v	...	s	chl s	B1[3], 672
e410	—,1,1-dibromo-2-ethoxy-*	$C_2H_5OCH:CBr_2$	229.91	....		170–2[747] (cor) 73–5[15]	1.7697[18]		i		v				B1[2], 473
Ω e411	—,1,1-dichloro-* ..	Vinylidene chloride. $CH_2:CCl_2$	96.94	λ^{vap}<200	−122.1	37[760] (32)	1.218[20]	1.4249[20]	i	s	s	...	s	chl v	B1[3], 647
Ω e412	—,1,2-dichloro-(*cis*)*	*Sym*-Dichloroethylene. $ClCH:CHCl$	96.94	λ^{vap}<200	−80.5	60.3[760]	1.2837[20]	1.4490[20]	δ	∞	∞	∞	v	chl v	B1[3], 651
Ω e413	—,—(*trans*)* ...	$ClCH:CHCl$	96.94	λ^{vap}<200	−50	47.5	1.2565[20/4]	1.4454[20]	δ	∞	∞	∞	v	chl v	B1[3], 651
Ω e414	—,1,1-difluoro-* ...	Vinylidene fluoride. $CH_2:CF_2$	64.04	gas	....	< −84			i	s	v	...			B1[3], 638
e415	—,1,1-dinitro-2,2-diphenyl-*	$(C_6H_5)_2C:C(NO_2)_2$	270.25	ye nd (aa or al)	149	....			s[h]	s	s	...			B5[2], 545
Ω e416	—,1,1-diphenyl-* ..	$(C_6H_5)_2C:CH_2$	180.25	λ^{al} 236 sh (4.2), 255 (4.0)	8.2	277[760] 94–5[11]	1.0284[16]	1.6100[20]	i	...	s	...		chl s	B5[2], 543
—	—,1,2-diphenyl-* ..	*see* **Stilbene**													
Ω e417	—,fluoro-*	Vinyl fluoride. $CH_2:CHF$ ...	46.05	gas	−160.5	−72.2			i	s	...	s			B1[1], 77
e418	—,iodo-*	Vinyl iodide. $CH_2:CHI$ ...	153.95	gas		56	2.037[20]	1.5385[20]	i	∞	∞	...			B1, 199
Ω e419	—,tetrabromo-* ...	Perbromoethylene. $Br_2C:CBr_2$	343.66	pl (dil al), nd (al) λ^{vap}<200	56.5	226–7[] 100[15] sub			i	s	s	...		chl v	B1[3], 673
Ω e420	—,tetrachloro-* ...	Perchloroethylene. $Cl_2C:CCl_2$	165.83	....	−19 fr −22	121[760] 14[10]	1.6227[20]	1.5053[20]	i	∞	∞	...	∞	....	B1[3], 664
e421	—,tetrafluoro-* ...	Perfluoroethylene. $F_2C:CF_2$	100.02	gas	−142.5	−76.3[760]	1.519[76.3]		i						B1[3], 638
e422	—,tetraiodo-* ...	Periodoethylene. $I_2C:CI_2$ ...	531.64	lemon ye lf, pr (eth)	192	sub	2.983[20]		i	δ	δ	...	s	CS_2 v chl s	B1[3], 676
Ω e423	—,tetraphenyl-* ...	$(C_6H_5)_2C:C(C_6H_5)_2$	332.45	mcl or rh (bz-eth or chl-al) λ^{diox} 310 (4.4)	225 (cor)	415 25[760]	1.155[0]		i	δ	δ	v[h]			B5[2], 679
e424	—,tribromo-* ...	$BrCH:CBr_2$	264.76	....		163–4[760] 75[15]	2.708[20.5]	1.6045[16]	δ	s	s	...	s	chl s	B1[2], 164
Ω e425	—,trichloro-* ...	$ClCH:CCl_2$	131.39	λ^{vap}<200	−73 fr −86.4	87[760]	1.4642[20/4]	1.4773[20]	δ	∞	∞	s	...	chl s	B1[3], 656
Ω e426	—,triphenyl-* ...	$C_6H_5CH:C(C_6H_5)_2$	256.35	lf (al or MeOH) λ^{al} 231 (4.1), 299 (4.2)	72–3	220–1[14]	1.0373[78/4]	1.6292[78]	i	s	v	...		MeOH s	B5[2], 630
Ω e427	Ethenetetra-carboxylic acid, tetraethyl ester*	$(C_2H_5O_2C)_2C:C(CO_2C_2H_5)_2$	316.31	tcl pr (eth)	58	325–8 δd 210[22]			i	v	v	...			B2[2], 709
e428	Ether, allyl butyl, 3'-methyl-	Allyl isoamyl ether. $(CH_3)_2CHCH_2CH_2OCH_2CH:CH_2$	128.22	....	....	120–2			i	∞	∞	...			B1[2], 477

For explanations, symbols and abbreviations see beginning of table. For structural formulas see end of table.

Ether

No.	Name	Synonyms and Formula	Mol. wt.	Color, crystalline form, specific rotation and λ_{max} (log ε)	m.p. °C	b.p. °C	Density	n_D	w	al	eth	ace	bz	other solvents	Ref.
Ω e429	—,allyl ethyl	3-Ethoxypropene.* $C_2H_5OCH_2CH:CH_2$	86.14			66^{761}	0.7651^{20}_4	1.3881^{20}	i	∞	∞	s			B1^3, 1881
e430	—,allyl isopropyl	$C_3H^i_7OCH_2CH:CH_2$	100.16			83–4	0.7764^{20}	1.3946^{20}	i	v	∞	s			B1^3, 1882
e431	—,allyl methyl	$CH_3OCH_2CH:CH_2$	72.12			46^{760}	0.77^{11}_{11}	1.3778^{20}	i	∞	∞	s			B1^3, 1881
e432	—,allyl 2-naphthyl	$C_{10}H^\beta_7OCH_2CH:CH_2$	184.24		16	d 210		1.600^{25}	i						B6^1, 313
Ω e433	—,allyl phenyl	$C_6H_5OCH_2CH:CH_2$	134.18			191.7^{760} 74^5	0.9811^{20}_4	1.5223^{20}	i	s	∞	s			B6^2, 146
e434	—,—,4'-chloro-		168.63			d^{760} $106–7^{12}$	1.131^{15}	1.5348^{25}	i	s	s	s	s		B6^1, 101
e434^1	—,—,2',4',6'-tri-bromo-		370.88	nd (al)	33–4				i		i				B6^2, 194
e435	—,allyl propyl	$CH_3CH_2CH_2OCH_2CH:CH_2$	100.16			90–2	$0·7764^{20}$	1.3919^{20}	i	s	∞				B1^3, 1882
Ω e436	—,allyl 2-tolyl		148.21			205–8 85^{12}	0.9698^{15}_{15}	1.5188^{15}	i			s			B6^2, 329
e437	—,allyl 3-tolyl		148.21			211–4 93.5^{13}	0.9564^{20}	1.5179^{20}	i			s			B6^1, 186
Ω e438	—,allyl 4-tolyl		148.21			214.5^{760} $97–8^{16}$	0.9728^{15}_{15}	1.5157^{24}	i			s			B6^2, 377
e439	—,benzyl butyl	$C_6H_5CH_2O(CH_2)_3CH_3$	164.25			223^{760} 92^{10}	0.9227^{20}_4	1.4833^{20}	i	∞	∞	s			B6^2, 410
e440	—,—,2'-methyl-(d)	$C_6H_5CH_2OCH_2CH(CH_3)CH_2CH_3$	178.28	$[\alpha]^{22}_D$ +1.82		231^{722}	0.911^{22}_2	1.4854^{22}	i	v	v				B6, 431
Ω e441	—,—,3'-methyl-	Benzyl isoamyl ether. $C_6H_5CH_2OCH_2CH_2CH(CH_3)_2$	178.28			236–7^{748} $117–9^{19}$	0.9098^{20}_4	1.4792^{20}	i	v	v		δ		B6^2, 410
Ω e442	—,benzyl ethyl	α-Ethoxytoluene. $C_6H_5CH_2OC_2H_5$	136.20			185^{760} 70^{15}	0.9490^{20}_4	1.4955^{20}	i	∞	∞				B6^2, 409
e443	—,benzyl isobutyl	$C_6H_5CH_2OCH_2CH(CH_3)_2$	164.25			211–2^{743}	$0·9233^{20}_4$	1.4826^{20}	i		v			chl v	B6^2, 410
e444	—,benzyl methyl	α-Methoxytoluene. $C_6H_5CH_2OCH_3$	122.17		−52.6	170^{760} $59–60^{12}$	0.9634^{20}_4	1.5008^{20}	i	v	v			lig i	B6^2, 409
e445	—,—,1'-chloro-	$C_6H_5CH_2OCH_2Cl$	156.61			103^{13}	1.1350^{20}_4	1.5192^{20}		δ					B6^2, 414
e446	—,benzyl 1-naphthyl	$C_6H_5CH_2OC_{10}H^\alpha_7$	234.30	cr (al)	61 (77)	200^{12}			i	δ v^h					B6^2, 579
e447	—,benzyl 2-naphthyl	$C_6H_5CH_2OC_{10}H^\beta_7$	234.30	lf or nd (al)	101–2				i	s	s	s	s	chl s oos ∞	B6^2, 599
e448	—,butyl ethenyl	Butoxyethene.* $CH_3(CH_2)_3OCH:CH_2$	100.16		−92	93.8^{760}	0.7888^{20}_4	1.4026^{20}	i	v	∞	v	s	glycol, glycerol δ	B1^3, 1860
e449	—,—,3-methyl-	Isoamyl vinyl ether. $(CH_3)_2CHCH_2CH_2OCH:CH_2$	114.19			$112–3^{760}$	0.7826^{20}_4	1.4072^{20}	i	s	v				B1^3, 1863
Ω e450	—,butyl ethyl	1-Ethoxybutane.* $CH_3(CH_2)_3OC_2H_5$	102.18		−124	96^{760}	0.7490^{20}_4	1.3818^{20}	i	∞	∞	v			B1^3, 1502
e451	—,sec-butyl ethyl	$CH_3CH(C_2H_5)OC_2H_5$	102.18			81^{760}	0.7503^{20}_4	1.3802^{20}	i	v	v				B1^3, 1533
e452	—,tert-butyl ethyl	$(CH_3)_3COC_2H_5$	102.18		−94	73.1^{760}	0.7519^{25}	1.3794^{20}	i	v	v				B1^3, 1577
e453	—,butyl ethyl, 2'-chloro-	$CH_3(CH_2)_3OCH_2CH_2Cl$	136.62			154.5^{750}d (cor) $49–50^{11}$	0.9335^{20}_4	1.4155^{20}							B1^3, 1502
e454	—,—,3-methyl-	Ethyl isoamyl ether. $(CH_3)_2CHCH_2CH_2OC_2H_5$	116.21			$112–3^{760}$	0.7695^{21}_{15}		i	∞	∞				B1^2, 432
e454^1	—,sec-butyl ethyl, 2-methyl-	Ethyl tert-amyl ether. $CH_3CH_2C(CH_3)_2OC_2H_5$	116.21			101^{760}	0.7657^{20}_4	1.3912^{20}	δ	v	v				B1, 389
e455	—,butyl ethynyl	Butoxyacetylene. $CH_3(CH_2)_3OC:CH$	98.15			$102–4^{760}$ exp ca. 100 $41–2^{78}$	0.8200^{20}_4	1.4020^{20}	d^h	v	s				B1^3, 1969
e456	—,butyl furfuryl		154.21			189.90^{765}	0.9516^{20}	1.4522^{20}	i	s	v				B17^2, 114
e457	—,butyl isobutyl	$CH_3(CH_2)_3OCH_2CH(CH_3)_2$	130.23			148–52^{730}	0.7980^{22}_2	1.4077^{21}	i	s	∞	s			B1, 376
e458	—,butyl isopropyl	$CH_3(CH_2)_3OCH(CH_3)_2$	116.21			108^{738}	0.7594^{15}	1.3870^{15}	i	s	s	s		os, con sulf s	B1^3, 1503
Ω e458^1	—,butyl methyl	$CH_3(CH_2)_3OCH_3$	88.15		−115.5	71^{760}	0.7443^{20}_4	1.3736^{20}	i	∞	∞	s			B1^2, 395
e459	—,sec-butyl methyl	$CH_3CH_2CH(CH_3)OCH_3$	88.15			60 (cor)	0.7415^{20}_2	1.3680^{25}	δ	v	v	s			B1^3, 1532
e460	—,tert-butyl methyl	$(CH_3)_3COCH_3$	88.15		−109	55.2^{760} (cor)	0.7405^{20}_4	1.3690^{20}	s	v	v				B1^3, 1576
e461	—,butyl methyl, 3-methyl-	Isoamyl methyl ether. $(CH_3)_2CHCH_2CH_2OCH_3$	102.18			91^{765}	0.7517^{20}	1.3830^{20}		s	s				B1^2, 432
e462	—,sec-butyl methyl, 2-methyl-	Methyl tert-amyl ether $CH_3CH_2C(CH_3)_2OCH_3$	102.18			86.3^{760}	0.7703^{20}_4	1.3885^{20}	δ	v	∞			MeOH v	B1, 389
e462^1	—,butyl propyl	$CH_3(CH_2)_3OCH_2CH_2CH_3$	116.21			117.1	0.7773^0_0		i	v	v				B1^3, 1503
e463	—,—,3-methyl-	Isoamyl propyl ether. $(CH_3)_2CHCH_2CH_2OCH_2CH_2CH_3$	130.23			130			i	s	∞				B1^2, 432
e464	—,butyl 2-tolyl		164.25			223^{760}	0.9437^0_0		i						B6, 353
e465	—,2-butynyl methyl	$CH_3C:CCH_2OCH_3$	84.13			$99–100^{760}$ 33^{27}	0.8496^{20}_4	1.4262^{20}	i	s	s		s		B1^3, 1973
e466	—,cyclohexyl 2-furyl		166.22			118.9^{28}	1.0200^{28}_4	1.4861^{28}	i	s	s	s		MeOH s	C51, 3550
e467	—,cyclohexyl methyl	Hexahydroanisole	114.19		−74.37	133^{760}	0.8756^{20}_4	1.4355^{20}	i	s	s	s		MeOH s	B6^2, 9
e468	—,—,2-bromo- (dl, trans)		193.09			$78–9^{12}$	1.3314^{20}_4	1.4871^{20}	i	s	s				B6^2, 13
Ω e469	—,diallyl	Allyl ether. $CH_2:CHCH_2OCH_2CH:CH_2$	98.15			94	0.8260^{20}_4	1.4163^{20}	i	∞	∞	v			B1^2, 477
Ω e470	—,dibenzyl	Benzyl ether. $C_6H_5CH_2OCH_2C_6H_5$	198.27	λ^{cy} 252 (2.5), 259 (2.6), 265 (2.5)	3.60	298^{760} 160^{11}	1.0428^{20}_4	1.5168^{20}	i	∞	∞				B6^2, 412

For explanations, symbols and abbreviations see beginning of table. For structural formulas see end of table.

Ether

No.	Name	Synonyms and Formula	Mol. wt.	Color, crystalline form, specific rotation and λ_{max} (log ε)	m.p. °C	b.p. °C	Density	n_D	w	al	eth	ace	bz	other solvents	Ref.
Ω e471	—,dibutyl	Butyl ether. $CH_3(CH_2)_3O(CH_2)_3CH_3$	130.23	....	−95.3	142^{760} 47^{24}	0.7689_4^{20}	1.3992^{20}	i	∞	∞	v	...		$B1^2$, 396
e472	—,di-sec-butyl (dl)	sec-Butyl ether. $CH_3CH(C_2H_5)OCH(C_2H_5)CH_3$	130.23	....		$120–1^{760}$	0.756^{25}	1.393^{25}	i	∞	∞	v	...		$B1^2$, 402
e473	—,dibutyl, 3,3′-dimethyl-	Isoamyl ether. $(CH_3)_2CHCH_2CH_2OCH_2CH_2CH(CH_3)_2$	158.29	....		$172–3^{760}$ 60^{10}	0.7777_4^{20}	1.4085^{20}	i	∞	∞	...	chl ∞		$B1^3$, 1638
e474	—,—,3-methyl-	Butyl isoamyl ether. $CH_3(CH_2)_3OCH_2CH_2CH(CH_3)_2$	144.26	....		157^{756}	....	....	i	s	∞	...			B1, 401
Ω e475	—,diethenyl	Ethenyloxyethene*. Vinyl ether. $CH_2:CHOCH:CH_2$	70.09	λ^{gas} 164 (3.82), 302 (4.19)	−101	28^{760} (39)	0.773_4^{20}	1.3989^{20}	i	∞	∞	...	chl ∞		$B1^2$, 473
e476	—,—,hexachloro-	$Cl_2C:CClOCCl:CCl_2$	276.76	....		210	1.654^{21}								B1, 725
Ω e477	—,diethyl	Ether. Ethoxyethane*. $CH_3CH_2OCH_2CH_3$	74.12	λ^{gas} 171 (3.60), 188 (3.30)	fr −116.2	34.51^{760}	0.7137_4^{20}	1.3526^{20}	δ	∞	∞	v	∞	chl, oils, lig ∞	$B1^2$, 311
e478	—,—,borofluoride	$(C_2H_5)_2O\cdot BF_3$	141.93	....	−60.4	$125–6^{760}$d 60^{20}	1.125_4^{25}	1.348^{20}	d	d	s	...			$B1^3$, 1308
Ω e479	—,—,2-bromo-	$BrCH_2CH_2OC_2H_5$	153.03	ye nd (al)		$127–8^{755}$ 40^{24}	1.3572_4^{20}	1.4447^{20}	δ	∞	∞	...			$B1^3$, 1361
Ω e480	—,—,1-chloro-	$CH_3CHClOC_2H_5$	108.57	λ^{hx} < 180		$92–5$	0.950_4^{20}	1.4053^{20}	d	d^h	∞	...			$B1^2$, 674
e481	—,—,2-chloro-	$ClCH_2CH_2OC_2H_5$	108.57	λ^{hx} < 180		$107–8$	0.9894_4^{20}	1.4113^{20}	δ	...	∞	...	chl s		$B1^3$, 1349
e482	—,—,decachloro-	Perchloroether. $Cl_3CCCl_2OCCl_2CCl_3$	418.57	oct or tetr pym	69	d	$1.900^{14.5}$								B2, 210
e483	—,—,2,2′-dl-benzoyloxy-	Oxybis(β-ethylbenzoate). $C_6H_5CO_2CH_2CH_2OCH_2CH_2O_2CC_6H_5$	314.34	....	33.5	$279–81^{24}$ 250^3	1.1701_{15}^{15}								$B9^2$, 108
e484	—,—,1,2-dibromo-	$BrCH_2CHBrOC_2H_5$	231.94	....		80^{20} $55–8^9$	1.7320_4^{20}	1.5044^{20}	d				chl s		B1, 625
—	—,—,1,1′-dicarboxy-	see Dilactic acid													
e485	—,—,1,1′-dichloro-	$CH_3CHClOCHClCH_3$	143.02	....		$116–7$	1.1060_4^{25}	1.4186^{25}	d	v	∞	...	chl s		B1, 607
e486	—,—,1,2-dichloro-	$ClCH_2CHClOC_2H_5$	143.02	λ^{hx} 230 (1.6), 298 (−0.8)		145^{760} $66–8^{45}$	1.1370_4^{20}	1.4435^{20}	d	v	v	...	chl s		$B1^2$, 676
e487	—,—,1,2′-dichloro-	$ClCH_2CH_2OCHClCH_3$	143.02	....		d^{760} $55–7^{17}$	1.1867_4^{20}	1.4473^{20}	d	v	v	...	chl s		$B1^2$, 674
e488	—,—,2,2′-dichloro-	$ClCH_2CH_2OCH_2CH_2Cl$	143.02	....	−24.5 (−46.8)	178^{760} 75^{20}	1.2199_4^{20}	1.4575^{20}	i $δ^h$	s	s	s	∞	MeOH ∞ oos s	$B1^3$, 1349
—	—,—,2,2′-dihydroxy-	see Diethylene glycol													
e489	—,—,2,2′-diphenoxy-	$C_6H_5OCH_2CH_2OCH_2CH_2OC_6H_5$	258.32	nd (dil al)	66–7	....				s					$B6^2$, 150
e490	—,—,1,1′-diphenyl-(dl)	$C_6H_5CH(CH_3)OCH(CH_3)C_6H_5$	226.32	....		280.2 $167–8^{23}$	1.0058_4^{15}	1.5454^{21}	i		s		chl s		$B6^2$, 445
e491	—,—,2,2′-diphenyl-	$C_6H_5CH_2CH_2OCH_2CH_2C_6H_5$	226.32	vt-bl flr		$317–20^{760}$ 194.5^{20}	1.0141_4^{18}	1.5488^{18}	i		s		chl s		$B6^2$, 450
—	—,—,2-methoxy-	see Ethane, 1-ethoxy-2-methoxy-*													
e492	—,—,1,1′,2,2,2,2′,2′-octachloro-	$Cl_3CCHClOCHClCCl_3$	349.68	cr (al or MeOH)	40–2	$130–1^{11}$			i	δ		v	peth, MeOH v		$B1^2$, 681
e493	—,difurfuryl	Furfuryl ether.	178.19	....		101^2 $88–9^1$	1.1405_4^{20}	1.5088^{20}	i						$B17^2$, 116
e494	—,diheptyl	Heptyl ether. $CH_3(CH_2)_6O(CH_2)_6CH_3$	214.40	....		258.5^{769}	0.8008_4^{20}	1.4275^{20}	i	s	s	...			$B1^3$, 1683
Ω e495	—,dihexadecyl	Dicetyl ether. Hexadecyl ether. $CH_3(CH_2)_{15}O(CH_2)_{15}CH_3$	466.89	lf (al)	55	270 d	0.978^{19}		i	s	s	...			$B1^2$, 467
Ω e496	—,dihexyl	Hexyl ether. $CH_3(CH_2)_5O(CH_2)_5CH_3$	186.34	....		223^{768}	0.7936_4^{20}	1.4204^{20}	i	s	s	...			$B1^3$, 1656
e496¹	—,diisobutyl, α,β-dichloro-	$(CH_3)_2CClCHClOC_4H_9^i$	199.12	....		192.5 83^{15}	1.031_4^{5}		d		s	s	...	os v	B1, 675
Ω e497	—,diisopropyl	Isopropyl ether. $(CH_3)_2CHOCH(CH_3)_2$	102.18	....	−85.89	68^{760}	0.7241_4^{20}	1.3679^{20}	δ	∞	∞	s	...	dil sulf i	$B1^3$, 1459
e498	—,—,β,β′-dichloro-	$ClCH_2CH(CH_3)OCH(CH_3)CH_2Cl$	171.07	....		187^{760}	1.103_4^{20}	1.4505^{20}	i	∞	∞	∞	v	oos ∞	$B1^3$, 1470
Ω e499	—,dimethyl	Methoxymethane*. Methyl ether. CH_3OCH_3	46.07	gas λ^{gas} 162.5 (3.60), 184 (3.40)	−138.5	$−23^{760}$	....	....	s	s	s	s	δ	chl s	$B1^2$, 1180
e500	—,—,borofluoride	$(CH_3)_2O\cdot BF_3$	113.88	....	−14 (−12)	127^{760} d	1.2410_4^{20}	1.302^{20}	d	d	s	...			$B1^3$, 1192
Ω e501	—,—,chloro-	$ClCH_2OCH_3$	80.52	....	−103.5	59.15^{760}	1.0605_4^{20}	1.3974^{20}	d	...	s	s	...	chl s	$B1^2$, 645
e502	—,—,1,1′-dichloro-	$ClCH_2OCH_2Cl$	114.96	....	−41.5	104^{760}	1.328_4^{15}	1.435^{21}	d	∞	∞	...			$B1^2$, 646
e503	—,—,1,1,1′,1′-tetraphenyl-	Benzhydryl ether. $(C_6H_5)_2CHOCH(C_6H_5)_2$	350.47	mcl (bz)	110	315^{745} d 267^{15}			i	$δ^h$	δ	v	chl s		$B6^2$, 634
e504	—,—,1,1,1 tri-2-tolyl-	, , , , , , , , , , ,	316.45	cr (peth)	108.6				i	s	s		MeOH s, peth s^h		Am 73, 3644
e505	—,1,1′-dinaphthyl-	α-Naphthyl ether. $C_{10}H_7^αOC_{10}H_7^α$	270.34	lf (al or al-eth)	110	$280–5^{23}$			i	δ s^h	s	...	s	aa $δ^h$	$B6^3$, 2926
e506	—,1,2′-dinaphthyl	α,β′-Naphthyl ether. $C_{10}H_7^αOC_{10}H_7^β$	270.34	nd (al or al-eth)	81	264^{15}			i	δ	v	s	v	chl v sulf s aa $δ^h$	$B6^2$, 600
e507	—,2,2′-dinaphthyl	β-Naphthyl ether. $C_{10}H_7^βOC_{10}H_7^β$	270.34	nd or lf (al)	105	250^{19} δd			i	δ s^h	v	...	v	aa δ, s^h	$B6^3$, 2976

For explanations, symbols and abbreviations see beginning of table. For structural formulas see end of table.

No.	Name	Synonyms and Formula	Mol. wt.	Color, crystalline form, specific rotation and λ_{max} (log ε)	m.p. °C	b.p. °C	Density	n_D	w	al	eth	ace	bz	other solvents	Ref.
	Ether														
Ω e508	—,dioctyl	Octyl ether $CH_3(CH_2)_7O(CH_2)_7CH_3$	242.45	....		$286-7^{760}$	0.8063_4^{20}	1.4327^{20}	δ	s	s	...	...	....	**B1, 419**
Ω e509	—,dipentyl	Amyl ether. $CH_3(CH_2)_4O(CH_2)_4CH_3$	158.29	....	-69	190^{760} 70^{12}	0.7833_4^{20}	1.4119^{20}	i	∞	∞	...	...	....	**B1[2], 417**
Ω e510	—,diphenyl	Phenyl ether	170.21	mcl, rh λ^{a1} 265 (3.20), 272 (3.28), 279 (3.23)	26.84	257.93^{760} 121^{10}	1.0748^{20}	1.5787^{25}	i	s	s	...	s	aa s	**B6, 146**
—	—,—,amino-	see **Aniline, phenoxy-**													
Ω e511	—,—,4-bromo-	$C_{12}H_9BrO$. See e510	249.11	λ^{a1} 272 (3.18), 279 (3.18)	18.72	310.14^{760} 163^{10}	1.4208_4^{20}	1.6084^{20}	i	...	s	...	...	....	**B6[2], 185**
e512	—,—,4,4'-dibromo-	$C_{12}H_8Br_2O$. See e510	328.03	lf (al) λ^{a1} 273 (3.26), 280 (3.26), 290 (3.18)	60.5	$338-40$ 210^{11}	1.8 (so)		i	s	v	...	s	aa δ	**B6[2], 185**
e513	—,—,4,4'-dichloro-	$C_{12}H_8Cl_2O$. See e510	239.11	nd (al)	30	$312-4$ 168.72^7	1.1231^{20}	1.611^{20}	i						**B6[2], 176**
e514	—,—,2,2'-di-hydroxy-	o-Diphenol ether. 2,2'-Oxydiphenol. $C_{12}H_{10}O_3$. See e510	202.21	nd (w)	121	....			δ^h	s		...	s	lig δ	**B6, 773**
e515	—,—,4,4'-di-hydroxy-	p-Diphenol ether. 4,4'-Oxydiphenol. $C_{12}H_{10}O_3$. See e510	202.21	lf (w or to)	$165-7$	....			δ s^h	v	v	v	v^h i	to i	**B6, 845**
e516	—,—,2,2'-di-methoxy-	o-Anisyl ether. $C_{14}H_{14}O_3$. See e510	230.27	pl (lig)	$79-80$	$330-1$			i	v	v			lig i, s^h	**B6, 773**
e517	—,—,2,3'-di-methoxy-	$C_{14}H_{14}O_3$. See e510	230.27	pr (bz-peth)	54	$326-9^{760}$ 152^2				s	s	...	s	lig δ	**B6[2], 816**
e518	—,—,3,3'-di-methoxy-	m-Anisyl ether. $C_{14}H_{14}O_3$. See e510	230.27	pa br liq λ^{diox} 275 (3.6)	....	$332-4$ 258^{16}			i	δ	v	...	v	lig δ	**B6[2], 816**
e519	—,—,2,2'-dinitro-	$C_{12}H_8N_2O_5$. See e510	260.22	pl or nd (al)	119				δ v^h						**B6, 219**
e520	—,—,2,4-dinitro-	$C_{12}H_8N_2O_5$. See e510	260.22	pl (al), nd (al-ace) λ^{a1} 293 (4.15)	71	$230-50^{27}$			δ	v	s	...	...	....	**B6[2], 242**
e521	—,—,2,4'-dinitro-	$C_{12}H_8N_2O_5$. See e510	260.22	nd (al)	103.5				δ s^h						**B6[2], 222**
e522	—,—,2,6-dinitro-	$C_{12}H_8N_2O_5$. See e510	260.22	lf (al)	$99-100$				δ s^h						**B6[2], 245**
e523	—,—,3,4-dinitro-	$C_{12}H_8N_2O_5$. See e510	260.22	pa ye lf	89						s	...	...	....	**B6[1], 127**
e524	—,—,4,4'-dinitro-	$C_{12}H_8N_2O_5$. See e510	260.22	ye nd (al), pr (bz) λ^{a1} 218 (4.20), 301 (4.33)	144 (cor)				i	δ s^h	δ	...	s	aa, bz s	**B6[2], 222**
e525	—,—,2-methoxy-	$C_{13}H_{12}O_2$. See e510	200.24	cr (MeOH), nd (lig)	79	288^{745} $91-2^7$			i	s	s	...	s	MeOH, lig s^h	**B6[2], 781**
Ω e526	—,—,2-nitro-	$C_{12}H_9NO_3$. See e510	215.21	ye liq λ^{a1} 255 (3.79), 315 (3.45)	< -20	235^{60} $183-5^8$	1.2539^{22}	1.575^{20}	i	s	s	...	s	chl, aa s	**B6[2], 222**
Ω e527	—,—,4-nitro-	$C_{12}H_9NO_3$. See e510	215.21	pl (peth or MeOH) λ^{a1} 303 (4.06)	61 (56)	$188-90^8$			i	δ	s	...	s	aa s	**B6[2], 210**
e528	—,dipropyl	Propyl ether. $CH_3CH_2CH_2OCH_2CH_2CH_3$	102.18	....	fr -122	91^{760}	0.7360_4^{20}	1.3809^{20}	δ	∞	∞	...	...	....	**B1[2], 367**
e529	—,—,1,2-dichloro-	$CH_3CHClCHClOC_3H_7^n$	171.07	....		176^{760}	1.129_4^{15}	1.447^{16}	i	s	s	...	...	....	**B1[1], 334**
e530	—,—,1,3-dichloro-	$ClCH_2CH_2CHClOC_3H_7^n$	171.07	....		65^{12}	1.112^{20}	1.4476^{20}	i	s	s	...	...	....	**B1[2], 690**
e531	—,—,2,2'-dichloro-	$CH_3CHClCH_2OCH_2CHClCH_3$	171.07	....		188^{760}	1.109_4^{20}	1.4467^{20}		s	s	...	...	....	**B1[2], 370**
e532	—,—,3,3'-dichloro-	$Cl(CH_2)_3O(CH_2)_3Cl$	171.07	....		215^{745} 90.5^{11}	1.140_{20}^{20}	1.4158^{20}		s	s	...	...	....	**B1[2], 370**
Ω e534	—,ethenyl ethyl	Ethyl vinyl ether. $C_2H_5OCH:CH_2$	72.12	....	-115.8	$35-6^{760}$	0.7589_4^{20}	1.3767^{20}	δ	s	∞	...	...	....	**B1[3], 1857**
Ω e535	—,—,2'-chloro-	$ClCH_2CH_2OCH:CH_2$	106.55	....		108^{760}	1.0475_4^{20}	1.4378^{20}	...	v	v	...	...	....	**B1[3], 1859**
e536	—,—,1,2-dichloro-	$C_2H_5OCCl:CHCl$	141.00	....		128.2	1.1972_4^{25}	1.4558^{17}	d^h s						**B1[2], 780**
Ω e537	—,ethenyl isobutyl	Isobutyl vinyl ether. $(CH_3)_2CHCH_2OCH:CH_2$	100.16	....	-112	83^{760}	0.7645_4^{20}	1.3966^{20}	δ	v	∞	v	v	oos ∞ glycol, glycerol δ	**B1[3], 1862**
Ω e538	—,ethenyl isopropyl	Isopropyl vinyl ether. $(CH_3)_2CHOCH:CH_2$	86.14	....		$55-6^{760}$	0.7534_4^{20}	1.3840^{20}	δ	v	v	v	v	....	**B1[3], 1859**
Ω e539	—,ethenyl methyl	Methoxyethene*. Methyl vinyl ether. $CH_3OCH:CH_2$	58.08	....	-122	12^{760}	0.7725_4^0	1.3730^0	δ	v	v	v	v	os v glycol, glycerol i	**B1[3], 1857**
e540	—,ethenyl phenyl	Phenyl vinyl ether. $C_6H_5OCH:CH_2$	120.16	λ^{cy} 225 (4.3), 271 (3.2), 274 (3.0)	....	$155-6$	0.9770_4^{20}	1.5224^{20}	i	...	v	...	v	....	**B6[2], 146**
e541	—,ethyl ethynyl	Ethoxyacetylene. $C_2H_5OC:CH$	70.09	....		50^{760} exp 100	0.8000_4^{20}	1.3796^{20}		v	v	...	v	....	**B1[3], 1968**
e542	—,ethyl furfuryl	....	126.16	....		$149-50^{770}$	0.9844_4^{20}	1.4523^{20}	i	s	s	...	...	....	**B17[2], 114**
e543	—,ethyl heptyl	$CH_3(CH_2)_6OC_2H_5$	144.26	....		166.6	0.790_4^{16}	1.4111^{20}	i	s	s	...	...	....	**B1[3], 1682**
e544	—,ethyl hexyl	$CH_3(CH_2)_5OC_2H_5$	130.23	....		$142-3^{773}$ 42^{14}	0.7722_4^{20}	1.4008^{20}	i	v	v	...	v	....	**B1[3], 1656**

For explanations, symbols and abbreviations see beginning of table. For structural formulas see end of table.

Ether

No.	Name	Synonyms and Formula	Mol. wt.	Color, crystalline form, specific rotation and λ_{max} (log ε)	m.p. °C	b.p. °C	Density	n_D	w	al	eth	ace	bz	other solvents	Ref.
e545	—,ethyl isobutyl	$(CH_3)_2CHCH_2OC_2H_5$	102.18			81^{760}	0.7512^{20}_4	1.3739^{25}	i	∞	∞	s		chl s	B1[3], 1559
e546	—,ethyl isopropyl	$(CH_3)_2CHOC_2H_5$	88.15			63–4	0.7202^{25}_5	1.3698^{25}	s	∞	∞	s		chl s	B1[3], 1458
e547	—,ethyl methyl	$CH_3OC_2H_5$	60.10			10.8^{760}	0.7252^{20}_0	1.3420^4	s	∞	∞	s		chl s	B1[3], 1288
e548	—,—,1'-bromo-	$BrCH_2OC_2H_5$	139.00			109^{746}	1.4402^{20}_4	1.4515^{20}			v				B1[2], 647
e549	—,—,1-chloro-	$CH_3OCHClCH_3$	94.54			$72–3^{751}$	0.9902^{20}_0	1.4004^{20}	d		s	v			B1[3], 2654
e550	—,—,1'-chloro-	$ClCH_2OC_2H_5$	94.54			83^{763}	1.0372^{20}_0	1.4040^{20}	d		s	v			B1[2], 645
e551	—,—,2-chloro-	$CH_3OCH_2CH_2Cl$	94.54			92–3	1.0345^{20}_4	1.4111^{20}	s		s	v			B1[2], 335
e552	—,—,1'-diethyl-amino-	$(CH_3CH_2)_2NCH_2OC_2H_5$	131.22			136^{760} $76^{11.5}$			i	v	s	s		os v	B4[2], 598
—	—,—,2-methyl-amino-	see Ethane, 1-ethoxy-2-methylamino-													
e553	—,ethyl octyl	$CH_3(CH_2)_7OC_2H_5$	158.29		12.5	186.3^{760} 74^9	0.7847^{20}_4	1.4127^{20}	i	s				AcOEt s	B1[3], 1708
e554	—,ethyl pentyl	Amyl ethyl ether. $CH_3(CH_2)_4OC_2H_5$	116.21			119–20	0.7622^{20}_0	1.3927^{20}	δ	∞	∞				B1[3], 1602
e555	—,—,1-chloro-	$CH_3(CH_2)_4OCHClCH_3$	150.65			$63–6^8$	0.9200^{20}_4	1.4218^{20}	d		s				Am 53, 4077
e556	—,ethyl phenyl, 2-bromo-	$C_6H_5OCH_2CH_2Br$	201.07		39	240–50 d $125–30^{20}$			i	v	v				B6[2], 145
e557	—,ethyl propyl	$CH_3CH_2CH_2OC_2H_5$	88.15		< −79	63.6^{760}	0.7386^{20}_0	1.3695^{20}	δ	∞	∞			aa ∞	B1[3], 1414
e558	—,—,1-chloro-	$C_3H_7^nOCHClCH_3$	122.60			$112–5^{731}$ δd	0.9322^{20}_0	1.4013^{20}	d		s	v			B1, 607
e560	—,—,2',3'-epoxy-		102.13			128^{760}	0.9700^{20}_0	1.4320^{20}	s	s					B17, 105
e561	—,ethyl 1-propynyl	Ethoxymethylacetylene. $CH_3C:COC_2H_5$	84.13			84^{760}	0.8276^{20}_4	1.4130^{20}	i d^h		v	v	v	os v	B1[3], 1969
e562	—,ethyl 3-propynyl	Ethyl propargyl ether. $C_2H_5OCH_2C:CH$	84.13			82^{760}	0.8326^{20}_4	1.4039^{20}	i	s	s				B1[2], 504
e563	—,ethynyl methyl	Methoxyacetylene. $CH_3OC:CH$	56.07			50^{760}	0.8001^{20}_0	1.3812^{20}			s	v			B1[3], 1968
e564	—,ethynyl phenyl	Phenoxyacetylene. $C_6H_5OC:CH$	118.14		−36	$61–2^{25}$ $43–4^{10}$	1.0614^{20}_4	1.5125^{20}	i	s	s				B6, 145
e565	—,ethynyl propyl	Propoxyacetylene. $CH_3CH_2CH_2OC:CH$	84.13			75	0.8080^{20}_4	1.3935^{20}	d^h	v	v				B1[3], 1969
e566	—,furfuryl methyl		112.14			$131–3^{760}$	1.0163^{20}_4	1.4570^{20}	i	s	v				B17[2], 114
e567	—,2-furyl octyl		196.29			$129–30^{18}$	0.9214^{28}_4	1.4520^{28}			s				C51, 3550
e568	—,2-furyl phenyl		160.18	λ^{al} 224 (4.06)		$105–6^{18}$	1.1010^{23}_4	1.5418^{23}			s				C51, 3550
e569	—,heptyl methyl	$CH_3(CH_2)_6OCH_3$	130.23			151^{760}	0.7869^{15}_{15}	1.4073^{20}	i	∞	∞	s			B1[3], 1682
e570	—,heptyl phenyl	$CH_3(CH_2)_6OC_6H_5$	192.31			267 $128–30^{12}$	0.9178^{15}_{15}	1.4912^{20}	i	∞	∞	s			B6, 144
—	—,—,4'-hydroxy-	see Phenol, 4-heptoxy-													
e572	—,hexadecyl phenyl	Cetyl phenyl ether. $CH_3(CH_2)_{15}OC_6H_5$	318.55	lf (al)	41.8	200^1	$0.8434^{8.2}$	1.4556^{87}							B6, 144
e573	—,hexyl phenyl	$CH_3(CH_2)_5OC_6H_5$	178.28		−19	240^{760} 130^{22}	0.9174^{20}_4	1.4921^{20}	i						B6[2], 146
e575	—,isobutyl methyl	$(CH_3)_2CHCH_2OCH_3$	88.15			58^{760}(cor)	0.7311^{20}_0		i	s					B1[3], 1559
e576	—,isobutyl propyl	$(CH_3)_2CHCH_2OCH_2CH_2CH_3$	116.21			$105–6^{720}$	0.7549^{20}	1.3852^{25}	δ	s	∞				B1[2], 410
e577	—,isopropyl methyl	$(CH_3)_2CHOCH_3$	74.12			32.5^{777}	0.7237^{15}_{15}	1.3576^{20}	δ	∞	∞				B1[2], 1458
e578	—,isopropyl propyl	$(CH_3)_2CHOCH_2CH_3$	102.18			83	0.7370^{20}_0	1.376^{21}	δ	v	s	s			B1[2], 381
e579	—,methyl 2-octyn-1-yl	$CH_3OCH_2C:C(CH_2)_4CH_3$	140.23			77^{19}	0.8370^{20}_0	1.4380^{20}	i		s				B1[3], 1996
e580	—,methyl pentyl	$CH_3(CH_2)_4OCH_3$	102.18			$99–100^{760}$	0.767^{19}	1.3855^{19}		v	s	s			B1[2], 417
e581	—,methyl propyl	$CH_3CH_2CH_2OCH_3$	74.12			38.9^{760}	0.738^{20}_4	1.3579^{20}	s	∞	∞	s			B1[3], 1413
e582	—,—,1-chloro-	$CH_3CH_2OCH_2Cl$	108.57			109^{760}	0.9884^{20}_0	1.4125^{20}	d	v	v				B1[1], 305
e583	—,—,2',3'-dibromo-	$CH_3CHBrCHBrOCH_3$	231.94			185^{760} 84^{15}	1.8320^{12}_4	1.5123^{20}	i	s	s				B1[3], 1428
e585	—,—,2',3'-epoxy-	Epimethylin.	88.12			115–8	0.9890^{20}	1.4320^{20}	s	s	s	s			B17, 104
e586	—,1-naphthyl pentyl	$C_{10}H_7O(CH_2)_4CH_3$	214.31	nd (al)	30	322^{760}			i	s	s		s	chl s	B6[3], 2925
e587	—,2-naphthyl pentyl	$C_{10}H_7O(CH_2)_4CH_3$	214.31	lf (al)	24.5	335^{760} $(32?.5$ cor) 159^{10}		1.5587^{30}	i	s	s		s	chl s	B6[3], 2973
e588	—,octyl phenyl	$C_6H_5O(CH_2)_7CH_3$	206.33		8	285^{760} $164–7^{20}$	0.9139^{15}_{15}	1.4875^{20}	i	s	s				B6, 144
e590	Ethionic acid, anhydride	Carbyl sulfate. 1,3,2,4-Dioxadithian 2,2,4,4-tetroxide	188.18	dlq	ca. 80				d						B19, 433
—	Ethyl acetate	see Acetic acid, ethyl ester													
—	Ethyl acetoacetate	see Butanoic acid, 3-oxo-, ethyl ester*													
—	Ethyl alcohol	see Ethanol*													
—	Ethylamine*	see Ethane, amino-*													
—	Ethyl cellosolve	see Ethanol, 2-ethoxy-*													
—	Ethylene	see Ethene*													
—	Ethylene bromide	see Ethane, 1,2-dibromo-*													
—	Ethylene bromohydrin	see Ethanol, 2-bromo-*													
—	Ethylene chloride	see Ethane, 1,2-dichloro-*													

For explanations, symbols and abbreviations see beginning of table. For structural formulas see end of table.

Ethylene chlorohydrin

No.	Name	Synonyms and Formula	Mol. wt.	Color, crystalline form, specific rotation and λ_{max} (log ε)	m.p. °C	b.p. °C	Density	n_D	w	al	eth	ace	bz	other solvents	Ref.
—	Ethylene chloro-hydrin	see Ethanol, 2-chloro-*													
—	Ethylenediamine	see Ethane, 1,2-diamino-*													
—	Ethylene dicyanide	see Succinic acid, dinitrile													
—	Ethylene fluoride	see Ethane, 1,2-difluoro-*													
—	Ethylene fluoro-hydrin	see Ethanol, 2-fluoro-*													
—	Ethylene glycol*	see 1,2-Ethanediol*													
—	—,monoallyl ether	see Ethanol, 2-allyloxy-													
—	—,monoethyl ether	see Ethanol, 2-ethoxy-*													
—	Ethylene iodide	see Ethane, 1,2-diiodo-*													
—	Ethylene iodohydrin	see Ethanol, 2-iodo-*													
—	Ethylene oxide	see Ethane, 1,2-epoxy-*													
—	Ethylene urea	see 2-Imidazolidone													
—	Ethylenimine	see Aziridine													
—	Ethyl ether	see Ethyl, diethyl													
—	Ethylidene acetate	see Acetaldehyde, diacetate													
—	Ethyl vanillin	see Benzaldehyde, 3-ethoxy-4-hydroxy-													
Ω e591	Ethyne*	Acetylene. Ethine. HC:CH	26.04	....	−80.8	−84.0[760] sub	0.6181_4^{-32}	1.00051^0	δ	δ	...	s	s	chl s CS$_2$ δ	B1[3], 887
e592	—,bis(1-hydroxy-cyclohexyl)-*		222.33	nd (CCl$_4$)	112–3	182[13]			i	v	v	v	s[h]	MeOH v CCl$_4$ s[h] lig δ	B6[2], 909
e593	—,bromo-*	Bromoacetylene. Ethynyl bromide. HC:CBr	104.94			4.7	0.0047 (760 mm.)		δ		s			dil HNO$_3$ s dil HCl δ	B1[3], 919
e594	—,chloro-*	Chloroacetylene. Ethynyl chloride. HC:CCl	60.48		−126	−30	0.002 (760 mm.)		d	δ					B1[3], 917
e599	—,dibromo-*	BrC:CBr	183.84	nd	−25– −23	76 (exp)			i	s	s	s	s	oos s	B1[3], 919
e600	—,dichloro-*	ClC:CCl	94.93		−66– −64.2	exp					s	s	s		B1[3], 918
e601	—,diiodo-*	IC:CI	277.83	rh nd (lig)	81–2	32–3[748] exp			i	s	s	s	s	oss lig δ	B1[3], 919
Ω e602	—,diphenyl-*	Tolane. C$_6$H$_5$C:CC$_6$H$_5$	178.24	mcl pr or pl (al) λ^{hx} 270 (4.4), 280 (4.5), 290 (4.4), 298 (4.4)	63.5	300[760] 170[19]	0.9657_4^{100}		i	δ v[h]	v				B5[2], 568
e603	—,1(2-naphthyl)-2-phenyl-*	C$_{10}$H$_7^\beta$C:CC$_6$H$_5$	228.30	cr (al)	117										B5[2], 628
e604	α-Eucaine	C$_{19}$H$_{27}$NO$_4$	333.43	pr (eth or al)	104–5				s	s	s		s	peth, lig, chl s	B22, 194
e605	—,hydrochloride	C$_{19}$H$_{27}$NO$_4$·HCl. See e604.	369.89	pl (w + 1), pr (MeOH + 2)	ca. 200 d				v	v	δ				B22, 194
e606	β-Eucaine (d)	C$_{15}$H$_{21}$NO$_2$	247.34	pr (peth)	57–8				i	s	s		s	chl, peth s	B21[2], 14
e607	—(dl)	Betacaine. C$_{15}$H$_{21}$NO$_2$. See e606.	247.34	pl (peth)	70–1 (78)				i	s	s		s	chl, peth s	B21[2], 13
e608	—(l)	C$_{15}$H$_{21}$NO$_2$. See e606	247.34	pr (peth)	57–8				i	s	s		s	chl, peth s	B21[2], 14
e609	—,hydrochloride (dl)	C$_{15}$H$_{21}$NO$_2$·HCl. See e606	283.80	pl (w)	277–9				s	s	s			chl s	B21[2], 13
e610	—,lactate (dl)	C$_{15}$H$_{21}$NO$_2$·CH$_3$CH(OH)CO$_2$H. See e606	337.42	wh pw	ca. 152				v	s	δ			chl s	B21[2], 13
—	Eucalyptol	see 1,8-Cineole													
Ω e611	Eugenol	5-Allylguaiacol	164.21	cr (hx)	−7.5	253.2[760] 130.5[18]	1.0652_4^{20}	1.5405^{20}	i	∞	∞			chl, aa, oil s	B6[2], 921
Ω e612	—,acetate	C$_{12}$H$_{14}$O$_3$. See e611	206.25	pl (al) λ^{iso} 229.5 (3.81), 278 (3.45), 281.5 (3.48), 287.5 (3.34)	30–1	127.1–7.8[4]	1.0806_4^{20}	1.5205^{20}	i	s					B6[3], 5029
—	Eugenic acid	see Benzoic acid, 5-allyl-2-hydroxy-3-methoxy-													
e613	Eupittone	Eupittonic acid. C$_{25}$H$_{26}$O$_9$	470.48	nd (al-eth) $\lambda^{10\% HCl}$ 560 (4.43)	200	....				δ[h]				aa, alk s (bl)	B8, 574
e614	Euxanthic acid	C$_{19}$H$_{16}$O	404.43	ye nd (w + 1) [α] −108 (+1w)	130 d (+w) 162 δd (anh)				δ s[h]	v[h]				alk s	B31, 277
—	Euxanthone	see Xanthone, 1,7-dihydroxy-													
—	Euxanthonic acid	see Benzophenone, 2,2′,5,6′-tetrahydroxy-													

For explanations, symbols and abbreviations see beginning of table. For structural formulas see end of table.

No.	Name	Synonyms and Formula	Mol. wt.	Color, crystalline form. specific rotation and λ_{max} (log ε)	m.p. °C	b.p. °C	Density	n_D	Solubility						Ref.
									w	al	eth	ace	bz	other solvents	
	Evernic acid														
e615	**Evernic acid**......	Orselinic acid 4-everitate. Lecanoric acid monomethyl ether. $C_{17}H_{16}O_7$.	332.31	nd (w or ace), pr (al)	170	....	....	....	i δ^h	δ s^h	i δ^h	... ∞	...	....	**B10²**, 274
—	**Everninic acid**.....	*see* **Benzoic acid, 2-hydroxy-4-methoxy-6-methyl-**													
e616	**Evodiamine** (*d*)....	Rhetsine. $C_{19}H_{17}N_3O$.	303.37	yesh lf (al) $[\alpha]_D^{15}+352$ (ace, c = 0.5)	278	....	....	....	i	δ	δ	s	i	chl, aa δ peth i	**B26²**, 103
e617	—,hydrate (*d*).....	$C_{19}H_{17}N_3O \cdot H_2O$.........	321.38	pl (al)	146–7	....	....	....						....	**B24²**, 72
—	**Exaltone**.........	*see* **Cyclopentadecanone***													

For explanations, symbols and abbreviations see beginning of table. For structural formulas see end of table.

No.	Name	Synonyms and Formula	Mol. wt.	Color, crystalline form, specific rotation and λ_{max} (log ε)	m.p. °C	b.p. °C	Density	n_D	w	al	eth	ace	bz	other solvents	Ref.
	Fagaramide														
f1	Fagaramide......	....	247.30	nd (bz, dil al or peth) pl (AcOEt)	119.5	....			δ	s^h	...	...	s	peth i AcOEt s^h	B19[2], 299
f2	β-Fagarine.......	Skimmianine. $C_{14}H_{13}NO_4$.	259.27	pym, oct (al) λ^{al} 244 (4.43), 320 (3.90), 331 (3.90)	177	....			i	s	δ	...	...	chl s CS_2 δ peth i	B27, 134
f3	γ-Fagarine.......	Haplophine. $C_{13}H_{11}NO_3$.	229.24	pr (al) λ^{al} 238 (4.76), 370 (3.89), 332 (3.88)	142	....			δ	s^h	s	...	s	chl s peth δ	C51, 4402
f4	α-Farnesene......	3,7,11-Trimethyl-1,3,6,10-dodecatetraene. $(CH_3)_2C{:}CH(CH_2)_2C(CH_3){:}CHCH_2CH{:}C(CH_3)CH{:}CH_2$	204.36		....	129–32[12]	0.8410_4^{20}	1.4836^{20}	i	...	s	s	...	peth ∞ lig ∞	B1[3], 1067
f5	β-Farnesene......	$CH_2{:}CHC({:}CH_2)(CH_2)_2CH{:}C(CH_3)(CH_2)_2CH{:}C(CH_3)_2$	204.36	....	121–2[9]		0.8363_4^{20}	1.4899^{20}	i	...	s	s	...	chl v aa s os s	B1[3], 1067
Ω f6	Farnesol (trans, trans)	$(CH_3)_2C{:}CH(CH_2)_2C(CH_3){:}CH(CH_2)_2C(CH_3){:}CHCH_2OH$	222.38	λ^{al} 215 (3.30), 235 (2.65), 325 sh (0.45)	160[10]	$120^{0.3}$	0.8846_4^{20}	1.4877^{20}	i	v	s	...	...	os s	B1[3], 2040
f7	α-Fenchene(d)....	....	136.24	$[\alpha]_D^{14} + 29$ (1 = 10 cm)	....	155–6	0.8660_4^{20}	1.4713^{20}	i	∞	s	s	...		B5[1], 86
f8	—(dl)...........	Isopinene. $C_{10}H_{16}$. See f7 ...	136.24		....	154–6	0.8660_4^{20}	1.4705^{20}	i	∞	s	s	...		B5[1], 86
f9	—(l)...........	$C_{10}H_{16}$. See f7	136.24	$[\alpha]_D^{20} - 43.8$	....	158.5–8.8	0.8670_4^{20}	1.4713^{20}	i	∞	s	s	...		B5[2], 109
Ω f10	Fenchone(d)	d-2-Fenchanone. d-1,3,3-Trimethylnorcamphor.	152.24	$[\alpha]_D^{20} + 66.9$ (al)	6	193.5^{760} 80^{20}	0.9465_4^{20}	1.4623^{20}	i	v	v	s	...		E12A, 724
f11	—(dl)...........	$C_{10}H_{16}O$. See f10	152.24	λ^{MeOH} 288 (1.34)	−18 to −16	193–4 72–3[12]	0.9501^{15}_{15}	1.4702^{20}	i	v	v	s	...		B7[2], 93
f12	—(l)...........	$C_{10}H_{16}O$. See f10	152.24	$[\alpha]_D^{23} - 66.94$ (al) λ^{al} 285 (1.32)	5 (8.5)	192–4	0.948^{20}	1.4636^{20}	i	v	v	s	...		B7[2], 92
Ω f13	Fenchyl alcohol (dl)	....	154.26		α38–9 β6	α 202–3 β 201			i	v	v	...	...	peth	B6, 71
—	Ferulaldehyde	see **Cinnamaldehyde, 4-hydroxy-3-methoxy-**													
—	Ferulic acid	see **Cinnamic acid, 4-hydroxy-3-methoxy-**													
—	Filicinic acid	see **1,3,5-Cyclohexane-trione, 2,2-dimethyl-**													
f15	Filixic acid BBB....	Filicic acid BBB. Filicin.	652.70	cr (AcOEt-ace)	172–4	....			i	i d^h	δ	...	s	CS_2, chl, xyl s	J1952, 3102
—	Fisetin	see **Flavone,3,3′,4′,7-tetrahydroxy-**													
f16	Flavaniline.......	2(p-Aminophenyl) lepidine.	234.30	pr (bz)	97	133–41[15]			δ	s	...	...	s		B22, 469
Ω f17	Flavanone	2,3-Dihydro-2-phenyl-1,4-benzopyrone. 4-Oxo-2-phenylchroman.	224.26	nd (lig) λ^{al} 252 (3.94), 320 (3.53)	76	....			i	...	...	s	s		B17[2], 387
Ω f18	—,4′-methoxy-3′,5,7-tri-hydroxy-	Hesperetin. $C_{16}H_{14}O_6$. See f17	302.29	pl (dil al + ½w), pl (AcOEt)	227–8 (233d)	sub $205^{0.004}$			i	v	s	...	δ	chl δ dil alk s	B8[2], 580 B18[2], 204
Ω f19	—,3′,4′,5,7-tetra-hydroxy-	Eriodictyol. $C_{15}H_{12}O_6$. See f17	288.26	pa br nd (dil al + 1.5 w or dil aa + 2.5w), pl (al) λ^{MeOH} 250 (3.28), 292 (4.24)	267d 257d (+1.5w)				$δ^h$	s^h	δ	...	...	dil alk s os δ aa s	B8, 543 B18[2], 204
—	Flavianic acid	see **2-Naphthalenesulfonic acid, 5,7-dinitro-8-hydroxy-**													
—	Flavinium, 3,4′,5,7-tetra-hydroxy-, chloride	see **Pelargonidine, chloride**													
—	Flavol...........	see **Anthracene, 2,6-dihydroxy-**													
Ω f20	Flavone	2-Phenyl-γ-benzopyrone. 2-Phenylchromone.	222.25	nd (lig), cr (30 % al), λ^{al} 252 (4.33), 295 (4.41)	100 (97)	....			i	s	s	s	s	os s chl s lig s	B17[2], 395
f21	—,6-bromo-......	$C_{15}H_9BrO_2$. See f20........	301.15	nd (al)	191–2	....			i	s^h	...	...	δ	CS_2, chl δ	B17, 373
f22	—,5,7-dihydroxy-.	Chrysin. $C_{15}H_{10}O_4$. See f20	254.25	pa ye pl or pr (MeOH), nd (sub) λ^{al} 270 (4.46), 318 (4.08)	275	sub			i	s^h δ	δ	s	δ	CS_2, chl δ aa s^h lig δ	B18[2], 97
f23	—,5,7-dihydroxy-4′-methoxy-	Acacetin, $C_{16}H_{12}O_5$. See f20	284.27	pa ye nd (al)	261	....			i	δ s^h	i	v	δ	AcOEt δ alk s lig δ	B18[3], 173
f24	—,5,7-dihydroxy-6-methoxy-	Oroxylin-A. $C_{16}H_{12}O_5$. See f20	284.27	ye nd (al)	231–2	....			i	s	s	s	s^h	alk s aa s	J1936, 591

For explanations, symbols and abbreviations see beginning of table. For structural formulas see end of table.

No.	Name	Synonyms and Formula	Mol. wt.	Color, crystalline form, specific rotation and λ_{max} (log ε)	m.p. °C	b.p. °C	Density	n_D	w	al	eth	ace	bz	other solvents	Ref.
	Flavone														
Ω f25	—,3-hydroxy-.....	Flavonol. $C_{15}H_{10}O_3$. See f20	238.25	pa ye nd (al, MeOH) λ^{al} 240 (4.30), 307 (4.25)	169–70	.....			...	s^h	...	...	...		B17[2], 498
—	—,7-methoxy-3,3',4',5-tetra-hydroxy-	see **Rhamnetin**													
f26	—,2',3,3',5,7-pentahydroxy-	$C_{15}H_{10}O_7$. See f20........	302.24	ye nd (aa + 1.5w) λ^{MeOH} 262 (4.5), 365 (4.3)	300				δ^h	s^h					B18[2], 235
Ω f27	—,2',3,4',5,7-pentahydroxy-	Morin. $C_{15}H_{10}O_7$. See f20 ..	302.24	pa ye nd (+ 1w, dil al) λ^{al} 265 (4.24), 273 (4.24)	303–4 (286)				δ^h	v	δ	...	s	CS_2 i aa δ alk s	B18, 239
f28	—,2',3,5,5',7-pentahydroxy-	$C_{15}H_{10}O_7$. See f20........	302.24	red-ye cr (dil al + 1w)	306–8				...	...	...	...	...		C48, 2055
Ω f29	—,3,3',4',5,7-pentahydroxy-	Quercetin. Meletin. Sophoretin. $C_{15}H_{10}O_7$. See f20	302.24	ye nd (dil al + 2w) λ^{al} 256 (4.32), 301 (3.89), 373 (4.32)	316–7 (anh)	sub			δ^h	s^h	δ	s		MeOH δ Py s aa s	B18[2], 236
f30	—,3,3',4',7,8-pentahydroxy-	$C_{15}H_{10}O_7$. See f20........	302.24	ye nd (dil al + 1w)	308d				δ^h	s^h		s			B18, 250
f31	—,3,3',5,5',7-pentahydroxy-	$C_{15}H_{10}O_7$. See f20........	302.24	ye nd	>300				...	...	...	...	...		B18[2], 239
f32	—,3',4',5,5',7-pentahydroxy-	Tricetin. $C_{15}H_{10}O_7$. See f20 .	302.24	ye nd (dil al + w)	>330 d				...	δ	i	...	i		B18[1], 423
f33	—,2',3,5,7-tetra-hydroxy-	Datiscetin. $C_{15}H_{10}O_6$. See f20	286.24	pa ye nd (al, aq aa)	277–8				δ^h	v	v	s		os, alk, con sulf s	B18[2], 214
Ω f34	—,3,3',4',7-tetra-hydroxy-	Fisetin. $C_{15}H_{10}O_6$. See f20	286.24	lt ye nd (dil al + 1w)	330 (>360)	sub^{vac}			i	s	δ	s	δ	peth δ	B18[2], 216
f35	—,3',4',5,7-tetra-hydroxy-	Luteolin. $C_{15}H_{10}O_6$. See f20	286.24	ye nd (dil al + 1w) λ^{al} 256 (4.20), 355 (4.25)	329–30d (anh)	sub^{vac}			δ^h	s	δ	...		alk s con sulf s	B18[2], 212
Ω f36	—,3,4',5,7-tetra-hydroxy-	Kaempferol. $C_{15}H_{10}O_6$. See f20	286.24	ye nd (al + 1w) (aa) λ^{al} 235 sh (4.15), 273 (4.20), 320 sh (3.72)	276–8				δ	v^h	v	v	i	chl δ aa s^h alk s	B18[2], 214
f37	—,4',5,7-tri-hydroxy-	Apigenin, $C_{15}H_{10}O_5$. See f20	270.25	ye nd (Py-w or w, + ½w), lf (al) $\lambda^{w(hyd)}$ 269 (4.30), 335 (4.32)	347–8 (352)	sub^{vac}			i	s^h	...	...	...	Py s dil alk v con sulf s	B18[2], 172
f38	—,5,6,7-tri-hydroxy-	Baicalein. $C_{15}H_{10}O_5$. See f20	270.25	ye pr (al, MeOH or aa) λ^{al} 276 (4.42), 324 (4.18)	264–5d				δ	s v^h	s	s	δ	AcOEt s alk s (og-red) aa s^h chl δ	B18[2], 172
—	Flavopurpurin	see **9,10-Anthraquinone, 1,2,6-trihydroxy-**													
f39	Floridoside	Glycerol-2-α-D-mono-galactoside.	254.24	pr (al) $[\alpha]_D$ + 15.1 (w)	86–7	.....			v	δ	...	...	...		C31, 3878
Ω f40	Fluoran	9-Hydroxy-9-xanthene-o-benzoic acid lactone.	300.32	nd (al + 2 al)	182–3				i	s	s	...		con sulf s	B19[2], 173
f41	—,1,6-dihydroxy-..	$C_{20}H_{12}O_5$. See f40	332.32	ye nd	>280				...	...	...	...	...		B19[2], 247
f42	—,2,6-dihydroxy-..	$C_{20}H_{12}O_5$. See f40........	332.32	ye nd (al)	177				...	...	...	...	...		B19[2], 247
f43	—,3,5-dihydroxy-..	$C_{20}H_{12}O_5$. See f40........	332.32	ye-gr nd (aa)	179				...	...	...	...	...		B19[2], 248
Ω f44	Fluoranthene......	1,2-Benzacenaphthene. Idryl.	202.26	pa ye nd or pl (al) λ^{cy} 237 (4.75), 254 (4.22), 263 (4.18), 277 (4.41), 288 (4.73)	111	ca. 375 217[30]	1.252^0_4		i	s	s	...	s	chl, CS_2 s aa s	E14s, 54
Ω f45	Fluorene	2,3-Benzindene. Diphenyl-enemethane.	166.23	lf (al) λ^{chl} 266 (4.3), 290 (3.8), 301 (4.0)	116–7	293–5[760]	1.203^0_4		i	δ s^h	s	s	s	CS_2 CCl_4 s, to s, v^h aa, Py s, v^h MeOH δ	E13, 25
Ω f46	—,2-acetamido-..	N(2-Fluorenyl) acetamide. $C_{15}H_{13}NO$. See f45	223.28	nd (50 % al or 50 % aa) λ^{al} 287 (4.4), 300 sh (4.2)	194	.....			i	s	s	...	...	aa s	B12, 1331
f47	—,9-acetamido-..	$C_{15}H_{13}NO$. See f45........	223.28	nd (aa)	262				...	...	...	...	...	con sulf s	B12[2], 781
f48	—,2-amino-......	$C_{13}H_{11}N$. See f45........	181.24	lo pl or nd (dil al) λ^{al} 287,5 (4.32), 315 sh (3.94)	131–2	.....			i	s	s	...	...		B12[2], 779

For explanations, symbols and abbreviations see beginning of table. For structural formulas see end of table.

Fluorene

No.	Name	Synonyms and Formula	Mol. wt.	Color, crystalline form, specific rotation and λ_{max} (log ε)	m.p. °C	b.p. °C	Density	n_D	w	al	eth	ace	bz	other solvents	Ref.
f49	—,9-amino-	$C_{13}H_{11}N$. See f45	181.24	nd (lig) λ 258 (4.37), 293 (3.82), 304 (3.79)	α 64–5 γ 46–7 (unst)				δ	v	s	s	s	MeOH, chl v con sulf s (gr)	B12[2], 780
f50	—,1-amino-9-hydroxy-	$C_{13}H_{11}NO$. See f45	197.24	dk red nd (w)	142				δ	v	v		s	con sulf s aa v	B13[2], 435
f51	—,2-amino-9-hydroxy-	$C_{13}H_{11}NO$. See f45	197.24	irid nd (al)	200.5–1.0					s^h	δ			chl s^h con sulf s	B13[2], 435
f52	—,4-amino-9-hydroxy-	$C_{13}H_{11}NO$. See f45	197.24	ye (60 % al)	183–4					s					B13[2], 436
f53	—,9-benzhydryl-idene-	β,β-Diphenyl-α,α-biphenylene ethylene. ω,ω-Diphenyl dibenzofulvene. $C_{26}H_{18}$. See f45	330.43	ye (bz) λ^{al} 235 (4.6), 260 (4.4), 338 (4.0)	229.5				i	δ	δ			chl s	E13, 37
Ω f54	—,9-benzylidene-	ω-Phenyldibenzofulvene. $C_{20}H_{14}$. See f45	254.34	lf (al) λ^{al} 227 (4.6), 256 (4.4), 325 (4.1)	76				i	s^h			s		E13, 35
Ω f55	—,2-bromo-	$C_{13}H_9Br$. See f45	245.13	nd or pl (al) λ^{al} 270 (4.39), 295 (3.90), 306 (3.98)	113–4	ca. 185[135]			i	s^h				chl v aa s	B5[2], 534
Ω f56	—,9-bromo-	$C_{13}H_9Br$. See f45	245.13	(lig or al) λ^{hx} 241 (4.7), 279 (4.4)	104–5				i	s^h		s		con sulf s^h	B5[2], 534
f57	—,9(3-bromo-benzylidene)-	$C_{20}H_{13}Br$. See f45	333.24	ye nd (aa)	92–3				i	s				MeOH s con sulf s^h	B5[1], 358
f58	—,9(4-bromo-benzylidene)-	$C_{20}H_{13}Br$. See f45	333.24	ye nd (aa, AcOEt-chl) λ^{diox} 258 (4.54), 330 (4.24)	147–8				i					con sulf s^h aa s^h	B5[2], 640
f59	—,9(2-chloro-benzylidene)-	$C_{20}H_{13}Cl$. See f45	288.78	ye nd (aa, MeOH)	69–70 (176)	180[0.7]			i	v				con sulf s^h aa s^h	B5[1], 358
f60	—,9(3-chloro-benzylidene)-	$C_{20}H_{13}Cl$. See f45	288.78	pa ye pr or pym (MeOH)	90.5				i	v				con sulf s^h lig v	B5[1], 358
f61	—,9(4-chloro-benzylidene)-	$C_{20}H_{13}Cl$. See f45	288.78	ye nd (aa, al)	151				i	s				con sulf s^h aa s^h	B5[1], 358
f62	—,9-cinnamyl-idene-(trans)	$C_{22}H_{16}$. See f45	280.37	pa ye nd (aa) λ^{hx} 240 (4.6), 373 (4.67), 390 sh (4.5)	155					s^h				chl s^h sulf s (og)	E13, 36
f63	—,2,7-diamino-	$C_{13}H_{12}N_2$. See f45	196.26	nd (w), pr (bz), pl (eth) λ^{al} 293 (4.46), 330 sh (3.88)	165–7				i s^h	s				chl s	B13[2], 123
f64	—,2,7-dichloro-	$C_{13}H_8Cl_2$. See f45	235.13	pl or nd (bz)	128	sub			i				s^h	chl, CCl_4 s	B5[2], 533
f65	—,9,9-dichloro-	$C_{13}H_8Cl_2$. See f45	235.13	rh pr (bz, eth) nd (peth) λ^{hx} 234 (4.6), 244 (4.62)	103				d^h	v	s	v	v	os v con sulf s	B5[2], 534
f66	—,1,8-dimethyl-9-(2-tolyl)-	$C_{22}H_{20}$. See f45	299.40		168–9					s	s	s			C50, 11293
Ω f67	—,2-hydroxy-	$C_{13}H_{10}O$. See f45	182.23	lf (w), nd (chl or 60 % al) λ^{cy} 271 (4.33), 304 (3.74), 315 (3.76)	171–4				i	v	v			alk v aa v lig i	B6[2], 655
Ω f68	—,9-hydroxy-	Diphenylenecarbinol. 9-Fluorenol. $C_{13}H_{10}O$. See f45	182.23	hex nd (w or peth) λ^{sulf} 480 (3.30), 660 (3.49)	154				δ	δ	s	s	v	peth δ	E13, 63
f69	—,9-hydroxy-9-phenyl-	$C_{19}H_{14}O$. See f45	258.32	ye or col pr (lig) λ^{diox} 242 (3.22), 272 (3.06), 280 (3.08), 311 (2.76)	108–9								s	con sulf s (ye) aa s	E13, 64
f70	—,9-methyl-	$C_{14}H_{12}$. See f45	180.25	pr λ 263 (4.40), 290 (3.61), 300 (3.89)	46–7	154–6[15]	1.0263_4^{66}	1.610^{66}	i	s	s	s	s	chl s	E13, 29
f71	—,9(2-methyl-benzylidene)-	$C_{21}H_{16}$. See f45	268.38	nd or pr (aa) λ^{al} 258 (4.62), 298 (4.21), 312 (4.24)	109.5				i	s^h			s^h	con sulf s^h	B5[1], 359
f72	—,9(4-methyl-benzylidene)-	$C_{21}H_{16}$. See f45	268.38	nd (aa), pr (al) λ^{al} 258 (4.55), 330 (4.30)	97.5				i	s^h			s^h	con sulf s^h	B5[1], 359
f73	—,9-methylene-	Biphenyleneethylene. Dibenzofulvene. $C_{14}H_{10}$. See f45	178.24		53				i	s	s	s	s	os v	E13, 34

For explanations, symbols and abbreviations see beginning of table. For structural formulas see end of table.

No.	Name	Synonyms and Formula	Mol. wt.	Color, crystalline form, specific rotation and λ_{max} (log ε)	m.p. °C	b.p. °C	Density	n_D	w	al	eth	ace	bz	other solvents	Ref.
	Fluorene														
Ω f74	—,2-nitro-	$C_{13}H_9NO_2$. See f45	211.22	nd (50 % aa or ace) λ^{al} 234 (3.98), 332 (4.25)	158				i			s^h	s^h		$B5^2$, 535
f75	—,3-nitro-	$C_{13}H_9NO_2$. See f45	211.22	pa ye nd (al, chl-peth)	106					s^h		s^h			E13, 48
f76	—,9-nitro-	$C_{13}H_9NO_2$. See f45	211.22	gr-ye nd (al). lf (bz) λ 248 (4.6), 305 (3.4), 340 (4.0) (*aci* form)	181–2d				i	s^h	s	s	s	chl s aa s, lig i	E13, 48
—	—,9 oxo-	*see* 9-Fluorenone													
f77	—,9-phenyl-	$C_{19}H_{14}$. See f45	242.32	nd or lf (al or bz) λ^{al} 265 (4.2), 292 (3.7), 305 (3.9)	148				i	s^h	δ		s	aa, chl s peth s	E13, 29
—	Fluorenecarboxylic acid, 9-oxo	*see* 9-Fluorenonecarboxylic acid													
f78	2-Fluorenesulfonic acid		246.29	nd (aa)	155 (+1w)				v	s		s		chl s alk s	E13, 114
	Fluorenol	*see* Fluorene, hydroxy-													
Ω f80	9-Fluorenone	Diphenylene ketone. 9-Oxofluorene.	180.22	ye rh bipym (al, bz-peth) λ^{diox} 258 (4.90), 294 (3.62), 328 (2.89), 378 (2.43)	84 (86)	341.5^{760}	1.1300_4^{99}	1.6369^{99}	i	s	v	δ v^h	ε to v	E13, 77
Ω f81	—,oxime	9-Isonitrosofluorene. 9-Oximinofluorene.	195.22	nd (chl-peth or bz)	195–6				i	s				chl s dil alk v	$B7^2$, 407
f82	—,1-amino-	$C_{13}H_9NO$. See f80	195.22	ye nd (dil al)	118.5–20				s^h	s	s	v		oos v	B14, 113
Ω f83	—,2-amino-	$C_{13}H_9NO$. See f80	195.22	red-vt pr (al)	163				i	s^h	s^h		s^h	peth δ, aa s	$B14^2$, 68
f84	—,3-amino-	$C_{13}H_9NO$. See f80	195.22	ye nd (w or dil al)	158–9				s^h	s					$B14^2$, 69
f85	—,4-amino-	$C_{13}H_9NO$. See f80	195.22	red nd (al)	145					v	v	s		chl v, aa v	$B14^2$, 69
f86	—,2-bromo-	$C_{13}H_7BrO$. See f80	259.11	ye nd (al or aa) λ^{diox} 262 (4.92), 304 (3.63), 380 (2.76)	149				i	s^h		s	s	chl, aa s	E13, 83
f87	—,2-chloro-	$C_{13}H_7ClO$. See f80	214.65	og-ye nd (dil al)	125–6	sub					s			sulf s (vt-red)	E13, 83
f88	—,1,8-dimethyl-	$C_{15}H_{12}O$. See f80	208.24	ye	197–8					i				chl s, aa s	C62, 7611
f89	—,2-nitro-	$C_{13}H_7NO_3$. See f80	225.21	ye nd or lf (aa) λ^{al} 284 (4.46), 336 (3.79)	222–3	sub				δ		s		sulf s aa s^h (red-ye)	E13, 85
f90	—,2,3,7-trinitro-	$C_{13}H_5N_3O_7$. See f80	315.20	pa ye nd (aa)	180–1				i	δ	δ		v	chl v	$B7^1$, 254
Ω f91	—,2,4,7-trinitro-	$C_{13}H_5N_3O_7$. See f80	315.20	pa ye nd (aa or bz) λ^{aa} 350 sh (3.9), 380 sh (3.5)	176				δ			v	v	chl v	$B7^2$, 410
f92	9-Fluorenone-1-carboxylic acid		224.23	og-red nd (dil al)	192–4				i	v	v			sulf s (red)	$B10^2$, 534
f93	—,amide		223.23	ye nd (al)	229–30				δ	δ s^h		s			B10, 774
f94	—,chloride	$C_{14}H_7ClO_2$. See f92	242.66	pa ye nd (bz)	140				d^h	s	s		v^h		B10, 774
f95	—,ethyl ester	$C_{16}H_{12}O_3$. See f92	252.27	ye nd (dil al)	84–5				i	s	s			sulf s	B10, 774
Ω f96	9-Fluorenone-2-carboxylic acid		224.23	ye nd (al or aa)	338	sub 340			i	s^h δ				aa s^h	E13, 108
f97	—,methyl ester	$C_{15}H_{10}O_3$. See f96	238.25	ye nd (MeOH)	181				i	s	s			sulf s	B10, 774
f98	9-Fluorenone-3-carboxylic acid		224.23	ye (aa, MeOH)	299 (286)					s^h				aa s^h	E13, 108
Ω f99	9-Fluorenone-4-carboxylic acid		224.23	ye nd (al)	227				i	s^h				sulf s (red) aa s^h	$B10^2$, 535
Ω f100	Fluorescein	3′,4′-Dehydroxyfluoran. Resorcinolphthalein.	332.32	red rh pr (stable form) ye gran (MeOH) (labile form) λ^{diox} 225 (4.8) 227.5 (3.8), 490 (2.1)	314–6 d (sealed tube)				δ^h	δ	δ	v	δ	peth i l'y s MeOH s	$B19^2$, 249
—	—,sodium salt	*see* Uranine													
f102	Fluorescin	2(3,6-Dihydroxyxanthyl)-benzoic acid.	334.33	col or ye nd (aa or eth) pl (bz) λ^w 490 (4.5)	125–7				i	s	s	s	s^h	aa s^h	$B18^2$, 307

For explanations, symbols and abbreviations see beginning of table. For structural formulas see end of table.

No.	Name	Synonyms and Formula	Mol. wt.	Color, crystalline form, specific rotation and λ_{max} (log ε)	m.p. °C	b.p. °C	Density	n_D	w	al	eth	ace	bz	other solvents	Ref.
	Fluoroform														
—	Fluoroform	*see* **Methane, trifluoro-**													
f103	Fluorophosphoric acid, diisopropyl ester	$(C_3H_7O)_2POF$	184.15	λ^{al} 243 (0.28), 255 (0.33), 261 (0.30)	....	62^9	1.055	1.3830^{25}	δ d^h	...	s	...	...	oils v lig δ	C41, 1233
—	Fluoroprene	*see* **1,3-Butadiene, 2-fluoro-**													
Ω f104	Folic acid	P.G.A. Pteroylglutamic acid. Vitamin Bc. $C_{19}H_{19}N_7O_6$	441.41	ye-og nd (w) $[\alpha]_D^{25}$ +23 (0.1 N NaOH, c = 0.5) $\lambda^{w,pH=13}$ 259 (4.51), 368 (3.87)	darkens 250 d	....			δ s^h	s	i	i	i	Py, aa s chl i alk δ	Am 69, 1476
f105	Folinic acid (*d*)	5-Formyl-5,6,7,8-tetrahydropteroyl-L-glutamic acid. Leucovorin.	473.45	cr (w +3) $[\alpha]_D^{25}$ +16.76 (5 % Na_2CO_3 sol, c = 3.5) $\lambda^{w,pH=13}$ 287	248–50 d	....			δ						Am 73, 1979
Ω f106	Formaldehyde	Methanal*. HCHO	30.03	gas λ^{vap} 155.5 (4.37), 175 (4.26)	−92	$−21^{760}$ $−79.6^{20}$	$0.815_4^{−20}$		s	s	∞	∞	∞	chl s	B1², 619 B6², 1244
f107	—,β,β′-dichloroisopropyl ethyl acetal	$(ClCH_2)_2CHOCH_2OC_2H_5$	187.07	....		$96–8^{16}$	1.182_{17}^{17}	1.4491^{17}			s				B1², 640
Ω f108	—,diethyl acetal	Diethoxymethane*. Diethyl formal. Ethylal. $CH_2(OC_2H_5)_2$	104.15	....	−66.5	89	0.8319_4^{20}	1.3748^{18}	s	∞	∞	v	v		B1², 639
Ω f109	—,dimethyl acetal	Methylal. $CH_2(OCH_3)_2$	76.11	λ 288 (−2.4)	−104.8	45.5^{760}	0.8593_4^{20}	1.3513^{20}	v	∞	∞	∞	∞	oos ∞	B1², 638
Ω f110	—,2.4-dinitrophenylhydrazone	....	210.15	ye cr (al), pr (lig) λ^{chl} 346 (4.31)	167				i	s^h	δ				B15, 490
f111	—,dipropyl acetal	Dipropoxymethane*. $CH_2(OCH_2CH_2CH_3)_2$	132.21	....	−97.3	140.5^{760}	0.8345^{20}	1.3939^{19}		v	v	v	v		B1², 639
f112	—,oxime	Formaldoxime. $CH_2:NOH$	45.04	....	2.5	109^{15} (84)	1.133		s	v	v				B1, 590
f113	—,fluoro-	Formyl fluoride. FCHO	48.02	gas	....	$−24^{760}$ (−29)					d				Am 77 5278
—	—,thio, trimer	*see* **1,3,5-Trithiane**													
f114	Formaldomedone	....	292.38	nd (al or bz) λ^{al} 257 (4.42)	189–90				i	δ s^h	...	...	δ s^h	peth δ	B7², 852
—	Formamide	*see* **Formic acid, amide**													
—	Formamidine	*see* **Formic acid, amidine**													
—	Formanilide	*see* **Formic acid, amide, N-phenyl-**													
Ω f115	Formic acid	Methanoic acid*. HCO_2H	46.03	λ^{undil} 205 (1.65)	8.4	100.7^{760} 50^{120}	1.220_4^{20}	1.3714^{20}	∞	∞	∞	v	s	to s	B2³, 3
Ω f116	—,allyl ester	$HCO_2CH_2CH:CH_2$	86.09	....		83.6	0.9460_4^{20}		δ	s	∞				B2³, 46
Ω f117	—,amide	Formamide. $HCONH_2$	45.04	λ^{undil} 205 sh (2.20)	2.55	111^{20}	1.1334_4^{20}	1.4472^{20}	∞	∞	δ	s	i	chl i peth i	B2, 26
Ω f119	—,—,N,N-diethyl-	$HCON(C_2H_5)_2$	101.15	....		$177–8^{760}$ 68^{15}	0.9080^{19}	1.4321^{25}	∞	v	v	∞	∞		B4, 109
Ω f120	—,—,N,N-dimethyl-	$HCON(CH_3)_2$	73.09	λ^{gas} 162 (3.84), 197.4 (3.94)	−60.48	$149–56^{760}$ 39.9^{10}	0.9487_4^{20}	1.4305^{20}	∞	∞	∞	∞	∞	chl ∞ lig δ	B4, 58
Ω f121	—,—,N,N-diphenyl-	N-Formyldiphenyl amine. $HCON(C_6H_5)_2$	197.24	rh (dil al) λ^{bz} 324 (4.22)	73–4	337.5^{762} 190^{13}			i s^h	s	s	s	s		B12¹, 190
f122	—,—,N-ethyl-	$HCONHC_2H_5$	73.09	....		$197–9$ 109.6^{30}	0.9552^{20}	1.4320^{20}	∞	∞	∞	∞			B4, 109
f123	—,—,N(1-hydroxy-2,2,2-trichloroethyl)-	Chloral formamide. $HCONHCHOHCCl_3$	192.43	cr	....	118			s d^h	v d^h	v	v		AcOEt s	B2², 37
Ω f124	—,—,N-methyl-	$HCONHCH_3$	59.07	....		$180–5$ $102–3^{20}$	1.011^{19}	1.4319^{20}	s	s	i	∞			B4², 563
Ω f125	—,—,N-phenyl-	Formanilide. $HCONHC_6H_5$.	121.14	mcl pr (lig-xyl) λ^{al} 242 (4.14)	50	271 166^{14}	1.1437_4^{17} 1.1322_{50}^{50}		s	s	v	s			B12¹, 190
Ω f126	—,—,N-2-tolyl-	Form-*o*-toluidide. N-Formyl-*o*-toluidine	135.17	lf (al)	62	288^{760}	1.086_4^{25}		s	v					B12², 439
Ω f127	—,—,N-3-tolyl-	Form-*m*-toluidide.	135.17	....	< −18	278^{724} δd $176–8^{17}$			s					NaOH s	B12², 468
Ω f128	—,—,N-4-tolyl-	Form-*p*-toluidide.	135.17	nd	53				s	v	s				B12¹, 419
f129	—,amidine	Formamidine. $HN:CHNH_2$	44.06	pr	81	d			v	s					B2, 90
Ω f130	—,—,N,N′-diphenyl-	$C_6H_5N:CHNHC_6H_5$	196.26	nd (al) λ^{al} 282 (4.34)	142 (136–7)	>250			δ	s	v	s	s	chl s, lig δ CS_2, peth δ	B12, 236
f130¹	—,amidoxime.	Isoretin. $HON:CHNH_2$	60.06	rh nd (al)	114–5	d			v	δ	δ		i		B2², 89
Ω f131	—,benzyl ester	Benzyl formate. $HCO_2CH_2C_6H_5$	136.16	....		$202–3^{747}$ $84–5^{10}$	1.081_4^{20}	1.5154^{20}	i	s	∞	s			B6², 415
Ω f132	—,butyl ester	Butyl formate. $HCO_2CH_2CH_2CH_2CH_3$	102.13	....	−91.9	106.8^{760}	0.8885_4^{20}	1.3912^{20}	δ	∞	∞	s			B2³, 39
f133	—,sec-butyl ester. (*dl*)	$HCO_2CH(CH_3)C_2H_5$	102.13	....		97	0.8846_4^{20}	1.3865^{20}	δ	∞	∞	s			B2³, 41
Ω f134	—,cyclohexyl ester	....	128.17	....		162.5^{750}	1.0057_4^{20}	1.4430^{20}	i	s	v	...		HCO_2H s aa s	B6², 10

For explanations, symbols and abbreviations see beginning of table. For structural formulas see end of table.

No.	Name	Synonyms and Formula	Mol. wt.	Color. crystalline form. specific rotation and λ_{max} (log ε)	m.p. °C	b.p. °C	Density	n_D	w	al	eth	ace	bz	other solvents	Ref.
	Formic acid														
Ω f135	—,ethyl ester	$HCO_2C_2H_5$	74.08	,,,,,,,,,	−80.5	54.5^{760}	0.9168^{20}	1.3598^{20}	s	∞	∞	v			B2[3], 31
Ω f136	—,heptyl ester	$HCO_2(CH_2)_6CH_3$	144.22			178.12^{760} 83^{30}	0.8784^{20}	1.4140^{20}	i	∞	∞				B2[3], 44
Ω f137	—,hexyl ester	$HCO_2(CH_2)_5CH_3$	130.19		−62.65	155.5^{760}	0.8813^{20}_4	1.4071^{20}	i	∞	∞				B2[3], 44
f138	—,hydrazide	Formyl hydrazide. $HCONHNH_2$	60.06	ye lf or nd (al)	54				i	v	v^h		v	chl v	B2, 93
Ω f139	—,isobutyl ester	$HCO_2CH_2CH(CH_3)_2$	102.13		−95.8	98.4^{760} 33^{54}	0.8854^{20}_4	1.3857^{20}	δ	∞	∞	v			B2[2], 30
Ω f140	—,isopropyl ester	Isopropyl formate. $HCO_2CH(CH_3)_2$	88.12			68.2^{760}	0.8728^{20}	1.3678^{20}	δ	∞	∞	v			B2[2], 29
Ω f141	—,methyl ester	Methyl formate. HCO_2CH_3	60.05		−99	31.5^{760}	0.9742^{20}	1.3433^{20}	v	∞	s			MeOH s	B2[2], 25
Ω f142	—,3-methylbutyl ester	Isoamyl formate. $HCO_2(CH_2)_2CH(CH_3)_2$	116.16		−93.5	124.2^{760}	0.8857^{20}_4	1.3976^{20}	δ	s	∞				B2[3], 43
f143	—,4-nitrobenzyl ester		181.15	(dil al)	31					s^h					B6[1], 223
Ω f144	—,octyl ester	$HCO_2(CH_2)_7CH_3$	158.24		−39.1	198.8	0.8744^{20}	1.4208^{15}_4	i	∞	∞				B2, 22
Ω f145	—,pentyl ester	Amyl formate. $HCO_2(CH_2)_4CH_3$	116.16		−73.5	132.1 (130)	0.8853^{20}	1.3992^{20}	δ	∞	∞				B2[3], 42
Ω f146	—,propyl ester	Propyl formate. $HCO_2CH_2CH_2CH_3$	88.12		−92.9	81.3^{760}	0.9058^{20}_4	1.3779^{20}	δ	∞	∞	v			B2[2], 28
—	—,amino-	see Carbamic acid													
—	—,azodi-	see Azodicarboxylic acid													
—	—,chloro-, amide	see Carbamic acid, chloride													
Ω f150	—,—,benzyl ester	Carbobenzoxy chloride. $ClCO_2CH_2C_6H_5$	170.60			103^{20}	1.20	1.5160^{20}	d	d^h	s	s	s		B6, 437
Ω f151	—,—,butyl ester	$ClCO_2(CH_2)_3CH_3$	136.58			138^{756} 35.5^{13}	1.0513^{20}	1.4121^{20}	d	d	∞	s			B3[2], 111
Ω f152	—,—,2-chloroethyl ester	$ClCO_2CH_2CH_2Cl$	142.97			$155.7-$ 6.0	1.3847^{20}	1.4465^{20}	i	s	s	s	s	oos s	B2[2], 193
f153	—,—,chloromethyl ester	$ClCO_2CH_2Cl$	128.94			107^{760}	1.465^{15}	1.4286^{22}	d^h		s	v			B3[2], 11
f154	—,—,3-chloropropyl ester	$ClCO_2(CH_2)_3Cl$	157.00			177	1.2949^{25}_{20}	1.4456^{20}	i						B3[2], 10
f155	—,—,cyclohexyl ester		162.62			87.5^{27}					s				B6[2], 11
f156	—,—,dichloromethyl ester	$ClCO_2CHCl_2$	163.39			$110-1^{760}$			d^h			v			B3[2], 11
f157	—,—,2-ethoxyethyl ester	Cellosolve chloroformate. $ClCO_2CH_2CH_2OC_2H_5$	152.58			67.2^{14}	1.1341^{25}	1.4169^{25}	i	s					B3[2], 29
Ω f158	—,—,ethyl ester	Ethyl chloroformate. $ClCO_2C_2H_5$	108.53		−80.6	95^{760} (93.1)	1.1352^{20}_4	1.3974^{20}	d	d		s		chl s	B3[2], 10
Ω f159	—,—,isobutyl ester	$ClCO_2CH_2CH(CH_3)_2$	136.58			128.8	1.0426^{18}_4	1.4071^{18}_{He}	d	s^h	∞		s	chl s	B3[2], 11
f160	—,—,isopropenyl ester	$ClCO_2C(CH_3):CH_2$	120.53			100^{760}	1.1032^{20}				s				C28, 6702
f161	—,—,isopropyl ester	$ClCO_2CH(CH_3)_2$	122.55			$104.6-$ 0.9^{761} 66.3^{200}		1.4013^{20}	i		s				B3[2], 10
f162	—,—,2-methoxyethyl ester	$ClCO_2CH_2CH_2OCH_3$	138.55			58.7^{13}	1.1905^{25}	1.4163^{25}	i		v				B3[3], 29
Ω f163	—,—,methyl ester	Methyl chloroformate. $ClCO_2CH_3$	94.50			$70.4-$ 0.9^{752}	1.2231^{20}_4	1.3868^{20}	d	∞	∞	s		chl s	B3[2], 9
f164	—,—,3-methylbutyl ester	Isoamyl chloroformate. $ClCO_2CH_2CH_2CH(CH_3)_2$	150.61			154.3^{760} 60^{15}	1.0288^{17}	1.4176^{20}	d	∞	∞				B3[2], 11
Ω f165	—,—,pentyl ester	Amyl chloroformate. $ClCO_2(CH_2)_4CH_3$	150.61			$60-2^{15}$		1.4181^{18}			s				B3[3], 27
f166	—,—,propyl ester	$ClCO_2CH_2CH_2CH_3$	122.55			115.2^{760} (105^{759})	1.0901^{20}_4	1.4035^{20}	d	∞	∞				B3[2], 10
f167	—,—,trichloromethyl ester	Diphosgene. Perchloromethyl formate. Superpalite. $ClCO_2CCl_3$	197.83		−57	128^{760} 49^{50}	1.6525^{14}	1.4566^{22}	i	s	v				B3[2], 16
—	—,cyano-, ethyl ester	see Oxalic acid, monoethyl ester mononitrile													
f168	—,(ethoxy)dithio-	Ethylxanthic acid. $C_3H_6OCS_2H$	122.21		ca. −53	25d			δ					chl. CS_2 s $PhNO_2$ s	B3[2], 151
—	—,fluoro-, fluoride	see Carbonyl fluoride													
f169	Formimidic acid, N-phenyl-, ethyl ester	N-Phenylformiminoethyl ether. $C_6H_5N:CHOC_2H_5$	149.19	λ^{hx} 250 (3.7)		$213-5^{761}$	1.0051^{20}_4	1.5279^{20}			s	s			C21, 387
f170	Formonitrolic acid	Methyl nitrolic acid. $HON:CHNO_2$	90.04	nd (eth or eth-peth)	68d				s	s	s			alk s (red)	B2, 92
f171	Frangulin A	$C_{21}H_{20}O_9$	416.39	ye or red (al or AcOEt) λ 225 (4.52), 264 (4.28), 282 (4.15), 300 (3.97), 430 (4.05)	228				i s^h	s^h			s^h	chl s^h aa s	B31, 74
	Fraxetin	see Coumarin 7,8-dihydroxy-6-methoxy-													
f173	Fraxin	8-Glucosidofraxetin.	370.32	ye nd (al) ye nd (w + 3)	205 (anh)				δ v^h	δ s^h	i			alk s	B31, 249

For explanations, symbols and abbreviations see beginning of table. For structural formulas see end of table.

No.	Name	Synonyms and Formula	Mol. wt.	Color, crystalline form, specific rotation and λ_{max} (log ε)	m.p. °C	b.p. °C	Density	n_D	Solubility						Ref.
									w	al	eth	ace	bz	other solvents	
	Freon														
—	Freon	see **Methane, dichloro-** **difluoro-**													
—	Freon 114	see **Ethane, 1,1-dichloro-** **1,2,2,2-tetrafluoro-**													
f 174	1-**Fructosamine** (D)	Isoglucosamine.	179.17	syr	. . . .	. . . .				i	i	. . . . . .		dil ac s	**B31**, 342, 345
Ω f 175	β-**Fructose** (D)	Fruit sugar. Levulose.	180.16	pr or nd (w) orh pr (al) $[\alpha]_D^{20} -133$ → −92 (w, c = 2) λ^w 279 (−0.42)	103–5d	. . . .	1.60_4^{20}		v	s	. . .	v^h δ	. . .	MeOH s Py s	**B31**, 321
Ω f 176	α-**Fucose** (L)	6-Deoxygalactose.	164.16	nd (al) $[\alpha]_D^{20}$ (mut) −124.1 → 75.6 (w, c = 9)	145	. . . .			v	δ s^h	i				**B31**, 76, 78
—	—,3-methyl-(D) . . .	see **Digitalose**													
f 177	**Fucoxanthin**	$C_{40}H_{60}O_6$.	632.89	red-br pl (eth-peth) hex pl (+2w, dil al, dil ace), nd (MeOH +3) $[\alpha]_D^{18} +72.5$ (chl) λ^{chl} 475, 492	168	. . . .				s	s			MeOH δ peth δ con sulf → bl	**B30**, 105
—	**Fulminuric acid**	see **Malonic acid, nitro-,** monoamide, mononitrile													
Ω f 178	**Fumaric acid**	trans-Butenedioic acid*. $HO_2CCH:CHCO_2H$	116.07	nd, mcl pr or lf (w) λ^w 208 (4.20)	300–2 (286–7) (sealed tube)	$165^{1.7}$ sub	1.635_4^{20}		δ s^h	s	δ	δ	. . .	chl, CCl_4 δ con sulf s	**B2²**, 631
Ω f 179	—,dichloride.	Fumaryl chloride. ClCOCH:CHCOCl	152.97	pa ye liq	. . . .	$158–60^{760}$ 63^{13}	1.408^{20}	1.5004^{18}	d	d					**B2³**, 1907
f 180	—,diisobutyl ester .	$(CH_3)_2CHCH_2O_2CCH:CHCO_2CH_2CH(CH_3)_2$ 228.29		. . . .	170^{160} 122^5	0.9760_4^{20}	1.4432^{20}	i	s	s	s	s		**B2**, 742
f 181	—,diisopropyl ester	$(CH_3)_2CHO_2CCH:CHCO_2CH(CH_3)_2$ 200.24		. . . .		$225–6^{760}$				s	s	s			**B2**, 742
Ω f 182	—,dinitrile	trans-1,2-Dicyanoethylene. Fumaronitrile. NCCH:CHCN	78.07	nd (bz-peth) λ^{al} 232 sh (4.06), 292 (0.60)	96.8	186^{760}	0.9416^{111}	1.4349^{111}	s	s	s	s	s	peth δ	**B2¹**, 302
f 183	—,diphenyl ester . .	$C_6H_5O_2CCH:CHCO_2C_6H_5$	268.27	nd (al)	161–2	219^{14}			i	δ s^h					**B6**, 156
Ω f 184	—,dipropyl ester. . .	$CH_3CH_2CH_2O_2CCH:CHCO_2CH_2CH_2CH_3$ 200.24		. . . .		110^5	1.0129_4^{20}	1.4435^{20}		s	s				**B2²**, 639
f 185	—,piperazinium salt	$C_4H_{10}N_2 . HO_2CCH:CHCO_2H$	202.21		240d	. . . .			s^h	s	i				**Am 70**, 2758
f 185¹	—,**bromo-**	$HO_2CCBr:CHCO_2H$	194.98	pr (AcOEt)	185–6	d 200			s	s	s				**B2²**, 640
f 185²	—,**chloro-**	$HO_2CCCl:CHCO_2H$	150.52	pl (aa)	192–3	sub			v	v	v	δ			**B2²**, 640
f 186	—,—,dichloride . . .	ClCOCCl:CHCOCl.	187.41	pa gr	. . . .	$184–7$ δd $73–5^{20}$	1.564_4^{20}	1.5206^{20}	d	d	v			aa s	**B2²**, 640
f 187	—,—,diethyl ester	$C_2H_5O_2CCH:CClCO_2C_2H_5$.	206.63		. . . .	250 δd 127^{10}	1.1880_4^{20}	1.4571^{20}	i	v	v				**B2²**, 640
f 188	—,—,dimethyl ester	$CH_3O_2CCH:CClCO_2CH_3$	178.57		. . . .	224^{760} 108^{15}	1.2899^{25}	1.4720_{Hc}^{18}		s	s				**B2²**, 640
f 189	—,**dimethyl-**	$HO_2C(CH_3)C:C(CH_3)CO_2H$	144.14	nd (w)	241	. . . .			δ s^h	δ			i	chl, lig i	**B2²**, 660
Ω f 190	—,**methyl-**	Mesaconic acid. $HO_2CC(CH_3):CHCO_2H$	130.10	rh nd or mcl pr (eth, AcOEt, w) rods (sub)	204.5 (cor)	sub	1.466_4^{20}		δ v^h	v	s		δ	chl, CS_2 δ lig δ	**B2²**, 651
f 191	—,—,diethyl ester .	$C_2H_5O_2CC(CH_3):CHCO_2C_2H_5$	186.21		. . . .	229^{760} $93–5^{10}$	1.0453_{20}^{20}	1.4488^{20}	δ	s	s	s	s		**B2²**, 652
f 192	—,—,dimethyl ester	$CH_3O_2CC(CH_3):CHCO_2CH_3$ 158.16			. . . .	203.5 100^{16}	1.0914_4^{20}	1.4512^{20}	δ	s	s	s	s		**B2²**, 652
—	**Fumigatin**	see **1,4-Benzoquinone, 3-** hydroxy-2-methoxy-5-methyl-*													
Ω f 193	**Furan**	1,4-Epoxy-1,3-butadiene*. Furfuran.	68.08	λ^{al} 208 sh (3.9)	−85.65	31.36^{760}	0.9514_4^{20}	1.4214_0^2	i	v	v	s	s		**B17²**, 34
Ω f 194	—,**2-acetyl-**	2-Furyl methyl ketone. $C_6H_6O_2$. See f 193	110.11	cr (lig) λ^{al} 225.5 (3.37), 270 (4.11)	33	173 67^{10}	1.098^{20}	1.5017^{20}	i	s	s	s	s		**B17²**, 314
Ω f 194'	—,**2-(amino-** methyl)-	Furfurylamine. C_5H_7NO. See f 193	97.12			$145–6^{761}$ 80^{84}	1.0995^{20}	1.4908^{20}	∞	s	s				**B18²**, 416
f 195	—,**2-(amino-** methyl)tetra- hydro-	Tetrahydrofurfuryl amine. $C_5H_{11}NO$. See f 220	101.15		. . . .	$151–2^{735}$	0.9770_4^{20}	1.4551^{20}	∞	∞	s				**Am 67**, 693
f 196	—,**2-bromo-**	α-Furyl bromide. C_4H_3BrO. See f 193	146.98	λ^{al} 215.5 (3.99)		102^{744}	1.6500^{20}	1.4980^{20}	δ	s	s	s	s		**Am 52**, 2083

For explanations, symbols and abbreviations see beginning of table. For structural formulas see end of table.

No.	Name	Synonyms and Formula	Mol. wt.	Color, crystalline form, specific rotation and λ_{max} (log ε)	m.p. °C	b.p. °C	Density	n_D	w	al	eth	ace	bz	other solvents	Ref.
	Furan														
f 197	—,3-bromo-	β-Furyl bromide. C_4H_3BrO. See f 193	146.98			103^{760}	1.6606_4^{20}	1.4958^{20}	i	s	s	s	s		**B17**, 27
f 198	—,2(bromomethyl)-	Furfuryl bromide. C_5H_5BrO. See f 193	161.00	pa ye		$33-4^2$	1.560_{20}^{20}	1.5380^{20}			s				**B17²**, 39
Ω f 199	—,2(bromomethyl)tetrahydro-	1-Bromo-2,5-epoxypentane*. C_5H_9BrO. See f 220	165.03			$168-70^{744}$ $69-70^{22}$	1.3653_4^{20}	1.4850^{20}		s	s				**B17²**, 21
f 200	—,2-tert-butyl-	$C_8H_{12}O$. See f 193	124.19			$119-20^{760}$	0.869_4^{20}	1.4373^{20}	i	s	s	s	s		**C49**, 2419
f 200¹	—,2-chloro-	α-Furyl chloride. C_4H_3ClO. See f 193	102.52			77.5^{744}	1.1923_4^{20}	1.4569^{20}	i	s	s	s			**C42**, 2284
f 201	—,3-chloro-	β-Furyl chloride. C_4H_3ClO. See f 193	102.52			79^{742}	1.2094_4^{20}	1.4601^{20}	δ	s	s	s			**C49**, 2419
f 201¹	—,2-(chloromethyl)-	Furfuryl chloride. C_5H_5ClO. See f 193	116.55			49^{26} 37^{15}	1.1783_4^{20}	1.4941^{20}	i	s	s	s	s	os s	**B17²**, 39
f 202	—,2,5-dibromo-	$C_4H_2Br_2O$. See f 193	225.88	pl	9–10	$164-5^{764}$ 62^{15}	2.272_4^{20}	1.5455^{20}			s				**B17**, 28
f 203	—,2,5-di-tert-butyl-	$C_{12}H_{20}O$. See f 193	180.29			210^{760} $61-2^{17}$	0.837_4^{20}	1.4369^{20}	i	s	s	s			**C51**, 12875
f 204	—,2,5-dichloro-	$C_4H_2Cl_2O$. See f 193	136.97			115	1.371^{25}								**C42**, 2284
f 205	—,2,2-diethyl-(tetrahydro)-	$C_8H_{16}O$. See f 220	128.22			146	0.8703_4^{20}	1.4317^{20}	i	s	s	v	v	os v	**B17²**, 25
Ω f 206	—,2,5-dimethyl-	C_6H_8O. See f 193	96.14	λ^{al} 220 (3.90)	−62.84	$93-4^{760}$	0.8883_4^{20}	1.4363^{20}	i	s	s	s	s	chl s aa s	**B17¹**, 20
f 207	—,2,4-dioxo-(tetrahydro)-	Tetronic acid. β-Ketobutyrolactone. $C_4H_4O_3$. See f 202	100.08	pl (al-lig) λ^w 233 (3.41), 310 (4.15)	141				v^h	v^h	δ		δ	chl δ lig δ	**B17**, 403
f 207¹	—,2,5-dinitro-	$C_4H_2N_2O_5$. See f 193	158.07	nd (w), pr (al)	102–2.5				δ	i	s				**B17**, 29
Ω f 207²	—,2,5-diphenyl-	$C_{16}H_{12}O$. See f 193	220.27	nd or lf (dil al) λ^{iso} 324 (4.46)	91	343–5			i	v	v	s	s	oos s	**C40**, 4705
f 208	—,2-ethoxy-	Ethyl 2-furyl ether. $C_6H_8O_2$. See f 193	112.14			125–6	0.9849_4^{23}	1.4500^{23}							**C51**, 3549
f 209	—,2-ethyl-	C_6H_8O. See f 193	96.14			$92-3^{768}$	0.912_{13}^{13}	1.4466^{13}							**C49**, 10918
f 210	—,2-ethyl-(tetrahydro)-	$C_6H_{12}O$. See f 220	100.16			109^{760}	0.8570_4^{19}	1.4147^{19}		s	s	s	s	os s	**B17²**, 23
—	—,2-(hydroxymethyl)-	see Methanol, 2-furyl-													
f 210¹	—,2-iodo-	C_4H_3IO. See f 193	193.97			$43-5^{15}$	2.024_4^{20}	1.5661^{20}			s				**C51**, 14672
f 210²	—,3-iodo-	C_4H_3IO. See f 193	193.97			132.2^{732} $37-8^{22}$	2.045_4^{20}	1.5610^{20}	i		s				**C56**, 11536
f 211	—,2-isopropoxy-	2-Furyl isopropyl ether. $C_7H_{10}O_2$. See f 193	126.16			135–6	0.9689_4^{20}	1.4419^{20}							**C51**, 3550
f 212	—,2-methoxy-	2-Furyl methyl ether. $C_5H_6O_2$. See f 193	98.10	λ^{al} 221 (3.82)		110–1	1.0646_4^{25}	1.4468^{25}							**C49**, 6217
Ω f 213	—,2-methyl-	Sylvan. C_5H_6O. See f 193	82.10	λ^{MeOH} <220		(i) 63^{737} (ii) 79^{42} (unst)	0.9132_4^{20}	1.4342^{20}	δ	s	s				**B17²**, 39
f 214	—,3-methyl-	C_5H_6O. See f 193	82.10			65.5^{749}	0.923_4^{18}	1.4330^{19}	i	s	s				**B17²**, 40
Ω f 215	—,2-methyl-(tetrahydro)-	$C_5H_{10}O$. See f 220	86.14			80^{761}	0.8552_4^{20}	1.40595^{21}	s	v	v	v	v	chl, os v	**B17²**, 21
f 216	—,3-methyl-(tetrahydro)-	$C_5H_{10}O$. See f 220	86.14			86–7	0.8642_4^{20}	1.4122^{20}	s	v	v	v	s	os v	**B17²**, 21
f 217	—,2-nitro-	$C_4H_3NO_3$. See f 193	113.07	yesh mcl cr (peth) λ^w 225 (3.53), 315 (3.91)	29	$133-5^{123}$				s	s				**B17**, 28
f 218	—,2-phenyl-	$C_{10}H_8O$. See f 193	144.19			$107-8^{18}$	1.083_4^{20}	1.5920^{20}			s	s			**B17²**, 64
Ω f 219	—,2-propyl-	$C_7H_{10}O$. See f 193	110.16			$114-5^{750}$	0.8876_4^{20}	1.4549^{20}			s	s			**C33**, 1316³
f 219¹	—,2-propyl(tetrahydro)-	$C_7H_{14}O$. See f 220	114.19			139.4^{758}	0.8547_4^{20}	1.4242^{20}	i						**B17¹**, 11
Ω f 220	—,tetrahydro-	1,4 Epoxybutane*. Tetramethylene oxide.	72.12		fr 65	67 (64.5)	0.8892_4^{20}	1.4050^{20}	s	v	v	v	v	os v	**B17²**, 15
f 220¹	—,tetraiodo-	C_4I_4O. See f 193	571.66	nd	165				i		s			lig δ	**B17²**, 34
f 221	—,2,3,5-trichloro-	C_4HCl_3O. See f 193	171.41			147	1.50^{25}								**C42**, 2284
—	2-Furanacrylic acid	see Propenoic acid, 3(2-furyl)-													
—	2-Furancarboxaldehyde	see Furfural													
Ω f 222	2-Furancarboxylic acid	α-Furoic acid. Pyromucic acid	112.09	mcl nd or lf (w) λ^{al} 214 sh (3.58), 242.5 (4.03)	133–4	230–2 141–4²⁰ (sub 130–40⁵⁰)			s v^h	s	v				**B18²**, 265
Ω f 223	—,allyl ester	$C_8H_8O_3$. See f 222	152.16	λ^w 225 (3.53), 315 (3.91)		$206-9^{760}$	1.118_{25}^{25}	1.4945^{20}				s	s		**C36**, 5812
f 224	—,benzyl ester	$C_{12}H_{10}O_3$. See f 222	202.21	ye		$179-81^{18}$	1.1632_4^{20}	1.5550^{20}	i		s	s	s		**B18²**, 267

For explanations, symbols and abbreviations see beginning of table. For structural formulas see end of table.

2-Furancarboxylic acid

No.	Name	Synonyms and Formula	Mol. wt.	Color, crystalline form, specific rotation and λ_{max} (log ε)	m.p. °C	b.p. °C	Density	n_D	w	al	eth	ace	bz	other solvents	Ref.
Ω f225	—,butyl ester	$C_9H_{12}O_3$. See f222	168.20			233 83–4[1]	1.0555[20]	1.4740	i	s	s	...	s	peth s	B18[2], 266
f226	—,sec-butyl ester	$C_9H_{12}O_3$. See f222	168.20			67–9[1]	1.0465[20]		i	∞	∞				B18[2], 266
Ω f227	—,chloride	$C_5H_3ClO_2$. See f222	130.53		−2 (+1)	173 66[10]			i d[h]	d	s			chl s	B18[2], 267
Ω f228	—,ethyl ester	$C_7H_8O_3$. See f222	140.15	lf or pr λ^{al} 220 sh (3.46), 251 (4.13)	34–5	196.8[760] 128[95]	1.1174[20]	1.4797[21]	i	∞	∞	∞	s	peth ∞	B18[2], 266
f229	—,furfuryl ester		192.18	dimorphic	27.5	122[2]	1.2384[25/25]	1.5280[20]	i	s	s	v	∞	chl ∞	B18[2], 267
f230	—,heptyl ester	$C_{12}H_{18}O_3$. See f222	210.28			116–7[1]	1.0005[20]		i	s	s				B18[2], 267
Ω f231	—,hexyl ester	$C_{11}H_{16}O_3$. See f222	196.25			105–7[1]	1.0170[20]		i	s	s		∞	MeOH s	B18[2], 267
f232	—,isobutyl ester	$C_9H_{12}O_3$. See f222	168.20			221–3[760] 97[13.5]	1.0388[28]	1.4676[28]	i	s	s	s	v		B18[2], 266
f233	—,isopropyl ester	$C_8H_{10}O_3$. See f222	154.17			198–9[760]	1.0655[24]	1.4682[24]	i	s	s	s	s		B18, 275
Ω f234	—,methyl ester	$C_6H_6O_3$. See f222	126.11	λ^{al} 252 (4.13)		181.3[760]	1.1786[21]	1.4860[20]	i	s	s	s	s		B18[2], 266
f235	—,3-methylbutyl ester	Isoamyl α-furoate. $C_{10}H_{14}O_3$. See f222	182.22			282[760] (232)	1.030[20]	1.4274[20]	i	∞			s	peth ∞ aa s	B18[2], 266
f236	—,nitrile	α-Furyl cyanide.	93.09			146[738]	1.0822[20]	1.4798[20]	i	s	s				B18[2], 268
Ω f237	—,octyl ester	$C_{13}H_{20}O_3$. See f222	224.30			126–7[1]	0.9885[20]		i	s	s				B18[2], 267
Ω f238	—,pentyl ester	Amyl furoate. $C_{10}H_{14}O_3$. See f222	182.22			95–7[1]	1.0335[20]		i	∞					B18[2], 266
f239	—,piperazinium salt	2($C_5H_4O_3$)·$C_4H_{10}N_2$. See f222	310.31		234–6				s	s	δ				Am 70, 2758
Ω f240	—,propyl ester	$C_8H_{10}O_3$. See f222	154.17			210.9	1.0745[26]	1.4737[26]	i	s	s	s	s	peth s	B18[2], 266
f241	3-Furancarboxylic acid	β-Furoic acid	112.09	nd (w) λ^{al} 232 (3.36)	122–3	105–10[12] sub			δ s[h]	s	v			AcOEt s	B18[1], 439
f242	—,methyl ester	$C_6H_6O_3$. See f241	126.11	λ^{al} 238 (3.40)		160[760] 79[42]	1.1744[15/15]	1.4676[20]	i	s	s	s	s	chl s lig δ CS_2 δ	B18[1], 439
f244	—,4-bromo-	$C_5H_3BrO_3$. See f222	190.99	nd (w)	129				s	s	s		s	chl s lig δ CS_2 δ	B18[2], 268
Ω f245	—,5-bromo-	$C_5H_3BrO_3$. See f222	190.99	lf (w) λ^{al} 251 (4.08)	190–1				δ	s	v		δ	chl δ, lig i peth i	B18, 284
f246	—,—,ethyl ester	$C_7H_7BrO_3$. See f222	219.04	pr	17	235[767] 134–6[34]	1.528[20]		i	s	s				B18, 284
f247	—,3-chloro-	$C_5H_3ClO_3$. See f222	146.53	pl or pr (w)	149.5				δ	s	s	s[h]		chl s[h]	B18, 282
f248	—,4-chloro-	$C_5H_3ClO_3$. See f222	146.53	pl or pr (w)	149 (146)				δ	s	s	s[h]		chl s[h]	C31, 2207
f249	—,5-chloro-	$C_5H_3ClO_3$. See f222	146.53	lf (w)	179–80				δ s[h]	s	s	s[h]			B18, 282
f250	—,—,methyl ester	$C_6H_5ClO_3$. See f222	160.56	λ^{al} 260.5 (4.23)	40–1				i		s				C52, 1990
f251	—,5(cyclohexyloxy)	$C_{11}H_{14}O_4$. See f222	210.23		138–9				δ d[h]	s					C51, 3549
f252	3-Furancarboxylic acid, 2,5-dimethyl-	Pyrotritaric acid. $C_7H_8O_3$. See f241	140.15	nd (w)	135	sub			s[h]	s	v				B18, 297
f253	2-Furancarboxylic acid, 5-ethoxy-	$C_7H_8O_4$. See f222	156.15		140–1				δ d[h]	s					C51, 3549
f254	—,5-iodo-	$C_5H_3IO_3$. See f222	237.98		197d										C53, 12267
f255	—,5-methoxy-	$C_6H_6O_4$. See f222	142.11		136–8d				δ d[h]	s					C51, 3549
f256	—,3-methyl-	$C_6H_6O_3$. See f222	126.11	nd (w)	134	sub			s[h]						B18[1], 439
f257	—,—,ethyl ester	$C_8H_{10}O_3$. See f222	154.17	pl	47–8	205[760]				s					B18[2], 271
f258	—,—,methyl ester	$C_7H_8O_3$. See f222	140.15	pl (al)	36–8	72–6[8]				s					B18, 293
f259	—,4-methyl-	$C_6H_6O_3$. See f222	126.11	nd (bz-peth)	131–2										C26, 1603
Ω f260	—,5-methyl-	$C_6H_6O_3$. See f222	126.11	pl or nd (w) λ^w 257 (4.10)	109–10	105[1]			δ v[h]	s	s	ace	δ	chl s	B18[2], 272
Ω f261	—,—,methyl ester	$C_7H_8O_3$. See f222	140.14	λ^w 272 (4.06)		205[760] 98[15]				s	s				B18[2], 272
f262	3-Furancarboxylic acid, 2-methyl-	$C_6H_6O_3$. See f241	126.11	cr (w)	102–3						s	s		peth s aa s	B18[2], 271
f263	—,—,ethyl ester	$C_8H_{10}O_3$. See f241	154.17			85–7[20]	1.0102[25/4]	1.4620[25]	i	s					B18[1], 439
f264	—,4-methyl-	$C_6H_6O_3$. See f241	126.11	nd (bz-peth)	138–9				s		s				C26, 1603
f265	—,5-methyl-	$C_6H_6O_3$. See f241	126.11	(w)	119	sub			s		s				C33, 4983
Ω f266	2-Furancarboxylic acid, 5-nitro-	$C_5H_3NO_5$. See f222	157.08	pa ye pl (w) λ^{al} 212 (3.98), 314 (4.06)	184	sub			s[h]	s	s	...	δ	chl i	B18, 287
f267	—,5-octyloxy-	$C_{13}H_{20}O_4$. See f222	240.30		125–6				δ d[h]	s					C51, 3549
—	3-Furancarboxylic acid, 5-oxo(tetrahydro)-	see Paraconic acid													

For explanations, symbols and abbreviations see beginning of table. For structural formulas see end of table.

No.	Name	Synonyms and Formula	Mol. wt.	Color, crystalline form, specific rotation and λ_{max} (log ε)	m.p. °C	b.p. °C	Density	n_D	w	al	eth	ace	bz	other solvents	Ref.
	3-Furancarboxylic acid														
f268	**2-Furancarboxylic acid, 5-phenoxy-**	$C_{11}H_8O_4$. See f222	204.19	. . . .	122–3	. . . .			δ d[h]	s		. . .	. . .		C51, 3549
f269	—,tetrahydro-		116.13		21	145[25]	1.1933_{20}^{20}	1.4612^{20}	s	s	. . .	. . .			B18[2], 262
f270	**2,3-Furandicarboxylic acid**		156.10	pr (aa or sub) λ^{al} 263 (4.14)	226	sub			v	v	δ	. . .		AcOEt v aa δ v[h]	B18[2], 287
f271	—,dimethyl ester	$C_8H_8O_5$. See f270	184.16	(MeOH) λ^{al} 254 (3.96)	39				i	s	v				B18[2], 288
f272	**2,4-Furandicarboxylic acid**		156.10	lf (w + l) λ^w 240 (4.02)	266 (anh)	sub			δ v[h]	v	. . .	v		chl δ CS$_2$ δ aa δ	B18, 327
f273	—,dimethyl ester	$C_8H_8O_5$. See f272	184.16	pr (MeOH) λ^{al} 242.5 (4.09)	109–10										B18, 327
f273[1]	**2,5-Furandicarboxylic acid**	Dehydromucic acid.	156.10	nd (w), lf (al) λ^{al} 263 (4.20)	> 320	sub			δ	δ					B18[2], 288
f274	—,dichloride	Dehydromucyl chloride. $C_6H_2Cl_2O_3$. See f273[1]	192.99	nd (sub)	80	245[760]			v	v	v			chl v	B18, 330
f275	—,dimethyl ester	$C_8H_8O_5$. See f273[1]	184.16	nd (w), cr (MeOH) λ^{al} 263 (4.19)	112	154–6[15]			i	s	s			chl s	B18, 329
f275[1]	**3,4-Furandicarboxylic acid**		156.10	λ^{al} 240 (3.43)	217–8 (212)										C54, 9876
Ω f276	**Furazan, 3,4-dimethyl-**	3,4-Dimethyl-1,2,5-oxadiazole	98.11		−7	156[744]	1.0528_4^{14}	1.4237^{20}	δ	v	v				B27[2], 628
Ω f277	**Furfural**	α-Furaldehyde. Fural. 2-Furancarboxaldehyde.	96.09	λ^{sat} 280 (3.07) (initial)	−38.7	161.7[760] 90[65]	$1\,1594_4^{20}$	1.5261^{20}	s v[h]	v	∞	v	s	chl s	B17[2], 305
f278	—,diacetate	Furfurylidiene diacetate.	198.17	nd or pl (eth-peth)	52–3	220[760] 143–4[20]			δ	s	v		v	peth δ	B17[2], 309
f279	—,diethyl acetal	$C_9H_{14}O_3$. See f277	170.21			191–2[760] 62–4[3]	0.9994_{20}^{20}	1.4451^{20}	i	s					B17[2], 309
f280	—,oxime (anti)	α-Furaldoxime. $C_5H_5NO_2$. See f277	111.10	nd (lig) λ^{al} 270 (4.2)	75–6				s	v	v		v	lig δ s[h]	B17[2], 311
f281	—,—(syn)	β-Furaldoxime. $C_5H_5NO_2$. See f277	111.10	nd (lig) λ^{al} 265 (4.23)	91–2	201–8 d 98[9]			δ	v	v		v	CS$_2$ v aa v lig s[h]	B17[2], 311
Ω f282	—,phenylhydrazone	$C_{11}H_{10}N_2O$. See f277	186.22	ye lf (al) λ 302 (4.0), 345 (4.4)	97–8				i	v	v			lig δ	B17[2], 312
f283	—,5-bromo-	$C_5H_3BrO_2$. See f277	174.99	cr (50 % al)	82	112[16]			δ	s	s				C35, 2508
f284	—,5-chloro-	$C_5H_3ClO_2$. See f277	130.53		31.5–33	70[1]									C40, 1825
Ω f285	—,5-hydroxymethyl-	$C_6H_6O_3$. See f277	126.11	nd (eth-peth) λ^w 284 (4.26)	35–5.5	114–6[0.5] 72[0.002]	1.2062^{25}	1.5627^{18}	s	s	δ		s	chl, AcOEt s CCl$_4$ δ	B18[2], 6
f286	—,5-methyl-	$C_6H_6O_2$. See f277	110.11	λ 225 (3.45), 283.5 (4.23)		187[760] 79–81[12]	1.1072_4^{18}	1.5264^{20}	s	v	∞				B17[2], 315
f287	—,5-nitro-	$C_5H_3NO_4$. See f277	141.08	pa ye (peth) λ^w 297 (4.06)	35–6	128–32[10]			δ					peth s	Am 52, 2550
f288	—,—,semicarbazone	Furacin. Nitrofurazone. $C_6H_6N_4O_4$. See f277	198.14	pa ye nd (w) darkens in light	237 d				i	δ	i			alk s	C46, 4029
f289	—,tetrahydro-		100.13			142–3[779] 45–7[29]	1.0727_4^{20}	1.4366^{20}	s		s				C38, 2336
Ω f290	**Furfurin**	Furin. 2,4,5-Tris(2-furyl) 2-imidazoline.	268.28	lt br nd or rh pr (w or eth)	116–7				δ[h]	v	v				B27[2], 918
—	**Furfuryl alcohol**	see Methanol, 2-furyl-													
—	**Furfurylamine**	see Furan, 2(aminomethyl)-													
—	**2-Furfurylfuran**	see Methane, di-2-furyl-													
—	**Furfuryl mercaptan**	see Methanethiol, 2-furyl-													
—	**Furil**	see 1,2-Ethanedione, 1,2-di(2-furyl)-													
—	**Furoic acid**	see Furancarboxylic acid													
Ω f291	**Furoin**	Furoylfurylcarbinol.	192.18	nd (al)	138–9 (cor)	. . . .			δ[h] s[h]	δ s	s			MeOH s	B19[2], 224

For explanations, symbols and abbreviations see beginning of table. For structural formulas see end of table.

Gaidic acid

No.	Name	Synonyms and Formula	Mol. wt.	Color, crystalline form, specific rotation and λ_{max} (log ε)	m.p. °C	b.p. °C	Density	n_D	w	al	eth	ace	bz	other solvents	Ref.
—	Gaidic acid	see 2-Hexadecenoic acid													
Ω g1	Galactitol(D)	D-Dulcitol.............	182.18	mcl pr (w)	189	275–8[1] sub	1.466	....	s v^h	δ	i	...	i	Py δ	B1[2], 612
Ω g2	Galactonic acid, γ-lactone (D)	....	178.14	nd (w + 1), nd (al or AcOEt) $[\alpha]_D^{20}$ −65.5 (w)	112 (anh) 66 (hyd)	....			s					AcOEt v	B18[1], 408
Ω g3	Galactose(D)......		180.16	pl or pr (al), pr or nd (w + 1) $[\alpha]$ +83.3 (w) $\lambda^{w, pH=11}$ 290 (2.36)	170 (anh) 118–20 (hyd)	....			v^h	δ	i		i	Py s	B1, 909 B31, 295
g4	—,3,6-an-hydro-(D)	....	162.14	lf (PrOH) $[\alpha]_D$ +24(w)	123–5				s						C41, 3062
g5	—,2,3,4,6-tetra-O-methyl-(D, α)		236.27	$[\alpha]_D^{20}$ +150 → +114 (w) (mut)	71–3	172[12]			s	s	s			mut	B31, 304
Ω g6	Galacturonic acid(D)	nd (w + 1)	194.14	α: $[\alpha]_D^{20}$ +98 → +53.4 (w, c = 10) (mut) β: $[\alpha]_D^{20}$ +27 (w) $\lambda^{79\% sulf}$ 277	α: 156–9 d β: 160 d				s	s^h	i				B3[1], 306
g7	Galegine	4-Guanidino-2-methyl-2-butene. γ,γ-Dimethylallyl-guanidine. $(CH_3)_2C:CHCH_2N:C(NH_2)_2$	127.19	hyg	60–5	d			v	v	δ			chl, peth i	B4[2], 672
g8	Galipine	Galipoline methyl ether. $C_{20}H_{21}NO_3$.	323.40	pr (al, eth), nd (peth)	115.5				δ	v	v	v	v	chl v peth δ	B21[2], 171
—	Gallamide	see Benzoic acid, 3,4,5-tri-hydroxy-, amide													
—	Gallanilide.......	see Benzoic acid, 3,4,5-tri-hydroxy-, amide, N-phenyl-													
g9	Gallein	4,5-Dihydroxyfluorescein. Pyrogallophthalein. $C_{20}H_{12}O_7$.	364.32	br-red pw (+1.5w), red (anh)	>300 (darkens 180)				i	v	δ	s	i	alk s aa δ chl i	B19[2], 282
—	Gallic acid	see Benzoic acid, 3,4,5-tri-hydroxy-*													
g10	Gallin..........	4,5-Dihydroxyfluorescin. $C_{20}H_{14}O_7$.	365.33	nd (eth), turns red in air	....				δ	v	δ	v	...	aa v	B18, 368
—	Gammexane	see Cyclohexane, 1,2,3,4,5,6-hexachloro-*													
—	Gelseminic acid....	see Coumarin, 7-hydroxy-6-methoxy-													
Ω g12	Gelsemine(d).....	Gelseminin. $C_{20}H_{22}N_2O_2$.	322.41	cr (ace), $[\alpha]_D^{20}$ +15.9 (chl) λ^{al} 252 (3.87), 280 (3.15)	178	....			i	s	s	s^h	s	chl s	B27[2], 720
Ω g13	—,hydrochloride(d)	$C_{20}H_{22}N_2O_2 \cdot HCl$. See g12..	358.87	pr (w) $[\alpha]_D^{20}$ +2.6 (w) λ^{al} 255 (3.8), 288 (3.2)	326				s	δ			...		B27, 720
—	Genistein	see Isoflavone, 4′,5,7-trihydroxy-													
—	Gentianin........	see Xanthone, 1,7-dihydroxy-3-methoxy-													
—	Gentisic acid	see Benzoic acid, 2,5-dihydroxy-													
—	Gentisic aldehyde ..	see Benzaldehyde, 2,5-dihydroxy-													
—	Gentisin........	see Xanthone, 1,7-dihydroxy-3-methoxy-													
—	Gentisyl alcohol ...	see Toluene, α,2,5-trihydroxy-													
—	Geranial	see Citral a													
Ω g14	Geraniol	3,7-Dimethyl-2,6-octadien-1-ol*.	154.26	λ^{al} 215 (3.25), 238 (2.30), 325 sh (−1.99)	< −15	230[760] 121[18]	0.8894[20]	1.4766[20]	i	s	s	s		....	B1[2], 508
Ω g15	—,formate	$C_{11}H_{18}O_2$. See g14.	182.27	....		229d 113–4[15]	0.9086[25]	1.4659[20]	i	v	s	s			B2[2], 33
g16	—,tetrahydro-(dl).	3,7-Dimethyl-1-octanol*. $(CH_3)_2CH(CH_2)_3CH(CH_3)CH_2CH_2OH$	158.29	λ^{al} 237 (1.1)	....	212–3 106[12]	0.8308[20]	1.4367[20]	i	s	s	s	s		B1[2], 460
g17	Geranyl bromide ...	8-Bromo-2,6-dimethyl-2,6-octadiene*. $BrCH_2CH:C(CH_3)CH_2CH_2CH:C(CH_3)_2$	217.16	....		101–2[12] 47–8[0.005]	1.0940[22]	1.5027[20]	d^h	s	s				B1[2], 240
g18	Germanidine	$C_{37}H_{57}NO_{10}$.............	675.87	nd, $[\alpha]_D^{24}$ −30 ±2 (al)	221–2 (vac)	....			i						Am 75, 4925

For explanations, symbols and abbreviations see beginning of table. For structural formulas see end of table.

No.	Name	Synonyms and Formula	Mol. wt.	Color. crystalline form. specific rotation and λ_{max} (log ε)	m.p. °C	b.p. °C	Density	n_D	Solubility						Ref.
									w	al	eth	ace	bz	other solvents	

Germanitrine

No.	Name	Synonyms and Formula	Mol. wt.	Color etc.	m.p.	b.p.	Density	n_D	w	al	eth	ace	bz	other	Ref.
g19	Germanitrine......	Germine-3-angelate-7-acetate-15-[(−)2-methylbutyrate]. $C_{39}H_{59}NO_{11}$. See g22	717.91	nd (aq ace) $[\alpha]_D^{24}$ −61 (Py, c = 1)	228–9 (vac)				i						Am 75, 4925
g20	Germerine.......	Germine-3[(+)-2-methylbutyrate]-15-[(+)2-hydroxy-2-methylbutyrate]. $C_{37}H_{59}NO_{11}$. See g22	693.88	cr (ace), lf (bz, +1w) $[\alpha]_D^{25}$ +15.7 (chl, c = 1.02)	193–5d (cor) (202–5d)				i	s	δ	s	s	MeOH, chl v alk, ac s	Am 72, 4625
g21	Germidine.......	Germine-3-acetate-15-[(−)-2-methylbutyrate]. $C_{34}H_{53}NO_{10}$. See g22	635.81	pl (aq MeOH) $[\alpha]_D^{25}$ +13 (chl), −11 (Py)	(i) 242–4 (ii) 202–3					s^h			s	MeOH s^h ac s	Am 72, 4625
g22	Germine.......	$C_{27}H_{43}NO_8$	509.65	pr or cr (MeOH +2) $[\alpha]_D^{25}$ +5 (95 % al) λ^{al} 276 (0.6)	220								s	MeOH s^h alk, ac s	Am 71, 3260
g23	Germinitrine......	$C_{39}H_{57}NO_{11}$	715.89	pr (dil ace) $[\alpha]_D^{24}$ −36 (Py, c = 1.12)	175 (vac)				i						Am 75, 4925
g24	Germitrine.......	Germine 3[(−)-2-methylbutyrate]-7-acetate-15-[(+)-2-hydroxy-2-methylbutyrate]. $C_{42}H_{67}NO_{13}$. See g22	735.92	cr (dil al) $[\alpha]_D^{25}$ +11 (chl)	197–9				i	d^h		s^h	s	chl, ac s	Am 72, 4625
g25	Gitogenin........	Digine. $C_{27}H_{44}O_4$	432.65	lf (bz), nd (eth) $[\alpha]_D^{20}$ −75 (chl, c = 1) λ^{sulf} 399 (3.09)	271–2				i	s^h	δ			chl s	Am 77, 5661
g26	Gitoxigenin......	Bigitaligenin. Hydroxy-digitoxin. $C_{23}H_{34}O_5$.	390.53	pr (AcOEt), pr (+w, dil al) $[\alpha]_{546}^{20}$ +38.5 (MeOH, c = 0.7) λ^{al} 220 (4.12), 278 sh (2.2)	222 (cor) (234 anh)				i		δ			chl s	E14, 242
g27	Gitoxin........	Anhydrogitalin. Bigitalin. $C_{41}H_{64}O_{14}$.	780.96	pr (chl-MeOH) $[\alpha]_D^{24}$ +5 (Py, c = 1)	285d				δ	δ		i		chl δ	E14, 243
—	Glucitol..........	see Sorbitol													
g28	Gluco-ascorbic acid(D)		206.15	rods (+1w, ace-MeOH-peth) $[\alpha]_D^{20}$ −22 (MeOH, c = 1), −80 (NaOH, c = 0.75)	191 (anh) 140 (hyd)				s	s				MeOH s	J1937, 549
g29	Gluco-α-heptose(D)		210.19	rh pl (w) $[\alpha]_D^{20}$ −19.7 (w) (mut)	193 (210–5)				v	δ					B31, 359
g30	Gluco-methylose(D)	Epifucose. D-Isorhamnose. D-Isorhodeose. Quinovose.	164.16	cr (AcOEt) $[\alpha]_D^{20}$ +73 → +29.7 (w) (mut)	139–40				v	v	i	i		AcOEt δ^h	B31, 63
g31	Gluconal(d)......		146.14	hyg nd $[\alpha]_D^{22}$ −7 (w)	60				δ	δ	i			MeOH δ	B31, 116 B17², 214
Ω g32	Gluconic acid(D)...	Dextronic acid........	196.16	nd (al-eth) $[\alpha]_D^{25}$ −3.49 → +12.95 (w) (mut)	131				s d^h	δ	i		i		B3², 352
g33	—,γ-lactone		178.14	nd (al) $[\alpha]_D$ +67.5 → +6.2 (w) (mut)	134–6				d	v^h					B18, 203
Ω g34	—,δ-lactone		178.14	nd (al) $[\alpha]_D^{23}$ +63.5 → +6.2 (w) (mut)	153	1.610⁻⁵			d^h v	δ	i	i			B18², 190
g35	—,nitrile(d).......	d-Gluconitrile........	177.16	(i) cr (al, aa) $[\alpha]_D^{24}$ +10.0 (w, c = 1.8) (ii) pl (al) $[\alpha]_D^{21}$ + 8.8 (w) λ^w 278 (0.85)	(i) 146–8 (ii) 120.5				v	δ		δ		MeOH, Py s	B3², 351
g36	—,phenyl-hydrazide(D)		286.29	pr (w) $[\alpha]$ +12 (+18) (w)	204–5				s	δ^h	i				B15², 122
g37	—,5-oxo-(D).....		194.14	cr or syr $[\alpha]_D$ −14.5 (w)	125–6				s	s	δ				B3, 883

For explanations, symbols and abbreviations see beginning of table. For structural formulas see end of table.

No.	Name	Synonyms and Formula	Mol. wt.	Color. crystalline form. specific rotation and λ_{max} (log ε)	m.p. °C	b.p. °C	Density	n_D	Solubility						Ref.
									w	al	eth	ace	bz	other solvents	
	Glucosamine														
—	**Glucosamine** . . . . . . **Glucose**(*D*) (equilibrium mixture)	*see* **Glucose, amino-** Dextrose.	180.16	$[\alpha]_D^{20} +52.7$ (w) λ^w 282 (1.2)	146 (150)	. . . .			s	s^h	. . .	δ	. . .	Py, MeOH s^h	**B1,** 879
Ω g38															
g39	—(*D*, α)		180.16	rods, cubes, orh, nd (al) $[\alpha]_D^{20} +112.2 \to +52.7$ (w, c = 4) (mut)	146d	. . . .	1.5620_4^{18}	. . . .	v	δ s^h	. . .	i	. . .	Py s^h MeOH δ AcOEt i	**B31,** 83
g40	—,mono-hydrate(*D*, α)	$C_6H_{12}O_6 \cdot H_2O$. *See* g39	198.18	lf or pl or orh (w) $[\alpha]_D^{20} +102 \to +47.9$ (mut)	86	. . . .	1.54_4^{25}		v	δ	i	. . .	. . .	. . . .	**B31,** 86
g41	—(*D*, β) . . .	$C_6H_{12}O_6$. *See* g39	180.16	nd (al), (w + 1) $[\alpha]_D^{20} +17.5 \to +52.7$ (w, c = 4) (mut)	150	. . . .	1.5620_4^{18}		v	δ s^h	i	. . .	. . .	Py s^h MeOH δ	**B31,** 87
g43	—,penta-acetate(*D*, α)	$C_{16}H_{22}O_{11}$. *See* g39	390.35	pl or nd (al) $[\alpha]_D^{20} +100.9$ (al, c = 0.5) λ^{chl} 292 (1.51)	112–3	sub			δ	δ	s	. . .	. . .	chl, aa s $CS_2 \delta$ lig δ	**B31,** 119
Ω g44	—,—(*D*, β)	$C_{16}H_{22}O_{11}$. *See* g41	390.35	nd (al) $[\alpha]_D +3.9$ (chl, c = 6)	134	sub vac			i	δ	δ	. . .	s	chl ∞ peth δ	**B31,** 120
g45	—,pentamethyl-ether(*D*)	$C_{11}H_{22}O_6$. *See* g38 . . .	250.30	$[\alpha]_D^{20} +147.4$ (w, p = 10)	. . . .	$180^{0.4}$	1.0944_4^{20}	1.4466^{20}	s	s	s	s	. . .	. . . .	**B31,** 180
g46	—,phenyl-hydrazone(*D*, α)	. . . .	270.29	pl (al) $[\alpha]_D^{25} -8.7 \to -52.5$ (w, c = 2) (mut) $\lambda^{50\% al}$ 237 (3.95), 278 (3.4)	160	. . . .			s	δ^h	δ^h	. . .	δ	. . . .	**B31,** 173
g47	—,phenyl-hydrazone(*D*, β)	$C_{12}H_{18}N_2O_5$. *See* g46	270.29	pr, nd (al) $[\alpha]_D^{19} -4.5 \to -53.7$ (w-Py) (mut) $\lambda^{50\% al}$ 235 (3.7), 277 (4.14)	140–1	. . . .			s	δ	i	. . .	δ	. . . .	**B31,** 173
g48	—,phenyl-osazone(*D*)	*D*-Fructosazone. *D*-Glucosazone. *D*-Mannosazone.	358.40	ye nd (dil al) $[\alpha]_D -41$ (MeOH), $[\alpha]_D^{20} -0.62 \to -0.35$ (al-Py, c = 2) λ 256 (4.30), 310 (4.02), 397 (4.31)	210	d213			i	s^h	i	. . .	. . .	Py s^h lig, SO$_2$ i	**B31,** 350
g49	—,—(*DL*)	$C_{18}H_{22}N_4O_4$. *See* g48	358.40	ye nd (al)	. . . .	. . . .			i	δ	i	. . .	i	. . . .	**B31,** 355
g50	—,2-amino-(*D*, β) . .	Chitosamine. *D*-Glucosamine.	179.17	nd (al, MeOH) $[\alpha]_D +28 \to +47.5$ (w, c = 0.4) (mut) λ 530	110d	. . . .			v	δ	i	. . .	i	MeOH δ, s^h chl i	**B31,** 167
Ω g51	—,—,hydro-chloride(*D*, β)	$C_6H_{13}NO_5 \cdot HCl$. *See* g50	215.64	mcl (w or dil al) $[\alpha]_D^{20} +25 \to +72.6$ (w) (mut)	. . . .	. . . .			v	s^h	. . .	. . .	. . .	. . . .	**B31,** 169
—	—,6-benzoyl-(*D*) . . .	*see* **Vacciniin**													
g52	—,2(methyl-amino)-	*N*-Methyl-2-glucosamine. . . .	193.20	gummy $[\alpha]_D^{25} -65$ (MeOH, c = 1) (mut)	130–2d	. . . .			s					. . . .	**B31,** 186
g53	—,thio-	Glucothiose.	196.22	hyg pw (w + 1) $[\alpha]_D^{30} +48.7$ (w, c = 1.4) (mut)	70	. . . .			s					. . . .	**B31,** 474
g54	**Glucoside,** **α-methyl-**(*D*)	Methyl-α-*D*-glucopyranoside	194.18	rh nd (al) $[\alpha]_D^{20} +158.9$ (w) λ^w 280 (−1.4)	168 (166)	$200^{0.2}$	1.46_4^{20}	. . . .	v	δ	i	. . .	. . .	MeOH s	**B31,** 179
g55	—,β-methyl-(*D*) . . .	Methyl-β-*D*-glucopyranoside.	194.19	tetr pr (al) $[\alpha]_D^{20} -34.2$ (w, p = 10)	115–6 (105)	. . . .			v	δ	i	. . .	. . .	MeOH s	**B31,** 182
—	**Glucothiose**	*see* **Glucose, thio-**													
—	**Glucurone**	*see* **Glucuronic acid, γ-lactone.**													

For explanations, symbols and abbreviations see beginning of table. For structural formulas see end of table.

No.	Name	Synonyms and Formula	Mol. wt.	Color, crystalline form, specific rotation and λ_{max} (log ε)	m.p. °C	b.p. °C	Density	n_D	w	al	eth	ace	bz	other solvents	Ref.

Glucuronic acid (D)

No.	Name	Synonyms and Formula	Mol. wt.	Color, crystalline form, specific rotation and λ_{max} (log ε)	m.p. °C	b.p. °C	Density	n_D	w	al	eth	ace	bz	other solvents	Ref.
Ω g56	Glucuronic acid(D)	....	194.14	nd (al, AcOEt) $[\alpha]_D^{20} +11.7 \rightarrow +36.3$ (w, c = 6) (mut)	165	....			s	s	...	...	...		B31, 261
g57	—, γ-lactone	Glucurone...............	176.13	mcl pl (w), cr (al) $[\alpha]_D^{25} +19.8$ (w, c = 5.2)	177–8	....	1.76_4^{30}	....	s	δ	...	...	i	MeOH, aa δ	B31, 264
Ω g58	Glutamic acid(D, −)	α-Aminoglutaric acid. 2-Aminopentanedioic acid.* $HO_2CCH_2CH_2CH(NH_2)CO_2H$	147.13	lf (w), $[\alpha]_D^{25}$ −31.7 (1.7N HCl)	213d		1.538_4^{20}		δ s^h	i	i	i	i	MeOH, aa i	B4², 910
Ω g59	—(DL)	$HO_2CCH_2CH_2CH(NH_2)CO_2H$	147.13	rh (al, w)	199d (225–7)		1.4601_4^{20}		δ s^h	i	δ	...	...	CS_2, lig i	B4², 911
Ω g60	—(L, +)	$HO_2CCH_2CH_2CH(NH_2)CO_2H$	147.13	orh (dil al) $[\alpha]_D^{22} +31.4$ (6N HCl, c = 1) $\lambda^{w,pH=0}$ 206 (2.0)	224–5d (247–9d)	sub 175¹⁰	1.538_4^{20} (vac)		δ s^h	i	δ	i	i	MeOH, aa i	B4², 902
g61	—, hydrochloride(L)	Acidulin. $HO_2CCH_2CH_2CH(NH_2)CO_2H \cdot HCl$	183.59	rh pl (w) $[\alpha]_D^{19} +31.1$ (dil HCl)	214d				s	s	...	...	...		B4³, 1537
Ω g62	—, N-acetyl-(L)	$HO_2CCH_2CH_2CH(NHCOCH_3)CO_2H$	189.17	pr (w), $[\alpha]_D$ −15.3 (w, c = 2) $\lambda^{w,pH=1}$ 215 sh (2.7)	199				s^h	s^h	...	...	...		B4², 911
g63	—, 3-hydroxy-(D)	$HO_2CCH_2CH(OH)CH(NH_2)CO_2H$	163.13	hyg pr (w)	135 (sinters 100)	d			v	i	i	...	i	aa v	B4², 946
Ω g64	—, —(DL)	$HO_2CCH_2CH(OH)CH(NH_2)CO_2H$	163.13	rh pr or nd (w)	198d	d			v^h	i	i	...	i	os i	B4¹, 550
—	—, pteroyl-	see Folic acid													
Ω g65	Glutamine(L, +)	α-Aminoglutaramic acid. $HO_2CCH(NH_2)CH_2CH_2CONH_2$	146.15	nd (w or dil al) $[\alpha]_D^{20} +32.5$ (5% HCl) $[\alpha]_D^{25} +6.5$ (w, c = 2) λ^w 220 sh (2.0)	185–6d (205)				s	i	i	...	i	MeOH i	B4³, 1540
—	α-Glutamylcysteinylglycine	see Glutathione													
—	Glutaraldehyde	see Pentanedial													
—	Glutaric acid	see Pentanedioic acid*													
—	Glutaronitrile	see Pentanedioic acid, dinitrile													
—	Glutaryl chloride	see Pentanedioic acid, dichloride													
Ω g66	Glutathione	α-Glutamylcysteinylglycine. $HO_2CCH(NH_2)CH_2CH_2CONHCH(CH_2SH)CONHCH_2CO_2H$	307.33	rh (w), cr (50% al) $[\alpha]_D^{27}$ −21.3 (w, c = 2) $\lambda^{w,pH=9}$ 236 (3.5)	195	....			v	i	i	...	...	DMF s	B4², 931
g67	Glyceraldehyde(D)	D-2,3-Dihydroxypropanal*. $HOCH_2CH(OH)CHO$	90.08	syr $[\alpha]_D +14$(w) λ^w 294 (0.1)	....				s				i	....	B1¹, 427
Ω g68	—(DL)	$HOCH_2CH(OH)CHO$	90.08	nd or pr (40% MeOH, al-eth) λ^w 294 (0.1)	145 (142)	140–50⁰·⁸	1.455_{18}^{18}		s	δ	δ	...	i	peth, lig i	B1², 888
g68¹	—(L)	$HOCH_2CH(OH)CHO$	90.08	$[\alpha]$ −13.8 (w, c = 11) λ^w 294 (0.1)	....	....			s	δ	δ	...	i	....	B1¹, 427
g69	—, diethyl acetal (D)	3,3-Diethoxy-1,2-propanediol*. $HOCH_2CH(OH)CH(OC_2H_5)_2$	164.20	$[\alpha]_D^{15} +21.2$ (w, c = 18)	....	127–9¹⁷			∞	∞	∞	v		....	B1², 889
—	Glyceric acid	see Propanoic acid, 2,3-dihydroxy-*													
—	Glycerin	see Glycerol													
Ω g70	Glycerol	Glycerin. 1,2,3-Propanetriol*. $HOCH_2CH(OH)CH_2OH$	92.11	syr, rh pl λ^{undil} 270 (−1.2)	20	290d 182²⁰	1.2613_4^{20}	1.4746^{20}	∞	∞	δ	...	i	chl, CCl_4, CS_2, peth i	B1³, 2297
g71	—, borate	$(C_3H_5BO_3)_n$	(99.88)	glass	ca. 150	....			d^h	...	...	...	...	....	B1, 519
g72	—, 1(2-chlorophenyl) ether	....	202.64	nd (bz)	71–2	250¹⁹			s^h	...	v	...	s^h	....	B6¹, 99
g73	—, 1(4-chlorophenyl) ether	....	202.64	nd(eth-peth), lf (bz) λ^{cy} 281 (3.26), 289 (3.17)	76	214–5¹⁹			i	v	v	...	s^h	con sulf s	B6¹, 101

For explanations, symbols and abbreviations see beginning of table. For structural formulas see end of table.

Glycerol

No.	Name	Synonyms and Formula	Mol. wt.	Color. crystalline form. specific rotation and λ_{max} (log ε)	m.p. °C	b.p. °C	Density	n_D	w	al	eth	ace	bz	other solvents	Ref.
g74	—,1,3-diacetate	Diacetin. $HOCH(CH_2O_2CCH_3)_2$	176.17	....	40	280 155–6[15]	1.1779[15]	1.4395[20]	v	v	δ	...	...	CS_2 i	B2[2], 160
g75	—,1,2-dibutanoate (d)	α,β-Dibutyrin. $C_3H_7^nCO_2CH_2CH(CH_2OH)O_2CC_3H_7^n$ (Py, c = 7)	232.28	$[\alpha]_D + 1.7$	....	273.5 167[20]	....	1.4422[20]	i						B2, 273
g76	—,1,3-dido-decanoate	α,γ-Dilaurin. Glycerol-1,3-dilaurate. $HOCH[CH_2O_2C(CH_2)_{10}CH_3]_2$	456.72	pl (al), nd (eth-al) β: 56.5 (st)	α: 49.5 (unst) β: 56.5 (st)	....	....	....		s	s		s	chl, lig s	B2[2], 320
g77	—,1,3-dihexa-decanoate	α,γ-Dipalmitin. Glycerol-1,3-dipalmitate. $HOCH[CH_2O_2C(CH_2)_{14}CH_3]_2$	568.93	cr (al or chl)	72–4 (α: 50 β: 63.5)	....	....	....	δ s^h	s^h	s		...	chl s^h	B2[3], 968
g78	—,1,2-dimethyl ether(dl)	2,3-Dimethoxy-1-propanol*. $CH_3OCH_2CH(OCH_3)CH_2OH$	120.15	....	....	180[760] 100[40]	1.016[25]₄	1.4200[20]	∞	s	s	...	...		B1[3], 2317
g79	—,1,3-dimethyl ether	1,3-Dimethoxy-2-propanol*. $CH_3OCH_2CH(OH)CH_2OCH_3$	120.15	....	....	169[760] 88[40]	1.0085[20]₄	1.4192[20]	∞	v	s	...	...		B1[3], 2318
g80	—,1,3-dinitrate	$O_2NOCH_2CH(OH)CH_2ONO_2$	191.10	pr (w), cr (eth +1w)	26 (hyd)	148[15] 116[0.6]	1.523[20]₄	1.4715[20]₄	s	v	v				B1[2], 591
Ω g81	—,1,3-diocta-decanoate	α,γ-Distearin. Glycerol-1,3-distearate. $HOCH[CH_2O_2C(CH_2)_{16}CH_3]_2$	625.04	nd or pl (eth, chl, lig)	79.1	....	....	....		δ s^h	δ s^h	s^h		os s^h	B2[2], 356
g82	—,1,3-diphenyl ether	$C_6H_5OCH_2CH(OH)CH_2OC_6H_5$	244.29	lf (al)	81–2	224.5[17.5] 175[2]	1.179[24]₄	....	i	v^h	v		v	chl v	B6[2], 152
g83	—,—,2-acetate	$CH_3CO_2CH(CH_2OC_6H_5)_2$	286.33	(dil al)	70–1	190[160]	....	....	i	v	v		v	chl v	B6, 149
g84	—,1,3-dipropanoate	α,γ-Dipropioin. $HOCH(CH_2O_2CC_2H_5)_2$	204.23	....	....	170–3[10]	....	....		s					B2[1], 107
g85	—,1-hexadecyl ether	Chimyl alcohol. 3-Hexadecyl-oxy-1,3-propanediol. $HOCH(CH_2OH)CH_2O(CH_2)_{15}CH_3$	316.53	lf (hx) $[\alpha]_D^{20} + 3$ (chl)	64	120[0.005]	....	....					s	chl, peth s	H27, 674
g86	—,1(2-methoxy-phenyl) ether	Guaiacol α-glyceryl ether. Guaiamar. $HOCH(CH_2OH)CH_2OC_6H_4OCH_3$	198.22	rh pr (eth, eth-peth)	78.5–9	215[19] 126–8[0.2]	....	....	s v^h	v	v	...	s	chl s peth i	B6[1], 382
g87	—,1-methyl ether	3-Methoxy-1,2-propanediol*. $HOCH_2CH(OH)CH_2OCH_3$	106.12	hyg liq	....	220[760] (198–200) 110–2[13]	1.1830[20]₄	1.442[25]	v	v	s	v	...	os s	B1[3], 2317
g88	—,2-methyl ether	2-Methoxy-1,3-propanediol*. $HOCH_2CH(OCH_3)CH_2OH$	106.12	hyg liq	....	232[760] 119–20[9]	1.124[25]₄	1.4505[17]	v	v	s	v	...	os v	B1[3], 2317
Ω g89	—,1-mono-acetate(dl)	α-Monoacetin. $HOCH_2CH(OH)CH_2O_2CCH_3$	134.13	....	....	158[165] 129–31[3]	1.2060[20]₄	1.4157[20]	s	s	δ	...	i		B2[2], 159
g90	—,1-mono-butanoate(dl)	α-Monobutyrin. $HOCH_2CH(OH)CH_2O_2CC_2H_5CH_3$	162.19	....	....	269–71[18] 163[16]	1.129[18]	1.4531[20]	v	s					B2[2], 249
g91	—,1-monodo-decanoate(dl)	α-Monolaurin. $HOCH_2CH(OH)CH_2O_2C(CH_2)_{10}CH_3$	274.41	lf (CCl_4 or peth)	α:44 (unst) β':59.5 (unst) β:63 (st)	186[1]	0.9248[97]	1.4350[86]	...	δ s^h	v	v	s	chl v	B2[2], 320
g92	—,—(l)	$HOCH_2CH(OH)CH_2O_2C(CH_2)_{10}CH_3$	274.41	cr (eth or peth) $[\alpha]_D - 4.9$ (Py)	54–5	....	....	....		δ s^h	v	v	s	chl v	B2[3], 890
g93	—,monohexa-decanoate(dl)	α-Monopalmitin. $HOCH_2CH(OH)CH_2O_2C(CH_2)_{14}CH_3$	330.51	pl or lf (eth, lig)	α:66.5 (unst) β':74.6 (unst) β:77 (st)	....	....	....	i	v	δ				B2[2], 338
g94	—,—(l)	$HOCH_2CH(OH)CH_2O_2C(CH_2)_{14}CH_3$	330.51	cr (eth or peth) $[\alpha]_D - 4.37$ (Py)	71–2	....	....	....							B2[3], 966
g95	—,1-mono(2-hydroxybenzoate)	Glycosal. α-Glyceryl salicylate.	212.21	nd (eth)	76	....	....	....	δ v^h	v	δ	...	v^h	chl, peth δ	B10[2], 53
g96	—,1-mono(12-hydroxy-9-octadecenoate)	Glycerol-1-monoricinoleate. α-Monoricinolein. $HOCH_2CH(OH)CH_2O_2C(CH_2)_7CH:CHCH_2CH(OH)(CH_2)_5CH_3$	372.55	ye	....	....	1.028[20]₄	....		s	s	s	s	chl, AcOEt s lig, MeOH, CS_2 δ	B3[1], 138
g97	—,1-mononitrate	$HOCH_2CH(OH)CH_2ONO_2$	137.09	pr (w, al or eth)	61	155–60 102[1]	1.4164[29]₄	1.4698[20]	v	v	δ				B1[2], 591
g98	—,2-mononitrate	$HOCH_2CH(ONO_2)CH_2OH$	137.09	lf (w)	54	155–60	1.402[20]	....	s	s	s				B1[2], 591
g99	—,1-mono(9,12-octadecadienoate)	Glycerol-α-monolinoleate. α-Monolinolein. $HOCH_2CH(OH)CH_2O_2C(CH_2)_7CH:CHCH_2CH:CH(CH_2)_4CH_3$	354.54	cr (bz)	14–5	....	....	1.4758[20]		δ	v		v	chl v lig, MeOH, CS_2 δ	B2[1], 213
Ω g100	—,1-monoocta-decanoate(dl)	α-Monostearin. $HOCH_2CH(OH)CH_2O_2C(CH_2)_{16}CH_3$	358.57	pl (MeOH)	α:74 (unst) β':79 (unst) β:81 (st)	....	0.9841[20]₄	1.4400[86]	i	δ s^h	δ v^h	...	...	lig s peth δ	B2[2], 354
g101	—,—(l)	$HOCH_2CH(OH)CH_2O_2C(CH_2)_{16}CH_3$	358.57	cr (eth or peth) $[\alpha]_D - 3.58$ (Py)	76–7	....	....	....							B2[3], 1024

For explanations, symbols and abbreviations see beginning of table. For structural formulas see end of table.

Glycerol

No.	Name	Synonyms and Formula	Mol. wt.	Color, crystalline form, specific rotation and λ_{max} (log ε)	m.p. °C	b.p. °C	Density	n_D	w	al	eth	ace	bz	other solvents	Ref.
g102	—,1-mono(9-octa-decenoate)	Glycerol 1-monooleate. α-Monoolein. $HOCH_2CH(OH)CH_2O_2C(CH_2)_7CH:CH(CH_2)_7CH_3$	356.55	pl (al)	α:25 (unst) β':32 (unst) β:35.5 (st)	238–40[3]	0.9420[20]	1.4626[40]	i	s	s	. . .	. . .	chl s	B2[2], 439
—	—,1-monooleate	see **Glycerol**, 1-mono(9-octadecenoate)													
—	—,1-monoricin-oleate	see **Glycerol**, 1-mono(12-hydroxy-9-octadecenoate)													
Ω g103	—,1-octadecyl ether (d)	Batyl alcohol. 3-Octadecyl-oxy-1,2-propanediol*. $HOCH_2CH(OH)CH_2O(CH_2)_{17}CH_3$	344.59	pl (bz, ace) $[\alpha]_D^{20}$ +1.14 (chl, c = 6.6)	70–1	215–20[2]			i	s[h]	s	s[h]	s[h]	. . .	B1[2], 590
g104	—,1-phenyl ether	Antodyne. $HOCH_2CH(OH)CH_2OC_6H_5$	168.20	nd (eth, peth or bz-lig)	67–8 (62–4)	200[22] 145–8[0.6]	1.2225[20]		v	v	s[h]	. . .	v	peth δ con sulf s	B6[2], 152
g105	,1(2-tolyl)ether	. . . .	182.22	nd (bz-peth)	70–1d (cor)	. . . .			δ	s	δ	. . .	. . .	. . . .	B6, 354
g106	—,triacetate	Triacetin. $CH_3CO_2CH(CH_2O_2CCH_3)_2$	218.21	cr (al)	4.1	258–60[760] 130.5[7]	1.1596[20]	1.4301[20]	δ	∞	∞	v	∞	chl ∞ lig, CS_2 δ	B2[2], 160
g107	—,tribenzoate	Tribenzoin. $C_6H_5CO_2CH(CH_2O_2CC_6H_5)_2$	404.43	nd (MeOH)	76	. . . .	1.228[12]		δ	s[h]	v	v	v	chl v	B9[2], 122
Ω g108	—,tributanoate	Tributyrin. $CH_3CH_2CH_2CO_2CH(CH_2O_2CCH_2CH_2CH_3)_2$	302.37	. . . .	−75	305–10 (287–8) 190[15]	1.0350[20]	1.4359[20]	i	s	v	s	s	. . . .	B2[2], 249
g109	—,tridodecanoate	Glycerol trilaurate. Trilaurin. $CH_3(CH_2)_{10}CO_7CH[CH_2O_2C(CH_2)_{10}CH_3]_2$	639.03	nd (al)	α:35.6 (unst) β:32.9 (unst) β:46.4 (st)	. . . . . .	0.8986[55]	1.4404[60]	i	s	s	v	v	chl, peth s	B2[2], 320
—	—,trielaidate	see **Glycerol**, tri(trans-9-octadecenoate)													
Ω g110	—,trihexadecanoate	Glycerol tripalmitate. Tripalmitin. $CH_3(CH_2)_{14}CO_2CH[CH_2O_2C(CH_2)_{14}CH_3]_2$	807.35	nd (eth)	α:44.7 (unst) β:56.6 (unst) β:66.4 (st)	310–20	0.8752[70]	1.4381[80]	i	δ	v	. . .	s v[h]	chl s	B2[2], 340
g111	—,trihexanoate	Glycerol tricaproate. Tricaproin. $CH_3(CH_2)_4CO_2CH[CH_2O_2C(CH_2)_4CH_3]_2$	386.54	. . . .	−60	>200	0.9867[20]	1.4427[20]	i	∞	∞	v	∞	peth, chl ∞	B2[2], 285
g112	—,tri(3-methyl-butanoate)	Glycerol isovalerate. Triisovalerin. $(CH_3)_2CHCH_2CO_2CH[CH_2O_2CCH_2CH(CH_3)_2]_2$	344.45	. . . .	. . . .	330–5[763] 194[15]	0.9984[20]	1.4354[20]	. . .	s	s	v	s	. . . .	B2[2], 277
g113	—,trimethyl ether	1,2,3-Trimethoxypropane*. $CH_3OCH_2CH(OCH_3)CH_2OCH_3$	134.18	. . . .	. . . .	148	0.9460[15]	1.4055[15]	∞	s	s	v	s	sulf v	B1[3], 2318
g114	—,trinitrate	Nitroglycerin. Trinitrin. $O_2NOCH_2CH(ONO_2)CH_2ONO_2$	227.09	pa ye tcl or rh	13 (st) 2 (unst)	256 exp 125[2]	1.5931[20]	1.4786[12]	δ	s	∞	v	s	MeOH s CS_2, lig, peth δ chl v	B1[3], 2328
g115	—,trioctadecanoate	Glycerol tristearate. Tristearin. $CH_3(CH_2)_{16}CO_2CH[CH_2O_2C(CH_2)_{16}CH_3]_2$	891.51	cr (eth, peth)	α:55 β':64.5 β:73	. . . . . .	0.8559[90]	1.4399[80]	i	i	. . .	s	δ s[h] s[h]	CCl_4 δ, s[h] chl, CS_2 s AcOEt i lig, peth i, s[h]	B2[3], 1035
g116	—,tri(cis-9-octa-decenoate)	Glycerol trioleate. Triolein. $CH_3(CH_2)_7CH:CH(CH_2)_7CO_2CH[CH_2O_2C(CH_2)_7CH:CH(CH_2)_7CH_3]_2$	885.47	polymorphic	235–40[18] α: −32 (unst) β': −12 (unst) β: −5.5 (st)		0.8988[40]	1.4621[40]	i	δ	v	. . .	. . .	chl, peth s	B2[2], 440
Ω g117	—,tri(trans-9-octadecenoate)	Glycerol trielaidate. Trielaidin. $CH_3(CH_2)_7CH:CH(CH_2)_7CO_2CH[CH_2O_2C(CH_2)_7CH:CH(CH_2)_7CH_3]_2$	885.47	. . . .	α:16.6 β:42.8	. . . . . .	. . . . . .	i	δ	v	. . .	s	chl s	B2, 470
g118	—,trioctanoate	Glycerol tricaprylate. Tricaprylin. $CH_3(CH_2)_6CO_2CH[CH_2O_2C(CH_2)_6CH_3]_2$	470.70	. . . .	9.8–10.1 (st) −21 (metast)	233.1	0.9540[20]	1.4482[20]	i	∞	v	. . .	v	peth, lig, chl v	B2[2], 303
g119	—,tripropanoate	Tripropionin. Tripropin. $CH_3CH_2CO_2CH(CH_2O_2CCH_2CH_3)_2$	260.29	. . . .	. . . .	175–6[20] 130–2[3]	1.100[20 over 18]	1.4318[19]	i	s	v	. . .	. . .	chl s	B2[2], 222
Ω g120	—,tritetradecanoate	Glycerol trimyristate. trimyristin. $CH_3(CH_2)_{12}CO_2CH[CH_2O_2C(CH_2)_{12}CH_3]_2$	723.19	polymorphic (al-eth)	α:32 (unst) β:44 (unst) β':56.5 (st)	311	0.8848[40]	1.4428[60]	i	δ	s	s	s	chl s lig, CS_2 δ	B2[2], 328
—	—,1,2-dithio-	see **1-Propanol, 2,3-dimercapto-**													

For explanations, symbols and abbreviations see beginning of table. For structural formulas see end of table.

Glycerophosphoric acid

No.	Name	Synonyms and Formula	Mol. wt.	Color, crystalline form, specific rotation and λ_{max} (log ε)	m.p. °C	b.p. °C	Density	n_D	w	al	eth	ace	bz	other solvents	Ref.
g121	Glycerophosphoric acid(L)	$HOCH_2CH(OH)CH_2OPO(OH)_2$	172.08	syr $[\alpha]_D -1.45$ (Ba salt in 2N HCl, c = 10.3)	....				s	s	i	...	i	MeOH s	B1[3], 2335
—	Glycidic acid......	see Propanoic acid, 2,3-epoxy-*													
g122	Glycidol(d)......	2,3-Epoxy-1-propanol*. Glycide. 3-Hydroxy-propylene oxide.	74.08	$[\alpha]_D +15$ (undil)	56.5[11]		1.117_4^{20}	1.4293^{16}	s	s	s	s	s	chl s	B17[1], 50
g123	—(l)......	$C_3H_6O_2$. See g122	74.08	$[\alpha]_D^{18} -8.6$ (undil)	56–6.5[11]		1.1050^{18}	1.4293^{16}	s	s	s	s	s	chl s	B17[1], 50
Ω g124	Glycine	Aminoacetic acid. Glycocoll. $H_2NCH_2CO_2H$	75.07	mcl or trg pr (dil al), $\lambda^{al.pH=2}$ 285 (3.76)	262d (br at 228)		0.828^{17} 1.1607		v	i	i	δ	...	Py δ	B4[1], 462
g125	—,amide......	Glycinamide. $H_2NCH_2CONH_2$	74.08	hyg nd (chl) $\lambda^{w.pH=6}$ 210 sh (2.1)	67–8				v	v	δ	s	δ	MeOH v AcOEt s chl s[h]	B4[2], 783
g125[1]	—,—,N'(4-ethoxyphenyl)-	Glycine-p-phenetidide. Phenocoll.	194.24	nd (+1w)	100.5 (anh) 95 (hyd)				δ	s	s				B13[2], 268
g126	—,—,hydrochloride	$H_2NCH_2CONH_2 . HCl$.....	110.54	nd (al)	203–4 (189)				v	δ					B4[1], 468
—	—,anhydride......	see 2,5-Piperazinedione													
g127	—,ethyl ester......	Ethyl glycinate. $H_2NCH_2CO_2C_2H_5$	103.12	$\lambda^{w.pH=9}$ 218 sh (1.9)		148–9[750] 57.6[18]	1.0275_4^{10}	1.4242^{20}	∞	∞	∞	∞	∞	lig v	B4[2], 780
Ω g128	—,—,hydrochloride	$H_2NCH_2CO_2C_2H_5 . HCl$....	139.58	nd (al)	144	sub			v	v					B4[2], 781
g129	—,hydrochloride ..	$H_2NCH_2CO_2H . HCl$.......	111.53	hyg rh nd (w)	200–1 (187)				v	δ					B4, 340
g130	—,methyl ester	Methyl glycinate. $H_2NCH_2CO_2CH_3$	89.10	....	130d 45[20]					s					B4[2], 780
g131	—,nitrile	Aminoacetonitrile. H_2NCH_2CN	56.07	....	58[15] δd					s				ac v	B4[3], 1120
g132	—,N(p-acetamidophenyl)-		208.22	....	241–2				s						Am 39, 1457
Ω g133	—,N-acetyl-	Acetamidoacetic acid. Aceturic acid. $CH_3CONHCH_2CO_2H$	117.11	lo nd (w, MeOH) $\lambda^{w.pH=1}$ 215 sh (2.4)	206				δ	s	i	δ	i	chl, aa δ	B4[2], 789
g134	—,N-acetyl-N-phenyl-	N-Phenylaceturic acid. $CH_3CON(C_6H_5)CH_2CO_2H$	193.21	lf (w)	194				δ	s	δ	...	δ	AcOEt s chl, lig δ	B12, 476
g136	—,N(4-aminophenyl)-, monohydrate	$C_8H_{10}N_2O_2 . H_2O$. See g167 ..	184.20	pl (dil aa)	222–3d				s[h]						B13[1], 34
g137	—,N(2-arsonophenyl)-, amide		274.11	sc (w)	198–9d				v[h]	δ[h]	...	...	...	MeOH δ[h]	B16[2], 487
g138	—,N(3-arsonophenyl)-, amide		274.11	nd (w)	175–7d				v[h]	v	...	i	...	aa v	B16[2], 489
—	—,N-benzoyl-	see Hippuric acid													
g142	—,N-benzyl-		165.19	nd (w)	198–9				δ s[h]				i	alk s	B12[2], 567
Ω g143	—,—,ethyl ester	$C_{11}H_{15}NO_2$. See g142 .	193.25			175–9[50] 165[16]		1.5041^{20}	...	v	v		v		B12[2], 567
Ω g144	—,N,N-bis(2-hydroxyethyl)-	$(HOCH_2CH_2)_2NCH_2CO_2H$.	163.18	nd (al)	193–5d				v	i s[h]					B4[2], 787
g145	—,N-bromoacetyl-N-phenyl-	$BrCH_2CON(C_6H_5)CH_2CO_2H$	272.11	pl (w)	153d				δ	s			s		B12, 477
Ω g148	—,N(2-carboxyphenyl)-	N-Carboxymethylanthranilic acid. Anthranilidoacetic acid. $C_9H_9NO_4$. See g167	195.18	nd (MeOH)	218–20				δ	s	s	...	i	chl i aa s	B14[2], 225
g149	—,N-chloroacetyl-N-phenyl-	$ClCH_2CON(C_6H_5)CH_2CO_2H$	227.65	pl or pr (bz)	132–3				δ	s			s		B12, 476
g150	—,—,methyl ester .	$ClCH_2CON(C_6H_5)CH_2CO_2CH_3$	241.68	pr (lig)	59–60				δ	v	v		v	chl v	B12, 477
—	—,cholyl-.........	see Glycocholic acid													
g151	—,N,N-dicarbethoxy-, ethyl ester	$(C_2H_5O_2C)_2NCH_2CO_2C_2H_5$	247.25	pr (peth)	36.5	152–3[10]			δ	v	v		v	AcOEt v peth δ	B4, 365
g153	—,—,nitrile.......	Diethylaminoacetonitrile. $(C_2H_5)_2NCH_2CN$	112.18			170 70[24]		1.4260^{20}	s	s	s				B4[2], 787
g154	—,N,N-dimethyl- ..	Dimethylaminoacetic acid. $(CH_3)_2NCH_2CO_2H$	103.12	hyg nd (PrOH)	185–6 (157–60)				v	s	s	s[h]	...	MeOH v	B4[2], 785
g155	—,—,nitrile.......	Dimethylaminoacetonitrile. $(CH_3)_2NCH_2CN$	84.13		137–8 42[21]		0.8650_0^{20}	1.4095^{20}	s	s	s			HCl s	B4, 346
g156	—,N-ethyl-	Ethylaminoacetic acid. $C_2H_5NHCH_2CO_2H$	103.12	pl (al)	181–2d				s	s					B4[2], 787
g157	—,—,nitrile.......	Ethylaminoacetonitrile. $C_2H_5NHCH_2CN$	84.13		166–7[760] 81–3[29]				s	s				dil HCl v	B4[2], 787
g158	—,N-formyl-N-phenyl-	$C_6H_5N(CHO)CH_2CO_2H$ ...	179.18	nd (w)	125				s	s					B12, 476

For explanations, symbols and abbreviations see beginning of table. For structural formulas see end of table.

No.	Name	Synonyms and Formula	Mol. wt.	Color, crystalline form, specific rotation and λ_{max} (log ε)	m.p. °C	b.p. °C	Density	n_D	w	al	eth	ace	bz	other solvents	Ref.
	Glycine														
—	—,$N(N$-γ-gluta-mylcysteinyl)-,	*see* **Glutathione**													
—	—,$N(N$-glycyl-glycine)-	*see* **Triglycine**													
—	—,N-guanyl-	*see* **Glycocyamine**													
Ω g159	—,N(4-hydroxy-phenyl)-	$C_8H_9NO_3$. See g167	167.17	pl (w)	245–7d (200d)				δ s^h	δ	i	δ	δ	AcOEt, chl, alk s	B13[2], 259
g160	—,N(4-hydroxy-phenylacetyl)-		209.20	pl (w)	153–5				s^h	s	δ	...	i	AcOEt s	B10[1], 83
Ω g161	—,N-leucyl-(DL)	DL-Leucylglycine. $(CH_3)_2CHCH_2CH(NH_2)CONHCH_2CO_2H$	188.23	cr (w) λ^w 300 (0.8) (<220)	243d				s	δ	δ	i	i	chl i	B4[2], 872
Ω g162	—,—(L)	$(CH_3)_2CHCH_2CH(NH_2)CONHCH_2CO_2H$	188.23	lf or nd (w-al) $[\alpha]_D^{20}$ +85.8 (w, c = 2.4)	248d				s	δ	δ	i	i	chl i	B4, 444
g163	—,N,N'-methyl-enedi-	$CH_2(NHCH_2CO_2H)_2$	162.15	pl	199d					s				HCl s	B4[1], 473
g164	—,N(2-naphthyl)-	$C_{10}H_7^\beta NHCH_2CO_2H$	201.23	(w)	134–5				v^h	v	v			aa v	B12, 1298
Ω g165	—,N(2-nitro-phenyl)-	....	196.17	dk red pr (al)	192–3d				δ	v^h	δ				B12, 695
g167	—,N-phenyl-	Anilinoacetic acid.	151.17	....	127–8				s	s	δ				B12, 468
g168	—,—,amide	$C_6H_5NHCH_2CONH_2$	150.18	nd (w), lf (al)	141 (136)				v^h	v	δ	v			B12[2], 249
g169	—,—,ethyl ester	$C_6H_5NHCH_2CO_2C_2H_5$	179.22	lf (dil al)	58	273–4 163[18]			δ^h	s	s				C48, 719
g170	—,—,methyl ester	$C_6H_5NHCH_2CO_2CH_3$	165.19	nd (al)	48				i	s	s				C49, 1337
Ω g171	—,—,nitrile	Anilinoacetonitrile. $C_6H_5NHCH_2CN$	132.18	pl (lig-eth)	48				δ	δ	δ		s	lig δ	B12, 472
Ω g173	—,N-phthaloyl-	Phthalimide-N-acetic acid.	205.17	nd or pr (w or al)	193 (193–6)				δ v^h	s^h	s^h			peth, lig, chl i	B21, 481
g174	—,—,chloride	$C_{10}H_6ClNO_3$. See g173	223.62	nd (lig)	84–5	distb vac			d	v			v		B21[2], 358
g175	—,—,ethyl ester	$C_{12}H_{11}NO_4$. See g173	233.23	nd (w, al or eth)	112–3 (104–5)	300			δ	v^h	v		v	chl v lig δ	B21[2], 357
g176	—,$N(N$-phthaloyl-glycyl)-	Phthaloyldiglycine.	262.22	nd (w)	232				δ	s	δ	i		chl i aa v	B21[2], 358
g177	—,—,ethyl ester	$C_{14}H_{14}N_2O_5$. See g176	290.28	nd (al)	193.5–4.5				i	v^h	v		v	chl v	B21[2], 358
g178	—,N-succinyl-, ethyl ester	Ethyl succinimide-N-acetate.	185.18	nd (eth)	67	198[32]			v	δ	v				B21[2], 305
g179	**Glycocholic acid**	Cholylglycine. $C_{26}H_{43}NO_6$.	465.64	nd (w), $[\alpha]_D^{23}$ +32.3 (al, c = 1) $\lambda^{65\% \text{ sulf}}$ 318 (4.18)	165–8 (anh) 154–5d (+1.5w) 132–4 (+6w)				δ	v	δ				E14, 194
—	**Glycocoll**	*see* **Glycine**													
Ω g180	**Glycocyamine**	Guanidoacetic acid. N-Guanylglycine. $NH{:}C(NH_2)NHCH_2CO_2H$	117.11	pl or nd (w)	>300 (250–66)				δ s^h	δ	δ				B4[2], 793
Ω g181	**Glycogen**	Animal starch. $(C_6H_{10}O_5)_n$	(162.14)$_n$	wh pw, $[\alpha]_D^{25}$ +196.5 (w) λ^w 420					v	i s^h	i				C25, 4940
—	**Glycol**	*see* **1,2-Ethanediol**													
—	**Glycolaldehyde**	*see* **Acetaldehyde, hydroxy-**													
—	**Glycolic acid**	*see* **Acetic acid, hydroxy-**													
g182	**Glycolide**	2,5-p-Dioxanedione.	116.07	lf (al-chl or al)	86–7 (83)				s^h	δ s^h	δ	v		chl s s^h	B19[2], 175
Ω g183	**Glycoluril**	Acetylenediurea. Glyoxaldiurene.	142.12	nd or pr (w)	300d				δ^h	i	s			HCl, NH_4OH s aa i	B26[2], 260
—	**Glycolylurea**	*see* **Hydantoin**													
—	**Glycylglycine**	*see* **Diglycine**													
g184	**18α-Glycyr-rhetinic acid**	Glycyrrhetic acid. $C_{30}H_{46}O_4$.	470.70	α: pl (dil al) β: nd (al-peth) pl (chl-MeOH) α: $[\alpha]_D^{20}$ +140 (al) β: $[\alpha]_D^{20}$ +145.5 (diox) λ^{al} 242 (4.09)	α: 283 β: 296 (331–5)					s				chl, diox, aa s peth i	E14, 561
g185	—,glycoside	Glycyrrhizic acid. Glycyrrhizin. $C_{42}H_{62}O_{16}$. See g184	822.96	pl or pr (aa)	220d				v^h	i	δ				H4, 100

For explanations, symbols and abbreviations see beginning of table. For structural formulas see end of table.

Glyoxal

No.	Name	Synonyms and Formula	Mol. wt.	Color, crystalline form, specific rotation and λ_{max} (log ε)	m.p. °C	b.p. °C	Density	n_D	w	al	eth	ace	bz	other solvents	Ref.
g186	Glyoxal	Ethanedial*. Biformyl. OCHCHO	58.04	ye pr	15	50.4	1.14^{20} (1.26^{20})	1.3826^{20}	v	s	s	...	...	...	B1[3], 3076
Ω g187	—,dioxime	Diisonitrosoethane. Glyoxime. HON:CHCH:NOH	88.07	rh pl (w) λ^{al} 233 (4.23)	178d (181)	sub	....	....	v^h	v^h	v^h	...	...	...	B1[2], 818
g188	—,phenyl-	Benzoylformaldehyde. C₆H₅COCHO	134.14	nd (+w)	91 (hyd) 142^{125} (anh) 95–7^{25}		....	....	s d^h	s	s	s	s	chl s	B7[1], 360
—	Glyoxaline.......	see Imidazole													
—	Glyoxime........	see Glyoxal, dioxime													
—	Glyoxylic acid....	see Acetic acid, oxo-													
—	Gnoscopine	see Narcotine(dl)													
Ω g189	Gramine	3(Dimethylaminomethyl)-indole. Donaxine.	174.25	lf (eth), nd (ace) λ^{al} 280 (3.80), 289 (3.68)	138–9				i	s	s	...	...	chl s peth i	C30, 4502
g190	Griseofulvin......	Fulvicin. C₁₇H₁₇ClO₆.	352.78	oct or rh (bz) $[\alpha]_D^{17} +376$ (chl sat sol) $[\alpha]_D^{21} +337$ (ace) λ^{al} 291 (4.37), 325 (3.77)	220				i	δ	δ	δ	δ s^h	AcOEt, chl, aa δ	J1952, 3949
—	Guaethol	see Phenol, 2-ethoxy-*													
—	Guaiacol	see Phenol, 2-methoxy-*													
—	Guaiacol, 4-propenyl-	see Benzene, 1-hydroxy-3-methoxy-4-propenyl-													
—	Guaiazulene	see Azulene, 1,4-dimethyl-7-isopropyl-													
—	Guaiene	see Naphthalene, 2,3-dimethyl-*													
g191	Guaiol	Champacol. 3,8-Dimethyl-5[α-hydroxypropyl]-Δ⁹-octahydroazulene. C₁₅H₂₆O.	222.38	trg pr (al) $[\alpha]_D^{20} -30$ (al, c = 4)	91	288^{760} δd 165^{17}	0.9074^{100}_{20}	1.4716^{100}	i	s	s	...	...	...	E12A, 431
g192	Guanidine	Aminomethanamidine. Carbamamidine. HN:C(NH₂)₂	59.07	cr λ^w 209	ca. 50				v	v	...	...	...	...	B3[2], 69
Ω g193	—,acetate	HN:C(NH₂)₂.CH₃CO₂H ...	119.13	nd (al-eth)	229–30				v	v	i	...	...	...	B3[2], 69
Ω g194	—,carbonate......	2[HN:C(NH₂)₂].H₂CO₃	180.17	oct tetr pr (w)	198		1.24^4		v	i	...	...	...	...	B3[2], 72
Ω g195	—,hydrochloride ..	HN:C(NH₂)₂.HCl	95.53	rh bipym (al) λ^w 262 (1.25)	178–85		1.354^{20}_4		v	s	...	...	...	...	B3[2], 71
Ω g196	—,nitrate........	HN:C(NH₂)₂.HNO₃	122.08	lf (w)	217	d			v	s v^h	...	δ	...	...	B3[2], 72
g197	—,picrate	HN:C(NH₂)₂. C₆H₃N₃O₇.	288.19	og-ye pl or nd (w)	333d				$δ^h$	δ	δ	...	...	...	B6[2], 265
Ω g198	—,thiocyanate	HN:C(NH₂)₂.HCNS.	118.16	lf	118				v	...	...	...	...	...	B3[2], 121
g199	—,1-amino-*	Guanylhydrazine. HN:C(NH₂)NHNH₂	74.09	cr	d				s	s	s	...	...	...	B3[2], 95
Ω g200	—,1-cyano-*	Dicyanodiamide. Param. NH:C(NH₂)NHCN	84.08	rh lf or pl (al)	211–2	d	1.404^{14}		s	s	s	s	i	AcOEt δ chl, CS₂, CCl₄ i	B3[2], 75
Ω g201	—,1,3-diphenyl-* ..	Melaniline. HN:C(NHC₆H₅)₂	211.27	mcl nd (al or to) λ^{al} 251 (4.4), 286 sh (1.1)	150	d 170	1.13^{20}_4		δ	s	v	...	...	CCl₄, chl s to s^h	B12[2], 216
Ω g202	—,1,3-di(2-tolyl)-		239.32	cr (dil al) λ^{chl} 252 (4.08)	179		1.10^{20}_4		$δ^h$	δ s^h	v	...	...	chl s	B12, 803
g203	—,1-methyl-, sulfate*	[HN:C(NH₂)NHCH₃]₂. H₂SO₄	244.27	(w)	238–40				v	δ	i	...	i	os i	B4[2], 570
Ω g204	—,1-nitro-*	HN:C(NH₂)NHNO₂	104.07	nd or pr (w) λ^w 264 (4.16)	239d (slow htng), 246–7 (rapid htng)				δ s^h	δ	i	...	...	alk v	B3[2], 100
g205	—,1-phenyl-3(2-tolyl)-		225.30	nd (aa)	123–5 (130)				s	v	v	...	v	chl v	B12[2], 445
g206	—,1,1,3,3-tetra-phenyl-*	HN:C[N(C₆H₅)₂]₂	363.47	rh (lig)	130–1				i	v	v	...	v		B12, 430
g207	—,1,1,3-tri-phenyl-*	HN:C(NHC₆H₅)N(C₆H₅)₂	287.37	ta (dil al)	134				δ	v	v	...	δ		B12[2], 242
Ω g208	—,1,2,3-tri-phenyl-*	C₆H₅N:C(NHC₆H₅)₂	287.37	nd or pr (al)	146–7	d	1.163^{20}_4		$δ^h$	s	...	...	...		B12[2], 246
g209	—,—.hydrochloride monohydrate	C₆H₅N:C(NHC₆H₅)₂. HCl. H₂O	341.85	pr (w + 1)	241–2d				δ	...	i	...	i	HCl δ	B12[2], 246
g210	—,1-ureido-*	1-Carbamoylguanidine. Guanylurea. Dicyandiamidine. HN:C(NH₂)NHCONH₂	102.10	pr (al) $\lambda^{0.1 N NaOH}$ 218 (4.29)	105	160d			s^h	δ	i	...	i	Py s chl, CS₂ i	B3, 89

For explanations, symbols and abbreviations see beginning of table. For structural formulas see end of table.

No.	Name	Synonyms and Formula	Mol. wt.	Color, crystalline form, specific rotation and λ_{max} (log ε)	m.p. °C	b.p. °C	Density	n_D	Solubility						Ref.
									w	al	eth	ace	bz	other solvents	
	Guanine														
Ω g211	**Guanine**	2-Aminohypoxanthine. 6-hydroxy-2-aminopurine.	151.13	nd or pl (NH₄OH) $\lambda^{w, pH=11}$ 245 (3.81), 273 (3.85)	360d	sub	. . . .		i	δ	δ	. . .	. . .	NH₄OH, alk, ac s aa i	**B26²**, 262
Ω g212	**Guanosine**	9-D-Ribosidoguanine. Vernine. C₁₀H₁₃N₅O₅.	283.25	nd (w), $[\alpha]_D^{20}$ −60.5 (0.1N NaOH, p = 3) λ^w 254 (4.13)	239d (250d)		. . . .		δ sʰ	i	i	. . .	. . .	aa vʰ	**B31**, 28
	Guanosine phosphoric acid	*see* **Guanylic acid**													
g213	**Guanylic acid**	Guanosine 3'-phosphate. Guanosine phosphoric acid. GMP. C₁₀H₁₄N₅O₈P.	363.23	nd or pr (w + 2) $[\alpha]_D^{20}$ −7.5 (w, p = 1) $[\alpha]_D^{25}$ −65 (5 % NaOH, c = 2) λ^w 260 (4.07)	208d (anh) (218d)		. . . .		s vʰ	. . .	. . .	. . .	. . .		**B31**, 29
—	**Gulitol**	*see* **Sorbitol**													
g214	**Gulonic acid,** γ-lactone(*d*)		178.14	pr ta (w) $[\alpha]_D^{20}$ +55.1(w)	180–1		. . . .		ʒ	δ	i	., .	i		**B18²**, 193
g215	—,—(*l*)	C₆H₁₀O₆. *See* g214	178.14	rh pr (w) $[\alpha]_4^{20}$ −57.1(w)	185		. . . .		vʰ	δʰ	i	. . .	i		**B18²**, 193
g216	—,phenyl-hydrazide(*D*)	. . . .	286.29	(w), $[\alpha]_D^{20}$ +13.45	147–9	d 195			vʰ	vʰ					**B15**, 332
g217	—,1-oxo-(*L*)		194.14	cr (w), $[\alpha]_D^{18}$ −48 (w. c = 1)	171 δd		. . . .		δ			δ	. . .	alk s aa δ	**B3²**, 522
g218	**Gulose**(*D*)		180.16	syr $[\alpha]_D^{20}$ +61.6	. . . .	d			s	δ				MeOH δ	**B31**, 282
g219	—(*L*)	C₆H₁₂O₆. *See* g218 . .	180.16	syr $[\alpha]_D^{20}$ −20.4	. . . .	d			s	δ				MeOH δ	**B31**, 282
g220	—,osazone(*D*)	D-Idosazone	358.40	$[\alpha]$ +0.5 (al-Py) (mut)	168 (180d)		. . . .								**B31**, 355
g221	**Guvacine**	1,2,5,6-Tetrahydronicotinic acid.	127.14	pr (w), rods (+1w, dil al)	295d (285d)				s	i	i		i	chl i	**B22¹**, 489

For explanations, symbols and abbreviations see beginning of table. For structural formulas see end of table.

C-318

No.	Name	Synonyms and Formula	Mol. wt.	Color. crystalline form. specific rotation and λ_{max} (log ε)	m.p. °C	b.p. °C	Density	n_D	Solubility						Ref.
									w	al	eth	ace	bz	other solvents	

Halazone

No.	Name	Synonyms and Formula	Mol. wt.	Color/form	m.p.	b.p.	Density	n_D	w	al	eth	ace	bz	other	Ref.
—	Halazone..........	see Benzoic acid, 4(dichlorosulfamyl)-*													
h1	Halostachine(l)....	$C_6H_5CH(OH)CH_2NHCH_3$	151.21	[α] −47	43–5	....	....	....	s	s	s	i	....	....	C42, 2245
Ω h2	Harmaline........	3,4-Dihydroharmine. $C_{13}H_{14}N_2O$.	214.27	ta (MeOH), rh, pr (al) $\lambda^{0.1 NHCl}$ 264 (4.07), 380 (4.49)	250d	....	....	....	δ	δ s^h	δ	....	....	chl δ Py s	B23², 345
Ω h3	Harmine	Banisterine. Telepathine. Yageine. $C_{13}H_{12}N_2O$.	212.55	rh (al), pr (MeOH) λ^{MeOH} 240 (4.63), 301 (4.13), 322 (4.11)	272–4 (264–5d)	sub	....	....	δ	δ	δ	....	....	Py s chl δ	B23², 348
h4	Hecogenin	$C_{27}H_{42}O_4$	430.64	pl (eth), $[α]_D^{22} +7$ λ^{sulf} 351 (3.86), 396 (4.20)	265–8 (253)	....	....	....		s	s	s	....	lig, MeOH s	J1955, 1966
h5	—,acetate	$C_{29}H_{44}O_5$. See h4.	472.67	cr (MeOH)	243 (252)	....	....	....	i	s^h					Am 77, 5196
h6	Hederagenin	$C_{30}H_{48}O_4$	472.72	pr (al), $[α]_D^{21}$ +70.1 (chl-MeOH), $[α]_D^{23} +80$ (Py, c = 0.7)	332–4	....	....	....	i	s	δ	δ	δ	Py, aa, alk s	B10², 305
Ω h7	Helenine	Alantolactone............	232.33	nd	76	275^{760} 197^{10}	....	....	$δ^h$	v	v	....	s	chl, aa, alk, lig s	Am 79, 1009
h8	Helicin	Salicylaldehyde-D-glucoside.	284.27	nd (w), $[α]_D^{20}$ −60.4 (w)	175	....	....	....	v^h	s	δ s^h	....	....		B31, 223
h9	Helvolic acid	Fumigacin. $C_{33}H_{44}O_8$	554.69	nd (dil aa) $[α]_D^{18}$ −125 (chl, c = 1) λ^{al} 231 (4.29), 322 (1.99)	212d	....	....	....	δ	δ s^h	s	s	s	aa, diox s MeOH s^h peth δ	Am 78, 5275
Ω h10	Hematein........	Haematein. $C_{16}H_{12}O_6$.	300.27	red-br cr λ^{diox} 277.5 (3.86), 295 (3.51), 308.5 (3.46), 430 (4.6)	250d	....	....	....	i	δ	i	....	i	NH_3 v aa δ chl i	B18², 221
h11	Hematin	Hydroxyhemin. Ferri-porphyrin hydroxide. $C_{34}H_{32}N_4O_4$.FeOH	633.51	br pw (Py) λ^w 550, 575	>200	....	....	....	i	s^h	i	....	....	alk s Py $δ^h$ aa δ	M, 508
h12	Hematommic acid..	nd (aa)	244.17	nd (aa)	172–3	....	....	....				....	....	aa s^h	H16, 282
Ω h13	Hematoporphyrin ..	Photodyn. $C_{34}H_{38}N_4O_6$	598.71	red λ^{al} 494 (2.7), 529 (2.5)	....	....	....	....	i	s	δ	....	....	chl δ	M, 509
Ω h14	Hematoxylin......	Hydroxybrasilin. Haematoxylin. $C_{16}H_{14}O_6$.3H₂O	356.33	yesh cr, [α] +11 (w, c = 3.7) $\lambda^{0.1NKOH}$ 499, 534.4, 565, 615.5	140 (120)	....	....	....	δ s^h	s^h	δ	....	....	alk s	B17², 273
—	Hemellitic acid	see Benzoic acid, 2,3-dimethyl-													
—	Hemimellitene.....	see Benzene 1,2,3-trimethyl-*													
—	Hemimellitic acid ..	see 1,2,3-benzenetri-carboxylic acid*													
h15	1,10-Hendeca-diyne*	HC:C(CH₂)₇C:CH.........	148.25	....	−17.0	83^{12}	0.8182_4^{21}	1.453^{21}	....	....	....	s	s		B1², 248
Ω h16	Hendecanal*......	n-Undecylaldehyde. $CH_3(CH_2)_9CHO$	170.30	....	−4	117^{18}	0.8251_4^{23}	1.4520^{20}	i	s	s	....	....		B1, 712
h17	—,oxime*	$CH_3(CH_2)_9CH:NOH$	185.31	wh nd (dil MeOH)	72	....	....	....	s	s	s	....	....		B1, 713
h18	—,2-methyl-*	$CH_3(CH_2)_8CH(CH_3)CHO$	184.33	....		114^{10}	0.830_4^{15}	1.4321^{20}	δ	s	s	....	....		C47, 831
Ω h19	Hendecane*.......	Undecane*. $CH_3(CH_2)_9CH_3$	156.32	....	−25.59	195.9^{760} 75^{10}	0.74017_4^{20}	1.4172^{20}	i	∞	∞	....	....		B1³, 534
h20	—,1-amino-*	$CH_3(CH_2)_{10}NH_2$	171.33	cr (eth or al)	17 (15.5)	242^{760} 112.3^{10}	0.7979_4^{20}	1.4398^{20}	s^h	s	i	....	....		B4², 658
h21	—,1-bromo-11-fluoro-*	$F(CH_2)_{11}Br$	253.21	....		$95^{0.6}$		1.4518^{25}	i	v	v	....	....		C51, 7300
Ω h22	Hendecanoic acid ..	Undecanoic acid.* Undecylic acid. $CH_3(CH_2)_9CO_2H$	186.30	cr (ace)	28.6 α 13.4 β 16.3	280^{760} 164^{15}	0.8907_4^{30}	1.4294^{45}	i	v	s	v	∞	chl v	B2², 314
Ω h23	—,ethyl ester*.....	$CH_3(CH_2)_9CO_2C_2H_5$	214.35	....	(i) −19.5 (unst) (ii) −15 (st) (iii) −27.8	131^{14}	0.8633_4^{20}	1.4285^{20}	i	s	s	s	s	os s	B2¹, 154

For explanations, symbols and abbreviations see beginning of table. For structural formulas see end of table.

No.	Name	Synonyms and Formula	Mol. wt.	Color, crystalline form, specific rotation and λ_{max} (log ε)	m.p. °C	b.p. °C	Density	n_D	w	al	eth	ace	bz	other solvents	Ref.

Hendecanoic acid

No.	Name	Synonyms and Formula	Mol. wt.	Color/rotation	m.p.	b.p.	Density	n_D	w	al	eth	ace	bz	other	Ref.
h24	—,nitrile	Decyl cyanide. $CH_3(CH_2)_9CN$	167.30			253^{760} 143^{22}	0.8254_4^{30}	1.4293^{30}	i	s	s				B2, 358
h25	—,2-bromo-*	$CH_3(CH_2)_8CHBrCO_2H$	265.20		10	178–183^{14}			i					alk s	B2[1], 155
h26	—,10-bromo-*	$CH_3CHBr(CH_2)_8CO_2H$	265.20	cr (peth-eth, bz or ace)	35.7				i	v				os v	B2[2], 315
Ω h27	—,11-bromo-*	$Br(CH_2)_{10}CO_2H$	265.20	nd (lig)	57 (52)	188^{18}			i	v	s	s	s	os v	B2[2], 315
h28	—,10,11-di-bromo-*	$BrCH_2CHBr(CH_2)_8CO_2H$	344.10	cr	38				i	s					B2[2], 315
h29	—,11-fluoro-*	$F(CH_2)_{10}CO_2H$	204.29		36	$113-5^{0.25}$				v	v			lig v	C52, 1918
Ω h30	—,4-hydroxy-, lactone*	γ-Undecalactone.	184.28			286 162^{13}	0.9494_4^{20}	1.4512^{20}	i	s					B17[2], 294
Ω h31	1-Hendecanol*	1-Undecyl alcohol. $CH_3(CH_2)_9CH_2OH$	172.31		19	243^{760} 131^{15}	0.8298_4^{20}	1.43918^{20}	i	s	v				J1948, 1814
h32	2-Hendecanol(d)*	2-Undecanol. $CH_3(CH_2)_8CH(OH)CH_3$	172.31	$[\alpha]_D^{20}+10.29$ (bz)	12	128^{20}	0.8270_4^{20}	1.4369^{20}	i	s	s				B1[3], 1774
h33	—(dl)*	$CH_3(CH_2)_8CH(OH)CH_3$	172.31		0	228^{760} 119^{12}	0.8268^{19}	1.4369^{20}	i	s	s				B1[3], 1774
h34	—(l)*	$CH_3(CH_2)_8CH(OH)CH_3$	172.31	$[\alpha]_D -0.02$		$231-3$	0.8302^{20}	1.4381^{20}	i	s	s				B1[3], 1774
h35	3-Hendecanol(l)*	3-Undecanol. $CH_3(CH_2)_7CH(OH)CH_2CH_3$	172.31	$[\alpha]_D^{20} -6.22$ (al), -7.08 (bz)	17	229 117^{16}	0.8295_4^{20}	1.4367^{20}	i	s	s		s		B1[2], 462
h36	5-Hendecanol*	5-Undecanol. $CH_3(CH_2)_5CH(OH)(CH_2)_3CH_3$	172.31		-3.5	229^{760} 107^{12}	0.8292_4^{20}	1.4354^{24}	i	s	s				B1[2], 462
h37	6-Hendecanol*	6-Undecanol. $CH_3(CH_2)_4CH(OH)(CH_2)_4CH_3$	172.31	cr (ace)	25	228^{760} (235^{754}) $117-8^{16}$	0.8334_4^{20}	1.4374^{20}	i	s		s			B1[2], 462
h38	1-Hendecanol, 2-methyl-*	$CH_3(CH_2)_8CH(CH_3)CH_2OH$	186.34		$129-31^{12}$		0.8300_4^{15}	1.4382^{20}	δ	s	s				C54, 2880
Ω h39	2-Hendecanone*	2-Undecanone. $CH_3(CH_2)_8COCH_3$	170.30		15	$231.5-2.5^{760}$ 106^{12}	0.8250_4^{20}	1.42907^{20}	i	s	s	s	s	chl s	B1[3], 2109
Ω h40	3-Hendecanone*	3-Undecanone. $CH_3(CH_2)_7COCH_2CH_3$	170.30		12	227^{760} $104-6^{11}$	0.8272_4^{20}	1.4296^{20}	i	s	s				B1[2], 767
Ω h41	4-Hendecanone*	4-Undecanone. $CH_3(CH_2)_6COCH_2CH_2CH_3$	170.30		4–5	106^{13}	0.8274_4^{25}	1.4248^{24}	i	s	s				B1[2], 767
Ω h42	5-Hendecanone*	5-Undecanone. $CH_3(CH_2)_5CO(CH_2)_3CH_3$	170.30		2	227^{760} $105-6^{12}$	0.8278_4^{19}	1.4275^{18}	i	s	s				B1[2], 767
Ω h43	6-Hendecanone*	n-Caprone. 6-Undecanone. $CH_3(CH_2)_4CO(CH_2)_4CH_3$	170.30	lf λ^{MeOH} 278 (1.69)	14–5	228^{760} 145.7^{29}	0.8308_4^{20}	1.4270^{20}	i	v	v				B1[2], 768
h44	4-Hendecanone, 7-ethyl-2-methyl-*	$CH_3(CH_2)_3CH(C_2H_5)CH_2CH_2COCH_2CH(CH_3)_2$	212.38			$252-3^{760}$ $101-3^4$	0.8362^{20}	1.4370^{20}	i	v	v	v	v	os v	C31, 6773
h45	Hendecasiloxane, tetracosamethyl-	$(CH_3)_3SiO[Si(CH_3)_2O]_9Si(CH_3)_3$	829.78			322.8^{760} $202^{4.7}$	0.930^{20}	1.3994^{20}	δ				s		Am 68, 691
h46	1-Hendecene*	1-Undecene. α-Undecylene. $CH_3(CH_2)_8CH:CH_2$	154.30		-49.19	192.7^{760} 72^{10}	0.7503_4^{20}	1.42609^{20}	i	s				chl, lig s	B1[3], 866
h47	2-Hendecene(trans)*	2-Undecene. $CH_3(CH_2)_7CH:CHCH_3$	154.30		-48.3	$192-3^{760}$ 75^{10}	0.7528_4^{20}	1.4292^{20}	i	s					B1, 225
h48	5-Hendecene(trans)*	5-Undecene. $CH_3(CH_2)_4CH:CH(CH_2)_3CH_3$	154.30		-61.1	192^{760} 73^{10}	0.7497_4^{20}	1.4285^{20}	i	s		s		chl, lig s	B1[3], 867
h49	9-Hendecenoic acid(trans)*	$CH_3CH:CH(CH_2)_7CO_2H$	184.28		19	273 $121-3^{0.7}$	0.9119_0^{25}	1.4519^{20}	i	s	s				B2[2], 420
Ω h50	10-Hendecenoic acid*	$CH_2:CH(CH_2)_8CO_2H$	184.28	cr	24.5	275^{760} 165^{15}	0.9072_4^{20}	1.4486^{24}	i	s	s				B2[2], 419
Ω h51	—,ethyl ester*	$CH_2:CH(CH_2)_8CO_2C_2H_5$	212.34		-38	$263.5-5.5^{760}$ 131.5^{16}	0.88271^{15}	1.4449^{23}	i	s	s			aa s	B2[2], 420
Ω h52	—,methyl ester*	$CH_2:CH(CH_2)_8CO_2CH_3$	198.31		-27.5	248^{760} 124^{10}	0.889^{15}	1.43928^{20}	i	s	s			aa s	B2[2], 420
Ω h53	10-Hendecen-1-ol*	Undecenyl alcohol. $CH_2:CH(CH_2)_8CH_2OH$	170.30		-2	250 $132-3^{15}$	0.8495_4^{15}	1.4500^{20}	i	s	s				C53, 21717
h54	1-Hendecen-3-yne*	$CH_3(CH_2)_6C:CCH:CH_2$	150.27			74^9	0.7962_4^{20}	1.4606^{20}							C35, 3499
h55	1-Hendecyne*	1-Undecyne. $CH_3(CH_2)_8C:CH$	152.28		-25 (-17.7)	195^{760} 73.2^{10}	0.7720_4^{20}	1.4306^{20}	i	s	s	s	s	oos s	B1, 240
h56	5-Hendecyne*	5-Undecyne. $CH_3(CH_2)_4C:C(CH_2)_3CH_3$	152.28		-74.1	198.1^{760} 78.3^{10}	0.7753_4^{20}	1.4369^{20}							Am 61, 2897
h57	9-Hendecynoic acid*	$CH_3C:C(CH_2)_7CO_2H$	182.27	pl (dil al)	61	170^{15} $132^{0.1}$			v	v	v				B2[2], 457
h58	10-Hendecynoic acid*	$HC:C(CH_2)_8CO_2H$	182.27	lf	43–4	175^{15} 130^3	0.9060^{25}		i	s					B2[2], 456
h59	Heneicosane*	$CH_3(CH_2)_{19}CH_3$	296.59	cr (w)	40.5	356.5^{760} 203^{10}	0.7917_4^{20}	1.4441^{20}	i	δ				peth s	B1[3], 573
h60	Heneicosanoic acid*	$CH_3(CH_2)_{19}CO_2H$	326.57	nd (ace)	82 (75)				δ		s	s[h]		chl s aa s[h]	B2[2], 372
h61	Hentriacontane*	$CH_3(CH_2)_{29}CH_3$	436.86	lf (AcOEt)	67.9	458^{760} 302^{15}	0.8111_4^{20} 0.7814^{68}	1.4543^{20} 1.4278^{90}	i	δ	δ		δ	peth s chl δ	B1[3], 585
Ω h61[1]	Hentriacontanoic acid*	Melissic acid. $CH_3(CH_2)_{29}CO_2H$	466.84	sc or nd (al or ace)	93–3.2				i	δ	δ[h]	δ	s	MeOH δ[h] s[h]	B2[2], 382
h62	16-Hentriacontanone	Palmitone. $CH_3(CH_2)_{14}CO(CH_2)_{14}CH_3$	450.84	lf (al) λ^{hx} 275 (1.50)	83		0.7947_4^{91}	1.4297^{94}	i	δ	s	δ	δ	chl δ	B1[2], 776

For explanations, symbols and abbreviations see beginning of table. For structural formulas see end of table.

No.	Name	Synonyms and Formula	Mol. wt.	Color, crystalline form, specific rotation and λ_{max} (log ε)	m.p. °C	b.p. °C	Density	n_D	w	al	eth	ace	bz	other solvents	Ref.
	Heptachlor														
—	Heptachlor	see **Dicyclopentadiene, 3,4,5,6,7,8,9-heptachloro-**													
h63	Heptacosane*	$CH_3(CH_2)_{25}CH_3$	380.75	cr (al, bz), lf (AcOEt)	59.5	422.1[760] 270[15]	0.8050[20] 0.7796[60]	1.4511[20] 1.4345[65]	i	i	δ	...	...	...	B1[3], 581
h64	7,10-Heptadecadiyne*	$CH_3(CH_2)_5C:CCH_2C:C(CH_2)_5CH_3$ 232.41				150[6]	0.841[9]	1.4700[19]	...	...	...	...	...	...	C28, 4035
h65	Heptadecanal*	Margaraldehyde. $CH_3(CH_2)_{15}CHO$	254.46	nd (peth), cr (al + 1)	36 52 (+al)	204[26]	...	...	i	δ	s	δ	s	aa v AcOEt δ	B1, 717
Ω h66	Heptadecane*	$CH_3(CH_2)_{15}CH_3$	240.48	hex lf	22	301.8[760] 161.75[10]	0.7780[20]	1.4369[20]	i	δ	s	...	s	aa δ	B1[3], 563
Ω h67	—,1-amino-*	Heptadecylamine. $CH_3(CH_2)_{16}NH_2$	255.49		49	336[760] 188.9[10]	0.8510[20]	1.4510[20]	i	s	s	...	v	chl v	B4[2], 660
Ω h68	—,1-bromo-*	n-Heptadecyl bromide. $CH_3(CH_2)_{16}Br$	319.38		32	349[760] 199[10]	0.9916[20]	1.4625[20]	i	...	...	...	...	chl v	B1[3], 564
h69	—,1,17-dibromo-*	$Br(CH_2)_{17}Br$	398.28	lf (al)	38–8.4	208–10[3]	...	...	i	δ	...	...	...	chl v	B1[3], 564
Ω h70	Heptadecanoic acid*	Margaric acid. $CH_3(CH_2)_{15}CO_2H$	270.46	pl (peth)	62–3	227[100]	0.8532[60]	1.4342[60]	...	δ	s	s	s	chl s	Am 64, 2739
h71	—,ethyl ester*	$CH_3(CH_2)_{15}CO_2C_2H_5$	298.52	pl (dil al)	28	185[5]	...	...	i	s	v	s	s	os s	B2[2], 344
Ω h72	—,methyl ester*	$CH_3(CH_2)_{15}CO_2CH_3$	284.49	pl (al)	30	184–7[9]	...	...	i	s	v	s	v	os s	B2[1], 169
h73	—,nitrile	Cetyl cyanide. Margaronitrile. $CH_3(CH_2)_{15}CN$	251.46	cr (al)	34	349[760] 183[10]	0.8315[20]	1.4467[20]	i	δ v[h]	v	...	...	...	B2[2], 345
Ω h74	1-Heptadecanol*	$CH_3(CH_2)_{16}OH$	256.48	lf (al), cr (ace)	54	308[760]	0.8475[20]	...	i	s	s	...	s	...	B1[3], 1830
h75	2-Heptadecanol*	$CH_3(CH_2)_{14}CH(OH)CH_3$	256.48	pl (dil al)	54 (46–7)	140[0.5]	...	1.4407[37]	i	s	s	...	...	...	C30, 8255
h76	9-Heptadecanol*	$CH_3(CH_2)_7CH(OH)(CH_2)_7CH_3$ 256.48	pl (dil al)	61	174[9]	...	1.4262[80]	i	s	s	s	s	os s		B1, 430
Ω h77	2-Heptadecanone*	Methyl heptadecyl ketone. $CH_3(CH_2)_{14}COCH_3$	254.46	pl (dil al)	48	320 246[110]	0.8140[48 48]	...	i	δ	v	s	v	peth s chl v	B1[2], 772
Ω h78	9-Heptadecanone*	Nonylone. Pelargone. $CH_3(CH_2)_7CO(CH_2)_7CH_3$	254.46	pl (MeOH)	53	250–3 142[1]	...	...	...	δ	...	...	...	MeOH s[h]	B1[2], 772
h79	1-Heptadecanone, 1-phenyl-*	Stearophenone. $CH_3(CH_2)_{15}COC_6H_5$	330.56		56–6.5	...	...	...	i	...	...	...	s		B7[2], 272
h80	1-Heptadecene*	$CH_3(CH_2)_{14}CH:CH_2$	238.46		11.2	300[760] 160[10]	0.7852[20]	1.4432[20]	i	...	v	...	s	lig ∞	B1[3], 878
h81	1,4-Heptadiene*	$CH_3CH_2CH:CHCH_2CH:CH_2$	96.17			93[772] (101)	0.7270[20]	1.4370[20]	i	...	s	...	s	peth s	B1[3], 999
h82	1,5-Heptadiene*	$CH_3CH:CHCH_2CH_2CH:CH_2$	96.17			94[760]	0.7186[20]	1.4200[20]	i	s	s	s	s	os s	B1[3], 999
h83	2,4-Heptadiene*	$CH_3CH_2CH:CHCH:CHCH_3$	96.17	λ^{al} 227 (4.41)		108[760]	0.7384[20]	1.4578[20]	i	s	s	s	s	peth s	B1[3], 1000
h84	1,5-Heptadien-4-ol*	$CH_3CH:CHCH(OH)CH_2CH:CH_2$ 112.17			155–6[742] 68[24]	0.8598[20]	1.4510[25]	δ	...	s	...	s			B2[3], 1992
h85	3,5-Heptadien-2-one*	Crotonylideneacetone. $CH_3CH:CHCH:CHCOCH_3$	110.16	λ^{al} 271 (4.34)		88[28] 63[10]	0.8946[19]	1.51767[19]	...	...	...	...	...		B1[2], 809
Ω h86	2,5-Heptadien-4-one-2,6-dimethyl-*	Diisopropylideneacetone. Phorone. $CH_3C(CH_3):CHCOCH:C(CH_3)CH_3$	138.21	ye gr pr	28	197.8[760]	0.8850[20]	1.49982[20]	δ	s	s	...	s		B1, 810
h87	1,6-Heptadien-3-yne*	$CH_2:CHCH_2C:CCH:CH_2$	92.14			110[750]	0.7872[25]	1.4694[25]	i	...	...	...	s	peth s	Am 58, 612
h88	1,5-Heptadiyne*	$CH_3C:CCH_2CH_2C:CH$	92.14		26[30]	0.8100[21]	1.4521[21]	i	...	...	...	s	peth s		B1[2], 247
h89	1,6-Heptadiyne*	$HC:CCH_2CH_2CH_2C:CH$	92.14		–85	112[760] 36[20]	0.8164[17]	1.451[17]	i	...	...	...	s	aa s	B1[3], 1061
Ω h90	Heptanal*	Enanthaldehyde. Heptaldehyde. $CH_3(CH_2)_5CHO$	114.19		–43.3	152.8[760] 59.6[30]	0.8495[20]	1.4113[20]	δ	∞	∞	...	...		B1[2], 750
h91	—,oxime*	$CH_3(CH_2)_5CH:NOH$	129.20	pl (al)	57–8	195[760] 100.5[14]	0.8583[55]	1.4210[20]	δ	s	s	...	...		B1[1], 752
Ω h92	—,2-benzylidene-	α-Pentylcinnamaldehyde. $CH_3(CH_2)_4C(:CHC_6H_5)CHO$	202.30	ye oil	80	174–5[20] 140[5]	0.97108[20]	1.5381[20]	i	...	...	...	s		Am 53, 3122
Ω h93	Heptane*	$CH_3(CH_2)_5CH_3$	100.21		–90.61	98.42[760] –2.1[10]	0.68376[20]	1.38777[20]	i	v	∞	∞	∞	chl, peth ∞	B1[3], 415
Ω h94	—,1-amino-*	$CH_3(CH_2)_6NH_2$	115.22		–18	156.9[760] 45.6[10]	0.7754[20]	1.4251[20]	δ	∞	∞	...	...		B4[2], 652
h95	—,2-amino-*	$CH_3(CH_2)_4CH(NH_2)CH_3$	115.22			142[760]	0.7665[19]	1.41997[19]	δ	s	s	...	...	peth s	B4[3], 374
Ω h96	—,1-bromo-*	$CH_3(CH_2)_6Br$	179.11		–56.1	178.9[760] 59.7[10]	1.1400[20]	1.4502[20]	i	v	v	...	...	chl s	B1[3], 431
h97	—,1-bromo-7-fluoro-*	$F(CH_2)_7Br$	197.10			85[11]	...	1.4463[20]	i	v	v	...	...		JOC, 1956, 739
Ω h98	—,1-chloro-*	$CH_3(CH_2)_6Cl$	134.65		–69.5	159[760] 45[10]	0.8758[20]	1.4256[20]	i	∞	∞	...	...	chl s	B1[2], 117
h99	—,2-chloro-*	$CH_3(CH_2)_4CHClCH_3$	134.65			46[19]	0.8672[20]	1.4221[20]	i	...	v	...	s	chl, aa s	B1[3], 429
h100	—,3-chloro-*	$CH_3(CH_2)_3CHClCH_2CH_3$	134.65			144[751] 48.3[20]	0.8960[20]	1.4228[20]	i	...	v	...	s	chl v	B1[2], 430
h101	—,4-chloro-*	$(CH_3CH_2CH_2)_2CHCl$	134.65			144[758] 48.9[21]	0.8710[20]	1.4237[20]	i	...	v	...	s	chl s	B1[2], 117
h102	—,3-chloro-2,3-dimethyl-*	$CH_3(CH_2)_3CCl(CH_3)CH(CH_3)_2$ 162.71			54[8] 42[2]	0.8395[20]	1.4391[20]		...	...	...	s	chl s		Am 55, 812
h103	—,5-chloro-2,5-dimethyl-*	$CH_3CH_2CCl(CH_3)CH_2CH_2CH(CH_3)_2$ 162.71			63[15]	0.8692[18]	1.43457[15]	i	...	...	...	s	chl s		B1[1], 64
h104	—,3-chloro-3-ethyl-*	$CH_3(CH_2)_3CCl(C_2H_5)CH_2CH_3$ 162.71			46[3]	0.8856[20]	1.4400[20]		...	...	...	s	chl s		B1[3], 510
h105	—,4-chloro-4-ethyl-*	$(CH_3CH_2CH_2)_2CClCH_2CH_3$ 162.71			67[12]	0.8821[20]	1.4438[20]	i	...	v	...	s	chl s		B1[3], 511

For explanations, symbols and abbreviations see beginning of table. For structural formulas see end of table.

No.	Name	Synonyms and Formula	Mol. wt.	Color, crystalline form, specific rotation and λ_{max} (log ε)	m.p. °C	b.p. °C	Density	n_D	w	al	eth	ace	bz	other solvents	Ref.
	Heptane														
h106	—,1-chloro-7-fluoro-*	F(CH₂)₇Cl	152.64			70¹⁰	0.993²⁰	1.4222²⁵	i	v	v	...	s	chl s	C51, 7300
h107	—,2-chloro-2-methyl-*	CH₃(CH₂)₄CCl(CH₃)₂	148.68			50¹⁵	0.8568²⁵	1.4240²⁵	i	v	v	...	s	chl s	B1³, 472
h108	—,2-chloro-6-methyl-*	(CH₃)₂CH(CH₂)₃CHClCH₃	148.68			74³⁵		1.4260¹⁵	i	v	v	...	s	chl s	B1³, 472
h109	—,3-chloro-3-methyl-*	CH₃(CH₂)₃CCl(CH₃)CH₂CH₃	148.68			64²⁷	0.8764²⁰	1.4317²⁰	i	v	v	...	s	chl s	B1³, 474
h110	—,4-chloro-4-methyl-*	(CH₃CH₂CH₂)₂CClCH₃	148.68			50¹²	0.8690²⁰	1.43098¹⁵	i	v	s	...	s	chl s	B1³, 477
Ω h110¹	—,3(chloromethyl)-*	CH₃(CH₂)₃CH(C₂H₅)CH₂Cl	148.68			174⁷⁶⁰	0.8769²⁰	1.4319²⁰	i	s	s	s	s	os s	C31, 7408
h111	—,1,1-dichloro-*	CH₃(CH₂)₅CHCl₂	169.10			187⁷⁶⁰ 82²⁰	1.0008²⁰	1.4440²⁰	i	s	s	...	s	chl v	B1³, 430
h112	—,1,2-dichloro-*	CH₃(CH₂)₄CHClCH₂Cl	169.10			68–72⁷	1.064²⁰	1.4490²⁰	i	s	s	...	s	chl v	B1³, 430
h113	—,2,2-dichloro-*	CH₃(CH₂)₄CCl₂CH₃	169.10			77²⁵	1.0122²⁰	1.4440²⁰	i	s	s	...	s	chl s	B1³, 430
h114	—,4,4-dichloro-*	(CH₃CH₂CH₂)₂CCl₂	169.10			86²⁷	1.008¹⁷	1.448¹⁷	i			...	s	chl s	B1, 154
h115	—,2,6-dichloro-2,6-dimethyl-*	(CH₃)₂CCl(CH₂)₃CCl(CH₃)₂	197.15		43	93¹⁶			i				s	chl s	B1³, 513
h116	—,2,3-dimethyl-*	CH₃(CH₂)₂CH(CH₃)CH(CH₃)₂	128.26		−116	140.5⁷⁶⁰ 29.4¹⁰	0.7260²⁰	1.4088²⁰	i	∞	∞	∞	∞	chl, peth ∞ os v	B1³, 511
h117	—,2,4-dimethyl-*	CH₃CH₂CH₂CH(CH₃)CH₂CH(CH₃)₂	128.26			133.5⁷⁶⁰ 23.8¹⁰	0.7143²⁰	1.4031²⁰	i	∞	∞	∞	∞	os, peth, chl ∞	B1³, 512
h118	—,2,5-dimethyl (d)-*	CH₃CH₂CH(CH₃)CH₂CH₂CH(CH₃)₂	128.26	[α]²⁷_D +4.2		136⁷⁶⁰	0.7198²⁰	1.4033²⁰	i	∞	∞	∞	∞	os, chl ∞ peth v	B1², 128
Ω h119	—,2,6-dimethyl-*	Diisobutylmethane. Isobutyl-isoamyl. (CH₃)₂CH(CH₂)₃CH(CH₃)₂	128.26		−102.9	135.2⁷⁶⁰ 25.5¹⁰	0.7089²⁰	1.4011²⁰	i	∞	∞	∞	∞		B1², 512
h120	—,3,3-dimethyl-*	CH₃(CH₂)₃C(CH₃)₂CH₂CH₃	128.26			137.3⁷⁶⁰ 26¹⁰	0.7254²⁰	1.4087²⁰	i	∞	s	v	v	os v	B1³, 513
h122	—,4-ethyl-*	Ethyldipropylmethane. CH₃(CH₂)₂CH(C₂H₅)(CH₂)₂CH₃	128.26			141.2⁷⁶⁰ 31¹⁰	0.7270²⁰	1.4096²⁰	i	∞	s	∞	∞	chl, lig ∞	C37, 2631
h123	—,1-fluoro-*	CH₃(CH₂)₅CH₂F	118.20		−73	117.9⁷⁶⁰	0.8062²⁰	1.3854²⁰	i	s	s	s	s	peth v	B1, 56
h124	—,hexadeca-fluoro-*	Perfluoroheptane. CF₃(CF₂)₅CF₃	388.05		−78	82.43⁷⁶⁰	1.7333²⁰	1.2618²⁰	i						B1³, 429
Ω h125	—,1-iodo-*	CH₃(CH₂)₅CH₂I	226.10		−48.2	204⁷⁶⁰ 76.16¹⁰	1.3791²⁰	1.4904²⁰	i	s	s	s	s	chl s	B1³, 433
Ω h126	—,2-methyl-*	CH₃(CH₂)₄CH(CH₃)₂	114.23		−109	117.65⁷⁶⁰ 12.3¹⁰	0.6980²⁰	1.39494²⁰	i	∞	s	∞	∞	chl, peth ∞	B1³, 471
h127	—,3-methyl-(d)*	CH₃(CH₂)₃CH(CH₃)CH₂CH₃	114.23	[α]²⁶_D +9.34		115–8	0.7075¹⁶	1.4002¹⁸	i	∞	s	∞	∞	chl ∞	B1³, 475
Ω h128	—,(dl)*	CH₃(CH₂)₃CH(CH₃)CH₂CH₃	114.23		−120.5	119 13.3¹⁰	0.70583²⁰	1.3985²⁰	i	∞	s	∞	∞	chl, peth ∞	B1³, 476
h129	—,(l)*	CH₃(CH₂)₃CH(CH₃)CH₂CH₃	114.23	[α]²⁵_D −3.87		117–8⁷⁴⁵		1.3990²⁰	i	∞	s	∞	∞	chl ∞	C40, 2048
Ω h130	—,4-methyl-*	(CH₃CH₂CH₂)₂CHCH₃	114.23		−121	117.7⁷⁶⁰ 12.4¹⁰	0.70463²⁰	1.39792²⁰	i	∞	s	∞	∞	chl, peth ∞	B1³, 476
h131	—,2(methyl amino)-	CH₃(CH₂)₄CH(NHCH₃)CH₃	129.25			155⁷⁶⁰			δ						C36, 222
Ω h132	**Heptanedioic acid***	Pimelic acid. HO₂C(CH₂)₅CO₂H	160.17	pr (w)	106	272¹⁰⁰ sub 212¹⁰	1.329¹⁵		s	s	s		i	sʰ	B2², 586
h133	—,dichloride	ClCO(CH₂)₅COCl	197.06			137¹⁵			d	d					B2, 671
Ω h134	—,diethyl ester*	C₂H₅O₂C(CH₂)₅CO₂C₂H₅	216.28		−24	252–5⁷⁴⁸ 139–41¹⁵	0.99448²⁰	1.43052²⁰	i	s	s			AcOEt s	B2¹, 282
Ω h135	—,dimethyl ester*	CH₃O₂C(CH₂)₅CO₂CH₃	188.23		−21	120¹⁰ 80¹	1.0625²⁰	1.4309²⁰	δ	s	s				B2², 587
Ω h136	—,dinitrile	1,5-Dicyanopentane. NC(CH₂)₅CN	122.17		−31.4	175¹⁴	0.949¹⁸	1.4472²⁰	i	∞	∞	s		chl ∞	B2², 587
h137	—,monoethyl ester.	HO₂C(CH₂)₅CO₂C₂H₅	188.23	cr (eth)	10	182¹⁸ 160⁴		1.4415²⁰	δ	δ	δ	...	δ	chl δ	B2¹, 282
h138	—,4-oxo-*	OC(CH₂CH₂CO₂H)₂	174.16	rh pl (w)	143 (141.5)				sʰ	s	δ	δ	i		B3², 487
h139	**1,7-Heptanediol***	Heptamethyleneglycol. HOCH₂(CH₂)₅CH₂OH	132.21		22	262 151¹⁴	0.9569²⁵	1.4520²⁵	s	s	δ				B1³, 2214
Ω h140	**2,4-Heptanediol, 3-methyl-***	CH₃CH₂CH₂CH(OH)CH(CH₃)CH(OH)CH₃	146.23			115³	0.928²⁰	1.4459²⁰	i						B1, 491
h141	**2,4-Heptanedione***	CH₃CH₂CH₂COCH₂COCH₃	128.17			174⁷⁶⁰ 70²⁰	0.9411¹⁵								B1, 792
Ω h142	**1-Heptanethiol***	CH₃(CH₂)₆SH	132.27	λ 225 sh (2.2)	−43	177⁷⁶⁰ 70²⁰	0.8427²⁰	1.4521²⁰	i	∞	∞	∞	∞		B1³, 1684
h143	**2,4,6-Heptanetrione***	Diacetylacetone. CH₃COCH₂COCH₂COCH₃	142.16	lf	49	121¹⁰	1.0681²⁰	1.4930²⁰	s dʰ	s	s			alk s	C41, 1917
Ω h144	**Heptanoic acid***	Enanthic acid. n-Heptylic acid. CH₃(CH₂)₅CO₂H	130.19		−7.5	223⁷⁶⁰ 116¹¹	0.9200²⁰	1.4170²⁰	δ	s	s	s	s		B2², 294
h145	—,amide	CH₃(CH₂)₅CONH₂	129.20	nd (al), lf (w)	96	250–8	0.8521¹¹⁰	1.4217¹¹⁰	s	s	s				B2², 296
h146	—,anhydride*	[CH₃(CH₂)₅CO]₂O	242.36	λ^MeOH 274 (3.93), 314 (3.68)	−12.4	268–71 164¹².⁵	0.9321²⁰	1.4335¹⁵	i	s	s				B2, 340

For explanations, symbols and abbreviations see beginning of table. For structural formulas see end of table.

No.	Name	Synonyms and Formula	Mol. wt.	Color, crystalline form, specific rotation and λ_{max} (log ε)	m.p. °C	b.p. °C	Density	n_D	w	al	eth	ace	bz	other solvents	Ref.
	Heptanoic acid														
h147	—,butyl ester*	$CH_3(CH_2)_5CO_2C_4H_9^n$	186.30		−67.5	226.18[760]	0.86382[20]	1.4204[25]	i	s	s	s	s	os s	B2, 340
h148	—,chloride*	$CH_3(CH_2)_5COCl$	148.63		−83.8	125.2[760]	0.9590[20]	1.4345[15]	d	d	s			lig v	J87, 93
Ω h149	—,ethyl ester*	$CH_3(CH_2)_5CO_2C_2H_5$	158.24		−66.1	187[760] 78[14]	0.8817[20]	1.4100[20]	δ	s	s				B2², 295
h150	—,heptyl ester*	$CH_3(CH_2)_5CO_2(CH_2)_6CH_3$	228.38		−33	276–8[760]	0.86492[19]	1.4320[20]	i	s	s	s	s	os s	B2², 145
h151	—,hexyl ester*	$CH_3(CH_2)_5CO_2(CH_2)_5CH_3$	214.35		−48	261[760]	0.86114[20]	1.429[15]	i	s	s	s	s	os s	B2², 295
Ω h152	—,methyl ester*	$CH_3(CH_2)_5CO_2CH_3$	144.22		−56	172[760]	0.8815[20]	1.4152[20]	δ	s	s	s	s	os s	B2², 296
h153	—,2-methylpropyl ester*	$CH_3(CH_2)_5CO_2CH_2CH(CH_3)_2$	186.30			209[759]	0.8593[20]		i	s	s	s	s	os s	B2¹, 145
h154	—,nitrile*	$CH_3(CH_2)_5CN$	111.19			183[765] (187) 70–2[10]	0.8107[20]_0	1.41037[30]	i		s	s	s	aa s	B2², 296
h155	—,octyl ester*	$CH_3(CH_2)_5CO_2(CH_2)_7CH_3$	242.41		−22.5	290[760]	0.85961[20]	1.43488[15]	i	s	s	s	s	os s	B2, 340
h156	—,pentyl ester*	$CH_3(CH_2)_5CO_2(CH_2)_4CH_3$	200.33		−50	245.44[760]	0.86232[20]	1.42627[15]	i	s	s	s	s	os s	B2³, 766
h157	—,p-phenylphenacyl ester		324.43		62										Am 52, 3715
h158	—,propyl ester*	$CH_3(CH_2)_5CO_2CH_2CH_2CH_3$	172.27	cr (peth)	−63.5	207.9[760]	0.86412[15]	1.41835[15]	i	s	s	s	s	os s	B2, 340
h159	—,7-amino-*	$H_2N(CH_2)_6CO_2H$	145.20	cr (w, MeOH-peth)	195 (188)				s[h]	s[h]	i	s[h]			B4, 459
h160	—,2-bromo-*	$CH_3(CH_2)_4CHBrCO_2H$	209.09			250d 147[12]	1.319[18]	1.471[18]			s		s		B2², 296
h161	—,7-bromo-*	$Br(CH_2)_6CO_2H$	209.09	wh cr (dil al)	31	280			i	s	s	s	s	os s lig i	B2, 341
h162	—,7-fluoro-*	$F(CH_2)_6CO_2H$	148.18			133[10]	1.039[20]	1.4207[25]	δ	δ	δ				C50, 14528
h163	—,3-hydroxy-4-methyl-*	$CH_3CH_2CH(CH_3)CH(OH)CH_2CH_2CO_2H$	160.22	ye pw (w)	95–100				δ	s	i	v	i	aa s peth i	B3¹, 127
h164	—,7-iodo-*	$I(CH_2)_6CO_2H$	256.09	lf (dil al)	49–51				δ	s	s	s	s	os s	B2, 341
h165	—,6-oxo-*	$CH_3CO(CH_2)_4CO_2H$	144.17		40–2	250–3[280] 135[1]		1.4306[25]	s	s	s	s	s		B3¹, 242
Ω h166	1-Heptanol*	$CH_3(CH_2)_6OH$	116.21		−34.1	176[760]	0.8219[20]	1.4249[20]	δ	∞	∞				B1³, 1679
h167	2-Heptanol(d)*	$CH_3(CH_2)_4CH(OH)CH_3$	116.21	$[\alpha]_D^{20} +11.4$ (al), $+13.7$ (bz)		160–2 73[20]	0.8190[20]	1.4209[20]	δ	s	s				B1³, 1687
Ω h168	—(dl)*	$CH_3(CH_2)_4CH(OH)CH_3$	116.21			160[760] 66[20]	0.8167[20]_4	1.4210[20]	δ	s	s				B1³, 1686
h169	—(l)*	$CH_3(CH_2)_4CH(OH)CH_3$	116.21	$[\alpha]_D^{12} -10.5$		74[23]	0.8184[20]_4	1.4208[20]	δ	s	s				B1³, 1687
Ω h170	3-Heptanol(d)*	$CH_3(CH_2)_3CH(OH)CH_2CH_3$	116.21	$[\alpha]_D^{20} +6.7$ (w) $[\alpha]_D^{25} -3.78$ (undil)	−70	157[750] 66[18]	0.8227[20]_4	1.4201[20]	δ	s	s				B1², 444
Ω h171	4-Heptanol*	$(CH_3CH_2CH_2)_2CHOH$	116.21		−41.2	161[760] (154) 63.8[16]	0.8183[20]	1.4205[20]	i	s	s				B1³, 1685
h172	2-Heptanol, 6-amino-2-methyl-, hydrochloride*	$CH_3CH(NH_2)(CH_2)_3COH(CH_3)_2 \cdot HCl$	181.71	cr	154–5				v	s	i		i		C54, 8627
h173	1-Heptanol, 7-chloro-*	$Cl(CH_2)_7OH$	150.65	cr (peth or bz)	11	150[20] 120[13]	0.9998[15]	1.4537[25]	δ	v	s			peth s	B1³, 1684
Ω h174	4-Heptanol, 2,6-dimethyl-*	$[(CH_3)_2CHCH_2]_2CHOH$	144.26			176–7[760]	0.809[21]_4	1.4242[20]	i	s	s				B1³, 1753
h175	4-Heptanol, 4-ethyl-*	$(CH_3CH_2CH_2)_2C(C_2H_5)OH$	144.26			182[760]	0.8350[20]	1.4332[20]	i	s	s				B1², 457
h176	1-Heptanol, 7-fluoro-*	Heptamethylene fluorohydrin. $F(CH_2)_7OH$	134.20			98–9[12]	0.956[20]_4	1.4197[25]	δ	v	v				C51, 7299
h177	—,4-methyl-*	$CH_3CH_2CH_2CH(CH_3)(CH_2)_3OH$	130.23			183[760] 71.6[20]	0.8065[25]	1.4258[20]	i	s	s			os s	B1³, 1734
h178	—,6-methyl-*	$(CH_3)_2CH(CH_2)_5OH$	130.23		−106	188[764] 95.8[20]	0.8176[25]	1.4251[25]	i	s	s				Am 63, 3100
Ω h179	2-Heptanol, 2-methyl-*	$CH_3(CH_2)_4COH(CH_3)_2$	130.23			156[760] 66–8[15]	0.8142[20]_4	1.4250[20]	i	s	s				B1³, 1725
Ω h180	3-Heptanol, 3-methyl-*	$CH_3(CH_2)_3COH(CH_3)CH_2CH_3$	130.23		−83	163[760] (159) 64–5[16]	0.8282[20]_4	1.4279[20]	i	s	s				B1³, 1729
Ω h181	4-Heptanol, 4-methyl-*	$(CH_3CH_2CH_2)_2C(CH_3)OH$	130.23		−82	161[760] 61–3[12]	0.8248[20]_4	1.4258[20]	i	s	s				B1³, 1735
h182	1-Heptanol, 1-phenyl-*	$CH_3(CH_2)_5CH(OH)C_6H_5$	192.31			275 153–5[18]	0.946	1.5024[20]	i						B6², 513
h183	4-Heptanol, 4-propyl-*	$(CH_3CH_2CH_2)_3COH$	158.29			190–2 89–90[15]	0.8338[21]_4	1.43551[21]	i	s	s				B1³, 1769
Ω h184	2-Heptanone*	$CH_3(CH_2)_4COCH_3$	114.19	λ^{MeOH} 274 (1.34)	−35.5	151.45[760] 111[21]	0.8111[20]	1.4088[20]	λ	s	s				B1², 753
Ω h185	3-Heptanone*	$CH_3(CH_2)_3COCH_2CH_3$	114.19	λ^{al} 277.5 (1.34)	−39	147[765] (149)	0.8183[20]	1.4057[20]	i	∞	∞				B1², 754
Ω h186	4-Heptanone*	$(CH_3CH_2CH_2)_2CO$	114.19	λ^{al} 279.5 (1.38)	−33	144[760]	0.8174[20]	1.4069[20]	i	∞	∞				B1², 754
h187	2-Heptanone, 1-chloro-*	$CH_3(CH_2)_4COCH_2Cl$	148.63	λ^{al} 284 (1.43)		83[16]	0.802[20]	1.4371[20]	δ	s	s			chl s	Am 67, 1944
Ω h187¹	4-Heptanone, 2,6-dimethyl-*	Isovalerone. $[(CH_3)_2CHCH_2]_2CO$	142.24	λ^{vap} 179, 192, 195		168[760] 60–1[18]	0.8053[20]	1.412[21]	i	∞	∞				B1², 763
h188	3-Heptanone, 6-dimethyl-amino-4,4-diphenyl-(l)*	l-Amidon. l-Methadone. $(CH_3)_2NCH(CH_3)CH_2C(C_6H_5)_2COC_2H_5$	309.46	$[\alpha]_D^{20} -32$ (al) λ^{al} 295 (2.66)	99–100					s				dil HCl s	Am 71, 1648

For explanations, symbols and abbreviations see beginning of table. For structural formulas see end of table.

No.	Name	Synonyms and Formula	Mol. wt.	Color, crystalline form, specific rotation and λ_{max} (log ε)	m.p. °C	b.p. °C	Density	n_D	w	al	eth	ace	bz	other solvents	Ref.
	3-Heptanone														
h189	—,—hydrochloride (dl)*	Physopeptone. $(CH_3)_2NCH(CH_3)CH_2C(C_6H_5)_2COC_2H_5 \cdot HCl$ 345.92		pl (al-eth) λ^{al} 292	236–6.5				v	s	i	...	...	chl s	Am 69, 2941
h190	—,—,—(l)*	$(CH_3)_2NCH(CH_3)CH_2C(C_6H_5)_2COC_2H_5 \cdot HCl$ 345.92		$[\alpha]_D^{20}$ −169 (al, c = 2.1)	245–6				s	s	i	...	...	chl s	Am 71, 1648
Ω h191	2-Heptanone, 4-isopropyl-*	$CH_3(CH_2)_2CH[CH(CH_3)_2]CH_2COCH_3$ 156.27				82–4[14]			δ	s	v	s	s	os v	B1[2], 2902
Ω h192	—,3-methyl-*	$CH_3(CH_2)_3CH(CH_3)COCH_3$	128.22			167[760]	0.8218[20]	1.4172[20]	δ	s	s	s	s	os s	B1[2], 759
Ω h193	3-Heptanone, 6-methyl-*	$(CH_3)_2CHCH_2CH_2COC_2H_5$	128.22			163–3.5[734]	0.8304[20]	1.4209[20]	i	s	s	s	s	os s	B1[2], 759
h194	4-Heptanone, 2-methyl-*	$CH_3CH_2CH_2COCH(CH_3)_2$	128.22	λ^{al} 282 (1.40)		155[750]	0.813[22]		i	s	s	s	s		B1[1], 363
h194[1]	1-Heptanone, 1-phenyl-*	Enanthophenone. $CH_3(CH_2)_5COC_6H_5$	190.29	lf	16.4	283.3 155[15]	0.9516[20]	1.5060[20]	i	s	s	s			B7[2], 264
h195	Heptasiloxane, hexadecamethyl-	$CH_3[Si(CH_3)_2O]_6Si(CH_3)_3$	533.06		−78	270[760] 165[20]	0.9012[20]	1.3965[20]	i	δ				peth s lig s	Am 68, 2284
h196	1,4,6-Heptatrien-3-one, 1(4-methoxy-phenyl)-7-phenyl-*	....	290.37	ye lf (al)	139				i	s[h]				chl s lig s	B8, 208
Ω h197	1-Heptene*	α-Heptylene. $CH_3(CH_2)_4CH:CH_2$	98.19	λ^{ht} 237 sh (0.3), 263 (−1.4)	119	93.64[760]	0.6970[20]	1.3998[20]	i	s	s				B1[3], 820
h198	2-Heptene(cis)*	β-Heptylene. $CH_3(CH_2)_3CH:CHCH_3$	98.19			98.5[760]	0.708[20]	1.406[20]	i	s	s	s	s	chl s peth s	B1[3], 824
h199	—(trans)*	$CH_3(CH_2)_3CH:CHCH_3$	98.19		−109.48	98[760]	0.7012[20]	1.4045[20]	i	s	s	s	s	chl s peth s	B1[3], 825
h200	3-Heptene(cis)*	$CH_3CH_2CH_2CH:CHCH_2CH_3$	98.19			95.75[760]	0.7030[20]	1.4059[20]	i	s	s			chl s peth s	B1[3], 826
h201	—(trans)*	$CH_3CH_2CH_2CH:CHCH_2CH_3$	98.19		−136.63	95.67[760]	0.6981[20]	1.4043[20]	i	s	s			chl s peth s	B1[3], 827
h202	1-Heptene, 1-chloro-*	$CH_3(CH_2)_4CH:CHCl$	132.64			155 78–82[75]	0.8948[20]	1.4380[20]	i	s	s			chl v to v	B1[2], 196
h203	—,2-chloro-*	$CH_3(CH_2)_4CCl:CH_2$	132.64			138[748]	0.8895[20]	1.4349[20]	i	s	s			chl s	B1[3], 823
h204	2-Heptene, 4-chloro-*	$CH_3CH_2CH_2CHClCH:CHCH_3$	132.64			140–145 49[21]	0.879[18]	1.4430[21]	i	s				MeOH v chl v	B1[3], 825
h205	3-Heptene, 4-chloro-*	$CH_3CH_2CH_2CCl:CHCH_2CH_3$	132.64			139	0.883[14]	1.437[14]	i	s				chl s	B1[3], 827
h206	2-Heptene, 6-chloro-2-methyl-*	$CH_3CHCl(CH_2)_2CH:C(CH_3)_2$	147.67			60–61[15]	0.8931[18]	1.4458[18]	i	s	s	s	s	os s	B1[2], 200
h207	2-Heptene, 2-methyl-6-methylamino-*	$CH_3CH(NHCH_3)CH_2CH_2CH:C(CH_3)_2$	141.26	....		176–8 58–9[17]			i	v	v				B4[3], 467
h208	1-Heptene-2-car-boxaldehyde, 1-phenyl-*	α-m-Amylcinnamaldehyde. Jasminaldehyde. $CH_3(CH_2)_4C(CHO):CHC_6H_5$	203.30			174–5[20] 140[5]	0.9718[20]	1.5381[20]	i	s	s				B7[2], 310
Ω h209	2-Hepten-4-ol(dl)*	$CH_3CH_2CH_2CH(OH)CH:CHCH_3$	114.19			152–4[760] 64[14]	0.8445[20]	1.4373[20]	...	s	s				B1, 447
Ω h210	1-Hepten-4-ol, 4-methyl-*	$CH_3CH_2CH_2COH(CH_3)CH_2CH:CH_2$	128.22			159–60	0.8345[20]	1.4479[18]	i	s	s				B1[3], 1945
h211	3-Hepten-2-one (trans)*	$CH_3CH_2CH_2CH:CHCOCH_3$	112.17	λ^{al} 222 (4.09)		62[15] 52[11]	0.8496[20]	1.4436[20]	i	v	v				B1[3], 3003
Ω h212	5-Hepten-2-one, 6-methyl-*	$(CH_3)_2C:CHCH_2CH_2COCH_3$	126.20		−67	173[760] 58.6[10]	0.8546[16]	1.4445[20]	i	∞	∞				B1[2], 797
h213	1-Hepten-3-yne*	$CH_3CH_2CH_2C:CCH:CH_2$	94.16			110[760] 44[75]	0.7603[20]	1.4520[25]	i	s	s	s	s	peth s	Am 61, 572
h214	1-Hepten-4-yne, 6,6-dimethyl-*	$CH_2:CHCH_2C:CC(CH_3)_3$	122.21			125[760] 68[100]	0.758[20]	1.4312[20]	i	s		s	s	peth s	C55, 23329
h215	6-Hepten-4-yne-3-ol,3-ethyl-*	$CH_2:CHC:CCOH(C_2H_5)CH_2CH_3$	138.21			62[4]	0.8875[20]	1.4800[20]	i	v	v				B1[3], 2034
—	Heptyl alcohol.	see **Heptanol***													
—	Heptyl amine*.	see **Heptane, amino-***													
—	Heptylene	see **Heptene***													
—	Heptyl thiocyanate	see **Thiocyanic acid**, heptyl ester													
h216	1-Heptyne*	$CH_3(CH_2)_4C:CH$	96.17		−81	99.74[760] 6.0[10]	0.7328[20]	1.4087[20]	δ	∞	∞		s	chl s peth s	B1[3], 995
h217	2-Heptyne*	$CH_3(CH_2)_3C:CCH_3$	96.17			112[760]	0.7480[20]	1.4230[20]	i	∞	∞		s	chl s peth s	B1[3], 998
h218	3-Heptyne*	$CH_3CH_2CH_2C:CCH_2CH_3$	96.17			105–6[760]	0.7527[20]	1.4220[20]	i	∞	∞		s	chl s peth s	B1[3], 999
h219	1-Heptyne, 1-bromo-*	$CH_3(CH_2)_4C:CBr$	175.08			164[758] 69[25]	1.2120[24]	1.4678[22]	i	s	s	s		chl s	B1[3], 998
h220	2-Heptyne, 1-bromo-*	$CH_3(CH_2)_3C:CCH_2Br$	175.08			104[56] 84[40]		1.4878[25]	i	s	s	s	s		B1[3], 998
h221	1-Heptyne, 1-chloro-*	$CH_3(CH_2)_4C:CCl$	130.62			141[760]	0.9250[24]	1.4411[24]	i	v	v			MeOH v	B1[3], 997

For explanations, symbols and abbreviations see beginning of table. For structural formulas see end of table.

No.	Name	Synonyms and Formula	Mol. wt.	Color. crystalline form. specific rotation and λ_{max} (log ε)	m.p. °C	b.p. °C	Density	n_D	w	al	eth	ace	bz	other solvents	Ref.
	2-Heptyne														
h222	2-Heptyne, 1-chloro-*	$CH_3(CH_2)_3C{:}CCH_2Cl$	130.62			167^{760} 73^{24}		1.4570^{25}	i	s	s				B1[3], 998
h223	—,7-chloro-*	$ClCH_2(CH_2)_3C{:}CCH_3$	130.62			166^{760}		1.4507^{20}	i	s	s				B1[3], 998
h224	3-Heptyne, 1-chloro-*	$CH_3CH_2CH_2C{:}CCH_2CH_2Cl$	130.62			162^{760} $90-93^{70}$		1.4520^{25}	i	s	s				B1[3], 999
h225	—,7-chloro-*	$Cl(CH_2)_3C{:}CCH_2CH_3$	130.62			164^{760} $74-5^{31}$		1.4517^{20}	i	s	s				B1[3], 999
h226	—,2,6-dimethyl-*	$(CH_3)_2CHCH_2C{:}CCH(CH_3)_2$ $|124.23$				$130-6^{760}$	0.785_4^{20}		i		s	s			B1[3], 1005
h227	—,5,5-dimethyl-*	$CH_3CH_2C(CH_3)_2C{:}CCH_2CH_3$ $|124.23$				69^{100}	0.7610_4^{20}	1.4360^{20}	i		s	s			Am 62, 1800
h228	—,5-ethyl-5-methyl-*	$(CH_3CH_2)_2C(CH_3)C{:}CCH_2CH_3$	138.25			88^{100}	0.7714_4^{20}	1.4386^{20}	i		s	s			Am 62, 1800
h229	2-Heptyn-1-ol*	Butyl propargyl alcohol. $CH_3(CH_2)_3C{:}CCH_2OH$	112.17			94^{22}		1.4523^{25}							Am 71, 1294
—	Herniarin	see Coumarin, 7-methoxy-													
—	Heroin	see Morphine, diacetyl-													
—	Hesperetin	see Flavanone, 4'-methoxy-,3',5,7-trihydroxy-													
—	Hesperetol	see Styrene, 4-hydroxy-3-methoxy-													
h232	Hesperidin	Hesperetin-1-rhamnosido-D-glucose. $C_{28}H_{34}O_{15}$.	610.58	wh nd (dil MeOH or aa) $[\alpha]_D^{30}$ −77.5 (Py, c = 4.28)	261-3 (254d)				δ	s	i		i	Py v aa s chl, CS_2 i	Am 68, 2108
—	Heteroxanthine	see Xanthine, 7-methyl-													
h233	Hexacene	Anthraceno-2':3',2:3-anthracene.	328.42	dk bl-gr cr (sub)	ca. 380	sub			i	i					E14s, 789
—	Hexachlorophene	see Methane, bis(2-hydroxy-3,5,6-trichlorophenyl)-*													
h234	Hexacosane*	Cerane. $CH_3(CH_2)_{24}CH_3$	366.72	mcl, tcl or rh (bz), cr (eth)	56.4	412.2^{760} 248.22^{10}	0.8032_4^{20} 0.7783^{60}	1.4501^{20} 1.4357^{60}	i	s^h δ			s	lig v chl s	B1[2], 143
Ω h235	Hexacosanoic acid*	Cerotic acid. Phthioic acid. $CH_3(CH_2)_{24}CO_2H$	396.71	nd (al)	88-9		0.8198_4^{100}	1.4301^{100}	i	v^h	v				B2[2], 380
Ω h236	1-Hexacosanol*	Cerotin. Ceryl alcohol. $CH_3(CH_2)_{25}OH$	382.72	rh pl (dil al)	80	305^{20}d			i	s	s				B1[2], 470
h237	1,15-Hexadecadiyne*	$HC{:}C(CH_2)_{12}C{:}CH$	218.39	fl (al)	44-5	$152-5^{12}$									B1[2], 249
h238	6,9-Hexadecadiyne*	$CH_3(CH_2)_5C{:}CCH_2C{:}C(CH_2)_4CH_3$ $|218.39$				169^{15}	0.845_4^{18}	1.4694^{18}							C28, 4035
h239	6,10-Hexadecadiyne*	$CH_3(CH_2)_4C{:}CCH_2CH_2C{:}C(CH_2)_4CH_3$ $|218.39$				157^{10} 130.6^6	0.7907_4^{20}	1.4523^{20}							C45, 3638
h240	Hexadecanal*	Palmitaldehyde. $CH_3(CH_2)_{14}CHO$	240.43	pl (eth), nd (peth) λ^{cy} 293 (1.45)	34	$200-2^{29}$			i	s	s	s	s	os s	B1[2], 771
h241	—,dimethyl acetal	$CH_3(CH_2)_{14}CH(OCH_3)_2$	286.50		10	144^2	0.8542^{20}	1.4382^{25}	v	s	v	s		MeOH v	C49, 161
h242	—,oxime	$CH_3(CH_2)_{14}CH{:}NOH$	255.45	nd (dil al)	88				i	s			δ	chl s peth δ	B1[2], 771
Ω h243	Hexadecane*	Cetane. $CH_3(CH_2)_{14}CH_3$	226.45	lf (ace)	18.17	287^{760} 149^{10}	0.77331_4^{20}	1.4345	i	δ^h	∞				B1[3], 555
Ω h244	—,1-amino-*	Cetylamine. $CH_3(CH_2)_{15}NH_2$	241.47	lf	46.77	322.5^{760} 177.9^{10} 144^2	0.8129_4^{20}	1.4496^{20}	i	v	v	s	v	chl s	B4[2], 660
Ω h245	—,1-bromo-*	Cetyl bromide. $CH_3(CH_2)_{15}Br$	305.35		17-9	336^{760} 188^{10}	0.9991_4^{20}	1.4618^{20}	i	s	s				B1[2], 138
Ω h246	—,1-chloro-*	Cetyl chloride. $CH_3(CH_2)_{15}Cl$	260.90		17.9	322^{760} 177^{10}	0.8652_4^{20}	1.4505^{20}	i	s	s				B1[3], 558
h247	—,1,16-dibromo-*	$Br(CH_2)_{16}Br$	384.25	lf (al)	56	204^4			i	δ v^h				chl v	B1[2], 138
h248	—,1-fluoro-*	Cetyl fluoride. $CH_3(CH_2)_{15}F$	244.44		18	289^{760} 152.63^{10}	0.8321_4^{20}	1.4317^{20}	i		s			lig s	B1[2], 138
h249	—,1-iodo-*	Cetyl iodide. $CH_3(CH_2)_{15}I$	352.35	lf (al)	24.7	357^{760} 202^{10}	1.1257_4^{20}	1.4818^{20}	i	δ	s	s	∞	chl v	B1[3], 560
h250	—,1-phenyl-*	Cetylbenzene. $CH_3(CH_2)_{15}C_6H_5$	302.55		27	237^{16}	0.8560_4^{20}	1.4814^{20}	i	δ	v		v	CS_2, lig v	B5, 472
h251	Hexadecanedioic acid*	Thapsic acid. $HO_2C(CH_2)_{14}CO_2H$	286.42	pl (al, AcOEt)	126				i	s^h	δ	s^h	i	AcOEt s^h s^h CS_2 i	B2, 733
Ω h252	1-Hexadecanethiol*	Cetyl mercaptan. $CH_3(CH_2)_{15}SH$	258.52	(lig) λ^{hx} 225 sh (2.2)	18-20	$123-8^{0.5}$			i	δ	s				B2[2], 330
Ω h253	Hexadecanoic acid*	Palmitic acid. $CH_3(CH_2)_{14}CO_2H$	256.43	nd (al) λ^{al} 210 (1.70)	63	390^{760} 267^{100}	0.8527_4^{62}	1.4335^{60}	i	s	∞	s	s	chl v	Am 64, 2739
Ω h254	—,amide	Palmitamide. $CH_3(CH_2)_{14}CONH_2$	255.45	lf	107	236^{12}			i	δ	δ	δ	δ		B2[2], 341
h255	—,—,N-phenyl-*	Palmitanilide. $CH_3(CH_2)_{14}CONHC_6H_5$	331.55	nd (al)	90.5	$282-4^{17}$ 132^{10}			i	v	δ	v	v	chl v aa v^h	B12[2], 148
h256	—,anhydride*	$[CH_3(CH_2)_{14}CO]_2O$	494.85	lf (peth)	64		0.8383_5^{83}	1.4364^{68}	i	δ	v		v	peth δ^h	B2[2], 341
h257	—,benzyl ester*	$CH_3(CH_2)_{14}CO_2CH_2C_6H_5$	346.56	cr (al)	36		0.9136_{25}^{25}	1.4689^{50}	i	s	s	s		chl v	B6[2], 417
h258	—,butyl ester*	$CH_3(CH_2)_{14}CO_2C_4H_9^n$	312.54	cr (dil al)	16.9			1.4312^{50}	i	s	s	s			B2[2], 336
Ω h259	—,chloride	$CH_3(CH_2)_{14}COCl$	274.88		12	199^{20}		1.4514^{20}	d	d	v				B2[2], 341

For explanations, symbols and abbreviations see beginning of table. For structural formulas see end of table.

No.	Name	Synonyms and Formula	Mol. wt.	Color, crystalline form, specific rotation and λ_{max} (log ε)	m.p. °C	b.p. °C	Density	n_D	w	al	eth	ace	bz	other solvents	Ref.
	Hexadecanoic acid														
h260	—,ethyl ester*	$CH_3(CH_2)_{14}CO_2C_2H_5$	284.49	nd	α: 24 β: 19.3	191^{10}	0.8577_4^{25}	1.4347^{34}	i	s	s	s	s	chl s	B2², 336
h261	—,hentriacontyl ester*	Myricyl palmitate. $CH_3(CH_2)_{14}CO_2(CH_2)_{30}CH_3$	691.28	cr (eth)	72	....	....	....	i	i	s	...	...	....	B2, 373.
h262	—,hexadecyl ester*	Cetyl palmitate. $CH_3(CH_2)_{14}CO_2(CH_2)_{15}CH_3$	480.87	pl (eth)	53–4	360	0.8324_4^{50}	1.4425^{50}	i	s^h	s	...	s	chl, CS_2 s	B2², 337
h262¹	—,2-hydroxyethyl ester*	$CH_3(CH_2)_{14}CO_2CH_2CH_2OH$	300.49	....	51	$173–4^3$	0.8786_4^{60}	....	i	v	s^h	...	...	....	C42, 2927
h263	—,isopropyl ester*	$CH_3(CH_2)_{14}CO_2C_3H_7^i$	298.52	....	13–4	160^2	0.8404^{38}	1.4364^{25}	i	v	s	v	v	chl v	B2², 336
Ω h264	—,methyl ester*	$CH_3(CH_2)_{14}CO_2CH_3$	270.46	....	30	$415–8^{747}$ 148^2	....	....	i	v	s	v	v	chl v	B2, 372
Ω h265	—,nitrile	$CH_3(CH_2)_{14}CN$	237.43	hex	31	333^{760} 251^{100} 142^1	0.8303_4^{20}	1.4450^{20}	i	v	v	v	v	chl v	B2², 341
h266	—,propyl ester*	$CH_3(CH_2)_{14}CO_2C_3H_7^n$	298.52	nd	20.4	190^{12}	0.8455^{38}	1.4392^{25}	i	v	s	v	v	chl v	B2², 336
Ω h267	—,16-hydroxy-*	$HO(CH_2)_{15}CO_2H$	272.43	cr (bz-eth)	95	....	....	....	i	s	δ ε^h	s	δ^h	....	B3, 362
Ω h268	—,9,10,16-tri-hydroxy*	Aleuritic acid. $HO(CH_2)_6CH(OH)CH(OH)(CH_2)_7CO_2H$	304.43	lf (dil al), nd(w)	102	....	....	....	δ					....	B3², 272
Ω h269	1-Hexadecanol*	Cetyl alcohol. $CH_3(CH_2)_{15}OH$	242.45	fl (AcOEt)	50	344^{760} 190^{15}	0.8176_4^{50}	1.4283^{79}	i	δ	v	s	v	chl v	B1², 466
Ω h270	1-Hexadecene*	Cetene. Cetylene. $CH_3(CH_2)_{13}CH:CH_2$	224.44	lf	4.1	284.4^{760} 155^{15}	0.7811_4^{20}	1.4412^{20}	i	s	s	...	...	peth s	B1², 206
h271	2-Hexadecenoic acid (form I)*	Gaidic acid. $CH_3(CH_2)_{12}CH:CHCO_2H$	254.42	lf (al)	39	....	....	....	v					chl v peth s	B2, 461
h272	2-Hexadecenoic acid (form II)*	Δ-α,β-Hypogeic acid. $CH_3(CH_2)_{12}CH:CHCO_2H$	254.42	fl (al)	49	....	....	....	s	s	v	...	...	chl, peth v	B2, 460
h273	7-Hexadecenoic acid*	Hypogeic acid (artificial). $CH_3(CH_2)_7CH:CH(CH_2)_5CO_2H$	254.42	cr	33	230^{10}	....	....	i	v	v	...	...	....	B2, 460
h274	1-Hexadecyne*	$CH_3(CH_2)_{13}C:CH$	222.42	....	15	284^{760} 147.8^{10}	0.7965_4^{20}	1.4440^{20}	i				s	....	B1³, 1028
h275	2-Hexadecyne*	$CH_3(CH_2)_{12}C:CCH_3$	222.42	fl	20	160^{15} (184^{15})	0.8039_4^{20}	....						....	B1, 262
h276	7-Hexadecynoic acid*	$CH_3(CH_2)_7C:C(CH_2)_5CO_2H$	252.40	nd (w), cr (al)	47	214^{15}	....	....	i	v	v	...	...	....	B2, 494
h277	2,4-Hexadien-1-al*	Sorbaldehyde. $CH_3CH:CHCH:CHCHO$	96.14	λ^{al} 271 (4.99)	....	$173–4^{754}$ 76^{30}	0.898^{20}	1.5384^{20}						chl s	B1², 809
h278	1,2-Hexadiene*	Propylallene. $CH_3CH_2CH:CH:C:CH_2$	82.15	....	....	76^{760}	0.7149^{20}	1.4282^{20}	i		s			chl s	B1³, 981
h279	1,3-Hexadiene*	$CH_3CH_2CH:CHCH:CH_2$	82.15	....	....	73^{760}	0.7050_4^{20}	1.4380^{20}	i		s			chl s	B1³, 981
h280	1,4-Hexadiene*	1-Allylpropene. $CH_3CH:CHCH_2CH:CH_2$	82.15	....	....	65^{760}	0.7000_4^{20}	1.4150^{20}	i		s			chl s	B1³, 982
Ω h281	1,5-Hexadiene*	Biallyl. $H_2C:CHCH_2CH_2CH:CH_2$	82.15	λ^{vap} 177 (4.4)	-141	59.5^{760}	0.6880_4^{20}	1.4042^{20}	i	s	s	...	s	chl s	B1³, 982
h282	2,4-Hexadiene*	Bipropenyl. $CH_3CH:CHCH:CHCH_3$	82.15	....	-79	80^{760}	0.7196_4^{20}	1.4500^{20}	i	s	s	...	s	chl s	B1³, 985
h283	1,3-Hexadiene,3-chloro-*	$CH_3CH_2CH:CClCH:CH_2$	116.59	....	....	68^{117}	0.9390_4^{20}	1.4770^{20}	i				s	chl s	B1³, 981
h284	1,4-Hexadiene,5-chloro-2-isopropyl-*	$CH_3CCl:CHCH_2C[CH(CH_3)_2]:CH_2$	158.67	....	95¹⁸	0.9310_4^{25}	1.4730^{25}	i			s		chl s	C33, 3362
h285	2,4-Hexadiene, 6-chloro-2-methyl-*	$ClCH_2CH:CHCH:C(CH_3)_2$	130.62	....	57¹¹	0.9416_4^{20}	1.5120^{20}	i			s		chl s	B1³, 1000
h286	1,5-Hexadiene, decachloro-*	Perchlorodiallyl. $Cl_2C:CClCCl_2CCl_2CCl:CCl_2$	426.60	cr (ace)	49	$121^{0.03}$	1.905_4^{51}	1.6012^{51}	i	s	s	...	s	chl s	B1³, 984
h287	2,4-Hexadiene, 1,3-dichloro-*	$CH_3CH:CHCCl:CHCH_2Cl$	151.05	....	....	$80–2^{17}$	1.1456_4^{20}	1.5271^{20}	i			s		chl s	B1³, 987
Ω h288	1,5-Hexadiene, 2,5-dimethyl-*	Diisobutenyl. $CH_2:C(CH_3)CH_2CH_2C(CH_3):CH_2$	110.20	....	-75.6	134^{760}	0.7512^{20}	1.43995^{21}	i	s	s	...	s	chl s	B1², 239
Ω h289	2,4-Hexadiene, 2,5-dimethyl-*	Diisocrotyl. $(CH_3)_2C:CHCH:C(CH_3)_2$	110.20	....	14.5–.8	134^{760} 75^{100}	0.7625_4^{20}	1.4785^{20}	i	s	s	...	s	chl s	B1³, 1011
h290	—,1,3,4,6-tetrachloro-*	$ClCH_2CH:CClCCl:CHCH_2Cl$	219.93	....	$84–9^1$	1.4013_4^{20}	1.5465^{20}	i			...		chl, MeOH s	B1³, 987
h291	1,4-Hexadiene, 3,3,6-trichloro-*	$ClCH_2CH:CHCCl_2CH:CH_2$	185.48	....	....	$100–3^4$	1.3036_4^{20}	1.5585^{20}	i			s		chl s	B1³, 982
h292	2,4-Hexadiene-1,6-dioic acid (cis, cis)*	cis-Muconic acid. $HO_2CCH:CHCH:CHCO_2H$	142.11	....	194–5	....	....	....						aa s	B2, 803
Ω h293	—(trans, trans)*	trans-Muconic acid. $HO_2CCH:CHCH:CHCO_2H$	142.11	nd (al)	305d	320	....	....	δ	δ		...		AcOEt, aa s	B2, 803
h294	—,dimethyl ester (trans, trans)*	$CH_3O_2CCH:CHCH:CHCO_2CH_3$	170.17	nd (dil al)	157	....	....	....	δ	s	s	...		aa s	B2², 672
h295	1,5-Hexadiene-3,4-diol(d)*	Divinyl glycol. $H_2C:CHCH(OH)CH(OH)CH:CH_2$	114.15	$[\alpha]_4^{17}$ +94.8 (al)	-60	198^{760} 97^{13}	1.006_4^{20}	1.4700^{20}	s	s	s			chl s	B1³, 2272
h296	—(dl)*	$H_2C:CHCH(OH)CH(OH)CH:CH_2$	114.15	hyg	21.7	$90.5–.7^8$	1.017_4^{19}	1.4790^{19}	s	s	s	...		chl s	B1³, 2272
h297	—(meso)*	$CH_2:CHCH(OH)CH(OH)CH:CH_2$	114.15	hyg	18	100^{14}	1.023_4^{19}	1.4810^{19}	v	v	v	...		chl v	B1³, 2272

For explanations, symbols and abbreviations see beginning of table. For structural formulas see end of table.

No.	Name	Synonyms and Formula	Mol. wt.	Color, crystalline form, specific rotation and λ_{max} (log ε)	m.p. °C	b.p. °C	Density	n_D	w	al	eth	ace	bz	other solvents	Ref.
	2,4-Hexadienoic acid														
Ω h298	2,4-Hexadienoic acid (trans, trans)	Sorbic acid. CH₃CH:CHCH:CHCO₂H	112.14	nd (dil al)	134.5	228d 153[50]	1.204[19]₄	....	s[h] δ	s	v	...	...	....	B2, 489
h299	—,amide	CH₃CH:CHCH:CHCONH₂	111.15	nd (w)	171.5–2.5	....	....	....	s	s					B2², 453
h300	—,chloride	CH₃CH:CHCH:CHCOCl	130.58	....	....	78[15]	1.0666[19]₄	1.5545[20]	d	...	...	s			B2², 453
Ω h301	—,ethyl ester*	CH₃CH:CHCH:CHCO₂C₂H₅	140.19	....	....	195.5 85[20]	0.9506[20]₄	1.4951[20]	i	s	s	...	...	chl s	B2², 452
h302	—,methyl ester*	CH₃CH:CHCH:CHCO₂CH₃	126.16	lf	15	180[759] 70[20]	0.9777[20]₄	1.5025[22]	i	s	s				B2², 452
h303	2,4-Hexadien-1-ol*	Sorbyl alcohol. CH₃CH:CHCH:CHCH₂OH	98.15	nd	30.5–1.5	76[12]	0.8967[23]₄	1.4981[20]	i	s	s				B1³, 1988
h304	3,5-Hexadien-2-ol*	H₂C:CHCH:CHCH(OH)CH₃	98.15	λ^{al} 225 (4.33)	....	77–8[26] 44–5[8]	0.8678[20]	1.4816[20]		v					B1³, 1987
h306	3,5-Hexadien-2-one, 6-phenyl-*	Cinnamylideneacetone. C₆H₅CH:CHCH:CHCOCH₃	172.23	wh lf (eth) λ^{al} 234 (3.65), 319 (4.56)	68	170–2[15]	....	....	i	s	s	s	s	chl, MeOH s	B7², 321
h308	1,5-Hexadien-3-yne*	Divinyl acetylene. H₂C:CHC:CCH:CH₂	78.12	....	−88	85[760]	0.7851[20]	1.5035[20]	i				s		B1³, 1058
h309	3,5-Hexadien-1-yne*	HC:CCH:CHCH:CH₂	78.12	....	....	83.4[760] 32[100]	0.7806[20]	1.5095[20]	i				s	sulf s	B1³, 1058
h310	1,5-Hexadien-3-yne, 2,5-di-methyl-*	Diisopropenyl acetylene. CH₂:C(CH₃)C:CC(CH₃):CH₂	106.17	ye	....	123[760]	0.7863[25]	1.4845[20]	i				s	chl s	B1³, 1062
h311	1,4-Hexadiyne-	HC:CCH₂C:CCH₃	78.12	....	< −80	78–83[760]	0.825[0]₄	....	i				s	chl s	B1³, 1057
h312	1,5-Hexadiyne*	Dipropargyl. HC:CCH₂CH₂C:CH	78.12	....	−6	86[760] 20[46]	0.8049[20]₄	1.4380[23]	i	s	s	s	s	os s	B1³, 1057
h313	2,4-Hexadiyne*	Dimethyl diacetylene. CH₃C:CC:CCH₃	78.12	pr (sub) λ^{al} 218.5 (2.48), 236 (2.52), 250 (2.20)	68.5	129–30	....	....		v	v				B1², 247
h314	1,5-Hexadiyne,1,6-diamino-	H₂NC:CCH₂CH₂C:CNH₂	108.13	....	104–5	....	....	....	s[h]	...	...			s	C53, 10036
—	Hexahydrobenzyl alcohol	see **Methanol, cyclohexyl-***													
—	Hexahydro-p-cymene	see **p-Menthane**													
—	Hexahydrothymol	see **Menthol**													
—	Hexamethylene-diamine	see **Hexane, 1,6-diamino-***													
—	Hexamethylene glycol	see **1,6-Hexanediol***													
—	Hexamethylene-imine	see **Cycloheptane, 1-aza-***													
Ω h315	Hexamethylene-tetramine	Aminoform. Formin. Hexamine. Urotropine.	140.19	rh (al)	285–95 sub	sub	1.331[-5]	....	v s[h]	s	δ	s	δ	chl s	B1², 648
Ω h316	Hexanal*	Caproaldehyde. n-Caproic aldehyde. CH₃(CH₂)₄CHO	100.16	λ^{vap} 184.5	−56	128[760] (131) 28[12]	0.81392[20]₄	1.4039[20]	δ	v	v	s			B1², 745
h317	—,oxime*	CH₃(CH₂)₄CH:NOH	115.18	cr (MeOH)	51	....	....	....		s	s				B1, 689
Ω h318	—,2-ethyl-*	CH₃(CH₂)₃CH(C₂H₅)CHO	128.22	....	< −100	163[760] 65[15]	0.8540[20]	1.4142[20]	i	s	s				B1, 707
Ω h319	Hexane*	Dipropyl. CH₃(CH₂)₄CH₃	86.18	....	−95 (−93.5)	68.95[760]	0.6603[20]₄	1.37506[20]	i	v	s			chl s	B1³, 374
—	neo-Hexane	see **Butane, 2,2-dimethyl-***													
Ω h320	Hexane, 1-amino-*	n-Hexylamine. CH₃(CH₂)₅NH₂	101.19	....	−19	130[762]	0.7660[20]	1.4180[20]	δ	∞	∞				B4², 649
h321	—,2-amino-(d)*	d-α-Methylamylamine. CH₃(CH₂)₃CH(NH₂)CH₃	101.19	$[\alpha]_D^{27}$ +4.30	....	114–5 64[90]	0.755[27]₄	....							C50, 4782
Ω h322	—,-(dl)*	CH₃(CH₂)₃CH(NH₂)CH₃	101.19	....	−19	117–8	0.7534[20]₄	1.4080[25]	...	s	s				B4, 190
h323	—,2-amino-4-methyl-*	CH₃CH₂CH(CH₃)CH₂CH(NH₂)CH₃	115.22	....	....	130–5[760]	0.7655[20]	1.4150[25]	δ	v	v			chl, dil ac v	Am 66, 1516
h324	—,3,4-bis(4-hydroxy-3-methylphenyl)-	Dimethylhexestrol. Promethestrol.	298.43	cr (dil aa)	145	....	....	....	i	v	v			aa δ	Am 70, 508
h325	—,2,4-bis(4-hydroxyphenyl)-3-ethyl-	Benzestrol. Octofollin.	298.43	cr (al)	162–6	....	....	....	i	v	v	v	δ	MeOH v aa s chl, peth δ	Am 68, 729
Ω h326	—,1-bromo-*	n-Hexyl bromide. CH₃(CH₂)₅Br	165.08	....	−84.7	155.3[760] 41[10]	1.1744[20]₄	1.44781[20]	i	∞	∞	s		chl v	B1³, 391
Ω h327	—,2-bromo-*	sec-Hexyl bromide. CH₃(CH₂)₃CHBrCH₃	165.08	....	....	144[749] 78[90]	1.1658[20]₄	1.4832[25]	i	v	s	s		chl v	B1³, 392
Ω h328	—,3-bromo-*	CH₃CH₂CH₂CHBrCH₂CH₃	165.08	....	....	141–3[760]	1.1799[20]	1.4472[20]	i	s	s	s		chl v	B1, 144
h329	—,1-bromo-6-fluoro-*	F(CH₂)₆Br	183.07	....	....	67–8[11]	1.293[20]₄	1.4435[25]	i	v	v	s		chl s	C51, 7300
Ω h330	—,1-chloro-*	n-Hexyl chloride. CH₃(CH₂)₅Cl	120.62	....	−94.0	134.5[760]	0.8785[20]	1.41991[20]	i	v	s	s		chl v	B1³, 388
h331	—,2-chloro-*	sec-Hexyl chloride. CH₃(CH₂)₃CHClCH₃	120.62	....	....	122–3[760] 61[100]	0.8694[21]₄	1.4142[22]	i	s	s	s		chl v	B1³, 389
h332	—,3-chloro-*	CH₃CH₂CH₂CHClCH₂CH₃	120.62	....	....	123[760] 60[95]	0.8700[20]₂₀	1.4163[20]	i	s	v	s	s	chl v	Am 61, 940

For explanations, symbols and abbreviations see beginning of table. For structural formulas see end of table.

No.	Name	Synonyms and Formula	Mol. wt.	Color, crystalline form, specific rotation and λ_{max} (log ε)	m.p. °C	b.p. °C	Density	n_D	Solubility						Ref.
									w	al	eth	ace	bz	other solvents	
	Hexane														
h333	,2-chloro-2,5-dimethyl-*	$(CH_3)_2CHCH_2CH_2CCl(CH_3)_2$ 148.68		....	....	86^{100} 44^{14}	0.8476_4^{18}	1.4232^{20}	i	s	s	s	s	....	B1[3], 485
h334	—,3-chloro-2,3-dimethyl-*	$CH_3CH_2CH_2CCl(CH_3)CH(CH_3)_2$ 148.68		....	....	$41-3^{12}$	0.8869_4^{20}	1.4333^{25}	i	s	...	...	...	....	B1[3], 481
h336	—,1-chloro-3-ethyl-(d)*	$CH_3CH_2CH_2CH(C_2H_5)CH_2CH_2Cl$ 148.68		$[\alpha]_D^{27} +1.15$	....	85^{40}	0.879_4^{21}	1.4335^{25}	i	...	s	...	...	chl s	B1[3], 478
h337	—,3-chloro-3-ethyl-*	$CH_3CH_2CH_2CCl(C_2H_5)_2$.... 148.68		....	....	155d $62-3^{24}$	0.9018^0	1.4358^{20}	i	...	s	...	...	chl s	B1[3], 479
h338	—,1-chloro-6-fluoro-*	$F(CH_2)_6Cl$ 138.61		....	....	167^{740} 62^{15}	1.015_2^{20}	1.4168^{25}	i	v	v	v	...	chl s	C51, 7300
h339	—,1-chloro-3-methyl-*	$CH_3CH_2CH_2CH(CH_3)CH_2CH_2Cl$ 134.65		....	....	$150-2^{758}$	0.8766_4^{20}	1.4274^{20}	i	v	v	v	...	chl s	B1[2], 119
h340	—,2-chloro-2-methyl-*	$CH_3(CH_2)_3CCl(CH_3)_2$ 134.65		....	....	$135^{760} \delta d$ 59.5^{52}	0.8635_4^{20}	1.4200^{20}	i	v	v	v	...	chl s	B1, 156
h341	—,2-chloro-5-methyl-*	$(CH_3)_2CHCH_2CH_2CHClCH_3$ 134.65		....	....	$138^{735}d$	0.863_4^{20}	....	i	v	v	v	...	chl s	B1, 156
h342	—,3-chloro-3-methyl-*	$CH_3CH_2CH_2CCl(CH_3)CH_2CH_3$ 134.65		....	....	135^{760}	0.8787_4^{20}	1.4250^{20}	i	v	v	v	...	chl s	B1[2], 119
h343	—,3-chloro-2,2,3-trimethyl-*	$CH_3(CH_2)_2CCl(CH_3)C(CH_3)_3$ 162.71		....	....	$64-5^{13}$	0.9010_4^{20}	1.4465^{20}	i	v	v	v	...	chl s	B1[3], 515
b344	—,1,6-diamino-*	Hexamethylenediamine. $H_2N(CH_2)_6NH_2$ 116.21		rh bipym pl	41–2	204–5 100^{70}			v	s	...	...	s		B4[2], 710
h345	—,—,dihydrochloride*	$H_2N(CH_2)_6NH_2.2HCl$ 189.13		nd (al-eth)	248–50	....			v	δ	i	...	i	chl i	B4[2], 710
h346	—,2,5-diamino-*	$CH_3CH(NH_2)CH_2CH_2CH(NH_2)CH_3$ 116.21		....	....	175			v	v	v	...	...		B4, 269
h347	—,1,2-dibromo-*	$CH_3(CH_2)_3CHBrCH_2Br$.. 243.98		....	....	$103-5^{36}$ 87^{16}	1.5774_4^{20}	1.5024^{20}	...	s	∞	...	s	chl s	B1[2], 109
h348	—,1,2-dichloro-*	$CH_3(CH_2)_3CHClCH_2Cl$.. 155.07		....	....	$172-4^{760}$ $73-4^{0.3}$	1.085^{15}	....	...	...	s	...	s	chl s	B1, 144
Ω h349	—,1,6-dichloro-*	$Cl(CH_2)_6Cl$........... 155.07		....	....	$203-5$ 94^{22}	1.0677_4^{20}	1.4572^{20}	i	...	s	...	...	chl s	B1[3], 389
h350	—,2,2-dichloro-*	$CH_3(CH_2)_3CCl_2CH_3$... 155.07		....	....	68^{49}	1.0150_4^{25}	1.4353^{25}	i	...	s	...	...	chl s	B1[3], 390
h351	—,2,3-dichloro-*	$CH_3CH_2CH_2CHClCHClCH_3$ 155.07		....	....	$162-5$	1.0527^{11}	....	...	...	s	...	...	chl s	B1[2], 109
h352	—,2,5-dichloro-(dl)*	$CH_3CHClCH_2CH_2CHClCH_3$ 155.07		....	fp -38.36	177^{751} (cor) 106^{91}	1.0474_4^{20}	1.4491^{20}	i	...	s	...	...	chl s	B1, 144
h353	—,2,5-dichloro-(meso)*	$CH_3CHClCH_2CH_2CHClCH_3$ 155.07		....	19.88	178^{752} (cor) 109^{99}	1.0474_4^{20}	1.4484^{20}	i	...	s	...	...	chl s	B1, 144
h354	—,3,4-dichloro-(dl)*	$CH_3CH_2CHClCHClCH_2CH_3$ 155.07		....	....	167.7 62^{20}	1.0617^{20}	1.4541^{20}	i	...	...	s	...	chl s	B1[3], 390
h355	—,2,5-dichloro-2,5-dimethyl-*	$(CH_3)_2CClCH_2CH_2CCl(CH_3)_2$ 183.12		lf, nd	67–8	....	0.9543^{70}	....	...	s	s	...	s	chl s	B1[2], 127
h356	—,3,4-dichloro-3,4-dimethyl-*	$CH_3CH_2CCl(CH_3)CCl(CH_3)CH_2CH_3$ 183.12		....	....	165^{760} $114-5^{18}$			...	...	...	...	...	chl s	B1[2], 62
Ω h357	—,1,6-diiodo-*	$I(CH_2)_6I$ 337.97		nd	10	$141-2^{10}$ 113^3	2.03_2^{22}	1.585^{20}	i	v	v	...	...	....	B1[2], 110
h358	—,2,2-dimethyl-*	$CH_3(CH_2)_3C(CH_3)_3$ 114.23		....	-121.18	106.84^{760} 3.1^{10}	0.69528_4^{20}	1.39349^{20}	i	∞	∞	∞	∞	chl, lig ∞	B1[3], 479
h359	—,2,3-dimethyl-(dl)*	$CH_3CH_2CH_2CH(CH_3)CH(CH_3)_2$ 114.23		....	....	115.6^{760} 9.9^{10}	0.71214_4^{20}	1.40113^{20}	i	∞	s	∞	∞	chl, lig ∞	B1[3], 480
h360	—,—(l)*	$CH_3CH_2CH_2CH(CH_3)CH(CH_3)_2$ 114.23		$[\alpha]_D^{25} -0.92$	....	113^{760}			i	∞	s	∞	∞	chl, lig ∞	B1[3], 482
h361	—,2,4-dimethyl-(d)*	$CH_3CH_2CH(CH_3)CH_2CH(CH_3)_2$ 114.23		$[\alpha]_D^{30} +2.99$	....	111^{760}	0.696_4^{30}	1.3810^{20}	i	∞	v	∞	∞	chl, lig ∞	B1[3], 483
h362	—,—(dl)*	$CH_3CH_2CH(CH_3)CH_2CH(CH_3)_2$ 114.23		....	....	109.4^{760} 5.2^{10}	0.70036_4^{20}	1.39534^{20}	i	∞	s	∞	∞	chl, lig ∞	B1[3], 482
h363	—,—(l)*	$CH_3CH_2CH(CH_3)CH_2CH(CH_3)_2$ 114.23		$[\alpha]_D^{21} -10.85$	....	110^{760}	0.703_4^{21}	....	i	∞	s	∞	∞	chl, lig ∞	B1[3], 483
Ω h364	—,2,5-dimethyl-*	$(CH_3)_2CHCH_2CH_2CH(CH_3)_2$ 114.23		....	-91.2	109^{760} 5.3^{10}	0.69354_4^{20}	1.39246^{20}	i	∞	s	∞	∞	chl, lig ∞	B1[3], 483
h365	—,3,3-dimethyl-*	$CH_3CH_2CH_2C(CH_3)_2CH_2CH_3$ 114.23		....	-126.1	112^{760} 6.1^{10}	0.71000_4^{20}	1.40009^{20}	i	∞	v	v	v	os s	B1[3], 486
Ω h366	—,3,4-dimethyl-*	$CH_3CH_2CH(CH_3)CH(CH_3)CH_2CH_3$ 114.23		....	....	117.72^{760} 11.3^{10}	0.7200_4^{20}	1.4046^{70}	i	∞	s	∞	∞	chl, lig ∞	B1[3], 488
h367	—,1,6-dinitro-*	$O_2N(CH_2)_6NO_2$ 176.17		cr (MeOH) $\lambda^{95\% al}$ 276 (1.65)	37.5	$100-3^{0.3}$			i					aa s	B1[3], 396
h368	—,3-ethyl-*	$CH_3CH_2CH(CH_2CH_3)_2$ 114.23		....	....	118.53^{760} 12.8^{10}	0.7136_4^{20}	1.4018^{20}	i	∞	∞	∞	∞	chl, lig ∞	B1[3], 478
h369	—,1-fluoro-*	$CH_3(CH_2)_5F$ 104.17		....	-103	91.5^{760}	0.7995^{20}	1.3738^{20}	i	...	s	...	s	....	B1[3], 387
Ω h370	—,1-iodo-*	$CH_3(CH_2)_5I$ 212.08		....	-75	181.33^{760} 58.23^{10}	1.4397_4^{20}	1.49290^{20}	i	...	s	...	s	....	B1[3], 394
h371	—,2-methyl-*	Isoheptane. $CH_3(CH_2)_3CH(CH_3)_2$ 100.21		....	-118.27	90^{760} -9.09^{10}	0.67869_4^{20}	1.38485^{20}	i	s	∞	∞	∞	chl, lig ∞	B1[3], 434
h372	—,3-methyl-(d)*	$CH_3CH_2CH_2CH(CH_3)CH_2CH_3$ 100.21		$[\alpha]_D^{20} +9.5$	-119	92^{760}	0.6860^{20}	1.3887^{20}	i	s	∞	∞	∞	chl, lig ∞	B1[3], 439

For explanations, symbols and abbreviations see beginning of table. For structural formulas see end of table.

No.	Name	Synonyms and Formula	Mol. wt.	Color, crystalline form. specific rotation and λ_{max} (log ε)	m.p. °C	b.p. °C	Density	n_D	Solubility w	al	eth	ace	bz	other solvents	Ref.
	Hexane														
Ω h373	—,—(dl)*	$CH_3CH_2CH_2CH(CH_3)CH_2CH_3$ 100.21			ca. −173	92[760]	0.6872[20]	1.3885[20]	i	∞	∞	∞	∞	chl, lig ∞	B1[3], 437
h374	—,—(l)*	$CH_3CH_2CH_2CH(CH_3)CH_2CH_3$ 100.21		$[\alpha]_D^{21}$ −7.75		92[760]	0.6872[21]	1.3854[25]	i	s	∞	∞	∞	chl, lig ∞	B1[3], 440
h375	—,1,1,1,2,2-pentachloro-*	$CH_3(CH_2)_3CCl_2CCl_3$ 258.40				129–31[10]	1.370[25]	1.4872[25]	i	...	s			chl s	B1[3], 390
h376	—,1-phenyl-*	Hexylbenzene. $CH_3(CH_2)_5C_6H_5$ 162.28			−62	227[760]	0.8613[20]	1.4900[20]	i		∞	...	s	peth s	B5[2], 337
h377	—,1,1,2,2-tetrachloro-*	$CH_3(CH_2)_3CCl_2CHCl_2$ 223.96				99–101[14]	1.3096[25]	1.488[25]	i		s	s	s	chl s	B1[3], 390
Ω h378	—,2,2,5-trimethyl-*	$(CH_3)_2CHCH_2CH_2C(CH_3)_3$ 128.26			−105.78	124[760] 16.17[10]	0.7072[20]	1.3997[20]	i	v	v	v	v	lig ∞ os v	B1[3], 516
h379	1,6-Hexanedial*	Adipaldehyde. $OCH(CH_2)_4CHO$ 114.15			−8	92–4[9] 70[3]	1.0031[19]	1.4350[20]	δ	v	v	...	s	aa s	B1[2], 839
Ω h380	Hexanedioic acid*	Adipic acid. $HO_2C(CH_2)_4CO_2H$ 146.14		mcl pr (w, ace-lig)	153	265[100] 205[10] sub	1.360[25]		δ s[h]	s	v	s		aa, lig i	B2[2], 572
Ω h381	—,diamide	Adipamide. $H_2NCO(CH_2)_4CONH_2$ 144.18		pl	220				δ	v	δ				B2[2], 576
h382	—,diazide	$N_3OC(CH_2)_4CON_3$ 196.18			−1	d				v	v				B2[1], 278
Ω h383	—,dibutyl ester*	$C_4H_9^nO_2C(CH_2)_4CO_2C_4H_9^n$ 258.36			−32.4	165[10] 145[4]	0.9615[20]	1.4369[20]	i	∞	∞				B2[2], 575
Ω h384	—,dichloride	$ClCO(CH_2)_4COCl$ 183.05				126[12]			d	d					B2[2], 575
Ω h385	—,diethyl ester*	$C_2H_5O_2C(CH_2)_4CO_2C_2H_5$ 202.25		λ^{al} 210 (2.0)	−19.8	245[760] 127[13]	1.0076[20]	1.4272[20]	i	s	s	s		aa s	B2[2], 574
h386	—,di(2-ethylbutyl) ester*	$(C_2H_5)_2CHCH_2O_2C(CH_2)_4CO_2CH(C_2H_5)_2$ 314.47			−15	200[10]	0.934[25]	1.4434[20]	i	s		s		aa s	C41, 4298
h387	—,di(2-ethylhexyl) ester	$C_4H_9^nCH(C_2H_5)CH_2O_2C(CH_2)_4CO_2CH_2CH(C_2H_5)C_4H_9^n$ 370.58			−67.8	214[5]	0.9222[25]	1.4474[20]	i	s	s	s		aa s	B2[2], 1715
h388	—,dihydrazide	$H_2NNHOC(CH_2)_4CONHNH_2$ 174.20		lf (w)	182–2.5				s	s[h]	i		s	aa i	B2[3], 1724
Ω h389	—,diisopropyl ester	$C_3H_7^iO_2C(CH_2)_4CO_2C_3H_7^i$ 230.31			−1.1	120[6.5]	0.9659[20]	1.4247[20]	i	s	s	s		aa s	B2[3], 1713
Ω h390	—,dimethyl ester*	$CH_3O_2C(CH_2)_4CO_2CH_3$ 174.20		cr	10.3	115[13] 105[7]	1.0600[20]	1.4283[20]	i	s	s	s		aa s	B2, 365
Ω h391	—,dinitrile	$NC(CH_2)_4CN$ 108.15		nd (eth)	1	295[760] 180[20]	0.9676[20]	1.4380[20]	δ	s	δ			chl s	B2[2], 576
' 392	—,dipropyl ester*	$C_3H_7^nO_2C(CH_2)_4CO_2C_3H_7^n$ 230.31			−15.7	151[11]	0.9790[20]	1.4314[20]	i	s	s			chl s	B2[2], 574
h393	—,monoamide*	Adipamic acid. $HO_2C(CH_2)_4CONH_2$ 145.16		nd (w)	161–2										J1934, 1101
h394	—,monoethyl ester*	$HO_2C(CH_2)_4CO_2C_2H_5$ 174.20		hyg (eth-peth)	29	285[760] 170[17]	0.9796[20]	1.4311[20]		s	s[h]			peth s[h]	B2[2], 574
Ω h395	—,monomethyl ester*	$HO_2C(CH_2)_4CO_2CH_3$ 160.17		lf (Me$_3$N-MeOH)	9	158[10]	1.0623[20]	1.4283[20]		s	s				B2, 652
h396	—,piperazinium salt	$HO_2C(CH_2)_4CO_2H.C_4H_{10}N_2$ 232.28			244d				s		i				Am 56, 1759
Ω h397	—,2-amino-(dl)*	$HO_2C(CH_2)_3CH(NH_2)CO_2H$ 161.16		pl (w)	206 (anh)				δ s[h]	δ	δ				Am 75, 1994
h398	—,2-methyl-*	$HO_2C(CH_2)_3CH(CH_3)CO_2H$ 160.17		cr (peth-bz)	93	209[13]			s	s			δ	chl s peth δ	B2[3], 1745
h399	—,3-methyl-(d)*	$HO_2CCH_2CH_2CH(CH_3)CH_2CO_2H$ 160.17		cr (chl-bz), $[\alpha]_D^{25}$ +9.81 (w)	94–4.5	230[30]			v	v	v	v	s	chl, AcOEt v peth δ	B2[2], 588
Ω h400	—,—(dl)*	$HO_2CCH_2CH_2CH(CH_3)CH_2CO_2H$ 160.17		nd (bz), cr (ace-bz)	97	190–200[12]			v	v	v	v	δ	chl, AcOEt v lig δ	B2[2], 589
h401	—,2-oxo-*	$HO_2C(CH_2)_3COCO_2H$ 160.14		cr (al or eth)	127				v	v	δ	v	i	peth, chl i	B3[2], 485
h402	—,3-oxo-*	$HO_2CCH_2CH_2COCH_2CO_2H$ 160.14		pl (ace-chl)	125				δ	δ	δ	s	δ	chl δ	B3[2], 486
—	—,2,3,4,5-tetrahydroxy-*	*see* Mucic acid													
Ω h406	1,6-Hexanediol*	Hexamethylene glycol. $HO(CH_2)_6OH$ 118.18		nd (w)	43 (59)	250[760] 132[9]			s	s	δ	s	i		B1[3], 2201
h407	2,3-Hexanediol*	$CH_3CH_2CH_2CH(OH)CH(OH)CH_3$ 118.18		cr	60	204–6[760] 102[0.8]	0.9900[15]	1.4510[15]	s	s	s				B1, 484
Ω h408	2,5-Hexanediol*	$CH_3CH(OH)CH_2CH_2CH(OH)CH_3$ 118.18		cr (eth)	43	216–8[750] 85–7[1]	0.9610[20]	1.4475[20]	s	s	s				B1[2], 551
h409	3,4-Hexanediol, 3,4-diethyl-*	$(C_2H_5)_2C(OH)C(OH)(C_2H_5)_2$ 174.29		cr (eth)	28	230[760] 112[10]	0.9630[13]	1.467[13]	i	v	v				B1[3], 2235
Ω h410	2,5-Hexanediol, 2,5-dimethyl-*	$(CH_3)_2C(OH)CH_2CH_2C(OH)(CH_3)_2$ 146.23		pr (AcOEt), fl (peth)	92	214 118[15]	0.898[20]		s	s			v[h]	chl v	B1[2], 557
Ω h411	1,3-Hexanediol, 2-ethyl-*	$CH_3CH_2CH_2CH(OH)CH(C_2H_5)CH_2OH$ 146.23			−40	244[760]	0.9325[22]	1.4497[20]	δ	s	s				C37, 5020
h412	2,3-Hexanedione, 3-oxime*	$CH_3(CH_2)_2C(:NOH)COCH_3$ 129.16		cr (al)	60						s[h]				B1[1], 405
Ω h413	2,5-Hexanedione*	Acetonylacetone. $CH_3COCH_2CH_2COCH_3$ 114.15		λ 271 (2.09)	−5.5	194[754] 89[25]	0.9737[20]	1.4421[20]	∞	∞	∞	v	s	peth δ[h]	B1[2], 841
h414	—,dioxime*	$CH_3C(:NOH)CH_2CH_2C(:NOH)CH_3$ 144.18		pl (bz)	137				v[h]	v[h]	v[h]				B1, 790
Ω h415	1,6-Hexanedione, 1,6-diphenyl-*	1,4-Dibenzoylbutane. $C_6H_5CO(CH_2)_4COC_6H_5$ 266.34		nd (al), pr (chl-al), lf (dil al)	107						s[h]			MeOH, chl s[h]	B7[2], 705
h416	2,5-Hexanedione, 3-hydroxy-*	$CH_3COCH_2CH(OH)COCH_3$ 130.15				62–7[0.5]		1.4497[25]	δ		s		s		Am 71, 3171

For explanations, symbols and abbreviations see beginning of table. For structural formulas see end of table.

3,4-Hexanedione

No.	Name	Synonyms and Formula	Mol. wt.	Color, crystalline form, specific rotation and λ_{max} (log ε)	m.p. °C	b.p. °C	Density	n_D	w	al	eth	ace	bz	other solvents	Ref.
h417	3,4-Hexanedione, 2,2,5,5-tetra-methyl-*	Di-tert-butylglyoxal. Dipivaloyl. Pivalil. $(CH_3)_3CCOCOC(CH_3)_3$	170.25	$\lambda^{95\%al}$ 294 (1.67), 365 (1.31)	−2	168[745]	0.8776[20]	1.4157[20]	i		∞				B1[3], 3147
Ω h418	1,2,3,4,5,6-Hexanehexol*	Dulcite. Dulcitol. Melampyrin. $HOCH_2(CHOH)_4CH_2OH$	182.18	mcl pr	189	275–80[1]	1.466[15]		s v[h]	δ	i				B1[2], 612
h419	1,3,4,5-Hexane-tetrol*	Digitoxin. $CH_3(CHOH)_3CH_2CH_2OH$	150.18	pr, $[\alpha]_D^{15}$ −86.2	88				i	v	s[h]				B1[2], 603
Ω h420	1-Hexanethiol*	n-Hexyl mercaptan. $CH_3(CH_2)_5SH$	118.24	λ^{hx} 224 sh (2.1)	−81	151[760]	0.8424[20]	1.4496[20]	i	v	v				B1[3], 1659
h421	2-Hexanethiol*	sec-Hexyl mercaptan. 2-Mercaptohexane*. $CH_3(CH_2)_3CH(SH)CH_3$	118.24	λ^{iso} 223 sh (2.2)	−147	142[760] 60–6[50]	0.8345[20]	1.4451[20]	i	s	s		s		B1[3], 1662
h422	3-Hexanethiol*	3-Mercaptohexane*. $CH_3CH_2CH_2CH(SH)CH_2CH_3$	118.24			57[25]	0.9206[20]	1.4496[20]		s	s				B1[3], 1665
h423	1,2,3-Hexanetriol (threo)*	$CH_3CH_2CH_2CH(OH)CH(OH)CH_2OH$	134.18		64–4.5	130[0.05]	1.089[26]	1.472[26]	s	s	i				B1[3], 2349
h424	1,2,4-Hexanetriol*	$CH_3CH_2CH(OH)CH_2CH(OH)CH_2OH$	134.18			190–2[30]			s	s	i				B1, 521
h425	1,2,5-Hexanetriol*	$CH_3CH(OH)CH_2CH_2CH(OH)CH_2OH$	134.18			181[10] 150[3]	1.1012[20]		∞	∞	i				B1[3], 2349
h426	2,3,4-Hexanetriol*	$CH_3CH_2(CHOH)_3CH_3$	134.18			256–7[155–6.5[20]]			∞	∞	i				B1[3], 2349
Ω h427	Hexanoic acid*	n-Caproic acid. $CH_3(CH_2)_4CO_2H$	116.16		−2 −1.5	205[760]	0.9274[20]	1.4163[20]	i	s	s				B2[2], 281
Ω h428	—,amide	Caproamide. $CH_3(CH_2)_4CONH_2$	115.18	cr (ace)	101	255[760]	0.999[20]	1.4200[110]	δ s[h]	s	s		s	chl s	B2[2], 286
h429	—,—,N-phenyl-	Hexanilide. Capranilide. $CH_3(CH_2)_4CONHC_6H_5$	191.28	nd (peth), pr (al) λ^{al} 243 (4.18)	95		1.112		i	v	v			peth s[h]	B12[2], 147
h430	—,anhydride*	$[CH_3(CH_2)_4CO]_2O$	214.31		−41	254–7d (245) 143[15]	0.9240[15]	1.4297[20]	i	s	s				B2[2], 285
Ω h431	—,butyl ester*	$CH_3(CH_2)_4CO_2(CH_2)_3CH_3$	172.27		−64.3	208[760]	0.8653[20]	1.4153[25]	i	s	∞				B2, 323
h432	—,chloride	$CH_3(CH_2)_4COCl$	134.61		−87	153[760]	0.9754[20]	1.4264[20]	d	d	s	s			B2[2], 286
Ω h433	—,ethyl ester*	$CH_3(CH_2)_4CO_2C_2H_5$	144.22		−67	168[760]	0.8710[20]	1.4073[20]	i	s	s				B2[2], 285
h434	—,heptyl ester*	$CH_3(CH_2)_4CO_2(CH_2)_6CH_3$	214.35		−34.4	261[760]	0.8611[20]	1.4293[15]	i	s	s	s	s	os s	B2, 323
h435	—,hexyl ester*	$CH_3(CH_2)_4CO_2(CH_2)_5CH_3$	200.33		−55	246[761]	0.865[18]	1.4264[15]	i	s	s	s	s	os s	B2, 323
Ω h436	—,methyl ester*	$CH_3(CH_2)_4CO_2CH_3$	130.19		−71	151[760] 52[15]	0.8846[20]	1.4049[20]	i	v	v	s	s		B2[2], 284
Ω h437	—,3-methylbutyl ester*	Isoamyl caproate. $CH_3(CH_2)_4CO_2CH_2CH_2CH(CH_3)_2$	186.30			224–7[760]	0.861[20]		i		s				B2[3], 727
Ω h438	—,nitrile	Amyl cyanide. $CH_3(CH_2)_4CN$	97.16		−80.3	163.6[760] 47.3[10]	0.8051[20]	1.4068[20]	i	s	s				B2[2], 286
h439	—,octyl ester*	$CH_3(CH_2)_4CO_2(CH_2)_7CH_3$	228.38		−28	275[760]	0.8603[20]	1.4326[15]	i	s	s	s	s	os s	B2, 323
Ω h440	—,pentyl ester*	$CH_3(CH_2)_4CO_2(CH_2)_4CH_3$	186.30		−47	226[760] 116.6[20]	0.8612[25]	1.4202[25]	i	s	s				B2[2], 285
h441	—,4-phenyl-phenacyl ester*		310.40	cr (dil al)	69–70					s[h]					Am 52, 3715
h442	—,piperazinium salt	$2[CH_3(CH_2)_4CO_2H] \cdot C_4H_{10}N_2$	318.46		111				s	s	i	s[h]			Am 56, 1759
h443	—,propyl ester*	$CH_3(CH_2)_4CO_2CH_2CH_2CH_3$	158.24		−68.7	187[760]	0.8672[20]	1.4170[20]	i	s	s				B2, 323
Ω h444	—,2-acetyl-, ethyl ester	Ethyl α-butylacetoacetate. $CH_3(CH_2)_3CH(COCH_3)CO_2C_2H_5$	186.25			219–24 104[12]	0.9523[20]	1.4301[20]	i		s	s		AcOEt s	B1[3], 706
Ω h445	—,6-amino-*	$H_2N(CH_2)_5CO_2H$	131.18	lf (eth)	202–3				v	i				MeOH δ	B4[2], 856
h446	—,—,lactam*	ε-Caprolactam	113.16	lf (lig)	69–71	139[12]			s	v	v		s	chl v	B21[2], 216
h447	—,6-amino-3-methyl-, lactam*		127.19	cr (bz-peth) $[\alpha]_D^{20}$ −36.1	105–6				v				s		B21, 243
h448	—,6-amino-5-methyl-, lactam*		127.19	cr (peth, bz-lig) $[\alpha]_D^{20}$???	68–9				v				s		B21, 242
h449	—,6-benzoyl-amino-	$C_6H_5CONH(CH_2)_5CO_2H$	235.29	nd (al-eth)	79–80				δ[h]				δ	AcOEt s lig δ	B9[2], 181
h450	—,6-benzoyl-amino-2-bromo-(dl)	$C_6H_5CONH(CH_2)_4CHBrCO_2H$	314.19	cr (dil al)	166				δ	v[h]					B9[2], 182
h451	—,—,(l)	$C_6H_5CONH(CH_2)_4CHBrCO_2H$	314.19	nd (dil al), $[\alpha]_D^{18}$ −29.2 (al)	129				δ	s[h]					B9[2], 181
Ω h452	—,2-bromo-(dl)*	$CH_3(CH_2)_3CHBrCO_2H$	195.06		4	240[760] 140–2[23]				s	s				B2[2], 287
h453	—,—(l)*	$CH_3(CH_2)_3CHBrCO_2H$	195.06	$[\alpha]_D^{20}$ −27 (eth, c = 5)		129[14]				s	s				B2[2], 287
Ω h454	—,—,ethyl ester(dl)*	$CH_3(CH_2)_3CHBrCO_2C_2H_5$	223.12			205–10 95–6[9]					s				B2[1], 141
h455	—,3-bromo-*	$CH_3CH_2CH_2CHBrCH_2CO_2H$	195.06	nd (dil al)	35						s		v	chl, lig v	B2, 235
Ω h456	—,6-bromo-*	$Br(CH_2)_5CO_2H$	195.06	cr (peth)	35	165–70[20]					s			peth s[h]	B2[2], 287
h457	—,6-cyclohexyl-*		198.31		33–3.5	180[11]	0.9626[20]	1.4750[20]			s				B9[2], 21
—	—,2,6-diamino-*	see Lysine													

For explanations, symbols and abbreviations see beginning of table. For structural formulas see end of table.

No.	Name	Synonyms and Formula	Mol. wt.	Color, crystalline form, specific rotation and λ_{max} (log ε)	m.p. °C	b.p. °C	Density	n_D	w	al	eth	ace	bz	other solvents	Ref.
	Hexanoic acid														
h458	—,2,4-dioxo-*	Propionylpyruvic acid. $CH_3CH_2COCH_2COCO_2H$	144.14	cr (al, w + 1)	83				s	s	s	...	δ	peth i	B3[2], 437
h459	—,—,ethyl ester*	$CH_3CH_2COCH_2COCO_2C_2H_5$	172.19			163–5 108–11[11]			...	v	v	v	...		B3[2], 437
Ω h460	—,2-ethyl-*	$CH_3(CH_2)_3CH(C_2H_5)CO_2H$	144.22			228[755] 120[13]	0.9031[25/4]	1.4241[20]	s[h]	δ	s	...			B2[2], 304
h461	—,—,amide	$CH_3(CH_2)_3CH(C_2H_5)CONH_2$	143.23	nd (w)	102–3				s[h]						B2, 350
h462	—,6-fluoro-*	$F(CH_2)_5CO_2H$	134.15			138[26] 67–8[0.6]		1.4166[25]	δ	v	v				C52, 1922
h463	—,2-hydroxy-(d)*	$CH_3(CH_2)_3CH(OH)CO_2H$	132.16	$[\alpha]_D^{20}$ +0.7 (w, c = 14)	60				v	v	s				B3[2], 231
Ω h464	—,—(dl)*	$CH_3(CH_2)_3CH(OH)CO_2H$	132.16	pr (eth-al, peth)	61	270			v	v	s			chl v	B3[2], 232
h465	—,—(l)*	$CH_3(CH_2)_3CH(OH)CO_2H$	132.16	pr (eth) $[\alpha]_D^{20}$ −3.8 (w, c = 4.5)	60–1				v	v	v			chl v	B3[2], 232
h466	—,4-hydroxy-, lactone*	γ-Caprolactone	114.15		−18	215–6 103[14]		1.4495[20]	s	s				alk s	B17[2], 290
h467	—,2-methyl-(d)*	$CH_3(CH_2)_3CH(CH_3)CO_2H$	130.19	$[\alpha]_D^{22}$ +19.6 (eth)		105[5]	0.909[25]	1.4189[20]	∞	∞	∞	∞	∞	chl ∞	B2[2], 296
h468	—,—(dl)*	$CH_3(CH_2)_3CH(CH_3)CO_2H$	130.19			215–6[760] 100[12]	0.9612[20/4]	1.4193[20]	∞	∞	∞	∞	∞	chl ∞	B2[2], 297
h469	—,—(l)*	$CH_3(CH_2)_3CH(CH_3)CO_2H$	130.19	$[\alpha]_D^{25}$ −4.3 (w, c = 26) $[\alpha]_D^{25}$ −15.25 (eth)		121[20] 105[5]	0.909[25]	1.4189[25]	∞	∞	∞	∞	∞	chl ∞	B2[2], 296
h470	—,3-methyl-, chloride	$CH_3CH_2CH_2CH(CH_3)CH_2COCl$	148.63			163[751] 82[50]	0.967[20]	1.4293[25]	d	d	...	s		to s[h]	B2[2], 295
h471	—,4-methyl-(d)*	act-Amylacetic acid. $CH_3CH_2CH(CH_3)CH_2CH_2CO_2H$	130.19	$[\alpha]_D^{20}$ +7.6 (MeOH)		221[760] 115[16]	0.9228[20]	1.4198[20]	δ	s	...	s	s	MeOH s	B2[1], 146
h472	—,—(dl)*	$CH_3CH_2CH(CH_3)CH_2CH_2CO_2H$	130.19		−80	217–8[760] 85[2]	0.9215[20]	1.4211[20]	δ	s	s	s	s	os s	B2[2], 298
h473	—,—,chloride(dl)	$CH_3CH_2CH(CH_3)CH_2CH_2COCl$	148.63			167[767]	0.9677[20]				s				C19, 464
h474	—,5-methyl-*	$(CH_3)_2CH(CH_2)_3CO_2H$	130.19		< −25	216 (207[752]) 109[14]	0.9138[21]	1.4220[20]	δ	s	s	s	s	peth s	B2[2], 297
h475	—,—,chloride	$(CH_3)_2CH(CH_2)_3COCl$	148.63			168[739] 76–82[34]			i		s				B2, 342
h476	—,4-oxo-	Homolevulinic acid. $CH_3CH_2COCH_2CH_2CO_2H$	130.15	hyg ta or lf (eth-peth)	41–2	183[20] 89[0.4]			s	s	s				B3[2], 435
—	—,2,3,4,5,6-pentahydroxy-*	see **Idonic acid**													
Ω h478	1-Hexanol*	n-Hexyl alcohol. $CH_3(CH_2)_5OH$	102.18		−46.7	158[760]	0.8136[20/4]	1.4178[20]	δ	s	∞	s	∞	chl s	B1[3], 1650
h479	2-Hexanol(d)*	$CH_3(CH_2)_3CH(OH)CH_3$	102.18	$[\alpha]_D^{25}$ +14.1 (eth, c = 11) $[\alpha]_D^{20}$ +12.70 (al)		138[760]	0.81036[25]	1.4126[25]	δ	s	s				B1[2], 437
Ω h480	—(dl)*	$CH_3(CH_2)_3CH(OH)CH_3$	102.18			140[760]	0.8159[20]	1.4144[20]	δ	s	s				B1[3], 1660
h481	—(l)*	$CH_3(CH_2)_3CH(OH)CH_3$	102.18	$[\alpha]_{5780}^{18}$ −12.04		136–8[754]	0.8178[18]		δ	s	s				B1[3], 1663
h482	3-Hexanol(d)*	$CH_3CH_2CH_2CH(OH)CH_2CH_3$	102.18	$[\alpha]_D^{20}$ +6.81 (chl)		131–3	0.8213[20]	1.4150[20]	δ	s	∞	s			B1[3], 1663
Ω h483	—(dl)*	$CH_3CH_2CH_2CH(OH)CH_2CH_3$	102.18			135[760]	0.81825[20/4]	1.4167[20]	δ	s	∞	s			B1[3], 1663
h484	—(l)*	$CH_3CH_2CH_2CH(OH)CH_2CH_3$	102.18	$[\alpha]_D^{18}$ −7.17		135[760]	0.8213[20]	1.4140[22]	δ	s	∞	s			B1[3], 1665
Ω h485	1-Hexanol, 6-chloro-*	Hexamethylene chlorohydrin. $Cl(CH_2)_6OH$	136.62			107[12] 94[2]	1.0241[20/4]	1.4550[20]	δ	v	v				B1[3], 1658
h486	2-Hexanol, 1-chloro-*	$CH_3(CH_2)_3CH(OH)CH_2Cl$	136.62			73–5[12]	1.0139[20/4]	1.4478[20]	δ	v	v	s	δ		B1[2], 1661
h487	3-Hexanol, 1-chloro-*	$CH_3CH_2CH_2CH(OH)CH_2CH_2Cl$	136.62			120[35] 78[6]	1.003[25]	1.446[25]	δ s[h]	s	s	s	s	os v	B1[3], 1664
h488	—,2-chloro-*	$CH_3(CH_2)_3CH(OH)CHClCH_3$	136.62			171[760]	1.0143[11]		i	s	s	s	s	os s	B1[2], 438
h489	—,5-chloro-*	$CH_3CHClCH_2CH(OH)CH_2CH_3$	136.62			78–9[13]	1.0012[19]	1.4433[19]	δ	s	v	s	s	os ∞	B1[3], 1664
Ω h491	—,2-ethyl-*	$CH_3(CH_2)_3CH(C_2H_5)CH_2OH$	130.23		< −76	185 84–6[15]	0.8328[20]	1.4328[20]	i	s	s	s	s		Am 58, 586
h492	3-Hexanol, 3-ethyl-*	$CH_3CH_2CH_2COH(C_2H_5)_2$	130.23	λ^{sulf} 224 (1.20), 291 (3.08)		160[760]	0.8373[20/4]	1.4300[20]	i	s	s			os s	B1[3], 1736
h493	—,3-ethyl-5-methyl-*	$(CH_3)_2CHCH_2COH(C_2H_5)_2$	144.26			272	0.8396[27]	1.43457[13]	i	s	s				B1[3], 1755
h494	1-Hexanol, 6-fluoro-*	Hexamethylene fluorohydrin. $F(CH_2)_6OH$	120.17			85–6[14]	0.975[20]	1.4141[25]	δ	v	v				C51, 7300
Ω h495	—,2-isopropyl-5-methyl-*	$(CH_3)_2CHCH_2CH_2CH_2CH(C_3H_7^i)CH_2OH$	158.29			211[760]	0.8345[20/4]	1.4369[20]	i	s	v				B1[1], 215
h496	—,2-methyl-(d)*	$CH_3(CH_2)_3CH(CH_3)CH_2OH$	116.21	$[\alpha]_D^{25}$ +2.45 (al)		164–5[??] 71–2[15]	0.8313[13]	1.4245[17]	i	∞	s				B1[2], 444

For explanations, symbols and abbreviations see beginning of table. For structural formulas see end of table.

No.	Name	Synonyms and Formula	Mol. wt.	Color, crystalline form, specific rotation and λ_{max} (log ε)	m.p. °C	b.p. °C	Density	n_D	w	al	eth	ace	bz	other solvents	Ref.
	1-Hexanol														
h497	—,—(dl)*	$CH_3(CH_2)_3CH(CH_3)CH_2OH$	116.21			164^{750}	0.8270_4^{20}	1.4226^{20}	i	∞	s				B1[3], 1689
h498	—,4-methyl-(d)*	$CH_3CH_2CH(CH_3)(CH_2)_3OH$	116.21	$[\alpha]_D^{28}+2.2$		77^{20}	0.809_2^{23}	1.4233^{25}	i	s	s	s	s	os s	B1[3], 1695
h499	—,—(dl)*	$CH_3CH_2CH(CH_3)(CH_2)_3OH$	116.21			173^{761} 83^{24}	0.8239_2^{20}	1.4219^{20}	i	s	s	s	s	os s	B1[3], 1695
Ω h500	—,5-methyl-*	$(CH_3)_2CH(CH_2)_4OH$	116.21			170^{755}	0.8192_5^{25}	1.4251^{23}	δ	s	s				B1[3], 1692
Ω h501	2-Hexanol, 2-methyl-*	$CH_3(CH_2)_3COH(CH_3)_2$	116.21			143^{760} $53-5^{15}$	0.8119_4^{20}	1.4175^{20}	δ	∞	∞				B1[3], 1690
Ω h502	—,5-methyl-*	$(CH_3)_2CHCH_2CH_2CH(OH)CH_3$	116.21			150^{744} 78^{28}	0.814_4^{20}	1.4180^{20}	i	s					B1[2], 1692
Ω h503	3-Hexanol, 3-methyl-*	$CH_3CH_2CH_2C(OH)(CH_3)CH_2CH_3$	116.21			143^{760} 56^{18}	0.8234_0^{20}	1.4231^{20}	δ	s					B1[3], 1693
h504	—,5-methyl-(d)*	$(CH_3)_2CHCH_2CH(OH)CH_2CH_3$	116.21	$[\alpha]_D^{35}+21.23$		81^{60}		1.4171^{25}							B1[3], 1692
Ω h505	—,—(dl)*	$(CH_3)_2CHCH_2CH(OH)CH_2CH_3$	116.21			$147-8^{756}$	0.827^0	1.4128^{20}	i	s					B1[3], 1692
h506	—,—(l)*	$(CH_3)_2CHCH_2CH(OH)CH_2CH_3$	116.21	$[\alpha]_D^{23}-3.88$		$93-6^{105}$ 63^{19}		1.4171^{25}							B1[3], 1691
h507	1-Hexanol, 1-phenyl-*	$CH_3(CH_2)_4CHOH(C_6H_5)$	178.28	λ^{al} 242 (1.78)		170^{50} $110^{0.3}$	0.9477_4^{25}	1.5105^{20}		s	s				C46, 8005
h508	3-Hexanol, 2,2,5,5-tetra-methyl-*	$(CH_3)_3CCH_2CHOHC(CH_3)_3$	158.29	cr (peth)	52.5-3.0	166-70			i	s	s	s		peth s	B1[3], 1772
h509	2-Hexanol, 2,3,4-trimethyl-*	$CH_3CH_2CH(CH_3)CH(CH_3)COH(CH_3)_2$	144.26			57^5	0.853_4^{15}	1.4415^{15}		s	s	s		peth s	B1[3], 1756
h510	—,2,3,5-tri-methyl-*	$(CH_3)_2CHCH_2CH(CH_3)COH(CH_3)_2$	144.26			171^{755} 72^{21}	0.8271_{20}^{20}	1.4321^{20}							B1, 212
Ω h511	3-Hexanol, 2,2,3-trimethyl-*	$CH_3CH_2CH_2COH(CH_3)C(CH_3)_3$	144.26			170^{760}	0.8474_4^{20}	1.4402^{20}		s	s				B1[3], 1755
h512	—,2,3,5-tri-methyl-*	$(CH_3)_2CHCH_2COH(CH_3)CH(CH_3)_2$	144.26			72^{21}	0.8271_{20}^{20}	1.4321^{20}		s	s				B1[3], 1756
Ω h513	—,2,4,4-tri-methyl-*	$CH_3CH_2C(CH_3)_2CH(OH)CH(CH_3)_2$	144.26			170^{760}	0.8489^{20}	1.4395^{20}		s	s				B1[2], 458
h514	—,2,5,5-tri-methyl-*	$(CH_3)_3CCH_2CH(OH)CH(CH_3)_2$	144.26			77^{32}	0.8250^{20}	1.4286^{20}		s	s				B1[3], 1756
Ω h515	—,3,4,4-tri-methyl-*	$CH_3CH_2C(CH_3)COH(CH_3)CH_2CH_3$	144.26			$165-6^{760}$	0.8323_0^{21}	1.43407^{21}		s	s				B1, 425
h516	—,3,5,5-tri-methyl-*	$(CH_3)_3CCH_2COH(CH_3)CH_2CH_3$	144.26			62^{14}	0.8350^{20}	1.4352^{20}		s	s				B1[3], 1755
Ω h517	2-Hexanone*	$CH_3(CH_2)_3COCH_3$	100.16	λ^{al} 275.5 (1.31)	-57	128^{760}	0.8112_7^{20}	1.4007^{20}	δ	∞	∞	s			B1[2], 745
Ω h518	3-Hexanone*	$CH_3CH_2CH_2COCH_2CH_3$	100.16	λ^{al} 277.5 (1.34)		125^{760}	0.8182^{20}	1.4004^{20}	δ	∞	∞	s			B1[2], 746
Ω h519	1-Hexanone, 1(2,4-dihydroxy-phenyl)-*		208.24	pl (to-peth)	56	343d			i	s	s	s		chl s	B8[2], 314
h520	2-Hexanone, 3,3-dimethyl-*	$CH_3CH_2CH_2C(CH_3)_2COCH_3$	128.22			149^{745}	0.838_4^0	1.4098^{20}		s	s				B1[3], 2881
Ω h521	—,3,4-dimethyl-*	$CH_3CH_2CH(CH_3)CH(CH_3)COCH_3$	128.22			158^{760} (155)	0.8295_2^{22}	1.4193^{20}		s	s				B1[1], 760
h522	3-Hexanone, 2,2-dimethyl-*	$CH_3CH_2CH_2COC(CH_3)_3$	128.22	λ^{al} 285.5 (1.47)		$145-8^{745}$	0.8105_2^{25}	1.4119^{20}		s	s				B1[2], 760
h523	—,—,oxime*	$CH_3CH_2CH_2C(:NOH)C(CH_3)_3$	143.23	nd (al)	78-8.5					δ					B1[1], 364
h524	—,2,5-dimethyl-*	$(CH_3)_2CHCH_2COCH(CH_3)_2$	128.22			$147-8^{760}$	0.8270_0^0	1.4049^{20}		s	s				B1[2], 760
h525	—,4,4-dimethyl-*	$CH_3CH_2C(CH_3)_2COCH_2CH_3$	128.22			151	0.8285^{20}	1.4203^{25}	s	s	s			chl s	B1[2], 760
h526	—,6-dimethyl-amino-4,4-diphenyl-5-methyl-(l)*	l-Isomethadone. l-Isoamidon. Liden. $(CH_3)_2NCH_2CH(CH_3)C(C_6H_5)_2COCH_2CH_3$	309.46	$[\alpha]_D^{25}-20$ (95% al, c = 1.5) λ^{al} 225 (4.0), 252 sh (2.8), 265 (2.3), 299 (2.8)		$162-5^{0.6}$									C51, 7420
h527	—,4-hydroxy-*	Propioin. $CH_3CH_2CH(OH)COCH_2CH_3$	116.16			$173-4^{747}$ 73^{20}	0.9560_1^{21}	1.4340^{21}		s		s			B1, 835
h528	—,4-hydroxy-2,2,5,5-tetra-methyl-*	Pivaloin. $(CH_3)_3CCH(OH)COC(CH_3)_3$	172.27	cr (sub)	81 sub	80^{10}			s^h		s			peth i	B1[2], 884
h529	2-Hexanone, 3-methyl-*	$CH_3CH_2CH_2CH(CH_3)COCH_3$	114.19			$142-5^{760}$	0.828^{25}	1.4035^{20}		s	s	s	s	os v	B1[1], 360
h530	—,4-methyl-*	$CH_3CH_2CH(CH_3)CH_2COCH_3$	114.19			142^{760} (139[762] $35-7^{11}$)		1.4081^{24}	δ	v	v	v	v	os v	B1[2], 756
Ω h531	—,5-methyl-*	$(CH_3)_2CHCH_2CH_2COCH_3$	114.19	$\lambda^{v.p}$ 176, 188, 192, 196 sh		144^{760}	0.888_4^{20}	1.4062^{20}	δ	∞	∞	v	v		B1[2], 756
h532	—,—,oxime*	$(CH_3)_2CHCH_2CH_2C(:NOH)CH_3$	129.20			$195-6^{761}$	0.8881_4^{20}	1.4448^{20}							B1, 701

For explanations, symbols and abbreviations see beginning of table. For structural formulas see end of table.

3-Hexanone

No.	Name	Synonyms and Formula	Mol. wt.	Color, crystalline form, specific rotation and λ_{max} (log ε)	m.p. °C	b.p. °C	Density	n_D	w	al	eth	ace	bz	other solvents	Ref.
h533	3-Hexanone, 4-methyl-*	$CH_3CH_2CH(CH_3)COCH_2CH_3$	114.19	....		134–5	0.8162^{20}	1.4069^{20}	δ	v	v	v	v	os v	B1, 701
Ω h534	—,5-methyl-*	$(CH_3)_2CHCH_2COCH_2CH_3$	114.19	λ^{al} 280 (1.39)		134^{735}	0.8090^{20}	1.4047^{20}	i	∞	∞	...	...		B1[1], 360
Ω h535	1-Hexanone, 1-phenyl-*	Caprophenone. $CH_3(CH_2)_4COC_6H_5$	176.24	fl	27	265^{760} $122–4^{15}$	0.9576^{20}	1.5027^{25}	δ	s	s	s	...		B7[2], 257
h536	Hexasiloxane tetradeca-methyl-	$(CH_3)_3SiO[-Si(CH_3)_2O-]_4Si(CH_3)_3$	443.97	....	−59	245.5^{760} 142^{20}	0.8910^{20}_4	1.3948^{20}	i	δ			s		C41, 1998
h538	1,2,3,5-Hexa-tetraene, 4-chloro-*	$CH_2{:}CHCCl{:}C{:}C{:}CH_2$	112.56	......		127^{760}d 55^{54}	0.9997^{20}_4	1.5280^{20}	i	...	s	s		chl s	B1[3], 1061
h539	1,2,4,5-Hexa-tetraene, 3,4-dichloro-*	$CH_2{:}C{:}CClCCl{:}C{:}CH_2$	147.01			$38–40^8$	1.1819^{20}_4	1.5456^{20}	i	...	s	s		chl s	B1[3], 1061
h540	1,3,5-Hexatriene (cis)*	Divinylethylene. $CH_2{:}CHCH{:}CHCH{:}CH_2$	80.14	λ^{hx} 247 (4.21), 256 (4.35), 266 (4.27)	−12	78^{760}	0.7175^{20}_4	1.4577^{20}	i	...	s	...	s	peth, chl s	B1[2], 243
h541	—(trans)*	$CH_2{:}CHCH{:}CHCH{:}CH_2$	80.14	λ^{hx} 247 (4.53), 258 (4.64), 268 (4.56)	−12	78.5^{760}	0.7369^{15}_4	1.5135^{20}	i	...	s	...	s	peth, chl s	B1[3], 1041
h542	1,3,4-Hexatriene, 3,6-dichloro-*	$ClCH_2CH{:}C{:}CClCH{:}CH_2$	149.02	....	$45–6^3$		1.1807^{20}_4	1.5195^{20}	i	...	s	s		AcOEt s	C27, 2932
h543	1,3,5-Hexatriene, 2,5-dimethyl-*	$CH_2{:}C(CH_3)CH{:}CHC(CH_3){:}CH_2$	108.19	λ^{hx} 252 (4.49), 261 (4.62), 272 (4.51)	−9	145^{747}	0.7822^{20}_4	1.5122^{20}	i	...	s		s	MeOH, lig s	B1[3], 1047
Ω h544	—,1,6-diphenyl-*	$C_6H_5CH{:}CHCH{:}CHCH{:}CHC_6H_5$	232.33	lf (ace) λ^{bz} 343 (4.69), 360 (4.83), 380 (4.7)	200–3				i	i	i	s^h δ	δ	chl δ aa i	B5[2], 605
h545	1,2,4-Hexatriene, 3,4,6-trichloro-*	$ClCH_2CH{:}CClCCl{:}C{:}CH_2$	183.47	....	50^1		1.3132^{20}_4	1.5517^{20}	i	...	...	s	s	chl s	C27, 2932
Ω h546	2-Hexen-1-al (trans)*	$CH_3CH_2CH_2CH{:}CHCHO$	98.15			$146–7^{760}$ 43^{12}	0.8491^{20}_4	1.4480^{20}							B1, 382
h546³	1-Hexene*	$CH_3CH_2CH_2CH_2CH{:}CH_2$	84.16		−139.82	63.35^{760}	0.6731^{20}_4	1.3837^{20}	i	s	s	s	s	peth, chl s	B1[3], 800
h547	2-Hexene(cis)*	$CH_3CH_2CH_2CH{:}CHCH_3$	84.16	λ^{gas} 178 (4.2), 186 (3.9), 194 sh (3.4)	−141.35	68.84^{760}	0.6869^{20}_4	1.3977^{20}	i	s	s	...	s	lig, chl s	Am 63, 2683
h548	—(trans)*	$CH_3CH_2CH_2CH{:}CHCH_3$	84.16	λ^{gas} 170 (3.8), 179 (4.1), 201 (3.0)	−133	68^{750}	0.6784^{20}_4	1.3935^{20}	i	s	s	...	s	lig, chl s	Am 63, 2683
h549	3-Hexene(cis)*	$CH_3CH_2CH{:}CHCH_2CH_3$	84.16	λ^{gas} 179 (4.17)	−137.82	66.44^{760}	0.6796^{20}_4	1.3947^{20}	i	s	s	...	s	lig, chl s	Am 63, 2683
Ω h550	—(trans)*	$CH_3CH_2CH{:}CHCH_2CH_3$	84.16		−113.43	67.08^{760}	0.6772^{20}_4	1.3943^{20}	i	s	s	...	s	lig, chl s	Am 63, 2683
h551	1-Hexene, 5-amino-4-methyl-*	$CH_3CH(NH_2)CH(CH_3)CH_2CH{:}CH_2$	113.20			$133–6^{760}$	0.793^{15}_0	....	s						B4, 226
h552	—,1-chloro-*	$CH_3(CH_2)_3CH{:}CHCl$	118.61			121	0.8872^{22}	1.4300^{22}	i	...	v	s	s	chl v	B1[3], 803
h553	—,2-chloro-*	$CH_3(CH_2)_3CCl{:}CH_2$	118.61			113^{740} 63^{110}	0.8886^{25}	1.4278^{25}	i	...	...	s	s	chl v	B1[3], 803
h554	—,5-chloro-*	$CH_3CHClCH_2CH_2CH{:}CH_2$	118.61			120.7^{760} $28–30^{13}$	0.8891^{25}_4	1.4305^{20}	i	...	...	s	s	chl v	B1[3], 803
h555	2-Hexene, 4-chloro-*	$CH_3CH_2CHClCH{:}CHCH_3$	118.61			123^{760} 30^{10}	0.8934^{20}_4	1.4400^{20}	i	...	v	v	s	chl v	B1[2], 192
h556	3-Hexene, 1-chloro-*	$CH_3CH_2CH{:}CHCH_2CH_2Cl$	118.61			$61–1.5^{60}$	0.900^{24}_4	1.435^{24}	i	...	v	v	s	chl v	B1[3], 807
h557	—,3-chloro-(cis)	$CH_3CH_2CH_2CCl{:}CHCH_2CH_3$	118.61			119.6^{760}	0.9009^{20}_4	1.4360^{20}	i	...	s	s	s	chl s	B1[3], 807
h558	—,2-chloro-2,5-dimethyl-*	$(CH_3)_2CHCH{:}CHCCl(CH_3)_2$	146.66			$45–60^{15}$		1.450^{20}	i	...	s	s	s	chl s	Am 63, 3474
h559	—,1-chloro-4-ethyl-*	$CH_3CH_2C(C_2H_5){:}CHCH_2CH_2Cl$	146.66			173	0.9102^{20}	1.4524^{20}	δ	...	...	...	s	chl s	B1[2], 201
h560	1-Hexene, 1,2-dichloro-(cis)*	$CH_3(CH_2)_3CCl{:}CHCl$	153.05			88^{30}	1.0812^{25}	1.4631^{25}	i	...	...	...	s	CCl_4, chl s	B1[3], 803
h561	—,—(trans)*	$CH_3(CH_2)_3CCl{:}CHCl$	153.05			$63–5^{22}$	1.1167^{25}_4	1.4576^{25}	i	...	...	s	s	chl s	B1[3], 803
h562	—,dodecafluoro-*	Perfluoro-1-hexene. $F_3C(CF_2)_3CF{:}CF_2$	300.05			57			i					chl s	J1952, 4259
h563	3-Hexene, dodecafluoro-*	Perfluoro-3-hexene. $F_3CCF_2CF{:}CFCF_2CF_3$	300.05			49			i					chl s	J1953, 1592
Ω h564	1-Hexene, 2-ethyl-*	$CH_3(CH_2)_3C(C_2H_5){:}CH_2$	112.22			120^{760}	0.7270^{20}_4	1.4157^{20}	i	...	v	...	v	peth v	Am 77, 5443
h565	3-Hexene, 1,2,3,4,5,6-hexa-chloro-*	$ClCH_2CHClCCl{:}CClCHClCH_2Cl$	290.83	cr (peth)	58–9	$110–12^2$			i	s	v	v		MeOH, chl v^k	B1[3], 808
h566	—,3(4-hydroxyphenyl)-4(4-methoxyphenyl)-*	Mestilbol.	282.39	(i) nd (bz-lig), (ii) lf 70% al	(i) 117–8 (120–1) (ii) 114	$185–95^{0.3}$			i	s	v	v			Am 64, 1625
h567	1-Hexene, 1,1,2-trichloro-*	$CH_3(CH_2)_3CCl{:}CCl_2$	187.50			$90–93^{10}$	1.225^{25}	1.4760^{25}	i	...	...	s		....	B1[3], 803

For explanations, symbols and abbreviations see beginning of table. For structural formulas see end of table.

3-Hexenoic acid

No.	Name	Synonyms and Formula	Mol. wt.	Color, crystalline form, specific rotation and λ_{max} (log ε)	m.p. °C	b.p. °C	Density	n_D	Solubility						Ref.
									w	al	eth	ace	bz	other solvents	
h568	3-Hexenoic acid*	Hydrosorbic acid. $CH_3CH_2CH:CHCH_2CO_2H$	114.15	....	12	208 $81-2^2$	0.9640_4^{23}	1.4935^{20}	...	...	...	...	...		B2, 435
Ω h569	4-Hexenoic acid, 2-acetyl-5-hydroxy-3-oxo-, lactone	Dehydracetic acid.........	168.16	nd (w), rh nd or pr (al)	109	270^{760} $132-3^5$			v^h	δ s^h	v				B17², 524
h570	2-Hexenoic acid, 3-phenyl-	$CH_3(CH_2)_2C(C_6H_5):CHCO_2H$	190.25	cr (peth)	94	$183-4^{14}$							s	peth δ	B9², 477
h571	1-Hexen-3-ol*	$CH_3CH_2CH_2CH(OH)CH:CH_2$	100.16	....		134^{760} 50^{20}	0.834_4^{22}	1.4297^{18}		s	s	s			B1³, 1924
h572	3-Hexen-1-ol(cis)*	$CH_3CH_2CH:CHCH_2CH_2OH$	100.16	....		$156-7$ 58^{12}	0.8478_4^{22}	1.4380^{20}	s	v	s				B1³, 1925
h573	1-Hexen-3-yne*	$CH_3CH_2C:CCH:CH_2$	80.14	lf		85^{758}	0.7492_4^{20}	1.4522^{20}	i	s	s		s	peth, chl s	B1³, 1041
h574	1-Hexen-5-yne*	Diallylene. $HC:CCH_2CH_2CH:CH_2$	80.14	....		70^{760}	0.7650_4^{20}	1.4318^{20}	i	s	s		s	peth, chl s	C54, 3272
h575	1-Hexen-3-yne, 5-chloro-5-methyl-*	$(CH_3)_2CClC:CCH:CH_2$	128.60	....		48^{28}	0.9375^{15}	1.4778^{20}	i	s	s	v^h	s	peth s	B1³, 1045
h576	3-Hexen-1-yne, 3-propyl-*	$CH_3CH_2CH:C(C_3H_7^n):C:CH.$	122.21	....		136^{760}	0.7799_4^{25}	1.4432^{25}					s	peth, chl s	Am 64, 365
h577	4-Hexen-1-yn-3-ol(d)*	$CH_3CH:CHCH(OH)C:CH..$	96.14	$[\alpha]_D^{20} +16.06$		$157-9$	0.9090_4^{20}	1.4645^{17}	s	s	s	s	s		J1945, 273
h578	—(dl)*	$CH_3CH:CHCH(OH)C:CH..$	96.14	....		$154-6$ 60^{18}	0.9148_4^{23}	1.4651^{23}		s	s	s	s		Am 66, 1289
—	Hexestrol, dimethyl-	see Hexane, 3,4-bis(4-hydroxy-3-methyl-phenyl)-*													
—	Hexeton	see 2-Cyclohexen-1-one, 5-isopropyl-3-methyl-*													
Ω h579	1-Hexyne*	n-Butylacetylene. $CH_3(CH_2)_3C:CH$	82.15	....	-131.9	71.3^{760}	0.7155_4^{20}	1.3989^{20}	i	s	s		s	peth, chl s	B1³, 977
h580	2-Hexyne*	$CH_3CH_2CH_2C:CCH_3$.....	82.15	....	-89.58	84^{760}	0.73146_4^{20}	1.41382^{20}	i	∞	∞		s	peth, chl s	B1³, 980
h581	3-Hexyne*	Diethylacetylene. $CH_3CH_2C:CCH_2CH_3$	82.15	....	-103	81.5^{744}	0.7231_4^{20}	1.4115^{20}	i	s	s		s	peth, chl s	B1³, 980
h582	—,2,5-dichloro-2,5-dimethyl-*	$(CH_3)_2CClCH:CHCCl(CH_3)_2$	181.11	....	29	$175-8^{745}$								chl s	B1³, 847
h583	—,1:2,5:6-diepoxy-		110.11	....	-16	98^{20}	1.1189^{23}	1.4871^{23}						chl s	B19², 19
h584	1-Hexyne, 5-methyl-*	Isoamylacetylene. $(CH_3)_2CHCH_2CH_2C:CH$	96.17	....	-125	92^{760}	0.7274_4^{20}	1.4059^{20}	i	s	s		s	peth, chl s	B1³, 1000
h585	2-Hexyne, 5-methyl-*	$(CH_3)_2CHCH_2C:CCH_3$	96.17	....	-92.91	102.46^{760}	0.73776_4^{20}	1.41762^{20}	i	s	s	s	s	peth, chl s	B1³, 1000
h586	3-Hexyne, 2-methyl-*	$CH_3CH_2C:CCH(CH_3)_2$	96.17	....	-116.7	95.2^{760}	0.7263_4^{20}	1.4114^{20}	i	s	s		s	peth, chl s	B1³, 1000
Ω h587	3-Hexyne-2,5-diol, 2,5-dimethyl-*	Acetylenepinacol. $(CH_3)_2C(OH)C:CC(OH)(CH_3)_2$	142.20	nd (w)	95	205^{759}	0.949_{20}^{20}	....	s	v	v	v	v	chl s	B1², 572
h588	1-Hexyn-3-ol, 3-methyl-*	$CH_3CH_2CH_2COH(CH_3)C:CH$	112.17	....		137^{760}	0.8620^{20}	1.4338^{20}	s	s	s				B1³, 1994
h589	3-Hexyn-2-ol, 2-methyl-*	$CH_3CH_2C:CCOH(CH_3)_2..$	112.17	....		$145-7$ $46-7^7$	0.962^0	1.4392^{25}	s	s	s				B1³, 1993
Ω h589¹	Hippuric acid	Benzamidoacetic acid. N-benzoylglycine.	179.18	pr (w or al) λ 226 (4.03), 269 (2.8)	$190-3$	....	1.371_4^{20}	....	s	s	δ		δ	AcOEt s chl δ peth, CS₂ i	B9², 174
h589²	—,4-phenylphenacyl ester		373.41	....	163										Am 52, 3715
h589³	—,piperazinium salt	$2(C_6H_5CONHCH_2CO_2H).C_4H_{10}N_2$	444.49	wh cr	$182-4d$				s^h	s^h	i				Am 70, 2758
Ω h589⁴	—,p-amino-	$C_9H_{10}N_2O_3$. See h589¹	194.19	pr or nd (w) $\lambda^{1 N NaOH} 273$ (4.21)	$198-9$				i	s	i				B14², 258
h589⁵	—,m-bromo-	$C_9H_8BrNO_3$. See h589¹	258.09	nd (w)	$146-7$				s^h	s			δ	MeOH s	B9², 233
h589⁶	—,o-bromo-	$C_9H_8BrNO_3$. See h589¹	258.09	nd (w)	$192-3$				s^h	s	i			AcOEt v	B9², 231
h589⁷	—,p-bromo-	$C_9H_8BrNO_3$. See h589¹	258.09	nd (w)	162				s^h	v					B9, 353
Ω h590	Histamine	4-Imidazolethylamine. β-Aminoethylglyoxaline.	111.15	wh nd (chl)	86 $(83-4)$	209^{18} $167^{0.8}$	....		s	s	δ			chl s^h	B23³, 302
Ω h591	—,dihydrochloride	$C_5H_9N_3.2HCl$. See h590.	184.07	pl (eth-ace), pr (w)	$249-52$				v	δ	i		i	MeOH v	B25², 303
h592	Histidine(d)		155.16	ta (w), $[\alpha]_D^{20}$ +40.2 (w)	287d				s	i	i	i	i	chl i	B25², 404
Ω h593	—(dl)	$C_6H_9N_3O_2$. See h592.	155.16	ta, tetr pr (w)	285d				s	δ	i	i	i	os i	B25², 409
Ω h594	—(l)	$C_6H_9N_3O_2$. See h592.	155.16	nd or pl (dil al) $[\alpha]_D^{20} -39.7$ (w, c = 1.13) $\lambda^{w, pH=0} 211$ (3.8)	287d				s	δ	i	i	i	chl i	B25², 409

For explanations, symbols and abbreviations see beginning of table. For structural formulas see end of table.

No.	Name	Synonyms and Formula	Mol. wt.	Color, crystalline form, specific rotation and λ_{max} (log ε)	m.p. °C	b.p. °C	Density	n_D	Solubility						Ref.
									w	al	eth	ace	bz	other solvents	

Histidine

No.	Name	Synonyms and Formula	Mol. wt.	Color, crystalline form	m.p. °C	b.p. °C	Density	n_D	w	al	eth	ace	bz	other solvents	Ref.
h595	—,bis(3,4-dichloro-benzene-sulfonate)(*l*)	$C_6H_9N_3O_2 \cdot 2C_6H_4Cl_2O_3S$. See h592	609.29	rh nd (w)	280d				s^h	i					C51, 5184
h596	—,diflavianate(*l*)	$C_6H_9N_3O_2 \cdot 2C_{10}H_6N_2O_8S$. See h592	783.62	nd (w)	251–4d				δ	i	i				B25², 427
h597	—,dihydrochloride(*dl*)	$C_6H_9N_3O_2 \cdot 2HCl$. See h592	228.08	. . . .	237d										B25¹, 718
Ω h598	—,—(*l*)	$C_6H_9N_3O_2 \cdot 2HCl$. See h592	228.08	rh pl	252d				s	s	i				B25, 513
h599	—,monohydro-chloride mono-hydrate(*l*)	$C_6H_9N_3O_2 \cdot HCl \cdot H_2O$. See h592	209.63	pl (w) $[\alpha]_D^{26} +8.0$ (3N HCl, c = 2)	259d (254d)				s	i	i				B25², 407
—	—,β-alanyl-	see Carnosine													
h600	Holocaine	N,N-Bis(p-ethoxyphenyl)-acetamidine. $C_{18}H_{22}N_2O_2$.	298.39	nd (al)	117–8				δ	v	v	s	v	lig δ	B13², 247
h601	—,hydrochloride	Phenacaine. $C_{18}H_{22}N_2O_2 \cdot HCl$. See h600	334.85	cr (w + 1)	190–2 (anh)				v^h	v	i			chl s	B13², 248
Ω h602	Homatropine	Homotropine. Mandelyltropine. $C_{16}H_{21}NO_3$.	275.35	pr (al or eth)	99–100				δ	s	s	s	δ	chl s	B21², 18
Ω h603	—,hydrobromide	$C_{16}H_{21}NO_3 \cdot HBr$. See h602	356.27	rh pym or pl (w)	217–8d				s	s	i			chl δ	B21, 23
h604	—,hydrochloride	$C_{16}H_{21}NO_3 \cdot HCl$. See h602	311.81	wh pr (w) λ^{al} 266	220–27d				s	s				chl δ	B21², 18
—	Homoanisic acid	see Acetic acid, (4-methoxyphenyl)-													
—	Homocaine	see Ecgonine, benzoate ethyl ester													
—	Homogentisic acid	see Acetic acid, (2,5-dihydroxyphenyl)-													
—	Homoisophthalic acid	see Acetic acid, (3-carboxyphenyl)-													
—	Homoisovanillic acid	see Acetic acid, (3-hydroxy-4-methoxyphenyl)-													
—	Homophthalic acid	see Acetic acid, (2-carboxyphenyl)-													
—	Homopyro-catechol	see Toluene, 3,4-dihydroxy-													
—	Homosaligenine	see Benzene, 1-hydroxy-2-hydroxymethyl-4-methyl-													
—	Homotere-phthalic acid	see Acetic acid, (4-carboxyphenyl)-													
—	Homoveratric acid	see Acetic acid, (3,4-dimethoxyphenyl)-													
h605	Hordenine	Anhaline. 1(Dimethylamino)-2(4-hydroxyphenyl)ethane*. $C_{10}H_{15}NO$.	165.24	rh pr (al or bz-peth), nd (w)	117–8	173–4¹¹ sub 140–50			s^h	v	v		δ	chl, lig s	B13², 356
Ω h606	—,sulfate	$2(C_{10}H_{15}NO) \cdot H_2SO_4$. See h605	428.54	fl	210–11 (205)				s	δ	i				B13¹, 236
Ω h607	—,sulfate, dihydrate	$2(C_{10}H_{15}NO) \cdot H_2SO_4 \cdot 2H_2O$. See h605	464.58	pr or pl	197				s	δ	i				B13¹, 236
h608	Humulon	α-Lupulic acid. $C_{21}H_{30}O_5$.	362.47	yesh cr (eth) $[\alpha]_D^{20} -232$ (bz), -212 (al) $\lambda^{aq\ ac}$ 260 (3.70)	66.5				δ^h	s	s	s		os, alk s	B8², 537
Ω h609	Hydantoic acid	N-Carbamoylglycine. Ureidoacetic acid. $H_2NCONHCH_2CO_2H$	118.09	mcl pr	180d (163)				v^h s	v^h δ	δ				B4², 792
h610	—,ethyl ester	$H_2NCONHCH_2CO_2C_2H_5$	146.15	nd (w)	135				v^h	s^h	i				B4², 794
h611	—,phenylthio-	N-Phenylpseudothio-hydantoic acid. $C_6H_5N:C(NH_2)SCH_2CO_2H$	210.26	wh (al)	159–61	175⁷⁶⁰			s^h	δ	δ		δ		B12¹, 248
Ω h612	Hydantoin	Glycolylurea.	100.18	nd (MeOH), lf (w) $\lambda^{0.02N\ NaOH}$ 223 (3.9)	220				v^h δ	s^h	δ			alk s peth i	B24², 127
Ω h613	—,1-acetyl-2-thio-	$C_5H_6N_2O_2S$. See h612	158.18	pl (al) $\lambda^{w,\ pH = 3}$ 235 (4.2), 278 (4.2)	175–6					s^h					B24¹, 293
Ω h614	—,1-benzoyl-2-thio-	$C_{10}H_8N_2O_2S$. See h612	220.26	pr (al) λ^{al} 240 (4.3), 287 (3.7)	165d					s^h					B24¹, 294
h615	—,5-benzylidene-2-thio-	$C_{10}H_8N_2OS$. See h612	204.26	ye nd (al) λ^{al} 240 (4.08), 295 sh (3.86), 365 (4.53)	258d					s^h				aa δ	B24¹, 355
Ω h616	—,5,5-dimethyl-	$C_5H_8N_2O_2$. See h612	128.14	pr (w-al) $\lambda^{al\ KOH}$ 219 (3.82)	178	sub			v	v	v	v	v	chl v	B24², 157

For explanations, symbols and abbreviations see beginning of table. For structural formulas see end of table.

No.	Name	Synonyms and Formula	Mol. wt.	Color, crystalline form, specific rotation and λ_{max} (log ε)	m.p. °C	b.p. °C	Density	n_D	Solubility						Ref.
									w	al	eth	ace	bz	other solvents	
	Hydantoin														
Ω h617	—,5,5-diphenyl-	$C_{15}H_{12}N_2O_2$. See h612	252.28	nd (al) λ^w 252 sh (2.99), 258 (2.85), 269 sh (2.38)	286 (cor)	....			i	s	δ	s	δ	aa s chl δ	B24², 227
h618	—,3,5-diphenyl-2-thio-	$C_{15}H_{12}N_2OS$. See h612	268.34	λ^{al} 266 (4.23), 271 (4.25)	233				δ	v	v	...	v	....	B24, 385
h619	—,5-ethyl-5-phenyl-(d)	d-Nirvanol. $C_{11}H_{12}N_2O_2$. See h612	204.23	pl (10 % al) $[\alpha]_D$ +123 (al), +169 (aq alk)	237	....					s				Am 54, 4697
Ω h620	—,—(dl)	dl-Nirvanol. $C_{11}H_{12}N_2O_2$. See h612	204.23	pr (dil al)	199–200				δ^h	s	δ	s^h	i	aa s	B24², 206
h621	—,5(2-hydroxy-benzylidene)-2-thio-	$C_{10}H_8N_2O_2S$. See h612	220.26	nd (aa)	248									aa s^h	B25¹, 502
Ω h622	—,1-methyl-	$C_4H_6N_2O_2$. See h612	114.11	cr (w), pl (al)	157–9				s	s^h	δ			chl s	B24², 128
Ω h623	—,5-methyl-(dl)	α-Lactylurea. $C_4H_6N_2O_2$. See h612	114.11	pr (+w, w)	145–6 (anh)				s	s	δ				B24², 155
h624	—,—(l)	$C_4H_6N_2O_2$. See h612	114.11	(w) $[\alpha]_D^{20}$ −50.6	175				v	s	δ			chl s	B24¹, 304
h625	—,—hydrate(dl)	$C_4H_6N_2O_2 \cdot H_2O$. See h612	132.12	rh (w)	155–6				v	v		v			B24², 155
Ω h626	—,2-thio-	Glycolylthiourea. $C_3H_4N_2OS$. See h612	116.14	wh nd (w) λ^{al} 222 (3.96), 264 (4.23)	229–31d				v^h	v^h	s			alk s	B24², 138
—	—,5-ureido-	see Allantoin													
—	Hydracrylic acid	see Propanoic acid, 3-hydroxy-*													
Ω h627	β(-)-Hydrastine	$C_{21}H_{21}NO_6$	383.41	yesh pr (al) $[\alpha]_D^{17}$ −67.8 (chl, c = 2.5) λ^{MeOH} 295 (3.88)	132 (135)				i	δ	s		s	chl v AcOEt s CCl₄ δ peth i	B27², 603
Ω h628	—,hydrochloride	$C_{21}H_{21}NO_6 \cdot HCl$. See h627	419.87	micr pw $[\alpha]_D$ +158.0 (w, c = 2)	116				v^h	...	δ			chl δ	B27², 604
h629	Hydrastinine	$C_{11}H_{13}NO_3$	207.23	nd (lig), cr (eth) $\lambda^{aq HCl}$ 250 (4.3), 307 (3.8)	116–7				s^h	v	v			chl v HCl s	B27², 530
h630	—,bisulfate	$C_{11}H_{13}NO_3 \cdot H_2SO_4$. See h629	287.29	gr-flr ye cr (al)	216d	....			s	s					B27, 465
h631	—,hydrochloride	$C_{11}H_{13}NO_3 \cdot HCl$. See h629	225.68	pa ye nd	212d				v	v	i			chl δ	B27², 530
—	Hydratrop-aldehyde	see Propanal, 2-phenyl-*													
Ω h633	Hydrazine, 1-acetyl-2-phenyl-	Acetic acid β-phenyl hydrazide. Hydracetin. $C_6H_5NHNHCOCH_3$	150.18	hex pr (eth) λ 246 (3.9), 290 (3.3)	130–2				v^h δ	v	δ		s	chl s	B15², 92
h634	—,allyl-	$CH_2:CHCH_2NHNH_2$	72.12			122–4[757]			s	s				chl s	B4¹, 562
—	—,benzoyl-	see Benzoic acid, hydrazide													
h635	—,benzyl-	$C_6H_5CH_2NHNH_2$	122.17	fl or pr (al)	26	103[41]			∞	∞	∞				B15², 244
h636	—,1-benzyl-2(4-tolyl)-		212.30			212[17]									B15, 533
h637	—,1,2-bis(3-aminophenyl)-*	m,m'-Hydrazodianiline. $C_{12}H_{14}N_4$. See h669	214.27	pym (al)	151	....			i	δ	i				B15², 309
h638	—,1,2-bis(4-aminophenyl)-*	p,p'-Hydrazodianiline. Diphenine. $C_{12}H_{14}N_4$. See h669	214.27	ye cr	145				s^h	v	v				B15, 653
—	—,1,2-bis(car-boxyphenyl)-*	see Benzoic acid, hydrazodi-													
h640	—,1,2-bis(1-cyanocyclo-hexyl)-		246.36	cr (al)	145d						s^h				B15², 294
h641	—,2-(bromo-phenyl)-*	$C_6H_7BrN_2$. See h694	187.05	nd	48	....									B15¹, 117
h643	—,(4-bromo-phenyl)-*	$C_6H_7BrN_2$. See h694	187.05	nd (w), lf (lig), cr (al)	108				s^h	s	s			lig v^h peth δ	B15², 160
h644	—,1-butyl-1-phenyl-*	$H_2NN(C_6H_5)C_4H_9$	164.25			250[763]									B15¹, 28
h645	—,1,2-diallyl-	$CH_2:CHCH_2NHNHCH_2CH:CH_2$	112.18			145[752]									B4², 963
Ω h646	—,1,2-dibenzoyl-	$C_6H_5CONHNHCOC_6H_5$	240.27	nd (al) λ^{MeOH} 232 (4.27)	241				δ^h	i	i			MeOH s^h chl i	B9², 216
Ω h647	—,1,2-dibenzoyl-1,2-dimethyl-	$C_6H_5CON(CH_3)N(CH_3)COC_6H_5$	268.32	pr (al)	85–6				i	s^h	i				B9², 217
h648	—,1,1-dibenzyl-	$H_2NN(CH_2C_6H_5)_2$	212.30	cr (peth)	65				i	v	v				B15², 245
h649	—,1,2-dibenzyl-	$C_6H_5CH_2NHNHCH_2C_6H_5$	212.30	lf (dil al)	47				i	s	δ				B15², 246
h650	—,(2,4-dichloro-phenyl)-*	$C_6H_6Cl_2N_2$. See h694	177.03	nd (eth or peth)	94				s^h	v	v			aa v	B15, 431
h651	—,1,1-diethyl-*	$H_2NN(C_2H_5)_2$	88.15		98–9.6[736]		0.8804$^{20}_4$	1.4214[20]	v	v	v		v	chl v	B4, 550
h652	—,1,2-diethyl-*	$C_2H_5NHNHC_2H_5$	88.15		85–6 (106 7)		0.797[26]	1.4204[20]		s	s		s		B4, 550
Ω h653	—,1,2-diformyl-	Hydrazodiformic acid. OCHNHNHCHO	88.07	pr (al)	160				v	δ	i				B2¹, 38

For explanations, symbols and abbreviations see beginning of table. For structural formulas see end of table.

No.	Name	Synonyms and Formula	Mol. wt.	Color. crystalline form. specific rotation and λ_{max} (log ε)	m.p. °C	b.p. °C	Density	n_D	w	al	eth	ace	bz	other solvents	Ref.
	Hydrazine														
h654	—,1,2-diisobutyl-	$(C_4H_9^i)NHNH(C_4H_9^i)$	144.26			170^{735} 63^{10}	0.8002_4^{20}	1.4276	δ	v	v	v	v	os s	B4², 962
h655	—,1,2-di-isopropyl-*	$(C_3H_7^i)NHNH(C_3H_7^i)$	116.21			125^{760} 63^{84}	0.7894_4^{20}	1.4173^{20}	δ	v	v	v	v	os ∞	B4², 960
Ω h656	—,1,1-dimethyl-*	$H_2NN(CH_3)_2$	60.11			63^{752}	0.7914^{22}	1.4075^{22}	v	v	v	....	....	MeOH v	B4², 958
h657	—,1,2-dimethyl-*	$CH_3NHNHCH_3$	60.11	λ^{al} 235 (4.0), 280 (3.1)		81^{753}	0.8274_4^{20}	1.4209^{20}	∞	∞	∞	....	....		B4², 958
Ω h658	—,—dihydro-chloride*	$CH_3NHNHCH_3 . 2HCl$	133.02	pr (w)	170d				v	v					B4¹, 560
h659	—,(2,3-dimethyl-phenyl)-*	$C_8H_{12}N_2$. See h694	136.20	nd (al)	111–2					v^h	s				B15¹, 171
h660	—,(2,4-dimethyl-phenyl)-*	$C_8H_{12}N_2$. See h694	136.20	nd (eth)	85				δ	v	s				B15¹, 173
h661	—,(2,5-dimethyl-phenyl)-*	$C_8H_{12}N_2$. See h694	136.20	nd (dil aa)	78				i	v	s	s	s	os s	B15¹, 175
h662	—,(2,6-dimethyl-phenyl)-*	$C_8H_{12}N_2$. See h694	136.20	nd (lig)	46									lig s	B15¹, 172
h663	—,(3,4-dimethyl-phenyl)-*	$C_8H_{12}N_2$. See h694	136.20	yesh nd (eth)	57										B15¹, 172
h664	—,1,2-di(1-naphthyl)-*	1,1'-Hydrazonaphthalene. $C_{10}H_7^a NHNHC_{10}H_7^a$	284.37	lf (bz), pl (peth)	153				i		s		s	peth δ	B15², 256
h665	—,1,2-di(2-naphthyl)-*	2,2'-Hydrazonaphthalene. $C_{10}H_7^\beta NHNHC_{10}H_7^\beta$	284.37	red pl (bz)	140–1 (133)					i	δ			os s	B15, 569
Ω h666	—,(2,4-dinitro-phenyl)-*	$C_6H_6N_4O_4$. See h694	198.14	blsh-red (al) λ^{diox} 261 (3.86), 349 (4.07)	194 (198d)				i	s^h	δ	....	δ	AcOEt s^h chl δ	B15, 489
h667	—,(2,6-dinitro-phenyl)-*	$C_6H_6N_4O_4$. See h694	198.14	red nd (dil al) λ^{chl} 409 (3.81)	145				i	s^h	δ		δ	chl δ	B15¹, 146
Ω h668	—,1,1-diphenyl-*	$H_2NN(C_6H_5)_2$	184.24	ta (lig) λ^{al} 287 (4.08)	49–52	220^{40-50}	1.190_4^{16}		δ	v	v		v	chl v con sulf s	B15², 52
Ω h669	—,1,2-diphenyl-*	Hydrazobenzene	184.24	ta (al-eth) λ^{al} 245 (4.3), 290 (3.6), 340 sh (2.8)	131		1.158_4^{16}			v			δ	aa i	B15², 52
h670	—,1,1-di(4-tolyl)-		212.30	lf (al)	93					s^h				sulf s	B15¹, 154
Ω h671	—,1,2-di(2-tolyl)-*	o-Hydrazotoluene	212.30	lf (al) λ^{al} 245 (4.3), 285 (3.6)	165				i	s	s		s		B15², 223
h672	—,1,2-di(3-tolyl)-*	m-Hydrazotoluene	212.30	cr (peth) λ^{al} 250 (4.2), 300 (3.6)	38	224			i	s	s		s		B15, 506
h673	—,1,2-di(4-tolyl)-*	p-Hydrazotoluene	212.30	lf (lig), cr (bz-al), pl (al-eth)	135		0.957_4^{20}		i	s	s		s		B15², 234
h674	—,ethyl-*	$H_2NNHC_2H_5$	60.11			101^{760}	1.0181^{21}	1.5711^{21}	v	v	v	s	v	chl v	B4², 959
h675	—,1-ethyl-1-phenyl-	$H_2NN(C_2H_5)C_6H_5$	136.20			237^{760} $115-9^{19}$	1.0151^{20}	1.5676^{20}	δ	v	v	s	v	chl v	B15², 50
h676	—,1-ethyl-2-phenyl-	$C_6H_5NHNHC_2H_5$	136.20			240^{750} 110^{14}	1.0150_4^{20}	1.5676^{20}	δ	v	v		v	chl v	B15², 50
h680	—,1-isobutyl-1-phenyl-	$H_2NN(C_6H_5)C_4H_9^i$	164.25	λ^{al} 235 (4.0), 280 (3.1)		$240-5$	0.9633_4^{15}								B15, 121
h681	—,isopropyl-*	$H_2NNHCH(CH_3)_2$	74.13			107^{750}			∞	∞	δ		∞	AcOEt ∞	B4², 960
h682	—,1-isopropyl-2-methyl-*	$(CH_3)_2CHNHNHCH_3$	88.15	cr (eth)		100^{760}									B4², 960
Ω h683	—,methyl-*	H_2NNHCH_3	46.07		< −80	87^{745}			s	∞	s			lig i	B4², 957
h684	—,1(3-methyl-butyl)-1-phenyl-*	$H_2NN(C_6H_5)CH_2CH_2CH(CH_3)_2$	178.28			236	0.9588^{15}								B15, 121
Ω h685	—,1-methyl-1-phenyl-*	$H_2NN(C_6H_5)CH_3$	122.17			227^{745} 131^{35}	1.0404_4^{20}	1.5691^{20}	δ	∞	∞		∞	chl ∞	B15², 49
h686	—,1-methyl-2-phenyl-*	$C_6H_5NHNHCH_3$	122.17			230^{728} 112^{14}	1.0320_4^{20}	1.5733^{20}	δ	v	v		v	chl s	B15², 50
h687	—,1-methyl-2(3-tolyl)-		136.20	ye	59–61		1.0265_4^{100}		i	v	δ		v		B15², 229
h687¹	—,1-methyl-2(4-tolyl)-		136.20	ye nd (eth), pl (lig)	91				i	s	s		s		B15¹, 154
h688	—,(1-naphthyl)-*	$H_2NNHC_{10}H_7^a$	158.21	lf (al), pl (w) sc (eth)	117	203^{20}			δ^h	v^h	s		v	chl v	B15², 256
h689	—,(2-naphthyl)-*	$H_2NNHC_{10}H_7^\beta$	158.21	lf (w)	124–5				s^h	v	δ		v	chl δ	E12B, 885
h690	—,(2-nitro-phenyl)-*	$C_6H_7N_3O_2$. See h694	153.14	red nd (bz) λ^{al} 280 (3.8), 430 (3.8)	90–2				v^h	δ	δ		δ	lig δ	B15², 177
h691	—,(3-nitro-phenyl)-*	$C_6H_7N_3O_2$. See h694	153.14	red nd or pr (ace), ye nd (al) λ^{al} 375 (3.0)	93				δ^h	δ	....		δ	chl, aa s	B15², 182

For explanations, symbols and abbreviations see beginning of table. For structural formulas see end of table.

No.	Name	Synonyms and Formula	Mol. wt.	Color, crystalline form, specific rotation and λ_{max} (log ϵ)	m.p. °C	b.p. °C	Density	n_D	w	al	eth	ace	bz	other solvents	Ref.
Ω h692	—,(4-nitrophenyl)-*	$C_6H_7N_3O_2$. See h694	153.14	og-red lf or nd (al) λ^{al} 230 (3.85), 384 (4.24)	158d				δ	s^h	s	...	s^h	chl, AcOEt s	B15², 183
h693	—,1-pentyl-2-phenyl-(d)*	$C_6H_5NHNH(CH_2)_4CH_3$	178.28	[α]$_D$ +4.45		173–5⁵⁰ 142–4¹²	0.986²⁰	1.5523²⁰	...	...	s	...	...		B15, 121
Ω h694	—,phenyl-*		108.15	mcl pr or pl λ^{al} 241 (3.97), 283 (3.2)	19.8	243⁷⁶⁰ 115¹⁰	1.0986²⁰$_4$	1.6084²⁰	s^h	∞	∞	v	∞	chl ∞ lig δ	B15², 44
h695	—,—,hemihydrate*	$C_6H_5NHNH_2.\frac{1}{2}H_2O$	117.15	fl (w)	24	120¹²	1.0970²⁵$_{25}$	1.6081²⁰	δ						B15, 68
h696	—,—,hemihydrochloride*	$2(C_6H_5NHNH_2).HCl$	252.75	nd	225				s	s	δ				B15, 108
Ω h697	—,—,hydrochloride*	$C_6H_5NHNH_2.HCl$	144.61	lf (al)	243–6d	sub			v	s	i				B15², 48
h698	—,1-phenyl-2(2-tolyl)-	2-Methylhydrazobenzene	198.27	pl (al)	101–2				i	δ	v	...	v	peth δ	B15, 497
h699	—,1-phenyl-2(3-tolyl)-	3-Methylhydrazobenzene	198.27	ye cr (peth)	61		1.0265¹⁰⁰$_4$		i	v	δ	...	s	lig s	B15², 229
h700	—,1-phenyl-2(4-tolyl)-	4-Methylhydrazobenzene	198.27	pl (lig), cr (al)	91				i	v	v	...	v		B15¹, 154
h701	—,propyl-*	$H_2NNHCH_2CH_2CH_3$	74.13		119										B4², 960
h702	—,tetraphenyl-	$(C_6H_5)_2NN(C_6H_5)_2$	336.44	pr (chl-al) λ^{al} 258.5 (4.16), 292.5 (4.31)	149d				i	δ	s	v	v	chl v	B15¹, 29
h703	—,(2-tolyl)-		122.17	nd (dil al)	59					v	v			chl v lig δ	B15², 222
Ω h704	—,(3-tolyl)-		122.17			244δd	1.057²⁰$_4$		δ	v	v		v		B15², 229
Ω h705	—,(4-tolyl)-		122.17	lf (w or eth)	66	244δd			δ	v	v		v		B15², 233
h706	—,1(3-tolyl)-2(4-tolyl)-		212.30	ta (lig)	74										B15, 511
h707	—,(2,4,6-tribromophenyl)-*	$C_6H_5Br_3N_2$. See h694	344.85	nd (peth), cr (lig)	146				$δ^h$				v	chl v lig s aa s^h	B15¹, 126
h708	—,(2,4,6-trichlorophenyl)-*	$C_6H_5Cl_3N_2$. See h694	211.48	cr (bz)	143				s^h				s^h		B15², 156
Ω h709	—,(2,4,6-trinitrophenyl)-*	$C_6H_5N_5O_6$. See h694	243.14	red pl (al) λ^{chl} 337 (4.38), 385 (3.72)	186				δ	s	δ	...	δ	aa s chl δ	B15², 221
h710	—,triphenyl-*	$C_6H_5NHN(C_6H_5)_2$	260.34	nd (bz-peth), cr (al)	142d		0.869²⁰$_4$		i	s	δ	...	v		B15², 54
h711	Hydrazinecarboxylic acid, ethyl ester*	N-Aminourethane. $H_2NNHCO_2C_2H_5$	104.12	cr	46	198d 93⁹									B3², 79
h712	1,1-Hydrazinedicarboxylic acid, diethyl ester*	$H_2NN(CO_2C_2H_5)_2$	176.17	pr (w)	29	138¹²									B3², 79
Ω h713	1,2-Hydrazinedicarboxylic acid, diamide	Dicarbonamide. $H_2NCONHNHCONH_2$	118.10	pl (w)	257–9 (248)				s^h	i	i	...		30% KOH s	B3², 95
h714	—,diethyl ester*	$C_2H_5O_2CNHNHCO_2C_2H_5$	176.17	nd (chl), pr (w)	135	250d	1.324⁸		s^h	v	v	...		chl s^h	B3², 79
—	Hydrazobenzene	see Hydrazine, 1,2-diphenyl-*													
—	Hydrazo compounds	see Hydrazine derivatives													
h715	Hydrindane (trans, l)	Hexahydroindane. Octahydroindene.	124.23	[α]$_D^{21}$ −5.98		161.08⁷⁶⁰ 71.7⁴⁰	0.86268²⁰$_4$	1.46363²⁰	i		s		s	peth s	B5², 50
h716	2-Hydrindanone (cis)	$C_9H_{14}O$. See h715	138.21		10	225⁷⁵⁴ 109²³		1.4830²⁰		s			s	lig s	E12A, 221
h717	—(trans)	$C_9H_{14}O$. See h715	138.21		−12	218⁷⁵⁴	0.9807¹⁷$_4$	1.4769¹⁷		s			s	lig s	E12A, 222
—	Hydrindene	see Indan													
—	Hydrindene, 1,2,3-triketo-, monohydrate	see Ninhydrin													
Ω h718	Hydrobenzamide	Tribenzaldiamine. $C_6H_5CH(N:CHC_6H_5)_2$	298.39	nd (bz), cr (al,w)	110	130⁷⁶⁰			i	s	v				B7⁷, 166
—	Hydrobenzoin	see 1,2-Ethanediol, 1,2-diphenyl-*													
h719	Hydroberberine(d)	d-Canadine(D). Tetrahydroberberine. $C_{20}H_{21}NO_4$	339.40	nd (dil al) [α]$_D^{20}$ +297.4 (chl, c = 1)	132				i	v			s	chl s	B27², 556
h720	—(l)	$C_{20}H_{21}NO_4$. See h719	339.40	nd (al), [α]$_D^{20}$ −298.2 (chl, c = 1)	134				i	v			s	chl s lig $δ^h$	B27², 557
—	Hydrocerulignone	see Biphenyl, 4,4'-dihydroxy-3,3',5,5'-tetramethoxy-													
h721	Hydrocinchonidine	Cinchamidine. Dihydrocinchonidine $C_{19}H_{24}N_2O$.	296.42	lf (al), [α]$_D^{20}$ −98.4 (al)	229				i	s	δ	δ	δ		B23², 357
—	Hydrocinnamaldehyde	see Propanal, 3-phenyl-*													

For explanations, symbols and abbreviations see beginning of table. For structural formulas see end of table.

Hydrocinnamic acid

No.	Name	Synonyms and Formula	Mol. wt.	Color, crystalline form, specific rotation and λ_{max} (log ε)	m.p. °C	b.p. °C	Density	n_D	w	al	eth	ace	bz	other solvents	Ref.
—	Hydrocinnamic acid	see Propanoic acid, 3-phenyl-*													
—	Hydrocortisone	see Corticosterone, 17-hydroxy-													
h722	Hydrocotarnine, hemihydrate	$C_{12}H_{15}NO_3 \cdot \frac{1}{2}H_2O$	230.27	pr (eth) λ 283 (3.23)	56				i	v	v	v	...	chl, aa v	B27[2], 541
h723	Hydrocupreine	$C_{19}H_{24}N_2O_2$	312.42	pl (dil al) $[\alpha]_D^{13} -159.2$ (abs al)	230				δ	...	s			chl s	B23[1], 151
h724	Hydrocyanic acid*	Hydrogen cyanide. Formonitrile. HCN	27.04	....	−13.24	25.7[760]	0.6876_4^{20} 0.925^{-40} (sol)	1.2614^{20}	∞	∞	∞				B2[2], 37
Ω h725	Hydrofuramide	Furfuralhydramide. Furfuramide. Trifurfuraldiamine.	268.28	nd (al)	117				i	v	v				B17[2], 311
—	Hydrogen cyanide	see Hydrocyanic acid*													
h726	Hydrohydrastinine	$C_{11}H_{13}NO_2$	191.23	nd (lig), cr (peth)	66	303[752]			i	v	v	v	s	AcOEt, CS_2, aa v	B27[2], 528
h727	Hydrolapachol	$C_{15}H_{16}O_3$	244.29	ye nd (al), cr (peth) λ^{al} 252 (4.32), 282 (4.15)	94						s			peth s[h]	E12B, 3082
—	Hydroperoxide, acetyl	see Acetic acid, per-													
h728	—,tert-butyl-	$(CH_3)_3COOH$	90.12	....	6	d at 89 35–7[17]	0.8960^{20}	1.4015^{20}	s	s	s			chl s	C55, 22109
h729	—,cyclohexyl-		116.16		−20	42[0.1]	1.019^{20}	1.4645^{25}	...	s	s			aa s	Am 72, 3333
h730	—,ethyl-	C_2H_5OOH	62.07		−100	93–7[760] exp >100	0.9332_4^{20}	1.3800^{20}	∞	∞	∞		s		B1[3], 1312
h731	—,methyl-	CH_3OOH	48.04		38–40[65]		1.9967_4^{15}	1.3641^{15}	∞	∞	∞		s	chl, aa δ	B1[2], 270
—	Hydrophlorone	see Benzene, 1,4-dihydroxy-2,5-dimethyl-*													
Ω h732	Hydroquinidine	$C_{20}H_{26}N_2O_2$	326.44	nd (al) $[\alpha]_D^{18} +229.26$	168–9					s	s	s	...	chl s	Am 41, 826
h733	Hydroquinine(d)	Quinotine. $C_{20}H_{26}N_2O_2$. See h732	326.44	$[\alpha]_D^{16} +143.5$	171				i	s	s	s	...	chl s	Am 41, 819
h734	—(dl)	$C_{20}H_{26}N_2O_2$. See h732	326.44	nd (al, chl)	175–7				i	s	s	s	...	chl s	Am 41, 819
h735	—(l)	$C_{20}H_{26}N_2O_2$. See h732	326.44	nd (eth, chl) $[\alpha]_D^{20} -142.2$ (anh)	172.3				i	s	s	s	...	chl s	B23[2], 400
—	Hydroquinol	see Benzene, 1,2,4-trihydroxy-*													
—	Hydroquinone	see Benzene, 1,4-dihydroxy-*													
Ω h736	Hydroquinonephthalein	2,7-Dihydroxyfluoran	332.32	nd (eth)	228–9				δ[h]	v	v	v	...	aa v	B19[2], 247
—	Hydrosorbic acid	see 3-Hexenoic acid*													
h737	Hydroxyamphetamine	Paredrine. $C_9H_{13}NO$	151.21		125–6				δ		s			chl s	C55, 14473
h738	—,hydrobromide	$C_9H_{13}NO \cdot HBr$. See h737	232.13		189				v	s					C46, 6603
h739	Hydroxycitronellal	$(CH_3)_2COH(CH_2)_3CH(CH_3)CH_2CHO$	172.27			103[3] 91[0.3]	0.9220^{20}	1.4494^{20}	δ	s		s			C52, 3855
—	Hydroxyditan	see Methane, (hydroxyphenyl)phenyl-*													
—	Hydroxyhemin	see Hematin													
h742	Hyenic Acid	$C_{25}H_{50}O_2$	382.68	cr (eth), nd (bz)	77–8				i	δ	v				B2[2], 380
h743	Hygrine(l)	2-Acetonyl-1-methyl pyrrolidine	141.22	$[\alpha]_D -1.3$		193–5[760] 92–4[20]	0.935_4^{17}		δ	s				chl, dil ac s	B21[2], 218
—	Hyodeoxycholic acid	see Cholanic Acid, 3α,6α-dihydroxy-													
h744	Hyoscine(dl)	Atroscine. Scopolamine. $C_{17}H_{21}NO_4$	303.36	syr					δ	v	v	v	v	chl s	B27[1], 248
h745	—,dihydrate(dl)	$C_{17}H_{21}NO_4 \cdot 2H_2O$. See h744	339.39	nd (w +2)	36–7							δ			B27, 101
h746	—,hydrobromide(d)	$C_{17}H_{21}NO_4 \cdot HBr$. See h744	384.28	$[\alpha]_D +26.3$ (w)	195										B27[1], 247
h747	—,—(dl)	$C_{17}H_{21}NO_4 \cdot HBr$. See h744	384.28	eff (ace)	185 (182)				s	s	i	δ		chl δ	B27[1], 248
h748	—,—(l)	$C_{17}H_{21}NO_4 \cdot HBr$. See h744	384.28	lf (al), $[\alpha]_D -26$	209 (194)				v	δ	i				B27[1], 247
h749	—,hydrobromide trihydrate(d)	$C_{17}H_{21}NO_4 \cdot HBr \cdot 3H_2O$. See h744	438.33	ta (w), $[\alpha]_D +26.3$ (w, c = 3)	55										B27[1], 247
h750	—,—(dl)	$C_{17}H_{21}NO_4 \cdot HBr \cdot 3H_2O$. See h744	438.33		55–8										B27[1], 248
h751	—,—(l)	$C_{17}H_{21}NO_4 \cdot HBr \cdot 3H_2O$. See h744	438.33	ta (w +3), $[\alpha]_D -22.8$ (w, c = 2)					v	δ					B27[2], 64
h752	—,hydrochloride(l)	$C_{17}H_{21}NO_4 \cdot HCl$. See h744	339.82	cr (al)	200				v	v					B27[2], 64
h753	—,hydrochloride dihydrate(l)	$C_{17}H_{21}NO_4 \cdot HCl \cdot 2H_2O$. See h744	375.85	pr (w)	80				v	v					B27, 101

For explanations, symbols and abbreviations see beginning of table. For structural formulas see end of table.

No.	Name	Synonyms and Formula	Mol. wt.	Color, crystalline form, specific rotation and λ_{max} (log ε)	m.p. °C	b.p. °C	Density	n_D	Solubility						Ref.
									w	al	eth	ace	bz	other solvents	

Hyoscine (*dl*)

No.	Name	Synonyms and Formula	Mol. wt.	Color etc.	m.p. °C	b.p. °C	Density	n_D	w	al	eth	ace	bz	other solvents	Ref.
h754	—,monohydrate(*dl*)	$C_{17}H_{21}NO_4 \cdot H_2O$. *See* h744..	321.38	cr (w + 1)	56–7	....			δ	v	v	...	...	chl v	B27, 101
h755	—,—(*l*)	$C_{17}H_{21}NO_4 \cdot H_2O$. *See* h744..	321.38	cr (w + 1), $[\alpha]_D^{20}$ −28 (w, c = 2.7), −18 (abs al, c = 5.2)	59	....			v^h	v	v	v	v	chl v	B27², 63
h756	—,nitrate(*l*)	$C_{17}H_{21}NO_4 \cdot HNO_3$. *See* h744	366.38	nd (al)	213	....									B27², 64
h757	—,sulfate dihydrate	$(C_{17}H_{21}NO_4)_2 \cdot H_2SO_4 \cdot 2H_2O$. *See* h744	740.83	nd (w, ace)	....										B27, 101
h758	**Hyoscyamine**(*d*)...	$C_{17}H_{23}NO_3$.............	289.38	nd (dil al) $[\alpha]_D +31.3$ (c = 4)	106	....			δ	v	v	...	v	chl v	B21², 18
h759	—(*l*).........	Daturine. *l*-Tropyltropeine. $C_{17}H_{23}NO_3$. *See* h758	289.38	tetr nd (dil al) $[\alpha]_D^{20}$ −1 (al, c = 1) λ^{MeOH} 252 (2.24), 258 (2.30), 264 (2.20)	108.5 (109–13)	....			δ	v	δ	...	δ	chl v dil ac s	B21², 18
h760	—,hydrobromide(*l*)	$C_{17}H_{23}NO_3 \cdot HBr$. *See* h758..	370.30	pr	152	....			v	v	i	...		chl v	B21¹, 198
Ω h761	—,hydrochloride(*l*)	$C_{17}H_{23}NO_3 \cdot HCl$. *See* h758 .	325.84	$[\alpha]_D$ −23.2 (w, c = 0.5)	149–51	....			s	s		...		....	B21, 26
h762	—,sulfate(*l*)	$(C_{17}H_{23}NO_3)_2 \cdot H_2SO_4 \cdot 2H_2O$ *See* h758	712.86	dlq nd (al or w) $[\alpha]_D$ −28.3 (w)	206 (anh)	....			v	v^h	i	v^h		chl δ	B21², 19
h763	**Hypaphorine**(*d*)...	*N,N*-Dimethyl-*L*-tryptophane betaine.	246.31	cr (dil al) $[\alpha]_D^{25} +113.4$ (w, c = 1.6)	255d (anh)	....			v	v	i	...	i	os i	B22², 469
h764	**Hypnal**.........	Antipyrine chloral hydrate.	353.64	wh	68	....			v	v					C23, 141
h765	**Hypochlorous acid,** *tert*-butyl ester	*tert*-Butyl hypochlorite. $(CH_3)_3COCl$	108.57	ye liq λ^{CCl_4} 280 (2.1), 340 sh (1.5)		77–8⁷⁶⁰	0.9583₄¹⁸	1.403²⁰	i	d	v	s	v	aa d	B1³, 1581
h766	—,ethyl ester*	CH_3CH_2OCl	80.52	ye liq λ^{CCl_4} 260 (1.5), 310 (1.2)	....	36⁷⁵²	1.013₄⁻⁶	....	i	s	∞		∞	chl ∞	B1², 325
h767	—,methyl ester* ...	CH_3OCl	66.49			12⁷²⁶d			i	s	v	...	s	chl s	Am 48, 2166
h768	**Hypofluorous acid,** trifluoromethyl ester*	F_3COF	104.00	....	< −215	−95⁷⁶⁰									Am 70, 3986
—	$\Delta^{\pi,8}$-**Hypogeic acid**	*see* **2-Hexadecenoic acid***													
h769	**Hypophosphoric acid,** tetraethyl ester*	Tetraethyl hypophosphate. $(C_2H_5O)_2POOP(OC_2H_5)_2$	274.19	....	......	116–7² 89⁰·⁰⁰⁵	1.1283¹⁸	1.4284²⁰	d	d	...	...	s		B1³, 1330
Ω h770	**Hypoxanthine**.....	6-Hydroxypurine. 6(1)-Purinone. Sarcine. $C_5H_4N_4O$.	136.11	oct nd (w) $\lambda^{0.01\ NaOH}$ 250 (4.04)	d at 150				δ s^h			...		alk, dil ac s	B26², 252
—	—,riboside	*see* **Inosine**													
—	—,2-amino-	*see* **Guanine**													
—	**Hystarazin**	*see* **9,10-Anthraquinone, 2,3-dihydroxy-***													

For explanations, symbols and abbreviations see beginning of table. For structural formulas see end of table.

No.	Name	Synonyms and Formula	Mol. wt.	Color, crystalline form, specific rotation and λ_{max} (log ε)	m.p. °C	b.p. °C	Density	n_D	Solubility						Ref.
									w	al	eth	ace	bz	other solvents	
	Iditol														
i1	Iditol	$L(+)$-Idite. 1,2,3,4,5,6-Hexanehexol.	182.18	mcl pr (al) $[\alpha]_D^{20} + 3.5$ (w)	73.5	. . . .			s		i		i	. . . .	B1[3], 2405
i1[1]	Idonic acid (L)	2,3,4,5,6-Pentahydroxy-hexanoic acid.	196.16	nd (w, al) $[\alpha]_D^{20} + 5.2 \rightarrow -13.7$ (mut)	205d	. . . .			s		i		i	. . . .	B3[2], 354
i2	—,γ-lactone(d)		178.14	pl, $[\alpha]_D^{20} -52.6$ (w)	174				s						Am 76, 3543
i3	—,phenylhydrazide (L)	. . . .	286.29	$[\alpha]_D^{20} -15.3$ (w, c = 1)	115–7 (117–20)				v	v[h]	,			AcOEt δ^h	B15[1], 82
i4	Idose(D)		180.16	syr, $[\alpha]_D^{13} + 16$ (w)	. . . .				s				i	. . . .	B31, 294 B1, 909
i5	—(L)	$C_6H_{12}O_6$. See i4	180.16	syr, $[\alpha]_D^{20} + 52.7$ (w, c = 6.2)	. . . .				s				i	. . . .	B1, 909
—	Ignotine	*see* **Carnosine**													
i6	Imesatin	Isatin-3-imide.	146.15	dk ye pr (dil al)	175–6	. . . .			i s^h	v	δ	. . .	i	lig i	B21[2], 332
Ωi7	Imidazole	1,3-Diazole. Glyoxaline. Iminazole.	68.08	mcl pr (bz) λ^{al} 207 (3.70)	90–1	257^{760} 138.2^{12}	1.0303_4^{101}	1.4801^{101}	v	v	s	s	δ	Py s chl s peth δ	B23[2], 34
—	—,4-ethylamino- . . .	*see* **Histamine**													
i8	—,2-mercapto-1-methyl-	Methimazol. Topazole. $C_4H_6N_2S$. See i7	114.17	lf (al) λ^{chl} 267 (4.23)	142	$280\ \delta d$			v	s	δ	. . .	δ	chl s lig δ	B24, 17
Ωi9	—,1-methyl-	Oxalmethyline. $C_4H_6N_2$. See i7	82.11	λ^{al} 212 (3.63)	−6	$195–6$ $94–5^{15}$	$1.0325_4^{20.5}$	1.4970^{20}	∞	v	s	s	. . .	. . . .	B23[2], 35
—	—,2,4,5-triphenyl-	*see* **Lophine**													
i10	4,5-Imidazoledi-carboxylic acid	1,3-Diazole-4,5-dicarboxylic acid.	156.10	pr	. . . .	288d	1.749		δ^h	i	i	. . .	i	Py δ con ac s os i	B25[2], 159
Ωi11	2-Imidazolidine-thione	N,N'-Ethylenethiourea.	102.16	nd (al), pr (AmOH) λ^{al} 235 (4.18)	200–3	. . . .			v	s	i	. . .	i	chl, lig i	B24[2], 4
i12	2-Imidazolidone	Ethylenurea.	86.09	nd (chl)	131–3	. . . .			v	v[h]	δ	. . .	. . .	chl δ	B24[2], 3
Ωi13	Δ^2-Imidazoline, 2-methyl-	Lysidine. 2-Methyl-2-glyoxalidine.	84.13	hyg	107 (103)	$195–8^{760}$ (222) ca. 120^{65}			v	v	s	. . .	. . .	chl s	B23[2], 26
i14	Imperatorin	Ammidin. $C_{16}H_{14}O_4$	270.29	cr (al)	102	. . . .			i	s	s	s	s	os s alk s	B19[2], 277
i15	Indaconitine	Acetylbenzoylpseudoaconine. $C_{34}H_{47}NO_{10}$	629.76	cr	202–3d	. . . .			i	s	s	s	s	peth i chl s	J 1905, 1620
Ωi16	Indan	2,3-Dihydroindene. Hydrindene.	118.18	λ^{cy} 262 (2.8), 268 (3.1), 273 (3.0)	−51.4	178 73^{13}	0.9639_4^{20}	1.5378^{20}	i	∞	∞				B5[2], 376
i17	—,1-amino-	dl-1-Hydrindamine. $C_9H_{11}N$. See i16	133.20	oil	. . . .	220.5^{747} $96–7^8$	1.038_4^{15}	1.5613^{20}	δ		s	s	s		E12A, 149
i18	—,5-amino-	5-Hydrindamine. $C_9H_{11}N$. See i16	133.20	nd (peth)	37–8	$247–9^{745}$ 131^{15}			δ		s	s	s	ac s os v	E12A, 154
i19	—,2,3-dibromo- . . .	Indene dibromide. $C_9H_8Br_2$. See i16	275.99	pr (peth)	31.5–2.5	144^{10} $100–5^1$	1.747_4^{25}	1.6290^{25}	d^h	d^h	s	. . .	. . .	sulf s (red)	E12A, 142
i20	—,2,3-dichloro-	Indene dichloride. $C_9H_8Cl_2$. See i16	187.07	. . . .		$87–90^2$	1.254_4^{25}	1.5715^{23}	d^h	d^h					E12A, 142
—	—,hexahydro-	*see* **Hydrindane**													
i21	—,1-hydroxy-	1-Indanol. $C_9H_{10}O$. See i16	134.18	pl (peth)	54	255 128^{12}			δ^h	v	v	. . .	v	chl v peth δ	B6[2], 530
Ωi22	—,4-hydroxy-	4-Indanol. $C_9H_{10}O$. See i16	134.18	(i) tcl pr (peth) (ii) nd (peth) λ^{MeOH} 269 (2.88), 277 (2.88)	(i) 50 (ii) 40	120^{12}									B6[2], 530
Ωi23	—,5-hydroxy-	5-Indanol. $C_9H_{10}O$. See i16	134.18	nd (peth) λ^{MeOH} 282 (3.45)	56	255 110^8			δ	v	v	. . .	. . .	sulf s (ye) peth δ	B6[3], 2428
Ωi24	—,1-methyl-	$C_{10}H_{12}$. See i16	132.21	λ^{iso} 260 (3.5), 273 (3.7)	. . . .	$188–90$ 60^{10}	0.9402_4^{20}	1.5260^{20}	i						B5[3], 1230
Ωi25	—,2-methyl-	$C_{10}H_{12}$. See i16	132.21	λ^{iso} 260 (2.8), 273 (3.0), 292 (1.5)	. . . .	187^{760} 70^{10}	0.9034_4^{20}	1.5070^{20}	i						B5[3], 1231
i26	—,4-nitro-	$C_9H_9NO_2$. See i16	163.18	wh cr (al)	44–4.5	139^{10}			i					os v	B5[3], 1204
i27	—,1-phenyl-1,3,3-trimethyl-	$C_{18}H_{20}$. See i16	236.36	tcl pr (al, MeOH)	52–3	$307–10$ $161–5^{12}$	1.0009_4^{20}	1.5681^{20} 1.5433^{70}	i	s^h			s	MeOH s	B5[3], 2038
i28	1,2-Indandione	α,β-Dioxohydrindene. Oxindone.	146.15	gold ye pl or lf (bz, eth)	114–6	. . . .			s^h	v				chl v MeOH v	B7[2], 631
i29	—,β-oxime		161.16	nd (al), (bz)	215–20d				δ	s^h	. . .	. . .	s^h	dil alk s (ye)	B7[2], 631
Ωi30	1,3-Indandione	1,3-Dioxohydrindene. Oxindone.	146.15	nd (eth, lig) $\lambda^{1\ NHCl}$ 227 (4.59), 255 (3.97), 300 (3.05)	131–2d	. . . .	1.37^{21}		δ	v^h	s^h	. . .	s^h	alk s (ye) lig δ	B7[2], 632
i31	—,dioxime	$C_9H_8N_2O_2$. See i30	176.19	nd (w)	ca. 225d	. . . .			δ^h	δ	i	. . .	. . .		B7, 695

For explanations, symbols and abbreviations see beginning of table. For structural formulas see end of table.

No.	Name	Synonyms and Formula	Mol. wt.	Color, crystalline form, specific rotation and λ_{max} (log ε)	m.p. °C	b.p. °C	Density	n_D	w	al	eth	ace	bz	other solvents	Ref.
	1,3-Indandione														
Ω i32	—,2,2-dimethylpropoxy-	Pivalyl indandione. Pivalyl valone. $C_{14}H_{14}O_3$. See i30	230.27	(dil al)	108.5–10.5	....			i	s	s	s	...	aq alk s (bt ye)	C53, 21830
i33	—,2(3-methylbutoxy)-	Valone. $C_{14}H_{14}O_3$. See i30	230.27	ye (dil al) λ^{al}237 (4.24), 274 (4.36), 283 (4.57), 323 (3.91)	67–8				i	s	s	s	...	...	C55, 12371
Ω i34	—,2-phenyl-	Danilone. $C_{15}H_{10}O_2$. See i30	222.25	lf (al or bz) λ^{al} 269 (4.35), 320 (3.53)	149–51				i δ^h	s	s	s	s	chl, MeOH s	B7², 732
Ω i35	1-Indanone	α-Hydrindone. 1-Keto-hydrindene.	132.17	ta, nd (w +3) λ^{al}244 (4.16), 286 (3.48), 291.5 (3.49)	42	241–2^{739} 129^{13}	1.1028$^{40}_{40}$	1.561^{25}	δ	v	v	v	...	chl v lig s	B7², 283
i36	2-Indanone	β-Hydrindone. 2-Keto-hydrindene.	132.17	nd (al or eth) λ^{hx} 296–316 (1.0)	59 (61)	218d	1.0712$^{69}_4$	1.538^{67}	i	v	v	v	...	chl v	B7², 286
Ω i37	1-Indanone, 2-nitro-	$C_9H_7NO_3$. See i35	177.16	ye nd (bz-lig)	117d				s	s	s	s	s	os s lig δ^h	B7¹, 192
i38	—,6-nitro-	$C_9H_7NO_3$. See i35	177.16	ye lf or nd (peth, al or AcOEt)	74				δ	v	v	s	v	AcOEt s chl v peth δ	B7², 285
i39	2-Indanone, 5-nitro-	$C_9H_7NO_3$. See i36	177.16	br nd (al)	141–1.5				δ	v	v	v	v	aa v	B7, 364
i40	Indanthrene	Dihydroanthraquinonazine. Indanthrone.	442.43	bl nd λ^{al} 216 (4.98), 255 (4.92), 292.5 (5.17), 371 (4.21)	470–500d				i	i	i	i	i	dil alk s PhNO₂ s (gr-bl)	B24¹, 317
Ω i41	Indazole	1,2-Benzodiazole. 1,2-Benzo-pyrazole	118.14	nd (al or w) λ^{MeOH} 250 (3.65), 285 (3.66)	147–9	26¹/–70$^{/43}$			s^h	s	s				B23², 117
i42	—,3-chloro-	$C_7H_5ClN_2$. See i41	152.58	nd (w or lig) λ^{al} 254 (3.49), 290 (3.72), 300 (3.61)	148–8.5	sub			s^h	v	v		v	lig s^h	B23², 139
i43	—,4-chloro-	$C_7H_5ClN_2$. See i41	152.58	nd (to) λ^{al} 256 (3.62), 288 (3.67), 299 (3.61)	156				s	s	s	s	s^h	os s, to s^h	B23², 139
i44	—,4-nitro-	$C_7H_5N_3O_2$. See i41	163.14	nd (w) λ^{al} 228 (4.09), 399 (3.83)	205–7				δ	s	s	v		aa v lig i	B23², 144
Ω i45	—,5-nitro-	$C_7H_5N_3O_2$. See i41	163.14	yesh nd or col nd (al) λ^{al} 232 (4.12), 254 (4.21), 304 (3.85)	208					s	s	v	s	aa v lig i	B23², 145
i46	—,6-nitro-	$C_7H_5N_3O_2$. See i41	163.14	nd (w, al, aa or xyl) λ^{al} 288 (3.97), 337 (3.44)	181d				s^h	s	s	v	s	NaOH, xyl s^h lig i	B23², 146
Ω i47	—,7-nitro-	$C_7H_5N_3O_2$. See i41	163.14	cr (al) λ^{al} 310 (3.48), 356 (3.91)	188–90 sub							s	v	2N NaOH v	B23², 150
i48	3-Indazolinone	Benzopyrazolone. Indazolone.	134.14	nd or lf (MeOH or w), pl or nd (al) λ^{MeOH} 215 (4.32), 306 (3.62)	250–2				δ^h	s^h δ	δ			MeOH s^h	B24², 59
Ω i49	Indene	Indonaphthene.	116.16	(aa) λ^{al} 249 (3.97), 279 (2.72), 290 (2.26)	−1.8 to −1.5	182.6^{760}	0.9960$^{20}_4$	1.5768^{20}	i	∞	∞	s	s	Py s CS₂ s	B5², 410
i50	—,1-benzhydrylidene-	ω,ω-Diphenylbenzofulvene.	280.37	og-ye (al)	114.5	.....	....	....		δ	s	s	s	os s aa δ	B5³, 2532
—	—,2,3-dihydro-	see Indan													
i51	—,1,2-diphenyl-	$C_{21}H_{16}$. See i49	268.38	lo nd (aa)	177–8				i	s^h δ	s	...	δ	sulf s(gr) peth δ aa s^h	B5³, 2473
i52	—,1,3-diphenyl-	$C_{21}H_{16}$. See i49	268.38	(i) nd (aa) (ii) pym (aa)	(i) 68–9 (ii) 85	230^{15}			i	s^h	s	s	s	aa s^h	B5³, 2474
i53	—,2,3-diphenyl-	$C_{21}H_{16}$. See i49	268.38	pr (aa) λ^{diox} 235 (4.3), 310 (4.2)	108–9	235–40^{12}			i	s^h	s	s	s	sulf s (gr) aa s^h	B5³, 2473
i54	—,2-methyl-	$C_{10}H_{10}$. See i49	130.19	oil	....	187^{760} 62–5^{20}	0.9034$^{20}_4$	1.5070^{20}	i	...	s	s	s	....	B5³, 1371
i55	—,3-methyl-	$C_{10}H_{10}$. See i49	130.19	λ^{al} 252 (3.97), 284 (2.5), 291 (2.4)	....	198.5d 70^{10}	0.9640$^{20}_4$	1.5591^{27}	i	...	s	s	s	....	B5³, 1372

For explanations, symbols and abbreviations see beginning of table. For structural formulas see end of table.

1-Indenecarboxylic acid

No.	Name	Synonyms and Formula	Mol. wt.	Color. crystalline form. specific rotation and λ_{max} (log ε)	m.p. °C	b.p. °C	Density	n_D	w	al	eth	ace	bz	other solvents	Ref.
Ω i56	1-Indenecarboxylic acid	$C_{10}H_8O_2$. See i49	160.18	pa ye nd (bz)	161	193–5[12]			δ	v	δ	...	δ	to, chl δ	E12A, 356
i57	2-Indenecarboxylic acid	$C_{10}H_8O_2$. See i49	160.18	nd or lf (bz)	234 sub				δ	v	v	...	δ	chl δ	E12A, 357
i58	1-Indenone, 2,3-diphenyl-		282.35	og-red (lig or al) λ^{al} 260 (4.50), 440 (3.24)	153–5 (151)				i	s	...	s	s	lig s[h]	B7[2], 501
i59	Indican	Indoxyl-β-glucoside. $C_{14}H_{17}NO_6 \cdot 3H_2O$	349.34	orh nd (w + 3), $[\alpha]_{546}^{19}$ −65.6 (w, c = 1)	57–8 (hyd) 178–80d (anh)				s	s	δ	s	δ	MeOH s AcOEt, CS_2, chl δ	B31, 258
—	Indigo carmine	see 5,5′-Indigotindisulfonic acid													
—	Indigo red	see Indirubin													
i60	Indigo white	2,2′-Diindoxyl. Leucoindigo.	264.29	ye cr (dil al)					δ	s	s	...	...	alk s	B23[2], 429
i61	4,4′-Indigotindi-carboxylic acid		350.29	bl nd					i	i	i	...	...	sulf s chl i	B25, 273
Ω i62	5,5′-Indigotindi-sulfonic acid, sodium salt	Indigo carmine	466.4	dk bl amor or br-red cr λ^w 260 (3.8), 310 (4.5), 600 (3.8)					s	s				....	B25[2], 298
i63	Indigotinsul-fonic acid		342.33	amor	200d				s	s				dil ac i	B25[2], 296
i64	Indirubin	Indigo red.	262.27	red or br rh nd (sub) λ^{chl} 285 (3.3), 603 (3.0)	sub				i	δ	s	...		con sulf s aa δ	B24[2], 246
—	Indogenic acid	see 2-Indolecarboxylic acid, 3-hydroxy-													
Ω i65	Indole	1-Benzo[b]pyrrole.	117.15	lf (w, peth), cr (eth) λ^{al} 218 (4.44), 271 (3.79), 287 (3.66)	52.5	254 123–4[5]	1.22		s[h]	v	v	...	s	lig s to v	B20[2], 196
i66	—,1-acetyl-	$C_{10}H_9NO$. See i65	159.19			152–3[14] 100[0.001]						s	s		B20[2], 200
i67	—,3(2-amino-ethyl)-	Tryptamine. $C_{10}H_{12}N_2$. See i65	160.22	nd (al-bz or lig) λ^w 279 (3.72)	120 (146)	137[0.15]			i	s	i	s	i	chl i	B22[2], 346
—	—,2,3-dihydro-	see Indoline													
i68	—,1,3-dimethyl-	N-Methylskatole. $C_{10}H_{11}N$. See i65	145.21	nd λ^{al} 282.5 (3.74), 292 (3.74)	141–3	257–60 119[7]					s				B20[2], 204
—	—,3(dimethyl-aminomethyl)-	see Gramine													
i69	—,3-hydroxy-	3-Indolol. Indoxyl. C_8H_7NO. See i65	133.15	bt ye pr	85				s	s	s	v	s	chl s lig δ	B21[2], 42
—	—,—,β-glucoside	see Indican													
i70	—,2-hydroxy-3-nitroso-	β-Isatoxime. $C_8H_6N_2O_2$. See i65	162.15	gold-ye nd	214				δ	s				KOH s	B21, 443
i71	—,2-methyl-	C_9H_9N. See i65	131.18	pl (dil al), nd or lf (w) λ^{al} 220 (4.51), 270 (3.89), 288 (3.70)	61	272	1.072[20]		δ[h]	v	v	s	s	sulf s	B20[2], 201
Ω i72	—,3-methyl-	Skatole. C_9H_9N. See i65	131.18	lf (lig) wh-br sc λ^{al} 223 (4.51), 281 (3.80), 290 (3.94)	97–8	265–6[755]			s	s	s	s	s	chl s	B20[2], 203
Ω i73	2-Indolecar-boxylic acid		161.16	ye pl (bz or eth-peth) λ^{al} 219 (4.40), 291 (4.21)	205–8 (203)				δ	s	s			aa δ	B22[2], 45
i74	—,3-hydroxy-	Indogenic acid. Indoxylic acid. $C_9H_7NO_3$. See i73	177.16	cr (sub)		122–3 sub d			δ d[h]						B22[2], 168
Ω i75	Indoline	2,3-Dihydroindole.	119.17	λ^{MeOH} 243 (3.8), 291 (3.3)		228–30 (220–1) 70–5[2]	1.069[20]	1.5923[20]	δ	s	s	s	s		B20[2], 170
—	2,3-Indolinedione	see Isatin													
—	Indolol	see Indole, hydroxy-													
—	Indonaphthene	see Indene													
i76	Indone, 2,3-dibromo-		287.95	og-ye nd (al, aa)	123				i	s	v	...		chl v	B7[1], 205
i77	Indophenin		426.20	bl nd or pw (PhOH-al) λ^{MeOH} 262 (4.19), 314 (3.97), 503 (3.93)	d				i	δ	δ	...	δ	chl δ aa δ	B21[2], 330

For explanations, symbols and abbreviations see beginning of table. For structural formulas see end of table.

Indophenol

No.	Name	Synonyms and Formula	Mol. wt.	Color, crystalline form, specific rotation and λ_{max} (log ε)	m.p. °C	b.p. °C	Density	n_D	Solubility						Ref.
									w	al	eth	ace	bz	other solvents	
i78	Indophenol........	....	199.21	red br pl (ace-peth) λ^{MeOH} 262 (4.19), 314 (3.97), 503 (3.93)	160	....	....	....	s	s	s	...	s	chl s aa s	C47, 7456
i79	Indoxazene	4,5-Benzoisoxazol.	119.12	oil	....	100^{26} $86–7^{11}$	1.1727^{21}_4	1.5570^{20}	i	...	s	...	...	....	B27[2], 15
—	Indoxylic acid	see 2-Indolecarboxylic acid, 3-hydroxy-													
Ω i82	Inosine.........	Hypoxanthosine. Hypoxanthine riboside.	268.23	pl (w +2), nd (80 % al) $[\alpha]^{20}_D -73$ (dil NaOH) λ^w 249 (4.13)	90 (+2w) 218d (anh)	....	....	....	δ s^h	s	...	...	...	dil alk s	B31, 25
i83	Inositol(D)........	d-Inosite. 1,2,3,4,5,6-Cyclo-hexanehexol*.	180.16	pr (w +2), (al) $[\alpha]_D +65.0$ (w, 12%)	249–50 (cor)	....	....	....	v	δ	i	...	i	aa v	B6[2], 1157
Ω i84	—(DL)..........	i-Inosite. Mesoinosite. Phaseomannitol. $C_6H_{12}O_6$. See i83	180.16	mcl pr (w), cr (gl aa)	253 (225)	319 vac	1.752^{15}	....	v	δ	i	...	i	aa v	B6[2], 1158
i85	—(L)	l-Inosite. $C_6H_{12}O_6$. See i83	180.16	nd (w +2) $[\alpha]^{28}_D -64.1$ (w, 4%)	247 (238)	250 vac	1.598^{20}	....	v	δ	i	...	i	aa v	B6[2], 1157
i86	Inulin..........	Plant starch. $(C_6H_{10}O_5)_n$	7000	wh amor or pw, $[\alpha]^{21}_D -38.3$	178d	....	1.35^{20}_4	....	δ s^h	i	δ	δ	i	HCO_2H s	J1932, 2384
—	Iodisan..........	see 2-Propanol, 1,3-bis(dimethylamino)-, dimethyl iodide													
—	Iodival	see Urea, 1(2-iodo-3-methylbutanoyl)-*													
—	Iodoalphionic acid	see Propanoic acid, 3(3,5-diiodophenyl-4-hydroxy)-2-phenyl-													
—	Iodoform	see Methane, triiodo-*													
i87	Iodogorgoic acid(d)	3,5-Diiodotyrosine(d). Dityrin.	432.99	yesh nd (w or 70% al), $[\alpha]^{20}_D +2.9$ (HCl, c = 5)	213 (204 cor)	....	....	....	δ	i	i	...	i	....	B14[2], 378
i88	—(dl)	$C_9H_9I_2NO_3$. See i87........	432.99	nd (50 % aa), pl (w), cr (70 % al) $\lambda^{al -NaOH}$ 315 (3.82)	200d (195d)	....	....	....	δ	i	i	...	i	....	B14[2], 384
i89	—(l)	$C_9H_9I_2NO_3$. See i87........	432.99	nd (w or 70 % al), $[\alpha]^{20} -2.98$ (4 % HCl, c = 5) $\lambda^{w, pH = 12.2}$ 311 (3.76)	213d (204 cor)	....	....	....	δ	i	i	...	i	....	B14[2], 366
i90	Iodonium fluoride didiphenyl-	$(C_6H_5)_2IF$	300.12	dlq rh (ace)	85d	....	....	....	v	v	i	s^h δ	...	....	J1946, 1129
Ω i91	Iodonium iodide, diphenyl-	$(C_6H_5)_2II$	408.02	ye nd (al)	182	....	....	....	...	s^h	...	...	...	....	C36, 5790
—	Iodophen	see Phenolphthalein, 3,3″,5,5″-tetraiodo-													
—	Iodoprene	see 1,3-Butadiene, 2-iodo-*													
—	Ionol	see Benzene, 1,3-di-tert-butyl-2-hydroxy-5-methyl-													
i92	α-Ionol..........	....	194.32	oil	....	127^{15}	0.9474^{20}_4	1.4735^{20}	...	s	s	s	...	....	C42, 5428
i93	β-Ionol	....	194.32	λ^{al} 234 (3.72)	....	131^{15} $89^{0.7}$	0.9243^{20}_4	1.4969^{20}	...	s	s	s	...	....	C32, 2090
i94	α-Ionone(d, trans)..	4(2,6,6-Trimethyl-2-cyclo-hexenyl)-3-buten-2-one*	192.31	$[\alpha]^{23}_D +347$	....	....	....	1.5016^{20}	δ	∞	∞	v	...	....	Am 46, 119
Ω i95	—(dl)	$C_{13}H_{20}O$. See i94	192.31	λ^{al} 232 (4.2)	....	$146.5–7.5^{28}$ $73–7^{0.15}$	0.9298^{21}	1.5041^{20}	δ	∞	∞	v	...	chl i	B7[2], 140
i96	—(l)	$C_{13}H_{20}O$. See i94	192.31	$[\alpha]^{27}_D -406$	....	....	....	1.5000^{25}	δ	∞	∞	v	...	....	Am 65, 2061
i97	—,semicarbazone (dl)	$C_{14}H_{23}N_3O$. See i94.......	249.36	(60 % al) λ^{al} 263.5 (4.48)	(i) 107–8 (ii) 143	....	....	....	...	...	...	...	...	....	B7, 169
Ω i98	β-Ionone	$C_{13}H_{20}O$	192.31	λ^{al} 228 (3.81), 295 (4.03)	....	140^{18} $72–4^{0.1}$	0.9462^{20}_4	1.5198^{20}	δ	∞	∞	...	...	....	B7[2], 140
i99	—,semicarbazone..	$C_{14}H_{23}N_3O$. See i98.......	249.36	nd (al) λ^{al} 282 (4.47), 291 (4.49)	149	....	....	....	i	s	s	...	s	chl s lig i	B7, 168
—	Ipral............	see Barbituric acid, 5-ethyl-5-isopropyl-													

For explanations, symbols and abbreviations see beginning of table. For structural formulas see end of table.

No.	Name	Synonyms and Formula	Mol. wt.	Color, crystalline form, specific rotation and λ_{max} (log ε)	m.p. °C	b.p. °C	Density	n_D	Solubility w	al	eth	ace	bz	other solvents	Ref.
	β-Irone														
i100	β-Irone	4(2,5,6,6-Tetramethyl-1-cyclohexenyl)-3-buten-2-one. $C_{13}H_{20}O$	192.31	$[\alpha]_D$ +41.6 λ^{al} 226(3.98), 295 (4.05)	....	85–90[0.1]	0.9434[21/4]	1.5017[20]	δ	v	v	...	v	chl, lig v	B7[1], 110
i101	Isatic acid	2-Aminobenzoylformic acid	165.15	pw	d	....	....	....	s d[h]						B14[2], 410
Ω i102	Isatin	2,3-Indolinedione. Isatic acid lactam.	147.14	yesh-red pr (sub) λ^{chl} 245 (4.2), 310 (3.4), 420 (2.7)	203.5	sub	....	....	s[h] δ	v[h]	δ	s	s	alk s, d[h]	B21[2], 327
i103	—,chloride	2-chloro-3-indolone	165.58	br nd	180d	....	....	....	i	v	v	...	δ v[h]	aa v lig δ	B21[2], 259
—	—,3-imide	see Imesatin													B21[1], 353
i104	—,2-oxime	$C_8H_6N_2O_2$. See i102	162.15	ye-og nd (al or w)	198–200d	....	....	....	δ v[h]	s[h]	v	v	δ	alk s lig i chl δ aa v	B21[1], 353
Ω i105	—,3-oxime	$C_8H_6N_2O_2$. See i102	162.15	gold ye nd	225d	....	....	....	v[h]	v	δ			alk, ac s lig i	B21[2], 334
Ω i106	—,1-acetyl-	$C_{10}H_7NO_3$. See i102	189.17	ye pr or nd λ^{al} 236 (4.36), 272 (3.91), 342 (3.56)	144–5	....	....	....	δ	s	δ	s			B21[2], 338
i107	—,1-methyl-	$C_9H_7NO_2$. See i102	161.16	red-ye orh nd (w) λ^{al} 242 (4.35), 304 (3.32), 426 (2.70)	134	....	....	....	s[h]	s	s	s	s	MeOH s	B21[2], 336
Ω i108	—,5-methyl-	$C_9H_7NO_2$. See i102	161.16	red pl (w), nd (w or al) λ^{diox} 294 (3.43), 418 (2.95)	187	....	....	....	δ	s	δ	...		HCl, alk s	B21[2], 375
Ω i109	—,5-nitro-	$C_8H_4N_2O_4$. See i102	192.13	ye nd (al)	254–5d	....	....	....	δ	v				KOH s	B21[2], 346
Ω i110	Isatoic acid, anhydride	N-Carboxyanthranilic anhydride.	163.13	pr (al or gl aa), cr (al or diox) λ^{diox} 239 (3.95), 315 (3.58)	243d	....	....	....	δ	δ[h]	i	δ	i	chl i	B27[2], 299
—	α-Isatropic acid	see 1,4-Tetralindicarboxylic acid, 1-phenyl-													
—	Isoanthraflavin	see 9,10-Anthraquinone, 2,7-dihydroxy-*													
i111	Isoapiol		222.24	mcl pr, lf or nd (al)	56 (fp 46)	303–4 189[33]	....	....	i	v[h]	v	v	v	con sulf s AcOEt s aa v[h]	B19[2], 97
—	Isobarbituric acid	see Uracil, 5-hydroxy-													
i112	Isobergaptene	$C_{12}H_8O_4$	216.21	cr (al) λ^{diox} 255 (4.3), 270 (4.2), 310 (4.0), 355 sh (2.9)	222–3	....	....	....			s		...	diox, MeOH s	C50, 12037
i113	Isoborneol(d)	2-Hydroxybornane	154.26	cr (peth), $[\alpha]_D^{20}$ −34.6 (al, c = 5)	212 (sealed tube) (214)	....	....	....	δ	s	s	...	s	lig, to s chl s	B6[2], 89
Ω i114	—(dl)	α,β-Camphol. $C_{10}H_{18}O$. See i113	154.26	ta(peth)	212 (sealed tube)	sub	....	....	i	v	v		δ	chl v	B6, 87
i115	—(l)	β-Camphol. $C_{10}H_{18}O$. See i113	154.26	(peth), $[\alpha]_D$ +33.9 (al)	214 (218)	....	....	....	i	v	v		δ	chl v	B6, 87
i116	—,acetate(d)	$C_{12}H_{20}O_2$. See i113	196.29	$[\alpha]^{20}$ −50.2 (al)	....	112[17]	0.9905[20/4]	1.4633[20]	i	s		s			B6[2], 90
Ω i117	—,—(dl)	$C_{12}H_{20}O_2$. See i113	196.29	....	....	115–7[22] 102–3[15]	0.9841[20/4]	1.4640[20]	i	s		s			B6[2], 91
i118	—,—(l)	$C_{12}H_{20}O_2$. See i113	196.29	....	< −50	225 123–7[35]	1.002[0/0]	....	i	s		s			B6, 89
i119	—,formate(d)	$C_{11}H_{18}O_2$. See i113	182.27	$[\alpha]_D^{20}$ +29.5 (al, c = 5)	....	94[15]	1.0136[20/4]	1.4678[22/6708]	i	s		s			E12A, 681
—	Isobornylamine	see Neobornylamine													
—	Isobutane	see Propane, 2-methyl													
—	Isobutylphosphonic acid	see 1-Propanephosphonic acid, 2-methyl-*													
—	Isobutyranilide	see Propanoic acid, 2-methyl-, amide, N-phenyl-													
—	Isobutyric acid	see Propanoic acid, 2-methyl-*													
—	Isobutyrophenone	see 1-Propanone 2-methyl-1-phenyl-*													
i120	Isocalycanthine	$C_{22}H_{28}N_4 \cdot H_2O$	183.26	rh	235–6	....	....	....	i	s	s	s		chl s	Am 31, 1305

For explanations, symbols and abbreviations see beginning of table. For structural formulas see end of table.

No.	Name	Synonyms and Formula	Mol. wt.	Color, crystalline form, specific rotation and λ_{max} (log ε)	m.p. °C	b.p. °C	Density	n_D	w	al	eth	ace	bz	other solvents	Ref.
	Isocamphane														
i121	Isocamphane(d)....	Dihydrocamphene. 2,2,3-Trimethylnorcamphane.	138.25	cr (MeOH), $[\alpha]_D^{20}$ +8.68 (bz, p=20)	62–3	166–6.5[750] (cor)	....	....	i	v		v	...	...	B5[2], 67
i122	—(dl)...........	$C_{10}H_{18}$. See i121	138.25	cr (MeOH)	65–7(cor)	165.5–5.7[730]	0.8276[67]	1.4419[67]	i	v		v	v	MeOH s AcOEt v	B5[1], 52
i123	—(l)...........	$C_{10}H_{18}$. See i121	138.25	cr (al) $[\alpha]_D^{20}$ −8.50 (al)	64	164–5[757] 62–3[17]	....	....	i	s		v	δ	lig δ	B5[2], 67
i124	Isocamphoric acid (d)	α-trans-1,2,2-Trimethyl-1,3-cyclopentane-dicarboxylic acid*.	200.24	lf(w), $[\alpha]_D^{20}$ +48.6	171–2	....	....	....	δ	v				aa v	B9, 762
Ω i125	—(dl)...........	$C_{10}H_{16}O_4$. See i124	200.24	pr (al or gl aa), cr (w)	197 (191)	....	1.249	....	δ[h]	δ	v	...	i[h]	peth i	B9[1], 334
i126	—(l)...........	$C_{10}H_{16}O_4$. See i124	200.24	tetr $[\alpha]_D^{17}$ −48.4 (MeOH, p=9.9)	173	....	....	....	δ	s				aa v	B9[1], 333
—	Isocaproamide	see **Pentanoic acid, 4-methyl-, amide**													
—	Isocaproic acid	see **Pentanoic acid, 4-methyl-***													
—	—,α-amino-......	see **Leucine**													
—	Isocarbostyril	see **Isoquinoline, 1-hydroxy-**													
Ω i127	Isocarotene	Dehydro-β-carotene. $C_{40}H_{54}$	534.88	vt pr (bz-MeOH), vt nd +lf (bz) λ^{hx} 220 (2.7), 320 (2.5), 445 (3.2), 470 (3.4), 495 (3.2)	192–3 cor	....	....	....							B30, 88
i128	Isocarvomenthol(d)	$C_{10}H_{20}O$.	156.27	$[\alpha]_D$ +20.2	....	110[20]	0.904[20]	1.4669[18]	...	s	s	s			B6[3], 131
i129	—(l)	$C_{10}H_{20}O$. See i128	156.27	$[\alpha]_D^{16}$ −17.7	....	106[17]	0.9109[20]	1.4662[20]	...	s	s	s			B6[2], 39
—	Isocholesterol	see **Lanosterol**													
—	Isocinchomeronic acid	see **2,5-Pyridinedicarboxylic acid**													
—	Isocinnamic acid ...	see **Cinnamic acid(cis)**													
—	Isocitric acid	see **1,2,3-Propanetricarboxylic acid, 1-hydroxy-***													
i130	Isocodeine	$C_{18}H_{21}NO_3$.	299.37	pl (bz), pr (AcOEt or aa) $[\alpha]_D^{15}$ −152 (chl, c=2)	171–2	d	1.87[4]	1.675							B27[2], 175
i131	Isocorybulbine.....	$C_{21}H_{25}NO_4$.	355.44	lf(al) $[\alpha]_D^{15}$ +301 (chl, c=1) λ^{MeOH} 283 (3.80)	187.5–8.5 (180)	....	1.045[20]	....	i	s	...	...	...	chl s ac s	B21[2], 200
i133	Isocorydine	Corytuberine methyl ether. Luteanine. $C_{20}H_{23}NO_4$.	341.41	pl, $[\alpha]_D^{20}$ +195.3 (chl) λ^{MeOH} 268 (4.3), 300 (3.8)	185	....	....	....					δ	chl s	B21[2], 192
—	Isocotin	see **Benzophenone, 2,4-dihydroxy-6-methoxy-**													
i134	Isocoumarin	2,1-Benzopyrone. o-(β-Hydroxyvinyl) benzoic acid lactone.	146.15	pl (bz) λ 239 (4.22), 261 (3.87), 318 (3.58)	47	285–6[719]	....	....	i	v	v	...	v	CS_2 v	B17, 333
—	Isocrotonic acid....	see **2-Butenoic acid(cis)***													
i135	Isocyanic acid, 4-bromophenyl ester	p-Bromophenyl isocyanate. C_7H_4BrNO. See i149	198.03	nd	42	226 158[14]	....	....	d[h]	d[h]	v				B12[1], 321
i136	—,tert-butyl ester..	tert-Butyl isocyanate. $(CH_3)_3CNCO$	99.13	....	85.5(cor)	....	0.8670[9]	1.4061[20]						HCl d	B4, 175
Ω i137	—,2-chlorophenyl ester	o-Chlorophenyl isocyanate. C_7H_4ClNO. See i149	153.57	λ^{hx} 231 (3.99), 274 (2.63), 283 (2.56)	....	114–5[43]	....	....							B12, 601
Ω i138	—,3-chlorophenyl ester	m-Chlorophenyl isocyanate. C_7H_4ClNO. See i149	153.57	λ^{hx} 229 (3.97), 276 (2.88), 284 (2.71)	....	113–4[43]	....	....							B12, 606
Ω i139	—,4-chlorophenyl ester	p-Chlorophenyl isocyanate. C_7H_4ClNO. See i149	153.57	λ^{hx} 233 (4.22), 273 (2.82), 287 (2.64)	30–1	115–7[45]	....	....							B12, 616
Ω i140	—,ethyl ester......	Ethyl isocyanate. C_2H_5NCO.	71.08	....	....	60	0.9031[20]	1.3808[20]	i	∞	∞				B4[2], 613
Ω i141	—,hendecyl ester ..	Undecyl isocyanate. $CH_3(CH_2)_{10}NCO$	197.32	....	....	103[3]	....	....	d[h]					lig v	B4[2], 658
i142	—,isobutyl ester ...	Isobutyl isocyanate. $(CH_3)_2CHCH_2NCO$	99.13	....	....	106	....	....							B4[2], 641

For explanations, symbols and abbreviations see beginning of table. For structural formulas see end of table.

No.	Name	Synonyms and Formula	Mol. wt.	Color, crystalline form, specific rotation and λ_{max} (log ε)	m.p. °C	b.p. °C	Density	n_D	w	al	eth	ace	bz	other solvents	Ref.
	Isocyanic acid														
i143	—,methyl ester	Methylcarbylamine. Methyl isocyanate. CH_3NCO	57.05	....	−45	59.6 (43–5)	0.9230_4^{27}	1.3419^{18}	s			...			B4[2], 578
Ω i144	—,1-naphthyl ester	α-Naphthylcarbylamine. α-Naphthyl isocyanate. $C_{10}H_7^\alpha NCO$	169.19	λ^{cy} 227 (4.86), 291 (3.94), 322 (2.75)	....	269–70	1.1774_4^{20}	....			s	...	s		E12B, 478
i145	—,2-naphthyl ester	β-Naphthylcarbylamine. β-Naphthyl isocyanate. $C_{10}H_7^\beta NCO$	169.19	lf	55–6	....	....	....			v	...	v		B12, 1297
i146	—,2-nitrophenyl ester	o-Nitrophenyl isocyanate. $C_7H_4N_2O_3$. See i149	164.12	wh nd (peth) λ^{hx} 222 (4.23), 259 (3.64), 314–8 (3.36)	41	135^7			d	d	s	...	s	chl s	B12[2], 373
i147	—,3-nitrophenyl ester	m-Nitrophenyl isocyanate. $C_7H_4N_2O_3$. See i149	164.12	wh lf (lig) λ^{hx} 222 (4.37), 253 (3.84), 300 (3.17), 335 (2.22)	51	$130–1^{11}$			d	d	s	...	s	chl, to s lig s^h,	B12[2], 382
Ω i148	—,4-nitrophenyl ester	p-Nitrophenyl isocyanate. $C_7H_4N_2O_3$. See i149	164.12	pa ye nd λ^{hx} 215 (4.01), 276 (4.14), 324 sh (2.74)	57	$137–8^{11}$			d	d	v	...	v	chl, to s lig s^h	B12[2], 394
Ω i149	—,phenyl ester	Phenyl isocyanate. Carbanil. Phenylcarbylamine.	119.12	λ^{hx} 226 (4.04), 263 (2.66), 277 (2.67)	....	$162–3^{751}$ (cor) 55^{13}	1.0956_4^{20}	1.5368^{20}	d	d	v	...			B12[2], 244
i150	—,2-tolyl ester	o-Tolyl isocyanate	133.15	λ^{hx} 228 (4.01), 273 (2.80), 280 (2.75)	....	$184–6^{760}$		1.5282^{20}	i d^h	d^h	s	...			B12, 812
i151	—,3-tolyl ester	m-Tolyl isocyanate	133.15	λ^{hx} 229 (3.98), 273 (2.74), 281 (2.69)	....	195–8			d	d	s	...	s		B12, 864
i152	—,4-tolyl ester	p-Tolyl isocyanate	133.15	λ^{hx} 230 (4.12), 274 (2.89), 283 (2.88)	....	187^{751}			d	d	s	...	s		B12[1], 427
i153	Isocyanuric acid, trimethyl ester	Tricarbonimide trimethyl ester.	171.16	mcl pr (w or al)	176–7	274			i δ^h	s		...			B26[2], 134
	Isocyclene	see Cyclocamphane													
i154	Isoderritol	$C_{21}H_{22}O_6$	370.41	ye lf (MeOH)	150							...		alk s	B18[2], 223
	Isodurene	see Benzene, 1,2,3,5-tetramethyl-*													
	Isodurenol	see Benzene, 1-hydroxy-2,3,4,6-tetramethyl-*													
	Isoduridine	see Benzene, 1-amino-2,3,4,6-tetramethyl-*													
	α-Isodurylic acid	see Benzoic acid, 3,4,5-trimethyl-													
	β-Isodurylic acid	see Benzoic acid, 2,4,6-trimethyl-													
	γ-Isodurylic acid	see Benzoic acid, 2,3,5-trimethyl-													
	Isoergosterone	see $\Delta^{4,6,22}$-Ergostatrienone													
i155	8-Isoestradiol	$\Delta^{1,3,5}$-8-α-Epiestratrien-3,17-β-diol. 8-Epiestradiol. $C_{18}H_{24}O_2$.	272.39	cr (dil MeOH-chl), $[\alpha]_D^{20}$ +18 (diox) λ^{al} 280 (3.31)	181						s	...		diox s	E14s, 1982
i156	8-Isoestrone	8-Epiestrone. $C_{18}H_{22}O_2$.	270.38	cr (MeOH or MeOH-eth), $[\alpha]_D^{20}$ +94 (diox)	247	....			i		s	...		diox s	E14s, 2559
i157	Iso-β-eucaine(dl)	4-Benzoyloxy-2,2,6-trimethylpiperidine. $C_{15}H_{21}NO_2$.	247.34	....	< −5	188^{19}	1.0467_{22}^{22}		i	s		...			B21[2], 15
i158	—,hydrochloride(d)	$C_{15}H_{21}NO_2$.HCl. See i157.	283.80	nd (w), $[\alpha]_{5461}$ +17 (w, c = 1)	271–3				s			...			B21[2], 16
i159	—,—(dl)	$C_{15}H_{21}NO_2$.HCl. See i157.	283.80	unst nd or st ta (w), pl (aq al or al-eth)	269–71				s			...			B21[2], 15
i160	—,—(l)	$C_{15}H_{21}NO_2$.HCl. See i157.	283.80	nd, $[\alpha]_{5461}$ − 16.3 (w, c = 1)	271–3				s			...			B21[2], 15
	Isoeugenol	see Benzene, 1-hydroxy-2-methoxy-4-propenyl-*													
	Isoeuxanthone	see Xanthone, 1,6-dihydroxy-													
	Isoeuxanthonic acid	see Benzophenone, 2,2′,4,6′-tetrahydroxy-													
i161	Isoflavone, 4′,7-dihydroxy-	Daidzein. $C_{15}H_{10}O_4$.	254.25	pa ye pr (50 % al) λ^{al} 249.5 (4.43), 303 (4.05)	323d	sub					s	s			B18[2], 100

For explanations, symbols and abbreviations see beginning of table. For structural formulas see end of table.

No.	Name	Synonyms and Formula	Mol. wt.	Color, crystalline form, specific rotation and λ_{max} (log ε)	m.p. °C	b.p. °C	Density	n_D	w	al	eth	ace	bz	other solvents	Ref.
	Isoflavone														
i162	—,4′,5,7-tri-hydroxy-	Genistein. Prunetol. $C_{15}H_{10}O_5$.	270.25	nd (eth), pr (dil al) λ^{al} 263 (4.50), 325 sh (3.71)	301–2d	....			δ^h	δ			os s	dil alk s aa δ	B18², 176
i163	Isofurfurine	$C_{15}H_{12}N_2O_3$.	268.28	nd (w)	143	....									B27, 764
i164	Isogeraniolene	2,6-Dimethyl-1,3-heptadiene. $CH_2{:}C(CH_3)CH{:}CHCH_2CH(CH_3)_2$	124.23	λ^{al} 230 (4.36)	....	143–4⁷⁵⁵ (140–2) 31⁷	0.7561²⁰₄	1.4520²⁰	i	...	s	...	s	....	B1³, 1015
—	Isohemipinic acid	see 1,3-Benzenedicarboxylic acid, 4,5-dimethoxy-													
—	Isohydroanisoin	see 1,2-Ethanediol, 1,2-bis(4-methoxyphenyl)-*													
—	Isoindoledione	See Phthalic acid, imide													
i165	Isolysergic acid (d)	$C_{16}H_{16}N_2O_2$.	268.32	cr (w + 2), $[\alpha]_D^{20}$ +281 (Py, c = 1) λ^{al} 312 (3.97)	218d	....			δ	δ				Py s	J 1936, 1440
—	α-Isomalic acid	see Malonic acid, hydroxy-(methyl)-													
i166	Isomannide	1:4, 3:6-Dianhydro-D-mannitol.	146.14	mcl cr, $[\alpha]_D^{26.2}$ +62.2 (chl) $[\alpha]_D$ +91 (w)	87–9.5	274d			v	δ	i	...	i	chl δ	B1³, 2402
i167	Isomenthol(d)	2-Isopropyl-5-methylcyclo-hexanol. p-Menthanol-3.	156.27	nd (dil al) $[\alpha]_D^{20}$ +26.5 (al, c = 4)	82.5 (85)	218.6⁷⁶⁰ 96.5¹⁰			δ	3	s	...		aa s	B6, 41
Ω i168	—(dl)	$C_{10}H_{20}O$. See i167	156.27	nd	53–4	218.5⁷⁶⁰ 97.4¹⁰·⁵	0.9040³⁰	1.4510⁶⁰	δ	s	s	...		aa s	B6², 51
i169	—(l)	$C_{10}H_{20}O$. See i167	156.27	$[\alpha]_D^5$ −24.1	82.5				δ	s	s	...		aa s	B6², 51
—	Isomethadone	see 3-Hexanone, 6-dimethylamino-4,4-diphenyl-5-methyl-*													
i170	α-Isomorphine	$C_{17}H_{19}NO_3$.	285.35	nd (MeOH-AcOEt) $[\alpha]_D^{15}$ −167 (MeOH, c = 3)	248	....			s^h	s				MeOH v	B27², 174
—	Isonicoteine	see 2,3′-Bipyridyl													
—	Isonicotinalde-hyde	see 4-Pyridinecarboxalde-hyde													
i171	Isonicotine	4(4-Pyridyl)piperidine.	162.24	hyg wh nd	80	292			δ	v	s	...	s	lig s	B23, 119
—	Isonicotinic acid	see 4-Pyridinecarboxylic acid													
—	Isonipecotic acid	see 4-Piperidinecarboxylic acid													
i172	Isopapaverine, N-benzyl-	$C_{27}H_{27}NO_4$.	429.52	ye lf (al)	139–40	....				s^h	s	...		....	B21, 229
i173	—,N-ethyl-	$C_{22}H_{25}NO_4$. See i172	367.45	pr (al)	ca. 101	....					s	...	s	....	B21, 229
i174	—,N-methyl-	$C_{21}H_{23}NO_4$. See i172	353.42	ye hyg mcl pr (al)	129–31	....			s	δ		...		os s dil al v	B21, 229
i175	Isopelletierine(dl)	2-Acetonylpiperidine. Isopimicine.	141.22	oil liq	....	91–2¹⁴ 62⁰·⁸	0.9624²⁰₄	1.4683²⁰		...	s	...		chl s dil ac s	B21², 219
i176	—,N-methyl-	$C_9H_{17}NO$. See i175	155.24		....	96–8¹³	0.9478²⁰₄	1.4674²⁰	s					dil ac s lig s	B21², 219
—	Isopentane	see Butane, 2-methyl-*													
—	Isopeonol	see Acetophenone, 4-hydroxy-2-methoxy-													
i177	Isophenolph-thalein	3-[o-Hydroxyphenyl]-3-(p-hydroxyphenyl)-phthalide.	320.35	(dil aa)	189–90	....				v^h	...	v^h		....	B10², 322
i178	3-Isopheno-thiazin-3-one	Azthione. Thiazone.	213.26	red (dil al) λ^{al} 280 (4.2), 370 (4.0), 510 (3.9)	164				s^h	v			v^h	chl s	B27¹, 251
i179	—,7-hydroxy-	Thionol. $C_{12}H_7NO_2S$. See i178	229.26	red br pw or nd (aa) $\lambda^{al-0.04NHCl}$ 248 (4.4), 280 (4.34), 440 (4.08), 520 (4.20)	>360				i	s			chl i aa s^h Ac₂O s	B27², 109
Ω i180	Isophorone	Isoacetophorone. 3,5,5-Tri-methyl-2-cyclohexen-1-one	138.21	λ^{al} 236 (4.09)	....	214⁷·³* 99¹⁸	0.9229²⁰	1.4759²⁰	i	s	s	s		....	B7², 64
—	Isophthaldehyde	see 1,3-Benzenedicarbox-aldehyde													
—	Isophthaldehydic acid	see Benzoic acid, 3-formyl-													
—	Isophthalic acid	see 1,3-Benzenedicar-boxylic acid*													
i181	Isopilocarpine	N-Methylisopilocarpidine. $C_{11}H_{16}N_2O_2$.	208.26	pr $[\alpha]_D^{18}$ +50 (w, c = 2)	....	261¹⁰			v	v			s	chl v peth i	B27², 697

For explanations, symbols and abbreviations see beginning of table. For structural formulas see end of table.

No.	Name	Synonyms and Formula	Mol. wt.	Color, crystalline form, specific rotation and λ_{max} (log ε)	m.p. °C	b.p. °C	Density	n_D	w	al	eth	ace	bz	other solvents	Ref.
	Isopimpinellin														
i182	Isopimpinellin	$C_{13}H_{10}O_5$	246.22	ye nd (MeOH) λ^{diox} 245 (4.2), 270 (4.2), 365 sh (3.1)	151	....	....	....						MeOH s	J 1945, 540
—	Isopinene	see α-Fenchene													
i183	Isopomiferin	$C_{25}H_{24}O_6$	270.25	nd (dil al) λ^{al} 268	265d	....	....	....		s					Am 61, 2832
—	Isoprene	see 1,3-Butadiene, 2-methyl-*													
—	Isopropyl alcohol	see 2-Propanol*													
—	Isopropyl bromide	see Propane, 2-bromo-*													
—	Isopropyl chloride	see Propane, 2-chloro-*													
i184	Isopulegol(d)	Δ^{8(9)}-p-Menthenol-3.	154.26	$[\alpha]_{5461}$ +29.3	....	212 93–4[14]	0.9110^{20}_{20}	1.4723^{20}	δ	s	s				B6[2], 70
i185	—(l)	$C_{10}H_{18}O$. See i184	154.26	$[\alpha]^{20}_{5461}$ −25.90	....	212 94[14]	0.9110^{20}_{20}	1.4723^{20}	δ	s	s				B6[3], 257
i186	α-Isoquinine		324.43	(bz-peth) $[\alpha]^b_D$ −245 (al, c = 1), −248 (al, c = 0.5)	196.5				i	v	v				B23[2], 414,423
i187	β-Isoquinine	$C_{20}H_{24}N_2O_2$. See i186	324.43	pr (dil al), or amor $[\alpha]^7_D$ −187 (97 % al, c = 1)	190–1				i	v	δ		v	chl v lig s	B23[2], 413
Ω i188	Isoquinoline	2-Benzazine*.Benzo(c)pyridine. Leucoline.	129.16	hyg pl λ^{al} 220 (4.80), 268 (3.56), 280 (3.37), 319 (3.45)	26.5	243.25[743] 142[40]	1.0986^{20}	1.6148^{20}	i	v	∞	v	∞	chl v dil ac s	B20[2], 236
i189	—, hydrochloride	Isoquinolinium chloride. $C_9H_7N.HCl$. See i188	165.63	pr or pl (al)	209–9.5	....			s	s^h					B20, 381
i190	—, hydrogen sulfate	$C_9H_7N.H_2SO_4$. See i188	227.15	pr or pl (al)	209–9.5				v	s^h	i				B20[2], 237
i191	—, 1-amino-	$C_9H_8N_2$. See i188	144.19	pl (w) λ^{al} 300 (3.8), 330 (3.7)	123				δ	v	δ				B22[1], 640
Ω i192	—, 5-amino-	$C_9H_8N_2$. See i188	144.19	pa ye nd (peth) $\lambda^{w, pH = 9}$ 238 (4.22), 332 (3.70)	128	sub								lig s^h	B22[2], 359
Ω i193	—, 4-bromo-	C_9H_6BrN. See i188	208.09	(peth)	40–3	280–5					v^h	s			B20[2], 238
i194	—, 6,7-dimethoxy-1,2-dimethyl-1,2,3,4-tetrahydro-	Carnegine. $C_{13}H_{19}NO_2$. See i188	221.30	pa br syr $[\alpha]^{25}_D$ +20 (w)	262–3	170[1]			s	s	s			chl, con sulf, HCl s	B21[2], 110
i195	—, 1-hydroxy-	Isocarbostyril. 1-Isoquinolinol. C_9H_7NO. See i188	145.16	mcl (bz), nd (bz, al, w) λ^{al} 270 (3.90), 328 (3.67)	209–10	240 sub			δ	v^h s^h	δ s^h	δ	δ	lig i	B21[2], 58
i196	—, 1-methyl-	$C_{10}H_9N$. See i188	143.19	λ^{al} 217 (4.80), 270 (3.66), 307 (3.45), 320 (3.57)	10.1–10.4	248 (253) 124–5[10]	1.0777^{20}_4	1.6095^{20}	δ	s	s	s	s		B20[2], 247
Ω i197	—, 3-methyl-	$C_{10}H_9N$. See i188	143.19	cr (eth)	68	246[761]			δ	s	s				B20[2], 247
i198	—, 4-methyl-	$C_{10}H_9N$. See i188	143.19	λ^{hx} 271 (3.64), 321.5 (3.62)	< −75	256			δ	s	s	s			B20[1], 152
i199	—, 6-methyl-	$C_{10}H_9N$. See i188	143.19	cr	85–6 (83)	265.5			δ	s	s	s	s	os s	B20[2], 247
i200	—, 7-methyl-	$C_{10}H_9N$. See i188	143.19		67–8	245			δ	s	s	s			B20[2], 248
i201	—, 8-methyl-	$C_{10}H_9N$. See i188	143.19		258				δ	s	s	s			B20, 404
Ω i202	—, 5-nitro-	$C_9H_6N_2O_2$. See i188	174.16	nd (w + 1) λ 235 (4.12), 333 (3.70)	110	sub			δ v^h	v	v			CS_2, chl, aa v	B20[2], 238
Ω i203	—, 1,2,3,4-tetrahydro-	2-Azatetralin. $C_9H_{11}N$. See i188	133.20	λ^{al} 266 (2.61), 273 (2.61)	< −15	232–3	1.0642^{24}	1.5668^{20}	i	s			s^h	dil ac s xyl s^h	B20[2], 176
i204	1-Isoquinoline-carboxylic acid, nitrile	1-Cyanoisoquinoline.	154.17	nd (w + 1), nd (MeOH)	78 (93)	....			δ	v	v		v	lig δ peth s^h MeOH s	B22[1], 511
i205	5-Isoquinoline-carboxylic acid, nitrile		154.17	nd (w or dil al)	135	100–20 sub			δ	v	v			dil ac v	B22[2], 58
i207	Isoraunescine	$C_{31}H_{36}N_2O_8$	564.64	wh nd, $[\alpha]_D$ −70 (chl) λ^{al} 218 (4.76), 270 (4.24)	241–2.5	....			i	δ				chl, aa s	C50, 1267
i208	Isoreserpiline	$C_{23}H_{28}N_2O_5$	412.49	wh pr, $[\alpha]^{20}_D$ −84 (Py) λ^{al} 228 (4.58), 304 (4.02)	210–2				i						C53, 14134
—	Isorhamnose	see Glucomethylose													

For explanations, symbols and abbreviations see beginning of table. For structural formulas see end of table.

No.	Name	Synonyms and Formula	Mol. wt.	Color, crystalline form, specific rotation and λ_{max} (log ε)	m.p. °C	b.p. °C	Density	n_D	w	al	eth	ace	bz	other solvents	Ref.
	Isorubijervine														
i209	Isorubijervine	Δ^5-3β-18-Dihydroxysolanidene. $C_{27}H_{43}NO_2$	413.65	pr (al), $[\alpha]_D$ +9.2 (al)	241–4	. . . .	. . . .	. . . .		i s[h]			s	ac s alk i chl s	Am 75, 2133
i210	Isorubijervosine	3-β-D-Glucosylisorubijervine. 3-β-D-Glucosyl-Δ^5-solanidene-18-ol. $C_{33}H_{53}NO_7$. See i209	575.80	wh nd, $[\alpha]_D^{24}$ −20 ±2 (Py, c = 1.45)	279–80	. . . .	. . . .	. . . .	i						Am 75, 2134
i211	Isosaccharic acid′.	3,4-Dihydroxytetrahydro 2,5-furandicarboxylic acid.	192.14	rh, $[\alpha]_D^{20}$ +46.1 (w, p = 4.2)	185	d	. . . .	. . . .	v	v	δ				B18², 309
Ω i212	Isosafrole(trans)		162.19	λ^{al} 259.5 (4.08), 267 (4.06), 305 (3.73)	fp 6.8	253[760] 111–2[6]	1.1224[20]	1.5782[20]	i	∞	∞	v	∞	chl s	B19², 27
i213	Isoserine(l)	$H_2NCH_2CH(OH)CO_2H$.	105.10	cr (dil al, w) $[\alpha]_D^{20}$ −32.58 (w, p = 1.3)	199–201d	. . . .	. . . .	. . . .	s	. .	i	i			B4, 503
—	Isosuccinic acid	see Malonic acid, 2-methyl-													
i214	Isothebaine(d)	$C_{19}H_{21}NO_3$.	311.39	rh cr (al), $[\alpha]_D^{18}$ 285.1 (al, c = 2) λ 398.5	203–4	. . . .	. . . .	. . . .	i	∞	δ			MeOH s chl ∞	B21², 169
i215	—,sulfate(d)	$(C_{19}H_{21}NO_3)_2.H_2SO_4$.	720.85	nd	120–1d	. . . .	. . . .	. . . .	v						B21¹, 250
Ω i216	Isothiocyanic acid, allyl ester	Allyl mustard oil. $CH_2{:}CHCH_2NCS$	99.16	λ^{cy} 250 (3.00), 275 sh (1.65)	−80 (−102.5)	152[760] 44[12]	1.0126[20]	1.5306[20]	δ	∞	∞		v		B4², 667
i217	—,benzyl ester	Benzyl mustard oil. $C_6H_5CH_2NCS$	149.22	ye oil λ^{al} 247.5 (3.12)	. . . .	243 124–5[12]	1.1246[15]	1.6049[13]	i	∞	s				B12², 567
i218	—,4-biphenylyl ester		211.29	nd (eth)	60								v		B12, 1319
i219	—,4-bromophenyl ester	C_7H_4BrNS. See i236	214.09	nd	60–1				i	s[h]					B12², 354
i220	—,butyl ester	Butyl mustard oil. n-Butyl thiocarbimide. $CH_3(CH_2)_2CH_2NCS$	115.20	λ^{cy} 248 (3.24) 270 sh (2.10)	. . . .	168 64–6[12]	0.9546[20]	1.501[20]	i	v	v				B4², 635
i221	—,sec-butyl ester(d)	sec-Butyl mustard oil. $CH_3CH_2CH(CH_3)NCS$	115.20	$[\alpha]_D^{20}$ +61.88		159	0.943[20]								B4, 161
i222	—,—(dl)	$CH_3CH_2CH(CH_3)NCS$	115.20			159.5	0.944[12]		i	s	s				B4, 162
i223	—,—(l)	$CH_3CH_2CH(CH_3)NCS$	115.20	$[\alpha]_D^{20}$ −61.80		159	0.942[20]								B4, 161
i224	—,tert-butyl ester . .	tert-Butyl mustard oil. $(CH_3)_3CNCS$	115.20		10.5–1.5	140[770] 64[12]	0.9187[10]		i	i	s				B4, 175
Ω i225	—,4-chloro-phenyl ester	C_7H_4ClNS. See i236	169.63	nd (al) λ^{cy} 228 (4.48), 276 (4.18), 288 (4.17), 304 (3.25)	45	249–50	. . . .	. . . .	i	s[h]					B12², 330
Ω i226	—,cyclohexyl ester .		141.24	λ^{cy} 249 (3.08), 275 sh (1.65)		219[746]		1.5375[20]	i	s	s				B12², 12
i227	—,4(dimethyl-amino)phenyl ester	$C_9H_{10}N_2S$. See i236	178.26	ye pr λ^{cy} 256 (3.75), 297 (4.46), 310 (4.41)	67										B13³, 53
Ω i228	—,ethyl ester	Ethyl mustard oil. C_2H_5NCS.	87.14	λ^{diox} 245 (2.86)	−5.9	131–2 (cor)	0.9990[20]	1.5130[20]	i	∞	∞				B4², 614
i229	—,isobutyl ester . . .	Isobutyl mustard oil. $(CH_3)_2CHCH_2NCS$	115.20	. . . .		160 (cor)	0.9638[14]	1.5005[14]	i	s	s				B4², 641
i230	—,isopropyl ester . .	Isopropyl mustard oil. $(CH_3)_2CHNCS$	101.17			138 29–30[10]			i	s	s				B4, 155
Ω i231	—,methyl ester	Methyl mustard oil. CH_3NCS	73.12		36	119[758]	1.0691[37]	1.5258	δ	∞	v				B4², 579
i232	—,3-methylbutyl ester	Isoamyl mustard oil. $(CH_3)_2CHCH_2CH_2NCS$	129.23			182–4	0.9419[17]		δ	v	v				B4², 649
i233	—,1-naphthyl ester	α-Naphthyl mustard oil. $C_{10}H_7NCS$	185.25	wh nd (al)	58				i	v[h]	v	v	v	chl v CCl_4 s lig δ	B12², 698
Ω i234	—,2-naphthyl ester	β-Naphthyl mustard oil. $C_{10}H_7NCS$	185.25	yesh nd (al)	62–3				i	v[h]	v		v	chl s	B12², 724
i235	—,pentyl ester	n-Amyl mustard oil. $CH_3(CH_2)_4NCS$	129.23	bt ye	. . . .	193.4 (cor)			δ	v	v				B4², 642
Ω i236	—,phenyl ester	Phenyl mustard oil.	135.19	λ^{hx} 221 (4.52), 270 (4.03), 280 (4.04)	−21 (cor)	221 (cor) 95[12]	1.1303[20]	1.6492[23]	i	s	s				B12², 247
i237	—,propyl ester	n-Propyl mustard oil. $CH_3CH_2CH_2NCS$	101.17	. . . .		153 (cor)	0.9781[16]	1.5085[16]	δ	∞	∞				B4², 627
i238	—,4-propylphenyl ester	$C_{10}H_{11}NS$. See i236	177.27	. . . .		263				v	v				B12, 1144
—	Isothiourea	see Urea, 2-thio-(S-substituted)													
—	Isovaleraldehyde . . .	see Butanal, 3-methyl-*													
—	Isovaleric acid	see Butanoic acid, 3-methyl-*													
—	Isovaleronitrile	see Butanoic acid, 3-methyl-, nitrile													

For explanations, symbols and abbreviations see beginning of table. For structural formulas see end of table.

No.	Name	Synonyms and Formula	Mol. wt.	Color, crystalline form, specific rotation and λ_{max} (log ε)	m.p. °C	b.p. °C	Density	n_D	w	al	eth	ace	bz	other solvents	Ref.
	Isovalerophenone														
—	Isovalerophenone ..	see **1-Butanone,3-methyl-1-phenyl-***													
—	Isovaleryl chloride	see **Butanoic acid, 3-methyl-,chloride**													
i241	Isovaline(d)	2-Amino-2-methylbutanoic acid*. $CH_3CH_2C(CH_3)(NH_2)CO_2H$	117.15	nd (aq al +1w) $[\alpha]_D +13$ (w, c = 2)	ca 300	sub	. . . . . .	. . . . . .	s	...	δ	...	i	. . . . . .	**B4²,** 851
Ω i242	—(dl)	$CH_3CH_2C(CH_3)(NH_2)CO_2H$	117.15	rh nd (al-eth, +1w), mcl pr	315 (307–8 sealed tube)	sub 300	. . . . . .	. . . . . .	s	s	δ	...	i	. . . . . .	**B4²,** 851
i243	—(l)	$CH_3CH_2C(CH_3)(NH_2)CO_2H$	117.15	lo nd (w-ace) $[\alpha]_D^{20} -9.1$ (w, c = 2)	ca. 300	sub	. . . . . .	. . . . . .	v	v	δ	...	i	. . . . . .	**B4²,** 851
—	Isovanillic acid	see **Benzoic acid, 3-hydroxy-4-methoxy-**													
—	Isovanillin	see **Benzaldehyde, 3-hydroxy-4-methoxy-***													
i244	Isoxanthen-3-one, 9-phenyl-2,6,7-trihydroxy-	9-Phenyl-2,6,7-trihydroxy-fluorone.	320.31	og red (al-HCl)	>300	. . . . . .	. . . . . .	. . . . . .	...	δ	δ	...	δ	os δ alk s	**B18¹,** 404
i245	Isoxazole		69.06	λ^{al} 211 (3.60)	. . . . . .	95–5.5	1.0782²⁰	1.4298¹⁷	s	...	...	...	...	. . . . . .	**B27²,** 9
—	Isoxylic acid	see **Benzoic acid, 2,5-dimethyl-**													
—	Itaconic acid	see **Succinic acid, methylene-**													

For explanations, symbols and abbreviations see beginning of table. For structural formulas see end of table.

C-351

Jacareubin

No.	Name	Synonyms and Formula	Mol. wt.	Color, crystalline form, specific rotation and λ_{max} (log ε)	m.p. °C	b.p. °C	Density	n_D	w	al	eth	ace	bz	other solvents	Ref.
j1	Jacareubin........	$C_{18}H_{14}O_6$	326.32	ye pr (MeOH) λ^{al} 240 (4.03), 279 (4.60), 334 (4.26)	256–7d	....	....	....		s	δ	s^h	δ	AcOEt s MeOH s chl δ	**J1953,** 3932
j2	Jaconecic acid.....	$C_{10}H_{16}O_6$	232.24	nd (eth), $[\alpha]_D^{25}$ +28.1 (95% al) λ^w 211 (2.43)	183–4	....	....	....	...	s	s^h	...	...	....	**Am 78,** 3518
j3	Japaconitine-A	Acetyl benzoyl aconitine. $C_{34}H_{47}NO_{11}$	645.76	rh $[\alpha]_D^{13}$ +20.7 (chl)	202–3d	....	....	....	i	s^h	s^h	v	...	chl s peth i	**Ber 57,** 1462
j4	—-A1..........	$C_{34}H_{47}NO_{11}$	645.76	rh (MeOH) $[\alpha]_D^{12}$ +26.4	208–9	....	....	....	i	s	s	...	...	MeOH s chl s peth i	**Ber 57,** 1462
j5	—-B..........	$C_{34}H_{47}NO_{11}$	645.76	rh (MeOH) $[\alpha]_D^{11}$ +26.9	208–9d	....	....	....	i	s	s	...	...	MeOH, chl s peth i	**Ber 57,** 1462
—	Jasminaldehyde ...	see 1-Heptene-2-carboxaldehyde, 1-phenyl-													
j6	Jasmone	3-Methyl-2-(2-pentenyl)-2-cyclopenten-1-one	164.25	ye oil λ^{al} 235 (4.14)	....	$257–8^{755}$ $134–5^{12}$	0.9437_4^{22}	1.4979^{22}	δ	s	s	...	...	CCl_4 s lig s	**B7[2],** 135
j7	Javanicin........	$C_{15}H_{14}O_6$	290.28	red (al) λ^{al} 303 (3.97), 505 (3.90)	208d	....	....	....	...	...	...	...	...	alk s (red)	**J1947,** 1021
—	Jervasic acid	see Chelidonic acid													
Ω j8	Jervine.........	$C_{27}H_{39}NO_3 \cdot 2H_2O$	461.65	nd (w + 2, MeOH-w) $[\alpha]_D^{23}$ −158.5 (al, c = 0.99) λ^{al} 247 (4.1), 370 (1.8)	243–4d (cor) 247–8	....	....	....	i	s	δ	s	...	chl s	**Am 73,** 2970
—	Juglone	see 1,4-Naphthoquinone, 5-hydroxy-*													
j9	Julolidine........	$C_{12}H_{15}N$	173.25	λ^{al} 225 (4.4), 300 (3.4), 405 (3.8)	40	280d $155–6^{17}$	1.003^{20}	1.568^{23}	...	...	...	...	...	....	**B20[2],** 214
j10	—,1,6-dioxo-......	1,6-Diketojulolidine. $C_{12}H_{11}NO_2$	201.23	ye (al) λ^{al} 250 (3.5), 305 (3.5)	145–6	190– $210^{0.3}$	....	....	...	...	s^h	...	...	MeOH s	**J1951,** 1898
j11	Junipal.........	5(α-Propynyl)-2-formyl thiophene. C_8H_6OS	150.20	nd (pet eth or dil al) λ^{al} 286 (3.91), 320 (4.27)	80	....	....	....	δ s^h				...	os s	**C49,** 13354
j12	Juniperol	Kuromatsuol. Macrocarpol. $C_{15}H_{26}O$.	220.38	tcl (EtOH) $[\alpha]_D^{30}$ +25.4 (al) + 18.4 (chl)	112	286–8d	1.0460_{20}^{20}	1.519	i	...	...	...	...	os s	**B6[2],** 516
j13	Junipic acid	5(α-Propynyl)-2-thiophenecarboxylic acid. $C_8H_6O_2S$.	166.20	ye nd (pet eth), cr (aq EtOH) λ^{al} 293 (4.02)	180	....	....	....	i	...	s	...	...	$NaHCO_3$ s lig s^h	**C54,** 9880
j14	—,methyl ester ...	$C_9H_8O_2S$. See j13	180.22	(aq MeOH)	62	sub 50–5	....	....	...	...	s	...	...	....	**C49,** 13354

For explanations, symbols and abbreviations see beginning of table. For structural formulas see end of table.

No.	Name	Synonyms and Formula	Mol. wt.	Color, crystalline form, specific rotation and λ_{max} (log ε)	m.p. °C	b.p. °C	Density	n_D	w	al	eth	ace	bz	other solvents	Ref.
	Kaempferol														
—	Kaempferol	see **Flavone, 3,4′,5,7-** **tetrahydroxy-**													
—	Kairoline	see **Quinoline, 1-methyl-** **1,2,3,4-tetrahydro-**													
—	Kavahin	see **Methysticin**													
k1	Ketene	Carbomethene. Ethonone*. CH_2:CO	42.04	λ^{gas} 330 (1.0)	−151	−56 (−41^{760})			d	d	δ	δ	...	NH_3 d	B1[2], 779
k2	—, diethyl acetal	1,1-Diethoxyethene*. CH_2:C$(OC_2H_5)_2$	116.16	λ^{vap} 250 (2.4), 380 (1.0)	....	68^{100} (76–7)	0.7932$^{20}_4$	1.3643^{21}	d	d					B1[3], 2948
k3	—, dimethyl-*	$(CH_3)_2$C:CO	70.09	ye	−97.5	34 −49^{12}			d	d					B1[2], 789
k3[1]	—, diphenyl-*	$(C_6H_5)_2$C:CO	193.24	ye-red	....	265–70d 146^{12}	1.1107$^{14}_4$	1.615^{14}			s		s		B7[2], 412
k4	—, methyl-*	CH_3CH:CO	56.07		−80						s				B1[2], 782
—	Ketine	see **Pyrazine, 2,5-dimethyl-**													
k5	Ketone, benzyl 1-naphthyl	α-Phenyl-1-acetonaphthone. $C_6H_5CH_2COC_{10}H_7^\beta$	246.31	ta, lf (al or MeOH)	66–7	194–6$^{0.05}$			i	δ v^h	s			chl s	B7[2], 461
k6	—, benzyl 2-naphthyl	β-Phenyl-2-acetonaphthone. $C_6H_5CH_2COC_{10}H_8^\beta$	246.31	nd (al)	99.5	....				s^h	s		s	chl s	B7[2], 461
Ω k7	—, benzyl phenyl	Desoxybenzoin. α-Phenyl acetophenone. $C_6H_5CH_2COC_6H_5$	196.25	pl (al) λ^{al} 240 (4.2)	60	320 177^{20}	1.201$^0_4$		δ^h	s	s			chl, CCl_4 s	B7[2], 368
Ω k8	—, —, α-chloro-	Desyl chloride. $C_6H_5COCHClC_6H_5$	230.70	nd (al) λ^{hx} 281 (2.94), 290 (2.75), 332 (2.2)	68.5	d				s^h				alk i	B7[2], 369
k9	—, —, α-diazo-	Azibenzil. Diazodesoxy-benzoin. N_2:C$(C_6H_5)COC_6H_5$	222.25	red pl (eth) λ^{eth} 267 (4.3), 317 sh (3.7), 417 (2.0)	79	....				δ s^h	δ	...	δ	....	B7[2], 683
Ω k10	—, cyclobutyl phenyl	Benzoylcyclobutane.	160.22	λ^{iso} 239 (4.11), 278 (2.94), 287 (2.84)	....	260 121.5–2^{10}	1.0457$^{25}_{25}$	1.5472^{20}							B7, 374
k11	—, 1,1′-dinaphthyl	....	282.35	wh nd, yesh pr (aa)	104					v^h s	s	...	v	aa s^h lig δ^h chl, sulf s	B7[2], 503
k12	—, 1,2′-dinaphthyl	....	282.35	nd (al, bz-lig)	136–7	235$^{0.6}$				δ			v	chl s	B7[2], 504
k13	—, 2,2′-dinaphthyl	$C_{10}H_7^\beta COC_{10}H_8^\beta$	282.35	(i) nd (eth). (ii) lf (chl-eth)	(i) 125.5 (ii) 164.5	....				δ	δ			chl s	B7[2], 504
k14	—, 1,1′-dinaph-thyl,2-methyl	$C_{22}H_{16}O$. See k11	296.37	gr-yesh nd (al)	171	230–5^5			i	s^h				con sulf s	B7[2], 506
k15	—, 1,2′-dinaph-thyl,2-methyl-	$C_{22}H_{16}O$. See k12	296.37	gr-yesh nd (aa or al)	142–3	....			i					con sulf s aa s^h	B7[2], 506
—	—, diphenyl	see **Benzophenone**													
k16	—, di(2-thienyl)	Thienone.	194.28	nd (al)	90–0.5	326			i	s^h	s	s		oos s	B19, 135
—	—, ethyl methyl	see **2-Butanone***													
—	—, ethyl styryl	see **1-Penten-3-one, 1-phenyl-***													
k18	—, 2-furyl phenyl	2-Benzoylfuran.	172.20	br λ^{al} 289 (4.2)	< −15	285 164^{19}	1.1732^{20}	1.6055^{20}	i	s	s		s	....	B17[2], 372
—	—, methyl phenyl	see **Acetophenone**													
k20	—, 1-naphthyl 2-tolyl	....	246.31	(al)	64	365			i	s^h	v			lig δ	B7[2], 462
k21	—, 1-naphthyl 3-tolyl	....	246.31	nd (al)	74–5	....			i	s				oos s	B7[1], 284
k22	—, phenyl 4′-piperidyl, 1′-methyl-	4-Benzoyl-N-methyl piperidine. $C_{13}H_{17}NO$.	203.29	nd λ^{alHBr} 245 (4.15), 281 (3.05)	35–7	160–3^{13} 130–7^2		1.5430^{23}	s^h	s	v	s	s	....	C49, 12472
—	—, phenyl 4-pyridyl	see **Pyridine, 4-benzoyl-**													
Ω k23	—, phenyl 2-thienyl	2-Benzoylthiophene. ...... $C_{11}H_8OS$.	188.26	nd (dil al) λ^{al} 263 (4.11), 293 (4.13)	56–7	300	1.1890$^{54}_4$	1.6181$^{54}_a$	i	v^h	v	s		....	B17[2], 372
Ω k24	Khellin	$C_{14}H_{12}O_5$	260.25	(MeOH or eth) λ^{al} 250 (4.6), 290 (3.6), 340 (3.6)	154–5 (vac)	180–200$^{0.05}$			s^h i	s^h	δ	s		MeOH s, v^h	B19[2], 236
—	Kojic acid	see **4-Pyrone, 5-hydroxy-** **2-hydroxymethyl-**													
—	Kynurenic acid	see **2-Quinolinecarboxylic** **acid, 4-hydroxy-**													
k25	Kynurenine(l)	3-Anthranyloylalanine. $C_{10}H_{12}N_2O_3$.	208.22	lf ($+\frac{1}{3}$w, w) $[\alpha]^{20}_D - 29$ (w, c = 4) λ^w 260 (2.3), 360 (2.0)	191d	....			δ						B14[2], 415
—	Kynurine	see **Quinoline, 4-hydroxy-**													

For explanations, symbols and abbreviations see beginning of table. For structural formulas see end of table.

No.	Name	Synonyms and Formula	Mol. wt.	Color, crystalline form, specific rotation and λ_{max} (log ε)	m.p. °C	b.p. °C	Density	n_D	Solubility						Ref.
									w	al	eth	ace	bz	other solvents	
	Lactamide														
—	**Lactamide**	see **Propanoic acid, 2-hydroxy-, amide**													
—	**Lactaric acid**	see **Octadecanoic acid, 6-oxo-***													
—	**Lactic acid**	see **Propanoic acid, 2-hydroxy-***													
—	**β-Lactic acid**	see **Propanoic acid, 3-hydroxy-***													
Ω 11	**Lactide**(d)	Dilactide. 2,5-Dimethyl-3,6-dioxo-1,4-dioxane.	144.14	hyg rh (eth) $[\alpha]_D^{18}$ −298 (bz, c = 1.17)	95	150^{25}	. . . .	. . . . .		δ	δ	. . .	δ	chl δ	**B19**, 154
12	—(dl)	$C_6H_8O_4$. See 11	144.14	pa ye tcl or nd (al)	124.5	255^{757} $138{-}42^8$	0.862_4^{10}	. . . . .	δ	δ	δ	s	s	peth δ	**B19**[2], 176
13	—(l)	$C_6H_8O_4$. See 11	144.14	rh (eth) $[\alpha]_D^{16}$ +281.6 (bz, c = 0.82)	95	150^{25}	. . . .	. . . . .		δ		. . .	δ		**B19**, 154
Ω 14	**Lactobionic acid** . . .		358.30	syr	. . . .	. . . .	. . . .	. . . . .	v	δ	i	. . .	. . .	aa δ MeOH δ	**B31**, 415
—	**Lactobiose**	see **Lactose**													
—	**Lactoflavin**	see **Riboflavin**													
15	**Lactose**(α)	Lactobiose. Milk sugar.	342.30	pw $[\alpha]_D^{20}$ +92.6 (w, c = 4.5) → + 52.3 (final) (mut)	222.8	. . . .	. . . .	. . . . .	v	δ	i	. . .	. . .	chl i	**B31**, 408
16	—(β)		342.30	$[\alpha]_D^{20}$ +34.2 (5 min)→ 52.3 (final) (w) (mut)	253	. . . .	1.59^{20}	. . . . .	v	δ	i	. . .	. . .	chl i	**B31**, 408
17	—,monohydrate(α)	$C_{12}H_{22}O_{11}.H_2O$. See 15	360.31	mcl (w) $[\alpha]_D^{20}$ +83.5 (w, 10 min)	201–2 (→ w, 130) d	. . . .	1.525^{20}	. . . . .	v	i	i	. . .	. . .	MeOH i chl i	**B31**, 408
18	**Lanosterol**	Cryptosterol. Isocholesterol. Zanosterol. $C_{30}H_{50}O$.	386.67	nd (eth), cr (MeOH-ace) $[\alpha]_D^{20}$ +62 (chl, c = 1)	140–1	. . . .	. . . .	. . . . .		s^h	v	δ	. . .	aa s^h chl s	**B6**[3], 2880
19	—,benzoate	Isocholesterol benzoate. $C_{34}H_{50}O_2$. See 18	490.78	pw or nd (eth) $[\alpha]_D^{17}$ +72.2	191.5	. . . .	. . . .	. . . . .		s	s		. . .	. . . .	**B4**[3], 2881
110	**Lanthionine**(D)	d-β,β-Thiodialanine. $[HO_2CCH(NH_2)CH_2]_2S$	208.24	hex pl $[\alpha]_D^{21}$ −8.0 (2.4N NaOH, c = 5)	293–5d darkens 245	. . . .	. . . .	. . . . .	δ	i	i	i	i	dil alk s dil ac s	**B4**[3], 1618
111	—(DL)	$[HO_2CCH(NH_2)CH_2]_2S$.	208.24	hex pl	282–95d chars 240	. . . .	. . . .	. . . . .	δ	i	i	i	i	dil alk s dil ac s chl i	**B4**[3], 1620
112	—(L)	$[HO_2CCH(NH_2)CH_2]_2S$.	208.24	hex pl $[\alpha]_D^{22}$ +8.6 (2.4N NaOH, c = 5)	293–5d darkens 245	. . . .	. . . .	. . . . .	δ	i	i	i	i	dil alk s dil ac s	**B4**[3], 1593
113	—(meso)	$[HO_2CCH(NH_2)CH_2]_2S$.	208.24	hex pl (dil NH$_4$OH)	304d softens 270	. . . .	. . . .	. . . . .	δ	i	i	i	i	dil alk s dil ac s chl i	**B4**[3], 1620
114	**Lanthopine**	$C_{23}H_{25}NO_4$.	379.46	pw	200	. . . .	. . . .	. . . . .	. . .	δ	δ	. . .	. . .	chl s	**C20**, 2715
115	**Lapachol**	Taiguic acid. Tecomine	242.28	ye pr (eth or bz), pl (aa or al) λ^{al} 252 (4.38), 278 (4.28), 331 (3.43), 382 sh (3.17)	139.5–140.5 (142–3)	. . . .	. . . .	. . . . .	i	v^h s	s	. . .	v^h s	alk s aa v chl s	**E12 B** 3083
116	—,δ-hydroxy-	$C_{15}H_{14}O_4$. See 115 .	258.28	ye nd (bz or w)	127	. . . .	. . . .	. . . . .	s^h	v	v	. . .	v^h		**E12B**, 3170
117	**Lappaconitine**	$C_{32}H_{44}N_2O_9$.	600.72	hex pl (al) $[\alpha]_D^{18}$ +27 (chl) λ^{MeOH} 224 (4.41), 251 (4.17), 307 (3.74)	223 (215–6)	. . . .	. . . .	. . . . .	i	δ	δ	. . .	s	chl s	**C18**, 2899
118	**Laudanidine**(d)	$C_{20}H_{25}NO_4$.	343.43	(MeOH) $[\alpha]_D^{17}$ +93.5 (chl, c = 1)	184–5	. . . .	. . . .	. . . . .		δ	δ	. . .	. . .		**B21**[2], 184
119	—(l)	Tritopine. $C_{20}H_{25}NO_4$. See 118	343.43	hex pr (al) $[\alpha]_D^{17}$ −94.8 (chl, c = 2)	184–5	. . . .	. . . .	. . . . .		s	δ	δ	. . .	s	peth δ con sulf s → ye-red	**B21**[2], 183
120	**Laudanine**	dl-Laudanidine. $C_{20}H_{25}NO_4$. See 118	343.43	ye wh pr (dil al or al-chl) λ^{al} 225 sh (4.2), 283 (3.8)	167	. . . .	1.26_4^{20}	. . . . .	δ	v^h δ	δ	. . .	. . .	chl s	**B21**[2], 184

For explanations, symbols and abbreviations see beginning of table. For structural formulas see end of table.

Laudanosine (d)

No.	Name	Synonyms and Formula	Mol. wt.	Color, crystalline form, specific rotation and λ_{max} (log ε)	m.p. °C	b.p. °C	Density	n_D	w	al	eth	ace	bz	other solvents	Ref.
121	Laudanosine(d)....	N-Methyltetrahydro-papaverine. $C_{21}H_{27}NO_4$.	357.46	nd (peth), pr (al) $[\alpha]_D^6 +106$ (al, c = 1.6) λ^{MeOH} 231 (4.20), 282 (3.78)	89	....			i	s	s	s	s[h]	chl s	B21[2], 184
122	—(dl)...........	$C_{21}H_{27}NO_4$. See 121.......	357.46	nd (al)	115–6				i	v[h]	s	s	s	chl v peth δ[h]	B21[2], 185
123	—(l)...........	$C_{21}H_{27}NO_4$. See 121.......	357.46	cr (al) $[\alpha]_D^{15} -105.4$ (al, c = 3)	89	....									B21[2], 185
—	Lauramide........	see Dodecanoic acid, amide*													
124	Laureline	$C_{19}H_{19}NO_3$	309.35	ta (al) cubes (peth) $[\alpha]_D^{18} -99$ (abs al, c = 0.7) λ 350 (1.8), 394 (1.65)	114 (97)				i	s	s			dil ac s con sulf s→red	B27[1], 461
—	Lauric acid	see Dodecanoic acid*													
—	Laurone..........	see 12-Tricosanone*													
—	Laurophenone.....	see 1-Dodecanone, 1-phenyl-													
—	Lawsone	see 1,4-Naphthoquinone, 2-hydroxy-*													
—	Lawsone anilide....	see 1,4-Naphthoquinone, 2(phenylamino)-*													
125	Lecithin..........	α(Dimyristoyl)lecithin	677.92	$[\alpha]_D^{24} +7.0$	236–7				i		s	i	δ	chl s peth s	Am 74, 158
126	Ledol...........		222.38	nd (al) $[\alpha]_D^{20} +28$ (chl, c = 10) $[\alpha]_D^{20} +7.98$ (al)	105–6.5 δsub	292[760] (282–3) with sub	0.9094[100]20	1.4667[110]	δ[h] i	v	s	s	...	oos s	E13, 5
—	Lepidine..........	see Quinoline, 4-methyl-													
—	p-Leucaniline, N,N,N',N'-tetra-methyl-	see Methane, bis(4-di-methylaminophenyl) (4-amino phenyl)-*													
—	Leucaurine	see Methane, tris-(4-hydroxyphenyl)-*													
—	Leucenol	see Mimosine													
127	Leucic acid(D)....	4-Hydroxy-4-methylvaleric acid. Leucinic acid. $(CH_3)_2CHCH_2CHOHCO_2H$	132.16	nd (bz), pr (eth-peth) $[\alpha]_D^{125} +10.7$ (w, c = 5) $[\alpha]_D^{18} +26.1$ (1N NaOH, c = 2)	80–1	....									B3[2], 233
Ω 128	—(DL)...........	$(CH_3)_2CHCH_2CHOHCO_2H$	132.16	pl (eth-peth)	77				v	v	v				B3[2], 234
129	—(L)	$(CH_3)_2CHCH_2CHOHCO_2H$	132.16	rh (eth) $[\alpha]_D^{20} -11.3$ (w, c = 1)	81–2	<100			v	v	v				B3[2], 233
130	Leucinamide(dl) ...	α-Aminoisocaproamide. $(CH_3)_2CHCH_2CH(NH_2)CONH_2$	130.19	pr (bz)	106–7				s	v		v	δ		B4, 448
Ω 131	Leucine(D)	D-α-Aminoisocaproic acid. $(CH_3)_2CHCH_2CH(NH_2)CO_2H$	131.18	pl (al) $[\alpha]_D^{20} +10.34$	293 sealed tube	sub			δ						B4, 446
Ω 132	—(DL)...........	$(CH_3)_2CHCH_2CH(NH_2)CO_2H$	131.18	lf (w) $\lambda^{w,pH=1}$ 207 (1.82)	293–5 sealed tube (332d)	sub	1.2931[18]		s	δ	i				B4[2], 870
Ω 133	—(L)	$(CH_3)_2CHCH_2CH(NH_2)CO_2H$	131.18	hex pl (dil al) $[\alpha]_D^{25} -10.42$ (w, p = 22) $[\alpha]_D^{15} +17.3$ (20 % HCl)	293–5 sealed tube	sub	1.2931[18]		δ	i	i				B4[2], 859
—	—,amide..........	see Leucinamide													
Ω 134	—,N-acetyl-(dl) ...	$(CH_3)_2CHCH_2CH(NHCOCH_3)CO_2H$	173.21	nd (dil al) $\lambda^{w,pH=1}$ 215 (2.8)	161	....				v	δ				B4, 451
135	—,N-benzoyl-(dl)..	$(CH_3)_2CHCH_2CH(NHCOC_6H_5)CO_2H$	235.29	nd (dil al)	137–41	....			s	s	s	...	δ	chl s lig i	B9, 253
Ω 136	—,N-glycyl-(dl) ...	$(CH_3)_2CHCH_2CH(NHCOCH_2NH_2)CO_2H$	188.23	tetr (dil al)	242d	....	1.181		v	i					B4, 453
Ω 137	—(l)	$(CH_3)_2CHCH_2CH(NHCOCH_2NH_2)CO_2H$	188.23	pl (dil al) $[\alpha]_D^{20} -35.2$ (w)	256d				v	i					Am 74, 3818
—	Leuco indigo	see Indigo white													

For explanations, symbols and abbreviations see beginning of table. For structural formulas see end of table.

Leucomethylene blue

No.	Name	Synonyms and Formula	Mol. wt.	Color, crystalline form, specific rotation and λ_{max} (log ε)	m.p. °C	b.p. °C	Density	n_D	w	al	eth	ace	bz	other solvents	Ref.
138	Leucomethylene blue	. . . .	285.42	ye nd (eth or al) λ^w 256	185	. . . .	. . . .	. . . . .	δ	s	. . .	. . .	. . .	. . . . .	B27, 393
—	Leucylglycine	see Glycine, N-leucyl-,													
139	Levopimaric acid, methyl ester	Methyl sapietate. $C_{21}H_{32}O_2$.	316.49	(MeOH or eth) $[\alpha]_D -190.4$ (al) $[\alpha]_D -268$ (eth)	63–4	$166-9^{0.5}$	1.0312_2^{22}	1.5232^{22}	. . .	s	s^h	. . .	. . .	MeOH s^h	B9², 433
—	Levulinaldehyde . . .	see Pentanal, 4-oxo-*													
140	Levulin	Fructosin. Laevulin. Levulosin. $(C_6H_{19}O_5)_n$	(162.14)	amor $[\alpha] -52.1$	140–45d	. . . .	. . . .	. . . . .	∞	s	i	. . .	. . .	. . . . .	B1, 925
—	Levulinic acid	see Pentanoic acid, 4-oxo-*													
—	Lewisite	see Ethene, 1-chloro- 2-dichloroarsino-*													
—	Limettin	see Coumarin, 5,7-dimethoxy-													
Ω 141	Limonene(d)	Citrene. Carvene. 4-Isopropenyl-1-methylcyclohexene.	136.24	$[\alpha]_D^{20} +125.6$ (undil) λ^{iso} 220 (2.41), 250 (1.36)	−74.35	178^{760} 61^{13}	0.8411_4^{20}	1.4730^{20}	i	∞	∞	. . .	. . .	. . . . .	B5², 88
Ω 142	—(dl)	Cinene. Dipentene. $C_{10}H_{16}$. See 141	136.24	λ^{iso} 220 (2.41), 250 (1.36)	−95.5	178^{760} 64.4^{15}	0.8402_4^{21}	1.4727^{20}	. . .	. . .	. . .	. . .	. . .	. . . . .	B5², 89
143	— (l)	$C_{10}H_{16}$ See 141	136.24	$[\alpha]_D^{20} -122.1$ (undil) λ^{iso} 220 (2.4), 250 (1.1)	. . . .	$177.6-$ 7.8^{755} 64.4^{15}	0.8422_4^{20}	1.4746^{20}	. . .	. . .	. . .	. . .	. . .	. . . . .	B5², 89
Ω 144	Linalool(d)	Coriandrol. 3,7-Dimethyl-1,6-octadien-3-ol. $CH_2{:}CHCOH(CH_3)CH_2CH_2CH{:}C(CH_3)_2$	154.26	$[\alpha]_D^{20} +19.18$ λ^{al} 243 sh (1.58), 272 sh (0.44)	. . . .	$198-$ 200^{760} $87-8^{12}$	0.8700_4^{20}	1.4636^{20}	δ	∞	∞	. . .	. . .	. . . . .	B1³, 2012
Ω 145	—,acetate(l)	Bergamol. Linalyl acetate. Licareol acetate. $C_{12}H_{20}O_2$. See 144	196.29	$[\alpha]_D^{20} -9.45$	. . . .	220^{762}	0.8951_4^{20}	1.4544^{21}	i	∞	∞	. . .	. . .	. . . . .	B2², 153
146	—,formate(l)	Linalyl formate. $C_{11}H_{18}O_2$. See 144	182.27	. . . .	. . . .	$100-3^{10}$	0.915_4^{25}	$1.456^{20}-$	i	s	. . .	. . .	. . .	. . . . .	B2³, 47
147	β-Linaloolene	Dihydromyrcene. $CH_2{:}CHCH(CH_3)CH_2CH_2CH{:}C(CH_3)_2$	138.25	. . . .	. . . .	$165-8$ $(161-2)$	0.7601_4^{20}	1.4362^{20}	. . .	. . .	. . .	. . .	. . .	. . . . .	B1³, 1020
148	Linamarin	Acetone cyanohydrin-β-d-glycopyranoside. Phaseolunatin.	247.25	nd (w, al or AcOEt) $[\alpha]_D^{18} -29.1$ (w, p = 5)	145 (142–3)	. . . .	. . . .	. . . . .	v	s^h δ	i	v^h	δ	chl δ peth i	B31, 197
—	Lindane	see Cyclohexane, 1,2,3,4,5,6-hexachloro-													
—	Linoleic acid	see 9,12-Octadecadienoic acid*													
—	Linolenic acid	see 9,12,15-Octadecatrienoic acid*													
—	Linolenin	see Glycerol, 1-mono-(9.12-octadecadienoate)													
Ω 149	α-Lipoic acid(d) . . .	6.8-Epidithiooctanoic acid*. Thioctic acid.	206.33	pa ye pl $[\alpha]_D^{25} +96.7$ λ^{MeOH} 333 (2.18)	47.5	. . . .	. . . .	. . . . .	δ	. . .	. . .	. . .	v	MeOH v AcOEt v	Am 76, 1270
150	Lithocholic acid	3α-Hydroxycholanic acid. $C_{24}H_{40}O_3$.	376.59	hex lf(al), pr (dil al or aa) $[\alpha]_D^{20} +32.14$ (al) $\lambda^{con\,sulf}$ 326 (3.53)	186	. . . .	. . . .	. . . . .	i	v^h s	δ	. . .	. . .	chl s aa s lig i	C30, 2575
152	Lobelanidine	$C_{22}H_{29}NO_2$	339.48	sc (al or eth) λ^{MeOH} 252 (2.58), 258 (2.63), 263 (2.55)	150	distb vac	. . . .	. . . . .	$δ^h$ i	s	δ	v	v	Py v chl v peth δ	B21², 136
153	Lobelanine	$C_{22}H_{25}NO_2$	335.45	nd (peth or eth)	99	. . . .	. . . .	. . . . .	i	v	δ	v	v	MeOH. aa, chl v	B21², 394
Ω 154	Lobeline(dl)	$C_{22}H_{27}NO_2$	337.47	ye pl (eth), pr (al)	110	. . . .	. . . .	. . . . .	δ	v	v	. . .	s	chl s	B21², 434
155	—(l)	$C_{22}H_{27}NO_2$. See 155	337.47	nd (al, eth or bz) $[\alpha]_D^{15} -42.85$ (al, c = 1) λ^{MeOH} 245 (4.12), 261 (3.15)	130–1	. . . .	. . . .	. . . . .	δ	s^h	s	v	s	peth δ chl s	B21², 434
Ω 156	Longifolene(d)	$C_{15}H_{24}$	204.36	$[\alpha]_D^{18} +42.73$	. . . .	$254-6^{706}$ $126-7^{15}$	0.9319_4^{18}	1.5040^{20}	i	. . .	. . .	. . .	s	. . . . .	B5³, 1097
157	Lophine	2,4,5-Triphenylimidazole . . .	296.38	nd (al)	275	sub	. . . .	. . . . .	i	s	s	. . .	. . .	. . . . .	B23², 280
—	Loretine	see 5-Quinolinesulfonic acid, 8-hydroxy-7-iodo-													

For explanations, symbols and abbreviations see beginning of table. For structural formulas see end of table.

No.	Name	Synonyms and Formula	Mol. wt.	Color, crystalline form, specific rotation and λ_{max} (log ε)	m.p. °C	b.p. °C	Density	n_D	w	al	eth	ace	bz	other solvents	Ref.

Luciculine

158	Luciculine	$C_{22}H_{35}NO_3$	361.51	cr (+1w, ace) $[\alpha]_D^{1.5}-11.4$ (al)	148–50	$165^{0.02}$			i	s					C46, 1008
159	—, hydrochloride	$C_{22}H_{35}NO_3 \cdot HCl$	397.97	cr (w + 1.5) $[\alpha]_D = -9.4$ (w)	198–203d (anh)				i^h	s					C46, 1008
—	Luminal	see **Barbituric acid, 5-ethyl-5-phenyl-**													
Ω 160	Luminol	5-Amino-2,3-dihydro-1,4-phthalazinedione. 3-Amino-phthalhydrazide.	177.16	ye nd (al) λ^{ac} 240 (3.9), 280 sh (3.6), 290 (3.7), 350 (3.65), λ^{al} 235 (4.1), 320 (3.8)	329–32				i	s	δ			alk v dil ac δ aa s^h	B25², 389
161	Lumisterol	$C_{28}H_{44}O$	396.67	nd (ace-MeOH) $[\alpha]_D^{18}+197$ (chl) λ^{al} 278.5 (3.95), 294 (3.63)	118				i	s	v	v		aa s chl v MeOH s	E14, 76
162	Lupanine(d)	$C_{15}H_{24}N_2O$	248.37	hyg nd $[\alpha]_D^{20}+82.4$ (w, c = 3)	40–44	$190–3^3$		1.5444^{24}	s	v	v			chl v lig i	B24², 53
163	—(dl)	$C_{15}H_{24}N_2O$. See 162	248.37	nd (peth), rh pr (ace)	98–9	$233–4^{18}$			v	v	v			peth s chl v	B24², 55
Ω 164	Lupeol	Lupenol. 2-Hydroxy-$\Delta^{20,29}$-lupene. $C_{30}H_{50}O$.	426.74	nd (al or ace) $[\alpha]_D^{20}+27.2$ (chl) λ^{al} 206 (3.40)	215–7		0.9457_4^{218}	1.4910^{218}	i	v^h	v	v	v	chl v lig v	E14s, 1115
—	Lupetidine	see **Piperidine, dimethyl-**													
Ω 165	Lupinine(l)	$C_{10}H_{19}NO$.	169.27	rh (peth) $[\alpha]_D^{17}-20.35$ (al)	70	$269–70^{754}$			s	s	s		s	chl s peth δ	B21², 28
166	—, hydrochloride	$C_{10}H_{19}NO \cdot HCl$. See 165	205.73	pr (aq al) $[\alpha]_D-14$ (w)	212–3				s	s					B21², 29
167	—, des-N-methyl-	$C_{11}H_{21}NO$.	183.30			$145–6^{15}$			i	s					B21², 27
—	Lupulic acid	see **Humulon**													
168	Lupulone	β-Bitter acid. β-Lupulinic acid. $C_{26}H_{38}O_4$.	414.59	pr (MeOH) λ^{al} 228 (4.15), 280 (3.79), 338 (4.01)	93				i					peth s hx s	B7², 856
—	Lutein	see **Xanthophyll**													
—	Luteolin	see **Flavone, 3′,4′,5,7-tetrahydroxy-**													
—	Lutidine	see **Pyridine, dimethyl-**													
169	Lycaconitine	$C_{27}H_{34}N_2O_6$	566.61	amor $[\alpha]_D$ +31.5	111–4				δ	s	δ		s	peth, chl s	C53, 9266
170	Lycomarasmine	$HO_2CCH_2CH(CO_2H)NHCH_2CH(CO_2H)NHCH_2CONH_2$	277.24	$[\alpha]_D^{20}-48$ (w)		227–9d			δ					dil ac, dil alk v	H46, 60
Ω 171	Lycopene	Lycopin. Neolycopene. $C_{40}H_{56}$.	536.90	red pr or nd (peth or CS_2-al) λ^{hx} 412 (4.9), 433 (4.9), 460 sh (4.7), (all cis) λ^{hx} 418 sh (4.8), 442 (5.1), 473 (5.3), 504 (5.2), (all trans)	175					$δ^h$	s		v^h	chl v^h peth δ CS_2 s	B30, 81
172	Lycorine(l)	Amarylline. Narcissine. $C_{16}H_{17}NO_4$.	287.32	pr (al or Py) $[\alpha]_D^{16}-129$ (al, c = 0.16) λ^{MeOH} 233 (3.54), 293 (3.68)	280 (262–3)	sub			i	δ	δ			chl δ	B27², 547
173	Lycoxanthin	$C_{40}H_{56}O$.	552.93	purple or red br nd (CS_2), (bz-peth), red pl (bz-MeOH) λ^{CS_2} 473, 507, 547	168				i	δ			s	CS_2 s peth δ	C30, 3832
—	Lysergamide	see **Ergine**													
174	Lysergic acid	$C_{16}H_{16}N_2O_2$.	268.32	lf or hex sc (w) $[\alpha]_D^{20}+40$ (Py, c = 0.5) $\lambda^{aq\,NaOH}$ 223 (4.3), 238 (4.31), 310 (3.96)	240d				δ	s	δ		δ	Py s	J1955, 1626

For explanations, symbols and abbreviations see beginning of table. For structural formulas see end of table.

No.	Name	Synonyms and Formula	Mol. wt.	Color, crystalline form, specific rotation and λ_{max} (log ε)	m.p. °C	b.p. °C	Density	n_D	Solubility						Ref.
									w	al	eth	ace	bz	other solvents	
	Lysidine														
—	**Lysidine**.........	*see* Δ^2-**Imidazoline, 2-methyl-**													
Ω 175	**Lysine**(*L*)........	*L*-α,ε-Diaminocaproic acid. $H_2N(CH_2)_4CH(NH_2)CO_2H$	146.19	nd (w or dil al) $[\alpha]_D^{20} +14.6$ (w, c = 6)	224–5 d darkens 210	....	....		v	i	i	i	i	....	**B4**[2], 857
Ω 176	—,dihydro-chloride(*L*)	$H_2N(CH_2)_4CH(NH_2)CO_2H \cdot 2HCl$	219.11	(al-eth or aq HCl) $[\alpha]_D^{20}$ $+15.29$ (w)	201–2 (193)	....	....		v	s^h	...	...	i	....	**B4**[2], 857
177	—,N^α-**benzoyl-**(*dl*) .	$H_2N(CH_2)_4CH(NHCOC_6H_5)CO_2H$	250.30	nd (w)	235 (235– 249)	....	....		v^h	δ	i	...	i	chl i	**B9**[2], 193
178	—,N^ε-**benzoyl-**(*dl*) .	$C_6H_5CONH(CH_2)_4CH(NH_2)CO_2H$	250.30	cr (w)	268 (254)	....	....		s^h	i	i	...	...	chl i	**B9**[2], 193
179	—,—(*L*).........	$C_6H_5CONH(CH_2)_4CH(NH_2)CO_2H$	250.30	lf (w) $[\alpha]_D^{19}$ $+20.1$ (aq HCl)	240d	....	....		s^h	i	i	...	i	chl i	**B9**[2], 193
—	**Lyxitol**..........	*see* **Arabitol**													

For explanations, symbols and abbreviations see beginning of table. For structural formulas see end of table.

Malachite green

No.	Name	Synonyms and Formula	Mol. wt.	Color, crystalline form, specific rotation and λ_{max} (log ε)	m.p. °C	b.p. °C	Density	n_D	w	al	eth	ace	bz	other solvents	Ref.
—	Malachite green, leuco-	see Methane, bis(4-dimethylaminophenyl)-(phenyl)-													
Ω m1	Malathion	S(1,2-Dicarboxyethyl)-O, O-dimethyldithiophosphate.	330.36	ye-br	2.85	156–7[0.7] δd	1.2076[20]	1.4960[20]	δ	s	s	...	s	. . . .	C48, 5572
Ω m2	Maleic acid	cis-Butenedioic acid*. $HO_2CCH{:}CHCO_2H$	116.07	mcl pr (w) λ^w 210 (4.14)	139–40 (131)	. . . .	1.590[20]	. . . .	v	v	s	v	i	con sulf, aa s chl i	B2², 641
Ω m3	—,anhydride.		98.06	nd (chl or eth) λ^{iso} 208 (3.90), 290 (1.11)	60 (56)	197–9 82[14]	1.314[60]	. . . .	s d[h]	s	s	s	. . .	chl s lig δ	B17², 445
Ω m3¹	—,diethyl ester	Ethyl maleate. $C_2H_5O_2CCH{:}CHCO_2C_2H_5$	172.19	λ^{al} 250 sh (2.7)	−8.8	223[760] 105–6[14]	1.0662[20]	1.4416[20]	i	s	s	. . .	. . .	. . . . .	B2³, 1923
Ω m3²	—,dimethyl ester . . .	Methyl maleate. $CH_3O_2CCH{:}CHCO_2CH_3$	144.14	λ^{al} 205 (3.90)	−19	202[762] 102[17]	1.1606[20]	1.4416[20]	i	. . .	s	. . .	. . .	lig i	B2³, 1921
m4	—,diphenyl ester . . .	$C_6H_5O_2CCH{:}CHCO_2C_6H_5$.	268.27	pl (lig)	73	226[15]	. . . . . .	. . . . . .	i	v	v	v	v	chl v	B6, 156
—	—,hydrazide.	see Pyridazine, 3,6-dioxo-1,2,3,6-tetrahydro-													
Ω m5	—,imide	Maleimide.	97.07	pl (bz) λ^{al} 216 (4.13), 230 sh (3.70), 280 (2.64)	93–5	sub	. . . . . .	. . . . . .	s	s	s	. . .	. . .	. . . . .	B21², 311
Ω m6	—,—,N-ethyl-	$C_6H_7NO_2$. See m5	125.13	cr (bz) λ^{al} 217 (4.10), 224 sh (4.03), 310 (2.71)	45.5	. . . . . .	. . . . . .	. . . . . .	δ	v	v	. . .	. . .	. . . . .	B21, 399
Ω m6¹	—,—,N-phenyl- . . .	Maleanil. $C_{10}H_7NO_2$. See m5	173.17	ye nd (bz-lig) λ^{cy} 205 (3.98), 220 (3.97), 275 (3.48)	90–1	162[12]	. . . . . .	. . . . . .	δ	s	s	. . .	s	chl, CS_2 δ	B21, 400
m6²	—,monoamide	Maleamic acid $HO_2CCH{:}CHCONH_2$	115.09	lf (w)	178 (d 153)	. . . . . .	. . . . . .	. . . . . .	v	s[h]	i	. . .	i	chl i	B2³, 1927
m6³	—,bromo-	$HO_2CCH{:}CBrCO_2H$	194.98	nd or pr	140–1 (rapid htng) 136–8 (slow htng)	d	. . . . . .	. . . . . .	v	v	v	. . .	. . .	. . . . .	B2³, 1929
m6⁴	—,chloro-	$HO_2CCH{:}CClCO_2H$	150.52	pr (eth-chl)	108 (114)	. . . . . .	. . . . . .	. . . . . .	s[h]	v	v	s	δ	aa s chl δ peth i	B2³, 1928
m7	—,—,diethyl ester .	$C_2H_5O_2CCH{:}CClCO_2C_2H_5$.	206.63	. . . .	. . . . . .	235δd 125[19]	1.1741[20]	. . . . . .	. . .	v	v	. . .	. . .	. . . . .	B2², 646
m8	—,—,dimethyl ester	$CH_3O_2CCH{:}CClCO_2CH_3$	178.57	. . . .	. . . . . .	106.5[18]	1.2775[25]	. . . . . .	. . .	v	v	. . .	. . .	. . . . .	B2², 646
m9	—,dichloro-	$HO_2CCCl{:}CClCO_2H$	184.96	nd (lig or eth) λ^{al} 218 sh (3.7), 242 (3.8)	119–20	. . . . . .	. . . . . .	. . . . . .	v	s	s	. . .	i	chl, CS_2 i	B2, 753
Ω m10	—,dihydroxy-	$HO_2CC(OH){:}C(OH)CO_2H$	148.07	pl (w + 2) $\lambda^{w,pH=5.8}$ 291 (3.7)	155 (anh)	. . . . . .	. . . . . .	. . . . . .	δ	s	δ	. . .	. . .	MeOH δ	B3², 346
Ω m11	—,dimethyl-, anhydride	Pyrocinchonic anhydride. $C_6H_6O_3$. See m3	126.11	pl or lf (dil al)	96	223 105[12]	1.107[100] 0.90912[219]	. . . . . .	δ	v	v	. . .	v	chl v	B17², 450
Ω m12	—,methyl-	Citraconic acid. $HO_2CCH{:}C(CH_3)CO_2H$	130.10	tcl pr or pl (eth-bz), nd (eth-lig)	93–3.8	. . . . . .	1.617	. . . . . .	v	. . .	δ	. . .	i	chl δ CS_2 i	B2², 652
Ω m13	—,—,anhydride . . .	Citraconic anhydride. $C_5H_4O_3$. See m3	112.09	. . . .	7–8	213–4[760] 99–100[15]	1.2469[16]	1.4710[21]	d	v	s	s	. . .	. . . . .	B17², 448
m14	—,—,diethyl ester . .	Diethyl citraconate. $C_2H_5O_2CCH{:}C(CH_3)CO_2C_2H_5$	186.21	λ^{al} 230 sh (3.4), 263 sh (2.0)	. . . . . .	228[766] 120[20]	1.0491[20]	1.44676[20]	δ	s	s	. . .	. . .	aa s	B2², 653
m15	—,—,dimethyl ester	Dimethyl citraconate. $CH_3O_2CCH{:}C(CH_3)CO_2CH_3$	158.16	λ^{al} 233 (3.37)	. . . . . .	210.5[758] 92.8[10]	1.1153[20]	1.44733[20]	δ	s	s	. . .	. . .	aa s	B2², 653
m16	—,phenyl-, anhydride	$C_{10}H_6O_3$. See m3	174.16	ye nd (CS_2)	122	. . . . . .	. . . . . .	. . . . . .	. . .	. . .	s	s	. . .	chl s CS_2, lig δ	B17², 481
—	Malonanilic acid	see Malonic acid, monoamide, N-phenyl-													
Ω m17	Malonic acid	Propanedioic acid*. $CH_2(CO_2H)_2$	104.06	tcl (al) λ^{MeOH} 228 (2.34)	135.6 δ sub	d at 140	1.619[16]	. . . . . .	v	v	v	. . .	i	Py v	B2², 516
Ω m19	—,diamide	Malonamide. $CH_2(CONH_2)_2$	102.09	mcl st pr (w), unst tetr	171.5–2.5 (st)	. . . . . .	. . . . . .	. . . . . .	s	i	i	. . .	i	. . . . .	B2², 530
Ω m20	—,—,N,N'-diphenyl-	Malonanilide. $CH_2(CONHC_6H_5)_2$	254.29	nd (al)	226	. . . . . .	. . . . . .	. . . . . .	i	v[h]	i	. . .	v	aa s	B12², 167
Ω m21	—,dibutyl ester	Dibutyl malonate. $CH_2(CO_2CH_2CH_2CH_2CH_3)_2$	216.28	. . . .	−83	251–2[760] 137[14]	0.9824[20]	1.4262[20]	i	s	s	s	s	aa s	B2², 528
m22	—,dichloride.	Malonyl chloride. $CH_2(COCl)_2$	140.95	λ^{diox} 280 (2.76), 293 (2.64), 304 (2.57)	. . . . . .	58[26]	1.4509[20]	1.4639[20]	d[h]	d[h]	. . .	. . .	. . .	AcOEt s	B2², 529

For explanations, symbols and abbreviations see beginning of table. For structural formulas see end of table.

No.	Name	Synonyms and Formula	Mol. wt.	Color, crystalline form, specific rotation and λ_{max} (log ε)	m.p. °C	b.p. °C	Density	n_D	Solubility						Ref.
									w	al	eth	ace	bz	other solvents	
	Malonic acid														
Ω m23	—,diethyl ester	Ethyl malonate. Malonic ester. $CH_2(CO_2C_2H_5)_2$	160.17	λ^{MeOH} 235 (1.70)	−48.9	199.3^{760} 96^{22}	1.0551_4^{20}	1.4139^{20}	δ	∞	∞	v	v	chl, aa s	B2[2], 524
Ω m24	—,dimethyl ester ..	Methyl malonate. $CH_2(CO_2CH_3)_2$	132.13		−61.9	181.4^{760} 78.4^{15}	1.528_4^{20}	1.41348^{20}	δ	∞	∞	v	v	chl s	B2[2], 522
Ω m25	—,dinitrile	Malononitrile. Methylene cyanide. Dicyanomethane. $CH_2(CN)_2$	66.06	λ^w 267 (0.5)	32	$218-9^{760}$ 109^{20}	1.1910_2^{20}	1.4146^{34}	s	v	v	s	s	chl, aa s	B2[2], 535
m26	—,dipropyl ester...	Propyl malonate. $CH_2(CO_2CH_2CH_2CH_3)_2$	188.23	glass	−77.1	229^{760} 113^{13}	1.0097_4^{20}	1.42061^{20}	v	v	v	v	v		B2[2], 528
m27	—,monoamide, N-phenyl-	Malonanilic acid. $C_6H_5NHCOCH_2CO_2H$	179.18	cr (w, eth, al)	132	....			s^h	s^h	s^h		s^h		B12[1], 208
Ω m28	—,monoamide mononitrile	Cyanoacetamide. H_2NCOCH_2CN	84.08	pl (w)	121–2	....			s	δ					B2[2], 534
m29	—,—,N-phenyl-	α-Cyanoacetanilide. $C_6H_5NHCOCH_2CN$	160.19	nd (al)	199–200	....			δ						B12[2], 167
m30	—,monochloride monoethyl ester	Carbethoxyacetyl chloride. $ClCOCH_2CO_2C_2H_5$	150.56			$170-80d$ $75-7^{15}$			d	d	d				B2[2], 529
m31	—,monochloride monomethyl ester	$ClCOCH_2CO_2CH_3$	136.54			71^{15}			d	d	d				B2[1], 252
Ω m32	—,monoethyl ester mononitrile	Ethyl cyanoacetate. $NCCH_2CO_2C_2H_5$	113.12		−22.5	205^{760} 99^{15}	1.0654_4^{20}	1.4175^{20}	i	∞	∞				B2[2], 531
m33	—,monoethyl ester piperazinium salt	$C_4H_{10}N_2.2HO_2CCH_2CO_2C_2H_5$	350.37		144	....			s	s^h	i				Am 56, 150
Ω m34	—,monomethyl ester mononitrile	Methyl cyanoacetate. $NCCH_2CO_2CH_3$	99.09		−22.5	$200.4-$ $.9^{761}$ 115^{36}	1.1128^{20}	1.4176^{20}	i	∞	∞				B2[2], 530
Ω m35	—,mononitrile	Cyanoacetic acid. $NCCH_2CO_2H$	85.06	dlq dimorphic cr λ^{al} 208 (1.6)	70–1	$108^{0.15}δd$			s	s	s			chl, aa δ	B2[2], 530
m36	—,piperazinium salt	$C_4H_{10}N_2.CH_2(CO_2H)_2$	190.20		180d	....			s	s^h	i				Am 56, 150
Ω m37	—,**acetamido-**, diethyl ester	$CH_3CONHCH(CO_2C_2H_5)_2$	217.22	cr (al or bz peth)	95 6	185^{20}			$δ^h$	s^h	δ				B4[2], 891
m38	—,**acetyl-**, diethyl ester	$CH_3COCH(CO_2C_2H_5)_2$	202.21			232^{760} 120^{17}	1.0834_4^{26}	1.4435^{25}	i			s		Na_2CO_3 s	B3[2], 485
m39	—,**allyl-**	3-Butene-1,1-dicarboxylic acid.* $CH_2:CHCH_2CH(CO_2H)_2$	144.14	tcl (eth)	105	$>180d$			s	s	v		s^h		B2[2], 658
Ω m40	—,—,diethyl ester .	$CH_2:CHCH_2CH(CO_2C_2H_5)_2$	200.24			$222.5-$ 3^{766} 93^6	1.0098_4^{20}	1.4305^{20}	i	v	v				B2[2], 658
m41	—,**amino-**, monohydrate	$H_2NCH(CO_2H)_2.H_2O$	137.09	pr (w+1)	112d	....			δ	δ					B4[2], 890
m42	—,—,diethyl ester .	$H_2NCH(CO_2C_2H_5)_2$	175.19			$122-3^{16}$ 88^4	1.100_4^{16}	1.4353^{16}	v	v	v	s	s	os s lig i	B4[2], 890
Ω m43	—,**benzoyl-amino-**, diethyl ester	Ethyl benzamidomalonate. $C_6H_5CONHCH(CO_2C_2H_5)_2$	279.30	nd (peth)	61	....			i	v	s			peth δ	B9[2], 185
Ω m44	—,**benzyl-**	$C_6H_5CH_2CH(CO_2H)_2$ ...	194 19	pr (bz, eth, chl-peth)	121–2				v	v	v		v^h		B9[2], 619
m45	—,—,diamide	$C_6H_5CH_2CH(CONH_2)_2$	192.22	nd (al)	225					δ	i				B9, 869
Ω m46	—,—,diethyl ester .	$C_6H_5CH_2CH(CO_2C_2H_5)_2$	250.30			300 169^{212}	1.0750_4^{20}	1.4872^{20}	i						B9[2], 620
m47	—,—,dinitrile	Benzylmalononitrile. $C_6H_5CH_2CH(CN)_2$	156.20	pl (al), nd (w or lig)	91	174^{23}				s	s		s	AcOEt s lig δ	B9, 870
m48	—,**benzyl-(hydroxy)-**	Benzyltartronic acid. $C_6H_5CH_2COH(CO_2H)_2$	210.19	pr	147d				s	s	s				B10, 515
m49	—,**benzylidene-**	$C_6H_5CH:C(CO_2H)_2$	192.18	pr (w)	195–6d				δ s^h	δ	s	δ	AcOEt s CS_2, chl δ	B9[2], 638
Ω m50	—,—,diethyl ester .	$C_6H_5CH:C(CO_2C_2H_5)_2$.	248.28		32(27)	$308-12δd$ 180^{10}	1.1045_4^{20}	1.5389^{20}	i	s	s	s	s	os s	B9[2], 639
m51	—,—,monoethyl ester mononitrile	Ethyl α-cyanocinnamate. Ethyl benzalcyanoacetate. $C_6H_5CH:C(CN)CO_2C_2H_5$	201.23	(i) oil (ii) nd (al)	(ii) 51	(i) $118^{0.4}$ 188^{15}	(i) 1.0762	(i) 1.5033	i	δ s^h	s		v	aa v chl s	B9[2], 640
Ω m52	—,—,mononitrile..	Benzalcyanoacetic acid. α-Cyanocinnamic acid. $C_6H_5CH:C(CN)CO_2H$	173.17	cr (al)	183					s^h				dil NH_3 s	B9[2], 639
m53	—,**bromo-**	$BrCH(CO_2H)_2$	182.96	nd (eth), pl (ace-bz)	113d				s^h	v	v				B2[2], 538
Ω m54	—,—,diethyl ester .	$BrCH(CO_2C_2H_5)_2$	239.07		−54	$233-5d$ 123^{20}	1.4022_4^{20}	1.4521^{20}	i	∞	∞	s			B2[2], 538
Ω m55	—,**butyl-**	1,1-Pentanedicarboxylic acid.* $CH_3(CH_2)_3CH(CO_2H)_2$	160.17	pr (w)	104–5				v	s	s				B2[2], 588
Ω m56	—,—,diethyl ester .	$CH_3(CH_2)_3CH(CO_2C_2H_5)_2$	216.28			$235-40^{760}$ 122^{12}		1.4250^{20}		v	v				B2[2], 588
m57	—,—,monoethyl ester mononitrile	Ethyl α-cyanocaproate. $CH_3(CH_2)_3CH(CN)CO_2C_2H_5$	169.23	syr		$230-3^{734}$ $128-9^{25}$	0.9537_4^{25}	1.4262^{20}		s			s		B2[2], 588
Ω m58	—,**sec-butyl-**, diethyl ester	$CH_3CH_2CH(CH_3)CH(CO_2C_2H_5)_2$	216.28			$245-50^{762}$ 105^9	0.988^{15}	1.4248^{20}	i	v	v				B2[2], 590

For explanations, symbols and abbreviations see beginning of table. For structural formulas see end of table.

No.	Name	Synonyms and Formula	Mol. wt.	Color, crystalline form, specific rotation and λ_{max} (log ε)	m.p. °C	b.p. °C	Density	n_D	w	al	eth	ace	bz	other solvents	Ref.
	Malonic acid														
m59	—,chloro-	ClCH(CO$_2$H)$_2$	138.51	pr (w)	133	d	1.2040$_4^{20}$	1.4327^{20}	v	v	v			chl ∞	B2^2, 537
Ω m60	—,—,diethyl ester	Ethyl chloromalonate. ClCH(CO$_2$C$_2$H$_5$)$_2$	194.62			222^{760} 118^{16}	1.2040$_4^{20}$	1.4327^{20}	i	∞	∞			chl ∞ CS$_2$ s	B2^2, 537
Ω m61	—,(3-chloropropyl)-, diethyl ester	ClCH$_2$CH$_2$CH$_2$CH(CO$_2$C$_2$H$_5$)$_2$	236.71			147–9^{10}		1.4429^{20}	i	s	s			chl, CS$_2$ s	B2^1, 278
Ω m62	—,cinnamylidene-(trans)	Cinnamalmalonic acid. C$_6$H$_5$CH:CHCH:C(CO$_2$H)$_2$	218.21	dk ye nd	212d				i	s				chl, AcOEt s	B9^2, 649
m63	—,1-cyclohexenyl-, mononitrile	1-Cyclohexenylcyanoacetic acid	165.19	nd (bz)	109–10				δ v^h	s		s	s^h		B9^2, 560
m64	—,cyclohexyl-, diethyl ester		242.32			163–5^{20}	1.0281$_4^{19}$	1.4478^{25}	i	s	s	s	s	os s	B9^2, 526
Ω m65	—,2-cyclopentenyl-, diethyl ester		226.28			141^{16}	1.0507$_4^{20}$	1.4536^{20}	i		s	s			B9^2, 559
m66	—,cyclopentylidene-, diethyl ester		226.28			140^{10}	1.0616$_4^{20}$	1.4724^{20}	i		s	s			B9^2, 559
Ω m67	—,dibenzyl-, diethyl ester	(C$_6$H$_5$CH$_2$)$_2$C(CO$_2$C$_2$H$_5$)$_2$	340.42		14	234–5^{23}	1.093^{20}		i	s	s				B9^1, 408
m68	—,dibromo-, diethyl ester	Br$_2$C(CO$_2$C$_2$H$_5$)$_2$	317.97			250–6δd 154^{28}			i	s	s				B2^2, 539
Ω m69	—,dibutyl-, diethyl ester	(CH$_3$CH$_2$CH$_2$CH$_2$)$_2$C(CO$_2$C$_2$H$_5$)$_2$	272.39			153–4^{14}	0.9457$_4^{20}$	1.4341^{20}	i	s	s				B2^2, 614
Ω m70	—,diethyl-	3,3-Pentanedicarboxylic acid*. (C$_2$H$_5$)$_2$C(CO$_2$H)$_2$	160.17	pr (w or bz)	127	d			v	v	v		δ^h	chl δ	B2^2, 593
Ω m71	—,—,diethyl ester	(C$_2$H$_5$)$_2$C(CO$_2$C$_2$H$_5$)$_2$	216.28			230 (225) 100^{12}	0.9643^{30}	1.4240^{20}	i	∞	∞				B2^2, 593
m72	—,—,monoethyl ester mononitrile	(C$_2$H$_5$)$_2$C(CN)CO$_2$C$_2$H$_5$	169.23			214–5 100–1^{15}		1.4200^{27}	i	∞	∞				B2^2, 594
m73	—,—,piperazinium salt	(C$_2$H$_5$)$_2$C(CO$_2$H)$_2$ · C$_4$H$_{10}$N$_2$	246.31		80–1				s	s	i	s^h			Am 56, 150
—	—,dihydroxy-	see **Malonic acid, oxo-, hydrate**													
m74	—,dimethyl-, diethyl ester	(CH$_3$)$_2$C(CO$_2$C$_2$H$_5$)$_2$	188.23		–30.4	197^{760} 97–8^{22}	0.9964$_4^{20}$	1.4129^{20}	i	∞	∞				B2^2, 572
m75	—,(2,4-dinitrophenyl)-, diethyl ester		326.27	pr (al)	51				i	v^h	v^h			alk s	B9^1, 378
Ω m76	—,(ethoxymethylene)-, diethyl ester	C$_2$H$_5$OCH:C(CO$_2$C$_2$H$_5$)$_2$	216.24			279–81d 165.5^{19} 109$^{0.5}$		1.4600^{20}	i	s	s				B3^2, 300
Ω m77	—,ethyl-	1,1-Propanedicarboxylic acid*. CH$_3$CH$_2$CH(CO$_2$H)$_2$	132.13	pr (w + 1)	114 (112) (anh)	160d			v	s	s	i	s	MeOH, AcOEt, chl s	B2^2, 569
Ω m78	—,—,diethyl ester	CH$_3$CH$_2$CH(CO$_2$C$_2$H$_5$)$_2$	188.23			207–9^{755} 98–9^{12}	1.0047$_4^{20}$	1.4166^{20}	δ	v	v	s		chl s	B2^2, 570
m79	—,ethyl(isopropyl)-, diethyl ester	(CH$_3$)$_2$CHC(C$_2$H$_5$)(CO$_2$C$_2$H$_5$)$_2$	230.31			232–4^{742} 108–10^{11}		1.4280^{25}							B2, 706
m80	—,ethyl(methyl)-	2,2-Butanedicarboxylic acid*. C$_2$H$_5$C(CH$_3$)(CO$_2$H)$_2$	146.14	pr or nd (eth)	122				s	s	s				B2^2, 585
Ω m81	—,ethyl(phenyl)-, diethyl ester	C$_6$H$_5$C(C$_2$H$_5$)(CO$_2$C$_2$H$_5$)$_2$	264.33			170^{19}	1.071$_4^{20}$	1.4896^{25}	i	s	s				B9^2, 630
m82	—,ethylidene-, diethyl ester	CH$_3$CH:C(CO$_2$C$_2$H$_5$)$_2$	186.21	λ^{a1} 225 (3.75)		115–8^{17}	1.0194$_4^{17}$	1.4308^{17}	i	s	s				B2^2, 654
m83	—,(formylamino)-, diethyl ester	Diethyl formamidomalonate. HCONHCH(CO$_2$C$_2$H$_5$)$_2$	203.20	pl (MeOH)	48–9	173–4^{11} 130–2$^{2–3}$									B4^2, 891
m84	—,heptyl-	1,1-Octanedicarboxylic acid*. CH$_3$(CH$_2$)$_6$CH(CO$_2$H)$_2$	202.25	pr (bz-peth)	96.5–8.0				i	v	v	v	i		B2^2, 610
m85	—,hexadecyl-	Cetylmalonic acid. 1,1-Heptadecanedicarboxylic acid*. CH$_3$(CH$_2$)$_{15}$CH(CO$_2$H)$_2$	328.50	nd (lig), lf (aa)	121–2				i	δ	v		v^h	aa v^h lig s^h peth δ	B2^2, 627
m86	—,—,diethyl ester	CH$_3$(CH$_2$)$_{15}$CH(CO$_2$C$_2$H$_5$)$_2$	384.61	amor	(i) 25.1 (ii) 12.7	238–40^{14} 204–8^2		1.4433^{20}	i	s					B2^1, 299
m87	—,hexyl-, diethyl ester	1,1-Heptanedicarboxylic acid. CH$_3$(CH$_2$)$_5$CH(CO$_2$C$_2$H$_5$)$_2$	244.34			268–70 143^{15}	0.9577$_4^{21}$	1.4278^{21}	i	s	s	s	s	os s	B2^2, 604
Ω m88	—,hydroxy-	Tartronic acid. HOCH(CO$_2$H)$_2$	120.06	pr (w + 1)	156–8d (rapid htng) 141–2 (slow htng) (anh)	sub			s	s	δ				B3, 415
m89	—,—,diethyl ester	HOCH(CO$_2$C$_2$H$_5$)$_2$	176.17		–2.5	222–5 121^{15}	1.152^{15}			s	s	s	s	os s	B3^1, 148
m90	—,—,dimethyl ester	HOCH(CO$_2$CH$_3$)$_2$	148.13	cr (eth-peth)	45	122^{19}			s	s	v	s	s	chl v os s peth δ	B3^3, 905

For explanations, symbols and abbreviations see beginning of table. For structural formulas see end of table.

No.	Name	Synonyms and Formula	Mol. wt.	Color, crystalline form, specific rotation and λ_{max} (log ε)	m.p. °C	b.p. °C	Density	n_D	w	al	eth	ace	bz	other solvents	Ref
	Malonic acid														
m91	—,(2-hydroxy-cyclohexyl)- lactone, monoethyl ester	. . . .	212.25	pa ye	. . . .	199[30] (195[10])	1.0735[17]	. . . .							B18[2], 322
Ω m92	—,hydroxy-(methyl)-	α-Isomalic acid. $CH_3COH(CO_2H)_2$	134.09		142d	170d			v	v	v				B3, 440
m93	—,isobutyl-	$(CH_3)_2CHCH_2CH(CO_2H)_2$	160.17	cr (bz)	115d (108)	d			v	v	v				B2[1], 284
Ω m94	—,—,diethyl ester .	$(CH_3)_2CHCH_2CH(CO_2C_2H_5)_2$	216.28			255 119–20[16]	0.9804[20]	1.4236[20]	i	v	v		. . .	chl s	B2, 683
Ω m95	—,isopropyl-, diethyl ester	$(CH_3)_2CHCH(CO_2C_2H_5)_2$	202.25			215[760] 107–9[18]	0.9970[20]	1.4188[21]	δ	v	v		. . .	chl s	B2[2], 586
m96	—,isopropylidene-. .	$(CH_3)_2C{:}C(CO_2H)_2$	144.14	cr (ace-chl)	170–1	d					s			alk v chl i	B2[1], 312
m97	—,—,diethyl ester .	$(CH_3)_2C{:}C(CO_2C_2H_5)_2$	200.24			175–8 140–1[20]	1.0282[18]	1.4486[17]			s	s	. . .	CCl_4 s	B2[2], 661
Ω m98	—,methyl-	1,1-Ethanedicarboxylic acid*. Isosuccinic acid. $CH_3CH(CO_2H)_2$	118.09	nd (AcOEt-bz), pr (eth-bz)	135d	. . . .	1.455[20]	. . . .	v	v	v		δ	aa v AcOEt s	B2[2], 562
Ω m99	—,—,diethyl ester .	Ethyl isosuccinate. $CH_3CH(CO_2C_2H_5)_2$	174.20	$\lambda^{MeOH-KOH}$ 268 (2.0)	. . . .	201 94[16]	1.0225[20]	1.4126[20]	δ	v	v	s	. . .	chl s	B2[2], 563
m100	—,—,dimethyl ester	Methyl isosuccinate. $CH_3CH(CO_2CH_3)_2$	146.14			176.5[761]	1.0977[20]	1.4128[20]	δ	∞	∞	s	. . .	chl s	B2[2], 562
m101	—,(3-methyl-butyl)-, diethyl ester	Ethyl isoamylmalonate. $(CH_3)_2CHCH_2CH_2CH(CO_2C_2H_5)_2$	230.31			240–2[760] 137.5[19]	0.9580[25]	1.4255[25]	i	v	v	v	s		B2[2], 599
m102	—,nitro-, mono-amide mononitrile	Cyanonitroacetamide. Ful-minuric acid. $NCCH(NO_2)CONH_2$	129.08	pr (al)	145 exp (136–49)				s	s	δ		i	chl, lig i	B2[1], 258
m103	—,octyl-	1,1-Nonanedicarboxylic acid*. $CH_3(CH_2)_7CH(CO_2H)_2$	216.28	pr (bz-peth)	116		1.173[17]		s[h]	s	s	s	s[h]	chl s[h]	B2[2], 613
Ω m104	—,oxo-, hydrate . . .	Mesoxalic acid. Dihydroxy-malonic acid. $(HO)_2C(CO_2H)_2$	136.06	dlq nd (w)	120–1				v	v	v				B3[2], 472
Ω m105	—,—,diethyl ester .	Ethyl mesoxalate. $OC(CO_2C_2H_5)_2$	174.16	pa ye gr oil	ca −30	208–10[220] 105[19]	1.1419[16]	1.4310[22]	v	s	v		. . .	chl s CS_2 i	B3[1], 267
m106	—,—,diethyl ester hydrate	Ethyl dihydroxymalonate. $(HO)_2C(CO_2C_2H_5)_2$	192.17	pl (bz)	57	ca. 200			s	s	v	s	s	chl s lig δ CS_2 i	B3[2], 474
m107	—,—,diethyl ester, oxime	Ethyl isonitrosomalonate. $HON{:}C(CO_2C_2H_5)_2$	189.17		172[12] 151[4.8]		1.1821[18]	1.4544[18]	i	s	v	v	s	os ∞, alk s	B3[2], 475
Ω m108	—,pentyl-, diethyl ester	$CH_3(CH_2)_4CH(CO_2C_2H_5)_2$	230.31			134–6[14]	0.9652[20]	1.4253[20]	i	v	v		. . .		B2[2], 597
m109	—,(3-pentyl)-, diethyl ester	Ethyl sec-amylmalonate. $(C_2H_5)_2CHCH(CO_2C_2H_5)_2$	230.31			130[16]		1.4291[20]	i	v	v		. . .		B2[3], 1781
Ω m111	—,phenyl-, diethyl ester	$C_6H_5CH(CO_2C_2H_5)_2$	236.27		16–7	205δd 168[12]	1.0950[20]	1.4977[20]	i	s		s			B9[2], 615
m112	—,—,dimethyl ester	$C_6H_5CH(CO_2CH_3)_2$	208.22	cr (lig)	51	145–7[13]			. . .	s	s			lig δ[h]	B9[2], 615
m113	—,—,dinitrile	$C_6H_5CH(CN)_2$	142.16	cr (dil al)	70–1	152–3[21]			δ	v	δ v[h]			lig δ	B9[2], 616
m114	—,—,monoethyl ester mononitrile	Ethyl phenylcyanoacetate. $C_6H_5CH(CN)CO_2C_2H_5$	189.22	oil		275δd 165[20]	1.0912[20]	1.5012[25]	i	∞	∞	v	v	os ∞	B9[2], 615
m115	—,(phenyl-amino)-, diethyl ester	Ethyl anilinomalonate. $C_6H_5NHCH(CO_2C_2H_5)_2$	251.29	cr (al or lig)	45				i	v	v		v	CS_2, chl v	B12[1], 271
m116	—,phthalimido-, diethyl ester	. . . .	305.29	pr (al)	74				δ	v[h]	s	v	v	chl v CS_2 s peth δ	B21[1], 379
m117	—,(4-phthali-midobutyl)-, diethyl ester	. . . .	361.40	nd (peth)	46				i		s	v	v	peth s[h]	B21, 489
m118	—,propyl-	1,1-Butanedicarboxylic acid*. $CH_3CH_2CH_2CH(CO_2H)_2$	146.14	pl (bz)	96–7.5	d			v	s	s		δ	chl s	B2[2], 581
Ω m119	—,—,diethyl ester	$CH_3CH_2CH_2CH(CO_2C_2H_5)_2$	202.25	. . . .		221–1.5[767] 114[22]	0.9873[20]	1.4197[20]	δ	v	v		. . .		B2[2], 582
—	**Maltobiose**	see **Maltose**													
—	**Maltol**	see **4-Pyrone, 3-hydroxy-2-methyl-**													
m120	**α-Maltose,** (pyranose form) anhydrous	Glucose-4-α-glucoside. Maltobiose	342.30	nd (abs al) $[\alpha]_D +140.7$ (w, c = 10)	160 5	. . . .			s	i	i		i		B31, 386
Ω m121	—,monohydrate. . .	$C_{12}H_{22}O_{11} \cdot H_2O$. See m120	360.32	nd (w), $[\alpha]_D^{20}$ +111.7 → +130.4 (c = 4) (mut)	102–3	. . . .	1.540	. . . .	v	δ	i				B31, 386

For explanations, symbols and abbreviations see beginning of table. For structural formulas see end of table.

Malvidine chloride

No.	Name	Synonyms and Formula	Mol. wt.	Color, crystalline form, specific rotation and λ_{max} (log ε)	m.p. °C	b.p. °C	Density	n_D	w	al	eth	ace	bz	other solvents	Ref.
Ω m122	Malvidine chloride	Syringidine chloride. $C_{17}H_{15}ClO_7$.	366.76	rh ta or pr (al-aq HCl + 1w) λ^{al-HCl} 560 (1.77)	>300	....	....	....	δ	s	...	...	...	MeOH s (red)	B18[2], 247
—	Mandelic acid	see Acetic acid, hydroxy-(phenyl)-													
—	l-Mandelo-nitrile-β-gentio-bioside	see Neoamygdalin													
m123	Mannitane........	3,6(1,4)-Anhydro-D-mannitol.	164.16	(i) amor (ii) pl $[\alpha]_D^{20}$ −26.2 (w)	146–7 (137)	....	....	....	v	(i) s (ii) i	i	...	i	....	B1[1], 284
—	Mannite........	see Mannitol													
Ω m124	Mannitol (D)......	D-Mannite.	182.18	rh nd or pr (w) $[\alpha]_D^5$ −0.49 (w)	168	295[3.5] sub 130	1.489[20]$_4$	1.3330	v	δ^h	i	...	...	Py δ	B1[3], 2392
m125	—(DL)..........	α-Acritol. $C_6H_{14}O_6$. See m124	182.18	cr (al)	168	....	....	....	s^h	δ	...	...	...	....	B1[3], 2405
m126	—(L)..........	L-Mannite. $C_6H_{14}O_6$. See m124	182.18	nd (al)	163–4	....	....	....	v	δ	...	...	...	MeOH δ^h	B1[3], 2405
m127	—,hexanitrate(D)..	Manexin. Nitranitol. Nitro-mannitol. $C_6H_8N_6O_{18}$. See m124	452.17	nd (al), $[\alpha]_{546}^{22}$ +46.8 (ClCH₂CH₂Cl, c = 0.33)	112–3	120 exp	1.82[20] 1.604[0]		i	s^h	s^h	...	s^h	aa s	B1[3], 2404
—	—,1,4:3,6-dianhydro-(D)	see Isomannide													
m128	Mannoheptose-(d, α)	....	210.19	nd (al), $[\alpha]_D^{20}$ +85 to +68.6 (w, c = 10) (mut)	134–5	....	....	....	v	δ	...	...	...	....	B31, 361
m129	—(d, β), mono-hydrate	....	244.20	cr (w +1), $[\alpha]_D^{20}$ +45.7	83	....	....	....	s	δ	...	...	...	....	B31, 362
m132	Mannonic acid, γ-lactone(D)	....	178.14	nd (96 % al), pr (abs al) $[\alpha]_D^{20}$ +54 (w, c = 2)	151	....	....	....	v	δ^h	...	...	i	MeOH δ	B18[1], 407
m133	—,—(L).........	$C_6H_{10}O_6$. See m132	178.14	rh nd (w) $[\alpha]_D$ −51.8	151	....	....	....	v	δ	...	...	...	....	B18[2], 199
m134	Mannosaccharic acid, γ,γ′-di-lactone(d)	....	174.11	nd (w +2), $[\alpha]_D^{23}$ +202 (w) $\lambda^{aq\,NaOH}$ 263 (3.72)	190d	....	....	....	δ v^h	s^h	i	...	...	....	B19[2], 266
m135	—,—(l).........	$C_6H_6O_6$. See m134	174.11	nd (w or al) $[\alpha]_D^{20}$ −202.5 (w)	183–5d (anh) 68 (hyd)	....	....	....	s v^h	δ	i	...	...	....	B19[2], 266
Ω m136	Mannose(D)......	Carubinose. Seminose	180.16	nd or orh pr (al or aa) $[\alpha]_D^{20}$ −17 to +14.6 (w, p = 3) (mut) λ^w <220	132d	....	1.539[20]$_4$	....	v	δ	i	...	i	MeOH δ	B31, 284
m137	—(DL)..........	$C_6H_{12}O_6$. See m136	180.16	cr (al)	132–3	....	....	....	v	δ	i	...	i	MeOH δ	B31, 294
m138	—(L)..........	$C_6H_{12}O_6$. See m136	180.16	cr (al) $[\alpha]_D$ +14 → −14 (mut)	132	....	....	....	v	δ	i	...	i	MeOH δ	B31, 293
m139	—,phenyl-hydrazone(D)	$C_{12}H_{18}N_2O_5$. See m136	270.29	ye pr (w), nd (al), $[\alpha]_D$ +26.3 → +33.8 (Py) (mut)	199–200	....	....	....	i s^h	s^h	...	...	i	....	B31, 290
m140	—,—(L)..........	$C_{12}H_{18}N_2O_5$. See m136	270.29	ye pr (w)	195	....	....	....	i s^h	s^h	...	...	i	....	B31, 294
m141	Mannuronic acid(D, α)	....	194.14	hyg nd (al-eth) $[\alpha]_D^{25}$ +16 → −6 (w) (mut)	120–30d	....	....	....	s	...	i	...	i	....	C27, 3451
m142	—(β)..........	$C_6H_{10}O_7$. See m141	194.14	cr (w +½, w-ace-eth) $[\alpha]_D^{25}$ −47.9 → −23.9 (w) (mut)	165–7	....	....	....	s	...	i	...	i	....	C27, 3457
—	Maraniol........	see Coumarin, 7-ethoxy-4-methyl-													
—	Maretine........	see Semicarbazide, 1(3-tolyl)-													
—	Margaraldehyde...	see Heptadecanal*													
—	Margaric acid	see Heptadecanoic acid*													
m144	Matrine	Sophocarpidine. $C_{15}H_{24}N_2O$.	248.37	(4 forms) α: nd or pl, $[\alpha]_D^{15}$ +40.93 (w) β: orh pr $[\alpha]_D^{19}$ −28.73 (w) γ: liq δ: pr or lf (peth)	α 76–7 β 87 δ 84	γ223[6]	γ1.088[20]$_4$	γ1.52865[85.4]	v s δ^h	s	s	v	CS₂, chl v peth δ	B24[2], 58

For explanations, symbols and abbreviations see beginning of table. For structural formulas see end of table.

No.	Name	Synonyms and Formula	Mol. wt.	Color, crystalline form, specific rotation and λ_{max} (log ε)	m.p. °C	b.p. °C	Density	n_D	w	al	eth	ace	bz	other solvents	Ref.
	Meconic acid														
Ω m145	Meconic acid	3-Hydroxy-γ-pyrone-2,6-dicarboxylic acid.	200.11	rh pl (w or dil HCl + 3w), pr (con HCl + 1w) λ^w 212 (4.2), 235 (4.15), 305 (3.95)	−w at 100	d at 120	....	....	δ v^h	s	δ	δ	s	MeOH δ	B18[2], 372
m146	Meconidine	$C_{21}H_{23}NO_4$	353.42	ye amor	58	....			i	s	s	s	s	chl, peth s	M, 641
m147	Meconin	6,7-Dimethoxyphthalide. Opianyl.	194.19	wh nd (w) λ^{al} 213 (4.40), 308 (3.58)	102–3	155 sub			s^h δ	s	s	s	s	chl, aa s	B18[2], 62
m148	Medicagenic acid	2β,3β-Dihydroxy-Δ[12]-oleanene-23,28-dioic acid. $C_{30}H_{46}O_6$.	502.70	pr or nd $[\alpha]_D^{25} + 106$	352–3	....			i	δ^h	δ	...			Am 76, 2271
m149	—, diacetate	$C_{34}H_{50}O_8$. See m148	586.78	mcl, $[\alpha]_D^{22}$ +92 (chl)	210–2 (207)		1.190_{25}^{25}		i^h	δ^h	i				Am 79, 5292
m150	Melam	$C_6H_8N_{11}$	235.21	pw					i	δ				ac s	B3[2], 121
Ω m151	Melamine	Cyanurotriamide. Cyanuramide. 2,4,6-Triamino-1,3,5-triazine*.	126.12	mcl pr (w) $\lambda^{0.1N HCl}$ 235 (4.01) $\lambda^{w, \rho H = 7}$ 236 (3.4)	354d (cor)	sub	1.573^{14}	1.872^{20}	δ v^h	δ^h	i	...			B26[2], 132
—	Melaniline	see Guanidine, 1,3-diphenyl-													
m152	Melene	$C_{30}H_{60}$	420.82	nd (ace), cr (peth)	62–3	380	0.9037_{25}^{25}	1.4228^{90}	i	δ^h	δ^h	δ^h	δ	to δ	B1[3], 885
m153	Melezitose	Melizitose. $C_{18}H_{32}O_{16}$	504.45	cr (w + 2) $[\alpha]_D^{20}$ +88 (w, c = 4)	153–4 (anh)		1.5565^0		s	δ	i	...	i	peth i	B31, 466
m154	Melibiose(α)	Glucose-6-α-galactoside. $C_{12}H_{22}O_{11}$.	342.30	amor (anh) $[\alpha]^{15}$ +145.8 → +141.6 (w, c = 2) (mut)					v	δ	i	...	i	peth i	B31, 422
m155	—(β), dihydrate	$C_{12}H_{22}O_{11}$.2H_2O. See m154	378.33	mcl cr (w + 2) $[\alpha]_D^{20}$ +111.7 → +129.5 (w, c = 4) (mut)	84–5	....			v	δ	i	...	i	MeOH s	B31, 421
—	Melilotic acid	see Propanoic acid, 3(2-hydroxyphenyl)-*													
—	Melitotol	see Coumarin, 3,4-dihydro-													
—	Melissic acid	see Hentriacontanoic acid*													
—	Melitoxin	see Dicoumarol													
—	Mellitene	see Benzene, hexamethyl-*													
—	Mellitic acid	see Benzenehexacarboxylic acid*													
—	Mellophanic acid	see 1,2,3,4-Benzenetetracarboxylic acid*													
—	Menadione	see 1,4-Naphthoquinone, 2-methyl-*													
Ω m157	p-Menthane(cis)	Hexahydro-p-cymene. 1-Isopropyl-4-methylcyclohexane.	140.27	λ^{iso} 220 (−0.67), 250 (−1.38)	−89.84	170.9^{725}	0.8039_4^{20}	1.4431^{20}	i	v	v	...	s	peth s	B5[2], 26
Ω m158	—(trans)	$C_{10}H_{20}$. See m157	140.27	λ^{iso} 220 (−1.15), 250 (−2.40)	....	170.6^{760} (161) 58.5^{15}	0.7928_4^{20}	1.4366^{20}	i	v	v	...	s	lig s	B5[2], 27
—	Menthanone	see Menthone													
m159	Δ[3]-p-Menthene(d) (one form)	1-Isopropyl-4-methylcyclohexane.	138.25	$[\alpha]_D^{20}$ +115.6 (undil)	....	168	0.8118_4^{20}	1.4524^{20}	i	s	s	...	s	aa s	B5[2], 52
m160	—(d) (one form)	$C_{10}H_{18}$. See m159	138.25	$[\alpha]_D$ +29.6 → +54.4 (mut)	....	167–8	0.8078_4^{20}	....	i	s	s	...	s	peth s	B5[3], 237
Ω m161	—(dl)	$C_{10}H_{18}$. See m159	138.25		168^{751} 60.5^{12}		0.8069_4^{20}	1.4503^{20}	i	s	s	...	s	peth s	B5[2], 53
m162	—(l)	$C_{10}H_{18}$. See m159	138.25	$[\alpha]_D$ −13.46 (al)	....	167–8	0.8112_{19}^{19}	1.4511^{20}	i	s	s	...	s	peth s	B5, 89
—	Δ[8(9)]-p-Menthenol	see Isopulegol													
—	Menthenone	see Piperitone													
m163	Menthol(d)	3-p-Menthanol. Hexahydrothymol.	156.27	$[\alpha]_D$ +49.2 (al, c = 5)	42–3	$103–4^9$			s	s	s	s	s	os s	B6[2], 49
m164	—(dl)	$C_{10}H_{20}O$. See m163	156.27	nd (peth)	(i) 28 (ii) 38	216^{760} $103–5^{16}$	0.904_{15}^{15}	1.4615^{20}	i	v	v	v	v	os, chl v	B6[2], 49
Ω m165	—(l)	$C_{10}H_{20}O$. See m163	156.27	nd (MeOH) $[\alpha]_D^{20}$ −48 (al, c = 2.5)	(i) 44 (ii) 35 (iii) 33 (iv) 31	216.4^{760} 111^{20}	0.904_{15}^{15}	1.460^{22}	δ	v	v	v	v	peth, aa s chl v	B6[2], 39
Ω m166	—,3-methylbutanoate	Menthyl isovalerate. $C_{15}H_{28}O_2$. See m163	240.39	$[\alpha]_D^{20}$ −64.02 (bz, c = 10)	....	129^9	0.9089^{15}	1.4486^{20}	i	s	...	...	...		B6[1], 22
m167	Menthone(d)	2-Isopropyl-5-methylcyclohexanone. d-3-p-Menthanone.	154.26	$[\alpha]_D^{18}$ +24.85 λ^{al} 236 (1.40), 287 (1.38)	....	204^{750} 85^{14}	0.8963_{20}^{20}	1.4503^{20}	δ	s	s	s	∞	aa s	B7[1], 35

For explanations, symbols and abbreviations see beginning of table. For structural formulas see end of table.

No.	Name	Synonyms and Formula	Mol. wt.	Color, crystalline form, specific rotation and λ_{max} (log ε)	m.p. °C	b.p. °C	Density	n_D	Solubility						Ref.
									w	al	eth	ace	bz	other solvents	

Menthone

No.	Name	Synonyms and Formula	Mol. wt.	Color...	m.p.	b.p.	Density	n_D	w	al	eth	ace	bz	other	Ref.
Ω m168	—(dl)	$C_{10}H_{18}O$. See m167	154.26	....	....	210.5^{760}	0.911^0	....	δ	s	s	s	∞	aa s	**B7²**, 41
m169	—(l)	$C_{10}H_{18}O$. See m167	154.26	$[\alpha]_D^{20} -29.6$ λ^{hx} 293 (1.3)	−6.6	209.6^{760} 96^{20}	0.8954_4^{20}	1.4505^{20}	δ	∞	∞	s	∞	CS_2 ∞	**B7¹**, 35
—	Mepheridine	see 4-Piperidinecarboxylic acid, 1-methyl-4-phenyl-, ethyl ester, hydrochloride													
—	Mesaconic acid	see Fumaric acid, methyl-													
m170	Mescaline	Mezcaline. 3,4,5-Tri-methoxy-β-phenethylamine. $C_{11}H_{17}NO_3$.	211.26	cr λ^{al} 225 sh (4.2), 270 (3.2)	35–6	180^{12} $120-$ $30^{0.05}$	....	....	s	s	i	...	s	chl s lig s peth i	**B13²**, 521
—	Mesidine	see Benzene, 2-amino-1,3,5-trimethyl-*													
—	Mesitoic acid.....	see Benzoic acid, 2,4,6-trimethyl-													
—	Mesitol	see Benzene, 2-hydroxy-1,3,5-trimethyl-*													
—	Mesitylaldehyde ...	see Benzaldehyde, 2,4,6-trimethyl-													
—	Mesitylene........	see Benzene, 1,3,5-trimethyl-*													
—	Mesitylenic acid ...	see Benzoic acid, 3,5-dimethyl-													
—	Mesityl oxide	see 3-Penten-2-one, 4-methyl-*													
—	Mesorcinol	see Benzene, 2,4-dihydroxy-1,3,5-trimethyl-*													
—	Mesoxalic acid	see Malonic acid, oxo-													
—	Mestilbol.........	see 3-Hexene, 3(4-hydroxyphenyl)-4(4-methoxyphenyl)-*													
—	Metacetaldehyde, (tetramer)	see Metaldehyde II													
m171	Metacrolein.......	2,4,6-Triethenyl-1,3,5-trioxane.	168.20	pl (al)	50 (45)	170^{760}	....	....	i δ^h	s	s	...	...		**B1¹**, 378
—	Metahemipinic acid	see Phthalic acid, 4,5-dimethoxy-													
Ω m172	Metaldehyde......	Metacetaldehyde. $(C_2H_4O)_{4-6}$	$(44.05)_{4-6}$	tetr nd or pr (al)	246.2 (sealed tube)	sub $112-5$	....	....	i	δ^h	δ^h	i	δ	chl δ, s^h CS_2, aa i	**B1²**, 671
m173	Metaldehyde II	Metacetaldehyde (tetramer).	176.22	....	47	710^{760} δd 65^{15}	....	....	δ	s	s	s	s	os s	**B1³**, 2640
m174	Metameconin	5,6-Dimethoxyphthalide.	194.19	cr (dil al) λ^{al} 220 (4.38), 258 (3.97), 294 (3.86)	155–7	....	....	....	i s^h		δ	...	...	KOH v	**B18²**, 62
—	Metanilic acid	see Benzenesulfonic acid, 3-amino-*													
—	Methacrylic acid ...	see Propenoic acid, 2-methyl-*													
—	Methadone	see 3-Heptanone, 6-dimethylamino-4,4-diphenyl-*													
—	Methanal*........	see Formaldehyde													
Ω m175	Methane*	Marsh gas. CH_4	16.04	gas	−182.48	$−164^{760}$	0.466^{-164} 0.5547^0	....	s	s	s	δ	s	MeOH, to s	**B1³**, 1
m176	—,amino-*	Methylamine. CH_3NH_2	31.06	gas λ^{gas} 190.5 (3.51), 215 (2.77)	−93.5	$−6.3^{760}$	0.699^{-11} 0.6628^{20}	....	v	s	∞	s	s	....	**B4²**, 546
Ω m177	—,—,hydrochloride	$CH_3NH_2 \cdot HCl$	67.52	dlq tetr ta (al)	227–8	sub^{760} $225-$ 30^{15}	....	....	s	s	i	i	...	AcOEt, chl i	**B4³**, 90
Ω m178	—,amino-(diphenyl)-*	Benzhydrylamine. $(C_6H_5)_2CHNH_2$	183.26	hex pl	34	304^{763} (288) 176^{23}	1.0635_{20}^{20}	1.5963^{22}	δ	s	s	...	...		**B12²**, 768
—	—,amino(2-furyl)-	see Furan, 2(aminomethyl)-													
m180	—,aminooxy-, hydrochloride.	Methoxyamine hydrochloride. O-Methylhydroxylamine hydrochloride. $CH_3ONH_2 \cdot HCl$	83.52	pr	149	....	....	....	s	s				s	**B1²**, 275
m181	—,(2-amino-phenyl)-bis(4-aminophenyl)-*	$C_{19}H_{19}N_3$. See m312	289.38	cr (al)	165	....	....	....	s^h	v	i	...	...	lig i	**B13**, 311
m182	—,(3-amino-phenyl)-bis(4-aminophenyl)-*	$C_{19}H_{19}N_3$. See m312	289.38	nd (eth or eth-lig)	150	....	....	....	i	s	δ	...	...	lig i	**B13**, 312
m183	—,(3-amino-phenyl)-diphenyl*	3-Aminotritan. $C_{19}H_{17}N$. See m312	259.36	nd (eth)	120	....	....	....	i	s	s	...	...		**B12²**, 790

For explanations, symbols and abbreviations see beginning of table. For structural formulas see end of table.

No.	Name	Synonyms and Formula	Mol. wt.	Color, crystalline form, specific rotation and λ_{max} (log ε)	m.p. °C	b.p. °C	Density	n_D	w	al	eth	ace	bz	other solvents	Ref.
	Methane														
m184	—,(4-amino-phenyl)-diphenyl-*	4-Aminotritan. p-Benzhydrylaniline. $C_{19}H_{17}N$. See m312	259.36	pr or lf (eth, lig), ta (path), pr (bz + l)	84.5	ca. 248[12]	....	....	i	...	s	...	s	lig s	B12[2], 790
m185	—,(3-amino-phenyl)phenyl-*	3-Aminoditan. m-Benzyl-aniline. $C_{13}H_{13}N$. See m271	183.26	cr (lig)	46									lig s	B12, 1323
m186	—,(4-amino-phenyl)phenyl-*	4-Aminoditan. p-Benzyl-aniline. $C_{13}H_{13}N$. See m271	183.26	mcl (lig)	34–5	300	1.038[55]	....	i	v	v	...	v	lig s	B12, 1323
—	—,biphenylyl-(phenyl)-	see Biphenyl, benzyl-													
m187	—,bis(4-amino-cyclohexyl)-(cis, cis)	4,4'-Methylenebiscyclo-hexylamine.	210.37	....	60.5–1.9	141[2]		1.5014[27] (mixture of isomers)	i						Am 73, 741
m188	—,—(cis, trans)	$C_{13}H_{26}N_2$. See m187	210.37	cr	36–7	127–8[1.2]	0.9608[25]	1.5046[25]	i						Am 73, 741
m189	—,—(trans, trans)	$C_{13}H_{26}N_2$. See m187	210.37	cr (peth)	64–5.4	130–1[0.8]		1.5032[25]	i						Am 73, 741
m190	—,bis(4-amino-2-nitrophenyl)-	$C_{13}H_{12}N_4O_4$. See m271	288.27	og pl (al)	205					v^h	δ	...	δ	aa v lig δ	B13[2], 113
m191	—,bis(4-amino-3-nitrophenyl)-	$C_{13}H_{12}N_4O_4$. See m271	288.27	red nd (PhOH-al)	232–3					i			i	$PhNO_2$ s^h chl i	B13[2], 113
Ω m192	—,bis(4-amino-phenyl)-*	4,4'-Diaminoditan. $C_{13}H_{14}N_2$. See m271	198.27	pl or nd (w), pl (bz)	92–3	398–9[768] 257[18]			δ	v	v		v		B13[2], 111
m193	—,bis(4-amino-phenyl)phenyl-*	4,4'-Diaminotritan. $C_{19}H_{18}N_2$. See m312	274.37	pr (bz or eth)	139–40				δ^h	v	v			chl, lig s	B13[2], 134
Ω m194	—,bis(3 carboxy-4-hydroxy-phenyl)-*	5,5'-Methylenedisalicylic acid.	288.26	nd (bz)	243–4				δ	s	s	s	δ		B10[2], 397
m195	—,bis(5-chloro-2-hydroxyphenyl)-*	Dichlorophene. Dihydroxane $C_{13}H_{10}Cl_2O_2$. See m271	269.13	cr (bz, to, path)	177–8				i	s		s			B6[3], 5406
m196	—,bis(4-chloro-phenoxy)-*	Neotran. Oxythane	269.13	....	69.7–70.2	189–94[6]			i	δ	v	v	s		Am 73, 1872
m197	—,bis(4-dimethyl-aminophenyl)-*	$C_{17}H_{22}N_2$. See m271	254.38	pl or ta (al, lig)	91–2	390d 182–5[3]			i	δ s^h	v	...	v	CS_2 v ac s	B13[2], 111
m198	—,bis(4-dimethyl-aminophenyl)(4-aminophenyl)-*	N,N,N',N'-Tetramethyl-p-leucaniline. $C_{23}H_{27}N_3$. See m312	345.49	(al)	151–2										B13, 314
m198[1]	—,[2,4-bis(di-methylamino)phenyl]diphenyl-*	$C_{23}H_{26}N_2$. See m312	330.48	pl (peth)	122–3				i	s	s	s	s	os s	B13, 273
m199	—,bis(4-dimethyl-aminophenyl)(2-hydroxy-phenyl)-*	$C_{23}H_{26}N_2O$. See m312	346.48	nd (al)	127–8				δ	δ v^h			v	lig δ	B13[2], 440
m200	—,bis(4-dimethyl-aminophenyl)(3-hydroxy-phenyl)-*	$C_{23}H_{26}N_2O$. See m312	346.48	cr (al)	149				δ	δ			v		B13[2], 440
m201	—,bis(4-dimethyl-aminophenyl)-(4-hydroxy-phenyl)-*	$C_{23}H_{26}N_2O$. See m312	346.48	cr (al)	165				δ	v^h			v	alk s lig δ	B13[2], 440
m202	—,bis(4-dimethyl-aminophenyl)-phenyl-	Leucomalachite green. $C_{23}H_{26}N_2$. See m312	330.48	nd or lf (al, bz)	102 (94)				i	δ	v		v	to v lig δ	B13[2], 135
Ω m203	—,bis(2,4-dinitro-phenyl)-*	2,2',4,4'-Tetranitroditan. $C_{13}H_8N_4O_8$. See m271	348.24	ye pr (aa)	181					i	i	...	δ	alk s aa δ	B5[2], 503
m204	—,bis(3-formyl-4-hydroxy-phenyl)-	5,5'-Methylene-disalicylaldehyde. $C_{15}H_{12}O_4$. See m271	256.26	pa ye (aa or ace)	142–3									aa s^h	B8, 436
m205	—,bis(3-hydroxy-phenyl)-*	m,m'-Methylenediphenol. $C_{13}H_{12}O_2$. See m271	200.24	nd (dil aa)	102–3	230–40[3]			s^h	v	v		δ	aa v lig δ	B6, 995
m206	—,bis(4-hydroxy-phenyl)-*	p,p'-Methylenediphenol. $C_{13}H_{12}O_2$. See m271	200.24	lf or nd (w) λ^{al} 225 (4.7), 280 (3.6)	162–3	sub				s	s			chl, alk s CS_2 i	B6[2], 964
m207	—,bis(2-hydroxy-3,5,6-trichloro-phenyl)-*	Gamophen. Hexa-chlorophen. Hexosan. $C_{13}H_6Cl_6O_2$. See m271	406.91	nd (bz, to)	166–7				i	s	s	s		dil alk, chl s	B6[3], 5407
m209	—,bis(2-nitro-phenyl)-*	2,2'-Dinitroditan. $C_{13}H_{10}N_2O_4$. See m271	258.24	cr	83.5					s	s			lig i	B5[3], 1796
m210	—,bis(3-nitro-phenyl)-*	3,3'-Dinitroditan. $C_{13}H_{10}N_2O_4$. See m271	258.24	lf (aa)	175.5					s	δ	...	v^h	aa v^h	B5[3], 503
m211	—,bis(4-nitro-phenyl)-*	4,4'-Dinitroditan. $C_{13}H_{10}N_2O_4$. See m271	258.24	nd (bz, peth, aa)	188 (184)					i	δ	v^h		aa v^h	B5, 595
—	—,bis(phenyl-imino)-*	see Carbodiimide, N,N'-diphenyl-													
m212	—,bis(trichloro-silyl)-	$Cl_3SiCH_2SiCl_3$	282.92	....		182.7[745]	1.5567[20]	1.4740[20]		s	v				B1[3], 2587
Ω m213	—,bromo-*	Methyl bromide. CH_3Br	94.94	λ^{gas} 204 (2.26)	–93.6	3.56[760] 64[10]	1.6755[20]₄	1.4218[20]	δ	∞	∞			chl, CS_2 ∞	B1[3], 79

For explanations, symbols and abbreviations see beginning of table. For structural formulas see end of table.

No.	Name	Synonyms and Formula	Mol. wt.	Color, crystalline form, specific rotation and λ_{max} (log ε)	m.p. °C	b.p. °C	Density	n_D	w	al	eth	ace	bz	other solvents	Ref.
	Methane														
Ω m214	—,bromochloro-*	ClCH$_2$Br	129.39	....	−86.5	68.11[760]	1.9344[20]	1.4838[20]	i	s	s	s	s	os s	B1[3], 83
m215	—,bromochloro-dinitro-*	BrCCl(NO$_2$)$_2$	219.38		9.2–9.3	75–6[15]	2.0394[20]	1.4793	...	v					B1[3], 115
m216	—,bromochloro-fluoro-*	BrCHClF	147.38		−115	36.1[756]	1.9771[20]	1.4144[25]	i		s	s	...	chl s	B1[3], 84
Ω m217	—,bromodi-chloro-*	BrCHCl$_2$	163.83		−57.1	90[760]	1.980[20]	1.4964[20]	i	v	v	v	v	chl ∞ os v	B1[3], 84
m218	—,bromodi-fluoro-*	BrCHF$_2$	130.93	$\lambda^{gas} < 208$	−14.5	....	1.55[16]			s	v				B1[3], 83
m219	—,bromodi-fluoronitroso-*	BrCF$_2$(NO)	159.92	bl gas	....	ca. −12[760]									J1953, 2075
m220	—,bromodiiodo-*	BrCHI$_2$	346.74	ye (peth)	60	110[25]			i					peth δ	B1, 72
Ω m221	—,bromo-(diphenyl)-*	Benzhydryl bromide. α-Bromoditan. (C$_6$H$_5$)$_2$CHBr	247.14	tcl (peth)	45	193[26]δd 111[0.3]			d[h]	s			v		B5[2], 502
m222	—,bromofluoro-*	BrCH$_2$F	112.94			18–20				s				chl v	B1[3], 83
m223	—,bromoiodo-*	BrCH$_2$I	220.84			138–41[760]	2.926[17]	1.6410[20]						chl v	B1[3], 99
m224	—,bromonitro-*	BrCH$_2$NO$_2$	139.94			148–9[742] 70–2[45]		1.4880[20]	i	v				alk s	B1[3], 115
Ω m225	—,bromotri-chloro-*	BrCCl$_3$	198.28	λ^{iso} 240 (2.3)	−5.65	104.7[760] 0.6[10]	2.0122[20]	1.5063[20]	i	∞	∞			chl s	B1[3], 85
Ω m226	—,bromotri-fluoro-*	BrCF$_3$	148.92	gas λ^{gas} 208 (1.52)		−59[740]								chl v	B1[3], 83
m227	—,bromotri-nitro-*	BrC(NO$_2$)$_3$	229.94	....	17–8	56[10]	2.0313[20]	1.4808[20]	δ	s	s			chl s	B1[3], 116
Ω m228	—,chloro-*	Methyl chloride. CH$_3$Cl	50.49	gas	−97.73	−24.2[760]	0.9159[20]	1.3661[−10] 1.3389[20]	s	s	∞	∞	∞	chl, aa ∞	B1[3], 36
m229	—,chlorodi-bromo-*	ClCHBr$_2$	208.29			119–20[748]	2.451[20]	1.5482[20]	i	s	s	s	s	os s	B1[3], 87
Ω m230	—,chlorodi-fluoro-*	Freon 22. ClCHF$_2$	86.47	gas	−146–7 (−160)	−40.8[760]	1.4909[−69]	....	v		s	s		chl s	B1[3], 41
m231	—,chlorodifluoro-nitro-*	ClCF$_2$(NO$_2$)	131.47			25[760]								chl s	J1953, 2075
m232	—,chlorodifluoro-nitroso-*	ClCF$_2$(NO)	115.47	bl gas	....	ca. −35[760]									J1953, 2075
m233	—,chlorodiiodo-*	ClCHI$_2$	302.28		−4	200d[760] 88[30]					s	s	...	chl v	B1, 72
m234	—,chlorodinitro-*	ClCH(NO$_2$)$_2$	140.48			34–6[13]	1.6123[20]	1.4575[20]						alk s	B1[3], 115
Ω m235	—,chloro-(diphenyl)-*	Benzhydryl chloride. α-Chloroditan. (C$_6$H$_5$)$_2$CHCl	202.69	nd	20.5 (18)	173[19] 141[4]	1.1398[20]	1.5959[20]							B5[2], 500
m237	—,chlorofluoro-*	ClCH$_2$F	68.48	gas		−9.1								chl v	B1[3], 41
m238	—,chloroiodo-*	ClCH$_2$I	176.39			109[760]	2.422[20]	1.5822[20]	i	s	s	s	s	chl v liq HF δ	B1[2], 99
m239	—,chloronitro-*	ClCH$_2$NO$_2$	95.49			122–3	1.466[15]		s					alk v	B1[3], 112
m239[1]	—,(4-chloro-phenyl)phenyl-	4-Chloroditan. C$_{13}$H$_{11}$Cl. See m271	202.69		7.5	298[742] 147–8[8]	1.1247[20]		i			s			B5[2], 500
m240	—,chlorotri-bromo-*	ClCBr$_3$	287.19	lf (eth)	55	158–9	2.71[15]		i		s				B1[3], 91
Ω m241	—,chlorotri-fluoro-*	Freon −13. ClCF$_3$	104.46	gas	−181	−81.1[760]									B1[3], 42
m242	—,chlorotri-nitro-*	ClC(NO$_2$)$_3$	185.48		4.5	133–5δd 56[40]	1.6769[20]	1.4500[20]	δ	s	s			chl s	B1[3], 116
Ω m243	—,chloro(tri-phenyl)-*	Trityl chloride. (C$_6$H$_5$)$_3$CCl	278.79	nd or pr (bz-peth) $\lambda^{98\% sulf}$ 430 (4.58)	113–4	310[760] 230–5[20]			i d[h]	δ d[h]	v	s	v	chl, CCl$_4$, CS$_2$ v	B5[2], 615
—	—,cyano-	see **Acetic acid**, nitrile													
m243[1]	—,deuterotri-chloro-	Chloroform-d. CDCl$_3$	120.39		−64.12	61.3–1.5	1.5004[20]	1.4450[20]	i						B1[3], 63
m244	—,diazo-*	Azomethylene. CH$_2$N$_2$	42.04	ye gas λ^{gas} 380 (0.5), 408 (0.5), 435 (0.5)	−145	ca. 0			d	s[h]					B1[2], 650
m245	—,diazo-(diphenyl)-*	(C$_6$H$_5$)$_2$CN$_2$	194.24	bl-red nd (peth)	30–2	exp					s	v	v	v	os v	B7[2], 358
—	—,dibenzoyl-	see **1,3-Propanedione, 1,3-diphenyl-***													
Ω m246	—,dibromo-*	Methylene bromide. CH$_2$Br$_2$	173.85		−52.55	97[760]	2.4970[20]	1.5420[20]	δ	∞	∞	∞	∞		B1[3], 85
Ω m247	—,dibromodi-chloro-*	Br$_2$CCl$_2$	242.74	nd	38 (22)	150.2	2.42[25]		i	s	s	s	s	os s	B1[3], 88
Ω m248	—,dibromodi-fluoro-*	F$_2$CBr$_2$	209.83	λ^{gas} 227 (2.86)		24.5[760]				s	s	s	s		B1[1], 16
m249	—,dibromo-dinitro-*	Br$_2$(CNO$_2$)$_2$	263.84	nd	5.5	158d 77[21]	2.4440[20]	1.5280[20]	i	∞					B1[3], 115
m250	—,dibromo-fluoro-*	FCHBr$_2$	191.84			64.9[757]	2.421[20]	1.4685[20]	i	s	s	s	s	chl s	B1[3], 87
m251	—,dibromoiodo-*	ICHBr$_2$	299.74	pl (peth)	22.5	91[42]								peth δ	B1[3], 99
Ω m252	—,dichloro-*	Methylene chloride. CH$_2$Cl$_2$	84.93	$\lambda^{vap} < 200$	−95.1	40[760]	1.3266[20]	1.4242[20]	δ	∞	∞				B1[2], 13
Ω m253	—,dichlorodi-fluoro-*	Freon 12. Cl$_2$CF$_2$	120.91	$\lambda^{vap} < 200$	−158	−29.8[760]	1.75[−115] 1.1834[57]		s	s	s			aa s	B1, 61

For explanations, symbols and abbreviations see beginning of table. For structural formulas see end of table.

No.	Name	Synonyms and Formula	Mol. wt.	Color, crystalline form, specific rotation and λ_{max} (log ε)	m.p. °C	b.p. °C	Density	n_D	w	al	eth	ace	bz	other solvents	Ref.
	Methane														
m254	—,dichloro-dinitro-*	$Cl_2C(NO_2)_2$	174.93	....	....	121–2.5 46^{20}	1.6124^{20}_4	1.4575^{20}	i	s	s	...	s	chl, CS_2 s	B1[3], 115
Ω m255	—,dichloro-(diphenyl)-*	Benzophenone dichloride. $(C_6H_5)_2CCl_2$	237.13	....	305d	190^{21}	1.235^{18}	....			s	s	s		B5[2], 501
Ω m256	—,dichloro-fluoro-*	Freon 21. $FCHCl_2$	102.92	....	−135	9^{760}	1.405^9	1.3724^9	i	s	s		...	aa, chl s	B1[3], 47
m257	—,dichloroiodo-*	$ICHCl_2$ ..	210.83	....	....	132^{760} 40^{30}	2.392^{20}_4	1.5840^{20}	i	s	s	s	s	chl v	B1[3], 99
m258	—,dichloronitro-*	Cl_2CHNO_2 ..	129.93	....	....	107^{760}	....	....							B1[3], 113
m259	—,difluoro-*	Methylene fluoride. CH_2F_2 ..	52.02	....	−51.6^{760}		0.909^{20}	1.190^{20}	i	s					B1, 59
m260	—,(difluoro-amino)trifluoro-	Perfluoromethylamine. F_3CNF_2	121.01	....	−75^{760}										J1950, 1966
m261	—,difluoroiodo-*	$ICHF_2$	177.92	....	−122	21.6^{760}	3.238^{-19}								B1[3], 98
m262	—,di(2-furyl)-	2-Furfurylfuran	148.17	....	$94^{22.5}$ 75^{13}		1.102^{20}_4	1.5049^{20}	i	s	s	s	...	MeOH s	Am 55, 3302
Ω m263	—,diiodo-*	Methylene iodide. CH_2I_2 ..	267.84	ye nd or lf	6.1	182^{760} 60^{10}	3.3254^{20}_4	1.7425^{20}	δ	s	s	s	s	chl s	B1[2], 99
m264	—,diiodofluoro-*	$FCHI_2$	285.83	pa ye	−34.5	$100-1^{760}$ 50^{50}	3.1969^{22}		δ	s	s	s	s	chl s	B1[3], 102
m265	—,[3(dimethyl-amino)phenyl] [4(dimethyl-amino)phenyl]-*	$C_{23}H_{26}N_2$. See m312	330.48	cr (abs al)	83–4					δ^h	δ^h				B13, 274
m267	—,di(1-naphthyl)-	$C_{10}H_7^\alpha CH_2C_{10}H_7^\alpha$	268.38	pr or nd (al) $\lambda^{liqNH_3-KNH_2}$ 645 (4.9)	109	>360 270^{14}			δ s^h	δ s^h	s		s	chl s peth δ	B5[2], 650
m268	—,di(2-naphthyl)-	$C_{10}H_7^\beta CH_2C_{10}H_7^\beta$	268.38	nd (al or eth)	93								s		B5[1], 360
m269	—,dinitro-*	$CH_2(NO_2)_2$ ..	106.04	ye nd λ^w 360 (4.22)	< −15	100 exp			i δ^h	s	s	...	...		B1[3], 115
m270	—,dinitro-(diphenyl)-*	$(C_6H_5)_2C(NO_2)_2$ ..	258.24	pl (dll al)	79–80				i	v^h	v		v	chl v	B5, 596
Ω m271	—,diphenyl-*	Ditan	168.24	pr nd λ^{al} 260 (2.70), 268.5 (2.61)	25.35	264.3^{760} 125.5^{10}	1.0060^{20}_4	1.5753^{20}	i	s	s	...	s	chl s	B5[2], 498
m272	—,diphenyl(3-tolyl)-	3-Methyltritan	258.37	pr (al or MeOH)	62	354^{706}	1.07^{16}		i	δ	v		v	chl, aa v lig s	B5, 710
m273	—,di(α-pyrryl)-	2,2′-Methylenedipyrrole. 2,2′-Pyrromethane.	146.19	lf or nd (al)	73 (66)	$163-7^{12}$				s	s			lig s s^h	B23, 167
m274	—,disilano-	2-Carbatrisilane. Disilyl-methane. $CH_2(SiH_3)_2$	76.25	....		14.7^{754}	0.6979^4_4	1.4115^4							C48, 5080
m275	—,di(4-tolyl)phenyl-*	4,4′-Dimethyltritan	272.40	nd (MeOH) λ^{al} 270 (4.0), 358 (4.5)	56	$218-20^{12}$			i	s	s		v	chl, CS_2 v aa, lig s	B5[1], 352
m276	—,fluoro-*	Methyl fluoride. CH_3F	34.03	....	−141.8	−78.4^{760}	0.8428^{-60} 0.5786^{20}_0	1.1727^{20}	v	v	v		s	chl s	B1[3], 33
m277	—,fluoroiodo-*	FCH_2I	159.93	....		53.4	2.366^{20}_0	1.4911^{20}	i		s	s	s	chl v	B1[3], 98
m278	—,fluorotri-bromo-*	$FCBr_3$	270.74	....		106^{760}	2.7648^{20}_4	1.5256^{20}	i		s	s	s	chl v	B1[3], 91
m279	—,hydroxyl-amino-*	N-Methylhydroxylamine. CH_3NHOH	47.06	hyg nd	42 (rapid htng) (87–8)	62.5^{13}	1.0003^{20}_4	1.4164^{20}	v	v	δ		δ	MeOH v lig δ	B4[2], 952
m280	—,(2-hydroxy-phenyl)(4-hydroxy-phenyl)-*	2,4′-Dihydroxyditan. $C_{13}H_{12}O_2$. See m271	200.24	nd (dil al, bz or w) λ^{al} 277.5 (3.65)	119–20				δ	v	v		s		B6, 994
Ω m281	—,(4-hydroxy-phenyl)-phenyl-*	4-Benzylphenol. p-Hydroxy-ditan. $C_{13}H_{12}O$. See m271	184.24	nd or pl (al)	84	325–30 198–200^{10}			δ^h	s v^h	s		s	chl, aa, alk s	B6[2], 629
Ω m282	—,iodo-*	Methyl iodide. CH_3I ..	141.94	....	−66.45	42.4^{760}	2.2792^{20}_0	1.5380^{20}	δ	∞	∞	s	s	....	B1[2], 35
m283	—,iodotrichloro-*	$ICCl_3$ ..	245.27	....	142^{760}		2.355^{20}_4	1.5854^{20}	i	s	s	s	s	chl v	B1[3], 99
m284	—,(1-naphthyl)phenyl-*	α-Benzylnaphthalene. $C_{10}H_7^\alpha CH_2C_6H_5$	218.30	mcl lf or ta (al) λ^{al} 273 (3.8), 283 (3.9), 290 (3.75), 312 (2.6)	59	350^{760} 220^{20}	1.166^{17}		i	δ	s		s	CS_2 v chl s	B5[2], 604
m285	—,(2-naphthyl)phenyl-*	β-Benzylnaphthalene. $C_{10}H_7^\beta CH_2C_6H_5$	218.30	mcl pr (al or MeOH)	58	350^{760}	1.176^0		i	δ v^h		...	v	chl s	B5, 690
Ω m286	—,nitro-*	CH_3NO_2 ..	61.04	mcl λ^{al} 260 (1.59)	fr −17 (−28.5)	100.8^{760}	1.1371^{20}_4	1.3817^{20}	s	s	s		s	alk s	B1[2], 40
m287	—,(2-nitro-phenyl) (4-nitro-phenyl)-*	2,4′-Dinitroditan. $C_{13}H_{10}N_2O_4$. See m271	258.24	ye mcl pr (bz)	118				i		δ		δ s^h		B5, 595
m288	—,(3-nitro-phenyl) (4-nitro-phenyl)-*	3,4′-Dinitroditan. $C_{13}H_{10}N_2O_4$. See m271	258.24	nd (al)	103–4				i	δ s^h					B5, 595
m289	—,nitrosotri-fluoro-*	F_3CNO ..	99.01	λ^{chl} 680 (1.3), 700 (1.3)	−197 (−205)	−84^{760} (−93^{760})									B1[3], 105

For explanations, symbols and abbreviations see beginning of table. For structural formulas see end of table.

No.	Name	Synonyms and Formula	Mol. wt.	Color. crystalline form. specific rotation and λ_{max} (log ε)	m.p. °C	b.p. °C	Density	n_D	Solubility						Ref.
									w	al	eth	ace	bz	other solvents	
	Methane														
m290	—,nitrotribromo-*	Bromopicrin. Nitrobromoform. Br_3CNO_2	297.74	pr λ^{peth} (not max) 240 (3.28), 260 (3.00), 300 (1.90)	10.25	exp[760] 89–90[20]	2.7930[20]	1.5790[20]	i	s	s	v	v	aa v	B1[3], 115
m291	—,nitrotrichloro-*	Chloropicrin. Nitrochloroform. Cl_3CNO_2	164.38	λ^{al} 276.5 (1.79)	−64.5	111.84[760] −8.9[10]	1.6566[20]	1.4622[20]	s[h]	∞	...	∞	∞	MeOH, aa ∞	B1[3], 113
m291¹	—,nitrotrifluoro-*	Fluoropicrin. F_3CNO_2	115.01	λ^{gas} 277.5 (1.05)	....	−31.1 (−20)	....	....							J1953, 2075
m292	—,(pentafluorothio)trifluoro-	$F_3C(SF_5)$	196.06	....	....	−20[760]	....	....	i					CS_2 s	J1953, 2372
Ω m293	—,phenyl(3-tolyl)-	m-Benzyltoluene. 3-Methylditan.	182.27	....	(i) −27.83 (ii) −34.46	279.24[760] 120[0.2]	0.99135[20]	1.5712[20]	i	s	s	...	s	aa, chl s	B5, 607
Ω m294	—,phenyl(4-tolyl)-	p-Benzyltoluene. 4-Methylditan.	182.27	λ^{iso} 260.5 (2.77), 266 (2.80), 274.5 (2.75)	−30	286[760] 114–5[3]	0.9976[20]	1.5712[20]	i	s	s	...	s	chl, aa s	B5[2], 511
Ω m295	—,tetrabromo-*	Carbon tetrabromide. CBr_4	331.65	mcl ta (dil al) $\lambda^{Bu'OH}$ 228	α 90–1 β 94.3	α 189–90[760] 102[50]	α 2.9609[100] 3.273[18]	α 1.59419[100]	i	s	s	...	s	CS_2 v chl s liq HF δ	B1[3], 92
Ω m296	—,tetrachloro-*	Carbon tetrachloride. CCl_4	153.82	λ^{vap} <200	−22.99	76.54[760]	1.5940[20]	1.4601[20]	i	s	∞	s	∞	chl ∞	B1[3], 65
Ω m297	—,tetrafluoro-*	Carbon tetrafluoride. CF_4	88.01	....	−150	−129[754]	3.034[0]	....	δ				s	chl s	B1[3], 35
m298	—,tetraiodo-*	Carbon tetraiodide. CI_4	519.63	red lf (bz or chl)	171d	130–40[1–2] sub	4.23[20]	....	i	i				chl, CCl_4, Py s	B1[3], 104
—	—,tetrakis (hydroxymethyl)-*	see **Pentaerythritol**													
Ω m299	—,tetranitro-*	$C(NO_2)_4$	196.03	λ^{cy} <220	14.2	126 21–3[22]	1.6380[20]	1.4384[20]	i	s	s				B1[2], 47
Ω m300	—,tetraphenyl-*	$C(C_6H_5)_4$	320.44	rh nd (bz, sub, Ac_2O) λ^{cy} 262 (3.11), 272.5 (2.95)	285 (282)	431[760] (sub)	....	....	i	i	i	...	s[h]	to s[h] aa i, s[h] lig i	B5[2], 672
m301	—,tribenzoyl- (enol form)	$(C_6H_5CO)_3CH$	328.37	....	155 (in Jena, 240–5 in soft glass)	....	....	....						chl v	B7[1], 485
m302	—,—,(keto form)	$(C_6H_5CO)_3CH$	328.37	nd (al or ace)	231 245–50 (in soft glass)	sub	....	....	i	i δ[h]	...	δ	δ	chl δ	B7[2], 842
Ω m303	—,tribromo-*	Bromoform. $CHBr_3$	252.75	hex sc $\lambda^{Bu'OH}$ 224	8.3	149.5[760] 46[15]	2.8899[20]	1.5976[20]	δ	∞	∞	...	s	chl, lig s	B1[3], 88
Ω m306	—,trichloro-*	Chloroform. $CHCl_3$	119.38	λ^{vap} <200	−63.5	61.7[760]	1.4832[20]	1.4459[20]	δ	∞	∞	s	∞	lig ∞	B1[2], 14
—	—,—,d	see **Methane, deuterotrichloro-***													
Ω m308	—,trifluoro-*	Fluoroform. CHF_3	70.01	....	−160	−82.2[760]	1.52[−100]	....	s	v	∞	s	s	chl δ	B1[3], 34
Ω m310	—,triiodo-*	Iodoform. CHI_3	393.73	ye hex pr or nd (ace) λ^{chl} 244 (3.0), 307 (3.2), 347 (3.2)	123	ca. 218[760]	4.008[20]	....	i	s[h]	s	s	i	chl, CS_2, aa s	B1[3], 102
m310¹	—, trimethyl	see **Propane, 2-methyl**													
m311	—,trinitro-*	Nitroform. $CH(NO_2)_3$	151.04	....	19 (15)	exp[760] 45–7[22]	1.479[20]	1.44511[24 He]	s		...	s		alk s	B1[3], 116
Ω m312	—,triphenyl-*	Tritan.	244.34	rh (al) λ^{cy} 256 (2.86), 262.5 (2.92), 269.5 (2.81)	(i) 94 (st) (ii) 81 (unst)	358–9[754] 190–215[10]	1.014[99]	1.5839[99]	i	δ v[h]	v	...	s v[h]	chl, CS_2, Py v	B5[2], 613
m313	—,tris(4-aminophenyl)-*	p-Leucaniline. $C_{19}H_{19}N_3$. See m312	289.38	lf (w, al or bz)	208	....	....	....	i	s	s				B13[2], 150
m314	—,tris(4-dimethylaminophenyl)-*	Leucocrystal violet. $C_{25}H_{31}N_3$. See m312	373.55	lf (al), nd (bz or lig)	175	....	....	....	i	δ v[h]	v		v	chl, aa v	B13[2], 150
—	—,tris(ethylthio)-*	see **Orthoformic acid, trithio-**, triethyl ester													
m315	—,tris(4-hydroxyphenyl)-*	Leucoaurin. $C_{19}H_{16}O_3$. See m312	292.34	pr (aa or dil al)	240 (235)	....	....	....	δ	v	s			aa v	B6[2], 1106
m316	—,tris(4-nitrophenyl)-*	$C_{19}H_{13}N_3O_6$. See m312	379.33	sc (bz) λ^{hp} 382 (3.2)	212.5 (207)	....	....	....			δ		δ	aa δ	B5[2], 618
m317	—,tri(2-tolyl)-		286.42	nd (al)	130.5–1.5	....	....	....			s	s	s	MeOH s	B5[3], 2347
m319	**Methanearsonic acid***	Methylarsonic acid. $CH_3AsO(OH)_2$	139.97	lf (al)	160–1	....	....	....	s	s					B4[2], 996
m320	**Methanedisulfonic acid*,** dihydrate	Methionic acid. $CH_2(SO_3H)_2.2H_2O$	212.18	hyg nd (w + 2)	....	220–70[15–20]d	....	....	s	s[h]					B1[2], 644
m323	**Methanephosphonic acid***	Methylphosphonic acid. $CH_3PO(OH)_2$	96.02	hyg pl	108–9 (105)	d	....	....	v	v	v	...	i	peth i	Am 74, 5540

For explanations, symbols and abbreviations see beginning of table. For structural formulas see end of table.

No.	Name	Synonyms and Formula	Mol. wt.	Color, crystalline form, specific rotation and λ_{max} (log ε)	m.p. °C	b.p. °C	Density	n_D	w	al	eth	ace	bz	other solvents	Ref.
	Methanephosphonic acid														
m324	—,diethyl ester*	Diethyl methylphosphonate. $CH_3PO(OC_2H_5)_2$	152.13	....	....	194^{763} 85^{15}	1.0406_4^{30}	1.4101^{30}	s	s	s	...	i	....	**J1954,** 3222
m325	—,dimethyl ester*	Dimethyl methylphosphonate. $CH_3PO(OCH_3)_2$	124.08	λ^{al} 217 (1.12)	....	181^{754} 79.5^{20}	1.1507_4^{20}	1.4099^{30}	s	s	s	...	i	....	**J1954,** 3222
m326	—,trifluoro-, diammonium salt*	$F_3CPO(ONH_4)_2$	184.06	....	212–6d				s						**J1954,** 3598
m328	**Methanesiliconic acid***	Silicoacetic acid. CH_3SiO_2H	76.13	amor	....	....			i		s			KOH s	**B4,** 629
Ω m329	**Methanesulfenic acid, trichloro-, chloride**	Perchloromethylmercaptan. Trichloromethanesulfenyl chloride. Cl_3CSCl	185.89	ye oil λ^{chl} 324 (1.08)	....	147–8^{760} 51^{25}	1.6947_4^{20}	1.5484^{20}			s				**B3²,** 106
m330	—,trifluoro-, chloride	Trifluoromethylsulfenyl chloride. F_3CSCl	136.52	ye λ^{gas} 214 (2.37), 333 (1.40)	....	-0.7^{760}			i d						**J1953,** 3219
Ω m331	**Methanesulfinic acid, amino-(imino)-***	$HN:C(NH_2)SO_2H$	108.12	nd (al)	144d				v		i		i	os i	**B3¹,** 36
m332	**Methanesulfonic acid***	Methylsulfonic acid. CH_3SO_3H	96.11	....	20	167^{10} 122^1	1.4812_4^{18}	1.4317^{16}	v	s	v	...			**B4²,** 524
Ω m333	—,chloride	Methanesulfonyl chloride*. CH_3SO_2Cl	114.55	....	....	161^{730} 55^{11}	1.48053_4^{18}	1.4573^{20}	i	s	s	...			**B4²,** 525
m334	—,phenyl-, amide, N-methyl-	N-Methylbenzylsulfonamide. $C_6H_5CH_2SO_2NHCH_3$	185.25	nd or lf (aa-lig)	108–9				s^h	s				alk s	**B11²,** 73
Ω m335	—,trichloro-, chloride	Cl_3CSO_2Cl	217.89	cr (al-w)	140–1	170 (δsub)			i d^h	d^h	s	s		CS_2 s	**B3²,** 16
m336	,trifluoro-*	F_3CSO_3H	150.08	hyg liq	....	162^{760} $81^{37.5}$				d	∞ d^h				**J1955,** 2901
m337	—,—,amide	$F_3CSO_2NH_2$	149.09	....	119				s		s			chl s	**J1956,** 173
m338	—,—,—,N,N-diethyl-	$F_3CSO_2N(C_2H_5)_2$	205.20	....	....	55^7			i		s				**J1956,** 173
m339	—,—,anhydride*	$(F_3CSO_2)_2O$	282.14	....	....	84^{760}			d	d	s				**J1957,** 4069
m340	—,—,chloride	F_3CSO_2Cl	168.52	....	....	31.6^{760}			i		s				**J1955,** 2901
m341	—,—,ethyl ester	$F_3CSO_3C_2H_5$	178.13	....	....	115^{760}			d		s				**J1956,** 173
m342	—,—,fluoride	F_3CSO_2F	152.07	....	....	-21.7^{760} 42^{40}			d	i^h					**J1956,** 173
m343	—,—,potassium salt	CF_3SO_3K	188.19	cr (ace)	230				s						**J1957,** 4069
m344	—,—,sodium salt	CF_3SO_3Na	172.06	cr (ace)	248				s			s			**J1957,** 4069
m345	**Methanethiol***	Methylmercaptan. CH_3SH	48.11	λ^{cy} 228.5 (2.15)	−123	6.2	0.8665_4^{20}		$δ^h$	v	v			chl s	**B1³,** 1212
m346	—,(2-furyl)-	Furfurylmercaptan. $C_5H_4OCH_2SH$	114.17	....	....	155^{760} 47^{12}	1.1319_4^{20}	1.5329^{20}	i		s	s			**B17²,** 116
m348	**Methanetricarboxylic acid, trimethyl ester***	Tricarbomethoxymethane. $CH(CO_2CH_3)_3$	190.15	pr (MeOH)	46–7	242.7^{760} 128^{15}				v	v		v	chl v MeOH s^h	**B2²,** 680
—	**Methanal***	see **Formaldehyde**													
—	**Methanoic acid***	see **Formic acid**													
Ω m349	**Methanol***	Carbinol. Methyl alcohol. Wood alcohol. CH_3OH	32.04	λ^{gas} 183.3 (2.18)	−93.9	64.96^{760} 15^{73}	0.7914_4^{20}	1.3288^{20}	∞	∞	∞	∞	v	chl s	**B1³,** 1147
m349¹	**Methanol-d**	O-Deuteromethanol. CH_3OD.	33.05	....	−100	65.5^{760}	0.8127_4^{20}		∞	∞	∞	∞	v	chl s	**B1³,** 1186
m349²	**Methan-d^3-ol-d**	Deuteroxy(trideutero)-methane*. Tetradeutero-methanol. D_3COD	36.07	....	....	65.4^{760}			∞	∞	∞	∞	v	chl s	**B1³,** 1187
m350	**Methanol, (2-amino-3-methylphenyl)-***	2-Amino-3-methylbenzyl alcohol.	137.18	nd (bz)	71	135–45^{12}							δ s^h		**B13²,** 367
m351	—,(2-amino-4-methyl-phenyl)-*	2-Amino-4-methylbenzyl alcohol.	137.18	nd (bz)	141	140–50^{13}							δ s^h		**B13²,** 369
m352	—,(2-amino-5-methyl phenyl)-*	2-Amino-5-methylbenzyl alcohol.	137.18	nd (bz)	123	145–50^{13}							δ s^h		**B13²,** 367
m353	—,(4-amino-3-methylphenyl) bis(4-amino-phenyl)-*	Rosaniline. $C_{20}H_{21}N_3O$. See m381	319.41	nd (w) $\lambda^{aq\,HCl}$ 540 (3.1)	186d				δ	s	i				**B13,** 763
m355	—,(4-amino-phenyl)phenyl-*	p-Aminobenzhydrol. $C_{13}H_{13}NO$. See m366	199.16	nd (w or bz)	121					v	δ			MeOH, AcOEt v lig δ	**B13,** 696
m356	—,bis[4(dimethyl-amino)phenyl]-*	Michler's hydrol. $C_{17}H_{22}N_2O$. See m366	270.38	lt gr lf or pr (bz) λ^{aa} 607.5 (5.17)	98 (102–3)				i	v^h	s		s	aa s	**B13²,** 423
m357	—,bis[2(dimethyl-amino)phenyl] phenyl-*	$C_{23}H_{26}N_2O$. See m381	346.48	pr (lig)	105					δ	...			ac s lig δ	**B13,** 741

For explanations, symbols and abbreviations see beginning of table. For structural formulas see end of table.

No.	Name	Synonyms and Formula	Mol. wt.	Color, crystalline form, specific rotation and λ_{max} (log ε)	m.p. °C	b.p. °C	Density	n_D	w	al	eth	ace	bz	other solvents	Ref.
	Methanol														
m358	—,bis[3(dimethylamino) phenyl] phenyl-*	$C_{23}H_{26}N_2O$. See m381	346.48	cr (eth)	128–9						v^h			aa s	B13, 742
m359	—,bis[4(dimethylamino)phenyl] phenyl-*	$C_{23}H_{26}N_2O$. See m381	346.48	cr (eth, bz, lig, MeOH or peth) λ^{aa} 320 (4.25), 428 (4.28), 620 (5.00)	121–3 (110)						v		v^h	ac s lig v^h	B13², 442
m360	—,bis(4-hydroxyphenyl)phenyl-*	Benzaurin. $C_{19}H_{16}O_3$. See m381	292.34	ye-red pw λ^{chl} 414 (4.3)	110–20				i	δ	δ		δ		B8², 245
m362	—,cyclohexyl-	Hexahydrobenzyl alcohol. Hydroxymethylcyclohexane.	114.19		−43	183⁷⁶⁰ 83¹⁴	0.9297²⁰₄	1.46439²⁰		s	s				B6³, 76
m363	—,[2(dimethylamino)phenyl][3(dimethylamino)phenyl]phenyl-*	$C_{23}H_{26}N_2O$. See m381	346.48	pl (bz)	183–4					δ	δ		s	HCl s	B13, 742
m364	—,[2(dimethylamino)phenyl][4(dimethylamino)phenyl]phenyl-*	$C_{23}H_{26}N_2O$. See m381	346.48	(al)	169–70					δ	δ		v	ac s	B13, 742
m365	—,[3(dimethylamino)phenyl][4(dimethylamino)phenyl]phenyl-*	$C_{23}H_{26}N_2O$. See m381	346.48	pr (bz-al)	140					δ	δ		v	ac s	B13, 742
Ω m366	—,diphenyl-*	Benzhydrol.	184.24	nd (lig) λ^{MeOH} 220 sh (4.0), 259 (2.67) λ^{sulf} 442 (4.60)	69	297–8⁷⁴⁸ 180²⁰			δ^h	v	v			CCl₄, chl v aa s lig δ	B6², 631
m367	—,diphenyl-(1-naphthyl)-*	$C_{10}H_7^1COH(C_6H_5)_2$	310.40	cr (lig or bz)	136.5	d			i	s^h	s		s	lig i, s^h	B6², 721
m368	—,diphenyl-(2-naphthyl)-*	$C_{10}H_7^\beta COH(C_6H_5)_2$	310.40	pr (eth-lig)	118				i	s	s	s	v	oos s lig δ	B6², 722
m368¹	—,di(4-tolyl)-		212.30	nd (al) λ^{sulf} 472 (4.87)	69				i	s	s	s		chl, aa s	B6, 688
m369	—,(2-furyl)-	Furfuryl alcohol. 2-Hydroxymethylfuran.	98.10	col-ye λ^w 217 (3.9)		171⁷⁵⁰ 68–9²⁰	1.1296²⁰₄	1.4868²⁰	∞ d	v	v				B17², 113
m370	—,(4-methoxyphenyl)phenyl-*	p-Anisylphenylcarbinol. p-Methoxybenzhydrol. $C_{14}H_{14}O_2$. See m366	214.27	nd (w, lig or dil al)	66–8				s^h	v	v			chl s lig s^h	B6², 965
m371	—,(5-methyl-2-furyl)-	5-Methylfurfuryl alcohol	112.14			194–6⁷⁴⁴ δd 81¹³	1.0769²⁰₄	1.4853²⁰	δ^h	v	v				Am 54, 2554
m373	—,(1-naphthyl)-*	1(Hydroxymethyl)naphthalene*. $C_{10}H_7^1CH_2OH$	158.20	nd (w or al), cr (bz-lig)	64 (61)	301⁷¹⁵ 163¹²	1.1039⁸⁰₄		δ^h	v	v				B6², 617
m374	—,(1-naphthyl)phenyl-(dl)*	$C_{10}H_7^1CH(OH)C_6H_5$	234.30	cr (al or lig)	86.5	ca. 360			i	s	s		v	lig δ	B6², 681
m375	—,(2-naphthyl)phenyl-(dl)*	$C_{10}H_7^\beta CH(OH)C_6H_5$	234.30	nd (al or lig)	87–8 (83)				i	s	s		s	to s lig δ	B6², 681
Ω m376	—,(2-tetrahydrofuryl)-(dl)	Tetrahydrofurfuryl alcohol.	102.13	hyg		177–8⁷⁵⁰ 80–2²⁰	1.0544²⁰₄	1.4517²⁰			s	s			B17², 106
m377	—,(2-thienyl)-		114.17			207⁷⁶⁰ 96¹²		1.5280²⁰	i	v	v				B17, 113
m378	—,(2-tolyl)-	o-Methylbenzyl alcohol	122.17	nd λ^{iso} 263 (2.4), 275 (2.3)	37–9	223⁷⁵⁰ 117–9²⁰	1.023⁴⁰		δ v^h	v	v			chl v	B6², 457
Ω m379	—,(3-tolyl)-	m-Methylbenzyl alcohol	122.17		< −20	215–6⁷⁶⁰ (218–9⁷⁴³) 110–2¹⁷	0.9157¹⁷		δ s^h	v	v				B6², 465
Ω m380	—,(4-tolyl)-	p-Methylbenzyl alcohol	122.17	nd (hp)	61–2.1	217⁷⁶⁰ 116–8²⁰	0.978²²₄		δ s^h	v	v				B6², 469
Ω m381	—,triphenyl-*	Triphenylcarbinol. Tritanol	260.34	pl (al), trig (bz), rh (CCl₄) λ^{diox} 240 (3.16), 253 (3.26), 260 (3.28) λ^{sulf} 405 (4.6), 435 (4.5)	164.2	380⁷⁶⁰	1.199⁰₄		i	v	v	s	s	aa s peth i	B6², 686
m382	—,tris(4-aminophenyl)-*	Pararosaniline. $C_{19}H_{19}N_3O$. See m381	305.38	col to red lf $\lambda^{w,pH=1.3}$ 260 sh (3.0), 410 (2.7), 540 (3.0)	189 ca. (205)					δ	s	δ			B13², 447
m383	—,tris-(4-biphenylyl)-	Tri-p-xenylcarbinol	488.64	nd (aa or bz)	212						δ		v	aa s^h	B6², 741

For explanations, symbols and abbreviations see beginning of table. For structural formulas see end of table.

No.	Name	Synonyms and Formula	Mol. wt.	Color, crystalline form, specific rotation and λ_{max} (log ε)	m.p. °C	b.p. °C	Density	n_D	w	al	eth	ace	bz	other solvents	Ref.
	Methanol														
m384	—,tris(3-nitro-phenyl)-*	$C_{19}H_{13}N_3O_7$. See m381	395.33	rhd (MeOH, chl or AcOEt-lig)	167	....	....		...	δ^h	δ	...	s	aa s CS_2 δ	B6[1], 352
m385	—,tris(4-nitro-phenyl)-*	$C_{19}H_{13}N_3O_7$. See m381	395.33	mcl pr (bz or aa) λ^{sulf} 265 (4.4), 425 (4.6), 450 sh (4.5)	(i) 190–1 (ii) 167	....	....		i	δ^h	δ	...	s	aa s CS_2 δ	B6[1], 352
m386	Methantheline bromide	Banthine bromide	420.36	cr (i-PrOH) λ^{al} 246, 282	172–7	....	....		σ	σ	i	...	...	chl σ	Am 65, 1582
m387	Methapyrilene, (base)	Histadyl base. Tenalin base. Thenylene base.	261.39	λ^w 238 (4.17), 304 (3.60)	....	173–5[3]		1.5915^{20}							Am 71, 333
—	Methionic acid	see Methanedisulfonic acid*													
Ω m388	Methionine(DL)	dl-2-Amino-4-(methylthio)-butanoic acid. $CH_3SCH_2CH_2CH(NH_2)CO_2H$	149.21	pl (al) λ^w <200	281d (272)	....	1.340		v	δ	i	...	i	peth i	B4[2], 938
Ω m389	—(L)	$CH_3SCH_2CH_2CH(NH_2)CO_2H$	149.21	hex pl (dil al) $[\alpha]_D^{25}$ −8.2 (w, c = 1) $[\alpha]_D^{25}$ +22.5 (1N HCl) $\lambda^{0.01N\,HCl}$ 208 sh (3.2)	283d	sub 186			s	i	i	i	i	aa δ peth i	B4[2], 938
—	Methone	see 1,3-Cyclohexanedione, 5,5-dimethyl-*													
—	Methoxychlor	see Ethane, 2,2-bis(4-methoxyphenyl)-1,1,1-trichloro-*													
—	Methyl alcohol	see Methanol*													
—	Methylamine	see Methane, amino-*													
—	Methyl cellosolve	see Ethanol, 2-methoxy-*													
m390	Methylene blue	3,9-Bisdimethylamino-phenazothionium chloride.	319.86	dk gr cr or pw (chl-eth) λ^{al} 655 (4.95)	....	....			s	s	i	...	...	chl s Py δ	B27[2], 448
—	Methylene bromide	see Methane, dibromo-*													
—	Methylene chloride	see Methane, dichloro-*													
—	Methylene cyanide	see Malonic acid, dinitrile													
—	5,5'-Methylene disalicylaldehyde	see Methane, bis(3-formyl-4-hydroxyphenyl)-													
—	Methylene fluoride	see Methane, difluoro-*													
Ω m391	Methyl green	Paris green. Heptamethyl pararosaniline chloride.	458.48	gr pw (al)	....	....			s	δ	i	...	...	....	B13[2], 451
—	Methylhydroxyl-amine	see Methane, hydroxylamino-*													
—	Methyl mercaptan	see Methanethiol*													
Ω m392	Methyl orange	Sodium 4'-dimethyl-aminoazobenzene-4-sulfonate. Helianthin-β. Orange III.	327.34	og, ye pl or sc (w) λ^{al} 265 (4.2), 305 (3.9), 420 (4.6)	d	....			δ	δ	i	...	...	Py δ	B16, 331
Ω m393	Methyl red	4'-Dimethylaminoazo-benzene-2-carboxylic acid.	269.31	vt or red pr (to or bz), nd (aq aa), lf (dil al) $\lambda^{MeOH-0.4N\,HCl}$ 521 (4.76) $\lambda^{MeOH-NaOMe}$ 410 (4.4)	183	....			δ	s	...	v^h	v^h	chl, aa v lig δ, peth δ	B16[2], 164
m394	Methysticin	Kavahin. Kavatin. $C_{15}H_{14}O_5$.	274.28	nd (MeOH), pr (ace) $[\alpha]_D^{20}$ +94.3 (ace, p = 5)	137	....			i δ^h	v^h	δ	s	s^h	chl s^h peth δ alk i	B19[2], 431
Ω m395	Metrazol	Cardiazole. Leptazole.	138.17	cr (bz-lig)	59–60	194[12]			v	v	s	v	s	os s	B26[2], 213
m396	Metycaine	Piperocaine hydrochloride.	292.78	....	172–5				s	s	i	...	...	chl s	C25, 1037
—	Michler's ketone	see Benzophenone, 4,4'-bis(dimethylamino)													
m397	Mimosine(l)	l-Leucenol	198.18	ta (w) $[\alpha]_D^{22}$ −21 (w, c = 0.5) λ^w 215 (4.6), 280 (4.6)	228–9d	....			δ	i	i	i	i	dil ac, dil alk s oos, aa, diox i	Am 71, 705

For explanations, symbols and abbreviations see beginning of table. For structural formulas see end of table.

No.	Name	Synonyms and Formula	Mol. wt.	Color, crystalline form, specific rotation and λ_{max} (log ε)	m.p. °C	b.p. °C	Density	n_D	w	al	eth	ace	bz	other solvents	Ref.
	Monolaurin														
—	**Monolaurin**	*see* **Glycerol,** monododecanoate													
—	**Monoolein**	*see* **Glycerol,** mono(9-octadecenoate)													
—	**Monopalmitin**	*see* **Glycerol,** monohexadecanoate													
—	**Monoricinolein**	*see* **Glycerol,** mono(12-hydroxy-9-octadecenoate)													
—	**Monostearin**	*see* **Glycerol,** monooctadecanoate													
—	**Morin**	*see* **Flavone, 2′,3,4′,5,7,8-pentahydroxy-**													
—	**Morindone**	*see* **9,10-Anthraquinone, 6-methyl-1,2,5-tri-hydroxy-***													
m399	**Morphine**	$C_{17}H_{19}NO_3$	285.35	pr (PhOMe) λ^{al} 210 sh (4.4), 236 sh (3.7), 287 (3.2)	(i) 254–6.4d (st) (ii) 197 (unst)	....	....	....	i δ^h	δ	i	i	i	MeOH, Py s chl, peth i	B27², 118
m400	—,acetate tri-hydrate(*l*)	$C_{17}H_{19}NO_3 \cdot CH_3CO_2H \cdot 3H_2O.$ *See* m399	398.44	col to ye cr (dil al) $[\alpha]_D^5 -77$ (w)	200d	....	....	....	v v^h	s	i	...	...	chl δ	B27², 134
m401	—,hydrate.......	$C_{17}H_{19}NO_3 \cdot H_2O.$ *See* m399	303.36	orh pr (dil al) $[\alpha]_D^{25} -132$ (MeOH, c = 1)	–w, 130 ; 254–6.4 (anh)	d	1.32_4^{20}	1.58–1.64	s^h	δ	i	...	...	...	B27², 122
m402	—,hydrochloride trihydrate	$C_{17}H_{19}NO_3 \cdot HCl \cdot 3H_2O.$ *See* m399	375.85	nd or fl (dil HCl) $[\alpha]_D^{25} -113.5$ (w, c = 2.2) λ^w 230 (3.85), 286 (3.2)	200d (250d)	....	....	....	s v^h	s	i	...	...	chl i	B27², 132
m403	—,N-oxide	Genomorphine. $C_{17}H_{19}NO_4.$ *See* m399	301.35	pr (50 % al) λ^w 208 (4.4), 235 sh (3.7), 284 (3.2)	274–5	....	....	....	δ	δ	...	i	i	NH_4OH v chl i	B27², 159
m404	—,sulfate penta-hydrate	$2(C_{17}H_{19}NO_3) \cdot H_2SO_4 \cdot 5H_2O.$ *See* m399	758.85	pw or cubes $[\alpha]_D^{25} -107.8$ (w, c = 4) λ^{al} 285	*ca.* 250d	....	....	....	s v^h	δ	i	...	i	chl i	B27², 133
m405	—,O,O-diacetyl-...	Diamorphine. Heroin. $C_{21}H_{23}NO_5.$ *See* m399	369.42	rh $[\alpha]_D^{15} -166$ (MeOH) λ^{al} 230 sh (3.8), 281 (3.3)	173	$272–4^{12}$	1.56–1.61	....	i	s^h	δ	...	s	chl v MeOH s	B27², 151
m406	—,—hydrochloride monohydrate	$C_{21}H_{23}NO_5 \cdot HCl \cdot H_2O.$ *See* m399	423.90	$[\alpha]_D^{20} -153$ (w, c = 1.17) λ^w 227 (3.85), 279.5 (3.25)	231–2 (243–4)	....	....	....	v	s	i	...	...	chl v	B27², 153
m407	—,3-ethyl ether, hydrochloride dihydrate	Dionin. $C_{19}H_{23}NO_3 \cdot HCl \cdot 2H_2O.$ *See* m399	385.89	cr $\lambda^{0.2N\ HCl}$ 244 (3.5), 286 (3.2)	123–5d (170 anh)	....	....	....	s	s	δ	...	...	chl δ	B27², 148
—	**Morphol**	*see* **Phenanthrene, 3,4-dihydroxy-***													
Ω m408	**Morpholine**	Diethylenimide oxide. Tetrahydro-1,4-isoxazine.	87.12	hyg	–4.75	128.3^{760} 24.86^{10}	1.0005_4^{20}	1.4548^{20}	∞	s	s	s	s	os s	B27², 3
Ω m409	—,4-acetyl-......	$C_6H_{11}NO_2.$ *See* m408	129.16	....	14.5	152^{50} 118^{12}	1.1165_{20}^{20}	1.4827^{20}	∞	s	s	...	s	...	C50, 7112
Ω m410	—,4(2-amino-ethyl)-	$C_6H_{14}N_2O.$ *See* m408	130.19	....	25.6	116^{50}	0.9915_{20}^{20}	1.4715^{20}	∞	∞	...	s	∞	lig ∞	C42, 6747
Ω m411	—,4(3-amino-propyl)-	$C_7H_{16}N_2O.$ *See* m408	144.22	....	–15	219^{733} 134^{50}	0.9872_{20}^{20}	1.4762^{20}	∞	∞	...	s	∞	lig ∞	Am 66, 725
m412	—,4-benzyl-......	$C_{11}H_{15}NO.$ *See* m408	177.25	....	260–1 128–9¹³	....	1.0387_4^{20}	1.5302^{20}	δ	...	...	s	s	ac s	B27¹, 203
m413	—,4-butyl-.......	$C_8H_{17}NO.$ *See* m408	143.23	....	–57.1	$213–4^{760}$ $67–8^{10}$	0.9068_4^{20}	1.4451^{20}	v	s	s	s	s	...	Am 61, 171
Ω m414	—,2,6-dimethyl-...	$C_6H_{13}NO.$ *See* m408	115.18	....	fr –85	146.6^{760} 58^{30}	0.9346_{20}^{20}	1.4460^{20}	∞	s	s	...	∞	lig ∞	Am 80, 1257
m415	—,4(2-ethoxy-ethyl)-	$C_8H_{17}NO_2.$ *See* m408	159.23	....	–100	206^{760} $93–7^{11}$	0.963^{20}	....	∞	...	s	s	s	...	Am 63, 298
Ω m416	—,4-ethyl-......	$C_6H_{13}NO.$ *See* m408	115.18	....	...	$138–9^{763}$	0.8996_4^{20}	1.4400^{20}	∞	∞	∞	s	s	...	B27¹, 203
Ω m417	—,4(2-hydroxy-ethyl)-	4-Morpholineethanol. $C_6H_{13}NO_2.$ *See* m408	131.18	....	...	227^{757}	1.0710_4^{20}	1.4763^{20}	s	s	s	...	s	...	B27, 7
m418	—,4(2-hydroxy-propyl)-	$C_7H_{15}NO_2.$ *See* m408	145.20	....	...	$92–4^{13}$	1.0174_4^{20}	1.4638^{20}	s	s	s	s	s	MeOH s	Am 64, 970
Ω m419	—,4-methyl-......	$C_5H_{11}NO.$ *See* m408	101.15	....	...	$115–6^{750}$	0.9051_4^{20}	1.4332^{20}	s	s	s	...	...	...	B27, 6
Ω m420	—,4-phenyl-......	$C_{10}H_{13}NO.$ *See* m408	163.22	cr (al-eth)	57–8	$259–60^{745}$ $165–70^{45}$	....	....	i	i	v	...	...	...	B27², 3
m421	—,4(4-tolyl)-......	$C_{11}H_{15}NO.$ *See* m408	177.25	cr (dil al)	51	167^{30}	....	....	...	v	s	...	...	...	B27², 4

For explanations, symbols and abbreviations see beginning of table. For structural formulas see end of table.

No.	Name	Synonyms and Formula	Mol. wt.	Color, crystalline form, specific rotation and λ_{max} (log ε)	m.p. °C	b.p. °C	Density	n_D	Solubility						Ref.
									w	al	eth	ace	bz	other solvents	
	Mucic acid														
Ω m422	Mucic acid.......	Galactosaccharic acid. 2,3,4,5-Tetrahydroxy-hexanedioic acid*.	210.14	pr (w)	255 (rapid htng) 225 (208) (slow htng)	....	....		δ s^h	i	i	....	....	alk s Py i	B3[3], 1122
—	Mucobromic acid ..	see 2-Butenoic acid, 2,3-dibromo-4-oxo-*													
—	Mucochloric acid ..	see 2-Butenoic acid, 2,3-dichloro-4-oxo-*													
—	Muconic acid.....	see 2,4-Hexadienedioic acid*													
Ω m423	Murexide........	Ammonium purpurate	302.21	red-gr pr (aq NH₄Cl) λ^w 510 (0.7)	....	....			δ s^h	i	i	....	....	alk s (bl)	B25, 499
—	Muscone	see Cyclopentadecanone, 3-methyl-*													
—	Musk baur.......	see Benzene, 2-tert-butyl-4-methyl-1,3,5-trinitro-													
—	Musk ketone......	see Acetophenone, 4-tert-butyl-2,6-dimethyl-3,5-dinitro-													
—	Musk xylene......	see Benzene, 1-tert-butyl-3,5-dimethyl-2,4,6-trinitro-													
—	Mustard gas	see Sulfide, diethyl, 2,2'-dichloro-													
m424	Mycophenolic acid	$C_{17}H_{20}O_6$	320.35	nd (w)	141	....	....		i δ^h	v	v	....	δ	chl v to δ, v^h	B18[2], 393
m425	Myrcene	7-Methyl-3-methylene-1,6-octadiene. $(CH_3)_2C{:}CH(CH_2)_2C({:}CH_2)CH{:}CH_2$	136.24	λ^{al} 225 (4.30)	....	167[760] 65[20]	0.8013[15]	1.4722[20]	i	s	s	....	s	chl, aa s	B1, 264
—	Myricyl alcohol....	see 1-Triacontanol*													
—	Myrlstaldehyde....	see Tetradecanal*													
—	Myristic acid......	see Tetradecanoic acid*													
m426	Myristicin	....	192.22	....	< −20	276–7[760] 157[21]	1.1437[20]	1.5403[20]	i	δ	s	....	s	....	B19[2], 84
—	Myristyl bromide ..	see Tetradecane, 1-bromo-*													

For explanations, symbols and abbreviations see beginning of table. For structural formulas see end of table.

No.	Name	Synonyms and Formula	Mol. wt.	Color, crystalline form, specific rotation and λ_{max} (log ε)	m.p. °C	b.p. °C	Density	n_D	Solubility						Ref.
									w	al	eth	ace	bz	other solvents	
	Naphthacene														
Ω n1	Naphthacene......	2,3-Benzanthracene. Benz[b]anthracene. Tetracene.	228.30	og-ye lf (bz or xyl) λ^{bz} 396 (3.35), 418 (3.64), 444.5 (3.91), 475.5 (3.98)	357 (341)	sub	....	....	δ	...	...	...	δ s[h]	con sulf s oos δ	B5[3], 2372
n2	—,9,10-dihydro-...	$C_{18}H_{14}$. See n1	230.31	nd (xyl), lf (bz)	212	ca. 400				δ[h]	δ[h]	...	s[h]	PhNO₂ v sulf s (ye) aa s[h]	E14s, 76
n3	—,9,10-diphenyl-...	$C_{30}H_{20}$. See n1	380.50	og (eth + ½) λ^{bz} 407 (3.32), 434 (3.73), 461 (3.96), 493 (3.98)	207–8	....					s[h]	...	...	os v	E14s, 77
n4	—,9,11-diphenyl-..	$C_{30}H_{20}$. See n1	380.50	ye λ^{bz} 408 (3.3), 435 (3.8), 462 (4.1), 493 (4.1)	301–2				i		s	...	s	CS₂ s	E14, 313
n5	—,9,10,11-tri-phenyl-	$C_{36}H_{24}$. See n1	456.60	og (eth), (bz + 1) λ^{bz} 417 (3.48), 442 (3.80), 472 (4.08), 504 (4.14)	236–7 177–8 (+1 bz)				i		s	...	s	CS₂ s	E14, 313
Ω n6	9,10-Naphthacenequinone	2,3-Benzanthraquinone.....	258.28	ye nd (PhNO₂ or aa)	294 (285)	sub	....				s	...	δ[h]	δ[h]	sulf s (red-vt) aa δ[h]	E14, 319
n7	9,11-Naphthacenequinone	....	258.28	dk red (aa or xyl)	322 part δ				i					os δ xyl, aa δ	E14s, 86
Ω n8	1-Naphthaldehyde	1-Formylnaphthalene. α-Naphthaldehyde. 1-Naphthalenecarbonal*.	156.20	pa ye	33–4	292⁷⁶⁰ 160¹⁵	1.1503_4^{20}	1.6507^{20}	i	s	s	s	s	sulf s	E12B, 2197
Ω n9	2-Naphthaldehyde	2-Formylnaphthalene. β-Naphthaldehyde. 2-Naphthalenecarbonal.*	156.20	lf (w) λ^{chl} 384 (4.51)	61–3	160¹⁹	1.0775_4^{99}	1.6211^{99}	δ[h]	v	v	s	...	....	E12B, 2204
n10	1-Naphthaldehyde, 2-ethoxy-	$C_{13}H_{12}O_2$. See n8	200.24	yesh nd (al or aa)	115	185–7²⁵				s[h]		...	...	aa s[h]	B8[1], 564
n11	—,4-ethoxy-......	$C_{13}H_{12}O_2$. See n8	200.24	yesh cr (aa or AcOEt)	75 (72)	....				s[h]		...	...	aa s[h]	B8[2], 174
n12	—,2-hydroxy-.....	β-Naphthol-1-aldehyde. $C_{14}H_8O_2$. See n8	172.20	pr (al), nd (AcOEt) $\lambda^{MeOH-HCl}$225 (4.7), 230 (3.8), 270 sh (3.7)	82	192²⁷			i	s	s	...	...	aq alk s sulf s(ye) peth s	B7[2], 171
n13	2-Naphthaldehyde, 1-hydroxy-	α-Naphthol-2-aldehyde. $C_{14}H_8O_2$. See n9	172.20	grsh-ye nd (dil aa, dil al or lig) $\lambda^{MeOH-HCl}$ 260 (4.6), 295 (3.8), 375 (3.8)	60	....			δ s[h]	s	s	...	...	os v alk s aa s[h]	E12B, 2369
Ω n14	Naphthalene*.....	....	128.19	mcl pl (al) λ^{al} 221 (5.04), 275.5 (3.76), 286 (3.59), 311 (2.38)	80.55	218⁷⁶⁰ 87.5¹⁰	1.0253_4^{20} 0.9625_4^{100}	$1.4003^{24`}$ 1.5898^{85}	i	s v[h]	v[h]	v	v	CS₂, CCl₄, chl v aa s, v[h]	B5[3], 1549
Ω n15	—,picrate	$C_{10}H_8 \cdot C_6H_3N_3O_7$. See n14 ..	357.28	ye pr or pl (aa), cr (eth) $\lambda^{C_2H_4Cl_2}$ 230 (4.30), 240 (4.30), 340 (3.60)	152	....	1.53	....	δ d[h]	d	s	...	s	....	B5[3], 1568
n16	—,1-acetamido-2-nitro-*	$C_{12}H_{10}N_2O_3$. See n14	230.23	lt ye nd (aa or al)	200					s[h]		...	...	aa s	E12B, 746
n17	—,1-acetamido-4-nitro-*	$C_{12}H_{10}N_2O_3$. See n14	230.23	pa ye nd (ace)	192.5–3.5					s[h]	...	s[h]	...	....	E12B, 751
n18	—,1-acetamido-5-nitro-*	$C_{12}H_{10}N_2O_3$. See n14	230.23	br pr (aa), ye cr (al)	220				δ	s[h]	δ	...	δ	....	E12B, 755
n19	—,1-acetamido-8-nitro-*	$C_{12}H_{10}N_2O_3$. See n14	230.23	nd (w)	191				s[h]					....	E12B, 756
n20	—,2-acetamido-1-nitro-*	$C_{12}H_{10}N_2O_3$. See n14	230.23	ye rh bipym nd or pl (al)	123.5				δ	s	δ	...	s	aa s lig δ	B12[2], 731
n21	—,2-acetamido-5-nitro-*	$C_{12}H_{10}N_2O_3$. See n14	230.23	ye-br rh (al), ye nd (bz)	186					s		...	s	aa s	E12B, 764
n22	—,2-acetamido-6-nitro-*	$C_{12}H_{10}N_2O_3$. See n14	230.23	lt ye nd (dil al)	224				i	v	i	...	s	aa v xyl s	E12B, 765
n23	—,2-acetamido-8-nitro-*	$C_{12}H_{10}N_2O_3$. See n14	230.23	ye nd (al)	195.5				δ s[h]			...	δ	aa s	E12B, 766
Ω n24	—,1-acetyl-.......	1-Acetonaphthone. Methyl 1-naphthyl ketone. $C_{12}H_{10}O$. See n14	170.21	λ^{al} 242 (4.4), 290 (3.9)	34	296–8⁷⁶⁰ 170–0.5²⁰	$1.1171_4^{21.5}$	1.6280^{22}	i	s	s	s	...	os s	B7[2], 337

For explanations, symbols and abbreviations see beginning of table. For structural formulas see end of table.

Naphthalene

No.	Name	Synonyms and Formula	Mol. wt.	Color, crystalline form, specific rotation and λ_{max} (log ε)	m.p. °C	b.p. °C	Density	n_D	w	al	eth	ace	bz	other solvents	Ref.
Ω n25	—,2-acetyl-	2-Acetonaphthone. Methyl 2-naphthyl ketone. $C_{12}H_{10}O$. See n14	170.21	nd (lig, dil al or xyl) λ^{al} 247 (4.8), 280 (3.9), 290 (3.9)	56	301–3 171–3[17]				δ				CS_2 s lig δ, s[h]	B7[2], 338
n26	—,2-acetyl-1-amino-, hydrochloride	$C_{12}H_{11}NO \cdot HCl$. See n14	186.21	cr (w)	220d					s				chl, CS_2, aa s	C34, 5086
n27	—,2-acetyl-4-bromo-1-hydroxy-	$C_{12}H_9BrO_2$. See n14	265.11	ye nd (al)	126–7				i	s	s		s	CS_2, chl, lig s	B8[2], 178
n28	—,1-acetyl-2-hydroxy-	1-Acetyl-2-naphthol. $C_{12}H_{10}O_2$. See n14	186.21	pa ye lf (peth), rh (lig), nd or pl (gasoline) λ^{al} 227 (4.71), 299 (3.60), 337 (3.58)	64–5					v	v		v	os, con sulf v	B8[2], 175
n29	—,1-acetyl-4-hydroxy-	4-Acetyl-1-naphthol. $C_{12}H_{10}O_2$. See n14	186.21	yesh pr (aa, to or al)	198								s	alk s aa s[h]	B8[2], 176
Ω n30	—,2-acetyl-1-hydroxy-	2-Acetyl-1-naphthol. $C_{12}H_{10}O_2$. See n14	186.21	(i) pr (bz or lig) (ii) gr-ye nd (al) λ^{al} 256 (4.38), 284 (3.71), 366 (3.66)	(i) 98 (ii) 103	325δd			i	δ			s	chl, CS_2, aa s	B8[1], 567
n31	—,2-acetyl-3-hydroxy-	3-Acetyl-2-naphthol. $C_{12}H_{10}O_2$. See n14	186.21	ye lf or nd (al, peth) λ^{al} 250 (4.46), 304 (3.82), 390 (3.18)	112					δ s[h]		v	v	dil NaOHs lig δ	B8[2], 179
n32	—,2-acetyl-6-hydroxy-	6-Acetyl-2-naphthol. $C_{12}H_{10}O_2$. See n14	186.21	pr (bz)	172					s			s[h]	NaOH s	B8[2], 179
n33	—,3-acetyl-1-hydroxy-	3-Acetyl-1-naphthol. $C_{12}H_{10}O_2$. See n14	186.21	nd (bz)	173–4					s			δ s[h]	alk, aa, con sulf s	B8, 150
n34	—,2-acetyl-1-hydroxy-4-nitro-	$C_{12}H_9NO_4$. See n14	231.21	ye nd (al)	159				i	δ s[h]	s		s		B8[2], 179
Ω n35	—,1-allyl-	4-α-Naphthylpropene. $C_{13}H_{12}$. See n14	168.24	λ^{al} 228 (4.73), 296 (3.97)		265–7 129–30[10]	1.0228[20]	1.6140[20]		s			v	chl s	E12B, 118
Ω n36	—,1-amino-*	1-Naphthylamine*. α-Naphthylamine. $C_{10}H_9N$. See n14	143.19	nd (dil al, eth) λ^{al} 242 (4.27), 320 (3.71) sub	50	300.8[760] 160[12] sub	1.1229[25/25]	1.67034[51]	δ	v	v		v		B12[2], 675
Ω n37	—,—,hydrochloride	$C_{10}H_9N \cdot HCl$. See n14	179.65	nd $\lambda^{w,1N HCl}$ 302 (2.7), 311 (2.5), 317 (2.3)		sub			δ	s	δ				B12[2], 678
Ω n38	—,2-amino-*	2-Naphthylamine* β-Naphthylamine. $C_{10}H_9N$. See n14	143.19	lf (w) λ^{al} 236 (4.78), 280 (3.82), 292 (3.73), 340 (3.28)	113	306.1 (294)	1.0614[98/4]	1.64927[98]	s v[h]	v					B12[2], 710
Ω n39	—,—,hydrochloride	$C_{10}H_9N \cdot HCl$. See n14	179.65	lf	254				v	v	v		i		B12[2], 712
Ω n42	—,1-amino-4-bromo-*	$C_{10}H_8BrN$. See n14	222.10	nd (al, bz or peth)	102					s		s	s	lig s	E12B, 713
n43	—,1-amino-5-bromo-*	$C_{10}H_8BrN$. See n14	222.10	lf or pl (w or lig)	69 (cor) sub				δ[h]	s	s		v	chl v lig s	E12B, 717
n44	—,2-amino-1-bromo-*	$C_{10}H_8BrN$. See n14	222.10	rh nd (dil al or lig)	63–4				δ	v	s		v	chl v	B12, 1310
n45	—,2-amino-3-bromo-*	$C_{10}H_8BrN$. See n14	222.10	pl (al)	169					s				aa s	E12B, 729
n46	—,2-amino-6-bromo-*	$C_{10}H_8BrN$. See n14	222.10	lf (al, w or peth)	128				δ[h]	s[h]		s	s	peth s[h]	E12B, 731
n47	—,3-amino-1-bromo-*	$C_{10}H_8BrN$. See n14	222.10	nd (bz-peth or 90% aa)	72				i	v	v		v	peth δ	B12, 1311
n48	—,6-amino-1-bromo-*	$C_{10}H_8BrN$. See n14	222.10	cr $\lambda^{\ast?}$ 218 (4.82), 247 (4.19), 331 (3.76)	38	207–10[16]			i	v		s		os v lig δ	E12B, 730
n49	—,1-amino-4-bromo-2-nitro-*	$C_{10}H_7BrN_2O_2$. See n14	267.09	og cr (al or aa)	200					v[h]			v	to, chl v aa s[h] CS_2 δ	E12B, 775
n50	—,1-amino-2-chloro-*	$C_{10}H_8ClN$. See n14	177.65	nd (peth or dil al)	60 (56)				δ[h]	s		s		pcth s[h]	E12B, 709
Ω n51	—,1-amino-4-chloro-*	$C_{10}H_8ClN$. See n14	177.65	nd (al, bz or lig)	99–100					s	s		s[h]	lig s[h]	E12B, 711
n52	—,2-amino-1-chloro-*	$C_{10}H_8ClN$. See n14	177.65	nd (al or peth)	60					s				aa s lig s[h]	E12B, 720
n53	—,1-amino-2,4-dibromo-*	$C_{10}H_7Br_2N$. See n14	300.99	nd or pl (dil al)	118–9				i	v	v		v	chl, lig v	E12B, 735
n54	—,2-amino-1,4-dibromo-*	$C_{10}H_7Br_2N$. See n14	300.99	nd (al or bz)	106–7					v	v		v	os v	E12B, 737

For explanations, symbols and abbreviations see beginning of table. For structural formulas see end of table.

No.	Name	Synonyms and Formula	Mol. wt.	Color, crystalline form, specific rotation and λ_{max} (log ε)	m.p. °C	b.p. °C	Density	n_D	w	al	eth	ace	bz	other solvents	Ref.
	Naphthalene														
n55	—,2-amino-1,6-dibromo-*	$C_{10}H_7Br_2N$. See n14	300.99	nd (al or peth)	121	....			δ	v	...	...	v	aa s	E12B, 737
n56	—,1-amino-2,4-dichloro-*	$C_{10}H_7Cl_2N$. See n14	212.08	nd (al)	83–4	....			i	v	...	...	...	to s^h	E12B, 734
n57	—,5-amino-1,4-dihydro-*	$C_{10}H_{11}N$. See n14	145.21	pl or nd (to), turns pink in air	37.5 (cor)	247[408]				s	...	...	...	chl, ac s	E12B, 667
n58	—,1-amino-2,4-dinitro-*	$C_{10}H_7N_3O_4$. See n14	233.19	ye nd (al), pr (aa), cr (ace) λ^{HClO_4} 400 (4.04)	242	....			i	δ	δ	v	δ	chl, aa δ lig i Py s^h	E12B, 784
n59	—,2-amino-1,6-dinitro-*	$C_{10}H_7N_3O_4$. See n14	233.19	gold-ye nd (al or aa), ye pw (Py)	248	....			δ	δ	δ	δ	δ	Py s^h chl δ lig i	E12B, 793
n60	—, 1-amino-4-fluoro-*	$C_{10}H_8FN$. See n14	161.19	lt ye	48	162[16]								ac s	E12B, 710
n61	—,1-amino-2-hydroxy-*	1-Amino-2-naphthol. $C_{10}H_9NO$. See n14	159.19	silvery lf (bz, eth)	150d (175d)	....			δ^h	s	δ s^h	...	...	dil alk, dil ac v	B13[2], 412
n62	—,1-amino-6-hydroxy-*	5-Amino-2-naphthol. $C_{10}H_9NO$. See n14	159.19	nd or og pr (w)	190.6 (185)	....			s	s	s	s	s	NH_3, os s	E12B, 1688
Ω n63	—,1-amino-7-hydroxy-*	8-Amino-2-naphthol. $C_{10}H_9NO$. See n14	159.19	nd (w, al)	205–7	sub			s^h	v^h	s	...	δ	lig δ	E12B, 1696
n64	—,2-amino-3-hydroxy-*	3-Amino-2-naphthol. $C_{10}H_9NO$. See n14	159.19	silvery lf (bz), nd (al, w)	235	....			δ s^h	v	δ s^h	...	δ	dil ac, dil alk v	E12B, 1677
n65	—,2-amino-6-hydroxy-*	6-Amino-2-naphthol. $C_{10}H_9NO$. See n14	159.19	br (dil al), pr (w)	192–4 212–3d (sealed tube)	....			s	s					B13[2], 412
n66	—,2-amino-7-hydroxy-*	7-Amino-2-naphthol. $C_{10}H_9NO$. See n14	159.19	nd or lf (al)	201 (208)	....			δ	v	v	...	...	....	E12B, 1691
n67	—,2-amino-3-iodo-*	$C_{10}H_8IN$. See n14	269.10	cr (al)	137	....			δ	...	...	...	s	chl, aa s	E12B, 729
n68	—,1-amino-2-methyl-*	$C_{11}H_{11}N$. See n14	157.22	nd (peth), turns red in air	32	....			δ		s	...	...	os v lig s	B12[2], 742
n69	—,1-amino-3-methyl-*	$C_{11}H_{11}N$. See n14	157.22	cr (peth) λ^{al} 234 (4.6), 299 (3.78)	51–2	....				s	s	...	...	os, lig s	B12[2], 743
n70	—,1-amino-4-methyl-*	$C_{11}N_{11}N$. See n14	157.22	nd (peth)	51–2	176[12]			δ		s	...	...	os v lig s^h	B12[2], 740
n71	—,2-amino-1-methyl-*	$C_{11}H_{11}N$. See n14	157.22	nd (lig), pr (peth)	51	....			δ^h	v	s	v	v	chl v lig s	B12[2], 740
n72	—,2-amino-6-methyl-*	$C_{11}H_{11}N$. See n14	157.22	lf (peth, w) turns red in air	129–30	....			δ					os, min ac v	B12[2], 743
n73	—,1-amino-2-nitro-*	$C_{10}H_8N_2O_2$. See n14	188.20	ye-red mcl pr (al)	144	....				s^h		...	...		B12[2], 703
n74	—,1-amino-3-nitro-*	$C_{10}H_8N_2O_2$. See n14	188.20	og-ye nd (50 % al)	137	....				v	...	...	s	chl s	E12B, 748
Ω n75	—,1-amino-4-nitro-*	$C_{10}H_8N_2O_2$. See n14	188.20	og-ye nd (al) λ^{al} 269 (3.94), 443 (4.18)	195 (192)	....			δ^h	v	...	...	...	aa v	B12[2], 704
n76	—,1-amino-5-nitro-*	$C_{10}H_8N_2O_2$. See n14	188.20	red nd (w)	118–9	....			s^h	...	s	...	...	aa s	B12[2], 705
n77	—,1-amino-6-nitro-*	$C_{10}H_8N_2O_2$. See n14	188.20	og-red nd (chl) λ^{al} 290 (4.11) 353 (3.49), 429 (3.29)	172–3	....					s	...	...	chl s^h	B12[2], 705
n78	—,1-amino-8-nitro-*	$C_{10}H_8N_2O_2$. See n14	188.20	red lf (peth)	96–7	....					s	...	...	dil sulf s lig s^h	B12[2], 705
Ω n79	—,2-amino-1-nitro-*	$C_{10}H_8N_2O_2$. See n14	188.20	og-ye nd (al)	126–7	....			s^h	v	...	v	...	aa v	B12, 1313
n80	—,2-amino-6-nitro-*	$C_{10}H_8N_2O_2$. See n14	188.20	lt og pl (al), ye pl (aa) λ^{al} 292 (3.81), 429 (4.14)	207.5	....			δ			...	s	diox s aa s^h	E12B, 765
n81	—,6-amino-1-nitro-*	$C_{10}H_8N_2O_2$. See n14	188.20	red nd (al) λ^{al} 277 (4.20), 352 (3.55)	143.5	....				v^h	...	...	v	aa v lig i	B12, 1314
n82	—,7-amino-1-nitro-*	$C_{10}H_8N_2O_2$. See n14	188.20	red nd (aa) λ^{al} 275 (4.22), 347 (3.42), 427 (3.46)	104.5	....				s	s	...	s	os v aa s^h lig i	B12, 1315
n83	—,2-amino-1-nitroso-*	$C_{10}H_8N_2O$. See n14	172.20	gr nd (dil al), dk gr nd (bz)	150–2	....			δ^h	v^h	...	...	...	dil ac v os s^h	B7, 717
n84	—,2-amino-1,3,6-tribromo-*	$C_{10}H_6Br_3N$. See n14	379.89	pa red cr (chl, al or al-eth)	143	....			δ^h	δ^h	v	...	...	chl v peth δ	E12B, 741
n85	—,1(2-amino-ethyl)-*	$C_{12}H_{13}N$. See n14	171.25			182–3[18]				v	...	...	...	xyl s	E12B, 425
n86	—,2(2-amino-ethyl)-*	$C_{12}H_{13}N$. See n14	171.25			174[25]				s	...	...	...	aa s	E12B, 426

For explanations, symbols and abbreviations see beginning of table. For structural formulas see end of table.

Naphthalene

No.	Name	Synonyms and Formula	Mol. wt.	Color, crystalline form, specific rotation and λ_{max} (log ε)	m.p. °C	b.p. °C	Density	n_D	w	al	eth	ace	bz	other solvents	Ref.
n87	—,1(2-amino-ethylamino)-*	N-α-Naphthylethylenedi-amine $C_{10}H_7^4NHCH_2CH_2NH_2$	186.26	ye	....	320d 204[9]	1.114$_4^{25}$	1.6648[25]	δ	s	...	v	...	os v lig i	E12B, 518
n88	—,1(amino-methyl)-*	$C_{11}H_{11}N$. See n14.........	157.22	yesh turns red in air	....	294–5 162–3[12]				s	s	...	...	sulf s (bl) CS_2 s	B12[2], 741
n89	—,2(amino-methyl)-*	$C_{11}H_{11}N$. See n14.	157.22	pr (eth)	59–60	180[24] 149[12]			δ	v	v	...	...		E12B, 421
n90	—,1-benzyl-2-hydroxy-	1-Benzyl-2-naphthol. $C_{17}H_{14}O$. See n14	234.30	nd (bz, dil HCO_2H)	115 (110)	247–50[15]			i	s	v	v	s	chl s	B6[2], 680
n91	—,1-benzyl-4-hydroxy-	4-Benzyl-1-naphthol. $C_{17}H_{14}O$. See n14	234.30	pl or nd (dil aa-lig), pr (bz)	125–6	237[9–10]			δ					os s lig δ	B6[2], 680
n92	—,2-benzyl-1-hydroxy-	2-Benzyl-1-naphthol. $C_{17}H_{14}O$. See n14 λ^{MeOH} 220 (4.52), 236 (4.60), 270 (3.48), 295 (3.64)	234.30	nd (lig), pr (bz)	73.5–4.0	237–40[12]			i				s^h	lig δ	B6[2], 681
n92[1]	—,1(benzylidene-amino)-	Benzaldehyde α-naph-thylimide. $C_{17}H_{13}N$. See n14	231.30	ye lf (al)	73.5				i	s^h	s	...	s	MeOH s	E12B, 507
n92[2]	—,2(benzylidene-amino)-	Benzaldehyde β-naph-thylimide. $C_{17}H_{13}N$. See n14 $\lambda^{decalin}$ 335 (4.1)	231.30	yesh nd (al)	103				i	s^h	s	...	s	chl, aa s	E12B, 602
Ω n93	—,1-bromo-*.....	$C_{10}H_7Br$. See n14.........	207.08	pr (β form)	−6.2(α) 2–2.7(β)	281 139[16]	1.4826$_4^{20}$	1.658[20]	s^h	∞	∞	s	∞	chl s	B5[3], 1580
Ω n94	—,2-bromo-*.....	$C_{10}H_7Br$. See n14.........	207.08	pl or rh lf (al) λ^{Me-cy} 410 (−1.2)	59, fp 55.2	281–2[760] 147[18]	1.605[0]	1.6382[60]	i	s	s	...	s	chl, CS_2 s	B5[3], 1583
n95	—,1-bromo-2(bromo-methyl)-*	$C_{11}H_8Br_2$. See n14.	300.02	nd (al), cr (peth)	107–8	....			d^h	s	s	...	s	lig s^h	B5[3], 1633
Ω n96	—,1-bromo-2-hydroxy-*	1-Bromo-2-naphthol. $C_{10}H_7BrO$. See n14	223.08	rh pr (bz-lig), nd (aa, lig)	84	d130			i	s	s	...	s	aa v lig s	E12B, 1484
n97	—,1-bromo-4-hydroxy-*	4-Bromo-1-naphthol. $C_{10}H_7BrO$. See n14	223.08	nd (dil al), nd (hx)	128	....				s^h		...		chl, aa s	B6[3], 2935
n98	—,1-bromo-5-hydroxy-*	5-Bromo-1-naphthol. $C_{10}H_7BrO$. See n14	223.08	nd (w)	137	....			s^h		s	...			B6[3], 2936
n99	—,1-bromo-6-hydroxy-*	5-Bromo-2-naphthol. $C_{10}H_7BrO$. See n14	223.08	nd (w)	105	....			s^h		s	...			B6[2], 605
n100	—,1-bromo-8-hydroxy-*	8-Bromo-1-naphthol. $C_{10}H_7BrO$. See n14	223.08	pl (peth)	61	....				s	s	s		oos s lig s^h	B6, 614
n101	—,2-bromo-3-hydroxy-*	3-Bromo-2-naphthol. $C_{10}H_7BrO$. See n14	223.08	nd (lig)	84–5	....			δ^h	v		...	v	oos s lig s^h	B6[2], 605
Ω n102	—,2-bromo-6-hydroxy-*	6-Bromo-2-naphthol. $C_{10}H_7BrO$. See n14	223.08	nd (bz)	127 (130)	....					s	...	s^h		B6[2], 605
n103	—,2-bromo-7-hydroxy-*	7-Bromo-2-naphthol. $C_{10}H_7BrO$. See n14	223.08	cr (peth)	132–3	....						s	s	lig s^h	B6[2], 605
n104	—,6-bromo-1-hydroxy-*	6-Bromo-1-naphthol. $C_{10}H_7BrO$. See n14	223.08	nd (w)	129.5–30	....			v^h			...			B6[3], 2936
n105	—,7-bromo-1-hydroxy-*	7-Bromo-1-naphthol. $C_{10}H_7BrO$. See n14	223.08	cr (w)	105.6–6.5	....			s^h			...			B6[2], 583
n106	—,6-bromo-2-hydroxy-1-methyl-*	$C_{11}H_9BrO$. See n14.........	237.10	nd (bz)	129				i	v^h s	v^h s	v	δ^h	chl v aa s, v^h peth δ	E12B, 1501
n107	—,1(bromo-methyl)-*	$C_{11}H_9Br$. See n14.........	221.10	cr (peth or al)	56	183[18] 145–50[1]			i^h	s	s	v	s	aa s^h	B5[2], 462
n108	—,2(bromo-methyl)-*	$C_{11}H_9Br$. See n14.........	221.10	lf (al)	56	213[100] 165–9[14]			δd	al	s	...	s	chl s aa s^h	B5[2], 464
Ω n109	—,1-chloro-*.....	$C_{10}H_7Cl$. See n14.........	162.62	cr (al, ace, CCl_4) λ^{cy} 225 (4.83), 285.5 (3.83), 295 (3.61)	−2.3	258.8[753] 106.5[5]	1.1938$_4^{20}$	1.6326[20]	i	s	s	...	s	CS_2 s	B5[3], 1570
Ω n110	—,2-chloro-*.....	$C_{10}H_7Cl$. See n14.........	162.62	pl (dil al), lf λ^{MeOH} 226 (4.91), 270 (3.67), 288 (3.47), 322 (2.25)	61	256 121–2[12]	1.1377$_4^{71}$	1.6079[71]	i	s	s	...	s	chl, CS_2 s	B5[3], 1573
n111	—,1-chloro-2-hydroxy-*	1-Chloro-2-naphthol. $C_{10}H_7ClO$. See n14	178.62	nd (lig), pr (chl), pl (w)	71	....			δ v^h	v^h	...	...	v^h	chl v lig s^h	B6[3], 2990
n112	—,1-chloro-2-nitro-*	$C_{10}H_6ClNO$. See n14.......	207.62	pa ye nd (al, lig) λ^{MeOH} 220 (4.73), 257 (4.13), 284 (3.73)	81					s^h		...		lig s^h	E12B, 374
n113	—,1-chloro-3-nitro-*	$C_{10}H_6ClNO$. See n14.......	207.62	ye nd (HCO_2H, al)	129.5	....				s^h		...	...	HCO_2H s^h	E12B, 376

For explanations, symbols and abbreviations see beginning of table. For structural formulas see end of table.

Naphthalene

No.	Name	Synonyms and Formula	Mol. wt.	Color, crystalline form, specific rotation and λ_{max} (log ε)	m.p. °C	b.p. °C	Density	n_D	w	al	eth	ace	bz	other solvents	Ref.
n114	—,1-chloro-4-nitro-*	$C_{10}H_6ClNO_2$. See n14	207.62	br ye nd (peth or al) λ^{MeOH} 230 (4.24), 250 (4.05)	87–7.5 (85)				i	s	s			peth s[h]	E12B, 370
n115	—,1-chloro-5-nitro-*	$C_{10}H_6ClNO_2$. See n14	207.62	nd (dil al or aa)	111	>360 181[2]			i	s				aa s[h]	E12B, 372
n116	—,1-chloro-6-nitro-*	$C_{10}H_6ClNO_2$. See n14	207.62	ye nd (dil al)	131 (120)					v	δ	v	v	chl, lig v	E12B, 377
Ω n117	—,1-chloro-8-nitro-*	$C_{10}H_6ClNO_2$. See n14	207.62	lt ye nd (gl aa bz or lig)	94–5	>360 175[2]				s			s[h]	aa s lig δ, s[h]	E12B, 373
n118	—,2-chloro-1-nitro-*	$C_{10}H_6ClNO_2$. See n14	207.62	nd (peth), ye nd (al) λ^{MeOH} 226 (4.93), 265 (3.60)	99–100	>360				v	v	v	v	aa v peth δ, s[h]	E12B, 368
n119	—,2-chloro-3-nitro-*	$C_{10}H_6ClNO_2$. See n14	207.62	br cr or nd (al)	94.5 (79)										E12B, 375
n120	—,2-chloro-6-nitro-*	$C_{10}H_6ClNO_2$. See n14	207.62	ye nd	170	180–90[15]									C41, 5492
n121	—,2-chloro-7-nitro-*	$C_{10}H_6ClNO_2$. See n14	207.62	pa ye nd	136										C41, 5492
n122	—,3-chloro-1-nitro-*	$C_{10}H_6ClNO_2$. See n14	207.62	grsh-br nd (PhNO$_2$ or 90 % HCO$_2$H)	105				δ					PhNO$_2$ s[h]	E12B, 369
n123	—,6-chloro-1-nitro-*	$C_{10}H_6ClNO_2$. See n14	207.62	nd (aq ace)	!00.5				δ		s				E12B, 373
n124	—,7-chloro-1-nitro-*	$C_{10}H_6ClNO_2$. See n14	207.62	ye nd (al)	116				i	s	s				E12B, 373
Ω n126	—,1(chloromethyl)-*	$C_{11}H_9Cl$. See n14	176.65	pr	32	291–2 135–9[6]									B5[3], 1622
n127	—,2(chloromethyl)-*	$C_{11}H_9Cl$. See n14	176.65	lf (al)	48–9	170[20]			δ^h	s[h]			s		B5[3], 1632
—	—,decahydro-*	see Decalin													
Ω n128	—,1,2-diamino-*	1,2-Naphthylenediamine $C_{10}H_{10}N_2$. See n14	158.21	lf (w), rose to br in air	98–5	214[13] 150–1[0.5]			δ^h	v	v			chl v	E12B, 805
n129	—,1,4-diamino-*	1,4-Naphthylenediamine. $C_{10}H_{10}N_2$. See n14	158.21	ye nd (w)	120			1.6441[18]	δ^h	v	v		v	chl v	B13[2], 82
Ω n130	—,1,5-diamino-*	1,5-Naphthylenediamine. $C_{10}H_{10}N_2$. See n14	158.21	pr (eth, al, w)	190	sub	1.4		s[h] v[h]	s v[h]				chl v	E12B, 824
n131	—,1,6-diamino-*	1,6-Naphthylenediamine. $C_{10}H_{10}N_2$. See n14	158.21	nd (w, eth)	85–6		1.1477[99]	1.7083[99]	δ s[h]	s s[h]	δ s[h]		s		E12B, 828
n132	—,1,7-diamino-*	1,7-Naphthylenediamine. $C_{10}H_{10}N_2$. See n14	158.21	lf (bz), nd (w)	117.5				δ^h	s	δ		s[h]	lig δ	B13, 204
Ω n133	—,1,8-diamino-*	1,8-Naphthylenediamine. $C_{10}H_{10}N_2$. See n14	158.21	nd (dil al)	66.5	205[12] sub	1.1265[99]	1.6828[99]	δ s[h]	v	v				B13[2], 85
Ω n134	—,2,3-diamino-*	2,3-Naphthylenediamine. $C_{10}H_{10}N_2$. See n14	158.21	lf (eth or w)	199		1.0968[26]	1.6342[26]	δ	v	s				B13[2], 86
n135	—,2,6-diamino-*	2,6-Naphthylenediamine. $C_{10}H_{10}N_2$. See n14	158.21	nd or lf (w), lf (al)	222 d				δ^h	δ	δ				B13[2], 86
n136	—,1,4-diamino-2-methyl-*	$C_{11}H_{12}N_2$. See n14	172.23	ye cr (peth)	113–4				δ					aa, ac s peth s[h]	E12B, 846
n137	—,—,dihydrochloride	Vitamin K$_6$. $C_{11}H_{12}N_2$.2HCl. See n14	245.15	cr (dil HCl)	300 d				v						E12B, 846
n138	—,1,5-diamino-2-methyl-*	$C_{11}H_{12}N_2$. See n14	172.23	red-ye lf (dil al)	136 (128d)				δ	v	v		v		E12B, 847
n139	—,1,3-diamino-2-phenyl-*	$C_{16}H_{14}N_2$. See n14	234.30	pl (MeOH or bz) turns red in air	116					v	δ		s[h]	lig i	E12B, 843
n140	—,2,6-dibromo-1,5-dihydroxy-,diacetate	$C_{14}H_{10}Br_2O_4$. See n14	402.05	nd	147.5									lig s[h]	B6[2], 951
Ω n141	—,1,6-dibromo-2-hydroxy-*	1,6-Dibromo-2-naphthol. $C_{10}H_6Br_2O$. See n14	301.98	nd (peth, bz), lf (al), nd (aa +1)	106 84 (+1 aa)				i	s	s	s			E12B, 1512
n142	—,1,2-dichloro-*	$C_{10}H_6Cl_2$. See n14	197.07	pl (al) λ^{hx} 273, 284, 316, 325	35–7	295–8 151–3[19]	1.3147[49]	1.6338[49]		s	s				E12B, 302
n143	—,1,3-dichloro-*	Dichloronaphthalene. $C_{10}H_6Cl_2$. See n14	197.07	nd or pr (al) λ^{hx} 272, 277, 312, 319, 326	61.5	291[775]				s					E12B, 304
n144	—,1,4-dichloro-*	β-Dichloronaphthalene. $C_{10}H_6Cl_2$. See n14	197.07	nd or pr (al, aa or ace)	68	286–7[740] 147[12]	1.2997[76]	1.6228[76]	i	δ	s	v	s	aa s	E12B, 306
n145	—,1,5-dichloro-*	γ-Dichloronaphthalene. $C_{10}H_6Cl_2$. See n14	197.07	nd or lf (al, MeOH, aa), pr (sub) λ^{hx} 280, 292, 320, 324	107	sub			i	δ	s				E12B, 309

For explanations, symbols and abbreviations see beginning of table. For structural formulas see end of table.

No.	Name	Synonyms and Formula	Mol. wt.	Color. crystalline form. specific rotation and λ_{max} (log ε)	m.p. °C	b.p. °C	Density	n_D	w	al	eth	ace	bz	other solvents	Ref.
	Naphthalene														
n146	—,1,6-dichloro-*	η-Dichloronaphthalene. $C_{10}H_6Cl_2$, See n14	197.07	nd or pr (al, peth, sub) λ^{hx} 276, 288, 317, 325	49	sub	......	......	...	s	s	...	s	aa s	E12B, 310
n147	—,1,7-dichloro-*	θ-Dichloronaphthalene. $C_{10}H_6Cl_2$. See n14	197.07	nd or pr (al, aa) λ^{hx} 267, 273, 296, 320, 326	63.5–4.5	285–6	1.2611_4^{100}	1.6092^{100}	...	s	s	...	s	aa s	E12B, 312
n148	—,1,8-dichloro-*	ζ-Dichloronaphthalene. peri-Dichloronaphthalene. $C_{10}H_6Cl_2$. See n14	197.07	rh pl (hx), nd (al, sub) λ^{hx} 296, 308 319, 324, 329	89–9.5	d sub	1.2924_4^{100}	1.6236^{100}	...	s^h	s	...	...	peth s^h	E12B, 313
n149	—,2,3-dichloro-*	ι-Dichloronaphthalene. $C_{10}H_6Cl_2$. See n14	197.07	rh lf (al) λ^{hx} 272, 283, 312, 326	120		......	......	i	δ s^h	v	...	...		E12B, 315
n150	—,2,6-dichloro-*	ϵ-Dichloronaphthalene. $C_{10}H_6Cl_2$. See n14	197.07	pr (aa), nd or lf (al), pl (eth, bz) λ^{hx} 277, 301, 313, 330	140–1	285	......	......	...	δ	s	...	s	chl, aa s	E12B, 317
n151	—,2,7-dichloro-*	δ-Dichloronaphthalene. $C_{10}H_6Cl_2$. See n14	197.07	pl or lf (al) λ^{hx} 260, 270, 281, 311, 327	114		......	......	...	v^h	...	...	...	hx, aa s^h	E12B, 318
Ω n152	—,1(diethyl-amino)-*	N,N-Diethyl-1-naphthyl-amine*. $C_{14}H_{17}N$. See n14	199.30			285 155–65^{30}	1.015_{20}^{20}	1.5961^{20}	i	s	s	...	...	aa s	C37, 1397
n153	—,2,3-di-hydrazino-*	$C_{10}H_{12}N_4$. See n14	188.23	red-br (al or w), col nd (bz), br-ye (AmOH)	167–8d (w, AmOH) 155–6 (bz, al)		......	......	...	v	...	...	...	dil ac s sulf s(red) aa δ	E12B, 908
Ω n154	—,1,2-dihydro-*	Δ^1-Dialin. Δ^1-Dihydro-naphthalene. $C_{10}H_{10}$. See n14	130.19	lf, pl on cooling	–8 – –7	206–7 78^9	0.9974_4^{20}	1.58137^{20}	...	...	...	...	...		E12B, 53
n155	—,1,4-dihydro-*	Δ^2-Dialin $C_{10}H_{10}$. See n14	130.19	pl	25 (30)	211–2^{760} 94^{17}	0.9928_4^{23}	1.5577^{20}	...	...	...	...	...	aa s^h	E12B, 54
n156	—,1,2-dihydroxy-*	β-Naphthohydroquinone. 1,2-Naphthalenediol*. $C_{10}H_8O_2$. See n14	160.18	lf or nd (CS_2), lf (w + l), nd (lig)	103–4 (anh) 58–60 (+1w)	......	......		δ	...	s	...	...	sulf v alk s lig s^h	E12B, 1962
Ω n157	—,1,4-dihydroxy-*	1,4-Naphthalenediol*. α-Naphthohydroquinone. $C_{10}H_8O_2$. See n14	160.18	mcl nd (bz, w)	192 (176)	......			s^h	s	s	...	i	aa s CS_2, lig i	E12B, 1973
Ω n158	—,1,5-dihydroxy-*	1,5-Naphthalenediol*. $C_{10}H_8O_2$. See n14	160.18	pr (w), nd (sub)	265d	sub	......	......	δ	δ	v	v	i	aa s lig i	E12B, 1980
n159	—,—,diacetate	$C_{14}H_{12}O_4$. See n14	244.25	nd (bz)	161				...	...	...	...	s^h	aa s^h	E12B, 1982
Ω n160	—,1,6-dihydroxy-*	1,6-Naphthalenediol*. $C_{10}H_8O_2$. See n14	160.18	pr (bz)	138	sub	......	......	δ	δ	s	s		MeOH s chl δ lig i	E12B, 1987
Ω n161	—,1,7-dihydroxy-*	1,7-Naphthalenediol*. $C_{10}H_8O_2$. See n14	160.18	nd (bz or sub)	178–81	sub	......	......	δ s^h	v	v	...	s	aa s	E12B, 1989
n162	—,1,8-dihydroxy-*	1,8-Naphthalenediol*. peri-Dihydroxy-naphthalene. $C_{10}H_8O_2$. See n14	160.18	lf or nd (w)	144 (140)		......	......	δ^h	s^h	v	...	v	to v lig δ	E12B, 1991
Ω n163	—,2,3-dihydroxy-*	2,3-Naphthalenediol*. $C_{10}H_8O_2$. See n14	160.18	lf (w)	163.5–4		......	......	s^h	s	s	...	s	aa, lig s	E12B, 1994
Ω n164	—,2,6-dihydroxy-*	2,6-Naphthalenediol*. $C_{10}H_8O_2$. See n14	160.18	rh pl (w)	222	sub	......	......	δ s^h	s	s	s	δ	aa s lig i	E12B, 2003
Ω n165	—,2,7-dihydroxy-*	2,7-Naphthalenediol*. $C_{10}H_8O_2$. See n14	160.18	nd (w or dil al), pl (dil al)	190 (nd) 194 (pl)	sub	......	......	s^h	s	s	...	s	chl, to s lig, CS_2 i	E12B, 2007
Ω n166	—,1,4-dihydroxy-2-methyl-, diacetate	$C_{15}H_{14}O_4$. See n14	258.28	pr (al)	113		......	......	i	s^h	...	...	δ		B6^2, 958
n167	—,1,5-di-mercapto-*	1,5-Naphthalenedithiol*. $C_{10}H_8S_2$. See n14	192.31	ye lf (al, eth, bz)	119				...	s	s	...	s	dil HCl v	B6^2, 952
n168	—,1,4-dimethyl-*	α-Dimethylnaphthalene. $C_{12}H_{12}$. See n14	156.23	....	7.66	268^{760} 129^{10}	1.0166_4^{20}	1.6127^{20}	i	v	∞	∞	∞	CCl_4, lig ∞	B5^3, 1645
Ω n169	—,2,3-dimethyl-*	Guaiene. $C_{12}H_{12}$. See n14	156.23	lf (al, MeOH)	105	268^{760} 128.7^{10}	1.003_4^{20}	1.5060^{20}	i	δ s^h	s	s	s	aa δ	B5^3, 1650
Ω n170	—,1(dimethyl-amino)-*	N,N-Dimethyl-1-naphthyl-amine*. $C_{12}H_{13}N$. See n14	171.25	vt flr λ^{al} 236 (4.13), 305 (3.68)		274.5^{711} 139–40^{15}	1.0423^{20}	1.624^{15}	i	s	s	...	...	aa s	B12, 521
Ω n171	—,2(dimethyl-amino)-*	N,N-Dimethyl-2-naphthyl-amine*. $C_{12}H_{13}N$. See n14	171.25	dk red nd λ^{al} 240 (4.65), 282 (3.86), 345 (3.35)	52–3 (46–7)	305 160–2^{12}	1.0455_{40}^{40}	1.6443^{53}	i	s	s	...	s	aa s	B12, 1273
n172	—,1,6-dimethyl-4-isopropyl-*	Cadalene. $C_{15}H_{18}$. See n14	198.31	....		291–2^{720} 165^{20}	0.9792_4^{19}	1.5851^{19}	...	...	...	...	...		B5^3, 1683
n173	—,1,3-dinitro-*	γ Nitronaphthalene. $C_{10}H_6N_2O_4$. See n14	218.17	ye nd (bz or Py-w)	147–9	sub	......	......	i	s	s	...	s		B5^3, 1605

For explanations, symbols and abbreviations see beginning of table. For structural formulas see end of table.

No.	Name	Synonyms and Formula	Mol. wt.	Color, crystalline form, specific rotation and λ_{max} (log ε)	m.p. °C	b.p. °C	Density	n_D	w	al	eth	ace	bz	other solvents	Ref.
	Naphthalene														
Ω n174	—,1,5-dinitro-*	$C_{10}H_6N_2O_4$. See n14	218.17	hex nd (aa or ace) λ^{al} 233 (4.32), 327 (3.81)	219	sub	....		i	δ	v	δ	s[h]	Py s[h], CS$_2$ δ	B5[3], 1606
Ω n175	—,1,8-dinitro-*	$C_{10}H_6N_2O_4$. See n14	218.17	ye rh pl (chl) λ^{al} 231 (4.44), 313 (3.81)	173–3.5	445d			i	δ	...	s	δ	Py s chl δ	B5[3], 1607 B14[2], 653
n176	—,1,6-dinitro-2-hydroxy-*	$C_{10}H_6N_2O_5$. See n14	234.17	pa ye nd (chl)	195d	....			i	s[h]	v	...	...	Py, chl v lig i	E12B, 1581
n177	—,2,4-dinitro-1-triazo-*	$C_{10}H_5N_5O_4$. See n14	259.18	ye rh nd (al)	105d					s[h]	s	s	...	chl, to s lig s[h]	B5[2], 460
n178	—,5,8-dioxo-1,4,5,8,9,10-hexa-hydro-1,4-methylene-*	Cyclopentadienebenzo-quinone.	174.20	gr-ye lf (MeOH) λ 285 (1.40)	77–8	....				s	s	s	s	os s	E13, 1033
Ω n179	—,1-ethoxy-*	Ethyl α-naphthyl ether. $C_{12}H_{12}O$. See n14	172.23	nd	5.5	280.5 136–8[14]	1.0602[20]	1.5953[25]	i	v	v				B6[3], 2924
Ω n180	—,2-ethoxy-*	Ethyl β-naphthyl ether Nerolin II. $C_{12}H_{12}O$. See n14	172.23	pl (al)	37–8	282 148[10]	1.0640[20]/20	1.5975[36]	i	s	s		...	to, lig, CS$_2$, s	B6[3], 2972
Ω n181	—,1-ethyl-*	$C_{12}H_{12}$. See n14	156.23	λ^{iso} 224 (4.9), 282 (3.8), 323 (1.4)	−13.88	258.67[760] 120[10]	1.00816[20]/4	1.6062[20]	i	∞	∞				B5[3], 1639
Ω n182	—,2-ethyl-*	$C_{12}H_{12}$. See n14	156.23	....	−7.4	257.9[760] 119[10]	0.9922[20]/4	1.5999[20]	i	∞	∞				B5[3], 1641
n183	—,1(ethyl-amino)-*	Ethyl α-naphthylamine. $C_{12}H_{13}N$. See n14	171.25	....		303[723] 191[16]	1.060[20]	1.6477[15]	i	s	s				B12[2], 682
n184	—,2(ethyl-amino)-*	Ethyl β-naphthylamine. $C_{12}H_{13}N$. See n14.	171.25	....	<15	316–7 191[25]	1.0545[21]	1.6544[21]		s	s				B12[2], 715
Ω n185	—,1-fluoro-*	$C_{10}H_7F$. See n14.	146.17	....	−9	215[756] 80[11]	1.1322[20]	1.5939[20]	i	s	s		s	chl, aa s	B5[3], 1569
Ω n186	—,2-fluoro-*	$C_{10}H_7F$. See n14.	146.17	nd (al)	61	211.5[737] 90[16] sub			i	s	s		s	chl, aa s	B5[3], 1569
n187	—,1(formyl-amino)-*	$C_{11}H_9NO$. See n14	171.20	nd (w)	137.5	....			s[h]	s	s	s	...	os s	E12B, 459
n188	—,2(formyl-amino)-*	$C_{11}H_9NO$. See n14	171.20	lf (bz-peth)	129						s	s	s	peth δ	E12B, 562
n189	—,1,2,3,4,9,10-hexahydro-*	Naphthalene hexahydride. $C_{10}H_{14}$. See n14	134.22			200 82[2]	0.934[23]	1.5260[16]	i		s		s		B5, 433
Ω n190	—,1-hydroxy-*	1-Naphthol. α-Naphthol. $C_{10}H_8O$. See n14	144.19	ye mcl nd (w) λ^{al} 292 (3.67), 308 (3.52), 322 (3.31)	96 (94)	288[760] sub	1.0989[99]/4	1.6224[99]	i δ[h]	v	v	s	s	chl v CCl$_4$ δ	E12B, 1148
Ω n191	—,2-hydroxy-*	2-Naphthol. β-Naphthol. $C_{10}H_8O$. See n14	144.19	mcl lf (w), pl (CS$_2$) λ^{al} 226 (4.86), 265 (3.59), 274 (3.67), 285 (3.52)	123–4	295[760]	1.28[20]	....	i δ[h]	v	v	...	s	chl s SO$_2$, CCl$_4$ δ lig δ[h]	E12B, 1210
n192	—,—,acetate	2-Acetoxynaphthalene. $C_{12}H_{10}O_2$. See n14	186.21	nd (al)	71–2	132–4[2]	....		i	v	v			chl v	E12B, 1256
Ω n193	—,—,benzoate	2-Benzoyloxynaphthalene. $C_{17}H_{12}O_2$. See n14	248.29	nd or pr (al), cr (lig) λ^{al} 221 (4.88), 274 (3.71), 303 (2.59), 317 (2.50)	108	....			i	v[h]	δ				E12B, 1260
Ω n197	—,2-hydroxy-1-methyl-*	1-Methyl-2-naphthol. $C_{11}H_{10}O$. See n14	158.20	nd (w, bz-lig, dil aa)	112	180[12] sub	....		δ s[h]	v	v	v	v	aa, chl v peth s	E12B, 1388
n198	—,1-hydroxy-8-nitro-*	8-Nitro-1-naphthol. $C_{10}H_7NO_3$. See n14	189.17	grsh ye nd (al, chl, bz-hx)	130–3	....			s	v	v	v	v	alk s	E12B, 1547
Ω n199	—,2-hydroxy-1-nitro-*	1-Nitro-2-naphthol. $C_{10}H_7NO_3$. See n14	189.17	ye nd, lf or pr (al) λ^{al} 330 (3.50)	104	115[0.05]	....		s[h]	s	v				E12B, 1547
n199[2]	—,2-hydroxy-5-nitro	5-Nitro-2-naphthol. $C_{10}H_7NO_3$. See n14	189.17	lt ye nd (w)	147–9				v[h]	δ	v	v	...	oos v	E12B, 1556
Ω n201	—,1-hydroxy-4-nitroso-*	1,4-Naphthoquinone 1-oxime*. 4-Nitroso-1-naphthol. $C_{10}H_7NO_2$. See n14	173.17	pa ye nd (bz), nd (dil al) λ^{al} 263 (4.08), 372.5 (3.70)	198	....			i	v	v	v	δ[h]	MeOH v chl, CS$_2$ δ	E12B, 2786
Ω n202	—,2-hydroxy-1-nitroso-*	1,2-Naphthoquinone 1-oxime*. 1-Nitroso-2-naphthol. $C_{10}H_7NO_2$. See n14	173.17	ye nd (bz), og pr or pl (al) $\lambda^{w, pH=7}$ 260 (3.78)	112 (109.5)	....			i	v v[h]	v	s	v	aa v lig δ	E12B, 2731
n203	—,2-hydroxy-1,3,6-tribromo-*	1,3,6-Tribromo-2-naphthol. $C_{10}H_5Br_3O$. See n14	380.88	nd (aa or al)	133					s	s		s	MeOH, CCl$_4$ s	B6[3], 3000
n204	—,2-hydroxy-1,4,6-tribromo-*	Providoform. 1,4,6-Tribro-mo-2-naphthol. $C_{10}H_5Br_3O$. See n14	380.88	nd (bz)	157–8	....				s	s		s[h]	chl, aa s	E12B, 1522

For explanations, symbols and abbreviations see beginning of table. For structural formulas see end of table.

No.	Name	Synonyms and Formula	Mol. wt.	Color, crystalline form, specific rotation and λ_{max} (log ε)	m.p. °C	b.p. °C	Density	n_D	Solubility					Ref.
									w	al	eth	ace	bz	other solvents	

Naphthalene

No.	Name	Synonyms and Formula	Mol. wt.	Color...	m.p.	b.p.	Density	n_D	w	al	eth	ace	bz	other	Ref.
n205	—,3-hydroxy-1,2,7-tribromo-*	3,4,6-Tribromo-β-naphthol. $C_{10}H_5Br_3O$. See n14	380.88	nd (bz)	127–8	....				s			v^h		B6[2], 607
n206	—,1-hydroxy-2,3,4-trichloro-*	2,3,4-Trichloro-α-naphthol. $C_{10}H_5Cl_3O$. See n14	247.51	nd (aa or lig)	168				i	s^h	s			aa, lig δ^h	B6[2], 582
Ω n207	—,2-hydroxy-1,3,4-trichloro-*	1,3,4-Trichloro-β-naphthol. $C_{10}H_5Cl_3O$. See n14	247.51	nd	162	....				s				aa s	B6[7], 604
Ω n208	—,1-iodo-*	$C_{10}H_7I$. See n14	254.07	λ^{hp} 225 (4.6), 280 (3.9), 287 (4.0), 299 (3.6)	4.2	302	1.7399_4^{20}	1.70256^{20}	i	∞	∞		∞	CS_2 ∞	B5[3], 1590
n209	—,2-iodo-*	$C_{10}H_7I$. See n14	254.07	lf (dil al) λ^{hp} 236 (4.4), 275 (3.6), 292 (3.5)	54.5	308 172[21]	1.6319_4^{29}	1.6662^{99}	i	v	v			aa v	B5[3], 1591
n210	—,1-mercapto-*	1-Naphthalenethiol*. 1-Thionaphthol. $C_{10}H_8S$. See n14	160.24	λ^{iso} 297 (4.34)	....	285d 208.5[200] 161[20]	1.1607_4^{20}	1.6802^{20}	δ	v	v			dil alk δ	B6[3], 2943
Ω n211	—,2-mercapto-*	2-Naphthalenethiol*. 2-Thionaphthol. $C_{10}H_8S$. See n14	160.24	pl (al) λ^{chl} 273 (3.8), 292 (3.7), 336 (2.8)	81	288 162.7[20]	1.550	....	δ	v	v			lig v	B6[3], 3006
Ω n215	—,1-methoxy-*	Methyl α-naphthyl ether. $C_{11}H_{10}O$. See n14	158.20	λ^{cy} 293 (3.5), 306 (3.3), 320 (3.1)	< –10	269 (cor) 135[10]	1.0964_4^{14}	1.6940^{25}	i	s	s		s	CS_2 v chl ε	B6[3], 2922
Ω n216	—,2-methoxy-*	Methyl β-naphthyl ether. Nerolin. $C_{11}H_{10}O$. See n14	158.20	lf (eth), pl (peth) λ^{al} 227 (4.85), 271 (3.65), 314 (3.19), 328 (3.30)	73 4	274 138[10] sub			δ	δ	s		v	chl v CS_2 s MeOH δ	B6[3], 2926
Ω n217	—,1-methyl-*	$C_{11}H_{10}$. See n14	142.20	λ^{diox} 267 (3.6), 279 (3.6), 314 (2.4)	–22 (–30.5)	244.64[760] 107.4[10]	1.0202_4^{20}	1.6170^{20}	i	v	v		s		B5[3], 1620
Ω n218	—,2-methyl-*	$C_{11}H_{10}$. See n14	142.20	mcl (al) λ^{al} 224 (4.38), 274 (3.72), 305 (2.66), 319 (2.65)	34.58	241.05[760] 104.7[10]	1.0058_4^{20}	1.6019^{40}	i	v	v		s		B5[3], 1627
n219	—,1(methyl-amino)-*	Methyl α-naphthylamine. $C_{11}H_{11}N$. See n14	157.22	oil	....	293 165–75[15]		1.6722^{20}	i	s	s			CS_2 s	B12[2], 681
n220	—,2(methyl-amino)-*	Methyl β-naphthylamine. $C_{11}H_{11}N$. See n14	157.22	dk in air	....	317 (308–10) 165–70[12]			i	s	s				B12, 1273
n221	—,1(3-methyl-butoxy)-*	Isoamyl α-naphthyl ether. $C_{15}H_{18}O$. See n14	214.31	....		317–9[742] 148–53[3]	1.0069_4^{14}	1.5705^{14}							B6, 607
n222	—,2(3-methyl-butoxy)-*	Isoamyl β-naphthyl ether. $C_{15}H_{18}O$. See n14	214.31	lf	26.5	323–6d 155–60[6]	1.0155_4^{12}	1.5768^{12}	i	s	s				B6, 642
n223	—,1-methyl-2-nitro-*	$C_{11}H_9NO_2$. See n14	187.20	lt ye nd (al)	58–9	....			i	s					E12B, 363
n224	—,1-methyl-3-nitro-*	$C_{11}H_9NO_2$. See n14	187.20	ye nd (al)	81–2				i	v					E12B, 364
n225	—,1-methyl-4-nitro-*	$C_{11}H_9NO_2$. See n14	187.20	pa ye nd (al)	71–2	182–3[18]			i	s	s	s		os s	E12B, 362
n226	—,1-methyl-5-nitro-*	$C_{11}H_9NO_2$. See n14	187.20	brsh nd (al)	82–3				i	s	s			os s	E12B, 363
n227	—,1-methyl-6-nitro-*	$C_{11}H_9NO_2$. See n14	187.20	ye nd (dil al)	76–7				i	s					E12B, 364
n228	—,1-methyl-7-nitro-*	$C_{11}H_9NO_2$. See n14	187.20	ye nd (al)	98–9				i	s^h					E12B, 364
n229	—,1-methyl-8-nitro-*	$C_{11}H_9NO_2$. See n14	187.20	br lf (al)	65				i	s^h					E12B, 363
Ω n230	—,2-methyl-1-nitro-*	$C_{11}H_9NO_2$. See n14	187.20	yesh pr or nd (al)	81–2	188[20]			i	s		v		os v	E12B, 362
n231	—,2-methyl-3-nitro-*	$C_{11}H_9NO_2$. See n14	187.20	yesh pl (al)	117–8				i	s^h					E12B, 364
n232	—,2-methyl-6-nitro-*	$C_{11}H_9NO_2$. See n14	187.20	ye nd (al)	119				i	s^h					E12B, 364
n233	—,2-methyl-7-nitro-*	$C_{11}H_9NO_2$. See n14	187.20	ycsh pl (al)	105 (102)				i	s^h					E12B, 364
n234	—,3-methyl-1-nitro-*	$C_{11}H_9NO_2$. See n14	187.20	pa ye nd (al)	49–50				i	v^h					E12B, 362
n235	—,6-methyl-1-nitro-*	$C_{11}H_9NO_2$. See n14	187.20	ye nd (al)	61–2				i	s^h					E12B, 363
n236	—,7-methyl-1-nitro-*	$C_{11}H_9NO_2$. See n14	187.20	ye nd (al)	36–8				i	s^h					E12B, 363
n237	—,1-nitramino-*	1-Diazonaphthalenic acid. $C_{10}H_7^\prime NHNO_2$	188.20	lt ye nd (w)	123 4				s^h			s		alk, os v lig i	E12B, 862
n238	—,2-nitramino-*	2-Diazonaphthalenic acid. $C_{10}H_7^\prime NHNO_2$	188.20	lf or nd	131.5–6										E12B, 862

For explanations, symbols and abbreviations see beginning of table. For structural formulas see end of table.

No.	Name	Synonyms and Formula	Mol. wt.	Color, crystalline form, specific rotation and λ_{max} (log ε)	m.p. °C	b.p. °C	Density	n_D	w	al	eth	ace	bz	other solvents	Ref.
	Naphthalene														
Ω n239	—,1-nitro-*	$C_{10}H_7NO_2$. See n14	173.17	ye nd (al) λ^{al} 243 (4.02), 343 (3.60)	61.5	304 sub 30–40[0.01]	1.3322[20]	....	i	v	v	...	v	chl, CS_2, Py v	B5[3], 1593
n240	—,2-nitro-*	$C_{10}H_7NO_2$. See n14	173.17	ye rh nd or pl (al) λ^{al} 258 (4.40), 306 (3.93), 352 (3.44)	79	312.5[734] 165[15]	....	....	i	v	v	...	...		B5[3], 1596
n241	—,1-nitro-5-triazo-*	$C_{10}H_6N_4O_2$. See n14	214.19	gold-ye nd (al)	121	....	....	....	δ s^h	s^h	...	s			B5[2], 459
n242	—,2-nitro-1-triazo-*	$C_{10}H_6N_4O_2$. See n14	214.19	ye nd (dil ace)	103–4d	....	....	....	...	v	...	v	v	aa v lig δ^h	B5, 565
n243	—,1(nitroso-hydroxyl-amino)-*	$C_{10}H_7^{a}N(NO)OH$. See n14	188.20	nd (peth)	54–5	....	....	....						chl, NH_3 s peth s^h	E12B, 863
n244	—,2(nitroso-hydroxyl-amino)-*	$C_{10}H_7^{a}N(NO)OH$. See n14	188.20	nd (AcOEt-peth)	88–92	....	....	....				s		NH_3, aa s	E12B, 863
n245	—,octachloro-*	Perchloronaphthalene. $C_{10}Cl_8$. See n14	403.74	nd (bz-CCl_4) λ^{al} 275 (4.67), 332 (3.87), 345 sh (3.79)	197.5–8 (cor)	440–2[7.4] δd 246[0.5]	....	....		δ	...		v	chl, lig v	B5[3], 1579
Ω n246	—,1-phenyl-*	$C_{16}H_{12}$. See n14	204.28	cr λ^{al} 225 (4.70), 288 (3.95)	ca. 45	334[760] 190[12]	1.0962[20]	1.6664[20]	i	v	v	...	v	aa v	B5[3], 2230
Ω n247	—,2-phenyl-*	$C_{16}H_{12}$. See n14	204.28	lf (al) λ^{al} 250 (4.70), 285 (4.00)	103–4	345–6 (357–8) 185–90[5]	....	....		s	v	...	s	aa, chl s	B5[3], 2231
n248	—,1-propoxy-*	α-Naphthyl propyl ether. $C_{13}H_{14}O$. See n14	186.26	....	....	293.5[760] 167[18]	1.0447[18]	1.5928[18]			v	...			B6[3], 2924
n249	—,2-propoxy-*	β-Naphthyl propyl ether. $C_{13}H_{14}O$. See n14	186.26	nd (al)	41	305[760] 144[10]	....	....		s^h					B6[3], 2973
—	—,1,2,3,4-tetra-hydro-*	see **Tetralin**													
n251	—,1,3,5,8-tetra-nitro-*	γ-Tetranitronaphthalene. $C_{10}H_4N_4O_8$. See n14	308.17	lt ye tetr (ace)	194–5	....	....	....		δ	...	v		HNO_3 s chl, aa δ	E12B, 410
n252	—,1,3,6,8-tetra-nitro-*	β-Tetranitronaphthalene. $C_{10}H_4N_4O_8$. See n14	308.17	ye nd (al, bz)	207	exp	....	....	i	δ s^h	...	...	s^h	aa, to s^h	B5[3], 1614
n253	—,1-triazo-*	α-Naphthyl azide. $C_{10}H_7N_3$. See n14	169.19	pa ye pr λ^{al} 300 (3.85)	12	d	1.1713[25]	1.6550[25]		v	∞	∞			E12B, 1041
n254	—,2-triazo-*	β-Naphthyl azide. $C_{10}H_7N_3$. See n14	169.19	pr (al), nd (peth) ye in air	33	....	....	....	δ^h	s	s	s	s	MeOH, os s peth s^h	E12B, 1041
n255	—,1,2,5-tri-methyl-*	$C_{13}H_{14}$. See n14	170.26	nd (al) λ^{hx} 231 (4.98), 289 (3.80), 325 (2.94)	33.5	140[12]	1.0103[22]	1.6093[22]	i	δ	v	...	v	MeOH,	B5[3], 1661
n256	—,1,2,6-tri-methyl-*	$C_{13}H_{14}$. See n14	170.26	lf λ^{peth} 229 (4.92), 282 (3.69), 327 (3.03), 355 (0.94)	14	146[10]	....	1.6010[20]	i	δ			s		B5[3], 1662
n257	—,1,2,7-tri-methyl-*	Sapotalin. $C_{13}H_{14}$. See n14	170.26	λ^{eth} 230.5 (5.0), 280–5 (3.74), 326 (2.36)	....	147–8[16]	1.0087[20]	1.6097[20]	i	s			s		B5[3], 1662
Ω n258	—,2,3,6-tri-methyl-*	$C_{13}H_{14}$. See n14	170.26	λ 229 (5.04), 275 (3.76), 309 (2.78), 323 (2.83)	100–2 (92–3)	263–4[760] 146–8[14]	....	....	i	s			s		B5, 572
n259	—,1,2,5-trinitro-*	$C_{10}H_5N_3O_6$. See n14	263.17	lt ye nd (al)	112–3	....	....	....	i	s		s		CCl_4 s	B5[2], 457
n260	—,1,3,5-trinitro-*	$C_{10}H_5N_3O_6$. See n14	263.17	ye rh (chl)	122	364 exp	....	....	i	v	δ	v	...	aa v chl s	B5[3], 1612
n261	—,1,3,8-trinitro-*	$C_{10}H_5N_3O_6$. See n14	263.17	yesh mcl pr (al, ace or aa), wh nd (80 % HNO_3)	218	....	....	....	i^h δ^h	i	δ	s	δ	Py s to, chl δ	E12B, 405
n262	—,1,4,5-trinitro-*	$C_{10}H_5N_3O_6$. See n14	263.17	ye lf, nd or rh pl (al, aa, bz or HNO_3)	154	....	....	....	i	δ	δ	v^h	δ	AcOEt s Py v^h chl δ lig i	E12B, 406
—	**Naphthalene car-boxylic acid***	see **Naphthoic acid**													
n263	1,2-Naphthalene-dicarboxylic acid*		216.21	nd (al), cr (w)	175d	....	....	....	s^h	s	s	...	δ	aa s lig, chl, CS_2 δ	E12B, 4681
n264	1,4-Naphthalene-dicarboxylic acid*		216.21	rods (aa or $PhNO_2$)	309 (320)	....	....	....	i δ^h	v		...		os δ aa, $PhNO_2$ s^h	E12B, 4690
n265	1,5-Naphthalene-dicarboxylic acid*		216.21	nd ($PhNO_2$)	320–2 d (cor)	....	....	....	i	δ^h	δ^h	...	i^h	chl δ^h lig i^h os i	E12B, 4693

1,6-Naphthalenedicarboxylic acid

No.	Name	Synonyms and Formula	Mol. wt.	Color. crystalline form. specific rotation and λ_{max} (log ε)	m.p. °C	b.p. °C	Density	n_D	w	al	eth	ace	bz	other solvents	Ref.
n266	**1,6-Naphthalene-dicarboxylic acid***	....	216.21	nd (aa)	310 (sinters ca. 290)	....			i	s[h]	i	....	....	aa s[h] os δ	**E12B,** 4695
n267	**1,7-Naphthalene-dicarboxylic acid***	....	216.21	ye pw (dil al or aa)	308d (294–6d)	....			...	s	s	s	....	aa, os s	**E12B,** 4696
Ω n268	**1,8-Naphthalene-dicarboxylic acid***	Naphthalic acid	216.21	nd (al)	260 (270d)	....			i	δ s[h]	δ	....	....		**E12B,** 4697
Ω n269	—,anhydride......	Naphthalic anhydride. $C_{12}H_6O_3$. See n268	198.18	nd (al), pr (aa), lf (sub)	274	sub			i	δ[h]	i	...	i	aa s[h]	**E12B,** 4705
n270	—,dichloride....	Naphthaloyl chloride. $C_{12}H_6Cl_2O_2$. See n268	253.09	pr (CS_2)	84–6	195–200[0.2]							s	chl s CS_2 s[h] peth δ	**E12B,** 4713
n271	—,diethyl ester	Diethyl naphthalate. $C_{16}H_{16}O_4$. See n268	272.30	yesh mcl pr or lf (dil al)	59–60	238–9[19] 202–4[11]	1.1399[70]	1.5586[70]	i	s	s	....		AcOEt s con sulf s (bl flr)	**B9²,** 652
n272	—,dimethyl ester ..	Dimethyl naphthalate. $C_{14}H_{12}O_4$. See n268	244.25	nd (al), pr (MeOH)	104	....			i	s				MeOH v aa s	**E12B,** 4703
n273	—,imide	Naphthalimide. $C_{12}H_7NO_2$. See n268	197.20	nd (chl-al)	300	....			i	δ	i	....	i	....	**E12B,** 4724
Ω n274	**2,3-Naphthalene-dicarboxylic acid***	pr (aa or w), pr (sub)	216.21	pr (aa or w), pr (sub)	246 (sub) 239–41 (aa)	....			i δ[h]	δ s[h]	δ	...	i	aa δ[h] CS_2, chl, lig i	**E12B,** 4723
n275	**2,6-Naphthalene-dicarboxylic acid***	....	216.21	nd (al or sub)	>300d	....			δ[h]	s[h]	i	...	i	to δ[h] aa i	**E12B,** 4728
n276	**2,7-Naphthalene-dicarboxylic acid***	....	216.21	nd (w, al or dil HCl)	>300d	....			i[h]	s[h]	i	...	i	aa, to i	**E12B,** 4730
n277	**1,2-Naphthalene-dicarboxylic acid, 3,4-dihydro-, anhydride**	$C_{12}H_8O_3$. See n263........	200.21	pa ye nd (lig or al)	126–7	227–30[23]							v	MeOH, aa s lig δ, s[h]	**B17²,** 487
n278	**1,8-Naphthalene-dicarboxylic acid, 3,6-dinitro-***	3,6-Dinitronaphthalic acid. $C_{12}H_6N_2O_3$. See n268	306.19	silvery lf (w)	212	....			δ[h]	v[h]	i	...	i	AcOEt, $PhNO_2$, aa v[h]	**E12B,** 4775
n279	—,3-nitro-, anhydride	3-Nitronaphthalic anhydride. $C_{12}H_5NO_5$. See n268	243.18	yesh nd (aa or $PhNO_2$)	252–3	....			i[h]	i[h]	i	....	i[h]	aa s[h]	**E12B,** 4771
n280	—,4-nitro-*......	4-Nitronaphthalic acid. $C_{12}H_7NO_6$. See n268	261.19	ye nd	d 140–50	....			...	δ	δ	....	....	aa s[h] lig δ	**E12B,** 4772
n281	**1,5-Naphthalene-disulfonic acid***	γ-Naphthalenedisulfonic acid.	288.31	pl (+4w, dil aa or dil HCl) λ^{al} 277 (4.82), 298 (3.98), 318 (2.93)	240–5d (anh)	....	1.493		v	s	i	....	....		**B11²,** 119
n282	**1,6-Naphthalene-disulfonic acid***	δ-Naphthalenedisulfonic acid	288.31	og pr (+4w, aa or w) $\lambda^{5\%HCl-al}$ 237 (4.89), 273 (3.62), 342 (3.23)	125d (anh)	....			v	s	i	....	....		**B11²,** 121
n283	**2,7-Naphthalene-disulfonic acid***	....	288.31	hyg nd (con HCl) λ^{al} 233 (4.94), 266 (3.59), 308 (2.41), 323 (2.25)	199	....			s					con HCl δ	**B11²,** 122
n284	**1,3-Naphthalene-disulfonic acid, 7-amino-***	β,γ-Acid. Amino-G-acid.	303.32	mcl pr or nd (w +4)	273–5	....			s	s					**B14,** 784
n285	**2,7-Naphthalene-disulfonic acid, 4-amino-5-hydroxy-***	H acid. $C_{10}H_9NO_7S_2$. See n283	319.31			....			δ	δ	δ				**B14²,** 502
Ω n286	—,4,5-dihydroxy-*	Chromotropic acid. $C_{10}H_8O_8S_2 \cdot 2H_2O$. See n283	356.33	nd or lf (w +2) λ^{sulf} 235 (4.7), 316 (3.7), 335 (3.8), 351 (4.0)		....			s	i	i			alk s (bl-vi flr)	**B11⁷,** 72
n287	**1,3-Naphthalene-disulfonic acid, 7-hydroxy-***	G Acid. β-Naphthol-γ-disulfonic acid.	304.31	$\lambda^{5\%HCl-al}$ 237 (4.75), 287 (3.75), 338 (3.48)		....									**B11²,** 165
n288	**2,7-Naphthalene-disulfonic acid, 3-hydroxy-***	R-Acid. $C_{10}H_8O_7S_2$. See n283	304.31	dlq nd	d	....			s	s	i				**B11²,** 164

For explanations, symbols and abbreviations see beginning of table. For structural formulas see end of table.

1-Naphthalenephosphonic acid

No.	Name	Synonyms and Formula	Mol. wt.	Color, crystalline form, specific rotation and λ_{max} (log ε)	m.p. °C	b.p. °C	Density	n_D	w	al	eth	ace	bz	other solvents	Ref.
n289	1-Naphthalene-phosphonic acid*	. . . .	208.16	cr (w)	189	. . . .	. . . .		δ	v	. . .	. . .	. . .	. . . . . .	B16[2], 392
n290	—,dichloride.	$C_{10}H_7Cl_2OP$. See n289	245.05	. . . .	ca. 60	. . . .	. . . .		d	d^h	. . .	. . .	. . .	. . . . . .	B16[2], 392
n291	1-Naphthalene-sulfinic acid*		192.25	nd (w)	104 (96)	. . . .	. . . .		s	s	δ	. . .	. . .	dil HCl δ	B11[1], 5
n292	2-Naphthalene-sulfinic acid*		192.25	nd (w)	98(105)	. . . .	. . . .		s	s	s	. . .	. . .		B11[2], 10
n293	1-Naphthalene-sulfonic acid*	. . . .	208.25	pr (+2w, dil HCl) λ^w 228 (4.69), 275 (3.98), 320 3.32)	90 (hyd) 139–40 (anh)	. . . .	. . . .		s	s	δ	. . .	. . .		B11[2], 91
n294	—,chloride	$C_{10}H_7ClO_2S$. See n293	226.68	lf (eth)	68	195^{13} $147.5^{0.9}$	. . . .		i	s	v	. . .	v	peth i	B11[2], 93
Ωn295	2-Naphthalene-sulfonic acid*	. . . .	208.25	dlq pl (+1w), cr (+3w, dil HCl) $\lambda^{5\%HCl-al}$ 227 (4.98), 275 (3.69), 320 (2.62)	124–5 (+1w) 83 (+3w)	d	1.4412_4^{25}		v	s	s	. . .	$δ^h$	. . . . . .	B11[2], 96
Ωn296	—,chloride	$C_{10}H_7ClO_2S$. See n295	226.68	pw or lf(bz-peth)	79	201^{13} $148^{0.6}$	. . . .		i	s	v	. . .	s	chl, CS_2 s peth δ	B11[2], 99
Ωn297	1-Naphthalene-sulfonic acid, 4-amino-*	Naphthionic acid. $C_{10}H_9NO_3S.\frac{1}{2}H_2O$. See n293	232.26	wh nd (w + ½), red-br cr λ^{1NHCl} 283 (3.9)	d	. . . .	1.6703_4^{25}		i $δ^h$	δ	. . .	. . .	. . .	MeOH, Py s	E12B, 5033
n298	—,7-amino-*	δ-Acid. Amino-F-acid. Bayer's acid. Cassela's acid. $C_{10}H_9NO_3S.H_2O$. See n293	241.27	nd (w + 1), pl (aq ace)	. . . .	. . . .		i $δ^h$	δ	δ	. . .	. . .	aa s	E12B, 5106
n299	2-Naphthalene-sulfonic acid, 4-amino-*	Cleve's acid. $C_{10}H_9NO_3S.H_2O$. See n295	241.27	nd (w + 1)		. . . .	. . . .								E12B, 5031
n300	1-Naphthalene-sulfonic acid, 4-amino-5-hydroxy-*	S-acid. $C_{10}H_9NO_4S$. See n293	239.25	nd		. . . .	. . . .		δ	δ	i	. . .	. . .		B14, 835
n301	2-Naphthalene-sulfonic acid, 5,7-dinitro-8-hydroxy-*	Flavianic acid. $C_{10}H_6N_2O_8S$. See n295	314.23	pa ye nd (con HCl, +3w), cr (w) λ^w 358 (4.30), 380 (3.99)	100(+3w) 151 (anh)	. . . .	. . . .		v	v	. . .	. . .	. . .	BuOH s con HCl δ	B11[2], 156
n302	1-Naphthalene-sulfonic acid, 4-hydroxy-*	Nevile-Winther acid. NW-Acid. $C_{10}H_8O_4S$. See n293	224.25	ta or pl (w) $\lambda^{5\%HCl-al}$ 234 (4.50), 300 (3.85), 320 sh (3.64)	170 d (rapid htng)	. . . .	. . . .		v	. . .	i	. . .	. . .		B11, 271
n303	—, 5-hydroxy-*	α-Naphtholsulfonic acid L. $C_{10}H_8O_4S$. See n293	224.25	dlq $\lambda^{5\%HCl-al}$ 241 (4.46), 311.5 (3.66), 323 sh (3.62)	120(112)	. . . .	. . . .		s	. . .	. . .	. . .	. . .	aa s	B11[2], 155
n304	—,7-hydroxy-*	Croceic acid. $C_{10}H_8O_4S$. See n293	224.25	λ^w 278(3.6), 330 (3.1)		. . . .	. . . .		s	. . .	. . .	. . .	. . .		B11[2], 163
n305	—,8-hydroxy-*	α-Naphtholsulfonic acid S. $C_{10}H_8O_4S$. See n293	224.25	cr (w + 1)	106–7 (+1w)	. . . .	. . . .		s	. . .	. . .	. . .	. . .		B11, 275
n306	—,—,lactone.	1-Naphthol-8-sulfonic acid, sultone. Naphthosultone. $C_{10}H_6O_3S$. See n293	206.22	pr (bz)	154	>360	. . . .		δ	δ	. . .	. . .	s v^h	chl v CS_2 i	B19, 43
n307	2-Naphthalene-sulfonic acid, 1-hydroxy-*	α-Naphtholsulfonic acid. $C_{10}H_8O_4S$. See n295	224.25	pl (w) $\lambda^{5\%HCl-al}$ 237 (4.58), 294 (3.64), 328 (3.57)	>250	. . . .	. . . .		s^h δ	s	i	. . .	. . .	dil HCl δ	E12B, 5262
n308	—,6-hydroxy-*	Schaeffer acid. β-Naphtholsulfonic acid S. $C_{10}H_8O_4S$. See n295	224.25	lf, cr (w + 1) $\lambda^{5\%HCl-al}$ 233 (4.85), 280 (3.71), 332 (3.13)	167 (anh) 129 (+1w) 118 (+2w)	. . . .	. . . .		v	v	i	. . .	. . .	aa s	B11, 282
n309	—,7-hydroxy-*	F acid. β-Naphtholsulfonic acid. $C_{10}H_8O_4S$. See n295	224.25	nd (HCl), cr (w + 1,2 or 4)	115–6 (anh) 108–9 (+1w) 95 (+2w), 67 (+4w)	150d	. . . .		v	v	i	. . .	i		B11, 285
n309[1]	—,6-hydroxy-5-nitroso-*	$C_{10}H_7NO_5S$. See n295	253.23	og	d	. . . .	. . . .		v	. . .	. . .	. . .	$δ^h$	. . . . . .	B11[2], 190
—	—,5,6,7,8-tetrahydro-	see 5-Tetralinsulfonic acid													

For explanations, symbols and abbreviations see beginning of table. For structural formulas see end of table.

C-385

No.	Name	Synonyms and Formula	Mol. wt.	Color, crystalline form, specific rotation and λ_{max} (log ε)	m.p. °C	b.p. °C	Density	n_D	w	al	eth	ace	bz	other solvents	Ref.
	1,4,5,8-Naphthalenetetracarboxylic acid														
Ω n310	1,4,5,8-Naph-thalenetetra-carboxylic acid*	....	304.23	lf or nd (w, dil HCl or dil HNO₃)	320	....			δ s[h]	δ[h]		v	δ[h]	aa s[h] CS₂, chl δ[h]	E12B, 4833
Ω n311	—,1,8:4,5-dianhydride*	C₁₄H₄O₆. See n310	268.19	nd (aa), pr (PhNO₂)	>300	sub 320[3]			i					Na₂CO₃ s aa s[h]	E12B, 4835
n312	1,2,5-Naph-thalenetricar-boxylic acid*		260.22	nd (MeOH or sub)	270–2				s		δ			MeOH s	E12B, 4829
n313	1,4,5-Naph-thalenetricar-boxylic acid*		260.22	cr (eth or con HCl)	266 8				δ	v	s[h]				E12B, 4830
—	Naphthalic acid	*see* 1,8-Naphthalenedicar-boxylic acid*													
—	Naphthazarin	*see* 1,4-Naphthoquinone, 5,8-dihydroxy-*													
—	Naphthionic acid ..	*see* 1-Naphthalenesulfonic acid, 4-amino-*													
n314	Naphthocaine, hydrochloride		322.84	pa ye	212–6				δ						C35, 4003
—	Naphthohydro-quinone	*see* Naphthalene, dihydroxy-*													
Ω n315	1-Naphthoic acid.	α-Naphthalenecarboxylic acid.* α-Naphthoic acid.	172.20	nd (aa-w, w or al) λ^{al} 293 (3.9)	161	>300 231[50]	1.398	....	δ	s v[h]	s			chl s lig δ	E12B, 3966
Ω n316	—,amide	1-Naphthalenecarbonamide*. C₁₁H₉NO. See n315	171.20	nd or pl (al or gl aa)	204–5	sub			δ[h] s[h]	δ				con HCl, aa s[h]	E12B, 3992
n317	—,amidine	1-Naphthamidine*. C₁₁H₁₀N₂. See n315	170.22	lf (dil al)	154				δ[h]	s	s	s	δ	chl s lig δ	E12B, 4002
n318	—,anhydride	1-Naphthoic acid anhydride. C₂₂H₁₄O₃. See n315	326.36	pr (bz)	145–6				i	δ	s		s		E12B, 3988
n319	—,chloride	1-Naphthoyl chloride. C₁₁H₇ClO. See n315	190.63		20	297.5 172[15]			d[h]	d[h]					B9², 450
n320	—,ethyl ester ...	C₁₃H₁₂O₂. See n315	200.24			310[760] 183–6[20]	1.1274[15/15]	1.5966[15]	i	s	s				B9², 449
n321	—,methyl ester ..	C₁₂H₁₀O₂. See n315	186.21		59.5	167–9[20] 100–2[0.04]	1.1290[20/4]	1.6086[20]		s	s		s		E12B, 3981
Ω n322	—,nitrile	1-Cyanonaphthalene. 1-Naphthonitrile. C₁₁H₇N. See n315	153.19	nd (lig)	37.5	299 148[12]	1.1113[25/25]	1.6298[18]	i	v	v			lig s[h]	B9², 450
Ω n324	2-Naphthoic acid...	2-Naphthalenecarboxylic acid.* β-Naphthoic acid.	172.20	nd (lig, chl, sub), pl (ace)	185.5	>300	1.077[100/4]		δ[h]	s	s			chl s lig δ[h]	E12B, 4021
n325	—,amide	2-Naphthalenecarbonamide.* C₁₁H₉NO. See n324	171.20	lf (al)	195 (cor)	....			δ	s	s		s	chl, CS₂, lig s	E12B, 4039
n326	—,amidine	2-Naphthamidine.* C₁₁H₁₀N₂. See n324	170.22	cr (bz)	133–6				δ	s	δ		v[h]	aa v[h]	E12B, 4047
n327	—,anhydride......	2-Naphthoic acid anhydride. C₂₂H₁₄O₃. See n324	326.36	nd (eth)	135				i		δ s[h]		v[h]	aa v	E12B, 4037
n328	—,chloride	2-Naphthoyl chloride. C₁₁H₇ClO. See n324	190.63	cr (peth)	51	304–6 142–3[5]			i d[h]		s		s	chl, aa s	B9, 657
n329	—,ethyl ester ...	C₁₃H₁₂O₂. See n324	200.24		32	308–9 (315–6) 224[74]	1.1143[23/23]	1.5951[23]	i	s	s			chl s aa s[h]	B9², 453
n330	—,methyl ester ..	C₁₂H₁₀O₂. See n324	186.21	lf (MeOH)	77	290 141–3[4]				v	v		v	MeOH, chl v	E12B, 4031
Ω n331	—,nitrile	2-Cyanonaphthalene. 2-Naphthonitrile. C₁₁H₇N. See n324	153.19	lf (lig)	66	306.5[760] 156–8[12]	1.0939[60/60]		δ	s	s			lig s[h]	B9, 659
n333	2-Naphthoic acid, 4-acetyl-3-hydroxy-	C₁₃H₁₀O₄. See n324	230.22	ye pr (aa)	194				δ[h]	v			δ	chl δ aa δ, s[h]	E12B, 4589
n334	1-Naphthoic acid, 2-amino-	C₁₁H₉NO₂. See n315	187.20	nd (dil al)	126d				δ	v	v		s[h]	aa v[h]	E12B, 4184
n335	—,3-amino-.......	C₁₁H₉NO₂. See n315	187.20	ye or pksh nd (eth)	181–2					s				MeOH s	E12B, 4185
n336	—,4-amino-.......	C₁₁H₉NO₂. See n315	187.20	brsh nd (w or al)	177				δ s[h]	s	s	s	δ	aa s lig δ	E12B, 4188
n337	—,5-amino-.......	C₁₁H₉NO₂. See n315	187.20	og nd (w or dil al), nd (sub)	211–2 (217–20) 196 (sub)	sub			δ[h]	s	δ		s	aa s	E12B, 4198
n338	—,6-amino-.......	C₁₁H₉NO₂. See n315	187.20	pa ye nd (al or w)	205–6				δ	v	s	s	δ	AcOEt, aa s	E12B, 4200
n339	—,7-amino-.......	C₁₁H₉NO₂. See n315	187.20	pa br pr (al)	223–4					v	s	s	δ	aa v AcOEt s	B14², 322
n340	2-Naphthoic acid, 1-amino-	C₁₁H₉NO₂. See n324	187.20	nd (dil al or aa)	205 (rapid htng)				δ	s	s		s	....	B14², 323
Ω n341	—,3-amino-.......	C₁₁H₉NO₂. See n324	187.20	ye lf (dil al)	216–7					s	s			....	B14², 323
n342	—,4-amino-.......	C₁₁H₉NO₂. See n324	187.20	nd (dil al)	215–6 (204–6)					s[h]	s	s	s	AcOEt s	B14², 323

For explanations, symbols and abbreviations see beginning of table. For structural formulas see end of table.

2-Naphthoic acid

No.	Name	Synonyms and Formula	Mol. wt.	Color, crystalline form, specific rotation and λ_{max} (log ε)	m.p. °C	b.p. °C	Density	n_D	w	al	eth	ace	bz	other solvents	Ref.
n343	—,5-amino-	$C_{11}H_9NO_2$. See n324	187.20	ye lf (al)	291–2 (232)				δ	s^h	s	s	s	aa i	B14[2], 324
n344	—,6-amino-	$C_{11}H_9NO_2$. See n324	187.20	pa ye nd (w or dil al)	225				δ s^h	v	v	s	v	dil ac, aa v	B14[2], 324
n345	—,7-amino-	$C_{11}H_9NO_2$. See n324	187.20	pa ye nd or lf (al)	245				...	v	s	s	δ	NH_3, aa v AcOEt s	B14[2], 324
n346	—,8-amino-	$C_{11}H_9NO_2$. See n324	187.20	grsh-ye nd (aa)	220				...	s	s	s	δ	AcOEt s	B14[2], 324
n347	1-Naphthoic acid, 4-bromo-	$C_{11}H_7BrO_2$. See n315	251.09	nd (aa, dil al or xyl) λ^{diox} 305 (3.97)	220				δ^h	v	s	s	s	xyl, aa s^h	E12B, 4121
n348	—,5-bromo-	$C_{11}H_7BrO_2$. See n315	251.09	nd (aa or al) λ^{diox} 305 (3.9)	261	sub			δ^h	δ	δ	...	v	aa δ	E12B, 4123
n349	—,8-bromo-	$C_{11}H_7BrO_2$. See n315	251.09	pr (w or bz) λ^{diox} 282.5 sh (3.79), 292 (3.89), 302.5 sh (3.81)	178				s^h	v	δ	s	s^h	aa v chl, lig δ	E12B, 4130
n350	2-Naphthoic acid, 1-bromo-	$C_{11}H_7BrO_2$. See n324	251.09	nd (aa or bz)	191				δ	s	s	s	s^h	aa s	E12B, 4133
n351	—,5-bromo-	$C_{11}H_7BrO_2$. See n324	251.09	nd (al, sub)	270 (cor)	sub			δ^h	s	s	s	s	aa s	E12B, 4138
n352	1-Naphthoic acid, 2-chloro-	$C_{11}H_7ClO_2$. See n315	206.63	cr (w, bz) λ^{diox} 282 (3.75), 292.5 (3.78)	153				s^h	s	s	...	s^h	E12B, 4120
n353	—,4-chloro-	$C_{11}H_7ClO_2$. See n315	206.63	nd (al) λ^{diox} 298 (3.73)	210 (223–4)				δ	v	δ	...	δ	aa v chl δ	E12B, 4121
n354	—,5-chloro-	$C_{11}H_7ClO_2$. See n315	206.63	nd (dil al) λ^{diox} 303 (3.85)	245	sub			δ	v	δ	...	δ	aa δ	E12B, 4122
n355	—,8-chloro-	$C_{11}H_7ClO_2$. See n315	206.63	pl (al, w or bz) λ^{diox} 280 sh (3.78), 290 (3.85), 312.5 sh (3.74)	171–2	sub			s^h	s^h	...	v	s^h	aa s xyl s^h	E12B, 4128
n356	2-Naphthoic acid, 1-chloro-	$C_{11}H_7ClO_2$. See n324	206.63	nd (bz)	196				δ	s	s	s		aa v	E12B, 4132
n357	—,3-chloro-	$C_{11}H_7ClO_2$. See n324	206.63	cr (dil MeOH)	216.5					s	s	v	s	MeOH v chl, aa, AcOEt s	E12B, 4134
n358	—,5-chloro-	$C_{11}H_7ClO_2$. See n324	206.63	nd (al or aa)	270 (cor)					s^h	...	...	s	aa s	E12B, 4137
n359	—,4-chloro-1-hydroxy-	$C_{11}H_7ClO_3$. See n324	222.63	nd (al or aa)	234 (229)				i^h	s	δ	s	δ	aa s^h	B10[1], 146
n360	—,4-chloro-3-hydroxy-	$C_{11}H_7ClO_3$. See n324	222.63	ye nd	231d										B10, 336
n361	1-Naphthoic acid, 1,2-dihydro-	$C_{11}H_{10}O_2$. See n315	174.20	cr (50 % al)	138				s					sulf s (red)	B9[2], 443
n362	—,1,4-dihydro-	$C_{11}H_{10}O_2$. See n315	174.20	nd or pl (lig)	91				δ	v	s	v	δ	AcOEt, CS_2 v lig δ	B9[2], 442
n363	—,3,4-dihydro-	$C_{11}H_{10}O_2$. See n315	174.20	nd (w, AcOEt), cr (peth) λ^{al} 223 (4.10) 274 (3.78)	125	305–6[748]			δ	s				MeOH, chl, CS_2 s	B9[2], 442
Ω n364	2-Naphthoic acid, 1,2-dihydro-(dl)	$C_{11}H_{10}O_2$. See n324	174.20	nd or pr (dil al, w or peth) λ^{al} 211.5 (4.37), 260.5 (3.99)	105–6				i v^h	s	...	...		chl v aa s	B9[2], 443
Ω n365	—,1,4-dihydro-	$C_{11}H_{10}O_2$. See n324	174.20	pl (bz, w or dil al) λ^{al} 273 (2,61)	162–3				i s^h	s	s	...	δ	lig δ CS_2 i	B9[2], 443
Ω n366	—,3,4-dihydro-	$C_{11}H_{10}O_2$. See n324	174.20	nd (dil aa, dil al, or dil MeOH) λ^{al} 225 (4.30), 291 (4.18)	120				δ s^h	s	...	...		chl v aa s	B9[2], 443
n367	—,1,3-dihydroxy-, ethyl ester	$C_{13}H_{12}O_4$. See n324	232.24	nd (dil al or dil aa)	83–4				i	v	v	...		alk s lig v^h	B10[2], 310
n368	1-Naphthoic acid, 4,5-dinitro-	$C_{11}H_6N_2O_6$. See n315	262.18	yesh nd or pl (al)	266.7 sub				δ^h	v^h	δ	...	δ	aa v	B9, 654
n369	—,5-hydroxy-	$C_{11}H_8O_3$. See n315	188.20	pr or nd (w), cr (bz)	236				δ^h	v	s	...		chl, aa s	B10[2], 208
n370	—,6-hydroxy-	$C_{11}H_8O_3$. See n315	188.20	nd or pr (w)	212.5–13				s^h	s	s	s	δ	aa s^h chl δ	B10[2], 208
n371	—,7-hydroxy-	$C_{11}H_8O_3$. See n315	188.20	nd (w or gl aa)	256				δ s^h	v	δ	...	i	aa s	B10[2], 208
Ω n372	2-Naphthoic acid, 1-hydroxy-	$C_{11}H_8O_3$. See n324	188.20	cr (dil al, w, aa), nd (al, eth, bz), pw (chl)	195 (188)				δ s^h	v	v	...	s		B10[2], 210
n373	—,—,phenyl ester	$C_{17}H_{12}O_3$. See n324	264.28	....	96				s^h	s^h	...	...	s		B10, 332

For explanations, symbols and abbreviations see beginning of table. For structural formulas see end of table.

No.	Name	Synonyms and Formula	Mol. wt.	Color, crystalline form, specific rotation and λ_{max} (log ε)	m.p. °C	b.p. °C	Density	n_D	w	al	eth	ace	bz	other solvents	Ref.
	2-Naphthoic acid														
Ω n374	—,3-hydroxy-	$C_{11}H_8O_3$. See n324	188.20	ye lf (dil al), ye lf (w), nd (dil al) λ^{al} 232 (4.80), 266 (3.78), 328 (3.28)	222–3				δ	v	v	...	s	to, chl s	B10², 211
n375	—,—,ethyl ester	$C_{13}H_{12}O_3$. See n324	216.24	nd or mcl pr (aa)	85	291			i^h	s^h		s	...	chl s aa s^h	B10², 213
n376	—,—,hexadecyl ester	$C_{27}H_{40}O_3$. See n324	412.62	grsh-wh pr	72–3				i	δ		...	s	lig s	C42, 2108
n377	—,—,methyl ester	$C_{12}H_{10}O_3$. See n324	202.21	pa ye rh nd (dil MeOH) λ^{al} 240 (4.6), 290 (3.8), 365 (3.3)	75–6	205–7			i	s		...		os s	B10², 213
n378	—,5-hydroxy-	$C_{11}H_8O_3$. See n324	188.20	wh nd (w, dil al)	213				i s^h	s	s	s	i	aa s chl i	B10², 216
n379	—,7-hydroxy-	$C_{11}H_8O_3$. See n324	188.20	wh lf or pl (dil al), pa ye nd (al)	269–70				i s^h	s	s	s	i	aa s chl i	B10², 217
n380	1-Naphthoic acid, 8-iodo-	$C_{11}H_7IO_2$. See n315	298.08	br pr (w) λ^{diox} 299 (3.91), 312.5 sh (3.84)	164.5				s^h	s		...	s	aa s	E12B, 4131
n381	—,3-nitro-	$C_{11}H_7NO_4$. See n315	217.18	cr (al) λ^{diox} 308 (3.86), 351 (3.40)	271.5				δ^h	s^h					B9², 451
n382	—,4-nitro-	$C_{11}H_7NO_4$. See n315	217.18	yesh nd (al or aa) λ^{diox} 335 (3.65)	225–6 (221)				δ^h	v			δ	chl, aa s lig δ	B9², 451
n383	—,5-nitro-	$C_{11}H_7NO_4$. See n315	217.18	yesh nd (al) λ^{diox} 310 (3.81), 328 (2.70)	241–2	sub			i s^h	s^h	δ		δ	aa s chl, CS_2 δ	B9², 452
n384	—,8-nitro-	$C_{11}H_7NO_4$. See n315	217.18	nd (w), pr (al) λ^{diox} 281 (3.74), 308 (2.85)	217				i	s	δ		δ	aa s^h	B9², 452
n385	**2-Naphthoic acid, 5-nitro-**	$C_{11}H_7NO_4$. See n324	217.18	yesh nd (al)	295 (287)				i	δ^h	δ	s	δ	chl, aa, peth δ	B9², 455
n386	—,8-nitro-	$C_{11}H_7NO_4$. See n324	217.18	yesh nd (al)	295	sub			δ	δ					B9², 455
—	α-Naphthol	see **Naphthalene, 1-hydroxy-***													
—	β-Naphthol	see **Naphthalene, 2-hydroxy-***													
—	**β-Naphthol-1-aldehyde**	see **1-Naphthaldehyde, 2-hydroxy-**													
—	**α-Naphtholsulfonic acid**	see **2-Naphthalenesulfonic acid, 1-hydroxy-***													
—	**α-Naphtholsulfonic acid L**	see **1-Naphthalenesulfonic acid, 5-hydroxy-***													
—	**α-Naphtholsulfonic acid S**	see **1-Naphthalenesulfonic acid, 8-hydroxy-***													
—	**β-Naphtholsulfonic acid**	see **2-Naphthalenesulfonic acid, 7-hydroxy-***													
—	**β-Naphtholsulfonic acid S**	see **2-Naphthalenesulfonic acid, 6-hydroxy-***													
—	**1-Naphthol-8-sulfonic acid, sultone**	see **1-Naphthalenesulfonic acid, 8-hydroxy-, lactone***													
—	**Naphthonitrile**	see **Naphthoic acid, nitrile**													
n387	**Naphtho-(2′,3′:5,6)quinoline**	β-Anthraquinoline.	229.29	lf or ta (al)	170	446			i	v^h	v	...	v		B20, 506
Ω n388	**1,2-Naphtho-quinone-***	1,2-Dihydro-1,2-diketo-naphthalene*. β-Naphthoquinone.	158.16	ye-red nd (eth), og lf (bz) λ^{al} 240 (4.4), 340 (3.4), 415 (3.3)	146 (125)		1.450		s	s	s	...		sulf s (gr) lig δ	B7², 645
n389	—,dioxime*	$C_{10}H_8N_2O_2$. See n388	188.20	ye nd (bz-lig or dil al) λ^{al} 260 (4.30), 270 (4.27), 300 (3.50), 330 (3.83), 350 (3.95)	169 (152)					s^h		...	s	diox s sulf s (red) alk s (ye)	B7², 649
—	—,1-oxime*	see **Naphthalene, 2-hydroxy-1-nitroso-**													
Ω n390	**1,4-Naphtho-quinone***	1,4-Dihydro-1,4-diketo-naphthalene*. α-Naphthoquinone.	158.16	bt ye nd (al or peth), ye (sub) λ^{al} 255 (4.2), 330 (3.4)	128.5 (125)	sub			δ	v^h	s	...	s	CS_2, chl, aa s lig δ	B7², 651

For explanations, symbols and abbreviations see beginning of table. For structural formulas see end of table.

No.	Name	Synonyms and Formula	Mol. wt.	Color, crystalline form, specific rotation and λ_{max} (log ε)	m.p. °C	b.p. °C	Density	n_D	w	al	eth	ace	bz	other solvents	Ref.
	1,4-Naphthoquinone														
n391	—,dioxime*	$C_{10}H_8N_2O_2$. See n390	188.20	nd (dil al)	207d				s	s				alk s	B7[2], 653
—	—,1-oxime*	see **Naphthalene, 1-hydroxy-4-nitroso-***													
n392	2,6-Naphtho-quinone*	2,6-Dihydro-2,6-diketo-naphthalene.*	158.16	ye-red pr (bz or pz-peth)	135d					v	δ	d	δ	MeOH v Py, aa d	B7[2], 656
n393	1,4-Naphtho-quinone, 4-anil-, 2-anilino-	Naphthoquinone dianilide	324.39	ye-red nd (bz- or al)	182.5–3				i	δ		s	s	os s dil ac i	B14[2], 91
n394	1,2-Naphtho-quinone, 3-bromo-*	$C_{10}H_5BrO_2$. See n388	237.06	red nd or pl (aa or al)	178	sub				s			s^h	aa s^h	B7, 721
n395	—,4-bromo-*	$C_{10}H_5BrO_2$. See n388	237.06	red nd (bz-lig)	154					s			v	sulf s (red) aa s lig δ	E12B, 2890
n396	—,6-bromo-*	$C_{10}H_5BrO_2$. See n388	237.06	og-red or ye pr or pl (bz or AcOEt), nd (w)	168d (150d)					s	s^h	s		xyl, aa, lig s^h	B7, 722
n397	1,4-Naphtho-quinone, 2-bromo-*	$C_{10}H_5BrO_2$. See n390	237.06	ye pl or nd (al or dil aa)	132				i	s^h	δ	s	v	chl, aa s $CS_2\,\delta$	B7[2], 655
n398	—,5-bromo-2,3-dichloro-*	$C_{10}H_3BrCl_2O_2$. See n390	305.95	ye pr (al)	180					s^h		v	v		B7[2], 655
n399	—,2-bromo-3-hydroxy-*	$C_{10}H_5BrO_3$. See n390	253.06	ye mcl pr (al), nd (al, w or aa)	202	sub			i δ^h	δ s^h	δ	s	δ		B8[1], 636
n400	—,2-bromo-3-methyl-*	$C_{11}H_7BrO_2$. See n390	251.09	ye-br nd (al)	151	sub 100			i	s	v	s	s	chl v aa s alk i	B7[2], 657
n401	1,2-Naphtho-quinone, 3-chloro-*	$C_{10}H_5ClO_2$. See n388	192.60	red nd (al, aa, bz or chl)	172d				i	s^h			s	aa, chl s^h Na_2CO_3 i	B7, 720
Ω n402	1,4-Naphtho-quinone, 2-chloro-*	$C_{10}H_5ClO_2$. See n390	192.60	ye nd (w, al or aa)	117–8				s^h	δ	s	s	aa s^h Na_2CO_3 i	B7[2], 653
n403	—,5-chloro-*	$C_{10}H_5ClO_2$. See n390	192.60	ye nd (lig)	163	sub			i	s				aa, lig s	B7[2], 653
n404	—,6-chloro-*	$C_{10}H_5ClO_2$. See n390	192.60	red-br (al or eth), ye cr (dil MeOH)	109–10				v		δ		v	sulf s (red) chl δ	E12B, 2896
n405	—,2-chloro-3-hydroxy-*	$C_{10}H_5ClO_3$. See n390	208.60	ye nd (al or aa)	215	sub			δ s^h	s	s	s			B8[2], 347
n406	1,2-Naphtho-quinone, 3,4-dibromo-*	$C_{10}H_4Br_2O_2$. See n388	315.96	red lf or pl (aa or bz)	172–4					δ	δ		s^h	alk s aa s^h	B7, 722
n407	—,3,6-dibromo-*	$C_{10}H_4Br_2O_2$. See n388	315.96	red pr (AcOEt)	176					s				aa, AcOEt s^h	B7[2], 650
n408	—,4,6-dibromo-*	$C_{10}H_4Br_2O_2$. See n388	315.96	og-red pr (bz, peth), nd (AcOEt)	153					δ			v	aa v lig δ, s^h	B7[2], 650
n409	1,4-Naphtho-quinone, 2,3-dibromo-*	$C_{10}H_4Br_2O_2$. See n390	315.96	ye nd (aa)	218					δ	δ			aa s^h lig δ	B7, 731
n410	—,5,8-dibromo-*	$C_{10}H_4Br_2O_2$. See n390	315.96	ye nd (al)	171–3					δ					B7, 732
n411	1,2-Naphtho-quinone, 3,4-dichloro-*	$C_{10}H_4Cl_2O_2$. See n388	227.05	red lf or pl (aa or bz), nd (bz or chl)	184	sub				δ			s^h	chl s aa s^h	B7[2], 650
Ω n412	1,4-Naphtho-quinone, 2,3-dichloro-*	$C_{10}H_4Cl_2O_2$. See n390	227.05	ye nd (al)	195				i s^h	δ	δ		δ s^h	chl s^h	B7[2], 653
n413	—,2,6-dichloro-*	$C_{10}H_4Cl_2O_2$. See n390	227.05	dk ye nd (al)	148–9				i	s^h					B7, 730
n414	—,5,6-dichloro-*	$C_{10}H_4Cl_2O_2$. See n390	227.05	ye nd (al)	181	sub			i	δ s^h	s				B7, 730
n415	—,5,8-dichloro-*	$C_{10}H_4Cl_2O_2$. See n390	227.05	ye nd (al)	173–4	sub			i	s^h	s				B7, 730
n416	2,6-Naphtho-quinone, 1,5-dichloro-*	$C_{10}H_4Cl_2O_2$. See n392	227.05	og pr (chl), gold-ye nd (al)	206.5d				i	s^h	δ	v	v	chl, aa v AcOEt s lig i	B7, 733
n417	1,4-Naphtho-quinone, 2,3-dihydroxy-*	Isonaphthazarin. $C_{10}H_6O_4$. See n390	190.16	red og nd or lf (sub) λ^{al} 268 (4.32), 330 (3.32), 440 (3.26)	282	sub			δ^h	δ	δ	s	δ	alk s chl δ	B8[2], 461
n418	—,5,8-di-hydroxy-*	Naphthazarin. $C_{10}H_6O_4$. See n390	190.16	dk red mcl pr (bz), red-br nd (al) λ^{diox} 270 (3.9), 520 (3.8)	276–80	sub			δ^h	δ^h	δ^h			aa s^h	B8[2], 463

For explanations, symbols and abbreviations see beginning of table. For structural formulas see end of table.

No.	Name	Synonyms and Formula	Mol. wt.	Color. crystalline form. specific rotation and λ_{max} (log ε)	m.p. °C	b.p. °C	Density	n_D	Solubility						Ref.
									w	al	eth	ace	bz	other solvents	

1,4-Naphthoquinone

No.	Name	Synonyms and Formula	Mol. wt.	Color...	m.p.	b.p.	D	n_D	w	al	eth	ace	bz	other	Ref.
n419	—,3,5-di-hydroxy-2-methyl-*	Droserone. $C_{11}H_8O_4$. See n390	204.19	og-ye nd (al or aa) λ^{al} 232 (4.12), 285 (4.08), 409 (3.66)	181	sub 100³			s^h	s	s	...	...	peth s aa s^h	B8², 465
n420	—,5,8-dihydroxy-2-methyl-*	$C_{11}H_8O_4$. See n390	204.19	gr pl	173	....			i	s^h					E12B, 3195
Ω n421	—,2,3-dimethyl-*	$C_{12}H_{10}O_2$. See n390	186.21	ye pr (al) λ^{al} 249 (4.26), 267 (4.24), 330 (3.38)	127				i	s^h			s	aa s	B7², 658
n422	—,2,5-dimethyl-*	$C_{12}H_{10}O_2$. See n390	186.21	ye nd (peth, eth or MeOH)	95									diox s lig δ	B7¹, 386
n423	—,2,6-dimethyl-*	$C_{12}H_{10}O_2$. See n390	186.21	ye pr or nd (AcOEt)	136–7					s	s	s	s		B7¹, 386
n424	—,2,8-dimethyl-*	$C_{12}H_{10}O_2$. See n390	186.21	pr (peth), nd (MeOH)	135–6				δ^h	s					E12B, 2850
n425	—,2-ethyl-*	$C_{12}H_{10}O_2$. See n390	186.21	pr (al), nd (aa, MeOH, peth)	88–9					s^h				MeOH, aa s^h	B7², 658
n426	—,2-ethyl-3-hydroxy-*	$C_{12}H_{10}O_3$. See n390	202.21	ye nd (dil MeOH)	141					s		s^h			E12B, 3075
n427	—,2-ethyl-3,5,6,7,8-penta-hydroxy-*	Echinochrome A. $C_{12}H_{10}O_7$. See n390	266.21	red (diox-w, to) $\lambda^{w, pH=7}$ 400 (3.7), 465 (3.7), 480 (3.8), 550 (3.5)	220 δd	sub 120¹⁰			δ	s	v	s	v	con sulf s	E12B, 3230
n428	1,2-Naphtho-quinone, 6-hy-droxy-*	$C_{10}H_6O_3$. See n388	174.16	red lf (ace), og-ye nd λ^{chl} 280 (4.18), 370 (3.79)	165d				δ	s	s	s^h	δ	aa s	B8¹, 634
n429	—,7-hydroxy-*	$C_{10}H_6O_3$. See n388	174.16	br nd λ^{chl} 265 (4.47), 335 (3.11)	194					v	i	...	i	chl i	B8¹, 634
Ω n430	1,4-Naphtho-quinone, 2-hy-droxy-*	Lawsone. $C_{10}H_6O_3$. See n390	174.16	redsh-br (aa) λ^{MeOH} 275 (4.5), 335 (3.8)	192d (194–6)					v	i	...	i	aa s^h chl i	B8², 344
n431	—,—,acetate	$C_{12}H_8O_4$. See n390	216.21	ye lf (al)	131				δ	s	s	...		$CS_2 s^h$	B8², 346
Ω n432	—,5-hydroxy-*	Juglon. Nucin. $C_{10}H_6O_3$. See n390	174.16	redsh-ye nd or pr (chl or bz) λ^{al} 245 (4.1), 330 sh (3.0), 420 (3.5)	154 (161–3)	sub			i	s	s	s^h		chl. aa v^h lig δ	B8², 347
n433	—,6-hydroxy-*	$C_{10}H_6O_3$. See n390	174.16	gold-ye or red ye nd (w, bz-al, bz-ace) λ^{chl} 270 (4.37), 390 (3.60)	170d					v	v	v	δ	MeOH v sulf s (red) lig δ	B8², 348
n434	—,2-hydroxy-3-methyl-*	Phthiocol. $C_{11}H_8O_3$. See n390	188.20	ye pr (eth-peth, MeOH)	173–4	sub			δ	...	s	s	...	os s lig i	E12B, 3069
n435	—,5-hydroxy-2-methyl-*	Plumbagin. $C_{11}H_8O_3$. See n390	188.20	gold pr or og-ye nd (dil al)	78–9	sub			i	s v^h	v	v	v	chl, CS_2, lig v	B8², 350
Ω n436	—,2-hydroxy-3-phenyl-*	$C_{16}H_{10}O_3$. See n390	250.26	gold-ye or og pr or nd (al, bz, MeOH) $\lambda^{0.1 N NaOH}$ 480 (3.41)	147					v^h	v		v	chl v alk. lig s	B8², 409
n437	1,2-Naphtho-quinone, 3-methyl-*	$C_{11}H_8O_2$. See n388	172.20	red or og nd (abs al), lf (bz, peth) λ^{al} 253 (4.4), 340 (3.3)	116 (122–2.5)					s	...	...	s^h	alk. sulf s (gr)	E12B, 2814
n438	—,4-methyl-*	$C_{11}H_8O_2$. See n388	172.20	og nd (MeOH), nd (aa) λ^{al} 252 (4.4), 345 (3.4)	248–50d					s				alk s (bl) MeOH s^h	B8¹, 565
Ω n439	1,4-Naphtho-quinone, 2-methyl-*	Menadione, Vitamin K_3. $C_{11}H_8O_2$. See n390	172.20	ye nd (al, peth) λ^{al} 246 (4.28), 262 sh (4.23), 333 (3.42)	107	....			i	δ	s		s	sulf s aa, lig δ	B7², 656
n440	1,2-Naphtho-quinone, 3-nitro-*	$C_{10}H_5NO_4$. See n388	203.16	red pl (aa)	158				s^h	s^h	δ	...	s	aa v^h CS_2, lig i	B7², 651
n441	1,4-Naphtho-quinone, 2-phenyl-*	$C_{16}H_{10}O_2$. See n390	234.26	gold-ye nd (al)	111					v	v		v	chl v sulf s (red) lig δ	B7, 822
n442	—,2(phenyl-amino)-*	Lawsone anilide. $C_{16}H_{11}NO_7$. See n390	249.27	red nd (dil al)	193	sub				s^h	s		s	sulf s (red) lig δ	B14², 91
n443	—,5,6,7,8-tetra-hydro-*	$C_{10}H_{10}O_2$. See n390	162.19	gold-ye nd (peth)	55–6	....				s	s			aa s	B7², 625

For explanations, symbols and abbreviations see beginning of table. For structural formulas see end of table.

No.	Name	Synonyms and Formula	Mol. wt.	Color. crystalline form. specific rotation and λ_{max} (log ε)	m.p. °C	b.p. °C	Density	n_D	Solubility						Ref.
									w	al	eth	ace	bz	other solvents	

1,4-Naphthoquinone

No.	Name	Synonyms and Formula	Mol. wt.	Color etc.	m.p.	b.p.	Density	n_D	w	al	eth	ace	bz	other	Ref.
n444	—,2,5,8-tri-hydroxy-*	Naphthopurpurin. $C_{10}H_6O_5$. *See* n390	206.16	red nd (bz or MeOH) λ^{al} 480 (3.8)	195	....			δ v^h	v	....	....	s^h	aa, NH_4OH s sulf s (red)	B8[2], 537
—	Naphthosultone....	*see* 1-Naphthalenesulfonic acid, 8-hydroxy-, lactone*													
—	α-Naphthylamine	*see* Naphthalene, 1-amino-*													
—	β-Naphthylamine ..	*see* Naphthalene, 2-amino-*													
—	α-Naphthylazide ...	*see* Naphthalene, 1-triazo-*													
—	Naphthylene-diamine	*see* Naphthalene, diamino-*													
—	Naphthyl red	*see* Azo, benzene 1-naphthalene, 4′-amino-													
n445	Narceine	Narcein. Narcéne. Pseudonarcéne. $C_{23}H_{27}NO_8 \cdot 3H_2O$.	499.52	nd or pr (w +3) $\lambda^{w, pH=2}$ 278 (3.0)	145.2 (155) (anh) 176–7 (+3w)	....			δ s^h	s^h	i	...	i	chl, peth i	B19[2], 386
n447	—,bisulfate decahydrate	$C_{23}H_{27}NO_8 \cdot H_2SO_4 \cdot 10H_2O$. *See* n445	723.71	nd (sulf), pw	d	....			s	s^h	s				B19[2], 386
n448	—,hydrochloride trihydrate	$C_{23}H_{27}NO_8 \cdot HCl \cdot 3H_2O$. *See* n445	535.98	pr (HCl) λ^w 208 (4.76), 277 (4.19)	192 (anh)	....			δ^h	s^h	δ				B19[1], 372
n449	α-Narcotine(dl)....	$C_{22}H_{23}NO_7$........	413.43	nd (al, chl, MeOH) λ^{chl} 290 (3.6), 309 (3.7)	232–3				...	δ	....	...	δ	chl v^h peth i	B27[2], 607
n450	—(l)	$C_{22}H_{23}NO_7$. *See* n449	413.43	pr or nd (al), $[\alpha]$ −200 (chl) λ^{MeOH} 291 (3.60), 309 (3.69)	176				i	s	δ	v	s	chl s CCl_4 δ	B27[2], 605
n451	—,hydrochloride ..	$C_{22}H_{23}NO_7 \cdot HCl$	449.89	(w +3), $[\alpha]$ +100 λ^w 211 (4.76), 291 (3.40), 313 (3.55)	193 (anh)				v	δ					B27[2], 605
n452	β-Narcotine(dl)....	β-Gnoscopine. $C_{22}H_{23}NO_7$. *See* n449	413.43	nd, pr (MeOH, al)	180	....			...	s^h				MeOH s^h	B27[1], 559
n452[1]	—,hydrochloride ...	$C_{22}H_{23}NO_7 \cdot HCl$. *See* n449 ..	449.89	pr	86–8 (224–6 on standing)										B27[1], 559
n453	Naringin	Naringenin-7-rhamno-glucoside. Naringoside. $C_{27}H_{32}O_{14} \cdot 2H_2O$.	616.58	nd (w +8) $[\alpha]_D^{19}$ −82.11 (al) λ^{al} 283 (4.37)	82 (+8w), 171 (+2w)	....			δ s^h	δ v^h	i	...	i	aa s^h chl i	C54, 25366
n454	Neoabietic acid, methyl ester	Methyl neoabietate. $C_{21}H_{32}O_2$.	316.49	cr (MeOH)	61.5–2	....			...	...				MeOH v	B9[2], 433
n455	Neoamygdalin.....	l-Mandelonitrile-β-gentobioside. $C_{20}H_{27}NO_{11}$.	457.44	cr (al), $[\alpha]_D^{25}$ −61.4 (w, c = 8.5)	212				v	v					B31, 404
n456	Neobornyl amine	Isobornylamine............	153.27	pw $[\alpha]_D$ −47.7 (4 % al) −27 (bz)	184	....			i	...	s	s		os s	B12[2], 40
n457	Neocarvo-menthol(dl)	....	156.27			....		1.4637[20]	...	s					B6[3], 130
n458	—(l).............	$C_{10}H_{20}O$. *See* n457........	156.27	$[\alpha]_D^{21}$ −41.7 λ^{eth} 270 (2.5)	....	102[18] 90[9]	0.9012[20]/4	1.4632[20]	...	s					B6[3], 130
—	Neocholestene.....	*see* 2-Cholestene													
n458[1]	Neoergosterol	$C_{26}H_{38}O$.............	380.62	pr or nd (al) $[\alpha]_D^{17}$ −12 (chl, c = 2)	154.5 (157)				i	...	s	s		os s	B6[3], 3474
n459	Neogermitrine.....	$C_{38}H_{55}NO_{11}$.	677.84	wh nd $[\alpha]_D^{25}$ −79.2 (Py)	237–9				i	d^h				chl s	C54, 6780
—	Neohexane.......	*see* Butane, 2,2-dimethyl-* ...													
n460	Neoisocarvo-menthol(l)	....	156.27	$[\alpha]_D^{17}$ −34.7	< −25	87–8[4]	0.9102[20]/4	1.4676[20]	i	s	...	s			B6[3], 130
n461	Neoisomenthol(d) ..	p-Menthol-3	156.27	$[\alpha]_D^5$ +2.2 (al, c = 2)	−8	214.6[760] 91.5[11]	0.9131[18]/4	1.4670[20]	i	s	...	s			B6[3], 132
n462	—(dl).............	$C_{10}H_{20}O$. *See* n461........	156.27		14	214.5[760] 81[6]	0.8854[35]/4	1.4649[20]	i	s	...	s			B6[3], 132
n463	Neomenthol(d)	d-β-Pulegomenthol.	156.27	$[\alpha]_D^{20}$ +19.6 (al)	−15	211.7[760] 95[12]	0.897[22]/2	1.4600[20]	i	s	...	s		oos s	B6[3], 139
n464	—(dl).............	$C_{10}H_{20}O$. *See* n463........	156.27	pl or pr (peth)	52	211.7[760] 103–5[16]	0.903[15]/15	1.4600[20]	i	s	...	s		oos s	B6[3], 140

For explanations, symbols and abbreviations see beginning of table. For structural formulas see end of table.

No.	Name	Synonyms and Formula	Mol. wt.	Color, crystalline form, specific rotation and λ_{max} (log ε)	m.p. °C	b.p. °C	Density	n_D	Solubility						Ref.
									w	al	eth	ace	bz	other solvents	
	Neomenthol														
n465	—(l)	$C_{10}H_{20}O$. See n463	156.27	$[\alpha]_D^{18}$ −19.62 (al)	. . . .	211.7^{760} 97.6^{10}		1.4603^{20}	i	s	. . .	s	. . .	oos s	$B6^3$, 140
—	Neonicotine	see **Anabasine**													
—	Neopentane	see **Propane, 2,2-dimethyl-***													
—	Neopentyl alcohol	see **1-Propanol, 2,2-dimethyl-***													
—	Neopentyl chloride	see **Propane, 1-chloro-2,2-dimethyl-***													
—	Neopine	see **β-Codeine**													
—	Neral	see **Citral b**													
—	Neriine	see **Conessine**													
Ω n466	Nerol	3,7-Dimethyl-2,6-octadien-1-ol*. $C_{10}H_{18}O$. $(CH_3)_2C{:}CH(CH_2)_2\overset{\underset{\mid}{CH_3}}{C}{:}CHCH_2OH$	154.26	λ^{hp} 189–94 (4.26)	< −15	$224–5^{745}$ 125^{25}	0.8756_4^{20}	1.4746^{20}	i	s					$B1^3$, 2008
n467	Nerolidol(d)	Peruviol. α-3,7,11-Tri-methyl-1,6,10-dodecatrien-3-ol*. $C_{15}H_{26}O$. $(CH_3)_2C{:}CH(CH_2)_2\overset{\underset{\mid}{CH_3}}{C}{:}CH(CH_2)_2\overset{\underset{\mid}{OH}}{C}CH{:}CH_2$	222.38	$[\alpha]_D^{20}$ +15.5 (undil)		276^{760} $128–9^6$	0.8778_4^{20}	1.48982^{20}		v	s	s	. . .	os, aa s	$B1^3$, 2041
Ω n468	—(dl)	$C_{15}H_{26}O$. See n467 .	222.38	λ^{al} 273 sh (1.74), 280 sh (1.70)	. . . .	$145–6^{12}$ $75–6^{0.1}$	0.8756_4^{19}	1.4801^{16}		s	s	s	. . .	os, aa s	$B1^3$, 2042
n469	—(l)	$C_{15}H_{26}O$. See n467 .	222.38	$[\alpha]_D$ −6.5 (undil)		$124–6^3$	0.8881_{15}^{15}	1.4799^{20}		s	s	s	. . .	os, aa s	$B1^3$, 2042
n470	Neurine	Trimethylethenylammonium hydroxide*. $CH_2{:}CHN^+(CH_3)_3OH^-$	103.17	syr					s	s	s				$B4^3$, 442
—	Neuronal	see **Butanoic acid, 2-bromo-2-ethyl-, amide**													
—	Nevile-winther acid	see **1-Naphthalenesulfonic acid, 4-hydroxy-**													
—	Niacinamide	see **3-Pyridinecarboxylic acid, amide**													
—	Nicotinamide	see **3-Pyridinecarboxylic acid, amide**													
n471	Nicotine(d)	α-N-Methyl-d-β-pyridyl-pyrrolidine. $C_{10}H_{14}N_2$	162.24	hyg, $[\alpha]_D^{20}$ +163.2 λ^{al} 262 (3.47)	. . . .	$245.5–$ 6.5^{729}	1.0094_4^{20}	1.5280^{20}	∞	v	v	. . .	. . . .	chl v lig s	**B23**, 117
n472	—(dl)	Tetrahydronicotyrine. $C_{10}H_{14}N_2$. See n471	162.24	λ^{al} 262 (3.47)	. . . .	$242–3$	1.0082_4^{20}	1.5289^{20}	∞	v	v	. . .	. . . .	chl v lig s	**B23**, 117
Ω n473	—(l)	$C_{10}H_{14}N_2$. See n471	162.24	hyg, br in air, $[\alpha]_D^{20}$ −169 λ^{al} 262 (3.47)	−79	246.7^{745} $124–5^{18}$	1.0097_4^{20}	1.5282^{20}	∞	v	v	. . .	. . . .	chl v lig s	**B23**, 110
n474	—,hydrochloride(d)	$C_{10}H_{14}N_2 \cdot HCl$. See n471 . . .	198.70	dlq, $[\alpha]_D^{20}$ +104 (w, p = 10)	. . . .		1.0337								**B23**, 114
—	Nicotinic acid	see **3-Pyridinecarboxylic acid**													
—	Nicotinonitrile	see **3-Pyridinecarboxylic acid, nitrile**													
n475	2,2′-Nicotyrine (solid)	N-Methyl-2(2-pyridyl)-pyrrole. α-Nicotyrine. $C_{10}H_{10}N_2$	158.21	cr, br in air λ^{al} 288 (3.99)	43.4–4.5				i	v	s		v	dil HCl s	$B23^2$, 192
n476	—(liquid)	$C_{10}H_{10}N_2$. See n475	158.21	λ^{al} 288 (3.99)	−28	273^{764} $149–50^{22}$			δ			s	bz	os s	$B23^2$, 191
n477	3,2′-Nicotyrine	N-Methyl-2(3-pyridyl)-pyrrole. β-Nicotyrine. $C_{10}H_{10}N_2$	158.21	br in air λ^{al} 288 (3.99)	. . . .	$280–1^{744}$ 150^{15}	1.2411_2^{20}	1.6057^{20}	δ s^δ	s	s	s	. . .	os s	$B23^2$, 192
Ω n478	Ninhydrin	1,2,3-Triketohydrindene monohydrate. λ^{al} 228 (4.64) 357 (2.00)	178.15	pr (w)	241–3d (250d)				v*	s	. . .	. . .	. . . .	alk s	$B7^2$, 831
—	Nioxime	see **1,2-Cyclohexanedione, dioxime*.**													
—	Nirvanol	see **Hydantoin, 5-ethyl-5-phenyl-**													
Ω n479	Nitranilic acid	2,5-Dihydroxy-3,6-dinitro-p-benzoquinone.	230.09	gold-ye pl (+w, dil HNO$_3$)	86–7d (hyd) (100d)	exp	. . . .	. . . . .	v	v	i	. . .	. . . .		$B8^3$, 433
Ω n480	**Nitric acid, butyl ester***	n-Butyl nitrate. $CH_3(CH_2)_3ONO_2$	119.12	. . . .	. . . .	135.5^{763} (cor) $70–1^{86}$	1.0228^{30}	1.4013^{23}	i	s	s	. . .	. . . .		$B1^2$, 397
n481	—,sec-butyl ester (dl)	sec-Butyl nitrate. $CH_3CH_2CH(CH_3)ONO_2$	119.12	λ^{al} 270 sh (1.23)	. . . .	124 59^{80}	1.0264_4^{20}	1.4015^{20}	. . .	∞	∞	. . .	. . . .		$B1^3$, 1533
n482	—,decyl ester*	n-Decyl nitrate. $CH_3(CH_2)_9ONO_2$	203.28	. . . .	. . . .	$127–8^{11}$ $88–9^1$	0.9510^0	. . . . .	. . .	. . .	s	s	. . .		$B1$, 425
n483	—,ethyl ester *	Ethyl nitrate. $CH_3CH_2ONO_2$.	91.07	inflam λ^{al} 266 sh (1.17)	−94.6	87.2^{762}	1.1084_4^{20}	1.3852^{20}	s	∞	∞	. . .	. . . .		$B1^2$, 328

For explanations, symbols and abbreviations see beginning of table. For structural formulas see end of table.

C-392

No.	Name	Synonyms and Formula	Mol. wt.	Color, crystalline form, specific rotation and λ_{max} (log ε)	m.p. °C	b.p. °C	Density	n_D	w	al	eth	ace	bz	other solvents	Ref.
	Nitric acid														
n484	—, isopropyl ester*	Isopropyl nitrate. $(CH_3)_2CHONO_2$	105.10	....		100–1.4[760]	1.036^{19}_{19}	1.3912^{16}	...	s	s				B1[3], 1465
n485	—, methyl ester*	Methyl nitrate. CH_3ONO_2	77.04	explosive vapor	−82.3 exp	64.6^{760} exp	1.2075^{20}_4	1.3748^{20}	δ	s	s				B1[1], 284
Ω n486	—, 3-methylbutyl ester*	Isoamyl nitrate. $(CH_3)_2CHCH_2CH_2ONO_2$	133.15	....		147–8	0.9961^{22}_4	1.4122^{22}	δ	∞	∞				B1[3], 1642
n487	—, octyl ester*	n-Octyl nitrate. $CH_3(CH_2)_7ONO_2$	175.23	λ^{al} 270 sh (1.18)	....	110–2[20]	0.8419^{17}_{17}	....	δ	s	s				B1, 419
n488	—, propyl ester*	n-Propyl nitrate. $CH_3CH_2CH_2ONO_2$	105.10	....		110[762]	1.0538^{20}_4	1.3973^{20}	δ	s	s				B1[2], 369
—	**Nitroform**	see Methane, trinitro-*													
—	**Nitrofurazone**	see Furfural, 5-nitro-, semicarbazone													
—	**Nitrogen mustard**	see Amine, triethyl, 2,2′2″-trichloro-													
—	**Nitroglycerin**	see Glycerol, trinitrate													
—	**N-Nitroguanidine**	see Guanidine,1-nitro-*													
Ω n489	**Nitron**	4,5-Dihydro-1,4-diphenyl-3,5-phenylimino-1,2,4-triazole	312.38	ye lf (al), nd (+chl)	189d	....	....	....	i	s	δ	s	s	chl, CCl₄, dil ac s	B26[2], 76, 199
n490	**Nitrous acid, butyl ester***	n-Butyl nitrite. $CH_3(CH_2)_3ONO$	103.12	λ^{cy} 223 (3.15), 333 (1.72), 356 (1.93), 384 (1.51)	....	77.8^{760} 27[88]	0.8823^{20}_4	1.3762^{20}		∞	∞				B1[2], 397
n491	—, sec-butyl ester (dl)	sec-Butyl nitrite. $C_2H_5CH(CH_3)ONO$	103.12	....		68–9 28[180]	0.8726^{20}_4	1.3710^{20}	δ	v	v			CCl₄, CS₂, chl s	B1[2], 402
Ω n492	—, tert-butyl ester	tert-Butyl nitrite. $(CH_3)_3CONO$	103.12	pa ye λ^{cy} 221 (3.23), 353 (1.68), 382 (1.91), 397 (1.72)	....	62.8–3.2 34[250]	0.8670^{20}_4	1.3687^{20}	δ	s	s			chl, CS₂ s	B1[2], 415
n493	—, decyl ester*	n-Decyl nitrite. $CH_3(CH_2)_9ONO$	187.29	yesh λ^{hp} 357 (1.92), 384 (1.53)		105–8[12] 95[4]	....	1.4247^{20}							B1, 425
n494	—, ethyl ester*	Ethyl nitrite. CH_3CH_2ONO	75.07	yesh or col		16.5–17[725]	0.90^{15}_{15}	1.3418^{10}	d	∞	∞				B1[2], 328
n495	—, heptyl ester*	n-Heptyl nitrite. $CH_3(CH_2)_6ONO$	145.20	λ^{eth} 315 (1.38), 356 (1.93), 382.5 (1.52)		155–8 44[18]	0.8939^0_4	1.4032^{20}	i		s				B1[2], 443
n496	—, hexyl ester*	n-Hexyl nitrite. $CH_3(CH_2)_5ONO$	131.18	ye λ^{hp} 357 (1.91), 387 (1.52)		129–30[774] (cor) 52[44]	0.8778^{20}_4	1.3987^{20}	i	s	s				B1[3], 1657
n497	—, isopropyl ester*	Isopropyl nitrite. $(CH_3)_2CHONO$	89.10	λ^{eth} 327 (1.20), 359 (1.70), 387 (1.45)		45[762]	0.8684^{15}_1	....	i	s	s				B1[3], 1464
n498	—, methyl ester*	Methyl nitrite. CH_3ONO	61.04	gas	−16	−12	0.991^{15} (liq)	....		s	s				B1, 284
Ω n499	—, 3-methylbutyl ester*	Isoamyl nitrite. $(CH_3)_2CHCH_2CH_2ONO$	117.15	yesh, inflam λ^{cy} 224 (3.29), 333 (1.71), 369 (1.83), 384 (1.52)	....	99.2^{760} 30[60]	0.8828^{20}_4	1.3918^{20}	δ	∞	∞				B1[3], 1641
n500	—, octyl ester*	n-Octyl nitrite. $CH_3(CH_2)_7ONO$	159.23	ye λ^{hp} 357 (1.92), 384 (1.52)		174–5[760] 60[10]	0.862^{17}	1.4127^{20}	δ	v	v				Am 78, 1501
n501	—, pentyl ester*	n-Amyl nitrite. $CH_3(CH_2)_4ONO$	117.15	ye λ^{cy} 224 (3.25), 334 (1.66), 356 (1.87), 383 (1.45)		104.5[763] (cor) 29[40]	0.8817^{20}_4	1.3851^{20}	δ	∞	∞				B1[3], 1604
n502	—, propyl ester*	n-Propyl nitrite. $CH_3CH_2CH_2ONO$	89.10	....		79[760] (57)	0.935^{21}	1.3604^{20}	δ	s	s				B1[2], 369
Ω n502¹	**Nonacosane***	$CH_3(CH_2)_{27}CH_3$	408.80	rh cr (peth)	63.7	440.8^{760} 271.4[10]	0.7630^{100}_4 0.8083^{20}_4	1.4529^{20}	i	v[h]	v	v	s	chl δ	B1[2], 144
n503	—, 2-methyl-*	$(CH_3)_2CH(CH_2)_{26}CH_3$	422.83	pl (lig)	73–4	222[0.3]	....	....	i		s	s	s	chl δ	B1[1], 72
n504	**1-Nonacosanol***	$CH_3(CH_2)_{27}CH_2OH$	424.80	cr (al)	84.6–5.0	sub 200–50[1]	....	....		s[h]					B1[2], 471
Ω n505	**Nonadecane***	$CH_3(CH_2)_{17}CH_3$	268.53	wax	32.1	329.7^{760} 193[15]	0.7774^{32}_4 0.7855^{20}_4	1.4409^{20}	i	δ	s	s	s		B1[3], 568
Ω n506	**1,2,3-Nonadecanetricarboxylic acid, 2-hydroxy-***	Agaric acid. Agaricin. Laricic acid. $CH_3(CH_2)_{15}CH(CO_2H)C(OH)(CO_2H)CH_2(CO_2H)$	416.56	lf (+1.5w, dil al) $[\alpha]^9_D$ −8.8 (NaOH)	142d	....	....	....	s[h]	δ	δ		i	chl i	B3[2], 372
n507	—, triethyl ester	$C_{28}H_{52}O_7$. See n506.	500.73	nd	36–7	....	....			s[h]			s		B3[2], 373
n508	—, trimethyl ester	$C_{25}H_{46}O_7$. See n506.	458.64	nd (al)	63–4	....	....			s[h]			s		B3[2], 373
Ω n509	**Nonadecanoic acid***	n-Nonadecylic acid. $CH_3(CH_2)_{17}CO_2H$	298.52	lf (al)	69.4	297–8[100] 227–30[10]	....	....	i	v[h]	v		v	chl, lig v	B2[2], 368
n510	**1-Nonadecanol***	n-Nonadecyl alcohol. $CH_3(CH_2)_{17}CH_2OH$	284.53	cr (ace)	62–3	166–7[0.32]	....	1.4328^{75}		s	s[h]				B1[3], 1841

For explanations, symbols and abbreviations see beginning of table. For structural formulas see end of table.

No.	Name	Synonyms and Formula	Mol. wt.	Color. crystalline form. specific rotation and λ_{max} (log ε)	m.p. °C	b.p. °C	Density	n_D	Solubility						Ref.
									w	al	eth	ace	bz	other solvents	
	2-Nonadecanone														
Ω n511	2-Nonadecanone*	Methyl n-heptadecyl ketone. $CH_3(CH_2)_{16}COCH_3$	282.52	pl (al)	57	266.5^{110} 165^2	0.8108^{56}	....	i	δ s^h	v	s v^h	....	chl, CCl_4 v to v^h bz s, v^h	B1[2], 773
n512	—, oxime*	$CH_3(CH_2)_{16}C(:NOH)CH_3$	297.53	cr (al)	76.5–7.5	....	....	....		s^h	s				B1, 718
n513	4-Nonadecanone*	n-Propyl n-pentadecyl ketone. $CH_3(CH_2)_{14}COCH_2CH_2CH_3$	282.52	lf (al)	50.5	$211^{11}\delta$d	....	....	i	δ	v	v			B1[2], 773
Ω n514	10-Nonade-canone*	Caprinone. Dinonyl ketone. $[CH_3(CH_2)_7CH_2]_2CO$	282.52	lf (al)	65.5 (58)	>350 $155.6^{1.1}$	....	....	i	δ s^h	s	s	v	chl, lig s	B1, 718
Ω n515	1-Nonadecyne*	$CH_3(CH_2)_{16}C\colon CH$	264.50	....	37–8 (33)	327^{760} 181.6^{10}	0.8054^{20}_4	1.4488^{20}			s	s			B1[3], 1030
n516	1,8-Nonadiyne*	$HC\colon C(CH_2)_5C\colon CH$	120.20	....	−27.3	162^{760} 55^{13}	0.8158^{20}_4	1.4490^{20}			s	s			B1[3], 1063
Ω n517	Nonanal*	n-Nonylaldehyde. Pelargonaldehyde. $CH_3(CH_2)_7CHO$	142.24	....	....	$190–2$ 93.5^{23}	0.8264^{22}_4	1.4273^{20}			s				B1[2], 761
n518	—, oxime*	$CH_3(CH_2)_7CH\colon NOH$	157.26	lf (dil al)	64	....	....	....	i	s	s	s		os s	B1[2], 761
Ω n519	Nonane*	$CH_3(CH_2)_7CH_3$	128.26	....	−51	150.798^{760} 39^{10}	0.7176^{20}_4	1.4054^{20}	i	v	v	∞	∞	chl, hp ∞	B1[3], 502
Ω n520	—, 1-amino-*	n-Nonylamine. $CH_3(CH_2)_7CH_2NH_2$	143.28	....	−1	202.2^{760} 80.8^{10}	0.7886^{20}_4	1.4336^{20}	δ	s	s				B4[3], 393
n521	—, 1-chloro-*	n-Nonyl chloride. $CH_3(CH_2)_7CH_2Cl$	162.71	....	−39.4	203.4^{760} 80.5^{10}	0.8720^{20}_4	1.4345^{20}	i		s	s		chl s	B1[2], 128
n522	—, 2-chloro-*	2-Nonyl chloride. $CH_3(CH_2)_6CHClCH_3$	162.71	....	....	190^{764}	0.8790^{20}	1.4420^{20}	i		s	s		chl s	B1, 166
n523	—, 5-chloro-*	5-Nonyl chloride. $(CH_3CH_2CH_2CH_2)_2CHCl$	162.71	....	....	$85–7^{14}$	0.8639^{15}	1.4314^{15}	i		v				B1[2], 128
n524	—, 1-chloro-9-fluoro-*	$FCH_2(CH_2)_7CH_2Cl$	180.70	....	....	$102–2.5^{11}$	0.9662^{20}	1.4301^{25}	i	v	v				C51, 7300
Ω n525	Nonanedioic acid*	Azelaic acid. 1,7-Heptanedi-carboxylic acid*. $HO_2C(CH_2)_7CO_2H$	188.23	lf or nd	106.5	>360d 287^{100} 225.5^{10}	1.225^{25}_4	1.4303^{111}	δ s^h	s	δ	....	δ v^h		B2[2], 602
Ω n526	—, dichloride	Azelayl dichloride. $ClCO(CH_2)_7COCl$	225.12	....	....	166^{18} $140^{0.4}$	....	1.4680^{20}	d	d^h	s	s	v^h		B2, 709
Ω n527	—, diethyl ester*	Ethyl azelate. $C_2H_5O_2C(CH_2)_7CO_2C_2H_5$	244.34	λ^{al} 255 (0.7), 262 (0.8), 273 (0.7)	−18.5	$291–2$ $174–5^{20}$	0.97294^{20}_{20}	1.43509^{20}	i	s	s	s	s		B2[2], 603
Ω n528	—, di(2-ethylbutyl) ester*	Di-2-ethylbutyl azelate. $CH_2[(CH_2)_3CO_2CH_2CH(C_2H_5)_2]_2$	356.55	....	−45	230^5	0.928^{25}_4	1.443^{25}	i		s	s	s		B2[3], 1787
n529	—, di(2-ethylhexyl) ester*	Di-2-ethylhexyl azelate. $CH_2[(CH_2)_3CO_2CH_2CH(C_2H_5)C_4H_9]_2$	412.66	....	−78	237^5	0.915^{25}_4	1.446^{25}	i		s	s	s		B2[3], 1787
Ω n530	—, dimethyl ester*	Dimethyl azelate. $CH_3O_2C(CH_2)_7CO_2CH_3$	216.28	....	....	156^{20} 128^5	1.0082^{20}_{20}	1.4367^{20}	i	s	s	s	s	os s	B2[1], 290
Ω n531	—, dinitrile	Azelanitrile. $NC(CH_2)_7CN$	150.23	....	....	$198–9^{23}$ 160^3	0.9290^{19}	1.4518^{19}	i	v	v		v		B2[1], 290
n532	—, diphenyl ester*	Diphenyl azelate. $C_6H_5O_2C(CH_2)_7CO_2C_6H_5$	340.42	nd (al)	59–60 (49)	....	....	....	i	δ s^h	s		v		B6[3], 606
Ω n533	1,9-Nonanediol*	Nonamethylene glycol. $HOCH_2(CH_2)_7CH_2OH$	160.26	cr (bz)	45.8	$173–5^{20}$	....	....	δ	v	v	....	s^h	lig i	B1[3], 2226
Ω n534	Nonanoic acid*	n-Nonylic acid. Pelargonic acid. $CH_3(CH_2)_7CO_2H$	158.24	....	fp 12.24 15	255^{760} 150^{20}	0.9057^{20}_4	1.4343^{19}	i	s	s			chl s	B2[2], 360
n535	—, amide	Nonanamide*. Pelargon-amide. $CH_3(CH_2)_7CONH_2$	157.26	....	99.2–9.7	sub	0.8394^{110}	1.4248^{110}	i	δ	δ				B2[3], 822
Ω n536	—, chloride	Nonanoyl chloride*. Pelargonyl chloride. $CH_3(CH_2)_7COCl$	176.69	....	−60.5	215.35^{760} 98^{15}	0.9463^{15}_4	....	d	d	s	s			B2[2], 308
Ω n537	—, ethyl ester*	$CH_3(CH_2)_7CO_2C_2H_5$	186.30	....	−36.7	227^{760} $96–8^{10}$	0.8657^{20}_4	1.4220^{20}	i	s	s	s	s		B2[2], 307
Ω n538	—, methyl ester*	$CH_3(CH_2)_7CO_2CH_3$	172.27	....	....	$213–4^{757}$ $104–6^{23}$	0.8799^{15}	1.4214^{20}	i	s	s	s	s		B2[2], 307
Ω n539	—, nitrile	Nonanonitrile*. Octyl cyanide. Pelargonitrile. $CH_3(CH_2)_7CN$	139.24	....	−34.2	224.4^{760} 91.9^{10}	0.8178^{20}_4	1.4255^{20}	i	s	s	s			B2[3], 828
n540	—, piperazinium salt	$2[CH_3(CH_2)_7CO_2H].C_4H_{10}N_2$	402.62	wh	95.1–6.2	....			s^h	s	i				Am70, 2758
n541	—, 9-amino*	$H_2NCH_2(CH_2)_7CO_2H$	173.26	....	185.6–6.6				s	s					B4[3], 1479
n542	—, 9-fluoro-*	ω-Fluoropelargonic acid. $FCH_2(CH_2)_7CO_2H$	176.23	....	ca. 18	$89–90^{0.2}$		1.4289^{25}	δ	v	v				C52, 1918
Ω n543	1-Nonanol*	Nonyl alcohol. $CH_3(CH_2)_7CH_2OH$	144.26	....	−5.5	213.5^{760} 118^{15}	0.8273^{20}_4	1.4333^{20}	i	s	s				B1[3], 1743
n549	5-Nonanol, 5-butyl-*	Tri-n-butyl carbinol. $[CH_3(CH_2)_3]_3COH$	200.37	....	20	$230–5$d 118 20^{17}	0.8408^{20}_4	1.4445^{20}	i	s	s				B1[3], 1802
n550	1-Nonanol, 9-chloro-*	Nonamethylene chloro-hydrin. $ClCH_2(CH_2)_7CH_2OH$	178.71	....	28	$146–8^{14}$		1.4575^{20}	i	v	v				C51, 7300
n551	—, 9-fluoro-*	Nonamethylene fluorohydrin. $FCH_2(CH_2)_7CH_2OH$	162.25	....	....	$125–6^{15}$	0.9282^{20}_4	1.4279^{25}	i	v	v				C51, 7300
Ω n552	2-Nonanone*	Heptyl methyl ketone. $CH_3(CH_2)_6COCH_3$	142.24	λ <200	−7.46	195.3^{760} 73.8^{10}	0.8208^{20}_4	1.42096^{20}	i	s	s	v	s	chl, MeOH v	B1[3], 2887

For explanations, symbols and abbreviations see beginning of table. For structural formulas see end of table.

No.	Name	Synonyms and Formula	Mol. wt.	Color, crystalline form, specific rotation and λ_{max} (log ε)	m.p. °C	b.p. °C	Density	n_D	w	al	eth	ace	bz	other solvents	Ref.
	4-Nonanone														
Ω n553	4-Nonanone*	n-Propyl n-amyl ketone. $CH_3(CH_2)_4CO(CH_2)_2CH_3$	142.24	λ^{MeOH} 279 (1.42)	....	187–8 75–6[20]	0.8190_4^{25}	1.4189^{20}	i	s	s	v	...	chl s	B1[3], 2888
n554	5-Nonanone*	Dibutyl ketone. $CH_3(CH_2)_3CO(CH_2)_3CH_3$	142.24	λ^{MeOH} 278 (1.46)	−4.8	188.4 88[22]	0.8217_4^{20}	1.4195^{20}	i	s	v	...	...	chl v	B1[2], 762
n555	Nonasiloxane, eicosamethyl-	$CH_3[Si(CH_3)_2O-]_8Si(CH_3)_3$.	681.47			307.5[760] 198.8[16]	0.9173^{20}	1.3980^{20}	i	δ	...	...	s		C43, 4402
Ω n556	1,3,6,8-Nona-tetraen-5-one, 1,9-diphenyl-*	Dicinnamylidene acetone, $(C_6H_5CH:CHCH:CH)_2CO$	286.38	ye nd (abs al) λ^{al} 266 (4.74)	144	....		δ s^h	δ			con sulf s	B7, 524
n557	1-Nonen-3-yne*	$CH_3(CH_2)_4C:CCH:CH_2$.	122.21			27.2–8.2[4]	0.7602_4^{25}	1.4487^{25}	i	...	s	s	...		B1[3], 1048
n558	1-Nonen-4-yne*	$CH_3(CH_2)_3C:CCH_2CH:CH_2$	122.21			58.0[22]	0.777_4^{25}	1.4413^{25}	i	...	s	s	...		B1[3], 1048
n559	2-Nonen-4-yne*	$CH_3(CH_2)_3C:CCH:CHCH_3$	122.21			70–0.5[29]	0.7832_4^{25}	1.4590^{25}	i	...	s	s	...		B1[3], 1048
n560	1-Nonyne*	$CH_3(CH_2)_6C:CH$.	124.23		−50	150.8[760] 33.3[10]	0.7568_4^{20}	1.4217^{20}	i	...	s	s	...	os s	B1[3], 1012
n561	2-Nonyne*	$CH_3(CH_2)_5C:CCH_3$	124.23			158–9[760]	0.7690_4^{20}	1.4331^{20}	i	...	s	...	...	lig s	B1[3], 1013
n562	3-Nonyne*	$CH_3(CH_2)_4C:CCH_2CH_3$.	124.23			153–5[745] 92[97]	0.7616_4^{20}	1.4299^{20}	i	...	s	...	...	lig s	B1[3], 1013
n563	4-Nonyne*	$CH_3(CH_2)_3C:CCH_2CH_2CH_3$	124.23			150–4[750]	0.757^{25}	1.4296^{25}	i	...	s	...	...		B1[3], 1013
n564	1-Nonyne, 1-chloro-*	$CH_3(CH_2)_6C:CCl$	158.67			75–7[15]	0.906^{20}	1.450^{20}	i	...	v	...	...		B1[3], 1012
n565	4-Nonyne,3,3-di-methyl-*	$CH_3(CH_2)_3C:CC(CH_3)_2CH_2CH_3$	152.28			82[40]	0.7667_4^{20}	1.4317^{20}	...	...	s	...	s		B1[3], 1024
n566	—,8-methyl-*	2-Methyl-5-nonyne. $(CH_3)_2CHCH_2CH_2C:CCH_2CH_2CH_3$	138.25			104.5[97]	0.7681_4^{20}	1.4311^{20}	...	...	s	...	s		B1[3], 1018
—	Nopinene	see β-Pinene													
n567	Nopinone(d)		138.21	$[\alpha]_D^{20}$ +34 (chl), +11.5 (eth)	0	209[760] 87–8[14]	0.9807_4^{20}	1.4787^{20}	s	s	s	...	...		B7[2], 69
n568	Noradrenaline(l)	l-Arterenol. l-Norepinephrine.	169.18	$[\alpha]_D^{25}$ −37.3 (dil HCl) $\lambda^{w, pH=7}$ 280	216.5–8d	....		δ	δ	δ	...	alk, dil HCl v	B13[2], 523
—	Norbornane	see Bicyclo(2.2.1)heptane													
—	Norbornylane	see Bicyclo(2.2.1)heptane													
—	Norcamphane	see Bicyclo(2.2.1)heptane													
—	Norcamphane dicarboxylic acid	see Bicyclo(2.2.1)heptane-2,3-dicarboxylic acid													
—	Norcamphoric acid	see 1,3-Cyclopentane-dicarboxylic acid*													
n569	Nordihydro-guaiaretic acid	NDGA	302.38	nd (w, al, aa)	185–6			δ^h	s	s	s	i	alk s chl δ^h to i	B6[1], 577
Ω n570	Norephedrine, hydrochloride(dl)	2-Amino-1-phenyl-1-propanol hydrochloride. $C_6H_5CH(OH)CH(CH_3)NH_2$.HCl	187.67	pl (abs al), cr (dil HCl, al or al-AcOEt)	194			v	s	i	...	chl i	B13[2], 371
n571	—,N,N-di-ethyl-hydro-chloride(dl)	$C_6H_5CH(OH)CH(CH_3)N(C_2H_5)_2$.HCl	243.78	cr (al-ace, AcOEt-al)	205–6				s					B13[2], 380
n572	—,N-ethyl-	$C_6H_5CH(OH)CH(CH_3)NHCH_2CH_3$	179.26	cr (lig)	51.5	143[18]						s		B13[2], 380
n573	Normorphine	Desmethylmorphine. $C_{16}H_{17}NO_3$.	271.32	(w + 1½), (MeOH + 1)	273 (w + 1½) 263–4 (anh) (277)	....		i^h	i^h			i	chl i	B27[2], 117
n574	Nornicotine(l)	l-3(2-Pyrrolidyl)pyridine. $C_9H_{12}N_2$.	148.21	hyg $[\alpha]_D^{22}$ −88.8 (undil) λ^{al} 262 (3.47)	....	270 130.5–1.3[11]	$1.0737^{19.5}$	$1.5378^{18.5}$	∞	v	v	v	...	chl, peth v	B23[2], 107
—	Norvaline	see Pentanoic acid, 2-amino-*													
—	Novocaine	see Benzoic acid, 4-amino-2-diethylaminoethyl ester, hydrochloride													
—	Novonal	see 4-Pentenoic acid, 2,2-diethyl-, amide													

For explanations, symbols and abbreviations see beginning of table. For structural formulas see end of table.

No.	Name	Synonyms and Formula	Mol. wt.	Color, crystalline form, specific rotation and λ_{max} (log ε)	m.p. °C	b.p. °C	Density	n_D	Solubility						Ref.
									w	al	eth	ace	bz	other solvents	
	Octacosane														
o1	**Octacosane***	$CH_3(CH_2)_{26}CH_3$	394.78	mcl or rh (bz-al)	64.5 fr 61.4	431.6^{760} 264^{10}	0.8067_4^{20} 0.7750^{70}	1.4520^{20} 1.4330^{70}	i	...	...	∞	s	chl s	B1[3], 582
o2	**Octacosanoic acid***	$CH_3(CH_2)_{26}CO_2H$	424.76		90.4		0.8191^{100}	1.4313^{100}							B2[3], 1095
o3	**1-Octacosanol***	$CH_3(CH_2)_{27}OH$	410.78	(ace or peth)	83.3	sub $200–50^1$									B1[3], 1849
Ω o4	**9,12-Octade-cadienoic acid** (cis,cis)*	Linoleic acid $CH_3(CH_2)_4CH:CHCH_2CH:CH(CH_2)_7CO_2H$	280.46	pa ye or col λ^{al} 232 (3.8), 275 (2.9)	−5	$229–30^{16}$	0.9022_4^{20}	1.4699^{20}	i	∞	∞	∞	∞	chl, CCl_4, MeOH ∞	B2[2], 459
o5	—,ethyl ester*	Ethyl linoleate. $CH_3(CH_2)_4CH:CHCH_2CH:CH(CH_2)_7CO_2C_2H_5$	308.49	ye or col λ^{hx} 198 (4.6), λ^{al} 233 sh (2.1) 270 (1.79)		$270–5^{180}$ 212^{12}	0.8865_4^{20}		i	s	s				B2[2], 461
Ω o6	—,methyl ester*	Methyl linoleate. $CH_3(CH_2)_4CH:CHCH_2CH:CH(CH_2)_7CO_2CH_3$	294.48	ye or col λ^{al} 232 (3.78)	−35	215^{20} $168–70^1$	0.8886_4^{18}	1.4638^{20}	i	s	s				B2[2], 461
o7	**10,12-Octade-cadienoic acid** (trans,trans)*	10,12-Linoleic acid. $CH_3(CH_2)_4CH:CHCH:CH(CH_2)_8CO_2H$	280.45	(bz or al) λ^{al} 233 (3.51)	56–7.5		0.8686_4^{70}	1.4689^{60}							B2[3], 1476
o8	**7,11-Octa-decadiyne***	$CH_3(CH_2)_5C:CCH_2CH_2C:C(CH_2)_5CH_3$	246.44			$167–8^7$	0.8411_4^{19}	1.4698^{19}	i						B2[3], 1068
o9	**Octadecanal***	Stearaldehyde. $CH_3(CH_2)_{16}CHO$	268.49	nd (peth)	55 (38–9)	261 $212–3^{12}$			i						B1[2], 772
o10	—,dimethyl acetal	1,1-Dimethoxyoctadecane* $CH_3(CH_2)_{16}CH(OCH_3)_2$	314.56			$168–70^3$		1.4410^{25}	...	v	v			MeOH v	Am 80, 6613
Ω o11	**Octadecane***	$CH_3(CH_2)_{16}CH_3$	254.51	nd (al or eth-MeOH)	28.18	316.1^{760} 173.5^{10}	0.7768_4^{28}	1.4390^{20}	i	δ	s	s	...	lig s	B1[3], 565
Ω o12	—,1-amino-*	$CH_3(CH_2)_{17}NH_2$	269.52	(w)	fr 52.86	348.8^{760} 199.5^{10}	0.8618_4^{20}	1.4522^{20}	i	s	s	δ	s	chl v	B4[3], 431
o13	—,—,acetate	$CH_3(CH_2)_{17}NH_2 . CH_3CO_2H$	329.57	nd (al), cr (bz)	fr 84.5				i s^h	v			s		B4[3], 433
o14	—,—,hydrochloride	$CH_3(CH_2)_{17}NH_2 . HCl$	305.98	orh pl (al)	162–3				i v^h	δ v^h	i		i		B4[3], 432
Ω o15	—,1-bromo-*	$CH_3(CH_2)_{17}Br$	333.41	cr (al)	28.2	210^{10}	0.9848_4^{20}	1.4631^{20} 1.4594^{30}	i	s	s			peth, AcOEt s	B1[3], 567
Ω o16	—,1-chloro-*	$CH_3(CH_2)_{17}Cl$	288.95		28.6	348^{760} 199^{10}	0.8641_4^{20}	1.4531^{20}	i						B1[3], 566
o17	—,1,18-dibromo-*	$Br(CH_2)_{18}Br$	412.31	nd or lf (al)	64	$205–7^{15}$			i	δ v^h				chl v	B1[2], 139
o18	—,1-iodo-*	$CH_3(CH_2)_{17}I$	380.40	lf (lig), nd (ace or al-ace)	34	383^{760} 223^{10}	1.0994_4^{20}	1.4810^{20}	i	δ	δ				B1[3], 567
o19	**Octadecanedioic acid, diethyl ester***	Diethyl eicosanedioate. $C_2H_5O_2C(CH_2)_{16}CO_2C_2H_5$	370.58		54.5–5.0	240^{12}			i	s	s				B2[2], 626
o20	**1,18-Octa-decanediol***	$HO(CH_2)_{18}OH$	286.50	lf (al, AcOEt or bz), nd (bz, diox)	97–9	$210–1^2$			i						B1[3], 2247
o21	**1-Octa-decanethiol***	n-Octadecyl mercaptan. $CH_3(CH_2)_{17}SH$	286.57		(i) 24–6 (ii) 28	188^{1-2}	0.8475^{20}	1.4645^{20}	i	δ	s				B1[3], 1838
Ω o22	**Octadecanoic acid***	Stearic acid. $CH_3(CH_2)_{16}CO_2H$	284.50	mcl lf (al) λ^{al} 210 (1.69)	71.5–2.0	360d 232^{15}	0.9408_4^{20}	1.4299^{80}	i	s^h δ	v	s	δ	chl, CCl_4, CS_2, to s	B2[2], 346
Ω o23	—,amide	Stearamide. $CH_3(CH_2)_{16}CONH_2$	283.50	lf (al)	109	$250–1^{12}$			i	s^h δ	s	δ	δ	chl s	B2, 384
o24	—,—,N-phenyl-	Stearanilide. $CH_3(CH_2)_{16}CONHC_6H_5$	359.60	nd (al)	94	153.5^{10}			i	v	v	s	v	chl s peth δ	B12[2], 148
o24[1]	—,anhydride*	Stearic anhydride. $[CH_3(CH_2)_{16}CO]_2O$	550.96	λ^{al} 243 (4.17)	72		0.8368_4^{82}	1.4362^{80}	i	i	δ	...	δ		B2[2], 360
o25	—,benzyl ester	Benzyl stearate. $CH_3(CH_2)_{16}CO_2CH_2C_6H_5$	374.61	pa ye	28 (45–6)		0.9075_{23}^{50}	1.4663^{50}	i	δ	δ			chl δ	B6[2], 418
Ω o26	—,butyl ester*	n-Butyl stearate. $CH_3(CH_2)_{16}CO_2(CH_2)_3CH_3$	340.60		27.5	223	0.855_4^{20}	1.4328^{50}	i	s	δ	v			B2[2], 352
Ω o27	—,chloride	Stearoyl chloride. $CH_3(CH_2)_{16}COCl$	302.93		23	215^{15} $202–3^6$		1.4523^{24}		s^h					B2, 384
o28	—,cyclohexyl ester*		366.64		44 (28–9)		0.890_{23}^{23}		i	i	s				B6[2], 11
Ω o29	—,ethyl ester*	Ethyl stearate. $CH_3(CH_2)_{16}CO_2C_2H_5$	311.50		(i) 33.4 (ii) 30.9	199^{10}	1.0577^{10} (0.8973^{31})	1.4342^{60}	i	s	s	v			B2[2], 379
o30	—,hexadecyl ester*	Cetyl stearate. $CH_3(CH_2)_{16}CO_2(CH_2)_{15}CH_3$	508.92	lf or pl (eth, aa)	57			1.4410^{70}	i	i	s	s	i	chl, CS_2 s s^h aa i	B2[2], 353
o30[1]	—,2-hydroxyethyl ester*	Glycol monostearate. $CH_3(CH_2)_{16}CO_2CH_2CH_2OH$	328.54	(peth)	60–1	$189–91^3$	0.8780_6^{60}	1.4310^{60}	...	δ	s^h				B2[3], 1020
o31	—,isobutyl ester	Isobutyl stearate. $CH_3(CH_2)_{16}CO_2CH_2CH(CH_3)_2$	340.60	wax	(i) 22.5 (ii) 28.9	223^{15} 199^5	0.8498_4^{20}		i		s				B2[2], 353

For explanations, symbols and abbreviations see beginning of table. For structural formulas see end of table.

No.	Name	Synonyms and Formula	Mol. wt.	Color, crystalline form, specific rotation and λ_{max} (log ε)	m.p. °C	b.p. °C	Density	n_D	Solubility					Ref.
									w	al	eth	ace	bz	other solvents	

Octadecanoic acid

No.	Name	Synonyms and Formula	Mol. wt.	Color/form	m.p.	b.p.	Density	n_D	w	al	eth	ace	bz	other	Ref.
o32	—,isopropyl ester*	Isopropyl stearate. $CH_3(CH_2)_{16}CO_2CH(CH_3)_2$	326.57	....	28	207^6	0.8403^{38}	....		s	s	v		chl s	$B2^2$, 352
Ω o33	—,methyl ester*	Methyl stearate. $CH_3(CH_2)_{16}CO_2CH_3$	298.52	....	39.1	$442-3^{747}$ 215^{15}	0.8498^{40}_4	1.4367^{40}	i	s	s	v		chl v	$B2^3$, 1011
Ω o34	—,3-methylbutyl ester*	Isoamyl stearate. $CH_3(CH_2)_{16}CO_2CH_2CH_2CH(CH_3)_2$	354.62	....	25.5	192^2	0.855^{20}_{20}	1.433^{50}	i	δ	s	s			$B2^2$, 353
Ω o35	—,nitrile	Stearonitrile. $CH_3(CH_2)_{16}CN$	265.49	....	41	362^{760} 193^{10}	0.8325^{20}_4	1.4389^{45} 1.4481^{20}	i	v	v	v		chl v	$B2$, 384
o36	—,pentyl ester*	n-Amyl stearate. $CH_3(CH_2)_{16}CO_2(CH_2)_4CH_3$	354.62	pl	30	....	....	1.4342^{50}	i	s	v				$B2^2$, 353
o37	—,phenyl ester*	Phenyl stearate. $CH_3(CH_2)_{16}CO_2C_6H_5$	360.59	....	51.5-3.0	267^{15}	....	....	i	s	s				$B6^2$, 155
o38	—,p-phenyl-phenacyl ester	....	478.72	....	97	....	....	....				s			C32, 4944
o39	—,propyl ester*	Propyl stearate. $CH_3(CH_2)_{16}CO_2CH_2CH_2CH_3$	326.57	cr (eth or PrOH), pr (peth)	fr 28.9	186.8^2	0.8452^{38}	1.4400^{30}	i	s	v	v		chl, CCl_4 v	$B2^2$, 352
o40	—,tetrahydro-furfuryl ester	....	368.61	....	22	....	0.917^{25}_{25}	....	i	s	s				Am 50, 134
o41	—,9,10-dibromo-* (trans, dl)	Elaidic acid dibromide. $CH_3(CH_2)_7CHBrCHBr(CH_2)_7CO_2H$	442.29	col or ye	29-30 (27)	....	1.2458^{30}_4	1.4893^{42}	i	i	s				$B2^2$, 362
o42	—,2,3-dihydroxy-*	$CH_3(CH_2)_{14}CH(OH)CH(OH)CO_2H$	316.49	nd (aa)	α: 107 β: 126	....	....	....	δ^h	δ	δ	δ		chl δ^h peth δ	B3, 406
o43	—,9,10-di-hydroxy-*	$CH_3(CH_2)_7CH(OH)CH(OH)(CH_2)_7CO_2H$	316.49	llf λ^{al} 220 (2.1)	95	....	....	....	i	δ	δ				$B3^3$, 876
o44	—,9,10-dioxo-*	Stearoxylic acid. $CH_3(CH_2)_7COCO(CH_2)_7CO_2H$	312.46	ye pl (al) λ^{al} 270 (1.7)	86	....	....	....	i	v^h	v^h	v		lig v	$B3^3$, 1350
Ω o45	—,9,10,12,13,15,16-hexabromo-*	α-Linolenic acid hexa-bromide. $CH_3[CH_2CHBrCHBr]_3(CH_2)_7CO_2H$	757.89	cr (diox)	182	....	....	....	i	δ	i		δ	chl i aa δ xyl s^h	$B2^2$, 364
o46	—,2-hydroxy-*	$CH_3(CH_2)_{15}CH(OH)CO_2H$	300.49	flat nd (chl, AcOEt)	93	....	....	....		s	s	s	s^h	chl, AcOEt s	B3, 364
o47	—,3-hydroxy-*	$CH_3(CH_2)_{14}CH(OH)CH_2CO_2H$	300.49	pl (chl)	89-90	....	....	....		s^h	s			chl s^h	$B3^2$, 249
o48	—,10-hydroxy-*	$CH_3(CH_2)_7CH(OH)(CH_2)_8CO_2H$	300.49	pl	84	....	....	....	i	s	δ				$B3^2$, 249
o49	—,11-hydroxy-*	$CH_3(CH_2)_6CH(OH)(CH_2)_9CO_2H$	300.49	ta or pl (al)	81-2	....	....	....	i	δ	δ			lig δ	$B3^3$, 670
Ω o50	—,12-hydroxy-*	$CH_3(CH_2)_5CH(OH)(CH_2)_{10}CO_2H$	300.49	(al)	82	....	....	....	i	s	s			chl s	$B3^2$, 250
o51	—,10-methyl-* (D, −)	Tuberculostearic acid. $CH_3(CH_2)_7CH(CH_3)(CH_2)_8CO_2H$	298.52	$[\alpha]_D^{22}$ −0.11 (ace), $[\alpha]_D^{19}$ −0.41 (Py, c = 17)	12-3	$175-8^{0.7}$	0.8771^{25}_4	1.4512^{25}		s^h	s^h	s^h			$B2^2$, 369
o52	—,3-oxo-*	Palmitoylacetic acid. $CH_3(CH_2)_{14}COCH_2CO_2H$	298.47	....	102-3	....	....	....		s^h					$B3^2$, 457
o53	—,—,ethyl ester*	Ethyl palmitoylacetate. $CH_3(CH_2)_{14}COCH_2CO_2C_2H_5$	326.53	(al or peth)	37-8	....	....	....	i	s^h				peth s^h	$B3^2$, 457
o54	—,6-oxo-*	Lactaric acid. $CH_3(CH_2)_{11}CO(CH_2)_4CO_2H$	298.47	pl (al or peth-al)	87	....	....	....	i	s			δ	chl s	$B3^2$, 457
o55	—,—,ethyl ester*	$CH_3(CH_2)_{11}CO(CH_2)_4CO_2C_2H_5$	326.53	cr	41	....	....	....	i	v	v				$B3^1$, 253
Ω o56	—,10-oxo-*	$CH_3(CH_2)_7CO(CH_2)_8CO_2H$	298.47	pl (al)	76 (82)	....	....	....		δ					$B3^2$, 457
o57	—,—,ethyl ester*	$CH_3(CH_2)_7CO(CH_2)_8CO_2C_2H_5$	326.53	pl (al)	41	....	....	....	i	s^h					B3, 725
o58	—,12-oxo-*	$CH_3(CH_2)_5CO(CH_2)_{10}CO_2H$	298.47	llf (aa), cr (lig)	82	....	....	....		s^h				aa s^h	$B3^2$, 458
o59	—,—,ethyl ester*	$CH_3(CH_2)_5CO(CH_2)_{10}CO_2C_2H_5$	326.53	llf (al)	38	$199-200^5$	....	....	i	s^h					$B3^2$, 458
Ω o60	—,9,10,12,13-tetrabromo-*	Linoleic acid tetrabromide. $CH_3(CH_2)_4[CHBrCHBrCH_2]_2(CH_2)_6CO_2H$	600.09	pl or llf (aa)	114-5	....	....	....	i	v	v		v	chl, aa v	$B2^2$, 362
o61	—,—,ethyl ester*	$CH_3(CH_2)_4[CHBrCHBrCH_2]_2(CH_2)_6CO_2C_2H_5$	628.15	nd	63	....	....	....	i	δ				peth δ	$B2^2$, 363
o62	—,—,methyl ester*	$CH_3(CH_2)_4[CHBrCHBrCH_2]_2(CH_2)_6CO_2CH_3$	614.12	llf	63	215^{15}	....	1.4346^{45}	i	s	s			chl s	$B2^2$, 351
Ω o63	1-Octadecanol*	Stearyl alcohol. $CH_3(CH_2)_{17}OH$	270.50	llf (al)	59.4-9.8 fr 57.95	210.5^{15}	0.8124^{59}	....	i	s	s	δ	δ	chl s	$B1^3$, 1833
o64	9,11,13-Octa-decatrienoic acid (cis)*	α-Eleostearic acid. $CH_3(CH_2)_3[CH:CH]_3(CH_2)_7CO_2H$	278.44	nd (al) λ^{al} 261 (4.56), 271 (4.67), 281 (4.58)	49	235^{12} δd 170^1	0.9028^{20}_{20}	1.5112^{50}	i	s	s				$B2^2$, 465
o65	—(trans)*	β-Eleostearic acid. $CH_3(CH_2)_3[CH:CH]_3(CH_2)_7CO_2H$	278.44	llf (al, MeOH or CCl_4) λ^{al} 259 (4.67), 268 (4.78), 279 (4.69)	71-2	188^1	0.8839^{80}_4	1.5000^{80}	i	s^h	i			MeOH s	$B2^2$, 467
Ω o66	9,12,15-Octade-catrienoic acid (cis, cis, cis)*	α-Linolenic acid. $CH_3[CH_2CH:CH]_3(CH_2)_7CO_2H$	278.44	λ 195 (4.4), 233 (2.1)	−11.3	$230-2^{17}$ $125^{0.05}$	0.9164^{20}_{20}	1.4800^{20}	i	s	s		δ		$B2^2$, 463
Ω o67	—,ethyl ester (cis, cis, cis)*	Ethyl linolenate. $CH_3[CH_2CH:CH]_3(CH_2)_7CO_2C_2H_5$	306.49	λ^{al} 260 (1.7)	....	218^{15} $174^{2.5}$	0.8919^{20}_4	1.4694^{20}	i	s	s				$B2^2$, 465

For explanations, symbols and abbreviations see beginning of table. For structural formulas see end of table.

9-Octadecenal*

No.	Name	Synonyms and Formula	Mol. wt.	Color, crystalline form, specific rotation and λ_{max} (log ε)	m.p. °C	b.p. °C	Density	n_D	w	al	eth	ace	bz	other solvents	Ref.
Ω 068	9-Octadecenal*....	Olealdehyde. $CH_3(CH_2)_7CH:CH(CH_2)_7CHO$	266.47	ye nd	....	168–9[3-4]	0.8509[20]	1.4558[20]	i			s^h			B1, 749
Ω 069	1-Octadecene*	$CH_3(CH_2)_{15}CH:CH_2$.......	252.49	....	17.5	179[15] 145[8]	0.7891[20]	1.4448[20]	i	....		s^h			B1[3], 878
o70	9-Octadecene*	$CH_3(CH_2)_7CH:CH(CH_2)_7CH_3$	252.49	....	−30.5	162[9]	0.7916[20]	1.4470[20]	i						B1[3], 879
Ω 071	9-Octadecenoic acid(cis)*	Oleic acid. $CH_3(CH_2)_7CH:CH(CH_2)_7CO_2H$	282.47	nd λ^{hx} 185 (3.8) (13.4)	16.3	286[100] 228–9[15]	0.8935[20]	1.4582[20]	i	∞	∞	∞	∞	chl, CCl_4, MeOH ∞	B2[3], 1387
Ω 072	—(trans)*	Elaidic acid. $CH_3(CH_2)_7CH:CH(CH_2)_7CO_2H$ λ^{hx} 189 (3.9)	282.47	pl (al)	45	288[100] 234[15]	0.8734[45]	1.4499[45] 1.4308[100]	i	s	s	...	s	chl s	B2[2], 441
o73	—,amide(cis)	Oleamide. $CH_3(CH_2)_7CH:CH(CH_2)_7CONH_2$	281.49	....	76	....			i	s^h	v				B2[3], 1425
o74	—,—,(trans)	Elaidamide. $CH_3(CH_2)_7CH:CH(CH_2)_7CONH_2$	281.49		93–4				i	s	v				B2[3], 1433
o75	—,—,N-phenyl-(cis)	Oleanilide. $CH_3(CH_2)_7CH:CH(CH_2)_7CONHC_6H_5$	357.59	nd	41	143.5[10]			i	s^h	v	s^h	v^h	MeOH, aa s	B12[1], 198
o76	—,benzyl ester(cis).	Benzyl oleate. $CH_3(CH_2)_7CH:CH(CH_2)_7CO_2CH_2C_6H_5$	372.60			237[1]	0.9330[25]	1.4875[25]	i	s	v				B6[2], 418
Ω 077	—,butyl ester(cis)*	Butyl oleate. $CH_3(CH_2)_7CH:CH(CH_2)_7CO_2(CH_2)_3CH_3$	338.58	ye	−26.4	227–8[15]	0.8704[15]	1.4480[25]	i		v				B2[2], 439
Ω 078	—,ethyl ester(cis)* .	Ethyl oleate. $CH_3(CH_2)_7CH:CH(CH_2)_7CO_2C_2H_5$ λ^{al} 237 (1.5)	310.53		....	207[13]	0.8720[20]	1.4515[20]	i	∞	∞				B2[3], 1410
Ω 079	—,—,(trans)*	Ethyl elaidate. $CH_3(CH_2)_7CH:CH(CH_2)_7CO_2C_2H_5$	310.53		5.8	217–9[15]	0.8664[25]	1.4480[25]	i	s	s				B2[2], 443
Ω 080	—,methyl ester (cis)*	Methyl oleate. $CH_3(CH_2)_7CH:CH(CH_2)_7CO_2CH_3$ λ^{al} 230 (3.5)	296.50		−19.9	218.5[20]	0.8739[20]	1.4522[20]	i	∞	∞				B2[3], 1407
Ω 081	—,—,(trans)*	Methyl elaidate. $CH_3(CH_2)_7CH:CH(CH_2)_7CO_2CH_3$	296.50			213–5[15]	0.8730[20]	1.4513[20]	i	s	s				B2[2], 443
o82	—,3-methylbutyl ester(cis)*	Isoamyl oleate. $CH_3(CH_2)_7CH:CH(CH_2)_7CO_2CH_2CH_2CH(CH_3)_2$	352.61			223–4[10]	0.897[15]		i	s	v				B2[2], 439
o83	—,nitrile(cis)......	Oleonitrile. $CH_3(CH_2)_7CH:CH(CH_2)_7CN$	263.47	....	−1	330–5d 204[12]	0.848[17/17]	1.4566[20]	i	s	s				B2[2], 443
o84	11-Octadecenoic acid(trans)*	Vaccenic acid. $CH_3(CH_2)_5CH:CH(CH_2)_9CO_2H$ λ <210	282.47	pl (ace)	44			1.4439[60]	i			s^h			B2[3], 1384
o85	6-Octadecenoic acid, 6,7-diiodo-*	6,7-Diiodotariric acid. Iodostarin. $CH_3(CH_2)_{10}CI:CI(CH_2)_4CO_2H$	534.27	nd (al)	48.5	d			i	δ v^h	v	...	v	chl. CS_2 v alk δ	B2[2], 428
Ω 086	9-Octadecenoic acid, 12-hydroxy-(cis)*	Ricinoleic acid. $CH_3(CH_2)_5CH(OH)CH_2CH:CH(CH_2)_7CO_2H$ $[\alpha]_D^{22}$ + 5.05 (+7.86) λ <210	298.47		α: 7.7 β: 16 γ: 5.5	226–8[10]	0.9450[21]	1.4716[21]	i	s	s				B3, 385
o87	—,—,butyl ester (cis)*	Butyl ricinoleate. $CH_3(CH_2)_5CH(OH)CH_2CH:CH(CH_2)_7CO_2(CH_2)_3CH_3$ $[\alpha]_D^{22}$ + 3.73	354.58		....	278[13]	0.9058[22]	1.4566[22]	i	s	s				B3, 388
o88	—,—,ethyl ester (cis)*	Ethyl ricinoleate. $CH_3(CH_2)_5CH(OH)CH_2CH:CH(CH_2)_7CO_2C_2H_5$ $[\alpha]_D^{22}$ + 5.28	326.53		....	258[13]	0.9145[22]	1.4618[22]	i	s^h	s				B3[2], 259
o89	—,—,(trans)*	Ethyl ricinelaidate. $CH_3(CH_2)_5CH(OH)CH_2CH:CH(CH_2)_7CO_2C_2H_5$	326.53		16				i	s	s				B3, 389
o90	—,—,isobutyl ester(cis)*	Isobutyl ricinoleate. $CH_3(CH_2)_5CH(OH)CH_2CH:CH(CH_2)_7CO_2C_4H_9^i$	354.58			282[9]	0.9078[22]	1.4538[22]	i	s	s				B3, 388
Ω 091	9-Octadecen-1-ol(cis)*	Oleyl alcohol. $CH_3(CH_2)_7CH:CH(CH_2)_8OH$	268.49		6–7	205–10[15]	0.8489[20]	1.4606[20]	i	s	s				B1[3], 1962
o92	—(trans)*	Elaidyl alcohol. $CH_3(CH_2)_7CH:CH(CH_2)_8OH$	268.49	(al or ace)	36–7 (34)	ca. 333 198[10]	0.8338[40]	1.4552[40]	i	s^h	...	s^h		dil NaOH s	B1[3], 1965
o93	1-Octadecyne*	$HC:C(CH_2)_{15}CH_3$	250.47	(al)	22.5 fr 27	313[760] 180[15]	0.8025[20]	1.4774[20]							B1[3], 1029
o94	2-Octadecyne*	$CH_3(CH_2)_{14}C:CCH_3$.......	250.47		30	184[15]	0.8016[30]	1.4488[25]							B1, 262
o95	9-Octadecyne*	$CH_3(CH_2)_7C:C(CH_2)_7CH_3$..	250.47		3	163–4[7]	0.8012[20]	1.4488[25]							B1[3], 1029
o96	9-Octadecynoic acid*	Stearolic acid. $CH_3(CH_2)_7C:C(CH_2)_7CO_2H$	280.46	pr (al, peth) nd (dil al) λ 220 (1.8), 265 (1.0)	48	260 189–90[1.8]		1.4510[54]	i	s^h	v				B2[3], 1474
o97	—,ethyl ester*.....	Ethyl stearolate. $CH_3(CH_2)_7C:C(CH_2)_7CO_2C_2H_5$	308.51			180[2.5]		1.4555[20]							B2[2], 458
o98	—,methyl ester* ...	Methyl stearolate. $CH_3(CH_2)_7C:C(CH_2)_7CO_2CH_3$	294.48			175[3]		1.4562[20]							B2[3], 1475
o99	1,3-Octadiene, 3-chloro-*	$CH_3(CH_2)_3CH:CClCH:CH_2$	144.65			64–5[18]	0.9366[20]	1.4794[20]	i		s				B1[3], 1007
Ω o100	2,6-Octadiene, 2,6-dimethyl-*	Dihydroocimene. $CH_3CH:C(CH_3)(CH_2)_2CH_2CH:C(CH_3)_2$	138.25	λ^{hx} 223 (2.0)	....	168 75[30]	0.7752[21]	1.4498[20]	i	s	s	s		aa s	B1[3], 1018
o101	2,7-Octadiene, 2,6-dimethyl-*	Linaloolen. $(CH_3)_2C:CHCH_2CH_2CH(CH_3)CH:CH_2$	138.25			168 58[12]	0.7882[20]	1.4561[20]	...	s					B1, 261
o102	2,4-Octadiene, 7-methyl-*	$(CH_3)_2CHCH_2CH:CHCH:CHCH_3$	124.23			149	0.7521[18]	1.4543[18]	i						B1[2], 239
—	1,6-Octadien-2-ol, 3,7-dimethyl-	see Linalool													
—	2,6-Octadien-1-ol, 3,7-dimethyl-	see Geraniol, Nerol													
o103	1,5-Octadien-3-yne, 5-propyl-*	$CH_3CH_2CH:C(C_3H_7^n)C:CCH:CH_2$	148.25			57–8[6]	0.8047[20]	1.4949[20]			s	s			B1[3], 1065

For explanations, symbols and abbreviations see beginning of table. For structural formulas see end of table.

No.	Name	Synonyms and Formula	Mol. wt.	Color, crystalline form, specific rotation and λ_{max} (log ε)	m.p. °C	b.p. °C	Density	n_D	Solubility						Ref.
									w	al	eth	ace	bz	other solvents	
	2,6-Octadien-4-yne														
o104	2,6-Octadien-4-yne, 3,6-diethyl-*	$CH_3CH{:}C(C_2H_5)C{:}C(C_2H_5)C{:}CHCH_3$	162.28	....	....	$169-71^{760}$ 99^{12}	0.8196_4^{20}	1.4965^{20}	...	..	s	s	...	....	**B1**[3], 1066
o105	—,3,6-dimethyl-*	$CH_3CH{:}C(CH_3)C{:}C(CH_3)C{:}CHCH_3$	134.22		−45	170^{760}	0.8071_4^{22}	1.4998^{20}	...	..	s	s	...	....	**B1**[3], 1065
o106	**1,7-Octadiyne***	$HC{:}C(CH_2)_4C{:}CH$	106.17	....	....	$135-6^{760}$ $93-5^{16}$	0.8169_4^{21}	1.4521^{18}	...	..	s	...	...	....	**B1**[3], 1061
o107	**2,6-Octadiyne***	$CH_3C{:}CCH_2CH_2C{:}CCH_3$	106.17	λ^{al} 227.5 (2.56)	27	62^{19}	0.828_4^{80}	1.4658^{30}	...	..	s	...	...	....	**B1**[2], 248
o108	**3,5-Octadiyne***	$CH_3CH_2C{:}CC{:}CCH_2CH_3$	106.17	238.5 (2.53), 253 (2.36)	....	$163-4^{760}$ 78^{34}	0.826_4^0	1.4968^0	...	..	s	...	...	....	**B1**[3], 1064
o109	—,2,7-dimethyl-*	$(CH_3)_2CHC{:}CC{:}CCH(CH_3)_2$	134.22		....	74^{12}	0.8090^{20}		...	..	s	...	...	....	**B1**, 128
—	**Octalene**	*see* **Aldrin**													
Ω o110	**Octanal***	Capryl aldehyde. $CH_3(CH_2)_6CHO$	128.22	λ^{hx} 295 (1.11)	....	171^{760} 72^{20}	0.8211_4^{20}	1.4217^{20}	δ	s	∞	∞	v	os s	**B1**[2], 757
o111	—,oxime	Caprylaldoxime. $CH_3(CH_2)_6CH{:}NOH$	143.23	nd (peth, MeOH, dil al)	60	112^9			δ	s	..	s	...	MeOH s	**B1**[2], 758
Ω o112	**Octane***	$CH_3(CH_2)_6CH_3$	114.23	....	−56.79	125.66^{760} 19.2^{10}	0.7025_4^{20}	1.3974^{20}	i	∞	∞	∞	∞	chl, peth ∞	**B1**[3], 457
Ω o113	—,1-amino-*	Octylamine. $CH_3(CH_2)_7NH_2$	129.25	....	0.0	179.6^{760} 63.2^{10}	0.7826_4^{20}	1.4924^{20}	δ	v	v	..	...	....	**B4**[3], 379
o114	—,2-amino-(d)*	$CH_3(CH_2)_5CH(NH_2)CH_3$	129.25	$[\alpha]_D^{} +8.62$ (undil)	....	70^{25}	0.771_4^{25}	1.4220^{25}	...	v	v	..	...	....	**B4**[3], 384
o115	—,—(dl)	$CH_3(CH_2)_5CH(NH_2)CH_3$	129.25		....	$163-5^{760}$ $58-9^{13}$	0.7745_4^{20}	1.4232^{25}	i	v	v	..	...	....	**B4**, 196
—	—,1(4-aminophenyl)-	*see* **Benzene, 1-amino-4-octyl-**													
Ω o116	—,1-bromo-*	$CH_3(CH_2)_7Br$	193.13	....	−55	200.8^{760} 77.3^{10}	1.1122_4^{20}	1.4524^{20}	i	∞	∞	..	...	....	**B1**[3], 466
o117	—,2-bromo-(d)*	$CH_3(CH_2)_5CHBrCH_3$	193.13	$[\alpha]_D^{25} +34.2$	....	71^{14}	1.0982_4^{25}	1.4500^{20}	i	∞	∞	..	...	....	**B1**[2], 125
Ω o118	—,—(dl)	$CH_3(CH_2)_5CHBrCH_3$	193.13		....	$188-9^{760}$ 72^{14}	1.0878_4^{25}	1.4442^{25}	i	∞	∞	..	...	....	**B1**[2], 125
o119	—,—(l)	$CH_3(CH_2)_5CHBrCH_3$	193.13	$[\alpha]_D^{25} -37.46$	....	$72-3^{18}$ 46^1	1.0920_4^{20}	1.4475^{25}	i	∞	∞	..	...	....	**B1**[2], 125
o120	—,1-bromo-8-fluoro*	$F(CH_2)_8Br$	211.13		....	$118-20^{22.5}$		1.4500^{20}	i	v	..	..	...	....	**C51**, 7300
Ω o121	—,1-chloro-*	$CH_3(CH_2)_7Cl$	148.68	....	−57.8	182^{760} 78^{15}	0.8738_4^{20}	1.4305^{20}	i	v	v	..	...	....	**B1**, 159
o122	—,2-chloro-(d)*	$CH_3(CH_2)_5CHClCH_3$	148.68	$[\alpha]_D^{20} +33.7$	....	$171-3$ 75^{28}	0.8658_4^{17}	1.4273^{21}	i	v	v	..	...	....	**B1**, 160
o123	—,4-chloro-(d)*	$CH_3(CH_2)_3CHClCH_2CH_2CH_3$	148.68	$[\alpha]_D^{} +0.28$ (undil. 1 = 10 cm)	....	92^{50}			i	v	s	..	...	chl s	**B1**[3], 466
o124	—,1-chloro-8-fluoro-*	$F(CH_2)_8Cl$	166.67		....	87^{10}	0.978_4^{20}	1.4266^{25}	i	v	v	s	...	....	**C51**, 7300
o125	—,3-chloro-3-methyl-*	$CH_3(CH_2)_4CCl(CH_3)CH_2CH_3$	162.71		....	$73-4^{15}$	0.8680_4^{25}	1.4351^{20}	...	..	s	s	s	chl s	**B1**[3], 508
o126	—,4-chloro-4-methyl-*	$CH_3(CH_2)_3CCl(CH_3)CH_2CH_2CH_3$	162.71		....	$71^{14.5}$	0.8723_4^{20}	1.4360^{20}	...	..	s	s	s	chl s	**B1**[3], 509
o127	—,1,2-dibromo-*	$CH_3(CH_2)_5CHBrCH_2Br$	272.04	....	....	$240-2$ 118.5^{15}	1.4580_4^{20}	1.4970^{20}	...	..	s	..	...	....	**B1**[2], 125
o128	—,2,7-dimethyl-*	Di-isoamyl. $(CH_3)_2CH(CH_2)_4CH(CH_3)_2$	142.29	....	−54.6	159.6^{760}	0.7240_4^{20}	1.4092^{20}	...	..	s	..	...	aa s	**B1**[2], 131
o129	—,1-fluoro-*	$CH_3(CH_2)_7F$	132.22	....	....	$142-3^{760}$	0.8103_4^{20}	1.3935^{20}	...	..	..	..	...	....	**B1**[2], 124
Ω o130	—,1-iodo-*	$CH_3(CH_2)_7I$	240.13	....	−45.7	225.5^{760} 86.5^5	1.3297_4^{20}	1.4889^{20}	...	s	s	..	...	....	**B1**[2], 185
o131	—,2-iodo-(D, −)*	sec-Octyl iodide. $CH_3(CH_2)_5CHICH_3$	240.13	$[\alpha]_D^{28} -45.47$	....	92^{12}	1.3219_4^{20}	1.4863^{25}	i	s	s	..	...	lig s	**B1**[3], 470
o132	—,—(DL)	$CH_3(CH_2)_5CHICH_3$	240.13		....	210 $95-6^{16}$	1.3251_4^{20}	1.4896^{20}	i	s	s	..	...	lig s	**B1**[3], 470
o133	—,—(L, +)*	$CH_3(CH_2)_5CHICH_3$	240.13	$[\alpha]_D^{26} +46.33$	....	101^{22}	1.3314_4^{17}	1.4877^{22}	i	s	s	..	...	lig s	**B1**[3], 470
o134	—,2-methyl-*	$CH_3(CH_2)_5CH(CH_3)_2$	128.26	....	−80.1	142.8^{760}	0.7107_4^{20}	1.4029^{20}	i	s	s	..	...	peth, lig v	**B1**[3], 507
o135	—,3-methyl-(d)*	$CH_3(CH_2)_4CH(CH_3)CH_2CH_3$	128.26	$[\alpha]_D^{17} +9.38$	−107.6	$143-4^{760}$	0.7206_4^{17}	1.4068^{20}	...	..	..	s	s	....	**B1**, 166
o136	—,—(l)	$CH_3(CH_2)_4CH(CH_3)CH_2CH_3$	128.26	$[\alpha]_D^{27} -8.5$	....	143^{760}	0.714_4^{27}	1.4052^{25}	...	..	..	s	s	....	**B1**[3], 509
Ω o137	—,4-methyl-(dl)*	$CH_3(CH_2)_3CH(CH_3)CH_2CH_2CH_3$	128.26	....	−113.2	142.4^{760} 32^{10}	0.7199_4^{20}	1.4061^{20}	...	..	s	v	v	os v	**B1**[3], 509
o138	—,—(l)	$CH_3(CH_2)_3CH(CH_3)CH_2CH_2CH_3$	128.26	$[\alpha]_D^{19} -1.06$	....	141^{760}	0.7171_4^{19}		i	..	v	v	v	os v	**B1**[3], 510
o139	—,1(4-nitrophenyl)-*	1-Nitro-4-octylbenzene*.	235.33	....	−5	200^{10}			i	..	∞	..	...	....	**B5**, 454
Ω o140	—,1-phenyl-*	Octylbenzene*. $C_6H_5(CH_2)_7CH_3$	190.33	....	−7	$264-5^{760}$ $131-4^{12}$	0.8582_4^{20}	1.4851^{20}	i	..	∞	..	∞	....	**B5**[2], 343
o141	**Octanedial***	Suberaldehyde. $OHC(CH_2)_6CHO$	142.20	....	....	$230-40d$ $96-8^3$		1.4439^{20}	v	v	..	..	...	....	**B1**[2], 845
o142	—,dioxime	Suberaldoxime. $HON{:}CH(CH_2)_6CH{:}NOH$	172.23	pr (al)	155−6	....			δ^h	s^h	..	..	...	....	**B1**[2], 845
Ω o143	**Octanedioic acid***	Suberic acid. $HO_2C(CH_2)_6CO_2H$	174.20	lo nd or pl (w)	144	300 sub 219.5^{10}			δ s^h	s	δ	..	...	MeOH s chl i	**B2**[2], 595

For explanations, symbols and abbreviations see beginning of table. For structural formulas see end of table.

Octanedioic acid

No.	Name	Synonyms and Formula	Mol. wt.	Color, crystalline form, specific rotation and λ_{max} (log ε)	m.p. °C	b.p. °C	Density	n_D	w	al	eth	ace	bz	other solvents	Ref.
Ω o144	—,diethyl ester	Diethyl suberate. $C_2H_5O_2C(CH_2)_6CO_2C_2H_5$	230.31	....	5.9	$282-6^{760}$ $140-1^8$	0.9811_4^{20}	1.4328^{20}	i	s	s	...	...		B2[2], 596
Ω o145	—,dimethyl ester ..	Dimethyl suberate. $CH_3O_2C(CH_2)_6CO_2CH_3$	202.25	....	-3.1	268 120^6	1.0217_4^{20}	1.4341^{20}	i	s	s	s		oss	B2, 693
Ω o146	1,8-Octanediol* ...	$HO(CH_2)_8OH$	146.23	nd (bz-lig), pr	63	172^{20}	....	....	δ	v	δ		s	lig δ	B1[2], 556
Ω o147	4,5-Octanediol (dl)*	1,2-Dipropylethylene glycol. $CH_3CH_2CH_2CH(OH)CH(OH)CH_2CH_2CH_3$	146.23		28	110^8	....	1.4419^{25}							B1[3], 2219
o148	—(meso)*	$CH_3CH_2CH_2CH(OH)CH(OH)CH_2CH_2CH_3$	146.23	lf (bz, al, lig)	123-4	....	....	....	i	δ	δ		δ	lig δ	B1[3], 2219
o149	2,3-Octanedione* ..	Acetylcaproyl. $CH_3COCO(CH_2)_4CH_3$	142.20	....		$172-3^{733}$	....	....						lig δ	B1, 795
o150	—,dioxime*	Methylpentylglyoxime. $CH_3C(:NOH)C(:NOH)(CH_2)_4CH_3$	172.23	nd (dil al) $\lambda^{al}229$ (4.15)	173	....			i	s	s				B1, 795
o151	—,3-oxime*	$CH_3COC(:NOH)(CH_2)_4CH_3$	157.22	(lig)	59	133^{11}	....	....			v			lig s[h]	B1, 795
o152	2,7-Octanedione* ..	1,4-Diacetylbutane. $CH_3CO(CH_2)_4COCH_3$	142.20	pl (bz)	44	114^{10}	....	....	δ	s				lig δ	B1[1], 408
o153	—,dioxime*	$CH_3C(:NOH)(CH_2)_4C(:NOH)CH_3$	172.23	(al)	158	....	....	....	i	s[h]					B1, 795
o154	3,6-Octanedione* ..	sym-Dipropionylethane. $CH_3CH_2COCH_2CH_2COCH_2CH_3$	142.20	pl (al)	35-6	98^{14} sub	....	....	δ[h]						B1[2], 845
o155	4,5-Octanedione* ..	Dibutyryl. Dipropylglyoxal. $CH_3CH_2CH_2COCOCH_2CH_2CH_3$	142.20	ye oil $\lambda^{al}268$ (1.67), 425 (1.16)	....	168^{760} 60^{12}	0.934_4^0	....		v	v	v			B1[2], 845
o156	—,dioxime*	Dipropylglyoxime. $CH_3CH_2CH_2C(:NOH)C(:NOH)CH_2CH_2CH_3$	172.23		186-7	sub	....	....	i	s	s			lig i	B1[2], 846
o157	3,6-Octanedione, 2,2,7,7-tetra-methyl-	Dipivaloylethane. $(CH_3)_3CCOCH_2CH_2COC(CH_3)_3$ Dipivaloylethane.	198.31	nd	2.5	$115-7^{17}$ $55-60^{0.5}$	0.900_4^{27}	1.4400^{20}	i	s	s				B1[3], 3151
Ω o158	1-Octanethiol*	Octyl mercaptan. $CH_3(CH_2)_7SH$	146.30	....	-49.2	199.1^{760} 86^{15}	0.8433_4^{20}	1.4540^{20}		s	s				B1[3], 1710
o159	2-Octanethiol (dl)*	$CH_3(CH_2)_5CH(SH)CH_3$	146.30	....	-79	186.4^{760} 88.9^{30}	0.8366_4^{20}	1.4504^{20}		s	s				B1[3], 1717
o160	—(l)*	$CH_3(CH_2)_5CH(SH)CH_3$	146.30	$[\alpha]_{546}^{25}$ -36.4	....	$78-80^{22}$	0.830^{25}	....		s	s				B1[3], 1722
Ω o161	Octanoic acid*	Caprylic acid*. $CH_3(CH_2)_6CO_2H$	144.22	....	16.5	239.3 140^{23}	0.9088^{20}	1.4285^{20}	δ[h]	∞				chl, CH_3CN ∞	B2[2], 301
Ω o162	—,amide	Caprylamide. $CH_3(CH_2)_6CONH_2$	143.23	lf lf, pl	fr 105.9 110	239^{760}	0.8450^{110}	....	δ[h]	v	s	s	δ	chl δ	B2[2], 303
o163	—,anhydride*	Caprylic anhydride. $[CH_3(CH_2)_6CO]_2O$	270.42	....	-1	$280-5$ 186^{15}	0.9065^{18}	1.4358^{18}	d	s	∞	s		oos s	B2[2], 303
o164	—,butyl ester*	Butyl caprylate. $CH_3(CH_2)_6CO_2(CH_2)_3CH_3$	200.33	....	-42.9	240.5 $121-2^{20}$	0.8628^{20}	1.4232^{25}	i	s	s			oss	B2, 348
Ω o165	—,chloride	Caprylyl chloride. $CH_3(CH_2)_6COCl$	162.66	....	63	195.6^{760} 89^{20}	0.9535_4^{15}	1.4335^{20}	d	d					B2[2], 303
Ω o166	—,ethyl ester*	Ethyl caprylate. $CH_3(CH_2)_6CO_2C_2H_5$	172.27	....	-43.1	208.5^{760} 104^{80}	0.8693^{20}	1.4178^{20}	i	v	v				B2[2], 302
o167	—,heptyl ester*	$CH_3(CH_2)_6CO_2(CH_2)_6CH_3$	242.41	....	-10.6	290.6 160^{14}	0.8596^{20}	1.4340^{20}	i	s	s			oss	B2, 348
o168	—,hexyl ester*	$CH_3(CH_2)_6CO_2(CH_2)_5CH_3$	228.38	....	-30.6	277.4	0.8603^{20}	1.4323^{15}	i	s	s			oss	B2[3], 794
o169	—,isopropyl ester* .	Isopropyl caprylate. $CH_3(CH_2)_6CO_2CH(CH_3)_2$	186.30	....		93.8^{10}	0.8555^{20}	1.4147^{25}							B2[3], 794
Ω o170	—,methyl ester*	Methyl caprylate. $CH_3(CH_2)_6CO_2CH_3$	158.24	....	-40	192.9^{760} 83^{15}	0.8777_4^{20}	1.4170^{20}	i	v	v				B2[2], 302
Ω o171	—,2-methylallyl ester*	Isoamyl caprylate. $CH_3(CH_2)_6CO_2CH_2C(CH_3):CH_2$	198.31	....		147.8^{50}	0.8703	1.4308	δ	s					B2[3], 795
o172	—,nitrile	Caprylonitrile. $CH_3(CH_2)_6CN$	125.22	....	-45.6	205.2^{760} 77.8^{10}	0.8136_4^{20}	1.4203^{20}	i	δ	s				B2[2], 303
o173	—,octyl ester*	$CH_3(CH_2)_6CO_2(CH_2)_7CH_3$	256.43	....	-18.1	306.8^{760} 192.5^{30}	0.8554_4^{20}	1.4352^{20}	i	s	s	s		oss	B2, 348
Ω o174	—,pentyl ester*	Amyl caprylate. $CH_3(CH_2)_6CO_2(CH_2)_4CH_3$	214.35	....	-34.8	260.2 $124-6^{20}$	0.8613^{20}	1.4262^{25}	i	s	s	s		oss	B2[3], 794
o175	—,piperazinium salt	$C_4H_{10}N_2 \cdot 2[CH_3(CH_2)_6CO_2H]$	374.59	....	98	....	....	....	s	s	i				Am 70, 2758
o176	—,propyl ester* ...	Propyl caprylate. $CH_3(CH_2)_6CO_2CH_2CH_2CH_3$	186.30	(peth)	-46.2	226.4 112^{20}	0.8659^{20}	1.4191^{25}	i	s	s	s		oss	B2, 348
o177	—,2-amino-(d)* ...	$CH_3(CH_2)_5CH(NH_2)CO_2H$.	159.23	$[\alpha]_D^{26}$ + 23.5 (6N HCl, c = 1) $[\alpha]_D^{20}$ + 12.3 (1N NaOH, c = 0.5)	....	....	....	....	δ	δ	δ		δ	aa s	B4[2], 886
Ω o178	—,—(dl)	$CH_3(CH_2)_5CH(NH_2)CO_2H$.	159.23	lf(w)	270 (263-5)	sub d	....	....	δ	δ	δ		δ	aa s	B4[2], 886
o179	—,—(l)	$CH_3(CH_2)_5CH(NH_2)CO_2H$	159.23	$[\alpha]_D$ -13 (1N NaOH, c = 2) $[\alpha]_D$ -23 (5N HCl)	276	....	....	....	δ	δ	δ		δ	aa s	B4[2], 886
o180	—,8-amino-*	$H_2N(CH_2)_7CO_2H$	159.23		172	....	....	....	δ v[h]	v					B4[1], 527
o181	—,2-bromo *......	$CH_3(CH_2)_5CHBrCO_2H$	223.12	....		140^5	1.2785^{24}	1.4613^{24}							B2[2], 303

For explanations, symbols and abbreviations see beginning of table. For structural formulas see end of table.

Octanoic acid

No.	Name	Synonyms and Formula	Mol. wt.	Color, crystalline form, specific rotation and λ_{max} (log ε)	m.p. °C	b.p. °C	Density	n_D	w	al	eth	ace	bz	other solvents	Ref.
o182	—.8-fluoro-*	$F(CH_2)_7CO_2H$	162.21		35	132–3[4]			δ	v	v			lig s[h]	C51, 7300
Ω o183	—.2-hydroxy-*	$CH_3(CH_2)_5CH(OH)CO_2H$	160.22	pl	70	160–5[10]			δ	v	v				B3[2], 237
Ω o184	—.4-hydroxy-, lactone*	γ-Caprylolactone	142.20			132–3[20]	0.9796_4^{19}	1.4451^{19}		s					B17[1], 133
o185	—.2-methyl-3-oxo-, ethyl ester*	$CH_3(CH_2)_4COCH(CH_3)CO_2C_2H_5$	200.28			128–9[12]	0.963_4^0			s					B3, 713
Ω o186	1-Octanol*	Octyl alcohol. $CH_3(CH_2)_7OH$	130.23	λ^{vap} 197	−16.7	194.45[760] 98[19]	0.8270_4^{20}	1.4295^{20}	i	∞	∞				B1[3], 1703
o187	2-Octanol(d)*	$CH_3(CH_2)_5CH(OH)CH_3$	130.23	$[\alpha]_D^{17}$ +9.9		86[20]	0.8216_4^{20}	1.4264^{20}	δ	s	s	s			B1[1], 208
Ω o188	—(dl)*	$CH_3(CH_2)_5CH(OH)CH_3$	130.23	λ^{vap} 196 λ^{hx} 175 (2.5)	−31.6	180[760] 87[20]	0.8193_4^{20}	1.4203^{20}	δ	s	s	s			B1[2], 449
o189	—(l)*	$CH_3(CH_2)_5CH(OH)CH_3$	130.23	$[\alpha]_D^{17}$ −9.9		86[20]	0.8201_4^{20}	1.4264^{20}	δ	s	s	s			B1[2], 451
o190	1-Octanol, 8-chloro-*	Octamethylene chlorohydrin. $Cl(CH_2)_8OH$	164.68			139[19]		1.4563^{25}	δ	v	v				B1[3], 1710
o191	—.3,7-dimethyl-(d)*	Tetrahydrogeraniol. $(CH_3)_2CH(CH_2)_3CH(CH_3)CH_2CH_2OH$	158.29	λ^{al} 237 (1.09) $[\alpha]_D^{20}$ +4.09 (+5.57)		212–3[760] 105–6[10]	0.8285_4^{20}	1.4355^{20}			v				B1[2], 460
o192	—,—(l)*	$(CH_3)_2CH(CH_2)_3CH(CH_3)CH_2CH_2OH$	158.29	$[\alpha]_{546}^{11}$ −3.67 λ^{al} 237 (1.09)		212–3[760] 109[15]	0.830^{18}	1.4370^{15}			v				B1[2], 461
Ω o193	3-Octanol, 3,7-dimethyl-(dl)*	Tetrahydrolinalool. $(CH_3)_2CH(CH_2)_3C(OH)(CH_3)CH_2CH_3$	158.29		31–2	196–7 87–8[10]	0.8280^{20}	1.4335^{20}	i	s					B1[3], 1767
o194	—.3-ethyl-*	$CH_3(CH_2)_4C(OH)(C_2H_5)_2$	158.29			199 84[12]	0.8361_4^{25}	1.4390^{20}	i	s					B1, 426
o195	1-Octanol, 8-fluoro-*	Octamethylene fluorohydrin. $F(CH_2)_8OH$	148.22			106–7[10]	0.945_4^{20}	1.4248^{25}	δ	v	v				C51, 7300
Ω o196	2-Octanol, 2-methyl-*	$CH_3(CH_2)_5C(OH)(CH_3)_2$	144.26			178 81–3[16]	0.8210_4^{20}	1.4280^{20}	i	s	s				B1[2], 457
Ω o197	2-Octanone*	Hexyl methyl ketone. $CH_3(CH_2)_5COCH_3$	128.22		−16	173[760] 59–60[11]	0.8202_4^{20}	1.4151^{20}	δ	∞	∞				B1[2], 758
Ω o198	3-Octanone*	Amyl ethyl ketone. $CH_3(CH_2)_4COC_2H_5$	128.22	λ^{MeOH} 278 (1.38)		167[749]	0.8221_4^{20}	1.4153^{20}	i	∞	∞				B1[1], 362
Ω o199	4-Octanone*	Butyl propyl ketone. $CH_3(CH_2)_3COCH_2CH_2CH_3$	128.22	λ^{al} 280 (1.36)		163[760] 70[26]	0.8146_4^{25}	1.4173^{14}	i	∞	∞				B1[2], 759
o200	—.5-hydroxy-*	Butyroin. $CH_3CH_2CH_2CH(OH)COCH_2CH_2CH_3$	144.22		−10	180–90[760] 95[20]	0.9231^{20}	1.4290^{20}	s	s	s	s			B1[2], 880
o201	—.7-methyl-*	Isoamyl propyl ketone. $(CH_3)_2CHCH_2CH_2COCH_2CH_2CH_3$	142.24			177–9[760]	0.8239_4^{20}	1.4210^{20}	i	s	s				B1[1], 366
o202	Octasiloxane, octadeca-methyl-	$CH_3[-Si(CH_3)_2O-]_7Si(CH_3)_3$	607.32			153[5.1]	0.913	1.3970^{20}	i	δ			s	peth, lig s	Am 68, 362
o203	1,3,5,7-Octa-tetraene*	$CH_2{:}CHCH{:}CHCH{:}CHCH{:}CH_2$	106.17	(bz) λ^{cy} 278, 290, 302	ca. 50	sub								peth s[h] aa s	B1[3], 1062
o204	2,4,6-Octatriene (trans, trans, trans)*	$CH_3CH{:}CHCH{:}CHCH{:}CHCH_3$	108.19	lf λ^{iso} 253 (4.7), 263 (4.22), 274 (4.7)	52	147–8[764] 43[10]	0.7961_4^{23}	1.5131^{27}	i	s	s			chl, lig s	B1[3], 1047
o205	1,3,7-Octatriene, 3,7-dimethyl-*	Ocimene. $CH_2{:}C(CH_3)CH_2CH_2CH{:}C(CH_3)CH{:}CH_2$	136.24	λ^{iso} 235 (4.22)		176–8d 73–4[21]	0.8000^{20}	1.4862^{20}	i	s	s			chl, aa s	B1[3], 1052
o206	2,4,6-Octatriene, 2,6-dimethyl-(4-trans, 6-trans)*	Alloocimene A. $CH_3CH{:}C(CH_3)CH{:}CHCH{:}C(CH_3)_2$	136.24	λ^{iso} 270 (4.50), 278 (4.60), 289 (4.48)	−35.4	188[750] 91[20]	0.8118_4^{20}	1.5446^{20}							B1[3], 1050
o207	—,—(4-trans, 6-cis)*	Alloocimene B. $CH_3CH{:}C(CH_3)CH{:}CHCH{:}C(CH_3)_2$	136.24	λ^{iso} 265 (4.52), 273 (4.63), 285 (4.53)	−20.6	89[20]	0.8060^{20}	1.5446^{20}							B1[3], 1050
Ω o208	1-Octene*	$CH_3(CH_2)_5CH{:}CH_2$	112.22	λ^{hp} 177 (4.1), λ^{al} 210 (2.60)	−101.73	121.3[760] 15.4[10]	0.7149_4^{20}	1.4087^{20}	i	∞	s	s	s	chl, os v	B1[3], 835
o209	2-Octene(cis)*	$CH_3(CH_2)_4CH{:}CHCH_3$	112.22	λ^{hx} 179 (4.15)	−100.2	125.6[760] 16.5[10]	0.7243_4^{20}	1.4150^{20}	i	s	s	s	s	chl s	B1[3], 839
o210	—(trans)*	$CH_3(CH_2)_4CH{:}CHCH_3$	112.22	λ^{hx} 183 (4.11)	−87.7	125.0[760] 16.0[10]	0.7199_4^{20}	1.4132^{20}	i	s	s	s	s	chl v	B1[3], 839
o211	3-Octene(cis)*	$CH_3(CH_2)_3CH{:}CHCH_2CH_3$	112.22		−126	122.9[760] 14.3[10]	0.7189_4^{20}	1.4135^{20}	i	s	s	s	s	lig s	B1[3], 840
Ω o212	—(trans)	$CH_3(CH_2)_3CH{:}CHCH_2CH_3$	112.22	λ^{al} 185 (3.91)	−110	123.3[760] 14.6[10]	0.7152_4^{20}	1.4126^{20}	i	s	s	s	s	lig s	B1[3], 841
o213	4-Octene(cis)*	$CH_3CH_2CH_2CH{:}CHCH_2CH_2CH_3$	112.22		−118.7	122.5[760] 14[10]	0.7212_4^{20}	1.4148^{20}	i	s	s	s	s	lig s	B1[3], 841
Ω o214	—(trans)*	$CH_3CH_2CH_2CH{:}CHCH_2CH_2CH_3$	112.22		−93.8	122.3[760] 13.7[10]	0.7141_4^{20}	1.4118^{20}	i	s	s	s	s	lig s	B1[3], 841
o215	1-Octene, 2-chloro-*	$CH_3(CH_2)_5CCl{:}CH_2$	146.66			168–70	0.9274_0^0			s	s	s	s		B1[3], 840
o216	2-Octene, 2-chloro-*	$CH_3(CH_2)_4CH{:}CClCH_3$	146.66			167–8	0.8923_{16}^{16}	1.4424^{16}		s	s	s	s		B1[3], 840

For explanations, symbols and abbreviations see beginning of table. For structural formulas see end of table.

No.	Name	Synonyms and Formula	Mol. wt.	Color, crystalline form, specific rotation and λ_{max} (log ε)	m.p. °C	b.p. °C	Density	n_D	w	al	eth	ace	bz	other solvents	Ref.
	2-Octene														
o217	—,4-chloro-*	$CH_3(CH_2)_3CHClCH:CHCH_3$	146.66			153 65–6[15]	0.8924[20]	1.4452[20]	i		s	s	s	chl s	B1[3], 840
o218	4-Octene, 4-chloro-(cis)*	$CH_3CH_2CH_2CH:CClCH_2CH_3$	146.66			165.33[760]	0.8912[20]	1.4447[20]			s			chl s	Am 73, 3329
o219	1-Octen-3-yne*	$CH_3(CH_2)_3C:CCH:CH_2$	108.19			62[60]	0.7830[20]	1.4592[20]			s				B1[3], 1046
o220	1-Octen-3-yn-5-ol, 5-methyl-*	$CH_2:CHC:CC(CH_3)(OH)CH_2CH_2CH_3$	138.21			80[13]	0.8851[15]	1.4735[20]		s					B1[3], 2034
o221	1-Octyne*	n-Hexylacetylene. $CH_3(CH_2)_5C:CH$	110.20	λ^{hp} 185 (3.3), 222.5 (2.1)	–79.3	125.2[760] 19.7[10]	0.7461[20]	1.4159[20]	i	s	s				B1, 258
o222	2-Octyne*	Methylpentylacetylene. $CH_3(CH_2)_4C:CCH_3$	110.20	λ^{hp} 177.5 (4.0), 196 sh (3.3), 222.5 (2.2)	–61.6	138[760]	0.7596[20]	1.4278[20]	i	s	s				B1, 258
o223	3-Octyne*	n-Butylethylacetylene. $CH_3(CH_2)_3C:CC_2H_5$	110.20		–103.9	133[760] 85[169]	0.7529[20]	1.4250[20]	i	s	s				B1[3], 1006
o224	4-Octyne*	Di-n-propylacetylene. $CH_3CH_2CH_2C:CCH_2CH_2CH_3$	110.20		–102.55	131.5[760]	0.7509[20]	1.4248[20]	i	s	s				B1[3], 1006
o225	1-Octyne, 1-chloro-*	$CH_3(CH_2)_5C:CCl$	144.65			61–2[17]	0.912[20]	1.445[20]		v[h]	v				B1[3], 1005
o226	3-Octyne, 2-chloro-2-methyl-*	$CH_3(CH_2)_3C:CCCl(CH_3)_2$	158.67			68[15]	0.8929[20]	1.4480[20]			v				B1[3], 1014
o227	—,2,2-dimethyl-*	$CH_3(CH_2)_3C:CC(CH_3)_3$	138.25			79[60]	0.7491[20]	1.4270[20]	i		s				B1[3], 1018
o228	—,7-methyl-*	$(CH_3)_2CH(CH_2)_2C:CCH_2CH_3$	124.23			87[99]	0.7599[20]	1.4280[20]	i		v				B1[3], 1014
o229	2-Octyn-1-ol*	Pentylpropargyl alcohol. $CH_3(CH_2)_4C:CCH_2OH$	126.20		–18	98–9[15]	0.8805[20]	1.4556[20]			∞				B1[7], 506
—	Octhracene	see Anthracene, 1,2,3,4,5,6,7,8-octahydro-													
—	Olealdehyde	see 9-Octadecenal*													
—	Oleanilide	see 9-Octadecenoic acid, amide. N-phenyl-(cis)													
—	Oleanolic acid	see Caryphyllin													
—	Oleic acid	see 9-Octadecenoic acid(cis)*													
—	Oleyl alcohol	see 9-Octadecen-1-ol(cis)*													
—	Olivetol	see Benzene, 1,3-dihydroxy-5-pentyl-*													
—	Olivetolcarboxylic acid	see Benzoic acid, 2,4-dihydroxy-6-pentyl-													
o230	Orcein	Orcin. $C_{28}H_{24}N_2O_7$	500.51	br-red pw					i	s	i	s	i	chl, CS_2 i	B6[2], 876
—	Orcinol	see Toluene, 3,5-dihydroxy-													
o231	Ornithine(L)	L-2,5-Diaminopentanoic acid*. $H_2N(CH_2)_3CH(NH_2)CO_2H$	132.16	cr (al-eth) $[\alpha]_D^{25}$ +11.5 (w, c = 6.5)	140				s	s	δ				B4[2], 844
o232	—,monohydrochloride(L)	$H_2N(CH_2)_3CH(NH_2)CO_2H \cdot HCl$	168.63	nd, $[\alpha]_D^{23}$ +11.0 (w, c = 5.5)	215 (230–2)				s						B4[3], 1347
o233	—,sulfate(L)	$H_2N(CH_2)_3CH(NH_2)CO_2H \cdot H_2SO_4$	230.24	$[\alpha]_D^{25}$ +8.4 (w)	234d				v	δ	i				B4[3], 1347
—	Orotic acid	see 6-Uracilcarboxylic acid													
—	Oroxylin	see Flavone, 5,7-dihydroxy-6-methoxy-													
—	Orsellinic acid	see Benzoic acid, 2,4-dihydroxy-6-methyl-													
—	Orthanilic acid	see Benzenesulfonic acid, 2-amino-*													
Ω o234	Orthoacetic acid, triethyl ester	1,1,1-Triethoxyethane*. $CH_3C(OC_2H_5)_3$	162.23			144–6[740] 66.5[41]	0.8847[25]	1.3980[20]	i	∞	∞			chl, CCl_4 ∞	B2[2], 137
o235	—,trimethyl ester	1,1,1-Trimethoxyethane*. $CH_3C(OCH_3)_3$	120.15			107–9	0.9438[25]	1.3859[25]		v	v				B2[2], 128
Ω o236	Orthocarbonic acid, tetraethyl ester	Tetraethoxymethane*. $C(OC_2H_5)_4$	192.26			160–1 62[28]	0.9186[20]	1.3928[20]		∞	∞				B3[1], 4
Ω o237	—,tetrapropyl ester	Tetrapropoxymethane*. $C(OCH_2CH_2CH_3)_4$	248.37			224.2	0.897[20]	1.4100[20]		v	v				B3, 6
—	Orthoform	see Benzoic acid, 4-amino-3-hydroxy-, methyl ester													
Ω o238	Orthoformic acid, triethyl ester	Triethoxymethane*. $HC(OC_2H_5)_3$	148.20			143[765] 60[30]	0.8909[20]	1.3922[20]	d	s	s				B2[3], 35
o239	—,triisobutyl ester	Triisobutoxymethane. $HC[OCH_2CH(CH_3)_2]_3$	232.37			224–6	0.8582[20]	1.4120[20]		s	s				B2[2], 31
o240	—,triisopropyl ester	Triisopropoxymethane*. $HC[OCH(CH_3)_2]_3$	190.29			166.0	0.8621[20]	1.4088[20]		s	s				B2[3], 39
Ω o241	—,trimethyl ester	Trimethoxymethane*. $HC(OCH_3)_3$	106.12			103–5[760]	0.9676[20]	1.3793[20]		s	s				B2, 19
o242	—,tri(3-methylbutyl) ester	Triisoamyl orthoformate. $HC[OCH_2CH_2CH(CH_3)_2]_3$	274.45			267–9d 166[25]	0.8628[20]	1.4233[20]		s	s				B2[2], 31
o243	—,triphenyl ester	Triphenoxymethane.* $HC(OC_6H_5)_3$	292.34		76–7	269–70[50] d				s[h]	s		s[h]	chl s	B6[3], 595
o244	—,tripropyl ester	Tripropoxymethane.* $HC(OCH_2CH_2CH_3)_3$	190.29			190–1[745] 93[30]	0.8805[20]	1.4072[20]		s	s				B2[3], 38

For explanations, symbols and abbreviations see beginning of table. For structural formulas see end of table.

No.	Name	Synonyms and Formula	Mol. wt.	Color. crystalline form. specific rotation and λ_{max} (log ε)	m.p. °C	b.p. °C	Density	n_D	Solubility						Ref.
									w	al	eth	ace	bz	other solvents	

Orthoformic acid

No.	Name	Synonyms and Formula	Mol. wt.	Color etc.	m.p.	b.p.	Density	n_D	w	al	eth	ace	bz	other	Ref.
o245	—,trithio-, triethyl ester	Ethyl orthothioformate. Tris(ethylthio)methane*. $HC(SC_2H_5)_3$	196.40	....		235^{760}d $127-8^{12}$	1.053_4^{20}	1.5410^{15}		s	s				B2[1], 39
Ω o246	Orthopropionic acid, triethyl ester	1,1,1-Triethoxypropane*. $CH_3CH_2C(OC_2H_5)_3$	176.26			161^{766} 44^9		1.4000^{25}		v	v				B2[2], 220
o247	Orthosilicic acid, tetraethyl ester	$(OC_2H_5)_4Si$ ..	208.33		−82.5	168.8^{760} 77^{32}	0.9320_4^{20}	1.3928^{20}	d	v	∞				B1, 334
o248	—,tetrakis(2-ethyl-butyl) ester	$[(C_2H_5)_2CHCH_2O]_4Si$	432.77	liq		358^{760}	0.8920_4^{20}	1.4307^{20}	i	δ	s	s			C54, 23706
o249	—,tetrakis(2-ethyl-hexyl) ester	$[CH_3(CH_2)_3CH(C_2H_5)CH_2O]_4Si$	544.99		−90	419^{760} 227^5	0.8803_4^{20}	1.4388^{20}	i	δ	s	s			C54, 23706
o250	—,tetramethyl ester	Methyl silicate. $(CH_3O)_4Si$ ..	152.22	nd	−2	121^{760} $25-7^{12}$	1.0232^{20}	1.3683^{20}		s					B1[2], 274
o253	Orthovanadic acid, triisopropyl ester	$[(CH_3)_2CHO]_3VO$	244.21	pa ye to col	−180	124^{21}	1.088^{15}		d	s	s		s	to s	B51, 751
o254	1,3,4-Oxadiazole, 2,5-dimethyl-		98.11			178−9			∞	∞	∞				B27, 565
Ω o255	Oxalic acid	Ethanedioic acid*. HO_2CCO_2H	90.04	mcl ta or pr (+2w, w) orh (anh) λ^w 250 sh (1.8)	α: 189.5 β: 182 (anh) 101.5 (hyd)	157 sub	α: 1.900_4^{17} β: 1.895 1.650$_4^{20}$ (hyd)		s	v	δ		i	chl, peth i	B2[3], 1534
Ω o256	—,diallyl ester.....	$CH_2:CHCH_2O_2CCO_2CH_2CH:CH_2$	170.17			217 86^3	1.1582^{20}	1.4481^{20}	i	s		s	s	chl δ	B2[3], 1581
Ω o257	—,diamide	Oxamide. $H_2NCOCONH_2$..	88.07	nd (w)	419d				δ	δ	i				B2[3], 1586
o258	—,—,N,N'-diethyl-	$C_2H_5NHCOCONHC_2H_5$....	144.18	nd (al)	175 (180)		1.169^4		δ	s	i				B4[2], 605
o259	—,—,N,N''-diisopropyl-	$(CH_3)_2CHNHCOCONHCH(CH_3)_2$	172.23	nd (al)	212					v^h					B4, 154
o260	—,—,N,N''-dimethyl-	$CH_3NHCOCONHCH_3$	116.13	pl or nd (al)	217	sub	1.3_4^4		v^h	δ	i		s^h	chl s^h	B4[2], 564
Ω o261	—,—,N,N''-diphenyl-	Oxanilide. $C_6H_5NHCOCONHC_6H_5$	240.27	lf (bz or PhNO₂)	254	>360			i	δ^h	i		s		B12[2], 165
Ω o262	—,dibutyl ester....	$CH_3(CH_2)_3O_2CCO_2(CH_2)_3CH_3$	202.25		−30.5	242^{773} 96^2	0.9873_4^{20}	1.4234^{20}	i	s	s	s			B2[2], 507
Ω o263	—,dichloride......	Oxalyl chloride. ClCOCOCl .	126.93	nd (eth or peth) λ^{hp} 306 (1.36), 316 (1.37), 320 (1.40), 330 (1.35), 340 (1.24), 351 (1.20), 369 (0.74)	−16 (−12)	$63-4^{763}$	1.4785_4^{20}	1.4316^{20}	d	d	s		s		B2[2], 508
o264	—,di(2-chloroethyl) ester	$ClCH_2CH_2O_2CCO_2CH_2CH_2Cl$.	215.04	lf (dil al)	45	132^3				s			s		B2[3], 1579
o265	—,dicyclohexyl ester	....	254.33	(MeOH)	42 (47)	$190-1^{73}$			i	v	v			MeOH s	B6[1], 6
Ω o266	—,diethyl ester	Oxalic ester. $C_2H_5O_2CCO_2C_2H_5$	146.14	λ^{al} 225 (2.6)	−38.5	185.7^{760} 97^{20}	1.0785_4^{20}	1.4101^{20}	δ^h	∞	∞	∞			B2[2], 504
o267	—,dihydrazide	$H_2NNHCOCONHNH_2$....	118.10	nd (w)	243d		$1.458^{22.5}$		s^h	δ	δ		δ	chl δ	B2[2], 514
o268	—,diisobutyl ester .	$(CH_3)_2CHCH_2O_2CCO_2CH_2CH(CH_3)_2$	202.25			229^{758} 143^{20}	0.9737_4^{20}	1.4180^{20}	i	s	s	s			B2[2], 507
o269	—,diisopropyl ester	$(CH_3)_2CHO_2CCO_2CH(CH_3)_2$	174.20			191^{765}	1.0010_4^{20}	1.4100^{20}							B2[1], 234
Ω o270	—,dimethyl ester ..	$CH_3O_2CCO_2CH_3$	118.09	mcl ta	54	164.5^{760}	1.148^{15} 1.1716^{60}	1.379^{82}	δ^h s^h	s	s	s			B2[2], 503
o271	—,di(3-methyl-butyl) ester	Isoamyl oxalate. $(CH_3)_2CHCH_2CH_2O_2CCO_2CH_2CH_2CH(CH_3)_2$	230.30			$267-8^{14}$ 144^{14}	0.968^{11}_{11}		i	v	v				B2[3], 1580
—	—,dinitrile	see Cyanogen													
o273	—,dipropyl ester...	$CH_3CH_2CH_2O_2CCO_2CH_2CH_2CH_3$	174.20		−44.3	211^{749} $78-80^3$	1.0188_4^{20}	1.4168^{20}	δ	∞	s				B2[3], 1579
o274	—,di(2-tolyl) ester .	.....	270.29	nd (al)	91	distb			i	v	v	v	v	chl, CS_2, os v	B6[2], 330
o275	—,di(3-tolyl) ester .	.....	270.29	nd (al)	106	distb			i	v	v	v	v	os v, chl v	B6[2], 353
o276	—,di(4-tolyl) ester .	.....	270.29	lf or pl (al-eth)	148				i	s	v	v	v	os s, chl v	B6[2], 379
o277	—,imide	Oximide.	71.04	pr (al)					d^h	δ					B21, 368
Ω o278	—,monoamide ...	Oxamic acid. HO_2CCONH_2 ..	89.05	cr (w)	210d				δ	i	i				B2[2], 509
o279	—,—,N-sec-butyl-	$CH_3CH_2CH(CH_3)NHCOCO_2H$	145.16	cr (eth)	88−9						s^h				B4, 162
o280	—,—,N-phenyl-	Oxanilic acid. $C_6H_5NHCOCO_2H$	165.15	nd (bz)	150				s^h	v	s		δ	chl s lig δ	B12[2], 164
Ω o281	—,monoamide monoethyl ester	Ethyl oxamate. $C_2H_5O_2CCONH_2$	117.11	....	114−5				δ	s	s		i		B2[2], 509
o282	—,—,N-acetyl-	$C_2H_5O_2CCONHCOCH_3$ ...	159.14	pl (eth)	54−5					s	s				B2[2], 509
o283	—,—,N-phenyl-	$C_2H_5O_2CCONHC_6H_5$	193.21	pl or pr (al), nd (w)	65−6	260−300			δ	s	s	s	s	oos v	B12[2], 164
Ω o284	—,monoamide monohydrazide	Semioxamazide. $H_2NNHCOCONH_2$	103.08	lf	221d (232)				δ s^h	i	i			alk, ac v	B2[3], 1594
o285	—,monoamide monoureide	Oxalam. Oxaluramide. $H_2NCOCONHCONH_2$	131.09		>310				i					sulf s	B3[2], 54

For explanations, symbols and abbreviations see beginning of table. For structural formulas see end of table.

No.	Name	Synonyms and Formula	Mol. wt.	Color, crystalline form, specific rotation and λ_{max} (log ε)	m.p. °C	b.p. °C	Density	n_D	Solubility w	al	eth	ace	bz	other solvents	Ref.
	Oxalic acid														
o286	—,monochloride monoethyl ester	$ClCOCO_2C_2H_5$	136.54	hyg	....	135^{760} 30^{10}	1.2226_4^{20}		d	d	s	...	s		B2[2], 508
o287	—,monoethyl-monomethyl ester	$CH_3O_2CCO_2C_2H_5$	132.13		....	173.7	1.5505_0^0		i	v	s	...	...		B2[1], 232
Ω o288	—,monoethyl ester mononitrile	Ethyl cyanoformate. $C_2H_5O_2CCN$	99.09		....	116.5– .8[765]	1.0034_4^{20}	1.3821^{20}	i	s	s	...	...		B2[2], 510
o289	—,monoureide	Oxaluric acid. $H_2NCONHCOCO_2H$	132.08	cr	208–10d				s	i	δ	...	δ	oos δ	B3[2], 54
o290	—,piperazinum salt	$C_2H_2O_4 \cdot C_4H_{10}N_2$	176.17	(w)	>300				s^h	v	i				Am 56, 1759
o291	—,dithiono-, diamide	Dithiooxamide. $H_2NCSCSNH_2$	120.20	og-red	sub				δ	δ				con sulf s	B2[2], 515
—	**Oxaluramide**	*see* **Oxalic acid,** monoamide monoureide													
—	**Oxaluric acid**	*see* **Oxalic acid,** monureide													
—	**Oxamic acid**	*see* **Oxalic acid,** monoamide													
—	**Oxanilic acid**	*see* **Oxalic acid,** monoamide, *N*-phenyl-													
—	**Oxanthranol**	*see* **Anthracene,9,10-** dihydroxy-													
o292	**Oxazole**		69.06	λ^{cy} 303 (4.48)		69–70		$1.4285^{17.5}$							B27[2], 9
o292[1]	—,2,4 dimethyl-	C_5H_7NO. *See* o292	97.12			108	0.9352_5^{15}	$1.4166^{15.3}$	v	v	v				B27[2], 10
o293	—,2,5-dimethyl-	C_5H_7NO. *See* o292	97.12			117–8[760]	0.9958_4^{21}	1.4385^{21}	∞						B27[2], 10
o294	—,2,4-diphenyl-	$C_{15}H_{11}NO$. *See* o292	221.26	lf (al) λ^{al} 240 sh (4.2), 280 (4.2)	103	338–40			...	v^h	v	...	v		B27, 78
o295	—,2,5-diphenyl-	$C_{15}H_{11}NO$. *See* o292	221.26	nd (lig) λ^{cy} 223 (4.31), 303 (4.48)	74	360	1.0940_4^{100}	1.6231^{100}	i	v	v				B27[2], 43
Ω o296	—,4,5-diphenyl-	$C_{15}H_{11}NO$. *See* o292	221.26	pl or pr (lig) λ^{MeOH} 220 sh (4.27), 275 (4.09)	44	192–5[15]		1.6283^{100}	δ	v	v	...		con ac s	B27, 79
Ω o297	—,2,4,5-triphenyl-	Azobenzil. Benzilam. $C_{21}H_{15}NO$. *See* o292	297.36	pr λ^{cy} 235 (4.40), 310 (4.35)	116				...	δ		...	s		B27[2], 56
o298	**2,4-Oxazoli-** dinedione, 5,5-dipropyl-		185.23		42–3	$148–50^3$			i						Am 67, 522
o299	**Oxindole**		133.15	nd (w) λ^w 248.5 (3.89)	127	227^{23}			s^h	s	s				B21[2], 249
o300	—,1-ethyl-	$C_{10}H_{11}NO$. *See* o299	161.21	nd (ace or w)	97–8				δ	s	s	s^h			B21[1], 291
o301	—,3-ethyl-1-methyl-	$C_{11}H_{13}NO$. *See* o299	175.23			280–5[745] 103–7[0.5]		1.557^{25}	...	s	s				B21[2], 258
o302	—,3-hydroxy-	Dioxindole. $C_8H_7NO_2$. *See* o299	149.15	cr (w, al) $\lambda^{w,0.1N HCl}$ 252 (3.72), 292 (3.16)	180 (19s d)				...						B21[2], 415
o303	**Oxonium,** dimethyl-, bromide	$[(CH_3)_2OH]^+Br^-$	126.99		–13						s			liq HBr v	B1[3], 1192
o304	—,—,chloride	$[(CH_3)_2OH]^+Cl^-$	82.53	gas	–97	–2					s			liq HCl v	B1[3], 1192
o305	—,trimethyl-, fluoborate	$[(CH_3)_3O]^+BF_4^-$	147.91	hyg nd	148d				d		v^h			chl, CH_3NO_2, $PhNO_2$ v	B1[3], 1193
o306	**Oxyacanthine**	Vinetine. $C_{37}H_{40}N_2O_6$	608.71	nd (al or eth) $[\alpha]_D^{20}$ +131.5 (chl, c = 1) λ^{MeOH} 281 (4.04)	216–7				i	s	s	...	s	chl, min ac s lig I	B27[2], 892
o307	—,hydrochloride	$C_{37}H_{40}N_2O_6 \cdot HCl$. *See* o306.	645.17	nd, $[\alpha]_D^{15}$ +163.8 (w, c = 3)	270–1				s						B27[2], 893
o308	—,nitrate dihydrate	$C_{37}H_{40}N_2O_6 \cdot HNO_3 \cdot 2H_2O$. *See* o306	705.74	nd	195–200				δ						B27[2], 893
o309	**Oxynarcotine**	α-Narcotine-*N*-oxide. $C_{22}H_{23}NO_8$.	429.43	hyg nd $[\alpha]_D$ +135 (chl)					v	v	i	δ	...	chl v	B27[2], 607
o311	**Oxysparteine**	Isolupanine. $C_{15}H_{24}N_2O$.	248.36	ye to col hyg nd (peth) $[\alpha]_D^{14}$ –10.0 (al, c = 18) λ^w 230 sh (3.0)	111	209^{12}			v	v	v	...	...	chl s	B24[2], 56
o312	—,monohydro-chloride tetrahydrate	$C_{15}H_{24}N_2O \cdot HCl \cdot 4H_2O$. *See* o311	356.89	wh cr (w)	48–50				s	s					B24[2], 57
—	**Oxytetracycline**	*see* **Terramycin**													

For explanations, symbols and abbreviations see beginning of table. For structural formulas see end of table.

C-404

No.	Name	Synonyms and Formula	Mol. wt.	Color, crystalline form, specific rotation and λ_{max} (log ε)	m.p. °C	b.p. °C	Density	n_D	w	al	eth	ace	bz	other solvents	Ref.
	Palmitaldehyde														
—	Palmitaldehyde....	*see* **Hexadecanal***													
—	Palmitanilide......	*see* **Hexadecanoic acid, amide, N-phenyl-***													
—	Palmitic acid.....	*see* **Hexadecanoic acid***													
p1	Paludrine........	Chloroguanide. Proguanil. BPC. $C_{11}H_{16}ClN_5$. λ^w 240 (4.16)	253.74	pl (dil al)	130–1	....			i	s				to s[h]	C40, 2931
p2	—, hydrochloride..	$C_{11}H_{16}ClN_5 \cdot HCl$. *See* p1 ...	290.20	nd (w)	245 (248–52)				δ	s	i			chl i	J1946, 729
p3	Panthesin........	$C_{18}H_{32}N_2O_5S$........	388.53	pa ye pw (al) $\lambda^{w, pH=9.5}$ 289 (4.7)	157–9				v	s					C27, 808
p4	Pantothenic acid (d)	Chick antidermatitis factor. (D, +)-N(α,γ-Dihydroxy-β,β-dimethylbutyryl)-β-alanine. $C_9H_{17}NO_5 \cdot HOCH_2C(CH_3)_2CH(OH)CONH(CH_2)_2CO_2H$	219.24	ye visc oil $[\alpha]_D^{25}$ +37.5 (w)	....				v		s		v	AmOH, aa v diox s	C40, 7163
p5	—, calcium salt (d).	Calcium pantothenate. $[C_9H_{16}NO_5]_2Ca$. *See* p4	476.55	wh (MeOH) $[\alpha]_D^{26}$ +28.2(w)	195–6				s	i		i	i	MeOH s	C40, 7163
Ω p6	—, —(l).........	$[C_9H_{16}NO_5]_2Ca$. *See* p4....	476.55	cr (MeOH) $[\alpha]_D^{26}$ −27.8 (w)	187.5–9				s	i		i	i		C36, 406
Ω p7	Pantothenyl alcohol	Penthenol. $C_9H_{19}NO_4$. $HOCH_2C(CH_3)_2CH(OH)CONH(CH_2)_3OH$ $[\alpha]_D^{20}$ +29.5 (w, c=5)	205.26	slightly hyg oil	....	d 118–20[0.02]	1.2_{20}^{20}	1.497[20]	v	v	δ			MeOH v alk d	C40, 374
p8	Papaveraldine.....	Xanthaline. $C_{20}H_{19}NO_5$....	353.38	nd (al), cr (bz, peth) λ^{al} 265 (4.78), 305 (4.15), 385 (4.1)	210–1				i	δ	δ		s	min ac v aa v[h] chl s peth δ	B21², 479
p9	Papaverine.......	Papaveroline tetramethyl ether. $C_{20}H_{21}NO_4$. λ^{al} 240 (4.9), 280 (3.9), 315 (3.7), 327 (3.7)	339.40	wh pr (al-eth), nd (chl-peth)	147–8	d sub 135–40[11]	1.337_4^{20}	1.625	δ s[h]	v[h]	δ	s	s[h]	chl v Py s CCl_4, lig δ	B21², 202
p10	—, hydrochloride..	$C_{20}H_{21}NO_4 \cdot HCl$. *See* p9... λ^w 250 (4.69), 281 (3.80), 311 (3.82)	375.86	wh mcl pr (w)	224–5				s	s	δ			chl s	B21², 203
—	—, tetrahydro-N-methyl-	*see* **Laudanosine**													
Ω p11	Parabanic acid.....	Imidazoletrione. Oxalylurea. $\lambda^{w, pH=7.45}$ 272 (2.9)	114.06	mcl nd (w)	243–5 d	part sub 100			s	v					B24², 263
p12	Parabutyraldehyde		216.32			98–100[35] (105–8[12])	0.918								B19², 402
p13	Paraconic acid.....	Hydroxymethylsuccinic acid γ-lactone. Itamalic acid γ-lactone. Tetrahydro-5-oxo-3-furancarboxylic acid.	130.10	dlq	57–8	....			s						B18², 311
p14	Paracyanogen.....	$(CN)_x$.........	......	br pw	....	sub			i	i			s	KOH s	B2³, 1590
p14¹	Paraisobutyraldehyde	2,4,6-Triisopropyl-1,3,5-trioxane.	216.32	nd (al)	59–60	195 sub δd			i	s	v				B19, 390
Ω p15	Paraldehyde......	Paraacetaldehyde. 2,4,6-Trimethyl-1,3,5-trioxane.	132.16		12.6	128.0	0.9943_4^{20}	1.4049[20]	δ s[h]	∞	∞			chl ∞	B19², 394
p16	—, trichloro-	Chloroacetaldehyde trimer..	235.50	nd (eth)	87–7.5 (cor)	142–4[10]			i	δ v[h]	v				B19¹, 807
p17	Paraldol........		176.22	wh tcl pr	89–91	90[15]	1.116^{20}	1.4610[20]	v	v	s				B1², 869 B19², 93
—	Pararosaniline.....	*see* **Methanol, tris(4-aminophenyl)-***													
p18	Parasorbic acid....	2-Hexen-5,1-olide. 5-Hydroxy-2-hexenoic acid lactone* $[\alpha]_D^{19}$ +210 (al, c=2)	112.14	oily liq	....	110[15]	1.079_4^{18}	1.4730[19]	s	v	v				B17, 225
Ω p19	Parathion.......	Diethyl p-nitrophenyl monothiophosphate.	291.27	ye liq	6.1	375[760] 157–62[0.6] 115[0.04]	1.2704_{20}^{20}	1.5370[25]	i	∞	s	s		chl, AcOEt v lig i	Am 70, 3943
—	Paredrine........	*see* **Benzene, 1(2-aminopropyl)-4-hydroxy-***													
—	Paris green	*see* **Methyl green**													
—	α-Parvoline	*see* **Pyridine,3,5-dimethyl-2-ethyl-**													
—	β-Parvoline	*see* **Pyridine, tetramethyl-**													
p20	Patulin.........	Clavacin............. λ^{al} 277 (4.3)	154.12	pr or pl (eth, chl)	111	....			s	s	s	s	s	AcOEt v os s peth i	C38, 1321
p21	Paucine, hydrate...	$C_{27}H_{39}N_5O_5 \cdot 6\frac{1}{2}H_2O$	630.75	ye lf	126d				s[h]	s[h]	i			alk s[h] chl i	M775
—	Peganine........	*see* **Vasicine** (DL)													
—	Pelargonaldehyde ..	*see* **Nonanal***													
—	Pelargonic acid	*see* **Nonanoic acid***													

For explanations, symbols and abbreviations see beginning of table. For structural formulas see end of table.

No.	Name	Synonyms and Formula	Mol. wt.	Color, crystalline form, specific rotation and λ_{max} (log ε)	m.p. °C	b.p. °C	Density	n_D	w	al	eth	ace	bz	other solvents	Ref.
	Pelargonidin														
p22	Pelargonidin, chloride	$C_{15}H_{11}ClO_5$	306.70	red br hyg (anh), pr or pl (dil HCl), nd (al-HCl, +w), lf (MeOH-eth) λ^{al} 275 (4.2), 330 sh (3.7)	>350 (anh)	....	....	....	s v^h	v	...	...	...	conc sulf s MeOH, chl δ	B18[2], 200
p25	Pellotine	N-Methylanhalonidine. $C_{13}H_{19}NO_3$.	237.30	pl (al, peth)	111.5	....			δ	s	s	s	...	chl v peth s	B21[1], 249
p26	Penicillic acid	CH_2:$C(CH_3)COC(OCH_3)$:$CHCO_2H$	170.17	rh or hex pl (+1w), nd (peth) λ^{al} 225.5 (4.02)	64–5 (+1w) 87 (anh)	....	....	....	s v^h	v	v	s	v	chl v peth δ^h	B3[2], 519
Ω p27	Pentacene*	Benzo[b]naphthacene. 2,3,6,7-Dibenzanthracene.	278.36	deep vt-bl nd or lf (PhNO2), cr (bz) λ^{MeOH} 310 (5.4), 575 (4.1)	270–1 (>300 d)	290–300 sub (vac)			i	...	...	...	δ^h	PhNO2 s[h] os δ	E14s, 582
p28	—,6,13-diphenyl-* .	$C_{34}H_{22}$. See p27	430.56	vt-bl nd (PhNO2 +1)	....	318–20				s[h]	...	...	s	aa s CCl4 s[h]	E14s, 583
p29	6,9-Pentadecadiyne*	$CH_3(CH_2)_4C$:CCH_2C:$C(CH_2)_4CH_3$	204.34	....		135–6[4]	0.8401_4^{21}	1.4693^{21}		...	...	...	...	....	B1[3], 1067
p30	Pentadecanal*	n-Pentadecylaldehyde. $CH_3(CH_2)_{13}CHO$	226.41	nd	24–5	185[25]			i	s	v	v	...	os v	B1[3], 2920
p31	—,oxime*	$CH_3(CH_2)_{13}CH$:NOH.	241.42	nd (dil al)	86	....			i	δ	s	...	δ	peth δ	B1, 716
p32	Pentadecane*	$CH_3(CH_2)_{13}CH_3$	212.42	....	10	270.63[760] 136[10]	0.7685_4^{20}	1.4315^{20}	i	v	v	...	...	....	B1[3], 553
p33	—,1-amino-*	n-Pentadecylamine. $CH_3(CH_2)_{14}NH_2$	227.44	fl	37.3 (40)	307.6[760] 165.8[10] (suc)	0.8104_4^{20} (suc)	1.4480^{20} (suc)	i	s	s	...	...	....	B4[3], 422
Ω p34	—,1-bromo-*	n-Pentadecyl bromide. $CH_3(CH_2)_{14}Br$	291.33	....	19.0	322[760] 177[10]	1.0675_4^{20}	1.4611^{20}	i	...	...	s	...	chl v	B1[3], 553
p35	—,1,15-dibromo-* .	Pentadecamethylene bromide. $Br(CH_2)_{15}Br$	370.23	lf (al)	27.2–7.5	215–25[15] 192[2]			i	δ v^h	...	...	...	chl v	B1[3], 554
p36	—,1(2,3-dihydroxy-phenyl)-*	Tetrahydrourushiol.	320.52	nd (to, xyl, eth or peth)	59	....				v	v	...	v	aa, chl v lig δ, v^h	B6[2], 911
Ω p37	Pentadecanoic acid*	Pentadecylic acid. $CH_3(CH_2)_{13}CO_2H$	242.41	pl (aq al, ace), cr (peth)	53–4	257[100] 158[1]	0.8423^{80}	1.4254^{80}	i	s	v	v	v	CS_2, peth, chl s	B2[2], 329
Ω p38	—,methyl ester*	$CH_3(CH_2)_{13}CO_2CH_3$	256.43	nd (dil al)	18.5	153.5	0.8618_4^{25}	1.4390^{25}	i	s	s	...	...	os s	B2[2], 330
Ω p39	8-Pentadecanone...	Caprylone. Diheptyl ketone. $CH_3(CH_2)_6CO(CH_2)_6CH_3$	226.41	cr (MeOH, al)	43	291[760] 178[20]				s	s	s	s	chl, CCl4 s	B1[3], 2922
p40	1-Pentadecene*	$CH_3(CH_2)_{12}CH$:CH_2	210.41	....	2–8 (−3.73)	268.17[760] 133.7[10]	0.7764_4^{20}	1.4389_4^{20}	i	...	...	...	...	....	B1[3], 874
p41	1-Pentadecyne*	$CH_3(CH_2)_{12}C$:CH.	208.39	....	10	268[760] 129.8[10]	0.7928_4^{20}	1.4419^{20}	i	...	...	...	...	....	B1[3], 1028
p43	2,4-Pentadienal, 5-phenyl-*	Cinnamylideneacetaldehyde. C_6H_5CH:$CHCH$:$CHCHO$	158.20	nd λ^{bz} 320 (4.58)	42–3	155–65[3] 92–5[0.05]			i	∞	v	...	∞	....	B7[2], 320
p44	1,2-Pentadiene* ...	Ethylallene. CH_3CH_2CH:C:CH_2	68.13	λ^{gas} 177 (4.4), 181 (4.4)	−137.26	44.86[760]	0.6926_4^{20}	1.4209^{20}	i	∞	∞	∞	∞	hp, CCl4 ∞	B1[3], 958
Ω p45	1,3-Pentadiene* ...	Piperylene. CH_3CH:$CHCH$:CH_2	68.13	λ^{al} 223.5 (4.36)	−87.47	42.03[760]	0.6760_4^{20}	1.4301^{20}	i	∞	∞	...	∞	hp, CCl4 ∞	B1[3], 958
Ω p46	1,4-Pentadiene* ...	Allylethylene. Divinylmethane. CH_2:$CHCH_2CH$:CH_2	68.13	λ^{gas} 178 (4.23)	−148.28	25.97[760]	0.6608_4^{20}	1.3888^{20}	i	∞	∞	...	∞	....	B1[3], 963
p47	2,3-Pentadiene* ...	sym-Dimethylallene. CH_3CH:C:$CHCH_3$	68.13	λ^{gas} 171 (4.3), 180 (4.2), 194 (3.6), 202 sh (3.5)	−125.65	48.25[760]	0.6950_4^{20}	1.4284^{20}	i	∞	∞	∞	∞	hp, CCl4 ∞	B1[3], 964
p48	1,3-Pentadiene, 3-chloro-*	3-Methylchloroprene. CH_3CH:$C(Cl)CH$:CH_2	102.57	....		99.5–101.5[759]	0.9576_4^{20}	1.4785^{20}	i	...	v	v	v	chl s	B1[3], 962
p49	1,2-Pentadiene, 1-chloro-3-ethyl-*	$(C_2H_5)_2C$:C:$CHCl$ ...	130.62	....		85–8[100]	0.9297_4^{19}		i	...	s	...	...	chl s	B1[3], 1002
p50	—,1-chloro-3-methyl-*	$CH_3CH_2C(CH_3)$:C:$CHCl$.	116.59	....		68–70[100]	0.9562_4^{20}		i	...	s	...	...	chl s	B1[3], 990
p51	1,3-Pentadiene, 1-chloro-3-methyl-*	CH_3CH:$C(CH_3)CH$:$CHCl$	116.59	....		62–3[100]	0.9574_4^{20}		i	...	s	...	...	chl s	B1[3], 990
p52	—,2-chloro-3-methyl-*	CH_3CH:$C(CH_3)CCl$:CH_2	116.59	....		57–60[95]	0.9437_4^{20}	1.4671^{20}	i	...	s	...	...	chl s	B1[3], 991
p53	2,4-Pentadienoic acid*	β-Vinylacrylic acid. CH_2:$CHCH$:$CHCO_2H$	98.10	hyg pr (eth) λ^{al} 242 (4.39)	80	d110–5			v^h	v	v	...	v	peth s	B2, 451
p54	—,4-hydroxy-, lactone*	Protoanemonin.	96.09	pa ye oil λ^w 260 (4.15)	....	73[11] 45[11]			δ	...	...	...	...	chl s	C54, 7673
p55	—,5(3,4-methyl-enedioxyphenyl)-	Piperic acid.	218.21	ye in light, nd (al), ye nd (sub) λ^{al} 340 (4.5)	215	sub			i	s[h]	δ	...	δ	....	B19[2], 300
Ω p56	—,5-phenyl-*	Cinnamylideneacetic acid. C_6H_5CH:$CHCH$:$CHCO_2H$	174.20	pl (al), pr (bz) λ^{al} 307 (4.56)	166–7	....				s[h]	s	...	s	peth δ v^h	B9[2], 441

For explanations, symbols and abbreviations see beginning of table. For structural formulas see end of table.

2,4-Pentadienoic acid

No.	Name	Synonyms and Formula	Mol. wt.	Color, crystalline form, specific rotation and λ_{max} (log ε)	m.p. °C	b.p. °C	Density	n_D	w	al	eth	ace	bz	other solvents	Ref.
p57	—,—,ethyl ester	$C_6H_5CH:CHCH:CHCO_2C_2H_5$	202.26	ye oil	25–6.7	149–50[4]	1.0469[20]	1.5768[80]	...	s	s	...	...		B9[2], 441
p58	—,—,methyl ester	$C_6H_5CH:CHCH:CHCO_2CH_3$	188.23	lf or pl λ^{eth} 360 (4.57)	71	185[20]			i	v	...	...		MeOH v	B9[2], 441
p59	1,4-Pentadien-3-one, 1,5-bis-(2-ethoxy-phenyl)-*	$C_{21}H_{22}O_3$. See p72	322.41	ye lf (dil al)	89				i	v[h]	s[h]				B8, 352
p61	—,1,5-bis(2-hydroxyphenyl)-*	Disalicylidene acetone. $C_{17}H_{14}O_3$. See p72	266.30	ye nd (dil al)	168d				δ	v	s	v	s	Py v ac, chl, aa s	B8[2], 404
p62	—,1,5-bis(4-hydroxy-phenyl)-*	Bis(4-hydroxystyryl) ketone. $C_{17}H_{14}O_3$. See p72	266.30	(i) ye-og nd or lf (dil al) (ii) gr lf	(i) 237–8 (st)					v	δ	v	δ	aa, MeOH, alk, acs, chl δ	B8[2], 405
p63	—,1,5-bis(2-methoxy-phenyl)-*	Bis (2-methoxystyryl)ketone. $C_{19}H_{18}O_3$. See p72	294.35	ye nd or lf (al)	127				i	δ s[h]					B8[2], 405
p64	—,1,5-bis(3-methoxy-phenyl)-*	Bis(3-methoxystyryl) ketone. $C_{19}H_{18}O_3$. See p72	294.35	nd (chl-MeOH)	55–6				i			s		os v chl s lig δ	B8[1], 666
Ω p65	—,1,5-bis(4-methoxy-phenyl)-*	Dianisalacetone. $C_{19}H_{18}O_3$. See p72	294.35	ye lf (aa, AcOEt)	129–30					δ	δ		v	chl v aa s	B8[2], 406
Ω p66	—,1,5-bis(3,4-methylene-dioxyphenyl)-*	Dipiperonylideneacetone. $C_{19}H_{14}O_5$. See p72	322.32	ye nd (bz or AcOEt)	185				i	δ		v	s[h]	chl v con sulf s lig i	B19[2], 463
p67	—,1,5-bis(2-nitrophenyl)-*	Bis(2-nitrostyryl) ketone. $C_{17}H_{12}N_2O_5$. See p72	324.30	ye nd (aa)	170.5–1				i	δ				chl v con sulf s	B7[2], 455
p68	—,1,5-bis(3-nitrophenyl)-*	Bis(3-nitrostyryl) ketone. $C_{17}H_{12}N_2O_5$. See p72	324.30	ye, br (Ac₂O)	238							s		os s con sulf, Ac₂O δ	B7[2], 455
p69	—,1,5-bis(4-nitrophenyl)-*	Bis(4-nitrostyryl) ketone. $C_{17}H_{12}N_2O_5$. See p72	324.30	ye (Ac₂O)	254 (248)				i			s		os v Ac₂O δ	B7[2], 455
p70	—,1(2-chloro-phenyl)-5(3-chlorophenyl)-	$C_{17}H_{12}Cl_2O$. See p72	303.19	ye nd (dil al)	67–8					s		δ		CS₂, lig δ	B7[2], 454
p71	—,1(2-chloro-phenyl)-5(4-chlorophenyl)-	$C_{17}H_{12}Cl_2O$. See p72	303.19	ye nd (al)	109					δ					B7[2], 454
p71[1]	—,1,5-di(2-furyl)-	Difurfurylidene acetone	214.22	dlq pr (peth), ye pr (lig)	60–1	d			i	v	v			chl v con HCl, sulf s lig δ[h]	B19[2], 162
p72	—,1,5-diphenyl-*	Dibenzalacetone. Cinnamone. Distyryl ketone.	234.30	pl or lf (ace or AcOEt) λ^{al} 331 (4.55)	113d	d			i	δ	δ	s		chl s	B7[2], 452
p72[1]	2,4-Pentadiene-1-one, 1,5-diphenyl-	Cinnamalacetophenone. $C_6H_5CH:CHCH:CHCOC_6H_5$	234.30	(i) ye nd (al) (ii) ye cr	(i) 102–3 (ii) 235				i	δ s[h]	δ			con sulf s (red)	B7[2], 451
p73	1,3-Pentadiyne*	$CH_3C:CC:CH$	64.09	λ^{al} 227 (2.43), 236 (2.59), 249 (2.32)	55–6		0.7375[21]_4	1.4431[21]	i	...	s		s	chl s	B1[2], 247
Ω p74	Pentaerythritol	Tetrakis(hydroxymethyl)-methane*. Tetramethylol-methane. $C(CH_2OH)_4$	136.15	cr (dil HCl)	269 (260)	sub		1.548	s	δ	i		i		B1[2], 601
p75	—,tetraacetate	$C(CH_2O_2CCH_3)_4$	304.30	tetr nd (w or bz)	83–4 (84–6)		1.273[18]		s	v	v				B2[2], 162
Ω p76	—,tetranitrate	Penthrit. PETN. $C(CH_2ONO_2)_4$	316.15	tetr (ace), pr (ace-al)	140–1		1.773[20]_4		δ	δ	δ	v	s	to s Py s[h] MeOH δ	B1[2], 602 B9[2], 887
—	Pentalin	see Ethane, pentachloro-*													
Ω p77	Pentanal*	Valeral. Valeraldehyde. $CH_3(CH_2)_3CHO$	86.14	λ^{gas} 178, 182, 184	−91.5	103[760]	0.8095[20]_4	1.3944[20]	δ	s	s				B1[3], 2797
p78	—,oxime*	Valeraldoxime. $CH_3(CH_2)_3CH:NOH$	101.15	cr	52						s				B1, 676
p78[1]	—,4-hydroxy-(dl)*	$CH_3CH(OH)CH_2CH_2CHO$	102.13			63–5[10]	1.019[20]_4	1.4359[17]	s			s		os s	B1[2], 871
p78[2]	—,—(l)*	$CH_3CH(OH)CH_2CH_2CHO$	102.13	$[α]_D^{23}$ −7.8		43–6[1]			s			s		os s	B1[2], 872
p79	—,3-hydroxy-2-methyl-*	Propionaldol. $C_2H_5CH(OH)CH(CH_3)CHO$	116.16			94–6[23]	0.986[25]	1.4502[20]	s	v	v	v			B1[1], 423
Ω p80	—,2-methyl-*	$CH_3CH_2CH_2CH(CH_3)CHO$	100.16			116[737]			s	s	s	s			B1[1], 355
p81	—,4-methyl-2-oxo-*	Formyl isobutyl ketone. $(CH_3)_2CHCH_2COCHO$	114.15	ye-gr		45–6[12]								os s	B1[1], 406
p82	—,2-oxo-*	Butyrylformaldehyde. $CH_3(CH_2)_2COCHO$	100.13			112[760] 36[16]		1.4043[25]	∞	∞	∞	∞			B1[2], 830
p83	—,4-oxo-*	γ-Ketovaleraldehyde. Levulinaldehyde. Levulinic aldehyde. $CH_3COCH_2CH_2CHO$	100.13		< −21	186–8[760] δd 70[12]	1.0184[21]	1.4257[22]	s	s	s	s			B1[2], 830
Ω p84	Pentane*	$CH_3(CH_2)_3CH_3$	72.15		−129.72	36.07	0.6262[20]	1.3575[20]	δ	∞	∞	∞	∞	chl, hp ∞	B1[3], 238
Ω p85	—,1-amino-*	n-Amylamine. Pentylamine*. $CH_3(CH_2)_4NH_2$	87.17		−55	104.4[760] 5.9[10]	0.7547[20]_4	1.4118[20]	∞	∞	∞	v	v		B4[2], 641

For explanations, symbols and abbreviations see beginning of table. For structural formulas see end of table.

No.	Name	Synonyms and Formula	Mol. wt.	Color, crystalline form, specific rotation and λ_{max} (log ε)	m.p. °C	b.p. °C	Density	n_D	w	al	eth	ace	bz	other solvents	Ref.
	Pentane														
p86	—,2-amino-*	sec n-Amylamine. $CH_3(CH_2)_2CH(NH_2)CH_3$	87.17			91.5^{755}	0.7384^{20}	1.4027^{20}	∞	∞	∞	v	v		$B4^2$, 643
p87	—,3-amino-*	$(C_2H_5)_2CHNH_2$	87.17			91^{760}	0.7487^{20}_4	1.4063^{20}		s					$B4^3$, 339
p88	—,3(amino-methyl)-*	2-Ethyl-n-butylamine. $(C_2H_5)_2CHCH_2NH_2$	101.19			125.3									B4, 192
—	—,2,2-bis-(hydroxymethyl)-*	see 1,3-Propanediol, 2-methyl-2-propyl-*													
p89	—,3,3-bis(ethyl-sulfonyl)-*	Tetronal. $(C_2H_5)_2C(SO_2C_2H_5)_2$	256.39	lf (dil al)	85				δ	s	s				B4, 681
Ω p90	—,1-bromo-*	Amyl bromide. $CH_3(CH_2)_4Br$	151.05		−87.9	129.6^{760} 21^{10}	1.2182^{20}_4	1.4447^{20}	i	s	∞		s	chl s	$B1^3$, 344
Ω p91	—,2-bromo-(dl)*	sec-Amyl bromide. $CH_3(CH_2)_2CHBrCH_3$	151.05		−95.5	117.4^{760} 58.4^{100}	1.20754^{20}_4	1.4413^{20}	i	s	s		s	chl s	$B1^3$, 345
Ω p92	—,3-bromo-*	$(C_2H_5)_2CHBr$	151.05		−126.2	118.6^{760} 10.8^{10}	1.2124^{20}_4	1.4441^{20}	i	s	s		s	chl s	$B1^3$, 346
p93	—,1-bromo-5-fluoro-*	$F(CH_2)_5Br$	169.04			162	1.3604^{25}	1.4406^{25}	i	v	v				C51, 7300
p94	—,1-bromo-2-methyl-*	$CH_3(CH_2)_2CH(CH_3)CH_2Br$	165.08			$142–5^{748}$ $51–3^{25}$	1.1624^{20}_4	1.4495^{20}	i		v			chl v	$B1^3$, 399
Ω p95	—,1-bromo-3-methyl-*	$CH_3CH_2CH(CH_3)CH_2CH_2Br$	165.08			$148.6–$ 9.4^{766}	1.1829^{20}	1.4496^{20}	i		s			chl v	$B1^2$, 403
p96	—,1-bromo-4-methyl-*	Isohexyl bromide. $(CH_3)_2CH(CH_2)_3Br$	165.08			$147–8^{759}$	1.1683^{20}	1.4490	i		v			chl v	$B1^3$, 399
p97	—,2-bromo-2-methyl-*	$CH_3CH_2CH_2CBr(CH_3)_2$	165.08			$142–3^{760}$ 70^{100}		1.442^{23}	d^h		s			chl v	$B1^3$, 399
p98	—,3-bromo-3-methyl-*	$(C_2H_5)_2CBrCH_3$	165.08			$129–31$ $82–3^{145}$	1.1835^{20}	1.4525^{20}	d^h		v			chl v	$B1^1$, 54
Ω p99	—,1-chloro-*	n-Amyl chloride, Pentyl chloride. $CH_3(CH_2)_4Cl$	106.60		−99	107.8^{760} 4.9^{10}	0.8818^{20}	1.4127^{20}	i	∞	∞		s	chl v	$B1^3$, 339
p100	—,2-chloro-(d)*	sec-Amyl chloride. $CH_3CH_2CH_2CHClCH_3$	106.60	$[\alpha]_D +34.07$	−137	96.86^{760}	0.8698^{20}_4	1.4069^{20}	i	s	s		s	chl v	$B1^3$, 340
Ω p101	—,3-chloro-*	$(C_2H_5)_2CHCl$	106.60		−105	97.8^{760}	0.8731^{20}	1.4082^{20}	i	s	s		s	chl v	$B1^3$, 340
p102	—,2-chloro-2,3-dimethyl-*	$CH_3CH_2CH(CH_3)CCl(CH_3)_2$	134.65			$38–9^{20}$		1.4264^{20}	i		s		s		$B1^3$, 447
p103	—,2-chloro-2,4-dimethyl-*	$(CH_3)_2CHCH_2CCl(CH_3)_2$	134.65			$127–8^{733}d$ $33–4^{20}$	0.861^{20}	1.4180^{20}			v		s		$B1^3$, 451
p104	—,3-chloro-2,3-dimethyl-*	$CH_3CH_2C(CH_3)ClCH(CH_3)_2$	134.65			$135–8^{757}$ $δd$ $41–2^{20}$	0.884^{22}_{22}	1.4318^{20}	i		s		s	chl s	$B1^3$, 448
p105	—,4-chloro-2,2-dimethyl-*	$CH_3CHClCH_2C(CH_3)_3$	134.65			93^{250}	0.855^{20}_4	1.4180^{20}	i		s			chl s	$B1^3$, 444
p106	—,3-chloro-2,2-dimethyl-3-ethyl-*	$(C_2H_5)_2CClC(CH_3)_3$	162.71		$d53–4^6$			1.4528^{25}	d		s			chl s	$B1^3$, 517
p107	—,2-chloro-3-ethyl-*	$(C_2H_5)_2CHCHClCH_3$	134.65			83.5^{100}	0.8951^{25}_{25}	1.4318^{20}	i		s			chl s	$B1^2$, 120
p108	—,3-chloro-3-ethyl-*	$(C_2H_5)_3CCl$	134.65			$143–4^{760}$ $43–4^{20}$	0.8856^{20}_4	1.4400^{20}			v				$B1^3$, 510
p109	—,3-chloro-3-ethyl-2-methyl-*	$(C_2H_5)_2CClCH(CH_3)_2$	148.68			$150–5d$ $98–100^{98}$		1.4405^{25}	d	s				chl s	$B1^3$, 490
p110	—,1-chloro-5-fluoro-*	$F(CH_2)_5Cl$	124.59			143.2	1.0325^{25}	1.4120^{23}	i	v	v				C51, 7300
p111	—,2-chloro-2-methyl-*	$CH_3(CH_2)_2CCl(CH_3)_2$	120.62			$110–1^{734}d$ $36–7^{15}$	0.863^{20}_4	1.4126^{20}	d^h		v				$B1^3$, 399
p111¹	—,2-chloro-4-methyl-*	$(CH_3)_2CHCH_2CHClCH_3$	120.62			$111–2^{733}$	0.8610^{20}_4	1.4113^{20}	d		v				$B1^3$, 399
p112	—,3-chloro-2-methyl-*	$CH_3CH_2CHClCH(CH_3)_2$	120.62			$115–6.5^{752}$ d			i		s			chl s	$B1^2$, 111
p113	—,3-chloro-3-methyl-*	$(C_2H_5)_2CClCH_3$	120.62			116^{760} 35^{25}	0.8900^{20}_4	1.4210^{20}	d^h		v		s	chl v	$B1^3$, 403
p114	—,3(chloro-methyl)-*	$(C_2H_5)_2CHCH_2Cl$	120.62			$125–7$	0.8914^{20}	1.4222^{20}	i		v		s	chl v	$B1^3$, 403
p115	—,2-chloro-2,4,4-trimethyl-*	$(CH_3)_2CClCH_2C(CH_3)_3$	148.68		−26	$145–50d$ 44^{16}	0.8746^{20}	1.4308^{20}	d	s				alk d^h	$B1^3$, 498
p116	—,1,5-diamino-*	Cadaverine. Pentamethylene diamine. $H_2N(CH_2)_5NH_2$	102.18		9	$178–80$	0.867^{25}	1.4561^{23}	s	s	δ				$B4^3$, 588
Ω p117	—,1,5-dibromo-*	Pentamethylene bromide. $Br(CH_2)_5Br$	229.95		−39.5	222.3^{760} 98.6^{10}	1.7018^{20}_4	1.5126^{20}	i		s		s	chl s	$B1^3$, 374
p118	—,1,2-dichloro-*	$CH_3CH_2CH_2CHClCH_2Cl$	141.04			$148.4–.8$ $58–9^{28}$	1.0872^{20}_4	1.4485^{20}	i		s			chl v alk d	$B1^3$, 341
p119	—,1,3-dichloro-*	$CH_3CH_2CHClCH_2CH_2Cl$	141.04			80.4^{60}	1.0834^{20}_4	1.4485^{20}	i		v			chl v	$B1^3$, 342
p120	—,1,4-dichloro-*	$CH_3CHCl(CH_2)_2CH_2Cl$	141.04			$161–3^{760}$ $58–60^{13}$	1.0840^{20}_4	1.4503^{20}	d^h			s		chl s	$B1^3$, 342
Ω p121	—,1,5-dichloro-*	$Cl(CH_2)_5Cl$	141.04		−72.8	180^{760} 59^{10}	1.1006^{20}_4	1.4564^{20}	i		s		s	chl s	$B1^3$, 342
p122	—,2,2-dichloro-*	$CH_3CH_2CH_2CCl_2CH_3$	141.04			$128–9$ (cor) $36–7^{20}$	1.040^{20}	1.434^{20}	i		s		s	chl s	$B1^2$, 342
p123	—,2,4-dichloro-*	$CH_3CHClCH_2CHClCH_3$	141.04			$147–50^{760}$ 62^{12}	1.0634^{15}_4	1.447^{18}	i		v		s	chl v alk d	$B1^3$, 343

For explanations, symbols and abbreviations see beginning of table. For structural formulas see end of table.

Pentane

No.	Name	Synonyms and Formula	Mol. wt.	Color, crystalline form, specific rotation and λ_{max} (log ε)	m.p. °C	b.p. °C	Density	n_D	w	al	eth	ace	bz	other solvents	Ref.
p124	—,3,3-dichloro-*	$CH_3CH_2CCl_2CH_2CH_3$	141.04			131–2[750] 32[14]	1.053^{20}	1.442^{20}	i				s	chl s	B1[3], 343
p125	—,1,2-dichloro-4,4-dimethyl-*	$(CH_3)_3CCH_2CHClCH_2Cl$	169.10			173–5[745] 58–9[12]	1.0259^{20}_4	1.4489^{20}	i				s	chl s	B1[3], 445
p126	—,1,5-dichloro-3,3-dimethyl-*	$(ClCH_2CH_2)_2C(CH_3)_2$	169.10			135[80] 58–9[8]	1.0563^{20}_4	1.4652^{20}	i	s^h				chl s	B1[3], 454
p127	—,2,4-dichloro-2,4-dimethyl-*	$(CH_3)_2CClCH_2CCl(CH_3)_2$	169.10		23–4	51.5–.7[8]	1.0292^{20}_2	1.4537^{20}	i	δ				chl s	B1[3], 451
p128	—,3,3-dichloro-2,4-dimethyl-*	$(CH_3)_2CHCCl_2CH(CH_3)_2$	169.10			118–20δd	0.9513^9		i		s			chl s	B1, 158
p129	—,3,3-diethyl-*	Tetraethylmethane. $C(C_2H_5)_4$	128.26		−33.110	146.17[760] 30.71[10]	0.75359^{20}_4	1.4206^{20}	i		s	s	s	os s	B1[3], 518
Ω p130	—,1,5-diiodo-*	$I(CH_2)_5I$	323.94		9	149[20] 101–2[3]	2.1903^{15}	1.6046^{15}	i		s		s	chl s	B1[3], 350
Ω p131	—,2,2-dimethyl-*	$CH_3CH_2CH_2C(CH_3)_3$	100.21		−123.82	79.197[760]	0.6739^{20}_4	1.3822^{20}	i	s	s	∞	∞	chl, hp ∞	B1[3], 442
Ω p132	—,2,3-dimethyl-*	$CH_3CH_2CH(CH_3)CH(CH_3)_2$	100.21			89.8	0.6951^{20}_4	1.3919^{20}	i	s	s	∞	∞	chl, hp ∞	B1-, 445
Ω p133	—,2,4-dimethyl-*	$(CH_3)_2CHCH_2CH(CH_3)_2$	100.21		−119.24	80.5[760]	0.6727^{20}_4	1.3815^{20}	i	s	s	∞	∞	chl, hp ∞	B1[3], 449
Ω p134	—,3,3-dimethyl-*	$CH_3CH_2C(CH_3)_2CH_2CH_3$	100.21		−134.46	86.064	0.6936^{20}	1.3909^{20}	i	s	s	∞	s	chl, hp ∞	B1[3], 452
p135	—,1,5-dinitro-*	$O_2NCH_2(CH_2)_3CH_2NO_2$	162.15	λ^{al} 275 (1.69)		134[1.2]		1.461^{20}	i				s		B1[3], 350
p136	—,1,1-diphenyl-*	$CH_3(CH_2)_3CH(C_6H_5)_2$	224.35	λ^{iso} 262 (2.7), 269 (2.6)	−12.06	307.89	0.96594^{20}	1.5511^{20}	i						B5[2], 523
p137	—,1,5-diphenyl-*	$C_6H_5(CH_2)_5C_6H_5$	224.35	λ^{iso} 254 (2.6), 261.5 (2.7), 268 (2.6)		330.6 (cor) 187–9[10]	0.9814^{19}_0	1.559^{19}	i						B5[3], 1895
p138	—,1,5-dithiocyanato-	$NCS(CH_2)_5SCN$	186.30	yesh		221–2									B3[1], 72
p139	—,1,2-epoxy-2,4,4-trimethyl-*		128.22		−64	140.9 20[5.4]	0.8287^{20}_{20}	1.4097^{20}	δ		s		s		B1[3], 850
p140	—,3-ethyl-*	Triethylmethane. $(C_2H_5)_3CH$	100.21		−118.604	93.5[760]	0.6982^{20}_4	1.3934^{20}	i	s	s	∞	∞	chl, hp ∞	B1[3], 441
p141	—,3-ethyl-2-methyl-*	$(CH_3)_2CHCH(C_2H_5)_2$	114.23		−114.960	115.65[760] 9.5[10]	0.7193^{20}_4	1.4040^{20}	i	∞	s	∞	∞	chl, hp ∞	B1[3], 489
p142	—,3-ethyl-3-methyl-*	$(C_2H_5)_3CCH_3$	114.23		−90.87	118.26[760] 9.9[10]	0.7274^{20}_4	1.4078^{20}_4	i	∞	s	∞	∞	chl, hp ∞	B1[3], 490
p143	—,1-fluoro-*	n-Amyl fluoride. $CH_3(CH_2)_4F$	90.14		−120	62.8[760]	0.7907^{20}_4	1.3591^{20}	i	v	v				B1[3], 338
Ω p144	—,1-iodo-*	n-Amyl iodide $CH_3(CH_2)_4I$	198.05		−85.6	157[760] 39.31[10]	1.5161^{20}_4	1.4959^{20}	δ	s	s				B1[3], 348
p145	—,2-iodo-(dl)*	$CH_3(CH_2)_2CHICH_3$	198.05			144–5[760]	1.5096^{20}_4	1.4961^{20}	i		s	s	s	os s	B1[3], 349
p146	—,3-iodo-*	$(C_2H_5)_2CHI$	198.05			145–6 68[50]	1.5176^{20}_4	1.4974^{20}	i		s	s	s	os s	B1[3], 349
p147	—,1-isocyano-	n-Amylcarbylamine. Amyl isocyanide. $CH_3(CH_2)_4NC$	97.16		−51.1	155.5 (130[760]) 50[45]	0.806^{20}_4		i	s					C42, 869
Ω p148	—,2-methyl-*	$CH_3CH_2CH_2CH(CH_3)_2$	86.18		−153.67	60.271	0.6532^{20}_4	1.3715^{20}	i	s	s	∞	∞	hp, chl ∞	B1[3], 396
Ω p149	—,3-methyl-*	$(C_2H_5)_2CHCH_3$	86.18		−118	63.282	0.6645^{20}_4	1.3765^{20}	i	s	∞	∞	∞	hp, chl ∞	B1[3], 401
p150	—,3-nitro-*	$(C_2H_5)_2CHNO_2$	117.15			153–5	0.957^0		i	s	s	s			B1[3], 350
p151	—,2,2,4,4-tetramethyl-*	$(CH_3)_3CCH_2C(CH_3)_3$	128.26		−66.54	122.68[760] 12.5[10]	0.7195^{20}_4	1.4069^{20}	i	v			v	os v	B1[3], 519
p152	—,2,2,3-trimethyl-*	$CH_3CH_2CH(CH_3)C(CH_3)_3$	114.23		−112.27	109.841[760] 3.9[10]	0.7161^{20}_2	1.4030^{20}_2	i	∞	∞	∞	∞	chl, hp ∞	B1[3], 491
Ω p153	—,2,2,4-trimethyl-*	Isooctane. $(CH_3)_2CHCH_2C(CH_3)_3$	114.23		−107.38	99.238[760] −4.3[10]	0.6919^{20}_2	1.3915^{20}	i	∞	s	∞	∞	chl, hp ∞	B1[3], 492
p154	—,2,3,3-trimethyl-*	$CH_3CH_2C(CH_3)_2CH(CH_3)_2$	114.23		−100.7	114.76[760] 6.9[10]	0.7262^{20}_4	1.4075^{20}	i	v	∞	∞	∞	chl, hp ∞ os v	B1[3], 499
Ω p155	—,2,3,4-trimethyl-*	$(CH_3)_2CHCH(CH_3)CH(CH_3)_2$	114.23		−109.21	113.467[760] 7.1[10]	0.7191^{20}_4	1.4042^{20}	i	v	∞	∞	∞	chl, hp ∞ to, os v	B1[3], 500
p156	1,5-Pentanedial*	Glutaraldehyde. Glutaric aldehyde. $OCH(CH_2)_3CHO$	100.13			187–9d 71–2[10]			∞	∞			s		B1[2], 831
Ω p157	—,dioxime	Glutaraldoxime. $HON:CH(CH_2)_3CH:NOH$	130.15	nd (w or Py)	178	sub			s^h					Py s^h	B1[2], 831
Ω p158	Pentanedioic acid*	Glutaric acid. $HO_2C(CH_2)_3CO_2H$	132.13	nd (bz)	99	302–4δd 200[20]	1.424^{25}_4	1.4188^{106}	v	v	v		i	chl, con sulf s lig δ	B2[3], 1685
Ω p159	—,dichloride	Glutaryl chloride. $ClCO(CH_2)_3COCl$	169.01			216–8 (cor) 100[15]	1.324^{20}_4	1.4728^{20}	d	d	s				B2[3], 1691
Ω p160	—,diethyl ester*	Diethyl glutarate. $C_2H_5O_2C(CH_2)_3CO_2C_2H_5$	188.23	syr	−24.1 (cor)	236.5–7 103–4[7]	1.0220^{20}_4	1.4241^{20}	δ	δ	s				B2[3], 1689
Ω p161	—,dimethyl ester*	Dimethyl glutarate. $CH_3O_2C(CH_2)_3CO_2CH_3$	160.17		−42.5	214[751] 109[21]	1.0876^{20}_4	1.4242^{20}		v	v				B2[3], 1688
Ω p162	—,dinitrile	Glutaronitrile. Pentanedinitrile*. $NC(CH_2)_3CN$	94.12		−29	286 160.4[22]	0.99112^{15}_4	1.4295^{20}	s	s	i			chl s CS_2 i	B2[3], 1692
p163	—,diphenyl ester*	Diphenyl glutarate. $C_6H_5O_2C(CH_2)_3CO_2C_6H_5$	284.32	nd (lig)	54	236.5[15]			i	s	s		s	os, lig v	B6, 156
p164	—,piperazinium salt	$2[HO_2C(CH_2)_3CO_2H]\cdot C_4H_{10}N_2$	350.37		152				s	s^h	i				Am 56, 1759
Ω p165	—,2-acetyl-,diethyl ester	$CH_3COCH(CO_2C_2H_5)CH_2CH_2CO_2C_2H_5$	230.26			271–2δd 110–2[0.1]	1.0712^{20}_4	1.4420^{19}	δ	s	s				B3[2], 488
—	—,2-amino-*	see Glutamic acid													
Ω p166	—,2,2-dimethyl-*	$HO_2CCH_2CH_2C(CH_3)_2CO_2H$	160.17	nd (con HCl, bz-lig)	85				v	v				chl, aa s lig δ	B2[3], 1750

For explanations, symbols and abbreviations see beginning of table. For structural formulas see end of table.

No.	Name	Synonyms and Formula	Mol. wt.	Color, crystalline form, specific rotation and λ_{max} (log ε)	m.p. °C	b.p. °C	Density	n_D	w	al	eth	ace	bz	other solvents	Ref.

Pentanedioic acid

No.	Name	Synonyms and Formula	Mol. wt.	Color, crystalline form, specific rotation and λ_{max} (log ε)	m.p. °C	b.p. °C	Density	n_D	w	al	eth	ace	bz	other solvents	Ref.
Ω p167	—,3,3-dimethyl-*	$HO_2CCH_2C(CH_3)_2CH_2CO_2H$ 160.17		mcl pl, nd (bz)	103–4	$126–7^{4.5}$	1.4278_4^{20}		v	v	v		δ s^h	lig i	B2³, 1758
p168	—,3[2(3,5-di-methyl-2-oxo-cyclohexyl)2-hydroxyethyl]-, imide	Actidione. Cycloheximide.	281.36	wh pl (w) $[\alpha]_D^{29}$ −3.38 (al) λ^{al} 235 sh (2.3), 255 sh (2.6), 290 (1.5)	119.5–21				δ	s	s	s			Am 69, 474
p169	—,2-ethyl-3-methyl-*	$HO_2CCH_2CH(CH_3)CH(C_2H_5)CO_2H$ 175.20		(i) pr (w) (ii) pr (chl-lig)	(i) 100–1 (ii) 88				v		v				B2³, 1779
p170	—,2-ethyl-4-methyl (dl)*	Paramethylethylglutaric acid. $HO_2CCH(CH_3)CH_2CH(C_2H_5)CO_2H$ 175.20		nd (w)	107				s^h		v		i	os v lig s CS_2 i	B2³, 1775
p171	—,— (meso)*	Mesomethylethylglutaric acid. $HO_2CCH(CH_3)CH_2CH(C_2H_5)CO_2H$ 175.20		nd (w)	83.5–4.5				δ s^h		v			os v lig δ xy i	B2³, 1775
Ω p172	—,3-ethyl-3-methyl-*	$HO_2CCH_2C(CH_3)(C_2H_5)CH_2CO_2H$ 175.20		nd (w or bz), pl (bz-peth)	87	260^{740}			s^h	s	s		s^h		B2³, 1781
p173	—,2-hydroxy-(d)*	$HO_2CCH_2CH_2CH(OH)CO_2H$ 148.13		cr (eth), $[\alpha]_D^{19}$ +1.76 (w, c = 3)	72					s	v				B3³, 929
p174	—,— (dl)*	$HO_2CCH_2CH_2CH(OH)CO_2H$ 148.13		pr (AcOEt)	72				s	s	v				B3², 293
p175	—,— (l)*	$HO_2CCH_2CH_2CH(OH)CO_2H$ 148.13		$[\alpha]_D$ −1.98 (w)	72–3				s	s	v				B3², 93
Ω p177	—,2-oxo-*	2-Oxoglutaric acid. α-Keto-glutaric acid. $\lambda^{w.pH=8}$ 315 (1.49) $HO_2CCH_2CH_2COCO_2H$	146.10	cr (ace-bz)	115–6				v	v	s		s		B3², 481
Ω p178	—,3-oxo-*	Acetonedicarboxylic acid. β-Ketoglutaric acid. $HO_2CCH_2COCH_2CO_2H$	146.10	nd (al, AcOEt), rh (w)	135d (138)	d			s d^h	s	δ		i	AcOEt s^h chl, lig i	B3², 482
Ω p179	—,diethyl ester*	$C_2H_5O_2CCH_2COCH_2CO_2C_2H_5$	202.21			250 140^{13}	1.113_4^{20}		δ	∞					B3², 484
p181	—,2-phenyl-*	$C_6H_5CH(CO_2H)CH_2CH_2CO_2H$	208.22	cr (bz or eth-peth)	82–3					s^h		s^h			B9, 877
p182	—,—anhydride*		190.20	nd (eth)	95	$218–30^{13}$				s^h					B17, 494
p183	—,3-phenyl-, anhydride*		190.20	cr (bz)	105	$217–9^{15}$			d^h		s		s	chl s peth i	B17², 476
p184	—,2,3,4-tri-hydroxy-(d)*	D-Arabotrihydroxyglutaric acid. $HO_2C(CHOH)_3CO_2H$	180.13	cr (ace), pl (w) $[\alpha]_D^{21}$ +22.2	128				v	s	i	s^h		chl i	B3¹, 192
p185	—,— (dl)*	$HO_2C(CHOH)_3CO_2H$	180.13	cr (ace)	154.5d				v	v	i	s		chl i	B3, 553
p186	1,2-Pentanediol (d)*	1,2-Amylene glycol. $CH_3(CH_2)_2CH(OH)CH_2OH$	104.15	$[\alpha]_D^{20}$ +0.95		210.5–211.5⁷⁵¹ $99–102^{13}$	0.9802_{20}^{20}	1.4412^{19}							B1³, 2190
p187	1,4-Pentanediol (dl)*	γ-Pentylene glycol. $CH_3CH(OH)CH_2CH_2CH_2OH$	104.15			220^{713} $124–6^{10}$	0.9883_4^{20}	1.4452^{25}	∞	∞				chl ∞ lig i	B1³, 2191
Ω p188	1,5-Pentanediol*	Pentamethylene glycol. $HO(CH_2)_5OH$	104.15		−18	260 (240) $137–8^{12}$	0.9939_{20}^{20}	1.4494_4^{20}	s	s	δ		δ		B1³, 2192
Ω p189	2,3-Pentanediol*	β-n-Amylene glycol. $CH_3CH(OH)CH(OH)CH_2CH_3$	104.15			187.5 97^{17}	0.9800_0^{19}	1.4402^{25}	s	s	δ				B1³, 2194
p190	1,3-Pentanediol, 2,2-dimethyl-*	$CH_3CH_2CH(OH)C(CH_3)_2CH_2OH$	132.21	(eth)	60–3	212–4 119^{21}				s					B1, 190
p191	1,5-Pentanediol, 2,2-dimethyl-*	$HO(CH_2)_3C(CH_3)_2CH_2OH$	132.21			130^{12}					s				B1¹, 254
Ω p192	2,4-Pentanediol, 2-methyl-*	$CH_3CH(OH)CH_2C(OH)(CH_3)_2$	188.18			197^{760}	0.9254_{17}^{17}	1.4250^{20}	s	v	v				B1¹, 252
Ω p193	—,3-methyl-*	$CH_3CH(OH)CH(CH_3)CH(OH)CH_3$	118.18			$211–2^{760}$ 91^3	0.9640^{20}	1.4433^{20}	s	s	v				B1³, 2209
Ω p194	1,2-Pentanediol, 2,4,4-trimethyl-*	$(CH_3)_3CCH_2C(OH)(CH_3)CH_2OH$	146.23	pr or pl (bz)	62–3				s	v	v		s^h		B1³, 2226
Ω p195	1,3-Pentanediol, 2,2,4-trimethyl-*	$(CH_3)_2CHCH(OH)C(CH_3)_2CH_2OH$	146.23	pl (bz)	51.8–2.2	234^{737} $81–2^1$	0.937_{15}^{15}	1.4513^{15}	δ	v	v	ace	s^h		B1³, 2225
p196	1,4-Pentanediol, 2,2,4-trimethyl-*	$(CH_3)_2C(OH)CH_2C(CH_3)_2CH_2OH$	146.23	cr (eth)	86	209–11 $114–5^{13}$				v	s				B1, 493
Ω p197	2,3-Pentanediol, 2,4,4-trimethyl-*	$CH_3C(CH_3)_2CH(OH)C(CH_3)_2(OH)CH_3$	146.23	mcl pr (lig)	65–6					v	v			lig s^h	B1³, 2225
p198	2,3-Pentane-dione*	Acetylpropionyl. Ethyl methylglyoxal. $CH_3CH_2COCOCH_3$	100.13	dk ye liq		108	0.9565_4^{19}	1.4014^{19}	s	∞	∞	∞			B1³, 3112
p199	—,dioxime*	2,3-Diisonitrosopentane. $CH_3CH_2C(:NOH)C(:NOH)CH_3$	130.15	ye nd (al), pl (to, al)	172–3	sub			i	s	δ			to s^h	B1², 831
p200	—,2-oxime*	Isonitrosodiethyl ketone. $CH_3CH_2COC(:NOH)CH_3$	115.13	lf (dil al)	69–72					v	v				B1, 776
p201	—,3-oxime*	Isonitrosopropyl methyl ketone. $CH_3CH_2C(:NOH)COCH_3$	115.13	pl (lig)	58–9	183–7 part d			δ	v	v			chl v alk s (ye)	B1², 831
Ω p202	2,4-Pentane-dione*	Acetylacetone. Diacetyl-methane. $CH_3COCH_2COCH_3$	100.13	λ^{iso} 271 (4.00), λ^{chl} 274 (4.03)	−23	139^{746}	0.9721_4^{25}	1.4494^{20}	v	∞	∞	∞		chl ∞	B1, 777
p203	—,dioxime*	2,4-Diisonitrosopentane. $CH_3C(:NOH)CH_2C(:NOH)CH_3$	130.15	pr (eth)	149–50				δ	v	v				B1², 838
p204	—,monoimide	$CH_3COCH_2C(:NH)CH_3$	99.13		43	209			s d^h		v				B1², 838

For explanations, symbols and abbreviations see beginning of table. For structural formulas see end of table.

2,4-Pentanedione

No.	Name	Synonyms and Formula	Mol. wt.	Color, crystalline form, specific rotation and λ_{max} (log ε)	m.p. °C	b.p. °C	Density	n_D	w	al	eth	ace	bz	other solvents	Ref.
p205	—,3,3-dimethyl-*	$CH_3COC(CH_3)_2COCH_3$....	128.17		19	173 58^{10}	0.9575_4^{20}	1.4306^{20}	...	...	s	...	...	...	B1[3], 3137
p206	—,3-ethyl-*	$CH_3COCH(C_2H_5)COCH_3$..	128.17			$177-80$ $69-70^{13}$	0.95311_4^{19}	1.4408_4^{19}	...	s	s	...	...	chl s	B1[2], 844
p207	1,5-Pentanedione, 1,2,3,4,5-penta-phenyl-*	Benzamaron. Benzylidene-bis-desoxybenzoin. $C_6H_5CH[CH(C_6H_5)COC_6H_5]_2$	480.61	lf (w)	218–9				δ	δ	...	...	δ s^h		B7[2], 803
p208	1,4-Pentanedione, 1-phenyl-*	γ-Oxovalerophenone. Phenacylacetone. $C_6H_5COCH_2CH_2COCH_3$	176.22	ye oil		162^{12}		1.5250^{30}	s^h	...	s	...	s	alk i	B7[1], 368
Ω p209	1-Pentanethiol*	n-Amyl mercaptan. n-Thio-amyl alcohol. $CH_3(CH_2)_3CH_2SH$	104.22	λ^{iso} 230 (2.2)	−75.7	126.638^{460} 19.505^{10}	0.84209_4^{20}	1.4469^{20}	i	∞	∞	...	...	...	B1[3], 1607
p210	2-Pentanethiol*	(α-Methylbutyl) mercaptan. $CH_3CH_2CH_2CH(SH)CH_3$	104.22	λ^{iso} 227 (2.0)	−169	112.9^{760} 63.9^{150}	0.8327_4^{20}	1.4412^{20}	...	s	...	...	...	lig s	B1[3], 1615
p211	3-Pentanethiol*	(α-Ethylpropyl) mercaptan. $(C_2H_5)_2CHSH$	104.22		−110.8	105	0.8410_4^{20}	1.4447^{20}	...	s	...	...	...	...	B1[3], 1619
p212	1,3,5-Pentanetri-carboxylic acid, 3-acetyl-, 3-ethyl ester, 1,5-dinitrile*	$CH_3COC(CH_2CH_2CN)_2CO_2C_2H_5$	236.27	cr	83	$190-200^2$			i	s^h	...	...	...	...	B3[2], 512
p213	1,2,3-Pentane-triol*	$CH_3CH_2CH(OH)CH(OH)CH_2OH$	120.15	syr		192^{63}	1.0851_0^{34}		∞	∞	s	...	...	...	B1[3], 2346
Ω p214	Pentanoic acid*	Propylacetic acid. Valerianic acid. Valeric acid. $CH_3(CH_2)_3CO_2H$	102.13		−33.83	186.05^{760} 82.7^{10} $86-8^{15}$	0.93912_4^{20}	1.4085_4^{20}	s	s	s	...	...	...	B2[3], 664
Ω p215	—,amide	Pentanamide.* n-Valeramide. $CH_3(CH_2)_3CONH_2$	101.15	mica-like mcl pl (peth, al)	106 (114–6)		1.023 0.8735^{110}	1.4183^{110}	v	v	v	...	...	...	B2[3], 674
p216	—,—,N,N-dimethyl-	$CH_3(CH_2)_3CON(CH_3)_2$....	129.20		−51	141^{100}	0.8962^{25}	1.4419^{25}	∞	∞	∞	...	...	...	Am 59, 4012
p217	—,—,N-phenyl-	Valeranilide. $CH_3(CH_2)_3CONHC_6H_5$	177.25	mcl pr (al), cr (peth)	63				...	...	s	...	...	...	C51, 251
p218	—,anhydride*	Valeric anhydride. $[CH_3(CH_2)_3CO]_2O$	186.25		−56.1	218^{754} 111^{15}	0.924_4^{20}	1.4171^{26}	d^h	s	v	...	...	...	B2[3], 674
Ω p219	—,butyl ester*	n-Butyl valerate. $CH_3(CH_2)_3CO_2(CH_2)_3CH_3$	158.24		−92.8	185.8^{760} $84-5^8$	0.8710_4^{15}	1.4128^{20}	δ	s	s	...	...	...	B2[3], 671
p220	—,sec-butyl ester (d)*	d-sec-Butyl valerate. $CH_3(CH_2)_3CO_2CH(CH_3)C_2H_5$	158.24	$[\alpha]_D^{20} + 20.72$		174.5 67^{18}	0.8605_4^{20}	1.4070^{20}	i	s	s	...	s	Py s	B2[1], 131
p221	—,chloride	Pentanoyl chloride*. Valeryl chloride. $CH_3(CH_2)_3COCl$	120.58		−110.0	$107-10^{756}$	1.0155^{15}	1.4200^{20}							B2[3], 674
Ω p222	—,ethyl ester*	Ethyl valerate. $CH_3(CH_2)_3CO_2C_2H_5$	130.19		−91.2	144.6^{736} 50.5^{29}	0.8770_4^{20}	1.4120^{20}	i	∞	∞	...	...	...	B2[3], 669
p223	—,furfuryl ester*	Furfuryl valerate.	182.22			$228-9^{764}$ $82-3^1$	1.0284_4^{20}		i	s	s	...	...	...	B17[2], 115
p224	—,heptyl ester*	n-Heptyl valerate. $CH_3(CH_2)_3CO_2(CH_2)_6CH_3$	200.33		−46.4	245.2	0.8623^{20}	1.42536_{He}^{15}	i	s	s	s	...	os s	B2, 301
p225	—,hexyl ester*	n-Hexyl valerate. $CH_3(CH_2)_3CO_2(CH_2)_5CH_3$	186.30		−63.1	226.3	0.8635^{20}	1.42286^{15}	i	s	s	s	...	os s	B2, 301
p226	—,isobutyl ester	Isobutyl valerate. $CH_3(CH_2)_3CO_2CH_2CH(CH_3)_2$	158.24			179^{760}	0.8625^{25}	1.4046^{20}	i	∞	s	s	...	...	B2[3], 671
p227	—,isopropyl ester*	Isopropyl valerate. $CH_3(CH_2)_3CO_2CH(CH_3)_2$	144.22			153.5 (164.9)	0.8579_4^{20}	1.4061^{20}	i	s	s	...	...	...	B2[2], 266
Ω p228	—,methyl ester*	Methyl valerate. $CH_3(CH_2)_3CO_2CH_3$	116.16			126.5^{750}	0.8947_4^{20}	1.4003^{20}	δ	∞	∞	s	...	...	B2[3], 669
Ω p229	—,nitrile	Pentanonitrile*. Valeronitrile. $CH_3(CH_2)_3CN$	83.13	λ^{cy} 341 (2.1)	−96	141.3^{760} 30.9^{10}	0.8008_4^{20}	1.3971^{20}	s	s	s	s	...	...	B2[2], 267
p230	—,octyl ester*	n-Octyl valerate. $CH_3(CH_2)_3CO_2(CH_2)_7CH_3$	214.35		−42.3	261.6	0.8615^{20}	1.4273^{15}	i	s	s	s	...	os s	B2, 301
Ω p231	—,pentyl ester*	n-Amyl valerate. $CH_3(CH_2)_3CO_2(CH_2)_4CH_3$	172.27		−78.8	203.7^{760} 103^{23}	0.8638_4^{20}	1.4164^{20}	δ	∞	∞	...	...	...	B2[3], 671
p232	—,p-phenylphenacyl ester		296.37	cr (dil al)	67.5–8.0				δ	s	...	...	...	...	Am 52, 3715
p233	—,piperazinium salt	$2C_4H_9CO_2H.C_4H_{10}N_2$	290.41	wh (diox)	112–5.3				s	s	i	...	...	diox s^h	Am 56, 1759
p234	—,propyl ester*	n-Propyl valerate. $CH_3(CH_2)_3CO_2CH_2CH_2CH_3$.	144.22			167.5	0.8699_4^{20}	1.4065^{20}	i	s	s	...	...	chl s	B2[3], 670
p235	—,2-acetyl-, ethyl ester	Ethyl propylacetoacetate. $CH_3COCH(C_3H_7)CO_2C_2H_5$	172.23			$210-2^{749}$ $90.2-.5^{10}$	0.9682_4^{15}	1.4271^{20}	i	s	s	...	...	...	B3[2], 441
p236	—,2-amino-(D, +)*	$CH_3CH_2CH_2CH(NH_2)CO_2H$	117.15	lf (w) $[\alpha]_D^{23} + 32$ (6N HCl, c = 2)	ca. 307	sub			s v^h	i	i	...	...	chl, AcOEt, lig i	B4[3], 1532
Ω p237	—,—(DL)*	Norvaline. $CH_3CH_2CH_2CH(NH_2)CO_2H$.	117.15	lf (al, w)	303 (sealed tube)	sub			s v^h	i	i	...	...	chl, AcOEt, lig i	B4[2], 843
p238	—,—(L, −)*	$CH_3CH_2CH_2CH(NH_2)CO_2H$	117.15	cr (dil al, w) $[\alpha]_D^{20} − 23$ (20 % HCl, c = 10)	ca. 305	sub			s v^h	i	i	...	...	chl, AcOEt, lig i	B4[3], 1549

For explanations, symbols and abbreviations see beginning of table. For structural formulas see end of table.

Pentanoic acid

No.	Name	Synonyms and Formula	Mol. wt.	Color, crystalline form, specific rotation and λ_{max} (log ε)	m.p. °C	b.p. °C	Density	n_D	w	al	eth	ace	bz	other solvents	Ref.
p239	—,4-amino-(D)*	$CH_3CH(NH_2)CH_2CH_2CO_2H$ 117.15		cr (dil al), $[\alpha]_D^{20} +12.0$ (w, p = 10)	214 (cor)	. . . . . .			v	i	i		i	lig i	B4[2], 843
p240	—,—(DL)*	$CH_3CH(NH_2)CH_2CH_2CO_2H$ 117.15		cr (w)	199 (214)	d			v	i	i		i	lig i	B4[2], 843
Ω p241	—,5-amino-*	$H_2N(CH_2)_4CO_2H$ 117.15		lf (dil al)	157–8d	d	. . . . . .	. . . . . .	s	δ	i		i	lig i	B4[2], 844
—	—,—,lactam*	see 2-Piperidone													
—	—,2-amino-5-guanidino-*	see Arginine													
—	—,2-amino-4-methyl-*	see Leucine													
—	—,2-amino-3-sulfo-*	see Cysteic acid													
Ω p242	—,2-bromo-(dl)*	$CH_3CH_2CH_2CHBrCO_2H$ 181.04				118^{12}	1.381^{20}		δ	v	s				B2[3], 680
Ω p243	—,—,ethyl ester*	$CH_3CH_2CH_2CHBrCO_2C_2H_5$ 209.09				$190-2$ $92-4^{18}$	1.226_4^{18}	1.4496^{20}	i	s	s				B2[3], 681
p244	—,2-bromo-4-methyl-(d)*	$(CH_3)_2CHCH_2CHBrCO_2H$ 195.06		oil, $[\alpha]_D^{20} +29.8$ (eth, c = 6) 26.8 (20% dil al, c = 8)		$131-1.5^{16}$				v	v				B2[2], 290
p245	—,—(l)*	$(CH_3)_2CHCH_2CHBrCO_2H$ 195.06		oil, $[\alpha]_D^{20} -12.1$		$94^{0.2-0.4}$ (cor)				v	v				B2[2], 291
p246	—,—,amide(d)*	$(CH_3)_2CHCH_2CHBrCONH_2$ 194.08		(w), $[\alpha]_D^{20} -48.3$ (al, c = 5.9)	118 (cor)				v^h	s	s			chl, AcOEt s	B2[2], 291
p247	—,—,cthyl ester*	$(CH_3)_2CHCH_2CHBrCO_2C_2H_5$ 223.12		pa ye	. . . . . .	$202-4$ $86-7^{11}$									B2[1], 142
p248	—,2-chloro-(dl)*	$CH_3CH_2CH_2CHClCO_2H$ 136.58		. . . . . .	−15	222^{763} $133-5^{30}$	1.141^{13}	1.4481^{11}	i	s	s				B2, 302
p249	—,—,chloride(dl)	$CH_3CH_2CH_2CHClCOCl$ 155.03		. . . . . .		$155-7^{763}$ $61-2^{28}$	1.1765^{20}	1.4465^{20}	d	d	s				B2[3], 677
p250	—,—,ethyl ester	$CH_3CH_2CH_2CHClCO_2C_2H_5$ 164.63		cr	33	185^{752}	1.040^{12}	1.4307^{11}	i	s	s				B2, 302
p251	—,3-chloro-*	$CH_3CH_2CHClCH_2CO_2H$ 136.58		cr (bz)	33	112^{10}	1.1484_4^{20}	1.4462^{20}	i	s	s				B2[3], 678
p252	—,—,ethyl ester*	$CH_3CH_2CHClCH_2CO_2C_2H_5$ 164.63				189 $66-7^{10}$	1.0330_4^{20}	1.4278^{20}	i	s	s				B2[3], 678
p253	—,4-chloro-*	$CH_3CHClCH_2CH_2CO_2H$ 136.58				116^{10}	1.1514^{20}	1.4458^{20}	i	s	s				B2[3], 678
p254	—,—,chloride	$CH_3CHClCH_2CH_2COCl$ 155.03				61^8			d	d	v				B2[3], 679
p255	—,—,ethyl ester*	$CH_3CHClCH_2CH_2CO_2C_2H_5$ 164.63				196^{760} 70.5^9	1.0393_4^{20}	1.4310^{20}	i	s	s				B2[3], 678
p256	—,5-chloro-*	$Cl(CH_2)_4CO_2H$ 136.58			18	230^{760} $141-9^{12}$ δd	1.3416_4^{25}	1.4555^{20}	s v^h	s	v				B2[3], 679
p257	—,—,chloride	$Cl(CH_2)_4COCl$ 155.03				83^{12}	1.210^{18}	1.4639^{20}	d	d	s				B2[3], 679
Ω p258	—,—,ethyl ester	$Cl(CH_2)_4CO_2C_2H_5$ 164.63				$205-6^{760}$ 93^{16}	1.0561^{20}	1.4355^{20}	i	s	s				B2[3], 679
—	—,2,5-diamino-*	see Ornithine													
p259	—,4,4-dimethyl-, chloride	Neopentylacetyl chloride. $(CH_3)_3CCH_2CH_2COCl$ 148.63				$150-2^{760}$ 58^2		1.4294^{20}	d	d	s				C47, 6438
p260	—,2,4-dioxo-*	Acetoneoxalic acid. Acetyl-pyruvic acid. $CH_3COCH_2COCO_2H$ 130.10		nd (bz-chl), pr (bz) $\lambda^{w,pH=1.5}$ 285 (3.5) λ^{eth} 290 (3.95)	55–63 (+1w) 101(anh)	130^{37} sub par d			s	s	s	s	s	AcOEt, chl s lig i alk d	B3[2], 465
Ω p261	—,—,ethyl ester*	Ethyl acetoneoxalate. $CH_3COCH_2COCO_2C_2H_5$ 158.16		. . . . . .	18	$213-5$ $111-2^{16}$	1.1251^{20}	1.4757^{17}	. . .	s	s				B3[2], 465
p262	—,2-ethyl-(dl)*	3-Hexanecarboxylic acid* $CH_3CH_2CH_2CH(C_2H_5)CO_2H$ 130.19				209.2 $105-7^{18}$	0.9361_{33}^{33}		i	s	s				B2[3], 778
p263	—,—,chloride	$CH_3CH_2CH_2CH(C_2H_5)COCl$ 148.63				$158 \; 60$ 50^{11}			d						B2, 344
p264	—,3-ethyl-*	$(C_2H_5)_2CHCH_2CO_2H$ 130.19				212 $104-5^{13}$		1.4250^{20}		s	s				B2[3], 779
p265	—,5-fluoro-*	$F(CH_2)_4CO_2H$ 120.13				83^2		1.4080^{25}	δ	v	v				C50, 4063
Ω p266	—,2-hydroxy-*	Valerolactic acid. $CH_3CH_2CH_2CH(OH)CO_2H$ 118.13		hyg pl	34	sub			s	s	s				B3[2], 225
p267	—,4-hydroxy-, lactone(d)*	γ-Valerolactone. Tetrahydro-5-methyl-2-furanone. 100.12		$[\alpha]_D^{20} +13.5$ (undil)		$86-90^{14}$			∞	δ		s			B17[2], 288
Ω p268	—,—,—(dl)*	$C_5H_8O_2$. See p267 100.12			−31	206^{760} $83-4^{13}$	1.0465^{25}	1.4328^{20}	∞	δ		s			B17[2], 288
p269	—,—,—(l)*	$C_5H_8O_2$. See p267 100.12		$[\alpha]_D^{20} +4.6$ (eth, c = 10)		$78-80^8$		1.4322^{20}	∞	s		s			B17[2], 288
Ω p270	—,5-hydroxy-, lactone	δ-Valerolactone. 100.12		. . . . . .	12.5	$218-20$ $113-4^{14}$	1.0794^{20}	1.4503^{20}	s	∞	∞				B17[2], 287
—	—,2-hydroxy-4-methyl-*	see Leucic acid													
p271	—,2-hydroxy-2-propyl-, nitrile	4-Heptanone cyanohydrin. $(CH_3CH_2CH_2)_2C(OH)CN$ 141.22				$119-20^{21}$	0.9077^{18}	1.4337^{18}		s					B3[2], 238
p282	—,2-isobutyl-4-methyl-, amide	Diisobutylacetamide. $[(CH_3)_2CHCH_2]_2CHCONH_2$ 171.29		lf or nd (eth)	74–5	. . . . . .			δ	v				os v lig δ	B2[1], 153
p283	—,2-methyl-(d)*	Methylpropylacetic acid. $CH_3CH_2CH_2CH(CH_3)CO_2H$ 116.16		$[\alpha]_D^{25} +5.58$ (eth) $[\alpha]_D^{16}$ +18.5 (undil)		96^{15}	0.927^{16}	1.4112^{25}	s	s	s				B2[3], 739

For explanations, symbols and abbreviations see beginning of table. For structural formulas see end of table.

No.	Name	Synonyms and Formula	Mol. wt.	Color, crystalline form, specific rotation and λ_{max} (log ε)	m.p. °C	b.p. °C	Density	n_D	w	al	eth	ace	bz	other solvents	Ref.
	Pentanoic acid														
Ω p284	—,—(dl)*	$CH_3CH_2CH_2CH(CH_3)CO_2H$	116.16	....	....	$195-6^{760}$ $102-5^{12}$	0.9230^{20}_{20}	1.413^{20}	s	s	s				B2³, 740
p285	—,—(l)*	$CH_3CH_2CH_2CH(CH_3)CO_2H$	116.16	$[\alpha]^{25}_D - 7.08$ (eth)	....	$190-3$ 96^{15}	0.9781^{20}_4	1.4117^{25}	s	s	s				B2², 288
p286	—,—,chloride(dl)	$CH_3CH_2CH_2CH(CH_3)COCl$	134.61	....	....	$140.0-$ 0.8^{745}	0.9781^{20}_4	1.4330^{27}	d^h	d^h	s				B2³, 741
p287	—,3-methyl-(d)*	see-Butylacetic acid. $CH_3CH_2CH(CH_3)CH_2CO_2H$	116.16	$[\alpha]^{20}_D + 8.5$ (undil)	....	199 $92-3^{10}$	0.9276^{20}_{20}	1.4158^{20}		s	s				B2³, 749
Ω p288	—,—(dl)*	$CH_3CH_2CH(CH_3)CH_2CO_2H$	116.16	....	-41.6	$197.2-$ $.8^{760}$	0.9262^{20}	1.4159^{20}		s	s				B2³, 750
p289	—,—(l)*	$CH_3CH_2CH(CH_3)CH_2CO_2H$	116.16	$[\alpha]^{20}_D -8.9$ (al)	....	$196-7$ 105^{30}	0.9232^{25}_4	1.4152^{20}		s	s				B2³, 749
p290	—,—,chloride(dl)	sec-Butylacetyl chloride. $CH_3CH_2CH(CH_3)CH_2COCl$	134.61	....	....	$142.5-$ 3^{749}	0.9781^{20}_4			d	d	v		CS_2 v	B2³, 750
Ω p291	—,4-methyl-*	Isobutylacetic acid. Isocaproic acid. $(CH_3)_2CHCH_2CH_2CO_2H$	116.16	....	-33.0	$200-1^{760}$ $86-8^{11}$	0.9225^{20}_4	1.4144^{20}	δ	s	s				B2³, 743
p292	—,—,amide	Isocaproamide. $(CH_3)_2CHCH_2CH_2CONH_2$	115.18	nd (al)	$120-1$	....			s	s^h	s				B2², 290
p293	—,—,—,N-phenyl-	Isocaproanilide. $(CH_3)_2CHCH_2CH_2CONHC_6H_5$	191.28	nd (bz, dil al)	112	....			i	s^h	s		s^h		B12², 147
p294	—,—,chloride	Isocaproyl chloride. $(CH_3)_2CHCH_2CH_2COCl$	134.61	....	....	$143.8-$ 4.5^{745}	0.9725^{20}		d^h	d^h					B2³, 745
Ω p295	—,—,nitrile	Isoamyl cyanide. Isocapronitrile. $(CH_3)_2CHCH_2CH_2CN$	97.16	....	-51	$156-7^{761}$ 50^{13}	0.8030^{20}_4	1.4059^{20}	i	s	∞				B2³, 745
p296	—,4-methyl-2-phenyl-*	α-Phenylisocaproic acid. $(CH_3)_2CHCH_2CH(C_6H_5)CO_2H$	192.24	pr (peth)	$78-9$	$178-80^{30}$					s			alk s lig δ	B9², 369
p297	—,—,nitrile	α-Phenylisocapronitrile. $(CH_3)_2CHCH_2CH(C_6H_5)CN$	173.26	....	....	$263-6^{765}$ $136-8^{15}$	0.942^{16}		i	s	s	s		aa s	B9¹, 220
p298	—,3-oxo-, ethyl ester*	Ethyl propionylacetate. $CH_3CH_2COCH_2CO_2C_2H_5$	144.17	....	....	191 90^{13}		1.4230^{20}		s	s				B3², 430
Ω p299	—,4-oxo-*	β-Acetopropionic acid. Levulinic acid. $CH_3COCH_2CH_2CO_2H$	116.13	lf or pl λ^w 270 (1.40)	37.2	$245-6$ δd $139-40^8$	1.1335^{20}_4	1.4396^{20}	v	v	v				B3³, 1214
p299¹	—,—,benzyl ester	Benzyl levulinate. $CH_3COCH_2CH_2CO_2CH_2C_6H_5$	206.24	....	....	$132-4^2$	1.0935^{20}_{20}	1.5090^{20}						to s	Am 55, 4727
p300	—,—,butyl ester*	Butyl levulinate. $CH_3COCH_2CH_2CO_2(CH_2)_3CH_3$	172.23	....	....	237.8^{760}	0.9735^{20}_{20}	1.4290^{20}		s	s	s	s	CS_2 s	B3³, 1220
p301	—,—,sec-butyl ester	sec-Butyl levulinate. $CH_3COCH_2CH_2CO_2CH(CH_3)CH_2CH_3$	172.23	....	....	225.8^{760}	0.9669^{20}_4	1.4249^{20}		s	s	s	s		B3³, 1221
p302	—,—,isobutyl ester.	Isobutyl levulinate. $CH_3COCH_2CH_2CO_2CH_2CH(CH_3)_2$	172.23	....	....	230.9^{760} $(222-4)$	0.97047^{20}_4	1.4268^{20}		s	s	s	s	CS_2 s	B3³, 1221
p303	—,—,isopropyl ester*	Isopropyl levulinate. $CH_3COCH_2CH_2CO_2CH(CH_3)_2$	158.20	....	....	209.3^{760}	0.98422^{20}_4	1.4420^{20}	δ	s	s	s	s		B3³, 1220
Ω p304	—,—,methyl ester*.	Methyl levulinate. $CH_3COCH_2CH_2CO_2CH_3$	130.15	....	....	196^{760} $85-6^{14}$	1.05113^{20}_4	1.4233^{20}	δ	s	∞	s	s		B3³, 1217
Ω p305	—,—,propyl ester*.	Propyl levulinate. $CH_2COCH_2CH_2CO_2CH_2CH_2CH_3$	158.20	....	....	221.2^{760}	0.9896^{20}_4	1.4258^{20}	δ	s	s	s	s	CS_2 s	B3³, 1219
p306	—,5-oxo-5-phenyl-*	γ-Benzoylbutyric acid. $C_6H_5CO(CH_2)_3CO_2H$	192.22	pl (w) λ^{al} 281 (1.41)	$128-9$	....			s^h						B10², 488
p307	—,2-phenyl-(d)*	α-Phenylvaleric acid. $CH_3CH_2CH_2CH(C_6H_5)CO_2H$	178.23	$[\alpha]_D + 58.81$ (chl), $+33.1$ (eth)	....	165^{14}	1.047^{20}_2				s	s		chl s lig s^h	B9, 557
p308	—,—(dl)*	$CH_3CH_2CH_2CH(C_6H_5)CO_2H$	178.23	nd (lig)	58	280				s	s			chl s lig s^h	B9, 557
p309	—,—,nitrile	$CH_3CH_2CH_2CH(C_6H_5)CN$	159.23	....	....	$254-5^{750}$ $125-8^{13}$	0.9425	1.5000^{20}	i	∞	s	s	∞		B9¹, 216
Ω p310	—,4-phenyl-*	γ-Phenylvaleric acid. $C_6H_5CH(CH_3)CH_2CH_2CO_2H$	178.23	....	ca. 13	210^{85} 165^{12}	1.0554^{15}_{15}	1.5167^{20}	δ	s	s				B9², 362
Ω p311	—,5-phenyl-*	δ-Phenylvaleric acid. $C_6H_5(CH_2)_4CO_2H$	178.23	pl (w), pr (peth)	$57-8$ (61)	$190-3^{30}$			δ^h	v	s			os s	B9¹, 216
p312	—,2,2,4-tri-methyl-, amide	$(CH_3)_2CHCH_2CH(CH_3)_2C(CH_3)_2CONH_2$	143.23	lf (lig)	71	....				s^h	s			lig δ	B2², 305
Ω p313	1-Pentanol*	Butyl carbinol. n-Amyl alcohol. $CH_3(CH_2)_4OH$	88.15	λ^{undil} 178 (2.4), 215 (1.55)	-79	137.3^{748} 50^{13}	0.8144^{20}	1.4101^{20}	i δ^h	∞	∞	s	v		B1³, 1598
Ω p314	2-Pentanol*	Methyl n-propyl carbinol. $CH_3CH_2CH_2CH(OH)CH_3$	88.15	....	....	118.9 62^{60}	0.81032^{20}_4	1.4053^{20}	v	s	s				B1³, 1609
Ω p315	3-Pentanol*	Diethyl carbinol. $(CH_3CH_2)_2CHOH$	88.15	....	....	116.1^{760} 30^{12}	0.8212^{20}_4	1.4104^{20}	δ	s	s	s			B1, 385
p317	—,4-amino-2-methyl-*	$(CH_3)_2C(OH)CH_2CH(NH_2)CH_3$	117.19	....	$35-6$	174^{745}			s^h	s	s	s	s	lig i	B4, 296
p318	1-Pentanol, 5-chloro-*	Pentamethylene chlorohydrin $Cl(CH_2)_5OH$	122.60	....	....	112^{12}		1.4518^{20}	δ	v	v				B1³, 1606
p319	2-Pentanol, 1-chloro-*	$CH_3CH_2CH_2CH(OH)CH_2Cl$	122.60	....	....	$157-60^{735}$ $59-62^{14}$	1.0372^{20}_{20}	1.4404^{25}	δ	s	v				B1², 419
p320	3-Pentanol, 1-chloro-*	$CH_3CH_2CH(OH)CH_2CH_2Cl$	122.60	....	....	173 77^{20}	1.0327^{25}_4	1.448^{25}	δ s^h	v	v				B1³, 1618
p321	1-Pentanol,2,4-dimethyl-(dl)*	$(CH_3)_2CHCH_2CH(CH_3)CH_2OH$	116.21	....	....	$160-2^{760}$ $65-7^{18}$	0.7932^{20}	1.427^{20}	i	s	s	s		os s	B1³, 1700

For explanations, symbols and abbreviations see beginning of table. For structural formulas see end of table.

No.	Name	Synonyms and Formula	Mol. wt.	Color. crystalline form. specific rotation and λ_{max} (log ε)	m.p. °C	b.p. °C	Density	n_D	w	al	eth	ace	bz	other solvents	Ref.
	1-Pentanol														
p322	—,—,(l)*	$(CH_3)_2CHCH_2CH(CH_3)CH_2OH$	116.21	$[\alpha]_D^{22} -1.1$ (undil)		157^{760}	0.816_4^{25}		i	s	s			os s	B1[3], 1700
Ω p323	2-Pentanol, 2,4-dimethyl-*	Dimethyl isobutyl carbinol. $(CH_3)_2CHCH_2C(OH)(CH_3)_2$	116.21		< −20	133.1^{760} $53.5-4.5^{25}$	0.8103_4^{20}	1.4172^{20}	i	s	s			os s	B1[3], 1700
Ω p324	3-Pentanol, 2,3-dimethyl-*	Ethyl isopropyl methyl carbinol. $(CH_3)_2CHC(OH)(CH_3)CH_2CH_3$	116.21		< −30	139.7^{760} $44-5^{14}$	0.833_4^{20}	1.4287^{20}		s	s				B1[3], 1698
Ω p325	—,2,4-dimethyl-*	Diisopropyl carbinol. $(CH_3)_2CHCH(OH)CH(CH_3)_2$	116.21		< 70	138.7^{760} 87.5^{125}	0.8288_4^{20}	1.4250^{20}	δ	s	s				B1[3], 1701
p326	—,2,4-dimethyl-3-phenyl-*	Diisopropylphenyl carbinol. $[(CH_3)_2CH]_2C(OH)C_6H_5$	192.31	ye		229^{760} 157^{760}	0.9755_4^{20}	1.5239^{20}	δ	i	s				B6[1], 273
Ω p327	—,3-ethyl-*	Triethyl carbinol. $(C_2H_5)_3COH$	116.21			$143.1-3.2$ 73^{52}	0.8407_4^{22}	1.4294^{20}		s	s				B1[3], 1696
Ω p328	—,3-ethyl-2-methyl-*	Diethylisopropyl carbinol. $(CH_3)_2CHCOH(C_2H_5)_2$	130.23			$159.5-61^{750}$ $55-7^{48}$	0.8295_{20}^{20}	1.4372^{20}		s	s				B1[3], 1740
p329	1-Pentanol, 5-fluoro-*	Pentamethylene fluorohydrin $F(CH_2)_5OH$	106.14			$70-1^{11}$		1.4057^{25}	s	v	v				C51, 7300
Ω p330	—,2-methyl-*	sec-Amyl carbinol. $CH_3CH_2CH_2CH(CH_3)CH_2OH$	102.18			148^{760}	0.8263_4^{20}	1.4182^{20}		s	ε	з			B1[3], 1665
Ω p331	—,3-methyl-(dl)*	$CH_3CH_2CH(CH_3)CH_2CH_2OH$	102.18			152.44^{760} $51-2.5^8$	0.8242_4^{20}	1.4112^{23}	i	s	s				B1[3], 1671
Ω p332	—,4-methyl-*	Isoamyl carbinol. Isohexyl alcohol. $(CH_3)_2CH(CH_2)_3OH$	102.18			151.6^{760}	0.8131_4^{20}	1.4134^{25}	i	s	s				B1[3], 1671
Ω p334	2-Pentanol, 2-methyl-*	Dimethyl n-propyl carbinol. $CH_3CH_2CH_2C(OH)(CH_3)_2$	102.18	col	−103	$120.5-1.5$ $49.5^{27.5}$	0.8350_4^{16}	1.4100^{20}	δ	s	s				B1[3], 1666
Ω p335	—,3-methyl-*	sec-Butyl methyl carbinol. $CH_3CH_2CH(CH_3)CH(OH)CH_3$	102.18			134.32^{760} 75.6^{50}	0.8307_4^{20}	1.4182^{20}	δ	s	s				B1[3], 1672
Ω p336	—,4-methyl-*	Methyl isobutyl carbinol. $(CH_3)_2CHCH_2CH(OH)CH_3$	102.18			133^{760} $50-5^{25}$	0.8075_4^{20}	1.4100^{20}	δ	s	s				B1[3], 1669
Ω p337	—,—,acetate	4-Methyl-2-pentyl acetate. $(CH_3)_2CHCH_2CH(CH_3)O_2CCH_3$	144.22			$147-8$ 76.5^{47}	0.8805_0^0	1.4066^{20}	i	s	s	s			C50, 4817
Ω p338	3-Pentanol, 2-methyl-*	Ethyl isopropyl carbinol. $(CH_3)_2CHCH(OH)CH_2CH_3$	102.18			126.68^{760}	0.8243_4^{20}	1.4175^{20}	δ	∞	∞				B16, 1037
Ω p339	—,3-methyl-*	Diethyl methyl carbinol. $(CH_3CH_2)_2C(OH)CH_3$	102.18		−23.6	122.4^{760}	0.8286_4^{20}	1.4186^{20}	δ	∞	∞				B1, 411
p340	1-Pentanol, 1-phenyl-(d)*	Butyl phenyl carbinol. $C_6H_5CH(OH)(CH_2)_3CH_3$	164.25	$[\alpha]_D^{20} +40.8$		$140-2^{25}$	0.9672_{20}^{20}	1.4086^{25}	i	s	s	s			B6[2], 504
p341	—,5-phenyl-*	$C_6H_5(CH_2)_5OH$	164.25			155^{20} $128-30^{2.5}$	0.9725^{20}	1.5156^{20}	i	v	v				B6[2], 505
p342	2-Pentanol, 2-phenyl-*	Methyl phenyl propyl carbinol. $C_6H_5C(OH)(CH_3)(CH_2)_2CH_3$	164.25			216 112^{14}	0.9723^{22}		i	v					B6[2], 505
p343	3-Pentanol, 1-phenyl-(d)*	$C_6H_5CH_2CH_2CH(OH)CH_2CH_3$	164.25	$[\alpha]_D^{20} +26.8$ (al), $+30.2$ (CS₂)	38	143^{19}	0.9687_4^{20}		i	v				CS₂ v	B6[2], 504
p344	—,3-phenyl-*	Diethyl phenyl carbinol. $(C_2H_5)_2C(OH)C_6H_5$	164.25		< −17	$223-4^{762}$ 110^{12}	0.9831_4^{20}	1.51655^{20}	i	v					B6[2], 506
Ω p345	2-Pentanol,2,4-trimethyl-*	Isodibutol. $(CH_3)_2CHCH_2C(OH)(CH_3)_2$	130.23		−20	147.5 $42-4^7$	0.8225_4^{20}	1.4284^{20}	i	δ	s				B1[3], 1741
Ω p346	2-Pentanone*	Methyl propyl ketone. $CH_3CH_2CH_2COCH_3$	86.14	λ^{a1} 280.3 (1.26)	−77.8	102	0.8089_4^{20}	1.3895^{20}	δ	∞	∞				B1[3], 2800
p347	—,oxime*	Methyl propyl ketoxime. $CH_3CH_2CH_2C(:NOH)CH_3$	101.15			167^{148}	0.9095^{20}	1.4450^{20}	s	∞	∞				B1[3], 2803
Ω p348	3-Pentanone*	Diethyl ketone. Propione. $CH_3CH_2COCH_2CH_3$	86.14	λ^{a1} 275 (1.30)	−39.8	101.7^{760}	0.8138_4^{20}	1.3924^{20}	v	∞	∞				B1[3], 2806
p349	2-Pentanone, 4-amino-4-methyl-*	Diacetonamine. $(CH_3)_2C(NH_2)CH_2COCH_3$	115.18			$25^{0.14}$	< 1		s	∞	∞				B4[2], 767
Ω p350	1-Pentanone, 1(4-amino-phenyl)-*	3-Aminovalerophenone	177.25	cr (bz-peth)	74−5	$160-3^3$			i	s	s				B14[2], 43
p351	2-Pentanone, 1-chloro-*	$CH_3CH_2CH_2COCH_2Cl$	120.58			$154.5-6$ δd $58-9^{17}$	δ							MeOH s	B1[3], 2804
Ω p352	—,5-chloro-*	$Cl(CH_2)_3COCH_3$	120.58			76^{34} (75^{73})	1.0323_4^{18}	1.4375^{20}			s	s			B1[3], 2804
p353	3-Pentanone, 1-chloro-*	$CH_3CH_2COCH_2CH_2Cl$	120.58			68^{20} $33^{2.5}$		1.4361^{20}		s	v			MeOH s alk d[h]	B1[3], 2812
p354	—,2-chloro-*	$CH_3CH_2COCHClCH_3$	120.58			$135 (145)$			i	s	s				B1[3], 2812
Ω p355	—,2,4-dimethyl-*	Diisopropyl ketone. Isobutyrone. Tetramethyl acetone. $(CH_3)_2CHCOCH(CH_3)_2$	114.19	λ^{a1} 286 (1.45)	−69.03	$124-5$	0.8108_4^{20}	1.39995^{20}	i	∞	∞		s		B1[3], 2868
Ω p356	2-Pentanone, 3-ethyl-4-methyl-*	$(CH_3)_2CHCH(C_2H_5)COCH_3$	128.22			$154-5^{760}$	0.812_4^{20}	1.4105^{10}	s	∞	∞		∞	aa, chl ∞ os v	B1[3], 2883
p357	—,1-hydroxy-*	$CH_3CH_2CH_2COCH_2OH$	102.13			152 $62-4^{18}$	0.9860_4^{10}	1.4234^{20}	s	s	s				B1[3], 3219
p358	—,3-hydroxy-*	$CH_3CH_2CH(OH)COCH_3$	102.13			$147-8^{761}$ 59^{27}	0.9500_4^{20}	1.4350^{26}	∞	∞	ε	в	з		B1[3], 3220

For explanations, symbols and abbreviations see beginning of table. For structural formulas see end of table.

No.	Name	Synonyms and Formula	Mol. wt.	Color, crystalline form, specific rotation and λ_{max} (log ε)	m.p. °C	b.p. °C	Density	n_D	w	al	eth	ace	bz	other solvents	Ref.
	2-Pentanone														
p359	—,4-hydroxy-*	$CH_3CH(OH)CH_2COCH_3$	102.13	λ^{al} 277.5 (1.38)	....	177^{760} $62–4^{12}$	1.0071_4^{20}	1.4265^{20}	s	s	s	...	...		B1[3], 3220
Ω p360	—,5-hydroxy-*	$HOCH_2CH_2CH_2COCH_3$	102.13	....	....	208^{730} $116–8^{33}$	1.0071_4^{20}	1.4390^{20}	∞	s	s	...	...		B1[3], 3221
p361	3-Pentanone, 2-hydroxy-*	$CH_3CH_2COCH(OH)CH_3$	102.13		....	152.5^{761} 63^{20}	0.9742_4^{20}	1.4128^{20}	s	s	s	...	...		B1[2], 873
Ω p362	2-Pentanone, 4-hydroxy-4-methyl-*	Diacetone alcohol. $(CH_3)_2C(OH)CH_2COCH_3$	116.16	λ^{al} 282 (1.40)	−44	164^{760} (168) $67–9^{19}$	0.9387_4^{20}	1.4213^{20}	∞	∞	∞	...	...		B1[3], 3234
p363	1-Pentanone, 5-hydroxy-1-phenyl-*	δ-Hydroxy-n-valerophenone. $C_6H_5CO(CH_2)_4OH$	178.23	pl (w)	40–1	....	....	....	s^h	v	v	...	v	MeOH v peth δ	B8, 123
Ω p364	2-Pentanone, 3-methyl-(dl)*	sec-Butyl methyl ketone. $CH_3CH_2CH(CH_3)COCH_3$	100.16	λ^{al} 282 (1.40)	....	118^{758}	0.8130_4^{20}	1.4002^{20}	δ	∞	∞	...	...	chl s	B1[3], 2837
Ω p365	—,4-methyl-*	Isobutyl methyl ketone. Isopropyl acetone. $(CH_3)_2CHCH_2COCH_3$	100.16	....	−84.7	116.85^{760} $35–40^{16}$	0.7978^{20}	1.3962^{20}	δ	∞	∞	∞	∞	chl s	B1[3], 2882
Ω p366	3-Pentanone, 2-methyl-*	Ethyl isopropyl ketone. $CH_3CH_2COCH(CH_3)_2$	100.16	λ^{al} 281 (1.41)	....	$114.5–5^{745}$	0.830_0^0	1.3975^{20}	δ	v	∞	∞	v	chl s	B1[3], 2831
p367	1-Pentanone, 4-methyl-1-phenyl-*	Isocaprophenone. Isopentyl phenyl ketone $(CH_3)_2CHCH_2CH_2COC_6H_5$	176.24	....	−2	$255–6$ $145–7^{30}$	0.9623^{15}	1.533^{20}	i	v	v	v	v	chl s	B7[2], 258
Ω p368	—,1-phenyl-*	n-Butyl phenyl ketone. Valerophenone. $CH_3(CH_2)_3COC_6H_5$	162.23	λ^{MeOH} 240 (4.11)	....	248.5 (cor) $131–3^{13}$	0.988_{20}^{20}	1.5158^{20}	i	v	v	...	...		B7[2], 251
Ω p369	3-Pentanone, 2,2,4,4-tetra-methyl-*	Hexamethylacetone. Pivalone. $(CH_3)_3COC(CH_3)_3$	142.24			152 (154) 70^{43}	0.8240^{18}	1.4194^{20}	i	s	s	s	...	chl, aa s	B7[2], 251
—	Pentaphene	see 2:3, 6:7-Dibenzophenanthrene													
p370	Pentaquine	$C_{18}H_{27}N_3O$	301.44			$165–70^{0.02}$	....	1.5785^{25}	...	...	...	...	...	dil HCl s	Am 68, 1529
p371	Pentasiloxane, dodecamethyl-	$CH_3[–Si(CH_3)_2O–]_4Si(CH_3)_3$	384.85		−80	229^{710} $103–7^{12}$	0.8755^{20}	1.3925^{20}	δ	...	...	...	s	lig s	Am 68, 2284
p372	Pentatri-acontane*	$CH_3(CH_2)_{33}CH_3$	492.97	cr (al)	75	490^{760} 311.36^{10}	0.8157_4^{20}	1.4568^{20} (suc)	i	...	$δ^h$	s	...		B1, 177
Ω p373	18-Pentatri-acontanone*	Diheptadecyl ketone. Stearone. $CH_3(CH_2)_{16}CO(CH_2)_{16}CH_3$	506.95	lf (lig)	88.4	....	0.793_4^{95}	....	i	$δ^h$	$δ^h$	$δ^h$	δ	chl, lig δ	B1, 720
p374	2-Pentenal, 2-methyl-*	Methylethyl acrolein. $CH_3CH_2CH:C(CH_3)CHO$	98.15	λ^{MeOH} 227.5 (4.14), 311 (1.51)	....	$136.4–7.1^{762}$ $38–9^{18}$	0.8581_4^{20}	1.4488^{20}	i	s	s	...	s	MeOH s	B1[3], 2995
Ω p375	1-Pentene*	1-Pentylene. Propylethylene. $CH_3CH_2CH_2CH:CH_2$	70.14	λ^{gas} 177 (4.22), 181.3 (4.14), 187.1 sh (3.65)	−138 (−165.2)	29.968^{760}	0.6405_4^{20}	1.3715^{20}	i	∞	∞	...	s	dil sulf v	B1[3], 770
p376	2-Pentene(cis)*	cis-β-n-Amylene. $CH_3CH_2CH:CHCH_3$	70.14	λ^{gas} 166.7 (4.03), 177 (4.26), 185 (4.1), 204.8 (2.95)	−151.39	36.9^{760}	0.6556_4^{20}	1.3830^{20}	i	∞	∞	...	s	dil sulf s	B1[3], 776
p377	—(trans)*	trans-β-n-Amylene. $CH_3CH_2CH:CHCH_3$	70.14	λ^{gas} 157.7 (4.08), 180.8 (4.15), 200.9 (3.11)	−136	36.353^{760}	0.6482_4^{20}	1.3793^{20}	i	∞	∞	...	s	dil sulf v	B1[3], 777
p378	1-Pentene, 1-bromo-*	$CH_3CH_2CH_2CH:CHBr$	149.04	....		$121.5–22^{760}$ 43.5^{30}	1.2606_4^{25}	1.4572^{20}	i	...	v	...	s	chl s	B1[3], 775
p379	—,2-bromo-*	$CH_3CH_2CH_2CBr:CH_2$	149.04			107–8	1.228^{20}	1.4535^{20}	i	...	...	s	s	chl, lig s	B1[2], 183
p380	—,3-bromo-*	$CH_3CH_2CHBrCH:CH_2$	149.04			30.5^{30}	1.2417_4^{25}	1.4626^{25}	i	...	...	s	s	chl v	B1[3], 775
p380[1]	2-Pentene, 1-bromo-*	$CH_3CH_2CH:CHCH_2Br$	149.04			$123–4$ (122) 35^{25}	1.2545^{20}	1.4731^{20}	i	...	...	s	s	chl v	B1[3], 783
p381	—,2-bromo-*	$CH_3CH_2CH:CBrCH_3$	149.04			110.5^{750}	1.277_{20}^{20}	1.4580^{20}	i	...	...	s	s	chl v	B1[3], 784
p382	—,3-bromo-*	$CH_3CH_2CBr:CHCH_3$	149.04			115.2^{750}	1.273_{20}^{20}	1.4628^{20}	i	...	...	s	s	chl v	B1[3], 784
p383	—,4-bromo-*	$CH_3CHBrCH:CHCH_3$	149.04			$116.7–9.2$ d 22^8	1.2312^{21}	1.4752^{21}	d	...	...	s	s	chl v	B1[3], 784
p384	—,5-bromo-*	$BrCH_2CH_2CH:CHCH_3$	149.04			121.7^{621}	1.2715_4^{20}	1.4695^{20}	i	...	...	s	s	chl v.	B1[3], 784
p385	1-Pentene, 2-chloro-*	$CH_3CH_2CH_2CCl:CH_2$	104.58			95–7	0.872^5	....	...	s	v	...	...		B1[3], 774
p386	—,3-chloro-*	$CH_3CH_2CHClCH:CH_2$	104.58			$93–4^{764}$	0.8978_4^{20}	1.4254^{20}	...	s	v	...	...		B1[3], 774
p387	—,4-chloro-*	$CH_3CHClCH_2CH:CH_2$	104.58	λ^{undil} 233 (1.25)	....	97–100	0.934^{15}	1.417^{15}	i	...	v	...	...	chl v	B1[3], 774
p388	—,5-chloro-*	$ClCH_2CH_2CH_2CH:CH_2$	104.58			$103.5–4.5^{773}$ 36.5^{61}	0.9125^{20}	1.4297^{20}	δ	...	s	v	...		B1[3], 775
p389	2-Pentene, 1-chloro-*	$CH_3CH_2CH:CHCH_2Cl$	104.58			109.5 62^{148}	0.908^{22}	1.4352^{22}	i	v^h	v	s	...	chl s	B1[2], 184
p390	—,2-chloro-*	$CH_3CH_2CH:CClCH_3$	104.58			95–7 45^{130}	0.9067_4^{20}	1.4261^{20}	i	...	v	v	...	xyl v^h	B1[2], 185
p391	—,3-chloro-*	$CH_3CH_2CCl:CHCH_3$	104.58			$90–2^{781}$	1.423^{20}	0.9125_{20}^{20}	i	...	v	v	...	xyl v^h	B1[2], 185

For explanations, symbols and abbreviations see beginning of table. For structural formulas see end of table.

No.	Name	Synonyms and Formula	Mol. wt.	Color. crystalline form. specific rotation and λ_{max} (log ε)	m.p °C	b.p. °C	Density	n_D	w	al	eth	ace	bz	other solvents	Ref.
	2-Pentene														
p392	—,4-chloro-*	Piperylene hydrochloride. $CH_3CHClCH:CHCH_3$	104.58	....		103 18–20[12]	0.9004_{20}^{20}	1.4322^{20}	i	...	v	v	...	chl s	B1[3], 782
p393	—,5-chloro-*	$ClCH_2CH_2CH:CHCH_3$	104.58	....		107.0–.6[755]	0.9043_4^{20}	1.4310^{20}	i	...	v	v	...	chl s	B1[3], 782
p394	—,3-chloro-2,4-dimethyl-*	$(CH_3)_2CHCCl:C(CH_3)_2$	132.64	....		118–20 44–5[30]	0.9513_9^{9}		i		v		s	chl v	B1, 221
p395	1-Pentene, 2-chloro-3-ethyl-3-methyl-*	$(C_2H_5)_2C(CH_3)CCl:CH_2$	146.66	....		147[743] 53[20]	0.9147_4^{20}	1.4450^{25}	i				s	chl s	B1[3], 847
p396	—,3-chloro-2-methyl-*	$CH_3CH_2CHClC(CH_3):CH_2$	118.61	....		121–4		1.4422^{20}	i				s	chl v	B1[3], 809
p397	2-Pentene, 5-chloro-2-methyl-*	$ClCH_2CH_2CH:C(CH_3)_2$	118.61	....		132–3[758]	0.9135_4^{20}	1.4419^{20}	i			s		chl s	B1[3], 810
p398	1-Pentene, decafluoro-*	Perfluoropentene. $F_3CCF_2CF_2CF:CF_2$	250.04	....		29–30[740]		1.2571^{25}	i					chl s	Am 73, 4054
p399	2-Pentene, 2,5-dichloro-*	$ClCH_2CH_2CH:CClCH_3$	139.04	....		40–1[8]	1.1182_{15}^{15}		i					chl s	B1[3], 783
p400	1-Pentene, 2,3-dimethyl-*	$CH_3CH_2CH(CH_3)C(CH_3):CH_2$	98.19	....	−134.8	84.26[760]	0.7051_4^{20}	1.4033^{20}	i	∞	∞	...	...	dil sulf v	B1[3], 832
Ω p401	—,2,4-dimethyl-*	$(CH_3)_2CHCH_2C(CH_3):CH_2$	98.19	....	−123.8	81.64[760]	0.6943_4^{20}	1.3986^{20}	i	∞	∞		s	chl s	B1[3], 833
p402	—,3,3-dimethyl-*	$CH_3CH_2C(CH_3)_2CH:CH_2$	98.19	....	−134.3	77.54[760]	0.6974_4^{20}	1.3984^{20}	i	∞	∞		s	chl s	B1[3], 834
Ω p403	—,4,4-dimethyl-*	Vinylneopentane. $(CH_3)_3CCH_2CH:CH_2$	98.19	....	−136.6	72.49[760]	0.6827_4^{20}	1.3918^{20}	i	∞	∞			os, chl s	B1[3], 832
p404	2-Pentene, 2,3-dimethyl-*	$CH_3CH_2C(CH_3):C(CH_3)_2$	98.19	....	−118.3	97.46[760]	0.7277^{20}	1.4208^{20}	i	s	s		s	chl s	B1[3], 832
Ω p405	—,2,4-dimethyl-*	$(CH_3)_2CHCH:C(CH_3)_2$	98.19	....	−127.7	83.44[760]	0.6954_4^{20}	1.4040^{20}	i	s	s		s	chl s	B1[3], 833
p406	—,3,3-dimethyl-*	$(CH_3)_3CC(CH_3):CHCH_3$	98.19	λ^{iso} <215	....	87[760]	0.7126_4^{20}	1.4070^{20}	i	s	s		s	chl s	B1[3], 833
p407	—,4,4-dimethyl-(trans)*	$(CH_3)_3CCH:CHCH_3$	98.19	....	−115.235	76.75[760]	0.6889_4^{20}	1.3982^{20}	i	s	s		s	chl s	B1[3], 831
p408	1-Pentene, 2-ethyl-*	$CH_3CH_2CH_2C(C_2H_5):CH_2$	98.19	....		94[760]	0.7079_4^{20}	1.405^{20}	i	s	s		s	chl s	B1[3], 830
p409	2-Pentene, 3-ethyl-*	$(C_2H_5)_2C:CHCH_3$	98.19	....		96.01[760]	0.7204_4^{20}	1.4148^{20}	i	s	s		s	chl s	B1[3], 832
Ω p410	1-Pentene, 2-methyl-*	$CH_3CH_2CH_2C(CH_3):CH_2$	84.16	λ^{gas} 184 (3.8), 189 (3.9), 194 sh (3.8)	−135.72	60.7[760]	0.6799_4^{20}	1.3920^{20}	i				s	chl, peth s	B1[3], 808
p411	—,3-methyl-*	$CH_3CH_2C(CH_3)CH:CH_2$	84.16	λ^{gas} 177 (4.2), 183 sh (4.0), 186 (3.7)	−153.0	51.14[760]	0.6675_4^{20}	1.3841^{20}	i				s	chl, peth s	B1[3], 812
p412	—,4-methyl-*	1-Isohexene. $(CH_3)_2CHCH_2CH:CH_2$	84.16	λ^{gas} 173 (3.9), 178 (4.0)	−153.63	53.88[760]	0.6642_4^{20}	1.3828^{20}	i				s	chl, peth s	B1[3], 811
Ω p413	2-Pentene, 2-methyl-*	$CH_3CH_2CH:C(CH_3)_2$	84.16	λ^{gas} 192 (4.0)	−135.07	67.29[760]	0.6863_4^{20}	1.4004^{20}	i	s	s		s	chl, peth s	B1[3], 809
p414	—,3-methyl-(cis)*	$CH_3CH_2C(CH_3):CHCH_3$	84.16	λ^{gas} 179 (4.0), 184 (4.0), 187 (3.9), 199 sh (3.6)	−138.445	70.45[760]	0.6986_4^{20}	1.4045^{20}	i	s	s		s	chl, peth s	B1[3], 813
Ω p415	—,—(trans)*	$CH_3CH_2C(CH_3):CHCH_3$	84.16	λ^{gas} 175 sh (4.0), 180 (4.1), 186 sh (4.0)	−134.84	67.63[760]	0.6942_4^{20}	1.4016^{20}	i	s	s		s	chl, peth s	B1[3], 813
Ω p416	—,4-methyl-(cis)*	2-Isohexene. $(CH_3)_2CHCH:CHCH_3$	84.16	λ^{gas} 177 (4.2), 197 sh (3.2), 204 (2.9)	−134.43	56.3[760]	0.6690_4^{20}	1.3880^{20}	i	s	s		s	chl, peth s	B1[3], 810
Ω p417	—,—(trans)*	$(CH_3)_2CHCH:CHCH_3$	84.16	λ^{gas} 180 (4.1), 186 sh (4.0)	−140.81	58.55[760]	0.6686_4^{20}	1.3889^{20}	i	s	s		s	chl, peth s	B1[3], 810
p418	1-Pentene, nonafluoro-2-trifluoromethyl-*	Perfluoro-2-methylpentene. $F_3C(CF_2)_2C(CF_3):CF_2$	300.05	....	....	60			i				s	....	J1955, 3005
Ω p419	—,2,4,4-trimethyl-*	"Diisobutylene." $(CH_3)_2CHC_2C(CH_3):CH_2$	112.22	λ^{al} 206 (2.91)	−93.48	101.44	0.7150_4^{20}	1.4086^{20}	i		s		s	lig, chl s	B1[3], 849
Ω p420	2-Pentene, 2,4,4-trimethyl-*	"Diisobutylene." $(CH_3)_3CCH:C(CH_3)_2$	112.22	λ^{al} 207 (3.40)	−106.33	104.91[760] 2.33[10]	0.7218_4^{20}	1.4160^{20}	i		s		s	lig v chl s	B1[3], 848
p421	2-Pentenedioic acid, diethyl ester(trans)*	Ethyl glutaconate. $C_2H_5O_2CCH_2CH:CHCO_2C_2H_5$	186.21	....		236–8 125[12]	1.0496_4^{20}	1.4411^{20}	...	s	s			....	B2[3], 1931
p422	—,3-methyl-, 5-ethyl 1-methyl ester*	Ethyl methyl 3-methylglutaconate. $C_2H_5O_2CCH_2C(CH_3):CHCO_2CH_3$	186.21	....		118[12]				s					B2, 778
Ω p423	4-Pentenoic acid*	Allylacetic acid. $CH_2:CHCH_2CH_2CO_2H$	100.13	....	−22.5	188.9 93[20]	0.9802_4^{20}	1.4281^{20}	δ	v	v			....	B2[3], 1297
p424	—,nitrile	Allylacetonitrile. Allylmethyl cyanide. $CH_2:CHCH_2CH_2CN$	81.12	....		140 60–1[40]	0.8239^{24}	1.4213^{14}	i	∞	∞			....	B2, 426
Ω p425	—,2-acetyl-, ethyl ester	Ethyl allylacetoacetate. $CH_2:CHCH_2CH(COCH_3)CO_2C_2H_5$	170.21	....		211–2δd 102[12]	0.9898_4^{20}	1.4388^{18}	i	∞	∞		∞	....	B3, 738
p426	—,2,2-diethyl-, amide	Novonal. $CH_2:CHCH_2C(C_2H_5)_2CONH_2$	155.24	wh pw, cr (eth-peth)	75–6	155[10]			δ	v	v			....	B2[3], 1951
Ω p428	2-Pentenoic acid, 4-hydroxy-, lactone*	β-Angelica lactone. Δ^1-Angelica lactone.	98.10	λ^{al} <214	< −17	208–9[751] 98[15]	1.0810_4^{20}	1.4454_{Hc}^{20}	∞	s	s		...	....	B17[2], 297

For explanations, symbols and abbreviations see beginning of table. For structural formulas see end of table.

No.	Name	Synonyms and Formula	Mol. wt.	Color, crystalline form, specific rotation and λ_{max} (log ε)	m.p. °C	b.p. °C	Density	n_D	w	al	eth	ace	bz	other solvents	Ref.
	3-Pentenoic acid														
p429	3-Pentenoic acid, 2-hydroxy-, nitrile (cis)	Angelactinonitrile. cis-Crotonaldehyde cyanohydrin. $CH_3CH:CHCH(OH)CN$	97.12	....	......	139^{70} 112^{12}	0.9675_{15}^{15}	1.4460^{21}	s	s	s	...	s	chl s CS_2, lig i	B3[2], 256
Ω p430	—,4-hydroxy-, lactone*	γ-Angelica lactone. Δ²-Angelica lactone.	98.10	nd λ^{peth} 217 (3.4)	18	167^{760} 53^{12}	1.084_4^{20}	1.4476^{20}	s^d	s	s	...	...	CS_2 s	B17[2], 297
p431	2-Pentenoic acid, 4-methyl-*	Isobutylideneacetic acid. α-Isohexenoic acid. $(CH_3)_2CHCH:CHCO_2H$	114.15	....	35	$217(211)$ $115-6^{20}$	0.9529_4^{21}	1.4489^{21}	...	v	v	v	...	os v	B2[2], 406
p432	1-Penten-3-ol*	Ethyl vinyl carbinol. $CH_2:CHCH(OH)CH_2CH_3$	86.14	....	......	$114-6^{760}$ 37^{20}	0.8395_4^{22}	1.4239^{20}	δ	∞	∞	...	...		B1[3], 1909
Ω p433	4-Penten-1-ol*	Allylethanol. $CH_2:CHCH_2CH_2CH_2OH$	86.14	....	......	$140-2$ (137)	0.8457_4^{20}	1.4309^{20}	δ	...	s	...	...		B1[3], 1910
Ω p434	4-Penten-2-ol*	Allyl methyl carbinol. $CH_2:CHCH_2CH(OH)CH_3$	86.14	....	......	$115-6^{750}$ $(139-42)$	0.8367_4^{20}	1.4225^{20}	v	∞	∞	...	...		B1[3], 1910
p435	3-Penten-2-ol, 2-methyl-*	Dimethyl propenyl carbinol. $CH_3CH:CH(OH)(CH_3)_2$	100.16	....	......	$121.6-2^{757}$ 37^{13}	0.8347_4^{20}	1.4302^{20}	s	∞	s	...	...		B1[3], 1932
Ω p436	4-Penten-2-ol, 2-methyl-*	Dimethyl allyl carbinol. $CH_2:CHCH_2C(OH)(CH_3)_2$	100.16	....	......	119.5	0.8300_4^{20}	1.4263^{20}	δ	s	s	...	...		B1[3], 1932
p437	3-Penten-2-one (trans)*	Ethylideneacetone. Methyl propenyl ketone. $CH_3CH:CHCOCH_3$	84.13	λ 220 (4.12), 310 (1.61)	......	122	0.8624_4^{20}	1.4350^{20}	s	s	s	s	...		B1[2], 791
p438	1-Penten-3-one, 5,5-dimethyl-1-phenyl-	Benzalpinacolone. 5-Methyl-1-phenyl-1-hexen-3-one*. $C_6H_5CH:CHCOCH_2CH(CH_3)_2$	188.27	cr	43	154^{25}	0.9509^{46}	1.5523^{25}	δ	...	...	s	...	chl s	B7[2], 308
Ω p439	—,1(4-methoxy-phenyl)-*	Ethyl 4-methoxystyryl ketone.	190.24	col-lt ye pl (eth-peth)	60	....			i	s	s	...	...	peth δ	B8[2], 159
p440	—,2-methyl-*	Ethyl isopropenyl ketone. $C_2H_5COC(CH_3):CH_2$	98.15	....	......	118.5	0.8530_4^{20}	1.4289^{20}	δ	s	s	...	...		B1[3], 2994
Ω p441	3-Penten-2-one,4-methyl-	Mesityl oxide. $(CH_3)_2C:CHCOCH_3$	98.15	λ 227.5 (3.87), 253 (3.88), 295 (3.59)	-52.85	129.76^{760} 41^{23}	0.8653_4^{20}	1.4440^{20}	s	∞	∞	v	...		B1[5], 2995
Ω p441¹	1-Penten-3-one,1-phenyl*	$C_6H_5CH:CHCOC_2H_5$	160.22	lf (lig)	38-9	142^{12}	0.8697_4^{20}	1.5684^{50}	δ	v	v	v	...		B7[2], 298
p442	1-Penten-3-yne*	Pyrylene. $CH_2:CHC:CCH_3$.	66.10	....	......	$59.2-60.1$	0.7401_4^{20}	1.4496^{20}	i	...	s	...	s		Am 55, 1622
p443	1-Penten-4-yne*	Allylacetylene. $CH_2:CHCH_2C:CH$	66.10	....	......	$42-3$	0.7773_{22}^{22}	1.3653^{22}	i	...	s	...	s		C47, 2682
p444	3-Penten-1-yne, 3-ethyl-*	$CH_3CH:C(C_2H_5)C:CH$	94.16	....	......	96.5 $41-3^{100}$	0.7886^{25}	1.4338^{25}		...	s	...	s		C34, 7844
p445	1-Penten-3-yne, 2-methyl-*	$CH_2:C(CH_3)C:CCH_3$	80.14	....	......	$81-2^{100}$		1.4002^{20}		...	s	...	s		C42, 1871
p446	3-Penten-1-yne, 3-methyl-*	$CH_3CH:C(CH_3)C:CH$	80.14	λ^{hx} 219 (3.95)	......	$66-7$ $(67-9)$	0.739^{20}	1.4332^{20}		...	s	...	s		C51, 4292
—	Pentobarbital	see **Barbituric acid, 5-ethyl-5(2-pentyl)-**													
p447	1-Pentyne*	n-Propyl acetylene. $CH_3CH_2CH_2C:CH$	68.13	....	-90.0 (-105.7)	40.18^{760}	0.6901_4^{20}	1.3852^{20}	i	v	∞	...	s	chl s	B1[3], 957
p448	2-Pentyne*	Ethyl-methyl acetylene. $CH_3CH_2C:CCH_3$	68.13	....	-101 (-109.3)	56.07^{760}	0.7107_4^{20}	1.4039^{20}	i	v	∞	...	s	chl s	B1[3], 958
p449	1-Pentyne, 3-chloro-3-ethyl-*	$(C_2H_5)_2CClC:CH$	130.62	....	......	$73-6^{100}$	0.9230_4^{19}	1.4437^{19}	i	...	s	...	s	chl s	B1[3], 1002
p450	—,3-chloro-3-methyl-*	$CH_3CH_2CCl(CH_3)C:CH$	116.59	....	......	$102.5-.7^{760}$ 55^{130}	0.9163_4^{20}	1.4330^{20}	i	...	s	...	s	chl s	B1[3], 990
p451	2-Pentyne, 4-chloro-4-methyl-*	Trimethylpropargyl chloride. $CH_3CCl(CH_3)C:CCH_3$	116.59	....	......	55^{70}		1.4143^{20}	...	...	...	v^h	s	chl s	C25, 1931
p452	1-Pentyne, 4,4-dimethyl-*	$(CH_3)_3CCH_2C:CH$	96.17	....	-75.68	76.08^{760}	0.7142_4^{20}	1.3983^{20}	i	...	s	...	s	chl s	C50, 776
p453	2-Pentyne, 4,4-dimethyl-*	$(CH_3)_3CC:CCH_3$	96.17	....	-82.37	$82.9-3.0^{760}$	0.7176_4^{20}	1.4071^{20}	i	...	s	...	s	chl s	C50, 776
p454	1-Pentyne, 3-ethyl-*	$(C_2H_5)_2CHC:CH$	96.17	....	......	$87-8.5$	0.7246^{25}	1.4043^{25}	i	...	s	...	s	chl s	B1[3], 1002
p455	—,3-ethyl-3-methyl-*	$(C_2H_5)_2C(CH_3)C:CH$	110.20	....	......	$101.5-2.5^{760}$	0.7422_4^{20}	1.4110^{20}	i	...	s	...	s	chl s	C51, 16284
p456	—,4-methyl-*	Isobutyl acetylene. $(CH_3)_2CHCH_2C:CH$	82.15	....	-105.1	$61.1-2$	0.7092_4^{15}	1.3936_4^{15}	i	...	s	...	s	chl s	B1[3], 987
p457	2-Pentyne, 4-methyl-*	Isopropyl methyl acetylene. $(CH_3)_2CHC:CCH_3$	82.15	....	-110.37	$72.0-.5$	0.7161_4^{19}	1.4078^{19}	i	...	s	...	s	chl s	B1[3], 987
p458	2-Pentynoic acid*	Ethylpropiolic acid. $CH_3CH_2C:CCO_2H$	98.10	cr (peth)	50	122^{10} $81-2^3$	0.978^{20}	1.4619^{20}	s	...	...	...	...	peth s^h	B2, 481
p459	4-Pentynoic acid*	Ethynylpropionic acid. $HC:CCH_2CH_2CO_2H$	98.10	....	57.7	102^{17}			v	v	v	...	...		B2[3], 1450
p460	1-Pentyn-3-ol, 3,4-dimethyl-*	Ethynyl methyl isopropyl carbinol. $(CH_3)_2CHC(OH)(CH_3)C:CH$	112.17	....	......	133^{735}	0.8691_4^{20}	1.4372^{20}	s	s	s	...	...		B1[3], 1996

For explanations, symbols and abbreviations see beginning of table. For structural formulas see end of table.

No.	Name	Synonyms and Formula	Mol. wt.	Color. crystalline form. specific rotation and λ_{max} (log ε)	m.p. °C	b.p. °C	Density	n_D	w	al	eth	ace	bz	other solvents	Ref.
	1-Pentyn-3-ol														
Ω p461	—,3-methyl-*	$CH_3CH_2C(OH)(CH_3)C:CH$	98.15	....	30–1	120–1 61^{70}	0.8688_4^{20}	1.4310^{20}	...						B1[3], 1990
—	Peonol	see Acetophenone, 2-hydroxy-4-methoxy-													
—	Peracetic acid	see Acetic acid, per-													
	Perbenzoic acid	see Benzoic acid, per-													
p462	Perchloric acid, ethyl ester*	Ethyl perchlorate*. $CH_3CH_2OClO_3$	128.51	oil	....	89	....		d	∞	∞				C30, 8057
p463	—,methyl ester*	Methyl perchlorate*. CH_3OClO_3	114.49	oil	....	ca. 52	....		d	∞	∞				C30, 8057
p464	—,trichloromethyl ester*	Trichloromethyl perchlorate* Cl_3COClO_3	217.82		−55	exp (40d)	....		d		∞			bz, al exp CCl_4 ∞	C24, 4506
p465	Pereirine	$C_{20}H_{26}N_2O.\frac{1}{2}H_2O$	323.44	pa ye amor pw, [α] +137.5 (al) λ^{al} 245 (3.93), 300 (3.47)	135d				i	v	v			chl v	C28, 5459
Ω p466	Perimidine	Peri-naphthimidazole	168.21	gr cr (dil al)	222	....			i	s	s	s	s	os, ac s	B23[1], 53
p467	Peroxide, acetyl benzoyl	$C_6H_5COOOCOCH_3$	180.17	wh nd (lig)	40–1	85–100 exp 130^{19}	....		d	d	s			chl, oils s	B9[2], 157
p468	—,diacetyl	Acetyl peroxide. $CH_3COOOCOCH_3$	118.09	nd (eth), lf	30 (26)	63^{21}	....		δ	s	s[h]			CCl_4 v NaOH d	B2[3], 380
Ω p469	—,dibenzoyl	Benzoyl peroxide	242.23	rh (eth), pr	106–8 (104)	exp		1.545	δ	s	s	s	s	CS_2 s MeOH δ	B9[2], 157
p470	—,—,3,3'-dinitro-	$C_{14}H_8N_2O_8$. See p469	332.24	nd (al)	139–40d	....					v	v	v	AcOEt s[h]	B9[2], 252
p471	—,—,4,4'-dinitro-	$C_{14}H_8N_2O_8$. See p469	332.24	ye cr (ace), nd (to)	156d	....					v	v	v	AcOEt, to s[h]	B9[2], 270
Ω p472	—,di(tert-butyl)	$(CH_3)_3COOC(CH_3)_3$	146.23		−40	111^{760} 70^{197}	0.794^{20}	1.3890^{20}	i			∞		os, lig s	Am 72, 337
Ω p473	—,didodecanoyl	Alperox c. Lauroyl peroxide. $CH_3(CH_2)_{10}COOOCO(CH_2)_{10}CH_3$	398.63	wh pl	49				i						C42, 1252
p474	—,diethyl	Ethyl peroxide. $C_2H_5OOC_2H_5$	90.12		−70	65^{760}	0.8240^{19}	1.3715^{17}	δ	∞	∞				B1[3], 1313
p475	—,dimethyl, hexafluoro-	Perfluorodimethyl peroxide. F_3COOCF_3	170.01		−32 (−37)				d					aq KOH i	C52, 6154
p476	—,di(1-naphthyl)	$C_{10}H_7COOOCOC_{10}H_7$	342.36	yesh pr (chl, ace, eth)	91d exp	....				s		s		chl s	E12B, 3989
p477	—,disuccinyl	$(HO_2CCH_2CH_2CO)_2O_2$	234.16	cr pw	127d	....			s	s	δ	s	i	chl i	B2, 613
Ω p478	Perseitol	α-Mannoheptitol, Perseite	212.20	nd, [α]^{20} +4.53 (w)	188 (cor)	....			s	s δ	δ s[h]	δ			B1[3], 2412
Ω p479	Perylene	peri-Dinaphthalene	252.32	gold-br ye pl (bz, to, aa) λ^{al} 251 (4.70), 368 (3.68), 387 (4.08), 406 (4.42), 434 (4.56)	277–9 (273–4)	sub 350– 400	1.35		i	δ	δ	v	s	chl, CS_2 v peth i	B5[2], 655
p480	3-Perylene-carboxylic acid	$C_{21}H_{12}O_2$. See p479.	296.33	og-br nd ($PhNO_2$)	330				i					sulf s (vt, red flr) os s (gr flr)	E14s, 743
—	Petn	see Pentaerythritol, tetranitrate													
p481	Peucedanin	....	258.28	pr or pl (bz peth), yesh cr (eth) λ^{MeOH} 255 (4.4), 298 (4.1), 340 (3.7)	109	$276–81^{17}$			δ	s[h]	s		δ	chl, CS_2 v aa s peth δ	B19[2], 228
Ω p482	α-Phellandrene(d)	5-Isopropyl-2-methyl-1,3-cyclohexadiene*. $\Delta^{1,5(0)}$-p-Menthadiene.	136.24	[α]$_D$ +49.1 (undil) $\lambda^{n-C_6H_{18}}$ 263 (3.52)	....	$175–6^{760}$ 61^{11}	0.8463^{25}	1.4777^{20}	i	i	s				B5, 129
p483	β-Phellandrene	3-Isopropyl-6-methylene-cyclohexene*. 2-p-Menthadiene.	136.24	[α]$_D^{20}$ +65.2 (undil)	....	$171–2^{760}$ 57^{11}	0.8520^{20}	1.4788^{20}	i	i	s				B5, 131
—	Phenacetin	see Acetic acid, amide, N(1-ethoxyphenyl)-													
—	Phenaceturic acid	see Glycine, N-acetyl-N-phenyl-													
—	Phenacyl alcohol	see Acetophenone, α-hydroxy-													
—	Phenacyl bromide	see Acetophenone, α-bromo-													
—	Phenacyl chloride	see Acetophenone, α-chloro-													

For explanations, symbols and abbreviations see beginning of table. For structural formulas see end of table.

No.	Name	Synonyms and Formula	Mol. wt.	Color, crystalline form, specific rotation and λ_{max} (log ε)	m.p. °C	b.p. °C	Density	n_D	w	al	eth	ace	bz	other solvents	Ref.
	Phenanthrene														
Ω p484	**Phenanthrene***		178.24	mcl pl (al), lf (sub) λ^{hp} 187.5 (4.48), 211.5 (4.57)	101	340 210–15[12]	0.9800[4]	1.59427	i	s	s	s	s	CS_2, chl, aa s Py s[h] MeOH δ, s[h]	B5, 667
p485	**—,2-acetyl-***	$C_{16}H_{12}O$. See p484........	220.27	nd (MeOH) λ^{al} 218 (4.26), 266 (4.77), 304 (3.98), 368 (3.98)	144–5	....			i	s	...	...	v	MeOH s[h]	E13, 878
p486	**—,3-acetyl-***	$C_{16}H_{12}O$. See p484........	220.27	nd (MeOH) λ^{al} 210 (4.11), 252 (4.61), 314 (4.07)	72				i	s	...	...	s	MeOH v, chl, aa s lig δ	E13, 879
p487	**—,9-acetyl-***	$C_{16}H_{12}O$. See p484........	220.27	bl flr nd (MeOH), lf (al)	74.5				i	s	v	...	s	MeOH s[h]	E13, 879
p488	**—,2-amino-***	2-Phenanthrylamine. $C_{14}H_{11}N$. See p484.	193.25	lt ye (lig)	85				i	i s[h]	i s[h]	...	...	lig s[h]	E13, 819
p489	**—,3-amino-***	3-Phenanthrylamine. $C_{14}H_{11}N$. See p484	193.25	α lf (lig), β cr (lig)	α 143 β 87.5 (st)				δ	s	...	...	...	HCl s lig s[h] xyl δ	E13, 820
p490	**—,9-amino- (a form)***	9-Phenanthrylamine. $C_{14}H_{11}N$. See p484	193.25	lt ye cr (al)	137–8	sub			i	v	v	...	v	chl v	E13, 819
p491	**—,—(b form)***	$C_{14}H_{11}N$. See p484..	193.25	lt ye nd (al)	104	sub			i	v	v	...	v	chl v	E13, 819
Ω p492	**—,9-bromo-***	$C_{14}H_9Br$. See p484	257.14	pr (al)	63.8–4.8	>360 190[1.2] sub	1.4093[10]		i	s	s	...	s	CS_2, aa s	B5[2], 583
p493	**—,9,10-diamino-*** ..	$C_{14}H_{12}N_2$. See p484...	208.27	pa ye lf	166	....									E13, 822
Ω p494	**—,9,10-dihydro-*** ..	$C_{14}H_{12}$. See p484	180.25	nd (MeOH) λ^{al} 267 (4.2), 297 sh (3.7)	34.5–5	168–9[15]	1.0757[20]	1.6415[20]	...	s	v	...	...	MeOH δ, s[h]	E13, 794
p495	**—,3,4-dihydroxy-*** .	3,4-Phenanthrenediol*. Morphol. $C_{14}H_{10}O_2$. See p484	210.24	col nd (peth), dk in air	143	sub 130 (vac)			i	s	s	...	s	alk s peth s[h]	E13, 846
p496	**—,3,4-di-methoxy-***	Dimethylmorphol. $C_{16}H_{14}O_2$. See p484.	238.29	bt ye lf (MeOH)	45	298–303[112]			i	v	v	...	...	MeOH s[h]	C34, 4072
p497	**—,4,5-dimethyl-*** .	$C_{16}H_{14}$. See p484	206.29	pr (MeOH)	76–7.2				δ					$PhNO_2$, chl s	E14, 309
p498	**—,9,10-dimethyl-*** .	$C_{16}H_{14}$. See p484	206.29	lt red pr (aa), nd (MeOH)	144	sub					δ	...	s	chl, aa s	E13, 803
p499	**—,9,10-diphenyl-*** .	$C_{26}H_{18}$. See p484	330.44	nd (eth, bz)	240 (235)	sub 270			i	δ	s	...	s	os s	E13, 810
p500	**—,1,2,3,4,5,6,7,8,9, 10,11,12-dodeca-hydro-***	$C_{14}H_{22}$. See p484	190.33	....		81–2[1.5]	0.9674[20]	1.5102[20]	i	...	...	s	s	os s	E13, 795
p501	**—,9-ethyl-***	$C_{16}H_{14}$. See p484	206.29	λ^{al} 252 (4.81), 274 (4.18), 296 (4.12), 350 (2.70)	62.5–3.0 (66)	199–200[11]	1.0603[78]	1.6582[78]	i	s	...	...	s	peth δ	E13, 799
p502	**—,1,2,3,4,11,12-hexahydro-***	$C_{14}H_{16}$. See p484	184.28	λ^{al} 247 (3.75)	(i) −3 (ii) −8	(i) 307 167[13] (ii) 290	1.045[20]	1.5810[15]	i	δ	s	...	s	os, aa, CS_2, chl, peth s	E13, 794
p503	**—,1-hydroxy-***	1-Phenanthrol*. $C_{14}H_{10}O$. See p484	194.24	nd (peth, bz-lig, eth) λ^{al} 245 (4.08), 308 (4.1), 335 (3.5)	157	....			i		s[h]	...	s[h]	sulf s (red)	E13, 829
Ω p504	**—,2-hydroxy-***	2-Phenanthrol*. $C_{14}H_{10}O$. See p484	194.24	pl, lf (al, eth, lig) λ^{al} 255 (4.82), 292 (4.15), 355 (3.00)	168				δ	s	s	...	s	lig δ	B6, 704
Ω p505	**—,3-hydroxy-***	3-Phenanthrol*. $C_{14}H_{10}O$. See p484	194.24	nd (al, lig) λ^{al} 248 (4.85), 305 (4.28), 355 (3.28)	122–3				i s[h]	v	s	...	s[h]	lig s[h]	B6, 705
Ω p506	**—,9-hydroxy-***	9-Phenanthrol*. $C_{14}H_{10}O$. See p484	194.24	nd (lig, bz) λ^{al} 248 (4.6), 305 (3.8), 355 (3.2)	158				δ	v	v	...	v	chl v lig s	E13, 831
Ω p506[1]	**—,7-isopropyl-1-methyl-***	Retene. $C_{18}H_{18}$. See p484 ...	234.34	pl (al) λ^{al} 259, 277, 301, 334, 351	100.5–1	390[760] 290[10]	1.035	....	i	s[h]	s[h]	...	s	CS_2, lig s aa s[h]	B5, 683
p507	**—,1-methyl-***	$C_{15}H_{12}$. See p484....	192.26	lf, pl (dil al)	123				i	s	...	...	...	os s	E13, 798
Ω p508	**—,3-methyl-***	$C_{15}H_{12}$. See p484....	192.26	pr or nd (al)	65	140–50[6]			i[h]	s[h]	...	s	...	os s	B5, 675
p509	**—,9-nitro-***	$C_{14}H_9NO_2$. See p484......	223.23	ye nd (al)	116–7	....			i	s	s	...	s	sulf s (red) MeOH s lig δ	E13, 817

For explanations, symbols and abbreviations see beginning of table. For structural formulas see end of table.

No.	Name	Synonyms and Formula	Mol. wt.	Color, crystalline form, specific rotation and λ_{max} (log ε)	m.p. °C	b.p. °C	Density	n_D	w	al	eth	ace	bz	other solvents	Ref.
	Phenanthrene														
Ω p510	—,1,2,3,4,5,6,7,8-octahydro-*	Octanthrene. $C_{14}H_{18}$. See p484	186.30	. . . .	16.7	295 169[15]	1.026_4^{20}	1.5569^{17}	i	. . .	. . .	s	s	CS_2, aa s	E13, 795
p511	—,1,2,3,4,9,10,11,12-octahydro-(cis)*	$C_{14}H_{18}$. See p484	186.30	. . . .		129[6] 88–90[0.1]	1.00072_4^{25}	1.5549^{21}	i	. . .	. . .	. . .	s		E13, 795
p512	—,—(trans)*	$C_{14}H_{18}$. See p484	186.30	nd	23–4	94–5[15]	1.0060_4^{20}	1.5528^{21}	i	. . .	. . .	. . .	s		E13, 795
Ω p513	—,tetra-decahydro-*	Perhydrophenanthrene. $C_{14}H_{24}$. See p484	192.35	. . . .	86–9[2]	86–9[2]	0.9447_4^{20}	1.5011^{20}	i	. . .	s	s	s	os s	E13, 796
p514	—,1,2,3,4-tetra-hydro-*	Tetranthrene. $C_{14}H_{14}$. See p484	182.27	lf (MeOH) λ^{al} 229 (4.87), 251 (3.82), 280 (3.77), 301 (3.95), 322 (2.87)	33–4	173[11]	1.0601_4^{20}	. . . .	i	s	s	s	s	chl, aa, lig s	E13, 794
p515	—,3,4,5-tri-hydroxy-*	3,4,5-Phenanthrenetriol*. $C_{14}H_{10}O_3$	226.24	lf or pl (w)	148	. . . .	. . . .	. . . .	i	v	s	. . .	. . .	chl s	E13, 862
p516	1-Phenanthrene-carboxylic acid*	1-Phenanthroic acid. $C_{15}H_{10}O_2$. See p484	222.25	nd (al) λ^{al} 232 (4.3), 251 (4.76), 275 (4.07), 300 (4.00)	232–3	. . . .	. . . .	. . . .		s	. . .	. . .	s		E13, 953
p517	2-Phenanthrene-carboxylic acid*	2-Phenanthroic acid. $C_{15}H_{10}O_2$. See p484	222.25	nd (aa) λ^{al} 251 sh (4.69), 255 (4.72)	258.5–60	. . . .	. . . .	. . . .		s	. . .	. . .	s	aa s	E13, 953
p518	—,nitrile	$C_{15}H_9N$. See p484	203.25	cr (bz-lig, al)	108–9.5	. . . .	. . . .	. . . .		v	s	s	. . .	os v	B9, 706
p519	3-Phenanthrene-carboxylic acid*	3-Phenanthroic acid. $C_{15}H_{10}O_2$. See p484	222.25	nd (al) λ^{al} 245 (4.07), 257 (4.11)	270	sub	. . . .	. . . .	i	s	s	. . .	s	aa s	E13, 954
p520	—,nitrile	$C_{15}H_9N$. See p484	203.27	nd (abs al)	102	. . . .	. . . .	. . . .		s^h	s	s	. . .	os v	B9, 706
p521	9-Phenanthrene-carboxylic acid*	9-Phenanthroic acid. $C_{15}H_{10}O_2$. See p484	222.25	nd (aa), lf (sub) λ^{al} 211 (4.66), 254 (4.88), 299 (4.24), 355 (3.61)	256.5–7	sub	. . . .	. . . .	i	s	s	. . .	s	aa s	E13, 955
Ω p522	—,nitrile	$C_{15}H_9N$. See p484	203.25	nd (al) λ^{al} 229 (4.65), 258 (4.73), 278 (4.08), 311 (4.16), 356 (3.00)	103	. . . .	. . . .	. . . .		s^h	s	s	. . .	os v	B9, 707
p523	2-Phenanthrene-sulfonic acid*	$C_{14}H_{10}O_3S$. See p484	258.30	cr (bz), cr (w + 1)	ca.150	. . . .	. . . .	. . . .	v	v	. . .	. . .	v^h	to, $PhNO_2$ s	E13, 995
p524	3-Phenanthrene-sulfonic acid*	$C_{14}H_{10}O_3S$. See p484	258.30	lf (bz), cr (w + 1 or w + 2)	88–9 (+2w) 120–1 (+1w) 175–6 (anh)	. . . .	. . . .	. . . .	s	. . .	. . .	. . .	s^h		E13, 995
p525	9-Phenanthrene-sulfonic acid*	$C_{14}H_{10}O_3S$. See p484	258.30	lf or nd (bz or w + 2)	134 (hyd) 174 (anh)	. . . .	. . . .	. . . .	s	s	. . .	. . .	δ s^h	aa s	E13, 996
Ω p526	Phenanthridine	9-Azaphenanthrene. 3,4-Benzoquinoline.	179.22	nd (dil al)	106–7	349[769]	. . . .	. . . .	δ	v	v	s	v	chl, CS_2 v	B20, 466
p527	—,6-hydroxy-	9-Phenanthridone. $C_{13}H_9NO$. See p526	195.22	nd (al, sub) λ^{al} 230 (4.7), 250 (4.1), 260 (4.3), 320 (4.0), 338 (3.9)	293–4	sub	. . . .	. . . .	i	δ s^h	δ	. . .	. . .	con sulf s $PhNO_2$ s^h aa δ	B21[2], 79
—	Phenanthrol*	see **Phenanthrene, hydroxy-***													
Ω p528	1,7-Phenan-throline	1,7-Diazaphenanthrene*. m-Phenanthroline.	180.22	pl (anh), nd (w + 2)	78–8.5 (anh) 65.5 (+2w)	>360	. . . .	. . . .	s^h	v	i	. . .	i δ^h	lig i	B23[1], 61
Ω p529	1,10-Phenan-throline	4,5-Diazaphenanthrene*. o-Phenanthroline.	180.22	wh nd (bz), cr (w + 1)	117 (anh)	>300	. . . .	. . . .	v^h	s	. . .	s	s	peth i	B23, 227
p530	4,7-Phenan-throline	1,8-Diazaphenanthrene*. p-Phenanthroline.	180.22	nd (w) $\lambda^{dil\ HCl}$ 221 (4.6), 275 (4.5), 304 (3.8), 336 (3.6)	177	sub 100	. . . .	. . . .	s^h	v	δ	. . .	δ	chl v lig s^h CS_2 δ	B23[1], 61
Ω p531	—,hydrate	$C_{12}H_8N_2 \cdot H_2O$. See p530 . . .	198.23	wh nd (w)	100–3 (94)	. . . .	. . . .	. . . .	δ s^h	δ	δ	. . .	. . .		B23[2], 235
p532	1,7-Phenan-throline, 9-nitro-	$C_{12}H_7N_3O_2$. See p528	225.21	nd (dil al)	168	. . . .	. . . .	. . . .	δ s^h	s^h	. . .	. . .	. . .	os s	B23[2], 236
Ω p533	9,10-Phenan-throquinone	9,10-Phenanthrenequinone*.	208.23	og nd (to), og-red pl (sub) λ^{al} 252 (4.5), 283 (3.0)	208.5–10	>360 sub	1.405_4^{20}	. . . .	i	δ	s	. . .	δ	aa s^h AcOEt δ	E13, 911

For explanations, symbols and abbreviations see beginning of table. For structural formulas see end of table.

No.	Name	Synonyms and Formula	Mol. wt.	Color, crystalline form, specific rotation and λ_{max} (log ε)	m.p. °C	b.p. °C	Density	n_D	w	al	eth	ace	bz	other solvents	Ref.
	9,10-Phenanthroquinone														
p534	—,—,2-bromo-*	$C_{14}H_7BrO_2$. See p533	287.12	red-ye cr (aa)	233–4					δ	δ	...	δ	sulf s (gr) aa s[h]	E13, 924
p535	—,—,3-bromo-*	$C_{14}H_7BrO_2$. See p533	287.12	ye nd (aa)	268–9				i	δ	δ	...	s	sulf s (dk br) aa δ, s[h] PhNO₂, chl s	E13, 925
p536	—,2-chloro-*	$C_{14}H_7ClO_2$. See p533	242.66	ye-red nd (aa)	252–3				i	s			...	sulf s (gr-br) aa s[h]	E13, 924
p537	—,3-chloro-*	$C_{14}H_7ClO_2$. See p533	242.66	og-ye nd (aa, bz-al)	264–5 (246)				i	s			s	aa s	E13, 925
p538	—,1,2-dihydroxy-*	$C_{14}H_8O_4$. See p533	240.23	dk red nd (ace)	d				δ	s		s	...	alk, aa, con sulf s	E13, 940
p539	—,2,5-dihydroxy-*	$C_{14}H_8O_4$. See p533	240.23	dk red nd (w)	400d				s[h]	s				alk, sulf s	E13, 941
p540	—,2,7-dihydroxy-*	$C_{14}H_8O_4$. See p533	240.23	dk red or br nd	>400d (293)					s	s	s	δ	NaOH, aa s	E13, 941
p541	—,4,5-dihydroxy-*	$C_{14}H_8O_4$. See p533	240.23	dk red (al), nd (w)	d >400				s[h]	s					B8², 508
p542	—,2,5-dinitro-*	$C_{14}H_6N_2O_6$. See p533	298.21	red ye pr (aa)	228				i					aa s	E13, 929
p543	—,2,7-dinitro-*	$C_{14}H_6N_2O_6$. See p533	298.21	gold ye nd (aa)	301–3				i	δ				aa δ, s[h]	E13, 929
p544	—,2-hydroxy-*	$C_{14}H_8O_3$. See p533	224.23	br-red or bk-vt nd (aa)	283 (cor)	sub				s				Ac₂O s al-KOH s (bl)	E13, 937
p545	—,3-hydroxy-*	$C_{14}H_8O_3$. See p533	224.23	ye-red or red nd (aa, MeOH, sub)	330d	sub				s	s			alk s (red) Ac₂O s	E13, 937
p546	—,7-isopropyl-1-methyl-*	Retenoquinone. $C_{18}H_{16}O_2$. See p533	264.33	og nd (chl-al)	197–9	sub				i	s	s	...	i	aa, chl i	B7, 819
p547	—,2-nitro-*	$C_{14}H_7NO_4$. See p533	253.22	ye lf or nd (aa)	260						i		δ		aa δ	E13, 927
p548	—,1,2,4-trihydroxy-*	$C_{14}H_8O_5 \cdot C_2H_5OH$. See p533	302.29	red (al + l)	d						v				alk, con sulf, Py s os δ	E13, 943
p549	—,2,3,4-trihydroxy-*	$C_{14}H_8O_5$. See p533	256.23	red br pw	185d					s	δ					E13, 943
—	**Phenanthryl-amine***	*see* **Phenanthrene, amino-***													
Ω p550	**Phenazine**	Azophenylene.	180.22	ye-red nd (aa) λ^{MeOH} 248 (5.10), 350 sh (4.03)	176–7	>360 sub			δ	s[h]	δ	...	s	sulf s (gr)	B23, 223
p551	—,9,10-dihydro-	Hydrazophenylene. $C_{12}H_{10}N_2$. See p550	182.23	rh lf	317 (sealed tube)				i	δ		i			B23, 209
p552	—,1,4-dihydroxy-, di(N-oxide)	$C_{12}H_8N_2O_4$. See p550	244.22	purp (chl)	236d				i					chl, dil alk, con sulf s	C50, 358
p553	—,1-hydroxy-	Hemipyocyanine. 1-Phenazinol. $C_{12}H_8N_2O$. See p550	196.22	ye nd (bz, dil MeOH), lf (dil MeOH) λ^{al} 240 (4.2), 265 (4.7), 370 (3.9)	158	sub			δ s[h]	δ			s[h]	os v dil alk, con ac, Py s	B23², 360
Ω p554	—,2-methyl-	$C_{13}H_{10}N_2$. See p550	194.24	lt ye nd or pr λ^{al} 251.5 (5.2), 364.5 (4.2)	117	350d			δ[h]	v	v	...		chl v lig δ	B23², 239
—	**Phenazinol**	*see* **Phenazine, hydroxy-**													
—	**Phenethyl alcohol**	*see* **Ethanol, 2-phenyl-***													
—	**Phenethyl amine**	*see* **Benzene, (1-amino-ethyl)-***													
—	**Phenethyl chloride**	*see* **Benzene, (chloro-ethyl)-***													
—	**Phenetidine**	*see* **Aniline, ethoxy-***													
—	**Phenetole**	*see* **Benzene, ethoxy-***													
—	**Phenetsal**	*see* **Benzoic acid, 2-hydroxy-, 4-acetamidophenyl ester**													
—	**Phenicin**	*see* **Biquinone, 3,3'-dihydroxy-5,5'-dimethyl-**													
—	**Phenobarbital**	*see* **Barbituric acid, 5-ethyl-5-phenyl-**													
—	**Phenocoll**	*see* **Glycine, amide, N'-ethoxyphenyl-**													
Ω p555	**Phenol***	Carbolic acid. Benzenol*. Hydroxybenzene*.	94.11	nd λ^{al} 218.5 (3.78), 266 sh (3.18), 271 (3.28), 276 sh (3.16)	43 (fr 41)	181.75[760] 70.86[10]	1.0722²⁰₂₀ 1.0576²⁰₄	1.5509²¹ 1.5418⁴¹	s ∞[h]	s	v	∞	∞[h]	CCl₄ ∞ chl, CS₂ s	B6², 116
Ω p556	—,2-amino-*	o-Hydroxyaniline. C_6H_7NO. See p555	109.13	wh rh bipym nd (bz) λ^w 229 (3.79), 281 (3.43)	174	sub 153[11]	1.328		s	v	s	...	δ		B13², 164

For explanations, symbols and abbreviations see beginning of table. For structural formulas see end of table.

No.	Name	Synonyms and Formula	Mol. wt.	Color, crystalline form, specific rotation and λ_{max} (log ε)	m.p. °C	b.p. °C	Density	n_D	w	al	eth	ace	bz	other solvents	Ref.
	Phenol														
Ω p557	—,3-amino-*	m-Hydroxyaniline. C$_6$H$_7$NO. See p555	109.13	pr (to) λ$^{0.1N HCl}$ 270 (326)	123	164^{11}	......	......	s^h	v	v	...	δ	alk s to s^h lig δ	B13^2, 209
p558	—,—,hydro-bromide*	C$_6$H$_7$NO. HBr. See p555	190.06	pr (w)	224										B13, 403
p559	—,—,hydro-chloride*	C$_6$H$_7$NO. HCl. See p555	145.60	pr (w)	229				s^h						B13, 403
p560	—,—,hydroiodide	C$_6$H$_7$NO. HI. See p555	237.05	pr (w)	209				s^h						B13, 403
Ω p561	—,4-amino-*	p-Hydroxyaniline. C$_6$H$_7$NO. See p555	109.13	wh pl (w) λ^w 229 (3.78), 294 (3.30)	186–7	sub par d 110$^{0.3}$	......	......	δ v^h	v	...	...	i	alk s chl i	B13^2, 220
p562	—,2-amino-3-chloro-*	C$_6$H$_6$ClNO. See p555	143.57	nd (aq NaHSO$_3$)	122				s						B13^2, 182
p563	—,2-amino-5-chloro-*	C$_6$H$_6$ClNO. See p555	143.57	nd (al), pr (dil al)	154–5				s^h	s	s		δ		B13^2, 184
p564	—,3-amino-2-chloro-*	C$_6$H$_6$ClNO. See p555	143.57		85–7				δ	s	s				B13, 420
p565	—,4-amino-2-chloro-*	C$_6$H$_6$ClNO. See p555	143.57	nd (al, eth, w)	153				δ	s	s			alk s	B13^2, 272
p566	—,4-amino-3-chloro-*	C$_6$H$_6$ClNO. See p555	143.57	nd (dil NaHSO$_3$)	160				δ	s	s				B13^2, 273
p567	—,2-amino-4-chloro-5-nitro-*	C$_6$H$_5$ClN$_2$O$_3$. See p555	188.57	ye nd λ^w 285 (3.29)	225d (dk at 200)				δ^h	v				alk s	B13^2, 196
p568	—,2-amino-4-chloro-6-nitro-*	C$_6$H$_5$ClN$_2$O$_3$. See p555	188.57	......	152				δ^h	v					B13^2, 196
p569	—,2-amino-6-chloro-4-nitro-*	C$_6$H$_5$ClN$_2$O$_3$. See p555	188.57	ye nd (w + l)	160				δ^h	v	v				B13^2, 195
p570	—,4-amino-2-chloro-6-nitro-*	C$_6$H$_5$ClN$_2$O$_3$. See p555	188.57		130				δ^h	v					B13, 524
p571	—,2-amino-3,5-dibromo-*	C$_6$H$_5$Br$_2$NO. See p555	266.93	nd (lig)	145 (142–3)				s					alk s lig s^h	B13^2, 187
p572	—,2-amino-4,6-dibromo-*	C$_6$H$_5$Br$_2$NO. See p555	266.93	ye nd (dil al)	99				δ	s	s			chl s	B13^2, 188
p573	—,4-amino-2,6-dibromo-*	C$_6$H$_5$Br$_2$NO. See p555	266.93	nd (al, bz) λ^w 315 (3.51)	192.5–3				i	s	δ		s^h		B13^2, 280
p574	—,2-amino-3,5-dichloro-*	C$_6$H$_5$Cl$_2$NO. See p555	178.02	nd (bz, w)	132–3				δ	s	s	s	s^h	oos, chl s peth i	B13^2, 185
p575	—,3-amino-4,6-dichloro-*	C$_6$H$_5$Cl$_2$NO. See p555	178.02	ye br pr (w)	135–6				i s^h	s	v	v		chl s	B13^1, 135
p576	—,4-amino-2,5-dichloro-*	C$_6$H$_5$Cl$_2$NO. See p555	178.02	cr (bz)	178–9				d^h	s	v		s^h	aa v alk s chl i	B13^2, 274
Ω p577	—,4-amino-2,6-dichloro-*	C$_6$H$_5$Cl$_2$NO. See p555	178.02	nd or lf (w, bz)	167	sub	......	......	i δ^h	v			δ s^h	aa δ	B13^2, 274
p578	—,4-amino-3,5-dichloro-*	C$_6$H$_5$Cl$_2$NO. See p555	178.02	nd (w, bz)	154				s	s	s			chl, CS$_2$, CCl$_4$, aa s	B13^2, 276
Ω p579	—,2-amino-4,6-dinitro-*	Picramic acid. C$_6$H$_5$N$_3$O$_5$. See p555	199.12	dk red nd (al), pr (chl)	169				s	s	δ		s	chl δ	B13^2, 196
p580	—,2-amino-3-nitro-*	C$_6$H$_6$N$_2$O$_3$. See p555	154.13	red nd (w)	216–7	sub			v^h						B13^1, 191
Ω p581	—,2-amino-4-nitro-*	C$_6$H$_6$N$_2$O$_3$. See p555	154.13	og pr (+w)	80–90 (+w) 145–7 (anh)				δ	v	s		s^h	MeOH, aa s	B13^2, 192
p582	—,2-amino-6-nitro-*	C$_6$H$_6$N$_2$O$_3$. See p555	154.13	red nd (dil al)	111–2				δ	s	v		v	chl, aa v	B13^1, 122
p583	—,3-amino-4-nitro-*	C$_6$H$_6$N$_2$O$_3$. See p555	154.13	og nd (w)	185–6				δ^h	s	v		v	chl v	B13^1, 136
Ω p584	—,4-amino-2-nitro-*	C$_6$H$_6$N$_2$O$_3$. See p555	154.13	dk red pl or nd (w, al)	131				s^h	s	s				B13^2, 839
p585	—,4-amino-3-nitro-*	C$_6$H$_6$N$_2$O$_3$. See p555	154.13	dk red pr (eth)	154				s	s	s			chl s	B13^1, 186
Ω p586	—,4(2-amino-propyl)-*	C$_9$H$_{13}$NO. See p555	151.21	cr (bz)	125–6				s	s	...	...	s^h	chl, AcOEt s	B13^1, 251
—	—,anilino-	see Amine, diphenyl, hydroxy-													
p587	—,2-benzylidene-amino-	C$_{13}$H$_{11}$NO. See p555	197.24	lf (al) λ^{al} 251 (4.1), 345 (3.8)	89				δ	v	...	v	con sulf s	B13^1, 112
p588	—,2-benzyloxy-	Pyrocatechol monobenzyl ether. C$_{13}$H$_{12}$O$_2$. See p555	200.24			173–4^{13}	1.154^{22}	1.5906^{18}		s	s			alk s	C53, 14106
p589	—,3-benzyloxy-	Resorcinol monobenzyl ether. C$_{13}$H$_{12}$O$_2$. See p555	200.24	cr (CCl$_4$)	69.2	200^3				s				5 % KOH s CCl$_4$ s^h	Am 53, 3997
Ω p590	—,4-benzyloxy-	Hydroquinone monobenzyl ether. C$_{13}$H$_{12}$O$_2$. See p555	200.24	pl (w)	122–2.5				δ v^h	v	v		v		B6, 845
p591	—,4[bis(2-hydroxyethyl)amino]-*	N-p-Phenoldiethanolamine. C$_{10}$H$_{15}$NO$_3$. See p555	197.24	cr (w or dil Na$_2$CO$_3$)	140				s					ac, alk s	B13^2, 233

For explanations, symbols and abbreviations see beginning of table. For structural formulas see end of table.

No.	Name	Synonyms and Formula	Mol. wt.	Color, crystalline form, specific rotation and λ_{max} (log ε)	m.p. °C	b.p. °C	Density	n_D	w	al	eth	ace	bz	other solvents	Ref.
	Phenol														
Ω p592	—,2-bromo-*	C_6H_5BrO. See p555	173.02	λ^{al} 214 sh (3.93), 275.5 (3.44), 281 sh (3.87)	5.6	194–5[760] 87.3[13]	1.4924[20/4]	1.5892[20]	δ	s	s	....	....	alk s	B6[3], 735
Ω p593	—,3-bromo-*	C_6H_5BrO. See p555	173.02	lf λ^{cy} 210 (3.88), 272 (3.36), 279 (3.35)	33	236.5[760] 135–40[12]	....	....	δ	v	v	....	....	chl, alk s	B6[3], 738
Ω p594	—,4-bromo-*	C_6H_5BrO. See p555	173.02	tetr λ^{cy} 224 (4.0), 279.5 (3.22), 287 (3.18)	66.4	238 118.2[11]	1.840[15]	....	s	v	v	....	....	chl s	B6[3], 739
p595	—,3-bromo-5-chloro-*	C_6H_4BrClO. See p555	207.46	nd (peth)	70	256–60[756]	....	....		s		....	....	10 % alk, aa s	B6[2], 187
Ω p596	—,4-bromo-2-chloro-*	C_6H_4BrClO. See p555	207.46	nd (lig, bz, aa)	50–1	233–4[760] 127–30[12]	1.6170[20/4]	1.5859[20]	...	v	v	v	v	to v lig δ[h]	B6[3], 750
p597	—,3-bromo-2,4-dinitro-*	$C_6H_3BrN_2O_5$. See p555	263.02	pa ye nd (w)	175	....	....	....	v		s	....	....		B6[2], 249
p598	—,3-bromo-2,6-dinitro-*	$C_6H_3BrN_2O_5$. See p555	263.02	nd (peth)	131	....	....	....	δ	s	s	....	v	lig δ, v[h]	B6[2], 250
p599	—,4-bromo-2,6-dinitro-*	$C_6H_3BrN_2O_5$. See p555	263.02	pa ye nd (w), nd (al), pr (aa)	78	sub	....	....	δ s[h]	s	v	....	v	chl v aa s[h] lig δ	B6[3], 872
p600	—,5-bromo-2,4-dinitro-*	$C_6H_3BrN_2O_5$. See p555	263.02	pr (al, eth)	92	....	....	....	s	v	v	....	....	con HNO_3 s	B6[3], 871
p601	—,6-bromo-2,4-dinitro-*	$C_6H_3BrN_2O_5$. See p555	263.02	pa ye cr (al), pr (eth), col nd (w, al)	118–9	sub	....	....	δ[h]	s[h]	v	....	....	lig s	B6[3], 871
p602	—,2-bromo-3-nitro-*	$C_6H_4BrNO_3$. See p555	218.01	pa ye nd (HCl)	147–8	sub	....	....	i δ[h]	v		....	....	CS_2, lig δ	B6, 244
p603	—,2-bromo-4-nitro-*	$C_6H_4BrNO_3$. See p555	218.01	cr (to, w), nd (chl, eth, dil al)	114	....	....	....	δ[h]	v	v	....	....	CCl_4, chl s	B6[3], 845
Ω p604	—,2-bromo-5-nitro-*	$C_6H_4BrNO_3$. See p555	218.01	pa ye nd (w), cr (peth)	129–30 (124)	....	....	....	δ	v	v	s	s	os s lig δ	B6[2], 234
p605	—,2-bromo-6-nitro-*	$C_6H_4BrNO_3$. See p555	218.01	pa ye nd (chl, al)	68	....	....	....	s[h]	v		....	....	aa s	B6[3], 844
p606	—,3-bromo-2-nitro-*	$C_6H_4BrNO_3$. See p555	218.01	ye nd (peth), col nd (+w)	65–7 (anh) 35 (hyd)	....	....	....	s	v		....	....	alk s lig δ, v[h]	B6[3], 842
p607	—,3-bromo-4-nitro-*	$C_6H_4BrNO_3$. See p555	218.01	pa ye nd (bz, peth)	129–30	....	....	....			v	v	s	lig s[h] v[h]	B6[2], 234
p608	—,3-bromo-5-nitro-*	$C_6H_4BrNO_3$. See p555	218.01	cr (w)	145	....	....	....	δ s[h]	v	s	....	δ		B6[2], 233
p609	—,4-bromo-2-nitro-*	$C_6H_4BrNO_3$. See p555	218.01	ye nd or lf (al), pr (eth)	92	sub	....	....	i	s	v	....	v	chl v lig δ	B6[3], 842
p610	—,4-bromo-3-nitro-*	$C_6H_4BrNO_3$. See p555	218.01	ye nd (w)	147	....	....	....	i δ[h]		s	....	s		B6[3], 845
p611	—,5-bromo-2-nitro-*	$C_6H_4BrNO_3$. See p555	218.01	ye pr or nd (lig)	44	....	....	....	s[h]	v	v	....	....	lig s	B6[3], 844
p612	—,2-butoxy-*	Pyrocatechol monobutyl ether. $C_{10}H_{14}O_2$. See p555	166.22	....	....	231–4 159[69]	1.026[25]	1.5113[25]							B6, 772
—	—,butyl-*	see Benzene, butyl-(hydroxy)-*													
Ω p613	—,2-chloro-*	C_6H_5ClO. See p555	128.56	λ^{al} 216 (3.81), 274.5 (3.37), 280 sh (3.30)	9.0	174.9[760] 56.4[10]	1.2634[20/4]	1.5524[20]	δ	s	s	....	v	....	B6[3], 671
Ω p614	—,3-chloro-*	C_6H_5ClO. See p555	128.56	nd λ^{cy} 216 (3.81), 272 (3.31), 279 (3.30)	33 (35–6)	214[760]	1.268[25]	1.5565[40]	δ s[h]	s	s	....	v	....	B6[3], 681
Ω p615	—,4-chloro-*	C_6H_5ClO. See p555	128.56	nd λ^{cy} 224 (3.94), 279 (3.27), 287 (3.23)	43.2–3.7	219.75 (217) 125[18]	1.2651[40]	1.5579[40]	i	v	eth	....	v	alk s	B6[3], 684
p616	—,4-chloro-2,3-dinitro-*	$C_6H_3ClN_2O_5$. See p555	218.55	pr	127	....	....	....	δ[h]	s	v	....	v	chl s	B6[2], 248
p617	—,5-chloro-2,4-dinitro-*	$C_6H_3ClN_2O_5$. See p555	218.55	nd (al, peth)	92	....	1.74[22]	....	δ	s v[h]	s	....	....	chl s peth s[h]	B6[2], 247
Ω p618	—,2-chloro-4-nitro-*	$C_6H_4ClNO_3$. See p555	173.55	wh nd (w, 50 % al) $\lambda^{0.1N HCl}$ 240 (4.11), 317 (3.93)	111	....	....	....	s[h]	s	s	....	δ	chl s	B6[3], 839
p619	—,2-chloro-5-nitro-*	$C_6H_4ClNO_3$. See p555	173.55	ye nd or pr (w), rosettes (bz)	121–2	....	....	....	s[h]			....	s[h]		B6[3], 838
Ω p620	—,4-chloro-2-nitro-*	$C_6H_4ClNO_3$. See p555	173.55	ye mcl pr (al)	88–9 (87)	....	....	....	i	s v[h]	s	....	v	chl s	B6[3], 834
Ω p621	—,5-chloro-2-nitro-*	$C_6H_4ClNO_3$. See p555	173.55	ye pr or nd (w)	41	sub	....	....	δ	s	s	....	....	aa s	B6[3], 836
p622	—,2,4-diamino-*	$C_6H_8N_2O$. See p555	124.14	lf	78–80d	....	....	....		s	δ	s	....	ac, alk s chl, lig δ	B13[2], 308

For explanations, symbols and abbreviations see beginning of table. For structural formulas see end of table.

No.	Name	Synonyms and Formula	Mol. wt.	Color, crystalline form, specific rotation and λ_{max} (log ε)	m.p. °C	b.p. °C	Density	n_D	w	al	eth	ace	bz	other solvents	Ref.
	Phenol														
Ω p623	—,—,-dihydro-chloride*	Amidol. $C_6H_8N_2O \cdot 2HCl$. See p555.	197.07	nd $\lambda^{w \cdot pH=3}$ 235 sh (3.6), 280 (3.3)	230–40d				v	δ	δ	...	...		B13[2], 308
p624	—,2,5-diamino-*	$C_6H_8N_2O$. See p555	124.15	nd	68				v						B13[2], 312
p625	—,3,4-diamino-*	$C_6H_8N_2O$. See p555	124.15	nd	170–2				v						B13[1], 210
p626	—,3,5-diamino-*	$C_6H_8N_2O$. See p555	124.15	nd or pr (chl)	168–70 (180)				v		δ		...	chl s[h]	B13, 567
Ω p627	—,2,4-dibromo-*	$C_6H_4Br_2O$. See p555	251.92	nd (peth)	40	238–9 177[17]			δ s[h]	v	v		v	CS_2 v	B6[2], 188
p628	—,2,6-dibromo-*	$C_6H_4Br_2O$. See p555	251.92	nd (w) $\lambda^{0.1N\,NaOH}$ 367.5 (3.57)	56–7	162[21] sub			s[h]	v	v		s		B6[2], 189
Ω p629	—,2,6-dibromo-4-nitro-*	$C_6H_3Br_2NO_3$. See p555	296.92	pa ye pr or lf (al)	145 6	d >144			i	v[h]	v[h]	...	δ	CS_2 v[h] aa δ lig i	B6[2], 234
Ω p630	—,2,3-dichloro-*	$C_6H_4Cl_2O$. See p555	163.00	cr (lig, bz) $\lambda^{0.1N\,HCl}$ 277 (3.52), 280 (3.30), 283 (3.29)	57–9					s	s		s[h]	lig s[h]	B6[3], 699
Ω p631	—,2,4-dichloro-*	$C_6H_4Cl_2O$. See p555	163.00	hex nd (bz) $\lambda^{0.1N\,NaOH}$ 304 (3.50)	45	210[760] 145–7[110]			δ	s	s		s	chl s	B6[3], 699
Ω p632	—,2,5-dichloro-*	$C_6H_4Cl_2O$. See p555	163.00	pr (bz, peth) $\lambda^{0.1N\,HCl}$ 280 (3.41)	59	211[744]			δ	v	v		s	peth s[h]	B6[3], 712
Ω p633	—,2,6-dichloro-*	$C_6H_4Cl_2O$. See p555	163.00	nd (peth) $\lambda^{0.1N\,NaOH}$ 238 (3.85), 301 (3.71)	68–9	219–20[740] 80–5[4]			δ	v	v		s	peth s[h]	B6[3], 713
Ω p634	—,3,4-dichloro-*	$C_6H_4Cl_2O$. See p555	163.00	nd (bz-peth) $\lambda^{0.1N\,NaOH}$ 244 (4.12), 302 (3.51)	68	253.5[767]			δ	v	v	...	s	peth s[h]	B6[3], 715
Ω p635	—,3,5-dichloro-*	$C_6H_4Cl_2O$. See p555	163.00	pr (peth) λ^{al} 220 (3.86), 278 (3.23)	68	233[757] 122–4[8]			δ	v	v		s	peth s[h]	B6[3], 715
Ω p637	—,2,6-dichloro-4-nitro-*	$C_6H_3Cl_2NO_3$. See p555	208.00	br nd (w) λ^{hp} 285 (3.81)	127d (exp <100)		1.822		δ s[h]	s[h]	s		δ	chl s	B6[3], 841
Ω p638	—,3(diethyl-amino)-*	$C_{10}H_{15}NO$. See p555	165.24	rh bipym (CS_2-lig)	78	276–80 170[15]			s	s	s		s	CS_2 s lig δ	B13[2], 212
p639	—,2,4-diiodo-*	$C_6H_4I_2O$. See p555	345.91	nd (w)	72–3	sub 100			δ	v	v		δ	chl δ	B6[3], 786
p640	—,2,3-dimeth-oxy-*	Pyrogallol 1,2-dimethyl ether. $C_8H_{10}O_3$. See p555	154.17			233–4[760] 124–5[17]		1.5392[20]	δ	s	v			aq alk s	B6, 1081
p641	—,2,6-dimeth-oxy-*	Pyrogallol 1,3-dimethyl ether. $C_8H_{10}O_3$. See p555	154.17	mcl pr (w) λ^{MeOH} 267.5 (3.04)	56–7	262–7			δ	s	v			aq alk s	B6[2], 1065
Ω p642	—,3,5-dimeth-oxy-*	Phloroglucinol dimethyl ether. $C_8H_{10}O_3$. See p555	154.17	cr (bz-lig)	36–8	198–200[15] 172–5[17]			δ	s	s		s	lig δ	B6[2], 1078
—	—,dimethyl-*	see **Benzene, dimethyl-(hydroxy)-***													
Ω p643	—,3(dimethyl-amino)-*	$C_8H_{11}NO$. See p555	137.18	nd (lig) λ^{cy} 252 (4.11), 294 (3.50)	87	265–8[760] 152–3[15]		1.5895[26]	i δ[h]	s	s	s	s	CS_2 s lig s[h]	B13[2], 211
p644	—,2,3-dinitro-*	$C_6H_4N_2O_5$. See p555	184.11	ye nd (w)	144–5		1.681[20]		δ s[h]	v[h]	v		s	...	B6[3], 854
Ω p645	—,2,4-dinitro-*	$C_6H_4N_2O_5$. See p555	184.11	pa ye pl or lf (w) λ^{AcOEt} 260 (3.91), 280 (3.76)	115–6 (113)	sub	1.683[24]		δ s[h]	s	s		s	chl, to, MeOH s Py s, v[h]	B6[3], 854
Ω p646	—,2,5-dinitro-*	$C_6H_4N_2O_5$. See p555	184.11	ye mcl pr or nd (dil al, w, lig) λ^{Py} 360 (3.5), 465 (2.5)	108				δ v[h]	δ v[h]	v		s v[h]	MeOH δ	B6[3], 866
Ω p647	—,2,6-dinitro-*	$C_6H_4N_2O_5$. See p555	184.11	pa ye rh nd or lf (dil al)	63–4				i δ[h]	v[h]	v	v	s[h] v[h]	chl, Py s CS_2, CCl_4 δ	B6[3], 867
p648	—,3,4-dinitro-*	$C_6H_4N_2O_5$. See p555	184.11	ye nd (w)	134		1.672		δ s[h]	s	s		s	...	B6[3], 868
p649	—,3,5-dinitro-*	$C_6H_4N_2O_5$. See p555	184.11	lf (w)	126.1		1.702		δ s[h]	s	s		s	chl s lig δ	B6[3], 869
Ω p650	—,2-ethoxy-*	Guaethol. Pyrocatechol monoethyl ether. $C_8H_{10}O_2$. See p555	138.17		29	217 68[4]			δ	∞	∞				B6, 771
Ω p651	—,3-ethoxy-*	m-Hydroxyphenetole. Resorcinol monoethyl ether. $C_8H_{10}O_2$. See p555	138.17	ye		246–7 117[5.5]	1.0705[4]		i	s	s		s		B6, 814
Ω p652	—,4-ethoxy-*	p-Hydroxyphenetole. Hydroquinone monoethyl ether. $C_8H_{10}O_2$. See p555	138.17	pr or lf (w)	66–7	246–7			δ s[h]	v	v				B6, 843

For explanations, symbols and abbreviations see beginning of table. For structural formulas see end of table.

No.	Name	Synonyms and Formula	Mol. wt.	Color, crystalline form, specific rotation and λ_{max} (log ε)	m.p. °C	b.p. °C	Density	n_D	w	al	eth	ace	bz	other solvents	Ref.
	Phenol														
—	—,ethyl-*	see **Benzene, ethyl-(hydroxy)-**													
p653	—,2(ethyl-amino)-*	$C_8H_{11}NO$. See p555	137.18	pl (bz)	113–4				i	v	δ	...	s[h]	chl δ	B13, 364
p654	—,3(ethyl-amino)-*	$C_8H_{11}NO$. See p555	137.18	cr (bz-peth)	62	176[12] 143[5]			s[h]	s	s		s	chl v peth δ	B13, 408
p655	—,4(ethyl-amino)-*	$C_8H_{11}NO$. See p555	137.18	nd (w)	110–2 (104)				s[h]	s	s				B13, 443
p655[1]	—,4(heptyloxy)-*	Hydroquinone monoheptyl ether. $C_{13}H_{20}O_2$. See p555	208.30	cr (lig)	60				δ					lig s[h]	Am 54, 298
p655[2]	—,4(hexyloxy)-*	Hydroquinone monohexyl ether. $C_{12}H_{18}O_2$. See p555	194.28	cr (lig)	48				δ					lig s[h]	Am 54, 298
p656	—,2-iodo-*	C_6H_5IO. See p555	220.01	nd λ^{cy} 218 (3.97), 229 (3.81), 274 (3.48), 281.5 (3.45)	43	186–7[160] 91–2[2]	1.8757[80]		s[h]	v	v		...	CS_2 v	B6[3], 768
p657	—,3-iodo-*	C_6H_5IO. See p555	220.01	nd (lig) λ^w 277 (3.26), λ^{alk} 297 (3.45)	118	d			δ	s	s				B6[3], 771
Ω p658	—,4-iodo-*	C_6H_5IO. See p555	220.01	nd (w or sub) λ^{cy} 230.5 (4.18), 273.5 (3.11), 279.5 (3.16), 288 (3.04)	93–4	138–40[5]d	1.8573[112]		δ	v	v		...		B6[3], 774
p659	—,2-mercapto-*	Monothiopyrocatechol. C_6H_6OS. See p555	126.18	oil	5–6	216–7[751] 88–90[8]	1.2373[0]		δ	s	s		...	alk s	B6, 793
p660	—,3-mercapto-*	Monothioresorcinol. C_6H_6OS. See p555	126.18	cr	16–7	168[35]			δ	s	s		...	os v alk, con sulf s	B6[2], 827
p661	—,4-mercapto-*	Monothiohydroquinone. C_6H_6OS. See p555	126.18	cr λ^{al} 255 (4.04)	29–30	166–8[45] 133–7[11]	1.1285[25]	1.5101[25]	s	s	s			alk, con sulf s	B6[1], 419
Ω p662	—,2-methoxy-*	Pyrocatechol monomethyl ether. Guaiacol. $C_7H_8O_2$. See p555	124.15	hex pr λ^{al} 274 (3.41)	32 (fr 28.65)	205.05[760] 106.5[24]	1.1287[21]	1.5429[20]	δ	s	s			os v chl s	B6[2], 776
p663	—,—,acetate	$C_9H_{10}O_3$. See p555	166.18			123–4[13] (107[22])	1.1285[25]	1.5101[25]	i	∞	∞				B6[2], 783
Ω p664	—,3-methoxy-*	m-Hydroxyanisole. Resorcinol monomethyl ether. $C_7H_8O_2$. See p555	124.15	λ^{cy} 220 (3.73), 271.5 (3.22), 278 (3.19)	< −17.5	244.3[760] 144[25]		1.5520[20]	δ	∞	∞		s		B6, 813
Ω p665	—,4-methoxy-*	Hydroquinone monomethyl ether. 4-Hydroxyanisole. $C_7H_8O_2$. See p555	124.15	pl (w) λ^{cy} 224 (3.85), 288 (3.50), 298 (3.37)	57 (66)	243[760]			s	v	v		s		B6, 843
p666	—,2-methoxy-3-nitro-*	6-Nitroguaiacol. $C_7H_7NO_4$. See p555	169.14	yesh rh pr (CS₂, peth)	102–3				δ	v				peth s[h] CS_2 δ, s[h]	B6[2], 789
p667	—,2-methoxy-4-nitro-*	5-Nitroguaiacol. $C_7H_7NO_4$. See p555	169.14	ye nd (w)	103–4				s[h]	v	v				B6[2], 790
p668	—,2-methoxy-5-nitro-*	4-Nitroguaiacol. $C_7H_7NO_4$. See p555	169.14	pa ye nd (w)	105				s[h]	s	s				B6[2], 790
p669	—,2-methoxy-6-nitro-*	3-Nitroguaiacol. $C_7H_7NO_4$. See p555	169.14	og-ye nd (sub)	62	sub			s	s	s			peth δ	B6[2], 789
p670	—,3-methoxy-4-nitro-*	$C_7H_7NO_4$. See p555	169.14	ye nd (al) λ^{al} 329.5 (3.98)	144					s[h]			s[h]		B6[2], 822
p671	—,3-methoxy-5-nitro-*	$C_7H_7NO_4$. See p555	169.14	ye cr (al)	144						s				B6, 825
p672	—,4-methoxy-2-nitro-*	$C_7H_7NO_4$. See p555	169.14	og ye nd or mcl cr (al, lig)	80 (83)					s[h]				lig s[h]	B6[2], 849
p673	—,4-methoxy-3-nitro-*	$C_7H_7NO_4$. See p555	169.14	pa ye nd (w), cr (bz)	98–100				δ v[h]	s[h]			δ v[h]		B6[2], 848
p674	—,5-methoxy-2-nitro-*	$C_7H_7NO_4$. See p555	169.14	yesh nd (al)	95					s[h]					B6[2], 822
—	—,methyl-*	see **Toluene, hydroxy-**													
p675	—,2(methyl-amino)-*	C_7H_9NO. See p555	123.16	pl (bz-peth)	96–7				i	s			s	peth δ	B13, 362
Ω p676	—,4(methyl-amino)-, sulfate*	Metol. Photol. Pictol. 2(C_7H_9NO). H_2SO_4. See p555	344.39	wh nd (w)	250–60d				v						B13, 441
p677	—,4(methyl-amino)-2-nitro-*	$C_7H_8N_2O_3$. See p555	168.15	dk red-br nd (al)	113–4					s[h]				alk s (red)	B13[1], 186
p678	—,4(2-methyl-aminopropyl)-*	$C_{10}H_{15}NO$. See p555	165.24	cr (MeOH)	164				δ	s	s		...	dil ac v MeOH s[h]	C43, 1741
Ω p679	—,2-nitro-*	$C_6H_5NO_3$. See p555	139.11	ye nd or pr (eth, al) λ^w 230 (3.57), 276 (3.80), 346 (3.48)	45.3–5.7	216[760] 96.4–.8[10]	1.485[14] 1.2942[40]	1.5723[50]	δ s[h]	v[h]	v	v	v	chl, Py v alk, to, CS_2 s	B6[3], 794

For explanations, symbols and abbreviations see beginning of table. For structural formulas see end of table.

No.	Name	Synonyms and Formula	Mol. wt.	Color, crystalline form, specific rotation and λ_{max} (log ε)	m.p. °C	b.p. °C	Density	n_D	w	al	eth	ace	bz	other solvents	Ref.
	Phenol														
Ω p680	—,3-nitro-*	$C_6H_5NO_3$. See p555	139.11	ye mcl (aq HCl, eth) λ^w 228 (3.88), 272 (3.77), 328 (3.29)	97	194[70]	1.2797[100]₄		δ v[h]	v	v	v	v[h]	dil ac, alk s chl s[h]	B6³, 805
Ω p681	—,4-nitro-*	$C_6H_5NO_3$. See p555	139.11	ye mcl pr (to) λ^{MeOH} 310 (4.00)	114.9–5.6	279d sub	1.479[20]		δ v[h]	v	v	v	δ s[h]	chl, to, Py s chl, CS_2 δ	B6³, 811
Ω p682	—,4-nitroso-*	1,4-Benzoquinone monoxime. $C_6H_5NO_2$. See p555	123.11	pa ye rh nd (ace, bz) λ^{MeOH} 303 (4.09)	d144 (br at 124)				δ s[h]	s	s	s	s[h]	dil alk s	B6², 205 B7², 574
p682¹	—,4-octyloxy-*	Hydroquinone monooctyl ether. $C_{14}H_{22}O_2$. See p555	222.33	cr (lig)	60–1					s				lig s[h]	Am 54, 298
Ω p683	—,pentabromo-*	C_6HBr_5O. See p555	488.62	mcl pr (aa), nd (al, CS_2)	229.5	sub			i	s[h]	δ		s[h]	CS_2, aa s[h]	B6³, 766
Ω p684	—,pentachloro-*	C_6HCl_5O. See p555	266.34	mcl pr (al + 1w), nd (bz) λ^{al} 300.5 (3.4), 308 (3.4)	174 (+1w), 191 (anh)	309–10[754] d	1.978[22]₄		δ	v	v		s[h]	lig δ	B6³, 731
p685	—,2-propoxy-*	Pyrocatechol monopropyl ether. $C_9H_{12}O_2$. See p555	152.20			228–9[760] 80–3[4]	1.0523[25]	1.5176[25]		s				lig s[h]	Am 54, 1204
p686	—,3-propoxy-*	Resorcinol monopropyl ether. $C_9H_{12}O_2$. See p555	152.20	cr (w, al)	55	256–7 120[5]			s[h]	s[h]				lig s[h]	Am 53, 3397
p687	—,4-propoxy-*	Hydroquinone monopropyl ether. $C_9H_{12}O_2$. See p555	152.20	cr (w, lig, al)	56–7				s[h]	s[h]				lig s[h]	Am 54, 298
—	—,propyl-*	see **Benzene, hydroxy-(propyl)-***													
p688	—,seleno-*	Selenylbenzene. C_6H_5SeH	157.08	λ^{al} 241 (3.94), 270 sh (3.35), 320–350 (3.67)		183.6[760]	1.4865[15]		i	s	v			CCl_4 v	B6³, 766
p689	—,2,3,4,6-tetra-bromo-*	$C_6H_2Br_4O$ See p555	409.72	nd (al, aa)	113–4 (120)	sub				v			s	alk s aa s[h]	B6³, 766
p690	—,2,3,4,5-tetra-chloro-*	$C_6H_2Cl_4O$. See p555	231.89	nd (peth, sub)	116–7	sub				v				alk, MeOH v peth s[h]	B6³, 729
p691	—,2,3,4,6-tetra-chloro-*	$C_6H_2Cl_4O$. See p555	231.89	nd (lig, aa)	70	150[15]			i δ[h]	s	s		s	NaOH v chl, lig s aa s[h]	B6³, 729
p692	—,2,3,5,6-tetra-chloro-*	$C_6H_2Cl_4O$. See p555	231.89	lf (lig)	115				δ				v	lig s[h]	B6³, 730
p693	—,2,3,4,6-tetra-nitro-*	$C_6H_2N_4O_9$. See p555	274.10	lt ye nd (chl)	140d	exp			v					chl s[h]	B6³, 973
p694	—,2,4,6-tri-amino-*	$C_6H_9N_3O$. See p555	139.16			257			v	s	s				B13², 317
p695	—,2,3,5-tri-bromo-*	$C_6H_3Br_3O$. See p555	330.82	nd or pl (w, lig)	94–5				δ	v	v	v		alk v lig v[h]	B6², 192
p696	—,2,4,5-tri-bromo-*	$C_6H_3Br_3O$. See p555	330.82	nd (lig)	87					s				alk, lig s	B6², 192
Ω p697	—,2,4,6-tri-bromo-*	Bromol. $C_6H_3Br_3O$. See p555	330.82	nd (al), pr (bz), cr (aa + 1)	95–6	282–90[764] sub	2.55[20]₂₀		δ	v	s		s[h]	chl s aa s[h]	B6, 203
p698	—,3,4,5-tri-bromo-*	$C_6H_3Br_3O$. See p555	330.82	tcl (bz-lig) $\lambda^{0.1N\ NaOH}$ 246 (3.85), 309 (3.45)	129					s			s	alk v aa s	B6², 195
p699	—,2,3,4-tri-chloro-*	$C_6H_3Cl_3O$. See p555	197.45	nd (sub, bz, lig)	83.5	sub				s	s		s	alk, aa s	B6³, 716
p700	—,2,3,5-tri-chloro-*	$C_6H_3Cl_3O$. See p555	197.45	nd (al) $\lambda^{0.1N\ HCl}$ 280 (3.28), 290 (3.28)	62	248.5–9.5[250]			δ	s	s				B6³, 716
p701	—,2,3,6-tri-chloro-*	$C_6H_3Cl_3O$. See p555	197.45	nd (dil al, lig) $\lambda^{0.1N\ HCl}$ 280 (3.28), 289 (3.29)	58				δ[h]	v	v		v	aa, lig s	B6³, 716
Ω p702	—,2,4,5-tri-chloro-*	$C_6H_3Cl_3O$. See p555	197.45	nd (al, peth) $\lambda^{0.1N\ NaOH}$ 244 (3.95), 310 (3.62)	68–70.5	sub			δ	s				os, lig s	B6³, 717
Ω p703	—,2,4,6-tri-chloro-*	$C_6H_3Cl_3O$. See p555	197.45	rh nd (aa) $\lambda^{0.1N\ NaOH}$ 244 (3.95), 311 (3.69)	69.5	246[760]	1.4901[75]₇		δ	s	s			aa s[h]	B6³, 722
p704	—,3,4,5-tri-chloro-*	$C_6H_3Cl_3O$. See p555	197.45	nd (lig) $\lambda^{0.1N\ NaOH}$ 204 (4.03), 307 (3.70)	101	271–7[746]			δ		s			lig δ, v[h]	B6³, 729
p705	—,2,3,5-triiodo-*	$C_6H_3I_3O$. See p555	471.80	nd (peth, bz-lig)	114					s	s	s	s	os v	B6, 211

For explanations, symbols and abbreviations see beginning of table. For structural formulas see end of table.

No.	Name	Synonyms and Formula	Mol. wt.	Color, crystalline form, specific rotation and λ_{max} (log ε)	m.p. °C	b.p. °C	Density	n_D	w	al	eth	ace	bz	other solvents	Ref.
	Phenol														
p706	—,2,4,6-triiodo-*	$C_6H_3I_3O$. See p555.	471.80	nd (dil al) λ^{al} 295 (3.51)	158–9	sub d			i	δ	s	s	...		B6³, 789
p707	—,2,3,6-tri-nitro-*	$C_6H_3N_3O_7$. See p555.	229.11	ye nd (w)	119				δ v^h	s	v	...	s	aa s	B6, 265
p708	—,2,4,5-trinitro-*	$C_6H_3N_3O_7$. See p555.	229.11	wh nd (w, dil al)	96				δ s^h	v	v	...	v	aa v	B6², 253
Ω p709	—,2,4,6-trinitro-*	Picric acid. $C_6H_3N_3O_7$. See p555	229.11	ye lf (w), pr (eth), pl (al), col cr (lig) λ^{al} 360 (4.20)	122–3	sub exp >300	1.763		δ s^h	s	s	v	s	aa, MeOH, Py s chl s^h	B6³, 873
Ω p710	Phenolphthalein	2,2-Bis(p-hydroxyphenyl) phthalide.	318.33	wh rh nd λ^{alk-al} 550 (3.90)	262–3		1.277^{32}_4		i	v	s	v	i	Py v chl, to s CS_2 δ peth i	B18, 143
Ω p711	—,3′,3″,5′,5″-tetrabromo-	$C_{20}H_{10}Br_4O_4$. See p710	633.94	nd (al, eth, aa)	295–7				i	δ^h	v	...	...	alk s aa s^h	B18², 124
p712	—,3′,3″,5′,5″-tetrachloro-	$C_{20}H_{10}Cl_4O_4$. See p710	456.11	cr (bz, aa)	225				i	s	...	s	v	$PhNO_2$ s aa s^h	B18², 123
Ω p713	—,3′,3″,5′,5″-tetraiodo-	Iodophen. Nosophen. $C_{20}H_{10}I_4O_4$. See p710	821.92	amor	277–9d		2.0246^{22}_{22}		i	i	i	...	...	chl δ	B18², 119
p714	Phenolphthalin		320.35	nd (w)	229–32 (225)				δ	s	s	...	...	NaOH s	B10², 322
Ω p715	Phenolsulfon-phthalein	Phenol red.	354.37	dk red nd or pl	>300				δ	δ	i	δ	δ	KOH s chl i	B19², 102
Ω p716	Phenothiazine	Thiodiphenylamine.	199.28	ye pr (al), ye lf or pl (to) λ^{MeOH} 254 (4.5), 285 (3.1), 318 (3.6)	185.5–.9	371^{760} 290^{40} (sub 130^1)			δ	δ	s	v	v	aa s^h lig δ CCl_4 i	B27, 63
p717	—,2,8-dinitro-, 5-oxide	$C_{12}H_7N_3O_5S$. See p716.	305.27	ye-red lf (aa), pr ($PhNH_2$)	d									$PhNO_2$ s^h os δ	B27¹, 229
p718	—,10(2-diethyl-aminoethyl)-	$C_{18}H_{22}N_2S$. See p716.	298.46	ye oil		195–208^{4-5} 161–$50^{.5}$			i					dil HCl s	Am 66, 888
p719	—,10(2-dimethyl-aminopropyl)-	Phenergan base. Prometha-zine. $C_{17}H_{20}N_2S$. See p716	284.43		60 (55)	190–$3^{0.5}$ (190–2^3)			i					dil HCl v	C42, 575
p720	—,—,hydrochloride	$C_{17}H_{20}N_2S$. HCl. See p716	320.89	λ 249	230–2				v	s				chl s	C42, 575
Ω p721	—,10-phenyl-	$C_{18}H_{13}NS$. See p716.	275.38	ye pr (al)	89–90				i	s^h				con sulf s	B27, 227
Ω p722	Phenoxanthin		200.27	nd, cr (MeOH)	59–60	311^{745} $183–4^{12}$				s	s	s	s	os v con sulf s	B19², 33
p723	Phenoxazine	Dibenzoxazine	183.21	lf (dil al, bz)	156	δd				v	v	...	s^h	chl, aa v con sulf, lig s	B27¹, 223
—	Phenoxytol	see Ethanol, 2-phenoxy-*													
Ω p724	Phenylalanine (D)	l-α-Aminohydrocinnamic acid. l-β-Phenyl-α-aminopropionic acid. $C_6H_5CH_2CH(NH_2)CO_2H$	165.19	nd or pr (w), $[\alpha]^{20}_D$ −69.5 (w) λ^w 242 (1.88), 257 (2.25), 267 (1.91)	283 d	sub at 295	1.600		s	δ^h	i			alk s dil ac δ os i	B14², 297
Ω p725	—(DL)	$C_6H_5CH_2CH(NH_2)CO_2H$	165.19	red-br lf (aq al), pr or nd (w) λ^w 242 (1.88), 257 (2.25), 267 (1.91)	284–8d (271–3)	sub par d			v	i	i	i	i	as i	B14², 299
Ω p726	—(L)	$C_6H_5CH_2CH(NH_2)CO_2H$	165.19	pr (w), $[\alpha]^{18}_D$ +70 (w) λ^w 242 (1.88), 2.57 (2.25), 267 (1.91)	283–4 d	sub at 295			s	i	i		...	MeOH δ os i	B14², 296
p727	—,N-acetyl-(d, +)	$C_6H_5CH_2CH(NHCOCH_3)CO_2H$	207.23	cr (w), $[\alpha]^{26}_D$ −50.9 λ^w 260 (2.3)	172				s^h	s					B14², 297
p728	—,—(dl)	$C_6H_5CH_2CH(NHCOCH_3)CO_2H$	207.23	nd or pl (w), hex tab (ace) λ^w 260 (2.3)	152.5–3				s	s					B14², 302
p729	—,—(l, −)	$C_6H_5CH_2CH(NHCOCH_3)CO_2H$	207.23	$[\alpha]^{26}_D$ +51.4 λ^w 260 (2.3)	172					s					B14², 298
—	Phenylenediamine	see Benzene, diamino-*													
—	Phenylglycidol	see 1-Propanol,2,3-epoxy-3-phenyl-*													
—	Phenylglycine	see Acetic acid, amino-(phenyl)-*													
—	Phenylisocyanide	see Benzene, isocyano-*													
—	Phloramin	see Benzene, 1-amino-3,5-dihydroxy-*													
Ω p730	Phloretin	Dihydronaringenin. $C_{15}H_{14}O_5$.	274.28	nd (dil al), cr (dil ace)	262–4d (274d)				δ^h	∞	i	s^h	∞	MeOH s chl δ	B8², 542

For explanations, symbols and abbreviations see beginning of table. For structural formulas see end of table.

No.	Name	Synonyms and Formula	Mol. wt.	Color, crystalline form, specific rotation and λ_{max} (log ε)	m.p. °C	b.p. °C	Density	n_D	Solubility						Ref.
									w	al	eth	ace	bz	other solvents	
	Phlorhizin														
p731	Phlorhizin, dihydrate	Asebotin. Ascbotoside. $C_{21}H_{24}O_{10}\cdot 2H_2O$	472.45	nd (w) $[\alpha]_D^{25}-52$ (96% al)	108 (+2w) 170d (anh)	....	1.4298	....	δ	s	i	s	i	Py s chl i	B31, 231
—	Phloroglucinol.....	see Benzene, 1,3,5-trihydroxy-*													
—	Phlorol.........	see Benzene, 1-ethyl-2-hydroxy-*													
—	Phorone......	see 2,5-Heptadiene-4-one, 2,6-dimethyl-*													
p732	Phosgene........	Carbonic acid dichloride. Carbonyl chloride. Chloroformyl chloride. Cl_2CO.	98.92	λ^{gas} 295, 297, 298	−118 (−127.76)	7.56^{760}	1.381_4^{20}	....	d	d	....	....	s	to, CCl_4, chl, aa s	B3³, 31
p733	—,thio-	Thiocarbonyl chloride. $SCCl_2$	114.98	red		73	1.508^{15}	1.5442^{20}	i	s	s				B3³, 246
p734	Phosphine, bis(trifluoromethyl)-	$(F_3C)_2PH$	169.99	spontaneously inflam	−137	1									J1954, 3896
p735	—,bis(trifluoromethyl)chloro-	$(F_3C)_2PCl$	204.44	spontaneously inflam	.,....	21			d						J1953, 1552
p736	—,bis(trifluoromethyl)cyano-	$(F_3C)_2PCN$	195.00	spontaneously inflam		48		1.3248^{20}							J1953, 1552
p737	—,bis(trifluoromethyl)iodo-	$(F_3C)_2PI$	295.89			73		1.403^{15}	d					Bu_2O s	J1953, 1552
p738	—,dichloro(2,4-dimethylphenyl)-	$C_8H_9Cl_2P$. See p741	207.04			256–8			d^h						B16, 773
p739	—,dichloro(2,5-dimethylphenyl)-	$C_8H_9Cl_2P$. See p741	207.04		−30	253–4	1.25_{18}^{18}		d^h						B16, 773
p740	—,dichloro(4-ethylphenyl)-	$C_8H_9Cl_2P$. See p741	207.04			250–2 $85^{0.4}$	1.237_4^{20}	1.584^{20}	d^h						B16, 772
p741	—,dichloro(phenyl)-	....	178.99			224.6^{760} $99–101^{11}$	1.356_4^{20}	1.6030^{20}	d				∞	CS_2 ∞	B16², 373
p742	—,dichlorotrifluoromethyl-	CF_3PCl_2	170.89			37			d						J1953, 1552
p743	—,diethyl-	$(C_2H_5)_2PH$	90.11			85									B4³, 1761
p744	—,diiodo(trifluoromethyl)-	F_3CPI_2	353.79	ye fum		d^{760} 73^{37}		1.630^{20}	i d		s			Bu_2O s	J1953, 1552
p745	—,dimethyl-	$(CH_3)_2PH$	62.05	λ^{gas} 189 (3.80)		25	<1		i	s	s	s			B4³, 1759
p746	—,diphenyl(ethyl)-	$(C_6H_5)_2PC_2H_5$	214.25			293			δ				δ		B16², 371
p747	—,ethyl-	$CH_3CH_2PH_2$	62.05			25	<1		d						B4³, 1761
p748	—,methyl-	CH_3PH_2	48.02	gas		-14^{759}			i	δ	v				B4³, 1759
p749	—,phenyl-	$C_6H_5PH_2$	110.10	λ^{al} 234 (3.54), 260.5 (2.8), 265.5 (2.84), 272 (2.72)		$160–1^{760}$ 40^{10}	1.001^{15}	1.5796^{20}							B16², 369
p750	—,triethyl-	$(C_2H_5)_3P$	118.16		−88– −85	129^{762}	0.8006_4^{19}	1.458^{15}	i	∞	∞				B4³, 1761
p751	—,—,oxide	$(C_2H_5)_3PO$	134.16	wh hyg nd	50	243			s	s	s				B4³, 1755
p752	—,—,sulfide	$(C_2H_5)_3PS$.	150.23	cr (al)	94				s						B4³, 1755
p753	—,(trifluoromethyl)-	F_3CPH_2	102.00	spontaneously inflam		−26.5									J1954, 3896
p754	—,trimethyl-	$(CH_3)_3P$	76.08	λ^{gas} 201 (4.27)	−85.3– −84.3	37.8	<1		i		s				B4³, 1759
Ω p755	—,triphenyl-	$(C_6H_5)_3P$	262.29	$\lambda^{dil\,al}$ 260 (4.0)	80	>360 188^1	1.0749_4^{80}	1.6358^{80}	i	s	v		s	chl s	B16², 371
Ω p756	—,—,oxide	$(C_6H_5)_3PO$	278.29	pr (hyd) λ^{MeOH} 228 (4.3), 267 (3.3)	156–7	>360	1.2124_4^{23}		δ^h	v	δ	..	v		B16², 379
p757	—,tris(chloromethyl)-	$P(CH_2Cl)_3$	179.41			100^7	1.414^{20}		i	s	v	v	v		B4³, 1760
p758	—,tris(trichloromethyl)-	$(CCl_3)_3P$	386.08		53				d						C47, 2685
p759	—,tris(trifluoromethyl)-	$(CF_3)_3P$	237.99	spontaneously inflam	−112	17.3			i					w d^{200}	J1953, 1565
p760	—,—,oxide	$(CF_3)_3PO$	253.99			23,6			d						J1955, 574
p761	Phosphinic acid, bis(trifluoromethyl)-*	$(F_3C)_2PO_2H$	201.99	visc liq		182^{760} $137–8^{238}$	<1.9		s					con sulf i	J1955, 563
p762	—,diethyl-*	$(C_2H_5)_2PO_2H$	122.11		18.5	320 $134^{0.7}$			v	v	v				B4³, 1776
p763	—,—,anhydride*	$[(C_2H_5)_2PO]_2O$	226.20			188^{14}	1.1053_4^{23}	1.4720^{23}	d	d	s				Am 73, 5466
p764	—,—,chloride.	$(C_2H_5)_2POCl$	140.55			104^{15}	1.1394_4^{20}	1.4647^{20}	d	d					Am 73, 5466
p765	—,—,ethyl ester*	$(C_2H_5)_2PO(OC_2H_5)$	150.16			95^{14}	0.9908_4^{20}	1.4337^{20}	δ	s	s				Am 73, 5466
p766	—,dimethyl-*	$(CH_3)_2PO_2H$	94.05	cr (bz)	92	377			v	v	v		s^h		B4³, 1776

For explanations, symbols and abbreviations see beginning of table. For structural formulas see end of table.

No.	Name	Synonyms and Formula	Mol. wt.	Color, crystalline form, specific rotation and λ_{max} (log ε)	m.p. °C	b.p. °C	Density	n_D	w	al	eth	ace	bz	other solvents	Ref.
	Phosphinic acid														
p767	—,—,anhydride*	[(CH₃)₂PO]₂O	170.09	nd (bz)	119–21	192¹⁵			d	d	...	...	sʰ	...	Am 73, 5466
p768	—,—,chloride	(CH₃)₂POCl	112.50	hyg nd (bz-peth)	66.8–8.4	204⁷⁶⁰			d	d	...	...	sʰ	peth δ	B4³, 1776
—	—,phenyl-*	*see* **Benzenephosphinic acid**													
—	phosphonic acid ethyl-*	*see* **Ethanephosphonic acid**													
—	—,methyl-*	*see* **Methanephosphonic acid**													
—	—,phenyl-*	*see* **Benzenephosphonic acid**													
p770	**Phosphoric acid,** diethyl ester*	(C₂H₅O)₂POOH	154.10	syr	...	203.3d	1.186²⁵₄	1.4170²⁰	i	...	s	...	...	CCl₄ i	B1³, 1328
p771	—,dimethyl ester*	(CH₃O)₂POOH	126.05	...	172–6d	1.335²⁵	1.408²⁵	s	s	i	s	...	to, CCl₄ i	B1³, 1205
p772	—,monoethyl ester*	(C₂H₅O)PO(OH)₂	126.05	hyg cr	...	d	1.430²⁵₄	1.427	s dʰ	s	s	s	...	CCl₄, to i	B1³, 1327
p773	—,monophenyl ester*	(C₆H₅O)PO(OH)₂	174.09	pl (chl), nd (w)	99.5	...			v	v	v	...	v	chl s	B6³, 657
p774	—,triamide, hexamethyl-*	[(CH₃)₂N]₃PO	179.20	...	98–100⁶ 66⁰·⁵	...	1.024²⁵₂₅	1.4579²⁰	...	s	s	...	...		C53, 4132
Ω p775	—,tributyl ester*	(C₄H₉ⁿ)₃PO	266.32	...	...	289 160–2¹⁵	0.9727²⁵₄	1.4224²⁵	s	∞	...	...	s	CS₂ s	B1³, 1511
Ω p776	—,triethyl ester*	(C₂H₅)₃PO	182.16	...	−56.4	215–6⁷⁶⁰ 103²⁵	1.0695²⁰₄	1.4053²⁰	sᵈᵈ	v	s	...	...		B1³, 1328
p777	—,triisobutyl ester	(C₄H₉ⁱ)₃PO	266.32	...	...	264⁷⁶⁰ 138¹⁰	0.9681²⁰₄	1.4193²⁰	v	s	s	...	s		B1³, 1563
p778	—,triisopropyl ester*	(C₃H₇ⁱO)₃PO	224.24	...	...	218–20⁷⁶³ 95–6⁸	0.9867²⁰₄	1.4057²⁰	...	...	s	...	...		B1³, 1466
p779	—,trimethyl ester*	(CH₃O)₃PO	140.08	λ^{al} 229 (1.74), 263 (0.97)	α: −46 (st) β: −62 (unst)	197.2⁷⁶⁰ 85²⁴	1.2144²⁰₄	1.3967²⁰	v	δ	s	...	...		B1³, 1205
p780	—,tripentyl ester*	[CH₃(CH₂)₄O]₃PO	308.40	...	...	225⁵⁰ 167⁵	0.9608²⁰₄	1.4319²⁰	i	s	s	...	...	to, CS₂ s	B1³, 1605
Ω p781	—,triphenyl ester*	...	326.29	cr (abs al-lig), pr (al), nd (eth-lig)	50–1	245¹¹	1.2055⁵⁰₄		i	s	v	...	v	chl, CCl₄ v	B6³, 658
Ω p782	—,tripropyl ester*	(C₃H₇ⁿO)₃PO	224.24	...	...	252⁷⁶⁰ 107.5⁵	1.0121²⁰₄	1.4165²⁰	δ	s	s	...	...	to, CS₂ s	B1³, 1422
p783	—,tris(2,4-dimethylphenyl) ester*	C₂₄H₂₇O₄P. See p781	410.46	glassy on fr	...	232–5	1.142²⁸₈	1.5550²⁰	i	...	...	...	s	hx s	B6, 488
p784	—,tris(2,5-dimethylphenyl) ester*	C₂₄H₂₇O₄P. See p781	410.46	cr (dil al)	78.6–81 (77)	260–5⁸	1.197²⁵		i	δ	...	...	s	to, CCl₄ s hx δ	B6³, 1773
p785	—,tris(2,6-dimethylphenyl) ester*	C₂₄H₂₇O₄P. See p781	410.46	...	136–8	262–4⁶			i	δ	...	...	s	hx̃ δ	J1956, 3043
p786	—,tris(3,4-dimethylphenyl) ester*	C₂₄H₂₇O₄P. See p781	410.46	wax	71.5–2.5	260–3⁷			i	δ	...	...	s	hx δ	B6, 482
p787	—,tris(3,5-dimethylphenyl) ester*	C₂₄H₂₇O₄P. See p781	410.46	wax	46–6.5	290¹⁰			i	δ	...	...	...	aa s hx δ	C31, 187
p788	—,tris(2,2,2-trichloroethyl) ester*	(Cl₃CCH₂O)₃PO	492.16	...	73–4				...	...	...	v	...	lig δ	B1, 338
Ω p789	—,tri(2-tolyl) ester	Tri-*o*-cresyl phosphate. C₂₁H₂₁O₄P. See p781	368.37	col or pa ye	11	410 283–5²⁰	1.1955²⁰₄	1.5575²⁰	i	v	v	...	...	CCl₄, to v aa s	B6³, 1261
Ω p790	—,tri(3-tolyl) ester	Tri-*m*-cresyl phosphate. C₂₁H₂₁O₄P. See p781	368.37	wax	25–6	260¹⁵	1.150²⁵	1.5575²⁰	i	δ	v	...	...	to, CCl₄ v aa s	B6³, 1312
Ω p791	—,tri(4-tolyl) ester	T.P.C. Tri-*p*-cresyl phosphate. C₂₁H₂₁O₄P. See p781	368.37	nd (al), ta (eth)	77–8	244³·⁵	1.247²⁵		i	δ	v	...	s	chl, aa s	B6³, 1372
p794	—,thiono-, tri(2-tolyl) ester		384.44	nd (al)	45–6	260–5¹			i	s	...	...	...	aa v	B6³, 1262
p795	—,—,tri(3-tolyl) ester		384.44	nd (al)	40–1	270–2¹²			i	δ sʰ	...	...	...	aa v MeOH, lig δ	B6², 354
p796	—,—,tri(4-tolyl) ester		384.44	nd (al)	93–4				i	δ sʰ	...	...	δ	chl, aa v lig δ	B6³, 1372
Ω p797	**Phosphorous acid,** diethyl ester*	(C₂H₅O)₂POH	138.10	...	...	87²⁰ 51–2²	1.0720²⁰₄	1.4101²⁰	dʰ	s	s	...	...		B1³, 1324
Ω p798	—,dimethyl ester*	(CH₃O)₂POH	110.05	...	...	170–1 70²⁵	1.2004²⁰₄	1.4036²⁰	...	...	s	...	...	Py s	B1³, 1203
Ω p799	—,tributyl ester*	[CH₃(CH₂)₃O]₃P	250.32	...	...	122¹²	0.9259²⁰₄	1.4321¹⁹	dʰ	s	v	...	...		B1³, 1510
Ω p800	—,triethyl ester*	(C₂H₅O)₃P	166.16	λ^{al} 260 (0.16)	...	157.9 49¹²	0.9629²⁰₄	1.4127²⁰	i	v	v	...	...		B1³, 1325
Ω p801	—,triisopropyl ester*	[(CH₃)₂CHO]₃P	208.24	λ^{al} 261 (0.60)	...	60–1¹⁰ 43.5¹	0.9687¹⁸·⁵₀	1.4085²⁵	...	s	s	...	...		B1³, 1465
Ω p802	—,trimethyl ester*	(CH₃O)₃P	124.08	λ^{al} 251 (2.76), 257 (2.80), 263 (2.66)	...	111–2 22²³	1.0520²⁰₄	1.4095²⁰	dʰ	v	v	...	...		B1³, 1203
Ω p803	—,triphenyl ester*	(C₆H₅O)₃P	310.29	...	ca. 25	360⁷⁶⁰ 200–1⁵	1.1844²⁰₄	1.5900²⁰	i dʰ	v	...	...	...	os v	B6³, 656
p804	—,tripropyl ester*	(CH₃CH₂CH₂O)₃P	208.24	...	...	206–7⁷⁶⁰ 92¹⁴	0.9417²⁰	1.4282²⁰	...	s	s	...	...		B1³, 1420
p805	—,tris(2,2,2-trichloroethyl) ester*	(Cl₃CCH₂O)₃P	476.16	...	263 127–31⁰·¹			1.5174²⁰							B1, 338

For explanations, symbols and abbreviations see beginning of table. For structural formulas see end of table.

No.	Name	Synonyms and Formula	Mol. wt.	Color, crystalline form, specific rotation and λ_{max} (log ε)	m.p. °C	b.p. °C	Density	n_D	w	al	eth	ace	bz	other solvents	Ref.
	Phosphorous acid														
p806	—,tri(2-tolyl) ester.	Tri-o-cresyl phosphite......	352.38	ye	....	238^{11} $197–9^2$	$1.1423^{20}_{?}$	1.5740^{28}	δd	δd	s	...	...	...	B6[3], 1260
p807	—,tri(4-tolyl) ester..	Tri-p-cresyl phosphite......	352.38	pa ye	....	$250–5^{10}$	1.1313^{25}_{25}	1.5703^{28}	...	...	s	...	...	...	B6[3], 1371
p808	**Phthalaldehyde**	1,2-Benzene dicarbonal*. o-Phthalic aldehyde.	134.14	ye cr or nd (lig) λ^w 210 (3.9), 219 (3.7), 260 (3.0), 300 (2.3)	(i) 53.2 (ii) 56–7				s	s	s	...	...	os s peth δ	B7[2], 605
—	**Phthalaldehydic acid**	*see* Benzoic acid, 2-formyl-													
—	**Phthalamic acid** ...	*see* Phthalic acid, monoamide													
—	**Phthalamide**	*see* Phthalic acid, diamide													
—	**Phthalanil**	*see* Phthalic acid, imide, N-phenyl-													
—	**Phthalazine, 6-amino-1,4-dioxo-1,2,3,4-tetrahydro-**	*see* Phthalic acid, 4-amino-, hydrazide													
Ω p810	**—,1,2-dihydro-1-oxo**	1(2H)-Phthalazinone. Phthalazone.	146.15	nd (w), pr (sub)	184–5	337^{755} sub			v^h	s v^h	...	...	s v^h	alk, ac s	B24[7], 70
Ω p812	**Phthalic acid**	1,2-Benzenedicarboxylic acid*.	166.14	pl (w) λ^{al} 225 (3.88), 275 (3.08)	210–11d 231 (rapid htng) 191 (sealed tube)	d	1.593	....	δ v^h	s	δ	...	...	chl i	B9[2], 580
Ω p813	—,anhydride	Phthalandione. Phthalic anhydride. $C_8H_4O_3$. See p812 λ^{CCl_4} 287 (3.2), 295 (3.3)	148.12	wh nd (al, bz)	131.61	295.1 (284^{740}) sub	1.527^4		δ	s	δ	s^h	...		B17[2], 463 B21[2], 466
Ω p814	—,diamide	Phthalamide. Phthalic diamide. $C_8H_8N_2O_2$. See p812	164.18	cr	222	d			δ	δ	i	...	...		B9[2], 601
p815	—,—,N,N,N',N'-tetraethyl-	$C_{16}H_{24}N_2O_2$. See p812	276.38	....	36	204^{16}			s	...	...	...	...	os v	B9[2], 602
p816	—,dibenzyl ester...	$C_{22}H_{18}O_4$. See p812........	346.39	pr (al) λ^{al} 276 (3.1)	42–3	277^{15}			i	v	v	...	...	lig i	B9[2], 595
Ω p817	—,dibutyl ester...	$C_{16}H_{22}O_4$. See p812.	278.35	λ^{al} 226 (3.98), 272 (3.18)		340 206^{20}	1.047^{20}_{20}	1.4911^{20}	i	∞	∞	...	∞		B9[2], 586
p818	—,dichloride......	Phthalyl chloride. $C_8H_4Cl_2O_2$. See p812	203.03	λ^{eth} 235 (3.8), 272 sh (2.9), 278 (3.0), 286 (3.0)	15–6 (fr 12)	281.1 $131–3^9$	1.4089^{20}_4	1.5684^{20}	d	d	...	...	...		B9[2], 599
Ω p819	—,dicyclohexyl ester	$C_{20}H_{26}O_4$. See p812.	330.43	pr (al)	66	....	1.383^{20}	1.451^{20}	i	s	s	...	...		B9, 799
p820	—,di(2-ethoxy-ethyl) ester...	$C_{16}H_{22}O_6$. See p812.	310.35	....	34	345 $233–5^{23}$	1.1229^{21}		i	...	...	...	...		B9[2], 597
Ω p821	—,diethyl ester....	$C_{12}H_{14}O_4$. See p812.	222.24	λ^{al} 225 (3.9), 275 (3.1)	....	298 (290) 172^{12}	1.1175^{20}_4	1.5000^{20}	i	∞	∞	s	s		B9[2], 584
Ω p822	—,diisobutyl ester	$C_{16}H_{22}O_4$. See p812.	278.35	....		295–8 $182–4^{10}$	1.0490^{15}		i						B9[2], 587
p823	—,di(2-methoxy-ethyl) ester	$C_{14}H_{18}O_6$. See p812.	282.30	....		230^{10}	1.1708^{15}								B9[2], 597
Ω p824	—,dimethyl ester ..	$C_{10}H_{10}O_4$. See p812.	194.19	pa ye λ^{al} 225 (3.92), 274 (3.10)	0–2	283.8^{760}	$1.1905^{20.7}_4$	1.5138^{20}	i	∞	∞	...	s		B9[2], 584
p825	—,di(3-methyl-butyl) ester	$C_{18}H_{26}O_4$. See p812.	306.41	....		330–8d 225^{40}	1.0220^{16}_{16}	1.4871^{20}	i	s	...	...	...	os s	B9[2], 587
Ω p826	—,dinitrile	Phthalonitrile. $C_8H_4N_2$. See p812	128.14	nd (w, lig) λ^{MeOH} 237 (4.02), 276 (3.05), 280.5 (3.22), 290 (3.23)	141	....			δ	v	s	s	v	lig δ, s^h	B9[2], 602
Ω p827	—,diphenyl ester ..	$C_{20}H_{14}O_4$. See p812.	318.33	pr (al, lig)	73	$250–7^{14}$ sub			i	δ	δ	...	...		B9[2], 594
Ω p828	—,dipropyl ester...	$C_{14}H_{18}O_4$. See p812.	250.30	....		304–5			i	s	s	...	...		B9[2], 586
p829	—,hydrazide......	Phthalhydrazide. 1,4-Dioxo-1,2,3,4-tetra-hydrophthalazine.	162.15	mcl nd (w, dil al, aa) λ^{al} 251 (3.6), 262 (3.64), 300 (3.78)	342–4 (cor)	....			δ^h	s δ^h	...	...	i	aa, dil alk s aa s^h chl i	B24[2], 194
Ω p830	—,imide	1,3-Isoindoledione. Phthalimide.	147.14	nd (w), pr (aa). If (sub) λ^{al} 215 (3.61), 229.5 (4.21), 238 (4.03), 291 (3.15)	238	....			δ	...	...	...	i	alk s aa s lig i	B21[2], 348
p831	—,—,N-acetyl-....	$C_{10}H_7NO_3$. See p830.......	189.17	nd (bz), cr (al, aa)	135–6	....			i	...	s	...	v^h	chl v	B21[2], 357

For explanations, symbols and abbreviations see beginning of table. For structural formulas see end of table.

No.	Name	Synonyms and Formula	Mol. wt.	Color. crystalline form. specific rotation and λ_{max} (log ε)	m.p. °C	b.p. °C	Density	n_D	Solubility						Ref.
									w	al	eth	ace	bz	other solvents	
	Phthalic acid														
Ω p832	—.—,N-benzyl-	$C_{15}H_{11}NO_2$. See p830	237.26	ye nd (al), cr (aa) λ^{al} 222 (4.65), 240 (3.74), 297 (3.28)	116	....	1.343[16]	....	...	s[h]	...	...	...	aa s[h]	B21[2], 351
Ω p833	—.—,N(2-bromoethyl)-	$C_{10}H_8BrNO_2$. See p830	254.10	nd (w) λ 291 (3.4)	82.0–3.5	....			d[h]		v	...	...		B21[2], 349
p834	—.—,N(2-bromoisobutyl)-	$C_{12}H_{12}BrNO_2$. See p830	282.14	nd (al), lf (chl)	97					s v[h]	...	...	v	AcOEt, chl v	B21[2], 349
Ω p835	—.—,N(bromomethyl)-	$C_9H_6BrNO_2$. See p830	240.06	pr (chl, bz, aa, AcOEt)	151.5				d[h]			s	δ	AcOEt v[h] chl δ	B21[2], 354
p836	—.—,N(2-bromopropyl)-	$C_{11}H_{10}BrNO_2$. See p830	268.12	nd (MeOH, al)	110–11				δ[h]	v	v	...	...	lig δ	B21[2], 349
Ω p837	—.—,N(3-bromopropyl)-	$C_{11}H_{10}BrNO_2$. See p830	268.12	nd (lig)	72–3				i	v[h]	v[h]	...	...	lig δ peth i	B21[2], 349
p838	—.—,N-carbethoxy-	Ethyl N,N-phthalyl-carbamate. $C_{11}H_9NO_4$. See p830	219.20	(bz-peth)	87–9						v	...	v	chl v con ac s peth δ	B21[2], 35
p839	—.—,N-ethyl-	$C_{10}H_9NO_2$. See p830	175.19	nd (al) λ^{al} 219 (4.6)	79	285.6[758] (cor)				s[h]	s	...	...		B21[2], 349
Ω p840	—.—,N(2-hydroxyethyl)-	$C_{10}H_9NO_3$. See p830	191.19	nd (al), lf (w)	129.5 (cor)				δ			...	...		B21[2], 352
Ω p841	—.—,N(hydroxymethyl)-	$C_9H_7NO_3$. See p830	177.16	lf, pr (to)	141–2				i s[h]	δ s[h]	i	...	δ s[h]	to s[h] CCl_4 i	B21[2], 354
p842	—.—,N-isobutyl-	$C_{12}H_{13}NO_2$. See p830	203.24	....	93	293–5			i			...	...		B21, 463
p843	—.—,N-methyl-	$C_9H_7NO_2$. See p830	161.16	nd (al), lf (sub)	134	285–7 (cor) sub			i	δ v[h]		...	...		B21[2], 348
p844	—.—,N(1-naphthyl)-	$C_{18}H_{11}NO_2$. See p830	273.30	pr, pl (al-aa)	180–1					s[h]	s[h]	...	...		B21, 469
p845	—.—,N(2-naphthyl)-	$C_{18}H_{11}NO_2$. See p830	273.30	nd (aa)	216					s		...	...	aa v[h]	B21[2], 352
Ω p846	—.—,N(4-nitrophenyl)-	$C_{14}H_8N_2O_4$. See p830	268.24	cr (aa) λ^{al} 222 (4.36), 317 (4.15)	271–2 (266)					i[h]		...	...	xyl i aa i, s[h]	B21[2], 350
Ω p847	—.—,N-phenyl-	$C_{14}H_9NO_2$. See p830	223.23	wh nd (al) λ^{al} 215 (4.54), 230 (4.22), 295 (3.26)	210	sub			i	δ	...	...	...	chl ∞	B21[2], 350
p849	—,monoamide	Phthalamic acid. $C_8H_7NO_3$. See p812	165.15	pr	148–9				s[h]	s	δ	...	δ	lig i	B9[2], 600
Ω p850	—.—,N(1-naphthyl)-	Alanap-1. $C_{18}H_{13}NO_3$. See p812	291.31	....	185				i	δ	...	δ	δ		B12[1], 525
p851	—,monoamide mononitrile	o-Cyanobenzamide. Phthalamic nitrile. $C_8H_6N_2O$. See p812	146.15	nd (MeOH), cr (aa)	173				i	v	...	v	...	MeOH, aa s[h] AcOEt δ	B9, 815
p852	—,monobutyl ester	$C_{12}H_{14}O_4$. See p812	222.24	pl (al, ace)	73–4					s[h]	...	s[h]	...	os s	B9[2], 586
p853	—,mono-sec-butyl ester(d)	$C_{12}H_{14}O_4$. See p812	222.24	$[\alpha]_D^{20}$ +38.4 (al)	48					s		...	...	chl s	B9[2], 586
p854	—,—(dl)	$C_{12}H_{14}O_4$. See p812	222.24	cr (peth)	63–3.5				δ	s	s	...	...	peth s[h]	B9[2], 587
p855	—,monoethyl ester.	$C_{10}H_{10}O_4$. See p812	194.19	d	2		1.1877[22]	1.509[22]	δ	s	s	...	...		B9[2], 587
p856	—,mononitrile	$C_8H_5NO_2$. See p812	147.14	nd (al)	187d (192d)				s[h]	v[h]	δ	s	δ	peth δ	B9[2], 602
p857	—,mono(2-octyl)ester(d)	$C_{16}H_{22}O_4$. See p812	278.35	pr (peth), $[\alpha]_D^{20}$ +48.7 (al)	75		1.027[22]₄			v	...	...	v	AcOEt, chl v CS_2 s peth s[h]	B9[2], 587
p858	—,—(dl)	$C_{16}H_{22}O_4$. See p812	278.35	pr (peth)	55					v	v	v	v	chl v peth s[h]	B9[1], 353
p859	—,—(l)	$C_{16}H_{22}O_4$. See p812	278.35	pr (peth), $[\alpha]_D$ −48.26 (al)	75					v	...	...	v	chl v peth s[h]	B9[2], 587
p860	—,3-amino-	$C_8H_7NO_4$. See p812	181.15	nd	231–2				δ	δ	δ	...	i	chl i	B14[2], 336
p861	—,4-amino-, dimethyl ester	$C_{10}H_{11}NO_4$. See p812	209.20	pl (al, bz), pr (w)	84 (cor)				δ[h]	s	δ	...	s[h]	chl, Py s peth δ	B14, 554
p862	—.—,hydrazide	$C_8H_7N_3O_2$. See p829	177.16	ye nd (w +1)	>305				...	δ	i	...	i	chl, lig i	B25, 487
p863	—,3-benzoyl-	2,3-Benzophenone dicarboxylic acid. $C_{15}H_{10}O_5$. See p812	270.25	pl, nd (w +1)	140–1	d			s[h]	s	δ	...	s	....	B10, 880
p864	—,4-benzoyl-	3,4-Benzophenone dicarboxylic acid. $C_{15}H_{10}O_5$. See p812	270.25	lf (xyl)	177					s	s	...	...	xyl s[h]	H29, 1413
p865	—,3-bromo-	$C_8H_5BrO_4$. See p812	245.04	nd	188d				s	s	s	...	...	chl i	B9[2], 604
p866	—,4-bromo-	$C_8H_5BrO_4$. See p812	245.04		173–5				δ[h]	v	s	...	...		B9[2], 605
p867	—,3-chloro-	$C_8H_5ClO_4$. See p812	200.58	nd (w)	186–7				δ	v	v	...	...		B9[2], 603
p868	—.—,anhydride	$C_8H_5ClO_3$. See p812	182.56	nd (sub)	124–5	sub				s	s	...	...		B17[2], 466
p869	—,4-chloro-	$C_8H_5ClO_4$. See p812	200.58	nd (dil al)	157					s	s	...	...		B9[2], 603
p870	—.—,anhydride	$C_8H_5ClO_3$. See p812	182.56	pr	98.5	294–5[720]				s	s	...	...	chl s	B17[2], 466
p871	—,3,4-dichloro-	$C_8H_4Cl_2O_4$. See p812	235.03	pl (w)	195				v	s	v	...	...		B9, 817
p871[1]	—.—,anhydride	$C_8H_2Cl_2O_3$. See p812	217.01	pl	121	329				s		...	...	chl, to s	B17[2], 467
p872	—,3,5-dichloro-	$C_8H_4Cl_2O_4$. See p812	235.03	nd, ta (aq HCl)	164d	sub			s	v	v	v	δ	chl s	B9, 817
p873	—.—,anhydride	$C_8H_2Cl_2O_3$. See p812	217.01	nd	89				d[h]			...	s	chl s	B17, 483

For explanations, symbols and abbreviations see beginning of table. For structural formulas see end of table.

No.	Name	Synonyms and Formula	Mol. wt.	Color, crystalline form, specific rotation and λ_{max} (log ε)	m.p. °C	b.p. °C	Density	n_D	w	al	eth	ace	bz	other solvents	Ref.
	Phthalic acid														
p874	—,3,6-dichloro-	$C_8H_4Cl_2O_4$. See p812	235.03	pl (w)	d at 100 → anh				v^h	v	v				B9, 817
p875	—,—,anhydride	$C_8H_2Cl_2O_3$. See p812	217.01	nd	194.5	339[760]									B17[2], 467
p876	—,4,5-dichloro-	$C_8H_4Cl_2O_4$. See p812	235.03	nd (w)	ca. 200d					s v^h		v				B9[2], 604
p877	—,—,anhydride	$C_8H_2Cl_2O_3$. See p812	217.01	ta or pr (to, CCl_4)	187.5–8.8 (cor)	313					s	s	δ v^h	to v alk s CCl_4 δ	B17[2], 467
—	—,dihydro-	see Cyclohexadiene-dicarboxylic acid*													
Ω p878	—,3,6-dihydroxy-, dinitrile	$C_8H_4N_2O_2$. See p812	160.13	yesh lf (w +2)	230				δ	v	v		δ	chl δ	B10[2], 383
Ω p879	—,—,imide	$C_8H_5NO_4$. See p830	179.13	gr-ye nd (w +3)	273–4				v^h						B21[1], 478
p880	—,4,5-dimethoxy-	m-Hemipic acid. m-Hemipinic acid. $C_{10}H_{10}O_6$. See p812	226.19	nd (w) or pr (w +2)	174–5 (206) (179–82, rapid htng)				δ						B10[2], 382
p881	—,3-hydroxy-	$C_8H_6O_5$. See p812	182.13	nd, pr (eth-peth, w) λ^{al} 235 (3.4), 311 (3.3)	150d→ anh	sub			s^h	v	v			peth δ	B10[2], 352
p882	—,4-hydroxy-	$C_8H_6O_5$. See p812	182.13	rosettes (w)	204–5d→ anh				δ s^h	s	s		δ	peth δ	B10[1], 255
p882[1]	—,monoper-	$C_8H_6O_5$. See p812	182.13	nd (w)	110–2d				v	v			s	chl s	B9[2], 599
Ω p883	—,3-nitro-	$C_8H_5NO_6$. See p812	211.13	pa ye pr (w)	218				δ s^h	s^h	δ		i	chl, peth i	B9, 823
Ω p884	—,—,anhydride	$C_8H_3NO_5$. See p812	193.12	nd (aa, ace, al)	164				i	s^h		s	δ	aa s^h	B17[2], 468
p885	—,—,diethyl ester	$C_{12}H_{13}NO_6$. See p812	267.24	pr (al), nd (peth)	46				i	v	v				B9[2], 607
Ω p887	—,4-nitro-	$C_8H_5NO_6$. See p812	211.13	pa ye nd (w, eth)	165–6				s	s			i	AcOEt s^h chl, peth, CS_2 i	B9[2], 606
Ω p888	—,—,imide	$C_8H_4N_2O_4$. See p830	192.13	col nd (w), ye lf (al-ace) λ^{al} 231 (4.25)	202				$δ^h$	δ s^h		s		aa s	B21[2], 373
p889	—,—,dimethyl ester	$C_{10}H_9NO_6$. See p812	239.19	cr (dil al)	69–71 (66)				i	s				MeOH s	B9[2], 607
p890	—,—,piperazinium salt	$C_8H_5NO_6 \cdot C_4H_{10}N_2$. See p812	297.27	wh cr	201.5–4.5 d				s^h	s^h	δ				Am 70, 2758
p891	—,tetrabromo-	$C_8H_2Br_4O_4$. See p812	481.74	nd (w)	266d→ anh				δ s^h	δ				os δ	B9[1], 367
Ω p892	—,—,anhydride	$C_8Br_4O_3$. See p812	463.72	nd (aa-xyl) λ^{cy} 255 (1.55), 326 (0.15), 345 (0.25)	279.5–80.5				i	i			δ	$PhNO_2$ s os $δ^h$	B17[2], 468
Ω p893	—,tetrachloro-	$C_8H_2Cl_4O_4$. See p812	303.92	pl (w)	98d→ anh 250d				δ d^h			v	δ	chl δ	B9[2], 604
Ω p894	—,—,anhydride	$C_8Cl_4O_3$. See p812	285.90	pr, nd (sub) $\lambda^{Pr_2O-Me_2C}$ 240 (4.7), 310 sh (3.1), 335 (3.6)	255–6.5	sub			d^h		δ				B17[2], 467
p895	—,—,monoethyl ester	$C_{10}H_6Cl_4O_4$. See p812	331.97	pr (dil al)	94–5	d 150			δ	v	v				B9[2], 604
p896	—,tetraiodo-, anhydride	$C_8I_4O_3$. See p812	651.71	ye pr, nd (aa, $PhNO_2$), nd (sub) λ^{cy} 270 (0.9), 322 (0.15), 342 (0.1)	327–8 (325)	sub			i	i			i	aa $δ^h$ oos i	B17[2], 468
—	**Phthalic anhydride**	see Phthalic acid, anhydride													
Ω p897	Phthalide	α-Hydroxy-o-toluic acid lactone. 1(2)-Isobenzofuranone.	134.14	(i) nd or pl (w) λ^{al} 272 (3.0), 285 (3.0)	(i) 75 (st) (ii) 65.8 (unst)	290	1.1636[29 over 4]	1.536[99]	s^h	v	v				B17[2], 332
Ω p898	—,3-benzylidene-(trans)	$C_{15}H_{10}O_2$. See p897	222.25	mcl pr λ^{al} 239 (4.13), 296 (4.31), 340 (4.32)	108				i	s^h					B17[1], 399
Ω p899	—,3,3-diphenyl-	Phthalophenone. Triphenylcarbinol-o-carboxyhc lactone.	286.33	lf (al)	120	235[15]									B17, 391
Ω p900	—,6-nitro-	$C_8H_5NO_4$. See p897	179.13	ye nd (al, aa)	145				i	s	s		s	aa s chl s^h	B17[2], 334
—	**Phthalimide**	see Phthalic acid, imide													

For explanations, symbols and abbreviations see beginning of table. For structural formulas see end of table.

No.	Name	Synonyms and Formula	Mol. wt.	Color, crystalline form, specific rotation and λ_{max} (log ε)	m.p. °C	b.p. °C	Density	n_D	w	al	eth	ace	bz	other solvents	Ref.
	Phthalocyanine														
Ωp901	**Phthalocyanine**	Tetrabenzoporphyrazine.	514.55	grsh-bl mcl with purp luster (quinoline) $\lambda^{1-Bromonaphthalene}$ 549 (3.85), 575 (4.06), 600 (4.66), 632 (4.86)	does not melt	sub 550d (vac)	....	....	i	i	i	....	....	PhNH₂ s os i	**J1938**, 1151
—	**Phthalonic acid**	see **Acetic acid, (2-carboxyphenyl)-2-oxo-***													
—	**Phthalyl chloride**...	see **Phthalic acid, dichloride**													
—	**Phthiocol**........	see **1,4-Naphthoquinone, 2-hydroxy-3-methyl-***													
Ωp902	**Physostigmine**.....	Eserine. $C_{15}H_{21}N_3O_2$	275.35	orth pr (eth, bz) $[\alpha]_D^{17}-82$ (chl, c = 1.3), $[\alpha]_D^{25}-120$ (bz, c = 1) λ^{MeOH} 252 (4.11), 309 (3.50)	(i) 105–6 (st) (ii) 86–7 (unst)	....	....	....	δ	s	s	....	s	chl s	**B23²**, 330
Ωp903	**—,2-hydroxy-benzoate**	Eserin salicylate. $C_{15}H_{21}N_3O_2 \cdot C_7H_6O_3$. See p902	413.48	pr (al), lt, air, heat → red pr	185–7	....	....	....	δ sʰ	s vʰ	δ	....	....	chl s	**B23²**, 332
p904	**—,sulfate**........	$2(C_{15}H_{21}N_3O_2) \cdot H_2SO_4$. See p902	648.79	dlq sc (ace-eth) $[\alpha]_D-130$ (w)	140–2 (anh)	....	....	....	v	v	δ	s	....	....	**B23²**, 332
p905	**Phytadiene(d)**	2,6,10,14-Tetramethyl-13,15-hexadecadiene. $C_{20}H_{38}$	278.53	col $[\alpha]_D+0.89$ (undil) λ^{al} 230 (4.20)	....	186–8¹⁴	0.8260	....	....	....	....	....	....	peth, MeOH, aa ∞	**B1³**, 1030
Ωp906	**Phytol (dl)**........	3,7,11,15-Tetramethyl-2-hexadecen-1-ol*. $C_{20}H_{40}O$	296.54	λ^{al} 212 (3.04)	....	202–4¹⁰ 140–1⁰·⁰³	0.8497₄²⁵	1.4595²⁵	i	....	....	....	....	os s	**B1³**, 1966
p907	**Picein**..........	p-Hydroxyacetophenone-D-glucoside. $C_{14}H_{18}O_7$	298.30	nd (w + 1), nd (MeOH) $[\alpha]_D-86.5$	195–6	....	....	....	sʰ δ	s	s	....	....	aa s AcOEt δ chl i	**B31**, 226
Ωp908	**Picene**..........	Dibenzo[a,i]phenanthrene. 3,4-Benzochrysene. $C_{22}H_{14}$	278.36	lf, pl (xyl, Py cumene, sub), cr (w + 1) λ^{bz} 287 (2.99), 304 (4.53), 315 (4.28), 329 (4.35), 358 (3.92), 376 (2.92)	367–9	518–20 sub 300²	....	....	i	δ	....	....	δʰ	cumene s con sulf s (bl flr) chl, aa δʰ	**B5³**, 2555
—	**Picoline**	see **Pyridine, methyl-**													
—	**Picolinic acid**.....	see **2-Pyridinecarboxylic acid***													
—	**Picramic acid**	see **Phenol, 2-amino-4,6-dinitro-***													
—	**Picric acid**	see **Phenol, 2,4,6-trinitro-***													
Ωp909	**Picrolonic acid**	....	264.21	ye nd (al)	116–7 (d125)	....	....	....	δʰ	sʰ	sʰ	....	....	MeOH sʰ	**B24²**, 25
Ωp910	**Picropodophyllin**...	$C_{22}H_{22}O_8$	414.42	col nd (al, MeOH, bz) λ^{al} 208.5 (4.76), 289.5 (3.66)	228	....	....	....	i	vʰ	s	v	s	chl, MeOH v alk s peth i	**B19**, 424
Ωp911	**Picrotoxin**	Cocculin. $C_{30}H_{34}O_{13}$	602.60	rh lf, $[\alpha]_D^{16}-29.3$ (absal, c = 4)	203–4	....	....	....	δ vʰ	s vʰ	δ	....	....	Py v chl δ	**Am 79**, 5550
—	**Picryl chloride**.....	see **Benzene, 2-chloro-1,3,5-trinitro-***													
p912	**Pilocarpidine (d)**...	$C_{10}H_{14}N_2O_2$	194.24	syr, $[\alpha]_D^{20}+81.3$ (w, al, chl)	....	....	....	....	s	v	δ	....	....		**B27²**, 694
p913	**—,nitrate (d)**......	$C_{10}H_{14}N_2O_2 \cdot HNO_3$. See p912	257.25	pr (w), $[\alpha]_D^{20}+73.2$ (w)	137	....	....	....	s	s	....	....	....		**B27²**, 694
p914	**Pilocarpine**	$C_{11}H_{16}N_2O_2$	208.26	nd, $[\alpha]_D^{20}+100.5$ (w) λ^{MeOH} 216 (3.75)	34	260⁵	....	....	s	s	δ	....	δ	chl v peth i	**B27²**, 694
Ωp915	**—,hydrochloride** ..	$C_{11}H_{16}N_2O_2 \cdot HCl$. See p914	244.72	hyg cr	204–5 (198)	....	....	....	v	s	i	....	....	chl δ	**B27²**, 695
p916	**—,2-hydroxy-benzoate**	Pilocarpine salicylate. $C_{11}H_{16}N_2O_2 \cdot C_7H_6O_3$. See p914	346.39	nd or lf (al) $[\alpha]_D+63$	120	....	....	....	v	s	s	....	....		**B27**, 635
p917	**—,nitrate**........	$C_{11}H_{16}N_2O_2 \cdot HNO_3$. See p914	271.28	wh pw or cr (al) $[\alpha]_D+80$ (w, c = 4)	178 (cor)	....	....	....	v	sʰ δ	i	....	....	chl i	**B27²**, 695
p918	**—,sulfate**........	$(C_{11}H_{16}N_2O_2)_2 \cdot H_2SO_4$. See p914	514.60	hyg cr (al-eth) $[\alpha]_D^{20}+85$ (w, c = 7)	132	....	....	....	s	s	....	....	....		**B27**, 635
—	**Pilosine**	see **Carpiline**													

For explanations, symbols and abbreviations see beginning of table. For structural formulas see end of table.

Pimaric acid

No.	Name	Synonyms and Formula	Mol. wt.	Color, crystalline form, specific rotation and λ_{max} (log ε)	m.p. °C	b.p. °C	Density	n_D	w	al	eth	ace	bz	other solvents	Ref.
p919	**Pimaric acid** (d) ...	Dextropimaric acid. $C_{20}H_{30}O_2$	302.46	orh (ace), pr (al) $[\alpha]_D^{20} +87.3$ (chl) $\lambda <215$	218–9 (215.4 cor)	282[18]	....		i	s	s	...	..	Py v MeOH δ peth δ[h]	B9[2], 433
—	Pimelic acid........	see Heptanedioic acid*													
—	Pinacol	see 2,3-Butanediol, 2,3-dimethyl-*													
—	Pinacolone........	see 2-Butanone, 3,3-dimethyl-*													
p920	**Pinane** (d, cis)	....	138.26	$[\alpha]_D^{20} +23.3$ (undil) $\lambda <220$	−53	169[760] 60.1[18]	0.8560_4^{20}	1.4629^{20}	i	...	s	...	s	os s	B5[3], 254
Ω p921	—(dl).........	Pincocampane. $C_{10}H_{18}$. See p920	138.26	$\lambda <220$	....	164.5– 5.0[760]	0.8551_4^{20}	1.4609^{20}	i	...	s	...	s	os s	B5[1], 47
p922	—(l, cis).........	$C_{10}H_{18}$. See p920	138.26	$[\alpha]_D^{20} -47$ (undil) $\lambda <220$	....	167–8[757]	0.8556^{21}	1.4645^{20}	i	...	s	...	s	os s	B5[3], 254
Ω p923	**α-Pinene** (dl)	$C_{10}H_{16}$	136.24	oil λ^{al} 210 (3.64)	−55	156.2[760] 51.4[20]	0.8582_4^{20}	1.4658^{20}	i	∞	∞	...	...	chl ∞	B5[3], 366
Ω p924	**β-Pinene** (d)	Nopinene. Pseudopinene. $C_{10}H_{16}$	136.24	$[\alpha]_D +28.6$ λ^{al} 208 (3.72)	....	164–6[760] 59.7[20]	0.8654_4^{20}	1.4789^{20}	i	s	s	...	s	chl v os s	B5[3], 378
p925	—(l)...........	$C_{10}H_{16}$. See p924	136.24	$[\alpha]_D^{25} -21.5$ λ^{al} 208 (3.72)	....	164[760] 59.7[20]	0.8694_4^{20}	1.4762^{20}	i	s	s	...	s	chl v os s	B5[3], 376
p926	**Pinic acid** (dl) (a form)	3-Carboxy-2,2-dimethylcyclo-butylacetic acid.	186.21	wh pr (w)	101–2.5	214–6[9]	1.0925_4^{109}	1.4458_4^{109}	δ	...	...	...	..		B9[2], 529
p927	—(dl) (b form).....	$C_9H_{14}O_4$. See p926	186.21	....	68	214–6[9]	....								B9[2], 529
p928	—(dl) (c form).....	$C_9H_{14}O_4$. See p926	186.21	pl	58	214–6[9]	....								B9[2], 529
p929	—,—(l).........	$C_9H_{14}O_4$. See p926	186.21	nd (w)	135–6	....	....		s[h]	...	...	...	..		B9[1], 320
p930	**Pinol** (dl).......	dl-Sobrerone. 6,8-Epoxy-1-p-menthene.	152.24	$[\alpha]_D -7.1$ (ace)	....	183–4[760] 76–7[14]	0.9515_4^{20}	1.4695^{20}	...	s	s	...	..		B17[2], 44
p931	—,hydrate (trans,dl)	$C_{10}H_{16}O. H_2O.$ See p930....	170.25	pl or nd (w)	132 (128)	270–1 157–8[12]	....		s	v	v	...	..		C55, 4569
—	Pinosylvin........	see Stilbene, 3,5-dihydroxy- (trans)													
—	Pipecoline........	see Piperidine, methyl-*													
—	Pipecolyl carbinol .	see Piperidine, 2(2-hydroxyethyl)-													
Ω p932	**Piperazine**........	Diethylenediamine. Hexahydropyrazine.	86.14	hyg pl or lf (al) λ^{gas} 196 (3.7)	106 (106–9)	146[760]	....	1.446^{113}	v	s	i	...	..	glycols v	B23[2], 3
p933	—,dihydrobromide	$C_4H_{10}N_2. 2HBr.$ See p932...	247.97	wh nd	d	....	....		v	i	i	...	..		J1957, 1881
p934	—,dihydrochloride monohydrate	$C_4H_{10}N_2. 2HCl. H_2O.$ See p932	177.07	nd (dil al)	82.5–3	....	....		v	i	i	...	..		B23[2], 4
Ω p935	—,hexahydrate....	Arthriticine. $C_4H_{10}N_2. 6H_2O.$ See p932	194.23	wh (w)	44–5	125–30	....		s	s	s	...	..		C47, 10014
Ω p936	—,1-benzyl-	$C_{11}H_{16}N_2.$ See p932........	176.26			145–7[12] 88–9[0.3]	....	1.5430^{28}	s	s	s	...	..		Am 77, 753
p937	—,1,4-bis(4-methoxy-benzoyl)	1,4-Dianisoylpiperazine. $C_{20}H_{22}N_2O_4.$ See p932	354.41	wh	192.5–3.5	....			i	s[h]	i	...	..		Am 56, 150
p938	—,1,4-bis-(phenylacetyl)-	N,N'-Di-α-toluylpiperazine. $C_{20}H_{22}N_2O_2.$ See p932	322.41	wh	150–1	....			δ	s[h]	δ	...	..		Am 56, 150
p939	—,1,4-bis-(3-phenyl-propanoyl)-	1,4-Bis(hydrocinnamyl)-piperazine. $C_{22}H_{26}N_2O_2.$ See p932	350.47	wh	122.5–3	....			i	s[h]	δ	...	..		Am 56, 150
p940	—,1,4-dimethyl-	$C_6H_{14}N_2.$ See p932	114.19			131–2[764]	0.8600_4^{20}	1.4474^{20}	v	s	s	...	..		B23[2], 5
Ω p941	—,2,5-dimethyl- (cis)	$C_6H_{14}N_2.$ See p932	114.19	rh bipym nd or pr (chl) λ^{iso} 277 (1.3), 308 (0.4), 313 (0.5), 319 (0.4)	114	162 sub	....	1.4720^{20}	v	v	δ	...	δ	chl v	B23[2], 21
Ω p942	—,—(trans).......	$C_6H_{14}N_2.$ See p932	114.19	mcl pl or pr (bz, chl)	118–9	162 sub	....		v	v	δ	...	δ s[h]	chl s	B23[2], 19
Ω p943	—,2,6-dimethyl- (cis)	$C_6H_{14}N_2.$ See p932	114.19	lf or pl (bz)	111–3	162	....		s	s	i	...	δ	peth v chl s	B23[1], 8
Ω p944	—,1,4-dinitroso-	$C_4H_8N_4O_2.$ See p932	144.14	pa ye pl (w)	158	....	....		δ	v[h]	δ	...	..		B23[1], 7
p945	—,1-ethyl-.......	$C_6H_{14}N_2.$ See p932	114.19			154[753]	....		v	s	s	...	..		B23[2], 5
Ω p946	—,1-methyl-	$C_5H_{12}N_2.$ See p932	100.17			138[760]	....	1.4378^{10}	v	v	v	...	..		C51, 10538
Ω p947	—,2-methyl-.....	$C_5H_{12}N_2.$ See p932	100.17	hyg lf (al)	62	155[763]	....		v	s	s	...	s	chl s	B23[2], 16
Ω p948	—,1-phenyl-	$C_{10}H_{14}N_2.$ See p932	162.24	pa ye oil	....	286.5[760] 156–7[10]	1.0621^{20}	1.5875^{20}	i	∞	∞	...	..		C49, 11667
Ω p949	**1-Piperazine-carboxylic acid, ethyl ester**	....	158.20			237 116–7[12]	....	1.4760^{25}	s	s	s	...	..		B23[2], 9
Ω p950	**1,4-Piperazine-dicarboxylic acid, diethyl ester**	....	230.27	nd (hx)	49	315 131–3[3]	....		s	s	s	...	..		B23, 12
Ω p951	**2,5-Piperazine-dione**	Glycine anhydride.	114.11	ta or pl (w)	318–20d sub 260	....	....		δ	δ[h]	...	...	..	HCl s	B24[2], 141

For explanations, symbols and abbreviations see beginning of table. For structural formulas see end of table.

No.	Name	Synonyms and Formula	Mol. wt.	Color. crystalline form. specific rotation and λ_{max} (log ε)	m.p. °C	b.p. °C	Density	n_D	w	al	eth	ace	bz	other solvents	Ref.
	Piperic acid														
—	Piperic acid	see 2,4-Pentadienoic acid, 5(3,4-methylene-dioxyphenyl)-*													
Ω p952	Piperidine	Hexahydropyridine. Pentamethyleneimine.	85.15	λ^{gas} 198 (3.5)	−9	106.0 17.7[20]	0.8606_4^{20}	1.4530^{20}	∞	∞	s	s	s	chl s	B20[2], 6
—	—,2-acetonyl-	see Isopelletierine													
p953	—,1-acetyl-	$C_7H_{13}NO$. See p952	127.19			226–7[760] 109[18]	1.011[9]	1.4790^{25}	∞	s					B20[2], 33
p954	—,2-allyl-	$C_8H_{15}N$. See p952	125.22			170–1	0.8823_4^{15}								B20, 147
Ω p955	—,1-benzoyl-	$C_{12}H_{15}NO$. See p952	189.26	tcl	49	320–1 180[15]			i	s	s				B20[2], 34
—	—,4-benzoxy-2,2,6-trimethyl-	see Iso-β-eucaine													
p956	—,1-butyl-	$C_9H_{19}N$. See p952	141.26			175–7 47–8[20]	0.8245_4^{20}	1.4467^{20}							B20[2], 13
p957	—,2-butyl-(d)	$C_9H_{19}N$. See p952	141.26	$[\alpha]_D$ + 15.7			0.8512								B20, 127
p958	—,—(dl)	$C_9H_{19}N$. See p952	141.26			191–3 75[14]	0.8529_4^{15}		i					os s	B20, 128
p959	—,—(l)	$C_9H_{19}N$. See p952	141.26	$[\alpha]_D^{16}$ − 18.7		196–7	0.8533								B20, 127
p960	—,3-butyl-	$C_9H_{19}N$. See p952	141.26			196–7			i	s	s	s		chl s	B20[1], 33
p961	—,1-sec-butyl-(dl)	$C_9H_{19}N$. See p952	141.26			175–6[768]	0.8378_4^{20}	1.4506^{20}			s	s			B20[2], 13
p962	—,—(l)	$C_9H_{19}N$. See p952	141.26	$[\alpha]_D^{25}$ − 54.59		175[760] 75–6[25]	0.835_4^{25}	1.4486^{21}			s	s			J1935, 1072
p963	—,1-tert-butyl-	$C_9H_{19}N$. See p952	141.26			166[763]	0.8465_4^{20}	1.4532^{20}	δ	∞	∞				B20[2], 13
p964	—,2,4-diethyl-	$C_9H_{19}N$. See p952	141.26			174–9	0.8722^0		δ						B20, 128
p965	—,2,5-diethyl-	$C_9H_{19}N$. See p952	141.26			190 100–5[22]	0.8722^0				v			chl v	B20, 128
p966	—,3,4-diethyl-(cis)	$C_9H_{19}N$. See p952	141.26	$[\alpha]_D^{22}$ + 26.0 (95 % al, c = 4.35)	70[12]										Am 66, 1881
p967	—,—(trans)	$C_9H_{19}N$. See p952	141.26			193[720]									B20, 128
p969	—,1,2-dimethyl-(d)	N-Methyl-α-pipecoline. $C_7H_{15}N$. See p952	113.20	$[\alpha]_D^{15}$ + 68.8 (undil)		127	0.825[16]	1.4395^{20}							C24, 3240
p970	—,—(dl)	$C_7H_{15}N$. See p952	113.20			127.9[760]	0.824_4^{15}	1.4395^{20}	s	s	s			CS_2 s	B20, 95
p971	—,1,3-dimethyl-(dl)	N-Methyl-β-pipecoline. $C_7H_{15}N$. See p952	113.20			124–6	0.818[15]								B20, 100
p972	—,2,3-dimethyl-	α,β-Lupetidine. $C_7H_{15}N$. See p952	113.20			138–40[720]			s	v					B20[1], 29
p973	—,2,4-dimethyl-(d)	α,γ-Lupetidine. $C_7H_{15}N$. See p952	113.20	$[\alpha]_D$ + 23.2		140–2	0.845								B20, 108
p974	—,—(dl)	$C_7H_{15}N$. See p952	113.20			140–2	0.8615^0	1.4366^{25}		v	v			ac s	B20[1], 29
p975	—,2,5-dimethyl-	α,β'-Lupetidine. $C_7H_{15}N$. See p952	113.20			138–40 (cor)		1.4452^{25}		v				ac s	B20, 108
Ω p976	—,2,6-dimethyl-	α,α'-Lupetidine. $C_7H_{15}N$. See p952	113.20			127.5– 8.3[768]	0.8158_4^{25}	1.4377^{20}						ac s	B20[2], 60
p977	—,3,3-dimethyl-	β,β-Lupetidine. $C_7H_{15}N$. See p952	113.20			137 45–6[33]		1.4452^{25}		v					B20[1], 29
p978	—,4,4-dimethyl-	γ,γ-Lupetidine. $C_7H_{15}N$. See p952	113.20			145–6 30–2[12]		1.4489^{25}	∞					os v	B20[1], 29
p979	—,4(dimethylamino)-1-phenyl-	Irenal. $C_{13}H_{20}N_2$. See p952	204.32	lf (bz)	47.5–8.5	123–6[0.5]								s[h] dil HCl v	H26, 1132
p980	—,1(2,2-dimethylpropyl)-	N-Neopentylpiperidine. $C_{10}H_{21}N$. See p952	155.29			188	0.8608_4^{20}	1.4593^{20}		s	s				B20[2], 13
p981	—,1-dodecyl-	$C_{17}H_{35}N$. See p952	253.48	pa ye		161[5] 114–6[0.4]	0.8378_4^{20}	1.4588^{20}							J1952, 1057
Ω p982	—,1-ethyl-	$C_7H_{15}N$. See p952	113.20			130.8	0.8237_4^{20}	1.4480^{20}							B20[2], 13
p983	—,2-ethyl-(d)	$C_7H_{15}N$. See p952	113.20	$[\alpha]_D$ + 17.1		142–3.5	0.8680^4		δ						B20, 104
Ω p984	—,—(dl)	$C_7H_{15}N$. See p952	113.20			142–3[719] 73–5[52]	0.8651_4^0	1.4494^{21}	δ						B20[1], 28
p985	—,—(l)	$C_7H_{15}N$. See p952	113.20	$[\alpha]_D$ − 14.9		143[720]	0.8680^4	1.4544^{20}	δ						B20[1], 28
p986	—,3-ethyl-(dl)	$C_7H_{15}N$. See p952	113.20	fum in air		152.6	0.8565_4^{23}	1.4531^{20}	δ			s			B20[1], 29
p987	—,—(l)	$C_7H_{15}N$. See p952	113.20	$[\alpha]_D^{15}$ − 4.5		155			δ			s			B20, 106
p988	—,4-ethyl-	$C_7H_{15}N$. See p952	113.20			156–8[760]	0.8759^0	1.4503^{25}	δ						B20, 108
—	—,1,4-ethylene-	see Quinuclidine													
p989	—,1-heptyl-	$C_{12}H_{25}N$. See p952	183.34			239.5 100–3[9]	0.8316^{20}	1.4531^{20}							C45, 2940
p990	—,1-hexyl-	$C_{11}H_{23}N$. See p952	169.31			219.2 103–4[20]	0.8292^{20}	1.4522^{20}							C55, 2465
p991	—,1(2-hydroxyethyl)-	2-N-Piperidylethanol. $C_7H_{15}NO$. See p952	129.20			200–2[742] 90[12]	0.9732_{25}^{25}	1.4749^{20}	∞	v					B20[2], 18
p992	—,2(1-hydroxyethyl)-	Methyl-2-piperidylcarbinol. $C_7H_{15}NO$. See p952	129.20			106–10[18]									B21[2], 9
p993	—,2(2-hydroxyethyl)-	Pipecolyl carbinol. $C_7H_{15}NO$. See p952	129.20		39–40	234.5 145–6[36]	1.01[17]		v	v	v				B21[2], 9
p994	—,3(2-hydroxyethyl)-	$C_7H_{15}NO$. See p952	129.20			121–3[6]	1.0106_4^{25}	1.4888^{25}	v	v	v				B21[2], 10
p995	—,4(2-hydroxyethyl)-	$C_7H_{15}NO$. See p952	129.20	syr	132–3.5	227–8 120–5[15]	1.0059_4^{15}	1.4907^{20}	s	v	v				B21[2], 10
—	—,2(1-hydroxypropyl)-	see Conhydrine													

For explanations, symbols and abbreviations see beginning of table. For structural formulas see end of table.

No.	Name	Synonyms and Formula	Mol. wt.	Color, crystalline form, specific rotation and λ_{max} (log ε)	m.p. °C	b.p. °C	Density	n_D	w	al	eth	ace	bz	other solvents	Ref.
	Piperidine														
p996	—,1-isobutyl-	$C_9H_{19}N$. See p952	141.26			$160-1^{740}$ 87^{43}	0.8161^{25}	1.4382^{25}	v						B20, 20
p997	—,2-isobutyl-	$C_9H_{19}N$. See p952	141.26			181–2	0.8510_4^{22}	1.4553^{22}		v	v				B20, 128
p998	—,1-isopropyl-	$C_8H_{17}N$. See p952	127.23			$149-50^{757}$	0.8389_4^{20}	1.4491^{20}	s						B20², 13
p999	—,2-isopropyl- (dl)	$C_8H_{17}N$. See p952	127.23			162	0.8668^0		δ i^h						B20, 120
p1000	—,—(l)	$C_8H_{17}N$. See p952	127.23	$[\alpha]_D -13.1$		161.5	0.8503^{19}		δ i^h						B20, 121
p1001	—,4-isopropyl-	$C_8H_{17}N$. See p952	127.23			168–71 $66-70^{15}$			δ i^h						B20, 121
p1002	—,1-methyl-	$C_6H_{13}N$. See p952	99.18	λ^{eth} 213 (3.20)		107	0.8159_4^{20}	1.4355^{20}	v s^h	∞	∞				B20², 12
Ω p1003	—,2-methyl-(d)	d-α-Pipecoline. $C_6H_{13}N$. See p952	99.18	$[\alpha]_D^{15} +18.7$ (chl), $(\alpha)_D^{22}$ $+5.6$ (al)		$117-$ 7.5^{745}		1.4459^{20}							B20², 57
p1004	—,—(dl)	α-Pipecoline. $C_6H_{13}N$. See p952	99.18		−4.9	$117-8^{747}$	0.8436_4^{24}	1.4459^{20}	v	s	s			dil KOH i	B20², 57
Ω p1005	—,3-methyl-(dl)	β-Pipecoline. $C_6H_{13}N$. See p952	99.18	λ^{iso} 268 (2.63)	0–5	$125-6^{763}$	0.8446_4^{24}	1.4470^{20}	v						B20², 58
p1006	—,—(l)	$C_6H_{13}N$. See p952	99.18	$[\alpha]_D^{25} -4$ λ^{iso} 268 (2.63)		124			v						B20², 58
Ω p1007	—,4-methyl-	γ-Pipecoline. $C_6H_{13}N$. See p952	99.18			132–4 (127–9)	0.8674^0	1.4458^{20}	v						B20, 101
p1008	—,1(3-methyl-butyl)-	N-Isoamylpiperidine. $C_{10}H_{21}N$. See p952	155.29			188–9 $76-9^{20}$			δ			s			B20², 14
p1009	—,1(2-methyl-2-pentyl)-	$C_{11}H_{23}N$. See p952	169.31			205–7	0.8517_4^{20}	1.4592^{20}				s			B20², 14
p1010	—,1(3-methyl-3-pentyl)-	$C_{11}H_{23}N$. See p952	169.31			214^{752}	0.8614_4^{20}	1.4637^{20}							B20², 14
—	—,1-methyl-2-propyl-	see Coniine, N-methyl-													
Ω p1011	—,1-nitroso-	$C_5H_{10}N_2O$. See p952	114.15	pa ye λ^{hx} 354 (1.91), 366 (2.04), 377 (2.00)		217^{721} 109^{20}	$1.0631_4^{18.5}$	$1.4933^{18.5}$	s					HCl s	B20¹, 24
p1012	—,1-nonyl-	$C_{14}H_{29}N$. See p952	211.40			$135-7^{11}$	0.8313^{25}	1.4538^{25}							Am 56, 2419
p1013	—,1-octyl-	$C_{13}H_{27}N$. See p952	197.37			$136-8^{13}$ 89^1	0.8324_4^{20}	1.4544^{20}							C43, 3378
p1014	—,1-pentyl-	$C_{10}H_{21}N$. See p952	155.29			198.2^{760} 80^8	0.8282^{20}	1.4498^{20}							B20², 13
p1015	—,1-phenyl-	$C_{11}H_{15}N$. See p952	161.25	λ^{MeOH} 253 (4.0)		$257-8^{752}$ 126.5^{15}				v	v		v	chl v	B20², 14
p1016	—,2-propenyl-(d)	β-Coniceine. $C_8H_{15}N$. See p952	125.22	nd, $[\alpha]_D^{15} +49.9$	39	168–9			δ	s	s				B20, 147
p1017	—,—(dl)	$C_8H_{15}N$. See p952	125.22	nd	8	$168.5-$ 70^{753}	0.8716_4^{15}		δ	s	s				B20, 147
p1018	—,—(l)	$C_8H_{15}N$. See p952	125.22	nd, $[\alpha]_D^{15} -50.47$	39.5–40	168–9	0.8672_4^{15}		δ	s	s				B20, 147
p1019	—,1-propyl-	$C_8H_{17}N$. See p952	127.23			151.2	0.8231^{20}	1.4446^{20}	s	v	v				B20², 13
—	—,2-propyl-	see Coniine													
p1020	—,3-propyl-(d)	$C_8H_{17}N$. See p952	127.23	$[\alpha]_D^{16} +5.9$		174^{752}	0.8517_4^{19}		s	s	s				B20, 120
p1021	—,—(dl)	$C_8H_{17}N$. See p952	127.23			174^{758}	0.8475_4^{26}		s	s	s				B20, 119
p1022	—,—(l)	$C_8H_{17}N$. See p952	127.23	oil, $[\alpha]_D^{16} -6.6$		174^{752}	0.8517_4^{19}		s	s	s				B20, 120
Ω p1023	—,4-propyl-	$C_8H_{17}N$. See p952	127.23			172^{748} (179)	0.864^{23}	1.4465^{23}							B20, 120
Ω p1024	—,2,2,6,6-tetra-methyl-	$C_9H_{19}N$. See p952	141.26		155.5–6.5		0.8367_4^{16}	1.4455^{20}				s			B20, 129
p1025	—,2,2,4-tri-methyl-	$C_8H_{17}N$. See p952	127.23			148	0.832^{15}	1.4458^{20}	δ	s	s				B20, 124
p1026	—,2,3,6-tri-methyl-	$C_8H_{17}N$. See p952	127.23			36^8	0.8302_4^{20}	1.4434^{20}							C43, 2959
p1027	—,2,4,6-tri-methyl-	$C_8H_{17}N$. See p952	127.23			165–6 (151–3)	0.8315_4^{19}	1.4412^{20}	δ	∞	∞				B20², 64
p1028	1-Piperidinecar-boxaldehyde	N-Formylpiperidine	113.16	pa ye		222 $106-$ 10^{17}	1.0205_4^{25}	1.4700^{20}	∞	∞	∞		∞	chl, aa, lig ∞	B20², 33
p1029	1-Piperidinecar-bodithioic acid, piperidinium salt	Piperidinium cyclopenta-methylenedithiocarbamate.	246.44	pa ye lf (al), cr (CS₂-eth)	174				v^h	v			v		B20², 37
p1030	4-Piperidinecar-boxylic acid	Hexahydroisonicotinic acid. Isonipecotic acid.	129.16	nd (w)	ca. 326				s	i					D22¹, 480
p1031	—,ethyl ester	Ethyl isonipecotate. $C_8H_{15}NO_2$. See p1030	157.22	col oil		$100-1^{10}$		1.4591^{20}	s	s	s		s		C49, 12473
p1032	—,methyl ester	Methyl isonipecotate. $C_7H_{13}NO_2$. See p1030	143.19	col oil		$107-10^{22}$ $88-9^9$		1.4635^{25}	s	s	s		s		C49, 12473
p1033	—,1-methyl-, methyl ester	$C_8H_{15}NO_2$. See p1030	157.22	λ^{al} 204 (3.0)		$96-100^{20}$ $82-6^{10}$		1.4539^{24}	s	s	s		s		B22, 486
p1034	—,1-methyl-4-phenyl-, ethyl ester hydro-chloride	Demerol hydrochloride. Meperidine hydrochloride. Pethidine hydrochloride.	283.80	cr (al)	186–9				s	δ	i	s	i	AcOEt s	C33, 9442

For explanations, symbols and abbreviations see beginning of table. For structural formulas see end of table.

No.	Name	Synonyms and Formula	Mol. wt.	Color, crystalline form, specific rotation and λ_{max} (log ε)	m.p. °C	b.p. °C	Density	n_D	Solubility						Ref.
									w	al	eth	ace	bz	other solvents	

2,4-Piperidinedione

No.	Name	Synonyms and Formula	Mol. wt.	Color etc.	m.p.	b.p.	Density	n_D	w	al	eth	ace	bz	other	Ref.
p1034[1]	2,4-Piperidine-dione, 3,3-diethyl-	Piperidione.............	169.23	nd (w)	103–5 (102–7)	....	....		v	v	.	.	.	MeOH, chl v	C44, 1506
—	Piperidinic acid	see Butanoic acid 4-amino-*													
—	Piperidinium, cyclopenta-methylene dithio-carbamate	see 1-Piperidinecarbodithoic acid, piperidinium salt													
Ω p1035	2-Piperidone	5-Aminopentanoic acid lactam*. δ-Valerolactam.	99.13	hyg λ^{al} <217 (3.0)	39–40	256[760] 137[14]	....		v	v	v	.	.	dil ac s con ac i	B21, 238
p1036	4-Piperidone, hydrochloride	....	135.60	cr (+1.5 al, al-eth), cr (w+1)	147–9 139–41d (+al) 140–5d (+w)				v						B21[2], 215
p1037	2-Piperidone, 3-hydroxy-(dl)	$C_5H_9NO_2$. See p1035...	115.13	nd or pr (AcOEt)	141–2				v	v	δ	.	.	AcOEt, chl δ	B21[2], 411
p1038	—,5-hydroxy-.....	$C_5H_9NO_2$. See p1035.	115.13	(al, al-AcOEt)	145–6 (cor)				v	v	i	.	i	AcOEt, chl δ	B21[2], 412
Ω p1039	4-Piperidone, 2,2,6,6-tetra-methyl-	Triacetoneamine. $C_9H_{17}NO.H_2O$. See p1036	173.26	rh pl (moist eth, +1w), nd (eth)	58 (hyd), 34.9 (anh)	205			s	s	s	.	.	....	B21[2], 222
Ω p1040	Piperine	1-Piperylpiperidine. $C_{17}H_{19}NO_3$	285.35	pr (AcOEt), pl or mcl pr (al), cr (bz-lig) λ^{al} 345 (4.5)	130–2.5 (129.5)				i	s v^h	δ	.	s	chl v Py, aa, MeOH s peth i	B20[2], 53
p1041	—,hydroiodide diiodide	$2(C_{17}H_{19}NO_3).HI.I_2$. See p1040	952.42	bl nd	145				s	v^h	v	.	.	chl, CS_2 v	B20, 80
—	Piperitenone	see 3-Terpinolenone													
p1042	Piperitone(d)	Δ^1-p-Methanone-3. 1-Methyl-4-isopropylcyclohexenone-3. $C_{10}H_{16}O$	152.24	yesh in air $[\alpha]_D^{20}$ +49.13 (undil) λ^{al} 234 (4.18)	......	222–30 116– 8.5[20]	0.9344[20]₄	1.4848[20]	.	.	.	.	s	....	B7[2], 74
p1043	—(dl)	$C_{10}H_{16}O$. See p1042.......	152.24	λ^{al} 234 (4.18)		232–3[769] 113[18]	0.9331[20]₄	1.4845[20]							B7[2], 75
p1044	—(l)	$C_{10}H_{16}O$. See p1042.......	152.24	$[\alpha]_D^{20}$ −51.53 (undil) λ^{al} 234 (4.18)		235 109.5– 10.5[15]	0.9324[20]	1.4848[20]							B7[2], 75
Ω p1045	Piperolidine(dl)	δ-Coniceine. Indolizidine. Octahydropyrrocoline.	125.22		......	161.5[750] 65–7[18]	0.9012[15]₄	1.4748	δ	s	s	.	.	....	B20, 150
p1046	—(l)	$C_8H_{15}N$. See p1045........	125.22	$[\alpha]_D^{27}$ −7.89 (c = 1)	......	158[729] 65–7[18]	0.8976[23]₄	1.4748[20]	δ	s	s	.	.	....	B20, 150
—	Piperonal........	see Benzaldehyde,3,4-methylenedioxy-													
—	4-Piperone.......	see Verbenone													
—	Piperonyl alcohol .	see Toluene, α-hydroxy-3,4-methylenedioxy-													
—	Piperonylic acid ...	see Benzoic acid, 3,4-methylenedioxy-													
—	Pivalaldehyde	see Propanal,2,2-dimethyl-*													
—	Pivalic acid	see Propanoic acid, 2,2-dimethyl-*													
—	Pivalil	see 3,4-Hexanedione, 2,2,5,5-tetramethyl-*													
—	Pivalilindandione ..	see 1,3-Indandione, 2-tert-butyl-													
—	Pivaloin.........	see 3-Hexanone, 4-hydroxy-2,2,5,5-tetramethyl-*													
—	Pivalophenone.....	see 1-Propanone, 2,2-dimethyl-1-phenyl-*													
—	Plasmocid	see Antimalarine													
—	Plumbagin........	see 1,4-Naphthoquinone, 5-hydroxy-2-methyl-*													
Ω p1047	Podophyllotoxin ...	$C_{22}H_{22}O_8$	414.42	nd (MeOH, dil ace), wh cr (w+1 or 2) $[\alpha]_D^{20}$ −132.7 (chl, c = 2) λ^{al} 291 (3.64)	114–8 (hyd) 183–4 (anh)	....			δ	v	i	s	s^h	chl v aa s lig i	B19[2], 443
p1048	Polyglycolid	[-O-CH₂CO-]x		wh (PhNO₂)	223				.	.	i	.	i	....	B19[1], 679
p1049	Populin	Salicin benzoate..........	390.40	nd (w+2), pr (al) $[\alpha]_D$ −2.0 (Py, c = 5)	180	....			δ s^h	s^h	v	.	.	aa s	B31, 216

For explanations, symbols and abbreviations see beginning of table. For structural formulas see end of table.

No.	Name	Synonyms and Formula	Mol. wt.	Color. crystalline form. specific rotation and λ_{max} (log ε)	m.p. °C	b.p. °C	Density	n_D	Solubility						Ref.
									w	al	eth	ace	bz	other solvents	

Porphin

p1050	Porphin.........	Tetramethenetetrapyrrole. $C_{20}H_{14}N_4$	310.36	met red or og lf (chl-MeOH) λ^{bz} 396.5 (5.42), 489.5 (4.20), 519.5 (3.42), 563 (3.70), 569 (3.62), 616.5 (2.93)	darkens 360	300^{12} sub	1.336	....	i	i	i	i	s	diox s chl, aa δ Py	B26[2], 228
p1051	5β-Pregnane.....	17β-Ethyletiocholane. $C_{21}H_{36}$	288.52	mcl sc or pl (MeOH) $[\alpha]_D^{19}$ +21.2 (chl, c = 2)	83.5	....	1.032_4^{15}	....	i					chl s MeOH s[h]	E14, 17
p1052	5β-Pregnane-3α, 20α-diol	$C_{21}H_{36}O_2$. See p1051......	320.52	pl (ace) $[\alpha]_D^{20}$ +27.4 (al, c = 0.7) λ^{sulf} 320 (4.94), 430 (4.73)	243-4	....	1.15	....	...	δ	δ	s[h]	...	os δ	E14, 95
Ωp1053	5β-Pregnane-3α-20β-diol	$C_{21}H_{36}O_2$. See p1051	320.52	cr (al), $[\alpha]_D^{20}$ + 10 $\lambda^{97\%sulf}$ 239 (3.56), 323 (3.84), 428 (3.69), 496 sh (3.10)	244-6	....	....	....	...	s[h]					E14, 95
p1054	5β-Pregnane-3β, 20α-diol	$C_{21}H_{16}O_2$. See p1051......	320.52	cr (al, ace)	182	....	....	....	...	s[h]		s[h]	...		E14, 95
p1055	5β-Pregnane-3β, 20β-diol	$C_{21}H_{36}O_2$. See p1051	320.52	cr (AcOEt-peth or dil al)	174-6	....	....	....	δ	s[h]	...	...	...	AcOEt s peth δ	E14, 95
p1056	5β-Pregnane-3,20-dione	$C_{21}H_{32}O_2$. See p1051......	316.49	nd (dil al), cr (dil ace) $\lambda^{97\%sulf}$ 237 sh (3.70)	123	....	....	....	i	v[h]	s	s	...	os v	E14, 152
Ωp1057	5β-Pregnan-3α-ol-20-one	$C_{21}H_{14}O_3$. See p1051	318.51	nd (bz), cr (dil al), rosetts or nd (hx) $\lambda^{97\%sulf}$ 233 sh (3.62), 331 (3.86), 396 sh (2.76)	149.5	....	....	....	i	s[h]	...	...	s[h]	peth s[h]	E14, 115
p1058	5β-Pregnan-3β-ol-20-one	$C_{21}H_{34}O_2$. See p1051......	318.51	cr (dil al)	149	....	....	....	i	s[h]	...	...	s[h]		E14, 115
p1059	5β-Pregnan-20α-ol-3-one	$C_{21}H_{34}O_7$. See p1051	318.51	pr (ace)	152	....	....	....	...	...	...	s[h]	...		E14, 132
p1060	5β-Pregnan-20β-ol-3-one	$C_{21}H_{34}O_2$. See p1051	318.51	cr (dil MeOH)	172	....	....	....	...	...	...	...	...	MeOH s[h]	E14, 132
Ωp1061	5-Pregnene-3β-ol-20-one	$C_{21}H_{32}O_2$. See p1051	316.49	nd (dil al) $[\alpha]_D^{20}$ + 28 (al) λ^{al} 205 (3.52)	193	....	....	....	δ	δ	...	δ	δ	CCl_4 δ lig i	E14, 114
p1062	4-Pregnene-11β, 17α,20β,21-tetrol-3-one	Reichstein's substance E. $C_{21}H_{32}O_5$. See p1051	364.49	cr (aq ace + w) $[\alpha]_D^{20}$ +87 (al) $\lambda^{97\%sulf}$ 240 (4.31), 283 (4.23), 330 sh (3.73), 405 (3.66), 468 (3.63), 515 sh (3.51)	ca.125d	....	....	....	...	s	...	s[h]	...		E14, 150
p1063	4-Pregnene-17α, 20β,21-triol-3-one	$C_{21}H_{32}O_4$. See p1051......	348.49	cr (MeOH) $[\alpha]_D$ +63 (diox, c = 1) λ^{al} 240 (4.1)	190	....	....	....	...	...	...	...	...	diox, chl MeOH s	H22, 755
—	Prehnitene........	see Benzene,1,2,3,4-tetramethyl-*													
—	Prehnitic acid	see 1,2,3,4-Benzenetetra-carboxylic acid*													
—	Prehnitylic acid....	see Benzoic acid, 2,3,4-trimethyl-													
p1064	Primeverose	6(β-D-Xylosido)-D-glucose. $C_{11}H_{20}O_{10}$.	312.28	cr (MeOH, 80% al), $[\alpha]_D^{20}$ +23 $\rightarrow$ 3.2 (w, c = 5) (mut)	210 (darkens 190)	....	....	....	s	δ				MeOH s	B31, 372
—	Procaine	see Benzoic acid, 4-amino-, (2-diethylaminoelthyl) ester													
Ωp1065	α-Progesterone	17α-Progesterone. $C_{21}H_{30}O_2$.	314.47	orh pr (dil al) $[\alpha]_D$ +192 λ^w 249 (4.23)	128.5-31	....	1.166^{23}	....	δ					os δ	E14, 151
p1066	β-Progesterone	17β-Progesterone. $C_{21}H_{30}O_2$. See p1065	314.47	nd (peth) $[\alpha]_D^{20}$ +172-82 (diox, c = 2)	121-2	....	1.171^{20}	....	i	s	...	...	s	con sulf, diox s	E14, 151

For explanations, symbols and abbreviations see beginning of table. *For structural formulas see end of table.

No.	Name	Synonyms and Formula	Mol. wt.	Color, crystalline form, specific rotation and λ_{max} (log ε)	m.p. °C	b.p. °C	Density	n_D	w	al	eth	ace	bz	other solvents	Ref.
	Progesterone														
p1067	**Progesterone, dioxime**	$C_{21}H_{32}N_2O_2$. See 1065	344.50	pl (dil al)	243				i	s[h]	...	...	...	...	**E14**, 151
p1068	**Proline**(D)	d-2-Pyrrolidinecarboxylic acid. $[\alpha]_D^{20} +81.9$ (w)	115.13	hyg pr (al-eth)	215–20d				v	s[h]	i	δ	δ	...	**B22**, 1
p1069	—(DL)	$C_5H_9NO_2$. See p1068	115.13	hyg nd (al-eth), cr (+w)	205d (anh), 190 (hyd)				v	s v[h]	i	δ	δ	chl δ	**B22²**, 5
Ωp1070	—(L)	$C_5H_9NO_2$. See p1068	115.13	nd (al-eth), pr (w), $[\alpha]_D^{20} -80.9$ (w, c = 1)	220–2d				v	δ	i	δ	δ	BuOH, PrOH i	**B22²**, 3
p1071	—,4-hydroxy- (D, cis)	Allo-4-hydroxyproline. $C_5H_9NO_3$. See p1068. $[\alpha]_D^{18} +58.6$ (w, p = 5)	131.13	nd (w +1)	237–41				v		i				**B22¹**, 546
p1072	—,—,(DL, cis)	Allo-4-hydroxyproline. $C_5H_9NO_3$. See p1068	131.13	cr (w, dil al)	250				s		i			MeOH δ	**B22²**, 144
p1073	—,—,(L, cis)	Allo-4-hydroxyproline. $C_5H_9NO_3$. See p1068. $[\alpha]_D^{18} -58.1$ (w, p = 5.2)	131.13	nd (w +1)	238–41				v	δ				MeOH δ	**B22**, 546
Ωp1074	—,—,(D, trans)	α-4-Hydroxyproline. $C_5H_9NO_3$. See p1068. $[\alpha]_D^{21} +75.2$ (w)	131.13	lf (dil al)	274				v	δ					**B22¹**, 545
p1075	—,—,(DL, trans)	α-4-Hydroxyproline. $C_5H_9NO_3$. See p1068	131.13	pl (MeOH)	270 (261)				v	δ				MeOH s[h]	**B22²**, 143
p1076	—,—,(L, trans)	α-4-Hydroxyproline. $C_5H_9NO_3$. See p1068. $[\alpha]_D -76.5$ (w, c = 2.5)	131.13	lf (dil al), pr (w)	274				v	δ					**B22²**, 143
p1077	—,—,betaine(d)	$C_7H_{13}NO_3$. See p1068. $[\alpha]_D^{21} +36$	159.19	pr (w +1)	249d				δ s[h]	δ					**B22¹**, 546
—	**Prominal**	see **Barbituric acid, 5-ethyl-1-methyl-5-phenyl-**													
p1078	**Prontosil**	$C_{12}H_{13}N_5O_2S.HCl$.	327.80	og-red pw $\lambda^{w, pH = 0.8}$ 273 (3.86) $\lambda^{w, pH = 1.8}$ 262 (4.10), 297 (3.67)	248–51				δ	s		s		oils, fats s	**C29**, 4135
p1079	**Propadiene***	Allene. Dimethylenemethane. $CH_2:C:CH_2$	40.07	gas	−136	−34.5[760]	1.787	1.4168	i				s	peth s	**B1³**, 922
p1080	—,1,3-dioxo-*	Carbon suboxide. Dioxoallene. $O:C:C:C:O$	68.03	gas	−107	6.8	1.114[0]₄	1.4538[0]	d	d			s	CS_2 s HCO_2H, MeOH d	**B1³**, 3163
p1081	—,tetrafluoro-*	Perfluoroallene. $F_2C:C:CF_2$	112.03	gas		−38									**Am81**, 606
Ωp1082	—,tetraphenyl-*	$(C_6H_5)_2C:C:C(C_6H_5)_2$	344.46	nd, pr (dil ace, al),	166				i	δ	s	s		CS_2, chl v	**B5²**, 692
—	**Propaesin**	see **Benzoic acid, 4-amino-, propyl ester**													
Ωp1083	**Propanal***	Propionaldehyde. Propional. CH_3CH_2CHO	58.08	λ^w 282 (0.9)	−81	48.8	0.8058[20]₄	1.3636[20]	s	∞	∞				**B1³**, 2682
p1084	—,diethyl acetal*	1,1-Diethoxypropane*. Propylal. $CH_3CH_2CH(OC_2H_5)_2$.	132.21			122.8[744]	0.8232[20]₄	1.3924[19]	s	v	v	s	s		**B1³**, 2689
p1085	—,oxime*	Propionaldoxime. $CH_3CH_2CH:NOH$	73.10		40	131.5 77[0.5]	0.9258[20]	1.4287[20]	s	v	v				**B1³**, 2689
p1086	—,2-bromo-*	$CH_3CHBrCHO$	136.98			109–10 52–4[80]	1.592[20]	1.4813[20]			v				**B1³**, 2693
p1087	—,2-chloro-*	$CH_3CHClCHO$	92.53			86	1.182[15]₄	1.431[17]	δ		∞		∞		**B1³**, 2691
p1088	—,3-chloro-*	$ClCH_2CH_2CHO$	92.53			130–1 40[19] (40–50[10])	1.268[15]	1.475[15]	i	s	s				**B1³**, 2691
Ωp1089	—,—,diethyl acetal*	$ClCH_2CH_2CH(OC_2H_5)_2$.	166.65			84[25] 52[9]	0.9951[19]	1.4268[20]			s	s			**B1³**, 2692
p1090	—,2-chloro-2-methyl-*	2-Chloroisobutyraldehyde. $(CH_3)_2CClCHO$	106.55		90		1.053[15]₄	1.4160[16]		v	v				**B1**, 675
Ωp1091	—,2,3-dibromo-*	Acrolein dibromide. $BrCH_2CHBrCHO$	215.88	pa ye fum liq		73–5[10]	2.198[15]	1.5082[20]			v				**B1³**, 2694
p1092	—,2,2-dichloro-*	CH_3CCl_2CHO	126.97	(peth)	38–9	77.8–8.0								peth δ	**B1³**, 2692
p1093	—,2,3-dichloro-*	$ClCH_2CHClCHO$	126.97	hyd (w)		73[50] 48[14]	1.400[20]	1.4762[20]		d				CCl_4 s	**B1³**, 2693
—	—,2,3-dihydroxy-*	see **Glyceraldehyde**													
p1094	—,2,2-dimethyl-*	Pivalaldehyde. $(CH_3)_3CCHO$	86.14	λ^{al} 193 (1.65)	6	77–8	0.7923[17]	1.3791[20]		s	s				**B1²**, 742
p1095	—,—,oxime*	Pivaldoxime. $(CH_3)_3CCH:NOH$	101.15		48	65[20]				s	s				**B1²**, 744
Ωp1096	—,3-ethoxy-, diethyl acetal*	1,1,3-Triethoxypropane*. $C_2H_5OCH_2CH_2CH(OC_2H_5)_2$	176.26			184–6 δd 78[14]	0.898[15]₄	1.4067[20]	δ		s	s			**B1³**, 3190
—	—,2-ethyl-3-phenyl-*	see **Butanal, 2-benzylidene-**													
Ωp1097	—,3-hydroxy-2-oxo-*, enol form	Propanolonal. Reductone. $HOCH:C(OH)CHO$	88.06	ye nd (w)	200–20d				s	s					**B1³**, 3310

For explanations, symbols and abbreviations see beginning of table. For structural formulas see end of table.

No.	Name	Synonyms and Formula	Mol. wt.	Color, crystalline form, specific rotation and λ_{max} (log ε)	m.p. °C	b.p. °C	Density	n_D	w	al	eth	ace	bz	other solvents	Ref.
	Propanal														
p1098	—,3(4-isopropyl-phenyl)-2-methyl-	Cyclamen aldehyde. Cyclomal.	190.29	....	....	133–7[99] 115[5]	0.951[15]	1.5068[20]	i	s	s	...	s	....	C55, 25834
p1099	—,2-oxo-*......	Methylglyoxal. Pyruvaldehyde. CH_3COCHO	72.06	ye hyg liq	....	72	1.0455[24]	1.4002[18]	...	s	s	...	s		B1[2], 819
p1100	—,—,dioxime* ...	Methyl glyoxime. $CH_3C(:NOH)CH:NOH$	102.09	nd (to, w, sub), pr (al) λ^{al} 231 (4.32)	157	sub			δ s[h]	s	s	...	s[h]	to s[h]	B1[2], 822
Ωp1101	—,—,1-oxime*....	Isonitrosoacetone. $CH_3COCH:NOH$	87.08	nd (CCl_4), lf (eth-peth)	69	sub	1.0744[67]		s		s		δ	chl, CCl_4 δ	B1[3], 3092
p1102	—,2-phenoxy-*	$C_6H_5OCH(CH_3)CHO$......	150.18		....	229–30 99–101[16]			i	v	v	v	v	....	B6, 151
p1103	—,—,oxime*	$C_6H_5OCH(CH_3)CH:NOH$.	165.19	nd (dil al)	110				δ	v	v				B6, 151
Ωp1104	—,2-phenyl-*	Hydratropic aldehyde. $C_6H_5CH(CH_3)CHO$	134.18	λ 239 (2.87), 259 (2.34), 287 (2.18), 314 (2.00),		202–5 92.5[10]	1.0089[20/4]	1.5176[20]	i	s					B7[2], 237
Ωp1105	—,3-phenyl-*	Hydrocinnamaldehyde. $C_6H_5CH_2CH_2CHO$	134.18	mcl λ^{al} 252 (2.3), 259 (2.4)	47	223[745] 104–5[13]			i	v	∞		v		B7[2], 236
p1106	—,2,2,3-tri-chloro-*	$ClCH_2CCl_2CHO$	161.42			63–5[45]	1.470[25]	1.473[25]			v			CCl_4 s	B1[2], 691
Ω p1107	Propane*........	$CH_3CH_2CH_3$	44.11		−189.69	−42.07	0.5005[20] (liq) 0.5853[−45/4]	1.2898[20]	s	s	v	δ	v	chl v	B1[3], 204
Ωp1108	—,1-amino-*......	Propylamine. $CH_3CH_2CH_2NH_2$	59.11		−83.0	47.8[760]	0.7173[20/4]	1.3870[20]	s	v	v	v	s	chl s	B4[3], 250
Ωp1109	—,2-amino-*......	Isopropylamine. $(CH_3)_2CHNH_2$	59.11		−95.2	32.4[760]	0.8889[20]	1.3742[20]	∞	∞	∞	v	s	chl s	B4[3], 271
p1110	—,1-amino-3-cyclohexyloxy *		159.28		....	115[20]			i			s	s		C55, 22136
p1111	—,1-amino-2,2-dimethyl-*	Neopentylamine. $(CH_3)_3CCH_2NH_2$	87.17		....	81–2[741]	0.7455[20/4]	1.4023[20]	δ	s	s				B4[3], 355
p1112	—,1-amino-3-dodecyloxy-*	$CH_3(CH_2)_{11}O(CH_2)_3NH_2$.	243.44		....	140[3]	0.8439[20/4]	1.4487[20]	i		s		s	MeOH, chl s	C55, 22136
Ω p1113	—,1-amino-3-methoxy-*	$CH_3OCH_2CH_2CH_2NH_2$.....	89.14		....	116–9	0.8727[20/4]	1.4191[20]	s			s	s	MeOH, chl, CCl_4 s	C55, 22136
Ωp1114	—,2-amino-2-methyl-*	tert-Butylamine. $(CH_3)_3CNH_2$	73.14		−67.5	44.4[760]	0.6958[20/4]	1.3784[20]	∞	∞	∞				B4[3], 323
—	—,2-amino-1-phenyl-*	see **Amphetamine**													
,Ωp1114[1]	—,2,2-bis(bromo-methyl)-1,3-dibromo-*	Pentaerythrityl tetrabromide. $C(CH_2Br)_4$	387.76	cr (ace), nd (lig), tcl (bz + 1)	163	305–6	2.596[15]		...	s[h]	δ	...	s[h]	to s[h] os δ	B1[2], 105
Ωp1115	—,2,2-bis(chloro-methyl)-1,3-dichloro-*	Pentaerythrityl tetrachloride. $C(CH_2Cl)_4$	209.94		97	110[12]			i		s			chl s	Am 67, 942
p1116	—,1,1-bis(ethyl-sulfonyl)-2-methyl-*	$(C_2H_5SO_2)_2CHCH(CH_3)_2$ ..	242.36	nd (al)	94	....			s[h]						B1, 676
p1117	—,1,1-bis(4-hydroxy-phenyl)-*	4,4′-Propylidenediphenol. ..	228.29	nd (w)	130	275[20]			i	v	v			alk v aa s	B6[2],977
Ωp1118	—,2,2-bis(4-hydroxy-phenyl)-*	4,4′-Isopropylidenediphenol.	228.29	pr (dil aa), nd (w) λ^{al} 227 (4.4), 275 (3.8)	152–3	250–2[13]			i	v	v	v		alk v aa s	B6[2], 978
Ωp1118[1]	—,2,2-bis(iodo-methyl)-1,3-diiodo-*	Pentaerythrityl tetraiodide. $C(CH_2I)_4$	575.75	nd (to)	225	....			...	δ	δ			to s[h]	B1[3], 373
Ωp1119	—,1-bromo-*......	n-Propyl bromide. $CH_3CH_2CH_2Br$	123.00		−109.85	71.0[760]	1.3537[20/4]	1.4343[20]	δ	s	s	s	s	chl s	B1[3], 239
Ω p1120	—,2-bromo-*......	Isopropyl bromide. $CH_3CHBrCH_3$	123.00		−89.0	59.38[760]	1.3140[20/4]	1.4251[20]	δ	∞	∞	s	s	chl s	B1[3], 242
p1121	—,1-bromo-2-chloro-*	$CH_3CHClCH_2Br$........	157.44			118	1.531[20]	1.4745[20]	δ	v	v	s	s		B1[3], 245
Ω p1122	—,1-bromo-3-chloro-*	$ClCH_2CH_2CH_2Br$........	157.44		−58.87	143.36[760] 32.4[10]	1.5969[20/4]	1.4864[20]	i	v	v	s	s	chl v	B1[3], 245
Ωp1123	—,2-bromo-1-chloro-*	$CH_3CHBrCH_2Cl$........	157.44			118[756]	1.537[20]	1.4795[20]	i	s	s	s	s	chl v	B1[3], 245
p1124	—,2-bromo-2-chloro-*	$(CH_3)_2CBrCl$........	157.44			93.0–5.5[745]	1.474[21]	1.4575[20]	i	v	v	v	s	chl v	B1[3], 246
Ωp1125	—,1-bromo-2,2-dimethyl-*	Neopentyl bromide. $(CH_3)_3CCH_2Br$	151.05			106[760] 34.6[100]	1.1997[20/4]	1.4370[20]	i	s	s	s	s	chl s	B1, 141
Ωp1126	—,1-bromo-2,3-epoxy-*(d)*	Epibromohydrin........	136.98	$[\alpha]_D^{16}$ +45.4 (undil); +6.5 (al, p = 5.5)		134–6[50]			i	s[h]	s	...	s	chl s	B17[2], 14
p1127	—,—,(dl)	C_3H_5BrO. See p1126.	136.98			138–40 (134–6) 61–2[50]	1.615[14]	1.4841[20]	i	s[h]	s	...	s	chl s	B17[2], 14

For explanations, symbols and abbreviations see beginning of table. For structural formulas see end of table.

No.	Name	Synonyms and Formula	Mol. wt.	Color. crystalline form. specific rotation and λ_{max} (log ε)	m.p. °C	b.p. °C	Density	n_D	w	al	eth	ace	bz	other solvents	Ref.
	Propane														
p1128	—,1-bromo-3-fluoro-*	FCH₂CH₂CH₂Br	140.99			101.4	1.542²⁵₄	1.4290²⁵	i	v	v	...	s	chl v	B1³, 244
Ω p1129	—,2-bromo-2-methyl-*	tert-Butyl bromide. (CH₃)₃CBr	137.03		−16.2	73.25⁷⁶⁰	1.2209²⁰₄	1.4278²⁰	i				s		B1³, 322
p1130	—,2(bromo-methyl)-1,2,3-tribromo-*	(BrCH₂)₃CBr	373.73		25	150–1¹⁴	2.5595²⁰₄	1.6246²⁰	i	...	s	s			B1², 91
p1131	—,1-bromo-1-nitro-*	CH₃CH₂CHBrNO₂	168.00			160–5 82.5⁵⁰				s	s			KOH s	B1³, 260
p1132	—,2-bromo-2-nitro-*	(CH₃)₂CBrNO₂	168.00			151.7 −.8⁷⁴⁵ 73–5⁵⁰	1.6562⁰			s	s			alk i	B1³, 260
Ω p1133	—,1-chloro*	n-Propyl chloride. CH₃CH₂CH₂Cl.	78.54		−122.8	46.60⁷⁶⁰	0.8909²⁰₄	1.3879²⁰	δ	∞	∞		s	chl s	B1³, 219
Ω p1134	—,2-chloro-*	Isopropyl chloride. CH₃CHClCH₃.	78.54		−117.18	35.74⁷⁶⁰	0.8617²⁰₄	1.3777²⁰	δ	∞	∞		s	chl s	B1³, 221
p1135	—,1-chloro-2,2-dimethyl-*	Neopentyl chloride. (CH₃)₃CCH₂Cl.	106.60		−20	84.3⁷⁶⁰	0.8660²⁰₄	1.4044²⁰	δ	s	v		s	chl s	B1³, 370
Ω p1136	—,1-chloro-2,3-epoxy-(dl)*	α-Epichlorohydrin.	92.53		−48	116.5⁷⁶⁰ 60–1¹⁰⁰	1.1801²⁰₄	1.4361²⁰	δ dʰ	∞	∞		s		B17², 13
p1137	—,—(l)	C₃H₅ClO. See p1136	92.53	[α]ᴅ¹⁸ −25.6		92–3³⁶⁰	1.2007		δ dʰ	∞	∞		s		B17¹, 4
p1138	—,2-chloro-1,3-epoxy-*	3-Chloro-1-oxacyclobutane. 3-Chlorooxetane. β-Epichlorohydrin.	92.53		132–4					v	v			chl s	B17, 6
p1139	—,3-chloro-1,2-epoxy-2-methyl-*		106.55			122.0 51⁵⁵	1.1011²⁰₄	1.4340²⁰	s		v				C55, 18694
p1140	—,1-chloro-3-fluoro-*	FCH₂CH₂CH₂Cl.	96.53			79.5⁷⁴⁰		1.3871²⁵	i	v	v		s	chl s	C51, 260
Ω p1141	—,2-chloro-2-methyl-*	tert-Butyl chloride. (CH₃)₃CCl.	92.57		−25.4	52	0.8420²⁰₄	1.3857²⁰	δ	s	s		s	chl s	B1³, 316
p1142	—,(2-chloro-methyl)-1,1,2,3-tetrachloro-*	(ClCH₂)₂CClCHCl₂	230.35			226.3–.4⁷³⁷ 95⁹	1.5686²⁵₄	1.5165²⁵		s			s	chl s	B1³, 321
p1143	—,(2-chloro-methyl)-1,2,3-trichloro-*	(ClCH₂)₃CCl	195.91			209.8–10.5⁷³⁷ 87⁹	1.5036²⁵₄	1.508²⁰						chl s	B1³, 321
Ω p1144	—,1-chloro-1-nitro-*	CH₃CH₂CHClNO₂	123.54	λ^{al} 280.5 (1.48)		141–3 67⁵⁶	1.209²⁰₂₀	1.4251²⁰	δ	s	s			glycols, oils s	B1³, 259
p1145	—,1-chloro-2-nitro-*	CH₃CH(NO₂)CH₂Cl	123.54			172–3 94⁴⁶	1.245²²	1.4432²⁵		s	s			chl s	B1³, 259
p1146	—,1-chloro-3-nitro-*	O₂NCH₂CH₂CH₂Cl	123.54			197 δd 115–6⁴⁰	1.267²⁰			s	s			chl s	B1, 116
p1147	—,2-chloro-1-nitro-*	CH₃CHClCH₂NO₂	123.54			172⁷⁶⁰ 75¹⁵	1.2361¹⁵	1.4447²⁰	δ	s	s				B1³, 259
Ω p1148	—,2-chloro-2-nitro-*	CH₃CCl(NO₂)CH₃	123.54			134 δd 57⁵⁰	1.230¹⁹	1.4378¹⁹	δ	s	s			glycerol, oils s KOH i	B1³, 259
Ω p1149	—,1-chloro-3-phenyl-*	C₆H₅CH₂CH₂CH₂Cl	154.64			219–20 110²¹	1.056²⁵₄	1.5160²⁵						chl s	B5², 305
p1150	—,1,2-di-acetamido-*	CH₃CONHCH(CH₃)CH₂NHCOCH₃	158.20	nd (bz)	138–9	190¹⁸			v	v	i	δ sʰ	chl v lig i	B4, 261
Ω p1151	—,1,2-di-amino-(d)*	1,2-Propanediamine*. CH₃CH(NH₂)CH₂NH₂	74.13	[α]ᴅ²⁵ +29.78		120.5	0.8584²⁵₄		v		i			chl v	B4², 697
Ω p1152	—,1,3-diamino-*	Trimethylenediamine. H₂NCH₂CH₂CH₂NH₂	74.13			135.5⁷³⁸	0.884²⁵₄	1.4600²⁰	s	∞	∞			chl v	B4³, 552
p1153	—,1,1-dibromo-*	Propylidene bromide. CH₃CH₂CHBr₂	201.90			133.5⁷⁶⁰ 28.4¹⁰	1.9822⁰	1.5100²⁰	...	s	s			chl s	B1³, 246
Ω p1154	—,1,2-dibromo-*	Propylene bromide. CH₃CHBrCH₂Br	201.90		−55.25	140.0⁷⁶⁰ 35.7¹⁰	1.9324²⁰₄	1.5201²⁰		s	s			chl s	B1³, 246
Ω p1155	—,1,3-dibromo-*	Trimethylene bromide. BrCH₂CH₂CH₂Br	201.90		fr −34.2	167.3⁷⁶⁰ 56.6¹⁰	1.9822²⁰₄	1.5232²⁰		s	s			chl s	B1³, 248
p1156	—,2,2-dibromo-*	Isopropylidene bromide. CH₃CBr₂CH₃	201.90			114–5⁷⁴⁰	1.7825²⁰			s	s			chl s	B1³, 250
p1157	—,1,1-dibromo-2,2-dimethyl-*	Neopentylidene bromide. (CH₃)₃CCHBr₂	229.95		14	180⁷⁶⁰ 66¹⁰	1.6695²⁰	1.5047²⁰	i				s	chl s	B1³, 371
p1158	—,1,3-dibromo-2,2-dimethyl-*	(CH₃)₂C(CH₂Br)₂	229.95			185–90d 72¹⁴	1.6934²⁰	1.5050²⁰	i				s	chl s	B1³, 371
Ω p1159	—,1,2-dibromo-2-methyl-*	Isobutylene bromide. (CH₃)₂CBrCH₂Br	215.94		9–12	149–51 61⁴⁰	1.759²⁰₄	1.509					s	chl s	B1³, 324
p1160	—,1,1-dichloro-*	Propylidene dichloride. CH₃CH₂CHCl₂	112.99			88.1⁷⁶⁰	1.1321²⁰	1.4289²⁰		s	s			chl s	B1³, 225
Ω p1161	—,1,2-dichloro-*	Propylene chloride. CH₃CHClCH₂Cl	112.99		−100.44	96.37⁷⁶⁰ −3.69¹⁰	1.1560²⁰₄	1.4394²⁰	δ	s	s			chl s	B1³, 225
Ω p1163	—,1,3-dichloro-*	Trimethylene chloride. ClCH₂CH₂CH₂Cl	112.99		−99.5	120.4⁷⁶⁰ 14¹⁰	1.1878²⁰₄	1.4487²⁰	δ	v	v		s	chl s	B1³, 227
Ω p1164	—,2,2-dichloro-*	Acetone dichloride. Isopropylidene chloride. CH₃CCl₂CH₃	112.99		−33.8	69.3⁷⁶⁰	1.1120²⁰₄	1.4148²⁰	i	s	∞		s	chl s	B1³, 228

For explanations, symbols and abbreviations see beginning of table. For structural formulas see end of table.

No.	Name	Synonyms and Formula	Mol. wt.	Color, crystalline form, specific rotation and λ_{max} (log ε)	m.p. °C	b.p. °C	Density	n_D	w	al	eth	ace	bz	other solvents	Ref.
	Propane														
p1165	—,1,1-dichloro-2-methyl-*	Isobutylidene chloride. $(CH_3)_2CHCHCl_2$	127.03	....		105–6 (108–10)	1.0111_{12}^{12}	1.4330^{25}	i	s	s	...	s	chl s	B1[3], 319
p1166	—,1,2-dichloro-2-methyl-*	Isobutylene chloride. $(CH_3)_2CClCH_2Cl$	127.03	....	> −130	108 38–9[70]	1.093_2^{20}	1.4370^{20}	i	∞	∞	∞	∞	CCl_4 ∞	B1[3], 319
p1167	—,1,3-dichloro-2-methyl-*	$CH_3CH(CH_2Cl)_2$..........	127.03	....		134.6^{760} 60[49]	1.1325_4^{25}	1.4488^{25}	i	s	v	...	v	CCl_4 s	B1[3], 319
—	—,1,1-diethoxy-* .	see **Propanal, diethyl acetal***													
p1168	—,2,2-di(ethyl-sulfonyl)-*	Acetone diethyl sulfone. Sulfonal. $(CH_3)_2C(SO_2C_2H_5)_2$	228.33	mcl (w), pr (al)	125.8	300d			δ s[h]	δ	δ		s	to, chl, AcOEt s CCl_4 δ CS_2 i	B1[1], 345
p1169	—,1,3-difluoro-* ...	Trimethylene fluoride. $FCH_2CH_2CH_2F$	80.08	....		41.6^{760}	1.0057_4^{25}	1.3190^{26}			s			....	B1[3], 218
p1170	—,2,2-difluoro-* ...	Isopropylidene fluoride. $CH_3CF_2CH_3$	80.08	gas	−104.8	$−0.4^{760}$	0.9205_4^{20} (liq at sat pressure)	1.2904^{20} (liq at sat pressure)							B1[3], 218
p1171	—,1,2-diiodo-*	Propylene iodide. CH_3CHICH_2I	295.89	....				$2.490^{18.5}$		s	s			MeOH s	B1, 115
Ω p1172	—,1,3-diiodo-*	Trimethylene iodide. $ICH_2CH_2CH_2I$	295.89	fr −20		227^{760} δd 110^{19}	2.5755_4^{20}	1.6423^{20}	i		s			CCl_4, chl s	B1[3], 255
p1173	—,2,2-diiodo-*	Isopropylidene iodide. $CH_3CI_2CH_3$	295.89	....		173^{760} 53^{10}	2.5755_4^{20}	1.651^{20}	i		s			CCl_4, chl s	B1[3], 255
Ω p1174	—,2,2-dimethyl-* ..	Neopentane. $C(CH_3)_4$	72.15	gas	−16.55	9.50	0.61350^{20}	1.3476^6	i	s	s			chl s	B1[3], 369
p1175	—,1(dimethyl-amino)-*	Dimethyl propylamine*. $CH_3CH_2CH_2N(CH_3)_2$	87.17	....		65.5^{757}	0.7152_4^{20}	1.3860^{20}	...	s	s		s	chl s	B4[2], 621
p1176	,1(dimethyl-amino)-2-methyl	Dimethyl isobutylamine*. $(CH_3)_2CHCH_2N(CH_3)_2$.	101.19	....		81.0^{753}	0.7097_4^{20}	1.3907^{20}	...	s	s		s	chl s	B4[2], 638
p1177	—,1,1-dinitro-*	$CH_3CH_2CH(NO_2)_2$	134.09	λ^{hx} 280 (1.76)	−42	184	1.2610^{25}	1.4339^{20}						alk s	B1[3], 260
p1178	—,1,3-dinitro-*	$O_2NCH_2CH_2CH_2NO_2$	134.09	λ^{al} 273 (1.60)	−21.4	103[1]	1.353_4^{26}	1.4654^{20}	i		s				B1[3], 261
p1179	—,2,2-dinitro-*	$CH_3C(NO_2)_2CH_3$	134.09	λ^{al} 278 (1.72)	53	185.5 48–50[2]	1.30^{25}		δ						B1[3], 261
p1179[1]	—,1,2-di-phenoxy-*	$CH_3CH(OC_6H_5)CH_2OC_6H_5$	228.29	rh (MeOH)	32	$175–8^{12}$	$1.0748_4^{33.3}$	$1.5542^{33.3}$	i	s	s	s	s	MeOH, chl s	B6[2], 151
p1179[2]	—,1,3-di-phenoxy-*	$C_6H_5OCH_2CH_2CH_2OC_6H_5$	228.29	lf (al)	61	$338–40^{760}$ 160^{25}			i	s	s				B6[2], 151
Ω p1180	—,1,2-epoxy-(dl)* .	Methyloxiran. Propylene oxide.	58.08	....		34.3	0.859_0^0	1.3670^{20}	∞	∞	∞				B17, 6
p1181	—,1,3-epoxy-*	Oxetane. Trimethylene oxide.	58.08	λ^{gas} 167 (3.04), 170.5 (3.29), 174.2 (3.44), 184 (3.1), 187.5 (3.30)		47.8 (cor)	0.8930_4^{25}	1.3961^{20}	∞	∞	s	v		os v	B17[2], 12
p1182	—,1,2-epoxy-3-iodo-*	Epiiodohydrin.	183.98	....		160–2	1.982^{24}								B17[2], 15
p1183	—,1,2-epoxy-2-methyl-*	Isobutylene oxide. 2,2-Dimethyl oxiran.	72.12	....		52	0.8650^0	1.3712^{22}		s	s				B17[2], 17
Ω p1184	—,1,2-epoxy-3,3,3-trichloro-*		161.42	....		149^{764} 44–5[13]	1.495_4^{20}	1.4737^{25}			v				B17[2], 14
p1184[1]	—,1-ethoxy-3-phenoxy-	$C_6H_5OCH_2CH_2CH_2OC_2H_5$.	180.25	oil		328–30					s	s			B6, 147
p1185	—,1-fluoro-*	n-Propyl fluoride. $CH_3CH_2CH_2F$	62.09	....	−159	2.50^{760}	0.7956_4^{20}	1.3115^{20}	δ	v	v				B1[3], 217
Ω p1186	—,1,1,1,2,2,3,3-heptachloro-*	$Cl_2CHCCl_2CCl_3$	285.21	amor	29.4	247–8 132[30]	1.8048_4^{34}							chl s	B1[3], 238
p1187	—,1,1,1,2,3,3,3-heptachloro-*	$Cl_3CCHClCCl_3$	285.21		11–1.5	249 93[3]	1.7921_4^{34}	1.5427^{21}						chl s	B1[3], 239
p1188	—,heptafluoro-1-nitro-*	$F_3CCF_2CF_2NO_2$	215.03	λ^{vap} 282 (1.56)		25									C51, 14790
p1189	—,heptafluoro-1-nitroso-*	$F_3CCF_2CF_2NO$	199.03	deep bl λ^{vap} 686 (1.34)	−151	−12									C51, 14790
p1190	—,1,1,1,2,2,3-hexafluoro-*	$FCH_2CF_2CF_3$	152.04			1.2									B4, 537
p1191	—,1(hydroxyl-amino)-*	$CH_3CH_2CH_2NHOH$.......	75.11	nd (eth)	46				v		s			lig δ	B4, 537
Ω p1192	—,1-iodo-*	n-Propyl iodide. $CH_3CH_2CH_2I$	169.99	λ^{al} 254.5 (2.69)	−101.3	102.45	1.7489_4^{20}	1.5058^{20}	δ	∞	∞				B1[3], 252
Ω p1193	—,2-iodo-*	Isopropyl iodide. CH_3CHICH_3	169.99		−90.1	89.45	1.7033_4^{20}	1.5026^{20}	δ	∞	∞		∞	chl ∞	B1[3], 253
p1194	—,1-iodo-2,2-dimethyl-*	Neopentyl iodide. $(CH_3)_3CCH_2I$	198.05			127–9d 47–4[20]	1.4940^{20}	1.4890^{20}	i	s	s				B1[3], 373
p1195	—,2-iodo-2-methyl-*	tert-Butyl iodide. $(CH_3)_3CI$	184.02		−38.70	100.6d 20.8[30]	1.5443_4^{20}	1.4918^{20}	d	∞	∞				B1[3], 326
Ω p1196	—,1-isocyano-*	Propylcarbylamine. Propyl isocyanide. $CH_3(CH_2)_2NC$	69.11			99.5			i	∞	∞				B4[2], 625
p1197	—,2-isocyano-*	Isopropylcarbylamine. Isopropyl isocyanide $(CH_3)_2CHNC$	69.11			87	0.7596^0			s	s			chl s	B4, 154
p1198	—,2-isocyano-2-methyl-*	tert-Butyl carbylamine. tert-Butyl isocyanide $(CH_3)_3CNC$	83.13			167–70 91[38]				∞	∞			HCl d	B4[2], 641

No.	Name	Synonyms and Formula	Mol. wt.	Color, crystalline form, specific rotation and λ_{max} (log ε)	m.p. °C	b.p. °C	Density	n_D	Solubility w	al	eth	ace	bz	other solvents	Ref.
	Propane														
p1198[1]	—, 2-methyl	Isobutane	58.12	Col. gas	−138.3	−0.50	0.579^{20}		s	v	v			chl v	B1, 124
p1198[2]	—,1-methoxy-3 phenoxy-	$CH_3OCH_2CH_2CH_2OC_6H_5$	166.22	oil		230–1									B6, 147
p1199	—,1(2-methoxy-phenyl)-2(methyl-amino)-, hydrochloride.		215.73	cr (al-eth)	128				v	v	δ		δ	chl v	C55, 24677
p1200	—,2-methyl-1-nitro-*	Nitroisobutane. $(CH_3)_2CHCH_2NO_2$.	103.12			140.5^{760} $61–2^{45}$	0.9625^{25}_{25}	1.4066^{20}	δ	∞	∞			chl s	B1[3], 327
p1201	—,2-methyl-1,1,1,2,3-penta-chloro-*	$ClCH_2CCl(CH_3)CCl_3$	230.35	(al)	73.5	213^{737} $90–3^{10}$	1.5686^{25}_4	1.5165^{25}	i					chl s	B1[3], 321
p1202	—,2-methyl-1,1,1,2-tetra-bromo-*	$(CH_3)_2CBrCBr_3$	373.73	lf	217				i	v	v				B1, 128
p1203	—,2-methyl-1,1,2,3-tetra-bromo-*	$BrCH_2CBr(CH_3)CHBr_2$	373.73			134^{11}	2.4545^{20}	1.5990^{20}	i					chl s	B1[3], 325
p1204	—,2-methyl-1,1,1,2-tetra-chloro-*-	$(CH_3)_2CClCCl_3$	195.91	cr (al)	178.6–9.6	$192^{117.5}$ (cor) sub			i	v	v			chl s	B1[3], 320
p1205	—,2-methyl-1,1,2,3-tetra-chloro-*	$ClCH_2CCl(CH_3)CHCl_2$	195.91		−46	$190.6–$ 1.3^{760} 69^{12}	1.4393^{25}_4	1.4963^{20}	i		s		s	chl s	B1[3], 321
p1206	—,2-methyl-1,1,2-tribromo-*	$(CH_3)_2CBrCHBr_2$	294.83			$208–15$d 96^{14}	2.0169^{20}_4		i		s			chl s	B1[3], 325
p1207	—,2-methyl-1,2,3-tribromo-*	$(BrCH_2)_2CBrCH_3$	294.83			88.5^9	2.1750^{20}_4	1.5652^{20}	i		s			chl s	B1[3], 325
p1208	—,2-methyl-1,1,2-trichloro-*	$(CH_3)_2CClCHCl_2$	161.46		−6	$144.5–$ 5.5^{760} $46–7^{18}$	1.2588^{20}_4	1.4666^{20}	i		s			chl v	B1[3], 320
p1209	—,2-methyl-1,2,3-trichloro-*	$CH_3CCl(CH_2Cl)_2$	161.46			$162–3^{760}$ 81^{50}	1.3012^{25}_4	1.4765^{20}	i					chl s	B1[3], 320
Ω p1210	—,1-nitro-*	$CH_3CH_2CH_2NO_2$	89.09	$\lambda^{al} 270 (1.59)$	−108	$130.5–$ 1.5^{760}	1.00812^4_4	1.4016^{20}	δ	∞	∞			chl s	B1[3], 256
Ω p1211	—,2-nitro-*	$CH_3CH(NO_2)CH_3$	89.09	$\lambda^{al} 260 (1.66)$	−93	120^{760}	0.9876^{20}	1.3944^{20}	δ	∞	∞			chl s	B1[3], 258
p1212	—,1(nitro-amino)-*	n-Propylnitramine. $CH_3CH_2CH_2NHNO_2$	104.12		−21	$128–9^{40}$	1.1046^{15}	1.4610^{20}	δ	∞	∞^{40}				B4[1], 569
p1213	—,3-nitro-1,1,1-trifluoro-*	$O_2NCH_2CH_2CF_3$	143.07			135^{760}	1.4203^{20}_{20}	1.3549^{20}	i		s				C51, 1868
Ω p1214	—,octachloro-*	Perchloropropane. $Cl_3CCCl_2CCl_3$	319.66	wh cr (dil al)	160	$268–9^{734}$			i	v	v				B1[3], 239
p1215	—,1,1,1,2,3-penta-chloro-*	$ClCH_2CHClCCl_3$	216.32	nd (al)	179–80	$84–5^{20}$ sub		1.513^{20}	i	s	s	s		os, chl s	B1, 107
Ω p1216	—,1,1,2,3,3-penta-chloro-*	$Cl_2CHCHClCHCl_2$	216.32		$198–$ 200^{760} $98–100^{20}$		1.6086^{14}_4	1.5131^{17}	i	v	s			chl s	B1[3], 236
Ω p1218	—,1,1,1,2-tetra-chloro-*	$CH_3CHClCCl_3$	181.88		−64	150^{760} (152) 37^{10}	1.4732^{20}_4	1.4867^{20}	i	v	s			chl s	B1[3], 233
p1219	—,1,1,2,2-tetra-chloro-*	$CH_3CCl_2CHCl_2$	181.88			153^{760}	1.47^{13}	1.4850^{25}	i	∞	∞			chl s	B1[3], 234
p1220	—,1,1,2,3-tetra-chloro-*	$ClCH_2CHClCHCl_2$	181.88			$179–$ 80^{760} (cor)61^{12}	1.513^{17}	1.5037^{17}	i	s	v			chl s alk d[h]	B1[3], 234
p1221	—,1,2,2,3-tetra-chloro-*	$ClCH_2CCl_2CH_2Cl$	181.88			165^{760} 51^{12}	1.500^{18}	1.4940^{18}	i	v	v			chl s	B1[3], 234
Ω p1222	—,1,1,2-tri-bromo-*	$CH_3CHBrCHBr_2$	280.80			$200–1$ 83^6	2.3548^{20}_4	1.5790^{20}	i	s	v			chl, aa s	B1[3], 251
p1223	—,1,2,2-tri-bromo-*	$CH_3CBr_2CH_2Br$	280.80			$190–1$ 81^{20}	2.2985^{20}_4	1.5670^{20}	i	s	v			chl, aa s	B1[2], 77
Ω p1224	—,1,2,3-tri-bromo-*	$BrCH_2CHBrCH_2Br$	280.80		16.9	222.16^{760} 98.47^{10}	2.4209^{20}_4	1.5862^{20}	i	v	v			chl s	B1[3], 251
p1225	—,1,1,1-tri-chloro-*	$CH_3CH_2CCl_3$	147.43			$106.5–8.5$	1.287^{23}_4		i	v	v			chl v	B1[3], 230
Ω p1226	—,1,1,2-tri-chloro-*	$CH_3CHClCHCl_2$	147.43			140 (131–3)	1.372^{25}		i	s	v			chl s	B1[3], 230
p1227	—,1,1,3-tri-chloro-*	$ClCH_2CH_2CHCl_2$	147.43		−58.98	145.55^{760} 33.42^{10}	1.3557^{20}_4	1.4718^{20}	i	s	v			chl v aa s	B1[3], 330
Ω p1228	—,1,2,2-tri-chloro-*	$CH_3CCl_2CH_2Cl$	147.43			$123–5^{762}$	1.318^{25}	1.4609^{25}	i	s	s			chl v	B1[3], 231
Ω p1229	—,1,2,3-tri-chloro-*	Trichlorohydrin. $ClCH_2CHClCH_2Cl$	147.43		−14.7	156.85^{760} 41.92^{10}	1.3889^{20}_4	1.4832^{20}	δ	s	s			chl v	B1[3], 231
—	—,1,3,3-tri-ethoxy-*	see Propanal, 3-ethoxy-, diethyl acetal*													
p1230	—,1,1,1-tri-phenyl-*	$(C_6H_5)_3CCH_2CH_3$	272.40	pr	51										B5[3], 2340

For explanations, symbols and abbreviations see beginning of table. For structural formulas see end of table.

No.	Name	Synonyms and Formula	Mol. wt.	Color, crystalline form, specific rotation and λ_{max} (log ε)	m.p. °C	b.p. °C	Density	n_D	w	al	eth	ace	bz	other solvents	Ref.
	1-Propanearsonic acid														
Ω p1231	1-Propanearsonic acid*	$CH_3CH_2CH_2AsO_3H_2$	168.03	nd (al), pl (w)	134.6–5.2	....			v	v	i				B4[2], 997
p1232	1-Propaneboronic acid*	n-Propylboric acid. $CH_3CH_2CH_2B(OH)_2$	87.92	wh nd	107	d			v	s	s				B4[2], 1023
p1233	—,2-methyl-*	Isobutylboric acid. $(CH_3)_2CHCH_2B(OH)_2$	101.94	lo pl (w), cr $(ClCH_2CH_2Cl)$	112	....			δ	s	s				B4[3], 1965
—	**Propanedioic acid***	see **Malonic acid**													
Ω p1234	1,2-Propanediol* ..	Propylene glycol. $CH_3CH(OH)CH_2OH$	76.11	....	....	189 96–8[21]	1.0361[20/4]	1.4324[20]	∞	∞	s	...	s		B1[3], 2142
Ω p1235	—,carbonate......	4-Methyl-1,3-dioxolan-2-one.	102.09	....	−48.8	240 110[10]	1.2041[20/4]	1.4189[20]	v	v	v	v	s		C49, 12303
p1236	—,diacetate.	$CH_3CO_2CH(CH_3)CH_2O_2CCH_3$ 160.17		....	....	190–1[762]	1.059[20/4]	1.4173[20]	v	s	s				B2[3], 312
p1243	—,sulfite		122.14	....	< −60	175 85[25]	1.2960[20/4]	1.4370[20]	v d[h]	v	v	v	v	AcOEt v	C51, 1036
Ω p1244	1,3-Propanediol*	Trimethylene glycol. $HOCH_2CH_2CH_2OH$.	76.11	....	....	213.5[760] 110[12]	1.0597[20/4]	1.4398[20]	∞	∞	v	δ s[h]			B1[2], 540
p1245	—,diacetate.	$CH_3CO_2CH_2CH_2CH_2O_2CCH_3$ 160.17		....	....	209–10[760] 84.5[10]	1.070[19]	1.4192	v	s	s				B2[2], 156
Ω p1250	—,2-amino-2-ethyl-*	$CH_3CH_2C(CH_2OH)_2NH_2$	119.17	ye	37.5–8.5	143–5[10]	1.099[20/4]	1.490[20]	∞						C34, 1305
Ω p1251	—,2-amino-2(hydroxymethyl)-*	$H_2NC(CH_2OH)_3$	121.14	nd of fl (MeOH)	170.5–1.5	219–20[18] (230–4[12])			v					MeOH s[h]	C49, 1357
Ω p1252	—,2-amino-2-methyl-*	$CH_3C(CH_2OH)_2NH_2$	105.14	....	109–11	151.2[10]			v	s					C34, 1305
Ω p1253	—,2-butyl-2-ethyl-*	$CH_3(CH_2)_3C(C_2H_5)(CH_2OH)_2$ 160.26		wh	43.8	262 123[15]	0.929[50/20]	1.4587[25]	δ						Am 70, 3121
Ω p1254	1,2-Propanediol, 3-chloro-*	α-Chlorohydrin. $ClCH_2CH(OH)CH_2OH$	110.54	yesh liq	....	213d 116[11]	1.326[18/15]	1.4809[20]	s	s	s				B1[3], 2150
p1255	—,—,diacetate	$ClCH_2CH(O_2CCH_3)CH_2O_2CCH_3$ 194.62		....	....	245 116[12]	1.199[15/25]	1.4407[20]		s	s				B2[3], 313
p1256	1,3-Propanediol, 2-chloro-*	$HOCH_2CHClCH_2OH$	110.54	....	....	146[18]	1.3219[20/4]	1.4831[20]	v	v		v			B1[2], 542
p1257	1,2-Propanediol, 3-chloro-2-methyl-*	$ClCH_2C(OH)(CH_3)CH_2OH$	124.57	....	....	114–7[20] 80[1.6]	1.2362[20/4]	1.4748[20]	∞	∞	∞				B1[3], 2188
—	—,3,3-diethoxy-* ..	see **Glyceraldehyde, diethyl acetal**													
Ω p1258	1,3-Propanediol, 2,2-diethyl-*	$HOCH_2C(C_2H_5)_2CH_2OH$ ..	132.21	wh	61.3–.6	240–1 131[13]	1.052[20/20]	....	v	v	v		os s lig i		Am 70, 946
p1259	1,2-Propanediol, 3(diethylamino)-*	$(C_2H_5)_2NCH_2CH(OH)CH_2OH$ 147.22		syr	....	233–5			s	s	s		chl s		B4, 302
Ω p1260	1,3-Propanediol, 2,2-dimethyl-*	$HOCH_2C(CH_3)_2CH_2OH$ ...	104.15	nd (bz)	130	206[747] 120–30[15]			s	v	v	s[h]			B1[3], 2199
p1261	1,2-Propanediol, 3(dimethylamino)-*	$(CH_3)_2NCH_2CH(OH)CH_2OH$ 119.17		....	....	220[749]			s	s	s		chl s		B4, 302
p1262	1,3-Propanediol, 2,2-dinitro-*	$HOCH_2C(NO_2)_2CH_2OH$ ...	166.09	wh pl (bz)	142				s[h]	s[h]		s[h]	diox, $PhNO_2$ s[h]		C45, 9473
Ω p1263	—,2-ethyl-2-hydroxymethyl-*	TMP. Trimethylolpropane. $CH_3CH_2C(CH_2OH)_3$	134.18	wh pw or pl	58	160[5]			∞	∞			i	CCl_4 i	C54, 2177
Ω p1264	—,2-ethyl-2-nitro-*	$CH_3CH_2C(NO_2)(CH_2OH)_2$.	149.15	nd (w) λ^{al} 280 sh (1.61)	57–8	d			v	v	v				B1, 483
—	1,2-Propanediol, 3-hexadecyloxy-*	see **Glycerol, 1-hexadecyl ether**													
Ω p1265	1,3-Propanediol, 2(hydroxymethyl)-2-methyl-*	Pentaglycerol. Trimethylolethane. $CH_3C(CH_2OH)_3$.	120.15	wh pw or nd (al)	204	135–7[15]			∞	∞	i	...	i	aa v[h]	B1[3], 2348
Ω p1266	—,2(hydroxymethyl)-2-nitro-*	$O_2NC(CH_2OH)_3$	151.12	nd or pr	165 (144)	d			v	v	s				B1[2], 596
p1267	1,2-Propanediol, 3-mercapto-*	1-Thioglycerol. $HSCH_2CH(OH)CH_2OH$.	108.17	visc	....	100–1[1]	1.2455[20]	1.5268[20]	δ	∞	δ	v	δ		B1[3], 2339
p1268	—,2-methyl-*	Isobutylene glycol. $(CH_3)_2C(OH)CH_2OH$	90.12	....	....	176[760] 79–80[12]	1.0024[20/4]	1.4350[20]	s	s	v				B1[3], 2187
p1269	1,3-Propanediol, 2-methyl-2-nitro-*	$CH_3C(NO_2)(CH_2OH)_2$	135.12	mcl	149 50	d			v	v					B1[3], 2190
p1270	—,2-methyl-2-propyl-*	2,2-bis(hydroxymethyl)-pentane. $(HOCH_2)_2C(CH_3)(CH_2)_2CH_3$	132.21	cr (hx)	62–3	234			s					os s hx s[h]	Am 72, 3716
—	1,2-Propanediol, 3-octadecyloxy-*	see **Glycerol, 1-octadecyl ether**													
p1271	1,3-Propanedione, 2,2-dibromo-1,3-diphenyl-*	$C_6H_5COCBr_2COC_6H_5$	382.06	pr (eth)	95					δ	s[h]			os δ	B7, 772

For explanations, symbols and abbreviations see beginning of table. For structural formulas see end of table.

1,2-Propanedione

No.	Name	Synonyms and Formula	Mol. wt.	Color, crystalline form, specific rotation and λ_{max} (log ε)	m.p. °C	b.p. °C	Density	n_D	w	al	eth	ace	bz	other solvents	Ref.
p1272	1,2-Propanedione, 1(3,5-dimethoxy-4-hydroxy-phenyl)-	Syringoyl methyl ketone	224.22	ye nd	80–1	....			δ^h	s	....	...	s	peth s^h	Am 62, 986
p1273	1,3-Propanedione, 1,3-diphenyl-(one enol form)*	Dibenzoylmethane. $C_6H_5COCH:C(OH)C_6H_5$	224.26	unst nd λ^{al} 245 (3.65), 342 (4.38)	70–1	....					s			peth, chl, dil NaOH s	B7², 689
p1274	—,—(one enol form)*	$C_6H_5COCH:C(OH)C_6H_5$ ..	224.26	metast mcl	72–3	....					s	v		chl v	B7², 689
p1275	—,—(one enol form)*	$C_6H_5COCH:C(OH)C_6H_5$ ..	224.26	st rh bipym (eth)	78–9	219–21¹⁸ 165–70³					s	v		chl v NaOH s Na₂CO₃ i	B7², 689
p1276	—,—,(keto form)...	$C_6H_5COCH_2COC_6H_5$	224.26	metast nd or pl (eth)	81	....					s	s		chl, dil NaOH s	B7², 690
p1277	1,2-Propanedione, 1-phenyl-*	Acetyl benzoyl.	148.17	ye oil	....	222⁷⁶⁰ 101¹²	1.0065²⁰₄	1.537¹⁰	s	s	s				B7², 608
p1278	—,—,dioxime*	Methyl phenyl glyoxime. $C_6H_5C(:NOH)C(:NOH)CH_3$	178.19	nd (dil al)	238–40	....			i	s					B7², 609
p1279	—,—,1-oxime*....	$C_6H_5C(:NOH)COCH_3$.....	163.18	pa ye nd or lf (aa, al)	166–7	....			δ	s^h			δ	aa s^h	B7², 608
Ω p1280	—,—,2-oxime*....	α-Isonitrosopropiophenone. $C_6H_5COC(:NOH)CH_3$	163.18	wh nd (w)	115	....			s^h					to s^h	B7², 608
p1281	1,3-Propanedithiol*	$HSCH_2CH_2CH_2SH$.	108.24		–79	172.9 63¹⁵	1.0783²⁰₄	1.5392²⁰	δ	∞	∞		∞	chl ∞	B1³, 2164
p1282	1-Propanephos-phonic acid*	n-Propylphosphonic acid. $CH_3CH_2CH_2PO_3H_2$	124.08	pl (bz)	73	d			v	v	v		δ	peth δ	Am 75, 3379
p1283	2-Propanephos-phonic acid*	Isopropylphosphonic acid. $(CH_3)_2CHPO_3H_2$	124.08	pl (bz)	74–5	d			v	v	v		δ s^h		Am 75, 3379
p1284	1-Propanephos-phonic acid, 2-methyl-*	Isobutylphosphonic acid. $(CH_3)_2CHCH_2PO_3H_2$	138.10	pl (xyl)	119	d			v	v	s		δ	xyl s^h	Am 75, 3379
p1285	2-Propanephos-phonic acid, 2-methyl-*	tert-Butylphosphonic acid. $(CH_3)_3CPO_3H_2$	138.10	wh nd (xyl, aa-lig)	192	d			v	v				aa s xyl s^h peth δ	Am 75, 3379
p1286	1-Propanesul-fonic acid, amide	1-Propansulfonamide. $CH_3CH_2CH_2SO_2NH_2$	123.18	pr (eth), cr (bz)	53.5				s	s	δ s^h		s^h		B4³, 18
p1287	—,chloride	1-Propanesulfonyl chloride*. $CH_3CH_2CH_2SO_2Cl$	142.61			180d 77¹³	1.2826¹⁵₄	1.452²⁰	d^h	d^h					B4³, 18
p1288	2-Propanesul-fonic acid*	Isopropylsulfonic acid. $(CH_3)_2CHSO_3H$	124.17		–37	159¹·⁴	1.187²⁵	1.4332²⁰	v						B4³, 19
p1289	—,amide........	Isopropylsulfonamide*. $(CH_3)_2CHSO_2NH_2$	123.18	cr (eth-peth)	67.5 (60)				v	s	s		i	peth i	B4³, 19
p1290	1-Propanesul-fonic acid, 2-methyl-, chloride	Isobutanesulfonyl chloride*. $(CH_3)_2CHCH_2SO_2Cl$	156.63			189–91⁷⁶⁰ 87¹⁵			1.4520²⁵	d	d^h					B4³, 22
p1291	1,1,2,3-Propane-tetracarboxylic acid, tetraethyl ester*	$C_2H_5O_2CCH_2CH(CO_2C_2H_5)CH(CO_2C_2H_5)_2$	332.36			203–4¹⁸ 187⁵	1.1184²⁰₄	1.4393²⁰	...	s					B2³, 2077
p1292	1,1,3,3-Propane-tetracarboxylic acid, tetraethyl ester*	Ethyl methanedimalonate. $(C_2H_5O_2C)_2CHCH_2CH(CO_2C_2H_5)_2$	332.36		–30	300–10d 195⁸	1.116²⁰	1.4398²⁰	...	s					B2³, 2077
Ω p1293	1-Propanethiol*	n-Propylmercaptan. $CH_3CH_2CH_2SH$	76.17	$\lambda^{w,pH\approx10.2}$ 240 (3.20)	–113.3	67–8⁷⁶⁰	0.8411²⁰	1.4380²⁰	δ	s	s	s	s		B1³, 1430
Ω p1294	2-Propanethiol*	Isopropylmercaptan. $(CH_3)_2CHSH$	76.17		–130.54	52.56⁷⁶⁰	0.8143²⁰	1.4255²⁰	δ	∞	∞	v			B1³, 1477
Ω p1295	1-Propanethiol, 2-methyl-*	Isobutylmercaptan. $(CH_3)_2CHCH_2SH$	90.19	λ^{iso} 225–30 (2.20)	< –79	88.72⁷⁶⁰	0.8339²⁰	1.4387²⁰	δ	v	v	v			B1³, 1565
Ω p1296	2-Propanethiol, 2-methyl-*	tert-Butylmercaptan. $(CH_3)_3CSH$	90.19	λ^{cy} 226 sh (2.2)	1.11	64.22⁷⁶⁰	0.8002²⁰	1.4232²⁰	i					hp s	B1³, 1589
Ω p1297	1,2,3-Propanetri-carboxylic acid*	Tricarballylic acid. $HO_2CCH_2CH(CO_2H)CH_2CO_2H$	176.14	orh (w, eth)	166	....			v	s	δ		v		B2³, 2027
p1298	—,1,2-di-hydroxy-*(l)	$HO_2CCH_2C(OH)(CO_2H)CH(OH)CO_2H$	208.14	nd.$[\alpha]_D$ –17.7 (ac)	159–60	....	1.39³⁵		v	δ	v				B3³, 1127
p1299	—,1-hydroxy-*	Isocitric acid. $HO_2CCH_2CH(CO_2H)CH(OH)CO_2H$	192.14	yesh syr	105	....			δ	δ	δ				B3², 359
—	—,2-hydroxy-*	see Citric acid													
—	1,2,3-Propane-triol*	see Glycerol													
p1301	Propanetrione, diphenyl-*	Diphenyltriketone. $C_6H_5COCOCOC_6H_5$	238.25	ye nd (lig)	68–70	289¹⁷⁵ 248⁶⁰			i	δ	s				B7, 871
Ω p1302	Propanoic acid* ...	Propionic acid. $CH_3CH_2CO_2H$	74.08	....	–20.8	140.99⁷⁶⁰ 41.65¹⁰	0.9930²⁰	1.3869²⁰	∞	∞	s				B2³, 502
Ω p1303	—,allyl ester	$CH_3CH_2CO_2CH_2CH:CH_2$	114.15			124– 4.5⁷⁷⁴	0.9140²⁰	1.4105²⁰	s	s	s	s	s		B2³, 532
p1304	—,amide.........	Propanamide*. Propionamide. $CH_3CH_2CONH_2$	73.10	rh, pl (bz) $\lambda^{bz-C_2H_5CN}$ 175 (3.85)	81.3	213	0.9262¹¹⁰	1.4160¹¹⁰	v	v	v			chl v	B2³, 542

For explanations, symbols and abbreviations see beginning of table. For structural formulas see end of table.

No.	Name	Synonyms and Formula	Mol. wt.	Color, crystalline form, specific rotation and λ_{max} (log ε)	m.p. °C	b.p. °C	Density	n_D	w	al	eth	ace	bz	other solvents	Ref.
	Propanoic acid														
p1305	—,—,N,N-diethyl-.	$CH_3CH_2CON(C_2H_5)_2$......	129.20	....	.....	191 $81-5^{20}$		1.4425^{20}	...	v	...	...	...	ac v	B4³, 210
p1306	—,—,N-phenyl-...	Propionanilide. $CH_3CH_2CONHC_6H_5$	149.19	pl (eth, al, bz) $\lambda^{al}243$ (4.16)	105–6	222.2	1.175		δ	v	v	...	...		B12, 250
p1307	—,—,N-propionyl-	Dipropionamide $CH_3CH_2CONHCOCH_2CH_3$	129.16	nd (w, eth) $\lambda^{chl}281$ (2.12)	154 (sub 100)	210–20			δ s^h		δ	...	...		B2², 224
p1308	—,—,N(2-tolyl)-...		163.22	nd (bz)	89.5	298–9			...	v	v	...	s^h	chl, aa v	B12², 440
p1309	—,—,N(3-tolyl)-...		163.22	nd (eth)	81	....			...	v	s	...	...	lig s	B12, 861
Ω p1310	—,anhydride......	Propionic anhydride. $(CH_3CH_2CO)_2O$	130.15	....	−45	$168.1-.4^{712}$ 67.5^{18}	1.0110^{20}_4	1.4038^{20}	d	d	∞	...	...		B2³, 539
p1311	—,bromide......	Propionyl bromide. CH_3CH_2COBr	136.98	....	$103.0-.6^{770}$		1.5210^{16}_4	1.4578^{16}	...	...	s	...	...		B2², 108
Ω p1312	—,butyl ester*....	$CH_3CH_2CO_2(CH_2)_3CH_3$	130.19	....	−89.55	145.5^{760}	0.8754^{20}_4	1.4014^{20}	δ	∞	∞	...	...		B2³, 526
p1313	—,sec-butyl ester	$CH_3CH_2CO_2CH(CH_3)CH_2CH_3$	130.19			$132.0-.5^{760}$	0.8657^{20}	1.3952^{20}	...	s	s	...	...		B2, 241
Ω p1314	—,chloride......	Propionyl chloride. CH_3CH_2COCl	92.53	....	−94	80^{760}	1.0646^{20}	1.4032^{20}	d	d	s	...	...		B2³, 540
Ω p1315	—,cyclohexyl ester*		156.23	....		193^{750} 93^{35}	0.9359^{20}_4	1.4403^{20}	i	s	s	s	...		B6³, 24
Ω p1316	—,ethyl ester*...	$CH_3CH_2CO_2C_2H_5$	102.13	....	−73.9	99.10^{760}	0.8917^{20}	1.3839^{20}	δ	∞	∞	s	...		B2³, 520
p1317	—,fluoride......	Propionyl fluoride. CH_3CH_2COF	76.07	....		44	0.972^{15}	1.329^{13}	d	...	s	...	...		B2³, 540
Ω p1318	—,furfuryl ester...		154.17	$\lambda^w<220$		$195-6^{762}$	1.1085^{20}_4		δ	s	∞	s	...		B17², 115
p1319	—,heptyl ester*....	$CH_3CH_2CO_2(CH_2)_6CH_3$	172.27	....	−50.9	210.04^{760} $124-5^{14}$	0.8679^{20}	1.4201^{15}	i	s	s	s	...	os s	B2³, 530
p1320	—,hexyl ester*	$CH_3CH_2CO_2(CH_2)_5CH_3$	158.24	....	−57.5	190^{760} $73-4^{10}$	0.8698^{20}	1.4162^{15}	i	s	s	s	...	AcOEt s	B2³, 529
p1321	—,iodide........	Propionyl iodide. CH_3CH_2COI	183.98	....		127–8			...	...	...	...	...		B2, 243
Ω p1322	—,isobutyl ester...	$CH_3CH_2CO_2CH_2CH(CH_3)_2$	130.19	....	−71.4	136.8^{760} 66.5^{60}	0.8687^{20}_4	1.3973^{20}	δ	...	...	...	...		B2³, 527
Ω p1323	—,isopropyl ester*.	$CH_3CH_2CO_2CH(CH_3)_2$	116.16	....		$109-10^{760}$	0.8660^{20}_4	1.3872^{20}	δ	∞	∞	...	...		B2³, 526
Ω p1324	—,methyl ester*...	$CH_3CH_2CO_2CH_3$	88.12	....	−87.5	79.85^{760}	0.9150^{20}	1.3775^{20}	δ	∞	∞	s	...	os s	B2³, 519
Ω p1325	—,3-methylbutyl ester*	Isoamyl propionate. $CH_3CH_2CO_2CH_2CH_2CH(CH_3)_2$	144.22	....		160.7^{760}	0.8697^{20}_4	1.4069^{20}	δ	s	s	...	...		B2³, 529
Ω p1326	—,nitrile........	Ethyl cyanide. Propionitrile. CH_3CH_2CN	55.08	....	−92.89	97.35^{760} 1.32^{10}	0.7818^{20}_4	1.3655^{20}	v	s	s	s	s	os s	B2³, 547
Ω p1327	—,octyl ester*....	$CH_3CH_2CO_2(CH_2)_7CH_3$	186.30	....	−41.6	227.93^{760}	0.8663^{20}	1.4221^{15}_4	i	s	s	s	s	os s	B2³, 531
p1328	—,pentyl ester*....	$CH_3CH_2CO_2(CH_2)_4CH_3$	144.22	....	−73.1	168.65	0.8761^{15}	1.4096^{15}	i	∞	∞	s	s		B2², 221
Ω p1329	—,phenyl ester*...	$CH_3CH_2CO_2C_6H_5$	150.18	pr	20	211^{760} 100^{16}	1.0467^{25}_{23}	1.4980^{20}	i	v	v	s	...		B6³, 599
Ω p1330	—,4-phenylphenacyl ester*		268.32	cr	102	....			i	...	...	...	...		Am 52, 3715
p1331	—,piperazinium salt	$2(CH_3CH_2CO_2H).C_4H_{10}N_2$	234.30	cr (diox)	124–5				...	...	...	...	...	diox s^h	Am 56, 1759
Ω p1332	—,propyl ester*...	$CH_3CH_2CO_2CH_2CH_2CH_3$.	116.16	....	−75.9	122.3^{760}	0.8809^{20}_4	1.3935^{20}	δ	∞	∞	s	...	chl v	B2³, 524
p1333	—,tetrahydrofurfuryl ester*		158.20	....		$204-7^{756}$ $85-7^3$	1.044^{20}_0		i	∞	∞	...	...	chl ∞	B17², 107
—	—,2-amino-*......	see **Alanine**													
—	—,3-amino-*......	see **β-Alanine**													
p1335	—,2(2-amino-acetamido)-2-methyl-	$(CH_3)_2C(CO_2H)NHCOCH_2NH_2$	160.17	nd (al)	260d				...	...	s^h	...	...		B4², 841
—	—,2-amino-3-hydroxy-*	see **Serine**													
—	—,2-amino-3(4-hydroxyphenyl)-*	see **Tyrosine**													
Ω p1336	—,2-amino-2-methyl-*	$(CH_3)_2C(NH_2)CO_2H$......	103.12	ta or pr (w)	337 (cor)	sub 280	....	....	v	δ	i	...	...		B4³, 1322
—	—,2-amino-3-phenyl-*	see **Phenylalanine**													
p1337	—,3-amino-3-phenyl-(d)*	β-Aminohydrocinnamic acid. $C_6H_5CH(NH_2)CH_2CO_2H$	165.19	pl (w), $[\alpha]_D -9.2$ (1N NaOH, p = 9) $[\alpha]^{20}_D +7$ (w, p = 1)	234–5d	....	....		δ s^h	δ s^h	δ	...	...		B14¹, 602
p1338	—,—(dl)*	$C_6H_5CH(NH_2)CH_2CO_2H$	165.19	cr (w)	231d				δ s^h	δ s^h	δ	...	...	dil ac s	B14², 295
p1339	—,—(l)*	$C_6H_5CH(NH_2)CH_2CO_2H$..	165.19	cr (w), $[\alpha]^{25}_D$ −7.5 (w, c = 1) $[\alpha]_D$ +8.9 (1N NaOH, p = 10)	234–5d				δ s^h	δ s^h	δ	...	...		B14¹, 602

For explanations, symbols and abbreviations see beginning of table. For structural formulas see end of table.

No.	Name	Synonyms and Formula	Mol. wt.	Color. crystalline form. specific rotation and λ_{max} (log ε)	m.p. °C	b.p. °C	Density	n_D	Solubility						Ref.
									w	al	eth	ace	bz	other solvents	
	Propanoic acid														
—	—,3(2-amino-phenyl)-, lactam*	*see* **Quinoline, 2-oxo-1,2,3,4-tetrahydro-**													
—	—,2-benzylidene-	*see* **Cinnamic acid, α-methyl-**													
p1340	—,2-benzyl-3-phenyl-	Dibenzylacetic acid. $(C_6H_5CH_2)_2CHCO_2H$	240.31	pl (peth, dil aa), nd (w)	89	235^{18}	....	....	δ^h	s	s	....	s	chl, aa s	B9², 475
p1341	—,—,amide	$(C_6H_5CH_2)_2CHCONH_2$	239.32	nd (al, w)	129	259^{18}			s	s	s		s		B9, 683
p1342	—,—,methyl ester	$(C_6H_5CH_2)_2CHCO_2CH_3$	254.33	nd (al)	42–3				i	δ				os v peth δ	B9², 475
p1343	—,—,nitrile	$(C_6H_5CH_2)_2CHCN$	221.31	lf or pl (al)	89–91				i	s	s				B9, 683
Ω p1344	—,2-bromo-(dl)*	$CH_3CHBrCO_2H$	152.98	pr	(i) 25.7(st) (ii) −3.9 (unst)	203.5 96^{10}	1.7000_4^{20}	1.4753^{20}	v	v	v				B2³, 565
p1345	—,—,amide, N(2-tolyl)-	....	242.12	nd	131					s	v		s	chl v	B12, 794
Ω p1346	—,—,bromide	$CH_3CHBrCOBr$	215.88			$152-4$ (cor) 59^{15}	2.0612_4^{16}		d	d					B2³, 569
p1347	—,—,chloride	$CH_3CHBrCOCl$	171.43	pl		$131-3$	1.697^{11}	....	d	d^h	s			chl s	B2³, 569
Ω p1348	—,—,ethyl ester*	$CH_3CHBrCO_2C_2H_5$	181.04			$159-61$ δd 71^{26}	1.4135_4^{20}	1.4490^{20}	i	∞	∞			chl s	B2³, 568
p1349	—,—,methyl ester(d)*	$CH_3CHBrCO_2CH_3$	167.01	$[\alpha]_D^{17}$ +42.65	....	144^{760} $61-2^{36}$	1.482^{17}			s	s	s		chl s	B2, 253
p1350	—,—,—(dl)*	$CH_3CHBrCO_2CH_3$	167.01			$143-5^{760}$ 51.5^{19}	1.4966_4^{21}	1.4451^{22}		s	s	s		MeOH s	B2³, 567
p1351	—,—,—(l)*	$CH_3CHBrCO_2CH_3$	167.01	$[\alpha]_{578}^{20}$ −55.5		$61-3^{32}$	1.484^{20}			s	s	s			B2², 229
p1352	—,—,nitrile	$CH_3CHBrCN$	133.98			59^{24}	1.5505_4^{20}	1.4585^{20}			s	s			B2³, 567
p1353	—,—,piperazinium salt	$2(CH_3CHBrCO_2H) \cdot C_4H_{10}N_2$	392.10	wh cr	195d (cor)		....		s	s	i				Am 70, 2758
Ω p1354	—,3-bromo-*	$BrCH_2CH_2CO_2H$	152.98	pl (CCl_4)	62.5	$140-2^{45}$	1.48		s	s	s	s		chl s	B2³, 569
p1355	—,—,amide	$BrCH_2CH_2CONH_2$	152.00	cr (w)	111				s^h	s	s	s			B2², 231
p1356	—,—,butyl ester*	$BrCH_2CH_2CO_2(CH_2)_3CH_3$	209.09			130^{26}	1.4549^{20}	1.3051^{20}		s	s	s		os s	B2², 231
p1357	—,—,ethyl ester*	$BrCH_2CH_2CO_2C_2H_5$	181.04			179 70^{12}		1.4516^{20}		s	s	s		os v	B2³, 570
Ω p1358	—,—,methyl ester*	$BrCH_2CH_2CO_2CH_3$	167.01			105.5^{60} 80^{27}	1.4897^{15}	1.4542^{20}		s	s	s		os v	B2³, 570
p1359	—,—,3-methylbutyl ester*	Isoamyl β-bromopropionate. $BrCH_2CH_2CO_2CH_2CH_2CH(CH_3)_2$	223.12			$110-1^{11}$	1.2217_4^{15}	1.4556^9		s	s	s		os s	B2², 231
Ω p1360	—,—,nitrile	$BrCH_2CH_2CN$	133.98			92^{25} 69^7	1.6152_4^{20}	1.4800^{20}		v	v				B2³, 571
p1361	—,2-bromo-2-methyl-*	2-Bromoisobutyric acid. $(CH_3)_2CBrCO_2H$	167.01	cr (peth)	48–9	$198-200^{760}$ 115^{24}	1.5225_{60}^{60}	....	v	s	s	s		os v peth s^h	B2³, 659
p1362	—,—,amide	$(CH_3)_2CBrCONH_2$	166.03	pr (chl)	148	145^{17}			s	s				chl s	B2², 263
p1363	—,—,—,N-methyl-N-phenyl-	$(CH_3)_2CBrCON(CH_3)C_6H_5$	256.15	cr (lig)	44									to s lig s^h	B12, 254
p1364	—,—,bromide	$(CH_3)_2CBrCOBr$	229.91			$162-4$ $91-8^{100}$	1.4067_4^{14}	1.4552^{14}	d	d^h			s	AcOEt, CS_2 s	B2³, 661
Ω p1365	—,—,ethyl ester*	$(CH_3)_2CBrCO_2C_2H_5$	195.06			164^{762} 70^{20}	1.3182_4^{20}	1.4446^{20}	i	s	∞				B2³, 660
p1366	—,—,nitrile	$(CH_3)_2CBrCN$	148.01			$139-40$ $61.2-.6^5$	1.4796_4^{15}	1.4739^{15}		s	s		s		B2³, 661
p1367	—,2-bromo-2-phenyl-(dl)*	$C_6H_5CBr(CH_3)CO_2H$	229.08	pl (CS_2)	$93-4$ $(90-1)$				i				v	CS_2 s lig δ	B9, 525
p1368	—,3-bromo-2-phenyl-(dl)*	$C_6H_5CH(CH_2Br)CO_2H$	229.08	pr (CS_2)	$93-4$				i	v	v			CS_2 s	B9, 526
p1369	—,3-bromo-3-phenyl-(dl)*	$C_6H_5CHBrCH_2CO_2H$	229.08	mcl pr (al)	137				s	s					B9², 343
p1370	—,—,methyl ester*	$C_6H_5CHBrCH_2CO_2CH_3$	243.11	pr	37.5–8.5				s	s	δ			os s lig δ	B9¹, 201
p1371	—,3(2-carboxy-phenyl)-*	....	194.19	nd (w)	167				s	s		δ			B9², 622
p1372	—,3(4-carboxy-phenyl)-*	....	194.19	nd (al)	294	sub			s^h	s^h					B9², 622
Ω p1373	—,2-chloro-*	$CH_3CHClCO_2H$	108.53			186 84^{12}	1.2585_4^{20}	1.4380^{20}	∞	∞	∞	s			B2³, 554
p1374	—,—,amide, N(2-tolyl)-	....	197.67	nd (abs al)	111					v^h					B12, 794
p1375	—,—,butyl ester*	$CH_3CHClCO_2C_4H_9^n$	164.63	....		$183.5-5.0$ $71.6-2.6^{10}$	1.0253_4^{20}	1.4263^{20}	i	s	s				B2³, 555
p1376	—,—,chloride(d)	$CH_3CHClCOCl$	126.97	$[\alpha]_D^{18}$ +0.2 $(l = 10)$		110^{744}	$1.2394^{7.5}$		d	d					B2¹, 110
Ω p1377	—,—,ethyl ester*	$CH_3CHClCO_2C_2H_5$	136.58			$147-8$ $52-4^{18}$	1.0793_4^{20}	1.4178^{20}	i	∞	∞				B2³, 555
p1378	—,—,isobutyl ester(d)*	$CH_3CHClCO_2CH_2CH(CH_3)_2$	164.63	$[\alpha]_D$ +5.21	....	$175-7$	1.0312_4^{20}	1.4247^{20}		s	s	s		os s	B2, 248

For explanations, symbols and abbreviations see beginning of table. For structural formulas see end of table.

No.	Name	Synonyms and Formula	Mol. wt.	Color, crystalline form, specific rotation and λ_{max} (log ε)	m.p. °C	b.p. °C	Density	n_D	w	al	eth	ace	bz	other solvents	Ref.
	Propanoic acid														
p1379	—,—,isopropyl ester*	$CH_3CHClCO_2CH(CH_3)_2$	150.61			$151.5-2.5^{760}$ $46.1-.9^{12}$	1.0315_4^{20}	1.4149^{20}	i	s	s				B2³, 555
p1380	—,—,methyl ester(d)*	$CH_3CHClCO_2CH_3$	122.55	$[\alpha]_D +19.88$ (undil)		$133-4$ 50^{35}	1.1815_4^{20}			s					B2, 248
Ω p1381	—,—, (dl)*	$CH_3CHClCO_2CH_3$	122.55			132.5^{760}	1.209_4^{20}	1.4182^{20}		s				0.1N HCl s	B2³, 554
p1382	—,—,—(l)*	$CH_3CHClCO_2CH_3$	122.55	$[\alpha]_D -26.83$ (undil)		$79-80^{120}$	1.158_4^{20}			s					B2, 248
p1383	—,—,nitrile	$CH_3CHClCN$	89.53			$123-4$ 73^{144}	1.0792^{10}								B2³, 556
Ω p1384	—,3-chloro-*	$ClCH_2CH_2CO_2H$	108.53	lf (w), hyg cr (lig)	41 (61)	204 δd			s	s	∞				B2³, 556
p1385	—,—,amide, N(2-tolyl)-		197.67	(w, dil al)	78				s^h	v^h					B12², 441
p1386	—,—,butyl ester*	$ClCH_2CH_2CO_2C_4H_9^n$	164.63			104^{22} 77^6	1.0370_4^{20}	1.4321^{20}		s		s		os s	B2³, 559
Ω p1387	—,—,chloride	$ClCH_2CH_2COCl$	126.97	yesh		$143-5^{763}$ 82^{102}	1.3307^{13}	1.4549^{20}	δ	v d^h	v			chl v	B2³, 560
p1388	—,—,ethyl ester*	$ClCH_2CH_2CO_2C_2H_5$	136.58			162^{760} 56^{11}	1.1086_4^{20}	1.4254^{20}	δ	∞	∞			os s	B2³, 558
p1389	—,—,isobutyl ester	$ClCH_2CH_2CO_2CH_2CH(CH_3)_2$	164.63			$191-3$	1.0323_4^{20}	1.4295^{20}	i	s	s				B2³, 559
Ω p1390	—,—,methyl ester*	$ClCH_2CH_2CO_2CH_3$	122.55			$155-7^{760}$ (150) $40-2^{10}$	1.1861_4^{15}	1.4263^{20}		s					B2³, 558
p1391	—,—,3-methyl-butyl ester*	Isoamyl β-chloropropionate. $ClCH_2CH_2CO_2CH_2CH_2CH(CH_3)_2$	178.66			$207-8^{740}$ 87^{12}	1.0171_4^{20}	1.4343^{20}	i	s	s				B2³, 559
Ω p1392	—,—,nitrile	$ClCH_2CH_2CN$	89.53			$175-6$ $85-7^{20}$	1.1573^{20}	1.4360^{20}							B2², 227
p1393	—,—,propyl ester*	$ClCH_2CH_2CO_2CH_2CH_2CH_3$	150.61			180 $77-8^{12}$	1.0656_4^{20}	1.4290^{20}	i	s	s				B2³, 559
p1394	—,3-chloro-2(chloromethyl)-2-hydroxy-*	$(ClCH_2)_2C(OH)CO_2H$	173.00	ta (chl)	93					v	v			chl s^h peth δ	B3², 224
Ω p1395	—,3-chloro-2,2-dimethyl-*	Chloropivalic acid. $ClCH_2C(CH_3)_2CO_2H$	136.58		$41-2$	$126-9^{30}$ $108-12^{10}$								CCl_4 v	C47, 11126
p1396	—,—,chloride	$ClCH_2C(CH_3)_2COCl$	155.04			$85-6^{60}$		1.4539^{20}	d	d				CCl_4 s	C34, 3677
p1397	—,3-chloro-2-hydroxy-2-methyl-, nitrile	Chloroacetone cyanohydrin. $ClCH_2C(CH_3)(OH)CN$	119.55			110^{27}	1.2027^{15}	1.45362^{11}	v		v	v		os v peth i	B3, 317
p1398	—,2-chloro-2-methyl-*	2-Chloroisobutyric acid. $(CH_3)_2CClCO_2H$	122.55		31	118^{50} $80-2^{12}$		1.450^{20}	v	v					B2³, 657
p1399	—,—,chloride	$(CH_3)_2CClCOCl$	141.00			$126-7$ $(113-4)$		1.4369^{20}	d	d	s				B2³, 657
p1400	—,—,ethyl ester*	$(CH_3)_2CClCO_2C_2H_5$	150.61			$148.5-9$ (cor)	1.062^0	1.4109^{16}		s	s				B2³, 657
p1401	—,—,methyl ester*	$(CH_3)_2CClCO_2CH_3$	136.58			135 $42-4^{17}$	1.0893_{13}^{13}	1.4122^{21}			s				B2³, 657
p1402	—,3-chloro-2-methyl-*	$ClCH_2CH(CH_3)CO_2H$	122.55			$128-33^{50}$	1.0153^{20}	1.4310^{20}		s	v			CCl_4 s	B2³, 658
p1403	—,—,chloride	$ClCH_2CH(CH_3)COCl$	141.00			$151-2^{765}$		1.4542^{20}	d	d				CCl_4 s	B2³, 658
p1404	—,3-cyclohexyl-*		156.23		16	$275-8$ $(268$ (cor)) 143.5^{11}	0.9966_4^{20}	1.4634^{20}	s			s			B9², 13
p1405	—,2,3-diamino-*	$H_2NCH_2CH(NH_2)CO_2H$	104.12	hyg rosettes	ca. 110–20				s	i	i				B4¹, 500
Ω p1406	—,2,3-dibromo-*	Acrylic acid dibromide. $BrCH_2CHBrCO_2H$	231.88	(i) st pl (ii) labile pr	(i) 66.5–7 (ii) 51	$220-40$d 160^{20}			s	s	s		s	CS_2 s	B2, 258
Ω p1407	—,—,ethyl ester*	$BrCH_2CHBrCO_2C_2H_5$	259.95			$214-5$ 112^{23}	1.7966_4^{20}	1.5007^{20}		s					B2³, 572
Ω p1408	—,—,methyl ester*	$BrCH_2CHBrCO_2CH_3$	245.91			206^{760} 115^{25}	1.9333_4^{20}	1.5127^{20}		s					B2³, 572
p1410	—,2,3-dibromo-3-phenyl-(d)*	d-Cinnamic acid dibromide. $C_6H_5CHBrCHBrCO_2H$	307.99	pr (chl), $[\alpha]_D^{15}$ +45.8 (abs al)	182					v	v			chl s^h	B9², 344
Ω p1411	—,— (dl)*	$C_6H_5CHBrCHBrCO_2H$	307.99	mcl pr (chl)	240d	sub			d^h	v	v			chl s^h CS_2 δ	B9², 344
p1412	—,— (meso)*	$C_6H_5CHBrCHBrCO_2H$	307.99	nd	91–3				d^h				v	CS_2 v lig i	B9², 344
p1413	—,—,ethyl ester(d)*	$C_6H_5CHBrCHBrCO_2C_2H_5$	336.04	cr (CS_2), $[\alpha]_D$ +59.1	71					s				CS_2 s^h	B9, 518
p1414	—,—,— (dl)*	$C_6H_5CHBrCHBrCO_2C_2H_5$	336.04	mcl pr or pl	75–6				i	s	v			chl v	B9², 345
Ω p1415	—,2,2-dichloro-*	$CH_3CCl_2CO_2H$	142.97			$185-90$ $90-2^{14}$	$1.389_4^{22.8}$		v	v	s			alk v	B2², 228
p1416	—,—,chloride	CH_3CCl_2COCl	161.42			$117.4-.8^{753}$	1.4062_4^{20}	1.4524^{20}	d	d					B2³, 561
Ω p1417	—,2,3-dichloro-*	$ClCH_2CHClCO_2H$	142.97	hyg nd (peth)	50	210 part d 113^{12}		1.4650^{20}	s	s	s			peth δ, s^h	B2³, 561
p1418	—,—,chloride	$ClCH_2CHClCOCl$	161.42			$52-4^{16}$	1.4757_4^{20}	1.4764^{20}	d	d	s				B2³, 562

For explanations, symbols and abbreviations see beginning of table. For structural formulas see end of table.

No.	Name	Synonyms and Formula	Mol. wt.	Color. crystalline form. specific rotation and λ_{max} (log ε)	m.p. °C	b.p. °C	Density	n_D	Solubility						Ref.
									w	al	eth	ace	bz	other solvents	
	Propanoic acid														
p1419	—,—,ethyl ester* ..	ClCH$_2$CHClCO$_2$C$_2$H$_5$	171.03	....	....	183–4 76–7^{15}	1.2461$_4^{20}$	1.4482^{20}	...	s	s	...	...		B2^3, 561
p1420	—,—,methyl ester(d)*	ClCH$_2$CHClCO$_2$CH$_3$	157.00	[α]$_D^{20}$ +1.70	....	92^{50}	1.3282$_4^{20}$	....	...	s	s	s	...		B2^1, 111
p1421	—,3,3-dichloro-*...	Cl$_2$CHCH$_2$CO$_2$H	142.97	pr	56	....	....	....	v	v	v	...	v	chl v	B2, 252
p1422	—,—,chloride.....	Cl$_2$CHCH$_2$COCl	161.42	....	....	43–4^{10}	1.4557$_4^{20}$	1.4738^{20}	d	d	s	...		diox s	B2^3, 562
p1423	—,3,3-dichloro-2-hydroxy-2-methyl-*	Cl$_2$CHC(CH$_3$)(OH)CO$_2$H ..	173.00	pr (al-eth)	82–3	d	....	....	s	s	s	...			B3^2, 224
Ω p1423^1	—,3(3,5-diiodo-4-hydroxy-phenyl)-2-phenyl-*	Iodoalphionic acid........	494.07	pa ye cr (aa, bz, dil al)	163.5–.8	....	....	....	i	s	s	...	δ	alk s aa s^h chl δ	C40, 1883
p1423^2	—,2,3-di-hydroxy-*	Glyceric acid. HOCH$_2$CH(OH)CO$_2$H	106.08	syr	....	d	....	....	∞	∞	i	∞			B3^3, 845
p1424	—,—,ethyl ester(D)*	D-Ethyl glycerate. HOCH$_2$CH(OH)CO$_2$C$_2$H$_5$	134.13	[α]$_D^{1.1}$ −22.73 (1 = 19.84 cm)	....	....	....	....							B3^1, 141
p1425	—,—,—(DL)*	HOCH$_2$CH(OH)CO$_2$C$_2$H$_5$.	134.13	....	....	230–40 120–1^{14}	1.1909$_{15}^{15}$	....	s	v	v	...			B3^3, 854
p1426	—,—,methyl ester (DL)*	DL-Methyl glycerate. HOCH$_2$CH(OH)CO$_2$CH$_3$	120.12	....	....	239–44 119–20^{14}	1.2814$_{15}^{15}$	1.4502^{20}	∞	∞	δ	...			B3^1, 141
p1427	—,—,—(L)*	HOCH$_2$CH(OH)CO$_2$CH$_3$.	120.12	[α]$_D^{15}$ −6.44	....	119–20^{14} 74.5$^{0.5}$	1.2798$_{15}^{15}$	....	∞	∞	δ	...			B3^3, 853
p1428	—,3(2,5-dimeth-oxyphenyl)-2-oxo-*		224.22	yesh cr (aa)	166–70d	....	....	....	...	...	...	s	δ	MeOH s aa s^h	B10^2, 723
p1429	—,3(3,4-dimeth-oxyphenyl)-2-oxo-*		224.22	lf (aa)	ca. 187d	....	....	....	s^h	v	δ	v	δ	chl δ	B10^2, 723
Ω p1430	—,2,2-dimethyl-* ..	Pivalic acid. Trimethylacetic acid. (CH$_3$)$_3$CCO$_2$H	102.13	nd	35.3–.5	163.7–.8^{760} 70^{14}	0.905^{50}	1.3931$^{36.5}$	δ	v	v	...			B2^3, 708
p1431	—,—,amide,N,N-diethyl-	(CH$_3$)$_3$CCON(C$_2$H$_5$)$_2$	157.26	....	....	203	0.891^{15}	....	s	s	s	...			B4, 111
Ω p1432	—,—,chloride.....	Pivalyl chloride. (CH$_3$)$_3$CCOCl	120.58	....	....	107^{760} 48^{100}	1.003^{20}	1.4139^{20}	d	d	v	...			B2^3, 712
p1433	—,—,ethyl ester* ..	(CH$_3$)$_3$CCO$_2$C$_2$H$_5$	130.19	....	−89.55	118–8.2^{760}	0.856$_4^{20}$	1.3906^{20}	δ	∞	∞	...			B2^3, 710
p1434	—,—,methyl ester*	(CH$_3$)$_3$CCO$_2$CH$_3$.	116.16	....	....	100.8–1.4^{760}	0.891$_4^0$	1.3880^{20}	δ	∞	∞	...			B2^3, 709
Ω p1435	—,—,nitrile.......	tert-Butyl cyanide. Pivalonitrile. (CH$_3$)$_3$CCN	83.13	....	15–6	105–6	0.7586$_4^{25}$	1.3774^{20}	δ	v	v	...			B2^3, 713
p1436	—,2(dimethyl-amino)-, nitrile	N,N-Dimethyl-dl-alanine nitrile. (CH$_3$)$_2$NCH(CH$_3$)CN	98.15	....	....	144	....	....	s	s	s	...			B4, 392
Ω p1437	—,2,2-diphenyl-* ..	(C$_6$H$_5$)$_2$C(CH$_3$)CO$_2$H ..	226.28	pl (bz-peth), nd (w), lf (dil al)	175–7	sub >300	....	....	δ^h	s v^h	v	...	s	chl, to v peth δ	B9^2, 474
p1438	—,2,3-diphenyl-(d)*	C$_6$H$_5$CH$_2$CH(C$_6$H$_5$)CO$_2$H .	226.28	cr (dil al) [α]$_D^{15}$ +94 (bz)	83–9	....	....	....	δ^h	s	s	...	s		B9^1, 284
p1439	—,—(dl)*	C$_6$H$_5$CH$_2$CH(C$_6$H$_5$)CO$_2$H. .	226.28	(i) pr (chl), (ii) pl (chl), (iii) cr (MeOH)	(i) 88–9 (ii) 95–6 (iii) 82	330–40	(i) 1.1481 (ii) 1.1495 (iii) 1.1430	....	i δ^h	v	s	...	s	CS$_2$ s chl s^h	B9^1, 285
p1440	—,—(l)*	C$_6$H$_5$CH$_2$CH(C$_6$H$_5$)CO$_2$H. .	226.28	nd (dil al) [α]$_D^{20}$ −85.1 (bz)	83–9	....	....	....	δ^h	s	s	...	s		B9^1, 285
Ω p1441	—,3,3-diphenyl-* ..	Benzhydrylacetic acid. (C$_6$H$_5$)$_2$CHCH$_2$CO$_2$H	226.28	nd (dil al)	155	....	....	....	δ	s	s	...			B9^2, 473
p1442	—,2,3-diphenyl-2-hydroxy-*	α-Benzylmandelic acid. C$_6$H$_5$CH$_2$C(OH)(C$_6$H$_5$)CO$_2$H	242.28	nd (bz), cr (dil al)	165–6	....	....	....	δ^h	v	v	...	s^h	aa v	B10^2, 227
p1443	—,3,3-diphenyl-2-hydroxy-*	β,β-Diphenyllactic acid. (C$_6$H$_5$)$_2$CHCH(OH)CO$_2$H	242.28	nd (w)	159d	....	....	....	δ s^h	s	s	...			B10^2, 228
Ω p1444	—,3,3-diphenyl-3-hydroxy-*	(C$_6$H$_5$)$_2$C(OH)CH$_2$CO$_2$H ..	242.28	nd (dil al)	212	....	....	....	δ^h	v	δ	v	δ	aa v	B10^1, 156
p1445	—,—,ethyl ester* ..	(C$_6$H$_5$)$_2$C(OH)CH$_2$CO$_2$C$_2$H$_5$	270.33	pr (dil al)	87	....	....	....	δ s^h	v	...	...		os v con sulf s	B10^2, 228
p1446	—,2,3-epoxy-*	Acrylic acid oxide. Glycidic acid.	88.06	....	....	....	....	....	∞	∞	∞	...			B18^1, 435
p1447	—,2-ethoxy-, nitrile	CH$_3$CH(OC$_2$H$_5$)CN	99.13	....	....	131^{765}	0.8743$_4^{20}$	1.3890^{22}	δ	v	v	...		aa v	B3^3, 498
Ω p1448	—,3-ethoxy-, nitrile	C$_2$H$_5$OCH$_2$CH$_2$CN......	99.13	....	....	171.3–.5^{760} 65^{15}	0.9285$_4^{15}$	1.4068^{20}	...	v	v	...		ac d	B3^3, 538
p1449	—,3-fluoro-*	FCH$_2$CH$_2$CO$_2$H	92.07	....	....	83–4^{14} 51–2^2	....	1.3889^{25}	s	v	v	...			C42, 866
p1451	—,3(2-furyl)-..	Furfurylacetic acid........	140.15	cr (chl-lig, w, peth), ye in HCl	58	229 108–10^{10}	....	....	s	s	s	...		chl s lig δ	B18^2, 272
p1452	—,—,ethyl ester ...	C$_9$H$_{12}$O$_3$. See p1451	168.20	....	....	212 108–10^{10}	....	1.4812^{25}							B18^2, 272

For explanations, symbols and abbreviations see beginning of table. For structural formulas see end of table.

No.	Name	Synonyms and Formula	Mol. wt.	Color, crystalline form, specific rotation and λ_{max} (log ε)	m.p. °C	b.p. °C	Density	n_D	w	al	eth	ace	bz	other solvents	Ref.
	Propanoic acid														
Ω p1452[1]	—,3(2-furyl)-3-oxo-, ethyl ester	$C_9H_{10}O_4$. See p1451	182.18	lt ye		142–3[10]	1.165[17]		i	s	s				B18[2], 327
p1453	—,—,methyl ester	$C_8H_8O_4$. See p1451	168.16	ye in air		144–5[20] 96–8[7]				s	s				B18[2], 327
p1454	—,2-hydroxy-(D)*	l-(−)-Lactic acid. Sarcolactic acid. $CH_3CH(OH)CO_2H$	90.08	pl (chl or aa) $[\alpha]_D -2.26$ (w, c = 1.24)	53	103[2]			v	v	δ				D3[3], 442
Ω p1455	—,—(DL)*	$CH_3CH(OH)CO_2H$	90.08	ye	18	122[15]	1.2060[25/4]	1.4392[20/a]	v	v	δ				B3[3], 454
p1456	—,—(L)*	$CH_3CH(OH)CO_2H$	90.08	hyg pr (eth-Pr_2^iO), $[\alpha]_D^{15}$ +3.82 (w, c = 10.5)	52.8	119[12]d			∞	∞	δ				B3[3], 448
p1457	—,—,acetate (dl)	$CH_3CO_2CH(CH_3)CO_2H$	132.13	dlq	57–60	167–70[78] 127[11]	1.17582[20/4]	1.4240[20]	d[h]	s			s	peth δ	B3[3], 467
p1458	—,—,acetate chloride(d, +)	$CH_3CO_2CH(CH_3)COCl$	150.56	$[\alpha]_{578}^{18}$ +32.4		51–3[11]	1.177[20]		d[h]	d[h]					B3[2], 189
p1459	—,—,—(dl)	$CH_3CO_2CH(CH_3)COCl$	150.56			150δd 56[11]	1.1920[17]	1.4241[17]	d[h]	d[h]					B3[3], 495
Ω p1460	—,—,allyl ester	Allyl lactate. $CH_3CH(OH)CO_2CH_2CH:CH_2$	130.15			56–60[8]	1.0452[20/4]	1.4369[20]	d[h]	d[h]				Py s	B3[3], 486
p1461	—,—,amide (d)	Lactamide. Lactic amide. $CH_3CH(OH)CONH_2$	89.09	cr (AcOEt) $[\alpha]_{578}^{18}$ +22.2	49–51				s	s					B3[3], 450
Ω p1462	—,—,—(dl)	$CH_3CH(OH)CONH_2$	89.09	pl (AcOEt)	75.5 (78.5–9.5)		1.1381[80/4]		s	s				AcOEt s[h]	B3[3], 495
p1463	—,—,—,N(4-ethoxyphenyl)-	Lactophenin. N-Lactyl-β-phenetidide.	209.25	nd (w) λ^{MeOH} 249 (4.20)	118				s[h]	v	δ		δ	peth δ	B13[2], 262
p1464	—,—,anhydride*	Lactic anhydride. $[CH_3CH(OH)CO]_2O$	162.14	pa ye amor or syr		d250			δ	v	v				B3, 282
p1465	—,—,butyl ester(d)*	d-Butyl lactate. $CH_3CH(OH)CO_2C_4H_9^n$	146.19	$[\alpha]_D^{27.3}$ +13.63		77[10]	0.9744[27.6]		s	∞	∞				B3[2], 188
Ω p1466	—,—,—(dl)*	$CH_3CH(OH)CO_2C_4H_9^n$	146.19		−43	83[13]	0.98032[22]	1.4217[20]	s	∞	∞				B3[3], 480
p1467	—,—,ethyl ester(D)*	Ethyl lactate. $CH_3CH(OH)CO_2C_2H_5$	118.13	$[\alpha]_D^{19}$ +14.52		58[20]	1.0324[20.4/4]	1.4125[20]	∞	v	v				B3[3], 446
Ω p1468	—,—,—(DL)*	$CH_3CH(OH)CO_2C_2H_5$	118.13			154.5 (cor) 58[19]	1.0302[20/4]	1.4124[20]	∞	v	v				B3[3], 473
p1469	—,—,—(L)*	$CH_3CH(OH)CO_2C_2H_5$	118.13	$[\alpha]_D^{19}$ −11.33		69–70[36]	1.0314[20]	1.4156[20]	∞	v	v				B3[3], 449
p1470	—,—,isopropyl ester*	Isopropyl lactate. $CH_3CH(OH)CO_2CH(CH_3)_2$	132.16			166–8 75–80[32]	0.9980[20]	1.4082[25]	s	s	s		s		C24, 1843
p1471	—,—,methyl ester(D)*	d-Methyl lactate. $CH_3CH(OH)CO_2CH_3$	104.12	$[\alpha]_D^{20}$ +7.46		40[15]	1.0857[26/4]		∞	v	v				B3[2], 187
Ω p1472	—,—,—(DL)*	$CH_3CH(OH)CO_2CH_3$	104.12			144.8 (cor)	1.09282[20/4]	1.4141[20]	∞	v	v				B3[3], 471
p1473	—,—,—(L)*	l-Methyl lactate. $CH_3CH(OH)CO_2CH_3$	104.12	$[\alpha]_D^{20}$ −8.25		58[19]	1.0895[20]	1.4139[20]	∞	v	v				B3[3], 444
p1474	—,—,3-methyl-butyl ester*	Isoamyl lactate. $CH_3CH(OH)CO_2CH_2CH_2CH(CH_3)_2$	160.22			202.4 82[7]	0.9617[25/25]	1.4240[25]	i	s	s				B3[3], 483
Ω p1475	—,—,nitrile	Acetaldehyde cyanohydrin. Lactonitrile. $CH_3CH(OH)CN$	71.08	ye liq λ^{undil} 270 (−0.7)	−40	182–4δd 102[30]	0.9877[20]	1.4058[18]	∞	∞				CS_2, peth i	B3[2], 209
p1476	—,—,—,acetate	$CH_3CO_2CH(CH_3)CN$	113.12			172–3 76–7[25]	1.0278[20/4]	1.4027[20]	s	δ	δ			aa δ	B3[3], 499
p1477	—,—,4-phenyl-phenacyl ester*		284.32	cr	145				i						C24, 3051
p1478	—,—,piperazinium salt	$2[CH_3CH(OH)CO_2H] \cdot C_4H_{10}N_2$	266.30		96–6.5				s	s[h]	i			cellosolve s[h]	Am 56, 1759
Ω p1479	—,3-hydroxy-*	Hydracrylic acid. β-Lactic acid. $HOCH_2CH_2CO_2H$	90.08	syr		d		1.4489[20]	v	s	∞				B3[2], 212
Ω p1480	—,—,lactone*	β-Propiolactone.	72.06		−33.4	162d 51[16]	1.1460[20/3]	1.4105[20]	d	d	∞			chl s	B17[1], 130
Ω p1481	—,—,nitrile	Ethylene cyanohydrin. Hydracrylonitrile. $HOCH_2CH_2CN$	71.08			230[760] 110[15]	1.0588[20]	1.4240[20]	∞	∞	δ			CS_2 i	B3[2], 213
p1483	—,3(4-hydroxy-3-methoxy-phenyl)-*	Hydroferulic acid	196.21	pl (w)	89–90				s[h]	s	s				B10, 424
Ω p1484	—,2-hydroxy-2-methyl-*	Acetonic acid. 2-Hydroxyisobutyric acid. $(CH_3)_2C(OH)CO_2H$	104.12	hyg pr (eth), nd (bz)	82–3	212 108[11]			v	v	v		δ v[h]		B3[3], 587
Ω p1485	—,—,ethyl ester*	$(CH_3)_2C(OH)CO_2C_2H_5$	132.16			150 (cor) 46[14]	0.987[20]	1.4080[20]	∞	∞	∞				B3[3], 591
Ω p1486	—,—,methyl ester*	$(CH_3)_2C(OH)CO_2CH_3$	118.13			137 62–4[12]		1.4056[20]	v	v					B3[3], 590
Ω p1487	—,—,nitrile	Acetone cyanohydrin. $(CH_3)_2C(OH)CN$	85.11	λ^{al} 263 (0.1)	−19	82[23]	0.932[20]	1.3996[20]	v	v	v	s	s	os v peth i	B3[3], 597
p1488	—,2-hydroxy-3-oxo-3-phenyl-*	Benzoylglycolic acid. $C_6H_5COCH(OH)CO_2H$	180.17	lo pr (lig)	112				δ s[h]	s	s			chl s	B9[2], 147

For explanations, symbols and abbreviations see beginning of table. For structural formulas see end of table.

No.	Name	Synonyms and Formula	Mol. wt.	Color. crystalline form. specific rotation and λ_{max} (log ε)	m.p. °C	b.p. °C	Density	n_D	Solubility						Ref.
									w	al	eth	ace	bz	other solvents	
	Propanoic acid														
p1490	—,2-hydroxy-2-phenyl-(D)*	Atrolactic acid. $C_6H_5C(OH)(CH_3)CO_2H$	166.18	pr (w) $[\alpha]_D^{16.5} +37.7$ (al, c = 3.5)	116.5–7	....			s	s[h]	...	v	v[h]	....	B10[2], 156
p1491	—,—(DL)*	$C_6H_5C(OH)(CH_3)CO_2H$ ...	166.18	nd, pl (lig)	93–5				s	s[h]	...	v	v[h]	lig s[h]	B10[2], 157
p1492	—,—(L)*	$C_6H_5C(OH)(CH_3)CO_2H$ ...	166.18	nd (bz, w) $[\alpha]_D^{13.8} -37.7$ (al, c = 3.4)	116–7				s	v s[h]	...	v	v[h]	....	B10[2], 157
p1493	—,—,hemihydrate (DL)*	$C_6H_5C(OH)(CH_3)CO_2H \cdot \frac{1}{2}H_2O$	175.19	nd or pr (w)	67–8				s ∞^h	s[h]					B10[2], 157
p1494	—,2-hydroxy-3-phenyl-(d)*	α-Hydroxyhydrocinnamic acid. $C_6H_5CH_2CH(OH)CO_2H$	166.18	nd (w) $[\alpha]_D^{20} +22.2$ (w, c = 2.2)	124–6				v[h]	s	s[h]	s	s[h]	MeOH s CS_2, chl, peth δ	B10[2], 152
p1495	—,—(dl)*	$C_6H_5CH_2CH(OH)CO_2H$ ...	166.18	cr (chl, bz), pr (w)	98	148–50[15]			δ	s	s	s	s[h]	CCl_4, chl s[h]	B10[2], 154
p1496	—,—(l)*	$C_6H_5CH_2CH(OH)CO_2H$ ...	166.18	nd (w) $[\alpha]_D^{20} -19.9$ (w, c = 3.2)	124–5				s[h]	s	s	s	s[h]		B10[2], 153
p1497	—,3-hydroxy-2-phenyl-(d)*	$HOCH_2CH(C_6H_5)CO_2H$ ...	166.18	nd (w, bz), pr (eth or w) $[\alpha]_D^{16} +72.2$ (al, c = 2.7)	130				s[h]	s	s		δ		B10[2], 158
Ω p1498	—,—(dl)*	Tropaic acid. Tropic acid. $HOCH_2CH(C_6H_5)CO_2H$	166.18	nd, pl (al, bz, w)	118	d			s ∞^h	s	s		δ	peth, CS_2 i	B10[2], 158 B23[2], 534
p1499	—,—(l)*	$HOCH_2CH(C_6H_5)CO_2H$ ...	166.18	pl (AcOEt), nd (w), $[\alpha]_D^{15} -81.2$ (w, c = 1.5)	130					s	s		δ	AcOEt s	B10[2], 158
p1500	—,3-hydroxy-3-phenyl-(d)*	$C_6H_5CH(OH)CH_2CO_2H$ ...	166.18	cr (bz), $[\alpha]_D^{18} +20.6$ (MeOH, c = 5.04)	116				δ	s	s		...	MeOH s chl δ	B10[2], 148
p1501	—,—(dl)*	$C_6H_5CH(OH)CH_2CO_2H$ ...	166.18	pr (w)	96				δ ∞^h	v		v	δ	MeOH v chl s peth δ	B10[2], 148
p1502	—,—(l)*	$C_6H_5CH(OH)CH_2CO_2H$ ...	166.18	nd (bz) $[\alpha]_D^{18} -19.8$ (al, c = 4.7)	115–6				δ				δ	chl δ	B10[2], 147
p1502[1]	—,3(2-hydroxyphenyl)-*	o-Hydrocoumaric acid. Melilotic acid.	166.18	pr (w)	82–4				s v[h]	v	v		...	chl v	B10[2], 143
p1503	—,2-hydroxy-3,3,3-trichloro-*	$Cl_3CCH(OH)CO_2H$	193.42	pr (eth)	125	140–70[45]			v	v	v		...	chl v	B3[2], 210
p1504	—,—,monohydrate	$Cl_3CCH(OH)CO_2H \cdot H_2O$ ...	211.43		105–10 (115–8)				s						B3, 287
p1505	—,—,nitrile	Chloral cyanohydrin. $Cl_3CCH(OH)CN$	174.42	pl (w, CS_2)	61	215–20d			v	v	v		...	CS_2 s	B3[2], 210
p1506	—,2,2'-iminodi-(dl)*	$HN[CH(CH_3)CO_2H]_2$	161.16	(i) nd (w), pr (eth), (ii) cr	(i) 234–5d (ii) 254–5				v	i s[h]	i	i	...	os i	B4[2], 824
p1507	—,—,dinitrile	$HN[CH(CH_3)CN]_2$	123.16	nd (eth)	68				δ	s	s		...		B4[2], 825
p1508	—,3,3-iminodi-, N-methyl-, diethyl ester*	$(C_2H_5O_2CCH_2CH_2)_2NCH_3$	231.30			136–8[4]	1.0190[20]	1.4421[20]		s	s		...		B4[2], 829
Ω p1509	—,β(3-indolyl)-* ...		189.22	pl (w) λ^w 280 (3.7)	134				δ s[h]	v	v	v	v	AcOEt, chl v	B22[2], 53
p1510	—,—,methyl ester	$C_{12}H_{13}NO_2$. See p1509	203.24	pr (MeOH)	79–80	93–6[0.2]				s			...	MeOH s[h]	B22[2], 53
p1511	—,2-iodo-(dl)* ...	CH_3CHICO_2H	199.98	nd (bz, w, al)	45–7		2.073[18]_4		δ	v	v		...		B2[3], 573
Ω p1512	—,3-iodo-*	$ICH_2CH_2CO_2H$	199.98	lf (w)	85				δ s[h]	v	s	s	...		B2[3], 574
p1513	—,—,methyl ester*	$ICH_2CH_2CO_2CH_3$ ...	214.00			188[756]	1.8408[7]			s			...		B2[3], 574
Ω p1514	—,3-mercapto-* ...	$HSCH_2CH_2CO_2H$	106.14	amor	17–9	110.5–1.5[15]	1.218[21]	1.4911[20]	s	s	s		...		B3[2], 214
p1515	—,2-methoxy-, nitrile	$CH_3CH(OCH_3)CN$	85.11			118[740]	0.8928[20]_4	1.3818[20]		s	s		...		B3[3], 497
Ω p1516	—,3-methoxy-, nitrile	$CH_3OCH_2CH_2CN$	85.11			165.5[763] 85.5[49]	0.9379[20]_4	1.4043[20]		s	s		...		B3[3], 538
p1517	—,2-methoxy-3-methyl-, 3-p-menthyl ester*	....	256.39			124–6[10]	0.9466			s	s		...		C25, 984
Ω p1518	—,2-methyl-*	Isobutyric acid. $(CH_3)_2CHCO_2H$	88.11		–46.1	153.2[760] 53.74[10]	0.96815[20]_4	1.3930[20]	v	∞	∞		...		B2[3], 637
p1519	—,—,allyl ester	Allyl isobutyrate. $(CH_3)_2CHCO_2CH_2CH:CH_2$	128.17			133–5[755]			δ	∞	∞	s	...		B2[3], 650
Ω p1521	—,—,amide, N-phenyl-	Isobutyranilide. $(CH_3)_2CHCONHC_6H_5$	163.22	mcl pr (al, eth), nd (lig)	106–7				δ[h]	v	v		...	lig s[h]	B12[2], 147
Ω p1522	—,—,anhydride* ..	Isobutyric anhydride. $[(CH_3)_2CHCO]_2O$	158.20	....	–53.5	181.5[734] 89–90[32]	0.9535[20]_4	1.4061[19]	d	d	∞		...		B2[3], 653
p1523	—,—,bromide	Isobutyryl bromide. $(CH_3)_2CHCOBr$	151.01	....		116–8	1.4067[15]_4	1.4552[15]	d	d			...		B2[2], 262
p1524	—,—,tert-butyl ester	tert-Butyl isobutyrate. $(CH_3)_2CHCO_2C(CH_3)_3$	144.22	....		126.7[760]		1.3921[20]	i	s	s		...		B2[3], 648

For explanations, symbols and abbreviations see beginning of table. For structural formulas see end of table.

Propanoic acid

No.	Name	Synonyms and Formula	Mol. wt.	Color, crystalline form, specific rotation and λ_{max} (log ε)	m.p. °C	b.p. °C	Density	n_D	w	al	eth	ace	bz	other solvents	Ref.
Ω p1525	—,—,chloride*....	Isobutyryl chloride. $(CH_3)_2CHCOCl$	106.55	....	−90.0	92^{760}	1.0174_4^{20}	1.4079^{20}	d	d	s	...	...		B2³, 653
p1526	—,—,cyclohexyl ester*	Cyclohexyl isobutyrate.	170.25	....	....	204^{750} $87–8^{15}$	0.9489_4^0		i	s	s	...	...	os s	B6², 11
Ω p1527	—,—,ethyl ester*...	Ethyl isobutyrate. $(CH_3)_2CHCO_2C_2H_5$	116.16	....	−88.2	111.0^{760}	0.8693_4^{20}	1.3869^{20}	δ	∞	∞	s	...		B2², 260
p1528	—,—,furfuryl ester.	Furfuryl isobutyrate	168.20	....	....	$85–6^{15}$	1.0313_4^{20}		δ	s	s	...	...		B17², 115
p1529	—,α,α′,1,2-hydrazodi-, dinitrile,	α,α′-Hydrazodiisobutyro-nitrile. $(CH_3)_2C(CN)NHNHC(CN)(CH_3)_2$	166.23	pl (eth)	92–3	....			i	v	s	...	...		B4, 561
Ω p1530	—,—,isobutyl ester	Isobutyl isobutyrate. $(CH_3)_2CHCO_2CH_2CH(CH_3)_2$	144.22	....	−80.66	148.6^{760} $36–40^{11}$	0.8750_4^0	1.3999_4^{20}	δ	∞	∞	s	...		B2³, 647
p1531	—,—,isopropyl ester*	Isopropyl isobutyrate. $(CH_3)_2CHCO_2CH(CH_3)_2$	130.19	....	....	120.76^{760}	0.8471_2^{21}		i	s	s	s	...		B2³, 646
Ω p1532	—,—,methyl ester*	Methyl isobutyrate. $(CH_3)_2CHCO_2CH_3$	102.13	....	−84.7	92.3^{760}	0.8906_2^{20}	1.3840^{20}	δ	∞	∞	s	...		B2³, 642
Ω p1533	—,—,3-methylbutyl ester*	Isoamyl isobutyrate. $(CH_3)_2CHCO_2CH_2CH_2CH(CH_3)_2$	158.24	....	....	168.9	0.8627^{20}		δ	s	s	s	...		B2³, 649
Ω p1534	—,—,nitrile.......	Isobutyronitrile. Isopropyl cyanide. $(CH_3)_2CHCN$	69.11	....	−71.5	103.8^{760} $(107–8)$	0.7608_4^{20}	1.3720^{20}	δ	v	v	s	...		B2³, 655
p1535	—,—,2-nitropentyl ester	2-Nitroamyl isobutyrate. $(CH_3)_2CHCO_2CH_2CH(NO_2)(CH_2)_2CH_3$	202.24	....	....	$248–51^{760}$ 122^{10}	1.0329_{20}^{20}	1.4315^{20}	δ	∞	∞	s	...		B2³, 648
p1536	—,—,piperazinium salt	$2[(CH_3)_2CHCO_2H]\cdot C_4H_{10}N_2$	262.35	wh cr (diox)	89.5–90	....			s	s	iʰ	...	...	diox sʰ	Am 56, 1759
p1537	—,—,propyl ester*.	n-Propyl isobutyrate. $(CH_3)_2CHCO_2CH_2CH_2CH_3$	130.19	....	....	$135–5.5^{760}$	0.8843^0	1.3955^{20}	δ	s	v	s	...		B2³, 646
p1538	—,2-methyl-3-phenyl-*	$C_6H_5CH(CH_3)CO_2H$	164.21	pl (dil al)	36.5	272 $155–6^{11}$			δ vʰ	v	v	...	...		B9², 357
Ω p1539	—,3(1-naphthyl)-*	$C_{10}H_7^aCH_2CH_2CO_2H$	200.24	cr (bz), nd (al)	156–6.7 (148)	179^{11}			sʰ	s	...	sʰ	...		E12B, 3283
p1540	—,3(2-naphthyl)-*	$C_{10}H_7^bCH_2CH_2CO_2H$	200.24	lf or nd (w, al)	135	....			vʰ	s	...	...	...		E12B, 3285
Ω p1541	—,3(2-nitro-phenyl)-2-oxo-*		209.16	ye nd or lf (w, al, bz)	130	....			δ sʰ	s	v	δ sʰ	...	aa v chl δ lig i	B10², 476
Ω p1542	—,2-oxo-*........	Acetylformic acid. Pyruvic acid. CH_3COCO_2H	88.06	....	13.6	165 part d 54^{10}	1.2272_4^{20}	1.4280^{20}	∞	∞	∞	s	...		B3³, 1146
Ω p1543	—,—,ethyl ester*	Ethyl pyruvate. $CH_3COCO_2C_2H_5$	116.13	....	−50	155 $69–71^{42}$	$1.0596_4^{15.6}$	1.4052^{20}	δ	∞	∞	s	...		B3³, 1161
Ω p1544	—,—,methyl ester*	Methyl pyruvate. $CH_3COCO_2CH_3$	102.09	....	....	$134–7$ 53^{15}	1.154_4^0	1.4046^{25}	δ	∞	∞	s	...		B3³, 1160
Ω p1545	—,—,nitrile.......	Acetyl cyanide. Pyruvonitrile. CH_3COCN	69.06	rh	....	92.3	0.9745_4^{20}	1.3764^{20}	d	d	s	...	...	CH_3CN s	B3³, 1165
Ω p1545¹	—,3(2-oxocyclo-hexyl)-, nitrile		151.21	....	....	$138–42^{10}$	1.0181_4^{20}	1.4755^{20}							Am 73, 724
p1546	—,2-oxo-3-phenyl-*	Phenylpyruvic acid. $C_6H_5CH_2COCO_2H$	164.17	lf (chl, bz) λ^{MeOH} 287.5 (4.28)	157–8	....			δʰ	v	v	sʰ	...	chl sʰ lig i	B10², 471
p1546¹	—,3-oxo-2-phenyl-, ethyl ester*	Ethyl phenylmalonalde-hydate. $C_6H_5CH(CHO)CO_2C_2H_5$	192.22	pl (chl)	70–1	136^{16}	1.1204_{20}^{20}	1.532^{21}	i	∞	∞	...	...	chl sʰ	B10², 478
p1547	—,3-oxo-3-phenyl-*	Benzoylacetic acid. $C_6H_5COCH_2CO_2H$	164.17	nd (bz-peth)	103–4d	....			δ vʰ	v	v	...	s	lig δ	B10², 466
Ω p1548	—,—,amide,N-phenyl-*	α-Benzoylacetanilide. $C_6H_5COCH_2CONHC_6H_5$	239.28	lf (bz) λ^{al} 235 (4.2), 325 (3.4)	108	....			δ	v	v	δ vʰ	...	alk, chl v	B12², 270
Ω p1549	—,—,ethyl ester*	$C_6H_5COCH_2CO_2C_2H_5$	192.22	<0	....	$265–70$ part d 165^{14}	1.1220_4^{20}	1.5312^{16}	δ	s	s	...	...		B10², 467
p1550	—,—,methyl ester (enol form)*	$C_6H_5C(OH){:}CHCO_2CH_3$	178.19	....	ca. 40	....		1.5620^{16}							B10², 467
p1551	—,—,(keto + enol forms)*	$C_6H_5COCH_2CO_2CH_3$	178.19	pa ye	....	265d 151.5^{13}	1.158^{29}	1.537^{25}	i	∞	∞	s	...	dil alk s	B10², 467
Ω p1552	—,—,nitrile......	Benzoylacetonitrile. α-Cyanoacetophenone. $C_6H_5COCH_2CN$	145.16	pr or lf (w) λ^{al} 245 (4.11), 280 (3.30)	80–1	160^{10}			δ	s	s	...	s	chl, aq KCN, alk s	B10², 468
p1553	—,pentachloro-*...	$Cl_3CCCl_2CO_2H$	246.31	cr(CCl_4)	200–15d	....			v					CCl_4 δ, vʰ	B2², 228
p1554	—,—,chloride*.....	Cl_3CCCl_2COCl	264.75	nd	42	....			d	d		s	...		B2¹, 112
p1555	—,2-phenoxy-(D)*	$CH_3CH(OC_6H_5)CO_2H$.....	166.18	nd (w) $[\eta]_D^{21}$ +39.3 (al, c = 1.2)	87	$265–6^{758}$			δ vʰ	v	v	...	...		B6³, 614
p1556	—,—(DL)*	$CH_3CH(OC_6H_5)CO_2H$.....	166.18	nd (w)	115–6	$265–6^{758}$ $105–6^5$	1.1865_4^{20}	1.5184^{20}	δ sʰ	s	s	...	...		B6³, 614
p1557	—,—,amide*	$CH_3CH(OC_6H_5)CONH_2$ ...	165.19	nd or pl (to, w)	132–3	....			sʰ	v	v	...	...	aa s to sʰ lig vʰ	B6, 163
Ω p1558	—,—,chloride.....	$CH_3CH(OC_6H_5)COCl$	184.62	....	....	$146–7^{55}$ $115–7^{10}$	1.1865_4^{20}	1.5178^{20}	d	d	s	...	...		B6³, 615
p1559	—,—,ethyl ester* ..	$CH_3CH(OC_6H_5)CO_2C_2H_5$.	194.23	....	....	$243–4^{760}$ $120–5^6$	1.360_4^{17}		i	s	s	...	...		B6³, 615

For explanations, symbols and abbreviations see beginning of table. For structural formulas see end of table.

No.	Name	Synonyms and Formula	Mol. wt.	Color, crystalline form, specific rotation and λ_{max} (log ε)	m.p. °C	b.p. °C	Density	n_D	w	al	eth	ace	bz	other solvents	Ref.
	Propanoic acid														
Ω p1560	—,3-phenoxy-*	$C_6H_5OCH_2CH_2CO_2H$	166.18	nd (w), lf (lig)	97.5–8	234–45[771] 188–9[26]			s[h]					lig s[h]	B6[3], 615
p1561	—,—,amide	$C_6H_5OCH_2CH_2CONH_2$..	165.19	nd (w)	119				s[h]	v[h]	v[h]				B6[3], 616
p1562	—,—,ethyl ester*	$C_6H_5OCH_2CH_2CO_2C_2H_5$ ..	194.23	nd (peth)	24	170[40] 142[11]	1.0821[25]	1.5007[18]	i	s	s				B6[3], 616
p1563	—,2-phenyl-(d)*	Hydratropic acid. $C_6H_5CH(CH_3)CO_2H$	150.18	$[\alpha]_D^{20}$ +9.14; +81.1 (al, c = 3)	....	152[16]			δ						B9[2], 347
Ω p1564	—,—(dl)*	$C_6H_5CH(CH_3)CO_2H$	150.18		< −20	260–2 160[25]	1.1[0]	1.5237[20]	δ						B9[2], 348
p1565	—,—(l)*	$C_6H_5CH(CH_3)CO_2H$	150.18	$[\alpha]_D^{20}$ −7.0; −58 (al)		152[16]			δ						C53, 5179
p1566	—,—,amide	Hydratropamide. $C_6H_5CH(CH_3)CONH_2$	149.19	lo nd (w, dil al) $[\alpha]_D^{28}$ +57.9 (chl, c = 1.6)	100.5	....			i δ[h]	s				chl s	B9, 525
p1567	—,—,nitrile	Hydratroponitrile. $C_6H_5CH(CH_3)CN$	131.18	....		230–2 116–7[20] (127– 8[12])	0.9854[20]	1.5095[25]	i	s	s				B9[2], 348
Ω p1568	—,3-phenyl-*	Hydrocinnamic acid. $C_6H_5CH_2CH_2CO_2H$	150.18	pr (peth)	48.6	279.8[760] 169– 70[28]	1.0712[49]	......	s	s	s	...	v	CCl_4, CS_2, chl s	B9[2], 337
p1569	—,—,amide	Hydrocinnamamide. $C_6H_5CH_2CH_2CONH_2$	149.19	nd (w)	106–8	....			s[h]	v	v				B9[2], 340
p1570	—,—,benzyl ester	Benzyl hydrocinnamate. $C_6H_5CH_2CH_2CO_2CH_2C_6H_5$	240.13			310–40 198–9[20]	1.090[15]				s				B9[2], 339
p1571	—,—,chloride	Hydrocinnamyl chloride. $C_6H_5CH_2CH_2COCl$	168.63			225 d 105[10]	1.135[21]		d	d[h]				CS_2 s	B9[2], 340
p1572	—,—,ethyl ester*	Ethyl hydrocinnamate. $C_6H_5CH_2CH_2CO_2C_2H_5$	178.23			247.2[760] 123[16]	1.0147[20]	1.4954[20]	i	s	s				B9[2], 339
p1573	—,—,isopropyl ester*	Isopropyl hydrocinnamate. $C_6H_5CH_2CH_2CO_2CH(CH_3)_2$	192.24			126[11]	0.9860[25]		i	s	s				B9[2], 339
Ω p1574	—,—,methyl ester*	Methyl hydrocinnamate. $C_6H_5CH_2CH_2CO_2CH_3$	164.21			238–9[757]	1.0455[0]						s	AcOEt s	B9[2], 338
Ω p1575	—,—,nitrile	Hydrocinnamonitrile. $C_6H_5CH_2CH_2CN$	131.17			261 125–6[15]	1.0016[20]	1.5266[20]		s	s				B9[2], 341
p1576	—,—,piperazinium salt	$2[C_6H_5CH_2CH_2CO_2H]. C_4H_{10}N_2$	386.50	wh cr	122.5–3				δ	s[h]	i				Am 56, 150
p1577	—,—,propyl ester*	Propyl hydrocinnamate. $C_6H_5CH_2CH_2CO_2CH_2CH_2CH_3$	192.26			262.1 135[16]	1.008[12]		i	s	s				B9[2], 339
p1578	—,2-propoxy-, nitrile	$CH_3CH_2CH_2OCH(CH_3)CN$	113.16			150[727]	0.866[20]	1.398[20]							B3, 285
Ω p1579	—,3(3-pyrenyl)-		274.32	pl(aa)	180				i		s	s	...	con sulf, dil alk, aa s	E14s, 441
p1580	—,2,2,3,3-tetra-chloro-*	$Cl_2CHCCl_2CO_2H$	211.86	cr (CS_2-chl)	76				s					CS_2 v	B2, 253
p1581	—,3(2-tetra-hydrofuryl)-		144.17			263 118–20[2]	1.1155[20]	1.4578[25]	...	s				alk v	B18[2], 263
p1582	—,—,ethyl ester*	$C_9H_{16}O_3$. See p1581	172.23			221–2[750] 73[2]	1.024[7] [15]	1.440[20]		s	s	s			B18[2], 263
p1584	—,2,2,3-tri-chloro-*	$ClCH_2CCl_2CO_2H$	177.42	hyg pr (CS_2)	65–6	140[40]			s	s			s	CS_2 s[h]	B2[3], 563
p1585	—,2,3,3-tri-phenyl-*	$(C_6H_5)_2CHCH(C_6H_5)CO_2H$	302.38	nd (dil al, peth)	222–3				i	v	v			peth δ	B9, 715
Ω p1586	—,3,3,3-tri-phenyl-*	$(C_6H_5)_3CCH_2CO_2H$	302.38	pr (al)	179–80				i	s	v				B9[2], 504
Ω p1587	1-Propanol-*	n-Propyl alcohol. $CH_3CH_2CH_2OH$	60.11	λ^{gas} 183 (2.38)	−126.5	97.4[760]	0.8035[20]	1.3850[20]	∞	∞	∞	s	v		B1[3], 1397
Ω p1588	2-Propanol*	Isopropanol. Isopropyl alcohol. $CH_3CH(OH)CH_3$	60.11	λ^{gas} 181 (2.79)	−89.5	82.4[760]	0.7855[20]	1.3776[20]	∞	∞	∞	s	v		B1[3], 1439
Ω p1589	1-Propanol, 2-amino-(dl)*	$CH_3CH(NH_2)CH_2OH$	75.11			173–6 80[18]		1.4502[20]	v	v	v				B4[3], 736
Ω p1590	—,3-amino-*	$H_2NCH_2CH_2CH_2OH$	75.11			187–8[756] (cor)	0.9824[26]	1.4617[20]	s	s	s				B4[3], 738
Ω p1591	2-Propanol, 1-amino-(dl)*	$CH_3CH(OH)CH_2NH_2$	75.11		1.74	159.46[760] 59.5[10]	0.9611[20]	1.4479[20]	∞	∞	∞	∞	∞	CCl_4 ∞	B4[3], 754
p1592	—,—(l)*	$CH_3CH(OH)CH_2NH_2$	75.11			156–8[758]	0.973[18]		∞	∞	∞	∞	∞		B4[2], 736
p1593	1-Propanol, 2-amino-1(4-aminophenyl)-, dihydrochloride*	p-Aminonoeephedrine dihydrochloride.	239.15	lf (al-eth)	192–3d				v	s	i				C27, 2762
Ω p1594	2-Propanol, 1-amino-3-(diethylamino)-*	$H_2NCH_2CH(OH)CH_2N(C_2H_5)_2$	146.24			223 116–8[25]	0.9372[20]	1.465[20]	...	s	s				B4[3], 767
p1595	1-Propanol, 2-amino-2-methyl-*	$(CH_3)_2C(NH_2)CH_2OH$	89.14		25–6	165.5 69–70[10]	0.9342[20]	1.449[20]	∞						C49, 1537
—	—,2-amino-1-phenyl-*	*see* **Norephedrin**													

For explanations, symbols and abbreviations see beginning of table. For structural formulas see end of table.

No.	Name	Synonyms and Formula	Mol. wt.	Color, crystalline form, specific rotation and λ_{max} (log ε)	m.p. °C	b.p. °C	Density	n_D	w	al	eth	ace	bz	other solvents	Ref.
	2-Propanol														
p1596	**2-Propanol, 2-benzyl-**	$C_6H_5CH_2C(OH)(CH_3)_2$....	150.22	nd	24	214–6 103–5[10]	0.9790[20/25]	1.5174[20]	δ	s	..	..	..		**B6**[2], 489
p1597	**—,1,3-bis(di-methylamino)-***	$(CH_3)_2NCH_2CH(OH)CH_2N(CH_3)_2$	146.24	....		178–85 79–81[18]	0.8788[20/4]	1.4418[20]	v						**B4**[3], 766
p1598	**—,—,dimethiodide**	Endoiosin. Iodisan $HOCH[CH_2N(CH_3)_3I]_2$	430.14	wh cr	270–5d	....			v	δ	i	i	..		**C19**, 1757
p1599	**1-Propanol, 3-bromo-***	Trimethylene bromohydrin. $BrCH_2CH_2CH_2OH$	139.00	....		98–112[185] 62[5]	1.5374[20/4]	1.4834[25]	s	∞	∞				**B1**[3], 1427
Ω p1600	**2-Propanol, 1-bromo-***	Propylene bromohydrin. $CH_3CH(OH)CH_2Br$	139.00	....		145–8 49.6[12]	1.5585[30]	1.4801[20]	s	v	v				**B1**[3], 1474
Ω p1601	**—,1-butoxy-***	1,2-Propyleneglycol, 1-monobutyl ether. $CH_3CH(OH)CH_2O(CH_2)_3CH_3$	132.21	....		168–75	1.0035[20/4]	1.4168[20]	..	s	s		s	MeOH, CCl_4 s	**B1**[2], 537
p1602	**1-Propanol, 2-chloro-***	Propylene chlorohydrin. $CH_3CHClCH_2OH$	94.54	....		133–4	1.103[20]	1.4390[20]	s	s	s			os s	**B1**[3], 1424
Ω p1603	**—,3-chloro-***	Trimethylene chlorohydrin. $ClCH_2CH_2CH_2OH$	94.54	....		165 53[6]	1.1309[20/4]	1.4459[20]	v	s	s				**B1**[3], 1425
Ω p1604	**2-Propanol, 1-chloro-***	Propylene chlorohydrin. $CH_3CH(OH)CH_2Cl$	94.54	....		126–7[750] (cor)	1.115[20/20]	1.4392[20]	∞	∞	∞				**B1**[3], 1469
Ω p1605	**—,1-chloro-3-isopropoxy-***	$ClCH_2CH(OH)CH_2OCH(CH_3)_2$	152.62			87–7.5[20]	1.0530[25]	1.4370[25]	..	s	s				**B1**[3], 2153
p1606	**1-Propanol, 2-chloro-2-methyl-**	β-Isobutylene chlorohydrin. $(CH_3)_2CClCH_2OH$	108.57	visc		132–3d 59–61[50]	1.0472[20/4]	1.4388[20]	d					con HCl s	**B1**[3], 1564
p1607	**—,3-chloro-2-methyl-***	$ClCH_2CH(CH_3)CH_2OH$	108.57	....		76–8[21]	1.083[25/4]	1.4460[25]	..	v	v				**B1**[3], 1564
p1608	**2-Propanol, 1-chloro-2-methyl-***	$(CH_3)_2C(OH)CH_2Cl$	108.57		−20	128–9 71[100]	1.0628[20/0]	1.4380[24]	v δd[h]	v					**B1**[3], 1584
p1609	**—,1-chloro-3-propoxy-***	$CH_3CH_2CH_2OCH_2CH(OH)CH_2Cl$	152.63			92–5[15]	1.0526[25/4]	1.4378[25]	..		s	s			**B1**[3], 2153
Ω p1610	**—,1,3-diamino-***	$H_2NCH_2CH(OH)CH_2NH_2$	90.13	cr	42–5	235 93–5[2]					i		i		**B4**[2], 739
p1611	**—,—,dihydro-chloride**	$H_2NCH_2CH(OH)CH_2NH_2 \cdot 2HCl$	163.05	hyg pr or nd (dil al)	184.5	....			s	i	i		i		**B4**[2], 739
p1612	**1-Propanol, 2,3-dibromo-(d)***	$BrCH_2CHBrCH_2OH$	217.90	$[\alpha]_D$ + 7.27		219δd	2.11		δ	∞	∞	∞	∞		**B1**[2], 371
Ω p1613	**—,—,(dl)***	$BrCH_2CHBrCH_2OH$	217.90	....		219δd 118[17]	2.0739[20/0]	1.5466[20]	δ	∞	∞	∞	∞		**B1**[3], 1428
p1614	**2-Propanol, 1,3-dibromo-***	$BrCH_2CH(OH)CH_2Br$	217.90	yesh liq		219δd 105[16]	2.1202[25/4]	1.5495[25]	δ	∞	∞	∞	∞		**B1**[3], 1475
p1615	**1-Propanol, 2,3-dichloro-***	$ClCH_2CHClCH_2OH$	128.99	visc		183–5 70–80.5[17]	1.3607[20/0]	1.4819[20]	δ	∞	∞	∞	∞	lig δ	**B1**[3], 1426
p1617	**2-Propanol, 1,1-dichloro-***	$CH_3CH(OH)CHCl_2$	128.99	....		146–8[763]	1.3334[22/4]		δ	v	v	s			**B1**[2], 383
Ω p1618	**—,1,3-dichloro-***	$ClCH_2CH(OH)CH_2Cl$	128.99	....		176[760] 69[12]	1.3506[17]	1.4837[20]	v	v	∞	s			**B1**[3], 1471
p1620	**—,1,1-dichloro-2-methyl-***	$(CH_3)_2C(OH)CHCl_2$	143.02		8	150–5 52[10]	1.2363[19/9]	1.4598[19]		v			v[h]		**B1**[3], 1586
p1621	**—,1,3-dichloro-2-methyl-***	$(ClCH_2)_2C(OH)CH_3$	143.02	....		174–5 55–6[10]	1.2745[20/0]	1.4744[21]	s	v	s				**B1**[3], 1586
p1622	**—,1(diethyl-amino)-***	$CH_3CH(OH)CH_2N(C_2H_5)_2$	131.22	....		158–9[756] (167–72) 63[22]	0.8511[20/0]	1.4255[20]	..	s	s	s			**B4**[2], 737
Ω p1623	**1-Propanol, 2,3-dimercapto-***	BAL. British antilewisite. 1,2-Dithioglycerol. $HSCH_2CH(SH)CH_2OH$	124.24	visc liq		120[15] 100[8]	1.2463[20/0]	1.5733[20]	d	s	s			oils s	**B1**[3], 2340
p1624	**—,3(3,5-di-methoxy-4-hydroxy-phenyl)-***	Hydrosinapyl alcohol. 2-Syringylethanol.	212.25	wh nd (eth-peth)	75.5–6.5	....			s				δ	lig i	**Am 70**, 57
Ω p1625	**—,2,2-dimethyl-***	tert-Butylcarbinol. Neopentyl alcohol. $(CH_3)_3CCH_2OH$	88.15	....	52–3	113–4[760]	0.812		δ	v	v				**B1**[3], 1648
p1626	**—,2,2-dimethyl-1-phenyl-***	$C_6H_5CH(OH)C(CH_3)_3$	164.25	nd	45	114–6[16]			i	s	s			os s	**B6**[1], 270
p1627	**—,2,2-dimethyl-3-phenyl-***	$C_6H_5CH_2C(CH_3)_2CH_2OH$	164.25	nd	34–5	125–6[14.5]			i	s	s			os s	**B6**[2], 507
Ω p1628	**—,2,3-epoxy-***	Glycide. Glycidol. 3-Hydroxypropylene oxide.	74.08	....		166–7d 65–6[2.5]	1.1143[25]	1.4287[20]	∞	∞	s	s	s	chl s xyl, peth δ	**B17**[2], 104
p1629	**—,2,3-epoxy-3-phenyl-***	Phenyl glycidol..........	150.18	....	26.5	138[3]	1.512[27]	1.5432[27]	..	s	s			CCl_4 s	**C26**, 3493
p1630	**—,2-ethoxy-***	$CH_3CH(OC_2H_5)CH_2OH$	104.15	....		140–1[760]	0.9044[20/0]	1.4122[20]	s	s	s				**B1**[3], 2147
p1630[1]	**2-Propanol, 1-ethoxy-***	$CH_3CH(OH)CH_2OC_2H_5$	104.15	....		131[760] (136)	0.9028[20/0]	1.4075[20]	s	s	s				**B1**[3], 2147
p1631	**1-Propanol, 3-fluoro-***	Trimethylene fluorohydrin. $FCH_2CH_2CH_2OH$	78.09	....		127.8	1.0390[25/5]	1.3771[25]	s	v	v		δ		**B1**[3], 1424
Ω p1632	**—,3(4-hydroxy-3-methoxy-phenyl)-***	Hydroconiferyl alcohol.....	182.22	λ^{al} 281.6 (3.45)	65	197[15]		1.5545[25]	..	s	s				**C22**, 3884

For explanations, symbols and abbreviations see beginning of table. For structural formulas see end of table.

No.	Name	Synonyms and Formula	Mol. wt.	Color. crystalline form. specific rotation and λ_{max} (log ε)	m.p. °C	b.p. °C	Density	n_D	Solubility						Ref.
									w	al	eth	ace	bz	other solvents	
	2-Propanol														
Ω p1632[3]	2-Propanol, 1-methoxy-*	$CH_3CH(OH)CH_2OCH_3$	90.12	....	....	118–8.5[740]	0.9620^{20}	1.4034^{20}							B1[3], 2146
Ω p1633	—,2-methyl-*	tert-Butyl alcohol. $(CH_3)_3COH$	74.12	rh pr or pl λ^{sulf} 237 (2.48), 300 (3.13)	25.5	82.2–.3[760] 20[31]	0.7887^{20}_4	1.3878^{20}	∞	∞	∞				B1[3], 1568
Ω p1634	1-Propanol, 2-methyl-2-nitro-*	$(CH_3)_2C(NO_2)CH_2OH$	119.12	nd or pl (MeOH)	89.5–90	94.5–5.5[10]	....	....	δ	v	v				B1[3], 1564
Ω p1635	—,2-methyl-1-phenyl-*	α-Isopropylbenzyl alcohol. $C_6H_5CH(OH)CH(CH_3)_2$	150.22	$d:[\alpha]^{20}_D +47.7$ $l:[\alpha]^{20}_D -25.2$	....	222–4 112–3[15]	0.9869^{14}	1.5193^{14}	i	s		s			B6[3], 1859
p1636	2-Propanol, 2-methyl-2-phenyl-*	$(CH_3)_2C(OH)CH_2C_6H_5$	150.22	nd	24	214–6 104–5[17]	0.9840^{20}_4	1.5170^{20}	i	s	s		s		B6[3], 1860
Ω p1637	—,2-methyl-1,1,1-tribromo-*	Brometone. $(CH_3)_2C(OH)CBr_3$	310.83	nd (lig), cr (dil al)	168–70 (167–76)	sub	....	....	δ	s	s	s	s		B1[3], 1588
Ω p1638	—,2-methyl-1,1,1-trichloro-*	Chloretone. $(CH_3)_2C(OH)CCl_3$	177.46	hyg nd (w + 1)	98.5–9.5 77 (hyd)	167	....	....	i s^h	s	s	s	s	chl, lig s	B1[3], 1586
Ω p1639	—,—,hemihydrate*	$(CH_3)_2C(OH)CCl_3 \cdot \frac{1}{2}H_2O$ ..	186.47	wh	80–1	167	....	....	i s^h	v	s	s	s	chl, lig s	B1[2], 415
p1640	1-Propanol, 2-nitro-*	$CH_3CH(NO_2)CH_2OH$	105.10	λ^{al} 275 (1.49)	....	120–2[32] 100[12]	1.1841^{25}_4	1.4379^{20}	s	s	s				B1[3], 1429
p1641	2-Propanol, 3-nitro-1,1,1-trichloro-*	$O_2NCH_2CH(OH)CCl_3$	208.43	pr or pl (chl)	44.7–5.7	105.5–6.5[3.5]	....	....	i	s	s				B1[3], 1477
p1642	1-Propanol, 2-phenoxy-*	$CH_3CH(OC_6H_5)CH_2OH$	152.20		....	244 124–6[20]	0.9830^{25}_{25}	1.4760^{25}							B6[3], 577
p1642[1]	—,3-phenoxy-	$C_6H_5OCH_2CH_2CH_2OH$ ..	152.20	oil	....	249–50[764] 170[60]	....	1.491^{20}							B6[3], 577
p1642[2]	2-Propanol, 1-phenoxy-	$CH_3CH(OH)CH_2OC_6H_5$ ...	152.20		....	134.5[20]	1.0622^{20}	1.5232^{20}							B6[1], 85
p1643	1-Propanol, 1-phenyl-(dl)*	$CH_3CH_2CH(OH)C_6H_5$.	136.20		....	213–5[740] 98[10]	0.9938^{23}_{23}	1.5210^{23}	i	s	s				B6[3], 1793
Ω p1644	—,3-phenyl-*	$C_6H_5CH_2CH_2CH_2OH$	136.20		< –18	236–7[750] 132[21]	1.008^{20}_4	1.5278^{20}	s	∞	∞				B6[3], 1800
Ω p1645	2-Propanol, 2-phenyl-*	$C_6H_5C(OH)(CH_3)_2$	138.20	pr	35–7	202 93[13]	0.9735^{20}_4	1.5325^{20}	i	s	s	s	s	aa s	B6[3], 1813
p1646	—,1,1,1,3-tetrachloro-*	$ClCH_2CH(OH)CCl_3$	197.88		....	95–6[17]	1.610^{20}_4	1.5145^{20}							B1[3], 1474
p1647	—,1,1,3,3-tetrachloro-*	$Cl_2CHCH(OH)CHCl_2$	197.88		....	80–90[14]	1.612^{20}_4	1.5133^{20}							B1[3], 1474
Ω p1648	—,1,1,1-trichloro-*	Isopral. $CH_3CH(OH)CCl_3$ ..	163.43		50–1	161.8[773] 53–5[12]	....	....	δ	v	v	s	s	oos s	B1[3], 1474
Ω p1649	2-Propanone*	Acetone. Dimethyl ketone. CH_3COCH_3	58.08		–95.35	56.2[760]	0.7899^{20}_4	1.3588^{20}	∞	∞	∞	∞	∞	chl ∞	B1[3], 2696
p1650	—,azine*	Acetone azine. $(CH_3)_2C:NN:C(CH_3)_2$	112.18	λ^w 217 (3.47)	–12.5	133 54[37]	0.8389^{20}	1.4535^{20}	∞	∞	∞	s	...	min ac d	B1[3], 2745
Ω p1651	—,diethyl acetal* ...	2,2-Diethoxypropane*. $(CH_3)_2C(OC_2H_5)_2$	132.21		....	114[760] 46[60]	0.8200^{21}_4	1.3891^{20}	...	s	v	s	s		B1[3], 2741
Ω p1652	—,2,4-dinitro-phenylhydrazone*.	Acetone DNP. λ^{iso} 344 (4.23)	238.21	ye nd or pl (al)	128		....	....	i	s^h	s^h		s	AcOEt, chl s	B15[2], 216
p1653	—,4-nitrophenyl-hydrazone*	....	193.21	og-br or og-ye nd or lf (al)	152 (149)		....	....	δ^h	s^h	s^h			aa δ	B15[2], 184
p1654	—,oxime*	Acetoxime. $(CH_3)_2C:NOH$..	73.10	pr (al) λ^{al} 190 (3.70)	61	134.8[728] 61[20]	0.9113^{62}_2	1.4156^{20}	s	s	s			lig s	B1[3], 2743
Ω p1655	—,phenyl-hydrazone*	$C_6H_5NHN:C(CH_3)_2$	148.21	rh	42	163[50] 140[16]	....	....		s	s			dil ac s	B15[2], 55
p1656	—,—,hydrate*	$C_6H_5NHN:C(CH_3)_2 . H_2O$..	166.23		35		....	....	δ						B15[1], 30
Ω p1657	—,semicarbazone*	Acetone semicarbazone. $(CH_3)_2C:NNHCONH_2$	115.14	nd (w, ace)	190–1d		....	....	δ s^h	v	s	s^h			B3[2], 81
p1658	1-Propanone, 1(4-acetamido-phenyl)-*	$C_{11}H_{13}NO_2$. See p1696	191.23	pa ye nd (w)	172–3		....	....	s	v	v				B14[1], 375
p1659	2-Propanone, 1-amino-, hydrochloride*	Acetonylamine hydrochloride $CH_3COCH_2NH_2 . HCl$	109.56	hyg pl (al-eth)	75		....	....	v	s					B4, 314
p1660	1-Propanone, 1(2-amino-phenyl)-*	o-Aminopropiophenone. $C_9H_{11}NO$. See p1696	149.19	pa ye lf (peth), pl (dil al)	46–7	93[0.8]	....	....	i	s	s			ac, os s chl i	B14[2], 37
p1661	2-Propanone, 1(4-amino-phenyl)-*	p-Aminopropiophenone. $C_9H_{11}NO$. See p1696	149.19	pl (al, w), nd (w)	140		....	....	s	s	δ			chl s	B14[1], 375
p1662	—,2-amino-1-phenyl-, hycrochloride	α-Aminopropiophenone hydrochloride. $C_6H_5COCH(CH_3)NH_2 . HCl$	185.66	nd (al-eth)	187		....	....	δ	δ	i				B14[2], 37
Ω p1663	2-Propanone, 1-bromo-*	Bromoacetone. CH_3COCH_2Br	136.98	....	–36.5	136.5[725] 31.5[8]	1.634^{23}	1.4697^{15}	δ	s	s	s			B1[3], 2752
p1664	1-Propanone, 1(4-bromo-1-hydroxy-2-naphthyl)-*	....	279.14	ye nd (al)	98		....	....	i	s	s				B8, 152

For explanations, symbols and abbreviations see beginning of table. For structural formulas see end of table.

No.	Name	Synonyms and Formula	Mol. wt.	Color, crystalline form, specific rotation and λ_{max} (log ε)	m.p. °C	b.p. °C	Density	n_D	Solubility						Ref.
									w	al	eth	ace	bz	other solvents	
	1-Propanone														
p1665	—,2-bromo-2-methyl-1(2,4,6-trimethylphenyl)-*	α-Bromoisobutyryl-mesitylene.	269.19	gold-ye oil	27	160–70[24]					s				Am 52, 5036
Ω p1666	—,1(4-bromophenyl)-*	p-Bromopropiophenone. C_9H_9BrO. See p1696	213.08	nd	48	169[15]			i	s	s	s		CS_2 s	B7, 302
Ω p1667	—,2-bromo-1-phenyl-*	α-Bromopropiophenone. $C_6H_5COCHBrCH_3$	213.08	ye		245–50 134–5[18]	1.4298[20 over 4]	1.5720[20]	i	s	s	s	s		B7[2], 233
Ω p1668	2-Propanone, 1-chloro-*	Acetonyl chloride. Chloroacetone. CH_3COCH_2Cl	92.53	λ^{cy} 292 (1.49)	−44.5	119[763]	1.15[20]		s	s	s	s		chl s	B1[3], 2746
Ω p1669	1-Propanone, 1(4-chlorophenyl)-*	p-Chloropropiophenone. C_9H_9ClO. See p1696	168.63		36–7	134–7[31] 114–8[2]			i		s	s		CS_2 s	B7, 301
Ω p1670	—,—,oxime*	$C_9H_{10}ClNO$. See p1696	183.64	pl (al)	62–3				i	s[h]					B7, 301
p1671	—,3-chloro-1-phenyl-*	ω-Chloropropiophenone. $C_6H_5COCH_2CH_2Cl$	168.63	lf (eth), cr (peth, al)	49–50					s[h]	s[h]			peth s[h]	B7[2], 233
p1672	2-Propanone, 1-chloro-3-phenyl-*	$C_6H_5CH_2COCH_2Cl$	168.63	nd (chl)	72–3	159–61[17]								chl s[h]	B7[2], 235
p1673	—,1,3-diamino-, dihydrochloride*	$(H_2NCH_2)_2CO.2HCl$	161.03	(dil al, dil aa), pr (w +1 or 1½)	180d				v	i	i		i	chl δ aa i	B4[2], 763
p1674	1-Propanone, 2,3-dibromo-1,3-diphenyl-* (one form)	threo-Chalcone dibromide. $C_6H_5CHBrCHBrCOC_6H_5$	386.08	nd (al) λ^{iso} 253 (4.17)	122–3				δ	s					B7[2], 381
p1675	—,—(one form)*	erythro-Chalcone dibromide. $C_6H_5CHBrCHBrCOC_6H_5$	386.08	pr or nd (al) λ^{iso} 253 (4.14)	159–60				δ v[h]						B7[2], 381
p1676	2-Propanone, 1,1-dichloro-*	asym-Dichloroacetone. $CH_3COCHCl_2$	126.97	λ^{dios} 294 (1.8)		120 47[76]	1.305[18 over 15]		δ	s	∞				B1[3], 2749
Ω p1677	—,1,3-dichloro-*	sym-Dichloroacetone. $ClCH_2COCH_2Cl$	126.97	pl or nd λ^{cy} 300 (1.62)	45	173.4 86–8[12]	1.3826[46 over 4]	1.4714[46]	ε	s	s	s			B1[3], 2749
p1678	—,1(diethylamino)-*	$CH_3COCH_2N(C_2H_5)_2$	129.20			155–6δ 64[16]	0.8620[20]	1.4249[20]	∞	∞	∞				B4[3], 877
Ω p1679	—,1,3-dihydroxy-*	Dihydroxyacetone. $HOCH_2COCH_2OH$	90.08	λ^w 270 (1.35)	89–91.5 (80)				s[h]	s[h]	s[h]	s		lig i	B1[3], 3292
p1680	1-Propanone, 1(2,4-dihydroxyphenyl)-*	4-Propionylresorcinol. $C_9H_{10}O_3$. See p1696	166.18	ye nd (al)	97 (anh) 56 (hyd)	176–8[6]			δ	v	s		s	aa s peth, chl, CCl_4 δ	B8[2], 305
p1681	—,2,2-dimethyl-1-phenyl-*	tert-Butyl phenyl ketone. Pivalophenone. $C_6H_5COC(CH_3)_3$	162.23	λ^{hx} 263 (3.91)		219–21[760] 97–8[16]	0.963[26]	1.5086[19]			s				B7[2], 253
Ω p1682	2-Propanone, 1,3-diphenyl-*	Dibenzyl ketone. $C_6H_5CH_2COCH_2C_6H_5$	210.28	cr (al, peth, eth) λ^{hx} 294 (2.34)	35	331 112–25[0.1]	1.195[0 over 4]		i	s	s	s		peth s[h]	B7[2], 382
Ω p1683	1-Propanone, 1(2-furyl)-	2-Propionylfuran.	124.15	cr λ^{al} 270 (4.0), 315 (2.0)	28	88[14]	1.0626[28]	1.4922[25]			s				B17[1], 157
Ω p1684	2-Propanone, hexachloro-*	Perchloroacetone. $Cl_3CCOCCl_3$	264.75		−2 15 (hyd)	202–4 110[40]	1.7444[12 over 12]	1.5112[20]	δ d[h]						B1[3], 2751
p1685	—,1-hydroxy-*	Acetol. CH_3COCH_2OH	74.08	λ^{al} 269 (1.67)	−17	145–6d 54[18]	1.0824[20 over 20]	1.4295[20]	v	v	v				B1[3], 3191
p1686	1-Propanone, 1(1-hydroxy-2-naphthyl)-		200.26	grsh ye lf or pl (al)	81				i		s				B8[2], 179
Ω p1687	—,1(2-hydroxyphenyl)-*	o-Propionylphenol. $C_9H_{10}O_2$. See p1696	150.18	λ^{al} 250 (3.9), 325 (3.5)		150[80] 115[15]		1.5501[20]	δ	s	s			alk s	B8[2], 103
Ω p1688	—,1(4-hydroxyphenyl)-*	p-Propionylphenol. $C_9H_{10}O_2$. See p1696	150.18	wh nd or pr (w) λ^{al} 220 (4.0), 277 (4.1)	149				δ v[h]	s	s	s		alk s	B8[2], 104
p1689	2-Propanone, 1-iodo-*	Iodoacetone. CH_3COCH_2I	183.98	yesh liq λ^{hx} 268 (2.6)		62[12]	2.17[15]								B1[3], 2753
p1690	—,—,oxime*	Iodoacetoxime. $CH_3C(:NOH)CH_2I$	198.99	pr (peth)	64.5									peth s[h]	B1, 660
p1691	—,1(3-methoxyphenyl)-*		164.21	λ^{al} 250 (3.8), 310 (3.3)		258–60 95–7[0.7]	1.0812[0]	1.5230[25]		s	s				B8, 106
p1692	—,1(4-methoxyphenyl)-*		164.21	λ^{al} 270 (4.2)	< −15	267–9 142[14]	1.0670[18 over 4]	1.5253[20]	δ	s	s				B8[2], 104
Ω p1693	1-Propanone, 2-methyl-1-phenyl-*	Isobutyrophenone. $(CH_3)_2CHCOC_6H_5$	148.21	λ^{al} 242 (4.11), 275 (2.99)		221[760] 86[11]	0.9860[17]	1.5116[19]	i	s	s			oy s	B7[2], 245
p1694	2-Propanone, pentachloro-*	$Cl_2CHCOCCl_3$	230.31	cr (w +4)	2.1 (anh) 15–7 (hyd)	192[753] 97.5–8.5[40]	1.69[15]		s			v			B1[3], 2751
p1695	—,1-phenoxy-*	$CH_3COCH_2OC_6H_5$	150.18			229–30 117–9[20]	1.0903[20]	1.5228[20]	δ		s	s			B6[3], 589
Ω p1696	1-Propanone, 1-phenyl-*	Propiophenone.	134.18	λ^{hx} 238 (4.06), 277 (2.94)	18.61	217.48[760] 91.6[10]	1.0096[20]	1.5269[20]	i	s	s				B7[2], 231
p1697	—,—,oxime*	$C_6H_5C(:NOH)CH_2CH_3$	149.19	pl (peth) λ^{al} 245 (4.00)	53–5	245–6d 165[38]			i	s	s				B7[2], 232

For explanations, symbols and abbreviations see beginning of table. For structural formulas see end of table.

No.	Name	Synonyms and Formula	Mol. wt.	Color, crystalline form, specific rotation and λ_{max} (log ε)	m.p. °C	b.p. °C	Density	n_D	w	al	eth	ace	bz	other solvents	Ref.
	2-Propanone														
Ωp1698	2-Propanone, 1-phenyl-*	Acetonylbenzene. Phenylacetone. $CH_3COCH_2C_6H_5$	134.18	λ^{al} 285 (2.18)	−15	216.5 101[14]	1.0157_4^{20}	1.5168^{20}	i	v	v	...	∞	xyl ∞	B7[2], 233
p1699	—,1,1,1,3-tetrachloro-*	asym-Tetrachloroacetone. $ClCH_2COCCl_3$	195.86	liq (anh), pr (w +4), pl (w +2)	46 (+4w) 65 (+2w)	183[760] 71–2[13]	1.624_4^{15}	1.497^{18}	δ	...	v	v	...	...	B1[3], 2751
p1700	—,1,1,3,3-tetrachloro-*	sym-Tetrachloroacetone. $Cl_2CHCOCHCl_2$	195.86			180–2[718] (cor)	...	...	v	v	v	v	v	...	B1[3], 2751
p1701	—,—,tetrahydrate*	$Cl_2CHCOCHCl_2 \cdot 4H_2O$	267.92	tcl pl (w)	48–9	...	...	...	s						B1, 656
Ωp1702	1-Propanone, 1(3-tolyl)-*	...	148.21	λ^{al} 245 (4.0), 285 (3.0)	...	234[745] 130–5[33]	1.0059_0^0	...	i	s	s	s	s	...	B7[2], 246
p1703	—,1(4-tolyl)-*	...	148.21	λ^{al} 255 (4.0), 315 (1.7)	...	238–9[760] 120[18]	0.9926_4^{20}	1.5278^{20}	i	s	s	s	s	CS_2 s	B7[2], 246
p1704	2-Propanone, 1,1,1-trichloro-*	CH_3COCCl_3	161.42			149[764] (134) 28[10]	1.435_4^{20}	1.4633^{17}	i	v	v				B1[3], 2751
Ωp1705	1-Propanone, 1,3,3-triphenyl-*	$(C_6H_5)_2CHCH_2COC_6H_5$	286.38	nd (al) λ^{al} 252.5 (4.22), 257 (4.22)	96	...	...	...	...	δ v[h]	δ	v	v	chl v lig δ	B7[2], 485
p1706	—,1-ureido-*	Propionylurea. $CH_3CH_2CONHCONH_2$	116.13	cr (w)	210–11	...	...	...	s	s[h]					C37, 5934
—	**Propargyl alcohol**	see **2-Propyn-1-ol***													
—	**Propargyl aldehyde**	see **Propynal***													
Ωp1707	**Propenal***	Acrolein. Acrylaldehyde. $CH_2{:}CHCHO$	56.07	λ^{al} 207 (4.05)	−86.95	52.5–3.5	0.8410_4^{20}	1.4017^{20}	v	s	s	s	...	...	B1[3], 2953
—	—,diacetate	see **2-Propene-1,1-diol, diacetate**													
Ωp1708	—,diethyl acetal	3,3-Diethoxy-1-propene*. $CH_2{:}CHCH(OC_2H_5)_2$	130.19			123.5[760]	0.8543^{15}	1.4000^{20}	δ	∞	∞				B1[3], 2960
p1709	—,2-chloro-*	$CH_2{:}CClCHO$	90.51	ye or wh nd		40[30]	1.199^{20}	1.463^{20}	...	...	v			CCl_4 v	B1[3], 2960
Ωp1711	—,3(2-furyl)-*	Furacrolein	122.13	ye or wh nd (lig) λ^{diox} 312 (4.42)	54	>200d 135[14]	...	...	i s[h]	∞	s				B17[2], 325
Ωp1712	—,2-methyl-*	Methacrolein. $CH_2{:}C(CH_3)CHO$	70.09	λ^{al} 216 (4.04)	...	68.4	0.837_4^{20}	1.4144^{20}	∞	∞	v				B1[3], 2981
—	—,3-phenyl-*	see **Cinnamaldehyde**													
Ωp1713	**Propene***	Propylene. $CH_3CH{:}CH_2$	42.08	gas	−185.25	−47.4[760] (liq at sat pressure)	0.5193_4^{20}	1.3567^{-70}	v	v	...	...	...	aa v	B1[3], 677
Ωp1714	—,3-amino-*	Allylamine. $H_2NCH_2CH{:}CH_2$	57.09			58	0.7612_4^{20}	1.4205^{20}	∞	∞	∞			chl s	B4[3], 444
Ωp1715	—,1-bromo-(cis)*	Propenyl bromide. $CH_3CH{:}CHBr$	120.98		−113	57.8[760]	1.4291_4^{20}	1.4560^{20}	i	...	s	s		chl s	B1[3], 710
Ωp1716	—,2-bromo-*	Isopropenyl bromide. $CH_3CBr{:}CH_2$	120.98		−124.8	48.4[748]	1.362_4^{20}	1.4440^{20}	i	...	s	s		chl s	B1[3], 710
Ωp1717	—,3-bromo-*	Allyl bromide. $BrCH_2CH{:}CH_2$	120.98		−119.4	70[753]	1.398_4^{20}	1.4697^{20}	i	...	s	s		chl, CS_2, CCl_4 s	B1[3], 711
p1718	—,2-bromo-3-cyclohexyl-*	...	203.13			90[15]	1.215^{17}	1.495^{17}			s				B5[3], 224
p1719	—,1-chloro-(cis)*	cis-Propenyl chloride. $CH_3CH{:}CHCl$	76.53		−134.8	32.8[760]	0.9347_4^{20}	1.4055^{20}	i	...	s	s	s	chl s	B1[3], 697
p1720	—,—(trans)*	trans-Propenyl chloride. $CH_3CH{:}CHCl$	76.53		−99	37.4[760]	0.9350_4^{20}	1.4054^{20}	i	...	s	s	s	chl s	B1[3], 697
p1721	—,2-chloro-*	Isopropenyl chloride. $CH_3CCl{:}CH_2$	76.53		−137.4	22.65[760]	0.9017_4^{20}	1.3973^{20}	i	...	s	s	s	chl s	B1[3], 698
Ωp1722	—,3-chloro-*	Allyl chloride. $ClCH_2CH{:}CH_2$	76.53	λ 230	−134.5	45[760]	0.9376_4^{20}	1.4157^{20}	i	∞	∞	∞	∞	lig ∞	B1[3], 699
p1723	—,3-chloro-2-(chloromethyl)-*	$(ClCH_2)_2C{:}CH_2$	125.00		−15 (−13)	138–8.5 30–1[9]	1.1782_4^{20}	1.4754^{20}	...	v				chl v	B1[3], 768
p1724	—,1-chloro-2-methyl-*	Isocrotyl chloride. $(CH_3)_2C{:}CHCl$	90.55			68[754]	0.9186_4^{20}	1.4221^{20}	i	...	s	s	s	chl v	B1[3], 765
Ωp1725	—,3-chloro-2-methyl-*	Isobutenyl chloride. $ClCH_2C(CH_3){:}CH_2$	90.55			71.5–2.5	0.9165_4^{20}	1.4291^{20}	i	...	s	s	s	chl v	B1[3], 765
p1726	—,1-chloro-1-phenyl-*	$C_6H_5CCl{:}CHCH_3$	152.63	λ^{cy} 253 (3.28)		90.5[0.9]	1.085_4^{20}	1.5635^{15}	i	...	s	s	s	to s	B5[2], 372
p1727	—,1-chloro-3-phenyl-*	$C_6H_5CH_2CH{:}CHCl$	152.63	λ^{hx} 253 (3.48)		212–4[760] (cor) 97[18]	1.073_4^{14}	1.545^{14}	i	...	s	s	s	to s	B5[3], 1191
p1728	—,2-chloro-1-phenyl-*	$CH_3CCl{:}CHC_6H_5$	152.63			118–23[28] 61.5–2.5[2]	1.0738_4^{19}	1.5565^{19}	i	...	s	s	s	chl v	B5[3], 1186
p1729	—,3-chloro-1-phenyl-(trans)*	trans-Cinnamyl chloride. $ClCH_2CH{:}CHC_6H_5$	152.63	nd λ^{cy} 253 (4.31)	8–9	106.7[13]	1.0926_4^{20}	1.5851^{20}	i	∞	∞	v	s	...	B5[3], 1186
Ωp1730	—,2,3-dibromo-*	α-Epidibromhydrin. $BrCH_2CBr{:}CH_2$	199.88			141–1.5[760] 37–7[11]	2.0346_4^{25}	1.5416^{25}	i	...	s	s	s	chl s	B1[3], 713
Ωp1731	—,1,1-dichloro-*	$CH_3CH{:}CCl_2$	110.97			76–7[760] (78)	1.1864_4^{25}	1.4430^{25}	i	...	s	s	s	chl s	B1[3], 704
Ωp1732	—,1,2-dichloro-(trans)*	$CH_3CCl{:}CHCl$	110.97			77.0[757]	1.1818_4^{20}	1.4471^{20}	i	v	...	...	...	MeOH, CCl_4 v	B1[3], 704

For explanations, symbols and abbreviations see beginning of table. For structural formulas see end of table.

Propene

No.	Name	Synonyms and Formula	Mol. wt.	Color, crystalline form, specific rotation and λ_{max} (log ε)	m.p. °C	b.p. °C	Density	n_D	w	al	eth	ace	bz	other solvents	Ref.
Ωp1733	—,1,3-dichloro-(cis)*	ClCH₂CH:CHCl	110.97			104.3	1.217_4^{20}	1.4730^{20}	i	…	s	…	s	chl s	B1[3], 704
p1734	—,—(trans)*	ClCH₂CH:CHCl	110.97			112	1.224_4^{20}	1.4682^{20}	i	…	s	…	s	chl s	B1[3], 705
Ωp1735	—,2,3-dichloro-*	ClCH₂CCl:CH₂	110.97			94^{760}	1.211_4^{20}	1.4603^{20}	i	∞	s	…	s	chl s	B1[3], 705
p1736	—,3,3-dichloro-*	Acrolein dichloride. Cl₂CHCH:CH₂	110.97			84.4 (cor)	1.175_4^{20}	1.4510^{20}	i	v	v	…	s	chl s	B1[3], 706
p1737	—,1,1-dichloro-2-methyl-*	(CH₃)₂C:CCl₂	125.00			108.7–9.1[760] 42–3[75]	1.1449_6^{20}	1.4580^{20}	i	…	s	…	s	chl s	B1[3], 767
p1738	—,3,3-dichloro-2-methyl-*	Cl₂CHC(CH₃):CH₂	125.00			108–12[762] 49–50[120]	1.1363_4^{24}	1.4523_a^{24}	i	…	s	…	s	chl v	B1[3], 767
p1739	—,1,1-dichloro-3-phenyl-*	Cinnamylidene chloride. C₆H₅CH:CHCHCl₂	187.08	cr (eth, chl), pl (peth) λ^{al} 258 (4.28), 295 sh (3.30)	59	142–3[30] 121–2[14]			d	…	s	…	s	chl s peth s[h]	B5[3], 1188
—	3,3-diethoxy-*	see Propenal, diethyl acetal													
p1741	—,1,1-diphenyl-*	CH₃CH:C(C₆H₅)₂	194.28	lf (al) λ^{al} 235 (3.87), 248 (3.94)	52	280–1 149[11]	1.0250_4^{20}	1.5880^{20}	i	s	…	…	s		B5[3], 1998
p1742	—,1,2-epoxy-*	Allylene oxide. Methyloxirene.	56.07			63			δ	∞	∞				B17, 20
p1743	—,3-fluoro-*	Allyl fluoride. FCH₂CH:CH₂	60.07	gas		−3			δ	v	v	…		chl s	B1[3], 696
Ωp1744	—,hexafluoro-*	Perfluoropropene. CF₃CF:CF₂	150.02	gas	−156.2	−29.4	1.583_4^{-40}								B1[3], 697
p1745	—,3-iodo-*	Allyl iodide. ICH₂CH:CH₂	167.98	pa ye	−99.3	102[760]	1.8494_4^{20}	1.5530^{20}	i	s	s	…	s	chl s	B1[3], 714
p1746	—,3-isocyano-	Allyl carbylamine. Allyl isocyanide. CNCH₂CH:CH₂	67.09			98	0.794_4^{17}		δ	∞	∞				B4, 208
Ωp1747	—,2-methyl-*	Isobutylene. (CH₃)₂C:CH₂	56.11	gas λ^{gas} 159 (3.9), 184 (4.1), 188 (4.1), 192 sh (3.9), 200 sh (3.9)	−140.35	−6.9	0.5942_4^{20} (liq)	1.3926^{-25}	i	v	v	…	s	sulf, peth s	B1[3], 749
p1748	—,—(trimer)	Triisobutylene. (C₄H₈)₃	168.33		−76	179–81 56[10]	0.7590_4^{20}	1.4314^{20}							B1[3], 762
p1749	—,—(tetramer)	Tetraisobutylene. (C₄H₈)₄	224.44		−98	243–6 109.5[15]	0.7944_4^{20}	1.4482^{20}							B1[3], 763
p1750	—,2-methyl-1,1,3-trichloro-*	ClCH₂C(CH₃):CCl₂	159.44			156 45–6[12]	1.346^{20}	1.4990^{20}	i	…	…	v	s	chl v	B1[3], 768
p1751	—,2-methyl-3,3,3-trichloro-*	Cl₃CC(CH₃):CH₂	159.44			132–4	1.293^{20}	1.4770^{20}	i	…	…	s	s	chl v aa s	B1[3], 768
p1752	—,2-nitro-1-phenyl-*	CH₃C(NO₂):CHC₆H₅	163.18	ye nd (peth) $\lambda^{95\% al}$ 223 (3.90), 276 (3.80), 283 (3.89), 291 (3.96), 307 (4.02)	65–6				i	v	δ	…	…	peth s[h] alk i	B5[3], 1189
p1753	—,1,1,2,3,3-pentachloro-*	Cl₂CHCCl:CCl₂	214.31			185[760] 116[9]	1.6317_4^{24}	1.5313^{20}	i	…	s	…	…	to v[h]	B1[3], 708
Ωp1754	—,2-phenyl-*	α-Methylstyrene. C₆H₅C(CH₃):CH₂	118.18	λ^{al} 242 (4.08)	24.5	163.4[760] 60[17]	0.9082_4^{20}	1.5303^{20}	i	…	s	…	s	chl s	B5[3], 1192
—	—,3-phenyl-*	see Benzene, allyl-*													
p1755	—,1,1,2-trichloro-*	CH₃CCl:CCl₂	145.42			118 41[52]	1.382_4^{20}	1.4827^{20}	i	s	s	…	s	chl s	B1[3], 707
p1756	—,1,2,3-trichloro-*	ClCH₂CCl:CHCl	145.42			142 (145) 32–3[14]	1.414_{20}^{20}	1.5020^{20}	i	v	v	…	s	chl s	B1[3], 707
p1757	—,3,3,3-trichloro-*	Cl₃CCH:CH₂	145.42		−30	114–5 57[103]	1.369_{20}^{20}	1.4827^{20}	i	s	s	…	s	chl s	B1[3], 707
p1758	2-Propene-1-arsonic acid*	Allylarsonic acid. CH₂:CHCH₂AsO₃H₂	166.01	nd (w), pr (al)	130–1				v[h]	v[h]	…	…	…		B4[3], 1826
Ωp1758[1]	2-Propene-1,1-diol, diacetate	Allylidene diacetate. CH₂:CHCH(O₂CCH₃)₂	158.16		−37.6	180[760] 76[13]	1.0760_4^{20}	1.4193^{20}	δ	∞	∞	…	∞	lig ∞	B2[3], 356
Ωp1759	2-Propene-1-thiol*	Allyl mercaptan. CH₂:CHCH₂SH	74.15			67–8	0.925_4^{23}	1.4832^{20}	i	∞	∞	…	s	chl s	B1[2], 478
p1760	1,2,3-Propenetricarboxylic acid-(cis)*	cis-Aconitic acid. HO₂CCH₂C(CO₂H):CHCO₂H	174.11	nd (w) λ^w 389 (2.69), 411 (? 78)	130 (125)				s	…	δ	…	…		D2[1], 2063
Ωp1761	—(trans)*	HO₂CCH₂C(CO₂H):CHCO₂H	174.11	lf (w), nd (w, eth) λ^w 411 (2.88), 432 (2.88)	198–9 (195 cor)				v	s	δ	…	…		B2[3], 2063
p1762	—,triamide (trans)*	Aconitamide. H₂NOCCH₂C(CONH₂):CHCONH₂	171.16	ye nd (w)	sinters 260				v[h]	i	i	…	…	chl i	B2, 853
p1763	—,triethyl ester (trans)*	C₂H₅O₂CCH₂C(CO₂C₂H₅):CHCO₂C₂H₅	258.27			275d 159[9]	1.1064_4^{20}	1.4556^{20}	…	v	s	…	…		B2[3], 2065
p1764	—,trimethyl ester (trans)*	CH₃O₂CCH₂C(CO₂CH₃):CHCO₂CH₃	216.19			270–1[760] 161[14]			i	s	s	…	…		B2[3], 2064
p1765	—,tripropyl ester (trans)*	C₃H₇O₂CCH₂C(CO₂C₃H₇):CHCO₂C₃H₇	300.36			195[13]	1.0501^{15}	$1.4521^{1.1}$	i	s	s	…	…		B2[3], 2065
Ωp1766	Propenoic acid*	Acrylic acid. CH₂:CHCO₂H	72.06	λ^{MeOH} 252 (1.96)	13	141.6[760] 48.3[1f]	1.0511_4^{20}	1.4224^{20}	∞	∞	∞	δ	s		B2[3], 1215

For explanations, symbols and abbreviations see beginning of table. For structural formulas see end of table.

No.	Name	Synonyms and Formula	Mol. wt.	Color, crystalline form, specific rotation and λ_{max} (log ε)	m.p. °C	b.p. °C	Density	n_D	w	al	eth	ace	bz	other solvents	Ref.
	Propenoic acid														
p1767	—,allyl ester	Allyl acrylate. $CH_2:CHCO_2CH_2CH:CH_2$	112.14			$122-4^{760}$ 47^{40}	0.9441_4^{20}	1.4320_4^{20}	δ	s	s			ac s	B2³, 1230
Ω p1768	—,amide	Acrylamide. Propenamide*. $CH_2:CHCONH_2$	71.08	lf (bz)	84–5				v	s	s			chl v	B2², 388
Ω p1769	—,benzyl ester*	Benzyl acrylate. $CH_2:CHCO_2CH_2C_6H_5$	162.19			228^{760} 94^6	1.0573_4^{20}	1.5143^{20}	i	s	s	s			B6³, 1481
Ω p1770	—,butyl ester*	n-Butyl acrylate. $CH_2:CHCO_2C_4H_9^n$	128.17		−64.6	$146-8^{760}$ 39^{10}	0.8898_4^{20}	1.4185^{20}	i	s	s				B2³, 1226
Ω p1771	—,chloride	Acrylyl chloride. $CH_2:CHCOCl$	90.51			75–6	1.1136_4^{20}	1.4343^{20}	d	d				chl v	B2³, 1233
Ω p1772	—,cyclohexyl ester*	Cyclohexyl acrylate.	154.21			$182-4^{750}$ 88^{20}	1.0275_4^{20}	1.4673^{20}	i	∞	∞			chl s	C40, 5697
Ω p1773	—,ethyl ester*	Ethyl acrylate. $CH_2:CHCO_2C_2H_5$	100.13	λ^{al} 208 (3.84)	−71.2	99.8	0.9234_4^{20}	1.4068^{20}	δ	∞	∞			chl s	B2³, 1223
Ω p1774	—,isobutyl ester*	Isobutyl acrylate. $CH_2:CHCO_2CH_2CH(CH_3)_2$	128.17			132 62^{50}	0.8896_4^{20}	1.4150^{20}	δ	s	s			MeOH s	B2³, 1227
Ω p1775	—,methyl ester*	Methyl acrylate. $CH_2:CHCO_2CH_3$	86.09		< −75	80.5^{760}	0.9535_4^{20}	1.4040^{20}	δ	s	s	s	s		B2³, 1218
Ω p1776	—,nitrile	Acrylonitrile. Vinyl cyanide. $CH_2:CHCN$	53.06	λ^{al} 203 (3.79)	−83.5	$77.5-9^{760}$	0.8060_4^{20}	1.3911^{20}	s v^h	∞	∞	s	s		B2³, 1234
p1777	—,2-chloro-*	$CH_2:CClCO_2H$	106.51	nd (peth), pr (sub)	65 sub	176–81d			s	s	s				B2³, 1244
Ω p1778	—,—,ethyl ester*	$CH_2:CClCO_2C_2H_5$	134.56			$51-3^{18}$ 52^{51}	1.1404_4^{20}	1.4384^{20}		v	v				B2³, 1245
p1779	—,—,methyl ester*	$CH_2:CClCO_2CH_3$	120.54			52^{51}	1.189_4^{20}	1.4420^{20}		v	v				B2³, 1244
p1780	—,3-chloro-(cis)*	$ClCH:CHCO_2H$	106.51	lf or nd (HCl)	63–4	$107^{17.5}$				s	s				B2³, 1243
p1781	—,—,(trans)*	$ClCH:CHCO_2H$	106.51	lf	86 (92–4)	94^{18}				s	s				B2³, 1243
Ω p1782	—,2,3-dichloro-*	$ClCH:CClCO_2H$	140.95	mcl pr (chl), cr (peth, CS_2)	87–8				v	s	s	s	δ s^h	chl v lig s^h CS_2 δ CCl_4 i	B2³, 1246
p1783	—,3,3-dichloro-*	$Cl_2C:CHCO_2H$	140.95	nd (peth, sub), pr (chl)	76–7	sub			δ		v			chl v	B2³, 1246
Ω p1783¹	—,2,3-diphenyl-(trans)*	α-Phenylcinnamic acid. $C_6H_5CH:C(C_6H_5)CO_2H$	224.26	nd (lig, dil al) λ^{al} 228 (4.11) 294 (4.38)	172.5–3	sub			δ s^h	s	s				B9², 482
p1784	—,3(2-furyl)-(cis)*	2-Furanacrylic acid	138.12	wh pr or pl (unst) λ^{al} 230 (3.25), 300 (4.36)	103–4	sub vac at 95			δ s^h	s			δ		B18, 301
p1785	—,—,(trans)*	$C_7H_6O_3$. See p1784	138.12	nd (w) (st)	141	286 (sub vac at 112)		1.5286^{20}	δ s^h	s			s	aa s lig, CS_2 i	B18², 273
p1786	—,—,benzyl ester*	$C_{14}H_{12}O_3$. See p1784	228.25	pa ye	42–3	$201-3^{12}$ $155-6^3$		1.5872^{25}	i	s^h	s	s	s		B18², 274
p1787	—,—,butyl ester*	$C_{11}H_{14}O_3$. See p1784	194.23			$147-50^{15}$ $117-8^3$	1.045^{20}	1.5129^{20}	i	s			s		C48, 2114
p1788	—,—,ethyl ester*	$C_9H_{10}O_3$. See p1784	166.18	pa ye λ^{al} 225 (3.33), 302.5 (4.37)	24.5	232^{760} 120^{17}	1.0891_4^{25}	1.5286^{20}	i	∞	∞				B18¹, 440
p1789	—,—,methyl ester*	$C_8H_8O_3$. See p1784	152.16	λ^{al} 302 (4.37)	35–7 (27.5)	$227-8^{774}$ 112^{15}		1.4447^{20}	i	v	v		v		B18¹, 440
p1790	—,—,pentyl ester*	$C_{12}H_{16}O_3$. See p1784	208.24			$116.5-8^2$	1.0322_4^{20}	1.5289^{24}	i	s			s		Am 69, 460
p1791	—,—,propyl ester*	$C_{10}H_{12}O_3$. See p1784	180.21			$91-4^3$	1.0744_4^{20}	1.5392^{24}	i	s			s		Am 69, 460
Ω p1792	—,2-methyl-*	Methacrylic acid. $CH_2:C(CH_3)CO_2H$	86.09	pr λ^{MeOH} 244 (1.8)	16	$162-3^{757}$ 60^{12}	1.0153_4^{20}	1.4314^{20}	s v^h	∞	∞				B2³, 1278
Ω p1793	—,—,amide	Methacrylamide. $CH_2:C(CH_3)CONH_2$	85.11	cr (bz), pl (CH_2Cl_2)	110–1					s	δ s^h			CH_2Cl_2 s^h	B2³, 1293
Ω p1794	—,—,anhydride*	Methacrylic anhydride. $[CH_2:C(CH_3)CO]_2O$	154.17			89^5 (87^{13})		1.4540^{20}	d	∞	∞				B2³, 1293
Ω p1795	—,—,butyl ester*	Butyl methacrylate. $CH_2:C(CH_3)CO_2(CH_2)_3CH_3$	142.20	λ^{al} 214 (3.83)		160^{760} 52^{11}	0.8936_4^{20}	1.4240^{20}	i	∞	∞				B2³, 1286
Ω p1796	—,—,ethyl ester*	Ethyl methacrylate. $CH_2:C(CH_3)CO_2C_2H_5$	114.15	λ^{al} 208 (3.93)		117^{760} 30^{18}	0.9135_4^{20}	1.4147^{20}	δ	∞	∞				B2³, 1284
Ω p1797	—,—,isobutyl ester*	Isobutyl methacrylate. $CH_2:C(CH_3)CO_2CH_2CH(CH_3)_2$	142.20			155^{760} 45^{11}	0.8858_4^{20}	1.4199^{20}	i	∞	∞				B2³, 1287
Ω p1798	—,—,isopropyl ester*	Isopropyl methacrylate. $CH_2:C(CH_3)CO_2CH(CH_3)_2$	128.17			125^{760}	0.8847_4^{20}	1.4122^{20}	i	∞	∞	∞	∞		B2³, 1286
Ω p1799	—,—,methyl ester*	Methyl methacrylate. $CH_2:C(CH_3)CO_2CH_3$	100.13		−48	$100-1^{760}$ 24^{32}	0.9440_4^{20}	1.4142^{20}	δ	∞	∞	∞		glycol δ	B2³, 1280
Ω p1800	—,—,nitrile	Methacrylonitrile. $CH_2:C(CH_3)CN$	67.09	λ^{al} 215 (2.83)	−35.8	90.3^{760}	0.7998_4^{20}	1.4003^{20}	i	∞	∞			peth, to ∞	B2³, 1294
Ω p1801	—,—,propyl ester*	Propyl methacrylate. $CH_2:C(CH_3)CO_2CH_2CH_2CH_3$	128.17			141^{760}	0.9022_4^{20}	1.4190^{20}	i	∞	∞				B2³, 1286
p1802	—,3(1-naphthyl)-(cis)*	$C_{10}H_7^1CH:CHCO_2H$	198.22	col pl (al) λ^{MeOH} 307 (3.84)	156						s				E12B, 3287
p1803	—,—,(trans)*	$C_{10}H_7^1CH:CHCO_2H$	198.22	nd (al, w, aa) λ^{MeOH} 317 (4.06)	211–2	sub			δ^h	s^h	s			chl s	B9², 465

For explanations, symbols and abbreviations see beginning of table. For structural formulas see end of table.

No.	Name	Synonyms and Formula	Mol. wt.	Color, crystalline form, specific rotation and λ_{max} (log ε)	m.p. °C	b.p. °C	Density	n_D	w	al	eth	ace	bz	other solvents	Ref.
	Propenoic acid														
p1804	,3(2-naphthyl)-(trans)*	$C_{10}H_7^\beta CH{:}CHCO_2H$	198.22	nd (al, w) λ^{MeOH} 269 (4.6), 308 (4.4)	210 (203)	....			s^h	s					B9, 672
p1805	—,3(2-nitrophenyl)-2-phenyl-(trans)*	o-Nitro-α-phenylcinnamic acid.	269.26	ye cr (al) λ^{al} 262 (4.06)	196–7				δ^h s^h	δ	s		s	to s^h chl δ, s^h	B9[2], 483
p1806	—,3(3-nitrophenyl)-2-phenyl-(cis)*	m-Nitro-α-phenylcinnamic acid.	269.26	nd (al, aa)	195–6					δ s^h					B9[2], 483
p1807	—,—(trans)*	$C_{15}H_{11}NO_4$. See p1806	269.26	ye pr (eth), nd (dil al)	182					s^h			s	CS_2, peth, chl s	B9[2], 483
p1808	—,3(4-nitrophenyl)-2-phenyl-(cis)*	p-Nitro-α-phenylcinnamic acid.	269.26	ye-gr pr (dil al + 1w), cr (abs al + ½), lf (bz + ½) λ^{al} 270 (4.3)	144				δ	v	s		s^h	....	B9[2], 484
p1809	—,—,(trans)*	$C_{15}H_{11}NO_4$. See p1808	269.26	ye pr or nd (al)	213–4				δ	s^h	δ		δ	chl δ	B9, 696
p1810	—,2-phenyl-*	Atropic acid. $CH_2{:}C(C_6H_5)CO_2H$	148.17	lf (al), nd (w) λ^{al} 246 (3.75)	106–7	267d			δ	s	s		s	chl, CS_2 s	B9[2], 407
—	—,3-phenyl-*	see **Cinnamic acid**													
p1811	—,trichloro-*	$Cl_2C{:}C(Cl)CO_2H$	175.40	pr (CS_2, eth)	76	221–3 133[30] (cor)			s^h	s	s			CCl_4 s CS_2 s^h	B2[3], 1247
p1812	—,—,chloride	$Cl_2C{:}C(Cl)COCl$	193.85			158		1.5271[18.5]	d				s	CS_2 v	B2[1], 187
p1813	—,triphenyl-, nitrile	$(C_6H_5)_2C{:}C(C_6H_5)CN$	281.36	nd (al), pr	166–7					s^h			s		B9[2], 507
Ωp1814	**2-Propen-1-ol***	Allyl alcohol. $CH_2{:}CHCH_2OH$	58.08	$\lambda^{98\% sulf}$ 273 (3.67)	−129 (fr−50)	97	0.8540[20/4]	1.4135[20]	∞	∞	∞				B1[3], 1874
p1815	—,2-bromo-*	$CH_2{:}CBrCH_2OH$	136.98			153–4[755] 62[21]	1.621[18]	1.500[18]						chl s	B1[3], 1888
Ωp1816	—,2-chloro-*	$CH_2{:}CClCH_2OH$	92.53			136–40 47[10]	1.1618[20/20]	1.4588[20]	d^h	s^h					B1[3], 1887
p1817	—,3-chloro-*	$ClCH{:}CHCH_2OH$	92.53			(i) 146[746] (ii) 153[756]	(i) 1.1769[4/20] (ii) 1.1729[4/20]	(i) 1.4638[20] (ii) 1.4664[20]	δ						B1[3], 1887
p1818	—,3(3,5-dimethoxy-4-hydroxyphenyl)-*	Sinapyl alcohol. Syringenin.	210.23	nd (eth-peth)	66–7	....			i		s			peth δ	B6[3], 6690
—	—,3(4-hydroxy-3-methoxyphenyl)-*	see **Coniferyl alcohol**													
p1819	—,3(4-hydroxyphenyl)-*	p-Coumaryl alcohol.	150.18	pr (dil al) λ^{al} 260 (4.30)	124	....			δ	s	s	s	s	to, MeOH s	C45, 3359
Ωp1820	—,2-methyl-*	Methallyl alcohol. $CH_2{:}C(CH_3)CH_2OH$	72.12			114.49[760]	0.8515[20]	1.4255[20]	v	∞	∞				B1[3], 1903
p1821	—,1-phenyl-*	α-Vinylbenzyl alcohol. $CH_2{:}CHCH(C_6H_5)OH$	134.18	λ^{al} 242 sh (2.88), 248 (2.92), 251 (2.92), 257 sh (2.88)	....	215 6 111[18]	1.0251[21/0]	1.5406[20]	δ	s	s		s	chl s	B6[3], 2417
Ωp1822	—,3-phenyl-(trans)*	Cinnamic alcohol. Cinnamyl alcohol. $C_6H_5CH{:}CHCH_2OH$	134.18	wh nd (eth-peth) λ^{eth} 252 (4.08), 275 sh (3.3), 282 (3.2), 292 (3.0)	34	257.5 127–8[10]	1.0440[20/4]	1.5819[20]	δ	v	v				B6[3], 2401
p1823	—,—,acetate (trans)	$C_6H_5CH{:}CHCH_2O_2CCH_3$	176.22	λ^{al} 250 (4.24)	....	145–6[15] 114[1]	1.0567[20]	1.5425[20]	i	s	s	s	s	chl s	B6[3], 2406
p1824	**2-Propen-1-one, 3(2-furyl)-1-phenyl-***	Furfurylideneacetophenone.	198.22	λ^{al} 260 (3.93), 344 (4.43)	....	317 181–2[9]	1.1140[20]			s	s				B17[2], 377
p1825	—,1(2-hydroxynaphthyl)-3-phenyl-*	....	274.32	og-red lf or pl (al)	129	....			i	s	s			con sulf s	B8[2], 246
—	Proploin	see **3-Hexanone, 4-hydroxy-***													
—	Propiolactone	see **Propanoic acid, 3-hydroxy-, β-lactone***													
	Propiolaldehyde	see **Propynal***													
—	Propiolic acid	see **Propynoic acid***													
—	Propionaldehyde	see **Propanal***													
—	Propionaldol	see **Pentanal, 3-hydroxy-2-methyl-***													
—	Propionamide	see **Propanoic acid, amide***													
—	Propionic acid	see **Propanoic acid***													
—	Propiophenone	see **1-Propanone, 1-phenyl-***													
—	Propylal	see **Propynal, diethyl acetal**													
—	Propyl alcohol	see **1-Propanol***													
—	Propyl bromide	see **Propane, 1-bromo-***													
—	Propyl chloride	see **Propane, 1-chloro-***													

For explanations, symbols and abbreviations see beginning of table. For structural formulas see end of table.

No.	Name	Synonyms and Formula	Mol. wt.	Color, crystalline form, specific rotation and λ_{max} (log ε)	m.p. °C	b.p. °C	Density	n_D	w	al	eth	ace	bz	other solvents	Ref.
	Propylene														
—	Propylene	*see* **Propene***													
—	Propylene glycol . . .	*see* **1,2-Propanediol***													
—	Propylene oxide . . .	*see* **Propane, 1,2-epoxy-***													
p1826	Propyl hexedrine . . .	. . . .	155.29		. . . . . .	205[760] 92–3[20]	0.8501[20/4]	1.4600[20]	δ	s	. . .	. . .	. . .	dil ac s	**Am 69,** 1117
—	Propyl iodide	*see* **Propane, 1-iodo-***													
p1827	Propyl red	4'-Dipropylaminoazo-benzene-2-carboxylic acid.	325.42	vt-bl or purp-red cr (al)						s[h]				KOH s	**B16²,** 165
p1828	Propynal*	Propargylaldehyde. Propiolaldehyde. HC:CCHO	54.05	λ^{iso} 212 (3.7), 335 (1.3), 382 (0.7)	. . . . . .	59–61 (55–6)		1.4033[25]	∞	s	s	s	s	to s	**B1³,** 3040
p1829	—,diethyl acetal . . .	3,3-Diethoxypropyne. CH:CCH(OC₂H₅)₂	128.17		. . . . . .	130.45 37[11]	0.8942[22/4]	1.4140[20]	. . .	s	s	s		chl s	**B1²,** 808 **B4²,** 1135
Ω p1830	—,1-phenyl-*	C₆H₅C:CCHO	130.15	λ 240 (4.5), 250 (4.4), 300 (4.05)		127–8[28] 65[0.1]	1.0639[16/4]	1.6079[18]							**B7²,** 317
p1831	Propyne*	Methylacetylene. Propine. CH₃C:CH	40.07	gas	−101.5 (cor)	−23.2[760]	0.7062[−50/4] 0.66[−13]	1.3863[−40]	δ	v	. . .	. . .	s	chl s	**B1³,** 919
Ω p1832	—,3-bromo-*	Propargyl bromide. BrCH₂C:CH	118.97	. . . .		88–90 33[130]	1.579[19]	1.4922[20]	. . .	s	s		s	chl s	**B1³,** 922
Ω p1833	—,3-chloro-*	Propargyl chloride. ClCH₂C:CH	74.51	. . . .		65 (56–7)	1.0297[20/0]	1.4320[20]	i	∞	∞		s	chl s	**B1³,** 922
p1834	—,3-cyclohexyl-* .	. . . .	122.21	λ^{al} 236.5 (3.90)	. . . . .	157–8[760] 48[11]	0.8449[20/4]	1.4605[20]		. . .	s		. . .		**B5³,** 329
p1835	—,1,3-dibromo-* .	BrCH₂C:CBr	197.88	. . . .		73–4[30] 53–4[10]	2.1894[20]	1.5690[20]	i	. . .	. . .	. . .	s	chl s	**B1,** 248
—	—,3,3-diethoxy-* . .	*see* **Propynal**, diethyl acetal													
p1836	—,1-iodo-*	CH₃C:CI	165.96		. . . . . .	110[760]	2.08[22]	. . . . . .	δ	v	v				**B1³,** 922
p1837	—,3-iodo-*	Propargyl iodide. ICH₂C:CH	165.96		. . . . .	115	2.0177[0]	. . . . . .			s				**B1³,** 922
p1838	—,3-methoxy-* . . .	Methyl propargyl ether. CH₃OCH₂C:CH	70.09			63	0.83[12]	1.5035[20]	δ	∞	∞				**B1³,** 1971
p1839	—,1-phenyl-*	Phenylallylene. CH₃C:CC₆H₅	116.17	λ^{al} 238 (4.22), 249 (4.22)		183 77[17]	0.9388[20/4]	1.5650[20]	i		s				**B1³,** 1353
p1840	—,3,3,3-trifluoro-*	F₃CC:CH	94.04	gas		−48.3	. . . . . .	. . . . . .							**Am 82,** 543
p1841	Propynoic acid* . . .	Propargylic acid. Propiolic acid. HC:CCO₂H	70.05	cr (CS₂)	18 (anh) +0.3 (+1w)	144d 83–4[50]	1.1380[20/4]	1.4306[20]	∞	∞	∞	v	. . .	chl ∞	**B2³,** 1447
p1842	—,ethyl ester*	HC:CCO₂C₂H₅	98.10		. . . . . .	119[745]	0.9583[25/25]	1.4105[20]	i	v	v			chl v	**B2³,** 1448
p1843	—,chloro-*	ClC:CCO₂H	104.50	cr (peth)	69–70						v			peth δ, v[h]	**B2³,** 1448
p1844	—,(2-chloro-phenyl)-*	C₉H₅ClO₂. *See* p1849	180.59	cr (50 % aa, bz)	132.7–3.8				i				v[h]	aa v	**Am 77,** 5549
p1845	—,(3-chloro-phenyl)-*	C₉H₅ClO₂. *See* p1849	180.59	cr (aa, bz-peth)	144.3–5.1				i				s[h]	aa v	**Am 77,** 5549
p1846	—,(4-chloro-phenyl)-*	C₉H₅ClO₂. *See* p1849	180.59	cr (aa), pl (bz)	192–3				i				s[h]	aa v[h]	**Am 77,** 5549
Ω p1847	—,(2-nitro-phenyl)-*	C₉H₅NO₄. *See* p1849	191.15	nd or lf (w)	157d	exp			s[h]	s	s			chl δ CS₂, lig i	**B9,** 637
p1848	—,(4-nitro-phenyl)-*	C₉H₅NO₄. *See* p1849	191.15	nd (eth, al)	181				δ	s[h]	s		δ	aa, chl s CS₂ δ peth i	**B9,** 637
Ω p1849	—,phenyl-*	. . . .	146.15	nd (w, CS₂) λ^{al} 253 (4.1)	137	sub			δ	v	v				**B9,** 633
p1850	—,—,ethyl ester* . .	C₆H₅C:CCO₂C₂H₅	174.20	λ 258 (4.18)	. . . . . .	260–70δd 144[13]	1.0550[25/4]	1.5535[20]			s				**B9,** 634
Ω p1851	2-Propyn-1-ol*	Propargyl alcohol. Propiolic alcohol. HC:CCH₂OH	56.07	. . . .	−48	113.6[760] 30[21]	0.9485[20]	1.4322[20]	s	∞	∞				**B2¹,** 234
p1852	—,acetate*	Propargyl acetate. HC:CCH₂O₂CCH₃	98.10	. . . .		124–5 (110–2)	1.0052[20/4]	1.4205[20]	δ	s	s				**B2³,** 294
p1853	Prostigmine bromide	Neostigmine bromide	303.21	(al-eth)	167d				v	s					**C47,** 4908
—	Protoanemonin	*see* **2,4-Pentadienoic acid, 4-hydroxy-, lactone***													
—	Protocatechu-aldehyde	*see* **Benzaldehyde, 3,4-dihydroxy-**													
—	Protocatechuic acid	*see* **Benzoic acid, 3,4-dihydroxy-**													
p1854	Protopine	Fumarine. Macleyine. C₂₀H₁₉NO₅	353.38	mcl pr (al-chl) λ^{al} 290 (4.0)	208				i	δ	δ	. . .	δ	chl s peth, CS₂ AcOEt δ	**B27¹,** 568
p1855	Protoveratridine . . .	C₃₂H₅₁NO₉	593.76	cr (al-chl), $[\alpha]_D^{20}$ −14 (Py, c = 1)	272–3					s[h]	i			aq ac s	**Am 74,** 2382

For explanations, symbols and abbreviations see beginning of table. For structural formulas see end of table.

No.	Name	Synonyms and Formula	Mol. wt.	Color, crystalline form, specific rotation and λ_{max} (log ε)	m.p. °C	b.p. °C	Density	n_D	w	al	eth	ace	bz	other solvents	Ref.

Protoveratrine

No.	Name	Synonyms and Formula	Mol. wt.	Color etc.	m.p.	b.p.	Density	n_D	w	al	eth	ace	bz	other	Ref.
p1856	Protoveratrine	$C_{39}H_{61}NO_{13}$	751.93	pl (ace) $[\alpha]_D^{24} -8.3$ (chl) $\lambda^{al} 260$ (1.1), 290 (0.8)	225d				i	s^h				chl s^h	Am 74, 5107
p1857	Protoveratrine A	$C_{41}H_{63}NO_{14}$	793.96	lf (al) $[\alpha]_D^{20} -44.1$ (Py, c = 1.12), -12.1 (chl, c = 3.2)	305d				i						H36, 718
p1858	Protoveratrine B	Neoprotoveratrine. $C_{41}H_{63}NO_{15}$	809.96	lf (chl-al) $[\alpha]_D^{20} -39.8$ (Py, c = 1.24), -3.5 (chl, c = 3.1) $\lambda 260$ (1.2), 290 (0.9)	285–90d (267–9)				i	s^h				chl, Py s	H36, 718
p1859	Protoverine	$C_{27}H_{43}NO_9$	525.65	nd (MeOH) $[\alpha]_D^{20} -15.7$ (Py, c = 1.1) $\lambda^{al} 260$ (1.0), 330 (0.5)	220–2				i	s			s	aq ac s MeOH s^h	C37, 5726
—	Provitamin A	see β-Carotene													
—	Provitamin D₃	see 5,7-Cholestadien-3β-ol													
p1860	Prulaurasin	dl-Mandelonitrile glucoside. $C_{14}H_{17}NO_6$	295.30	wh nd or pr (al) $[\alpha]_D -54$	122–2.5				s	s	i				B31, 240
p1861	Prunasin	d-Mandelonitrile-β-d-glucoside. $C_{14}H_{17}NO_6$. See p1860	295.30	nd (chl or AcOEt–CCl₄) $[\alpha]_D^{21} -27.0$	149–50				s	s	i	s		AcOEt s^h chl δ^h	B31, 238
—	Prunetol	see Isoflavine, 4′,5,7-trihydroxy-													
—	Pseudocholestane	see Coprostane													
p1862	Pseudoaconitine	$C_{36}H_{51}NO_{12}$	687.79	tcl (MeOH–AmOH) $[\alpha]_D^{15} +18.36$ (al), $+22.75$ (chl)	214				i	v	s				J1928, 1105
p1863	Pseudocodeine	Neoisocodeine. $C_{18}H_{21}NO_3$	299.37	wh nd $[\alpha]_D -96.6$ (al)	181–2		1.290⁸⁰	1.574	δ	s	δ				B27², 112
p1864	Pseudoconhydrine	5-Hydroxyconine. $C_8H_{17}NO$	143.23	hyg nd (eth) $[\alpha]_D^{20} +11.0$ (al, c = 10)	106 (anh) 60 (+1w)	236			s	s	s				B21¹, 191
p1865	Pseudoconiceine(L)	γ-Coniceine.	125.22	hyg, $[\alpha]_D^{15} +122.6$		171–2	0.8776¹⁵	1.4607¹⁸	δ	s	s			chl s	B20, 146
—	Pseudocumene	see Benzene, 1,2,4-trimethyl-*													
—	Pseudocumenol	see Benzene, 1-hydroxy-2,4,5-trimethyl-*													
—	Pseudocumidine	see Benzene, 1-amino-2,4,5-trimethyl-*													
p1866	Pseudoephedrine(d)	Isoephedrine. ψ-Ephedrine. $C_{10}H_{15}NO$	165.24	pr or lf (eth) $[\alpha]_D^{20} +51.9$ (abs al, c = 0.6)	118.7				δ	s	s		v		B13², 376
Ω p1867	—(dl)	$C_{10}H_{15}NO$. See p1866	165.24	nd (eth)	118.2	130¹⁶			δ	v	s		v		B13², 372
p1868	—(l)	$C_{10}H_{15}NO$. See p1866	165.24	lf or pr (eth) $[\alpha]_D^{20} -51.9$ (abs al, c = 0.6)	118.7				δ	s	s		v		B13², 377
p1869	—, hydrochloride(d)	$C_{10}H_{15}NO\cdot HCl$. See p1866	201.70	rh pl or nd (al) $[\alpha]_D^{20} +62$ (w, c = 0.8)	181–2				s	s	s			25% HCl v	B13², 373
Ω p1870	—, —(dl)	$C_{10}H_{15}NO\cdot HCl$. See p1866	201.70	nd (abs al)	164				v	s	s				B13², 377
p1871	—, —(l)	$C_{10}H_{15}NO\cdot HCl$. See p1866	201.70	nd (abs al or AcOEt) $[\alpha]_D^{20} -62.1$ (w, c = 1.8)	182–2.5				v					chl i	B13², 377
—	Pseudoergostane	see Coproergostane													
p1872	Pseudohyoscyamine	Norhyoscyamine. $C_{16}H_{21}NO_3$	275.34	nd, $[\alpha]_D -21$ to 14 (al)	140.5				δ	s	δ			chl s	B21¹, 197
p1873	Pseudoionone	Citrylideneacetone. $C_{13}H_{20}O$. $(CH_3)_2C{:}CHCH_2CH_2C(CH_3){:}CHCH{:}CHCOCH_3$	192.31	pa ye oil $\lambda 290$ (4.4)		143–5¹² 114–6²	0.8984²⁰	1.5335²⁰						chl, MeOH s	B1³, 3067
p1874	Pseudojervine	$C_{33}H_{49}NO_8$	587.73	wh nd or hex pl $[\alpha]_D -133$ (al-chl, 1:3) $\lambda^{MeOH} 250$ (4.18)	304–5d				i	s	i		i	chl s peth, to i	C39, 1413

For explanations, symbols and abbreviations see beginning of table. For structural formulas see end of table.

Pseudomorphine

No.	Name	Synonyms and Formula	Mol. wt.	Color, crystalline form, specific rotation and λ_{max} (log ε)	m.p. °C	b.p. °C	Density	n_D	w	al	eth	ace	bz	other solvents	Ref.
p1875	Pseudomorphine	2,2'-Bimorphine. $C_{34}H_{36}N_2O_6$	568.68	cr (aq NH_3 + 3w) $[\alpha]_D^{24}$ + 44.8 (1 N HCl, c = 0.86) $\lambda^{1 N \, sulf}$ < 320	282–3 (327d)	....			i	i	i	.....	...	Py s NH_3 s[h] sulf, chl i	B27[2], 886
p1876	—, hydrochloride	$C_{34}H_{36}N_2O_6 \cdot 2HCl \cdot 2H_2O$. See p1876	677.64	pw $[\alpha]_D$ −114.76					δ						B3, 910
p1877	Pseudopelletierine	Pseudopunicine. $C_9H_{15}NO$	153.23	orh pr (peth)	54	246	1.001[100]	1.4760[100]	v	s	s	....	...	chl s	B21, 261
p1878	Pseudoreserpine	$C_{32}H_{38}N_2O_9$	594.67	$[\alpha]_D^{24}$ − 65 (chl) λ^{MeOH} 217 (4.78), 266 (4.23), 293 (4.00)	257–8				i			s			C52, 2876
Ωp1879	Pseudo-thiohydantoin	2-Imino-4-thiazolidinone	116.14	pr or nd (w) λ 220 (4.17), 250 (3.82)	255–8d				δ v[h]	i	i				B27[2], 284
Ωp1880	Pseudotropine	Pseudotropanol. $C_8H_{15}NO$	141.22	rh ta or pr (eth), rh bipym (peth-bz)	109	24[760]			v	v	δ s[h]	...	s	chl s	C48, 2724
p1881	Psicose	d-Allose. Pseudofructose. $C_6H_{12}O_6$	180.16	$[\alpha]_D^{25}$ +4.7 (w, c = 4.3)	58				s	s	...	i		MeOH s	B31, 349
p1882	Pteridine	Pyrimido[4,5-b]pyrazine	132.13	ye pl (bz, sub) λ^{a1} 267 sh (3.6), 300 (3.9), 380 sh (1.9)	139.5–40	sub 125–30[20]			s	s	δ		δ		J1951, 474
p1883	—, 2-amino-4,6-dihydroxy-	Xantopterin. Uropterin. $C_6H_5N_5O_2$. See p1882	179.14	og-ye (w + 1) λ^{aa} 270 (4.07), 380 (3.55)	>410d (darkens 360)				i					ac, alk v	Am 73, 1497
p1884	—, 2-amino-4-hydroxy-	2-Amino-4-pteridonol. $C_6H_5N_5O$. See p1882	163.14	ye $\lambda^{w, \, pH=1}$ 312 (3.91) $\lambda^{w, \, pH=11}$ 252 (4.34), 358 (3.88)	>360										C47, 5945
p1885	Pukateine(l)	4-Hydroxy-5,6-methylene-dioxyaporphin. $C_{18}H_{17}NO_3$	295.34	cr (al, eth) $[\alpha]_D^{15}$ − 200 (al, c = 6)	200	210–5[2]			l	δ s[h]	δ s[h]			Py v chl s peth δ	B27[1], 461
p1886	Pulegenone	4-Methyl-1-isopropyl-cyclopentenone-5.	138.21			188.5–9[760]	0.9144[20]	1.4660[20]	...	s	s	s		chl s	C34, 92
Ωp1887	Pulegone	4(8)-p-Menthen-3-one. $C_{10}H_{16}O$	152.24	$[\alpha]_D^{20}$ +23.4 (undil) λ^{hx} 244.5 (390), 331 (1.70)	....	224[760] 103[17]	0.9346[65]	1.4894[20]	i	∞	∞			chl ∞	B7, 81
Ωp1888	Purine	7-Imidazo[4,5-d]pyrimidine	120.11	nd (to or al) $\lambda^{w, \, pH=1}$ 260 (3.79) $\lambda^{w, \, pH=7}$ 263 (3.90)	216–7	sub			v	v[h]	δ	s		chl, AcOEt δ	B26, 354
Ωp1889	—, 6-amino-	Adenine. $C_6H_5N_5$. See p1888	135.13	nd or lf (w + 3) $\lambda^{w, \, pH=7}$ 260 (4.13)	360–5d (anh)	sub at 220			δ v[h]	δ	i			ac, alk v chl i	B26[2], 252
—	—, 1,3-dimethyl-2,6-dihydroxy-	see Theophylline													
p1890	—, 6-mercapto-	6-Purinethiol. $C_5H_4N_4S$. See p1888	152.18	ye pr (w + 1) dk ye hyd λ^{a1} 330 (4.28)	313–4d (−w140)				i δ[h]					alk s	Am 74, 411
p1891	—, 2,6,8-trichloro-	$C_5HCl_3N_4$. See p1888	223.45	nd (al)	159–61	....			δ[h]	v[h]	v	v	v[h]	chl v[h]	B26, 356
—	—, 2,6,8-trihydroxy-	see Uric acid													
—	6(1)-Purinone	see Hypoxanthine													
—	Purpurin	see 9,10-Anthraquinone, 1,2,4-trihydroxy-*													
—	Purpuroxanthin	see 9,10-Anthraquinone, 1,3-dihydroxy-*													
—	Putrescine	see Butane, 1,4-diamino-*													
p1892	Pyocyanine		210.24	dk bl nd (w + 1 or chl-peth) λ^{a1} 231 (4.4) 315 (4.4), 740 (4.0)	133d	sub			δ s[h]	s[h]	i	s	δ	chl v Py, AcOEt, $PhNO_2$ s CCl_4, peth i	J123, 3279
p1893	Pyraconitine	$C_{32}H_{43}O_9N$	585.70	nd	171				δ	s					C51, 17963
p1893[1]	γ-Pyran	C_5H_6O	82.10	col oil λ^{a1} 222 (3.85), 238 (3.71)		80[760]		1.4559[20]	...	s	s	s			B17, 36

For explanations, symbols and abbreviations see beginning of table. For structural formulas see end of table.

No.	Name	Synonyms and Formula	Mol. wt.	Color. crystalline form. specific rotation and λ_{max} (log ε)	m.p. °C	b.p. °C	Density	n_D	Solubility w	al	eth	ace	bz	other solvents	Ref.
	γ-Pyran														
p1894	—,2,3-dihydro-	C_5H_8O. See p1893[1]	84.13	λ^{hx} 195 (3.58)	....	86–7	0.922^{19}_{15}	1.4402^{19}	s	s					C28, 4056
—	—,2,3-dihydro-3,4-dihydroxy-2-hydroxy-methyl-	see **Gluconal**													
—	—,4-oxo-	see **4-Pyrone**													
p1895	—,tetrahydro-	Pentamethylene oxide. $C_5H_{10}O$. See p1893[1]	86.14	λ^{vap} 175 (3.3), 187 (2.8)	....	88^{760}	0.8810^{20}_4	1.4200^{20}	.,.	s	s	...	a		B17[2], 18
p1896	Pyranthrone	8,16-Pyranthenedione	406.45	red-ye or red-br nd (PhNO₂)	d	sub vac	....		i					sulf s (bl) PhNO₂ s[h] 50 % Py δ	E14s, 887
Ω p1897	**Pyrazine**	1,4-Diazine*. Paradiazine	80.09	pr (w) λ^{al} 261 (3.78), 310 (2.93)	54	115.5 –.8[768]	1.0311^{01}_5	1.4953^{61}	s	s	s	s			B23, 91
Ω p1898	—,2,5-dimethyl-	Ketine. $C_6H_8N_2$. See p1897	108.15	λ^{cy} 271 (3.76), 314 (2.96)	15	155^{760} (cor)	0.9887^{20}_4	1.4980^{20}	∞	∞	∞	s			B23[2], 80
Ω p1899	—,2-methyl-	$C_5H_6N_2$. See p1897	94.12	λ^{cy} 266 (3.76), 320 (2.92)	....	136–7	1.0290^{20}_4	1.5067^{19}	∞	∞	∞	s			B23, 94
Ω p1900	Pyrazine-carboxylic acid, amide	Pyrazinamide	123.12	wh nd (w, al) λ^{al} 268 (3.95), 322 (2.75)	191–3	sub			s[h]	s[h]					C48, 2074
Ω p1901	2,3-Pyrazinedi-carboxylic acid	....	168.11	pr (w +2) λ^{al} 269 (3.79), 314 (2.84)	193d (188d)				v	δ	δ	s	δ	MeOH s chl d	B25[2], 164
p1902	2,5-Pyrazinedi-carboxylic acid	....	168.11	nd (w +2)	255–6d (sealed tube) (272)				δ	δ	δ	...	δ	chl δ	B25[2], 164
p1903	2,6-Pyrazinedi-carboxylic acid	....	168.11	mcl nd (w +2)	217 8d				δ s[h]	δ	s[h]				B25, 168
Ω p1904	2,3-Pyrazinedi-carboxylic acid, 5-methyl-	$C_7H_6N_2O_4$. See p1901	182.14	(w, ace, dil al-eth)	174–5				v[h]	s	...	s[h]			B25[2], 165
Ω p1905	**Pyrazole**	1,2-Diazole	68.08	nd or pr (lig) λ^{diox} 212 (3.45)	69.5–70	$186–8^{760}$		1.4203	s	s	s	s			B23, 39
p1906	—,4-bromo-1,3-dimethyl-	$C_5H_7BrN_2$. See p1905	175.03	....		$76–7^{10}$	1.4976^{15}_4	1.5214^{15}	...	s	s	s		os v	B23[2], 54
p1907	—,4-bromo-1,5-dimethyl-	$C_5H_7BrN_2$. See p1905	175.03	cr	38.5–9.5	85^{10}			δ					os, dil ac s peth i	B23[2], 54
Ω p1908	—,4-bromo-3,5-dimethyl-	$C_5H_7BrN_2$. See p1905	175.03	nd (dil al)	123				s[h]	...	v	v		os s	B23[2], 68
p1909	—,4-bromo-3-methyl-	$C_4H_5BrN_2$. See p1905	161.00	cr (dil al)	76–7	....	1.5638^{100}_4	1.5182^{100}	s[h]	s	v	v			B23[2], 54
p1910	—,3-chloro-1,5-dimethyl-	$C_5H_7ClN_2$. See p1905	130.58	pl (w)	47–6	210–2 138[72]	1.0823^{100}_4	1.4648^{100}	δ	v	v	v	v		B23[2], 49
p1911	—,4-chloro-3,5-dimethyl-	$C_5H_7ClN_2$. See p1905	130.58	pr (w), cr (al)	117.5–8.5	220–22			δ s[h]	v	v	v	v	os v	B23[2], 67
p1912	—,5-chloro-1,3-dimethyl-	$C_5H_7ClN_2$. See p1905	130.58	....		157–8 (cor)	1.1367^{18}_4	1.4877^{18}	s						B23[2], 49
p1913	—,5-chloro-3-methyl-	$C_4H_5ClN_2$. See p1905	116.55	cr (eth, lig)	118–9	258 138[15]			v[h]					os v	B23[2], 49
—	—,dihydro-	see **Pyrazoline**													
—	—,dihydro(oxo)-	see **Pyrazolone**													
p1914	—,1,3-dimethyl-	$C_5H_8N_2$. See p1905	96.14	λ^{al} 221 (3.67)		136–8 (143–5) 31[1]	0.9561^{17}_4	1.4734^{15}_a	v						B23[2], 44
p1915	—,1,5-dimethyl-	$C_5H_8N_2$. See p1905	96.14	λ^{al} 217 (3.64)	....	153 (cor)	0.9813^{17}_4	1.4782^{16}_a	v	v	v				B23[2], 44
Ω p1916	—,3,4-dimethyl-	$C_5H_8N_2$. See p1905	96.14	(peth) λ^{al} 222 (3.65)	58	111^{10}			s	s	s	s	s	os s	B23[2], 64
Ω p1917	—,3,5-dimethyl-	$C_5H_8N_2$. See p1905	96.14	cr (peth, MeOH, al)	107.5–8.5	218^{758}	0.8839^{26}		s	v	v	s	v	chl, MeOH v	B23[2], 65
p1918	—,1-ethyl-	$C_5H_8N_2$. See p1905	96.14	....		139^{760}	0.9537^{20}_4	1.4700^{20}	v	v	v	v	v	Py v	C55, 22291
p1919	—,1-isopropyl-	$C_6H_{10}N_2$. See p1905	110.16			143			s	v					C53, 21043
p1920	—,3-methyl-	$C_4H_6N_2$. See p1905	82.11	λ^{al} 213 (3.60)	36–7	204[752] (cor) 108[25]	1.0203^{16}_4	1.4915^{20}	∞	∞	∞				B23[2], 44
p1921	**2-Pyrazoline**	4,5-Dihydropyrazole	70.10	....		144[100]	1.0200^{17}_4	1.4796^{17}	∞	∞	s				B23, 28
p1922	—,1-phenyl-	$C_9H_{10}N_2$. See p1921	146.19	pl (lig) λ^{al} 242 (4.06), 281 (4.41)	52	273[754] 151[17]	1.0689^{58}_4	1.6015^{58}	i	s		s	s		B23[2], 25
p1923	5-Pyrazolone	2-Pyrazolin-5-one	84.08	nd (to, w, xyl)	165	sub			s	s	δ				B24[1], 186
—	3-Pyrazolone, 1,5-dimethyl-2-phenyl-	see **Antipyrine**													

For explanations, symbols and abbreviations see beginning of table. For structural formulas see end of table.

No.	Name	Synonyms and Formula	Mol. wt.	Color. crystalline form. specific rotation and λ_{max} (log ε)	m.p. °C	b.p. °C	Density	n_D	Solubility						Ref.
									w	al	eth	ace	bz	other solvents	

5-Pyrazolone

No.	Name	Synonyms and Formula	Mol. wt.	Color...	m.p.	b.p.	Density	n_D	w	al	eth	ace	bz	other	Ref.
Ω p1925	5-Pyrazolone, 3-methyl-	$C_4H_6N_2O$. See p1923......	98.11	pr (w), nd (al), lf (sub) λ^{al} 240 (3.5)	215 (219)	sub			v^h	δ^h	...	...	...		B24, 19
p1926	—,3-methyl-1(3-nitrophenyl)-	$C_{10}H_9N_3O_3$. See p1923.....	219.20	ye amor (aa)	185	....			δ	δ	δ	...	...	alk s aa s^h	B24[1], 191
p1927	—,3-methyl-1-phenyl-	$C_{10}H_{10}N_2O$. See p1923.....	174.20	mcl pr (w) λ^{al} 245 (1.1), 280 sh (3.6)	127	287^{105} 191^{17}		1.637	s^h	s^h	...	...	δ	peth i	B24, 20
p1928	—,3-methyl-1(4-sulfophenyl)-	$C_{10}H_{10}N_2O_4S$. See p1923...	254.27	nd (w + 1)	290–320d	....			s^h	i	i	...	...	alk v aa i	B24[2], 20
p1929	5-Pyrazolone-3-carboxylic acid, 1-phenyl-	....	204.20	nd (w, al)	261	....			i δ^h	s	i	...	...		B25[2], 219
Ω p1930	Pyrene*..........	Benzo[d,e,f]phenanthrene .	202.26	pa ye pl (to, sub) λ^{cy} 273 (4.77), 306 (5.07), 320 (4,51), 335 (4.78)	156 (cor) (150)	393^{760} 260^{60}	1.271^{23}_4		i	s	s	...	s	CS_2, to, lig s	B5[3], 2279
Ω p1931	—,1-acetyl-......	$C_{18}H_{12}O$. See p1930	244.30	gr-ye lf (al, MeOH)	89–90	....			...	...	s	...	v	to v sulf s (og-red)	E14s, 434
p1932	—,1-amino-......	$C_{16}H_{11}N$. See p1930	217.27	ye nd (hx), lf (dil al) λ^{eth} 238 (4.6), 286 (4.4), 357 (4.2), 400 (4.1)	117–8	....			...	s	...	s	s	hx, ac s	E14s, 422
—	3-Pyrenebutyric acid	see Butanoic acid, 4(3-pyrenyl)-*													
p1933	3-Pyrenecarboxylic acid	$C_{17}H_{10}O_2$. See p1930.......	246.27	ye nd (PhCl, eth-al, sub)	274	sub			δ	δ	s	...	...	con sulf, dil alk, chl s	E14s, 447
p1934	4-Pyrenecarboxylic acid	$C_{17}H_{10}O_2$. See p1930.......	246.27	gr lf or nd (PhNO_2, aa-PhCl)	327–8	....			δ	...	...	...	...	chl, con sulf s	C52, 11081
p1935	Pyrethrin I	Chrysanthemummono-carboxylic acid, pyrethrolone ester. $C_{21}H_{28}O_3$.	328.46	visc liq $[\alpha]^{25}_D$ −32.3 (eth, c = 5.66)	....	$170^{0.1}$ d		1.5192^{18}	i	s	s	...	...	peth, CH_3NO_2, CCl_4 s	B9[2], 46
p1936	Pyrethrin II	Chrysanthemumdicarboxylic acid, methyl ester, pyrethrolone ester. $C_{22}H_{28}O_5$.	372.47	visc liq $[\alpha]^{20}_D$ −6 (eth, c = 5)	....	$200^{0.1}$ d		1.5258^{20}	i	s	s	...	...	peth, CH_3NO_2, CCl_4 s	B9[2], 565
Ω p1937	Pyridazine........	1,2-Diazine*. Orthodiazine..	80.09	λ^{al} 261 (3.78), 310 (2.93)	−8	208^{760} $47–8^1$	1.1035^{28}_4	1.5218^{20}	∞	∞	v	v	v	peth i	B23, 89
p1938	—,3,6-dioxo-1,2,3,6-tetrahydro-	Maleic acid hydrazide. $C_4H_4N_2O_2$. See p1937	112.09	cr (w) $\lambda^{w-pH=8}$ 215 (4.2), 340 (3.4)	>300d (296 −8d)	....			δ s^h	δ^h	...	...	...		Am 80, 3790
Ω p1939	Pyridine	Azine*....................	79.10	λ^{cy} 251 (3.1), 256 (3.1), 279 sh (2.0), 284 sh (1.8), 288 sh (1.4)	−42	115.5	0.9819^{20}	1.5095^{20}	∞	∞	∞	∞	∞	chl ∞	B20, 181
Ω p1940	—,hydrochloride ..	Pyridinium hydrochloride. $C_5H_5N.HCl$. See p1939	115.56	hyg pl or sc (al) λ^{al} 266 (3.7)	82	218–9			s	s	i	...	i	chl s	B20, 189
p1941	—,nitrate	Pyridinium nitrate. $C_5H_5N.HNO_3$. See p1939	142.12	nd (al)	sub	....			v	s	i	...	i		B20[1], 59
Ω p1942	—,picrate	Pyridinium picrate. $C_5H_5N.C_6H_3N_3O_7$. See p1939	308.22	ye nd (al)	167–8	....			s^h	s^h	...	...	...		B20[2], 122
p1943	—,sulfate	Pyridinium sulfate. $C_5H_5N.H_2SO_4$. See p1939	177.18	cr (al) λ^{2Nsulf} 250 sh (3.7), 255 (3.8), 262 sh (3.6)	....	....			∞	∞	i	...	...		B20, 190
p1944	—,2-acetyl-......	Methyl 2-pyridyl ketone. C_7H_7NO. See p1939	121.14	ye in air λ^{hx} 227.5 (3.84), 267.5 (3.50)	....	192^{760} 78^{12}		1.5203^{20}	...	s	s	...	...	min ac s	B21[2], 247
p1945	—,3-acetyl-......	Methyl 3-pyridyl ketone. C_7H_7NO. See p1939	121.14	ye in air λ^{ac-al} 235 (4.0), 276 (3.6)	13–4	220^{760} 106^{12}		1.5341^{20}	s	s	s	...	...	ac s	B21[2], 247
p1946	—,—,oxime	$C_7H_8N_2O$. See p1939.......	136.17	cr (al, bz)	113 (130.5)	....			s^h	s	s	...	...	min ac s	B21[2], 247
p1947	—,2-allyl-........	C_8H_9N. See p1939	119.17	....	....	190 $58–8.5^{10}$	0.959^{20}		δ	∞	∞	...	...		C52, 15520
Ω p1948	—,2-amino-......	α-Pyridylamine. $C_5H_6N_2$. See p1939	94.12	lf (lig) λ^{al} 234 (4.1), 297 (3.6)	57.5–87 (59–60)	204 $104–6^{20}$ sub			...	s	s	s	s	os s	B22, 428
Ω p1949	—,3-amino-......	β-Pyridylamine. $C_5H_6N_2$. See p1939	94.12	lf (bz-lig) λ^{al} 241 (4.0), 301 (3.4)	64–5	252 $131–2^{12}$			s	s	s	...	s	lig δ	B22, 431

For explanations, symbols and abbreviations see beginning of table. For structural formulas see end of table.

Pyridine

No.	Name	Synonyms and Formula	Mol. wt.	Color, crystalline form, specific rotation and λ_{max} (log ε)	m.p. °C	b.p. °C	Density	n_D	w	al	eth	ace	bz	other solvents	Ref.
Ω p1950	—,4-amino-	γ-Pyridylamine. $C_5H_6N_2$. See p1939	94.12	nd (bz) λ^{al} 246 (4.2)	158–9	180[13]			s	v	s	...	s	lig δ	B22, 433
Ω p1951	—,2-amino-5-bromo-	$C_5H_5BrN_2$. See p1939	173.02	cr (bz)	137					v	i	...	s	lig i	B22, 431
Ω p1952	—,5-amino-2-butoxy-	$C_9H_{14}N_2O$. See p1939	166.23			148–50[12] (146–7[2])	1.037[25]	1.5373[20]	...	s	s			dil ac s	C46, 10285
Ω p1953	—,2-amino-5-chloro-	$C_5H_5ClN_2$. See p1939	128.56	pl	136–8	127–8[11]			s	s				peth, lig i	B22[2], 332
p1954	—,2-amino-3,5-dibromo-	$C_5H_4Br_2N_2$. See p1939	251.92	nd (dil al, peth)	104–4.5				δ	s	s			lig δ	B22[2], 333
p1955	—,2-amino-3,5-dichloro-	$C_5H_4Cl_2N_2$. See p1939	163.01	nd or pr (dil al)	84–5				δ	s		s		lig s	B22[2], 333
p1956	—,4-amino-2,6-dichloro-	$C_5H_4Cl_2N_2$. See p1939	163.01	nd (dil al)	176				i s[h]	s	s	s	s		B22[1], 632
p1957	—,4-amino-3,5-dinitro-	$C_5H_4N_4O_4$. See p1939	184.11	ye pl (dil al)	170–1				δ[h]	δ					B22[2], 341
p1958	—,2-amino-5-iodo-	$C_5H_5IN_2$. See p1939	220.01	nd or lf (dil al)	129				δ	s	v				B22[2], 334
Ω p1959	—,2-amino-3-methyl-	α-Amino-β-picoline. $C_6H_8N_2$. See p1939	108.15	hyg λ^w 230 (3.8), 294 (3.7)	33.5	221.5[748] 95[8]			v	s	s	s	s	os s lig δ	B22[2], 342
Ω p1960	—,2-amino-4-methyl-	α-Amino-γ-picoline. $C_6H_8N_2$. See p1939	108.15	lf or pl (lig)	100–0.5 (cor)	115–7[11] (cor)			v	s	s	s	s	os s lig i	B22[2], 342
Ω p1961	—,2-amino-6-methyl-	α'-Amino-α-picoline. $C_6H_8N_2$. See p1939	108.15	hyg (lig)	41	208–9			v	s	s	s	s	lig s[h]	B22[2], 342
p1962	—,3-amino-4-methyl-	β-Amino-γ-picoline. $C_6H_8N_2$. See p1939	108.15	pr (bz-peth)	106	254[735]			v	v	v	v	v	chl v lig i	B22[2], 343
p1963	—,2-amino-3-nitro-	$C_5H_5N_3O_2$. See p1939	139.12	ye nd (dil al)	165–7				δ	s	δ				B22[2], 335
Ω p1964	—,2-amino-5-nitro-	$C_5H_5N_3O_2$. See p1939	139.12	ye lf (dil al)	188				δ	s	δ	...	δ	lig δ	B22[1], 631
p1965	—,4-amino-3-nitro-	$C_5H_5N_3O_2$. See p1939	139.12	ye nd (w)	200				s[h]	s					B22[2], 341
Ω p1966	—,4-benzoyl-	Phenyl 4-pyridyl ketone $C_{12}H_9NO$. See p1939	183.21	nd (peth), pl (w)	71.5–3	314[742] 170–2[10]			δ[h]	s	s	s			B21[2], 277
Ω p1967	—,2-benzyl-	$C_{12}H_{11}N$. See p1939	169.23	nd λ^{al} 262.5 (3.67), 270 (3.54)	11–4	276[742] 149[16]	1.067[0]	1.5785[20]	i	s	s	s			B20, 425
p1968	—,3-benzyl-	$C_{12}H_{11}N$. See p1939	169.23	nd	34	286[740]	1.061		i	s	s				B20, 426
Ω p1969	—,4-benzyl-	$C_{12}H_{11}N$. See p1939	169.23	λ^{al} 259 (3.5)		287[742] 180–1[31]	1.0614[20]	1.5818[20]	i	s	v				B20[2], 272
Ω p1970	—,2-bromo-	C_5H_4BrN. See p1939	158.00	λ^{al} 260 sh (3.4), 265 (3.4), 270 sh (3.3)		193–4[764] 74–5[13]	1.657[15]	1.5734[20]	δ	s	s			os s	B20[2], 153
Ω p1971	—,3-bromo-	C_5H_4BrN. See p1939	158.00	nd (al) λ^{al} 265 sh (3.3), 268 (3.4), 275 sh (3.2)	142–3	172–3[752] 68–70[18]	1.645[0]	1.5694[20]	s	v	v				B20, 233
p1972	—,5-bromo-2-hydroxy-	C_5H_4BrNO. See p1939	174.00	pr (w, al)	177–8				δ v[h]	v[h]	δ			dil alk, con ac v	B21[1], 202
Ω p1973	—,2-chloro-	C_5H_4ClN. See p1939	113.55	oil λ^{al} 260 sh (3.4), 265 (3.5), 270 (3.3)		170[760] 54–8[10]	1.205[15]	1.5320[20]	δ	s	s				B20, 230
Ω p1974	—,3-chloro-	C_5H_4ClN. See p1939	113.55	λ^{al} 265 (3.4), 268 (3.4), 275 (3.3)		148[744] 85–7[100]		1.5304[20]	δ						B20, 230
Ω p1975	—,4-chloro-	C_5H_4ClN. See p1939	113.55	λ^{al} 258 (3.30)	−42.5	147–8[760] 85–7[100]			s	∞					B20, 231
Ω p1976	—,2,3-diamino- (one form)	$C_5H_7N_3$. See p1939	109.13	lf or pl (dil al)	122	148–50[5]			δ	s			δ	peth i	B22[1], 647
Ω p1977	—,— (one form)	$C_5H_7N_3$. See p1939	109.13	nd (bz)	116	sub			s	s			s[h]		B22[2], 394
p1978	—,2,4-diamino-	$C_5H_7N_3$. See p1939	109.13	hyg lf or nd	107				v				δ	peth i	B22[2], 394
p1979	—,2,5-diamino-	$C_5H_7N_3$. See p1939	109.13	nd	109–10	180–5[12]			s	s			δ	peth i	B22[2], 394
p1980	—,3,4-diamino-	$C_5H_7N_3$. See p1939	109.13	nd or lf	218–9				i[h]				δ		B22[2], 395
p1981	—,3,5-diamino-	$C_5H_7N_3$. See p1939	109.13	hyg nd or lf	119–20				v				δ	peth i	B22[1], 648
Ω p1982	—,3,5-dibromo-	$C_5H_3Br_2N$. See p1939	236.90	nd (al)	112	222 sub 100			δ[h]	s[h]	s				B20, 233
p1983	—,1,2-dihydro-1-methyl-2-oxo-	C_6H_7NO. See p1939	109.13	nd λ^{al} 228.5 (3.66) 303 (3.57)	7	250[740] 121[10]			∞					peth, lig δ	B21[1], 229
p1984	—,2,4-dihydroxy-	2,4-Pyridinediol. $C_5H_5NO_2$. See p1939	111.10	rh bipym (al or w)	260–5 d				s	s	i				B21, 160
p1985	—,2,6-dihydroxy-, hydrate	2,6-Pyridinediol hydrate $C_5H_5NO_2 \cdot H_2O$. See p1939	129.12	ye pr	202–3 (195)				s	s	i			alk, ac δ	B21[2], 108
p1986	—,3,5-diiodo-2-hydroxy-	$C_5H_3I_2NO$. See p1939	346.89	bt br nd (AmOH)	261–2				δ[h]	...	δ			AmOH s[h] chl δ	B21[2], 32
p1987	—,2,3-dimethyl-	2,3-Lutidine. C_7H_9N. See p1939	107.15	λ^{al} 266 (3.56)		163–4[760] (160.7)	0.9319[25]	1.5057[20]	s	s	s				B20, 243

For explanations, symbols and abbreviations see beginning of table. For structural formulas see end of table.

No.	Name	Synonyms and Formula	Mol. wt.	Color, crystalline form, specific rotation and λ_{max} (log ε)	m.p. °C	b.p. °C	Density	n_D	w	al	eth	ace	bz	other solvents	Ref.
	Pyridine														
Ω p1988	—,2,4-dimethyl-	2,4-Lutidine. C_7H_9N. See p1939	107.16	λ^{MeOH} 265 (3.4), 270 (3.3)	....	159–9.5[760]	0.9309[20/4]	1.5010[20]	v i[h]	v	v	s	...	...	B20[2], 160
Ω p1989	—,2,5-dimethyl-	2,5-Lutidine. C_7H_9N. See p1939	107.16	λ^{MeOH} 260 sh (2.5), 270 (3.6), 280 (3.4)	−16	156.8–.9[760] (159–60)	0.9297[20/4]	1.5006[20]	δ v[h]	v	∞	s	...	...	B20, 244
Ω p1990	—,2,6-dimethyl-	2,6-Lutidine. C_7H_9N. See p1939	107.16	λ^{MeOH} 267 (3.64)	−6.1	145.7[760]	0.9226[20/4]	1.4953[20]	∞ s[h]	δ	s	s	...	chl s	B20[2], 160
p1991	—,3,4-dimethyl-	3,4-Lutidine. C_7H_9N. See p1939	107.16	$\lambda^{0.1 NH_2SO_4}$ 258 (3.7)	....	163.5–4.5[760] (178.8)	0.9281[25/4]	1.5096[20]	δ	s	s	s	...	chl s	B20[2], 161
Ω p1992	—,3,5-dimethyl-	3,5-Lutidine. C_7H_9N. See p1939	107.16	$\lambda^{0.1 NH_2SO_4}$ 268 (3.8)	....	171.6[760]	0.9419[20]	1.5061[20]	s	s	s	s	...	...	B20[2], 161
Ω p1993	—,2(dimethyl-amino)-	$C_7H_{10}N_2$. See p1939	122.17	λ^{al} 250 (4.2), 312 (3.8)	....	196 88[15]	1.0157[14/14]	1.5663[20]	...	s	s	...	s	dil ac s	B22[1], 629
Ω p1994	—,4(dimethyl-amino)-	$C_7H_{10}N_2$. See p1939	122.17	pl (eth) $\lambda^{72\% diox}$ 258 (4.39), 290 (3.30)	114	....	....	....	v	s	v	...	v	chl v	B22[2], 341
p1995	—,2(dimethyl-amino) 6-methyl-	$C_8H_{12}N_2$. See p1939	136.20	....	....	198–200[760] 88[15]	....	....	δ	s	s	...	...	...	B22[2], 342
Ω p1996	—,3,5-dimethyl-2-ethyl-	α-Parvoline. $C_9H_{13}N$. See p1939	135.21	λ^{MeOH} 255 (3.3), 265 (3.2)	....	198–9[764] 85–7[15]	0.9338[0]	....	s	v	v	v	...	chl v	B20[2], 166
Ω p1997	—,2-ethenyl-	α-Vinylpyridine. C_7H_7N. See p1939	105.14	λ^{al} 238 (4.1), 282 (3.8)	....	159–60 50–5[4]	0.9985[20/0]	1.5495[20]	δ	v	v	v	...	chl v	B20, 256
Ω p1998	—,4-ethenyl-	γ-Vinylpyridine. C_7H_7N. See p1939	105.14	red to dk-br λ^{al} 242.5 (4.12)	....	65[15]	0.9800[20/4]	1.5449[20]	s[h]	s[h]	δ	...	...	...	B20[2], 170
Ω p1999	—,2-ethyl-	C_7H_9N. See p1939	107.16	$\lambda^{0.1 NHCl}$ 263 (3.85)	−63.1	148.6[760]	0.9502[0]	1.4964[20]	s	∞	v	v	...	...	B20, 241
Ω p2000	—,3-ethyl-	C_7H_9N. See p1939	107.16	λ^{cy} 257 (3.4), 262 (3.4), 268 sh (3.2)	−76.9	165[760]	0.9539[0]	1.5021[20]	s	s	s	v	...	...	B20, 242
p2001	—,4-ethyl-	C_7H_9N. See p1939	107.16	λ^{MeOH} 255 (3.3), 265 (3.2)	−90.5	167.7[760]	0.9417[20]	1.5009[20]	s	s	s	s	...	dil ac s	B20, 243
p2002	—,2-ethyl-4-methyl-	2-Ethyl-γ-picoline. $C_8H_{11}N$. See p1939	121.18	....	....	173–5[748]	0.9239[20/0]	....	δ	s	s	s	...	...	B20[2], 162
p2003	—,2-ethyl-6-methyl-	6-Ethyl-α-picoline. $C_8H_{11}N$. See p1939	121.18	....	....	160–1.5[760] 73–6[12]	0.9207[25/4]	1.4920[25]	δ	s	s	s	...	...	B20[2], 162
Ω p2004	—,3-ethyl-4-methyl-	β-Collidine. 3-Ethyl-γ-picoline. $C_8H_{11}N$. See p1939	121.18	....	....	198[760] 76[12]	0.9286[17]	....	δ	s	s	v	...	chl s	B20[2], 163
p2005	—,4-ethyl-2-methyl-	α-Collidine. 4-Ethyl-α-picoline. $C_8H_{11}N$. See p1939	121.18	....	....	179[760]	0.9130[25]	....	s δ[h]	s	s	s	s	...	B20[2], 162
Ω p2006	—,5-ethyl-2-methyl-	Aldehyde collidine. Aldehydine. 5-Ethyl-α-picoline. $C_8H_{11}N$. See p1939	121.18	λ^{MeOH} 270 (3.6), 280 (3.5)	....	178.3[760] 65–6[17]	0.9219[20/20]	1.4971[20]	δ[h]	s	s	s	s	con sulf, dil ac s	B20, 248
—	—,hexahydro-	see Piperidine													
Ω p2007	—,2-hydroxy-	2-Pyridol. α-Pyridone. C_5H_5NO. See p1939	95.10	nd (bz) λ^{al} 227 (4.00), 297 (3.80)	106–7	280–1	....	....	s	s	δ	...	s	chl s lig δ	B21[2], 30
Ω p2008	—,3-hydroxy-	3-Pyridol. C_5H_5NO. See p1939	95.10	nd (bz) λ^{al} 215 (3.81), 279 (3.65)	129	....	....	....	s	s	δ	...	...	...	B21[2], 33
Ω p2009	—,4-hydroxy-	4-Pyridol. γ-Pyridone. C_5H_5NO. See p1939	95.10	pr or nd (w +1) λ^{al} 260 (4.2)	148.5 (anh) 65 (hyd)	>350 257–60[10]	....	....	s	s	i	...	i	...	B21[2], 34
Ω p2010	—,2(2-hydroxy-ethyl)-	2(2-Pyridyl)ethanol. C_7H_9NO. See p1939	123.16	hyg	....	118–21[15]	1.1111[4]	1.5368[20]	v	v	δ	...	...	chl v	B21, 50
p2011	—,2(β-hydroxy-isopropyl)-	2(2-Pyridyl)-1-propanol. $C_8H_{11}NO$. See p1939	137.18	....	....	128–31[17]	....	....	v	v	δ	...	...	...	B21, 57
p2012	—,3(α-hydroxy-isopropyl)-	2(3-Pyridyl)-2-propanol. $C_8H_{11}NO$. See p1939	137.18	cr	58	140–1[12]	....	....	s	s	...	...	...	chl s	B21[2], 37
Ω p2013	—,2(hydroxy-methyl)-	2-Pyridylmethanol. C_6H_7NO. See p1939	109.13	λ^{al} 260 (4.58), 266.5 (4.58)	....	112–3[16] 102.5[8]	1.1317[20]	1.5444[20]	∞	v	v	v	v	os v	B21[1], 203
p2014	—,2(1-hydroxy-propyl)-	1(2-Pyridyl)-1-propanol. $C_8H_{11}NO$. See p1939	137.18	pa ye	....	213–6 112–3[13]	1.0501[20/4]	1.5197[20]	v	v	...	...	...	chl v	B21[2], 37
p2015	—,2(2-hydroxy-propyl)-	1(2-Pyridyl)-2-propanol. $C_8H_{11}NO$. See p1939	137.18	pr	32	123.5[20]	....	....	v	v	...	...	...	chl v	B21[2], 37
Ω p2016	—,2-isopropyl-	$C_8H_{11}N$. See p1939	121.18	$\lambda^{0.1N NaOH}$ 261.5 (3.58), 268 (3.43)	....	159.8	0.9342[0]	1.4915[20]	δ	∞	∞	v	...	...	B20, 247
Ω p2017	—,4-isopropyl-	$C_8H_{11}N$. See p1939	121.18	λ^{al} 252 sh (3.3), 256 (3.3), 262 (3.2)	−54.9	178 (181.5)	0.9382[25]	1.4962[20]	δ	∞	∞	v	...	...	B20, 248
p2018	—,4-methoxy-	C_6H_7NO. See p1939	109.13	λ^{MeOH} 220 (3.9)	....	191[738] 95[45]	....	....	∞	...	...	...	...	...	B21, 49

For explanations, symbols and abbreviations see beginning of table. For structural formulas see end of table.

Pyridine

No.	Name	Synonyms and Formula	Mol. wt.	Color, crystalline form, specific rotation and λ_{max} (log ε)	m.p. °C	b.p. °C	Density	n_D	w	al	eth	ace	bz	other solvents	Ref.
Ωp2019	—,2-methyl-	α-Picoline. C_6H_7N. See p1939	93.13	λ^{al} 256 (3.31), 262 (3.34), 269 (3.24)	−66.8	128.8^{760}	0.9443$^{20}_4$	1.4957^{20}	v	∞	∞	v	...		B20^2, 155
Ωp2020	—,3-methyl	β-Picoline. C_6H_7N. See p1939	93.13	λ^{MeOH} 260 (3.4), 265 (3.5), 270 (3.3)	−18.3	144.1^{760}	0.9566$^{20}_4$	1.5040^{20}	∞	∞	m	v	...		B20^7, 157
Ωp2021	—,4-methyl-	γ-Picoline. C_6H_7N. See p1939	93.13	λ^{cy} 255 (3.20), 260 sh (3.12)	3.6	144.9^{760}	0.9548$^{20}_4$	1.5037^{20}	∞	∞	∞	s	...		B20^2, 158
p2022	—,2(methyl-amino)-	$C_6H_8N_2$. See p1939	108.15	λ^{eth} 300 (3.7)	15	200–1 90^9	1.052$^{29}_{29}$	...	s	v	v	...	s	aa v	B22^2, 325
p2023	—,4(methyl-amino)-	$C_6H_8N_2$. See p1939	108.15	pl (eth)	117–8	...	...	...	s	s	s	s	s	aa v	B22^2, 340
—	—,2(N-methyl-2-pyrrolidyl)-	see 2,2′-Nicotyrine													
—	—,3(N-methyl-2-pyrrolidyl)-	see Nicotine													
—	—,3(N-methyl-2-pyrrolidyl)-	see 2′,3-Nicotyrine													
Ωp2024	—,2-phenyl-	α-Pyridylbenzene. $C_{11}H_9N$. See p1939	155.20	λ^{al} 277 (4.02)		270–2^{760} 146^{15}	1.0833^{25}	1.6210^{20}	δ	∞	∞				B20, 424
p2025	—,3-phenyl-	β-Pyridylbenzene. $C_{11}H_9N$. See p1939	155.20	pa ye oil λ^{al} 246 (4.1), 276 sh (3.8)		273–4^{760} 118^5	...	1.6123^{25}	δ	s	s				B20, 424
Ωp2026	—,4-phenyl-	γ-Pyridylbenzene. $C_{11}H_9N$. See p1939	155.20	pl (w) λ^{al} 261 (4.22)	77–8	280–2^{762}			s^h	s	s				B20, 424
p2027	—,2-propyl-	Conyrine. $C_8H_{11}N$. See p1939	121.18	λ^{al} 262 (3.6)	2	166–8^{760} 60^{11}	0.9119$^{20}_4$	1.4925^{20}	δ	∞	∞	v			B20^2, 161
p2028	—,4-propyl-	$C_8H_{11}N$. See p1939	121.18			184–6 80^{20}	0.9381^{15}	1.4966^{20}	δ	v	v				B20^2, 161
—	—,3(2-pyrrolidyl)-	see Nornicotine													
p2029	—,2,3,4,6-tetra-methyl-	β-Parvoline. Parvuline. $C_9H_{13}N$. See p1939	135.21			203^{750}	0.9322$^{25}_4$	1.5087^{25}	...	s	s				C46, 5587
p2030	—,2,4,6-trihydroxy-	2,4,6-Pyridinetriol. $C_5H_5NO_3$. See p1939	127.10	ye nd or pw	230d	...	...	...	δ	s	s	s			B21, 197
p2031	—,2,3,5-trimethyl-	$C_8H_{11}N$. See p1939	121.18			186.7 (184)	0.9352$^{19}_4$	1.5057^{25}	δ	s	s	s	s		B20^2, 163
p2032	—,2,3,6-trimethyl-	$C_8H_{11}N$. See p1939	121.18	λ^{cy} 273 (3.5)		176–8^{759}	0.9220$^{25}_4$	1.5053^{20}	s^h	s	s	s	s		B20^2, 163
p2033	—,2,4,5-trimethyl-	$C_8H_{11}N$. See p1939	121.18			188^{760}	0.9330$^{25}_4$	1.5054^{25}	δ	s	s	s	s		B20^2, 164
Ωp2034	—,2,4,6-trimethyl-	γ-Collidine. sym-Collidine. $C_8H_{11}N$. See p1939	121.18	λ^{MeOH} 264 (3.58)	−44.5	170.5^{762} (175–8)	0.9166$^{20}_4$	1.4959^{25}	s δ^h	s	s	s			B20^2, 164
Ωp2035	4-Pyridinecarbox-aldehyde	Isonicotinaldehyde	107.11	λ^{al} 258 (3.35)		77.3–8.1^{12}	...	1.5423^{20}	s		s				B21, 287
Ωp2036	2-Pyridine-carboxylic acid	Picolinic acid	123.11	nd (w, al, bz) λ^{al} 264 (3.51)	136–7	sub	...	...	δ s^h	s	i		δ^h	aa v chl, CS$_2$ i	B22^2, 30
Ωp2037	—,amide	Picolinamide. $C_6H_6N_2O$. See p2036	122.13	mcl pr (w) $\lambda^{w, pH = 6}$ 265 (3.6)	107–8	...	...	...	δ	s			s	lig i	B22^2, 31
p2038	—,ethyl ester	$C_8H_9NO_2$. See p2036	151.17	ye in air $\lambda^{95\% al}$ 262 (3.55)	0–2	243 122^{13}	1.1194^{20}	1.5104^{20}	∞	∞	∞				B22^2, 31
Ωp2039	—,nitrile	Picolinonitrile. $C_6H_4N_2$. See p2036	104.11	nd or pr (eth) λ^{cy} 265 (3.44), 278 sh (2.53)	29	222–7 (212–5)	1.0810$^{25}_4$	1.5242^{25}	s	v	v		v	chl s lig δ	B22, 36
Ωp2040	3-Pyridine-carboxylic acid	Nicotinic acid. Niacin	123.11	nd (w, al) λ^{al} 257 (3.36), 262 (3.42)	236–7	sub	1.473	...	δ s^h	δ s^h	δ				B22^2, 32
Ωp2041	—,amide	Niacin amide. Nicotamide. Nicotine amide. Pellagra preventive vitamin. P. P. factor. $C_6H_6N_2O$. See p2040	122.13	wh pw, nd (bz) λ^{al} 255 (3.4), 262.5 (3.4)	129–31	150–60$^{5.10^{-4}}$	1.400	1.466	v	v	...	...		glycerol v	B22^2, 34
Ωp2042	—,—,N,N-diethyl-	Coramine. Cardiamine. $C_{10}H_{14}N_2O$. See p2040	178.24	yesh	24–6	280 d 175^{25}	1.060$^{25}_4$	1.525^{20}	∞	∞	∞	∞	...	chl ∞	B22^2, 34
p2043	—,ethyl betaine		151.17	hyg pl	84–6	...	...	...	v	δ	i		...	os i	B22, 43
Ωp2044	—,ethyl ester	$C_8H_9NO_2$. See p2040	151.17	λ^{al} 262 (3.46)	8–9.5	224^{760} 103–5^5	1.1070^{20}	1.5034^{20}	v	v	v		v		B22^2, 33
Ωp2045	—,hydrochloride	$C_6H_5NO_2$.HCl. See p2040.	159.57	pr or pl, rh bipym (w)	274				s	s					B22^2, 33
Ωp2046	—,methyl ester	$C_7H_7NO_2$. See p2040	137.14	oi λ^{al} 261 (3.4)	42–3	204 118.5^{25}			s	s	s				B22^2, 33
Ωp2047	—,nitrile	Nicotinonitrile. $C_6H_4N_2$. See p2040	104.11	nd (peth-eth, lig) λ^{cy} 265 (3.35), 279 sh (2.63)	50–2	240–5	...	...	v	v	v		v	lig δ, s^h	B22^2, 35
Ωp2048	4-Pyridine-carboxylic acid	Isonicotinic acid.	123.11	nd (w) λ^{al} 271.5 (3.41)	319 (325–6 sealed tube)	sub at 260^{15}	...	...	δ s^h	δ^h	δ		δ		B22^2, 37

For explanations, symbols and abbreviations see beginning of table. For structural formulas see end of table.

No.	Name	Synonyms and Formula	Mol. wt.	Color, crystalline form, specific rotation and λ_{max} (log ε)	m.p. °C	b.p. °C	Density	n_D	Solubility w	al	eth	ace	bz	other solvents	Ref.
	4-Pyridine carboxylic acid														
p2049	—,anhydride	$C_{12}H_8N_2O_3$. See p2048	228.22	nd	103–4 (302d sealed tube)	....	....								B22², 37
p2050	—,ethyl betaine ...	....	151.17	nd	241d	....			v	v	...	...		chl v	B22, 47
Ω p2051	—,ethyl ester	$C_8H_9NO_2$. See p2048	151.17	nd	23	220⁷⁶⁰ 110¹⁵	1.1052²⁰	1.5177²⁰	δ	s	v	...	s	chl v	B22², 37
Ω p2052	—,hydrazide......	Isoniazid. $C_6H_7N_3O$. See p2048	137.14	nd (al) λᵃˡ 263 (3.6)	171 (163)				δ	s	s	...	s		B22², 37
Ω p2053	—,methyl ester	$C_7H_7NO_2$. See p2048	137.14	λ$^{w, pH=6}$ 278 (3.44)	8.5	209⁷⁶⁰ δd 104²¹	1.1599₄²⁰	1.5135²⁰	δ	s	s	...	s		B22, 46
Ω p2054	—,nitrile	Isonicotinonitrile. $C_6H_4N_2$. See p2048	104.11	nd (lig-eth) λ^{cy} 271 (3.45) 290 sh (2.70)	83	....			s	s	s	...	s	lig δ	B22, 46
p2055	3-Pyridine-carboxylic acid, 6-amino-	$C_6H_6N_2O_2$. See p2040	138.13	cr (dil aa +2w)	312					δ				os δ	B22², 464
Ω p2056	4-Pyridine-carboxylic acid, 2,6-dihydroxy-	Citrazinic acid. $C_6H_5NO_4$. See p2048	155.11	yesh-grsh pw (w)	>330d				s^h					alk s HCl δ^h	B22, 254
p2057	3-Pyridine-carboxylic acid, 2-hydroxy-	$C_6H_5NO_3$. See p2040	139.11	nd (w) λᵃˡ 234 (3.7), 328 (3.8)	α 259–61d β 301–2d				δ s^h	δ	δ	...	...	chl i	B22², 165
p2058	—,4-hydroxy-	$C_6H_5NO_3$. See p2040	139.11	nd (w + 2), cr (al + 2w)	254–5				s^h	δ		...		chl δ	B22, 214
Ω p2059	—,6-hydroxy-	$C_6H_5NO_3$. See p2040	139.11	nd (w) λ$^{w, pH=6.8}$ 250 (4.1), 295 (3.7)	304 d	sub			δ^h	i	i	...	i	chl i	B22², 165
p2060	4-Pyridine-carboxylic acid, 3-hydroxy-5(hydroxy-methyl)-2-methyl-, lactone	$C_8H_7NO_3$. See p2048	165.15	cr (MeOH)	273–3.5d (260d)				s					MeOH δ, s^h	C43, 3045
p2061	3-Pyridine-carboxylic acid, 5-hydroxy-4(hydroxy-methyl)-6-methyl-, lactone	$C_8H_7NO_3$. See p2040	165.15	nd (al)	282–3d				s	δ s^h					C53, 21931
p2062	—,1-methyl-	Trigonelline	137.14	pr (aq al +1w) λᵃˡ 265 (3.6), 272 sh (3.5)	218d (anh) 130 (hyd)				v	δ v^h	δ	...	δ	chl δ	B22², 35
p2063	2-Pyridine-carboxylic acid, 1,2,3,6-tetrahydro-	Baikiain. $C_6H_9NO_2$. See p2036	127.14	pr (MeOH) [α]$_D^{20}$ −201.6	274d				v	δ	i	i	i	MeOH s^h AcOEt i	J1950, 3590
Ω p2064	2,3-Pyridinedicar-boxylic acid	Quinolinic acid...........	167.12	mcl pr (w) λ^{MeOH} 274 (3.57)	228–9 (191) (rapid htng)				δ	i	i	...	i	....	B22, 150
Ω p2065	2,4-Pyridinedicar-boxylic acid	Lutidinic acid.............	167.12	lf (w +1) λ^{MeOH} 219 (3.63), 258 (3.36)	248–50 (anh)		0.942		δ s^h	s^h	i	...	i	CS₂ i	B22², 105
Ω p2066	2,5-Pyridine-dicarboxylic acid	Isocinchomeronic acid	167.12	lf (w +1), (al, dil HCl) λ^{MeOH} 223 (3.97), 272.5 (3.85)	256–8d	sub			s^h	δ^h	i	...	i	HCl s^h	B22², 105
Ω p2067	2,6-Pyridine-dicarboxylic acid	Dipicolinic acid	167.12	nd (w + 1½) λ^{MeOH} 219 (3.85), 270 (3.79)	252 (anh) (228d sealed tube)	....			δ s^h	δ^h	i	...	i	aa δ	B22², 106
Ω p2068	3,4-Pyridine-dicarboxylic acid	Cinchomeronic acid	167.12	pr, nd or lf (w) λ^{MeOH} 263.5 (3.57)	262d	sub			δ^h	δ	i	...	δ	chl i	B22², 106
Ω p2069	3,5-Pyridine-dicarboxylic acid	Dinicotinic acid	167.12	cr (ac-w), pr (gl aa) λ^{MeOH} 268.5 (3.48)	325d	sub			i	...	δ			HCl s^h aa δ	B22², 107
p2070	3,4-Pyridine-dicarboxylic acid, 4,5-dihydro-2,6-dimethyl-, diethyl ester	$C_{13}H_{19}NO_4$. See p2068	253.30	bl flr, pl (eth)	85	....			i	v	s^h	s		os s lig i	B22², 98

For explanations, symbols and abbreviations see beginning of table. For structural formulas see end of table.

3,5-Pyridinedicarboxylic acid

No.	Name	Synonyms and Formula	Mol. wt.	Color, crystalline form, specific rotation and λ_{max} (log ε)	m.p. °C	b.p. °C	Density	n_D	w	al	eth	ace	bz	other solvents	Ref.
Ω p2071	3,5-Pyridine-dicarboxylic acid, 1,4-dihydro-2,6-dimethyl-, diethyl ester	$C_{13}H_{19}NO_4$. See p2069	253.30	ye nd or lf (al) λ^{al} 232 (4.3), 375 (3.8)	184–5				δ^h	s^h	δ	...	...	chl v	B22[7], 98
Ω p2072	—,1,4-dihydro-2,4,6-trimethyl-, diethyl ester	$C_{14}H_{21}NO_4$. See p2069	267.33	lt bl flr pl (al) λ^{al} 234 (4.3), 350 (3.9)	131				δ	δ v^h	δ	...	...	chl v $CS_2 \delta$	B22[2], 100
p2073	3,4-Pyridine-dicarboxylic acid, 2,6-dimethyl-, diethyl ester	$C_{13}H_{17}NO_4$. See p2068	251.29	...	16	270d 163[13]			...	...	...	...	...		B22[2], 109
Ω p2074	3,5-Pyridine-dicarboxylic acid, 2,6-dimethyl-, diethyl ester	$C_{13}H_{17}NO_4$. See p2069	251.29	nd (al), pr (eth) λ^{MeOH} 233 (4.1), 275 (3.6)	75–6 (73)	301–2 180[16]			i	s	s	...	s	chl, lig s	B22[2], 110
p2075	3,4-Pyridine-dicarboxylic acid, 5-methoxy-6-methyl-	$C_9H_9NO_5$. See p2068	211.18	cr (w-ace)	213–5				s^h	...	...	s^h	...	chl v	C40, 1636
p2076	2,4-Pyridine-dicarboxylic acid, 6-methyl-	Uvitonic acid. $C_8H_7NO_4$. See p2065	181.15	cr (w)	282d (>330)				δ	...	...	...	i	HCl s aa s^h chl δ^h CS_2 i	B22[2], 107
—	Pyridinediol	see Pyridine, dihydroxy-													
p2077	Pyridinepenta-carboxylic acid, dihydrate	....	335.18	cr (eth, w)	220d				v	δ	i	...	...		B22, 190
p2078	3-Pyridinesulfonic acid	....	159.16	orh $\lambda^{50\% al}$ 208 (3.8), 262 (3.45)	357d		1.718^{25}_{25}		v	δ	i	...	...		B22, 387
p2079	2,3,4,5-Pyridine-tetracarboxylic acid	....	255.14	cr (w + 2 or 3)	160d (−w115)				s	...	...	...	...		B22, 188
p2080	2,3,4,6-Pyridine-tetracarboxylic acid	....	255.14	nd (w + 3)	236d				v	δ	δ	...	...	aa s	B22[2], 142
p2081	2,3,5,6-Pyridine tetracarboxylic acid	....	255.14	cr (w + 2)	200d				v	...	...	...	...		B22[1], 544
p2082	2,3,4-Pyridine-tricarboxylic acid	α-Carbocinchomeronic acid	211.13	lf (w + 1½)	250 (anh)				s^h s^h	δ	i	...	i		B22[2], 136
p2083	2,3,5-Pyridine-tricarboxylic acid	Carbodinicotinic acid	211.13	pl, lf or nd (w + 2, dil al + 2w)	323 (anh)				v	δ	δ	...	...	dil al v aa δ	B22[2], 136
p2084	2,4,5-Pyridine-tricarboxylic acid	Berberonic acid	211.13	tcl pr (dil HCl + 2w) λ^{MeOH} 275 (3.04)	243 (anh) 235 (hyd)				δ s^h	δ^h	i	...	i	dil ac s chl i	B22[2], 136
p2085	2,4,6-Pyridine-tricarboxylic acid	Trimesitic acid	211.13	nd (w + 2)	227d	sub			δ s^h	δ s^h	δ	...	...		B22[2], 136
p2086	3,4,5-Pyridine-tricarboxylic acid	β-Carbocinchomeronic acid	211.13	lf or pl (w + 3), ta (w)	261d (−w115)				δ s^h	δ s	...	...	...		B22, 186
p2087	Pyridinium, 1-ethyl-, bromide	....	188.08	cr (al)	111–2				s	s	i	...	...		B20, 214
Ω p2088	—,1-hexadecyl-, chloride	....	340.00	wh pw	77–83				v	...	δ	...	δ	chl v	C51, 4370
—	Pyridone	see Pyridine, hydroxy-													
p2089	Pyridoxal, hydrochloride	....	203.63	rh λ^w 318 (3.91), 390 (2.30) $\lambda^{0.1 NHCl}$ 288 (3.93)	165d				v	...	...	...	...		C55, 17657
p2090	—,oxime	....	182.18	cr (al)	225–6d				...	s^h	...	...	...		C44, 10740
Ω p2091	Pyridoxamine, dihydrochloride	....	241.12	pl (al) λ^w 253 (3.66), 328 (3.89) $\lambda^{0.1 NHCl}$ 293 (3.93)	226–7d				v	δ s^h	...	...	...		C51, 14833
—	Pyridoxin	see Vitamin B_6													
Ω p2092	Pyrimidine	1,3-Diazin*. Miazine	80.09	λ^{al} 243 (3.47), 280 (2.57)	22	123.5–4[760]		1.4998^{20}	∞	s	...	...	...		B23, 89
Ω p2093	—,2-amino-	$C_4H_5N_3$. See p2092	95.11	nd (AcOEt) λ^{MeOH} 227 (4.22), 297 (3.59)	127–8	sub			s	...	...	...	...		B24, 80
p2094	—,4-amino-	$C_4H_5N_3$. See p2092	95.11	pl (AcOEt) λ^{MeOH} 236 (4.30), 272 (3.71)	151–2				s	s	...	...	...	AcOEt s^h	B24, 81

For explanations, symbols and abbreviations see beginning of table. For structural formulas see end of table.

No.	Name	Synonyms and Formula	Mol. wt.	Color, crystalline form, specific rotation and λ_{max} (log ε)	m.p. °C	b.p. °C	Density	n_D	w	al	eth	ace	bz	other solvents	Ref.
	Pyrimidine														
p2095	—,2-amino-4,6-dihydroxy-	$C_4H_5N_3O_2$. See p2092	127.10	pl (w + 1) λ^w 257 (4.14)	>330	....	....	....	i	i	...	...	...	ac, alk s $PhNO_2 \delta^h$	B24, 468
p2096	—,6-amino-2,4-dihydroxy-	4-Aminouracil. $C_4H_5N_3O_2$. See p2092	127.10	cr (w)	d	....	....	....	s^h	...	...	...	...	min ac v aa i	B24, 469
p2097	—,2-amino-4,5-dimethyl-	$C_6H_9N_3$. See p2092	123.16	nd (w)	214–5	sub	....	....	s^h	s	δ	s	s	chl s lig δ	B24, 91
Ω p2098	—,4-amino-2,6-dimethyl-	Kyanmethin. $C_6H_9N_3$. See p2092	123.16	nd (al), pl (bz) λ^{al} 235 (4.02), 267 (3.62)	183 (191–2)	sub	....	....	δ	δ s^h	...	...	δ s^h		B24, 89
p2099	—,6-amino-4,5-dimethyl-	$C_6H_9N_3$. See p2092	123.16	nd (w)	230	....	....	....	s^h	s^h	δ	s	s	chl s lig i	B24, 92
Ω p2100	—,2-amino-4-methyl-	$C_5H_7N_3$. See p2092	109.13	pl (w), nd (sub) $\lambda^{w, pH = 6.8}$ 290 (3.6)	159–60	sub	....	....	s^h	s	i	s^h		lig s^h	B24, 84
p2101	—,2-amino-5-methyl-	$C_5H_7N_3$. See p2092	109.13	pl (sub), pr (w)	193.5	sub	....	....	s^h	s	i	s	s^h	lig s^h	B24, 87
p2102	—,4-amino-2-methyl-	$C_5H_7N_3$. See p2092	109.13	rh (ace)	205	....	....	....	v	s	...	s	s		B24, 84
p2103	—,4-amino-5-methyl-	$C_5H_7N_3$. See p2092	109.13	pl (al, AcOEt)	176	....	....	....	v	s^h	δ	...	s	AcOEt s^h chl, peth, lig δ	B24, 87
p2104	—,4-amino-6-methyl-	$C_5H_7N_3$. See p2092	109.13	pr (w), nd, lf (sub) $\lambda^{w, pH = 13}$ 234 (3.95), 264 (3.45)	197–7.5	sub	....	....	s	s	...	...	...		B24, 85
Ω p2105	—,2-amino-5-nitro-	$C_4H_4N_4O_2$. See p2092	140.10	nd (al) λ^w 317.5 (4.18)	236–7	....	....	....	δ	s	i	s	i	alk s chl i	B24[1], 231
p2106	—,2-chloro-4(dimethyl-amino)-6-methyl-	$C_7H_{10}ClN_3$. See p2092	171.63	br wx so	87	140–7[4]	....	....	i	s	...	...	...		C36, 911
Ω p2107	—,2,4-dichloro-5-methyl-	$C_5H_4Cl_2N_2$. See p2092	163.01	pl (al)	25–7	235[759]	....	....	δ	v	v	...	v	chl v	B23, 93
p2108	—,2,4-dichloro-6-methyl-	$C_5H_4Cl_2N_2$. See p2092	163.01	nd (lig)	46–7	219	....	....	δ	v	v	...	v	chl v lig s^h	B23, 92
p2109	—,2-hydroxy-, hydrochloride	2-Pyrimidone hydrochloride. $C_4H_4N_2O.HCl$. See p2092	132.55	rods (al)	205	....	....	....	v	s^h	...	...	...		B24[1], 231
p2110	—,2-methyl-	$C_5H_6N_2$. See p2092	94.12	λ^{hx} 245 (3.39), 249 (3.43), 255 (3.24), 295 (2.55)	−4	138[758]	....	....	∞						B23, 92
p2111	—,4(methyl-amino)-	$C_5H_7N_3$. See p2092	109.13	lf (al), nd (peth) $\lambda^{w, pH = 2.1}$ 254 (4.20)	74–5	142–4[16]	....	....	v	s^h	s^h	...	...		B24[2], 28
—	2,4-Pyrimidine-dione	see **Uracil**													
—	2(1)-Pyrimidone, 4-amino-	see **Cytosine**													
p2112	Pyrocalciferol	9α-Lumisterol. $C_{28}H_{44}O$	396.67	nd (MeOH), $[\alpha]_D^{20}$ + 512 (al) λ^{al} 274 (2.44), 284.5 (2.45), 296 (2.47)	93–5	....	....	....	i	s	...	...	...	chl s MeOH s^h	E14, 77
—	Pyrocatechol	see **Benzene, 1,2-dihydroxy-***													
—	o-Pyrocatechuic acid	see **Benzoic acid, 2,3-dihydroxy-**													
—	Pyrocinchonic acid, anhydride	see **Maleic acid, dimethyl-, anhydride**													
p2113	Pyrocoll	....	186.17	ye mcl pl (aa)	268	sub	....	....	i	δ	δ	...	δ	chl s aa δ, s^h	B24[1], 360
—	Pyrogallol	see **Benzene, 1,2,3-trihydroxy-***													
—	Pyrogallo-phthalein	see **Gallein**													
—	Pyromellitic acid	see **1,2,4,5-Benzenetetra-carboxylic acid***													
—	Pyromucic acid	see **2-Furancarboxylic acid**													
p2114	4-Pyrone	4H-Pyran-4-one. 4-Oxo-1,4-pyran. γ-Pyrone.	96.09	hyg cr λ^{MeOH} 246 (4.2)	32.5	215–7[742] 105[23]	1.190	1.5238	v	s	v	...	s	aa, chl v peth, CS_2 δ	B17, 271
p2116	2-Pyrone, 4,6-dimethyl-	5-Hydroxy-3-methyl-2,4-hexadienoic acid lactone.* Mesitenlactone.	124.15	lf (eth)	51.5	245 126[11]	....	....	v	v	s	...	...	CS_2 δ	B17, 291
p2117	4-Pyrone, 2,6-dimethyl-	$C_7H_8O_2$. See p2114	124.15	pl, nd (sub) λ^{MeOH} 208 (3.81), 245 (4.09)	132	248–9[713] 139–40[25] sub	0.9953[137]	....	s	s	s	s			B17[2], 315
p2118	2-Pyrone, 3-hydroxy-	2,5-Dihydroxy-2,4-hexadienoic acid 5-lactone*. Isopyromucic acid.	112.09	nd (w + 2)	95 (anh) 80–5 (hyd)	112[20]	....	....	s	s	s	...	s^h	chl s lig s^h CS_2 δ	B17[1], 233

For explanations, symbols and abbreviations see beginning of table. For structural formulas see end of table.

No.	Name	Synonyms and Formula	Mol. wt.	Color, crystalline form, specific rotation and λ_{max} (log ε)	m.p. °C	b.p. °C	Density	n_D	w	al	eth	ace	hz	other solvents	Ref.
	4-Pyrone														
p2119	4-Pyrone, 5-hydroxy-2(hydroxymethyl)-	Kojic acid. $C_6H_6O_4$. See p2114	142.11	nd, pr (ace) λ^{al} 268 (3.92)	153–5	sub	....	....	δ s^h	s	s	s^h	δ	AcOEt, chl, Py s aa δ	B18[2], 57
p2120	—,3-hydroxy-2-methyl-	Larixinic acid. Maltol. $C_6H_6O_3$. See p2114	126.11	red mcl pr (chl), bipym pr (50 % al, sub), nd (to)	162–4	sub at 93	....	....	δ v^h	...	δ	...	δ	chl v alk, ac s aa δ peth i	B17[2], 450
—	2-Pyrone-5-carboxylic acid	see **Coumalic acid**													
p2121	4-Pyrone-2-carboxylic acid, 5,6-dihydro-6,6-dimethyl-, butyl ester	Butopyronoxyl. Indalone...	226.28	ye or pa red-br λ^{al} 283 (4.00)	....	256–70 113–4[14]	1.052[25]	1.4745[25]	i	∞	∞		∞	chl ∞	C53, 6145
p2122	,5-hydroxy-.....	Comenic acid	156.10	ye cr λ^w 224 (4.32), 290 (3.76)	>270d		....	....	s^h	i s^h					B18[2], 352
—	4-Pyrone-2,6-dicarboxylic acid	see **Chelidonic acid**													
p2123	Pyrophosphoric acid, tetraamide, octamethyl-	OMPA. Scharadan. $[(CH_3)_2N]_4P_2O_3$	286.25			118–22[0.3]	1.1343[25]	1.462[25]	s	s				chl s	C52, 243
p2124	—,tetraethyl ester..	$(C_2H_5O)_4P_2O_3$	290.19			155[3] 104–10[0.08]	1.1847[20 4]	1.4180[20]	$\infty^{\delta d}$	∞	∞	∞		chl, xyl lig i ∞	B1[3], 1330
p2125	—,dithiono-, tetraethyl ester	Sulfotep. $(C_2H_5O)_4P_2OS_2$...	322.32	col oil	....	136–9[2] 110–3[0.2]	1.196[25]	1.4753[25]	i	s				....	C51, 8641
—	Pyrotartaric acid...	see **Succinic acid, methyl-**													
—	Pyrrocoline, octahydro-	see **Piperolidine**													
Ω p2126	Pyrrole	Azole*	67.09	λ^{cy} 324 (4.47)	....	130–1[761]	0.9691[20 4]	1.5085[20]	δ	s	s	s	s	....	B20, 159
p2127	—,1-acetyl-	C_6H_7NO. See p2126....	109.13	λ^{al} 238.5 (4.03), 288sh (2.88)		181–2			i	...	...	...		HCl d	B20, 165
p2128	—,2-acetyl-	C_6H_7NO. See p2126.	109.13	mcl nd (w) λ^{MeOH} 251 (3.61), 290 (2.41)	90	220[760]			s	s	s				B21[2], 236
p2129	—,1-benzyl-	$C_{11}H_{11}N$. See p2126....	157.22	λ^{al} 208 (4.14)	15	247 138[27]		1.5655[24]	i	v	v				B20[1], 39
p2130	—,1-butyl-	$C_8H_{13}N$. See p2126.	123.20	oil	....	170–1[760] 53–4[11]		1.4727[20]							B20[2], 83
—	,dihydro-	see **Pyrroline**													
p2131	—,2,4-dimethyl-	C_6H_9N. See p2126.	95.15	pa bl flr λ^{al} 218 (3.67)	....	171 62–3[10]	0.9236[20 4]	1.5048[20]	δ	v	v	...	v	aa δ	B20, 172
p2132	—,2,5-dimethyl-	C_6H_9N. See p2126.	95.15	λ^w 212 (3.89)	....	170–2[765] (165) 50–3[8]	0.9353[20 4]	1.5036[20]	i	v	v			chl s	B20, 173
p2133	—,2,3-dimethyl-4-ethyl-	Hemopyrrole. $C_8H_{13}N$. See p2126	123.20	....	16–7	198[725] 113[16]	0.915[20]	....	v^h						B20[2], 91
Ω p2134	—,2,4-dimethyl-3-ethyl-	Kryptopyrrole. $C_8H_{13}N$. See p2126	123.20	pr λ^{al} 213 (3.85)	0	197[710] 96[16]	0.913[20 4]	1.4961[20]	δ	s	s	...	s	chl s	B20[2], 91
p2135	—,1,3-diphenyl-	$C_{16}H_{13}N$. See p2126.	219.29	pl (al)	122–3	....			s^h	v	v		v	chl s	B20[1], 148
Ω p2136	—,2,5-diphenyl-	$C_{16}H_{13}N$. See p2126.	219.29	lf (aa, dil al) λ^{al} 230 (4.08), 325 (4.42), 330 (4.43)	143.5	....			i	v	v		v	chl s aa v HCl δ (red) alk i	B20[2], 313
p2137	—,1-ethyl-	C_6H_9N. See p2126	95.15		....	129–30[762]	0.9009[20]	1.4841[20]	i	s					B20, 163
p2138	—,2-ethyl-	C_6H_9N. See p2126	95.15		....	163–5[760] 59–60[15]	0.9042[20 4]	1.4942[20]	i	s					B20[2], 85
p2139	—,3-ethyl-4-methyl-	Opsopyrrole. $C_7H_{11}N$. See p2126	109.17	ye oil	3	70[11]	0.9059[20 4]	1.4913[20]	i	s	s				B20[2], 89
p2140	—,3-ethyl-2,4,5-trimethyl-	Phyllopyrrole. $C_9H_{15}N$. See p2126	137.23	pl (sub), lf (eth), wh lf (peth)	67.5–8.5	213[725] 92–3[12]			i	s	s			lig δ	B20[2], 93
p2141	—,2-isopropyl-	$C_7H_{11}N$. See p2126.	109.17	....		171–2[741]	0.908[25]	1.491[25]	i	s	s				B20[2], 89
Ω p2142	—,1-methyl-	C_5H_7N. See p2126.	81.12	....		114–5[747] (cor)	0.9145[15 4]	1.4875[20]	i	∞	∞				B20, 163
p2143	—,2-methyl-	C_5H_7N. See p2126.	81.12	....		147–8[750]	0.9446[15]	1.503[16]	i	∞	∞				B20[2], 170
p2144	—,3-methyl-	C_5H_7N. See p2126.	81.12	....		142–3[743] 45[11]		1.4970[20]		∞	∞				B20[2], 85 B21[2], 767
—	,oxo(tetrahydro)-	see **Pyrrolidone**													
Ω p2145	—,1-phenyl-	$C_{10}H_9N$. See p2126.	143.19	pl (sub) red in air	62	234 140[38] sub			i	s	s	s	s	peth v chl s	B20[2], 83
p2146	—,2-phenyl-	$C_{10}H_9N$. See p2126.	143.19	pl (al, sub) $\lambda^{95\%al}$ 290 (4.03)	129	271–2[726]			i	v	v	...	v	chl v lig δ	B20[2], 238

For explanations, symbols and abbreviations see beginning of table. For structural formulas see end of table.

Pyrrole

No.	Name	Synonyms and Formula	Mol. wt.	Color, crystalline form, specific rotation and λ_{max} (log ε)	m.p. °C	b.p. °C	Density	n_D	w	al	eth	ace	bz	other solvents	Ref.
p2147	—,1-propyl-	$C_7H_{11}N$. See p2126	109.17			145.5–6.5	0.8833_4^{20}		i	s	s				B20[1], 44
—	—,tetrahydro	see Pyrrolidine													
p2148	—,2,3,4,5-tetra-iodo-	Iodol. C_4HI_4N. See p2126	570.68	ye nd (al)	150d (162–4d)				i	s[h]	s	s		chl, aa s	B20[2], 84
p2149	—,2,3,4,5-tetra-methyl-	$C_8H_{13}N$. See p2126	123.20	lf (dil al, peth) λ^{al} 219 (3.74)	111	130[7]				∞	∞	∞	v	peth s[h]	B20[2], 92
p2150	2-Pyrrolcarboxaldehyde	2-Formylpyrrole	95.10	rh pr (peth) λ^{chl} 220 (3.9), 240 (3.9), 255 (3.9), 290 (4.7)	46–7	217–9 114[15]		1.5939[16]						os v lig δ, s[h]	B21[2], 236
p2151	2-Pyrrolecarboxylic acid		111.10	lf (w) λ^{al} 262 (4.08)	208.5d				s	s	s				B22[2], 15
p2152	—,4-acetyl-3,5-dimethyl, ethyl ester	$C_{11}H_{15}NO_3$. See p2151	209.25	wh nd (al) λ^{al} 235 (4.36), 255sh (4.08), 283 (4.07)	143–4				i	δ					B27[2], 233
p2152[1]	3-Pyrrolecarboxylic acid		111.10	nd (lig) λ^{al} 245 (3.68)	161–2										C50, 7830
p2153	2-Pyrrolecarboxylic acid, 3,5-dimethyl-, ethyl ester	$C_9H_{13}NO_2$. See p2151	167.21	cr (al) 240 sh (3.70), 276 (4.29)	125					s		s		os s	B22[2], 21
p2154	3-Pyrrolecarboxylic acid, 2,4-dimethyl-, ethyl ester	$C_9H_{13}NO_2$. See p2152[1]	167.21	cr (eth-lig or peth)	78–9	291 181–2[35]			δ	v	v			peth s[h]	B22[2], 18
p2155	—,2,5-dimethyl-, ethyl ester	$C_9H_{13}NO_2$. See p2152[1]	167.21	rh (al)	117–8	290[731] 130[15]			i	s				os s dil ac, alk i	B22[2], 22
p2156	—,4,5-dimethyl-, ethyl ester	$C_9H_{13}NO_2$. See p2152[1]	167.21	cr (dil al)	110–1				δ	v	v			chl v	B22[2], 20
p2156[1]	2,4-Pyrroledi-carboxylic acid		155.11	cr (w)	295d				s[h]						B22[1], 525
p2157	—,3,5-dimethyl-, diethyl ester	$C_{12}H_{17}NO_4$. See p2156[1]	239.27	lo nd (dil al) λ^{al} 221 (4.44), 273 (4.22)	136–7				i	δ	δ	s	s	chl, aa s lig δ	B22[2], 94
p2158	—,3,5-dimethyl-1-ethyl-, diethyl ester	$C_{14}H_{21}NO_4$. See p2156[1]	267.33	cr (dil al) λ^{chl} 275 (4.2),	40.5–1.3				δ	s[h]					C52, 3866
p2159	—,5-formyl-3-methyl-, diethyl ester	$C_{12}H_{15}NO_5$. See p2156[1]	253.26	nd λ^{al} 237 (4.33), 270 (3.88), 308 (4.04)	124–5				i	s				to s lig i	B22[2], 278
Ω p2160	Pyrrolidine	1-Azacyclopentane. Tetra-hydropyrrole. Tetra-methylenimine.	71.12	λ^{gas} 171 (3.4), 196 (3.3)		88.5–9[760]	0.8520_4^{22}	1.4431[20]	∞	s	s			chl s	B20[2], 3
p2161	—,1-butyl-	$C_8H_{17}N$. See p2160	127.23			154–5[758]	0.816^{25}	1.4373[25]	δ	s				os s	B20[2], 4
p2162	—,2-butyl-	$C_8H_{17}N$. See p2160	127.23			173.5–4.5[741] 67[18]	0.8277_4^{20}	1.4490[20]	s δ[h]	∞				os ∞	B20[2], 65
p2163	—,1(chloro-acetyl)-	$C_6H_{10}ClNO$. See p2160	147.61		44–6	112[0.5]									C51, 1171
p2164	—,1,2-dimethyl-	$C_6H_{13}N$. See p2160	99.18			96[760]	0.7994_4^{20}	1.4252[20]	∞	v	v				B20[2], 55
p2165	—,2,4-dimethyl-	$C_6H_{13}N$. See p2160	99.18			115–7[760]	0.8297_4^{20}	1.4325[20]	v	v	v				B20, 102
p2166	—,2,5-dimethyl- (cis)	$C_6H_{13}N$. See p2160	99.18			106–6.7[760]	0.8205_4^{20}	1.4299[20]	∞	∞	∞				B20[2], 60
Ω p2167	—,1-methyl-	$C_5H_{11}N$. See p2160	85.15			81–3[760]	0.8188_4^{20}	1.4247[20]	∞		s				B20[2], 4
—	—,oxo-	see Pyrrolidone													
p2168	—,1-phenyl-	$C_{10}H_{13}N$. See p2160	147.22	λ^{iso} 260 (4.27)		119–20.5[12] 110–6[9]	1.0260^{25}	1.5813[20]			s				C53, 1338
—	2-Pyrrolidine carboxylic acid	see Proline													
Ω p2169	2-Pyrrolidone	γ-Butyrolactam. 2-Oxopyr-rolidine.	85.11	cr (peth)	24.6	250.5[742] 133[12]	1.120_4^{20}	1.4806[30]	v	v			v	CS_2, chl v	B21[2], 213
Ω p2170	—,1,5-dimethyl-	N-Methyl-γ-valerolactam. $C_6H_{11}NO$. See p2169	113.16			215–7[743] 87.5[10]		1.4650[20]	∞		∞				B21, 239
p2171	—,3,3-dimethyl-	$C_6H_{11}NO$. See p2169	113.16	lf (bz)	65–7	237			v	v	s	s	v[h]		B21, 242
Ω p2172	—,1-methyl-	C_5H_9NO. See p2169	99.13	λ^{MeOH} 205 (3.46)	−23	202[760] 845[14]	1.0260_{25}^{25}	1.4684[20]	v		s	s		os s	B21[2], 213
p2173	3-Pyrroline	Dihydropyrrole	69.11			90–1[760]	0.9097_4^{20}	1.4664[20]	s	∞	∞				B20[2], 67
—	Pyruvaldehyde	see Propanal, 2-oxo-*													
—	Pyruvic acid	see Propanoic acid, 2-oxo-*													
—	Pyruvonitrile	see Propanoic acid, 2-oxo-, nitrile													

For explanations, symbols and abbreviations see beginning of table. For structural formulas see end of table.

No.	Name	Synonyms and Formula	Mol. wt.	Color, crystalline form, specific rotation and λ_{max} (log ε)	m.p. °C	b.p. °C	Density	n_D	w	al	eth	ace	bz	other solvents	Ref.
	Quaterphenyl														
Ω q1	o,o'-Quaterphenyl	o,o'-Diphenylbiphenyl	306.41	pr (al) λ^{hx} 203.5 (4.73), 227 (4.50), 248 sh (4.35)	118–9	420			i	δ	s	s	s	MeOH δ chl v aa s	B5², 669
Ω q2	p,p'-Quaterphenyl	Tetraphenyl	306.41	lf (bz) λ^{hx} 206.5 (4.82), 294 (4.64)	320	428[18]			i	i	i	...	s^h	chl i aa s^h PhNO₂ s	B5², 669
—	Quercitin	see Flavone, 3,3',4',5,7-pentahydroxy-													
—	Quercitol	see 1,2,3,4,5-Cyclohexane-pentol*													
q3	Quercitrin	Quercetin 3-rhamnoside. C₂₁H₂₀O₁₁.	448.39	pa ye nd or pl (+2w, dil al) [α]₅₇₈ −73.5 (al, c = 4) λ^{al} 258 (4.30), 350 (4.18)	182 5 (hyd) 250–2 (anh)				s^h i	s	i	...	...	aa s^h MeOH s AcOEt i alk s (ye)	B31, 75
q4	Quillaic acid	Quillaja sapogenin. C₃₀H₄₆O₅.	486.70	nd (dil al) $[α]_D^{20}$ +56.1 (Py, c = 2.9)	294				i	s	s	s	...	Py, aa s	B10², 737
q5	Quinacrine, dihydrochloride (dl)	Atebrine. C₂₃H₃₀ClN₃O. 2HCl. 2H₂O	508.90	yesh nd (w), ye cr pw $\lambda^{w, pH=6.5}$ 343 (3.7), 424 (3.9), 444 (3.9)	248–50d				s v^h	δ	ι	i	i	MeOH s	C28, 2126
—	Quinaldine	see Quinoline, 2-methyl-													
—	Quinaldinic acid	see 2-Quinolinecarboxylic acid													
—	Quinalizarin	see 9,10-Anthraquinone, 1,2,5,8-tetrahydroxy-													
q6	Quinamine	C₁₉H₂₄N₂O₂	312.42	pr (bz), nd (80 % al) $[α]_D^{15}$ +93 (chl, c = 2), $[α]_D^{15}$ +105 (al, c = 2) λ^{al} 245 (4.0), 299 (3.4)	185–6 (172)				i	v^h	s	s	v^h	lig v	B27², 667
Ω q7	Quinazoline	1,3-Benzodiazine. Benzo(a)-pyrimidine.	130.15	ye pl (peth) λ^{cy} 218 (4.64), 259 (3.43), 267 (3.45), 303 (3.29), 312 (3.32)	48.0–8.5	241.5[764] 117 20[15]			v	s	s	s	s	oos v	B23, 175
q8	—,3,4-dihydro-4-oxo-	Quinazolinone. C₈H₆N₂O. See q7	146.15	nd (dil aa)	216–8	360			s^h	s^h		...	...		B24, 143
q9	—,3,4-dihydro-2-phenyl-	C₁₄H₁₂N₂. See q7	208.27	lf (dil al)	142					v	v			chl v aa v	B23, 239
q10	—,3,4-dihydro-3-phenyl-	Orexin. Phenzoline. Cedra-rine. C₁₄H₁₂N₂. See q7	208.27	pl (eth-lig)	96	d	1.290[4]		i	v	v		v	chl, CS₂ v	B23², 155
q11	—,3,4-dihydro-4-phenyl-	C₁₄H₁₂N₂. See q7	208.27	pl (al, AcOEt)	166–7				i	v	v				B23, 239
q12	—,2,4-dihydroxy-6,8-dinitro-	C₈H₄N₄O₆. See q7	252.15	ye gr pr (aa)	274–5d				s^h	δ	δ		δ	chl δ aa s^h	B24¹, 344
Ω q13	—,2,4-dioxo-1,2,3,4-tetra-hydro-	2,4-Quinazolinedione. Benzoyleneurea. C₈H₆N₂O₂. See q7	162.15	nd (w, al), lf (aa) λ^{al} 217 (4.63), 310 (3.56)	356(cor)				$δ^h$	δ	δ			alk s	B24², 197
Ω q14	Quinhydrone	Benzoquinhydrone	218.21	red br nd $\lambda^{w, pH=2.5}$ 440 (2.95)	171	sub	1.401₄²⁰		s^h δ	v	v			chl δ lig, peth i	B7², 572
—	Quinic acid	see Cyclohexanecarboxylic acid, 1,3,4,5-tetra-hydroxy-*													
q15	Quinicine	Quinotoxin. C₂₀H₂₄N₂O₂	324.43	red ye amor $[α]_D^{15}$ +44.1 (chl) λ 256, 344	ca. 60				δ	v	v			chl v	B25², 20
q16	—,oxalate(d)	(C₂₀H₂₄N₂O₂)₂. H₂C₂O₄. 9H₂O See q15	901.03	pr (19w, chl), nd (al), $[α]_D^{13}$ +19.5 (al-chl) (+9.5(w))	149				v^h	s				chl v	B25, 39
q17	Quinidine	C₂₀H₂₄N₂O₂	324.43	cr (+2.5w, dil al) cr (+1 al, al) $[α]_D^{15}$ +230 (chl, c = 1.8) +262 (al, c = 1) λ^{MeOH} 230 (4.53), 280 (3.54), 336 (3.69)	174–5 (anh)				δ	s	δ	...	s	chl v peth i MeOH δ	B23², 414

For explanations, symbols and abbreviations see beginning of table. For structural formulas see end of table.

No.	Name	Synonyms and Formula	Mol. wt.	Color, crystalline form, specific rotation and λ_{max} (log ε)	m.p. °C	b.p. °C	Density	n_D	w	al	eth	ace	bz	other solvents	Ref.
	Quinidine														
q18	—,hydrate.......	Conquinine. $C_{20}H_{24}N_2O_2 \cdot 2\frac{1}{2}H_2O$. *See* q17	369.47	cr (dil al)	171.5d (168)	....	....		δ	s	s	...	v	chl s	B23², 414
q19	—,bisulfate.....	$C_{20}H_{24}N_2O_2 \cdot H_2SO_4 \cdot 4H_2O$. *See* q17	494.57	pr, nd (w) flr in sol, $[\alpha]_D + 184$ (chl)	....				s	v	δ				M, 887
q20	—,hydrochloride ..	$C_{20}H_{24}N_2O_2 \cdot HCl \cdot H_2O$. *See* q17	378.91	pr (w), $[\alpha]_D^{20} + 200$ (w, c = 1)	258–9d (anh)				s^h	s^h	i	...	...	chl s	M, 887
q21	—,sulfate(d)......	$(C_{20}H_{24}N_2O_2)_2 \cdot H_2SO_4 \cdot 2H_2O$. *See* q17	782.97	pr, nd (w) sol flr bl, $[\alpha]_D^{25} + 212$ (al)	....				s	v	δ	...	...	chl s	B23², 415
Ω q22	**Quinine**	$C_{20}H_{24}N_2O_2 \cdot 3H_2O$.	378.47	cr (+3w, eth), nd (+3w, al) rh nd (abs al) $[\alpha]_D^{15} - 145.2$ (al), $[\alpha]_D^{57} - 117$ (chl, c = 1.5) λ^w 347.5 (3.74)	57 (hyd) 177 (anh)	sub		1.625	δ	v	s	δ	δ	Py, MeOH v chl s peth i	B23¹, 166
q23	—,bisulfate.......	$C_{20}H_{24}N_2O_2 \cdot H_2SO_4 \cdot 7H_2O$. *See* q22	548.62	pr (+w, w) pr (+5w, al) $[\alpha]_D^{15} + 168.4$ (w)	160d				i	δ	δ	...	...	chl s	B23, 522
Ω q24	—,o-ethyl carbonate	$C_{23}H_{28}N_2O_4$. *See* q22	396.49	nd (w), cr (dil al)	95 (91)	....			δ	v	v	...	...	chl v	B23², 424
q25	—,formate .⸱.....	Quinoform. $C_{20}H_{24}N_2O_2 \cdot HCOOH$. *See* q22	370.45	nd, $[\alpha]_D^{20} - 144.2$ (w, c = 1)	149–50 (anh) 126 (+1w)				s	s	δ	...	...	chl s CCl_4 δ	B23¹, 169
Ω q26	—,hydrobromide ..	$C_{20}H_{24}N_2O_2 \cdot HBr \cdot H_2O$. *See* q22	423.36	silky efflor nd λ^w 332 (3.70)	*ca.* 200 softens at 152	....			s	v	δ	...	...	chl v	B23¹, 168
q27	—,hydrochloride ..	$C_{20}H_{24}N_2O_2 \cdot HCl$. *See* q22..	360.89	silky efflor nd (w), $[\alpha]_D^{15} - 145$ (al) $\lambda^{w,0.02NHCl}$ 249 (4.5), 310 (3.6), 345 (3.7)	158–60 (anh)				s	v	δ	...	...	chl, alk s	M, 891
Ω q28	—,hydrochloride hydrate	$C_{20}H_{24}N_2O_2 \cdot HCl \cdot 2H_2O$. *See* q22	396.92	silky efflor nd (w), $[\alpha]_D^{20} - 149.8$ (w, c = 1.3) λ^{al} 278 (3.40), 331 (3.51)	156–90 (120)				v	v	δ	...	...	chl v	B23, 168
q29	—,2-hydroxy-benzoate	Quinine salicylate. $C_{20}H_{24}N_2O_2 \cdot C_7H_6O_3 \cdot H_2O$ *See* q22	480.55	wh pr (al) cr (+2w, w)	195	....			δ	v	δ	...	...	chl, glycerol v	B23, 526
q30	—,pentanoate.....	Quinine valerate. $C_{20}H_{24}N_2O_2 \cdot CH_3(CH_2)_3COOH \cdot H_2O$. *See* q22	444.58	wh	*ca.* 95				δ	v	v	...	...		M, 892
q31	—,sulfate........	$2(C_{20}H_{24}N_2O_2) \cdot H_2SO_4$. *See* q22	746.93	silky nd (w)	235.2	....			s^h	s	δ	...	i	chl i	B23, 522
Ω q32	—,sulfate dihydrate	$2(C_{20}H_{24}N_2O_2) \cdot H_2SO_4 \cdot 2H_2O$. *See* q22	782.97	silky nd (w) $[\alpha]_D^{15} - 220$ (0.5N HCl) λ^w 274	205				s^h	s	δ	...	...	chl δ	B23, 522
—	**Quininic acid**	*see* **4-Quinolinecarboxylic acid, 6-methoxy-**													
q33	**Quininone**	$C_{20}H_{22}N_2O_2$............	322.41	nd, lf (eth) $[\alpha]_D^{20} + 75.5$ (al, c = 2)	108 (rapid htng) 101 (slow htng)				i	v	v	...	v	chl v peth i	B25², 23
—	**Quinitol**	*see* **1,4-Cyclohexanediol***													
—	**Quinizarin**	*see* **9,10-Anthraquinone, 1,4-dihydroxy-***													
Ω q34	**Quinoline**	1-Benzazine*. Benzo[b]-pyridine.	129.16	λ^w 275 (3.51), 299 (3.46), 312 (3.52)	fr −15.6	238.05⁷⁶⁰ 114¹⁷	1.0929²⁰	1.6268²⁰	s^h i	∞	∞	∞	∞	CS_2 ∞	B20², 222
q35	—,hydrochloride ..	Quinolinium chloride. $C_9H_7N \cdot HCl$. *See* q34	165.63	pr (+½w, w) λ^w 233 (4.5), 312 (3.9)	94 (hyd) 134.5 (anh)				v	s	s^h	...	s^h	chl s	B20², 226
q36	—,hydrogen sulfate	Quinolinium bisulfate. $C_9H_7N \cdot H_2SO_4$. *See* q34	227.24	cr (al, aa)	164–4.5				s	s^h		...		aa s^h	B20², 226
Ω q37	—,3-acetamido-	$C_{11}H_{10}N_2O$. *See* q34	186.22	cr (w)	166–7				δ	s					B22², 352
q38	—,4-acetamido-	$C_{11}H_{10}N_2O$. *See* q34	186.22	nd (w + 1) λ^{al} 227 (4.65), 299 (3.98), 314 (3.85)	176 (anh)	sub			δ	s	...	...	...		B22, 445

For explanations, symbols and abbreviations see beginning of table. For structural formulas see end of table.

Quinoline

No.	Name	Synonyms and Formula	Mol. wt.	Color, crystalline form, specific rotation and λ_{max} (log ε)	m.p. °C	b.p. °C	Density	n_D	w	al	eth	ace	bz	other solvents	Ref.
q39	—,5-acetamido-	$C_{11}H_{10}N_2O$. See q34	186.22	pl (w), pr (dil al)	178				δ	s					B22[2], 353
q40	—,6-acetamido-	$C_{11}H_{10}N_2O$. See q34	186.22	nd (w)	138				v^h	v	δ		s^h		B22[2], 355
q41	—,7-acetamido-	$C_{11}H_{10}N_2O$. See q34	186.22	cr (w, al)	167.5				s^h	s^h					B22[2], 356
q42	,8-acetamido-	$C_{11}H_{10}N_2O$. See q34	186.22	nd (al)	103					s^h					B22[1], 640
Ω q43	—,2-amino-	α-Quinolylamine. $C_9H_8N_2$. See q34	144.19	lf (w) $\lambda^{95\%\,al}$ 219 (4.60), 314 (3.70)	131.5	sub			v^h	s	s	s	δ	chl, aa s	B22[2], 350
q44	—,3-amino- (stable form)	β-Quinolylamine. $C_9H_8N_2$. See q34	144.19	rh (w, dil al)	94				δ	v	v			chl v	B22[2], 352
q45	—,— (unstable form)	$C_9H_8N_2$. See q34	144.19	mcl cr (to) $\lambda^{95\%\,al}$ 242 (4.48), 350 (3.60)	84				δ	v	v			chl v	B22[2], 352
q46	—,4-amino-	γ-Quinolylamine. $C_9H_8N_2 \cdot H_2O$. See q34	144.19	nd (w + 1), nd (dil al, bz) λ^{al} 233 (4.28), 320 (4.01)	70 (hyd) 154 (anh)	180[12-3]				s	v	v^h	s^h	chl s CS_2 δ	B22[2], 353
Ω q47	—,5-amino-	5-Quinolylamine. $C_9H_8N_2$. See q34	144.19	ye nd (al), lf (eth) λ^{al} 252 (4.42), 352 (3.46)	110	310 sub 184[10]			δ	v	v		s	MeOH s lig i	B22[2], 353
q48	,6-amino-	6-Quinolylamine. $C_9H_8N_2$. See q34	144.19	cr (w + 2), pr (eth) λ^{al} 245 (4.61), 285 (3.64), 355 (3.65)	114 (anh)	187[11] 146[0.3]			δ	s	δ			NH_3 s	B22[2], 355
q49	—,7-amino-	7-Quinolylamine. $C_9H_8N_2$. See q34	144.19	ye nd (+1w) λ^{al} 246 (4.63), 285 (3.70), 354 (3.68)	93.5–94 (anh) 74–75.5 (hyd)					s				ac s	B22[2], 355
q50	,8-amino-	8-Quinolylamine. $C_9H_8N_2$. See q34	144.19	pa ye nd (sub), cr (al, lig) λ^{al} 250 (4.44), 340 (3.48)	70 (65)	157–8[19]			s	s					B22[2], 356
q51	—,2-amino-4-hydroxy-	$C_9H_8N_2O$. See q34	160.19	nd (w + 1), rh (al)	303–4					δ s^h			δ	AcOEt, chl δ alk, ac s	B22[1], 653
q52	—,5-amino-6-hydroxy-	$C_9H_8N_2O$. See q34	160.19	gr nd (w + 2)	185 (anh)				s^h	v	δ		δ	chl δ	B22, 501
q53	—,5-amino-8-hydroxy-	$C_9H_8N_2O$. See q34	160.19	nd (bz)	143				d^h	d^h			δ		B22[1], 653
q54	—,7-amino-8-hydroxy-	$C_9H_8N_2O$. See q34	160.19	br pr (eth, dil al) λ^{hp} 260 (4.7), 345 (3.5)	124				i	s	s		s	chl s	B22[2], 417
Ω q55	—,8-amino-6-methoxy-	$C_{10}H_{10}N_2O$. See q34	174.20	cr	41	137–8[1]									B22[2], 413
q56	—,2-amino-4-methyl-	2-Aminolepidine. $C_{10}H_{10}N_2$. See q34	158.21	cr pw (bz)	133	320			δ^h	v	v		v^h	chl, aa v	B22[2], 364
q57	—,3-amino-2-methyl-	3-Aminoquinaldine. $C_{10}H_{10}N_2$. See q34	158.21	pa ye nd (eth, peth)	160–0.5	278[760] δd 198[16]			i	s	v		v	chl v	B22[2], 359
Ω q58	—,4-amino-2-methyl-	4-Aminoquinaldine. $C_{10}H_{10}N_2$. See q34	158.21	nd (bz-lig), pr (eth-bz)	168	333			δ	v	v	v	v^h	lig δ	B22[2], 359
q59	—,5-amino-2-methyl-	5-Aminoquinaldine. $C_{10}H_{10}N_2$. See q34	158.21	grsh pl or nd (w + 1)	117–8 (anh)				v^h	v	δ		v	lig s	B22[2], 360
q60	—,5-amino-8-methyl-	$C_{10}H_{10}N_2$. See q34	158.21	yesh nd (w or dil al)	143				δ^h	v					B22, 456
q61	—,6-amino-2-methyl-	6-Aminoquinaldine. $C_{10}H_{10}N_2$. See q34	158.21	pa br (w or dil al)	187.5				v^h	v				chl v	B22[2], 361
q62	—,6-amino-4-methyl-	6-Aminolepidine. $C_{10}H_{10}N_2$. See q34	158.21	nd (w)	169–70				s^h	v	s			chl v ac s	B22, 455
q63	—,7-amino-2-methyl-	7-Aminoquinaldine. $C_{10}H_{10}N_2$. See q34	158.21	nd (w + 1)	148 (anh)				v^h		δ		s	lig s	B22[2], 363
q64	—,7-amino-8-methyl-	$C_{10}H_{10}N_2$. See q34	158.21	pr (dil al)	129	304			δ	v	v	v	v	lig δ	B22, 456
Ω q65	—,8-amino-2-methyl-	8-Aminoquinaldine. $C_{10}H_{10}N_2$. See q34	158.21	pr (lig)	57–8				δ	v	v	v	v	lig s	C1d, 5045
q65[1]	—,8-amino-6-methyl-	$C_{10}H_{10}N_2$. See q34	160.21	nd	73 (62–4)	sub			s	v	v	v	v	oos v	B22[2], 365
—	—,5-benzamido-8-ethoxy-	see Analgen													
q66	—,2-bromo-	C_9H_6BrN. See q34	208.06	nd (al) $\lambda^{10\%\,al}$ 277 (3.53), 319 (3.62)	49				δ	v^h	v		v	chl v	B20, 362
q67	—,3-bromo-	C_9H_6BrN. See q34	208.06	ye oil $\lambda^{10\%\,al}$ 279 (3.53), 323 (3.51)	13–5	274–6 95[0.5]	1.6641[20]							aa v^h	B20, 363
q68	—,4-bromo-	C_9H_6BrN. See q34	208.06	cr	29–30	270d			δ					dil ac v	B20, 364

For explanations, symbols and abbreviations see beginning of table. For structural formulas see end of table.

Quinoline

No.	Name	Synonyms and Formula	Mol. wt.	Color, crystalline form, specific rotation and λ_{max} (log ε)	m.p. °C	b.p. °C	Density	n_D	w	al	eth	ace	bz	other solvents	Ref.
q69	—,5-bromo-	C_9H_6BrN. See q34	208.06	nd $\lambda^{10\%\,al}$ 293 (3.70), 317 (3.46)	52 (48)	280[756] 105–7[1.2]								ac s	B20[2], 235
Ω q70	—,6-bromo-	C_9H_6BrN. See q34	208.06	$\lambda^{10\%\,al}$ 273 (3.58), 320 (3.53)	24	278 155–6[15]				s	s			ac s	B20, 364
q71	—,7-bromo-	C_9H_6BrN. See q34	208.06	nd $\lambda^{10\%\,al}$ 269 (3.61), 320 (3.58)	34 (52)	290				s	s			ac v	B20, 365
q72	—,8-bromo-	C_9H_6BrN. See q34	208.06	$\lambda^{10\%\,al}$ 291 (3.70), 315 (3.46)	< –10 (80)	302–4 165–6[18]				v				ac s	B20[2], 235
q73	—,3-bromo-2-hydroxy-	β-Bromocarbostyril. C_9H_6BrNO. See q34	224.06	pr (al)	253	sub				s^h			s^h		B21, 80
q74	—,4-bromo-2-hydroxy-	γ-Bromocarbostyril. C_9H_6BrNO. See q34	224.06	nd (al)	266–7	sub				v^h					B21, 80
q75	—,5-bromo-2-hydroxy-	5-Bromocarbostyril. C_9H_6BrNO. See q34	224.06	nd (al)	300					δ s^h					B21, 80
q76	—,5-bromo-6-hydroxy-	C_9H_6BrNO. See q34	224.06	nd (dil al)	186					δ				dil ac δ	B21[1], 221
Ω q77	—,5-bromo-8-hydroxy-	C_9H_6BrNO. See q34	224.06	nd (al), nd or lf (sub)	124	sub			v^h	v^h			v	chl v	B21[1], 222
q78	—,6-bromo-2-hydroxy-	C_9H_6BrNO. See q34	224.06	ye nd (al)	269				v	v^n				chl, ac, alk s	B21, 80
q79	—,7-bromo-2-hydroxy-	7-Bromocarbostyril. C_9H_6BrNO. See q34	224.06	nd (aa), pl (al)	228	sub				v^h	s			chl s	B21, 80
q80	—,8-bromo-5-hydroxy-	C_9H_6BrNO. See q34	224.06	nd (al)	190d					v				chl s	B21, 85
Ω q81	—,2-chloro-	C_9H_6ClN. See q34	163.61	nd (aq al) $\lambda^{10\%\,al}$ 282 (3.52), 318 (3.66)	38	265–6[753] 153–4[22]	1.2464[25]	1.6342[25]	i	v	v		s	lig s	B20[2], 233
q82	—,3-chloro-	C_9H_6ClN. See q34	163.61	hyg cr $\lambda^{10\%\,al}$ 283 (3.48), 323 (3.55)		255[743] 141[15]									B20[2], 234
q83	—,4-chloro-	C_9H_6ClN. See q34	163.61	cr $\lambda^{10\%\,al}$ 289 (3.69), 316 (3.45)	34–5	261[744] 130[15]	1.251		δ	v	v			dil HCl s	B20[2], 234
q84	—,5-chloro-	C_9H_6ClN. See q34	163.61	cr (al) $\lambda^{10\%\,al}$ 292 (3.66), 317 (3.50)	45	256–7[56]				s^h					B20, 360
Ω q85	—,6-chloro-	C_9H_6ClN. See q34	163.61	pr (eth), nd (al) $\lambda^{10\%\,al}$ 276 (3.56), 319 (3.54)	44–5	262–4[760]		1.6110[56]							B20[2], 234
q86	—,7-chloro-	C_9H_6ClN. See q34	163.61	nd or pr $\lambda^{10\%\,al}$ 279 (3.55), 319 (3.56)	31–2	267–8	1.2158[58]	1.6108[58]_a	δ	v	v	v	v	chl v	B20[2], 234
Ω q87	—,8-chloro-	C_9H_6ClN. See q34	163.61	$\lambda^{10\%\,al}$ 292 (3.65), 315 (3.47)	fr. –20	288–9[760]	1.2834[14]_a	1.6408[14.3]_a	s	v	v	v	v	chl v	B20[2], 234
Ω q88	—,7-chloro-4-hydroxy-	C_9H_6ClNO. See q34	179.61	nd (al-w) λ^{chl} 246 (4.28), 290 (3.37), 320 (4.01), 333 (4.08)	276–80										C44, 2572
Ω q89	—,5-chloro-8-hydroxy-7-iodo-	Vioform. C_9H_5ClINO. See q34	305.50	ye br nd (al, aa) λ^{chl} 326 (3.41)	178–9					$δ^h$				aa s^h	B21[2], 58
Ω q90	—,2-chloro-4-methyl-	2-Chlorolepidine. $C_{10}H_8ClN$. See q34	177.65	nd (dil al)	59	296			i	v	v			chl v	B20[2], 245
q91	—,2-chloro-6-methyl-	$C_{10}H_8ClN$. See q34	177.65	nd (dil al)	112 (116)				δ	v	v		v	chl v	B20[1], 151
q92	—,2-chloro-8-methyl-	$C_{10}H_8ClN$. See q34	177.65	nd (eth)	61	286[734]			δ	v	v		v	chl v	B20[1], 152
q93	—,3-chloro-2-methyl-	3-Chloroquinaldine. $C_{10}H_8ClN$. See q34	177.65	nd (dil al)	71–2				δ	v	v				B20, 392
q94	—,3-chloro-4-methyl-	3-Chlorolepidine. $C_{10}H_8ClN$. See q34	177.65	nd (dil al)	55					s				HCl v	B20[1], 150
q95	—,3-chloro-6-methyl-	$C_{10}H_8ClN$. See q34	177.65	nd (dil MeOH)	85.5				δ					MeOH s	B20[2], 246
q96	—,4-chloro-2-methyl-	4-Chloroquinaldine. $C_{10}H_8ClN$. See q34	177.65	nd (+1w)	42–3 (hyd) 25–6 (anh)	269–70			δ	s	s		s	chl, CS_2 s	B20[2], 241
q97	—,6-chloro-2-methyl-	5-Chloroquinaldine. $C_{10}H_8ClN$. See q34	177.65	lf or nd (dil al)	91					s^h	s				B20[2], 242
q98	—,6-chloro-4-methyl-	6-Chlorolepidine. $C_{10}H_8ClN$. See q34	177.65	nd (al)	71–2 (65–6)				δ	v	v	v	v	oos v	B20[2], 245

For explanations, symbols and abbreviations see beginning of table. For structural formulas see end of table.

No.	Name	Synonyms and Formula	Mol. wt.	Color, crystalline form, specific rotation and λ_{max} (log ε)	m.p. °C	b.p. °C	Density	n_D	w	al	eth	ace	bz	other solvents	Ref.
	Quinoline														
q99	—,7-chloro-2-methyl-	7-Chloroquinaldine. $C_{10}H_8ClN$. See q34	177.65	nd (eth), cr (lig)	75–6	$87^{0.5}$					s^h			lig s^h	B20[2], 242
q100	—,8-chloro-5-methyl-	$C_{10}H_8ClN$. See q34	177.65	nd (w)	49				s^h	v	v		v		B20[2], 246
q101	—,8(chloromethyl)-	$C_{10}H_8ClN$. See q34	177.65	nd or pl (peth)	56						s			peth s^h	B20, 402
q102	—,decahydro-(cis)	$C_9H_{17}N$. See q34	139.24		−40	205^{735} 90^{20}	0.9426^{20}	1.4926^{20}	δ	s	s				B20[2], 73
q103	—,—(trans, d)	$C_9H_{17}N$. See q34	139.24	$[\alpha]_D^{25} +4.8$ (al, c = 3–4)	75	200–2			δ	s	s	v	s	oos v	B20[1], 35
q104	—,—(trans, dl)	$C_9H_{17}N$. See q34	139.24	pr (lig, sub)	48	203^{735} sub	0.9610^{22}	1.4692_a^{56}	s^h	v	v	v		alk δ oos v	B20[2], 72
q105	—,—(trans, l)	$C_9H_{17}N$. See q34	139.24	$[\alpha]_D^{25} -4.5$ (al, c = 3–7)	74–5	200–1			δ						B20[1], 35
Ω q106	—,5,7-dibromo-8-hydroxy-	$C_9H_5Br_2NO$. See q34	302.96	nd (al) λ^{chl} 328 (3.47)	196	sub			i	s	δ	s	s	aa, chl s	B21[2], 58
q107	—,6,8-dibromo-2-hydroxy-	6,8-Dibromocarbostyril. $C_9H_5Br_2NO$. See q34	302.96	nd (dil al)	230					v^h					B21, 81
q108	—,2,3-dichloro-	$C_9H_5Cl_2N$. See q34	198.05	(dil al)	104–5				i	v	v		s	lig δ	B20, 361
q109	—,2,4-dichloro-	$C_9H_5Cl_2N$. See q34	198.05	nd (dil al)	67–8	280–2			i	v	v		s	chl v	B20[2], 234
q110	—,2,6-dichloro-	$C_9H_5Cl_2N$. See q34	198.05	nd (eth)	156 (161.5)				i	s	s				B20, 361
q111	—,2,7-dichloro-	$C_9H_5Cl_2N$. See q34	198.05	nd (al)	120	sub 100^2			δ	s	s				B20[2], 234
q112	—,3,4-dichloro-	$C_9H_5Cl_2N$. See q34	198.05	(skellysolve B)	69–70						s	s			Am 68, 2570
q113	—,4,5-dichloro-	$C_9H_5Cl_2N$. See q34	198.05		118	$134^{5.5}$					s	s			Am 68, 113
q114	—,4,6-dichloro-	$C_9H_5Cl_2N$. See q34	198.05	(peth)	104						s	s			Am 68, 1277
Ω q115	—,4,7-dichloro-	$C_9H_5Cl_2N$. See q34	198.05	cr (MeOH), nd(80 % al) λ^{chl} 279 (3.68), 310 (3.46), 324 (3.52)	93	148^{10}					s	s			Am 68, 1206
q116	—,4,8-dichloro-	$C_9H_5Cl_2N$. See q34	198.05		155–6				δ	s	s				Am 68, 1277
q117	—,5,6-dichloro-	$C_9H_5Cl_2N$. See q34	198.05	nd (al)	85				δ	v	s			peth v	B20, 361
q118	—,5,7-dichloro-	$C_9H_5Cl_2N$. See q34	198.05	nd (al)	117				δ		s				B20, 361
q119	—,5,8-dichloro-	$C_9H_5Cl_2N$. See q34	198.05	nd (al)	97–8	sub			δ	s	s				B20, 362
Ω q120	—,6,8-dichloro-	$C_9H_5Cl_2N$. See q34	198.05	nd (al), pl (eth)	104–5				δ	s	s				B20, 362
q121	—,7,8-dichloro-	$C_9H_5Cl_2N$. See q34	198.05	nd	85.5					s^h	s				Prak 48, 279
Ω q122	—,5,7-dichloro-8-hydroxy-	$C_9H_5Cl_2NO$. See q34	214.05	nd (al)	183					δ		δ	s	peth, alk s chl, aa δ	B21[2], 58
—	—,8(3-diethylaminopropylamino-6-methoxy-	see **Antimalarine**													
Ω q123	—,1,2-dihydro-1-methyl-2-oxo-	N-Methyl-2(1H)-quinolone. N-Methylcarbostyril. N-Methyl-o-aminocinnamic acid lactam.	159.19	nd (lig) λ^w 228 (4.53), 245 (4.01), 272 (3.84), 325 (3.81)	74	324^{728}			δ	s	s	s	v	chl s lig δ	B21[1], 297
Ω q124	—,5,7-diiodo-8-hydroxy-	Diodoquin. Embequin. Floraquin. $C_9H_5I_2NO$. See q34	396.96	yesh nd (aa, xyl)	210 (200–15d)				δ	v	δ		δ	chl, aa δ alk s	B21[2], 58
q125	—,5,8-diiodo-6-hydroxy-	$C_9H_5I_2NO$. See q34	396.96	yesh	191				i	v	v		δ	chl, aa δ alk v	B21[2], 54
q126	—,2,3-dimethyl-	3-Methylquinaldine. $C_{11}H_{11}N$. See q34	157.22	ye rh (eth)	68–9	261^{729}	1.1013		i	v	v			lig s	B20, 406
Ω q127	—,2,4-dimethyl-	4-Methylquinaldine. $C_{11}H_{11}N$. See q34	157.22			$264–6^{758}$ 143^{15}	1.0611^{15}	1.6075^{20}	δ	v	v				B20, 407
Ω q128	—,2,6-dimethyl-	6-Methylquinaldine. $C_{11}H_{11}N$. See q34	157.22	rh pr (eth) λ^{MeOH} 240 (4.5), 310 (3.5), 320 (3.5), 330 (3.6)	60	$266–7$ $152–5^{13}$			$δ^h$	δ	δ		v		B20, 408
Ω q129	—,2,8-dimethyl-	o-Toluquinaldine. $C_{11}H_{11}N$. See q34	157.22		27	255.3^{760} $103–4^5$	1.0394_4^{20}	1.6022^{20}	δ	v	v				B20[1], 154
q130	—,3,4-dimethyl-	3-Methyllepidine. $C_{11}H_{11}N$. See q34	157.22	cr (eth)	73–4	290^{737}			i	s	s				B20, 410
q131	—,5,8-dimethyl-	$C_{11}H_{11}N$. See q34	157.22	nd	4–5	265^{736}	1.070^{21}		δ	v	v				B20, 411
q132	—,6,8-dimethyl-	β-Cytisolidine. $C_{11}H_{11}N$. See q34	157.22			$268–9^{760}$ $133–4^{14}$	1.0665^4		δ	s	s				B20, 411

For explanations, symbols and abbreviations see beginning of table. For structural formulas see end of table.

Quinoline

No.	Name	Synonyms and Formula	Mol. wt.	Color, crystalline form, specific rotation and λ_{max} (log ε)	m.p. °C	b.p. °C	Density	n_D	w	al	eth	ace	bz	other solvents	Ref.
q133	—,6(dimethylamino)-2-methyl-	6(Dimethylamino)-quinaldine. $C_{12}H_{14}N_2$. See q34	186.26	ye pr (aa, AcOEt)	101	319^{760}				v	v		v	peth i	B22², 361
q134	—,2,3-dimethyl-4-hydroxy-	$C_{11}H_{11}NO$. See q34	173.22	pr (w+1) λ^{chl} 248 (4.29), 288 (3.35), 324 (4.03), 337 (4.07)	319–20	sub			δ^h	δ^h				lig δ^h	B21², 68
q135	—,2,4-dimethyl-6-hydroxy-	$C_{11}H_{11}NO$. See q34	173.22	pr or pl (al)	214	360d			i	s	δ	v	i	ac, alk v	B21², 68
q136	—,2,4-dimethyl-7-hydroxy-	$C_{11}H_{11}NO$. See q34	173.22	nd (al)	218					s					B21, 116
q137	—,2,4-dimethyl-8-hydroxy-	$C_{11}H_{11}NO$. See q34	173.22	pr (eth) λ^{cy} 246 (4.70), 309 (3.52)	65	281 sub			i	v	v	v	v	peth δ chl v	B21, 116
q138	—,2,6-dimethyl-4-hydroxy-	$C_{11}H_{11}NO$. See q34	173.22	nd (w+1)	279 (anh)				v^h					ac s	B21², 68
q139	—,2,8-dimethyl-4-hydroxy-	$C_{11}H_{11}NO$. See q34	173.22	lf or pl (w+1)	260–1 (anh)	sub			δ	v	δ		δ	chl δ dil ac, alk v	B21, 116
q140	—,4,6-dimethyl-2-hydroxy-	$C_{11}H_{11}NO$. See q34	173.22	pr (al)	249–50				δ	s^h	δ		δ	chl, alk, dil ac δ	B21², 225
q141	—,4,7-dimethyl-2-hydroxy-	$C_{11}H_{11}NO$. See q34	173.22	cr (aa)	220				δ^h	v^h				alk s aa v^h	B21¹, 225
q142	—,4,8-dimethyl-2-hydroxy-	$C_{11}H_{11}NO$. See q34	173.22	pl (aq aa)	217–8				δ s^h	s				alk s	B21¹, 225
q143	—,6,8-dimethyl-2-hydroxy-	$C_{11}H_{11}NO$. See q34	173.22	nd (al)	201–2				s^h	s				dil ac i	B21¹, 225
q144	—,6,8-dimethyl-5-hydroxy-	Cytisoline. $C_{11}H_{11}NO$. See q34	173.22	pl (chl), cr (al)	197–8	sub			δ s^h	v			s	chl, ac s	B21, 117
q145	—,3-ethyl-2-hydroxy-	3-Ethylcarbostyril. $C_{11}H_{11}NO$. See q34	173.22	(dil HCl)	168					δ			s	chl s	B21, 115
q146	—,2-hydrazino-	$C_9H_9N_3$. See q34	159.19	(bz)	142–3					v	δ			lig δ	B22¹, 690
q147	—,5-hydrazino-	$C_9H_9N_3$. See q34	159.19	ye nd (w)	150–1				s^h	v			δ	peth i	B22, 565
Ωq148	—,2-hydroxy-	o-Aminocinnamic acid lactam. Carbostyril. 2-Quinolinol. α-Quinolone. C_9H_7NO. See q34	145.16	pr (al, dil al +1w), nd (sub) $\lambda^{w, pH=5.5}$ 224 (4.43), 2.5 (3.93), 270 (3.82), 324 (3.80)	199–200 (anh)	sub			δ s^h	v	v			dil HCl s	B21², 51
q149	—,3-hydroxy-	3-Quinolinol. C_9H_7NO. See q34	145.16	cr (bz, to or dil al) λ^{al} 272 (3.49), 329 (3.68)	200–1				s^h i	s	δ		v^h	chl δ to v^h	B21², 52
q150	—,4-hydroxy-	Kynurine. 4-Quinolinol. 4(1)-Quinolone. C_9H_7NO. See q34	145.16	nd (w+3) λ^{al} 225 (4.3), 315 (4.1), 325 (4.1)	210 (anh) 100 (hyd)				v^h	v^h	δ		δ	peth δ	B21², 53
q151	—,5-hydroxy-	5-Quinolinol. C_9H_7NO. See q34	145.16	nd (al), pl λ^{al} 242 (4.75), 323 (3.53)	224d	sub			s^h	δ	δ		s^h	chl s^h lig i MeOH v	B21, 84
q152	—,6-hydroxy-	6-Quinolinol. C_9H_7NO. See q34	145.16	pr (al or eth) λ^{al} 227 (4.51), 274 (3.45), 331 (3.61)	193	>360			δ^h i	δ	δ		i	chl i ac, alk s	B21, 85
q153	—,7-hydroxy-	7-Quinolinol. C_9H_7NO. See q34	145.16	pr (al), nd (dil al-eth)	238–40	sub			δ	v				alk v chl s^h	B21, 91
Ωq154	—,8-hydroxy-	8-Quinolinol. Quinophenol. Oxine. C_9H_7NO. See q34	145.16	nd (dil al) λ^{al} 240 (4.60), 308 (3.47)	75–6	266.6^{752} sub	1.034^{209}		i	v	i	s	v^h	chl v^h alk, ac s	B21, 91
Ωq155	—,—,sulfate	Chinosol. $2(C_9H_7NO) \cdot H_2SO_4$	388.40	ye pw (w)	177.5				v	s	i				B21, 92
q156	—,—,sulfate monohydrate	ye pr (w-al) $2(C_9H_7NO) \cdot H_2SO_4 \cdot H_2O$	406.42		176–9				v	δ^h					B21², 56
Ωq157	—,2-hydroxy-3-methyl-	3-Methylcarbostyril. $C_{10}H_9NO$. See q34	159.19	yesh nd (dil al or ace)	234–5	sub				s		s^h		chl	B21, 107
q158	—,2-hydroxy-4-methyl-	2-Hydroxylepidine. $C_{10}H_9NO$. See q34	159.19	nd (w)	245 (223)	$>360^{760}$ 270^{17}			s^h δ	v^h	δ		δ	chl, lig δ	B21², 65
Ωq159	—,2-hydroxy-6-methyl-	6-Methylcarbostyril. $C_{10}H_9NO$. See q34	159.19	nd (al)	237	$240–1^{12}$				v	s	s	s	oos s	B21¹, 65
q161	—,—(high m.p.)	$C_{10}H_9NO$. See q34	159.19	nd (aq ace)	260d				δ	v^h	δ	v^h	δ	lig δ	B22², 59
q162	—,3-hydroxy-2-methyl-(low m.p.)	3-Hydroxyquinaldine. $C_{10}H_9NO$. See q34	159.19	nd (al)	203–5				δ	s	s			chl s	B21, 104
Ωq163	—,4-hydroxy-2-methyl-	4-Hydroxyquinaldine. $C_{10}H_9NO$. See q34	159.19	pr (w+2) λ^{chl} 247 (4.14), 285 (3.43), 329 (4.06), 317 (4.03)	232	$>360d^{760}$			s^h	v	i		i	lig i	B21, 104

For explanations, symbols and abbreviations see beginning of table. For structural formulas see end of table.

Quinoline

No.	Name	Synonyms and Formula	Mol. wt.	Color, crystalline form, specific rotation and λ_{max} (log ε)	m.p. °C	b.p. °C	Density	n_D	w	al	eth	ace	bz	other solvents	Ref.
q164	—.5-hydroxy-2-methyl-	5-Hydroxyquinaldine. $C_{10}H_9NO$. See q34	159.19	pl (al)	246–7 (233)	....			i	δ	v	...	...	alk s Na_2CO_3 i	B21, 106
q165	—.5-hydroxy-6-methyl-	$C_{10}H_9NO$. See q34	159.19	nd (al or sub)	230	sub			$δ^h$	v	v	v		oos v	B21, 111
q166	—.5-hydroxy-8-methyl-	$C_{10}H_9NO$. See q34	159.19	nd (dil al or sub)	262–3	sub								NaOH s^h chl δ	B21, 112
q167	—.6-hydroxy-2-methyl-	6-Hydroxyquinaldine. $C_{10}H_9NO$. See q34	159.19	(w)	213	$304–5^{760}$ 186^{35}	1.1665^0		δ	v	v			ac, alk s	B21, 106
q168	—.6-hydroxy-4-methyl-	6-Hydroxylepidine. $C_{10}H_9NO$. See q34	159.19	nd (w or dil al)	222–4	....			δ s^h	v^h		v		chl v^h	B21, 109
q169	—.6-hydroxy-8-methyl-	$C_{10}H_9NO$. See q34	159.19	nd (dil al)	200					s^h					B21, 113
q170	—.7-hydroxy-6-methyl-	$C_{10}H_9NO$. See q34	159.19	nd (al)	244	240^{22} 210^{11} sub			i	v^h	v		v	alk s	B21, 111
Ω q171	—.8-hydroxy-2-methyl-	8-Hydroxyquinaldine. $C_{10}H_9NO$. See q34	159.19	pr (dil al) λ^{cy} 246 (4.72), 309 (3.46)	74–5	267^{760} 145–60^{22-8} sub 100			i	s^h	s		s	alk s	B21, 106
Ω q172	—.8-hydroxy-4-methyl-	8-Hydroxylepidine. $C_{10}H_9NO$. See q34	159.19	nd (lig) λ^{cy} 242 (4.68), 319 (3.52)	141	....			s^h	s^h		v		ac, alk, chl, aa v	B21, 109
q173	—.8-hydroxy-5-methyl-	$C_{10}H_9NO$. See q34 ...	159.19	nd (dil al)	122–4	sub 100			i					ac, alk s	B21, 110
q174	—.8-hydroxy-6-methyl-	$C_{10}H_9NO$. See q34	159.19	nd (chl or bz)	95–6	sub			δ	v				alk s^h	B21, 111
q175	—.8-hydroxy-7-methyl-	$C_{10}H_9NO$. See q34	159.19	nd (dil al)	72–4	sub 100			δ	v					B21, 111
Ω q176	—.8-hydroxy-5-nitroso-	$C_9H_6N_2O_2$. See q34 ...	174.16	nd (al)	245d				i		δ		δ	chl δ	B21¹, 405
q177	—.4-hydroxy-2-phenyl-	$C_{15}H_{11}NO$. See q34	221.26	pl or pr (al), nd (aa) λ^{al} 257 (4.55), 325 sh (4.06), 334 (4.08)	256–7	....			i	v^h	i			alk s	B21², 84
q178	—.2-iodo-	C_9H_6IN. See q34	255.06	nd (dil al)	52–3				δ	v	v	v		oos v	B20, 370
q179	—.4-iodo-	C_9H_6IN. See q34	255.06	nd or pr	97 (100)	sub			i	v	v				B20, 370
q180	—.5-iodo-	C_9H_6IN. See q34	255.06	nd (al or eth)	101–2	sub			$δ^h$	s^h	s^h	...		B20¹, 141
q181	—.6-iodo-	C_9H_6IN. See q34	255.06	lf (w), nd (sub)	91	sub			s^h	v	v				B20, 370
q182	—.8-iodo-	C_9H_6IN. See q34	255.06	lo nd (al)	36					v	v	v	v	lig s	B20¹, 141
q183	—.4-methoxy-	$C_{10}H_9NO$. See q34	159.19	λ^{al} 275 (3.8)	41	245 167^{20}			i	s	s		s		B21², 53
q184	—.5-methoxy-	$C_{10}H_9NO$. See q34	159.19			282^{758}				v	v				B21, 84
Ω q185	—.6-methoxy-	p-Quinanisole. $C_{10}H_9NO$. See q34	159.19	hyg lf λ^w 223 (4.51), 268 (3.47), 325 (3.59)	26.5	305^{740} 153^{12}	1.1542^{20}_{20} 1.000^{209}			s	s			dil HCl s	B21², 53
q186	—.8-methoxy-	o-Quinanisole. $C_{10}H_9NO$. See q34	159.19	nd (peth) λ^{al} 240 (4.6), 360 (3.52)	49–50	282^{750} 164^{14}	1.034^{29}			s	s		s	peth s	B21¹, 222
q187	—.2-methoxy-6-nitro-	$C_{10}H_8N_2O_3$. See q34	204.20	nd (dil aa, bz or sub)	189–90	....			i	s	s		s	con sulf, chl v lig s	B21¹, 219
q188	—.2-methoxy-8-nitro-	$C_{10}H_8N_2O_3$. See q34	204.20	nd (dil al)	124–5					v			v		B21, 82
q189	—.6-methoxy-5-nitro-	$C_{10}H_8N_2O_3$. See q34	204.20	cr (al)	104–5					s^h		v			B21, 90
Ω q190	—.6-methoxy-8-nitro-	$C_{10}H_8N_2O_3$. See q34	204.20	yesh nd (al)	159–60									chl s MeOH δ	B21², 54
q191	—.8-methoxy-5-nitro-	$C_{10}H_8N_2O_3$. See q34	204.20	cr (al)	151.5				i	v^h					B21, 98
q192	—.6-methoxy-1,2,3,4-tetrahydro-	Thalline. $C_{10}H_{13}NO$. See q34	163.22	pr (peth or al), rh pym (w)	42–3	283^{735} $127–30^1$		1.5718^{50}	s^h δ	v	v		v	peth δ	B21, 61
Ω q193	—.2-methyl-	Quinaldine. $C_{10}H_9N$. See q34	143.19	λ^{MeOH} 230 (4.0), 270 (3.5), 300 (3.6), 310 (3.4), 320 (3.6)	−2 to −1	247.6^{760} 118^{10}	1.0585^{20}_4	1.6116^{20}	δ	s	s	s		chl s	B20², 238
q194	—.3-methyl-	β-Methylquinoline. $C_{10}H_9N$. See q34	143.19	pr $\lambda^{0.2\,N\,HCl}$ 316 (3.83)	16–7	259.6^{760} $140–2^{25}$	1.0673^{20}_4	1.6171^{20}	δ	s	s	s	s	min ac s alk i	B20, 394
Ω q195	—.4-methyl-	Lepidine. $C_{10}H_9N$. See q34	143.19	red br λ^{al} 280 (3.68)	9–10	264.2^{760} 133^{15}	1.0862^{20}_4	1.6206^{20}	δ	∞	∞	s	s	lig s	B20², 244
q196	—.5-methyl-	ana-Methylquinoline. $C_{10}H_9N$. See q34	143.19	$\lambda^{0.2\,N\,HCl}$ 315 (3.76)	19	262.7^{760} 130^{15}	1.0832^{20}_4	1.6219^{20}	δ	∞	∞	s			B20², 246
Ω q197	—.6-methyl-	p-Toluquinoline. $C_{10}H_9N$. See q34	143.19	$\lambda^{0.2\,N\,HCl}$ 318 (3.85)	ca. −22	258.6^{760} 130^{15}	1.0654^{20}_4	1.6157^{20}	δ	s	s	s			B20, 397
q198	—.7-methyl-	m-Toluquinoline. $C_{10}H_9N$. See q34	143.19	ye $\lambda^{0.2\,N\,HCl}$ 316 (3.82)	39	257.6^{760} 144^{18}	1.0609^{20}_4	1.6150^{20}	δ	s	s	s			B20², 246
q199	—.8-methyl-	o-Toluquinoline. $C_{10}H_9N$. See q34	143.19	$\lambda^{0.2\,N\,HCl}$ 315 (3.76)	....	247.8^{760} 143^{34}	1.0719^{20}_4	1.6164^{20}	δ	∞	∞	s			B20¹, 247

For explanations, symbols and abbreviations see beginning of table. For structural formulas see end of table.

Quinoline

No.	Name	Synonyms and Formula	Mol. wt.	Color, crystalline form, specific rotation and λ_{max} (log ε)	m.p. °C	b.p. °C	Density	n_D	w	al	eth	ace	bz	other solvents	Ref.
q200	—,2-methyl-5-nitro-	5-Nitroquinaldine. $C_{10}H_8N_2O_2$. See q34	188.20	nd (dil al)	82	....			δ	v	v	...	...		B20[2], 243
q201	—,2-methyl-6-nitro-	6-Nitroquinaldine. $C_{10}H_8N_2O_2$. See q34	188.20	cr (80 % MeOH)	165 (173–4)	....			s^h	s	i	...	...	dil HCl v	B20[2], 243
q202	—,2-methyl-8-nitro-	8-Nitroquinaldine. $C_{10}H_8N_2O_2$. See q34	188.20	pa ye nd (dil al)	137	....			δ	v	v	...	v		B20[2], 244
q203	—,4-methyl-3-nitro-	3-Nitrolepidine. $C_{10}H_8N_2O_2$. See q34	188.20	pr (w)	118	....			s^h	s					B20[2], 245
q204	—,4-methyl-8-nitro-	8-Nitrolepidine. $C_{10}H_8N_2O_2$. See q34	188.20	lf (abs al) λ^{al} 283 (3.70), 314 (3.60)	126–7	....			δ	s^h δ	s				B20, 397
Ω q205	—,6-methyl-5-nitro-	$C_{10}H_8N_2O_2$. See q34	188.20	pa ye nd (al)	116–7	....			i	s	s	s	s	oos v	B20[1], 151
q206	—,6-methyl-8-nitro-	$C_{10}H_8N_2O_2$. See q34	188.20	pa ye nd (w)	122	....			s^h	v	s	s	s	oos v	B20, 400
q207	—,8-methyl-5-nitro-	$C_{10}H_8N_2O_2$. See q34	188.20	pa ye nd (al)	93	....				s	s	s	s	oos v	B20, 403
q208	—,8-methyl-6-nitro-	$C_{10}H_8N_2O_2$. See q34	188.20	cr (al)	129	....			δ	v					B20, 403
q209	—,1-methyl-1,2,3,4-tetrahydro-	Kairoline. $C_{10}H_{13}N$. See q34	147.22	....	....	247–50[758] 123–6[14]	1.0222[20]	1.5802[23]	...	v	δ				B20[2], 174
q210	—,3-nitro-	$C_9H_6N_2O_2$. See q34	174.16	nd (dil al) λ^{cy} 242.5 (4.45), 295 (4.0)	128	....			δ^h	s	...	v			B20[2], 235
q211	—,4-nitro-, oxide	....	190.16	ye nd, pl or nd (ace)	154	....									C50, 13925
Ω q212	—,5-nitro-	$C_9H_6N_2O_2$. See q34	174.16	pl (w or al), nd (+w, w) λ 305 (3.80)	73–5 (anh)	sub			δ^h	s^h			s		B20[2], 235
Ω q213	—,6-nitro-	$C_9H_6N_2O_2$. See q34	174.16	ye pl (HCl-aa), nd (w or dil al) λ 249 (4.40), 257 (4.34), 286 (3.98)	153–4	sub			s^h	s^h	δ	...	v	dil ac v lig δ	B20[2], 235
q214	—,7-nitro-	$C_9H_6N_2O_2$. See q34	174.16	nd or lf (w or al), pl (sub) λ^{cy} 248 (4.37), 256.5 (4.3), 284 sh (3.97)	132–3	sub			s^h	s^h	s			chl v	B20, 372
Ω q215	—,8-nitro-	$C_9H_6N_2O_2$. See q34	174.16	mcl pr (al) λ 275 (3.74), 301 (3.54), 315 (3.52)	91–2	....			δ	s	s	...	s	dil ac s	B20, 373
q216	—,2-oxo-1,2,3,4-tetrahydro-	3(2-Aminophenyl)propionic acid lactam. Hydrocarbostyril. C_9H_9NO. See q34	147.18	pr (al or eth) λ^{al} 251 (4.1)	163–4	201[45]			i	v	v	...		alk δ^h	B21[2], 253
q218	—,2-phenyl-	$C_{15}H_{11}N$. See q34	205.26	nd (dil al) λ^{al} 252 (4.6), 325 (3.9)	86	363[760] 310[187]			δ	v^h	v	v	v	peth δ	B20[2], 311
q219	—,3-phenyl-	$C_{15}H_{11}N$. See q34	205.26	pl (eth) λ^{al} 253 (4.5)	52	205–7[12]			δ	s	s	v	s	chl s aa δ	B20[2], 312
q220	—,5-phenyl-	$C_{15}H_{11}N$. See q34	205.26	nd (dil al)	83	....			δ	s	s	v			J1943, 441
q221	—,6-phenyl-	$C_{15}H_{11}N$. See q34	205.26	pl (al, bz or $PhNH_2$), pym (eth) λ^{al} 253 (4.64)	111	260[77]	1.1945[20]	n_D	δ	v	δ	v	v	chl v peth δ	B20, 483
q222	—,8-phenyl-	$C_{15}H_{11}N$. See q34	205.26	ye gr oil λ^{al} 233 (4.50), 300 (3.80)		283[187]			δ	v	v	v	v	chl v CS_2 s	B20, 484
Ω q223	—,1,2,3,4-tetrahydro-	Py-Tetrahydroquinoline. $C_9H_{11}N$. See q34	133.20	nd λ^{al} 250 (3.85), 300 (3.30)	20	251[760]	1.0588[20]	1.6062[19]	s	∞	∞				B20[2], 173
q224	—,5,6,7,8-tetrahydro-	Bz-Tetrahydroquinoline. $C_9H_{11}N$. See q34	133.20	λ^{al} 268 (3.66)		222[760] 92–5[12]	1.0304[20]	1.5435[20]	δ	s	s	s	s		B20[2], 176
q225	—,2,3,4-trimethyl-	3,4-Dimethylquinaldine. $C_{12}H_{13}N$. See q34	171.25	....	92 (65)	285[760] 156–8[12]									B20[2], 255
q226	—,2,4,6-trimethyl-	4,6-Dimethylquinaldine. $C_{12}H_{13}N$. See q34	171.25	nd (w or dil al +1w)	65.5 (anh) 40 (44) (hyd)	281–2[760] 146–8[13.5]			δ	v	v	v	v	chl, peth v	B20[2], 256
q227	—,2,4,7-trimethyl-	4,7-Dimethylquinaldine. $C_{12}H_{13}N$. See q34	171.25	nd (w)	63–4 (anh) 48 (hyd)	280–1	1.0337[20]	1.5973[24]	δ	v	v	v	v		B20[2], 256
q228	—,2,4,8-trimethyl-	4,8-Dimethylquinaldine. $C_{12}H_{13}N$. See q34	171.25	....	50–1	287[758]		1.5855[50]							B20[2], 257
q229	—,2,5,6- or -2,6,7-trimethyl-	$C_{12}H_{13}N$. See q34	171.25	nd	69–70	....			δ	v	v	...	v		B20, 415

For explanations, symbols and abbreviations see beginning of table. For structural formulas see end of table.

No.	Name	Synonyms and Formula	Mol. wt.	Color, crystalline form, specific rotation and λ_{max} (log ε)	m.p. °C	b.p. °C	Density	n_D	w	al	eth	ace	bz	other solvents	Ref.
	Quinoline														
q230	—,2,5,7-tri-methyl-	Tetracoline. $C_{12}H_{13}N$. See q34	171.25	pr	....	286.6^{746} $107-8^{1.2}$		1.5980^{20}	i	v	v	...	...		Am 81, 152
q231	—,2,6,8-tri-methyl-	$C_{12}H_{13}N$. See q34.........	171.25	pr (peth), lf (dil al) λ^{al} 238 (4.63), 285 (3.59), 311 (3.50), 325 (3.46)	46	260^{719}			i	v	v	...	v	peth v	B20, 415
q232	—,4,5,8-tri-methyl-	$C_{12}H_{13}N$. See q34.	171.25		73.4	155^{13}			i	v	v	v	v		Am 68, 644
Ω q233	2-Quinoline-carboxylic acid	Quinaldinic acid.	173.17	nd (w + 2w) (bz)	157 (anh)				v^h s				v^h		B22², 55
q234	—,amide	Quinaldinamide. $C_{10}H_8N_2O$. See q233	172.20	nd (dil al, bz-lig)	133				δ^h	v	δ	...	v	chl, dil HCl v aa s	B22, 73
q235	—,chloride	Quinaldinyl chloride. $C_{10}H_6ClNO$. See q233	191.62	nd (eth or lig)	(i) 97–8 (ii) 175–6				δ	d^h	v	...	v	lig δ	B22¹, 509
q236	—,methyl ester ...	Methyl quinaldinate. $C_{11}H_9NO_2$. See q233	187.20	nd (lig)	86					s				lig s^h	B22², 55
q237	—,nitrile	2-Cyanoquinoline. $C_{10}H_6N_2$. See q233	154.17	nd (lig, chl)	94	$160-$ 70^{20-23}			s	v	v	...	v	chl v lig s	B22¹, 509
q238	3-Quinoline-carboxylic acid	....	173.17	pl (al or dil al) λ^{al} 233 (4.56), 275 (3.62), 322 sh (3.02)	275δd				s^h δ	δ	...	...		dil ac, alk v	B22², 56
q239	—,nitrile	3-Cyanoquinoline. $C_{10}H_6N_2$. See q238	154.17	(al or sub)	108				δ	s^h	v	s	s	oos s	B22², 57
q240	4-Quinoline-carboxylic acid	Cinchoninic acid.	173.17	mcl pr (w), nd (+1w), mcl or tcl (+2w)	257–8 (anh)				δ	δ	i	...	...		B22², 57
q241	—,nitrile	4-Cyanoquinoline. Cinchoninonitrile. $C_{10}H_6N_2$. See q240	154.17	cr (chl, eth or lig) nd (sub)	103–4	240–5			δ	v	v	v	v	oos v	B22², 76
q242	5-Quinoline-carboxylic acid	....	173.17	cr (aa or sub)	342	sub < 338			δ	δ	i	...	i	dil ac, dil alk v CS_2 i	B22¹, 511
q243	—,nitrile	5-Cyanoquinoline. $C_{10}H_6N_2$. See q242	154.17	nd (lig), nd (+1.5 w, dil al)	89 (anh) 70 (hyd)				δ	v		...	v	CS_2 v lig δ	B22, 79
q244	6-Quinoline-carboxylic acid	....	173.17	nd, pr or pl (sub)	291–2	sub < 290			δ	s^h		...	...	dil ac, dil alk v	B22¹, 511
q245	7-Quinoline-carboxylic acid	....	173.17	nd (w or al)	249–50	sub			δ^h i	s	i	...	δ	....	B22, 81
q246	8-Quinoline-carboxylic acid	....	173.17	nd (w)	187	sub			s^h	s		...	...	dil ac, dil alk v	B22, 81
q247	—,nitrile	8-Cyanoquinoline. $C_{10}H_6N_2$. See q246	154.17	nd (dil al)	84				i	v		...	...		B22, 81
q248	4-Quinoline-carboxylic acid, 2(3-carboxy-4-hydroxyphenyl)-	Hexophan. $C_{17}H_{11}NO_5$. See q240	309.28	yesh pw	283–4 δd				i	δ		...	...	chl, alk v lig i	B22², 206
Ω q249	2-Quinoline-carboxylic acid, 4,8-dihydroxy-	Xanthurenic acid. Xanthuric acid. $C_{10}H_7NO_4$. See q233	205.17	ye micr cr (w) λ^{al} 243 (4.4), 345 (3.8)	289 (297)				i	s	δ	...	δ	dil HCl s^h alk, Na_2CO_3 s	Am 73, 3520
q250	—,4-hydroxy-	Kynurenic acid. 4-Hydroxyquinaldinic acid. $C_{10}H_7NO_3$. See q233	189.17	ye nd (+w, dil aa) λ^{al} 243 (4.4), 345 (4.0)	282–3				δ^h	s^h	i	...	...	oos δ alk v	B22², 174
Ω q251	4-Quinoline-carboxylic acid, 6-methoxy-	Quininic acid. $C_{11}H_9NO_3$. See q240	203.20	pa ye pr (dil al)	285d	sub			δ	s^h	δ	...	δ	chl i alk, ac s	B22², 176
q252	—,8-methoxy-2-phenyl-	Isatophan. $C_{17}H_{13}NO_3$. See q240	279.30	ye nd (al)	216				i	s	i	...	...	chl, alk, ac s	B22¹, 559
Ω q253	—,6-methyl-2-phenyl-, ethyl ester	6-Methylcinchophene ethyl ester. Neocinchophene. Novatophan. $C_{19}H_{17}NO_2$. See q240	291.35	ye cr (al)	75–6				i	s^h	v	s	s	chl v oos s	B22¹, 520
q254	3-Quinoline-carboxylic acid, 2-phenyl-	$C_{16}H_{11}NO_2$. See q238	249.27	nd (al)	230d (226)				δ^h	a	...	s	δ	aa, MeOH, phNO₂ s	B22¹, 70
Ω q255	4-Quinoline-carboxylic acid, 2-phenyl-	Artamin. Atophan. Cinchophene. $C_{16}H_{11}NO_2$. See q240	249.27	nd (MeOH or dil al), ye in air λ^{al} 260 (>4.5), 330 (3.9)	218				i	s^h	s	δ^h	δ^h	peth i alk s	B22², 70
q256	—,—,allyl ester ...	Atoquinol. $C_{19}H_{15}NO_2$. See q240	289.34	nd (dil al)	30	265^{15} $215^{0.8}$			i	s	v	v	v	alk i ac δ	B22², 71
q257	5-Quinoline-sulfonic acid, 6-hydroxy-	....	225.23	ye nd (+0.5 w, w or al)	270d	....			s^h	δ	i	...	i	chl i aa δ	B22, 407

For explanations, symbols and abbreviations see beginning of table. For structural formulas see end of table.

No.	Name	Synonyms and Formula	Mol. wt.	Color, crystalline form, specific rotation and λ_{max} (log ε)	m.p. °C	b.p. °C	Density	n_D	w	al	eth	ace	bz	other solvents	Ref.
	5-Quinoline Sulfonic acid														
Ω q258	—,8-hydroxy-	$C_9H_7NO_4S$. See q257	225.23	ye (+2w, con HCl) lf, nd (+1w, dil HCl) λ^w 362 (3.9), $\lambda^{w, pH=10.5}$ 359 (5.0)	322–3				δ^h	...					B22[2], 313
q259	7-Quinoline-sulfonic acid, 8-hydroxy-		225.23	ye nd (al)	314–5				s^h	δ		...	i		B22, 408
Ω q260	5-Quinoline-sulfonic acid, 8-hydroxy-7-iodo-	Loretin. $C_9H_6INO_4S$. See q257	351.12	ye pr or lf (al) $\lambda^{w, pH=1}$ 327 (3.4), 355 (3.4), $\lambda^{w, pH=9}$ 335 (4.2), 362 (4.8)	260d				δ	δ	i	...	i	chl i con sulf s	B22[2], 314
q261	8-Quinoline-sulfonic acid, 5-hydroxy-6-iodo-	Lorenite	351.13	ye nd or lf	210–30d									con sulf s	B22, 406
—	Quinolinic acid	see 2,3-Pyridinedicarboxylic acid													
Ω q262	Quinolinium, N-ethyl-, iodide		285.13	ye pr (al or MeCN) λ^{MeOH} 316 (3.87)	158				v	s^h	i	...		chl s	B20[2], 231
q263	—, N-methyl-, chloride		179.65	cr (+w, al) λ^{al} 232 (4.5), 315 (4.0), 375 sh (2.2)	126				s	s^h		...		chl s	B20[1], 139
—	Quinolinol	see Quinoline, hydroxy-													
—	Quinone	see Benzoquinone													
q264	Quinovic acid	Quinovaic acid. $C_{30}H_{46}O_5$	486.67	pl or nd $[\alpha]_D^{16}$ +87 (aq KOH)	298d				i	δ^h				alk, Ac_2O s aa δ	E14, 580
Ω q265	Quinoxaline	1,4-Benzodiazine. Benzo-pyrazine. Quinazine.	130.15	cr (peth) cr (+w, peth-w) λ^{al} 232 (4.4), 305 sh (3.7), 315 (3.8)	28 (anh) 37 (hyd)	229.5[760] 108–11[12]	1.1334[48]$_4$	1.6231[48]	s	∞	∞	∞	∞	aa s	B23[2], 177
q266	—,6-amino-	$C_8H_7N_3$. See q265	145.17	ye nd (eth) λ^{al} 236 (4.35), 321 (3.69)	159	sub			v	v	s	...	δ	aa δ chl s	B25, 326
q267	—,6-chloro-	$C_8H_5ClN_2$. See q265	164.60	nd (w) λ^{al} 236 (4.35), 321 (3.69)	63.8–4.3	117–9[10] sub			δ						B23[2], 177
q268	—,2,3-dichloro-	$C_8H_4Cl_2N_2$. See q265	199.04	cr (al, bz) λ^{al} 245 (4.5), 315 sh (3.7), 325 (3.8), 340 (3.8)	151–3				i	v^h		...	v	chl, aa v^h	B23[2], 177
Ω q269	—,2,3-dihydroxy-	$C_8H_6N_2O_2$. See q265	162.15	nd (w) $\lambda^{w, pH=5}$ 262 (3.63), 312 (4.07), 326 (4.00)	410				v	δ	δ	...	s^h	MeOH, aa s^h alk v	B24[2], 200
Ω q270	—,2,3-dimethyl-	$C_{10}H_{10}N_2$. See q265	158.21	nd (w +3), (ace) λ^{al} 237 (4.41), 316 (3.86), 322.5 sh (3.75)	106 (anh) 85 (hyd)					s	s	s	s	oos, ac s	B23[2], 197
q271	—,2,6-dimethyl-	$C_{10}H_{10}N_2$. See q265	158.21		54	267–9			v	v	v	s	s		B23, 192
q273	—,2-hydroxy-	2-Quinoxalinol. $C_8H_6N_2O$. See q265	146.15	lf (al) $\lambda^{w, pH=4}$ 250 (3.79), 287 (3.70), 343 (3.74)	271	sub 200[0.5]									C40, 341
q274	—,5-hydroxy-	5-Quinoxalinol. $C_8H_6N_2O$. See q265	146.15	(eth) λ^{ae} 263 (4.53), 338 (3.68), 416 (3.05)	101–2	184[7] sub 90[25]									C48, 8232
q275	—,6-methoxy-	$C_9H_8N_2O$. See q265	161.19	nd (w)	57.5	128[7] sub						s	s		B23, 387
Ω q276	—,2-methyl-	$C_9H_8N_2$. See q265	144.19	ye λ^{al} 234 (4.48), 250 (4.44), 297 sh (3.61), 309 (3.74), 317 (3.77)	180–1	245–7[760] 118[16]			∞	v	∞	∞	∞		B23[2], 190
q277	—,6-methyl-	$C_9H_8N_2$. See q265	144.19		218–9	248[748] 141.5[29]	1.1164[20]$_4$	1.6211[18.4]	∞	∞	∞	∞	∞		B23, 184

For explanations, symbols and abbreviations see beginning of table. For structural formulas see end of table.

No.	Name	Synonyms and Formula	Mol. wt.	Color, crystalline form, specific rotation and λ_{max} (log ε)	m.p. °C	b.p. °C	Density	n_D	Solubility						Ref.
									w	al	eth	ace	bz	other solvents	
	Quinoxaline														
Ω q278	—,1,2,3,4-tetra-hydro-	Ethylene-o-phenyl-enediamine. $C_8H_{10}N_2$. *See* q265	134.18	lf (w, eth or peth)	99.0–9.5	288.5–9.5 153–4[14]	....	....	s^h	v	v	...	v	CCl_4 v chl s peth δ^h	B23[2], 106
q279	Quinuclidine	1-Azabicyclo[2,2,2]octane. 1,4-Ethylenepiperidine. Nuclidine.	111.19	(eth)	158 (sealed tube)	....	....	....	v	v	v	v	v	oos v	B20[2], 71
Ω q280	—,3-hydroxy-	$C_7H_{13}NO$. *See* q279	127.19	cr (bz)	221–3	....	....	....			...	s	...	....	C48, 11499
q281	2-Quinuclidine-carboxylic acid	$C_8H_{13}NO_2$. *See* q279	155.20	col hyg cr (al-ace)	280d	....	....	....			...	...		....	C32, 166

For explanations, symbols and abbreviations see beginning of table. For structural formulas see end of table.

Raffinose

No.	Name	Synonyms and Formula	Mol. wt.	Color, crystalline form, specific rotation and λ_{max} (log ε)	m.p. °C	b.p. °C	Density	n_D	Solubility w	al	eth	ace	bz	other solvents	Ref.
r1	**Raffinose**	Gossypose. Melitose. Melitriose.	594.50	wh pw, pr or nd ($+5$w, dil al) $[\alpha]_D^{20} +105.2$ (w, c = 4) (hyd) $[\alpha]_D$ $+123$ (w) (anh)	80 (hyd) 118–9 (anh)	d 130	1.465^0	....	v	δ	i	...	...	MeOH v Py s	**B31**, 462
r2	**Raunescine, hydrate**	$C_{31}H_{36}N_2O_8 \cdot$	582.61	wh hex pr (90 % MeOH) $[\alpha]_D^{25}$ -74 (chl, c = 1) λ^{al} 218 (4.77), 271 (3.82)	160–70	....	....	....	i	δ	...	...	...	chl s aa s	**Am 79**, 250
—	**Reductone**	see **Propanal, 3-hydroxy-2-oxo-***													
r3	**Resazurin**	Diazoresorcinol. 3-Isophenoxazinone 10-oxide. Resazoin. $C_{12}H_7NO_4 \cdot$	229.18	dk red to grsh pr or pl (aa or (AcOEt) $\lambda^{w,pH=4}$ 355 (3.6), 425.5 (3.6), 520 (3.9)	d	sub vac	....	....	i	δ	i	...	...	alk s aa δ	**B27**, 128
r4	**Rescinnamine**	Moderil. $C_{35}H_{42}N_2O_9$	634.74	nd (bz) $[\alpha]_D^{24}$ -98 (chl, c = 0.1) λ^{al} 229 (4.73), 302 (4.39)	238–9	....	....	....	i	δ	...	s	...	chl, AcOEt s	**Am 77**, 2241
r5	**Reserpic acid**	Reserpinolic acid. $C_{22}H_{28}N_2O_5 \cdot$	400.48	(MeOH) $[\alpha]_D^{23}$ (of hydrochloride) -81 $\lambda^{al\ HCl}$ 225 (4.43), 269 (3.71), 295 (3.81)	241–3	....	....	....							**Am 78**, 2023
Ω r6	**Reserpine**	Rivasin. Serparsin. $C_{33}H_{40}N_2O_9 \cdot$	608.70	lo pr (dil ace) $[\alpha]_D -117.7$ (chl, c = 1), -164 (Py, c = 0.96) λ^{chl} 268 (3.15), 295 (4.02)	264–5, 277–7.5 sealed tube	....	....	....	δ^h	s^h	δ	δ	s	chl s AcOEt s	**H37**, 67
—	**—,11-desmethoxy-**	see **Deserpidine**													
r7	**Reserpinine**	Raubasinine. $C_{22}H_{26}N_2O_4 \cdot$	382.47	pa ye pl (aq ace) $[\alpha]_D^{20} -131$ (chl, c = 1.18) $[\alpha]_D^{22} -129$ (Py, c = 0.5) λ^{al} 229 (4.58), 299 (3.74)	243–4d	....	....	....	i	s	...	...	...	chl s	**C49**, 11672
—	**Resodiacetophenone**	see **Benzene, 1,5-diacetyl-2,4-dihydroxy-**													
—	**Resorcinol**	see **Benzene, 1,3-dihydroxy-***													
—	**Resorcylaldehyde** ..	see **Benzaldehyde, 2,4-dihydroxy-**													
—	**Resorcylic acid**	see **Benzoic acid, dihydroxy-**													
r8	**Resorufin**	7-Hydroxy-2-phenoxazone.	213.20	br nd (PhNH$_2$), red pr (HCl) $\lambda^{w,pH=4}$ 413 sh (3.8), 493 (4.0) $\lambda^{w,pH=8}$ 561 (4.4)			....	....	i	δ	i	...	...	alk v	**B27²**, 108
—	**Retene**	see **Phenanthrene, 7-isopropyl-1-methyl-***													
—	**Retenoquinone**	see **9,10-Phenanthroquinone, 7-isopropyl-1-methyl-***													
r10	**Retronecine**	Senecifolinene.	155.20	pr (ace) $[\alpha]_D$ $+27.4$ (w), $[\alpha]_D^{26} +50.2$ (al)	121–2 (130–1)	$80^{0.01}$	....	....	v	v	δ	s	...	....	**J1936**, 744
r11	**Rhamnetin**	$C_{16}H_{12}O_7 \cdot$	316.27	ye nd (al, PhOH) $\lambda^{alk\ al}$ 238 sh (4.35)	294–6	....	....	....	δ^h	s^h	...	s	...	dil alk v PhOH s^h	**B18²**, 237
r12	**Rhamnitol**(D)	Rhamnite.	166.18	pr (ace) $[\alpha]_D^{20}$ -12.4 (w, c = 0.5)	123	....	....	....	s	s	i	...	...	chl δ Py s	**B1**, 532

For explanations, symbols and abbreviations see beginning of table. For structural formulas see end of table.

No.	Name	Synonyms and Formula	Mol. wt.	Color, crystalline form, specific rotation and λ_{max} (log ε)	m.p. °C	b.p. °C	Density	n_D	w	al	eth	ace	bz	other solvents	Ref.
	α-Rhamnose														
r13	α-Rhamnose(d), hydrate	....	182.18	(w + 1), $[\alpha]_D^{20}$ + 3.76 → −0.82 (3 hours), (mut) $[\alpha]_D^{6.5}$ −8.25 (w)	90–1	....	....		s		i				B1[1], 439
r14	—(dl)...........	$C_6H_{12}O_5$. See r13	164.16	(w)	151.3–3 (anh)				s	s	i				C25, 84
r15	—(l), hydrate	$C_6H_{12}O_5 \cdot H_2O$. See r13	182.18	mcl pl (al, w + 1) $[\alpha]_D^{20}$ −77 → + 8.9 (mut)	92	105^2 sub	1.4708^{20}	....	s	s	...			MeOH s	B1[2], 901 B31, 66
r16	β-Rhamnose(l)	$C_6H_{12}O_5$. See r13	164.16	nd (ace) $[\alpha]_D^{20}$ + 38.4 → + 8.9 (w) (mut)	122–6							s^h δ			B1[1], 439
—	Rhamnoxanthin ...	see **Frangulin**													
r17	**Rheadin**..........	Rhoeadine. $C_{21}H_{21}NO_6$	383.41	nd (chl, eth, al) $[\alpha]_D^{17.5}$ +232 (chl, c = 0.025) λ^{MeOH} 242 (4.0), 291 (4.0)	256–7.5	sub	....		δ	δ	δ				C35, 6060
r18	**Rhizopterin**	12-Formylpteroic acid. $C_{15}H_{12}N_6O_4$.	340.31	lt ye pl (aq AcONH₄), lf (aq aa) $\lambda^{w, pH=7}$ 248 (4.34), 265 (4.30), 348 (3.69)	>300 285 darkens	....	....		i	i	i			aq alk s aq NH₃ s Py s	Am 69, 2751
Ω r19	**Rhodamine B**.....	Tetraethylrhodamine.	442.57	gr lf (w +4), col pr (al, xyl) λ^{al} 546 (4.86)	165 (anh)	....	....		s	s	s		s	os i xyl s^h	B19[2], 373
r20	—, hydrochloride .	$C_{26}H_{30}N_2O_3 \cdot HCl$. See r19 ..	479.03	gr or red vt pw (w), lf (dil HCl)					v	v			s	w (red) dil HCl δ	B19[2], 373
Ω r21	**Rhodanine**	4-Oxo-2-thioxothiazolidine. Rhodanic acid. 4-Thioxo-4-thiazolidone.	133.19	lt ye pr (al, w, aa) λ^{al} 250.5 (4.12), 294 (4.24)	170		0.868		δ v^h	v	v			MeOH v aa s lig i	B27[2], 288
Ω r22	—,5[4(dimethyl-amino)-benzylidene]-	$C_{12}H_{12}N_2OS_2$. See r21	264.37	red or og nd (al, Py-w)	296 (282)				i	$δ^h$	v	s	δ	min ac s lig i CCl_4^v chl δ	B27[2], 484
r23	—,5-ethyl-	$C_5H_7NOS_2$. See r21	161.25	ye amor (dil al) λ^{al} 253 (4.1), 296 (4.3)	105				i	v	v	v		peth i aa v	B27[1], 313
Ω r24	—,3-phenyl-	$C_9H_7NOS_2$. See r21	209.29	ye pl (aa), nd or pr (al) λ^{al} 220 (3.9), 230 (3.9), 250 (4.0), 295 (4.1)	194–5				i	δ s^h	δ	s^h		chl s^h lig δ aa s^h	B27[2], 288
—	**Rhodinal**	see **Citronellal**													
—	**Rhodinol**	see **Citronellol**													
r25	**Rhodizonic acid**....	5,6-Dihydroxy-5-cyclohexene-1,2,3,4-tetrone*.	170.08	dk og nd (sub)	155–60 (anh)				d	s					B8[2], 572
—	**Ribitol**	see **Adonitol**													
Ω r26	**Riboflavin**	Lactoflavin. Vitamin B₂. Vitamin G. $C_{17}H_{20}N_4O_6$.	376.37	ye or og-ye nd (w, dil aa) $[\alpha]_D^{25}$ −112 → −122 (0.02N NaOH, c = 0.5) (mut) $[\alpha]_D$ −8.80 (w) λ^w 267 (4.51), 373 (4.02), 447 (4.09)	280d	....	....		i	$δ^h$	i	i		chl i	C28, 2036
Ω r27	**Ribose**(D)		150.13	pl (abs al) $[\alpha]_D$ −21.5 (w) $[\alpha]_D^{20}$ −38.2 → + 43.1 (Py) (mut)	95 (87)	....	....		s	δ	...				B1[1], 434
r29	**Ricinidine**	1-Methyl-2-pyridone-3-carbonitrile.	134.14	nd (sub), (chl, al)	140	243^{28}				s^h				chl s^h	B22[2], 222

For explanations, symbols and abbreviations see beginning of table. For structural formulas see end of table.

No.	Name	Synonyms and Formula	Mol. wt.	Color, crystalline form, specific rotation and λ_{max} (log ε)	m.p. °C	b.p. °C	Density	n_D	Solubility						Ref.
									w	al	eth	ace	bz	other solvents	
	Ricinine														
r30	**Ricinine**	Ricidine. $C_8H_8N_2O_2$.	164.18	pr or lf (w, al) λ^{MeOH} 256 (3.50), 313 (3.89)	201.5	sub 170– 80[20]	. . . .		s^h	δ	. . .	. . .	δ^h	chl s^h Py v^h peth i	B22[1], 371
—	**Ricinoleic acid**	see **9-Octadecenoic acid, 12-hydroxy-(cis)***													
—	**Rivanol**	see **Acridine, 6,9-diamino-2-ethoxy-**													
—	**Roccelic acid**	see **Succinic acid, 2-dodecyl-3-methyl-**													
—	**Rosaniline**	see **Methanol,(4-amino-3-methylphenyl)bis(4-aminophenyl)**													
r31	**Rosinduline, anhydro base**	$C_{22}H_{17}NO_3$.	337.39	red-br lf (eth, bz)	198–9	. . . .			i	v	v	. . .	v	. . . .	B25[2], 322
Ω r32	**Rotenone**	Tubotoxine. $C_{23}H_{22}O_6$.	394.43	nd or lf (al, aq ace), (CCl_4 +1) $[\alpha]_D^{9.5}$ −225.2 (bz) $[\alpha]_D$ −132 (al, c = 0.125) λ^{al} 237 (4.15), 293.5 (4.25), 330.5 (3.80)	(i) 163 (ii) 176	210–20[0.5]			i	s	δ	s	s	chl v, aa s os s	B19[2], 438
r33	**Rubicene**		326.40	red nd (xyl or Ph NO_2) λ^{al} 230 (5.10), 251 (5.00)	306					i	i		δ	PhNO_2 v^h CS_2 s peth i con sulf i	B5[2], 707
r34	**Rubijervine**	$C_{27}H_{43}NO_2$.	413.65	nd (+1w, dil al) $[\alpha]_D^5$ +19.0 (al, c = 1.0)	242				i	s	δ	. . .	s	chl s aq ac s aq alk i con sulf (red) peth δ	C32, 5996
r35	**Rubixanthin**	3-Hydroxy-γ-carotene. $C_{40}H_{56}O$.	552.90	dk red nd (bz-MeOH), og-red (bz-peth) λ^{CS_2} 461, 494, 533	160						δ		s	chl s peth δ	B30, 93
Ω r36	**Rubrene**	9,10,11,12-Tetraphenyl-naphthacene. $C_{42}H_{28}$	532.69	og red (bz-lig) λ^{bz} 439 (3.40), 464 (3.76), 495 (4.06), 529 (4.05)	331		Ω		i	δ	δ	δ	s	CS_2 δ Py δ aa i	B5[2], 725
—	**Rufigallic acid**	see **9,10-Anthraquinone, 1,2,3,5,6,7-hexahydroxy-**													
—	**Rufiopin**	see **9,10-Anthraquinone, 1,2,5,6-tetrahydroxy-***													
—	**Rufol**	see **Anthracene, 1,5-dihydroxy-***													
r37	**Rutaecarpine**	$C_{18}H_{13}N_3O$.	287.33	yesh nd (al or AcOEt) λ^{MeOH} 232 (4.45), 276 (3.93), 288 (3.97), 328 (4.50), 343 (4.57), 358 (4.47)	259–60	. . . .				δ	. . .	δ	δ	ac v con sulf → ye	B26[2], 104
r38	**Rutinose**	6(β-1-L-Rhamnosido) D-glucose.	326.30	hyg pw (al, eth) $[\alpha]_D^{20}$ + 3.2 → −0.8 (w, c = 4) (mut) $[\alpha]_D^{20}$ −10 (al)	189–92d	. . . .			v	s	i	. . .	. . .	. . . .	B31, 376
—	**Rutonal**	see **Barbituric acid, 5-methyl-5-phenyl-**													

For explanations, symbols and abbreviations see beginning of table. For structural formulas see end of table.

Sabadine

No.	Name	Synonyms and Formula	Mol. wt.	Color, crystalline form, specific rotation and λ_{max} (log ε)	m.p. °C	b.p. °C	Density	n_D	w	al	eth	ace	bz	other solvents	Ref.
s1	**Sabadine**	$C_{29}H_{48}NO_8$	541.73	nd (eth) $[\alpha]_D -11$ (al)	256–60				δ	s	δ	s			**C54,** 2386
—	**Sabinane**	*see* **Thujane**													
s2	**Sabinene**(d)	4(10)-Thujene	136.24	$[\alpha]_D^{20} +101.4$		$163-5^{758}$ 49^{13}	0.8437_4^{20}	1.4676^{20}	i	∞	s		s		**B5²,** 96
s3	—(l)	$C_{10}H_{16}$. See s2	136.24	$[\alpha]_D^{15} -42.5$		$162-6$	0.8468^{20}	1.4674^{17}	i	∞	s		s		**B5²,** 96
Ω s4	**Sabinol**(d)	4(10)-Thuien-3-ol $C_{10}H_{16}O$	152.24	$[\alpha]_D^{18} +3.94$		208 90^{11}	0.9488_4^{19}	1.4871^{25}		s	s		s		**E12A,** 13
s5	**Saccharic acid**(d)		210.14	nd (95 % al), $[\alpha]_D +6.86 \rightarrow +20.60$ (w, c = 2.5) (mut)	125–6				v	v	δ			chl δ	**B3²,** 377
Ω s6	**Saccharin**	2-Sulfobenzoic acid imide.	183.19	mcl (ace), pr (al), lf (w) $\lambda^{MeOH} 230$ sh (3.8), 260 sh (2.9)	228.8–9.7d	sub vac	0.828		δ s^h	s	δ	s	δ	alk v chl δ	**B27,** 168
Ω s7	**Safrole**	1-Allyl-3,4-Methylene-dioxybenzene. Shikimole.	162.19	mcl $\lambda^{al} 236$ (3.62), 285 (3.58)	11.2	234.5^{760} $104-5^6$	1.1000_4^{20}	1.5383^{20}	i	v	∞			chl ∞	**B19²,** 29
—	**Salicin**	*see* **Toluene,** α,2-dihydroxy-, glucoside													
—	**Salicylaldehyde**	*see* **Benzaldehyde,** 2-hydroxy-													
—	**Salicylic acid**	*see* **Benzoic acid,** 2-hydroxy-													
—	**Saligenin**	*see* **Toluene,** α,2-dihydroxy-													
—	**Salipyrine**	*see* **Antipyrine,** 2-hydroxybenzoate													
—	**Salol**	*see* **Benzoic acid,** 2-hydroxy-, phenyl ester													
—	**Salophen**	*see* **Benzoic acid,** 2-hydroxy-, 4-acetamido-phenyl ester													
s8	**Salsoline**	$C_{11}H_{15}NO_2$	193.26	pw or cr (al) $[\alpha]_D^{20} +34.5$ (0.1 N HCl, c = 1) $\lambda^{MeOH} 226$ (3.79), 285 (3.55)	221–2				δ	s	i		δ	chl, NaOH s peth i	**C53,** 14039
s9	**Salvarsan**	606. Arsphenamine.	475.03	gy pw	185–95d				v^h	δ	i		i	dil HCl s MeOH δ con HCl i	**B16²,** 560
s10	**Sambunigrin**	d-Mandelonitrile glucoside. $C_6H_5CH(CN)O.C_6H_{11}O_5$	295.30	nd (bz-peth), $[\alpha]_D^{18} -75.1$	151.5–2.5				s	s				AcOEt s	**B31,** 239
s11	**Samidin**	$C_{21}H_{22}O_7$	386.41	cubic, $[\alpha]_D^{21} +49.1$ (chl, c = 1.59) $\lambda^{al} 322$ (3.15)	138–9				i	δ	s			MeOH s	**Ber 92,** 2338
—	**Sandoptal**	*see* **Barbituric acid,** 5-allyl-5-isobutyl-													
s12	**Sanguinarine**	ψ-Chelerythrine. $C_{20}H_{15}NO_5$	351.36	cr (eth) cr (al + 1)	266 (242–3 slow htng) 195–7 (+al)				i	s	s	s	s		**C54,** 13552
s13	**Santalic acid**	Guerbet's acid.	234.34	red		β:202 γ:189		β:1.5136^{20} γ:1.5055^{20}							
s14	**α-Santalol**	Arheol. $C_{15}H_{24}O$	220.36	$[\alpha]_D^{20} +17.0$		$301-2^{760}$ 167^{14}	0.9769_4^{20}	1.5023^{20}	i i	∞ s					**B9,** 571 **B6¹,** 275
s15	**β-Santalol**	$C_{15}H_{24}O$	220.36	$[\alpha]_D^{20} -90.5$		$167-8^{10}$ 133^1	0.9750^{20}	1.5115^{20}							**B6²,** 517
s16	**Santene**	2,3-Dimethyl-2-norbornene.	122.21		140–1 35^{15}		0.8698_4^{17}	1.4688^{17}			s	s	s		**E12A,** 540
s17	**Santenic acid** (cis, d)	π-Norcamphenic acid.	186.21	pl (w), $[\alpha]_D^{3.3} +38.3$ (al)	170–1				a^h	s				alk s	**B9²,** 529
s18	**β-Santenol** (cis, exo)	2,3-Dimethyl-2-norbor-nanol.	140.23	nd (al) tab (lig)	101–2	192			i		s				**E12A,** 632
s19	**α-Santenone**(cis)	1,7-Dimethyl-2-norbor-nanone.	138.12	pl, $[\alpha]_D^{22} +11.4$ (al)	55	191				s		s	s		**E12A,** 271
s20	**Santonin**	Santonic acid. $C_{15}H_{18}O_3$	246.31	orh (w, al, eth) $[\alpha]_D^{18} -173$ (al, c = 2) $\lambda^{al} 240$ (4.0), 268 (3.8)	174–6 (120 sub)		1.187_4^{26}	1.590 (1.640)	δ^h	δ s^h	δ s^h		s	chl, Py s peth i	**E12B,** 3736

For explanations, symbols and abbreviations see beginning of table. For structural formulas see end of table.

No.	Name	Synonyms and Formula	Mol. wt.	Color. crystalline form. specific rotation and λ_{max} (log ε)	m.p. °C	b.p. °C	Density	n_D	Solubility						Ref.
									w	al	eth	ace	bz	other solvents	

Sarmentogenin

s21	Sarmentogenin	$C_{23}H_{34}O_5$	390.53	pr (85 % al or MeOH-eth), nd (al), $[\alpha]_D^{19}$ +21.1 ± 4 (MeOH, c = 0.5) λ^{al} 217 (4.24), 288 (1.00)	270–5	....	....	....	i	s	i	δ	i	MeOH, Py s chl δ	E14, 237
s22	Sarpagine	Raupine. $C_{19}H_{22}N_2O_2$	310.40	nd, $[\alpha]_D^{20}$ + 54 (Py) λ^{al} 231 (4.2), 280 (3.95)	320				i	s^h	...	...	...		Am 84, 622
s23	Sarsasapogenin	Parigenin. $C_{27}H_{44}O_3$	416.65	lo pr nd (ace), $[\alpha]_D^{25}$ − 75 (chl, c = 0.5) λ^{al} <230 λ^{sulf} 398 (3.44)	200–1.5					s	...	s	s	chl s	E14, 282
s24	Scarlet red		380.46	dk br pw or nd	186 δd	d 260			i	δ	...	δ	δ	chl, peth s	B16, 172
s25	Scilliroside	$C_{32}H_{44}O_{12}$	620.67	lo pr (dil MeOH), $[\alpha]_D^{20}$ − 59.4 (MeOH, c = 1) λ^{al} 302 (3.65)	168–70	d			δ	v	i	δ	...	diox v chl, AcOEt δ	H42, 1620
—	Scopolamine	see Hyoscine													
—	Scopoletin	see Coumarin, 7-hydroxy-6-methoxy-													
s26	Scopoline	Oscin.	155.20	hyg nd (lig, eth, peth or chl)	108–9	248	1.089_4^{134}	....	s	s	s^h	s	...	chl, peth δ	B27[2], 61
s27	Scyllitol	$C_6H_{12}O_6$	180.16	pr (+3w)	353d	1.659_4^{19}			δ	i	i	...	i	chl, MeOH i	B6[2], 1160
—	Sebacic acid	see Decanedioic acid*													
s28	Sedormide	$H_2NCONHCOCH(CH_2CH:CH_2)CH(CH_3)_2$	184.24	nd (al)	194				δ	s^h	δ	...	...	chl s	B3[2], 53
s29	Selenanthrene	Diphenyldiselenide.	310.13	pr (al), nd (ace) $\lambda^{96 \%}$ ^{al} 240 (4.22), 330 (2.99)	181	223^{11}				δ s^h	δ	...	...	CS_2 s	B19, 47
s30	Selenide, diethyl ...	$(C_2H_5)_2Se$	137.06	pa ye	....	108	1.2300_4^{20}	1.4768^{20}	i	v	v	...	v	chl v	B1[3], 357
s31	—,dimethyl	$(CH_3)_2Se$	109.03	....	54–5[753]	1.4077_4^{15}			i	s	s	δ	...	chl s to, MeOH δ	B1, 291
s32	—,—,hexachloro-..	$(Cl_3C)_2Se$	315.70	....	37							...	...	CCl_4 s	J1947, 1080
s33	—,diphenyl	$(C_6H_5)_2Se$	233.17	ye nd (bz) λ^{al} 235 (3.78), 255 (3.97), 275 sh (3.67)	2.5	301–2[760] 126–7[5]	1.3512_4^{20}	1.6500^{20}	i	∞	∞	...	s	xyl s	B6[2], 318
s34	—,di(2-tolyl)		261.23	pl or lf (al)	65	186^{16}			i	s^h	δ	...	...	chl δ	B6[2], 343
s35	—,di(4-tolyl)		261.23	rods or nd (al) λ^{al} 257 (4.00), 275 sh (3.68)	69–70	196^{16}			i	s^h	δ	...	...	chl δ	B6[2], 402
s36	Selenonium, diphenyl-, dichloride	$(C_6H_5)_2SeCl_2$	304.08	pa ye pr (xyl or ace), nd (al-HCl)	183 (142d)				s	s	i	s	...	chl, CCl_4 i	B6[2], 318
s37	—,triphenyl-, chloride	$(C_6H_5)_3SeCl$	345.71	orh (AcOEt)	230d	....			v	v	δ	δ	...	chl s	J1946, 1126
s38	—,—,fluoride	$(C_6H_5)_3SeF$	329.26	oct deliq	145d				v	v	...	s	...	chl v	J1946, 1126
s39	—,—,hydrogen fluoride	$(C_6H_5)_3SeF. HF$	349.27	nd (ace)	99						...	s	...		J1946, 1126
—	Selenophenol......	see Phenol, seleno-													
Ω s39[1]	Semicarbazide*....	Aminourea. Carbamyl-hydrazine. $H_2NCONHNH_2$	75.07	pr (al) λ^{al} 231 (1.2)	96				v	s	i	...	i	chl i	B3[2], 80
Ω s39[2]	—,hydrochloride ..	$H_2NCONHNH_2 . HCl$	111.52	pr (dil al) λ^w 278 sh (−0.7) 357 sh (−1.1)	175–7d				v $δ^h$	i	i	...	...		B3, 100
s40	—,1,1-diphenyl-*	$H_2NCONHN(C_6H_5)_2$	227.27	nd (al or bz)	195	....				v^h	...	...	v^h	con sulf s	B15, 304
s41	—,1,4-diphenyl-*	$C_6H_5NHCONHNHC_6H_5$	227.27	nd or lf (al, bz) λ^{al} 275 (3.4)	177				$δ^h$	v	i	...	...		B15[2], 106
s42	—,2,4-diphenyl-*	$C_6H_5NHCON(NH_2)C_6H_5$	227.27	lf (al)	165.5					s	s	...	s	chl v	B15, 277
s43	—,1,1-diphenyl-3-thio-*	$H_2NCSNHN(C_6H_5)_2$	243.33	cr (al or bz)	202				i	v^h	v	...	v	chl v lig i	B15, 304
s44	—,2,4-diphenyl-3-thio-*	$C_6H_5NHCSN(NH_2)C_6H_5$	243.33	lf (al)	139					δ v^h	v	...	v^h		B15[2], 103
s45	—,2-phenyl-*	$H_2NCON(NH_2)C_6H_5$	151.17	nd (bz or al) λ^{al} 242 (4.00)	120				v^h	v	δ	...	δ	chl v	B15[2], 103
Ω s46	—,4-phenyl-*	$C_6H_5NHCONHNH_2$	151.17	nd (bz), pl (w) λ^{al} 238 (4.3), 280 (2.9)	128				$δ^h$	v	i	...	...	chl v	B12[2], 221

For explanations, symbols and abbreviations see beginning of table. For structural formulas see end of table.

No.	Name	Synonyms and Formula	Mol. wt.	Color, crystalline form, specific rotation and λ_{max} (log ε)	m.p. °C	b.p. °C	Density	n_D	w	al	eth	ace	bz	other solvents	Ref.
	Semicarbazide														
Ω s47	—,1-phenyl-3-thio-*	$H_2NCSNHNHC_6H_5$	167.23	pr (al) λ^{al} 245 (4.2), 275 sh (3.3)	200–1d	....	....	....	δ	s[h]	δ	...	δ	chl δ	B15[2], 110
s48	—,2-phenyl-3-thio-*	$H_2NCSN(NH_2)C_6H_5$	167.23	(w) λ^{al} 255 (3.91)	153					δ	s			δ		B15[1], 70
s49	—,4-phenyl-3-thio-*	$C_6H_5NHCSNHNH_2$	167.23	pl (al) λ^{al} 256 (4.3)	140d					s[h]	i			δ	lig i	B12[2], 232
s50	—,3-thio-*	Thiosemicarbazide. $H_2NCSNHNH_2$	91.14	lo nd (w) λ^{al} 244 (4.2), 280 sh (2.4)	183					s	s					B3[2], 134
Ω s51	—,1(3-tolyl)-	Maretine	165.19	lf (w or dil al) λ^{al} 234.5 (4.00), 282.5 (3.30)	183–4					δ	v[h]	i				B15, 508
s52	—,1,1,4-tri-phenyl-*	$C_6H_5NHCONHN(C_6H_5)_2$	303.37	nd (al)	206–7						δ v[h]					B15[2], 115
s53	—,1,4,4-tri-phenyl-*	$(C_6H_5)_2NCONHNHC_6H_5$	303.37	pl (al)	151–2					i	v[h]					B15[1], 71
s54	—,2,4,4-tri-phenyl-*	$(C_6H_5)_2NCON(NH_2)C_6H_5$	303.37	cr (dil al)	128					i	v				peth i	B15, 277
—	Seminose	see **Mannose**													
s55	Serine(D)	2-Amino-3-hydroxy-propanoic acid*. $HOCH_2CH(NH_2)CO_2H$	105.10	nd or hex pr (w) $[\alpha]_D^{20} +6.87$ (w, c = 10)	228d	d				v	i	i		i	aa i	B4[2], 919
Ω s56	—(DL)	$HOCH_2CH(NH_2)CO_2H$	105.10	mcl pr or lf (w)	246d (sealed tube)			$1.603^{22.5}$		s	i	i		i	aa i	B4[2], 934
s57	—(L)	$HOCH_2CH(NH_2)CO_2H$	105.10	hex pl or pr (w) $[\alpha]_D^{20} -6.83$ (w, c = 10)	228d	sub $150^{10^{-4}}$				v	i	i		i	aa i	B4[2], 919
Ω s58	Serpentine	$C_{21}H_{20}N_2O_3$	348.41	ye rods or lf (al) $[\alpha]_D^{25} +292 \pm 2$ (MeOH) λ^{al} 252 (4.3), 310 (4.35), 370 (3.55)	175					i	s	s	s		MeOH v aq aa s	Am 76, 2843
s59	Sesamin	Asaranin. $C_{20}H_{18}O_6$	354.34	nd (al) $[\alpha]_D^{20} +68.4$ (chl, c = 24) λ^{al} 235 (3.97), 288 (3.92)	123–4					i	δ	δ	s	s	chl s peth δ	B19[2], 490
s60	Shikonine	d-Alkannin	288.30	br-red nd (bz) $[\alpha]_{644}^{20} +135$ (bz, c = 1.3) λ^{CCl_4} 488 (3.8), 524 (3.9), 543 sh (3.7), 560 (3.7)	147	....				i	s	s	s	s	oos s	B8[2], 543
s61	Silane, butyl-(trichloro)-	Butylsilicon trichloride. $CH_3(CH_2)_3SiCl_3$	191.56		....	148.9^{760}	1.1606_4^{20}	1.4363^{20}	d	d[h]	s	...	s	to, AcOEt s	B4[1], 582
s62	—,chloro(tri-ethoxy)-	Orthosiliconic acid mono-chloride, triethyl ester. $(C_2H_5O)_3SiCl$	198.72		−51	$156–6.5^{760}$ 69^{32}	1.032_{20}^{20}	1.3999^{20}	d	s					B1[3], 1336
s63	—,dichloro-(diethoxy)-	$(C_2H_5O)_2SiCl_2$	189.12		−130	135.9^{760} 51.6^{32}	1.1290_4^{20}		d	s					B1[3], 1336
Ω s63[1]	—,dichloro-(diethyl)-	$(C_2H_5)_2SiCl_2$	157.12		−96.5	128–30d	1.0504_4^{20}	1.4309^{20}	d	d					B4, 629
Ω s64	—,dichloro-(diphenyl)-	$(C_6H_5)_2SiCl_2$	253.21			$302–5^{757}$ $163–5^{10}$	1.2216_4^{20}	1.5819^{20}	d	d					B16[2], 608
s65	—,diethoxy-(difluoro)-	Diethyl difluorosilicate. $(C_2H_5O)_2SiF_2$	156.21		−122	83^{760}d			d						Am 68, 76
s67	—,diethyl-(difluoro)-	$(C_2H_5)_2SiF_2$	124.21		−78.7	60.9^{755}	0.9348_4^{20}	1.3385^{20}	i d[h]						J1944, 454
s68	—,difluoro-(diphenyl)-	$(C_6H_5)_2SiF_2$	220.30			252^{760} 158^{50}	1.145_4^{17}	1.5221^{25}	i d[h]				s		J1944, 454
s69	—,dimethyl-	Dimethylsilicane. $(CH_3)_2SiH_2$	60.17	gas	−155.2	-19.6^{760}	0.68^{-80}								B4[1], 579
s70	—,ethoxy(tri-chloro)-	$(C_2H_5O)SiCl_3$	179.51		−135	101.9^{760}	1.2274^{20}	1.4045^{20}	d	s					B1, 335
s71	—,ethoxy(tri-ethyl)-	$(C_2H_5O)Si(C_2H_5)_3$	160.34			154–5	0.8160^{20}	1.4140^{20}	i	∞	∞			sulf s	B4, 627
s72	—,ethoxy(tri-fluoro)-	$(C_2H_5O)SiF_3$	130.15	gas	−122	-7^{760}									J1949, 1696
Ω s73	—,ethyl(tri-chloro)-	$C_2H_5SiCl_3$	163.51		−105.6	97.9^{760}	1.2381_4^{20}	1.4257^{20}	d	d					B4[1], 582
s74	—,ethyl(tri-ethoxy)-	Triethyl ethaneorthosili-conate. $C_2H_5Si(OC_2H_5)_3$	192.33			158.9	0.8594_4^{20}	1.3955^{20}	i	∞	∞				B4, 630
s74[1]	—,ethyl(tri-fluoro)-	$C_2H_5SiF_3$	114.14		−105	-4.4^{760}	1.227^{-76}		d						J1944, 454
s74[2]	—,ethyl(tri-methoxy)-	Trimethyl ethaneortho-siliconate. $C_2H_5Si(OCH_3)_3$	150.25			124.3^{760}	0.9488_4^{20}	1.3838^{20}	...	s					B4, 629

For explanations, symbols and abbreviations see beginning of table. For structural formulas see end of table.

No.	Name	Synonyms and Formula	Mol. wt.	Color, crystalline form, specific rotation and λ_{max} (log ε)	m.p. °C	b.p. °C	Density	n_D	w	al	eth	ace	bz	other solvents	Ref.
	Silane														
s75	—,fluoro(tri-ethoxy)-	$(C_2H_5O)_3SiF$	182.27	....	....	134.6^{760}	....	....	d	...	...				J1944, 1696
s76	—,fluoro(tri-ethyl)-	$(C_2H_5)_3SiF$	134.27	....	....	110^{760}	0.8354^{25}_4	1.3900^{25}	i	...	...			peth, lig ∞	Am 58, 897
—	—,hydroxy-	*see* Silicol													
s77	—,methyl-	Methylsilicane. CH_3SiH_3	46.15	....	−156.5	−57			i	...	...				B4[1], 579
Ω s77[1]	—,methyl(tri-ethoxy)-	Trimethyl methaneortho-siliconate. $CH_3Si(OC_2H_5)_3$	178.31	....	....	143^{760}	0.8923^{20}	1.3835^{20}	...	s					B4[3], 1895
s78	—,phenyl(tri-fluoro)-	$C_6H_5SiF_3$	162.19	....	....	101.5^{760} 16.5^{24}	1.2169^{20}_4	1.4110^{20}	d	s			s		J1944, 454
s79	—,tetraethyl-	$(C_2H_5)_4Si$	144.34	....	....	153^{760} 108^{200}	0.7658^{20}_4	1.4268^{20}	i						B4[2], 1007
Ω s80	—,tetramethyl-	$(CH_3)_4Si$	88.23	....	α: −102.2 β: −99.1	26.5^{760}	0.648^{19}_4	1.3587^{20}	i	v	v			sulf i	B4[1], 579
s81	—,triethyl-	$(C_2H_5)_3SiH$	116.27	....	....	109^{755}	0.7302^{20}	1.4117^{20}	i					sulf i	B4, 625
—	Silicane	*see* Silane													
s82	Silicol, triethyl-	$(C_2H_5)_3SiOH$	132.28	....	....	154^{760} 46.6^9	0.8647^{20}_4	1.4329^{20}	i	∞	∞				B4[1], 581
—	Sinapic acid	*see* Cinnamic acid, 3,5-dimethoxy-4-hydroxy-													
s83	Sinapine, hydrogen sulfate	$C_{16}H_{23}NO_5.H_2SO_4$	407.44	lf(al)	186–7d	....	....		s	s[h]	i				B10, 509
s84	—,hydrogen sulfate trihydrate	$C_{16}H_{23}NO_5.H_2SO_4.3H_2O.$ *See* s83	461.48	lf(al)	127d	....	....		s	s[h]	i				B10, 509
s85	—,thiocyanate monohydrate	$C_{16}H_{23}NO_5.HSCN.H_2O.$ *See* s83	386.45	ye nd	180–1				δ	δ					B10[2], 354
—	Sinapyl alcohol	*see* 2-Propen-1-ol, 3(3,5-dimethoxy-4-hydroxyphenyl)-*													
s86	Sinomenine	Cuculine. $C_{19}H_{23}NO_4$.	329.40	nd (bz), $[\alpha]_D^{26}$ −71 (al, c = 2.1) $\lambda^{aq.HCl}$230 sh (3.8), 266 (3.7)	162 (182 after melting)	....	....		δ	s	δ	s	δ	chl, dil alk s	B21[2], 470
s87	α_1-Sitosterol	$C_{29}H_{48}O$.	412.71	nd (al), $[\alpha]_D^{28}$ −1.7 (chl, c = 2)	166	....				s				chl s	E14, 89
s88	α_2-Sitosterol	$C_{30}H_{50}O$.	426.74	cr (al-peth), $[\alpha]_D^{25}$ +3.5 (chl, c = 2)	156	....								oos s peth δ	E14, 89
s89	α_3-Sitosterol	$C_{29}H_{48}O$.	412.71	pl (al), $[\alpha]_D^{20}$ +5.2 (chl)	142–3	....				s				chl s	E14, 90
s90	β-Sitosterol	Cinchol. Vorosterol. $C_{29}H_{50}O$.	414.72	pl (al), nd (MeOH) $[\alpha]_D^{25}$ −37 (chl, c = 2) λ^{al} 267 (3.61)	140 (137)	....				s	s			aa s	E14, 90
—	Skatole	*see* Indole, 3-methyl-													
s91	Skimmin	7-Hydroxycoumarin-7-D glucoside. Umbelliferone-D glucoside.	324.29	cr (w + 1) $[\alpha]_D^{18}$ −80 (Py, c = 10) λ^{al} 319 (4.1)	219–21	....			s[h]	s	i			chl i	B31, 245
s92	Smilagenin	Isosarsapogenin.$C_{27}H_{44}O_3$.	416.65	silky nd (ace), $[\alpha]_D^{25}$ −69 (chl, c = 0.5)	185	....					s	s	s	chl s	E14, 284
s94	Solanidine-T	Solatubine. $C_{27}H_{43}NO$	397.65	lo nd (chl-MeOH) $[\alpha]_D^{21}$ −29 (chl, c = 0.5)	218–9	sub δd			i	δ	i		v	chl v MeOH δ	J1936, 1299
s95	Solanine-S	Purapurine. Solatunine. $C_{45}H_{73}NO_{16}.$ $C_6H_{11}O_4-O-C_6H_{10}O_4-O-C_6H_{10}O_4-O-C_{27}H_{42}N$ rhamnose galactose glucose solanidine-T	884.09	nd (al), fl (diox) $[\alpha]_D^{20}$ −69 (al) $[\alpha]_D^{20}$ −60 (Py, c = 1)	*ca.* 190 (284.5d)	....			i δ^h	s[h]	i		i	diox s[h] chl i	J1963, 745
s96	Solasodine	Purapuridine. Solanidine-S. $C_{27}H_{43}NO_2$.	413.65	hex pl (sub) $[\alpha]_D^{20}$ −92.4 (bz) $[\alpha]_D^{?}$ +109.8 (chl)	202	....				s[h]	δ	s	s	chl v MeOH, diox, aq ac, Py s	J1942, 13
—	Solatubine	*see* Solanidine-T													
—	Solatunine	*see* Solanine-S													
—	Sorbic acid	*see* 2,4-Hexadienoic acid*													
s98	Sorbierite(D, −) ...	Iditol.	182.18	pr (al), $[\alpha]_D$ −3.53 (w, p = 2)	73–4	....			s						B1, 544
Ω s99	Sorbitol(D)	D-Glucitol. D-Sorbite.	182.18	nd (w + 0.5) $[\alpha]_D^{25}$ −1.98 (w) λ^w < 220	110–2 (anh) 75 (hyd)	$295^{3.5}$	1.489^{20}_4	1.3330^{20}	v	δ^h	i	s		Py v[h] aa s	B1[3], 2385
s100	—(L)	Gulitol. $C_6H_{14}O_6$. *See* s99.	182.18	nd (w + 0.5) $[\alpha]$ + 1.7 (w)	77	....			v	δ^h	i	s		aa s	B1, 534

For explanations, symbols and abbreviations see beginning of table. For structural formulas see end of table.

Sorbitol

No.	Name	Synonyms and Formula	Mol. wt.	Color, crystalline form, specific rotation and λ_{max} (log ε)	m.p. °C	b.p. °C	Density	n_D	w	al	eth	ace	bz	other solvents	Ref.
Ω s101	—,hexaacetate(D)	$C_{18}H_{26}O_{12}$. See s99	434.38	pr (w), $[\alpha]_D^{18}$ +6.8 (ace)	99.5 (120)				δ^h	v	δ			AcOEt s	B2², 163
s102	Sorbose(D)	Pseudotagatose. D-Sorbinose.	180.16	rh (al), $[\alpha]_D^{20}$ +42.9 (w)	165		1.612¹⁷		s	δ	δ			MeOH δ	B31, 345
s103	—DL	β-Acrose. $C_6H_{12}O_6$. See s102	180.16	rh (dil al)	162–3 (154)		1.638¹⁷		s	δ^h	δ			MeOH δ	B31, 348
Ω s104	—(L)	$C_6H_{12}O_6$. See s102	180.16	rh (al), $[\alpha]_D^{20}$ −43.2 (w, c = 5) $\lambda^{79\ \%sulf}$ 243 (3.34), 299 (3.70)	165		1.612¹⁷		s	δ^h	δ			MeOH δ	B31, 346
—	Sorbyl alcohol	see 2,4-Hexadien-1-ol*													
—	Sparassol	see Benzoic acid, 2-hydroxy-4-methoxy-6-methyl-, methyl ester													
s105	Sparteine(D)	Lupinidine. $C_{15}H_{26}N_2$	234.39	$[\alpha]_D^{20}$ −19.5 (al) λ^{eth} 214 (3.71)	30–1	325⁷⁵⁴ 173⁸	1.0196²⁰	1.5312²⁰	δ	v	v			chl v	B2², 621
s106	—,sulfate pentahydrate	$C_{15}H_{26}N_2 . H_2SO_4 .5H_2O$. See s105	422.53	pr, $[\alpha]_D^{17}$ −15.3	242			1.5289	i	v					B23², 99
—	Spinacane	see Squalene, perhydro-													
—	Spinacene	see Squalene													
—	Spinulosin	see 1,4-Benzoquinone, 2,5-dihydroxy-3-methoxy-6-methyl-*													
s107	Spiro[5,5]hendecane, 2,4,8,10-tetraoxa-	Pentaerythritol dimethylene ether. Spiro-bi(1,3-dioxane).	160.17		46.5	147⁵³			v	v	s	s	s	CCl_4 s	B19², 449
s108	Squalene	Spinacene. $C_{30}H_{50}$	410.74	λ^{cy} < 220	< −20	280¹⁷ 241⁴	0.8584²⁰₄	1.4990²⁰	i	δ	s	s		CCl_4 s	B1², 250
Ω s109	—,perhydro	2,6,10,15,19,23-Hexamethyltetracosane*. Spinacane. $C_{30}H_{62}$. See s108	422.83	oil	−38	ca. 350⁷⁶⁰ 263¹⁰	0.8125¹⁵	1.4525²⁰	i	s^h δ	s	δ	∞	peth v MeOH, chl s aa δ	B1², 145
s110	Stachydrine(L)	Hygric acid methylbetaine. N-Methylproline methylbetaine. $C_7H_{13}NO_2$.	143.19	cr (w +1) $[\alpha]_D^{25}$ −40.25 (w, c = 4)	235d (anh) 116–8 (hyd)				s	s				chl i	B22², 4
s111	—,oxalate	$C_7H_{13}NO_2 . H_2C_2O_4$	233.22	nd	105–7					i					M, 974
s112	Starch	Amylum. $(C_6H_{10}O_5)_n$		amor pw	d				i	i					C51, 11746
s113	—,triacetate	$C_{216}H_{288}O_{144}$	7801.3	pw $[\alpha]_D^{25}$ +72.5	180 (>270 δd)				δ	δ		s	s	chl i	C46, 8401
—	Stearic acid	see Octadecanoic acid*													
—	Stearolic acid	see 9-Octadecynoic acid*													
—	Stearone	see 18-Pentatriacontanone*													
—	Stearoxylic acid	see Octadecanoic acid, 9,10-dioxo-*													
s114	Stibine, bis(trifluoromethyl)-bromo-*	$(F_3C)_2SbBr$	339.67			113⁷⁶⁰									J1957, 3708
s115	—,bis(trifluoromethyl)-chloro-*	$(F_3C)_2SbCl$	295.22			ca. 88⁷⁶⁰ 17²⁰			d^h						J1957, 3708
s116	—,bis(trifluoromethyl)iodo-*	$(F_3C)_2SbI$	386.67		−42	ca. 129 16⁸									J1957, 3708
s117	—,dibromo(trifluoromethyl)-*	F_3CSbBr_2	350.57			ca. 157⁷⁶⁰ 34²·⁵									J1957, 3708
s118	—,dichloro-(phenyl)-*	$C_6H_5SbCl_2$	269.71	nd or ta	69–70	110–5¹⁰			d	v		s		MeOH, aa s	B16², 574
s119	—,diiodo(trifluoromethyl)-*	F_3CSbI_2	444.57	bt ye	4–8	>200⁷⁶⁰d			i						J1957, 3708
s120	—,triethyl-*	$(C_2H_5)_3Sb$	208.94		−98 (−29)	161.4⁷⁶⁰	1.3224¹⁶		i	s	s				B4, 618
s121	—,trimethyl-*	$(CH_3)_3Sb$	166.85	pr (peth)	−62.0	80.6⁷⁶⁰	1.523¹⁵	1.42¹⁵	i	s	s			CS_2 s	B4, 1004
Ω s122	—,triphenyl-*	$(C_6H_5)_3Sb$	353.07	53.5 λ^{al} 233 (4.11)		>360 >220¹	1.4343²⁵	1.6948⁴²	i	δ	v	v	v	chl, CS_2 aa v	B16², 573
s123	—,tris(trifluoromethyl)-	$(F_3C)_3Sb$	328.77		−58	73⁷⁶⁰			i						J1957, 3708
s124	—,tri(2-tolyl)-		395.15	(al)	102					s^h	v		v	chl, peth v	B16, 892
s125	—,tri(3-tolyl)-		395.15	(peth)	72		1.3957¹⁶			s	v		v	chl, peth v	B16, 892
s126	—,tri(4-tolyl)-		395.15	rh (eth, MeOH)	127–8		1.3595¹⁶		δ	s			s	chl s peth δ	B16², 574
s127	Stigmastanol	Fucostanol. β-Sitostanol. $C_{29}H_{52}O$.	416.74	pl (al), cr (+1 w), $[\alpha]_D^{20}$ +24.8 (chl, c = 1.1)	144–5 (anh) 138–9 (hyd)									chl s	E14, 91

For explanations, symbols and abbreviations see beginning of table. For structural formulas see end of table.

Stigmasterol

No.	Name	Synonyms and Formula	Mol. wt.	Color, crystalline form, specific rotation and λ_{max} (log ε)	m.p. °C	b.p. °C	Density	n_D	w	al	eth	ace	bz	other solvents	Ref.
Ω s128	Stigmasterol	$C_{29}H_{48}O$.	412.71	cr (al + 1 w), $[\alpha]_D^{2} - 51$ (chl, c = 2) λ^{al} 205 (3.74)	170	....	....	....	i	s^h	s	s	s	chl, oos s	E14, 88
Ω s129	Stilbene(trans)	trans-1,2-Diphenylethene.*	180.25	cr (al) λ^{al} 244 (4.39), 280 (4.02)	124.5–4.8	305^{720} 166–7^{12}	0.9707	1.6264^{17}	i	δ s^h	v	...	v	....	B5^2, 537
s130	—,2,2'-diamino-(cis)	$C_{14}H_{14}N_2$. See s129	210.28	red nd (w)	123 (107)	....	....	....	...	s^h	...	s	...	....	B13^1, 85
s131	—,—(trans)	$C_{14}H_{14}N_2$. See s129	210.28	gold-ye pr (al) λ^{al} 228 (4.21), 295 (4.46), 307 (4.45)	176	....	....	....	...	s^h	...	s	...	....	B13^1, 85
s132	—,4,4'-diamino-(trans)	$C_{14}H_{14}N_2$. See s129	210.28	ye nd or lf (al) λ^w 328 (4.60)	231	sub	....	....	δ^h	...	...	...	δ	MeOH s CS_2 δ	B13, 267
s133	—,2,2'-dihydroxy-(α-form)	$C_{14}H_{12}O_2$. See s129	212.25	nd (al)	95	....	....	....	...	v	v	...	...	....	B6^2, 987
s134	—,—(β-form)	$C_{14}H_{12}O_2$. See s129	212.25	flat nd (al)	197	....	....	....	...	δ	s	...	s	MeOH s^h	B6, 1022
s135	—,3,5-dihydroxy-(trans)	Pinosylvin. $C_{14}H_{12}O_2$. See s129	212.25	nd (aa)	156	....	....	....	i	...	...	s	s	chl, aa s	C33, 8989
s136	—,4,4'-dihydroxy-(trans)	Stilbestrol. $C_{14}H_{12}O_2$. See s129	212.25	nd (aa), ta (al) λ^{al} 228 (4.10), 300 (4.46), 307 (4.46), 325 (4.40)	284	....	....	....	...	δ s^h	δ	v	s	aa δ	B6, 1022
Ω s137	—,4,4'-di-methoxy-	Bianisal. Photoanethole. $C_{16}H_{16}O_2$. See s129	240.31	lf (bz or aa) λ^{al} 228 (4.11), 306 (4.54), 325 (4.53)	214–5	sub	....	....	i	...	...	s	s^h	aa s^h	B6^2, 988
s138	—,α,β-dinitro-(cis)	$C_{14}H_{10}N_2O_4$. See s129	270.25	ye pym pr (al) λ^{al} 265 (4.5)	108–9	d	....	....	i	s	s	v	v	chl v MeOH s	B5^2, 542
s139	—,—(trans)	$C_{14}H_{10}N_2O_4$. See s129	270.25	pa ye nd or pr (al) λ^{al} 262 (4.4)	187–8	....	....	....	i	δ s^h	δ	s	s	chl, aa s MeOH δ	B5^2, 541
s140	—,2,2'-dinitro-(cis)	$C_{14}H_{10}N_2O_4$. See s129	270.25	ye nd (aa)	126	....	....	....	i	...	...	...	...	aa s^h	B5, 637
s141	—,—(trans)	$C_{14}H_{10}N_2O_4$. See s129	270.25	pa ye nd (chl)	199	420 exp	....	....	...	δ	δ	...	s^h	CS_2 s chl s^h	B5^1, 306
s142	—,2,4-dinitro-(cis)	$C_{14}H_{10}N_2O_4$. See s129	270.25	ye pl (aa)	127	....	....	....	...	...	...	...	v	chl s aa s^h	B5^2, 541
Ω s143	—,—(trans)	$C_{14}H_{10}N_2O_4$. See s129	270.25	pa ye (aa) λ^{Py} 368 (4.40)	143–5	412 exp	....	....	...	δ	i	...	δ	CS_2, chl, xyl s	B5^2, 540
s144	—,2,6-dinitro-(trans)	$C_{14}H_{10}N_2O_4$. See s129	270.25	ye nd (bz, aa) λ^{bz} 330 sh (3.7)	114 (86)	....	....	....	i	...	...	...	s^h	chl s	B5^1, 306
s145	—,3,4'-dinitro-(cis)	$C_{14}H_{10}N_2O_4$. See s129	270.25	ye nd (aa)	155	....	....	....	...	δ	...	s	s	chl s aa s^h	B5^2, 541
s146	—,—(trans)	$C_{14}H_{10}N_2O_4$. See s129 PhNO$_2$ or Py)	270.25	ye nd (aa)	220–2	....	....	....	...	δ^h	...	δ	δ^h	chl c, AcOEt δ	B5^2, 541
s147	—,4,4'-dinitro-(cis)	$C_{14}H_{10}N_2O_4$. See s129	270.25	ye nd (aa, chl or PhNO$_2$) λ^{al} 224 (4.15), 330 (4.18)	186–6.5	....	....	....	i	δ	δ	s	s	chl s lig δ	B5^2, 541
s148	—,—(trans)	$C_{14}H_{10}N_2O_4$. See s129	270.25	pa ye lf (aa), nd (aa or PhNO$_2$) λ^{al} 235 (4.20), 356 (4.45)	303–4 (294–5)	....	....	....	i	s	s	s	s	chl s aa s^h	B5^2, 541
—	Stilbestrol	see Stilbene, 4,4'-dihydroxy-(trans)													
s151	Strophanthidin	Corchorgenin. $C_{23}H_{32}O_6$	404.51	orh ta (MeOH-w), lf (w + 2) $[\alpha]_D^{25} + 43.1$ (MeOH, c = 2.8) λ^{al} 216 (4.23)	235 (anh) 171–5 (hyd)	....	....	....	i	s	i	s	s	chl, aa s peth i	E14, 252
Ω s152	g-Strophanthin	Ouabain. $C_{29}H_{44}O_{12}$	584.67	hyg pl (+9w) $[\alpha]_D^{25} - 34$	200 (180)	....	....	....	δ s^h	v	...	...	...	....	E14, 251
Ω s153	Strychnine	$C_{21}H_{22}N_2O_2$	334.42	orh pr (al), $[\alpha]_D^{18} - 139.3$ (chl, c = 1) λ^{al} 255 (4.10), 280 (3.63), 290 (3.53)	286–8 (270 slow htng)	270^5	1.36$_4^{20}$	....	δ^h	δ	i	δ	δ	chl s peth i to, MeOH δ	B27^2, 723
Ω s154	—,hydrochloride	$C_{21}H_{22}N_2O_2$.HCl.2H$_2$O. See s153.	406.91	nd (w) $[\alpha]_D - 28.3$ (w, c = 0.7) λ^{al} 254 (4.1), 279 (3.6), 287 (3.5)	....	....	....	....	s	δ	i	δ	...	chl δ	B27^2, 730

For explanations, symbols and abbreviations see beginning of table. For structural formulas see end of table.

No.	Name	Synonyms and Formula	Mol. wt.	Color, crystalline form, specific rotation and λ_{max} (log ε)	m.p. °C	b.p. °C	Density	n_D	w	al	eth	ace	bz	other solvents	Ref.
	Strychnine														
Ω s155	—,nitrate........	$C_{21}H_{22}N_2O_2.HNO_3$. See s153.	397.44	nd (w) $\lambda^{w, pH=2}$ 249 (4.5), 310 (3.6), 345 (3.7)	280–310	....	1.627	....	v^h s	s^h δ	i	....	...	MeOH s chl δ	B27², 732
s156	—,sulfate........	$(C_{21}H_{22}N_2O_2)_2.H_2SO_4.5H_2O$ See s153.	857.00	wh mcl $[\alpha]_D$ 13.25 λ^w 255 (4.03)	200d (anh)				s v^h	s^h δ	i	...		MeOH s chl δ	C48, 4963
—	Styphnic acid.....	see Benzene ,2,4-dihydroxy-1,3,5-trinitro-*													
—	Styptol.........	see Cotarnine, phthalate													
Ω s157	Styracin.........	Cinnamyl cinnamate. $C_6H_5CH:CHCO_2CH_2CH:CHC_6H_5$	264.33	nd	44	....	1.1565⁴	....	i	s	v				B9², 388
s158	Styracitol........	$C_6H_{12}O_5$.	164.16	pr (90 % al) $[\alpha]_D^{20} -71.72$ (w)	157	....	....	....	v	δ	i	i	i	MeOH δ, s^h	B17², 235 B18², 620
Ω s159	Styrene.........	Ethenylbenzene*. Phenylethylene. Vinylbenzene.	104.16	λ^{al} 245.3 (4.18)	−30.63	145.2⁷⁶⁰ 33.6¹⁰	0.9060²⁰	1.5468²⁰	i	s	s	s	∞	peth ∞ MeOH, CS₂ s	B5², 362
s160	—,α-bromo-......	$C_6H_5CBr:CH_2$	183.05		−44	86–7¹⁴	1.4025²³	1.5881²⁰	....	s	s				B5², 367
Ω s161	—β-bromo-(trans) .	$C_6H_5CH:CHBr$	183.05	λ^{al} 253 (4.34), 256 (4.36), 260 (4.34)	7	219 δd 108²⁰	1.4269¹⁶	1.6093²⁰	i	∞	∞				B5⁷, 368
Ω s162	—,2-bromo-......	C_8H_7Br. See s159	183.05	λ^{chl} 248 (1.84)	fı −52.8	206.2⁷⁶⁰ 98²⁰	1.4160²⁰	1.5927²⁰	i	s	s				B5³, 1176
s163	—,3-bromo-......	C_8H_7Br. See s159	183.05	λ^{chl} 248 (1.84)	....	90–4²⁰ 48.3⁰·⁵	1.4059²⁰	1.5933²⁰							Am 59, 1176
Ω s164	—,4-bromo-......	C_8H_7Br. See s159	183.05	lf λ^{chl} 259 (2.19)	4.5 (−7.7)	103²⁰ 50²·⁵	1.3984²⁰	1.5947²⁰	i					chl v aa s	B5², 367
s165	—,α-chloro-......	$C_6H_5CCl:CH_2$	138.60		−23	199⁷⁶⁰ 73¹⁶	1.1016¹⁸	1.5612²⁰	i	s	s				B5², 367
s166	—,β-chloro-(trans)	$C_6H_5CH:CHCl$	138.60	λ^{al} 254 (4.22)	....	199⁷⁶⁰ 90¹⁸	1.1095¹⁸	1.5648²⁰	i	s	s	s			B5², 367
Ω s167	—,2-chloro-......	C_8H_7Cl. See s159	138.60	λ^{chl} 246.5 (1.92)	−63.15	188.7⁷⁶⁰ 64.6¹⁰	1.1000²⁰	1.5649²⁰	...	s	s	s		peth ∞ CCl₄, aa s	Am 66, 1295
Ω s168	—,3-chloro-......	C_8H_7Cl. See s159	138.60	λ^{chl} 250 (1.98)	....	62–3⁶ 51³	1.1168²⁰	1.5625²⁰	i	s	s				Am 66, 1296
Ω s169	—,4-chloro-......	C_8H_7Cl. See s159	138.60	λ^{al} 253 (4.29)	−15.90	192.0⁷⁶⁰ 66.3¹⁰	1.0868²⁰	1.5660²⁰	i	s	s	∞	∞	CCl₄, peth ∞	B5², 367
s170	—,2-fluoro-......	C_8H_7F. See s159	122.14		....	46³² 32–4³	1.0282²⁰	1.5200²⁰	i	s	s		s		Am 66, 1295
s171	—,3-fluoro-......	C_8H_7F. See s159	122.14	λ^{chl} 248 (1.99)	....	30–1⁴	1.0177²⁰	1.5170²⁰	i	s	s				Am 66, 1295
Ω s172	—,4-fluoro-......	C_8H_7F. See s159	122.14		−34.5	67.4⁵⁰ 29–30⁴	1.0220²⁰	1.5150²⁰	i	s	s				Am 68, 1159
s173	—,2-hydroxy-.....	o-Vinylphenol. C_8H_8O. See s159	120.16	nd	29–9.5	101¹⁴ 77¹⁵	1.0609¹⁸ 1.0468³⁶	1.5851²⁰	s	v	v				B6, 560
s174	—,3-hydroxy-.....	m-Vinylphenol. C_8H_8O. See s159	120.16		....	114 6¹⁶	1.0353³¹	1.5804³¹							B6, 561
s175	—,4-hydroxy-3-methoxy-	5-Vinylguaiacol. Hesperetol. $C_9H_{10}O_2$. See s159	150.18	cr	57	....			δ	v	v				B6, 954
s176	—,2-methoxy-.....	o-Vinylanisole. $C_9H_{10}O$. See s159	134.18	nd	29–9.5	195–200 83–4¹²	1.0049¹⁷ 18	1.5388²⁰	i	s	s	s	s	oos s	B6¹, 277
s177	—,3-methoxy-.....	m-Vinylanisole. $C_9H_{10}O$. See s159	134.18	λ^{al} 250 (3.93), 293 (3.33)	....	114–6¹⁶⁻⁷ 90–3¹⁵	0.9991¹⁶	1.5586²³	i	s	s				B6, 561
Ω s178	—,4-methoxy-.....	p-Vinylanisole. $C_9H_{10}O$. See s159	134.18	$\lambda^{al−HCl}$ 260 (4.17), 292 sh (3.3)	....	204–5⁷⁵⁶ 91¹³	1.0001¹³	1.5642¹³	i	s	s				B6², 520
Ω s179	—,β-nitro-(trans) ..	$C_6H_5CH:CHNO_2$	149.15	ye pr (peth or al) λ^{al} 228 (3.89), 311 (4.22)	60 (58)	250– 60⁷⁶⁰d 150¹⁴			i δ^h	s	v	s		chl, CS₂ v peth s	B5², 368
s180	—,4-nitro-.......	$C_8H_7NO_2$. See s159	149.15	pr (lig) λ^{al} 301 (4.16)	29	d			...	v^h	v			aa, chl, lig s	B5³, 1180
—	Styrene oxide	see Benzene, (1,2-epoxyethyl)-*													
s181	β-Styrenesulfonic acid, chloride (trans)	$C_6H_5CH:CHSO_2Cl$	202.66	fl (bz) λ^{iso} 273.7 (4.33)	88	....				d			s^h		B11², 87
s182	Subboric acid, tetramethyl ester	$(CH_3O)_2BB(OCH_3)_2$	145.76	....	−24.3	93⁷⁶⁰ (extrap 18³³)			d						Ber 94, 509
—	Suberaldehyde	see Octanedial*													
—	Suberic acid......	see Octanedioic acid*													
s183	Succinaldehyde....	1,4-Butanedial*. $OCHCH_2CH_2CHO$	86.09	....	....	169–70⁷⁶⁰ δd 56.5⁹	1.064²⁰	1.4262¹⁸	s	s	s	v	s	os v	B1², 824
—	Succinamic acid	see Succinic acid, monoamide													
—	Succinamide	see Succinic acid, diamide													
—	Succinanil	see Succinic acid, imide, N-phenyl-													

For explanations, symbols and abbreviations see beginning of table. For structural formulas see end of table.

Succinanilic acid

No.	Name	Synonyms and Formula	Mol. wt.	Color, crystalline form, specific rotation and λ_{max} (log ε)	m.p. °C	b.p. °C	Density	n_D	w	al	eth	ace	bz	other solvents	Ref.
—	Succinanilic acid	see Succinic acid, mono-amide, N-phenyl-													
Ω s185	Succinic acid	Butanedioic acid*. $HO_2CCH_2CH_2CO_2H$	118.09	tcl or mcl pr λ^w 208 (2.0)	188 (185)	235d (→an-hydride)	1.572_4^{25}	1.450	δ v^h	s	s	s	i	MeOH s to i	B2², 540
Ω s186	—,anhydride	Succinic anhydride.	100.08	nd (al), rh pym (chl or CCl₄) λ^{bz} 278 (3.15)	119.6	261 139¹⁵	1.2340_4^{20}		i	s	δ			chl s	B17², 429
s187	—,diamide	Succinamide. $H_2NCOCH_2CH_2CONH_2$	116.12	orh nd (w)	268–70d (260)	125.5 sub			δ s^h	i	i				B2², 554
Ω s188	—,dibenzyl ester	$C_6H_5CH_2O_2CCH_2CH_2CO_2CH_2C_6H_5$	298.33	orh pl or ta (PrOH)	49–50 (45)	245¹⁵	1.256	1.596	i	s	s	s	s		B6², 418
Ω s189	—,dibutyl ester	$C_4H_9O_2CCH_2CH_2CO_2C_4H_9^n$	230.31		−29.25	274.5⁷⁶⁰ 145⁴	0.9752_4^{20}	1.4299^{20}	i	s	s	s	s		B2², 551
s190	—,di-sec-butyl ester	$C_4H_9O_2CCH_2CH_2CO_2C_4H_9^s$	230.31			256⁷⁶⁰	0.9735_4^{20}	1.4238^{25}	i	δ	s	s	s		B2², 559
s191	—,di(2-carboxy-phenyl) ester	Diaspirin. Succinylsalicylic acid.	358.29	nd (aa or al)	176–8				δ	δ s^h	δ			aa δ, s^h	B10², 43
Ω s192	—,dichloride	Succinyl chloride. $ClCOCH_2CH_2COCl$	154.98	pl or lf	20	193.3 88.5¹⁵	1.3748_4^{20}	1.4683^{20}	d	d	s	s	s		B2, 613
Ω s193	—,diethyl ester	Ethyl succinate. $C_2H_5O_2CCH_2CH_2CO_2C_2H_5$	174.20		−20.6	216.5⁷⁶⁰ 105¹⁵	1.0402_4^{20}	1.4198^{20}	i	∞	∞	s			B2², 550
Ω s195	—,dimethyl ester	Methyl succinate. $CH_3O_2CCH_2CH_2CO_2CH_3$	146.14		19	196.4⁷⁶⁰ 80¹¹	1.1198_4^{20}	1.4197^{20}	δ	s	v	s			B2², 549
Ω s196	—,dinitrile	Succinonitrile. Ethylene dicyanide. $NCCH_2CH_2CN$	80.09		57.15–.20	265–7⁷⁶⁰ 124⁵	0.9867_4^{60}	1.4173^{60}	v	s	δ	s	s	chl s	B2, 615
s197	—,diphenyl ester	$C_6H_5O_2CCH_2CH_2CO_2C_6H_5$	270.29	lf (al)	121	222.5¹⁵			i	s^h	s	s	s		B6, 155
s198	—,dipropyl ester	$C_3H_7O_2CCH_2CH_2CO_2C_3H_7^n$	202.25		−5.9	250.8⁷⁶⁰ 101.5³	1.0020_4^{20}	1.4250^{20}	i	s	s	s	s	os s	B2², 551
s199	—,di(4-tolyl)ester		298.34	nd or lf (al)	121				i	s	s	s	s	aa, os s lig δ	B6², 379
Ω s200	—,imide	Succinimide.	99.09	pl (+1w, al), rh (ace) λ^{al} 218 sh (2.27), 243 (1.96)	126–7	287–8d	1.418		s v^h	δ s^h	δ				B21, 369
s201	—,—,N-benzyl-	$C_{11}H_{11}NO_2$. See s200	189.22	nd (w), pr (al)	103	390–400			v^h	v	s		v^h	chl v CS₂ δ peth i	B21², 304
Ω s202	—,—,N-bromo-	NBS. $C_4H_4BrNO_2$. See s200	177.99	cr (bz)		173.5d	2.098		δ		δ	v		AcOEt v Ac₂O δ	B21², 306
s203	—,—,N(2-bromo-phenyl)-	$C_{10}H_8BrNO_2$. See s200	254.10	dil al)	91				i	s					B21², 304
s204	—,—,N(3-bromo-phenyl)-	$C_{10}H_8BrNO_2$. See s200	254.10	nd (al)	118				s^h	v^h					B21², 304
s205	—,—,N(4-bromo-phenyl)-	$C_{10}H_8BrNO_2$. See s200	254.10	pr (al)	172				i^h		s	s	os v		B21², 304
s206	—,—,N-carbethoxy-	$C_7H_9NO_4$. See s200	171.15	(eth-lig)	44				v		s	s	os v		B21², 305
Ω s207	—,—,N-chloro-	NCS. $C_4H_4ClNO_2$. See s200	133.53	pl (CCl₄)	150		1.65		δ	δ		s	δ	aa s, lig δ	B21², 306
s208	—,—,N(chloro-methyl)-	$C_5H_6ClNO_2$. See s200	147.56		58	158–60¹²			v		s	v	oos v		B21², 305
s209	—,—,N(4-chloro-phenyl)-	$C_{10}H_8ClNO_2$. See s200	209.64	nd (dil al)	170					v	s	v	os v		B21², 303
s210	—,—,N(ethoxy-methyl)-	$C_7H_{11}NO_3$. See s200	157.17	nd	31–2	262 151–2¹⁴			v	v	δ				B21², 304
s211	—,—,N(4-ethoxy-phenyl)-	$C_{12}H_{13}NO_3$. See s200	219.24	pr (al)	155				δ^h	s^h	i			aa s^h	B21, 377
s212	—,—,N-ethyl-	$C_6H_9NO_2$. See s200	127.14	(eth)	26	236			v	v	v				B21, 373
s213	—,—,N(hydroxy-methyl)-	$C_5H_7NO_3$. See s200	129.12	lf (bz)	66				v					os s δ	B21², 304
Ω s214	—,—,N-iodo-	$C_4H_4INO_2$. See s200	224.99	(ace)	135		2.245		v	s	δ	s			B21², 306
s215	—,—,N-methyl-	$C_5H_7NO_2$. See s200	113.12	nd (eth-peth, al, ace) λ^{MeOH} 224 (2.7), 252 (2.0)	71 (66)	234			s	s	v				B21², 303
s216	—,—,N(1-naphthyl)-	$C_{14}H_{11}NO_2$. See s200	225.25	nd (dil al)	153				i	v^h				MeOH v^h	B21, 376
s217	—,—,N(2-naphthyl)-	$C_{14}H_{11}NO_2$. See s200	225.25	nd (al or AcOEt)	183				i	s			s	AcOEt δ	B21, 376
s218	—,—,N-phenyl-	Succinanil. $C_{10}H_9NO_2$. See s200	175.19	mcl pr or nd (w or al) λ^{hx} 262 (2.90), 273 (1.97)	156	ca. 400	1.356		i δ^h	s^h	s				B21², 303
s219	—,monoamide	Succinamic acid. $HO_2CCH_2CH_2CONH_2$	117.11	nd (w or ace)	156.3–7.8				s	δ		s^h	δ	lig δ	B2², 554
Ω s220	—,—,N-phenyl-	Succinanilic acid. $HO_2CCH_2CH_2CONHC_6H_5$	193.20	nd (w) λ^{al} 242 (4.11)	148.5				δ s^h	s	v				B12, 295
s221	—,monobenzyl ester	$HO_2CCH_2CH_2CO_2CH_2C_6H_5$	208.22	cr (bz)	59 (47)				i				δ	lig δ	B6², 418

For explanations, symbols and abbreviations see beginning of table. For structural formulas see end of table.

No.	Name	Synonyms and Formula	Mol. wt.	Color, crystalline form, specific rotation and λ_{max} (log ε)	m.p. °C	b.p. °C	Density	n_D	w	al	eth	ace	bz	other solvents	Ref.
	Succinic acid														
s222	—,monochloride monomethyl ester	$CH_3O_2CCH_2CH_2COCl$	150.56	....		102^{35} $53-4^1$	....	1.4412^{20}	d^h	d^h	....	....	....		B2², 553
s223	—,monoethyl ester(dl)	$HO_2CCH_2CH_2CO_2C_2H_5$ ..	146.14	pr or nd	8	172^{42} 119^3	1.1466_2^{20}	1.4327^{20}	v	v	v	....	....	chl δ peth i	B2², 549
s224	—,monoethyl ester monomethyl ester	$CH_3O_2CCH_2CH_2CO_2C_2H_5$.	160.17	....	< −20	208.2^{760} $90-5^3$	1.076_4^{20}	....	i	v	v	....	....		B2, 609
s226	—,piperazinium salt	$HO_2CCH_2CH_2CO_2H.C_4H_{10}N_2$	204.23	....	205–6d	....	....	....	s	s^h	i	....	....		Am 56, 1759
Ω s227	—,acetyl-, diethyl ester	$C_2H_5O_2CCH(COCH_3)CH_2CO_2C_2H_5$	216.24	....		$254-6^{760}$ 139^{12}	1.081_4^{20}	1.438^{16}	i	s	s	....	s	CS_2 s	B3², 486
—	—,amino-	*see* **Aspartic acid**													
s228	—,benzyl-(dl)	$C_6H_5CH_2CH(CO_2H)CH_2CO_2H$	208.22	nd or lf $\lambda^{a\,c}$ 261 (2.35)	163–4				s^h	s	s	....	δ		B9², 628
Ω s229	—,bromo-(dl)	$HO_2CCH_2CHBrCO_2H$	196.99	(w)	161	....	2.073		s	s	s	....	....	aa δ	B2², 560
s230	—,2,3-diacetyl-, diethyl ester (diketo form)	Ethyl diacetosuccinate. $C_2H_5O_2CCH(COCH_3)CH(COCH_3)CO_2C_2H_5$ λ^{MeOH} 250 (3.7)	258.27	mcl pr or nd (al)	90	....			δ	s	s	s	s	chl v lig δ	B3², 505
s231	—,2,3-dibromo-(d) .	$HO_2CCHBrCHBrCO_2H$ ...	275.89	pl (aa-CCl_4) $[\alpha]_D^{24} +147.8$ (AcOEt) $[\alpha]_D^{18} +64.4$ (w, c = 5)	157–8				s	v	....	v			B2², 561
Ω s232	—,—(dl)	$HO_2CCHBrCHBrCO_2H$ ...	275.89	(w or AcOEt)	171 (166–7)				s	v	....	v			B2, 561
s233	—,—(l)	$HO_2CCHBrCHBrCO_2H$ ...	275.89	nd (bz), $[\alpha]_D^{18} -148$ (AcOEt, c = 5.79)	157–8d				v	v	,..	v	...	AcOEt, MeOH v, chl, CCl_4, peth δ	B2¹, 268
s234	—,—(meso)......	$HO_2CCHBrCHBrCO_2H$	275.89	....	255 (sealed tube)	sub 275			δ v^h	v	v	....	....	chl δ	B2², 561
s235	—,2,3-dichloro-(d)	$HO_2CCHClCHClCO_2H$....	186.98	mcl, $[\alpha]_D^{19}$ +3.6 (w, c = 3)	168	....	1.820^{15}		s	δ	s	s	δ	chl s	B2², 556
s236	—,—(dl)	$HO_2CCHClCHClCO_2H$....	186.98	pr (w or eth-peth)	175d		1.844^{15}		s	δ	s	s	δ	chl s	B2², 557
Ω s237	—,—(meso)......	$HO_2CCHClCHClCO_2H$....	186.98	hex pr (w)	221d				s	v	v	v	δ	chl v lig δ	B2², 558
s238	—,—,dichloride(dl)	$ClCOCHClCHClCOCl$....	223.87	....	39	78.5^7			d	d	s	....	....		B2², 558
s239	—,—,—(meso)	$ClCOCHClCHClCOCl$....	223.87	....	$105-6^{45}$ $79-80^{15}$				d	d	....	....	....	CCl_4 s	B2², 558
s240	—,—,diethyl ester(dl)	$C_2H_5O_2CCHClCHClCO_2C_2H_5$	243.09	....		132^{15}	1.1963_4^{27}	1.4512^{20}			v	....	....		B2², 558
s241	—,—,—(meso)	$C_2H_5O_2CCHClCHClCO_2C_2H_5$	243.09	nd (dil al)	63	$125.5^{12.5}$	1.1490_4^{29}	1.4266^{65}	i	v	v	....	....		B2², 558
s242	—,2,3-diethyl-, diphenyl ester	3,4-Dicarbophenoxyhexane. $C_6H_5O_2CCH(C_2H_5)CH(C_2H_5)CO_2C_6H_5$	326.40	nd (lig)	107–8	....			i	δ	s	s	s	to, CS_2 s	B6, 156
—	—,2,3-dihydroxy-	*see* **Tartaric acid**													
s243	—,2,3-dimethoxy-, dimethyl ester(d)	$CH_3O_2CCH(OCH_3)CH(OCH_3)CO_2CH_3$	206.20	pr, $[\alpha]_D^{18} +79.9$ (MeOH, c = 2)	53–4	$130-2^{12}$	1.1317_4^{60}	1.4340^{20}	....	....	....	....	....	MeOH s	B3², 328 B16², 871
—	—,dioxo-, dihydrate	*see* **Succinic acid, tetrahydroxy-**													
s244	—,2-dodecyl-3-methyl-	2,3-Pentadecanedicarboxylic acid*. Roccellic acid. $CH_3(CH_2)_{11}CH(CO_2H)CH(CH_3)CO_2H$	300.44	lf (aa, bz or al), rods (ace) wh pl (peth) $[\alpha]_D^{20} +17.4$ (al)	132–3				i	s	v	s	s^h	$NaHCO_3$ s peth i	B2, 734
s245	—,ethyl-(d)	$HO_2CCH_2CH(C_2H_5)CO_2H$.	146.14	pr or nd, $[\alpha]_D^{16} +20.6$ (aa, c = 3.7) $[\alpha]_D^{17} +26$ (ace, c = 4)	96	180–3	1.0017_4^{20}		v	v	v	....	....	chl δ peth i	B2², 584
s246	—,—(l)	$HO_2CCH_2CH(C_2H_5)CO_2H$.	146.14	pr or nd $[\alpha]_D^{24} -20.8$ (ace, c = 4.6)	96	180–3	1.0018^{20}		v	v	v	....	....	chl δ peth i	B2², 584
s247	—,formyl-, diethyl ester (aldo form)	$C_2H_5O_2CCH_2CH(CHO)CO_2C_2H_5$	202.21	....		$130-4^{15}$ $114-9^5$		1.4486^{25}	i	∞	∞	....	....		B3², 485
—	—,(hydroxymethyl)-,γ-lactone	*see* **Paraconic acid**													
s248	—,2-hydroxy-3-methyl-(d)-	d-Citramalic acid. $HO_2CC(CH_3)OHCH_2CO_2H$	148.13	$[\alpha]_D^{24} +34.67$ (w)	108–9				v	s	....	s	i	peth i	B3, 443
s249	—,—(dl)	$HO_2CC(CH_3)OHCH_2CO_2H$	148.13	mcl pr (AcOEt)	123	sub			v	s	....	s	i	AcOEt s peth i	B3², 294
s250	—,isopropylidene-..	Teraconic acid. $(CH_3)_2C{:}C(CO_2H)CH_2CO_2H$	158.16	tcl nd (eth)	160–1 (165–6)	....			s^h	s	s	....	δ	....	B2, 786

For explanations, symbols and abbreviations see beginning of table. For structural formulas see end of table.

No.	Name	Synonyms and Formula	Mol. wt.	Color, crystalline form, specific rotation and λ_{max} (log ε)	m.p. °C	b.p. °C	Density	n_D	Solubility						Ref.
									w	al	eth	ace	bz	other solvents	
	Succinic acid														
s250[1]	—,**mercapto**-(d)	d-Thiomalic acid. $HO_2CCH_2CH(SH)CO_2H$	150.15	cr (AcOEt-bz) $[\alpha]_D^{17}+64.4$ (al), $+76.1$ (ace)	154	....	....	....	s	s	...	s	...	....	B3[2], 287
Ω s250[2]	—,—(dl)	$HO_2CCH_2CH(SH)CO_2H$	150.15	cr (eth)	151				v	v	s	v	i	....	B3[2], 291
s250[3]	—,—(l)	$HO_2CCH_2CH(SH)CO_2H$	150.15	$[\alpha]_D^{17}-64.8$ (al), -75.8 (ace)	152–3				s	s	δ	s	δ	....	B3[2], 287
Ω s251	—,**methyl**-(dl)	Pyrotartaric acid. $HO_2CCH_2CH(CH_3)CO_2H$	132.13	pr	115	d	....	1.4303	v	v	s	...	...	MeOH v chl δ	B2, 637
s252	—,**2-methyl-3-oxo**-,diethyl ester	Diethyl methyloxalacetate. $C_2H_5O_2CCOCH(CH_3)CO_2C_2H_5$	202.21			137–8[23] 75–8[2]	1.0970_4^{20}	1.4313^{20}	i	∞	∞	...	...	....	B3[2], 484
Ω s253	—,**methylene**-	Itaconic acid. $CH_2{:}C(CO_2H)CH_2CO_2H$	130.10	rh (bz)	175 (162–4)	d	1.632	....	s	s	δ	s	δ	chl s peth, CS_2 δ	B2[2], 650
Ω s254	—,—,**anhydride**	Itaconic anhydride.	112.09	rh bipym pr (eth or chl), sc (aa)	68.5 (70)	139–40[30] 114–5[18]	....	....	d^h	d^h	δ	...	...	chl v	B17[2], 449
Ω s255	—,—,**dichloride**	Itaconyl chloride. $CH_2{:}C(COCl)CH_2COCl$	166.99			89[17] 72[2]	....	1.4919^{20}	d^h	d^h	...	...	...	....	B2, 762
s256	—,—,**diethyl ester**	Diethyl itaconate. $CH_2{:}C(CO_2C_2H_5)CH_2CO_2C_2H_5$	186.21	λ^{al} 265 sh (2.1)	58–9	228 111[13]	1.0467_4^{20}	1.4377^{20}	...	∞	s	v	s	....	B2[2], 651
Ω s257	—,—,**dimethyl ester**	Dimethyl itaconate. $CH_2{:}C(CO_2CH_3)CH_2CO_2CH_3$	158.16	hyg mcl (MeOH) λ^{al} 205 (3.88), 240 sh (2.2)	38	208[760] 108[11]	1.1241_4^{18}	1.4457^{20}	...	s	s	v	...	MeOH s	B2, 762
s258	—,**oxo**-,diethyl ester	Diethyl oxaloacetate. $C_2H_5O_2CCH_2COCO_2C_2H_5$	188.18	λ^w 265 (2.25)	....	131–2[24]	1.1312_4^{20}	1.4561^{17}	i	∞	∞	...	∞	....	B3[2], 479
s259	—,**2-oxo-3-phenyl**-, 1-ethyl ester 4-nitrile	Ethyl phenylcyanopyruvate. $C_6H_5CH(CN)COCO_2C_2H_5$	217.23	(eth-lig)	130	206[20]			...	...	v	δ	...	chl, alk s	B10[2], 607
s260	—,**phenyl**-(d)	$HO_2CCH_2CH(C_6H_5)CO_2H$	194.19	pr (w), $[\alpha]_D^{16.5}+148.3$ (al, c = 1.5) λ^{al} 260 (2.05)	173–4				δ v^h	s	v	v	δ	MeOH s	B9[1], 380
Ω s261	—,—(dl)	$HO_2CCH_2CH(C_6H_5)CO_2H$	194.19	lf or nd (w) λ^{al} 260 (2.06)	168	d			δ v^h	v	v	v	i	aa v chl δ CS_2, peth i	B9[2], 619
s262	—,—(l)	$HO_2CCH_2CH(C_6H_5)CO_2H$	194.19	$[\alpha]_D^{15}-173.3$ (ace) λ^{al} 260 (2.06)	173–4				...	v	v	v	i	MeOH s	B9[1], 381
s263	—,—,**anhydride**(d)	....	176.18	nd (bz-peth), $[\alpha]_D^{15}+100.9$ (bz) λ^{al} 258 (2.2)	83.5–4.5				d^h	s	...	...	v	chl v peth, CCl_4 δ	B17[1], 259
s264	—,—,—(dl)	$C_{10}H_8O_3$. See s263	176.18	mcl pr or nd (eth)	54	204–6[22] 191–2[12]			i	v	s	v	v	oos v	B17[2], 473
s265	—,—,—(l)	$C_{10}H_8O_3$. See s263	176.18	$[\alpha]_D^{14}-100.9$ (bz)	83.5–4.5				d^h	...	...	...	v	chl v	B17[1], 259
s266	—,**(3-phenyl-propenyl)**-	$C_6H_5CH_2CH{:}CHCH(CO_2H)CH_2CO_2H$	234.25	lf (eth), (bz)	112	....	....	....	s	v	v	v	...	....	B9, 909
Ω s267	—,**tetrahydroxy**-	$HO_2CC(OH)_2C(OH)_2CO_2H$	182.09	....	114–5	d	....	....	d	v	...	...	...	....	B3[2], 500
s268	—,**tetramethyl**-	$HO_2CC(CH_3)_2C(CH_3)_2CO_2H$	174.20	tcl (60 % MeOH, lig or AcOEt), mcl and tcl (eth or ace)	200	sub	1.30	....	δ	v	...	...	v	chl s	B2[2], 601
s269	—,—,**dinitrile**	$NCC(CH_3)_2C(CH_3)_2CN$	136.20	mcl pl, lf and pr (dil al)	170.5–1.5	....	1.070	....	...	s^h	...	...	...	....	B2[1], 290
—	**Succinimide**	see **Succinic acid**, imide													
Ω s273	**Sucrose**	Cane sugar. Saccharose.	342.30	mcl, $[\alpha]_D^{20}+66.37$ (w)	185–6		$1.5805^{17.5}$	1.5376	s v^h	δ	i	...	...	Py s	B31, 424
Ω s274	—,**octaacetate**	$C_{28}H_{38}O_{19}$. See s273	678.61	nd (al), $[\alpha]_D^{20}+59.6$ (chl)	86–87	d 285 260[1]	1.27^{16}	1.4660	$δ^h$	s^h	s	s	s	chl, oos s	B31, 453
s275	**Sudan III**	Tetrazobenzene-β-naphthol.	352.40	br lf with gr lustre (aa) $\lambda^{cellosolve}$ 345 (4.22), 505 (4.49)	195	....	....	....	i	s	s	s	s	xyl, chl, aa, peth s	B16[2], 75
—	**Sudan G**	see **Azobenzene, 2,4-dihydroxy**-													
—	**Sudan yellow**	see **Azobenzene 1-naphthalene, 2'-hydroxy**-													
Ω s276	**Sulfadiazine**	2-Sulfanilamidopyrimidine. Sulfapyrimidine.	250.28	cr (w), wh pw $\lambda^{0.1N\ HCl}$ 244 (4.15)	255–6d (cor)	....	....	....	δ	...	...	δ	...	ac s	C55, 25956
s277	**Sulfaguanidine**	Sulfoguenil.	214.25	nd (w)	190–3 (anh)	....	....	....	δ s^h	δ	...	δ	...	dil ac s	C55, 22204

For explanations, symbols and abbreviations see beginning of table. For structural formulas see end of table.

No.	Name	Synonyms and Formula	Mol. wt.	Color, crystalline form, specific rotation and λ_{max} (log ε)	m.p. °C	b.p. °C	Density	n_D	w	al	eth	ace	bz	other solvents	Ref.

Sulfaguanidine

No.	Name	Synonyms and Formula	Mol. wt.	Color etc.	m.p. °C	b.p. °C	Density	n_D	w	al	eth	ace	bz	other	Ref.
s278	—monohydrate	$C_7H_{10}N_4O_2S.H_2O$	232.27	nd (w)	143 (sealed tube)				δ s^h	δ	i	δ			M, 993
Ω s279	Sulfamerazine	Sulfamethyldiazine.	264.31	cr $\lambda^{w,pH=2.1}$ 239 (4.16), 315 (3.53)	234–8				δ	δ	i	δ		chl i	C55, 5501
Ω s280	Sulfamethazine		278.34	pa ye (w + ½), cr (diox-w) λ^w 241 (4.20), 260 (4.23)	198–9 (cor) (205–7)				s					ac, alk s	Am 64, 567
—	Sulfanilamide	see Benzenesulfonic acid, 4-amino-, amide													
—	Sulfanilic acid	see Benzenesulfonic acid, 4-amino-*													
Ω s281	Sulfapyrazine	N'(2-Pyrazinyl)sulfanilamide.	250.28	nd ($PhNO_2$)	251 (251–4)				i	i	i	δ	i	Py s diox δ chl i	Am 63, 3153
s282	Sulfapyridine		249.29	ye og (al) λ^w 262 (4.2), 310 (4.0)	191–3				s^h i	s^h			i	CCl_4 i	C34, 1814
Ω s283	Sulfaquinoxaline		300.34	$\lambda^{w,pH=6.6}$ 255 (4.52), 362 (3.93)	247–8				δ	δ		δ		aq alk s	C49, 5525
s284	Sulfathiadiazole		256.32		218				δ	s				Py s	C40, 5411
Ω s285	Sulfathiazole		255.32	br pl, rods or pw (45 % al) λ^{al} 260 (4.16), 290 (4.27)	202.5 (form I) 175 (form II)				δ	δ					C40, 7518
Ω s286	—,phthalyl-		403.44	λ^w 270 (4.30)	272–7d				i	δ	i			ac, alk s chl i	C51, 9689
s287	—,4-nitro-	Nisulfazole.	285.30	pa ye pw	255–62				i	δ	i		i	dil alk v chl i	C53, 12281
Ω s288	—,succinyl-		355.39	cr λ^w 257 (4.26), 275.5 (4.23)	192–5 (184–6)				i	δ	i	δ		alk s chl i	C51, 12148
Ω s289	Sulfide, benzyl phenyl	Benzylthiobenzene. $C_6H_5CH_2SC_6H_5$	200.31	lf (al) λ^{al} 255 (3.83)	42–3.5	197^{27}			i	s^h	s			con sulf s	$B6^2$, 428
—	—,bis(2-amino-2-carboxyethyl)	see Lanthionine													
—	—,bis(dimethylarsine)	see Cacodyl sulfide													
s290	—,butyl ethyl	1(Ethylthio)butane*. $CH_3(CH_2)_3SC_2H_5$	118.24		−95.13	144.2^{760} 33.3^{10}	0.8376^{20}_4	1.4491^{20}		v				chl s	$B1^3$, 1522
s291	—,butyl methyl	1(Methylthio)butane*. $CH_3(CH_2)_3SCH_3$	104.22		−97.8	123.2^{760}	0.8426^{20}_4	1.4477^{20}		v				MeOH v^h	$B1^3$, 1521
Ω s292	—,diallyl	Allyl sulfide. $(CH_2:CHCH_2)_2S$	114.21	λ^{al} 221 (3.33)	−83	139^{758} 35^6	0.8877^{27}_4	1.4870^{25}	δ	∞	∞			CCl_4, CS_2 s	$B1^2$, 478
s293	—,dibenzoyl	Thiobenzoic anhydride. $C_6H_5COSCOC_6H_5$	242.30	pr (al, eth)	48	d			i	v					$B9^2$, 289
Ω s294	—,dibenzyl	Benzyl sulfide. $(C_6H_5CH_2)_2S$	214.33	pl (eth or chl) λ^{al} 238 sh (3.30), 260 (2.85), 266 sh (2.66)	49–50	d	1.0712^{50}_{50}		i	s	s				$B6^2$, 429
Ω s295	—,dibutyl (α-form)	1(Butylthio)butane*. Butyl sulfide. $CH_3(CH_2)_3S(CH_2)_3CH_3$	146.30		−79.7	185–5.5	0.8386^{20}_4	1.4530^{20}	i	v	v			chl, CCl_4 v	$B1^2$, 399
s296	—,—(β-form)	$CH_3(CH_2)_3S(CH_2)_3CH_3$	146.30	λ^{iso} 251 sh (1.0)		190–230d			i	s	s	s		oos s	Ber 62, 2168
s297	—,—,2,2'-dimethyl-(d)	d-Di-act-amyl sulfide. $CH_3CH_2CH(CH_3)CH_2SCH_2CH(CH_3)CH_2CH_3$	174.35	$[\alpha]^{20}_D +24.5$	98		0.8362^{20}_0								B1, 387
Ω s298	—,—,3,3'-dimethyl-	Isoamyl sulfide. $(CH_3)_2CHCH_2CH_2SCH_2CH_2CH(CH_3)_2$	174.35	col-pa ye		216^{760} 85.5^5	0.8323^{20}_4	1.4520^{20}	i	∞	v				$B1^3$, 1646
s299	—,di-sec-butyl	sec-Butyl sulfide. $CH_3CH_2CH(CH_3)SCH(CH_3)CH_2CH_3$	146.30			165	0.8348^{20}_4	1.4506^{20}	i	v	v				B1, 373
Ω s300	—,di(dimethylthiocarbamyl)	$(CH_3)_2NCSSCSN(CH_3)_2$	208.37	ye mcl λ^{MeOH} 279 (4.21)	109–10		1.37		i	s	δ	s	s	chl s	B4, 76
s301	—,diethenyl	Vinyl sulfide. $CH_2:CHSCH:CH_2$	86.16	λ^{al} 240 (4.62), 255 (4.52)		84^{759}	0.9174^{15}		δ	∞	v	v			$B1^2$, 444
s302	—,diethoxy	Ethoxyl sulfide. $C_2H_5OSOC_2H_5$	122.19	λ <308		117^{733}	0.9940^{20}_4	1.4234^{20}	s	v	v	v	v	os v	$B1^3$, 1314
Ω s303	—,diethyl	Ethyl sulfide. $C_2H_5SC_2H_5$	90.19	λ^{al} 210 (3.25), 229 sh (2.14)	−103.9	92.1^{760}	0.8362^{20}_4	1.4430^{20}	δ	s	s				$B1^2$, 343
s305	—,—,2-chloro-	$ClCH_2CH_2SC_2H_5$	124.63			156^{760} $63–5^{47}$	1.0663^{20}_4	1.4878^{20}						chl s	$B1^2$, 348
s306	—,—,2,2'-diamino-	$H_2NCH_2CH_2SCH_2CH_2NH_2$	120.22	ye		$231–3^{755}$ $118–20^{17}$			∞						B4, 287

For explanations, symbols and abbreviations see beginning of table. For structural formulas see end of table.

No.	Name	Synonyms and Formula	Mol. wt.	Color, crystalline form, specific rotation and λ_{max} (log ε)	m.p. °C	b.p. °C	Density	n_D	w	al	eth	ace	bz	other solvents	Ref.
	Sulfide														
	—,—,2,2'-diamino-2,2'-dicarboxy-	*see* **Lanthionine**													
s307	—,—,2,2'-dichloro-	Mustard gas. Yperite. $ClCH_2CH_2SCH_2CH_2Cl$	159.09	ye pr	13–4	217^{760} 95^{10}	1.2741^{20}_4	1.5312^{20}	i	v	s	v	v	lig ∞	B1[2], 349
Ω s308	—,—,2,2'-dihydroxy-	2,2'-Thiodiethanol. Thiodiglycol. $HOCH_2CH_2SCH_2CH_2OH$	122.19	$\lambda^{al} < 210$	−10 (−16)	$164–6^{20}$ 133^1	1.1819^{20}_4	1.5203^{20}	∞	∞	s		δ	chl, AcOEt ∞	B1[3], 2122
s309	—,—,2,2'-diphenoxy-	$C_6H_5OCH_2CH_2SCH_2CH_2OC_6H_5$	274.39	nd (al)	42	....			i	s	s				B6[2], 150
s310	—,diheptyl	Heptyl sulfide. $CH_3(CH_2)_6S(CH_2)_6CH_3$	230.46			298 164^{20}	0.8416^{20}_4	1.4606^{20}	i		s				B1[3], 1685
s311	—,dihexyl	Hexyl sulfide. $CH_3(CH_2)_5S(CH_2)_5CH_3$	202.41			230 113.5^4	0.8411^{20}_4	1.4586^{20}			s				B1[3], 1659
s312	—,diisopropyl	Isopropyl sulfide. $(CH_3)_2CHSCH(CH_3)_2$	118.24	λ^{iso} 213 (3.4)	−78.08	120.02^{760}	0.8142^{20}_4	1.4438^{20}	i	s	s			MeOH s	B1[3], 1479
Ω s313	—,dimethyl	Methyl sulfide. CH_3SCH_3	62.13	λ^{al} 215 (3.0)	−98.27	37.3^{760}	0.8483^{20}_4	1.4355^{20}	i	s	s			MeOH s	B1, 288
s313[1]	—,—,hexafluoro-	F_3CSCF_3	170.08	λ^{vap} 210 (0.84)	....	$−22.2^{760}$									J1952, 2198
s314	—,1,1'-dinaphthyl	α-Naphthyl sulfide. $C_{10}H_7^\alpha SC_{10}H_7^\alpha$	286.40	nd or pr (al)	110	$289–90^{15}$				δ s^h			v	CS_2, aa v	B6[2], 588
Ω s315	—,2,2'-dinaphthyl	β-Naphthyl sulfide. $C_{10}H_7^\beta SC_{10}H_7^\beta$	286.40	pl (al), lf (bz)	151	$295–6^{15}$				$δ^h$ i			v	CS_2, aa v	B6[2], 611
s316	—,dipentyl	Amyl sulfide. $CH_3(CH_2)_4S(CH_2)_4CH_3$	174.35		−51.3	230^{760} 84.5^4	0.8409^{20}_4	1.4556^{20}	i		s				B1[3], 1608
Ω s317	—,diphenyl	Phenyl sulfide.	186.28	λ^{hx} 240 (3.8), 255 (4.1), 280 (3.7)	−25.9	296 145^8	1.1136^{20}_4	1.6334^{20}	i	s^h	∞		∞	CS_2 ∞	B6, 299
s318	—,—,2-amino-	$C_{12}H_{11}NS$. *See* s317	201.29	pl (al)	35–6	257.5^{100} 212^{25}				s v^h					B13[2], 200
s319	—,—,4-amino-	$C_{12}H_{11}NS$. *See* s317	201.39	nd (dil al) cr (lig)	95.8	282.3^{100} 242.5^{29}			$δ^h$	v	v				B13[2], 298
s320	—,—,2,4'-diamino-	$C_{12}H_{12}N_2S$. *See* s317	216.31	nd (w or al), pr (dil al)	62.5				s^h	v	v		v	peth δ	B13[2], 299
Ω s321	—,—,4,4'-diamino-	p,p'-Thiodianiline. $C_{12}H_{12}N_2S$. *See* s317	216.31	nd (w) λ^{al} 264 (4.39)	108–9				$δ^h$	v	v		v^h		B13[2], 299
s322	—,—,4,4'-dichloro-2,2'-dinitro-	$C_{12}H_6Cl_2N_2O_4S$. *See* s317	345.16	br-ye nd (90 % aa)	149–50					i			v		B6[2], 312
s323	—,—,4,4'-dihydroxy-	$C_{12}H_{10}O_2S$. *See* s317	218.28	mcl pr or lf (al)	151				i s^h	v					B6, 860
s324	—,—,2,2'-dimethoxy-	o-Anisyl sulfide. $C_{14}H_{14}O_2S$. *See* s317	246.33	lf (al)	73	$252–3^{10}$			s^h	v	v		v	aa s peth i	B6, 794
s325	—,—,2,2'-dinitro-	$C_{12}H_8N_2O_4S$. *See* s317	276.28	gold-ye pl (aa)	122–3	sub δd				δ				aa δ	B6[2], 305
s326	—,—,2,4-dinitro-	$C_{12}H_8N_2O_4S$. *See* s317	276.28	pa ye nd (ace or bz-al) λ^{al} 270 sh (3.89), 331 (4.07)	121				i	δ		s	v	aa v	B6[2], 315
Ω s327	—,—,4,4'-dinitro-	$C_{12}H_8N_2O_4S$. *See* s317	276.28	og pl (aa) λ^{al} 235 (4.08), 250 (4.06), 341 (4.18)	160–1				i	δ s^h				con sulf s	B6[2], 311
s328	—,—,2-nitro-	$C_{12}H_9NO_2S$. *See* s317	231.28	ye-og nd (lig or al-eth) λ^{sulf} 414 (4.28), 575 (3.73), 611 (3.75)	82	210^{15}				s	s			con sulf s peth i	B6[2], 305
Ω s329	—,—,4-nitro-	$C_{12}H_9NO_2S$. *See* s317	231.28	pa ye mcl pr (lig) λ^{sulf} 480 (4.30)	55	288.2^{100} 240^{25}				s	s				B6[2], 311
Ω s330	—,—,2,2'4,4'-tetranitro-	$C_{12}H_6N_4O_8S$. *See* s317	366.27	ye nd or pl (aa)	197					i			i	con HNO_3 s CS_2 i	B6[2], 315
s332	—,dipropyl	Propyl sulfide. $CH_3CH_2CH_2SCH_2CH_2CH_3$	118.24		−102.5	142.38^{760} 32.31^{10}	0.8377^{20}_4	1.4487^{20}	i	s	s				B1[2], 372
s333	—,—,2,2'-dichloro-	$CH_3CHClCH_2SCH_2CHClCH_3$	187.13		−40	122^{23} $95–7^{4.5}$	1.1569^{25}_4	1.5020^{20}		s	s				B1[3], 1437
s334	—,—,3,3'-dichloro-	$Cl(CH_2)_3S(CH_2)_3Cl$	187.13			162^{43} $111–2^7$	1.1774^{25}_4	1.5075^{20}		s	s			to s	B1[3], 1438
s335	—,2,2'-ditolyl	o-Tolyl sulfide. λ^{al} 248 (4.11), 274 (3.70)	214.33	pl (al)	64	285 174^{15}			i	s^h δ	v			chl, CS_2 v	B6[2], 342
s336	—,2,4'-ditolyl		214.33			173^{11}	1.0774^{15}			s					B6, 418
s337	—,3,4'-ditolyl		214.33	nd (al)	28	179^{11}				s	s				B6, 418
Ω s338	—,4,4'-ditolyl	p-Tolyl sulfide. λ^{al} 252 (4.16), 276 (3.83)	214.33	nd (al)	57.3	>300 179^{11} (cor)			i	s^h	v	s	s^h	aa s^h	B6[2], 395
s340	—,ethyl isobutyl	$C_2H_5SCH_2CH(CH_3)_2$	118.24			134.22^{760} 24.8^{10}	0.8306^{20}_4	1.4450^{20}						chl s	B1[3], 1566
s341	—,ethyl methyl	$CH_3SC_2H_5$	76.16	λ^{iso} 212 (3.0), 240 sh (1.6)	−105.91	66.65^{760}	0.8422^{20}_4	1.4404^{20}	i	∞	s				B1, 343

For explanations, symbols and abbreviations see beginning of table. For structural formulas see end of table.

No.	Name	Synonyms and Formula	Mol. wt.	Color, crystalline form, specific rotation and λ_{max} (log ε)	m.p. °C	b.p. °C	Density	n_D	Solubility w	al	eth	ace	bz	other solvents	Ref.

Sulfide

Ω s342	—,—,2-chloro-	$CH_3SCH_2CH_2Cl$	110.61		....	140 44^{20}	1.1097_4^{25}	1.4902^{20}	...	s	s	s	...	...	B1[2], 347
—	—,ethyl phenyl	*see* **Benzene, (ethylthio)-***													
s343	—,ethyl propyl	$C_2H_5SCH_2CH_2CH_3$	104.22	λ^{ey} 216 (2.49)	−117.04	118.5^{760} 13.49^{10}	0.8370_4^{20}	1.4462^{20}	...	s					B1[3], 1432
s345	—,2-furyl phenyl		176.23		....	$119-20^8$ $97-8^{2.5}$	1.1341^{26}	1.5976^{20}	...	s	s				Am 81, 4927
s346	—,isobutyl methyl	$CH_3SCH_2CH(CH_3)_2$	104.22			112.5^{760}	0.8335_4^{20}	1.4433^{20}	...	s	s	s			B1[3], 1565
s347	—,isopropyl methyl	$CH_3SCH(CH_3)_2$	90.19	λ^{iso} 215 (2.96)	−101.51	84.75^{760}	0.8291_4^{20}	1.4932^{20}	...	s	s	s			B1, 367
—	—,methyl phenyl	*see* **Benzene, (methylthio)-***													
s348	—,methyl propyl	$CH_3SCH_2CH_2CH_3$	90.19	λ^{ey} 210–15 (3.00)	−113	95.54^{760} -4.09^{10}	0.8424^{20}	1.4442^{20}	s	s	s	s	...		B1[3], 1432
Ω s350	—,penta-methylene	Tetrahydrothiopyran. Thiacyclohexane. Thiane.	102.20	λ^{al} 230 sh (2.2)	19	141.75^{760} 93^{82}	0.9861_4^{20}	1.5067^{20}	i	s	s	s	s	os s	B17[2], 18
s351	—,trimethylene	Thiacyclobutane.	74.15	λ^{al} 272 (1.4)	−73.25	94.67^{760} 14.01^{30}	1.0200_4^{20}	1.5102^{20}	i	v	s		v	os v	B17[2], 12
s352	**Sulfone, benzyl phenyl**	$C_6H_5CH_2SO_2C_6H_5$	232.30	nd (al) λ^{al} 219 (4.12), 259 (2.85), 265 (3.03), 272 (2.90)	146–6.5	....	1.126_4^{153}	....	i s^h	δ	δ	...	δ		B6[2], 428
s353	—,benzyl (4-tolyl)		246.33	nd (al)	144–5					v^h		...	v	aa v	B6, 455
Ω s354	—,dibenzyl	Benzyl sulfone. $C_6H_5CH_2SO_2CH_2C_6H_5$	246.33	nd (al-bz) λ^{al} 219 (4.32), 259 (2.68), 265 (2.61), 269 (2.41)	155	290 δd			s^h i	δ	...	v	s	aa s	B6[2], 430
Ω s355	—,dibutyl	Butyl sulfone. $CH_3(CH_2)_3SO_2(CH_2)_3CH_3$	178.30	pl (w or al)	46	....			i	s	s				B1[2], 400
s356	—,diethyl	Ethyl sulfone. $C_2H_5SO_2C_2H_5$	122.19	rh pl λ < 208	73–4	248	1.357_4^{20}		s	s	s^h		v	peth i	B1[2], 345
s356[1]	—,—,2,2′-diphenoxy-	$C_6H_5OCH_2CH_2SO_2CH_2CH_2OC_6H_5$	306.38	pink lf (al)	180				i	s					B6[2], 150
Ω s357	—,diisopropyl	Isopropyl sulfone. $(CH_3)_2CHSO_2CH(CH_3)_2$	150.24	(eth)	36	....			v		s^h		v		B1[2], 387
Ω s358	—,dimethyl	Methyl sulfone. $CH_3SO_2CH_3$	94.13	pr	110	238^{760}	1.1702_{10}^{110}	1.4226	s	s			s		B1, 289
Ω s359	—,diphenyl	Phenyl sulfone.	218.28	mcl pr (bz), pl (al), nd (w) λ^{al} 235 (4.20), 261 (3.23), 267 (3.30), 274 (3.11)	128–9	379 232^{18}	1.252_4^{20}	....	i δ^h	s^h	s		s		B6[3], 992
s360	—,—,2-amino-	$C_{12}H_{11}NO_2S$. *See* s359	233.29	lf (dil al) λ^{ey} 228 (4.33), 274 (2.94), 280 (2.40), 318–20 (3.62)	122–4				i	v			v	aa v	B13, 399
s361	—,—,4-amino-	$C_{12}H_{11}NO_2S$. *See* s359	233.29	nd (al) λ^{ey} 270 (4.27)	176	....			i	s			v^h	aa v	B13[2], 298
Ω s362	—,—,4-chloro-	Sulphenone. $C_{12}H_9ClO_2S$. *See* s359	252.72	cr (al) λ^{al} 239 (4.21), 273 sh (3.19)	98 (95)	....			i	δ	s	v	v	os s	B6[3], 1036
s363	—,—,4,4′-diacetamido-	$C_{16}H_{16}N_2O_4S$. *See* s359	332.38	pa ye nd (eth or dil aa), lf (aq al) λ^{al} 257 (4.41), 285 (4.55)	282–5	....			i	s					B13[2], 303
s364	—,—,2,4-diamino-	$C_{12}H_{12}N_2O_2S$. *See* s359	248.31	nd (al)	188	....			i	v^h	i		δ		B13, 553
Ω s365	—,—,3,3′-diamino-	$C_{12}H_{12}N_2O_2S$. *See* s359	248.31	pr λ^{al}231 (4.52), 315 (3.67)	168	....			v^h	v^h					B13[2], 219
Ω s366	—,—,4,4′-diamino-	$C_{12}H_{12}N_2O_2S$. *See* s359	248.31	lf (dil al, MeOH) λ^{al} 261 (4.25), 295 (4.43)	178	....				s					B13[2], 300
Ω s367	—,—,4,4′-dichloro-	$C_{12}H_8Cl_2O_2S$. *See* s359	287.18	mcl	148–9	sub			i	δ s^h					B6[2], 297
s368	—,—,4,4′-diethoxy-	$C_{16}H_{18}O_4S$. *See* s359	306.38	pl (al or aq)	169	....			v^h	v	...	...	aa s^h		B6, 861
Ω s369	—,—,2,2′-dihydroxy-	$C_{12}H_{10}O_4S$. *See* s359	250.28	nd (bz)	164–5 (179)	....			s	v	v	...	δ	aa v peth i	B6[1], 396
s370	—,—,2,5-dihydroxy-	$C_{12}H_{10}O_4S$. *See* s359	250.28	pr (w), nd (dil al)	196				δ s^h	v	δ				B6[2], 1072
s371	—,—,3,3′-dihydroxy-	$C_{12}H_{10}O_4S$. *See* s359	250.28		190–1				δ s^h				aa δ		B6[2], 827
Ω s372	—,—,4,4′-dihydroxy-	$C_{12}H_{10}O_4S$. *See* s359	250.28	nd (w), rh bipym λ^{al} 236 (4.12), 262 (4.30), 295 (3.35)	240–1	....	1.3663^{15}	....	i s^h	s	s	...	δ	alk s	B6[2], 853

For explanations, symbols and abbreviations see beginning of table. For structural formulas see end of table.

No.	Name	Synonyms and Formula	Mol. wt.	Color, crystalline form. specific rotation and λ_{max} (log ε)	m.p. °C	b.p. °C	Density	n_D	Solubility						Ref.
									w	al	eth	ace	bz	other solvents	
	Sulfone														
Ω s373	—,—,2,2'-dimethoxy-	$C_{14}H_{14}O_4S$. See s359	278.33	nd (bz) λ^{al} 233 sh (4.01), 289 (3.88)	157–8					v^h			δ^h	aa s con sulf s^h xyl δ^h peth i	B6, 794
s374	—,—,4,4'-dimethoxy-	Anisyl sulfone. $C_{14}H_{14}O_4S$. See s359	278.33	lf or pr (al), nd (al-eth) λ^{al} 237 (4.16), 260 (4.35)	130	sub			i	v^h					B6, 861
Ω s375	—,dipropyl	Propyl sulfone. $CH_3CH_2CH_2SO_2CH_2CH_2CH_3$	150.24	sc	29.5–30.5		1.0278_4^{50}	1.4456^{30}	δ	s	s				B1², 373
s376	—,2,2'-ditolyl	o-Tolyl sulfone.	246.33	nd (al) λ^{al} 233 (4.16), 273 (3.43), 280 (3.40)	134–5 (104.5–5.5)				i	v	v		v	chl, CS_2 s	B6², 342
s377	—,3,4'-ditolyl		246.33	nd (aa) λ^{al} 233 (4.00), 245 (4.30)	116										B6¹, 208
s378	—,4,4'-ditolyl	p-Tolyl sulfone.	246.33	pr (bz), nd (w or al), pl (al)	159	405⁷¹⁴			δ s^h	s^h	δ		s	chl, CS_2 s	B6², 395
s381	—,phenyl (2-tolyl)		232.30	pl (al) λ^{al} 234 (4.15), 266 (3.31), 273 (3.35)	81				i	s	v		v	lig δ	B6, 371
Ω s382	—,phenyl (4-tolyl)		232.30	pl (al)	127–8 (124.5)				i	δ			δ	aa δ	B6², 395
Ω s383	**Sulfoxide, dibenzyl**	$C_6H_5CH_2SOCH_2C_6H_5$	230.33	lf (al or w) λ^{al} 222 (4.29), 260 (2.68), 265 (2.55)	134–5	210d			i s^h	v	s				B6², 429
Ω s384	—,dibutyl	Butyl sulfoxide. $CH_3(CH_2)_3SO(CH_2)_3CH_3$	162.30	nd (dil al)	32.6	d	0.8317_4^{23}	1.4669^{20}	i	s	s				B1², 400
s385	—,diethyl	Ethyl sulfoxide. $C_2H_5SOC_2H_5$	106.19	syr	14 (4–6)	104²⁵ 88–9¹⁵			s	s	s				B1², 345
Ω s386	—,dimethyl	Methyl sulfoxide. CH_3SOCH_3	78.13		18.45	189⁷⁶⁰ 85–7²⁰	1.1014_4^{20}	1.4770^{20}	s	s	s	s		AcOEt s	B1, 289
Ω s387	—,diphenyl	Phenyl sulfoxide.	202.28	pr (lig) λ^{al} 233 (4.15), 265 (3.32)	70.5	340 δd 210¹⁵				v	v		v	aa v peth i	B6², 290
s388	—,—,4-amino-	$C_{12}H_{11}NOS$. See s387	217.29	nd (w) λ^{al} 278 (4.01)	152				s^h	v	v				B13, 534
s389	—,—,4-amino-4'-nitro-	$C_{12}H_{10}N_2O_3S$. See s387	262.29	ye (al) λ^{al} 277 (4.33)	132				δ	v					Am 73, 4356
s390	—,—,4,4'-diamino-	p,p'-Sulfinyldianiline. $C_{12}H_{12}N_2OS$. See s387	232.31	pr (w or al) λ^{al} 264 (4.17), 300 (4.25)	175d				s^h	s^h					B13, 53
s391	—,—,4,4'-dihydroxy-	$C_{12}H_{10}O_3S$. See s387	234.28	nd (ace)	195					s		s			B6, 860
s392	—,dipropyl	Propyl sulfoxide. $CH_3CH_2CH_2SOCH_2CH_2CH_3$	134.24	nd	22–3	80²	0.9654_4^{20}	1.4663^{20}	δ	s	s				B1², 373
Ω s393	—,4,4'-ditolyl	p-Tolyl sulfoxide.	230.33	cr (lig, peth) λ^{al} 275 (3.35)	94–4.5					v	v		v	chl, aa v lig δ, s^h	B6², 395
s394	**Sulfuric acid, diamide, N,N,N',N'-tetramethyl-**	Tetramethylsulfamide. $(CH_3)_2NSO_2N(CH_3)_2$	152.22	pl or nd (dil al)	73	225⁷⁶⁰ (extrap 126³⁰·⁶)			δ	s					Am 76, 220
s395	—,dibutyl ester*	Butyl sulfate. $[CH_3(CH_2)_3O]_2SO_2$	210.30			109.5⁴	1.0616^{20}	1.4192^{20}	i						J1943, 16
s396	—,didecyl ester*	1-Decanol sulfate. Decyl sulfate. $[CH_3(CH_2)_9O]_2SO_2$	378.62		37.6–7.8										Am 56, 1204
s397	—,didodecyl ester*	Dodecyl sulfate. $[CH_3(CH_2)_{11}O]_2SO_2$	434.73		48.5										Am 56, 1204
Ω s398	—,diethyl ester*	Ethyl sulfate. $(C_2H_5O)_2SO_2$	154.19		−24.5	208 δd 96¹⁵	1.1774_4^{20}	1.4004^{20}	i d^h	∞ d^h	∞				B1², 327
s399	—,diheptyl ester*	Heptyl sulfate. $[CH_3(CH_2)_6O]_2SO_2$	294.46	cr (peth)	13	146.6¹·⁵	0.9819_{25}^{25}	1.4362^{25}							B1³, 1683
s400	—,dihexadecyl ester*	Cetyl sulfate. $[CH_3(CH_2)_{15}O]_2SO_2$	546.95		66.2				s						B1³, 1823
s401	—,dihexyl ester*	Hexyl sulfate. $[CH_3(CH_2)_5O]_2SO_2$	266.40			125.3²	1.0036_0^{21}	1.433^{21}							B1³, 1656
Ω s402	—,dimethyl ester*	Methyl sulfate. $(CH_3O)_2SO_2$	126.13	λ^{undil} 265	−31.75 fr −27	188.5⁷⁶⁰d 76¹⁵	1.3283^{20}	1.3874^{20}	s	∞	s		s	CS_2 i	B1, 283
s403	—,di(3-methylbutyl) ester*	Isoamyl sulfate. $[(CH_3)_2CHCH_2CH_2O]_2SO_2$	238.35		−20	139–41¹²									B1², 434
s404	—,dioctadecyl ester*	Octadecyl sulfate $[CH_3(CH_2)_{17}O]_2SO_2$	603.06		70.5										B1³, 1837
s405	—,dipentyl ester*	Amyl sulfate. $[CH_3(CH_2)_4O]_2SO_2$	238.35		14	117³·⁵	1.029^{20}	1.4290^{20}							B1², 418
s406	—,dipropyl ester*	Propyl sulfate. $(CH_3CH_2CH_2O)_2SO_2$	182.24			121²⁰ 93–4⁴	1.1064_4^{20}	1.4135^{20}	i δd					peth v	B1², 368

For explanations, symbols and abbreviations see beginning of table. For structural formulas see end of table.

No.	Name	Synonyms and Formula	Mol. wt.	Color, crystalline form, specific rotation and λ_{max} (log ε)	m.p. °C	b.p. °C	Density	n_D	w	al	eth	ace	bz	other solvents	Ref.
	Sulfuric acid														
s407	—,ethylene ester...	Ethylene sulfate. Glycol sulfate.	124.12	nd or pr (bz-lig)	99 (97)	sub	1.735_4^{13}	....	d	s	v	v	s	os v	B1³, 2110
Ω s408	—,monoamide, N-cyclohexyl-	Cyclohexylsulfamic acid.	179.24	(al)	169–70	....	....	....	δdʰ					alk v	C53, 5157
Ω s409	—,mono(2-amino-ethyl) ester*	$H_2NCH_2CH_2OSO_3H$	141.15	mcl pr (w-al)	230d	....	....	....	s	i				....	B4², 718
s410	—,monobutyl ester*	Butyl hydrogen sulfate. $CH_3(CH_2)_3OSO_3H$	154.19	syr	....	d	....	....	v	s	s				B1², 397
s411	—,monochloride monoethyl ester	Ethyl chlorosulfonate*. $C_2H_5OSO_2Cl$	144.58	....		151–4 52¹⁴	1.3502_4^{25}	1.416^{20}	d	d	s			chl, lig s	B1², 327
s412	—,monochloride monomethyl ester	Methyl chlorosulfonate*. CH_3OSO_2Cl	130.55	....		133–5⁷⁶⁰d 48²⁹	1.4805_4^{25}	1.4138^{18}	i dʰ	dʰ	s	v	s	os s	B1³, 1199
s413	—,monoethyl ester*	Ethylsulfuric acid. Ethyl hydrogen sulfate. $C_2H_5OSO_3H$	126.13			280d	1.3657_4^{20}	1.4105^{20}	v	δ	δ				B1², 326
s414	—,monomethyl ester*	Methyl bisulfate. Methyl hydrogen sulfate. CH_3OSO_3H	112.11	....	< −30	130–40d	....	....	v	s	∞			CCl₄ s	B1, 283
s415	**Sulfurous acid,** diamide, N,N,N',N'-tetra-methyl-	Tetramethylthionamide. $(CH_3)_2NSON(CH_3)_2$	136.22		31	209⁷⁶⁰ 70¹⁰					s			oos s	Am 76, 220
Ω s416	—,dibutyl ester*...	Butyl sulfite. $[CH_3(CH_2)_3O]_2SO$	194.30	λ^{iso} < 230	....	230 116¹⁹	0.9957_4^{20}	1.4310^{20}		s	s				B1³, 1506
s417	—,diethyl ester*...	Ethyl sulfite. $(C_2H_5O)_2SO$	138.19			157⁷⁶⁸ 55¹³	1.0829_4^{20}	1.4144^{20}	d	s	s				B1², 326
s418	—,diisobutyl ester*	Isobutyl sulfite. $[(CH_3)_2CHCH_2O]_2SO$	194.30			209⁷⁴¹ 92–4¹³	0.9862_4^{20}	1.4268^{20}		s	s				B1³, 1561
s419	—,dimethyl ester*	Methyl sulfite. $(CH_3O)_2SO$ ...	110.13	λ^{al} 280 (0.90)		126⁷⁶⁰ 52⁴⁵	1.2129_4^{20}	1.4093^{20}	sʰ	s	s				B1, 282
Ω s420	—,ethylene ester...	Ethylene sulfite. Glycol sulfite.	108.12	....	−11	173⁷⁶⁰ 70–1²⁰	1.4402_4^{20}	1.4463^{20}	v dʰ	v	v	v	v	AcOEt v	B1³, 2110
s421	—,monochloride, monoethyl ester	Ethyl chlorosulfinate. $C_2H_5OS(O)Cl$	128.58	....		52.5⁴⁴ 32¹⁶	1.2766_4^{25}	1.4550^{25}	d	d	s				B1³, 1316
s422	**Sylvestrene**(d)	Carvestrene. 3-Isopropenyl-1-methylcyclohexene d-1,8(9)-m-Menthadiene.	136.24	$[\alpha]_D^{18}$ +83.18 (undil), +66.3 (chl, c = 4.3)	....	175⁷⁵¹	0.8479_4^{18}	1.4760^{18}	i	∞	∞				B5², 84
—	Syntomycetin	see **Chloromycetin**													
—	Syringaldehyde ...	see **Benzaldehyde, 3,5-dimethoxy-4-hydroxy-**													
—	Syringenin........	see **2-Propen-1-ol, 3(3,5-dimethoxy-4-hydroxyphenyl)-**													
—	Syringic acid	see **Benzoic acid, 3,5-dimethoxy-4-hydroxy-**													
—	Syringidin	see **Malvidin**													
s423	Syringin.........	Methoxyconiferine........	372.38	cr (w), nd (al), nd (w +1), $[\alpha]_D$ −17.1	192				δ sʰ	s	i			con HNO₃, con sulf s	B31, 222

For explanations, symbols and abbreviations see beginning of table. For structural formulas see end of table.

No.	Name	Synonyms and Formula	Mol. wt.	Color, crystalline form, specific rotation and λ_{max} (log ε)	m.p. °C	b.p. °C	Density	n_D	w	al	eth	ace	bz	other solvents	Ref.
	Tachysterol														
t1	Tachysterol	$C_{28}H_{44}O$	396.67	$[\alpha]_D^{18} -70$ (bz) λ^{eth} 280 (4.44)		220 vac			i	s	s	s	s	os s MeOH i	E12A, 175
t2	Tagatose(D)	$C_6H_{12}O_6$	180.16	cr (dil al), $[\alpha]_D^{20} -5$ (w, c=1)	134–5				s	δ	i	...	i	MeOH δ	B31, 348
t3	Talitol(D)	D-Altritol. D-Talite. $C_6H_{14}O_6$	182.18	pr (al, MeOH) $[\alpha]_D^{18} +3.2$ (w)	87–8				s	s	i	...	i		B1³, 2384
t4	Talonic acid, hemihydrate(D)	$C_6H_{12}O_7 \cdot \frac{1}{2}H_2O$	205.17	cr (aq al + ½w) $[\alpha]_D^5 +16.7 \rightarrow -21.6$ (w, c=4) (mut)	138–9				v		i		i		B3³, 1068
Ω t5	—,γ-lactone(D)	$C_6H_{10}O_6$	178.14	pr (al), $[\alpha]_D^{25} -34.65 \rightarrow -28.4$ (w) (mut)	135–7										Am 54, 1593
t6	Talose(D)	$C_6H_{12}O_6$	180.16	α: cr (al), β: cr (MeOH) $[\alpha]_D^{67} +29 \rightarrow +19.7$ (w, c=1) (mut) β: $[\alpha]_D^{20} +11.5 \rightarrow +21$ (w, c=4) (mut)	α: 130–5 β: 120–1				s	s^h	i	...	i		B31, 283
Ω t7	Tannic acid	Gallotannic acid. Tannin. $C_{76}H_{52}O_{46}$.	1701.24	pa ye-br amor or fl $\lambda^{w, pH=8}$ 280 (2.2), 420 (1.8), 500 (1.8)	210–5 δd				s	v	i	v	i	chl, CS_2 i	B31, 133
—	Tannin	see Tannic acid													
t8	Taraxanthin	$C_{40}H_{56}O_4$	600.89	ye pr (MeOH) $[\alpha]_{Cd}^{20} +200$ (AcOEt) λ^{bz} 428.5 (4.96), 455 (5.14), 485 (5.12)	185–6					s^h	v	...	s	CS_2, peth s MeOH δ	B30, 100
t9	Tartaric acid(d)	L-2,3-Dihydroxybutanedioic acid*. d-2,3-Dihydroxy-succinic acid. $HO_2CCH(OH)CH(OH)CO_2H$	150.09	mcl (anh), rh pr (w+1), $[\alpha]_D^{20} +12.7$ (w, c=17.4)	171–4		1.7598^{20}	1.4955	v	v	δ	s	i	MeOH s	B3³, 994
Ω t10	—(dl)	Racemic acid. $HO_2CCH(OH)CH(OH)CO_2H$	150.09	mcl pr (w or al +1w)	206 (210d) (anh) 203–4 (+1w)		1.788		s	s^h	δ	...	i		B3³, 1025
t11	—(meso)	$HO_2CCH(OH)CH(OH)CO_2H$	150.09	tcl pl (w)	146–8 (140)		1.666_4^{20}	1.5–1.6	v	s	δ	...			B3³, 1029
t12	—,anhydride diacetate(d)	α,α'-Diacetoxysuccinic anhydride.	216.16	nd (bz)	135					v	v	s	...	aa δ	B18², 143
t13	—,dibenzyl ester(d)	$C_6H_5CH_2O_2CCH(OH)CH(OH)CO_2CH_2C_6H_5$	330.34	$[\alpha]_D^{15} +19.26$	50	250–70⁴	1.2036^{72}		...	s	...	...	...	Py s	B6³, 1537
t14	—,dibutyl ester(d)	$CH_3(CH_2)_3O_2CCH(OH)CH(OH)CO_2(CH_2)_3CH_3$	262.31	pr, $[\alpha]_D^{20} +11.3$ (al)	22–2.5	320⁷⁶⁰ 178¹²	1.0909_4^{20}	1.4451^{20}	s	s	...	s	...	os s	B3³, 1021
Ω t15	—,—(dl)	$CH_3(CH_2)_3O_2CCH(OH)CH(OH)CO_2(CH_2)_3CH_3$	262.31			320⁷⁶⁵ 185¹²	1.0879_4^{18}	1.4474^{15}	s	s	...	s	...	os s	B3³, 1032
t16	—,diethyl ester(d)	$C_2H_5O_2CCH(OH)CH(OH)CO_2C_2H_5$	206.20	$[\alpha]_D^{16} +7.9$ (undil)	18.7	280⁷⁶⁰ 142⁸	1.2036_4^{20}	1.4468^{20}	s	s	s	s	...	aa ∞ os s	B3², 329
Ω t17	—,—(dl)	Diethyl racemate. $C_2H_5O_2CCH(OH)CH(OH)CO_2C_2H_5$	206.20		18.7	281⁷⁶⁵ 158¹⁴	1.2046^{20}	1.4438^{20}	δ	∞	∞	s	...	oos s	B3², 337
t18	—,—(l)	$C_2H_5O_2CCH(OH)CH(OH)CO_2C_2H_5$	206.20	$[\alpha]_D^{20} -7.55$ (undil)	18	280⁷⁶⁰ 162¹⁹	1.2054^{20}	1.4468^{20}	...	s	s	s	...	os s	B3³, 1020
t19	—,—(meso)	$C_2H_5O_2CCH(OH)CH(OH)CO_2C_2H_5$	206.20		60 (55)	157.5¹⁴	1.1350^{29}	1.4315^{65}	...	s	...	s	...		B3³, 1031
t20	—,diethyl ester diacetate(d)	$C_2H_5O_2CCH(O_2CCH_3)CH(O_2CCH_3)CO_2C_2H_5$	290.27	mcl cr (lig) $[\alpha]_D^{100} +6.3$ (undil) $[\alpha]_{546}^{20} -17.3$ (bz, c=5)	67.3–7.6 (cor)	296⁷⁶⁴ 163¹⁰	1.1149_4^{66}		δ	s	v	...	...	lig s^h	B3³, 1021
t21	—,diisobutyl ester (d)	$(CH_3)_2CHCH_2O_2CCH(OH)CH(OH)CO_2CH_2CH(CH_3)_2$	262.31	$[\alpha]_D +11.8$ (al) $[\alpha]_{546}^{22} +67.1$ (Py, p=7)	72.7–2.9	323–5 183¹¹	1.0265_4^{81}		s^h	s	...	s	...	os s	B3³, 1021
t22	—,—(dl)	$(CH_3)_2CHCH_2O_2CCH(OH)CH(OH)CO_2CH_2CH(CH_3)_2$	262.31	cr (bz)	311⁷⁶⁸ 195¹³ 63		1.0386_4^{68}		s^h	v	...	s	...	os s	B3³, 1028

For explanations, symbols and abbreviations see beginning of table. For structural formulas see end of table.

No.	Name	Synonyms and Formula	Mol. wt.	Color, crystalline form, specific rotation and λ_{max} (log ε)	m.p. °C	b.p. °C	Density	n_D	w	al	eth	ace	bz	other solvents	Ref.
	Tartaric acid														
t23	—,diisopropyl ester(d)	$(CH_3)_2CHO_2CCH(OH)CH(OH)CO_2CH(CH_3)_2$	234.25	$[\alpha]_D^{20}+14.9$	....	275^{765} 152^{12}	1.1300_4^{20}	....		s	s	s		os s	B3[2], 331
t24	—,—,(dl)	$(CH_3)_2CHO_2CCH(OH)CH(OH)CO_2CH(CH_3)_2$	234.25		34	275^{765} 154^{12}	1.1166_4^{20}	....		s	s	s		os s	B3[2], 337
t25	—,dimethyl ester(d)	$CH_3O_2CCH(OH)CH(OH)CO_2CH_3$	178.14	(i) cr (bz) (ii) cr (bz) (iii) cr (w) $[\alpha]_D^{50}+6.72$ (MeOH, c=16), $[\alpha]_D^{20}-9.1$ (bz, c=1)	(i) 48 (ii) 50 (iii) 61	280^{760} 166^{12}	1.306_4^5	....	s	v	s	s		chl v	B3[3], 1018
t26	—,—,(dl)	$CH_3O_2CCH(OH)CH(OH)CO_2CH_3$	178.14	orh nd (bz), ta (chl)	90 (st) 80 (unst)	282^{760} 169^{20}	1.2604^{90}	....	s	v	s	s		os s	B3[3], 1027
t27	—,—,(meso)	$CH_3O_2CCH(OH)CH(OH)CO_2CH_3$	178.14	nd (chl), cr (MeOH)	114	$98^{0.01}$ sub	....	....	s	v		s		os v	B3[3], 1031
t28	—,di(2-methyl-butyl) ester(d)	$C_2H_5CH(CH_3)CH_2O_2CCH(OH)CH(OH)CO_2CH_2CH(CH_3)C_2H_5$	290.36	$[\alpha]_D^{20}+14.10$	....	208^{20}	1.0636_4^{20}	....		s	s	s		s	B3, 519
t29	—,dinitrate(d)	$HO_2CCH(ONO_2)CH(ONO_2)CO_2H$	240.08	nd (eth-bz) $[\alpha]_D^{20}+13.7$ (MeOH, p=9)	d	....	....	....	d	v	v	v	i	peth i	B3[2], 328
t30	—,dipropyl ester(d)	$CH_3CH_2CH_2O_2CCH(OH)CH(OH)CO_2CH_2CH_2CH_3$	234.25	$[\alpha]_D^{20}+12.44$ (w)	....	303^{760} 181^{23}	1.1390_4^{20}	....	s	v	v	s		os s	B3, 516
t31	—,—,(dl)	$CH_3CH_2CH_2O_2CCH(OH)CH(OH)CO_2CH_2CH_2CH_3$	234.25	pr (al-eth)	25	286^{765} 167^{11}	1.1256_4^{20}	....	s	v	v	s		os s	B3[2], 337
t32	—,monoethyl ester (d)	$HO_2CCH(OH)CH(OH)CO_2C_2H_5$	178.14	$[\alpha]_D+21.8$ (w)	90	....	....	....	s	s	i				B3, 512
t33	—,piperazinium salt (d)	$HO_2CCH(OH)CH(OH)CO_2H \cdot C_4H_{10}N_2$	236.23	cr	248–54 (cor)	....	....	....	s^h	s	δ				Am 70, 2758
t34	—,—,(meso)	$HO_2CCH(OH)CH(OH)CO_2H \cdot C_4H_{10}N_2$	236.23	cr	140–1 (cor)		....	....	s	s	δ				Am 70, 2758
—	**Tartronic acid**	see **Malonic acid, hydroxy-**													
Ω t35	**Taurine**	2-Aminoethanesulfonic acid*. $H_2NCH_2CH_2SO_3H$	125.15	mcl pr (w)	328 (317d)				s v^h	i	i				B4, 528
t36	—,N,N-dimethyl- ..	2(Dimethylamino)ethane-sulfonic acid*. $(CH_3)_2NCH_2CH_2SO_3H$	153.20	pr (MeOH), pl (w+1)	315–6 (anh) 270–80d (hyd)				v	i	i			aa v MeOH δ^h	B4[2], 951
t37	—,N-methyl-	2(Methylamino)ethane-sulfonic acid*. $CH_3NHCH_2CH_2SO_3H$	139.18	pr	241–2				v	i	i				B4, 529
t38	—,N-methyl-N-phenyl-	$C_6H_5N(CH_3)CH_2CH_2SO_3H$	215.27	pa vt (al)	239–40				v^h						B12[2], 285
t39	—,N-phenyl-	$C_6H_5NHCH_2CH_2SO_3H$	201.25	lf (w), pr (al)	277–80d				v	i	i				B12[2], 284
t40	**Taurocholic acid** ...	Cholaic acid. Cholyltaurine. $C_{26}H_{45}NO_7S$	515.72	pr (al-eth) $[\alpha]_D^{18}+38.8$ (al, c=2) $\lambda^{con\,sulf}$ 303 (3.64), 389 (4.45), 480 (3.46)	ca. 125d	....	....	....	v	v^h	δ			AcOEt δ	E14, 195
t41	**Telluride, diethyl-** ...	Ethyl telluride. $C_2H_5TeC_2H_5$	185.73	red-ye	....	$137–8^{760}$	1.599_4^{15}	1.5182^{15}	δ	s					B1[2], 359
t42	—,dimethyl	Methyl telluride. CH_3TeCH_3	157.67	pa ye	....	93.5^{749}	>1	....	d	v	i				B1, 291
t43	**Tephrosin**	Hydroxydeguelin. $C_{23}H_{22}O_7$.	410.43	pr (chl-MeOH)	198 (218–20)		....	....	i		s	s		chl s MeOH δ	Am 55, 759
—	**Teraconic acid**	see **Succinic acid, iso-propylidene-**													
t44	**Terebic acid**(dl)	3,3-Dimethylparaconic acid. Teribinic acid. $C_7H_{10}O_4$	158.16	mcl pr (al)	176	....	0.8155_4^{24}	....	δ s^h	s^h	δ				B18[2], 314
—	**Terephthalaldehyde**	see **1,4-Benzenedicarbox-aldehyde**													
—	**Terephthalaldehydic acid**	see **Benzoic acid, 4-formyl-**													
—	**Terephthalic acid**	see **1,4-Benzenedicarboxylic acid***													
t45	**Terpenolic acid**	Terpenylic acid.	172.19	lf or pr (w+1)	90 (anh) 57 (+1w)	sub 130–40			s v^h						B18[2], 316
Ω t46	**o-Terphenyl**	1,2-Diphenylbenzene.	230.31	mcl pr (MeOH) λ^{al} 231.5 (4.42), 250.5 (4.06)	58	332^{760} $160–70^2$	....	....	i			s	s	MeOH, chl s	B5[3], 2292
Ω t47	**m-Terphenyl**	1,3-Diphenylbenzene.	230.31	ye nd (al) λ^{al} 246.8 (4.59), 290.7 (3.24)	89	365^{760}	....	....	i	s	s	s		aa s	B5[3], 2294
Ω t48	**α-Terpinene**	p-Mentha-1,3-diene. $C_{10}H_{16}$.	136.24	λ^{al} 265 (3.84)	....	177.2^{760} $68–70^{12}$	0.8502_4^{20}	1.4784^{20}	i	∞	∞			peth s	B5[3], 337

For explanations, symbols and abbreviations see beginning of table. For structural formulas see end of table.

No.	Name	Synonyms and Formula	Mol. wt.	Color, crystalline form, specific rotation and λ_{max} (log ε)	m.p. °C	b.p. °C	Density	n_D	w	al	eth	ace	bz	other solvents	Ref.
	α-Terpineol														
Ω t49	α-Terpineol(dl)	dl-p-Menth-1-en-8-ol. $C_{10}H_{18}O$.	154.26	cr (peth) λ^{al} 215 (2.25), 260 (0.26)	40–1	220[760] 85[3]	0.9337[20]	1.4831[20]	δ	v	v	s	s	chl s peth s[h]	B6[3], 247
Ω t50	—,acetate	$C_{12}H_{20}O_2$. See t49	196.29	d:[α]_D +52.5 (undil) l:[α]_D[20] −73 (undil)		140[40] 104–6[11]	0.9659[20]	1.4689[21]	i	s	s	...	s		B6[2], 66
t51	**Terpinol, hydrate** (cis)	cis-Terpin hydrate	214.31	rh cr	123d	sub 100	1.51–1.52		δ	s	δ				B6[2], 754
Ω t52	**Terpinolene**		136.24			185[760] 76[10]	0.8623[20]	1.4883[20]	i	∞	∞		s		B5[3], 345
t53	**3-Terpinolenone**	Piperitenone. $C_{10}H_{14}O$	150.22	[α]_546 −0.1 λ^{al} 242 (4.10), 278 (3.90), 353 sh (2.05)		120–2[14]	0.9774[20]	1.5294[20]		v	v				J1939, 1496
t54	**Terramycin**	Oxytetracycline. $C_{22}H_{24}N_2O_9$	498.49		184.5–5.5	1.634[20]			δ	δ					Am 87, 134
Ω t55	**Testosterone**	17β-Hydroxy-4-androsten-3-one. $C_{19}H_{28}O_2$.	288.44	nd (dil ace) [α]_D[24] +109 (al, c =4) λ^{al} 240.5 (4.23)	155				i	s	s	s		os s	Am 76, 1962
t56	—,4,5-dihydro-17-methyl-	$C_{20}H_{32}O_2$. See t55	304.48	cr (AcOEt) λ 283 (4.15)	192–3 (cor)									AcOEt δ	E14, 145
t57	—,17-ethenyl-	17-Vinyltestosterone. $C_{21}H_{30}O_2$. See t55	314.47	pr nd (peth-eth) [α]_D +87.6	140–1						s	s		MeOH, chl s	C31, 2224
t58	—,17-ethyl-	$C_{21}H_{32}O_2$. See t55	316.49	nd (AcOEt) [α]_D[20] +71.2	143–4				i			s[h]		AcOEt s[h]	E14, 145
t59	—,17-ethynyl-	$C_{21}H_{28}O_2$. See t55	312.46	cr (chl-MeOH, AcOEt) [α]_D[20] +22.5 (diox) λ^{al} 238.5	270–2 (cor)	sub vac			i	δ				diox, Py s AcOEt s[h]	C34, 18213
t60	—,17-methyl-	$C_{20}H_{30}O_2$. See t55	302.46	nd (hx) [α]_D[20] +82 (al) $\lambda^{97\% sulf}$ 298 (4.26), 497 (2.86)	165–6 (cor)				i	s	s	s		MeOH, os s	E14s, 2645
t61	**Tetrabenzotriaza-porphyrin**		513.57	purple nd and pl (quinoline)										Py δ	J1939, 1809
—	**Tetracaine,** hydrochloride	see **Benzoic acid, 4(butyl-amino)-, (2-dimethyl-aminoethyl) ester, hydrochloride**													
—	**Tetracene**	see **Naphthacene**													
Ω t62	**Tetracosane***	$CH_3(CH_2)_{22}CH_3$	338.67	cr (eth)	54 (51)	391.3[760] 231.3[10]	0.7665[70] 0.7991[20] (suc)	1.4283[70] 1.4480[20] (suc)	i	δ	v				B1[3], 575
—	**Tetracyclone**	see **Cyclopentadienone, tetraphenyl-***													
t63	**6,8-Tetradeca-diyne***	$CH_3(CH_2)_4C\vdots CC\vdots C(CH_2)_4CH_3$	190.33		2	118–9[4]	0.8699[16]					s			B1[3], 1067
Ω t64	**Tetradecanal***	Myristaldehyde. Tetradecyl aldehyde. $CH_3(CH_2)_{12}CHO$	212.38	lf	30 (23)	166[24]			i	s	s	s		oos s	B1[3], 2919
t65	—,dimethyl acetal	1,1-Dimethoxytetradecane*. $CH_3(CH_2)_{12}CH(OCH_3)_2$	258.45			134–6[4]		1.4342[25]		v	v			MeOH v	C53, 12168
t66	—,oxime	Myristaldoxime. $CH_3(CH_2)_{12}CH\vdots NOH$	227.39	fl or nd (al)	82–3				i	v			δ	chl δ	B1, 716
Ω t67	**Tetradecane***	$CH_3(CH_2)_{12}CH_3$	198.40		5.86	253.7[760] 121.9[10]	0.7628[20]	1.4290[20]	i	v	v				B1[3], 549
Ω t68	—,1-amino-*	Myristylamine. $CH_3(CH_2)_{13}NH_2$	213.41		83.1	291.2[760] 162[15]	0.8079[20]	1.4463[20]	i	v	v		v	chl v	B4[3], 419
Ω t69	—,1-bromo-*	Myristyl bromide. $CH_3(CH_2)_{13}Br$	277.30		5.6	307[760] 181[21]	1.0170[20]	1.4603[20]	i	s		∞	∞	chl v	B1[2], 136
Ω t70	—,1-chloro-*	Myristyl chloride. $CH_3(CH_2)_{13}Cl$	232.84		4.9	292[760] 153[10]	0.8665[20]	1.4473[20]	i	s		v	v	chl, os s	B1[3], 550
t71	—,1,14-dibromo-*	Tetradecamethylene bromide. $Br(CH_2)_{14}Br$	356.20	lf(al-eth), cr (al)	50.4	190–2[8]			i	v[h]	s			chl v	B1[3], 551
t72	—,1-phenyl-*	Tetradecylbenzene* $CH_3(CH_2)_{13}C_6H_5$	274.50		16.1	358.9[760] 210[12]	0.8559[20]	1.4818[20]							C50, 4869
t73	**Tetradecanedioic acid,** dimethyl ester*	$CH_3O_2C(CH_2)_{12}CO_2CH_3$.	286.42	nd (MeOH)	43–5	191–2[10]			i		δ			MeOH i, s[h]	B2[3], 1858
t74	**1,14-Tetrade-canediol***	Tetradecamethylene glycol. $HO(CH_2)_{14}OH$	230.40	nd (bz)	84.5	200[9]				s	s			s[h]	B1[3], 2241
t75	**1-Tetradecane-sulfonic acid***	$CH_3(CH_2)_{13}SO_3H$	278.46		65.5 (anh) 55–6 (+1w)		0.9996[25]		s						Am 57, 1905
Ω t76	**1-Tetradecane-thiol***	n-Tetradecyl mercaptan. $CH_3(CH_2)_{13}SH$	230.45			176–80[22]	0.8484[20]	1.4597[20]	i	s	s				Am 55, 1090

For explanations, symbols and abbreviations see beginning of table. For structural formulas see end of table.

No.	Name	Synonyms and Formula	Mol. wt.	Color, crystalline form, specific rotation and λ_{max} (log ε)	m.p. °C	b.p. °C	Density	n_D	Solubility						Ref.
									w	al	eth	ace	bz	other solvents	
	Tetradecanoic acid														
Ω t77	**Tetradecanoic acid***	Myristic acid. $CH_3(CH_2)_{12}CO_2H$	228.38	lf (eth, 80 % aa) λ^{hp} 210 (1.85)	58	250.5^{100} 149.3^1	0.8439^{80}_4	1.4305^{60}	i	s	δ	s	v	chl s MeOH s, v^h	B2[3], 911
Ω t78	—,amide	Myristamide. $CH_3(CH_2)_{12}CONH_2$	227.39	lf (ace) λ^{al} < 200	105–7	217^{12}			i	s	δ	δ $\frac{}{\delta^h}$	δ	CCl_4 δ	B2[3], 929
t79	—,anhydride*	$[CH_3(CH_2)_{12}CO]_2O$.	438.74	lf (peth)	53.4	vac distb	0.8502^{70}	1.4335^{70}	i	s	s			peth s^h	B2[3], 929
t80	—,benzyl ester	Benzyl myristate. $CH_3(CH_2)_{12}CO_2CH_2C_6H_5$	318.51		20.5	229.3^{11}	0.9321^{25}_{25}		i	s	v		v	chl v	B6[2], 417
Ω t81	—,chloride	Myristoyl chloride. $CH_3(CH_2)_{12}COCl$	246.83		–1	174^{16}			d	d	s				B2[3], 929
Ω t82	—,ethyl ester*	Ethyl myristate. $CH_3(CH_2)_{12}CO_2C_2H_5$	256.43		12.3	295^{760} 162.5^9	0.8573^{25}_4	1.4362^{20}	i	s	δ			lig s	B2[3], 922
Ω t83	—,isopropyl ester*	Isopropyl myristate. $CH_3(CH_2)_{12}CO_2CH(CH_3)_2$	270.46			192.6^{20} 140.2^2	0.8532^{20}	1.4325^{25}	i	s	v	s	v	chl s	B2[3], 923
Ω t84	—,methyl ester*	Methyl myristate. $CH_3(CH_2)_{12}CO_2CH_3$	242.41	λ^{hp} 212 (1.85)	19	295^{751} (323) $155–7^7$		1.425^{45}	i	∞	∞	∞	v	chl, CCl_4, MeOH, AcOEt ∞	B2[3], 921
Ω t85	—,nitrile	Myristonitrile. $CH_3(CH_2)_{12}CN$	209.38		19.25	226.5^{100} 119^1	0.8281^{19}_4	1.4392^{25}	i	∞	∞	∞	∞	chl ∞	B2[3], 930
t86	—,propyl ester*	Propyl myristate. $CH_3(CH_2)_{12}CO_2CH_2CH_2CH_3$	270.46			147^2	0.8592^{20}	1.4356^{25}	i	v	v	v	v	solvents	B2[3], 923
Ω t87	**1-Tetradecanol***	Myristyl alcohol. $CH_3(CH_2)_{13}OH$	214.40	lf	39–40	263.2 167^{15}	0.8236^{38}_4		i	v	v	v	v	chl v	B1[3], 1803
Ω t88	**2-Tetradecanone***	n-Dodecyl methyl ketone. $CH_3(CH_2)_{11}COCH_3$	212.38	cr (dil al)	33–4	$205–6^{100}$ 134^{13}			i	s		s		os s	B1[3], 2919
Ω t89	**3-Tetradecanone***	Ethyl n-undecyl ketone. $CH_3(CH_2)_{10}COC_2H_5$	212.38	cr (MeOH)	34	152^{16}			i	s		s		os s	B1[3], 2919
Ω t90	**1-Tetradecene***	1-Tetradecylene. $CH_3(CH_2)_{11}CH:CH_2$	196.38		–12	$232–4^{760}$ 125^{15}	0.7745^{15}_4	1.4351^{20}	i		s		v	chl v	B1[3], 873
t91	**5,9-Tetradeca-dien-7-yne, 6,9-dimethyl-***	$CH_3(CH_2)_3CH:C(CH_3)C:CC(CH_3):CH(CH_2)_3CH_3$	218.39		$95–8^{0.5}$		0.8241^{20}_4	1.4866^{20}	i		s		s		Am 55, 1655
t92	**2-Tetradecyne***	$CH_3(CH_2)_{10}C:CCH_3$	194.36		6.5	252.5 134^{15}	0.8000^{20}_4		i	v	v				B1, 262
t93	**7-Tetradecyne***	$CH_3(CH_2)_5C:C(CH_2)_5CH_3$	194.36			144^{30}	0.7991^{25}	1.4330^{25}	i	v	v				B1[3], 1067
Ω t94	**Tetraethylene glycol**	$HOCH_2(CH_2OCH_2)_3CH_2OH$	194.23		–6.2	328^{760} 198^{14}	1.1285^{15}_4	1.4577^{20}	v	s	s			diox s	B1[3], 2106
Ω t95	—,dimethyl ether	$CH_3OCH_2(CH_2OCH_2)_3CH_2OCH_3$	222.29			275.8	1.0132^{20}_{20}		∞	s	s				B1[3], 2107
t96	—,monoocta-decanoate	Tetraethylene glycol mono-stearate. $CH_3(CH_2)_{16}CO_2CH_2(CH_2OCH_2)_3CH_2OH$	476.72		40 (35)	328^{760}	1.1285^{15}_4	1.4593^{20}	i						C37, 3202
Ω t97	**Tetraethylene-pentamine**	$H_2NCH_2(CH_2NHCH_2)_3CH_2NH_2$	189.31			340.3^{760} $186–$ 92^{14}		1.5042^{20}							C51, 5821
Ω t98	**Tetralin**	1,2,3,4-Tetrahydronaph-thalene*.	132.21	λ^{al} 259 (2.69), 266 (2.84), 274 (2.90), 286 (2.28)	–35.79 (–31)	207.57^{760} 79.36^{10}	0.9702^{20}_4	1.54135^{20}	i	s	s		s	$PhNH_2$ s	B5[3], 1219
t99	—,6-acetyl-	$C_{12}H_{14}O$. See t98	174.25			$289–91d$ 182^{20}									B7[2], 305
t100	—,2-amino-(dl)	$C_{10}H_{13}N$. See t98	147.22		38	249^{710} 140^{20}	1.0295^{22}_4	1.5604^{22}	δ s^h	v	s	s	s		B12, 1200
Ω t101	—,5-amino-	$C_{10}H_{13}N$. See t98	147.22			276.8^{760} 155^{22}	1.0625^{16}	1.6050^{20}	δ	s	s			ac s	C50, 4112
t102	—,1,4-dioxo-	2,3-Dihydro-1,4-naphtho-quinone. $C_{10}H_8O_2$. See t98	160.18	lf (hx), nd (peth) λ^{al} 228 (4.0), 253 (4.0), 294 (3.2)	98–9						s				E12B, 2806
t103	—,1,2,3,4-tetra-bromo-	Naphthalene tetrabromide. $C_{10}H_8Br_4$. See t98	447.81	mcl pr (chl)	111d				i δ^h	i	i		s^h	CS_2 s chl s^h	B5[3], 1229
t104	**1-Tetralincar-boxylic acid (dl)**	1,2,3,4-Tetrahydro-1-naphthoic acid.	176.22	tcl pr (AcOEt)	85				δ s^h	v	v	v	s	os v AcOEt s^h	B9[2], 415
Ω t105	**2-Tetralincar-boxylic acid (dl)**	1,2,3,4-Tetrahydro-2-naphthoic acid.	176.22	nd (dil al) λ^{al} 266 (2.65), 273.5 (2.70)	97	$168–70^{15}$			δ	s	s		δ	CS_2, chl s	B9[2], 416
t106	**5-Tetralincar-boxylic acid**	5,6,7,8-Tetrahydro-1-naphthoic acid.	176.22	pr (w), wh nd (dil aa) λ^{al} 235 (3.78), 285 (3.11)	150				δ s^h	v			s	chl s	E12D, 4079
t107	**6-Tetralincar-boxylic acid**	5,6,7,8-Tetrahydro-2-naphthoic acid.	176.22	nd (al), cr (aa or bz) λ^{al} 240 (4.1), 272 (3.2), 286 (3.1)	154	216^{14}				v			s	aa s peth i	E12B, 4082
t108	**1,4-Tetralindicar-boxylic acid, 1-phenyl-(d, α)**	d-α-Isatropic acid.	296.33	pr, $[\alpha]^{20}_D$ +9.44 (al, c = 12.6)	239d				δ^h	δ	i		i		B9[1], 417
t109	—,—(dl,α)	$C_{18}H_{16}O_4$. See t108	296.33	cr (chl-peth)	238–9				δ^h	δ	i		i	CS_2, aa s lig i	B9[1], 416

For explanations, symbols and abbreviations see beginning of table. For structural formulas see end of table.

No.	Name	Synonyms and Formula	Mol. wt.	Color, crystalline form, specific rotation and λ_{max} (log ε)	m.p. °C	b.p. °C	Density	n_D	w	al	eth	ace	bz	other solvents	Ref.
	1,4-Tetralindicarboxylic acid														
t110	—, -(dl,β)	$C_{18}H_{16}O_4$. See t108	296.33	pl (w)	208–9	....			i s^h	s	. See .	...	...	aa s	B9[1], 417
t111	—, -(l,β)	$C_{18}H_{16}O_4$. See t108	296.33	$[\alpha]_D -8.8$ (al, c = 5)	197	....			s^h	s	...	...	...	aa s	B9[1], 417
—	**Tetralindione**	see **Tetralin, dioxo-**													
t112	**5-Tetralinsulfonic acid**	....	212.27	cr (chl + 1w), cr (w or min ac + 2w)	105–10 (+1w)	....			v^h					chl δ^h	B11[2], 87
t113	—, amide	$C_{10}H_{13}NO_2S$. See t112	211.29	lf (al or 30 % aa)	139–40					s^h				dil NaOH v	B11[2], 87
t114	—, chloride	$C_{10}H_{11}ClO_2S$. See t112	230.72	pl (peth)	70.5				d^h	d^h	s	...	...	peth δ	B11[2], 87
t115	**6-Tetralinsulfonic acid**	....	212.26	cr (chl or dil sulf)	75				s		s			chl v	B11[2], 88
t116	—, chloride	$C_{10}H_{11}ClO_2S$. See t115	230.72	pl (eth)	58	197–200[18]			d^h		s	...	...		B11[2], 88
Ω t117	**1-Tetralone**	1-Oxo-1,2,3,4-tetrahydronaphthalene*.	146.19	λ^{hx} 247.5 (4.06), 290 (3.28)	8	255–7[760] 129[12]	1.0988_4^{16}	1.5672^{20}							B7[2], 292
Ω t118	**2-Tetralone**	2-Oxo-1,2,3,4-tetrahydronaphthalene*.	146.19	λ^{al} 245 (4.0), 290 (3.2)	18	234–40[760] 138[16]	1.1055_4^{17}	1.5598^{20}	i		s		s		B7[2], 295
t119	**1-Tetralone, 7-ethyl-**	$C_{12}H_{14}O$. See t117	174.25	....		152–3[12]	1.0556_4^{17}	1.5599^{17}	i		s		s		B7[2], 305
—	**Tetranthrene**	see **Phenanthrene, 1,2,3,4-tetrahydro-***													
t120	**Tetraphenylene**	Tetrabenzocyclooctatetraene.	304.40	cr (al or AcOEt) λ^{cy} 300 sh (2.3)	233	200[0.2] sub				s^h	δ			AcOEt, PhNO$_2$ s^h oos δ	E14s, 752
t121	**Tetraphosphoric acid, hexaethyl ester**	$[(C_2H_5O)_2P(O)O]_3PO$	506.26	hyg	ca. −40	>150d	1.2917_2^{27}	1.4273^{27}	d	∞	...	∞	∞	oos ∞ peth i	C41, 2692
t122	**Tetrasiloxane, decamethyl-**	$(CH_3)_3Si(—OSi(CH_3)_2—)_3CH_3$	310.69	....	−76	194[760] 88[20]	0.8536_4^{20}	1.3895^{20}	i	δ			s	peth s	Am 68, 358
t123	**1-Tetratriacontanol***	n-Carnatyl alcohol. $CH_3(CH_2)_{33}OH$	494.94	nd (ace)	91.9	....							s^h		B1[3], 1852
t124	**1,2,4,5-Tetrazine**	s-Tetrazine	82.07	dk red pr λ^w 253 (3.4), 511 (2.56)	99	sub			s	s				sulf s (red)	B26[2], 212
t125	**1,2,3,4-Tetrazole**		70.05	pl (al)	156	sub			s	s	δ	s	δ	aa s	B26[2], 196
t126	**1,2,3,4-Tetrazolium, 2,3,5-triphenyl-, chloride**	Tetrazolium salt. T.T.C.	334.81	nd (al or chl) λ^{al} 250, 290, 300	243d	....			s	s	i	s	...	chl s^h	C51, 11334
—	**Tetrolic acid**	see **2-Butynoic acid***													
—	**Tetronal**	see **Pentane, 3,3-bis(ethylsulfonyl)-***													
—	**Tetronic acid**	see **Furan, 2,4-dioxotetrahydro-**													
—	**Tetryl**	see **Aniline, N-methyl-N, 2,4,6-tetranitro-**													
—	**Thalline**	see **Quinoline, 6-methoxy-1,2,3,4-tetrahydro-**													
—	**Thapsic acid**	see **Hexadecanedioic acid***													
Ω t127	**Thebaine**	Paramorphine. $C_{19}H_{21}NO_3$	311.39	pl (eth), pr (dil al), $[\alpha]_D^{15}$ −218.5 (al, p = 2) λ^{al} 225 sh (4.2), 285 (3.9)	193	sub 91[0.01]	1.3052^{20}	....	i	v^h	δ	...	s	chl, Py, PhNH$_2$ v	B27[2], 177
t128	—, hydrochloride monohydrate	$C_{19}H_{21}NO_3 \cdot HCl \cdot H_2O$	365.86	orh pr (al) $[\alpha]_D^{20}$ −157 (al)		....			s	s	s				C55, 8764
Ω t129	**Thebainone A**	$C_{18}H_{21}NO_3$	299.37	nd (dil al + ½w) nd or pr (al, aa, AcOEt) $[\alpha]_D^{28}$ −47 (95 %) al, c = 1.16 ($[\alpha]_D^{20}$ +9.6 (al)) λ 283 (3.25)	151–2				δ	δ s^h	δ	s	s	chl s AcOEt s^h MeOH δ	B21[2], 448
—	**Theine**	see **Caffeine**													
t130	**Theobromine**	3,7-Dimethylxanthine. $C_7H_8N_4O_2$.	180.18	rh or mcl nd (w) $\lambda^{0.1N HCl}$ 274 (5.57)	351 (cor) (357)	sub 290			δ	δ	i	...	i	CCl$_4$, chl, lig i	B26[2], 264
t131	**Theophylline**	1,3-Dimethyl-2,6-dihydroxypurine. 1,3-Dimethylxanthine. $C_7H_8N_4O_2$.	180.18	nd or pl (w + 1) λ^{al} 270 (3.98)	272–4 (264)				v^h	δ	δ	...	...	chl δ	B26[2], 263

For explanations, symbols and abbreviations see beginning of table. For structural formulas see end of table.

No.	Name	Synonyms and Formula	Mol. wt.	Color, crystalline form, specific rotation and λ_{max} (log ε)	m.p. °C	b.p. °C	Density	n_D	w	al	eth	ace	bz	other solvents	Ref.
	Thevetin														
t132	Thevetin.........	$C_{42}H_{66}O_{18}$	858.99	nd (al), pl or nd (i-PrOH + 3w), $[\alpha]_D^{26}$ −62.5 (MeOH, c = 2)	210	....	....	....	δ	s	i	i	i	MeOH, Py s chl i	E14, 231
t134	Thialdine........	Thioacetaldehyde ammonia .	163.31	pl (al-eth)	46 (43)	d	1.0632_{20}^{50}	....	δ	s	s	...	...		B27², 525
—	Thiamine hydrochloride	see Vitamin B₁													
Ω t135	Thianthrene......	Diphenylene disulfide	216.34	mcl pr or pl (al) λ^{al} 242 (4.22), 257 (4.63), 275 sh (3.35)	158–9	366⁷⁶⁰ 204¹¹			i	δ s^h	s	...	s	CS₂ s conc sulf s (vt)	B19², 34
t136	Thiazole........		85.13	λ^{al} 240 (3.60)	....	116.8	1.1998_4^{17}	1.5969^{20}	δ	s	s	s	...		B27², 9
Ω t137	—,2-amino-	Abadol. $C_3H_4N_2S$. See t136	100.14	ye pl (al) λ^{al} 257 (3.79)	93	140¹¹			δ s^h	δ	s	...	...	dil HCl v	B27², 205
Ω t138	—,2-amino-4-methyl-	$C_4H_6N_2S$. See t136...	114.17	hyg cr λ^{al} 257 (3.74)	45–6	281–2δd 136³⁰⁻⁴⁰			v	v	v	...	...		B27², 206
t139	—,2-amino-5-methyl-	$C_4H_6N_2S$. See t136...	114.17	pl (w) λ^{al} 260 (3.84)	96				δ s^h	v	s	...	...		B27, 162
t140	—,2-amino-5-sulfanilyl-	....	255.32	nd (al)	219–21δd				i	s	s	v	...	diox v AcOEt, dil ac s	C41, 447
—	—,dihydro-	see Thiazoline													
t141	—,2,4-dimethyl-	C_5H_7NS. See t136	113.18	λ 253 (3.65)	....	144–5⁷¹⁹ 70–3⁵⁰	1.0562_4^{15}	1.5091^{20}	δ^h	s	s	...	...		B27², 10
t142	—,4,5-dimethyl-	C_5H_7NS. See t136	113.18		83–4	158 81–3⁵⁹									Am 74, 5778
t143	—,2,4-diphenyl-	$C_{15}H_{11}NS$. See t136	237.33	lf (al)	92–3	>360	1.1554_4^{98}			v	v	...	...	ac s	B24², 43
t144	—,5(2-hydroxyethyl)-4-methyl-	C_6H_9NOS. See t136	143.21	col to pa ye λ^w 249 (4.61)		135⁷ 103¹	1.196_4^{24}		v	s	s	s	s	chl s	Am 71, 2931
t145	—,2-mercapto-4-methyl-	$C_4H_5NS_2$. See t136	131.22	ye (dil al)	88–9	188³			δ	s		...	...		B27², 208
t146	—,2-methyl-	C_4H_5NS. See t136	99.16	λ^{MeOH} 234 (3.8), 275 (3.0)		128–9⁷⁶⁰ 65–70⁸⁰		1.510	∞	s	...	s	...		B27, 16
t147	—,4-methyl-	C_4H_5NS. See t136	99.16	λ^{al} 250 (3.54)		132⁷⁴³ 70⁹⁰	1.112^{25}		s	s	s	...	...		B27², 9
—	—,tetrahydro-	see Thiazolidine													
t149	5-Thiazolecarboxylic acid	....	129.14	lt ye nd (dil HCl)	217–18 (196–7)				s^h	...	s	...	...	dil HCl s	C48, 2688
t150	—,2-amino-, ethyl ester	$C_6H_8N_2O_2S$. See t149	172.22		163–4	213–5d			δ						C47, 7453
t151	—,4-methyl-	$C_5H_5NO_2S$. See t149	143.17	pr or pl (w), nd (al) λ 255 (3.78)	280d	suh >250			δ^h	s^h	s^h	...	δ	lig δ	B27², 376
t152	—,—,ethyl ester	$C_7H_9NO_2S$. See t149	171.22	pr	28	232–3⁷³⁵ (215–20) 110–5¹⁵			s	s	s	s	...	oos v	B27, 316
t153	—,—,—,hydrochloride	$C_7H_9NO_2S$. HCl. See t149	207.68	nd (al)	155d	....			s	s^h	...	...	...		J1939, 443
t154	—,4-methyl-2-sulfanilamido-	....	313.36	cr	241–2				δ						C38, 2250
t155	Thiazolidine......	Tetrahydrothiazole	89.16			164–5⁷⁶⁰	1.1312_4^{25}	1.551^{30}	∞	s	v	v	...		Am 59, 200
Ω t156	2,4-Thiazolidinedione	2,4-Dioxothiazolidine	117.13	pl (w), pr (al)	128	179¹⁹			δ s^h	δ v^h	s	...	...		B27², 284
t157	2-Thiazolidinethione	....	119.21	nd (w or MeOH) λ 270 (4.11)	106–7				s^h	δ	i	...	s^h	alk v chl δ CS₂ i	B27², 198
—	4-Thiazolidone, 2-thioxo-	see Rhodanine													
t158	2,3-Thiazoline.....	4,5-Dihydrothiazole. Δ²-Thiazoline.	87.14			138⁷⁵⁰			...	...	s	s	s		B27¹, 206
Ω t159	—,2-amino-	S,N-Ethyleneisothiourea. $C_3H_6N_2S$. See t158	102.16	nd or fl (bz)	84–5	d			v	v	...	...	v^h	chl v	B27², 194
Ω t160	—,2-mercapto-	2-Thiazolinethiol. $C_3H_5NS_2$. See t158	119.21	nd (w or MeOH)	106–7				s^h	s^h	δ	...	s^h	chl s^h CS₂ i	B27², 198
—	Thiazone........	see 3-Isophenothiazin-3-one													
—	Thiazone	(ketone, di(2-thienyl))													
t161	Thiirane........	Ethylene sulfide	60.12	λ^{al} 258 (1.5)		55–6d	1.0368_4^9	1.4937^{20}	...	δ	δ	s	...	chl s	B17², 12
—	Thioacetic acid	see Acetic acid, thio-													
—	Thioanisole	see Benzene, (methylthio)-													
—	Thiocarbazide	see Carbazide, 3-thio-													
t162	Thiochrome.......	....	262.34	ye pr (chl) $\lambda^{w,pH=7}$ 367 (3.97) $\lambda^{w,pH=3}$ 392 (4.13)	227–8	sub vac			s	δ	δ	δ	...	MeOH s chl δ	C29, 6242
t163	Thiocyanic acid	Sulfocyanic acid. HSCN	59.09	....	5	d			∞	∞	∞	...	...		B3³, 251
t164	—,allyl ester	Allyl rhodanate $CH_2{:}CHCH_2SCN$	99.16	....		161	1.056^{15}	....	δ	v	v	...	...		B3, 177

For explanations, symbols and abbreviations see beginning of table. For structural formulas see end of table.

Thiocyanic acid

No.	Name	Synonyms and Formula	Mol. wt.	Color, crystalline form, specific rotation and λ_{max} (log ε)	m.p. °C	b.p. °C	Density	n_D	w	al	eth	ace	bz	other solvents	Ref.
t165	—,4-aminophenyl ester	p-Thiocyanatoaniline. $C_7H_6N_2S$. See t180	150.20	nd (w), cr (dil al) λ^{al} 262 (4.20), 280 sh (3.75)	57–8	....			δ	v	s	...	s	....	B13[2], 299
Ω t166	—,benzyl ester	Benzyl rhodanate. Benzyl thiocyanate. $C_6H_5CH_2SCN$	149.22	pr (al) λ^{cy} 222 (3.91), 258 (2.84)	43	256			i	s^h	s			CS_2 s	B6[3], 1600
Ω t167	—,butyl ester	n-Butyl thiocyanate. $CH_3(CH_2)_3SCN$	115.20	....		185[743]	0.9563[25]	1.4630[20]	i	s	s				B3[3], 281
t168	—,tert-butyl ester..	$(CH_3)_3CSCN$	115.20	....	10.5	140[770]d 39–40[10]	0.9187[10]								B3[3], 282
t169	—,4-chlorophenyl ester	C_7H_4ClNS. See t180	169.63	nd (al) λ^{al} 238 (4.09)	35–6	....			i	v				os v	B6[3], 1038
t170	—,4(dimethyl-amino)phenyl ester	$C_9H_{10}N_2S$. See t180	178.26	nd (lig, w, al)	73–4	....			s^h	δ s^h	s^h			lig s^h	B13[2], 301
Ω t171	—,ethyl ester	Ethyl rhodanate. Ethyl thiocyanate. C_2H_5SCN	87.14	....	−85.5	145[758]	1.0071[22]₄	1.4684[15]	i	∞	∞				B3[3], 281
t172	—,heptyl ester.....	n-Heptyl rhodanate. $CH_3(CH_2)_6SCN$	157.28	....		234–6 136[28]	0.92[20]		i	∞	∞				B3[2], 122
t173	—,isobutyl ester ...	Isobutyl rodanate. $(CH_3)_2CHCH_2SCN$	115.20	....	−59	175.4[760] 66[15]			i	v	v				B3, 177
Ω t174	—,isopropyl ester..	Isopropyl rodanate. $(CH_3)_2CHSCN$	101.17	....		152–3[754]	0.9784[20]		i	∞	∞				B3[3], 281
Ω t175	—,methyl ester	Methyl rhodanate. Methyl thiocyanate. CH_3SCN	73.12	....	−51	132.9[757]	1.0678[25]₄	1.4669[25]	δ	∞	∞				B3[3], 280
t176	—,3-methylbutyl ester	Isoamyl rhodanate. Isoamyl thiocyanate. $(CH_3)_2CHCH_2CH_2SCN$	129.23	....		197[760]			i	s	s				B3[3], 282
t177	—,1-naphthyl ester.	α-Naphthyl thiocyanate. $C_{10}H_7SCN$	185.25	cr (peth) λ^{al} 225 (4.75), 280 sh (3.83), 287 (3.93), 315 (2.98)	55	....								peth s^h	B6[2], 588
t178	—,2-naphthyl ester.	β-Naphthyl thiocyanate. $C_{10}H_7SCN$	185.25	....	35	....									B6[2], 611
Ω t179	—,octyl ester......	n-Octyl rhodanate. $CH_3(CH_2)_7SCN$	171.31	....	105	141–2[19] 122–4[11]	0.9149[25]₄	1.4649[20]	i	v	v		s^h		B3[3], 282
t180	—,phenyl ester	Thiocyanatobenzene. Phenyl rhodanide. Phenyl thiocyanate.	135.19	λ^{cy} 226 (3.97), 270 (3.13)		232–3[760] 71–3[1.5]	1.155[18]₁₈		i	s	s				B6[3], 1011
t181	—,propyl ester	Propyl rhodanate. Propyl thiocyanate. $CH_3CH_2CH_2SCN$	101.17	....		163			i	s	s				B3[3], 281
t182	—,4-tolyl ester	p-Tolyl rhodanide.	149.22			240–5 116–8[10]			i				s	chl s	B6[2], 398
—	Thiocyanuric acid ..	see Cyanuric acid, thio-													
Ω t183	Thiodiglycolic acid	Dimethyl sulfide α,α-dicarboxylic acid. Thiodiacetic acid. $S(CH_2CO_2H)_2$	150.15	cr (w, AcOEt-bz)	129	....			v	v			s^h		B3[3], 422
—	Thioglycolic acid...	see Acetic acid, mercapto-													
—	Thiohydantoin.....	see Hydantoin, thio-													
t184	Thioindigo........		296.38	br-red nd (xyl), red mcl nd (bz) λ^{chl} 283 sh (4.1), 300 (4.4), 490 (4.3)	359	sub			i	i δ^h			s^h	xyl s PhNO₂ v^h CS₂, chl δ^h	B19[2], 192
—	Thioisatin	see 2,3-Benzothiophene-quinone													
—	Thiomalic acid.....	see Succinic acid, 2-mercapto-													
t185	Thiomorpholine....	1,4-Thiazan..............	103.19	....		174[746] 110[100]	1.0882[20]₄	1.5386[20]	∞	s	s	s	s	oos ∞	B17[2], 4
—	Thionol	see 3-Isophenothiazin-3-one, 7-hydroxy													
—	Thionaphthene	see 2,3-Benzothiophene													
t186	Thionin, hydro-chloride	7-Amino-3-imino-3H-2-phenothiazine hydro-chloride. Lauth's violet.	263.76	dk br or gr pl or nd λ^{al} 602 (4.74)	....				δ s^h	δ	δ	...	s	chl, ac s	B27[2], 447
Ω t187	Thiophene	Thiofuran...............	84.14	λ^{al} 215 (3.8), 231 (3.87)	−38.25	84.16[760]	1.06494[20]₄	1.5289[20]	..	∞	∞	∞	∞	oos, CCl₄, hp, Py, diox, to ∞	B17[2], 35
t188	—,2-acetamido-	C_6H_7NOS. See t187........	141.19	lf (w)	161–2	....			δ^h	v	δ	v	δ		B17[1], 136
Ω t189	—,2-acetyl-	Methyl 2-thienyl ketone. C_6H_6OS. See t187	126.18	λ^{al} 260 (4.01), 283 (3.87)	10–11	213.5[760] 94.5–6.5[13]	1.1679[22]₄	1.5667[20]	δ	∞	∞	...			B17[2], 314

For explanations, symbols and abbreviations see beginning of table. For structural formulas see end of table.

No.	Name	Synonyms and Formula	Mol. wt.	Color, crystalline form, specific rotation and λ_{max} (log ε)	m.p. °C	b.p. °C	Density	n_D	w	al	eth	ace	bz	other solvents	Ref.
	Thiophene														
Ω t190	—,2-acetyl-5-bromo-	C_6H_5BrOS. See t187	205.08	nd (al) λ^{al} 268 (3.92), 293 (4.09)	94–5	105–7[4.5]			...	δ v^h					B17, 288
Ω t191	—,2-acetyl-5-chloro-	C_6H_5ClOS. See t187	160.62	ta (al or eth) λ^{al} 264.5 (3.94), 292 (4.05)	52	88–9[4.5]			v	v	v				B17, 287
Ω t192	—,2-amino-	Thiophenine. C_4H_5NS. See t187	99.16	pa ye tab (al)		77–9[11] 61–2[1]			v	v	i				B17, 248
t192¹	—,2-benzoyl-	Phenyl 2-thienyl ketone. $C_{11}H_8OS$. See t187	188.26	nd (dil al or peth) λ^{al} 263 (4.11), 293 (4.13)	56.5–7	300[760]	1.1890_4^{54}		i	s	s				B17², 372
Ω t193	—,2-bromo-	C_4H_3BrS. See t187	163.04	λ^{al} 236 (3.90)		149–51 42–6[13]	1.684_4^{20}	1.5868^{20}	i		v	v			B17, 39
t194	—,2-bromo-5-chloro-	C_4H_2BrClS. See t187	197.49		−20	70[18]	1.803_{25}^{25}	1.5925^{25}	...		s	s			Am 70, 2379
t195	—,2-bromo-5-iodo-	C_4H_2BrIS. See t187	288.94			116[13]									C32, 3391
t196	—,2-bromo-3-methyl-	C_5H_5BrS. See t187	177.07			175[729] 27[1.8]	1.5844_4^{18}	1.5714^{20}	...		s		s		B17², 40
t197	—,2-bromo-5-methyl	C_5H_5BrS. See t187	177.07	col to pa ye		177[740] 29[1.8]	1.5529_4^{20}	1.5673^{20}			s		s		B17², 39
Ω t198	—,2-chloro-	C_4H_3ClS. See t187	118.59	λ^{iso} 236 (3.94)	−71.9	128.3[760]	1.2863_4^{20}	1.5487^{20}	i	∞	∞				B17, 32
t199	—,2-chloro-5-butyl-	$C_8H_{11}ClS$. See t187	174.69			117–8[88]	1.0842_4^{17}	1.5162^{20}	i				s		B17, 44
t200	—,2-chloro-5-iodo-	C_4H_2ClIS. See t187	244.48		−25	95 6[14]									C32, 3391
t201	—,2-chloro-5-methyl-	C_5H_5ClS. See t187	132.61			154–5[747] 55[19]	1.2147_4^{25}	1.5372^{20}		s	s	s	s	os s	B17, 37
Ω t202	—,2,5-dibromo-	$C_4H_2Br_2S$. See t187	241.94	λ^{iso} 252 (3.96)	−6	210.3[760] 76–80[10]	2.147_{23}^{23}	1.6288^{20}	i	v	v				B17, 33
t203	—,2,5-dibromo-3,4-dinitro-	$C_4Br_2N_2O_4S$. See t187	331.94	cr (al)	139–40					δ					B17, 36
Ω t204	—,2,5-dichloro-	$C_4H_2Cl_2S$. See t187	153.03	λ^{iso} 252 (3.87)	−40.5	162[760]	1.4422_4^{20}	1.5626^{20}	i	∞	∞				B17, 33
t205	—,2,5-diiodo-	$C_4H_2I_2S$. See t187	335.93	lf (al) λ^{iso} 266 (4.15), 315 (2.43)	40.5–1.5	139–40[15]			i	v					B17, 35
t206	—,2,3-dimethyl-	2,3-Thioxene. C_6H_8S. See t187	112.21	λ^{iso} 233 (3.77)	−49.0	141.6[760] 29.3[10]	1.0021_4^{20}	1.5192^{20}	i	v	v		s		B17, 40
t207	—,2,4-dimethyl-	2,4-Thioxene. C_6H_8S. See t187	112.21	λ^{iso} 234.5 (3.80)		140.7[760] 29.9[10]	0.9956_{20}^{20}	1.5104^{20}	i	s	s		s		B17, 41
t208	—,2,5-dimethyl-	α,α-Thioxene. C_6H_8S. See t187	112.21	λ^{iso} 238 (4.8)	−62.6	136.7[760] 26.2[10]	0.985_4^{20}	1.5129^{20}	i	s	s		s		B17, 41
t209	—,2,5-dinitro-	$C_4H_2N_2O_4S$. See t187	174.14	(i) ye lf (al) (ii) ye nd (al, w)	(i) 52 (ii) 80–2	290[760]			s^h	s	v				B17, 35
Ω t210	—,2-ethyl-	C_6H_8S. See t187	112.21	λ^{iso} 233 (3.89)		134[760] 24[10]	0.9930_4^{20}	1.5122^{20}	i	v	v				B17, 39
t211	—,3-ethyl-	C_6H_8S. See t187	112.21	λ^{iso} 235 (3.6)	−89.1	136[760] 26[10]	0.9980_4^{20}	1.5146^{20}	i	s	v				B17, 40
t212	—,2-hydroxy-5-methyl-	2,5-Thiotenol. C_5H_6OS. See t187	114.17			85[40]			δ	v	v				B17, 252
Ω t213	—,2-iodo-	C_4H_3IS. See t187	210.04	λ^{iso} 243 (3.97), 285 sh (2.4)	−40	180–2[760] 73[15]		1.6465^{25}		v	v				B17, 34
t214	—,2-iodo-5-nitro-	$C_4H_2INO_2S$. See t187	255.04	ye pr (al)	74					s					B17, 35
Ω t215	—,2-methyl-	α-Thiotolene. C_5H_6S. See t187	98.17	λ^w 234 (3.58)	−63.4	112.56[760] 9.2[10]	1.0193_4^{20}	1.5203^{20}	i	∞	∞	∞	∞	CCl_4, hp ∞	B17, 37
Ω t216	—,3-methyl-	β-Thiotolene. C_5H_6S. See t187	98.17	λ^{cy} 234.5 (3.75)	−69	115.4[760] 10.96[10]	1.0218_4^{20}	1.5204^{20}	i	∞	∞	∞	∞	chl v	B17, 38
t217	—,2(methyl-amino)-	N-Methyl-2-thiophenine. C_5H_7NS. See t187	113.18			88–92[15]				s	s				B17¹, 136
t218	—,2-methyl-5-phenyl-	$C_{11}H_{10}S$. See t187	174.27	nd λ 225 sh (3.79), 291 (4.21)	51	270–2[760]				v	v			lig v	B17, 67
Ω t219	—,2-nitro-	$C_4H_3NO_2S$. See t187	129.14	lt ye mcl nd (peth) λ^{al} 270 (3.80), 296 (3.78)	46.5	224–5	1.3644_4^{43}							alk s^h peth δ, s^h	B17, 35
t220	—,4-nitro-2,3,5-tribromo	$C_4Br_3NO_2S$. See t187	365.84	red-ye nd (al)	106					δ	v				B17, 35
t221	—,3-nitro-2,4,5-trichloro-	$C_4Cl_3NO_2S$. See t187	232.47	red-ye nd (al)	86					s	v		v		B17, 35
Ω t222	—,tetrabromo-	C_4Br_4S. See t187	399.74	nd (al)	117–8	326 170–3[13]			i	s^h	v				B17, 34
Ω t223	—,tetrachloro-	C_4Cl_4S. See t187	221.92	nd (dil al)	30–1	233.4[760] 75–7[2]	1.7036_3^{30}	1.5915^{30}	i	v	∞				B17, 33
Ω t224	—,tetrahydro-	Tetramethylene sulfide	88.18	λ^{al} 240 sh (1.7)	−96.16	121.12[760] 14.48[10]	0.9987_4^{20}	1.5048^{20}	i	∞	∞	∞	∞	os ∞	B17², 15
t225	—,2,3,5-tribromo-	C_4HBr_3S. See t187	320.84	nd (al)	29	260[760]			i	v^h	v				B17, 34
t227	—,2,3,5-trichloro-	C_4HCl_3S. See t187	187.48		−16.1	198.7[760]	1.5856_4^{20}	1.5791^{20}	i	∞	∞				B17, 33

For explanations, symbols and abbreviations see beginning of table. For structural formulas see end of table.

No.	Name	Synonyms and Formula	Mol. wt.	Color. crystalline form. specific rotation and λ_{max} (log ε)	m.p. °C	b.p. °C	Density	n_D	w	al	eth	ace	bz	other solvents	Ref.
	Thiophene														
t228	—,2,3,5-tri-methyl-	$C_7H_{10}S$. See t187	126.22	λ^{hx} 237 (3.83)	....	164.5[760] 46.8[10]	0.9753[20][4]	1.5112[20]	i	v	v	v	v	os s	B17[2], 43
—	Thiopheneacetic acid	see Acetic acid, thienyl-													
Ω t229	2-Thiophene-carboxaldehyde	2-Formylthiophene. 2-Thiophenealdehyde.	112.15	pa ye liq λ^{iso} 265 (4.12), 278.5 (3.81)	....	198[760] 85–6[16]	1.215[21][21]	1.5920[20]	i	v	s	...	...		B17, 285
Ω t230	—,oxime(syn)	2-Thiophenealdoxime	127.17	nd λ 265 (4.1)	133	....					v	...	...		B17, 285
t231	—,phenylhydrazone	....	202.28	ye nd (al)	134.5	....			i	s	...	...	...		B17, 286
Ω t232	2-Thiophene-carboxylic acid	α-Thiophenic acid	128.15	nd (w) λ^{al} 246 (3.96), 260 (3.84)	129–30	260d			v[h]	v	v	...	...	chl s peth δ	B18, 289
Ω t233	—,chloride	C_5H_3ClOS. See t232.	146.60			201 (206 –8) 77[10]			d	d[h]	s	...	...		B18[2], 269
Ω t234	—,ethyl ester	$C_7H_8O_2S$. See t232.	156.22	λ^{al} 249 (3.95), 269 (3.89)		218 94[10]	1.1623[16][4]	1.5248[20]		s	...	s	...	os s	B18[2], 269
t235	—,3-methyl-	$C_6H_6O_2S$. See t232.	142.18	nd (dil al, w)	144	....			δ v[h]	s	s	s	s		B18, 293
t236	2,3-Thiophenedi-carboxylic acid		172.16	pr or nd (w)	272–4	....			δ[h]	...	v	...	...		B18, 327
t237	2,4-Thiophenedi-carboxylic acid		172.16	cr	280d (>300)	sub >200			δ v[h]						B18, 327
Ω t238	2,5-Thiophenedi-carboxylic acid		172.16	λ^{iso} 271 (4.2)	358.5–9.5 (sealed tube)	sub at 150–300			δ	s	s	...	...		B18, 330
t239	—,diethyl ester	$C_{10}H_{12}O_4S$. See t238.	228.27	nd (al)	51.5	....				s	...	...	...		B18, 331
t240	2-Thiophene-sulfonic acid, amide		163.22	nd (w)	147	....			δ s[h]					alk s Na_2CO_3 i	B18, 567
t241	—,chloride		182.65		28	99–101[6] sub			d	d[h]	s	...	...		B18, 567
t242	3-Thiophene-sulfonic acid, amide		163.22	pl (w)	152–3 (146)	....			δ						B18, 568
t243	—,chloride		182.65	cr (eth)	43	98–9[0.5]			d[h]	d[h]	v	...	...	lig i	B18, 568
—	Thiophenine	see Thiophene, amino-													
—	Thiophenol	see Benzene, mercapto-*													
—	Thiophosphoric acid	see Phosphoric acid, thiono-*													
t244	Thiophthene (solid).	Thieno[3,2-b]thiophene.....	140.23	bipym orh (lig) λ^{iso} 259 (4.1), 268 (4.0), 278 (4.0)	56	221–4[760]			i	...	s	...	...	lig δ, s[h]	J1953, 1837
t245	—(liquid)	Thieno[2,3-b]thiophene.....	140.23	nd (eth-so CO_2)	6.5	224–6[760] 106[16]			i	...	s	...	...		B19[1], 612
—	Thiopyran, tetrahydro-	see Sulfide, pentamethylene													
t246	Thiopyrine	1,5-Dimethyl-2-phenyl-3-thio-3-pyrazolone.	204.30	cr (w)	166	....			δ s[h]	s	s	...	...		B24[2], 28
—	Thiosemi-carbazide	see Semicarbazide, 3-thio-													
—	Thiosinamine	see Urea, 1-allyl-2-thio-													
—	Thiourea	see Urea, 2-thio-													
—	Thiourethan	see Carbamic acid, thiono-, ethyl ester													
t248	Thioxanthene	Thiaxanthene. Dibenzthiopyran.	198.29	nd (al-chl)	128–9	340[730] sub			i	δ s[h]	δ s[h]	...	...	chl, peth s	B17, 74
Ω t249	Thioxanthone	9-Oxothioxanthene	212.28	ye nd (chl) λ^{al} 219 (3.87), 257 (4.28), 286 (3.37), 299 (3.20), 379 (3.48)	209 (212)	371–3[715] sub			i	δ	...	...	s	CS_2, aa s chl s[h] peth i	B17[1], 191
—	Threite(D)	see Erithritol (l)													
t250	Threonic acid(D)...	2,3,4-Trihydroxybutyric acid*.	136.12	nd (al), $[\alpha]_D$ ca. −30 (w)	197–8	....			s	s[h]	...	s[h]	...	AcOEt s[h]	B3[2], 272
t251	—(DL)...........	$C_4H_8O_5$. See t250.	136.12	cr (al, ace)	99	....			s	s[h]	...	s[h]	...	AcOEt s[h]	B3[3], 895
t252	—(L)	$C_4H_8O_5$. See t250.	136.12	nd (al-eth) $[\alpha]_D$ +9.54 (w)	169.5–70.5	....			s	s[h]	...	s	...	AcOEt s[h]	B3[3], 894
t253	Threonine(D)	D-2-Amino-3-hydroxybutyric acid. $CH_3CH(OH)CH(NH_2)CO_2H$	119.12	cr (80 % al) $[\alpha]_D^{26}$ −28.3 (w, c = 1.1)	255–7d	....			s	i	i	...	...	chl i	C31, 6199
Ω t254	—(DL)...........	$CH_3CH(OH)CH(NH_2)CO_2H$	119.12	cr (dil al)	229–30 (+½w) 234–5d	....			s v[h]	i	i	...	...	chl i	B4, 514
t255	Threose(D)	Trihydroxybutyraldehyde.	120.12	hyg syr or nd (w), $[\alpha]_D^{22}$ +29.1 → +19.6 (w) (mut)	126–32	....			v	δ	i	...	...	peth i	B1, 855 B31, 13

For explanations, symbols and abbreviations see beginning of table. For structural formulas see end of table.

No.	Name	Synonyms and Formula	Mol. wt.	Color, crystalline form, specific rotation and λ_{max} (log ε)	m.p. °C	b.p. °C	Density	n_D	Solubility						Ref.
									w	al	eth	ace	bz	other solvents	
	Thujane														
Ω t256	Thujane(d)	Sabinane	138.26	$[\alpha]_D$ +73.1 (+62)		157^{758}	0.8139^{20}_4	1.4376^{20}	...	s	s	s	s		B5[3], 253
t257	4(10)-Thujene(d)	Sabinene	136.24	$[\alpha]_D$ +80.17		$163-5^{760}$ 66^{30}	0.842^{20}	1.4678^{20}	...	s	s	s	s	chl s	B5[3], 365
t258	—(l)	$C_{10}H_{16}$. See t257	136.24	$[\alpha]_D^{15}$ −42.5		$163-5^{760}$	0.8464^{20}	1.4515^{20}	...	s	s	s	s	chl s	B5[3], 365
Ω t259	α-Thujone		152.24	$[\alpha]_D^{18}$ −19.94		$200-1^{760}$ 75^9	0.9152^{20}	1.4490^{25}	i	∞	∞	s	...		B7, 92
Ω t260	Thymidine	Thymine-2-desoxyriboside. $C_{10}H_{14}N_2O_5$.	242.23	nd (AcOEt) $[\alpha]_D^{25}$ +30.6 (w, c = 1.03) λ^w 269 (3.97)	186–7				s	s^h	...	s^h	...	Py, MeOH, aa s AcOEt s^h chl δ^h	C48, 226
—	Thymine	see Uracil, 5-methyl-													
—	Thymohydroquinone	see Benzene, 1,4-dihydroxy-2-isopropyl-5-methyl-*													
—	Thymol	see Benzene, 2-hydroxy-1-isopropyl-4-methyl-*													
Ω t263	Thymol blue	Thymolsulfonephthalein. $C_{27}H_{30}O_5S$	466.60	gr-red (al, eth, aa) λ 450, 600	221–4d				δ	s	δ	δ	δ	aniline, aa s chl, CCl_4 to δ	B19[2], 112
Ω t264	Thymolphthalein	$C_{28}H_{30}O_4$	430.55	pr or nd (al)	253				i	s^h	s	s	...	alk s (bl)	B18[2], 130
—	Thymoquinone, dioxime	see 1,4-Benzoquinone, 2-isopropyl-5-methyl-, dioxime*													
—	o-Thymotic acid	see Benzoic acid, 2-hydroxy-3-isopropyl-6-methyl-													
—	Thymylamine	see Benzene, 2-amino-1-isopropyl-4-methyl-*													
t266	Thyroxine(d)	$C_{15}H_{11}I_4NO_4$	776.88	nd, $[\alpha]_D^{25}$ +2.97 (al-NaOH) $\lambda^{0.02N\,KOH}$ 325 (3.8)	237d				δ	i	i		i		B14[2], 366
t267	—(l)	$C_{15}H_{11}I_4NO_4$. See t266	776.88	nd, $[\alpha]_D^{20}$ −4.4 (al-NaOH) $\lambda^{0.02N\,KOH}$ 325 (3.8)	235–6				δ	i	i		i		B14[2], 378
—	Tiglaldehyde	see 2-Butenal, 2-methyl-*													
—	Tiglic acid	see 2-Butenoic acid, 2-methyl-(trans)*													
t268	Tigogenin	5α, 22α-Spirostan-3 β-ol. $C_{27}H_{44}O_3$.	416.65	lf(al + 1w), pr (ace) $[\alpha]_D^{25}$ −49 (Py, c = 1) $[\alpha]_D^{18}$ −67.2 (chl) λ^{sulf} 394 (3.50)	205–6				i	s^h	s	s	...	MeOH, peth s CCl_4 s^h	E14, 280
—	TNT	see Toluene, 2,4,6-trinitro-													
Ω t269	α-Tocopherol	Vitamin E. 5,7,8-Trimethyltocol. $C_{29}H_{50}O_2$.	430.69	pa ye visc oil $[\alpha]_D^{25}$ +0.65 (al) λ^{MeOH} 292 (3.54)	2.5–3.5	350d $140^{10^{-6}}$			i	s	s	s	...	os s	H21, 520
t270	β-Tocopherol	Vitamin E. 5,8-Dimethyltocol. $C_{28}H_{48}O_2$.	416.70	pa ye visc oil $[\alpha]_D^{20}$ +6.37 λ 296 (3.57)		$200-10^{0.1}$			i	∞	∞	∞	...	chl ∞	H21, 1234
t271	γ-Tocopherol	Vitamin E. 7,8-Dimethyltocol. $C_{28}H_{48}O_2$.	416.70	pa ye visc oil $[\alpha]_D^{20}$ −2.4 (al) λ 298 (3.58)	−3 − −2	$200-10^{0.1}$			i	∞	∞	∞	...	chl ∞	H22, 260
t272	δ-Tocopherol	8-Methyltocol. $C_{27}H_{46}O_2$	402.67	pa ye visc oil $[\alpha]_{546}^{25}$ +3.4 (al, c = 15.5) λ 298 (3.54)		$150^{0.001}$			i	v	v	v	...	chl v	J1959, 3374
t273	α-Tocopherolquinone	α-Tocoquinone.	446.72	ye oil λ 259, 269		$120^{0.002}$					s		...	peth s MeOH δ, s^h	Am 73, 5148
—	Tolan	see Ethyne, diphenyl-*													
t274	Tolbutamide	Artosin. 1-Butyl-3-(p-tolyl-sulfonyl)urea.	270.35	orh cr λ^{al} 228 (4.11), 256 (2.8), 263 (2.8), 274 (2.8)	128.5–9.5		1.245^{25}		δ^h	s	s			chl s	C54, 13084
—	Tolidine	see Biphenyl, diamino(dimethyl)-													
—	α-Tolualdehyde	see Acetaldehyde, phenyl-													
—	Tolualdehyde	see Benzaldehyde, methyl-													
Ω t275	Toluene	Methylbenzene*. Phenylmethane*.	92.15	λ^{al} 207 (3.97), 260 (2.48)	−95	110.6^{760} $14.5^{14.5}$	0.8669^{20}_4	1.4961^{20}	i^{al}	∞	∞	s	∞	CS_2, lig s	B5[3], 651
t276	—,2-acetamido-3-bromo-	6-Bromo-o-acetotoluidide. $C_9H_{10}BrNO$. See t275	228.10	nd (bz)	166					s		s^h			B12[2], 455
t277	—,2-acetamido-4-bromo-	5-Bromo-o-acetotoluidide. $C_9H_{10}BrNO$. See t275	228.10	nd (bz)	165.5					s		v^h			B12[2], 456

For explanations, symbols and abbreviations see beginning of table. For structural formulas see end of table.

No.	Name	Synonyms and Formula	Mol. wt.	Color, crystalline form, specific rotation and λ_{max} (log ε)	m.p. °C	b.p. °C	Density	n_D	w	al	eth	ace	bz	other solvents	Ref.
	Toluene														
Ω t278	—,2-acetamido-5-bromo-	4-Bromo-o-acetotoluidide. $C_9H_{10}BrNO$. See t275	228.10	nd (dil al or lig)	159–60	....	....	....	s^h	v	....	....	....	lig s^h	B12[2], 456
Ω t279	—,4-acetamido-2-bromo-	3-Bromo-p-acetotoluidide. $C_9H_{10}BrNO$. See t275	228.10	nd (bz or dil al)	113	....	....	....	s	v	....	....	v^h	....	B12[1], 436
t280	—,4-acetamido-3-bromo-	2-Bromo-p-acetotoluidide. $C_9H_{10}BrNO$. See t275	228.10	nd (al)	118	....	....	....	....	v^h	....	....		xyl v^h	B12[2], 532
Ω t281	—,α-amino-	Benzylamine. $C_6H_5CH_2NH_2$	107.16	λ 255 (2.1), 262 (2.2), 270 (2.0)	....	185[770] 90[12]	0.9813[20/4]	1.5401[20]	∞	∞	∞	v	s	....	B12[2], 540
Ω t282	—,—,hydrochloride	Benzylamine hydrochloride. $C_6H_5CH_2NH_2 \cdot HCl$	143.62	pl (al)	255–8 (248)	....	....	....	s	s^h	....	....		chl i	B12[2], 540
Ω t283	—,2-amino-	2-Methylaniline. o-Toluidine. C_7H_9N. See t275	107.16	α: −23.7 (unst) (3.88), 281.5 (3.16) $\lambda^{w.pH=10}$ 232.5 β: −14.7 (st)		200.23[760] 80.14[10]	0.9984[20/4]	1.5725[20]	δ	∞	∞			CCl_4 ∞	B12[2], 429
Ω t285	—,—,hydrochloride	o-Toluidine hydrochloride. $C_7H_9N \cdot HCl$. See t275	143.62	mcl pr (w^c), rh pym (w^h)	215	242.2[760]	....	....	v	s	i	....	i	....	B12[2], 432
Ω t286	—,3-amino-	3-Methylaniline. m-Toluidine. C_7H_9N. See t275	107.16	....	−30.4	203.35[760] 82.33[10]	0.9889[20/4]	1.5681[20]	δ	∞	∞	∞	∞	CCl_4, hp ∞	B12[2], 463
t287	—,—,hydrochloride	m-Toluidine hydrochloride. $C_7H_9N \cdot HCl$. See t275	143.62	lf (w)	228	250[760]	....	....	v	v	....	....		....	B12, 856
Ω t288	—,4-amino-	4-Methylaniline. p-Toluidine. C_7H_9N. See t275	107.16	lf (w + l) λ^{iso} 237 (3.98), 293 (3.28)	43.7 (45)	200.55[760] 79.63[10]	0.9619[20/4]	1.5534[45] 1.5636[20]	δ	v	s	s	....	Py v	B12[2], 482
Ω t289	—,—,hydrochloride	p-Toluidine hydrochloride. $C_7H_9N \cdot HCl$. See t275	143.62	mcl nd (aa-eth)	243	257.5[760]	....	....	v	v	i	....	i	CS_2 i	B12[2], 487
—	—,4-amino-N-benzylidene-	see **Benzaldehyde**, imine, N(4-tolyl)-													
t291	—,α-amino-3-bromo-	m-Bromobenzylamine. C_7H_8BrN. See t275	186.07	....	....	244–5 84[15]	....	....	....	....	v	....		ac s	B12[2], 575
t292	—,α-amino-4-bromo-	p-Bromobenzylamine. C_7H_8BrN. See t275	186.07	....	20	250–1 126–7[15]	....	....	....	....	v	....		ac s	B12[2], 575
t293	—,2-amino-3-bromo-	6-Bromo-o-toluidine. C_7H_8BrN. See t275	186.07	....	....	130[16] 107[3]	....	....	....	....	v	....		ac s	B12[2], 455
t294	—,2-amino-4-bromo-	5-Bromo-o-toluidine. C_7H_8BrN. See t275	186.07	lf λ^w 293 (3.24)	33	253–7δd 139[17]	....	....	....	s	v	....		ac s	B12[2], 456
Ω t295	—,2-amino-5-bromo-	4-Bromo-o-toluidine. C_7H_8BrN. See t275	186.07	cr (al)	59.5	240	....	....	δ	s	v	....		aa v	B12[2], 456
t296	—,3-amino-4-bromo-	6-Bromo-m-toluidine. C_7H_8BrN. See t275	186.07	pr	46	129–30[15]	1.474[25/25]	1.5990[25]	....	v	....	....		ac s	B12[2], 474
t297	—,3-amino-5-bromo-	5-Bromo-m-toluidine. C_7H_8BrN. See t275	186.07	....	37–8	255–60 150–1[15]	1.1422[19]	....	....	s	....	....		ac s	B12[2], 474
t298	—,4-amino-2-bromo-	3-Bromo-p-toluidine. C_7H_8BrN. See t275	186.07	....	26	254–7	....	....	....	....	v	....		con ac s	B12[2], 532
Ω t299	—,4-amino-3-bromo-	2-Bromo-p-toluidine. C_7H_8BrN. See t275	186.07	lf λ^w 298 (3.33)	26	240 120–2[30]	1.510[20]	1.5999[20]	i	s	s	....		....	B12[2], 532
t300	—,5-amino-2-bromo-	4-Bromo-m-toluidine. C_7H_8BrN. See t275	186.07	pl (50 % al), cr (al)	81	240	....	....	i	v	....	....		....	B12[2], 474
t301	—,4-amino-5-bromo-2-nitro-	$C_7H_7BrN_2O_2$. See t275	231.06	br to pa ye nd (al or aa)	121	....	....	....	....	....	....	....		....	B12[1], 441
Ω t302	—,2-amino-4-chloro-	5-Chloro-o-toluidine. C_7H_8ClN. See t275	141.61	....	26 (22)	237[722] 140[38]	....	....	....	s^h	....	....		....	B12[2], 453
Ω t303	—,2-amino-5-chloro-	4-Chloro-o-toluidine. C_7H_8ClN. See t275	141.61	lf (al)	29–30	241[760]	....	....	....	s^h	....	....		....	B12[2], 455
Ω t304	—,2-amino-6-chloro-	3-Chloro-o-toluidine. C_7H_8ClN. See t275	141.61	....	0–2	245[760] 96–9[10]	....	1.5880[20]	s^h	s	i	....	i	....	B12[2], 456
t305	—,3-amino-4-chloro-	6-Chloro-m-toluidine. C_7H_8ClN. See t275	141.61	pl	29–30	228–30	....	....	....	s^h	....	....		....	B12[2], 473
Ω t306	—,4-amino-2-chloro-	3-Chloro-p-toluidine. C_7H_8ClN. See t275	141.61	....	26	242–4[760] (238) 112–3[13]	....	....	....	s	....	....		....	B12[2], 530
t307	—,4-amino-3-chloro-	2-Chloro-p-toluidine. C_7H_8ClN. See t275	141.61	....	7	219[732]	1.151[20]	1.5748[22]	....	δ	....	δ		....	B12[2], 531
t308	—,5-amino-2-chloro-	4-Chloro-m-toluidine. C_7H_8ClN. See t275	141.61	nd (peth)	83–4	241	....	....	δ	v	....	s	s	os s lig δ	B12[1], 404
t309	—,4-amino-2,6-dinitro-	3,5-Dinitro-p-toluidine. $C_7H_7N_3O_4$. See t275	197.15	ye nd (w or aa)	171	....	....	....	$δ^h$	v	s	s	s	chl s aa s^h CS_2 δ	B12[2], 538
t310	—,2-amino-3-hydroxy-	2-Amino-m-cresol. C_7H_9NO. See t275	123.16	pl (w)	150	sub	....	....	s^h	....	....	....		....	B13[2], 324
t311	—,2-amino-4-hydroxy-	3-Amino-p-cresol. C_7H_9NO. See t275	123.16	cr (w or eth), lf (sub)	156–7 (144–5)	sub	....	....	s^h	....	s	....		....	B13[2], 337
Ω t312	—,2-amino-5-hydroxy-	4-Amino-m-cresol. C_7H_9NO. See t275	123.16	pr (dil al), cr (bz)	179	....	....	....	δ	v	v	....		....	B13[2], 330
t313	—,2-amino-6-hydroxy-	3-Amino-o-cresol. C_7H_9NO. See t275	123.16	nd (w)	129	....	....	....	δ	s	δ	....		....	B13, 579
t314	—,3-amino-2-hydroxy-	6-Amino-o-cresol. C_7H_9NO. See t275	123.16	pl (w)	89	....	....	....	s^h	s	s	s	s	MeOH, chl, CCl_4 s peth i	B13[1], 212

For explanations, symbols and abbreviations see beginning of table. For structural formulas see end of table.

No.	Name	Synonyms and Formula	Mol. wt.	Color, crystalline form. specific rotation and λ_{max} (log ε)	m.p. °C	b.p. °C	Density	n_D	Solubility						Ref.
									w	al	eth	ace	bz	other solvents	
	Toluene														
t315	—,3-amino-4-hydroxy-	2-Amino-p-cresol. C_7H_9NO. See t275	123.16	cr (w), rh (bz), sc (eth), lf or nd (sub)	137	sub	....	....	δ	s	s	...	δ	chl s lig i	B13², 338
t316	—,3-amino-5-hydroxy-	5-Amino-m-cresol. C_7H_9NO. See t275	123.16	cr (dil MeOH)	139	245	....	....	δ	sʰ				MeOH sʰ	C47, 9300
t318	—,4-amino-3-hydroxy-	6-Amino-m-cresol. C_7H_9NO. See t275	123.16	nd (bz, dil al)	162d	....	....	....	sʰ	s	s	s		MeOH s lig i	B13², 326
Ω t319	—,5-amino-2-hydroxy-	4-Amino-o-cresol. C_7H_9NO. See t275	123.16	nd or lf (bz)	175	sub	....	....	δ	s	s	...	δ sʰ	....	B13², 319
t320	—,α-amino-2-hydroxy-5-nitro-	2-Hydroxy-5-nitrobenzylamine. $C_7H_8N_2O_3$. See t275	168.16	ye nd or lf (w or dil NH₃)	253d	....	....	....	sʰ	sʰ					B13, 587
t321	—,α-amino-4-hydroxy-3-nitro-	4-Hydroxy-3-nitrobenzylamine. $C_7H_8N_2O_3$. See t275	168.16	og red nd (w + 1)	225d (−w 115)	....	....	....	sʰ						B13, 610
t322	—,3-amino-2-hydroxy-5-nitro-	$C_7H_8N_2O_3$. See t275	168.16	red-br nd (bz)	176	....	....	....		sʰ			sʰ		B13², 319
t323	—,3-amino-4-hydroxy-5-nitro-	$C_7H_8N_2O_3$. See t275	168.16	red-br (al)	119	....	....	....		sʰ					B13², 345
t324	—,5-amino-2-hydroxy-3-nitro-	$C_7H_8N_2O_3$. See t275	168.16	br-red nd (al)	118	....	....	....		sʰ					B13, 578
t325	—,5-amino-2-hydroxy-2-nitro-	$C_7H_8N_2O_3$. See t275	168.16	ye-og cr (al)	199–200d	....	....	....	sʰ	sʰ				dil HCl s	B13², 346
t326	—,6-amino-3-hydroxy-2-nitro-	$C_7H_8N_2O_3$. See t275	168.16	red-br nd (al)	201	....	....	....		sʰ				dil ac v dil alk v	B13, 595
t327	—,2-amino-4-iodo-	5-Iodo-o-toluidine. C_7H_8IN. See t275	233.06	nd (aq al)	48–9	273d	....	....	δ	s				dil ac, aa s	B12¹, 391
Ω t328	—,2-amino-5-iodo-	4-Iodo-o-toluidine. C_7H_8IN. See t275	233.06	nd (dil al), pr (lig)	91–2 (87.2)	....	....	....	sʰ	v	v	...	v	aa, lig s	B12², 457
t329	—,3-amino-2-iodo-	2-Iodo-m-toluidine. C_7H_8IN. See t275	233.06	pr	41–2	....	....	....	i	s	s	s	...	os s	B12², 475
t330	—,3-amino-4-iodo-	6-Iodo-m-toluidine. C_7H_8IN. See t275	233.06	nd (dil al), br in air	48 (38)	....	....	....		s	s	s		chl s	B12², 475
t331	—,3-amino-5-iodo-	5-Iodo-m-toluidine. C_7H_8IN. See t275	233.06	nd (peth)	78.5	....	....	....	s	s	s	s		oos s peth sʰ	B12¹, 406
t332	—,4-amino-2-iodo-	3-Iodo-p-toluidine. C_7H_8IN. See t275	233.06	nd (dil al or peth)	39–40	....	....	....		s	s	s		aa v oos s	B12², 533
t333	—,4-amino-3-iodo-	2-Iodo-p-toluidine. C_7H_8IN. See t275	233.06	pr	40	d	....	....		v	v	v	v	os, chl, peth v	B12², 533
t334	—,5-amino-2-iodo-	4-Iodo-m-toluidine. C_7H_8IN. See t275	233.06	lf or pl (al or peth)	46	....	....	....	δʰ	s	s			aa, lig v	B12², 474
t335	—,α-amino-3-methoxy-	m-Methoxybenzylamine. $C_8H_{11}NO$. See t275	137.18	....	....	141³⁰ 81⁰·⁸	....	....	i	s				os s	B13², 335
t336	—,α-amino-4-methoxy-	p-Methoxybenzylamine. $C_8H_{11}NO$. See t275	137.18	....	....	236–7⁷⁶⁰ (220–3) 133–4³³	1.050¹⁵	1.5462²⁰	s	s	s				B13², 347
t337	—,2-amino-3-methoxy-	6-Methyl-o-anisidine. $C_8H_{11}NO$. See t275	137.18	nd (w)	31	119–21¹⁶	....	....	sʰ	v				os v	B13², 324
t338	—,2-amino-4-methoxy-	6-Methyl-m-anisidine. $C_8H_{11}NO$. See t275	137.18	nd (w)	47	253 140²⁰	....	....	sʰ	s					B13², 337
Ω t339	—,2-amino-5-methoxy-	2-Methyl-p-anisidine. $C_8H_{11}NO$. See t275	137.18	cr (lig)	29–30	248–9 146–7²³	....	1.5647²⁰		s	s			lig sʰ	B13², 330
Ω t340	—,3-amino-4-methoxy-	Cresidine. 5-Methyl-o-anisidine. $C_8H_{11}NO$. See t275	137.18	nd or lf (al, lig or peth)	93–4 (52–4)	235⁷⁶⁰	....	....	δʰ	s	s		s	peth sʰ	B13², 338
t341	—,4-amino-2-methoxy-	4-Methyl-m-anisidine. $C_8H_{11}NO$. See t275	137.18	....	58	250–2	....	....	δ	v	s		v	lig v	B13¹, 213
t342	—,4-amino-3-methoxy-	4-Methyl-o-anisidine. $C_8H_{11}NO$. See t275	137.18	pa ye	....	237–9 179–80⁴⁶	....	....		s	s	s		oos s	B13², 326
t343	—,5-amino-2-methoxy-	3-Methyl-p-anisidine. $C_8H_{11}NO$. See t275	137.18	cr (dil al)	59–60	....	....	....	δ sʰ	s	s				B13², 320
Ω t344	—,2-amino-3-nitro-	6-Nitro-o-toluidine. $C_7H_8N_2O_2$. See t275	152.16	og-ye pr (dil al) λ^{al} 208 (3.62), 283.5 (3.65), 330 (4.17)	97	....	1.1900⁴¹⁰⁰	....	δ	s	s		s	chl s	B12², 458
Ω t345	—,2-amino-4-nitro-	5-Nitro-o-toluidine. $C_7H_8N_2O_2$. See t275	152.16	ye ncl pr (al) λ^{al} 385 (3.78)	107–8	....	....	....	δ	s	s	s	s	chl s	B12², 459
Ω t346	—,2-amino-5-nitro-	4-Nitro-o-toluidine. $C_7H_8N_2O_2$. See t275	152.16	ye ncl pr or nd (w, al or lig) λ^{al} 231 (4.08), 253 (4.08), 288.5 (3.69), 373 (3.23)	134–5 (129)	....	1.1586⁴¹⁴⁰	....	δʰ	s			s	aa s	B12², 459
Ω t347	—,2-amino-6-nitro-	3-Nitro-o-toluidine. $C_7H_8N_2O_2$. See t275	152.16	ye rh nd (w), ye lf (al) λ^{al} 235 (4.20), 352 (3.14)	92 (97)	305d	....	....	δʰ	s	s		s	chl s	B12², 460

For explanations, symbols and abbreviations see beginning of table. For structural formulas see end of table.

No.	Name	Synonyms and Formula	Mol. wt.	Color, crystalline form, specific rotation and λ_{max} (log ε)	m.p. °C	b.p. °C	Density	n_D	w	al	eth	ace	bz	other solvents	Ref.
	Toluene														
t348	—,3-amino-2-nitro-	2-Nitro-m-toluidine. $C_7H_8N_2O_2$. See t275	152.16	ye-og pr or nd (bz-peth) λ^{al} 282.5 (3.53), 404 (3.50)	108	. . . .			δ	v	s	. . .	. . .		B12[2], 476
t349	—,3-amino-4-nitro-	6-Nitro-m-toluidine. $C_7H_8N_2O_2$. See t275	152.16	ye lf (w), pl (dil al) λ^{al} 233 (4.11), 373.5 (3.87)	112	. . . .			s^h	s	s	. . .	s	chl s	B12[2], 476
t350	—,3-amino-5-nitro-	5-Nitro-m-toluidine. $C_7H_8N_2O_2$. See t275	152.16	ye-red or red-br nd (al) λ^{al} 235 (4.18), 287 (3.59), 375 (3.07)	98	. . . .			δ	s	v	. . .	s		B12[2], 476
Ω t352	—,4-amino-2-nitro-	3-Nitro-p-toluidine. $C_7H_8N_2O_2$. See t275	152.16	ye nd (w) λ^{al} 230 (4.30), 280 (3.80), 417.5 (3.76)	78–9	. . . .			δ s^h	s^h	s	. . .	s	CS_2 δ	B12[2], 534
Ω t353	—,4-amino-3-nitro-	2-Nitro-p-toluidine. $C_7H_8N_2O_2$. See t275	152.16	red lf (dil al), mcl pr (al) $\lambda^{dil\,MeOH}$ 227.5 (4.26), 287 (3.75), 428 (3.63)	117	. . . .	1.164_4^{121}	. . . . . .	δ^h	s	. . .	. . .		B12[2], 535
Ω t354	—,5-amino-2-nitro-	4-Nitro-m-toluidine. $C_7H_8N_2O_2$. See t275	152.16	lt ye nd (w or dil al) λ^{al} 233 (3.87), 373.5 (4.12)	138 (134)	. . . .			δ s^h	s	s	. . .		ac v	B12[2], 476
Ω t355	—,3-amino-α,α,α-trifluoro-	m-Aminobenzotrifluoride. $C_7H_6F_3N$. See t275	161.13	λ^{al} 296 (3.45)	. . . . . .	187.5^{764} 74–5[10]		1.4787^{20}	δ	s	s				B12[2], 473
t356	—,α-azido-	Benzyl azide. $C_6H_5CH_2N_3$	133.15		. . . . . .	108^{23} 74[11]	1.0655^{25}	1.5341^{25}	i	∞	∞				B5[3], 773
Ω t357	—,α-bromo-	Benzyl bromide. $C_6H_5CH_2Br$	171.04	pr λ^{iso} 224.5 (3.87)	–3 –1	201^{760} 114[15]	1.4380_0^{22}	1.5752^{20}	i	∞	∞				B5[3], 709
Ω t358	—,2-bromo-	o-Tolyl bromide. C_7H_7Br. See t275	171.04	λ^{chl} 260 sh (2.6), 272 (2.7), 280 (2.6)	–27.73 (–26)	181.7^{760} 59.1[10]	1.4232_4^{20}	1.5565^{20}	i	v	v		v	CCl_4 ∞	B5[3], 704
Ω t359	—,3-bromo-	m-Tolyl bromide. C_7H_7Br. See t275	171.04	λ^{hx} 267 (2.59), 276 (2.53)	–39.8	183.7	1.4099_4^{20}	1.5510^{20}	i	s	∞	s	. . .	chl s	B5[3], 706
Ω t360	—,4-bromo-	p-Tolyl bromide. C_7H_7Br. See t275	171.04	cr (al) λ^{al} 220 (4.02), 262 (2.59), 269 (2.68), 277 (2.59)	28.5 (24.8)	184.35^{760} 61.9[10]	1.3995_4^{20}	1.5477^{20}	i	s	s	s	s	chl s	B5[3], 707
t361	—,α-bromo-2-chloro-	o-Chlorobenzyl bromide. C_7H_6BrCl. See t275	205.49	. . . .	. . . . . .	120^{10}			d^h			s		chl s	B5[3], 714
t362	—,2-bromo-α-chloro-	o-Bromobenzyl chloride. C_7H_6BrCl. See t275	205.49		. . . . . .	124–6^{20}			i	v	v				B5[3], 713
t363	—,3-bromo-α-chloro-	m-Bromobenzyl chloride. C_7H_6BrCl. See t275	205.49	. . . .	22–3	119^{18}			d	s					B5[3], 714
Ω t364	—,4-bromo-α-chloro-	p-Bromobenzyl chloride. C_7H_6BrCl. See t275	205.49	nd (al or peth)	50	236^{760} 110–1[9]			i	v^h	v			peth s^h	B5[3], 714
t365	—,5-bromo-$\alpha,2$-dihydroxy-	5-Bromosaligenin. Bromo-salisol. $C_7H_7BrO_2$. See t275	203.04	lf (bz)	113 (109)	. . . .			δ v^h	v	v		s	AcOEt v chl s	B6[2], 879
t366	—,2-bromo-α-hydroxy-	o-Bromobenzyl alcohol. C_7H_7BrO. See t275	187.04	nd (lig)	80	. . . .			s^h	v	v			lig s^h	B6[2], 423
t367	—,2-bromo-4-hydroxy-	3-Bromo-p-cresol. C_7H_7BrO. See t275	187.04	nd (peth)	56	245–7			δ	v	s	s	v	MeOH v peth s^h	B6[3], 1377
t368	—,2-bromo-5-hydroxy-	4-Bromo-m-cresol. C_7H_7BrO. See t275	187.04	nd (peth or w)	63.5	137–43^{16}			δ	. . .	s			Py v peth, lig δ	B6[3], 1321
t369	—,2-bromo-6-hydroxy-	3-Bromo-o-cresol. C_7H_7BrO. See t275	187.04	nd (peth)	95	55–7^4			δ	s	s	s	s	peth s^h	B6, 360
Ω t370	—,3-bromo-4-hydroxy-	2-Bromo-p-cresol. C_7H_7BrO. See t275	187.04	nd (peth)	56–7	213–4 (218–9)	1.5468_{25}^{25}	1.5772^{20}	δ	s	. . .	s			B6[3], 1378
t371	—,3-bromo-5-hydroxy-	5-Bromo-m-cresol. C_7H_7BrO. See t275	187.04	nd (w)	56–7	161–2^{28}			δ	s	s				B6[2], 357
t372	—,4-bromo-α-hydroxy-	p-Bromobenzyl alcohol. C_7H_7BrO. See t275	187.04	nd (lig)	77	. . . .			i	v	v		v	CS_2 v	B6[3], 1560
t373	—,4-bromo-2-hydroxy-	5-Bromo-o-cresol. C_7H_7BrO. See t275	187.04	nd (lig or peth)	80					s	s	s		oos s lig δ, s^h	B6[2], 333
t374	—,4-bromo-3-hydroxy-	6-Bromo-m-cresol. C_7H_7BrO. See t275	187.04	cr (peth)	38	206–8^{731} 81–2[4]				v	s	s	. . .	os s	B6[3], 1320
t375	—,5-bromo-2-hydroxy-	4-Bromo-o-cresol. C_7H_7BrO. See t275	187.04	nd (al or peth)	64	235 137–43[18] sub				v	s	s		os s	B6[3], 1269
Ω t376	—,α-bromo-2-nitro-	o-Nitrobenzyl bromide. $C_7H_6BrNO_2$. See t275	216.04	pl (dil al)	46–7	. . . .			i	s	s	. . .	s	lig s	B5[3], 752
Ω t377	—,α-bromo-3-nitro-	m-Nitrobenzyl bromide. $C_7H_6BrNO_2$. See t275	216.04	nd or pl (al)	58–9	153.5–4.5[8]			i	s	. . .	. . .	s		B5[3], 752

For explanations, symbols and abbreviations see beginning of table. For structural formulas see end of table.

No.	Name	Synonyms and Formula	Mol. wt.	Color, crystalline form, specific rotation and λ_{max} (log ε)	m.p. °C	b.p. °C	Density	n_D	w	al	eth	ace	bz	other solvents	Ref.
	Toluene														
Ω t378	—,α-bromo-4-nitro-	p-Nitrobenzyl bromide. $C_7H_6BrNO_2$. See t275	216.04	nd (al) λ^{al} 270.5 (4.08)	99–100	....			δ	v	v	...	...	aa s	B5[3], 753
t379	—,2-bromo-3-nitro-	$C_7H_6BrNO_2$. See t275......	216.04	ye pr (al)	41–2	157^{22} $135-6^8$			i	s	...	...	...		B5[3], 752
Ω t380	—,2-bromo-4-nitro-	$C_7H_6BrNO_2$. See t275	216.04	nd (al)	78	$150-1^{20}$			i	δ v^h	s	...	...	CS_2 s	B5[3], 753
t381	—,2-bromo-5-nitro-	$C_7H_6BrNO_2$. See t275	216.04	cr (al)	78	$140-3^{17}$			...	δ v^h	s	...	...	CS_2 s	B5[3], 752
t382	—,2-bromo-6-nitro-	$C_7H_6BrNO_2$. See t275	216.04	pa ye nd (dil al)	42	143^{22}			i	s v^h	s	...	...		B5[3], 751
t383	—,3-bromo-2-nitro-	$C_7H_6BrNO_2$. See t275	216.04	pa ye nd	28	$129-30^{10}$			i	s	s	...	...		B5[3], 751
t384	—,3-bromo-2-nitro-	$C_7H_6BrNO_2$. See t275	216.04	pa ye pr or nd (MeOH)	37	$154-5^{20}$			i	s	s	...	...		B5[3], 753
t385	—,3-bromo-5-nitro-	$C_7H_6BrNO_2$. See t275	216.04	pa ye nd or pr (MeOH)	84	$269-70^{760}$			i	s	s	...	...	MeOH δ	B5[3], 752
t386	—,4-bromo-2-nitro-	$C_7H_6BrNO_2$. See t275	216.04	pa ye nd (dil al)	47	$256-7^{760}$ 130^{12}			i	s	s	...	...	con sulf s	B5[3], 751
t387	—,4-bromo-3-nitro-	$C_7H_6BrNO_2$. See t275	216.04	pa ye nd (MeOH)	35			1.5682^{50}	i			...	...	con sulf s MeOH s^h	B5[3], 752
t388	—,5-bromo-2-nitro-	$C_7H_6BrNO_2$. See t275	216.04	cr (al)	56	267 143^{10}			i	δ s^h		...	...		B5[3], 751
t389	,3-butoxy-	Butyl m-tolyl ether. $C_{11}H_{16}O$. See t275	164.25	....	....	229.2^{760}	0.9407_0^0	1.4970^{20}				s			B6[3], 1300
t390	,4-butoxy-	Butyl p-tolyl ether. $C_{11}H_{16}O$. See t275	164.25	λ^{al} 218 (3.83), 254 (2.31), 260 (2.39), 266 (2.34)	....	229.5^{760} 88^3	0.9232_{25}^{25}	1.4970^{20}				s			B6[3], 1354
Ω t391	—,α-chloro-	Benzyl chloride. $C_6H_5CH_2Cl$	126.59	λ^{al} 217 (3.85)	−39	179.3^{760} 66^{11}	1.1002_{20}^{20}	1.5391^{20}	i d^h	∞	∞	...	...	chl ∞	B5[3], 685
Ω t392	—,2-chloro-	o-Tolyl chloride. C_7H_7Cl. See t275	126.59	λ^{cy} 265 (2.48)	−35.1	159.15^{760} 42.6^{10}	1.0825_4^{20}	1.5268^{20}	i	s	∞	∞	s	chl, CCl_4, hp ∞	B5[3], 680
Ω t393	—,3-chloro-	m-Tolyl chloride. C_7H_7Cl. See t275	126.59	λ^{iso} 254 (2.13), 261 (2.33), 268 (2.47), 275 (2.45)	−47.8	162^{760}	1.0722_4^{20}	1.5214^{19}	i	s	∞	...	s	chl s	B5[3], 682
Ω t394	—,4-chloro-	p-Tolyl chloride. C_7H_7Cl. See t275	126.59	λ^{iso} 264 (2.54), 270 (2.68), 277.5 (2.70)	7.5	162^{760} 44^{10}	1.0697_4^{20}	1.5150^{20}	i	s	∞	...	s	chl, aa s	B5[3], 683
t395	—,α-chloro-α,α-difluoro-	Benzodifluorochloride. $C_6H_5CClF_2$	162.57	....	−49.8	140.6^{760} $79-81^{100}$	1.2509^{20}	1.4648^{20}	i	s	s	...	...		B5[3], 692
t397	—,2-chloro-α-hydroxy-	o-Chlorobenzyl alcohol. C_7H_7ClO. See t275	142.59	lf or nd (dil al)	74	230 $100-5^{28}$			δ	v	v	...	...	lig v^h	B6[3], 1554
t398	—,2-chloro-3-hydroxy-	2-Chloro-m-cresol. C_7H_7ClO. See t275	142.59	pr (peth)	55–6	196^{760} $53-7^4$			δ			...	...	aa v peth s^h	B6[3], 1315
t399	—,2-chloro-4-hydroxy-	3-Chloro-p-cresol. C_7H_7ClO. See t275	142.59	nd (al)	55–6	228^{760}			s^h	s	s	...	...	aa v	B6[3], 1374
Ω t400	—,2-chloro-5-hydroxy-	4-Chloro-m-cresol. C_7H_7ClO. See t275	142.59	nd (peth)	66–8	235^{760}			δ	s	s	...	...	peth s^h	B6[3], 1315
t401	—,2-chloro-6-hydroxy-	3-Chloro-o-cresol. C_7H_7ClO. See t275	142.59	lo nd (w)	86	225			δ s^h	s	s	s	...		B6[3], 1267
Ω t402	—,3-chloro-2-hydroxy-	6-Chloro-o-cresol. C_7H_7ClO. See t275	142.59	λ^{peth} 275, 282		$188-9^{740}$ $80-1^{20}$		1.5449^{20}				s	...		B6[3], 1263
t403	—,3-chloro-4-hydroxy-	2-Chloro-p-cresol. C_7H_7ClO. See t275	142.59	....		$195-6^{760}$	1.1785_4^{25}	1.5200^{27}	δ	s	s	s	s	aa s	B6[3], 1374
t404	—,4-chloro-α-hydroxy-	p-Chlorobenzyl chloride. C_7H_7ClO. See t275	142.59	nd (w), pr (bz or bz-lig), cr (al) λ^{al} 266 (2.42)	75	235			$δ^h$	s	s	s^h	...	lig δ	B6[3], 1555
t405	—,4-chloro-2-hydroxy-	5-Chloro-o-cresol. C_7H_7ClO. See t275	142.59	nd (peth or gasoline)	73–4	....				v		...	v	alk, aa v	B6[3], 1263
t406	—,4-chloro-3-hydroxy-	6-Chloro-m-cresol. C_7H_7ClO. See t275	142.59	pr (peth)	45–6	196	1.215^{15}		δ			...	...	peth s^h	B6[3], 1315
Ω t407	—,5-chloro-2-hydroxy-	4-Chloro-o-cresol. C_7H_7ClO. See t275	142.59	nd (peth) λ^{peth} 286, 292	51	223			δ			...	...	peth s^h	B6[3], 1264
t408	—,α-chloro-4-hydroxy-3-nitro-	$C_7H_6ClNO_3$. See t275	187.58	ye nd (bz, lig or al), lf (peth)	75	....				s^h		...	s^h	aa, lig s^h	B6, 413
Ω t409	—,α-chloro-4-methoxy-	p-Methoxybenzyl chloride. C_8H_9ClO. See t275	156.61	....	....	$116-20^{15}$ $83-4^2$	1.159^{20}	1.553				...	...		B6[3], 1375
Ω t410	—,α-chloro-2-nitro-	o-Nitrobenzyl chloride. $C_7H_6ClNO_2$. See t275	171.58	cr (lig)	50–2	....		1.5557^{62}	i	s	s	v	v	AcOEt v aa s	B5[3], 745
t411	—,α-chloro-3-nitro-	m-Nitrobenzyl chloride. $C_7H_6ClNO_2$. See t275	171.58	pa ye nd (lig)	45–7	$175-$ 83^{30-5}		1.5577^{62}	i	s	s	v	s	AcOEt v aa s	B5[3], 746
Ω t412	—,α-chloro-4-nitro-	p-Nitrobenzyl chloride. $C_7H_6ClNO_2$. See t275	171.58	pl or nd (al) λ^{al} 265 (4.08)	71	....		1.5647^{62}	i	s	s	v	v	AcOEt v MeOH s	B5[3], 747
Ω t413	—,2-chloro-4-nitro-	$C_7H_6ClNO_2$. See t275	171.58	nd (al)	68	260^{760}		1.5470^{69}	$δ^h$	s	s	...	...	aa s	B5[3], 747
Ω t414	—,2-chloro-6-nitro-	$C_7H_6ClNO_2$. See t275	171.58	nd (dil al)	37–40	238^{760}		1.5377^{69}	i	s	s	...	...		B5[3], 745
Ω t415	—,3-chloro-4-nitro-	$C_7H_6ClNO_2$. See t275	171.58	pa ye nd	24	146^{19}			i			...	...		B5[2], 253

For explanations, symbols and abbreviations see beginning of table. For structural formulas see end of table.

No.	Name	Synonyms and Formula	Mol. wt.	Color, crystalline form, specific rotation and λ_{max} (log ε)	m.p. °C	b.p. °C	Density	n_D	w	al	eth	ace	bz	other solvents	Ref.
	Toluene														
t416	—,3-chloro-5-nitro-	$C_7H_6ClNO_2$. See t275	171.58	ye nd (al)	61	....		1.5404^{69}	i	s^h	...	...	...		$B5^3$, 746
Ω t417	—,4-chloro-2-nitro-	$C_7H_6ClNO_2$. See t275	171.58	mcl nd $\lambda^{dil\,MeOH}$ 213 (4.26), 262 (3.68), 315 (3.23)	38	240^{720} 115.5^{11}	1.2559^{80}	....	i	s^h	s	...	...		$B5^2$, 251
Ω t418	—,4-chloro-3-nitro-	$C_7H_6ClNO_2$. See t275	171.58		7	260^{745} 118^{11}		1.5572^{20}	i	...	...	...	...		$B5^2$, 252
t419	—,5-chloro-2-nitro-	$C_7H_6ClNO_2$. See t275	171.58	ye	24.9	....		1.5496^{65}	i	...	...	...	...		$B5^1$, 162
t420	—,2,3-diamino-	$C_7H_{10}N_2$. See t275	122.17	cr	63–4	255			s	s	s	...		oos s	$B13^2$, 60
Ω t421	—,2,4-diamino-	$C_7H_{10}N_2$. See t275	122.17	nd (w), or (al)	99	292 $148–50^8$			v^h	v	v	...	v^h		$B13^2$, 60
t422	—,2,5-diamino-	$C_7H_{10}N_2$. See t275	122.17	pl (bz)	64	273–4			s	s	s	δ s^h		aa δ, v^h	$B13^2$, 62
Ω t423	—,2,6-diamino-	$C_7H_{10}N_2$. See t275	122.17	pr (bz or w)	106				s	s	s	s^h			$B13^2$, 64
Ω t424	—,3,4-diamino-	$C_7H_{10}N_2$. See t275	122.17	lf (lig)	89–90	265 sub			v			...		lig s^h	$B13^2$, 64
t425	—,3,5-diamino-	$C_7H_{10}N_2$. See t275	122.17		<0	283–5			v	s	s	...			$B13$, 164
t426	—,—,hydrochloride	$C_7H_{10}N_2$. 2HCl. See t275	195.09	nd (dil al)	255–60d				v	i	i	...			$B13$, 164
t427	—,α,α-dibromo-	Benzal bromide. Benzylidene bromide. $C_6H_5CHBr_2$	249.94	λ^{iso} 276 sh	....	156^{23}	1.51^{15}	1.6147^{20}	i	∞	∞	...	...		$B5^3$, 717
t428	—,α,2-dibromo-	o-Bromobenzyl bromide. $C_7H_6Br_2$. See t275	249.94	cr (al, lig)	31	129^{19}			d^h	∞	∞	...		CS_2, aa ∞	$B5^3$, 717
t429	—,α,3-dibromo-	m-Bromobenzyl bromide. $C_7H_6Br_2$. See t275	249.94	nd or lf	41				d^h	s	v	...		CS_2, aa v	$B5^3$, 717
Ω t430	—,α,4-dibromo-	p-Bromobenzyl bromide. $C_7H_6Br_2$. See t275	249.94	nd (MeOH or al)	63				δ d^h	s^h	v	...	s	CS_2, aa v	$B5^3$, 717
t431	—,2,5-dibromo-	$C_7H_6Br_2$. See t275	249.94	fr 5.62	236^{760} $135–6^{35}$		1.8127^{19}	1.5982^{18}	i	...	...	...			$B5^3$, 716
t432	—,3,5-dibromo-	$C_7H_6Br_2$. See t275	249.94	nd	39	246^{760}			i	...	...	...			$B5^3$, 717
t433	—,2,4-dibromo-6-hydroxy-	3,5-Dibromo-o-cresol. $C_7H_6Br_2O$. See t275	265.94	nd (peth)	98–101	$283–7^{758}$				...	...	...		peth s^h	$B6^3$, 1271
t434	—,3,5-dibromo-2-hydroxy-	4,6-Dibromo-o-cresol. $C_7H_6Br_2O$. See t275	265.94	nd (peth or 50 % al)	58	$263–6^{745}$d			δ	s	s	s		oos, aa s	$B6^2$, 334
t435	—,3,6-dibromo-2-hydroxy-	3,6-Dibromo-o-cresol. $C_7H_6Br_2O$. See t275	265.94	cr	38	255–60				...	...	...		os v	$B6^1$, 176
Ω t436	—,α,α-dibromo-4-nitro-	p-Nitrobenzylidene bromide. $C_7H_5Br_2NO_2$. See t275	294.94	nd (al) λ^{hx} 263.5 (4.23)	84 (82)				i	v	v	...			$B5^3$, 755
Ω t437	—,α,α-dichloro-	Benzal chloride. Benzylidene chloride. $C_6H_5CHCl_2$	161.03	λ^{cy} 260 (2.4), 265 (2.5), 272 (2.3)	−16.4	205.2^{760}	1.2557^{14}	1.5502^{20}	i	s	s	...			$B5^3$, 696
Ω t438	—,α,2-dichloro-	o-Chlorobenzyl chloride. $C_7H_6Cl_2$. See t275	161.03		−17	217^{760} $94–5^{10}$	1.2699^0_4	1.5530^{20}		...	...	...			$B5^3$, 694
t439	—,α,3-dichloro-	m-Chlorobenzyl chloride. $C_7H_6Cl_2$. See t275	161.03			$215–6^{753}$ $110–1^{25}$	1.2695^{15}_4	1.5554^{20}	i d^h	v	...	...			$B5^3$, 695
Ω t440	—,α,4-dichloro-	p-Chlorobenzyl chloride. $C_7H_6Cl_2$. See t275	161.03	nd (dil al)	31	222 (214) 117^{20}			i	δ s^h	v	...	v	aa v CS_2 s	$B5^3$, 695
t441	—,2,3-dichloro-	$C_7H_6Cl_2$. See t275	161.03			$207–8^{760}$ $61–2^3$		1.5511^{20}	i	...	...	...	v		$B5^3$, 693
Ω t442	—,2,4-dichloro-	$C_7H_6Cl_2$. See t275	161.03		−13.5	$196–7^{760}$	1.2498^{20}_{20}	1.5511^{20}	i	...	...	...			$B5^3$, 693
t443	—,2,5-dichloro-	$C_7H_6Cl_2$. See t275	161.03		5	200^{770}	1.2535^{20}	1.5449^{20}	i	...	...	...	s		$B5^3$, 694
Ω t444	—,2,6-dichloro-	$C_7H_6Cl_2$. See t275	161.03	λ^{MeOH} 267 (2.26)		198^{760}		1.5507^{20}	i	...	...	...		chl s	$B5^3$, 694
Ω t445	—,3,4-dichloro-	$C_7H_6Cl_2$. See t275	161.03		−15.25	208.92^{760} 81.8^{10}	1.2564^{20}_4	1.5471^{20}	i	∞	∞	∞	∞	CCl_4, lig ∞	$B5^3$, 694
t446	—,3,5-dichloro-	$C_7H_6Cl_2$. See t275	161.03		26	$201–2^{760}$			i	...	...	...			$B5^3$, 694
t447	—,α,α-dichloro-α-fluoro-	Benzodichlorofluoride. $C_6H_5CCl_2F$	179.02			178–80	1.3138^{11}	1.5180^{11}	d	s^h	...	...			$B5^3$, 698
t448	—,2,4-dichloro-3-hydroxy-	2,6-Dichloro-m-cresol. $C_7H_6Cl_2O$. See t275	177.03		58–9	$235–6^{745}$ $75–80^4$				...	s	...		chl v	$B6^3$, 1319
Ω t449	—,2,4-dichloro-5-hydroxy-	4,6-Dichloro-m-cresol. $C_7H_6Cl_2O$. See t275	177.03	pr (peth)	72–4	235–6 110^{18}		1.572^{20}		...	...	...		chl v peth s^h	Am 55, 4216
t450	—,2,6-dichloro-3-hydroxy-	2,4-Dichloro-m-cresol. $C_7H_6Cl_2O$. See t275	177.03	pr (peth)	27	241–2.5				...	s	...		chl v peth s^h	$B6^3$, 1319
Ω t451	—,3,5-dichloro-2-hydroxy-	4,6-Dichloro-o-cresol. $C_7H_6Cl_2O$. See t275	177.03	nd (w or peth)	55	266.5 $73–8^4$			δ s^h	v	v	...	s	chl, CS_2 v peth s^h	$B6^3$, 1267
t452	—,3,5-dichloro-4-hydroxy-	2,6-Dichloro-p-cresol. $C_7H_6Cl_2O$. See t275	177.03	nd (lig)	39 (42)	$138–9^{28}$			δ	s	s	...		aa s lig s^h	$B6^3$, 1377
t453	—,4,5-dichloro-2-hydroxy-	4,5-Dichloro-o-cresol. $C_7H_6Cl_2O$. See t275	177.03	nd (peth)	101	....			δ	s	s	...	s	aa v peth δ	$B6^2$, 333
t454	—,α,α-dichloro-3-nitro-	m-Nitrobenzylidene chloride. $C_7H_5Cl_2NO_2$. See t275	206.03	mcl (al)	65				i	s^h	s	...			$B5^3$, 750
t455	—,α,α-dichloro-4-nitro-	p-Nitrobenzylidene chloride. $C_7H_5Cl_2NO_2$. See t275	206.03	pr (al) λ^{hx} 256 (4.16)	46				i	v	v	...			$B5^3$, 750
t456	—,2,5-diethoxy-	$C_{11}H_{16}O_2$. See t275	180.25	nd (lig)	24–5	$247–9^{760}$	1.0134^{15}		∞	∞	...	∞	chl ∞	$B6^3$, 4499
t457	—,2(diethyl-amino)-	N,N-Diethyl-o-toluidine. $C_{11}H_{17}N$. See t275	163.26			$208–9^{755}$			δ	s	s	...			$B12^2$, 436
t458	—,4(diethyl-amino)-	N,N-Diethyl-p-toluidine. $C_{11}H_{17}N$. See t275	163.26		<0	229^{770}	0.9242^{16}		δ	∞	∞	...			$B12^2$, 492

For explanations, symbols and abbreviations see beginning of table. For structural formulas see end of table.

No.	Name	Synonyms and Formula	Mol. wt.	Color, crystalline form, specific rotation and λ_{max} (log ε)	m.p. °C	b.p. °C	Density	n_D	w	al	eth	ace	bz	other solvents	Ref.
	Toluene														
t459	—,α,α-difluoro-	Benzal fluoride. Benzylidene fluoride. $C_6H_5CHF_2$	128.12	λ^{iso} 239 (2.02), 261 (2.47), 284 (0.78)	....	139.9^{760}	1.1357^{20}	1.4577^{20}	i	s					B5², 224
Ω t460	—,α,2-dihydroxy-	Saligenin. Salicyl alcohol. $C_7H_8O_2$. See t275	124.15	lf (bz), nd or pl (w, eth), pl (sub)	87	sub	1.1613^{25}	....	s v^h	s	s	s		chl v	B6³, 4537
Ω t461	—,—,glucoside	Salicin. Saligenin-β,D-glucoside.	286.29	rh nd or lf (w) $[\alpha]_D^{20}$ +62.6 (w, c = 3) $\lambda^{w, pH=4}$ 271 (3.0)	204.7–8.7	240d	1.434^{26}	....	s v^h	s	i		i	aa, Py s chl i	B31, 214
Ω t461¹	—,α,3-dihydroxy-	$C_7H_8O_2$. See t275	124.15	nd (bz), cr (CCl_4)	73	300^{760}d	1.161^{25}	....	v^h	v	v		...	chl δ	B6³, 4545
Ω t462	—,α,4-dihydroxy-	$C_7H_8O_2$. See t275	124.15	pr or nd (w) λ^w 289 (3.43)	124.5–5.5	252^{760}			v	v	v		δ	chl, peth i	B6³, 4546
Ω t463	—,2,3-dihydroxy-	Isohomocatechol. $C_7H_8O_2$. See t275	124.15	lf (bz) λ^{cy} 275 (3.26)	68 (47)	241^{760} 127^{12}			v	v	s		v	chl v	B6³, 4492
t464	—,2,4-dihydroxy-	Cresorcinol. $C_7H_8O_2$. See t275	124.15	cr (bz-peth) λ^{al} 283 (3.48)	105–7	267–70			s	s	s		δ	peth δ	B6³, 4495
Ω t465	—,2,5-dihydroxy-	Toluhydroquinone. 2-Methylhydroquinone. $C_7H_8O_2$. See t275	124.15	rh pl (bz)	126–7	163^{11} sub			v	v	v		δ	lig δ	B6³, 4498
t466	—,—,diacetate	2,5-Diacetoxytoluene. $C_{11}H_{12}O_4$. See t275	208.22	nd (aa), pr (lig) nd or pr (w)	52	....				v	v		δ	aa s lig s^h	B6³, 4501
Ω t467	,3,4-dihydroxy-	4-Homopyrocatechol. $C_7H_8O_2$. See t275	124.15	lf (bz-lig), pr (bz) λ^{cy} 283 (3.45)	65	251^{766} $143–6^{26}$ sub	1.1287_4^{74}	1.5425^{74}	s	s	s	s	...	os s lig δ	B6³, 4514
Ω t468	—,3,5-dihydroxy-	Orcinol. $C_7H_8O_2$. See t275	124.15	pr (w + 1), lf (chl) λ^{al} 278 (2.97)	107–8 (anh) 58 (hyd)	289–90 147^5	1.290^4		s	s	s		s	lig, peth δ	B6³, 4531
Ω t469	—,α,4-dihydroxy-3-methoxy-	Vanillyl alcohol. $C_8H_{10}O_3$. See t275	154.17	pr (w), nd (bz) λ^{al} 230 (3.8), 280 (3.6)	115	d			s^h	s^h	s^h		s^h		B6³, 6323
t470	—,2,4-dimercapto-	Dithiocresorcinol. $C_7H_8S_2$. See t275	156.28	....	36–7	263^{760}				s	s				B6, 873
t471	—,2,3-dimethoxy-	Isohomoveratrol. $C_9H_{12}O_2$. See t275	152.20	....		$202–3^{760}$ (214) $92–3^{18}$	1.0335_4^{20}	1.5121^{25}		s	s				B6³, 4493
Ω t472	—,2,4-dimethoxy-	$C_9H_{12}O_2$. See t275	152.20	....		211 110–20³⁰			δ	s	s				B6³, 4496
Ω t473	—,3,4-dimethoxy-	Homoveratrol. $C_9H_{12}O_2$. See t275	152.20	pr (eth)	24	$219–21^{760}$ $122–4^{27}$	1.0509_4^{25}	1.5257^{25}	i					os v	B6³, 4516
t474	—,3,5-dimethoxy-	$C_9H_{12}O_2$. See t275	152.20	....		244^{760} 102^8	1.0478^{15}	1.5234^{29}	i	v	v		v	CS_2, aa v	B6³, 4533
Ω t475	—,α(dimethyl-amino)-	N,N-Dimethylbenzylamine. $C_6H_5CH_2N(CH_3)_2$	135.21			$180–2^{760}$ $73–4^{15}$	0.9152_4^{0}	1.5011^{20}	δ^h	∞	∞				B12², 545
Ω t476	—,2(dimethyl-amino)-	N,N-Dimethyl-o-toluidine. $C_9H_{13}N$. See t275	135.21	λ^{iso} 248 (3.80)	–60	185.3^{760} $70–2^{15}$	0.9286_4^{20}	1.5153^{20}	δ	∞	∞				B12², 435
Ω t477	—,3(dimethyl-amino)-	N,N-Dimethyl-m-toluidine. $C_9H_{13}N$. See t275	135.21	λ^{cy} 253 (4.12), 298 (3.38)	....	212^{760}	0.9410_4^{20}	1.5492^{20}		∞	∞				B12², 466
Ω t478	—,4(dimethyl-amino)-	N,N-Dimethyl-p-toluidine. $C_9H_{13}N$. See t275	135.21	λ^{hx} 255 (5.0), 305 (3.8)		211^{760}	0.9366_4^{20}	1.5366^{20}	i	∞	∞				B12², 491
Ω t479	—,2,4-dinitro-	$C_7H_6N_2O_4$. See t275	182.14	ye nd or mcl pr (CS_2) $\lambda^{5\% \, al}$ 252 (4.15)	71	300 δd	1.3208^{71}	1.442 (1.756)	i	s	s	v	s	Py v to, chl, CS_2, AcOEt s	B5³, 759
t480	—,2,5-dinitro-	$C_7H_6N_2O_4$. See t275	182.14	nd (al) $\lambda^{5\% \, al}$ 266.5 (4.06)	52.5	....	1.282^{111}			s			s	CS_2 v	B5³, 760
Ω t481	—,2,6-dinitro-	$C_7H_6N_2O_4$. See t275	182.14	rh nd (al) $\lambda^{5\% \, al}$ 241 (3.95)	66	....	1.2833^{111}	1.479 (1.734)		s	s		s		B5³, 761
Ω t482	—,3,4-dinitro-	$C_7H_6N_2O_4$. See t275	182.14	ye nd (CS_2) $\lambda^{5\% \, al}$ 219 (4.00)	58.3	....	1.2594^{111}		i	s				CS_2 s	B5³, 761
t483	—,3,5-dinitro-	$C_7H_6N_2O_4$. See t275	182.14	ye rh nd (aa) $\lambda^{5\% \, al}$ 248 (4.08)	93	sub	1.2772^{111}		δ	s	s		s	CS_2, chl s	B5³, 762
t484	—,2,4-dinitro-6-hydroxy-	3,5-Dinitro-o-cresol. Sinox. $C_7H_6N_2O_5$. See t275	198.14	ye pr (al) $\lambda^{0.1N \, HCl}$ 268 (4.10)	85.8	....			δ	s	s	s	...	peth δ	C51, 10414
Ω t484¹	—,3,5-dinitro-2-hydroxy-	4,6-Dinitro-o-cresol. $C_7H_6N_2O_5$. See t275	198.14	ye pr or nd (al) $\lambda^{0.1N \, HCl}$ 268 (4.10)	86.5	....			δ	s	s	s	...	peth δ	B6³, 1276
t485	—,3,5-dinitro-4-hydroxy-	2,6-Dinitro-p-cresol. $C_7H_6N_2O_5$. See t275	198.14	ye nd (eth or peth) λ^{al} 241 (4.02), 354 (3.72)	85	....			i	s	s	s	...		B6³, 1390
	—,α-ethoxy-	see Ether, benzyl ethyl													

For explanations, symbols and abbreviations see beginning of table. For structural formulas see end of table.

No.	Name	Synonyms and Formula	Mol. wt.	Color, crystalline form, specific rotation and λ_{max} (log ε)	m.p. °C	b.p. °C	Density	n_D	w	al	eth	ace	bz	other solvents	Ref.
	Toluene														
t486	—,2-ethoxy-	Ethyl o-tolyl ether. o-Cresyl ethyl ether. $C_9H_{12}O$. See t275	136.20	λ^{hx} 260 sh (2.90), 272 (3.24), 278 (3.22)	....	184^{760} 70^{12}	0.9592_4^{13}	1.508^{13}	i	s	s				B6³, 1246
t487	—,3-ethoxy-	Ethyl m-tolyl ether. m-Cresyl ethyl ether. $C_9H_{12}O$. See t275	136.20			192^{760}	0.949^{20}	1.513^{20}	i	s	s				B6³, 1299
Ω t488	—,4-ethoxy-	Ethyl p-tolyl ether. p-Cresyl ethyl ether. $C_9H_{12}O$. See t275	136.20			$188–9^{760}$	0.9509_4^{18}	1.5058^{18}	i	s	s				B6³, 1353
Ω t489	—,2(ethylamino)-	N-Ethyl-o-toluidine. $C_9H_{13}N$. See t275	135.21	λ^{al} 244 (3.86), 291 (3.33)	< −15	218^{760} 95.5^{10}	0.948_4^{25}	1.5456^{20}	...	s	s				B12², 435
Ω t490	—,3(ethylamino)-	N-Ethyl-m-toluidine. $C_9H_{13}N$. See t275	135.21			221 $111–2^{20}$		1.5451^{20}	...	s	s				B12², 466
Ω t491	—,4(ethylamino)-	N-Ethyl-p-toluidine. $C_9H_{13}N$. See t275	135.21			217	0.9391^{16}		...	s	s				B12², 492
t492	—,α-fluoro-	Benzyl fluoride. $C_6H_5CH_2F$	110.13	nd (fr) λ^{iso} 244 (2.27), 250 (2.31), 264 (2.23), 289 (1.27)	−35	139.8^{753} 40^{14}	1.0228_4^{25}	1.4892^{25}	d						B5³, 678
Ω t493	—,2-fluoro-	o-Tolyl fluoride. C_7H_7F. See t275	110.13	λ^{cy} 206 (3.90), 262 (3.00), 268 (3.00)	−62	114 30^{26}	1.0041_4^{13}	1.4704^{20}	i	v	v				B5³, 676
Ω t494	—,3-fluoro-	m-Tolyl fluoride. C_7H_7F. See t275	110.13	λ^{cy} 207 (3.88), 262 (2.93), 269 (2.98)	−87.7	116^{760}	0.9986^{20}	1.4691^{20}	i	v	v				B5³, 676
Ω t495	—,4-fluoro-	p-Tolyl fluoride. C_7H_7F. See t275	110.13	λ^{cy} 206 (3.86), 264 (3.04), 273 (3.22)	−56.8	116.6^{760}	1.0007_4^{16}	1.4699^{20}	i	v	v				B5³, 677
Ω t496	—,α,α,2,3,4,5,6-heptachloro-	Pentachlorobenzylidene chloride. C_7HCl_7. See t275	333.26	lf (al) λ^{al} 307 (2.95)	119.5	334 199^{13}				δ v^h					B5¹, 153
Ω t497	—,α-hydroxy-	Benzyl alcohol. $C_6H_5CH_2OH$	108.15	λ^{al} 243 (1.91), 258.5 (2.26), 268 (1.95)	−15.3	205.35^{760} 93^{10}	1.0419_4^{20}	1.5396^{20}	s	s	s	s	s	MeOH, chl s	B6³, 1445
Ω t498	—,2-hydroxy-	o-Cresol. 2-Methylphenol*. C_7H_8O. See t275	108.15	λ^w 219 (3.71), 275 (3.22)	30.94	190.95^{760} 74.9^{10}	1.02734_4^{20}	1.5361^{20}	s	v	∞	∞	∞	CCl_4 ∞ oos s	B6³, 1233
Ω t499	—,3-hydroxy-	m-Cresol. 3-Methylphenol*. C_7H_8O. See t275	108.15	λ^{hx} 214 (3.79), 271 (3.20), 277 (3.27)	11.5	202.2^{760} 86^{10}	1.03362_0^{20}	1.5438^{20}	δ s^h	∞	∞	∞	∞	CCl_4 ∞ os s	B6³, 1286
Ω t500	—,4-hydroxy-	p-Cresol. 4-Methylphenol*. C_7H_8O. See t275	108.15	pr λ^{cy} 280 (3.23)	34.8	201.9^{760} 85.7^{10}	1.0178_4^{20}	1.5312^{20} (suc)	δ s^h	∞	∞	∞	∞	CCl_4 ∞ os s	B6³, 1341
t502	—,α-hydroxyl-amino-	N-Benzylhydroxylamine. $C_6H_5CH_2NHOH$	123.16	nd (peth or lig) λ^{al} 209 (3.86), 258 (2.31), 264 (2.21)	57				δ	s				lig s^h	B15², 17
t503	—,2-hydroxyl-amino-	o-Tolylhydroxylamine. C_7H_9NO. See t275	123.16	nd (eth-bz)	44				i	s	s		s	lig δ	B15², 14
t504	—,3-hydroxyl-amino-	m-Tolylhydroxylamine. C_7H_9NO. See t275	123.16	lf (bz-peth)	68.5				s^h	s	s		s^h	chl s lig δ	B15², 15
Ω t505	—,4-hydroxyl-amino-	p-Tolylhydroxylamine. C_7H_9NO. See t275	123.16	lf (bz)	98 (94)	$115–20d$			δ	s	s		s^h	chl s lig i	B15², 16
t506	—,2-hydroxyl-amino-6-nitro-	$C_7H_8N_2O_3$. See t275	168.18	col or ye (bz)	120–1				δ	v	v		δ s^h	peth δ	B15², 14
t507	—,4-hydroxyl-amino-2-nitro-	$C_7H_8N_2O_3$. See t275	168.18	ye (bz)	108–9					s	s		s^h		B15², 16
Ω t508	—,α-hydroxy-2-methoxy-	o-Methoxybenzyl alcohol. Saligenin 2-methyl ether. $C_8H_{10}O_2$. See t275	138.17			249^{760} 119^8	1.0395_{15}^{15}	1.5455^{20}	i	s	∞				B6², 878
Ω t509	—,α-hydroxy-4-methoxy-	Anisyl alcohol. $C_8H_{10}O_2$. See t275	138.17	nd	25	259.1^{760} $134–5^{12}$	1.109_4^{26}	1.5420^{25}	s	v	v				B6², 883
t511	—,4-hydroxy-3-methoxy-	Cresolol. $C_8H_{10}O_2$. See t275	138.17	pr	5.5	221 113.5^{22}	1.098_4^{20}	1.5353^{25}	δ	∞	∞		∞	chl, aa ∞	B6², 865
t512	—,4-hydroxy-2-(methylamino)-	$C_8H_{11}NO$. See t275	137.18	cr (bz-lig)	108					s	s		s	lig δ	B13, 599
Ω t513	—,α-hydroxy-3,4-methylenedioxy-	Piperonyl alcohol. $C_8H_8O_3$. See t275	152.16	nd (peth)	58	157^{16}			δ	s	s		s	chl, MeOH s lig i	B19², 77
Ω t514	—,α-hydroxy-2-nitro-	o-Nitrobenzyl alcohol. $C_7H_7NO_3$. See t275	153.14	nd (w) $\lambda^{0.1N HCl}$ 267.5 (3.75)	74	270^{760} 168^{20}			δ	s	s		s		B6³, 1563
t515	—,α-hydroxy-3-nitro-	m-Nitrobenzyl alcohol. $C_7H_7NO_3$. See t275	153.14	rh nd (w)	30.5 (27)	$175–80^3$	1.296_{15}^{19}		s	s	s		s		B6³, 1565
Ω t516	—,α-hydroxy-4-nitro-	p-Nitrobenzyl alcohol. $C_7H_7NO_3$. See t275	153.14	nd (w) $\lambda^{0.1N HCl}$ 276 (3.96)	96–7	$250–60d$ 185^{12}			δ s^h	s	s		s		B6³, 1567
Ω t517	—,2-hydroxy-3-nitro-	6-Nitro-o-cresol. $C_7H_7NO_3$. See t275	153.14	ye pr (dil al or peth)	70	$102–3^9$			i	v	v			peth s^h	B6³, 1273
t518	—,2-hydroxy-4-nitro-	5-Nitro-o-cresol. $C_7H_7NO_3$. See t275	153.14	ye nd (lig) λ^{MeOH} 320 (3.99)	118				δ	s	s		s	CS_2, lig δ	B6³, 1273

For explanations, symbols and abbreviations see beginning of table. For structural formulas see end of table.

No.	Name	Synonyms and Formula	Mol. wt.	Color. crystalline form. specific rotation and λ_{max} (log ε)	m.p. °C	b.p. °C	Density	n_D	Solubility						Ref.
									w	al	eth	ace	bz	other solvents	
	Toluene														
Ω t519	—,2-hydroxy-5-nitro-	4-Nitro-o-cresol. $C_7H_7NO_3$. See t275	153.14	ye or col nd (w or aq al +w), pl (bz)	96 (anh) 30–40 (hyd)	186–90[9]	....	....	δ	v	v	...	v	aa v	B6[3], 1274
Ω t521	—,2-hydroxy-6-nitro-	3-Nitro-o-cresol. $C_7H_7NO_3$. See t275	153.14	pa ye nd (w)	147	....	....	....	δ[h]	s	s	...	...	....	B6[1], 178
t522	—,3-hydroxy-4-nitro-	6-Nitro-m-cresol. $C_7H_7NO_3$. See t275	153.14	ye mcl pl (eth or bz)	56	....	....	....	δ	s	s	s	s	....	B6[3], 1326
t523	—,3-hydroxy-5-nitro-	5-Nitro-m-cresol. $C_7H_7NO_3$. See t275	153.14	pa ye cr (bz)	90–1	....	....	....	δ[h]		s		s[h]	....	B6[2], 361
t524	—,—,monohydrate	$C_7H_7NO_3 \cdot H_2O$. See t275 ...	171.16	pa ye nd (w)	60–2	....	....	....	δ[h]	v	v		s	....	B6, 385
Ω t525	—,4-hydroxy-2-nitro-	3-Nitro-p-cresol. $C_7H_7NO_3$. See t275	153.14	ye pr (eth)	79	....	....	....	δ	v	v		δ	CS_2, lig δ	B6[3], 1384
Ω t526	—,4-hydroxy-3-nitro-	2-Nitro-p-cresol. $C_7H_7NO_3$. See t275	153.14	ye nd (al or w)	36.5	125[22]	1.2399_4^{39}	1.574^{40}	δ[h]	v	v	v	os s		B6[3], 1384
Ω t527	—,5-hydroxy-2-nitro-	4-Nitro-m-cresol. $C_7H_7NO_3$. See t275	153.14	nd or pr (w)	129	....	....	....	δ[h]		s		s	chl s	B6[3], 1327
Ω t528	—,2-hydroxy-5-nitroso-	1,4-Toluquinone 4-oxime. $C_7H_7NO_2$. See t275	137.14	nd (w) λ^{MeOH} 305 (4.26)	134–5d	....	....	....	δ v[h]	v	s		s	chl. alk v CCl_4 s	B7[2], 589
Ω t529	—,5-hydroxy-2-nitroso-	1,4-Toluquinone 1-oxime. $C_7H_7NO_2$. See t275	137.14	nd (w or bz), pr (aa)	165d	....	....	....	δ s[h]	s	s		s	aa s	B7[2], 589
t530	—,2-hydroxy-3,4,5,6-tetrabromo-	3,4,5,6-Tetrabromo-o-cresol. $C_7H_4Br_4O$. See t275	423.75	ye nd (chl or aa)	208	d	....	....	i		s		s	chl s aa, lig δ	B6[3], 1272
t531	—,3-hydroxy-2,4,5,6-tetrabromo-	2,4,5,6-Tetrabromo-m-cresol. $C_7H_4Br_4O$. See t275	423.75	nd (chl, aa)	194	....	....	....			s		s	alk s chl, aa s[h]	B6[3], 1324
t532	—,4-hydroxy-2,3,5,6-tetrabromo-	2,3,5,6-Tetrabromo-p-cresol. $C_7H_4Br_4O$. See t275	423.75	nd (al or chl)	198–9 (209)	....	....	....			s	v		chl, alk v aa v[h]	B6[3], 1383
t533	—,2-hydroxy-3,4,5,6-tetrachloro-	3,4,5,6-Tetrachloro-o-cresol. $C_7H_4Cl_4O$. See t275	245.92	nd (lig)	190	....	....	....			s		s	aa s lig s[h]	B6[2], 333
t534	—,3-hydroxy-2,4,5,6-tetrachloro-	2,4,5,6-Tetrachloro-m-cresol. $C_7H_4Cl_4O$. See t275	245.92	nd (peth)	189–90	....	....	....			s	s	s	os, KOH s	B6[3], 1320
t535	—,4-hydroxy-2,3,5,6-tetrachloro-	2,3,5,6-Tetrachloro-p-cresol. $C_7H_4Cl_4O$. See t275	245.92	nd (dil al, aa, bz-lig) λ^{chl} 295 (3.4)	190	....	....	....			s		s	chl, alk v aa s lig δ	B6[3], 1377
t536	—,2-hydroxy-3,4,5-trinitro-	4,5,6-Trinitro-o-cresol. $C_7H_5N_3O_7$. See t275	243.13	og-ye pr (ace)	102	....	....	....	δ[h]	s	s	s	...	chl, AcOEt v	B6, 369
t537	—,3-hydroxy-2,4,6-trinitro-	Methylpicric acid. $C_7H_5N_3O_7$. See t275	243.13	pa ye nd (w or al) λ^{iso} 257 (4.00), 335 (3.54)	109–10	150 exp	....	....	δ[h]	s	s	s	s	chl s	B6[3], 1331
t538	—,α-iodo-	Benzyl iodide. $C_6H_5CH_2I$ ...	218.04	col or ye nd (MeOH)	24.5	93[10]	1.7335^{25}	1.6334^{25}	i	s	s	...	s	MeOH s[h] CS_2 δ	B5[3], 724
Ω t539	—,2-iodo-	o-Tolyl iodide. C_7H_7I. See t275	218.04	λ^{cy} 232 (4.07)	....	211–2[760] 73–5[7]	1.713_4^{20}	1.6079^{20}	i	∞	∞	...	...		B5[3], 720
Ω t540	—,3-iodo-	m-Tolyl iodide. C_7H_7I. See t275	218.04	λ^{hx} 260 (2.93), 297 (2.78)	−27.2	213[760] 80–2[10]	1.705^{20}	1.6053^{20}	i	∞	∞	...	...		B5[3], 721
Ω t541	—,4-iodo-	p-Tolyl iodide. C_7H_7I. See t275	218.04	lf (al) λ^{hx} 262 (3.06), 280 (2.85)	36–7	211 sub	1.678_4^{40}		i	s	s	ace	...	CS_2 s	B5[3], 722
t542	—,α-isocyano-	Benzyl isocyanide. Benzyl carbylamine. $C_6H_5CH_2NC$	117.15	λ^{al} 210 (3.90)	....	198–200 δd 93–3[1]	0.972^{15}	....							B12, 1041
Ω t543	—,α-mercapto-	Benzyl mercaptan. $C_6H_5CH_2SH$	124.22	....	....	194–5	1.058^{20}	1.5751^{20}	i	v	v		...	CS_2 s	B6[3], 1573
Ω t544	—,2-mercapto-	o-Toluenethiol. o-Thiocresol. C_7H_8S. See t275	124.22	pl or lf λ^{iso} 236 (3.88), 271 (2.83), 279 (2.86), 280.5 (2.76)	15	194.2[760] 67.1[10]	1.041_4^{20}	1.5702^{20}	i	s	v		...		B6[3], 1279
Ω t545	—,3-mercapto-	m-Toluenethiol. m-Thiocresol. C_7H_8S. See t275	124.22	λ^{iso} 237 (4.89), 281 (3.80), 289.5 (3.52)	< −20	195.1[760] 67.8[10]	1.044_4^{20}	1.5722^{20}	i	s	∞		s		B6[3], 1332
Ω t546	—,4-mercapto-	p-Toluenethiol. p-Thiocresol. C_7H_8S. See t275	124.22	lf (eth or dil al) λ^{cy} 271 (3.3), 278 (3.3)	44	195[760] 67.6[10]	....	....	i	s	v		s		B6[3], 1391
—	—,α-methoxy-	see Ether, benzyl methyl													
Ω t547	—,2-methoxy-	o-Methylanisole. $C_8H_{10}O$. See t275	122.17	λ^{hx} 272 (3.26), 278 (3.25)	....	171.3[760]	0.9851_{15}^{15}	1.5161^{20}	i	s	s		...		B6[3], 1244
Ω t548	—,3-methoxy-	m-Methylanisole. $C_8H_{10}O$. See t275	122.17	λ^{cy} 273 (3.3), 280 (3.3)	....	177.2[760]	0.9697_{23}^{23}	1.5164^{13}	i	s	s	s	s		B6[3], 1297

For explanations, symbols and abbreviations see beginning of table. For structural formulas see end of table.

No.	Name	Synonyms and Formula	Mol. wt.	Color, crystalline form, specific rotation and λ_{max} (log ε)	m.p. °C	b.p. °C	Density	n_D	w	al	eth	ace	bz	other solvents	Ref.
	Toluene														
Ω t549	—,4-methoxy-	p-Methylanisole. $C_8H_{10}O$. See t275	122.17	λ^{cy} 270.5 (3.2), 280 (3.4), 286 (3.3)	....	176.5[760]	0.9689[25/25]	1.5124[19]	i	s	s	...	...	...	B6[3], 1351
Ω t550	—,2(methyl-amino)-	N-Methyl-o-toluidine. $C_8H_{11}N$. See t275	121.18	λ^{al} 244 (4.1), 294 (3.4)	....	207–8[760] 99[17]	0.9769[20/4]	1.5649[20]	i	∞	∞	s	...	...	B12[2], 435
t551	—,3(methyl-amino)-	N-Methyl-m-toluidine. $C_8H_{11}N$. See t275	121.18		....	206–7[760] 120–1[40]		1.5557[25]	i	∞	∞	s	...	...	B12[1], 398
Ω t552	—,4(methyl-amino)-	N-Methyl-p-toluidine. $C_8H_{11}N$. See t275	121.18	λ^{iso} 246 (4.12), 302 (3.35)	....	209–11[761] 102[20]	0.9348[55]	1.5568[20]	i	∞	∞	s	...	...	B12[2], 491
t553	—,α-nitro-	Phenylnitromethane*. $C_6H_5CH_2NO_2$	137.14	ye liq	....	225–7 118–9[16]	1.1598[20/0]	1.5323[20]		...	s	s	...	...	B5[3], 741
Ω t554	—,2-nitro-	$C_7H_7NO_2$. See t275	137.14	(i) nd (ii) cr λ^{al} 259 (3.72)	(i) −9.55 (ii) −2.9	220.4[760] 118[16]	1.1629[20]	1.5450[20]	i	∞	∞	...	...	...	B5[3], 730
Ω t555	—,3-nitro-	$C_7H_7NO_2$. See t275	137.14	pa ye $\lambda^{5\%al}$ 274 (3.86)	16	232.6[760]	1.1571[20/4]	1.5466[20]	i	s	s	...	s		B5[3], 734
Ω t556	—,4-nitro-	$C_7H_7NO_2$. See t275	137.14	orh cr (al, eth) λ^{hx} 265 (4.02)	54.5	238.3[760] 105[9]	1.1038[25/4]		i	s	v	v	v	CCl_4, Py, to, chl, CS_2 v	B5[3], 736
t557	—,2-nitroso-	C_7H_7NO. See t275	121.14	nd or pr λ 286 (3.80)	72.5	....			δ	v	v	...	...	chl v	B5[3], 728
t558	—,3-nitroso-	C_7H_7NO. See t275	121.14	nd λ 282 (3.76)	53.5				i	δ	s	...	...	chl s MeOH s[h] lig δ, s[h]	B5[3], 728
t559	—,4-nitroso-	C_7H_7NO. See t275	121.14	nd (lig) λ^{chl} 745 (1.66)	48.5				i			...	v	chl v lig s[h]	B5[3], 729
t560	—,3-nitro-4-triazo-	$C_7H_6N_4O_2$. See t275	178.15	ye nd or pl (lig or dil al)	38				i	s		...	...	lig s[h]	B5[1], 174
Ω t561	—,2-nitro-α,α,α-trifluoro-	o-Nitrobenzotrifluoride. $C_7H_4F_3NO_2$. See t275	191.11	cr (al)	32.5	216.3[765]			i	v		...	v	aa v	B5[2], 251
Ω t564	—,3-nitro-α,α,α-trifluoro-	m-Nitrobenzotrifluoride. $C_7H_4F_3NO_2$. See t275	191.11	λ^{al} 247 (3.84)	−2.4	202.75[760] 81.6[10]	1.4357[15/4]	1.4719[20]	i	s	s	...	s		B5[2], 251
t565	—,α,α,2,3,4-pentachloro-	$C_7H_3Cl_5$. See t275	264.37	cr (lig)	84	275–85			i			...	δ v[h]	lig δ, s[h]	B5[1], 153
t566	—,α,α,2,3,6-pentachloro-	$C_7H_3Cl_5$. See t275	264.37	nd (MeOH)	83	145–50[12]			i			...	s	MeOH δ	B5[3], 703
t567	—,α,α,2,4,5-pentachloro-	$C_7H_3Cl_5$. See t275	264.37	....	<0	280–1 153–5[15]	1.5956[20/4]	1.5992[20]	i			...	s		B5[1], 153
t568	—,α,α,2,4,6-pentachloro-	$C_7H_3Cl_5$. See t275	264.37	cr (MeOH)	27	158[15]			i			...	...	MeOH s[h]	B5[3], 704
t569	—,2,3,4,5,6-pentachloro-	$C_7H_3Cl_5$. See t275	264.37	nd (bz or peth) λ^{al} 280 (2.38)	224	301				δ[h]	δ[h]	...	s[h]	to s peth s[h] CS_2 δ	B5[3], 703
t570	—,2-propoxy-	Propyl o-tolyl ether. o-Cresyl propyl ether. $C_{10}H_{14}O$. See t275	150.22	....		204.1	0.9517[0/0]			...	...	...	...		B6[3], 1246
t571	—,3-propoxy-	Propyl m-tolyl ether. m-Cresyl propyl ether. $C_{10}H_{14}O$. See t275	150.22	....		210.6	0.9484[0/0]			...	...	...	...		B6[3], 1299
t572	—,4-propoxy-	Propyl p-tolyl ether. p-Cresyl propyl ether. $C_{10}H_{14}O$. See t275	150.22	....		210.4	0.9497[0/0]			...	...	...	...		B6[3], 1354
t573	—,2,3,5,6-tetra-bromo-	$C_7H_4Br_4$. See t275	407.75	nd	116–7	....			i	δ s[h]	...	s	s	os s	B5, 310
Ω t574	—,α,α,α,2-tetra-chloro-	o-Chlorobenzotrichloride. $C_7H_4Cl_4$. See t275	229.92	....	30	264.27[760] 129.5[13]	1.5187[20]	1.5836[20]	i d[h]	...	s	s	s	os s	B5[3], 703
Ω t575	—,α,α,α,3-tetra-chloro-	m-Chlorobenzotrichloride. $C_7H_4Cl_4$. See t275	229.92	....		255 (247–50)	1.495[14]	1.4461[20]	i d[h]	...	s	s	s	os s	B5, 303
Ω t576	—,α,α,α,4-tetra-chloro-	p-Chlorobenzotrichloride. $C_7H_4Cl_4$. See t275	229.92	....		245 108–12[8]		1.4463[20]	i	...	s	s	s	os s	B5, 303
t577	—,α,α,2,5-tetra-chloro-	$C_7H_4Cl_4$. See t275	229.92	cubic cr (chl)	42	....			i	v	v	...	v	os s	B5[3], 702
t578	—,α,α,3,4-tetra-chloro-	$C_7H_4Cl_4$. See t275	229.92	....		257	1.518[22/22]		i	s	s	...	s	aa s	B5[3], 702
t579	—,α,α,3,5-tetra-chloro-	$C_7H_4Cl_4$. See t275	229.92	cr (MeOH or dil aa)	36.5	....			i	s	s	...	s	oos s	B5[3], 703
t580	—,α,2,4,5-tetra-chloro-	$C_7H_4Cl_4$. See t275	229.92	....		273	1.547[20]		i	s	s	...	s	os s	B5, 302
t581	—,2,3,4,5-tetra-chloro-	$C_7H_4Cl_4$. See t275	229.92	nd (MeOH or dil al)	98.1				i	v	s	...	s	os s	B5[2], 233
t582	—,2,3,4,6-tetra-chloro-	$C_7H_4Cl_4$. See t275	229.92	nd (al or eth)	96 (92)	276.5			i	s	s	...	v	CS_2 v	B5[3], 702
t583	—,2,3,5,6-tetra-chloro-	$C_7H_4Cl_4$. See t275	229.92	nd (MeOH)	93–4	sub			i	s	v	...	s	MeOH s[h]	B5[3], 702
—	—,triacetoxy-	see **Toluene, trihydroxy-, triacetate**													
t586	—,3,4,5-triamino-	$C_7H_{11}N_3$. See t275	137.19	col nd (bz), red in air	105					v	v	...	s		B13[2], 147
t587	—,α-triazo-	Benzyl azide. $C_6H_5CH_2N_3$	133.15	....		108[23] 74[11]	1.0655[25/25]	1.53414[25]	i	∞	∞	...	...		B5[3], 773

For explanations, symbols and abbreviations see beginning of table. For structural formulas see end of table.

No.	Name	Synonyms and Formula	Mol. wt.	Color, crystalline form, specific rotation and λ_{max} (log ε)	m.p. °C	b.p. °C	Density	n_D	Solubility						Ref.
									w	al	eth	ace	bz	other solvents	
	Toluene														
t588	—,2-triazo-.......	o-Tolyl azide. $C_7H_7N_3$. See t275	133.15	pa ye liq	< −10	90.5[30]	....	....			s	...	s[h]	....	B5[3], 773
t589	—,3-triazo-.......	m-Tolyl azide. $C_7H_7N_3$. See t275	133.15	....		92.5[31]					s				B5[2], 273
t590	—,4-triazo-.......	p-Tolyl azide. $C_7H_7N_3$. See t275	133.15	....		d 180 80[10]	1.0527[23]₄	....	i	s	s				B5[3], 773
t591	—,α,2,4-tribromo-.	$C_7H_5Br_3$. See t275	328.85	....	40–1		....	....	i		s			oos v	B5[2], 240
t592	—,α,3,5-tribromo-.	$C_7H_5Br_3$. See t275	328.85	pl or nd (al)	96	173[19]	....	....	i	v				os s	B5[3], 719
t593	—,2,3,4-tribromo-.	$C_7H_5Br_3$. See t275	328.85	rh pl (lig-CS_2, aa)	45–6	....	2.456[20]	....	i					aa s[h]	B5[1], 156
t594	—,2,3,5-tribromo-.	$C_7H_5Br_3$. See t275	328.85	mcl pr (eth-to)	53–4	....	2.467[17]	....	i		v				B5[3], 719
t595	—,2,3,6-tribromo-.	$C_7H_5Br_3$. See t275	328.85	mcl pr or lf (lig or chl)	60.5	....	2.471[17]	....	i					lig s[h] chl δ	B5[1], 156
t596	—,2,4,5-tribromo-.	$C_7H_5Br_3$. See t275	328.85	mcl pr (eth-al), nd (al)	113.5	....	2.472[17]	....	i	δ					B5[3], 719
t597	—,2,4,6-tribromo-.	$C_7H_5Br_3$. See t275	328.85	lo nd or mcl pr (eth-AcOEt)	70	290	2.479[17]	....	i	δ	s				B5[3], 719
Ω t598	—,α,α,α-trichloro-.	Benzotrichloride. $C_6H_5CCl_3$.	195.48	λ^{cy} 262 (2.6), 267 (2.7), 274 (2.6)	−4.75	220.6[760] (214) 150[100]	1.3723[20]	1.5580[20]	i	s	s		s		B5[3], 699
t599	—,α,α,2-trichloro-.	o-Chlorobenzylidene chloride. $C_7H_5Cl_3$. See t275	195.48	....		228.5	1.399[15]	....	i					os s	B5, 300
Ω t600	—,α,2,6-trichloro-.	$C_7H_5Cl_3$. See t275	195.48	cr (lig, eth, al-eth)	39–40	117–9[14]				v	v			lig s[h]	C53, 21809
Ω t601	—,α,3,4-trichloro-.	$C_7H_5Cl_3$. See t275	195.48	....	37–7.5	241	....	....	i	s				os s	B5, 300
t602	—,α,3,5-trichloro-.	$C_7H_5Cl_3$. See t275	195.48	cr (MeOH)	36	60[0.35]								MeOH s[h]	C28, 754
t603	—,2,3,4-trichloro-.	$C_7H_5Cl_3$. See t275	195.48	nd (al or MeOH)	43–4	244[760]	....	....	i	s	s	s		oos s	B5[2], 232
t604	—,2,3,5-trichloro-.	$C_7H_5Cl_3$. See t275	195.48	nd (al)	45–6	229–31[757]			i	s		s		os s	B5, 299
Ω t605	—,2,3,6-trichloro-.	$C_7H_5Cl_3$. See t275	195.48	nd (al)	45–6	....			i	s		s		os s	B5, 299
t606	—,2,4,5-trichloro-.	$C_7H_5Cl_3$. See t275	195.48	nd or lf (al)	82.4	229–30[716]			i	s		s		os s	B5[2], 232
t607	—,2,4,6-trichloro-.	$C_7H_5Cl_3$. See t275	195.48	nd (al)	38	....			i	s		s		os s	B5[2], 232
t608	—,3,4,5-trichloro-.	$C_7H_5Cl_3$. See t275	195.48	....	45–5.5	246–7[768]			i	s		s		os s	B5, 299
Ω t609	—,α,α,α-trifluoro-.	Benzotrifluoride. $C_6H_5CF_3$.	146.11	λ^{iso} 250 (2.34), 260 (2.70), 266.5 (2.58)	−29.11	102.06[760] 10[10]	1.1884[20]	1.4146[20]	d	∞	∞	∞	∞	CCl_4 ∞	B5[2], 224
t610	—,α,α,2-tri-hydroxy-, triacetate	Salicylaldehyde triacetate. $C_{13}H_{14}O_6$. See t275	266.25	nd or pl (al or Ac_2O), pr (al)	107	....			i	δ v[h]	s		s	chl, CCl_4 s	B8[2], 41
t610[1]	—,α,α,3-tri-hydroxy-, triacetate	m-Acetoxybenzal acetate. $C_{13}H_{14}O_6$. See t275	266.25	lf (w-al)	76	....			δ	s	s			....	B8, 60
t611	—,α,α,4-tri-hydroxy-, triacetate	p-Acetoxybenzal acetate. $C_{13}H_{14}O_6$. See t275	266.25	pr (eth or lig)	94	....			i s[h]	δ s[h]	v			lig s[h]	B8[1], 530
t611[1]	—,α,2,5-tri-hydroxy-	Gentisyl alcohol. $C_7H_8O_3$. See t275	140.15	nd (chl)	100	sub vac			v	v	v		δ	chl v lig i	H30, 124
Ω t612	—,2,4,5-tri-hydroxy-, triacetate	2,4,5-Triacetoxytoluene. $C_{13}H_{14}O_6$. See t275	266.25	cr (al)	114–5	....			s	s	s			....	B6, 1109
t613	—,2,4,6-tri-hydroxy-, triacetate	2,4,6-Triacetoxytoluene. $C_{13}H_{14}O_6$. See t275	266.25	(i) cr (eth-peth) (ii) nd (peth)	(i) 76 (ii) 58	....			δ[h]	v[h]			v	AcOEt v lig s[h]	B6[3], 6320
t614	—,3,4,5-tri-hydroxy-	5-Methylpyrogallol. $C_7H_8O_3$. See t275	140.15	pa br nd (bz) λ^w 280 (1.6)	129 (125)	sub								s[h]	B6[3], 6320
t615	—,2,3,4-triiodo-...	$C_7H_5I_3$. See t275	469.83	pa br nd (al)	92	....			i	s			s		B5[1], 157
t616	—,2,3,5-triiodo-...	$C_7H_5I_3$. See t275	469.83	og pl (al)	72–3	....			i	δ s[h]					B5[1], 157
t617	—,2,3,6-triiodo-...	$C_7H_5I_3$. See t275	469.83	nd (al)	80.5	....			i	δ					B5[1], 158
t618	—,2,4,5-triiodo-...	$C_7H_5I_3$. See t275	469.83	pa br nd (al)	118–20	....			i	δ					B5[1], 158
t619	—,2,4,6-triiodo-...	$C_7H_5I_3$. See t275	469.83	nd (al or bz)	118–9	300d			i	δ					B5, 317
t620	—,3,4,5-triiodo-...	$C_7H_5I_3$. See t275	469.83	nd (al)	122–3	....			i	s					B5, 317
t621	—,2,3,4-trinitro-...	$C_7H_5N_3O_6$. See t275	227.13	tcl lf (al), pr (ace) $\lambda^{5\%al}$ 238.5 (4.09)	112	....	1.62		i	δ	s	s	s		B5[3], 766
t622	—,2,4,5-trinitro-...	$C_7H_5N_3O_6$. See t275	227.13	yesh pl (ace), pa ye rh bipym (al) $\lambda^{3\%al}$ 237 (4.15)	104	exp 290–300			i	δ	s	s	s	aa e[h]	B5[1], 767
Ω t623	—,2,4,6-trinitro-...	TNT. $C_7H_5N_3O_6$. See t275	227.13	orh (al) λ^{al} 225 (4.36)	82	240 exp	1.654		i	δ s[h]	s	v	v	to, Py v	B5[3], 767
t624	α-Toluenearsonic acid	Benzylarsonic acid. Phenylmethanearsonic acid*. $C_6H_5CH_2AsO(OH)_2$	216.07	nd (al)	167–8	....			δ s[h]	δ s[h]				chl, AcOEt v CS_2 δ CCl_4 δ, s[h]	B16[2], 461
t625	2-Toluenearsonic acid	o-Tolylarsinic acid	216.07	nd (w)	163–4 (160)	....			δ[h]	v					B16[2], 460
t626	3-Toluenearsonic acid	m-Tolylarsinic acid	216.07	nd (w)	150	....			s[h]	s				aa s[h]	B16[2], 460

For explanations, symbols and abbreviations see beginning of table. For structural formulas see end of table.

No.	Name	Synonyms and Formula	Mol. wt.	Color, crystalline form, specific rotation and λ_{max} (log ε)	m.p. °C	b.p. °C	Density	n_D	w	al	eth	ace	bz	other solvents	Ref.
	4-Toluenearsonic acid														
t627	**4-Toluenearsonic acid**	p-Tolylarsinic acid	216.07	nd (w)	d (−w 105−10)				δ v^h	s	...	...	...	aa s^h	B16^2, 460
t628	α-**Tolueneboronic acid**	Benzylboric acid. $C_6H_5CH_2B(OH)_2$	135.96	cr (w or bz)	140 (195−215) 104 (hyd)				δ	s	...	...	s	....	B16^2, 639
t629	**2-Tolueneboronic acid**	o-Tolylboronic acid	135.96	nd or pl (w)	165−8	d				δ	s	s	...	s		B16, 921
t630	**3-Tolueneboronic acid**	m-Tolylboronic acid	135.96	cr (w)	137−40				δ s^h	v	v				B16, 921
t631	**4-Tolueneboronic acid**	p-Tolylboronic acid	135.96	nd (w)	245 (226)				δ v^h		s				B16^2, 638
t632	**2-Toluenesulfinic acid**	o-Tolylsulfinic acid.......	156.22	nd (w)	80	d				s	v	s	s	...	os v	B11^2, 6
t633	**4-Toluenesulfinic acid**	p-Tolylsulfinic acid......	156.22	rh pl or lo nd (w) λ^{a1} 223 (4.05), 262 (3.14)	86−7				s^h	v	v	δ^h			B11^2, 6
t634	—,chloride	p-Toluenesulfinyl chloride...	174.65	nd	54−8	115−20^4			d^h	d^h	...	...	chl s		B11^2, 9
Ω t635	α-**Toluenesulfonic acid, amide**	Benzylsulfonamide. $C_6H_5CH_2SO_2NH_2$	171.22	pr or nd (w), nd (al)	105				v^h	v					B11^2, 73
t636	—,—,N(2-tolyl)-...	....	261.35	cr (dil al)	83					v				alk s	B12^2, 45
t637	—,—,N(3-tolyl)-...	....	261.35	cr (al)	75					v				alk s	B12^2, 47
t638	—,—,N(4-tolyl)-...	....	261.35	pr (al)	113					s^h	s			alk s	B12^2, 52
Ω t639	—,chloride	Benzylsulfonyl chloride. $C_6H_5CH_2SO_2Cl$	190.65	pr (eth), nd (bz)	93				d^h	d^h	v		v		B11^2, 73
t640	**2-Toluenesulfonic acid**	o-Toluenesulfonic acid	172.21	hyg pl (w +2) λ^w 222 (4.0)	67.5	128.8^{25}			v	s	i				B11^2, 39
Ω t641	—,amide	o-Toluenesulfonamide......	171.22	oct (al), pr (w) $\lambda^{0.1N HCl}$ 270 (3.1), 276 (3.0)	156.3				δ	s	δ				B11^2, 39
t642	—,—,N-methyl-	$C_8H_{11}NO_2S$. See t641	185.25	pl (bz-lig)	74−5				δ^h	v	...	v	i	chl v lig δ	B11, 87
t643	—,—,N-phenyl-	$C_{13}H_{13}NO_2S$. See t641...	247.32	pr (dil al)	136				i	v					B12, 566
t644	—,bromide	o-Toluenesulfonyl bromide.. $C_7H_7BrO_2S$. See t640	235.11	cr	13	138^{10}			i d^h	d^h			...	os ∞	B11, 86
Ω t645	—,chloride	o-Toluenesulfonyl chloride. $C_7H_7ClO_2S$. See t640	190.65	....	10.2	154^{36}	1.3383$_4^{20}$	1.5565^{20}	i d^h	s^h	s	s			B11^2, 39
t646	—,2-tolyl ester	$C_{14}H_{14}O_3S$. See t640	262.33	cr (al) λ^{a1} 260 (3.01), 271.5 (3.27), 279.5 (3.16)	50−1					s^h			s		B11, 85
t647	—,3-tolyl ester	$C_{14}H_{14}O_3S$. See t640	262.33	cr (al) λ^{a1} 272 (3.27), 280 (3.17)	60					s^h			s		B11, 85
t648	—,4-tolyl ester	$C_{14}H_{14}O_3S$. See t640	262.33	cr (al) λ^{a1} 272 (3.27), 279.5 (3.14)	70−1					s^h			s		B11, 85
t649	**3-Toluenesulfonic acid**	m-Toluenesulfonic acid	172.21	oil λ^w 222 (3.8), 277 (2.8)	....				v	s	s				B11^2, 23
Ω t650	—,amide	m-Toluenesulfonamide	171.22	pl (w), mcl pr (al) $\lambda^{0.1N HCl}$ 262 (2.9), 270 (3.0), 279 (3.0)	108				δ s^h	s					B11^2, 42
t651	—,—,N-phenyl- ...	m-Toluenesulfonanilide. $C_{13}H_{13}NO_2S$. See t650	247.32	pr (al)	96	....			i	s	s				B12, 566
Ω t652	**4-Toluenesulfonic acid**	p-Toluenesulfonic acid	172.21	hyg pl (w +1), mcl lf or pr λ^w 222 (4.0), 261 (2.5), 272 (2.2)	104−5	140^{20}			v	s	s				B11^2, 43
Ω t653	—,amide	p-Toluenesulfonamide......	171.22	mcl pl (w +2) λ^{a1} 224 (4.08), 263 (2.7), 275 sh (2.5)	138.5−9 (anh) 105 (hyd)				δ	s	δ				B11^2, 55
Ω t654	—,—,N,N-dichloro-	Dichloramine T. $C_7H_7Cl_2NO_2S$. See t653	240.11	pa ye pr (peth-chl)	83				i	s d^h			s	aa, chl, CCl_4 s peth δ	B11^2, 63
Ω t655	—,—,N-ethyl-.....	$C_9H_{13}NO_2S$. See t653	199.27	pl (dil al or lig)	64					s					B11^2, 56
Ω t656	—,—,N-methyl-...	$C_8H_{11}NO_2S$. See t653	185.25	pl (dil al)	78−9		1.340		δ	v	s				B11^2, 56
Ω t657	—,—,N-methyl-N-nitroso-	$C_8H_{10}N_2O_3S$. See t653......	214.25	cr	60				i	v^h	v				B11^1, 29
t658	—,—,N-methyl-N-phenyl-	$C_{14}H_{15}NO_2S$. See t653......	261.35	pl or mcl pr (AcOEt)	95				i	v	v			AcOEt s^h	B12^2, 305
t659	—,—,N-methyl-N(2-tolyl)-	$C_{15}H_{17}NO_2S$. See t653......	275.37	pr (al)	119−20				i	v^h					B12^1, 388
t660	—,—,N-methyl-N(4-tolyl)-	$C_{15}H_{17}NO_2S$. See t653	275.37	pr	60				i	δ	...	...		oos δ	B12^2, 529

For explanations, symbols and abbreviations see beginning of table. For structural formulas see end of table.

No.	Name	Synonyms and Formula	Mol. wt.	Color, crystalline form, specific rotation and λ_{max} (log ε)	m.p. °C	b.p. °C	Density	n_D	w	al	eth	ace	bz	other solvents	Ref.
	4-Toluenesulfonic acid														
t661	—,—,N-phenyl-	p-Toluenesulfonanilide. $C_{13}H_{13}NO_2S$. See t653	247.32	dimorphic, α: tcl β: mcl pr (dil al or bz)	103–4	....			i	v			s^h	aa s	B12[2], 298
t662	, N(2-tolyl)-	$C_{14}H_{15}NO_2S$. See t653	261.35	rh bipym (al), nd (dil aa)	110					s	v	v	v	chl v	B12[2], 452
Ω t663	—,—,N(4-tolyl)-	$C_{14}H_{15}NO_2S$. See t653	261.35	tcl pr or nd (aa)	118–9				..	v^h	...	s	s	chl s	B12[2], 528
Ω t664	—,butyl ester	$C_{11}H_{16}O_3S$. See t652	228.31	λ^{al} 225.5 (4.09), 263 (2.78), 274 (2.70)	....	164–6[6]	1.1319^{20}_4	1.5050^{20}	i	.	s		v		B11[2], 46
Ω t665	—,chloride	p-Toluenesulfonyl chloride. $C_7H_7ClO_2S$. See t652	190.65	tcl (eth or peth)	71	145–6[15]			i	s	s	s	v		B11[2], 54
Ω t666	—,2-chloroethyl ester	$C_9H_{11}ClO_3S$. See t652	234.70	....		210[21]			i						B11[2], 45
t667	—,2-chloropropyl ester	$C_{10}H_{13}ClO_3S$. See t652	248.73	....		216–7[17]	1.2674^{20}_4	1.5225^{21}							B11[2], 45
Ω t668	—,ethyl ester	$C_9H_{12}O_3S$. See t652	200.26	mcl pr (aa, AcOEt) λ^{hp} 257 (2.5), 261 (2.6), 267 (2.6)	34–5	173[15]	1.166^{48}_4	....	i	s	s			aa, AcOEt s^h	B11[2], 45
t669	—,ethylene ester	Ethylene p-toluenesulfonate.	370.44	cr (bz)	128	....									Am 77, 4899
Ω t670	—,isopropyl ester	$C_{10}H_{14}O_3S$. See t652	214.29		21		1.5065^{20}								Am 77, 4899
Ω t671	—,methyl ester	$C_8H_{10}O_3S$. See t652	186.23	mcl lf or pr (eth-lig) λ^{hp} 261 (2.7), 273 (2.6)	28–9	292[760] 140[20]			i	v	s		v	chl v lig δ	B11[2], 44
t672	—,propyl ester	$C_{10}H_{14}O_3S$. See t652	214.29	λ^{al} 225 (4.09), 263 (2.77), 272 (2.93), 274 (2.69)	< −20	189[9] 155[3]	1.144^{20}_4	1.4998^{20}							B11[2], 45
Ω t673	—,2-tolyl ester	$C_{14}H_{14}O_3S$. See t652	262.33	nd λ^{al} 228 (4.13), 264 (3.03), 275 (2.81)	54–5						s^h				B11, 100
t674	—,2,4,6-tribromophenyl ester	$C_{13}H_9Br_3O_3S$. See t652	485.01	cr (al)	113						s^h				B11[2], 47
t675	3-Toluenesulfonic acid, 6-acetamido-, chloride	$C_9H_{10}ClNO_3S$. See t649	247.70	nd (bz)	159				d	d^h			δ s^h		B14[2], 448
Ω t676	2-Toluenesulfonic acid, 4-amino-	$C_7H_9NO_3S$. See t640	187.22	mcl pr (w +1)	d				δ	i					B14[2], 446
t677	—,—,amide	$C_7H_{10}N_2O_2S$. See t641	186.23	nd or pl (w)	164				δ v^h	v^h					B14, 721
t678	—,5-amino-	$C_7H_9NO_3S$. See t640	187.22	pl (w +1)	>275				δ						B14[2], 446
t679	—,6-amino-	$C_7H_9NO_3S$. See t640	187.22	nd (+½w)	130d				δ	i					B14, 723
t680	3-Toluenesulfonic acid, 4-amino-	$C_7H_9NO_3S$. See t649	187.22	lt ye nd (w + ⅓)	132d (hyd)				s						B14[2], 447
t681	4-Toluenesulfonic acid, 2-amino-	$C_7H_9NO_3S$. See t652	187.22	pl, nd or pr (w +1)					δ	i					B14[2], 450
t682	—,—,amide	$C_7H_{10}N_2O_2S$. See t653	186.23	pr (w)	176				δ s^h	δ	i		i		B14, 729
t683	2-Toluenesulfonic acid, 5-isopropyl-, amide	$C_{10}H_{15}NO_2S$. See t641	213.30	pl (al), pr or lf (dil al)	75				$δ^h$	s^h				lig s	B11, 140
t684	3-Toluenesulfonic acid, 4-isopropyl-, amide	$C_{10}H_{15}NO_2S$. See t650	213.30	fl (dil al)	149.9				$δ^h$	v^h	v				B11[2], 84
t685	4-Toluenesulfonic acid, 3-isopropyl-, amide	$C_{10}H_{15}NO_2S$. See t653	213.30	nd (w)	162				$δ^h$	v					B11, 139
t686	2-Toluenesulfonic acid, 4-nitro-, dihydrate	$C_7H_7NO_5S$. $2H_2O$. See t640	253.23	pl (w)	133.5				v	s	s			chl s	B11[1], 23
t687	—,5-nitro-	$C_7H_7NO_5S$. See t640	217.20	pr or pl (w +2)	133.5 (anh) 130 (+2w)				v	v	v			chl v	B11[2], 41
t688	—,4-propyl-, amide	$C_{10}H_{15}NO_2S$. See t641	213.30	pl (dil al or bz)	101–2				v	s			δ s^h	....	B11, 138
—	α-Toluic acid	see **Acetic acid, phenyl-**													
—	Toluic acid	see **Benzoic acid, methyl-**													
—	Toluidine	see **Toluene, amino-**													
—	Toluquinone	see **Benzoquinone, methyl-***													
t689	Tomatidine	$C_{27}H_{45}NO_2$	415.67	pl, $[α]^{20}_D$ +5 (MeOH) $\lambda^{al-con\,sulf}$ 105, 470	210–1						s^h	s			Am 73, . 4018

For explanations, symbols and abbreviations see beginning of table. For structural formulas see end of table.

No.	Name	Synonyms and Formula	Mol. wt.	Color, crystalline form, specific rotation and λ_{max} (log ε)	m.p. °C	b.p. °C	Density	n_D	w	al	eth	ace	bz	other solvents	Ref.
	Tomatine														
t690	**Tomatine**	Lycopersicin. $C_{50}H_{83}NO_{21}$	1034.22	nd (MeOH) $[\alpha]_D^{20} - 30$ (Py)	270				i	s	i	...	...	MeOH, dioxs	C41, 3502
t691	**Torularhodin**	Torulene. $C_{37}H_{48}O_2$	524.80	red nd (MeOH-eth), vt-bk (bz-MeOH)	201–3d				...	δ^h	...	s	...	peth i chl, CS_2, Py s	H42, 867
t692	**α-Toxicarol(dl)**	Hydroxydequelin. $C_{23}H_{22}O_7$	410.43	gr ye pl (al) λ^{al} 273 (4.53), 297 (4.04), 315 sh (4.00)	219–23 (231–2)			1.580	...	δ	...	...	...	peth i chl s^h	J1941, 878
t693	**—(l)**	$C_{23}H_{22}O_7$. See t691	410.43	gr-yesh pl or nd (AcOEt-al) $[\alpha]_D^{20} - 66$ (bz) $[\alpha]_D^{20} + 58$ (ace) λ^{al} 273 (4.53), 297 (4.04), 315 sh (4.00)	125–7				...	...	...	s	...	AcOEt s	J1941, 878
t694	**β-Toxicarol(dl)**	$C_{23}H_{22}O_7$	410.43	pa ye pl (al) λ 675 (4.08)	169–70				...	s^h	...	...	...		J1938, 528
t695	**α-Toxicarol, dihydro-(l)**	$C_{23}H_{24}O_7$	412.45	pa ye pl or rods $[\alpha]_D^{20} - 30$ (bz, c = 5)	179 (206)				...	...	...	...	...		J1940, 1178
t696	**Trasentin, hydrochloride**	Adiphenine. 2(Diethylamino)ethyl diphenylacetate hydrochloride. $(C_6H_5)_2CHCO_2CH_2CH_2N(C_2H_5)_2 \cdot HCl$	347.89	nd	114–5				s	δ	i	...	i		C54, 12062
—	**Traumatic acid**	see 2-Dodecenedioic acid*													
t697	**α,α-Trehalose**	Mycose. $C_{12}H_{22}O_{11}$	342.30	orh cr $[\alpha]_D^{20} + 199$ (w, c = 6)	214–6 (anh) 97 (hyd)		1.58_{24}^{24}		v^h	s^h	i	...	i		B31, 378
t698	**—,dihydrate**	$C_{11}H_{22}O_{11} \cdot 2H_2O$. See t697	378.33	cr (dil al), $[\alpha]_D^{20} + 178.3$ (w, c = 7)	103 (97)				v	s^h	i	...	...		B31, 378
—	**Triacetamide**	see Acetic acid, amide, N,N-diacetyl-													
—	**Triacetin**	see Glycerol, triacetate													
t699	**Triacontane***	$CH_3(CH_2)_{28}CH_3$	422.83	orh (eth, bz)	65.8	449.7^{760} 304^{15}	0.7750_4^{78} 0.8097_2^{20} (suc)	1.4352^{70} 1.4536^{20} (suc)	i	δ^h	s	...	v^h		$B1^3$, 584
t700	**1-Triacontanol***	Myricyl alcohol. $CH_3(CH_2)_{29}OH$	438.83	nd (eth), pl (bz)	88		0.777^{95}		i	s	v	v		oos s^h	$B1^3$, 1850
t701	**1,3,5-Triazine***		81.08	rh λ^{iso} 272 (3.0)	86	114^{760}	1.38		...	s	s	s	...		Am 76, 5646
Ω t701¹	**—,2,4-diamino-***	Formoguanamine. Guanamine. $C_3H_5N_5$. See t701	111.11	nd (w) $\lambda < 205$ (<4.54), 258 (3.56)	329d (315)				s^h	δ	...	...	...		$B26^1$, 65
Ω t702	**—,2,4-diamino-6-phenyl-***	Benzoquanamine. $C_9H_9N_5$. See t701	187.21	nd or pr (al) λ^{al} 249 (4.40)	226–8				...	s	s	...	...		$B26^1$, 69
t703	**—,hexahydro-1,3,5-trinitro-***	Cyclonite. Hexogen. $C_3H_6N_6O_6$. See t701	222.12	orh cr (ace)	205–6		1.82^{20}		i	i	δ	s	i	aa s MeOH, to, AcOEt δ CCl_4, CS_2 i	$B26^2$, 5
Ω t703¹	**—,hexahydro-1,3,5-triphenyl-***	$C_{21}H_{21}N_3$. See t701	315.42	nd (lig), pr (eth or chl-al)	143	185			i	δ	s	s	s	chl, to s	$B26^2$, 3
—	**—,trichloro-***	see Cyanuric acid, trichloride													
—	**—,trihydroxy-***	see Cyanuric acid													
t704	**1,3,5-Triazine-2,4,6-tricarboxylic acid**	Cyanuric tricarboxylic acid. Paracyanoformic acid.	213.11	pw	>250d				δ	i	i	...	i		$B26^2$, 168
t705	**—,triethyl ester**	$C_{12}H_{15}N_3O_6$. See t704	297.27	nd (al)	168	d			i	i δ^h	i	...	i		$B26^2$, 168
t706	**—,trinitrile**		156.11	mcl pr (bz + 1)	119 sub	262^{771} 119^1			d^h	...	...	...	s	CCl_4 s v^h	$B26^1$, 91
Ω t707	**1,2,3-Triazole**	Osotriazole	69.07	hyg cr λ^{al} 210 (3.64)	23	203^{739}	1.1861_4^{25}	1.4854^{25}	s	s	s	s	...	oos s lig i	$B26^1$, 5
Ω t708	**1,2,4-Triazole**	Pyrrodiazole	69.07	pr (w), nd (al, eth, chl or bz) λ^{THF} 216.5 (3.66)	120–1	260	1.132^{153}	1.4854^{25}	v	v	δ	...	δ		$B26^2$, 7
Ω t709	**—,3-amino-**	Amizol. ATA. $C_2H_4N_4$. See t708	84.08	cr (w, al or AcOEt)	159				v	v	i	i	...	chl s	$B26^2$, 76
AcΩ t710	**—,4-amino-**	$C_2H_4N_4$. See t708	84.08	hyg nd (al or chl)	82–3				s	s	...	...	...	AcOEt δ chl, peth δ	$B26^2$, 7
—	**Tribenzoin**	see Glycerol, tribenzoate													
—	**Tributyrin**	see Glycerol, tributanoate													
—	**Tricaproin**	see Glycerol, trihexanoate													
—	**Tricaprylin**	see Glycerol, trioctanoate													

For explanations, symbols and abbreviations see beginning of table. For structural formulas see end of table.

No.	Name	Synonyms and Formula	Mol. wt.	Color, crystalline form, specific rotation and λ_{max} (log ε)	m.p. °C	b.p. °C	Density	n_D	w	al	eth	ace	bz	other solvents	Ref.
	Tricarballylic acid														
—	Tricarballylic acid..	see 1,2,3-Propane-tricarboxylic acid*													
—	Tricarbonimide, trimethyl ester	see Isocyanuric acid, trimethyl ester													
—	Tricetin	see Flavone, 3′,4′,5,5′,7-pentahydroxy-													
Ω t711	Tricosane*	$CH_3(CH_2)_{21}CH_3$	324.64	lf (eth-al)	47.6	380.2^{760} 243^{15}	0.7785_4^{48} 0.7969^{20} (suc)	1.4468^{20} (suc)	i	δ	s	. . .	. . .		B1[2], 141
Ω t712	12-Tricosanone* . . .	Diundecyl ketone. Laurone. $[CH_3(CH_2)_{10}]_2CO$	338.63	lf (al)	69.3	. . . .	0.8086_4^{69}	1.4283^{80}	i	δ	s	δ	s	chl s	B1[2], 7.74
—	Tricyclodecane	see α-Dicyclopentadiene, tetrahydro-													
t713	1,12-Tri-decadiyne*	$HC{:}C(CH_2)_9C{:}CH$	176.31		−3	115.5^{12}	0.8262_4^{21}	1.454^{20}							B1[2], 284
t714	Tridecanal*	$CH_3(CH_2)_{11}CHO$	198.35		14	156^{23} 128^{10}	0.8356_4^{18}	1.4384^{18}	i	s	. . .	. . .		os v	B1[3], 2916
t715	—,oxime*	$CH_3(CH_2)_{11}CH{:}NOH$	213.37	nd (dil al)	80.5	. . . .			i	δ	v		δ	chl v peth δ	B1[2], 769
Ω t716	Tridecane*	$CH_3(CH_2)_{11}CH_3$	184.37		−5.5	235.4^{760} 107^{10}	0.7564_4^{20}	1.4256^{20}	i	v	v	. . .	. . .		B1[3], 547
Ω t717	—,1-amino-* . . .	$CH_3(CH_2)_{12}NH_2$	199.38		27.4	275.8^{760} 140.1^{10}	0.8049_4^{20}	1.4443^{20}	δ	s	s	. . .	. . .		B4[1], 388
Ω t718	—,1-bromo-*	Tridecyl bromide. $CH_3(CH_2)_{12}Br$	263.27		6.2	296^{760} 162^{16}	1.0177_4^{20}	1.4593^{20}	i			. . .		chl v	B1[3], 548
t719	—,1,13-dibromo-* .	$Br(CH_2)_{13}Br$	342.17		8–10	$188{-}92^{13}$ $155{-}7^1$	1.276^{15}	1.4880^{27}	i		s	. . .		chl v	B1[3], 548
t720	1,12-Tri-decanediol*	$CH_3CH(OH)(CH_2)_{11}OH$ . . .	216.37	cr (dil al)	60–1	$188{-}90^8$				v^h				peth δ	B1[2], 563
t721	1,13-Tri-decanediol*	Tridecamethylene glycol. $HO(CH_2)_{13}OH$	216.37	cr (bz)	76.5	$195{-}7^{10}$						s^h		aa v^h	B1[3], 2240
Ω t722	Tridecanoic acid* . .	$CH_3(CH_2)_{11}CO_2H$.	214.35	cr (peth, ace)	44.5–5.5	236^{100} 140.5^1			i	v	v	s		aa v peth s^h	B2[3], 904
t723	—,amide	$CH_3(CH_2)_{11}CONH_2$	213.37	lf (al)	100					v	v	. . .			B2[1], 159
Ω t724	—,methyl ester* . . .	$CH_3(CH_2)_{11}CO_2CH_3$	228.38	fr 6.5		$90{-}5^1$		1.4405^{20}		∞	v	v			B2[3], 905
Ω t725	—,nitrile	1-Cyanododecane. $CH_3(CH_2)_{11}CN$	195.35		9.7	293^{760} 142^{10}	0.8257_4^{20}	1.4378^{20}		v	v	v			B2[3], 906
t726	1-Tridecanol*	Tridecyl alcohol. $CH_3(CH_2)_{12}OH$	200.37	cr (al)	32.5–3.5	152^{14}	0.8223_4^{31}		i	s	s	. . .			B1[3], 1799
Ω t727	2-Tridecanone*	Hendecyl methyl ketone. $CH_3(CH_2)_{10}COCH_3$	198.35		30.5	263^{760} 160^{16}	0.8217_4^{30}	1.4318^{20}	i	v	v	v	v	CCl_4, chl, to, MeOH v	B1[3], 2916
Ω t728	3-Tridecanone*	Ethyl decyl ketone. $CH_3(CH_2)_9COCH_2CH_3$	198.35	pl	31	140^{17}			i			s			B1[3], 2916
Ω t729	7-Tridecanone*	Dihexyl ketone. Enanthone. $CH_3(CH_2)_5CO(CH_2)_5CH_3$	198.35	lf (al)	33	261^{760} 138^{12}	0.825^{30}		i		s	v		chl, lig s	B1[3], 2917
t730	1-Tridecene*	Tridecylene. $CH_3(CH_2)_{10}CH{:}CH_2$	182.35		−13 (−23)	232.8^{760} 104^{11}	0.7658_4^{20}	1.4340^{20}	i	v	v	. . .	s		B1[3], 872
—	Tridecylene	see 1-Tridecene													
t731	1-Tridecyne	$CH_3(CH_2)_{10}C{:}CH$	180.34		. . . . .	94.5^{25}	0.7729_4^{20}	1.4309^{20}	i		s	. . .	s		J1960, 4719
—	Triethanolamine . . .	see Amine, triethyl, 2,2′,2″-trihydroxy-													
Ω t732	Triethylene glycol . .	$HOCH_2CH_2OCH_2CH_2OCH_2CH_2OH$	150.18	hyg liq	−5 (−7.2)	278.3^{760} 165^{14}	1.1274_4^{15}	1.4531^{20}	∞	∞	δ	. . .	∞	to ∞ peth i	B1[3], 2102
t733	—,3-aminopropyl ether	$HOCH_2CH_2OCH_2CH_2OCH_2CH_2OCH_2CH_2CH_2NH_2$	207.27	glassy	−50	184^{10}	1.0682_{20}^{20}	1.4668^{20}	∞	∞					C55, 5935
t734	—,diacetate	$CH_3CO_2CH_2CH_2OCH_2CH_2OCH_2CH_2O_2CCH_3$	234.25		. . . . .	300			∞	∞	∞				B2[3], 309
t735	—,monobutyl ether	$HOCH_2CH_2OCH_2CH_2OCH_2CH_2OCH_2(CH_2)_3CH_3$	206.29		. . . . .	278^{760}	0.9890^{20}	1.4389^{20}	∞	v				MeOH, CCl_4 v	C53, 1154
Ω t736	Triethylene-tetramine	$H_2NCH_2(CH_2NHCH_2)_2CH_2NH_2$	146.24		12	$266{-}7^{760}$ 157^{20}		1.4971^{20}	s^h	s				ac s	B4[3], 542
Ω t737	Triglycine	N(N-Glycylglycyl)glycine. $H_2NCH_2CONHCH_2CONHCH_2CO_2H$	189.17	ns (dil al) λ 186 (4.1)	246d	. . . .			s^h	i	i	. . .			B4[3], 1198
t738	—,N-phthalyl-		319.28	nd (al)	234–5d	. . . .			v^h	v^h	i		i	chl, peth i	B21[2], 358
—	Triglycolamic acid	see Acetic acid, nitrilotri-													
—	Trigonelline	see 3-Pyridinecarboxylic acid, 1-methyl-													
—	Triisovalerin	see Glycerol, tri(3-methyl-butanoate)													
—	Trilaurin	see Glycerol, tridodecanoate													
—	Trimellitic acid	see 1,2,4-Benzenetricar-boxylic acid*													
—	Trimesic acid	see 1,3,5-Benzenetricar-boxylic acid*													

For explanations, symbols and abbreviations see beginning of table. For structural formulas see end of table.

No.	Name	Synonyms and Formula	Mol. wt.	Color, crystalline form. specific rotation and λ_{max} (log ε)	m.p. °C	b.p. °C	Density	n_D	w	al	eth	ace	bz	other solvents	Ref.
	Trimesitic acid														
—	Trimesitic acid	see **2,4,6-Pyridinetricar-boxylic acid**													
t739	Trimethadione.....	3,5,5-Trimethyl-2,4-oxazolidinedione. Tridione.	143.14	cr (50 % MeOH) λ^{MeOH} 226 (2.11)	46–6.5	78–80[5] 71–3[1]			s	v	v	v	v	chl v peth i	C45, 9528
—	Trimethylene glycol	see **1,3-Propanediol***													
—	Trimethylene-imine	see **Azetidine**													
—	Trimethyl-ethenylammonium hydroxide	see **Neurine**													
—	Trimyristin	see **Glycerol**, tritetra-decanoate													
—	Triolein	see **Glycerol**, tri(cis-9-octa-decenoate)													
—	Trional..........	see **Butane**, 2,2-bis(ethyl-sulfonyl)-*													
Ω t741	1,3,5-Trioxane	Metaformaldehyde	90.08	rh nd (eth)	64	114.5[759] sub 46[1]	1.17[65]	....	v	s	s	...	s	CCl$_4$, chl, CS$_2$ s peth i	B19[2], 392
—	—,triimine	see **Cyamelide**													
—	—,2,4,6-tri-ethenyl-	see **Metacrolein**													
—	—,2,4,6-triiso-propyl-	see **Paraisobutyraldehyde**													
—	—,2,4,6-tri-methyl-	see **Paraldehyde**													
—	—,2,4,6-tri-propyl-	see **Parabutyraldehyde**													
—	Tripalmitin	see **Glycerol**, trihexa-decanoate													
—	Triphenylene......	see **9,10-Benzophenan-threne**													
—	Triphenyl methane	see **Methane**, triphenyl-*													
—	Triphosgene.......	see **Carbonic acid**, bis(tri-chloromethyl) ester*													
—	Tripropionin	see **Glycerol**, tripropanoate													
t743	Trisiloxane, octamethyl-	(CH$_3$)$_3$SiOSi(CH$_3$)$_2$OSi(CH$_3$)$_3$	236.54		−80	153[774] 50–2[17]	0.8200[20/4]	1.3840[20]	...	δ	...	...	s	peth s	C54, 8602
t744	—,1,1,3,5,5-penta-methyl-1,3,5-triphenyl-	C$_6$H$_5$Si(CH$_3$)$_2$OSi(CH$_3$)(C$_6$H$_5$)OSi(CH$_3$)$_2$C$_6$H$_5$	422.75	....	....	169[0.7]	1.0227[20/4]	1.5280[20]	i				s	lig s	Am 70, 1116
—	Tristearin	see **Glycerol**, triocta-decanoate													
t745	Trisulfide, diallyl...	CH$_2$:CHCH$_2$S$_3$CH$_2$CH:CH$_2$	178.34		....	112–22[16]	1.0845[15]		i	i	∞				B1, 441
t746	—,diethyl........	CH$_3$CH$_2$S$_3$CH$_2$CH$_3$	154.32	ye λ^{hx} 250 (2.63)	....	96–7[26]	1.114[20]	1.5689[13]							B1[3], 1378
t747	—,dimethyl, hexabromo-	Br$_3$CS$_3$CBr$_3$	599.67	rh pr (eth)	125d	d			i	δ	δ		s	CS$_2$ v chl, peth s	B3[2], 107
t748	—,diphenyl,2,2′-dinitro-	....	340.41	ye nd (al)	175–6					δ				KOH s os δ	B6[3], 1062
—	Tritan	see **Methane**, triphenyl-*													
Ω t749	1,3,5-Trithiane	Trithioformaldehyde.......	138.27	hex (bz), pr (w), nd (al) λ^{al} 240 (3.16)	220 (cor)	sub	1.6374[24/4]		δ s[h]	δ	δ		s	....	B19[2], 393
t750	—,2,4,6-tri-methyl-(α-form)	Trithioacetaldehyde. C$_6$H$_{12}$S$_3$. See t749	180.36	mcl (al, ace) λ 238 (2.91)	101	245–8			i	s	s	s	v	chl v CS$_2$ s	B19[2], 399
t751	—,—(β-form).....	C$_6$H$_{12}$S$_3$. See t749	180.36	rh nd (ace)	126–7	245–8			i	s	s	s	v	chl v	B19[2], 399
Ω t753	—,2,4,6-tri-methyl-2,4,6-triphenyl-	Trithioacetophenone. C$_{24}$H$_{24}$S$_3$. See t749	408.65	nd (al)	122				i	δ s[h]	v	v	...	chl v	B19, 398
t754	—,2,4,6-tri-phenyl-(α-form)	Trithiobenzaldehyde. C$_{21}$H$_{18}$S$_3$. See t749	366.57	nd (bz-al)	167	d			i	δ	δ	δ	s	chl, AcOEt, CS$_2$ s MeOH δ	B19[1], 808
t755	—,—(β-form).....	C$_{21}$H$_{18}$S$_3$. See t749........	366.57	cr (bz or thiophene)	229–30				i	i	δ	δ	s[h]	chl, CS$_2$, AcOEt δ MeOH i	B19[2], 408
—	Trithioacetalde-hyde	see **1,3,5-Trithiane**, 2,4,6-trimethyl-													
—	Trithiobenzalde-hyde	see **1,3,5-Trithiane**, 2,4,6-triphenyl-													
—	Trithiocyanuric acid	see **Cyanuric acid**, thio-													
t756	α-Tritisterol......	C$_{30}$H$_{50}$O	426.74	nd (MeOH-ace), $[\alpha]_D^{20}$ +54.3 (al)	114–5	....	....	....		s				peth, chl s	H20, 424

For explanations, symbols and abbreviations see beginning of table. For structural formulas see end of table.

β-Tritisterol

No.	Name	Synonyms and Formula	Mol. wt.	Color, crystalline form, specific rotation and λ_{max} (log ε)	m.p. °C	b.p. °C	Density	n_D	Solubility						Ref.
									w	al	eth	ace	bz	other solvents	
t757	β-Tritisterol	$C_{30}H_{50}O$ ...	426.74	nd (MeOH) $[\alpha]_D +49.2$ (al)	97	......	......	......		s					H20, 424
t758	Tropacocaine	Benzoyl-ψ-tropeine. $C_{15}H_{19}NO_2$	245.33	pl or tab	49	d	1.0426_4^{100}	1.5080^{100}	δ^h	v	v	...	v	chl, peth, dil ac v	B21², 23
t759	—,hydrochloride ..	$C_{15}H_{19}NO_2 \cdot HCl$. See t758 ..	281.79	pl (al)	283d	......	......	......	s	δ	i				B21, 39
t760	Tropane	2,3-Dihydro-8-methylnor-tropidine.	125.22			167^{760}	0.9259_{15}^{15}	1.4732^{20}	δ^h						B20², 69
t761	Tropeine, benzoyl-		245.33	cr (eth)	41–2 37 ($+\frac{5}{3}$w)	175–80			s	s	s				B21², 17
t763	—,dihydrate	$C_{15}H_{19}NO_2 \cdot 2H_2O$. See t761	281.36	pl (w)	58				s	s	s				B21, 19
—	Tropic acid	see Propanoic acid, 3-hydroxy-2-phenyl-													
—	Tropilidene	see 1,3,5-Cycloheptatriene*													
Ω t764	Tropine	3-Tropanol.	141.22	hyg pl (eth)	64	229^{760}			v	v	s			chl s	B21², 17
t765	Tropinic acid(d) ...		187.20	cr (w or dil al) $[\alpha]_D +14.8$ (w)	253d (rapid htng) 247–8 (slow htng)				s	δ s^h	i		i	aa i	B22, 123
t766	—(dl)	$C_8H_{13}NO_4$. See t765 ...	187.20	nd (dil al)	251d	......	......	......	s	δ s^h	i		i	aa i	B22, 124
t767	—(l)	$C_8H_{13}NO_4$. See t765	187.20	cr (w), $[\alpha]_D^{20}$ -14.8 (w)	243				s	δ s^h	i		i	aa i	B22, 124
Ω t768	Tropinone	3-Tropanone.	139.20	lo nd (peth)	42–4	$224–5^{714}$ 113^{25}	1.9872_4^{100}	1.4598^{100}	s	s	s	s	s	oos v peth s^h	B21², 225
—	Tropolone	see 2,4,6-Cycloheptatrien-1-one, 2-hydroxy-													
—	Tropone	see 2,4,6-Cycloheptatrien-1-one*													
t769	Truxane	Diindene	232.33	pl (peth) λ^{diox} 273 (4.92), 297 (4.82), 335 (2.84)	116					v^h	v			aa v peth s^h	B5², 606
t770	—,tetraphenyl-	Dimer of triphenylallene	536.73	lf (bz-al)	210	......	......	......		δ			s^h	chl v	E14s, 494
t771	α-Truxilline	Cocamine. $C_{36}H_{46}N_2O_6$	658.80	amor pw $[\alpha]_D < 0$	ca. 80				δ	s	s		s	chl s peth δ	B22, 202
Ω t772	Tryptophan(D) ...	α-Amino-β-indolylpropionic acid. $C_{11}H_{12}N_2O_2$	204.23	pl (dil al) λ^w 280 (3.8) $[\alpha]_D^{20} +33$ (w)	281–2				δ s^h	s^h	i			aa δ	C43, 2656
Ωt773	—(DL)	$C_{11}H_{12}N_2O_2$. See t772	204.23	pl (50 % al) λ^w 280 (3.8)	282 (293)				δ s^h	δ	i				B22², 470
Ω t774	—(L)	$C_{11}H_{12}N_2O_2$. See t772	204.23	lf or pl (dil al), $[\alpha]_D^{20} +6.1$ (1N NaOH, p = 11), $[\alpha]_D^{20} -31.5$ (w, c = 0.5) λ^w 280 (3.7)	290–2.5d (278)				δ s^h	s^h	i			aa δ chl i	B22², 466
Ωt775	—,N-acetyl-(DL) ..	$C_{13}H_{14}N_2O_3$. See t772	246.27	pl (dil al) λ^w 279 (3.72)	206–7				s	v				NaOH v	B22², 469
Ωt776	—,—(L)	$C_{13}H_{14}N_2O_3$. See t772	246.27	nd (dil MeOH) $[\alpha]_D^5 +25$ (95 % al, c = 1) λ^w 279 (3.72)	189–90				s	s				alk s	Am 66, 350
t777	—,N-methyl-(DL) .	$C_{12}H_{14}N_2O_2$. See t772	218.26	nd (dil al)	297d				δ s^h	s	i				J1938, 1910
t778	—,—(L)	Abrin. $C_{12}H_{14}N_2O_2$. See t772	218.26	pr (w) $[\alpha]_D^{21} +44.4$ (dil HCl)	295d	......	......	......	δ s^h	s	i				J1938, 1910
—	Tuberculostearic acid	see Octadecanoic acid, 10-methyl-*													
t779	Tuduranine	$C_{18}H_{19}NO_3$	297.36	nd (eth) $[\alpha]_D^{20} -127.5$ (al)	204	......	......	......		s	s	s		os v	C49, 8317
t780	Turanose	3α-D-Glucosido-D-fructose. $C_{12}H_{22}O_{11}$	342.30	μ (w-al or MeOH $+\frac{1}{2}$) $[\alpha]_D^{20} +27.2$ → $+75.8$ (w, c = 4) (mut)	168 (157d) 65–70 ($+\frac{1}{2}$ MeOH)				v	s				MeOH s^h	B31, 454
Ω t781	Tyramine	p-(β-Aminoethyl)phenol. ...	137.18	pl or nd (bz), cr (al), nd (w) λ 535 (2.78)	164–5 165–7ᵃ	$205–7^{25}$			δ s^h	s v^h				δ xyl s to i	B13², 354

For explanations, symbols and abbreviations see beginning of table. For structural formulas see end of table.

C-528

Tyrosine

No.	Name	Synonyms and Formula	Mol. wt.	Color, crystalline form, specific rotation and λ_{max} (log ε)	m.p. °C	b.p. °C	Density	n_D	w	al	eth	ace	bz	other solvents	Ref.
t782	Tyrosine(D)	2-Amino-3(4-hydroxy-phenyl) propanoic acid*	181.19	cr (w) $[\alpha]_D^{25}+10.3$ (1N HCl, c = 4) $\lambda^{w,pH=6}$ 274.5 (3.15)	310–4d	....	....	....	δ^h	...	...	...	...	dil HCl s	B14², 365
Ω t783	—(DL)	$C_9H_{11}NO_3$. See t782	181.19	nd $\lambda^{w,pH=6}$ 274.5 (3.15)	340d (rapid htng) 290–5d (slow htng)	....	....	....	δ δ^h	i	i	...	...	....	B14², 379
Ω t784	—(L)	$C_9H_{11}NO_3$. See t782	181.19	nd (w) $[\alpha]_D^{22}-10.6$ (1N HCl, c = 4) $\lambda^{w,pH=6}$ 274.5 (3.15)	342–4d (sealed tube, rapid htng) 290–5 (slow htng)	sub	....	....	δ^h	i	i	...	...	aa δ	B14², 366
t785	—,amide(L)	$C_9H_{12}N_2O_2$. See t782	180.21	pl or pr (al) $[\alpha]_D^{20}+19.5$ (w)	153–4	....	....	....	s	v	...	...	...	MeOH v	B14, 612
Ω t786	—,ethyl ester(L)	$C_{11}H_{15}NO_3$. See t782	209.25	pr (AcOEt) $[\alpha]_D^{20}+20.4$ (MeOH)	108–9	....	....	....	δ^h	s	δ	...	v^h	MeOH v AcOEt, alk s	B14², 372
t787	—,methyl ester(L)	$C_{10}H_{13}NO_3$. See t782	195.21	pr (AcOEt) $[\alpha]_D^{20}+25.75$ (MeOH)	136–7	....	....	....	δ s^h	s	δ	...	δ	MeOH v AcOEt, alk s	B14², 372
t788	—,3-bromo-(L)	$C_9H_{10}BrNO_3$. See t782	260.09	cr (w + 1), nd (w + 2)	246–9d	....	....	....	δ v^h	...	...	...	...	....	B14², 377
Ω t789	—,3,5-dibromo-(L)	Bromotiren. $C_9H_9Br_2NO_3$. See t782	339.00	nd or pl (w + 2) $[\alpha]_D^{20}-5.5$ (1N HCl, c = 5)	245 (anh)	....	....	....	δ^h s^h	δ	i	...	...	ac, alk s	B14², 377
—	—,diiodo-	see **Iodogorgoic acid**													
t790	—,N-methyl-(L)	Andirine. Surinamine. $C_{10}H_{13}NO_3$. See t782	195.21	nd, $[\alpha]_D^{21}+19.8$ (dil HCl)	257 (d280)	....	....	....	i	δ	i	...	...	NH_4OH v dil ac s	B14¹, 665

For explanations, symbols and abbreviations see beginning of table. For structural formulas see end of table.

No.	Name	Synonyms and Formula	Mol. wt.	Color, crystalline form, specific rotation and λ_{max} (log ε)	m.p. °C	b.p. °C	Density	n_D	w	al	eth	ace	bz	other solvents	Ref.
	Umbellatine														
u1	Umbellatine......	$C_{21}H_{21}NO_8$	415.71	ye nd	206–7				δ s^h	s	...	δ	...	chl δ	C48, 10034
—	Umbellic acid	see Cinnamic acid, 2,4-dihydroxy-													
—	Umbelliferone ...	see Coumarin, 7-hydroxy-													
—	Undecane*........	see Hendecane*													
—	Undecanoic acid*..	see Hendecanoic acid*													
—	Undecanol*.......	see Hendecanol*													
—	Undecanone*......	see Hendecanone*													
—	Undecenoic acid*..	see Hendecenoic acid*													
—	Undecyl alcohol...	see 1-Hendecanol*													
—	Undecylic acid....	see Hendecanoic acid*													
—	Undecyne*........	see Hendecyne*													
Ω u2	Uracil	....	112.10	nd (w) $\lambda^{w,pH=2.4}$205 (3.9), 260 (3.9) $\lambda^{w,pH=7.2}$ 259.5 (3.91) $\lambda^{w,pH=12}$ 284 (3.79)	338	....			δ v^h	v	v	...	...	dil NH_3 s	B24², 168
Ω u3	—,5-amino-......	$C_4H_5N_3O_2$. See u2.	127.11	nd (w) λ^w 225 (4.02), 290 (3.93)	d				i $δ^h$					alk, ac s^h	B24², 266
Ω u4	—,5,6-dihydro-..	Hydrouracil. β-Lactylurea. $C_4H_6N_2O_2$. See u2	114.10	nd (w) λ^{NaOH} 230 (3.91)	275–6				v	s				MeOH, chl s	B24², 140
u4¹	—,5,6-dihydro-5-methyl-	Dihydrothymine. $C_5H_8N_2O_2$. See u2	128.14	(w or al) λ^{NaOH} 230 (3.91)	264–5				v^h	δ					B24¹, 306
Ω u5	—,5-hydroxy-.....	Isobarbituric acid. $C_4H_4N_2O_3$. See u2	128.09	pr (w) λ^w 210 (3.82), 278 (3.72)	d > 300				s					alk s	B24¹, 408
u6	—,1-methyl-.....	$C_5H_6N_2O_2$. See u2.	126.12	pr (w), λ^w 267.5 (3.99)	179				v	v	δ	...	i	alk s	B24², 170
Ω u7	—,3-methyl-.....	$C_5H_6N_2O_2$. See u2.	126.12	pr (al), nd (w) λ^w 278.5 (3.82)	232				v	v^h				dil alk s	B24², 170
Ω u7¹	—,5-methyl-.....	Thymine. $C_5H_6N_2O_2$. See u2	126.12	nd (al), pl (w) λ^w 265 (3.90)	326	sub			δ	δ	δ	...	...		B24, 353
Ω u8	—,6-methyl-.....	$C_5H_6N_2O_2$. See u2.	126.12	oct, pr or nd (w or al) λ^w 260 (4.0)	270–80d				s	s^h	δ	...	...	NH_3 v alk s	B24², 182
Ω u9	—,6-methyl-2-thio-	$C_5H_6N_2OS$. See u2.	142.18	pl (w)	299–303d				i s^h	δ	δ	...	δ	MeOH δ	B24², 183
u10	—,6-methyl-4-thio-	$C_5H_6N_2OS$. See u2.	142.18	ye pr (w) λ^{MeOH} 277 (4.20)	>250d				$δ^h$	δ					B24, 352
Ω u11	—,5-nitro-........	$C_4H_3N_3O_4$. See u2.	157.09	gold nd (al) λ^w 235 (3.90), 338 (4.02)	exp > 300				δ	s^h					B24², 171
Ω u12	—,6-propyl-2-thio-	$C_7H_{10}N_2OS$. See u2.	170.24	pw (w)	219				δ s^h	δ	i	...	i	chl δ	C43, 674
Ω u13	—,2-thio-........	$C_4H_4N_2OS$. See u2.	128.15	pr (w or al) λ^{MeOH} 273 (4.14)	>340d				δ	δ				anh HF s	B24², 171
u14	—,4-thio-........	$C_4H_4N_2OS$. See u2.	128.15	yesh nd or pr (w) λ^w 332 (4.25)	328d (289d)				δ s^h	δ					B24, 323
u15	6-Uracilcarboxylic acid	Orotic acid.	156.10	pr (w + 1) λ^{NaOH} 215 (4.40), 284 (3.77)	347d (322–5)				δ					os i	B25², 249
Ω u16	—,monohydrate...	$C_5H_4N_2O_4 \cdot H_2O$. See u15.	174.11	pr (w)	125–30d				δ s^h		...	i	i	os i	B25², 249
—	Uramil..........	see Barbituric acid, 5-amino-													
Ω u17	Uranin..........	Sodium salt of fluorescein.	376.28	yc pw λ^w 478 (4.51), 490 ah (3.59)					s	δ				glycerol, dil ace s	B19¹, 252
—	p-Urazine	see Diurea													
Ω u18	Urea*..........	Carbamide. Carbonyl diamide. H_2NCONH_2	60.06	tetr pr (al) λ^{NaOH} <220	135	d	1.3230²⁰	1.484 (1.602)	v	v	i	...	i	chl i MeOH v abs al, aa, Py s	B3², 35
Ω u19	—,nitrate*.......	$H_2NCONH_2 \cdot HNO_3$	123.07	mcl lf (w)	157d		1.690₄²⁰		δ v^h	s	i	...	i	chl i HNO_3 δ	B3², 45
u20	—,oxalate.......	$2(H_2NCONH_2) \cdot HO_2CCO_2H$	210.15	mcl (w + 1)	173d		1.585		s	δ	i				B3², 48
u21	—,1-acetyl-......	$CH_3CONHCONH_2$	102.09	nd (al) λ^{NaOH} 222 (3.11)	218	180 90 sub			δ s^h	s	δ				B3², 49
u22	—,1-acetyl-3-methyl-	$CH_3CONHCONHCH_3$	116.13	tcl (w, al or AcOEt), pr (w)	180–1	d			s v^h	δ	δ				B4², 568

For explanations, symbols and abbreviations see beginning of table. For structural formulas see end of table.

No.	Name	Synonyms and Formula	Mol. wt.	Color, crystalline form, specific rotation and λ_{max} (log ε)	m.p. °C	b.p. °C	Density	n_D	Solubility						Ref.
									w	al	eth	ace	bz	other solvents	
	Urea														
Ω u23	—,1-acetyl-2-thio-	N(Thiocarbamyl)acetamide. $CH_3CONHCSNH_2$	118.16	pr (w), rh (al)	165	....	....	....	δ s^h	s	δ	....	....	dil NaOH	B3², 131
u24	—,S-acetyl-2-thio-, hydrochloride	$H_2NC(:NH)SCOCH_3$.HCl..	154.62	pl	109d	....	....	....	v	δ	....	....	....	....	B3², 133
Ω u25	—,1-allyl-	$H_2NCONHCH_2CH:CH_2$	100.13	nd (al)	85	....	....	....	∞	∞	δ	....	....	chl δ peth i	B4², 664
u26	—,1-allyl-3-phenyl-	$C_6H_5NHCONHCH_2CH:CH_2$	176.22	nd (bz)	115–6	....	....	....	δ	s	....	....	s	....	B12, 350
Ω u27	—,1-allyl-2-thio-	$H_2NCSNHCH_2CH:CH_2$	116.20	mcl or rh pr (w) λ^{MeOH} 248 (2.82)	(i) 71 (ii) 78.4	....	1.219^{20}_{20}	1.5936^{78}_a	s	s	δ	....	i	....	B4, 211
u28	—,1(4-aminobenzenesulfonyl)-*	1-Sulfanylurea. Sulfacarbamide.	215.23	(w)	146–8δd	sub 320	....	....	s^h	s^h	....	....	....	alk s	Am 64, 1683
u29	—,1(4-aminobenzenesulfonyl)-2-thio-	1-Sulfamylthiourea. Sulfathiourea.	231.30	pw, la pl (w) λ^w 257 (4.3)	182 (200d)	....	....	....	i	δ s^h	....	....	....	....	Am 68, 761
Ω u30	—,1-benzoyl-	$H_2NCONHCOC_6H_5$	164.18	fl or lf (al)	214.5	....	....	....	s^h	s^h	i	....	....	....	B9², 172
u31	—,1-benzoyl-2-thio-	$H_2NCSNHCOC_6H_5$	180.24	pr (dil al)	171	....	....	....	δ	s	i	....	....	....	B9², 173
Ω u32	—,1-benzyl-	Phthalamic acid. $H_2NCONHCH_2C_6H_5$	150.18	nd (al)	149	d200	....	....	δ s^h	s	i	s	δ	....	B12², 563
u33	—,1-benzyl-2-thio-	$H_2NCSNHCH_2C_6H_5$	166.25	pr (w) λ^w 238 (4.15)	164.5–5.5	....	....	....	i	δ	....	....	....	....	B12², 564
u33¹	—,1,3-bis(2-ethoxyphenyl)-*	$C_{17}H_{20}N_2O_3$. See u71	300.36	pr (dil al)	125	....	....	....		s^h	....	....	....	....	B13², 179
u33²	—,1,3-bis(4-ethoxyphenyl)-*	$C_{17}H_{20}N_2O_3$. See u71	300.36	nd (aa), pr (abs al)	255–6	....	....	....	i	s^h	....	....	....	aa s^h	B13², 254
Ω u34	—,1,3-bis(2,4-dinitrophenyl)-*	$C_{13}H_8N_6O_9$. See u71	392.25	lf or pr (al), nd (con HNO_3)	204	....	....	....	δ	s	δ	....	....	....	B12², 410
Ω u35	—,1,3-bis(hydroxymethyl)-*	N,N'-Dimethylolurea. $HOCH_2NHCONHCH_2OH$	120.12	pr (abs al), pl (w-al)	126 (137–8)	d260	149^{25}		s	δ	i	....	....	MeOH s	B3², 49
u36	—,1,3-bis(1-hydroxy-2,2,2-trichloroethyl)-*	Dichloralurea. EH2. Crag herbicide. $Cl_3CCH(OH)NHCONHCH(OH)CCl_3$	354.83	....	196	....	....	....	i	s	δ	s	i	chl i	B3², 49
Ω u37	—,1(2-bromo-2-ethylbutanoyl)-*	Adalin. Carbromal. Uradal. $H_2NCONHCOCBr(C_2H_5)_2$	237.10	rh (dil al)	118	....	1.544^{25}		δ s^h	....	....	s	s	....	B3², 52
u38	—,1(2-bromo-3-methylbutanoyl)-*	Adabine. Bromoisovalum. Bromural. Pivadorm. $H_2NCONHCOCHBrCH(CH_3)_2$	223.08	nd or lf (to)	154 (160)	sub	1.56^{15}		δ v^h	s v^h	v	s	s	alk v lig i	B3², 51
u39	—,1(2-bromophenyl)-*	$C_7H_7BrN_2O$. See u110	215.06	nd (al)	202	....	....	....	i	δ	....	....	s	chl s	B12, 632
u40	—,1(3-bromophenyl)-*	$C_7H_7BrN_2O$. See u110	215.06	nd (abs al-eth-lig)	164–5	....	....	....		s	....	....	....	os i	B12, 634
Ω u41	—,1(4-bromophenyl)-*	$C_7H_7BrN_2O$. See u110	215.06	nd (bz), (al) λ^{al} 247 (4.40), 276 (3.14)	225–7	d ca. 260 (d 296)	....	....	$δ^h$	v^h	v	....	v	aa v lig δ	B12², 351
Ω u42	—,1-butyl-*	$H_2NCONH(CH_2)_3CH_3$	116.16	ta (w), nd (bz)	96	....	....	....	v	v	....	....	....	....	B4², 634
u43	—,1-sec-butyl-	$H_2NCONHCH(CH_3)CH_2CH_3$	116.16	d forms nd $[\alpha]^{20}_D +24.1$ (al, c = 1.5), $+27.6$ (chl, c = 0.3) dl form: pr. l form: $[\alpha]^{20}_D -27.3$ (w, c = 2)	166(d) 169–70 (dl) 168–9(l)	....	....	....		s	s	....	....	....	B4, 160
Ω u44	—,1-tert-butyl-	$H_2NCONHC(CH_3)_3$	116.16	nd (w or dil al)	191d	sub >100	....	....	s	v	....	....	δ	....	B4¹, 377
u45	—,1-butyl-3-phenyl-2-thio-*	$C_6H_5NHCSNH(CH_2)_3CH_3$	208.33	pr	85(63)	....	....	....			....	....	s	CCl_4 s	B12², 226
u48	—,1(2-chlorophenyl)-*	$C_7H_7ClN_2O$. See u110	170.60	pr (w) λ^{al} 269 (2.8), 283 (2.8)	152	....	....	....	s	v	δ	v	δ	....	B12, 600
u49	—,3(4-chlorophenyl)-1,1-dimethyl-*	CMU Weed killer (Du Pont).	198.65	gy-wh pl (MeOH)	170.5–1.5	....	....	....	i	δ	....	δ	....	....	C51, 16534
u50	—,1(2-chlorophenyl)-2-thio-*	$C_7H_7ClN_2S$. See u112	186.66	nd or pl	146–6.5	....	....	....		v	....	....	s	NH_3 δ	B12², 318
u51	—,1(4-chlorophenyl)-2-thio-*	$C_7H_7ClN_2S$. See u112	186.66	pl or nd (al)	178	....	....	....	i	s^h	....	....	s	....	B12², 329
u52	—,1,3-diacetyl-	$CH_3CONHCONHCOCH_3$	144.14	nd (al, 50 % aa)	154–5	sub d 179–80	....	....	δ	δ	s	s	s	os s	B3², 50
Ω u55	—,1,1-diethyl-*	$H_2NCON(C_2H_5)_2$	116.16	pl (abs eth), nd (eth)	75	$94–6^{0.02}$	....	....	v	v	s	....	v	lig v	B4², 611
Ω u56	—,1,3-diethyl-*	$CH_3CH_2NHCONHCH_2CH_3$	116.16	ta (lig), dlq nd (al)	112.5	263	1.0415	1.4616^{49}	v	v	v	....	....	....	B4², 608
Ω u57	—,1,3-diethyl-1,3-diphenyl-*	$C_6H_5N(C_2H_5)CON(C_2H_5)C_6H_5$	268.36	(al or w) λ^{al} 247 (3.94)	79	....	....	....	i	v	w	....	....	....	B12², 238

For explanations, symbols and abbreviations see beginning of table. For structural formulas see end of table.

Urea

No.	Name	Synonyms and Formula	Mol. wt.	Color, crystalline form, specific rotation and λ_{max} (log ε)	m.p. °C	b.p. °C	Density	n_D	w	al	eth	ace	bz	other solvents	Ref.
u58	—,1,3-diethyl-1,3-diphenyl-2-thio-*	$C_6H_5N(C_2H_5)CSN(C_2H_5)C_6H_5$ 284.43		rh pl (lig), pr (al)	75.5				i	v^h	...	...	...	lig s^h	B12, 424
Ω u59	—,1,3-diethyl-2-thio-*	$CH_3CH_2NHCSNHCH_2CH_3$ 132.23		λ^{MeOH} 234 (3.80), 265 (3.86)	144 (78) d				s	s	v				B4², 610
Ω u60	—,1,1-dimethyl-*	$H_2NCON(CH_3)_2$ 88.12		mcl pr (al or chl)	182		1.255		s	δ	i				B4², 573
Ω u61	—,1,3-dimethyl-*	$CH_3NHCONHCH_3$ 88.12		rh bipym (chl-eth)	108	268–70	1.142		v	v	i				B4², 568
Ω u62	—,1,3-dimethyl-1,3-diphenyl-*	$C_6H_5N(CH_3)CON(CH_3)C_6H_5$ 240.31		pl (al) λ^{al} 244 (3.95)	121	350			v	v	δ	v	δ	chl v, CS_2 δ	B12², 236
Ω u64	—,1,3-dimethyl-2-thio-*	$CH_3NHCSNHCH_3$ 104.19		dlq pl	62 (58)				v	v	δ	v	δ	chl v CS_2, peth i	B4², 573
u65	—,1,1-di(2-naphthyl)-*	$H_2NCON(C_{10}H_7^\beta)_2$ 312.38		nd (al)	192–3						δ		δ	aa δ	B12, 1297
u66	—,1,3-di(1-naphthyl)-*	$C_{10}H_7^\alpha NHCONHC_{10}H_7^\alpha$ 312.38		nd ($PhNO_2$, Py or aa)	296 (280)	sub			δ^h	...	...			Py s $PhNO_2$ s	B12², 692
u67	—,1,3-di(2-naphthyl)-*	$C_{10}H_7^\beta NHCONHC_{10}H_7^\beta$ 312.38		nd (ace, $PhNO_2$, aa)	310				δ^h	δ^h	δ		δ	$PhNO_2$ δ^h i AmOH s aa s^h	B12², 723
u68	—,1,3-di(1-naphthyl)-2-thio-*	$C_{10}H_7^\alpha NHCSNHC_{10}H_7^\alpha$ 328.44		nd ($PhNO_2$), lf (to)	207.5					δ^h			δ	to, $PhNO_2$ s^h CS_2 δ	B12², 696
u69	—,1,3-di(2-naphthyl)-2-thio-*	$C_{10}H_7^\beta NHCSNHC_{10}H_7^\beta$ 328.44		lf (aa, $PhNO_2$) λ^{al} 256 (4.56)	203 (192–3)				δ^h	δ^h	δ^h		δ	os δ	B12², 723
Ω u70	—,1,1-diphenyl-*	Acardite. $H_2NCON(C_6H_5)_2$. 212.25		ta (al) λ^{al} 242 (4.06)	189 d		1.276		δ	s	s			chl s	B12², 241
Ω u71	—,1,3-diphenyl-*	Carbanilide. 212.25		rh bipym, pr (al) λ^{al} 256 (4.56)	238	262⁷⁶⁰d	1.239		δ	δ	s	δ	i	chl δ aa s	B12², 207
u72	—,1,3-diphenyl-1-methyl-*	N-Methylcarbanilide. $C_6H_5NHCON(CH_3)C_6H_5$ 226.28		nd (al or xyl), cr (lig) λ^{al} 242 (4.2), 262 sh (3.8)	106	203–5⁷⁶⁰d			δ^h	δ	v		s	chl s bz-aa v lig i	B12¹, 251
u73	—,1,3-diphenyl-S-methyl-2-thio-	S-Methyl-N,N'-diphenylisothiourea. $C_6H_5N:C(SCH_3)NHC_6H_5$ 242.35		nd (al)	109–10					s^h					B12², 248
u74	—,1,1-diphenyl-2-thio-*	$H_2NCSN(C_6H_5)_2$ 228.32		pr (al)	210d (218)				i	s					B12², 242
Ω u75	—,1,3-diphenyl-2-thio-*	$C_6H_5NHCSNHC_6H_5$ 228.32		lf (al) λ^{al} 273 (4.3)	154 (189)				δ	v	v			chl, olive oil v	B12², 227
u76	—,1,1-dipropyl-2-thio-*	$H_2NCSN(CH_2CH_2CH_3)_2$. 160.28			67										B4, 144
u77	—,1,3-dipropyl-2-thio-*	$CH_3CH_2CH_2NHCSNHCH_2CH_2CH_3$ 160.28		lf (w)	71				δ s^h		s				B4, 143
Ω u78	—,1,3-diiso-propyl-2-thio-*	$(CH_3)_2CHNHCSNHCH(CH_3)_2$ 160.28		nd (w)	141				δ^h						B4, 155
Ω u79	—,1,3-di(2-tolyl)-2-thio-	256.37		nd (al, sub)	165–6	216–8⁷⁶⁰ (sub)			i	s^h	i		s	chl, aa s	B12², 446
u80	—,1,3-di(4-tolyl)-2-thio-	256.37		rh bipym pr	176(cor) (178)				i	δ	s			aa s	B12², 514
u81	—,1(3-ethoxy-phenyl)-*	$C_9H_{12}N_2O_2$. See u110 180.21		nd λ^{al} 240.5 (4.13), 280 (3.41)	112				δ s^h	δ	s		δ		B13, 418
u82	—,1(4-ethoxy-phenyl)-*	Dulcin. $C_9H_{12}N_2O_2$. See u110 180.21		lf (dil al), pl (w) λ^{al} 242 (4.26), 290 (3.30)	173–4 d				δ	s				AcOEt v	B13², 253
Ω u83	—,1-ethyl-*	$H_2NCONHCH_2CH_3$ 88.12		nd (al-eth), (bz)	92.1–0.4 d				v	v	s^h		v^h	abs eth, CS_2 i chl v	B4², 607
Ω u84	—,1-ethyl-1-phenyl-*	$H_2NCON(C_2H_5)C_6H_5$ 164.21		ta (peth), cr (ace) λ^{al} 236 (2.54)	62.3–0.5				s	s	s	s		oos s lig i	B12², 237
Ω u85	—,1-ethyl-3-phenyl-*	$C_6H_5NHCONHCH_2CH_3$. 164.21		nd (dil al) λ^{al} 240 (4.30), 275 (3.02)	104 (99)					s					B12², 205
u86	—,1-ethyl-3-phenyl-2-thio-*	$C_6H_5NHCSNHCH_2CH_3$ 180.27			107 (102)					s^h			s^h		B12², 226
u87	—,1-ethyl-2-seleno-	$H_2NCSeNHCH_2CH_3$ 151.08		nd (al-peth or w)	ca. 125				δ v^h	s^h					B4², 610
u88	—,1-ethylidene-2-thio-*	$H_2NCSN:CHCH_3$ 102.16		(al)	ca. 212d				i	δ s^h	δ			oos i	B3¹, 76
u89	—,1-hydroxy-*	Carbamide oxide. $H_2NCONHOH$ 76.06		nd (al)	141 d				v	δ s^h v^h	i		i		B3², 78
u90	—,1(hydroxy-methyl)-*	Methylolurea. $H_2NCONHCH_2OH$ 90.08		pr (al)	111				v	s^h	i			MeOH, aa s	B3¹, 27
u91	—,1(2-iodo-3-methyl-butanoyl)*	Iodival. α-Iodoisovalerylurea. $H_2NCONHCOCHICH(CH_3)_2$ 270.07		lf (al)	180–1				δ s^h	v	l		δ	dil NaOH s	B3¹, 29

For explanations, symbols and abbreviations see beginning of table. For structural formulas see end of table.

Urea

No.	Name	Synonyms and Formula	Mol. wt.	Color, crystalline form, specific rotation and λ_{max} (log ε)	m.p. °C	b.p. °C	Density	n_D	w	al	eth	ace	bz	other solvents	Ref.
u92	—,isobutyl-	$H_2NCONHCH_2CH(CH_3)_2$	116.16	pr (w), nd (ace)	141				i		i	δ	δ		B4[1], 376
u93	—,1(2-isopropyl-4-pentenoyl)-*	$H_2NCONHCOCH(C_3H_7^i)CH_2CH:CH_2$	184.24	nd (al)	194–4.5				i δ^h	δ v^h	s	s	s	chl, aa v CCl_4, $CS_2\,\delta$	B3[2], 53
u94	—,1(4-methoxy-phenyl)-*	$C_8H_{10}N_2O_2$. See u110	166.18	pl (w) λ^{al} 243 (4.21), 289 (3.23)	168				δ		s				B13[2], 252
Ω u95	—,1-methyl-*	$H_2NCONHCH_3$	74.08	rh pr (w or al)	103	d			v	v	i		i	CS_2, lig s	B4[2], 567
Ω u95[1]	—,1(2-methyl-2-butyl)-*	tert-Amylurea. $H_2NCONHC(CH_3)_2CH_2CH_3$	130.19	mcl (w)	162 (151)				δ						B4[1], 379
u96	—,1(3-methyl-butyl)-*	Isoamylurea. $H_2NCONHCH_2CH_2CH(CH_3)_2$	130.19	pl (dil al)	96 (150)				δ	s	δ				B4[1], 383
u97	—,1-methyl-3(1-naphthyl)-2-thio-*	$C_{10}H_7^\alpha NHCSNHCH_3$	216.31	pl (al)	198 (191–2)					s^h					B12[2], 696
u98	—,1-methyl-1-nitroso-*	$H_2NCON(NO)CH_3$	103.08	col or yesh pl (eth)	123–4d				i v^h	v	v	v	s	chl s	B4[1], 342
u99	—,1-methyl-3-phenyl-2-thio-*	$C_6H_5NHCSNHCH_3$	166.25	ta, pl	112–3					s					B12[2], 225
u100	—,S-methyl-2-thio-	2-Methylthiopseudourea. $H_2NC(:NH)SCH_3$	90.15	lf (ace) $\lambda^{pH=7}$ 220 (4.58), $\lambda^{pH=12}$ 238 (3.74)	79				s	s		s			B3[2], 132
u100[1]	—,—,hydroiodide	S-Methylisothiouronium iodide. $H_2NC(:NH)SCH_3.HI$	218.06	pr	117				v	v					B3, 192
u100[2]	—,—,nitrate	S-Methylisothiouronium nitrate. $H_2NC(:NH)SCH_3.HNO_3$	153.16	(NHO_3)	109–10				s	v				MeOH v $HNO_3\,s^h$	B3[1], 78
u101	—,—,sulfate	S-Methylisothiouronium sulfate. $2[H_2NC(:NH)CSH_3].H_2SO_4$	278.37	nd (al or w)	244d				δ s^h	i s^h					B3[2], 132
Ω u102	—,1-methyl-2-thio-*	$H_2NCSNHCH_3$	90.15	pr λ^w 235 (4.08)	120.5–1.0				v	v	δ				B4[2], 572
Ω u103	—,1(1-naphthyl)-*	$H_2NCONHC_{10}H_7^\alpha$	186.22	nd (al)	219–20				i	v	s				B12, 1238
Ω u104	—,1(2-naphthyl)-*	$H_2NCONHC_{10}H_7^\beta$	186.22	nd (al)	219				i	v^h					B12, 1292
u105	—,1(1-naphthyl)-3-phenyl-2-thio-*	$C_6H_5NHCSNHC_{10}H_7^\alpha$	278.38	lf	162–3					i					B12, 1241
Ω u106	—,1(1-naphthyl)-2-thio-*	$H_2NCSNHC_{10}H_7^\alpha$	202.28	pr (al)	198				i	δ	δ	δ			C42, 4560
Ω u107	—,1(2-naphthyl)-2-thio-*	$H_2NCSNHC_{10}H_7^\beta$	202.28	lf (al)	186					s^h				os δ	B12[2], 723
u108	—,1-nitro-*	$H_2NCONHNO_2$	105.05	pl (al-peth), lf or pr (al)	158.4–.8d	exp			δ d^h	v	v	v	δ	peth, chl δ aa v	B3[2], 99
—	—,1-oxalyl-	see Parabanic acid													B6[1], 91
u109	—,1(2-phenoxy-ethyl)-*	$H_2NCONHCH_2CH_2OC_6H_5$	180.21	nd (w + 2), cr (50 %al)	120–1				s^h	s					B6[1], 91
Ω u110	—,1-phenyl-	Phenylcarbamide.	136.17	nd or pl (w), tab (al) λ^{al} 238 (4.19)	147	238			δ s^h	s^h	δ			AcOEt s	B12[2], 204
Ω u111	—,1(phenyl-acetyl)-	$H_2NCONHCOCH_2C_6H_5$	178.19	(al)	209 (212–6)					s^h					Am 70, 4189
u112	—,1-phenyl-2-thio-*	Phenylthiocarbamide.	152.23	nd (w), pr (al) λ^{al} 245 sh (4.0), 266 (4.19)	154				δ s^h	s				NaOH s	B12[2], 225
u112[1]	—,S-phenyl-2-thio-*	S-Phenylisothiourea. $C_6H_5SC(:NH)NH_2$	152.23	nd (bz)	96–7d								s		B6[1], 146
Ω u113	—,1-propyl-*	$H_2NCONHCH_2CH_2CH_3$	102.14	pr (al)	110				δ	s					B4[3], 261
u114	—,2-seleno-	Selenourea. $H_2NCSeNH_2$	123.02	pr or nd (w)	200d (213d)				s v^h	δ s^h				abs al s^h	B3[1], 87
—	—,1(sulfonamyl-phenyl)-*	see Benzenesulfonic acid, ureido-, amide													
u115	—,1,1,3,3-tetra-ethyl-*	$(C_2H_5)_2NCON(C_2H_5)_2$	172.27		103	209[760] 94–5[12]	0.9192[20]	1.4474[20]	i					alk, aci	B4[2], 611
Ω u116	—,1,1,3,3-tetra-methyl-*	$(CH_3)_2NCON(CH_3)_2$	116.16	λ^{cy} 217.5 (3.29)	–1.2	166–7.2[760] 63–4[12]	0.9687[20]	1.4496[23]	δ	δ	δ				B4[2], 574
u117	—,1,1,3,3-tetra-methyl-2-thio-*	$(CH_3)_2NCSN(CH_3)_2$	132.23	λ^{al} 255.5 (4.23)	78–9	245			s v^h	s	δ				B4[2], 576
Ω u118	—,1,1,3,3-tetra-phenyl-*	$(C_6H_5)_2NCON(C_6H_5)_2$	364.45	rh (bz) λ^{al} 266.5 (4.31)	183		1.222		i	δ^h					B12[2], 242
u119	—,1,1,3,3-tetra-phenyl-2-thio-*	$(C_6H_5)_2NCSN(C_6H_5)_2$	380.52	nd (al or MeOH)	194.5–5.5				i	δ	s		v	con sulf s	B12[2], 242

For explanations, symbols and abbreviations see beginning of table. For structural formulas see end of table.

No.	Name	Synonyms and Formula	Mol. wt.	Color, crystalline form, specific rotation and λ_{max} (log ε)	m.p. °C	b.p. °C	Density	n_D	w	al	eth	ace	bz	other solvents	Ref.
	Urea														
Ω u120	—,2-thio-*	Thiourea*. H_2NCSNH_2	76.12	rh (al) $\lambda^{w,pH=7.4}$ 238 (4.1)	182		1.405		s v^h	s	i				B3², 128
Ω u121	—,2-thio-1(2-tolyl)-		166.25	nd (dil al), (w)	162				v^h	v	δ				B12², 445
u122	—,2-thio-1(3-tolyl)-		166.25	pr (al)	110–1				s^h	δ	δ				B12², 470
Ω u123	—,2-thio-1(4-tolyl)-		166.25	pl (al)	188–9				δ s^h	s^h					B12², 514
u123¹	—,2-thio-1,1,3-trimethyl-*	$CH_3NHCSN(CH_3)_2$	118.20	pr (bz-lig)	87–8				v	v			s	chl s	B4², 576
u124	—,2-thio-1,1,3-triphenyl-*	$C_6H_5NHCSN(C_6H_5)_2$	304.42	nd (al)	152					δ					B12, 432
Ω u125	—,1(2-tolyl)-		150.18	lf (al or w) λ^{al} 236 (4.02), 270 (2.82)	195–6				i $δ^h$	v	v	δ			B12², 444
Ω u126	—,1(3-tolyl)-		150.18	lf (w) λ^{al} 240 (4.25), 277 (2.89)	142				s	v	δ				B12², 470
Ω u127	—,1(4-tolyl)-		150.18	nd (w), pl (w-aa) λ^{al} 240 (4.26), 281 (3.04)	183 (187)				$δ^h$	v	i	s	i		B12², 511
u128	—,1,1,3-tri-methyl-*	$CH_3NHCON(CH_3)_2$	102.14	pr (eth)	75.5(cor)	232.5⁷⁶⁴			s	s	δ		δ		B4¹, 335
Ω u129	1-Ureacarboxylic acid, ethyl ester*	Allophanic acid ethyl ester. $H_2NCONHCO_2C_2H_5$	132.13	nd (w), (bz)	195	d			i s^h	δ	i		δ s^h		B3², 56
u130	—,3-phenyl-, nitrile	1-Cyano-3-phenylurea. $C_6H_5NHCONHCN$	161.17	nd	125					s					B12², 210
—	Urethan	see **Carbamic acid**, ethyl ester													
—	Urethytan	see **Carbamic acid**, methyl ester													
Ω u131	Uric acid	2,6,8-Purinetrione. 2,6,8-Trihydroxypurine. $C_5H_4N_4O_3$.	158.12	rh pr or pl $\lambda^{w,pH=5.5}$ 235 (4.01), 290 (4.04) $\lambda^{w,pH=9.4}$ 292 (4.10)	d	d	1.89		i $δ^h$	i	i			alk v aq Na_2CO_3, glycerol s ac δ	B26², 293
u132	—,1-methyl-	$C_6H_6N_4O_3$. See u131	182.14	nd	400				i^h						B26², 299
u133	—,3-methyl-	$C_6H_6N_4O_3$. See u131	182.14	pr (w + 1) λ^w 241 (2.36), 296 (1.80)	> 350		1.6104²⁵ (anh) 1.6334⁷⁵ (hyd)		$δ^h$	δ				alk s	B26², 299
u134	,7-methyl-	$C_6H_6N_4O_3$. See u131	182.14	pl (w) $\lambda^{w,pH=1}$ 234 (2.07), 286 (1.95) $\lambda^{w,pH=7}$ 238 (1.99), 294 (1.92) $\lambda^{w,pH=14}$ 297 (1.87)	370–80d		1.7064²⁵		$δ^h$					NaOH s	B26², 299
Ω u135	Uridine	3(d)-Ribofuranosidouracil. $C_9H_{12}N_2O_6$.	244.21	nd (aq al) $[\alpha]_D^{20}$ +4 (w) λ^w 262 (4.00) $\lambda^{w,pH=11}$ 262 (3.87)	165				s	s^h				Py s	J1947, 338
u136	Uridylic acid	Uridine-3′-phosphate. $C_9H_{13}N_2O_9P$.	324.19	pr (MeOH) $[\alpha]_D^{20}$ +10.5(w) λ^w 262 (4.02)	202d				v					MeOH s^h	J1940, 746
u137	Urocanic acid	4-Imidazolylacrylic acid. Urocaninic acid. $C_6H_6N_2O_2$.	138.13	pr (w + 2) λ^w 277 (4.27)	cis: 175–6 trans: 218–24 (hyd)				s^h	i	i	s^h			B25², 121
u138	Urochloralic acid	β,β,β-Trichloroethyl-D-glucuronide. $C_8H_{11}Cl_3O_7$.	325.23	nd	142				v	v	δ				B31, 266
—	Uronium, S-methyl-2-thio-, inorganic salt	see **Urea**, S-methyl-2-thio-, inorganic salt													
—	Uropterin	see **Xanthopterin**													
—	Urotropine	see **Hexamethyl-enetetramine**													
—	Ursocholanic acid	see **Cholanic acid**													
u139	Ursodesoxycholic acid	$3\alpha,7\beta$-Dihydroxy-5β-cholanic acid. $C_{24}H_{40}O_4$.	392.58	pl (al) $[\alpha]_D^{20}$ +57 (abs al, c = 2)	203					v	δ				E14, 180

For explanations, symbols and abbreviations see beginning of table. For structural formulas see end of table.

No.	Name	Synonyms and Formula	Mol. wt.	Color, crystalline form, specific rotation and λ_{max} (log ε)	m.p. °C	b.p. °C	Density	n_D	Solubility						Ref.
									w	al	eth	ace	bz	other solvents	
	Ursolic acid														
u140	Ursolic acid	Malol. Prunol. Urson. $C_{30}H_{48}O_3$.	456.72	(i) pr (eth) $[\alpha]_D^{21} +66$ (1N al KOH) (ii) (al) $[\alpha]_D^{21} +72.4$ (MeOH)	(i) 291 (ii) 284.5 –5	. . . .		. . . .	i	δ^h	s	s	. . .	peth, CS_2 i MeOH, chl s aa s^h	**B10**², 202
u141	Usnic acid(d)	Usninic acid. $C_{18}H_{16}O_7$.	344.33	ye orh pr (ace) $[\alpha]_D^{20} +469$ $[\alpha]_D^{16} +509$ (chl, c = 0.7)	204	. . . .		. . . .	i	s	s	δ	. . .	os δ chl s^h aa δ, s^h	**B18**², 241
Ω u142	—(dl)	$C_{18}H_{16}O_7$. See u141	344.33	λ^{al} 234 (4.52), 282 (4.39)	193–4	. . . .		1.710$_\beta$, 1.611$_\alpha$	i	s	s	. . .	. . .	chl s	**B18**², 241
u143	—(l)	$C_{18}H_{16}O_7$. See u141	344.33	$[\alpha]_D^{20} -480$ $[\alpha]_D^{20} -367$ (chl)	203	. . . .		. . . .	i	s	s	. . .	. . .	chl v	**B18**², 241
—	Uvitic acid	see **1,3-Benzenedi-carboxylic acid, 5-methyl-***													
—	Uvitonic acid	see **2,4-Pyridinedicarboxylic acid, 6-methyl-**													
u144	Uzarin	$C_{35}H_{54}O_{14}$.	698.82	pr $[\alpha]_D -27$ (Py)	268–70	. . . .		. . . .	δ	. . .	i	i	. . .	Py v chl i	**E14**, 233

For explanations, symbols and abbreviations see beginning of table. For structural formulas see end of table.

No.	Name	Synonyms and Formula	Mol. wt.	Color, crystalline form, specific rotation and λ_{max} (log ε)	m.p. °C	b.p. °C	Density	n_D	Solubility						Ref.
									w	al	eth	ace	bz	other solvents	
	Vaccenic acid														
—	**Vaccenic acid**	*see* **11-Octadecenoic acid**(*trans*)*													
v1	**Vacciniin**	6-Benzoyl-*D*-glucose. $C_{13}H_{16}O_7$.	284.27	amor (aq ace +1w) $[\alpha]_D^{21}$ +48 (al)	104–6	....	....		s	s	i	s	δ	peth i chl δ AcOEt s	**B31**, 123
—	**Valeraldehyde**	*see* **Pentanal***													
—	**Valeric acid**	*see* **Pentanoic acid***													
—	**Valerolactone**	*see* **Pentanoic acid, hydroxy-**, lactone*													
—	**Valeronitrile**	*see* **Pentanoic acid**, nitrile													
—	**Valerophenone**	*see* **1-Pentanone, 1-phenyl-***													
v2	**Valine**(*D*)	*l*-α-Aminoisovaleric acid. *l*-2-Amino-3-methyl-butanoic acid*. $(CH_3)_2CHCH(NH_2)CO_2H$	117.15	pl (aq al) $[\alpha]_D^{20}$ −29.04 (20 % al)	156–7.5 (293d, sealed tube)	....	....		s	δ	δ	...	δ	....	**B4²**, 853
Ω v3	—(*DL*)	$(CH_3)_2CHCH(NH_2)CO_2H$.	117.15	tcl pl (al)	298d (sealed tube)	sub	1.316		s	δ	δ	...	δ	....	**B4²**, 854
v4	—(*L*)	*d*-α-Aminoisovaleric acid. $(CH_3)_2CHCH(NH_2)CO_2H$	117.15	lf (w–al) $[\alpha]_D^{23}$ +22.9 (20 % al, c = 0.8)	93–6 (315 sealed tube)	....	1.230		s	δ	δ	...	δ	....	**B4²**, 852
v5	—, β-**hydroxy**-(*dl*) ..	*dl*-2-Amino-3-hydroxy-3-methylbutanoic acid. $(CH_3)_2C(OH)CH(NH_2)CO_2H$	133.15	pl (dil al)	240d	....	....		s	i	i	...	i	AcOEt i	**B4²**, 942
—	**Valone**	*see* **1,3-Indandione, 2(3-methylbutyl)-**													
—	**Valylene**	*see* **1-Buten-3-yne, 2-methyl-***													
—	**Vanillic acid**	*see* **Benzoic acid, 4-hydroxy-3-methoxy-**													
—	**Vanillyl alcohol**....	*see* **Toluene,α,4-dihydroxy-3-methoxy-**													
—	**Vanillin**	*see* **Benzaldehyde, 4-hydroxy-3-methoxy-**													
v7	**Vasicine**(*dl*)	Peganine. $C_{11}H_{12}N_2O$.	188.23	nd (al) λ^{al} 285 (3.51)	209–10	....	....		δ	s	δ	s	δ	chl s	**B23²**, 342
v8	—(*l*)	$C_{11}H_{12}N_2O$. *See* v7	188.23	nd (al) $[\alpha]_D^{14}$ −62 (al, c = 2.4), −254 (chl)	211–2	....	....		δ	s	δ	...	δ	chl s	**B23²**, 342
—	**Veratraldehyde**	*see* **Benzaldehyde,3,4-dimethoxy-**													
v9	**Veratramine**	$C_{27}H_{39}NO_2$.	409.62	nd $[\alpha]_D^{19}$ −70 (MeOH) λ^{al} 268 (2.8)	209.5–10.5 (hyd)	....	....			s^h		...	s	dil ac s dil alk i chl s	**C55**, 17675
—	**Veratric acid**	*see* **Benzoic acid, 3,4-dimethoxy-**													
v10	**Veraridine**	3-Veratroylveracerive. $C_{36}H_5NO_{11}$.	673.80	yesh amor $[\alpha]_D^{22}$ +8 (al)	130 (anh) 180 (hyd)	....	....		s^h	s^h	δ	...			**C49**, 569
v11	**Veratrine**	Cevadine. $C_{32}H_{49}NO_9$.	591.75	rh (+2 al) $[\alpha]_D^{17}$ +12.5 (al) λ^{al} 290.5 (2.1)	205d	....	....		i δ^h	s	δ	...		chl s Py v	**C53**, 18148
—	**Veratrole**	*see* **Benzene, 1,2-dimethoxy-***													
—	**Veratrophenone**	*see* **Benzophenone, 3,3′,4,4′-tetramethoxy-**													
v13	**Veratrosine**	Veratramine *D*-glucoside. $C_{33}H_{49}NO_7$. *See* v9	571.76	nd (aqu MeOH) $[\alpha]_D^{24}$ −55 (al-chl, c = 0.94)	242–3d	....	....		i			...			**C39**, 1413
v14	**Verbenone** (*d*)	*d*-4-Piperone. $C_{10}H_{14}O$.	150.22	$[\alpha]_D^{18}$ +249.6 λ^{MeOH} 253 (3.01)	9.8	227–8 103.4¹⁶	0.9978^{20}	1.4993^{18}	s	s	...	s	s	oos s	**B7¹**, 104
v15	—(*l*)	$C_{10}H_{14}O$. *See* v14	150.22	$[\alpha]_D$ −144 (l = 10)	6.5	253.5 (227–8) 100¹⁶	0.9731^{20}	1.4961^{20}	s	s	...	s	s		**E12A**, 515
—	**Vernine**	*see* **Guanosine**													
—	**Veronal**	*see* **Barbituric acid, 5,5-diethyl-**													
—	**Vetivazulene**	*see* **Azulene, 4,8-dimethyl-2-isopropyl-**													
v16	α-**Vetivone**	α-Vetiverone. $C_{15}H_{22}O$	218.34	(peth) $[\alpha]_D$ +238.2 (al, c = 10) λ^{hx} 328 (2.22)	51.5	144.0–4.5²	1.00352_4^{20} (suc)	1.5370^{20}		...	...	s			**E12A**, 436

For explanations, symbols and abbreviations see beginning of table. For structural formulas see end of table.

β-Vetivone

No.	Name	Synonyms and Formula	Mol. wt.	Color, crystalline form, specific rotation and λ_{max} (log ε)	m.p. °C	b.p. °C	Density	n_D	Solubility						Ref.
									w	al	eth	ace	bz	other solvents	
v17	β-Vetivone	β-Vetiverone. $C_{15}H_{22}O$. See v16	218.34	(pentane) $[\alpha]_D^{20} -38.9$ (al, c = 10.6) $\lambda^{hx} 330 (1.52)$	44.5	141–2²	1.0001_4^{20}	1.5309^{20}	...	...	...	s	...	....	E12A, 436
v18	Vicianose	6(β-Arabinoside)D-glucose. $C_{11}H_{20}O_{10}$	312.28	nd (dil al) $[\alpha]_D^{20}$ +56.5 → +39.7 (w) (mut)	ca. 210d	....			s	δ					B31, 371
v19	Vicine	$C_{10}H_{16}N_4O_7$.	304.26	nd (w or dil al, +1w) $[\alpha]_D^{25} -12$ (w, c = 10) $\lambda^{0.1NHCl} 274$ (4.21)	239–42d (anh)				δ	δ	...	...	...	ac v alk v	B31, 163
—	Vinaconic acid	see 1,1-Cyclopropanedicarboxylic acid*													
—	Vinetine	see Oxyacanthine													
—	Vinyl acetate	see Acetic acid, ethenyl ester													
—	Vinyl amine	see Ethene, amino-*													
—	Vinyl bromide	see Ethene, bromo-*													
—	Vinyl chloride	see Ethene, chloro-*													
—	Vinyl ether	see Ether, diethenyl*													
—	Vinyl fluoride	see Ethene, fluoro-*													
—	Vinyl iodide	see Ethene, iodo-*													
—	Violanthrone	see Dibenzanthrone													
v20	Violaxanthin	Zeaxanthin diepoxide. $C_{40}H_{56}O_4$	600.89	red pr (MeOH, al-eth or CS_2) $[\alpha]_{Cd}^{20} +35$ (chl, c = 0.08) $\lambda^{bz} 428 (4.95), 453.5 (5.13), 483 (5.11)$	208	....			...	s	s	...	...	CS_2 s peth i	B30, 99
v21	Violuric acid	Alloxan-5-oxime. 5-Isonitrosobarbituric acid. Oximidomesoxalylurea. $C_4H_3N_3O_4$	157.09	pa ye rh $\lambda^{al} 310 (3.3)$	203–4d	....			δ	s		...	...	....	B24², 304
v22	Visnadin	$C_{21}H_{24}O_7$.	388.42	nd $[\alpha]_D +9$ (al) $\lambda^{al} 323 (4.14)$	85–6	....			i	s	s	...	...	....	Am 79, 3534
v23	Visnagin	5-Methoxy-2-methylfuranochromone. $C_{13}H_{10}O_4$	230.22	nd (w or MeOH) λ^{al} 245 (3.5), 320 (2.6)	144–5				δ	δ		...	...	chl v	C53, 6220
Ω v24	Vitamin A₁	Axerophthol. $C_{20}H_{30}O$	286.46	ye pr (peth) $\lambda^{al} 326 (4.66)$	63–4	137–8¹⁰⁻⁶			i	s	s	s	s	oos v	B6³, 2787
Ω v25	Vitamin B₁	Aneurin. Thiamine hydrochloride. Thiamine chloride. $C_{12}H_{18}Cl_2N_4OS$.	337.27	(i) mcl pl (MeOH-al) (ii) pl (MeOH-al, w-al) $\lambda^{w,pH=8} 235 (4.1), 268 (3.9)$	(i) 233–4 (ii) 250				v	δ	i	δ	i	chl i	Am 74, 2409
—	Vitamin B₂	see Riboflavin													
v26	Vitamin B₆	Adermin. Pyridoxin. $C_8H_{11}NO_3$.	169.18	nd (ace) $\lambda^{al} 286 (3.76)$ $\lambda^{w,pH=6.8} 254 (3.59), 324 (3.86)$	160	sub			v	s	δ	s	...	chl δ	C53, 2225
Ω v27	—,hydrochloride	Adermine hydrochloride. Pyridoxin hydrochloride. $C_8H_{11}NO_3 \cdot HCl$. See v26	205.64	pl (al, ace) $\lambda^{w,pH=7} 253 (3.57), 325 (3.85)$	206–8 (205–12d)	sub			v	δ	i	δ	...	chl i	Am 61, 1245
—	Vitamin C	see Ascorbic acid(l)													
—	Vitamin D₂	see Calciferol													
—	Vitamin E	see Tocopherol													
—	Vitamin K	see 1,4-Naphthoquinone, 2-hydroxy-3-methyl-*													
Ω v28	Vitamin K₁	Natural vitamin K. Phylloquinone. $C_{31}H_{46}O_2$.	450.71	ye visc oil $[\alpha]_D^{20} -0.4$ (bz, 57.5 %) $\lambda^{MeOH} 263 (4.20), 270 (4.22), 328 (3.50)$	−20	140–45¹⁰⁻³ >100–120d	0.967_{25}^{25}	1.5250^{25}	i	s	s	s	s	peth, chl s	Am 76, 4529
—	Vitamin K₃	see 1,4-Naphthoquinone, 2-methyl-*													
—	Vitamin K₆	see Naphthalene, 1,4-diamino-2-methyl-, dihydrochloride*.													

For explanations, symbols and abbreviations see beginning of table. For structural formulas see end of table.

No.	Name	Synonyms and Formula	Mol. wt.	Color, crystalline form, specific rotation and λ_{max} (log ε)	m.p. °C	b.p. °C	Density	n_D	Solubility						Ref.
									w	al	eth	ace	bz	other solvents	
	Vomicine														
v29	Vomicine.........	$C_{22}H_{24}N_2O_4$.	380.45	nd (80 % al), pr (ace) $[\alpha]_D^{22} +80.4$ (al, p = 0.4) λ 266 (3.95), 291 (3 62)	282	....	....	....	...	δ s^h	δ	δ	...	chl v AcOEt s	B27², 795

For explanations, symbols and abbreviations see beginning of table. For structural formulae see end of table.

C-538

No.	Name	Synonyms and Formula	Mol. wt.	Color, crystalline form, specific rotation and λ_{max} (log ε)	m.p. °C	b.p. °C	Density	n_D	w	al	eth	ace	bz	other solvents	Ref.
	Xanthaline														
—	Xanthaline.......	*see* **Papaveraldine**													
Ω x1	Xanthene........	Dibenzo-1,4-pyran. Diphenylmethane oxide. $C_{13}H_{10}O$.	182.23	wh ye lf (al) λ^{cy} 248 (3.9), 283 (3.4), 287 (3.4), 293 (3.3)	100.5	310–2 (315 sub)	....	....	i	δ	s	...	s	aa, chl, lig s	**B17², 72**
Ω x2	—,9-hydroxy-.....	Dibenz-γ-pyranol. Xanthydrol. $C_{13}H_{10}O_2$. *See* x1	198.22	nd (aq al) λ^{al} 290 (3.59), 336 (2.69)	*ca.* 125	....			δ	s	s	...	...	chl s	**B17¹, 72**
Ω x3	—,9-phenyl-.....	$C_{19}H_{14}O$. *See* x1	258.32	(al) λ^{al} 250 (3.91), 284 (3.47)	145.1–5.5					s^h	...	...	s	aa s lig s^h	**B17¹, 38**
Ω x4	9-Xanthene-carboxylic acid	Xanthanoic acid. $C_{14}H_{10}O_3$.	226.24	nd (dil al or MeOH)	223–4					s^h	s	...	...	peth s^h	**B18², 279**
Ω x5	*peri*-Xantheno-xanthene	1,1-Binaphthylene, 2:8′,2:8-dioxide. $C_{20}H_{10}O_2$.	282.30	ye pr (chl)	242	400²⁰⁻²⁵						...	s	chl s^h	**B19², 52**
—	Xantic acid	*see* **Xanthogenic acid**													
Ω x6	Xanthine........	2,6-Purinedione. $C_5H_4N_4O_2$	152.11	yesh pl (w) $\lambda^{w,pH=2}$ 266 (3.96) $\lambda^{w,pH=10}$ 240 (3.91), 277 (3.95)	d	sub			δ	δ	i	...	...	ac, alk s chl i	**B26², 260**
—	—,3,7-dimethyl-...	*see* **Theobromine**													
Ω x7	—,7-methyl-......	Heteroxanthine. $C_6H_6N_4O_2$. *See* x6	166.14	nd (w)	380d	....			δ	i	i	...	...	chl i NH₃ s HCl s^h	**B26², 263**
—	—,1,3,7-trimethyl-.	*see* **Caffeine**													
x9	Xanthione.......	9-Xanthenethione. $C_{13}H_8OS$.	212.28	red nd (al)	156				i	δ	s	...	s		**B17², 382**
—	Xanthogenamide...	*see* **Carbamic acid, thiono-, ethyl ester**													
Ω x10	Xanthogen, diethyl-	Auligen. Lenisarin. $C_2H_5OC(:S)SSC(:S)OC_2H_5$	242.40	ye nd or pl (al)	31.5–32	107–9⁰·⁰⁵	1.2604²⁵	....	i	δ v^h	v	s	v	peth v chl, CS₂ s	**B3², 154**
x11	Xanthogenic acid...	Ethoxydithioformic acid. Ethylxanthogenic acid. Xanthic acid. C_2H_5OCSSH	122.21	unst	fr −53	25d	....	....	δ						**B3², 151**
Ω x12	Xanthone........	Diphenylene ketone oxide. Dibenzopyrone. 9-Xanthenone. $C_{13}H_8O_2$	196.22	nd (al) λ^{al} 260 (4.11), 288 (3.66), 366 (3.85)	174	349–50⁷³⁰ 143–6³			i	s		...	s	chl s peth δ	**B17², 378**
x13	—,1,2-dihydroxy-..	$C_{13}H_8O_4$. *See* x12	228.22	pa ye nd (aq al + 3w)	166–7					s		...	...	Py s	**J1958, 1790**
x14	—,1,3-dihydroxy-..	$C_{13}H_8O_4$. *See* x12	228.22	nd (aq al + 1w)	259	sub				s	δ	...	...	alk v	**B18², 85**
x15	—,1,6-dihydroxy-..	Isoeuxanthone. $C_{13}H_8O_4$. *See* x12	228.22	ye nd (dil al)	245–6				i	s	s	...	...		**B18, 113**
Ω x16	—,1,7-dihydroxy-..	Euxanthone. $C_{13}H_8O_4$. *See* x12	228.22	yel nd (to), pl (al) λ^{al} 263 (4.0), 305 (4.1), 355 (3.8)	240	sub, δd			i	s^h	δ	...	...	con alk s	**B18², 87**
x17	—,1,8-dihydroxy-..	$C_{13}H_8O_4$. *See* x12	228.22	ye lf (bz) λ^{al} 252 (3.90), 334 (3.30), 380 (2.90)	187	....			i	s^h	δ	...	s^h	alk, chl s	**B18², 87**
x18	—,2,3-dihydroxy-..	$C_{13}H_8O_4$. *See* x12	228.22	ye nd (al)	294				i	v	δ	v	v	chl δ aa v	**B18, 116**
x19	—,2,7-dihydroxy-..	β-Isoeuxanthone. $C_{13}H_8O_4$. *See* x12	228.22	ye nd (al or eth)	>330	sub			i	s	s	...	...	alk s	**B18², 88**
x20	—,3,4-dihydroxy-..	$C_{13}H_8O_4$. *See* x12	228.22	pa red-ye nd (dil al + 3w)	240 (anh)				i	v		...	...	alk s sulf s (ye)	**B18², 88**
x21	—,3,6-dihydroxy-..	$C_{13}H_8O_4$. *See* x12	228.22	nd (dil al), pr (sub)	300–50d	sub			i	v	...	...	i	chl δ aa s	**B18¹, 357**
x22	—,1,7-dihydroxy-3-methoxy-	Gentianin. Gentisin. $C_{14}H_{10}O_5$. *See* x12	258.23	ye rh λ^{al} 260 (4.7), 315 (4.2)	266–7	400 sub			i	v	...	...	i	Py s	**B28², 158**
x23	Xanthophyll......	Lutein. Luteol. $C_{40}H_{56}O_2$	568.89	ye or vt pr (eth-MeOH) $[\alpha]_{Cd}$ +160 (chl)	196	....			i	s	s	...	s	peth s	**B30, 94**
Ω x24	Xanthopterin......	2-Amino-4,6-pteridinediol. Uropterin. $C_6H_5N_5O_2$.	179.14	hyg ye amor or og (aa) λ^{alk} 255 (4.25), 392 (3.82)	>410d	98–100¹⁸	1.559	....	i	δ	δ	...	...	NH₃ s alk s (ye)	**B26², 313**
—	Xanthopurrin....	*see* **9,10-Anthraquinone, 1,3-dihydroxy-**													
x25	Xanthotoxin	Ammoidin. 8-Methoxypsoralen. Zanthotoxin. $C_{12}H_8O_4$	216.21	pr (dil al), nd (peth or bz-peth) λ^{al} 249 (4.35), 300 (4.06)	148	....			δ	v^h	δ	δ	...	peth δ	**B19¹, 711**

For explanations, symbols and abbreviations see beginning of table. For structural formulas see end of table.

Xanthotoxol

No.	Name	Synonyms and Formula	Mol. wt.	Color, crystalline form, specific rotation and λ_{max} (log ε)	m.p. °C	b.p. °C	Density	n_D	w	al	eth	ace	bz	other solvents	Ref.
x26	**Xanthotoxol**	8-Hydroxy-4':5', 6:7-furocoumarin. $C_{11}H_6O_4$	202.17	....	251–2	....	....	....	i	...	...	....	....	diox s[h]	**Am 72,** 4826
x27	**Xanthoxyletin**	Alloxanthylethin. Xanthoxylin-N. $C_{15}H_{14}O_4$	258.28	pr (MeOH or peth) λ^{al} 272 (4.33), 348 (4.05)	133	....	....	....	i	s[h]	δ	s	v	alk v chl v	**J1936,** 627
—	**Xanthurenic acid** ...	see **2-Quinolinecarboxylic acid, 4,8-dihydroxy-**													
—	**Xanthuric acid**	see **2-Quinolinecarboxylic acid, 4,8-dihydroxy-**													
—	**Xanthydrol**	see **Xanthene, 9-hydroxy-**													
x28	**Xanthyletin**	2,2-Dimethyl-chromenocoumarin. $C_{14}H_{12}O_3$	228.25	pr λ^{al} 266 (4.34), 348 (4.15)	131.5	140–5[0.1]	....	....		s[h]	...	....	....	peth s[h]	**J1936,** 1828
—	**Xenylamine**	see **Biphenyl, 4-amino-**													
—	**Xylene**	see **Benzene, dimethyl-***													
—	**Xylenol**	see **Benzene, dimethyl(hydroxy)-***													
—	**Xylic acid**	see **Benzoic acid, 2,4-dimethyl-***													
—	**Xylidine**	see **Benzene, amino(dimethyl)-***													
Ω x29	**Xylitol**	Xylit. $C_5H_{12}O_5$.	152.15	(i) rh (al) (metast) (ii) mcl (al) (st)	(i) 61–1.5 (ii) 93–4.5	(ii) 215–7[f]	....	....	v	s	...	....	....	Py s	**B31²,** 604
—	**Xyloquinone**	see **Benzoquinone, dimethyl-***													
Ω x30	**Xylose**(D) (aldehydo form)	Wood sugar. $C_5H_{10}O_5$.	150.13	mcl nd $[\alpha]_D^{20}$ +22.5 (chl)	90–1	....	1.525_4^{20}	....	v	s[h]	δ	....	....	....	**B31,** 47
x31	—,osazone	$C_{11}H_{20}N_4O_3$.	328.38	pa ye nd $[\alpha]_D$ −40.9 (al) λ 310 (4.02), 397 (4.31)	159 (167d)	....	....	....	δ	s	s	s	....	....	**B31,** 61

For explanations, symbols and abbreviations see beginning of table. For structural formulas see end of table.

No.	Name	Synonyms and Formula	Mol. wt.	Color. crystalline form. specific rotation and λ_{max} (log ε)	m.p. °C	b.p. °C	Density	n_D	Solubility						Ref.
									w	al	eth	ace	bz	other solvents	
	Yamogenin														
y1	Yamogenin	$C_{27}H_{42}O_3$.	414.64	pl $[\alpha]_D^{25} - 123$ λ^{sulf} 412 (4.13), 512 (3.40)	201	. . . .	. . . .	. . .	. . .		s^h	. . .	. . .	MeOH s^h	Am 77, 3086
—	Yellow AB	*see* Azo, benzene 1-naphthalene, 2-amino-													
y2	Yobyrine	Yobirine. 1-*o*-Methylbenzyl-9H-pyrid-[3,4-b]indole. $C_{19}H_{16}N_2$.	272.35	nd (dil al) λ^{al} 236 (4.53), 289 (4.23), 338 (3.66), 351 (3.65)	218–9	$150^{0.01}$	. . . .	. . .	. . .	s	s^h	. . .	s^h	chl s	B23², 263
Ω y3	Yohimbine	Corynine. Quebrachine. Hydroergotocin. Aphrodine. $C_{21}H_{26}N_2O_3$	354.45	nd (dil al) $[\alpha]_D^{20} + 108$ (Py, c = 1) λ^{MeOH} 225 (4.7), 275 (3.9)	241	$159^{0.01}$ sub	. . . .	. . .	δ	s	s	. . .	δ s^h	chl s	B25², 201
Ω y4	—,hydrochloride . .	$C_{21}H_{26}N_2O_3 \cdot HCl$. *See* y3 . . .	390.92	orh nd or pl (w or dil HCl), pr (al) $[\alpha]_D^{22} + 103.3$ (w, c = 2)	302	. . . .	. . . .	. . .	s^h	δ	i	i	. . . .		B25², 201
y5	—,nitrate	$C_{21}H_{26}N_2O_3 \cdot HNO_3$. *See* y3	417.47	pr (w)	276	. . . .	. . . .	. . .	v	. . .	. . .	. . .	. . . .		B25², 201
—	Yperite	*see* Sulfide, diethyl, 2,2'-dichloro-													
y6	Yuccagenin	$C_{27}H_{42}O_4$.	430.64	nd (al) $[\alpha]_D^{25} - 113$ λ^{sulf} 345 (3.67), 404 (3.91)	252	. . . .	. . . .	. . .		s^h	s^h	. . .	. . .	diox s	J1956, 1167

For explanations, symbols and abbreviations see beginning of table. For structural formulas see end of table.

No.	Name	Synonyms and Formula	Mol. wt.	Color, crystalline form, specific rotation and λ_{max} (log ε)	m.p. °C	b.p. °C	Density	n_D	Solubility						Ref.
									w	al	eth	ace	bz	other solvents	
	Zagadinine														
z1	**Zagadinine**	$C_{27}H_{43}NO_7$	493.65	orh (al), nd (bz) [α] -45 (chl)	201–4	....	....	......λ.	δ	s^h	δ	...	s^h	ac, chl s alk, lig i	**Am 35,** 258
z2	**Zeaxanthin**	Zeaxanthol. $C_{40}H_{56}O_2$	568.89	ye pr (MeOH), rh (chl-eth) λ^{al} 275 (4.34), 453 (5.12), 480 (5.07)	215.5 (cor)	$226–9^{0.06}$	....	....	i	δ	s	s	s	chl, Py s peth i^h	**B30, 97**
—	**Zymostanone**	*see* **3-Cholestanone**													
z3	**Zymosterol**	$\Delta^{8(14).24(25')}$-Cholestadienol. $C_{27}H_{44}O$	384.65	pl (MeOH), nd [α]$_D^{20}$ $+49$ (chl) λ^{al} 209 (3.54)	110	$160^{0.001}$ sub	....	... ...			...	s^h	...	MeOH s^h chl s	**E14s,** 1559

For explanations, symbols and abbreviations see beginning of table. For structural formulas see end of table.

STRUCTURAL FORMULAS OF ORGANIC COMPOUNDS

In Alpha Numeric as they occur in Organic Compounds Table

a1

a3

a4

a13

a14

a15

a16

a17

a23

a63

a64

a68

a70

a71

a73

a77

a78

a79

a82

a83

a84

a85

a86

a87

a89

a90

a91

a92

a93

a94

a95

a96

a97

a98

a99

a103

a104

a105

a106

a107

a108

a109

a110

a113

a114

a115

a116

a117

a118

a119

a120

a122

a123

a126

a127

a128

a129

a130

a131

a132

a133

a135

a136

a137

a138

a139

a140

a141

a142

a143

a144

a145

a146

a147

a151

a153

a154

a155

a158

CH_3CONH–(ring, NO_2 ortho) **a159**

$CH_3CO_2CH_2$–(furan) **a204**

CH_3CO_2–(naphthalene) **a240**

H_2N–(ring)–CH_2CN **a271**

CH_3CONH–(ring, NO_2 meta) **a160**

CH_3CO_2–(ring)–OH **a213**

CH_3CO_2–(ring, NO_2 ortho) **a243**

$\left(NO_2\text{-(ring)-}NO_2 \right)_2 CHCO_2CH_2CH_3$ **a273**

CH_3CONH–(ring)–NO_2 **a161**

CH_3CO_2–(cyclohexane, $C_3H_7^i$, CH_3) **a218**

CH_3CO_2–(ring)–NO_2 (meta) **a244**

$\left(NO_2\text{-(ring)-}NO_2 \right)_2 CHCO_2CH_3$ **a274**

CH_3CONH–(ring, NO_2, CH_3) **a162**

CH_3O–(ring)–CH_3CO_2 **a220**

CH_3CO_2–(ring)–NO_2 (para) **a245**

(ring, Br)–OCH_2CO_2H **a292**

CH_3CONH–(ring)–$(CH_2)_7CH_3$ **a163**

CH_3CO_2–(naphthalene, CH_3) **a229**

$CH_3CO_2CH_2$–(tetrahydrofuran) **a260**

Br–(ring)–OCH_2CO_2H **a293**

CH_3CONH–(ring, CH_3 ortho) **a166**

CH_3CO_2–(naphthalene, CH_3) **a230**

CH_3CO_2–(ring, CH_3 ortho) **a261**

(ring, Br)–CH_2CO_2H **a295**

CH_3CONH–(ring, CH_3 meta) **a167**

CH_3CO_2–(naphthalene, CH_3) **a231**

CH_3CO_2–(ring)–CH_3 (meta) **a262**

(ring, Br)–CH_2CN **a296**

CH_3CONH–(ring)–CH_3 **a168**

CH_3CO_2–(naphthalene, CH_3) **a232**

CH_3CO_2–(ring)–CH_3 (para) **a263**

Br–(ring)–CH_2CO_2H **a297**

CH_3CO_2–(cyclohexane) **a189**

CH_3CO_2–(naphthalene) **a239**

H_2NCOCH_2O–(ring)–$NHCOCH_3$ **a266**

Br–(ring)–CH_2CO_2H **a298**

CH_3CO_2–(ring, NO_2, NO_2) **a195**

(ring, NH_2)–CH_2CN **a269**

Br–(ring)–CH_2CN **a299**

CH_3CO_2–(ring, NO_2, NO_2) **a196**

H_2N–(ring)–CH_2CO_2H **a270**

Br–(ring)–$CH(OH)CO_2H$ **a300**

a301

a302

a303

a304

a305

a306

a307

a308

a329

a330

a337

a338

a339

a340

a347

a351

a362

a377

a380

a385

a386

a387

a388

a389

a393

a394

a395

a396

a397

a398

a399

a400

a401

a418

a421

a423

a424

a425

a426

a427

a428

a429

a430

In Alpha Numeric as they occur in Organic Compounds Table

NO_2, NO_2 ring—CH_2COCl
a431

OH, ring—CH_2CO_2H, NO_2
a490

HO—ring—CH_2CN
a500

OCH_3, ring—OCH_2CO_2H
a530

NO_2, NO_2 ring—$CH_2CO_2CH_2CH_3$
a432

OH, ring—$CH_2CO_2CH_2CH_3$, NO_2
a491

HO—ring—CH_2CO_2H
a501

CH_3O—ring—OCH_2CO_2H
a531

NO_2, ring—CH_2CO_2H, NO_2
a433

HO—ring—OCH_2CO_2H
a492

HO—ring—CH_2CN
a502

OCH_3, ring—CH_2CO_2H
a532

CH_3—ring—$C_3H_7^i$, $O_2CCH_2CHOC_2H_5$
a447

HO—ring—$OCH_2CO_2CH_2CH_3$
a493

indole ring—CH_2CO_2H, N—H
a505

OCH_3, ring—CH_2CN
a533

OC_2H_5, ring—CH_2CO_2H
a450

HO—ring—OCH_2CO_2H
a494

$CH(CH_3)_2$, ring—OCH_2CO_2H, CH_3
a509

CH_3O—ring—CH_2CO_2H
a534

fluorene ring, CH_2CO_2H
a452

OH, ring—CH_2CO_2H
a495

$C_3H_7^i$—ring—CH_2CONH_2
a510

CH_3O—ring—CH_2CN
a535

furan ring O—CH_2CO_2H
a456

OH, ring—CH_2CONH_2
a496

CH_3—ring—$C_3H_7^i$, OCH_2CO_2H
a513

indole ring—CO_2H, CH_3, N—H
a537

furan ring O—CH_2CN
a457

OH, ring—$CH_2CONHNH_2$
a497

CH_3—ring—$C_3H_7^i$, OCH_2COCl
a514

NO_2, ring—OCH_2CO_2H
a547

I—ring—$CH(OH)CO_2H$
a466

OH, ring—CH_2CN
a498

SH, ring—CH_2CO_2H
a519

NO_2, ring—CH_2CO_2H
a549

CH_3, CH_3 CH—ring—$CH(OH)CO_2H$
a467

HO—ring—CH_2CO_2H
a499

C_2H_5O—ring—$NHCOCH_2OCH_3$
a521

NO_2, ring—CH_2CN
a550

HO, CH_3O—ring—CH_2CO_2H
a489

NO_2, CH_3O—ring—CH_2CO_2H
a529

NO_2, ring—CH_2CO_2H
a551

a552

a553

a554

a556

a562

a586

a588

a595

a597

a598

a599

a600

a601

a602

a603

a604

a609

a635

a636

a645

a719

a721

a727

a741

a742

a743

a744

a745

a/46

a748

a749

a750

a751

a752

a762

a764

a772

a773

In Alpha Numeric as they occur in Organic Compounds Table

a775

a776

$CH_2:CHCH_2S \cdot SCH_2CH:CH_2$

a777

$HOCH_2-C-C-C-C-CH_2OH$ (OH OH OH OH / H H H H)

a778

a781

$HOCH_2-C-C-C-C-CHO$ (OH OH OH OH / H H H H)

a782

a784

a785

a786

a787

a788

a789

$HOCH_2-C-C-C-C-CHO$ (OH OH OH H / H H H OH)

a790

a792

C_6H_5 ... C_6H_5

a793

C_6H_5 ... C_6H_5
C_6H_5 ... C_6H_5

a795

$N(C_2H_5)CH_2C_6H_5$

a799

$N(CH_3)CH_2C_6H_5$

a800

$NHCH_2C_6H_5$

a803

$NHCH_2C_6H_5$

a804

CH_3—$NHCH_2C_6H_5$

a805

NH

a825

CH_2NHCH_2

a840

NH (two indanol groups)

a844

NH

a863

$\left[\quad \right]_2 NH$ (CH_3)

a900

$\left[\quad \right]_2 NH$ (CH_3)

a901

$\left[CH_3 \quad \right]_2 NH$

a902

NH—CH_3·HCl

a903

$NHCH_2CH_2OH$

a908

CH_3—$NHCH_2CH_2OH$

a909

$C_{10}H_7^{\alpha}NH$

a914

$C_{10}H_7^{\alpha}NH$—CH_3

a915

$C_{10}H_7^{\beta}NH$

a916

$C_{10}H_7^{\beta}NH$—CH_3

a917

$\left[\quad CH_2 \quad \right]_3 N$

a935

$\left[CH_3 \quad \right]_2 N$—$CH_3$

a951

$\left[CH_3 \quad \right]_3 N$

a952

a953

a954

a982

a984

a985

a986

a988

a989

a990

a991

a992

a993

a994

a995

a996

a1000

a1003

a1009

a1066

a1112

a1119

a1165

a1193

a1241

a1243

a1244

a1245

a1246

a1247

a1248

a1342

a1349

a1350

a1351

a1352

a1353

a1354

a1377

a1391

a1454

a1358

a1378

a1394

a1455

a1359

a1380

a1397

a1458

a1366

a1398

a1466

a1367

a1382

a1400

a1401

a1467

a1368

a1383

a1444

a1469

a1369

a1386

a1447

a1473

a1372

a1388

a1448

a1476

a1374

a1390

a1453

a1478

a1479

a1513

a1617[1]

a1645

a1480

a1604

a1619[1]

a1647

a1481   a1482   a1483

a1605

a1629

a1648

a1485[1]

a1606

a1634

a1485[2]

a1612

a1636

a1653

a1510

a1613

a1638

a1654

a1511

a1614

a1643

a1655

a1512

a1614[1]

a1644

a1658

b1

b2

b4

b9

STRUCTURAL FORMULAS OF ORGANIC COMPOUNDS (Continued)

In Alpha Numeric as they occur in Organic Compounds Table

b11

b19

b25

b26

b31

b32

b35

b41

b49

b51

b55

b58

b140

b160

b161

b163

b164

b166

b167

b169

b170

b181

b193

b194

b195

b196

b197

b202

b216

b570

b985

b1006

b1014

b1015

b1016

b1016^1

b1021

b1022

b1024

b1025

In Alpha Numeric as they occur in Organic Compounds Table

ClCO—⟨⟩—COCl
b1027

NC—⟨⟩—CN
b1030

H₂NCO—⟨⟩—CO₂H
b1031

NC—⟨⟩—CO₂H
b1032

HO₃S—⟨⟩—SO₃H, NH₂
b1064

HO₃S—⟨⟩—SO₃H, OH
b1065

HO₂C, CO₂H, HO₂C, CO₂H, HO₂C, CO₂H
b1066

HO₂C, CO₂H, HO₂C, HO₂C, CO₂H
b1067

C₆H₅—P(=S)(OC₂H₅)—O—⟨⟩—NO₂
b1073

⟨⟩—SCl
b1078

⟨⟩—SO₂H
b1082

⟨⟩—SO₃H
b1091

⟨⟩—SO₂NH₂
b1093

NH₂, naphthyl—N:N—⟨⟩—SO₃H
b1129

NH₂, naphthyl—N:N—⟨⟩—SO₂H
b1130

NH₂—⟨⟩—SO₂NH—⟨⟩—SO₂NH₂
b1131

HO₂C, CO₂H, HO₂C, CO₂H
b1182

CH₃O₂C, CO₂CH₃, CO₂CH₃, CH₃O₂C
b1184

HO₂C, CO₂H, HO₂C, CO₂H
b1185

HO₂C, CO₂H, CO₂H
b1188

HO₂C, CO₂H, HO₂C, CO₂H
b1190

HO₂C, CO₂H, HO₂C, CO₂H
b1191

HO₃S, SO₃H, HO₃S
b1197

HON NOH
C₆H₅C—CC₆H₅
b1199

NOH HON
C₆H₅C   CC₆H₅
b1200

NOH NOH
C₆H₅C   CC₆H₅
b1201

C₆H₅COCC₆H₅
‖
HON
b1202

C₆H₅COCC₆H₅
‖
NOH
b1203

C₆H₅NIIN NNHC₆H₅
‖   ‖
C₆H₅C—CC₆H₅
b1204

NNHC₆H₅ C₆H₅NHN
‖   ‖
C₆H₅C—————CC₆H₅
b1205

b1206

b1219

b1220

b1221

b1222

b1223

b1224

b1225

b1226

b1227

STRUCTURAL FORMULAS OF ORGANIC COMPOUNDS (Continued)

In Alpha Numeric as they occur in Organic Compounds Table

b1228

b1229

b1231

b1237

b1239

b1244

b1291

b1298

b1300

b1409

b1547

b1548

b1558

b1598

b1605

b1646

b1647

b1648

b1699

b1791

b1799

b1807

b1880

b1944

b1956

b1957

b1958

b1959

b2062

b2066

b2067

b2068′

b2069

b2070

b2072

b2073

b2115

b2116

b2143

b2144

b2145

b2172

b2183

b2199

b2148

b2173

b2185

b2202

b2149

b2186

b2205

b2150

b2174

b2188

b2151

b2175

b2189

b2207

b2161

b2176

b2190

b2208

b2162

b2179

b2191

b2212

b2180

b2192

b2214

b2163

b2181

b2194

b2329

b2169

b2182

b2196

b2197

b2330

b2331

b2332

b2333

b2335

b2341

b2342

b2343

b2345

b2347

b2353

b2354

b2355

b2356

b2359

b2361

b2362

b2363

b2364

b2365

b2366

b2367

b2368

b2369

b2370

b2372

b2373

b2374

b2375

b2376

b2377

b2378

b2379

b2381

b2398

b2414

b2421

b2422

b2423

b2425

b2426

b2427

b2428

b2432

b2433

b2469

$CH_3CH_2CH_2CH \left(\underset{}{\underbrace{}} -OH \right)_2$

b2498

$CH_3CH_2C(CH_3) \left(\underset{}{\underbrace{}} -OH \right)_2$

b2499

b2550

b2551

$\left(\underset{}{\underbrace{}} \right)_2 C(CH_3)CH_2CH_3$

b2554

$CH_3CHCHCH_3$ (epoxide)

b2561

$CH_3CHCHCH_3$ (epoxide)

b2562

$CH_3CH_2CHCH_2$ (epoxide)

b2563

b2620

$CH_3CH_2CH_2CO_2CH_2CO-\underset{}{\underbrace{}}-Br$

b2660

$CH_3CH_2CH_2CO_2-\underset{}{\underbrace{}}$

b2666

$CH_3CH_2CH_2CO_2CH_2-\underset{}{\underbrace{O}}$

b2669

$CH_3CH_2CH_2CO_2CH_2O-\underset{}{\underbrace{}}-\underset{}{\underbrace{}}$

b2684

b2687

$Cl-\underset{}{\underbrace{}}-COCH(OH)CHC(C_6H_5)CO_2H$

b2747

CH_2CHCH_2CN (epoxide)

b2770

$CH_3C(C_6H_5)CHCO_2C_2H_5$ (epoxide)

b2771

b2778

b2793

b2794

b2821

b2823

b2824

$CH_3COCH_2CONH-\underset{}{\underbrace{}}-CH_3$

b2825

$CH_3O-\underset{}{\underbrace{}}-COCH_2CH_2CO_2H$

b2833[1]

b2855

b2925

$CH_3CH_2CH_2CO-\underset{}{\underbrace{}}-CH_3$

b2932

$O_2N-\underset{}{\underbrace{}}-C(CH_3):CHCO_2H$

b3042[1]

b3057

b3065

c7

c8

c20

c21

c22

c64

c85

c178 $OC\left(-O-\underset{CH_3}{\bigcirc}\right)_2$

c23

c70

CH_3O — HO — $CH_2NHCO(CH_2)_4CH:CHCH(CH_3)_2$

c86

c179 $OC\left(-O-\bigcirc-CH_3\right)_2$

c26

c71

$H_2NCO_2-\bigcirc-CH_2-\bigcirc$

c88

c187

c27

c72 SO_3CH_3

$\underset{C_2H_5}{N}-CS_2NH(CH_2)_5CH_3$

c103

c188

c30 CO_2H

c73 CH_2SO_3H

$(CH_3)_2NCS_2-\bigcirc\underset{O_2N}{-NO_2}$

c111

c190

c31

c76 $CH_2CH_2NH_2$

c141

HO HO_2C CH_3 O O HO OH HO $CO(CHOH)_4CH_3$

c191

c34 $=NOH$

c77 $CH_2CH_2NH_2$

c53 CO_2H

c78 CH_3O CH_3O

c166 $OC\left(-O-\bigcirc\right)_2$ CH_3O

c193 $NHCOCH_2CH_2NH_2$ CH_2CHCO_2H

c56 HO_2C CO_2H

c83 CH_3 OH $(CH_2)_4CH_3$ H_3C CH_2 OH

c195 CH_3 CH_3 $[CH:CHC(CH_3):CH]_2CH:CH[CH:C(CH_3)CH:CH]_2$ CH_3 CH_3 H_3C CH_3

c59

c177 $OC\left(-O-\bigcirc\right)_2$ H_3C

c196 $\left[\underset{CH_3}{CH_3\ CH_3}[CH:CHC(CH_3):CH]_2CH:\right]_2$

c63 HO_2C $CONH_2$

c84 CH_3 H_3C H_3C O OH $(CH_2)_4CH_3$

c197 $CH_3\ CH_3$ $[CH:CHC(CH_3):CH]_2CH:CH[CH:C(CH_3)CH:CH]_2$ CH_3 $CH_3\ CH_3$ H_3C

c199

c201

c202

c204

c206

c207

c208

c210

c211

c214

c219

c221

c222

c223

c224

c226

c227

c230

c231

c241

c243

c244

c245

c257

c259

c260

c262

c264

c266

c267

c268

c270

c275

c279

c298

c320

c347

c280

c300

c321

c350

c281

c304

c322

c358

c282

c305

c326

c366 $C_6H_5CH:CHCO_2CH_2CO$—

c368 $C_6H_5CH:CHCO_2$—NHCONH$_2$

c283

c311

c333

c425

c312

c334

c426

c291

c313

c427

c292

c318

c335

c436

c336

c437

c297

c319

c339

c445 C_6H_5OCO, CH_3O_2C N—CH$_3$

c451

c464

c478

c502

c453

c454

c465

c481

c455

c482

c503

c466

c504

c467

c483

c508

c460

c468

c496

c510

c461

c470

c497

c511

c462

c473

c498

c512

c474

c500

c463

c477

c501

c513

c518

c519

c523

c524

c525

c526

c543

c547

c548

c551

c554

c555

c556

c557

c558

c559

c563

c564

c565

c566

c567

c569

c570

c586

c588

c589

c590

c594

c595

c597

c601

c603

c605

c606

c607

c608

c609

c610

c611

c612

c614

c618

c619

c620

c627

c628

c629

c633

c634

c635

c636

c637

c652

c670

c691

c697

c698

c703

c707

c713

c719

c723

c725

c727

c729

c731

c736

c736[1]

c737

c739

c740

c741

c742

c786

c810

c811

c824

c825

c826

c827

c828

c829

c830

c831

In Alpha Numeric as they occur in Organic Compounds Table

c832

c835

c836

c841

c845

c850

c851

c852

c854

c855

c856

c857

c859

c860

c861

c862

c863

c865

c867

c868

c879

c880

c883

c887

c892

c894

c898

c899

c902

c903

c904

c905

c907

c912

c913

c920

c922

c929

c930

c931

c932

c933

c934

c935

c945

c946

c947

c949

d6

d82

d87

d105

d12

d14

d83

d90

d106

d17

d84

d91

d107

d79

d102

d109

d80

d85

d103

d110

d81

d86

d104

d111

d112

d134

d154

d166

d113

d138

d155

d167

d128

d139

d156

d181

d129

d140

d159

d182

d130

d143

d160

d183

d131

d148

d161

d184

d132

d150

d162

d163

d186

d133

d151

d164

d152

d165

d187

d190

d208

d231

d265

d191

d211

d234

d266

d193

d212

d240

d267

d197

d214

d248

d268

d198

d216

d263

d270

d229

d264

d306

e1

e8¹

e11

e15

e2

e5

e10

e12

e30

e32

e43

e68

e79

e33

e53 NO_2—⬡—$CON(CH_3)CH(CH_3)CH(OH)C_6H_5$

e70 H_3C CH_3 / CH_3—C—$CH_2CH_2NH_2$

e81

e34

e54

e71

e82 CH_3—$\overset{H}{\underset{OH}{C}}$—$\overset{OH}{\underset{H}{C}}$—$\overset{OH}{\underset{H}{C}}$—$\overset{OH}{\underset{H}{C}}$—$CH_2OH$

e35

e55 CH_3CO_2

e74

e84 CH_3—$\overset{OH}{\underset{H}{C}}$—$\overset{H}{\underset{OH}{C}}$—$\overset{H}{\underset{OH}{C}}$—$\overset{H}{\underset{OH}{C}}$—$CHO$

e57 HO

e36

e58 CH_3CO_2

e75

e85

e86

e37

e59

e76

e88

e38 C_6H_5—$\left[NH—⬡ \right]_6$—N=⬡=NH

e60

e77

e89 HO HO—⬡—$CH_2CH_2NHCH_3$

e63 HON

e39

e66 $H_2NCONHN$

e78

e90

C-569

STRUCTURAL FORMULAS OF ORGANIC COMPOUNDS (Continued)

In Alpha Numeric as they occur in Organic Compounds Table

e93

e94

e97

e98

e99

e100

e101

e102

e103

e104

e107

e109

e111

e113

e114

e116

e117

e119

e120

e121

e122

e123

e124

e125

e126

e127

e128

e129

e130

e131

e133

e134

e135

e137

e139

$R_1 = CH_3$ or H
$R_2 = H$ or CH_3

e140

$R_1 = CH_3$ or H
$R_2 = H$ or CH_3

e141

e142

$R_1 = CH_3$ or H
$R_2 = H$ or CH_3

e144

e145

e146

e147

$HOCH_2$—C—CH_2OH

e148

e148¹

e148²

e149

e150

e152

$HOCH_2$—C——C—CHO

e154

e158

e159

e160

e161

e177

H_2N——CH_2CH_2——NH_2

e179

e180

e182

$(Cl$——$)_2 CHCHCl_2$

e183

$(Cl$——$)_2 CHCCl_3$

e185

$(CH_3O$——$)_2 CHCCl_3$

e186

e190

e191

e206

e230

In Alpha Numeric as they occur in Organic Compounds Table

$(CH_3-C_6H_4-)_2CHCH_3$
e239

$H_2N-C_6H_4-CH_2CH_2OH$
e345

Br, Br, $OCH_2CH:CH_2$, Br
e434[1]

$C_6H_4-O-C_6H_4$ (3 2 / 2' 3' / 4 5 6 / 6' 5' 4')
e510

$CH_3-C_6H_4-CH_2CH_2-C_6H_4-CH_3$
e240

$(Cl-C_6H_4-)_2C(OH)CH_3$
e346[1]

$CH_3-C_6H_4-OCH_2CH:CH_2$
e436

$C_4H_3O-CH_2OC_2H_5$
e542

$(CH_3-C_6H_4-)_2CHCCl_3$
e240[1]

cyclohexane$-CH(OH)CH_3$
e353

$CH_3-C_6H_4-OCH_2CH:CH_2$
e437

$C_4H_3O-CH_2OCH_3$
e566

CH_2-CH_2 over O
e241

cyclohexane$-CH_2CH_2OH$
e354

$CH_3-C_6H_4-OCH_2CH:CH_2$
e438

$C_4H_3O-O(CH_2)_7CH_3$
e567

$C_6H_5CH-CH_2$ over O
e242

cyclopentane$-CH_2CH_2OH$
e355

$C_6H_5-OCH_2CH:CH_2$
e438

$C_4H_3O-O-C_6H_5$
e568

$CH_3O-C_6H_4-CH(C_6H_5)CH_3$
e254[1]

OCH_3, $C_6H_4-CH(OH)CH_3$
e374

$C_4H_3O-CH_2O(CH_2)_3CH_3$
e456

$CH_2CHCH_2-OCH_3$ over O
e585

NO_2, $C_6H_4-CH_2CH_2-C_6H_4-NO_2$
e258

$CH_3O-C_6H_4-CH(OH)CH_3$
e375

CH_3, $C_6H_4-O(CH_2)_3CH_3$
e464

$O_2S-O-SO_2$ ring with O
e590

$CH_3O-C_6H_4-CH(OH)CH(OH)-C_6H_4-OCH_3$
e301

$CH_3O-C_6H_4-CH(OH)CH_3$
e376

cyclohexane$-O-C_4H_3O$
e466

OH, HO, cyclohexane$-C:C-$cyclohexane
e592

cyclohexane$-CH(OH)CH(OH)-$cyclohexane
e304

CH_3, $C_6H_4-CH(OH)CH_3$
e393

cyclohexane$-OCH_3$
e467

$C_6H_5CO_2$, CO_2CH_3, CH_3, CH_3, CH_3, CH_3, N, CH_3
e604

$C_6H_5-CH(OH)CH(OH)-C_6H_5$
e305

$CH_3-C_6H_4-CH(OH)CH_3$
e394

Br, cyclohexane$-OCH_3$
e468

$C_6H_5CO_2$, CH_3, NH, CH_3, CH_3
e606

$C_4H_3O-COCO-C_4H_3O$
e310

$CH_3-C_6H_4-3CH_2CH_2OH$
e395

$C_4H_3O-CH_2OCH_2-C_4H_3O$
e493

NH_2, $C_6H_4-CH_2CH_2OH$
e344

$Cl-C_6H_4-OCH_2CH:CH_2$
e434

CH_3, $(C_6H_4-)_3COCH_3$
e504

OCH_3, $CH_2:CHCH_2-C_6H_3-OH$
e611

e613 e615 e616 e617 e614

f1 f13 f40 f93 f44 f96 f15

f2 f16 f45 f98 f3 f78 f80 f99 f100

f7 f20 f81 f10 f39 f92 f102 f17

f104

f105

f110

f143

f155

f114

f126

f171

f127

f173

f128

f174

f134

f175

f176

f193

f220

f222

f224

f236

f241

f269

f270

f272

f273 [1]

f275 [1]

f276

f277

f278

f288

f290

f291

g1

g2

g3

g4

STRUCTURAL FORMULAS OF ORGANIC COMPOUNDS (Continued)

In Alpha Numeric as they occur in Organic Compounds Table

g5

g25

g34

g50

g6

g26

g35

g52

g8

g9

g28

g36

g53

g10

g29

g37

g54

g30

g38

g55

g12

g31

g39

g56

g22

g32

g41

g57

g33

g46

g72

g48

g73

In Alpha Numeric as they occur in Organic Compounds Table

$HOCH_2CH(OH)(CH_2O$—[benzene ring with CH_3O]
g86

[benzene ring, positions 2,3,4,5,6] $NHCH_2CO_2H$
g167

[indole ring with N-H] $CH_2N(CH_3)_2$
g189

[purine with OH, H_2N, N, N, N-H] CH—C—C—C—CCH_2OH (with OH, OH, H, H, H, H and O bridge)
g212

$HOCH_2CH(OH)(CH_2O_2C$—[benzene ring with HO]
g95

[isoindoline-1,3-dione with two O] NCH_2CO_2H
g173

[purine with OH, H_2N, N, N, N-H] CH—C—C—C—CH_2OH (with OH, OPO(OH)$_2$, H, H and O bridge)
g213

$HOCH_2CH(OH)CH_2O$—[benzene ring with CH_3]
g105

[isoindoline dione] $NCH_2CONHCH_2CO_2H$
g176

CH_2—$CHCH_2OH$ (with O epoxide)
g122

g190 [benzofuran spiro structure with OCH_3, OCH_3, CH_3O, Cl, CH_3, two O]

[structure with O bridge] $HOCH_2$—C—C—C—C—CO (with OH, H, OH, OH)
g214

H_2NCH_2CONH—[benzene ring]—OC_2H_5
g125[1]

[succinimide ring with two O] $NCH_2CO_2C_2H_5$
g178

CH_3CONH—[benzene ring]—$NHCH_2CO_2H$
g132

[steroid structure with OH, OH, HO, and $NHCH_2CO_2H$, O]
g179

$HOCH_2$—C—C—C—C—$CONHNHC_6H_5$ (with H, OH, H, H and OH, H, OH, OH)
g216

[benzene ring with AsO(OH)$_2$] $NHCH_2CONH_2$
g137

[cyclopentane fused ring with OH]
g191

$(HO)_2OAs$—[benzene ring]—$NHCH_2CONH_2$
g138

[1,4-dioxane-2,6-dione with two O]
g182

$HOCH_2$—C—C—C—$COCO_2H$ (with H, OH, H and OH, H, OH)
g217

[benzene ring, positions 2,3,4,5,6] $CH_2NHCH_2CO_2H$
g142

CH_3—[benzene ring]—NH—C(=NH)—NH—[benzene ring]—CH_3
g203

$HOCH_2$—C—C—C—C—CHO (with H, OH, H, H and OH, H, OH, OH)
g218

[glycoluril structure with H, H, two O, N, N, N, N, H, H]
g183

[benzene ring] NH—C(=NH)—NH—[benzene ring with CH_3]
g206

HO—[benzene ring]—$CH_2CONHCH_2CO_2H$
g160

$HOCH_2$—C—C—C—C=CH:NNHC$_6$H$_5$ (with H, OH, H, NHNC$_6$H$_5$ and OH, H, OH)
g220

[benzene ring with NO_2] $NHCH_2CO_2H$
g165

[triterpene steroid structure with CO_2H, O, HO]
g184

[purine with OH, H_2N, N, N, N-H]
g211

[tetrahydropyridine ring with N-H] CO_2H
g221

CH_3O ... CH_3

h2

H_3C $CH=CH_2$ CH_3 $CH=CH_2$

CH N CH N CH

$FeOH$

CH N CH N CH

CH_3 $(CH_2)_2CO_2H$ $(CH_2)_2COOH$ CH_3

h11

h233

HO

$CH_3(CH_2)_4O$ ... OH

h519

CH_3O ... CH_3

h3

N CH_2

CH_2 N CH_2 N

CH_2

N CH_2

h315

CH_3O ... C_2H_5 $C:C$ ... OH C_2H_5

h566

HO_2C OH

CH_3 CHO

OH

h12

HO ... $CH(C_2H_5)CHC(C_2H_5)$ ... OH

CH_3 CH_3

h324

h4

$HOCH_2$

HO ... CO_2H

h6

H_3C $CH(OH)CH_3$ CH_3

$CH(OH)CH_3$

N CH N

CH CH

N N

CH CH

CH_3 $(CH_2)_2CO_2H$ $(CH_2)_2CO_2H$ CH_3

h13

HO ... $CH(C_2H_5)CHC(C_2H_5)CH(CH_3)$ ... OH

h325

$CH_3(CH_2)_4CO_2CH_2CO$ ... biphenyl

h441

CH_3 ... O ... $COCH_3$ ... O

h569

CH_3

O O

CH_3

h7

OH

HO

HO

HO OH

h14

NH O

h446

$CH_2CHC:CCHCH_2$

O O

h583

CHO

$O.C_6H_{11}O_5$

h8

$CH_3(CH_2)_6$ O O

h30

NH O

CH_3

h447

p ... $CONHCH_2CO_2H$

m o

h589[1]

H_2OC

CH_3COO

O

$OCOCH_3$

O

h9

$CH_3(CH_2)_5CO_2CH_2CO$ ... O ... biphenyl

h157

CH_3

NH O

h448

... $CONHCH_2CO_2CH_2CO$ ... biphenyl

h589[2]

CH_3O ... O ...

h196

$(CH_2)_5CO_2H$

h457

$CH_2CH_2NH_2$

N NH

h590

OH

O

HO

HO OH

h10

$C_{12}H_{21}O_9 \cdot O$ ... OH O ... OH OCH_3

h232

C_2H_5 O O

h466

$CH_2CH(NH_2)CO_2H$

N NH

h592

C_2H_5O —⟨⟩— NHC:N —⟨⟩— OC_2H_5 | CH_3

h600

H_2NN ⟨⟩ CH_3)$_2$

h670

⟨⟩—HNNH$_2$ | CH_3

h703

CH:N—CH—N:CH

h725

CH_3—N⟨⟩—O_2CCH(OH)C_6H_5

h602

⟨⟩—NHNH—⟨⟩ | CH_3 | CH_3

h671

⟨⟩—NHNH$_2$ | CH_3

h704

h726 N—CH_3

HO—⟨⟩—$CH_2CH_2N(CH_3)_2$

h605

⟨⟩—NHNH—⟨⟩ | CH_3 | CH_3

h672

CH_3—⟨⟩—NHNH$_2$

h705

OH $CH_2CH_2CH(CH_3)_2$

h727

$(CH_3)_2C:CHCH_2$ | HO | COCH$_2$CH(CH$_3$)$_2$ | HO | O | $CH_2CH:C(CH_3)_2$

h608

CH_3—⟨⟩—NHNH—⟨⟩—CH_3

h673

H_3C—⟨⟩—NHNH—⟨⟩—CH_3

h706

⟨⟩—OOH

h729

5 4 O
HN 1 NH 3
2 O

h612

⟨⟩—NHNHCH$_3$ | H_3C

h687

5 4 8 3
6 9 2
7 1

h715

CH_3O—⟨⟩ C_2H_5—N⟨⟩—CH(OH)—⟨⟩N

h732

h627 CH_3—N ... OCH$_3$ OCH$_3$ O O O

CH_3—⟨⟩—NHNHCH$_3$

h687¹

CH_3O CH_3O N O O—CH_2

h719

OH O O OH

h736

h629 OH N—CH_3 O O

4 5 6
3 2 —NHNH$_2$

h694

C_2H_5—N⟨⟩—CH(OH)—⟨⟩N

h721

H_3C—⟨⟩—NHNHCH$_2C_6H_5$

h636

⟨⟩—NHNH—⟨⟩ | CH_3

h698

O O N—CH_3 OCH$_3$

h722

$CH_3CH(NH_2)CH_2$—⟨⟩—OH

h737

CN NC
⟨⟩—NHNH—⟨⟩

h640

⟨⟩—NHNH—⟨⟩ | CH_3

h699

CH_3—N⟨⟩—CH_2COCH_3

h743

3' 2' 2 3
4' 1' NHNH 1 4
5' 6' 6 5

h669

CH_3—⟨⟩—NHNH—⟨⟩

h700

C_2H_5—N⟨⟩—CH(OH)—⟨⟩N HO

h723

O CH_3—N⟨⟩—O_2CCHC$_6H_5$ | CH_2OH

h744

STRUCTURAL FORMULAS OF ORGANIC COMPOUNDS (Continued)

In Alpha Numeric as they occur in Organic Compounds Table

h758

h763

h764

h770

i1

i1^1

i2

i3

i4

i6

i7

i10

i11

i12

i13

i14

i16

i28

i29

i30

i35

i36

i40

i41

i48

i49

i50

i58

i59

i60

i61

i62

i63

i64

i65

In Alpha Numeric as they occur in Organic Compounds Table

i73

i75

i76

i77

i78

i79

i82

i83

i87

i92

i93

i94

i98

i100

i101

i102

i103

i110

i111

i112

i113

i121

i124

i128

i130

i131

i133

i134

i149

i150

i151

i152

i153

i154

i155

i156

i157

i161

i162

i163

i165

i166

i167

i170

i171

i175

i172

i177

i178

i180

i181

i182

i183

i184

i186

i188

i204

i205

i207

i208

i209

i211

i212

i214

i218

i226

i236

i244

i245

j1

j7

j9

j12

j2

j6

j8

j11

j13

k11

k16

k21

k24

k18

k22

k25

k12

k20

k23

l1

l4

l5

l6

l8

138

153

165

115

139

154

167

118

141

156

168

121

148

157

171

124

149

160

172

126

150

161

173

152

162

174

m1

m3

m5

m63

m64

m65

m66

m75

m91

m116

m117

m120

m122

m123

m124

m128

m129

m132

m134

m136

m141

m144

m145

m147

m148

m151

m153

m154

m157

m159

m163

m167

m170

m171

m173

m174

m187

m194

m196

m262

m271

m272

m273

m275

m293

m294

m312

m317

m346

m350

m351

m352

m362

m366

m368[1]

m369

m371

m376

m377

m378

m379

m380

m381

m383

m386

m387

m390

m391

m392

m393

m394

m395

m396

m397

m408

m423

m426

m399

m422

m424

n1

n178

n268

n284

n6

n263

n274

n287

n7

n264

n275

n289

n8

n265

n276

n291

n9

n266

n281

n292

n14

n267

n282

n293

n283

n295

n310

n390

n457

n477

n312

n392

n458[1]

n478

n313

n393

n459

n479

n314

n445

n460

n489

n315

n449

n461

n567

n324

n463

n568

n387

n455

n471

n569

n388

n456

n475

n573

n574

CH₃(CH₂)₁₆CO₂— (cyclohexyl)

o28

CH₃(CH₂)₁₆CO₂CH₂CO— (biphenyl)

o38

CH₃(CH₂)₁₆CO₂CH₂— (tetrahydrofuran)

o40

NO₂— (benzene) —(CH₂)₇CH₂

o139

CH₃(CH₂)₃— (γ-butyrolactone)

o184

CH₃—(1,3,4-oxadiazole)—CH₃

o254

(cyclohexyl)—O₂CCO₂—(cyclohexyl)

o265

(o-tolyl)—O₂CCO₂—(o-tolyl)

o274

(m-tolyl)—O₂CCO₂—(m-tolyl)

o275

H₃C—(benzene)—O₂CCO₂—(benzene)—CH₃

o276

(aziridinedione NH)

o277

(oxazole)

o292

CH₃CH₂CH₂—, CH₃CH₂CH₂— (oxazolidinedione NH)

o298

(oxindole, positions 2–7, N–H)

o299

o306

o309

o311

Cl—(benzene)—NHC(:NH)NHC(:NH)NHCH(CH₃)₂

p1

HN—(hydantoin)—O, NH, O

p11

CH₃O, OCH₃ (isoquinoline) C=O (benzene)—OCH₃, OCH₃

p8

CH₃O, OCH₃ (isoquinoline)—CH₂—(benzene)—OCH₃, OCH₃

p9

H₃C—(1,3,5-trioxane)—CH₃, CH₃

p15

CH₃CH₂CH₂—(1,3,5-trioxane)—CH₂CH₂CH₃, CH₂CH₂CH₃

p12

O=(tetrahydrofuran)—CO₂H

p13

(CH₃)₂CH—(1,3,5-trioxane)—CH(CH₃)₂, CH(CH₃)₂

p14

CH₃ (1,3-dioxane) CH₃

p15

ClCH₂—(1,3,5-trioxane)—CH₂Cl, CH₂Cl

p16

CH₃CH(OH)CH₂—(1,3-dioxane)—CH₃, OH

p17

CH₃—(pyranone)=O

p18

(C₂H₅O)₂PO—(benzene)—NO₂ (P=S)

p19

(furanopyran)—O, OH

p20

HO, OH (chromenylium)—OH, (benzene)—OH   Cl⁻

p22

CH₃O, OCH₃ (tetrahydroisoquinoline N—CH₃) OH, CH₃

p25

C-588

In Alpha Numeric as they occur in Organic Compounds Table

p26

p27

p36

p54

p55

p71[1]

p72

p139

p168

p182

p183

p223

p232

p267

p270

p350

p370

p428

p430

p439

p466

p469

p478

p479

p481

p482

p483

p484

p526

p528

p529

p530

p533

p550

p555

p710

p714

p781

p829

p908

p715

p794

p830

p909

p716

p795

p897

p910

p722

p796

p901

p912

p723

p806

p902

p914

p730

p807

p905

p919

p731

p808

p810 or p906

p920

p741

p812

p907

p923

p924

p1030

p1050

p1117

p926

p1034[1]

p1118

p930

p1035

p1051

CH_2CHCH_2Br

p1126

p932

p1036

p1064

CH_2CHCH_2Cl

p1136

Cl

p1138

p949

p1040

p1065

p950

p1042

p1068

$CH_2CH(CH_3)CH_2Cl$

p1139

CH_2CHCH_3

p1180

p951

p1045

p1078

p1181

p952

p1047

C_3H_7—CH_2CH(CH_3)CHO

p1098

CH_2CHCH_2I

p1182

p1028

$OCH_2CH_2CH_2NH_2$

p1110

$CH_2CHC(CH_3)_2$

p1183

p1029

p1049

CH_2CHCCl_3

p1184

STRUCTURAL FORMULAS OF ORGANIC COMPOUNDS (Continued)

In Alpha Numeric as they occur in Organic Compounds Table

OCH$_3$ · CH$_2$CH(NHCH$_3$)CH$_3$·HCl
p1199

CH$_3$CHBrCONH— (CH$_3$)
p1345

CH$_2$CH$_2$CO$_2$H (furan)
p1451

NO$_2$ · CH$_2$COCO$_2$H
p1541

CH$_3$ — O — C=O (cyclic carbonate)
p1235

CO$_2$H · CH$_2$CH$_2$CO$_2$H
p1371

CH$_3$CH(OH)CONH— —OC$_2$H$_5$
p1463

O (cyclohexanone) —CH$_2$CH$_2$CN
p1545[1]

CH$_3$ — O — SO (cyclic)
p1243

HO$_2$C— —CH$_2$CH$_2$CO$_2$H
p1372

CH$_3$CH(OH)CO$_2$CH$_2$CO— —biphenyl
p1477

(pyrene) CH$_2$CH$_2$CO$_2$H
p1579

CH$_3$O, HO, CH$_3$O — COCOCH$_3$
p1272

H$_3$C · CH$_3$CHClCONH—
p1374

O — C=O
p1480

CH$_3$CH$_2$CONH— (CH$_3$)
p1308

H$_3$C · ClCH$_2$CH$_2$CONH—
p1385

HO— —CH$_2$CH$_2$CO$_2$H, CH$_3$O
p1483

(furan)—CH$_2$CH$_2$CO$_2$H
p1581

CH$_3$CH$_2$CONH— (CH$_3$)
p1309

(cyclohexyl)—CH$_2$CH$_2$CO$_2$H
p1404

OH · CH$_2$CH$_2$CO$_2$H
p1502[1]

H$_2$N— —CH(OH)CH(NH$_2$)CH$_3$. 2HCl
p1593

CH$_3$CH$_2$CO$_2$ (cyclohexyl)
p1315

I, HO, I — CH$_2$CH(C$_6$H$_5$)CO$_2$H
p1423[1]

(indole)—CH$_2$CH$_2$CO$_2$H
N H
p1509

CH$_3$O, HO, CH$_3$O —CH$_2$CH$_2$CH$_2$OH
p1624

.CH$_3$CH$_2$CO$_2$CH$_2$ (furan)
p1318

OCH$_3$ —CH$_2$COCO$_2$H, CH$_3$O
p1428

(CH$_3$)$_2$C(OCH$_3$)CO$_2$ (cyclohexyl-CH$_3$) C$_3$H$_7$
p1517

O CH$_2$CHCH$_2$OH
p1628

CH$_3$CH$_2$CO$_2$CH$_2$CO— —biphenyl
p1330

CH$_3$O, CH$_3$O —CH$_2$COCO$_2$H
p1429

(CH$_3$)$_2$CHCO$_2$ (cyclohexyl)
p1526

O C$_6$H$_5$CH —CHCH$_2$OH
p1629

CH$_3$CH$_2$CO$_2$CH$_2$ (tetrahydrofuran)
p1333

O CH$_2$CHCO$_2$H
p1446

(CH$_3$)$_2$CHCO$_2$CH$_2$ (furan)
p1528

CH$_3$O, HO —CH$_2$CH$_2$CH$_2$OH
p1632

C-592

p1652

p1653

p1664

p1665

p1683

p1686

p1691

p1692

p1696

p1702

p1703

p1711

p1718

p1742

p1772

p1784

p1805

p1806

p1808

p1818

p1819

p1824

p1825

p1826

p1827

p1834

p1849

p1853

p1854

p1855

p1857

p1858

p1859

p1863

p1864

p1865

p1882

p1897

p1929

p1872

p1885

p1900

p1930

p1874

p1886

p1901

p1935

p1875

p1887

p1936

p1877

p1888

p1902

p1937

p1878

p1892

p1903

p1939

p1879

p1893[1]

p1905

p2035

p1880

p1896

p1921

p2036

p1881

p1923

p2040

STRUCTURAL FORMULAS OF ORGANIC COMPOUNDS (Continued)

In Alpha Numeric as they occur in Organic Compounds Table

p2043

p2069

p2085

p2113

p2048

p2077

p2086

p2114

p2050

p2078

p2087

p2116

p2062

p2079

p2088

p2118

p2064

p2080

p2089

p2121

p2065

p2081

p2090

p2122

p2066

p2082

p2091

p2126

p2067

p2083

p2092

p2150

p2068

p2084

p2112

p2151

p2152[1]

p2156[1]

p2160

p2169

p2173

q1

q14

q123

q244

q2

q15

q211

q245

q3

q233

q246

q4

q17

q238

q257

q5

q22

q259

q6

q33

q240

q261

q7

q34

q242

q262

STRUCTURAL FORMULAS OF ORGANIC COMPOUNDS (Continued)

In Alpha Numeric as they occur in Organic Compounds Table

q263

q264

q265

q279

r1

r10

r19

r11

r21

r2

r6

r25

r3

r7

r12

r26

r4

r13

r27

r5

r8

r18

r29

r30

r31

r33

r35

r36

r32

r34

r37

r38

s1

s8

s15

s21

s2

s9

s16

s22

s5

s12

s17

s23

s6

s13

s18

s19

s7

s14

s20

s24

s25

$C_6H_{11}O_5.O$

OH

O_2CCH_3

s59

s94

HO

s108

s26

HO

CH_3N

s60

OH

O

$CH(OH)CH_2CH:C(CH_3)_2$

OH

O

s96

HO

HN

s110

H

$^{\ominus}O_2C$ $N^{\oplus}$

CH_3 CH_3

s27

H OH

HO OH H

H H

OH H

OH OH

H

s83

CH_3O

HO

$CH:CHCO_2CH_2CH_2N(CH_3)_2.H_2SO_4$

OCH_3

s124

$\left(\begin{array}{c} CH_3 \end{array} \right)_3 Sb$

s29

Se

Se

s86

NCH_3

CH_3O OH

OCH_3

O

s98

$HOCH_2-\overset{OH}{\underset{H}{C}}-\overset{H}{\underset{OH}{C}}-\overset{OH}{\underset{H}{C}}-\overset{H}{\underset{OH}{C}}-CH_2OH$

s125

$\left(\begin{array}{c} CH_3 \end{array} \right)_3 Sb$

s34

$\left(\begin{array}{c} CH_3 \end{array} \right)_2 Se$

s87

HO

s99

$HOCH_2-\overset{OH}{\underset{H}{C}}-\overset{H}{\underset{OH}{C}}-\overset{OH}{\underset{H}{C}}-\overset{OH}{\underset{H}{C}}-CH_2OH$

s126

$\left(\begin{array}{c} CH_3 \end{array} \right)_3 Sb$

s35

$\left(\begin{array}{c} CH_3 \end{array} \right)_2 Se$

s90

HO

s102

$HOCH_2-\overset{OH}{\underset{H}{C}}-\overset{H}{\underset{OH}{C}}-\overset{OH}{\underset{H}{C}}-COCH_2OH$

s127

HO

s51

$H_2NCONHNH$ CH_3

s91

$C_6H_{11}O_5.O$ O O

s105

N

N

s128

HO

s58

N

N

CH_3O_2C

CH_3

O

s92

HO

O

s107

O O

O O

s129

$_{4'}^{3'} \quad _{2'}^{2'}$ β α $_{2}^{2} \quad _{3}^{3}$

$_{5'}^{} \quad _{6'}^{}$ CH:CH $_{6}^{} \quad _{5}^{} \quad _{4}^{}$

In Alpha Numeric as they occur in Organic Compounds Table

s151

s152 } rhamnose

s153

s158

s159

s186

s191

s199

s200

s254

s263

s273

s275

s276

s277

s279

s280

s281

s282

s283

s284

s285

s286

s287

s288

s317

s335

s336

s337

s338

s345

s350

s351

s353

s359

s376

s377

CH_3—⬡—SO_2—⬡—CH_3

s378

⬡—SO—⬡

s387

⬡—$NHSO_3H$

s408

s422

⬡—SO_2—⬡—CH_3

s381

CH_3—⬡—SO—⬡—CH_3

s393

O—SO (ring with O, O)

s420

$HOCH_2CH:CH$—⬡—O $C_6H_{11}O_5$ (with OCH_3, OCH_3)

s423

⬡—SO_2—⬡—CH_3

s382

O—SO_2 (ring with O, O)

s407

t1

$HOCH_2$—C—C—C—C—CHO (with H OH OH OH / OH H H H)

t6

(lactone with CH_2CO_2H, CH_3, CH_3)

t45

HO—⬡—OH · H_2O

t51

$HOCH_2COC$—C—C—CH_2OH (with OH OH H / H H OH)

t2

CH_3CO_2—⬡—O_2CCH_3 (anhydride)

t12

t46

t52

$HOCH_2$—C—C—C—C—CH_2OH (with OH H H H / H OH OH OH)

t3

t40 (steroid with H_3C, CH_3, CH_3, HO, HO, OH, $CONHCH_2CH_2SO_3H$)

t53

$HOCH_2$—C—C—C—C—CO_2H · ½H_2O (with H OH OH OH / OH H H H)

t4

t43

t47

t48

t54

$HOCH_2$—C—C—C—C—CO (ring with O, with H OH OH / OH H H H)

t5

(lactone with CO_2H, CH_3, CH_3)

t44

HO—⬡—CH_3

t49

t55 (steroid numbered)

t61

t98

t104

t105

t106

t107

t108

t112

t115

t117

t118

t120

t124

t125

t126

t127

t129

t130

t131

t132

thevetose
glucose
glucose

t134

t135

t136

t140

t149

t154

t155

t156

t157

t158

t161

t162

t180

t182

t184

t185

STRUCTURAL FORMULAS OF ORGANIC COMPOUNDS (Continued)

In Alpha Numeric as they occur in Organic Compounds Table

t186

t187

t224

t229

t230

t231

t232

t236

t237

t238

t240

t241

t242

t243

t244

t245

t246

t248

t249

t250

t255

t256

t257

t259

t260

t263

t264

t266

t268

t269

t270

t271

t272

t273

t274

t275

t461

t625

t626

C-603

CH_3—⟨⟩—$AsO(OH)_2$

t627

CH_3 ... —SO_3H (positions 3,4,5,6)

t640

(complex structure with H_3C, CH_3 groups, $(CH:CHC:CH)_2CH:CH(CH:CCH:CH)_2$, CH_3, CH_3, CO_2H)

t691

CH_3—⟨⟩—$B(OH)_2$

t629

CH_3—⟨⟩—SO_2NH_2 (positions 3,4,5,6)

t641

(polycyclic structure with OCH_3, CH_3O, O, OH, O, O, CH_3, CH_3)

t692

$N≡C$, C≡N, $N≡C$ triazine ring

t706

CH_3—⟨⟩—$B(OH)_2$

t630

CH_3 ... —SO_3H (positions 2,4,5,6)

t649

triazole ring (NH)

t707

CH_3—⟨⟩—$B(OH)_2$

t631

CH_3 ... —SO_2NH_2 (positions 2,4,5,6)

t650

(polycyclic structure with CH_3O, OCH_3, O, OH, O, O, CH_3, CH_3)

t694

triazole ring (HN, N, positions 1-5)

t708

CH_3—⟨⟩—SO_2H

t632

CH_3 ... —SO_3H (positions 2,3,5,6)

t652

(phthalimide structure) $NCH_2CONHCH_2CONHCH_2CO_2H$ with two O

t738

CH_3—⟨⟩—SO_2H

t633

CH_3 ... —SO_2NH_2 (positions 2,3,5,6)

t653

(polycyclic structure with CH_3O, OCH_3, O, OH, O, O, CH_3, CH_3)

t695

(oxazolidinedione structure) CH_3, CH_3, O, O, NCH_3

t739

CH_3—⟨⟩—$SOCl$

t634

CH_3—⟨⟩—$SO_3CH_2CH_2O_3S$—⟨⟩—CH_3

t669

(disaccharide structure with CH_2OH, H, HO, OH, H, H, OH, OH, HOCH_2, OH, H, H, O)

t697

(steroid alkaloid structure with CH_3, H_3C, H_3C, CH_3, N, H, HO, O)

t689

CH_2SO_2NH—⟨⟩—CH_3

t636

triazine ring (positions 1-6, N)

t701

dioxane/trioxane ring (positions 1-6, O)

t741

CH_2SO_2NH—⟨⟩—CH_3

t637

(steroid alkaloid structure with CH_3, H_3C, H_3C, CH_3, N, H, xylose—O, glucose, galactose)

t690

CH_2SO_2NH—⟨⟩—CH_3

t638

triazine ring with CO_2H, HO_2C, CO_2H, N

t704

NO_2 ... O_2N ... S$_3$ (two benzene rings)

t748

t749

t765

t771

t758

t768

t772

t780

t760

t769

t781

t761

t779

t782

t764

t770

u2

u29

u110

u125

u15

u49

u112

u126

u17

u71

u121

u127

u79

u122

u131

u28

u80

u123

u135

u138

u144

u136

u137

u139

u140

u141

v1

v20

v7

v11

v21

v14

v18

v22

v9

v16

v10

v19

STRUCTURAL FORMULAS OF ORGANIC COMPOUNDS (Continued)

In Alpha Numeric as they occur in Organic Compounds Table

v23

v25

v28

v24

v26

v29

x1

x9

x25

x28

x4

x12

x26

x29

x5

x23

x30

x6

x24

x27

x31

y1

y2

y3

y6

z2

z3

CAsBr$_2$F$_3$: a1423
CAsCl$_2$F$_3$: a1426
CAsF$_3$I$_2$: a1432
CBrClN$_2$O$_4$: m215
CBrCl$_3$: m225
CBrF$_2$NO: m219
CBrF$_3$: m226
CBrN: c582
CBrN$_3$O$_6$: m227
CBr$_2$Cl$_2$: m247
CBr$_2$F$_2$: m248
CBr$_2$F$_3$Sb: s117
CBr$_2$N$_2$O$_4$: m249
CBr$_3$Cl: m240, m304
CBr$_3$F: m278, m305
CBr$_3$NO$_2$: m290
CBr$_4$: m295
CClF$_2$NO: m232
CClF$_2$NO$_2$: m231
CClF$_3$: m241
CClF$_3$O$_2$S: m340
CClF$_3$S: m330
CClN: c 583
CClN$_3$O$_6$: m242
CCl$_2$F$_2$: m253
CCl$_2$F$_3$P: p742
CCl$_2$N$_2$O$_4$: m254
CCl$_2$O: p732
CCl$_2$S: p733
CCl$_3$D: m243[1]
CCl$_3$I: m283
CCl$_3$NO$_2$: m291
CCl$_4$: m296
CCl$_4$O$_2$S: m335
CCl$_4$O$_4$: p464
CCl$_4$S: m329
CD$_4$O: m349[2]
CF$_3$I$_2$P: p744
CF$_3$I$_2$Sb: s119
CF$_3$KO$_3$S: m343
CF$_3$NO: m289
CF$_3$NO$_2$: m291[1]
CF$_3$NaO$_3$S: m344
CF$_4$: m297
CF$_4$O: h768
CF$_4$O$_2$S: m342
CF$_5$N: m260
CF$_8$S: m292
CHBrClF: m216
CHBrCl$_2$: m217
CHBrF$_2$: m218
CHBrI$_2$: m220
CHBr$_2$Cl: m229
CHBr$_2$F: m250
CHBr$_2$I: m251
CHBr$_3$: m303
CHClF$_2$: m230
CHClI$_2$: m233
CHClN$_2$O$_4$: m234
CHCl$_2$F: m256
CHCl$_2$I: m257
CHCl$_2$NO$_2$: m258
CHCl$_3$: m306
CHFI$_2$: m264
CHFO: f113
CHF$_2$I: m261

CHF$_3$: m308
CHF$_3$O$_3$S: m336
CHI$_3$: m310
CHN: h724
CHNO: c580
CHNS: t163
CHN$_3$O$_6$: m311
CH$_2$AsF$_3$: a1439
CH$_2$BrCl: m214
CH$_2$BrF: m222
CH$_2$BrI: m223
CH$_2$BrNO$_2$: m224
CH$_2$Br$_2$: m246
CH$_2$ClF: m237
CH$_2$ClI: m238
CH$_2$ClNO: c90
CH$_2$ClNO$_2$: m239
CH$_2$Cl$_2$: m252
CH$_2$Cl$_6$Si$_2$: m212
CH$_2$FI: m277
CH$_2$F$_2$: m259
CH$_2$F$_3$NO$_2$S: m337
CH$_2$F$_3$P: p753
CH$_2$I$_2$: m263
CH$_2$N$_2$: c571, m244
CH$_2$N$_2$O$_3$: f170
CH$_2$N$_2$O$_4$: m269
CH$_2$N$_4$: t125
CH$_2$O: f106
CH$_2$O$_2$: f115
CH$_2$S$_3$: c183
CH$_3$AsCl$_2$: a1424
CH$_3$AsF$_2$: a1430
CH$_3$AsO: a1445
CH$_3$Br: m213
CH$_3$Cl: m228
CH$_3$ClO: h767
CH$_3$ClO$_2$S: m333
CH$_3$ClO$_3$S: s412
CH$_3$ClO$_4$: p463
CH$_3$DO: m349[1]
CH$_3$F: m276
CH$_3$I: m282
CH$_3$NO: f112, f117
CH$_3$NO$_2$: m286, n498
CH$_3$NO$_3$: n485
CH$_3$NS$_2$: c115
CH$_3$N$_3$O$_3$: u108
CH$_4$: m175
CH$_4$N$_2$: f129
CH$_4$N$_2$O: f130[1], f138, u18
CH$_4$N$_2$O$_2$: u89
CH$_4$N$_2$O$_2$S: m331
CH$_4$N$_2$S: u120
CH$_4$N$_2$Se: u114
CH$_4$N$_4$O$_2$: g204
CH$_4$O: m349
CH$_4$O$_2$: h731
CH$_4$O$_2$Si: m328
CH$_4$O$_3$S: m332
CH$_4$O$_4$S: s414
CH$_4$S: m345
CH$_5$As: a1437
CH$_5$AsO$_3$: m319
(CH$_5$BS)$_n$: b2407

CH$_5$P: p748
CH$_5$N: m176
CH$_5$NO: m279
CH$_5$N$_3$: g192
CH$_5$N$_3$O: s39[1]
CH$_5$N$_3$O$_4$: u19
CH$_5$N$_3$S: s50
CH$_5$O$_3$P: m323
CH$_6$ClN: m177
CH$_6$ClNO: m180
CH$_6$ClN$_3$: g195
CH$_6$ClN$_3$O: s39[2]
CH$_6$N$_2$: h683
CH$_6$N$_4$: g199
CH$_6$N$_4$O: c136
CH$_6$N$_4$O$_3$: g196
CH$_6$N$_4$S: c140
CH$_6$Si: s77
CH$_8$B$_2$S: d158
CH$_8$F$_3$N$_2$O$_3$P: m326
CH$_8$O$_8$S: m320
CH$_8$Si$_2$: m274
ClN: c584
Cl$_4$: m298
(CN)$_n$: p14
CN$_4$O$_8$: m299
CO: c184
COF$_2$: c185
COS: c186
CO$_2$: c159
CS$_2$: c161
CSe$_2$: c160

C$_2$

C$_2$AsBrF$_6$: a1417
C$_2$AsClF$_6$: a1418
C$_2$AsF$_6$I: a1420
C$_2$AsF$_7$: a 1419
C$_2$BrCl$_3$O: a616
C$_2$BrF$_6$Sb: s114
C$_2$Br$_2$: e599
C$_2$Br$_4$: e419
C$_2$Br$_4$O: a607
C$_2$Br$_6$: e247
C$_2$Br$_6$S$_3$: t747
C$_2$ClF$_3$N$_2$O$_4$: e201
C$_2$ClF$_5$: e204
C$_2$ClF$_6$P: p735
C$_2$ClF$_6$Sb: s115
C$_2$Cl$_2$: e600
C$_2$Cl$_2$F$_2$N$_2$O$_4$: e217
C$_2$Cl$_2$F$_4$: e218
C$_2$Cl$_2$O$_2$: o263
C$_2$Cl$_3$F$_3$: e275, e276
C$_2$Cl$_3$N: a630
C$_2$Cl$_4$: e420
C$_2$Cl$_4$F$_2$: e223, e224
C$_2$Cl$_4$O: a620
C$_2$Cl$_4$O$_2$: f167
C$_2$Cl$_5$F: e246
C$_2$Cl$_6$: e248
C$_2$Cl$_6$Se: s32
C$_2$F$_3$N: a640

C$_2$F$_4$: e421
C$_2$F$_4$N$_2$O$_4$: e234
C$_2$F$_5$NO: e259
C$_2$F$_5$NO$_2$: e256
C$_2$F$_6$: e249
C$_2$F$_6$IP: p737
C$_2$F$_6$ISb: s114
C$_2$F$_6$O$_2$: p475
C$_2$F$_6$O$_5$S$_2$: m339
C$_2$F$_6$S: s313[1]
C$_2$F$_6$S$_2$: d243
C$_2$F$_7$N: a853, e225
C$_2$HAsF$_6$: a1416[1]
C$_2$HAsF$_6$O$_2$: a1449
C$_2$HBr: e593
C$_2$HBrF$_2$O$_2$: a287
C$_2$HBr$_3$: e424
C$_2$HBr$_3$O: a49
C$_2$HBr$_3$O$_2$: a605
C$_2$HBr$_5$: e260
C$_2$HCl: e594
C$_2$HCl$_2$N: a416
C$_2$HCl$_3$: e425
C$_2$HCl$_3$O: a52, a411
C$_2$HCl$_3$O$_2$: a610, f156
C$_2$HCl$_5$: e261
C$_2$HF$_3$N$_2$: e210
C$_2$HF$_3$O$_2$: a637
C$_2$HF$_6$N: a852
C$_2$HF$_6$O$_2$P: p761
C$_2$HF$_6$P: p734
C$_2$HI$_3$O$_2$: a641
C$_2$HI$_5$: e262
C$_2$HNO$_2$: o277
C$_2$H$_2$: e591
C$_2$H$_2$AsClF$_2$: a1428
C$_2$H$_2$AsCl$_3$: e406
C$_2$H$_2$BrClO$_2$: a285
C$_2$H$_2$BrFO$_2$: a290
C$_2$H$_2$BrN: a282
C$_2$H$_2$Br$_2$: e408, e409
C$_2$H$_2$Br$_2$Cl$_2$: e213, e214
C$_2$H$_2$Br$_2$O: a277
C$_2$H$_2$Br$_2$O$_2$: a403
C$_2$H$_2$Br$_3$NO: a606
C$_2$H$_2$Br$_4$: e264, e265
C$_2$H$_2$ClN: a375
C$_2$H$_2$Cl$_2$: e411, e412, e413
C$_2$H$_2$Cl$_2$O: a33, a367
C$_2$H$_2$Cl$_2$O$_2$: a407, f153
C$_2$H$_2$Cl$_3$N: e252
C$_2$H$_2$Cl$_3$NO: a611
C$_2$H$_2$Cl$_4$: e266, e267
C$_2$H$_2$F$_2$: e414
C$_2$H$_2$F$_2$O$_2$: a420
C$_2$H$_2$F$_3$NO$_2$: e257
C$_2$H$_2$F$_4$: e268
C$_2$H$_2$I$_2$O$_2$: a422
C$_2$H$_2$NO: e339
C$_2$H$_2$N$_4$: t124
C$_2$H$_2$O: k1
C$_2$H$_2$O$_2$: g186
(C$_2$H$_2$O$_2$)$_n$: p1048
C$_2$H$_2$O$_3$: a557
C$_2$H$_2$O$_4$: o255

$C_6H_{14}O_7$: g10
$C_6H_{14}S$: h420, h421, h422, s312, s290, s332, s340
$C_6H_{14}S_2$: d241, d262, e184
$C_6H_{15}As$: a1438
$C_6H_{15}AsO_3$: a1415
$C_6H_{15}AsO_4$: a1414
$C_6H_{15}B$: b2408
$C_6H_{15}BF_4O$: o305
$C_6H_{15}BO_3$: b2388
$C_6H_{15}Br_2N$: a928
$C_6H_{15}ClN_2O_2$: c310
$C_6H_{15}ClO_3Si$: s62
$C_6H_{15}Cl_2N$: e200
$C_6H_{15}FO_3Si$: s75
$C_6H_{15}FSi$: s76
$C_6H_{15}N$: a810, a811, a812, a813, a848, a854, a893, a925, b2490, b2491, h321, h320, h322, p88, p1176
$C_6H_{15}NO$: a836, e349, e358, e369
$C_6H_{15}NO_2$: a28, a814, a815, a895, a930, p317
$C_6H_{15}NO_3$: a933
$C_6H_{15}OP$: p751
$C_6H_{15}O_2P$: p765
$C_6H_{15}O_3P$: e315, p800
$C_6H_{15}O_4P$: p776
$C_6H_{15}P$: p750
$C_6H_{15}PS$: p752
$C_6H_{15}Sb$: s120
$C_6H_{16}ClN$: a926, b2492
$C_6H_{16}ClNO$: a965
$C_6H_{16}ClNO_3$: a934
$C_6H_{16}Cl_2N_2O_2$: l76
$C_6H_{16}IN$: a927
$C_6H_{16}N_2$: e169, h344, h346, h655
$C_6H_{16}OSi$: s82
$C_6H_{16}Si$: s81
$C_6H_{18}Cl_2N_2$: h345
$C_6H_{18}N_3OP$: p774
$C_6H_{18}N_4$: t736
$C_6H_{24}As_3B_3$: b2400
$C_6H_{24}B_3P_3$: b2406
$C_6H_{26}O_8$: b2627
C_6I_6: b790
C_6N_6: t706
C_6O_6: c736[1]

C_7

C_7Cl_6O: b1868
C_7F_{14}: c677
C_7F_{16}: h124
C_7HCl_5O: b171
$C_7HCl_5O_2$: b1867

C_7HCl_7: t496
$C_7H_2Cl_4O$: b172
$C_7H_2Cl_4O_2$: b1889
$C_7H_3BrN_2O_6$: b1440
$C_7H_3Br_3O_2$: b1901, b1902, b1903, b1904, b1905, b2109
$C_7H_3ClN_2O_2$: b1519
$C_7H_3ClN_2O_5$: b1596
$C_7H_3Cl_3O$: b173, b174, b175, b176, b177, b178, b1539
$C_7H_3Cl_3O_2$: b1906, b1907, b1908, b1909, b1910, b1911
$C_7H_3Cl_5$: t565, t566, t567, t568, t569
$C_7H_3I_3O_2$: b1926, b1927, b1928
$C_7H_3N_3O_7$: b180
$C_7H_3N_3O_8$: b1940, b1941, b1942, b1943
C_7H_4BrClO: b1412, b1425
$C_7H_4BrClO_2$: b1430, b1431, b1432, b1433, b1434, b1435
C_7H_4BrN: b1415, b1421, b1428
C_7H_4BrNO: i135
$C_7H_4BrNO_4$: b1449, b1450, b1451, b1452, b1453, b1454, b1455, b1456, b1457
C_7H_4BrNS: i219
$C_7H_4Br_2O_2$: b1530, b1531, b1532, b1533, b1534, b2086
$C_7H_4Br_2O_5$: b1536
$C_7H_4Br_3NO_2$: b1394
$C_7H_4Br_4$: t573
$C_7H_4Br_4O$: b865, t530, t531, t532
C_7H_4ClN: b1471, b1479, b1486
C_7H_4ClNO: b2152, i137, i138, i139
$C_7H_4ClNO_3$: b1848, b1857
$C_7H_4ClNO_4$: b1514, b1515, b1516, b1517, b1518, b1520
C_7H_4ClNS: b2125, i225, t169
$C_7H_4Cl_2O$: b80, b81, b82, b83, b84, b85, b1468, b1476, b1481
$C_7H_4Cl_2O_2$: b86, b87, b88, b90, b91, b1537, b1538, b1540, b1541, b1542, b1544
$C_7H_4Cl_2O_3$: b1545, b1546
$C_7H_4Cl_2O_3S$: b1885
$C_7H_4Cl_4$: t574, t575, t576, t577, t578,

t579, t580, t581, t582, t583
$C_7H_4Cl_4O$: b866, b867, b868, t533, t534, t535
C_7H_4FN: b1631
$C_7H_4F_3NO_2$: t561, t564
$C_7H_4INO_4$: b1752, b1753, b1754, b1755, b1756
$C_7H_4I_2O_3$: b1559, b1561
$C_7H_4N_2O_2$: b1843, b1852, b1861
$C_7H_4N_2O_2S_2$: b2138
$C_7H_4N_2O_3$: b1529, i146, i147, i148
$C_7H_4N_2O_5$: b112, b113
$C_7H_4N_2O_6$: b1589, b1590, b1591, b1592, b1593
$C_7H_4N_2O_7$: b1606, b1607, b1608
$C_7H_4N_4O_3$: b1839, b1847
$C_7H_4O_3$: b570
$C_7H_4O_4S$: b1880
$C_7H_4O_6$: c260
$C_7H_4O_7$: m145
C_7H_5BrO: b54, b56, b57, b1266
$C_7H_5BrO_2$: b59, b60, b61, b62, b63, b64, b65, b1410, b1417, b1423, b2074, b2075, c622
$C_7H_5BrO_3$: b1441, b1442, b1443, b1444, b1445, b1446, b1447, b1448
$C_7H_5BrO_4$: b1436, b1437, b1438, b1439
$C_7H_5Br_2NO_2$: t436
$C_7H_5Br_3$: t591, t592, t593, t594, t595, t596, t597
$C_7H_5Br_3O$: b869, b870, b871, b872, b873
$C_7H_5ClF_2$: t395
$C_7H_5ClN_2$: i42, i43
C_7H_5ClO: b67, b68, b69, b1268
$C_7H_5ClO_2$: b70, b71, b72, b73, b74, b75, b76, b77, b1465, b1473, b1480, b1660, b1684, b2080, b2081, b2082
$C_7H_5ClO_3$: b1489, b1490, b1491, b1492, b1493, b1496, b1497, b1498, b1499
$C_7H_5ClO_3S$: b1163
$C_7H_5ClO_4S$: b1884, b1888
$C_7H_5Cl_2F$: t447

$C_7H_5Cl_2N$: a1083
$C_7H_5Cl_2NO_2$: b89, b1343, b1344, b1345, b1346, b1347, b1348, t454, t455
$C_7H_5Cl_2NO_4S$: b1547, b1548
$C_7H_5Cl_3$: t598, t599, t600, t601, t602, t603, t604, t605, t606, t607, t608
$C_7H_5Cl_3O$: a709, b813, b814, b815, b874, b875, b876, b877
C_7H_5FO: b1274
$C_7H_5FO_2$: b1628, b1629, b1630
$C_7H_5F_3$: t609
C_7H_5IO: b1281
$C_7H_5IO_2$: b1746, b1748, b1750
$C_7H_5IO_3$: b1700, b1701, b1702, b1703, b1704, b1705, b1706, b1707, b1757, b1758, b1759
$C_7H_5I_2NO_2$: b1349, b1351, b1353
$C_7H_5I_3$: t615, t616, t617, t618, t619, t620
$C_7H_5I_3O$: b878
C_7H_5N: b1291
C_7H_5NO: a1247, b844, b1676, b1687, b1694, b2151, i79, i149
C_7H_5NOS: b2129, b2159
$C_7H_5NO_3$: b162, b165, b168, b1863, b1864, b1865
$C_7H_5NO_3S$: b1881, s6
$C_7H_5NO_4$: b141, b142, b144, b146, b148, b149, b1836, b1844, b1853, p2064, p2065, p2066, p2067, p2068, p2069
$C_7H_5NO_5$: b1731, b1732, b1733, b1734, b1736, b1737, b1738, b1739, b1740
C_7H_5NS: b2116, i236, t180
$C_7H_5NS_2$: b2132
$C_7H_5N_3$: b1011
$C_7H_5N_3O$: b1263
$C_7H_5N_3O_3$: b1217, i44, i45, i46, i47
$C_7H_5N_3O_6$: t621, t622, t623
$C_7H_5N_3O_7$: b879, b880, b881, b882, t536, t537
$C_7H_5N_5O_8$: a1165
C_7H_6BrCl: t361, t362, t363, t364
C_7H_6BrNO: b1411, b1418, b1424

$C_{17}H_{20}N_2O$: b1974, u57
$C_{17}H_{20}N_2O_3$: u33[1], u33[2]
$C_{17}H_{20}N_2O_4$: a1388, a1390
$C_{17}H_{20}N_2S$: b1975, p719, u58
$C_{17}H_{20}N_4O_3$: x31
$C_{17}H_{20}N_4O_6$: r26
$C_{17}H_{20}O_6$: m424
$C_{17}H_{21}ClN_2S$: p720
$C_{17}H_{21}NO_2$: a1369
$C_{17}H_{21}NO_4$: c445, c446, c447, h744, h745, h754, h755, m400
$C_{17}H_{21}N_3$: a1473
$C_{17}H_{22}BrNO_4$: h746, h747, h748, h749, h750, h751
$C_{17}H_{22}ClNO_2$: a1370
$C_{17}H_{22}ClNO_4$: c449, c450, h752, h753
$C_{17}H_{22}ClN_3$: a1474
$C_{17}H_{22}N_2$: m197
$C_{17}H_{22}N_2O$: m356
$C_{17}H_{22}N_2O_7$: h756
$C_{17}H_{23}ClN_2O_2$: n314
$C_{17}H_{23}CrNO_8$: c448
$C_{17}H_{23}NO_3$: a1469, h758, h759
$C_{17}H_{24}BrNO_3$: h760
$C_{17}H_{24}ClNO_3$: a1470, h761
$C_{17}H_{24}N_2O_5S$: s85
$C_{17}H_{24}O_2$: c362, c363, c364
$C_{17}H_{24}O_3$: b1668
$C_{17}H_{24}O_4$: f114
$C_{17}H_{24}O_9$: s423
$C_{17}H_{25}ClN_2O$: d193
$C_{17}H_{25}N_3O$: a1358
$C_{17}H_{26}N_2S_4$: c107
$C_{17}H_{28}$: h64
$C_{17}H_{28}O$: b301
$C_{17}H_{30}O$: c610
$C_{17}H_{32}O_4$: s244
$C_{17}H_{33}N$: h73
$C_{17}H_{34}$: h80
$C_{17}H_{34}Br_2$: h69
$C_{17}H_{34}N_2S_2$: c103
$C_{17}H_{34}O$: h65, h77, h78
$C_{17}H_{34}O_2$: h70, h264, t83, t86
$C_{17}H_{35}Br$: h68
$C_{17}H_{35}N$: p981
$C_{17}H_{36}$: h66
$C_{17}H_{36}O$: h74, h75, h76
$C_{17}H_{37}N$: h67

C_{18}

$C_{18}H_{10}N_2O_6$: i61
$C_{18}H_{10}O_2$: b194, b195, c318, c319, n6, n7
$C_{18}H_{10}O_4$: b2179, b2202
$C_{18}H_{11}NO_2$: p844, p845
$C_{18}H_{12}$: b181, b1956, b1957, c313, e603, n1

$C_{18}H_{12}N_2$: b2367, b2368, b2369, b2370, b2371, b2372, b2373, b2374, b2375, b2376, b2377, b2378
$C_{18}H_{12}N_2O$: a1382
$C_{18}H_{12}O$: b184, p1931
$C_{18}H_{12}O_2$: a586, b2100
$C_{18}H_{12}O_3$: b1834, b1835
$C_{18}H_{12}O_4$: d159, d160
$C_{18}H_{13}N$: c153
$C_{18}H_{13}NO_3$: p850
$C_{18}H_{13}NS$: p721
$C_{18}H_{13}N_3O$: r37
$C_{18}H_{13}N_3O_2$: b1215
$C_{18}H_{14}$: b182, n2, t46, t47
$C_{18}H_{14}N_4O_2$: b306, b307
$C_{18}H_{14}O$: k5, k6, k20, k21
$C_{18}H_{14}O_3$: b1786[1], c353
$C_{18}H_{14}O_6$: j1
$C_{18}H_{14}O_8$: s191
$C_{18}H_{15}As$: a1441
$C_{18}H_{15}B$: b2411
$C_{18}H_{15}ClSe$: s37
$C_{18}H_{15}FSe$: s38
$C_{18}H_{15}N$: a947
$C_{18}H_{15}N_3$: a1602
$C_{18}H_{15}OP$: p756
$C_{18}H_{15}O_3P$: p803
$C_{18}H_{15}O_4P$: p781
$C_{18}H_{15}P$: p755
$C_{18}H_{15}Sb$: s122
$C_{18}H_{16}$: c906, h544, t769
$C_{18}H_{16}F_2Se$: s39
$C_{18}H_{16}N_2$: h710
$C_{18}H_{16}N_2O$: a1489, a1490, a1491, a1492, a1493
$C_{18}H_{16}N_2O_2$: a989
$C_{18}H_{16}N_2O_6S$: q155, q156
$C_{18}H_{16}O_2$: p546, s157
$C_{18}H_{16}O_4$: e93, t108, t109, t111
$C_{18}H_{16}O_7$: u141, u142, u143
$C_{18}H_{17}Cl_4N_3O_8S_2$: h595
$C_{18}H_{17}NO_3$: p1885
$C_{18}H_{17}N_3$: a1494
$C_{18}H_{18}$: p506[1]
$C_{18}H_{18}N_2O_4$: a1361
$C_{18}H_{18}N_6$: b1
$C_{18}H_{18}O_4$: e94, e95, e96, h415
$C_{18}H_{18}O_3$: b2684
$C_{18}H_{18}O_4$: b2287, b2338, s188, s199
$C_{18}H_{18}O_5$: e483
$C_{18}H_{18}O_6$: t13
$C_{18}H_{19}NO_2$: a844, a845, a846, a1374

$C_{18}H_{19}NO_3$: e144, t779
$C_{18}H_{19}N_3O_2$: a1535
$C_{18}H_{20}$: i27
$C_{18}H_{20}Br_2N_2O_4$: b1416, b1422, b1429
$C_{18}H_{20}Cl_2N_2O_4$: b1472, h1487
$C_{18}H_{20}N_{10}O_{16}$: a1407, a1408
$C_{18}H_{20}O_2$: e97
$C_{18}H_{21}NO_3$: c455, c456, c460, e138, e139, e143, e145, i130, p1863, t129
$C_{18}H_{21}NO_4$: e146
$C_{18}H_{22}ClNO_3$: c457
$C_{18}H_{22}N_2O_2$: h600
$C_{18}H_{22}N_2O_5$: p916
$C_{18}H_{22}N_2S$: p718
$C_{18}H_{22}N_4O_4$: g48, g49, g220
$C_{18}H_{22}O_2$: b2270, b2271, b2272, b2281, e98, e161, i156
$C_{18}H_{22}O_4$: n569
$C_{18}H_{22}O_8$: b1186
$C_{18}H_{23}ClN_2O_2$: h601
$C_{18}H_{23}NO_3$: c461
$C_{18}H_{23}NO_4$: c456, e6
$C_{18}H_{23}N_3$: a1475
$C_{18}H_{24}NO_7P$: c458
$C_{18}H_{24}O_2$: e159, e159[1], i155
$C_{18}H_{24}O_3$: e160
$C_{18}H_{26}O_4$: p825
$C_{18}H_{26}O_{12}$: s101
$C_{18}H_{27}NO_3$: c86
$C_{18}H_{27}NO_5$: e610
$C_{18}H_{27}N_3O$: p370
$C_{18}H_{28}N_2O_4S$: a980, a981
$C_{18}H_{28}O$: d314
$C_{18}H_{28}O_2$: d305
$C_{18}H_{28}O_4$: b2095
$C_{18}H_{29}NO$: d297
$C_{18}H_{30}$: b788, o8
$C_{18}H_{30}Br_6O_2$: o45
$C_{18}H_{30}O$: b824
$C_{18}H_{30}O_2$: o64, o65, o66
$C_{18}H_{30}O_4$: a1480
$C_{18}H_{32}Br_4O_2$: o60
$C_{18}H_{32}CaN_2O_{10}$: p5, p6
$C_{18}H_{32}I_2O_2$: o85
$C_{18}H_{32}N_2O_5S$: p3
$C_{18}H_{32}O_2$: c257, c258, o4, o7, o96
$C_{18}H_{32}O_4$: o44
$C_{18}H_{32}O_5$: a1479
$C_{18}H_{32}O_6$: g112
$C_{18}H_{32}O_{16}$: m153, r1
$C_{18}H_{33}N$: o83
$C_{18}H_{34}$: o93, o94, o95
$C_{18}H_{34}Br_2O_2$: o41
$C_{18}H_{34}O$: o68
$C_{18}H_{34}O_2$: o71, o72, o84

$C_{18}H_{34}O_3$: o52, o54, o56, o58, o86
$C_{18}H_{34}O_4$: d33, h386
$C_{18}H_{35}ClO$: o27
$C_{18}H_{35}N$: o35
$C_{18}H_{35}NO$: o73, o74
$C_{18}H_{36}$: o69, o70
$C_{18}H_{36}Br_2$: o17
$C_{18}H_{36}ClNO$: a318
$C_{18}H_{36}N_2S_4$: d225
$C_{18}H_{36}O$: o9, o91, o92
$C_{18}H_{36}O_2$: a207, d55, h72, h260, o22
$C_{18}H_{36}O_3$: h262[1], o46, o47, o48, o49, o50
$C_{18}H_{36}O_4$: o42, o43
$C_{18}H_{37}Br$: o15
$C_{18}H_{37}Cl$: o16
$C_{18}H_{37}I$: o18
$C_{18}H_{37}NO$: o23
$C_{18}H_{38}$: o11
$C_{18}H_{38}O$: o63
$C_{18}H_{38}O_2$: h241, o20
$C_{18}H_{38}S$: o21
$C_{18}H_{39}N$: a937, o12
$C_{18}H_{40}ClN$: o14
$C_{18}H_{54}O_7Si_8$: o202
$C_{18}H_{54}O_9Si_9$: c851

C_{19}

$C_{19}H_{10}Br_4O_5S$: b2427
$C_{19}H_{12}O$: b193
$C_{19}H_{12}O_2$: b1224, b1225
$C_{19}H_{12}O_5$: i244
$C_{19}H_{12}O_6$: d161
$C_{19}H_{12}O_7$: c552
$C_{19}H_{13}N$: a740
$C_{19}H_{13}NO$: c143
$C_{19}H_{13}N_3O_6$: m316
$C_{19}H_{13}N_3O_7$: m384, m385
$C_{19}H_{14}$: b185, b186, b187, b188, b189, b190, b191, b192, c315, c316, c317, f77
$C_{19}H_{14}N_2O_2$: a1578, a1581, a1584
$C_{19}H_{14}O$: f69, x3
$C_{19}H_{14}O_2$: p1579, p1825
$C_{19}H_{14}O_3$: a1478
$C_{18}H_{14}O_5$: p66
$C_{19}H_{14}O_5S$: p715
$C_{19}H_{15}Cl$: m243
$C_{19}H_{15}ClN_4$: t126
$C_{19}H_{15}N$: c144
$C_{19}H_{15}NO$: b1246
$C_{19}H_{15}NO_2$: q256
$C_{19}H_{15}N_3$: a733
$C_{19}H_{16}$: b2234, b2235, m312
$C_{19}H_{16}N_2$: b1257, b1259, b1962, y3
$C_{19}H_{16}N_2S$: u124
$C_{19}H_{16}O$: m381
$C_{19}H_{16}O_3$: m315, m360, o243

C_{38}

$C_{38}H_{26}$: b2198
$C_{38}H_{30}$: e250
$C_{38}H_{44}N_2O_{10}S$: i215
$C_{38}H_{46}N_2O_8$: t771
$C_{38}H_{50}N_4O_8S$: c332
$C_{38}H_{53}NO_{13}$: a722
$C_{38}H_{58}N_4O_{12}S$: c325
$C_{38}H_{74}O_4$: e295
$C_{38}H_{74}O_5$: d171

C_{39}

$C_{39}H_{57}NO_{11}$: g23
$C_{39}H_{59}NO_{11}$: g19
$C_{39}H_{61}NO_{12}$: g24
$C_{39}H_{61}NO_{13}$: p1856
$C_{39}H_{74}O_6$: g109
$C_{39}H_{76}O_5$: g81

C_{40}

$C_{40}H_{42}N_2O_{15}S$: b2167
$C_{40}H_{50}N_4O_8S$: q21, q31, q32
$C_{40}H_{54}$: i127

C_{40}

$C_{40}H_{54}O$: a1366
$C_{40}H_{56}$: c195, c196, c197, l71
$C_{40}H_{56}O$: c558, r35
$C_{40}H_{56}O_2$: x23, z2
$C_{40}H_{56}O_4$: t8, v20
$C_{40}H_{56}O_6$: f177
$C_{40}H_{60}O$: l73
$C_{40}H_{74}O_5$: d172

C_{41}

$C_{41}H_{61}NO_{13}$: e157
$C_{41}H_{63}NO_{14}$: p1857
$C_{41}H_{63}NO_{15}$: p1858
$C_{41}H_{64}O_{13}$: d185
$C_{41}H_{64}O_{14}$: g27

C_{42}

$C_{42}H_{28}$: r36
$C_{42}H_{32}$: t770
$C_{42}H_{46}N_4O_8S$: s156
$C_{42}H_{50}N_4O_8$: q16
$C_{42}H_{62}O_{16}$: g185
$C_{42}H_{66}O_{18}$: t132

C_{43}

$C_{43}H_{76}O_2$: c303

C_{44}

$C_{44}H_{87}O_3$: d280

C_{45}

$C_{45}H_{86}O_6$: g120
$C_{45}H_{73}NO_{15}$: s93
$C_{45}H_{73}NO_{16}$: s95

C_{46}

$C_{46}H_{68}N_4O_{19}S$: b2431

C_{47}

$C_{47}H_{94}O_2$: h261

C_{48}

$C_{48}H_{38}N_8$: e38
$C_{48}H_{40}O_4Si_4$: c931
$C_{48}H_{102}O_7Si_2$: d222

C_{50} to C_{216}

$C_{50}H_{83}NO_{22}$: d196
$C_{51}H_{98}O_6$: g110
$C_{53}H_{83}NO_{21}$: t690
$C_{54}H_{111}N$: a945
$C_{55}H_{70}MgN_4O_6$: c267
$C_{55}H_{72}MgN_4O_5$: c266
$C_{56}H_{86}O_2$: e116
$C_{57}H_{104}O_6$: g116, g117
$C_{57}H_{110}O_6$: g115
$C_{68}H_{96}N_2O_{26}S$: a726
$C_{76}H_{52}O_{46}$: t7
$C_{90}H_{154}$: e42
$C_{216}H_{288}O_{144}$: s113

MELTING POINT INDEX OF ORGANIC COMPOUNDS

Temperatures in °C; where values are not precisely known, or where there is a range of melting points, the compound is listed according to the lower temperature.

−215: h768

−205: c184, m289

−197: m289

−190: p1107

−185: b2940, p1713

−183: e162

−182: m175

−181: m241

−180: o253

−177: c911

−173: h373

−169: b2992, e401, p210

−165: p375

−162: b2410

−160: b2759, e417, m230, m253, m308

−159: p1185

−157: b2983, s77

−156: p1744

−155: s69

−154: e405, p148, p412

−153: p411

−151: k1, p376, p1189

−148: p46

−147: h421

−146: b2461, m230

−145: m244

−144: e328

−143: a1437, e245

−142: c876, e421, m276

−141: b2513, h54, h281, p417

−140: e403, h558, p1747

−139: b2941, b2995

−138: b2485, b2991, c186, c874, e499, h549, p375, p414

−137: h201, p44, p100, p734, p1721

−136: b2435, e199, p377, p403, p410, p1079

−135: c899, m256, p400, p413, p415, p1719, p1722, s70

−134: b2564, b2993, p134, p137, p401, p402

−133: a1642, h548

−132: b2454, b2583, b2987

−131: b2512, p1294

−130: a852, p84, s63

−129: b2557, b2995, p1814

−128: c907, p405, p732

−127: c688, p1587

−126: b3070, e544, h365, o211, p47, p92

−125: h584, p1716

−124: e450, p131

−123: b2511, m345, p1133

−122: e411, e528, e539, m261, s65, s72

−121: a18, c817

−120: b2460, h128, p143

−119: c910, e195, o213, p133, p140, p1717

−118: p404

−117: a939, b2957, b3078, c878, e221, e336, p1134, s343

−116: b2643, c819, c820, e477, e534, p407

−115: a925, b2866, b2984, e458[1], m216, p141

−114: c185

−113: a22, e592, o137, p1293, p1715, s348

−112: a183, b2500, b2501, b2510, b2680, c161, d67, e537, p152, p759

−111: c674, c875, e241, e253, e277, p211

−110: b3001, o212, p221, p457, p1119

−109: b2436, c909, e460, p155

−108: c871, e253, o135, p1210

−107: c691, c696, p153, p1080

−106: b2942, b2958, e204, p420, s73, s341

−105: a813, b2487, b2494, c877, f109, p101, p456, p1170, s74[1]

−104: b2522, b2569, c811, o223, s303

−103: b2568, e501, i216, o224, p334

−102: d238, o208, p1831, s80, s332, s347

−101: b2668, e475, p154, p448, p1192

−100: b2556, b2810, c673, d158, e365, h318, o209, p1161, p1163

−99: a215, b928, b2471, b2806[1], f141, p99, p1720, p1745, s80

−98: a221, m228, p1749, s120, s291, s313

−97: b2686, c150, c865, e215, f111, k3, o304, s63[1]

−96: a174, b771, b847, c825, c873, f139, l42, p91, p229, t224

−95: a208, a259, b758, c686, c694, m252, p1109, p1649, s290, t275

−94: a948, c868, e218, e249, e452, m176, m213, m349, n483, o214, p1314

−93: a197, a201, a216,

a850, b2408, f142, f146, h319, p219, p419, p1211, p1326

−92: b2401, b2661, b2662, b2926, e448, f106, f132, p76, p77

−91: c667, p142, p222, p2001

−90: b2864, b3079, c687, m157, o249, p447, p1193, p1312, p1433, p1525, p1588

−89: b2665, c628, c665, p1120, t211

−88: b372, o210, p90, p750, p1324, p1527

−87: a1440, c668, p45, p1707

−86: b2912, e497, f139, m214, p144, t171

−85: b401, b2563, b2674, b2820, e373, p365, p754, p1532

−84: a199, b566, b672, b2404, b3018, d242, p1766

−83: b374, m21, p1108, s292

−82: n485, o247, p453

−81: a208, b770, b3077, e163, e591, f158, p1083, p1530

−80: b2542, b2562, e384, e412, f135, h311, h683, i216, k4, o134, p371, s295, t743

−79: c619, n473, o159, o221, p231, p313, p1281, s67

−78: a178, a223, a1641, b2671, n529, p346, s312

−77: m26, p2000

−76: b2447, c666, h491, p209, p452, p1332, p1748, t122

−75: b373, b374, b924, b2657, c647, c895, g108

−74: a847, b568, b2523, b2541, b2933, b2985, c807, e467, l41, p1316

−73: a172, a217, b2682, d68, d77, e425, f145, p121, p1328, s351

−72: b848, b2924, p1534, t198

−71: a253, p1322, p1773

−70: c854, e266, p474

−69: e509, h98, p355, t216

−68: b850, c908, d173, p1114

−67: b671, e213, e350, h147, p151, p2019

−66: b960, d66, e600, f108, m282

−65: a639, b2533, f220, p1770

−64: a1128, b247, b849, b889, b3089, m243[1], m291, m306, p139, p1218, t215

−63: a893, b257, b447, b642, b674, e211, f137, f206, h158, o165, p225, p1999, s167, t208

−62: a198, b772, m24, o222, s121, t493

−61: a848, n536

−60: a820, b887, b925, b2887, c604, e478, f120, g111, t476

−59: b2395, c862, p1122, p1227, t173

−58: b376, b2670, c693, c896, e292, o121, p1320, s123

−57: a52, a1157, b541, c159, c642, f167, m217, m413, o112, t495

−56: b35, b2412, b2681, c627, p218, p776

−55: o116, o128, p85, p464, p923, p1154, p2017

−54: b673, b3063, m54, p1522

−53: e408, e444, f168, m246, p441, p920, s162, x11

−52: a173, a415, b403, b648, b1299, b3015

−51: b843, b2481, c894, d268, i16, n519, p147, p216, p295, p1319, s62, s316, t175

−50: a205, b2827, b2921, c664, c695, e255, e413, n560, p1543, t395, t733

−49: b2486, c629, d213, e27, m23, o158, t206

−48: a827, b661, b2596, b2976, d37, p1136, p1799, p1851, t393

−47: b2907, c160, e488

−46: a241, b407, o130, o172, o176, p224, p1205, p1518

−45: b778, b782, b945, c677, c785, e367, e471, i143, n528, o105, p1310, p1668, p1974, p2034

−44: a823, b974, b2394, c651, e267, o273, s160

−43: a1424, b246, b449, b567, c170, d6, m362, o164, o166, p161, p1466

−42: a630, b2788, b3014, d197, e234, e502, p230,

107: a791, a872, a1095, a1591, b294, b333, b880, b1290, b1785, b1831, b2041, b2823, c622, c636, h254, h415, i13, i97, n95, n145, n439, o42, p170, p953, p1232, p1978, p2037, s130, s242, t345, t468, t610, u86

108: a8, a75, a352, a730, a912, a1058, a1180, a1194, a1589, b418, b574, b1157, b1407, b2263, d43, e183, e345, e504, f69, h643, h759, i32, i53, m6[4], m93, m323, m334, n193, n477, p646, p731 p898, p1548, p1917, q33, q239, s26, s138, s248, s321, t348, t507, t512, t650, t786, u61

109: a689, a1590, b141, b685, b1179, b1334, b1826, b1968, b2039, b2423, b2567, b3061, c28, c134, e6, e165, e182, f71, f260, f273, h569, h759, m63, m267, n202, n404, o23, p71, p481, p518, p1252, p1880, p1979, q25, s300, t365, t537, u24, u73, u100[2]

110: a166, a388, a422, a668, a1095, a1593, a1600, b72, b325, b383, b622, b1096, b1315, b1770, b1935, b1963, b2163, b2275, c37, c107, d118, d296, e125, e400, e503, g50, h718, i202, l54, m359, m360, n90, o162, p655, p836, p882[1], p1103, p1405, p1793, p2156, q47, s99, s314, s358, t662, u113, u122, z3

111: a516[1], a517, a727, a834, a1037, a1210, b234, b273, b574, b1184, b1360, b1792, b1843, b1969, b2024, b2113, b2815, b3006, b3064, c706, d265, e311, e323, f44, h442, h659, l69, n115, n441, o311, p20, p25, p582, p618, p943, p1355, p1374, p2087, p2149, q221, t103, u90

112: a1052, a1557, a1567, b17, b176, b182, b612, b904, b1257, b1594, b1601, b1626, b1970, b2704, c461, c654, c683, d186, d192, f275, g2,

g43, g175, j12, m41, m77, m127, n31, n197, n202, n259, n303, p233, p293, p1233, p1488, p1982, q91, s266, t349, t621, u56, u81, u99

113: a1124, b106[1], b542, b865, b1203, b1276, b1324, b1624, b1694, b1824, b1871, b1955, b2203, b2282, b2317, b2329, b2424, c658, c725, c801, e90, f55, m53, m243, n136, n166, p645, p653, p677, p689, p1946, t279, t365, t596, t638, t674

114: a164, a344, a347, a762, a885, a1169, a1394, a1444, a1560, b233, b383, b490, b858, b938, b1087, b1163, b1214, b1309, b1338, b1428, b1645, b1751, b2048, b2110, b2141, b2325, b2366, b3061, c144, c396, f130[1], h566, i28, i50, l24, m6[4], m77, n151, o60, o281, p215, p603, p705, p941, p1047, p1994, q48, s144, s267, t27, t612, t696, t756

115: a164, a382, a425, a593, a676, a697, a1127, a1562, b304, b430, b587, b598, b631, b2058, b2104, b2304, b2371, b2563, c20, c34, c179, c301, c915, e180, g8, g55, i3, l22, m93, n10, n90, n139, n309, p177, p645, p681, p692, p1280, p1502, p1556, p2086, t321, t469, u26

116: a142, a298, a305, a340, a377, a426, a554, a658, a867, a1060, a1188, a1525, a1636, b136, b293, b482, b538, b968, b1015, b1583, b1692, b2011, b2069, b2101, b2229, b2239, b2836, c264, c345, e120, e404, f45, f290, h628, h629, m103, n124, n437, o297, p509, p690, p832, p909, p1492, p1500, p1977, q91, q205, s110, s377, t573, t769

117: a498, a577, a952, a1189, a1537, a1549[1], a1579, b128, b416, b576, b965, b1761, b2086, c605, c793, d190, e77, e407, e603, h566, h600, h605,

h688, h725, i3, i37, n132, n231, n402, p529, p554, p1490, p1932, p2023, p2155, q59, q118, t222, t353, u100[1]

118: a123, a300, a312, a329, a381, a496, a531, a1150, a1164, a1179, a1396, a1469, a1532, b100, b190, b243, b665, b725, b736, b823, b1264, b1406, b1566, b1852, b2203, b2593, c35, c36, c47, c144, d98, d267, e15, f82, g3, g198, l61, m287, m368, n53, n76, p246, p601, p657, p942, p1463, p1498, p1867, p1911, p1913, q1, q113, q203, r1, s204, t280, t324, t518, t618, t619, t663, u37

119: a397, a425, a471, a805, a867, a1197, a1652, b180, b610, b734, b900, c274, e519, f1, f265, h701, m9, m280, m337, n167, n232, p707, p767, p1284, p1561, p1866, p1868, p1981, t323, t496, t659, t706

120: a385, a449, a461, a781, a1154, b570, b685, b1064, b1152, b1363, b1730, b1741, b1742, b1744, b2091, b2161, b2239, b2269, c156, c187, c267, c376, d94, d119, d125, g35, h14, i67, i215, m104, m141, m183, n116, n129, n149, n303, n366, p168, p292, p524, p689, p899, p916, q111, s20, s45, s101, s186, t6, t506, t708, u102, u109

121: a16, a106, a107, a312, a471, a606, a632, a1065, a1576, b76, b950, b981, b2148, b2215, b2219, b2628, b2685, c199, c452, c467, c887, e148[1], e514, m28, m44, m85, m355, m359, n55, n241, p619, p871, p1066, r10, s197, s199, s326, t301, u62

122: a551, a677[2], a734, a1093, a1123, a1158, a1182, a1587, b183, b690, b1239, b1600, b2012, b2025, b2045, b2261, b2375, c251, d135, e190, e306, f241,

m16, m80, m198[1], n260, n437, p505, p562, p590, p709, p1674, p1860, p1976, p2135, q173, q206, r16, s325, s360, t620, t753

123: a116, a158, a530, a532, a556, a736, a1184, a1619, b113, b236, b268, b578, b670, b1060, b1562, b1841, b1923, b2158, b2278, b2840, c418, g4, g205, i76, i191, m310, m352, m407, n20, n191, n237, o148, p507, p557, p939, p1056, p1576, p1908, r12, s59, s130, s249, t51, u98

124: a878, a1152, a1529, b53, b62, b100, b223, b500, b910, b1074, b1629, b1908, b1965, b2070, b2794, b2918, c434, d12, e17, h689, l2, n295, p604, p868, p1331, p1494, p1496, p1819, p2159, q54, q77, q188, s129

125: a106, a144, a749, a983, a1096, a1487, a1489, b586, b903, b1253, b1371, b1993, b2044, b2228, b2251, b2261, b2303, b3034, c110, c252, c465, e17, e301, f87, f102, f267, g37, g158, h402, h737, k13, n91, n282, n363, n387, n390, p586, p909, p1062, p1503, p1760, p2153, s5, t462, t614, t693, t747, u16, u33[1], u87, u130, x2

126: a158, a196, a305, a905, a1062, b142, b186, b1095, b1161, b1628, b1990, b2021, b2041, b2071, c120, c424, c829, c906, d127, d137, h251, n27, n79, n277, n334, o42, p21, p649, p1168, q25, q204, q263, s140, s200, t255, t465, t751, u35

127: a561, a947, a1446, a1522, a1528, a1629, a1656, b169, b258, b485, b979, b1026, b1312, b1398, b1459, b1581, b1708, b1812, b1934, b2245, b2305, b2769, b3035, c55, c246, c299, c344, c448, c454, c460, e190, g167, h401, l16, m70, m199, n102, n205, n421,

o299, p63, p477, p616,
p637, p1927, p2093,
s84, s126, s142, s382

128: a104, a462, a782,
a783, a1073, a1530,
a1531, a1592, b3, b78,
b146, b816, b1372,
b1730, b1731, b2143,
b2261, b2355, b2499,
c53, c251, c253, c288,
c314, c833, d115, f64,
f243, i192, m358, n46,
n97, n138, n390, p184,
p306, p931, p1199,
p1652, q210, s46, s54,
s359, t156, t248, t669

129: a47, a99, a530,
a756, a1022, a1155,
a1228, b788, b1764,
b1880, b1917, b1954,
b3058, c902, d136,
e304, f244, h451, i174,
n72, n106, n113, n188,
p65, p604, p607, p698,
p840, p1065, p1341,
p1825, p1928, p2008,
p2041, p2146, q64,
q208, t183, t232, t274,
t313, t346, t527, t614

130: a147, a489, a695,
a943, a972, a1197,
a1633, a1637, b23,
b42, b91, b137, b502,
b511, b602, b650,
b1157, b1170, b1278,
b1893, b1998, b2023,
b2038, b3005, c358,
c834, e9, e614, g52,
g206, h633, l7, l55,
m317, n102, n104,
n198, p1, p570, p1040,
p1117, p1260, p1497,
p1499, p1541, p1758,
p1760, p2062, r10,
s259, s374, t6, t679,
t687, v10

131: a171, a499, a1165,
a1485[2], a1539, b64,
b264, b501, b640, b655,
b824, b1037, b1237,
b1693, b2264, b2273,
b2761, c559, c769,
e126, f48, f259, g32,
h669, i12, i30, m2,
n116, n431, p584,
p598, p953, p1345, q43,
x28

132: a70, a720, a1038,
a1558, b384, b1244,
b1556, b1582, b1610,
b2117, b2131, b2133,
b2218, b2422, b2528,
c50, c78, e134, e324,
g149, g179, h579,
h627, h719, m27, m136,
m137, m138, n103,
n238, n323, n397, p574,
p813, p918, p931,

p995, p1138, p1557,
p2117, q214, s244,
s389, t680

133: a92, a288, a470,
a540, a605, a666, a886,
a1063, a1475, a1499,
b155, b245, b487, b614,
b961, b1183, b1192,
b1560, b1884, b1944,
b1946, b2050, b2499,
b2716, c350, d162, e9,
e68, f222, h665, m59,
n203, n326, p1844,
p1892, q56, q234, t230,
t686, t687, x27

134: a157, a473, a477,
a739, a1536, b253,
b631, b1041, b1983,
b2020, b2265, b2328,
b2764, b3005, c80,
c110, c714, c716, d31,
e126, f256, g33, g44,
g164, g207, h298, h720,
i107, m128, p525, p648,
p843, p1509, q35,
s376, s383, t2, t231,
t346, t354, t528

135: a5, a427, a466,
a605, a660, a1241,
a1453, a1561, a1601,
b22, b49, b60, b386,
b1057, b1242, b1279,
b1332, b1474, b1651,
b2012, b2287, c350,
c379, c903, e10, e55,
e84, e104, e176, f252,
g63, h610, h627,
h673, h714, i205, m17,
m98, n327, n392, n424,
p178, p465, p575, p831,
p929, p1231, p1540,
s214, t5, t12, u18

136: a93, a604, a793,
a1473, a1644, b498,
b587, b630, b938,
b957, b1653, b1711,
b1799, b2200, b2528,
c54, c191, c262, c353,
c377, d232, f130, f255,
g168, k12, m6[3], m102,
m367, n121, n138,
n423, p785, p1953,
p2036, p2157, t643,
t787

137: a120, a1510, b912,
b1131, b1202, b1352,
b1613, b1774, b1945,
b1962, b2230, b2262,
b2290, b2498, b2743,
b2803, b3038, c14,
c948, d229, h414, l35,
m123, m394, n67, n74,
n98, n187, p490, p913,
p1369, p1849, p1951,
q202, s90, t315, t630,
u35

138: a452, a696, a1501,
a1584, b5, b191, b308,

b2029, b2129, b2154,
b2720, c49, c277,
c336, c338, c340, c353,
c389, c597, d127, e80,
e327, f251, f264, f291,
g189, n160, n361, p178,
p1150, q40, s11, s127,
t4, t354

139: a83, a97, a876,
a1149, b4, b70, b74,
b724, b933, b1077,
b1536, b1541, b1614,
b1866, b2193, b2747,
c48, c922, d246, e186,
e308, g30, h196, i172,
m2, m193, n293, p470,
p1036, s44, t113, t203,
t316, t653

140: a95, a418, a1213,
a1306, b239, b494,
b963, b1457, b1514,
b1525, b1844, b2051,
b2268, b3059, c78,
c883, c920, f94, f253,
g47, h14, h665, l8, l15,
l40, m335, m365, n150,
n162, n280, o231, p76,
p591, p693, p863,
p904, p1661, p1872,
p1882, r29, s49, s90,
t11, t34, t57

141: a549, a1035, a1114,
b86, b192, b625, b1029,
b1169, b1260, b1564,
b1817, b1875, b1877,
b1882, b2153, c287,
c346, c420, c429, c684,
c834, d86, e76, e127,
f207, g168, h138, i39,
i68, i207, m89, m351,
m424, n426, p826, p841,
p1037, p1785, q172,
u78, u89, u92

142: a292, a424, a611,
a1399, b87, b668,
b1075, b1111, b1363,
b1465, b1466, b1518,
b1652, b1958, b2124,
b2353, b2411, c706[2],
c726, e48, e79, f3, f50,
f130, g68, h710, i8,
k15, l15, m20, m92,
n506, p571, p1262,
p1971, q9, q146, s36,
s89, u126, u138

143: a887, a1152, a1603,
b604, b1187, b1360,
b1430, b1753, b1786,
b1845, b2095, c18,
c274, c281, c307,
c601, c726, e269, h138,
h708, i97, i163, n81,
n84, n489, n495,
p2136, p2152, q53,
q60, s143, s278, t58,
t703[1], u28

144: a109, a741, a1446,
a1514, a1549, a1594,

a1644, h149, h896,
b1193, b1535, b1541,
b1580, b1654, b1931,
b1961, b1991, b2201,
b2207, b2369, c891,
e123, e168, e524, g128,
i106, m33, m331, n73,
n162, n556, o143, p485,
p498, p644, p670,
p671, p682, p1266,
p1808, s127, s353, t235,
u59, v23

145: a85, a378, a424,
a1097, a1199, a1447,
b252, b283, b1085,
b1143, b1165, b1213,
b1252, b1603, b1724,
b2026, b2047, b2106,
b2122, b2123, b2163,
b2164, b2189, b2279,
b2298, c88, c241, c254,
e250, f85, f176, g68,
h324, h623, h638,
h640, h667, j10, l48,
m102, n318, n388,
n445, p571, p581,
p608, p629, p900,
p1038, p1041, p1477,
p1845, s38, x3

146: a24, a308, a767,
a1232, a1492, b15,
b161, b222, b543,
b1259, b1314, b1547,
b1753, b1895, b1991,
b2005, b2046, b2253,
c287, c411, d80, d193,
d214, e617, f248, g35,
g38, g39, g208, h589[5],
h707, i67, m123, s352,
t11, t242, u50

147: a428, a495, a585,
a674, a677, a1053,
b71, b589, b668,
b1461, b1517, b1557,
b1664, b1709, b1786,
b1836, b1988, c427,
f58, g216, i41, m48,
n140, n173, n200,
n436, p9, p602, p610,
p1036, s60, t240, t521,
u110

148: a129, a168, a387,
a434, a563, a650, a788,
a966, a1200, a1213,
a1631, b193, b939,
b1141, b1354, b1356,
b1488, b1570, b1731,
b2267, b2281, b2377,
c300, c352, c391, e128,
e168, e305, e307, f77,
i42, l58, n413, o276,
o305, p515, p849,
p1362, p1539, p2009,
q63, s220, s367, x25

149: a501, a505, a773,
a1097, a1100, a1170,
a1235, b509, b582,
b636, b1008, b1107,

d138, d253, f67, g217,
h299, h733, i124, i130,
k14, m298, n355, n410,
n453, p67, p1251,
p1893, p2052, q14,
q18, s151, s232, t9,
t309, u31

172: a103, a858, a963,
a964, a1402, a1541,
b11, b145, b295, b540,
b921, b1367, b1740,
b1782, b1876, b2217,
c68, c317, c402, c706[3],
c835, f15, h12, h735,
m386, m396, n32, n77,
n401, n406, o180, p199,
p727, p729, p1060,
p1658, q6, s205

173: a1, a710, a774,
a1172, b577, b694,
b990, b1206, b1245,
b1340, b1499, b1509,
b1706, b1723, b1984,
b2168, b2295, c406,
e302, i126, m405, n33,
n175, n415, n420,
n434, o150, p851,
p866, p1783[1], q201,
s260, s262, u20, u82

174: a1007, a1195, a1494,
b12, b25, b698, b727,
b837, b1005, b1323,
b1531, b1607, b1728,
b1918, b2469, c79,
c275, d110, e167, e311,
i2, p525, p556, p684,
p880, p1029, p1055,
p1904, q17, s20, x12

175: a1036, b700, b802,
b992, b1369, b1574,
b1634, b1758, b2155,
b2359, c372, c393,
c923, c924, c925, c928,
d167, e61, e98, e109,
g23, g138, h8, h613,
h624, h734, i6, l71,
m210, m314, n263,
o258, p524, p597,
p1437, q235, s39[2],
s58, s236, s253, s285,
s390, t319, t748

176: a780, a1129, b14,
b21, b29, b982, b1039,
b1167, b1212, b1348,
b1555, b1620, b1834,
b2062, b2085, c19, c31,
c64, d85, e56, e133,
f91, i153, n157, n407,
n445, n450, p550,
p1956, p2103, q38,
q156, r32, s131, s191,
s361, t44, t322, t682,
u80

177: a170, a636, b699,
b1331, b1445, b1590,
b1627, b1727, b1837,
b1897, b1986, b2054,
b2368, c227, c229,

c296, e56, f2, f42,
g57, i51, m191, n5,
n161, n336, p530, p864,
p1972, q22, q155, s41

178: a137, a1032, a1129,
a1239, a1402, a1450,
a1596, b198, b201,
b254, b911, b1491,
b1508, b1721, b1736,
b2428, c197, c437,
c462, c934, e143, e334,
g12, g187, g195, h616,
i59, i86, m6[2], n349,
n394, p157, p576,
p917, q39, q89, s366,
u51, u80

179: a91, a430, a934,
b637, b1481, b1638,
b1809, b1974, b2161,
b3081, c32, c33, c634,
c708, f43, f249, g202,
p1204, p1215, p1586,
s369, t312, t695, u6

180: a46, a541, a724,
a957, a1008, a1113,
a1219, a1693, b29,
b132, b696, b1004,
b1246, b1323, b1404,
b1451, b1493, b1736,
b2132, c31, c269, c278,
c388, c738, c886, d191,
d231, e191, e193, f90,
g214, g220, h609, i103,
i131, j13, m36, n398,
n452, o258, o302, p626,
p844, p1049, p1579,
p1673, q276, s85,
s113, s152, s356[1], u22,
u91, v10

181: a927, a1009, a1028,
b10, b1395, b1520,
b1567, b2136, b2224,
b2376, c371, c884,
d126, e57, f76, f97,
g156, g187, i46, i155,
m203, n335, n414,
n419, p1848, p1863,
p1869, s29

182: a715, a888, a1253,
a1460, a1509, b199,
b697, b930, b1002,
b1114, b1493, b1607,
b1800, c366, d260, e60,
e107, e121, e262,
e309[1], f40, h388,
h589[3], h747, i91, o45,
p1054, p1410, p1807,
p1871, q3, s86, u29,
u60, u120

183: a1480, a1646, b14,
b189, b1330, b1589,
b2204, c63, c392, f52,
j2, m52, m363, m393,
n393, p2098, q122, s36,
s50, s51, s217, u118,
u127

184: a133, a306, a740,
a1380, b723, b970,

b1387, b1444, b1723,
b1872, b2079, h2137,
c82, c196, e62, f266,
l18, l19, l38, m211,
n411, n456, p810,
p1611, p2071, s288

185: a304, a992, a1190,
b489, b491, b902, b955,
b977, b1304, b1443,
b1630, b1729, b1775,
c369, c371, e75, f185[1],
g65, g154, g215, h747,
i133, i211, m135, n63,
n324, n569, p66, p549,
p583, p850, p903,
p1926, q6, q52, s9,
s92, s185, s273, t8,
t54

186: a984, a1029, a1030[1],
a1196, a1493, a1516,
b984, b991, b1133,
b1572, b1644, b1739,
b1971, b2134, b2334,
c320, d151, e62, h709,
l50, m353, n21, n541,
o156, p561, p716,
p867, p1034, q76,
s24, s83, s147, t269,
u107

187: a105, a888, a994,
a1278, b1437, b1558,
b1650, b1748, b1906,
b2208, c58, c149,
c195, c201, c390,
c449, e74, i108, i131,
p856, q61, q246, s139,
u127, x17

188: a1113, a1258, b1140,
b1329, b1544, b2009,
c56, c286, c713, c732,
e89, e166, h159, i147,
m211, n372, p6, p478,
p865, p877, p1964,
s185, s364, u123

189: a1455, a1457, a1489,
b1229, b1710, e49,
e100, f114, g1, g126,
h418, h738, i177,
m382, n289, q187,
r38, t534, t776, u70,
u75

190: a301, a538, a1005,
a1195, a1251, a1381,
a1643, b14, b994,
b1152, b1308, b1524,
b1769, b2289, b2373,
b2383, b2855, c933, e37,
f245, h589[1], h601, i187,
m134, m385, n130,
n165, p1063, p1067,
p1657, q80, s95, s277,
s371, t533, t535

191: a110, a877, a1084,
b14, b1449, b2157,
c373, c728, f21, g28,
i125, k25, l9, n19, n62,
n350, p684, p812,
p1900, p2064, p2098,

q125, s282, u44, u97

192: a3, a1192, a1455,
a1457, b96, b621,
b1424, b1754, b2183,
b2642, c233, c394,
c707, e422, f92, f185,
g165, h589[2], i127,
n65, n75, n157, n430,
n448, p856, p1285,
p1593, p1846, s288,
s423, t56, u65, u69

193: a1292, b983, b1482,
b1878, b1902, b2383,
b2384, b2693, c369,
c398, e309[1], g20, g29,
g144, g173, g177, l76,
n17, n442, n451, p573,
p937, p1061, p1901,
p2101, q152, t127,
u142

194: a1261, a1472, a1622,
b623, b1643, b1889,
b1941, b2199, c75,
c296, c320, d141, f46,
g134, h292, h666,
h748, n165, n251, n332,
n333, n429, n430,
n570, p875, r24, s28,
t531, n93, u119

195: a537, a744, a1183,
a1378, b51, b89, b285,
b1230, b1903, c73, e5,
e31, e99, e114, f81,
g66, h159, h746, i88,
m49, m140, n23, n75,
n176, n325, n372, n412,
n444, o308, p5, p871,
p907, p1353, p1806,
q29, s40, s275, s391,
u125, u129

196: a537, a1207, a1298,
a1407, a1479, b408,
b1381, b2031, b2159,
b2367, e115, i186,
n356, p1805, q106,
s370, t149, u36, x23

197: a108, a985, b1188,
b1453, b1576, b1702,
b1901, b2162, c337,
c450, d107, f88, f254,
g24, h607, i125, m399,
p546, p2104, q144,
s134, s330, t111, t250,

198: a780, a1004, b1403,
b1616, b1690, b1707,
b1742, b1904, b2238,
b2386, c65, c273,
c305, c332, c408, d82,
d258, e4, e92, g64,
g137, g142, g194,
h589[4], h666, i104, l59,
n29, n201, n245, p915,
p1761, r31, s280, t43,
t532, u97, u106

199: a114, a270, a756[1],
b508, b1250, b1307,
b1700, b1957, b2385,
b2433, c71, d122, g59,

g62, g163, h620, i213,
m29, m139, n134, n283,
p240, q148, s141,
t325
200: a609, a725, a983,
a1225, a1238, a1288,
a1379, a1398, a1409,
a1411, a1544, a1635,
b1002, b1507, b1526,
b1553, b2032, b2033,
b2052, b2307, b2696,
c309, c931, c944, d104,
d194, e247, e605, e613,
f51, g129, g159, h11,
h544, h752, i11, i63,
i88, l14, m400, m402,
n16, n49, p1097, p1553,
p1885, p1965, p2081,
q26, q124, q149, q169,
s23, s47, s152, s156,
s268, u29, u114
201: a141, a433, a889,
b95, b990, b1681,
b1690, b1854, b2226,
b2856, l7, l76, n66,
p876, q143, q150, r30,
t326, t691, t750, y1,
z1
202: a113, a543, a903,
a1282, a1406, b171,
b1436, b1578, b1591,
b1924, b2034, b2096,
b2225, c74, c233, g20,
h445, i15, j3, n399,
p888, p890, p1985, s43,
s96, s285, u39, u136
203: a1280, b18, b1456,
b1808, b2233, b2695,
c57, c408, e2, e81,
g126, i73, i102, i204,
p911, p1804, q162, t10,
u69, u139, u143, v21
204: a675, a721, a1240,
a1259, a1390, a1413,
b579, b1549, b1606,
b1975, b2040, c368,
c416, e59, e92, e139,
f190, g36, i87, n316,
n342, p882, p915,
p1265, p1411, t779,
u34, u141
205: a555, a789, a845,
a1488, a1500, b1209,
b1217, b1551, b1593,
b1646, b2358, b2378,
c150, c310, c325, d104,
e3, e116, e158, f173,
g65, i1[1], i44, i73, m190,
n63, n338, n340,
n571, p1069, p2102,
p2109, q32, s226, s280,
t268, t461, t703, v7,
v11, v27
206: a302, a714, a989,
a1389, a1504, a1523,
b1180[1], b1181, b1617,
b1647, b1752, b1995,
b2206, c332, e12, g133,

h397, h762, l51, m641,
n416, p880, s52, t10,
t695, t775, u1, v27
207: a161, a429, a756[1],
a1074, a1388, a1542,
b1200, b1497, b1912,
b1921, b2064, c259,
c385, e41, m149, m316,
n3, n80, n252, n391,
u68
208: a258, a266, a744,
a1236, a1645, b999,
b1365, b1384, b1542,
b1725, b1743, b1867,
b2223, b2414, b2687,
c57, c380, c409, g213,
i45, j4, j5, j7, m313,
n66, o289, p1854,
p2151, t110, t530, v20
209: a128, a723, a928,
a1230, a1277, b976,
b1217, b1390, b1510,
b2416, b2434, d130,
h148, i189, i190, i195,
p533, p560, t249, t532,
v9
210: a1307, a1498, b838,
b1205, b1310, b1351,
b1359, b1366, b1726,
b1863, b1869, b1911,
b1996, b2036, b2415,
c247, c284, c310, c322,
c430, d32, d154, e200,
g29, g48, h606, i208,
m149, n353, o278, p8,
p812, p847, p1064,
p1804, q124, q261, t7,
t10, t132, t689, t770,
v18
211: a747, a1264, a1632,
b740, b1855, b2094,
g200, n337, p1803, v8
212: a1209, a1285, a1466,
b30, b591, b1438,
b1759, c228, c680,
d252, e2, e111, f275[1],
h9, h631, i113, i114,
l66, m62, m316, m326,
m383, n2, n65, n278,
n314, n455, o259,
p1444, t249, u88, u111
213: a728, a960, a1281,
b527, b1346, b1440,
b1548, b1714, b1743,
b1755, b2209, c741,
g58, h756, i87, i89,
n370, n378, p1809,
q167, u114
214: b27, b123, b1446,
b1688, b1859, b1863,
b2100, b2348, b2697,
c81, c150, d112, e270,
g61, i113, i115, i170,
p239, p240, p1862,
p2097, q135, s137,
t697, u30
215: a746, a1202, a1608,
b24, b987, b1433,

b1437, b1527, b1705,
b1912, b1939, c215,
c330, c399, i29, l17, l64,
n342, n405, o232, p55,
p919, p1068, p1925,
s251, t285, z2
216: a161, a874, a962,
a982, a1193, a1477,
a1543, b1104, b1362,
b2120, b2156, b2341,
e35, h630, n341, n357,
o306, p580, p845,
p1888, q252
217: a873, a1246, a1404,
a1410, a1412, b307,
b585, b1022, b1228,
b1472, b1915, b2336,
b2350, b2699, c397,
f275[1], g196, h603,
n384, n568, o260,
p1202, p1903, q142,
t149
218: a942, a1003, a1625,
b249, b965, b1006,
b1434, b2426, b2698,
c85, e48, e50, g148,
g213, i82, i115, i165,
n261, n409, p207, p883,
p919, p1980, p2062,
q136, q255, q277, s94,
s284, t43, u21, u74,
u137, y2
219: a871, b1032, b1106,
b1487, b1498, b1550,
b2340, n174, p1925,
s91, t140, t692, u12,
u103, u104
220: a13, a586, a1607,
a1623, b28, b1172,
b1545, b1645, b2210,
b2692, b2694, c453,
c458, c867[1], c929, e8[1],
e118, e159, g22, g185,
g190, h381, h604, h612,
n18, n26, n346, n347,
n427, p1070, p1859,
p2077, q141, s146,
t749
221: a1047, b32, b33,
c60, c61, g18, n382,
o284, q280, s8, s237,
t263
222: a711, a750, a761,
a871, a1621, a1626,
b306, b1030, b2291,
c444, d187, f89, g26,
g136, i112, n135, n164,
n374, p466, p814,
p1585, q168
223: a844, a846, a982,
a1202, a1296, a1405,
a1411, b1188, b1258,
b1545, b1757, b2292,
b2432, c59, l5, l17,
n339, n353, p1048,
q158, x4
224: a729, a962, b27,
b584, b1207, b1429,

b1926, b2188, d139,
e71, g60, l75, n22,
p10, p558, q151, t569
225: a503, a1217, b143,
b184, b1639, c200,
c231, c386, e54, e423,
g59, h696, i31, i84,
i105, m45, n344,
n382, p567, p712, p714,
p1118[1], p2090, t321,
u33[2], u41
226: a1000, a1208, a1257,
a1312, b1403, b1704,
b2065, e110, e233,
f270, m20, p2091,
q254, t631, t702
227: a828, b951, b1416,
b1550, b2037, b2130,
c709, f18, f99, l70,
m177, m398, p2085,
t162
228: b917, b1000, b1067,
b1750, b1898, b2332,
e108, e117, e118, f171,
g19, h736, m397, p542,
p910, p2064, q79,
s55, s57, t287
229: a765, a1296[1], b1409,
b1733, b1819, b1942,
b2288, b2335, c232,
c316, c374, d84, d147,
f53, f59, g193, h626,
h721, n359, p559, p683,
p714, s6, t254, t755
230: a864, a969, b592,
b787, b1204, b1439,
b1659, b1701, b1864,
b2127, b2349, b2379,
b2430, c945, e325,
h723, m343, o232,
p623, p720, p878,
p2030, p2099, q107,
q165, q254, s37, s409
231: a1495, b1344, f24,
m302, m406, n360,
p812, p860, p1338,
s132, t692
232: a1143, a1174, a1400,
a1627, b626, b937,
b988, b1349, b1554,
b2212, d128, d216,
g176, m191, n449,
o284, p516, q163, u7
233: b628, b2335, c946,
d133, h618, p534,
q164, t120, v25
234: a731, a1459, b1534,
b1640, c444, d111, e30,
g26, i57, n359, o233,
p1337, p1339, p1506,
q157, s279, t738
235: a126, a743, a748,
a955, a1045, a1636,
b13, b31, b1001, b1158,
b1358, b1393, b1559,
b1732, b1737, b2103,
b2109, b2633, c737,
e1, e40, e157, e233,

i120, l77, m315, n64, p72[1], p499, p2084, q31, s110, s151, t267

236: a1148, a1461, b840, b2641, e140, h189, l25, n5, n369, p552, p2040, p2080, p2105

237: a732, a1609, b250, b1343, b1516, b1561, b1888, d79, e66, e67, e110, f288, h597, h619, n459, p62, p1071, q159, t266

238: a775, a1198, b1, b978, b1190, b1199, b1554, b1883, b1999, c8, e97, g203, i85, p68, p830, p1073, p1278, q153, r4, t109, u71

239: a307, b129, b1053, b2063, c318, g212, n274, t38, t108, v19

240: a1001, a1003, a1310, a1524, b1361, b1391, b1528, b1633, b1905, b2072, b2308, c239, c737, c940, d99, f185, l74, l79, m315, n281, p499, s372, v5, x16, x20

241: a732, a1606, b1182, c326, e141, f189, g132, g209, h646, i209, n383, n478, p2050, r5, t37, t154, y3

242: a242, a1308, a1507, b1185, b1343, b1588, b1853, c139, c244, c324, c412, e72, n58, s12, s106, r34, v13, x5

243: a956, a1254, b1480, b2594, g161, h5, h697, i110, j8, m194, m406, o267, p11, p1052, p1067, p2084, r7, t126, t289, t767

244: a880, a1299, a1456, b622, b1053, b1588, b1639, b1920, b1985, b2241, e11, h396, p1053, q170, u101

245: a132, a792, a1098, a1297, a1456, a1612, b1051, b2633, c387, d123, e51, e72, e112, g159, h190, m302, n345, n354, p2, q158, q176, t631, t789, x15

246: a795, a959, a1310, b1883, b2035, c194, c244, d129, e8, e33, m172, p537, q164, s56, t737, t788

247: a503, b2197, c141, c941, e178, f37, g60, i85, i156, s283, t765

248: a72, a1098, a1276, a1382, b2, b722, b1305, b1608, b1927, b2352, f105, g162, h345, h621, h713, i170, m344, n59, n438, p2, p69, p1078, p2065, q5, t33, t282

249: a1606, e33, h591, p1077, q140, q245

250: a752, a1538, a1638, b998, b1053, b1306, b1452, b1641, b1642, b2350, b2425, e94, f104, g180, g212, h2, h10, i48, m402, m404, n478, p676, p893, p1072, p2082, q3, t704, v25

251: a1244, b2173, h596, s281, t766, x26

252: a976, a1221, a1279, a1496, b722, b997, b1023, b1357, b1396, b2172, e136, h5, h598, i194, n279, p536, p2067, y6

253: a786, a1249, b1919, c679, d184, h4, i84, l6, q73, t264, t320, t765

254: a999, a1653, b940, b1423, h232, h599, i109, l78, m399, m401, n39, o261, p69, p1506, p2058

255: a941, a1225, a1497, b593, b1655, b1713, b2138, c313, c327, d124, d155, d185, h763, p1856, p1879, p1902, s234, s276, s287, t253, t282, t426

256: a784, a1409, a1638, b9, b1306, b1636, b2097, b2176, b2198, c315, c405, d184, j1, l37, n371, p894, p2066, q177, r17, s1

257: a1503, a1610, b2382, d132, d152, f19, h713, p52[1], p1878, q240, q249, t790

258: a242, a267, a751, a1617[1], a1628, b627, b1160, e94, e96, h615, q20

259: b1886, h599, p517, p2057, r37, x14

260: a733, a926, a1260, b1058, b1119, c193, c234, c384, c938, c942, c943, e161, n268, p74, p547, p1335, p1984, p2060, q139, q161, q260, s187

261: a14, a751, d156, f23, h3, h432, n348, p1075,

p1762, p1929, p1986, p2086

262: b194, b721, c260, d105, d159, f43, g124, i194, l72, p710, p730, q166

263: b2121, d106, n574, o173

264: a1452, c381, f38, p537, r6, t131, u4[1]

265: a1173, a1216, a1271, c327, h4, i83, n158

266: a1533, b1007, b1052, b1063, f272, n313, p891, q74, s12, x22

267: a643, a1474, b2351, f19, n368, p1858, q86

268: a742, a1112, a1267, a1287, b129, b1386, c333, d181, l78, p535, p2113, s187, u144

269: a1462, b1385, b1546, d105, e40, i159, n379, p74, q78

270: a1302, a1464, b1009, b1061, b1750, b2202, c950, d270, n268, n312, n351, n358, o178, o307, p27, p519, p1075, p1592, q257, s21, s153, t36, t59, t690, u8

271: a643, a1283, g25, i158, i160, n381, p725, p846, q273

272: b2342, c939, h3, m388, p1855, s286, t131, t236

273: a1533, b129, b2225, d150, n284, n573, p479, p879, p2060

274: b1383, b2280, c375, m403, n269, p1074, p1076, p1933, p2045, p2063, q12

275: c381, f22, l57, q238, u4

276: a1290, b1185, e95, f36, n418, o179, q88, y5

277: a940, a1508, b2175, e609, f33, n574, p479, p713, r6, t39

278: b1046, b1194, b1195, b1397, c459, e616, t744

279: b1881, b2427, i210, q138

280: a303, a766, a779, a977, a981, b1048, b1116, b1289, b1386, d183, h595, l72, m300, p892, q281, r26, s155, t151, t237, u66

281: a1245, a1451, b1185, m338, t772

282: l11, n417, p1875, p2061, p2076, p250, r22, s363, t773, v29

283: a1275, b1043, b1364,

b2093, g184, m389, p544, p724, p726, q248, t759

284: a735, b1392, p725, s95, s136, u140

285: a764, a787, a1013, b1194, b2354, e93, g221, h315, h593, m300, n6, p1858, q251, r18

286: a1248, b1066, b1164, b1648, c419, f27, f98, f178, h617, n452[1], s153

287: b1043, c457, h592, h594, n385

288: a1242, a1618, b1062, b1112, c313, d161, e160

289: a754, a1286, a1300, c419, q249, u14

290: a267, a1266, a1270, b989, b1126, b1887, b2111, b2530, e137, p1928, t774

291: a1284, b1042, b1347, n343, q244, u140

292: a1291, b1928, b2689, b2691

293: b1055, b1218, b2170, l10, l12, l31, l32, l33, p527, p540, t773, v2

294: a1502, b200, b1125, b1159, d131, n6, n267, p1372, q4, r11, s148, x18

295: a754, a1218, b1045, e13, e43, g221, n385, n386, p711, p2156[2], t778

296: g184, p1938, r22, u66

297: a755, a1269, b2202, t777

298: a757, b1003, b1056, b1210, b1389, c436, q264, v3

299: b1044, f98, u9

300: b1117, b1218, b2211, b2357, b2492, d271, f26, f178, g183, i241, i243, i244, m122, n137, n273, q75, x21

301: i102, n4, p543, p2057

302: y4

303: a1250, a1265, b2689, d261, f27, p237, q51, s148

304: b1210, h2690, l13, p1874, p2059

305: a1615, b1123, d82[1], h293, p238, p1154

306: b786, b1009, b1049, b1196, f28, r33

307: b2690, i242, p236

308: a1478, c194, f30, n267

309: n264

310: b1054, b1115, b2170, b2326, c226, n266, t782, u67
311: a1468
312: a1301, c720
313: p1890
314: a753, a755, c682, f100, q259
315: b1122, b2530, i242, t36, v4
316: b2174, f29, t783
317: p551, t35
318: b1208, p951
319: a1268, q134, p2048
320: a1654, b1047, c949, n264, n265, n310, q2, s22

322: n7, q258, u15
323: i161, p2083
324: b1040
325: p2048, p2069
326: g13, u7[1]
327: b786, d143, p896, p1875, p1934
328: b2256, t35, u14
329: f35, l60, t701[1]
330: a1614, f34, p480, p545
331: a1252, g184, r36
332: h6, l32
333: b2402, g197
334: b2345
336: b1036
337: d157, p1336

338: a1463, f96, u2
340: a1468, a1613, u13
341: n1
342: p829, q242, t784
347: u15
348: b1016
350: a1295, b790
351: t130
352: m148
353: a1272, s27
354: a738, m151
356: b2343, q13
357: n1, p2078
358: c382
359: t184, t238
360: a1294, a1655, b1462, g211, p1050, p1889

361: d148
367: p908
370: u134
380: b1191, h323, x7
383: b993
385: a1311
400: p539, u132
410: q269
415: d108
419: o257
420: a970
422: a1311
450: b1103, e36
470: i40
490: d109

BOILING POINT INDEX OF ORGANIC COMPOUNDS

Temperatures in °C; where there is a range of values, the compound is listed according to the lower value.

−191: c184

−164: m175

−127: m297

−123: m345

−104: e101

−100: m349[1]

−95: h768

−93: m289

−89: e162

−84: e591, m289

−83: c185

−82: m308

−81: m241

−79: c159, e249

−78: m276

−76: e421

−75: m260

−72: e417

−64: a640

−63: m176

−59: m226

−57: s77

−56: k1

−52: m259

−50: c186

−48: p1713, p1840

−47: e277

−42: e259, p1107

−41: k1, m230

−39: e204

−38: e245, p1081

−37: a853

−35: e225, m232, p1079

−32: a1064, c907

−31: m291[1]

−30: e594, m253

−29: f113, m297, p1744

−27: p753

−26: e268

−25: b3078, e221

−24: f113, m228

−23: e499, p1831

−22: m342, s313[1]

−21: f106

−20: m291[1], m292, s69

−14: p748

−13: e405

−12: a1439, m219, n498, p1189

−9: m237

−7: a852, a944, p1747, s72

−6: b2940, m176

−4: b2436, s74[1]

−3: p1743

−2: o304

−1: p2485, m330

0: b2995, e256, p1170

1: a1641, b2942, p1190

2: a1437, p1185

3: a939, c604, e546

4: b2941, c911, e218

5: b2994, b3066

6: b2454, m345

7: a850, e253, p1080

8: b3070, p732

9: m256

10: b2468

11: b2435, e547

12: b2452, c199, e539, h767

13: e241

15: m274

16: e403

17: e163, p759

19: a1416[1]

20: b2410, b2992, c909

21: a18, a203, b2403, p735

22: m261

23: p1721

24: m248, p760

25: a1419, f25, p745, p747, p1188, x11

26: h724, p46, s80

27: b3071

28: b2579, e475

29: b3079, p398

30: e222, p375

31: b2991, f141, f193

32: b2564, e411, e577, e601, m340, p1109

33: a1442, f198, p1719

34: b2461, b3069, k3, p1180

35: d243, e328, e477, e534

36: a904, a1433, a1436, h766, m216, p84, p377, p1134

37: p376, p742, s313

38: e195, p754, p1720

39: b2462, b2993, b3077

40: a639, b2460, c865, e581, m252, p447

41: b2984, p1169

42: m282, p45, p443

43: i143

44: c899, c910, p1114, p1317

45: f109, n497, p44, p1722

46: a1418, c161, e275, e431

47: e276, e413, p1133

48: p47, p736, p1108, p1181, p1716

49: c868, e271, h563, n502, p1083

50: b2556, e541, e563, g186, p448

51: a183, p411

52: a1421, a1440, e814, p1141, p1183, p1294

53: d158, f158, m277, p1707

54: f135, p412, s31

55: b3067, e402, e460, e538, p73, p1828, t161

56: a827, a1483, b2563, b2983, e418, p416, p1649, p1833

57: a221, c183, c632, e202, e215, h562

58: a1434, b2557, b2562, b2952, e234, e575, p1714, p1715

59: a1417, b2441, e501, f162, h281, p417, p1120, p1828

60: e412, e459, i140, i143, p148, p418, p442

61: a910, m306, p410, p456, s67

62: c90

63: a1482, b2487, b2488, b2489, b2561, b2950, b2958, c631, f213, h456[1], h656, n492, o263, p143, p149, p1742, p1838

64: a22, b2953, e557, f220, n485, p1296

65: a796, b2401, b2987, f214, h280, m250, m349, m349[1], m349[2], p474, p1175, p1833

66: a833, e429, h549, p466

67: b2390, f220, h550, p413, p1293, p1759, s341

68: b2440, b2512, b2513, b2951, e497, f140, h548, m214, n491, p415, p1712, p1724

69: b2447, h319, h547, o292, p1164

70: a931, b2986, h574, p414, p1717

71: a40, a197, a1426, b2404, b2957, e458[1], f163, h579, p1119

72: a197, a637, c876, e549, p403, p457, p1099, p1725

73: b2985, e452, h279, p733, p737, p1129, s123

74: e273

75: b2459, b2954, c662, e565

76: a174, a1430, b2471, c677, e599, h278, k2, m296, p452, p1731

77: a199, b2994, b3073, f200[1], h765, p407, p1094, p1732

78: b2486, b2511, b3001, e336, e337, d308, h311, h540, h541, n490, p402, p1092, p1731, p1776

79: e254, f201, p131, p1140

80: a854, b202, b2106, b2912, c628, f215, h282, p133, p1314, p1324, p1775, p1893[1]

81: a174, b2611, b3054, d210, e451, e545, f146, h581, h657, p1111, p1176, p2167, s121

82: a241, e562, h124, p401, p1588, p1633

83: b2646, c811, e216, e292, e430, e537, e550, e578, h309, p453, s65

84: a848, b2495, b2955, d215, e561, f116, h580, m339, p400, p405, p1135, p1736, s301, t187

85: a30, a630, b779, b2644, b2645, b2956, c628, h308, h373, h652, p743, s347

86: b2523, b2962, e459[1], f216, h312, p134, p1087, p1894

87: a589, b2457, e425, h683, n483, p406, p454, p1197

88: b2439, b2632, b2961, c637, h93, p1160, p1832, p1895, s115

89: a925, b2180, b2988, f108, p462, p1193, p1295, p2160

90: a33, a217, b2502, c173, e435, h371, m217, p132, p1090, p1800, p2173

91: b2458, b2501, e223, e461, e528, h369, p86, p87, p391

92: a44, a216, a1420, b2480, b2481, e450, 480, e551, f209, h372, h373, h374, h584, p1525, p1532, p1545, s303

93: a45, b2444, b2524, e224, e448, f206, h81, h730, p140, p386, p1124, s182, t42

94: a1429, b2451, b2926, b2963, b2966, e448, e469, h82, h197, p408, p1735

95: a810, b2408, b2493, e171, f158, h586, i245, p385, p390, s351

96: a56, b2961, b3047, e257, h200, h201, p109, p444, p1161, p2164, s348

97: a37, a182, a813, a1427, a1443, b2966, b3048, f133, p100, p387, p404, p1326, p1587, p1814

98: a52, a812, b2397, b2446, b2643, b2943,

Temperatures in °C; where there is a range of values, the compound is listed according to the lower value.

b3063, e201, e294,
f139, h198, h199,
h651, m246, p101,
p1746, s73
99: a522, b2443, b2522,
b2865, b2866, b2867,
e465, e580, n499,
p153, p1196, p1316
100: a1012, b1102,
b2520, b2521, c4, e342,
f160, h216, h682,
m264, m269, p48,
p1195, p1773, p1799
101: b2979, c630, c688,
d198, e454[1], f115,
h81, h674, m286,
n484, p419, p1128,
p1434, s78
102: a259, b2491, b2500,
b2526, b2665, b2674,
b2896, b2933, c691,
e243, e455, f196,
h585, p345, p348,
p450, p455, p1192,
p1745, s70, t609
103: a21, a59, c820,
c874, e366, f150,
f197, o241, p77, p392,
p1311
104: b2389, b2490,
b2541, b2933, b3072,
b3091, c818, c819,
e502, n501, p85, p388,
p1534
105: a566, a1427, b2944,
d197, e576, f161, h218,
m225, p211, p420,
p1165, p1435
106: b2178, b2394,
b2601, b2921, h652,
i142, m278, p952,
p1125, p2166
107: a367, b2442, b3090,
e181, e196, e481, f132,
f153, h358, h681,
m258, o235, p221,
p379, p393, p1002,
p1225, p1432, p1534
108: a214, a367, a411,
a811, e170, e211, e409,
e458, e535, h83, o292[1],
p198, p760, p1165,
p1166, p1738, s30
109: a36, a893, b2437,
b2450, b2729, b2965,
c2, e548, e582, f210,
h362, h364, m238,
p389, p1086, p1323,
p1737, s81
110: b2964, c817, d242,
e339, f156, f212, h87,
h213, h363, n488,
p53, p111, p152, p381,
p1376, p1836, s76
111: a816, b2456, b2517,
b2960, h361, p111[1],

p472, p802, p1527,
t275
112: a179, a180, a416,
b2516, b2897, b2970,
c408, e449, e454, e558,
h89, h217, h365,
m291, p82, p1733,
p1734, s346
113: b2898, b3046, c872,
e274, e331, h360, h553,
p155, p210, p1625,
s114, t215
114: b2537, b2806, c908,
d204, e244, f219, h321,
p432, p1156, p1651,
p1757, p1820, p1851,
p2142, t493, t741
115: a25, a55, a187,
b2515, b2519, b2915,
c627, d200, e255, e585,
f166, f200, f204, h127,
m341, p112, p154,
p366, p382, p434,
p1837, p1939, p2165,
t216, t505
116: a181, a591, a836,
b2514, b2542, b2799,
b2938, b2973, e207,
e485, h359, o288,
p80, p113, p141, p315,
p365, p383, p1113,
p1523, p1897, p1990,
t494
117: a215, b2478, b2570,
b2809, b2864, b2915,
b2917, c619, e462,
h129, h322, o293,
p1003, p1004, p1796,
s302, t136, t495
118: a37, a58, a525,
a1423, b2577, b2647,
b2648, b2680, b2888,
c611, e208, f123,
h123, h126, h130,
h366, p128, p142,
p364, p394, p440,
p1121, p1123, p1433,
p1515, p1632[1], p1755,
s343
119: b2946, b3014, b3017,
b3018, c669, e554,
h128, h368, i231,
m229, p92, p314, p436,
p1668, p1842, t224
120: a1416, b2388,
b2509, b2510, b2569,
b2833, b2889, b2916,
b3015, c663, c666,
e187, e428, e472, h557,
h564, m127, p461,
p1151, p1163, p1211,
p1676, s312
121: a184, b3014, b3045,
e420, h552, h554,
o208, o250, p334,
p396, p1531

122: b2508, b2668,
b3068, h331, h634,
o213, o214, p378,
p380[1], p384, p435,
p437, p1139, p1332,
p1767
123: a445, a857, c665,
e289, h332, h555,
m239, o211, o212,
p151, p380[1], p1084,
p1228, p1383, p1708, s291
124: a222, b2538,
b2574, b3012, c667,
c668, c670, e203, f142,
h378, k2, p355, p971,
p1006, p1303, p1852,
p2092, s74[2]
125: a178, b2801, b2969,
b2971, b2978, e373,
e478, f208, h148, h214,
h518, h655, o210,
o221, p88, p114, p935,
p1005, p1798
126: a178, a375, b2467,
c160, c170, c875, m299,
o112, o209, p228,
p441, p1604, s419
127: a32, b2893, e203,
e479, e500, h538,
p103, p209, p338,
p969, p1007, p1321,
p1194, p1524
128: b281, b2398,
b2659, b2765, b2892,
b2895, c816, e350,
e536, e560, f167, h316,
h517, m408, p122,
p970, p976, p1608,
p1631, s63[1], t146, t198
129: a53, b2894, b2945,
b3089, f159, h313,
n496, p98, p750,
p2019, p2137, s116
130: a176, a253[1], a374,
a949, b450, b2455,
b2545, b2673, b2810,
b2972, b2974, b2975,
c664, c878, c894, e266,
e463, f145, g130, h226,
h320, h323, h718, p90,
p147, p1088, p1829,
p2126, s414, t45
131: a524, b2568, b2800,
b2911, c671, e212,
e566, h316, h482,
i228, o224, p124,
p940, p982, p1085,
p1210, p1226, p1347,
p1447, p1630[1]
132: a177, a254, b407,
b2192, b2396, b2506,
b2759, c674, f145,
f210[2], m257, p397,
p1007, p1313, p1381,
p1606, p1751, p1774,
t147

133: a1424, b2546, b2939,
c879, e467, h117,
h551, p336, p460,
p1153, p1380, p1519,
p1602, p1650, s412, t175
134: a253[2], a420, b2265,
b2507, b2539, b2595,
c614, c640, e246, e359,
h288, h289, h330,
h533, h534, h571,
p335, p1148, p1544,
p1704, s340, t210
135: a821, b2762,
b2806[1], b2879, c913,
e363, f211, h119, h340,
h342, h483, h484,
n480, o106, o286,
p104, p354, p1152,
p1167, p1213, p1401,
p1537, p1654, s75
136: b758, b3012[1],
b3013, d223, e552,
h118, h481, h576,
p374, p1663, p1816,
p1899, p1914, s63, t211
137: b2191, b2884, b2914,
c870, g155, h120, h588,
p313, p433, p977,
p1322, p1486, t41, t208
138: a1438, b449, b662,
b2505, b2549, b2550,
b2575, b2878, c612,
c695, c861, f151, h203,
h341, h479, i230, m223,
m416, o222, p946,
p972, p975, p1127,
p1723, p2110, t158
139: a847, b661, c895,
f219[1], h205, h530,
p202, p325, p1366,
p1918, s292
140: a172, a402, b2274,
b2578, b2583, c126,
c696, c892, f111, h116,
h204, h480, i164, i224,
p286, p324, p424,
p433, p973, p974,
p1154, p1200, p1226,
p1630, s342, t168,
t459, t492
141: a264, b2877, b2882,
c860, h122, h221, h328,
o138, p139, p229,
p1144, p1302, p1730,
s350, t207, t395
142: a226, a253[2], b778,
b2652, b2808, b2885,
b3031, e217, e471,
e544, f289, h95, h421,
h529, h530, m283,
o129, o137
p94, p97, p290, p983,
p984, p1756, p1766,
p2144, s332, t206
143: a265, a415, a616,
b2610, b2686, b2805,

BOILING POINT INDEX OF ORGANIC COMPOUNDS (Continued)

Temperatures in °C; where there is a range of values, the compound is listed according to the lower value.

b2887, b2924, b3088, c651, c862, c896, h501, h503, i164, o134, o135, o136, p108, p110, p327, p1350, p1387, p1914, p1919, s77[1]

144: a219, a281, a369, b660, b2551, b2572, b2737, b2886, b3052, c897, e169, e370, h100, h101, h186, h327, h531, o234, o238, p145, p294, p1349, p1436, p1841, p1921, p2020, s290, t141

145: a185, a287, b2547, b2664, b2726, b2775, c689, c815, e486, f194[1], h522, h543, h589, h645, p115, p146, p222, p354, p978, p1208, p1312, p1472, p1600, p1685, p1756, p2021, s159, t171

146: a897, b2423, b2424, b2504, b2890, b3041, e267, e312, e356, f205, h546, p129, p932, p1227, p1617, p1770, p1817, p2147

147: a237, a448, b2573, b2934, b2936, c172, f221, h185, h505, h524, m329, m414, n484, o204, p96, p123, p337, p345, p358, p395, p1377, p1530, p1975, p2143

148: a233, a234, b1678, b2571, b2740, b2863, c855, e457, g113, g127, m224, p330, p1025, p1974

149: a186, a211, a253, e347, e542, h185, h520, m303, o102, p95, p998, p1159, p1184, p1400, p1704, p1999, s61, t193

150: a277, a282, a372, a1485, b2706, b2881, c3, c605, c854, e391, f120, h339, h502, m247, n309, n563, p109, p259, p1218, p1459, p1485, p1578, p1620

151: a464, b2662, b2980, b2981, c474, c639, e348, e569, f195, h184, h420, h436, h525· n519, n560, o269, p332, p1019, p1027, p1403, s411

152: a193, a446, b341, b847, b2472, b2608, b2663, b2913, b2976, c877, h209, i216, p331, p357, p361, p369, p1132, p1346, p1379, t174

153: a627, b2582, b2923, h90, h432, i237, n562, o217, p38, p150, p227, p986, p1518, p1815, p1817, p1915, s79, t743

154: a856, b781, b782, b1274, b2540, b2874, c687, c873, d238, e453, f8, f164, h171, h578, p356, p369, p945, p1219, p2161, s71, s82, t201

155: a412, a918, b859, b2730, b2959, b2977, c758, c785, e540, f7, f137, g97, g98, h84, h131, h194, h202, h326, h337, h521, m346, n495, p147, p249, p351, p947, p987, p1390, p1468, p1543, p1678, p1797, p1898

156: a198, a518, a948, b203, b309, b2811, b3042, c469, c643, f152, f276, h179, h572, p923, p988, p1024, p1592, p1750, s62, s305

157: a31, a210, b2672, b2927, c694, c871, e372, e474, h94, h170, h577, o255, p144, p295, p319, p322, p1229, p1834, p1912, p1989, s117, s417, t256

158: a209, a412, a446, b2195, b2529, c24, c25, c169, c468, c739, c869, e377, f9, f179, h478, h521, m240, m249, n561, p263, p800, p1046, p1622, p1812, t142

159: a820, b928, b2412, b2872, b3049, c697, e338, e368[1], h98, h210, i221, i222, i223, p1348, p1591, p1988, p1997, s74, t392

160: a202, a463, b1707, b2923, c23, c24, f242, g210, h167, h168, h492, i229, m77, o128, o236, p321, p328, p749, p996, p1131, p1182, p1795, p2003, p2016

161: a379, b771, b2482,

b2536, b3026, b3029, c21, c742, h171, h181, h715, l47, m158, m333, o246, p120, p1000, p1045, p1325, p1987, s120, t164

162: a175, a200, a238, a1481, b772, b844, e261, f134, f277, h224, h351, i149, m336, n516, p771, p943, p999, p1209, p1364, p1388, p1480, p1648, p1792, s3, t204, t393, t394

163: a28, a188, a366, b2483, b2725, b3016, b3087, c1, c869, e358, e424, h180, h193, h318, h459, h470, o108, o115, o199, p1754, p1987, p2138, s2, t181, t257, t258

164: a224, a414, b975, b2651, b2677, c675, c825, c836, f202, h219, h225, h438, h496, h497, i123, o270, p924, p925, p1365, p1430, p1991, t155, t228

165: a38, a102, a453, b770, b845, b2609, b2667, b2781, b3075, c1, c759, c804, h356, h515, i122, l47, o218, p227, p921, p1027, p1221, p1516, p1542, p1595, p1603, p2000, s299

166: b2533, b2676, b2919, c642, c752, c760, c762, d298, g157, h223, h508, i121, o240, p963, p1470, p1628, p2027, u116

167: a43, b2661, b2782, c188, c190, c761, c803, c852, e360, e543, h192, h222, h338, h473, m160, m162, o198, o216, p234, p347, p430, p922, p1155, p1198, p1622, p1638, p1639, t760

168: a279, a614, a623, b2496[1], b2548, c176, c189, c470, c471, c472, c807, d1, f199, h187[1], h417, h433, h475, i220, m159, m161, o100, o101, o155, o215, p1001, p1016, p1018, p1310, p1601

169: a20, b376, b854, b974, b2189, b2190, b2910, b3007, b3016, c673, c806, c841, e364, g79, o104, o247, p920, p1328, p1533, s183

170: a38, a206, a252, a371, a487, b746, b2708, c124, c808, d67, d68, d164, e340, e410, e444, f180, g153, g201, h500, h511, h513, h654, m30, m92, m171, o105, p798, p954, p1017, p1973, p2034, p2132

171: a208, b748, b749, b2807, c105, c649, c686, c798, d66, e319, e348, h488, h510, m157, m158, m335, m369, o110, o122, p483, p1448, p1865, p2141, t547

172: a225, b2552, b2705, b2832, c797, e371, h152, h348, o149, p1023, p1145, p1147, p1476, p1971, p1992

173: a189, a625, b373, b374, b536, b750, b843, b2732, b3037, c334, c473, c765, c766, e473, f194, f227, h96, h212, h277, h439, h559, o197, p125, p205, p320, p1173, p1281, p1589, p1677, p2002, s202, s420

174: a49, a286, a1132, b537, b1213, b2503, b2534, b2626, b2869, c755, c763, c764, d20, d74, h110, h141, n500, o287, p220, p317, p964, p1020, p1021, p1022, p1621, t185

175: a1484, b849, b925[1], b2631, b2734, b2738, c207, c930, d75, d268, h346, h582, h611, m67, p482, p613, p956, p961, p1243, p1378, p1392, s422, t173, t196, t761

176: a284, a417, a837, b973, b2718, b2796, b2798, b3025, c117, c335, d203, e368, e529, h166, h174, h207, m100, o205, p1268, p1618, p1777, p2032, t549

177: a204, b846, b850, b2707, b2797, b2802, b2813, c94, d77, d241,

Temperatures in °C; where there is a range of values, the compound is listed according to the lower value.

f119, f154, h142, h352, m376, o201, p206, p359, t48, t197, t548
178: a508, b848, b2624, b2678, b2741, b2787, b2869, c8, c617, c847, e213, e488, f136, h353, i16, l41, l42, l43, o196, o254, p116, p1597, p2006, p2017, t447
179: a41, a460, a921, b2391, b2675, c648, e227, p227, p1220, p1357, p1748, p2005, t391, u52
180: a29, a441, a1134, b535, b2622, b2828, c638, c685, c699, e352, h302, o113, o188, o200, p121, p1157, p1287, p1393, p1700, p1758[1], s245, s246, t213, t475, t590, u21
181: a406, b566, c93, c644, c647, c773, h370, m24, m325, p555, p997, p1522, p2017, p2127
182: b709, b780, b888, b1316, b2151, b2581, b2596, b2623, b2625, b2778, c912, e189, h175, i232, m263, o121, p761, p1475, p1772, t358
183: a35, a290, a365, a465, a730, a1432, b372, b565, b889, b2580, c701, e355, h154, h177, i148, m211, m362, p201, p930, p1419, p1615, p1699, p1839
184: a228, a1002, b245[3], b447, b567, b672, b2766, b2785, b3030, b3082, c699, e365, f186, i150, p688, p1096, p1177, p1375, p2028, p2031, t359, t360, t486
185: a101, a226, a807, b887, b2177, b2620, b2634, b2655, b2831, b3009, b3039, c91, c92, c616, d266, e442, e583, h491, p250, p1158, p1179, p1415, p1753, p295, t52, t167, t281, t476, t703[1]
186: b767, b1858, b2682, b2709, b2717, b2733, b2758, c106, c777, d22, e248, e553, f182, o159, o266, p83, p214,

p219, p1373, p1905
187: a212, a227, a624, a633, a855, a1164, a1133, b245[1], b245[2], b420, b421, b422, b432, b673, b2812, c776, d7, d209, e498, f286, h111, h149, h154, h443, i25, i54, i152, n553, p156, p189, p1590, p2031, t355
188: a280, a309, a310, a311, a823, b346, b674, b828, b2409, b2464, c842, e272, e531, h178, i24, n554, o118, o206, p423, p980, p1008, p1513, p2033, s402, t488
189: b1631, b2735, b3009, c660, c784, d170, e353, e456, m295, p252, p1234, p1290, p1886, s13, s167, s386
190: b671, b927, b1236, b2380, b2615, b2763, b2777, b2937, b3080, c106, c171, e285, e509, h183, n517, n522, o244, p243, p285, p965, p1205, p1223, p1236, p1320, p1947, s296
191: a251, a628, a634, a938, b1291, b2760, c781, f279, p298, p958, p1305, p2018, s19, t498
192: a205, a844, b422, b712, b765, b884, b2614, c133, c662, e433, e496[1], f12, h47, h48, p1389, p1694, p1944, s18, s169, t487
193: a410, b403, b462, b890, c26, c727, c780, d166, d179, d262, f10, f11, f16, h46, h743, i235, o170, p284, p967, p1315, p1970, s192
194: a19, a66, a249, a405, a407, a849, a929, a1105, b371, b423, b710, b711, b745, b2772, b2820, c76, c845, c857, e242, h413, m324, m371, o186, p592, t122, t543, t544
195: a48, a65, a806, b469, b769, b2636, b2777, b3027, b3038, c809, d176, e86, e87, e214, g216, h55, h91, h301, h532, i9, i13,

i151, n552, p283, p1318, s176, t403, t545, t546
196: a248, a250, a256, a1157, b313, b2904, b2906, b3004, c97, c690, c700, c782, d6, d201, e406, h19, o165, o193, p255, p289, p304, p960, p1993, s195, t398, t406, t442
197: a610, b122, b248[1], b402, b446, b463, b468, b766, b943, b1233, b1235, b1268, b2535, b2744, c182, e293, f122, f228, m3, m74, p192, p288, p779, p1146, t176
198: a793, b457, b461, b784, b924[1], b942, b3040, e283, e315, g87, h56, h86, h295, h711, l44, p1014, p1216, p1361, p1995, p2001, p2004, p2133, t229, t444, t542
199: a201, a419, a1229, b158, b329, b707, b885, b2657, b2900, d265, e332, e349, e369, f144, m23, o194, p287, s165, s166, t227
200: b43, b157, b470, b789, b1202, b1286, b1763, b2160, b2421, b2606, b2736, c848, d11, e228, e322, f185[1], m34, m106, m233, n189, p291, p991, p1222, p2022, q103, q105, t259, t283, t443, u32
201: b2152, b2795, c783, c812, f281, m99, o116, t233, t288, t357, t446
202: a191, a368, a645, a707, a861, b339, b2630, c693, e388, f131, m3[2], n520, p247, p1104, p1474, p1645, p1684, p2172, s13, t471, t500
203: a363, a520, a978, a979, a1130, a1140, b338[1], b642, b1099, b3086, c167, d63, e386, e387, f192, h349, n521, p770, p1344, p1431, p2029, g104, t286, t499, t564, t707, u72
204: a148, a260, b159, b312, b440, b481, b641, b708, b2617, c31, c33, c89, h125, h344, h407,

m167, p231, p768, p1333, p1384, p1526, p1920, p1948, p2046, s178, t570
205: a54, a121, a1128, b328, b329, b400, b458, b459, b460, b568, b776, b777, b924, b941, b1790, b2710, b2755, b2968, c440, c692, e436, f257, f261, h427, h454, h587, m111, n377, o172, p258, p662, p1009, p1039, p1826, q102, t437, t497
206: a444, a560, a837, a899, b647, b785, b2607, b2629, b2654, b2788, b2871, b3028, c77, c93, c659, c786, d64, f223, m415, n154, p268, p804, p1408, s162, t233, t374, t551
207: b401, b759, b2422, b2618, c92, c168, c438, c439, c650, d180, e354, h474, m78, m377, p1391, t441, t550
208: a261, a275, b399, b954, b2671, b2776, c843, e367, h158, h431, h568, o166, p360, p428, p1206, p1937, p1961, s4, s224, s257, s398, t98, t457
209: a112, a1043, a1044, a1401, b246, b763, b2688, b3036, d322, h153, n567, p196, p204, p262, p303, p1245, s415, s418, t445, t552, u115
210: a247, a607, a1083, b350, b370, b439, b643, b682, b1635, b1996, b2416, b2721, b2739, b3019, c898, d59, d62, e432, f203, m15, m168, m169, o132, p235, p631, p1143, p1307, p1319, p1417, p1910, s383, t202, t572
211: b680, b747, b764, b891, c5, d58, e296, e437, e443, f240, h495, n155, n186, p425, p632, p1329, t472, t478, t539, t571
212: a262, a263, b67, b354, b441, b649, b678, b2414, b2666,

Temperatures in °C; where there is a range of values, the compound is listed according to the lower value.

b2669, b2859, b3023, c880, g16, i184, i185, n463, n464, n465, o190, o191, o192, o273, p187, p190, p264, p1452, p1484, p1727, t477

213: a920, a1460, b68, b69, b794, b953, b1273, b1787, b1798, d315, e57, e62, f169, g48, m19, m413, n538, n543, p261, p1201, p1244, p1254, p1304, p1643, p2014, p2140, t150, t189, t370, t540

214: a409, a703, b225, b227, b228, b247, b327, b330, b760, b886, b2603, c311, c921, e438, h410, i180, m72, n462, p161, p614, p1010, p1407, p1596, p1636

215: a173, a285, a512, a1247, a1459, b351, b466, b783, b1789, b1797, b2094, b2453, b2605, b2756, b2804, b2903, c652, c702, d319, e532, h466, h468, m95, m379, n185, n461, n536, p776, p1505, p1821, p2114, p2170, t439

216: a1085, b349, b353, b883, b960, b2602, b2653, c130, d284, h408, h474, m164, m165, p342, p659, p679, p1698, s193, s298, t561

217: a621, a624, a1014, b248, b340, b442, b648, b959, b2187, b2703, c209, c184, h472, m380, o256, p431, p650, p1011, p1696, p2150, s307, t438, t491

218: a582, a687, b107, b230, b355, b513, b514, b675, b952, b1266, b1283, b1806, b2393, c210, c882, d177, e389, h717, i36, l168, m25, m310, n14, p218, p270, p778, p1917, p1940, t234, t370, t489

219: a1055, b345, b488, b562, b679, b761, b1795, c927, e394, h444, i167, i226, p633, p990, p1149, p1612, p1613, p1614, p1681,

p2108, s161, t307, t473

220: a631, a642, a704, a1401, b108, b110, b207, b226, b256, b819, b2604, b2683, b2746, b2773, c87, c96, d21, f278, g87, i17, i75, l45, m320, p615, p1261, p1406, p1911, p1945, p2051, p2128, t49, t554

221: a60, a61, b224, b393, b428, b827, b1797, b2145, c219, c220, h471, i236, m119, p138, p305, p1582, p1693, p1811, p1959, t244, t490, t511, t598

222: a615, a1178, b204, b336, b337, b471, b715, b1483, b1805, c208, c441, i13, m40, m60, m89, p117, p248, p1028, p1042, p1224, p1277, p1306, p1635, p2039, q224

223: a62, b109, b349, b367, b1486, b1671, b2417, b2418, b2419, d25, e439, e464, e496, m11, m31, m378, o26, p344, p685, p1105, p1594, t407

224: a312, a1145, b272, b396, b892, b2803, b2838, c180, c596, d49, f188, h437, h672, n466, n539, o237, o239, p1887, p2044, t219, t245, t768

225: a570, a608, a1042, a1139, a1163, b257, b266, b369, b512, b570, b676, b883, b1288, b1421, b1476, b1803, c204, e45, e47, f181, h716, i118, m71, m94, o130, p741, p1571, p394, t401, t553

226: a705, b229, b271, b683, b762, b2670, c467, d235, e419, h147, h440, i135, o176, p226, p301, p953, p1142

227: a580, a662, b456, b705, b855, b876, b1788, b1796, b2683, c672, h40, h42, h685, m417, n537, p995, p1172, p1789, v14, v15

228: a678, b215, b337, b701, b773, b795, b796, b820, b1243, b2116, b2842, b2849,

b2929, h33, h37, h43, h298, h460, i75, p223, p1327, p1769, s256, t305, t399, t599

229: a80, a1016, b214, b352, b3057, c425, c596, d57, d163, d217, f191, g15, h35, m26, o268, p326, p371, p1102, p1451, p1695, q265, t389, t390, t458, t604, t764

230: a376, a613, a922, a1046, b54, b120, b153, b338, b348, b455, b703, b704, b706, b822, b923, b2387, b2587, b2621, b2713, b2714, b2930, c98, c165, e158, e181, f222, g14, h409, h686, m6, m57, m71, n549, o141, p256, p1198[1], p1425, p1481, p1567, s311, s316, s416, t397

231: a1050, a1086, a1139, b82, b311, b702, b714, b1299, b1478, b2116, c47, c211, c212, c213, c751, d173, e440, h34, h39, p302, p612, s306

232: a403, a679, a1048, a1116, b277, b318, b825, b922, b1254, b1471, b2908, c166, c698, g88, i203, m38, m79, p783, p1043, p1788, t90, t152, t180, u128

233: a257, a408, a1050, b56, b213, b368, b551, b553, b797, b821, b1746, b2931, d220, f225, g118, h144, m54, p596, p635, p640, t223, t555, t730

234: a583, a1141, b260, b276, b347, b454, b742, b864, b1470, b1662, b1796, p195, p993, p1270, p1560, p1702, p2145, s7, s215, t118, t172

235: a923, a1414, a1498, b85, b151, b208, b320, b389, b398, b473, b484, b563, b677, b793, b971, b1069, b1428, b1804, b2621, b2901, b3002, c202, e313, f246, m7, m56, o245, p1044, p1610, p2107, s185, t340, t375, t400, t404, t448, b449, t716

236: b689, b1727, b2858,

b2928, e441, h684, p421, p593, p1644, p1864, s212, t336, t364, t431

237: a732, b179, b321, b397, b525, b550, b681, b832, b1484, c129, c827, e385, h675, p160, p949, p2171, t302, t342

238: a611, a829, b212, b255, b258, b367, b644, b753, b754, b800, b1468, b2139, b2186, b2658, b2850, b3084, e343, p300, p1574, p1703, q34, s358, t414, t556, u110

239: a573, b287, b395, b717, b830, b1680, c866, o162, p990, p1427

240: a370, a495, a700, a713, a946, a1539, b125, b215, b289, b392, b394, b713, b877, b933, b1667, b1781, c30, c227, c826, e287, e556, e573, h452, h676, h680, i195, m101, o127, o164, p1235, p1258, p2047, q241, t182, t295, t299, t300, t417, t461

241: a663, b259, b524, b609, c102, d22, d41, d47, i35, n218, p1880, q7, t303, t308, t450, t463, t601

242: a294, a601, a1041, b319, b474, b774, b1243, b1282, b1543, d213, h20, i196, n472, o262, t285, t306

243: a683, a1135, a1147, b152, b316, b933, b1469, b1771, d50, e265, h31, h694, i188, i217, m348, p665, p751, p1559, p2038

244: a190, a400, a597, a698, b831, b1414, b2681, c37, c46, c441, c704, c846, h411, h704, h705, p664, p1642, t274, t291, t603

245: a572, a587, a599, a605, a646, a671, a699, a1004, a1077, a1115, b115, b283, b478, b569, b645, b718, b751, b775, b798, b801, b826, b1014, b1412, b1425, b1477, b1767, b2492,

Temperatures in °C; where there is a range of values, the compound is listed according to the lower value.

b2816, c164, c810, c917, d169, d174, d207, f274, h156, h385, h536, i200, m58, m217, p224, p299, p1255, p1667, p1697, p2116, q183, q276, t304, t316, t367, t576, t750, t751, u117

246: a559, a680, a712, a835, a930, b430, b472, b564, b932, b3011, d313, h435, i197, h471, n473, p651, p652, p703, p1877, t432, t608

247: a581, a661, b84, b114, b135, b823, b1015, i18, p1186, p1572, p2129, q209, t456, t575

248: a1117, b382, b390, b391, b2125, b2148, c422, d212, h52, p188, p368, p1535, p2117, q153, q199, q277, s26, s356, t339

249: a648, a669, a895, b116, b154, b380, b752, b812, b1239, b1501, c36, c360, i225, p1187, p1642[1], t100, t508

250: a484, a571, a647, b288, b387, b817, b818, b935, b1031, b1267, b1680, b2841, c29, d236, f187, h53, h78, h145, h160, h406, h644, h714, m21, m68, p179, p740, p1464, p1983, p2169, s179, t287, t292, t341, t516

251: a394, a1017, a1078, a1146, b743, b934, b1097, b1415, b1611, b2932, c823, q223, s198, t467

252: a1076, b343, b344, b875, b1773, d206, h44, h134, p782, p1949, s68, t92, t462

253: a152, a243, a481, b209, c339, e611, h24, i196, i212, p634, p739, t67, t294, t338, v15

254: a1118, a1159, b206, b542, b714, b931, b1270, b1284, b1413, b1765, b2274, b2392, h430, l56, p309, p1962, s227

255: a655, a1425, b275, b515, b552, b555, b811, b916, b972, b1419, b1768, b1811,

b2320, c27, d311, h428, i21, i23, i65, l2, n534, p367, q82, q129, t117, t297, t420, t435, t575

256: a709, a825, b358, b492, b744, b1319, b1780, b1781, b2214, b2299, d205, e346, g114, h426, i198, n110, p595, p686, p738, p1035, p2121, s190, t166, t386

257: b265, b342, b388, b554, i7, i67, j6, p694, p1015, p1822, t289, t578

258: a124, a701, b103, b359, b559, b862, b863, b1071, b1512, b1619, b1785, b2839, c355, e414, e494, e510, g106, i201, n182, p1691, p1913, q198

259: a1026, b274, b378, b415, b451, b1622, d285, n109, n181, q197, t509

260: a153, a667, a1056, a1080, b2, b221, b299, b1272, b1495, b1561, b1612, b1658, b1666, b1772, b2381, b2780, d290, e183, k10, o96, o174, o283, p172, p188, p1564, p1850, q194, q231, s24, t225, t232, t413, t418, t708, u35, u41

261: b211, b1419, b1766, b2635, c359, h151, h434, o9, p1575, q83, q126, s186

262: a134, a1070, a1187, b232, b809[1], b1287, b1426, b1778, b3065, c230, d303, h139, p641, p1253, p1577, q85, q196, s210, t706, t729, u71

263: a937, b117, b160, b418, b530, b1320, b1513, b1792, c361, i238, n258, p297, p805, p1581, t87, t434, t470, t727, u56

264: a1027, b379, b610, b756, b1615, c62[1], m271, o140, p777, q127, q195, t574

265: a17, a574, a600, b133, b357, b506, b531, b603, b791, b809[1], b815, b915, c41, c44, c163, c348, h535, i72, i199, k3[1], n35,

p643, p1549, p1551, p1555, p1556, q81, q131, s196, t424

266: a165, b1810, q128, t451, t736

267: a73, b494, b558, b755, b816, b1034, b1276, b1581, b2322, e570, i41, o242, o271, p1692, p1810, q154, q171, q271, t388, t464

268: a1087, b231, b560, b1317, b1582, c357, h146, m87, n168, n169, o145, p40, p1214, q132, u61

269: b532, b1494, b1779, g90, i144, l65, q96, t385

270: a255, a670, a686, a1024, a1186, a1658, b601, b605, b659, b1322, b1658, b1693, b1784, b2300, b2847, c60, d42, e495, h464, n574, p931, p1764, p2021, p2073, q68, t218, t514

271: a830, a841, b950, c356, f125, p32, p165, p704, p2146

272: a1079, a1166, b526, b1275, b1663, b1874, b2361, b2771, c264, e309, h493, i71, p1538

273: a664, a809, a1019, b716, b1822, b2301, b2321, d301, g75, g169, h49, n476, p125, p205, p320, p1173, p1581 p1922, t327, t422, t580

274: a493, b164, b863, b1583, b2248, b2318, c7, c38, i153, i166, n170, n216, q67, s189

275: a1075, a1081, a1445, b636, b842, b949, b1618, b1775, b1800, b1840, b1842, b1848, c304, h7, h50, h182, h439, m114, p1404, p1763, t23, t24, t565

276: a986, b220, b574, b586, b1018, b1673, b1749, b2310, d288, h150, n467, p638, p1967, t95, t582, t717

277: b270, b583, b861, b919, b920, b1747, d178, d304, e416, o168, t101

278: b93, b284, b575, f127, q57, q70, t732, t735

279: a4, a1066, t1851, m76, m293, p681

280: a1109, a1137, b298, b836, b1686, b2302,

b2363, c125, e490, g47, h22, h151, i8, i193, j9, n179, n477, o163, o301, p308, p1568, p1741, p2007, p2026, p2042, q69, q109, q227, s413, t16, t18, t25, t567

281: a81, a860[1], c421, n93, n94, p818, q137, q226, t17, t138

282: b493, b534, b809, b1020, b1960, c203, e395, n8, n180, o144, p697, q184, q186, t26

283: a155, a213, b301, b486, b757, h194[1], q192, t425, t433

284: b756, b2249, h270, h274, p813, p824

285: a567, a798, a908, b139, b523, b577, b639, b640, b1271, b1716, b1821, c367, e237, e588, g27, h394, i134, k18, n147, n210, p839, p843, q225, s274, s335

286: a536, a677[1], a909, b638, b1211, b2312, c62, c351, c718, e236, e390, e508, h30, j12, m294, n144, p162, p948, p1968, q92, t31

287: a1168, b2846, c433, h248, p1969, q228, q230, s200

288: a1087, a1088, b835, b906, b1328, c403, c681, c717, e525, f126, g191, i10, m288, n190, n211, q87, q278

289: a648, b837, h248, n215, p775, t99, t468

290: b604, b1244, b2852, c859, g70, h155, n330, p27, p897, p2155, q71, q130, s354, t209, t597

291: b726, b1715, b2250, b2364, n126, n172, n375, n527, o167, p39, p2154, t68

292: a1185, b2303, i171, t70, t421, t671

293: a649, a891, a1233, a1513, b487, b522, f45, n248, p746, p842, t725

294: b170, b1219, b1326, c432, n38, n88, p870

295: a697, a831, a890, b1685, b1776, b2303, b2362, b2701, h391, n191, p510, p813, p823, t82, t84

296: a166, a688, b517,

BOILING POINT INDEX OF ORGANIC COMPOUNDS (Continued)

Temperatures in °C; where there is a range of values, the compound is listed according to the lower value.

b732, b926, b1849,
b2242, c240, n24,
q90, s317, t20, t718
297: a860, b278, b872,
b1692, b2365, m366,
n319
298: b788, d292, e239,
e470, m239[1], p821,
p1308, s310
299: b727, b1295, b2220,
b2243, n322
300: a737, a803, a817,
a1182, b873, b1300,
b1315, b1931, c350,
e602, g175, h80, k23,
m46, m186, o143,
p1168, p1292, t461,
t479, t619, t734
301: b1540, m373, n25,
n36, p2074, s14, s33
302: a863, b1019, b1028,
b2222, b3044, h66,
n208, p33, p158, s64
303: a145, a167, h726,
i111, t30
304: a164, m178, n239,
n328, p828, q64, q167
305: a1210, a1169, b870,
b2311, b2314, b2366,
e326, m255, n171,
n249, n363, q185,
s129, t347
306: a818, b871, b1959,
c175, d35, n38, n331
307: a801, a1175, b1301,
b2293, i27, n556, o173
308: h74, m50, n209,
n220, n329
309: b961, b2016, p684
310: a1015, b269, b1337,
b1566, b1845, b2244,
b2922, d248, e376,
e511, g110, m243,
n320, p1570, q47, x1
311: g120, p722, t22

312: a271, a804, a865,
a900, b219, b279, c513
313: o93, p877
314: b1295, b1297, b1302,
b2017, p1966
315: a39, a1176, b435,
b437, b438, b981,
b2267, e165, e502,
n329, p950, x1
316: a913, b1303, n184,
o11
317: b1837, b2252, e491,
n220, n221, p1824
318: p28
319: a10, a805, a901,
b725, q133
320: a828, a1211, b280,
b331, b1656, b2317,
b2323, h77, h293, k7,
n87, p955, q56, t14,
t15, u28
321: a802
322: b787, e586, h244,
h246, p34
323: b1265, h45, m272,
n222, t21
324: b2068, q123
325: b2219, b2275, c156,
e427, m281, n30, s105
326: e517, k16, t222
327: b2018, c864, n515
328: b2294, e18, p1184[1],
t94, t96
329: b929, e148[1], n505,
p871[1]
330: a502, a883, a902,
a936, b1979, b1989,
e516, g112, o83, p137,
p825, p1439
331: c158, p1682
332: a1170, b1981, d134,
e518, t46
333: a1422, b595, b2006,
h265, o92, q58
334: n246, t496

335: a9, b1533, b2144,
e587
336: b945, h67, h245
337: f121, p810
338: b2067, b2158,
e512, o294, p1179[2]
339: a1571, p875
340: a882, a1193, a1599,
b865, b946, b2325,
b3056, e29, f96, p484,
p817, s387, t97, t248
341: e28, f80
342: b2014, b2276, c610
343: b2329, e16, f207[2],
h519
344: b1945, d33, d36,
h269
345: a727, b1976, c245,
h73, n247, p820
346: b1198
348: e280, o16
349: h68, o12, p526, x12
350: b1401, b1978, b2066,
b2449, c354, m284,
m285, s109, t269,
u62
351: t130
353: b1988
354: a866, b2015
355: b1871, b2215, b2266,
c141
356: h59
357: e22, h249, t130
358: e270, m312, o248
359: t72
360: a1441, b1262, b2129,
c114, c300, h262,
m376, o22, o295,
p803, q8, q135, q152,
q158, q163
362: o35
363: b2258, q218
364: n260
365: a947, k20, t47
366: t135

369: d272, e21
371: p716, t249
374: b721
375: f44, p19
379: s359
380: a919, b1248, m152,
m381, t711
383: o18
385: b1672
390: h253, m197, s201,
p506[1]
391: t62
393: p1930
395: a912, b1986
398: b1229, m192
400: a916, b2261, s218
405: s378
410: b724, p789
412: h234, s143
413: b1229
415: b978, e423, h264
417: a1234
418: b418
419: o249
420: q1, s141
422: h63
425: b1957
430: a1286
431: m300, o1
435: b181
441: n502[1]
442: o33
445: n175
446: n387
448: c313
450: t699
452: b2208
458: h61
459: b982
467: d323
471: a858
480: b1228
518: p908
546: s132

Spectra Index of Organic Compounds

This index is a listing of the Sadtler Standard Spectra, infrared prism, and also contains the infrared grating (HR), the UV, and NMR numbers of many compounds listed in the Table of Physical Constants of Organic Compounds of the Handbook of Chemistry and Physics. In the NMR column of this index, the Varian numbers are preceded by the letter V and the JEOL numbers either by the symbol * which represents 100 Mc spectra, or the letter F (F-19 spectra) or J (60 Mc spectra). The various media in which some spectra were run are designated at the end of the reference number by one of the following abbreviations:

B, Between salts (Neat)		K, KBr
C, Cell		M, Mull
F, Film		S, Solution
G, Gas		

HCP No.	Prism	HR	UV	NMR
a1	3963			
a2	5151		1399	
a4	875	548	272	65
	7458	175		
a9	20181			
a14	14633		4140	
a17	13704		3631	
a18	5824			V6
a21	5274			V143
a22	5273			2949
a23	4128	8324	1193	
a25	15391			V373
a31	2395			3001
a32	8000			3827
a33	8040			
a39	18393			
a48	5176			
a52	4626			
a58	76			V8
a59	6476			
a60	69			4280
	13207			
	2217			
a62	26009	1854		427
a69	19170			
a72	5756			
a73	1818	281	510	
a79	4590	416	1271	
a80	1903			
a81	6633		1831	V601
a85	34756	12739		
a87	34758	12741		
a89	7335(K)		2070	
a89	2729(M)		2070	
a90	20856		8039	3015
a105	11270		3078	
a106	20128		6707	
a121	2296			146
a124	24023			1345
a128	24126	794	8443	2921
a129	19561		6428	
a130	1602	261	2913	
a142	13934		3810	
a145	9706		2573	
a147	22087			
a148	15060			
a150	9768			
a152	20972	10488	8130	2403
a156	2164	297	571	
a157	2165	298	572	131
a159	5855	8419	1638	3184
a160	12384			
a161	11426(K)		3138	5129

HCP No.	Prism	HR	UV	NMR
a162	7489			
a164	160	49	63	5235
a166	2899	350	830	175
a167	2900	351	831	
a168	2901		832	V239
a170	6474			
a172	70			
a173	859	167	260	V530
a174	1867			4980
a178	1041	10971		V140
a180	5250			
a182	18668			V141
a183	6030(gas)			
a185	6640			
a188	14890	10036		4924
a189	22788	10579		
a190	2973			
a197	982	8112		V65
a198	5284			
a199	4	3		V79
a200	58			
a201	108			
a203	11912			
a204	1475	249	420	V167
a205	5249			
a207	5166			
a208	4574	10946		217
a212	15649			
a213	5552		1546	
a215	164	50		
a216	772	10769		V440
a217	1473	10939		99
a218	11299			
a219	18372	10112	5831	4226
a221	2228			
a223	6650			281
a240	9683		2571	
a241	269			
a242	13213			
a245	17371		7321	
a247	3875			
a253	1911	10975		
a255	19118			
a256	5152		1400	
a259	1643	10940		115
a260	5968			
a262	8043		2175	
a263	1649	267	1458	
a275	2325			
a277	9717			

HCP No.	Prism	HR	UV	NMR
a279	6338			
a281	6334	10988		4205
a309	2094			
a312	2975			
a365	1302			92
a367	2993			
a369	1301	234		91
a374	1318			95
a375	5183			
a387	13137		3424	
a388	13138		3425	
a389	13139	259	457	V500
a391	25003	1003		
a395	26035	1878	9443	411
a402	17518			
a403	23667			
a407	2806			166
a408	12551			4967
a411	6264			
a412	5248			V59
a415	4561			
a418	13141	8174	3427	
a420	14891			
a421	25710	1584	9298	
a423	11174	132	176	
a430	1947	8213	11441	
a434	2112		560	129
a435	19246			
a437	10958			
a440	10650		2918	
a441	1938	289	534	
a444	7392			V417
a446	22898	10593		
a451	9766			
a453	17442			
a456	3990			
a458	5829			
a464	695			
a465	5141			
a471	13457		3518	4410
a475	23517			V554
a476	19191	708		
a481	2346			
a484	25017	1010		
a492	26717	2468	10026	1603
a495	17420		7333	
a499	796	8096	11410	
a503	10591			
a504	30353	6346		4312
a506	4562			214
a507	26608	2373		1754
a508	22423			
a509	20584		7915	

HCP No.	Prism	HR	UV	NMR	HCP No.	Prism	HR	UV	NMR	HCP No.	Prism	HR	UV	NMR
a515	7248				a688	15183		4491		a870	8963			
a516¹	21997				a689	3415		1066		a871	19698			
a517	29288	5284	12029	1330	a692	27912	3638	10858		a880	10524			
a518	22483				a693	32461	9457		4363	a882	20343	10374	6837	2328
a520	6533				a697	19571		6437	V234	a884	1292	232	388	681
a522	25206				a699	20308		6817		a886	34522	12506		5762
a523	6953	8490		2863	a700	20309	10362	6818	2314	a887	9744			
a524	6265				a701	3883		1177		a892	390		153	
a525	19936			V28	a702	20467	10387	6914	2340	a893	2243			
a534	6263	8454	1727	3192	a703	23784				a907	24683			
a535	18504		5928	4141	a704	22460	10575		2758	a911	179	58	72	21
a538	5870	8422	1646		a705	872	174	270		a912	155	48	61	
a539	5871	504	1647		a706	21154		8267		a918	15374			
a540	5874	585	2965		a707	5857		1639	531	a919	18406		5864	1899
a542	17537				a708	5112				a920	1187			84
a549	24457		8611		a710	20551		7894		a921	30298	6294		
a553	8441	505	2237	3223	a711	20552		7895		a923	23726			
a554	1801		503	V495	a712	20573				a925	227	76		29
a558	22237	10524		2512	a713	20574		7908	2368	a926	6605			
a559	23016				a721	7536				a928	23641	10622		3630
a560	32069	9067		4324	a727	1153		342	81	a929	18732	8882		2068
a567	5852	500	1637	264	a732	7591		2125		a931	1322			
a570	4723				a737	10786	10790	13286		a939	9718			
a574	1655		474	117	a738	7560		2117		a940	6377			
a575	2236	308	599		a742	27864	3590		835	a946	6375	521		
a579	4575			J106	a743	5446		1497		a947	24568	4808		
a580	882	10770	275	66	a744	5473				a948	2244			
a581	13594	8186	3579		a745	10784				a949	1313			
a582	165	4764	64	19	a752	23488				a953	8887			
a583	2231	307	598	135	a754	794	164			a954	8962			
a584	1633	265	467	720	a756	23489				a955	25746	1615	9315	
a589	417			V7	a756¹	795				a956	23636			
a591	7865				a759	23283	10910	13329		a957	11279			
a593	5970	8440	11494		a764	10623				a960	23618	10615	13339	3622
a597	20772	10425	7993	3052	a772	1935				a966	10266			
a600	6517		1810	272						a967	21884			
a601	31679	7665		2398	a773	23495				a969	5957			
a602	8336				a775	6488				a970	5958			
a603	17479		5550		a779	21948				a975	5959			
a605	22002				a788	3555				a977	21995			
					a795	18248								
a608	7387									a982	16450		5152	
a610	11346			6						a992	718			
a623	22016				a798	288		114	1178	a1002	3695	392	1129	191
a625	927				a802	2323	8251	618	148	a1003	8948		2299	
a635	13148	8175	3432		a816	11301				a1004	10645	582		
					a817	10943	8585	2978	3277					
a636	13149		3433			17113				a1008	6291		1731	
a640	2503				a819	17392	680	5526		a1011	5447	8397	1498	1217
a643	20686		7953							a1014	13702			
a645	3226	8290	953	V192						a1015	2731	339	743	1208
a646	5780		1618		a820	3195				a1016	9779			
					a821	3196								
a647	18351		5845	4987	a825	1033	208			a1017	16154			
a648	1843		518	119	a827	3194				a1018	6630	8481	1829	278
a649	5111	8370	1387	242		8960				a1022	25596	1473	9229	
a650	5023		1384		a828	5451			257	a1024	12473			
a652	24148	807	8459	2673						a1025	12410			
					a830	5830								
a653	8489		2228	240	a831	24492	4752	8634		a1027	12442			
a654	8626	561		1889	a832	277		110		a1030	32013	9014		4317
a655	4580	414	1267	219	a836	34412	12397			a1034	25572	1449	11540	
a657	6642	8483	1835	3206	a841	24958				a1035	1517			
a661	4576	8338	1264	3174						a1041	6643	532	1836	280
					a843	24957								
a664	1769	272	494	V188	a847	2246			136	a1042	21769			V568
a668	6641	531	1834	279	a848	1059				a1046	1262		376	88
a669	27877	3603		866	a850	1140				a1047	16545		5193	
a671	28837	4539	11355		a851	5452				a1048	1317	8140	393	V123
a672	28838	4540	11356	376						a1049	9752			
					a856	20605			V375					
a674	8764	8379		1555	a860	3198				a1053	21003		8154	
a675	19180	10815	6276	4286	a861	9728				a1057	8926		2291	
a678	3884				a863	68	8009	30	11	a1058	13917	8634	3799	3257
a685	9770				a865	20665		6963	3588	a1059	21922			
a687	6011	512	1695	532						a1060	10564	8344	2909	3237

HCP No.	IR Prism	IR HR	UV	NMR
a1061	21913			
a1068	23709			2378
a1069	24256	884	8517	2568
a1070	19145		6258	
a1074	21004		8155	
a1075	2304	321	612	147
a1076	19095		6233	5005
a1078	780	8093	253	58
a1079	6459		1794	271
a1080	19146	8973	6259	2164
a1084	6529		1814	
a1085	216	72	83	716
a1090	5890	508	1655	3186
a1098	24026			
a1102	19181		7705	5012
a1104	18927	8944	6158	2138
a1105	6	4	3	1
a1109	25194	1108	8994	
a1110	14894		4313	
a1111	5891		2908	
a1113	1287	231	387	3290
a1114	17483		5551	
a1115	26402	2180	9792	431
a1116	4674	8340	1285	236
a1118	4675	8341	1286	V208
a1128	9167		2378	1890
a1132	19615			5031
a1133	19616	715	9650	5032
a1134	19617		6459	5033
a1135	8418		2234	
a1136	17451			
a1137	17800		5637	
a1138	18976		6181	
a1140	30297	6293	12762	1335
a1141	1568		449	
a1157	6365	8463	1754	3203
a1158	10647			
a1162	18329		5832	V489
a1164	20537			V488
a1165	21134	750	9663	
a1166	19425			
a1168	1276	229	385	
a1169	205	70	80	
a1170	8451		2243	
a1175	4493		1246	
a1176	4494		1247	
a1177	4495		1248	
a1182	9769		2576	
a1186	20524		7882	
a1193	1319	239	394	
a1208	3506	381	1084	V618
a1210	19205	709	6290	V307
a1214	5436			254
a1220	19880		6579	
a1221	19875		6574	
a1224	11383			
a1230	21292		9681	
a1231	20504	10402	6940	V317
a1232	20358		6850	
a1233	15221	628	4511	550
a1246	24157	814	8465	
a1248	1815	279	508	
a1249	13893	8629	3787	
a1250	13894	8630	3788	
a1261	5770		1611	
a1263	2984		859	182
a1264	1855			
a1267	14895		4314	
a1268	2983	8283	858	
a1273	14896			

HCP No.	IR Prism	IR HR	UV	NMR
a1279	19109	8962	6238	
a1282	19122		6244	
a1288	8810		2284	
a1292	5420		4318	
a1294	3585			
a1295	3588			
a1298	3579			
a1307	22405	10560		2738
a1314	11414			
a1315	11256		3068	
a1316	6342	8459	1746	3200
a1317	18319	10108	5830	4221
a1333	21103			
a1336	3598			
a1337	3596			
a1342	14897	8695	4315	
a1353	18664			
a1354	18163	8824		
a1370	15657	4702	4443	
a1379	7520			
a1391	25687	1563		
a1393	15309			
a1398	15662		4704	4444
a1402	9603			
a1403	18700			2078
a1404	25689	1565		
a1405	13418			
a1454	2384			V276
a1457	13217	470	3455	3126
a1459	15266			
a1461	17219			
a1463	5425			
	7919			
a1465	6793			
a1469	18670	8857	5999	2070
a1477	4816			
a1478	21993			
a1599	23694		9711	
a1601	4847		1345	
a1643	11578		3203	
a1645	11577		3203	
a1652	6649		1837	
a1655	19108	8961		
a1658	10783			V551
b2	11337	8346	3094	
b8	22214	10511		
b9	6471		1798	
b11	24419	990		
b14	17178		5423	1173
b15	27744	3479	11668	1121
b21	27981	3705	10887	
b25	483		171	
b26	31693	7677		
b31	5971		1679	
b35	3010	364	868	V151
b36	5702	485	1584	702
b43	25698	1574	9290	
b44	20678		7948	3606
b48	15304		4569	
b50	15643			
b54	9988			
b56	19509			
b57	18083	10081	5724	4047
b65	5767	495	1609	
b67	625	8076	208	50
b68	13491			

HCP No.	IR Prism	IR HR	UV	NMR
b69	624	8075	207	V146
b81	620	10845	205	3151
b84	622		2066	
b94	7203	542	2044	534
b95	14539			
b97	19175		6271	
b98	19176	10196	6272	4283
b102	17472		7344	
b103	3887	8313	1179	V236
b111	6652		1838	V238
b118	5178	211	318	1320
b121	16462	10048	5155	4218
b122	9989	8567	2646	3232
b123	5705		1586	
b124	5985			V156
b125	2126		562	
b128	4579		1266	
b133	1273	9997	383	528
b136	18980		6183	
b139	8703			197
b151	5973	510	1680	
b152	13224	8614	3456	1895
b154	1946	10848	536	126
b157	32149	9147	13722	3936
b159	21549			
b160	3885		1178	V187
b162	3516		1091	V148
b165	9990(K)		626	
b168	3517	384	1092	
b181	1124		335	
b185	9268		2412	
b186	9269			
b187	9259			
b188	9260		2404	
b190	9261		2405	
b191	9262		2406	
b192	9263		2407	
b197	11260		3071	
b202	6402		1765	3429
b203	13701	10873	3630	3248
b206	17520		5557	4257
b209	3880			V260
b215	15603		4680	
b224	17119	663	5403	893
b225	4677	10778	1288	237
b226	34116	12106		5580
b227	7555	10785		
b228	17112	8718	5399	3276
b229	17391	679	5525	5577
b236	18768	8896	6054	2099
b245[2]	5859	8420	1640	V207
b246	1601		3239	111
b248	28862	4564	11849	493
b248[1]	280	8027	113	35
b256	15599		4676	1896
b260	1568		449	
b262	18932		6159	
b276	5340		1462	
b277	5555		1549	
b278	8240			
b281	4560			1882
b282	19167		6269	
b283	4887		1364	
b287	28918	4620		497
b288	32737	9732		4612
b289	13674		3624	3254
b293	20546	10412	7890	2362
b309	3227	366	954	1212
b310	32858	9852		4585
b311	2107			

HCP No.	Sadtler Reference Number IR Prism	HR	UV	NMR	HCP No.	Sadtler Reference Number IR Prism	HR	UV	NMR	HCP No.	Sadtler Reference Number IR Prism	HR	UV	NMR
b312	20098	10311	6684	2268	b487	6455		1791		b699	19653	10253	7802	2228
b313	16343				b490	1996		6636	3839	b706	12172	601	11527	
b314	4555	10776	3519	3251	b492	1604	262	460	112	b707	19395			
b325	16566		5203		b493	6522		1813	V458	b708	19398		9642	
b329	9736				b494	4111	8322	1187		b709	18712	8874	6024	2082
b330	20131		6710		b503	2971		855		b710	18926	8943	6157	2139
b338	2268	317	607	V198	b507	25940	1788	9405		b711	19397		9641	
b339	4617	424	1279	223	b508	5862		1641		b712	19396		9640	
b340	4682	434	1289		b512	12459	605			b713	20289	10357	6805	2311
b341	5727			V121	b513	2394	324			b714	20290		6806	
b342	5728		1590		b514	2393	323	625		b715	23688	775	9710	320
b344	6387	522	1764		b520	24259	7989	8520	2571	b717	17346		5498	
b345	21358				b523	22989	10598		2548	b718	2397			
b348	19440		7785		b525	25092	1067			b725	12397			
b351	2258	8249	605	141	b527	708		233		b726	81	27	33	
b353	4737	441	1305	239	b529	7244	8498	2053	3127	b727	3657			
b354	18666		5997	J114	b530	24266	887	8523	2574	b731	33630	11621	14277	5794
b355	6345	8460	1748	3201	b535	1003	201	303	746	b732	3511	383	1087	712
b356	20969	10485	8128	2426	b536	5934		1671		b739	7033		1983	V149
b357	16554		5198		b537	146	44	55	715	b740	20321	10365	7864	
b358	7897(K)		505		b542	11926				b742	2888	346	821	
b368	18806		6078		b554	19172	10195	6270	4282	b744	19706		6494	
b370	2720	334	735		b555	3655	387	1114	687	b745	9730(C)	10788	2303	V193
b372	6318	8457	1739	3425	b558	3656	388	1115	688	b746	192	4826	77	26
b374	247	83	98	31	b559	17387		5521		b748	26404	2182	9794	434
b376	679	152	228	53	b562	2890	347	823	171	b750	27954	3679	10871	335
b385	18719	8877	6029	2085	b564	711	157	235	309	b757	8446		2240	
b389	20023		6648		b565	24283		8528		b758	246	82	97	V505
b390	16264		5046		b566	18713		6025	4993	b759	2340			
b391	20162	10331	6731	2285	b567	24284		8529		b760	2339			
b392	13668		3618	J130	b568	19517				b761	2341			
b393	11626				b569	268		108	V124	b768	31977	7957		3943
b394	21107		8229	J131	b571	2861		802		b770	19677	722	9655	
b395	522	133	179	47	b574	467	125	2572		b773	1579		455	109
b396	257	89	103	525	b575	5551	481	1545	699	b775	19659			5040
b397	14511	622	4124	V288	b576	1624(C)	263	2103		b778	4615	8339	1278	222
b398	1061	8118	322	527	b577	153	47	60		b779	3509			
b403	8311		2215	V586	b578	5189	455	2078	252	b780	21875			
b407	34	19	16	714	b594	8318		2216		b781	15345	638	4587	3271
b413	13916	8633	3798		b595	8339	10856	2223	3219	b782	4670			233
b415	5553	8404	1547		b601	20311		6819		b783	21876			
b417	26968	2714	10217	3299	b605	13502				b784	19614	714	9649	5030
b418	1625	264	9787		b606	20276	10355			b785	4618	425	1280	224
b422	13675		3625		b609	19974				b787	4545	410		
b423	23015				b610	20540	10410	7885		b788	26949	2695	11601	
b435	964	196	5204		b613	9807				b789	33623	11614	14272	
b437	25163	1087	8976		b620	24849				b791	16015	648	4937	
b439	4671	431	1283	234	b621	21378				b794	11624			1893
b441	4672	432	1284	235	b626	7847	552	2154		b796	1073		326	
b442	13922		3802		b637	9534				b797	1916	286	531	V270
b446	8637				b640	4544		1258	207	b800	2470	325	653	684
b449	21856				b642	2958	356			b808	1017	8115	311	76
b450	21858				b643	2957	355			b816	487			
b451	6627	10855	1827	3205	b647	1658	8189	476	1112	b820	16263		5045	
b454	2892	348	825	690	b648	11030		2999	1891	b823	486		172	
b456	6871	535	10886		b649	1508				b824	488	130	173	707
b458	21703				b654	19576			5028	b825	3821			
b459	21704				b657	25106	1074			b827	295	8029	115	
b460	6760				b658	19579		7797		b828	2891	8270	824	172
b461	8802		2281		b660	11	9	7	V201	b830	9737			
b463	2727	338	741	164	b661	1045	210	317	V202	b831	20115		6696	
b465	4597	419	1274		b662	2276	319	609	V203	b832	19431	710	7778	V153
b470	895	178	279	68	b675	2342				b835	20984		8140	
b472	3231				b676	3819	393	1162	193	b836	2894			
b473	3232		958		b678	294	100		36	b837	6869		1919	
b474	4683	435	1290	V122	b679	8080	349	83		b838	6704			
b483	18318	10107	7579	4220	b680	1065	10846	323	82	b840	6703		1863	
b484	8033	8520	2712	J188	b682	521		178		b843	26669	2427	9995	
b485	19704		6492		b688	23629				b844	1075			80
b486	17169		5417		b692	19411		7773		b846	11619			

HCP No.	Prism	HR	UV	NMR	HCP No.	Prism	HR	UV	NMR	HCP No.	Prism	HR	UV	NMR
b847	242	8023	95	V240	b1032	19477	8999	6376	2177	b1239	779	162	252	57
b850	1066		324	V268	b1038	18164		5766		b1243	13700		3626	
b854	317		2919		b1039	28929	4631	11386		b1244	2732	340	744	689
b855	19428				b1043	32444	9440	13794		b1247	3630		1102	
b859	2988	362	861	J101	b1044	2910		838		b1251	3624	385		
b861	5864		1643	1887	b1047	16400		5128		b1256	18879	8918	6124	2117
b862	9757(C)				b1049	16401		7079		b1262	2702	565	2267	155
b863	5865	8421	1644	3185	b1054	19977		6623		b1265	1509	253	427	V627
b864	1467	8156	419	V258	b1056	20141		6714		b1267	2711	331	732	158
b872	4598	420	1275	696	b1058	20285		6801		b1268	3	5402	2	3417
b877	13471		3520		b1060	28932	4634	11875	873	b1273	1506	252	426	1204
b882	34871	12853			b1061	9716				b1274	34847	12830		5819
b884	1574			*160	b1066	2668				b1276	15671		4706	
b891	12	10	8	4	b1067	2667				b1278	29349	5315	12058	1009
b893	24813	4969	8786		b1068	201	69	2285		b1279	3888			
b894	21426				b1079	6165				b1282	1006	202	304	75
b895	20450		7878	2341	b1080	6166				b1283	9724			
b896	1879		525		b1083	13396				b1286	1052	212	319	78
b897	1884				b1086	19598	10240	6455	5029	b1287	1866	283	524	
b898	1885		526		b1091	13662		3616		b1290	8453			
b905	28878	4580	11853		b1092	5733		1593		b1291	2255	312	602	138
b906	20523	10406	6944	2356	b1093	5760	493	1606	1174	b1295	3856	8311	1171	3173
b916	21414			V287	b1094	7646		2142	3214	b1298	2881		814	
b922	9755				b1095	5670				b1299	20990			
b924	23608	772	9709	*157	b1097	415	118	154	3150	b1303	921	185	285	1187
b925	12455				b1098	15653		4700		b1306	5736	489	1595	1218
b926	34263				b1099	1379				b1314	2703	330	729	3159
b927	34920	12890			b1101	15277		4550		b1315	10971	8588	2987	
b928	5654				b1103	5735	488	1594		b1316	910	182	283	655
b931	5935				b1108	18667				b1317	3868			
b933	2976	360	856	1179	b1110	17193		5427		b1318	949	193	295	
b941	20568	10417	6956	815	b1112	2435		3235		b1319	897	280	1200	
b942	23781				b1113	301	102	117		b1323	6493	526	1802	2822
b943	1199	224	355	85	b1139	6623		1826		b1326	28938	4640		801
b944	24595	4825	8694	2698	b1143	14531	8692	4127	3263	b1329	1542		441	
b950	17183		5424		b1144	6457				b1333	5154		1402	243
b952	5936	509	1673	266	b1145	34349	12335	14458		b1335	7605		2131	V302
b953	4600	422	1277	221	b1157	22724				b1336	7542	550	2115	1219
b954	2493				b1162	20100	731	11530	898	b1337	3059	8286	888	1856
b960	24553	4796	8670		b1163	15766		4769		b1338	5433	473	1490	585
b961	8766	8542	2278	3225	b1164	9712				b1344	19445	8980	6353	
b965	3845				b1174	14532		4128		b1349	9715			
b971	3844				b1177	7360		2084		b1353	22220	10514		
b972	26606	2371			b1178	5876				b1355	10876			
b974	1038	8116	316	3417	b1179	1830		515		b1359	30548	6537	13226	
b975	4539	407	1256	V241	b1180	1817				b1360	30543	6531	12849	
b981	1086		328		b1182	2664				b1361	1477	8560	3162	3244
b982	15226	629	4513		b1183	2669				b1364	13598			
b985	5822		1628	672	b1184	2671				b1366	18123	8803	5739	2003
b986	5785		1622		b1185	2666		721		b1367	21254		8331	
b988	5474		1505		b1187	2672				b1379	27666	3401	10684	3045
b992	15166		4477		b1188	17449		5545		b1385	24015			
b993	19961		7842		b1191	18429	8842	5881		b1390	20669		6966	
b996	478		169		b1193	33611	11602	14261	5780	b1394	18489		5920	2052
b1001	20253		6784		b1198	922	186	286	73	b1398	3973			
b1003	20254				b1199	6624				b1400	5157			
b1005	17321	10057	5482	4441	b1206	1685		491	4270	b1401	3974			
b1006	11874				b1209	24484		8626		b1403	18582	10153	5952	2038
b1007	11867				b1212	4578(C)				b1406	26061	1899	9458	467
b1014	31886	7865	13666	3790	b1214	25489		9158		b1409	18599	10159	596	2060
b1015	16651		5240	4508	b1217	20269				b1410	4563(M)	8337	3297	
b1016	9179		2384		b1218	14331		4063		b1411	26471	2241	9845	457
b1018	13750				b1225	20375		6862		b1412	22162			
b1019	10551				b1229	25473	1357			b1415	19969		6617	3831
b1020	10550		2905		b1231	3739				b1417	20992	10501	8146	
b1021	25026	1017	8891		b1233	3740				b1421	20110		6691	
b1024	9178		2383		b1234	3741				b1423	4564(M)		3296	
b1027	7467				b1235	3743				b1424	12372			
b1028	10642		2917		b1236	3745				b1425	21935			
b1029	11093(K)	352	3015	3242	b1237	8125	10011	2190		b1428	20111	10315	6692	2272

HCP No.	IR Prism	IR HR	UV	NMR	HCP No.	IR Prism	IR HR	UV	NMR	HCP No.	IR Prism	IR HR	UV	NMR
b1448	4568(M)		3294		b1633	19471	8995	7787		b1819	20547		7891	
b1460	5955	8436	1676	3287	b1636	24355	934	8545		b1836	11480(K)	8237	3158	3243
b1465	251	85	101		b1637	19652		6467		b1840	2681			
b1466	8398				b1642	8393				b1841	21423			
b1468	618				b1645	15120				b1842	24737	10692		5742
b1471	9756				b1649	17414	328	671		b1843	17570		5573	
b1473	6617	8479	1824		b1651	51		25		b1844	11481(K)	295	3159	703
b1476	15045		4412		b1652	3253	373	973		b1848	1258			
b1480	147	45	56		b1656	1523	256	433	719	b1849	30544	6532	12850	1635
b1481	12373				b1658	2253	311	601		b1850	12462(M)			
b1483	2949		847	3167	b1662	3870	396	1174	196	b1851	8425	559	11507	
b1484	6499				b1664	23213	10757	13315		b1852	17357		5502	4948
b1486	2893	349	826	V483	b1665	14024				b1853	1826	8203	513	
b1488	13912		3795		b1666	1007	203	305	724	b1854	6252		1725	
b1496	30542	6530	12848		b1668	1008	204	306		b1857	11648(K)			
b1499	3248		968		b1671	2238				b1858	9475			
b1514	17166		5416		b1673	1522	255	432	1189	b1859	8689		2265	
b1515	4565(M)	599	3298		b1679	2931	353	841	178	b1860	4899	444	1366	584
b1518	18476	10151	5913	2047	b1681	3247	368	967	1624	b1861	24453	4723	8608	
b1519	5331	8389	11477		b1682	17370		5510		b1867	582			
b1520	18616		7649		b1683	5972	8441	2903	3235	b1871	8633			
b1521	21911				b1685	23763	782	11533	2773	b1875	30124	6124	12621	
b1527	10865		2962		b1686	4081	8320	11462	514	b1879	12935			
b1528	19506	711	7790	587	b1687	19484	8713	6381	2182	b1882	18665		7670	4033
b1534	20993	10502			b1688	5252	9999	3277	3160	b1887	20116	10318	6697	
b1538	585	138	200	3340	b1691	5434	474	972	1214	b1889	10912		2971	
b1539	2950	8277	848	3164	b1692	3250	370	970	1192	b1906	10909		2968	
b1540	2157		2972		b1693	18045	369	969	1191	b1907	10910		2969	
b1541	584				b1694	19970		6618		b1909	10908		2967	
b1542	583	137	199		b1695	18051	371	971	1213	b1912	4577		1265	
b1543	2951	8278	849	3165	b1714	1975	8217	546		b1916	1122		334	
b1546	19149	8975	6262	2166	b1715	1954		538		b1922	17496		7347	
b1550	17377	8722	7324		b1716	11795(K)				b1923	23625			
b1551	7173	8495	2028	3210	b1719	17527	8578	2910	3281	b1924	17494			
b1552	10967	8587	2986	540	b1721	13925		3804		b1925	9163			
b1553	11298				b1737	24707	4891	8760		b1926	32151	9149	13723	
b1554	19530	10214	6407	2197	b1739	30541	6973	12847		b1928	20532		6951	
b1555	31749	7730			b1746	4567	413	1262	3092	b1932	8449		2242	
b1559	6540		1817		b1747	9734				b1937	11925			
b1566	19512	10208	6398	2189	b1748	12374	602	9629		b1942	1112	217	331	
b1567	19540	10216	6412	2194	b1749	9767				b1945	2722		736	
b1568	19599	10241	6456	2218	b1750	20994		8147	2411	b1947	17366			
b1569	19486		6383	2183	b1751	9804				b1952	13599	333	734	1207
b1577	1961	8216	542	3158	b1757	18820		6084		b1955	6616	8478	1823	V655
b1584	24490	4750	8632		b1761	30118	6118	12615		b1956	9271		2414	
b1585	17476		7345		b1762	327		125		b1957	7334		2069	
b1587	13931	8637	3807		b1763	5427		1487	V195	b1959	14800	326	659	153
b1589	17106		5398		b1764	25854	1706	9342	825	b1961	5781		1619	
b1590	23753	779	9713		b1765	1805				b1963	18349	8832	5843	2020
b1592	19635		6462	4502	b1770	23695				b1965	18120	8802	5737	2001
b1593	15328	8705	4583	3273	b1775	11181	8258	730	V196	b1974	5974	8541	1681	V329
b1594	14553		4129		b1778	2948	10849	846	180	b1978	16552		5197	
b1595	9488				b1779	8018				b1981	13913	8632	4051	3260
b1596	460				b1780	1936	288	533	124	b1987	13914		3797	
b1597	9480				b1781	14300		4049		b1988	1014	206	309	
b1598	17372		7322		b1785	139	41	51	17	b1991	19552	10220	6420	2199
b1599	21126		8246		b1786	2153	8236	566	3163	b2001	8460			
b1600	20991	10300	8143		b1790	2898	8271	829	174	b2005	6294			
b1601	21117				b1792	140	42	52	18	b2006	5662		1570	
b1602	21120		8240		b1793	2154		567	692	b2010	6779		1909	
b1604	21118		8238		b1797	23802			2788	b2012	8332		2220	
b1605	10730				b1798	2886	8268	819	168	b2016	4734			
b1607	17383		5518		b1800	2152	293	565	1113	b2017	5656		1566	
b1610	19676		6477		b1801	2155	294	568	693	b2018	4868			
b1616	1623		462		b1803	32045	9044		3882	b2024	12920			
b1618	26711	2462	10020	476	b1804	11320		3085		b2029	25210	1117	9004	
b1628	11953				b1805	11319				b2031	20586		6958	
b1629	17454		5546		b1806	2887	8269	820	169	b2062	1189	8245	594	704
b1630	4566		3299		b1814	24526	4783	8661	2652	b2066	7521			
b1631	25468	1353	9141	906	b1817	862				b2067	14260	8691	4023	3261

HCP No.	IR Prism	IR HR	UV	NMR	HCP No.	IR Prism	IR HR	UV	NMR	HCP No.	IR Prism	IR HR	UV	NMR
b2069	751		248		b2324	20340		6834		b2623	4660			V87
b2071	10758		2947		b2325	8448	8531		3084	b2626	14254			
b2072	18459		7603		b2331	18852		6110		b2627	5979			
b2078	29004	5004	11908		b2332	18853				b2632	2977		857	
b2083	5144				b2335	7081	538	2008		b2633	7201		2042	
b2087	713	159	237	V314	b2339	20998		8151	2415	b2634	5782		1620	V72
b2090	29005	5005	11909		b2353	16067				b2635	5437	476	1492	
b2091	29006	5006	11910	3392	b2361	13298	8616	3468	3247	b2636	20090			2267
b2092	23677				b2363	15551		4661		b2642	5737			
b2093	11917	594			b2381	25973	1819		3113	b2643	6613			274
b2094	10874		2963		b2383	12988				b2645	14801			3437
b2096	22029				b2415	2143				b2648	6362			
b2097	10283				b2418	2180				b2649	4662			
b2098	34084	12074		5927	b2420	2177				b2650	4663			
b2099	34086	12076		5929	b2426	9529				b2651	125	37		
b2100	8194				b2427	9595				b2652	10155			
b2111	6634	530	1832		b2428	2252	8248	600	683	b2653	5761			
b2112	18321	10109			b2436	893				b2656	5762	494	1607	261
b2113	22413				b2444	2427				b2657	5148			
b2116	2256	313	603	139	b2447	14901			1859	b2658	930	188	288	726
b2117	5467		1502	V150	b2449	3512	8298	1088	5140	b2660	2867			
b2119	24145	806	8456		b2453	3229		956		b2661	338	112		
b2124	7529		2112		b2458	11018		2995		b2663	10545			
b2125	1796				b2461	688	154			b2665	6031			
b2131	20190		6751		b2471	333			V78	b2666	22381	10552		2726
b2132	11493	8139	390		b2472	13643			V420	b2668	341	114		42
b2139	6162		1722	V191	b2473	5779				b2671	23774	10662		2779
b2140	20127	10322	6706	2275	b2478	942			74	b2672	2713			159
b2141	8634		2251		b2479	5719				b2673	10546			
b2149	1631		465		b2480	9181				b2674	337			
b2151	9732			V147	b2481	648				b2678	10675			
b2160	19932		7835		b2484	9549				b2680	261			33
b2170	16563	479			b2485	2286				b2682	886			
b2183	5921				b2486	6648	8485		V89	b2684	2879		812	
b2197	11824		3275		b2488	13484			V88	b2686	336			
b2205	6555	527			b2493	10987				b2690	2954			
b2206	25728	1600			b2500	4619	10947		V418	b2691	23502			
b2208	23539	765			b2501	4620	10948		*124	b2693	15270			
b2210	20074	730	6677		b2503	20087	10310		2266	b2695	15271			
b2212	25729	1601			b2510	1858	10941		121	b2703	2259			V66
b2214	783	163	255	V289	b2511	4621				b2706	2262			
b2219	22092				b2512	13902				b2707	4698			V137
b2225	32556	9551		4401	b2522	1859	10942		122	b2710	2261			V58
b2235	20073	10303	6676	2261	b2523	6477			V447	b2711	34876			
b2243	12171				b2533	1844			V74	b2714	2710			
b2244	13650		3610	142	b2534	3210				b2717	4704			
b2248	8048		3351		b2535	3211				b2723	21372			
b2250	15043		4410		b2538	23668				b2727	18484	8850		2488
b2257	32555	9550		4400	b2539	4623				b2732	16159			
b2261	6632	8482	1830		b2540	508				b2734	18502			
b2262	6316	517	1738	3193	b2542	12165				b2735	5186			
b2264	6379	8468	1760	269	b2550	21359				b2750	4005			
b2266	14554(K)		3282		b2555	19097	8957		2150	b2751	19622			
b2267	15044		4411		b2556	683	5000		3406	b2757	17635			
b2274	13493		3526	541	b2557	687	153			b2758	18782	8901		2102
b2280	23754	10654		3661	b2561	15718				b2763	9187			
b2294	19573		6438	2210	b2568	4624	10949		V81	b2764	24493	4753		
b2299	25471				b2569	4625	10950		V82	b2772	67			
b2302	18935	8947	6161	2141	b2573	4556				b2777	14640			
b2303	21289		9678		b2577	10661			5086	b2780	17506			
b2305	20180	10335	6742	3083	b2579	691	8087		*141	b2783	5280			
b2308	22809	10580	13303		b2582	23683				b2785	17507			4253
b2312	1192(K)		341		b2592	5421				b2788	5330			*129
b2313	5832		1629	262	b2607	23711			2761	b2791	18968			
b2314	1107		330		b2611	11835				b2794	5430		1488	
b2318	6367	8465	1756	3196	b2612	5786				b2797	9199			317
b2320	12194				b2615	5314				b2802	1835			
b2321	21078		8208		b2618	265	91		V86	b2806	4736			
b2322	9393	8550	13281	2860	b2620	18671				b2806¹	7394			
b2323	1253		373	86	b2621	4112	10982		5127	b2807	6622			277

HCP No.	IR Prism	IR HR	UV	NMR
b2809	17502			
b2810	17382			
b2812	19648			5039
b2813	22464			
b2817	17740			
b2821	14638		4144	
b2822	14636	8693	4142	V256
b2823	6494	8475	1803	
b2825	20657		6959	3782
b2828	101	32	40	
b2832	65			
b2833	269			
b2836	12553			
b2839	7796		2150	
b2847	5873	8423	1648	3147
b2848	26059	1897	9457	443
b2852	2774			
b2854	24821		8790	
b2864	75	10934		
b2866	5278	10984		
b2869	3683			
b2871	15640			
b2872	18162			
b2876	4891			241
b2877	2250			
b2884	3431			
b2886	3432			
b2887	3433			
b2888	3435	12976		4944
b2889	3436			
b2890	103	10963		14
b2893	805	9996		
b2895	806			
b2896	919			
b2898	9195			
b2905	18438			
b2907	16558	8716	5200	4018
b2912	297	101		V76
b2913	5784			
b2918	18584		5953	
b2920	24821			
b2921	5975	10008		
b2922	4817			
b2924	7362	545	2086	536
b2926	5287			1885
b2929	5772	8415	1613	3199
b2930	14662	624	4153	547
b2931	13494		3527	
b2932	19862		6568	
b2933	1457		418	V60
b2934	22378			
b2940	7857			
b2941	7859			
b2942	7860			
b2983	1606			3418
b2984	1605			5318
b2986	299			
b2987	14643			5315
b2991	6320			3426
b2992	7856	553		J140
b2993	681	12975		3411
b2995	14551			
b3009	749	8091	247	V61
b3010	10732			
b3011	17150	10049		4494
b3012	14587			
b3013	14585			J143
b3014	14586			J142
b3015	11902			
b3016	15368			

HCP No.	IR Prism	IR HR	UV	NMR
b3019	19628			1861
b3035	23595	770		3608
b3040	22001			
b3043	6530			1815
b3045	14583			V414
b3054	13667			
b3056	8687		2264	
b3057	9053(K)			
b3058	9536			
b3062	9760			
b3063	14584			
b3064	13044			5416
b3065	1466			V251
b3069	17302			V99
b3074	23663			2793
b3075	19168			5010
b3078	31117			
b3081	19603			
b3082	22098			
b3083	14652		4151	5095
b3084	5332			
b3089	32794	9789		4548
b3091	8008	10990		V636
c8	1036	209	315	V204
c20	14471			
c24	11919			
c25	1474	248		
c32	244		96	30
c39	4582			
c42	11035			
c44	11037			
c48	11038			
c57	1499			
c59	2701			
c60	15618			
c71	9614			
c79	26825	2573	10103	
c85	13498			
c88	18455		5903	
c89	5747			
c91	11180			245
c93	3402			
c94	12994	607		5240
c98	30325	6320		3482
c106	11592			
c109	3224			
c111	14806			
c117	22419	10565		2748
c120	19184	707		4288
c133	19967			3830
c136	5701			
c141	1311	237	13550	
c142	10962			
c147	14645		4148	
c153	13268			
c156	8396			
c159	1924			
c161	2223	10977	596	
c165	5748			
c168	13481	10026		V243
c170	8024			290
c173	13477	10022		4466
c175	12993			1894
c177	9759	8562	2575	3231
c178	15324	8703	4581	3269
c179	15325	8704	4582	3270
c184	1142			
c188	31914	7892		
c191	23370			
c194	21933			

HCP No.	IR Prism	IR HR	UV	NMR
c196	11591			
c207	4608			
c211	6626			V271
c213	21371			
c227	19913		6600	
c231	1020	207		
c245	2723	335	737	160
c250	18778	8897	6063	2100
c251	13124		3419	
c260	20112	10316	6693	
c264	20799			V425
c273	721			
c298	7178		2031	J217
c300	723			J218
c301	5199			J225
c305	722			
c306	5450			
c307	6480			
c308	5956			
c309	25704	1579	9293	
c310	21			
c312	34477	12461		5745
c313	1188	221	351	
c327	9521	8554	175	
c334	8580			
c339	1490		424	101
c340	20882		8601	
c350	29		3452	V230
c351	13697		3628	
c352	19485	8838	6382	
c354	1520		430	104
c355	6033			
c356	884	177	276	718
c357	18097	10092	5728	4246
c359	167	52	66	20
c366	2882		815	
c369	19543		6413	
c372	18350		5844	
c386	17668		5609	
c392	1386			
c394	10002			
c397	17173	8719	5419	
c398	19985		6628	
c399	9915		2612	
c400	9919		2615	
c402	8405	10013		4945
c419	23684	10633	13349	
c424	10535			
c425	5275	8385	1448	
c428	765			
c432	2402			150
c439	5179			
c442	16021			
c444	14889			
c463	17152		5410	V689
c466	31646	7632		
c477	3276			
c482	5948		1674	
c483	17131			
c488	17158			
c501	7178		2031	J217
c502	10787			
c505	8758			
c523	203		79	
c526	1691	270	492	V225
c528	7622			
c529	13593		3578	
c532	8192			
c533	8417			
c534	3157		926	

HCP No.	IR Prism	IR HR	UV	NMR
c535	11616		3223	
c536	19701		6489	V294
c537	13757			
c539	20137		6712	
c542	465	8041	2232	3220
c544	1260		375	87
c545	8403		2231	
c548	1463			
c550	3747		1147	
c553	21934			
c554	7198			
c555	26680	2436	10002	
c566	13460			
c573	953	195		1034
c575	5794			
c576	5715			
c586	7027			
c588	380			
c589	27902	3628	10845	
c590	2496			
c593	16925			
c594	2385			
c595	19621	10248		
c596	14903			4926
c597	15453			
c599	15454			
c600	15455			
c608	22379			
c611	12046			
c612	23773	10661		2778
c613	20681			
c616	17154			
c617	11956			
c624	21999			1902
c627	23593			
c637	180	59		*150
c639	31987	7967		3949
c640	845			
c642	2263	8250		313
c644	4628			
c645	4629			
c647	11838			
c648	11837			
c649	11836			
c650	6449			
c651	191	8019		25
c652	3386			
c653	19155			
c654	17125			
c657	23664			
c658	23664			
c660	24271			
c663	11843			
c664	12999	8610		3407
c665	12998	8609		
c666	21745			
c668	31992	7972		3954
c669	31993	7973		
c671	3449			
c674	4540			315
c675	6445			
c681	9699			
c682	9698			
c683	9697	574		
c684	9696			
c685	22448			
c686	12047			
c687	11841			
c688	194	68		27
c689	5967			
c690	12054			
c691	31997			
c692	6315			
c693	12051			
c694	11842			
c698	26686	2441		2830
c699	22380			
c700	23760			
c704	13511			V173
c706	13199(CI$)			
c706¹	16546			
c720	22276	10545		
c723	7837	8512		
c724	7838	8513		
c726	22861			
c727	17130			
c728	3472	378	1072	710
c729	17349	5500		
c731	17177	670	5422	559
c735	14904	8697	4319	V512
c736	256			
c739	19137			5009
c742	41	10960		7
c746	20168	10332		2287
c749	18468			
c750	2540			
c752	27910	3636		486
c755	6464	10989		V211
c758	11911			
c759	13370			
c761	13371			
c763	13372			
c764	13362			
c765	13373			
c766	13363			
c767	468	126	161	
c768	3439			
c769	9510			
c783	13369			
c784	13368			
c785	166	51	65	
c786	276	95		
c788	18889	8925		2120
c789	1887		7682	
c790	19503			5023
c800	19663		7804	
c804	8401			
c807	8402			
c808	42		19	8
c809	20475			
c811	196			3409
c814	30248	6247		
c817	3387			3420
c820	7853			
c825	5721			
c827	25777	164		
c828	20179			
c830	24579	4814	8682	2696
c832	6217			
c835	10592			
c841	19138		7699	
c843	18785		6066	
c848	25016			
c854	18835			V511
c855	17144			
c856	17148			
c857	17139	665	5408	557
c860	13043		3365	
c861	4452			
c862	4451			
c863	1314			
c867	21399			
c868	680			3435
c870	438			
c872	6025			
c874	11829			
c876	689	155		3436
c880	19102	8958		2151
c882	13513			
c887	22825			
c892	376	12974		44
c894	171	55	67	1195
c897	23787			
c899	19781			5162
c901	23852	10920		
c907	30064			
c908	1306			
c909	11831(gas)			
c912	13924			
c913	11885			
c921	2333			
c922	22060			
c924	22059			
c930	1710			
c940	13419			
c941	17161			
c942	17180			
c943	323	111		
c944	17160			
c945	16947		5343	
c947	10785			
c949	17162		5414	V402
c950	9355	8549	2483	
d5	19594		7799	
d18	1524			
d20	4527	8332		*149
d21	7170			
d22	2981			
d23	31985	7965		3948
d25	2982			
d28	2980(C)			
d30	22449	10571		2754
d31	7037	537		
d32	17136			
d33	983			
d34	14296			
d35	5174		250	
d38	999			
d39	18811	8914		V570
d40	2979			
d41	3668			
d42	2705			
d45	6032			
d47	16160			
d49	16347			
d57	159	10965		V282
d58	23657	774		565
d59	32088	9086		3909
d62	22387	10557		2733
d63	22388			2743
d64	23658			
d66	1309			
d68	31991	7971		3953
d74	1671	8193		359
d79	7177		2030	
d81	4509			
d84	10561			
d85	7175			
d89	5416			
d113	5986			V589

HCP No.	IR Prism	IR HR	UV	NMR	HCP No.	IR Prism	IR HR	UV	NMR	HCP No.	IR Prism	IR HR	UV	NMR
d126	13221			652	e51	7559				e309[1]	7506		2102	
d129	12456				e97	1235				e310	3665	389	1120	
d134	2455		640		e105	2351	8252	11446		e312	15284			
d136	5817		1625		e109	4835	8351	11468		e323	17524			
d137	7261		2059		e110	4836	8352			e326	14647			
d151	13222		642		e114	2229	8247			e328	6306			3424
d153	6994				e130	7385				e330	17171			
d164	1143				e136	4840	8353			e332	9061		2307	
d166	24551				e148[1]	1030				e336	188	64		V14
d167	15769				e152	6169	8449			e338	19613			
d168	2945	10980		179	e154	9547				e339	5776			
d176	2290	10943			e155	9522				e340	123			
d180	5318				e158	19728		7811		e341	22917			
d185	2588				e159	9512				e343	97			
d186	17466				e160	773				e347	4724			
d194	5787				e161	1288				e348	2292	10979		4023
d198	40	21		1193	e162	7989				e349	16342			
d199	9761				e165	7373				e350	73			V12
d200	18812				e168	24369	948			e352	8187			
d204	19960				e169	26610	2375		836	e353	23654			3635
d205	8031	8518	11505	V75	e170	14480	10028		4391	e354	2978			
d207	2348				e171	22453			2757	e355	32087	9085		3906
d208	9684				e177	20065	10299	6670	2258	e356	17127			
d212	3296	375			e181	77				e358	143			
d213	3297	376		4885	e183	127		47	15	e359	5618			V91
d221	14704				c184	19633				e363	5291	10992		
d225	24574	4812			e185	17345		5497		e364	14666			V92
d226	1244				e187	18783				e365	14802			
d227	10588				e190	24657	4867	8733		e366	270			
d229	24276	892			e195	4631	10951		V10	e367	383			
d231	1344				e196	4685	10983		V5	e369	18392			
d239	17637			4438	e199	533			V11	e372	6351			
d252	9709				e203	944	190	292		e373	254	87		32
d258	9242				e204	2440				e377	19906			
d259	9241		2395		e207	5319				e385	248	84	99	V506
d260	9240		2394		e209	8183				e387	2191	8242	582	133
d261	13660		7007		e212	996				e389	1632	8184	466	113
d265	27950	3675		330	e215	3205			J118	e390	8636		2252	295
d269	3293		988		e216	35	20			e391	15307			
d271	17422				e221	30866	6838			e397	18320			4224
d272	17453				e224	6524				e399	24183	824	8474	2678
d273	15645	644			e228	22906				e401	1131			
d276	15644									e404	34471	12456		5738
d278	3504	379		711	e235	6245				e405	1119	10973		
d279	16560				e236	9982				e409	7190			
d282[1]	1534			106	e237	3203	365	950	184	e411	11632			
d284	7103	8492		3433	e238	1488				e412	3645			
d285	367				e240	30454	6445			e413	3646			
d288	11630				e241	1109				e414	30862			
d290	4684	10954			e248	4546	411			e416	19518		6401	*111
d293	24956				e249	30863	6836			e417	30864			
d294	6363				e253	57			V13	e419	5422	469	1485	
d295	8486				e254	23483				e420	237	79		
d300	5675				e255	7	5	4	2	e423	20510	10404	7881	2355
d301	3851	10775		194	e260	5244				e425	185	62		
d303	1937				e261	178				e426	21396			
d304	20585				e265	1465	247			e427	15279	630	4552	548
d311	1492	251		103	e267	182	60			e429	22899			
d313	23756	10655		3662	e272	4633			1883	e433	1863		522	
d314	28849	4551	11366	1138	e273	19461				e436	34462	12447		5733
d315	4528			202	e274	9721			V2	e438	34463	12448		5760
d323	10567				e276	23717	10998			e441	1861		521	
e16	16457	10045		4217	e283	2166	299			e442	11515			
e17	11722				e285	8012				e450	5297			
e18	8465			260	e286	7092	539	2016		e458[1]	22452			
e19	24967				e289	8803				e469	1862			V134
e21	24968			1317	e290	2230				e470	1656	8187	3530	118
e28	24951				e292	10604				e471	106			
e40	936				e306	8333	557	2221		e475	8021			
e48	7550	8507			e309	22919				e477	1335(liquid)	241		

HCP No.	IR Prism	IR HR	UV	NMR
e479	13379			
e480	16348			
e495	8691			
e496	95			
e497	102			
e499	1128			
e501	9682			
e508	5867			
e509	2487			151
e510	4492		1245	200
e511	2269		608	
e526	12234			
e527	4497		1250	
e534	228	10936		*110
e535	221	73		
e537	968			
e538	220			
e539	292			
e591	3961			
e602	4537	406	1255	205
e611	3880			
e612	5257	8384	1447	3183
f6	17489			
f10	6395			522
f13	4994			
f17	34500	12484		5759
f18	20108		6689	
f19	596			
f20	7526			
f25	9412		2519	
f27	21430			
f29	594			
f34	17433		7337	
f36	31626	7613		
f40	10563			
f44	901	180	281	
f45	7540	240	2114	288
f46	2458	8590	4150	
f54	9994			
f55	11938			
f56	7618		2139	
f67	20350		6843	
f68	11386			
f74	8442			
f80	7390		2095	287
f81	25075	1051	8923	
f83	10466		2890	
f91	3518		1093	
f96	22427	10568	8354	
f99	24783	4961		
f100	9792			
f104	17431			
f106	2538			
f108	17522			561
f109	9685	572		
f110	4127	400	1192	
f115	25	15		
f116	9775			
f117	2232			
f119	5051			
f120	156			V39
f121	1989	8218		360
f124	10961			
f125	1031		314	
f126	19981		6626	
f127	19657		6470	
f128	19658		7803	
f130	17511		5556	
f131	1531		436	
f132	2077			

HCP No.	IR Prism	IR HR	UV	NMR
f134	15273			
f135	2515			
f136	2529			
f137	2513			
f139	2716			
f140	5259			V415
f141	693			V9
f142	5258			
f144	1641			114
f145	885			
f146	2514			
f150	16344			
f151	5750			
f152	1552	8166		1552
f158	8312			
f159	5751			
f163	13474			4463
f165	5749			
f175	2755			
f176	1105			
f178	472	127	165	4407
f179	1876			
f182	7236		2051	538
f184	5163			
f190	5520			4982
f193	3664			V50
f194	3135			
f194¹	8081	8523	2184	V104
f199	10520			
f206	9256			
f207²	14146		3936	
f213	210		82	
f215	581	10970		
f219	12862			
f220	74			V77
f222	126	38	46	
f223	13691			
f225	10516			
f227	3667	390	1121	
f228	3129			
f231	10514			
f234	1423			V125
f237	10513			
f238	10515			
f240	10517			
f245	18729		6036	
f260	3130			
f261	3131			
f266	1424	244	410	
f276	18702	694	7673	1257
f277	113	35	42	V95
f282	17226		5442	
f285	22440	757	8361	
f290	3682	391		
f291	17441		5543	V247
g1	1044			
g2	21697			
g3	989	8113		
g6	17499			
g12	12213			
g13	509	8047		
g14	8087			V279
g15	18088	10086		
g32	8335			
g34	5145			
g38	5455	199		
g44	17512			4255
g51	5122			
g56	8951			
g58	8657	482		

HCP No.	IR Prism	IR HR	UV	NMR
g59	17530			
g60	2154	8050		
g62	23515			
g64	4517	8330		
g65	11489	591		
g66	7391			
g68	5180			
g70	169	10001		4979
g81	8654	8012		2400
g89	7594			
g100	6408	8046		
g103	18673			
g108	10269			
g110	8653	719		
g117	6852			
g120	6354			
g124	6475			
g128	6702			
g133	6490	40		
g143	26030	1873	9440	
g144	25751	1618		
g148	8632			
g159	8688			
g161	31643	7629		
g162	31642	7628		
g165	22814			
g166	5892			
g171	7404		2096	
g173	22588			
g180	2151			
g181	8671			
g183	19605	10242		
g187	24880	5992		
g189	3824		1163	
g193	5194			
g194	4588			
g195	8676	544		
g196	452			
g198	8323		2218	
g200	13632			
g201	1337	8143	396	97
g202	2218		592	
g204	21412			
g208	6374	8467	1759	
g211	17446			
g212	17443		7339	
h2	2969	8281	11453	
h3	3358	8292	11456	
h7	11498	8599		
h10	3885		1178	V187
h13	2928	8274	11450	
h14	2968	8280	11452	
h16	2717			
h19	7851			289
h22	5579			
h23	5260			3181
h27	3805			
h30	1525	257		
h31	7039			
h39	5310	461	1454	663
h40	23728	10643		3656
h41	23729	10644		3657
h42	26812	2561		2835
h43	16753			
h50	5580			
h51	6874			
h52	5583			
h53	20576			
h61¹	19912	10275		
h66	24326	7997		2596

SPECTRA INDEX OF ORGANIC COMPOUNDS (Continued)

HCP No.	IR Prism	IR HR	UV	NMR
h67	21345			
h68	21351			
h70	24327	926		2594
h72	3448	8295		1549
h74	7321			
h77	5311			
h78	16752			
h86	24837			
h90	306			
h92	952	194		
h93	271	93		679
h94	12004			
h96	4547			208
h98	4548			209
h110[1]	32154	9152		3938
h119	33859			5425
h125	4549			210
h126	5110	8369		
h128	11833			5320
h130	33851			5056
h132	5961			
h134	22398			
h135	18494	8853		2065
h136	9060			316
h140	19984			3836
h142	8686			297
h144	544			49
h149	6873			283
h152	5255			
h166	4571			215
h168	111			
h170	389	10767		45
h171	9192			
h174	378	10968		
h179	6191			
h180	28947	4649		876
h181	32007	9008		3962
h184	340	10966		41
h185	2034	290	548	1311
h186	9191			
h187[1]	6230	31	39	
h191	20169			
h192	34863	12846		5874
h193	22462	10576		2742
h197	542			
h209	32120	9118		
h210	32128	9126		3929
h212	1645			
h235	1399			
h236	3522	8300		
h243	15329			5313
h244	16685			
h245	11631			
h246	9725			
h252	3558	8301		
h253	11336	8007		
h254	2293			
h259	6035			
h264	5172			248
h265	24948			
h267	12045			
h268	17311	10050		
h269	222			5175
h270	4529	8393		1343
h281	15330			4419
h288	15617			
h289	5315	464	1457	V515
h293	20258			
h298	3674	8305		V462

HCP No.	IR Prism	IR HR	UV	NMR
h301	5271			
h315	2150			
h316	342			
h318	5720			
h319	678	151		
h320	433			46
h322	211			28
h326	4550	412		
h327	16033	10041		4212
h328	16032			
h330	4551	10945		211
h349	24273	889		2577
h357	22400			2736
h364	23741	10649		2765
h366	11832			
h370	4552			212
h373	19929			5312
				*145
h378	684	8085		3413
h380	281			4406
h381	14642			
h383	14660			
h384	6478			
h385	5251			
h389	181			
h390	7571			
h391	1875			
h395	18131			
h397	23499			
h400	5423			
h406	15337			
h408	4573			216
h410	5299	10985		
h411	4226			
h413	121		43	2709
h415	19119	8964	6242	2155
h418	1044			
h420	6364			
h427	308			37
h428	2733			
h431	16162			
h432	18325			
h433	931			
h436	6339			
h437	1642			
h438	2902			176
h440	23609			3614
h444	8013			
h445	15194(K)			4445
h452	16346			
h454	6141			
h456	2985			
h460	11287			
h464	18824			
h478	4064			198
h480	9196			
h483	5293			
h485	18478			
h491	1472	10974		98
h495	20480	10392		
h500	9185			
h501	6192			
h502	9188			
h503	32087	9028		3875
h505	32008	9009		4503
h511	8503			

HCP No.	IR Prism	IR HR	UV	NMR
h513	8507			
h515	8508			
h517	6343			
h518	9197			
h519	24544			
h521	8510			
h531	17523	10876		5997
h534	23482			
h535	9701	575	6986	415
h544	7383	8502	2093	
h546	22438			
h550	15061			5321
h564	15300	633		
h569	7172			V504
h579	23775			
h587	6746	10944		
h589[1]	2802	344	773	
h589[4]	1819	8202	511	
h589[7]	23272		5115	
h590	5860			V443
h591	16250		5040	4939
h593	5456	8396	11479	
h594	13420			
h598	24332	7998	8540	
h602	20211		6764	
h603	7162			
h606	19587		6448	2492
h607	33858		14368	
h609	8334			
h612	13497			
h613	18400	10137	7597	4050
h614	8601			
h616	2095			
h617	5470	478	2168	3215
h620	8086		2186	
h622	26019	1863	9435	831
h623	19939			
h626	18405			
h627	3774	8308	6093	
h628	7163			
h633	6492	8474	1801	3285
h646	19113		6240	
h647	24250	881		
h653	2470	4735		
h656	7647			
h658	23745			
h666	18317	377	989	
h668	17447		7340	
h669	15427	8707	4611	
h671	20362			
h683	7650			
h685	19921		6603	
h692	21427			
h694	3670			
h697	8631			
h704	25023	1015	8889	
h705	20543		7888	
h709	9538			
h713	5700			
h718	20378		6864	
h725	3019			
h732	3837	8310	11458	1551
h736	33119	11112	14024	
h761	7533			
h770	7007			
i1a	8335			
i7	7001			V20
i9	7205			
i11	5619		4571	
i13	19909		6599	

HCP No.	IR Prism	IR HR	UV	NMR
i16	15219	8701	4509	V527
i22	20144		6717	
i23	17526		5558	
i24	10926			
i25	10927			
i30	3505	380	1083	V224
i32	11597			
i34	23613	10612	13337	3618
i35	4890			V229
i37	3333		1022	
i41	18970		6176	
i45	23545			
i47	23546			V485
i49	1012	10938	308	V227
i56	3400			
i62	6219			
i65	4586	415	1269	473 / J189
i66	21265		8340	
i72	3823			V231 / J190
i73	24575	10688		2692
i75	22446			
i82	9340			
i84	1060	215		
i91	8193			
i95	5906			
i98	5907			
i102	2214	304	590	
i105	11603		3213	
i106	19212	10825	6295	4298
i108	21694			
i109	20294		6809	
i110	10143		2746	
i114	1383			
i117	207	71		524
i125	1499			
i127	14675			
i137	22269			
i138	22270			2527
i139	22271			
i140	23483			
i141	15366			
i144	6251		2052	
	7237			
i148	8436			
i149	1075			80
i168	586	9995		V281
i180	122	36	44	
i188	1144			V520
i192	33672	11663	14296	5447
i193	18728		6035	
i197	15220		4510	
i202	20300		6810	
i203	15886		4845	
i212	9062		2308	V252
i216	1603	8182	459	3155
i225	31857	7836		3771
i226	19174			5011
i228	15275		4548	
i231	19922			
i234	5908	8434		
i236	9063	8545	2309	3228
i242	24151	7983		2674
j8	8162			
k7	7197		2041	
k8	20060	10297	6666	2257
k10	31982	7962		

HCP No.	IR Prism	IR HR	UV	NMR
k23	1627	9998	463	
k24	2986			V628
l4	31634	7620		
l11	21949			
l28	18821			
l31	19911	729		
l32	5459			
l33	790			
l34	10916	586		
l36	564	8065		
l37	563	8064		
l41	12958	10018		2852
l42	15333			
l44	1005	8114		
l45	8341			
l49	17458			
l54	31656	7642		
l56	7217			
l60	8410			
l64	10338			
l65	3100			
l71	14679		4158	
l75	788			
l76	8699			
m1	11587			
m2	6253			
m3	462	8040	163	V48 / V212
m3[1]	1097		300	723
m3[2]	986		632	
m5	13219		6387	5021
m6	19491			
m6[1]	6225			
m10	17393		7343	
m11	17471			
m12	17143		3514	V427
m13	13445			
m17	2960			
m19	18323	10110		4222
m20	8698		2271	
m21	19907	728		3594
m23	7367			V181
m24	5261			
m25	5188			
m28	2237			
m32	2235	10773		4600
m34	5247	10780		V57
m35	7625			
m37	5169	453	1406	730
m40	3212			
m43	15281		4554	
m44	5739	491	1597	
m46	8380	10012		4983
m50	857			
m52	24407	979	8581	
m54	3217			1880
m55	31692	7676		
m56	7998			
m58	14909			4927
m60	24285	895		
m61	32812	9807		4558
m62	20036	10287	6654	
m65	18735			
m67	3214		951	
m69	27239	2983		519
m70	32100	9098		
m71	3213			1879
m76	6008			V573
m77	15280	631		891

HCP No.	IR Prism	IR HR	UV	NMR
m78	5262			
m81	264	8025	1728	302
m82	19125			
m83	19183			4287
m88	22014			
m92	19753			
m94	3216			
m95	15615	10809		5076
m98	22463			3607
m99	5263			
m104	19915			
m105	8567			
m108	14912			4417
m111	7183	8497	2034	3211
m119	21816			
m121	1019			
m122	4513			
m124	992			
m136	993			
m145	20113	10317	6694	
m151	5460	477	1499	
m157	20221			
m158	1846			
m161	4099			
m165	9599	995		V281
	586			
m166	17529			
m168	5190			
m172	6400	8469		
m175	4063			
m177	6369	520		
m178	9251		2402	
m192	7846			
m194	11341		3097	
m203	21006	747	8157	
m213	1098	10972		
m214	204			
m217	1898			
m221	1897		528	V606
m225	1845			
m226	2478			
m228	842			
m230	3701			
m235	9252	8548	2403	V176
m241	4083			
m243	4557	8336	1259	213
m246	5939	10956		
m247	3204			
m248	6523			
m252	6620			
m253	30865	6837		
m255	24272		8525	2385
m256	1129			2429
m263	4636	426		226
m271	3389			
m281	7608	551	2133	537
m282	59			
m286	61	25	29	
m293	8236			
m294	8237			
m295	13900			
m296	2210	302		
m297	4082			
m299	2492			
m300	11997			

HCP No.	IR Prism	IR HR	UV	NMR
m303	10	8		
m306	2224	305		
m308	3722			
m310	4553			
m312	4584		2945	220
m329	6740			
m331	17513			
m333	13515			
m335	14535			
m349	1918	287		V1
m366	3508	382	1085	V607
m376	112	10964		1554
m379	894		278	67
m380	32840	9835		4573
m381	6347	8461	1749	3202
m388	131	39		
m389	5565			
m391	7401	8504		
m392	8110			
m393	7156			
m395	4982			5951
m408	100	10962		V83
m409	879			
m410	11310			
m411	900			69
m414	881			
m416	11309			
m417	3295			185
m419	15541			
m420	9170		2380	
m422	8432			
m423	5938			
n1	1211		360	
n6	11258		3069	
n8	8444		2239	
n9	21406			
n14	865	169	265	62
n15	21007		8158	
n24	8695		2268	298
n25	1245		371	1202
n30	7525		2109	
n35	12169			
n36	9508	571	2545	539
n37	6370	8466	1757	
n38	46		22	
n39	9739		2574	
n42	18124	8804	5740	2004
n51	18361	8837	5850	2024
n63	5441	8394		1494
n75	18934	8946	6160	2140
n79	18674	8859	6000	
n93	2267	316	606	143
n94	14913	625	4321	546
n96	18803		6076	2109
n102	18804	8909	7677	
n109	3659		1117	
n110	23646	10624	13346	3632
n117	18424	8839	5877	2031
n126	23645	11997		1903
n128	19994		7845	
n130	19995		7846	
n133	17146	668	9632	
n134	34395	12381		5860
n141	19457	8989	6364	2174
n152	16249	8714	5039	3275
n154	21667			
n157	21419			
n158	1519		429	
n160	994		301	
n161	19547		6415	

HCP No.	IR Prism	IR HR	UV	NMR
n163	6759	8486	1889	3207
n164	19536		6410	2193
n165	19575	10231	6440	2206
n166	20206		6761	2298
n169	1145	219	340	
n170	1926	8210	11440	517
n171	22408			
n174	9038		2305	
n175	9037		2304	
n179	9810			
n180	918		284	72
n181	8207			
n182	19700		6488	V292
n185	12168			
n186	25445	1330	9120	797
n190	30	8004	2045	5
n191	18	8001	2551	3230
n193	11517		3168	
n197	8424			
n199	1416			
n202	1417			
n207	31481	7472		
n208	9735		11510	
n211	331		126	
n215	6870			
n216	1026		313	77
n217	2175			
n218	1277	230	12432	
n230	11628		3229	
n239	5850	499	1636	263
n246	21084		8214	
n247	21105		8227	
n258	1168			
n268	18841		6099	
n269	10072	8568	2710	
n274	24452	4722	8607	2933
n286	8045			
n295	6333		1742	
n296	21408			4311
n297	5853			
n310	20357		6849	2330
n311	25857	1709	13422	
n315	2162			
n316	17374		5512	
n322	31625	7612		
n324	11483	8238	3161	
n331	19488	10202	6385	2185
n341	18876	8916	6121	
n364	2036			
n365	2037			
n366	2038			
n372	16455	8715	5154	
n374	1829		514	
n388	8458			
n390	5879		1651	V550
n402	31711	7695	13586	1574
n412	11563	8600	3190	
n421	8288		2212	
n430	20150		6771	
n432	20315		6820	
n436	17626		5585	
n439	8077	8522	2183	3217
n466	23805	10669		2790
n468	20208			
n473	1355	8148	401	V269
n478	6361		1753	
n479	11584			
n480	13495			4411
n486	6486	525		
n489	21415			

HCP No.	IR Prism	IR HR	UV	NMR
n492	16165			
n499	5147		1398	
n502[1]	10566			
n505	24949			5311
n506	7534			
n509	24461	4730		2634
n511	5312	462	1455	664
n514	23691	10635		2760
n517	1489			100
n519	4530	8333		*148
n520	12000			
n525	142			
n526	14295			
n527	25695	1571		
n528	7565			
n530	5676			
n531	18731	8881		2089
n533	20608			
n534	60			9
n536	4888			
n537	887	10771		5218
n538	5173			249
n539	24463	10678		2635
n543	1491			102
n552	543			48
n553	25681	1557		
n556	8198		2198	
n570	27968	3692	10881	
o4	914			
o6	913			
o11	4531			5310
o12	20374			
o15	4637			
o16	9056			
o22	50			
o23	17362			
o26	1321			96
o27	14298			
o29	16467			
o33	24966			
o34	12504			
o35	21883			
o45	3451	8296		
o50	507			
o56	22762			
o60	20507			
o63	170	54		
o66	916	184		
o67	31652	7638		
o68	20372			2335
o69	4532			
o71	915			
o72	5329			
o77	7597			
o78	20816			3583
o79	2074	8232		1560
o80	917			71
o81	2113	8233		1632
o86	21992			
o91	20372			2335
o100	25044			
o110	1526			105
o112	5245	457		V216
o113	5861			
o116	4638			
o118	4639			227
o121	13423			4505
o130	23779			
o137	33852			
o140	32043	9042		3881

SPECTRA INDEX OF ORGANIC COMPOUNDS (Continued)

HCP No.	IR Prism	IR HR	UV	NMR
o143	18977			4448
o144	18982	10173		4260
o145	24955			
o146	23599			3610
o147	240			
o158	14804			4388
o161	2707			157
o162	16555			
o165	6034			
o166	5159			244
o170	6340	518		
o171	18078	10078		4234
o174	4699			
o178	23503			
o183	4198	8327		512
o184	20213	10344		2500
o186	161			
o188	6188			
o193	3879			
o196	6194			
o197	1634			
o198	10632		2915	
o199	26813	2562		2836
o208	4533	8334		3422
o212	32000	9001		3959
o214	26412	2190		
o234	6269			
o236	5799			
o237	5802			
o238	3273			
o241	5265			
o246	6270			
o255	2962	8279		
o256	1167			
o257	479			
o261	5856			
o262	5266			
o263	6653			
o266	5267			
o270	5171			
o278	5854			
o281	24311	915		2589
o284	24467	4732		
o288	26016	1860		410
o295	14056		3868	3355
o297	14103	8666	3904	3371
p6	524			
p7	17635			
p11	21014			
p15	5181			V474
p19	503			
p27	15223			
p34	23639			
p37	24814			5721
p38	24965			
p39	23604	10608		3612
p45	15377			
p46	23605			
p56	26671	10753	9997	
p65	8046			
p66	8028			5185
p74	2480			
p76	10553			
p77	9490			
p80	14530	10034		4387
p84	690	8086		*140
p85	10988			
p90	1857			120
p91	4641			
p92	21355			

HCP No.	IR Prism	IR HR	UV	NMR
p95	2265			
p99	63			
p101	23648			
p117	3654	386		
p121	5851			
p130	9726			
p131	31996	7976		
p132	7862			5317
p133	677	8084		52
p134	11834			
p144	4642			228
p148	686			*142
p149	682			3412
p153	4681	433		3432
p155	18508	12981		
p157	17452			
p158	7386			4409
p159	24323	923		2593
p160	17521			4258
p161	692			
p162	5187			251
p165	19116			5008
p166	17484			4252
p167	10897			
p172	19665	10256		2231
p177	8680		2261	
p178	14649			
p179	14650		4149	
p188	1907			
p189	22964			
	22965			
p192	239			
p193	20266	10353		
p194	17549			4019
p195	6527			V217
p197	17550			4020
p202	5774	497	1615	
p209	6612			
p214	304	10844		5995
p215	22009			
p219	2075			
p222	22010			
p228	24944	10712		
p229	20785	12982		3696
p231	1530			
p237	2326			
p241	15269			
p242	2709			
p243	6145			
p258	34406	12392		5839
p261	23514			
p266	4831	8349		
p268	3407			
p270	15064			
p284	10606	10789		5433
p288	23560			
p291	2706			156
p295	2728			165
p299	17491			
p304	8694			
p305	9058			
p310	21072		8203	
p311	2775			
p313	52	205		
p314	803			60
p315	804			

HCP No.	IR Prism	IR HR	UV	NMR
p323	27948	3673		329
p324	8522			4274
p325	8512			
p327	9189			
p328	2400			
p330	10607			
p331	9194			
p332	9193			
p334	6195	8451		
p335	23795			
p336	66	10933		4279
p337	144	43		521
p338	9186			
p339	19759	10274		3976
p345	3445			
p346	2903	8272	833	177
p348	880		274	
p350	20804		8006	
p352	19115			5007
p355	163			
p356	20134			
p360	24137	801		
p362	356	116	139	303
p364	9190			
p365	44	23	21	V139
p366	9183			
p368	11920			
p369	5681			
p373	16751			
p375	685			3414
p401	32004	9005		4315
p403	3390			5319
p405	32005	9006		4316
p410	7988			3393
p413	7987			5316
p415	15315			5314
p416	23796			V471
p419	3391			3421
p420	298			
p423	23090			
p425	6009		1693	
p428	18902			
p430	15287		4558	
p433	27133	2879		968
p434	8511			
p436	32030	9031		3878
p439	3882			
p441	109		41	
p441[1]	15302	634	4568	572
p461	5300			
p466	32038	9037		
p469	332	127		
p472	1333			
p473	334	9994		3845
p478	34418	12403		
p479	5253	458		
p482	12959			2853
p484	810	8035	256	61
p492	7603		2130	
p494	19206			V622
p504	23258			5112
p505	23259			5113
p506	13119		3414	
p506[1]	25474	1358	9145	
p508	20364	10380	6855	2332
p510	15222			
p513	27896	3622		
p522	19725		6504	
p526	15224		4512	
p528	20577		6957	

HCP No.	IR Prism	IR HR	UV	NMR
p529	21074		8204	
p531	5894			
p533	21389			
p550	14219			
p554	28702	4404	11797	
p555	843	165	258	3152
p556	6764		1894	1176
p557	709	8088	3509	
p561	712	158	236	717
p577	18173	8829	5772	2018
p579	5982	8443	1685	3189
p581	2161	296	570	2824
p584	20670		6967	
p586	30633	6615	13258	
p590	474		167	
p592	4665		1281	
p593	21356			
p594	4892	443	1365	678
p596	18724		6032	
p604	1515			
p613	2800	343	772	1209
p614	4666	10852	1282	232
p615	1418	243	409	
p618	6456	8471	1792	270
p620	1419	8155	1982	3209
p621	15185			
p623	6766	8488	1896	
p627	22392		8249	2735
p629	7191		2037	
p630	17464			
p631	1315	238	9786	
p632	22395	755	9704	
p633	17465	681	9634	
p634	17124		5405	
p635	17468			
p637	19142	8971	6255	2162
p638	13923	8636	3803	
p642	33636	11627	14278	
p643	5444		1496	255
p645	253	86	3234	
p646	17486		5553	
p647	17463		5547	4250
p650	2889		822	170
p651	5980		1683	267
p652	85		35	12
p658	24717	4901	8770	
p662	90	8013	36	3149
p664	5554		1548	259
p665	1482	10768	423	3154
p676	6765	8487	1895	3208
p679	13456	10853	3517	3250
p680	2160		569	
p681	5887	506	1684	
p682	23689	10634	13350	3644
p683	5277	459	1449	
p684	279	96	112	
p697	5323	466	1459	667
p702	14019	616	4839	
p703	29001	5001	11905	
p709	3891	397	1181	1753
p710	8113		2188	
p711	9171	568		
p713	9395			
p715	7157			
p716	321	109	122	
p721	8642			
p722	8623		2240	
p724	5556			
p725	11496			
p726	5557			

HCP No.	IR Prism	IR HR	UV	NMR
p730	23620			
p755	12192			
p756	12191		4852	4473
p775	138			
p776	377			V482
p781	9066			
p782	3008			
p789	22			
p790	20	8002	10	301
p791	676	150	227	
p797	110	34		
p798	3003			
p799	104	33		
p800	105			
p801	6739			
p802	13950			
p803	18408		5865	
p810	13930		3806	
p812	6272	8442	1730	
p813	8656		18	
p814	21064		8200	
p817	1902	285	529	721
p819	37	3837	225	1199
p821	375	117	150	705
p822	3228	367	955	709
p824	1265	8135	378	89
p826	9204		2385	
p827	1304	235	391	93
p828	9778			
p830	6227		516	9886
p832	1812	278	507	
p833	16548		5195	V246
p835	6635		1833	
p837	18797	8906	6071	2106
p840	18823	699	6086	
p841	20138		6713	
p846	27760	3495	10766	
p847	16607	658	5220	
p850	5962	8438	1678	3198
p878	20019			
p879	19545	10217	6414	
p883	21424	10837		5579
p884	8445			
p887	26607	2372		
p888	8700		2272	
p892	13001	8611	3355	
p893	9394			
p894	1271	228	382	
p897	13929	10874	3805	V496
p898	14538			
p899	11032		3001	
p900	31895	7873	13668	3795
p901	8760			
p902	6218	8452	11498	
p903	6236	8453	11499	
p906	18334			V346
p908	15225			
p909	9517			
p910	1442		309	
p911	7548			
p915	7161			
p921	22476			
p923	928			V272
p924	2188			V274
p932	15000			
p935	7194			
p936	34387	12373		5828
p941	368			
p942	9507			
p943	439			

HCP No.	IR Prism	IR HR	UV	NMR
p944	7480			
p946	11022			V119
p947	14478			
p948	8770		2279	300
p949	18497			4139
p950	23277			5117
p951	18335			
p952	5991			*135
p955	23634	10620	13344	3628
p976	8303			
p982	15285			
p984	24312			
p1003	8304			V477
p1005	8032	8519		
p1007	23799	10761		V479
p1011	20247			
p1023	34421	12406		5818
p1024	31908	7886		3800
p1035	20522			
p1039	25053			
p1040	8771			V328
p1045	29192	5189		
p1047	1343			
p1053	724			
p1057	763			
p1061	9600			
p1065	2518			
p1070	1905			
p1074	14542			
p1082	8269			
p1083	8348			
	302			
p1089	18482			4496
p1091	26036			
p1096	22883	10590		2541
p1097	4607			
p1101	7014			
p1104	16244	653	5037	
p1105	17410			V529
	17410		5535	*127
p1107	6404			
p1108	2242			
p1109	1081			
p1113	1130			
p1114	4719			V90
p1114[1]	20244			2300
p1115	26024	1868		400
p1118	1070	216	325	
p1118[1]	20246	10349		
p1119	11352			1892
p1120	4644	10952		V392
p1122	11042	10959		V29
p1123	16034			
p1125	1856			
p1126	22414			
p1129	4643	427		
p1133	193	66		
p1134	243			
p1136	129	10935		16
p1141	4646	429		
p1144	943	189	291	V385
p1148	946	192	294	
p1149	7245		2054	
p1151	9059			
p1152	8904			
p1154	3649			187
p1155	3650			188

HCP No.	IR Prism	IR HR	UV	NMR
p1159	9777			V412
p1161	3208	10981		V30
p1163	3209			V31
p1164	17517			
p1172	23736	10648		2762
p1174	7986			5309
p1180	387			V32
	2211			V32
	2212			V32
p1184	34404	12390		5837
p1186	5143	448		1215
p1192	4647			230
p1193	4651			V392
p1196	10652			V408
p1210	43	22	20	V42
p1211	1	1	1	
p1214	23596			
p1216	5246			V377
p1218	23630			
p1222	11351			
p1224	4652			231
p1226	23714	10638		3652
p1228	23715			V383
p1229	4653	10777		
p1231	9707			
p1234	267	92		V45
p1235	3297	376		4885
p1244	2804			
p1250	7898			
p1251	7246			
	11184(K)			
p1252	7899			
p1253	18722			
p1254	13919			
p1258	11297			
p1260	5085			
p1263	10749			
	6350			
p1264	5884	8430	1652	3188
p1265	1921			
p1266	1346	242	399	1203
p1280	22451	10572		2756
p1293	5983			
	328			
p1294	329			V396
p1295	330			3410
p1296	14803			3438
p1297	11296			
p1302	307	104		5996
p1303	9801			
p1310	107			
p1312	2170	300		
p1314	5965			
	5966			
p1315	22385	10556		2732
p1316	303	103		
p1318	1432			
p1322	698			55
p1323	5969			
p1324	5270			1884
p1325	2350			149
p1326	190			1877
p1327	23602			3611
p1328	339	113		40
p1329	8759			
p1330	2828		811	
p1332	309	105		38
p1336	9783			
p1344	2271	318		144
p1346	9776			
p1348	6144			

HCP No.	IR Prism	IR HR	UV	NMR
p1354	2251			137
p1358	16157			
p1360	2272			145
p1365	16156			
p1373	6618			V25
p1377	23758	10656		2770
	5268			
p1381	4707			
p1384	3647			
p1387	6553			
p1390	1596	8180		358
p1392	363			304
p1395	27940	3665		846
p1406	3648			
	10903(K)			
p1407	4001			
p1408	27238	2982		
p1411	23665	10628	13347	3637
p1415	5673			
p1417	18755			
p1423¹	19593		6452	
p1430	6355			
p1432	24888	6000		
p1435	22127			
p1437	24668	4873	8738	5333
p1441	20769	10422	7990	3049
p1444	11349		3099	
p1448	15334	10807		4933
p1452¹	3133			
p1455	5338	467		
p1460	768			
p1462	22444			2755
p1466	5167	10955		246
p1468	14027			
p1472	24952			
p1475	5276			
p1479	832	8098		
p1480	115			V409
p1481	388	10766		306
p1484	14541			
p1485	4703			
p1486	20096			
p1487	385			V70
	385			305
p1498	23727	10642		3655
p1509	5431		1489	
	10719		1489	
p1512	28899	4601		V27
p1514	15547			
p1516	1057			V69
p1518	697			54
p1521	27611	3346	10648	
p1522	11317			V516
p1525	14299			
p1527	18085	10083		4239
p1530	4702			238
p1532	8668			
p1533	17525			
p1534	10652			V408
p1539	11278		3080	
p1541	24458	4727	8612	
p1542	5963			
p1543	16153	651		
p1544	25732	1604		
p1545	27899	3625		
p1545¹	19188			5016
p1548	24986	10731		
p1549	8017			
p1552	8905			

HCP No.	IR Prism	IR HR	UV	NMR
p1558	26058			
p1560	24818	4972	8787	5628
p1564	2495			
p1568	8697		2270	299
p1574	3866			
p1575	24832		8797	5726
p1579	23627			
p1586	26028	1871	9438	428
p1587	64			10
	64	10961		V43
p1588	189	65		V44
p1589	23490			
p1590	5826			
p1591	5977			4273
p1594	7558			
p1600	8765			
p1601	25767			
p1603	9489			
p1604	2249	310		
p1605	25770	1636		
p1610	8050			
p1613	16246	10042		4214
p1618	17455			V386
p1623	17122			
p1625	15720			1897
p1628	15765			
p1632	2089		558	
p1632³	6371			
p1633	2	2		V423
	2219	2		V423
p1634	8678	8539	2259	V422
	8678			296
p1635	9398			
p1637	6372			
	6356			
p1638	266	10937		
	4570	10937		
p1639	289	99		
p1644	1651	268	470	116
p1645	15283		4556	
p1648	34872			
p1649	233	77	89	
	6309	77	89	
p1651	13948			
p1652	4135			199
p1655	5944			
p1657	2719			
p1663	16158			
p1666	22248	10531		2515
p1667	27936	3661	10863	496
p1668	8049			
p1669	5669	483	1575	700
p1677	17394			
p1679	18249			
p1682	3881		1176	V638
p1683	25975	1821		1483
p1684	15347			
p1687	833	8099	11411	361
p1688	8329		2219	
p1693	5773	496	1614	V559
p1696	272	94	109	34
p1698	2927	8273	839	1855
p1702	9969	8565	11513	2843
p1705	12170			
p1707	6646			
	6645			
p1708	14668			

HCP No.	IR Prism	IR HR	UV	NMR	HCP No.	IR Prism	IR HR	UV	NMR	HCP No.	IR Prism	IR HR	UV	NMR
p1711	10521			V152	p1904	3061		890		p2048	5644	8408	1564	
p1712	8350				p1905	21056		8194	V379	p2051	18978	10172	6182	4259
	8349				p1908	24207	847	8493	2683	p2052	7547			
p1713	6403				p1916	34266	12255	14418		p2053	18975		6180	
p1714	1100			V38	p1917	8625			1858	p2054	17175		5421	3283
p1715	4654													
					p1925	5457				p2056	8039			
p1716	13406			V23	p1930	870	173	269	64	p2059	20252	10351	6783	569
	2270			V23	p1931	34705	12688	14498		p2064	5964	8439	3163	
p1717	2539			V24	p1937	4834	8350	11467		p2065	27970	3694	10882	
p1722	275				p1939	15	12	9	V96	p2066	13499		3528	
	7848													
p1725	4689				p1940	21879				p2067	17440		5542	
p1730	3652			V17	p1942	21019		8166		p2068	21061	10836	8197	
					p1948	1788	8199	500	V431	p2069	168	53		
p1731	13903				p1949	8394		2230	293	p2071	8189			
p1732	23674				p1950	9495				p2072	19121	8966	6243	2157
p1733	23676													
p1735	13904			V18	p1951	18347	8831	5841	2019	p2074	7508			
p1744	7366				p1952	18145	8817	5756	2011	p2088	2419		627	
					p1953	5465		1501		p2091	21880			
p1747	7858	8514			p1959	12481	8608	3354	3246	p2092	2121		561	
p1754	195	8020	78	V232	p1960	13897		3791		p2093	1783		498	V401
p1758[1]	5192			V492										
p1759	871				p1961	13895	612	3789		p2098	15641		4697	5098
	13687				p1964	16588		5210		p2100	7517		2107	
p1761	23512				p1966	15314		4575		p2105	24016			
					p1967	13644	608	3607	V593	p2107	27244	2988		
p1766	11017		2994	5298	p1969	13646				p2126	1010		307	V55
p1768	2998	8284	3515	3166										
	13447	8284	3515		p1970	4728				p2134	18498		5924	
p1769	14038		3864		p1971	16341		5112		p2136	14149			
p1770	4694	10779	1294	5141	p1973	1795		501		p2142	6851		1911	
p1771	11400				p1974	17133		5406		p2145	8640		2254	
					p1975	18955				p2160	1908			
p1772	14564													
p1773	1310				p1976	18956		6170						
p1774	14041				p1977	18956		6170		p2167	16581			5091
p1775	1117			V64	p1982	3201				p2169	7235			V68
p1776	386			V15	p1988	1042				p2170	28861	4563		818
					p1989	3298				p2172	6528			V116
p1778	14574									q1	11995	596	6997	1614
p1782	26553	2318	9911	593	p1990	8009			V169					
p1783[1]	12487	606	9630		p1992	11029		2998		q2	4771	442	9885	
p1792	5342	8390	1464	V62	p1993	16586		5208		q7	34527	12511		
p1793	14604			V71	p1994	32021	9022		3873	q13	7527		2110	
					p1996	6654		1839	V154	q14	5976	511	1682	
p1794	1123									q22	7456			
p1795	14049				p1997	15806			V155		5993			
p1796	1082			V135	p1998	1249								
p1797	1120				p1999	1250		372		q24	9525			
p1798	15352				p2000	1251				q26	7504			
					p2004	5614		1559		q28	7455			
p1799	2226			V113						q32	7546			
p1800	14000			V97	p2006	4450	404	1241	571	q34	1053	213	320	
p1801	15351				p2007	18960		6173						
p1814	284	97		V34	p2008	17490		5554	V428	q37	9719			
p1816	26703			479	p2009	18961		6174		q43	7522			
					p2010	8188				q47	20672		6968	3589
p1820	12158									q55	18144	8816	5755	2010
p1822	184	8018	74	23	p2013	20453				q58	18682		6006	
p1830	8639				p2016	1283								
p1832	6603	529		273	p2017	1247				q65	33628	11619	14276	5791
p1833	18580			5998	p2019	9	7	6	566	q70	7610			
					p2020	32	18	14	890	q77	34388	12374		
p1847	12394									q81	1794			
p1849	21017		8164		p2021	31	17	13	889	q85	9762			
p1851	1111			V21	p2024	21070								
p1867	520		177		p2026	11397		3126		q87	8321			
p1870	7550	8507			p2034	10656		2920		q88	32735	9730	13970	
					p2035	20451	10383	6903	1344	q89	4585		1268	
p1879	20514									q90	18422		5875	2030
p1880	24059				p2036	3515		1090		q106	7168			
p1887	23626			1475	p2037	32726	9721		4607					
p1888	14700		4171	4021	p2039	19132	8969	6251	2160	q115	13310			
p1889	7006				p2040	434	120	161	942	q120	2813			
					p2041	860	8106	261	V453	q122	19446	8981	6354	5020
p1897	15548	642	4658	553						q123	19928		6606	
p1898	14476		4111	V459	p2042	8761		2277		q124	7179	8496	2032	
p1899	14477		4112	4390	p2044	5170	454	1407	697					
p1900	3068		895		p2045	8452								
p1901	20525	10407	6945		p2046	23791								
					p2047	17192	8720	5126	3278					

HCP No.	IR Prism	IR HR	UV	NMR
q127	8010		2163	V578
q128	10544	578	9625	V579
q129	19690			3971
q148	13899		3792	
q154	187	63	76	24
q155	8628			
q157	26313	2109		
q159	26314	2110		
q163	4214	8328		
q171	2573	329	9883	314
q172	11199		3050	
	2575		3050	
q176	33687	11677	14307	5486
q185	8340			V249
q190	6344		1747	
q193	1055		321	*138
q195	2174		575	*139
	2174			132
q197	8407			
q205	2819			
q212	20301		6811	
q213	5893	8433	1656	265
q215	20302		7862	
q223	22130			
q233	16571		5205	
q249	20021	10281		
q251	6519		1812	
q253	11645			
q255	11644	128	166	
	473	128	166	
q258	8682	8540	2262	
q260	10872			
	13309			
q262	26558	2323	9916	1168
q265	10727			V494
q269	3169			
q270	9467		2542	
q276	31609	7596		2855
q278	34823	12806		
q280	31686	7672		
r1	1032			
r6	7379			
	11280			
r19	11293			
r21	255	88	2964	
	10901	88	2964	
r22	8540			
r24	20687			3668
r26	10526			
r27	8952			
r32	373		149	
r36	25477	1361		
s4	4995			
s6	322	110		
s7	5990			V253
s39[1]	29947	5934		
s39[2]	481			
s46	20541		7886	
s47	23617	10614	13338	3621
s51	25024	1016	8890	
s56	10625			
	454			
s58	10560			
s63[1]	1226			
s64	1702			
s73	24004			
s77[1]	11470			V184

HCP No.	IR Prism	IR HR	UV	NMR
s80	1611			
s99	991	200		
s101	9027			
s104	1069			
s109	17336	10755		5411
s122	9758			
s128	5978			
s129	11985	8603		V306
s137	1827			
s143	20058	10295	6665	2256
s152	7549			
s153	3801			
s154	9471			
s155	13218			
	3803			
s157	2181		577	
s159	241	81	94	
s161	1529	8158	435	V497
s162	25739	1609		
s164	20123		6702	
s167	14032		3862	
s168	14033	617	3863	
s169	14034			V498
s172	22434		8360	
s178	14630		4139	
s179	3301		991	
s185	11335			
	2805			4531
s186	5150	449		
s188	2257	314	604	140
s189	3218			
s192	6312			
s193	3001			V215
	3001			183
s195	14918			4930
s196	500			
s200	482	129	170	
s202	7619			
s207	1431			
s214	15719	646	4732	4381
s220	23902		8382	
s227	1831			V277
s229	18586	10155		
s232	7189	540		
s237	19169	10194		4281
s250[2]	6187			
s251	19937			
s253	5519			4408
s254	18984			4261
s255	28869	4571		
s257	1307			
s261	11334			
s267	19500			
s273	8659	563		
s274	21882			
s276	9514			
s279	49		24	
	9024		24	
s280	423			
s281	312			
s283	3685			
s285	311	106	119	
s286	21089			
	21088		8218	
s288	20468		6915	
	20469			

HCP No.	IR Prism	IR HR	UV	NMR
s289	24186		8477	
s292	9781			V136
	14631			V136
s294	18221		5779	1898
s295	6614			275
s298	8037			
s300	1300			
s303	17151			
s308	11300			
s313	6300			
	6299			
s315	18230		7561	
s317	320	108	121	39
s321	18683	8866	6007	2074
s327	9234		2389	
s329	9231		2386	
s330	34489	12473		
s338	9235		2390	
s342	6655			
s350	23704			V118
s354	15577		4668	
s355	422			
	7459			
s357	20107			
s358	14501			
s359	53	24	26	
s362	17818		5649	
s365	13485		3522	
s366	2991		864	
	13393			
	4873		864	
s367	4875		1356	
s369	17827		5655	
s372	9548			
	1352		400	
s373	17826		5654	
s375	15062			
s382	9705			
s383	15576		4667	
s384	18723			
s386	7031	536		535
s387	16313		5090	
	418		5090	
s393	20593		7917	
s398	8023			
s402	15332			
s408	19478	9000		
s409	461			
s416	9765			
s420	19601			V371
t7	656	147	222	
t10	22011			
t15	5272			
t17	20815			1904
t35	10275			
t46	4543	409	1257	V670
t47	4542			206
	4542	408	2171	V669
	8030	408	2171	206
t48	22478			
t49	1369			
t50	1365			
t52	1364			
t55	727			
	13203			J128
t62	10565			
t64	31621	7608		
t67	4535	8335		204
t68	20503			
t69	4687			

HCP No.	Sadtler Reference Number			
	IR Prism	IR HR	UV	NMR
t70	4688			
t76	24576			2690
t77	21400			167
	2807			167
	8501			167
t78	20502			
t81	209			
t82	5264			
t83	7596			
t84	3852			195
t85	23699			3648
t87	8502			294
t88	23700			
t89	23701			
t90	4536			
t94	32144	9142		3934
t95	5612			
	10601			
t97	5320			
t98	12388			V557
t101	18893		6132	
t105	2035			
t117	8618			
t118	1392			
t127	4104	10007		
t129	4107			
t135	7505			
t137	1787		499	V380
t138	7552			
t156	20513			2359
t159	7512			
t160	3121			
t166	18591	8854	5959	J112
	18591			2055
t167	5753	10781	1601	5217
t171	15274			V384
t174	20086			
t175	20002			
t179	32063	9061		3897
t183	6092	514		1554
t187	172			V52
	172			*134
t189	8476	10847	523	123
	1865	10847	523	123
t190	25976	1822		1484
t191	25979	1825		1485
t192	17538		5560	
t193	1800	276	502	1408
t198	1802		504	
t202	13504			
t204	1809	277	506	1319
t210	19745		6521	
t213	8346			V49
t215	25980	1826		V103
t216	23801			
t219	177	57	71	
t222	20606			
t223	16580			
t224	14805			V80
	14805			*133
t229	174	56	69	V94
t230	25971	1817		1482
t232	176	963	70	523
t233	173			
t234	26712	2463	10021	475
t238	23256			
t249	7058			1994

HCP No.	Sadtler Reference Number			
	IR Prism	IR HR	UV	NMR
t254	784			
t256	12963			
t259	22000			
t260	21800			
t263	9543			
t264	1532	8159	437	
t269	10277			V366
t275	419	119	155	V157
t278	5757		1605	
t279	20973	10489		2404
t281	866	170	266	63
t282	28773	4475	11822	
t283	1543	8160	442	107
	7460	8160	422	107
t285	6330		1740	
t286	1544	8161	443	108
t288	3817	8309	1161	3172
t289	6341	8458	1745	3288
t295	21022		8169	
t299	21023			
t302	4721		1302	
t303	17155	669	5411	558
t304	4720		1301	
t306	14921	8699	4325	3266
t312	20668		6965	
t319	24010			
t328	11627			3228
t339	20460			6909
t340	4716			
t344	24433	4703	8592	
t345	13670	8626	3620	3252
	4722	8626	3620	
t346	13669	8625	3619	
t347	28904	4606	11379	
t352	212		4691	
	15634		4691	
t353	13671	611	3621	543
t354	21815			
t355	863	168	263	
t357	2504	327	660	154
t358	2724	336	738	161
t359	2725	8259	739	162
t360	2726	337	740	163
t364	4559	10851	1261	
t370	18680	8864	6004	2072
t376	32763	9758		4628
t377	20270	6793		
t378	8443	8530	2238	3222
t380	20880	8060		
t391	8	6	5	3
t392	91	29	37	13
t393	3658	8302	1116	3168
t394	629	145	212	51
t400	4726	440	1303	
	9809	440	1303	
t402	15736			
t407	15735			
t409	19934		6608	
t410	20271	11091	6794	
t412	13918	8635	3800	3258
t413	18905		6140	5000
t414	4690	436	1291	675
t415	21917			
t417	4691		3293	
	12065		3293	
t418	18798		6072	2107
t421	8047	8304	2177	3216
	3671	8304	2177	
t423	17467			
t424	13958	614	3815	
t430	13908	8631	3793	3256

HCP No.	Sadtler Reference Number			
	IR Prism	IR HR	UV	NMR
t436	4558		1260	
t437	2489		657	685
t438	621			1182
	621	141	206	J116
t440	626			1183
	626	142	209	J117
t442	628	144	211	1185
t444	17120	664	5404	894
t445	627	143	210	574
t449	19448	8983	6356	2169
t451	15737		4745	
t460	4572		1263	
t461	20387			
t461¹	18817		6083	
t462	18827	10812	6088	4996
t463	19974			
t465	707		232	
t467	19975		6622	
t468	24466	4731	8615	
t469	2092			
t472	11031		3000	
t473	24448	4718	8604	2626
t475	4718	8345	1300	3178
t476	3662		1118	
t477	23751			
t478	3663	8303	1119	3171
t479	175	8017	2550	3229
	258	8017	2350	3229
	9596	8017	2550	3229
t481	17378	676	5514	895
t482	1949	8214		
t484¹	287	98	2907	
	10554	98	2907	3236
t488	7188		2036	284
t489	8090			
t490	15318		4577	
t491	8313			
t493	4658			
t494	4657			
t495	4659			
t496	775		250	
t497	157	985	62	V161
t498	844	166	259	3153
t499	2338	322	622	V160
t500	33	8005	15	
t505	8122		2189	
t508	25712	1585	9299	
t509	6349	8462	1750	3194
t513	20147	10326	6719	2278
t514	20273			
t516	21403			
t517	19409	8977	7771	
t519	19410		7772	
t521	32463	9459	13799	
t525	20272		7860	
t526	11921		3280	
t527	23685			
t528	20534			
t529	20535			
t539	2896		828	
t540	2895	10774	827	
t541	2897		3100	173
	11353		3100	173
t543	6615	8477	1822	J111
	6615			276
t544	21700			
t545	313			

HCP No.	IR Prism	IR HR	UV	NMR
t546	45	8006	11403	V168
	12448	3353		
t547	28945	4647	11389	505
t548	2987	361	860	1180
t549	8044	10772	2176	V205
	8044	10772	2176	292
	1366	10772	2176	292
t550	21401			
t552	8409			
t554	4692	437	1292	676
t555	183	61	73	22
t556	4693	438	1293	677
t561	28374	4084	11732	1371
t564	236	8022	92	
t574	1768	271	493	1190
t575	18486	8852	5918	2051
t576	619	140	204	1181
t598	1268	227	380	90
t600	25215			
t601	630			
t605	23716			
t609	232		88	
t612	22032			
t623	21886			V486
t635	869	172	268	
t639	868			
t641	6337	8607	1744	
t645	10657		2921	
t650	28350	4064		
t652	19785		6540	
t653	2289	320	611	666
t654	16248		5038	
t655	23373			
t656	6860		1918	
t657	13453		3516	
t663	17363	675	5505	
t664	5754	492	1602	671
t665	6357			
t666	32049	9048	13694	3886
t668	8956	8544	2302	3227
t670	13518		3533	
t671	1572		451	
t673	9753			
t676	22370	10549		
t701[1]	22278	10547		
t702	2511	615	3855	544
	14013	615	3855	544
t703[1]	4729		1304	
t707	4114			
t708	10626			
t709	8667			
t710	10536			
t711	24950			1419
t712	23718	10639		3653
t716	18328	8830		3440
t717	24552			
t718	18686			
t722	22004			
t724	24445	4715		
t725	24946			
t727	5313	463	1456	
t728	22903			
t729	23719			
t732	5686	10986		5543
t736	5321			
t737	13213			
	5940			
t741	466			
t749	310			
t753	2801			

HCP No.	IR Prism	IR HR	UV	NMR
t764	21887			
t768	21888			
t772	21889			
t773	432	8612	3453	
	13210	8612	3453	
t774	5568			
t775	455	592		
	11497	592	11525	
t776	535	134	187	
t781	7501			
t783	10624			
t784	5569			
t786	21891			
t789	17385		5520	
u2	6335		1743	
u3	15638		4695	
u4	24877	5989		
u5	1136	8127	11420	
u7	31616	7603		
u7[1]	8683			
u8	7514	8506	2105	2801
u9	8429		2236	
u11	26885	2631	10150	
u12	25719	1591	9305	
u13	9400		2508	
u16	6467		1796	
u17	1836		517	
u18	447	123		
u19	9795			
u23	28912	4614	11381	
u25	7524			
u27	1823			
u30	18601	10160	5968	
u32	3902			
	11739			
u34	3939			
u35	13656			
u37	14717			
u41	34472	12457		5739
u42	6757			282
u44	9751			
u55	1837			
u56	11732			
	3895			
u57	3219		952	
	11751			
u59	3661			190
	11236			190
u60	3892	10864		
	12493	10864		4957
u61	3660			189
u62	3911			
u64	965			
u70	3898			
u71	3899		1182	
u75	21489			
	8029	554	2170	1220
u78	11234			
u79	202			4399
u83	3894			
	11731			
u84	3912			
	11749			
u85	3913			
	11750			
u95	19919			
u95[1]	13891			
u102	19941		6610	
u103	20330		6827	
u104	20331		6828	
u106	21417			

HCP No.	IR Prism	IR HR	UV	NMR
u107	20333	10369	7865	
u110	4591	417	1272	
u111	32139	9137	13717	
u113	20447			
u116	23703		3649	
u118	3901			
	11738			
u120	3962	8315	3292	
	12062	8315	3292	
u121	20553		6954	
u123	22015			
u125	3904			
	11741			
u126	3905			
	11742			
u127	3906			
	11743			
u129	19606			2221
u131	2963	358	853	
u135	22008			
u142	17640		7370	4032
v3	453			
	11495			
v24	16101			
v25	324		123	
v27	8085	30	38	
	92	30	38	
v28	16104			
x1	6855		1913	533
x2	6359		1715	
	6358		1715	
x3	6857		1915	
x4	20592			2373
x5	31476	7467	13160	
x6	645			
x7	31618	7605		
x10	18462			
x12	5608		1555	
x16	13753			
x24	4299			
x29	1039			
x30	1068			
y3	12279			
	12280			
y4	12281			

PHYSICAL CONSTANTS OF ORGANOMETALLIC COMPOUNDS

Metallic salts of organic acids will be found in Physical Constants of Organic Compounds table.

No.	Name	Formula	Mol. wt.	Crystalline form, color and index of refraction	Sp. gr. or density	Melting point, °C	Boiling point, °C	Solubility in grams per 100 ml of		
								Cold water	Hot water	Alcohol, acids, etc.
	Aluminum									
1	Aluminum isopropoxide	Al[OCH(CH₃)₂]₃	204.25	col. liq		118	145–150[5] solidifies			
2	Aluminum isopropylate	Al(OC₃H₇)₃	204.25	brittle wh. solid		118	125–130[4]	d.		s. bz.
3	Aluminum magnesium ethoxide	Mg[Al(OC₂H₅)₄]₂	438.77	iceblue cr.		129	225[4]			s. bz.
4	Diethylaluminum chloride	(C₂H₅)₂AlCl	120.56	col. liq.		−50	125–126[60]			
5	Diethylaluminum malonate	Al(C₇H₁₁O₄)₃	504.48	wh. need. or pr.	1.084[100]	98		i.		s. org. solv.
6	Dimethylaluminum chloride	(CH₃)₂AlCl	92.50	col. liq.		−50	83–84[200]			
7	Methylaluminum dichloride	CH₃AlCl₂	112.92		1.00[22]	72.7	97–100[100]			
8	Triethoxyaluminum	Al(OC₂H₅)₃	162.17	sol.	1.142[20]	150–160	d.			i. al., sl. s. bz., v. sl. s. eth.
9	Triethylaluminum	Al(C₂H₅)₃	114.17	col. liq., ign. in air, 1.480[6.5]	0.837	<−18 (−50.5)	194	exp.; d. to Al(OH)₃ + C₂H₆		
10	Triethylaluminum etherate	4Al(C₂H₅)₃.3(C₂H₅)₂O	679.04	col. liq			112[16]	exp.		d. al; s. bz., eth.
11	Trimethylaluminum	Al(CH₃)₃	72.09	col. liq, ign. in air, 1.432[12]	0.752	0(15)	130 (125[26])	d. to Al(OH)₃ + CH₄		s. eth., al.
12	Triphenylaluminum	Al(C₆H₅)₃	258.30	wh. need.		196–200		d.		d. al., chl., CCl₄; s. bz.
	Antimony									
1	Antimony ethoxide(ous) (triethyl antimonite)	Sb(C₂H₅O)₃	256.93	col. liq.	1.524[17]		95[11]	d.		s. org. liqs.
2	Pentamethylantimony	Sb(CH₃)₅	196.93	(exist?)		96–100		i.	i.	
3	Phenyldimethyl- antimony	C₆H₅Sb(CH₃)₂	228.93	col. oil, fumes in air			112[15–18]			
4	Phenylstibinic acid	(C₆H₅SbO₂)₃H₂O]2H₂O	746.61	wh. fine cr.				i.		s. chl., al., dil. a.; sl. s. acet.
5	Tetramethyldistibyl	(C₆H₅)₂Sb.Sb(C₆H₅)₂	551.93	col.		121–122 (in N₂)				
6	Tributylstibene	(C₄H₉)₃Sb	293.10	col. liq.			133–134[14]	i.	i.	s. org. solv.
7	Triethylantimony	Sb(C₂H₅)₃	208.94	liq. 15 1.42	1.324[16]	<−29 (−98)	159.5	i.	i.	s. al., eth.
8	Triethylantimony chloride	(C₂H₅)₃SbCl₂	279.84	col. liq.	1.540[17]		d.	i.		s. al., eth.; d. conc. H₂SO₄
9	Trimethylantimony	Sb(CH₃)₃	166.86	liq. n_D^{15}	1.523[15]		80.6	sl. s.	sl. s.	s. eth.; i. al.
10	Triphenylantimony	Sb(C₆H₅)₃	353.07	col. tricl. pl.	1.4343[25] (1.4998)	50, (46–53)	>220[1]; >360[760]	i.	i.	s. org. solv.; sl. s. al.
11	Triphenylantimony dichloride	(C₆H₅)₃SbCl₂	123.98	wh. sol.		143		i.	i.	s. bz., CS₂, hot al.
12	Triphenylantimony sulfide	(C₆H₅)₃SbS	385.13	wh. cr.		108–110		i.	i.	s. org. solv.
	Arsenic									
1	Acetylarsanilic acid	CH₃CONHC₆H₄AsO(OH)₂	259.09	cryst		>200				s. NaCO₃; v. sl. s. HCl; i. eth.
2	3-Amino-4-hydroxy- phenylarsonic acid	H₂O₃AsC₆H₃(OH)(NH₂)	233.06	col. prism		d.290		sl. s.		s. alk.; min. a.; i. org. solv.
3	2-Aminophenylarsonic acid (Arsanilic acid)	H₂NC₆H₄AsO(OH)₂	217.06	need.		153		s.		s. al.; alk., ac.; sl. s. eth.
4	4-Aminophenylarsonic acid (p-Arsanilicacid)	H₂NC₆H₅AsO(OH)₂	217.06	wh. need.		d. 300		sl. s.	s.	s. alk., dil. a.; sl. s. al.; i. eth., acet.
5	Arsanilic acid (p)(p- aminophenylarsinic acid)	H₂NC₆H₄AsO(OH)₂	217.06	wh. need.		232				s. eth., MeOH; sl. s. al., acet; i. bz., chl.
6	Arsenoacetic acid	(AsCH₂COOH)₂	267.93	sm. yel. need.		>260, d. 205		i.		s. pyr., alks., alk. carb; i. al., eth., chl.

No.	Name	Formula	Mol. wt.	Crystalline form, color and index of refraction	Sp. gr. or density	Melting point, °C	Boiling point, °C	Solubility in grams per 100 ml of		
								Cold water	Hot water	Alcohol, acids, etc.
	Arsenic									
7	Arsenobenzene........	$C_6H_5As: AsC_6H_5$.....	304.06	wh. need.....	....	212	....	i.	....	s. bz., chl., CS_2; sl. s. al.; i. eth.
8	Arsenophenyl-glycinamide	$H_2NCOCH_2NHC_6H_4AsO(OH)_2$ 274.11		....	280	....		v. s.	v. sl. s. al.	
9	Benzophenone-4-arsonic acid	$H_2O_3AsC_6H_4COC_6H_5$.	306.15	lustr. pl......	....	260	....	i.		s. al., alk; i. bz., eth.
10	Cacodyl oxide(di-cacodyl oxide)	$[(CH_3)_2As]_2O$.....	225.98	col. liq......	1.486^{15}	−25	149-51	sl s.		s. al., eth.
11	Cacodyl sulfide (dicacodyl sulfide)	$[(CH_3)_2As]_2S$........	242.05	oil........			211	sl. s.		s. al., eth.
12	β-Chlorovinyl dichlorarsine	$C_2H_2Cl_3As$..........	207.32	liq.....	1.8648^{20}_4	0.1	76.1^{10}	....		....
13	Dimethylarsine (cacodyl hydride)	$(CH_3)_2AsH$........	106.00	col. liq., ign. in air	1.213^{29}	....	35.6^{747}			s. al., eth., chl., bz., CS_2
14	Dimethylarsinic acid (cacodylic acid)	$As(CH_3)_2O.OH$.....	138.00	odorl., col. pr.	....	200	....	82.9^{22}	v. s.	s. al.; i. eth.
15	Dimethylbromarsine (cacodyl bromide)	$(CH_3)_2AsBr$........	184.90	yel. oil......			130	....		....
16	Dimethylchlorarsine (cacodyl chloride)	$(CH_3)_2AsCl$........	140.44	col. liq., infl.	>1	<−45	106.5-107, (109)	i.		v. s. al.; i. eth.
17	Dimethylcyanoarsine (Cacodylcyanide)	$(CH_3)_2AsCN$........	131.01	lustr., col. pr., very pois.	....	33	140	sl. s.		s. al., eth.
18	Diphenylarsinic acid...	$(C_6H_5)_2AsO(OH)$....	262.14	wh. need.....	....	174	subl. 190-200	s.		s. al., alk.; i. eth.; bz.
19	Diphenylchloroarsine.	$(C_6H_5)_2AsCl$.......	264.59	pa. yel. liq...	1.4223^{26}		333 (in CO_2)	i.		s.abs.al.;eth.; bz.;NH_4OH.
20	Ethylarsinedisulfide....	$C_2H_5AsS_2$.........	168.11	yel. oil......	1.836^{24}			i.		s. bz.; chl.; i. al., eth.
21	Ethylarsonic acid.....	$C_2H_5AsO(OH)_2$......	154.00	need........	....	99.9	....	70^{25}		39.4^{25} 95 % al.
22	p-Hydroxybenzene-arsonic acid (Phenol-p-arsonic acid)	$HO(C_6H_4)AsO(OH)_2$.	218.04	monocl. pr...	....	d. 174		s.	s.	s. al.; acet. a.; dil. a.; sl. s. acet. v. sl. s. eth.
23	Methylarsine........	CH_3AsH_2........	91.97	col. liq.	....		2	0.00085	....	s. al., eth.
24	Methyldichloroarsine..	CH_3AsCl_2........	160.86	col. liq.	....		133	d.	....	....
25	Phenylarsine.........	$C_6H_5AsH_2$........	154.04	col. oil......	1.356^{25}_{25}		148	....	....	sl. a., eth., CS_2
26	Phenylarsonic acid (benzenearsonic acid)	$C_6H_5AsO_3H_2$.	202.04	col. pr.	1.760	158-62 d.		3.36^{28}	31.6^{84}	18.4^{25} 95 %al
27	Phenylcyclotetra-methylenearsine	$C_4H_8AsC_6H_5$.....	208.14	col. oil......	1.2794^{20}_4	....	128.5^{15-16}	sl. s.		s. al., eth.
28	Phenyldimethylarsine..	$(C_6H_5)(CH_3)_2As$..	182.10	col. liq.	....		200	i.		s. al., bz.
29	Sodiumarsenophenyl-glycine	$(AsC_6H_5NHCH_2COONa)_2$ 494.12		liq.........		d.		s.		
30	Tetraethyldiarsine (ethyl cacodyl)	$[(C_2H_5)_2As]_2$	266.09	oil........	....		185-90	i.		s. al, eth..
31	Tetramethylbiarsine (Tetramethyl-biarsine)	$[As(CH_3)_2]_2$......	209.98	col.-yel. oily liq., highly poisonous	1.447^{15}	−5	163	sl. s.		s. al., eth.
32	Tribenzylarsine.......	$(C_6H_5CH_2)_3As$....	348.32	col. monocl.	....	104		i.		s. eth., bz.; sl. s. al.
33	Tri(β-chlorovinyl)arsine	$(CHClCH)_3As$.....	259.40	col. liq......	3-4	$151-158^{28}$	$151-158^{25}$	i.		i. al., dil. a.
34	Triethylarsine (arsenic triethyl)	$As(C_2H_5)_3$..........	162.11	col. liq. n^{20}_D 1.467	1.152	....	140^{736}	i.		....
35	Trimethylarsine (arsenic trimethyl)	$As(CH_3)_3$...........	120.03	col. liq.	1.124		70	sl. s.	....	s. eth.
36	Triphenylarsine (arsenic triphenyl)	$As(C_6H_5)_3$.........	306.24	wh. need. or rhomb. pl., 1.6139^{48}	1.2225^{48}	60-60.5(57)	>360 (In CO_2)	i.		v. s. eth., bz.; sl. s. cold. al.
37	Triphenylarsine-dihydroxide	$(C_6H_5)_3As(OH)_2$....	340.26	col. hex. pr.	....	115-116		s.		s. al.; u. sl. s. eth.
38	Triphenylarsinesulfide.	$(C_6H_5)_3AsS$........	338.31	lustr. need.	....			i.		sl. s. hot al.; i. eth., a.

No.	Name	Formula	Mol. wt.	Crystalline form, color and index of refraction	Sp. gr. or density	Melting point, °C	Boiling point, °C	Solubility in grams per 100 ml of		
								Cold water	Hot water	Alcohol, acids, etc.
	Beryllium									
1	Di-n-butylberyllium...	$Be(C_4H_9)_2$	123.24	col. liq........	....		170^{25}	d.	d.	....
2	Diethylberyllium.....	$Be(C_2H_5)_2$	67.14	col. liq........	....	12	110^{15}	d. to C_2H_6		....
3	Dimethylberyllium....	$Be(CH_3)_2$	39.09	wh. need.....	....		subl. 200	d. to CH_4		....
4	Dipropylberyllium.....	$Be(C_3H_7)_2$	95.19	liq..........	....	<-17	245	....	....	....
	Bismuth									
1	Bismuthethyl- camphorate	$C_{36}H_{57}BiO_{12}$	890.83	wh. amorph. solid	....	61–67	....	i.	i.	s. eth., chl.
2	Diphenylbismuthyl iodide	$(C_6H_5)_2BiI$	490.10	yel. flakes....	....	132–134		i.		s. acet.
3	Methylbismuthine.....	CH_3BiH_2	226.03	liq. (exist ?)	2.30^{18}		110	i.	i.	s. al., eth.
4	Triethylbismuthine (bismuth triethyl)	$Bi(C_2H_5)_3$	296.17	liq........	1.82		107^{79}	i.		s. al., eth.
5	Trimethylbismuthine (bismuth trimethyl)	$Bi(CH_3)_3$	254.09	liq........	2.300^{18}		110	i.	i.	s. al., eth.
6	Trinitrotriphenyl- bismuth dinitrate	$p-(NO_2C_6H_4)_3Bi(NO_3)_2$	699.30	pa. yel. cr....		d. 140–147				s. eth. ac., gla. ac. a.
7	Triphenylbismuth diacetate	$(C_6H_5)_3Bi(CH_3COO)_2$	558.39	wh. cr.....		152–153				s. acet.
8	Triphenylbismuthine (bismuth triphenyl)	$Bi(C_6H_5)_3$	440.30	monocl., tan. cr.	1.585	78				v. s. chl.; s. eth., acet.; sl. s. al.
9	Tri-n-propylbismuth...	$(C_3H_7)_3Bi$	338.25	col. liq......	1.621		$86–87^8$			s. eth,
10	Tri-m-tolylbismuth dichloride	$m-(CH_3C_6H_4)_3BiCl_2$	553.20	wh. cr. (from acet.)	....	132–133	....			s. acet., al-chl.
	Boron									
1	Aminophenylboric acid (m)	$(NH_2C_6H_4)B(OH)_2$	136.95	wh. hex. pl.	....	d.	d.	sl. s		s. al.; sl. s eth.
2	Amylboric acid (n)....	$(C_5H_{11})B(OH)_2$	115.97	col. fl........	....	93–4, d.	d.	s.	s.	s. eth., di- chloroethane
3	Anisylboric acids, o,m,p (methoxyphenyl- boric acids)	$CH_3OC_6H_4B(OH)_2$	151.96	wh. cr.....	....	d.	d.	sl. s		s. al., eth., bz.
4	Benzeneboronic acid...	$C_6H_5B(OH)_2$	121.93		....	215–216		s.	....	s. bz., CCl_4; v. s. eth., MeOH
5	Borine carbonyl.......	BH_3CO	41.85	col. unst. gas.	....	-137.0	-63	d.	d.	....
6	Butylboric acid (n)....	$C_4H_9B(OH)_2$	101.94	col. cr........	....	92–4	d.	s.	s.	v. s. al., eth., chl., acet., acet. a. and esters; sl. s bz., CCl_4, pet. eth.
7	Butylboric acid (tert)	$C_4H_9B(OH)_2$	101.94	wh. cr......	....	105 d.	d.	s.	....	s. eth.
8	n-Butylphenylchloro- boronite	$n-C_4H_9O(C_6H_5)BCl$	196.49	n_D^{20} 1.4996....	1.021^{20}_4	-32	$65^{0.4}$	d.		....
9	Diethoxyboron chloride	$(C_2H_5O)_2BCl$	136.29	col. liq.....	....		112.3	d.	d.	....
10	Diisoamyloxyboron chloride	$(C_5H_{11}O)_2BCl$	220.55	col. liq.....	....		$110–15^{14}$	d.	d.	....
11	Dimethoxyborine......	$(CH_3O)_2BH$	73.89	col. liq., unst.	....	-130.6	25.9	d.	d.	....
12	Dimethoxyboron chloride	$(CH_3O)_2BCl$	108.33	col. liq.....	....	-87.5	74.7	d.	d.	....
13	Dimethylboric acid (dimethylhydroxy- borine)	$(CH_3)_2BOH$	57.89	col. liq.....	....	....	0^{26}	v. s		....
14	Dimethylboric anhydride	$(CH_3)_2BOB(CH_3)_2$	97.76	col........	....	-37.3	43	hyd.	hyd.	....
15	Dimethylborine trimethylamine	$(CH_3)_3NBH(CH_3)_2$	101.00	col. liq.....	....	-18.0	d. 172	d.	d.	s. eth.
16	Dimethylboron bromide	$(CH_3)_2BBr$	120.79	col. liq. or gas	....	-123.4	22	d.	d.	....
17	Dimethylboron iodide	$(CH_3)_2BI$	167.79	col. liq.....	....	-110.7	65	d.	d.	....
18	Dimethyldiborane(1,1) (unsym.)	$B_2H_4(CH_3)_2$	55.72	col. gas.....	....	-150.2	-2.6	d.	d.	....
19	Dimethyldiborane(1,2) (sym.)	$B_2H_4(CH_3)_2$	55.72	col. unst. gas	....	-125	4.9	d.	d.	....

No.	Name	Formula	Mol. wt.	Crystalline form, color and index of refraction	Sp. gr. or density	Melting point, °C	Boiling point, °C	Solubility in grams per 100 ml of		
								Cold water	Hot water	Alcohol, acids, etc.
	Boron									
20	Dimethyltriborine triamine (B)	$(CH_3)_2B_3N_3H_4$	108.55	col. liq.		−48	107	hyd.	hyd.	
21	Dimethyltriborine triamine (N)	$(CH_3)_2B_3N_3H_4$	108.55	col. liq.			108	hyd.	hyd.	
22	Dimethyltriborine triamine (N-B)	$(CH_3)_2B_3N_3H_4$	108.55	col. liq.			124	hyd.	hyd.	
23	Diphenylboric acid (diphenylhydroxyborine)	$(C_6H_5)_2BOH$	182.03	col. radiating cr.		264–67	215–35[17]	i.	i.	s. eth., al., pet. eth.
24	Diphenylboron bromide	$(C_6H_5)_2BBr$	244.93	col. visc. liq. or cr.		25	150–60[8]	d.	d.	s. bz.
25	Diphenylboron chloride	$(C_6H_5)_2BCl$	200.48	col. visc. liq.			271	d.	d.	s. bz., pet. eth.
26	Di-p-tolylboric anhydride	$(C_7H_7)_2BOB(C_7H_7)_2$	402.16	wh. powd.		78		i.		s. al., eth., bz.
27	Ethoxyboron dichloride	$C_2H_5OBCl_2$	126.78	col. liq.			77.9	d.	d.	
28	Ethyl boric acid	$(C_2H_5)B(OH)_2$	73.89	wh. cr.		subl. 40		s.	s.	s. al., eth.
29	Furanylboric acid (β)	$(C_4H_3O)B(OH)_2$	111.89	wh. cr.		110 d.	d.	s.		v. s. eth., al., acet.; sl. s. bz., tol.
30	Hexylboric acid (n)	$C_6H_{13}B(OH)_2$	130.00	wh. cr.		88–90, d.	d.	sl. s.		s. eth.
31	Isobutylboric acid	$C_4H_9B(OH)_2$	101.94	col. cr.		106–12, d.	d.	s.		s. eth., dichloroethane
32	Isopropylamineborine	$(CH_3)_2CHNH_2BH_3$	72.95	wh. cr.	0.829_4^{25}	62	d. 75	sl. s.	sl. s.	s. al., eth.
33	Methoxyboron dichloride	CH_3OBCl_2	112.75	col. liq.		−15	58.0	d.	d.	
34	Methoxyboron difluoride	CH_3OBF_2	79.84	col. liq.	$1.417^{35.5}$; $1.354^{76.5}$	41.9	86	d.	d.	
35	Methylboric acid	$CH_3B(OH)_2$	59.86	wh. pl.		d.	d.	sl. s.		s. al., eth.
36	Methylborine trimethylammine	$(CH_3)_3NBH_2CH_3$	86.97	col. liq.		0.8	177	d.	d.	s. eth.
37	Methyldiborane	$B_2H_5CH_3$	41.70	col. very unst. gas			−80[50]; d. appr. −20	d.	d.	
38	Methyltriborine triamine (B)	$CH_3B_3N_3H_5$	94.53	col. liq.		−59	87	hyd.	hyd.	
39	Methyltriborine triamine (N)	$CH_3B_3N_3H_5$	94.53	col. liq.			84	hyd.	hyd.	
40	Nitrophenylboric acids, o, m, p	$NO_2C_6H_4B(OH)_2$	166.93	yel. need. or pr.		d.	d.	sl. s.	s.	s. al., eth.
41	Phenylboron dibromide	$C_6H_5BBr_2$	247.74	col. cr.		34	100[20]	d	d.	s. bz.
42	Phenylboron dichloride	$C_6H_5BCl_2$	158.82	col. liq. n_D^{20} 1.5385	1.194_4^{20}	7	175	d.	d.	s. bz.
43	Sodium tri-α-naphthyl boride	$Na_2B(C_{10}H_7)_3$	438.29	bl. cr. (purple in dil. soln.)			d.	d.	d.	s. eth.; sl. s. lgr.
44	Tetramethoxydiborine	$(CH_3O)_4B_2$	145.76	col. liq.		−24	d. 93; 21[44]	d.	d.	
45	Tetramethylammoniumborane	$(CH_3)_4NBH_4$	88.99	wh. cr.	0.813_4^{25}		>150	48[20]	61[40]	0.39; 1.04 abs. al. 95 % al.
46	Tetramethyldiborane (1,1,2,2)	$B_2H_2(CH_3)_4$	83.78	col. liq.		−72.5	68.6	d.	d.	
47	Tetramethyltriborine triamine (N-B'-B'')	$(CH_3)_4B_3N_3H_2$	136.61	col. liq.			158	hyd.	hyd.	
48	Thiophenylboric acid (α) ("thienylboric" acid)	$(C_4H_3S)B(OH)_2$	127.96	col. star-formed need.		134	d.	s.		s. eth., al., acet., bz., CCl_4
49	Tribenzylborine	$B(C_6H_5CH_2)_3$	284.21	prismatic need. or col. oily liq.		47	230[13]	i.		v. s. al., bz.; sl. s. eth.
50	Tri-n-butylborine	$B(C_4H_9)_3$	182.16	col. mobile liq.			90–1[9]; 108–110[20]	i.	i.	v. s. eth., al.
51	Tri-tert-butylborine	$B(C_4H_9)_3$	182.16	col. mobile liq.		glass at low temp.	71[12]	i.		s. eth.
52	Tri-n-butyltriborine trioxane (n-butyl boron oxide)	$(C_4H_9)_3B_3O_3$	251.78	col. liq.			154[20]	hyd.	hyd.	v. s. eth.

No.	Name	Formula	Mol. wt.	Crystalline form, color and index of refraction	Sp. gr. or density	Melting point, °C	Boiling point, °C	Cold water	Hot water	Alcohol, acids, etc.
	Boron									
53	Tri-*tert*-butyltriborine trioxane (*tert*-butyl boric oxide)	$(C_4H_9)_3B_3O_3$........	251.78	col. liq......	....	20	$66-8^5$	hyd.	hyd.	s. eth.
54	Trichloroborine dimethyletherate	$(CH_3)_2OBCl_3$........	163.24	col. cr......	....	d. 76	d.	d.	....	....
55	Trichloroborine trimethylammine	$(CH_3)_3NBCl_3$......	176.28	col. cr......	....	243	....		s.	s. al.
56	Tricyclohexylborine (boron tricyclohexyl)	$B(C_6H_{11})_3$.....	260.27	col. interlocking cr.	....	100	194^{15}	i.		s. eth.
57	Triethyl borate (triethoxyborine)	$B(OC_2H_5)_3$........	146.00	col. liq., 1.381	0.8746^{10}; $0.864^{26.5}$	-84.8	117.4, (120)	d.	....	....
58	Triethylboron (triethylborine)	$B(C_2H_5)_3$......	98.00	col. liq......	0.6961^{23}	-92.9	$0^{12.5}$	i.	i.	s. al., eth.
59	Tri-*n*-hexyltriborine trioxane (hexylboric oxide)	$(C_6H_{13})_3B_3O_3$......	335.94	col. liq., 1.4323^{20}	0.8876	....	$178-82^{24}$	hyd.	hyd.	s. org. solv.
60	Triisoamyl borate (triisoamyloxyborine)	$B(OC_5H_{11})_3$......	272.24	liq., 1.421....	0.872^0	....	255	....	....	....
61	Triisoamylborine......	$B(C_5H_{11})_3$......	224.24	col. mobile liq., $1.43207^{22.6}$	0.76	....	119^{14}	i.	....	s. eth.
62	Tri-*p*-anisylborine.....	$B(CH_3OC_6H_4)_3$....	332.21	wh. need.....	....	128	....	i.	i.	s. al., eth., bz.
63	Triisobutyl borate (triisobutoxyborine)	$B(OC_4H_9)_3$.......	230.16	liq., 1.408....	0.864^0	....	212	i.	....	....
64	Triisobutylborine......	$B(C_4H_9)_3$........	182.16	col., mobile liq., $1.41882^{22.8}$	0.74	....	188.86^{20}	i.	i.	s. eth.
65	Trimethoxyboroxine...	$(BO)_3(OCH_3)_3$....	173.55	col. liq., 1.3986	1.216^{25}	-30	(flashpt. 37)	....	....	v. s. bz., tol., CCl_4
66	Trimethylamminoborine	$(CH_3)_3NBH_3$........	72.94	col. hex., columns or need.	0.792^{25}_4	94	172	i.	sl. s.	s. eth., al., bs., NH_3
67	Trimethyl borate (trimethoxyborine)	$B(OCH_3)_3$..........	103.92	col. liq. n_D^{20} 1.3610	0.915; $0.9205^{24.3}$	-29	68.7, (65)	d.	....	s. al., eth.
68	Trimethylboron (trimethylborine)	$B(CH_3)_3$..........	55.92	col. gas......	1.9108 g/1, 0.625^{-100}	-161.5	-20.2	v. sl. s	....	v. s. al., eth.
69	Trimethyldiborane (1,1,2)	$B_2H_3(CH_3)_3$......	69.75	col. liq.	....	-123	45.5	d.	....	....
70	Trimethyltriborine triamine (*B*)	$(CH_3)_3B_3N_3H_3$......	122.58	col. cr. or liq.	....	31.5	129	hyd.	hyd.	....
71	Trimethyltriborine triamine (*N*)	$(CH_3)_3B_3N_3H_3$......	122.58	col. liq.	....		134	hyd.	hyd.	....
72	Trimethyltriborine triamine (*N-B-B'*)	$(CH_3)_3B_3N_3H_3$......	122.58	col. liq.	....		139	hyd.	hyd.	....
73	Trimethyltriborine trioxane (methylboric anhydride)	$(CH_3)_3B_3O_3$......	122.54	col. mobile liq.	....	-37vc,	79.3^{755}	hyd.	hyd.	s. eth.
74	Tri-*β*-naphthyl borate	$B(C_{10}H_7O)_3$........	440.31	col. leaflets ..	....	115		d.	....	s. bz.
75	Tri-*α*-naphthylborine ..	$B(C_{10}H_7)_3$.......	392.31	col. need.....	....	203	d.	i.		sl. s. eth., al.; v. s. bz., CCl_4, chl., CS_2
76	Triphenyl borate (triphenoxyborine)	$(C_6H_5O)_3B$........	280.13	col. cr......	....	ca. 35	>360	d.	....	s. eth., bz.
77	Triphenylborine ammine*	$(C_6H_5)_3BNH_3$......	259.16	col. cr......	....	d. 216	d.			s. al.; sl. s. bz.
78	Triphenylboron......	$B(C_6H_5)_3$........	242.13	hex. need....	....	136	203^{15}	d.		d. al.; s. bz.
79	Tripropyl borate (tripropoxyboron)	$B(OC_3H_7)_3$........	188.08	liq......	liq. 0.867^{16}	....	175			
80	Tri-*n*-propylborine.....	$B(C_3H_7)_3$........	140.08	col., mobile liq., $1.41352^{22.8}$	0.725	....	156, 60^{20}	i.	....	s. eth.
81	Tri-*sec*-propylborine...	$B(C_3H_7)_3$........	140.08	col., mobile liq.	......		$140-54$, $33-5^{12}$	i.	....	s. eth.

* This compound is the prototype of numerous stable complex compounds formed from organic amines and tri-aryl-borines.

No.	Name	Formula	Mol. wt.	Crystalline form, color and index of refraction	Sp. gr. or density	Melting point, °C	Boiling point, °C	Solubility in grams per 100 ml of		
								Cold water	Hot water	Alcohol, acids, etc.
	Boron									
82	Tri-*p*-tolylborine	B(CH₃C₆H₄)₃	284.21	separate wh. cr.	....	175	233¹²	i.	....	v. s. bz.; sl. s. eth.
83	Tri-*p*-xylylborine	B(CH₃C₆H₃CH₃)₃	326.29	col. bushed need.	....	147	221¹²	i.	....	v. s. bz., chl., CCl₄; sl. s. eth.
	Cadmium									
1	Dibutylcadmium	Cd(C₄H₉)₂	226.63	oil n_D 1.5155	1.3056¹⁹·⁵	−48	103.5¹²·⁵	d.	d.	....
2	Diethylcadmium	Cd(C₂H₅)₂	170.52	oil	1.6564¹⁸·¹	−21	64¹⁹	d.	d.	v. s. eth.
3	Diisoamylcadmium	Cd(C₅H₁₁)₂	254.69	oil n_D 1.5039	1.2210¹⁹	−115	121.5¹⁵			
4	Diisobutylcadmium	Cd(C₄H₉)₂	226.63	oil n_D 1.4997	1.2693¹⁸	−37	90.5²⁰	d.	d.	
5	Dimethylcadmium	Cd(CH₃)₂	142.47	oil	1.9846¹⁷·⁹	−4.5	105.5⁷⁵⁸	d.	d.	
6	Dipropylcadmium	Cd(C₃H₇)₂	198.58	oil n_D 1.5291	1.4201¹⁷·⁶	−83	84²¹·⁵	d.	d.	
	Calcium									
1	Dianilinecalcium	Ca(NHC₆H₅)₂	224.32	wh. cr.	....	d.	....	d.		i. eth., bz., lgr.
2	Ethylcalcium iodide	C₂H₅CaI	196.05	amor. powd.	....			d.		sl. s.
3	Glycocollcalcium	(CH₂NHCOO)Ca	113.13	cr.	....			s.		
	Chromium									
1	Anilinechromium tricarbonyl	H₂NC₆H₅Cr(CO)₃	229.16	yel. cr.	....	173–5	subl. 110–130	....	....	s. org. solv. HCl
2	Anisolechromium tricarbonyl	CH₃OC₆H₅Cr(CO)₃	244.17	yel. cr.	....	80–92	subl. 70–80 (vac.)			
3	Benzoic acid chromium tricarbonyl	HO₂CC₆H₅Cr(CO)₃	258.15	or. cr.	....	201–2	subl. 150 (vac.)			
4	Benzenechromium tricarbonyl	C₆H₆Cr(CO)₃	214.14	yel. monocl.	....	165.5–166.5 (162–3)	subl. 60–90			s. bz., s. org. solv.
5	Bis-cyclopentadienyl-chromium	(C₅H₅)₂Cr	182.19	red cr.	....	170–2	subl. 75–90 (vac.)	d.		d. in CS₂, CCl₄
6	Bis-diphenyl chromium iodide ("Tetraphenyl-chromium" iodide)	(C₆H₅C₆H₅)₂Cr⁺I⁻	487.33	or. yel.	....	177–8 (178)		s.		s. chl.; i. pet. eth.
7	Chlorobenzene-chromium tricarbonyl	ClC₆H₅Cr(CO)₃	248.59	yel.	....	96–8; 150–5 d.	50–8 (vac.)			
8	Cyclopentadienyl-chromium dinitrosomethyl	C₅H₅Cr(NO)₂CH₃	192.14	grn.	....	83.0				s. org. solv.
9	Dimethylanilinechromium tricarbonyl	(CH₃)₂NC₆H₅Cr(CO)₃	257.21	cr.	....	146–146.5				s. org. solv.
10	Diphenylbenzene-chromium iodide ("Triphenyl chromium" iodide)	C₆H₅C₆H₅Cr(I)(C₆H₅)	410.22	or. yel. pl.	....	110–2 (146–8)		s.		sl. s. et., al., chl., *m*-di-nitro-benzene.
11	Mesitylenechromium tricarbonyl	(CH₃)₃C₆H₃Cr(CO)₃	256.22	yel. cr.	....	177–8 (165, 170 d)	subl. 80–100			s. org. solv.
12	Methylbenzoate chromium tricarbonyl	CH₃O₂CC₆H₅Cr(CO)₃	272.18	red cr.	....	93–5	80–90 (vac.)			
13	Phenolchromium tricarbonyl	HOC₆H₅Cr(CO)₃	230.14	yel.	....	193–240				
14	Thiophenechromium tricarbonyl	C₄H₄SCr(CO)₃	220.17	red cr.	....		subl. 85–95 (vac.)			s. bz., eth, pet. eth.
15	Toluenechromium tricarbonyl	CH₃C₆H₅Cr(CO)₃	228.17	yel.	....	82–3 (80° d.)	subl.			s. org. solv.
16	*m*-Xylenechromium tricarbonyl	(CH₃)₂C₆H₄Cr(CO)₃	242.20	yel.	....	104–5	subl. 65			
17	*o*-Xylenechromium tricarbonyl	(CH₃)₂C₆H₄Cr(CO)₃	242.20	yel.	....	88–90	subl. 65			
18	*p*-Xylenechromium tricarbonyl	(CH₃)₂C₆H₄Cr(CO)₃	242.20	yel. cr.	....	97–8	subl. 65			
	Cesium									
1	Monocesiumacetylide	CsC₂H	157.94	col. cr.	....	300		d.		s. NH₃; i. bz.
	Cobalt									
1	Bis-dimethylglyoxime cobaltochloride	HON:C(CH₃)C(CH₃):NOH.Co HON:C(CH₃)C(CH₃):NOCl₂ 361.07			....		....	s.		s. al.
		lt. grn. cr.								

No.	Name	Formula	Mol. wt.	Crystalline form, color and index of refraction	Sp. gr. or density	Melting point, °C	Boiling point, °C	Solubility in grams per 100 ml of		
								Cold water	Hot water	Alcohol, acids, etc.
	Cobalt									
2	Cobalt(ous) hexa-methylenetetramine	$CoCl_2C_6H_{12}N_4$......	270.03	ultramarine blue	....	....	....	s.	....	
3	Cobalt(ous) hydroxy-quinone	$Co(C_{10}H_5O_3)_2$.......	405.23	ruby red.....		d. 210–15				
	Copper									
1	Cyclopentadienyl-triethylphosphine copper	$C_5H_5CuP(C_2H_5)_3$....	246.80	wh. cr.....		127–8			i.	s. dil. HCl, pet. eth., eth., bz, pyr.
2	Diazoamino-benzene(ous)	$CuN_3(C_6H_5)_2$........	259.77	or. cr.......		d. 270			i.	s. bz.; i. al., lgr.
	Gallium									
1	Dimethylgallium amide	$Ga(CH_3)_2NH_2$....	115.81	wh. cr.......			subl. 60 vac.			
2	Dimethylgallium chloride monammine	$Ga(CH_3)_2Cl.NH_3$....	152.27	wh. cr.......		54	....	d.	d.	v. s. NH_3; s. eth.
3	Dimethylgallium chloride diammine	$Ga(CH_3)_2Cl.2NH_3$...	169.30	wh. cr.......		112		d.	d.	v. s. NH_3; i. eth.
4	Methylgallium dichloride	$Ga(CH_3)Cl_2$.......	155.66	wh. cr.......		75		d.		v. s. eth.
5	Methylgallium dichloride monammine	$Ga(CH_3)Cl_2.NH_3$....	172.69	wh. cr.......				d.		i. eth.
6	Methylgallium dichloride pentammine	$Ga(CH_3)Cl_2.5NH_3$...	240.81	wh. cr.......		d. >80		d.	....	i. NH_3
7	Triethylgallium.......	$Ga(C_2H_5)_3$.......	156.91	col. liq......	1.0576^{30}	−82.3	142.6	d.	....	s. eth.
8	Triethylgallium monammine	$Ga(C_2H_5)_3.NH_3$	173.94	col. liq......				d.		
9	Triethylgallium monoetherate	$Ga(C_2H_5)_3.(C_2H_5)_2O$.	231.03	col. liq......				d.		s. eth.
10	Trimethylgallium......	$Ga(CH_3)_3$.......	114.83	col. liq......		−19	55.7 ± 2^{762}	d.		s. eth., NH_3
11	Trimethylgallium monammine	$Ga(CH_3)_3.NH_3$	131.86	wh. cr.......		31	subl. vac.	d.		s. eth., NH_3; i. pet. eth.
12	Trimethylgallium monoetherate	$Ga(CH_3)_3.(C_2H_5)_2O$.	188.95	col. liq......		<−76	99	d.		s. NH_3, eth.
	Germanium									
1	Amyltriphenyl-germanium (n)	$Ge(C_5H_{11})(C_6H_5)_3$....	375.05	col. pl......		42–3	i.	i.	i.	v. s. bz., pet. eth.; sl. s. me. al.
2	Benzyltriphenyl-germanium	$Ge(CH_2C_6H_5)(C_6H_5)_3$	395.04	col. pl......		82.5–3.5		i.	i.	v. s. bz., pet. eth., chl.; sl. s. iso-propyl al.; i. me. al.
3	Bis-acetylacetone germanium dibro-mide	$[CH(CCH_3O)_2]_2GeBr_2$	430.63	col. micr. cr..		226				sl. s. h. acetyl acet.; i. org. solv.
4	Bis-acetylacetone germanium dichloride	$[CH(CCH_3O)_2]_2GeCl_2$	341.72	col. pr.....		240d.				sl. s. org. solv.
5	Bis(5-oxy-2,8-dithio-octane) germanium	$[(SCH_2CH_2)_2O]_2Ge$...	354.06	col. cr.		159.0–.5				s. bz., abs. al.
6	Bis-propionylacetone germanium dichloride	$[CHC_2(C_2H_5)(CH_3)O_2]_2GeCl_2$	369.77	wh. cr. powd.		128–9				s. c. chl.; i. pet. eth.
7	Bis-tribenzyl germanyl sulfide	$[(C_6H_5CH_2)_3Ge]_2S$ ...	724.05	col. cr.....		124				s. al., me. al., bz.; i. alk.
8	Bis-tribiphenylyl germanyl sulfide	$[(C_6H_5C_6H_4)_3Ge]_2S$	1096.48	col. cr......		238	....	....	....	s. org. solv.; i. alk.
9	Bis-trichlorogermanyl methane	$CH_2(GeCl_3)_2$........	371.93	col. liq......		110^{18}	hyd.	hyd.		s. org. solv.
10	Bis-tricyclohexyl-germanium disulfide	$[(C_6H_{11})_3Ge]_2S_2$......	708.24	col. cr.....		87–8	....	i.	....	s. abs. al.
11	Bis-triethylgermanyl sulfide	$[(C_2H_5)_3Ge]_2S$.....	351.62	col. oily liq..			$148–50^{12}$			s. org. solv.; i. alk.
12	Bis-triphenylgermanyl sulfide	$[(C_6H_5)_3Ge]_2S$.....	639.88	col. cr.....		138				s. org. solv.; i. alk.
13	Bis-tritolylgermanyl sulfide	$[(C_6H_4CH_3)_3Ge]_2S$ ...	724.05	col. cr.....		156–7				s. org. solv.; i. alk.

No.	Name	Formula	Mol. wt.	Crystalline form, color and index of refraction	Sp. gr. or density	Melting point, °C	Boiling point, °C	Solubility in grams per 100 ml of		
								Cold water	Hot water	Alcohol, acids, etc.
	Germanium									
14	Butyltriphenyl-germanium (n)	$Ge(C_4H_9)(C_6H_5)_3$....	361.01	col. need.....	....	84.5–5.5	....	i.	i.	v. s. pet. eth., bz., chl., eth., sl. s. isopropyl al., i. me. al.
15	Cyclopentamethylene germanium dichloride	$(CH_2)_5GeCl_2$........	213.63	col. liq.			55–60[12]			
16	Diethylcyclopenta-methylenegermanium (1,1)	$(CH_2)_5Ge(C_2H_5)_2$....	200.85	col. liq.			52[13]			
17	Diethyldiphenyl-germanium	$Ge(C_2H_5)_2(C_6H_5)_2$....	284.93	col. liq.			316	i.	i.	v. s. org. solv.
18	Diethyldinylgermanium	$(C_2H_5)_2Ge)CH:CH_2)_2$	184.81	n_D^{20} 1.4575....	1.0193_4^{20}	....	149.8[760]			
19	Diethylgermanium bromide	$(C_2H_5)_2GeBr_2$........	290.53	col. liq......		< −33	202	d.	d.	d. liq. NH_3; s. org. solv.
20	Diethylgermanium chloride	$(C_2H_5)_2GeCl_2$........	201.62	col. liq......		−39 to −37	175	d.	d.	d. liq. NH_3; s. org. solv.
21	Diethylgermanium imine	$(C_2H_5)_2GeNH$......	145.73	col. liq......			100[0.01]			
22	Diethylgermanium iodide	$(C_2H_5)_2GeI_2$........	384.52	col. liq......		−2 to −1	252	d.	d.	d. liq. NH_3; s. org. solv.
23	Diethylgermanium oxide (α)	$[(C_2H_5)_2GeO]_x$......	146.71	stable wh. amor. sol.		175		i.	i.	i. org. solv., liq. NH_3
24	Diethylgermanium oxide (β)	$[(C_2H_5)_2GeO]_3$......	440.14	unst. col. liq..		18		i.	i.	s. org. solv.; i. liq. NH_3
25	Diphenylgermanium	$[(C_6H_5)_2Ge]_4$	907.21	wh. cr.		294–5	....	i.	i.	sl. s. bz., tol., chl.; i. pet. eth.
26	Diphenylgermanium dibromide	$(C_6H_5)_2GeBr_2$......	386.62	col. liq......			120[.007] 205–7[512]	hyd.	hyd.	s. org. solv.
27	Diphenylgermanium dichloride	$(C_6H_5)_2GeCl_2$......	297.71	col. liq......	71	9	223[13]	hyd.	hyd.	s. org. solv.
28	Diphenylgermanium difluoride	$(C_6H_5)_2GeF_2$......	264.80	col. liq....			100[0.007]	hyd.	hyd.	s. org. solv.
29	Diphenyl-sec-propyl-germanium bromide	$(C_6H_5)_2(C_3H_7)GeBr$..	349.80	col. liq......			215–50[13]			
30	Di-p-tolylgermanium dibromide	$(CH_3C_6H_4)_2GeBr_2$..	414.68	lt. yel. liq.....			230–33[13]	hyd.	hyd.	s. org. solv.
31	Di-p-tolylphenyl-germanium bromide	$(CH_3C_6H_4)_2(C_6H_5)GeBr$	411.87	col. pr......		119				
32	Di-triphenylgermanyl methane	$[(C_6H_5)_3Ge]_2CH_2$.....	621.85	lt. col. pr....		132–33	....	i.	....	v. s. bz., eth., pet. eth., chl.; i. liq. NH_3, al.
33	Ethyl-tris-p-biphenylyl-germanium	$Ge(C_2H_5)(C_6H_4C_6H_5)_3$	561.27	col. cr.....		154–6				
34	Ethylgermanium oxide.	$(C_2H_5GeO)_2O$......	251.30	wh. powd....		>300	d.	s.	s.	s. HCl, al.; i. pet. eth.
35	Ethylgermanium tri-bromide bromide	$C_2H_5GeBr_3$........	341.38	col. liq.		< −33	200[763]	d.	d.	d. liq. NH_3; s. bz., eth.
36	Ethylgermanium trichloride	$C_2H_5GeCl_3$........	208.01	col. liq.		< −33	144[762]	d.	d.	d. liq. NH_3; s. bz., eth.
37	Ethylgermanium trifluoride	$C_2H_5GeF_3$........	158.65	col. liq.		−16.5 to −15.5	112[750]	d.	d.	d. liq. NH_3; s. bz., eth.
38	Ethylgermanium triiodide	$C_2H_5GeI_3$........	482.37	yel. liq.....		−2.5 to −1.5	281[755] d. >350	d.	d.	d. liq. NH_3; s. bz., eth.
39	Ethylphenyldi-p-tolyl-germanium	$Ge(C_2H_5)(C_6H_5)(C_6H_4CH_3)_2$	361.03	wh. cr.....		55				
40	Ethyl-sec-propyl-diphenylgermanium	$Ge(C_2H_5)(C_3H_7)(C_6H_5)_2$	298.95	liq.		175–90	....			
41	Ethyltribenzyl-germanium	$Ge(C_2H_5)(CH_2C_6H_5)_3$	375.05	col. cr.....		56–7				s. meth. al.
42	Ethyltriphenyl-germanium	$Ge(C_2H_5)(C_6H_5)_3$....	332.97	col. sld......		78.0–.5	....	i.	i.	s. eth., pet. eth., bz., chl., acet.; i. meth. al.
43	Hexabenzyldigermane	$[(C_6H_5CH_2)_3Ge]_2$.....	691.98	col. cr.....		183–4	....			s. glac. acet. a.

No.	Name	Formula	Mol. wt.	Crystalline form, color and index of refraction	Sp. gr. or density	Melting point, °C	Boiling point, °C	Solubility in grams per 100 ml of		
								Cold water	Hot water	Alcohol, acids, etc.
	Germanium									
44	Hexaethyldigermane...	$[(C_2H_5)_3Ge]_2$.......	319.55	col. liq..........	....	< -60	265^{758}	i.	i.	s. bz., eth.
45	Hexaphenyldigermane .	$[(C_6H_5)_3Ge]_2$........	607.82	wh. cr..........	....	340	....	i.	i.	sl. s. h. bz., h. chl.; i. liq. NH_3, lgr. .s. bz.
46	Hexaphenyldigermane tribenzene	$[(C_6H_5)_3Ge]_2.3C_6H_6$	842.16	col. cr..........	....	$d. -C_6H_6$	....	i.		
47	Hexa-p-tolyldigermane.	$[(CH_3C_6H_4)_3Ge]_2$..	691.98	col. cr..........		226–7	....			
48	Hexavinylgermanium...	$(CH_2:CH)_6Ge_2$.....	307.44	n_D^{25} 1.5217	1.171_4^{25}	....	$55^{0.35}$	....		
49	Methyltriphenyl-germanium	$Ge(CH_3)(C_6H_5)_3$....	318.95	trans. col. cr..		70.5–1.0		i.	i.	v. s. bz., eth., acet., chl., pet. eth.; i. c. meth. al., liq. NH_3
50	Octaphenyltrigermane .	$(C_6H_5)_8Ge_3$.......	834.62	wh. cr..........		247–8		i.	i.	s. h. bz., h. chl.
51	Phenylethyl-sec-propyl-germanium bromide	$(C_6H_5)(C_2H_5)[CH(CH_3)_2]$ $GeBr$	301.76	col. oil; opt. act., d. & l. forms			$130–5^{13}$	....		
52	Phenylgermanium tribromide	$C_6H_5GeBr_3$........	389.42	col. liq..........			$120–2^{12}$	hyd.	hyd.	d. liq. NH_3; s. org. solv.
53	Phenylgermanium trichloride	$C_6H_5GeCl_3$........	256.06	col. liq..........			$105–6^{13}$	hyd.	hyd.	d. liq. NH_3; s. org. solv.
54	Phenylgermanium triiodide	$C_6H_5GeI_3$........	530.41	wh. sol., dec. by light		55–6		hyd.	hyd^4	d. liq. NH_3; s. glac. acet. a.; org. solv.
55	Phenyltri-p-tolyl-germanium	$Ge(C_6H_5)(C_6H_4CH_3)_3$	423.10	wh. pr..........		191		i.	i.	s. org. solv.
56	Propyltriphenyl-germanium(n)	$Ge(C_3H_7)(C_6H_5)_3$..	347.00	col. need.....		86.0–.5		i.	i.	v. s. chl., bz., pet. eth.; sl. s. isopropyl al.; i. meth. al., liq. NH_3
57	Tetra-i-amylgermanium	$Ge(C_5H_{11})_4$........	357.16	col. oily liq., $1.457^{17.5}$	0.9147_{20}^{20}	....	163–4	....		
58	Tetra-n-amylthio-germanium	$Ge[S(CH_2)_4CH_3]_4$..	485.42	col. liq., 1.5336^{25}	1.0697^{25}	....	$240–1^{3-4}$			s. bz., abs. al.
59	Tetraanhydro-tetrakisdiphenyl-germanediol (cyclo)	$[Ge(C_6H_5)_2O]_4$..	971.20	monocl. pr. & cubes		218				s. ethyl acetate, pet. eth., eth.
60	Tetrabenzylgermanium	$Ge(CH_2C_6H_5)_4$....	437.13	col. sol......		107–8				
61	Tetra-p-biphenylyl-germanium	$Ge(C_6H_4C_6H_5)_4$.....	685.41	wh. need.....		270–2		i.	i.	s. bz.
62	Tetra-p-bromophenyl-thiogermanium	$Ge(SC_6H_4Br)_4$.......	824.88	col. cr.......		196.0–.5				s. bz., abs. al.
63	Tetra-n-butyl-germanium	$Ge(C_4H_9)_4$.......	301.06	col. oily liq. .			$178–80^{733?}$			
64	Tetra-p-tert-butyl-phenylthiogermanium	$Ge[SC_6H_4C(CH_3)_3]_4$..	733.71	col. tetrag.		155–6				sl. s. al., glac. acet. a.; s. pet. eth., eth., acet.; v. s. chl., bz.
65	Tetra-n-butylthio-germanium	$Ge[S(CH_2)_3CH_3]_4$..	429.31	liq., 1.5439^{25}	1.1072^{25}		$222.5^{4.5}$			s. abs. al.
66	Tetra-sec-butylthio-germanium	$Ge[SCH(CH_3)(C_2H_5)]_4$	429.31	liq., 1.5497^{25}	1.1110^{25}		200.5^4	....		s. bz.
67	Tetra-tert-butylthio-germanium	$Ge[SC(CH_3)_3]_4$.....	429.31	tetrag. columns		172–73	subl. 170^4			s. abs. al.
68	Tetracetylthio-germanium	$Ge[SCH_2(CH_2)_{14}CH_3]_4$	1102.61	wh. cr........		50–1				v. s. chl., bz.; s. pet. eth., eth.; sl. s. acet. al., glac. acet. a.
69	Tetracyclohexylthio-germanium	$Ge(SC_6H_{11})_4$........	533.46	2 cr. mod. α (stab.) tetrag (metastab.) monocl.	$\alpha 1.270^{15}$ $\beta 1.259^{15}$	84 88		i. i.		s. abs. al., pet. eth. s. abs. al., pet. eth.

No.	Name	Formula	Mol. wt.	Crystalline form, color and index of refraction	Sp. gr. or density	Melting point, °C	Boiling point, °C	Solubility in grams per 100 ml of		
								Cold water	Hot water	Alcohol, acids, etc.
	Germanium									
70	Tetraethoxyl-germanium (tetraethyl germanate)	$Ge(OC_2H_5)_4$.......	252.84	col. liq......	....	−81	185–7	....		
71	Tetraethylgermanium..	$Ge(C_2H_5)_4$.........	188.84	col. oil, $1.443^{17.5}$; 1.554^0; 1.439^{30}	1.198^0 $0.991^{24.5}_{24.5}$	−90	162.5–3.0	d.	d.	s. bz., eth., HCl
72	Tetraethylthio-germanium	$Ge(SC_2H_5)_4$........	317.09	liq., 1.5886^{25}	1.2547^{25}	....	$164.5–5.0^5$	....		s. bz.
73	Tetra-iso-butylthio-germanium	$Ge[SCH_2CH(CH_3)_2]_4$.	429.31	liq., 1.5381^{25}	1.0984^{25}	....	$199–200^{4-5}$			s. al.
74	Tetraisopropylthio-germanium	$Ge[SCH(CH_3)_2]_4$....	373.20	liq., 1.5535^{25}	1.1478^{25}	15	$162–64^4$			s. abs. al.
75	Tetramethylgermanium	$Ge(CH_3)_4$.........	132.73	col. liq......	1.006^0	−88	43.4			s. al., eth., bz.
76	Tetramethylthio-germanium	$Ge(SCH_3)_4$........	260.90	liq., 1.6379^{25}	1.4364^{25}	−3	$138–40^4$			s. al., bz.
77	Tetraphenoxy-germanium	$Ge(OC_6H_5)_4$	445.01	col. oil	....		$210–20^{0.3}$			s. bz.
78	Tetraphenylgermanium	$Ge(C_6H_5)_4$.......	381.02	tetr., col.....	....	235.7	>400	i.	i.	s. chl., bz., tol.; sl. s. eth., acet., lgr.
79	Tetra(2-phenylethyl)-germanium	$Ge(C_6H_5C_2H_4)_4$.....	493.23	col. cr.....	....	56–7	....			s. eth., al.
80	Tetraphenylthio-germanium	$Ge(SC_6H_5)_4$.......	509.27	col., rhomb. cr., 1.7348, 1.782 (H green)		101.5				s. bz., abs. al., meth. al.
81	Tetra-n-propyl-germanium	$Ge(C_3H_7)_4$.........	244.95	col. mob. liq., $1.451^{17.5}$	0.9539^{20}_{20}	−73	225^{746}	....		
82	Tetrapropylthio-germanium	$Ge(SC_3H_7)_4$........	373.20	liq., 1.5612^{25}	1.1662^{25}	....	$191–92^5$			s. abs. al.
83	Tetra-N-pyrryl-germanium	$Ge(C_4H_4N)_4$.......	336.92	lt. yel. cr.....	....	202	....			s. pet. eth., chl.
84	Tetra-α-thienyl-germanium	$Ge(C_4H_3S)_4$.......	405.12	wh. need., doubly refract.	....	149–50	....	i.	i.	s. bz., tol., acet., chl., CCl_4; sl. s. al., meth. al.; i. pet. eth.
85	Tetra-o-tolylgermanium	$Ge(C_6H_4CH_3)_4$.....	437.13	wh. hex. cr.....	....	175–6	....	i.	i.	s. CCl_4, bz., xylene; sl. s. h. al.; i. pet. eth., al.
86	Tetra-m-tolyl-germanium	$Ge(C_6H_4CH_3)_4$.....	437.13	wh. need.....	....	146	....	i.	i.	s. bz., tol., CCl_4; sl. s. meth. al.
87	Tetra-p-tolyl-germanium	$Ge(C_6H_4CH_3)_4$.....	437.13	wh. rhbdr. tab.	....	227	....	i.	i.	s. bz.
88	Tetra-p-tolylthio-germanium	$Ge(SC_6H_4CH_3)_4$....	565.38	col., rhomb. cr., 1.726, 1.771 (H green)	....	110–11				s. bz., abs. al.
89	Tetravinylgermanium	$(CH_2:CH)_4Ge$......	180.77	n^{25}_D 1.4676.....	1.040^{25}_4	....	54^{27}			
90	Tolylgermanium tribromide(p)	$(CH_3C_6H_4)GeBr_3$....	403.45	col. liq.		$155–6^{13}$		hyd.	hyd.	d. liq. NH_3; s. org. solv.
91	Tolylgermanium trichloride(p)	$(CH_3C_6H_4)GeCl_3$....	270.08	col. liq......	....		$115–6^{12}$	hyd.	hyd.	d. liq. NH_3; s. org. solv.
92	Tolylgermanium triiodide(p)	$(CH_3C_6H_4)GeI_3$.....	544.44	col. cr., sensit. to light	....	72		hyd.	hyd.	d. liq. NH_3; s. org. solv.
93	Trianhydrotetrakis-diphenylgermanediol	$[HO-Ge(C_6H_5)_2-O-Ge(C_6H_5)_2]_2O$	989.23	....		149				s. eth. acetate
94	Tribenzylgermanium bromide	$(C_6H_5CH_2)_3GeBr$....	425.90	col. cr.....		145				
95	Tribenzylgermanium chloride	$(C_6H_5CH_2)_3GeCl$....	381.44	col. cr......	....	155	....			

No.	Name	Formula	Mol. wt.	Crystalline form, color and index of refraction	Sp. gr. or density	Melting point, °C	Boiling point, °C	Solubility in grams per 100 ml of		
								Cold water	Hot water	Alcohol, acids, etc.
	Germanium									
96	Tribenzylgermanium fluoride	$(C_6H_5CH_2)_3GeF$	364.99	col. need.....	....	96	....			
97	Tribenzylgermanium iodide	$(C_6H_5CH_2)_3GeI$	472.90	col. cr.	....	141	....			
98	Tribenzylgermanium oxide	$[(C_6H_5CH_2)_3Ge]_2O$	707.99	....	....	135	....			s. pet. eth.
99	Tri-p-biphenylyl-germanium bromide	$(C_6H_5C_6H_4)_3GeBr$ ...	612.12	wh. cr.	....	242	....			s. bz.
100	Tri-tert-butylthio-germanium chloride	$Ge[SC(CH_3)_3]_3Cl$ ..	375.58	col. cr.	....	66–7	$156–7^{3-4}$			s. al., org. solv.
101	Tri-n-butylvinyl-germanium	$(n-C_4H_9)_3Ge(CH:CH_2)$	270.99	n_D^{20} 1.4598....	0.9479_4^{20}	....	$108–109^2$			
102	Tricyclohexyl-germanium bromide	$(C_6H_{11})_3GeBr$	401.96	col. cr.	....	110	....	hyd.	hyd.	s. al.
103	Tricyclohexyl-germanium chloride	$(C_6H_{11})_3GeCl$	357.51	col. cr.	....	102	....	hyd.	hyd.	s. meth. al.
104	Tricyclohexyl-germanium fluoride	$(C_6H_{11})_3GeF$	341.05	col. need.	....	92	....	hyd.	hyd.	s. meth. al.
105	Tricyclohexyl-germanium hydroxide	$(C_6H_{11})_3GeOH$	339.06	....	....	176–7	....			s. al., bz., pet. eth.
106	Tricyclohexyl-germanium iodide	$(C_6H_{11})_3GeI$	448.96	col. cr.	....	99–100	....	hyd.	hyd.	s. meth. al.
107	Triethylgermanium bromide	$(C_2H_5)_3GeBr$	239.69	col. liq.	....	−33	190.9	hyd.	hyd.	s. bz., eth., chl., CCl_4
108	Triethylgermanium chloride	$(C_2H_5)_3GeCl$	195.23	col. liq.	....	< −50	175.9	hyd.	hyd.	s. bz., eth., chl., CCl_4
109	Triethylgermanium fluoride	$(C_2H_5)_3GeF$	178.77	col. liq.	....	....	149.0^{751}	hyd.	hyd.	s. bz., eth., chl., CCl_4
110	Triethylgermanium hydride	$(C_2H_5)_3GeH$	160.78	col. liq.	....	....	124.4^{751}	i.	i.	s. bz., eth.; i. liq. NH_3
111	Triethylgermanium-imine	$[(C_2H_5)_3Ge]_2NH$	334.57	col. liq.	....	....	$100^{0.1}$	hyd.	hyd.	s. bz., eth., CCl_4, chl.; i. liq. NH_3
112	Triethylgermanium-iodide	$(C_2H_5)_3GeI$	286.68	col. liq.	....	< −50	212.3	hyd.	hyd.	s. bz., eth., chl., CCl_4; i. liq. NH_3
113	Triethylgermanium oxide	$[(C_2H_5)_3Ge]_2O$	335.55	col. liq.	....	< −50	253.9	i.	i.	s. $C_2H_5NH_2$, bz., eth. org. solv.; i. liq. NH_3
114	Triethylphenyl-germanium	$Ge(C_2H_5)_3(C_6H_5)$	236.88	col. liq.	....	....	$116–7^{13}$	i.	....	s. org. solv.
115	Triethyl-p-tolyl-germanium	$Ge(C_2H_5)_3CH_3C_6H_4$ ..	250.91	col. liq.	....	....	$125–6^{12}$	i.	....	s. org. solv.
116	Triethyl-2,2,2,-tri-phenyldigermane-(1,1,1)	$(C_2H_5)_3GeGe(C_6H_5)_3$	463.69	rhomb. cr.	....	89.5–90.5	....	i.		v. s. bz., chl.; s. pet. eth., al.; sl. s. meth. al.
117	Triethylvinyl-germanium	$(C_2H_5)_3Ge(CH:CH_2)$	186.82	n_D^{20} 1.4501..	1.0048_4^{20}	....	61^{28}			
118	Trimethylgermanium bromide	$Ge(CH_3)_3Br$	197.60	col. oily liq., 1.4705	1.544_{40}^{18}	−25	113.7	d.	d.	s. org. solv.
119	Trimethylphenyl-germanium	$Ge(CH_3)_3(C_6H_5)$	194.80	col. liq.	....	....	182–3	i.	....	s. org. solv.
120	Trimethylstannyl-tri-phenylgermanium	$(CH_3)_3SnGe(C_6H_5)_3$	407.71	wh. cr.	....	88	....	i.		s. pet. eth., CCl_4, chl., bz.; sl. s. al.; i. liq. NH_3
121	Triphenylanisyl-germanium	$Ge(C_6H_5)_3(CH_3OC_6H_4)$	411.04	wh. sld.	....	158–9	....			s. al., glac. acet. a.
122	Triphenyldimethyl-aminophenyl-germanium	$Ge(C_6H_5)_3C_6H_4N(CH_3)_2$	424.09	wh. need.	....	140–1	....			
123	Triphenylgermanium amide	$(C_6H_5)_3GeNH_2$	319.93	wh. ppt.	....	d. −NH_3	....	d.	d.	i. liq. NH_3

No.	Name	Formula	Mol. wt.	Crystalline form, color and index of refraction	Sp. gr. or density	Melting point, °C	Boiling point, °C	Solubility in grams per 100 ml of		
								Cold water	Hot water	Alcohol, acids, etc.
	Germanium									
124	Triphenylgermanium bromide	$(C_6H_5)_3GeBr$.......	383.82	hex. col.....	....	138.7	....	i.	hyd.	s. bz., chl.; sl. s. lgr.
125	Triphenylgermanium chloride.	$(C_6H_5)_3GeCl$.......	339.36	wh. cr.....	....	117–8	285^{12}	i.	hyd.	s. bz., eth.
126	Triphenylgermanium fluoride	$(C_6H_5)_3GeF$........	322.91	wh. cr.....	....	76.6	....	i.	hyd.	v. s. bz., eth., lgr., chl.; i. liq. NH₃
127	Triphenylgermanium hydride	$(C_6H_5)_3GeH$.......	304.92	wh. cr. (two forms)	....	α, 47; β, 27	....	i.	i.	v. s. bz., tol., eth., chl., CCl₄; sl. s. liq. NH₃
128	Triphenylgermanium hydroxide	$(C_6H_5)_3GeOH$......	320.92	wh. cr.....	....	134.2	....	i.	i.	s. bz., chl.; sl. s. lgr.
129	Triphenylgermanium iodide	$(C_6H_5)_3GeI$........	430.81	wh. cr.....	....	157	....	hyd.	hyd.	s. bz., eth.
130	Triphenylgermanium oxide	$[(C_6H_5)_3Ge]_2O$......	623.82	col. pl.....	....	183–4	....	i.	i.	s. bz., lgr., eth.
131	Triphenylgermanium-sodium	$Ge(C_6H_5)_3Na$......	326.90	lt. yel.....	....	v. high	....	d.	d.	v. s. liq. NH₃; sl. s. eth., bz.
132	Triphenylgermanium-sodiumoxide	$Ge(C_6H_5)_3ONa$......	342.90	wh. sld.....	....	high	....	d.	d.	i. liq. NH₃
133	Triphenylgermanium-sodiumtriamine	$Ge(C_6H_5)_3Na.3NH_3$..	377.99	yel. sld.....	....	d.	....	d.	d.	v. s. liq. NH₃
134	Triphenyl-m-tolyl germanium	$Ge(C_6H_5)_3(C_6H_4CH_3)$	395.04	wh. aniso-tropic need.	....	136.5–8.5	....	i.	i.	s. bz., h. pet. eth.; i. meth. al.
135	Triphenyl-p-tolyl germanium	$Ge(C_6H_5)_3(C_6H_4CH_3)$	395.04	wh. sld.....	....	123–4	....			s. org. solv.
136	Tri-o-tolylgermanium bromide	$(CH_3C_6H_4)_3GeBr$....	425.90	col. oil, (blue fluores.)	....	....	$205–10^1$			
137	Tri-m-tolylgermanium bromide	$(CH_3C_6H_4)_3GeBr$....	425.90	wh. need., anisotropic	....	78.0–.9	$222–3^1$			s. CCl₄, bz., eth.
138	Tri-p-tolylgermanium bromide	$(CH_3C_6H_4)_3GeBr$....	425.90	col. cr.....	....	128–9	....			s. pet. eth.
139	Tri-o-tolylgermanium chloride	$(CH_3C_6H_4)_3GeCl$....	381.44	col. oil.....	....	....	$216–22^1$			
140	Tri-m-tolylgermanium chloride	$(CH_3C_6H_4)_3GeCl$....	381.44	sm. silky need.; opt. act.	....	84–5	$221–4^1$			s. pet. eth., bz.; i. c. meth. al.
141	Tri-p-tolylgermanium chloride	$(CH_3C_6H_4)_3GeCl$....	381.44	wh. cr.....	....	121	....			s. pet. eth.
142	Tri-o-tolylgermanium hydroxide	$(CH_3C_6H_4)_3GeOH$...	363.00	amor. powd..	....	....	$212–4^1$			
143	Tri-m-tolylgermanium oxide	$[(CH_3C_6H_4)_3Ge]_2O$...	707.98	wh. cr.....	....	125.0–.2	....	i.	i.	s. al., bz., pet. eth.
144	Tri-p-tolylgermanium oxide	$[(CH_3C_6H_4)_3Ge]_2O$...	707.98	wh. pr. aniso-tropic	....	148–50	....	i.	i.	s. h. lgr., c. bz.; sl. s. eth., al., meth. al.
145	Tri-m-tolyl-p-tolyl-germanium	$Ge(C_6H_4CH_3)_3(C_6H_4CH_3)$	437.13	wh. sld.....	....	98.5–100.5	....			s. meth. al.
146	Tri-p-tolyl-o-tolyl-germanium	$Ge(C_6H_4CH_3)_3(C_6H_4CH_3)$	437.13	wh. cr.....	....	164–6	....			....
147	Tri-triphenylgerma-nium nitride	$[(C_6H_5)_3Ge]_3N$......	925.74	col. need.....	....	163–4	....	hyd.	hyd.	s. lgr., eth., bz.
148	Tris-acetylacetone-germanium cupribromide	$[(C_5H_7O_2)_3Ge]CuBr_3$.	673.19	gr.-blk. cr....	....	139	....			i. chl.
149	Tris-acetylacetone-germanium cuprobromide	$[(C_5H_7O_2)_3Ge]CuBr_2$.	593.28	col. rect. pr..	....	165–6	....			s. chl.
150	Tris-acetylacetone-germanium cuprochloride	$[(C_5H_7O_2)_3Ge]CuCl_2$..	504.37	col. pr.....	....	147–8	....			s. chl.
151	Tris-acetylacetone-germanium dicuprobromide	$[(C_5H_7O_2)_3Ge]Cu_2Br_3$.	736.73	col. pr.....	....	195d.	....			s. h. acet. acet.; i. chl.

No.	Name	Formula	Mol. wt.	Crystalline form, color and index of refraction	Sp. gr. or density	Melting point, °C	Boiling point, °C	Solubility in grams per 100 ml of		
								Cold water	Hot water	Alcohol, acids, etc.
	Gold									
1	Aminopyridinotri-bromogold	$H_2NC_5H_4NAuBr_3$...	530.81	blk. pr.......	....	160d.	....	s.	....	s. chl.
2	α-Auromercapto-acetanilide	C_8H_8AuNOS........	363.19	gray-yel. powd.	....	238–241	....	i.		i. a., alk., eth., bz.
3	Diethylgold bromide...	$[(C_2H_5)_2AuBr]_2$......	670.00	col. need....	....	58; subl. vac.	d. 70, expl.			s. NH_4OH
4	Ethylenediaminodi-butylgold bromide	$(CH_2NH_2)_2Au(C_4H_9)_2Br$	451.21	col. need....	....	190 d.		s.		s. al.
5	Ethylenediaminodi-propylgold bromide	$(CH_2NH_2)_2Au(C_3H_7)_2Br$	423.15	col. cr.......	....	volat. 130	d. 190	....	....	....
6	Pyridinotribromogold.	$C_5H_5N\cdot AuBr_3$.......	515.80	red need.....	....	150 d.		s.		s. al., act.
7	Quinolinotribromogold.	$C_9H_7NBr_3Au$.......	565.86	deep red lust. pr.	....	d. >200				s. chl.
	Indium									
1	Trimethylindium	$In(CH_3)_3$.......	159.93	col. cr.......	1.568^{19}_{19}	89.0–.8	subl.	d.	....	s. eth.
	Iridium									
1	Cyclopenta-dienyliridium cyclopentadiene	$(C_5H_5)Ir(C_5H_6)$......	323.40	yel. cr.......	....	130–132	subl.			s. bz., acet., pet. eth.; sl. s. meth. alc.; alc.
	Iron									
1	(Acetylcyclo-pentadienyl) cyclo-pentadienyl iron (Monoacetyl-ferrocene)	$(C_5H_4COCH_3)FeC_5H_5$	228.08	lng. or. (red) need.	....	85–6	86–7			sl. s. iso-octane; s. H_2SO_4, HCl
2	Di(4-aminobutyl)-cyclopentadienyl iron	$[C_5H_4(CH_2)_4NH_2]_2Fe.$	328.28	or. cr.......	....	137–8				s. eth. al.; sl. s. n-heptane
3	(Aminocyclopenta-dienyl)cyclo-pentadienyliron (Aminoferrocene)	$(C_5H_4NH_2)FeC_5H_5$...	201.05	yel. cr.......	....	155				s. eth., al.
4	Mono(p-anisyliso-nitrile)tetra-carbonyliron	$Fe(CO)_4(NCC_6H_4OCH_3)$	301.04	yel. pr. need..	....	39–40				s. eth., pet. eth., bz., chl.
5	Azulene-di-iron pentacarbonyl	$C_{10}H_8Fe_2(CO)_5$	379.92	sld.........	....	100d.				
6	(Benzoylcyclopenta-dienyl)cyclopenta-dienyliron (Benzoyl ferrocene)	$(C_5H_5COC_5H_4)FeC_5H_5$	290.15	red need....	....	108.1–108.3 (108–9)				sl. s. meth. al.
7	(Benzylcyclopenta-dienyl)cyclopenta-dienyliron. (Phenyl-ferrocenylmethane)	$(C_5H_5CH_2C_5H_4)FeC_5H_5$	276.16	yel. cr.......	....	70–4 73.4				s. al.
8	Benzylcyclopenta-dienyliron dicarbonyl bromide	$C_5H_5CH_2C_5H_4Fe(CO)_2Br$	347.00	red cr.......	....	82				s. eth.; i. lgr.
9	Bicycloheptadieneiron tricarbonyl. (Bicyclo-[2:2:1] hepta-2:5-dieneiron tricarbonyl)	$C_7H_8Fe(CO)_3$.......	232.02	or.-red liq. (yel. liq.)	....		$60.2^{0.2}$			s. cold H_2SO_4
10	Butadieneiron tricarbonyl	$C_4H_6Fe(CO)_3$.......	193.97	pa. yel......	....	19				sl. s. meth. al. ligr.
11	(Carboxyaldehydin-pentadienyl)cyclo-pentadienyliron	$(C_5H_4CONO)Fe(C_5H_5)$	255.06	cr.........	....	74–5				s. eth.
12	(Carboxycyclopenta-dienyl)cyclopenta-dienyliron (Ferrocene monocarboxylic acid)	$(C_5H_4CO_2H)FeC_5H_5.$	230.05	rdsh. br. need.	....	225–330 (208.5 d.) (219–225)				sl. s. chl.
13	(Carboxylamidecyclo-pentadienyl) cyclo-pentadienyliron	$(C_5H_4CONH_2)FeC_5H_5$	229.06	cr.........	....	168–170				s. chl.

No.	Name	Formula	Mol. wt.	Crystalline form, color and index of refraction	Sp. gr. or density	Melting point, °C	Boiling point, °C	Solubility in grams per 100 ml of		
								Cold water	Hot water	Alcohol, acids, etc.
	Iron									
14	*Di*(3-Carboxypropionyl)cyclopentadienylIron	[C₅H₄CO(CH₂)₂CO₂H]₂Fe	386.19	cr.........	....	164–6 d.	....			
15	Chloromercuriferrocene	(C₅H₄HgCl)FeC₅H₅..	421.07	golden-yel. leaf.	....	193–4 d. (194–6)	....			
16	(*p*-Chlorophenylcyclopentadienyl) cyclopentadienyliron	(ClC₆H₄C₅H₄)FeC₅H₅	296.58	yel. cr.....	....	122	....			s. al., H₂SO₄; sl. s. ac. a.
17	(Cyanocyclopentadienyl)cyclopentadienyliron. (Ferrocenyl cyanide)	(C₅H₄CN)FeC₅H₅ ...	211.05	....	....	107–8 (103–4)	....			s. CH₂Cl₂; sl.. s. *n*-heptane
18	*Di*[(3-Cyanopropionyl)-cyclopentadienyl]iron	[C₅H₄CO(CH₂)₂CN]₂Fe	348.19	or. cr.	....	133–4	....			sl. s. tol., al.
19	Cycloheptatrienyliron dicarbonyl	C₇H₈Fe(CO)₂	204.01	yel. liq...	....	70⁰·⁴	....			
20	Cyclohexadieneiron tricarbonyl	C₆H₈Fe(CO)₃	220.01	yel. liq...	....		96¹²			s. acet.
21	Cyclooctatetraenediiron hexacarbonyl	C₈H₈Fe₂(CO)₆......	383.91	ye.-or.	....	d. <185	....			v. sl. s. common org. solv.; sl. s. bz.
22	Cyclooctatetraeneiron tricarbonyl	C₈H₈Fe(CO)₃	244.04	lng. red (deep red) need.	....	94–5(92) 155 d.	....			sl. s. hot hexane; s. common org. solv.
23	Cyclopentadienyliron dicarbonylbromide	C₅H₅FeBr(CO)₂	256.88	....	....	18–102 d.	....			s. chl.; i. lgr.
24	Cyclopentadienyliron dicarbonyliodide	C₅H₅FeI(CO)₂	303.88	....	....	117–8 d.	....			i. lgr.
25	(Cyclopentenylcyclopentadienyl) cyclopentadienyliron	(C₅H₇C₅H₄)FeC₅H₅ ..	252.14	cr......	....	64–5	....			sl. s. meth. al., bz. gasoline
26	(Cyclopentylcyclopentadienyl) cyclopentadienyliron	(C₅H₉C₅H₄)FeC₅H₅ ..	254.16	red liq......	....	16.3 frz.	....			s. bz.
27	1,1′-Di(acetylcyclopentadienyl)iron. (Diacetyl ferrocene)	(C₅H₄COCH₃)₂Fe..	270.12	red cr.....	....	130–1	....			....
28	1-1′Di(benzhydryldicyclopentadienyl)-iron. (1,1′-Dibenzhydrylferrocene)	[(C₆H₅)₂CHC₅H₄]₂Fe .	518.49	yel. need.....	....	162–3	....			s. eth., cyclohexane; sl. s. acet.
29	1,1′-Di(benzoylcyclopentadienyl)iron. (1,1′-Dibenzoyl ferrocene)	(C₆H₅COC₅H₄)₂Fe ...	394.26	purple need..	....	106.5–106.7 (105–106)	....			s. CH₂Cl₂
30	1,1′-Di(benzylcyclopentadienyl)iron. (1,1′-Dibenzyl ferrocene)	(C₆H₅CH₂C₅H₄)₂Fe ..	366.29	yel. need.....	....	102 (97–8) (105–6)	....			sl. s. meth. al.; s. *n*-butanol.
31	1,1′-Di(carboxycyclopentadienyl)iron (Ferrocene dicarboxylic acid)	(C₅H₄CO₂H)₂Fe.....	274.06	....	....		subl. <230			....
32	(1,3-Dicarboxycyclopentadienyl)iron (Ferrocene 1,3-dicarboxylic acid)	[C₅H₃(CO₂H)₂]FeC₅H₅	274.06	red need.....	....	206–206.5 d.	....			
33	1,1′-Di(chloromercuri)-ferrocene	(C₅H₄HgCl)₂Fe.....	656.11	sld. yel. powd.	....	no melt up to 300	....			
34	1,1′-Di(*p*-chlorophenylcyclopentadienyl)iron. (1,1′-Di′-*p*-chlorophenyl ferrocene).	(ClC₆H₄C₅H₄)₂Fe..	407.13	cr.....	....	192	....			s. me. al., H₂SO₄; sl. s. pet. eth.
35	Dicyclopentadienyl-di-iron tetracarbonyl	(C₅H₅)₂Fe₂(CO)₄.....	353.92	cr.....	....	192	....			s. pyr.

No.	Name	Formula	Mol. wt.	Crystalline form, color and index of refraction	Sp. gr. or density	Melting point, °C	Boiling point, °C	Solubility in grams per 100 ml of		
								Cold water	Hot water	Alcohol, acids, etc.
	Iron									
36	Diferrocenyl mercury	$(C_5H_5FeC_5H_4)_2Hg$	570.65	or. cr.		235–6 d. 248–9 233–4				s. bz. sl. s. xylene
37	1,1'-Di(hydroxybenzyl-cyclopentadienyl)-iron. (Ferrocenyl-bis-phenyl methanol)	$[C_6H_5CH(OH)C_5H_4]_2Fe$	398.29	yel. leaf		136–7				sl. s. meth. al., al.
38	(Dimethylamino-methylcyclopenta-dienyl)cyclopenta-dienyl iron. (Di-methylaminomethyl-ferrocene).	$[(CH_3)_2NCH_2C_5H_4]Fe\ C_5H_5$	243.13	amber oil 1.5839_4^{25}			$91–2^{0.45}$			s. eth.
39	1,1'-Di(methylcarboxy-cyclopentadienyl)iron	$(C_5H_4CO_2CH_3)_2Fe$	302.11	red cr.			114–5			
40	(1,3-Diphenylcyclo-pentadienyl) cyclo-pentadienyliron. (1,3-Diphenylferrocene)	$[(C_6H_5)_2C_5H_3]Fe(C_5H_5)$	338.24	or. need.		107				s. lgr.
41	1,2-Diphenyl-1,2-di-ferrocenylethanediol	$[C(C_5H_5FeC_5H_4)(OH)(C_6H_5)]_2$	582.31	yel. cr		125–145 d.				s. eth., chl., dioxane,; sl. s. bz.
42	1,1'-Diphenyl-dicyclo-pentadieenyliron. (1,1'-Diphenyl-ferrocene)	$(C_6H_5C_5H_4)_2Fe$	338.24	or.-yel.-br. leaf		154 (140–4)				s. bz.; sl. s. lt. pet.
43	1,1'-Di(trimethylsilyl) ferrocene	$[(CH_3)_3Si\ C_5H_4]_2Fe$	330.40	1.5454_D^{25}		16	$87–88^{0.06}$			s. eth.
44	bis-(Ethylisonitrile)tri-carbonyl iron	$Fe(CO)_3(CNC_2H_5)_2$	250.04	yel. pl. need.		65.5–66				s. eth., bz., al.
45	Ferrocene. (Dicyclo-pentadienyliron)	$C_5H_5FeC_5H_5$	186.04	yel. need.		172.5–173	subl.	i.	i.	s. al., eth., bz., MeOH
46	Ferrocenyl-acetic acid	$(C_5H_4CH_2CO_2H)FeC_5H_5$	244.08	lt. yel. (yel.) need		150–2 (125–135)				s. eth.; i. pentane; sl. s. meth. al.
47	1,1'-Ferrocenyl-diacetic acid	$(C_5H_4CH_2CO_2H)_2Fe$	302.11	yel.		sintered 140–3(d)				s. chl., eth.; i. pentane
48	β-Ferrocenyl-ethyl alcohol	$(C_5H_4CH_2CH_2OH)Fe(C_5H_5)$	230.09			49–50				s. eth.; i. pentane
49	β-Ferrocenyl-propionic acid	$[C_5H_4CO(CH_2)_2CO_2H]FeC_5H_5$	286.11	or. cr.		166.5–167.5				s. CH_2Cl_2; sl. s. meth. al.
50	(Formylcyclopenta-dienyl)cyclopenta-dienyliron. (Ferrocene monoaldehyde)	$(C_5H_4CHO)FeC_5H_5$	214.05	sld. red (rdsh br.)cr.		120–2 (130–2)				s. eth., chl.; sl. s. al.
51	(Hydroxybenzylcyclo-pentadienyl)cyclo-pentadienyliron. (Phenyl-ferrocenyl methanol)	$[C_6H_5CH(OH)C_5H_4]FeC_5H_5$	292.16	yel. cr.		81–2 (80–80.5)				s. eth.; i. pet. eth.
52	(Hydroxymethylcyclo-pentadienyl)cyclo-pentadienyliron. (Hydroxymethyl-ferrocene)	$(C_5H_4CH_2OH)FeC_5H_5$	216.06	yel. pl. lng. need.		81–2 (74–6)				s. chl.
53	p-Hydroxyphenyl-cyclopentadienyl)-cyclopentadienyliron	$(HOC_6H_4C_5H_4)FeC_5H_5$	278.14	cr. yel. grn. fluorescence		165				s. al.
54	(Methylcarboxycyclo-pentadienyl)cyclo-pentadienyliron	$(C_5H_4CO_2CH_3)FeC_5H_5$	244.08			70–1				s. meth. al.
55	bis(Methylisonitrile)-tricarbonyliron	$Fe(CO)_3(CNCH_3)_2$	221.98			100–130 d.				s. al., eth., bz., ac. a.
56	Mono(ethylisonitrile)-tetracarbonyliron	$Fe(CO)_4(CNC_2H_5)$	222.97	yel.		−3	i. d.			s. org. solv.

No.	Name	Formula	Mol. wt.	Crystalline form, color and index of refraction	Sp. gr. or density	Melting point, °C	Boiling point, °C	Solubility in grams per 100 ml of		
								Cold water	Hot water	Alcohol, acids, etc.
	Iron									
57	(p-Nitrophenylcyclopentadienyl)cyclopentadienyliron	$(NO_2C_6H_4C_5H_4)FeC_5H_5$	307.13	dk. purple cr.	....	163	....			s. al.
58	(Phenylcyclopentadienyl) cyclopentadienyliron (Phenylferrocene)	$(C_6H_5C_5H_5)FeC_5H_5$	263.14	yel. (or.) cr.	....	110–111 (109–110)	....			.. s. al.
59	Phenyl-diferrocenylmethane	$(C_5H_5FeC_5H_4)_2CHC_6H_5$	460.19	cr.	....	123–4				s. eth., al.
60	1,3,1′,3′-Tetraphenyldicyclopentadienyliron. (1,3,1′,3′-tetraphenylferrocene)	$[(C_6H_5)_2C_5H_3]_2Fe$	490.43	flat or. pr. (deep or. red)	....	219–220 (220–222)				sl. s. acet.
61	Thiopheniron dicarbonyl	$C_6H_4SFe(CO)_2$	220.03	pale red cr.	....	51	subl.			s. org. solv.
62	Trimethylsilylferrocene	$[C_5H_4Si(CH_3)_3]FeC_5H_5$	258.22	dk. or.-red liq. 1.5696_4^{25}	....	23	$64–5^{0.45}$			....
	Lanthanum									
1	Hexaantipyrineiodide	$La(COC_{10}H_{12}N_2)_6I_3$	1649.01	yel. cr.	....	268–9 d.	....	41.8^{20}		
	Lead									
1	Hexaethyldilead (triethyllead)	$Pb_2(C_2H_5)_6$	588.75	liq.	1.471	....	d.	i.		
2	Tetraethyllead	$Pb(C_2H_5)_4$	323.44	col. liq.; or. flame, grn. marg. 1.5195^{30}	1.659^{11}	-136.80	$200d.; 91^{19}$	i.		s. bz., pet., al., eth.
3	Tetra-iso-amyllead	$Pb(C_5H_{11})_4$	491.76	col. oily liq. 1.4946	n_D $1.2332_{4.5}^{20}$	....	....	i.		s. al., bz., eth
4	Tetraisobutyllead	$Pb[CH_2CH(CH_3)_2]_4$	435.66	col. liq., 1.5042	1.324	-23	....			
5	Tetraisopropyllead	$Pb[CH(CH_3)_2]_4$	379.55	col. liq., dec. in air, 1.5223	1.4504	-53.5	$120^{14}; 133–8^{27}$	i.		s. bz. pet. eth.
6	Tetramethyllead	$Pb(CH_3)_4$	267.33	liq. 1.5120^{20}	1.995	-27.5	110	i.		s. bz., pet. eth., al.
7	Tetraphenyllead	$Pb(C_6H_5)_4$	515.62	wh. need.	1.530^{20}	227.7	d. 270	i.		s. bz.
8	Tetra-n-propyllead	$Pb(C_3H_7)_4$	379.55	col. liq., 1.5094	1.44	....	126^{13}			s. bz., pet. eth.; sl. s. al.
9	Tetravinyllead	$(CH_2:CH)_4Pb$	315.37	n_D^{20} 1.5462	1.7882_4^{20}	....	$69–70^{11}$			
10	Tricyclohexyllead	$(C_6H_{11})_3Pb$	456.65	yel. hex. pl., decol. in light	....	d. 195				
11	Triphenylbenzyllead	$(C_6H_5)_3PbCH_2C_6H_5$	529.64	col. pl.	....	93	d. 205–210			v. s. bz., eth., chl.
12	Triphenylethyllead	$(C_6H_5)_3Pb(C_2H_5)$	467.57	wh. cr. $n_{H\infty}^{61}$ 1.6263 (vac)	1.5885_4^{61}	42				s. hot al.
13	Triphenylmethyllead	$(C_6H_5)_3PbCH_3$	453.55	col. rhomb. (from bz.)	....	60	d. 260			sl. sl al.; eth.; v. s. bz., chl.
14	Triphenylleadbromide	$(C_6H_5)_3PbBr$	518.42	need.	....	166		i.		s. al., bz., eth.
	Lithium									
1	n-Butyllithium	$n-C_4H_9Li$	64.06	inflamm. liq.	0.765^{25}	subl. vac. 80 100	d. 150	d.	d.	s. bz., eth.
2	Ethyllithium	LiC_2H_5	36.00	hex. transp. pl.	....	95 (in N_2)	subl. 95	d.	....	d. eth.; s. bz lgr.
	Magnesium									
1	Dimethylmagnesium	$(CH_3)_2Mg$(polymer?)	54.38	wh. sol., inflamm. in air	....	stable to 240	....			v. sl. s. eth.
2	Diphenylmagnesium	$(C_6H_5)_2Mg$	178.53	wh. sol.	....	d. ca, 280				i. bz., eth.
	Magnesiumaluminum ethoxide-see Aluminum(3)									

No.	Name	Formula	Mol. wt.	Crystalline form, color and index of refraction	Sp. gr. or density	Melting point, °C	Boiling point, °C	Solubility in grams per 100 ml of		
								Cold water	Hot water	Alcohol, acids, etc.
	Manganese									
1	Acetylcyclopentadienyl manganese tricarbonyl	$CH_3COC_5H_4Mn(CO)_3$	246.10	. . . .	. . . .	41.5–42.5 (39.5 40.0)	. . . .			s. pet. eth.
2	Acetylmanganese pentacarbonyl	$CH_3COMn(CO)_5$	238.04	wh. cr.		54–5				
3	(Benzoylcyclopenta-dienyl)manganese tricarbonyl	$C_5H_4COC_6H_5Mn(CO)_3$	308.17	yel. cr.		73.5–74.5				s. bz., hexane; i. pet. eth.
4	Benzoylmanganese pentacarbonyl	$C_6H_5COMn(CO)_5$	300.11	wh.		95.6				
5	Benzylmanganese pentacarbonyl	$C_6H_5CH_2Mn(CO)_5$ . . .	286.12	yel.		37.5–38.5				
6	(*tert*-Butylcyclopenta-dienyl) manganese tricarbonyl	$C_4H_9C_5H_4Mn(CO)_3$ . .	260.17	1.5600_D^{20}			150^{28-29}			
7	(γ-Butyrocyclopenta-dienyl)manganese tricarbonyl	$[C_5H_4(CH_2)_3CO_2H]Mn(CO)_3$	290.16	yel. cr.		63–5				s. bz., eth., al.
8	(Carboxycyclopenta-dienyl)manganese tricarbonyl	$(C_5H_4CO_2H)Mn(CO)_3$	248.08	yel. cr.		195–6				s. al.; sl. s. bz.
9	(Di-*tert*-butylcyclo-pentadienyl) manganese tricarbonyl	$(C_4H_9)_2C_5H_3Mn(CO)_3$	316.28	. . . .		70–1	$164–8^{10}$			
10	(Dicyclohexyl cyclo-pentadienyl) manganese tricarbonyl	$(C_6H_{11})_2C_5H_3Mn(CO)_3$	368.36	1.5804_D^{20}			$149–152^2$			
11	(Formylcyclopenta-dienyl)manganese tricarbonyl	$(C_5H_4CHO)Mn(CO)_3$	232.08	red oil.			$105^{0.15}$			s. org. solv.
12	(Hexylcyclopenta-dienyl)manganese tricarbonyl	$C_6H_{13}C_5H_4Mn(CO)_3$.	288.23	1.5686_D^{20}			$110–114^2$			s. eth.
13	(Methylcyclopenta-dienyl)manganese (benzene)	$CH_3C_5H_4MnC_6H_6$	212.18	red cr.		116–8	. . . .			
14	Methylmanganese pentacarbonyl	$CH_3Mn(CO)_5$	210.03	col. cr.		94.5–95				
15	Phenylmanganese pentacarbonyl	$C_6H_5Mn(CO)_5$	272.10	wh. cr.		52				
16	(Tri-*tert*-butylcyclo-pentadienyl) manganese tricarbonyl	$(C_4H_9)_3C_5H_2Mn(CO)_3$	372.39	1.5326_D^{20}			$160–3^{3.5}$			
17	(δ-Valerocyclopenta-dienyl)manganese tricarbonyl	$[C_5H_4(CH_2)_4CO_2H]Mn(CO)_3$	304.18	yel. cr.			69–71			s. bz., eth., al.
	Mercury									
1	Aminophenylmercuric acetate(*p*)	$C_6H_4(NH_2)HgO_2C_2H_3$	351.76	col. pr.		167		i.	i.	s. dil. a.; sl. s. chl., al.; i. eth.
2	Biphenylmercury	$Hg(C_6H_5C_6H_4)_2$	507.00	sm. scales		216		difficultly	soluble in	common solv.
3	*n*-Butylmercuric chloride	C_4H_9ClHg	293.16	wh. need.		130		14×10^{-4} $18°$	3.3×10^{-4} $100°$	0.5^{18} al.; 5.6^{18} $CHCl_3$
4	Chloromercuriphenol(*o*)	$C_6H_4OHHgCl$	329.15			152.5^0				s. NaOH
5	Di-*n*-amylmercury	$Hg(C_5H_{11})_2$	342.88	1.4998	1.6369		133^{10}			
6	Di-(*dl*)-amylmercury	$Hg(C_5H_{11})_2$ . . .	342.88	1.5014	1.6700		93^1			
7	Dibenzylmercury	$Hg(C_7H_7)_2$	382.86	long brittle col. need.						s. al., eth., chl., CS_2, ac. a., bz. eth. acet.; sl. s. lgr.

No.	Name	Formula	Mol. wt.	Crystalline form, color and index of refraction	Sp. gr. or density	Melting point, °C	Boiling point, °C	Solubility in grams per 100 ml of		
								Cold water	Hot water	Alcohol, acids, etc.
	Mercury									
8	Di-n-butylmercury	Hg(C$_4$H$_9$)$_2$	314.82	liq. 1.5057	1.7779	....	105^{10}			
9	Diethylmercury	Hg(C$_2$H$_5$)$_2$	258.71	col. liq. of hazel odor 1.5399	liq. 2.444	....	159	i.	i.	v. s. eth.; sl. s. al.
	Diferrocenylmercury- *see* **Iron** (36)									
10	Di-n-hexylmercury	Hg(C$_6$H$_{13}$)$_2$	370.94	1.4973	1.5361	....	158^{10}			
11	Diisoamylmercury	Hg(C$_5$H$_{11}$)$_2$	342.89	1.4989	1.6397	....	125^{10}			
12	Diisobutylmercury	Hg(C$_4$H$_9$)$_2$	314.82	col. liq., 1.4965	1.835^{15}; 1.7678	volat. 100	205–7; 86^{10}	v. sl. s.	....	s. eth. al.
13	Diisopropylmercury	Hg(C$_3$H$_7$)$_2$	286.78	1.5263	2.0024	....	63^{10}			
14	Dimethylaminophenyl-mercuric acetate(p)	C$_6$H$_4$N(CH$_3$)$_2$HgO$_2$C$_2$H$_3$	379.82	long. col. need	....	165	....	i.	i.	s. bz., chl., al., dil. a.
15	Dimethylaniline-mercury(p)	Hg[C$_6$H$_4$N(CH$_3$)$_2$]$_2$	440.95	lust. need	....	169				s. chl.; sl. s. al., eth., dil. HCl
16	Dimethylmercury	Hg(CH$_3$)$_2$	230.66	col. liq., sweet odor, 1.5327	3.069	....	96			s. al., eth.
17	Dinaphthylmercury(α)	Hg(C$_{10}$H$_7$)$_2$	454.92	wh. rhomb	1.929	188 (243)	249	i.	sl. s.	s. h. CS$_2$, chl.; sl. s. bz., eth. v. sl. s. h. bz
18	Dinaphthylmercury(β)	Hg(C$_{10}$H$_7$)$_2$	454.92	cryst. from bz.	....	247–8	....	i.		sl. s. al., eth.
19	Diphenylmercury	Hg(C$_6$H$_5$)$_2$	354.81	wh. glassy need.	2.318	121.8, subl.	204$^{10.5}$ >306 d.	i.	i.	s. chl., CS$_2$, bz.; sl. s. eth., h. al.
20	Dipropylmercury	Hg(C$_3$H$_7$)$_2$	286.78	col. mobile liq., 1.5170	2.0208	....	189–91; 73^{10}	i.		v. s. eth.; s. al.
21	Ditolylmercury(o)	Hg(C$_7$H$_7$)$_2$	382.86	wh. tabl.	....	107	219^{14}			s. h. bz.
22	Ditolylmercury(m)	Hg(C$_7$H$_7$)$_2$	382.86	col. or. lt. yel. need.	....	102	....	i.		s. bz., chl., acet., eth. acet.
23	Ditolylmercury(p)	Hg(C$_7$H$_7$)$_2$	382.86	need	....	238	....	i.		s. h. bz., chl., CS$_2$; sl. s. c. al.
24	Ethane hexamercarbide	C$_2$Hg$_6$O$_2$(OH)$_2$	1293.58	yelsh.-wh. powd.	....	exp. 230		i.	i.	i.
25	Ethylmercuric chloride	C$_2$H$_5$HgCl	265.10	silv. irid. leaf.	3.482	193	subl. 40	i.		v. s. h. al.; sl. s. eth.
26	Ethylmercuric hydroxide	C$_2$H$_4$HgOH	245.65	silv. irid. leaf.	....	37		i.	i.	v. s. h. al.; s. eth.; sl. s. c. al.
27	Ethylmercuric iodide	C$_2$H$_5$HgI	356.56	cr. from EtOH	....	186	....			s. al.
28	Mercury ethyl-mercaptide(ic)	Hg(SC$_2$H$_5$)$_2$	322.85	leaf.	....	76–7	d.	i.		d. a.
29	Mercuryphenyl-mercaptide(ic)	Hg(SC$_6$H$_5$)$_2$	418.93	yelsh. need.	....	153 d.	d.	i.		sl. s. h. al.; v. s. bz., pyr.
30	Methylmercuric chloride	CH$_3$HgCl	251.09	wh. cr., disg. odor	4.063	170	volat. 100			v. s. meth. al.; s. eth., al.
31	Methylmercuric iodide	CH$_3$HgI	342.53	col. pearly leaf.	....	143	....	i.		v. s. meth. al.; s. eth., al.
32	Naphthylmercuric acetate(α)	C$_{10}$H$_7$HgO$_2$C$_2$H$_3$	386.81	fine need.	....	154		i.	i.	s. al., ac. a., bz., CS$_2$, fats; sl. s. eth.
33	Naphthylmercuric chloride(α)	C$_{10}$H$_7$HgCl	363.22	silk quad. tabl.	....	188–9		i.	i.	sl. s. bz., al.
34	Phenylmercuric acetate	C$_6$H$_5$HgO$_2$C$_2$H$_3$	336.75	rhomb. sm. wh. lust. pr.	....	149		sl. s.	sl. s.	s. glac. ac. a. ac. a., bz., al.
35	Phenylmercuric bromide	C$_6$H$_5$HgBr	357.61	rhomb. wh. lust. tabl.	....	276		i.		s. al., bz., pyr.
36	Phenylmercuric chloride	C$_6$H$_5$HgCl	313.15	wh. satiny leaf.	....	251				sl. s. h. al., bz., pyr., eth.
37	Phenylmercuric cyanide	C$_6$H$_5$HgCN	303.73	rhomb. long pr.	....	204			sl. s.	s. h. al., bz.
38	Phenylmercuric iodide	C$_6$H$_5$HgI	404.60	rhomb. satiny tabl.	....	266		i.		s. chl., CS$_2$; sl. s. al., eth., bz.
39	Phenylmercuric nitrate	C$_6$H$_5$HgNO$_3$	339.70	rhomb. tabl.	....	176–86		i.	sl. s.	s. h. al., bz.

No.	Name	Formula	Mol. wt.	Crystalline form, color and index of refraction	Sp. gr. or density	Melting point, °C	Boiling point, °C	Solubility in grams per 100 ml of		
								Cold water	Hot water	Alcohol, acids, etc.
	Mercury									
40	Phenylmercuric nitrate, basic	$C_6H_5HgOH.C_6H_5HgNO_3$	634.41	wh.-grayish powd.	....	d. 178–184	....	0.8	....	sl. s. al., glyc.
41	Tolylmercuric bromide(p)	C_7H_7HgBr.........	371.63	thin lust. gray sc.	....	228				s. chl., al., bz.; i. c. CS_2
42	Tolylmercuric chloride(p)	C_7H_7HgCl.........	327.19	rhomb. silky tabl.	....	233	....	i.	i.	sl. s. h. al., bz , chl., acet., pyr.; i. eth.
	Molybdenum									
1	Benzenemolybdenum tricarbonyl	$C_6H_6Mo(CO)_3$	258.09	yel. monocl. .		120–5 d.				
2	Bicycloheptadiene-molybdenum tetra-carbonyl	$C_7H_8Mo(CO)_4$	300.12	yel. pl.		76–7				sl. s. pet. eth.
3	Cycloheptatriene-molybdenum tri-carbonyl	$C_7H_8Mo(CO)_3$	272.11	or.-red pl....	....	100.5–101.5				s. lt. pet.; chl., bz.
4	bis-Cyclopentadienyl-bimolybdenum pentacarbonyl (bis-Cyclopentadienyl-μ-pentacarbon monoxide bimolybdenum I)	$(C_5H_5)_2Mo_2(CO)_5$.	462.12	purp.-red..		215–7 d.				s. chl.; sl. s. CCl_4 al., CS_2, bz.
5	Mesitylenemolybdenum tricarbonyl	$(CH_3)_3C_6H_3Mo(CO)_3$.	300.17	yel..........		130–40 d.	90 subl.	....		....
6	Tropeniummolybdenum tricarbonyl fluoroborate	$C_7H_7Mo(CO)_3BF_4$ ...	357.91	lt. or. need...		>270				
	Neodymium									
1	Neodymium hexaanti-pyrine iodide	$[Nd(COC_{10}H_{12}N_2)_6I_2]$.	1654.34	rose cr.......		270–2	....	12.7^{20}		
	Nickel									
1	Dicyclopentadienyl-nickel	$(C_5H_5)_2Ni$	188.90	drk. grn. cr..			130 subl.			sl. s. lgr.; s. al.
2	bis(Cyclopentadienyl-nickel carbonyl)	$(C_5H_5NiCO)_2$	303.63	purple red. .		136		i.		s. bz., chl., pet. eth., eth., al.
3	Cyclopentadienylnickel carbonyl iodide	$C_5H_5Ni(CO)I$.......	278.72	blk. vlt.....		20 d.				sl. s. org. solv.
4	Dicyclopentadiene-nickel	$(C_5H_6)_2Ni$	190.92	red need....		41–42 cl. tube				....
	Niobium									
1	bis-Cyclopentadienylni-obium monohydroxy-dibromide	$(C_5H_5)_2Nb(OH)Br_2$.	399.92	or.-red....	....			s.		
2	bis-Cyclopentadienylni-obium tribromide	$(C_5H_5)_2NbBr_3$.......	462.82	reddsh. br. cr.	....	260 d.		s.		s. chl., al.; i. pet. eth.; sl. s. bz.;
	Palladium									
1	Cycloocta-1,5-dienedi-bromopalladium	$C_8H_{12}PdBr_2$......	374.40	or.-red. need...	....	210 d.	....	i.	....	sl. s. glac.; i. acet., ac. a.
2	Cycloocta-1,5-dienedi-chloropalladium	$C_8H_{12}PdCl_2$	285.49	pa. or. need..	d. 205–210					s. h. glac. ac. a.; sl. s. c. al., bx. sl. s. h. bz., chl., acet.
3	Cyclohexenepalladous chloride	$(C_6H_{10}PdCl_2)_2$.....	519.00	lt. br. cr.						v. i. in common org. solv.
4	Dicyclopentadienedi-chloropalladium	$(C_5H_6)_2PdCl_2$.......	309.51	....		165–70 d.	d.			s. bz., eth., chl.

No.	Name	Formula	Mol. wt.	Crystalline form, color and index of refraction	Sp. gr. or density	Melting point, °C	Boiling point, °C	Solubility in grams per 100 ml of		
								Cold water	Hot water	Alcohol, acids, etc.
	Palladium									
5	bis(Dicyclopentadiene-methoxide)dichlorodi-palladium	$C_{22}H_{30}O_2Pd_2Cl_2$	610.19	yel. pl.		166–70 d.		d.		i. meth. al.; s. boil. chl.; sl. s. c. chl., bz.
6	bis(Dicyclopentadiene-isopropoxide)di-chlorodipalladium	$C_{26}H_{38}O_2Pd_2Cl_2$	666.30	yel. pl.		150–60 d.		i.		i. meth. al.; s. boil. chl.; sl. s. cold chl.; bz.
7	bis(Dicyclopentadiene-n-propoxide) di-chlorodipalladium	$C_{26}H_{38}O_2Pd_2Cl_2$	666.30	yel. pl.		150–56 d.		i.		i. meth. al.; s. boil chl.; sl. s. cold chl.; bz.
8	Di(8-methoxycyclooct-4-enyl)dibromo-palladium	$(C_8H_{12}OMe)_2Pd_2Br_2$	651.06	pa. yel. cr.		125–35 d.				
9	Di(8-methoxycyclooct-4-enyl)dichloro-palladium	$(C_8H_{12}OMe)_2Pd_2Cl_2$	562.14	pa. yel. cr.		130–35 d.				sl. s. meth. al.,
10	Ethylenepalladous chloride	$C_4H_8Pd_2Cl_4$	410.72	lt. canary yel. need.						s. xylene; i. pet. eth.
11	1,5-Hexadienedichloro-palladium. (Biallyl-dichloropalladium)	$C_6H_{10}PdCl_2$	259.46	brnsh. yel. cr.						sl. s. bz.; i. pet. eth.
12	Styrenepalladous chloride	$C_{16}H_{16}Pd_2Cl_4$	562.92	lt. red. br. need.						sl. s. bz.; i. common org. solv.
13	Trimethylethylene-palladous chloride	$C_5H_{10}PdCl_2$	247.45	red. pr.		85–90 d.		s. with d.		s. bz.; i. isopentane, gasoline
	Platinum									
1	Bromochlorothylene amine platinum	$C_2H_4PtNH_3BrCl$	355.55	pa. grn. pr.		d. 163		sl. s.		i. c. HCl
2	cis-2-Buteneplatinous chloride	$(C_4H_8PtCl_2)_2$	644.21			d. 165–75				s. liq. butene
3	trans-2-Buteneplatinous chloride	$(C_4H_8PtCl_2)_2$	644.21	pink cr.		110–115 (d. 125–135)				s. liq. butene
4	Cyclohexenedibromo-platinum (Cyclo-hexene-platinous bromide)	$(C_6H_{10}PtBr_2)_2$	874.11	lng. slend. or need.		150–1				s. chl.; v. sl. s. bz., al.; i. eth. ac. a.
5	Cyclohexenedichloro-platinum (Cyclo-hexeneplatinous chloride)	$(C_6H_{10}PtCl_2)_2$	696.29	lng. sl. or. need.		145–6				v. s. al., acet.; s. chl., eth.; sl. s. bz. i. ac. a.
6	Cycloocta-1,5-dienedi-chloroplatinum	$C_8H_{12}PtCl_2$	374.18	wh. need.		d. >220				s. boil. chl., ac. a., CH_2Cl_2
7	Cycloocta-1,5-dienedi-iodoplatinum	$C_8H_{12}PtI_2$	557.08	or.-yel. need.		d. 250				s. boil. CH_2Cl_2
8	Cyclooctatetraene-dichloroplatinum	$C_8H_8PtCl_2$	370.15	or.						s. org. solv.
9	Cyclooctatetraenediido-platinum	$C_8H_8PtI_2$	553.05	or.-red. cr. powd.		Turns black (no change in cr. form)				s. boil. chl.
10	Cycloocta-1,5-dienedi-bromoplatinum	$C_8H_{12}PtBr_2$	463.09	pa. yel. need.		d. >200				s. h. ch., ac. ac. CH_2Cl_2
11	Cyclopropaneplatinous chloride	$C_3H_6PtCl_2$	308.08	br. powd.		d. >100		v. sl. s.		s. 10N HCl, al.; sl. s. eth., acet., chl., CCl_4
12	Diallyletherdichloro-platinum	$C_6H_{10}OPtCl_2$	364.14	wh. cr.		180 d.		i.	i.	s. h. chl.
13	trans-Dichloroethylene-dichloroplatinum (trans-Dichloroethyl-eneplatinous chloride)	$[C_2H_2Cl_2PtCl_2]_2$	725.88	or. cr.		155–60				s. acet., chl., bz., nitrobz.
14	Dicyclopentadienedi-bromoplatinum	$C_{10}H_{12}PtBr_2$	487.11	yel. pr.		d. 200–225		i.		s. h. chl.; i. eth.

No.	Name	Formula	Mol. wt.	Crystalline form, color and index of refraction	Sp. gr. or density	Melting point, °C	Boiling point, °C	Solubility in grams per 100 ml of		
								Cold water	Hot water	Alcohol, acids, etc.
	Platinum									
15	Dicyclopentadienedichloroplatinum	$(C_5H_6)_2PtCl_2$	398.21	sm. ivory need.	....	218–220 d.	....	....	....	i. al.; s. h. chl.
16	Dicyclopentadienediiodoplatinum	$(C_5H_6)_2PtI_2$	581.11	....	....	209–211 d.	....	i.	....	s. acet.
17	Dicyclopentadienemethoxy chloroplatinum	$C_{11}H_{13}OPtCl$	393.78	wh. cr.	....					i. eth.; s. chl.
18	Dimethylplatinum diiodide	$(CH_3)_2PtI_2$	478.97	blk.	....			i.	i.	i. eth.; et. ac. acet.
19	Dipentenedichloroplatinum (Dipenteneplatinous chloride)	$[C_{10}H_{16}PtCl_2]_2$	804.47	pa. yel. biax. pr.	....	151–2				v. s. chl.; s. acet.; i. eth., al., ac. a., bz.
20	β-Dipenteneplatinous iodide	$C_{10}H_{16}PtI_2$	585.14	red cr.	....	122–4 d.				i. chl.; s. acet.
21	Dipyridinecyclopropanedichloroplatinum	$C_{13}H_{16}N_2Cl_2Pt$	466.28		....	d. >100		i.	d.	s. warm 10N HCl
22	Dipyridinotrimethyliodoplatinum	$C_{13}H_{19}N_2PtI$	525.30	pa. yel. cr.	....	168		sl. s.	s. s.	sl. s. al.; s. bz., chl., acet., h. al.
23	Dipyridinotrimethylplatinic iodide	$(CH_3)_3Pt(Py)_2I$	525.31	col. pr.	....	168				....
24	Ethyl(trimethylplatinic) acetoacetate	$C_6H_9O_3Pt(CH_3)_3$	369.33	wh. hex. pl.	....	200 d.		i.		s. org. solv.
25	Ethylenedichloroplatinum (Ethyleneplatinous chloride)	$[C_2H_4PtCl_2]_2$	588.10	or. tabl.	....	170–180 d. 160–165		sl. s.		v. s. acet., al., eth.; s. bz., chl. sl. s. NaCl soln.
26	1,5-Hexadienedichloroplatinum (Biallyldichloroplatinum)	$C_6H_{10}PtCl_2$	348.15	or.-pa. yel.	....	172–3		i.	s. sl. with d.	s. chl.; v. sl. s. eth.; sl. s. bz.
27	1,5-Hexadienediiodoplatinum (Biallyldiiodoplatinum)	$C_6H_{10}PtI_2$	531.05	or. red cr.	....	d.		i.	....	s. chl.
28	Hexamethyldiplatinum	$(CH_3)_6Pt_2$	480.39	col. cr.	....	d.		i.	i.	v. s. bz., acet.; eth., sl. s. c. pet. eth.
29	Isobutylenedichloroplatinum (Isobutyleneplatinous chloride)	$[C_4H_8PtCl_2]_2$	644.21	or. rhomb. pl.	....	144–5		i.	....	v. s., chl., eth., bz., al. acet., NaCl soln.; sl. s. ac. a.; i. pet. eth.
30	8-Methoxycyclooct-4-enyl p-toluidinechloroplatinum	$(C_8H_{12}OCH_3)(CH_3C_6H_4NH_2)PtCl$	476.92	wh. need.	....	140–2				s. bz., meth. al., nitrobz.; i. lgr.
31	Methoxydicyclopentadiene-p-toluidinechloroplatinum	$C_{18}H_{24}ONPtCl$	500.93	wh. need.	....	160–170				v. s. c. chl.; s. bz., meth. al., acet. eth.; i. nitrobz.
32	Methylplatinum pentaiodide	CH_3PtI_5	844.65	blk. cr.	....			sl. s.	....	sl. s. acet., et. ac., s. eth.
33	Methylplatinum triiodide	CH_3PtI_3	590.84	blk. amor.	....				i.	s. HCl
34	Tetramethyl platinum	$(CH_3)_4Pt$	255.23	lg. col. hex.	....	d.		i.	i.	v. s. bz., acet., eth., pet. eth.
35	Sesquimethylenediaminotrimethylplatiniciodide	$C_{12}H_{34}N_6I_2Pt_2$	914.50	col. cr.	....	d. 269		s.		....
36	p-Toluidineethylenedichloroplatinum	$(C_2H_4)(CH_3C_6H_4NH_2)PtCl_2$	401.20	lem. yel. cr.	....	d. 125–135		i.		v. s. bz., acet., meth. al., eth., chl.; sl. s. cyclohexane; i. lt. pet.
37	Trimethylplatinicmonoethylenediamineiodide	$(CH_3)_3Pt(NH_2CH_2CH_2NH_2)I$	427.19	....	....	204 d.		s.		

No.	Name	Formula	Mol. wt.	Crystalline form, color and index of refraction	Sp. gr. or density	Melting point, °C	Boiling point, °C	Cold water	Hot water	Alcohol, acids, etc.
	Platinum									
38	Trimethylplatinum benzoylacetone	$C_{13}H_{18}O_2Pt$........	401.37	lng. wh. pr...	....	....	....	....		v. sl. s. lgr.; v. s. meth. al.
39	Trimethylplatinum chloride	$(CH_3)_3PtCl$........	275.64	wh. cr...	....	....	....	....		sl. s. c. pet. eth.; s. h. pet. eth.
40	Trimethylplatinum dipropionyl methane	$C_7H_{11}O_2Pt(CH_3)_3$....	367.36	wh. need....	....	d. 190	....	i.		s. org. solv.
41	Trimethylplatinum iodide	C_3H_9PtI...........	367.09	cr. yel. powd.	....	d. ca 250	....	i.	i.	sl. s. al. eth. acet., bz., s. warm bz.
42	Trimethylpyridino-platinum iodide	$[(CH_3)_3Pt(C_5H_5N)I]_2$.	892.40		....	d. >150	....			s. pyr., chl., bz.
43	Pinenedichloroplatinum (Pineneplatinous chloride)	$[C_{10}H_{16}PtCl_2]_2$	804.48	pr...	....	138–141				v. s. chl.; s. bz., acet.; sl. s. eth., et. ac., ac. a.
44	Stilbenedichloro-platinum (Stilbene-platinous chloride)	$[C_{14}H_{12}PtCl_2]_2$.......	892.50	sm. hex. or. pr.		191–2				w. s. chl., acet., nitrobz.; v. sl. s. bz., al.; i. ac. a.
45	Styrenedichloro-platinum (Styrene-platinous chloride)	$[C_8H_8PtCl_2]_2$	704.30	or. hex. pr...		169–171		i.		s. chl., eth., acet.; v. sl. s. ac. a., NaCl soln.; sl. s. bz.
46	Styrenedibromo-platinum (Styrene-platinous bromide)	$[C_8H_8PtBr_2]_2$.......	918.12	pink hex. pr..		153–4				s. chl.; sl. s., bz., acet.; i. eth., al., ac. a.
	Potassium									
1	Potassium saccharate, acid(d)	$KHC_6H_8O_8$........	248.23	rhomb. need,.	....	....	....	1.1^{16}	....	
2	Potassium-m-nitrophenoxide	$KOC_6H_4NO_2.2H_2O$..	213.23	flat or. need..	1.691^{20}	$-2H_2O$, 130	d.	16.3^{15}		s. al.
3	Potassium-p-nitrophenoxide	$KOC_6H_4NO_2.2H_2O$..	213.23	yel. leaf......	1.652^{20}	$-2H_2O$, 130	d.	7.5^{15}	....	sl. s. al.
	Rhenium									
1	Bis-2:2'-dipyridyl rhenichloride	$(C_{10}H_9N_2)_2ReCl_6$.....	713.31	pa. gr. cr...	....	sl. s.				
2	Dipyridyl per-rhenate(2:2')	$(C_5H_4N)_2HReO_4$....	407.39	col. need....		2.1				
3	Dipyridyl rheni-chloride(2:2')	$(C_5H_4N)_2ReCl_6$.....	555.12	yel. need....		sl. s.				
4	Trimethylrhenium....	$Re(CH_3)_3$...........	231.31	col. oil.....		60				
5	Tripyridyl rheni-chloride(2:2':2'')	$(C_5H_4N)_3HReCl_6$....	634.21	pa. grn. cr...		i.				
	Rubidium									
1	Monorubidium acetylide	$RbHC_2$........	110.50	col. cr., very hygr.	....	d. 300	....			s. NH_3; i. eth.
	Silicon									
1	Aminotrisilane........	$(H_3Si)_3N$........	107.34	liq.........	0.895^{-106}	-105.6	52	d.	....	s. eth.
2	Benzyltriethoxysilane..	$C_6H_5CH_2Si(OC_2H_5)_3$.	254.39	liq.........	0.9864_4^{20}	....	253	i.	i.	s. al., acet., eth.
3	Butyltrifluorosilane....	$C_4H_9SiF_3$...........	142.21	col. liq...	1.006_4^{25}	-96.6	52.4	d.		s. eth.
4	Carboxyethyl-dimethylsilane	$(CH_3)_2SiCH_2CH_2COOH$	131.23	n_D 1.4279....	....	22				
5	Chloromethylsilicane ..	SiH_2ClCH_3........	80.59	....	0.935^{-80}	-134.1	7			
6	Chlorotri-isocyanatesilane	$ClSi(NCO)_3$........	189.59	solid; n_D^{20} 1.437^{20} 1.4507	....	....				s. bz., CS_2, CCl_4

No.	Name	Formula	Mol. wt.	Crystalline form, color and index of refraction	Sp. gr. or density	Melting point, °C	Boiling point, °C	Cold water	Hot water	Alcohol, acids, etc.
	Silicon									
7	Di-p-aminoazobenzene fluosilicate	$(NH_2C_6H_4N_2C_6H_5)_2.H_2SiF_6$	538.57	long cinnamon br. need.	....	220 d.				187^3, 95 % al.
8	Di-p-aminobenzoic acid fluosilicate	$(NH_2C_6H_4COOH)_2.H_2SiF_6$	418.37	pr. wh. long, narrow		242				0.91^{25}, 95 % al.
9	Dianiline fluosilicate...	$(C_6H_5NH_2)_2.H_2SiF_6$.	330.33	irreg. wh. pl..	....	subl. 230	....	v. s.		s. h. al.
10	Di-p-biphenylyl diphenylsilane	$(C_6H_5)_2Si(C_6H_4C_6H_5)_2$	488.71	col. cr.......	1.14^{20}	170	570			0.40^{20} al., 36.46^{20} bz., 12.91^{20} pyr.
11	Dichloromethylsilicane.	$SiHCl_2CH_3$.........	115.02	....	0.93^0	−93	....			
12	Didiphenylamine fluosilicate	$[(C_6H_5)_2NH]_2H_2SiF_6$.	482.55	wh. rods forming rosettes		169				2.4492^{26}, 95 % al.
13	Diethoxydibutoxysilane	$(C_2H_5O)_2Si(C_4H_9O)_2$	264.45	col. liq.; n_D^{20} 1.4010	0.909	....	128^{32}	d.	d.	s. org. solv.
14	Diethylaniline fluosilicate	$(C_6H_5NHC_2H_5)_2.H_2SiF_6$	386.46	wh. pointed pr.	....	165.3	....			$.979^{26}$, 95 % al.
15	Diethyldichlorosilane ..	$(C_2H_5)_2SiCl_2$.......	157.13	col. liq.; n_D^{20} 1.4809	1.0504^{20}_4		129	d.		s. eth.
16	Diethylsilanediol......	$(C_2H_5)_2Si(OH)_2$.....	120.23	col. cr....		96	d. 140	s.		s. org. solv.
17	Dimethyoxdichlorosilane	$(CH_3O)_2SiCl_2$.......	161.07	col. liq......	1.2529^0_{15}	....	98–103			s. al., bz., eth.
18	Dimethylaniline fluosilicate	$(C_6H_5NHCH_3)_2.H_2SiF_6$	358.38	monocl. wh. need.						s. h. al.; i. c. al.
19	Dimethyldi(β-chloroethoxy)silane	$(CH_3)_2Si(OC_2H_4Cl)_2$	217.17	col. liq. n_D^{20} 1.4420	1.135^{25}_4		213	i.	i.	s. al., acet., eth.
20	Dimethylfluorochlorosilane	$(CH_3)_2SiFCl$.......	112.61	col. liq..,....	1.18^{25}_4	−85.1	36.4	d.	....	s. eth.
21	Dimethylsilicane	$SiH_2(CH_3)_2$.....	60.17	....	0.68^{-80}	−150	−20.1			
22	Di-α-naphthylamine fluosilicate	$(C_{10}H_7NH_2)_2.H_2SiF_6$.	430.47	rosettes of wh. need.	....	218	....			$.1504^{25}$, 95 % al.
23	Di-β-naphthylamine fluosilicate	$(C_{10}H_7NH_2)_2.H_2SiF_6$.	430.47	hex. wh. pl..	....	236.3	....			$.0816^{25}$; $.1248^{35}$, 95 % al.
24	Di-m-nitraniline fluosilicate	$(C_6H_4NH_2NO_2)_2.H_2SiF_6$	420.50	rhomb. wh. pl.	....	200				$.121^{25}$; $.4736^{35}$, 95 % al.
25	Dinitrosodiphenylamine	$[(C_6H_5)_2N=NO]_2.H_2SiF_6$	540.54	butterfly shaped indigo cr.		124.5				$.84^{25}$ 95 % al.
26	Diphenylarsinophenylene triethylsilane	$(C_2H_5)_3SiC_6H_4As(C_6H_5)_2$	420.51	liq., n_D^{20} 1.61455	1.1661^{21}_4	....	$279–281^{17}$			....
27	Diphenyldichlorophenoxysilane	$(C_6H_5)_2Si(OC_6H_4Cl)_2$.	437.40	col. liq., n_4^{20} 1.5510	1.2027^{20}_4	....	144	i.	i.	s. al., acet., eth.
28	Di-o-toluidine fluosilicate	$(C_6H_4NH_2CH_3)_2.H_2SiF_6$	358.41	wh. rhomb...						s. h. al.; i. c. al.
29	Di-m-toluidine fluosilicate	$(C_6H_4NH_2CH_3)_2.H_2SiF_6$	358.41	wh. rect. pr. pl.						s. h. al.; i. c. al.
30	Di-p-toluidine fluosilicate	$(C_6H_4NH_2CH_3)_2.H_2SiF_6$	358.41	wh. need., unst. irreg. outline						
31	Docosamethyl decasiloxane	$(CH_3)_{22}O_9Si_{10}$	755.63	n_D^{20} 1.3988....	0.926	....	100^{44}	i.	i.	s. bz.; sl. s. al.
32	Dodecamethylcyclohexasiloxane	$(CH_3)_{12}Si_6O_6$........	444.93	oily liq., n_D^{20} 1.4015	0.9672	−3	128^{20}	....		
33	Dodecamethylpentasiloxane	$(CH_3)_{12}O_4Si_5$........	384.85	liq., n_D^{20} 1.3925	0.8755	ca. −80	229^{710}	i.	i.	s. bz.; sl. s. al.
34	Eicosamethylnonasiloxane	$(CH_3)_{20}O_7Si_9$.......	665.47	liq., n_D^{20} 1.3980	0.918	....	$173^{4.9}$	i.	i.	s. bz.; sl. s. al.

No.	Name	Formula	Mol. wt.	Crystalline form, color and index of refraction	Sp. gr. or density	Melting point, °C	Boiling point, °C	Solubility in grams per 100 ml of		
								Cold water	Hot water	Alcohol, acids, etc.
	Silicon									
35	Ethyldiethoxy-acetoxysilane	$C_2H_5Si(OC_2H_5)_2(OCOCH_3)$ 206.31		liq., n_D^{20} 1.404	1.020_4^{20}	....	94^{16}	i.	i.	s. al., acet., eth.
36	Ethyldiethoxychloro-silane	$C_2H_5SiCl(OC_2H_5)_2$...	182.72	....	....	....	....	i.	i.	s. al., acet., eth.
37	Ethylisocyanatesilane..	$C_2H_5Si(NCO)_3$......	183.20	sol., n_D^{20} 1.4468	1.2192^{20}	183.5	....	sl. d.	....	s. bz., CS_2, CCl_4
38	Ethyltriethoxysilane...	$C_2H_5Si(OC_2H_5)_3$	192.33	liq., n_D^{20} 1.3853	0.9207_4^{20}	....	158.5	i.	i.	s. al., acet., eth.
39	Ethyltriphenylsilicane .	$(C_2H_5)(C_6H_5)_3Si$.....	288.47	rhomboidal pr.	....	76	....	i.		s. chl., bz., eth., acet.; sl. s. al.
40	Hexadecamethylcyclo-octasiloxane	$(CH_3)_{16}Si_8O_8$........	593.24	oily liq., n_D^{20} 1.4060	....	ca. 30	$175.^{20}$			
41	Hexamethylsilicane....	$Si_2(CH_3)_6$...........	146.38	col. liq......	0.723_4^{20}	12.5–14	112.5	i.	i.	s. acet., bz., eth.; col.
42	Hexamethylmethyl-enedisilane	$(CH_3)_3SiCH_2Si(CH_3)_3$	160.41	liq., n_D^{20} 1.4172	0.7520_4^{20}	....	134^{760}			
43	Hydroxymethyltri-methylsilane	$OHCH_2Si(CH_3)_3$....	104.23	liq., n_D^{25} 1.4169	0.8261_4^{20}	....	121.6			
44	Methylsilicane........	SiH_3CH_3......	46.14	....	0.62^{-67}	−156.4	31			
45	Methyltriethoxysilane .	$CH_3Si(OC_2H_5)_3$......	178.31	liq., n_D^{20} 1.3861	0.9383_4^{20}	....	151	i.	i.	s. al., acet., eth.
46	Methyltriphenyl-silicane	$(CH_3)(C_6H_5)_3Si$	274.44	....	....	67.3	....	i.		s. eth., chl., bz.; sl. s. al.
47	Octadecamethyl-octasiloxane	$(CH_3)_{18}O_7Si_8$........	607.31	liq., n_D^{20} 1.3970	0.913		$153^{5.1}$			s. bz., sl. s. al.
48	Octamethylcyclo-tetrasiloxane	$(CH_3)_8Si_4O_4$........	296.62	oily liq., n_D^{20} 1.3968	0.9558		175.0^0			
49	Octamethyltrisiloxane .	$(CH_3)_8O_2Si_3$......	236.54	liq., n_D^{20} 1.3848	0.8200	−80	153			s. bz.; sl. s. al.
50	Phenylenediamine fluosilicate(m)	$Si(C_6H_5CH_2)_4$	252.24	choc. br. need.-like pr.	....	243–4				0.065^{26}, 95% al.
51	Phenylenediamine fluosilicate(p)	$C_6H_4(NH_2)_2H_2SiF_6$...	252.24	pink irreg. six-sided pl.	....	d.				0.014^{26}, 95% al.
52	Phenylisocyanatesilane	$C_6H_5Si(NCO)_3$......	231.24	solid, n_D^{20} 1.5210	1.273^{20}	251.9	....	sl. d.	....	s. bz., CS_2, CCl_4
53	Phenyltrichlorosilicane.	$C_6H_5SiCl_3$...........	211.55	liq........	1.326_4^{13}	....	201.5	d.		s. eth., chl.; d. al.
54	Silicobenzoic acid......	C_6H_5SiOOH	138.20	col. flaky resin	....	40–50	215.6–			s. eth., bz., chl.; sl. s. al., ac. a.
55	Tetra-m-aminophenyl-silane	$(NH_2C_6H_4)_4Si$	396.57	solid		380				
56	Tetrabenzylsilicane....	$Si(C_6H_5CH_2)_4$........	392.62				127.5	i.		s. eth., chl., bz.; sl. s. al.
57	Tetra-p-Biphenylyl-silane	$Si(C_6H_4C_6H_5)_4$.....	640.91	col. cr.	....	283	600			0.049^{20} al.; 0.27^{20} bz.; 16.69^{20} pyr.
58	Tetradecamethylcyclo-heptasiloxane	$C_{14}H_{42}Si_7O_7$......	519.09	oily liq., n_D^{20} 1.4040	0.9730	−26	154^{20}			
59	Tetradecamethyl-hexasiloxane	$C_{14}H_{42}O_5Si_6$	459.00	liq., n_D^{20} 1.3948	0.8910	−100	142^{20}			s. bz.; sl. s. al.
60	Tetraethylsilicane.....	$Si(C_2H_5)_4$...........	144.33	liq., 1.4246	0.762^{25}	....	152.8–3.2			....

No.	Name	Formula	Mol. wt.	Crystalline form, color and index of refraction	Sp. gr. or density	Melting point, °C	Boiling point, °C	Solubility in grams per 100 ml of		
								Cold water	Hot water	Alcohol, acids, etc.
Silicon										
61	Tetraethylthiosilane	$(C_2H_5S)_4Si$	272.59	liq., n_D^{25} 1.5638	1.0860_4^{25}	−6	170^{12}	.....	.....	.....
62	Tetrahexyloxysilane	$(C_6H_{13}O)_4Si$	432.77	col. liq., n_D^{20} 1.4300	0.876	.....	$232-234^{13}$	d.	d.	s. org. solv.
63	Tetraisopropyl-mercaptane silicon	$C_{12}H_{28}S_5Si$	392.83	solid, n_D^{35} 1.5350	1.0099_4^{35}	335	$176-178^{13}$	.....	.....	.....
64	Tetramethoxysilane	$(OCH_3)_4Si$	152.22	col. liq., n_D^{20} 1.3681	1.0523	.....	$121-122^{759}$	d.	d.	s. org. solv.
65	Tetramethyl-mercaptanesilicon	$(CH_3)_4S_4Si$	216.48	solid, n_D^{20} 1.5989	1.1888_4^{25}	31	$144-146^{12}$	.....	.....	.....
66	Tetramethylsilicane	$Si(CH_3)_4$	88.23	col. liq.	0.651^{15}	.....	26.5	.....	.....	s. eth.; i. conc. H_2SO_4
67	Tetraphenoxysilane	$(C_6H_5O)_4Si$	400.51	col. cr.	.....	47-48	$415-420^7$	d.	d.	s. org. solv.
68	Tetraphenylsilicane	$Si(C_6H_5)_4$	336.51	col. flocc. amor. part.	.....	.....	.....	.....	.....	s. acet. anh. and chloro-sulphonic acid
69	Tetrapropoxysilane	$(OC_3H_7)_4Si$	264.44	col. liq., n_D^{20} 1.4015	0.918	.....	$225-227^{769}$	d.	d.	s. org. solv.
70	Tetratriethyl-siloxysilane	$Si[OSi(CH_3)_2C_2H_5]_4$	440.96	col. liq., 7_D^{20} 1.4112	$0.895_{15\ 6}^{20}$	−45	102^2	.....	.....	.....
71	Thioisocyanatotri-ethylsilane	$(C_2H_5)_3SiNCS$	173.35	liq., n_D^{20} 1.4944	0.934_4^{20}	.....	210.5	.....	.....	.....
72	Tolidine fluosilicate(o)	$(CH_3NH_2C_6H_3)_2H_2SiF_6$	356.39	tiny, micr. wh. pr.	.....	268-9	.....	.....	.....	$.013^{26}$, 0.41^{86} 95 % al.
73	Tri-p-Biphenylyl-phenylsilane	$(C_6H_5)_3SiC_6H_4C_6H_5$	412.61	col. cr.	1.10^{20}	174	580	.....	.....	0.238^{20} al.; 17.776^{20} bz.; 2.725^{20} pyr.
74	Trichloromethyl-triethyloxysilane	$CCl_3Si(OC_2H_5)_3$	281.64	col. liq., n_D^{20} 1.4320	1.8660_4^{20}	.....	81^3	i.	i.	s. al., acet., eth.
75	Triethylbromosilane	$(C_2H_5)_3SiBr$	195.18	col. liq., n_D^{20} 1.4561	1.777_4^{20}	.....	162	d.		s. eth.
76	Triethylchlorosilane	$(C_2H_5)_3SiCl$	150.73	col. liq., n_D^{20} 1.4314	0.8967_4^{20}	.....	144^{735}	d.		s. eth.
77	Triethylfluorosilane	$(C_2H_5)_3SiF$	134.27	col. liq., n_D^{20} 1.3915	0.9354_4^{20}	.....	$109-100^{745}$	d.		s. eth.
78	Triethylphenylsilicane	$(C_2H_5)_3(C_6H_5)Si$	192.38			149	230	.....	.....	.....
79	Trimethylchloro-methylsilane	$(CH_3)_3SiCH_2Cl$	122.67	col. liq., n_D^{20} 1.4180	0.8791_4^{20}	.....	97.1^{734}	.....	.....	.....
80	Trimethylethoxysilane	$(CH_3)_3Si(OC_2H_5)$	118.25	liq., n_D^{20} 1.3741	0.7573_4^{20}	.....	75^{745}	i.	i.	s. al., acet., eth.
81	Triphenylacetoxysilane	$(C_6H_5)_3SiOCOCH_3$	318.45	col. cr.	.....	91-92	.....	.....	.....	.....
82	Vinyltriphenoxysilane	$CH_2:CHSi(OC_6H_5)_3$	334.45	liq., n_D^{20} 1.5617	1.1300_4^{20}	.....	210.2^7	i.	i.	s. al., acet., eth.
	Silver									
1	Acetylene silver nitrate (complex.)	$Ag_2C_2.AgNO_3$	409.64	fine. nd. and crosses	.....	detonating pt. ca. 212				
2	Cycloocta-1,3-dienesilver nitrate	$C_8H_{12}.2AgNO_3$	447.94	col. need.	.....	150 d.				s. h. meth. al.
3	Cycloocta-1,4-dienesilver nitrate	$C_8H_{12}.2AgNO_3$	447.94	lg. col. hex. tab.	.....	110-1				sl. s. boil. meth. al.
4	Cycloocta-1,5-dienesilver nitrate	$C_8H_{12}.AgNO_3$	278.06	lng. col. need.	.....	135-6 (128.5-131)				v. s. meth. al.

No.	Name	Formula	Mol. wt.	Crystalline form, color and index of refraction	Sp. gr. or density	Melting point, °C	Boiling point, °C	Solubility in grams per 100 ml of		
								Cold water	Hot water	Alcohol, acids, etc.
	Silver									
5	cis-trans-1,3-Cyclo-octadienesilver nitrate	$C_8H_{12}.AgNO_3$......	278.06	wh. cr......		126–127.5 d.	....			sl. s. abs. al.
6	Cyclooctatetraene dimer silver nitrate	$C_{16}H_{16}.AgNO_3$......	378.18	pr......		153				s. h. al.
7	Cyclooctatetraenesilver nitrate	$C_8H_8.AgNO_3$......	274.03	lg. cr......		173 d.		d.		s. aq. $AgNO_3$; s. al.
8	Cyclooctatetraenyl-phenylketonesilver nitrate	$C_{15}H_{12}O.AgNO_3$.....	378.13	pa. yel. need.		121.4–122 d.				sl. s. abs. al.
9	Cycloocta-1,3,6-trienesilver nitrate	$C_8H_{10}.3AgNO_3$......	615.80	flat need....		138–9				sl. s. meth. al.
10	1,3,5-Cyclooctatriene-silver nitrate	$C_8H_{10}.AgNO_3$.....	276.04	cr......		125–6				sl. s. abs. al.
11	cis-Cyclooctenesilver nitrate	$(C_8H_{14})_2.AgNO_3$.....	390.28	lg. cr......		51				v. s. meth. al.
12	1,2-Dimethylcyclo-octatetraenesilver nitrate	$C_{10}H_{12}.2AgNO_3$......	471.95	cr......		142.5–144.5				s. h. abs. al.
13	Ethylcyclooctatetraene-silver nitrate	$C_{10}H_{12}.2AgNO_3$......	471.95	gray wh. cr...		124–125.5				i. eth.; sl. s. abs. al.
14	Ethylsilver......	C_2H_4Ag	135.93			d. >−40				
15	Methylcyclo-octatetraenesilver nitrate	$2C_9H_{10}.3AgNO_3$......	745.98	lt. yel. pr.....		123–124.5				sl. s. abs. al.; i. eth.
16	Methylsilver......	$AgCH_3$	122.90	yel.......		d. >−40				meth. al. 0.04^{-80}; al. 0.04^{-80}; amyl al. 0.06^{-80}
17	Phenylcyclo-octatetraenesilver nitrate	$C_6H_5.C_8H_7.AgNO_3$...	350.12	yel. gr. cr....		144.5 d.	....			i. c. eth.; s. h. abs. al.
18	n-Propylcyclo-octatetraenesilver nitrate	$C_{11}H_{14}.2AgNO_3$......	485.98	pa. yel. cr....		141 d.				s. h. abs. al.
19	Silver acetylide silver nitrate complex	$Ag_2C_2.6AgNO_3$......	1259.01	wh. rhomb....		d. >308		d.	....	i. acet.
	Sodium									
1	Bis(1-methylamyl)-sodium sulfosuccinate (Aerosol MA)	$C_{16}H_{29}NaO_7S$......	388.46	wh. waxlike pellets				34.3^{25}	44.7^{70}	s. acet., bz., glyc., CCl_4
2	Hydroxydionsodium (Viadril)	$C_{25}H_{35}NaO_6$......	454.54	wh. powd....		d. 193–203		s.	s.	s. acet., chl.
3	Sodium acetamide.....	$NaNHCOCH_3$......	81.05	wh. tabl.....		300–50 d.		d.	....	d. al.; sl. s. bz., liq. NH_3
4	Sodium acetylide (ethinylsodium)	$NaHC_2$..........	48.02	wh. cr.....		d. >210		d.		d. a.; s. liq. NH_3
5	Sodium anilide........	$NaNHC_6H_5$......	115.11	wh. cr. v. hygr.		d.		d.		d. a., al.; s. liq. NH_3
6	Sodium anthraquinone-β-sulfonate ("Silver salt")	$NaC_{14}H_7O_5S.H_2O$....	328.28	silvery leaf	....	d.		0.84	27	v. sl. s. al.
7	Sodium arsanilate (atoxyl, soamim)	$NaC_6H_7O_3NAs.6H_2O$	347.13	wh. cr. powd., monocl.				$16^{1.7}$		sl. s. al.; s. meth. al.
8	Sodium benzamide.....	$NaNHCOC_6H_5$......	143.12	wh. powd....		d.		d.		d. al.; i. eth., bz., chl.
9	Sodium-N-chloro-p-toluenesulfonamide	$NaC_7H_7O_2NClS.3H_2O$	281.69	col. pr......		expl. 175–180		s.	v. s.	....
10	Sodium ethoxide (sodium ethylate)	$NaOC_2H_5.2C_2H_5OH$	160.19	wh. powd. or need.		−$2C_2H_5OH$, 200	d.	d.	d.	v. s. al.; i. NH_3
11	Sodium, ethyl-.......	NaC_2H_5......	52.05	wh. cr., d. air		d.		d.		d. al., eth.; s. diethylzinc; i. bz., lgr.
12	Sodium-β-naphthoxide.	$NaOC_{10}H_7$......	166.16	wh. powd., v. hygr.		d.		s.		v. s. al., eth.; i. lgr.
13	Sodium-p-nitrobenzene isodiazotate	$NaC_6H_4O_3N_3.2H_2O$....	225.14	gold. leaf or need.	....	−H_2O over H_2SO_4	exp.	v. s.	....	

No.	Name	Formula	Mol. wt.	Crystalline form, color and index of refraction	Sp. gr. or density	Melting point, °C	Boiling point, °C	Solubility in grams per 100 ml of		
								Cold water	Hot water	Alcohol, acids, etc.
	Sodium									
14	Sodium-p-nitrophenoxide	$NaOC_6H_4NO_2.4H_2O$	233.15	yel. monocl. pr.	....	$-2H_2O$, 36; $-4H_2O$, 120	d.	5.97^{25}		sl. s. al.
15	Sodium-o-sulfo-benzoicimide (soluble saccharin)	$NaC_7H_4O_3NS.2H_2O$	241.20	wh. tabl....		$-H_2O$		v. s.		sl. s. h. al.
16	Triphenylborylsodium*	$NaB(C_6H_5)_3$	265.12	yel.-or. silky need.			d.	d.	d.	0.08^{18} eth.
17	Triphenylmethylsodium	$NaC(C_6H_5)_3$	266.32	red. cr.				d.		s. eth., bz., liq. NH_3
	Tantalum									
1	bis-Cyclopentadienyl-tantalum tribromide	$(C_5H_5)_2TaBr_3$	550.87	rust. cr.		280 d.		s.		sl. s. chl.;
2	Tantalumpenta-methoxide	$Ta(OCH_3)_5$	336.12	wh. solid.		50	189^{10}	d.		
	Tellurium									
1	Di-n-butyl telluride	$(C_4H_9)_2Te$	241.83	yel. oil	1.334^{40}		132–5			
2	Diethyl telluride	$(C_2H_5)_2Te$	185.72				137–8	sl. s.		
3	Diethyltelluroketone	$C_2H_5.CTe.C_2H_5$	197.74	yelsh., oily liq. n_D^{20} 1.5480	0.8821^{15}_4		$69–72^8$	i.	i.	v. s. eth., 95 % al. s.
4	Dimethyl telluride	$(CH_3)_2Te$	157.67	pa. yel. oil; garlic-like odor	....	sld. in liq. air	82.97^{770}			
5	Dimethyltelluroketone (Telluroacetone)	CH_3CTeCH_3	169.68	col. oily liq., n_D^{25} 1.4883	0.8578^{18}_4	....	$55–58^{10}$	i.	i.	s. eth., sl. s. 95 % al.
6	Dimethyltelluronium dibromide(α)	$C_2H_6Br_2Te$	317.49	or. leaf-like cr.		142 d.				s. al., eth.
7	Dimethyltelluronium dichloride(α)	$C_2H_6Cl_2Te$	228.58	leaf-like cr.		92		s.	s.	s. al., eth.
8	Dimethyltelluronium dichloride(β)	$C_2H_6Cl_2Te$	228.58	leaf-like cr.		134				s. al., eth.
9	Dimethyltelluronium diiodide(α)	$C_2H_6I_2Te$	411.48	red cr.		127 d.	....	i.	v. sl. s.	s. chl., bz.
10	Di-p-phenetyl ditelluride	$(C_2H_5OC_6H_4)_2Te_2$	497.52	or. brown need.	1.666	108	d. >108			s. lgr.
11	Ditelluromethane	CH_2Te_2	269.23	dk. red. amor. sld.	....	d. 124		i.	i.	i.
12	Ethylmethyl-tellurophetone	$C_2H_5CTeCH_3$	183.71	dark yel. oil, 1.5055²⁵	1.8711		63–6			
	Thallium									
1	Di-n-Butylthallium chloride	$(n-C_4H_9)_2TlCl$	354.06	col. pl. or flakes (from pyr.)	....	d. 240–250 (expl.)	....	sl. s.	....	s. hot bz.; 0.28^{30} al.; 2.98^{30} pyr; v. sl. s. eth.
2	Dicyclohexylthallium chloride	$(C_6H_{11})_2TlCl$	406.13	long col. need.	....	d. 210–230	....	v. sl. s.	i.	s. hot al., hot bz.; 1.34^{30} pyr.; i. eth.
3	Diethylthallium hydroxide	$Tl(C_2H_5)_2OH$	279.50	....		127–128		v. s.	....	v. s. al.
4	Di-n-hexylthallium chloride	$(n-C_6H_{13})_2TlCl$	410.16	col. pl.		d. 198		0.0117^{23}		s. pyr.; 0.123^{23} al.; 0.0304^{23} bz.; i. HNO_3
5	Di-n-hexylthallium nitrate	$(n-C_6H_{13})_2TlNO_3$	436.72	shiny flakes.		d. 271		0.008^{23}		0.1856^{22} al.; v. sl. s. bz.
6	Diisoamylthallium chloride	$(i-C_5H_{11})_2TlCl$	382.11	col. cr.		d. 253		sl. s.		0.31^{30} al.; 1.74^{30} pyr.
7	Dipropylyhallium chloride	$Tl(C_3H_7)_2Cl$	326.00	silvery leaflets		d. 200				s. eth.; i. HCl
8	Triethylthallium	$Tl(C_2H_5)_3$	291.56	yel. liq.	1.957^{23}_{23}	-63	192	....		....

* All of the tri-arylborines form analogous addition-salts of the alkali metals.

No.	Name	Formula	Mol. wt.	Crystalline form, color and index of refraction	Sp. gr. or density	Melting point, °C	Boiling point, °C	Solubility in grams per 100 ml of		
								Cold water	Hot water	Alcohol, acids, etc.
	Thallium									
9	Trimethylthallium.....	Tl(CH₃)₃..........	249.48	col. need....	....	38.5	147; may expl. 90	d.	....	v. s. bz., eth.
	Thorium									
1	Thoriumisotetra-propoxide	Th(OC₃H₇)₄.......	468.39	wh. cr.......	....	80⁰·¹	subl. 200–210⁰·¹	d.		s. bz.
	Tin									
1	Amyltetrathioortho-stannate(n)	Sn(SC₅H₁₁)₄....	531.52				162·⁰⁰⁴			
2	Amyltetrathioortho-stannate(tert)	[CH₃CH₂C(CH₃)₂S]₄Sn	531.52			44				
3	Bis(tributyltin) oxide..	(C₄H₉)₃Sn₂O.......	424.73	yel. liq.	1.17²⁵	....	254⁵⁰		0.1 %	
4	Bis(triphenytin) sulfide	(C₆H₅)₃Sn₂S.......	500.76	solid.		141–143				
5	Bromobenzenetetra-thioorthostannate(p)	Sn(SC₆H₄Br)₄.....	870.98			217				
6	Butylbenzenetetra-thioorthostannate(p)	Sn(SC₆H₄C₄H₉)₄...	779.81			106				
7	Butyltetrathioortho-stannate(n)	Sn(SC₄H₉)₄.......	475.41				136·⁰⁰¹			
8	Butyltetrathioortho-stannate(sec)	Sn(SC₄H₉)₄.......	475.41				111·⁰⁰¹			
9	Butyltin trichloride....	C₄H₉SnCl₃........	282.17	col. liq. 1.5244²⁰	1.7²⁰	–63	98¹⁰			s. org. solv.
10	n-Butylvinyltin dichloride	n-C₄H₉(CH₂:CH)SnCl₂	273.78	solid, n_D²⁵ 1.5334²⁵ 1.5254	1.533²⁵⁄₄	27–28	99–101³			
11	Carbomethoxyphenyl-trichlorostannane(o)	(CH₃OCOC₆H₄)SnCl₃	360.19	....	....	164				
12	Chlorobenzenetetra-thioorthostannate(p)	Sn(SC₆H₄Cl)₄.......	693.15			189				
13	Cyclohexyltetrathio-orthostannate	Sn(SC₆H₁₁)₄.......	579.56			53–4				
14	Diallylsdibutyltin.....	(C₄H₉)₂(CH₂:CHCH₂)₂Sn	315.07	liq., 1.4986	1.0999		93⁰·¹			
15	Diallyldiphenyltin.....	(C₆H₅)₂(CH₂:CHCH₂)₂Sn	355.05	liq., 1.6013²⁵ .	1.2688²⁵		173–174⁵			
16	Di-o-anisyldichloro-stannane	(CH₃OC₆H₄)₂SnCl₂ ..	403.86			113				
17	Dibenzyldiethyl-stannane	(C₆H₅CH₂)₂Sn(C₂H₅)₂	359.08	liq.........	1.+	<20	223–4²⁰	....	....	s. org. solv.
18	Dibenzylethylpropyl-stannane	(C₆H₅CH₂)₂(C₂H₅)(C₃H₇)Sn	373.11	liq..........	....	>0	220–5¹⁵			misc. all org. solv.
19	Dibenzyltin acetate....	(C₆H₅CH₂)₂Sn(OCOCH₃)₂	419.05	col. need. f. al.		136–7				s. acet. chl., bz.
20	Dibenzyltin dibromide.	(C₆H₅CH₂)₂SnBr₂....	460.78	col. need. f. pet.		130				s. acet., al., eth., chl., CCl₄
21	Dibenzyltin dichloride.	(C₆H₅CH₂)₂SnCl₂....	371.86	col. need. f. acet.-HCl		163–4				s. acet., al., eth., chl., CCl₄, h. ac. a.
22	Dibenzyltin diiodide...	(C₆H₅CH₂)₂SnI₂....	554.77	col. lng. silky yel. need. f. pet. eth.	....	86–7				s. acet., al., eth., chl., CCl₄
23	Dibutyldiphenyltin....	(C₄H₉)₂(C₆H₅)₂Sn....	387.14	col. liq., 1.5602	1.1882	....	180²			
24	Dibutyldivinyltin.....	(C₄H₉)₂(CH₂:CH)₂Sn	287.02	liq., 1.4824	1.1270	....	78–80²			
25	Dibutyltin diacetate...	(C₄H₉)₂Sn(OOCH₃)₂	326.99	col. liq., 1.482²⁰	1.32	10	142–145¹⁰	i.	i.	s. org. solv.
26	Dibutyltin dibromide...	(C₄H₉)₂SnBr₂.......	392.74	sm. need.....		20	118–170²⁸	i.	i.	....
27	Dibutyltin dichloride..	(C₄H₉)₂SnCl₂........	303.83	need. wh. 1.499⁵⁰	1.36⁵⁰	142¹⁰	d. 113.6⁶⁰	d.	d.	s. eth., bz., al.
28	Dibutyltin dilaurate...	(C₄H₉)₂Sn(OOC₁₁H₂₃)₂	631.55	oily liq., 1.474¹⁴	1.05	27	....		i.	s. ac., bz., eth., CCl₄
29	Dibutyltin oxide......	(C₄H₉)₂SnO........	248.92	wh. amorph. powd.	1.58	d.			i.	i. org. solv.

No.	Name	Formula	Mol. wt.	Crystalline form, color and index of refraction	Sp. gr. or density	Melting point, °C	Boiling point, °C	Solubility in grams per 100 ml of		
								Cold water	Hot water	Alcohol, acids, etc.
	Tin									
30	Dibutyltin sulfide.....	$(C_4H_9)_2SnS$........	264.99	col.-yel. lip., 1.58	1.417	....	....			
31	Dibutylvinyltin bromide	$(C_4H_9)_2(CH_2:CH)SnBr$	339.88	col. liq., 1.4970	1.3913	....	$96^{0.55}$			
32	Dibutylvinyltin chloride	$(C_4H_9)_2(CH_2:CH)SnCl$	295.42	liq. 1.4987^{20}..	1.2662^{20}	....	$112–114^4$			
33	Dichlorodi-m-tolyl stannane	$(CH_3C_6H_4)_2SnCl_2$....	371.86			39–40	....			
34	Diethyldibromo-dipyridinetin	$(C_2H_5)_2SnBr_2(C_5H_5N)_2$	494.84			140				
35	Diethyldiisoamyltin..	$(C_2H_5)_2Sn(C_5H_{11})_2$..	319.10		1.0725^{19}		$131^{13.5}$			
36	Diethyldiisobutyltin...	$(C_2H_5)_2Sn(C_4H_9)_2$....	291.05		1.1030		108.2^{13}			
37	Diethyldiphenyltin....	$(C_2H_5)_2(C_6H_5)_2Sn$....	331.03				$154–6^4$			
38	Diethylisoamyltin bromide	$(C_2H_5)_2(C_5H_{11})SnBr$	327.87		1.4881^{17}		137.5^{17}			
39	Diethylisoamyltin chloride	$(C_2H_5)_2(C_5H_{11})SnCl$..	283.41		$1.2994^{18.9}$		125.5^{13}			
40	Diethylisobutyltin bromide	$(C_2H_5)_2(C_4H_9)SnBr$..	313.84		1.5108		122^{17}			
41	Diethyl-n-propyltin bromide	$(C_2H_5)_2(C_3H_7)SnBr$..	299.81		1.5910^{21}		112.2^{16}			
42	Diethyl-n-propyltin chloride	$(C_2H_5)_2(C_3H_7)SnCl$..	255.36		$1.3848^{15.7}$		108^{17}			
43	Diethyl-n-propyltin fluoride	$(C_2H_5)_2(C_3H_7)SnF$...	238.90			271	....			6.93^{31}, meth. al.; 3.78^{12} al.; $.05^{31}$ bz.
44	Diethyltin...........	$Sn(C_2H_5)_2$........	176.81	sl. yel. oily liq.	1.654	< -12	150 d.	i.	i.	s. bz., eth., lgr., chl., CCl_4
45	Diethyltin dibromide..	$(C_2H_5)_2SnBr_2$....	336.63	col. need.....	2.068^{14}	63	232–3	s.	s.	s. eth., org. solv.
46	Diethyltin dichloride..	$(C_2H_5)_2SnCl_2$.......	247.72	wh. need....		84–5	220	s.	s.	s. HCl, org. solv.
47	Diethyltin difluoride...	$(C_2H_5)_2SnF_2$....	214.81	sp. pl. or long rhomb. tab. f. meth. al.		229	....			$.45^{31}$, al.; 2.64^{31}, meth. al.; 0.47^{31}, bz.
48	Diethyltin diiodide....	$(C_2H_5)_2SnI_2$....	430.62	wh. need.....		44.5–5.0	240–5 d.	v. sl. s.	sl. s.	s. org. solv.
49	Diethyltin oxide.......	$(C_2H_5)_2SnO$........	192.81	wh. powd....		infus...	....	i.	i.	s. HCl, dil. al., conc. alk.; i. org. solv.
50	Diisoamyltin dibromide	$(C_5H_{11})_2SnBr_2$....	420.79			−25 to −24				
51	Diisoamyltin dichloride	$(C_5H_{11})_2SnCl_2$....	331.88			28				
52	Diisoamyltin diiodide..	$(C_5H_{11})_2SnI_2$....	514.79	oily liq.....			$202–5^8$			
53	Diisobutyltin dichloride	$(CH_3)_2(CHCH_2)_2SnCl_2$	273.76	liq........	1.5012	9	135.5			
54	Diisobutyltin diiodide.	$(C_4H_9)_2SnI_2$........	486.73				290–5			
55	Diisopropyltin dibromide	$(C_3H_7)_2SnBr_2$..	364.69	pa. yel. hyg. cr.		54	....	d.	d.	i. org. solv.
56	Diisopropyltin dichloride	$(C_3H_7)_2SnCl_2$..	275.77	col. transp. cr.		80–4	....	s.	s.	s. al., h. bz., glac. ac. a.
57	Diisopropyltin oxide...	$(C_3H_7)_2SnO$........	220.87	d.			....	i.	i.	s. h. HCl; i. org. solv., alk.
58	Dimethyldibromo-dipyridinetin	$(CH_3)_2SnBr_2(C_5H_5N)_2$	466.78			172				
59	Dimethyldichloro-dipyridinetin	$(CH_3)_2SnCl_2(C_5H_5N)_2$	377.87			163				
60	Dimethyldiethyltin....	$(CH_3)_2Sn(C_2H_5)_2$....	206.88	col. liq......	1.2319^{19}	< -13	144–6	i.	i.	s. org. solv.
61	Dimethyldiisobutyltin..	$(CH_3)_2Sn(C_4H_9)_2$..	262.99		$1.1179^{20.1}$		$85^{16.5}$			
62	Dimethyldioctyltin....	$(CH_3)_2(C_8H_{17})_2Sn$....	375.21	liq., 1.4659	1.0168		$121–122^{0.2}$			
63	Dimethyldivinyltin....	$(CH_3)_2Sn(CH:CH_2)_2$	202.85	n_D^{25} 1.4720..	1.284_4^{25}		$120–121^{760}$			
64	Dimethylethylpropyltin	$(CH_3)_2(C_2H_5)C_3H_7Sn.$	220.91	....	1.2014_{20}^{20}		149–51			

No.	Name	Formula	Mol. wt.	Crystalline form, color and index of refraction	Sp. gr. or density	Melting point, °C	Boiling point, °C	Cold water	Hot water	Alcohol, acids, etc.
	Tin									
65	Dimethylethyltin iodide	$(CH_3)_2C_2H_5SnI$	304.73	1.5705[18]	2.0264$_{20}^{20}$		77–8[11]; 185–7[18]			
66	Dimethyltin	$[(CH_3)_2Sn]_x$	(148.76)$_x$	yel. sld				..i.	i.	i. org. solv.
67	Dimethyltin dibromide	$(CH_3)_2SnBr_2$	308.58	col. pr		74–6	208–13	s.	s.	s. org. solv.
68	Dimethyltin dichloride	$(CH_3)_2SnCl_2$	219.67	col. cr		90 (107)	188–90	s.		s. org. solv.
69	Dimethyltin difluoride	$(CH_3)_2SnF_2$	186.76	wh. fine pl			d. <360	4.66[30.7]		.08[31], al., 33[31], meth. al.
70	Dimethyltin diiodide	$(CH_3)_2SnI_2$	402.57	rhomb. wh	2.872	43 (30)	228	sl. s.	s.	s. org. solv.
71	Dimethyltin oxide	$(CH_3)_2SnO$	164.76	wh. powd	1.269	infus.	d.	i.	i.	s. a., NaOH; i. org. solv., NH$_4$OH
72	Dimethyltin sulfide	$(CH_3)_2SnS$	180.82			148				
73	Dimethylvinyltin bromide	$(CH_3)_2(CH_2:CH)SnBr$	255.72	solid n_D^{25} 1.5350	1.738[66]	59–61[27]				
74	Dimethylvinyltin iodide	$(CH_3)_2(CH:CH_2)SnI$	302.71	n_D^{25} 1.3762	2.033$_4^{25}$		57.5–59[5.2]			
75	Di-α-naphthyltin	$Sn(C_{10}H_7)_2$	373.02			200	d. 225			
76	Diphenyldivinyltin	$(C_6H_5)_2Sn(CH:CH_2)_2$	327.00	n_D^{25} 1.5949	1.3195$_4^{25}$		153–154[5]			
77	Diphenyldivinyltin	$(C_6H_5)_2Sn(CH:CH_2)_2$	326.98	liq., 1.5227[20]	1.3049[20]	143–144[5]				
78	Di(phenylthiol)-diphenylstannane	$Sn(C_6H_5)_2(SC_6H_5)_2$	491.25			65–65.5				
79	Diphenyltin	$Sn(C_6H_5)_2$	272.90	yel. amor. powd.		225.7; (126–30)		i.	i.	s. chl., bz., eth.; i. abs. al.
80	Diphenyltin dibromide	$(C_6H_5)_2SnBr_2$	432.72	col. cr		38	230[42]			s. al., eth.
81	Diphenyltin dichloride	$(C_6H_5)_2SnCl_2$	343.81	col. cr		42	333–7 d.	v. sl. s., d.		s. al., eth., lgr.
82	Diphenyltin difluoride	$(C_6H_5)_2SnF_2$	310.90			360				
83	Diphenyltin diiodide	$(C_6H_5)_2SnI_2$	526.71	col. cr		71–72	176–82[2]	i.	i.	s. org. solv.
84	Diphenyltin hydroxy-chloride	$(C_6H_5)_2Sn(OH)Cl$	325.36	amor. wh. powd.		187		i.	i.	s. conc. a.; i. org. solv.
85	Diphenyltin oxide	$(C_6H_5)_2SnO$	288.90	col. amor.		infus.		i.	i.	s. conc. a.; i. org. solv.
86	Diphenyltin sulfide	$(C_6H_5)_2SnS$	304.97	wh. cr		171–173				
87	Di-n-propyldibromodi-pyridinetin	$(C_3H_7)_2SnBr_2(C_5H_5N)_2$	522.89			128				
88	Dipropyltin dibromide	$(C_3H_7)_2SnBr_2$	364.69	col. need		49		v. sl. s.		s. org. solv.
89	Dipropyltin dichloride	$(C_3H_7)_2SnCl_2$	275.77	col. cr		81		v. sl. s.		s. org. solv.
90	Dipropyltin difluoride	$(C_3H_7)_2SnF_2$	242.87	leaf		205		0.22[32]		.93[32], al.. 1.91[32], meth. al.
91	Dipropyltin diiodide	$(C_3H_7)_2SnI_2$	458.68	col. oily liq		<−15	270–3	i.	i.	s. org. solv.
92	Di-m-tolylstannane	$(CH_3C_6H_4)_2SnO$	316.96	wh. amor. infus.				i.	i.	s. min. a.; i. org. solv.
93	Di-m-tolyl thiostannane	$(CH_3C_6H_4)_2SnS$	333.02			121.5–2				v. s. chl., bz., eth. acetate, pyr., eth.; s. HCl
94	Di-p-tolyltin	$(CH_3C_6H_4)_2Sn$	300.96	or.-yel. amor. powd.		111.5	d. <245			s. bz.
95	Di-o-tolyltin dichloride	$(CH_3C_6H_4)_2SnCl_2$	371.86			49–50				
96	Di-p-tolyltin dichloride	$(CH_3C_6H_4)_2SnCl_2$	371.86			49–50				
97	Ditriphenylstannyl-methane	$[(C_6H_5)_3Sn]_2CH_2$	714.05	wh. cr. sld		104.5				v. s. bz. eth., chl.; s. h. pet. eth.
98	Divinylbutyltin chloride	$(C_4H_9)(CH_2:CH)_2SnCl$	265.35	liq., 1.4970	1.370		82.84[3]			
99	Divinyltin dichloride	$(CH_2:CH)_2SnCl_2$	243.69	col. liq., 1.541	1.762		54–56[3]	i.	i.	s. bz., MeOH
100	Di-p-xylyltin	$[(CH_3)_2C_6H_3]_2Sn$	329.01			157	d. 240			
101	Dodecyltetrathioortho-stannate(n)	$Sn(SC_{12}H_{25})_4$	924.28			35.5				
102	Ethylchlorostannic acid	$H_2SnC_2H_5Cl_5$	327.03	col. deliq. pr		d.		d.		
103	Ethyldiisoamyltin bromide	$(C_2H_5)(C_5H_{11})_2SnBr$	369.95		1.3650		154–5[16]			

No.	Name	Formula	Mol. wt.	Crystalline form, color and index of refraction	Sp. gr. or density	Melting point, °C	Boiling point, °C	Solubility in grams per 100 ml of		
								Cold water	Hot water	Alcohol, acids, etc.
	Tin									
104	Ethyldiisobutyltin bromide	$(C_2H_5)(C_4H_9)_2SnBr$	341.90	....	$1.4089^{19.5}$	....	130.6^{11}			
105	Ethylmethylpropyltin-iodide	$(CH_3)(C_2H_5)(C_3H_7)SnI$	332.78	1.5548^{17}.....	1.8182^{20}_{20}	....	$108–11^{11}$; $226–307^{20}$ sl. d.			
106	Ethyl-n-propyldi-isoamyltin	$(C_2H_5)(C_3H_7)Sn(C_5H_{11})_2$	333.13		$1.0654^{21.9}$		141^{17}			
107	Ethylpropyltin dichloride	$(C_2H_5)(C_3H_7)SnCl_2$	261.76	need. f. lt. pet.	....	57-8	....	s.		s. eth., al.
108	Ethyl stannic acid	C_2H_5SnOOH	180.77	wh. amor. gel. or powd.		d. below red	heat	i.	i.	s. dil. min. a., KOH; i. al., eth., chl., xylene
109	Ethyltetrathioortho-stannate	$Sn(SC_2H_5)_4$	363.19					$105.^{001}$		
110	Ethyltin tribromide	$C_2H_5SnBr_3$	387.48	col. feath. cr.		310	....	s.		s. al.
111	Ethyltin triiodide	$C_2H_5SnI_3$	528.47				$181–4^{19}$			
112	Ethyltri-n-butyltin	$C_2H_5(C_4H_9)_3Sn$	319.10	1.4732	1.0783		129^{10}			
113	Ethyltri-n-propyltin	$C_2H_5(C_3H_7)_3Sn$	277.02				101^{10}			
114	Hexabutylditin	$[(C_4H_9)_3Sn]_2$	580.08	col. liq.	1.1480	198^{10}		i.	i.	s. org. solv.
115	Hexadecyltetrathio-orthostannate(n)	$Sn(SC_{16}H_{33})_4$	1148.71			53-54				
116	Hexaethyl disitannane	$[Sn(C_2H_5)_3]_2$	411.75				160^{23}			
117	Hexaethylditin	$[(C_2H_5)_3Sn]_2$	411.76	liq.	1.412^0		d. 270			
118	Hexaphenylditin	$[(C_6H_5)_3Sn]_2$	700.02	wh. cr.		232.5	d. <280	i.	i.	.029 eth.; 18.08 chl.; 7.82 bz.
119	Hexa-p-tolylditin	$[(C_6H_4CH_3)_3Sn]_2$	784.18	flat tabl. f. bz.		143.5	d. 335			sl. s. bz., eth.; v. sl. s. abs. al.
120	Hexa-p-xylylditin	$[(CH_3)_2C_6H_3)_3Sn]_2$	868.36	flat rhomb. tabl. f. bz.-al.		192.5	d. 368			$21^{30.4}$ bz.
121	Isopropylstannic acid	C_3H_7SnOOH	194.79	wh. amor.		d.	....	i.		s. dil. min. a., KOH; i. org. solv.
122	Isopropyltetrathio-orthostannate	$Sn(SC_3H_7)_4$	419.30				$92.^{001}$			
123	Isopropyltin tribromide	$C_3H_7SnBr_3$	401.51	pa. yel. deliq. pr.		112				s. glac. ac. a.; sl. s. h. bz., chl.; i. dry eth.
124	Isopropyltin trichloride	$C_3H_7SnCl_3$	268.14				75^{16}			
125	Methylstannic acid	$(CH_3)SnOOH$	166.73	wh. amor. powd.		infus.	....	i.	i.	s. a., alk.; i. org. solv.
126	Methyltetrathio-orthostannate	$Sn(SCH_3)_4$	307.09			31	$81.^{001}$			
127	Methyltin tribromide	CH_3SnBr_3	373.45	wh. need.		53-5	$210–11^{746}$	s.		s. eth., al., bz., lgr., hyd. by alk.
128	Methyltin trichloride	CH_3SnCl_3	240.08	col. cr.		43	171	s.		hyd. by alk.; s. org. solv.
129	Methyltin triiodide	CH_3SnI_3	514.44	lt. yel. need.		86.5		s.	s.	s. eth., al., bz., chl., meth. al.
130	Methyltribromo-dipyridinctin	$CH_3SnBr_3(C_5H_5N)_2$	531.66			203				
131	Methyltri-n-butyltin	$CH_3(C_4H_9)_3Sn$	305.07	1.4735	1.0898^{20}_{4}		121^{10}			
132	Methyltri-n-propyltin	$CH_3(C_3H_7)_3Sn$	262.99				93^{10}			
133	Phenylbenzyltin dichloride	$(C_6H_5)(C_6H_5CH_2)SnCl_2$	357.84	col. need. f. dil. HCl		83-4	80-100			
134	Phenyltetrathio-orthostannate	$Sn(SC_6H_5)_4$	555.37			67	....			
135	Phenyltin tribomide	$C_6H_5SnBr_3$	435.52				$182–3^{29}$			
136	Phenyltin trichloride	$C_6H_5SnCl_3$	302.16	col. liq.			$142–3^{26}$	i.	i.	s. bz., MeOH

No.	Name	Formula	Mol. wt.	Crystalline form, color and index of refraction	Sp. gr. or density	Melting point, °C	Boiling point, °C	Solubility in grams per 100 ml of		
								Cold water	Hot water	Alcohol, acids, etc.
	Tin									
137	Phenyltribenzyltin.....	$(C_6H_5)Sn(C_6H_5CH_2)_3$.	469.20	liq.........			290^5			s. all ord. org. solv. except al.
138	Propyltetrathioortho-stannate(n)	$Sn(SC_3H_7)_4$.........	419.30				$123^{.001}$			....
139	Propyltin triiodide.....	$C_3H_7SnI_3$.........	542.49				d. 200^{16}			
140	Propyltri-n-amyltin(n).	$C_3H_7(C_5H_{11})_3Sn$	375.21	1.4732.......	1.0368		163^{10}			
141	Stannic bisacetyl-acetone dibromide	$(C_5H_7O_2)_2SnBr_2$.....	476.73	col. six-sided cr.			187			s. bz., chl., acet.; sl. s. eth., CCl_4
142	Stannic bisacetyl-acetone dichloride	$(C_5H_7O_2)_2SnCl_2$......	387.82	col. six-sided cr.			202–3	s.		s. bz., acet.
143	Stannic bisbenzoyl-acetone dibromide	$(C_{10}H_{10}O_2)_2SnBr_2$....	614.98	pa. yel. powd.			213–4			sl. s. org. solv.
144	Stannic bisdibenzoyl-methane dibromide	$(C_{15}H_{10}O_2)_2SnBr_2$...	723.00	sulfur-yel. cr.			276–8	i.		sl. s. org. solv.
145	Stannic bis-3-ethyl-acetylacetone dibromide	$(C_7H_{11}O_2)_2SnBr_2$..	532.84	col. six-sided pr.		164–6				s. c. chl., bz.; sl. s. lt. pet.
146	Tetra-dl-amyltin......	$Sn(C_5H_{11})_4$.........	403.26	1.4730	1.0222		174^{10}			
147	Tetra-n-amyltin......	$Sn(C_5H_{11})_4$.........	403.26	col. stable liq., 1.4720	1.0206		181^{10}			
148	Tetraaquastannic bisacetylacetone stannibromide	$(C_5H_7O_2)_2Sn(OH)_4SnBr_6$	987.12	col. tab. pr...		105–7				s. bz.
149	Tetrabenzyltin........	$Sn(C_6H_5CH_2)_4$......	483.23	col. pr. f. lt. pet.		42–3		i.	i.	s. common org. solv.; sl. s. lt. pet.
150	Tetra-n-butyltin.....	$Sn(C_4H_9)_4$.......	347.16	col. stable liq., 1.4730	1.0572	< −70	145^{10}			
151	Tetracyclohexyltin....	$Sn(C_6H_{11})_4$.........	451.31	wh. micr. grains		263–4		i.	i.	6.25^{30} bz.; 0.86^{30} al.; s. chl. CS_2
152	Tetraethyltin.........	$Sn(C_2H_5)_4$.........	234.94	col. liq. $n_D^{19.7}$ 1.4724	1.187^{23}	−112	181	i.	i.	s. org. solv.
153	Tetra-n-heptyltin.....	$Sn(C_7H_{15})_4$......	515.48	1.4698.......	0.9748		239^{10}	i.	i.	
154	Tetra-n-hexyltin.....	$Sn(C_6H_{13})_4$......	459.37	1.4706.......	0.9959		209^{10}	i.	i.	
155	Tetraisoamyltin......	$Sn(C_5H_{11})_4$......	403.26	liq.........	$1.035^{19.6}$		188^{24}	i.	i.	
156	Tetraisobutyltin......	$Sn(C_4H_9)_4$......	347.16	col. liq......	1.054^{23}	−13	267; $143^{16.5}$	i.	i.	s. org. solv.
157	Tetralauryltin........	$(C_{12}H_{25})_4Sn$	796.02	1.4736^{20}	0.895	15–16		i.	i.	s. org. solv.
158	Tetramethyltin........	$Sn(CH_3)_4$......	178.83	col. liq. 1.4386	1.314^0	−54.8	78	i.	i.	s. org. solv.
159	Tetra-n-octyltin.....	$Sn(C_8H_{17})_4$......	571.59	1.4691.......	0.9605		268^{10}			
160	Tetraphenyltin........	$Sn(C_6H_5)_4$......	427.12	tetr. col. f. xylene	1.490^0	226	>420	i.	i.	s. h. bz., pyr., CCl_4, chl., ac. a.; sl. s. al.
161	Tetrapropyltin........	$Sn(C_3H_7)_4$......	291.05	col. liq.......	$1.1065^{20.2}$		222–5	i.	i.	s. org. solv.
162	Tetra-o-tolyltin......	$Sn(C_6H_4CH_3)_4$......	483.23	wh. cr. powd.		158–9 (215)		i.	i.	s. bz., eth.; i. al.
163	Tetra-m-tolyltin......	$Sn(C_6H_4CH_3)_4$......	483.23	col. need.....		128.5		i.	i.	s. bz., h. eth.; h. al.
164	Tetra-p-tolyltin......	$Sn(C_6H_4CH_3)_4$......	483.23	col. need.....		230–3		i.	i.	s. bz., chl., CS_2, pyr.; sl. s. al., eth.
165	Tetravinyltin.........	$(CH:CH_2)_4Sn$......	226.87	col. liq., n_D^{25} 1.4993	1.267_4^{25}		$55–57^{17}$			....
166	Tetra-m-xylyltin......	$[(CH_3)_2C_6H_3]_4Sn$.....	539.33	rhomb. need. f. bz.-al.		219.5	d. 360			$.314^{30}$ al.; 5.28^{30} eth.; 35.1^{30} bz.; 43.2^{30} chl.
167	Tetra-p-xylyltin.......	$[(CH_3)_2C_6H_3]_4Sn$......	539.33	wh. quad. pr.		272–3	d. 360	i.	i.	0.015^{30} al.; 1.73^{30} bz.; 2.80^{30} chl.; 0.29^{30} eth.; $.017^{30}$ meth. al.

No.	Name	Formula	Mol. wt.	Crystalline form, color and index of refraction	Sp. gr. or density	Melting point, °C	Boiling point, °C	Cold water	Hot water	Alcohol, acids, etc.
	Tin									
168	Tolylstannonic acid(o)	$CH_3C_6H_4SnO_2H$	242.83	amor. powd.		d. 295				
169	Tolylstannonic acid(m)	$CH_3C_6H_4SnO_2H$	242.83				d. 295	i.	i.	s. c. meth. al., al., eth., chl., eth. acet., pyr., a. and bases; i. pet. eth.
170	Tolyltetrathioortho-stannate(p)	$Sn(SCH_3C_6H_4)_4$	611.48		100					
171	Tolyltin trichloride(o)	$CH_3C_6H_4SnCl_3$	316.18		1.7619		$154-8^{20}$			
172	Tolyltin trichloride(p)	$CH_3C_6H_4SnCl_3$	316.18		1.7522		$156-7^{23}$	sl. d.		
173	Tolyltrichloro-stannane(m)	$CH_3C_6H_4SnCl_3$	316.18	col. liq.	1.7516	<-20	$150-1^{23}$			
174	Triallylbutyltin	$(CH_2:CHCH_3)_3(C_4H_9)Sn$	302.05	liq., 1.5162	1.3315		$116-119^{10}$			
175	Tri-n-amyltin bromide	$(C_5H_{11})_3SnBr$	412.03	1.4963	1.2678					
176	Tribenzylethyltin	$(C_6H_5CH_2)_3(C_2H_5)Sn$	421.15	col. tabl. f. al.-lt. pet.		$31-2$				s. eth. bz., chl.; sl. s. al.
177	Tribenzyltin chloride	$(C_6H_5CH_2)_3SnCl$	427.54	wh. need.		$142-4$	d.	i.	i.	s. ac. a., acet., bz., eth., chl. pyr.; i. al.
178	Tribenzyltin hydroxide	$(C_6H_5CH_2)_3SnOH$	409.10	rhomb., col. tabl.		$117-21$				s. h. al., CS_2, bz.; sl. s. eth., lgr.; i. KOH
179	Tribenzyltiniodide	$(C_6H_5CH_2)_3SnI$	519.00	need. like pr. f. glac. ac. a.		$102-3$				
180	Tributyltin acetate	$(C_4H_9)_3Sn(OOCH_3)$	349.08	wh., waxy solid	1.27	$80-83$		i.	i.	s. bz., MeOH
181	Tri-n-butyltin bromide	$(C_4H_9)_3SnBr$	369.95	1.5000	1.3365					
182	Tri-n-Butylvinyltin	$(n-C_4H_9)_3Sn(CH:CH_2)$	317.08	n_D^{25} 1.4761	1.085_4^{25}		114^3			
183	Triethyl-n-amyltin	$(C_2H_5)_3C_5H_{11}Sn$	277.02				102^{10}			
184	Triethyl(p-dimethyl-aminophenyl) stannane	$(C_2H_5)_3(CH_3)_2NC_6H_4Sn$	326.05	1.5610^{22}	1.2425		$172-3^3$			
185	Triethyl-o-hydroxy-phenyl stannane	$(C_2H_5)_3OHC_6H_4Sn$	298.98	1.5377^{25}	1.3229^{25}		$197-200^3$			
186	Triethylisoamyltin	$(C_2H_5)_3Sn(C_5H_{11})$	277.02		$1.1203^{20.1}$		$111^{18.5}$			
187	Triethylisobutyltin	$(C_2H_5)_3Sn(C_4H_9)$	262.99		$1.139^{20.3}$		96.5^{17}			
188	Triethylphenyltin	$(C_2H_5)_3Sn(C_6H_5)$	282.98	col. liq.	1.2639		254	i.	i.	s. al., eth., org. solv.
189	Triethyl-n-propyltin	$(C_2H_5)_3Sn(C_3H_7)$	248.97		$1.1680^{20.6}$		82^{13}			
190	Triethyltin	$(C_2H_5)_3Sn$	205.88	col. liq.	1.3774	<-75	161^{23}	i.	i.	s. al., org. solv.
191	Triethyltin bromide	$(C_2H_5)_3SnBr$	285.79	col. liq.	1.630	-13.5	$223-4$	v. sl. s.		s. org. solv.
192	Triethyltin chloride	$(C_2H_5)_3SnCl$	241.33	col. liq. $1.5017^{23.3}$	$1.4288^{23.3}$	15.5	$208-10$	i.		s. org. solv.
193	Triethyltin ethoxide	$(C_2H_5)_3Sn(OC_2H_5)$	250.94	col. liq.	1.2634		190	d.		s. org. solv.
194	Triethyltin hydroxide	$(C_2H_5)_3SnOH$	222.88	col. cr.		43	271	s.	s.	s. org. solv.
195	Triethyltin iodide	$(C_2H_5)_3SnI$	332.78	col. liq.	1.833	-34.5	225 (231)	v. sl. s.		s. org. solv.
196	Triisoamyltin bromide	$(C_5H_{11})_3SnBr$	412.03		$1.2613^{20.7}$	21	177^{15}			
197	Triisoamyltin chloride	$(C_5H_{11})_3SnCl$	367.57		$1.1290^{34.2}$	-30.2	174^{13}			
198	Triisoamyltin fluoride	$(C_5H_{11})_3SnF$	351.12	need.		288				1.03^{31} al.; $.967^{31}$ bz.; 1.22^{31} meth. al.
199	Triisoamyltin iodide	$(C_5H_{11})_3SnI$	459.02		$1.3777^{26.5}$	-22	182^{13}			
200	Triisobutylethyltin	$(C_4H_9)_3Sn(C_2H_5)$	319.10		1.0779^{21}		125^{16}			
201	Triisobutylisoamyltin	$(C_4H_9)_3Sn(C_5H_{11})$	361.18		$1.0356^{26.5}$		$152.9^{16.5}$			
202	Triisobutyltin bromide	$(C_4H_9)_3SnBr$	369.95		1.3523	-26.5	148^{13}			
203	Triisobutyltin chloride	$(C_4H_9)_3SnCl$	325.49		$1.1290^{34.2}$	$+30.2$	174^{13}			
204	Triisobutyltin fluoride	$(C_4H_9)_3SnF$	309.04	fine long pr.		244				$.414^{32}$ al.; 0.614^{32} meth. al., $.1^{32}$ bz.
205	Triisobutyltin iodide	$(C_4H_9)_3SnI$	416.94	col. liq.	$1.378^{26.5}$	-22	$284-6$			s. eth., org. solv.
206	Triisopropyltin bromide	$(C_3H_7)_3SnBr$	327.87		$1.4263^{25.2}$	-49	133^{12}			s. org. solv.
207	Triisopropyltin iodide	$(C_3H_7)_3SnI$	374.86		$1.4378^{22.2}$		151^{13}			

No.	Name	Formula	Mol. wt.	Crystalline form, color and index of refraction	Sp. gr. or density	Melting point, °C	Boiling point, °C	Solubility in grams per 100 ml of		
								Cold water	Hot water	Alcohol, acids, etc.
	Tin									
208	Trimethyldecyltin	$(CH_3)_3(C_{10}H_{21})Sn$	305.07	liq., 1.4602	1.0487	....	$67^{0.05}$	....	....	....
209	Trimethyldodecyltin	$(CH_3)_3(C_{12}H_{25})Sn$	333.13	liq., 1.4610	1.0285	....	$93-98^{0.15}$	....	....	....
210	Trimethylethyltin	$(CH_3)_3(C_2H_5)Sn$	192.86	col. liq.	....	....	108.2	i.	i.	s. org. solv.
211	Trimethyltin	$(CH_3)_3Sn$	163.80	col. liq.	1.570^{25}	23	182	i.	i.	s. org. solv.
212	Trimethyltin bromide	$(CH_3)_3SnBr$	243.70	col. cr. or liq.	....	27	165	s.	s.	s. org. solv.
213	Trimethyltin chloride	$(CH_3)_3SnCl$	199.24	col. cr.	....	37	154	s.	s.	s. org. solv.
214	Trimethyltin fluoride	$(CH_3)_3SnF$	182.79	wh. short. thick rect. pr.	....	360 seal. tube	d. <375	....	....	2.45^{31} meth. al.; 1.08^{31} al., 0.05^{31} bz.
215	Trimethyltin hydride	$(CH_3)_3SnH$	164.80	col. oily liq.	....	....	60	v. sl. s.	....	s. org. solv.
216	Trimethyltin hydroxide	$(CH_3)_3SnOH$	180.80	col. pr.	....	118 d.	subl. >80	s.	s.	s. a. al.,, bz., chl., CCl₄, alk.
217	Trimethyltin iodide	$(CH_3)_3SnI$	290.70	col. liq.	2.1432	3.4	170	v. sl. s.	....	s. bz., al., eth., acet.
218	Trimethyltin oxide	$[(CH_3)_3Sn]_2O$	343.59	wh. amor. powd.	....	d.	....	i.	i.	s. a., alk.; i. org. solv.
219	Trimethyltin sulfide	$[(CH_3)_3Sn]_2S$	359.65	lt. yel. oil	1.649^{25}	6	233.5	i.		s. org. solv., HNO₃
220	Triphenylallyltin	$(C_6H_5)_3(CH_2:CHCH_2)Sn$	391.08	wh. powd.	....	73-74	....	i.	i.	s. org. solv.
221	Triphenylbenzyltin	$(C_6H_5)_3Sn(C_6H_5CH_2)$	441.14	col. pl. f. al.	....	90	250^3	....	....	s. org. solv. except al.
222	Triphenylbutyltin	$(C_6H_5)_3(C_4H_9)Sn$	407.13	solid	....	59 60	222^3	....	....	sl. s. MeOH
223	Triphenylethyltin	$(C_6H_5)_3SnC_2H_5$	379.07	wh. pr. f. al.	1.2953^{62}	56	....	....	....	
224	Triphenylmethyltin	$(C_6H_5)_3SnCH_3$	365.05	col. tetr. f. eth.	$1.3113^{63.85}$	60-1	....	....	....	s. bz., chl., eth.
225	Triphenyl-α-naphthyltin	$(C_6H_5)_3Sn(C_{10}H_7)$	477.18	col. pr.	....	125	....	....	....	s. bz., chl., eth.
226	Triphenyltin	$(C_6H_5)_3Sn$	350.01	wh. powd.	....	232.5	d. 280	i.	i.	$.079^{30}$ al.; 7.82^{30} bz.; 0.92^{30} eth.; 18.1^{30} chl.
227	Triphenyltin bromide	$(C_6H_5)_3SnBr$	429.92	col. cr.	....	120.5	$249^{13.5}$	i.	i.	s. al., eth. org. solv.
228	Triphenyltin chloride	$(C_6H_5)_3SnCl$	385.46	col. cr.	....	106	$240^{13.5}$	i.	i.	s. org. solv.
229	Triphenyltin fluoride	$(C_6H_5)_3SnF$	369.01	fine pr.	....	357	....	sl. s.	....	sl. s. c. al., eth.
230	Triphenyltin hydroxide	$(C_6H_5)_3SnOH$	367.02	....	....	118	....	....	....	....
231	Triphenyltin iodide	$(C_6H_5)_3SnI$	476.91	4-sided monocl. wh.	....	121	$253^{13.5}$	i.	i.	s. org. solv.
232	Triphenyl-p-tolyltin	$(C_6H_5)_3Sn(C_7H_7)$	441.14	need. f. eth.	....	124	....	....	....	s. bz., chl., eth.
233	Triphenyl-p-xylytin	$(C_6H_5)_3Sn[C_6H_3(CH_3)_2]_2$	560.33	col. lng.hex. sheets f. al.	....	100.5	....	....	....	s. bz., chl., eth.
234	Tri-n-propyl-n-butyltin	$(C_3H_7)_3SnC_4H_9$	305.07	....	....	....	121^{10}	....	....	....
235	Tri-n-propylethyltin	$(C_3H_7)_3Sn(C_2H_5)$	277.02	....	$1.1225^{21.8}$	....	$117.5^{23.3}$	....	....	....
236	Tri-n-propylisobutyltin	$(C_3H_7)_3Sn(C_4H_9)$	305.07	....	$1.0841^{24.1}$	....	128^8	....	....	....
237	Tri-n-propyltin chloride	$(C_3H_7)_3SnCl$	283.41	col. liq.	1.2678^{28}	-23.5	123^{13}	....	....	s. org. solv.
238	Tri-n-propyltin fluoride	$(C_3H_7)_3SnF$	266.96	flat pr.	....	275	....	....	....	4.26^{31} meth. al.; 2.73^{31} al.; 0.118^{31} bz.
239	Tri-n-propyltin iodide	$(C_3H_7)_3SnI$	374.86	col. liq.	1.692^{13}	-53	$260-2; 141^{13}$	....	....	s. org. solv.
240	Tri-o-tolyltin bromide	$(C_6H_4CH_3)_3SnBr$	472.00	rhomb. tab f. al.	....	99.5	....	....	....	s. bz., eth.; sl. s. al.
241	Tri-p-tolyltin bromide	$(C_6H_4CH_3)_3SnBr$	472.00	rhbdr. f. al.	....	98.5	....	....	....	s. bz., eth.; sl. s. al.
242	Tri-o-tolyltin chloride	$(C_6H_4CH_3)_3SnCl$	427.54	short, thick pr. f. al.	....	99.5	....	....	....	s. bz., eth.; sl. s. al.
243	Tri-m-tolyltin chloride	$(C_6H_4CH_3)_3SnCl$	427.54	....	....	108	....	....	....	....
244	Tri-p-tolytin chloride	$(C_6H_4CH_3)_3SnCl$	427.54	rhomb. pl. f. al.	....	97.5	....	....	....	sl. s. al. bz., eth.
245	Tri-p-tolyltin fluoride	$(C_6H_4CH_3)_3SnF$	411.09	hairlike felted need	....	305	....	....	....	s. al.
246	Tri-p-tolyltin hydroxide	$(C_6H_4CH_3)_3SnOH$	409.10	....	....	108-9	....	....	....	....
247	Tri-o-tolytiniodide	$(C_6H_4CH_3)_3SnI$	519.00	rhomb. cr. fr. al.-eth	....	119.5	....	....	....	s. bz., eth.; sl. s. al.

No.	Name	Formula	Mol. wt.	Crystalline form, color and index of refraction	Sp. gr. or density	Melting point, °C	Boiling point, °C	Solubility in grams per 100 ml of		
								Cold water	Hot water	Alcohol, acids, etc.
	Tin									
248	Tri-p-tolyltiniodide....	$(C_6H_4CH_3)_3SnI$......	519.00	rhomb. pl. fr. eth.-al.	....	120.5	....			s. bz.,-eth.; sl. s. al.
249	Tritriphenylstannyl-methane	$[(C_6H_5)_3Sn]_3CH$.....	1063.05	wh. cr. sld...	....	128	....	i.	i.	v. s. bz., eth. chl.; s. h. pet. eth.; sl. s. c. pet. eth., al.
250	Trivinyldecyltin......	$(CH_2:CH)_3(C_{10}H_{21})Sn$	341.11	1.4820.......	1.0672	....	$90-94^{0.06}$			
251	Trivinylhexyltin......	$(CH_2:CH)_3(C_6H_{13})Sn$	285.00	1.4851.......	1.1266	....	$57-91^{0.03}$			
252	Trivinyloctylitin.....	$(CH_2:CH)_3(C_8H_{17})Sn$	313.05	1.4819.......	1.0865	$90-93^{02}$				
253	Trivinyltin chloride....	$(CH_2:CH)_3SnCl$.....	235.28	1.5235.......	1.5139	....	$59-60^5$			
254	Tri-p-xylyltin bromide.	$[(CH_3)_2C_6H_3]_3SnBr$...	514.08	lng. hex. cr. f. al.	....	151				s. bz., chl., eth.; i. c. al.
255	Tri-p-xylyltin chloride.	$[(CH_3)_2C_6H_3]_3SnCl$ ...	469.63	6-cornered col. f. al.	....	141.5				s. bz., chl., eth.; i. c. al.
256	Tri-m-xylyltin fluoride.	$[(CH_3)_2C_6H_3]_3SnF$ ...	453.17	fine felted need.	....	205				s. bz., eth., al.
257	Tri-p-xylyltin fluoride .	$[(CH_3)_2C_6H_3]_3SnF$....	453.17	fine lng. need.	....	247				sl. s. bz., h. eth., al.
258	Tri-p-xylyltin iodide...	$[(CH_3)_2C_6H_3]_3SnI$....	561.08	hex. tabl. f. al.	....	159.5				s. bz., chl., eth.; i. c. al.
259	Vinyltin trichloride....	$(CH_2:CH)SnCl_3$....	252.10	1.5361.......	1.9981	....	$63-65^{10}$			....
	Titanium									
1	bis-(cyclopentadienyl)-titanium diiodide	$(C_5H_5)_2TiI_2$........	431.90	purp..........		319 d.				sl. s. tol.; s. org. solv.
2	bis-(cyclopentadienyl)-titanium dichloride	$(C_5H_5)_2TiCl_2$.......	249.00	red-or......		289-291				sl. s. tol., chl., al., eth., bz., CS_2 CCl_4; i. pet. eth.
3	bis-(cyclopentadienyl)-titanium dibromide	$(C_5H_5)_2TiBr_2$........	337.91	dk. red cr....	1.920	240-3 (314 ± 2)	subl.			s. tol., org. solv.
4	Di(p-dimethylamino-phenol)[bis(cyclo-pentadienyl)]titanium	$[(CH_3)_2NC_6H_3OH]_2Ti(C_5H_5)_2$	450.44	maroon......		unst.				
5	Diphenyl[bis(cyclo-pentadienyl)]titanium	$(C_6H_5)_2Ti(C_5H_5)_2$....	332.30	or.-yel......		146-8 d.				s. CH_2Cl_2; i. pet. eth.
6	(Di-m-tolyl)[bis(cyclo-pentadienyl)]titanium	$(CH_3C_6H_4)_2Ti(C_5H_5)_2$	360.36	or.-yel......		135-40 d.				....
7	(Di-p-tolyl)[bis(cyclo-pentadienyl)]titanium	$(CH_3C_6H_4)_2Ti(C_5H_5)_2$	360.36	or.-yel......						i. pet. eth.
8	Methylaminotitanium trichloride	$(CH_3N)_2TiCl_3$......	213.34	bluish-grn. cr.	1.33^{25}	subl. 5-20	d. 75	s.		dil. HCl, dil. H_2SO_4
9	Monochlorotrieth-oxytitanium	$TiCl(OC_2H_5)_3$......	218.54	pa. yel. liq. ..			170^{16}			
10	Phenyltitanium triisopropylate	$(C_6H_5)Ti[(OCH(CH_3)_2)]_3$	302.27	wh. cr......		100-120 d.	....			s. pet. eth.
11	Tetraethoxytitanium ..	$Ti(OC_2H_5)_4$........	228.15	col. oily liq. supercooled, n_D^{25} 1.5082	1.1066^{25}	....	$133-135^5$			
12	Tetramethoxytitanium,	$Ti(OCH_3)_4$....	172.04	solid.......		210	243^{61}	i.	i.	i. bz.
13	Titanium isopropoxide,	$Ti(OC_3H_7)_4$........	284.25	liq.........	0.9550	20	58^1			
14	Titaniummonochloro-tri-2-ethoxyethoxide	$Ti(OCH_2CH_2OCH_2CH_3)Cl$	350.70	col. liq., n_D^{25} 1.516	1.203^{20}	....	182^1			
15	Titanium tetra-n-hexoide	$Ti[O:(CH_2)_5:CH_3]_4$	452.58	liq., n_D^{25} 1.483.	0.950^{25}	....	336			....
16	Titanium tetra-isobutoxide	$Ti[OCH_2CH(CH_3)_2]_4$	340.36	cr.; liq. n_D^{25} 1.475	liq., 0.960	30	269^{760}			....

No.	Name	Formula	Mol. wt.	Crystalline form, color and index of refraction	Sp. gr. or density	Melting point, °C	Boiling point, °C	Solubility in grams per 100 ml of		
								Cold water	Hot water	Alcohol, acids, etc.
Titanium										
17	Titanium tetra-*n*-pentoxide	Ti[O:(CH₂)₄:CH₃]₄...	396.47	liq. n_D^{25} 1.485	0.974²⁵	....	314	....	....	....
Tungsten										
1	*bis*-(Cyclopentadienyl)-hexacarbonmonoxide-bitungsten *bis*-(Cyclopentadienylbitungsten hexacarbonyl)	(C₅H₅)₂W₂(CO)₆.....	665.95	purp. red. cr.	....	240–2 d.	....			s. chl., CCl₄, CS₂; i. ligr.
2	Mesitylenetungsten tricarbonyl	(CH₃)₃C₆H₃W(CO)₃..	388.08	yel.........		160–165 d.	subl.			....
Uranium										
1	Uranium(IV)-dibenzoylmethane	U(C₆H₅COCH:COC₆H₅)₄	1131.04	vlt. blk. cr...	....	192–193	subl. vac.	....	....	v. s., bz.
2	Uranium(IV)-diethylamide	U[N(C₂H₅)₂]₄.......	526.55	grn. liq.....		35.5–36.5	....	d.		s. bz., s. eth.
3	Uranium(V)ethoxide...	U(OC₂H₅)₅.........	463.33	dk. brn. liq. .	1.711²⁵	....	160⁰·⁰⁵			s. al., eth. bz.; d. acet.
4	Uranium isipropoxide..	U(OC₄H₉)₅........	603.61	brn. cr......		100–104	192⁰·⁰⁰⁹			....
5	Uranium(V)methoxide.	U(OCH₃)₅........	393.20	red, cr. solid	....	210	subl. 190–210⁰·⁰¹	d.	....	s. eth., bz.
6	Uranium(V)2,2,2-trifluororethoxide	U(OCH₂CF₃)₅......	733.19	grn.-brn. solid	....	130⁰·⁰⁰⁸				s. eth., s. bz.
Vanadium										
1	*bis*-Cyclopentadienyl-vanadium dichloride	(C₅H₅)₂VCl₂.......	252.04	pa. gr. cr....		1.60 g/ml d >250				s. chl., al.; sl. s. eth., CS₂, CCl₄, bz.; i. pet. eth.
2	*bis*-Cyclopentadienyl-vanadium dibromide	(C₅H₅)₂VBr₂.....	340.95	dk. gn.		unst.				s. chl., CCl₄, lgr.
Zinc										
1	Di-*n*-butylzinc.......	Zn(CH₂CH₂CH₂CH₃)₂	179.60	liq........			81–2⁹	d.		
2	Diethylzinc..........	Zn(C₂H₅)₂..........	123.49	col. liq. ign. in air or Cl	1.182¹⁸	....	118	d.		
3	Dimethylzinc........	Zn(CH₃)₂..........	95.44	col. liq......	1.386¹⁰·⁵	−42.2	46	d.	....	d. al., a.; s. eth. xylene
4	Diphenylzinc........	Zn(C₆H₅)₂........	219.58	wh. cr......		107 (in H₂)	280–285 (in H₂)	d.		v. s. bz., eth., s. CHCl₃
5	Di-*n*-propylzinc......	Zn(CH₂CH₂CH₃)₂..	151.55	liq. n_4^{48} 1.4845		....	146; 39–40⁸	d.		
6	Di-*o*-tolylzinc........	Zn(C₆H₄CH₃)₂.....	247.64	wh. cr......		207–10	....			s. xylene; v. sl. s. pet. eth.
Zirconium										
1	*bis*-Cyclopentadienyl-zirconium dibromide	(C₅H₅)₂ZrBr₂........	381.23	col. cr......		260 d.	....	s.	....	....

SUBLIMATION DATA FOR ORGANIC COMPOUNDS

Compiled by Mansel Davies

The tables quote the parameters from what appear to be the best data in the literature expressed in the form

$$\log_{10} p(\text{mm}) = A - B/T$$

and the temperature range for which they apply. The corresponding heats and entropies (taking the standard state of the vapor to be

$$\Delta H \text{ (sublimation)} = 2.303 \, R.B. \text{ cal/mol.}$$
$$\Delta S \text{ (sublimation)} = 2.303R(A - 2.881) \text{ cal/mole } °K.$$

Compound	Temp. range °C	A	B	Ref.
Acenaphthene	18 to 37	11.758	4290.5	1
Acetamide	25 to 77	11.8468	4050.1	2
Acetic acid	−35 to +10	8.502	2177.4	3
" , m-cresyl ester	2 to 44	9.759	3170	14
Acetophenone, 1-chloro-	5 to 50	13.779	4740	14
" , 1-chloro-o-nitro	23 to 54	14.24	5413	14
" , 1-chloro-m-nitro	26 to 70	14.080	5700	14
" , p-methoxy	3 to 27	11.367	4056	1
Acetone, benzoyl	5 to 26	12.317	4375	1
Adipic acid	86 to 133	15.463	6757	4
Anthracene	65 to 80	12.638	5320	5
"	105 to 125	12.002	5102	6
" , 9.10 diphenyl	208 to 229	16.058	8213	22
Anthraquinone	224 to 286	12.305	5747	3
Arachidic acid	63 to 73	25.453	10,424	23
Arsine, diphenylcyano	23 to 53	10.724	4420	14
Azobenzene (cis)	30 to 60	9.652	3914	7
" (trans)	30 to 60	9.721	3911	7
Behenic acid	71 to 79	23.604	10,100	23
Benzanthrone	—	13.416	6030	8
Benzene	−30 to 5	9.846	2309	3
"	−58 to −30	9.556	2241	3
" , p-chloroiodo	30 to 50	9.819	3200	15
" , p-dichloro	10 to 50	11.985	3570	17
" , α-hexachloro	51 to 71	11.950	4850	14
" , β-hexachloro	95 to 117	11.790	5375	14
" , γ-hexchloro	60 to 92	15.515	6022	14
" , λ-hexachloro	55 to 75	12.635	5100	14
" , -hexamethyl		11.070	4215	37
" , 1,2,3-trichloro	16 to 30	10.662	3440	6
" , 1,2,4-trichloro	6 to 25	10.445	3254	6
" , 1,3,5-trichloro	9 to 28	9.176	2956	6
Benzil	45 to 67	12.708	5140	1
Benzoic acid	70 to 114	12.870	4776	9
" , p-hydroxy	125 to 160	13.623	6063	9
" , o-methoxy	80 to 95	11.871	4746	9
Benzophenone (stable)	16 to 42	17.46	4966	10
" (meta stable)	11 to 25	17.19	4818	10
Benzoquinone	—	10.00	3280	18
" , 2.6-dichloro	1 to 42	9.85	3670	18
" , trichloro	28 to 54	12.03	4630	18
" , tetrachloro	60 to 83	12.06	5170	18
" , p-xylo	0 to 20	11.53	4030	18
Bibenzyl	13 to 34	12.194	4386	1
Biphenyl	6 to 26	11.168	3959	1
Butyramide	25 to 68	12.739	4546	2
Butyramide	63 to 109	12.594	4513	2
Camphor	0 to 180	8.799	2797	3
Capramide	80 to 97	16.471	6577	2
" , N-methyl	30 to 52	14.594	5371	11
Capric acid	16 to 28	17.130	6119	23
Caproamide	65 to 95	13.328	4968	2
εCaprolactam	21 to 41	11.893	4339	34
Caprylamide	52 to 101	14.920	5783	2
Carbamic acid, n-butyl ester	19 to 43	14.582	4919	11
" , ethyl ester	19 to 43	14.090	4646	11
" , n-hexyl ester	18 to 41	14.748	5018	11
" , methyl ester	14 to 32	11.966	3883	11
Carbon tetrabromide (monoclinic)	22 to 46	9.3867	2841	12
(cubic)	48 to 56	8.5670	2579	12
Carbon tetrachloride	−64 to −48	9.089	2027	13
o-Cresol, 3,5-dinitro	17 to 51	14.140	5400	14
Cyclohexane	−5 to +5	8.594	1953	3
Cyclo-trimethylene-trinitramine	110 to 138	11.870	5850	16
Diphenylamine	25 to 51	12.434	4654	21
Dodecanedioic acid	102 to 123	17.728	8006	4
Eicosanedioic acid	107 to 122	18.185	8644	4
Enanthamide	72 to 93	13.617	5182	2
Ethane, 1.1:pp dichloro diphenyl tri-chloro	66 to 100	14.101	6160	14
" , hexachloro (cubic)	13 to 174	8.731	2677	26
" , hexachloro (triclinic)	13 to 174	9.890	3077	26
Ethylene dibromide	−21 to +8	9.884	2606	13
Ethylene, trans di-iodo	−8 to 20	5.86	2130	19
Fluorene	33 to 49	11.325	4324	5
Formic acid	−5 to +8	9.84	3160	36
2 Fuoric acid	44 to 55	14.62	5667	25
Hendecanoic acid	20 to 28	16.432	6037	24
Heneicosanoic acid	68 to 73	22.602	9642	24
Heptadecanoic acid	48 to 58	21.836	8769	24
Hydroquinone tetrachloro	77 to 86	10.08	4650	18
" , p-xylo	59 to 88	12.36	5280	18
Lauramide	76 to 95	19.169	7980	2
Lauric acid	22 to 41	19.897	7322	23

Compound	Temp. range °C	A	B	Ref.
Methane	−194 to −184	7.651	5169	3
" , triphenyl	52 to 76	12.661	5228	1
Myristamide	85 to 100	20.940	8746	2
Myristic acid	38 to 52	18.740	7291	23
Naphthalene	6 to 21	11.597	3783	5
1-Naphthol	25 to 39	13.074	4873	1
"	39 to 50	11.526	4389	1
2-Naphthol	25 to 39	13.356	5109	1
"	39 to 58	11.660	4579	1
Nonadecanoic acid	58 to 64	35.016	13,815	24
n-Octadecane	15 to 25	22.83	7995	27
Oxalic acid, anhyd.	60 to 105	12.223	4727	29
" , anhyd. (α)	38 to 52	13.17	5130	28
" , anhyd. (β)	38 to 50	12.57	4875	28
Oxamic acid	82 to 90	12.58	5639	30
Oxamide	80 to 96	12.57	5893	30
Palmitamide	91 to 105	22.690	9489	2
Palmitic acid	46 to 60	20.217	8069	23
Pelargonamide	80 to 97	15.249	5997	2
Pentadecanoic acid	38 to 48	23.110	8813	24
Pentaerythritol (tetrag.)	106 to 135	16.17	7528	28
" , tetranitrate	97 to 138	17.73	7750	16
Phenanthrene	37 to 50	11.388	4519	5
Phenol	5 to 32	11.421	3540	14
" , p-acetyl	47 to 75	12.216	5003	31
" , p-benzyl	40 to 62	12.600	5072	31
" , p-tert butyl	8 to 30	12.332	4402	31
" , 2-tert butyl-4-methyl	2 to 20	11.685	4036	31
" , 4-tert butyl-2-methyl	3 to 24	11.199	3952	31
Phenol, p-formyl	39 to 63	11.795	4762	31
" , p-methoxy	5 to 27	13.132	4624	31
" , o-phenyl	19 to 40	11.754	4331	31
" , p-phenyl	54 to 74	12.056	5068	31
" , 2:4:6-tritert butyl	18 to 40	11.507	4383	31
Phthalic anhydride	30 to 60	12.249	4632	32
Propionamide	45 to 73	12.041	4139	2
Pyrene	72 to 85	11.270	4904	5
Pyrrole 2-carboxylic acid	77 to 81	16.60	6633	25
Rubeanic acid	87 to 105	12.713	5515	30
Salicylic acid	95 to 134	12.850	4969	9
Sebacic acid	102 to 130	18.911	8395	4
Stearamide	94 to 106	24.449	10,230	2
Steraric acid	57 to 67	21.180	8696	23
Suberic acid	106 to 134	16.937	7472	4
Succinic acid	99 to 128	14.068	6132	4
d-Tartaric acid, dimethyl ester	35 to 44	16.610	5903	20
dl- "	42 to 85	16.127	5941	20
Thapsic acid	104 to 125	17.165	7885	4
2-Thenoic acid	42 to 50	13.53	5065	25
Thymol	0 to 40	14.201	4766	14
Toluene, 2,4,6-trinitro	50 to 143	15.34	6180	33
Tridecanoic acid	31 to 39	20.939	7764	24
Valeramide	60 to 101	12.846	4666	2

References

1. Aihara, Bull. Chem. Soc., Japan.
2. Davies, Jones and Thomas, Trans. Faraday Soc., 55, 1100 (1959).
3. This Handbook, 41st Edition, p. 2428 et seq.
4. Davies and Thomas, Trans. Faraday Soc., 56, 185 (1960).
5. Bradley and Cleasby, J. Chem. Soc., 1690 (1953).
6. Sears and Hopke, J. Amer. Chem. Soc., 71, 1632 (1949).
7. Bright et al., Research, 3, 185 (1950).
8. Inokuchi et al., Bull. Chem. Soc., Japan, 25, 299 (1952).
9. Davies and Jones, Trans. Farad. Soc., 50, 1042 (1954).
10. Neumann and Volker, Z. Physik. Chem. 161A, 33 (1932).
11. Davies and Jones, Trans. Farad. Soc., 55, 1329 (1959).
12. Bradley and Drury, ibid., 55, 1844 (1959).
13. Nitta and Seki, J. Chem. Soc., Japan, 69, 85 (1948).
14. Balson, Trans. Faraday Soc., 43, 54 (1947).
15. Ewald, ibid., 49, 1401 (1953).
16. Edwards, ibid., 49, 152 (1953).
17. Darkis et al., Ind. Eng. Chem., 32, 946 (1940).
18. Coolidge and Coolidge, J. Amer. Chem. Soc., 49, 100 (1927).
19. Broadway and Fraser, J. Chem. Soc., 429 (1933).
20. Crowell and Jones, J. Phys. Chem., 58, 666 (1954).
21. Aihara, J. Chem. Soc., Japan, 74, 437, 1953.
22. Stevens, J. Chem. Soc. 2973 (1953).
23. Davies, Malyaas and Blenhaym, Arkiv for Kemi
24. Thomas, M.Sc. thesis, Univ. of Wales, 1959.
25. Bradley and Care, J. Chem. Soc., 1688 (1953).
26. Ivin and Dainton, Trans. Farad. Soc., 43, 32 (1947).
27. Bradley and Shellard, Proc. Roy. Soc., 198A, 239 (1949).
28. Bradley and Cotson, J. Chem. Soc., 1684 (1953).
29. Noyes and Wobbe, J. Amer. Chem. Soc., 48, 1882 (1926).
30. Bradley and Cleasby, J. Chem. Soc., 1681 (1953).
31. Aihara, Bull Chem. Soc., Japan.
32. Crooks and Feetham, J. Chem. Soc., 899 (1946).
33. Edwards, Trans. Faraday Soc., 46, 423 (1950).
34. Aihara, J. Chem. Soc., Japan, 74, 631 (1953).
35. Seki and Suzuki, Bull. Chem. Soc., Japan, 70, 387 (1949).
36. Coolidge, J. Amer. Chem. Soc., 53, 1874 (1930).
37. Nitta et al. J. Chem. Soc., Japan, 70, 387 (1949).

HEAT OF FUSION OF SOME ORGANIC COMPOUNDS

Compiled by R. Loebel

Compounds in the following tables are listed in order of the increasing number of carbon and hydrogen atoms in the molecule. Melting points are listed in degrees Celcius and heats of fusion in calories per gram.

Formula	Name	M.P., °C	H_f, cal/g	Formula	Name	M.P., °C	H_f, cal/g
$CHCl_3$	Trichloromethane	−63.6	17.62	$C_4H_4O_3$	Succinic anhydride	119.0	48.74
CHN	Hydrogen cyanide	−13.4	74.38	C_4H_4S	Thiophene	−39.4	14.11
CH_2Cl_2	Dichloromethane	−95.14	16.89	C_4H_6	1,3-Butadiene	−108.9	35.28
CH_2N_2	Cyanamide	44.0	49.81	C_4H_6	2-Butyne	−32.26	40.80
CH_2O_2	Formic acid	8.3	66.05	$C_4H_6O_2$	Crotonic acid	72.0	25.32
CH_3D	Monodeuteromethane	−182.7	12.76	$C_4H_6O_2$	cis-Crotonic acid	71.2	34.90
CH_3Br	Methyl bromide	−93.7	15.05	$C_4H_6O_4$	Methyl oxalate	54.35	42.64
CH_4	Methane	−182.5	13.96	C_4H_8	Isobutene	−140.4	25.25
CD_4	Deuteromethane	−183.4	10.75	C_4H_8	cis-2-Isobutene	−138.9	32.30
CH_4O	Methanol	−97.8	23.70	$C_4H_8N_2S$	Thiosinamine	77.0	33.45
CH_4S	Methyl mercaptan	−121.0	29.35	$C_4H_8O_2$	Ethyl acetate	−83.6	28.43
CH_5N	Methylamine	−93.5	47.20	$C_4H_8O_2$	n-Butyric acid	−5.7	30.04
$CBrCl_3$	Bromotrichloromethane	−5.7	3.05	$C_4H_8O_2$	Dioxane	11.0	34.85
CCl_2O	Phosgene	−127.9	13.86	C_4H_9Br	sec-Butylbromide	−112.7	12.01
CCl_3NO_2	Chloropicrin	−64.0	48.16	C_4H_{10}	n-Butane	−138.3	19.18
CCl_4	Tetrachloromethane	−23.0	5.09	C_4H_{10}	Isobutane	−159.42	18.96
CS_2	Carbon disulfide	−111.5	13.80	$C_4H_{10}O$	n-Butanol	−89.8	29.93
$C_2HCl_3O_2$	Trichloroacetic acid	57.5	8.60	$C_4H_{10}O$	tert-Butyl alcohol	25.4	21.88
$C_2H_2Br_2Cl_2$	1,2-dibromo-1,1-dichloro-methane	−66.9	7.73	$C_4H_{10}O$	Ethyl ether	−116.3	23.45
				$C_4H_{12}Si$	Tetramethyl silane	−99.04	18.64
$C_2H_2Cl_2O_2$	Dichloroacetic acid	10.8	14.21	C_5H_8	Cyclopentene	−135.1	11.80
C_2H_3Br	Bromoethane	−139.5	11.44	C_5H_8	Isoprene	−145.9	16.80
$C_2H_3Br_3$	1,1,2-Tribromoethane	−29.2	8.16	C_5H_8	1,4-Pentadiene	−148.8	21.55
C_2H_3Cl	Chloroethane	−153.8	18.14	$C_5H_8O_3$	Levulinic acid	33.0	18.97
$C_2H_3ClO_2$	α-Chloroacetic acid	61.2	31.06	C_5H_{10}	1-Pentene	−166.2	19.81
$C_2H_3ClO_2$	β-Chloroacetic acid	56.0	35.12	C_5H_{10}	cis-2-Pentene	−151.4	24.25
$C_2H_3Cl_3$	Methyl chloroform	−30.4	4.90	C_5H_{10}	trans-2-Pentene	−140.2	28.48
$C_2H_3Cl_3$	1,1,2-Trichloroethane	−36.6	20.68	C_5H_{10}	Cyclopentane	−93.8	2.07
$C_2H_3Cl_3$	Chloral hydrate	47.4	33.18	$C_5H_{10}O_2$	Valeric acid	−59.0	27.83
$C_2H_3F_3$	1,1,1-Trifluoroethane	−111.3	17.61	C_5H_{12}	n-Pentane	−129.7	27.89
$C_2H_4Br_2$	1,2-Dibromoethane	9.93	13.79	C_5H_{12}	Isopentane	−159.9	17.05
$C_2H_4Cl_2$	1,2-Dichloroethane	−35.5	21.12	C_5H_{12}	2,2-Dimethylpropane	−16.7	10.79
C_2H_4O	Ethylene oxide	−112.5	28.07	$C_5H_{12}O$	Amyl alcohol	−78.9	26.65
$C_2H_4O_2$	Acetic acid	16.6	45.91	$C_6H_3Br_3O$	2,4,6-Tribromophenol	93.0	13.38
C_2H_5Cl	Ethyl chloride	−138.3	16.49	C_6H_4BrI	o-Bromoiodobenzene	21.0	12.18
C_2H_6	Ethane	−183.3	22.73	C_6H_4BrI	m-Bromoiodobenzene	9.3	10.27
C_2H_6O	Dimethyl ether	−141.5	25.62	C_6H_4BrI	p-Bromoiodobenzene	90.1	16.16
C_2H_6O	Ethanol	−114.5	26.05	$C_6H_4Br_2$	o-Dibromobenzene	1.8	12.78
$C_2H_6O_2$	Ethyleneglycol	−11.5	43.26	$C_6H_4Br_2$	m-Dibromobenzene	−6.9	13.38
C_2H_6S	Dimethyl sulfide	−98.3	30.73	$C_6H_4Br_2$	p-Dibromobenzene	86.0	20.55
C_2H_6S	Ethyl mercaptan	−121.0	19.14	$C_6H_4Br_2O$	2,4-Dibromophenol	12.0	13.97
$C_2H_6S_2$	Methyl disulfide	−120.5	23.32	$C_6H_4ClNO_2$	m-Chloronitrobenzene	44.4	29.38
C_2H_7N	Dimethylamine	−92.2	31.51	$C_6H_4ClNO_2$	p-Chloronitrobenzene	83.5	31.51
$C_3H_4O_2$	Acrylic acid	12.3	37.03	$C_6H_4Cl_2$	o-Dichlorobenzene	−16.7	21.02
$C_3H_5Br_3$	1,2,3-Tribromopropane	16.19	20.24	$C_6H_4Cl_2$	m-Dichlorobenzene	−24.8	20.55
$C_3H_5N_3O_9$	Trinitroglycerol	12.3	23.02	$C_6H_4Cl_2$	p-Dichlorobenzene	53.13	29.07
C_3H_6	Cyclopropane	−127.4	30.92	$C_6H_4I_2$	o-Diiodobenzene	23.4	10.15
C_3H_6	Propene	−185.3	17.06	$C_6H_4I_2$	m-Diiodobenzene	34.2	11.54
C_3H_6BrCl	Trimethylenebromochloride	−58.9	14.0	$C_6H_4I_2$	p-Diiodobenzene	129.0	16.20
$C_3H_6Br_2$	1,3-Dibromopropane	−34.2	16.10	$C_6H_4N_2O_4$	o-Dinitrobenzene	116.93	32.25
$C_3H_6Cl_2$	1,2-Dichloropropane	−100.5	13.53	$C_6H_4N_2O_4$	m-Dinitrobenzene	89.7	24.70
C_3H_6O	Acetone	−94.8	23.42	$C_6H_4N_2O_4$	p-Dinitrobenzene	173.5	39.99
C_3H_7Cl	2-Chloropropane	−117.2	22.48	$C_6H_4O_2$	Benzoquinone	112.9	40.97
$C_3H_7NO_2$	Urethane	48.7	40.85	C_6H_5Br	Bromobenzene	−30.6	16.17
C_3H_8	Propane	−181.7	19.11	C_6H_5BrO	p-Bromophenol	63.5	20.50
C_3H_8O	Propanol	−126.1	20.66	C_6H_5Cl	Chlorobenzene	−45.2	20.40
C_3H_8O	Isopropanol	−89.5	21.37	C_6H_5I	Iodobenzene	−31.3	11.43
$C_3H_8O_3$	Glycerol	18.2	47.95	$C_6H_5NO_2$	Nitrobenzene	5.7	22.50
C_3H_9N	Trimethylamine	−117.1	26.47	$C_6H_5NO_3$	p-Nitrophenol	113.8	41.70
$C_4H_4N_2$	Succinonitrile	54.5	11.71	$C_6H_5NO_3$	o-Nitrophenol	45.13	26.76

Formula	Name	M.P., °C	H_f, cal/g	Formula	Name	M.P., °C	H_f, cal/g
C_6H_6	Benzene	5.53	30.45	$C_8H_8O_2$	Phenylacetic acid	76.7	25.44
$C_6H_6N_2O_2$	o-Nitroaniline	71.2	27.88	$C_8H_8O_2$	o-Toluic acid	103.7	35.40
$C_6H_6N_2O_2$	p-Nitroaniline	147.0	36.50	$C_8H_8O_2$	m-Toluic acid	108.75	27.59
$C_6H_6N_2O_2$	m-Nitroaniline	114.0	40.97	$C_8H_8O_2$	p-Toluic acid	179.6	39.90
C_6H_6O	Phenol	40.9	28.67	$C_8H_9NO_2$	Hydroxyacetanilide	91.3	33.59
$C_6H_6O_2$	Pyrocatechol	105.0	49.40	C_8H_{10}	o-Xylene	−25.2	30.64
$C_6H_6O_2$	Quinol	172.3	58.84	C_8H_{10}	m-Xylene	−47.8	26.01
$C_6H_6O_2$	Resorcinol	110.0	46.22	C_8H_{10}	p-Xylene	13.2	37.83
C_6H_6S	Thiophenol	−14.9	24.90	C_8H_{16}	Ethylcyclohexane	−111.3	17.75
C_6H_7N	Aniline	−6.3	27.09	C_8H_{16}	trans-1,1-dimethylcyclohexane	−33.3	4.38
$C_6H_8N_2$	Phenylhydrazine	19.6	36.31	C_8H_{16}	cis-1,2-dimethylcyclohexane	−49.9	3.50
$C_6H_8O_4$	Glutaric acid	97.5	37.39	C_8H_{16}	trans-1,2-dimethylcyclohexane	−88.2	22.35
$C_6H_8O_4$	Methyl fumarate	102.0	57.93	C_8H_{16}	cis-1,3-dimethylcyclohexane	−75.6	23.05
C_6H_{10}	Cyclohexene	−103.5	9.58	C_8H_{16}	trans-1,3-dimethylcyclohexane	−90.1	21.01
$C_6H_{10}O_4$	Methyl succinate	19.5	35.72	C_8H_{16}	cis-1,4-dimethylcyclohexane	−87.4	19.82
$C_6H_{10}O_6$	d-Dimethyl tartrate	49.0	21.50	C_8H_{16}	trans-1,4-dimethylcyclohexane	−36.9	26.27
$C_6H_{10}O_6$	dl-Dimethyl tartrate	87.0	35.12	$C_8H_{16}O_2$	Caprylic acid	16.3	35.40
C_6H_{12}	Methylcyclopentane	−142.5	19.68	C_8H_{18}	n-Octane	−56.8	43.21
C_6H_{12}	Cyclohexane	6.6	7.47	C_8H_{18}	3-Methylheptane	−120.5	23.81
C_6H_{12}	Tetramethylethylene	−74.6	15.51	C_8H_{18}	4-Methylheptane	−121.0	22.68
$C_6H_{12}O$	Cyclohexanol	25.46	4.19	C_8H_{18}	2,2,4-Trimethylpentane	−107.3	18.92
$C_6H_{12}O_3$	Paraldehyde	10.5	25.02	C_9H_7N	Quinoline	−15.6	19.98
C_6H_{14}	2,2-Dimethylbutane	−99.0	1.61	$C_9H_8O_2$	Cinnamic acid	133.0	36.50
C_6H_{14}	2,3-Dimethylbutane	−128.8	2.22	$C_9H_8O_2$	Allocinnamic acid	68.0	27.35
C_6H_{14}	n-Hexane	−95.3	36.27	$C_9H_{10}O_2$	Hydrocinnamic acid	48.0	28.14
C_6H_{14}	Isohexane	−153.7	17.41	C_9H_{12}	Pseudocumene	−43.8	7.47
C_6H_{14}	2-Methylpentane	−153.7	17.38	C_9H_{12}	Hemimellitine	−25.4	16.65
$C_6H_{14}O$	Isopropyl ether	−86.8	25.79	C_9H_{12}	Mesitylene	−44.7	18.90
$C_6H_{14}O$	n-Propyl ether	−126.1	20.66	$C_9H_{18}O_2$	Pelargonic acid	12.35	30.63
$C_7H_5ClO_2$	o-Chlorobenzoic acid	140.2	39.27	C_9H_{20}	n-Nonane	−53.5	28.83
$C_7H_5ClO_2$	m-Chlorobenzoic acid	154.2	36.39	$C_{10}H_7NO_2$	Nitronaphthalene	56.7	25.44
$C_7H_5ClO_2$	p-Chlorobenzoic acid	239.7	49.23	$C_{10}H_8$	Naphthalene	80.2	35.06
$C_7H_5NO_4$	o-Nitrobenzoic acid	145.8	40.06	$C_{10}H_8O$	α-Naphthol	95.0	38.94
$C_7H_5NO_4$	m-Nitrobenzoic acid	141.1	27.59	$C_{10}H_8O$	β-Naphthol	120.6	31.30
$C_7H_5NO_4$	p-Nitrobenzoic acid	239.20	52.80	$C_{10}H_8O_2$	Methylphenyl propionate	18.0	22.86
$C_7H_5N_3O_6$	2,4,6-Trinitrotoluene	80.83	22.34	$C_{10}H_9N$	α-Naphthylamine	50.0	22.34
$C_7H_6N_2O_4$	2,4-Dinitrotoluene	70.14	26.40	$C_{10}H_{10}O_2$	Methyl cinnamate	36.0	26.53
$C_7H_6O_2$	Benzoic acid	122.4	33.89	$C_{10}H_{12}$	Camphene	51.0	57.0
C_7H_7Br	p-Bromotoluene	28.0	20.86	$C_{10}H_{12}O$	Anethole	22.5	25.80
C_7H_7I	9-Iodotoluene	34.0	18.75	$C_{10}H_{14}$	Durene	79.3	37.40
$C_7H_7NO_2$	o-Aminobenzoic acid	145.0	35.98	$C_{10}H_{14}$	Prehnitene	−7.7	20.0
$C_7H_7NO_2$	m-Aminobenzoic acid	179.5	38.03	$C_{10}H_{14}$	p-Cymene	−68.9	17.10
$C_7H_7NO_2$	p-Aminobenzoic acid	188.5	36.46	$C_{10}H_{14}O$	Thymol	51.5	27.47
C_7H_8	Toluene	94.99	17.17	$C_{10}H_{15}NO$	d-Carvoxime	71.5	23.29
C_7H_8O	Benzyl alcohol	−15.2	19.83	$C_{10}H_{15}NO$	1-Carvoxime	71.0	23.41
C_7H_8O	p-Cresol	34.6	26.28	$C_{10}H_{15}NO$	dl-Carvoxime	91.0	23.61
$C_7H_8O_2$	Dimethylpyrone	132.0	56.14	$C_{10}H_{20}O$	1-Menthol	43.5	18.63
C_7H_9O	p-Toluidine	43.3	39.90	$C_{10}H_{20}O_2$	n-Capric acid	31.99	38.87
C_7H_{14}	1-Heptene	−119.7	30.82	$C_{10}H_{22}$	n-Decane	−29.7	48.34
C_7H_{14}	Methylcyclohexane	−126.6	16.43	$C_{11}H_{10}$	2-Methylnaphthalene	−34.4	20.11
C_7H_{16}	n-Heptane	−90.6	33.78	$C_{11}H_{22}O_2$	n-Undecilic acid	28.25	32.20
C_7H_{16}	2-Methylhexane	−118.2	21.16	$C_{11}H_{24}$	Undecane	−25.6	34.12
C_7H_{16}	2,2-Dimethylpentane	−123.8	13.98	$C_{12}H_9N$	Carbazole	243.0	42.05
C_7H_{16}	2,4-Dimethylpentane	−119.9	15.95	$C_{12}H_{10}$	Diphenyl	165.5	30.40
C_7H_{16}	3,3-Dimethylpentane	−134.9	16.86	$C_{12}H_{10}N_2$	Azobenzene	67.1	28.91
C_7H_{16}	3-Ethylpentane	−118.6	22.78	$C_{12}H_{10}N_2O$	Azoxybenzene	36.0	21.62
C_7H_{16}	2,2,3-Trimethylbutane	−25.0	5.25	$C_{12}H_{11}N$	Diphenylamine	52.98	25.23
$C_8H_6Cl_4$	o-Tetrachloroxylene	86.0	21.02	$C_{12}H_{12}N_2$	Hydrazobenzene	134.0	22.89
$C_8H_6Cl_4$	p-Tetrachloroxylene	95.0	22.10	$C_{12}H_{14}O_4$	Apiol	29.5	25.80
C_8H_8	Cyclooctatetraene	−4.7	25.87	$C_{12}H_{24}O_2$	n-Lauric acid	43.22	43.72
$C_8H_8Br_2$	o-Xylenedibromide	95.0	24.25	$C_{12}H_{26}$	n-Dodecane	−9.6	51.33
$C_8H_8Br_2$	m-Xylenedibromide	77.0	21.45	$C_{13}H_{10}O$	Benzophenone	47.85	23.53
$C_8H_8Cl_2$	o-Xylenedichloride	55.0	29.03	$C_{13}H_{13}N$	Benzylaniline	32.37	21.86
$C_8H_8Cl_2$	m-Xylenedichloride	34.0	26.64	$C_{14}H_8O_2$	Anthraquinone	284.8	37.48
$C_8H_8Cl_2$	p-Xylenedichloride	100.0	32.73	$C_{14}H_{10}$	Anthracene	216.5	38.70

Formula	Name	M.P., °C	H_f, cal/g	Formula	Name	M.P., °C	H_f, cal/g
$C_{14}H_{10}$	Phenanthrene	96.3	25.0	$C_{19}H_{40}$	n-Nonadecane	32.1	40.78
$C_{14}H_{10}O_2$	Benzil	95.2	22.15	$C_{20}H_{42}$	n-Eicosane	36.8	59.11
$C_{14}H_{12}$	Stilbene	124.0	40.0	$C_{21}H_{44}$	n-Heneicosane	40.5	38.44
$C_{14}H_{28}O_2$	Myristic acid	53.96	47.49	$C_{22}H_{46}$	n-Docosane	44.4	37.67
$C_{16}H_{32}O_2$	Palmitic acid	61.82	39.18	$C_{23}H_{48}$	n-Tricosane	47.6	30.74
$C_{16}H_{34}O$	Cetyl alcohol	49.27	33.80	$C_{24}H_{50}$	n-Tetracosane	50.9	38.74
$C_{18}H_{14}O_3$	Cinnamic anhydride	48.0	28.14	$C_{25}H_{52}$	n-Pentacosane	53.7	39.13
$C_{18}H_{30}O_2$	Stearic acid	68.82	47.54	$C_{27}H_{56}$	n-Heptacosane	59.0	37.93
$C_{18}H_{34}O_2$	Elaidic acid	44.4	52.08	$C_{28}H_{58}$	n-Octacosane	61.4	39.14
$C_{18}H_{38}$	n-Octadiene	28.2	57.65	$C_{57}H_{110}O_6$	Tristearin	54.5	45.63

SOLUBILITY PARAMETERS OF
ORGANIC COMPOUNDS

While the solubility of organic compounds in selected solvents may be estimated from the "like dissolves like" rule of thumb, more useful information is available under the "Solubility" heading of the table "Physical Constants of Organic Compounds" in Section C of this book. This table provides qualitative data on solubility in water (w), ethanol (al), ethyl ether (eth), acetone (ace), and benzene (bz).

More quantitative solubility data for nonpolar organic compounds may be calculated from the Hildebrand expression for the square root of the cohesive energy density which is defined as the solubility parameter (δ). As shown by the following expression, δ values may be calculated if information for ΔH_v, Kelvin temperature (T), molecular weight (M), and density (D) is available:

$$\delta = \left(\frac{\Delta F_v}{V}\right)^{1/2} = \left(\frac{D(\Delta H_v - RT)}{M}\right)^{1/2}$$

The value for ΔH_v may be found in the table "Heats of Vaporization of Organic Compounds" immediately following this table. Values for D and M are listed under physical constants in Section C. Thus, the δ value for heptane may be calculated as follows:

$$\delta = \left[\frac{0.684\,(8670 - 1.99(298))}{100}\right]^{1/2} = 7.4\ H$$

The dimensions for δ are (cal cm^{-3})$^{1/2}$ but the Hildebrand unit (H) is used for convenience. It is important to note that the law of mixtures applies for δ values of mixed nonpolar solvents. Thus, the δ value for an equimolar mixture of heptane and carbon disulfide (δ = 10.0 H) is 8.7 H.

When ΔH_v values are not available, Small's molar attraction constants shown in Table I may be used.[a] As illustrated in the following expression which is solved for heptane, the summation of these constants (ΣG) may be used to estimate δ values at 298 K:

$$\delta = \frac{D\Sigma G}{M} = \frac{(2 \times 214) + 5(133)0.684}{100} = 7.5\ H$$

Solvents such as acetone (δ = 9.9 H) and water (δ = 23.4 H) are completely miscible when a large difference in δ values exists. The critical δ range for solubility of solid solutes and liquid solutes is less than that for liquids, and the critical δ range for nonpolar polymers in nonpolar liquids is less than 2 H at temperatures below 50°C.

These δ values are most useful for nonpolar solvents that are listed in Section A of Table II. Some consideration must be given to the dipole-dipole interactions in more polar solvents that are listed in Section B of Table II. The values shown for hydrogen-bonded solvents that are shown in Section C of Table II must be used with more discretion because of the stronger intermolecular forces present. However, these values are much more useful than the "like dissolves like" rule of thumb and can be used to predict the solubility of most solutes in most solvents.

[a]Small, P. A., *J. Appl. Chem.*, 3, 71, 1953.

Table I

MOLAR-ATTRACTION CONSTANTS AT 298 K

Group	G
-CH$_3$	214
-CH$_2$- single bonded	133
-CH<	28
>C<	-93
CH$_2$=	190
-CH= double bonded	111
>C=	19
CH≡C-	285
-C≡C-	222
Phenyl	735

Table I (continued)
MOLAR-ATTRACTION CONSTANTS AT 298 K

Group	G
Phenylene (o,m,p)	658
Naphthyl	1146
Ring, 5 membered	105–115
Ring, 6 membered	95–105
Conjugation	20–30
H (variable)	80–100
O ether	70
CO ketones	275
COO esters	310
CN	410
Cl (mean)	260
Cl single	270
Cl twinned as in >CCl$_2$	260
Cl triple as in –CCl$_3$	250
Br single	340
I single	425
CF$_2$ \} n-fluorocarbons only	150
CF$_3$ /	274
S sulfides	225
SH thiols	315
ONO$_2$ nitrates	~440
NO$_2$ (aliphatic nitro-compounds)	~440
PO$_4$ (organic phosphates)	~500
Si (in silicones)	–38

Table compiled by R. B. Seymour.

Table II
SOLUBILITY PARAMETER VALUES

A. Nonpolar Solvents

Name	δ (H)
Acetic acid nitrile (acetonitrile)	11.9
Anthracene	9.9
Benzene	9.2
Benzene, chloro	9.5
Benzene, 1,2-dichloro	10.0
Benzene, ethyl	8.8
Benzene, isopropyl (cumene)	8.5
Benzene, 1-isopropyl-4-methyl (ρ-cymene)	8.2
Benzene, nitro	10.0
Benzene, propyl	8.6
Benzene, 1,3,5-trimethyl (mesitylene)	8.8
Benzoic acid nitrile (benzonitrile)	8.4
Biphenyl, perchloro	8.8
1,3-Butadiene	7.1
1,3-Butadiene, 2-methyl (isoprene)	7.4

Table II (continued)
SOLUBILITY PARAMETER VALUES
A. Nonpolar Solvents

Name	δ (H)
Butane	6.8
Butanoic acid nitrile	10.5
Carbon disulfide	10.0
Carbon tetrachloride	8.6
Chloroform	9.3
Cyclohexane	8.2
Cyclohexane, methyl	7.8
Cyclohexane, perfluoro	6.0
Cyclopentane	8.7
Decalin	8.8
Decane	8.0
Dimethyl sulfide	9.4
Ethane	6.0
Ethane, bromo (ethyl bromide)	9.6
Ethane, chloro (ethyl chloride)	9.2
Ethane, 1,2-dibromo	10.4
Ethane, 1,1-dichloro (ethylidene chloride)	8.9
Ethane, difluoro-tetrachloro (Freon 112®)	7.8
Ethane, nitro	11.1
Ethane, pentachloro	9.4
Ethane, 1,1,2,2-tetrachloro	9.7
Ethanethiol (ethyl mercaptan)	9.2
Ethane, 1,1,2-trichloro	9.6
Ethane trichloro-trifluoro (Freon 113®)	7.3
Ethene, (ethylene)	6.1
Ethene, tetrachloro (perchloroethylene)	9.3
Ethene, trichloro	9.2
Heptane	7.4
Heptane, perfluoro	5.8
Hexane	7.3
Hexene-1	7.4
Malonic acid dinitrile (malononitrile)	15.1
Methane	5.4
Methane, bromo	9.6
Methane, dichloro (methylene chloride)	9.7
Methane, dichloro-difluoro (Freon 12®)	5.5
Methane, dichloro, manofluoro (Freon 21®)	8.3
Methane, nitro	12.7
Methane, tetrachloro-difluoro (Freon 112®)	7.8
Methane, trichloro-monofluoro (Freon 11®)	7.6
Naphthalene	9.9
Nonane	7.8
Octane	7.6
Pentane	7.0
Pentane, 1-bromo	7.6
Pentane, 1-chloro	8.3
Pentanoic acid, nitrile (valeronitrile)	9.6

Table II (continued)
SOLUBILITY PARAMETER VALUES

Name	δ (H)
Pentene-1	6.9
Phenanthrene	9.8
Propane	6.4
Propane, 1-bromo	8.9
Propane, 2,2-dimethyl (neopentane)	6.3
Propane, 1-nitro	16.3
Propane-2-nitro	9.9
Propene (propylene)	6.5
Propene, 2-methyl (isobutylene)	6.7
Propenoic acid nitrile (acrylonitrile)	10.5
Propionic acid nitrile	10.8
Styrene	9.3
Terphenyl, hydrogenated	9.0
Tetralin	9.5
Toluene	8.9
Xylene, m-	8.8

B. Moderately Polar Solvents

Name	δ (H)
Acetic acid, butyl ester	8.5
Acetic acid, ethyl ester	9.1
Acetic acid, methyl ester	9.6
Acetic acid, pentyl ester	8.0
Acetic acid, propyl ester	8.8
Acetic acid amide, N,N-diethyl	9.9
Acetic acid amide, N,N-dimethyl	10.8
Acrylic acid, butyl ester	8.4
Acrylic acid, ethyl ester	8.6
Acrylic acid, methyl ester	8.9
Adipic acid, dioctyl ester	8.7
Aniline, N,N-dimethyl	9.7
Benzene, 1-methoxy-4-propenyl (anethole)	8.4
Benzoic acid, ethyl ester	8.2
Benzoic acid, methyl ester	10.5
Butanal	9.0
Butane, 1-iodo	8.6
Butanoic acid, 4-hydroxylactone (butyrolactone)	12.6
2-Butanone	9.3
Carbonic acid, diethyl ester	8.8
Carbonic acid, dimethyl ester	9.9
Cyclohexanone	9.9
Cyclopentanone	10.4
2-Decanone	7.8
Diethylene glycol, monobutyl ether (butyl carbitol)	9.5
Diethylene glycol, monoethyl ether (ethyl carbitol)	10.2
Dimethyl sulfoxide	12.0
1,4-Dioxane	10.0

Table II (continued)
SOLUBILITY PARAMETER VALUES

B. Moderately Polar Solvents (continued)

Name	δ (H)
Ethene, chloro (vinyl chloride)	7.8
Ether, 1,1-dichloroethyl	10.0
Ether, diethyl	7.4
Ether, dimethyl	8.8
Ether, dipropyl	7.8
Ethylene glycol, monobutyl ether (butyl Cellosolve®)	9.5
Ethylene glycol, monoethyl ether (ethyl Cellosolve)	10.5
Ethylene glycol, monomethyl ether (methyl Cellosolve)	11.4
Formic acid amide, N,N-diethyl	10.6
Formic acid amide, N,N-dimethyl	12.1
Formic acid, ethyl ester	9.4
Formic acid, methyl ester	10.2
Formic acid, 2-methylbutyl ester	8.0
Formic acid, propyl ester	9.2
Furan	9.4
Furan, tetrahydro	9.1
Furfural	11.2
2-Heptanone	8.5
Hexanoic acid, 6-aminolactam (ε-caprolactam)	12.7
Hexanoic acid, 6-hydroxylactone (caprolactone)	10.1
Isophorone	9.1
Lactic acid, butyl ester	9.4
Lactic acid, ethyl ester	10.0
Methacrylic acid, butyl ester	8.3
Methacrylic acid, ethyl ester	8.5
Methacrylic acid, methyl ester	8.8
Oxalic acid, diethyl ester	8.6
Oxalic acid, dimethyl ester	11.0
Oxirane (ethylene oxide)	11.1
Pentane, 1-iodo	8.4
2-Pentanone	8.7
Pentanone-2,4-hydroxy,4-methyl (diacetone alcohol)	9.2
Pentanone-2,4-methyl (mesityl oxide)	9.0
Phosphoric acid, triphenyl ester	8.6
Phosphoric acid, tri-2-tolyl ester	8.4
Phthalic acid, dibutyl ester	9.3
Phthalic acid, diethyl ester	10.0
Phthalic acid, dihexyl ester	8.9
Phthalic acid, dimethyl ester	10.7
Phthalic acid, di-2-methylnonyl ester	7.2
Phthalic acid, dioctyl ester	7.9
Phthalic acid, dipentyl ester	9.1
Phthalic acid, dipropyl ester	9.7
Propane, 1,2-epoxy (propylene oxide)	9.2
Propionic acid, ethyl ester	8.4
Propionic acid, methyl ester	8.9
4-Pyrone	13.4

Table II (continued)
SOLUBILITY PARAMETER VALUES
B. Moderately Polar Solvents (continued)

Name	δ (H)
2-Pyrrolidone, 1-methyl	11.3
Sebacic acid, dibutyl ester	9.2
Sebacic acid, dioctyl ester	8.6
Stearic acid, butyl ester	7.5
Sulfone, diethyl	12.4
Sulfone, dimethyl	14.5
Sulfone, dipropyl	11.3

C. Hydrogen-bonded Solvents

Name	δ (H)
Acetic acid	10.1
Acetic acid amide, *N*-ethyl	12.3
Acetic acid, dichloro	11.0
Acetic acid, anhydride	10.3
Acrylic acid	12.0
Amine, diethyl	8.0
Amine, ethyl	10.0
Amine, methyl	11.2
Ammonia	16.3
Aniline	10.3
1,3-Butanediol	11.6
1,4-Butanediol	12.1
2,3-Butanediol	11.1
1-Butanol	11.4
2-Butanol	10.8
1-Butanol, 2-ethyl	10.5
1-Butanol, 2-methyl	10.0
Butyric acid	10.5
Cyclohexanol	11.4
Diethylene glycol	12.1
1-Dodecanol	8.1
Ethanol	12.7
Ethanol, 2-chloro (ethylene chlorohydrin)	12.2
Ethylene glycol	14.6
Formic acid	12.1
Formic acid amide, *N*-ethyl	13.9
Formic acid amide, *N*-methyl	16.1
Glycerol	16.5
2,3-Hexanediol	10.3
1,3-Hexanediol-2-ethyl	9.4
1-Hexanol	10.7
1-Hexanol-2-ethyl	9.5
Maleic acid anhydride	13.6
Methacrylic acid	11.2
Methacrylic acid amide, *N*-Methyl	14.6

Table II (continued)

SOLUBILITY PARAMETER VALUES

C. Hydrogen-bonded Solvents (continued)

Name	δ (H)
Methanol	14.5
Methanol, 2-furil (furfuryl alcohol)	12.5
1-Nonanol	8.4
Pentane, 1-amino	8.7
1,3-Pentanediol, 2-methyl	10.3
1-Pentanol	10.9
2-Pentanol	10.0
Piperidine	8.7
2-Piperidone	13.6
1,2-Propanediol	12.6
1-Propanol	11.9
2-Propanol	11.5
1-Propanol, 2-methyl	10.5
2-Propanol, 2-methyl	10.6
2-Propenol (allyl alcohol)	11.8
Propionic acid	9.9
Propionic acid anhydride	10.0
1,2-Propanediol	12.6
Pyridine	10.7
2-Pyrrolidone	14.7
Quinoline	10.8
Succinic acid anhydride	15.4
Tetraethylene glycol	9.9
Toluene, 3-hydroxy (meta cresol)	10.2
Water	23.4

Table compiled by R. B. Seymour.

HEATS OF VAPORIZATION OF ORGANIC COMPOUNDS

Numerical values in the following table are in the units of gram calories per gram mole. To convert to joules per gram mole, multiply the listed value by 4.184.

Formula	Name	ΔH_V	Formula	Name	ΔH_V
CBrN	Cyanogen bromide	10,882.8	CO_2	Carbon dioxide	5,539.0
CBr_4	Carbon tetrabromide	10,771.4	CSSe	Carbon selenosulfide	8,003.0
$CBrF_3$	Bromotrifluoromethane	–	CS_2	Carbon disulfide	6,786.8
CBr_2F_2	Dibromodifluoromethane	–	C_2BrCl_2O	Trichloroacetyl bromide	9,673.9
$CClF_3$	Chlorotrifluoromethane	3,996.3	C_2HClF_2	1-Chloro-2,2-difluoroethylene	–
CClN	Cyanogen chloride	5,243.4	C_2ClF_3	1-Chloro-1,2,2-trifluoroethylene	5,421.5
CCl_2F_2	Dichlorodifluoromethane	8,363.1	$C_2Cl_2F_2$	1,2-Dichloro-1,2-difluoroethylene	7,185.6
CCl_2O	Phosgene	6,224.3	C_2F_4	Tetrafluoroethylene	–
CCl_3F	Trichlorofluoromethane	6,424.1	$C_2Cl_2F_4$	1,1-Dichloro-1,2,2,2-tetrafluoroethane	–
CCl_3NO_2	Trichloronitromethane	9,109.7	$C_2Cl_2F_4$	1,2-Dichloro-1,1,2,2-tetrafluoroethane	6,134.6
CCl_4	Carbon tetrachloride	8,271.5	$C_2Cl_3F_3$	1,1,2-Trichloro-1,2,2-trifluoroethane	7,115.4
		7,628.8	C_2Cl_4	Tetrachloroethylene	9,240.5
CFN	Cyanogen fluoride	5,875.3	CCl_4F_2	Tetrachlorodifluoroethane	–
CF_4	Carbon tetrafluoride	3,016.5	$C_2Cl_4F_2$	1,1,2,2-Tetrachloro-1,2-difluoroethane	8,746.2
$CHBr_3$	Tribromomethane	9,673.3	$C_2Cl_3F_3$	1,1,2-Trifluoro-1,2,2-trichloroethane	–
$CHClF_2$	Chlorodifluoromethane	5,212.9			
			C_2Cl_6	Hexachloroethane	11,711.3
$CHCl_2F$	Dichlorofluoromethane	6,286.8	C_2ClF_5	Chloropentafluoroethane	–
$CHCl_3$	Chloroform	7,500.5	C_2F_6	Hexafluoroethane	–
CHF_3	Trifluoromethane	–	C_2HBr_3O	Tribromoacetaldehyde	11,057.8
CHN	Hydrogen cyanide	7,338.8	C_2HCl_3	Trichloroethylene	8,314.7
CH_2Br_2	Dibromomethane	8,722.0			
			C_2HCl_3O	Trichloroacetaldehyde	8,469.2
CH_2Cl_2	Dichloromethane	7,572.3	$C_2HCl_3O_2$	Trichloroacetic acid	13,817.9
CH_2O	Formaldehyde	5,917.9	C_2HCl_5	Pentachloroethane	9,800.1
CH_2O_2	Formic acid	9,896.5	C_2H_2	Acetylene	4,665.8
CH_3AsCl_2	Dichloromethylarsine	9,636.8	$C_2H_2Br_4$	1,1,1,2-Tetrabromoethane	14,517.3
CH_3BO	Borine carbonyl	4,867.6			
CH_3Br	Methyl bromide	5,925.9	$C_2H_2Br_4$	1,1,2,2-Tetrabromoethane	12,911.5
CH_3Cl	Methyl chloride	5,375.3	$C_2H_2O_4$	Oxalic acid	21,630.6
CH_3Cl_3Si	Trichloromethylsilane	7,450.0	$C_2H_2Cl_2$	cis-1,2-Dichloroethylene	7,420.6
CH_3F	Methyl fluoride	3,986.4	$C_2H_2Cl_2$	trans-1,2-Dichloroethylene	7,243.1
CH_3I	Methyl iodide	6,616.5	$C_2H_2Cl_2$	1,1-Dichloroethylene	7,211.8
CH_3NO	Formamide	15,556.6	$C_2H_2F_2$	1,1-Difluoroethylene	–
CH_3NO_2	Nitromethane	9,210.9	$C_2H_2Cl_2O_2$	Dichloroacetic acid	12,952.9
CH_4	Methane	2,128.8	$C_2H_2Cl_4$	1,1,1,2-Tetrachloroethane	9,296.5
CH_4Cl_2Si	Dichloromethylsilane	7,011.0			8,725.6
CH_4O	Methanol	9,377.2	$C_2H_2Cl_4$	1,1,2,2-Tetrachloroethane	9,917.1
		8,978.8	C_2H_3Br	1-Bromoethylene	6,076.9
CH_4S	Methanethiol	6,331.9	$C_2H_3BrO_2$	Bromoacetic acid	13,537.8
CH_5ClSi	Chloromethylsilane	6,349.5	$C_2H_3Br_3$	1,1,2-Tribromoethane	11,874.1
CH_5N	Methylamine	6,469.5	C_2H_3Cl	1-Chloroethylene	6,263.0
CH_6Si	Methylsilane	4,683.6	$C_2H_3ClO_2$	Chloroacetic acid	13,134.5
CH_9NSi_2	2-Methyldisilazane	7,185.6	$C_2H_3Cl_3$	1,1,1-Trichloroethane	8,012.7
CIN	Cyanogen iodide	14,065.4	$C_2H_3Cl_3$	1,1,2-Trichloroethane	9,163.2
CN_4O_8	Tetranitromethane	9,848.7	$C_2H_3ClF_2$	1-Chloro-1,1-difluoroethane	–
CO	Carbon monoxide	1,613.3	$C_2H_3F_3$	1,1,1-Trifluoroethane	–
COS	Carbonyl sulfide	4,992.2	$C_2H_3Cl_3O_2$	Trichloroacetaldehyde hydrate	12,141.5
COSe	Carbonyl selenide	5,366.5	C_2H_3F	1-Fluoroethylene	4,198.1

Formula	Name	ΔH_v	Formula	Name	ΔH_v
C_2H_3N	Acetonitrile	8,173.2	C_3H_4O	2-Propenal	7,628.8
C_2H_3NS	Methyl thiocyanate	9,424.1	$C_3H_4O_2$	Acrylic acid	10,955.1
C_2H_3NS	Methyl isothiocyanate	7,990.1	$C_3H_4O_3$	Pyruvic acid	11,815.7
C_2H_4	Ethylene	3,453.7			
C_2H_4BrCl	1-Bromo-2-chloroethane	9,314.9	$C_3H_5Br_3$	1,2,3-Tribromopropane	12,047.1
			C_3H_5Cl	1-Chloropropene	6,594.3
C_2H_4BrCl	1-Bromo-2-chloroethane	8,995.6	C_3H_5Cl	Allyl chloride	7,386.8
$C_2H_4Br_2$	1,2-Dibromoethane	9,229.4	C_3H_5ClO	Epichlorohydrine	9,815.4
$C_2H_4Cl_2$	1,1-Dichloroethane	7,288.0	$C_3H_5ClO_2$	Methyl chloroacetate	10,815.0
$C_2H_4Cl_2$	1,2-Dichloroethane	7,950.7			
$C_2H_4F_2$	1,1-Difluoroethane	6,068.8	$C_3H_5Cl_3$	1,1,1-Trichloropropane	8,933.9
			$C_3H_5Cl_3$	1,2,3-Trichloropropane	10,714.3
C_2H_4O	Acetaldehyde	7,267.8	$C_3H_5Cl_3Si$	Allyltrichlorosilane	9,386.1
		6,622.1	C_3H_5N	Propionitrile	8,769.0
C_2H_4O	Ethylene oxide	6,823.3	C_3H_5NO	3-Hydroxypropionitrile	13,287.2
$C_2H_4O_2$	Acetic acid	9,963.9			
		9,486.6	C_3H_5NS	Ethylisothiocyanate	9,574.7
$C_2H_4O_2$	Methyl formate	7,027.8	$C_3H_5N_3O_9$	Nitroglycerine	13,753.1
$C_2H_4O_2S$	Mercaptoacetic acid	13,790.7	C_3H_6	Propene	4,697.4
			C_3H_6	Cyclopropane	5,897.7
C_2H_5Br	Ethyl bromide	6,843.1	C_3H_6BrNO	2-Bromo-2-nitrosopropane	9,619.6
C_2H_5Cl	Ethyl chloride	6,310.6	$C_3H_6Br_2$	1,2-Dibromopropane	9,801.9
C_2H_5ClO	2-Chloroethanol	10,740.6	$C_3H_6Br_2$	1,3-Dibromopropane	10,374.4
$C_2H_5Cl_3Si$	Trichloroethylsilane	9,457.8	$C_3H_6Br_2O$	2,3-Dibromo-1-propanol	13,190.0
$C_2H_5Cl_3OSi$	Trichloroethoxysilane	8,811.4	$C_3H_6Cl_2$	1,2-Dichloropropane	8,428.5
			$C_3H_6Cl_2O$	1,3-Dichloro-2-propanol	12,067.6
C_2H_5F	Ethyl fluoride	5,519.5			
$C_2H_5F_3Si$	Ethyltrifluorosilane	6,945.7	C_3H_6O	Acetone	7,641.5
C_2H_5I	Ethyl iodide	7,851.8	C_3H_6O	Allyl alcohol	10,577.7
C_2H_5NO	Acetamide	14,025.3	C_3H_6O	Propylene oxide	7,295.8
C_2H_5NO	Acetaldoxime	11,317.8	$C_3H_6O_2$	Propanoic acid	12,454.4
			$C_3H_6O_2$	Methyl acetate	7,732.8
$C_2H_5NO_2$	Nitroethane	9,531.1			
$C_2H_5N_3O_2$	Di(nitrosomethyl)amine	10,326.7	$C_3H_6O_2$	Ethyl formate	7,511.7
C_2H_6	Ethane	3,739.5	$C_3H_6O_3$	Methyl glycolate	11,105.0
$C_2H_6Cl_2Si$	Dichlorodimethylsilane	7,995.7	$C_3H_6O_3$	Methoxyacetic acid	13,451.0
C_2H_6O	Ethyl alcohol	9,673.9	C_3H_7Br	n-Propyl bromide	8,029.8
			C_3H_7Br	2-Bromopropane	7,591.7
C_2H_6O	Dimethyl ether	5,409.8			
$C_2H_6O_2$	1,2-Ethanediol	14,032.4	C_3H_7Cl	n-Propyl chloride	7,485.7
C_2H_6S	Dimethyl sulfide	6,742.3			6,905.8
C_2H_6S	Ethane thiol	6,728.7	C_3H_7Cl	2-Chloropropane	6,855.2
C_2H_6Sb	Dimethylantimony	12,075.7	$C_3H_7Cl_3Si$	Trichloroisopropylsilane	8,973.3
			C_3H_7I	n-Propyl iodide	8,467.1
C_2H_7N	Ethylamine	6,845.1	C_3H_7I	2-Iodopropane	8,243.4
C_2H_7N	Dimethylamine	6,660.0			
$C_2H_8N_2$	1,2-Ethanediamine	10,510.5	C_3H_7NO	Propionamide	14,554.0
C_2H_8Si	Dimethylsilane	5,497.8	$C_3H_7NO_2$	1-Nitropropane	9,949.9
$C_2H_{10}B_2$	Dimethyldiborane	5,696.7	$C_3H_7NO_2$	2-Nitropropane	9,476.9
			$C_3H_7NO_2$	Ethyl carbamate	13,078.6
$C_2H_{11}NSi_2$	2-Ethyldisilazane	7,348.3	C_3H_8	Propane	4,550.0
C_2N_2	Cyanogen	6,597.3			4,811.8
C_3H_3N	Acrylonitrile	7,941.4			
C_3H_4	Propadiene	5,141.2	C_3H_8O	n-Propanol	11,298.8
C_3H_4	Propyne	5,632.4			10,421.1
			C_3H_8O	Isopropanol	10,063.5
$C_3H_4Br_2$	2,3-Dibromopropene	9,886.2	C_3H_8O	Ethyl methyl ether	6,388.3
$C_3H_4Cl_2O_2$	Methyl dichloroacetate	10,820.5	$C_3H_8O_2$	1,2-Propanediol	13,575.2

Formula	Name	ΔH_V	Formula	Name	ΔH_V
$C_3H_8O_2$	1,3-Propanediol	13,782.3	$C_4H_6O_2$	Vinyl acetate	8,470.4
			$C_4H_6O_2$	Acetic anhydride	10,930.4
$C_3H_8O_2$	2-Methoxyethanol	9,893.8			
$C_3H_8O_2$	Glycerol	18,188.9	$C_4H_6O_4$	Dimethyl oxalate	11,519.4
C_3H_8S	Methyl ethyl sulfide	–	C_4H_7Br	cis-1-Bromo-1-butene	8,300.2
C_3H_8S	Propanethiol	7,855.3	C_4H_7Br	trans-1-Bromo-1-butene	8,515.7
C_3H_9B	Trimethylborine	5,375.4	C_4H_7Br	2-Bromo-1-butene	8,389.7
			C_4H_7Br	cis-2-Bromo-2-butene	8,486.3
C_3H_9ClSi	Chlorotrimethylsilane	7,589.1			
C_3H_9Ga	Trimethylgallium	7,758.8	C_4H_7Br	trans-2-Bromo-2-butene	8,238.1
C_3H_9N	n-Propylamine	7,408.0	C_4H_7BrO	1-Bromo-2-butanone	10,980.7
C_3H_9N	Trimethylamine	6,361.7	C_4H_7BrO	2-Methylpropionyl bromide	10,974.6
$C_3H_9O_4P$	Trimethyl phosphate	11,019.7	$C_4H_7Br_3$	1,1,2-Tribromobutane	11,936.5
			$C_4H_7Br_3$	1,2,2-Tribromobutane	11,622.3
$C_3H_{12}B_2$	Trimethyldiborane	6,981.8			
C_3O_2	Carbon suboxide	6,446.3	$C_4H_7Br_3$	2,2,3-Tribromobutane	11,664.2
C_3S_2	Carbon subsulfide	10,466.0	$C_4H_7ClO_2$	Ethyl chloroacetate	10,522.6
$C_4Cl_6O_3$	Trichloroacetic anhydride	12,929.0	$C_4H_8Cl_2$	1,1-Dichloro-2-methylpropane	9,111.1
C_3F_8	Octafluoropropane	–	$C_4H_7Cl_3$	1,2,3-Trichlorobutane	9,447.0
			C_4H_7N	Butyronitrile	9,462.9
C_4H_4O	Furan	–			
C_4H_2	1,3-Butadiyne	7,761.0	$C_4H_7NO_2$	Diacetamide	14,508.1
$C_4H_2Br_2O_3$	α,β-Dibromomaleic anhydride	12,579.2	C_4H_8	1-Butene	5,996.7
$C_4H_2Cl_2O_2$	trans-Fumaryl chloride	11,251.0	C_4H_8	cis-2-Butene	6,401.0
$C_4H_2O_3$	Maleic anhydride	12,122.3	C_4H_8	trans-2-Butene	6,221.6
			C_4H_8	2-Methylpropene	5,742.9
$C_4H_3NO_2S$	2-Nitrothiophene	11,926.2			
C_4H_4	Butenyne	6,677.2	C_4H_8	Cyclobutane	6,464.8
$C_4H_4Cl_2O_2$	Succinyl chloride	12,466.1	C_4H_8BrClO	2-Bromoethyl-2-chloroethyl ether	12,010.5
$C_4H_4Cl_2O_3$	Chloroacetic anhydride	14,645.1	$C_4H_8Br_2$	1,2-Dibromobutane	10,182.1
$C_4H_4O_3$	Succinic anhydride	14,726.0	$C_4H_8Br_2$	dl-2,3-Dibromobutane	10,136.1
			$C_4H_8Br_2$	meso-2,3-Dibromobutane	9,966.9
$C_4H_4O_4$	1,4-Dioxane-2,6-dione	14,013.6			
C_4H_4S	Thiophene	8,748.3	$C_4H_8Br_2$	1,4-Dibromobutane	11,369.3
C_4H_4Se	Selenophene	7,766.1	$C_4H_8Br_2O$	Di(2-bromoethyl)ether	12,454.4
$C_4H_5ClO_2$	α-Chlorocrotonic acid	15,440.1	$C_4H_8Cl_2$	1,2-Dichlorobutane	8,850.6
$C_4H_5ClO_3$	Ethyl chloroglyoxylate	10,268.4	$C_4H_8Cl_2$	2,3-Dichlorobutane	8,975.3
			$C_4H_8Cl_2$	1,1-Dichloro-2-methylpropane	8,795.6
$C_4H_5Cl_3O_2$	Ethyl trichloroacetate	11,625.1			
C_4H_5N	3-Butenenitrile	9,447.8	$C_4H_8Cl_2$	1,2-Dichloro-2-methylpropane	9,260.1
C_4H_5N	Methacrylonitrile	8,083.8	$C_4H_8Cl_2$	1,3-Dichloro-2-methylpropane	10,519.7
C_4H_5N	cis-Crotononitrile	8,905.4	$C_4H_8Cl_2O$	Di(chloroethyl)ether	11,376.8
C_4H_5N	trans-Crotononitrile	9,277.1	C_4H_8O	1,2-Epoxy-2-methylpropane	7,066.6
			C_4H_8O	Methyl ethyl ketone	8,149.5
$C_4H_5NO_2$	Succinimide	16,422.0			
C_4H_5NS	Allylisothiocyanate	9,967.8	$C_4H_8O_2$	Dioxane	8,546.2
C_4H_6	1,2-Butadiene	6,539.1	$C_4H_8O_2$	n-Butyric acid	11,881.2
C_4H_6	1,3-Butadiene	5,688.2	$C_4H_8O_2$	Isobutyric acid	11,182.8
C_4H_6	Cyclobutene	6,167.5	$C_4H_8O_2$	Ethyl acetate	8,301.1
			$C_4H_8O_2$	Methyl propanoate	8,356.2
C_4H_6	1-Butyne	6,596.9			
C_4H_6	2-Butyne	7,868.5	$C_4H_8O_2$	n-Propyl formate	8,208.1
$C_4H_6Cl_2O_2$	Ethyl dichloroacetate	10,842.8	$C_4H_8O_2$	Isopropyl formate	8,230.2
$C_4H_6Cl_2O_2$	2-Chloroethyl chloroacetate	12,588.7	$C_4H_8O_3$	α-Hydroxyisobutyric acid	15,967.0
$C_4H_6O_2$	cis-Crotonic acid	12,964.7	$C_4H_8O_3$	Ethyl glycolate	11,318.1
			C_4H_9Br	n-Butyl bromide	8,789.1
$C_4H_6O_2$	trans-Crotonic acid	13,252.2			
$C_4H_6O_2$	Methyl acrylate	8,598.0	C_4H_9BrO	1-Bromo-2-butanol	13,473.7
$C_4H_6O_2$	Methacrylic acid	12,526.6	C_4H_9Cl	n-Butyl chloride	8,144.8

Formula	Name	ΔH_v	Formula	Name	ΔH_v
C_4H_9Cl	sec-Butyl chloride	7,407.9	$C_5H_6O_3$	Glutaric anhydride	14,814.1
C_4H_9Cl	Isobutyl chloride	8,045.1	$C_5H_6O_3$	Pyrotartaric anhydride	13,251.2
C_4H_9Cl	tert-Butyl chloride	6,876.0	C_5H_6S	2-Methylthiophene	8,884.2
			C_5H_6S	3-Methylthiophene	9,084.1
$C_4H_9ClO_2$	2-(2-Chloroethoxy)ethanol	14,082.1	$C_5H_7ClO_3$	Propyl chloroglyoxylate	11,430.0
C_4H_9I	n-Butyl iodide	–			
C_4H_9I	1-Iodo-2-methylpropane	9,650.7	C_5H_7N	Tiglonitrile	8,704.6
$C_4H_9NO_2$	Ethyl methylcarbamate	12,161.2	C_5H_7N	Angelonitrile	9,707.5
$C_4H_9NO_2$	Propyl carbamate	14,071.8	C_5H_7N	α-Ethylacrylonitrile	8,679.1
			$C_5H_7NO_2$	Ethyl cyanoacetate	15,615.6
$C_4H_9N_2O_2$	Di(nitrosoethyl)amine	10,894.8	C_5H_8	Cyclopentene	–
C_4H_{10}	n-Butane	5,801.2			
C_4H_{10}	2-Methylpropane	5,084.4	C_5H_8	Isoprene	6,901.8
		5,416.2	C_5H_8	1,3-Pentadiene	7,313.9
$C_4H_{10}Cl_2Si$	Dichlorodiethylsilane	10,038.6	C_5H_8	1,4-Pentadiene	6,826.6
$C_4H_{10}F_2Si$	Diethyldifluorosilane	8,214.9	C_5H_8O	Tiglaldehyde	9,009.2
			$C_5H_8O_2$	Levulinaldehyde	11,483.8
$C_4H_{10}O$	n-Butyl alcohol	10,970.5			
$C_4H_{10}O$	sec-Butyl alcohol	10,712.3	$C_5H_8O_2$	Tiglic acid	13,756.5
$C_4H_{10}O$	Isobutyl alcohol	10,936.0	$C_5H_8O_2$	α-Valerolactone	11,537.0
$C_4H_{10}O$	tert-Butyl alcohol	10,413.2	$C_5H_8O_2$	α-Ethylacrylic acid	14,417.8
$C_4H_{10}O$	Diethyl ether	6,946.2	$C_5H_8O_2$	Ethyl acrylate	9,259.4
			$C_5H_8O_2$	Methyl methacrylate	8,974.9
$C_4H_{10}O$	Methyl propyl ether	7,409.7			
$C_4H_{10}O_2$	1,3-Butanediol	10,479.1	$C_5H_8O_3$	Levulinic acid	17,795.0
$C_4H_{10}O_2$	2,3-Butanediol	13,708.6	$C_5H_8O_4$	Glutaric acid	22,085.2
$C_4H_{10}O_2$	1,2-Dimethoxyethane	7,681.0	$C_5H_8O_4$	Dimethyl malonate	12,608.1
$C_4H_{10}O_2S$	2,2-Thiodiethanol	6,597.0	$C_5H_9ClO_2$	Ethyl α-chloropropionate	11,032.8
			$C_5H_9ClO_2$	Isopropyl chloroacetate	10,575.7
$C_4H_{10}O_3$	Diethylene glycol	16,146.7			
$C_4H_{10}O_3$	1,2,3-Butanetriol	16,345.8	C_5H_9N	Valeronitrile	9,931.3
$C_4H_{10}O_3S$	Diethyl sulfite	10,783.0	C_5H_9NO	α-Hydroxybutyronitrile	13,577.0
$C_4H_{10}O_4S$	Diethyl sulfate	12,518.2	C_5H_{10}	1-Pentene	6,931.2
$C_4H_{10}S$	n-Butanethiol	–	C_5H_{10}	2-Pentene	–
			C_5H_{10}	3-Methyl-2-butene	7,112.8
$C_4H_{10}S$	Diethyl sulfide	8,210.8			
$C_4H_{10}Se$	Diethyl selenide	9,274.7	C_5H_{10}	2-Methyl-1-butene	6,474.6
$C_4H_{10}Zn$	Diethyl zinc	9,162.3	C_5H_{10}	3-Methyl-1-butene	–
$C_4H_{11}N$	Diethyl amine	7,307.5	C_5H_{10}	Cyclopentane	7,411.1
$C_4H_{11}N$	Isobutylamine	8,478.3	C_5H_{10}	Methylcyclobutane	6,413.2
			$C_5H_{10}Br_2$	1,2-Dibromopentane	11,130.0
$C_4H_{12}Cl_2Si_2$	1,3-Dichlorotetramethyldisiloxane	9,881.6			
$C_4H_{12}Pb$	Tetramethyllead	8,843.8	$C_5H_{10}Br_2$	1,2-Dibromo-2-methylbutane	7,616.9
$C_4H_{12}Si$	Tetramethylsilane	6,439.2	$C_5H_{10}Br_2$	1,3-Dibromo-3-methylbutane	10,639.6
$C_4H_{12}Sn$	Tetramethyl tin	7,897.8	$C_5H_{10}Cl_2Si$	Allyldichloroethylsilane	9,833.9
$C_4H_{14}B_2$	Tetramethyldiborane	7,517.1	$C_5H_{10}O$	Diethyl ketone	11,183.0
			$C_5H_{10}O$	Methyl n-propyl ketone	11,240.6
C_4F_8	Octafluorocyclobutane	–			
C_4F_{10}	Perfluoro-n-butane	–	$C_5H_{10}O$	Methyl isopropyl ketone	11,073.2
C_5H_4BrN	3-Bromopyridine	10,863.7	$C_5H_{10}Cl_2O$	2-Chloroethyl 2-chloroisopropyl ether	11,420.8
C_5H_4ClN	2-Chloropyridine	10,614.5	$C_5H_{10}Cl_2O$	2-Chloroethyl 2-chloropropyl ether	11,316.9
$C_5H_4O_2$	2-Furaldehyde	11,614.6	$C_5H_{10}Cl_2O_2$	Di(2-chloroethoxy)methane	12,908.0
			$C_5H_{10}O_2$	4-Hydroxy-3-methyl-2-butanone	13,639.4
$C_5H_4O_3$	Citraconic anhydride	12,307.8			
C_5H_5N	Pyridine	9,649.4	$C_5H_{10}O_2$	Valeric acid	13,370.3
$C_5H_6Cl_2O_2$	Glutaryl chloride	13,192.1	$C_5H_{10}O_2$	Isovaleric acid	12,951.1
$C_5H_6N_2$	Glutaronitrile	13,767.5	$C_5H_{10}O_2$	Ethyl propanoate	8,877.8
$C_5H_6O_2$	Furfuryl alcohol	12,815.8	$C_5H_{10}O_2$	n-Propyl acetate	8,921.1

Formula	Name	Δ H$_V$	Formula	Name	Δ H$_V$
C$_5$H$_{10}$O$_2$	Isopropyl acetate	8,794.8	C$_6$H$_4$Cl$_2$	1,3-Dichlorobenzene	10,446.8
			C$_6$H$_4$Cl$_2$	1,4-Dichlorobenzene	17,260.5
C$_5$H$_{10}$O$_2$	Methyl butyrate	8,886.0			10,611.0
C$_5$H$_{10}$O$_2$	Methyl isobutyrate	8,593.3			
C$_5$H$_{10}$O$_2$	n-Butyl formate	9,285.9	C$_6$H$_4$Cl$_2$O	2,4-Dichlorophenol	13,230.4
C$_5$H$_{10}$O$_2$	Isobutyl formate	8,678.8	C$_6$H$_4$Cl$_2$O	2,6-Dichlorophenol	13,472.0
C$_5$H$_{10}$O$_2$	sec-Butyl formate	8,975.7	C$_6$H$_4$Cl$_3$N	2,4,6-Trichloroaniline	22,297.3
			C$_6$H$_5$AsCl$_2$	Dichlorophenylarsine	12,229.5
C$_5$H$_{10}$O$_2$	tert-Butyl formate	8,955.3	C$_6$H$_5$Br	Bromobenzene	10,157.7
C$_5$H$_{10}$O$_3$	Diethyl carbonate	10,159.0			
C$_5$H$_{11}$Br	1-Bromopentane	—	C$_6$H$_5$Cl	Chlorobenzene	10,098.0
C$_5$H$_{11}$Br	1-Bromo-3-methylbutane	9,282.7			9,067.3
C$_5$H$_{11}$Br	1-Chloropentane	—	C$_6$H$_5$ClO	2-Chlorophenol	10,341.1
			C$_6$H$_5$ClO	3-Chlorophenol	11,979.7
C$_5$H$_{11}$I	1-Iodopentane	—	C$_6$H$_5$ClO	4-Chlorophenol	12,281.6
C$_5$H$_{11}$I	1-Iodo-3-methylbutane	9,951.6	C$_6$H$_5$ClO$_2$S	Benzenesulfonylchloride	12,621.0
C$_5$H$_{11}$N	Piperidine	8,911.8			
C$_5$H$_9$O$_2$	Pentanoic acid	—	C$_6$H$_5$Cl$_2$O$_2$P	Phenyl dichlorophosphate	13,319.6
C$_5$H$_{11}$NO$_2$	Isobutyl carbamate	13,897.1	C$_6$H$_5$Cl$_3$Si	Trichlorophenylsilane	11,385.9
			C$_6$H$_5$F	Fluorobenzene	7,980.4
C$_5$H$_{11}$NO$_3$	Isoamyl nitrate	10,817.2	C$_6$H$_5$F$_3$Si	Trifluorophenylsilane	9,171.6
C$_5$H$_{12}$	n-Pentane	6,595.1	C$_6$H$_5$I	Iodobenzene	10,277.2
C$_5$H$_{12}$	2-Methylbutane	6,470.8			10,377.8
C$_5$H$_{12}$	2,2-Dimethylpropane	5,648.6			
C$_5$H$_{12}$O	Amyl alcohol	12,495.5	C$_6$H$_5$NO$_2$	Nitrobenzene	12,168.2
			C$_6$H$_5$NO$_3$	2-Nitrophenol	12,497.3
C$_5$H$_{12}$O	Isoamyl alcohol	12,497.9	C$_6$H$_6$	1,5-Hexadiene-3-yne	8,288.0
C$_5$H$_{12}$O	2-Pentanol	12,086.2	C$_6$H$_6$	Benzene	10,254.3
C$_5$H$_{12}$O	tert-Amyl alcohol	11,239.2			8,146.5
C$_5$H$_{12}$O	Ethyl propyl ether	7,092.7	C$_6$H$_6$ClN	2-Chloroaniline	12,441.0
C$_5$H$_{12}$O	Methyl n-butyl ether	—			
			C$_6$H$_6$ClN	3-Chloroaniline	13,385.6
C$_5$H$_{12}$O$_3$	2,3,4-Pentanetriol	19,694.4	C$_6$H$_6$ClN	4-Chloroaniline	12,832.8
C$_5$H$_{12}$S	1-Pentanethiol	—	C$_6$H$_6$ClO	4-Chlorophenol	12,964.7
C$_5$H$_{14}$OSi	Ethoxytrimethylsilane	8,030.6	C$_6$H$_6$N$_2$O$_2$	2-Nitroaniline	15,284.0
C$_5$H$_{14}$Si	Ethyltrimethylsilane	7,633.4	C$_6$H$_6$N$_2$O$_2$	3-Nitroaniline	15,996.3
C$_5$H$_{14}$Sn	Ethyltrimethyltin	8,820.9			
			C$_6$H$_6$N$_2$O$_2$	4-Nitroaniline	17,220.2
C$_6$Cl$_4$O$_2$	Chloranil	21,514.3	C$_6$H$_6$O	Phenol	11,891.5
C$_6$Cl$_6$	Hexachlorobenzene	15,199.1	C$_6$H$_6$O$_2$	Pyrocatechol	13,779.7
C$_6$HCl$_5$	Pentachlorobenzene	15,124.2	C$_6$H$_6$O$_2$	Resorcinol	16,400.8
C$_6$HCl$_5$O	Pentachlorophenol	16,742.6	C$_6$H$_6$O$_2$	Hydroquinone	18,734.0
C$_6$H$_2$BrCl$_3$O	3-Bromo-2,4,6-trichlorophenol	15,231.9			
			C$_6$H$_6$O$_3$	Pyrogallol	15,731.8
C$_6$H$_2$Cl$_4$	1,2,3,4-Tetrachlorobenzene	12,872.5	C$_6$H$_6$S	Benzenethiol	11,320.1
C$_6$H$_2$Cl$_4$	1,2,3,5-Tetrachlorobenzene	11,982.1	C$_6$H$_7$N	Aniline	11,307.6
C$_6$H$_2$Cl$_4$	1,2,4,5-Tetrachlorobenzene	12,828.8	C$_6$H$_7$N	2-Picoline	9,933.2
C$_6$H$_2$Cl$_4$O	2,3,4,6-Tetrachlorophenol	15,362.7	C$_6$H$_7$N	3-Methylpyridine (β-picoline)	—
C$_6$H$_3$BrCl$_2$O	2-Bromo-4,6-dichlorophenol	13,829.1			
			C$_6$H$_8$	1,3-Cyclohexadiene	—
C$_6$H$_3$Cl$_3$	1,2,3-Trichlorobenzene	11,349.5	C$_6$H$_8$Cl$_2$O$_4$	Ethylene-bis-chloroacetate	16,499.1
C$_6$H$_3$Cl$_3$	1,2,4-Trichlorobenzene	11,425.1	C$_6$H$_8$N$_2$	1,3-Phenylenediamine	14,761.1
C$_6$H$_3$Cl$_3$	1,3,5-Trichlorobenzene	11,211.0	C$_6$H$_8$N$_2$	Phenylhydrazine	13,711.9
C$_6$H$_3$Cl$_3$O	2,4,5-Trichlorophenol	13,237.0	C$_6$H$_8$O$_3$	α-Methylglutaric anhydride	14,204.9
C$_6$H$_3$Cl$_3$O	2,4,6-Trichlorophenol	14,092.8			
			C$_6$H$_8$O$_3$	α,α-Dimethylsuccinic anhydride	13,683.1
C$_6$H$_4$Br$_2$	1,4-Dibromobenzene	13,047.8	C$_6$H$_8$O$_4$	Dimethyl maleate	12,615.7
C$_6$H$_4$BrCl	1,4-Bromochlorobenzene	16,671.8	C$_6$H$_{10}$	Cyclohexene	—
		11,451.1	C$_6$H$_{10}$	1,5-Hexadiene	—
C$_6$H$_4$Cl$_2$	1,2-Dichlorobenzene	10,943.0	C$_6$H$_{10}$Cl$_2$O$_2$	Isobutyl dichloroacetate	11,733.1

Formula	Name	ΔH_v	Formula	Name	ΔH_v
$C_6H_{10}Cl_2Si$	Diallyldichlorosilane	10,462.8	$C_6H_{14}O$	2-Methyl-2-pentanol	11,132.0
$C_6H_{10}O$	Cyclohexanone	10,037.6	$C_6H_{14}O$	2-Methyl-4-pentanol	10,985.5
$C_6H_{10}O$	Mesityl oxide	10,109.4	$C_6H_{14}O$	Ethyl butyl ether	–
$C_6H_{10}O_2$	Isocaprolactone	11,685.0	$C_6H_{14}O$	Di-n-propyl ether	8,229.6
$C_6H_{10}O_3$	Propionic anhydride	11,572.6	$C_6H_{14}O$	Diisopropyl ether	7,777.3
$C_6H_{10}O_3$	Ethyl acetoacetate	11,842.0	$C_6H_{14}O_2$	Acetal	9,853.9
$C_6H_{10}O_3$	Methyl levulinate	12,249.8	$C_6H_{14}O_2$	1,2-Diethoxyethane	8,102.6
$C_6H_{10}O_4$	Adipic acid	19,570.2	$C_6H_{14}O_3$	Di(2-methoxyethyl)ether	11,105.2
$C_6H_{10}O_4$	Diethyl oxalate	14,016.9	$C_6H_{14}O_3$	Diethyleneglycol diethyl ether	12,669.0
$C_6H_{10}O_4$	Glycol diacetate	12,496.1	$C_6H_{14}O_3$	Dipropyleneglycol	14,610.4
$C_6H_{10}O_5$	Dimethyl-l-malate	14,127.6	$C_6H_{14}O_4$	Triethyleneglycol	17,097.1
$C_6H_{10}O_6$	Dimethyl-d-tartrate	15,372.6	$C_6H_{15}N$	Dipropyl sulfide	–
$C_6H_{10}O_6$	Dimethyl-dl-tartrate	14,999.1	$C_6H_{15}N$	Di-n-Propylamine	–
$C_6H_{10}S$	Diallyl sulfide	9,652.6	$C_6H_{15}N$	Triethylamine	–
$C_6H_{11}BrO_2$	Ethyl α-bromoisobutyrate	10,635.8	$C_6H_{15}B$	Triethylboron	2,535.0
$C_6H_{11}ClO_2$	sec-Butylchloroacetate	11,152.0	$C_6H_{15}ClSi$	Chlorotriethylsilane	9,806.9
$C_6H_{11}N$	Capronitrile	10,492.3	$C_6H_{15}O_4P$	Triethyl phosphate	11,549.9
C_6H_{12}	1-Hexene	7,787.6	$C_6H_{15}Tl$	Triethylthallium	9,458.6
C_6H_{12}	2-Hexene	–	$C_6H_{16}O_2Si$	Diethoxydimethylsilane	9,758.2
C_6H_{12}	Cyclohexane	7,830.9	$C_6H_{16}Si$	Trimethylpropylsilane	7,964.6
C_6H_{12}	Methylcyclopentane	7,940.0	$C_6H_{16}Sn$	Trimethylpropyltin	9,659.6
$C_6H_{12}Cl_2O$	Dichlorodiisopropyl ether	11,881.1	$C_6H_{18}Cl_2O_2Si_3$	1,5-Dichlorohexamethyltrisiloxane	11,391.5
$C_6H_{12}Cl_2O_2$	bis(2-Chloroethyl)acetal	13,497.1	$C_6H_{18}O_3Si_3$	Hexamethylcyclotrisiloxane	10,503.3
$C_6H_{12}O$	2-Hexanone	12,358.3	$C_7H_3Cl_2F_3$	3,4-Dichloro-α,α,α-trifluorotoluene	10,253.5
$C_6H_{12}O$	4-Methyl-2-pentanone	11,669.6	$C_7H_4ClF_3$	2-Chloro-α,α,α-trifluorotoluene	10,016.9
$C_6H_{12}O$	Allyl propyl ether	8,621.5	$C_7H_4Cl_4$	2-α,α,α-Tetrachlorotoluene	12,501.3
$C_6H_{12}O$	Allyl isopropyl ether	8,637.5	C_7H_5BrO	Benzoyl bromide	12,070.8
$C_6H_{12}O$	Cyclohexanol	11,935.8	C_7H_5ClO	Benzoyl chloride	11,438.0
$C_6H_{12}O_2$	Caproic acid	16,189.4	$C_7H_5Cl_3$	α,α,α-Trichlorotoluene	12,168.6
$C_6H_{12}O_2$	Isocaproic acid	14,874.8	$C_7H_5F_3$	α,α,α-Trifluorotoluene	8,869.7
$C_6H_{12}O_2$	4-Hydroxy-4-methyl-2-pentanone	11,718.8	C_7H_5N	Benzonitrile	11,341.0
$C_6H_{11}O_2$	Methyl pentanoate	–	C_7H_5N	Phenyl isocyanide	10,736.7
$C_6H_{12}O_2$	Methyl isovalerate	9,567.5	C_7H_5NO	Phenyl isocyanate	10,556.7
$C_6H_{12}O_2$	Ethyl n-butyrate	9,468.5	$C_7H_5NO_3$	2-Nitrobenzaldehyde	13,773.6
$C_6H_{12}O_2$	Ethyl isobutyrate	8,945.7	$C_7H_5NO_3$	3-Nitrobenzaldehyde	14,726.9
$C_6H_{12}O_2$	n-Propyl propanoate	9,857.2	C_7H_5NS	Phenyl isothiocyanate	12,132.7
$C_6H_{12}O_2$	n-Butyl acetate	–	$C_7H_6Cl_2$	α,α-Dichlorotoluene	11,075.9
$C_6H_{12}O_2$	Isobutyl acetate	9,300.8	C_7H_6O	Benzaldehyde	11,657.8
$C_6H_{12}O_2$	n-Amyl formate	–	$C_7H_6O_2$	Benzoic acid	15,253.3
$C_6H_{12}O_2$	Isoamyl formate	9,438.2			16,295.1
			$C_7H_6O_2$	Salicylaldehyde	11,536.5
$C_6H_{12}O_3$	Paraformaldehyde	10,348.2			
C_6H_{14}	Hexane	7,627.2	$C_7H_6O_2$	4-Hydroxybenzaldehyde	16,043.4
C_6H_{14}	2-Methylpentane	7,676.6	$C_7H_6O_3$	Salicylic acid	18,920.7
C_6H_{14}	3-Methylpentane	7,743.9	C_7H_7Br	α-Bromotoluene	11,360.4
C_6H_{14}	2,2-Dimethylbutane	7,271.0	C_7H_7Br	2-Bromotoluene	11,365.0
			C_7H_7Br	3-Bromotoluene	10,537.1
C_6H_{14}	2,3-Dimethylbutane	7,120.0			
$C_6H_{14}O$	1-Hexanol	12,708.5	C_7H_7Br	4-Bromotoluene	10,076.2
$C_6H_{14}O$	2-Hexanol	12,386.5	C_7H_7BrO	4-Bromoanisole	12,075.4
$C_6H_{14}O$	3-Hexanol	11,157.9	C_7H_7Cl	α-Chlorotoluene	11,158.7
$C_6H_{14}O$	2-Methyl-1-pentanol	12,036.6	C_7H_7Cl	2-Chlorotoluene	10,279.3

Formula	Name	ΔH_V	Formula	Name	ΔH_V
C_7H_7Cl	3-Chlorotoluene	10,081.1	$C_7H_{14}O$	4-Heptanone	13,451.9
			$C_7H_{14}O$	2,5-Dimethyl-3-pentanone	12,266.9
C_7H_7Cl	4-Chlorotoluene	10,151.7	$C_7H_{14}O_2$	Enanthic acid	15,893.8
C_7H_7F	2-Fluorotoluene	9,164.8			
C_7H_7F	3-Fluorotoluene	9,251.8	$C_7H_{14}O_2$	Methyl caproate	10,676.8
C_7H_7F	4-Fluorotoluene	9,281.0	$C_7H_{14}O_2$	Ethyl isovalerate	10,183.9
C_7H_7I	2-Iodotoluene	11,380.7	$C_7H_{14}O_2$	Propyl butyrate	10,283.7
			$C_7H_{14}O_2$	Propyl isobutyrate	10,259.7
$C_7H_7NO_2$	2-Nitrotoluene	12,239.1	$C_7H_{14}O_2$	Isopropyl isobutyrate	9,717.6
$C_7H_7NO_2$	3-Nitrotoluene	11,831.1			
$C_7H_7NO_2$	4-Nitrotoluene	11,915.0	$C_7H_{14}O_2$	Isobutyl propionate	10,495.8
C_7H_8	Toluene	9,368.5	$C_7H_{14}O_2$	Isoamyl acetate	10,494.9
		8,580.5	C_7H_{16}	Perfluoro-n-Heptane	–
$C_7H_8Cl_2Si$	Benzyldichlorosilane	13,128.7	C_7H_{16}	n-Heptane	8,928.8
					8,409.6
$C_7H_8Cl_2Si$	Dichloromethylphenylsilane	11,464.7	C_7H_{16}	2-Methylhexane	8,538.7
$C_7H_8Cl_2Si$	Dichloro-4-tolylsilane	13,125.7			
C_7H_8O	Anisole	10,440.9	C_7H_{16}	3-Methylhexane	8,596.3
C_7H_8O	Benzyl alcohol	14,093.2	C_7H_{16}	3-Ethylpentane	8,642.8
C_7H_8O	o-Cresol	12,487.3	C_7H_{16}	2,2-Dimethylpentane	8,106.7
			C_7H_{16}	2,3-Dimethylpentane	8,390.9
C_7H_8O	m-Cresol	13,483.8	C_7H_{16}	2,4-Dimethylpentane	8,167.1
C_7H_8O	p-Cresol	13,611.7			
$C_7H_8O_2$	3,5-Dimethyl-1,2-pyrone	14,470.6	C_7H_{16}	3,3-Dimethylpentane	8,145.4
$C_7H_8O_2$	2-Methoxyphenol	13,425.8	C_7H_{16}	2,2,3-Trimethylbutane	7,767.1
$C_7H_8O_3$	Ethyl 2-furoate	12,144.0	$C_7H_{16}O$	n-Heptanol	13,920.9
			$C_7H_{16}O_3$	Triethyl orthoformate	10,935.0
C_7H_9N	2,6-Dimethylpyridine	–	$C_7H_{18}O_3Si$	Triethoxymethylsilane	10,306.7
C_7H_9N	Benzylamine	11,703.2			
C_7H_9N	N-Methylaniline	11,982.3	$C_7H_{18}Si$	Butyltrimethylsilane	9,206.0
C_7H_9N'	2-Toluidine	12,663.4	$C_7H_{18}Si$	Triethylmethylsilane	9,232.5
C_7H_9N	3-Toluidine	12,104.1	$C_8H_4Cl_2O_2$	Phthaloyl chloride	13,716.0
			$C_8H_4O_3$	Phthalic anhydride	13,919.0
$C_7H_{10}O_4$	Dimethyl citraconate	12,917.3	$C_8H_5Cl_2N$	α,α-Dichlorophenylacetonitrile	12,829.9
$C_7H_{10}O_4$	Dimethyl itaconate	15,613.7			
$C_7H_{10}O_4$	$trans$-Dimethyl mesaconate	12,688.1	$C_8H_5Cl_5$	Pentachloroethylbenzene	13,728.7
$C_7H_{11}NO_2$	2-Cyano-2-butyl acetate	12,720.8	$C_8H_6Cl_2$	2,3-Dichlorostyrene	12,827.2
$C_7H_{12}O_2$	Butyl acrylate	10,194.0	$C_8H_6Cl_2$	2,4-Dichlorostyrene	12,511.7
			$C_8H_6Cl_2$	2,5-Dichlorostyrene	12,592.5
			$C_8H_6Cl_2$	2,6-Dichlorostyrene	12,186.0
C_7H_9N	4-Toluidine	12,428.6			
C_7H_9NO	2-Methoxyaniline	13,684.6	$C_8H_6Cl_2$	3,4-Dichlorostyrene	12,626.5
$C_7H_{10}N_2$	Toluene-2,4-diamine	15,928.1	$C_8H_6Cl_2$	3,5-Dichlorostyrene	12,511.7
$C_7H_{10}N_2$	4-Tolylhydrazine	15,063.1	$C_8H_6Cl_4$	3,4,5,6-Tetrachloro-1,2-xylene	14,763.1
$C_7H_{10}O_3$	Trimethylsuccinic anhydride	12,196.7	$C_8H_6Cl_4$	1,2,3,5-Tetrachloro-4-ethylbenzene	12,980.3
			$C_8H_6O_2$	Phenylglyoxal	13,731.6
$C_7H_{12}O_3$	Ethyl levulinate	12,733.6			
$C_7H_{12}O_4$	Pimelic acid	19,840.8	$C_8H_6O_2$	Phthalide	14,021.6
$C_7H_{12}O_4$	Diethyl malonate	12,227.7	$C_8H_6O_3$	Piperonal	14,425.5
$C_7H_{13}ClO$	Enanthyl chloride	15,242.7	C_8H_7Cl	3-Chlorostyrene	10,990.2
$C_7H_{13}N$	Heptanonitrile	10,830.5	C_8H_7ClO	Phenylacetyl chloride	12,627.1
			C_8H_7N	2-Tolunitrile	11,557.7
C_7H_{14}	Ethylcyclopentane	8,797.7			
C_7H_{14}	2-Heptene	8,643.2	C_8H_7N	4-Tolunitrile	11,562.8
C_7H_{14}	Methylcyclohexane	8,549.2	C_8H_7N	Phenylacetonitrile	12,796.2
			C_8H_7N	2-Tolyl isocyanide	11,303.3
$C_7H_{14}O$	Enanthaldehyde	11,413.4	$C_8H_7NO_4$	2-Nitrophenyl acetate	16,875.3
$C_7H_{14}O$	2-Heptanone	12,478.9	C_8H_7NS	2-Methylbenzothiazole	14,492.3

Formula	Name	ΔH_V	Formula	Name	ΔH_V
C_8H_8	Styrene	9,634.7	$C_8H_{11}N$	2,4-Xylidine	13,099.2
$C_8H_8Br_2$	(1,2-Dibromoethyl)benzene	14,874.7	$C_8H_{11}N$	2,6-Xylidine	11,742.6
$C_8H_8Cl_2$	1,2-Dichloro-3-ethylbenzene	11,784.3	$C_8H_{11}NO$	2-Phenetidine	13,877.8
$C_8H_8Cl_2$	1,2-Dichloro-4-ethylbenzene	11,711.5	$C_8H_{11}NO$	2-Anilinoethanol	15,643.2
$C_8H_8Cl_2$	1,4-Dichloro-2-ethylbenzene	11,262.7	$C_8H_{12}AsNO_2$	Dimethyl arsanilate	11,277.7
C_8H_8O	Acetophenone	11,731.5	$C_8H_{12}Cl_2O_5$	Diethyleneglycol-bis-chloroacetate	19,830.5
$C_8H_8O_2$	Phenylacetate	12,174.9	$C_8H_{12}O_4$	Diethyl maleate	12,908.0
$C_8H_8O_2$	Phenylacetic acid	15,568.7	$C_8H_{12}O_4$	Diethyl fumarate	12,747.4
$C_8H_8O_2$	Anisaldehyde	13,581.8	$C_8H_{12}Si$	Dimethylphenylsilane	10,274.2
$C_8H_8O_2$	Methyl benzoate	12,077.2	$C_8H_{14}O_3$	Ethyl-α-ethylacetoacetate	12,344.2
$C_8H_8O_2$	Methyl salicylate	12,658.8	$C_8H_{14}O_4$	Propyl levulinate	13,354.4
$C_8H_8O_3$	Vanillin	15,703.2	$C_8H_{14}O_4$	Isopropyl levulinate	12,689.6
$C_8H_8O_4$	Dihydroacetic acid	14,663.8	$C_8H_{14}O_4$	Dipropyl oxalate	13,056.4
C_8H_9Br	2-Bromo-1,4-xylene	11,603.7	$C_8H_{14}O_4$	Diisopropyl oxalate	12,949.3
C_8H_9Br	1-Bromo-4-ethylbenzene	10,170.0	$C_8H_{14}O_4$	Diethyl succinate	13,076.1
C_8H_9Br	(2-Bromoethyl)benzene	12,152.5	$C_8H_{14}O_4$	Diethyl isosuccinate	12,087.6
C_8H_9Cl	1-Chloro-2-ethylbenzene	10,749.7	$C_8H_{14}O_4$	Suberic acid	21,089.8
C_8H_9Cl	1-Chloro-3-ethylbenzene	10,724.1	$C_8H_{14}O_5$	Diethyl malate	14,202.9
C_8H_9Cl	1-Chloro-4-ethylbenzene	10,659.9	$C_8H_{14}O_6$	Diethyl-dl-tartrate	15,150.4
C_8H_9ClO	1-Chloro-2-ethoxybenzene	12,411.1	$C_8H_{14}O_6$	Diethyl-d-tartrate	15,517.8
C_8H_9ClO	4-Chlorophenylethyl alcohol	14,298.5	$C_8H_{15}Br$	(2-Bromoethyl)cyclohexane	11,462.7
$C_8H_{10}Cl_2Si$	Dichlorophenylethylsilane	11,895.1	$C_8H_{15}N$	n-Caprylonitrile	12,221.8
C_8H_9NO	Acetanilide	15,474.1	$C_8H_{15}NO_3$	Ethyl-N,N-diethyloxamate	13,758.4
$C_8H_9NO_2$	Methyl anthranilate	13,186.3	C_8H_{16}	1-Octene	—
$C_8H_9NO_2$	4-Nitro-1,3-xylene	12,948.0	C_8H_{16}	2-Octene	—
C_8H_{10}	Ethylbenzene	9,301.3	C_8H_{16}	2-Methyl-2-heptene	9,643.8
C_8H_{10}	o-Xylene	9,998.5	C_8H_{16}	1,1-Dimethylcyclohexane	8,949.1
C_8H_{10}	m-Xylene	9,904.2	C_8H_{16}	cis-1,2-Dimethylcyclohexane	9,364.9
C_8H_{10}	p-Xylene	9,809.9	C_8H_{16}	trans-1,2-Dimethylcyclohexane	9,097.1
$C_8H_{10}Cl_2OSi$	Dichloroethoxyphenylsilane	12,516.5	C_8H_{16}	cis-1,3-Dimethylcyclohexane	9,232.6
$C_8H_{10}Cl_2Si$	Dichloroethylphenylsilane	11,721.2	C_8H_{16}	trans-1,3-Dimethylcyclohexane	9,080.3
$C_8H_{10}O$	2-Ethylphenol	12,516.7	C_8H_{16}	cis-1,4-Dimethylcyclohexane	9,188.9
$C_8H_{10}O$	3-Ethylphenol	13,856.4	C_8H_{16}	trans-1,4-Dimethylcyclohexane	8,951.2
$C_8H_{10}O$	4-Ethylphenol	13,437.9	C_8H_{16}	Ethylcyclohexane	9,441.2
$C_8H_{10}O$	Xylenol	—	$C_8H_{16}O$	Caprylaldehyde	21,201.0
$C_8H_{10}O$	2,3-Xylenol	13,106.9	$C_8H_{16}O$	Cyclohexaneethanol	13,152.4
$C_8H_{10}O$	2,4-Xylenol	13,130.2	$C_8H_{16}O$	6-Methyl-3-hepten-2-ol	13,864.1
$C_8H_{10}O$	2,5-Xylenol	13,130.2	$C_8H_{15}O$	6-Methyl-5-hepten-2-ol	13,999.1
$C_8H_{10}O$	3,4-Xylenol	13,991.0	$C_8H_{16}O$	2-Octanone	11,649.2
$C_8H_{10}O$	3,5-Xylenol	13,767.7	$C_8H_{16}O$	2,2,4-Trimethyl-3-pentanone	12,854.6
$C_8H_{10}O$	Phenetole	11,075.8	$C_8H_{16}O_2$	Caprylic acid	16,745.7
$C_8H_{10}O$	α-Methyl benzyl alcohol	13,087.4	$C_8H_{16}O_2$	Ethyl isocaproate	10,826.7
$C_8H_{10}O$	Phenylethylalcohol	13,307.4	$C_8H_{16}O_2$	Propyl isovalerate	10,715.7
$C_8H_{10}O_2$	4,6-Dimethylresorcinol	12,433.1	$C_8H_{16}O_2$	Isobutyl butyrate	10,283.9
$C_8H_{10}O_2$	2-Phenoxyethanol	14,368.3	$C_8H_{16}O_2$	Isobutyl isobutyrate	10,706.3
$C_8H_{10}O_6$	Diethyl dioxosuccinate	13,973.3	$C_8H_{16}O_2$	Amylisopropionate	10,567.2
$C_8H_{11}ClSi$	Chlorodimethylphenylsilane	11,382.2	$C_8H_{16}ClO_4$	Tetraethyleneglycol chlorohydrin	16,371.2
$C_8H_{11}N$	N-Ethylaniline	11,817.0	$C_8H_{17}I$	1-Iodooctane	11,625.1
$C_8H_{11}N$	N,N-Dimethylaniline	11,320.4	$C_8H_{17}NO_2$	Ethyl-l-leucinate	11,383.5
$C_8H_{11}N$	4-Ethylaniline	12,679.9	C_8H_{18}	Octane	9,221.0

Formula	Name	ΔH_v	Formula	Name	ΔH_v
C_8H_{18}	2-Methylheptane	9,362.0	$C_9H_{10}O$	2,4-Xylaldehyde	13,618.4
C_8H_{18}	3-Methylheptane	9,432.0	$C_9H_{10}O$	Cinnamyl alcohol	13,421.6
C_8H_{18}	4-Methylheptane	9,404.8	$C_9H_{10}O$	Propiophenone	12,407.6
C_8H_{18}	2,2-Dimethylhexane	8,927.8	$C_9H_{10}O$	3-Vinylanisole	12,756.4
C_8H_{18}	2,3-Dimethylhexane	9,224.9	$C_9H_{10}O$	3-Vinylanisole	12,735.8
C_8H_{18}	2,4-Dimethylhexane	9,086.6	$C_9H_{10}O$	4-Vinylanisole	12,554.7
C_8H_{18}	2,5-Dimethylhexane	9,110.2	$C_9H_{10}O_2$	Benzyl acetate	12,107.2
C_8H_{18}	3,3-Dimethylhexane	9,065.2	$C_9H_{10}O_2$	Ethyl benzoate	11,981.5
C_8H_{18}	3,4-Dimethylhexane	9,239.4	$C_9H_{10}O_2$	Hydrocinnamic acid	15,411.9
C_8H_{18}	3-Ethylhexane	9,416.3	$C_9H_{10}O_2$	Ethyl salicylate	13,030.1
C_8H_{18}	2,2,3-Trimethylpentane	8,861.1	$C_9H_{11}NO$	N-Methylacetanilide	13,235.2
C_8H_{18}	2,2,4-Trimethylpentane	8,548.0	$C_9H_{11}NO_2$	Ethyl carbanilate	19,791.8
C_8H_{18}	2,3,3-Trimethylpentane	8,960.9	C_9H_{12}	1,2,3-Trimethylbenzene	10,781.9
C_8H_{18}	2,3,4-Trimethylpentane	8,988.2	C_9H_{12}	1,2,4-Trimethylbenzene	10,710.2
C_8H_{18}	2-Methyl-3-ethylpentane	9,134.3	C_9H_{12}	1,3,5-Trimethylbenzene	10,516.8
C_8H_{18}	3-Methyl-3-ethylpentane	9,028.7	C_9H_{12}	o-Ethyl toluene	10,488.8
C_8H_{18}	2,2,3,3-Tetramethylbutane	10,351.5	C_9H_{12}	m-Ethyl toluene	10,416.6
$C_8H_{18}N_2$	Tetramethylpiperazine	11,187.5	C_9H_{12}	p-Ethyl toluene	10,461.1
C_8H_{18}	n-Octanol	14,262.4	C_9H_{12}	Isopropylbenzene	10,335.3
C_8H_{18}	2-Octanol	12,468.4	C_9H_{12}	N-Propylbenzene	10,424.1
$C_8H_{18}O$	Di n-butyl ether	–	$C_9H_{12}O$	2-Ethylanisole	11,642.8
$C_8H_{18}O$	Methyl heptyl ether	–	$C_9H_{12}O$	3-Ethylanisole	11,616.7
$C_8H_{18}O_2$	1,2-Dipropoxy ethane	6,370.7	$C_9H_{12}O$	4-Ethylanisole	11,625.7
$C_8H_{18}O_3$	Diethylene glycol butyl ether	14,127.0	$C_9H_{12}O$	3-Phenyl-1-propanol	14,493.9
$C_8H_{18}O_5$	Tetraethylene glycol	21,296.6	$C_9H_{12}O$	2-Isopropylphenol	13,402.3
$C_8H_{18}S$	Di n-butyl sulfide	11,183.6	$C_9H_{12}O$	3-Isopropylphenol	13,292.2
$C_8H_{18}S_2$	Dibutyl disulfide	8,254.1	$C_9H_{12}O$	4-Isopropylphenol	13,878.7
$C_8H_{19}N$	Diisobutylamine	10,058.3	$C_9H_{12}O$	Benzyl ethyl ether	11,315.5
$C_8H_{20}O_4Si$	Tetraethoxysilane	10,968.6	$C_9H_{13}ClOSi$	Chloroethoxymethylphenylsilane	12,270.3
$C_8H_{20}Pb$	Tetraethyllead	12,959.7	$C_9H_{13}N$	2,4,5-Trimethylaniline	13,975.0
$C_8H_{20}Si$	Amyltrimethylsilane	9,659.6	$C_9H_{13}N$	N,N-Dimethyl-O-toluidine	11,648.3
$C_8H_{20}Si$	Tetraethylsilane	9,893.0	$C_9H_{13}N$	N,N-Dimethyl-4-toluidine	12,738.4
$C_8H_{20}Sb_2$	Tetraethylbistibine	12,975.4	$C_9H_{13}N$	4-Cumidine	13,127.9
$C_8H_{22}O_3Si_2$	1,3-Diethoxytetramethyldisiloxane	11,261.9	$C_9H_{14}O$	Phorone	12,557.2
$C_8H_{24}Cl_2O_3Si_4$	1,7-Dichlorooctamethyltetrasiloxane	12,602.9	$C_9H_{14}O$	Isophorone	11,277.6
$C_8H_{24}O_2Si_3$	Octamethyltrisiloxane	10,956.0	$C_9H_{14}O_4$	cis-Diethyl citraconate	12,913.2
$C_8H_{24}O_4Si_4$	Octamethylcyclotetrasiloxane	11,515.0	$C_9H_{14}O_4$	Diethyl itaconate	12,075.8
$C_9H_6O_2$	Coumarin	15,202.7	$C_9H_{14}O_4$	Diethyl mesaconate	13,326.1
C_9H_7N	Quinoline	12,575.4	$C_9H_{14}O_7$	Trimethyl citrate	15,807.7
C_9H_7N	Isoquinoline	12,847.6	$C_9H_{16}O_3$	Isobutyl levulinate	13,571.2
C_9H_8	Indene	10,496.7	$C_9H_{16}O_4$	Azelaic acid	20,944.2
C_9H_8O	Cinnamylaldehyde	14,048.4	$C_9H_{16}O_4$	Diethyl ethylmalonate	12,842.0
$C_9H_8O_2$	trans-Cinnamic acid	17,492.9	$C_9H_{16}O_4$	Diethyl glutarate	13,261.5
C_9H_9N	Skatole	15,232.7	$C_9H_{18}O$	2-Nonanone	11,529.5
$C_9H_9NO_4$	Ethyl 3-nitrobenzoate	15,056.1	$C_9H_{18}O$	Di-isobutyl ketone	–
C_9H_{10}	α-Methyl styrene	10,214.6	$C_9H_{18}O$	Azelaldehyde	12,143.4
C_9H_{10}	β-Methyl styrene	10,701.3	$C_9H_{18}O_2$	Pelargonic acid	17,807.8
C_9H_{10}	2-Methyl styrene	–	$C_9H_{18}O_2$	Methyl caprylate	11,914.9
C_9H_{10}	3-Methyl styrene	–	$C_9H_{18}O_2$	Isobutyl isovalerate	10,999.7
C_9H_{10}	4-Methyl styrene	10,724.2	$C_9H_{18}O_2$	Isoamyl butyrate	11,104.5

Formula	Name	ΔH_v	Formula	Name	ΔH_v
$C_9H_{18}O_2$	Isoamyl isobutyrate	10,870.6	$C_{10}H_{14}$	1,2,3,5-Tetramethylbenzene	12,358.4
$C_9H_{19}I$	1-Iodononane	14,853.0	$C_{10}H_{14}$	1,2,4,5-Tetramethylbenzene	12,583.6
C_9H_{20}	n-Nonane	10,456.9	$C_{10}H_{14}$	4-Ethyl-1,3-xylene	11,070.4
C_9H_{20}	2,6-Dimethylheptane	—			
C_9H_{20}	2-Methyloctane	—	$C_{10}H_{14}$	5-Ethyl-1,3-xylene	11,045.5
			$C_{10}H_{14}$	2-Ethyl-1,4-xylene	11,144.6
C_9H_{20}	3-Methyloctane	—	$C_{10}H_{14}$	1,2-Diethylbenzene	11,695.5
$C_9H_{20}O$	1-Nonanol	13,849.2	$C_{10}H_{14}$	1,3-Diethylbenzene	10,993.9
$C_9H_{20}O$	Diisobutyl carbinol	—	$C_{10}H_{14}$	1,4-Diethylbenzene	10,746.3
$C_9H_{20}O_3$	Dipropyleneglycol isopropyl ether	12,583.8			
$C_9H_{20}O_4$	Tripropyleneglycol	15,291.4	$C_{10}H_{14}$	1-Methyl-2-isopropylbenzene	—
			$C_{10}H_{14}$	1-Methyl-4-isopropylbenzene	11,038.7
$C_9H_{22}Si$	Hexyltrimethylsilane	10,264.9	$C_{10}H_{14}$	N-Butylbenzene	11,052.1
$C_9H_{22}Si$	Triethylpropylsilane	10,709.3	$C_{10}H_{14}$	Isobutylbenzene	8,567.8
$C_{10}H_7Br$	1-Bromonaphthalene	13,274.9	$C_{10}H_{14}$	sec-Butylbenzene	11,069.3
$C_{10}H_7Cl$	1-Chloronaphthalene	13,570.5			
$C_{10}H_{12}$	Dicyclopentadiene	10,165.9	$C_{10}H_{14}$	tert-Butylbenzene	10,705.5
			$C_{10}H_{14}O$	Carvacrol	13,765.7
$C_{10}H_8$	Naphthalene	17,065.2	$C_{10}H_{14}O$	Carbone	12,796.2
		12,311.6	$C_{10}H_{14}O$	Cuminyl alcohol	13,799.2
$C_{10}H_8Cl_2Si$	Dichloro-1-naphthysilane	16,325.3	$C_{10}H_{14}O$	4-Ethylphenetole	12,766.4
$C_{10}H_8O$	1-Naphthol	14,205.6			
$C_{10}H_8O$	2-Naphthol	14,138.5	$C_{10}H_{14}O$	2-Isopropyl-5-methylphenol	13,352.8
$C_{10}H_9N$	1-Naphthylamine	14,529.5	$C_{10}H_{14}O$	4-Isobutylphenol	14,053.5
			$C_{10}H_{14}O$	4-sec-Butylphenol	13,690.2
$C_{10}H_9N$	2-Naphthylamine	14,679.6	$C_{10}H_{14}O$	2-sec-Butylphenol	12,781.3
$C_{10}H_9N$	2-Methylquinoline	14,154.0	$C_{10}H_{14}O$	2-tert-Butylphenol	13,112.3
$C_{10}H_{10}$	1,3-Divinylbenzene	11,384.7			
$C_{10}H_{10}O$	4-Phenyl-3-buten-2-one	13,913.9	$C_{10}H_{14}O$	4-tert-Butylphenol	13,787.7
$C_{10}H_{10}O_2$	α-Methylcinnamic acid	18,149.4	$C_{10}H_{14}N_2$	Nicotine	12,337.1
			$C_{10}H_{15}N$	N-Diethylaniline	12,539.2
$C_{10}H_{10}O_2$	Methyl cinnamate	13,325.5	$C_{10}H_{15}NO_2$	N-Phenyliminodiethanol	17,482.1
$C_{10}H_{10}O_2$	Safrole	13,255.8	$C_{10}H_{16}$	Camphene	10,505.4
$C_{10}H_{10}O_4$	1,2-Phenylene diacetate	14,986.0			
$C_{10}H_{10}O_4$	Dimethylphthalate	14,922.2	$C_{10}H_{16}$	Dipentene	10,538.3
$C_{10}H_{12}$	2,4-Dimethylstyrene	11,454.0	$C_{10}H_{16}$	d-Limonene	10,508.4
			$C_{10}H_{16}$	Myrcene	10,704.8
$C_{10}H_{12}$	2,5-Dimethylstyrene	11,283.5	$C_{10}H_{16}$	α-Phellandrene	11,139.5
$C_{10}H_{12}$	3-Ethylstyrene	11,285.7	$C_{10}H_{16}$	α-Pinene	9,813.6
$C_{10}H_{12}$	4-Ethylstyrene	11,146.6			
$C_{10}H_{12}$	Tetralin	11,613.0	$C_{10}H_{16}$	β-Pinene	10,235.8
$C_{10}H_{12}O$	Anethole	13,006.8	$C_{10}H_{16}$	Terpenoline	12,030.8
			$C_{10}H_{16}AsNO_3$	Diethyl arsanilinate	12,973.9
$C_{10}H_{12}O$	4-Methylpropiophenone	12,505.0	$C_{10}H_{16}O$	d-Camphor	12,800.9
$C_{10}H_{12}O$	Estragole	12,879.3			11,978.0
$C_{10}H_{12}O$	Cuminal	12,668.0	$C_{10}H_{16}O$	l-dihydrocarvone	11,825.9
$C_{10}H_{12}O$	4-Vinylphenetole	13,728.7			
$C_{10}H_{12}O_2$	Eugenol	13,907.8	$C_{10}H_{16}O$	α-Citral	13,255.5
			$C_{10}H_{16}O$	d-Fenchone	11,273.4
$C_{10}H_{12}O_2$	Isoeugenol	14,084.2	$C_{10}H_{16}O$	Pulegone	13,395.4
$C_{10}H_{12}O_2$	Chavibetol	14,527.7	$C_{10}H_{16}O$	α-Thujone	11,950.8
$C_{10}H_{12}O_2$	Propyl benzoate	12,318.7	$C_{10}H_{16}OSi$	Ethoxydimethylphenylsilane	11,718.6
$C_{10}H_{12}O_3$	2-Phenoxyethyl acetate	14,070.3			
$C_{10}H_{13}ClO$	2-Chloroethyl-α-methylbenzyl ether	12,969.2	$C_{10}H_{16}O_2$	Campholenic acid	16,324.1
			$C_{10}H_{16}O_2$	Diosphenol	13,644.0
$C_{10}H_{13}Cl_2O_2P$	4-tert-Butylphenyl dichlorophosphate	13,711.0	$C_{10}H_{16}O_2$	Fencholic acid	16,442.8
			$C_{10}H_{18}$	cis-Decalin	10,515.4
$C_{10}H_{14}$	1,2,3,4-Tetramethylbenzene	12,258.0	$C_{10}H_{18}$	trans-Decalin	8,749.1

Formula	Name	ΔH_v	Formula	Name	ΔH_v
$C_{10}H_{18}O$	d-Citronellal	12,305.1	$C_{11}H_{14}$	2,4,6-Trimethylstyrene	11,588.8
$C_{10}H_{18}O$	Cineol	10,570.8	$C_{11}H_{14}$	4-Isopropylstryene	11,471.0
$C_{10}H_{18}O$	Dihydrocarveol	13,698.5	$C_{11}H_{14}O$	Isobutyrophenone	12,878.8
$C_{10}H_{18}O$	dl-Fenchyl alcohol	12,955.9	$C_{11}H_{14}O$	Pivalophenone	13,221.3
$C_{10}H_{18}O$	Geraniol	14,060.7	$C_{11}H_{14}O$	2,3,5-Trimethylacetophenone	14,283.6
$C_{10}H_{18}O$	d-Linalool	12,269.7	$C_{11}H_{14}O_2$	Isobutyl benzoate	13,105.8
$C_{10}H_{18}O$	Nerol	13,366.1	$C_{11}H_{14}O_2$	4-Allylveratrole	15,027.1
$C_{10}H_{18}O$	α-Terpineol	12,754.5	$C_{11}H_{16}$	Pentamethylbenzene	–
$C_{10}H_{18}O_2$	Citronellic acid	16,455.4	$C_{11}H_{16}$	3,5-Diethyltoluene	11,167.4
$C_{10}H_{18}O_3$	Amyl levulinate	14,321.7	$C_{11}H_{16}$	1,2,4-Trimethyl-5-ethylbenzene	12,145.3
$C_{10}H_{18}O_3$	Isoamyl levulinate	13,867.9	$C_{11}H_{16}$	1,3,5-Trimethyl-2-ethylbenzene	11,677.3
$C_{10}H_{18}O_4$	Diethyl ethylmethylmalonate	12,345.6	$C_{11}H_{16}$	3-Ethylcumene	11,233.5
$C_{10}H_{18}O_4$	Diethyl adipate	14,240.6	$C_{11}H_{16}$	4-Ethylcumene	11,425.6
$C_{10}H_{18}O_4$	Diisobutyl oxalate	13,343.1	$C_{11}H_{16}$	sec-Amylbenzene	11,886.0
$C_{10}H_{18}O_4$	Dipropyl succinate	13,975.7	$C_{11}H_{16}O$	4-tert-Butyl-2-cresol	13,798.1
$C_{10}H_{18}O_4$	Sebacic acid	21,978.3	$C_{11}H_{16}O$	2-tert-Butyl-4-cresol	14,037.9
$C_{10}H_{18}O_6$	Dipropyl-d-tartrate	15,754.0	$C_{11}H_{16}O$	4-tert-Amylphenol	13,154.3
$C_{10}H_{18}O_6$	Diisopropyl-d-tartrate	15,836.6	$C_{11}H_{16}O_5$	Ethylcamphoronic anhydride	16,373.6
$C_{10}H_{19}N$	Camphylamine	13,224.1	$C_{11}H_{18}O_2$	Bornyl formate	12,276.0
$C_{10}H_{20}$	Menthane	10,293.1	$C_{11}H_{18}O_2$	Geranyl formate	13,189.7
$C_{10}H_{20}$	1-Decene	10,233.3	$C_{11}H_{18}O_2$	Neryl formate	12,959.3
$C_{10}H_{20}$	n-Decane	10,912.0	$C_{11}H_{18}O_2Si$	Diethoxymethylphenyl silane	13,267.3
$C_{10}H_{20}Br_2$	1,2-Dibromodecane	16,407.7	$C_{11}H_{18}O_5$	Diethyl-gamma-oxoazelate	17,543.6
$C_{10}H_{20}O$	Decanol	14,065.1	$C_{11}H_{20}O_2$	10-Hendecenoic acid	17,247.5
$C_{10}H_{20}O$	Citronellol	14,214.1	$C_{11}H_{20}O_2$	Menthyl formate	12,077.7
$C_{10}H_{20}O$	Capraldehyde	13,154.9	$C_{11}H_{20}O_2$	2-Ethylhexyl acrylate	12,522.5
$C_{10}H_{20}O$	l-Menthol	13,475.3	$C_{11}H_{20}O_2$	Octyl acrylate	12,957.5
$C_{10}H_{20}O$	Decan-2-one	12,114.7	$C_{11}H_{20}O_3$	Hexyl levulinate	14,626.2
$C_{10}H_{20}O_2$	Capric acid	19,372.6	$C_{11}H_{22}O$	Hendecan-2-one	14,353.5
$C_{10}H_{20}O_2$	Isoamyl isovalerate	11,040.8	$C_{11}H_{22}O_2$	Methyl caprate	13,831.7
$C_{10}H_{22}$	2,7-Dimethyloctane	10,339.3	$C_{11}H_{22}O_2$	Hendecanoic acid	14,689.9
$C_{10}H_{22}O$	Diisoamyl ether	11,072.2	$C_{11}H_{24}$	Undecane	11,481.7
$C_{10}H_{22}O_2$	2-Butyl-2-ethylbutane-1,3-diol	15,833.7	$C_{11}H_{24}O$	Hendecan-2-ol	14,216.2
$C_{10}H_{22}O$	Dihydrocitronellol	16,769.8	$C_{11}H_{26}Si$	Trimethyloctylsilane	12,285.8
$C_{10}H_{22}O_3$	Dipropylene glycol monobutyl ether	13,721.1	$C_{11}H_{26}Si$	Amyltriethylsilane	11,859.7
$C_{10}H_{22}S$	Diisoamyl sulfide	11,829.9	$C_{12}H_9Br$	4-Bromobiphenyl	13,493.4
$C_{10}H_{24}Si$	Heptyltrimethylsilane	10,987.3	$C_{12}H_9BrO$	2-Bromo-4-phenylphenol	13,589.9
$C_{10}H_{24}Si$	Butyltriethylsilane	11,124.0	$C_{12}H_9Cl$	2-Chlorobiphenyl	13,925.7
$C_{10}H_{28}O_4Si_3$	1,5-Diethoxyhexamethyl trisiloxane	12,586.4	$C_{12}H_9Cl$	4-Chlorobiphenyl	14,017.4
$C_{10}H_{30}O_3Si_4$	Decamethyltetrasiloxane	11,981.2	$C_{12}H_9ClO$	2-Chloro-3-phenylphenol	15,258.0
$C_{10}H_{30}O_5Si_5$	Decamethylcyclopentasiloxane	12,272.1	$C_{12}H_9ClO$	2-Chloro-6-phenylphenol	15,508.4
$C_{11}H_8O_2$	1-Naphthoic acid	22,581.4	$C_{12}H_9Cl_2PO$	2-Xenyl dichlorophosphate	17,127.6
$C_{11}H_8O_2$	2-Naphthoic acid	22,630.8	$C_{12}H_9N$	Carbazole	15,421.6
$C_{11}H_{10}$	1-Methylnaphthalene	–	$C_{12}H_{10}$	Acenaphthene	13,078.5
$C_{11}H_{12}O_2$	Ethyl-trans-cinnamate	13,639.9	$C_{12}H_{10}$	Diphenyl	12,910.0
$C_{11}H_{12}O_2$	1 Phenyl-1,3-pentanedione	15,033.9	$C_{12}H_{10}ClPO_3$	Diphenyl chlorophosphate	13,191.2
$C_{11}H_{12}O_3$	Ethyl benzoylacetate	17,115.4	$C_{12}H_{10}Cl_2Si$	Dichlorodiphenylsilane	14,968.5
$C_{11}H_{12}O_3$	Myristicine	14,471.4	$C_{12}H_{10}F_2Si$	Difluorodiphenylsilane	12,913.3
$C_{11}H_{14}$	1-Phenylpentane	–	$C_{12}H_{10}N_2$	Azobenzene	14,786.7
$C_{11}H_{14}$	2,4,5-Trimethylstyrene	12,076.1	$C_{12}H_{10}O$	1-Acetonaphthone	16,095.5

Formula	Name	ΔH_v	Formula	Name	ΔH_v
$C_{12}H_{10}O$	2-Acetonaphthone	16,496.7	$C_{12}H_{34}O_5Si_4$	1,7-Diethoxyoctamethyltetrasiloxane	14,095.9
$C_{12}H_{10}O$	Diphenyl ether	12,325.5	$C_{12}H_{36}O_4Si_5$	Dodecamethylpentasiloxane	12,942.6
$C_{12}H_{10}O$	2-Phenylphenol	15,397.8	$C_{12}H_{36}O_6Si_6$	Dodecamethylcyclohexasiloxane	13,760.6
$C_{12}H_{10}O$	4-Phenylphenol	16,974.3	$C_{13}H_9N$	Acridine	15,174.6
$C_{12}H_{10}S$	Diphenyl sulfide	13,974.8	$C_{13}H_{10}$	Fluorene	13,682.8
$C_{12}H_{10}S$	Diphenyl disulfide	17,452.0	$C_{13}H_{10}O$	Benzophenone	14,725.4
$C_{12}H_{10}Se$	Diphenyl selenide	14,603.4	$C_{13}H_{10}O_2$	Phenyl benzoate	14,181.7
$C_{12}H_{11}N$	Diphenylamine	14,920.3	$C_{13}H_{10}O_2$	Salol	15,441.6
$C_{12}H_{12}$	1-Ethylnaphthalene	12,751.3	$C_{13}H_{12}$	Diphenylmethane	13,089.4
$C_{12}H_{12}N_2$	1,1-Diphenylhydrazine	15,940.4	$C_{13}H_{12}O$	Benzhydrol	15,220.2
$C_{12}H_{14}N_2O_5$	2-Cyclohexyl-4,6-dinitrophenol	19,100.0	$C_{13}H_{12}O$	Benzyl phenyl ether	14,156.7
$C_{12}H_{14}O_3$	Eugenyl acetate	15,120.7	$C_{13}H_{12}O$	1-Proprionaphthone	16,630.8
$C_{12}H_{14}O_4$	Apiole	16,881.7	$C_{13}H_{13}ClSi$	Chloromethyldiphenylsilane	14,924.6
$C_{12}H_{14}O_4$	Diethyl phthalate	15,383.0	$C_{13}H_{14}Si$	Methyldiphenylsilane	15,396.8
$C_{12}H_{16}$	2,5-Diethylstyrene	12,150.3	$C_{13}H_{14}$	2-Isopropylnaphthalene	13,036.9
$C_{12}H_{16}$	Phenylcyclohexane	13,345.6	$C_{13}H_{18}O$	Enanthophenone	15,597.7
$C_{12}H_{16}O_2$	Isoamyl benzoate	12,782.9	$C_{13}H_{20}$	Heptylbenzene	13,535.4
$C_{12}H_{18}$	Hexamethylbenzene	–	$C_{13}H_{20}O$	α-Ionone	14,253.4
$C_{12}H_{18}$	1,2,4-Triethylbenzene	11,957.9	$C_{13}H_{22}O_2$	Bornyl propionate	13,245.0
$C_{12}H_{18}$	1,3,4-Triethylbenzene	12,215.0	$C_{13}H_{26}O$	2-Tridecanone	14,416.1
$C_{12}H_{18}$	1,3,5-Triethylbenzene	–	$C_{13}H_{26}O_2$	Methyl laurate	14,853.5
$C_{12}H_{18}$	1,2-Diisopropylbenzene	11,751.4	$C_{13}H_{26}O_2$	Tridecanoic acid	19,214.8
$C_{12}H_{18}$	1,3-Diisopropylbenzene	11,498.9	$C_{13}H_{28}$	Tridecane	12,991.3
$C_{12}H_{18}O$	2-tert-Butyl-4-ethylphenol	13,994.0	$C_{13}H_{28}O_4$	Tripropyleneglycol monobutyl ether	15,937.6
$C_{12}H_{18}O$	4-tert-Butyl-2,5-xylenol	14,477.9	$C_{13}H_{30}Si$	Decyltrimethylsilane	13,311.1
$C_{12}H_{18}O$	4-tert-Butyl-2,6-xylenol	14,142.5	$C_{13}H_{30}Si$	Triethylheptylsilane	13,298.3
$C_{12}H_{18}O$	6-tert-Butyl-2,4-xylenol	13,882.4	$C_{14}H_8O_2$	Anthraquinone	21,163.1
$C_{12}H_{18}O$	6-tert-Butyl-3,4-xylenol	14,848.3	$C_{14}H_8O_4$	1,4-Dihydroxyanthraquinone	17,677.9
$C_{12}H_{20}O_2$	d-Bornyl acetate	11,838.7	$C_{14}H_{10}$	Anthracene	16,823.6
$C_{12}H_{20}O_2$	Geranyl acetate	13,879.9	$C_{14}H_{10}$	Phenanthrene	14,184.0
$C_{12}H_{20}O_2$	Linalyl acetate	12,910.6	$C_{14}H_{10}O_2$	Benzil	15,046.4
$C_{12}H_{20}O_3Si$	Triethoxyphenylsilane	14,117.9	$C_{14}H_{10}O_3$	Benzoic anhydride	16,060.9
$C_{12}H_{20}O_7$	Triethyl citrate	14,818.4	$C_{14}H_{12}$	1,1-Diphenylethylene	13,778.1
$C_{12}H_{21}PO_4$	Trimethallyl phosphate	12,566.1	$C_{14}H_{12}$	trans-Diphenylethylene	15,010.1
$C_{12}H_{22}O_2$	Citronellyl acetate	15,781.3	$C_{14}H_{12}O$	Desoxybenzoin	15,642.1
$C_{12}H_{22}O_2$	Menthyl acetate	12,819.2	$C_{14}H_{12}O$	Benzoin	15,952.5
$C_{12}H_{22}O_4$	Dimethyl sebacate	14,861.3	$C_{14}H_{14}$	Dibenzyl	13,387.6
$C_{12}H_{22}O_4$	Diisoamyl oxalate	14,123.7	$C_{14}H_{14}O$	2-Isobutyronaphthone	17,133.8
$C_{12}H_{22}O_6$	Diisobutyl-d-tartrate	14,874.9	$C_{14}H_{15}O$	Dibenzylamine	16,260.1
$C_{12}H_{24}$	1-Dodecene	12,587.8	$C_{14}H_{15}N$	Ethyldiphenylamine	14,569.4
$C_{12}H_{24}$	Triisobutylene	10,790.4	$C_{14}H_{20}Cl_2$	1,2-Dichlorotetraethylbenzene	14,629.0
$C_{12}H_{24}O$	Dodecan-2-one	14,138.7	$C_{14}H_{20}Cl_2$	1,4-Dichlorotetraethylbenzene	13,397.5
$C_{12}H_{24}O$	Lauraldehyde	13,644.2	$C_{14}H_{20}O_3$	2-(4-tert-Butylphenoxy)ethyl acetate	16,017.6
$C_{12}H_{24}O_2$	Lauric acid	16,585.3	$C_{14}H_{22}$	1,2,3,4-Tetraethylbenzene	12,763.5
$C_{12}H_{26}$	n-Dodecane	11,857.7	$C_{14}H_{22}O$	2,4-Di-tert-butylphenol	14,237.7
$C_{12}H_{26}O$	Dodecyl alcohol	15,166.5	$C_{14}H_{24}O_2$	Bornyl butyrate	13,746.1
$C_{12}H_{26}O_4$	Tripropylene glycol monoisopropyl ether	14,171.5	$C_{14}H_{24}O_2$	Bornyl isobutyrate	13,501.8
$C_{12}H_{27}N$	Triisobutylamine	12,390.6	$C_{14}H_{24}O_2$	Geranyl butyrate	16,086.4
$C_{12}H_{27}N$	Dodecylamine	14,836.4	$C_{14}H_{24}O_2$	Geranyl isobutyrate	15,699.5
$C_{12}H_{28}Si$	Triethylhoxylsilane	12,119.4	$C_{14}H_{26}O_4$	Diethyl sebacate	16,819.6

Formula	Name	ΔH_v	Formula	Name	ΔH_v
$C_{14}H_{28}O$	2-Tetradecanone	15,102.7	$C_{16}H_{46}O_7Si_6$	1,1,1-Diethoxydodeca methylhexasiloxane	15,945.3
$C_{14}H_{28}O$	Myristaldehyde	14,088.9			
$C_{14}H_{28}O_2$	Myristic acid	18,380.1	$C_{16}H_{48}O_6Si_7$	Hexadecamethylheptasiloxane	14,841.5
$C_{14}H_{29}Cl$	1-Chlorotetradecane	14,083.5	$C_{16}H_{48}O_8Si_8$	Hexadecamethylcyclooctasiloxane	14,986.3
$C_{14}H_{30}$	Tetradecane	13,750.0	$C_{17}H_{10}O$	Benzanthrone	18,309.6
			$C_{17}H_{18}O_3$	4-tert-Butylphenyl salicylate	16,455.6
$C_{14}H_{31}N$	Tetradecylamine	14,840.8			
$C_{14}H_{32}Si$	Triethyloctysilane	12,954.8	$C_{17}H_{24}O_2$	Menthyl benzoate	16,804.5
$C_{14}H_{40}O_6Si_5$	1,9-Diethoxydeca methylpentasiloxane	15,296.9	$C_{17}H_{34}O$	2-Heptadecanone	16,559.8
			$C_{17}H_{34}O_2$	Methyl palmitate	17,003.5
$C_{14}H_{42}O_5Si_6$	Tetradecamethylhexasiloxane	13,800.0	$C_{17}H_{36}$	Heptadecane	15,608.5
$C_{14}H_{42}O_7Si_7$	Tetradecamethylcyclo heptasiloxane	14,263.8	$C_{17}H_{38}Si$	Tetradecyltrimethylsilane	16,439.7
			$C_{18}H_{12}Cl_3O_3PS$	Tri-2-chlorophenylthiophosphate	24,386.1
$C_{15}H_{14}O$	1,3-Diphenyl-2-propanone	15,429.8	$C_{18}H_{15}O_4P$	Triphenyl phosphate	19,272.3
$C_{15}H_{14}O_2$	1-Biphenyloxy-2,3-epoxypropane	16,160.6	$C_{18}H_{30}$	Hexaethylbenzene	14,184.9
$C_{15}H_{16}O_2$	4,4-Isopropylidenebisphenol	23,254.0	$C_{18}H_{30}O$	2,4,6-Tri-tert-butylphenol	14,703.7
$C_{15}H_{18}O$	Isocapronaphthone	17,360.3	$C_{18}H_{34}O_2$	Oleic acid	20,326.7
$C_{15}H_{18}OSi$	Ethoxymethyldiphenylsilane	16,106.4			
			$C_{18}H_{34}O_2$	Elaidic acid	19,538.0
$C_{15}H_{20}O_2$	Helenin	26,532.7	$C_{18}H_{36}O$	Stearaldehyde	16,555.6
$C_{15}H_{24}$	Cadinene	15,518.3	$C_{18}H_{36}O_2$	Stearic acid	19,306.6
$C_{15}H_{24}O$	2,6-Di-tert-butyl-4-cresol	14,338.6	$C_{18}H_{38}$	Octadecane	15,447.0
$C_{15}H_{24}O$	4,6-Di-tert-butyl-2-cresol	14,006.9	$C_{18}H_{38}$	2-Methylheptadecane	16,095.9
$C_{15}H_{24}O$	4,6-Di-tert-butyl-3-cresol	15,464.6			
			$C_{18}H_{38}O$	1-Octadecanol	17,508.0
$C_{15}H_{26}O$	Champacol	14,655.9	$C_{18}H_{39}N$	Ethylcetylamine	15,718.3
$C_{15}H_{26}O_6$	Triethyl camphoronate	16,112.2	$C_{18}H_{52}O_8Si_7$	1,1,3-Diethoxytetradeca methylheptasiloxane	16,765.8
$C_{15}H_{30}O_2$	Methyl myristate	16,051.0			
$C_{15}H_{32}$	Pentadecane	14,635.9	$C_{18}H_{54}O_7Si_8$	Octadecamethyloctasiloxane	15,270.3
$C_{15}H_{32}O_5$	Tetrapropylene glycol monoisopropyl ether	16,494.6	$C_{19}H_{16}$	Triphenylmethane	34,470.8
			$C_{19}H_{40}$	Nonadecane	16,497.3
$C_{15}H_{34}Si$	Dodecyltrimethylsilane	14,374.6	$C_{20}H_{20}OSi$	Ethoxytriphenylsilane	20,214.2
$C_{16}H_{14}O_2$	Benzyl cinnamate	20,840.6	$C_{20}H_{43}N$	Diethylhexadecylamine	15,871.3
$C_{16}H_{18}O$	Di(α-methylbenzyl)ether	14,628.1	$C_{20}H_{58}O_9Si_8$	1,1,5-Diethoxyhexadeca methyloctasiloxane	17,626.6
$C_{16}H_{20}O_2Si$	Diethoxydiphenylsilane	15,828.8			
$C_{16}H_{22}O_4$	Dibutyl phthalate	17,747.0	$C_{20}H_{60}O_8Si_9$	Eicosamethylnonasiloxane	19,522.9
$C_{16}H_{25}Cl$	Pentaethylchlorobenzene	13,707.3	$C_{21}H_{21}O_4P$	Tritolyl phosphate	20,835.9
$C_{16}H_{26}$	Pentaethylbenzene	13,670.1	$C_{21}H_{44}$	Heneicosane	17,702.2
$C_{16}H_{26}O$	2,6-Di-tert-butyl-4-ethylphenol	14,438.0	$C_{22}H_{42}O_2$	Erucic acid	23,655.2
$C_{16}H_{26}O$	4,6-Di-tert-butyl-3-ethylphenol	15,954.8	$C_{22}H_{42}O_2$	Brassidic acid	24,085.7
$C_{16}H_{30}O$	Muscone	14,722.5	$C_{22}H_{46}$	Docosane	16,941.1
$C_{16}H_{31}N$	Palmitonitrile	16,433.7	$C_{22}H_{56}O_9Si_{10}$	Docosamethyldecasiloxane	21,878.6
$C_{16}H_{32}$	1-Hexadecene	15,634.7	$C_{23}H_{48}$	Tricosane	19,082.1
$C_{16}H_{32}$	Tetraisobutylene	12,937.2	$C_{24}H_{50}$	Tetracosane	19,642.5
$C_{16}H_{32}O$	2-Hexadecanone	15,194.4	$C_{24}H_{72}O_{10}Si_{11}$	Tetracosamethylhendecasiloxane	23,941.2
$C_{16}H_{32}O$	Palmitaldehyde	15,454.2	$C_{25}H_{52}$	Pentacosane	20,815.9
$C_{16}H_{32}O_2$	Palmitic acid	17,603.6	$C_{26}H_{54}$	Hexacosane	21,605.7
$C_{16}H_{34}$	Hexadecane	15,405.5	$C_{27}H_{33}O_4P$	Dicarvacryl-2-tolyl phosphate	24,233.3
$C_{16}H_{34}O$	Cetyl alcohol	14,483.4	$C_{27}H_{56}$	Heptacosane	21,958.1
$C_{16}H_{36}N$	Cetylamine	15,238.0	$C_{28}H_{58}$	Octacosane	24,144.2
$C_{16}H_{36}Si$	Decyltriethylsilane	15,393.7	$C_{29}H_{60}$	Nonacosane	24,816.8
			$C_{32}H_{34}ClO_4P$	Dicarvacryl-mono-(6-chloro-2-xenyl)-phosphate	25,299.5

MISCIBILITY OF ORGANIC SOLVENT PAIRS
Table A

Doctor J. S. Drury

Industrial and Engineering Chemistry   Vol. 44, No. 11, Nov. 1952

(Reprinted by permission)

The classifications were made by shaking together 5 ml. of each of the solvents listed in a test tube for 1 minute, then allowing the mixture to settle. If no interfacial meniscus was observed, the solvent pair was considered miscible. If such a meniscus was present, the solvent pair was regarded as immiscible. The classification of immiscible is a qualitative one since solvent pairs may exhibit some degree of partial miscibility while existing as separate phases. Solvent pairs possessing a pronounced degree of partial miscibility are designated by the symbol Is.

#	Compounds	Acetone	Acetyl acetone	2-Amino-2-methyl-1-propanol	Aniline	Benzaldehyde	Benzene	Benzin	Benzyl alcohol	Butyl acetate	Butyl alcohol	n-Butyl ether	Capryl alcohol	Carbon tetrachloride	Diacetone alcohol	Diethanolamine	Diethyl cellosolve	Diethyl ether	Dimethylaniline	Ethyl alcohol	Ethyl benzoate	Ethylene glycol	2-Ethylhexanol	Formamide	Furfuryl alcohol	Glycerol	Hydroxyethyl-ethylenediamine	Isoamyl alcohol	Methyl isobutyl ketone	Nitromethane	Dibutoxytetra-ethylene glycol	Pyridine	Trietanolamine	Trimethylene glycol
1	Acetone	..	M	M	..	M	M	M	M	M	M	M	M	M	M	M	M	M	M	M	M	M	M	M	M	I	M	M	M	M	M	M	..	M
2	Acetyl acetone	M	..	R	..	M	M	M	M	M	M	M	M	M	M	M	R	M	M	M	M	M	M	M	M	I	M	R	M	M	M	M	..	M
3	Adiponitrile	M	M	M	M	..	M	..	M	..	M	M	I	..	I	M	..	M	I	M	M	M	I	I	M	M	I	R	M	I	M	..	M	M	M	M
4	2-Amino-2-methyl-1-propanol	M	R	..	..	M	M	I	M	M	M	Is	M	M	R	M	M	M	M	M	M	M	M	M	M	M	M	M	M	M	M	M	..	M
5	Benzaldehyde	M	M	M	..	..	M	M	M	M	M	M	M	M	M	I	M	M	M	M	M	Is	M	M	M	Is	M	R	M	M	M	M	M	..	M
6	Benzene	M	M	M	..	M	..	M	M	M	M	M	M	M	Is	I	M	M	M	M	M	I	M	I	M	I	R	I	M	M	I	M	M	..	I
7	Benzin	M	M	I	..	M	M	..	I	M	M	M	M	M	M	I	I	M	M	M	M	I	M	I	I	I	Is	M	M	I	M	M	M	..	I
8	Benzonitrile	M	M	M	M	..	M	..	M	M	M	M	..	M	..	M	M	M	M	M	M	I	M	I	M	I	M	M	M	M	M	M	M	M	I
9	Benzothiazole	M	M	M	M	..	M	M	M	M	M	M	M	..	M	..	M	I	M	M	M	I	M	I	M	I	M	M	M	M	..	M	M	M
10	Benzyl alcohol	M	M	M	..	M	M	I	..	M	M	M	M	M	M	M	M	M	M	M	M	M	M	M	M	M	M	M	M	M	M	M	..	M
11	Benzyl mercaptan	M	M	I	M	..	M	M	..	M	M	M	M	M	M	I	M	M	M	I	M	I	M	I	I	I	M	M	M	M	M	M	R	I
12	Butyl acetate	M	M	M	..	M	M	M	M	..	M	M	M	M	M	M	M	M	M	M	M	Is	M	I	M	I	I	M	M	M	M	M	M	..	Is
13	Butyl alcohol	M	M	M	..	M	M	M	M	M	..	M	M	M	M	M	M	M	M	M	M	M	M	M	M	M	M	M	M	M	M	M	..	M
14	n-Butyl ether	M	M	Is	..	M	M	M	M	M	M	..	M	M	M	I	M	M	M	M	M	I	M	I	I	I	M	M	M	I	M	M	M	..	I
15	Capryl alcohol	M	M	M	..	M	M	M	M	M	M	M	..	M	M	M	M	M	M	M	M	M	M	M	M	M	M	M	M	Is	M	M	..	M
16	Carbon tetrachloride	M	M	M	..	M	M	M	M	M	M	M	M	..	M	Is	I	M	M	M	M	M	I	I	M	I	M	M	M	M	M	M	..	M
17	Diacetone alcohol	M	M	R	..	M	Is	I	M	M	M	M	M	M	..	Is	..	M	M	M	M	M	M	M	M	I	R	M	M	M	M	M	..	M
18	Diethanolamine	M	R	M	..	I	I	I	I	M	I	M	I	M	I	..	M	..	I	I	Is	M	M	M	M	M	M	M	I	I	M	I	M	..	M
19	Diethyl Cellosolve	M	M	M	..	M	M	M	M	M	M	M	M	I	M	..	..	M	M	M	M	M	M	M	M	I	I	M	M	M	M	M	..	M
20	Diethyl ether	M	M	M	..	M	M	M	M	M	M	M	M	M	M	I	M	..	M	M	M	I	M	I	I	I	I	M	M	M	M	M	..	I
21	Dimethylaniline	M	M	M	..	M	M	M	M	M	M	M	M	M	Is	M	..	M	..	M	M	I	M	I	M	I	I	M	M	M	M	M	..	I
22	Di-N-propylaniline	M	M	I	M	..	M	M	M	M	M	M	M	M	I	..	M	M	M	..	M	I	M	I	I	I	I	M	M	M	M	M	I	I
23	Ethyl alcohol	M	M	M	..	M	M	M	M	M	M	M	M	M	M	..	M	M	M	..	M	M	M	M	M	M	M	M	M	M	M	M	..	M
24	Ethyl benzoate	M	M	M	..	M	M	M	M	M	M	M	M	M	M	Is	M	M	M	M	..	I	M	I	M	I	M	M	M	M	M	M	..	Is
25	Ethyl isothiocyanate	M	M	R	M	..	M	M	M	M	M	M	M	M	M	..	M	M	M	M	M	I	M	I	M	I	R	M	M	..	M	M	M	I
26	Ethyl thiocyanate	M	M	M	M	..	M	M	M	M	M	M	M	..	M	M	M	M	M	M	M	I	M	I	M	I	M	M	M	..	M	M	M	I
27	Ethylene glycol	M	M	M	..	Is	I	M	M	Is	M	I	M	I	M	M	I	I	M	M	I	..	M	M	M	M	M	M	M	M	I	M	..	M
28	2-Ethylhexanol	M	M	M	..	M	M	M	M	M	M	M	M	M	M	M	M	M	M	M	M	I	..	I	M	I	M	M	M	M	M	M	..	M
29	Formamide	M	M	M	..	M	I	I	M	I	M	I	I	M	I	M	I	M	I	I	M	M	I	..	M	M	M	M	Is	M	M	M	..	M
30	Furfuryl alcohol	M	M	M	I	..	M	M	M	M	M	M	M	M	M	M	M	M	M	M	M	M	M	M	..	M	M	M	M	M	M	M	..	M
31	Glycerol	I	I	M	..	I	I	I	M	I	M	I	I	I	I	M	I	I	I	M	I	I	M	I	M	..	M	I	I	I	I	M	..	M
32	Hydroxyethyl-ethylenediamine	M	R	M	..	R	I	Is	M	I	M	I	M	I	R	M	I	I	M	M	I	M	M	I	I	M	..	M	M	M	M	M	..	M
33	Isoamyl alcohol	M	M	M	..	M	M	M	M	M	M	M	M	M	M	M	M	M	M	M	M	M	M	I	M	I	M	..	M	M	M	M	..	M
34	Isoamyl sulfide	M	M	I	..	M	M	M	M	M	M	M	M	M	..	I	I	M	M	M	M	I	M	I	I	I	I	M	M	..	M	M	I	I
35	Isobutyl mercaptan	M	M	M	..	M	M	M	M	M	M	M	..	M	..	M	M	M	M	M	M	I	M	I	M	I	M	I	M	M	..	M	R	R
36	Methyl disulfide	M	M	M	..	M	M	M	M	M	..	M	M	M	M	M	M	M	M	I	M	I	M	I	M	I	I	M	M	..	M	M	I	R
37	Methyl isobutyl ketone	M	M	M	..	M	M	M	M	M	M	M	M	M	M	I	M	M	M	M	M	Is	M	I	M	I	M	M	..	M	M	M	M	..	I
38	Nitromethane	M	M	M	..	M	I	I	M	M	M	M	I	Is	M	M	I	M	M	M	M	I	M	I	M	I	M	M	M	..	M	M	M	..	I
39	Dibutoxytetra-ethylene glycol	M	M	M	..	M	M	M	M	M	M	M	M	M	M	I	M	M	M	M	M	I	M	I	M	I	M	M	M	M	..	M	..	M
40	Pyridine	M	M	M	..	M	M	M	M	M	M	M	M	M	M	M	M	M	M	M	M	M	M	M	M	I	M	M	M	M	M	..	..	M
41	Tri-n-butylamine	M	M	I	I	..	M	M	M	M	M	M	M	..	M	I	M	M	M	M	M	I	M	I	M	I	M	M	M	M	M	M	I	I
42	Trimethylene glycol	M	M	M	..	M	I	I	M	Is	M	I	M	I	M	M	M	I	I	M	Is	M	M	M	M	M	M	M	I	I	M	M	..	..

MISCIBILITY OF ORGANIC SOLVENT PAIRS (Continued)

Tables B and C

W. M. Jackson and J. S. Drury

Reprinted from Vol. 51 pp. 1491 to 1493, December 1959.
Copyright 1959 by the American Chemical Society and reprinted
by permission of the copyright owner.

The classifications were made at 20°C in the following manner. One-milliliter portions of each solvent comprising a pair were shaken together for approximately a minute. If no interfacial meniscus was observed after the contents of the tube were allowed to settle, the solvent pair was considered to be miscible, M. If a meniscus was observed without apparent change in the volume of either solvent, the pair was regarded as immiscible, I. This classification is a qualitative one, since solvent pairs may exhibit various degrees of partial miscibility while existing as separate phases. If an obvious change occurred in the volume of each solvent, but a meniscus was present, the pair was classified as partially miscible, S. The designation R indicates that the two solvents reacted.

Table B

Column key (1–33): 1 Acetone · 2 Isoamyl acetate · 3 n-Amyl cyanide · 4 Benzene · 5 Benzyl ether · 6 2-Bromoethyl acetate · 7 Chloroform · 8 Cinnamaldehyde · 9 Di-n-amylamine · 10 Di-n-butyl carbonate · 11 Diethylacetic acid · 12 Diethylenetriamine · 13 Diethyl formamide · 14 Diisobutyl ketone · 15 Diisopropylamine · 16 Di-n-propylaniline · 17 Ethyl alcohol · 18 Ethyl benzoate · 19 Ethyl ether · 20 Ethyl phenylacetate · 21 Heptadecanol[a] · 22 3-Heptanol · 23 n-Heptyl acetate · 24 n-Hexyl ether · 25 Methyl isopropyl ketone · 26 4-Methyl-n-valeric acid · 27 o-Phenetidine · 28 Sulfuric acid (concd.) · 29 Tetradecanol[a] · 30 Tri-n-butyl phosphate · 31 Triethylene glycol · 32 Triethylenetetramine · 33 2,6,8-Trimethyl 4-nonanone

No.	Compound	1	2	3	4	5	6	7	8	9	10	11	12	13	14	15	16	17	18	19	20	21	22	23	24	25	26	27	28	29	30	31	32	33	No.
1	Acetone	..	M	M	M	M	M	M	M	M	M	M	M	M	M	M	M	M	M	M	M	M	M	M	M	M	M	R	R	M	M	M	M	M	1
2	Isoamyl acetate	M	..	M	M	M	M	M	M	M	M	M	M	M	M	M	M	M	M	M	M	M	M	M	M	M	M	R	R	M	M	I	M	M	2
3	n-Amyl cyanide	M	M	..	M	M	M	M	M	M	M	M	M	M	M	M	M	M	M	M	M	M	M	M	M	M	M	R	R	M	M	I	M	M	3
4	Benzene	M	M	M	..	M	S	M	M	M	M	M	M	M	M	M	M	M	M	M	M	M	M	M	M	M	M	R	I	M	M	S	I	M	4
5	Benzyl ether	M	M	M	M	..	M	M	M	M	M	M	M	M	M	M	M	M	M	M	M	M	M	M	M	M	M	R	I	M	M	I	M	M	5
6	2-Bromoethyl acetate	M	M	M	S	M	..	M	M	R	M	M	R	M	R	M	R	M	M	M	M	M	M	M	S	M	M	R	I	M	M	M	R	M	6
7	Chloroform	M	M	M	M	M	M	..	M	M	M	M	R	M	M	M	M	M	M	M	M	M	M	M	M	M	M	R	I	M	M	M	R	M	7
8	Cinnamaldehyde	M	M	M	M	M	M	M	..	R	M	M	R	M	M	R	M	M	M	M	M	M	M	M	M	M	M	R	I	M	M	M	I	M	8
9	Di-n-amylamine	M	M	M	M	M	R	M	R	..	M	R	M	R	M	M	M	M	M	M	M	M	M	M	M	M	R	R	R	M	M	I	M	M	9
10	Di-n-butyl carbonate	M	M	M	M	M	M	M	M	M	..	M	M	M	M	M	M	M	M	M	M	M	M	M	M	M	M	R	R	M	M	I	I	M	10
11	Diethylacetic acid	M	M	M	M	M	M	M	M	R	M	..	R	M	M	R	M	M	M	M	M	M	M	M	M	M	M	R	R	M	M	M	R	M	11
12	Diethylenetriamine	M	M	M	M	M	R	R	R	M	M	R	..	M	R	M	R	M	M	M	M	M	M	R	I	M	R	R	R	M	M	M	M	I	12
13	Diethyl formamide	M	M	M	M	M	M	M	M	R	M	M	M	..	M	R	M	M	M	M	M	M	M	M	M	M	M	R	R	M	M	M	R	M	13
14	Diisobutyl ketone	M	M	M	M	M	R	M	M	M	M	M	R	M	..	M	M	M	M	M	M	M	M	M	M	M	M	R	R	M	M	I	M	M	14
15	Diisopropylamine	M	M	M	M	M	M	M	R	M	M	R	M	R	M	..	M	M	M	M	M	M	M	M	M	M	M	R	R	M	M	I	M	M	15
16	Di-n-propylaniline	M	M	M	M	M	R	M	M	M	M	M	R	M	M	M	..	M	M	M	M	M	M	M	M	M	M	R	M	M	M	I	M	M	16
17	Ethyl alcohol	M	M	M	M	M	M	M	M	M	M	M	M	M	M	M	M	..	M	M	M	M	M	M	M	M	M	R	R	M	M	M	M	M	17
18	Ethyl benzoate	M	M	M	M	M	M	M	M	M	M	M	M	M	M	M	M	M	..	M	M	M	M	M	M	M	M	R	R	M	M	I	M	M	18
19	Ethyl ether	M	M	M	M	M	M	M	M	M	M	M	M	M	M	M	M	M	M	..	M	M	M	M	M	M	M	R	M	M	M	I	M	M	19
20	Ethyl phenylacetate	M	M	M	M	M	M	M	M	M	M	M	M	M	M	M	M	M	M	M	..	M	M	M	M	M	M	R	M	M	M	I	M	M	20
21	Heptadecanol[a]	M	M	M	M	M	M	M	M	M	M	M	M	M	M	M	M	M	M	M	M	..	M	M	M	M	M	R	M	M	M	M	M	M	21
22	3-Heptanol	M	M	M	M	M	M	M	M	M	M	M	M	M	M	M	M	M	M	M	M	M	..	M	M	M	M	R	R	M	M	M	M	M	22
23	n-Heptyl acetate	M	M	M	M	M	M	M	M	M	M	M	R	M	M	M	M	M	M	M	M	M	M	..	M	M	M	R	R	M	M	I	R	M	23
24	n-Hexyl ether	M	M	M	M	M	S	M	M	M	M	M	I	M	M	M	M	M	M	M	M	M	M	M	..	M	M	R	R	M	M	I	M	M	24
25	Methyl isopropyl ketone	M	M	M	M	M	M	M	M	M	M	M	M	M	M	M	M	M	M	M	M	M	M	M	M	..	M	R	R	M	M	M	M	M	25
26	4-Methyl-n-valeric acid	M	M	M	M	M	M	M	M	R	M	M	R	M	M	M	M	M	M	M	M	M	M	M	M	M	..	R	R	M	M	R	R	M	26
27	o-Phenetidine	R	R	R	R	R	R	R	R	R	R	R	R	R	R	R	R	R	R	R	R	R	R	R	R	R	R	..	R	R	M	M	R	R	27
28	Sulfuric acid (concd.)	R	R	R	I	R	I	I	I	R	R	R	R	R	R	R	M	R	R	M	M	M	R	R	R	R	R	R	..	R	I	M	M	R	28
29	Tetradecanol[a]	M	M	M	M	M	M	M	M	M	M	M	M	M	M	M	M	M	M	M	M	M	M	M	M	M	M	R	R	..	M	M	M	M	29
30	Tri-n-butyl phosphate	M	M	M	M	M	M	M	M	M	M	M	M	M	M	M	M	M	M	M	M	M	M	M	M	M	M	M	I	M	..	M	M	M	30
31	Triethylene glycol	M	I	I	S	I	M	M	M	I	I	M	M	M	I	I	I	M	I	I	I	M	M	I	I	M	R	R	M	M	M	..	I	I	31
32	Triethylenetetramine	M	M	M	I	M	R	R	I	M	I	R	M	R	M	M	M	M	M	M	M	M	M	R	M	M	R	R	M	M	M	I	..	I	32
33	2,6,8-Trimethyl 4-nonanone	M	M	M	M	M	M	M	M	M	M	M	I	M	M	M	M	M	M	M	M	M	M	M	M	M	M	R	R	M	M	I	I	..	33

[a] Union Carbide name.

Compound number	Compounds	Acetone	Isoamyl acetate	n-Amyl cyanide	Anisaldehyde	Benzene	Benzyl ether	Chloroform	o-Cresol	Diisobutyl ketone	Diethylacetic acid	Diethyl formamide	Di-n-propyl aniline	Ethyl alcohol	Ethyl ether	3-Heptanol	n-Heptyl acetate	n-Hexyl ether	α-Methylbenzylamine	α-Methylbenzyldiethanolamine	α-Methylbenzyldimethylamine	α-Methylbenzylethanolamine	2-Methyl-5-ethylpyridine	Methyl isopropyl ketone	4-Methyl-n-valeric acid	o-Phenetidine	2-Phenylethylamine	Isopropanolamine	Pyridine	Salicylaldehyde	Tetradecanol[a]	Tri-n-butyl phosphate	Triethylenetetramine	2,6,8-Trimethyl 4-nonanone
1	1,3-Butylene glycol	M	I	M	I	I	I	M	M	I	M	M	M	I	M	S	M	I	I	M	M	M	M	M	M	M	M	M	M	M	M	M	M	I
2	2,3-Butylene glycol	M	M	M	M	S	I	M	M	M	M	M	I	M	M	M	M	I	M	M	M	M	M	M	M	M	M	M	M	M	M	M	M	I
3	2-Chloroethanol	M	M	M	M	M	M	M	M	M	M	M	M	M	M	M	M	M	R	M	M	M	R	M	M	M	R	R	M	M	M	M	M	M
4	3-Chloro-1,2-propanediol	M	M	M	M	I	M	M	M	M	M	M	I	M	M	M	M	I	R	M	M	M	M	M	M	M	R	R	M	M	S	M	R	S
5	Dibutyl hydrogen phosphite	M	M	M	M	M	M	M	M	M	M	M	M	M	M	M	M	M	M	M	M	M	M	M	M	M	M	M	M	M	M	M	M	M
6	Diethylene glycol dibutyl ether	M	M	M	M	M	M	M	M	M	M	M	M	M	M	M	M	M	R	M	S	M	M	M	M	M	R	R	M	M	M	M	R	M
7	Diethylene glycol diethyl ether	M	M	M	M	M	M	M	M	M	M	M	M	M	M	M	M	M	M	M	M	M	M	M	M	M	M	M	M	M	M	M	M	M
8	Diethylene glycol monobutyl ether	M	M	M	M	M	M	M	M	M	M	M	M	M	M	M	M	M	M	M	M	M	M	M	M	M	M	M	M	M	M	M	M	M
9	Diethylene glycol monoethyl ether	M	M	M	M	M	M	M	M	M	M	M	M	M	M	M	M	M	M	M	M	M	M	M	M	M	M	M	M	M	M	M	M	M
10	Diethylene glycol monomethyl ether	M	M	M	M	M	M	M	M	M	M	M	M	M	M	M	M	M	M	M	M	M	M	M	M	M	M	M	M	M	M	M	M	M
11	Dipropylene glycol	M	M	M	M	M	M	M	M	M	M	M	M	M	M	M	M	M	M	M	M	M	M	M	M	M	M	M	M	M	M	M	M	M
12	Ethylene diacetate	M	M	M	M	M	M	M	M	M	M	M	M	M	M	M	M	M	M	M	M	M	M	M	M	M	M	M	M	M	M	M	M	M
13	Ethylene glycol	M	I	I	I	I	I	S	M	I	M	M	M	I	M	I	M	I	I	M	M	M	M	M	I	M	M	M	M	M	I	I	S	M
14	Ethyl glycol ethylbutyl ether	M	M	M	M	M	M	M	M	M	M	M	M	M	M	M	M	M	M	M	M	M	M	M	M	M	M	M	M	M	M	M	M	M
15	Ethylene glycol monobutyl ether	M	M	M	M	M	M	M	M	M	M	M	M	M	M	M	M	M	M	M	M	M	M	M	M	M	M	M	M	M	M	M	M	M
16	Ethylene glycol monoethyl ether	M	M	M	M	M	M	M	M	M	M	M	M	M	M	M	M	M	M	M	M	M	M	M	M	M	M	M	M	M	M	M	M	M
17	Ethylene glycol monomethyl ether	M	M	M	M	M	M	M	M	M	M	M	M	M	M	M	M	M	M	M	M	M	M	M	M	M	M	M	M	M	M	M	M	M
18	Ethylene glycol monophenyl ether	M	I	M	M	M	M	I	M	I	I	M	I	M	M	M	M	M	M	M	M	M	M	M	M	M	M	M	M	M	M	M	M	M
19	Glycerol	I	I	I	I	I	I	I	M	I	M	I	I	M	I	I	I	I	M	M	I	M	I	I	M	M	M	M	M	I	I	I	M	I
20	1,2-Propanediol	M	M	M	M	M	I	I	M	M	I	M	M	M	I	S	M	I	I	I	M	M	M	M	M	M	M	M	M	M	I	I	M	I
21	1,3-Propanediol	M	I	I	I	I	I	M	M	I	M	M	I	M	I	M	I	I	I	M	M	M	M	M	M	M	M	M	M	I	S	M	M	I
22	Triethylene glycol	M	I	M	M	S	I	M	M	I	M	M	I	M	M	M	I	I	M	M	M	M	M	M	M	M	M	M	I	I	M	M	I	I
23	Triethyl phosphate	M	M	M	M	M	M	M	M	M	M	M	M	M	M	M	M	M	M	M	M	M	M	M	M	M	M	M	M	M	M	M	M	M
24	Trimethylene chlorohydrin	M	M	M	M	M	M	M	M	M	M	M	M	M	M	M	M	M	R	M	M	M	R	M	M	M	R	R	M	M	M	M	R	M

a Union Carbide name.

STEROID HORMONES AND OTHER STEROIDAL SYNTHETICS

Compiled by Erwin Di Cyan, Ph.D.

The field of steroids has expanded considerably and rapidly in degree and in kind, because synthetic steroids have been synthesized which though resembling the hormones in the body have no natural counterpart, but exert an effect comparable to those of the natural hormones.

In fact, the term *steroid hormone* thus becomes a misnomer when applied to the newer synthetically prepared steroids which do not have a counterpart in the body of man or other animals—as prednisone. (A hormone, by definition, is a material with certain functions and characteristics, *secreted by the ductless glands*. That part of the definition cannot be met by prednisone or by similar steroids as these are not secreted by the ductless, or endocrine glands.)

All the hormones as well as the synthetic analogues have in common the cyclopentanophenanthrene nucleus. Although chemically very similar, a comparatively slight structural change is in many instances productive of substances which have physiologically dissimilar effects, often acting upon different physiologic systems. But in many cases a small change in structure will result merely in an accentuation of certain effects.

The Cyclopentanophenanthrene Nucleus

Classification. Classification becomes a bizarre problem by reason of the (a) overlapping uses to which these substances are put, and (b) the multiple purposes for which the hormones or synthetic substances are used. Indeed, the steroids may be classified by structure; that however would be uninformative to the student as to their use. Classification by origin, as adrenal, would also be unsuitable because, for example, a number of the adrenal corticosteroids are not found in the adrenal cortex at all, but merely resemble the natural hormones found in the adrenal cortex.

For those reasons the hormonal or hormonelike entries in the tables are classified by-and-large, by their predominant pharmacologic effects. Even that classification has its disparities as for example, the use of male sex hormones, i.e. the androgens, is neither limited to men, nor to uses which entail their effect upon male sex characteristics.

Uses. Originally, the use of steroid hormones was largely based upon one or more of the following predicates:

(a) To supplement the progressively declining secretion of a specific hormone due to natural biologic aging of the organism; in the menopause as an example of such declining secretion, a female sex hormone is used for such supplementation;

(b) To make available to the body a specific hormone, the natural secretion of which is inhibited because of a congenital or developmental anomaly; the underdevelopment of male secondary sex characteristics is an example of such an inhibited secretion, in which a male sex hormone is used—and correspondingly, female sex hormones in underdevelopment in females;

(c) To cause a reversal of hormonal balance in the treatment of diseases peculiar to a sex; for example, in the case of cancer of the female breast, a male sex hormone is administered, and in cancer of the prostate, a female sex hormone is used;

(d) To mimic a natural function, as menstruation, by the administration of estrogens—on withdrawal of which bleeding occurs; or by the alternate use of estrogenic and progestational—both female sex hormones.

(e) To delay a function, as ovulation, as in oral contraceptives, or *birth control pills.*

Since the finding that cortisone ameliorates the symptoms of rheumatoid arthritis (1949) the adrenal corticosteroid hormones and especially the synthetically prepared steroid analogues which have no natural counterpart in the body, have been successfully employed in the treatment of diseases not related to sex or sex function.

Androgens and Anabolic Agents. The agents listed in the tables under this classification have the effect of male sex hormones (androgens) i.e., to stimulate sexual maturation, in the "male climacteric," etc. But all androgens have in greater or lesser degree the ability to stimulate muscle development, i.e., an anabolic effect. Among the synthetically prepared agents which have no counterpart in the body (Methandrostenolone or Oxymetholone) are those which have a lessened androgenic, but a heightened anabolic effect. These qualities are determined by biological tests on animals but principally confirmed by clinical use in man. The anabolic effect includes remineralization of bone, which may be partially demineralized (osteoporosis) by age, or by certain drugs, as the adrenal corticosteroids (q.v.).

Anabolic agents are used for muscle and bone nutrition in men as well as women. The reason for the high interest in synthetic steroidal substances for anabolic use, is based on the need for materials, which within a given effective dose have a greater anabolic-to-androgenic ratio than such androgens as methyl testosterone. Otherwise, the administration of androgens to women produces manifestations of virilism, such as growth of hair on the face, a deepening of the voice, etc. Androgens are also used in the female in the suppression of excessive bleeding and in the treatment of cancer of the breast and cervix. (For other androgen-like agents, see also Progestogens and Progestins.)

Estrogens. Estrogenic agents hasten sexual maturation in the female. Therefore, they are used in underdevelopment in the female. The widest use of estrogens is in the treatment of the menopause, in which they supplement from without, the secretion of natural estrogens by the ovary, which begins to decline at about the 40th year. The menopause is usually a slow process, and the declining secretion gives rise to various symptoms during the time that the secretion declines, until adjustment to the new status takes place. The menopause, a period of physical and psychological stress, is made less precipitous by estrogens.

Frequently, a menopause must be quickly induced, as in cancer of the ovary or in uterine hemorrhage. This is done by radiation or by the removal of the uterus. Severe vasomotor symptoms occur when the menopause is thus suddenly induced. Estrogens—among other drugs—are used in the amelioration of these symptoms.

Estrogens (especially diethylstilbestrol which though not a hormone has an estrogenic effect) are also used in the control of cancer of the prostate in the male. Note the inverse correspondence to the use of male sex hormones in cancer of the breast in the female.

Progestogens and Progestins (Including 19-Norsteroid Compounds). The agents under that listing include progesterone, a female sex hormone, as well as progestins, i.e., synthetic progesterone-like compounds which have no natural counterpart in the body. Their use includes a variety of conditions: functional uterine bleeding, absence of menstruation (amenorrhea) used at times with estrogens, painful menstruation (dysmenorrhea), infertility, habitual abortion in order to maintain pregnancy, and in fact, to suppress ovulation hence their use as antifertility drugs. Certain progestins—as norethindrone combined with an estrogen, are the principal components of birth control pills—suppressing ovulation, there is no egg to fertilize, hence conception does not take place.

Adrenal Corticosteroids, Including Antiinflammatory, Antiallergic and Antirheumatic Agents. The adrenal cortex secretes a large number of hormones. They usually differ from each other in the accentuation of some phases of their properties. Virtually all of the cortical hormones are catabolic, thus having an effect in this respect, diametrically opposed to the androgens which are anabolic. Nearly all the cortical hormones—differing in degree from each other—cause retention of sodium and water by the body and hasten the excretion of potassium. These effects are utilized in the treatment of adrenal insufficiency or Addison's disease, in which conversely, there is an undue excretion of sodium and a strong retention of potassium. Desoxycorticosterone is used in Addison's disease because it has a particularly strong sodium retaining and potassium excreting effect.

Since the finding in 1949 of the usefulness of cortisone in profoundly reducing the symptoms of rheumatoid arthritis, the adrenal corticosteroids, including hydrocortisone, a natural hormone secreted by the adrenal cortex, and particularly the synthetic analogues not found in the body, as prednisone, have been used in the treatment of a wide variety of inflammatory diseases—especially diseases of collagen tissue. The same antiinflammatory effect is also brought into use in the reduction of inflammations associated with diseases of the skin, allergy, asthma, and in such systematic diseases as disseminated lupus erythematosus, also a collagen disease.

The drawbacks of cortisone, also shared in lesser measure by hydrocortisone, gave the impetus to the synthesis of steroidal substances not native to the body but differing somewhat from cortisone and hydrocortisone, in order to reduce the drawbacks attendant to the use of the latter. The sideeffects—especially those of cortisone—are retention of water and sodium, excretion of potassium, loss of mineral from bone leading to osteoporosis and fractures, hypertension, at times diabetes, personality changes or gastric ulcer. Prednisone and prednisolone among others (see tables) are two such steroidal synthetics which have the effects of cortisone, but fewer or less severe sideeffects. Whereas the synthetic steroidal substances are superior to cortisone with respect to lessened sideeffects, it cannot be said that the sideeffects are absent—they vary in degree from substance to substance.

Diuretic, Antidiuretic and Local Anesthetic Agents. Aldosterone, a natural hormone of the adrenal cortex, promotes retention in the body of sodium and water, and facilitates excretion of potassium. Hence its effect is almost diametrically opposed to diuretics—especially the thiazide diuretics. Aldosterone is much more active in this respect than desoxycorticosterone, and is used in the treatment of Addison's disease, a hypofunction of the adrenal glands.

Spironolactone is an antagonist to aldosterone—the latter when elaborated in the body in excessive amounts gives rise to a syndrome called aldosteronism. Spironolactone, a synthetically produced steroid does not have a natural counterpart in the body, is diuretic when mercurial or thiazide diuretics are ineffective; it prevents sodium retention and potassium excretion—effects opposite to aldosterone. Hence spironolactone is used in aldosteronism, against edema, in the treatment of congestive heart failure and in other conditions in which an accumulation of water, and water-retaining salt, is to be corrected.

Doses. The amount of substance which comprises a dose of steroid hormones, or of the steroidal synthetics varies from substance to substance—from 0.1 mg for an estradiol ester, to 50 mg for a 19-norsteroid compound. The dose is conditioned upon the order of activity of the substance, the purpose for which it is administered, as well as the patient's response. However, as additional steroids for hormonal use are synthesized—especially those with adrenocortical activity, their average dose is usually smaller than the previously available steroid. The smaller effective dose of the more recent steroid is cited as an advantage over the previously available steroid.

However, a smaller dose cannot be claimed as an inherent advantage of a new steroid in comparison with an existing one, unless the lower dosage exhibits either greater or more prolonged activity or lesser sideeffects. One cannot meaningfully compare a dose, milligram for milligram, without taking into consideration if a heightened effect of the smaller dose produces fewer sideeffects. For example, it does not make any difference if a given effect and the same accompanying sideeffects are produced by a 50 mg or a 5 mg dose.

ADRENAL CORTICOSTEROIDS, INCLUDING ANTIINFLAMMATORY, ANTIALLERGIC AND ANTIRHEUMATIC AGENTS

Names & synonyms:	BETAMETHASONE; 9α-fluoro-16β-methylprednisolone; 16β-methyl-11β,17α,21-trihydroxy-9α-fluoro-1,4-pregnadiene-3,20-dione.	BETAMETHASONE ACETATE; 9α-fluoro-16β-methylprednisolone-21-acetate.	BETAMETHASONE DISODIUM PHOSPHATE; 9α-fluoro-16β-methylprednisolone-21-disodium phosphate.
Formulae:	$C_{22}H_{29}O_5F$	$C_{24}H_{31}O_6F$	$C_{22}H_{28}O_8FNa_2P$
Molecular weight	392.5	434.5	516.4
Melting point (°C)	240 (dec.)	200 to 220 (dec.)	decomposes
Specific rotation	$(\alpha)\frac{25}{D}+112$ to $+120$ (100 mg. in 10 ml. dioxane)	$(\alpha)\frac{25}{D}+120$ to $+128$ (100 mg. in 10 ml. dioxane)	$(\alpha)\frac{25}{D}+99$ to $+105$ (100 mg. in 10 ml. water)
Absorption max.	239 mμ, E(1 %, 1 cm) 390, methanol	239 mμ, methanol	241 mμ, water

Names & synonyms:	CHLOROPREDNISONE ACETATE; 6α-chloroprednisone acetate; 6α-chloro-Δ^{1,4}-pregnadien-17β,21-diol-3,11,20-trione 21-acetate.	CORTICOSTERONE; 11,21-dihydroxyprogesterone; Δ^4-pregnene-11β,21-diol-3,20-dione; 11β,21-dihydroxy-4-pregnene-3,20-dione; Kendall compound B; Reichstein substance H.	CORTISONE; 17-hydroxy-11-dehydrocorticosterone; 17α,21-dihydroxy-4-pregnene-3,11,20-trione; Δ^4-pregnene-17α,21-diol-3,11,20-trione; Kendall compound E; Wintersteiner compound F.
Formulae:		$C_{21}H_{30}O_4$	$C_{21}H_{28}O_5$
Molecular weight	436.6	346.40	360.4
Melting point (°C)	207–213	180–182	220–224
Specific rotation	$(\alpha)\frac{25}{D}+137$ to $+142$ (100 mg. in 10 ml. chloroform)	$(\alpha)\frac{15}{D}+222$ (110 mg. in 10 ml. alcohol)	$(\alpha)\frac{25}{D}+209$ (120 mg. in 10 ml. alcohol)
Absorption max.		240 mμ	237 mμ

Names & synonyms:	DESOXYCORTICOSTERONE; deoxycorticosterone; 11-desoxycorticosterone; 21-hydroxyprogesterone; 4-pregnen-21-ol-3,20-dione; Kendall desoxy compound B; Reichstein substance Q.	DESOXYCORTICOSTERONE ACETATE; DCA; 11-desoxycorticosterone acetate.	DESOXYCORTICOSTERONE PIVALATE; desoxycorticosterone trimethylacetate; 21-hydroxy-4-pregnene-3,20-dione pivalate.
Formulae:	$C_{21}H_{30}O_3$	$C_{23}H_{32}O_4$	$C_{26}H_{38}O_4$
Molecular weight	330.2	372.4	414.6
Melting point (°C)	140–142	154–160	198–204
Specific rotation	$(\alpha)\frac{22}{D} +176 - +178$ (100 mg. in 10 ml. alcohol)	$(\alpha)\frac{20}{D} +168 - +178$ (100 mg. in 10 ml. dioxane)	$(\alpha)\frac{25}{D} +157 \pm 4$ (1 % in dioxane)
Absorption max.	240 mμ		240 mμ (in ethanol)

Names & synonyms:	DEXAMETHASONE; hexadecadrol; 9α-fluoro-16α-methyl prednisolone; 9α-fluoro-11β,17α-21-trihydroxy-16α-methyl-1,4-pregnadiene-3,20-dione; 16α-methyl-9α-fluoro-1,4-pregnadiene-11β,17α-21-triol-3,20-dione; 16α-methyl-9α-fluoro-Δ¹-hydrocortisone; 1-dehydro-16α-methyl-9α-fluorohydro-cortisone.	DICHLORISONE ACETATE; 9α-11β-dichloro-1,4-pregnadiene-17α,21-diol-3,20-dione-21-acetate	FLUOCINOLONE ACETONIDE; 6α,9α-difluoro-16α hydroxyprednisolone-16,17-acetonide; 6α,9α-difluoro-16α,17α-isopropylidenediosy-1,4-pregnadiene-3,20-dione.
Formulae:	$C_{22}H_{29}FO_5$	$C_{23}H_{28}O_5Cl$	$C_{24}H_{30}O_6F_2$
Molecular weight	392.4	455.3	452.50
Melting point (°C)	262–264	235 (dec.)	255–266
Specific rotation	$(\alpha)\frac{25}{D} +78$ (100 mg. in 10 ml. dioxane)	$(\alpha)\frac{25}{D} +160 - 168$ (100 mg. in 10 ml. dioxane)	not less than $+95°$ and not more than $+105°$C at 25°C.
Absorption max.		237 mμ $- 316 - 337$ (ε_1^1)	237 mμ ± 1 mμ

Names & synonyms:	FLUOROHYDROCORTISONE; fludrocortisone; 9α-fluorohydrocortisone; 9α-fluorocortisol; fluohydrisone; 9α-fluoro-11β,17α,21-trihydroxy-4-pregnene-3,20-dione; 9α-fluoro-17-hydroxycorticosterone.	FLUOROMETHOLONE; 9α-fluoro-11β,17α-dihydroxy-6α-methyl-1,4-pregnadiene-3,20-dione; 21-desoxy-9α-fluoro-6α-methyl-prednisolone.	FLUPREDNISOLONE; 6α-fluoroprednisolone; 6α-fluoro-1-dehydrohydrocortisone; 6α-fluoro-11β,17α,21-trihydroxy-1,4-pregnadiene-3,20-dione.
Formulae:	$C_{21}H_{29}FO_5$	$C_{22}H_{24}FO_4$	$C_{21}H_{27}FO_5$
Molecular weight	380.4	376.4	378.4
Melting point (°C)	260–262 (dec.)	290 (dec.)	205–210
Specific rotation	$(\alpha)\frac{23}{D}$ +139 (55 mg. in 10 ml. alcohol)	$(\alpha)\frac{25}{D}$ +56 (pyridine)	$(\alpha)_D$ +88 (dioxane)
Absorption max.		239 mu (a_M = 15,050) methanol	λ_{max} 241.5 mu (ε 16,000)

Names & synonyms:	FLURANDRENOLONE; 6-fluoro-16α-hydroxyhydrocortisone-16,17-acetonide; 6α-fluoro-11β,21-dehydroxy-16α,17α-isopropylidenedioxy-pregna-4-ene-3,20-dione.	HYDROCORTISONE; cortisol; 17-hydroxycorticosterone; hydrocortisone free alcohol; 11β,17α,21-trihydroxy-4-pregnene-3,20-dione; 4-pregnene-11β,17α,21-triol-3,20-dione; Kendall compound F; Reichstein substance M.	HYDROCORTISONE ACETATE; cortisol acetate; hydrocortisone-21-acetate; 17-hydroxycorticosterone-21-acetate.
Formulae:	$C_{24}H_{33}O_6F$	$C_{21}H_{30}O_5$	$C_{23}H_{32}O_6$
Molecular weight	436.5	362.5	404.5
Melting point (°C)	240–250	215–220 (dec.)	223 (dec.)
Specific rotation	$(\alpha)\frac{25}{D}$ = +145 (1 % in CHCl₃)	$(\alpha)\frac{25}{D}$ +150 − +156 (100 mg. in 10 ml. dioxane)	$(\alpha)\frac{25}{D}$ +158 − +165 (100 mg. in 10 ml. dioxane)
Absorption max.	236 mμ (methanol)	242 mμ	242 mμ (methanol)

Names & synonyms:	HYDROCORTISONE SODIUM SUCCINATE; 11β, 17α, 21-trihydroxy-4-pregnene-3, 20-dione, 21 hydrogen succinate, sodium salt; hydrocortisone, 21 hydrogen succinate, sodium salt.	METHYLPREDNISOLONE; 6α-methylprednisolone; Δ^1-6α-methylhydrocortisone; 1-dehydro-6α-methylhydrocortisone; 11β, 17α,21-trihydroxy-6α-methyl-1,4-pregnadiene-3,20-dione.	METHYLPREDNISOLONE SODIUM SUCCINATE; 1-dehydro-6α-methylhydrocortisone, 21-hydrogen succinate, sodium salt; 6α-methylprednisolone 21-hydrogen succinate, sodium salt; 11β, 17α-trihydroxy-6α-methyl-1, 4-pregnadiene-3, 20-dione, 21-hydrogen succinate, sodium salt.
Formulae:	$C_{25}H_{33}O_8Na$	$C_{22}H_{30}O_5$	$C_{26}H_{33}O_8Na$
Molecular weight	484.5	374.5	496.5
Melting point (°C)	decomposes	230–240 (dec.)	decomposes
Specific rotation	$(\alpha)_D +140 \pm 5$ (alcohol)	$(\alpha)\frac{25}{D} +85$ (dioxane)	$(\alpha)_D +100 \pm 4$ (alcohol)
Absorption max.	λ 242 mμ (ε 15,700)	243 mμ	λ_{max} 242 mμ (ε 14,500)

Names & synonyms:	PARAMETHASONE; 6α-fluoro-16α-methylprednisolone; 6α-fluoro-11β-17α,21-trihydroxy-16α-methyl-1,4-pregnadiene-3,20-dione.	PARAMETHASONE ACETATE; 6α-fluoro-16α-methylprednisolone-21-acetate; 6α-fluoro-16α-methylpregna-1,4-diene-11β,21-diol-3,20-dione-21-acetate; 6α-fluoro-17β,17α,21-trihydroxy-16α-methyl-1,4-pregnadiene-3,20-dione-21-acetate.	PREDNISOLONE; metacortandralone; Δ^1-dehydrocortisol; delta F; Δ^1-hydrocortisone; Δ^1-dehydrohydrocortisone; 1,4-pregnadiene-3,20-dione-11β,17α,21-triol; 11β,17α,21-trihydroxy-1,4-pregnadiene-3,20-dione.
Formulae:	$C_{22}H_{30}O_5$	$C_{24}H_{31}O_6F$	$C_{21}H_{28}O_5$
Molecular weight	392.45	434.5	360.4
Melting point (°C)	228–241	233–246	240 (dec.)
Specific rotation	+59 to +69 at 25°C	$(\alpha)\frac{25}{D} +72$ (1 % in CHCl$_3$)	$(\alpha)\frac{25}{D} +97 +103$ (100 mg. in 10 ml. dioxane)
Absorption max.	242 mμ	242 mμ (methanol)	242 mμ (ε – 15,000) methanol

Names & synonyms:	PREDNISOLONE PHOSPHATE SODIUM; disodium prednisolone 21-phosphate.	PREDNISOLONE PIVALATE; prednisolone trimethylacetate; $11\beta,17\alpha,21$-trihydroxy-1,4-pregnadiene-3,20-dione 21-pivalate.
Formulae:	$C_{21}H_{27}Na_2O_8P$	$C_{26}H_{36}O_6$
Molecular weight	484.4	444.6
Melting point (°C)		229
Specific rotation	$(\alpha)\frac{25}{D}+102.5$ (100 mg. in 10 ml. H_2O)	$+108\pm4$ (1 % in dioxane)
Absorption max.	243 mμ	240 and 263 mμ (in absolute ethanol)

Names & synonyms:	PREDNISONE; metacortandricin; Δ^1-dehydrocortisone; delta E; Δ^1-cortisone; 1,4-pregnadiene-$17\alpha,21$-diol-3,11,20-trione; $17\alpha,21$-dihydroxy-1,4-pregnadiene-3,11,20-trione.	TRIAMCINOLONE; 9α-fluoro-16α-hydroxyprednisolone; 9α-fluoro-$11\beta,16\alpha,17\alpha,21$-tetrahydroxy-1,4-pregnadiene-3,20-dione.
Formulae:	$C_{21}H_{26}O_5$	$C_{21}H_{27}FO_6$
Molecular weight	358.4	394.4
Melting point (°C)	225 (dec.)	260–262.5 (dec.)
Specific rotation	$(\alpha)\frac{25}{D}+167 - +175$ (100 mg. in 10 ml. dioxane)	$(\alpha)\frac{25}{D}+75$ (200 mg. in 100 ml. acetone)
Absorption max.	239 mμ ($\varepsilon = 15,500$) methanol	238 mμ ($\varepsilon = 15,800$)

ADRENAL CORTICOSTEROIDS, INCLUDING ANTIINFLAMMATORY, ANTIALLERGIC AND ANTIRHEUMATIC AGENTS (Continued)

Names & synonyms:	TRIAMCINOLONE ACETONIDE; 9α-fluoro-11β,21-dihydroxy-16α,17-isopropylidene-dioxy-1,4-pregnadiene-3,20-dione; 9α-fluoro-16α-hydroxyprednisolone 16,17-acetonide.	TRIAMCINOLONE DIACETATE; 16α,21-diacetoxy-9α-fluoro-11β,17α-dihydroxy-1,4-pregnadiene-3,20-dione; 9α-fluoro-16α-hydroxyprednisolone 16,21-diacetate.
Formulae:	$C_{24}H_{31}FO_6$	$C_{25}H_{31}FO_8$
Molecular weight	434.4	478.49
Melting point (°C)	274–278 (dec.); 292–294	variable: 158–235
Specific rotation	$(\alpha)\frac{25}{D}+109 - +112$ (53.7 mg. in 10 ml. chloroform)	$(\alpha)\frac{25}{D}+22$ (78.8 mg. in 10 ml. chloroform)
Absorption max.	238–239 mμ ($\varepsilon = 14{,}600$)	239 mμ ($\varepsilon = 15{,}200$)

ANDROGENS AND ANABOLIC AGENTS

Names & synonyms:	ANDROSTERONE; cis-androsterone; 3α-hydroxy-17-androstanone; androstane-3α-ol-17-one.	FLUOXYMESTERONE; 9α-fluoro-11β-hydroxy-17α-methyltestosterone 9α-fluoro-11β,17β-dihydroxy-17α-methyl-4-androsten-3-one.	ALDOSTERONE; electrocortin; 18-oxocorticosterone; 18-formyl-11β,21-dihydroxy-4-pregnene-3,20-dione.
Formulae:	$C_{19}H_{30}O_2$	$C_{20}H_{29}FO_3$	$C_{21}H_{28}O_5$
Molecular weight	290.4	336.4	360.4
Melting point (°C)	185–185.5	270 (dec.)	108–112 (hydrate); 164 (anhydrous)
Specific rotation	$(\alpha)\frac{15}{D}+85 - +90$ (150 mg. in 10 ml. dioxane)	$(\alpha)\frac{25}{D}+107 - +109$ (alcohol)	$(\alpha)\frac{25}{D}+161$ (10 mg. in 10 ml. chloroform)
Absorption max.		240 mμ ($\varepsilon = 16{,}700$) alcohol	240 mμ (log $\varepsilon = 4.20$ monohydr.; ε mol. 15,000 anhydr.)

Names & synonyms:	HYDROXYDIONE SODIUM; 21-hydroxypregnane-3,20-dione-21-sodium hemisuccinate.	SPIRONOLACTONE; 3-(3-oxo-7α-acetylthio-17β-hydroxy-4-androsten-17α-yl)-propionic acid γ lactone.
Formulae:	$C_{25}H_{35}O_6Na$	$C_{24}H_{32}O_4S$
Molecular weight	454.5	416.5
Melting point (°C)	193–203 (dec.)	135 (preliminary)–202 (dec.)
Specific rotation	$(\alpha)\frac{25}{D}+95$ (chloroform) for free acid.	$(\alpha)\frac{25}{D}-34$ (chloroform)
Absorption max.	280 mμ ($\varepsilon = 93.2$)	$\varepsilon^{238} = 20,200$

Names & synonyms:	METHANDROSTENOLONE; 17α-methyl-17β-hydroxy-1,4-androstadien-3-one.	METHYLANDROSTENEDIOL; MAD; methandriol; 17α-methyl-5-androsten-3β,17β-diol.	METHYL TESTOSTERONE; 17-methyl testosterone; 17α-methyl-Δ⁴-androsten-17-β-ol-3-one; 17(β)-hydroxy-17(α-methyl-4-androsten-3-one.
Formulae:	$C_{20}H_{28}O_2$	$C_{20}H_{32}O_2$	$C_{20}H_{30}O_2$
Molecular weight	300.4	304.4	302.4
Melting point (°C)	166–167	205–207	161–166
Specific rotation	$(\alpha)\frac{20}{D}+9 - +17$ (100 mg. in 10 ml. alcohol)	$(\alpha)\frac{20}{D}-73$ (100 mg. in 10 ml. alcohol)	$(\alpha)\frac{25}{D}+69 - +75$ (100 mg. in 10 ml. dioxane)
Absorption max.			

Names & synonyms:	NORETHANDROLONE; 17α-ethyl-19-nortestosterone; 17α-ethyl-17-hydroxy-4-norandrosten-3-one; 17α-ethyl-17-hydroxy-19-norandrost-4-en-3-one.	OXANDROLONE; 17β-hydroxy-17α-methyl-2-oxa-5α-androstane-3-one.
Formulae:	$C_{20}H_{30}O_2$	$C_{19}H_{30}O_3$
Molecular weight	302.4	306.4
Melting point (°C)	130–136	230–233
Specific rotation	$(\alpha)\dfrac{25}{D} +21$ (dioxane)	$(\alpha)\dfrac{25}{D} -21$ (1 % in chloroform)
Absorption max.	240 mμ ($\varepsilon = 16{,}500$)	None

Names & synonyms:	OXYMETHOLONE; 17β-hydroxy-2-hydroxymethylene-17α-methyl-3-androstanone; 2-hydroxymethylene-17-α-methyl dihydrotestosterone.	PROMETHOLONE; 2α-methyl-dihydro-testosterone propionate; 2α-methyl-5α-androstane-17β-ol-3-one-propionate.
Formulae:	$C_{21}H_{32}O_3$	
Molecular weight	332.4	360.5
Melting point (°C)	182	124–130
Specific rotation	$(\alpha)\dfrac{25}{D} = +36$ (200 mg. in 10 ml. dioxane)	$(\alpha)\dfrac{25}{D} +22 - +29$ (200 mg. in 10 ml. chloroform)
Absorption max.	$E_1^1 = 547$ at 315 mμ (in alkaline methanol made 0.01 N with NaOH)	without significant absorption from 220–300 mμ (methanol)

Names & synonyms:	TESTOSTERONE; trans-testosterone; Δ^4-androsten-17-β-ol-3-one; 17β-hydroxy-4-androsten-3-one.	TESTOSTERONE CYPIONATE; testosterone cyclopentylpropionate; 17β-hydroxy-4-androsten-3-one, cyclopentanepropionate.
Formulae:	$C_{19}H_{28}O_2$	$C_{27}H_{40}O_3$
Molecular weight	288.4	412.6
Melting point (°C)	151–156	100–102
Specific rotation	$(\alpha)\frac{24}{D} + 109$ (400 mg. in 10 ml. alcohol)	$(\alpha)_D + 88.5 \pm 3.5$ (CHCl$_3$)
Absorption max.	238 mμ	λ_{max} 241 mμ (ϵ 16,125)

Names & synonyms:	TESTOSTERONE ENANTHATE; testosterone heptanoate; 17β-hydroxyandrost-4-en-3-one-17-enanthate.	TESTOSTERONE PHENYLACETATE; 17β-hydroxy-4-androsten-3-one phenyl-acetate; testosterone α-toluate.	TESTOSTERONE PROPIONATE; Δ^4-androstene-17-β-propionate-3-one.
Formulae:	$C_{26}H_{40}O_3$	$C_{27}H_{34}O_3$	$C_{22}H_{32}O_3$
Molecular weight	400.6	406.5	344.4
Melting point (°C)	34–39	129–131	118–122
Specific rotation	$(\alpha)\frac{25}{D} + 77 - + 82$ (2 % in dioxane)	$(\alpha)\frac{25}{D} + 101 \pm 3$ (1 % in chloroform)	$(\alpha)\frac{25}{D} + 83 - + 90$ (100 mg. in 10 ml. dioxane)
Absorption max.	241 mμ (in ethanol)	241 mμ (in ethanol)	

Names & synonyms:	EQUILENIN; 3-hydroxy-17-keto-$\Delta^{1,3,5-10,6,8}$ estrapentaene; 1,3,5–10,6,8-estrapentaen-3-ol-17-one.	EQUILIN; 3-hydroxy-17-keto-$\Delta^{1,3,5-10,7}$ estratetraene; 1,3,5,7-estratetraen-3-ol-17-one.	ESTRADIOL (formerly called α-estradiol); β-estradiol; dihydrofolliculin; dihydroxyestrin; 1,3,5-estratriene-3,17β-diol; 3,17-dihydroxy-$\Delta^{1,3,5-10}$-estratriene; 3,17-epidihydroxyestratriene.
Formulae:	$C_{18}H_{18}O_2$	$C_{18}H_{20}O_2$	$C_{18}H_{24}O_2$
Molecular weight	266.3	268.3	272.3
Melting point (°C)	258–259	236–240	173–179
Specific rotation	$(\alpha)\frac{25}{D} +89$ (dioxane)	$(\alpha)\frac{25}{D} +308$ (200 mg. in 10 ml. dioxane); $+325$ (200 mg. in 10 ml. alcohol).	$(\alpha)\frac{25}{D} +76 - +83$ (100 mg. in 10 ml. dioxane)
Absorption max.	231, 270, 282, 292, 325, 340 mμ	283–285 mμ	225, 280 mμ

Names & synonyms:	ESTRADIOL BENZOATE; β-estradiol-3-benzoate; estradiol monobenzoate.	ESTRADIOL CYPIONATE; estradiol cyclopentylpropionate; β-estradiol 17-cyclopentanepropionate; 1,3,5(10)-estratriene-3,17β-diol,17-cyclopentanepropionate.
Formulae:	$C_{25}H_{28}O_3$	$C_{26}H_{36}O_3$
Molecular weight	376.4	396.6
Melting point (°C)	191–196	151–154
Specific rotation	$(\alpha)\frac{25}{D} +58 - +63$ (200 mg. in 10 ml. dioxane)	$(\alpha)_D +41.5 \pm 3.5$ (dioxane)
Absorption max.		223 mμ

Names & synonyms:	ESTRADIOL DIPROPIONATE; α-estradiol dipropionate; 17β-estradiol dipropionate.	ESTRIOL; trihydroxyestrin; $\Delta^{1,3,5-10}$-estratriene-3-16-cis-17-trans-diol; 1,3,5-estratriene-3,16α,17β-triol.	ESTRONE; folliculin; ketohydroxyestrin; 1,3,5-estratrien-3-ol-17-one.
Formulae:	$C_{24}H_{32}O_4$	$C_{18}H_{24}O_3$	$C_{18}H_{22}O_2$
Molecular weight	384.5	288.3	270.3
Melting point (°C)	104–109	282	258–262
Specific rotation	$(\alpha)\frac{25}{D}+39\pm2$ (1 % in dioxane)	$(\alpha)\frac{25}{D}+53 - +63$ (40 mg. in 1 ml. dioxane)	$(\alpha)\frac{25}{D}+158 - +168$ (100 mg. in 10 ml. dioxane)
Absorption max.	268 mμ	280 mμ	283–285 mμ

Names & synonyms:	ESTRONE BENZOATE	ETHYNYL ESTRADIOL; 17-ethinyl estradiol; 17α-ethynyl-1,3,5-estratriene-3,17β-diol.	MESTRANOL; ethynylestradiol 3-methyl ether; 3-methoxy-17α-ethynyl-1,3,5(10)-estratriene-17β-ol; 17α-ethynyl-estradiol-3-methyl ether; 3-methoxy-19-nor-17α-pregna-1,3,5,trien-20-yn-17-ol.
Formulae:	$C_{25}H_{26}O_3$	$C_{20}H_{24}O_2$	$C_{21}H_{26}O_2$
Molecular weight	374.4	296.4	310.4
Melting point (°C)	220	141–146	148–154
Specific rotation	$(\alpha)\frac{25}{D}+120$ (dioxane)	$(\alpha)\frac{25}{D}+1 - +10$ (100 mg. in 10 ml. dioxane)	$(\alpha)\frac{25}{D}+2$ to $+8$ (200 mg. in 10 ml. dioxane)
Absorption max.		248 mμ	278 to 287 mμ (methanol)

Names & synonyms:	ACETOXYPREGNENOLONE; 21-acetoxypregnenolone; prebediolone acetate; Δ^5-pregnene-3β,21-diol-20-one-21-monoacetate; 21-acetoxy-5-pregnene-3-ol-20-one; 3-hydroxy-21-acetoxy-5-pregnen-20-one.	ANAGESTONE ACETATE; 6α-methyl-4-pregnen-17α-ol-20-one acetate; 17α-acetoxy-6α-methylpregn-4-en-20-one; 17α-acetoxy-6α-methyl-4-pregnen-20-one.	CHLORMADINONE ACETATE; 6-chloro-Δ^6-dehydro-17α-acetoxyprogesterone; 6-chloro-$\Delta^{4,6}$-pregnadiene-17α-ol-3,20-dioneacetate.
Formulae:	$C_{23}H_{34}O_4$	$C_{24}H_{36}O_3$	$C_{23}H_{29}ClO_4$
Molecular weight	374.5	372.6	404.9
Melting point (°C)	184–185	172–178	204–212
Specific rotation	(α) $\frac{20}{D}$ +37 – +43 (dioxane)	(α) $\frac{25}{D}$ +40 to +45 (10 mg. in 10 ml. chloroform)	(α) $\frac{25}{D}$ 0 to −6 (200 mg. in 10 ml. chloroform)
Absorption max.			284 mμ (methanol) Log ε = 4.34 ±0.02

Names & synonyms:	DIMETHISTERONE; 6α,21-dimethylethisterone; 6α,21-dimethyl-17β-hydroxy-17α-pregn-4-en-20-yn-3-one; 6α-methyl-17α-propynylandrost-4-en-17β-ol-3-one; 17β-hydroxy-6α-methyl-17α-(prop-1-ynyl)-androst-4-ene-3-one.	ETHISTERONE; anhydrohydroxyprogesterone; ethinyl testosterone; pregneninolone; 17α ethynyl testosterone; 17α-ethynyl-17β-hydroxy-4-androsten-3-one.	ETHYNODIOL DIACETATE; 17α-ethynyl-4-estrene-3β,17β-diol-17-diacetate; 19-nor-17α-pregn-4-en-20-yne-3β,17-diol diacetate.
Formulae:	$C_{23}H_{32}O_2 \cdot H_2O$	$C_{21}H_{28}O_2$	$C_{24}H_{32}O_4$
Molecular weight	358.5	312.4	384.5
Melting point (°C)	App. 100 (dec.)	266–273	126–132
Specific rotation	(α) $\frac{20}{D}$ +16.5 to +18.5 (2 % solution in chloroform) (calculated to the anhydrous basis)	(α) $\frac{25}{D}$ −32° (100 mg. in 10 ml. pyridine)	(α) $\frac{25}{D}$ −74 (1 % in chloroform)
Absorption max.	App. 240 mμ (anhydrous ethanol) E$\frac{\%}{1 cm}$ − 413	241 mμ (methanol)	None

Names & synonyms:	FLUROGESTONE ACETATE; 17α-acetoxy-9α-fluoro-11β-hydroxy-4-pregnene-3,20-dione.	HYDROXYMETHYLPRO-GESTERONE; medroxyprogesterone; 17α-hydroxy-6α-methylprogesterone; 17α-hydroxy-6α-methyl-4-pregnene-3,20-dione.	HYDROXYMETHYLPRO-GESTERONE ACETATE; medroxyprogesterone acetate; 17α-hydroxy-6α-methylprogesterone acetate; 17α-hydroxy-6α-methyl-4-pregnene-3,20-dione acetate.
Formulae:	$C_{23}H_{31}O_5F$	$C_{22}H_{32}O_3$	$C_{24}H_{34}O_4$
Molecular weight	406.5	344.5	386.5
Melting point (°C)	250–251	220–223.5	202–207
Specific rotation	$(\alpha)\frac{25}{D}+78$	$(\alpha)\frac{25}{D}+75$	$(\alpha)\frac{25}{D}+51$ (dioxane)
Absorption max.	238 mμ (ε = 17,100)	241 mμ (ε = 16,150)	241 mμ (a_M = 16,500) ethanol

Names & synonyms:	HYDROXYPROGESTERONE; 17α-hydroxyprogesterone; 17α-hydroxy-4-pregene-3,20 dione; 4-pregnen-17α-ol-3,20-dione.	HYDROXYPROGESTERONE ACETATE; 17α-acetoxyprogesterone; 17α-hydroxyprogesterone acetate; 17α-hydroxy-4-pregnene-3,20 dione acetate.
Formulae:	$C_{21}H_{30}O_3$	$C_{23}H_{32}O_4$
Molecular weight	330.4	372.5
Melting point (°C)	276	249–250
Specific rotation	$(\alpha)\frac{17}{D}+105$ (104 mg. in 10 ml. chloroform)	$(\alpha)\frac{25}{D}+72$ (chloroform)
Absorption max.		240 mμ (a_M = 16,875) ethanol

Names & synonyms:	HYDROXYPROGESTERONE CAPROATE; 17α-hydroxyprogesterone caproate; 17α-hydroxy-4-pregnene-3,20-dione caproate.	MELENGESTROL ACETATE: MGA; 17α-hydroxy-6-methyl-16-methylene-4,6-pregnadiene-3,20-dione acetate; 6-dehydro-17-hydroxy-6-methyl-16-methylene-progesterone acetate.
Formulae:	$C_{27}H_{40}O_4$	$C_{25}H_{32}O_4$
Molecular weight	428.6	396.51
Melting point (°C)	121–123	215–227
Specific rotation	$(\alpha)\frac{25}{D}+57$ (chloroform)	$(\alpha)_D-127$ to -135 (in $CHCl_3$)
Absorption max.		288 mμ ($\varepsilon_1^1 = 24{,}000$) (ethanol)

Names & synonyms:	NORETHINDRONE; Norethisterone; 17α-ethynyl-19-nortestosterone; 17α-ethynyl-17-hydroxy-19-nor-17α-4-en-20-yn-3-one.	NORETHINDRONE ACETATE; 17α-ethinyl-19-nortestosterone acetate.
Formulae:	$C_{20}H_{26}O_2$	$C_{22}H_{28}O_3$
Molecular weight	298.4	340.4
Melting point (°C)	202 and 208	157–163
Specific rotation	$(\alpha)\frac{25}{D}-30--35$ (200 mg. in 10 ml. dioxane)	$(\alpha)\frac{25}{D}-32--35$ (200 mg. in 10 ml. dioxane)
Absorption max.	α (1 %, 1 cm) $\lambda\,240 = 535\pm15$	α (1 %, 1 cm.) $\lambda\,240 = 490$ to 520 (505 ± 15) (ethanol)

Names & synonyms:	NORETHISTERONE; norethindrone; 19-norethisterone; 17α-ethynyl-19-nor-Δ^4-androstan-17β-ol-3-one; 17α-ethynyl-19-nor-testosterone; 17-hydroxy-3-oxo-19-nor-17α-pregn-4-ene-20-yne; 17-hydroxy-19-nor-17α-pregn-4-en-20-yn-3-one.	NORETHYNODREL; 17α-ethynyl-17β-hydroxy-5(10)-estren-3-one.
Formulae:	$C_{20}H_{26}O_2$	$C_{20}H_{26}O_2$
Molecular weight	298.4	298.4
Melting point (°C)	200–207	174–184
Specific rotation	$(\alpha)\frac{25}{D} - 30 - - 38$ (200 mg. in 10 ml. dioxane)	$(\alpha)\frac{25}{D} + 125$ (dioxane)
Absorption max.	240 mμ ($\varepsilon_1^1 = 576$)	

Names & synonyms:	NORMETHISTERONE; 19-normethisterone; normethandrolone; metalutin; normetandrone; 17α-methyl-19-nor-Δ^4-androsten-17β-ol-3-one; 17α-methyl-19-nor-testosterone; 17β-hydroxy-3-oxo-17α-methyl-estra-4-ene; 17β-hydroxy-17-methyl-estr-4-en-3-one.	PREGNENOLONE; Δ^5-pregnenolone; Δ^5-pregnen-3β-ol-20-one; 17β(1-ketoethyl)-Δ^5-androstene-3β-ol.	PROGESTERONE; progestin; progestone; pregnendione; Δ^4-pregnene-3,20-dione.
Formulae:	$C_{19}H_{28}O_2$	$C_{21}H_{32}O_2$	$C_{21}H_{30}O_2$
Molecular weight	288.4	308.4	314.4
Melting point (°C)	153–158	193	(β) isomer 121; (α) isomer 127–131
Specific rotation	$(\alpha)\frac{25}{D} + 25$ to $+ 29$ (200 mg. in 10 ml. chloroform)	$(\alpha)\frac{20}{D} + 28 - + 30$ (alcohol)	$(\alpha)\frac{20}{D} + 172 - + 182$ (200 mg. in 10 ml. dioxane)
Absorption max.	241 m$\mu - 565 \pm 15$		240 mμ

Names & synonyms:	ALDOSTERONE; electrocortin; 18-oxocorticosterone; 18-formyl-11β,21-dihydroxy-4-pregnene-3,20-dione.	HYDROXYDIONE SODIUM; 21-hydroxypregnane-3,20-dione-21-sodium hemisuccinate.	SPIRONOLACTONE; 3-(3-oxo-7α-acetylthio-17β-hydroxy-4-androsten-17α-yl)-propionic acid γ lactone.
Formulae:	$C_{21}H_{28}O_5$	$C_{25}H_{35}O_6Na$	$C_{24}H_{32}O_4S$
Molecular weight	360.4	454.5	416.5
Melting point (°C)	108–112 (hydrate); 164 (anhydrous)	193–203 (dec.)	135; 202 (dec.)
Specific rotation	$(\alpha)\frac{25}{D} +161$ (10 mg. in 10 ml. chloroform)	$(\alpha)\frac{25}{D} +95$ (chloroform) for free acid.	$(\alpha)\frac{25}{D} -34$ (chloroform)
Absorption max.	240 mμ (log ε = 4.20 monohydr.; ε mol. 15,000 anhydr.)	280 mμ (ε = 93.2)	ε^{238} = 20,200

PROPERTIES OF THE AMINO ACIDS

IONIZATION CONSTANTS AND pH VALUES AT THE ISOELECTRIC POINTS OF THE AMINO ACIDS IN WATER AT 25°C

The majority of the recorded values are true thermodynamic constants calculated from electrometric force measurements of cells without liquid junctions. The values for the constants given in the table were derived from the classical, the zwitterionic (Bjerrum), and the acidic (Brönsted) formulations of ionization and the corresponding mass law expressions. pH values at the isoelectric points were calculated from the expression, $pI = \frac{1}{2}(pk_{a1} + pk_w - pk_{b1})$. The error is approximately 0.5 per cent when this expression is used to calculate pI values for cystine, tyrosine, and diiodotyrosine.

Amino acid	Classical				Zwitterionic				Acidic				pI	Ref. no.
	pk_{a1}	pk_{a2}	pk_{b1}	pk_{b2}	pK_{A1}	pK_{A2}	pK_{B1}	pP_{B2}	pK_1	pK_2	pK_3	pK_4		
DL-Alanine	9.866	.....	11.649	.....	2.348	....	4.131	....	2.348	9.866	.....	....	6.107	1
L-Arginine	12.48	.....	4.96	11.99	2.01	....	1.52	4.96	2.01	9.04	12.48	....	10.76	2
L-Aspartic acid	3.86	9.82	11.93	.....	2.10	3.86	4.18	....	2.10	3.86	9.82	....	2.98	3
L-Cystine	8.00	10.25	11.95	12.96	1.04	2.05	3.75	6.00	1.04	2.05	8.00	10.25	5.02	4
Diiodo-L-tyrosine	6.48	7.82	11.88	.....	2.12	6.48	6.18	....	2.12	6.48	7.82	....	4.29	5,6
L-Glutamic acid	4.07	9.47	11.90	.....	2.10	4.07	4.53	....	2.10	4.07	9.47	....	3.08	7
Glycine	9.778	.....	11.647	.....	2.350	....	4.219	....	2.350	9.778	.....	....	6.064	8
L-Histidine	9.18	.....	7.90	12.23	1.77	....	4.82	7.90	1.77	6.10	9.18	....	7.64	3
Hydroxy-L-proline	9.73	.....	12.08	.....	1.92	....	4.27	....	1.92	9.73	.....	....	5.82	9
DL-Isoleucine	9.758	.....	11.679	.....	2.318	....	4.239	....	2.318	9.758	.....	....	6.038	1
DL-Leucine	9.744	.....	11.669	.....	2.328	....	4.253	....	2.328	9.744	.....	....	6.036	1
L-Lysine	10.53	.....	5.05	11.82	2.18	....	3.47	5.05	2.18	8.95	10.53	....	9.47	2
DL-Methionine	9.21	.....	11.72	.....	2.28	....	4.79	....	2.28	9.21	.....	....	5.74	10
DL-Phenylalanine	9.24	.....	11.42	.....	2.58	....	4.76	....	2.58	9.24	.....	....	5.91	11
L-Proline	10.60	.....	12.0	.....	2.00	....	3.40	....	2.00	10.60	.....	....	6.3	12
DL-Serine	9.15	.....	11.79	.....	2.21	....	4.85	....	2.21	9.15	.....	....	5.68	9
L-Tryptophan	9.39	.....	11.62	.....	2.38	....	4.61	....	2.38	9.39	.....	....	5.88	13
L-Tyrosine	9.11	10.07	11.80	.....	2.20	9.11	3.93	....	2.20	9.11	10.07	....	5.63	6
DL-Valine	9.719	.....	11.711	.....	2.286	....	4.278	....	2.286	9.719	.....	....	6.002	1

References

1. Smith, P. K., Taylor, A. C., and Smith, E. R. B., J. Biol. Chem., **122,** 109 (1937–38).
2. Schmidt, C. L. A., Kirk, P. L., and Appleman, W. K., J. Biol. Chem., **88,** 285 (1930).
3. Greenstein, J. P., J. Biol. Chem., **93,** 479 (1931).
4. Borsook, H., Ellis, E. L., and Huffman, H. M., J. Biol. Chem., **117,** 281 (1937).
5. Dalton, J. B., Kirk, P. L., and Schmidt, C. L. A., J. Biol. Chem., **88,** 589 (1930).
6. Winnek, P. S., and Schmidt, C. L. A., J. Gen. Physiol., **18,** 889 (1935).
7. Simms, H. S., J. Gen. Physiol., **11,** 629 (1928); **12,** 231 (1928).
8. Owen, B. B., J. Am. Chem. Soc., **56,** 24 (1934).
9. Kirk, P. L., and Schmidt, C. L. A., J. Biol. Chem., **81,** 237 (1929).
10. Emerson, O. H., Kirk, P. L., and Schmidt, C. L. A., J. Biol. Chem., **92,** 449 (1931).
11. Miyamoto, S., and Schmidt, C. L. A., J. Biol. Chem., **90,** 165 (1931).
12. McCay, C. M., and Schmidt, C. L. A., J. Gen. Physiol., **9,** 333 (1926).
13. Schmidt, C. L. A., Appleman, W. K., and Kirk, P. L., J. Biol. Chem., **85,** 137 (1929–30).

Ionization Constants of the Amino Acids in Aqueous Ethanol Solutions

Amino acid	pK_1	pK_2	pK_3	Volume per cent ethanol	Temperature °C	Ref. No.
Alanine	3.55	10.02	.....	72	25	1
Arginine	3.34	9.40	14.1	72	25	1
Aspartic acid	2.85	5.20	10.51	72	25	1
Glutamic acid	3.16	5.63	10.75	72	25	2
Glycine	2.66	9.82	.....	10	19.5	2
	2.96	9.76	.....	40	19.5	2
	3.46	9.82	.....	72	25	1
	3.79	9.99	.....	90	19.5	2
Histidine	3.00	5.85	9.45	72	25	1
Isoleucine	3.69	9.81	.....	72	25	1
Lysine	2.75	8.95	10.53	48	25	1
	3.56	8.95	10.49	84	25	1
Proline	3.04	10.55	.....	72	25	1
Valine	3.60	9.73	.....	72	25	1

References

1. Jukes, T. H., and Schmidt, C. L. A., J. Biol. Chem., **105,** 359 (1934).
2. Michaelis, L., and Mizutani, M., Z. physik. Chem., **116,** 135 (1925).

Ionization Constants of the Amino Acids in Aqueous Formaldehyde Solution[a]

Amino acid	Mole per cent formaldehyde				
	0.99	3.95	5.60	10.0	17.9
DL-Alanine	8.36	7.42	6.96[b]	6.56	6.10
L-Arginine	.....	3.45[c]	3.40[d]	....	....
L-Aspartic acid	.....	.....	7.21[d]	⌐3.8[e] 6.85[f]	....
L-Glutamic acid	.....	.....	6.91[d]	⌐4.2[e] 6.8[f]	....
Glycine	7.16	6.08	5.92[b]	5.34	5.04
L-Histidine	.....	7.90[e]	7.90[d]	....	....
Hydroxy-L-Proline	.....	.....	7.19[d]	....	....
L-Leucine	8.44	7.50	6.92[d]	6.62	6.20
DL-Leucine	8.44	7.48	.....	6.60	6.20
L-Lysine	.....	.....	7.35[c]	....	....
L-Phenylalanine	.....	.....	6.62[d]	5.9[e]	....
DL-Phenylalanine	8.09	7.16	6.80[d]	6.35	6.13
L-Proline	.....	.....	7.78[d]	....	....
DL-Serine	6.66	5.74	5.63[b]	....	4.94
L-Tryptophan	.....	.....	6.88[d]	....	....
L-Tyrosine	.....	.....	7.50[d]	6.2[e] >9[f]	....
DL-Valine	8.52	7.65	7.47[b]	....	6.52

(a) Dunn and Weiner (1), pK_2 at 22°.
(b) Dunn and Loshakoff (2), pK_2 at 22°.
(c) Levy (3) pK_2 at 30° for arginine and pK_3 at 30° for histidine and lysine.
(d) Levy and Silberman (4), pK_2 at 30°, pK_3 at 30° for histidine and lysine.
(e) Harris (5), pK_2 at 25° for aspartic acid, glutamic acid, phenylalanine and tyrosine.
(f) Harris (5), pK_3 at 30° for aspartic acid, glutamic acid, and tyrosine.

References

1. Dunn, M. S., and Weiner, J. G., J. Biol. Chem., **117,** 381 (1937).
2. Dunn, M. S., and Loshakoff, A., J. Biol. Chem., **113,** 691 (1936).
3. Levy, M., J. Biol. Chem., **109,** 365 (1935).
4. Levy M., and Silberman, D. E., J. Biol. Chem., **118,** 723 (1937).
5. Harris, L. J., Proc. Roy. Soc. London, Series B, **95,** 440 (1923–24).

Specific Rotations of the Amino Acids Using Sodium Light (5893 Å)

Abbreviations

c—grams of solute per 100 ml. of solution.
d—density of the solution.
p—grams of solute per 100 grams of solution.
l—length of the tube in decimeters.
α—observed rotation in angular degrees.
[α]—specific rotation in angular degrees calculated from

$$[\alpha]_\lambda^t = \frac{\alpha \times 100}{c \times l} = \frac{\alpha \times 100}{p \times d \times l}$$

where t is temperature in °C and λ is wave length of the incident light in Ångstroms.

A—prepared from a protein or other naturally occurring material.
B—prepared by resolution of the inactive synthetic form.
C—prepared by resolution of the inactive racemized form.
D—prepared from the inactive synthetic form by a biological method.
E—prepared from the inactive racemized form by a biological method.
?—source not given.

Source	c	Solvent	d	p	Moles acid or base per mole amino acid	l	Temp. °C.	α	[α]	Ref. No.
L-Alanine										
A	5.790	0.97 N HCl	1.033	5.605	1.5	2	15	+1.70	+14.7	1
A	10.3	Water	1.03	1.00	0	2	22	+0.55	+2.7	2
A	1.781	3 N NaOH	......	......	15	2	20	......	+3.0	3
D-Alanine										
B	1.344	6 N HCl	......	......	39.4	2	30.4	−0.392	−14.6	4
L-Arginine										
A	1.653	6.0 N HCl	......	......	63	4.001	23.4	+1.777	+26.9	5
A	3.48	Water	......	......	0	2	20	......	+12.5	6
A	0.87	0.50 N NaOH	......	......	10	2	20	......	+11.8	6
L-Aspartic acid										
A	2.002	6.0 N HCl	......	......	39	4.001	24.0	+1.972	+24.6	7
A	1.3300	Water	......	......	0	3	18	......	+4.7	3
A	1.3300	3 N NaOH	......	......	30	3	18	......	−1.7	3
D-Aspartic acid										
C	4.289	0.97 N HCl	1.032	4.156	3	1	20	−1.09	−25.5	8
L-Cystine										
A	0.9974	1.02 N HCl	1.0181	0.9797	24.6	2	24.35	−4.277	−214.40	9
A	0.400	0.20 N NaOH	......	......	12	2	18.5	......	−70.0	3
D-Cystine										
C	......	1 N HCl	......	1	24	...	20	......	+223	10
Diiodo-D-tyrosine										
A	5.08	1.1 N HCl	1.05	4.84	9.4	1	20	+0.15	+2.89	11
A	4.41	13.4 N NH₄OH	0.9779	4.51	132	1	20	+0.10	+2.27	11
L-Glutamic acid										
A	1.002	6.0 N HCl	......	......	87	4.001	22.4	+1.25	+31.2	12
A	1.471	Water	......	......	0	2	18	......	+11.5	3
A	1.471	1 N NaOH	......	......	10	2	18	......	+10.96	3
D-Glutamic acid										
C	5.425	0.37 N HCl	1.0233	5.3011	1	1	20	−1.63	−30.05	8
L-Histidine										
A	1.480	6.0 N HCl	......	......	63	4.001	22.7	+0.766	+13.0	7
A	1.128	Water	1.0012	1.127	0	4	25.00	−1.714	−39.01	13
A	0.775	0.50 N NaOH	......	......	10	2	20	......	−10.9	6
D-Histidine										
?	4.000	1.0 N HCl	......	......	4	1	20	−0.407	−10.2	14
B	2.66	Water	......	......	0	2	23	+2.11	+39.8	14
Hydroxy-L-proline										
A	1.31	1.0 N HCl	......	......	10	2	20	......	−47.3	6
A	1.001	Water	......	......	0	4.001	22.5	−3.009	−75.2	7
A	0.655	0.50 N NaOH	......	......	10	2	20	......	−70.6	6
Hydroxy-D-proline										
B	4.48	Water	1.03	4.35	0	1	21	+3.37	+75.2	16
Allo-Hydroxy-L-proline										
B	2.617	Water	1.014	2.581	0	1	18	−1.52	−58.1	16
Allo-Hydroxy-D-proline										
B	2.530	Water	1.013	2.998	0	1	17	+1.48	+58.5	16
L-Isoleucine										
B	5.09	6.1 N HCl	1.098	4.64	15	1	20	+2.07	+40.61	17
B	3.10	Water	1.008	3.08	0	1	20	+0.70	+11.29	17
A	3.34	0.33 N NaOH	1.017	3.28	1.3	2	20	+0.74	+11.09	18
D-Isoleucine										
B	4.53	6.1 N HCl	1.083	4.18	17	1	20	−1.85	−40.86	17
B	3.12	Water	1.006	3.10	0	1	20	−0.66	−10.55	17
D-allo-Isoleucine										
D	5.14	6.0 N HCl	1.094	4.70	15.0	2	20	−3.80	−36.95	19
E	2.00	Water	......	......	0	1	20	0.286	14.7	20
L-allo-Isoleucine										
B	3.97	6.0 N HCl	......	......	20	1	20	+1.50	+38.1	20
B	2.00	Water	......	......	0	1	20	+0.28	+14.0	20
L-Leucine										
A	1.999	6.0 N HCl	......	......	38	4.001	25.9	+1.212	+15.1	5
A	2.001	Water	......	......	0	4.001	24.7	−0.863	−10.8	5
A	1.31	3.00 N NaOH	......	......	30	2	20	......	+7.6	3
D-Leucine										
?	4.0	6.0 N HCl	1.1	3.664	19	2	20	+1.26	−15.6	21
?	......	Water	......	2.08	0	2	20	+0.43	+10.34	38
L-Lysine										
A	2.00	6.0 N HCl	......	......	43	4	22.9	+1.652	+25.9	5
A	6.496	Water	......	......	0	2	20	+1.90	+14.6	22
D-Lysine										
B	2.00	0.27 N HCl	......	......	2	1	20	−0.939	−23.48	23
L-Methionine										
B	0.80	Water	......	......	0	2	25	−0.13	−8.11	24
D-Methionine										
B	0.80	0.2001 N HCl	......	......	4	2	25	−0.34	−21.18	24
B	0.80	Water	......	......	0	2	25	+0.13	+8.12	24
B	0.80	0.6 N NaHCO₃	......	......	11	2	25	−0.12	−7.47	24
L-Phenylalanine										
B	1.936	Water	1.0040	1.928	0	2	20	−1.36	−35.14	27
D-Phenylalanine										
B	3.814	5.4 N HCl	1.0895	3.501	23	2	20	+0.54	+7.07	28
B	2.043	Water	1.0045	2.034	0	2	20	+1.43	+35.0	27
L-Proline										
A	0.575	0.50 N HCl	......	......	10	2	20	......	−52.6	6
A	1.001	Water	......	......	0	4.001	23.4	−3.402	−85.0	7
B	2.42	0.6 N KOH	1.031	2.35	3	1	20	−2.25	−93.0	29
D-Proline										
B	3.90	Water	1.01	3.865	0	1	20	+3.18	+81.5	29
L-Serine										
B	9.344	1 N HCl	1.0465	8.929	1	1	25	+1.35	+14.45	30
B	10.414	Water	1.0414	9.997	0	2	20	−1.42	−6.83	30
D-Serine										
B	9.359	1 N HCl	1.0465	8.943	1	1	25	−1.34	−14.32	30
B	10.412	Water	1.0414	9.998	0	2	20	+1.43	+6.87	30
D-Threonine										
B	......	Water	......	1.092	0	2	26	−0.625	−28.3	31
L-Threonine										
B	......	Water	......	1.331	0	2	26	+0.780	+28.4	31
D-allo-Threonine*										
B	......	Water	......	1.634	0	2	26	−0.302	−9.1	31
L-allo-Threonine										
B	......	Water	......	1.643	0	2	26	+0.320	+9.6	31
L-Thyroxine										
A	......	0.13 N NaOH in 70% EtOH by weight	......	3	3	1	......	−0.147	−4.4	32
L-Tryptophan										
A	1.02	0.50 N HCl	......	......	10	2	20	......	+2.4	6
A	1.004	Water	......	......	0	4.001	22.7	−1.266	−31.5	7
A	2.426	0.5 N NaOH	1.0243	2.368	4.2	1	20	+0.15	+6.17	33
D-Tryptophan										
C	0.5024	Water	......	......	0	2	25	+0.326	+32.45	34
L-Tyrosine										
B	4.40	6.3 N HCl	1.116	3.94	28	2	20	−0.76	−8.64	35
A	0.906	3.0 N NaOH	......	......	60	3	18	......	−13.2	3
D-Tyrosine										
B	5.1484	6.3 N HCl	1.1175	4.6071	24	2	20	+0.89	+8.64	35
L-Valine										
B	3.4	6.0 N HCl	1.1	3.05	20	2	20	+1.93	+28.8	36
B	3.58	Water	1.007	3.56	0	2	20	+0.46	+6.42	36
D-Valine										
B	3.2	6.0 N HCl	1.1	2.91	21	2	20	−1.86	−29.04	36
E	6.24	Water	1.00	6.24	0	1	20	−0.37	−6.06	37

* The levorotatory allothreonine probably belongs to the D family and its enantiomorph to the L family.

Specific Rotations of the Amino Acids Using Sodium
Light (5893 Å) (Continued)

References

1. Clough G. W., J. Chem. Soc., **113**, 526 (1918).
2. Fischer, E., and Raske, K., Ber, **40**, 3717 (1907).
3. Lutz, O., and Jirgensons, B., Ber., **63**, 448 (1930).
4. Dunn, M. S., Butler, A. W., and Naiditch, M. J., unpublished data.
5. Dunn, M. S., and Courtney, G., unpublished data.
6. Lutz, O., and Jirgensons, B., Ber., **64**, 1221 (1931).
7. Dunn, M. S., and Stoddard, M. P., unpublished data.
8. Fischer, E., Ber., **32**, 2451 (1899).
9. Toennies, G., and Lavine, T. F., J. Biol. Chem., **89**, 153 (1930).
10. Loring, H. S., and du Vigneaud, V., J. Biol. Chem., **107**, 267 (1934).
11. Abderhalden, E., and Guggenheim, M., Ber., **41**, 1237 (1908).
12. Dunn, M. S., and Sexton, E. L., unpublished data.
13. Dunn, M. S., and Frieden, E. H., unpublished data.
14. Cox, G. J., and Berg, C. P., J. Biol. Chem., **107**, 497 (1934).
15. Dakin, H. D., Biochem. J., **13**, 398 (1919).
16. Leuchs, H., and Bormann, K., Ber., **52**, 2086 (1919).
17. Locquin, R., Bull. Soc. Chim., (4), **1**, 601 (1907).
18. Ehrlich, F., Ber., **37**, 1809 (1904).
19. Ehrlich, F., Ber., **40**, 2538 (1907).
20. Abderhalden, E., and Zeisset, W., Z. physiol. Chem., **196**, 121 (1931)

21. Fischer, E., and Warburg, O., Ber., **38**, 3997 (1905).
22. Vickery, H. B., private communication, April, 1940.
23. Berg, C. P., J. Biol. Chem., **115**, 9 (1936); private communication, June, 1940.
24. Windus, W., and Marvel, C. S., J. Am. Chem. Soc., **53**, 3490 (1931).
27. Fischer, E., and Schoeller, W., Ann., **357**, 1 (1907).
28. Fischer, E., and Mouneyrat, A., Ber., **33**, 2383 (1900).
29. Fischer, E., and Zemplén, G., Ber., **42**, 2989 (1909).
30. Fischer, E., and Jacobs, W. A., Ber., **39**, 2942 (1906).
31. West, H. D., and Carter, H. E., J. Biol. Chem., **119**, 109 (1937); private communication from H. E. Carter, July, 1940.
32. Foster, G. L., Palmer, W. W., and Leland, J. P., J. Biol. Chem., **115**, 467 (1936).
33. Abderhalden, E., and Baumann, L., Z. physiol. Chem., **55**, 412 (1908).
34. Berg, C. P., J. Biol. Chem., **100**, 79 (1933); private communication, July, 1940.
35. Fischer, E., Ber., **32**, 3638 (1899).
36. Fischer, E., Ber., **39**, 2320 (1906).
37. Ehrlich, F., and Wendel, A., Biochem. Z. **8**, 399 (1908).
38. Ehrlich, F., Biochem. Z., **1**, 8 (1906).

Solubilities of the Amino Acids in Grams per 100 Grams of Water

Amino acid	Temperature, °C.					Ref. No.
	0°	25°	50°	75°	100°	
DL-Alanine	12.11	16.72	23.09	31.89	44.04	1
L-Alanine	12.73	16.65	21.79	28.51	37.30	1
DL-Aspartic acid	0.262	0.778	2.000	4.456	8.594	1
L-Aspartic acid	0.209	0.500	1.199	2.875	6.893	1
L-Cystine‡ × 10²	0.502	1.096	2.394	5.229	11.42	2
Diiodo-DL-tyrosine × 10.	0.149	0.340	0.773	......	......	3
Diiodo-L-tyrosine × 10..	0.204	0.617	1.862	5.62	17.00	1
DL-Glutamic acid	0.855	2.054	4.934	11.86	28.49	1
L-Glutamic acid	0.341	0.864	2.186	5.532	14.00	1
Glycine	14.18	24.99	39.10	54.39	67.17	1
L-Histidine	......	4.19	......	......	......	4
Hydroxy-L-Proline	28.86	36.11	45.18	51.67*	......	5
DL-Isoleucine	1.826	2.229	3.034	4.607	7.802	1
L-Isoleucine	3.791	4.117	4.818	6.076	8.255	2
DL-Leucine	0.797	0.991	1.406	2.276	4.206	1
L-Leucine	2.270	2.426†	2.887†	3.823	5.338	1
DL-Methionine	1.818	3.381	6.070	10.52	17.60	2
DL-Phenylalanine	0.997	1.411	2.187	3.708	6.886	1
L-Phenylalanine	1.983	2.965	4.431	6.624	9.900	2
L-Proline × 10⁻¹	12.74	16.23	20.67	23.90*	......	3
DL-Serine	2.204	5.023	10.34	19.21	32.24	2
L-Tryptophan	0.823	1.136	1.706	2.795	4.987	2
DL-Tyrosine × 10	0.147	0.351	0.836	......	......	3
L-Tyrosine × 10	0.196	0.453	1.052	2.438	5.650	1
D-Tyrosine × 10	0.196	0.453	1.052	......	......	3
DL-Valine	5.98	7.09	9.11	12.61	18.81	1
L-Valine	8.34	8.85	9.62	10.24*	......	6

* Value at 65°.

† Dunn and Stoddard (7) report 2.19 g. at 25° for L-Leucine rendered methionine-free by repeated recrystallization from 6 N HCl. Hlynka (8) found 2.20 g. at 25° and 2.66 g. at 50° for L-Leucine rendered methionine-free [by S. W. Fox (9)] by fractional crystallization of the formyl derivative and identical values for D-Leucine obtained by resolution of the DL form.

‡ The following values were found by Loring and du Vigneaud (10): DL-Cystine (0.0049 g), D-Cystine (0.0108 g), and meso-cystine (0.0056 g) at 25°.

References

1. Dalton, J. B., and Schmidt, C. L. A., J. Biol. Chem., **103**, 549 (1933).
2. Dalton, J. B., and Schmidt, C. L. A., J. Biol. Chem., **109**, 241 (1935).
3. Winnek, P. S., and Schmidt, C. L. A., J. Gen. Physiol., **18**, 889 (1934–35).
4. Dunn, M. S., Frieden, E. H., and Brown, H. V., unpublished data.
5. Tomiyama, T., and Schmidt, C. L. A., J. Gen. Physiol., **19**, 379 (1935–36).
6. Dalton, J. B., and Schmidt, C. L. A., J. Gen. Physiol., **19**, 767 (1935–36).
7. Dunn, M. S., and Stoddard, M. P., unpublished data.
8. Hlynka, I., Thesis (1939), California Institute of Technology, Pasadena, California.
9. Fox, S. W., Science, **84**, 163 (1936).
10. Loring, H. S., and du Vigneaud, V., J. Biol. Chem., **107**, 270 (1934).

Solubilities of the Amino Acids in Grams per 100 Grams of Water-Ethanol Mixtures

Per cent ethanol by volume	Temp. °C.	Grams amino acid per 100 grams solvent	Ref. No.	Per cent ethanol by volume	Temp. °C.	Grams amino acid per 100 grams solvent	Ref. No.	Per cent ethanol by volume	Temp. °C.	Grams amino acid per 100 grams solvent	Ref. No.	Per cent ethanol by volume	Temp. °C.	Grams amino acid per 100 grams solvent	Ref. No.
DL-Alanine				DL-Aspartic acid				L-Aspartic acid				Glycine			
24.93	0.00	3.84	1					20	25	0.204	3	24.93	0.02	3.95	1
50.10	0.00	1.16	1	24.93	0.03	0.0703	1	50	25	0.0633	3	50.10	0.02	1.03	1
74.50	0.00	0.305	1	50.10	0.03	0.0267	1	70	25	0.0224	3	74.50	0.02	0.200	1
95.14	0.00	0.0167	1	74.20	0.02	0.0111	1	90	25	0.0034	3	95.09	0.01	0.0080	1
10	25	12.25	2	24.55	25.06	0.266	1					10	25	17.13	2
24.93	24.97	7.09	1	50.25	25.06	0.0992	1	L-Glutamic acid				24.93	24.97	8.72	1
50.10	24.97	2.52	1	74.28	25.14	0.0317	1					50.10	24.97	2.47	1
74.20	24.97	0.573	1	95.14	25.07	0.0020	1	24.74	0.01	0.0855	1	74.20	24.97	0.448	1
95.14	25.09	0.0329	1	24.74	45.25	0.680	1	50.18	0.01	0.0371	1	95.14	25.09	0.0172	1
25.28	45.16	10.6	1	50.18	45.25	0.255	1	74.28	0.03	0.0163	1	24.93	44.98	15.0	1
50.10	44.96	4.25	1	74.28	45.27	0.0608	1	24.56	25.05	0.292	1	50.10	44.98	4.62	1
74.20	44.98	0.949	1	95.14	45.21	0.0042	1	50.25	25.08	0.131	1	74.20	44.97	0.756	1
95.14	45.19	0.0545	1	24.93	64.91	1.53	1	74.35	25.07	0.0370	1	95.14	45.19	0.0294	1
24.93	64.96	15.9	1	50.10	64.91	0.588	1	95.14	25.04	0.0044	1	24.93	65.11	24.5	1
50.10	64.94	6.68	1	74.20	65.07	0.132	1	24.55	45.01	0.811	1	50.10	65.10	8.03	1
74.20	64.94	1.48	1	95.14	65.00	0.0129	1	50.18	45.27	0.378	1	74.20	65.07	1.23	1
95.09	65.15	0.0851	1					74.35	44.93	0.0885	1	95.14	65.00	0.0488	1
								95.14	45.20	0.0127	1				

Solubilities of the Amino Acids in Grams per 100 Grams of Water-Ethanol Mixtures (Continued)

Per cent ethanol by volume	Temp. °C	Grams amino acid per 100 grams solvent	Ref. No.	Per cent ethanol by volume	Temp. °C	Grams amino acid per 100 grams solvent	Ref. No.	Per cent ethanol by volume	Temp. °C	Grams amino acid per 100 grams solvent	Ref. No.	Per cent ethanol by volume	Temp. °C	Grams amino acid per 100 grams solvent	Ref. No.
L-Isoleucine				L-Leucine				DL-Threonine				DL-Valine			
80	20	0.46	4	20	25	1.33	2	95	25	0.07*	6	24.93	0.02	2.10	1
80	78–80	1.16	4	60	25	0.641	2	DL-allo-Threonine				50.10	0.02	0.760	1
L-allo-Isoleucine				90	25	0.123	2	95	25	0.03*	6	74.20	0.02	0.269	1
80	20	0.81	4	L-Proline				L-Tyrosine				95.14	0.01	0.0277	1
80	78–80	1.97	4	100	19	1.5	5	95	17	0.10	7	10	25	5.50	2
DL-Leucine				DL-Serine				DL-Tyrosine				25.28	24.85	3.30	1
24.93	0.00	0.251	1	24.93	0.00	0.1530	1	95.09	0.00	0.0031	8	50.99	24.85	1.53	1
50.10	0.00	0.118	1	50.10	0.00	0.146	1	25.28	24.85	0.0285	8	74.35	24.93	0.570	1
74.50	0.00	0.0693	1	74.50	0.00	0.0304	1	50.99	24.75	0.0226	8	95.14	25.04	0.0569	1
95.14	0.00	0.0116	1	95.14	0.00	0.0008	1	74.63	24.75	0.0117	8	24.55	44.91	5.10	1
10	25	0.771	2	24.93	25.14	1.54	1	95.09	25.24	0.0032	8	50.25	44.92	2.74	1
24.93	24.97	0.493	1	50.10	25.14	0.461	1	25.28	45.15	0.0630	8	74.35	44.92	0.999	1
50.10	24.97	0.318	1	74.50	25.10	0.0840	1	50.99	45.16	0.0513	8	95.14	45.21	0.0979	1
74.20	24.97	0.175	1	95.14	25.09	0.0028	1	74.63	44.93	0.0230	8	24.55	65.07	7.44	1
95.14	25.09	0.0258	1	24.93	45.15	3.14	1	95.09	44.98	0.0035	8	50.10	64.94	4.49	1
24.93	45.24	0.853	1	50.10	45.04	0.985	1	95.09	65.06	0.0067	8	74.20	64.34	1.62	1
50.10	45.24	0.633	1	74.20	45.04	0.185	1					95.09	65.15	0.167	1
74.50	45.18	0.323	1	95.14	45.18	0.0058	1					L-Valine			
95.14	45.18	0.0471	1	24.93	65.26	5.99	1					20	25	5.11	2
24.93	65.16	1.45	1	50.10	65.25	1.88	1					40	25	2.93	2
50.10	65.20	1.16	1	74.50	65.24	0.318	1					60	25	1.61	2
74.20	65.15	0.584	1	95.14	65.01	0.0152	1					80	25	0.52	2
95.09	65.07	0.0844	1												

* Grams per 100 ml. of solution.

References

1. Dunn, M. S., and Ross, F. J., J. Biol. Chem., **125**, 309 (1938).
2. Cohn, E. J., McMeekin, T. L., Edsall, J. T., and Weare, J. H., J. Am. Chem. Soc., **56**, 2270 (1934).
3. McMeekin, T. L., Cohn, E. J., and Weare, J. H., J. Am. Chem. Soc., **57**, 626 (1935).
4. Abderhalden, E., and Zeisset, W., Z. physiol. Chem., **196**, 121 (1931).
5. Kapfhammer, J., and Eck, R., Z. physiol. Chem., **170**, 294 (1927).
6. West, H. D., and Carter, H. E., J. Biol. Chem., **119**, 109 (1937).
7. Stutzer, A., Z. anal. Chem., **31**, 501 (1892).
8. Dunn, M. S., and Ross, F. J., unpublished data.

Solubilities of the Amino Acids in Grams per 100 Grams of Organic Solvent

Solvent	Grams amino acid per 100 grams solvent	Temp. °C	Ref. No.	Solvent	Grams amino acid per 100 grams solvent	Temp. °C	Ref. No.
DL-Alanine				L-Isoleucine			
Ethanol	0.0087	25	1	Ethanol	0.09	20	5
L-Aspartic acid				Ethanol	0.13	78–80	5
Ethanol	0.000196	25	2	L-allo-Isoleucine			
L-Glutamic acid				Ethanol	0.13	20	5
Ethanol	0.000347	25	2	Ethanol	0.19	78–80	5
Ethanol	0.0056	44.93	3	L-Leucine			
Glycine				Ethanol	0.0217	25	1
Acetone	0.000291	25	4	L-Proline			
Butanol	0.000892	25	4	Ethanol	1.5	19	6
Ethanol	0.0037	25	1	DL-Valine			
Formamide	0.558	25	4	Ethanol	0.0136	0.03	3
Methanol	0.0407	25	4	Ethanol	0.019	25	1

References

1. Cohn, E. J., McMeekin, T. L., Edsall, J. T., and Weare, J. H., J. Am. Chem. Soc., **56**, 2270 (1934).
2. McMeekin, T. L., Cohn, E. J., and Weare, J. H., J. Am. Chem. Soc., **57**, 626 (1935).
3. Dunn, M. S., and Ross, F. J., J. Biol. Chem., **125**, 309 (1938).
4. McMeekin, T. L., Cohn, E. J., and Weare, J. H., J. Am. Chem. Soc., **58**, 2173 (1936).
5. Abderhalden, E., and Zeisset, W., Z. physiol. Chem., **196**, 121 (1931).
6. Kapfhammer, J., and Eck, R., Z. physiol. Chem., **170**, 294 (1927).

Densities of Crystalline Amino Acids

Amino acid	Density	Ref. No.	Amino acid	Density	Ref. No.
DL-Alanine	1.424	1	DL-Leucine	1.191	1
L-Alanine	1.401	2	L-Leucine	1.165	1
β-Alanine	1.404	1	DL-Methionine	1.340	5
DL-α-Amino-n-butyric acid	1.231	1	DL-Serine	1.537	1
α-Aminoisobutyric acid	1.278	1	L-Tyrosine	1.456	1
L-Arginine	1.1	3	DL-Valine	1.316	1
L-Aspartic acid	1.66	3	L-Valine	1.230	1
DL-Glutamic acid	1.460	4			
L-Glutamic acid	1.538	4			
Glycine*	1.601	3			
	1.607	1			

References

1. Cohn, E. J., McMeekin, T. L., Edsall, J. T., and Weare, J. H., J. Am. Chem. Soc., **56**, 2270 (1934).
2. Dalton, J. B., and Schmidt, C. L. A., J. Biol. Chem., **103**, 549 (1933).
3. Huffman, H. M., Ellis, E. L., and Fox, S. W., J. Am. Chem. Soc., **58**, 1728 (1936). Huffman, H. M., Fox, S. W., and Ellis, E. L., J. Am. Chem. Soc., **59**, 2144 (1937).
4. Schmidt, C. L. A., Chemistry of the Amino Acids and Proteins, C. C. Thomas, Springfield, Illinois, 1938, p. 900.
5. Albrecht, G., and Dunn, M. S., unpublished data.
6. Houck, R. C., J. Am. Chem. Soc., **52**, 2420 (1930).
7. Curtius, T., J. prakt. Chem., **26**, 145 (1882).

* The density of glycine at 50° is 1.5753 according to Houck (6) who concluded that the figure 1.1607, reported by Curtius (7) and reproduced in chemical handbooks, is a typographical error.

CARBOHYDRATES

These data for carbohydrates were compiled originally for the Biology Data Book by M. L. Wolfram, G. G. Maher and R. G. Pagnucco (1964). Data are reproduced here by permission of the copyright owners of the above publication, the Federation of American Societies for Experimental Biology, Washington, D.C. pp. 351–359.

All data are for crystalline substances, unless otherwise specified. Selection of substances was restricted to natural carbohydrates found free (or in chemical combination and released on hydrolysis) and to biological oxidation products of the natural carbohydrates. The nomenclature conforms with that of the British-American report as published in the *Journal of Organic Chemistry*, 28:281 (1963). Substances have been arranged alphabetically under the name of the parent sugar within groups formulated according to increasing carbon content (excluding carbon in substituents), with synonymous common names in parentheses. **Melting Point:** b.p. = boiling point; d. = decomposes; s. = sinters. **Specific Rotation** was determined in water at concentrations of 1–5 g per 100 ml. of solution and at 20°–25°C, unless otherwise specified; other temperatures or wavelengths are shown in brackets; c = grams solute per 100 ml of solution.

Part I. NATURAL MONOSACCHARIDES: ALDOSES AND KETOSES

	Substance (Synonym)	Chemical Formula	Melting Point °C	Specific Rotation $[\alpha]_D$
	(A)	(B)	(C)	(D)
		Aldoses		
1	D-Glyceraldehyde	$C_3H_6O_3$	....	+13.5 ± 0.5 (syrup)
2	D-Glyceraldehyde, 3-deoxy-3,3-*C*-bis-(hydroxymethyl)- (Cordycepose)	$C_5H_{10}O_4$	....	−26 (c 0.6, C_2H_5OH
3	D-Glyceraldehyde, 3,3-bis(*C*-hydroxy-methyl)- (Apiose)	$C_5H_{10}O_5$	....	+5.6 (c 10) [15°] syrup
4	β-D-Arabinose	$C_5H_{10}O_5$	155	−175 → −103
5	D-Arabinose, 2-*O*-methyl-	$C_6H_{12}O_5$	Syrup	−102
6	α-L-Arabinose	$C_5H_{10}O_5$	158 amorphous	+55.4 → +105
7	β-L-Arabinose	$C_5H_{10}O_5$	160	+190.6 → +104.5
8	DL-Arabinose	$C_5H_{10}O_5$	163.5–164.5	None
9	α-L-Lyxose	$C_5H_{10}O_5$	105	+5.8 → +13.5
10	L-Lyxose, 5-deoxy-3-*C*-formyl- (Streptose)	$C_6H_{10}O_5$	....	....
11	L-Lyxose, 3-*C*-formyl- (Hydroxy-streptose)	$C_6H_{10}O_6$	....	....
12	Pentose, 4,5-anhydro-5-deoxy-D-*erythro*-	$C_5H_8O_3$	....	....
13	Pentose, 2-deoxy-D-*erythro*-	$C_5H_{10}O_4$	96–98	−91 → −58
14	D-Ribose	$C_5H_{10}O_5$	87	−23.1 → −23.7
15	D-Ribose, 2-*C*-hydroxymethyl- (Hamamelose)	$C_6H_{12}O_6$	....	−7.1 [λ578]
16	α-D-Xylose	$C_5H_{10}O_5$	145	+93.6 → +18.8
17	D-Xylose, 5-deoxy-	$C_5H_{10}O_4$	....	+16
18	β-D-Xylose, 2-*O*-methyl-	$C_6H_{12}O_5$	137–138	−21 → +34
19	α-D-Xylose, 3-*O*-methyl-	$C_6H_{12}O_5$	95	+45 → +19
20	D-Allose, 6-deoxy-	$C_6H_{12}O_5$	140–143	+1.6 [18°] (c 0.6)
			146–148	−4.7 → 0
21	D-Allose, 6-deoxy-2,3-di-*O*-methyl- (Mycinose)	$C_8H_{16}O_5$	102–106	−46 → −29
22	Amicetose (a trideoxy hexose)	$C_6H_{12}O_3$	Oil, b.p. 65–70	+28.6 ($CHCl_3$)
23	Antiarose	$C_6H_{12}O_5$	....	Levo
24	α-D-Galactose	$C_6H_{12}O_6$	167	+150.7 → +80.2
25	β-D-Galactose	$C_6H_{12}O_6$	143–145	+52.8 → +80.2
26	D-Galactose, 3,6-anhydro-	$C_6H_{10}O_5$	....	+21.3 [10°]
27	α-D-Galactose, 6-deoxy- (D-Fucose; Rhodeose)	$C_6H_{12}O_5$	140–145	+127 → +76.3 (c 10)
28	D-Galactose, 6-deoxy-3-*O*-methyl- (Digitalose)	$C_7H_{14}O_5$	106[1], 119[2]	+106

	Substance (Synonym)	Chemical Formula	Melting Point °C	Specific Rotation $[\alpha]_D$
	(A)	(B)	(C)	(D)
	Aldoses (Con't)			
29	D-Galactose, 6-deoxy-4-O-methyl-	$C_7H_{14}O_5$	131–132	+82
30	D-Galactose, 6-deoxy-2,3-di-O-methyl-	$C_8H_{16}O_5$	. . . .	+73
31	α-D-Galactose, 3-O-methyl-	$C_7H_{14}O_6$	144–147	$+150.6 \to +108.6$
32	α-D-Galactose, 6-O-methyl-	$C_7H_{14}O_6$	122–123	$+117 \to +77.3$
33	L-Galactose	$C_6H_{12}O_6$	. . . .	See D-Galactose
34	α-L-Galactose, 3,6-anhydro-	$C_6H_{10}O_5$	. . . .	$-39.4 \to -25.2$
35	α-L-Galactose, 6-deoxy- (L-Fucose)	$C_6H_{12}O_5$	145	$-124.1 \to -76.4$
36	L-Galactose, 6-deoxy-2-O-methyl-	$C_7H_{14}O_5$	149–150	-75 ± 4 (c 0.5)
37	L-Galactose, 6-sulfate	$C_6H_{12}O_9S$	. . . .	−47 (c 0.2) (Na salt)
38	DL-Galactose	$C_6H_{12}O_6$	143–144, 163	None (racemic)
39	α-D-Glucose	$C_6H_{12}O_6$	146, 83 (H_2O)	$+112 \to +52.7$
40	β-D-Glucose	$C_6H_{12}O_6$	148–150	$+18.7 \to +52.7$
41	D-Glucose, 6-acetate	$C_7H_{14}O_7$	135	+48
42	D-Glucose, 2,3-di-O-methyl-	$C_8H_{16}O_6$	85–86, 121	+50
43	D-Glucose, 6-O-benzoyl- (Vaccinin)	$C_{13}H_{16}O_7$	Amorphous	+48 (C_2H_5OH)
44	α-D-Glucose, 6-deoxy- (Chinovose; Epirhamnose; Glucomethylose; Isorhamnose; Isorhodeose; Quinovose)	$C_6H_{12}O_5$	139–140	$+73.3 \to +29.7$ (c 8)
45	α-D-Glucose, 6-deoxy-3-O-methyl- (D-Thevetose)	$C_7H_{14}O_5$	116	$+84 \to +33$
46	D-Glucose, 6-sulfonic acid, 6-deoxy- (6-Sulfoquinovose)	$C_6H_{12}O_8S$	173–174	+87[3]
47	D-Glucose, 3-O-methyl-	$C_7H_{14}O_6$	162–167	$+98 \to +59.5$
48	α-L-Glucose	$C_6H_{12}O_6$	141–143	$-95.5 \to -51.4$
49	L-Glucose, 6-deoxy-3-O-methyl- (L-Thevetose)	$C_7H_{14}O_5$	126–129	-36.9 ± 2
50	D-Gulose, 6-deoxy-	$C_6H_{12}O_5$	. . . .	. . . .
51	Hexose, 2-deoxy-D-arabino-[4]	$C_6H_{12}O_5$	148	+46.6 [18°]
52	Hexose, 2,6-dideoxy-3-O-methyl-D-arabino- (D-Oleandrose)	$C_7H_{14}O_4$	. . . .	−11
53	Hexose, 3,6-dideoxy-D-arabino- (Tyvelose)	$C_6H_{12}O_4$	. . . .	$+24 \pm 2$
54	Hexose, 2,6-dideoxy-3-O-methyl-L-arabino- (L-Oleandrose)	$C_7H_{14}O_4$	62–63	$+11.9 \pm 2.5$
55	Hexose, 3,6-dideoxy-L-arabino- (Ascarylose)	$C_6H_{12}O_4$	. . . .	-24 ± 2
56	Hexose, 2,6-dideoxy-3-O-methyl-D-lyxo- (Diginose)	$C_7H_{14}O_4$	90–92	$+56 \pm 4$
57	Hexose, 2,6-dideoxy-L-lyxo- (L-Fucose, 2-deoxy-)	$C_6H_{12}O_4$	103–106	−61.6
58	Hexose, 2,6-dideoxy-3-O-methyl-L-lyxo-	$C_7H_{14}O_4$	78–85	−65
59	Hexose, 2,6-dideoxy-D-ribo- (Digitoxose; D-Altrose, 2,6-dideoxy-)	$C_6H_{12}O_4$	110	+46.4
60	Hexose, 2,6-dideoxy-3-O-methyl-D-ribo- (Cymarose)	$C_7H_{14}O_4$	93	+52
61	Hexose, 3,6-dideoxy-D-ribo- (Paratose)	$C_6H_{12}O_4$	. . . .	$+10 \pm 2$ (c 0.9)
62	Hexose, 4,6-dideoxy-3-O-methyl-D-ribo- (D-Gulose, 4,6-dideoxy-3-O-methyl-; Chalcose)	$C_7H_{14}O_4$	96–99	$+120 \to +76$
63	Hexose, 2,6-dideoxy-D-xylo- (Boivinose)	$C_6H_{12}O_4$	96–98	$-3.9 \to +3.9$

	Substance (Synonym)	Chemical Formula	Melting Point °C	Specific Rotation [α]$_D$
	(A)	(B)	(C)	(D)

	Aldoses (Con't)			
64	Hexose, 2,6-dideoxy-3-*O*-methyl-D-*xylo*- (Sarmentose)	$C_7H_{14}O_4$	78–79	$+12 \to +15.8$
65	Hexose, 3,6-dideoxy-D-*xylo*- (Abequose)	$C_6H_{12}O_4$	....	-3.2 ± 0.6
66	Hexose, 2,6-dideoxy-3-*C*-methyl-L-*xylo*- (Mycarose)	$C_7H_{14}O_4$	129–129	-31.1
67	Hexose, 2,6-dideoxy-3-*C*-methyl-3-*O*-methyl-L-*xylo*-(Cladinose)	$C_8H_{16}O_4$	oil, b.p. 120–132 (0.25 mm)	-23.1
68	Hexose, 3,6-dideoxy-L-*xylo*- (Colitose)	$C_6H_{12}O_4$	....	$+4$ (H_2O); -51 ± 2 (CH_3OH)
69	D-Idose[5]	$C_6H_{12}O_6$	....	....
70	L-Idose, 1,6-anhydro-	$C_6H_{10}O_5$		
71	α-D-Mannose	$C_6H_{12}O_6$	133	$+29.3 \to +14.5$
72	β-D-Mannose	$C_6H_{12}O_6$	132	$-16.3 \to +14.5$
73	D-Mannose, 6-deoxy- (D-Rhamnose)	$C_6H_{12}O_5$	86–90	-7.0
74	α-L-Mannose, 6-deoxy-monohydrate (L-Rhamnose)	$C_6H_{14}O_6$	93–94	$-8.6 \to +8.2$
75	β-L-Mannose, 6-deoxy-	$C_6H_{12}O_5$	123–125	$+38.4 \to +8.9$
76	L-Mannose, 6-deoxy-2-*O*-methyl-	$C_7H_{14}O_5$	....	....
77	L-Mannose, 6-deoxy-3-*O*-methyl- (L-Acofriose)	$C_7H_{14}O_5$	114–115	$+30$ [18°]
78	L-Mannose, 6-deoxy-2,4-di-*O*-methyl-	$C_8H_{16}O_5$	82	-19 [16°]
79	L-Mannose, 6-deoxy-5-*C*-methyl-4-*O*-methyl-(Noviose)	$C_8H_{16}O_5$	128–130	$+19.9$ (50% C_2H_5OH)
80	Rhodinose (a 2,3,6-trideoxyhexose)	$C_6H_{12}O_3$	....	-11 ± 1.6
81	D-Talose	$C_6H_{12}O_6$	128–132	$+16.9$
82	D-Talose, 6-deoxy- (D-Talomethylose)	$C_6H_{12}O_5$	129–131	$+20.6$
83	L-Talose, 6-deoxy- (L-Talomethylose)	$C_6H_{12}O_5$	116–118	-19.5 ± 2 [18°]
84	L-Talose, 6-deoxy-2-*O*-methyl- (L-Acovenose)	$C_7H_{14}O_5$	....	-19.4
85	Heptose, D-*glycero*-D-*galacto*-	$C_7H_{14}O_7$	139–140	$+47 \to +64$ (c 0.5)
86	Heptose, D-*glycero*-D-*manno*-	$C_7H_{14}O_7$	....	....
87	Heptose, D-*glycero*-L-*manno*-	$C_7H_{14}O_7$	....	....
	Ketoses			
88	Dihydroxyacetone	$C_3H_6O_3$	80 (dimer)	None
89	Tetrulose, L-*glycero*-[8] (L-Erythrulose; Ketoerythritol; L-Threulose)	$C_4H_8O_4$	Syrup	$+12$
90	Pentulose, D-*erythro*- (Adonose; D-Ribulose)	$C_5H_{10}O_5$	Syrup	$+16.6$ [27°]
91	Pentulose, L-*erythro*- (L-Ribulose)	$C_5H_{10}O_5$	....	-16.6
92	Pentulose, D-*threo*- (D-Xylulose)	$C_5H_{10}O_5$	....	-33
93	Pentulose, 5-deoxy-D-*threo*-	$C_5H_{10}O_4$	....	-5 ± 1 (CH_3OH)
94	Pentulose, L-*threo*- (L-Xylulose; L-Lyxulose; Xyloketose)	$C_5H_{10}O_5$	Syrup	$+33.1$
95	Hexulose, β-D-*arabino*-(β-D-Fructose; Levulose)	$C_6H_{12}O_6$	102–104[7]	$-133.5 \to -92$
96	Hexulose, 6-deoxy-D-*arabino*- (D-Rhamnulose)	$C_6H_{12}O_5$	....	-13 ± 2
97	Hexulose, D-*lyxo*- (D-Tagatose)	$C_6H_{12}O_6$	131–132	$+2.7 \to -4, -5$
98	5-Hexulose, D-*lyxo*	$C_6H_{12}O_6$	158	-86.6
99	Hexulose, 6-deoxy-L-*lyxo*- (L-Fuculose)	$C_6H_{12}O_5$	....	....

	Substance (Synonym)	Chemical Formula	Melting Point °C	Specific Rotation $[\alpha]_D$
	(A)	(B)	(C)	(D)
	Ketoses (Con't)			
100	Hexulose, D-*ribo*- (D-Psicose)	$C_6H_{12}O_6$	Amorphous	+4.7
101	Hexulose, L-*xylo*- (L-Sorbose)	$C_6H_{12}O_6$	159–161	−43.1
102	Hexulose, 6-deoxy-L-*xylo*-	$C_6H_{12}O_5$	88	−25 ± 2 (*c* 0.7)
103	Heptulose, D-*altro*- (Sedoheptulose; Sedoheptose)	$C_7H_{14}O_7$	Amorphous	+2.5 (*c* 10)
104	Heptulose·hemihydrate, L-*galacto*- (Perseulose)	$C_7H_{14}O_7 \cdot \frac{1}{2}H_2O$	110–115	−90 → −80
105	Heptulose, L-*gulo*-	$C_7H_{14}O_7$	. . . .	−28
106	Heptulose, D-*ido*-	$C_7H_{14}O_7$	172	−34 ± 8 (*c* 0.3)
107	Heptulose, D-*manno*- (Mannoketoheptose; D-Mannotagatoheptose)	$C_7H_{14}O_7$	152	+29.4
108	Heptulose, D-*talo*-	$C_7H_{14}O_7$	. . . .	. . . .
109	Octulose, D-*glycero*-L-*galacto*-	$C_8H_{16}O_8$	. . . .	−57, −43.4 → −13.4
110	Octulose, D-*glycero*-D-*manno*-	$C_8H_{16}O_8$	. . . .	+20 (CH_3OH)

[1] Original melting point. [2] Melting point after four-months' storage. [3] As a methyl glycoside cyclohexylamine salt. [4] Included because of speculations concerning it in biological processes. [5] Either D-idose or L-altrose is in the polysaccharide varianose. [6] Early literature refers to this as D-erythrose. [7] The $\cdot\frac{1}{2}H_2O$ and $\cdot 2H_2O$ forms also exist.

Part II. NATURAL MONOSACCHARIDES: AMINO SUGARS

	Substance (Synonym)	Chemical Formula	Melting Point °C	Specific Rotation $[\alpha]_D$
	(A)	(B)	(C)	(D)
	Aldosamines			
1	D-Ribose, 3-amino-3-deoxy-	$C_5H_{11}NO_4$	158–158.5 d.	−24.6 (hydrochloride)
2	D-Galactose, 2-amino-2-deoxy- (Galactosamine; Chondrosamine)	$C_6H_{13}NO_5$	185	+121 → +80 (hydrochloride)
3	α-L-Galactose, 2-amino-2,6-dideoxy- (L-Fucosamine)	$C_6H_{13}NO_4$	192–193 d.	−119 → −92 [27°] (hydrochloride)
4	α-D-Glucose, 2-amino-2-deoxy- (Glucosamine; Chitosamine)	$C_6H_{13}NO_5$	88	+100 → +47.5
5	β-D-Glucose, 2-amino-2-deoxy-	$C_6H_{13}NO_5$	110–111	+28 → +47.5
6	D-Glucose, 3-amino-3-deoxy- (Kanosamine)	$C_6H_{13}NO_5$	128 d.	+19 [14°]
7	D-Glucose, 6-amino-6-deoxy-	$C_6H_{13}NO_5$	161–162 d.	+23 → +50.1 (hydrochloride)
8	D-Glucose, 2,6-diamino-2,6-dideoxy- (Neosamine C)	$C_6H_{14}N_2O_4$	>230	+61.5 (dihydrochloride)
9	D-Glucose, 3,6-dideoxy-3-dimethylamino- (Mycaminose)	$C_8H_{17}NO_4$	115–116	+31 (hydrochloride)
10	D-Glucose, 4,6-dideoxy-4-dimethylamino-	$C_8H_{17}NO_4$	192–193	+45.5 (hydrochloride)
11	L-Glucose, 2-deoxy-2-methylamino-	$C_7H_{15}NO_5$	130–132	−64
12	D-Gulose, 2-amino-1,6-anhydro-2-deoxy-	$C_6H_{11}NO_4$	250–260 d.	+41 ± 2 (hydrochloride)
13	D-Gulose, 2-amino-2-deoxy-	$C_6H_{13}NO_5$	152–162 d.	+5.6 → −18.7 (hydrochloride)

Substance (Synonym)	Chemical Formula	Melting Point °C	Specific Rotation $[\alpha]_D$
(A)	(B)	(C)	(D)
Aldosamines (Con't)			
14 Hexose, 3,4,6-trideoxy-3-dimethyl-amino-D-*xylo*- (Desosamine; Picrocine)	$C_8H_{17}NO_3$	189–191 d.	+49.5 (*c* 10) (hydrochloride)
15 Hexose, a 4-acetamido-2-amino-2,4,6-trideoxy-	$C_8H_{16}N_2O_4$	216–219	+115 → +94 [26°] (*c* 0.05)
16 Hexose, an amino-deoxy-3-*O*-carboxyethyl-	$C_9H_{17}NO_7$	....	....
17 Hexose, a 2,6-diamino-2,6-dideoxy- (Neosamine B; Paramose)	$C_6H_{14}N_2O_4$	135–150 d.	+17.5 (*c* 0.9 (hydrochloride)
18 Hexose, a 3-dimethylamino-2,3,6-trideoxy- (Rhodosamine)	$C_8H_{17}NO_3$	....	....
19 D-Mannose, 2-amino-2-deoxy- (Mannosamine)	$C_6H_{13}NO_5$	142 d.	−4.3 (*c* 9) (hydrochloride)
20 D-Mannose, 3-amino-3,6-dideoxy- (Mycosamine)	$C_6H_{13}NO_4$	162	−11.5 (hydrochloride)
21 D-Talose, 2-amino-2-deoxy- (Talosamine)	$C_6H_{13}NO_5$	151–153	+3.4 → −5.7 (*c* 0.9) (hydrochloride)
22 L-Talose, 2-amino-2,6-dideoxy- (Pneumosamine)	$C_6H_{13}NO_4$	162–163	+6.9 → +10.4 (hydrochloride)
Ketosamines			
23 Pentulose, 1-(*o*-carboxyanilino)-1-deoxy-D-*erythro*-	$C_{12}H_{14}NO_6$	....	....
24 Hexulose, 1-(*o*-carboxyanilino)-1-deoxy-D-*arabino*-	$C_{13}H_{16}NO_7$	....	....
25 Hexulose, 5-amino-5-deoxy-L-*xylo*-	$C_6H_{13}NO_5$	174–176	−62
26 Hexulose, 6-deoxy-6-(*N*-methyl-acetamido)-L-*xylo*-	$C_9H_{17}NO_6$	....	....

Part III. NATURAL ALDITOLS AND INOSITOLS (with Inososes and Inosamines)

Substance (Synonym)	Chemical Formula	Melting Point °C	Specific Rotation $[\alpha]_D$
(A)	(B)	(C)	(D)
Alditols			
1 Glycerol	$C_3H_8O_3$	20	None
2 Glycerol, 1-deoxy- (1,2-Propane-diol)[1]	$C_3H_8O_2$	Oil, b.p. 188–189	None (racemic)
3 Erythritol	$C_4H_{10}O_4$	118–120	None (meso)
4 Erythritol, 1,4-dideoxy- (2,3-Butyleneglycol)	$C_4H_{10}O_2$	25, 34	None (meso)
5 D-Threitol, 1,4-dideoxy-	$C_4H_{10}O_2$	19	−13.0
6 L-Threitol, 1,4-dideoxy-	$C_4H_{10}O_2$	....	+10.2
7 DL-Threitol, 1,4-dideoxy-	$C_4H_{10}O_2$	7.6	None (racemic)
8 D-Arabinitol	$C_5H_{12}O_5$	103	+7.82 (*c* 8, borax solution)
9 L-Arabinitol	$C_5H_{12}O_5$	101–102	−32 (*c* 0.4, 5% molybdate)
10 Ribitol (Adomitol)	$C_5H_{12}O_5$	102	None (meso)
11 Galactitol (Dulcitol)	$C_6H_{14}O_6$	186–188	None (meso)

	Substance (Synonym)	Chemical Formula	Melting Point °C	Specific Rotation $[\alpha]_D$
	(A)	(B)	(C)	(D)

		Alditols (Con't)		
12	D-Glucitol (Sorbitol)	$C_6H_{14}O_6$	112	−1.8 [15°]
13	D-Glucitol, 1,5-anhydro- (Polygalitol)	$C_6H_{12}O_5$	140–141	+42.4
14	L-Iditol	$C_6H_{14}O_6$	73.5	−3.5 (c 10)
15	D-Mannitol	$C_6H_{14}O_6$	166	−0.21
16	D-Mannitol, 1,5-anhydro- (Styracitol)	$C_6H_{12}O_5$	157	−49.9
17	Heptitol, D-*glycero*-D-*galacto*- (Heptitol, L-*glycero*-D-*manno*-; Perseitol)	$C_7H_{16}O_7$	183–185, 188	−1.1
18	Heptitol, D-*glycero*-D-*gluco*- (Heptitol, L-*glycero*-D-*talo*-; β-Sedoheptitol)	$C_7H_{16}O_7$	131–132	+46 (5% NH₄ molybdate)
19	Heptitol, D-*glycero*-D-*manno*- (Heptitol, D-*glycero*-D-*talo*-; Volemitol)	$C_7H_{16}O_7$	153	+2.65
20	Octitol, D-*erythro*-D-*galacto*-	$C_8H_{18}O_8 \cdot H_2O$	169–170	−11 (5% NH₄ molybdate)
		Inositols		
21	Betitol (a dideoxy inositol)	$C_6H_{12}O_4$	224	. . . .
22	Bioinosose (*scyllo*-Inosose; *myo*-Inosose-2; a deoxy keto inositol)	$C_6H_{10}O_6$	198–200	None (meso)
23	h-Bornesitol (a *myo*-inositol monomethyl ether)	$C_7H_{14}O_6$	200	+31.6
24	l-Bornesitol (a *myo*-inositol monomethyl ether)	$C_7H_{14}O_6$	205–206	−32.1
25	Conduritol (a 2,3-dehydro-2,3-dideoxyinositol)	$C_6H_{10}O_4$	142–143	None (meso)
26	Cordycepic acid (a tetrahydroxycyclohexanecarboxylic acid)[2]	$C_7H_{12}O_6$	. . . .	. . . .
27	Dambonitol (a *myo*-inositol dimethyl ether)	$C_8H_{16}O_6$	206	None (meso)
28	DL-Inositol	$C_6H_{12}O_6$	253	None (racemic)
29	d-Inositol	$C_6H_{12}O_6$	. . . .	+60
30	l-Inositol	$C_6H_{12}O_6$	240	−65
31	Laminitol (a C-methyl *myo*-inositol)	$C_7H_{14}O_6$	266–269	−3
32	Liriodendritol (a *myo*-inositol dimethyl ether)	$C_8H_{16}O_6$	224	−25
33	*muco*-Inositol monomethyl ether	$C_7H_{14}O_6$	322–325	. . . .
34	*myo*-Inositol (*meso*-Inositol)	$C_6H_{12}O_6$	217–218	None (meso)
35	d-*myo*-Inosose-1 (a deoxy keto inositol)	$C_6H_{10}O_6$	138–139	+19.6
36	Mytilitol (a C-methyl *scyllo*-inositol)	$C_7H_{14}O_6$	259	None (meso)
37	*neo*-Inosamine-2 (a deoxy amino inositol)	$C_6H_{13}O_5N$	239–241 d.	None (meso)
38	d-Ononitol (a *myo*-inositol monomethyl ether)	$C_7H_{14}O_6$	172	+6.6
39	h-Pinitol (a *dextro*-inositol monomethyl ether)	$C_7H_{14}O_6$	186	+65.5
40	l-Pinitol (a *levo*-inositol monomethyl ether)	$C_7H_{14}O_6$	186	−65
41	l-Quebrachitol (a *levo*-inositol monomethyl ether)	$C_7H_{14}O_6$	190–191	−80.2 [28°]
42	d-Quercitol (a deoxy *dextro*-inositol)	$C_6H_{12}O_5$	235	+24.2
43	d-Quinic acid (a trideoxy carboxy *dextro*-inositol)	$C_7H_{12}O_6$	164	+44 (c 10)

Substance (Synonym)	Chemical Formula	Melting Point °C	Specific Rotation $[\alpha]_D$
(A)	(B)	(C)	(D)
Inositols (Con't)			
44 l-Quinic acid (a trideoxy carboxy *levo*-inositol)	$C_7H_{12}O_6$	162	-42.1
45 Quinic acid, 5-dehydro-	$C_7H_{10}O_6$	140–142 (138 s.)	-82.4 [28°]
46 Scyllitol (*scyllo*-Inositol; Cocositol)	$C_6H_{12}O_6$	352–353	None (meso)
47 Sequoyitol (a *myo*-inositol monomethyl ether)	$C_7H_{14}O_6$	234–235	None (meso)
48 Shikimic acid (a 3,4-anhydro-quinic acid)	$C_7H_{10}O_5$	183–184	-200 [16°]
49 Shikimic acid, 5-dehydro-	$C_7H_8O_5$	150–152	-57.5 [28°] (EtOH)
50 Streptamine (2,4-diaminodideoxy-scyllitol)	$C_6H_{14}O_4N_2$	88, 210–250 d.	None (meso)
51 Streptamine, 2-deoxy-	$C_6H_{14}O_3N_2$	....	None (meso)
52 Streptadine (1,3-Dideoxy-1,3-diguani-dino-scyllitol)	$C_8H_{18}N_6O_4$	....	None (meso)
53 Viburnitol (a deoxy *levo*-inositol)[3]	$C_6H_{12}O_5$	174	-73.9

[1] The 1-phosphate ester of this diol is said to occur in brain tissue and sea-urchin eggs. [2] Strong evidence that cordycepic acid is really D-mannitol. [3] Not an enantiomorph of *d*-quercitol; other isomeric relationship is involved.

Part IV. NATURAL ALDONIC, URONIC, AND ALDARIC ACIDS

Substance (Synonym)	Chemical Formula	Melting Point °C	Specific Rotation $[\alpha]_D$
(A)	(B)	(C)	(D)
Aldonic Acids			
1 D-Glyceric acid	$C_3H_6O_4$	Gum	Dextro
2 L-Glyceric acid	$C_3H_6O_4$	Gum	Levo
3 D-Arabinonic acid	$C_5H_{10}O_6$	114–116	$+10.5$ (*c* 6)
4 L-Arabinonic acid	$C_5H_{10}O_6$	118–119	$-9.6 \rightarrow -41.7$[1]
5 L-Arabinonic-1,4-lactone	$C_5H_8O_5$	97–99	-72
6 D-Ribonic acid	$C_5H_{10}O_6$	112–113	-17.0
7 D-Xylonic acid	$C_5H_{10}O_6$	....	$-2.9 \rightarrow +20.1$[1]
8 L-Xylonic acid	$C_5H_{10}O_6$	....	-91.8[1]
9 D-Altronic acid	$C_6H_{12}O_7$	....	$+11.5 \rightarrow +24.8$[1] (Ca salt, N HCl)
10 D-Galactonic acid	$C_6H_{12}O_7$	122	$-11.2 \rightarrow +57.6$[1]
11 D-Gluconic acid	$C_6H_{12}O_7$	130–132 (110–112 s.)	$-6.7 \rightarrow +11.9$[1]
12 L-Gulonic acid	$C_6H_{12}O_7$	Exists only in soln.	[ca. 0°]
13 Hexsonic acid, 2-deoxy-D-*arabino*-	$C_6H_{12}O_6$	93–95	$+68$ (lactone)
14 2-Hexulosonic acid, D-*arabino*-	$C_6H_{10}O_7$	....	-81.7 (Na salt)
15 2-Hexulosonic acid, 3-deoxy-D-*erythro*-	$C_6H_{10}O_6$	....	-29.2 (*c* 6, Ca salt)
16 2-Hexulosonic acid, D-*lyxo*-	$C_6H_{10}O_7$	169	-5
17 5-Hexulosonic acid, D-*arabino*-	$C_6H_{10}O_7$	108–109	....
18 5-Hexulosonic acid, D-*xylo*-	$C_6H_{10}O_7$	....	-14.5
19 D-Mannonic acid	$C_6H_{12}O_7$	....	-15.6
20 D-Gluconic acid, *O*-β-D-galactopyrano-syl- (1 → 4)- (Lactobionic acid)	$C_{12}H_{22}O_{12}$	....	$+25.1$ (Ca salt)

	Substance (Synonym)	Chemical Formula	Melting Point °C	Specific Rotation $[\alpha]_D$
	(A)	(B)	(C)	(D)
	Uronic Acids			
21	L-Lyxuronic acid	$C_5H_8O_6$	. . . .	. . . .
22	β-D-Galacturonic acid	$C_6H_{10}O_7$	160	$+27 \rightarrow +55.6$
23	α-D-Galacturonic acid·monohydrate	$C_6H_{12}O_8$	159–160 (110–115 s.)	$+97.9 \rightarrow +50.9$
24	D-Galacturonic acid, 2-amino-2-deoxy-	$C_6H_{11}O_6N$	160 d.	$+84.5$ (pH 2 HCl)
25	β-D-Glucuronic acid	$C_6H_{10}O_7$	156	$+11.7 \rightarrow +36.3$
26	D-Glucuronic acid, 2-amino-2-deoxy-	$C_6H_{11}O_6N$	120–172 d.	$+55$
27	D-Glucuronic acid, 3-O-methyl-	$C_7H_{12}O_7$	Syrup	$+6$
28	L-Guluronic acid	$C_6H_{10}O_7$	. . . .	. . . .
29	L-Iduronic acid	$C_6H_{10}O_7$	. . . .	$+30$
30	β-D-Mannuronic acid	$C_6H_{10}O_7$	165–167	$-47.9 \rightarrow -23.9$
31	α-D-Mannuronic acid·monohydrate	$C_6H_{12}O_8$	110 s., 120–130 d.	$+16 \rightarrow -6.1$ (c 6.8)
	Aldaric Acids			
32	D-Tartaric acid	$C_4H_6O_6$	170	-15
33	L-Tartaric acid	$C_4H_6O_6$	170	$+15$ [15°]
34	L-Malic acid	$C_4H_6O_5$	100	-2.3 (c 8.4)

[1] Equilibrates with the lactone.

WAXES

These data for waxes were compiled originally for the Biology Data Book by A. H. Warth. Data are reproduced here by permission of the copyright owners of the above publication, the American Societies for Experimental Biology, Washington, D.C. p. 382.

Specific Gravity (column C) was calculated at the specified temperature, degrees centigrade, and referred to water at the same temperature. **Density.** shown in parentheses (column C), and **Refractive Index** (column D) were measured at the specified temperature, degrees centigrade.

	Wax	Melting Point °C	Specific Gravity or (Density)	Refractive Index $n\frac{°C}{D}$	Iodine Value	Acid Value	Saponification Value
	(A)	(B)	(C)	(D)	(E)	(F)	(G)
1	Bamboo leaf	79–80	$(0.961^{25°})$	....	$7.8^{[1]}$	14.5	43.4
2	Bayberry (myrtle)	46.7–48.8	$(0.985^{15°})$	$1.436^{80°}$	$2.9^{[2]}$–$3.9^{[3]}$	3.5	20.5–21.7
3	Beeswax, crude	62–66	$(0.927$–$0.970^{15°})$	1.439–$1.483^{40°}$	6.8–$16.4^{[2]}$	16.8–35.8	89.3–149.0
4	Beeswax, white, U.S.P.	61–69	$(0.959$–$0.975^{15°})$	1.447–$1.465^{65°}$	7–$11^{[3]}$	17–24	90–96
5	Beeswax, yellow	62–65	$(0.960$–$0.964^{15°})$	1.443–$1.449^{65°}$	6–11	18–24	90–97
6	Candelilla, refined	67–69	$(0.982$–$0.986^{15°})$	1.454–$1.463^{85°}$	14.4–20.4	12.7–18.1	35–86
7	Cape berry[4]	40.5–45.0	$(1.004$–$1.007^{15°})$	$1.450^{45°}$	0.6–2.4	2.5–3.7	211–215
8	Carandá	79.7–84.5	$(0.990^{25°})$	....	8.0–8.9	5.0–9.5	64.5–78.5
9	Carnauba	83–86	0.990–$1.001^{15°}$	1.467–$1.472^{40°}$	7.2–13.5	2.9–9.7	78–95
10	Castor oil, hydrogenated	88–88	$(0.980$–$0.990^{20°})$	....	2.5–8.5	1.0–5.0	177–181
11	Chinese insect	81.5–84.0	0.950–$0.970^{15°}$	$1.457^{40°}$	1.4	0.2–1.5	73–93
12	Cotton	68–71	$0.959^{15°}$	....	24.5	32	70.6
13	Cranberry	207–218	$(0.970$–$0.975^{15°})$	....	44.2–$53.2^{[2]}$	42.2–59.1	131–134
14	Douglas-fir bark	59.0–72.8	$(1.030^{25°})$	$1.468^{80°}$	25.8–62.5	58.6–80.7	112–200
15	Esparto	67.5–78.1	$0.988^{15°}$	....	22–23	22.7–23.9	69.8–79.3
16	Flax	61.5–69.8	0.908–$0.985^{15°}$	....	21.6–28.8	17.5–48.3	77.5–101.5
17	Ghedda, E. Indian beeswax	60.5–66.4	0.956–$0.973^{15°}$	$1.440^{50°}$	5.6–12.6	5.8–7.9	84.5–118.3
18	Indian corn	80–81	....	....	$4.2^{[2]}$	1.9	120.3
19	Japan wax	48–53	0.975–$0.993^{15°}$	....	4.5–12.5	6–20	206.5–237.5
20	Jojoba	11.2–11.8	0.864–$0.899^{25°}$	$1.465^{25°}$	81.7–$88.4^{[2]}$	0.2–0.6	92.2–95.0
21	Madagascar	88	....	....	3.2–5.3	17.7–28.0	140.0–159.6
22	Microcrystalline, amber	64–91	0.913–$0.943^{15°}$	1.424–$1.452^{80°}$	0	0	0
23	Microcrystalline, white	71–89	0.928–$0.941^{15°}$	$1.441^{80°}$	0	0	0
24	Montan, crude	76–86	$(1.010$–$1.020^{25°})$	....	13.9–17.6	22.7–31.0	59.4–92.0
25	Montan, refined	77–84	$(1.010$–$1.030^{25°})$	....	10–14	24–43	72–103
26	Orange peel	44.0–46.5	$0.985^{15°}$	$1.502^{20°}$	$115.7^{[2]}$	48.3	120.9
27	Ouricury, refined	79.0–83.8	$1.053^{15°}$	....	6.9–$7.8^{[2]}$	3.4–21.1	61.8–85.8
28	Ozocerite, refined	74.4–75.0	0.907–$0.920^{15°}$	....	0	0	0
29	Palm	74–86	$(0.991$–$1.045^{15°})$	....	8.9–$16.9^{[2]}$	5.0–10.6	64.5–104.0
30	Paraffin, American	49–63	0.896–$0.925^{15°}$	1.442–$1.448^{80°}$	0	0	0
31	Peat wax, natural	73–76	$0.980^{15°}$	....	16–40	60.0–73.3	73.9–136.0
32	Rice bran, refined	75.3–79.9	....	$1.469^{30°}$	11.1–19.4	15–17	56.9–104.4
33	Shellac wax	79–82	0.971–$0.980^{15°}$	....	6.0–$8.8^{[3]}$	12.1–24.3	63.8–83.0
34	Sisal hemp	74–81	1.007–$1.010^{15°}$	....	28–$29^{[2]}$	16–$19^{[2]}$	56–58
35	Sorghum grain	77–82	....	....	15.7–20.9	10.1–16.2	16–44
36	Spanish moss	79–80	....	....	33.0	25.0	120.4
37	Spermaceti	42–50	0.905–$0.945^{15°}$	$1.440^{70°}$	4.8–5.9	2.0–5.2	108–134
38	Sugarcane, crude	52–67	0.988–$0.998^{25°}$	....	32–84	24–57	128–177
39	Sugarcane, double-refined	77–82	0.961–$0.979^{25°}$	$1.510^{25°}$	13–29	8–23	55–95
40	Wool wax, refined	36–43	0.932–$0.945^{15°}$	1.478–$1.482^{40°}$	15.0–46.9	5.6–22.0	80–127

[1] Wijs test. [2] Hanus test. [3] Hubl test. [4] *Myrica cordifolia*.

Trade name	Chemical name
A acid	1,7-Hydroxynaphthalene-3,6-disulfonic acid
Acetyl H acid	N-Acetyl-1-amino-8-naphthol-3,6-disulfonic acid
Alen's acid	1-Naphthylamine-3,6-disulfonic acid (also Freund's ac.)
Alizarin	1,2-Dihydroxyanthraquinone
Amido acid	2-Amino-7-hydroxynaphthalene-5-sulfonic acid
Amido J acid	2-Naphthylamine-5,7-disulfonic acid
Amino G acid	7-Amino-1,3-naphthalene disulfonic acid
	2-Naphthylamine-6,8-disulfonic acid
Amino R acid	3-Amino-2,7-naphthalene disulfonic acid
	2-Naphthylamine-3,6-disulfonic acid
Aminophenolic acid V	1-Amino-3-oxybenzene-5-sulfonic acid
Aminophenol sulfonic acid III	1-Amino-3-oxybenzene-6-sulfonic acid
Andresen's acid	1-Naphthol-3,8-disulfonic acid
Anisidine	o-Aminophenol methylether
Anthrachrysone	1,3,5,7-Tetrahydroanthraquinone
Anthraflavic acid	2,6-Dihydroxyanthraquinone
Anthranilic acid	o-Aminobenzoic acid
Anthrarufin	1,5-Dihydroxyanthraquinone
Anthranol	9-Hydroxyanthracene
α Anthrol	1-Hydroxyanthracene
Armstrong's acid	Naphthalene-1,5-disulfonic acid
Armstrong & Wynne acid	1-Naphthol-3-sulfonic acid
Armstrong & Wynne acid II	2-Naphthylamino-5,7-disulfonic acid
B acid	8-Amino-1-naphthol-4,6-disulfonic acid
Badische acid	2-Naphthylamino-8-sulfonic acid
Bayer's acid	2-Naphthol-8-sulfonic acid
Benzidine	p,p'-Diaminodiphenyl
Bronner's acid	2-Naphthylamino-6-sulfonic acid
β acid	Anthraquinone-2-sulfonic acid
C acid ⎫ CLT acid ⎰	6-Chloro-m-toluidine-4-sulfonic acid
Casella's acid	2-Naphthol-7-sulfonic acid (F acid)
Chicago acid	1-Amino-8-naphthyl-2,4-disulfonic acid
Chloro H acid	8-Chloro-1-naphthol-3,6-disulfonic acid
Chromogene I	4,5-Dihydroxy-2,7-naphthalene disulfonic acid
Chromotrope acid	1,8-Dihydronaphthalene-3,6-disulfonic acid
Chromotropic acid	4,5-Dihydroxy-2,7-naphthalene disulfonic acid
Chrysazine	1,8-Dihydroxyanthraquinone
Cleve's acid	1-Naphthylamine-3-sulfonic acid
Cleve's acid	1-Naphthylamine-5-sulfonic acid
Cleve's acid	1-Naphthylamine-6-sulfonic acid
Cleve's acid	1-Naphthylamine-7-sulfonic acid
α Coccinic acid	1-Methyl-5-oxybenzyl-2,4-dicarbonic acid
Cresidine	3-Amino-4-methoxytoluene
Cresotic acid	Cresol carboxylic acid
Croceine acid	2-Naphthol-1-sulfonic acid
DS	4,4'-Diamino-2,2'-stilbene disulfuric acid
DTS	Dihydrothio-p-toluidine sulfonic acid
Dahl's acid	2-Naphthylamine-5-sulfonic acid
Dahl's acid II	1-Naphthylamine-4,6-disulfonic acid
Dahl's acid III	1-Naphthylamino-4,7-disulfonic acid
Dimethyl-γ-acid	7-Dimethylamino-1-naphthol sulfonic acid
Dioxy G acid	1,7-Dihydroxynaphthalene-3-sulfonic acid
Dioxy J acid	1,6-Dihydroxynaphthalene-3-sulfonic acid
Dioxy S acid	1,8-Dihydroxynaphthalene-4-sulfonic acid
Diphenylblack base	p-Aminodiphenylamine
Disulfo acid S	1-Naphthylamine-4,8-disulfonic acid
δ acid	⎰1-Naphthol-4,8-disulfonic acid ⎱1-Naphthylamine-4,8-disulfonic acid

Trade name	Chemical name
Ebert & Merz acid	{ Naphthalene-2,7-disulfonic acid { Naphthalene-2,6-disulfonic acid
Ethyl-γ-acid	7-Ethylamino-1-naphthol-3-sulfonic acid
Ethyl F acid	7-Ethylamino-2-naphthalene sulfonic acid
Ewer & Pick's acid	Naphthalene-1,6-disulfonic acid
ε acid	{ 1-Naphthol-3,8-disulfonic acid { 1-Naphthylamine-3,8-disulfonic acid
F acid	2-Naphthol-7-sulfonic acid (Casella's acid)
Fast Black B base	4,4'-Diamino diphenylamine
Fast Blue base	Dianisidine
Fast Blue Red O base	3-Nitro-p-phenetidine
Fast Bordeaux GP	3-Nitro-p-anisidine
Fast Orange GR	o-Nitroaniline
Fast Orange R	m-Nitroaniline
Fast Red base AL	α-Aminoanthraquinone
Fast Red B base	5-Nitro-o-anisidine
Fast Red GG base	p-Nitroaniline
Fast Red GL base	3-Nitro-p-toluidine
Fast Red 3 GL base	4-Chloro-2-nitroaniline
Fast Red RL base	5-Nitro-o-toluidine
Fast Scarlet G base	4-Nitro-α-toluidine
Fast Scarlet R base	4-Nitro-O-anisidine
Forsling's acid I	2-Naphthylamine-8-sulfonic acid
Forsling's acid II	2-Naphthylamine-5-sulfonic acid
Freund's acid	1-Naphthylamine-3,6-disulfonic acid
G acid	2-Naphthol-6,8-disulfonic acid
GR acid	α-Naphthol-3,6-disulfonic acid
Gallic acid	3,4,5-Trihydroxybenzoic acid
γ acid	2-Amino-8-naphthol-6-sulfonic acid
H acid	1-Amino-8-naphthol-3,6-disulfonic acid
Histazarin	2,3-Dihydroxyanthraquinone
Isoanthraflavic acid	2,7-Dihydroxyanthraquinone
J acid	2-Amino-5-naphthol-7-sulfonic acid
K acid	1-Amino-8-naphthol-4,6-disulfonic acid
Kalle's acid	1-Naphthylamine-2,7-disulfonic acid
Ketone base	Tetramethyl aminobenzophenone
Koch's acid	1-Naphthylamine-3,6,8-trisulfonic acid
L acid	1-Naphthol-5-sulfonic acid
Laurent's acid	1-Naphthylamine-5-sulfonic acid
Lepidine	4-Methylquinoline
Leucotrop	Phenyldimethyl benzylammonium chloride
M acid	1-Amino-5-naphthol-7-sulfonic acid
Mesidine	2,4,6-Thimethylaniline
Metanilic acid	Aniline-m-sulfonic acid
Methyl-γ-acid	7-Methyl-8-naphthol disulfonic acid
Michler's hydrol	Tetramethyl diaminobenzohydrol
Michler's ketone	Tetramethyl diaminobenzophenone
Myrbane oil	Nitrobenzene
Naphthacetol	1-Acetylamino-4-naphthol
Naphthazarin	5,8-Dihydroxy-1,4-naphthoquinone
Naphthionic acid	1-Naphthylamine-4-sulfonic acid
o-Naphthionic acid	1-Naphthylamine-2-sulfonic acid
Naphthol AS	Anilide of hydronaphthoic acid
Naphthoresorcine	1,3-Dihydroxynaphthalene
Nekal BX	Na-salt of 1,4-bis,sec-butylnaphthalene-6-sulfonic acid
Nevile and Winther's acid	1-Naphthol-4-sulfonic acid
Nigrotic acid	1,3,6,7-Dihydroxysulfonaphthoic acid
Nitron 1,2,4-acid	1-Amino-8-nitro-7-naphthol-4-sulfonic acid
Nitroso base	p-Nitrodimethyl aniline

Trade name	Chemical name
NW acid	Nevile and Winther s acid
Oxy L acid	1-Naphthol-5-sulfonic acid
Oxy Tobias acid	β-Naphthol-1-sulfonic acid
Peri acid	1-Naphthylamine-8-sulfonic acid
p-Phenetidine	p-Aminophenol ethylether
Phenyl gamma acid	2-Phenylamine-8-naphthol-6-sulfonic acid
Phenyl Peri acid	Phenyl-1-naphthylamine-8-sulfonic acid
Phosxgene	Carbonyl chloride
Phthalic acid	O-Benzenedicarbolic acid
Picramic acid	2-Amino-4,6-dinitrophenol
Picric acid	2,4,6-Trinitrophenol
Pirio's acid	4-Amino-1-naphthalene sulfonic acid
Primuline base	p-Toluidine heated with sulfur
Purpurine	1,2,4-Trihydroxyanthraquinone
Pyrogallol	1,2,3-Trihydroxybenzene
Quinaldine	2-Methylquinoline
Quinazarin	1,4-Dihydroxyanthraquinone
R acid	2-Naphthol-3,6-disulfonic acid
2 R acid	2-Amino-8-naphthol-3,6-disulfonic acid
Red acid	1,5-Dihydroxynaphthalene-3,7-disulfonic acid
RG acid	1-Naphthol-3,6-disulfonic acid
Resorcinol	1,3-Dihydroxybenzene
Rumpff acid	2 Naphthol-8-sulfonic acid (Croceine acid)
S acid	1-Amino-8-naphthol-4-sulfonic acid
2 S acid	1-Amino-8-naphthol-2,4-disulfonic acid
Salicylic acid	o-Hydroxybenzoic acid
Schäffer's acid	2-Naphthol-6-sulfonic acid
Schäffer and Baum acid	α-Naphthol-2-sulfonic acid
Schollkopf's acid	$\begin{cases} \text{1-Naphthol-4,8-disulfonic acid} \\ \text{1-Naphthylamine-4,8-disulfonic acid} \\ \text{1-Naphthylamine-8-sulfonic acid} \end{cases}$
Sulfanilic acid	Aniline-p-sulfonic acid
Thiocarbanilide	Diphenylthiourea
Tobias acid	2-Naphthylamine-1-sulfonic acid
Tolidine	Di-p-aminoditolyl
Toluidine	Aminotoluene
Violet acid	α-Naphthol-3,6-disulfuric acid
Xylidine	Aminoxylene
Y acid	2-Naphthol-6,8-disulfuric acid
Yellow acid	1,3-Dihydroxynaphthalene-5,7-disulfuric acid
1:2:4 acid	1-Amino-2-naphthol-4-sulfonic acid

TRADE NAMES, COMPOSITION AND MANUFACTURERS OF SOME PLASTICS

Trade name	Composition	Manufacturer
A-100 SM	Acrylics	Resolite Corp.
Abson	Acrylonitrile-butadiene ABS polymers	B. F. Goodrich Chemical Co.
Acco	Polymers, copolymers of acrylics and methacrylate esters	Acco Polymers Company
Acetex	Synthetic resin latices	United States Rubber Co., Naugatuck Chemical Div.
Acrilan	Acrylic fiber	Monsanto Co.
Actol	Polyesters	Allied Chemical Corp.
Adipol BCA	Di-butoxyethyl adipate	Food Machinery and Chemical Corp.
Agile	Polyesters, polyethylenes, polypropylenes, polyvinyl chlorides	American Agile Corp.
Alathon	Polyethylene resins	E. I. duPont de Nemours & Co., Inc.
Alkor	Furane resin cement	Atlas Mineral Products
Alpex	Hydrocarbon resins	Alkydol Laboratories, Div. of Reichhold Chemicals, Inc.
Alpha	Nylons, polyethylenes, ABS-polymers, polypropylenes, polyvinyl chlorides	Alpha Plastics, Inc.
Ameripol	High density polyethylenes	Goodrich-Gulf Chemicals, Inc.
Ameripol CB	Polybutadienes	" " " "
Ameripol SBR	Butediene-styrene rubber	" " " "
Amerith	Cellulose nitrate	Celanese Corp. of America
Amphenol	Polystyrene	American Phenolic Co.
Amres	Phenolics, resorcinol, urea	American Marietta Co.
Anaconda	Polyethylenes, polyvinyl chlorides	Anaconda American Brass Co.
Aquaplex	Alkyd-resin emulsions	Rohm & Hass Company
Araldite	Epoxy resins	Ciba Products Corp.
Arcolite	Phenolic	Consolidated Molded Products Co.
Aritemp	Epoxy resins	Aries Laboratories, Inc.
Arociro	Polychlorinated polyphenyls	Monsanto Chemical Company
Arodures	Ureas	National Distillers & Chemical Corp.
Atlac	Polyester resins in solid state	Atlas Chemical Industries, Inc.
Avisco	Urea-formaldehyde compounds	American Viscose Corporation
AviSun	Polypropylene resins	AviSun Corporation
Bakelite	Acrylics, epoxies, phenolics, polyethylenes, copolymers	Union Carbide Corp., Plastics Div.
Bavick-11	Acrylics	J. T. Baker Chemical Co.
Beckacite	Maleic, fumaric, modified phenolic resins	Reichold Chemicals, Inc.
Beckamine	Alcohol-soluble urea-formaldehyde resins for laminates, adhesives, coating	" " "
Beckopol	High melt point modified phenolic resin	" " "
Blacar	Vinyl chloride resin; vinyl compound	Cary Chemicals, Inc.
Boltaflex	Supported and unsupported flexible vinyl sheeting	The General Tire & Rubber Co.
Boltaron	ABS polymers, polyethylenes, polypropylenes, polyvinyl chlorides	Bolta Products Company
Bondstrand	Epoxies, polyesters	Amercoat Corporation
Brea	Polyethylenes	" "
Budene	Polybutadiene	Goodyear Tire & Rubber Company
Butacite	Polyvinyl butyral resins	E. I. duPont de Nemours & Co.
Butakon	Butadiene-acrylonitriles	Imperial Chemical Ind. Ltd.
Buton	Thermosetting butadiene-styrene resins	Enjay Chemical Company, Div. Humble Oil & Refining Company
Butvar	Polyvinyl butyral resins	Shawinigan Resins Corporation

Trade name	Composition	Manufacturer
C-8 Epoxy	Epoxy resins	Union Carbide Corporation
Cadco	Acrylics, ABS polymers, nylons, phenolics, polyesters, polyethylenes, polypropylenes	Cadillac Plastic & Chemical Co.
Cadco Penton	Chlorinated polyethers	" " " "
Cadco Epoxy	Epoxies	" " " "
Cadco Teflon	Fluorocarbons	" " " "
Cadco PVC	Polyvinyl chlorides urethanes, elastomers	" " " "
Carbo-Korez	Phenolics	Atlas Mineral Products
Carbomix	Butadiene-styrene rubber	Copolymer Rubber & Chemical Corp.
Carbowax	Polyethylene glycols	Union Carbide Corporation
Cardolite	Phenol-aldehyde resins	Irvington Varnish Co.
Catabond	Phenolic resins	Catalin Corp. of America
Catalin	Acrylics, ABS polymers, nylons, phenolics, polyethylenes, polypropylenes, polystyrene	" " " "
Ceilcrete	Polyesters	The Ceilcote Co.
Centri-Cast	Epoxies, polyesters	Apex Fiberglass Products Co.
Chemigum	Butadiene-acrylonitrile rubber and latices	The Goodyear Tire & Rubber Co.
Chemline	Epoxies	A. O. Smith Corporation
Chempro	Fluorocarbons	Chemical & Power Products
Chemtite	Epoxies, phenolics	Johns-Manville Corp.
Cis-4	Polybutadienes	Phillips Petroleum Company
Cohrlastic	Silicon rubber	Connecticut Hardrubber Co.
Coltrock	Phenolics	Colt's Plastics Co.
Conolite	Polyester resins and laminates	Shellmar-Betner, Div. Continental Can Co.
Copo	Butadiene-styrene rubber	Copolymer Rubber & Chemical Corp.
Coroband	Furanes	The Ceilcote Company
Corocrete	Polyesters	" " "
Corvel	Epoxies, vinyls Fusion bond finishes	The Polymer Co.
Corvic	Polyvinyl chloride resins	Canadian Industries Limited
Cosmalite	Phenol-formaldehyde resins	Colton Chemical Co.
CR	Polyesters	Resolite Corp.
CR-39	Polycarbonates	Pittsburgh Plate Glass Co.
Crystalex	Acrylics	Rohm & Hass Company
Cumar	Paracoumarone-indene resins	Allied Chemical Corporation
Cycolac	ABS polymers Acrylonitrile-butadiene-styrene, copolymer	Borg-Warner Corporation
Cymel	Melamines molding compounds, adhesive and laminating resins	American Cyanamid Company
Dacovin	Polyvinyl chlorides	Diamond Alkali Company
Dapon	Diallyl phthalate	Food Machinery and Chemical Corp.
Delrin	Acetal resins	E. I. duPont de Nemours & Co., Inc.
D.E.R.	Epoxy resins	Dow Chemical Company
Devran	Epoxy resins	Devoe & Reynolds
Diamond PVS	Polyvinyl chloride resins; copolymer resins	Diamond Alkali Company
Dow Corning	Silicones	Dow Corning
Duradene	Butanediene-styrene rubber	Firestone Tire & Rubber Co.
Duragene 1203	Polybutadienes	The General Tire & Rubber Co.
Durcon	Epoxies	The Duriron Co.
Dur-X	Polyethylenes	Johns-Manville Company

Trade name	Composition	Manufacturer
Durez	Phenolic resins	Durez Plastic Division, Hooker Chemical Corporation
Dylan	Polyethylene	Koppers Company, Inc.
Dylene	Polystyrene	" " "
Dylite	Expandable polystyrene	" " "
Dyphene	Phenol-formaldehyde resins	The Sherwin-Williams Co.
Ebolene	Fluorocarbons	Chicago Gasket Co.
Enjay Butyl	Butylrubber	Enjay Chemical Company, Div. Humble Oil & Refining Co.
Enjay Butyl latex	Butylrubber in aqueous solution	Enjay Chemical Company, Div. Humble Oil & Refining Co.
Epikote	Epoxy resins	The Shell Chemical Company
Epiphen	Epoxide resins	The Borden Chemical Company
Epi-Rez	Epoxy resins	Jones-Dabney Company
Epi-Tex	Epoxy ester resins	" " "
Epolene	Low molecular weight polyethylene resins	Eastman Kodak Company
Epoxical	Epoxies	United States Gypsum Co.
Epon	Epoxy resins	The Shell Chemical Company
Escon	Polypropylene resins	Enjay Chemical Co., Div. Humble Oil & Refining Company
Estane	Polyurethane elastomers	B. F. Goodrich Chemical Company
Ethafoam	Polyethlene, low density	The Dow Chemical Company
eXtren 200	Polyesters	Universal Molded Fiberglass Co.
Fibercast	Epoxies, polyesters	Fibercast, Div. of Youngstown Sheet & Tube Co.
Fibestos	Cellulose acetate	Monsanto Chemical Co.
Fire-Snuf	Polyesters	Resolite Corp.
Flakoline	Polyesters	The Ceilcote Co.
Flamenol	Polyvinyl chlorides	General Electric Company
Flovic	Polyvinyl chlorides	Canadian Industries, Limited
Fluorogreen	Teflon with glass and ceramic fibers, fluorocarbons	John L. Dore Co.
Fluororay	Fluorocarbons	Raybestos-Manhattan, Inc.
Formica	Melamines	Formica Corp.
Formvar	Polyvinyl formal resins	Shawinigan Resins Corp.
Forticel	Cellulose propionate sheet films, molding powders	Celanese Polymer Co.
Fortiflex-A	Linear polyolefines	Celanese Polymer Company
Fortiflex-B	Linear copolymers	" " "
Fortiflex-C	Medium density polyethylenes	" " "
Fortiflex-D	Low-density polyethylenes	" " "
Fosta-Tuf-Flex	Polystyrene, high impact	Foster-Grant, Inc.
FR-N	Nitrile rubber	The Firestone Tire & Rubber Co., Firestone Plastics Company
FR-S	Butadiene-styrene rubber	The Firestone Tire & Rubber Co., Firestone Plastics Company
Frostwhite	Polystyrene, medium impact	Sheffield Plastics, Inc.,
Furnane	Furanes	Atlas Mineral Products Co.
Gabrite	Urea-formaldehyde	Chemore Corporation
Gaco	Epoxies	Gates Engineering Division, Glidden Company
GE Methylon	Phenolics	General Electric Company, Chemical Materials Dept.
Gelva	Polyvinyl acetate resins " " copolymers	Shawinigan Resins Corp.
Gelvatol	Polyvinyl alcohol resins	" " "

Trade name	Composition	Manufacturer
Genco	Acrylics, ABS polymers Polyethylenes, copolymers	General Plastics Corp.
GenEpoxy	Epoxy resins for adhesives, coatings, etc.	General Mills, Inc.
Genetron	Fluorinated hydrocarbons, monomers and polymers	Allied Chemical Corp., General Chemical Div.
Gen-Flo	Styrene-butadiene latex	General Tire & Rubber Co.
Genthanes	Urethane elastomers; prepolymers	" " " "
Geon	Polyvinyl chlorides	B. F. Goodrich Chemical Co.
Gering	Acrylics, ABS polymers, nylons, polyethylenes, polypropylenes polyvinyl chlorides, copolymers	Gering Plastics Company
Ger-Pak	Polyethylene film	Gering Plastics Company
Glykon	Polyester resins	The General Tire & Rubber Co.
GP excel	Polyvinyl chlorides	Glamorgan Plastics, Div. of Glamorgan Pipe & Foundry Co.
Grace	Polystyrenes	W. R. Grace & Company, Polymer Chemical Division
Grex	High density polyethylenes, polypropylenes	W. R. Grace & Company, Polymer Chemical Division
Halon	Fluorohalocarbon resins	Allied Chemical Corp.
Haveg	Phenolic resins, furanes	Haveg Industries, Inc.
Haysite	Reinforced polyester	Haysite Corp.
Hercose AP	Cellulose acetate-propionate	Hercules Powder Company
Herculoid	Cellulose nitrate	" " "
Hetrofoam	Polyurethane fire-retardant rigid foam	Hooker Chemical Corp., Durez Plastics Div.
Hetron	Fire retardant polyester resin	Hooker Chemical Corp., Durez Plastics Div.
Hi-flexible	Polyethylenes	Triangle Conduit & Cable Co.
Hycar	Butadiene-styrene, butadiene-acronitriles, acrylate emulsions	B. F. Goodrich Chemical Co.
Hystran	Epoxies, polyesters	Lamtex Industries of Koppers Co.
Iporca	Urea resin and foam	Badische Aniline & Soda Fabrik
Isothane	Urethane elastomers	Carborundum Company
J-M ABS	ABS polymers	Johns-Manville Company
J-M PVC	Polyvinyl chlorides	" " "
Kaylite	Polyvinyl chlorides	Kaykor Products Corp.
Kayrex	Polyvinyl chlorides	" " "
Kel-F	Chlorotrifluoroethylene, molding resins and dispersions	Minnesota Mining & Manufacturing Co.
Koroseal	Polyvinyl chlorides	B. F. Goodrich Industrial Products Co.
Kralac A-EP	High styrene resins	United States Rubber Co., Naugatuck Chemical Div.
Kralac Latex	Styrene-butadiene copolymers	United States Rubber Co., Naugatuck Chemical Div.
Kralastic	ABS Polymers, copolymers	United States Rubber Co., Naugatuck Chemical Div.
Kynar	Polyvinyldene fluoride	Pennsalt Chemical Corp.
La Favorite	Polyvinyl chlorides	La Favorita Rubber Mfg. Co.
Laminac	Polyester resins	American Cyanamid Company
Lemac	Polyvinyl acetate	Borden Chemical Company
Lexan	Polycarbonate resin	General Electric Company, Chemical Materials Dept.
Lucite	Acrylic resin	E. I. duPont de Nemours & Co.
Lustran	ABS polymers	Monsanto Chemical Company

Trade name	Composition	Manufacturer
Lustrex	Styrene molding and extrusion resins	Monsanto Chemical Company
Lytron RJ-100	Styrene molding and extrusion resins	" " "
Madurit	Melamine resins for plastic industry	Casella Farbwerke Mainkur, A.G.
Maplen	Polypropylenes	Chemore Corporation
Maraglas	Crystal clear epoxy resin	The Marblette Corporation
Marawood	Carvable epoxy resin	" " "
Marbon 8000	High styrene resins	Borg-Warner Corporation, Marbon Chemical Division
Marco	Polyester resins	Celanese Corp. of America
Marlex	Polyethylenes, polypropylenes, copolymers	Phillips Petroleum Company
Marvinol	Vinyl chloride resins and compounds	United States Rubber Company, Naugatuck Chemical Division
Melantine	Melamine resins	Ciba Limited
Melmac	Melamine resins	American Cyanamid Company
Melopas	Polyamide formaldehyde	Ciba Limited
Meltiplast 101	Polyethylenes	International Protected Metals
Meltiplast 301	Polyethylenes	" " "
Meltiplast 501	Chlorinated polyesters	" " "
Merlon	Polycarbonate resins	Mobay Chemical Co.
Methacrol	Acrylic emulsions	E. I. duPont de Nemours & Co., Inc.
Micarta	Melamines, phenolics, polyesters	Westinghouse Electric Co.
Microthene	Polyethylenes	U. S. Industrial Chemicals Co.
Monsanto	Polyethylene resins	Monsanto Chemical Company
MR Resin	Polyester resins	Celanese Corporation of America
Multrathane	Urethane elastomers	Mobay Chemical Company
Napcofoam	Polyurethane, flexible	Nopco Chemical Company
Natsyn	Polyisoprene	The Goodyear Tire & Rubber Co.
Naugatex 2700 series	Butadiene-styrene latices	United States Rubber Co., Naugatuck Chemical Division
Neville	Coumarone-indene resins	Neville Chemical Company
Niacet	Vinyl acetate, vinyl chloride	Union Carbide Corp.
Nopcofoam	Polyurethane plastics (flexible)	Nopco Chemical Co., Plastics Div.
Novodur	ABS copolymers	Farbenfabriken Bayer, A.G.
Nu-Klad	Epoxies	Amercoat Corporation
Nypene	Polystyrene resins	Neville Chemical Company
Opalon	Vinyl chloride resins and compounds	Monsanto Chemical Co.
Palmetto	Fluorocarbons	Greene, Tweed & Co.
Paracon	Polyester rubber	Bell Telephone Laboratories
Paracril	Nitrile rubber	United States Rubber Co., Naugatuck Chemical Div.
Paradene	Coumarone-indene resins	Neville Chemical Company
Paraplex	Polyester resins, acrylic modified polyester resin	Rohm & Haas Company
Pentacite	Pentaerythritol resins	Reichold Chemicals, Inc.
Permelite	Melamines	Melamine Plastics, Inc.
Petrothene	Polyethylene resin, polypropylene resin	U. S. Industrial Chemicals Co.
Pfaudlon 201	Epoxies	Pfaudler Co.
Pfaudlon 301	Chlorinated polyethers	" "
Philprene	Butadiene-styrene rubber	Phillips Petroleum Co.
Piccoflex	Styrene copolymer resins	Pennsylvania Industrial Chemical Corp.
Piccolastic	Styrene polymer resins	Pennsylvania Industrial Chemical Corp.
Plaskon	Nylons, melamines, phenolics polyesters	Allied Chemical Corp.
Pleogen	Polyester resins	American Petrochemical Corp.
Plexiglas	Acrylics	Rohm & Haas Company

Trade name	Composition	Manufacturer
Plioflex	Polyvinyl chlorides	The Goodyear Tire & Rubber Co.
Pliofoam	Expanded urea resins	" " " " "
Pliolite	Styrene-butadiene resins	" " " " "
Plio-Tuf series	Modified styrene resins	" " " " "
Pliovic	Polyvinyl chlorides	" " " " "
Plyophen	Phenol-formaldehyde resins	Reichhold Chemicals, Inc.
Poly-Eth	Polyethylene resins	Spencer Chemical Co.
Polylite	Polyester resins	Reichhold Chemicals, Inc.
Polypenco	Acrylics, chlorinated polyethers, fluorocarbons, nylons, polycarbonates,	Polymer Corp.
Red Thread	Epoxies, glassfiber filled	A. O. Smith Corp.
Resimene	Urea and melamine resins	Monsanto Chemical Co.
Resinox	Phenolic resins and compounds	" " "
Rezklad	Epoxies	Atlas Mineral Products, Div. Electric Storage Battery Co.
Rhonite	Urea resins	Rohm & Hass Company
Rock Island	Epoxies	Rock Island Fiberglass Pipe Co.
Root-Pruf	Butadiene-styrene	Triangle Conduit & Cable Co.
Roylar	Polyurethanes	United States Rubber Co., Naugatuck Chemical Division
RX	Epoxies, fluorocarbons, phenolics	Rogers Corp.
Ryercite	Phenolics	Joseph T. Ryerson & Son, Inc.
Ryertex	Phenolics	" " " "
Ryertex-Omicron	Polyvinyl chlorides	" " " "
S-4	Natural latex, liquid	Firestone Tire & Rubber Co.
Saran	Polyvinylidene chloride, vinylidene chloride copolymers	Saran Lined Pipe Co.
Sauercisen	Furanes	Sauereisen Cement Co.
Seilon ETH	Polyethylenes	Seiberling Rubber Co.
" PRO	Polypropylenes	" " "
" PVC	Polyvinyl chlorides	" " "
" S-3	ABS polymers	" " "
" UR	Urethane polymers	" " "
Semi-rigid	ABS polymers	Triangle Conduit & Cable Co.
Silastic	Silicone rubber	Dow Corning
Solprene	Fluoro elastomers	Phillips Petroleum Company
S-polymers	Butadiene-styrene copolymers	Esso Laboratories
Stauffer	ABS polymers, polyethylenes, polypylenes, polyvinyl chlorides	Stauffer Chemical Company, Molded Products Div.
Stylplast	Urea-formaldehyde compounds	American Viscose Corporation
Styrex	Styrene-acrylonitrile copolymer	The Dow Chemical Company
Super Beckamine	Melamine-formaldehyde resins	Reichhold Chemicals, Inc.
Super Dylan	Polyethylene	Koppers Company, Inc.
Supreme	Polyethylenes	Johns-Manville Company
Sylkyd	Silicone alkyd resins	Dow Corning
Sylplast	Urea formaldehyde	Food Machinery and Chemical Corp., Organic Chemicals Div.
Synthane	Epoxies, melamines, phenolics, silicones	Synthane Corporation
T/Na-100	Polyvinylfluorides	The Ruberoid Company
Teflon	Fluorocarbons, tetrafluoroethylene (TFE) fluorinated ethylpropylene resins (FEP)	E. I. duPont de Nemours & Co. Inc.
Tempron	Polybutadienes	Ace Molded Products Co.
Temp-R-Tape	Fluorocarbons	Connecticut Hardrubber Co.
Tenite	Cellulose acetate, cellulose-acetate-polyethylene, polypropylenes, urethane elastomers, copolymers	Eastman Chemical Products, Inc.

TRADE NAMES, COMPOSITION AND MANUFACTURERS OF SOME PLASTICS
(Continued)

Trade name	Composition	Manufacturer
Tetran	Fluorocarbons	Pennsalt Chemicals Corp.
Texin	Urethane elastomers	Mobay Chemical Company
Thermo-Seal	Polyethylenes, polypropylenes	Cabot Piping Systems, Plastics Division
Thioment	Polyisoprenes	Atlas Mineral Products Co.
Trans-4	Rubberlike materials	Phillips Petroleum Company, Bartlesville, Okla.
TPC	Polyvinyl chlorides	Thermoplastics Corp.
ttP	ABS polymers, chlorinated polyesters, fluorocarbons, polyvinylchlorides	Cabot Piping Systems, Plastics Division
Tyril	Styrene-acrylonitrile, copolymer molding resins	The Dow Chemical Company
Ultrapas	Melamine resins	Dynamite A.G.
Ultrathene	Ethylene vinyl acetate	U. S. Industrial Chemicals Co.
Ultron	Polyvinyl chlorides	Monsanto Chemical Company
Unox	Epoxides	Union Carbide Corporation
Upalon	Polyvinyl chlorides	Monsanto Chemical Company
Vibrathane	Urethane elastomers	United States Rubber Co., Naugatuck Chemical Div.
Vibrin	Polyester resins	United States Rubber Co., Naugatuck Chemical Div.
Vinelle	Vinyl compounds	The General Tire & Rubber Co.
Vipla	Polyvinyl chloride, vinyl acetate, co-polymers	Chemore Corp.
Vitalic	Chlorosulfonated polyethylenes, polybutadienes, polyisoprenes, ethylpropylenes, urethane elastomers	Continental Rubber Works
Vitel	Polyesters	Goodyear Chemical, Div., The Goodyear Tire & Rubber Co.
Viton	Synthetic rubbers	E. I. duPont de Nemours & Co., Inc.
Vitroplast	Polyester cement	Atlas Mineral Products Div.
Vygen	Polyvinyl chloride resins	The General Tire & Rubber Co.
Vyron	Polyvinyl chlorides	Monsanto Chemical Co.
X 2 B	Natural latex	The Firestone Tire & Rubber Co.
Yardley	ABS polymers, polyethylenes, polyvinyl chlorides	Celanese Plastics Co.
Zerlon	Methyl methacrylate styrene resins	The Dow Chemical Co.

Properties of Commercial Plastics

Of the many plastics commercially available in each chemical class only one or a very few individuals have been selected for this table as typical of the class. In some cases the range of properties has been expanded to include several grades or types. It is impractical to include a comprehensive list of materials or known properties of these materials in a table of convenient size. Properties vary widely with amount and kind of modifier such as filler and plasticizer. Within any type of thermoplastic resins molecular weight is an important variable. This property is controlled to afford the best physical properties available consistent with economical processing properties.

The information shown refers in all cases, except for "Forms available" and "Fabrication," to material in the fabricated form, which in the case of thermosetting materials means commercially cured. Physical and electrical properties will vary, to a greater or less degree with different materials, with humidity conditioning environment and with orientation. Strength values are quoted on the basis of short time tests at normal room temperature and are not suitable for engineering design purposes for load bearing applications. Maximum continuous service temperature refers to unloaded structures. The user of this table is referred to the specifications and test procedures of the American Society for Testing Materials.

FORMS AVAILABLE — Cs—castings, F—film, Fb—fibers, I—impregnants, L—laminations, Lq—lacquers, Mf—monofilaments, P—Powder, pellet, or granules, R—rods, tubes, or other extruded forms, S—sheets.

FABRICATION — Cl—calendering, Cs—casting, E—extrusion, F—hot forming or drawing, I—impregnation, MB—blow molding, MC—compression molding, MI—injection molding, S—spreading.

	Cellulose Acetate	Cellulose Acetate	Cellulose Acetate Butyrate
Resin Type	Thermoplastic	Thermoplastic	Thermoplastic
Subclass or Modification	Soft	Hard	Soft
Forms Available	F, Lq, P, R, S	F, Lq, P, R, S	F, Lq, P, R, S
Fabrication	Cs, E, F, MB, MC, MI, S	Cs, E, F, MB, MC, MI, S	Cs, E, F, MB, MC, MI, S
ELECTRICAL PROPERTIES			
D.C. Resistivity, ohm-cm	10^{10}–10^{13}	10^{10}–10^{13}	10^{10}–10^{12}
Dielectric constant, 60 cps	3.5–7.5	3.5–7.5	3.5–6.4
Dielectric constant, 10^6 cps	3.2–7.0	3.2–7.0	3.2–6.2
Dissipation factor, 60 cps	0.01–0.06	0.01–0.06	0.01–0.04
Dissipation factor, 10^6 cps	0.01–0.10	0.01–0.10	0.01–0.04
MECHANICAL PROPERTIES			
Modulus of elasticity, 10^3 psi	86–250	190–400	74–126
Tensile strength, psi	1,900–4,700	4,600–8,500	1,900–3,800
Ultimate elongation, %	32–50	6–40	60–74
Yield stress, psi	2,200–4,200	4,100–7,600	1,200–2,600
Yield strain, %			
Rockwell hardness	R 49–R 103	R 101–R 123	R 59–R 95
Notched Izod impact strength, ft.lb/in.	2.0–5.2	0.4–2.7	2.5–5.4
Specific gravity	1.27–1.34	1.27–1.34	1.15–1.22
THERMAL PROPERTIES			
Burning rate	Medium	Medium	Medium
Heat distortion 264 psi, °C	44–57	60–113	49–58
Specific heat, cal/g.	0.3–0.42	0.3–0.42	0.3–0.4
Linear thermal expansion coefficient, 10^{-5}, °C	8–16	8–16	11–17
Maximum continuous service temperature, °C			
CHEMICAL RESISTANCE			
Mineral acids, weak	Fair to good	Fair to good	Good
Mineral acids, strong	Poor	Poor	Fair to good
Oxidizing acids, concentrated	Very poor	Very poor	
Alkalies, weak	Poor	Poor	Good
Alkalies, strong	Very poor	Very poor	Poor
Alcohols	Poor	Poor	Poor
Ketones	Poor	Poor	Poor
Esters	Poor	Poor	Poor
Hydrocarbons, aliphatic	Fair to good	Fair to good	Fair to good
Hydrocarbons, aromatic	Poor to fair	Poor to fair	Poor
Oils, vegetable, animal, mineral	Fair to good	Fair to good	Good
MISCELLANEOUS PROPERTIES			
Clarity	Excellent	Excellent	Good to excellent
Color	Pale to colorless	Pale to colorless	Pale to colorless
Refractive index, n_D	1.46–1.50	1.46–1.50	1.46–1.49
Applicable ASTM specifications and test methods	D786, D706, D257, D150, D638, D785, D256, D792, D648, D696, D543, D542	D786, D706, D257, D150, D638, D785, D256, D792, D648, D696, D543, D542	D707, D257, D150, D638, D785, D256, D792, D648, D696

	Cellulose Acetate Butyrate	Nylon	Polycarbonates
Chemical Class			
Resin Type	Thermoplastic	Thermoplastic	Thermoplastic
Subclass or Modification	Hard	3/6	Unfilled
FORMS AVAILABLE	F, Lq, P, R, S	F, Fb, Mf, P, R, S	F, Fb, Mf, P, R, S
FABRICATION	Cs, E, F, MB, MC, MI, S	E, F, MB, MC, MI	Cs, E, F, MB, MC, MI

Cs—castings, F—film, Fb—fibers, I—impregnants, L—laminations, Lq—lacquers, Mf—monofilaments, P—Powder, pellet, or granules, R—rods, tubes, or other extruded forms, S—sheets.

Cl—calendering, Cs—casting, E—extrusion, F—hot forming or drawing, I—impregnation, MB—blow molding, MC—compression molding, MI—injection molding, S—spreading.

	Cellulose Acetate Butyrate	Nylon	Polycarbonates
ELECTRICAL PROPERTIES			
D.C. Resistivity, ohm-cm	10^{10}–10^{12}		2×10^{16}
Dielectric constant, 60 cps	3.5–6.4	4.0–4.6	3.17
Dielectric constant, 10^6 cps	3.2–6.2	3.4–3.6	2.96
Dissipation factor, 60 cps	0.01–0.04	0.014–0.04	0.0009
Dissipation factor, 10^6 cps	0.01–0.04	0.04	0.01
MECHANICAL PROPERTIES			
Modulus of elasticity, 10^3 psi	150–200		290–325
Tensile strength, psi	5,000–6,800	9,000–12,000	8,000–9,500
Ultimate elongation, %	38–54	60–300	20–100
Yield stress, psi	3,600–6,100		8,000–10,000
Yield strain, %			
Rockwell hardness	R 108–R 117	R 108–R 120	M 70–M 180
Notched Izod impact strength, ft.lb/in.	0.7–2.4	1.0–2.0	8–16
Specific gravity	1.19–1.25	1.13–1.15	1.2
THERMAL PROPERTIES			
Burning rate	Medium	Self extinguishing	Self extinguishing
Heat distortion 264 psi, °C	70–99		135–145
Specific heat, cal/g	0.3–0.4	0.4	0.3
Linear thermal expansion coefficient, 10^{-5}, °C	11–17	8.0	6.6
Maximum continuous service temperature, °C		80–150	138–143
CHEMICAL RESISTANCE			
Mineral acids, weak	Good	Very good	Excellent
Mineral acids, strong	Fair to good	Poor	Fair
Oxidizing acids, concentrated		Poor	
Alkalies, weak	Good	No effect	Poor
Alkalies, strong	Poor	No effect	Poor
Alcohols	Poor	Good	Poor
Ketones	Poor	Good	Poor
Esters	Poor	Good	Poor
Hydrocarbons, aliphatic	Fair to good	Very good	Poor
Hydrocarbons, aromatic	Poor	Fair to good	Poor
Oils, vegetable, animal, mineral	Good	Good	Poor
MISCELLANEOUS PROPERTIES			
Clarity	Good to excellent	Clear	Clear
Color	Pale to colorless	Pale amber to colorless	Colorless
Refractive index, n_D	1.46–1.49	1.53	1.60
Applicable ASTM specifications and test methods	D707, D257, D150, D638, D785, D256, D792, D648, D696, D543, D542	D257, D150, D638, D785, D256, D792, D648, D696, D543, D542	D257, D150, D638, D785, D256, D792, D648, D696, D543, D542

PROPERTIES OF COMMERCIAL PLASTICS

	Polyethylene	Polyethylene	Polyethylene
Chemical Class	Polyethylene	Polyethylene	Polyethylene
Resin Type	Thermoplastic	Thermoplastic	Thermoplastic
Subclass or Modification	Low density	Medium density	High density
FORMS AVAILABLE	F, Mf, P, R, S	F, Mf, P, R, S	F, Fb, Mf, P, R, S
FABRICATION	Cl, E, F, MB, MC, MI	Cl, E, F, MB, MC, MI	Cl, E, F, MB, MC, MI
ELECTRICAL PROPERTIES			
D.C. Resistivity, ohm-cm	$>10^{15}$	$>10^{15}$	$>10^{15}$
Dielectric constant, 60 cps	2.3–2.35	2.3	2.3–2.35
Dielectric constant, 10^6 cps	2.3–2.35	2.3	2.3–2.35
Dissipation factor, 60 cps	<0.0005	<0.0005	<0.0005
Dissipation factor, 10^6 cps	<0.0005	<0.0005	<0.0005
MECHANICAL PROPERTIES			
Modulus of elasticity, 10^3 psi	14–38	35–90	85–160
Tensile strength, psi	1,000–1,400	1,200–3,500	3,100–5,500
Ultimate elongation, %	400–700	50–600	15–100
Yield stress, psi	1,100–1,700	1,500–2,600	2,400–5,000
Yield strain, %	20–40	10–20	5–10
Rockwell hardness			R 30–R 50
Notched Izod impact strength, ft.lb/in	no break	0.5–>16	1.5–20
Specific gravity	0.91–0.925	0.926–0.941	0.941–0.965
THERMAL PROPERTIES			
Burning rate	Very slow	Slow	Slow
Heat distortion 264 psi, °C			
Specific heat, cal/g	0.55	0.55	0.55
Linear thermal expansion coefficient, 10^{-5}, °C	10–20	14–16	11–13
Maximum continuous service temperature, °C	60–77	71–93	92–200
CHEMICAL RESISTANCE			
Mineral acids, weak	Good	Excellent	Excellent
Mineral acids, strong	Good	Excellent	Excellent
Oxidizing acids, concentrated	Good to poor	Good to poor	Good to poor
Alkalies, weak	Good	Excellent	Excellent
Alkalies, strong	Good	Excellent	Excellent
Alcohols	Excellent to poor	Excellent to poor	Excellent to poor
Ketones	Excellent to poor	Excellent to poor	Excellent to poor
Esters	Excellent to poor	Excellent to poor	Excellent to poor
Hydrocarbons, aliphatic	Fair	Fair	Fair
Hydrocarbons, aromatic	Fair	Good	Fair
Oils, vegetable, animal, mineral	Good	Excellent	Good
MISCELLANEOUS PROPERTIES			
Clarity	Translucent	Translucent	Translucent
Color	Colorless	Colorless	Colorless
Refractive index, n_D	1.50–1.54	1.52–1.54	1.54
Applicable ASTM specifications and test methods	D702, D788, D257, D150, D412, D638, D696, D543, D542, D1248	D257, D150, D412, D638, D785, D256, D696, D543, D542, D1248	D257, D150, D412, D638, D785, D256, D696, D543, D542, D1248

FORMS AVAILABLE
Cs—castings, F—film, Fb—fibers, I—impregnants, L—laminations, Lq—lacquers, Mf—monofilaments, P—Powder, pellet or granules, R—rods, tubes, or other extruded forms, S—sheets.

FABRICATION
Cl—calendering, Cs—casting, E—extrusion, F—hot forming or drawing, I—impregnation, MB—blow molding, MC—compression molding, MI—injection molding, S—spreading.

PROPERTIES OF COMMERCIAL PLASTICS

	Methylmethacrylate	Polypropylene	Polypropylene
Chemical Class			
Resin Type	Thermoplastic	Thermoplastic	Thermoplastic
Subclass or Modification	Unmodified	Unmodified	Copolymer
FORMS AVAILABLE	Cs, P, R, S	F, Fb, Mf, P, R, S	F, Fb, Mf, P, R, S
FABRICATION	Cs, E, F, Lq, MB, MC, MI	Cl, E, F, MB, MC, MI	Cl, E, F, MB, MC, MI
ELECTRICAL PROPERTIES			
D.C. Resistivity, ohm-cm	$>10^{14}$	$>10^{16}$	10^{17}
Dielectric constant, 60 cps	3.5–4.5	2.2–2.6	2.3
Dielectric constant, 10^6 cps	3.0–3.5	2.2–2.6	2.3
Dissipation factor, 60 cps	0.04–0.06	<0.0005	0.0001–0.0005
Dissipation factor, 10^6 cps	0.02–0.03	0.0005–0.002	0.0001–0.002
MECHANICAL PROPERTIES			
Modulus of elasticity, 10^3 psi	350–500	1.4–1.7	
Tensile strength, psi	7,000–11,000	4,300–5,500	2,900–4,500
Ultimate elongation, %	2.0–10	>220	200–700
Yield stress, psi		4,900	
Yield strain, %		15	
Rockwell hardness	M 80–M 105	93	R 50–R 96
Notched Izod impact strength, ft.lb/in	0.3–0.6	1.0	1.1–12
Specific gravity	1.18–1.20	0.90	0.90
THERMAL PROPERTIES			
Burning rate	Slow	Medium	Medium
Heat distortion 264 psi, °C	66–99		
Specific heat, cal/g	0.35	0.5	0.5
Linear thermal expansion coefficient, 10^{-5}, °C	5.0–9.0	5.8–10	8–10
Maximum continuous service temperature, °C	60–93		190–240
CHEMICAL RESISTANCE			
Mineral acids, weak	Good	Excellent	Excellent
Mineral acids, strong	Fair to poor	Excellent	Excellent
Oxidizing acids, concentrated	Attacked	Good to poor	Poor
Alkalies, weak	Good	Excellent to good	Excellent
Alkalies, strong	Poor	Excellent to good	Good
Alcohols	Dissolves	Excellent to good	Good below 80°C
Ketones	Dissolves	Excellent to good	Good below 80°C
Esters		Excellent to good	Good below 80°C
Hydrocarbons, aliphatic	Good	Good to fair	Good below 80°C
Hydrocarbons, aromatic	Softens	Good to fair	Good below 80°C
Oils, vegetable, animal, mineral	Good	Good	Good below 80°C
MISCELLANEOUS PROPERTIES			
Clarity	Excellent	Transparent	Transparent
Color	Colorless	Colorless to sl. yellow	Colorless to sl. yellow
Refractive index, n_D	1.48–1.50	1.49	
Applicable ASTM specifications and test methods	D257, D150, D638, D785, D256, D792, D648, D696, D543, D542	D257, D150, D412, D638, D785, D256, D648, D543, D542	D257, D150, D412, D638, D785, D256, D648, D543, D542

FORMS AVAILABLE—Cs—castings, F—film, Fb—fibers, I—impregnants, L—laminations, Lq—lacquers, Mf—monofilaments, P—powder, pellet, or granules, R—rods, tubes, or other extruded forms, S—sheets.

FABRICATION—Cl—calendering, Cs—casting, E—extrusion, F—hot forming or drawing, I—impregnation, M—blow molding, MC—compression molding, MI—injection molding, S—spreading

PROPERTIES OF COMMERCIAL PLASTICS

Chemical Class	Polystyrene	Polystyrene-acrylonitrile	Polytetrafluoro ethylene
Resin Type	Thermoplastic	Thermoplastic	Thermoplastic
Subclass or Modification	Unmodified	Unmodified	Unmodified
FORMS AVAILABLE	F, Fb, Mf, P, R, S	F, Mf, P, R, S	F, L, P, R, S
FABRICATION	E, F, MB, MC, MI	Cl, E, F, MB, MC, MI	E, F, MC, MI
ELECTRICAL PROPERTIES			
D.C. Resistivity, ohm-cm.	$>10^{16}$	10^{12}–10^{17}	10^{18}
Dielectric constant, 60 cps.	2.5–2.65	2.6–3.4	2.
Dielectric constant, 10^6 cps.	2.5–2.65	2.5–3.1	2.
Dissipation factor, 60 cps.	0.0001–0.0003	0.006–0.008	0.0002
Dissipation factor, 10^6 cps.	0.0001–0.0004	0.007–0.01	0.0002
MECHANICAL PROPERTIES			
Modulus of elasticity, 10^3 psi.	400–600	$>10^{16}$	33–65
Tensile strength, psi.	5,000–10,000	9,000–12,000	2,000–4,500
Ultimate elongation, %.	1.0–2.5	1.0–2.5	200–400
Yield stress, psi.	...	...	1,600–2,000
Yield strain, %.	...	...	50–75
Rockwell hardness.	M 65–M 85	M 75–M 90	D 50–D 65
Notched Izod impact strength, ft.lb/in.	0.25–0.60	0.3–0.6	2.5–4.0
Specific gravity.	1.04–1.08	1.05–1.1	2.1–2.3
THERMAL PROPERTIES			
Burning rate.	Medium to slow.	Slow.	Self extinguishing
Heat distortion 264 psi, °C.		91–104.	60
Specific heat, cal/g.	0.32–0.35.	0.32–0.35.	0.25
Linear thermal expansion coefficient, 10^{-5}, °C.	6.0–8.0.	3.6–3.8.	10
Maximum continuous service temperature, °C.	66–82.	77–88.	260
CHEMICAL RESISTANCE			
Mineral acids, weak.	Excellent.	Excellent.	Excellent
Mineral acids, strong.	Excellent.	Good to excellent.	Excellent
Oxidizing acids, concentrated.	Poor.	Poor.	Excellent
Alkalies, weak.	Excellent.	Excellent.	Excellent
Alkalies, strong.	Excellent.	Good to excellent.	Excellent
Alcohols.	Excellent.	Good to excellent.	Excellent
Ketones.	Dissolves.	Dissolves.	Excellent
Esters.	Poor.	Dissolves.	Excellent
Hydrocarbons, aliphatic.	Poor.	Good.	Excellent
Hydrocarbons, aromatic.	Dissolves.	Fair to good.	Excellent
Oils, vegetable, animal, mineral.	Fair to poor.	Good to excellent.	Excellent
MISCELLANEOUS PROPERTIES			
Clarity.	Transparent.	Transparent.	Translucent
Color.	Colorless.	Colorless to amber.	Colorless to grey
Refractive index, n_D.	1.59–1.60.	1.56–1.57.	1.30–1.40
Applicable ASTM specifications and test methods.	D257, D150, D638, D785, D256, D792, D648, D696, D543, D542	D257, D150, D638, D785, D256, D792, D648, D696, D543, D542	

FORMS AVAILABLE
Cs—castings, F—film, Fb—fibers, I—impregnants, L—lamina-tions, Lq—lacquers, Mf—monofilaments, P—Powder, pellet, or granules, R—rods, tubes, or other extruded forms, S—sheets.

FABRICATION
Cl—calendering, Cs—casting, E—extrusion, F—hot forming or drawing, I—impregnation, MB—blow molding, MC—compression molding, MI—injection molding, S—spreading.

PROPERTIES OF COMMERCIAL PLASTICS

Chemical Class	Polytrifluorochloro ethylene	Polyvinylchloride and Vinylchloride acetate	Polyvinylchloride and Vinylchloride acetate
Resin Type	Thermoplastic	Thermoplastic	Thermoplastic
Subclass or Modification	Unmodified	Unmodified, rigid	Plasticized (non rigid)
FORMS AVAILABLE	F, Mf, P, R, S	F, Fb, I, Lq, Mf, P, R, S	F, L, P, R, S
FABRICATION	Cs, E, F, I, MC, MI, S	Cl, Cs, E, F, I, MB, MC, MI, S	Cl, Cs, E, MB, MC, MI, S
ELECTRICAL PROPERTIES			
D.C. Resistivity, ohm-cm	10^{18}	10^{12}–10^{16}	10^{11}–10^{14}
Dielectric constant, 60 cps	2.2–2.8	3.2–4.0	5.0–9.0
Dielectric constant, 10^6 cps	2.3–2.5	3.0–4.0	3.0–4.0
Dissipation factor, 60 cps	0.001	0.01–0.02	0.03–0.05
Dissipation factor, 10^6 cps	0.005	0.006–0.02	0.06–0.1
MECHANICAL PROPERTIES			
Modulus of elasticity, 10^3 psi	150	200–600	
Tensile strength, psi	4,500–6,000	5,000–9,000	1,500–3,000
Ultimate elongation, %	250	2.0–40	200–400
Yield stress, psi	4,200		
Yield strain, %	10	1.0–5.0	
Rockwell hardness	J 75–J 95	R 110–R 120	
Notched Izod impact strength, ft.lb/in.	2.5–4.0	0.4–2.0	
Specific gravity	2.1–2.3	1.36–1.4	1.15–1.35
THERMAL PROPERTIES			
Burning rate	Self extinguishing	Self extinguishing	Slow to self extinguishing
Heat distortion 264 psi, °C		60–80	
Specific heat, cal/g	0.22	0.2–0.28	0.36–0.5
Linear thermal expansion coefficient, 10^{-5}, °C	7.0	5.0–18	7.0–25
Maximum continuous service temperature, °C	200	70–74	80–105
CHEMICAL RESISTANCE			
Mineral acids, weak	Excellent	Excellent	Fair to good
Mineral acids, strong	Excellent	Good to excellent	Fair to good
Oxidizing acids, concentrated	Excellent	Fair to good	Poor to fair
Alkalies, weak	Excellent	Excellent	Fair to good
Alkalies, strong	Excellent	Good	Fair to good
Alcohols	Excellent	Excellent	Fair
Ketones	Excellent	Poor	Poor
Esters	Excellent	Poor	Poor
Hydrocarbons, aliphatic	Excellent	Excellent	Poor
Hydrocarbons, aromatic	Excellent	Poor	Poor
Oils, vegetable, animal, mineral	Excellent	Excellent	Poor
MISCELLANEOUS PROPERTIES			
Clarity	Transparent	Transparent	Transparent
Color	Colorless to pale	Colorless to amber	Colorless to amber
Refractive index, nD	1.43	1.54	1.50–1.55
Applicable ASTM specifications and test methods	D1430, D257, D150, D638, D785, D256, D792, D648, D696, D543, D542	D703, D728, D257, D150, D638, D256, D792, D648, D696, D543, D542	D1432, D257, D150, D412, D792, D543, D542

FORMS AVAILABLE
Cs—castings, F—film, Fb—fibers, I—impregnants, L—laminations, Lq—lacquers, Mf—monofilaments, P—Powder, pellet, or granules, R—rods, tubes, or other extruded forms, S—sheets.

FABRICATION
Cl—calendering, Cs—casting, E—extrusion, F—hot forming or drawing, I—impregnation, MB—blow molding, MC—compression molding, MI—injection molding, S—spreading.

PROPERTIES OF COMMERCIAL PLASTICS

	Epoxy	Melamine-Formaldehyde	Melamine-Formaldehyde
Chemical Class			
Resin Type	Thermosetting	Thermosetting	Thermosetting
Subclass or Modification	Unfilled	α-Cellulose filled	Mineral filled, (electrical)
FORMS AVAILABLE — Cs—castings, F—film, Fb—fibers, I—impregnants, L—laminations, Lq—lacquers, Mf—monofilaments, P—Powder, pellet, or granules, R—rods, tubes, or other extruded forms, S—sheets.	Cs, Lq	P, R, S	P, R, S
FABRICATION — Cl—calendering, Cs—casting, E—extrusion, F—hot forming or drawing, I—impregnation, MB—blow molding, MC—compression molding, MI—injection molding, S—spreading.	Cs, I, S	MC	MC
ELECTRICAL PROPERTIES			
D.C. Resistivity, ohm-cm	10^{12}–10^{14}	10^{12}–10^{14}	10^{12}–10^{14}
Dielectric constant, 60 cps	3.5–5.0	7.9–9.4	10.2
Dielectric constant, 10^6 cps	3.4–4.4	7.2–8.4	6.1
Dissipation factor, 60 cps	0.001–0.005	0.03–0.08	0.10
Dissipation factor, 10^6 cps	0.03–0.05	0.03–0.043	0.051
MECHANICAL PROPERTIES			
Modulus of elasticity, 10^3 psi	>300	1,300	1,950
Tensile strength, psi	4,000–13,000	7,000–13,000	5,500–6,500
Ultimate elongation, %	2.0–6.0	0.6–0.9	
Yield stress, psi			
Yield strain, %			
Rockwell hardness	M 75–M 110	M 110–M 124	E 90
Notched Izod impact strength, ft.lb/in	0.2–1.0	0.24–0.35	0.3–0.4
Specific gravity	1.115	1.47–1.52	1.78
THERMAL PROPERTIES			
Burning rate	Slow	Self extinguishing	Self extinguishing
Heat distortion 264 psi, °C	Up to 120	204	130
Specific heat, cal/g.	0.25–0.4	0.4	
Linear thermal expansion coefficient, 10^{-5}, °C	4.5–9.0	2.0–5.7	2.1–4.3
Maximum continuous service temperature, °C	80	99.0	149
CHEMICAL RESISTANCE			
Mineral acids, weak	Excellent	Good	Fair
Mineral acids, strong	Fair to good	Poor	Poor
Oxidizing acids, concentrated	Poor	Poor	Poor
Alkalies, weak	Excellent	Good	Fair
Alkalies, strong	Excellent	Poor	Poor
Alcohols	Excellent	Good	Good
Ketones	Poor	Good	Good
Esters		Good	Good
Hydrocarbons, aliphatic	Excellent	Good	Good
Hydrocarbons, aromatic	Excellent	Good	Good
Oils, vegetable, animal, mineral	Excellent	Good	Good
MISCELLANEOUS PROPERTIES			
Clarity	Transparent	Translucent	Opaque
Color	Colorless	Colorless	Dark
Refractive index, n_D	1.58		
Applicable ASTM specifications and test methods	D257, D150, D785, D256, D792, D648, D696, D543	D704, D257, D150, D638, D785, D256, D792, D648, D696, D543	D704, D257, D150, D638, D785, D256, D792, D648, D696, D543

PROPERTIES OF COMMERCIAL PLASTICS

	Phenol-Formaldehyde	Phenol-Formaldehyde	Phenol-Formaldehyde
Chemical Class	Thermosetting	Thermosetting	Thermosetting
Resin Type	Cordfilled	Cellulose filled	Unfilled Cast Phenolic, mechanical and chemical grade
Subclass or Modification			
FORMS AVAILABLE	L, P, S	L, P, S	Cs, R, S
FABRICATION	MC	MC	Cs, F
ELECTRICAL PROPERTIES			
D.C. Resistivity, ohm-cm	10^{11}–10^{12}	10^{11}–10^{13}	1.0–7.0 x 10^{12}
Dielectric constant, 60 cps	7.0–10.0	5.0–9.0	6.5–7.5
Dielectric constant, 10^6 cps	5.0–6.0	4.0–7.0	4.0–5.5
Dissipation factor, 60 cps	0.1–0.3	0.04–0.3	0.10–0.15
Dissipation factor, 10^6 cps	0.04–0.09	0.03–0.07	0.04–0.05
MECHANICAL PROPERTIES			
Modulus of elasticity, 10^3 psi	900–1,300	800–1,200	4.0–5.0
Tensile strength, psi	6,000–9,000	6,500–8,500	6,000–9,000
Ultimate elongation, %	0.5–1.0	0.6–1.0	1.5–2.0
Yield stress, psi			
Yield strain, %			
Rockwell hardness		M 110–M 120	M 93–M 120
Notched Izod impact strength, ft.lb/in	4.0–8.0	0.24–0.34	0.25–0.4
Specific gravity	1.36–1.43	1.32–1.55	1.307–1.318
THERMAL PROPERTIES			
Burning rate	Self extinguishing	Self extinguishing	Self extinguishing
Heat distortion 264 psi, °C	121–127	143–171	74–80
Specific heat, cal/g		0.35–0.40	0.35–0.40
Linear thermal expansion coefficient, 10^{-5}, °C	3.0–4.5	3.0–4.5	6.0–8.0
Maximum continuous service temperature, °C	121	149–177	
CHEMICAL RESISTANCE			
Mineral acids, weak	Variable	Variable	Fair to good
Mineral acids, strong	Poor	Poor	Poor to good
Oxidizing acids, concentrated	Poor	Poor	Poor
Alkalies, weak	Variable	Variable	Poor to good
Alkalies, strong	Poor	Poor	Poor
Alcohols	Good	Good to excellent	Good to excellent
Ketones	Poor to fair	Fair	Fair
Esters	Fair to good	Fair to good	Fair to good
Hydrocarbons, aliphatic	Fair to good	Excellent	Good to excellent
Hydrocarbons, aromatic	Fair to good	Excellent	Good
Oils, vegetable, animal, mineral	Good	Excellent	Excellent
MISCELLANEOUS PROPERTIES			
Clarity	Opaque	Opaque	Clear
Color			Colorless to amber
Refractive index, n_D			
Applicable ASTM specifications and test methods	D700, D257, D150, D638, D651, D785, D256, D792, D648, D543	D700, D257, D150, D638, D651, D785, D256, D792, D648, D696, D543	D257, D150, D638, D785, D256, D792, D648, D696, D543

FORMS AVAILABLE
Cs—castings, F—film, Fb—fibers, I—impregnants, L—laminations, Lq—lacquers, Mf—monofilaments, P—Powder, pellet, or granules, R—rods, tubes, or other extruded forms, S—sheets.

FABRICATION
Cl—calendering, Cs—casting, E—extrusion, F—hot forming or drawing, I—impregnation, MB—blow molding, MC—compression molding, MI—injection molding, S—spreading.

PROPERTIES OF COMMERCIAL PLASTICS

	Polyester (Styrene-Alkyd)	Silicones	Urea Formaldehyde
Chemical Class			
Resin Type	Thermosetting	Thermosetting	Thermosetting
Subclass or Modification	Glassfiber mat reinforced	Mineral filled	α-Cellulose filled
FORMS AVAILABLE	L, S	P	P, R, S
FABRICATION	I	MC	MC

Cs—castings, F—film, Fb—fibers, I—impregnants, L—laminations, Lq—lacquers, Mf—monofilaments, P—Powder, pellet, or granules, R—rods, tubes, or other extruded forms, S—sheets.
Cl—calendering, Cs—casting, E—extrusion, F—hot forming or drawing, I—impregnation, MB—blow molding, MC—compression molding, MI—injection molding, S—spreading.

ELECTRICAL PROPERTIES

	Polyester	Silicones	Urea Formaldehyde
D.C. Resistivity, ohm-cm	10^{11}	$>10^{12}$	0.5–5.0
Dielectric constant, 60 cps	4.0–5.5	3.5–3.6	7.7–9.5
Dielectric constant, 10^6 cps	4.0–5.5	3.4–3.6	6.7–8.0
Dissipation factor, 60 cps	0.01–0.04	0.004	0.036–0.043
Dissipation factor, 10^6 cps	0.01–0.06	0.005–0.007	0.025–0.035

MECHANICAL PROPERTIES

Modulus of elasticity, 10^3 psi	500–1,500		1,300–1,400
Tensile strength, psi	30,000–50,000	3,000–4,000	5,500–13,000
Ultimate elongation, %	0.5–1.5		0.6
Yield stress, psi			
Yield strain, %			
Rockwell hardness	M 80–M 120	M 85–M 95	E 94–E 97
Notched Izod impact strength, ft.lb/in	7.0–30	0.25–0.35	0.24–0.40
Specific gravity	1.5–2.1	1.8–2.8	1.47–1.52

THERMAL PROPERTIES

Burning rate	Self extinguishing	Self extinguishing	Self extinguishing
Heat distortion 264 psi, °C	93–288	>260	130
Specific heat, cal/g	0.2–0.4	0.2–0.3	0.6
Linear thermal expansion coefficient, 10^{-5}, °C	1.8–3.0	2.0–4.0	2.2–3.6
Maximum continuous service temperature, °C	121–204	288	77

CHEMICAL RESISTANCE

Mineral acids, weak	Good	Fair to good	Poor
Mineral acids, strong	Poor	Poor to good	Poor
Oxidizing acids, concentrated	Poor		Poor
Alkalies, weak	Good	Fair	Fair
Alkalies, strong	Poor	Poor	Poor
Alcohols	Good	Poor	Good
Ketones	Good	Poor	Good
Esters	Poor		Good
Hydrocarbons, aliphatic	Good	Fair to good	Good
Hydrocarbons, aromatic	Poor to fair	Poor	Good
Oils, vegetable, animal, mineral	Good	Good	Good

MISCELLANEOUS PROPERTIES

Clarity	Translucent	Opaque	Translucent
Color	Colorless	Pale to dark	Colorless
Refractive index, n_D			1.54–1.56
Applicable ASTM specifications and test methods	D257, D150, D638, D785, D256, D792, D648, D696, D543	D257, D150, D785, D256, D792, D648, D696, D543	D705, D257, D150, D638, D785, D256, D792, D648

C-793

	Acrylonitrile–Butadiene–Styrene (ABS)	Acetal	Alkyd resins
Chemical Class			
Resin Type	Thermoplastic	Thermoplastic	Thermosetting
Subclass or Modification	High Heat resistant	Homopolymer	Synthetic fiber filled
FORMS AVAILABLE	P, S, L, R	C, R	P,
FABRICATION	Cl, E, MB, MI	MI, E	Cs, MC, MI
ELECTRICAL PROPERTIES			
D.C. Resistivity, ohm-cm			
Dielectric constant, 60 cps	2.4–5.0		3.8–5.0
Dielectric constant, 10^6 cps	2.4–3.8	3.7	3.6–4.7
Dissipation factor, 60 cps	0.003–0.008		0.012–0.026
Dissipation factor, 10^6 cps	0.007–0.015	0.004	0.01–0.016
MECHANICAL PROPERTIES			
Modulus of elasticity, 10^3 psi			
Tensile strength, psi	7,000–8,000	10,000–12,000	4,500–6,500
Ultimate elongation, %	1.0–20	15–75	
Yield stress, psi	4,000–9,000	10,000–13,000	
Yield strain, %			
Rockwell hardness	R 110–115	M 94, R 120	E 76
Notched Izod impact strength, ft.lb/in	2.0–4.0	1.4–2.3	0.50–4.5
Specific gravity	1.06–1.08	1.43	1.24–2.6
THERMAL PROPERTIES			
Burning rate	Slow	Slow	Self extinguishing
Heat distortion 264 psi, °C	115–118		
Specific heat, cal/g	0.3–0.4	0.35	
Linear thermal expansion coefficient, 10^{-5}, °C	6.0–6.5	8.1	4.0–5.5
Maximum continuous service temperature, °C	88–110	84	149–220
CHEMICAL RESISTANCE			
Mineral acids, weak	Good	Fair	Good
Mineral acids, strong	Good	Poor	Fair
Oxidizing acids, concentrated	Poor	Poor	Good
Alkalies, weak	Good	Poor	Fair
Alkalies, strong	Good	Good	Fair to good
Alcohols	Good	Good	Fair to good
Ketones	Poor	Good	Fair to good
Esters	Poor	Good	Fair to good
Hydrocarbons, aliphatic	Fair	Good	Fair to good
Hydrocarbons, aromatic	Fair	Good	Fair to good
Oils, vegetable, animal, mineral	Good	Good	
MISCELLANEOUS PROPERTIES			
Clarity	Translucent to opaque	Translucent to opaque	Opaque
Color	Colorless	Colorless	Colorless
Refractive index, n_D		1.48	
Applicable ASTM specifications and test methods	D638, D150, D792, D651, D648, D256, D758, D696, D543	D638, D150, D792, D651, D648, D256, D758, D696, D543	D638, D150, D792, D651, D648, D256, D758, D543

FORMS AVAILABLE
Cs—castings, F—film, Fb—fibers, I—impregnants, L—laminations, Lq—lacquers, Mf—monofilaments, P—Powder, pellet, or granules, R—rods, tubes, or other extruded forms, S—sheets.

FABRICATION
Cl—calendering, Cs—casting, E—extrusion, F—hot forming or drawing, I—impregnation, MB—blow molding, MC—compression molding, MI—injection molding, S—spreading.

IONIC EXCHANGE RESINS

ANION EXCHANGE RESINS

The following table is divided into two parts; the first lists properties of some anionic resins and the second, properties of some cationic resins.

Character S=strong W=weak	Trade name	Manufacturer*	Active group	Matrix	Effective pH	Selectivity	Order of selectivity	Total exchange capacity; meq/ml	Total exchange capacity; meq/gm	Maximum thermal stability; °C	Physical form; s=sphere b=beads	Standard mesh range	Ionic form as shipped	Shipping density; lb./cu. ft.
S	Dowex 1	1	Trimethyl benzyl ammonium	Polystyrene	0–14	Cl/H approx. 25	I, NO_3, Br, Cl, Acetate, OH, F	1.33	3.5	OH^- 50 Cl^- 150	s	20–50 (wet)	Cl^-	44
S	Dowex 21 K	1	Trimethyl benzyl ammonium	Polystyrene	0–14	Cl/H approx. 15	I, NO_3, Br, Cl, Acetate, OH, F	1.25	4.5	OH^- 50 Cl^- 150	s	20–50 (wet)	Cl^-	43
S	Duolite A-101 D	2	Quaternary ammonium	Polystyrene	0–14	—	—	1.4	4.2	OH^- 60 Cl^- 100	b	16–50	Cl^-	—
S	Ionac A-540	3	Quaternary ammonium	Polystyrene	0–14	—	—	1.0	3.6	salt 100 OH^- 60	b	16–50	salt	43–66
S	Dowex 2	1	Dimethyl ethanol benzyl ammonium	Polystyrene	0–14	Cl/H approx. 1.5	I, NO_3, Br, Cl, Acetate, OH, F	1.33	3.5	OH^- 30 Cl^- 150	s	20–50 (wet)	Cl^-	44
S	Duolite A-102 D	2	Quaternary ammonium	Polystyrene	0–14	—	—	1.4	4.2	OH^- 40 Cl^- 100	b	16–50	Cl^-	—
S	Ionac A-550	3	Dimethyl ethanol benzyl ammonium	Polystyrene	0–14	—	—	1.3	3.5	salt 100 OH^- 40	b	16–50	salt	43–46
W	Duolite A-30 B	2	Tertiary amine; Quaternary ammonium	Epoxy polyamines	0–9	—	—	2.6	8.7	80	b	16–50	salt	—

IONIC EXCHANGE RESINS (Continued)

ANION EXCHANGE RESINS (Continued)

Character S = strong W = weak	Trade name	Manufacturer*	Active group	Matrix	Effective pH	Selectivity	Order of selectivity	Total exchange capacity; meq/ml	Total exchange capacity; meq/gm	Maximum thermal stability; °C	Physical form; s = sphere b = beads	Standard mesh range	Ionic form as shipped	Shipping density; lb./cu. ft.
W	Ionac A-300	3	Tertiary amine; Quaternary ammonium	Epoxy amine	0–12	—	—	1.8	5.5	40	g	16–50	salt	19–21
W	Duolite A-6	2	Tertiary amine	Phenolic	0–5	—	—	2.4	7.6	60	g	16–50	salt	—
W	Duolite A-7	2	Secondary amine	Phenolic	0–4	—	—	2.4	9.1	40	g	16–50	salt	—

* 1. Dow
2. Diamond Shamrock
3. Ionac
4. Nalco

CATION EXCHANGE RESINS

Character S = strong W = weak	Trade name	Manufacturer*	Active group	Matrix	Effective pH	Selectivity	Order of selectivity	Total exchange capacity; meq/ml	Total exchange capacity; meq/mg	Maximum thermal stability; °C	Physical form; s = sphere b = beads	Standard mesh range	Ionic form as shipped	Shipping density; lb./cu. ft.
S	Dowex 50	1	Nuclear sulfonic acid	Polystyrene	0–14	Na/H approx. 1.2	Ag, Cs, Rb, K, NH_4, Na, H, Li, Ba, Sr, Ca, Mg, Be	Na^+ 1.9 H^+ 1.7	Na^+ 4.8 H^+ 5.0	150	s	20–50 (wet)	H^+ or Na^+	H^+ 50 Na^+ 53
S	Dowex MPC-1	4	Nuclear sulfonic acid	Polystyrene	0–14	—	—	1.6–1.8 H^+ form	4.5–4.9 H^+ form	150	b	20–40 (wet)	Na^+	50
S	Duolite C-20	2	Nuclear sulfonic acid	Polystyrene	0–14	—	—	2.2	5.1	150	b	16–50	Na^+	—
S	Ionac 240	3	Nuclear sulfonic acid	Polystyrene	0–14	—	—	1.9	4.6	140 (Na^+) 130 (H^+)	b	16–50	Na^+	50–55

IONIC EXCHANGE RESINS (Continued)

CATION EXCHANGE RESINS (Continued)

Character S=strong W=weak	Trade name	Manu- facturer*	Active group	Matrix	Effective pH	Selectivity	Order of selectivity	Total exchange capacity; meq/ml	Total exchange capacity; meq/gm	Maximum thermal stability; °C	Physical form; s=sphere b=beads	Standard mesh range	Ionic form as shipped	Shipping density; lb./cu. ft.
S	Duolite C-3	2	Methylene sulfonic	Phenolic	0–9	—	—	1.1	2.9	60	g	16–50	H⁺	—
W	Dowex CCR-1	4	Carboxylic	Phenolic	0–9	—	—	—	—	38	g	20–50 (wet)	H⁺ (dry)	21
W	Duolite ES-63	2	Phosphonic	Polystyrene	4–14	—	—	3.3	6.5	100	b	16–50	H⁺	—
W	Duolite ES-80	2	Aliphatic	Acrylic	6–14	—	—	3.5	10.2	100	b	16–50	H⁺	—

* 1. Dow
2. Diamond Shamrock
3. Ionac
4. Nalco

AZEOTROPES

BINARY SYSTEMS

No.	Compounds	BP, °C	BP, °C	In azeo-trope	Upper layer	Lower layer	Relative volume of layers at 20°C	Specific gravity of layers or azeotrope
	Components			**Azeotrope**				
				Percent composition				
1	a. Acetal b. Chloroform	102–4 61.2	78.2	84.5 15.5				
2	a. Acetaldehyde b. Butane	20.9 −0.5	−7.0	16.0 84.0				
3	a. Acetaldehyde b. Ethyl ether	20.9 34.6	20.5	76.0 24.0				0.762
4	a. Acetaldehyde⎱ 1551 mm b. Ethyl ether ⎰	55.0 70.0	52.6	77.5 22.5				0.763
5	a. Acetamide b. Benzaldehyde	222.0 179.5	178.6	6.5 93.5				
6	a. Acetamide b. o-Bromophenol	222.0 195.0	223.0	50.0 50.0				
7	a. Acetamide b. p-Chloronitrobenzene	222.0 242.0	213.6	55.0 45.0				
8	a. Acetamide b. o-Chlorotoluene	222.0 159.0	157.8	8.0 92.0				
9	a. Acetamide b. p-Dichlorobenzene	222.0 219.0	199.4	18.0 82.0				
10	a. Acetamide b. Glycol monoacetate	222.0 182.0	190.7	5.0 95.0				
11	a. Acetamide b. 2-Methyl-5-ethyl pyridine	222.0 174.0	176.9	5.4 94.6				0.926
12	a. Acetamide b. o-Nitrotoluene	222.0 222.3	206.5	32.5 67.5				
13	a. Acetamide b. Nitrobenzene	222.0 210.9	202.0	24.0 76.0				
14	a. Acetamide b. Octyl alcohol	222.0 195.0	194.5	9.5 90.5				
15	a. Acetamide b. o-Toluidine	222.0 199.8	198.6	12.0 88.0				
16	a. Acetamide b. o-Xylene	222.0 144.1	142.6	11.0 89.0				
17	a. Acetic acid b. Benzene	118.1 80.1	80.1	2.0 98.0				0.882
18	a. Acetic acid b. Bromobenzene	118.1 156.0	118.4	95.0 5.0				
19	a. Acetic acid b. Butyl ether	118.1 142.0	116.7	81.0 19.0				0.983

No.	Components			Azeotrope					
	Compounds	BP, °C	BP, °C	Percent composition			Relative volume of layers at 20°C	Specific gravity of layers or azeotrope	
				In azeotrope	Upper layer	Lower layer			
20	a. Acetic acid b. Chlorobenzene	118.1 132.0	114.7	58.5 41.5					
21	a. Acetic acid b. Cyclohexane	118.1 81.4	79.7	2.0 98.0					
22	a. Acetic acid b. Cyclohexene	118.1 83.0	81.8	6.5 93.5					
23	a. Acetic acid b. 1,1-Dibromoethane	118.1 109.5	103.7	25.0 75.0					
24	a. Acetic acid b. 1,2-Dibromoethane	118.1 —	114.4	55.0 45.0					
25	a. Acetic acid b. Dibromomethane	118.1 98.2	94.8	16.0 84.0					
26	a. Acetic acid b. Dimethyl formamide	118.1 153.0	159.0	26.0 74.0					1.004
27	a. Acetic acid b. 1,4-Dioxane	118.1 101.5	119.5	77.0 23.0					1.05
28	a. Acetic acid b. Epichlorohydrin	118.1 117.0	115.1	34.5 65.5					
29	a. Acetic acid b. Ethyl benzene	118.1 136.2	114.7	66.0 34.0					0.882
30	a. Acetic acid b. Pyridine	118.1 115.3	139.7	35.0 65.0					1.024
31	a. Acetic acid b. Tetrachloroethylene	118.1 121.0	107.4	38.5 61.5					
32	a. Acetic acid b. Trichloroethylene	118.1 87.0	86.5	3.8 96.2					
33	a. Acetic acid b. Toluene	118.1 110.6	105.4	28.0 72.0					0.905
34	a. Acetic acid b. Triethyl amine	118.1 89.5	163.0	69.0 31.0					1.023
35	a. Acetic acid b. m-Xylene	118.1 139.1	115.4	27.0 73.0					0.908
36	a. Acetic acid b. Water	118.1 100	76.6	3.0 97.0					
37	a. Acetone b. Bromopropane	56.2 59.6	54.1	42.0 58.0					
38	a. Acetone b. Carbon disulfide	56.2 46.3	39.3	33.0 67.0					1.04
39	a. Acetone b. Carbon tetrachloride	56.2 76.8	56.1	88.5 11.5					

No.	Compounds	BP, °C	BP, °C	Percent composition In azeotrope	Upper layer	Lower layer	Relative volume of layers at 20°C	Specific gravity of layers or azeotrope
40	a. Acetone b. Chloroform	56.2 61.2	64.7	20.0 80.0				1.268
41	a. Acetone b. 1-Chloropropane	56.2 47.2	45.8	15.0 85.0				
42	a. Acetone b. Cyclohexane	56.2 81.4	53.0	67.0 33.0				
43	a. Acetone b. Cyclopentane	56.2 49.5	41.0	36.0 64.0				
44	a. Acetone b. Diethyl amine	56.2 55.5	51.3	38.2 61.8				0.732
45	a. Acetone b. Hexane	56.2 69.0	49.8	59.0 41.0				
46	a. Acetone b. Iodoethane	56.2 72.2	55.0	60.0 40.0				
47	a. Acetone b. Isobutyl amine	56.2 68.0	<56.0	<96.0 >4.0				
48	a. Acetone b. Isobutyl chloride	56.2 68.9	55.8	73.0 27.0				
49	a. Acetone b. Isopropyl ether	56.2 67.5	53.3	56.5 43.5				0.764
50	a. Acetone b. Isopropyl ether } 775.5 mm	78.3 91.9	75.0	55.0 45.0				0.769
51	a. Acetone b. Methanol	56.2 64.7	55.7	88.0 12.0				0.795
52	a. Acetone b. Methanol } 11.6 atm.	151.0	140.0	44.0 56.0				0.796
53	a. Acetone b. Methanol } 4.56 atm.	108.0 109.0	102.0	68.0 32.0				0.796
54	a. Acetone b. Methyl acetate	56.2 57.1	55.6	48.0 52.0				0.854
55	a. Acetone b. Pentane	56.2 36.0	32.0	21.0 79.0				
57	a. Acetone b. Water } 1034 mm	84.0 126.0	81.4	98.7 1.3				0.795
58	a. Acetone cyanohydrin b. Water	dec. 100.0	99.9	15.0 85.0				1.001
59	a. Acetonitrile b. Benzene	82.0 80.1	73.0	34.0 66.0				

No.	Components Compounds	BP, °C	BP, °C	Azeotrope Percent composition In azeotrope	Upper layer	Lower layer	Relative volume of layers at 20°C		Specific gravity of layers or azeotrope
60	a. Acetonitrile b. Diethyl amine	82.0 55.5	54.5	8.0 92.0					0.705
61	a. Acetonitrile b. Ethanol	82.0 78.5	72.9	43.0 57.0					0.788
62	a. Acetonitrile b. Ethyl acetate	82.0 77.2	74.8	23.0 77.0					
63	a. Acetonitrile b. Isopropyl ether	82.0 67.5	61.7	17.0 83.0					0.743
64	a. Acetonitrile b. Methanol	82.0 64.7	63.5	81.0 19.0					
65	a. Acetonitrile ⎱1240 mm b. Pentane ⎰	118.0 65.0	58.0	13.0 87.0	3.1 96.9	85.3 14.7	U 90.0 L 10		U 0.616 L 0.779
66	a. Acetonitrile ⎱152 mm b. Triethyl amine ⎰	36.5 43.4	29.0	36.8 63.2					0.749
67	a. Acetonitrile b. Water	82.0 100.0	76.5	83.7 16.3					0.818
68	a. Acetophenone b. Octyl alcohol	202.3 195.0	195.0	12.5 87.5					
69	a. Acetylene b. Ethane	−83.6 −88.3	−94.5	40.7 59.3					
70	a. Acrolein b. Water	52.5 100.0	52.4	97.4 2.6					
71	a. Acrylonitrile b. Benzene	78.0 80.1	73.3	47.0 53.0					
72	a. Acrylonitrile b. Isopropanol	78.0 82.3	71.7	56.0 44.0					
73	a. Acrylonitrile ⎱175 mm b. Methanol ⎰	37.0 31.3	29.0	53.0 47.0					
74	a. Acrylonitrile b. Water	78.0 100.0	70.6	85.7 14.3	96.8 3.2	7.3 92.7	U 89.5 L 10.5		U 0.813 L 0.99
75	a. Allyl acetate b. Water	104.1 100.0	83.0	83.3 16.7	98.4 1.6	3.0 97.0	U 84.0 L 16.0		U 0.930 L 0.998
76	a. Allyl acetone b. Water	129.5 100.0	92.1	64.7 35.3	97.75 2.25	2.2 97.8	U 69.0 L 31.0		U 0.849 L 0.997
77	a. Allyl alcohol b. Benzene	97.1 80.1	76.8	17.4 82.6					0.874
78	a. Allyl alcohol b. Carbon tetrachloride	97.1 76.8	72.3	11.5 88.5					1.450
79	a. Allyl alcohol b. Hexane	97.1 69.0	65.5	4.5 95.5					

No.	Compounds	BP, °C	BP, °C	Percent composition			Relative volume of layers at 20°C	Specific gravity of layers or azeotrope
	Components			In azeotrope	Upper layer	Lower layer		
80	a. Allyl alcohol b. Propyl acetate	97.1 101.6	94.6	52.0 48.0				
81	a. Allyl alcohol b. Toluene	97.1 110.6	91.5	50.0 50.0				
82	a. Allyl alcohol b. Trichloroethylene	97.1 87.0	81.0	16.0 84.0				1.313
83	a. Allyl alcohol b. Vinylallyl ether	97.1 67.4	66.6	5.0 95.0				
84	a. Allyl alcohol b. Water	97.1 100.0	88.2	72.9 27.1				0.905
85	a. Allyl chloride b. Water	44.9 100.0	43.0	97.8 2.2				
86	a. Allyl cyanide b. Water	118.9 100.0	89.4	66.0 34.0	97.5 2.5	3.6 96.4	U 70.0 L 30.0	U 0.837 L 0.994
87	a. 2-Aminoethanol b. Chlorobenzene	172.2 132.0	128.6	13.5 86.5				
88	a. 2-Aminoethanol b. o-Chlorotoluene	172.2 159.0	146.5	26.0 74.0				
89	a. Amyl acetate b. Glycol(1,2-ethanediol)	148.7 197.2	147.6	94.0 6.0				
90	a. tert. Amyl alcohol b. Cyclohexane	101.8 81.4	78.5	16.0 84.0				
91	a. tert. Amyl alcohol b. Toluene	101.8 110.6	100.5	56.0 44.0				
92	a. Aniline b. o-Cresol	184.4 191.5	191.3	8.0 92.0				
93	a. Aniline b. Glycol(1,2-ethanediol)	184.4 197.2	180.6	76.0 24.0				
94	a. Aniline b. Octyl alcohol	184.4 195.0	184.0	83.0 17.0				
95	a. Benzaldehyde b. α-Chlorotoluene	179.5 179.0	177.9	50.0 50.0				
96	a. Benzaldehyde b. Phenol	179.5 182.0	185.6	49.0 51.0				
97	a. Benzene b. 2-Butanol	80.1 99.5	78.8	84.0 16.0				
98	a. Benzene b. Cyclohexane	80.1 81.4	77.8	55.0 45.0				0.834
99	a. Benzene b. Ethanol	80.1 78.5	67.8	67.6 32.4				0.848

No.	Components Compounds	BP, °C	BP, °C	Azeotrope Percent composition In azeotrope	Upper layer	Lower layer	Relative volume of layers at 20°C	Specific gravity of layers or azeotrope
100	a. Benzene b. Ethyl nitrate	80.1 88.7	80.0	88.0 12.0				
101	a. Benzene b. Formic acid	80.1 100.7	71.1	69.0 31.0				
102	a. Benzene b. Heptane	80.1 98.4	80.1	99.3 0.7				
103	a. Benzene b. Isobutanol	80.1 108.3	79.8	90.7 9.3				0.870
104	a. Benzene b. Isopropanol	80.1 82.3	71.5	66.7 33.3				0.838
105	a. Benzene b. Methanol	80.1 64.7	58.3	60.5 39.5				0.844
106	a. Benzene b. Methylethyl ketone	80.1 79.6	78.4	62.5 37.5				0.853
107	a. Benzene b. 2-Methyl-2-propanol	80.1 82.8	74.0	63.4 36.6				0.842
108	a. Benzene b. Methyl propionate	80.1 79.6	79.5	48.0 52.0				
109	a. Benzene b. Nitromethane	80.1 101.0	79.2	86.0 14.0				
110	a. Benzene b. Propanol	80.1 97.2	77.1	83.1 16.9				0.865
111	a. Benzene b. Water	80.1 100.0	69.4	91.1 8.9	99.94 0.06	0.07 99.93	U 92.0 L 8.0	U 0.880 L 0.999
112	a. Benzonitrile b. p-Bromotoluene	190.7 185.0	184.3	15.0 85.0				
113	a. Benzonitrile b. o-Cresol	190.7 191.5	196.0	49.0 51.0				
114	a. Benzyl alcohol b. p-Cresol	205.2 202.5	206.8	62.0 38.0				
115	a. Benzyl alcohol b. Nitrobenzene	205.2 210.9	204.2	62.0 38.0				
116	a. Benzyl alcohol b. Water	205.2 100.0	99.9	9.0 91.0				
117	a. Bromobenzene b. Chloroacetic acid	156.0 189.0	154.3	89.0 11.0				
118	a. 1-Bromobutane b. Ethanol	101.6 78.5	75.0	57.0 43.0				
119	a. 1-Bromobutane b. Glycol	101.6 197.2	101.3	98.3 1.7				

No.	Components Compounds	BP, °C	BP, °C	Azeotrope Percent composition In azeo-trope	Upper layer	Lower layer	Relative volume of layers at 20°C	Specific gravity of layers or azeotrope
120	a. 1-Bromobutane b. Propyl acetate	101.6 101.6	99.9	52.0 48.0				
121	a. Bromodichloromethane b. Ethanol	90.2 78.5	75.5	72.0 28.0				
122	a. Bromoethane b. Ethanol	38.0 78.5	37.0	97.0 3.0				
123	a. o-Bromophenol b. o-Cresol	195.0 191.5	189.8	25.0 75.0				
124	a. o-Bromophenol b. Octyl alcohol	195.0 195.0	204.0	50.0 50.0				
125	a. 1-Bromopropane b. Hexane	70.9 69.0	67.2	50.0 50.0				
126	a. 2-Bromopropene b. Ethanol	48.4 78.5	46.2	94.0 6.0				
127	a. o-Bromotoluene b. Caproic acid	181.8 205.0	180.8	94.0 6.0				
128	a. o-Bromotoluene b. Chloroacetic acid	181.8 189.0	173.0	68.0 32.0				
129	a. o-Bromotoluene b. Ethylacetoacetate	181.8 180.0	174.7	49.0 51.0				
130	a. o-Bromotoluene b. Glycol	181.8 197.2	166.8	75.0 25.0				
131	a. m-Bromotoluene b. Octyl alcohol	183.7 195.0	184.1	91.0 9.0				
132	a. p-Bromotoluene b. Octyl alcohol	185.0 195.0	184.6	90.0 10.0				
133	a. Butane b. Ethylene oxide	−0.5 10.4	−6.5	78.0 22.0				
134	a. 2,3-Butanedione b. Ethanol	88.0 78.5	73.9	53.0 47.0				
135	a. 1-Butanol b. Butyl acetate	117.7 126.5	117.6	67.2 32.8				0.832
136	a. 1-Butanol b. Butyl ether	117.7 142.0	117.6	82.5 17.5				0.804
137	a. 1-Butanol b. Butyronitrile	117.7 118.0	113.0	50.0 50.0				
138	a. 1-Butanol b. Chlorobenzene	117.7 132.0	115.3	56.0 46.0				
139	a. 1-Butanol b. 1-Chloro-2-propanone	117.7 119.0	112.5	43.0 57.0				

No.	Components		Azeotrope					
	Compounds	BP, °C	BP, °C	Percent composition			Relative volume of layers at 20°C	Specific gravity of layers or azeotrope
				In azeo-trope	Upper layer	Lower layer		
140	a. 1-Butanol b. Cyclohexane	117.7 81.4	79.8	10.0 90.0				
141	a. 1-Butanol b. 1,1-Dibromoethane	117.7 109.5	104.5	20.0 80.0				
142	a. 1-Butanol b. 1,2-Dibromoethane	117.7 131.6	114.8	44.0 56.0				
143	a. 1-Butanol b. Epichlorohydrin	117.7 117.0	112.0	43.0 57.0				
144	a. 1-Butanol b. Ethylene diamine	117.7 116.9	124.7	64.3 35.7				0.849
145	a. 1-Butanol b. Ethyl nitrate	117.7 88.7	87.5	4.0 96.0				
146	a. 1-Butanol b. Heptane	117.7 98.4	93.3	18.0 82.0				0.701
147	a. 1-Butanol b. Hexaldehyde	117.7 128.5	116.8	77.1 22.9				0.829
148	a. 1-Butanol b. Hexane	117.7 69.0	67.0	3.0 97.0				0.69
149	a. 1-Butanol b. 1-Iodopropane	117.7 102.4	99.5	13.5 86.5				
150	a. 1-Butanol b. 3-Iodopropane	117.7 103.1	98.7	13.0 87.0				
151	a. 1-Butanol b. Methyl chloroacetate	117.7 130.0	116.3	74.0 26.0				
152	a. 1-Butanol b. Nitroethane	117.7 114.8	107.7	45.0 55.0				
153	a. 1-Butanol b. Nitromethane	117.7 101.9	97.8	30.0 70.0				
154	a. 1-Butanol b. Octane	117.7 125.8	110.2	50.0 50.0				
155	a. 1-Butanol b. Propylene diamine	117.7 120.9	126.5	51.0 49.0				0.843
156	a. 1-Butanol b. Pyridine	117.7 115.3	118.7	71.0 29.0				
157	a. 1-Butanol b. Tetrachloroethylene	117.7 121.2	110.0	32.0 68.0				
158	a. 1-Butanol b. Toluene	117.7 110.6	105.6	27.0 73.0				0.846
159	a. 1-Butanol b. Trichloroethylene	117.7 87.0	86.7	3.0 97.0				

No.	Compounds	BP, °C	BP, °C	Percent composition			Relative volume of layers at 20°C		Specific gravity of layers or azeotrope	
				In azeo-trope	Upper layer	Lower layer				
160	a. 1-Butanol	117.7	93.3	7.8						
	b. Vinylbutyl ether	94.2		92.2						
161	a. 1-Butanol	117.7	93.0	55.5	79.9	7.7	U	71.5	U	0.849
	b. Water	100.0		44.5	20.1	92.3	L	28.5	L	0.990
162	a. 1-Butanol } 30 mm	48.0	29.0	47.6	79.9	7.7	U	59.0	U	0.849
	b. Water	29.0		52.4	20.1	92.3	L	41.0	L	0.989
163	a. 1-Butanol	117.7	116.8	75.0						
	b. o-Xylene	144.4		25.0						
164	a. 2-Butanol	99.5	76.0	18.0						
	b. Cyclohexane	81.4		82.0						
165	a. 2-Butanol	99.5	91.0	35.0						
	b. Diisobutylene	102.3		65.0						
166	a. 2-Butanol	99.5	95.3	55.0						
	b. Toluene	110.6		45.0						
167	a. 2-Butanol	99.5	88.5	68.0						0.863
	b. Water	100.0		32.0						
168	a. tert. Butanol	82.8	74.0	36.6						
	b. Benzene	80.1		63.4						
169	a. tert. Butanol	82.8	71.3	37.0						
	b. Cyclohexane	81.4		63.0						
170	a. tert. Butanol	82.8	63.7	22.0						
	b. Hexane	69.0		78.0						
171	a. tert. Butanol	82.8	79.9	88.2						
	b. Water	100.0		11.8						
172	a. 2-Butanone	79.6	71.8	40.0						
	b. Cyclohexane	81.4		60.0						
173	a. 2-Butanone	79.6	77.0	18.0						
	b. Ethyl acetate	77.2		82.0						
174	a. 1-Butenylethyl ether, cis	72.0	64.0	93.9	99.8	0.32	U	95.2	U	0.777
	b. Water	100.0		6.1	0.2	99.68	L	4.8	L	1.000
175	a. 1-Butenylmethyl ether, trans	76.7	67.0	92.8	99.8	0.01	U	94.2	U	0.787
	b. Water	100.0		7.2	0.2	99.99	L	5.8	L	1.000
176	a. 1-Butoxy-2-propanol	170.1	98.6	28.0	80.8	6.4	U	31.0	U	0.910
	b. Water	100.0		72.0	19.2	93.6	L	69.0	L	0.997
177	a. Butyl acetate	126.5	125.9	95.0						0.879
	b. Butyl ether	142.1		5.0						
178	a. Butyl acetate	126.5	125.6	69.0						
	b. 2-Chloroethanol	128.0		31.0						

No.	Components			Azeotrope							
	Compounds	BP, °C	BP, °C	Percent composition			Relative volume of layers at 20°C		Specific gravity of layers or azeotrope		
				In azeotrope	Upper layer	Lower layer					
179	a. Butyl acetate b. 2-Ethoxy ethanol	126.5 135.6	125.8	64.3 35.7					0.896		
180	a. Butyl acetate b. Isoamyl alcohol	126.5 130.5	126.0	82.5 17.5							
181	a. Butyl acetate b. Octane	126.5 125.8	119.0	52.0 48.0							
182	a. Butyl acetate b. Water	126.5 100.0	90.7	72.9 27.1	98.8 1.2	0.68 99.32	U L	75.8 24.2	U L	0.882 0.998	
183	a. Butyl acetoacetate b. Water	213.9 100.0	99.4	15.9 84.1	97.2 2.8	0.4 99.6	U L	16.0 84.0	U L	0.970 1.000	
184	a. Butyl acrylate b. Water	118[2] 100.0	94.3	62.0 38.0	99.3 0.7	0.2 99.8	U L	65.0 35	U L	0.902 0.999	
185	a. Butyl amine b. Cyclohexane	77.1 81.4	76.5	60.0 40.0							
186	a. Butyl amine b. Ethanol	77.1 78.5	82.2	51.0 49.0					0.766		
187	a. Butyl amine b. Isopropanol	77.1 82.3	84.7	40.0 60.0					0.775		
188	a. Butyl amine }575 mm b. Water	69.0 92.4	69.0	98.7 1.3							
189	a. n-Butyl aniline b. Water	240.9 100.0	99.8	5.6 94.4	99.76 0.24	0.01 99.99	U L	6.0 94.0	U L	0.929 1.000	
190	a. Butyl benzoate b. Water	250.2 100.0	99.9	5.0 95.0	0.01 99.99	99.68 0.32	U L	95.0 5.0	U L	1.000 1.007	
191	a. Butyl butyrate b. Water	166.4 100.0	97.9	47.0 53.0	99.52 0.48	0.06 99.94	U L	50.6 49.4	U L	0.871 0.998	
192	a. Butyl-2-ethoxyethanol b. Dibutyl acetal	171.1 189.4	170.6	42.0 58.0					0.887		
193	a. Butyl-2-ethoxyethanol b. Water	171.1 100.0	98.8	20.8 79.2					0.989		
194	a. Butyl chloride b. Water	78.0 100.0	68.0	93.0 7.0	99.92 0.08	0.11 99.89	U L	94.0 6.0	U L	0.887 1.000	
195	a. Butyl ether b. 2-Ethoxy ethanol	142.0 135.1	127.0	50.0 50.0							
196	a. Butyl ether b. Ethylene glycol	142.0 197.2	139.5	93.6 6.4	98.0 2.0	1.0 99.0	U L	95.0 5.0	U L	0.777 1.114	
197	a. Butyl ether b. Morpholine	142.0 128.3	126.7	27.0 73.0					0.924		

No.	Components		BP, °C	BP, °C	Azeotrope						
	Compounds				Percent composition			Relative volume of layers at 20°C		Specific gravity of layers or azeotrope	
					In azeo-trope	Upper layer	Lower layer				
198	a.	Butyl ether	142.0	136.0	55.0						
	b.	Propionic acid	141.1		45.0						
199	a.	Butyl ether	142.0	94.1	66.6	99.97	0.19	U	72.0	U	0.769
	b.	Water	100.0		33.4	0.03	99.81	L	28.0	L	0.998
200	a.	Butylisopropenyl ether	114.8	86.3	81.2	0.01	99.99	U	84.7	U	0.790
	b.	Water	100.0		18.8	99.99	0.01	L	15.3	L	1.000
201	a.	2-Butyl octanol	253.4	99.9	2.5	98.9	0.01	U	3.0	U	0.85
	b.	Water	100.0		97.5	1.1	99.99	L	97.0	L	1.00
202	a.	Butyl salicylate	268.2	99.9	4.2	0.02	99.87	U	96.0	U	1.000
	b.	Water	100.0		95.8	99.98	0.13	L	4.0	L	1.075
203	a.	Butyraldehyde	75.7	70.7	39.4						0.835
	b.	Ethanol	78.5		60.6						
204	a.	Butyraldehyde	75.7	68.0	90.3	96.8	7.1	U	94.0	U	0.815
	b.	Water	100.0		9.7	3.2	92.9	L	6.0		
205	a.	Butyric acid	163.5	163.0	65.0						
	b.	o-Dichlorobenzene	180.0		35.0						
206	a.	Butyric acid	163.5	99.4	18.4						1.007
	b.	Water	100.0		81.6						
207	a.	Butyric acid	163.5	143.0	10.0						
	b.	o-Xylene	144.4		90.0						
208	a.	Butyric acid	163.5	138.1	6.6						
	b.	m-Xylene	139.1		93.4						
209	a.	Butyric acid	163.5	137.5	5.4						
	b.	p-Xylene	138.4		94.6						
210	a.	Butyronitrile	118.0	107.0	27.0						
	b.	Toluene	110.6		73.0						
211	a.	Butyronitrile	118.0	88.7	67.5	97.5	3.53	U	72.9	U	0.795
	b.	Water	100.0		32.5	2.5	96.47	L	27.1	L	0.994
212	a.	Caproic acid	205.0	201.9	13.0						
	b.	m-Cresol	202.8		87.0						
213	a.	Carbon disulfide	46.3	46.0	94.0						
	b.	1,1-Dichloroethane	57.2		6.0						
214	a.	Carbon disulfide	46.3	42.4	91.0						1.197
	b.	Ethanol	78.5		9.0						
215	a.	Carbon disulfide	46.3	46.1	97.0						1.249
	b.	Ethyl acetate	77.1		3.0						
216	a.	Carbon disulfide	46.3	34.4	1.0						0.719
	b.	Ethyl ether	34.6		99.0						
217	a.	Carbon disulfide	46.3	39.4	63.0						
	b.	Ethyl formate	54.3		37.0						

No.	Components	Compounds	BP, °C	BP, °C	Azeotrope Percent composition In azeotrope	Upper layer	Lower layer	Relative volume of layers at 20°C	Specific gravity of layers or azeotrope
218	a. Carbon disulfide		46.3	44.6	92.0				1.202
	b. Isopropanol		82.3		8.0				
219	a. Carbon disulfide		46.3	37.7	86.0	50.8	97.2	U 26.3	U 0.979
	b. Methanol		64.7		14.0	49.2	2.8	L 73.7	L 1.261
220	a. Carbon disulfide		46.3	40.2	70.0				1.126
	b. Methyl acetate		57.0		30.0				
221	a. Carbon disulfide		46.3	45.9	84.7				1.157
	b. Methylethyl ketone		79.6		15.3				
222	a. Carbon disulfide		46.3	45.3	94.0				1.219
	b. 2-Methyl-2-propanol		82.2		6.0				
223	a. Carbon disulfide		46.3	45.2	55.0				
	b. Propyl chloride		46.6		45.0				
224	a. Carbon disulfide		46.3	43.6	98.0	0.29	99.99	U 2.3	U 1.001
	b. Water		100.0		2.0	99.71	0.01	L 97.7	L 1.265
225	a. Carbon tetrachloride		76.8	65.0	84.2				1.377
	b. Ethanol		78.5		15.8				
226	a. Carbon tetrachloride		76.8	74.8	57.0				1.202
	b. Ethyl acetate		77.1		43.0				
227	a. Carbon tetrachloride ⎫286 mm		47.5	47.4	82.2				
	b. Ethyl acetate ⎭		50.5		17.8				
228	a. Carbon tetrachloride		76.8	75.3	78.0				1.500
	b. Ethylene dichloride		84.0		22.0				
229	a. Carbon tetrachloride		76.8	75.8	94.5				1.515
	b. Isobutanol		108.3		5.5				
230	a. Carbon tetrachloride		76.8	67.0	82.0				1.344
	b. Isopropanol		82.3		18.0				
231	a. Carbon tetrachloride		76.8	55.7	79.4				1.322
	b. Methanol		64.7		20.6				
232	a. Carbon tetrachloride		76.8	73.8	71.0				1.247
	b. Methylethyl ketone		79.6		29.0				
233	a. Carbon tetrachloride		76.8	69.5	83.0				1.358
	b. 2-Methyl-2-propanol		82.2		17.0				
234	a. Carbon tetrachloride		76.8	72.8	88.5				1.437
	b. Propanol		97.2		11.5				
235	a. Carbon tetrachloride		76.8	66.8	95.9	0.03	99.97	U 6.4	U 1.000
	b. Water		100.0		4.1	99.97	0.03	L 93.6	L 1.597
236	a. Chloral		98.0	93.0	53.0				
	b. Heptane		98.4		47.0				

No.	Components		BP, °C	BP, °C	Percent composition			Relative volume of layers at 20°C	Specific gravity of layers or azeotrope
	Compounds				In azeo-trope	Upper layer	Lower layer		
237	a. Chloral	98.0		95.0	93.0				
	b. Water	100.0			7.0				
238	a. Chloroacetic acid	189.0		156.8	12.0				
	b. o-Chlorotoluene	159.0			88.0				
239	a. Chloroacetic acid	189.0		187.1	78.0				
	b. Naphthalene	217.9			22.0				
240	a. Chloroacetic acid	189.0		186.3	3.0				
	b. Valeric acid	187.0			97.0				
241	a. Chloroacetic acid	189.0		143.5	12.0				
	b. o-Xylene	144.4			88.0				
242	a. Chlorobenzene	132.0		120.0	58.0				
	b. 2-Chloroethanol	128.0			42.0				
243	a. Chlorobenzene	132.0		127.2	68.0				
	b. 2-Ethoxy ethanol	135.1			32.0				
244	a. Chlorobenzene	132.0		124.4	66.0				
	b. Isoamyl alcohol	120.5			34.0				
245	a. Chlorobenzene	132.0		107.1	37.0				
	b. Isobutyl alcohol	108.4			63.0				
246	a. Chlorobenzene	132.0		131.2	92.0				
	b. Isobutyric acid	154.4			8.0				
247	a. Chlorobenzene	132.0		96.5	20.0				
	b. Propanol	97.2			80.0				
248	a. Chlorobenzene	132.0		128.9	82.0				
	b. Propionic acid	141.1			18.0				
249	a. Chlorobenzene	132.0		124.5	57.0				
	b. Pyrrole	131.0			43.0				
250	a. Chlorobenzene	132.0		90.2	71.6				
	b. Water	100.0			28.4				
251	a. 1-Chlorobutane	78.0		65.7	79.7				
	b. Ethanol	78.5			20.3				
252	a. 1-Chlorobutane	78.0		70.8	77.0				
	b. Isopropyl alcohol	82.3			23.0				
253	a. 2-Chloroethanol	128.0		121.0	62.0				
	b. Ethyl benzene	136.2			38.0				
254	a. 2-Chloroethanol	128.8		127.8	75.0				
	b. Isoamyl alcohol	130.5			25.0				
255	a. 2-Chloroethyl ether	179.2		141.2	28.0				
	b. 3-Heptanol	157.0			72.0				
256	a. 2-Chloroethyl ether	179.2		98.0	34.5	1.07	99.72	U 70.4	U 1.002
	b. Water	100.0			65.5	98.03	0.28	L 29.6	L 1.220

No.	Components		BP, °C	BP, °C	Azeotrope					
					Percent composition			Relative volume of layers at 20°C		Specific gravity of layers or azeotrope
	Compounds				In azeotrope	Upper layer	Lower layer			
257	a. Chloroform		61.2	59.4	93.0					1.403
	b. Ethanol		78.5		7.0					
258	a. Chloroform		61.2	60.0	72.0					1.101
	b. Hexane		68.7		28.0					
259	a. Chloroform		61.2	53.5	87.0					1.342
	b. Methanol		64.7		13.0					
260	a. Chloroform		61.2	79.9	17.0					0.877
	b. Methylethyl ketone		79.6		83.0					
261	a. Chloroform		61.2	56.3	97.0	0.8	99.8	U 4.4		U 1.004
	b. Water		100.0		3.0	99.2	0.2	L 95.6		L 1.491
262	a. Chloroisopropyl ether		187.0	98.5	37.4	0.17	99.86	U 65.0		U 1.00
	b. Water		100.0		62.6	99.83	0.14	L 35.0		L 1.11
263	a. o-Chloronitrobenzene		245.7	233.5	59.0					
	b. Diethylene glycol		244.5		41.0					
264	a. Chloronitromethane		122.5	115.2	45.0					
	b. Tetrachloroethylene		121.0		55.0					
265	a. o-Chlorophenol		122.5	115.2	48.0					
	b. o-Dichlorobenzene		180.0		52.0					
266	a. o-Chlorophenol		122.5	174.5	25.0					
	b. Phenol		182.0		75.0					
267	a. p-Chlorophenol		217.0	216.3	36.5					
	b. Naphthalene		217.9		63.5					
268	a. p-Chlorophenol		217.0	219.9	8.0					
	b. Nitrobenzene		210.9		92.0					
269	a. 1-Chloro-2-propanol		119.0	109.2	28.5					
	b. Toluene		110.6		71.5					
270	a. 1-Chloro-2-propanol		119.0	95.4	54.2					
	b. Water		100.0		45.8					
271	a. o-Chlorotoluene		159.0	155.5	62.0					
	b. Cyclohexanol		161.5		38.0					
272	a. o-Chlorotoluene		159.0	155.4	65.0					
	b. 2-Furaldehyde		161.7		35.0					
273	a. 1-Chlorotoluene		159.0	152.5	87.0					
	b. Glycol		197.2		13.0					
274	a. o-Chlorotoluene		159.0	153.5	56.0					
	b. Hexyl alcohol		157.2		44.0					
275	a. o-Chlorotoluene		159.0	157.5	88.0					
	b. Isovaleric acid		176.7		12.0					
276	a. o-Chlorotoluene		159.0	159.2	97.0					
	b. Phenol		182.0		3.0					

No.	Components			Azeotrope					
	Compounds	BP, °C	BP, °C	Percent composition			Relative volume of layers at 20°C		Specific gravity of layers or azeotrope
				In azeotrope	Upper layer	Lower layer			
277	a. o-Chlorotoluene	159.0	158.5	95.0					
	b. Valeric acid	187.0		5.0					
278	a. o-Cresol	191.5	196.9	38.0					
	b. Octyl alcohol	195.0		62.0					
279	a. m-Cresol	202.8	203.3	62.0					
	b. Octyl alcohol	195.0		38.0					
280	a. p-Cresol	202.5	202.3	70.0					
	b. Octyl alcohol	195.0		30.0					
281	a. Croton aldehyde	104.0	84.0	75.2	90.4	15.6	U	81.4	U 0.876
	b. Water	100.0		24.8	9.6	84.4	L	18.6	L 0.987
282	a. 1,3-Cyclohexadiene	80.5	79.0	45.0					
	b. Cyclohexane	81.4		55.0					
283	a. Cyclohexane	81.4	64.9	69.5					
	b. Ethanol	78.5		30.5					
284	a. Cyclohexanc	81.4	72.8	46.0					
	b. Ethyl acetate	77.2		54.0					
285	a. Cyclohexane	81.4	74.5	64.0					
	b. Ethyl nitrate	88.7		36.0					
286	a. Cyclohexane	81.4	78.1	86.0					
	b. Isobutanol	108.3		14.0					
287	a. Cyclohexane	81.4	68.6	67.0					0.777
	b. Isopropanol	82.3		33.0					
288	a. Cyclohexane	81.4	78.9	75.0					
	b. Isopropyl acetate	89.0		25.0					
289	a. Cyclohexane	81.4	45.2	63.0	97.0	39.0	U	43.0	
	b. Methanol	64.7		37.0	3.0	61.0	L	57.0	
290	a. Cyclohexane	81.4	70.2	72.0					
	b. Nitromethane	101.0		28.0					
291	a. Cyclohexane	81.4	74.2	80.0					
	b. Propanol	97.2		20.0					
292	a. Cyclohexane	81.4	67.4	38.7					0.850
	b. Vinyl acetate	72.0		61.3					
293	a. Cyclohexane	81.4	69.8	91.5	99.99	0.01	U	93.2	U 0.780
	b. Water	100.0		8.5	0.01	99.99	I	6.8	L 1.000
294	a. Cyclohexanol	161.5	156.5	94.5					
	b. 2-Furaldehyde	161.7		5.5					
295	a. Cyclohexanol	161.5	183.0	13.0					
	b. Phenol	182.0		87.0					
296	a. Cyclohexanol	161.5	159.0	53.0					
	b. Propylchloroacetate	163.5		47.0					

No.	Components				Azeotrope						
	Compounds	BP, °C	BP, °C	Percent composition			Relative volume of layers at 20°C		Specific gravity of layers or azeotrope		
				In azeo-trope	Upper layer	Lower layer					
297	a. Cyclohexanol	161.5	~97.8	~20.0							
	b. Water	100.0		~80.0							
298	a. Cyclohexanol	161.5	143.0	14.0							
	b. o-Xylene	144.4		86.0							
299	a. Cyclohexanone	155.4	159.0	55.0							
	b. 1,1,2,2-Tetrachloroethane	146.3		45.0							
300	a. Cyclohexanone	155.4	160.0	39.0							
	b. 1,2,3-Trichloropropane	156.3		61.0							
301	a. Cyclohexanone	155.4	95.0	38.4	92.0	2.3	U	41.5	U	0.953	
	b. Water	100.0		61.6	8.0	97.7	L	58.5	L	1.000	
302	a. Cyclohexylamine	134.0	96.4	44.2							
	b. Water	100.0		55.8							
303	a. Cyclopentanol	140.9	96.3	42.0							
	b. Water	100.0		58.0							
304	a. Cyclopentanol	140.9	132.8	40.0							
	b. m-Xylene	139.1		60.0							
305	a. Cyclopentanone	130.7	93.5	58.0	86.2	29.3	U	51.0	U	0.965	
	b. Water	100.0		42.0	13.8	70.7	L	49.0	L	0.998	
306	a. Diacetone alcohol	169.2	99.6	13.0						1.002	
	b. Water	100.0		87.0							
307	a. Diallyl acetal	150.9	95.3	59.0	99.3	0.7	U	62.0	U	0.876	
	b. Water	100.0		41.0	0.7	99.3	L	38.0	L	0.998	
308	a. Diallyl amine	110.5	87.2	76.0	71.1	5.09				0.852	
	b. Water	100.0		24.0	28.9	94.91					
309	a. p-Dibromobenzene	219.0	210.5	22.5							
	b. Nitrobenzene	210.9		77.5							
310	a. p-Dibromobenzene	219.0	218.0	73.0							
	b. o-Nitrotoluene	222.3		27.0							
311	a. 1,2-Dibromobutane	140.5	139.0	94.0							
	b. Glycol	197.2		6.0							
312	a. 1,2-Dibromethane	131.6	130.9	96.5							
	b. Glycol	197.2		3.5							
313	a. Dibromethane	98.2	76.0	62.0							
	b. Ethanol	78.5		38.0							
314	a. Dibutyl acetal	189.4	98.7	33.7	99.8	0.03	U	33.0	U	0.83	
	b. Water	100.0		66.3	0.2	99.97	L	67.0	L	1.000	
315	a. Dibutyl amine	159.6	97.0	49.5	93.8	0.47	U	58.0	U	0.780	
	b. Water	100.0		50.5	6.2	99.53	L	42.0	L	0.990	
316	a. Dibutyl ethanolamine	228.7	99.9	9.0	93.2	0.39	U	10.0	U	0.877	
	b. Water	100.0		91.0	6.8	99.61	L	90.0	L	0.999	

No.	Compounds	BP, °C	BP, °C	Percent composition			Relative volume of layers at 20°C		Specific gravity of layers or azeotrope	
				In azeo-trope	Upper layer	Lower layer				
317	a. Dibutyl formal	181.8	98.2	38.0						
	b. Water	100.0		62.0						
318	a. Dibutyl fumarate	285.1	99.9	1.5	99.62	0.1	U	1.5	U	0.987
	b. Water	100.0		98.5	0.38	99.9	L	98.5	L	1.000
319	a. Dibutyl maleate	280.6	99.9	1.6	99.36	0.01	U	1.7	U	0.996
	b. Water	100.0		98.4	0.64	99.99	L	98.3	L	1.000
320	a. o-Dichlorobenzene	180.0	161.0	22.0						
	b. 2-Furaldehyde	161.7		78.0						
321	a. o-Dichlorobenzene	180.0	165.8	80.0						
	b. Glycol	197.2		20.0						
322	a. o-Dichlorobenzene	180.0	173.7	65.0						
	b. Phenol	182.0		35.0						
323	a. o-Dichlorobenzene	180.0	175.8	78.0						
	b. Valeric acid	187.0		22.0						
324	a. p-Dichlorobenzene	173.4	172.5	30.0						
	b. Furfuryl alcohol	171.0		70.0						
325	a. p-Dichlorobenzene	173.4	171.1	74.8						
	b. Phenol	182.0		25.2						
326	a. 1,2-Dichloroethane	83.5	70.5	63.0						
	b. Ethanol	78.5		27.0						
327	a. 1,2-Dichloroethane	83.5	83.5	93.5						
	b. Isobutyl alcohol	108.4		6.5						
328	a. 1,1-Dichloroethane	57.2	49.1	88.5						
	b. Methanol	64.5		11.5						
329	a. 1,2-Dichloroethane	83.5	72.0	80.5						
	b. Water	100.0		19.5						
330	a. Di(2-chloroethyl) formal	218.1	99.4	13.2	0.78	99.56	U	89.0	U	1.002
	b. Water	100.0		86.8	99.22	0.44	L	11.0	L	1.233
331	a. Dichloromethane	40.1	<39.9	>95.0						
	b. Ethanol	78.5		<5.0						
332	a. Dichloromethane	40.1	168.7	86.0						
	b. Glycol	197.2		14.0						
333	a. 2,2-Dichloropropane	69.7	66.8	83.0						
	b. Isopropyl alcohol	82.3		17.0						
334	a. 2,3-Dichloropropanol	182.0	99.4	13.0	11.3	89.7	U	99.0	U	1.04
	b. Water	100.0		87.0	88.7	10.3	L	1.0	L	1.33
335	a. Dicyclopentadiene	170.0	98.0	32.3	99.99	0.05	U	33.0	U	0.978
	b. Water	100.0		67.7	0.01	99.95	L	67.0	L	1.000
336	a. Diethyl acetal	102.1	82.6	85.7	98.8	5.5	U	88.0	U	0.826
	b. Water	100.0		14.3	1.2	94.5	L	12.0	L	0.99

No.	Components Compounds	BP, °C	BP, °C	In azeo-trope	Upper layer	Lower layer	Relative volume of layers at 20°C		Specific gravity of layers or azeotrope
337	a. Diethyl amine }740 mm b. Methanol	54.7 63.8	66.2	40.0 60.0					
338	a. Diethylaminoethyl amine b. Water	144.9 100.0	99.8	20.5 79.5					0.988
339	a. Diethyl butyral b. Water	146.3 100.0	94.2	65.5 34.5	99.52 0.48	0.46 99.54	U 30.0 L 70.0		U 0.830 L 0.999
340	a. Diethylene glycol }50 mm b. Hexyl ether	163.0 137.0	129.0	15.5 84.5	0.2 99.8	99.6 0.4	U 89.0 L 11.0		U 0.795 L 1.117
341	a. Diethylene glycol b. Naphthalene	244.5 217.9	212.6	22.0 78.0					
342	a. Diethylene glycol b. Nitrobenzene	244.5 210.9	210.0	10.0 90.0					
343	a. Diethylene glycol b. o-Nitrotoluene	244.5 222.3	218.2	17.5 82.5					
344	a. Diethyleneglycol dibutyl ether b. Water	254.6 100.0	99.8	5.3 94.7	98.6 1.4	0.3 99.7	U 6.0 L 94.0		U 0.887 L 1.000
345	a. Diethyl ethanolamine b. Water	162.1 100.0	98.9	25.6 74.4					0.993
346	a. Diethyl formal b. Ethanol	87.5 78.5	74.2	43.0 57.0					
347	a. Diethyl fumarate b. Water	218.1 100.0	99.5	12.5 87.5	0.4 99.6	98.87 1.13	U 88.0 L 12.0		U 1.000 L 1.052
348	a. Di(2-ethylhexyl) acetate b. Water	dec. 100.0	99.9	1.0 99.0	99.9 0.1	0.1 99.9	U 1.2 L 98.8		U 0.845 L 1.000
349	a. Diethylisopropanol amine b. Water	150.5 100.0	97.2	45.0 55.0					0.962
350	a. Diethyl ketone b. Propanol	102.7 97.2	94.9	43.0 57.0					
351	a. Diethyl maleate b. Water	225.0 100.0	99.6	11.9 88.1	1.50 98.50	98.60 1.40	U 89.0 L 11.0		U 1.001 L 1.069
352	a. Diethyl phthalate b. Water	296.0 100.0	99.9	1.6 98.4	0.02 99.98	99.5 0.5	U 98.7 L 1.3		U 1.000 L 1.118
353	a. Diethyl pimelate b. Water	268.1 100.0	100.0	1.7 98.3	98.7 1.3	0.14 99.86	U 1.7 L 98.3		U 0.995 L 1.000
354	a. Diethyl succinate b. Water	217.7 100.0	99.9	9.0 91.0	2.05 97.95	98.2 1.8	U 93.0 L 7.0		U 1.005 L 1.04
355	a. Dihexyl amine b. Water	239.8 100.0	99.8	7.2 92.8	97.5 2.5	1.1 98.9	U 7.7 L 92.3		U 0.801 L 0.999

No.	Components Compounds	BP, °C	BP, °C	Percent composition In azeo-trope	Upper layer	Lower layer	Relative volume of layers at 20°C		Specific gravity of layers or azeotrope	
356	a. Diisobutylene b. Isopropanol	102.6 82.3	77.8	45.5 54.5						
357	a. Diisobutylene b. Water	102.6 100.0	82.0	88.0 12.0	99.99 0.01	0.01 99.99	U L	91.0 9.0	U L	0.721 1.000
358	a. Diisobutyl ketone b. Morpholine	168.0 128.3	128.0	2.0 98.0						0.996
359	a. Diisobutyl ketone b. Water	168.0 100.0	97.0	48.1 51.9	99.25 0.75	0.05 99.95	U L	53.4 46.6	U L	0.810 1.000
360	a. Diisopropyl amine b. Isopropanol	84.1 82.3	79.7	60.0 40.0						0.755
361	a. Diisopropyl amine b. Water	84.1 100.0	74.1	91.0 9.0						
362	a. Diisopropylethanol amine b. Water	190.0 100.0	99.2	15.0 85.0	81.8 18.2	1.28 98.72	U L	18.0 82.0	U L	0.90 0.998
363	a. Diisopropyl maleate b. Water	228.7 100.0	99.9	7.0 93.0	0.23 99.77	99.19 0.81	U L	93.0 7.0	U L	1.000 1.012
364	a. Dimethyl acetal b. Methanol	64.5 64.7	57.5	75.8 24.2						0.841
365	a. Dimethyl acetal b. Water	64.5 100.0	61.3	96.4 3.6						
366	a. 1,3-Dimethylbutyl amine b. Water	108.5 100.0	89.5	71.4 28.6						0.83
367	a. Dimethyl butyral b. Water	114.0 100.0	87.3	79.7 20.3	99.1 0.9	2.9 97.1	U L	82.3 17.7	U L	0.851 0.997
368	a. Dimethylethanol amine b. Water	123.4 90.7	91.0	4.8 95.2						
369	a. Dimethyl formal b. Methanol	42.3 64.7	41.8	92.1 7.9						0.860
370	a. 2,5-Dimethyl furan b. Methanol	93.3 64.7	61.5	49.0 51.0						0.841
371	a. 2,5-Dimethyl furan b. Water	93.3 100.0	77.0	88.3 11.7	99.87 0.13	0.13 99.87	U L	89.0 11.0	U L	0.902 1.000
372	a. 2,6-Dimethyl-4-heptanol b. Water	178.1 100.0	98.5	29.6 70.4	99.01 0.99	0.06 99.94	U L	34.4 65.6	L L	0.814 1.000
373	a. Dimethyl isobutyral b. Water	104.7 100.0	83.9	85.7 14.3	99.23 0.77	3.48 96.52	U L	87.7 12.3	U L	0.847 0.995
374	a. 2,6-Dimethyl morpholine b. Water	146.6 100.0	99.6	30.0 70.0						

Note (row 368): "540 mm" indicated as applying to the Dimethylethanol amine / Water pair.

No.	Components Compounds	BP, °C	BP, °C	Percent composition In azeotrope	Upper layer	Lower layer	Relative volume of layers at 20°C	Specific gravity of layers or azeotrope
375	a. Dimethyl phthalate b. Water	282.9 100.0	100.0	1.1 98.9	0.43 99.57	98.5 1.5	U 99.0 L 1.0	U 1.001 L 1.191
376	a. Dimethyl pimelate b. Water	248.9 100.0	99.9	3.2 96.8	0.99 99.01	98.0 2.0	U 97.8 L 2.2	U 1.005 L 1.04
377	a. 1,4-Dioxane b. Water	101.3 100.0	87.8	81.6 18.4				1.04
378	a. 1,3-Dioxolane b. Heptane	75.6 98.4	72.3	81.0 19.0				0.957
379	a. 1,3-Dioxolane b. Water	75.6 100.0	71.9	93.0 7.0				1.068
380	a. Dipropyl acetal b. Water	146.6 100.0	95.0	63.4 36.6	99.66 0.34	0.41 99.59	U 67.5 L 32.5	U 0.837 L 0.999
381	a. Dipropyl ketone b. Water	144.0 100.0	94.3	59.5 40.5	99.1 0.9	0.4 99.6	U 64.6 L 35.4	U 0.820 L 1.000
382	a. Epichlorohydrin b. Propanol	117.0 97.2	96.0	23.0 77.0				
383	a. Epichlorohydrin b. Toluene	117.0 110.6	108.3	26.0 74.0				
384	a. Epichlorohydrin b. Water	117.0 100.0	88.5	74.0 26.0	5.9 94.1	98.8 1.2	U 30.0 L 70.0	U 1.010 L 1.175
385	a. Ethanol b. Ethyl acetate	78.5 77.1	71.8	31.0 69.0				0.863
386	a. Ethanol b. Ethyl acrylate	78.5 99.3	77.5	72.7 27.3				
387	a. Ethanol b. Ethylbutyl ether	78.5 92.2	73.8	49.3 50.7				0.776
388	a. Ethanol b. Ethylene dichloride	78.5 83.5	71.0	33.5 66.5				1.049
389	a. Ethanol b. Ethyl nitrate	78.5 88.7	71.9	44.0 56.0				
390	a. Ethanol b. Heptane	78.5 98.4	72.0	48.0 52.0				0.729
391	a. Ethanol b. Hexane	78.5 69.0	58.7	21.0 79.0				0.687
392	a. Ethanol b. Iodoethane	78.5 72.2	63.0	14.0 86.0				
393	a. Ethanol b. Iodomethane	78.5 42.5	41.2	3.2 96.8				
394	a. Ethanol b. Isobutyl chloride	78.5 68.9	61.3	16.3 83.7				

No.	Compounds	BP, °C	BP, °C	Percent composition			Relative volume of layers at 20°C	Specific gravity of layers or azeotrope
				In azeo-trope	Upper layer	Lower layer		
395	a. Ethanol b. Isoprene	78.5 34.0	32.7	3.0 97.0				
396	a. Ethanol b. Isopropyl acetate	78.5 89.0	76.8	53.0 47.0				
397	a. Ethanol b. Isopropyl ether	78.5 67.5	64.0	17.1 82.9				0.741
398	a. Ethanol b. Methyl acrylate	78.5 80.9	73.5	42.4 57.6				
399	a. Ethanol b. Methylbutyl ether	78.5 70.3	65.5	20.0 80.0				
400	a. Ethanol b. Methylethyl ketone	78.5 79.6	74.8	34.0 66.0				0.802
401	a. Ethanol b. Nitromethane	78.5 101.0	76.0	73.2 26.8				
402	a. Ethanol b. Tetrachloroethylene	78.5 121.0	76.8	~63.0 ~37.0				
403	a. Ethanol b. Thiophene	78.5 84.1	70.0	45.0 55.0				
404	a. Ethanol b. Toluene	78.5 110.6	76.7	68.0 32.0				0.815
405	a. Ethanol b. Trichloroethylene	78.5 87.1	70.9	27.0 73.0				1.197
406	a. Ethanol b. 1,1,2-Trichloro-trifluoroethane	78.5 47.7	43.8	3.8 96.2				1.517
407	a. Ethanol b. Triethyl amine	78.5 89.5	76.9	51.0 49.0				0.775
408	a. Ethanol b. Vinylbutyl ether	78.5 94.2	73.0	48.0 52.0				0.786
409	a. Ethanol b. Vinylisobutyl ether	78.5 83.4	69.2	33.0 67.0				0.778
410	a. Ethanol b. Vinylpropyl ether	78.5 65.1	60.0	18.4 81.6				
411	a. Ethanol b. Water	78.5 100.0	78.2	95.6 4.4				0.804
412	a. Ethanol b. Water } 3 atm.	109.0 134.0	109.0	95.2 4.8				0.805
413	a. Ethanol b. Water } 95 mm	33.5 51.0	33.4	99.5 0.5				0.792

	Components			Azeotrope					
					Percent composition			Relative volume of layers at 20°C	Specific gravity of layers or azeotrope
No.	Compounds	BP, °C	BP, °C	In azeotrope	Upper layer	Lower layer			
414	a. Ethoxy diglycol	202.8	192.0	54.5					1.050
	b. Ethylene glycol	197.5		45.5					
415	a. 2-Ethoxy ethanol	135.1	110.2	10.8					0.874
	b. Toluene	110.6		89.2					
416	a. 2-Ethoxy ethanol	135.1	99.4	28.8					1.003
	b. Water	100.0		71.2					
417	a. 2-Ethoxy ethanol } 200 mm	96.5	66.4	15.0					
	b. Water	66.3		85.0					
418	a. 2-Ethoxy ethanol	135.1	130.8	55.0					
	b. o-Xylene	144.4		45.0					
419	a. 1-Ethoxy-2-propanol	132.2	97.3	49.9					0.98
	b. Water	100.0		50.1					
420	a. Ethyl acetate	77.2	70.0	22.0					
	b. Iodoethane	72.2		78.0					
421	a. Ethyl acetate	77.2	74.8	77.0					0.869
	b. Isopropanol	82.3		23.0					
422	a. Ethyl acetate	77.2	62.1	51.4					0.846
	b. Methanol	64.7		48.6					
423	a. Ethyl acetate	77.2	70.4	91.9	96.7	8.7	U 95.0	U 0.907
	b. Water	100.0		8.1	3.3	91.3	L 5.0	L 0.999
424	a. Ethyl acrylate	99.8	81.0	84.9	98.5	2.0	U 87.0	U 0.910
	b. Water	100.0		15.1	1.5	98.0	L 13.0	L 0.998
425	a. n-Ethyl aniline	204.8	99.2	16.1	99.3	0.2	U 16.6	U 0.963
	b. Water	100.0		83.9	0.7	99.8	L 83.4	L 1.000
426	a. Ethyl benzene	136.2	131.1	72.0					
	b. Propionic acid	141.6		28.0					
427	a. Ethyl benzene	136.2	92.0	67.0	99.95	0.02	U 70.0	U 0.870
	b. Water	100.0		33.0	0.05	99.98	L 30.0	L 1.000
428	a. 2-Ethyl butanol } 50 mm	77.0	77.0	61.0					
	b. 2-Ethylhexyl chloride	89.0		39.0					
429	a. 2-Ethyl butanol	146.0	96.7	42.0	95.44	0.43	U 48.0	U 0.841
	b. Water	100.0		58.0	4.56	99.57	L 52.0	L 0.999
430	a. 2-Ethylbutyl acetate	162.3	97.0	47.6	99.43	0.06	U 51.3	U 0.871
	b. Water	100.0		52.4	0.57	99.94	L 48.7	L 1.000
431	a. 2-Ethylbutyl acetate	162.3	154.4	27.5					0.838
	b. Hexanol	157.1		72.5					
432	a. 2-Ethylbutyl butyrate	199.6	98.6	25.1	99.5	0.1	U 27.8	U 0.873
	b. Water	100.0		74.9	0.5	99.9	L 72.2	L 0.999

No.	Components Compounds	BP, °C	BP, °C	Azeotrope Percent composition In azeotrope	Upper layer	Lower layer	Relative volume of layers at 20°C	Specific gravity of layers or azeotrope
433	a. Ethylbutyl ether b. Methanol	92.2 64.7	62.6	44.0 56.0				0.770
434	a. Ethylbutyl ether b. Water	92.2 100.0	76.6	88.1 11.9	99.6 0.4	0.44 99.56	U 91.0 L 9.0	U 0.753 L 0.998
435	a. Ethylbutyl ketone b. Water	148.5 100.0	94.6	57.8 42.2	99.2 0.8	1.4 98.6	U 62.5 L 37.5	U 0.822 L 0.997
436	a. 2-Ethylbutyraldehyde b. Water	116.9 100.0	87.5	76.3 23.7	99.2 0.8	0.4 99.6	U 80.2 L 19.8	U 0.816 L 0.997
437	a. 2-Ethylbutyric acid b. Water	194.2 100.0	99.7	13.0 87.0	96.7 3.3	1.55 98.45	U 12.0 L 88.0	U 0.929 L 1.000
438	a. Ethyl carbamate b. Octyl alcohol	180.0 195.0	183.5	72.5 27.5				
439	a. Ethyl carbamate b. Phenol	180.0 182.0	190.8	53.5 46.5				
440	a. Ethyl crotonate b. Water	137.8 100.0	93.5	62.0 38.0	98.48 1.52	0.63 99.37	U 65.0 L 35.0	U 0.921 L 1.000
441	a. n-Ethylcyclohexyl amine b. Water	164.0 100.0	97.1	42.0 58.0	77.0 23.0	1.5 98.5	U 56.0 L 44.0	U 0.895 L 0.998
442	a. Ethylene chlorohydrin b. Vinyl-2-chloroethyl ether	128.7 109.1	108.8	3.0 97.0				1.050
443	a. Ethylene chlorohydrin b. Water	128.7 100.0	97.8	42.3 57.7				1.093
444	a. Ethylene diamine b. Isobutanol	116.5 108.3	120.5	50.0 50.0				0.856
445	a. Ethylene diamine b. Toluene	116.5 110.6	103.0	30.0 70.0				
446	a. Ethylene diamine b. Water	116.5 100.0	119.0	81.6 18.4				0.953
447	a. Ethylene diamine }300 mm b. Water	90.5 75.9	94.5	77.1 22.9				0.963
448	a. Ethylene diamine }50 mm b. Water	49.0 38.0	55.0	71.0 29.0				
449	a. Ethylene dichloride b. Isopropanol	84.0 82.3	72.7	60.8 39.2				1.012
450	a. Ethylene dichloride b. Methanol	84.0 64.7	59.5	65.0 35.0				1.045
451	a. Ethylene dichloride b. Trichloroethylene	84.0 87.1	82.3	59.1 40.9				1.330

No.	Components Compounds	BP, °C	BP, °C	Percent composition In azeotrope	Upper layer	Lower layer	Relative volume of layers at 20°C		Specific gravity of layers or azeotrope	
452	a. Ethylene dichloride b. Water	84.0 100.0	71.6	91.8 8.2	0.8 99.2	99.8 0.2	U L	10.0 90.0	U L	1.002 1.254
453	a. Ethylene glycol b. 2-Ethylhexyl ether }10 mm	87.0 135.0					U L	50.0 50.0		
454	a. Ethylene glycol b. Hexyl ether }50 mm	123.0 137.0	112.8	35.6 64.4	0.1 99.9	99.9 0.1	U L	71.8 28.2	U L	0.795 1.115
455	a. Ethylene glycol b. Phenyl ether	197.5 257.4	192.3	64.5 35.5	0.22 99.78	98.28 1.72	U L	35.3 64.7	U L	1.068 1.108
456	a. Ethyl ether b. Isoprene	34.6 34.0	33.2	48.0 52.0						
457	a. Ethyl ether b. Methyl formate	34.6 31.5	28.2	44.0 56.0						
458	a. Ethyl ether b. Methyl sulfide	34.6 37.5	34.0	80.0 20.0						
459	a. Ethyl ether b. Water	34.6 100.0	34.2	98.8 1.2						0.720
460	a. Ethyl-3-ethoxy propionate b. Water	170.1 100.0	97.0	37.0 63.0	98.1 1.9	1.6 98.5	U L	38.0 62.0	U L	0.94 0.99
461	a. Ethyl formate b. Methanol	54.2 64.7	51.0	84.0 16.0						
462	a. Ethyl formate b. Water	54.2 100.0	52.6	95.0 5.0	95.5 4.5	13.6 86.4	U >99.5 L <0.5		U L	0.920 0.995
463	a. 2-Ethylhexanoic acid b. Water	228.0 100.0	99.9	3.6 96.4	98.77 1.23	0.25 99.75	U L	3.7 96.3	U L	0.906 1.000
464	a. 2-Ethyl hexanol b. Phenol }25 mm	95.6 89.6	95.0	66.0 34.0						0.900
465	a. 2-Ethyl hexanol b. Water	185.0 100.0	99.1	20.0 80.0	97.4 2.6	0.10 99.90	U L	23.0 77.0	U L	0.838 1.000
466	a. 2-Ethylhexyl acetate b. Water	199.0 100.0	99.0	26.5 73.5	99.45 0.55	0.03 99.97	U L	25.0 75.0	U L	0.873 1.000
467	a. 2-Ethylhexyl amine b. Water	169.1 100.0	98.2	36.0 64.0	74.7 25.3	0.25 99.75	U L	52.0 48.0	U L	0.848 1.000
468	a. n-Ethylhexyl aniline b. Water	dec. 100.0	100.0	0.7 99.3	99.9 0.1	0.01 99.99	U L	0.7 99.3	U L	0.848 1.000
469	a. 2-Ethylhexyl chloride b. Water	173.0 100.0	97.3	45.0 55.0	99.9 0.1	0.1 99.9	U L	48.0 52.0	U L	0.883 1.000
470	a. 2-Ethylhexyl crotonate b. Water	241.2 100.0	99.9	6.6 93.4	99.55 0.45	0.01 99.99	U L	7.2 92.8	U L	0.889 0.999

No.	Compounds	BP, °C	BP, °C	Percent composition			Relative volume of layers at 20°C		Specific gravity of layers or azeotrope	
				In azeotrope	Upper layer	Lower layer				
471	a. 2-Ethylhexyl ether	269.8	99.8	3.6	99.97	0.01	U	4.0	U	0.911
	b. Water	100.0		96.4	0.03	99.99	L	96.0	L	0.998
472	a. 2-Ethylhexyl hexanoate	267.2	99.9	3.6	99.81	0.01	U	4.1	U	0.865
	b. Water	100.0		96.4	0.19	99.99	L	95.9	L	1.000
473	a. Ethylidene acetone	123.5	92.0	71.4	82.8	38.0	U	76.3	U	0.892
	b. Water	100.0		28.6	17.2	62.0	L	23.7	L	0.975
474	a. N-Ethyl morpholine	138.3	96.7	53.8						1.000
	b. Water	100.0		46.2						
475	a. 4-Ethyl octanol	220.5	99.9	6.0	97.57	0.01	U	7.2	U	0.842
	b. Water	100.0		94.0	2.43	99.99	L	92.8	L	1.000
476	a. Ethyl propionate	99.0	93.4	49.0						
	b. Propanol	97.2		51.0						
477	a. Ethyl propionate ⎫ 350 mm	76.0	61.0	86.7	98.6	1.7	U	89.0	U	0.886
	b. Water ⎭	79.7		13.3	1.4	98.3	L	11.0	L	0.998
478	a. Formic acid	100.7	85.8	50.0						
	b. Toluene	110.6		50.0						
479	a. Formic acid	100.7	107.1	77.5						
	b. Water	100.0		22.5						
480	a. 2-Furaldehyde	161.7	140.5	13.0						
	b. o-Xylene	144.4		87.0						
481	a. Glycol	197.2	183.9	51.0						
	b. Naphthalene	217.9		49.0						
482	a. Glycol	197.2	185.9	59.0						
	b. Nitrobenzene	210.9		41.0						
483	a. Glycol	197.2	184.4	36.5						
	b. Octyl alcohol	195.0		63.5						
484	a. Glycol	197.2	196.4	79.5						
	b. Quinoline	237.7		20.5						
485	a. Glycol	197.2	139.5	16.5						
	b. Styrene	146.0		83.5						
486	a. Glycol	197.2	110.2	6.5						
	b. Toluene	110.6		93.5						
487	a. Glycol	197.2	186.5	42.5						
	b. o-Toluidine	199.8		57.5						
488	a. Glycol	197.2	139.6	16.0						
	b. o-Xylene	144.4		84.0						
489	a. Glycol diacetate	190.8	99.7	15.4						1.024
	b. Water	100.0		84.6						

No.	Components Compounds	BP, °C	BP, °C	Percent composition In azeotrope	Upper layer	Lower layer	Relative volume of layers at 20°C		Specific gravity of layers or azeotrope	
490	a. Heptane b. Methanol	98.4 64.7	59.1	48.5 51.5						
491	a. Heptane b. Vinyl acetate	98.4 72.7	72.0	16.5 83.5					0.880	
492	a. Heptane b. Water	98.4 100.0	79.2	87.1 12.9	99.98 0.02	0.01 99.99	U L	90.8 9.2	U L	0.685 1.000
493	a. 2-Heptyl acetate b. Water	176.4 100.0	97.8	41.1 58.9	99.49 0.51	0.03 99.67	U L	45.0 55.0	U L	0.864 1.000
494	a. 3-Heptyl acetate b. Water	173.8 100.0	97.5	42.4 57.6	99.56 0.44	0.03 99.97	U L	46.0 54.0	U L	0.863 1.000
495	a. Hexaldehyde b. Water	128.5 100.0	91.0	68.7 31.3	98.8 1.2	0.6 99.4	U L	73.4 26.6	U L	0.817 0.997
496	a. Hexane b. Isobutyl chloride	69.0 68.9	66.3	45.0 55.0						
497	a. Hexane b. Isopropanol	69.0 82.3	61.0	78.0 22.0					0.686	
498	a. Hexane b. Isopropyl ether	69.0 67.5	67.5	47.0 53.0						
499	a. Hexane b. Methanol	69.0 64.7	50.0	73.1 26.9	85.0 15.0	42.0 58.0	U L	67.8 32.2	U L	0.675 0.724
500	a. Hexane b. Methylethyl ketone	69.0 79.6	64.3	71.7 28.3					0.698	
501	a. Hexane b. 2-Methyl-2-propanol	69.0 82.6	63.7	75.0 25.0					0.691	
502	a. Hexane b. Nitromethane	69.0 101.0	62.0	79.0 21.0						
503	a. Hexane b. Propanol	69.0 97.2	65.7	96.0 4.0					0.67	
504	a. Hexane b. Propionitrile	69.0 97.1	63.5	91.0 9.0						
505	a. Hexane b. Water	69.0 100.0	61.6	**94.4** **5.6**			U L	96.2 3.8	U L	0.660 1.000
506	a. Hexanoic acid b. Water	205.0 100.0	99.9	7.9 92.1	94.6 5.4	1.1 98.9	U L	8.5 91.5	U L	0.934 0.999
507	a. Hexanol b. Water	158.0 100.0	97.8	32.8 67.2	92.8 7.2	0.58 99.42	U L	39.0 61.0	U L	0.835 0.999
508	a. 2-Hexenal b. Water	149.0 100.0	95.1	51.4 48.6	98.3 1.7	0.2 99.8	U L	56.3 43.7	U L	0.848 0.999
509	a. Hexyl acetate b. Water	169.2 100.0	97.4	39.0 61.0	99.44 0.56	0.05 99.95	U L	42.3 57.7	U L	0.873 1.000

No.	Components			Azeotrope					
	Compounds	BP, °C	BP, °C	Percent composition			Relative volume of layers at 20°C		Specific gravity of layers or azeotrope
				In azeotrope	Upper layer	Lower layer			
510	a. Hexyl amine	132.7	95.5	51.0					0.881
	b. Water	100.0		49.0					
511	a. Hexyl chloride	133.9	91.8	70.3	99.83	0.01	U	73.0	U 0.873
	b. Water	100.0		29.7	0.17	99.99	L	27.0	L 1.000
512	a. Hexyl-2-ethyl butyrate	230.3	99.7	11.2	99.76	0.01	U	13.0	U 0.861
	b. Water	100.0		88.8	0.24	99.99	L	87.0	L 1.000
513	a. Hexyl hexanoate	245.2	99.8	6.7	99.70	0.01	U	7.7	U 0.864
	b. Water	100.0		93.3	0.30	99.99	L	92.3	L 1.000
514	a. Hydrogen bromide	−67.0	126.0	47.5					1.481
	b. Water	100.0		52.5					
515	a. Hydrogen chloride	−83.7	108.6	20.2					1.102
	b. Water	100.0		79.8					
516	a. Hydrogen chloride ⎱6.8 atm	−31.0	177.0	14.8					
	b. Water ⎰	169.0		85.2					
517	a. Hydrogen fluoride	19.4	111.4	35.6					
	b. Water	100.0		64.4					
518	a. Hydrogen iodide	−35.5	127.0	57.0					
	b. Water	100.0		43.0					
519	a. Hydrogen nitrate	86.0	121.0	68.5					1.405
	b. Water	100.0		31.5					
520	a. Iodoethane	72.2	70.0	93.0					
	b. Propanol	97.2		7.0					
521	a. Iodomethane	42.5	42.4	98.2					
	b. Isopropyl alcohol	82.3		1.8					
522	a. Iodomethane	42.5	37.8	95.5					
	b. Methanol	64.7		4.5					
523	a. 1-Iodopropane	102.4	79.8	58.0					
	b. Isopropyl alcohol	82.3		42.0					
524	a. Isoamyl acetate	142.5	129.1	2.6					
	b. Isoamyl alcohol	130.5		97.4					
525	a. Isoamyl alcohol	130.5	95.2	50.4					
	b. Water	100.0		49.6					
526	a. Isoamyl alcohol	130.5	127.0	>52.0					
	b. o-Xylene	144.4		<48.0					
527	a. Isobutyl acetate	116.5	107.4	45.0					
	b. Isobutyl alcohol	108.4		55.0					
528	a. Isobutyl alcohol	108.4	101.0	17.0					
	b. Propyl acetate	101.6		83.0					

No.	Components Compounds	BP, °C	BP, °C	Azeotrope Percent composition In azeotrope	Upper layer	Lower layer	Relative volume of layers at 20°C		Specific gravity of layers or azeotrope	
529	a. Isobutyl alcohol b. Propylene diamine	108.4 120.9	123.0	35.0 65.0						
530	a. Isobutyl alcohol b. Toluene	108.4 110.6	101.2	44.5 55.5						0.836
531	a. Isobutyl alcohol b. Trichloroethylene	108.4 87.1	85.4	9.0 91.0						1.368
532	a. Isobutyl alcohol b. Water	108.4 100.0	89.7	70.0 30.0	85.0 15.0	8.7 91.3	U L	82.3 17.7	U L	0.839 0.988
533	a. Isobutyl chloride b. Isopropanol	68.9 82.3	63.8	81.0 19.0						
534	a. Isobutyl chloride b. Methanol	68.9 64.7	53.1	79.4 20.6						
535	a. Isophorone b. Water	215.2 100.0	99.5	16.1 83.9	95.7 4.3	1.2 98.8	U L	16.0 84.0	U L	0.929 0.999
536	a. Isoprene b. 2-Methyl-2-butene	34.0 38.4	34.0	86.0 14.0						
537	a. Isopropyl acetate b. Methanol	89.0 64.7	64.0	29.8 70.2						0.816
538	a. Isopropyl acetate b. Water	89.0 100.0	75.9	88.9 11.1	98.2 1.8	2.9 97.1	U L	91.4 8.6	U L	0.870 0.995
539	a. Isopropyl alcohol b. Isopropyl acetate	82.3 89.0	80.1	52.6 47.4						0.822
540	a. Isopropyl alcohol b. Methylethyl ketone	82.3 79.6	77.3	30.0 70.0						0.800
541	a. Isopropyl alcohol b. Methyl propionate	82.3 79.6	77.0	28.0 72.0						
542	a. Isopropyl alcohol b. Nitromethane	82.3 101.0	79.3	71.8 28.2						
543	a. Isopropyl alcohol b. Tetrachloroethylene	82.3 121.2	81.7	81.0 19.0						
544	a. Isopropyl alcohol b. Toluene	82.3 110.6	80.6	58.0 42.0						
545	a. Isopropyl alcohol b. Trichloroethylene	82.3 87.1	74.0	28.0 72.0						1.182
546	a. Isopropyl alcohol b. Vinyl acetate	82.3 72.7	70.8	22.4 77.6						0.899
547	a. Isopropyl alcohol b. Water	82.3 100.0	80.4	87.8 12.2						0.818
548	a. Isopropyl benzene b. Water	152.4 100.0	95.0	56.2 43.8	99.95 0.05	0.01 99.99	U L	60.0 40.0	U L	0.884 1.000

No.	Components Compounds	BP, °C	BP, °C	Percent composition			Relative volume of layers at 20°C		Specific gravity of layers or azeotrope	
				In azeotrope	Upper layer	Lower layer				
549	a. Isopropyl chloride b. Water	36.5 100.0	35.0	99.0 1.0	99.67 0.33	0.31 99.69	U L	99.0 1.0	U L	0.862 0.999
550	a. Isopropyl ether b. Water	67.5 100.0	62.2	95.4 4.6	99.43 0.57	0.90 99.10	U L	97.0 3.0	U L	0.727 0.998
551	a. Isopropyl ether }481 mm b. Water	54.8 87.7	50.0	96.0 4.0	99.4 0.6	0.90 99.10	U L	97.4 2.6	U L	0.727 0.998
552	a. Isoveralaldehyde b. Water	92.5 100.0	77.0	88.0 12.0						
553	a. Mesityl oxide b. Water	128.7 100.0	91.8	65.3 34.7	96.6 3.4	2.8 97.2	U L	69.8 30.2	U L	0.860 0.995
554	a. Methacrylaldehyde b. Water	67.5 100.0	63.6	92.3 7.7	98.02 1.98	2.65 97.35	U L	94.9 5.1	U L	0.845 0.996
555	a. Methanol b. Methyl acetate	64.7 57.0	54.0	18.7 81.3						0.908
556	a. Methanol }4.4 atm. b. Methyl acetate	107.0 107.0	99.0	29.0 71.0						0.890
557	a. Methanol b. Methylal	64.7 42.3	41.8	92.2 7.8						
558	a. Methanol b. Methyl acrylate	64.7 80.5	62.5	54.0 46.0						
559	a. Methanol b. Nitromethane	64.7 101.0	64.5	92.0 8.0						
560	a. Methanol b. Octane	64.7 125.8	63.0	72.0 28.0						
561	a. Methanol b. Toluene	64.7 110.6	63.7	72.4 27.6						0.813
562	a. Methanol b. Trichloroethylene	64.7 87.1	60.2	36.0 64.0						1.126
563	a. Methanol b. 1,1,2-Trichloro- trifluoroethane	64.7 47.7	39.9	6.0 94.0						1.476
564	a. Methanol b. Trimethyl borate	64.7 65.0	54.0	27.0 73.0						0.892
565	a. Methanol b. Vinyl acetate	64.7 72.7	58.5	36.6 63.4						0.880
566	a. Methanol b. 1-Methoxy-1,3-butadiene	64.7 90.9	62.0	57.5 42.5						
567	a. Methanol b. Vinylbutyl ether	64.7 94.2	62.0	52.0 48.0						

No.	Components Compounds	BP, °C	BP, °C	Percent composition In azeotrope	Upper layer	Lower layer	Relative volume of layers at 20°C		Specific gravity of layers or azeotrope	
568	a. 1-Methoxy-1,3-butadiene	90.9	76.2	87.3	99.74	0.31	U	89.4	U	0.832
	b. Water	100.0		12.7	0.26	99.69	L	10.6	L	0.999
569	a. 3-Methoxybutyl acetate	171.3	96.5	34.6	95.9	6.2	U	33.0	U	0.960
	b. Water	100.0		65.4	4.1	93.8	L	67.0	L	1.005
570	a. 2-Methoxy ethanol	124.6	105.9	25.0						0.887
	b. Toluene	110.6		75.0						
571	a. 2-Methoxy ethanol	124.6	99.9	15.3						1.005
	b. Water	100.0		84.7						
572	a. 1-Methoxy-2-propanol	118.5	97.5	51.0						0.994
	b. Water	100.0		49.0						
573	a. Methyl acetate	57.0	56.1	95.0						0.940
	b. Water	100.0		5.0						
574	a. Methylal	42.3	42.1	98.6						
	b. Water	100.0		1.4						
575	a. Methylamyl ketone	150.5	95.2	54.6	98.5	0.43	U	59.5	U	0.819
	b. Water	100.0		45.4	1.5	99.57	L	40.5	L	0.999
576	a. α-Methylbenzyl amine	187.4	99.4	16.2	52.0	4.8	U	26.0	U	0.994
	b. Water	100.0		83.8	48.0	95.2	L	74.0	L	1.000
577	a. α-Methylbenzyl ether	286.7	100.0	1.3	0.01	99.78	U	98.7	U	1.000
	b. Water	100.0		98.7	99.99	0.22	L	1.3	L	1.003
578	a. n-Methylbutyl amine	91.1	82.7	85.0						0.802
	b. Water	100.0		15.0						
579	a. n-Methyldibutyl amine	162.9	96.5	52.0	99.6	0.07	U	58.9	U	0.761
	b. Water	100.0		48.0	0.4	99.93	L	41.1	L	1.000
580	a. Methylene chloride	40.0	38.8	99.0	2.0	99.9	U	1.6	U	1.009
	b. Water	100.0		1.0	98.0	<0.1	L	98.4	L	1.328
581	a. Methylethyl ketone	79.6	73.4	88.0						0.834
	b. Water	100.0		12.0						
582	a. 2-Methyl-5-ethyl pyridine	177.8	98.4	28.0	80.6	1.22	U	35.0	U	0.960
	b. Water	100.0		72.0	19.4	98.78	L	65.0	L	1.002
583	a. 5-Methyl-2-hexanone	144.0	94.7	56.0	98.6	0.55	U	63.0	U	0.814
	b. Water	100.0		44.0	1.4	99.45	L	37.0	L	1.004
584	a. Methylisobutyl ketone	115.1	87.9	76.0	98.4	2.0	U	80.4	U	0.806
	b. Water	100.0		24.0	1.6	98.0	L	19.6	L	0.999
585	a. Methylisopropenyl ketone	97.9	81.5	81.6	97 0	0.91	U	96.0	U	0.853
	b. Water	100.0		18.4	3.0	99.09	L	4.0	L	0.997
586	a. N-Methyl morpholine	115.0	94.2	76.0						
	b. Water	100.0		24.0						

No.	Components		Azeotrope								
	Compounds	BP, °C	BP, °C	Percent composition			Relative volume of layers at 20°C		Specific gravity of layers or azeotrope		
				In azeo-trope	Upper layer	Lower layer					
587	a. 2-Methyl pentanal	118.3	95.0	14.0						0.814	
	b. Propanol	97.2		86.0							
588	a. 2-Methyl pentanal	118.3	88.5	77.0	99.17	0.42	U	81.0	U	0.811	
	b. Water	100.0		23.0	0.83	99.58	L	19.0	L	0.999	
589	a. 2-Methylpentanoic acid	196.4	99.4	12.1	97.1	1.3	U	13.0	U	0.924	
	b. Water	100.0		87.9	2.9	98.7	L	87.0	L	1.000	
590	a. 2-Methyl pentanol	148.0	97.2	40.0	94.6	0.3	U	47.0	U	0.826	
	b. Water	100.0		60.0	5.4	99.7	L	53.0	L	1.003	
591	a. 4-Methyl-2-pentanol	131.0	94.3	56.7	94.2	1.7	U	64.0	U	0.820	
	b. Water	100.0		43.3	5.8	98.3	L	36.0	L	0.999	
592	a. 4-Methyl-2-pentanol	131.0	109.0	1.0						1.004	
	b. Vinyl-2-chloryl ether	109.1		99.0							
593	a. 4-Methyl-2-pentanone	116.9	87.9	75.7							
	b. Water	100.0		24.3							
594	a. 4-Methyl-2-pentene	56.7	53.3	96.5	99.91	0.15	U	97.7	U	0.670	
	b. Water	100.0		3.5	0.09	99.85	L	2.3	L	0.999	
595	a. 4-Methyl-2-pentyl acetate	146.1	94.8	63.3	99.42	0.13	U	67.0	U	0.858	
	b. Water	100.0		36.7	0.58	99.87	L	33.0	L	0.998	
596	a. 4-Methyl-2-pentyl butyrate	182.6	98.2	39.2	97.2	0.81	U	43.0	U	0.859	
	b. Water	100.0		60.8	2.8	99.19	L	57.0	L	0.999	
597	a. Methylphenyl carbinol	205.0	99.7	11.0	2.3	94.1	U	91.0	U	1.000	
	b. Water	100.0		89.0	97.7	5.9	L	9.0	L	1.010	
598	a. Methylphenyl ketone	202.3	99.1	18.5	0.55	98.35	U	91.0	U	1.00	
	b. Water	100.0		81.5	99.45	1.65	L	9.0	L	1.03	
599	a. 2-Methyl-2-propanol	82.6	79.9	88.3						0.814	
	b. Water	100.0		11.7							
600	a. 2-Methylpropyl acetate	117.3	88.4	78.0	98.98	0.63	U	81.0	U	0.874	
	b. Water	100.0		22.0	1.02	99.37	L	9.0	L	1.000	
601	a. Methylpropyl ketone	101.7	83.8	80.4	96.7	4.3	U	85.0	U	0.812	
	b. Water	100.0		19.6	3.3	95.7	L	15.0	L	0.99	
602	a. Methylvinyl chloride (cis)	32.8	33.0	99.1	99.9	0.2	U	99.3	U	0.927	
	b. Water	100.0		0.9	0.1	99.8	L	0.7	L	1.000	
603	a. Methylvinyl ketone	80.0	75.8	85.0							
	b. Water	100.0		15.0							
604	a. Nitroethane	114.8	106.2	25.0							
	b. Toluene	110.6		75.0							
605	a. Nitromethane	101.0	96.5	55.0							
	b. Toluene	110.6		45.0							

No.	Components Compounds	BP, °C	BP, °C	Azeotrope Percent composition In azeotrope	Upper layer	Lower layer	Relative volume of layers at 20°C	Specific gravity of layers or azeotrope
606	a. Nitromethane b. Trichloroethylene	101.0 87.0	81.4	20.0 80.0				
607	a. o-Nitrophenol b. Propionamide	217.3 213.0	211.2	75.2 24.8				
608	a. Nonane b. Water	150.8 100.0	95.0	60.2 39.8	100.0	100.0	U 68.0 L 32.0	U 0.719 L 1.000
609	a. 1-Octanol b. Phenol	195.0 182.0	195.4	87.0 13.0				
610	a. 1-Octanol b. Water	195.0 100.0	99.4	10.0 90.0				
611	a. Paraldehyde b. Water	124.5 100.0	90.8	74.8 25.2	98.9 1.1	10,5 89.5	U 73.0 L 27.0	U 0.998 L 1.01
612	a. Pentachloroethane b. Phenol	162.0 182.0	160.9	90.5 9.5				
613	a. Pentane b. Water	36.1 100.0	34.6	98.6 1.4	99.95 0.05	0.04 99.96	U 99.1 L 0.9	U 0.627 L 1.000
614	a. 2,4-Pentanedione b. Water	140.6 100.0	94.4	59.0 41.0	95.5 4.5	16.6 83.4	U 55.0 L 45.0	U 0.981 L 1.011
615	a. 3-Pentanol b. Pyridine	115.6 115.5	117.4	55.0 45.0				
616	a. Pentanol b. Water	138.0 100.0	95.4	45.0 55.0				
617	a. 3-Pentanol b. Water	115.6 100.0	91.5	65.0 35.0	90.1 9.9	5.5 94.5	U 74.0 L 26.0	U 0.833 L 0.992
618	a. 2-Pentanone b. Water	102.0 100.0	83.3	80.5 19.5				
619	a. 4-Pentenal b. Water	106.2 100.0	84.3	79.0 21.0				
620	a. Phenol b. Water	182.0 100.0	99.5	9.21 90.79				
621	a. Phenyl ether b. Water	259.0 100.0	99.8	4.3 95.7	0.02 99.98	99.97 0.03	U 96.0 L 4.0	U 0.997 L 1.067
622	a. γ-Picoline b. Water	144.6 100.0	97.4	36.5 63.5				0.996
623	a. Propadiene b. Propane	−32.0 −42.1	−42.0	11.6 88.4	by volume by volume			
624	a. Propane b. Propyne	−42.1 −23.2	−42.0	88.3 11.7	by volume by volume			
625	a. Propanol b. Propyl acetate	97.2 101.6	94.0	63.0 37.0				0.833

No.	Compounds	BP, °C	BP, °C	Percent composition			Relative volume of layers at 20°C		Specific gravity of layers or azeotrope	
				In azeotrope	Upper layer	Lower layer				
626	a. Propanol b. Tetrachloroethylene	97.2 121.0	94.1	48.0 52.0						
627	a. Propanol b. Toluene	97.2 110.6	92.6	49.0 51.0					0.836	
628	a. Propanol b. Trichloroethylene	97.2 87.1	81.8	17.0 83.0					1.287	
629	a. Propanol b. Water	97.2 100.0	88.1	71.8 28.2					0.866	
630	a. Propanol b. m-Xylene	97.2 139.1	97.1	94.0 6.0						
631	a. Propionaldehyde b. Water	48.8 100.0	47.5	98.0 2.0					0.81	
632	a. Propionaldehyde }250 mm b. Water	21.0 71.6	19.0	99.5 0.5						
633	a. Propionamide b. o-Xylene	213.0 144.4	144.0	2.0 98.0						
634	a. Propionic acid b. Water	141.6 100.0	99.9	17.7 82.3					1.016	
635	a. Propionic acid b. o-Xylene	141.6 144.4	135.4	43.0 57.0						
636	a. Propionic acid b. p-Xylene	141.6 138.4	132.0	36.0 64.0						
637	a. Propionitrile b. Water	97.2 100.0	82.2	76.0 24.0	95.0 5.0	9.4 90.6	U 83.3 L 16.7		U 0.793 L 0.983	
638	a. Propyl acetate b. Water	101.6 100.0	82.4	86.0 14.0						
639	a. Propyl chloride b. Water	46.6 100.0	44.0	97.8 2.2	99.7 0.3	0.3 99.7	U 98.0 L 2.0		U 0.892 L 1.000	
640	a. Propylene chlorohydrin b. Water	127.0 100.0	95.4	54.2 45.8						
641	a. Propylene diamine b. Toluene	120.9 110.6	105.0	32.0 68.0					0.865	
642	a. Propylene dichloride b. Water	96.8 100.0	78.4	89.4 10.6	0.26 99.74	99.94 0.06	U 12.0 L 88.0		U 1.000 L 1.159	
643	a. Propylene oxide }60 psig b. Water	88.0 155.0	86.5	99.8 0.2						
644	a. Pyridine b. 3-Pentanol	115.5 115.6	117.4	45.0 55.0						
645	a. Pyridine b. Toluene	115.5 110.6	110.2	22.0 78.0						

No.	Components Compounds	BP, °C	BP, °C	Azeotrope Percent composition In azeotrope	Upper layer	Lower layer	Relative volume of layers at 20°C		Specific gravity of layers or azeotrope	
646	a. Pyridine b. Water	115.5 100.0	92.6	57.0 43.0						1.010
647	a. Styrene b. Water	145.2 100.0	93.9	59.1 40.9	99.95 0.05	0.03 99.97	U L	61.0 39.0	U L	0.91 1.00
648	a. Styrene oxide b. Water	194.2 100.0	99.2	22.4 77.6	0.3 99.7	99.5 0.5	U L	79.1 20.9	U L	1.000 1.054
649	a. Tetrachloroethylene b. Water	121.0 100.0	88.5	82.8 17.2	0.02 99.98	99.99 <0.01	U L	25.0 75.0	U L	1.000 1.625
650	a. 1,2,3,6- Tetrahydrobenzaldehyde b. Water	164.2 100.0	96.9	40.0 60.0	98.98 1.02	0.51 99.49	U L	41.0 59.0	U L	0.972 1.000
651	a. Tetrahydrobenzonitrile b. Water	195.1 100.0	98.8	21.7 78.3	99.46 0.54	0.63 99.37	U L	22.3 77.7	U L	0.958 0.999
652	a. 1,4-Thioxane b. Water	149.2 100.0	95.6	52.0 48.0	6.85 93.15	98.38 1.62	U L	53.0 47.0	U L	1.014 1.120
653	a. Toluene b. Water	110.6 100.0	85.0	79.8 20.2	99.95 0.05	0.06 99.94	U L	82.0 18.0	U L	0.868 1.000
654	a. Triallyl amine b. Water	151.1 100.0	95.0	62.0 38.0	99.57 0.43	0.13 99.87	U L	67.0 33.0	U L	0.802 1.000
655	a. Tributyl amine b. Water	213.9 100.0	99.8	18.0 82.0	99.7 0.3	0.01 99.99	U L	22.0 78.0	U L	0.781 1.000
656	a. 1,1,2-Trichloroethane b. Water	113.7 100.0	86.0	83.6 16.4	0.45 99.55	99.95 0.05	U L	22.0 78.0	U L	1.000 1.443
657	a. 1,1,2-Trichloroethylene b. Water	87.1 100.0	73.1	93.7 6.3	0.2 99.8	99.98 0.02	U L	9.0 91.0	U L	1.003 1.466
658	a. 1,1,2- Trichlorotri- fluoroethane b. Water	47.7 100.0	44.5	99.0 1.0	1.0 99.0	99.9 0.1	U L	2.0 98.0	U L	1.00 1.57
659	a. Tridecanol b. Water	244.0 100.0	100.0	2.2 97.8	98.74 1.26	0.01 99.99	U L	2.6 97.4	U L	0.843 1.000
660	a. Tridecyl acrylate b. Water	dec. 100.0	100.0	1.2 98.8	99.8 0.2	0.01 99.99	U L	1.3 98.7	U L	0.882 1.000
661	a. 1,1,3-Triethoxyethane b. Water	dec. 100.0	99.6	15.0 85.0	99.41 0.59	0.01 99.99	U L	17.0 83.0	U L	0.875 1.000
662	a. 1,1,3-Triethoxypropane b. Water	 100.0	99.0	30.0 70.0						
663	a. Triethyl amine b. Water	89.5 100.0	75.8	90.0 10.0						0.769
664	a. Triglycol dichloride b. Water	240.9 100.0	99.7	6.0 94.0	1.9 98.1	99.2 0.8	U L	96.5 3.5	U L	1.003 1.188

No.	Components		BP, °C	BP, °C	Azeotrope						
	Compounds				Percent composition			Relative volume of layers at 20°C		Specific gravity of layers or azeotrope	
					In azeo-trope	Upper layer	Lower layer				
665	a.	Trimethyltetrahydro-benzaldehyde	204.5	99.0	23.0	99.72	0.01	U	24.5	U	0.919
	b.	Water	100.0		77.0	0.28	99.99	L	75.5	L	1.000
666	a.	Valeraldehyde	103.3	83.0	81.0	98.7	1.35	U	85.0	U	0.810
	b.	Water	100.0		19.0	1.3	98.65	L	15.0	L	0.998
667	a.	Valeric acid	186.2	99.8	11.0	87.0	2.4	U	10.0	U	0.957
	b.	Water	100.0		89.0	13.0	97.6	L	90.0	L	1.000
668	a.	Vinyl acetate	72.7	66.0	92.7	98.97	2.0	U	94.0	U	0.933
	b.	Water	100.0		7.3	1.03	98.0	L	6.0	L	0.999
669	a.	Vinylallyl ether	67.4	60.0	94.6	99.73	0.4	U	95.8	U	0.806
	b.	Water	100.0		5.4	0.27	99.6	L	4.2	L	0.999
670	a.	Vinyl benzoate	dec.	99.3	17.4	0.01	99.68	U	83.5	U	1.000
	b.	Water	100.0		82.6	99.99	0.32	L	16.5	L	1.070
671	a.	Vinylbutyl ether	94.2	77.5	88.4	99.91	0.3	U	91.0	U	0.780
	b.	Water	100.0		11.6	0.09	99.7	L	9.0	L	1.000
672	a.	Vinyl butyrate	116.7	87.2	79.6	99.7	0.3	U	81.0	U	0.902
	b.	Water	100.0		20.4	0.3	99.7	L	19.0	L	0.999
673	a.	Vinyl-2-chloroethyl ether	109.1	84.0	83.0	0.61	99.63	U	17.0	U	1.000
	b.	Water	100.0		17.0	99.39	0.37	L	83.0	L	1.049
674	a.	Vinyl crotonate	133.9	92.0	69.0	98.9	0.3	U	71.0	U	0.944
	b.	Water	100.0		31.0	1.1	99.7	L	29.0	L	1.000
675	a.	Vinylethyl ether	35.5	34.6	98.5	99.8	0.9	U	99.3	U	0.754
	b.	Water	100.0		1.5	0.2	99.1	L	0.7	L	0.999
676	a.	Vinyl-2-ethyl hexanoate	185.2	98.6	32.0	99.8	0.01	U	35.0	U	0.875
	b.	Water	100.0		68.0	0.2	99.99	L	65.0	L	1.000
677	a.	Vinyl-2-ethylhexyl ether	177.7	97.8	40.9	99.95	0.01	U	46.0	U	0.810
	b.	Water	100.0		59.1	0.05	99.99	L	54.0	L	1.000
678	a.	2-Vinyl-5-ethyl pyridine	dec.	99.4	15.0	94.64	0.01	U	16.0	U	0.95
	b.	Water	100.0		85.0	5.36	99.99	L	84.0	L	1.00
679	a.	Vinylisobutyl ether	83.4	70.5	92.2	99.92	0.2	U	16.0	U	0.771
	b.	Water	100.0		7.8	0.08	99.8	L	84.0	L	1.000
680	a.	Vinyl isobutyrate	105.4	83.5	83.0	99.7	0.36	U	85.0	U	0.891
	b.	Water	100.0		17.0	0.3	99.64	L	15.0	L	1.000
681	a.	Vinyl isopropyl ether	55.7	51.8	97.3	99.81	0.64	U	98.0	U	0.760
	b.	Water	100.0		2.7	0.19	99.36	L	2.0	L	0.991
682	a.	Vinyl-2-methyl pentanoate	148.8	95.0	62.0	99.81	0.03	U	65.0	U	0.881
	b.	Water	100.0		38.0	0.19	99.97	L	35.0	L	1.000

BINARY SYSTEMS (Continued)

No.	Compounds	BP, °C	BP, °C	In azeo-trope	Upper layer	Lower layer	Relative volume of layers at 20°C		Specific gravity of layers or azeotrope	
	Components			Azeotrope						
				Percent composition						
683	a. Vinyl propionate	94.9	79.0	87.0	99.40	0.82	U	88.0	U	0.918
	b. Water	100.0		13.0	0.60	99.18	L	12.0	L	0.999
684	a. Vinylpropyl ether	65.1	59.0	95.0	99.8	0.4	U	96.0	U	0.770
	b. Water	100.0		5.0	0.2	99.6	L	4.0	L	0.999
685	a. m-Xylene	139.1	94.5	60.0	99.95	0.05	U	63.4	U	0.868
	b. Water	100.0		40.0	0.05	99.95	L	36.6	L	1.000

AZEOTROPES

TERNARY SYSTEMS

No.	Compounds	BP, °C	BP, °C	In azeo-trope	Upper layer	Lower layer	Relative volume of layers at 20°C	Specific gravity of layers or azeotrope
	Components			Azeotrope				
				Percent composition				
1	a. Acetal	103.6	77.8	61.0				
	b. Ethanol	78.5		27.6				
	c. Water	100.0		11.4				
2	a. Acetone	56.2	38.04	23.98				
	b. Carbon disulfide	46.3		75.21				
	c. Water	100.0		0.81				
3	a. Acetone	56.2	57.5	30.0				
	b. Chloroform	61.2		47.0				
	c. Methanol	64.7		23.0				
4	a. Acetone	56.2	60.4	38.4				
	b. Chloroform	61.2		57.6				
	c. Water	100.0		4.0				
5	a. Acetone	56.2	51.5	43.5				
	b. Cyclohexane	81.4		40.5				
	c. Methanol	64.7		16.0				
6	a. Acetone	56.2	32.5	7.6				
	b. Isoprene	34.0		92.0				
	c. Water	100.0		0.4				
7	a. Acetone, 775.5 mm	78.5	75.0	49.0				0.769
	b. Isopropyl ether	91.9		48.0				
	c. Water	120.9		3.0				
8	a. Acetone	56.2	53.7	5.8				0.898
	b. Methanol	64.7		17.4				
	c. Methyl acetate	57.0		76.8				
9	a. Acetonitrile	82.0	66.0	23.3				
	b. Benzene	80.1		68.5				
	c. Water	100.0		8.2				
10	a. Acetonitrile	82.0	70.1	34.0				0.757
	b. Ethanol	78.5		8.0				
	c. Triethyl amine	89.5		58.0				

No.		Components			Azeotrope						
	Compounds		BP, °C	BP, °C	Percent composition			Relative volume of layers at 20°C		Specific gravity of layers or azeotrope	
					In azeotrope	Upper layer	Lower layer				
11	a.	Acetonitrile	82.0	72.9	44.0						
	b.	Ethanol	78.5		55.0						
	c.	Water	100.0		1.0						
12	a.	Acetonitrile	82.0	59.0	13.0	13.0	13.0	U	97.0	U	0.742
	b.	Isopropyl ether	68.3		82.0	85.5	1.0	L	3.0	L	0.976
	c.	Water	100.0		5.0	1.5	86.0				
13	a.	Acetonitrile	82.0	67.0	20.5						
	b.	Trichloroethylene	87.0		73.1						
	c.	Water	100.0		6.4						
14	a.	Acetonitrile	82.0	68.6	31.0						0.77
	b.	Triethyl amine	89.5		63.0						
	c.	Water	100.0		6.0						
15	a.	Acrylonitrile	78.0	69.5	71.0						
	b.	Ethanol	78.5		20.3						
	c.	Water	100.0		8.7						
16	a.	Allyl alcohol	97.0	77.8	8.7						
	b.	Allyl ether	94.3		12.4						
	c.	Water	100.0		77.8						
17	a.	Allyl alcohol	97.0	68.2	9.2	8.7	17.7	U	91.2	U	0.877
	b.	Benzene	80.1		82.2	90.7	0.4	L	8.8	L	0.985
	c.	Water	100.0		8.6	0.6	80.9				
18	a.	Allyl alcohol	97.0	65.2	11.0	25.6	10.1	U	8.6	U	0.777
	b.	Carbon tetrachloride	76.8		84.0	2.7	89.1	L	91.4	L	1.464
	c.	Water	100.0		5.0	71.7	0.8				
19	a.	Allyl alcohol	97.0	66.2	81.0						
	b.	Cyclohexane	81.4		11.0						
	c.	Water	100.0		8.0						
20	a.	Allyl alcohol	97.0	68.0	11.0						
	b.	Cyclohexene	83.0		80.5						
	c.	Water	100.0		8.5						
21	a.	Allyl alcohol	97.0	59.7	5.0	3.6	34.8	U	98.2	U	0.668
	b.	Hexane	69.0		90.0	95.9	0.8	L	1.8	L	0.964
	c.	Water	100.0		5.0	0.5	64.4				
22	a.	Allyl alcohol	97.0	80.6	31.4	32.4	27.4	U	83.0	U	0.856
	b.	Toluene	110.6		53.4	64.9	2.2	L	17.0	L	0.95
	c.	Water	100.0		15.2	2.7	70.4				
23	a.	Allyl alcohol	97.0	71.4	12.5	21.6	12.5	U	11.8	U	0.983
	b.	Trichloro ethylene	87.0		80.0	4.7	86.5	L	88.2	L	1.354
	c.	Water	100.0		7.5	73.7	1.0				
24	a.	Benzene	80.1	64.6	74.1	86.0	4.8	U	85.5	U	0.866
	b.	Ethanol	78.5		18.5	12.7	52.1	L	14.2	L	0.892
	c.	Water	100.0		7.4	1.3	43.1				
25	a.	Benzene	80.1	65.7	72.0	77.5	0.5	U	93.6	U	0.855
	b.	Isopropanol	82.3		19.8	20.2	14.4	L	6.4	L	0.966
	c.	Water	100.0		8.2	2.3	85.1				

No.	Compounds	BP, °C	BP, °C	Percent composition			Relative volume of layers at 20°C		Specific gravity of layers or azeotrope	
				In azeotrope	Upper layer	Lower layer				
26	a. Benzene	80.1	68.2	65.1	71.3	0.1	U	92.5	U	0.858
	b. 2-Butanone (Methylethyl ketone)	79.6		26.1	28.1	5.2	L	7.5	L	0.992
	c. Water	100.0		8.8	0.6	94.7				
27	a. Benzene	80.1	67.3	70.5	76.7	0.1	U	92.4	U	0.857
	b. 2-Methyl-2-propanol	82.6		21.4	21.6	3.2	L	7.6	L	0.979
	c. Water	100.0		8.1	1.7	96.7				
28	a. Benzene	80.1	68.5	82.4	92.2	0.1	U	92.1	U	0.873
	b. Propanol	97.2		9.0	7.7	15.3	L	7.9	L	0.979
	c. Water	100.0		8.6	0.1	84.6				
29	a. Benzene	80.1	67.0	82.3						
	b. Propyl alcohol	97.2		10.1						
	c. Water	100.0		7.6						
30	a. Bromodichloromethane	90.2	72.0	>70.0						
	b. Ethanol	78.5		<22.5						
	c. Water	100.0		7.5						
31	a. 1-Bromopropane	70.8	60.0	83.0						
	b. Ethanol	78.5		12.0						
	c. Water	100.0		5.0						
32	a. 1-Butanol	117.7	90.7	8.0	11.0	2.0	U	75.5	U	0.874
	b. Butyl acetate	126.5		63.0	86.0	1.0	L	24.5	L	0.997
	c. Water	100.0		29.0	3.0	97.0				
33	a. 1-Butanol, 100 mm	69.8	46.0	26.0	41.0	2.6	U	65.0	U	0.862
	b. Butyl acrylate			33.0	53.0	0.4	L	35.0	L	0.990
	c. Water	51.6		41.0	6.0	97.0				
34	a. 1-Butanol	117.7	90.6	34.6	46.0	4.9	U	76.5	U	0.796
	b. Butyl ether	142.0		34.5	49.0	0.3	L	23.5	L	0.995
	c. Water	100.0		29.9	5.0	94.8				
35	a. 1-Butanol	117.7	77.4	2.0	2.0	2.0	U	92.0	U	0.78
	b. Vinylbutyl ether	94.2		88.0	98.0	0.3	L	8.0	L	1.00
	c. Water	100.0		10.0	0.1	98.0				
36	a. 2-Butanol	99.5	85.5	27.4	31.7	4.6	U	86.0	U	0.858
	b. 2-Butyl acetate	112.2		52.4	62.3	0.6	L	14.0	L	0.994
	c. Water	100.0		20.2	6.0	94.8				
37	a. 2-Butanol	99.5	86.6	56.1	65.0	10.0	U	86.0	U	0.816
	b. Butyl ether	142.0		19.2	23.0	0.2	L	14.0	L	0.981
	c. Water	100.0		24.7	12.0	89.8				
38	a. 2-Butanol	99.5	67.0							
	b. Cyclohexane	81.0								
	c. Water	100.0								
39	a. 2-Butanol	99.5	77.5	19.0	20.0	9.0±1	U	92.0	U	0.736
	b. Diisobutylene	102.6		70.0	78.8	0.5	L	8.0	L	0.987
	c. Water	100.0		11.0	1.2	91.0±1				

No.	Compounds	BP, °C	BP, °C	In azeotrope	Upper layer	Lower layer	Relative volume of layers at 20°C		Specific gravity of layers or azeotrope	
					Percent composition					
40	a. 2-Butanol	99.5	61.1							
	b. Hexane	69.0								
	c. Water	100.0								
41	a. 2-Butanone	79.6	65.7	22.2						
	b. Carbon tetrachloride	76.8		74.8						
	c. Water	100.0		3.0						
42	a. 2-Butanone	79.6	58.5	22.0						
	b. Hexane	68.0		74.0						
	c. Water	100.0		4.0						
43	a. Butenylmethyl ether		61.4	78.9	84.8	2.1	U	94.0	U	0.787
	b. Ethanol	78.5		14.3	12.6	37.1	L	6.0	L	0.996
	c. Water	100.0		6.8	2.6	60.8				
44	a. tert. Butyl alcohol	82.2	64.7	11.9						
	b. Carbon tetrachloride	76.8		85.0						
	c. Water	100.0		3.1						
45	a. Butyl amine	77.1	81.8	50.0						0.795
	b. Ethanol	78.5		42.5						
	c. Water	100.0		7.5						
46	a. Butyl amine	77.1	83.0	47.0						
	b. Isopropanol	82.3		40.5						
	c. Water	100.0		12.5						
47	a. Butyraldehyde	75.7	67.2	80.0	82.0		U	97.8		
	b. Ethanol	78.5		11.0	11.0		L	2.2	L	0.838
	c. Water	100.0		9.0	7.0					
48	a. Carbon disulfide	46.2	41.3	93.4						
	b. Ethanol	78.5		5.0						
	c. Water	100.0		1.6						
49	a. Carbon disulfide	46.2	37.0							
	b. Methanol	64.7								
	c. Methyl acetate	57.0								
50	a. Carbon disulfide	46.2	35.6	55.0						
	b. Methanol	64.7		7.0						
	c. Methylal	44.0		38.0						
51	a. Carbon tetrachloride	76.8	61.8	86.3	7.0	94.8	U	15.2	U	0.935
	b. Ethanol	78.5		10.3	48.5	5.2	L	84.4	L	1.519
	c. Water	100.0		3.4	44.5	<0.1				
52	a. Carbon tetrachloride	76.8	65.7	74.8	0.1	77.3	U	3.9	U	0.993
	b. 2-Butanone	79.6		22.2	5.5	22.6	L	96.1	L	1.413
	c. Water	100.0		3.0	94.4	0.1				
53	a. Carbon tetrachloride	76.8	65.4	84.0	0.1	88.0	U	7.0	U	0.979
	b. Propanol	97.2		11.0	15.0	11.0	L	93.0	L	1.436
	c. Water	100.0		5.0	84.9	1.0				
54	a. Chloroform	61.2	55.5	92.5	1.0	95.8	U	6.2	U	0.976
	b. Ethanol	78.5		4.0	18.2	3.7	L	93.8	L	1.441
	c. Water	100.0		3.5	80.8	0.5				

No.	Components Compounds	BP, °C	BP, °C	Percent composition In azeo-trope	Upper layer	Lower layer	Relative volume of layers at 20°C	Specific gravity of layers or azeotrope
55	a. Chloroform b. Methanol c. Water	61.2 64.7 100.0	52.6	81.0 15.0 4.0	32.0 41.0 27.0	83.0 14.0 3.0	U 3.0 L 97.0	U 1.022 L 1.399
56	a. 1-Chloro-2- methylpropane b. Ethanol c. Water	68.9 78.5 100.0	58.6	82.5 13.0 4.5				
57	a. Crotonaldehyde b. Ethanol c. Water	104.0 78.5 100.0	78.0	7.3 87.9 4.8				0.810
58	a. 1,3-Cyclohexadiene b. n-Propanol c. Water	80.5 97.1 100.0	67.8	79.0 12.0 9.0				
59	a. Cyclohexane b. Ethanol c. Water	81.0 78.5 100.0	62.1	76.0 17.0 7.0				
60	a. Cyclohexane b. Ethyl acetate c. Isopropanol	81.0 77.1 82.3	68.3					
61	a. Cyclohexane b. Methanol c. Methyl acetate	81.0 64.7 57.1	50.8	33.6 17.8 48.6				
62	a. Cyclohexane b. 2-Butanone c. Water	81.0 79.6 100.0	63.6	35.0 60.0 5.0	62.4 37.0 0.6	0.1 10.0 89.9	U 94.5 L 5.5	U 0.769 L 0.98
63	a. Cyclohexane b. 2-Methyl-2-propanol c. Water	81.0 82.6 100.0	65.0	71.0 21.0 8.0				
64	a. Cyclohexane b. Propanol c. Water	81.0 97.2 100.0	66.6	81.5 10.0 8.5				
65	a. Cyclohexane b. Isopropanol c. Water	81.0 82.3 100.0	66.1	71.0 21.5 7.5				
66	a. Cyclohexene b. Ethanol c. Water	82.9 78.5 100.0	64.1	73.0 20.0 7.0				
67	a. 1,2-Dichloroethane b. Ethanol c. Water	83.7 78.5 100.0	66.7	78.0 17.0 5.0				
68	a. cis-1,2-Dichloroethylene b. Ethanol c. Water	60.3 78.5 100.0	53.8	90.5 6.65 2.85				

No.	Compounds	BP, °C	BP, °C	In azeotrope	Upper layer	Lower layer	Relative volume of layers at 20°C		Specific gravity of layers or azeotrope	
				Percent composition						
69	a. trans-1,2-Dichloroethylene	47.5	44.4	94.5						
	b. Ethanol	78.5		4.4						
	c. Water	100.0		1.1						
70	a. Diethoxymethane	87.5	73.2	69.5						
	b. Ethanol	78.5		18.4						
	c. Water	100.0		12.8						
71	a. Diethyl formal	87.5	73.2	69.5						
	b. Ethanol	78.5		18.4						
	c. Water	100.0		12.1						
72	a. Diethyl ketone	102.7	81.2	60.0						
	b. Propanol	97.2		20.0						
	c. Water	100.0		20.0						
73	a. Diisobutylene	102.6	72.3	59.1	70.0	5.4	U	83.0		
	b. Isopropanol	82.3		31.6	26.9	55.2	L	17.0		
	c. Water	100.0		9.3	3.1	39.4				
74	a. Dipropyl acetal	146.6	87.6	21.0						
	b. Propanol	97.2		51.6						
	c. Water	100.0		27.4						
75	a. Dipropyl formal	137.4	86.4	47.2						
	b. Propanol	97.2		44.5						
	c. Water	100.0		8.0						
76	a. Ethanol	78.5	70.2	8.4						0.901
	b. Ethyl acetate	77.1		82.6						
	c. Water	100.0		9.0						
77	a. Ethanol		88.9	12.1						
	b. Ethyl acetate }1446 mm			77.6						
	c. Water			10.3						
78	a. Ethanol	78.5	77.1	48.3						0.867
	b. Ethyl acrylate	99.8		41.6						
	c. Water	100.0		10.1						
79	a. Ethanol	78.5	71.6	4.2	2.6	33.4	U	95.5	U	0.774
	b. Ethylbutyl ether	92.2		86.5	91.2	1.4	L	4.5	L	0.941
	c. Water	100.0		9.3	6.2	65.2				
80	a. Ethanol	78.5	81.4	61.7						
	b. Ethyl chloroacetate	143.5		20.8						
	c. Water	100.0		17.5						
81	a. Ethanol	78.5	67.8	15.7	41.8	12.5	U	13.3	U	0.941
	b. Ethylene dichloride	84.0		77.1	11.6	85.2	L	86.7	L	1.167
	c. Water	100.0		7.2	46.6	2.3				
82	a. Ethanol	78.5	66.0	15.8	14.6	33.0	U	94.5	U	0.747
	b. Ethylisobutyl ether	81.0		77.7	82.6	7.8	L	5.5	L	0.90
	c. Water	100.0		6.5	2.8	59.2				

No.	Compounds	BP, °C	BP, °C	In azeo-trope	Upper layer	Lower layer	Relative volume of layers at 20°C		Specific gravity of layers or azeotrope	
83	a. Ethanol	78.5	68.8	33.0	5.0	75.9	U	64.6	U	0.686
	b. Heptane	98.4		60.9	94.8	9.1	L	35.4	L	0.801
	c. Water	100.0		6.1	0.2	15.0				
84	a. Ethanol	78.5	56.0	12.0	3.0	75.0	U	90.0	U	0.672
	b. Hexane	69.0		85.0	96.5	6.0	L	10.0	L	0.833
	c. Water	100.0		3.0	0.5	19.0				
85	a. Ethanol	78.5	58.6	13.0						
	b. Isobutyl chloride	68.9		82.5						
	c. Water	100.0		4.5						
86	a. Ethanol	78.5	74.8	19.4						0.874
	b. Isopropyl acetate	93.0		70.8						
	c. Water	100.0		9.8						
87	a. Ethanol	78.5	61.0	6.5	5.9	20.2	U	97.1	U	0.737
	b. Isopropyl ether	67.5		89.5	92.9	1.8	L	2.9	L	0.967
	c. Water	100.0		4.0	1.2	78.0				
88	a. Ethanol	78.5	62.0	8.6	8.1	17.0	U	96.0	U	0.743
	b. Methylbutyl ether	71.0		85.1	89.6	2.2	L	4.0	L	0.95
	c. Water	100.0		6.3	2.3	80.8				
89	a. Ethanol	78.5	73.2	14.0						0.832
	b. Methylethyl ketone	79.6		75.0						
	c. Water	100.0		11.0						
90	a. Ethanol	78.5	66.0	14.7	13.7	30.5	U	95.0	U	0.745
	b. Propylisopropyl ether	83.0		78.3	83.3	0.7	L	5.0	L	0.925
	c. Water	100.0		7.0	3.0	68.3				
91	a. Ethanol	78.5	74.4	37.0	15.6	54.8	U	46.5	U	0.849
	b. Toluene	110.6		51.0	81.3	24.5	L	53.5	L	0.855
	c. Water	100.0		12.0	3.1	20.7				
92	a. Ethanol	78.5	74.7	15.0						0.774
	b. Triethyl amine	89.5		75.0						
	c. Water	100.0		10.0						
93	a. Ethanol	78.5	60.0	22.0	20.3	38.7	U	91.0	U	0.777
	b. Vinylisobutyl ether	83.4		70.0	77.6	3.6	L	9.0	L	0.90
	c. Water	100.0		8.0	2.1	57.7				
94	a. Ethanol	78.5	57.0	21.2	20.6	32.0	U	95.5	U	0.722
	b. Vinylpropyl ether	65.1		73.7	77.8	0.2	L	4.5	L	0.923
	c. Water	100.0		5.1	1.6	67.8				
95	a. 2-Ethoxyethanol	135.6	97.7	11.0	0.5	17.0	U	43.0	U	0.81
	b. Vinyl-2-ethylhexyl ether	177.7		38.0	99.4	0.1	L	57.0	L	1.00
	c. Water	100.0		51.0	0.1	82.9				
96	a. Ethyl acetate	77.1	68.3							
	b. Isopropanol	82.3								
	c. Cyclohexane	81.0								
97	a. Ethylbutyl ether	92.2	73.4	67.7	73.1	0.5	U	94.0	U	0.762
	b. Isopropanol	82.3		21.9	22.5	14.5	L	6.0	L	0.97
	c. Water	100.0		10.4	4.4	85.0				

No.	Compounds	BP, °C	BP, °C	In azeo-trope	Upper layer	Lower layer	Relative volume of layers at 20°C		Specific gravity of layers or azeotrope	
				Azeotrope						
				Percent composition						
98	a. Ethylene dichloride	84.0	69.7	75.3	0.9	78.1	U	7.0	U	0.968
	b. Isopropanol	82.3		19.0	20.7	18.8	L	93.0	L	1.117
	c. Water	100.0		7.7	78.4	3.1				
99	a. Ethyl ether	34.6	20.4	8.0						
	b. Methyl formate	31.5		40.0						
	c. Pentane	36.2		52.0						
100	a. Fluosilicic acid	d	116.1	36.0						
	b. Hydrofluoric acid	19.5		10.0						
	c. Water	100.0		54.0						
101	a. Formic acid	100.7	97.5	40.4						
	b. m-Xylene	139.0		49.0						
	c. Water	100.0		10.6						
102	a. Hexane	69.0	45.0	59.0						0.73
	b. Methanol	64.7		14.0						
	c. Methyl acetate	57.0		27.0						
103	a. Isoamyl acetate	142.5	93.6	24.0						
	b. Isoamyl alcohol	130.5		31.2						
	c. Water	100.0		44.8						
104	a. Isoamyl alcohol	130.5	89.8	19.6						
	b. Isoamyl formate	123.5		48.0						
	c. Water	100.0		32.4						
105	a. Isoamyl formate	123.5	117.6	25.0						
	b. Paraldehyde	124.0		30.0						
	c. Tetrachloroethylene	121.0		45.0						
106	a. Isobutyl acetate	116.5	86.8	46.5						
	b. Isobutyl alcohol	108.4		23.1						
	c. Water	100.0		30.4						
107	a. Isopropanol	82.3	75.5	13.0	13.0	11.5	U	94.0	U	0.870
	b. Isopropyl acetate	89.0		76.0	81.4	2.9	L	6.0	L	0.981
	c. Water	100.0		11.0	5.6	85.6				
108	a. Isopropanol	82.3	61.8	4.0	4.0	5.0	U	97.2	U	0.732
	b. Isopropyl ether	67.5		91.0	94.7	1.0	L	2.8	L	0.990
	c. Water	100.0		5.0	1.3	94.0				
109	a. Isopropanol	100.7	81.0	7.0	7.0	9.0	U	96.1	U	0.737
	b. Isopropyl ether }776 mm	91.9		87.0	91.5	1.0	L	3.9	L	0.984
	c. Water	120.9		6.0	1.5	90.0				
110	a. Isopropanol	82.3	73.4	1.0						0.834
	b. Methylethyl ketone	79.6		88.0						
	c. Water	100.0		11.0						
111	a. Isopropanol	82.3	76.3	38.2	38.2	38.0	U	92.0	U	0.845
	b. Toluene	110.6		48.7	53.3	1.0	L	8.0	L	0.930
	c. Water	100.0		13.1	8.5	61.0				
112	a. Isopropyl ether	67.5	61.0	92.4	97.4	3.0	U	97.0	U	0.724
	b. Propanol	97.2		2.0	2.0	3.0	L	3.0	L	0.990
	c. Water	100.0		5.6	0.6	94.0				

No.	Compounds	BP, °C	BP, °C	Percent composition			Relative volume of layers at 20°C		Specific gravity of layers or azeotrope	
				In azeo-trope	Upper layer	Lower layer				
113	a. Methanol	64.7	67.9	81.20						
	b. Methyl chloroacetate	131.5		13.54						
	c. Water	100.0		5.26						
114	a. 2-Methoxyethanol	124.6	97.7	4.0	0.2	6.0	U	45.0	U	0.81
	b. Vinyl-2-ethylhexyl ether	177.7		39.0	99.7	0.1	L	55.0	L	1.00
	c. Water	100.0		57.0	0.1	93.9				
115	a. 3-Pentanone	102.2	~81.2	~60.0						
	b. n-Propyl alcohol	97.2		~20.0						
	c. Water	100.0		~20.0						
116	a. Propanol	97.2	82.2	19.5						
	b. Propyl acetate	101.6		59.5						
	c. Water	100.0		21.0						
117	a. n-Propanol	97.2	70.8	5.0						
	b. Propyl formate	81.3		82.0						
	c. Water	100.0		13.0						
118	a. Propanol	97.2	71.6	12.0						
	b. Trichloroethylene	87.1		81.0						
	c. Water	100.0		7.0						
119	a. Propanol	97.2	74.8	20.2						
	b. Propyl ether	91.0		68.1						
	c. Water	100.0		11.7						

HEAT OF FORMATION OF INORGANIC OXIDES

The ΔH_o values are given in gram calories per mole. The a, b, and I values listed here make it possible for one to calculate the ΔF and ΔS values by use of the following equations:

$$\Delta F_t = \Delta H_o + 2.303aT \log T + b \times 10^{-3}T^2 + c \times 10^5 T^{-1} + IT$$
$$\Delta S_t = -a - 2.303a \log T - 2b \times 10^{-3}T + c \times 10^5 T^{-2} - I$$

Ref: Bulletin 542, U. S. Bureau of Mines, 1954.

Coefficients in Free-Energy Equations

Reaction and temperature range of validity	ΔH_o	2.303a	b	c	I
2 Ac(c) + 3/2 O₂(g) = Ac₂O₃(c) .... (298.16°–1,000° K.)	−446,090	−16.12	......	.....	+109.89
2 Al(c) + 1/2 O₂(g) = Al₂O(g) .... (298.16°–931.7° K.)	−31,660	+14.97	......		−72.74
2 Al(l) + 1/2 O₂(g) = Al₂O(g) .... (931.7°–2,000° K.)	−38,670	+10.36	......		−51.53
Al(c) + 1/2 O₂(g) = AlO(g) .... (298.16°–931.7° K.)	+10,740	+5.76	......		−37.61
Al(l) + 1/2 O₂(g) = AlO(g) .... (931.7°–2,000° K.)	+8,170	+5.76			−34.85
2 Al(c) + 3/2 O₂(g) = Al₂O₃ (corundum) .... (298.16°–931.7° K.)	−404,080	−15.68	+2.18	+3.935	+123.64
2 Al(l) + 3/2 O₂(g) = Al₂O₃ (corundum) .... (931.7°–2,000° K.)	−407,950	−6.19	−.78	+3.935	+102.37
2 Am(c) + 3/2 O₂(g) = Am₂O₃(c) .... (298.16°–1,000° K.)	−422,090	−16.12	......		+107.89
Am(c) + O₂(g) = AmO₂(c) .... (298.16°–1,000° K.)	−240,600	−4.61	......		+55.91
2 Sb(c) + 3/2 O₂(g) = Sb₂O₃ (cubic) ..... (298.16°–842° K.)	−169,450	+6.12	−6.01	−.30	+52.21
2 Sb(c) + 3/2 O₂(g) = Sb₂O₃ (orthorhombic) .... (298.16°–903° K.)	−168,060	+6.12	−6.01	−.30	+50.56
2 Sb(l) + 3/2 O₂(g) = Sb₂O₃ (orthorhombic) .... (903°–928° K.)	−175,370	+15.29	−7.75	−.30	+33.12
2 Sb(l) + 3/2 O₂(g) = Sb₂O₃(l) .... (928°–1,698° K.)	−173,940	−32.84	+.75	−.30	+166.52
2 Sb(l) + 3/2 O₂(g) = 1/2 Sb₄O₆(g) ..... (1,698°–1,713° K.)	−132,760	+10.91	+.75	−.30	+.96
2 Sb(g) + 3/2 O₂(g) = 1/2 Sb₄O₆(g) ..... (1,713°–2,000° K.)	−234,760	−.74	+.75	−.30	+98.17
2 Sb(c) + 2 O₂(g) = Sb₂O₄(c) .... (298.16°–903° K.)	−208,310	+6.31	−5.36	−.40	+73.02
2 Sb(l) + 2 O₂(g) = Sb₂O₄(c) .... (903°–1,500° K.)	−215,610	+15.47	−7.10	−.40	+55.61
6 Sb(c) + 13/2 O₂(g) = Sb₆O₁₃(c) .... (298.16°–903° K.)	−619,160	+38.46	−25.13	−1.30	+192.54
6 Sb(c) + 13/2 O₂(g) = Sb₆O₁₃(c) .... (903°–1,500° K.)	−691,370	+14.13	−30.35	−1.30	+315.93
2 Sb(c) + 5/2 O₂(g) = Sb₂O₅(c) .... (298.16°–903° K.)	−226,060	+37.12	−22.66	−.50	+18.61
2 Sb(l) + 5/2 O₂(g) = Sb₂O₅(c) .... (903°–1,500° K.)	−240,130	+29.01	−24.40	−.50	+59.74
2 As(c) + 3/2 O₂(g) = As₂O₃ (orthorhombic) .... (298.16°–542° K.)	−154,870	+29.54	−21.33	−.30	−8.83
2 As(c) + 3/2 O₂(g) = As₂O₃ (monoclinic) .... (298.16°–586° K.)	−150,760	+29.54	−21.33	−.30	−16.95
2 As(c) + 3/2 O₂(g) = As₂O₃(l) .... (542°–730.3° K.)	−156,260	−43.29	+2.97	−.30	+180.95
2 As(c) + 3/2 O₂(g) = 1/2 As₄O₆(g) ..... (730.3°–883° K.)	−135,930	+.46	+2.97	−.30	+26.88
1/2 As₄(g) + 3/2 O₂(g) = 1/2 As₄O₆(g) .. (883°–2,000° K.)	−154,450	−2.90	+.75	−.30	+59.71
2 As(c) + 2 O₂(g) = As₂O₄(c) .... (298.16°–883° K.)	−173,690	+21.52	−13.42	−.40	+34.38
1/2 As₄(g) + 2 O₂(g) = As₂O₄(c) .... (883°–1,500° K.)	−192,210	+18.15	−15.64	−.40	+67.22
2 As(c) + 5/2 O₂(g) = As₂O₅(c) .... (298.16°–883° K.)	−217,080	+12.32	−4.65	−.50	+80.50
1/2 As₄(g) + 5/2 O₂(g) = As₂O₅(c) ...... (883°–2,000° K.)	−235,600	+8.96	−6.87	−.50	+113.33
Ba(α) + 1/2 O₂(g) = BaO(c) .... (298.16°–648° K.)	−134,590	−7.60	+.87	+.42	+45.76
Ba(β) + 1/2 O₂(g) = BaO(c) .... (648°–977° K.)	−134,140	−3.34	−.56	+.42	+34.01
Ba(l) + 1/2 O₂(g) = BaO(c) .... (977°–1,911° K.)	−135,900	−2.19	−.56	+.42	+32.37
Ba(g) + 1/2 O₂(g) = BaO(c) .... (1,911°–2,000° K.)	−176,400	−8.01	−0.56	+0.42	+72.66
Ba(α) + O₂(g) = BaO₂(c) .... (298.16°–648° K.)	−154,830	−11.05	+.87	+.42	+74.48
Ba(β) + O₂(g) = BaO₂(c) .... (648°–977° K.)	−154,380	−6.79	−.56	+.42	+62.73
Ba(l) + O₂(g) = BaO₂(c) .... (977°–1,500° K.)	−156,140	−5.64	−.56	+.42	+61.09
Be(c) + 1/2 O₂(g) = BeO(c) .... (298.16°–1,556° K.)	−144,220	−1.91	−.46	+1.24	+30.64
Be(l) + 1/2 O₂(g) = BeO(c) .... (1,556°–2,000° K.)	−144,300	+6.06	−1.75	+1.485	+7.25
Bi(c) + 1/2 O₂(g) = BiO(c) .... (298.16°–544° K.)	−50,450	−4.61	......	.....	+35.51
Bi(l) + 1/2 O₂(g) = BiO(c) .... (544°–1,600° K.)	−52,920	−4.61	......	.....	+40.05
2 Bi(c) + 3/2 O₂(g) = Bi₂O₃(c) .... (298.16°–544° K.)	−139,000	−11.56	+2.15	−.30	+96.52
2 Bi(l) + 3/2 O₂(g) = Bi₂O₃(c) .... (544°–1,090° K.)	−142,270	+2.30	−3.25	−.30	+67.55
2 Bi(l) + 3/2 O₂(g) = Bi₂O₃(l) .... (1,090°–1,600° K.)	−147,350	−32.84	+.75	−.30	+174.59
2 B(c) + 3/2 O₂(g) = B₂O(c) .... (298.16°–723° K.)	−301,690	+11.72	−7.55	+.355	+34.25
2 B(c) + 3/2 O₂(g) = B₂O₃(gl) .... (298.16°–723° K.)	−298,670	+26.57	−15.90	−.30	−10.40
2 B(c) + 3/2 O₂(g) = B₂O₃(l) .... (723°–2,000° K.)	−308,100	−38.41	+5.15	−.30	+170.24
Cd(c) + 1/2 O₂(g) = CdO(c) .... (298.16°–594° K.)	−62,330	−3.05	+.71	−.10	+29.17
Cd(l) + 1/2 O₂(g) = CdO(c) .... (594°–1,038° K.)	−63,240	+2.07	−.76	−.10	+20.14
Cd(g) + 1/2 O₂(g) = CdO(c) .... (1,038°–2,000° K.)	−89,320	−2.83	−.76	−.10	+60.05
Ca(α) + 1/2 O₂(g) = CaO(c) .... (298.16°–673° K.)	−151,850	−6.56	+1.46	+.68	+43.93
Ca(β) + 1/2 O₂(g) = CaO(c) .... (673°–1,124° K.)	−151,730	−4.14	+.41	+.68	+37.63
Ca(l) + 1/2 O₂(g) = CaO(c) .... (1,124°–1,760° K.)	−153,480	−1.36	−.29	+.68	+31.49
Ca(g) + 1/2 O₂(g) = CaO(c) .... (1,760°–2,000° K.)	−194,670	−7.18	−.29	+.68	+73.84
Ca(α) + O₂(g) = CaO₂(c) .... (298.16°–500° K.)	−158,230	−12.32	+1.46	+.68	+78.28
C(graphite) + 1/2 O₂(g) = CO(g) .... (298.16°–2,000° K.)	−25,400	+2.05	+.27	−1.095	−28.79

Reaction and temperature range of validity	ΔH_o	2.303a	b	c	I
C(*graphite*) + O$_2$(g) = CO$_2$(g).......... (298.16°–2,000° K.)	−93,690	+1.63	−.07	−.23	−5.64
2 Ce(c) + 3/2 O$_2$(g) = Ce$_2$O$_3$(c)........ (298.16°–1,048° K.)	−435,600	−4.60	......	.....	+92.84
2 Ce(l) + 3/2 O$_2$(g) = Ce$_2$O$_3$(c)........ (1,048°–1,900° K.)	−440,400	−4.60	......	.....	+97.42
Ce(c) + O$_2$(g) = CeO$_2$(c)............... (298.16°–1,048° K.)	−245,490	−6.42	+2.34	−.20	+67.79
Ce(l) + O$_2$(g) = CeO$_2$(c)............... (1,048°–2,000° K.)	−247,930	+.71	−.66	−.20	+51.73
2 Cs(c) + 1/2 O$_2$(g) = Cs$_2$O(c)........ (298.16°–301.5°K.)	−75,900	.....	......	.....	+36.60
2 Cs(l) + 1/2 O$_2$(g) = Cs$_2$O(c)........ (301.5°–763° K.)	−76,900	.....	......	.....	+39.92
2 Cs(l) + 1/2 O$_2$(g) = Cs$_2$O(l)........ (763°–963° K.)	−75,370	−9.21	......	.....	+64.47
2 Cs(g) + 1/2 O$_2$(g) = Cs$_2$O(l)........ (963°–1,500° K.)	−113,790	−23.03	......	.....	+145.60
2 Cs(c) + O$_2$(g) = Cs$_2$O$_2$(c)........ (298.16°–301.5° K.)	−96,500	−2.30	......	.....	+62.30
2 Cs(l) + O$_2$(g) = Cs$_2$O$_2$(c)........ (301.5°–870° K.)	−97,800	−4.61	......	.....	+72.34
2 Cs(l) + O$_2$(g) = Cs$_2$O$_2$(l)........ (870°–963° K.)	−96,060	−18.42	......	.....	+110.94
2 Cs(g) + O$_2$(g) = Cs$_2$O$_2$(l)........ (963°–1,500° K.)	−134,000	−31.08	......	.....	+188.11
2 Cs(c) + 3/2 O$_2$(g) = Cs$_2$O$_3$(c)........ (298.16°–301.5° K.)	−112,690	−11.51	......	.....	+110.10
2 Cs(l) + 3/2 O$_2$(g) = Cs$_2$O$_3$(c)........ (301.5°–775° K.)	−113,840	−12.66	......	.....	+116.77
2 Cs(l) + 3/2 O$_2$(g) = Cs$_2$O$_3$(l)........ (775°–963° K.)	−110,740	−26.48	......	.....	+152.70
2 Cs(g) + 3/2 O$_2$(g) = Cs$_2$O$_3$(l)........ (963°–1,500° K.)	−148,680	−39.14	......	.....	+229.87
Cs(c) + O$_2$(g) = CsO$_2$(c)............ (298.16°–301.5° K.)	−63,590	−11.51	......	.....	+72.29
Cs(l) + O$_2$(g) = CsO$_2$(c)............ (301.5°–705° K.)	−64,240	−12.66	......	.....	+77.30
Cs(l) + O$_2$(g) = CsO$_2$(l)............ (705°–963° K.)	−61,770	−18.42	......	.....	+90.20
Cs(g) + O$_2$(g) = CsO$_2$(l)............ (963°–1,500° K.)	−80,500	−24.18	......	.....	+126.83
Cl$_2$(g) + 1/2 O$_2$(g) = Cl$_2$O(g)........ (298.16°–2,000° K.)	+17,770	−.71	−.12	+.49	+16.81
1/2 Cl$_2$(g) + 1/2 O$_2$(g) = ClO(g)........ (298.16°–1,000° K.)	+33,000	.....	......	.....	−.24
1/2 Cl$_2$(g) + O$_2$(g) = ClO$_2$(g)........ (298.16°–2,000° K.)	+24,150	−.76	−.105	−.665	+19.08
1/2 Cl$_2$(g) + 3/2 O$_2$(g) = ClO$_3$(g)........ (298.16°–500° K.)	+37,740	+5.76	......	.....	+21.42
Cl$_2$(g) + 7/2 O$_2$(g) = Cl$_2$O$_7$(g)........ (298.16°–500° K.)	+65,040	+12.66	......	.....	+78.01
2 Cr(c) + 3/2 O$_2$(g) = Cr$_2$O$_3$(β)........ (298.16°–1,823° K.)	−274,670	−14.07	+2.01	+.69	+105.65
2 Cr(l) + 3/2 O$_2$(g) = Cr$_2$O$_3$(β)........ (1,823°–2,000° K.)	−278,030	+2.33	−.35	+1.57	+58.29
Cr(c) + O$_2$(g) = CrO$_2$(c)............ (298.16°–1,000° K.)	−142,500	.....	......	.....	+42.00
Cr(c) + 3/2 O$_2$(g) = CrO$_3$(c)........ (298.16°–471° K.)	−141,590	−13.82	......	.....	+103.90
Cr(c) + 3/2 O$_2$(g) = CrO$_3$(l)........ (471°–600° K.)	−141,580	−32.24	......	.....	+153.14
Co(α, β) + 1/2 O$_2$(g) = CoO(c)........ (298.16°–1,400° K.)	−56,910	+.69	......	.....	+16.03
Co(γ) + 1/2 O$_2$(g) = CoO(c)........ (1,400°–1,763° K.)	−58,160	−1.15	......	.....	+22.71
Co(l) + 1/2 O$_2$(g) = CoO(c)........ (1,763°–2,000° K.)	−65,680	−6.22	......	.....	+43.43
3 Co(α, β, γ) + 2 O$_2$(g) = Co$_3$O$_4$(c)..... (298.16°–1,500° K.)	−207,300	−2.30	......	.....	+90.56
2 Cu(c) + 1/2 O$_2$(g) = Cu$_2$O(c)........ (298.16°–1,357° K.)	−40,550	−1.15	−1.10	−.10	+21.92
2 Cu(l) + 1/2 O$_2$(g) = Cu$_2$O(c)........ (1,357°–1,502° K.)	−43,880	+8.47	−2.60	−.10	−3.72
2 Cu(l) + 1/2 O$_2$(g) = Cu$_2$O(l)........ (1,502°–2,000° K.)	−37,710	−12.48	+.25	−.10	+54.44
Cu(c) + 1/2 O$_2$(g) = CuO(c)........ (298.16°–1,357° K.)	−37,740	−.64	−1.40	−.10	+24.87
Cu(l) + 1/2 O$_2$(g) = CuO(c)........ (1,357°–1,720° K.)	−39,410	+4.17	−2.15	−.10	+12.05
Cu(l) + 1/2 O$_2$(g) = CuO(l)........ (1,720°–2,000° K.)	−41,060	−11.35	+.25	−.10	+59.09
F$_2$(g) + 1/2 O$_2$(g) = F$_2$O(g)........ (298.16°–2,000° K.)	+5,070	−.41	−.15	+.535	+16.04
2 Ga(c) + 1/2 O$_2$(g) = Ga$_2$O(c)........ (298.16°–302.7° K.)	−81,110	+10.32	−5.75	−.10	−3.66
2 Ga(l) + 1/2 O$_2$(g) = Ga$_2$O(c)........ (302.7°–1,000° K.)	−83,360	+13.49	−5.75	−.10	−4.08
2 Ga(c) + 3/2 O$_2$(g) = Ga$_2$O$_3$(c)........ (298.16°–302.7° K.)	−256,240	+14.64	−3.75	−.30	+32.23
2 Ga(l) + 3/2 O$_2$(g) = Ga$_2$O$_3$(c)........ (302.7°–2,000° K.)	−258,490	+17.82	−3.75	−.30	+31.79
Ge(c) + 1/2 O$_2$(g) = GeO(c)........ (298.16°–1,200° K.)	−60,900	+1.27	−1.49	−.10	+17.19
Ge(c) + 1/2 O$_2$(g) = GeO(g)........ (298.16°–1,200° K.)	−21,870	+6.72	−.075	−.10	−41.25
Ge(c) + O$_2$(g) = GeO$_2$(gl)........ (298.16°–1,200° K.)	−127,830	+4.28	−2.52	−0.20	+30.54
2 Au(c) + 3/2 O$_2$(g) = Au$_2$O$_3$(c)........ (298.16°–500° K.)	−2,160	−10.36	......	.....	+95.14
Hf(c) + O$_2$(g) = HfO$_2$(*monocl.*)........ (298.16°–2,000° K.)	−268,380	−9.74	−.28	+1.54	+78.16
H$_2$(g) + 1/2 O$_2$(g) = H$_2$O(l)........ (298.16°–373.16° K.)	−70,600	−18.26	+.64	−.04	+91.67
H$_2$(g) + 1/2 O$_2$(g) = H$_2$O(g)........ (298.16°–2,000° K.)	−56,930	+6.75	−.64	−.08	−8.74
D$_2$(g) + 1/2 O$_2$(g) = D$_2$O(l)........ (298.16°–374.5° K.)	−72,760	−18.10	......	.....	+93.59
D$_2$(g) + 1/2 O$_2$(g) = D$_2$O(g)........ (298.16°–2,000° K.)	−58,970	+5.50	−.75	+.085	−3.74
1/2 H$_2$(g) + 1/2 O$_2$(g) = OH(g)........ (298.16°–2,000° K.)	+10,350	+.90	+.005	−.26	−6.69
H$_2$(g) + O$_2$(g) = H$_2$O$_2$(l)........ (298.16°–425° K.)	−47,140	−13.52	−7.13	.....	+99.39
H$_2$(g) + O$_2$(g) = H$_2$O$_2$(g)........ (298.16°–1,500° K.)	−32,570	+4.77	−.96	+.97	+13.84
2 In(c) + 3/2 O$_2$(g) = In$_2$O$_3$(c)........ (298.16°–429.6° K.)	−220,410	+5.43	−.50	−.30	+59.49
2 In(l) + 3/2 O$_2$(g) = In$_2$O$_3$(c)........ (429.6°–2,000° K.)	−220,970	+13.22	−3.00	−.30	+41.36
I$_2$(c) + 5/2 O$_2$(g) = I$_2$O$_5$(c)........ (298.16°–386.8° K.)	−42,040	+2.30	......	.....	+113.71
I$_2$(l) + 5/2 O$_2$(g) = I$_2$O$_5$(c)........ (386.8°–456° K.)	−43,490	+16.12	......	.....	+81.70
I$_2$(g) + 5/2 O$_2$(g) = I$_2$O$_5$(c)........ (456°–500° K.)	−58,020	−6.91	......	.....	+174.79
Ir(c) + O$_2$(g) = IrO$_2$(c)........ (298.16°–1,300° K.)	−39,480	+8.17	−6.39	−.20	+20.33
0.947 Fe(α) + 1/2 O$_2$(g) = Fe$_{0.947}$O(c)... (298.16°–1,033° K.)	−65,320	−11.26	+2.61	+0.44	+48.60
0.947 Fe(β) + 1/2 O$_2$(g) = Fe$_{0.947}$O(c)... (1,033°–1,179° K.)	−62,380	+4.08	−.75	+.235	+3.00
0.947 Fe(γ) + 1/2 O$_2$(g) = Fe$_{0.947}$O(c)... (1,179°–1,650° K.)	−66,750	−8.04	+.67	−.10	+42.28
0.947 Fe(γ) + 1/2 O$_2$(g) = Fe$_{0.947}$O(l)... (1,650°–1,674° K.)	−64,200	−18.72	+1.67	−.10	+73.45
0.947 Fe(δ) + 1/2 O$_2$(g) = Fe$_{0.947}$O(l).... (1,674°–1,803° K.)	−59,650	−6.84	+.25	−.10	+34.81

Reaction and temperature range of validity	ΔH_0	2.303a	b	c	I
$0.947\ Fe(l) + 1/2\ O_2(g) = Fe_{0.947}O(l)$ .... (1,803°–2,000° K.)	−63,660	−7.48	+.25	−.10	+39.12
$3\ Fe(\alpha) + 2\ O_2(g) = Fe_3O_4\ (magnetite)$ ... (298.16°–900° K.)	−268,310	+5.87	−12.45	+.245	+73.11
$3\ Fe(\alpha) + 2\ O_2(g) = Fe_3O_4(\beta)$ .... (900°–1,033° K.)	−272,300	−54.27	+11.65	+.245	+233.52
$3\ Fe(\beta) + 2\ O_2(g) = Fe_3O_4(\beta)$ .... (1,033°–1,179° K.)	−262,990	−5.71	+1.00	−.40	+89.19
$3\ Fe(\gamma) + 2\ O_2(g) = Fe_3O_4(\beta)$ .... (1,179°–1,674° K.)	−276,990	−44.05	+5.50	−.40	+213.52
$3\ Fe(\delta) + 2\ O_2(g) = Fe_3O_4(\beta)$ .... (1,674°–1,803° K.)	−262,560	−6.40	+1.00	−.40	+91.05
$3\ Fe(l) + 2\ O_2(g) = Fe_3O_4(\beta)$ .... (1,803°–1,874° K.)	−275,280	−8.74	+1.00	−.40	+104.84
$3\ Fe(l) + 2\ O_2(g) = Fe_3O_4(l)$ .... (1,874°–2,000° K.)	−257,240	−26.89	+1.00	−.40	+155.46
$2\ Fe(\alpha) + 3/2\ O_2(g) = Fe_2O_3\ (hematite)$. (298.16°–950° K.)	−200,000	−13.84	−1.45	+1.905	+108.26
$2\ Fe(\alpha) + 3/2\ O_2(g) = Fe_2O_3(\beta)$ .... (950°–1,033° K.)	−202,960	−42.64	+7.85	+.13	+188.48
$2\ Fe(\beta) + 3/2\ O_2(g) = Fe_2O_3(\beta)$ .... (1,033°–1,050° K.)	−196,740	−10.27	+.75	−.30	+92.26
$2\ Fe(\beta) + 3/2\ O_2(g) = Fe_2O_3(\gamma)$ .... (1,050°–1,179° K.)	−193,200	−.39	−.13	−.30	+59.96
$2\ Fe(\gamma) + 3/2\ O_2(g) = Fe_2O_3(\gamma)$ .... (1,179°–1,674° K.)	−202,540	−25.95	+2.87	−.30	+142.85
$2\ Fe(\delta) + 3/2\ O_2(g) = Fe_2O_3(\gamma)$ .... (1,674°–1,800° K.)	−192,920	−.85	−.13	−.30	+61.21
$2\ La(c) + 3/2\ O_2(g) = La_2O_3(c)$ .... (298.16°–1,153° K.)	−431,120	−13.31	+.80	+1.34	+112.36
$2\ La(l) + 3/2\ O_2(g) = La_2O_3(c)$ .... (1,153°–2,000° K.)	−434,330	−4.88	−.80	+1.34	+91.17
$Pb(c) + 1/2\ O_2(g) = PbO\ (red)$ .... (298.16°–600.5° K.)	−52,800	−2.76	−.80	−.10	+32.49
$Pb(l) + 1/2\ O_2(g) = PbO\ (red)$ .... (600.5°–762° K.)	−53,780	−.51	−1.75	−.10	+28.44
$Pb(c) + 1/2\ O_2(g) = PbO\ (yellow)$ .... (298.16°–600.5° K.)	−52,040	+.81	−2.00	−.10	+22.13
$Pb(l) + 1/2\ O_2(g) = PbO\ (yellow)$ .... (600.5°–1,159° K.)	−53,020	+3.06	−2.95	−.10	+18.08
$Pb(l) + 1/2\ O_2(g) = PbO(l)$ .... (1,159°–1,745° K.)	−53,980	−12.94	+.25	−.10	+64.22
$Pb(c) + 1/2\ O_2(g) = PbO(g)$ .... (298.16°–600.5° K.)	+10,270	+1.91	+1.08	+.295	−23.21
$Pb(l) + 1/2\ O_2(g) = PbO(g)$ .... (600.5°–2,000° K.)	+9,300	+4.17	+.13	+.295	−27.29
$3\ Pb(c) + 2\ O_2(g) = Pb_3O_4(c)$ .... (298.16°–600.5° K.)	−174,920	+8.82	−8.20	−.40	+72.78
$3\ Pb(l) + 2\ O_2(g) = Pb_3O_4(c)$ .... (600.5°–1,000° K.)	−177,860	+15.59	−11.05	−.40	+60.57
$Pb(c) + O_2(g) = PbO_2(c)$ .... (298.16°–600.5° K.)	−66,120	+.64	−2.45	−.20	+45.58
$Pb(l) + O_2(g) = PbO_2(c)$ .... (600.5°–1,100° K.)	−67,100	+2.90	−3.40	−.20	+41.50
$2\ Li(c) + 1/2\ O_2(g) = Li_2O(c)$ .... (298.16°–452° K.)	−142,220	−3.06	+5.77	−.10	+34.19
$2\ Li(l) + 1/2\ O_2(g) = Li_2O(c)$ .... (452°–1,600° K.)	−141,380	+16.97	−2.63	−.10	−17.05
$2\ Li(c) + O_2(g) = Li_2O_2(c)$ .... (298.16°–452° K.)	−151,880	−1.38	......	....	+54.83
$2\ Li(l) + O_2(g) = Li_2O_2(c)$ .... (452°–500° K.)	−153,260	−1.38	......	....	+57.88
$Mg(c) + 1/2\ O_2(g) = MgO\ (periclase)$ ... (298.16°–923° K.)	−144,090	−1.06	+.13	+.25	+29.16
$Mg(l) + 1/2\ O_2(g) = MgO\ (periclase)$ ... (923°–1,393° K.)	−145,810	+1.84	−.62	+.64	+23.07
$Mg(g) + 1/2\ O_2(g) = MgO\ (periclase)$ ... (1,393°–2,000° K.)	−180,700	−3.75	−.62	+.64	+65.69
$Mg(c) + O_2(g) = MgO_2(c)$ .... (298.16°–500° K.)	−150,230	−9.12	+.13	+.25	+70.84
$Mn(\alpha) + 1/2\ O_2(g) = MnO(c)$ .... (298.16°–1,000° K.)	−92,600	−4.21	+.97	+.155	+29.66
$Mn(\beta) + 1/2\ O_2(g) = MnO(c)$ .... (1,000°–1,374° K.)	−91,900	+1.84	−.39	+.34	+12.15
$Mn(\gamma) + 1/2\ O_2(g) = MnO(c)$ .... (1,374°–1,410° K.)	−89,810	+7.30	−.72	+.34	−6.05
$Mn(\delta) + 1/2\ O_2(g) = MnO(c)$ .... (1,410°–1,517° K.)	−89,390	+8.68	−.72	+.34	−10.70
$Mn(l) + 1/2\ O_2(g) = MnO(c)$ .... (1,517°–2,000° K.)	−93,350	+7.99	−.72	+.34	−5.90
$3\ Mn(\alpha) + 2\ O_2(g) = Mn_3O_4(\alpha)$ .... (298.16°–1,000° K.)	−332,400	−7.41	+.66	+.145	+106.62
$3\ Mn(\beta) + 2\ O_2(g) = Mn_3O_4(\alpha)$ .... (1,000°–1,374° K.)	−330,310	+10.75	−3.42	+.70	+54.07
$3\ Mn(\gamma) + 2\ O_2(g) = Mn_3O_4(\alpha)$ .... (1,374°–1,410° K.)	−324,050	+27.12	−4.41	+.70	−.50
$3\ Mn(\delta) + 2\ O_2(g) = Mn_3O_4(\alpha)$ .... (1,410°–1,445° K.)	−322,800	+31.27	−4.41	+.70	−14.46
$3\ Mn(\delta) + 2\ O_2(g) = Mn_3O_4(\beta)$ .... (1,445°–1,517° K.)	−328,870	−4.56	+1.00	−.40	+95.20
$3\ Mn(l) + 2\ O_2(g) = Mn_3O_4(\beta)$ .... (1,517°–1,800° K.)	−340,730	−6.63	+1.00	−.40	+109.60
$2\ Mn(\alpha) + 3/2\ O_2(g) = Mn_2O_3(c)$ .... (298.16°–1,000° K.)	−230,610	−5.96	−.06	+.945	+80.74
$2\ Mn(\beta) + 3/2\ O_2(g) = Mn_2O_3(c)$ .... (1,000°–1,374° K.)	−220,210	+6.15	−2.78	+1.315	+45.70
$2\ Mn(\gamma) + 3/2\ O_2(g) = Mn_2O_3(c)$ .... (1,374°–1,410° K.)	−225,030	+17.06	−3.44	+1.315	+9.33
$2\ Mn(\delta) + 3/2\ O_2(g) = Mn_2O_3(c)$ .... (1,410°–1,517° K.)	−224,200	+19.82	−3.44	+1.315	+0.05
$2\ Mn(l) + 3/2\ O_2(g) = Mn_2O_3(c)$ .... (1,517°–1,700° K.)	−232,110	+18.44	−3.44	+1.315	+9.65
$Mn(\alpha) + O_2(g) = MnO_2(c)$ .... (298.16°–1,000° K.)	−126,400	−8.61	+.97	+1.555	+70.14
$2\ Hg(l) + 1/2\ O_2(g) = Hg_2O(c)$ .... (298.16°–629.88° K.)	−22,400	−4.61	......	......	+43.29
$2\ Hg(g) + 1/2\ O_2(g) = Hg_2O(c)$ .... (629.88°–1,000° K.)	−53,800	−16.12	......	......	+125.36
$Hg(l) + 1/2\ O_2(g) = HgO\ (red)$ .... (298.16°–629.88° K.)	−21,760	+.85	−2.47	−.10	+24.81
$Hg(g) + 1/2\ O_2(g) = HgO\ (red)$ .... (629.88°–1,500° K.)	−36,920	−2.92	−2.47	−.10	+59.42
$Mo(c) + O_2(g) = MoO_2(c)$ .... (298.16°–2,000° K.)	−132,910	−3.91	......	......	+47.42
$Mo(c) + 3/2\ O_2(g) = MoO_3(c)$ .... (298.16°–1,068° K.)	−182,650	−8.86	−1.55	+1.54	+90.07
$Mo(c) + 3/2\ O_2(g) = MoO_3(l)$ .... (1,068°–1,500° K.)	−179,770	−36.34	+1.40	−.30	+167.61
$2\ Nd(c) + 3/2\ O_2(g) =$ Nd_2O_3 (hexagonal). .... (298.16°–1,113° K.)	−435,150	−16.19	+3.21	+1.78	+125.68
$2\ Nd(l) + 3/2\ O_2(g) =$ Nd_2O_3 (hexagonal). .... (1,113°–1,500° K.)	−437,090	+4.03	−2.13	+1.78	+71.77
$Np(c) + O_2(g) = NpO_2(c)$ .... (298.16°–913° K.)	−246,450	−3.45	......	......	+52.44
$Np(l) + O_2(g) = NpO_2(c)$ .... (913°–1,500° K.)	−249,010	−4.61	......	......	+58.68
$Ni(\alpha) + 1/2\ O_2(g) = NiO(c)$ .... (298.16°–633° K.)	−57,640	−4.61	+2.16	−.10	+34.41
$Ni(\beta) + 1/2\ O_2(g) = NiO(c)$ .... (633°–1,725° K.)	−57,460	−.14	−46	−.10	+23.27
$Ni(l) + 1/2\ O_2(g) = NiO(c)$ .... (1,725°–2,000° K.)	−58,830	+7.23	−1.36	−.10	+1.76
$2\ Nb(c) + 2\ O_2(g) = Nb_2O_4(c)$ .... (298.16°–2,000° K.)	−382,050	−9.67	......	......	+116.23

Reaction and temperature range of validity	ΔH_0	2.303a	b	c	I
2 Nb(c) + 5/2 O₂(g) = Nb₂O₅(c)........ (298.16°–1,785° K.)	−458,640	−16.14	− .56	+1.94	+157.66
2 Nb(c) + 5/2 O₂(g) = Nb₂O₅(l)........ (1,785°–2,000° K.)	−463,630	−66.04	+2.21	− .50	+317.84
N₂(g) + 1/2 O₂(g) = N₂O(g)........ (298.16°–2,000° K.)	+18,650	−1.57	− .27	+ .92	+23.47
1/2 N₂(g) + 1/2 O₂(g) = NO(g)........ (298.16°–2,000° K.)	+21,590	− .28	+ .45	− .03	−2.20
N₂(g) + 3/2 O₂(g) = N₂O₃(g)........ (298.16°–500° K.)	+17,390	− .35	......	......	+54.30
1/2 N₂(g) + O₂(g) = NO₂(g)........ (298.16°–2,000° K.)	+7,730	+ .53	− .265	+ .605	+13.74
N₂(g) + 2 O₂(g) = N₂O₄(g)........ (298.16°–1,000° K.)	+1,370	+2.14	−3.24	+1.38	+68.34
N₂(g) + 5/2 O₂(g) = N₂O₅(c)........ (298.16°–305° K.)	−10,200	......	......	......	+131.70
N₂(g) + 5/2 O₂(g) = N₂O₅(g)........ (298.16°–500° K.)	+3,600	......	......	......	+86.50
Os(c) + 2 O₂(g) = OsO₄ (yellow)........ (298.16°–329° K.)	−92,260	+14.97			+32.45
Os(c) + 2 O₂(g) = OsO₄ (white)........ (298.16°–315° K.)	−90,560	+14.97			+27.60
Os(c) + 2 O₂(g) = OsO₄(l)........ (315°–403° K.)	−88,970	+9.67			+35.78
Os(c) + 2 O₂(g) = OsO₄(g)........ (298.16°–1,000° K.)	−81,200	+8.17	−2.86	+1.94	+20.34
3/2 O₂(g) = O₃(g)........ (298.16°–2,000° K.)	+33,980	+2.03	− .48	+ .36	+11.45
P (white) + 1/2 O₂(g) = PO(g)........ (298.16°–317.4° K.)	−9,370	+2.53	......	......	−25.40
P(l) + 1/2 O₂(g) = PO(g)........ (317.4°–553° K.)	−9,390	+3.45	......	......	−27.63
1/4 P₄(g) + 1/2 O₂(g) = PO(g)........ (553°–1,500° K.)	−12,640	+2.30	......	......	−18.61
4 P (white) + 5 O₂(g) = (298.16°–317.4° K.) P₄O₁₀ (hexagonal).	−711,520	+95.67	−51.50	−1.00	−28.24
4 P(l) + 5 O₂(g) = P₄O₁₀ (hex.)........ (317.4°–553° K.)	−711,800	+97.98	−51.50	−1.00	−33.13
P₄(g) + 5 O₂(g) = P₄O₁₀ (hex.)........ (553°–631° K.)	−725,560	+87.45	−51.07	−2.405	+20.87
P₄(g) + 5 O₂(g) = P₄O₁₀(g)........ (631°–1,500° K.)	−722,330	−43.45	+2.93	−2.405	+348.20
Pu(c) + O₂(g) = PuO₂(c)........ (298.16°–1,500° K.)	−246,450	−3.45	......	......	+52.48
Po(c) + O₂(g) = PoO₂(c)........ (298.16°–900° K.)	−61,510	−9.21	......	......	+72.80
2 K(c) + 1/2 O₂(g) = K₂O(c)........ (298.16°–336.4° K.)	−86,400	......			+33.90
2 K(l) + 1/2 O₂(g) = K₂O(c)........ (336.4°–1,049° K.)	−87,380	+1.15			+33.90
2 K(g) + 1/2 O₂(g) = K₂O(c)........ (1,049°–1,500° K.)	−133,090	−16.12			+129.64
2 K(c) + O₂(g) = K₂O₂(c)........ (298.16°–336.4° K.)	−118,300	−2.30			+59.60
2 K(l) + O₂(g) = K₂O₂(c)........ (336.4°–763° K.)	−119,780	−4.61			+69.85
2 K(l) + O₂(g) = K₂O₂(l)........ (763°–1,049° K.)	−118,250	−18.42			+107.66
2 K(g) + O₂(g) = K₂O₂(l)........ (1,049°–1,500° K.)	−161,870	−31.08			+187.49
2 K(c) + 3/2 O₂(g) = K₂O₃(c)........ (298.16°–336.4° K.)	−126,640	−12.66			+111.75
2 K(l) + 3/2 O₂(g) = K₂O₃(c)........ (336.4°–703° K.)	−127,790	−12.66			+115.16
2 K(l) + 3/2 O₂(g) = K₂O₃(l)........ (703°–1,000° K.)	−125,330	−27.63			+154.28
K(c) + O₂(g) = KO₂(c)........ (298.16°–336.4° K.)	−68,940	−10.36			+66.45
K(l) + O₂(g) = KO₂(c)........ (336.4°–653° K.)	−69,510	−10.36			+68.15
K(l) + O₂(g) = KO₂(l)........ (653°–1,000° K.)	−67,880	−18.42			+88.34
K(c) + 3/2 O₂(g) = KO₃(c)........ (298.16°–336.4° K.)	−63,340	−10.36			+85.85
K(l) + 3/2 O₂(g) = KO₃(c)........ (336.4°–500° K.)	−63,910	−10.36			+87.55
2 Pr(c) + 3/2 O₂(g) = Pr₂O₃(c, C-type). (298.16°–1,205° K.)	−440,600	−4.60			+78.38
2 Pr(l) + 3/2 O₂(g) = Pr₂O₃(c, C-type). (1,205°–2,000° K)	−446,100	−4.60			+82.94
6 Pr(c) + 11/2 O₂(g) = Pr₆O₁₁(c)........ (298.16°–1,205° K.)	−1,374,000	......			+241.04
6 Pr(l) + 11/2 O₂(g) = Pr₆O₁₁(c)........ (1,205°–1,500° K.)	−1,390,500	......			+254.73
Pr(c) + O₂(g) = PrO₂(c)........ (298.16°–1,200° K.)	−230,990	−6.42	+2.34	− .20	+61.07
Ra(c) + 1/2 O₂(g) = RaO(c)........ (298.16°–1,000° K.)	−130,000	......			+23.50
Re(c) + 3/2 O₂(g) = ReO₃(c)........ (298.16°–433° K.)	−149,090	−16.12			+110.49
Re(c) + 3/2 O₂(g) = ReO₃(l)........ (433°–1,000° K.)	−146,750	−31.32			+145.16
2Re(c) + 7/2 O₇(g) = Re₂O₇(c)........ (298.16°–569° K.)	−301,470	−34.54			+250.57
2 Re(c) + 7/2 O₇(g) = Re₂O₇(l)........ (569°–635.5° K.)	−295,810	−73.68			+348.45
2 Re(c) + 7/2 O₂(g) = Re₂O₇(g)........ (635.5°–1,500° K.)	−256,460	+3.45			+70.33
2 Re(c) + 4 O₂(g) = Re₂O₈(c)........ (298.16°–420° K.)	−313,870	−41.45			+293.57
2 Re(c) + 4 O₂(g) = Re₂O₈(l)........ (420°–600° K.)	−318,470	−87.50			+425.32
2 Rh(c) + 1/2 O₂(g) = Rh₂O(c)........ (298.16°–2,000° K.)	−23,740	−8.06			+35.64
Rh(c) + 1/2 O₂(g) = RhO(c)........ (298.16°–1,500° K.)	−22,650	−7.37			+40.54
2 Rh(c) + 3/2 O₂(g) = Rh₂O₃(c)........ (298.16°–1,500° K.)	−70,060	−13.58			+101.72
2 Rb(c) + 1/2 O₂(g) = Rb₂O(c)........ (298.16°–312.2° K.)	−78,900	......			+32.20
2 Rb(l) + 1/2 O₂(g) = Rb₂O(c)........ (312.2°–750° K.)	−79,950	......			+35.56
2 Rb(l) + 1/2 O₂(g) = Rb₂O(l)........ (750°–952° K.)	−78,830	−10.36			+63.85
2 Rb(g) + 1/2 O₂(g) = Rb₂O(l)........ (952°–1,500° K.)	−120,290	−23.03			+145.14
2 Rb(c) + O₂(g) = Rb₂O₂(c)........ (298.16°–312.2° K.)	−102,000	−2.30			+57.40
2 Rb(l) + O₂(g) = Rb₂O₂(c)........ (312.2°–840° K.)	−103,360	−4.61			+67.52
2 Rb(l) + O₂(g) = Rb₂O₂(l)........ (840°–952° K.)	−101,680	−18.42			+105.91
2 Rb(g) + O₂(g) = Rb₂O₂(l)........ (952°–1,500° K.)	−143,130	−31.08			+187.16
2 Rb(c) + 3/2 O₂(g) = Rb₂O₃(c)........ (298.16°–312.2° K.)	−118,190	−11.51			+104.70
2 Rb(l) + 3/2 O₂(g) = Rb₂O₃(c)........ (312.2°–760° K.)	−119,400	−12.66			+111.43
2 Rb(l) + 3/2 O₂(g) = Rb₂O₃(l)........ (760°–952° K.)	−116,740	−27.63			+151.06
2 Rb(g) + 3/2 O₂(g) = Rb₂O₃(l)........ (952°–1,500° K.)	−157,720	−39.14			+228.39
Rb(c) + O₂(g) = RbO₂(c)........ (298.16°–312.2° K.)	−52,330	−10.36			+66.25
Rb(l) + O₂(g) = RbO₂(c)........ (312.2°–685° K.)	−65,120	−11.51			+71.30

Reaction and temperature range of validity	ΔH_o	2.303a	b	c	I
Rb(l) + O₂(g) = RbO₂(l)................(685°–952° K.)	−63,070	−18.42	......	.....	+87.89
Rb(g) + O₂(g) = RbO₂(l)...............(952°–1,500° K.)	−83,560	−24.18	......	.....	+126.57
Ru(α, β, γ) + O₂(g) = RuO₂(c)........(298.16°–1,500° K.)	−57,290	−6.91			+62.01
2 Sm(c) + 3/2 O₂(g) = Sm₂O₃(c).......(298.16°–1,623° K.)	−430,600	−4.60			+78.38
2 Sm(l) + 3/2 O₂(g) = Sm₂O₃(c).......(1,623°–2,000° K.)	−438,000	−4.60			+82.94
2 Sc(c) + 3/2 O₂(g) = Sc₂O₃(c).......(298.16°–1,673° K.)	−409,960	+7.78	−1.84	−0.30	+52.73
2 Sc(l) + 3/2 O₂(g) = Sc₂O₃(c).......(1,673°–2,000° K.)	−412,950	+18.47	−2.93	−.30	+21.88
Se(c) + 1/2 O₂(g) = SeO(g)...........(298.16°–490° K.)	+9,280	−3.04	+4.40	+.30	−14.78
Se(l) + 1/2 O₂(g) = SeO(g)...........(490°–1,027° K.)	+9,420	+8.70	......	+.30	−44.50
1/2 Se₂(g) + 1/2 O₂(g) = SeO(g)......(1,027°–2,000° K.)	−7,400	−.37		+.19	−.80
Se(c) + O₂(g) = SeO₂(c)..............(298.16°–490° K.)	−53,770	+14.94	−9.41	−.20	+6.94
Se(l) + O₂(g) = SeO₂(c)..............(490°–595° K.)	−53,640	+27.59	−14.31		−25.05
Se(l) + O₂(g) = SeO₂(g)..............(595°–1,027° K.)	−32,840	+6.79	......		−10.80
1/2 Se₂(g) + O₂(g) = SeO₂(g).........(1,027°–2,000° K.)	−49,000	−.74			+27.61
Si(c) + 1/2 O₂(g) = SiO(g)...........(298.16°–1,683° K.)	−21,090	+3.84	+.16	−.295	−33.14
Si(l) + 1/2 O₂(g) = SiO(g)...........(1,683°–2,000° K.)	−30,170	−7.78	−.12	+.25	−40.01
Si(c) + O₂(g) = SiO₂(α-quartz)........(298.16°–848° K.)	−210,070	+3.98	−3.32	+.605	+34.59
Si(c) + O₂(g) = SiO₂(β-quartz)........(848°–1,683° K.)	−209,920	−3.36	−.19	−.745	+53.44
Si(l) + O₂(g) = SiO₂(β-quartz)........(1,683°–1,883° K.)	−219,000	+.58	−.47	.20	+46.58
Si(l) + O₂(g) = SiO₂(l)...............(1,883°–2,000° K.)	−228,590	−15.66			+103.97
Si(c) + O₂(g) = SiO₂(α-crist.)........(298.16°–523° K.)	−207,330	+19.96	−9.75	−.745	−9.78
Si(c) + O₂(g) = SiO₂(β-crist.)........(523°–1,683° K.)	−209,820	−3.34	−.24	−.745	+53.35
Si(l) + O₂(g) = SiO₂(β-crist.)........(1,683°–2,000° K.)	−218,900	+.60	−.52	−.20	+46.49
Si(c) + O₂(g) = SiO₂(α-trid.)........(298.16°–390° K.)	−207,030	+22.29	−11.62	−.745	−15.64
Si(c) + O₂(g) = SiO₂(β-trid.)........(390°–1,683° K.)	−209,350	−1.59	−.54	−.745	+47.86
Si(l) + O₂(g) = SiO₂(β-trid.)........(1,683°–1,953° K.)	−218,430	+2.35	−.82	−.20	+41.00
2 Ag(c) + 1/2 O₂(g) = Ag₂O(c)........(298.16°–1,000° K.)	−7,740	−4.14	......		+27.84
2 Ag(c) + O₂(g) = Ag₂O₂(c)...........(298.16°–500° K.)	−6,620	−3.22			+52.17
2 Na(c) + 1/2 O₂(g) = Na₂O(c)........(298.16°–371° K.)	−99,820	−7.51	+5.47	−.10	+50.43
2 Na(l) + 1/2 O₂(g) = Na₂O(c)........(371°–1,187° K.)	−100,150	+4.97	−2.45	−.10	+22.19
2 Na(g) + 1/2 O₂(g) = Na₂O(c)........(1,187°–1,190° K.)	−156,200	−20.72			+145.48
2 Na(g) + 1/2 O₂(g) = Na₂O(l)........(1,190°–2,000° K.)	−150,250	−23.03			+147.58
2 Na(c) + O₂(g) = Na₂O₂(c)...........(298.16°–371° K.)	−122,500	−2.30			+57.51
2 Na(l) + O₂(g) = Na₂O₂(c)...........(371°–733° K.)	−124,320	−5.76			+71.30
2 Na(l) + O₂(g) = Na₂O₂(l)...........(733°–1,187° K.)	−123,220	−20.72			+112.66
2 Na(g) + O₂(g) = Na₂O₂(l)...........(1,187°–1,500° K.)	−174,800	−31.08			+187.97
Na(c) + O₂(g) = NaO₂(c)..............(298.16°–371° K.)	−63,040	−8.06			+56.98
Na(l) + O₂(g) = NaO₂(c)..............(371°–1,000° K.)	−64,220	−11.51	......		+69.04
Sr(c) + 1/2 O₂(g) = SrO(c)...........(298.16°–1,043° K.)	−142,410	−6.79	+.305	+.675	+44.33
Sr(l) + 1/2 O₂(g) = SrO(c)...........(1,043°–1,657° K.)	−143,370	−2.42	−.38	+.675	+32.77
Sr(g) + 1/2 O₂(g) = SrO(c)...........(1,657°–2,000° K.)	−181,180	−8.24	−.38	+.675	+74.32
Sr(c) + O₂(g) = SrO₂(c)..............(298.16°–1,000° K.)	−155,510	−11.40	+.305	+.675	+75.44
S(rh) + 1/2 O₂(g) = SO(g)............(298.16°–368.6° K.)	+19,250	−1.24	+2.95	+.225	−18.84
S(mon) + 1/2 O₂(g) = SO(g)...........(368.6°–392° K.)	+19,200	−1.29	+3.31	+.225	−18.72
S(lλ,μ) + 1/2 O₂(g) = SO(g)..........(392°–718° K.)	+20,320	+10.22	−.17	+.225	−50.05
1/2 S₂(g) + 1/2 O₂(g) = SO(g)........(298.16°–2,000° K.)	+3,890	+.07	......	......	−1.50
S(rh) + O₂(g) = SO₂(g)...............(298.16°–368.6° K.)	−70,980	+.83	+2.35	+.51	−5.85
S(mon) + O₂(g) = SO₂(g)..............(368.6°–392° K.)	−71,020	+.78	+2.71	+.51	−5.74
S(lλ,μ) + O₂(g) = SO₂(g).............(392°–718° K.)	−69,900	+12.30	−.77	+.51	−37.10
1/2 S₂(g) + O₂(g) = SO₂(g)...........(298.16°–2,000° K.)	−86,330	+2.42	−.70	+.31	+10.71
S(rh) + 3/2 O₂(g) = SO₃(c—I)..........(298.16°–335.4° K.)	−111,370	−6.45	......		+88.32
S(rh) + 3/2 O₂(g) = SO₃(c—II)........(298.16°–305.7° K.)	−108,680	−11.97	......		+94.95
S(rh) + 3/2 O₂(g) = SO₃(l)...........(298.16°–335.4° K.)	−107,430	−21.18			+113.76
S(rh) + 3/2 O₃(g) = SO₃(g)...........(298.16°–368.6° K.)	−95,070	+1.43	+0.66	+1.26	+16.81
S(mon) + 3/2 O₂(g) = SO₃(g)..........(368.6°–392° K.)	−95,120	+1.38	+1.02	+1.26	+16.93
S(lλ,μ) + 3/2 O₂(g) = SO₃(g).........(392°–718° K.)	−94,010	+12.89	−2.46	−1.26	−14.40
1/2 S₂(g) + 3/2 O₂(g) = SO₃(g).......(298.16°–1,500° K.)	−110,420	+3.02	−2.39	+1.06	+33.41
2 Ta(c) + 5/2 O₂(g) = Ta₂O₅(c).......(298.16°–2,000° K.)	−492,790	−17.18	−1.25	+2.46	+161.68
Tc(c) + O₂(g) = TcO₂(c)..............(298.16°–500° K.)	−103,400	.....		.....	+41.00
Tc(c) + 3/2 O₂(g) = TcO₃(c)..........(298.16°–500° K.)	−120,000	.....		.....	+64.50
2 Tc(c) + 7/2 O₂(g) = Tc₂O₇(c).......(298.16°–392.7° K.)	−266,000	.....		.....	+147.00
2 Tc(c) + 7/2 O₂(g) = Tc₂O₇(l).......(392.7°–500° K.)	−258,930	.....		.....	+129.00
Te(c) + 1/2 O₂(g) = TeO(g)...........(298.16°–723° K.)	+43,110	+1.91	+.84	+.315	−27.22
Te(l) + 1/2 O₂(g) = TeO(g)...........(723°–1,360° K.)	+39,750	+6.08	+.09	+.315	−33.94
1/2 Te₂(g) + 1/2 O₂(g) = TeO(g)......(1,360°–2,000° K.)	+23,730	−.90	+.09	+.315	−.29
Te(c) + O₂(g) = TeO₂(c)..............(298.16°–723° K.)	−78,090	−2.10	−2.35	−.20	+51.27
Te(l) + O₂(g) = TeO₂(c)..............(723°–1,006° K.)	−81,530	+1.84	−3.10	−.20	+45.30
Te(l) + O₂(g) = TeO₂(l)..............(1,006°–1,300° K.)	−82,090	−21.74	+.50	−.20	+113.04
2 Tl(α) + O₂(g) = Tl₂O(c)............(298.16°–505.5° K.)	−44,110	−6.91	......	.....	+42.30

Reaction and temperature range of validity	ΔH_0	2.303a	b	c	I
2 Tl(β) + O$_2$(g) = Tl$_2$O(c).............(505.5°–573° K.)	−44,260	−6.91	.....	.....	+42.60
2 Tl(β) + 1/2 O$_2$(g) = Tl$_2$O(l).........(573°–576° K.)	−40,880	−13.82	.....	.....	+55.76
2 Tl(l) + 1/2 O$_2$(g) = Tl$_2$O(l).........(576°–773° K.)	−42,320	−11.51	.....	.....	+51.89
2 Tl(l) + 1/2 O$_2$(g) = Tl$_2$O(g).........(773°–1,730° K.)	−18,400	+11.51	.....	.....	−45.55
2 Tl(g) + 1/2 O$_2$(g) = Tl$_2$O(g).........(1,730°–2,000° K.)	−104,670	.....	.....	.....	+41.59
2 Tl(α) + 3/2 O$_2$(g) = Tl$_2$O$_3$(c).........(298.16°–505.5° K.)	−99,410	−16.12	.....	.....	+119.09
2 Tl(β) + 3/2 O$_2$(g) = Tl$_2$O$_3$(c).........(505.5°–576° K.)	−99,560	−16.12	.....	.....	+119.39
2 Tl(l) + 3/2 O$_2$(g) = Tl$_2$O$_3$(c).........(576°–990° K.)	−101,010	−13.82	.....	.....	+115.55
2 Tl(l) + 3/2 O$_2$(g) = Tl$_2$O$_3$(l).........(990°–1,500° K.)	−94,550	−27.63	.....	.....	+150.39
2 Tl(α) + 2 O$_2$(g) = Tl$_2$O$_4$(c).........(298.16°–505.5° K.)	−117,680	−23.03	.....	.....	+161.19
2 Tl(β) + 2 O$_2$(g) = Tl$_2$O$_4$(c).........(505.5°–576° K.)	−117,830	−23.03	.....	.....	+161.49
2 Tl(l) + 2 O$_2$(g) = Tl$_2$O$_4$(c).........(576°–1,000° K.)	−119,270	−20.72	.....	.....	+157.63
Th(c) + O$_2$(g) = ThO$_2$(c).............(298.16°–2,000° K.)	−294,350	−5.25	+.59	+.775	+62.81
Sn(c) + 1/2 O$_2$(g) = SnO(c).........(298.16°–505° K.)	−68,600	−3.57	+1.65	−.10	+32.59
Sn(l) + 1/2 O$_2$(g) = SnO(c).........(505°–1,300° K.)	−69,670	+3.06	−1.50	−.10	+18.39
Sn(c) + 1/2 O$_2$(g) = SnO(g).........(298.16°–505° K.)	−1,000	−.97	+3.24	+.32	−17.41
Sn(l) + 1/2 O$_2$(g) = SnO(g).........(505°–2,000° K.)	−2,070	+5.66	+.09	+.32	−31.62
Sn(c) + O$_2$(g) = SnO$_2$(c).........(298.16°–505° K.)	−142,010	−14.00	+2.45	+2.38	+90.74
Sn(l) + O$_2$(g) = SnO$_2$(c).............(505°–1,898° K.)	−143,080	−7.37	−.70	+2.38	+76.53
Sn(l) + O$_2$(g) = SnO$_2$(l).........(1,898°–2,000° K.)	−139,130	−21.97	+.50	−.20	+120.11
Ti(α) + 1/2 O$_2$(g) = TiO(α).........(298.16°–1,150° K.)	−125,010	−4.01	−.29	+.83	+36.28
Ti(β) + 1/2 O$_2$(g) = TiO(α).........(1,150°–1,264° K.)	−125,040	+1.17	−1.55	+.83	+21.90
Ti(β) + 1/2 O$_2$(g) = TiO(β).........(1,264°–2,000° K.)	−125,210	−1.77	−1.25	−.10	+30.83
Ti(α) + 1/2 O$_2$(g) = TiO(g).........(298.16°–1,150° K.)	+11,710	+3.71	+1.07	−.10	−35.50
Ti(β) + 1/2 O$_2$(g) = TiO(g).........(1,150°–2,000° K.)	+11,680	+8.89	−.19	−.10	−49.88
2 Ti(α) + 3/2 O$_2$(g) = Ti$_2$O$_3$(α).........(298.16°–473° K.)	−360,660	+32.08	−23.49	−.30	−10.66
2 Ti(α) + 3/2 O$_2$(g) = Ti$_2$O$_3$(β).........(473°–1,150° K.)	−369,710	−30.95	+2.62	+4.80	+162.79
2 Ti(β) + 3/2 O$_2$(g) = Ti$_2$O$_3$(β).........(1,150°–2,000° K.)	−369,760	−20.59	+.10	+4.80	+134.03
3 Ti(α) + 5/2 O$_2$(g) = Ti$_3$O$_5$(α).........(298.16°–450° K.)	−587,980	−4.19	−9.72	−.50	+131.05
3 Ti(α) + 5/2 O$_2$(g) = Ti$_3$O$_5$(β).........(450°–1,150° K.)	−586,330	−18.31	+1.03	−.50	+159.98
3 Ti(β) + 5/2 O$_2$(g) = Ti$_3$O$_5$(β).........(1,150°–2,000° K.)	−586,420	−2.76	−2.75	−.50	+116.81
Ti(α) + O$_2$(g) = TiO$_2$ (rutile).........(298.16°–1,150° K.)	−228,360	−12.80	+1.62	+1.975	+82.81
Ti(β) + O$_2$(g) = TiO$_2$ (rutile).........(1,150°–2,000° K.)	−228,380	−7.62	+.36	+1.975	+68.43
W(c) + O$_2$(g) = WO$_2$(c).........(298.16°–1,500° K.)	−137,180	−1.38	.....	.....	+45.56
4 W(c) + 11/2 O$_2$(g) = W$_4$O$_{11}$(c).........(298.16°–1,700° K.)	−745,730	−32.70	.....	.....	+321.84
W(c) + 3/2 O$_2$(g) = WO$_3$(c).........(298.16°–1,743° K.)	−201,180	−2.92	−1.81	−.30	+70.89
W(c) + 3/2 O$_2$(g) = WO$_3$(l).........(1,743°–2,000° K.)	−203,140	−35.74	+1.13	−.30	+173.27
U(α) + O$_2$(g) = UO$_2$(c).........(298.16°–935° K.)	−262,880	−19.92	+3.70	+2.13	+100.54
U(β) + O$_2$(g) = UO$_2$(c).........(935°–1,045° K.)	−260,660	−4.28	−.31	+1.78	+55.50
U(γ) + O$_2$(g) = UO$_2$(c).............(1,045°–1,405° K.)	−262,830	−6.54	−.31	+1.78	+64.41
U(l) + O$_2$(g) = UO$_2$(c).........(1,405°–1,500° K.)	−264,790	−5.92	.....	.....	+63.50
3 U(α) + 4 O$_2$(g) = U$_3$O$_8$(c).........(298.16°–935° K.)	−863,370	−56.57	+10.68	+5.20	+330.19
3 U(β) + 4 O$_2$(g) = U$_3$O$_8$(c).........(935°–1,045° K.)	−856,720	−9.67	−1.35	+4.15	+195.12
3 U(γ) + 4 O$_2$(g) = U$_3$O$_8$(c).........(1,045°–1,405° K.)	−863,230	−16.44	−1.35	+4.15	+221.79
3 U(l) + 4 O$_2$(g) = U$_3$O$_8$(c).........(1,405°–1,500° K.)	−869,460	−10.91	−1.35	+4.15	+208.82
U(α) + 3/2 O$_2$(g) = UO$_3$ (hex).........(298.16°–935° K.)	−294,090	−18.33	+3.49	+1.535	+114.94
U(β) + 3/2 O$_2$(g) = UO$_3$ (hex).........(935°–1,045° K.)	−291,870	−2.69	−.52	+1.185	+69.90
U(γ) + 3/2 O$_2$(g) = UO$_3$ (hex).........(1,045°–1,400° K.)	−294,040	−4.95	−.52	+1.185	+78.80
V(c) + 1/2 O$_2$(g) = VO(c).............(298.16°–2,000° K.)	−101,090	−5.39	−.36	+.53	+38.69
V(c) + 1/2 O$_2$(g) = VO(g).........(298.16°–2,000° K.)	+52,090	+1.80	+1.04	+.35	−28.42
2 V(c) + 3/2 O$_2$(g) = V$_2$O$_3$(c).........(298.16°–2,000° K.)	−299,910	−17.98	+.37	+2.41	+118.83
2 V(c) + 2 O$_2$(g) = V$_2$O$_4$(α).........(298.16°–345° K.)	−342,890	−11.03	+3.00	−.40	+117.38
2 V(c) + 2 O$_2$(g) = V$_2$O$_4$(β).........(345°–1,818° K.)	−345,330	−24.36	+1.30	+3.545	+155.55
2 V(c) + 2 O$_2$(g) = V$_2$O$_4$(l).........(1,818°–2,000° K.)	−339,880	−59.59	+3.00	−0.40	+264.42
6 V(c) + 13/2 O$_2$(g) = V$_6$O$_{13}$(c).........(298.16°–1,000° K.)	−1,076,340	−95.33	.....	.....	+557.61
2 V(c) + 5/2 O$_2$(g) = V$_2$O$_5$(c).........(298.16°–943° K.)	−381,960	−41.08	+5.20	+6.11	+228.50
2 V(c) + 5/2 O$_2$(g) = V$_2$O$_5$(l).........(943°–2,000° K.)	−365,840	−38.91	+3.25	−.50	+207.54
2 Y(c) + 3/2 O$_2$(g) = Y$_2$O$_3$(c).........(298.16°–1,773° K.)	−419,600	+2.76	−1.73	−.30	+66.36
2 Y(l) + 3/2 O$_2$(g) = Y$_2$O$_3$(c).........(1,773°–2,000° K.)	−422,850	+13.36	−2.75	−.30	+35.56
Zn(c) + 1/2 O$_2$(g) = ZnO(c).........(298.16°–692.7° K.)	−84,670	−6.40	+.84	+.99	+43.25
Zn(l) + 1/2 O$_2$(g) = ZnO(c).........(692.7°–1,180° K.)	−85,520	−1.45	−.36	+.99	+31.25
Zn(g) + 1/2 O$_2$(g) = ZnO(c).........(1,180°–2,000° K.)	−115,940	−7.28	−.36	+.99	+74.94
Zr(α) + O$_2$(g) = ZrO$_2$(α).............(298.16°–1,135° K.)	−262,980	−6.10	+.16	+1.045	+65.00
Zr(β) + O$_2$(g) = ZrO$_2$(α).........(1,135°–1,478° K.)	−264,190	−5.09	−.40	+1.48	+63.58
Zr(β) + O$_2$(g) = ZrO$_2$(β).............(1,478°–2,000° K.)	−262,290	−7.76	+.50	−.20	+69.50

Name	Formula	Molecular weight	Melting point, °C	Crystalline form	Lattice parameter, Å	X-ray density, g/cm³
Chromium boride	CrB_2	73.65	1,850(29)a	Hexagonal $A1B_2$ type [C 32]	a = 2.969 c = 3.066(39)	5.16
Hafnium boride	HfB_2	200.14	3,100(31)	Hexagonal $A1B_2$ type [C 32]	a = 3.14(6) c = 3.47	10.5
Molybdenum boride	MoB	106.77	2,180(40)	Tetragonal	a = 3.110(41) c = 16.95	8.77
	MoB_2	117.59	2,100(40)	Hexagonal $A1B_2$ type [C 32]	a = 3.05 c = 3.113(42)	7.78
	Mo_2B	202.72	2,000(40)	Tetragonal $CuAl_2$ type [C 16]	a = 5.543(41) c = 4.735	9.31
Niobium boride	NbB	103.73	(decomposes) >2000(3)	Orthorhombic	a = 3.298 b = 8.724 c = 3.137(35)	
	NbB_2	114.55	2,900(36)	Hexagonal AlB_2 type [C 32]	a = 3.086(28) c = 3.306	7.21
Tantalum boride	TaB	191.77	(decomposes) >2000(3)	Orthorhombic	a = 3.276 b = 8.669 c = 3.157(37)	14.29
	TaB_2	202.59	3,000(6)	Hexagonal AlB_2 type [C 32]	a = 3.088(28) c = 3.241	12.60
Thorium boride	ThB_4	275.53	>2,500(6)	Tetragonal D^5_{4k}-P4/mbm	a = 7.256(43) c = 4.113	8.45
Titanium boride	TiB_2	69.54	2,980(6)	Hexagonal AlB_2 type [C 32]	a = 3.028(28) c = 3.228	4.52
Tungsten boride	WB	194.68	2,860(29)	Tetragonal	a = 3.115(6) c = 16.92	16.0
	W_2B	378.54	2,770(29)	Tetragonal $CuAl_2$ type [C 16]	a = 5.564(41) c = 4.740	16.72
Uranium boride	UB_{12}	367.91	>1,500(6)	Face-centered cubic	a = 7.473(44)	5.82
Vanadium boride	VB_2	72.59	(decomposes) 2,100(29)	Hexagonal AlB_2 type [C 32]	a = 2.998(28) c = 3.057	5.10
Zirconium boride	ZrB_2	112.86	3,040 ± 50(30)	Hexagonal AlB_2 type [C 32]	a = 3.169(28) c = 3.530	6.09
	ZrB_{12}	221.06	2,680(30)	Face-centered cubic	a = 7.408(33)	

Note: See end of table for footnotes.

REFRACTORY MATERIALS (Continued)

Borides (Continued)

Name	Thermal conductivity, cal-sec^{-1}-cm^{-2}-cm-°C^{-1}	Electrical resistivity, microhm-cm	Ductility relative scale[b]	Resistance to oxidation[c]	Hardness[d]
Chromium boride		21 at room temperature(38)	3(3)		1,800 kg/mm²(29)
Hafnium boride		10(31)	3(3)		8 Mohs(20)
Molybdenum boride		α-MoB = 45 at room temperature(40) β-MoB = 25 at room temperature 45 at room temperature(40) 40 at room temperature(40)		3(3)	1,570 kg/mm²(29) 1,280 kg/mm²(29) 8–9 Mohs(20)
Niobium boride	0.040 at 20°C(36)	6.45 at room temperature(36) 32.0 at room temperature(36)			>0.8 Mohs(36)
Tantalum boride	0.026 at 20°C(6)	100 at room temperature(38) 68 at room temperature(38)	3(3)	3(3)	
Thorium boride		28.4(28)			
Titanium boride	0.0624 at 200°C(28) (15% porosity)		3(3)	2–3(3)	3,400 kg/mm²(29)
Tungsten boride			3(3)	3(3)	9 Mohs(6)
Uranium boride	16 at 20°C(34)				
Vanadium boride					8–9 Mohs(6)
Zirconium boride	0.0550 at 200°C(28) 0.029 at room temperature(33)	9.2 at 20°C(31) 60–80 at room temperature(30)	2(3)	2–3(3)	8 Mohs(32)

Carbides

Name	Formula	Molecular weight	Melting point, °C	Crystalline form	Lattice parameter, Å	X-ray density, g/cm³
Boron carbide	B_4C	55.29	2,450	Hexagonal	$a_0 = 5.60(6)$ $c_0 = 12.12$	2.52
Chromium carbide	Cr_3C_2	180.05	1,895(15)	Orthorhombic (D5$_{10}$)	$a = 2.82$ $b = 5.53$ $c = 11.47(16)$	6.7
	Cr_7Cr_3	400.01	1,780(15)	Hexagonal [C_3v^4]	$a = 14.01$ $c = 4.532(17)$	6.92
Graphite	C	12.01	3,700 ± 100(3)	Hexagonal	Orthohexagonal axes $a_0 = 2.46$ $b_0 = 4.28$ $c_0 = 6.71$	2.25
Hafnium carbide	HfC	190.51	3,890(9)	Cubic NaCl type (B1)	$a = 4.46(10)$	12.7

REFRACTORY MATERIALS (Continued)
Carbides (Continued)

Name	Formula	Molecular weight	Melting point, °C	Crystalline form	Lattice parameter, Å	X-ray density, g/cm^3
Molybdenum carbide	MoC	107.96	2,695(9)	Face-centered cubic	a = 4.28(19)	
	Mo_2C	203.91	2,690(6)	Hexagonal (L'3)	a = 3.002, c = 4.724(18)	9.2
Niobium carbide	NbC	104.92	3,500(9)	Cubic NaCl type (B1)	a = 4.461	7.85
Silicon carbide β	SiC	40.07	Trans. to α at 2,100	Face-centered cubic	a_0 = 4.3590(6)	3.22
α	SiC		2,700(6)	Hexagonal (Wurtzite)	a_0 = 3.081(6), c_0 = 5.0394	
Tantalum carbide	TaC	192.96	3,880(9), 4,730(4)	Cubic NaCl type (B1)	a = 4.455(14)	14.5
Thorium carbide	ThC	244.06	2,625(23)	Cubic NaCl type (B1)	a = 5.34(9)	10.67
	ThC_2	256.07	2,655(29)	Monoclinic [C 2/e]	a = 6.53(24), b = 4.24	9.6
Titanium carbide	TiC	59.91	3,160(4)	Cubic NaCl type (B1)	a = 4.32(6)	4.938
Tungsten carbide	W_2C	379.73	2,730(21)	Hexagonal (L'3)	a = 2.98(6), c = 4.71	17.34
	WC	195.87	2,630(21) (decomposes)	Hexagonal (L'3)	a = 2.900(22), c = 2.831	15.77
Uranium carbide	UC	250.08	2,450–2,500(25)	Cubic NaCl type (B1)	a = 4.955(26)	13.6
	UC_2	262.09	2,350–2,400(25)	Body-centered tetragonal $CaCl_2$ type	a = 3.517(27), c = 5.987	11.68
Vanadium carbide	VC	62.96	2,830(1)	Cubic NaCl type (B1)	a = 4.16(6)	5.8
Zirconium carbide	ZrC	103.23	3,030(4)	Cubic NaCl type (B1)	a = 4.689(5)	6.44

Name	Thermal conductivity, cal-sec^{-1}-cm^{-2}-cm-°C^{-1}	Electrical resistivity, microhm-cm	Ductility relative scale[b]	Resistance to oxidation[c]	Hardness[d]
Boron carbide	0.05 at 20–425°C(1)	0.30–0.80(1)	3(3)	3(3)	9.3 Mohs
Chromium carbide			3(3)	3(3)	1,300 kg/mm^2(8)
Graphite	0.268–0.451 at room temperature	65 at room temperature(71)	3(3)	3(3)	
Hafnium carbide		109 at room temperature(1)	3(3)	4(3)	
Molybdenum carbide		97(6)	3(3)	3(3)	1,800 kg/mm^2(6)
Niobium carbide	0.034 at room temperature(7)	74(6)	3(3)	5(3)	>0.7 Mohs(20)
Silicon carbide		107–200 ohm cm(1) at room temperature	3(3)	5(3)	2,470 kg/mm^2(13)
β	0.10 at 20–425°C(1)		2–3(3)	3(3)	
Tantalum carbide			3(3)	2(3)	9.2 Mohs
Thorium carbide	0.053 at room temperature(6)	30(6)	2–3(3)	3(3)	1,800 kg/mm^2(8)

REFRACTORY MATERIALS (Continued)

Carbides (Continued)

Name	Thermal conductivity, $\text{cal-sec}^{-1}\text{-cm}^{-2}\text{-cm-°C}^{-1}$[6]	Electrical resistivity, microhm-cm	Ductility relative scale[b]	Resistance to oxidation[c]	Hardness[d]
Titanium carbide	0.049 at room temperature[6]	180–250[4]	3[3]	3[4]	3,200 kg/mm^2[8]
Tungsten carbide		80[6]	3[3]	5[3]	3,000 kg/mm^2[6]
		53[6]	3[3]	5[3]	2,400 kg/mm^2[6]
Uranium carbide			3[3]	5[3]	
Vanadium carbide		150[6]	3[3]		2,800 kg/mm^2[11]
					2,100 kg/mm^2[12]
Zirconium carbide	0.049 at room temperature[6]	70 at room temperature[6]	3[3]	3[3]	2,600 kg/mm^2[6]

Nitrides

Name	Formula	Molecular weight	Melting point, °C	Crystalline form	Lattice parameter, Å	X-ray density, g/cm^3
Boron nitride	BN	24.83	2,730[6]	Hexagonal (B 12)	a = 2.51 ± .02, c = 6.70 ± .04[52]	2.25
Chromium nitride	CrN	66.02	1,500 (decomposes)	Cubic NaCl type (B1)	a = 4.140[6]	6.14
Hafnium nitride	HfN	192.60	3,310[6]	Cubic NaCl type (B1)	a = 4.41–4.375[6]	7.28
Niobium nitride	NbN	106.92	2,050[46]	Cubic NaCl type (B1)		
Tantalum nitride	Ta$_2$N	375.77	3,090[46]	Hexagonal	a = 3.05[48], c = 4.95[53]	14.1
Thorium nitride	ThN	246.13	2,630[48]	Cubic NaCl type (B1)	a = 5.2[48]	
Titanium nitride	TiN	61.91	2,930 N$_2$ liberated on melting[46]	Cubic NaCl type (B1)	a = 4.23[53]	5.43
Uranium nitride	UN		2,650	Cubic NaCl type (B1)	a = 4.880[58]	14.32
Vanadium nitride	VN	64.96	2,050[46]	Cubic NaCl type (B1)	a = 4.129[6]	6.102
Zirconium nitride	ZrN	105.22	2,980[47]	Cubic NaCl type (B1)	a = 4.567[53]	7.349

REFRACTORY MATERIALS (Continued)

Nitrides (Continued)

Name	Thermal conductivity, cal-sec⁻¹-cm⁻²-cm-°C⁻¹	Electrical resistivity, microhm-cm	Ductility relative scale[b]	Resistance to oxidation[c]	Hardness[d]
Boron nitride		1,900 at 2,000°C[1]	3[3]	2[3]	2.0 Mohs
Chromium nitride					
Hafnium nitride					
Niobium nitride		200 at room temperature[46]	5[3]	3[3]	+8 Mohs[46]
Tantalum nitride		135 at room temperature[47]	3[3]	5[3]	+8
Thorium nitride					
Titanium nitride		21.7 at room temperature	3[3]	3[3]	Between 9 and 10 Mohs[46]
Uranium nitride		200 at room temperature[46]	3[3]	3[3]	
Vanadium nitride			3[3]		
Zirconium nitride		13.6 at room temperature[46]	3[3]	3[3]	+8 Mohs[6]

Oxides

Name	Formula	Molecular weight	Melting point, °C	Crystalline form	Lattice parameter, Å	X-ray density, g/cm³
Aluminum oxide	Al_2O_3	101.92	2,015[1]	Rhombohedral	a = 5.13 axial angle = 55° 6'	3.965
Beryllium oxide	BeO	25.02	2,550[1]	Hexagonal	a = 2.70 c = 4.39	3.03
Cerium oxide	CeO_2	172.3	2,600[1]	Face-centered cubic	a = 5.41	7.13
Chromic oxide	Cr_2O_3	152.02	2,265[1]	Rhombohedral	a = 5.38 axial angle = 54° 50'	5.21
Hafnium oxide	HfO_2	210.6	2,777[1]	Face-centered cubic	a = 5.11	9.68
Magnesium oxide	MgO	40.32	2,800[1]	Face-centered cubic	a = 4.20	3.58
Silicon oxide	SiO_2	60.06	1,728[1]	Hexagonal	a = 4.90 c = 5.39	2.32 (low cristobalite)
Thorium oxide	ThO_2	264.12	3,300[1]	Face-centered cubic	a = 5.59	9.69
Titanium oxide	TiO_2	79.90	1,840[1]	Tetragonal	a = 4.58 c = 2.98	4.24
Uranium oxide	UO_2	270.07	2,280[1]	Face-centered cubic	a = 5.47	10.96
Zirconium oxide	ZrO_2	123.22	2,677[1]	Monoclinic	a = 5.21 c = 5.37	5.56

REFRACTORY MATERIALS (Continued)

Oxides (Continued)

Name	Thermal conductivity, cal-sec^{-1}-cm^{-2}-cm-°C^{-1}	Electrical resistivity, microhm-cm	Ductility relative scale[b]	Resistance to oxidation[c]	Hardness[d]
Aluminum oxide	0.0723 at 100°C[2]	1×10^{22} at 14°C[1] 3×10^{19} at 300°C[1] 3.5×10^{14} at 800°C[1] 4×10^{14} at 600°C[1] 5×10^{12} at 1,100°C[1] 8×10^{8} at 2,100°C[1]	3[3]	1[3]	9 Mohs[1]
Beryllium oxide	0.525 at 100°C[2]	6.5×10^{10} at 800°C[1] 3.4×10^{8} at 1,200°C[1]			9 Mohs[1]
Cerium oxide		1.3×10^{9} at 350°C[1] 2.3×10^{7} at 1,200°C[1]			6 Mohs[1]
Chromium oxide		6.8×10^{3} at 600°C[1] 4.5×10^{3} at 1,100°C[1]	3[3]	1[3]	
Hafnium oxide		5×10^{15} at 400°C[1] 1×10^{3} at 1,500°C[1]			
Magnesium oxide	0.0860 at 100°C[2]	2×10^{14} at 850°C[1] 3×10^{13} at 980°C[1] 4.5×10^{8} at 2,100°C[1]			6 Mohs[1]
Silicon oxide		1×10^{21} at 20°C[1] 7×10^{12} at 600°C[1] 4×10^{5} at 1,300°C[1] (vitreous)	3[4] (vitreous)	1[4] (vitreous)	6–7 Mohs[1] (cristobalite)
Thorium oxide	0.0245 at 100°C[2]	2.6×10^{13} at 550°C[1] 8×10^{11} at 800°C[1]			6.5 Mohs[1]
Titanium oxide	0.0156 at 100°C[2]	1.5×10^{10} at 1,200°C[1] 1.2×10^{10} at 800°C[1] 8.5×10^{6} at 1,200°C[1]			5.5–6.0 Mohs[1]
Uranium oxide	0.0234 at 100°C[2]	3.8×10^{10} at 20°C[1] 5×10^{8} at 500°C[1]			
Zirconium oxide	0.00466 at 100°C[2]	1×10^{12} at 385°C[1] 2.2×10^{10} at 700°C[1] 3.6×10^{8} at 1,200°C[1]	3[3]	1[3]	6.5 Mohs[1]

Silicides

Name	Formula	Molecular weight	Melting point, °C	Crystalline form	Lattice parameter, Å	X-ray density g/cm³
Chromium silicide	$CrSi_2$	108.13	1,570[51]	Hexagonal	a = 4.42 c = 6.35[51]	
	CrSi	80.07	1,870 (decomposes in presence of C)	Tetragonal (C 11b)	a = 3.20 c = 7.86[6]	
Molybdenum silicide	$MoSi_2$	152.07	1,870 (decomposes in presence of C)	Tetragonal (C 11b)	a = 3.20 c = 7.86[64][51]	6.24
Niobium silicide	$NbSi_2$		1,950[50]	Hexagonal $CrSi_2$ type	a = 4.785 c = 6.576[51]	5.29
Tantalum silicide	$TaSi_2$	237.00	2,400[50]	Hexagonal $CrSi_2$ type	a = 4.773 c = 6.552[51]	8.83
Titanium silicide	$TiSi_2$	104.02	1,540[49]	Orthorhombic	a = 8.24 b = 4.79 c = 8.52[59]	4.13
	Ti_5Si_3	323.68	2,120[49]	Hexagonal	a = 7.465 c = 5.162[60]	4.32
Tungsten silicide	WSi_2	240.04	2,050[50]	Tetragonal $MoSi_2$ Structure (C 11b)	a = 3.21 c = 7.83[66]	9.3
Uranium silicide	βUSi_2	294.19	1,700[6]	Hexagonal	a = 3.85[6] c = 4.06	9.25
	U_3Si_2	770.33	1,665[6]	Tetragonal	a = 7.3151[6] c = 3.8925	12.20
Vanadium silicide	VSi_2	107.07	1,750[50]	Hexagonal $CrSi_2$ type	a = 4.562 c = 6.359[51]	4.71

REFRACTORY MATERIALS (Continued)

Silicides (Continued)

Name	Thermal conductivity, cal-sec⁻¹-cm⁻²-cm-°C⁻¹	Electrical resistivity, microhm-cm	Ductility relative scale[b]	Resistance to oxidation[c]	Hardness[d]
Chromium silicide					1,150 kg/mm²(50)
Molybdenum silicide	0.075 at room temperature to 200°C(6)	21.5 at room temperature; 18.9 at −80°C(69)	2(3)	1(3)	1,290 kg/mm²(50)
Niobium silicide		6.3(68)	2(3)	4(3)	1,050 kg/mm²(50)
Tantalum silicide		8.5(68)	2(3)	3(3)	1,560 kg/mm²(50)
Titanium silicide		123 (hot pressed)(1)	3(3)	4(3); 4(3)	870 kg/mm²(70); 986 kg/mm²(49)
Tungsten silicide		33.4(68)	3(3)	1–2(3)	1,310 kg/mm²(68); 1,090 kg/mm²(68)
Uranium silicide					
Vanadium silicide		9.5(68)			1,090 kg/mm²(50)

[a]Numbers in parentheses refer to references at end of table.

[b]Ductility — 1: capable of being severely drawn, rolled, or otherwise worked without failure; 2: capable of withstanding slight deformation, or consisting of individually ductile crystals fragilely bound together; 3: incapable of being worked, of glasslike brittleness.

[c]Resistance to oxidation — classed according to the temperature range in which the rate of attack by air would cause severe erosion or failure of the coated specimen within a few hours. 1: above 1,700°C; 2: 1,400 to 1,700°C; 1,100 to 1,400°C; 4: 800 to 1,000°C; 5: 500 to 800°C.

[d]Microhardness values taken with 100-g load.

REFRACTORY MATERIALS (Continued)

REFERENCES

1. Campbell, I. E., *High Temperature Technology*, Electrochemical Society, John Wiley & Sons, New York, 1956.
2. Kingery, W. D., Franch, J., Coble, R. L. and Vasilos, T., Thermal conductivity: X, data for several pure oxide materials corrected to zero porosity, *J. Am. Ceram. Soc.*, 37, 2, 107, 1954.
3. Fowel, C. F., Campbell, I. E., and Gonser, B. W., *Vapor Plating*, John Wiley & Sons, New York, 1955.
4. Friederich, E. and Sittig, L., *Z. Anorg. Allg. Chem.*, 144, 169, 1925.
5. Norton, J. T. and Morory, A. L., *Trans. Am. Inst. Min. Metall. Pet. Eng.*, 185, 133, 1949.
6. Schwarzkopf, P. and Kieffer, R., *Refractory Hard Metals*, Macmillan, New York, 1953.
7. Schwarzkopf, P. and Sindeband, S. J., Electrochemical Society, 97th Meeting, Cleveland, Ohio, 1950.
8. Kieffer, R. and Kölbl, F., *Powder Metall. Bull.*, 4, 4, 1949.
9. Agte, C. and Alterthum, H., *Z. Tech. Phys.*, 11, 182, 1930.
10. Becker, K. and Ebert, F., *Z. Phys.*, 31, 268, 1925.
11. Ruff, O. and Martin, W., *Z. Angew. Chem.*, 25, 49, 1912.
12. Hinnuber, J., *Z. VDI*, 92, 111, 1950.
13. Foster, L. S., Forbes, L. W., Jr., Friar, L. B., Moody, L. S., and Smith, W. H., *J. Am. Ceram. Soc.*, 33, 27, 1950.
14. Ellinger, F. H., *Trans. Am. Soc. Met.*, 31, 89, 1943.
15. Bloom, D. S. and Grant, N. J., *Trans. Am. Inst. Min. Metall. Pet. Eng.*, 188, 41, 1950.
16. Hellstrom, K. and Westgren, A., *Kem. Tidskr.*, 45, 141, 1933.
17. Westgren, A., *Jernkontorets Ann.*, 119, 231, 1935.
18. Xuo, K. and Hägg, G., *Nature*, 170, 245, 1952.
19. Nowotny, H. and Kieffer, R., *Z. Anorg. Allg. Chem.*, 267, 261, 1952.
20. Weiss, G., *Ann. Chem.*, 1, 446, 1946.
21. Brewer, L., Bromely, L. A., Gilles, P. W., and Lofgren, N. L., *The Chemistry and Metallurgy of Miscellaneous Materials: Thermodynamics*, McGraw-Hill, New York, 1950.
22. Becker, K., *Z. Phys.*, 51, 481, 1928.
23. Wilhelm, H. A. and Chiotti, P., *Trans. Am. Soc. Met.*, 42, 1295, 1950.
24. Hunt, E. B. and Rundle, R. E., *J. Am. Chem. Soc.*, 73, 4777, 1951.
25. Mallet, W., Gerds, A. F., and Nelson, H. R., *J. Electrochem. Soc.*, 99, 197, 1952.
26. Litz, L. M., Gurrett, A. B., and Croxton, F. C., *J. Am. Chem. Soc.*, 70, 1718, 1948.
27. Rundle, R. E., Baenziger, N. C., Wilson, A. S., and McDonald, R. A., *J. Am. Chem. Soc.*, 70, 99, 1948.
28. Norton, J. T., Blumenthal, H., and Sindeband, S. J., *Trans. Am. Inst. Min. Metall. Pet. Eng.*, 185, 749, 1949.
29. Honak, E. R., Thesis, Tech. Hochsch. Graz, 1951.
30. Glaser, F. W. and Post, B., *J. Met.*, 1953.
31. Moers, K., *Z. Anorg. Allg. Chem.*, 198, 262, 1931.
32. Andrieux, L., *Rev. Mét.*, 45, 49, 1948.
33. Post, B. and Glaser, F. W., *J. Met.*, 4, 631, 1952.
34. Moers, K., *Z. Anorg. Allg. Chem.*, 198, 243, 1931.
35. Anderson, L. H. and Kiessling, R., *Acta Chem. Scand.*, 4, 160, 209, 1950.
36. Glaser, F. W., *J. Met.*, 4, 391, 1952.
37. Kiessling, R., *Acta Chem. Scand.*, 3, 603, 1949.
38. Moers, K., *Z. Anorg. Allg. Chem.*, 198, 262, 1931.

REFRACTORY MATERIALS (Continued)

REFERENCES (Continued)

39. Kiessling, R., *Acta Chem. Scand.*, 3, 595, 1949.
40. Steintz, R., *J. Met.*, 4, 148, 1952.
41. Kiessling, R., *Acta Chem. Scand.*, 1, 893, 1947.
42. Bertaut, F. and Blum, P., *Acta Crystallogr.*, 4, 72, 1951.
43. Zalkin, A. and Templeton, D. H., *J. Chem. Phys.*, 18, 391, 1950.
44. Bertaut, F. and Blum, P., *Comptes rendus*, 229, 666, 1949.
45. Baumann, H. N., Jr., Electrochemical Society, 99th Meeting, Washington, D.C., April 1951.
46. Friederich, E. and Sittig, L., *Z. Anorg. Allg. Chem.*, 143, 293, 1925.
47. Agte, C. and Moers, K., *Z. Anorg. Chem.*, 198, 233, 1931.
48. Chiotti, P., *J. Am. Ceram. Soc.*, 35, 123, 1952.
49. Hansen, M., Klasler, H. D., and McPherson, D. J., *Trans. Am. Soc. Met.*, 44, 518, 1952.
50. Cerwenka, E., Thesis, Tech. Hochsch. Graz, 1951.
51. Wallbaum, H. J., *Z. Metallkd.*, 33, 378, 1941.
52. Pease, R. S., *Acta Crystallogr.*, 5, 356, 1952.
53. van Arkel, A. E., *Physica*, 4, 296, 1924.
54. Horn, F. H. and Ziegler, W. T., *J. Am. Chem. Soc.*, 69, 2762, 1947.
55. Pauling, L., Killeffer, D. H., and Linz, A., *Molybdenum Compounds*, Interscience, New York, 1952.
56. Hägg, G., *Z. Phys. Chem. Abt. B*, 7, 339, 1930.
57. Kiessling, R. and Lier, Y. H., *J. Met.*, 3, 639, 1951.
58. Rundle, R. E., Baenziger, N. C., Wilson, A. S., and McDonald, R. A., *J. Am. Chem. Soc.*, 70, 99, 1941.
59. Laues, F. and Wallbaum, H. J., *Z. Kristallogr. A*, 101, 78, 1939.
60. Pietrokowsky, P. and Duwez, P., *J. Met.*, 3, 772, 1951.
61. Naray Szako, S. V., *Z. Kristallogr. A*, 97, 223, 1937.
62. Lundin, C. E., McPherson, D. J., and Hansen, M., American Society for Metals, 34th Ann. Convention, Preprint No. 41, 1952.
63. Wallbaum, H. J., *Z. Metallkd.*, 31, 362, 1939.
64. Zachariasen, W. H., *Z. Phys. Chem.*, 128, 39, 1927.
65. Templeton, D. H. and Dauben, C. H., *Acta Crystallogr.*, 3, 261, 1950.
66. Nowotny, H., Kieffer, R., and Schachner, H., *Mh. Chem.*, 83, 1243, 1952.
67. Brauer, G. and Mitices, A., *Z. Anorg. Allg. Chem.*, 249, 325, 1942.
68. Gallistl, E., Thesis, Tech. Hochsch. Graz, 1951.
69. Glaser, F. W., *J. Appl. Phys.*, 22, 103, 1951.
70. Cerwenka, E., Thesis, Tech. Hochsch. Graz, 1951.
71. Currie, L. M., Hamister, V. C., and MacPherson, H. G., paper presented at the United Nations International Conference on The Peaceful Uses of Atomic Energy, Geneva, 1955.

THERMODYNAMIC PROPERTIES OF ELEMENTS AND OXIDES

Thermodynamic calculations over a wide range of temperatures are generally made with the aid of algebraic equations representing the characteristic properties of the substances being considered. The necessary integrations and differentiations, or other mathematical manipulations, are then most easily effected.

The most convenient starting point in making such calculations for a given substance is the heat capacity at constant pressure. From this quantity and a knowledge of the properties of any phase transitions, the other thermodynamic properties may be computed by the well-known equations given in standard texts on thermodynamics.

Users of the following equations and tables are cautioned that the units for a, b, c, and d are cal/g mole, whereas those for A are Kcal/g mole. The necessary adjustment must be made when the data are substituted into the equations.

Empirical heat capacity equations are generally of the form of a power series with the absolute temperature T as the independent variable:

$$C_p = a' + (b' \times 10^{-3})T + (c' \times 10^{-6})T^2$$

or

$$C_p = a'' + (b'' \times 10^{-3})T + \frac{d \times 10^5}{T^2}.$$

Since both forms are used in the ensuing, let

(1)
$$C_p = a + (b \times 10^{-3})T + (c \times 10^{-6})T^2 + \frac{d \times 10^5}{T^2}.$$

The constants a, b, c, and d are to be determined either experimentally or by some theoretical or semi-empirical approach.

The heat content or enthalpy H is determined from the heat capacity by a simple integration over the range of temperatures for which (1) is applicable. Thus, if 298° K is taken as a reference temperature,

(2)
$$H_T - H_{298} = \int_{298}^{T} C_p dT$$

$$= a(T - 298) + \tfrac{1}{2}(b \times 10^{-3})(T^2 - 298^2) + \tfrac{1}{3}(c \times 10^{-6})(T^3 - 298^3) - (d \times 10^5)\left(\frac{1}{T} - \frac{1}{298}\right)$$

$$= aT + \tfrac{1}{2}(b \times 10^{-3})T^2 + \tfrac{1}{3}(c \times 10^{-6})T^3 - \frac{d \times 10^5}{T} - A,$$

where all the constants on the right hand side of the equation have been incorporated in the term −A.

In general, the enthalpy is given by a sum of terms such as (2) for each phase of the substance involved in the temperature range considered plus terms which represent the heats of transitions.

$$H_T - H_{298} = \sum \int_{T_1}^{T_2} C_p dT + \sum \Delta H_{tr}.$$

In a similar manner, the entropy S is obtained from (1) by performing the integration

(3)
$$S_T - S_{298} = \int_{298}^{T} (C_p/T)dt$$

$$= a\ln(T/298) + (b \times 10^{-3})(T - 298) + \tfrac{1}{2}(c \times 10^{-6})(T^2 - 298^2) - \tfrac{1}{2}(d \times 10^5)\left(\frac{1}{T^2} - \frac{1}{298^2}\right)$$

$$= a\ln T + (b \times 10^{-3})T + \tfrac{1}{2}(c \times 10^{-6})T^2 - \left(\frac{\tfrac{1}{2}(d \times 10^5)}{T^2}\right) - B'$$

or

(4)
$$S_T = 2.303\, a \log T + (b \times 10^{-3})T + \tfrac{1}{2}(c \times 10^{-6})T^2 - \frac{\tfrac{1}{2}(d \times 10^5)}{T^2} - B$$

where

(5)
$$B = B' - S_{298}.$$

From the definition of free energy F:

$$F = H - TS$$

the quantity

$$F_T - H_{298} = (H_T - H_{298}) - TS_T$$

is obtained from (2) and (4):

(6)
$$F_T - H_{298} = -2.303aT \log T - \tfrac{1}{2}(b \times 10^{-3})T^2 - \tfrac{1}{6}(c \times 10^{-6})T^3 - \frac{\tfrac{1}{2}(d \times 10^5)}{T} + (B+a)T - A$$

and also the free energy function

(7)
$$\frac{F_T - H_{298}}{T} = -2.303a \log T - \tfrac{1}{2}(b \times 10^{-3})T - \tfrac{1}{6}(c \times 10^{-6})T^2 - \frac{\tfrac{1}{2}(d \times 10^5)}{T^2} + (B+a) - \frac{A}{T}$$

In the following two tables there has been collected values of the constants. The first column lists the element or the oxide. The second column gives the phase to which they are applicable. The third, fourth, and fifth columns supply the thermodynamic properties for the transition to the succeding phase. In column 6, the value of the entropy at 298.15° K, the reference temperature, is given. The remaining columns, except for the last, give the values of the constants a, b, c, d, A, and B required in the thermodynamic equations.

All values throughout the table which represent estimates have been enclosed in parentheses.

The heat capacities at temperatures beyond the range of experimental determination were estimated by extrapolation. Where no experimental values were found, use of analogy with compounds of neighboring elements in the Periodic Table was employed.

THERMODYNAMIC PROPERTIES OF THE ELEMENTS

Ref.: U. S. Atomic Energy Commission Report ANL-5750.

Element	Phase	Temperature of Transition (°K)	Heat of Transition (kcal/g mole)	Entropy of Transition (e.u.)	Entropy at 298°K (e.u.)	Element	cal/g mole a	cal/g mole b	cal/g mole c	cal/g mole d	A (kcal/g mole)	B (e.u.)
Ac	solid	(1090)	(2.5)	(2.3)	(13)	Ac	(5.4)	(3.0)	—	—	(1.743)	(18.7)
	liquid	(2750)	(70)	(25)	—		(8)	—	—	—	(0.295)	(31.3)
Ag	solid	1234	2.855	2.313	10.20	Ag	5.09	1.02	—	0.36	1.488	19.21
	liquid	2485	60.72	24.43	—		7.30	—	—	—	0.164	30.12
	gas	—	—	—	—		(4.97)	—	—	—	(−66.34)	(−12.52)
Al	solid	931.7	2.57	2.76	6.769	Al	4.94	2.96	—	—	1.604	22.26
	liquid	2600	67.9	26	—		7.0	—	—	—	0.33	30.83
Am	solid	(1200)	(2.4)	(2.0)	(13)	Am	(4.9)	(4.4)	—	—	(1.657)	(16.2)
	liquid	2733	51.7	18.9	—		(8.5)	—	—	—	(0.409)	(34.5)
As	solid	883	31/4	35.1/4	8.4	As	5.17	2.34	—	—	1.646	21.8
Au	solid	1336.16	3.03	2.27	11.32	Au	6.14	−0.175	0.92	—	1.831	23.65
	liquid	2933	74.21	25.30	—		7.00	—	—	—	−0.631	26.99
B	solid	2313	(3.8)	(1.6)	1.42	B	1.54	4.40	—	—	0.655	8.67
	liquid	2800	75	27	—		(6.0)	—	—	—	(−4.599)	(31.4)
Ba	solid, α	648	0.14	0.22	16	Ba	5.55	1.50	—	—	1.722	16.1
	solid, β	977	1.83	1.87	—		5.55	1.50	—	—	1.582	15.9
	liquid	1911	35.665	18.63	—		(7.4)	—	—	—	(0.843)	(25.3)
	gas	—	—	—	—		(4.97)	—	—	—	(−39.65)	(−11.7)
Be	solid	1556	2.919	1.501	2.28	Be	5.07	1.21	—	−1.15	1.951	27.62
	liquid						5.27	—	—	—	−1.611	25.68
Bi	solid	544.2	2.63	4.83	13.6	Bi	5.38	2.60	—	—	1.720	17.8
	liquid	1900	41.1	21.6	—		7.60	—	—	—	−0.087	25.6
	gas	—	—	—	—		(4.97)	—	—	—	(−46.19)	(−15.9)
C	solid	—	—	—	1.3609	C	4.10	1.02	—	−2.10	1.972	23.484
Ca	solid, α	723	0.24	0.33	9.95	Ca	5.24	3.50	—	—	1.718	20.95
	solid, β	1123	2.2	1.96	—		6.29	1.40	—	—	1.689	26.01
	liquid	1755	38.6	22.0	—		7.4	—	—	—	−0.147	30.28
	gas	—	—	—	—		(4.97)	—	—	—	(−43.015)	(−9.88)
Cd	solid	594.1	1.46	2.46	12.3	Cd	5.31	2.94	—	—	1.714	18.8
	liquid	1040	23.86	22.94	—		7.10	—	—	—	0.798	26.1
	gas	—	—	—	—		(4.97)	—	—	—	(−25.28)	(−11.7)
Ce	solid	1048	2.1	2.0	13.8	Ce	4.40	6.0	—	—	1.579	13.1
	liquid	2800	73	26	—		(7.9)	—	—	—	(−0.148)	(29.1)
Cl₂	gas	—	—	—	53.286	Cl₂	8.76	0.27	—	−0.65	2.845	−2.929
Co	solid, α	723	0.005	0.007	6.8	Co	4.72	4.30	—	—	1.598	21.4
	solid, β	1398	0.095	0.068	—		3.30	5.86	—	—	0.974	13.1
	solid, γ	1766	3.7	2.1	—		9.60	—	—	—	3.961	50.5
	liquid	3370	93	28	—		8.30	—	—	—	−2.034	38.7
Cr	solid	2173	3.5	1.6	5.68	Cr	5.35	2.36	—	−0.44	1.848	25.75
	liquid	2495	72.97	29.25	—		9.40	—	—	—	1.556	50.13
	gas	—	—	—	—		(4.97)	—	—	—	(−82.47)	(−13.8)
Cs	solid	301.9	0.50	1.7	19.8	Cs	7.42	—	—	—	2.212	22.5
	liquid	963	16.32	17.0	—		8.00	—	—	—	1.887	24.1
	gas	—	—	—	—		(4.97)	—	—	—	(−17.35)	(−13.6)
Cu	solid	1356.2	3.11	2.29	7.97	Cu	5.41	1.50	—	—	1.680	23.30
	liquid	2868	72.8	25.4	—		7.50	—	—	—	0.024	34.05
F₂	gas	—	—	—	48.58	F₂	8.29	0.44	—	−0.80	2.760	−0.76
Fe	solid, α	1033	0.410	0.397	6.491	Fe	3.37	7.10	—	0.43	1.176	14.59
	solid, β	1180	0.217	0.184	—		10.40	—	—	—	4.281	55.66
	solid, γ	1673	0.15	0.084	—		4.85	3.00	—	—	0.396	19.76
	solid, δ	1808	3.86	2.14	—		10.30	—	—	—	4.382	55.11
	liquid	3008	84.62	28.1	—		10.00	—	—	—	−0.021	50.73
Ga	solid	302.94	1.335	4.407	9.82	Ga	5.237	3.33	—	—	1.710	21.01
	liquid	2700	—	—	—		(6.645)	—	—	—	(0.648)	(23.64)
Ge	solid	1232	8.3	6.7	10.1	Ge	5.90	1.13	—	—	1.764	23.8
	liquid	2980	68	23	—		(7.3)	—	—	—	(−5.668)	(25.7)
H₂	gas	—	—	—	31.211	H₂	6.62	0.81	—	—	2.010	6.75
Hf	solid	(2600)	(6.0)	(2.3)	13.1	Hf	(6.00)	(0.52)	—	—	(1.812)	(21.2)
Hg	liquid	629.73	13.985	22.208	18.46	Hg	6.61	—	—	—	1.971	19.20
	gas	—	—	—	—		4.969	—	—	—	−13.048	−13.54
In	solid	430	0.775	1.80	13.88	In	5.81	2.50	—	—	1.844	19.97
	liquid	2440	53.8	22.0	—		7.50	—	—	—	1.564	27.34
	gas	—	—	—	—		(4.97)	—	—	—	(−58.42)	(−14.46)
Ir	solid	2727	6.6	2.4	8.7	Ir	5.56	1.42	—	—	1.721	23.4
K	solid	336.4	0.5575	1.657	15.2	K	1.3264	19.405	—	—	1.258	−1.86
	liquid	1052	18.88	17.95	—		8.8825	−4.565	2.9369	—	1.923	32.55
	gas	—	—	—	—		(4.97)	—	—	—	(−19.689)	(−9.46)
La	solid	1153	(2.3)	(2.0)	13.7	La	6.17	1.60	—	—	1.911	21.9
	liquid	3000	80	27	—		(7.3)	—	—	—	(−0.15)	(26.0)
Li	solid	459	0.69	1.5	6.70	Li	3.05	8.60	—	—	1.292	12.92
	liquid	1640	32.48	19.81	—		7.0	—	—	—	1.509	32.00
	gas	—	—	—	—		(4.97)	—	—	—	(−34.30)	(−2.84)
Mg	solid	923	2.2	2.4	7.77	Mg	5.33	2.45	—	−0.103	1.733	23.39
	liquid	1393	31.5	22.6	—		(8.0)	—	—	—	0.942	36.97
	gas	—	—	—	—		(4.97)	—	—	—	(−34.78)	(−7.60)
Mn	solid, α	1000	0.535	0.535	7.59	Mn	5.70	3.38	—	−0.37	1.974	26.11
	solid, β	1374	0.545	0.397	—		8.33	0.66	—	—	2.672	41.02
	solid, γ	1410	0.430	0.305	—		10.70	—	—	—	4.760	56.84
	solid, δ	1517	3.5	2.31	—		11.30	—	—	—	5.176	60.88
	liquid	2368	53.7	22.7	—		11.00	—	—	—	1.221	56.38
	gas	—	—	—	—		6.26	—	—	—	−63.704	−3.13
Mo	solid	2883	(5.8)	(2.0)	6.83	Mo	5.48	1.30	—	—	1.692	24.78
N₂	gas	—	—	—	45.767	N₂	6.76	0.606	0.13	—	2.044	−7.064
Na	solid	371	0.63	1.7	12.31	Na	5.657	3.252	0.5785	—	1.836	20.92
	liquid	1187	23.4	20.1	—		8.954	−4.577	2.540	—	1.924	36.0
	gas	—	—	—	—		(4.97)	—	—	—	(−24.40)	(−8.7)
Nb	solid	2760	(5.8)	(2.1)	8.3	Nb	5.66	0.96	—	—	1.730	24.24
Nd	solid	1297	(2.55)	(1.97)	13.9	Nd	5.61	5.34	—	—	1.910	19.7
	liquid	(2750)	(61)	(22)	—		(9.1)	—	—	—	−0.606	35.8
Ni	solid, α	626	0.092	0.15	7.137	Ni	4.06	7.04	—	—	1.523	18.095
	solid, β	1728	4.21	2.44	—		6.00	1.80	—	—	1.619	27.16
	liquid	3110	90.48	29.0	—		9.20	—	—	—	0.251	45.47

Element	Phase	Temperature of Transition (°K)	Heat of Transition (kcal/g mole)	Entropy of Transition (e.u.)	Entropy at 298°K (e.u.)	Element	cal/g mole a	cal/g mole b	cal/g mole c	cal/g mole d	A (kcal/g mole)	B (e.u.)
Np	solid	913	(2.3)	(2.5)	—	Np	(5.3)	(3.4)	—	—	(1.731)	(17.9)
	liquid	(2525)	(55)	(22)	(14)		(9.0)	—	—	—	(1.392)	(37.5)
O₂	gas	—	—	—	49.003	O₂	8.27	0.258	—	−1.877	3.007	−0.750
Os	solid	2970	(6.4)	(2.2)	7.8	Os	5.69	0.88	—	—	1.736	24.9
P₄	solid, white	317.4	0.601	1.89	42.4	P₄	13.62	28.72	—	—	5.338	43.8
	liquid	553	11.9	21.5	—		19.23	0.51	—	−2.98	6.035	66.7
	gas	—	—	—	—		(19.5)	(−0.4)	(1.3)	—	(−6.32)	(40.1)
Pa	solid	(1825)	(4.0)	(2.2)	(13.5)	Pa	(5.2)	(4.0)	—	—	(1.728)	(17.3)
	liquid	(4500)	(115)	(26)	—		(8.0)	—	—	—	(−3.823)	(28.8)
Pb	solid	600.6	1.141	1.900	15.49	Pb	5.64	2.30	—	—	1.784	17.33
	liquid	2023	42.5	21.0	—		7.75	−0.73	—	—	1.362	27.11
	gas	—	—	—	—		(4.97)	—	—	—	(−45.25)	(−13.6)
Pd	solid	1828	4.12	2.25	8.9	Pd	5.80	1.38	—	—	1.791	24.6
	liquid	3440	89	26	—		(9.0)	—	—	—	(1.215)	(43.8)
Po	solid	525	(2.4)	(4.6)	13	Po	(5.2)	(3.2)	—	—	1.693	17.6
	liquid	(1235)	(24.6)	(19.9)	—		(9.0)	—	—	—	(0.847)	(35.2)
	gas	—	—	—	—		(4.97)	—	—	—	(−28.73)	(−13.5)
Pr	solid	1205	(2.5)	(2.1)	(13.5)	Pr	(5.0)	(4.6)	—	—	(1.705)	(16.4)
	liquid	3563	—	—	—		(8.0)	—	—	—	(−0.519)	(30.0)
Pt	solid	2042.5	5.2	2.5	10.0	Pt	5.74	1.34	—	0.10	1.737	23.0
	liquid	4100	122	29.8	—		(9.0)	—	—	—	(0.406)	(42.6)
Pu	solid	913	(2.26)	(2.48)	(13.0)	Pu	(5.2)	(3.6)	—	—	(1.710)	(17.7)
	liquid	—	—	—	—		(8.0)	—	—	—	(0.506)	(31.0)
Ra	solid	1233	(2.3)	(1.9)	(17)	Ra	(5.8)	(1.2)	—	—	(1.783)	(16.4)
	liquid	(1700)	(35)	(21)	—		(8.0)	—	—	—	(1.284)	(28.6)
	gas	—	—	—	—		(4.97)	—	—	—	(−38.87)	(−14.5)
Rb	solid	312.0	0.525	1.68	16.6	Rb	3.27	13.1	—	—	1.557	5.9
	liquid	952	18.11	19.0	—		7.85	—	—	—	1.814	26.5
	gas	—	—	—	—		(4.97)	—	—	—	(−19.04)	(−12.3)
Re	solid	3440	(7.9)	(2.3)	(8.89)	Re	(5.85)	(0.8)	—	—	(1.780)	(24.7)
Rh	solid	2240	(5.2)	(2.3)	7.6	Rh	5.40	2.19	—	—	1.707	23.8
	liquid	4150	127	30.7	—		(9.0)	—	—	—	(−0.923)	(44.4)
Ru	solid, α	1308	0.034	0.026	6.9	Ru	5.25	1.50	—	—	1.632	23.5
	solid, β	1473	0	0	—		7.20	—	—	—	2.867	35.5
	solid, γ	1773	0.23	0.13	—		7.20	—	—	—	2.867	35.5
	solid, δ	2700	(6.1)	(2.3)	—		7.50	—	—	—	3.169	37.6
S	solid, α	368.6	0.088	0.24	7.62	S	3.58	6.24	—	—	1.345	14.64
	solid, β	392	0.293	0.747	—		3.56	6.95	—	—	1.298	14.54
	liquid	717.76	2.5	3.5	—		5.4	5.0	—	—	1.576	24.02
½S₂	gas	—	—	—	—	½S₂	(4.25)	(0.15)	—	(−1.0)	(−2.859)	(9.57)
Sb	solid (α,β,γ)	903.7	4.8	5.3	10.5	Sb	5.51	1.74	—	—	1.720	21.4
	liquid	1713	46.665	27.3	—		7.50	—	—	—	−1.992	28.1
½Sb₂	gas	—	—	—	—	½Sb₂	4.47	—	—	−0.11	−53.876	−21.7
Sc	solid	1670	(4.0)	(2.4)	(9.0)	Sc	(5.13)	(3.0)	—	—	1.663	21.1
	liquid	3000	80	27	—		(7.50)	—	—	—	(−2.563)	31.3
Se	solid	490.6	1.25	2.55	10.144	Se	3.30	8.80	—	—	1.375	11.28
	liquid	1000	14.27	14.27	—		7.0	—	—	—	0.881	27.34
Si	solid	1683	11.1	6.60	4.50	Si	5.70	1.02	—	−1.06	2.100	28.88
	liquid	2750	71	26	—		7.4	—	—	—	−7.646	33.17
Sm	solid	1623	3.7	2.3	(15)	Sm	(6.7)	(3.4)	—	—	(2.149)	(24.2)
	liquid	(2800)	(70)	(25)	—		(9.0)	—	—	—	(−2.296)	(33.4)
Sn	solid (α,β)	505.1	1.69	3.35	12.3	Sn	4.42	6.30	—	—	1.598	14.8
	liquid	2473	(55)	(22)	—		7.30	—	—	—	0.559	26.2
	gas	—	—	—	—		(4.97)	—	—	—	(−60.21)	(−14.3)
Sr	solid	1043	2.2	2.1	13.0	Sr	(5.60)	(1.37)	—	—	(1.731)	(19.3)
	liquid	1657	33.61	20.28	—		(7.7)	—	—	—	(0.976)	(30.4)
	gas	—	—	—	—		(4.97)	—	—	—	(−37.16)	(−10.2)
Ta	solid	3250	7.5	2.3	9.9	Ta	5.82	0.78	—	—	1.770	23.4
Tc	solid	(2400)	(5.5)	(2.3)	(8.0)	Tc	(5.6)	(2.0)	—	—	(1.759)	(24.5)
	liquid	(3800)	(120)	(32)	—		(11)	—	—	—	(3.459)	(59.4)
Te	solid, α	621	0.13	0.21	11.88	Te	4.58	5.25	—	—	1.599	15.78
	solid, β	723	4.28	5.92	—		4.58	5.25	—	—	1.469	15.57
	liquid	1360	11.9	8.75	—		9.0	—	—	—	−0.988	34.96
½Te₂	gas	—	—	—	—	½Te₂	4.47	—	—	−0.10	−19.048	−6.47
Th	solid	2173	(4.6)	(2.1)	12.76	Th	8.2	−0.77	2.04	—	2.591	33.64
	liquid	4500	(130)	(29)	—		(8.0)	—	—	—	(−7.602)	(26.84)
Ti	solid, α	1155	0.950	0.822	7.334	Ti	5.25	2.52	—	—	1.677	23.33
	solid, β	2000	(4.6)	(2.3)	—		7.50	—	—	—	1.645	35.46
	liquid	3550	(101)	(28)	—		(7.8)	—	—	—	(−2.355)	(35.45)
Tl	solid, α	508.3	0.082	0.16	15.4	Tl	5.26	3.46	—	—	1.722	15.6
	solid, β	576.8	1.03	1.79	—		7.30	—	—	—	2.230	26.4
	liquid	1730	38.81	22.4	—		7.50	—	—	—	1.315	25.9
	gas	—	—	—	—		(4.97)	—	—	—	(−41.88)	(−15.4)
U	solid, α	938	0.665	0.709	12.03	U	3.25	8.15	—	—	1.063	8.47
	solid, β	1049	1.165	1.111	—		10.28	—	—	0.80	3.493	48.27
	solid, γ	1405	(3.0)	(2.1)	—		9.12	—	—	—	1.110	39.09
	liquid	3800	—	—	—		(8.99)	—	—	—	(−2.073)	36.01
V	solid	2003	(4.0)	(2.0)	7.05	V	5.57	0.97	—	—	1.704	24.97
	liquid	3800	—	—	—		(8.0)	—	—	—	1.007	44.00
W	solid	3650	8.42	2.3	8.0	W	5.74	0.76	—	—	1.745	24.9
Y	solid	1750	(4.0)	(2.3)	(11)	Y	(5.6)	(2.2)	—	—	(1.767)	(21.6)
	liquid	3500	(90)	(26)	—		(7.5)	—	—	—	(−2.277)	(29.6)
Zn	solid	692.7	1.595	2.303	9.95	Zn	5.35	2.40	—	—	1.702	21.25
	liquid	1180	27.43	23.24	—		7.50	—	—	—	1.020	31.35
	gas	—	—	—	—		(4.97)	—	—	—	(−29.407)	(−9.81)
Zr	solid, α	1135	0.920	0.811	9.29	Zr	6.83	1.12	—	−0.87	2.378	30.45
	solid, β	2125	(4.9)	(2.3)	—		7.27	—	—	—	1.159	31.43
	liquid	(3900)	(100)	(26)	—		(8.0)	—	—	—	(−2.190)	(34.7)

For description of headings and symbols see preceding table.
Ref.: U. S. Atomic Energy Report ANL-5750.

Oxide	Phase	Temperature of Transition (°K)	Heat of Transition kcal/mole	Entropy of Transition (e.u.)	Entropy at 298°K (e.u.)	Oxide	cal/g mole a	cal/g mole b	cal/g mole c	cal/g mole d	A (kcal/mole)	B (e.u.)
Ac$_2$O$_3$	solid	(2250)	(20)	(8.9)	(36.5)	Ac$_2$O$_3$	(20.0)	(20.4)	—	—	(6.870)	(80.9)
	liquid	—	—	—			(40)				(−19.767)	(180.5)
Ag$_2$O	solid	dec. 460	—	—	29.09	Ag$_2$O	13.26	7.04	—	—	4.266	48.56
Ag$_2$O$_2$	solid	dec	—	—	(20.4)	Ag$_2$O$_2$	(16.4)	(12.2)	—	—	(5.432)	(76.7)
Al$_2$O$_3$	solid	2300	26	11	12.186	Al$_2$O$_3$	26.12	4.388	—	−7.269	10.422	142.03
	liquid	dec.					(33)				(−11.655)	(174.1)
Am$_2$O$_3$	solid	(2225)	(17)	(7.6)	(37)	Am$_2$O$_3$	(20.0)	(15.6)	—	—	(6.657)	(81.6)
	liquid	(3400)	(85)	(25)			(38.5)				(−7.796)	(181.8)
AmO$_2$	solid	dec.			(20)	AmO$_2$	(14.0)	(6.8)	—	—	(4.477)	(61.8)
As$_2$O$_3$	solid, α	503	4.1	8.2	25.6	As$_2$O$_3$	8.37	48.6	—	—	4.656	36.6
	solid, β	586	4.4	7.5			8.37	48.6	—	—	0.556	28.4
	liquid	730	7.15	9.79	—		(39)	—			(5.760)	(187.6)
	gas	—	—	—			(21.5)	—			(−14.164)	(62.5)
AsO$_2$	solid	(1200)	(9.0)	(7.5)	(13)	AsO$_2$	(8.5)	(9.4)	—	—	(2.952)	(38.2)
	liquid	(dec.)	—	—	—		(21)	—			(2.184)	(108.0)
As$_2$O$_5$	solid	dec. >1100	—	—	25.2	As$_2$O$_5$	(31.1)	(16.4)	—	(−5.4)	(11.813)	(159.9)
Au$_2$O$_3$	solid	dec.	—	—	30	Au$_2$O$_3$	(23.5)	(4.8)	—	—	(7.220)	(105.3)
B$_2$O$_3$	solid	723	5.27	7.29	12.91	B$_2$O$_3$	8.73	25.40	—	−1.31	4.171	45.04
	liquid	2520	(55)	(22)			30.50	—			7.822	161.59
Ba$_2$O	solid	(880)	(5.2)	(5.9)	(23.5)	Ba$_2$O	(20.0)	(2.2)	—	—	(6.061)	(91.1)
	liquid	(1040)	(20)	(19)			(22)	—			(1.769)	(96.8)
	gas	—	—	—			(15)	—			(−25.51)	(29.0)
BaO	solid	2196	13.8	6.28	16.8	BaO	12.74	1.040	—	−1.984	4.510	57.2
	liquid	3000	(62)	(21)			(13.9)	—			(−9.341)	(57.5)
BaO$_2$	solid	723	(5.7)	(7.9)	(18.5)	BaO$_2$	(13.6)	(2.0)	—	—	(4.144)	(59.6)
	liquid	dec. 1110	—	—			(21)	—			(3.241)	(99.0)
BeO	solid	dec.	—	—	3.37	BeO	8.69	3.65	—	−3.13	3.803	48.99
BiO	solid	(1175)	(3.7)	(3.1)	(15)	BiO	(9.7)	(3.0)	—	—	(3.025)	(41.2)
	liquid	(1920)	(54)	(28)			(14)	—			(2.306)	(64.9)
	gas	—	—	—			(8.9)	—			(−61.49)	(−1.8)
Bi$_2$O$_3$	solid	1090	6.8	6.2	36.2	Bi$_2$O$_3$	23.27	11.05	—	—	7.429	99.7
	liquid	(dec.)	—	—			(35.7)	—			(7.614)	(168.3)
CO	gas	—	—	—	47.30	CO	6.60	1.2	—	—	2.021	−9.34
CO$_2$	gas	—	—	—	51.06	CO$_2$	7.70	5.3	−0.83	—	2.490	−5.64
CaO	solid	2860	(18)	(6.3)	9.5	CaO	10.00	4.84	—	−1.08	3.559	49.5
CdO	solid	dec.	—	—	13.1	CdO	9.65	2.08	—	—	2.970	42.5
Ce$_2$O$_3$	solid	1960	(20)	(10)	(33.5)	Ce$_2$O$_3$	(23.0)	(9.0)	—	—	(7.258)	(100.2)
	liquid	(3500)	(80)	(23)			(37)	—			(−2.591)	(178.5)
CeO$_2$	solid	3000	(19)	(6.3)	17.7	CeO$_2$	15.0	2.5	—	—	4.579	68.5
CoO	solid	2078	(12)	(5.8)	10.5	CoO	(9.8)	(2.2)	—	—	(3.020)	(46.0)
	liquid	(2900)	(61)	(21)			(15.5)	—			(−1.886)	(79.2)
Co$_3$O$_4$	solid	dec., 1240	—	—	(35.5)	Co$_3$O$_4$	(29.5)	(17.0)	—	−3.736	(9.551)	(137.6)
Cr$_2$O$_3$	solid	2538	(25)	(10)	19.4	Cr$_2$O$_3$	28.53	2.20	—	—	9.857	145.9
CrO$_2$	solid	dec. 700	—	—	(11.5)	CrO$_2$	(16.1)	(3.0)	—	—	(5.946)	(82.8)
CrO$_3$	solid	460	(6.1)	(13)	(17.5)	CrO$_3$	(18.1)	(4.0)	—	−2.0)	(6.245)	(87.9)
	liquid	(1000)	(25)	(25)	—		(27)	—			(3.381)	(127.0)
	gas	—	—	—			(20)	—			(−28.62)	(53.6)
Cs$_2$O	solid	763	(4.58)	(6.0)	(23)	Cs$_2$O	(16.5)	(5.4)	—	—	(5.160)	(72.6)
	liquid	dec.	—	—			(22)	—			(3.205)	(99.0)
Cs$_2$O$_2$	solid	867	(5.5)	(6.3)	(40)	Cs$_2$O$_2$	(21.4)	(11.4)	—	—	(6.887)	(85.3)
	liquid	dec.	—	—			(29.5)	—			(4.125)	(123.8)
Cs$_2$O$_3$	solid	775	(7.75)	(10)	(47)	Cs$_2$O$_3$	(24.0)	(22.6)	—	—	(8.160)	(96.5)
	liquid	dec.	—	—			(35)	—			(2.148)	(142.2)
Cu$_2$O	solid	1503	13.4	8.92	22.44	Cu$_2$O	(13.4)	(8.6)	—	—	(4.378)	(54.9)
	liquid	dec.	—	—			(21.5)	—			(3.721)	(96.0)
CuO	solid	1609	(8.9)	(5.5)	10.4	CuO	14.34	6.2	—	—	4.551	61.11
	liquid	dec.	—	—			(22)	—			(−4.339)	(98.91)
FeO	solid	1641	7.5	4.6	12.9	FeO	9.27	4.80	—	—	(2.977)	(43.8)
	liquid	(2700)	(55)	(20)			(14.5)	—			(−3.721)	(69.2)
Fe$_3$O$_4$	solid, α	900	(0)	(0)	35.0	Fe$_3$O$_4$	12.38	1.62	—	−0.38	3.826	58.3
	solid, β	dec.	—	—	—		(14.5)	—			(−2.399)	(66.7)
Fe$_2$O$_3$	solid, α	950	0.16	0.17	21.5	Fe$_2$O$_3$	21.88	48.20	—	—	8.666	104.0
	solid, β	1050	0	0	—		48.00	—			12.652	238.3
	solid, γ	dec.	—	—			23.49	18.6	—	−3.55	9.021	119.9
Ga$_2$O	solid	(925)	(8.5)	(9.2)	(22.5)	Ga$_2$O	36.00	—	—	—	11.979	187.6
	liquid	(1000)	(20)	(20)			31.71	1.8	—	—	8.467	159.7
	gas	—	—	—			(13.8)	(8.6)			(4.497)	(58.7)
Ga$_2$O$_3$	solid	2013	(22)	(11)	20.23	Ga$_2$O$_3$	(21.5)	—	—	—	(−0.559)	(94.1)
	liquid	(2900)	(75)	(26)			(14)	—			(−28.06)	(22.3)
GeO	solid	983	(50)	(51)	(12.5)	GeO	11.77	25.2	—	—	(4.630)	(54.35)
	gas	—	—	—			(35.5)	—			(−20.66)	(173.2)
GeO$_2$	solid (α,β)	1389	10.5	7.56	(12.5)	GeO$_2$	(10.4)	(2.6)	—	(−0.5)	(3.384)	(47.8)
	liquid	(2625)	(61)	(23)			(8.2)	(0.4)	—	(−0.2)	(−49.67)	(−20.2)
H$_2$O	liquid	373.16	9.770	26.18	16.716	H$_2$O	11.2	7.17	—	—	(3.658)	(53.5)
							(21.7)	—			(1.149)	(111.9)
HfO$_2$	solid	3063	(17)	(5.6)	14.18	HfO$_2$	18.03	2.56	—	—	5.376	86.01
Hg$_2$O	solid	dec.	—	—	(30)	Hg$_2$O	7.17	2.56	—	−0.08	−8.290	−3.56
HgO	solid	dec.	—	—	16.839	HgO	17.39	2.08	—	−3.48	6.445	87.48
							(15.6)	(28)			(4.776)	(59.7)
In$_2$O	solid	(600)	(4.5)	(7.5)	(28)	In$_2$O	(8.5)	(7.0)	—	—	(2.846)	(33.7)
	liquid	(800)	(16)	(20)			(14.7)	(7.8)	—	—	(4.730)	(58.1)
	gas	—	—	—			(22)	—			(3.206)	(92.6)
InO	solid	(1325)	(4.0)	(3.0)	(14.5)	InO	(15)	—	—	—	(−18.39)	(25.8)
	liquid	(2000)	(60)	(30)			(10.0)	(3.2)	—	—	(3.124)	(43.4)
	gas	—	—	—			(14)	—			(1.615)	(64.9)
In$_2$O$_3$	solid	(2000)	(20)	(10)	30.1	In$_2$O$_3$	(9.0)	—	—	—	(−68.38)	(−3.1)
	liquid	(3600)	(85)	(24)			(22.6)	(6.0)	—	—	(7.005)	(100.5)
							(35)	—			(−0.195)	(172.8)

Oxide	Phase	Temperature of Transition (°K)	Heat of Transition kcal/mole	Entropy of Transition (e.u.)	Entropy at 298°K (e.u.)	Oxide	cal/g mole a	cal/g mole b	cal/g mole c	cal/g mole d	A (kcal/mole)	B (e.u.)
Ir₂O₃	solid	(1450)	(10)	(6.8)	(26.5)	Ir₂O₃	(21.8)	(14.4)	—	—	(7.140)	(102.0)
	liquid	(2250)	(50)	(22)	—		(35)				(0.706)	(170.3)
	gas	—	—	—	—		(20)	(10)	—	—	(−57.73)	(54.8)
IrO₂	solid	dec. 1373	—	—	(15.9)	IrO₂	9.17	15.20	—	—	3.410	40.9
K₂O	solid	(980)	(6.8)	(6.9)	(23)	K₂O	(15.9)	(6.4)	—	—	(5.025)	(69.5)
	liquid	dec.	—	—	—		(22)				(1.130)	(98.3)
K₂O₂	solid	763	(7.0)	(9.2)	(27)	K₂O₂	(20.8)	(5.4)	—	—	(6.442)	(93.1)
	liquid	(1800)	(45)	(25)	—		(29)				4.127	(134.2)
	gas	—	—	—	—		(20)				(−57.07)	(41.7)
K₂O₃	solid	703	(6.1)	(8.7)	(33.5)	K₂O₃	(19.1)	(23.2)	—	—	6.750	(82.2)
	liquid	(975)	(25)	(26)	—		(35.5)				6.447	(164.7)
	gas	—	—	—	—		(20)	(5.0)	—	—	(−31.29)	(37.3)
KO₂	solid	653	(4.9)	(7.5)	27.9	KO₂	(15.0)	(12.0)	—	—	(5.006)	(61.1)
	liquid	dec.	—	—	—		(24)				(3.424)	(105.5)
La₂O₃	solid	2590	(18)	(7)	(36.5)	La₂O₃	28.86	3.076	—	−3.275	9.840	(130.7)
Li₂O	solid	2000	(14)	(7)	9.06	Li₂O	(11.4)	(5.4)	—	—	(3.639)	(57.5)
	liquid	2600	(56)	(22)	—		(21)				(−1.961)	(112.7)
Li₂O₂	solid	dec. 470	—	—	(16.5)	Li₂O₂	(17.0)	(5.4)	—	—	(5.309)	(82.0)
MgO	solid	3075	18.5	5.8	6.4	MgO	10.86	1.197	—	−2.087	3.991	57.0
MgO₂	solid	dec. 361	—	—	(20.5)	MgO₂	(12.1)	(2.4)	—	—	(3.714)	(49.2)
MnO	solid	2058	13.0	6.32	14.27	MnO	11.11	1.94	—	−0.88	3.689	50.10
	liquid	dec.	—	—	—		(13.5)				(−8.543)	(58.02)
Mn₃O₄	solid, α	1445	4.97	3.44	35.5	Mn₃O₄	34.64	10.82	—	−2.20	11.312	166.3
	solid, β	1863	(33)	(18)	—		50.20				17.376	260.4
	liquid	(2900)	(75)	(26)	—		(49)				(−17.86)	(233.4)
Mn₂O₃	solid	dec. 1620	—	—	26.4	Mn₂O₃	24.73	8.38	—	−3.23	8.829	118.8
MnO₂	solid	dec. 1120	—	—	12.7	MnO₂	16.60	2.44	—	−3.88	6.359	84.8
MoO₂	solid	(2200)	(16)	(7.3)	(14.5)	MoO₂	(16.2)	(3.0)	—	(−3.0)	(5.973)	(80.4)
	liquid	dec. 2250	—	—	—		(23)				(−2.463)	(118.4)
MoO₃	solid	1068	12.54	11.74	18.68	MoO₃	13.6	13.5	—	—	4.655	62.83
	liquid	1530	33	22	—		(28.4)				(0.222)	(139.88)
	gas	—	—	—			(18.1)				(−48.54)	(42.8)
N₂O	gas				52.58	N₂O	10.92	2.06	—	−2.04	4.032	11.40
Na₂O	solid	1193	(7.1)	(6.0)	17.4	Na₂O	15.70	5.40	—	—	4.921	73.7
	liquid	dec.	—	—	—		(22)				(1.494)	(105.9)
Na₂O₂	solid	dec. 919	—	—	22.6	Na₂O₂	(20.2)	(3.8)	—	—	(6.192)	(93.6)
NaO₂	solid	(825)	(6.2)	(7.5)	27.7	NaO₂	(16.2)	(3.6)	—	—	(4.000)	(65.7)
	liquid	(1300)	(28)	(22)	—		(23)				(3.175)	(100.9)
	gas	—	—	—	—		(15)				(−35.22)	(22.0)
NbO	solid	(2650)	(16)	(6.0)	(12)	NbO	(9.6)	(4.4)	—	—	(3.058)	(44.0)
NbO₂	solid	(2275)	(16)	(7.0)	(12.7)	NbO₂	(17.1)	(1.6)	—	(−2.8)	(6.109)	(84.6)
	liquid	(3800)	(85)	(22)	—		(24)				(1.033)	(127.2)
Nb₂O₅	solid	1733	(28)	(16)	32.8	Nb₂O₅	21.88	28.2	—	—	7.776	100.3
	liquid	(3200)	(80)	(25)	—		(44.2)				(−24.09)	(201.6)
Nd₂O₃	solid	2545	(22)	(8.8)	(35.3)	Nd₂O₃	28.99	5.760	—	(−4.159)	10.295	(133.9)
NiO	solid	2230	(12.1)	(5.43)	9.22	NiO	13.69	0.83	—	−2.915	5.097	70.67
	liquid	dec.	—	—	—		(14.3)				(−7.861)	(67.91)
NpO₂	solid	(2600)	(15)	(5.7)	19.19	NpO₂	17.7	(3.2)	—	(−2.6)	(6.292)	(84.08)
Np₂O₅	solid	dec. 800–900°K	—	—	(43)	Np₂O₅	32.4	(12.6)	—	—	(10.22)	(145.4)
OsO₂	solid	dec. 923	—	—	(14.5)	OsO₂	(11.5)	(6.0)	—	—	(3.696)	(52.8)
OsO₄	solid	313.3	3.41	10.9	34.7	OsO₄	(16.4)	(23.1)	—	(−2.4)	(6.726)	(67.0)
	liquid	403	9.45	23.4	—		(33)				(6.612)	(143.0)
	gas	—	—	—	—		16.46	8.60	—	−4.6	(−7.644)	(25.3)
P₂O₃	liquid	448.5	4.5	10	(34)	P₂O₃	(34.5)				(10.287)	(162.6)
	gas	—	—	—	—		(15)	(10)	—	—	(−1.953)	(38.0)
PO₂	solid	(350)	(2.7)	(7.7)	(11.5)	PO₂	(11.3)	(5.0)	—	—	(3.591)	(54.4)
	liquid	(dec)	—	—	—		(20)				(3.640)	(95.9)
P₂O₅	solid	631	8.8	13.9	33.5	P₂O₅	8.375	5.40	—	—	4.897	30.3
	gas	—	—	—	—		36.80				3.284	165.6
PaO₂	solid	(2560)	(20)	(7.8)	(17.8)	PaO₂	(14.4)	(2.6)	—	—	(4.409)	(65.0)
Pa₂O₅	solid	(2050)	(26)	(13)	(37.5)	Pa₂O₅	(28.4)	(11.4)	—	—	(8.975)	(127.7)
	liquid	(3350)	(95)	(28)	—		(48)				(−0.800)	(241.1)
PbO	solid, red	762	(0.4)	(0.5)	16.2	PbO	10.60	4.00	—	—	3.338	45.4
	solid, yellow	1159	2.8	2.4	—		9.05	6.40			2.454	36.4
	liquid	1745	51	29	—		(14.6)				1.788	65.7
	gas	—	—	—	—		(8.1)	(0.4)	—	—	(−59.94)	(−11.0)
Pb₃O₄	solid	dec.	—	—	50.5	Pb₃O₄	(31.1)	(17.6)	—	—	(10.055)	(132.0)
PbO₂	solid	dec.	—	—	18.3	PbO₂	12.7	7.80	—	—	4.133	56.4
PdO	solid	dec. 1150	—	—	(9.1)	PdO	3.30	14.2	—	—	1.615	(13.9)
PoO₂	solid	(825)	(5.5)	(6.7)	(17)	PoO₂	(14.3)	(5.6)	—	—	(4.513)	(66.1)
	liquid	(dec.)	—	—	—		(22)				(3.460)	(106.5)
Pr₂O₃	solid	(2200)	(22)	(10)	(35.5)	Pr₂O₃	(29.0)	(4.0)	—	(−4.0)	(10.166)	(133.2)
	liquid	(4000)	(90)	(23)	—		(36)				(−6.298)	(168.3)
PrO₂	solid	dec. 700	—	—	(17)	PrO₂	(17.6)?	(3.4)	—	(−2.8)	(6.338)	(85.9)
PtO	solid	dec. 780	—	—	(13.5)	PtO	(9.0)	(6.4)	—	—	(2.968)	(39.7)
Pt₃O₄	solid	(dec.)	—	—	(41)	Pt₃O₄	(30.8)	(17.4)	—	—	(9.957)	(139.7)
PtO₂	solid	723	(4.6)	(6.4)	(16.5)	PtO₂	(11.1)	(9.6)	—	—	(3.736)	(49.6)
	liquid	dec. 750	—	—	—		(21)				(3.785)	(101.5)
PuO	solid	(1290)	(7.2)	(5.6)	(20)	PuO	(12.0)	(2.4)	—	—	(3.685)	(49.1)
	liquid	(2325)	(47)	(20)	—		(14.5)				0.007	(50.0)
	gas						(8.9)				(−62.307)	(−5.3)
Pu₂O₄	solid	(1880)	(16)	(8.5)	(38)	Pu₂O₃	(21.2)	(18.2)	—	—	(7.130)	(88.2)
	liquid	(3250)	(75)	(23)	—		(40)				(−5.691)	(187.2)
PuO₂	solid	(2400)	(15)	(6.2)	(19.7)	PuO₂	(17.1)	(3.4)	—	(−2.6)	(6.122)	(80.2)
	liquid	(3500)	(90)	(26)	—		(20.5)				(−10.62)	(92.2)
RaO	solid	(>2500)	—	—	(17)	RaO	10.5	(2.0)	—	—	(3.220)	(43.4)
Rb₂O	solid	(910)	(5.7)	(6.3)	(27)	Rb₂O	(15.4)	(5.8)	—	—	(4.850)	(62.5)
	liquid	dec.	—	—	—		(22)				(2.754)	(95.9)
Rb₂O₂	solid	843	(7.3)	(8.7)	(27.5)	Rb₂O₂	(20.9)	(8.0)	—	—	(6.587)	(94.0)
	liquid	(dec.)	—	—	—		(29)				(3.273)	(133.2)
Rb₂O₃	solid	762	(7.6)	(10)	(32.5)	Rb₂O₃	(20.5)	(13.0)	—	—	(6.690)	(88.2)
	liquid	dec.	—	—	—		(34)				(5.603)	(157.8)
RbO₂	solid	685	(4.1)	(6.0)	(21.5)	RbO₂	(13.8)	(6.4)	—	—	(4.399)	(59.0)
	liquid	dec.	—	—	—		(21)				(3.720)	(95.7)
ReO₂	solid	(1475)	(12)	(8.1)	(15)	ReO₂	(10.8)	(9.8)	—	—	(3.656)	(49.5)

THERMODYNAMIC PROPERTIES OF THE OXIDES

Oxide	Phase	Temperature of Transition (°K)	Heat of Transition kcal/mole	Entropy of Transition (e.u.)	Entropy at 298°K (e.u.)	Oxide	cal/g mole a	cal/g mole b	cal/g mole c	cal/g mole d	A (kcal/mole)	B (e.u.)
ReO_2	liquid	(3250)	(80)	(25)	—	ReO_2	(24.5)	—	—	—	(1.204)	(127.0)
ReO_3	solid	433	5.2	12	19.8	ReO_3	(18.0)	(5.8)	—	—	(5.625)	(84.5)
	liquid	dec.					29				(4.644)	(136.8)
Re_2O_7	solid	569	15.8	27.8	44	Re_2O_7	(41.8)	(14.8)	—	(−3.0)	(14.127)	(200.3)
	liquid	635.5	17.7	27.9	—		(65.7)	—	—	—	(9.203)	(314.7)
	gas	—					(38.2)	—	—	—	(−25.97)	(109.3)
ReO_4	solid	420	(4.2)	(10)	(34.5)	ReO_4	(21.4)	(10.8)	—	(−2.0)	(7.531)	(91.8)
	liquid	(460)	(9.3)	(20)	—		(33)	—	—	—	(6.775)	(146.7)
	gas	—					(16.5)	(8.6)	—	(−5.0)	(−8.118)	(30.6)
Rh_2O	solid	dec. 1400	—	—	(25.5)	Rh_2O	15.59	6.47	—	—	4.936	(65.3)
RhO	solid	dec. 1394	—	—	(12)	RhO	(9.84)	(5.53)	—	—	(3.179)	(45.7)
Rh_2O_3	solid	dec. 1388	—	—	(23)	Rh_2O_3	20.73	13.80	—	—	6.794	(99.2)
RuO_2	solid	dec. 1400	—	—	(12.5)	RuO_2	(11.4)	(6.0)	—	—	3.666	(54.2)
RuO_4	solid	300	(3.2)	(11)	(32.5)	RuO_4	(20)	—	—	—	(5.963)	(81.5)
	liquid	dec.					(33)	—	—	—	(6.663)	(144.9)
SO_2	gas	—	—	—	59.40	SO_2	11.4	1.414	—	−2.045	4.148	7.12
Sb_2O_3	solid	928	14.74	15.88	29.4	Sb_2O_3	19.10	17.1	—	—	6.455	84.5
	liquid	1698	8.92	5.25	—		(36)	—	—	—	(0.035)	(168.2)
	gas	—					(20.8)	—	—	—	(−34.70)	(49.9)
SbO_2	solid	dec.	—	—	15.2	SbO_2	11.30	8.1	—	—	3.725	51.6
Sb_2O_5	solid	dec.	—	—	29.9	Sb_2O_5	(22.4)	(23.6)	—	—	(7.728)	(104.8)
Sc_2O_3	solid	(2500)	(23)	(9.3)	24.8	Sc_2O_3	23.17	5.64	—	—	7.159	108.9
SeO	solid	(1375)	(7.6)	(5.5)	(11)	SeO	(9.1)	(3.8)	—	—	(2.882)	(42.0)
	liquid	(2075)	(45)	(22)	—		(15.5)	—	—	—	(0.490)	(77.5)
	gas	—					8.20	0.50	—	−0.80	(−58.54)	(0.7)
SeO_2	solid	603	(24.5)	(40.6)	(15)	SeO_2	(12.8)	(6.1)	—	(−0.2)	(4.150)	(59.9)
	gas	—					(14.5)	—	—	—	(−20.45)	(26.4)
SiO	solid	(2550)	(12)	(4.7)	(6.5)	SiO	(7.3)	(2.4)	—	—	(2.283)	(35.8)
SiO_2	solid, β	856	0.15	0.18	10.06	SiO_2	11.22	8.20	—	−2.70	4.615	57.83
	solid, α	1883	2.04	1.08			14.41	1.94	—	—	4.602	73.67
	liquid	dec. 2250					(20)	—	—	—	(9.649)	(111.08)
Sm_2O_3	solid	(2150)	(20)	(9.3)	(36.5)	Sm_2O_3	(25.9)	(7.0)	—	—	(8.033)	(113.2)
	liquid	(3800)	(80)	(21)			(36)	—	—	—	(−6.431)	(166.3)
SnO	solid	(1315)	(6.4)	(4.9)	13.5	SnO	9.40	3.62	—	—	2.964	41.1
	liquid	(1800)	(60)	(33)			(14.5)	—	—	—	(0.141)	(68.1)
	gas	—					(9.0)	—	—	—	(−69.76)	(−6.4)
SnO_2	solid	1898	(11.39)	(5.95)	12.5	SnO_2	17.66	2.40	—	−5.16	7.103	91.7
	liquid	(3200)	(75)	(23)			(22.5)	—	—	—	(0.304)	(117.7)
SrO	solid	2703	16.7	6.2	13.0	SrO	12.34	1.120	—	−1.806	4.335	58.7
SrO_2	solid	dec. 488	—	—	(14.8)	SrO_2	(16.8)	(2.2)	—	(−3.0)	(6.113)	(83.3)
Ta_2O_5	solid	2150	(16)	(7.4)	34.2	Ta_2O_5	29.2	10.0	—	—	9.151	135.2
	liquid	—					(46)	—	—	—	(6.158)	(235.1)
TcO_2	solid	(2400)	(18)	(7.5)	(13.5)	TcO_2	(10.4)	(9.2)	—	—	(3.510)	(48.6)
	liquid	(4000)	(105)	(26)			(25)	—	—	—	(−5.946)	(132.7)
TcO_3	solid	(dec. <1200)	—	—	(19.5)	TcO_3	(19.4)	(5.2)	—	(−2.0)	(6.686)	(93.7)
Tc_2O_7	solid	392.7	(11)	(28)	(42.5)	Tc_2O_7	(39.1)	(18.6)	—	(−2.4)	(13.29)	(187.2)
	liquid	583.8	(14)	(24)			(64)	—	—	—	(10.02)	(299.8)
	gas	—					(25)	(28)	—	—	(−21.98)	(43.8)
TeO	solid	(1020)	(7.1)	(7.0)	(13)	TeO	(8.6)	(6.2)	—	—	(2.840)	(37.8)
	liquid	(1775)	(50)	(28)			(15.5)	—	—	—	(−0.448)	(72.3)
	gas	—					(8.9)	—	—	—	(−62.16)	(−5.2)
TeO_2	solid	1006	3.2	3.2	16.99	TeO_2	13.85	6.87	—	—	4.435	63.97
	liquid	dec.					(20)	—	—	—	(3.940)	(96.4)
ThO	solid	(2150)	(13)	(6.0)	(16)	ThO	(11.0)	(2.4)	—	—	(3.386)	(47.4)
	liquid	(3250)	(65)	(20)			(15)	—	—	—	(−6.561)	(66.9)
ThO_2	solid	3225	(18)	(5.6)	15.59	ThO_2	16.45	2.346	—	−2.124	5.721	80.03
TiO	solid, α	1264	0.82	0.65	8.31	TiO	10.57	3.60	—	−1.86	3.935	54.03
	solid, β	dec. 2010	—	—			11.85	3.00	—	—	4.108	61.71
Ti_2O_3	solid, α	473	0.215	0.455	18.83	Ti_2O_3	7.31	53.52	—	—	4.559	38.78
	solid, β	2400	(24)	(10)			34.68	1.30	—	−10.20	13.605	184.48
	liquid	3300					(37.5)	—	—	—	(−7.796)	(193.2)
Ti_3O_5	solid, α	450	2.24	4.98	30.92	Ti_3O_5	35.47	29.50	—	—	11.887	179.98
	solid, β	(2450)	(50)	(20)			41.60	8.00	—	—	10.230	202.80
	liquid	(3600)	(85)	(24)			(60)	—	—	—	(−18.701)	(306.4)
TiO_2	solid	2128	(16)	(7.5)	12.01	TiO_2	17.97	0.28	—	−4.35	6.829	92.92
	liquid	dec. 3200					(21.4)	—	—	—	(−2.610)	(111.08)
Tl_2O	solid	573	(5.0)	(8.7)	23.8	Tl_2O	(15.8)	(6.0)	—	(−0.3)	(5.078)	(68.2)
	liquid	773	(17)	(22)	—		(22.1)	—	—	—	(2.651)	(96.0)
	gas	—					(13.7)	—	—	—	(−20.94)	(18.0)
Tl_2O_3	solid	990	(12.4)	(13)	(33.5)	Tl_2O_3	(23.0)	(5.0)	—	—	(7.080)	(99.0)
	liquid	(dec)					(35.5)	—	—	—	(4.604)	(167.8)
UO	solid	(2750)	(14)	(5.1)	(16)	UO	10.6	(2.0)	—	—	(3.249)	(45.0)
UO_2	solid	3000	—	—	18.63	UO_2	19.20	1.62	—	−3.957	7.124	93.37
U_3O_8	solid	dec.	—	—	(66)	U_3O_8	(65)	(7.5)	—	(−10.9)	(23.37)	(312.7)
UO_3	solid	dec. 925	—	—	23.57	UO_3	22.09	2.54	—	−2.973	7.696	104.72
VO	solid	(2350)	(15)	(6.4)	9.3	VO	11.32	1.61	—	−1.26	3.869	56.4
	liquid	(3400)	(70)	(21)			(14.5)	—	—	—	(−8.157)	(70.9)
V_2O_3	solid	2240	(24)	(11)	23.58	V_2O_3	29.35	4.76	—	−5.42	10.780	148.12
	liquid	dec. 3300					(38)	—	—	—	(−6.028)	(193.4)
V_3O_5	solid	(2100)	(42)	(20)	(32)	V_3O_5	(36)	(30)	—	—	(12.07)	(182.1)
	liquid	(dec.)					(55.6)	—	—	—	(−54.72)	(249.1)
VO_2	solid, α	345	1,02	2.96	12.32	VO_2	14.96	—	—	—	4.460	72.92
	solid, β	1818	13.60	7.48	—		17.85	1.70	—	−3.94	5.680	89.09
	liquid	dec. 3300					25.50	—	—	—	2.962	135.87
V_2O_5	solid	943	15.56	16.50	313	V_2O_5	46.54	−3.90	—	−13.22	18.136	240.2
	liquid	(2325)	(63)	(27)	—		45.60	—	—	—	2.122	220.1
	gas	—					(40)	—	—	—	(−73.90)	(149.6)
WO_2	solid	(1543)	(11.5)	(7.45)	(15)	WO_2	(17.6)	(4.2)	—	(−4.0)	(6.772)	(88.8)
	liquid	dec. 2125					(24)	—	—	—	(−0.112)	(121.2)
WO_3	solid	1743	(17)	(9.8)	19.90	WO_3	17.33	7.74	—	—	5.511	81.15
	liquid	(2100)	(43)	(20)			(30)	—	—	—	(−1.162)	(152.5)
	gas	—					(18)	—	—	—	(−69.36)	(40.2)
Y_2O_3	solid	(2500)	(25)	(10)	(29.5)	Y_2O_3	(26.0)	(8.2)	—	(−2.2)	(8.846)	(122.3)
ZnO	solid	dec.	—	—	10.4	ZnO	11.71	1.22	—	−2.18	4.277	57.88
ZrO_2	solid, α	1478	1.420	0.961	12.03	ZrO_2	16.64	1.80	—	−3.36	6.168	85.21
	solid, β	2950	20.8	7.0			17.80	—	—	—	4.270	89.96

VALUES OF CHEMICAL THERMODYNAMIC PROPERTIES

All values of energy in these tables are expressed, insofar as possible, in terms of the thermochemical calorie, now defined in terms of the absolute joule. 1 thermochemical calorie = 1 calorie = 4.1840 absolute joule = 4.1833 international joule. The notations used in these tables are as follows:

$\Delta Hf°$ = the standard heat of formation of a given substance from its elements at 25°C., kilo -cal/g mole.

$\Delta Ff°$ = the standard free energy of formation of a given substance from its elements at 25°C., kilo -cal/g mole.

$\log_{10} Kf$ = the logarithm of the equilibrium constant for the reaction for forming a given substance from its elements at 25°C.

$S°$ = the entropy of the given substance in its thermodynamic reference state at the reference temperature at 25°C., cal/deg. mole.

c = crystalline; in certain cases where a substance exists in more than one crystalline form there is an indication as to which form is concerned.

g = gaseous.

am = amorphous.

aq = aqueous; unless otherwise indicated the aqueous solution is taken as the hypothetical ideal state of unit molality.

gls = glass.

lq = liquid.

ppi = precipitate.

The values in these tables were taken from Circular of the National Bureau of Standards 500. "Selected Values of Chemical Thermodynamic Properties, issued February 1, 1952.

RELATIONSHIP TO SI UNITS

The symbols cal. mole^{-1} deg^{-1} and gibbs/mol are identical and refer to units of calories per degree-mole. These units can be converted to SI units of joules per degree-mole by multiplying the tabulated values by 4.184. Similarly values in kilocalories per mole can be converted to joules per mole by multiplying with the factor 4184. For further discussions of the SI system and for conversions from other units the reader should consult Pure and Applied Chemistry, 21, 1 (1970).

Substance	State	ΔHf°	ΔFf°	Log₁₀ Kf	S°
Aluminum					
Al	g	75.00	65.3	−47.86	39.303
	c	0.00	0.00	0.000	6.77
Al⁺⁺⁺	aq	1307.44	......	......	......
AlBr₃	c	−125.8	−120.7	88.47	44
	aq	−211.9			
Al₄C₃	c	−30.9	−29.0	21.26	25
Al(CH₃)₃	lq	−26.9	......		
Al₂Cl₆	g	−303.6			
AlCl₃	c	−166.2	−152.2	111.56	40
	aq, 600	−245.5			
AlCl₃·6H₂O	c	−641.1	−542.4	397.57	90
AlF₃	c	−311	−294	215.5	23
AlF₃·3H₂O	c	−549.1	−490.4	359.46	50
	aq	−361.4			
AlF₃·½H₂O	c	−357.4	−333.6	244.52	28
AlI₃	c	−75.2	−75.0	54.97	48
	aq	−165.8			
AlN	c	−57.7	−50.1	36.72	5
Al(NO₂)₃	aq	−273.65			
Al(NO₃)₃·6H₂O	c	−680.65	−525.82	385.419	111.8
Al(NO₃)₃·9H₂O	c	−897.34	−700.2	513.24	136
Al₂O₃(α)*	c	−399.09	−376.77	276.167	12.19
(γ)	c	−384.84			
Al₂O₃·H₂O	c	−471	−435	318.8	23.15
Al₂O₃·3H₂O†	c	−613.7	−547.9	401.60	33.51
Al(OH)₃	am	−304.2			
Al₂S₃	c	−121.6	−117.7	86.27	23
Al₂(SO₄)₃	c	−820.98	−738.99	541.670	57.2
	aq	−897.1			
Al₂(SO₄)₃·6H₂O	c	−1268.14	−1105.14	810.054	112.1
Al₂(SO₄)₃18H₂O	c	−2118.5			
AlNH₄(SO₄)₂	c	−561.24	−485.95	356.195	51.7
	aq	−591.74			
AlNH₄(SO₄)₂·12H₂O	c	−1419.40	−1179.02	864.207	166.6
Ammonium					
NH₃	g	−11.04	−3.976	2.914	46.01
	aq	−19.32	−6.37	−4.669	26.3
	aq ∞	−19.32			
NH₄⁺	aq	−31.74	−19.00	13.927	26.97
NH₄OH	aq	−87.64			
NH₄H₂AsO₄	c	−251.47	−197.24	144.574	41.12
	aq	247.9			
(NH₄)₂HAsO₄	c	−280.24			
	aq	−278.3			
(NH₄)₃AsO₄	c	−306.11			
	aq	−303			
(NH₄)₃AsO₄·3H₂O	c	−516.6			
NH₄BO₂	aq	−215.2			
NH₄BO₃	aq	−193.7			
NH₄BO₃·H₂O	c	−270.8			
(NH₄)₂HBO₃	aq	−305.5			
NH₄Br	c	−64.61			
	aq, ∞	−60.71			
(NH₄)₂CO₃	aq	−225.11	−164.22	120.371	41.2
NH₄HCO₃	c	−203.7			
	aq	−196.92	−159.31	116.772	49.7
NH₄CO₂NH₂	c	−154.21	−109.47	80.240	39.70
	aq	−150.4			
NH₄CN	c	0.0	......		
	aq	4.6	20.4		
NH₄CNO	c	−74.7			
	aq	−68.5			
NH₄CNS	c	−20.0			
	aq	−14.5	4.4		
NH₄C₂H₃O₂	c	−147.8			
	aq, 400	−148.1			
(NH₄)₂C₂O₄	c	−268.72			
	aq, 2100	−260.6			

Substance	State	ΔHf°	ΔFf°	Log₁₀ Kf	S°
Ammonium					
(NH₄)₂C₂O₄·H₂O	c	−340.62	......		
NH₄HC₂O₄	aq	−227.02			
NH₄Cl	c	−75.38	−48.73	35.718	22.6
	aq, ∞	−71.76			
NH₄ClO₄	c	−69.42			
NH₄F	c	−111.6			
	aq, ∞	−110.40			
NH₄I	c	−48.30			
	aq, ∞	−45.11			
NH₄NO₂	c	−63.1			
	aq	−57.1			
NH₄NO₃	c	−87.27			
	aq	−81.11			
NH₄H₂PO₄	c	−346.75	−290.46	212.903	36.32
	aq, 500	−342.91			
(NH₄)₂HPO₄	c	−376.12			
	aq, 500	−373.04			
(NH₄)₃PO₄	c	−401.8			
	aq, 660	−394.0			
(NH₄)₃PO₄·3H₂O	c	−612.8			
(NH₄)₂PtCl₄	c	−195.3			
	aq	−186.9			
(NH₄)₂S	aq	−54.5			
NH₄HS	c	−38.10			
	aq	−35.1			
NH₄S₄	c	−34.0			
	aq	−29.7			
(NH₄)₂S₅	c	−69.4			
	aq	−65.4			
(NH₄)₂SO₃	aq	−212.0			
	aq	−211.3			
(NH₄)₂SO₃·H₂O	c	−284.22			
NH₄HSO₃	c	−183.8			
	aq	−181.5			
(NH₄)₂SO₄	c	−281.86	−215.19	157.732	52.65
	aq, ∞	−280.38			
NH₄HSO₄	c	−244.83			
	aq	−245.6			
(NH₄)₂S₂O₈	aq	−396.4			
	aq	−387.8			
(NH₄)₂Se	aq	−26.2			
NH₄HSe	aq	−5.6			
(NH₄)₂SiF₆	c	−629.7			
	aq	−622.0			
NH₄VO₃	c	−251.2	−211.8	155.25	33.6
NH₂OH	c	−25.5			
	aq	−21.7			
NH₂OH·HCl	c	−74.0			
	aq	−70.7			
NH₂OH·HNO₂	c	−86.3			
	aq	−80.5			
(NH₂OH)₂·H₂SO₄	c	−282.5			
	aq	−276.7			
NH₂OH·H₂SO₄	c	−245.1			
	aq	−244.4			
N₂H₄	lq	12.05			
	aq, 300	8.16			
N₂H₄·H₂O	lq	−57.95			
N₂H₄·HCl	c	−46.93			
	aq	−41.7			
N₂H₄·2HCl	c	−90.0			
	aq	−84.0			
(N₂H₄)₂·H₂SO₄	c	−217.8			
N₂H₄·H₂SO₄	aq	−231.6			
	aq	−223.4			
HN₃	g	70.3	78.5	−57.54	56.74
	aq, 100	61.51			

* Corundum.
† Hydrargillite.

Substance	State	$\Delta Hf°$	$\Delta Ff°$	$\text{Log}_{10} Kf$	$S°$
Antimony					
Sb	g	60.8	51.1	−37.46	43.06
	c, III	0.00	0.00	0.000	10.5
SbO⁺	aq		−42.0	30.79	
Sb₂	g	52.	40	−29.32	60.9
SbBr₃	c	−62.1			
SbCl₃	g	−75.2	−72.3	52.99	80.8
	c	−91.34	−77.62	56.894	44.5
SbCl₅	g	−93.9			
	lq	−104.8			
SbOCl	c	−90.8			
SbF₃	c	−217.2			
	aq	−216.1			
SbI₃	c	−23.0			
	aq	−22.6			
Sb₂O₃	aq	−166.5			
Sb₂O₄	c	−214	−188	137.8	30.3
Sb₂O₅	c	−234.4	−200.5	146.96	29.9
	aq	−226.4			
Sb₂O₆	c	−336.8	−298.0	218.43	59.8
Sb₂S₃ (black)	c	−43.5			
(orange)	am	−36.0			
Sb₂(SO₄)₃	c	575.3			
H₃SbO₄	aq	−215.7			
Argon					
A	g	0.00	0.00	0.000	36.983
A·5H₂O	c	−357.2			
Arsenic					
As (gray)	c	0.00	0.00	0.000	8.4
(β)	am	1.6			
(yellow)	c	3.53			
AsO⁺	aq		−39.1	28.69	
As₂	g	29.6	17.5	−12.83	57.3
As₄	g	35.7	25.2	−18.47	69
AsBr₃	c	−46.61			
AsCl₃	g	−71.5	−68.5	50.21	78.2
	lq	−80.2	−70.5	51.68	55.8
AsF₃	g	−218.3	−214.7	157.37	69.08
	lg	−226.8	−215.5	157.96	43.31
AsH₃	g	41.0			
AsH₃·6H₂O	c	−386.7			
AsI₃	c	−13.7			
As₂O₅	c	−218.6	−184.6	135.41	25.2
	aq	−224.6			
As₂O₅·4H₂O	c	−500.3			
3As₂O₅·5H₂O	c	−1007.5			
As₂O₃·As₂O₅	c	−351.1			
As₄O₆ (oct)	c	−313.94	−275.36	201.835	51.2
(mon)	c	−312.8			
	aq	−299.4			
As₂S₃	c	−35			
H₃AsO₃	aq	−177.3	−152.9	112	47.0
H₃AsO₄	c	−215.2			
	aq	−214.8	−183.8	134.72	49.3
Barium					
Ba	g	41.96	34.60	−25.361	40.699
	c	0.00	0.00	0.000	16
Ba⁺⁺	aq	−128.67	−134.0	98.22	3
Ba₃(AsO₄)₂	c	−817.8			
BaHAsO₄·H₂O	c	−411.5			
Ba(H₂AsO₄)₂·2H₂O	c	−694.7			
Ba(C₂H₃O₂)₂	c	−355.1			
Ba(C₂H₃O₂)₂3H₂O	c	−567.3			
BaBr₂	c	−180.4			
	aq	−180.47	−183.1	134.21	42
BaBr₂·H₂O	c	−254.9			
BaBr₂·2H₂O	c	−326.3			
BaOBr₂	aq	−181.6			
Ba(HCO₂)₂	c	−326.5			
Ba(CN)₂	c	−47.9			
	aq	−50.7			
Ba(CN)₂·H₂O	c	−120.1			
Ba(CN)₂·2H₂O	c	−191.1			
BaCN₂	c	−63.8			
Ba(CNO)₂	c	−209.6			
BaCO₃	c	−291.3	−272.2	199.52	26.8
	aq	−290.30	−260.2	190.72	−10
Ba(HCO₃)₂	aq	−459.0	−414.6	303.90	48
BaC₂O₄·½H₂O	c	−363.7			
BaC₂O₄·2H₂O	c	−470.1			
BaC₂O₄·3½H₂O	c	−575.3			
BaCl₂	c	−205.56	−193.8	142.05	30
	aq	−208.72	−196.7	144.18	29
BaCl₂·H₂O	c	−278.4	−253.1	185.52	40
BaCl₂·2H₂O	c	−349.35	−309.7	227.01	48.5
BaOCl₂	aq	−194.0			
Ba(OCl)₂	aq	−176.1			
Ba(ClO₂)₂	c	−158.2			
Ba(ClO₃)₂	c	−181.7			
	aq	−175.6			

Substance	State	$\Delta Hf°$	$\Delta Ff°$	$\text{Log}_{10} Kf$	$S°$
Barium					
Ba(ClO₃)₂·H₂O	c	−254.9			
Ba(ClO₄)₂	c	−192.8			
Ba(ClO₄)₂·3H₂O	c	−405.4			
BaPtCl₆	c	−286.8			
	aq	−296.1			
BaPtCl₆·6H₂O	c	−707.2			
BaCrO₄	c	−341.3			
BaF₂	c	−286.9			
	aq	−286.0	−265.3		
BaSiF₆	c	−691.6			
BaH	g	52	46	−33.7	52.97
BaH₂	c	−40.9			
BaI₂	c	−144.0			
	aq	−155.41	−158.7	116.32	55
BaI₂·H₂O	c	−219.8			
BaI₂·2H₂O	c	−290.9			
BaI₂·2½H₂O	c	−326.0			
BaI₂·7H₂O	c	−640.1			
Ba(IO₃)₂	aq	−238.4			
Ba(IO₃)₂·H₂O	c	−319.6			
BaMoO₄	c	−373.8			
Ba(N₃)₂	c	−8.0			
	aq	0.2			
Ba₃N₂	c	−86.9			
Ba(NO₂)₂	c	−174.0			
Ba(NO₂)₂·H₂O	c	−254.5			
Ba(NO₃)₂	c	−237.06	−190.0	139.27	51.1
	aq	−227.41	−186.8	136.92	73
BaO	c	−133.4	−126.3	92.58	16.8
BaO₂	c	−150.5			
BaO₂·H₂O	c	−223.5			
BaO₂·8H₂O	c	−719.3			
Ba(OH)₂	c	−226.2			
	aq	−238.58	−209.2	153.34	−2
Ba(OH)₂·H₂O	c	−299.0			
Ba(OH)₂·8H₂O	c	−799.5			
Ba₃(PO₄)₂	c	−998.0			
BaHPO₄	c	−465.8			
Ba(H₂PO₄)₂	c	−749.6			
BaS	g	41			
	c	−106.0			
	aq	−118.4			
Ba(HS)₂	aq	−134.8			
Ba(HSO₃)₂	aq	−430.7			
BaSO₃	c	−282.6			
BaSO₄	c	−350.2	−323.4	237.05	31.6
	aq, ∞	−345.57	−311.3	228.18	7
BaS₂O₆	aq	−409.3			
BaS₂O₆·2H₂O	c	−552.5			
BaS₂O₃	aq	−454.0			
BaS₂O₃·4H₂O	c	−738.7			
BaS₄O₆	aq	−401.3			
BaS₄O₆·2H₂O	c	−554.5			
BaSe	c	−142.0			
BaSeO₄	c	−280.0			
BaSiO₃	c	−359.5			
Ba₂SiO₄	c	−496.8			
BaWO₄	c	−407.7			
Beryllium					
Be	g	76.63	67.60	−49.550	32.55
	c	0.00	0.00	0.000	2.28
Be⁺⁺	aq		−93		
(in acid solution)					
BeBr₂	c	−88.4			
BeBr₂ (in HCl)	aq	151			
BeCl₂	c	−122.3			
BeCl₂ (in HCl)	aq	173.4			
BeCl₂·4H₂O	c	−436.8			
BeF₂	aq	−251.4			
BeH	g	78.1	71.3	−52.26	40.84
BeI₂	c	−50.6			
BeI₂ (in HCl)	aq	−120			
BeMoO₄	c	−330			
Be₃N₂	c	−135.7	−122.4		
Be(NO₃)₂	aq	−188.3			
BeO	g	11.8	5.7	−4.18	47.18
	c	−146.0	−139.0	101.88	3.37
Be(OH)₂	c (α)	−216.8			
	c (β)	−216.1			
BeS	c	−55.9			
BeSO₄	c	−286.0			
BeSO₄·H₂O	c	−361			
BeSO₄·2H₂O	c	−433.2			
BeSO₄·4H₂O	c	−576.3			
BeSO₄·4BeO	c	−871.4			
Bismuth					
Bi	g	49.7	40.4	−29.61	44.67
	c	0.00	0.00	0.000	13.6
BiO⁺	aq		−35.54	25.317	
BiCl₃	g	−64.7	−62.2	45.59	85.3
	c	−90.61	−76.23	55.876	45.3

Substance	State	$\Delta Hf°$	$\Delta Ff°$	$Log_{10} Kf$	$S°$
Bismuth					
$BiCl_3$ (in HCl)	aq	−101.6	...	...	...
$BiOCl$	c	−87.3	−77.0	56.44	20.6
Bi_2O_3	c	−137.9	−118.7	87.01	36.2
$Bi(OH)_3$	c	−169.6	...	...	...
Bi_2S_3	c	−43.8	−39.4	28.88	35.3
Boron					
B	g	97.2	86.7	−63.55	36.649
B	c	0.00	0.00	0.000	1.56
B	am	0.4	...	...	...
BBr_3	g	−44.6	−51.0	37.38	77.49
BBr_3	lq	−52.8	−52.4	38.41	54.7
BCl_3	g	−94.5	−90.9	66.63	69.29
BCl_3	lq	−100.0	−90.6	66.41	50.0
B_4C	c	...	...	...	6.47
$B(CH_3)_3$	lq	−31.4	...	...	...
BF_3	g	−265.4	−261.3	191.53	60.70
BF_3	aq	−289.8	...	...	...
BF_4^-	aq	−365	−347	251.4	40
HBF_4	aq	−365	...	...	...
BH	g	73.8	67.1	−49.18	39.62
B_2H_6	g	7.5	19.8	−14.51	55.66
B_5H_9	g	15.0	39.6	−29.03	65.88
$B_{10}H_{14}$	c	8	...	...	...
BN	c	90.6	...	...	...
BO	g	−32.1	−27.2	19 94	8
	c	−5.3	−11.6	8 50	47.22
B_2O_3	c	−302.0	−283.0	207.44	12.91
B_2O_3	gls	−297.6	−280.4	205.53	18.8
B_2S_3	c	−57.0	...	...	...
HBO_2	c	−186.9	−170.5	124.97	11
	aq	−186.9	...	...	...
HBO_3	aq	−251.8	−217.63	159 520	7.3
$H_2B_4O_7$	c	−676.5	...	...	...
H_3BO_3	c	−260.2	−230.2	168.73	21.41
	aq	−255.2	−230.24	168.762	38.2
Bromine					
Br_2	g	7.34	0.75	−0.551	58.64
Br_2	lq	0.00	0.00	0.000	36.4
Br_2	aq	−1.1	...	...	...
$Br_2·10H_2O$	c	−700	...	...	...
$BrCl$	g	3 51	−0.21	0 154	57.34
HBr	g	−8.66	−12.72	9.327	47.44
HBr	aq, 1	−18.56	...	...	...
HBr	aq, 3	−24.36	...	...	...
HBr	aq	−28.90	−24.57	18.012	19.29
$HBrO_2$	aq	−11.63	5 00	...	...
Cadmium					
Cd	g	26.97	18.69	−13.700	40.07
Cd (α)	c	0.00	0.00	0.000	12.3
Cd (γ)	c	...	0.14	−0.103	...
$CdBr_2$	c	−75.15	−70.14	51.412	31.9
	aq	−75.822	−67.6	...	...
$CdBr_2·4H_2O$	c	−356.32	−297.64	218 166	74.7
$CdCl_2$	c	−93.00	−81.88	60.017	28.3
	aq	−97.39	−81.28	59.577	11.6
$CdCl_2·H_2O$	c	−164 13	−140.13	102.713	40.8
$CdCl_2·2\frac{1}{2}H_2O$	c	−269.97	−225 47	165.266	55.6
$Cd(CH_3)_2$	lq	16.2	...	...	...
$Cd(C_2H_5)_2$	lq	14.7	...	...	...
$Cd(CN)_2$	c	39.0	...	...	...
	aq	30.3	...	...	...
$Cd(ONC)_2$	c	37.7	...	...	...
$CdCO_3$	c	−178.7	−160.2	117.42	25.2
CdF_2	c	−164 9	−154.8	113.47	27
	aq	−173.6	...	...	...
CdH	g	62.54	55.73	−40.849	50.76
CdI_2	c	−48.0	−48.00	35.183	40.2
	aq, ∞	−44.66	...	...	...
$Cd(N_3)_2$	c	107.8	...	...	...
Cd_3N_2	c	38 6	...	...	...
$Cd(NO_3)_2$	c	−107 98	...	...	...
	aq	−116.04	−71.41	52.342	20.4
$Cd(NO_3)_2·2H_2O$	c	−251 19	...	...	...
$Cd(NO_3)_2·4H_2O$	c	−394.02	...	...	...
CdO	c	−60 86	−53.79	39.427	13.1
$Cd(OH)_2$	c	−133.26	−112.46	82.432	22.8
CdS	c	−34.5	−33.6	24.63	17
$CdSO_4$	c	−221.36	−195.99	143.657	32.8
	aq	−234.20	−195 92	143 607	−10.47
$CdSO_4·H_2O$	c	−294.37	−254.84	186.794	41.1
Cd_3Sb_2	c	7.83	1.59	−1.165	78.8
$CdₐOₐ$	g	1 6	...	...	...
$CdTe$	c	−24 30	−23.82	17.460	22.6
Calcium					
Ca	g	46.04	37.98	−27.839	36.99
Ca	c	0.00	0.00	0.000	9.95
Ca^{++}	aq	−129.77	−132.18	96.886	−13.2
$2CaO·Al_2O_3$	c	−704	...	...	...
$2CaO·Al_2O_3·5H_2O$	c	−1078	...	...	...
$3CaO·Al_2O_3$	c	−861	...	...	...
$3CaO·Al_2O_3·6H_2O$	c	−1329	...	...	...
$4CaO·Al_2O_3$	c	−1026	...	...	...
$Ca_3(AsO_4)_2$	c	−796	...	...	...
$CaHAsO_4$	aq	−344.1	...	...	...
$CaHAsO_4·H_2O$	c	−410	−363	266.1	35

Substance	State	$\Delta Hf°$	$\Delta Ff°$	$Log_{10} Kf$	$S°$
Calcium					
$Ca(H_2AsO_4)_2$	aq	−560.8	...	...	...
$CaBr_2$	c	−161.3	−156.8	114.93	31
	aq	−187.57	−181.33	132.912	25.4
$CaBr_2·6H_2O$	c	−597.2	...	...	...
$CaO·B_2O_3$	c	−483.3	−457.7	335.49	25.1
$CaO·2B_2O_3$	c	−798.8	−752.4	551.50	32.2
$2CaO·B_2O_3$	c	−651.6	−618.6	453.42	34.7
$3CaO·B_2O_3$	c	−817.7	−777.1	569.60	43.9
CaC_2	c	−15.0	−16.2	11.87	16.8
$CaCO_3$ (calcite)	c	−288.45	−269.78	197.745	22.2
(aragonite)	c	−288.49	−269.53	197 562	21.2
$Ca(HCO_3)_2$	aq	−460.13	−412.80	302.577	32.2
$Ca(HCO_2)_2$	c	−323.5	...	...	...
CaC_2O_4	c	−332.2	...	...	...
$CaC_2O_4·H_2O$	ppt	−399.1	−360.6	264.31	37.28
$CaC_2O_4·2H_2O$	c	−469.1	−416.9	305.58	47
$Ca(C_2H_3O_2)_2$	c	−355.0	...	...	...
	aq	−362.5	...	...	...
$Ca(C_2H_3O_2)_2H_2O$	c	−425.1	...	...	...
$Ca(CN)_2$	c	−44.2	...	...	...
	aq	...	−54	...	...
$CaCN_2$	c	−84.0	...	...	...
$CaCl_2$	c	−190.0	−179.3	131.42	27.2
$CaCl_2$	aq	−209.82	−194.88	142.884	13.1
$CaCl_2·H_2O$	c	−265.1	...	...	...
$CaCl_2·2H_2O$	c	−335.5	...	...	...
$CaCl_2·4H_2O$	c	−480.2	...	...	...
$CaCl_2·6H_2O$	c	−623.15	...	...	...
$CaCl_2·2CaO$	c	−505	...	...	...
$CaCl_2·3CaO$	c	−654	...	...	...
$CaCl_2·3CaO·3H_2O$	c	−910.6	...	...	...
$CaCl_2·3CaO·16H_2O$	c	−1833	...	...	...
$CaCl_2·3C_2H_5OH$	c	−399.8	...	...	...
$CaCl_2·4C_2H_5OH$	c	−467.4	...	...	...
$CaOCl_2$	c	−178.6	...	...	...
	aq	−189.1	...	...	...
$CaOCl_2·H_2O$	c	−249.2	...	...	...
$Ca(OCl)_2$	aq	−180.0	...	...	...
$CaCrO_4$	c	−329.6	−305.3	223.78	32
	aq	−336.0	...	...	...
CaF_2	c	−290.3	−277.7	203.55	16.46
	aq	−287.09	−264.34	193.758	−17.8
CaH	g	58.7	...	...	...
CaH_2	c	−45.1	−35.8	26.25	10
CaI_2	c	−127.8	−126.6	92.80	34
	aq	−156.51	−156.88	114.991	39.1
$CaI_2·8H_2O$	c	−700.7	...	...	...
CaN_6	c	75.8	...	...	...
Ca_3N_2	c	−103.2	−88.1	64.57	25
$Ca(NO_2)_2$	c	−178.3	...	...	...
	aq	−180.5	...	...	...
$Ca(NO_3)_2$	c	−224.0	−177.34	129.988	46.2
	aq	−228.51	−185.00	135.602	56.8
$Ca(NO_3)_2·2H_2O$	c	−368.00	−293.51	215.139	64.3
$Ca(NO_3)_2·3H_2O$	c	−437.18	−349.0	255.81	74
$Ca(NO_3)_2·4H_2O$	c	−509.37	−406.5	297.96	81
CaO	c	−151.9	−144.4	105.84	9.5
CaO_2	c	−157.5	...	...	...
$Ca(OH)_2$	c	−235.80	−214.33	157.101	18.2
	aq	−239.68	−207.37	152.000	−18.2
Ca_2P_2	c	−120.5	...	...	...
$Ca_3(PO_4)_2$	c (α)	−986.2	−929.7	681.46	57.6
$Ca_3(PO_4)_2$	c (β)	−988.9	−932.0	683.14	56.4
$CaHPO_4$	c	−435.2	−401.5	294.29	21
$CaHPO_4·2H_2O$	c	−576.0	−514.6	377.19	40
$Ca(H_2PO_4)_2$	ppt	−744.4	...	...	...
CaS	c	−115.3	−114.1	83.63	13.5
	aq	−119.8	...	...	...
$CaSO_3·2H_2O$	c	−421.2	−374.1	274.21	44
$CaSO_4$ (anhydrite)	c	−342.42	−315.56	231.301	25.5
(soluble α)	c	−340.27	−313.52	229.806	25.9
(soluble β)	c	−339.21	−312.46	229.029	25.9
	aq	−346.67	−309.52	226.874	−9.1
$CaSO_4·\frac{1}{2}H_2O$	c (α)	−376.47	−343.02	251.429	31.2
$CaSO_4·\frac{1}{2}H_2O$	c (β)	−375.97	−342.78	251.253	32.1
$CaSO_4·2H_2O$	c	−483.06	−429.19	314.590	46.36
$CaSr_2O_3$	aq, 1000	−283 4	...	...	...
$Ca_2SrO_6·6H_2O$	c	...	−602.2	441.40	...
$CaSe$	c	−74 7	−73.5	53.87	16
$CaSi_2$	c	−36	...	...	...
Ca_2Si	c	−50	...	...	...
$CaₐSiₐ$	c	−72	...	...	...
$CaSiO_3$*	c (α)	−377.4	−357.4	261.97	20.9
$CaSiO_3$	c (β)	−378.6	−358.2	262.55	19.6
Ca_2SiO_4	c (β)	−538.0	...	...	...
Ca_2SiO_4	c (γ)	−539.0	...	...	...
Ca_2SiO_5	c	−688.4	...	...	...
$CaWO_4$	c	−392.5	...	...	...
Carbon**					
C	g	171.70	160.85	−117.897	37.76
C (diamond)	c	0.45	0.69	−0.502	0.58
(graphite)	c	0.00	0.00	0.000	1.36
CO_2	g	−94 05	−94.26	69.092	51.06
CO_2	aq	−98.69	−92.31	67.662	29.0
CO	g	−26.42	−32.81	24.048	47.30

* (α) Pseudowollastonite; (β) wollast   ** For the values of organic compounds see table following zirconium compounds.

Substance	State	$\Delta Hf°$	$\Delta Ff°$	Log_{10} Kf	$S°$
Cerium					
Ce	c	0.00	0.00	0.000	13.8
Ce+++	aq	−173.7	−170.5	124.97	−44
CeCl₃	c (α)	−260.3	....	....	....
	aq	−293.9	−264 5	193.87	−5
Ce₂H₃	c	−170			
CeI₃	c (α)	−164.4			
	aq	−213.9	−207.5	152.09	34
CeO₂	c	−233			
CeO₃·2H₂O	c	−389			
CeS₂	c	−153.9			
Ce₂S₃	c	−298.7			
Ce(SO₄)₂	c	−560			
Ce₂(SO₄)₃	c	−998.3	−873.0	639.90	−76
Ce₂(SO₄)₃·5H₂O	c	−1308			
Ce₂(SO₄)₃·8H₂O	c	....	−1340.2	982.35	
Ce₂(SO₄)₃·9H₂O	c	....	−1396.8	1023.83	
Cesium					
Cs	c	0.00	0.00	0.000	19.8
Cs+	aq	−59.2	−67.41	49.111	31.8
CsBr	c	−94.3	−91.6	67.142	29
	aq	−88.1	−91.98	67.420	51
Cs₂CO₃	c	−267.4			
CsHCO₃	c	−228.4			
	aq	−224.4			
CsCl	c	−103.5			
	aq	−99.2	−88.76	65.060	45.0
CsClO₄	c	−103.86	−73.28	53.713	41.89
	aq	−90.6	−69.98	51.294	75.3
CsF	c	−126.9			
	aq	−135.9	−133.49	97.846	29.5
Cs₂SiF₆	c	−669.5			
CsH	g	29.0	24.3	−17.81	51.25
CsI	c	−80.5	−79.7	58.419	31
	aq	−72.6	−79.76	58.463	57.9
CsNH₂	c	−25.4			
CsNO₃	c	−118.11			
	aq	−108.6	−93.82	68.769	86.8
Cs₂O	c	−75.9			
Cs₂O₂	c	−96.2			
CsOH	c	−97.2			
	aq	−114.2	−105.00	76.964	29.3
CsOH·H₂O	c	−186.9			
CsReO₄	c	−257.2			
	aq	−249.5			
Cs₂S	c	−81.1			
	aq	−108.4			
CsHS	c	−62.9			
	aq	−63.2			
Cs₂SO₄	c	−339.38			
	aq	−335.3	−312.16	228.809	67.7
CsHSO₄	c	−274.0			
CsHSe	c	−36.7			
	aq	−34.6			
Chlorine					
Cl₂	g	0.00	0.00	0.00	53.29
Cl-	aq	−40.023	−31.350	22.98	13.17
ClF	g	−13.3	−13.6	9.97	52.05
ClO	g	33			
ClO₂	g	24.7	29.5	−21.623	59.6
ClO₃	g	37.0			
Cl₂O	g	18.20	22.40	−16.419	63.70
Cl₂O₇	g	63.4			
HCl	g	−22.06	−22.77	16.690	44.62
	aq	−40.02	−31.35	22.979	13.17
HClO	aq, 400	−28.18			
	aq, 1000	−27.83			
HClO₂	aq	−14.0			
HClO₃	aq	−23.50			
HClO₄	lq (lq)	−11.1			
	aq	−31.41			
HClO₄·H₂O	c	−92.1			
HClO·2H₂O	lq	−162.8			
Chromium					
Cr	g	80.5	69.8	−51.16	41.64
	c	0.00	0.00	0.000	5.68
Cr+++	aq	1310			
Cr₃C₂	c	−21.0	−21.2	15.54	20.4
Cr₄C	c	−16.4	−16.8	12.31	25.3
Cr₇C₃	c	−42.5	−43.8	32.10	48.0
CrCl₂	c	−94.56	−85.15	62.414	27.4
	aq	−113.2			
CrCl₂·2H₂O	c	−237			
CrCl₂·3H₂O	c	−309.0			
CrCl₂·4H₂O	c	−384.5			
CrCl₃	c	−134.6	−118.0	86.492	30.0
CrCl₄	g	−104.			
CrO₂Cl₂	lq	−135.7			
CrF₂	c	−181.0			
CrF₃	c	−265.2			
Cr₇H₂	c	−3.7			
CrI₂	c	−54 2			

Substance	State	$\Delta Hf°$	$\Delta Ff°$	Log_{10} Kf	$S°$
Chromium	aq	−59.9			
CrN	c	−29.8			
Cr₂N	c	−23.4			
Cr₂O₃	c	−269.7	−250.2	183.39	19.4
Cr₂O₃·H₂O	c	−358			
Cr₂O₃·2H₂O	c	−439			
Cr₂O₃·3H₂O	c	−517			
Cr(OH)₃	c	−247.1			
H₂CrO₄	aq	−213.3	−178.5	130.84	17.5
Cobalt					
Co	g	105	94	−68.9	42.88
	c	0.00	0.00	0.000	6.8
Co++	aq	−16.1	−12.3	9.016	−37.1
CoBr₂	c	−55.5			
CoBr₂·6H₂O	c	−73 9			
	aq	−485.1			
Co₃C	c	9.5	7.1	−5.20	29.8
CoCO₃	c	−172.7	−155.36		
CoCl₂	c	−77.8	−67.5	49.48	25.4
	aq	−96 1			
CoCl₂·2H₂O	c	−222 9			
CoCl₂·4H₂O	c	−367 2			
CoCl₂·6H₂O	c	−508.9			
CoF₂	c	−159			
	aq	−173.6			
CoF₂·4H₂O	c	....	−380.9	279.19	
CoF₃	c	−187			
CoH	c	−4.1			
CoH₂	c	−10.2			
CoI₂	c	−24.4			
	aq	−42.8			
Co(IO₃)₂	c	−124 3			
	aq	−125.9			
Co(IO₃)₂·2H₂O	c	−264.9			
Co(IO₃)₂·4H₂O	c	−401 9			
Co(NO₃)₂	c	−102.9			
	aq	−114 8			
Co(NO₃)₂·6H₂O	c	−529.7			
CoO	c	−57.2	−51.0	37.38	10.5
Co₃O₄	c	−210			
Co(OH)₂	c	−131 2	−108.9		
Co(OH)₃	c	−176 6	−142.0		
CoP	c	−35			
CoP₃	c	−65			
Co₂P	c	−47 3			
CoS	c	−20 2	−19.8		
	ppt	−21 4			
Co₂S₃	c	−51			
CoSO₄	c	−207.5	−182.1	133.48	27.1
	aq	−232 0			
CoSO₄·6H₂O	c	−643.2			
CoSO₄·7H₂O	c	−713.8			
Columbium (See Niobium)					
Copper					
Cu	g	81.52	72.04	−52.804	39.74
	c	0.00	0.00	0.000	7.96
Cu+	aq	12.4	12.0	−8.796	−6.3
Cu++	aq	15.39	15.53	−11.383	−23.6
CuBr	g	38	28	−20.5	59.22
	c	−25.1	−23.81	17.452	21.9
CuBr₂	c	−33.8			
CuBr₂·4H₂O	c	316.4			
CuCO₃	c	−142.2	−123.8	90.744	21
Cu(C₂H₃O₂)₂	c	−213.2			
Cu(C₂H₃O₂)₂·H₂O	c	−284.2			
CuONC	c	26.3			
CuCl	g	32	25	−18.3	56.50
	c	−32.5	−28.2	20.67	20.2
CuCl₂	c	−49.2			
CuF	g	44			
CuF₂	c	−126.9			
CuF₂·2H₂O	c	−274.5	−235.2	172.40	36.2
CuH	c	71	64	−46.9	46.89
CuI	g	62	50	−36.6	61.06
	c	−16.2	−16.62	12.182	23.1
CuI₂	c	−1.7			
CuN₃	c	60.5			
Cu₃N	c	17.8			
Cu(NO₃)₂	c	−73.4			
CuO	g	35			
	c	−37.1	−30.4	22.28	10.4
Cu₂O	c	−39.84	−34.98	25.640	24.1
Cu(OH)₂	c	107.2			
CuS	c	−11.6	−11.7	8.576	15.9
Cu₂S	c	−19.0	−20.6	15.10	28.9
CuSO₄	c	−184.00	−158.2	115.96	27.1
	aq	−201.51	−161 81	118.604	19.5
CuSO₄·H₂O	c	−259.00	−219.2	160.67	35.8
CuSO₄·3H₂O	c	−402.27	−334 6	245.26	53 8
CuSO₄·5H₂O	c	−544 45	−449.3	329 33	73.0
Cu₂SO₄	c	−179.2			
	aq	−190.8			
CuSe	c	−15.1			

* (α) Pseudowollastonite; (β) wollastonite.
** For the values of organic compounds see table following zirconium compounds.

Substance	State	ΔHf°	ΔFf°	Log₁₀ Kf	S°
Dysprosium					
Dy⁺⁺⁺	aq	−166.0	−161.2	118.16	......
DyCl₃	c (β)	−237.8	......	......	......
	c (γ)	−234.8	......	......	......
	aq	−286.1	−255.2	187.06	......
DyI₃	c (β)	−144.5	......	......	......
	aq	−206 1	−198.2	145.28	......
Dy(OH)₃	c	......	−305.8	224.15	......
Dy₂(SO₄)₃	aq	−982 7	−854.4	626.26	......
Dy₂(SO₄)₃·8H₂O	c	......	−1322.0	969.01	......
Erbium					
Er⁺⁺⁺	aq	−162.3	−157.5	115.45	......
ErCl₃	c (γ)	−231.8	......	......	......
	aq	−282	−251.5	184.35	......
ErI₃	c (β)	−140.0	......	......	......
	aq	−202.4	−194.5	142.57	......
Er(OH)₃	c	−340.5	......	......	......
Er₂(SO₄)₃	aq	−975.3	−847.0	620.84	......
Er₂(SO₄)₃·8H₂O	c	......	−1313.9	963.07	......
Europium					
Eu⁺⁺⁺	aq	−169.3	−165.1	121.02	......
EuCl₂	c (α)	−247.1	......	......	......
	aq	−289.4	−259.2	189.99	......
Eu₂(SO₄)₃	aq	−989.3	−862.2	631.98	......
Eu₂(SO₄)₃·8H₂O	c	......	−1331.0	975.60	......
Fluorine					
F₂	g	0.00	0.00	0.000	48.6
F⁻	aq	−78.66	66.08	48.435	−2.3
F₂O	g	5.5	9.7	−7.126	58.95
HF	g	64.2	64.7	47.402	41.47
	aq	−78.66	−66.08	48.435	−2.3
Gadolinium					
Gd	g	87	77	−56.4	46.41
Gd⁺⁺⁺	aq	−168.8	−164.6	120.65	−47.1
GdCl₃	c (α)	−245.5	......	......	......
	aq	−288.9	−258.6	189.55	−7.6
GdI₃	c (β)	−147.6	......	......	......
	aq	−208.9	−201.6	147.77	−31.3
Gd(OH)₃	c	......	−308.1	225.83	......
Gd₂(SO₄)₃	aq	−988.3	−861.2	631.25	−81.9
Gd₂(SO₄)₃·8H₂O	c	−1518.9	−1329.8	974 72	155.8
Gallium					
Ga	g	66.0	57.0	−41.78	40.38
Ga⁺⁺⁺	aq	50.4	36.6	26.83	−83
GaBr₃	c	−92.4	......	......	......
GaCl₃	c	−125.4	......	......	......
	aq	−170.5	−130.7	95.801	−43
GaI₃	c	−51.2	......	......	......
GaN	c	−25	......	......	......
GaO	g	66	......	......	......
Ga₂O	c	−82	......	......	......
Ga₂O₃	c	−258	......	......	......
Ga(OH)₃	c	......	−199	145.9	......
Germanium					
Ge	g	78.44	69.50	−50.943	40.11
	c	0.00	0.00	0.000	10.14
GeBr	g	34.8	......	......	......
GeCl	g	32.6	32.45	......	......
GeCl₄	lq	−130	......	......	......
GeH₄	g	......	......	......	51.21
Ge₃N₄	c	−14.8	......	......	......
GeO	g	−22.8	−28.2	20.63	52.56
GeO₂ (gls)	am	−128.3	......	......	......
(tetr.)	c	−128.3	......	......	......
GeS	g	1.35	......	......	......
H₂GeO₃	aq	−199.3	......	......	......
Gold					
Au	g	82.29	72.83	−53.383	43.12
AuO₂⁻⁻⁻	aq	......	−5.8	4.25	......
AuBr₃	c	−13.0	......	......	......
	aq	−9.2	......	......	......
HAuBr₄	aq	−45.5	−38.1	27.93	75
HAuBr₄·5H₂O	c	−398.5	......	......	......
AuCl₃	c	−28.3	......	......	......
	aq	−32.8	......	......	......
AuCl₃·2H₂O	c	−167.7	......	......	......
HAuCl₄	aq	−77.8	−56.2	41.19	61
HAuCl₄·3H₂O	c	−279.2	......	......	......
HAuCl₄·4H₂O	c	−356.9	......	......	......
AuI	c	0.2	......	......	......
Au₂O₃	c	19.3	39.0	−28.6	30
Au(OH)₃	c	−100.0	−69.3	50.80	29
Hafnium					
Hf	g	......	......	......	44.46
	c	0.00	0.00	0.000	13 1
HfO₂	c	−271.5	......	......	......
Helium					
He	g	0.00	0.00	0.000	30.13
Holmium					
Ho⁺⁺⁺	aq	−163.7	−159.2	116.69	......
HoCl₃	c (γ)	−232.8	......	......	......
	aq	−283.8	−253.2	185.59	......
HoI₃	c (β)	−141.7	......	......	......
	aq	−203.8	−196.2	143.81	......
Ho₂(SO₄)₃	aq	−978.1	−850.4	623.33	......
Ho₂(SO₄)₃·8H₂O	c	......	−1318.0	966.08	......

Substance	State	ΔHf°	ΔFf°	Log₁₀ Kf	S°
Hydrogen					
H₂ (mass 1)*	g	0.00	0.00	0.000	31.21
(mass 2)**	g	0.00	0.00	0.000	34.602
H*	g	52.09	48.58	−35.60	27.39
H**	g	52.98	49.36	−36.18	29.46
H₂O*	g	−57.80	−54.64	40.047	45.11
	lq	−68.32	−56.69	41.553	16.72
H₂O**	g	−59.56	−56.07	41.096	47.38
	lq	−70.41	−58.21	42.664	18.10
H*H**O	g	−58.74	−55.83	40.921	47.66
	lq	−69.39	−57.93	42.459	18.85
H₂O₂	g	−31.83	......	......	......
	lq	−44.84	−28.2	......	......
	aq	−45.68	......	......	......
Indium					
In	g	58.2	49.6	−36.36	41.51
In⁺⁺⁺	aq	27.3	−32.0	23.46	−62
InBr₃	c	−96.5	......	......	......
InCl	c	−18	−23	16.9	59.3
	c	−44.5	......	......	......
InCl₂	c	−86.8	......	......	......
InCl₃	c	−128.4	......	......	......
InH	g	51	45	−33.0	49.6
InI	g	20	9	−6.6	63.8
InI₃	c	−55.0	......	......	......
InN	c	−4.8	......	......	......
InO	g	91	......	......	......
In₂O₃	c	−222.5	......	......	......
In(OH)₃	c	−214	−182	133.4	25
In₂(SO₄)₃	c	695	......	......	......
Iodine					
I₂	g	14.88	4.63	−3.394	62.28
	c	0.00	0.00	0.000	27.9
I⁻	aq	−13.37	−12.35	9.252	26.14
IBr	g	9.75	0.91	0.667	61.80
ICl	g	4.20	−1.32	0.968	59.12
ICl₃	c	−21.1	−5.36	3.929	41.1
HI	g	6.20	0.31	−0.227	49.31
	aq	−13.37	−12.35	9.052	26.14
I₂O₅	c	−42.34	......	......	......
HIO₃	c	−57.03	......	......	......
Iridium					
Ir	g	165	154	−112.9	46.25
	c	0.00	0.00	0.000	8.7
IrCl	c	−22.3	......	......	......
IrCl₂	c	−42.8	......	......	......
IrCl₃	c	−61.5	......	......	......
IrF₆	lq	−130	......	......	......
IrO₂	c	−40.1	......	......	......
IrS₂	c	−30	......	......	......
Ir₂S₃	c	−51	......	......	......
Iron					
Fe	g	96.68	85.76	−62.861	43.11
	c	0.00	0.00	0.000	6.49
Fe⁺⁺	aq	−21.0	−20.30	14.88	−27.1
Fe⁺⁺⁺	aq	−11.4	−2.52	1.847	−70.1
FeBr₂	c	−60.02	......	......	......
FeBr₃	c	−98.1	......	......	......
Fe₃C (cementite)	c	5.0	3.5	−2.56	25.7
Fe(CO)₅	lq	−187.8	......	......	......
FeCO₃ (siderite)	c	−178.70	−161.06	118.055	22.2
H₃Fe(CN)₆	aq	153.	......	......	......
H₄Fe(CN)₆	aq	127.8	......	......	......
	aq	127.4	......	......	......
FeCl₂	c	−81.5	−72.2	52.92	28.6
	aq	−101.0	......	......	......
FeCl₂·2H₂O	c	−228.2	......	......	......
FeCl₂·4H₂O	c	−370.7	......	......	......
FeCl₃	c	−96.8	......	......	......
	aq	−127.9	−96.5	......	......
FeCl₃·6H₂O	c	−532.0	......	......	......
FeCr₂O₄	c	−341.9	−317.7	232.87	34.9
FeF₂	aq	−177.8	......	......	......
FeF₃	aq	−243.1	......	......	......
FeI₂	c	−29.98	......	......	......
	aq	−49.03	......	......	......
Fe₂N	c	−0.9	2.6	−1.91	24.2
Fe₄N	c	−2.55	0.89	−0.652	37.3
Fe(NO₃)₃	aq	−118.9	......	......	......
Fe₀.₉₅O "FeO" (wüstite)	c	−63.7	−58.4	42.81	12.9
Fe₂O₃ (hematite)	c	−196.5	−177.1	129.81	21.5
Fe₃O₄ (magnetite)	c	−267.0	−242.4	177 68	35.0
Fe(OH)₂	c	−135.8	−115.57	84.711	19
Fe(OH)₃	c	−197.0	......	......	......
FeP	c	−28	......	......	......
FeP₂	c	−42	......	......	......
Fe₂P	c	−36	......	......	......
Fe₃P	c	−40	......	......	......
FePO₄	c	−299.6	......	......	......
FePO₄·2H₂O	c	−440.8	......	......	......
FePO₄·4H₂O	c	−578.8	......	......	......
FeS	c (α)	−22.72	−23.32	17.093	16.1
	c (β)	−21.35	......	......	......
FeS₂ (pyrites)	c	−42.52	−39.84	29.202	12.7
(markasite)	c	−36.88	......	......	......

* Atomic weight 1.0078.
** Atomic weight 2.0142.

Substance	State	ΔHf°	ΔFf°	Log₁₀ Kf	S°
Krypton					
Kr	g	0.00	0.00	0.000	39.19
Kr·5H₂O	c	−357.1			
Lanthanum					
La	g	88	79	−57.9	43.57
	c	0.00	0.000	0.000	13.7
La⁺⁺⁺	aq	−176.2	−172.9	126.73	−44
La₂(CN)₃	c	−229			
LaCl₃	c (α)	−263.6			
	aq	−296.3	−266.9	195.63	−5
LaI₃	c (α)	−167.4			
	aq	−216.3	−209.9	153.85	34
LaN	c	−72.1			
La₂O₃	c	−458.			
La(OH)₃	c		−312.8	229.28	
La₂S₃	c	−306.8			
La₂(SO₄)₃	aq	−1003.1	−877.8	643.41	−76
Lanthanum					
La₂(SO₄)₃·9H₂O	c		−1403.1	1028.45	
Lead					
pb	g	46.34	38.47	−28.198	41.89
	c	0.00	0.00	0.000	15.51
Pb⁺⁺	aq	0.39	−5.81	4.259	5.1
PbBr₂	c	−66.21	−62.24	45.621	38.6
	aq	−57.41	−54.95	40.278	43.7
PbCO₃	c	−167.3	−149.7	109.73	31.3
PbCO₃·PbO	c	−220.0	−195.6	143.37	48.5
PbCO₃·2PbO	c	−273	−242	177.4	65
PbC₂O₄	c	−205.1			
Pb(C₂H₃O₂)₂	c	230.5			
	aq	−232.6			
Pb(C₂H₃O₂)₂·3H₂O	c	−443.1			
Pb(C₂H₅)₄	lq	52			
PbCl₂	c	−85.85	−75.04	55.003	32.6
	aq	−79.65	−68.51	50.217	31.4
PbF₂	c	−158.5	−148.1	108.55	29
PbF₄	c	−222.3			
PbI₂	c	−41.85	−41.53	30.441	42.3
	aq	−26.35	−30.51	22.363	57.8
Pb(N₃)₂	c	104.3			
Pb(NO₃)₂	c	−107.35			
	aq	−98.35	−58.64	42.982	75.1
PbO	g				57.4
(red)	c	−52.40	−45.25	33.168	16.2
(yellow)	c	−52.07	−45.05	33.021	16.6
PbO₂	c	−66.12	−52.34	38.364	18.3
Pb₂O	c	−51.2			
Pb₃O₄	c	−175.6	−147.6	108.19	50.5
Pb(OH)₂	c	−123.0	−100.6	73.738	21
Pb₃(PO₄)₂	c	−620.3	−581.4	426.16	84.45
PbS	c	−22.54	−22.15	16.236	21.8
PbSO₄	c	−219.50	−193.89	142.119	35.2
PbS₂O₃	c	−150.1			
PbSe	c	−18			
PbSeO₄	c	−148			
PbSiO₃	c	−258.8	−239.0	175.18	27
Pb₂SiO₄	c	−312.7	−285.7	209.41	43
Lithium					
Li	g	37.07	29.19	−21.396	33.14
	c	0.00	0.00	0.000	6.70
Li⁺	aq	−66.54	−70.22	51.470	3.4
LiBr	g	−41	−50	36.6	53.78
	c	−83.72			
	aq	−95.45	−94.69	69.483	22.7
LiBr·H₂O	c	−158.34			
LiBr·2H₂O	c	−229.94			
LiBr·3H₂O	c	−301.9			
Li₂CO₃	c	−290.54	−270.66	198.390	21.60
	aq	−294.74	−266.66	195.458	−5.9
LiHCO₃	aq	−231.73	−210.53	154.316	29.5
LiCl	g	−53	−58	42.5	51.01
	c	−97.70			
	aq	−106.58	−101.57	74.449	16.6
LiCl·H₂O	c	−170.31	−151.2	110.83	24.8
LiCl·2H₂O	c	−242.1			
LiCl·3H₂O	c	−313.5			
LiF	c	−146.3	−139.5	102.32	8.57
	aq	−145.21	−136.30	99.906	1.1
LiH	g	30.7	25.2	−18.47	40.77
	c	−21.61	−16.72	12.255	5.9
LiI	g	−16	−26	19.1	55.68
	c	−64.79			
	aq	−79.92	−82.57	−60.523	29.5
LiI·½H₂O	c	−103.8			
LiI·H₂O	c	−141.16			
LiI·2H₂O	c	−213.03			
LiI·3H₂O	c	−285.02			
Li₃N	c	−47.2			
LiNO₂	c	−96.6			
LiNO₃	c	−115.28			
	aq	−115.93	−96.63	70.828	38.4
LiNO₃·3H₂O	c	−328.6			
Li₂O	c	−142.4			
Li₂O₂	c	−151.7			
	aq	−159.0			

Substance	State	ΔHf°	ΔFf°	Log₁₀ Kf	S°
Lithium					
LiOH	c	−116.45	−106.1	77.77	12
	aq	−121.51	−107.82	79.031	0.9
LiOH·H₂O	c	−188.77	−164.8	120.80	22
Li₂SO₄	c	−342.83			
	dq	−350.01	−317.78	232.928	10.9
Li₂SO₄·H₂O	c	−414.20			
Lutetium					
Lu	g	87			44.14
	c	0.00	0.00	0.000	
Lu⁺⁺	aq	−160.1	−155.0	113.61	
LuCl₃	c (γ)	−227.9			
	aq	−280.2	−249.0	182.51	
LuI₂	c (β)	−133.2			
	aq	−200.2	−192.0	140.73	
Lu₂(SO₄)₃	aq, ∞	−970.9	−842.0	617.17	
Lu₂(SO₄)₃·8H₂O	c		−1308.1	958.82	
Magnesium					
Mg	g	35.9	27.6	−20.23	35.50
	c	0.00	0.00	0.000	7.77
Mg⁺⁺	aq	−110.41	−108.99	79.89	−28.2
Mg₃(AsO₄)₂	c	−731.3			
MgHAsO₄	aq	−349.2			
Mg(H₂AsO₄)₂	aq	−541.0			
Mg(NH₄)AsO₄·6H₂O	c	−800.7			
Mg₃Bi₂	c	−36.5			
MgBr₂	c	−123.7			
	aq	−168.21	−158.14	115.914	10.4
MgBr₂·6H₂O	c	−575.4	−491.0	359.90	95
Mg(CN)₂	aq	−31.9			
MgCN₂	c	−60.3			
MgCO₃	c	−266	−246	180.3	15.7
MgCl₂	c	−153.40	−141.57	103.769	21.4
	aq	−190.46	−171.69	125.846	−1.9
MgCl₂·H₂O	c	−231.15	−206.11	151.076	32.8
MgCl₂·2H₂O	c	−305.99	−267.32	195.942	43.0
MgCl₂·4H₂O	c	−454.00	−390.49	286.224	63.1
MgCl₂·6H₂O	c	−597.42	−505.65	370.635	87.5
Mg(OH)Cl	c	−191.3	−175.0	128.27	19.8
Mg(ClO₄)₂	c	−140.6			
Mg(ClO₄)₂·2H₂O	c	−290.7			
Mg(ClO₄)₂·4H₂O	c	−438.6			
Mg(ClO₄)₂·6H₂O	c	−583.2			
MgCrO₄	c	−318.3			
	aq	−321.2			
MgF₂	c	−263.5	−250.8	183.83	13.68
MgH	g	41	34	−24.9	47.61
MgI₂	c	−86.0			
	aq	−137.15	−133.69	97.993	24.1
Mg₃N₂	c	−110.24			
Mg(NO₃)₂	c	−188.72	−140.63	103.080	39.2
	aq	−209.15	−161.81	118.605	41.8
Mg(NO₃)₂·6H₂O	c	−624.36			
MgO	c	−143.84	−136.13	99.781	6.4
MgO₂	c	−148.9			
Mg(OH)₂	c	−221.00	−199.27	146.062	15.09
Mg₃(PO₄)₂	c	−961.5			
Mg(NH₄)PO₄·6H₂O	c	−881.0			
MgS	c	−83.0			
MgSO₄	c	−305.5	−280.5	152.83	21.9
	aq	−327.31	−286.33	209.876	−24.0
MgSO₄·2H₂O	c	−381.9			
MgSO₄·4H₂O	c	−595.5			
MgSO₄·6H₂O	c	−736.6			
MgSO₄·7H₂O	c	−808.7			
Mg₃Sb₂	c	−68.1			
MgSiO₃	c	−357.9	−337.2	247.16	16.2
Mg₂SiO₄ (forsterite)	c	−488.2	−459.8	337.03	22.7
Mg₂Sn	c	−17.0			
MgWO₄	c	−345.2			
Manganese					
Mn	g	68.34	58.23	−42.682	41.49
	c (α)	0.00	0.00	0.000	7.59
	c (γ)	0.33	0.33	−0.242	7.72
Mn⁺⁺	aq	−52.3	−53.4	39.14	−20
MnBr₂	c	−90.7			
	aq	−110.1			
MnBr₂·H₂O	c	−164.4			
MnBr₂·4H₂O	c	−367.5			
MnBr₃	aq	−111			
Mn₃C	c	−1	−1	0.73	23.6
MnCO₃	c	−213.9	−195.4	143.23	20.5
	ppt	−211.0			
	aq	−213.9	−179.6	131.64	−32.7
MnC₂O₄	c	−258.2			
MnC₂O₄·2H₂O	c	−388.6			
MnC₂O₄·3H₂O	c	−455.4			
Mn(C₂H₃O₂)₂	c	−273.0			
	aq	−285.2			
Mn(C₂H₃O₂)₂·4H₂O	c	−556.9			
MnCl₂	c	−115.3	−105.5	77.330	28.0
MnCl₂·H₂O	c	−188.5			
MnCl₂·2H₂O	c	−276.7			

Substance	State	ΔH_f°	ΔF_f°	$Log_{10}\ K_f$	S°
Manganese					
$MnCl_2\cdot4H_2O$	c	−407.0			
MnF_2	c	−189	−179	131.2	22.2
	aq	−209.2			
MnI_2	c	−59.3			
MnI_2	aq	−79.0			
$MnI_2\cdot H_2O$	c	−127.9			
$MnI_2\cdot2H_2O$	c	−194.5			
$MnI_2\cdot4H_2O$	c	−327.5			
$MnI_2\cdot6H_2O$	c	−451			
$Mn(N_3)_2$	c	92.2			
Mn_5N_2	c	−57.8			
Mn_3N_2	c	−81			
$Mn(NO_3)_2$	c	−166.32			
$Mn(NO_3)_2\cdot3H_2O$	c	−355.1			
$Mn(NO_3)_2\cdot6H_2O$	c	−566.50			
MnO	g	34.6			
	c	−92.0	−86.8	63.62	14.4
MnO_2	c	−124.5	−111.4	81.655	12.7
Mn_2O_3	c	−232.1			
Mn_3O_4	c	−331.4	−306.0	224.29	35.5
$Mn(OH)_2$	am	−165.8	−145.9	106.94	21.1
$Mn(OH)_3$	am	−212			
$Mn_3(PO_4)_2$	c	−771.			
MnS (green)	c	−48.8	−49.9	36.58	18.7
(red)	c	−47.6			
$MnSO_4$	c	−254.24	−228.48	167.473	26.8
$MnSO_4$	aq	−269.2	−230.7	169 10	−16
$MnSO_4\cdot H_2O$	c (I)	−328.5			
	c (II)	−322.4			
$MnSO_4\cdot4H_2O$	c	−539.3			
$MnSO_4\cdot5H_2O$	c	−609.6			
$MnSO_4\cdot7H_2O$	c	−750.0			
$Mn_2(SO_4)_4$	c	−666.9			
	aq	−699			
$MnSiO_3$	c	−302.5	283.3	207.65	21.3
	gls	−294.0			
Mercury					
Hg	g	14.54	7.59	−5.563	41.8
	lq	0.00	0.00	0.00	18.5
Hg^{++}	aq		39.38	−28.865	
Hg_2^{++}	aq		36.79	−26.967	
$HgBr$	g	23	18	−13.2	65.0
Hg_2Br_2	c	−49.42	−42.714	31.309	50.9
$HgBr_2$	c	−40.5	−38.8		
$Hg(CN)_2$	c	62.5			
$Hg(ONC)_2$	c	64			
$Hg(CNS)_2$	c	48.0			
HgC_2O_4	c	−161.8			
$Hg(C_2H_3O_2)_2$	c	−199.4			
$Hg_2(C_2H_3O_2)_2$	c	−201.1			
$Hg(CH_3)_2$	lq	18.			
$Hg(C_2H_5)_2$	lq	15			
$HgCl$	g	19	14	−10.3	62.2
Hg_2Cl_2	c	−63.32	−50.35	36 906	46.8
$HgCl_2$	c	−55.0	−42.2		
HgF	c	14			
HgH	g	58.06	52.60	−38.555	52.42
HgI	g	33	23	−16.9	67.1
Hg_2I_2 (yellow)	c	−28.91	−26.60	19.497	57 2
HgI_2 (red)	c	−25.2			
(yellow)	c	−24.55			
$Hg_2(N_3)_2$	c	133			
$Hg(NO_3)_2\cdot\frac{1}{2}H_2O$	c	−93.0			
$Hg(NO_3)_2\cdot2H_2O$	c	−206.9			
HgO (red)	c	−21.68	−13.990	10.255	17.2
(yellow)	c	−21.56	−13.959	10.232	17.5
Hg_2O	c	−21.8	−12.80		
$Hg(OH)_2$	aq		−66.0	43.38	
HgS (red)	c	−13.90	−11.67	8.554	18.6
(black)	c	−12.90	−11.05	8.100	19.9
$HgSO_4$	c	−168.3			
Hg_2SO_4	c	−177.34	−149.12	109.303	47.98
Molybdenum					
Mo	g	155.5	144.2	−105.70	43.46
	c	0.00	0.00	0.000	6.83
$MoBr_2$	c	−29			
$MoBr_3$	c	−41			
$MoBr_4$	c	−45			
$MoBr_5$	c	−51			
Mo_2C	c	4.3	2.9	−2.13	19.7
$MoCl_2$	c	−44			
$MoCl_3$	s				
$MoCl_4$	c	−79			
$MoCl_5$	c	−90.8			
$MoCl_6$	c	−90			
MoI_2	c	−12			
MoI_3	c	−15			
MoI_4	c	−18			
MoI_5	c	−18			
Mo_2N	c	−8 3			
MoO_2	c	−130			
MoO_3	c	−180.33	−161.95	118.707	18.68
	aq	−188.1			

Substance	State	ΔH_f°	ΔF_f°	$Log_{10}\ K_f$	S°
Molybdenum					
MoO_4	aq	−173.5			
MoO_4	aq	−155.1			
MoS_2	c	−55.5	−53.8	39.43	15.1
MoS_3	c	−61.2			
H_2MoO_4 (white)	c	−256.9			
$H_2MoO_4\cdot H_2O$ (yellow)	c	−331.4			
Neodymium					
Nd	g	87			
	c	0.00	0.00	0.000	
Nd^{+++}	aq	−171.2	−167.6	122.85	
$NdCl_3$	c (α)	−254.3			
	aq	−291.3	−261.6	191.75	
$NdCl_3\cdot6H_2O$	c	−692.3			
$Nd(OH)_3$	c		−309.6	226.93	
NdI_3	c (α)	−158.9			
	aq	−211.3	−204.6	149.97	
Nd_2O_3	c	−442.0			
Nd_2S_3	c	−281.8			
$Nd_2(SO_4)_3$	c	−948.1			
	aq	−993.1	−867.2	635.65	
$Nd_2(SO_4)_3\cdot5H_2O$	c	−1318.4			
$Nd_2(SO_4)_3\cdot8H_2O$	c	−1524.7	−1334.5	978.17	
Neon					
Ne	g	0.00	0.00	0.000	34.95
Neptunium					
Np	c	0.00	0.00	0.000	
$NpBr_3$	c	−174			
$NpBr_4$	c	−183			
$NpCl_3$	c	−216			
$NpCl_4$	c	−237			
$NpCl_6$	c	−246			
NpF_3	c	−360			
NpF_4	c	−428			
NpI_3	c	−120			
Nickel					
Ni	g	101.61	90.77	−66.533	43.59
	c	0.00	0.00	0.000	7.20
Ni^{++}	aq	−15.3	−11.1	8.136	−38.1
$NiBr_2$	c	−54.2			
$NiBr_2\cdot3H_2O$	c	−277.8			
Ni_3C	c	11.0			
$Ni(CN)_2$	c	27.1			
$NiCO_3$	c		−146.7	107.53	
$NiCl_2$	c	−75.5	−65.1	47.72	25.6
$NiCl_2\cdot2H_2O$	c	−220.8			
$NiCl_2\cdot4H_2O$	c	−364.7			
$NiCl_2\cdot6H_2O$	c	−505.8	−410.5	300.89	75.2
NiF_2	c	−159.5			
$NiF_2\cdot4H_2O$	c		−379.9	278.46	
NiH	g	93			
	c	−2.7			
NiH_2	c	−6.2			
NiI_2	c	−20.5			
$Ni(IO_3)_2$	c	−124.5			
$Ni(IO_3)_2\cdot2H_2O$	c (I)	−264.9			
	c (II)	−263.9			
$Ni(IO_3)_2\cdot4H_2O$	c	−401.7			
$Ni(NO_3)_2$	c	−102 2			
$Ni(NO_3)_2\cdot6H_2O$	c	−531.4			
NiO	g	59.3	51.8	−37.97	57
	c	−58.4	−51.7	37.90	9.22
$Ni(OH)_2$	c	−128.6	−108.3	79.382	19
$Ni(OH)_3$	c	−162.1			
NiS	c	−17.5			
$NiSO_4$	c	−213.0	−184.9	135.53	18.6
	aq	−232.2	−188.4	138.09	−34.0
$NiSO_4\cdot6H_2O$ (green)	c	−644.98			
(blue)	c	−642.5	−531.0	389.2	73.1
$NiSO_4\cdot7H_2O$	c	−712.9			
Niobium					
Nb	g	184.5	173.7	−127.32	44.49
	c	0.00	0.00	0.000	8.3
Nb_2O_4	c	−387.8			
Nb_2O_5	c	−463.2			
Nitrogen	(NH₄OH; NH₂OH; N₂H₄; and N₃H; see under ammonia)				
N_2	g	0.00	0.00	0.000	45.77
$NOBr$	g	19.56	19.70	−14.44	65.16
$NOCl$	g	12.57	15.86	−11.625	63.0
NF_3	g	−27 2			
NO	g	21.00	20.72	−15.187	50.34
NO_2	g	8.09	12.39	−9.082	57.47
N_2O_4	g	2.31	23.49	−17.219	72.73
N_2O	g	19.49	24.76	−18.149	52.58
N_2O_5	g	3.6			
	c	−10.0			
HNO_3	lq	−41.40	−19.10	14.000	37.19
	aq	−49.37	−26.41	19.36	35.0
$HNO_3\cdot H_2O$	lq	−112.96	−78.41	57.474	51.83
$HNO_3\cdot3H_2O$	lq	−252.20	−193.70	141.980	82.92
Osmium					
Os	g	174	163	−119.5	45.97
	c	0.00	0.00	0.000	7.8
OsO_4	g	−79.9	−67.9	49.77	65.6

Substance	State	ΔHf°	ΔFf°	$\log_{10} K_f$	S°
Osmium					
OsO_4	g	−79.9	−67.9	49.77	65.6
(white)	c	−91.7	−70.5	51.68	34.7
(yellow)	c	−93.4	−70.7	51.82	29.7
	aq		−68.59	50.276	
OsS_2	c	−35			
H_2OsO_5	aq		−125.28	91.829	
Oxygen					
O_2	g	0.00	0.00	0.000	49.003
O_3	g	34.0	39.06	−28.631	56.8
OH^-	aq	−54.957	−37.595	27.56	−2.519
Palladium					
Pd	g	93	84	−61.6	39.91
	c	0.00	0.00	0.000	8.9
$PdBr_2$	c	−24.9			
	aq	−205.6			
$Pd(CN)_2$	c	52.1			
$PdCl_2$	c	−45.4			
$PdCl_4^{--}$	aq	−128.3	−96.7	70.88	41.
H_2PdCl_4	aq	−129.3			
Pd_2H	c	−8.9			
PdO	c	−20.4			
$Pd(OH)_2$	c	−92.1			
$Pd(OH)_4$	c	−169.4			
Phosphorus					
P	g	75.18	66.71	−48.897	38.98
(white)	c	0.00	0.00	0.000	10.6
(red)	c	−4.4			
(black)	c	−10.3			
P_2	g	33.82	24.60	−18.031	52.13
P_4	g	13.12	5.82	−4.266	66.90
PBr_3	g	−35.9	−41.2	30.19	83.11
PBr_5	c	−66			
$POBr_3$	c	−114.6			
PCl_3	g	−73.22	−68.42	50.151	74.49
PCl_5	g	−95.35	−77.59	56.872	84.3
$POCl_3$	g	−141.5	−130.3	95.508	77.59
PH_3	g	2.21	4.36	−3.196	50.2
PI_3	c	−10.9			
PN	g	−20.2	−25.3	18.54	50.45
HPO_3	c	−228.2			
	aq	−234.9			
H_3PO_2	c	−145.5			
	aq	−145.6			
H_3PO_3	c	−232.2			
	aq	−232.2			
H_3PO_4	c	−306.2			
$H_4P_2O_7$	c	−538.0			
Platinum					
Pt	g	121.6	110.9	−81.288	45.96
	c	0.00	0.00	0.000	10.0
$PtBr_4$	c	−41.3			
$H_2PtBr_6·9H_2O$	c	−734.7			
$PtCl_2$	c	−35.5			
$PtCl_4$	c	−62.9			
$PtCl_4^{--}$	aq	−123.4	−91.9	67.36	42.
$PtCl_4·5H_2O$	c	−425.8			
$PtCl_6^{--}$	aq	−167.4	123.1	90.231	52.6
H_2PtCl_6	aq	−167.3			
$H_2PtCl_6·6H_2O$	c	−572.9			
PtI_4	c	−21.6			
$Pt(OH)_2$	c	−87.2	−68.2	49.99	26.5
PtS	c	−20.8			
PtS_2	c	−27.8			
Plutonium					
$PuBr_3$	c	−187.2			
$PuCl_3$	c	−230.0			
PuOCl	c	−222.8			
PuF_3	aq	−374.6			
PuH_2	c	−31.7			
PuI_3	c	−133			
PuO_2	c	−251			
Polonium					
PoO_2	c		−46.3	33.7	
Potassium					
K	g	21.51	14.62	−10.716	38.30
	c	0.00	0.00	0.000	15.2
K^+	aq	−60.04	−67.466	49.452	24.5
$KAl(SO_4)_2$	c	−589.24	−534.29	391.627	48.9
$KAl(SO_4)_2·12H_2O$	c	−1447.74	−1227.8	899.96	164.3
KH_2AsO_4	c	−271.5	−237.0	173.72	37.08
KBr	c	−93.73	−90.63	66.430	23.05
	aq	−88.94	−92.04	67.464	43.8
KBrO	aq	−82.0			
$KBrO_3$	c	−79.4	−58.2	42.66	35.65
	aq	69.6	−56.6	41.49	63.4
K_2CO_3	c	−273.93			
$K_2CO_3·\frac{1}{2}H_2O$	c	−210.43			
$K_2CO_3·1\frac{1}{2}H_2O$	c	−283.40			
$KHCO_3$	c	−229.3			
$KC_2H_3O_2$	c	−173.2			
$K_2C_2O_4$	c	−320.8			
$K_2C_2O_4·H_2O$	c	−392.17			
KCN	c	−26.90			
KCNO	c	−98.5			
Potassium					
KCNS	c	−48.62			
	g	−51.6	−56.2	41.19	57.24
KCl	c	−104.18	−97.592	71.534	19.76
	aq	−100.06	−98.82	72.431	37.7
KClO	aq	−85.4			
$KClO_3$	c	−93.50	−69.29	50.789	34.17
	aq, 100	−84.09			
	aq	−83.54	−68.09	49.909	63.5
$KClO_4$	c	−103.6	−72.7	53.29	36.1
	aq	−91.45	−70.04	51.338	68.0
K_2CrO_4	c	−330.49			
$K_2Cr_2O_7$	c	−485.90			
KF	c	−134.46	−127.42	93.397	15.91
$KF·2H_2O$	c	−277.0	−242.7	177.90	36
$KF·4H_2O$	c	−418.0			
KHF_2	c	−219.98	−203.73	149.331	24.92
KI	c	−78.31	−77.03	56.462	24.94
	aq	−73.41	−79.82	58.504	50.6
KIO_3	c	−121.5	−101.7	74.54	36.20
	aq	−115.0	−99.9	73.22	52.2
KIO_4	aq, 1200	−97.6			
$KMnO_4$	c	−194.4	−170.6	125.05	41.04
KNH_2	c	−28.3			
KNO_2	c	−88.5			
KNO_3	c	−117.76	−93.96	68.871	31.77
	c	−109.41	−93.88	68.813	69.5
K_2O	aq	−86.4			
K_2O_2	c	−118			
K_2O_4	c	−134			
KOH	c	−101.78			
	aq	−115.00	−105.06	77.008	22.0
K_2S	c	−100			
K_2S_4	c	−113.0			
K_2SO_3	c	−266.9			
K_2SO_4	c	−342.66	−314.62	230.612	42.0
$KHSO_4$	c	−276.8			
$K_2S_2O_6$	c	−413.6			
$K_2S_2O_3$	c	−458.3			
$K_2S_4O_6$	c	−422			
K_2Se	c	−79.3			
Praseodymium					
Pr	g	87			
	c	0.00	0.00	0.000	
Pr^{+++}	aq	−172.7	−169.1	123.95	
$PrCl_3$	c (α)	−257.8			
	aq	−292.8	−263.1	192.85	
$PrCl_3·H_2O$	c	−330.8			
$PrCl_3·7H_2O$	c	−764.5			
PrI_3	c (α)	−162.0			
	aq	−212.8	−206.1	151.07	
PrO_2	c	−234.0			
Pr_2O_3	c	−444.5			
$Pr(OH)_3$	c		−310.7	227.74	
$Pr_2(SO_4)_3$	aq	−996.1	−870.2	637.84	
$Pr_2(SO_4)_3·8H_2O$	c		−1337.0	980.00	
Promethium					
Pm^{+++}	aq	−170.4			
$PmCl_3$	c	−251.9			
	aq	−290.5			
Radium					
Ra	g	31	23	−16.8	42.15
	c	0.00	0.00	0.000	17
Ra^{++}	aq	−126.	−134.5	98.58	13
$RaCl_2·2H_2O$	c	−351	−311.7	228.47	50
$Ra(NO_3)_2$	c	−237	−190.3	139.49	52
RaO	c	−125			
$RaSO_4$	c	−352	−326.0	238.95	34
Radon					
Rn	g	0.00	0.00	0.000	42.10
Rhenium					
Re	g	189	179	−131.2	45.13
	c	0.00	0.00	0.000	10
ReF_6	g	−273			
Re_2O_7	c	−297.5			
Re_2O_8	c	−148.3			
ReS_2	c	−44.3			
ReO_4^-	aq	−190.3			
Rhodium					
Rh	g	138	127	−93.09	44.39
	c	0.00	0.00	0.000	7.6
RhCl	c	−16			
$RhCl_2$	c	−36			
$RhCl_3$	c	−56			
RhO	c	−21.7			
RH_2O	c	−22.7			
Rh_2O_3	c	−68.3			
Rubidium					
Rb	g	20.51	13.35	−9.785	40.63
	c	0.00	0.00	0.000	16.6
Rb^+	aq	−58.9	−67.45	47.974	29.7
RbBr	c	−93.03	−90.38	66.247	25.88
	aq	−87.8	−92.02	67.449	49.0
Rb_2CO_3	c	−269.6			
$Rb_2CO_3·H_2O$	c	−344.2			

Substance	State	ΔHf°	ΔFf°	Log₁₀ Kf	S°
Rubidium					
RbHCO₃	c	−228.5			
RbCNS	c	−54			
	aq	−41.7			
RbCl	c	−102.9	−98.48		
	aq	−98.9	−98.80	72.419	42.9
RbClO₃	c	−93.8	−69.8	51.16	36.3
	aq	−82.4	−68.07	49.894	68.7
RbClO₄	c	−100.87	−73.19	53.647	38.4
	aq	−90.3	−70.02	51.324	73.2
RbF	c	−131.28			
	c	−137.6	−133.53	97.876	27.4
RbHF₂	c	−217.3			
RbI	c	−78.5	−77.8	57.03	28.21
	aq	−72.3	−79.80	58.492	55.
RbNO₃	c	−117.04			
	aq	−108.5	−93.86	68.798	64.7
RbNH₂	c	−25.7			
Rb₂O	c	−78.9			
Rb₂O₂	c	−101.7			
RbOH	c	−98.9			
	aq	−113.9	−105.05	77.000	27.2
RbOH·H₂O	c	−177.8			
RbOH·2H₂O	c	−250.8			
Rb₂S	c	−83.2			
RbHS	c	−62.4			
RbHSO₄	c	−273.7			
Rb₂SO₄	c	−340.50			
	aq	−334.7	−312.24	228.868	33.8
Ruthenium					
Ru	g	160	149	−109.2	44.57
	c	0.00	0.00	0.000	6.9
RuCl₃	c	−63			
RuO₂	c	−52.5			
RuS₂	c	−48.1	−44.1		
Samarium					
Sm	g	87			43.74
Sm⁺⁺⁺	aq	−169.8	−165.9	121.60	
SmCl₂	c (α)	−249.8			
	aq	−289.9	−259.9	190.50	
SmI₂	c (β)	−153.4			
	aq	−209.9	−202.9	148.72	
Sm(OH)₃	c	......	−308.8	226.35	
Sm₂(SO₄)₃	aq	−990.3	−863.8	633.15	
Sm₂(SO₄)₃·8H₂O	c	......	−1332.6	976.78	
Scandium					
Sc	g	93			41.76
Sc⁺⁺⁺	aq	−148.8	−143.7	105.33	
ScBr₃	c	−179.4			
	aq	−235.5	−217.4	159.35	
ScCl₃	c	−220.8			
	aq	−268.9	−237.7	174.23	
Selenium					
Se	g	48.37	38.77	−28.42	42.21
Se (gray, hex.)	c	0.00	0.00	0.000	10.0
(red, mon.)	c	0.2			10.0
	gls	1.05			
	ppt	1.05			
H₂Se	g	20.5	17	−12.468	52.9
	aq	18.1	18.4	−13.49	39.9
SeO₂	c	−55.00			
H₂SeO₃	c	−126.5			
	aq	−122.39	−101.8	74.622	45.7
H₂SeO₄	c	−128.6			
	aq	−145.3	−105.42	77.276	5.7
Silicon					
Si	g	88.04	77.41	−56.740	40.12
	c	0.00	0.00	0.000	4.47
SiBr₄	lq	−95.1			
SiC	c	−26.7	−26.1	19.13	3.94
SiCl₄	g	−145.7	−136.2	99.83	79.2
	lq	−153.0	−136.9	100.34	57.2
SiF₄	g	−370	−360	263.9	68.0
SiH₄	g	−14.8	−9.4	6.89	48.7
SiI₄	c	−31.6			
Si₃N₄	c	−179.3	−154.7	113.39	22.4
SiO₂ (quarts)	c	−205.4	−192.4	141.03	10.00
(cristobalite)	c	−205.0	−192.1	140.81	10.19
(tridymite)	c	−204.8	−191.9	140.66	10.36
	gls	−202.5	−190.9	139.92	11.2
SiS₂ (white)	aq	−201.0			
H₂SiF₆	c	−34.7			
H₂SiO₃	aq	557.9			
	c	−270.7			
H₂SiO₄	c	−340.6			
H₄SiO₄	c	−472.4			
H₆Si₂O₇	c	−611.2			
Silver					
Ag	g	69.12	59.84	−43.862	41.32
	c	0.00	0.00	0.000	10.21
Ag⁺	aq	25.31	18.43	−13.51	17.67
AgBr	c	−23.78	−22.39	16.807	25.60
Ag₂CO₃	c	−120.97	−104.48	76.582	40.0
AgC₂H₃O₂	c	−93.41			
AgCN	c	34.94	39.20	−28.733	20.0

Substance	State	ΔHf°	ΔFf°	Log₁₀ Kf	S°
Silver					
AgCNO	c	−21.1			
AgONC	c	43.2			
AgCNS	c	21.0			
AgCl	g	23.23	16.79	−12.307	58.5
	c	−30.36	−26.22	19.222	22.97
AgClO₂	c	0.00	16.0	−11.73	32.16
AgClO₃	c	−5.73			
AgClO₄	c	−7.75			
Ag₂CrO₄	c	−170.15	−148.57	108.90	51.8
AgF	c	−48.5	−44.2	32.40	20
	aq	−53.35	−47.65	34.927	15.4
AgH	g	67.7	60.8	−44.56	48.86
AgI	c	−14.91	−15.85	11.618	27.3
AgIO₃	c	−42.02	−24.08		35.7
AgN₃	c	66.8			
AgNO₂	c	−10.61	4.74	−3.477	30.62
	aq	−0.09	9.79	−7.176	49.0
AgNO₃	c	−29.43	−7.69	5.637	33.68
	aq	−24.06	−7.98	5.849	52.67
Ag₂O	c	−7.31	−2.59	1.896	29.09
Ag₂O₂	c	−6.3			
Ag₂S	c (α)	−7.60	−9.62	7.051	34.8
	c (β)	−7.01	−9.36	6.860	35.9
Ag₂SO₄	c	−170.50	−147.17	107.873	47.8
Sodium					
Na	g	25.98	18.67	−13.685	36.72
	c	0.00	0.00	0.000	12.2
Na⁺	aq	−57.28	−62.59	45.88	14.4
Na₃AsO₄	c	−365			
Na₃AsO₄·12H₂O	c	−1213.9			
NaBO₂	c	−253			
NaBO₂·4H₂O	c	−504.8			
Na₂B₄O₇	c	−777.7			
Na₂B₄O₇·4H₂O	c	−1072.9			
Na₂B₄O₇·5H₂O	c	−1143.5			
Na₂B₄O₇·10H₂O	c	−1497.2			
Na₃BiO₄	c	−288.			
NaBr	c	−86.03			
	aq	−86.18	−87.16	63.889	33.7
NaBr·2H₂O	c	−227.25			
NaCN	c	−21.46			
NaCN·¼H₂O	c	−56.19			
NaCN·2H₂O	c	−162.25			
NaCNO	c	−95.6			
NaCNS	c	−41.73			
	aq	−40.1			
Na₂CO₃	c	−270.3	−250.4	183.53	32.5
Na₂CO₃·H₂O	c	−341.8			
Na₂CO₃·7H₂O	c	−765.1			
Na₂CO₃·10H₂O	c	−975.6			
NaHCO₃	c	−226.5	−203.6	149.24	24.4
NaC₂H₃O₂	c	−169.8			
NaC₂H₃O₂·3H₂O	c	−383.50			
Na₂C₂O₄	c	−314.3			
NaCl	g	−43.50			
	c	−98.23	−91.79	67.277	17.30
	aq	−97.302	−93.94	68.856	27.6
NaClO	aq	−82.7			
NaClO₂	c	−72.65			
NaClO₃	c	−85.73			
	aq, 400	−80.74	−62.8		
	aq, 1000	−80.73			
	aq, 5000	−80.74			
	aq	−80.78	−63.21	46.332	53.4
NaClO₄	c	−92.18			
	aq	−88.69	−65.16	47.688	57.9
Na₂CrO₄	c	−317.6			
Na₂CrO₄·4H₂O	c	−601.3			
Na₂Cr₂O₇	aq, 600	−463.4			
NaF	c	−136.0	−129.3	94.78	14.0
	aq	−135.94	−128.67	94.313	12.1
NaHF₂	c	−216.6			
NaH	g	29.88	24.78	−18.163	44.93
	c	−13.7			
NaI	g	−20.94			
	c	−68.84			
	aq	−70.65	−70.94	51.998	40.5
NaI·2H₂O	c	−211.05			
	aq, ∞	−112.3			
NaNH₂	c	−28.1			
NaNO₂	c	−85.0			
NaNO₃	c	−101.54	−87.45	64.100	27.8
	aq	−106.65	−89.00	65.236	49.4
Na₂O	c	−99.4	−90.0	65.97	17.4
Na₂O₂	c	−120.6			
NaOH	c	−101.99			
	aq	−112.24	−100.184	73.434	11.9
NaOH·H₂O	c	−175.17	−149.00	109.215	20.2
NaPO₃	c	−288.6			
NaH₂PO₂	c	−289.4			
NaH₂PO₂·2½H₂O	c	−454.8			
Na₂HPO₄	c	−338.0			
Na₂HPO₄·5H₂O	c	−684.2			
NaH₂PO₄	aq, 300	−367.7			

Substance	State	ΔHf°	ΔFf°	Log₁₀ Kf	S°
Sodium					
Na₂HPO₄	c	−417.4	....	....	
Na₂HPO₄·2H₂O	c	−560.2	....	....	
Na₂HPO₄·7H₂O	c	−913.3	....	....	
Na₂HPO₄·12H₂O	c	−1266.4	....	....	
Na₃PO₄	c	−460	....	....	
Na₃PO₄·12H₂O	c	−1309.0	....	....	
NaNH₄HPO₄·4H₂O	c	−682.7	....	....	
NaH₃P₂O₇	c	−602.7	....	....	
NaH₃P₂O₇H₂O	c	−670.6	....	....	
Na₂H₂P₂O₇	c	−663.4	....	....	
Na₂H₂P₂O₇·6H₂O	c	−1085.5	....	....	
Na₃HP₂O₇	c	−711.4	....	....	
Na₃HP₂O₇·H₂O	c	−788.2	....	....	
Na₃HP₂O₇·6H₂O	c	−1135.7	....	....	
Na₄P₂O₇	c	−760.8	....	....	
Na₄P₂O₇·10H₂O	c	−1468.2	....	....	
Na₂PbO₃	c	−205.	....	....	
Na₂PtCl₆	c	−273.6	....	....	
Na₂PtCl₆·2H₂O	c	−418.5	....	....	
Na₂PtCl₆·6H₂O	c	−702.5	....	....	
Na₂S	c	−89.2	....	....	
Na₂S·4½H₂O	c	−416.9	....	....	
Na₂S·5H₂O	c	−452.7	....	....	
Na₂S·9H₂O	c	−736.7	....	....	
Na₂S₄	c	−98.4	....	....	
Na₂SO₃	c	−260.6	−239.5	175.55	34.9
Na₂SO₃·7H₂O	c	−753.4	....	....	
Na₂SO₄	c	−330.90	−302.78	221.934	35.73
	aq	−331.46	−302.52	221.743	32.9
Na₂SO₄·10H₂O	c	−1033.48	−870.93	638.380	141.7
NaHSO₄	c	−269.2	....	....	
NaHSO₄·H₂O	c	−339.2	....	....	
Na₂S₂O₃	c	−267.0	....	....	
Na₂S₂O₃·5H₂O	c (I)	−621.89	....	....	
	c (II)	−620.60	....	....	
Na₂S₂O₅	c	−349.1	....	....	
Na₂S₂O₆	c	−399.9	....	....	
Na₂S₂O₆·2H₂O	c	−542.5	....	....	
Na₂S₃O₆·3H₂O	c	−623.0	....	....	
Na₂S₄O₆·2H₂O	c	−550.0	....	....	
Na₂Se	c	−63.0	....	....	
Na₂Se·4½H₂O	c	−398.2	....	....	
Na₂Se·9H₂O	c	−709.1	....	....	
Na₂Se·16H₂O	c	−1199.4	....	....	
NaHSe	c	−27.8	....	....	
Na₂SeO₄	c	−258.	....	....	
Na₂SiO₃	c	−363	−341	249.9	27.2
Na₂SiO₃·5H₂O	c	−720.0	....	....	
Na₂SiO₃·9H₂O	c	−1002.0	....	....	
Na₂SiF₆	c	−677	....	....	
Na₂SnO₃	c	−276	....	....	
Na₄SnO₄	aq, 1200	−455.5	....	....	
Na₂UO₄	c	−501	....	....	
Na₂U₂O₇·1½H₂O	c	−880	....	....	
Na₃VO₄	c	−420	....	....	
Na₂WO₄	c	−395	....	....	
Na₂ZnO₂	c	−188	....	....	
Strontium					
Sr	g	39.2	26.3	−19.28	39.33
	c	0.00	0.00	0.000	13.0
Sr⁺⁺	aq	−130.38	−133.2	97.49	−9.4
Sr₃(AsO₄)₂	c	−800.7	....	....	
SrBr₂	c	−171.1	....	....	
	aq	−188.2	−182.1	133.48	29.2
SrBr₂·H₂O	c	−246.2	....	....	
SrBr₂·6H₂O	c	−604.4	....	....	
SrCO₃	c	−291.2	−271.9	199.30	23.2
Sr(HCO₃)₂	aq	−460.7	−413.8	303.31	36.0
Sr(C₂H₃O₂)₂	c	−356.7	....	....	
	aq	−362.7	−311.8	....	
Sr(C₂H₃O₂)₂·½H₂O	c	−391.2	....	....	
SrC₂O₄	aq	−327.4	−294.3	215.72	3
SrC₂O₄·H₂O	c	....	360.8	264.46	....
SrC₂O₄·2½H₂O	c	−504.2	....	....	
Sr(CN)₂·4H₂O	c	−335.2	....	....	
SrCl₂	c	−198.0	−186.7	136.85	28
	aq	−210.43	−195.7	143.45	16.9
SrCl₂·H₂O	c	−271.7	....	....	
SrCl₂·2H₂O	c	−343.7	....	....	
SrCl₂·6H₂O	c	−627.1	....	....	
SrF₂	c	−290.3	....	....	
SrH	g	52.4	45.8	−33.57	49.43
SrH₂	c	−42.3	....	....	
SrI₂	c	−135.5	....	....	
	aq	−157.1	−157.7	115.59	42.9
SrI₂·H₂O	c	−212.2	....	....	
SrI₂·2H₂O	c	−282.8	....	....	
SrI₂·6H₂O	c	−571.2	....	....	
Sr(N₃)₂	c	48.9	....	....	
Sr₃N₂	c	−93.4	....	....	
Sr(NO₂)₂	c	−179.3	....	....	
Sr(NO₃)₂	c	−233.25	....	....	
	aq	−229.02	−185.8	136.19	60.06
Sr(NO₃)₂·4H₂O	c	−514.5	....	....	

Substance	State	ΔHf°	ΔFf°	Log₁₀ Kf	S°
Strontium					
SrO	c	−141.1	−133.8	98.07	13.0
SrO₂	c	−153.6	....	....	....
SrO₂·8H₂O	c	−722.6	....	....	
Sr(OH)₂	c	−229.3	....	....	
	aq	−240.29	−208.2	152.61	−14.4
Sr(OH)₂·H₂O	c	−302.3	....	....	
Sr(OH)₂·8H₂O	c	−801.2	....	....	
Sr₃(PO₄)₂	c	−987.3	....	....	
SrHPO₄	c	−431.3	....	....	
Sr(H₂PO₄)₂·H₂O	c	−819.4	....	....	
SrS	g	19	....	....	
	c	−108.1	....	....	
SrSO₄	c	−345.3	−318.9	233.75	29.1
	aq	−347.38	−310.3	227.45	−5.3
Sulfur					
S	g	53.25	43.57	−31.9362	40.085
(rhb)	c	0.00	0.00	0.000	7.62
(mon)	c	0.071	0.023	−0.017	7.78
S₂Br₂	lq	−3.6	....	....	
S₂Cl₂	lq	−14.4	....	....	
S₂Cl₄	lq	−24.0	....	....	
SOCl₂	lq	−49.2	....	....	
SO₂Cl₂	lq	−93.0	−75	....	
SF₆	g	−262	−237	173.7	69.5
H₂S	g	−4.815	−7.892	5.785	49.15
	aq	−9.4	−6.54	4.797	29.2
H₂S·6H₂O	c	−431.2	....	....	
SO₂	g	−70.96	−71.79	52.621	59.40
SO₃	g	−94.45	−88.52	64.8b4	61.24
	lq	−104.67	....	....	
S₂O₇	c	−194.3	....	....	
H₂SO₃	aq, 200	−146.82	−128.54	....	
	aq, 500	−147.17	....	....	
	aq, 1000	−147.59	....	....	
	aq, 5000	−148.73	....	....	
H₂SO₄	lq	−193.91	....	....	
	aq	−216.90	−177.34	129.99	4.1
S⁻⁻	aq	10	20	−14.660	5.3
SO₃⁻⁻	aq	−149.2	−118.8	87.08	10.4
SO₄⁻⁻	aq	−216.90	−177.34	129.99	4.1
S₂O₃⁻⁻	aq	−154.	−127.2	93.24	29.
HS⁻	aq	−4.22	3.01	−2.206	14.6
HSO₃⁻	aq	−150.09	−126.03	92.378	31.64
HSO₄⁻	aq	−211.70	−179.94	131.893	30.32
Tantalum					
Ta	g	185	175	−128.3	44.24
	c	0.00	0.00	0.000	9.9
TaN	c	−58.2	....	....	
Ta₂O₅	c	−499.9	−470.6	344.94	34.2
Technetium					
Tc	c	0.00	0.00	0.000	9
Tellurium					
Te	g	47.6	38.1	−27.93	43.64
	c	0.00	0.00	0.000	11.88
	(am. ppt)	2.7	....	....	
Te₂	g	41.0	29.0	−21.26	64.07
TeBr₄	c	−49.8	....	....	
TeCl₄	c	−77.2	....	....	
TeF₆	g	−315	−292	214.0	80.67
H₂Te	g	36.9	33.1	−24.26	56
TeO₂	c	−77.69	−64.60	47.353	16.99
H₂TeO₃	c	−144.7	−115.7	84.81	47.7
	aq	−144.7	....	....	
H₂TeO₄	aq	−166.7	....	....	
H₂TeO₄·2H₂O	c	−306.6	−245.3	179.80	47
Terbium					
Tb	g	87	....	....	
	c	0.00	0.00	0.000	
Tb⁺⁺⁺	aq	−168.4	−163.9	120.14	
TbCl₃	c (β)	−241.6	....	....	
	aq	−288.5	−257.9	189.04	
Tb₂(SO₄)₃	aq	−987.5	−859.8	630.22	
Tb₂(SO₄)₃·8H₂O	c	−1328.2	973.55		
Thallium					
Tl	g	44.5	36.2	−26.53	43.23
	c	0.00	0.00	0.000	15.4
Tl⁺	aq	1.38	−7.755	5.68	30.4
Tl⁺⁺⁺	aq	27.7	50.0	−36.65	−106
TlBr	g	−5.	−14	10.3	63.8
	c	−41.4	−39.7	29.10	26.6
	aq	−27.5	−32.3	23.68	49.7
TlBr₃	c	−59.0	....	....	
TlBr₃·4H₂O	c	−334.6	....	....	
TlBrO₃	c	−24.0	....	....	
	aq	−10.2	1.3	−0.953	68.6
TlCl	g	−16.	−22	16.1	61.1
	c	−48.99	−44.19	32.391	25.9
	aq	−38.64	−39.105	28.663	43.6
TlCl₃	c	−83.9	....	....	
TlCl₃·4H₂O	c	−367.7	....	....	
TlF	c	−33	....	....	
TlH	g	48	42	−30.8	51.39
TlI	c (II)	−29.7	−29.7	21.77	29.4
	aq	−12.0	−19.9	14.59	56.5

Substance	State	$\Delta Hf°$	$\Delta Ff°$	$Log_{10}\ Kf$	$S°$
Thallium					
$TlIO_3$	c	.....	-47.6	34.89	.....
	aq	-53.5	-40.1	29.39	58.1
$TlNO_3$	c	-58.01	-36.07	26.439	38.2
	aq	-47.99	-34.22	25.083	65.6
Tl_2O	c	-41.9	-32.5	23.82	23.8
$TlOH$	c	-56.9	-45.5	33.35	17.3
$Tl(OH)_3$	c	122.6			
Tl_2S	c	-20.8			
Tl_2SO_4	c	-221.7			
	aq	-214.14	-192.85	141.356	65.1
Thorium					
Th	c	0.00	0.00	0.000	13.6
Th^{++++}	aq	-183.0			
$ThBr_4$	c	-227.1			
ThC_2	c	-45			
$ThCl_4$	c	-285			
ThF_4	c	-477			
ThH_4	c	-43			
ThI_4	c	-131			
$Th(NO_3)_4$	aq, 100	-380.48			
ThO_2	c	-292			
$Th(OH)_4$	c*	-421.5			
Th_2S_3	c	-262.0			
$Th(SO_4)_2$	c	-602			
Thulium					
Tm	c	0.00	0.00	0.000	.....
Tm^{+++}	aq	-161.3	-156.5	114.71	.....
$TmCl_3$	c (γ)	-229.5			
	aq	281.4	-250.5	183.61	
TmI_3	c (β)	-137.8			
	aq	-201.4	-193.5	141.83	
Tin					
Sn	g	72	64	-47.6	40.25
(gray), cubic	c (III)	0.6	1.1	-0.806	10.7
(tet), white	c (II)	0.00	0.00	0.000	12.3
$SnBr_2$	c	-63.6			
$SnBr_4$	c (I)	-97.1			
$SnBr_4 \cdot 8H_2O$	lq	-656.6			
$Sn(C_2H_5)_4$	lq	-49			
$SnCl_2$	c	-83.6			
$SnCl_2 \cdot 2H_2O$	c	-225.9			
$SnCl_4$	lq	-130.3	-113.3	83.047	61.8
$SnOCl_2$	aq	-147.5			
SnI_2	c	-34.4			
SnO	c	-68.4	-61.5	45.08	13.5
SnO_2	c	-138.8	-124.2	91.037	12.5
$Sn(OH)_2$	c	-138.3	-117.6	86.199	23.1
$Sn(OH)_4$	c	-270.5			
SnS	c	-18.6	-19.7	14.44	23.6
$Sn(SO_4)_2$	c	-393.4			
Titanium					
Ti	g	112	101	-74	43.07
	c	0.00	0.00	0.000	7.24
$TiBr_2$	c	-95			
$TiBr_3$	c	-132			
$TiBr_4$	c	-155			
TiC	c	-54	-53	38.8	5.8
$TiCl$	g	122			
$TiCl_2$	c	-114			
$TiCl_3$	c	-165			
$TiCl_4$	g				84.4
	lq	-179.3	-161.2	118.16	60.4
TiF_2	c	-198			
TiF_3	c	-315			
TiF_4	c	-370			
H_2TiF_6	lq	-555.1			
TiI_2	c	-61			
TiI_3	c	-80			
TiI_4	c	-102			
TiN	c	-73.0	-66.1	48.45	7.2
TiO	g	43			
	c (II)	.....			8.31
TiO_2 (rutile)	c (III)	-218.0	-203.8	149.38	12.01
(hydrated)	(am. ppt)	-207.			
Ti_2O_3	c (II)	-367	-346	253.6	18.83
Ti_3O_5	c	-584	-550	403.1	30.92
Tungsten					
W	g	201.6	191.6	-140.44	41.55
	c	0.00	0.00	0.000	8.0
WC	c	-9.09			
WO_2	c	-136.3			
WO_3 (yellow)	c	-200.84	-182.47	133.748	19.90
$WO_3 \cdot H_2O$ (H_2WO_4)	c	-279.6			
W_2O_5	c	-337.9			
WS_2	c	-46.3	-46.2	33.86	23
Uranium					
U	g	125			
	c (III)	0.00	0.00	0.000	12.03
U^{+++}	aq	-123.0	-124.4	91.18	-30
U^{++++}	aq	-146.7	-138.4	101.44	-78
UBr_3	c	-170.1	-164.7	120.72	49
UBr_4	c	-196.6	-188.5	138.17	58
UC_2	c	-42	-42	30.8	14
UCl_3	c	-213.0	-196.9	144.32	37.99
UCl_4	c	-251.2	-230.0	168.59	47.4
Uranium					
UCl_5	c	-262.1	-237.4	174.01	62
UCl_6	c	-272.4	-241.5	177.02	68.3
UF_3	c	-357	-339	248.5	26
UF_4	c	-443	-421	308.6	36.1
UF_5	c	-488	-461	337.9	43
UF_6	g	-505	-485	355.5	90.76
UH_3	c	-30.4			
UI_3	c	-114.7	-115.3	84.51	56
UI_4	c	-127.0	-126.1	92.43	65
$UIBr_3$	c	-177.1			
$UICl_3$	c	-219.9	-204.4	149.82	54
UN	c	-80	-75	55	18
U_2N_3	c	-213	-194	142.2	29
UO_2	c	-270	-257	188.4	18.6
UO_2^+	aq	-247.4	-237.6	174.16	12
UO_2^{++}	aq	-250.4	-236.4	173.28	-17
UO_3	c	-302	-283	207.4	23.57
$UO_3 \cdot H_2O$	c	-375.4			
$UO_3 \cdot 2H_2O$	c	-446.2			
$UO_4 \cdot 2H_2O$	c	-436			
U_3O_8	c	-898			
$U(OH)_4^{+++}$	aq	-204.1	-193.5	141.83	-30
$U(SO_4)_2$	c	-563			
UO_2Br_2	aq (dil)	-308.2			
$UO_2(C_2H_3O_2)_2$	aq (dil)	-484.0			
$UO_2(C_2H_3O_2)_2 \cdot 2H_2O$	c	-624.9			
$UO_2(C_2H_3O_2)_2 \cdot NH_4C_2H_3O_2 \cdot 6H_2O$	c	-1045.8			
UO_2Cl_2	aq (dil)	-331			
UO_2CrO_4	aq (dil)	-456.7			
$UO_2CrO_4 \cdot 5\frac{1}{2}H_2O$	c	-838.8			
$UO_2(NO_3)_2$	c	-329.2	-273.1	200.18	66
	aq	-349.1	-289.2	211.98	53
$UO_2(NO_3)_2 \cdot H_2O$	c	-404.8	-335.3	245.77	76
$UO_2(NO_3)_2 \cdot 2H_2O$	c	-480.0	-396.6	290.70	85
$UO_2(NO_3)_2 \cdot 3H_2O$	c	-552.2	-454.7	333.29	94
$UO_2(NO_3)_2 \cdot 6H_2O$	c	-764.3	-625.0	458.12	120.85
UO_2SO_4	aq	-467.3	-413.7	303.24	-13
$UO_2SO_4 \cdot 3H_2O$	c	-666.8	-586.0	429.53	63
Vanadium					
V	g	120	109	-79.90	43.55
	c	0.00	0.00	0.000	7.05
VCl_2	c	-108	-97	71.1	23.2
VCl_3	c	-137	-120	87.96	31.3
VCl_4	lq	-138			
VN	c	-41	-35	25.7	8.91
VO	g	52			
V_2O_2	c	-200			
V_2O_3	c	-290	-271	198.6	23.58
V_2O_4	c (II)	-344	-318	233.1	24.65
V_2O_5	c	-373	-344	252.1	31.3
$VOCl_3$	c	-172			
$VOSO_4$	c	-312.5			
Wolfram (See Tungsten)					
Xenon					
Xe	g	0.00	0.00	0.000	40.53
$Xe \cdot 6H_2O$	c	-428			
Ytterbium					
Yb	g	87			41.30
	c	0.00	0.00	0.000	
Yb^{++}	aq	.....	-129.0	94.56	
Yb^{+++}	aq	-160.6	-155.5	113.98	
$YbCl_3$	c (γ)	-228.7			
	aq	-280.7	-249.5	182.88	
$Yb_2(SO_4)_3$	aq	-971.9	-843.0	617.91	
$Yb_2(SO_4)_3 \cdot 8H_2O$	c	.....	-1308.8	959.33	
Yttrium					
Y	g	103			42.87
	c	0.00	0.00	0.000	.....
Y^{+++}	aq	-168.0	-164.1	120.28	
YCl_3	c (γ)	-234.8			
	aq	-288.1	-258.1	189.18	
YI_3	c (β)	-143.2			
	aq	-208.1	-201.1	147.40	
$Y(OH)_3$	c	-337.6	-308.3	225.98	
$Y_2(SO_4)_3$	c	-986.7	-860.2	630.51	
$Y_2(SO_4)_3 \cdot 8H_2O$	c	-1512.6	-1327.3	972.89	
Zinc					
Zn	g	31.19	22.69	-16.631	38.45
	c	0.00	0.00	0.000	9.95
Zn^{++}	aq	-36.43	-35.184	25.79	-25.47
$ZnBr_2$	c	-76.17	-74.143	84.346	32.81
	aq	-94.23	-84.33	61.814	13.13
$ZnBr_2 \cdot 2H_2O$	c	-220.9	-190.6	139.71	56.2
$Zn(CN)_2$	c	18.4			
$ZnCO_3$	c	-194.2	-174.8	128.13	19.7
$Zn(C_2H_3O_2)_2$	c	-258.1			
$Zn(C_2H_3O_2)_2 \cdot H_2O$	c	-329.2			
$Zn(C_2H_3O_2)_2 \cdot 2H_2O$	c	-398.8			
$ZnC_2O_4 \cdot 2H_2O$	c	-373.8			
$Zn(CH_3)_2$	lq	6.0			
$Zn(C_2H_5)_2$	lq	5.0			
$ZnCl_2$	c	-99.40	-88.26	64.690	25.9
	aq	-116.48	-97.88	71.748	0.89

* Soluble.

Substance	State	ΔHf°	ΔFf°	Log₁₀ Kf	S°
Zinc					
ZnF₂	aq	−187.9	−166	....	....
ZnH	g	54.4	47.5	−34.82	48.70
ZnI₂	c	−49.98	−50.01	36.657	38.0
	aq	−63.17	−59.88	43.894	26.83
Zn(NO₃)₂	c	−115.12			
Zn(NO₃)₂·H₂O	c	−191.99	....	....	....
Zn(NO₃)₂·2H₂O	c	−264.94			
Zn(NO₃)₂·4H₂O	c	−405.76			
Zn(NO₃)₂·6H₂O	c	−550.92	....	....	....
ZnO	c	−83.17	−76.05	55.744	10.5
Zn(OH)₂ (stable)	c (I)	−153.5	....	....	....
(unstable)	c (II)	−153.1	....	....	....
ZnS	g	−14.0			
(sphalerite)	c (II)	−48.5	−47.4	34.74	13.8
(würtzite)	c (I)	−45.3			
ZnSO₄	c	−233.88	−208.31	152.688	29.8
	aq	−253.33	−212.52	155 774	−21.3
ZnSO₄·H₂O	c	−310.6	−269.9	197 83	34.9
ZnSO₄·6H₂O	c	−663.3	−555.0	406.81	86.8
ZnSO₄·7H₂O	c	−735.1	−611.9	448.51	92.4
Zirconium					
Zr	g	125	115	−84.29	43.31
	c	0.00	0.00	0.000	9.18
ZrBr₂	c	−120	....	....	....
ZrBr₃	c	−174	....	....	....
ZrBr₄	c	−192	....	....	....
ZrC	c	−45	....	....	....
ZrCl₂	c	−145	....	....	....
ZrCl₃	c	−208	....	....	....
ZrCl₄	c	−230	−209	153.2	44.5
ZrF₂	c	−230	....	....	....
ZrF₃	c	−350	....	....	....
ZrF₄	c	−445	....	....	....
ZrI₂	c	−90	....	....	....
ZrI₃	c	−128	....	....	....
ZrI₄	c	−130	....	....	....
ZrN	c	−82.2	−75.4	55.27	9.23
ZrO(NO₃)₂·2H₂O	c	−456.3	....	....	....
ZrO(NO₃)₂·3H₂O	c	−527.3	....	....	....
ZrO(NO₃)₂·3½H₂O	c	−562.8	....	....	....
ZrO(NO₃)₂·6H₂O	c	−737.6	....	....	....
ZrO₂	c	−258.2	−244.4	179.14	12.03
Zr(OH)₄	c	−411.2	....	....	....
Zr(OH)₄·H₂O	c	−482.9	....	....	....
Zr(OH)₄·2H₂O	c	−554.2	....	....	....
Zr(SO₄)₂	c	−597.4	....	....	....
Zr(SO₄)₂·H₂O	c	−677.9	....	....	....
Zr(SO₄)₂·4H₂O	c	−893.1	....	....	....

Formula	Name	State	ΔHf°	ΔFf°	Log₁₀ Kf	S°
C	Carbon	g	171.698	160.845	−117.897	37.761
	(diamond)	c	0.4532	0.6850	−0.5021	0.5829
	(graphite)	c	0.000	0.000	0.000	1.3609
CO	Carbon monoxide	g	−26.4157	−32.8079	24.048	47.301
CO₂	Carbon dioxide	g	−94.052	−94.260	69.091	51.061
		aq	−98.69	−92.31	67.662	29.0
CO₃⁻⁻	Carbonate ion	aq	−161.63	−126.22	92.517	−12.7
CH₃	Methyl	g	32.0	....	....	....
CH₄	Methane	g	−17.889	−12.140	8.8985	44.50
HCOO⁻	Formate ion	aq	−98.0	−80.0	58.64	21.9
HCO₃⁻	Bicarbonate ion	aq	−165.18	−140.31	102.845	22.7
CH₂O	Formaldehyde	g	−27.7	−26.3	19.28	52.26
CH₂O₂	Formic acid, monomer	g	−86.67	−80.24	58.815	60.0
	Formic acid	lq	−97.8	−82.7	60.62	30.82
		aq	−98.0	−85.1	62.38	39.1
H₂CO₃	Carbonic acid	aq	−167.0	−149.00	109.215	45.7
CH₃OH	Methanol	g	−48.08	−38.69	28.359	56.8
		lq	−57.02	−39.73	29.122	30.3
CF₄	Tetrafluoromethane	g	−162.5	−151.8	111.27	62.7
CCl₄	Tetrachloromethane	g	−25.5	−15.3	11.21	73.95
		lq	−33.3	−16.4	12.02	51.25
COCl₂	Carbonyl chloride	g	−53.30	−50.31	36.877	69.13
CH₃Cl	Chloromethane	g	−19.6	−14.0	10.26	55.97
CH₂Cl₂	Dichloromethane	g	−21.	−14.	10.3	64.68
		lq	−28	−15.1	11.07	42.7
CHCl₃	Trichloromethane	g	−24	−16	11.7	70.86
		lq	−31.5	−17.1	12.53	48.5
CBr₄	Tetrabromomethane	g	12.	8.6	−6.30	85.6
CH₃Br	Bromomethane	g	−8.5	−6.2	4.54	58.74
CH₂Br₂	Dibromomethane	g	−1.	−1.4	1.03	70.16
CHBr₃	Tribromomethane	g	6.	3.8	−2.78	79.18
		lq	−4.8	0.7	−0.51	53.0
CH₃I	Iodomethane	g	4.9	5.3	−3.88	60.85
		lq	−2.0	4.9	−3.59	38.9

Formula	Name	State	$\Delta Hf°$	$\Delta Ff°$	$Log_{10} Kf$	$S°$
CH_2I_2	Diodomethane	lq	15.9	....	....	....
CHI_3	Triodomethane	c	33.6	....	....	....
CS_2	Carbon disulfide	g	27.55	15.55	−11.398	56.84
		lq	21.0	15.2	−11.14	36.10
COS	Carbon oxysulfide	g	−32.80	−40.45	29.649	55.34
CN^-	Cyanide ion	aq	36.1	39.6	−29.03	28.2
CNO^-	Cyanate ion	aq	−33.5	−23.6	17.30	31.1
$C(NO_2)_4$	Tetranitromethane	lq	8.8	....	....	....
HCN	Hydrogen cyanide	g	31.2	28.7	−21.04	48.23
		lq	25.2	29.0	−21.26	26.97
	Hydrocyanic acid	aq	25.2	26.8	−19.64	30.8
CH_5N	Methyl amine	g	−6.7	6.6	−4.84	57.73
CH_2N_2	Cyanamide	c	9.2	....	....	....
CH_5N_3	Guanidine	c	−17.0	....	....	....
HCNO	Cyanic acid	aq	−35.1	−28.9	21 18	43.6
CH_3O_2N	Nitromethane	lq	−21.28	2.26	−1.656	41.1
CH_4ON_2	Urea	c	−79.634	−47.120	34.538	25.00
		aq	−76.30	−48.72	35.711	41.55
$CH_6O_2N_2$	Ammonium carbamate	c	−154.21	−109.47	80.240	39.70
CNCl	Cyanogen chloride	g	34.5	32.9	−24.12	56.31
CH_6NCl	Methylamine hydrochloride	c	−68.31	−35.09	25.720	33.13
CNI	Cyanogen iodide	g	54.6	47.7	−34.96	61.26
		c	40.4	42.6	−31.23	30.8
		aq	43.2	43.3	−31.74	37.9
CNS^-	Thiocyanate ion	aq (very dilute)	17.2	....	....	....
CH_4N_2S	Thiourea	c	−22.1	....	....	....
$C_2O_4^{--}$	Oxalate ion	aq	−197.0	−161.3	118.23	12.2
C_2H_2	Ethyne (acetylene)	g	54.194	50.000	−36.649	47.997
$C_2H_2·6H_2O$	Ethyne hexahydrate	c	−371.1	....	....	....
C_2H_4	Ethene (ethylene)	g	12.496	16.282	−11.935	52.45
C_2H_6	Ethane	g	−20.236	−7.860	5.7613	54.85
$HC_2O_4^-$	Bioxalate ion	aq	−195.5	−167.1	122.48	36.7
C_2H_2O	Ketene	g	−14.6	....	....	....
$C_2H_2O_2$	Glyoxal	c	−83.7	....	....	....
$C_2H_2O_4$	Oxalic acid	c	−197.6	−166.8	122.28	28.7
$C_2H_3O_2^-$	Acetate ion	aq	−116.843	....	....	....
C_2H_4O	Ethylene oxide	g	−12.19	−2.79	2.045	58.1
	Acetaldehyde	g	−39.76	−31.96	23.426	63.5
$C_2H_4O_2$	Acetic acid	lq	−116.4	−93.8	68.75	38.2
$C_2H_4O_4$	Formic acid dimer	g	−187.7	−163.8	120.09	83.1
C_2H_6O	Ethanol	g	−56.24	−40.30	29.536	67.4
		lq	−66.356	−41.77	30.617	38.4
	Dimethyl ether	g	−44.3	−27.3	19.98	63.72
$C_2H_6O_2$	1-2 Ethanediol	lq	−108.58	−77.12	56.528	39.9
C_2H_5Cl	Chloroethane	g	−25.1	−12.7	9.331	65.90
$C_2H_4Cl_2$	1-2 Dichloroethane	lq	−30.7	−19.2	14.11	49.84
C_2HOCl_3	Chloral trichloroacetaldehyde	lq	−51.1	....	....	....
$C_2HO_2Cl_3$	Trichloroacetic acid	c	−122.8	....	....	....
C_2H_5Br	Bromoethane	g	−13.0	....	....	....
		lq	−20.4	....	....	....
$C_2H_4Br_2$	1-2 Dibromoethane	lq	−19.30	−4.94	3.621	53.37
C_2H_5I	Iodoethane	lq	−7.4	....	....	....
$C_2H_4I_2$	1-2 Diiodoethane	c	0.1	....	....	....
C_2H_6S	Ethanethiol	lq	−16.	....	....	....
	Dimethyl sulfide	g	−6.9	3.7	−2.74	68.28
		lq	−13.6	3.4	−2.50	46.94
C_2N_2	Cyanogen	g	73.60	70.81	−51.903	57.86
C_2H_3N	Acetonitrile	g	21.0	25.2	−18.47	58.18
		lq	12.7	24.0	−17.59	34.5
	Methyl isocyanide	g	35.9	40.0	−29.32	58.78
C_2H_7N	Ethylamine	g	−11.6	....	....	....
$C_2H_5O_2N$	Aminoacetic acid (glycine)	c	−126.33	−88.61	64.950	26.1
	Nitroethane	lq	−30.	....	....	....
C_2H_3SN	Methyl thiocyanate	lq	25.	....	....	....
	Methyl isothiocyanate	c	18.	....	....	....
$C_2H_7O_3SN$	2-Aminoethylsulfonic acid (taurine)	c	−181.66	....	....	....

THERMODYNAMIC FUNCTIONS OF COPPER, SILVER AND GOLD

1 cal = 4.1840J H_0° is the enthalpy of the solid at 0°K and 1 atm pressure

T °K	C_P° J/deg-mol			$H_T^\circ - H_0^\circ$ J/mol			$(H_T^\circ - H_0^\circ)/T$ J/deg-mol		
	Cu	Ag	Au	Cu	Ag	Au	Cu	Ag	Au
1.00	0.000743	0.000818	0.00118	0.000359	0.000367	0.000478	0.000359	0.000367	0.000478
2.00	0.00177	0.00265	0.00504	0.00158	0.00197	0.00326	0.000790	0.000987	0.00163
3.00	0.00337	0.00650	0.0141	0.00409	0.00633	0.0123	0.00136	0.00211	0.00410
4.00	0.00582	0.0134	0.0306	0.00860	0.0160	0.0340	0.00215	0.00399	0.00849
5.00	0.00943	0.0243	0.0570	0.0161	0.0344	0.0768	0.00322	0.00689	0.0154
6.00	0.0145	0.0403	0.0955	0.0279	0.0663	0.152	0.00466	0.0110	0.0253
7.00	0.0213	0.0626	0.149	0.0456	0.117	0.273	0.00652	0.0167	0.0390
8.00	0.0301	0.0927	0.220	0.0712	0.194	0.456	0.00889	0.0243	0.0570
9.00	0.0414	0.132	0.313	0.107	0.306	0.720	0.0119	0.0340	0.0800
10.00	0.0555	0.183	0.431	0.155	0.462	1.090	0.0155	0.0462	0.109
11.00	0.0727	0.247	0.577	0.219	0.676	1.592	0.0199	0.0614	0.145
12.00	0.0936	0.325	0.755	0.302	0.961	2.255	0.0251	0.0801	0.188
13.00	0.119	0.421	0.963	0.407	1.332	3.112	0.0313	0.102	0.239
14.00	0.149	0.535	1.203	0.541	1.809	4.193	0.0386	0.129	0.299
15.00	0.184	0.670	1.474	0.706	2.409	5.529	0.0471	0.161	0.369
16.00	0.225	0.826	1.772	0.910	3.155	7.149	0.0569	0.197	0.447
17.00	0.273	1.002	2.096	1.158	4.067	9.081	0.0681	0.239	0.534
18.00	0.328	1.199	2.442	1.458	5.166	11.35	0.0810	0.287	0.630
19.00	0.390	1.414	2.807	1.816	6.471	13.97	0.0956	0.341	0.735
20.00	0.462	1.647	3.187	2.242	8.001	16.97	0.112	0.400	0.848
25.00	0.963	3.066	5.245	5.703	19.62	37.97	0.228	0.785	1.519
30.00	1.693	4.774	7.375	12.25	39.14	69.53	0.408	1.305	2.318
35.00	2.638	6.612	9.395	22.99	67.58	111.5	0.657	1.931	3.186
40.00	3.740	8.419	11.22	38.89	105.2	163.2	0.972	2.630	4.079
45.00	4.928	10.11	12.86	60.54	151.6	223.4	1.345	3.368	4.965
50.00	6.154	11.66	14.29	88.23	206.1	291.4	1.765	4.121	5.828
55.00	7.385	13.04	15.52	122.1	267.9	366.0	2.220	4.871	6.654
60.00	8.595	14.27	16.59	162.0	336.2	446.3	2.701	5.604	7.438
65.00	9.759	15.35	17.51	208.0	410.4	531.6	3.199	6.313	8.179
70.00	10.86	16.30	18.31	259.5	489.5	621.2	3.708	6.993	8.874
75.00	11.89	17.14	19.01	316.4	573.2	714.6	4.219	7.642	9.528
80.00	12.85	17.87	19.63	378.4	660.7	811.2	4.729	8.259	10.14
85.00	13.74	18.53	20.17	444.9	751.8	910.7	5.234	8.844	10.71
90.00	14.56	19.11	20.64	515.7	845.9	1013.	5.730	9.399	11.25
95.00	15.31	19.63	21.06	590.4	942.8	1117.	6.215	9.924	11.76
100.00	16.01	20.10	21.44	668.7	1042.	1223.	6.687	10.42	12.23
105.00	16.64	20.52	21.77	750.3	1144.	1331.	7.146	10.89	12.68
110.00	17.22	20.89	22.06	835.0	1247.	1441.	7.591	11.34	13.10
115.00	17.76	21.23	22.33	922.5	1353.	1552.	8.021	11.76	13.49
120.00	18.25	21.54	22.56	1013.	1460.	1664.	8.438	12.16	13.87
125.00	18.70	21.82	22.78	1105.	1568.	1777.	8.839	12.54	14.22
130.00	19.12	22.07	22.97	1199.	1678.	1892.	9.227	12.91	14.55
135.00	19.51	22.31	23.15	1296.	1789.	2007.	9.601	13.25	14.87
140.00	19.87	22.52	23.31	1395.	1901.	2123.	9.961	13.58	15.17
145.00	20.20	22.72	23.45	1495.	2014.	2240.	10.31	13.89	15.45
150.00	20.51	22.90	23.59	1597.	2128.	2358.	10.64	14.19	15.72
155.00	20.79	23.07	23.70	1700.	2243.	2476.	10.97	14.47	15.97
160.00	21.05	23.22	23.81	1804.	2358.	2595.	11.28	14.74	16.22
165.00	21.30	23.37	23.91	1910.	2475.	2714.	11.58	15.00	16.45
170.00	21.53	23.50	24.00	2017.	2592.	2834.	11.87	15.25	16.67
175.00	21.74	23.63	24.08	2125.	2710.	2954.	12.15	15.49	16.88
180.00	21.94	23.75	24.15	2235.	2828.	3075.	12.42	15.71	17.08
185.00	22.13	23.86	24.22	2345.	2947.	3196.	12.68	15.93	17.27
190.00	22.31	23.96	24.29	2456.	3067.	3317.	12.93	16.14	17.46
195.00	22.47	24.06	24.35	2568.	3187.	3438.	13.17	16.34	17.63
200.00	22.63	24.16	24.41	2681.	3308.	3650.	13.40	16.54	17.80
205.00	22.77	24.24	24.48	2794.	3429.	3683.	13.63	16.72	17.96
210.00	22.91	24.33	24.54	2908.	3550.	3805.	13.85	16.90	18.12
215.00	23.04	24.41	24.60	3023.	3672.	3928.	14.06	17.08	18.27
220.00	23.17	24.49	24.65	3139.	3794.	4051.	14.27	17.25	18.41
225.00	23.28	24.56	24.71	3255.	3917.	4174.	14.47	17.41	18.55
230.00	23.39	24.63	24.76	3372.	4040.	4298.	14.66	17.56	18.69
235.00	23.50	24.69	24.82	3489.	4163.	4422.	14.85	17.71	18.82
240.00	23.60	24.76	24.87	3607.	4287.	4546.	15.03	17.86	18.94
245.00	23.69	24.82	24.92	3725.	4411.	4671.	15.20	18.00	19.06
250.00	23.78	24.88	24.97	3844.	4535.	4796.	15.37	18.14	19.18
255.00	23.86	24.93	25.02	3963.	4659.	4921.	15.54	18.27	19.30
260.00	23.94	24.99	25.07	4082.	4784.	5046.	15.70	18.40	19.41
265.00	24.02	25.04	25.12	4202.	4909.	5171.	15.86	18.53	19.51
270.00	24.09	25.09	25.17	4322.	5035.	5297.	16.01	18.65	19.62
273.15	24.13	25.12	25.20	4398.	5114.	5376.	16.10	18.72	19.68
275.00	24.15	25.14	25.21	4443.	5160.	5423.	16.16	18.76	19.72
280.00	24.22	25.19	25.26	4564.	5286.	5549.	16.30	18.88	19.82
285.00	24.28	25.24	25.31	4685.	5412.	5676.	16.44	18.99	19.91
290.00	24.34	25.28	25.35	4807.	5538.	5802.	16.57	19.10	20.01
295.00	24.40	25.32	25.39	4929.	5665.	5929.	16.71	19.20	20.10
298.15	24.44	25.35	25.42	5005.	5745.	6009.	16.79	19.27	20.15
300.00	24.46	25.37	25.43	5051.	5792.	6056.	16.84	19.31	20.19

THERMODYNAMIC FUNCTIONS OF COPPER, SILVER AND GOLD (Continued)

From NSRDS-NBS   George T. Furukawa, William G. Saba and Martin L. Reilly

T °K	S_T° J/deg-mol			$-(G_T^\circ - H_0^\circ)$ J/mol			$-(G_T^\circ - H_0^\circ)/T$ J/deg-mol		
	Cu	Ag	Au	Cu	Ag	Au	Cu	Ag	Au
1.00	0.000711	0.000706	0.000880	0.000351	0.000339	0.000402	0.000351	0.000339	0.000402
2.00	0.00152	0.00175	0.00266	0.00145	0.00152	0.00206	0.000727	0.000762	0.00103
3.00	0.00251	0.00347	0.00620	0.00345	0.00406	0.00631	0.00115	0.00135	0.00210
4.00	0.00379	0.00619	0.0123	0.00657	0.00879	0.0153	0.00164	0.00220	0.00383
5.00	0.00546	0.0103	0.0218	0.0112	0.0169	0.0321	0.00223	0.00338	0.00641
6.00	0.00760	0.0160	0.0354	0.0176	0.0299	0.0603	0.00294	0.00498	0.0100
7.00	0.0103	0.0238	0.0539	0.0265	0.0496	0.104	0.00379	0.00709	0.0149
8.00	0.0137	0.0341	0.0782	0.0385	0.0783	0.170	0.00481	0.00979	0.0212
9.00	0.0179	0.0472	0.109	0.0542	0.119	0.263	0.00602	0.0132	0.0292
10.00	0.0229	0.0636	0.148	0.0746	0.174	0.391	0.00746	0.0174	0.0391
11.00	0.0290	0.0839	0.196	0.100	0.247	0.562	0.00913	0.0225	0.0511
12.00	0.0362	0.109	0.253	0.133	0.343	0.786	0.0111	0.0286	0.0655
13.00	0.0447	0.138	0.322	0.173	0.466	1.073	0.0133	0.0359	0.0825
14.00	0.0545	0.174	0.402	0.223	0.622	1.434	0.0159	0.0444	0.102
15.00	0.0660	0.215	0.494	0.283	0.815	1.880	0.0189	0.0544	0.125
16.00	0.0791	0.263	0.598	0.355	1.054	2.426	0.0222	0.0659	0.152
17.00	0.0941	0.318	0.715	0.442	1.344	3.081	0.0260	0.0790	0.181
18.00	0.111	0.381	0.845	0.544	1.693	3.861	0.0302	0.0940	0.214
19.00	0.131	0.452	0.987	0.665	2.109	4.775	0.0350	0.111	0.251
20.00	0.152	0.530	1.140	0.806	2.599	5.838	0.0403	0.130	0.292
25.00	0.305	1.043	2.069	1.917	6.446	13.76	0.0767	0.258	0.550
30.00	0.541	1.750	3.214	3.995	13.35	26.89	0.133	0.445	0.896
35.00	0.871	2.623	4.505	7.487	24.22	46.14	0.214	0.692	1.318
40.00	1.294	3.625	5.881	12.86	39 79	72.08	0.322	0.995	1.802
45.00	1.802	4.715	7.299	20.57	60.61	105.0	0.457	1.347	2.334
50.00	2.385	5.862	8.729	31.01	87.04	145.1	0.620	1.741	2.902
55.00	3.029	7.040	10.15	44.52	119.3	192.3	0.809	2.169	3.496
60.00	3.724	8.228	11.55	61.38	157.5	246.5	1.023	2.624	4.109
65.00	4.458	9.414	12.91	81.82	201.6	307.7	1.259	3.101	4.734
70.00	5.222	10.59	14.24	106.0	251 6	375.6	1.514	3.594	5.366
75.00	6.007	11.74	15.53	134.1	307.4	450.0	1.788	4.099	6.001
80.00	6.806	12.87	16.78	166.1	368.9	530.8	2.076	4.612	6.635
85.00	7.612	13.97	17.98	202.1	436.1	617.7	2.378	5.130	7.267
90.00	8.421	15.05	19.15	242.2	508.6	710.6	2.691	5.652	7.895
95.00	9.229	16.10	20.28	286.4	586.5	809.1	3.014	6.174	8.517
100.00	10.03	17.12	21.37	334.5	669.6	913.3	3.345	6.696	9.133
105.00	10.83	18.11	22.42	386.7	757.7	1023.	3.683	7.216	9.740
110.00	11.62	19.07	23.44	442.8	850.6	1137.	4.025	7.733	10.34
115.00	12.39	20.01	24.43	502.8	948.3	1257.	4.372	8.246	10.93
120.00	13.16	20.92	25.38	566.7	1051.	1382.	4.723	8.755	11.51
125.00	13.91	21.80	26.31	634.4	1157.	1511.	5.075	9.260	12.09
130.00	14.66	22.66	27.20	705.8	1269.	1645.	5.429	9.759	12.65
135.00	15.39	23.50	28.07	780.9	1384.	1783.	5.785	10.25	13.21
140.00	16.10	24.32	28.92	859.7	1504.	1925.	6.140	10.74	13.75
145.00	16.80	25.11	29.74	941.9	1627.	2072.	6.496	11.22	14.29
150.00	17.49	25.88	30.54	1028.	1755.	2223.	6.851	11.70	14.82
155.00	18.17	26.64	31.31	1117.	1886.	2377.	7.206	12.17	15.34
160.00	18.84	27.37	32.07	1209.	2021.	2536.	7.559	12.63	15.85
165.00	19.49	28.09	32.80	1305.	2160.	2698.	7.910	13.09	16.35
170.00	20.13	28.79	33.52	1404.	2302.	2864.	8.260	13.54	16.85
175.00	20.75	29.47	34.21	1506.	2448.	3033.	8.608	13.99	17.33
180.00	21.37	30.14	34.89	1612.	2597.	3206.	8.954	14.43	17.81
185.00	21.97	30.79	35.55	1720.	2749.	3382.	9.298	14.86	18.28
190.00	22.57	31.43	36.20	1831.	2904.	3561.	9.639	15.29	18.74
195.00	23.15	32.05	36.83	1946.	3063.	3744.	9.978	15.71	19.20
200.00	23.72	32.66	37.45	2063.	3225.	3930.	10.31	16.12	19.65
205.00	24.28	33.26	38.05	2183.	3390.	4118.	10.65	16.54	20.09
210.00	24.83	33.85	38.64	2306.	3558.	4310.	10.98	16.94	20.52
215.00	25.37	34.42	39.22	2431.	3728.	4505.	11.31	17.34	20.95
220.00	25.90	34.98	39.79	2559.	3902.	4702.	11.63	17.74	21.37
225.00	26.42	35.53	40.34	2690.	4078.	4903.	11.96	18.12	21.79
230.00	26.94	36.07	40.89	2824.	4257.	5106.	12.28	18.51	22.20
235.00	27.44	36.60	41.42	2960.	4439.	5312.	12.59	18.89	22.60
240.00	27.94	37.12	41.94	3098.	4623.	5520.	12.91	19.26	23.00
245.00	28.42	37.63	42.46	3239.	4810.	5731.	13.22	19.63	23.39
250.00	28.90	38.14	42.96	3382.	4999.	5945.	13.53	20.00	23.78
255.00	29.37	38.63	43.46	3528.	5191.	6161.	13.84	20.36	24.16
260.00	29.84	39.11	43.94	3676.	5386.	6379.	14.14	20.71	24.53
265.00	30.30	39.59	44.42	3826.	5582.	6600.	14.44	21.07	24.91
270.00	30.75	40.06	44.89	3979.	5782.	6823.	14.74	21.41	25.27
273.15	31.02	40.35	45.18	4076.	5908.	6965.	14.92	21.63	25.50
275.00	31.19	40.52	45.35	4134.	5983.	7049.	15.03	21.76	25.63
280.00	31.62	40.97	45.81	4291.	6187.	7277.	15.32	22.10	25.99
285.00	32.05	41.42	46.25	4450.	6393.	7507.	15.61	22.43	26.34
290.00	32.48	41.86	46.69	4611.	6601.	7739.	15.90	22.76	26.69
295.00	32.89	42.29	47.13	4775.	6811.	7974.	16.19	23.09	27.03
298.15	33.15	42.56	47.40	4879.	6945.	8123.	16.36	23.29	27.24
300.00	33.30	42.72	47.56	4940.	7024.	8211.	16.47	23.41	27.37

VALUES OF CHEMICAL THERMODYNAMIC PROPERTIES OF HYDROCARBONS

The values in this table are for the ideal gas state at 298.16 K and are expressed as kilocalorie per mole.

It is frequently possible to calculate values for compounds not listed since the following increments are known for an addition of a methylene group, CH_2, to the following types of compounds:

> Normal alkyl cyclohexanes
> Normal alkyl benzenes
> Normal alkyl cyclopentanes
> Normal monoolefins (1-alkenes)
> Normal acetylenes (1-alkynes)

For each of the above types of compounds the increments per CH_2 group are

ΔHf°:	−4.926 kcal/g mol
ΔFf°:	−2.048 kcal/g mol
$Log_{10} Kf$:	−1.5012 kcal/g mol
S°:	−9.183 kcal/g mol

Relationships to SI units — The symbols cal mole^{-1} deg^{-1} and gibbs/mol are identical and refer to units of calories per degree-mole. These units can be converted to SI units of joules per degree-mole by multiplying the tabulated values by 4.184. Similarly, values in kilocalories per mole can be converted to joules per mole by multiplying with the factor 4184. For further discussions of the SI system and for conversions from other units, see *Pure and Applied Chemistry*, 21, 1, 1970.

Formula	Compound	ΔHf°	ΔFf°	$Log_{10} Kf$	S°
CH_4	Methane	−17.889	−12.140	8.8985	44.50
C_2H_2	Ethyne (acetylene)	54.194	50.000	−36.6490	47.997
C_2H_4	Ethene (ethylene)	12.496	16.282	−11.9345	52.54
C_2H_6	Ethane	−20.236	− 7.860	5.7613	54.85
C_3H_4	Propadiene (allene)	45.92	48.37	−35.4519	58.30
C_3H_4	Propyne (methyl-acetylene)	44.319	46.313	−33.9469	59.30
C_3H_6	Propene (propylene)	4.879	14.990	−10.9875	63.80
C_3H_8	Propane	−24.820	− 5.614	4.1150	64.51
C_4H_6	1,2-Butadiene	39.55	48.21	−35.3377	70.03
C_4H_6	1,3-Butadiene	26.75	36.43	−26.7004	66.62
C_4H_6	1-Butyne (ethyl acetylene)	39.70	48.52	−35.5616	69.51
C_4H_6	2-Butyne (dimethylacetylene)	35.374	44.725	−32.7823	67.71
C_4H_8	1-Butene	0.280	17.217	−12.6199	73.48
C_4H_8	cis-2-Butene	−1.362	16.046	−11.7618	71.90
C_4H_8	trans-2-Butene	−2.405	15.315	−11.2255	70.86
C_4H_8	2-Methylpropane (isobutene)	− 3.343	14.582	−10.6888	70.17
C_4H_{10}	n-Butane	−29.812	− 3.754	2.7516	74.10
C_4H_{10}	2-Methylpropane (isobutane)	−31.452	− 4.296	3.1489	70.42
C_5H_8	1-Pentyne	34.50	50.17	−36.7712	79.10
C_5H_8	2-Pentyne	30.80	46.41	−34.0177	79.30
C_5H_8	3-Methyl-1-butyne	32.60	49.12	−36.0061	76.23
C_5H_8	1,2-Pentadiene	34.80	50.29	−36.861	79.7
C_5H_8	cis-1,3-Pentadiene (cis-piperylene)	18.70	34.88	−25.563	77.5
C_5H_8	trans-1,3-Pentadiene (trans-piperylene)	18.60	35.07	−25.707	76.4
C_5H_8	1,4-Pentadiene	25.20	40.69	−29.824	79.7
C_5H_8	2,3-Pentadiene	33.10	49.22	−36.074	77.6
C_5H_8	3-Methyl-1,2-butadiene	31.00	47.47	−34.657	76.4
C_5H_8	2-Methyl-1,3-butadiene (isoprene)	18.10	34.87	−25.560	75.44
C_5H_{10}	1-Pentene	− 5.000	18.787	−13.7704	83.08
C_5H_{10}	cis-2-Pentene	− 6.710	17.173	−12.5874	82.76

VALUES OF CHEMICAL THERMODYNAMIC PROPERTIES OF HYDROCARBONS (Continued)

Formula	Compound	$\Delta Hf°$	$\Delta Ff°$	$Log_{10} Kf$	$S°$
C_5H_{10}	trans-2-Pentene	− 7.590	16.575	−12.1495	81.81
C_5H_{10}	2-Methyl-1-butene	− 8.680	15.509	−11.3680	81.73
C_5H_{10}	3-Methyl-1-butene	− 6.920	17.874	−13.1017	79.70
C_5H_{10}	2-Methyl-2-butene	−10.170	14.267	−10.4572	80.90
C_5H_{10}	Cyclopentane	−18.46	9.23	− 6.7643	70.00
C_5H_{12}	n-Pentane	−35.00	− 1.96	1.4366	83.27
C_6H_6	Benzene	19.820	30.989	−22.7143	64.34
C_6H_{10}	1-Hexyne	29.55	52.19	−38.258	88.27
C_6H_{12}	1-Hexene	− 9.96	20.80	−15.2491	92.25
C_6H_{12}	cis-2-Hexene	−11.56	19.18	−14.0549	92.35
C_6H_{12}	trans-2-Hexene	−12.56	18.46	−13.5291	91.40
C_6H_{12}	cis-3-Hexene	−11.56	19.66	−14.4094	90.73
C_6H_{12}	trans-3-Hexene	−12.56	18.86	−13.8262	90.04
C_6H_{12}	2-Methyl-1-pentene	−13.56	17.48	−12.8135	91.32
C_6H_{12}	3-Methyl-1-pentene	−11.02	20.28	−14.8655	90.45
C_6H_{12}	4-Methyl-1-pentene	−11.66	19.90	−14.5865	89.58
C_6H_{12}	2-Methyl-2-pentene	−14.96	16.34	−11.9780	90.45
C_6H_{12}	cis-3-Methyl-2-pentene	−14.32	16.98	−12.4471	90.45
C_6H_{12}	trans-3-Methyl-2-pentene	−14.32	16.74	−12.2697	91.26
C_6H_{12}	cis-4-Methyl-2-pentene	−13.26	18.40	−13.4903	89.23
C_6H_{12}	trans-4-Methyl-2-pentene	−14.26	17.77	−13.0216	88.02
C_6H_{12}	2-Ethyl-1-butene	−12.92	18.51	−13.5690	90.01
C_6H_{12}	2,3-Dimethyl-1-butene	−14.78	17.43	−12.7782	89.39
C_6H_{12}	3,3-Dimethyl-1-butene	−14.25	19.04	−13.9578	83.79
C_6H_{12}	2,3-Dimethyl-2-butene	−15.91	16.52	−12.1073	86.67
C_6H_{12}	Methylcyclopentane	−25.50	8.55	− 6.2649	81.24
C_6H_{12}	Cyclohexane	−29.43	7.59	− 5.5605	71.28
C_6H_{14}	n-Hexane	−39.96	0.05	0.037	92.45
C_7H_8	Methylbenzene (toluene)	11.950	29.228	−21.4236	76.42
C_7H_{12}	1-Heptyne	24.62	54.24	−39.759	97.25
C_7H_{12}	1-Heptene	−14.85	22.84	−16.742	101.43
C_7H_{14}	Ethylcyclopentane	−30.37	10.59	− 7.7632	90.62
C_7H_{14}	1,1-Dimethylcyclopentane	−33.05	9.33	− 6.8372	85.87
C_7H_{14}	1,cis-2-Dimethylcyclopentane	−30.96	10.93	− 8.0107	87.51
C_7H_{14}	1,trans-2-Dimethylcyclopentane	−32.67	9.17	− 6.7224	87.67
C_7H_{14}	1,cis-3-Dimethylcyclopentane	−31.93	9.91	− 7.2648	87.67
C_7H_{14}	1,trans-3-Dimethylcyclopentane	−32.47	9.37	− 6.8690	87.67
C_7H_{14}	Methylcyclohexane	−36.99	6.52	− 4.7819	82.06
C_7H_{16}	n-Heptane	−44.89	2.09	− 1.532	101.64
C_8H_8	Ethenylbenzene (styrene)	35.32	51.10	−37.4532	82.48
C_8H_{10}	Ethylbenzene	7.120	31.208	−22.8750	86.15
C_8H_{10}	1,2-Dimethylbenzene (o-xylene)	4.540	29.177	−21.3860	84.31
C_8H_{10}	1,3-Dimethylbenzene (m-xylene)	4.120	28.405	−20.8203	85.49
C_8H_{10}	1,4-Dimethylbenzene (p-xylene)	4.290	28.952	−21.2214	84.23
C_8H_{14}	1-Octyne	19.70	56.29	−41.260	106.63
C_8H_{16}	1-Octene	−19.82	24.89	−18.244	110.61
C_8H_{16}	n-Propylcyclopentane	−35.39	12.54	− 9.195	99.80
C_8H_{16}	1,1-Dimethylcyclohexane	−43.26	8.42	− 6.174	87.24
C_8H_{16}	cis-1,2-Dimethylcyclohexane	−41.15	9.85	− 7.225	89.51
C_8H_{16}	trans-1,2-Dimethylcyclohexane	−43.02	8.24	− 6.038	88.65

VALUES OF CHEMICAL THERMODYNAMIC PROPERTIES OF HYDROCARBONS (Continued)

Formula	Compound	$\Delta Hf°$	$\Delta Ff°$	$Log_{10} Kf$	$S°$
C_8H_{16}	cis-1,3-Dimethylcyclohexane	−44.16	7.13	− 5.228	88.54
C_8H_{16}	trans-1,3-Dimethylcyclohexane	−42.20	8.68	− 6.363	89.92
C_8H_{16}	cis-1,4-Dimethylcyclohexane	−42.22	9.07	− 6.650	88.54
C_8H_{16}	trans-1,4-Dimethylcyclohexane	−44.12	7.58	− 5.552	87.19
C_8H_{18}	n-Octane	−49.82	4.14	− 3.035	110.82
C_8H_{18}	2-Methylheptane	−51.50	3.06	− 2.243	108.81
C_8H_{18}	3-Methylheptane	−50.82	3.29	− 2.412	110.32
C_8H_{18}	4-Methylheptane	−50.69	4.00	− 2.932	108.35
C_8H_{18}	3-Ethylhexane	−50.40	3.95	− 2.895	109.51
C_8H_{18}	2,2-Dimethylhexane	−53.71	2.56	− 1.876	103.06
C_8H_{18}	2,3-Dimethylhexane	−51.13	4.23	− 3.101	106.11
C_8H_{18}	2,4-Dimethylhexane	−52.44	2.80	− 2.052	106.51
C_8H_{18}	2,5-Dimethylhexane	−53.21	2.50	− 1.832	104.93
C_8H_{18}	3,3-Dimethylhexane	−52.61	3.17	− 2.324	104.70
C_8H_{18}	3,4-Dimethylhexane	−50.91	4.14	− 3.035	107.15
C_8H_{18}	2-Methyl-3-ethylpentane	−50.48	5.08	− 3.724	105.43
C_8H_{18}	3-Methyl-3-ethylpentane	−51.38	4.76	− 3.489	103.48
C_8H_{18}	2,2,3-Trimethylpentane	−52.61	4.09	− 2.998	101.62
C_8H_{18}	2,2,4-Trimethylpentane	−53.57	3.13	− 2.294	101.62
C_8H_{18}	2,3,3-Trimethylpentane	−51.73	4.52	− 3.313	103.14
C_8H_{18}	2,3,4-Trimethylpentane	−51.97	4.32	− 3.167	102.99
C_8H_{18}	2,2,3,3-Tetramethylbutane	−53.99	4.88	− 3.577	94.34
C_9H_{10}	Isopropenylbenzene (α-methylstyrene; 2-phenyl-1-propene)	27.00	49.84	−36.531	91.70
C_9H_{10}	1-Methyl-2-ethenylbenzene (o-Methylstyrene)	28.30	51.14	−37.484	91.70
C_9H_{10}	1-Methyl-3-ethenylbenzene (m-methylstyrene)	27.60	50.02	−36.665	93.1
C_9H_{10}	1-Methyl-4-ethenylbenzene (p-methylstyrene)	27.40	50.24	−36.825	91.7
C_9H_{12}	n-Propylbenzene	1.870	32.810	−24.049	95.74
C_9H_{12}	Isopropylbenzene (Cumene)	0.940	32.738	−23.996	92.87
C_9H_{12}	1,3,5-Trimethylbenzene (Mesitylene)	− 3.840	28.172	−20.6497	92.15
C_9H_{16}	1-Nonyne	14.77	58.34	−42.761	115.82
C_9H_{18}	1-Nonene	−24.74	26.94	−19.747	119.80
C_9H_{18}	n-Butylcyclopentane	−40.22	14.69	−10.768	108.99
C_9H_{20}	n-Nonane	−54.74	6.18	− 4.536	120.00
$C_{10}H_{14}$	n-Butylbenzene	− 3.30	34.62	−25.374	104.91
$C_{10}H_{18}$	1-Decyne	9.85	60.39	−44.262	125.00
$C_{10}H_{10}$	1-Decene	−29.67	28.99	−21.249	128.98
$C_{10}H_{22}$	n-Decane	−59.67	8.23	6.037	129.19
$C_{11}H_{22}$	1-Undecene	−34.60	31.03	−22.745	138.16
$C_{11}H_{24}$	n-Undecane	−64.60	10.28	− 7.539	138.37
$C_{12}H_{24}$	1-Dodecene	−39.52	33.08	−24.297	147.34

From Rossini, F. D., Pitzer, K. S., Arnett, R. L., Braun, R. M., and Pimentel, G. C., *Selected Values of Physical and Thermodynamic Properties of Hydrocarbons and Related Compounds,* Carnegie Press, Pittsburgh, 1953.

KEY VALUES FOR THERMODYNAMICS

In this report, the CODATA Task Group on Key Values for Thermodynamics presents recommended values for the quantities ΔH°_f(298.15 K), S°(298.15 K), and H°(298.15 K) − H°(0). The recommended values in the table below were given the approval of IUPAC Commission I.2 on Thermodynamics and Thermochemistry at the XXVIIth IUPAC Conference in Munich, August 1973. The values depend on the following values of the fundamental constants: gas constant, R, (8.31433 ± 0.00120) J K⁻¹ mol⁻¹; constant relating wave number and energy (0.1196256 ± 0.0000107) J m mol⁻¹. Relative atomic masses were taken from the recommendations of the IUPAC Commission on Atomic Weights (1970). Data in the table relate to the natural mixture of isotopic species. Nuclear spin contributions were ignored. The uncertainties in the table represent the Task Group's estimates of the overall uncertainties at a 95% confidence level.

In the table, the standard state for crystalline solids (symbolized as c) and for liquids (symbolized as l) is that of the pure substance under a pressure of 101,325 Pa (1 standard atmosphere). For gases (symbolized as g) the standard state is that of the ideal gas at a pressure of 101,325 Pa. For species in aqueous solution (symbolized as aq) the standard state is the hypothetical ideal solution at unit activity; the properties of ideal aqueous ionic solutions are taken equal to the sum of the properties of the individual ions.

The data listed in joules are the primary data. The values in calories (thermochemical) are derived from the corresponding values in joules by dividing by 4.184.

Recommended Key Values for Thermodynamics

Substance	State	ΔH°_f(298.15 K) kJ mol⁻¹	ΔH°_f(298.15 K) kcal mol⁻¹	S°(298.15 K) J K⁻¹ mol⁻¹	S°(298.15 K) cal K⁻¹ mol⁻¹	H°(298.15 K) − H°(0) kJ mol⁻¹	H°(298.15 K) − H°(0) kcal mol⁻¹
O	g	249.17 ± 0.10	59.553 ± 0.024	160.946 ± 0.020	38.467 ± 0.005	6.728 ± 0.003	1.608 ± 0.001
O_2	g	0	0	205.037 ± 0.033	49.005 ± 0.008	8.682 ± 0.004	2.075 ± 0.001
H	g	217.997 ± 0.006	52.103 ± 0.001	114.604 ± 0.015	27.391 ± 0.004	6.197 ± 0.002	1.481 ± 0.001
H^+	aq	0	0	0	0	—	—
H_2	g	0	0	130.570 ± 0.033	31.207 ± 0.008	8.468 ± 0.003	2.024 ± 0.001
OH^-	aq	−230.025 ± 0.045	−54.977 ± 0.011	−10.71 ± 0.20	−2.56 ± 0.05	—	—
H_2O	l	−285.830 ± 0.042	−68.315 ± 0.010	69.950 ± 0.080	16.718 ± 0.019	13.293 ± 0.021	3.177 ± 0.005
H_2O	g	−241.814 ± 0.042	−57.795 ± 0.010	188.724 ± 0.040	45.106 ± 0.010	9.908 ± 0.008	2.368 ± 0.002
He	g	0	0	126.039 ± 0.012	30.124 ± 0.003	6.197 ± 0.002	1.481 ± 0.001
Ne	g	0	0	146.214 ± 0.016	34.946 ± 0.004	6.197 ± 0.002	1.481 ± 0.001
Ar	g	0	0	154.732 ± 0.020	36.982 ± 0.005	6.197 ± 0.002	1.481 ± 0.001
Kr	g	0	0	163.971 ± 0.020	39.190 ± 0.005	6.197 ± 0.002	1.481 ± 0.001
Xe	g	0	0	169.573 ± 0.020	40.529 ± 0.005	6.197 ± 0.002	1.481 ± 0.001
Cl	g	121.290 ± 0.008	28.989 ± 0.002	165.076 ± 0.020	39.454 ± 0.005	6.272 ± 0.003	1.499 ± 0.001
Cl^-	aq	−167.080 ± 0.088	−39.933 ± 0.021	56.73 ± 0.16	13.56 ± 0.04	—	—
Cl_2	g	0	0	222.965 ± 0.040	53.290 ± 0.010	9.180 ± 0.008	2.194 ± 0.002
HCl	g	−92.31 ± 0.13	−22.063 ± 0.031	186.786 ± 0.033	44.643 ± 0.008	8.640 ± 0.004	2.065 ± 0.001
Br	g	111.86 ± 0.12	26.735 ± 0.029	174.904 ± 0.020	41.803 ± 0.005	6.197 ± 0.002	1.481 ± 0.001
Br^-	aq	−121.50 ± 0.15	−29.039 ± 0.035	82.84 ± 0.20	19.80 ± 0.05	—	—
Br_2	l	0	0	152.210 ± 0.040	36.379 ± 0.010	24.52 ± 0.13	5.860 ± 0.031
Br_2	g	30.91 ± 0.11	7.388 ± 0.026	245.350 ± 0.054	58.640 ± 0.013	9.724 ± 0.012	2.324 ± 0.003
HBr	g	−36.38 ± 0.17	−8.695 ± 0.041	198.585 ± 0.033	47.463 ± 0.008	8.648 ± 0.004	2.067 ± 0.001
I	g	106.762 ± 0.040	25.517 ± 0.010	180.673 ± 0.020	43.182 ± 0.008	6.197 ± 0.002	1.481 ± 0.001

Recommended Key Values for Thermodynamics (Continued)

Substance	State	$\Delta H°_f$ (298.15 K) kJ mol⁻¹	$\Delta H°_f$ (298.15 K) kcal mol⁻¹	$S°$ (298.15 K) J K⁻¹ mol⁻¹	$S°$ (298.15 K) cal K⁻¹ mol⁻¹	$H°$ (298.15 K) $- H°$ (0) kJ mol⁻¹	$H°$ (298.15 K) $- H°$ (0) kcal mol⁻¹
I⁻	aq	−56.90 ± 0.84	−13.60 ± 0.20	106.70 ± 0.20	25.50 ± 0.05	—	—
I₂	c	0	0	116.139 ± 0.080	27.758 ± 0.019	13.196 ± 0.040	3.154 ± 0.010
I₂	g	62.421 ± 0.080	14.919 ± 0.019	260.567 ± 0.063	62.277 ± 0.015	10.117 ± 0.021	2.418 ± 0.005
HI	g	26.36 ± 0.80	6.30 ± 0.19	206.480 ± 0.040	49.350 ± 0.010	8.657 ± 0.006	2.069 ± 0.001
S	g	276.98 ± 0.25	66.20 ± 0.06	167.715 ± 0.035	40.085 ± 0.008	6.657 ± 0.004	1.591 ± 0.001
S₂	g	128.49 ± 0.30	30.71 ± 0.07	228.055 ± 0.050	54.506 ± 0.012	9.088 ± 0.008	2.172 ± 0.002
SO₂	g	−296.81 ± 0.20	−70.94 ± 0.05	248.11 ± 0.06	59.300 ± 0.014	10.548 ± 0.013	2.521 ± 0.003
N	g	472.68 ± 0.40	112.97 ± 0.10	153.189 ± 0.020	36.613 ± 0.005	6.197 ± 0.002	1.481 ± 0.001
N₂	g	0	0	191.502 ± 0.025	45.770 ± 0.006	8.669 ± 0.003	2.072 ± 0.001
NO₃⁻	aq	—	—	146.94 ± 0.85	35.12 ± 0.20	—	—
NH₃	g	−45.94 ± 0.35	−10.980 ± 0.08	192.67 ± 0.08	46.049 ± 0.019	10.046 ± 0.008	2.401 ± 0.002
NH₄⁺	aq	−133.26 ± 0.25	−31.850 ± 0.06	111.17 ± 0.75	26.57 ± 0.18	—	—
C	c	0	0	5.74 ± 0.12	1.372 ± 0.029	1.050 ± 0.020	0.251 ± 0.005
C	g	716.67 ± 0.44	171.29 ± 0.11	157.988 ± 0.020	37.760 ± 0.03	6.535 ± 0.006	1.562 ± 0.002
CO	g	−110.53 ± 0.17	−26.417 ± 0.041	197.556 ± 0.032	47.217 ± 0.008	8.673 ± 0.008	2.073 ± 0.002
CO₂	g	−393.51 ± 0.13	−94.051 ± 0.031	213.677 ± 0.040	51.070 ± 0.010	9.364 ± 0.008	2.238 ± 0.002
Zn	c	0	0	41.63 ± 0.13	9.950 ± 0.031	5.657 ± 0.020	1.352 ± 0.005
Zn	g	130.42 ± 0.20	31.17 ± 0.05	160.875 ± 0.025	38.450 ± 0.006	6.197 ± 0.004	1.481 ± 0.001
Ag	c	0	0	42.55 ± 0.21	10.17 ± 0.03	5.745 ± 0.020	1.373 ± 0.003
Ag	g	284.9 ± 0.08	68.09 ± 0.19	172.883 ± 0.025	41.320 ± 0.006	6.197 ± 0.004	1.481 ± 0.005
Ag⁺	aq	105.750 ± 0.085	25.275 ± 0.020	73.38 ± 0.40	17.54 ± 0.10	—	—
AgCl	c	−127.070 ± 0.085	−30.370 ± 0.020	96.23 ± 0.20	23.00 ± 0.05	12.033 ± 0.040	2.876 ± 0.010
Li	c	0	0	29.12 ± 0.20	6.96 ± 0.05	4.632 ± 0.040	1.107 ± 0.010
Li⁺	aq	−278.455 ± 0.090	−66.552 ± 0.022	11.30 ± 0.35	2.70 ± 0.08	—	—
Na	c	0	0	51.30 ± 0.20	12.26 ± 0.05	6.460 ± 0.020	1.544 ± 0.005
Na⁺	aq	−240.300 ± 0.065	−57.433 ± 0.015	58.41 ± 0.20	13.96 ± 0.05	—	—
K	c	0	0	64.68 ± 0.20	15.46 ± 0.05	7.088 ± 0.020	1.694 ± 0.005
K⁺	aq	−252.17 ± 0.10	−60.271 ± 0.025	101.04 ± 0.25	24.15 ± 0.06	—	—
Rb	c	0	0	76.78 ± 0.30	18.35 ± 0.07	7.489 ± 0.020	1.790 ± 0.005
Rb⁺	aq	−251.12 ± 0.13	−60.018 ± 0.030	120.46 ± 0.40	28.79 ± 0.10	—	—
Cs	c	0	0	85.23 ± 0.40	20.37 ± 0.10	7.711 ± 0.020	1.843 ± 0.005
Cs⁺	aq	−258.04 ± 0.13	−61.673 ± 0.030	132.84 ± 0.40	31.75 ± 0.10	—	—

Data from CODATA Bulletin 10, December 1973. For information and references upon which these values are based, consult this bulletin, available at no cost from ICSU CODATA Central Office, 19 Westendstrasse, 6 Frankfurt/Main, Germany Federal Republic.

THERMODYNAMIC PROPERTIES OF ALKANE HYDROCARBONS[a]

Symbols and Units

$(G° - H°_0)/T$ = Gibbs energy function, cal K^{-1} mol^{-1}
$(H° - H°_0)/T$ = enthalpy function, cal K^{-1} mol^{-1}
$S°$ = entropy, cal K^{-1} mol^{-1}
C_p = heat capacity at constant pressure, cal K^{-1} mol^{-1}
$\Delta H_f°$ = enthalpy of formation, kcal mol^{-1}
$\Delta G_f°$ = Gibbs energy of formation, kcal mol^{-1}
$\log_{10} K_f$ = common logarithm of the equilibrium constant of formation
T = temperature, kelvins
$H° - H°_0$ = enthalpy, kcal mol^{-1}

Conversion Factors

The tabulated values may be converted to SI units by use of the relations:

calories $\times$ 4.184 = joules
kilocalories $\times$ 4184 = joules

Methane (CH_4)

T, K	$(G° - H°_0)/T$, cal K^{-1} mol^{-1}	$(H° - H°_0)/T$, cal K^{-1} mol^{-1}	$H° - H°_0$, kcal mol^{-1}	$S°$, cal K^{-1} mol^{-1}	$C_p°$, cal K^{-1} mol^{-1}	$\Delta H_f°$, kcal mol^{-1}	$\Delta G_f°$, kcal mol^{-1}	$\log_{10} K_f$
0	0	0	0	0	0	-15.9_5	-15.9_5	∞
200	-33.3_1	7.9_4	1.58_8	41.2_5	8.0_1	-17.1_8	-13.8_8	15.1_7
273.15	-35.7_9	7.9_9	2.18_4	43.7_3	8.3_3	-17.6_8	-12.6_0	10.0_8
298.15	-36.4_9	8.0_3	2.39	44.5_2	8.5_3	-17.8_6	-12.1_2	8.8_8
400	-38.8_8	8.3_0	3.32	47.1_8	9.7_1	-18.6_0	-10.0_4	5.4_9
600	-42.4	9.2	5.5_4	51.6	12.5	-19.9	-5.5	1.9_9
800	-45.2	10.4	8.3	55.6	15.2	-20.8	-0.5	0.1_4
1,000	-47.7	11.6	11.6	59.3	$17._4$	-21.4	4.6	-1.0_0
1,200	$-49._9$	$12._7$	$15._3$	$62._6$	$19._2$	$-21._7$	$9._8$	-1.7_9
1,500	$-52._9$	$14._2$	$21._3$	$67._1$	$21.$	$-21._8$	$17._7$	-2.5_9

[a]The original source of the data in this table contains the thermodynamic properties of all the alkane hydrocarbons through decane. Including the *meso*, (*d*, *l*), *cis*, and *trans* isomers, there are 182 compounds in the original source.

THERMODYNAMIC PROPERTIES OF ALKANE HYDROCARBONS (Continued)

Ethane (C$_2$H$_6$)

T, K	(G° − H°$_0$)/T, cal K^{-1} mol^{-1}	(H° − H°$_0$)/T, cal K^{-1} mol^{-1}	H° − H°$_0$, kcal mol^{-1}	S°, cal K^{-1} mol^{-1}	C°$_p$, cal K^{-1} mol^{-1}	ΔH°$_f$, kcal mol^{-1}	ΔG°$_f$, kcal mol^{-1}	log$_{10}$ K$_f$
0	0	0	0	0	0	−16.2$_6$	−16.2$_6$	∞
200	−41.6$_3$	8.6$_7$	1.73$_5$	50.3$_0$	10.1$_0$	−18.8$_0$	−11.4$_6$	12.5$_2$
273.15	−44.4$_2$	9.2$_8$	2.53$_4$	53.7$_0$	11.8$_5$	−19.7$_0$	−8.6$_3$	6.9$_1$
298.15	−45.2$_4$	9.5$_2$	2.84	54.7$_6$	12.5$_7$	−20.0$_0$	−7.6$_0$	5.5$_7$
400	−48.2$_0$	10.7$_1$	4.28	58.9$_1$	15.8$_3$	−21.1$_8$	−3.1$_8$	1.7$_4$
600	−53.1	13.5	8.0$_9$	66.6	22.2	−23.0	6.2	−2.2$_7$
800	−57.3	16.7	13.3	74.0	27.4	−23.7	16.1	−4.4$_1$
1,000	−61.3	19.0	19.0	80.3	31.$_7$	−24.3	26.2	−5.7$_3$
1,200	−65.$_0$	21.$_4$	25.$_7$	86.$_4$	35.$_1$	−24.$_1$	36.$_3$	−6.6$_1$
1,500	−70.$_1$	24.$_6$	36.$_9$	94.$_7$	39.	−23.$_1$	51.$_3$	−7.4$_7$

Propane (C$_3$H$_8$)

T, K	(G° − H°$_0$)/T, cal K^{-1} mol^{-1}	(H° − H°$_0$)/T, cal K^{-1} mol^{-1}	H° − H°$_0$, kcal mol^{-1}	S°, cal K^{-1} mol^{-1}	C°$_p$, cal K^{-1} mol^{-1}	ΔH°$_f$, kcal mol^{-1}	ΔG°$_f$, kcal mol^{-1}	log$_{10}$ K$_f$
0	0	0	0	0	0	−19.7$_4$	−19.7$_4$	∞
200	−48.3$_6$	10.2$_1$	2.04$_1$	58.5$_7$	12.6$_4$	−23.4$_2$	−11.8$_8$	12.9$_8$
273.15	−51.7$_0$	11.3$_3$	3.09$_6$	63.0$_3$	16.2$_2$	−24.6$_6$	−7.4$_7$	5.9$_7$
298.15	−52.7$_1$	11.8$_0$	3.52	64.5$_1$	17.4$_4$	−25.0$_7$	−5.8$_7$	4.3$_0$
400	−56.4$_6$	13.8$_8$	5.55	70.3$_4$	22.4$_6$	−26.6$_1$	0.9$_4$	−0.5$_1$
600	−62.9	18.2	10.9$_5$	81.1	31.2	−28.9	15.2	−5.5$_5$
800	−68.7	22.4	17.9	91.1	38.0	−30.2	30.2	−8.2$_5$
1,000	−74.1	26.1	26.1	100.2	43.$_4$	−30.8	45.4	−9.9$_2$
1,200	−79.$_2$	29.$_3$	35.$_2$	108.$_5$	47.$_6$	−30.$_7$	60.$_6$	−11.0$_4$
1,500	−86.$_2$	33.$_5$	50.$_2$	119.$_7$	52.	−29.$_7$	83.$_3$	−12.1$_4$

n-Butane (C$_4$H$_{10}$)

T, K	(G° − H°$_0$)/T, cal K^{-1} mol^{-1}	(H° − H°$_0$)/T, cal K^{-1} mol^{-1}	H° − H°$_0$, kcal mol^{-1}	S°, cal K^{-1} mol^{-1}	C°$_p$, cal K^{-1} mol^{-1}	ΔH°$_f$, kcal mol^{-1}	ΔG°$_f$, kcal mol^{-1}	log$_{10}$ K$_f$
0	0	0	0	0	0	−23.6$_3$	−23.6$_3$	∞
200	−52.5$_7$	13.4$_1$	2.68$_1$	65.9$_8$	18.3$_6$	−28.1$_3$	−12.2$_3$	13.3$_6$
273.15	−57.0$_1$	15.1$_8$	4.14$_5$	72.1$_9$	21.8$_9$	−29.5$_7$	−6.1$_9$	4.9$_5$
298.15	−58.3$_7$	15.8$_0$	4.71	74.1$_7$	23.3$_0$	−30.0$_5$	−4.0$_2$	2.9$_5$
400	−63.3$_8$	18.4$_9$	7.40	81.8$_7$	29.4$_5$	−31.9$_0$	5.1$_7$	−2.8$_2$
600	−71.9	24.0	14.4$_2$	95.9	40.4	−34.7	24.3	−8.8$_7$
800	−79.6	29.2	23.4	108.8	48.8	−36.3	44.3	−12.1$_0$
1,000	−86.6	33.8	33.8	120.4	55.$_2$	−37.0	64.5	−14.1$_0$
1,200	−93.$_1$	37.$_8$	45.$_4$	130.$_9$	60.$_1$	−37.$_0$	84.$_8$	−15.4$_5$
1,500	−102.$_1$	42.$_8$	64.$_3$	144.$_9$	66.	−36.$_1$	115.$_2$	−16.7$_8$

THERMODYNAMIC PROPERTIES OF ALKANE HYDROCARBONS (Continued)

2-Methylpropane (C$_4$H$_{10}$)

T, K	$(G^\circ - H^\circ_0)/T$, cal K^{-1} mol^{-1}	$(H^\circ - H^\circ_0)/T$, cal K^{-1} mol^{-1}	$H^\circ - H^\circ_0$, kcal mol^{-1}	S°, cal K^{-1} mol^{-1}	C°_p, cal K^{-1} mol^{-1}	ΔH°_f, kcal mol^{-1}	ΔG°_f, kcal mol^{-1}	$\log_{10} K_f$
0	0	0	0	0	0	-25.3_4	-25.3_4	∞
200	-50.7_9	11.7_2	2.34_4	62.5_1	16.8_5	-30.1_7	-13.5_8	14.8_4
273.15	-54.7_3	13.7_1	3.74_4	68.4_4	21.5_2	-31.6_7	-7.2_7	5.8_2
298.15	-55.9_7	14.4_1	4.30	70.4_1	23.1_3	-32.1_6	-5.0_0	3.6_7
400	-60.6_3	17.4_9	6.99	78.1_2	29.6_2	-34.0_0	4.5_6	-2.4_9
600	-68.9	23.4	14.0_7	92.3	40.8	-36.7	24.5	-8.9_2
800	-76.4	28.9	23.1	105.3	49.5	-38.2	45.1	-12.3_3
1,000	-83.3	33.8	33.8	117.1	$56._4$	-38.7	66.1	-14.4_4
1,200	$-89._9$	$38._0$	$45._6$	$127._9$	$61._7$	$-38._4$	$87._0$	-15.8_4
1,500	$-99._0$	$43._3$	$65._0$	$142._3$	$68.$	$-37._0$	$118._2$	-17.2_2

n-Pentane (C$_5$H$_{12}$)

T, K	$(G^\circ - H^\circ_0)/T$, cal K^{-1} mol^{-1}	$(H^\circ - H^\circ_0)/T$, cal K^{-1} mol^{-1}	$H^\circ - H^\circ_0$, kcal mol^{-1}	S°, cal K^{-1} mol^{-1}	C°_p, cal K^{-1} mol^{-1}	ΔH°_f, kcal mol^{-1}	ΔG°_f, kcal mol^{-1}	$\log_{10} K_f$
0	0	0	0	0	0	-27.3_5	-27.3_5	∞
200	-57.0_3	16.4_6	3.29_1	73.4_9	22.3_6	-32.7_0	-12.4_5	13.6_0
273.15	-62.4_7	18.6_5	5.08_3	81.0_8	26.9_0	-34.4_1	-4.7_7	3.8_2
298.15	-64.1_4	19.3_8	5.78	83.5_2	28.6_9	-34.9_8	-2.0_3	1.4_9
400	-70.2_9	22.7_4	9.10	93.0_3	36.4_6	-37.1_6	9.5_8	-5.2_3
600	-80.8	29.7	17.7_9	110.5	49.9	-40.3	33.7	-12.2_7
800	-90.3	36.0	28.8	126.3	59.9	-42.2	58.7	-16.0_3
1,000	-98.9	41.6	41.6	140.5	$67._3$	-43.0	84.0	-18.3_6
1,200	$-106._9$	$46._3$	$55._6$	$153._2$	$72._8$	$-43._0$	$109._4$	-19.9_2
1,500	$-117._9$	$52._3$	$78._4$	$170._2$	$79.$	$-42._1$	$147._4$	-21.4_8

2-Methylbutane (C$_5$H$_{12}$)

T, K	$(G^\circ - H^\circ_0)/T$, cal K^{-1} mol^{-1}	$(H^\circ - H^\circ_0)/T$, cal K^{-1} mol^{-1}	$H^\circ - H^\circ_0$, kcal mol^{-1}	S°, cal K^{-1} mol^{-1}	C°_p, cal K^{-1} mol^{-1}	ΔH°_f, kcal mol^{-1}	ΔG°_f, kcal mol^{-1}	$\log_{10} K_f$
0	0	0	0	0	0	-28.4_4	-28.4_4	∞
200	-58.1_6	14.3_4	2.86_7	72.5_0	20.3_0	-34.2_0	-13.7_6	15.0_3
273.15	-62.9_8	16.7_4	4.57_3	79.7_2	26.3_8	-36.0_0	-6.0_0	4.8_0
298.15	-64.4_9	17.6_4	5.26	82.1_3	28.4_1	-36.5_8	-3.2_1	2.3_6
400	-70.2_0	21.4_3	8.57	91.6_3	36.5_4	-38.7_6	8.5_3	-4.6_6
600	-80.3	28.8	17.3_0	109.1	50.2	-41.9	32.9	-11.9_9
800	-89.5	35.5	28.4	125.0	60.5	-43.7	58.2	-15.8_9
1,000	-98.1	41.3	41.3	139.4	$68._4$	-44.3	83.7	-18.3_0
1,200	$-106._1$	$46._3$	$55._6$	$152._4$	$74._4$	$-44._1$	$109._3$	-19.9_1
1,500	$-117._1$	$52._7$	$79._0$	$169._8$	$81.$	$-42._6$	$147._5$	-21.4_9

THERMODYNAMIC PROPERTIES OF ALKANE HYDROCARBONS (Continued)

T, K	$(G° - H°_0)/T$, cal K⁻¹ mol⁻¹	$(H° - H°_0)/T$, cal K⁻¹ mol⁻¹	$H° - H°_0$, kcal mol⁻¹	$S°$, cal K⁻¹ mol⁻¹	$C_p°$, cal K⁻¹ mol⁻¹	$\Delta H_f°$, kcal mol⁻¹	$\Delta G_f°$, kcal mol⁻¹	$\log_{10} K_f$
2,2-Dimethylpropane (C₅H₁₂)								
0	0	0	0	0	0	-32.3_8	-32.3_8	∞
200	-48.3_2	13.4_3	2.68_5	61.7_5	19.2_5	-38.3_3	-15.7_4	17.2_0
273.15	-53.0_1	17.4_6	4.77_0	70.4_7	26.6_8	-39.7_6	-7.2_2	5.7_8
298.15	-54.5_3	18.5_8	5.54	73.1_1	28.8_8	-40.2_5	-4.1_9	3.0_7
400	-60.3_3	22.7_2	9.09	83.0_5	37.2_8	-42.2_0	8.5_3	-4.6_6
600	-70.7	30.2	18.1_1	100.9	51.3	-45.0	34.7	-12.6_5
800	-80.2	36.9	29.6	117.1	62.4	-46.5	61.7	-16.8_6
1,000	-88.9	43.0	43.0	131.9	$71._2$	-46.6	88.9	-19.4_3
1,200	$-97._2$	$48._3$	$57._9$	$145._5$	$78._2$	$-45._7$	$116._0$	-21.1_3
1,500	$-108._7$	$55._1$	$82._7$	$163._8$	$86.$	$-42._9$	$156._2$	-22.7_6
n-Hexane (C₆H₁₄)								
0	0	0	0	0	0	-31.0_9	-31.0_9	∞
200	-61.4_5	19.5_6	3.91_1	81.0_1	26.4_3	-37.2_6	-12.6_8	13.8_5
273.15	-67.9_2	22.1_0	6.03_5	90.0_2	31.9_2	-39.2_5	-3.3_7	2.7_0
298.15	-69.9_0	23.0_1	6.86	92.9_1	34.0_8	-39.9_1	-0.0_5	0.0_3
400	-77.2_1	27.0_1	10.80	104.2_2	43.3_9	-42.4_2	13.9_7	-7.6_3
600	-89.7	35.3	21.1_5	125.0	59.3	-46.0	43.0	-15.6_7
800	-100.9	42.8	34.2	143.7	70.8	-48.1	73.1	-19.6
1,000	-111.2	49.3	49.3	160.5	$79._2$	-49.0	103.5	-22.6_2
1,200	$-120._7$	$54._8$	$65._8$	$175._5$	$85._4$	$-49._1$	$134._0$	-24.4_0
1,500	$-133._7$	$61._7$	$92._5$	$195._4$	$93.$	$-48._2$	$179._7$	-26.1_8
2-Methylpentane (C₆H₁₄)								
0	0	0	0	0	0	-32.1_6	-32.1_6	∞
200	-62.3_5	17.1_8	3.43_6	79.5_3	24.2_2	-38.8_1	-13.9_3	15.2_2
273.15	-68.1_2	20.0_4	5.47_3	88.1_6	31.5_2	-40.8_9	-4.5_0	3.6_0
298.15	-69.9_2	21.1_1	6.29	91.0_3	33.9_9	-41.5_5	-1.1_3	0.8_3
400	-76.7_5	25.6_7	10.27	102.4_2	43.8_6	-44.0_3	13.0_8	-7.1_5
600	-88.9	34.5	20.7_3	123.4	60.0	-47.5	42.5	-15.4_7
800	-99.9	42.5	34.0	142.4	71.8	-49.5	72.8	-19.8_8
1,000	-110.1	49.3	49.3	159.4	$80._6$	-50.1	103.5	-22.6_1
1,200	$-119._6$	$55._1$	$66._1$	$174._7$	$87._2$	$-49._9$	$134._2$	-24.4_3
1,500	$-132._7$	$62._3$	$93._4$	$195._0$	$95.$	$-48._4$	$180._0$	-26.2_3

THERMODYNAMIC PROPERTIES OF ALKANE HYDROCARBONS (Continued)

3-Methylpentane (C_5H_{14})

T, K	$(G°-H°_0)/T$, cal K⁻¹ mol⁻¹	$(H°-H°_0)/T$, cal K⁻¹ mol⁻¹	$H°-H°_0$, kcal mol⁻¹	$S°$, cal K⁻¹ mol⁻¹	$C°_p$, cal K⁻¹ mol⁻¹	$\Delta H°_f$, kcal mol⁻¹	$\Delta G°_f$, kcal mol⁻¹	$\log_{10} K_f$
0	0	0	0	0	0	-31.4_8	-31.4_8	∞
200	-63.1_3	17.1_0	3.41_9	80.2_3	23.6_4	-38.1_4	-13.4_0	14.6_4
273.15	-68.8_5	19.8_4	5.41_9	88.6_9	31.0_3	-40.2_6	-4.0_1	3.2_1
298.15	-70.6_3	20.8_9	6.23	91.5_2	33.4_9	-40.9_3	-0.6_5	0.4_8
400	-77.3_9	25.3_6	10.14	102.7_5	43.3_0	-43.4_6	13.5_1	-7.3_8
600	-89.3	34.2	20.5_0	123.5	59.5	-47.1	42.9	-15.6_1
800	-100.3	42.1	33.6	142.4	71.4	-49.1	73.2	-19.9_9
1,000	-110.4	48.9	48.9	159.3	$80._3$	-49.8	103.9	-22.7_0
1,200	$-119._9$	$54._7$	$65._6$	$174._6$	$87._0$	$-49._7$	$134._6$	-24.5_1
1,500	$-132._9$	$61._9$	$92._9$	$194._8$	$95.$	$-48._2$	$180._5$	-26.3_0

2,2-Dimethylbutane (C_6H_{14})

T, K	$(G°-H°_0)/T$, cal K⁻¹ mol⁻¹	$(H°-H°_0)/T$, cal K⁻¹ mol⁻¹	$H°-H°_0$, kcal mol⁻¹	$S°$, cal K⁻¹ mol⁻¹	$C°_p$, cal K⁻¹ mol⁻¹	$\Delta H°_f$, kcal mol⁻¹	$\Delta G°_f$, kcal mol⁻¹	$\log_{10} K_f$
0	0	0	0	0	0	-34.2_8	-34.2_8	∞
200	-58.3_5	15.8_2	3.16_3	74.1_7	24.2_5	-41.2_0	-15.2_4	16.6_6
273.15	-63.7_5	19.0_0	5.19_0	82.7_5	31.3_3	-43.2_8	-5.4_2	4.3_3
298.15	-65.4_7	20.1_5	6.01	85.6_2	33.8_1	-43.9_5	-1.9_1	1.4_0
400	-72.0_5	24.9_1	9.96	96.9_6	43.7_7	-46.4_4	12.8_5	-7.0_2
600	-83.9	34.1	20.4_6	118.0	60.5	-49.9	43.3	-15.7_8
800	-94.9	42.3	33.9	137.2	73.3	-51.7	74.7	-20.4_1
1,000	-105.1	49.6	49.6	154.7	$83._2$	-51.9	106.4	-23.2_5
1,200	$-114._7$	$55._8$	$67._0$	$170._5$	$90._9$	$-51._1$	$137._9$	-25.1_2
1,500	$-128._1$	$63._8$	$95._7$	$191._9$	$100.$	$-48._3$	$184._9$	-26.9_9

2,3-Dimethylbutane (C_6H_{14})

T, K	$(G°-H°_0)/T$, cal K⁻¹ mol⁻¹	$(H°-H°_0)/T$, cal K⁻¹ mol⁻¹	$H°-H°_0$, kcal mol⁻¹	$S°$, cal K⁻¹ mol⁻¹	$C°_p$, cal K⁻¹ mol⁻¹	$\Delta H°_f$, kcal mol⁻¹	$\Delta G°_f$, kcal mol⁻¹	$\log_{10} K_f$
0	0	0	0	0	0	-32.2_9	-32.2_9	∞
200	-60.8_6	15.5_6	3.11_1	76.4_2	22.2_6	-39.2_7	-13.7_6	15.0_4
273.15	-66.1_2	18.5_0	5.05_1	84.6_2	30.6_7	-41.4_4	-4.0_8	3.2_7
298.15	-67.8_0	19.6_3	5.85	87.4_3	33.3_2	-42.1_2	-0.6_2	0.4_6
400	-74.2_3	24.4_3	9.77	98.6_6	43.4_3	-44.6_5	13.9_6	-7.6_3
600	-85.9	33.6	20.1_7	119.5	59.8	-48.2	44.1	-16.0_7
800	-96.7	41.8	33.4	138.5	72.1	-50.1	75.2	-20.5_5
1,000	-106.8	48.8	48.8	155.6	$81._4$	-50.7	106.7	-23.3_1
1,200	$-116._3$	$54._8$	$65._8$	$171._1$	$88._6$	$-50._3$	$138._1$	-25.1_5
1,500	$-129._4$	$62._4$	$93._7$	$191._8$	$97.$	$-48._3$	$185._1$	-26.9_5

THERMODYNAMIC PROPERTIES OF ALKANE HYDROCARBONS (Continued)

n-Heptane (C_7H_{16})

T, K	$(G^\circ - H^\circ_0)/T$, cal K⁻¹ mol⁻¹	$(H^\circ - H^\circ_0)/T$, cal K⁻¹ mol⁻¹	$H^\circ - H^\circ_0$, kcal mol⁻¹	S°, cal K⁻¹ mol⁻¹	C°_p, cal K⁻¹ mol⁻¹	ΔH°_f, kcal mol⁻¹	ΔG°_f, kcal mol⁻¹	$\log_{10} K_f$
0	0	0	0	0	0	-34.8_3	-34.8_3	∞
200	-65.8_6	22.6_7	4.53_4	88.5_4	30.5_1	-41.8_3	-12.9_0	14.1_0
273.15	-73.3_5	25.5_8	6.98_8	98.9_4	36.9_6	-44.0_9	-1.9_6	1.5_7
298.15	-75.6_4	26.6_5	7.94	102.2_9	39.4_8	-44.8_4	1.9_4	-1.4_2
400	-84.1_1	31.3_0	12.52	115.4_1	50.3_5	-47.6_7	18.3_7	-10.0_4
600	-98.6	40.9	24.5_2	139.5	68.7	-51.7	52.4	-19.0_7
800	-111.6	49.6	39.6	161.2	81.8	-54.1	87.4	-23.8_8
1,000	-123.5	57.0	57.0	180.5	$91._2$	-55.1	123.0	-26.8_7
1,200	$-134._4$	$63._3$	$76._0$	$197._7$	$98._1$	$-55._2$	$158._6$	-28.8_8
1,500	$-149._4$	$71._1$	$106._6$	$220._5$	$106.$	$-54._4$	$212._0$	-30.8_8

2-Methylhexane (C_7H_{16})

T, K	$(G^\circ - H^\circ_0)/T$, cal K⁻¹ mol⁻¹	$(H^\circ - H^\circ_0)/T$, cal K⁻¹ mol⁻¹	$H^\circ - H^\circ_0$, kcal mol⁻¹	S°, cal K⁻¹ mol⁻¹	C°_p, cal K⁻¹ mol⁻¹	ΔH°_f, kcal mol⁻¹	ΔG°_f, kcal mol⁻¹	$\log_{10} K_f$
0	0	0	0	0	0	-35.9_1	-35.9_1	∞
200	-66.7_7	20.3_5	4.07_0	87.1_2	28.3_4	-43.3_8	-14.1_7	15.4_8
273.15	-73.5_8	23.5_8	6.43_9	97.1_6	36.5_1	-45.7_3	-3.1_1	2.4_9
298.15	-75.7_0	24.7_8	7.39	100.4_8	39.3_2	-46.4_8	0.8_4	-0.6_1
400	-83.6_9	29.9_4	11.98	113.6_3	50.6_6	-49.3_0	17.4_5	-9.5_4
600	-97.8	40.1	24.0_6	137.9	69.2	-53.3	51.8	-18.8_6
800	-110.6	49.1	39.3	159.7	82.6	-55.5	87.2	-23.8_1
1,000	-122.4	56.9	56.9	179.3	92.4	-56.3	123.0	-26.8_7
1,200	$-133._4$	$63._4$	$76._1$	$196._8$	$99._8$	$-56._2$	$158._8$	-28.9_2
1,500	$-148._4$	$71._6$	$107._4$	$220._0$	$108.$	$-54._7$	$212._4$	-30.9_5

3-Methylhexane (C_7H_{16})

T, K	$(G^\circ - H^\circ_0)/T$, cal K⁻¹ mol⁻¹	$(H^\circ - H^\circ_0)/T$, cal K⁻¹ mol⁻¹	$H^\circ - H^\circ_0$, kcal mol⁻¹	S°, cal K⁻¹ mol⁻¹	C°_p, cal K⁻¹ mol⁻¹	ΔH°_f, kcal mol⁻¹	ΔG°_f, kcal mol⁻¹	$\log_{10} K_f$
0	-1.38	0	0	1.38	0	-35.2_2	-35.2_2	∞
200	-68.6_8	19.9_5	3.98_9	88.6_3	27.5_8	-42.7_7	-13.8_5	15.1_4
273.15	-75.3_6	23.1_4	6.32_2	98.5_0	36.2_0	-45.1_5	-2.9_0	2.3_2
298.15	-77.4_4	24.3_6	7.26	101.8_0	39.1_0	-45.9_1	1.0_1	-0.7_4
400	-85.3_2	29.6_0	11.84	114.9_2	50.6_0	-48.7_4	17.5_0	-9.5_6
600	-99.3	39.9	23.9_2	139.2	69.2	-52.7	51.6	-18.7_8
800	-112.0	49.0	39.2	161.0	82.6	-54.9	86.7	-23.6_8
1,000	-123.8	56.7	56.7	180.5	92.4	-55.8	122.2	-26.7_1
1,200	$-134._8$	$63._3$	$76._0$	$198._1$	$99._8$	$-55._6$	$157._8$	-28.7_4
1,500	$-149._8$	$71._5$	$107._2$	$221._3$	$108.$	$-54._1$	$211._0$	-30.7_5

THERMODYNAMIC PROPERTIES OF ALKANE HYDROCARBONS (Continued)

T, K	$(G° − H°_0)/T$, cal K⁻¹ mol⁻¹	$(H° − H°_0)/T$, cal K⁻¹ mol⁻¹	$H° − H°_0$, kcal mol⁻¹	$S°$, cal K⁻¹ mol⁻¹	$C°_p$, cal K⁻¹ mol⁻¹	$ΔH°_f$, kcal mol⁻¹	$ΔG°_f$, kcal mol⁻¹	$\log_{10} K_f$
3-Ethylpentane (C_7H_{16})								
0	0	0	0	0	0	-34.8_4	-34.8_4	∞
200	-64.1_4	20.5_0	4.09_9	84.6_4	29.9_6	-42.2_8	-12.5_6	13.7_3
273.15	-71.0_4	23.9_5	6.54_1	94.9_9	37.0_6	-44.5_5	-1.3_4	1.0_7
298.15	-73.2_0	25.1_6	7.50	98.3_6	39.6_7	-45.2_9	2.6_6	-1.9_5
400	-81.2_9	30.2_5	12.10	111.5_4	50.5_6	-48.1_0	19.4_9	-10.6_5
600	-95.5	40.2	24.1_3	135.7	68.9	-52.1	54.2	-19.7_6
800	-108.3	49.1	39.3	157.4	82.2	-54.4	90.1	-24.6_1
1,000	-120.1	56.8	56.8	176.9	$92._1$	-55.3	126.3	-27.6_1
1,200	$-131._0$	$63._3$	$76._0$	$194._3$	$99._5$	$-55._2$	$162._6$	-29.6_2
1,500	$-146._1$	$71._4$	$107._2$	$217._5$	108.	$-53._8$	$217._0$	-31.6_2
2,2-Dimethylpentane (C_7H_{16})								
0	0	0	0	0	0	-38.0_2	-38.0_2	∞
200	-62.1_9	18.2_8	3.65_5	80.4_7	27.9_3	-45.9_0	-15.3_6	16.7_8
273.15	-68.4_3	22.0_3	6.01_7	90.4_6	36.7_9	-48.2_6	-3.8_1	3.0_5
298.15	-70.4_3	23.4_0	6.98	93.8_3	39.8_4	-49.0_0	0.3_0	-0.2_2
400	-78.1_0	29.1_4	11.66	107.2_4	51.8_1	-51.7_3	17.5_8	-9.6_1
600	-92.0	40.0	24.0_2	132.0	70.9	-55.4	53.1	-19.3_5
800	-104.9	49.6	39.7	154.5	84.9	-57.2	89.6	-24.4_8
1,000	-116.8	57.8	57.8	174.6	$95._6$	-57.5	126.4	-27.6_3
1,200	$-128._0$	$64._8$	$77._8$	$192._8$	$103._9$	$-56._6$	$163._1$	-29.7_1
1,500	$-143._5$	$73._6$	$110._4.$	$217._1$	114.	$-53._8$	$217._8$	-31.7_3
2,3-Dimethylpentane (C_7H_{16})								
0	-1.38	0	0	1.38	0	-35.2_0	-35.2_0	∞
200	-68.3_2	18.1_6	3.63_1	86.4_8	25.0_9	-43.1	-13.7_7	15.0_5
273.15	-74.4_4	21.4_0	5.84_6	95.8_4	35.2_8	-45.6_1	-2.6_4	2.1_1
298.15	-76.3_7	22.7_1	6.77	99.0_8	38.4_4	-46.3_9	1.3_4	-0.9_8
400	-83.8_1	28.2_8	11.31	112.0_9	50.4_4	-49.2_6	18.1_1	-9.9_0
600	-97.3	39.0	23.3_8	136.3	69.3	-53.3	52.7	-19.2_1
800	-109.9	48.4	38.7	158.3	83.1	-55.4	88.4	-24.1_6
1,000	-121.5	56.4	56.4	177.9	$93._5$	-56.1	124.5	-27.2_1
1,200	$-132._4$	$63._3$	$75._9$	$195._7$	$101._3$	$-55._7$	$160._6$	-29.2_4
1,500	$-147._5$	$71._8$	$107._7$	$219._3$	110.	$-53._6$	$214._4$	-31.2_4

THERMODYNAMIC PROPERTIES OF ALKANE HYDROCARBONS (Continued)

2,4-Dimethylpentane (C_7H_{16})

T, K	$(G° - H°_0)/T$, cal K^{-1} mol^{-1}	$(H° - H°_0)/T$, cal K^{-1} mol^{-1}	$H° - H°_0$, kcal mol^{-1}	$S°$, cal K^{-1} mol^{-1}	$C°_p$, cal K^{-1} mol^{-1}	$\Delta H_f°$, kcal mol^{-1}	$\Delta G_f°$, kcal mol^{-1}	$\log_{10} K_f$
0	0	0	0	0	0	-37.2	-37.2	∞
200	-63.1_8	18.1_2	3.62_3	81.3_0	27.5_9	-45.1_3	-14.7_5	16.1_2
273.15	-69.3_9	22.0_2	6.01_4	91.4_1	37.6_6	-47.4_5	-3.2_7	2.6_1
298.15	-71.3_9	23.4_7	7.00	94.8_6	40.8_1	-48.1_7	0.8_2	-0.6_0
400	-79.1_1	29.4_3	11.77	108.5_4	52.6_0	-50.8_0	17.9_8	-9.8_3
600	-93.2	40.3	24.2_1	133.5	70.8	-54.4	53.2	-19.3_9
800	-106.1	49.7	39.8	155.8	84.2	-56.3	89.5	-24.4_4
1,000	-118.0	57.7	57.7	175.7	$94._2$	-56.8	126.0	-27.5_4
1,200	$-129._2$	64.4	$77._3$	$193._6$	$101._9$	$-56._3$	$162._5$	-29.6_0
1,500	$-144._5$	$72._8$	$109._2$	$217._3$	$111.$	$-54._1$	$217._0$	-31.6_1

3,3-Dimethylpentane (C_7H_{16})

T, K	$(G° - H°_0)/T$, cal K^{-1} mol^{-1}	$(H° - H°_0)/T$, cal K^{-1} mol^{-1}	$H° - H°_0$, kcal mol^{-1}	$S°$, cal K^{-1} mol^{-1}	$C°_p$, cal K^{-1} mol^{-1}	$\Delta H_f°$, kcal mol^{-1}	$\Delta G_f°$, kcal mol^{-1}	$\log_{10} K_f$
0	0	0	0	0	0	-36.6_4	-36.6_4	∞
200	-63.7_0	18.2_4	3.64_8	81.9_4	27.1_8	-44.5_3	-14.2_8	15.6_0
273.15	-69.9_1	21.9_0	5.98_2	91.8_1	36.5_6	-46.9_1	-2.8_4	2.2_7
298.15	-71.8_9	23.2_7	6.94	95.1_6	39.6_2	-47.6_6	1.2_4	-0.9_1
400	-79.5_1	28.9_7	11.59	108.4_8	51.4_7	-50.4_2	18.3_9	-10.0_5
600	-93.3	39.8	23.8_9	133.1	70.7	-54.2	53.7	-19.5_6
800	-106.1	49.4	39.5	155.5	84.9	-56.0	90.0	-24.5_8
1,000	-118.1	57.6	57.6	175.7	$95._7$	-56.3	126.6	-27.6_6
1,200	$-129._2$	$64._7$	$77._6$	$193._9$	$104._1$	$-55._4$	$163._0$	-29.6_9
1,500	$-144._7$	$73._6$	$110._4$	$218._3$	$114.$	$-52._4$	$217._3$	-31.6_6

2,2,3-Trimethylbutane (C_7H_{16})

T, K	$(G° - H°_0)/T$, cal K^{-1} mol^{-1}	$(H° - H°_0)/T$, cal K^{-1} mol^{-1}	$H° - H°_0$, kcal mol^{-1}	$S°$, cal K^{-1} mol^{-1}	$C°_p$, cal K^{-1} mol^{-1}	$\Delta H_f°$, kcal mol^{-1}	$\Delta G_f°$, kcal mol^{-1}	$\log_{10} K_f$
0	0	0	0	0	0	-37.4_2	-37.4_2	∞
200	-61.3_4	17.3_0	3.45_9	78.6_4	26.6_4	-45.5_0	-14.5_5	15.9_4
273.15	-67.2_7	21.0_5	5.74_9	88.3_2	35.9_6	-47.9_3	-2.9_0	2.3_2
298.15	-69.1_8	22.4_4	6.69	91.6_2	39.0_2	-48.6_9	1.2_7	-0.9_3
400	-76.5_7	28.2_0	11.28	104.7_7	50.8_7	-51.5_1	18.7_9	-10.2_7
600	-90.1	39.1	23.4_7	129.2	70.2	-55.4	54.9	-19.9_8
800	-102.7	48.8	39.0	151.5	84.9	-57.3	91.9	-25.1_2
1,000	-114.5	57.2	57.2	171.7	$96._3$	-57.5	129.3	-28.2_6
1,200	$-125._6$	$64._5$	$77._4$	$190._1$	$105._2$	$-56._4$	$166._6$	-30.3_4
1,500	$-141._0$	$73._7$	$110._6$	$214._7$	$115.$	$-53._0$	$222._0$	-32.3_4

THERMODYNAMIC PROPERTIES OF ALKANE HYDROCARBONS (Continued)

n-Octane (C$_8$H$_{18}$)

T, K	$(G°-H°_0)/T$, cal K^{-1} mol^{-1}	$(H°-H°_0)/T$, cal K^{-1} mol^{-1}	$H°-H°_0$, kcal mol^{-1}	$S°$, cal K^{-1} mol^{-1}	$C°_p$, cal K^{-1} mol^{-1}	$\Delta H°_f$, kcal mol^{-1}	$\Delta G°_f$, kcal mol^{-1}	$\log_{10} K_f$
0	0	0	0	0	0	-38.5_7	-38.5_7	∞
200	-70.2_6	25.7_9	5.15_8	96.0_5	34.6_0	-46.4_0	-13.1_2	14.3_4
273.15	-78.7_7	29.0_9	7.94_5	107.8_6	41.9_5	-48.9_4	-0.5_6	0.4_5
298.15	-81.3_8	30.2_9	9.03	111.6_7	44.8_8	-49.7_7	3.9_2	-2.8_7
400	-91.0_0	35.5_9	14.24	126.5_9	57.3_0	-52.9_3	22.7_7	-12.4_4
600	-107.5	46.5	27.8_8	154.0	78.1	-57.4	61.7	-22.4_7
800	-122.3	56.3	45.1	178.6	92.8	-60.0	101.8	-27.8_2
1,000	-135.7	64.7	64.7	200.4	$103._1$	-61.2	142.4	-31.1_3
1,200	$-148._2$	$71._8$	$86._1$	$220._0$	110.7	$-61._4$	$183._2$	-33.3_6
1,500	$-165._2$	$80._5$	$120._7$	$245._7$	$119.$	$-60._5$	$244._3$	-35.5_9

2-Methylheptane (C$_8$H$_{18}$)

T, K	$(G°-H°_0)/T$, cal K^{-1} mol^{-1}	$(H°-H°_0)/T$, cal K^{-1} mol^{-1}	$H°-H°_0$, kcal mol^{-1}	$S°$, cal K^{-1} mol^{-1}	$C°_p$, cal K^{-1} mol^{-1}	$\Delta H°_f$, kcal mol^{-1}	$\Delta G°_f$, kcal mol^{-1}	$\log_{10} K_f$
0	0	0	0	0	0	-39.6_5	-39.6_5	∞
200	-71.1_5	23.4_7	4.69_3	94.6_2	32.4_2	-47.9_5	-14.3_9	15.7_2
273.15	-78.9_9	27.0_7	7.39_4	106.0_6	41.5_6	-50.5_7	-1.7_0	1.3_6
298.15	-81.4_2	28.4_2	8.47	109.8_4	44.7_5	-51.4_1	2.8_2	-2.0_7
400	-90.5_7	34.2_4	13.70	124.8_1	57.6_6	-54.5_5	21.8_6	-11.9_4
600	-106.7	45.7	27.4_4	152.4	78.7	-59.0	61.1	-22.2_6
800	-121.3	55.9	44.8	177.2	93.6	-61.4	101.5	-27.7_4
1,000	-134.7	64.6	64.6	199.3	$104._4$	-62.4	142.4	-31.1_3
1,200	$-147._1$	$72._0$	$86._3$	$219._1$	$112._5$	$-62._2$	$183._4$	-33.4_0
1,500	$-164._2$	$81._0$	$121._5$	$245._2$	$122.$	$-60._8$	$244._6$	-35.6_4

3-Methylheptane (C$_8$H$_{18}$)

T, K	$(G°-H°_0)/T$, cal K^{-1} mol^{-1}	$(H°-H°_0)/T$, cal K^{-1} mol^{-1}	$H°-H°_0$, kcal mol^{-1}	$S°$, cal K^{-1} mol^{-1}	$C°_p$, cal K^{-1} mol^{-1}	$\Delta H°_f$, kcal mol^{-1}	$\Delta G°_f$, kcal mol^{-1}	$\log_{10} K_f$
0	-1.38	0	0	1.38	0	-38.9_7	-38.9_7	∞
200	-73.1_0	23.1_3	4.62_5	96.2_3	31.7_1	-47.3	-14.0_9	15.4_0
273.15	-80.8_2	26.6_9	7.28_9	107.5_1	41.1_8	-50.0_0	-1.5_2	1.2_1
298.15	-83.2_2	28.0_4	8.36	111.2_6	44.4_1	-50.8_4	2.9_7	-2.1_8
400	-92.2_6	33.8_8	13.55	126.1_4	57.4_0	-54.0_1	21.8_6	-11.9_5
600	-108.2	45.4	27.2_5	153.6	78.4	-58.5	60.9	-22.1_7
800	-122.7	55.7	44.5	178.4	93.5	-60.9	101.0	-27.6_1
1,000	-136.1	64.4	64.4	200.5	$104._3$	-61.9	141.7	-30.9_7
1,200	$-148._5$	$71._7$	$86._1$	$220._2$	$112._4$	$-61._8$	$182._4$	-33.2_2
1,500	$-165._5$	$80._8$	$121._2$	$246._3$	$122.$	$-60._4$	$243._4$	-35.4_6

THERMODYNAMIC PROPERTIES OF ALKANE HYDROCARBONS (Continued)

T, K	$(G° − H°_0)/T$, cal K^{-1} mol^{-1}	$(H° − H°_0)/T$, cal K^{-1} mol^{-1}	$H° − H°_0$, kcal mol^{-1}	$S°$, cal K^{-1} mol^{-1}	$C_p°$, cal K^{-1} mol^{-1}	$\Delta H_f°$, kcal mol^{-1}	$\Delta G_f°$, kcal mol^{-1}	$\log_{10} K_f$
4-Methylheptane (C$_8$H$_{18}$)								
0	0	0	0	0	0	-38.9_6	-38.9_6	∞
200	-71.4_7	22.8_0	4.56_0	94.2_7	31.5_2	-47.3_9	-13.7_6	15.0_4
273.15	-79.1_0	26.4_5	7.22_5	105.5_5	41.3_7	-50.0_5	-1.0_4	0.8_3
298.15	-81.4_8	27.8_4	8.30	109.3_2	44.7_0	-50.8_9	3.5_0	-2.5_7
400	-90.4_8	33.8_5	13.54	124.3_3	57.9_2	-54.0_2	22.5_8	-12.3_4
600	-106.4	45.6	27.3_4	152.0	79.0	-58.4	61.9	-22.5_5
800	-121.0	55.9	44.7	176.9	93.9	-60.8	102.4	-27.9_8
1,000	-134.5	64.6	64.6	199.1	104.6	-61.7	143.4	-31.3_3
1,200	-146.9	$72._0$	86.4	218.9	112.6	$-61._5$	$184._3$	-33.5_7
1,500	-164.0	$81._0$	121.6	245.0	$122.$	-60.0	245.7	-35.7_9
2,2-Dimethylhexane (C$_8$H$_{18}$)								
0	0	0	0	0	0	-41.7_7	-41.7_1	∞
200	-66.6_3	21.5_8	4.31_5	88.2_1	32.2_0	-50.4_5	-15.6_1	17.0_5
273.15	-73.9_5	25.6_7	7.01_0	99.6_2	41.6_8	-53.0_8	-2.4_4	1.9_6
298.15	-76.2_7	27.1_5	8.10	103.4_2	45.0_0	-53.9_1	2.2_4	-1.6_4
400	-85.1_1	33.4_2	13.37	118.5_3	58.2_8	-57.0_0	21.9_2	-11.9_8
600	-101.0	45.5	27.2_8	146.5	79.8	-61.2	62.4	-22.7_3
800	-115.6	56.1	44.9	171.7	95.6	-63.4	104.0	-28.4_0
1,000	-129.1	65.3	65.3	194.4	107.4	-63.8	145.9	-31.8_9
1,200	-141.7	$73._1$	$87._7$	$214._8$	116.4	$-63._0$	$187._8$	-34.2_0
1,500	$-159._1$	$82._8$	$124._2$	$241._9$	$127.$	$-60._2$	$250._2$	-36.4_5
3,3-Dimethylhexane (C$_8$H$_{18}$)								
0	0	0	0	0	0	-40.3_8	-40.3_8	∞
200	-68.9_2	20.7_0	4.14_0	89.6_2	30.8_6	-49.2_4	-14.6_7	16.0_3
273.15	-75.9_7	24.9_3	6.80_7	100.9_0	42.0_0	-51.8_9	-1.6_1	1.2_8
298.15	-78.2_3	26.5_1	7.90	104.7_4	45.6_2	-52.7_1	3.0_5	-2.2_3
400	-86.9_4	33.1_8	13.27	120.1_2	59.4_4	-55.7_1	22.5_8	-12.3_4
600	-102.8	45.7	27.4_3	143.5	81.0	-59.7	62.7	-22.8_3
800	-117.5	56.6	45.2	174.1	96.5	-61.6	103.8	-28.3_6
1,000	-131.1	65.8	65.8	196.9	$108._1$	-61.9	145.3	-31.7_5
1,200	$-143._8$	$73._6$	$88._3$	$217._4$	$117._0$	$-61._0$	$186._6$	-33.9_8
1,500	$-161._3$	$83._4$	$125._0$	$244._7$	$127.$	$-58._0$	$248._2$	-36.1_6

THERMODYNAMIC PROPERTIES OF ALKANE HYDROCARBONS (Continued)

2,2,4-Trimethylpentane (Isooctane) (C_8H_{18})

T, K	$(G° − H°_0)/T$, cal K⁻¹ mol⁻¹	$(H° − H°_0)/T$, cal K⁻¹ mol⁻¹	$H° − H°_0$, kcal mol⁻¹	$S°$, cal K⁻¹ mol⁻¹	$C°_p$, cal K⁻¹ mol⁻¹	$\Delta H°_f$, kcal mol⁻¹	$\Delta G°_f$, kcal mol⁻¹	$\log_{10} K_f$
0	0	0	0	0	0	-41.2_3	-41.2_3	∞
200	-66.3_0	19.7_3	3.94_5	86.0_3	31.2_1	-50.2_8	-15.0_0	16.3_9
273.15	-73.1_0	24.1_8	6.60_6	97.2_8	41.5_8	-52.9_4	-1.6_7	1.3_3
298.15	-75.2_9	25.8_0	7.69	101.0_9	45.0_3	-53.7_7	3.0_7	-2.2_5
400	-83.7_9	32.4_4	12.98	116.2_3	58.4_6	-56.8_5	22.9_9	-12.5_6
600	-99.3	44.9	26.9_4	144.2	80.2	-61.0	63.9	-23.2_8
800	-113.8	55.8	44.7	169.6	96.4	-63.1	105.9	-28.9_4
1,000	-127.3	65.2	65.2	192.5	$108._7$	-63.3	148.2	-32.4_0
1,200	$-139._9$	$73._3$	$88._0$	$213._2$	$118._2$	$-62._2$	$190._4$	-34.6_8
1,500	$-157._4$	$83._4$	$125._1$	$240._8$	$129.$	$-58._7$	$253._2$	-36.9_0

n-Nonane (C_9H_{20})

T, K	$(G° − H°_0)/T$, cal K⁻¹ mol⁻¹	$(H° − H°_0)/T$, cal K⁻¹ mol⁻¹	$H° − H°_0$, kcal mol⁻¹	$S°$, cal K⁻¹ mol⁻¹	$C°_p$, cal K⁻¹ mol⁻¹	$\Delta H°_f$, kcal mol⁻¹	$\Delta G°_f$, kcal mol⁻¹	$\log_{10} K_f$
0	0	0	0	0	0	-42.3_2	-42.3_2	∞
200	-74.6_4	28.9_2	5.78_3	103.5_6	38.7_0	-50.9_8	-13.3_6	14.6_0
273.15	-84.2_0	32.5_9	8.90_2	116.7_9	47.0_3	-53.7_9	0.8_4	-0.6_7
298.15	-87.1_0	33.9_4	10.12	121.0_4	50.2_9	-54.7_1	5.9_0	-4.3_2
400	-97.8_9	39.8_8	15.95	137.7_7	64.2_5	-58.2_0	27.1_6	-14.8_4
600	-116.4	52.1	31.2_5	168.5	87.5	-63.2	71.0	-25.8_6
800	-132.9	63.1	50.5	196.0	103.7	-66.0	116.2	-31.7_4
1,000	-148.0	72.4	72.4	220.4	$115._1$	-67.3	161.9	-35.3_9
1,200	$-161._9$	$80._3$	$96._3$	$242._2$	$123._4$	$-67._5$	$207._8$	-37.8_4
1,500	$-180._9$	$89._9$	$134._8$	$270._8$	$133.$	$-66._7$	$276._5$	-40.2_9

2-Methyloctane (C_9H_{20})

T, K	$(G° − H°_0)/T$, cal K⁻¹ mol⁻¹	$(H° − H°_0)/T$, cal K⁻¹ mol⁻¹	$H° − H°_0$, kcal mol⁻¹	$S°$, cal K⁻¹ mol⁻¹	$C°_p$, cal K⁻¹ mol⁻¹	$\Delta H°_f$, kcal mol⁻¹	$\Delta G°_f$, kcal mol⁻¹	$\log_{10} K_f$
0	0	0	0	0	0	-43.4_0	-43.4_0	∞
200	-75.5_4	26.5_9	5.31_8	102.1_3	36.5_2	-52.5_3	-14.6_2	15.9_8
273.15	-84.4_0	30.5_8	8.35_8	114.9_8	46.6_0	-55.4_2	-0.3_0	0.2_4
298.15	-87.1_5	32.0_7	9.56	119.2_2	50.1_5	-56.3_5	4.8_0	-3.5_2
400	-97.4_5	38.5_4	15.41	135.9_9	64.6_1	-59.8_2	26.2_5	-14.3_4
600	-115.5	51.4	30.8_1	166.9	88.1	-64.7	70.4	-25.6_6
800	-131.9	62.7	50.2	194.6	104.6	-67.4	115.9	-31.6_7
1,000	-146.9	72.4	72.4	219.3	$116._4$	-68.4	161.9	-35.3_8
1,200	$-160._9$	$80._4$	$96._5$	$241._3$	$125._1$	$-68._4$	$208._0$	-37.8_7
1,500	$-180._0$	$90._4$	$135._6$	$270._4$	$135.$	$-66._9$	$276._9$	-40.3_5

THERMODYNAMIC PROPERTIES OF ALKANE HYDROCARBONS (Continued)

3-Methyloctane (C$_9$H$_{20}$)

T, K	$(G° − H°_0)/T$, cal K^{-1} mol^{-1}	$(H° − H°_0)/T$, cal K^{-1} mol^{-1}	$H° − H°_0$, kcal mol^{-1}	$S°$, cal K^{-1} mol^{-1}	$C°_p$, cal K^{-1} mol^{-1}	$\Delta H°_f$, kcal mol^{-1}	$\Delta G°_f$, kcal mol^{-1}	$\log_{10} K_f$
0	-1.38	0	0	1.38	0	-42.7_1	-42.7_1	∞
200	-77.4_8	26.2_4	5.24_8	103.7_2	35.7_9	-51.9_1	-14.3_2	15.6_4
273.15	-86.2_3	30.1_8	8.24_4	116.4_1	46.2_4	-54.8_3	-0.1_0	0.0_8
298.15	-88.9_3	31.6_9	9.45	120.6_2	49.8_5	-55.7_7	4.9_6	-3.6_4
400	-99.1_4	38.1_8	15.00	137.3_2	64.4_0	-59.2_6	26.2_7	-14.3_5
600	-117.1	51.0	30.6_3	168.1	87.9	-64.2	70.2	-25.5_7
800	-133.4	62.4	50.0	195.8	104.5	-66.9	115.4	-31.5_4
1,000	-148.4	72.1	72.1	220.5	$116._3$	-68.0	161.1	-35.2_2
1,200	$-162._3$	$80._2$	$96._3$	$242._5$	$125._0$	$-67._9$	$207._0$	-37.7_0
1,500	$-181._3$	$90._2$	$135._4$	$271._5$	$135.$	$-66._5$	$275._6$	-40.1_6

4-Methyloctane (C$_9$H$_{20}$)

T, K	$(G° − H°_0)/T$, cal K^{-1} mol^{-1}	$(H° − H°_0)/T$, cal K^{-1} mol^{-1}	$H° − H°_0$, kcal mol^{-1}	$S°$, cal K^{-1} mol^{-1}	$C°_p$, cal K^{-1} mol^{-1}	$\Delta H°_f$, kcal mol^{-1}	$\Delta G°_f$, kcal mol^{-1}	$\log_{10} K_f$
0	-1.38	0	0	1.38	0	-42.7_0	-42.7_0	∞
200	-77.2_7	25.9_7	5.19_4	103.2_4	35.6_4	-51.9_5	-14.2_6	15.5_9
273.15	-85.9_4	29.9_9	8.19_0	115.9_3	46.3_5	-54.8_8	-0.0_2	0.0_1
298.15	-88.6_3	31.5_2	9.40	120.1_5	50.0_2	-55.8_1	5.0_6	-3.7_1
400	-98.8_0	38.1_2	15.25	136.9_2	64.7_1	-59.2_8	26.4_2	-14.4_3
600	-116.8	51.1	30.6_7	167.9	88.2	-64.1	70.4	-25.6_5
800	-133.1	62.5	50.1	195.6	104.7	-66.8	115.7	-31.6_0
1,000	-148.1	72.2	72.2	220.3	$116._5$	-67.8	161.5	-35.2_9
1,200	$-162._0$	$80._4$	$96._4$	$242._4$	$125._2$	$-67._8$	$207._3$	-37.7_6
1,500	$-181._0$	$90._4$	$135._5$	$271._4$	$135.$	$-66._3$	$276._0$	-40.2_1

3-Ethylheptane (C$_9$H$_{20}$)

T, K	$(G° − H°_0)/T$, cal K^{-1} mol^{-1}	$(H° − H°_0)/T$, cal K^{-1} mol^{-1}	$H° − H°_0$, kcal mol^{-1}	$S°$, cal K^{-1} mol^{-1}	$C°_p$, cal K^{-1} mol^{-1}	$\Delta H°_f$, kcal mol^{-1}	$\Delta G°_f$, kcal mol^{-1}	$\log_{10} K_f$
0	0	0	0	0	0	-42.3_4	-42.3_4	∞
200	-74.9_0	26.5_0	5.30_0	101.4_0	38.0_7	-51.4_8	-13.4_3	14.6_7
273.15	-83.8_0	30.7_9	8.41_0	114.5_9	47.2_7	-54.3_0	0.9_3	-0.7_4
298.15	-86.5_6	32.3_2	9.64	118.8_7	50.6_4	-55.2_1	6.0_4	-4.4_3
400	-96.9_4	38.7_8	15.51	135.7_2	64.6_2	-58.6_6	27.5_2	-15.0_4
600	-115.1	51.4	30.8_6	166.5	87.7	-63.6	71.8	-26.1_4
800	-131.5	62.6	50.1	194.1	104.2	-66.3	117.3	-32.0_5
1,000	-146.5	72.2	72.2	218.7	$116._0$	-67.5	163.4	-35.7_2
1,200	$-160._4$	$80._3$	$96._3$	$240._7$	$124._8$	$-67._5$	$209._6$	-38.1_7
1,500	$-179._5$	$90._2$	$135._4$	$269._7$	$135.$	$-66._1$	$278._8$	-40.6_1

THERMODYNAMIC PROPERTIES OF ALKANE HYDROCARBONS (Continued)

T, K	$(G°-H°_0)/T$, cal K^{-1} mol^{-1}	$(H°-H°_0)/T$, cal K^{-1} mol^{-1}	$H°-H°_0$, kcal mol^{-1}	$S°$, cal K^{-1} mol^{-1}	$C_p°$, cal K^{-1} mol^{-1}	$\Delta H_f°$, kcal mol^{-1}	$\Delta G_f°$, kcal mol^{-1}	$\log_{10} K_f$
			4-Ethylheptane (C$_9$H$_{20}$)					
0	0	0	0	0	0	-42.3$_4$	-42.3$_4$	∞
200	-74.6$_3$	26.1$_7$	5.23$_3$	100.8$_0$	37.9$_3$	-51.5$_6$	-13.3$_8$	14.6$_2$
273.15	-83.4$_3$	30.5$_7$	8.34$_9$	114.0$_0$	47.5$_2$	-54.3$_6$	1.0$_2$	-0.8$_2$
298.15	-86.1$_8$	32.1$_3$	9.58	118.3$_1$	50.9$_8$	-55.2$_7$	6.1$_5$	-4.5$_1$
400	-96.5$_3$	38.7$_5$	15.50	135.2$_8$	65.0$_9$	-58.6$_7$	27.6$_8$	-15.1$_2$
600	-114.7	51.6	30.9$_4$	166.3	88.1	-63.5	72.0	-26.2$_2$
800	-131.1	62.9	50.3	194.0	104.5	-66.2	117.6	-32.1$_3$
1,000	-146.2	72.4	72.4	218.6	116.$_2$	-67.3	163.7	-35.7$_8$
1,200	-160.$_1$	80.$_5$	96.$_6$	240.$_6$	124.$_9$	-67.$_3$	209.$_9$	-38.2$_3$
1,500	-179.$_2$	90.4	135.$_6$	269.$_6$	135.	-65.$_9$	279.$_1$	-40.6$_6$
			n-Decane					
0	0	0	0	0	0	-46.0$_6$	-46.0$_6$	∞
200	-79.0$_2$	32.0$_5$	6.40$_8$	111.0$_7$	42.8$_0$	-55.5$_6$	-13.5$_8$	14.8$_4$
273.15	-89.6$_1$	36.1$_0$	9.86$_1$	125.7$_1$	52.0$_8$	-58.6$_3$	-2.2$_5$	-1.8$_0$
298.15	-92.8$_3$	37.5$_9$	11.21	130.4$_2$	55.7$_0$	-59.6$_4$	7.8$_8$	-5.7$_8$
400	-104.7$_7$	44.1$_8$	17.67	148.9$_5$	71.2$_2$	-63.4$_5$	31.5$_6$	-17.2$_4$
600	-125.3	57.7	34.6$_3$	183.0	97.0	-68.8	80.3	-29.2$_6$
800	-143.6	69.9	55.9	213.5	114.7	-71.9	130.6	-35.6$_7$
1,000	-160.3	80.2	80.2	240.5	127.$_1$	-73.3	181.4	-39.6$_4$
1,200	-175.$_7$	88.$_8$	106.$_5$	264.$_5$	136.$_1$	-73.$_6$	232.$_4$	-42.3$_2$
1,500	-196.$_7$	99.$_3$	149.$_9$	296.$_0$	146.	-72.$_8$	308.$_8$	-44.9
			2-Methylnonane (C$_{10}$H$_{22}$)					
0	0	0	0	0	0	-47.1$_5$	-47.1$_5$	∞
200	-79.9$_2$	29.7$_2$	5.94$_4$	109.6$_4$	40.6$_2$	-57.1$_0$	-14.8$_5$	16.2$_2$
273.15	-89.8$_1$	34.0$_9$	9.31$_0$	123.9$_0$	51.6$_5$	-60.2$_6$	1.1$_0$	-0.8$_2$
298.15	-92.8$_7$	35.7$_2$	10.65	128.5$_9$	55.5$_6$	-61.2$_8$	6.7$_8$	-4.9$_7$
400	-104.3$_4$	42.8$_4$	17.13	147.1$_8$	71.5$_8$	-65.0$_8$	30.6$_4$	-16.7$_4$
600	-124.4	57.0	34.1$_9$	181.4	97.5	-70.4	79.8	-29.0$_5$
800	-142.6	69.5	55.6	212.1	115.6	-73.3	130.3	-35.6$_0$
1,000	-159.2	80.1	80.1	239.3	128.$_4$	-74.5	181.4	-39.6$_4$
1,200	-174.$_7$	88.$_9$	106.$_8$	263.$_6$	137.$_8$	-74.$_5$	232.$_5$	-42.3$_5$
1,500	-195.$_7$	99.$_9$	149.$_8$	295.$_6$	149.	-73.$_0$	309.$_2$	-45.0$_4$

THERMODYNAMIC PROPERTIES OF ALKANE HYDROCARBONS (Continued)

3-Methylnonane ($C_{10}H_{22}$)

T, K	$(G°-H°_0)/T$, cal K^{-1} mol^{-1}	$(H°-H°_0)/T$, cal K^{-1} mol^{-1}	$H°-H°_0$, kcal mol^{-1}	$S°$, cal K^{-1} mol^{-1}	$C°_p$, cal K^{-1} mol^{-1}	$\Delta H°_f$, kcal mol^{-1}	$\Delta G°_f$, kcal mol^{-1}	$\log_{10} K_f$
0	-1.38	0	0	1.38	0	-46.4_5	-46.4_5	∞
200	-81.8_6	29.3_7	5.87_3	111.2_3	39.8_8	-56.4_8	-14.5_4	15.8_9
273.15	-91.6_4	33.6_9	9.20_2	125.3_3	51.2_8	-59.6_7	1.3_0	-1.0_4
298.15	-94.6_6	35.3_3	10.54	129.9_9	55.2_5	-60.7_0	6.9_5	-5.0_9
400	-106.0_2	42.4_8	16.99	148.5_0	71.3_5	-64.5_2	30.6_7	-16.7_6
600	-125.9	56.7	34.0_0	182.6	97.3	-69.9	79.5	-28.9_7
800	-144.1	69.2	55.4	213.3	115.4	-72.8	129.8	-35.4_7
1,000	-160.7	79.8	79.8	240.5	$128._3$	-74.0	180.7	-39.4_8
1,200	$-176._0$	$88._7$	$106._5$	$264._7$	$137._7$	$-74._0$	$231._6$	-42.1_8
1,500	$-197._1$	$99._6$	$149._5$	$296._9$	149.	$-72._6$	$307._9$	-44.8_6

4-Methylnonane ($C_{10}H_{22}$)

T, K	$(G°-H°_0)/T$, cal K^{-1} mol^{-1}	$(H°-H°_0)/T$, cal K^{-1} mol^{-1}	$H°-H°_0$, kcal mol^{-1}	$S°$, cal K^{-1} mol^{-1}	$C°_p$, cal K^{-1} mol^{-1}	$\Delta H°_f$, kcal mol^{-1}	$\Delta G°_f$, kcal mol^{-1}	$\log_{10} K_f$
0	-1.38	0	0	1.38	0	-46.4_5	-46.4_5	∞
200	-81.6_5	29.0_9	5.81_7	110.7_4	39.7_2	-56.5_3	-14.5_0	15.8_4
273.15	-91.3_5	33.4_8	9.14_6	124.8_3	51.4_1	-59.7_3	1.3_8	-1.1_1
298.15	-94.3_5	35.1_6	10.48	129.5_1	55.4_5	-60.7_5	7.0_4	-5.1_6
400	-105.6_8	42.4_2	16.97	148.1_0	71.7_1	-64.5_4	30.8_1	-16.8_3
600	-125.6	56.8	34.0_5	182.4	97.7	-69.8	79.7	-29.0_4
800	-143.7	69.4	55.5	213.1	115.7	-72.7	130.1	-35.5_3
1,000	-160.4	80.0	80.0	240.4	$128._5$	-73.9	180.9	-39.5_4
1,200	$-175._8$	$88._9$	$106._7$	$264._7$	$137._8$	$-73._8$	$231._9$	-42.2_3
1,500	$-196._8$	$99._8$	$149._7$	$296._6$	149.	$-72._4$	$308._2$	-44.9_0

5-Methylnonane ($C_{10}H_{22}$)

T, K	$(G°-H°_0)/T$, cal K^{-1} mol^{-1}	$(H°-H°_0)/T$, cal K^{-1} mol^{-1}	$H°-H°_0$, kcal mol^{-1}	$S°$, cal K^{-1} mol^{-1}	$C°_p$, cal K^{-1} mol^{-1}	$\Delta H°_f$, kcal mol^{-1}	$\Delta G°_f$, kcal mol^{-1}	$\log_{10} K_f$
0	-1.38	0	0	1.38	0	-46.4_3	-46.4_3	∞
200	-80.3_3	29.1_5	5.82_9	109.4_8	39.7_5	-56.5_1	-14.2_2	15.5_4
273.15	-90.0_4	33.5_2	9.15_5	123.5_6	51.3_1	-59.7_0	1.7_6	-1.4_0
298.15	-93.0_5	35.1_8	10.49	128.2_3	55.3_2	-60.7_3	7.4_4	-5.4_6
400	-104.3_8	42.3_9	16.96	146.7_7	71.5_2	-64.5_4	31.3_4	-17.1_3
600	-124.3	56.7	34.0_0	181.0	97.5	-69.8	80.5	-29.3_4
800	-142.4	69.3	55.4	211.7	115.6	-72.8	131.2	-35.8_3
1,000	-159.0	79.9	79.9	238.9	$128._4$	-73.9	182.3	-39.8_4
1,200	$-174._4$	$88._8$	$106._6$	$263._2$	$137._8$	$-73._9$	$233._6$	-42.5_4
1,500	$-195._4$	$99._7$	$149._6$	$295._1$	149.	$-72._5$	$310._3$	-45.2_1

Data from Scott, D. W., U.S. Bureau of Mines Bulletin 666 (stock number 2404-01547), U.S. Government Printing Office, Washington, D.C., 1974.

HEAT OF DILUTION OF ACIDS

From National Standards Reference Data Systems NSRDS-NBS 2
Vivian B. Parker

ΔH_{diln}, the integral heat of dilution, is the change in enthalpy, per mole of solute, when a solution of concentration m_1 is diluted to a final finite concentration m_2. When the dilution is carried out by addition of an infinite amount of solvent, so the final solution is infinitely dilute, the enthalpy change is the integral heat of dilution to infinite dilution. Since Φ_L, the relative apparent molal enthalpy, is equal to and opposite in sign to this, only Φ_L is referred to here.

Φ_L, cal/mole, at 25°C

n	m	HF	HCl	HClO₄	HBr	HI	HNO₃	CH₂O₂	C₂H₄O₂
∞	0.00	0	0	0	0	0	0	0	0
500,000	.000111	300	5	5	5	5	5	9	40
100,000	.000555	900	10	10	9	9	11	13	50
50,000	.00111	1,300	16	14	13	12	15	20	53
20,000	.00278	1,800	25	22	22	20	23	23	55
10,000	.00555	2,130	34	30	31	29	31	25	58
7,000	.00793	2,250	40	35	37	34	36	26	59
5,000	.01110	2,360	47	40	44	41	42	26	61
4,000	.01388	2,450	54	43	49	46	46	27	62
3,000	.01850	2,550	60	47	56	52	51	28	62
2,000	.02775	2,700	74	54	68	63	59	28	63
1,500	.03700	2,812	85	58	77	71	65	29	64
1,110	.05000	2,927	97	62	89	81	73	29	65
1,000	.05551	2,969	102	62	92	84	76	29	65
900	.0617	2,989	107	63	97	88	78	30	66
800	.0694	3,015	113	64	102	92	81	31	67
700	.0793	3,037	120	65	108	96	84	32	68
600	.0925	3,057	129	65	115	102	88	32	68
555.1	.1000	3,060	133	65	119	105	89	32	69
500	.1110	3,077	140	65	124	108	92	32	70
400	.1388	3,097	156	64	135	116	97	33	72
300	.1850	3,126	176	61	150	125	103	34	76
277.5	.2000	3,129	182	59	155	128	105	35	79
200	.2775	3,142	212	50	176	140	117	36	82
150	.3700	3,148	242	36	197	154	118	39	88
111.0	.5000	3,156	280	18	225	170	119	42	97
100	.5551	3,160	295	+12	235	176	120	44	101
75	.7401	3,167	343	−14	270	194	121	49	113
55.51	1.0000	3,179	405	−48	314	223	121	54	130
50	1.1101	3,184	431	−61	331	234	121	56	147
40	1.3877	3,192	493	−91	379	260	121	60	155
37.00	1.5000	3,194	518	−103	398	269	121	62	162
30	1.8502	3,200	595	−138	455	301	124	65	183
27.75	2.0000	3,203	627	−149	477	315	126	66	192
25	2.2202	3,208	674	−162	510	336	130	67	204
22.20	2.5000	3,211	732	−173	550	365	139	68	218
20	2.7753	3,214	792	−182	590	396	149	69	233
18.50	3.0000	3,216	838	−187	624	427	159	69	245
15.86	3.500	3,221	946	−196	709	503	189	69	268
15	3.7004	3,227	988	−195	743	536	203	69	277
13.88	4.0000	3,234	1,052	−188	796	588	229	69	291
12.33	4.5000	3,246	1,171	−175	887	676	265	69	313
12	4.6255	3,249	1,190	−170	911	700	277	69	318
11.10	5.0000	3,256	1,271	−150	983	764	313	69	333
10	5.5506	3,265	1,396	−117	1,097	855	368	68	353
9.5	5.8427	3,269	1,462	−97	1,156	920	400	68	363
9.251	6.0000	3,272	1,498	−84	1,196	950	418	67	368
9.0	6.1674	3,274	1,535	−72	1,230	980	437	67	373
8.5	6.5301	3,278	1,618	−40	1,313	1,050	480	66	383
8.0	6.9383	3,282	1,710	+4	1,401	1,115	530	65	392
7.929	7.0000	3,283	1,725	11	1,416	1,130	538	65	394

n	m	HF	HCl	HClO$_4$	HBr	HI	HNO$_3$	CH$_2$O$_2$	C$_2$H$_4$O$_2$
7.5	7.4008	3,286	1,820	61	1,497	1,210	595	63	402
7.0	7.9295	3,290	1,942	135	1,608	1,325	661	61	411
6.938	8.0000	3,291	1,960	146	1,622	1,340	667	61	412
6.5	8.5394	3,296	2,090	229	1,738	1,450	745	58	420
6.167	9.0000	3,302	2,202	306	1,845	1,570	805	55	426
6.0	9.2510	3,305	2,265	348	1,903	1,630	840	53	429
5.551	10.0000	3,316	2,447	481	2,078	1,820	940	49	436
5.5	10.0920	3,317	2,472	499	2,102	1,850	950	49	437
5.0	11.1012	3,335	2,721	730	2,344	2,100	1,098	43	445
4.5	12.3346	3,362	3,025	1,144	2,655	2,460	1,270	37	453
4.0	13.8765	3,400	3,404	1,574	3,089	2,960	1,495	29	462
3.700	15.0000	3,428	3,680	1,893	3,415	3,350	1,645	26	469
3.5	15.8589	3,450	3,882	2,150	3,668	3,660	1,770	21	473
3.25	17.0788	3,483	4,160	2,460	4,005	4,110	1,920	17	481
3.0	18.5020	3,520	4,460	2,880	4,370	4,630	2,101	13	488
2.775	20.0000	3,557	4,750	3,300	4,760	5,190	2,270	9	496
2.5	22.2024	3,607	5,180	4,000	5,300	6,000	2,520	+4	506
2.0	27.7530	3,712	6,260	5,500	6,650	.....	3,060	−5	528
1.5	37.0040	.....	8,240	.....	8,530	.....	3,770	−13	532
1.0	55.506	.....	10,900	.....	11,670	.....	4,715	+11	518
0.5	111.012	.....	......	.....	......	.....	.....	77	495
0.25	222.02	.....	......	.....	......	.....	.....	129	......

HEATS OF SOLUTION

From National Standards Reference Data Systems NSRDS-NBS 2

Vivian B. Parker

ΔH°_∞ 25°C for uni-univalent electrolytes in H$_2$O

Substance	State	ΔH°_∞	Substance	State	ΔH°_∞	Substance	State	ΔH°_∞
		cal/mole			*cal/mole*			*cal/mole*
HF	g	−14,700	LiBr·2H$_2$O	c	−2,250	KCl	c	4,115
HCl	g	−17,888	LiBrO$_3$	c	340	KClO$_3$	c	9,890
HClO$_4$	l	−21,215	LiI	c	−15,130	KClO$_4$	c	12,200
HClO$_4$·H$_2$O	c	−7,875	LiI·H$_2$O	c	−7,090	KBr	c	4,750
HBr	g	−20,350	LiI·2H$_2$O	c	−3,530	KBrO$_3$	c	9,830
HI	g	−19,520	LiI·3H$_2$O	c	140	KI	c	4,860
HIO$_3$	c	2,100	LiNO$_2$	c	−2,630	KIO$_3$	c	6,630
HNO$_3$	l	−7,954	LiNO$_2$·H$_2$O	c	1,680	KNO$_2$	c	3,190
HCOOH	l	−205	LiNO$_3$	c	−600	KNO$_3$	c	8,340
CH$_3$COOH	l	−360				KC$_2$H$_3$O$_2$	c	−3,665
			NaOH	c	−10,637	KCN	c	2,800
NH$_3$	g	−7,290	NaOH·H$_2$O	c	−5,118	KCNO	c	4,840
NH$_4$Cl	c	3,533	NaF	c	218	KCNS	c	5,790
NH$_4$ClO$_4$	c	8,000	NaCl	c	928	KMnO$_4$	c	10,410
NH$_4$Br	c	4,010	NaClO$_2$	c	80			
NH$_4$I	c	3,280	NaClO$_2$·3H$_2$O	c	6,830	RbOH	c	−14,900
NH$_4$IO$_3$	c	7,600	NaClO$_3$	c	5,191	RbOH·H$_2$O	c	−4,310
NH$_4$NO$_2$	c	4,600	NaClO$_4$	c	3,317	RbOH·2H$_2$O	c	210
NH$_4$NO$_3$	c	6,140	NaClO$_4$·H$_2$O	c	5,380	RbF	c	−6,240
NH$_4$C$_2$H$_3$O$_2$	c	−570	NaBr	c	−144	RbF·H$_2$O	c	−100
NH$_4$CN	c	4,200	NaBr·2H$_2$O	c	4,454	RbF·1½H$_2$O	c	320
NH$_4$CNS	c	5,400	NaBrO$_3$	c	6,430	RbCl	c	4,130
CH$_3$NH$_3$Cl	c	1,378	NaI	c	−1,800	RbClO$_3$	c	11,410
(CH$_3$)$_2$NHCl	c	350	NaI·2H$_2$O	c	3,855	RbClO$_4$	c	13,560
N(CH$_3$)$_4$Cl	c	975	NaIO$_3$	c	4,850	RbBr	c	5,230
N(CH$_3$)$_4$Br	c	5,800	NaNO$_2$	c	3,320	RbBrO$_3$	c	11,700
N(CH$_3$)$_4$I	c	10,055	NaNO$_3$	c	4,900	RbI	c	6,000
			NaC$_2$H$_3$O$_2$	c	−4,140	RbNO$_3$	c	8,720
AgClO$_4$	c	1,760	NaC$_2$H$_3$O$_2$·3H$_2$O	c	4,700			
AgNO$_2$	c	8,830	NaCN	c	290	CsOH	c	−17,100
AgNO$_3$	c	5,400	NaCN·½H$_2$O	c	790	CsOH·H$_2$O	c	−4,900
			NaCN·2H$_2$O	c	4,440	CsF	c	−8,810
LiOH	c	−5,632	NaCNO	c	4,590	CsF·H$_2$O	c	−2,500
LiOH·H$_2$O	c	−1,600	NaCNS	c	1,632	CsF·1½H$_2$O	c	−1,300
LiF	c	1,130				CsCl	c	4,250
LiCl	c	−8,850	KOH	c	−13,769	CsClO$_4$	c	13,250
LiCl·H$_2$O	c	−4,560	KOH·H$_2$O	c	−3,500	CsBr	c	6,210
LiClO$_4$	c	−6,345	KOH·1½H$_2$O	c	−2,500	CsBrO$_3$	c	12,060
LiClO$_4$·3H$_2$O	c	7,795	KF	c	−4,238	CsI	c	7,970
LiBr	c	−11,670	KF·2H$_2$O	c	1,666	CsNO$_3$	c	9,560
LiBr·H$_2$O	c	−5,560						

HEAT CAPACITY OF AQUEOUS SOLUTIONS OF VARIOUS ACIDS

From National Standards Reference Data Systems NSRDS-NBS 2

Vivian B. Parker

Φ_C is the apparent molal heat capacity of the solute, equal to $[(1000 + mM_2)C - 1000C°]/m$ where C and C° are the specific heats (per unit mass) of the solution and pure solvent, respectively, m is the molality, and M_2 is the molecular weight of the solute.

Φ_C, cal/deg mole, at 25°C

n	m	HF	HCl	HBr	HI	HIO₃	HNO₃	CH₂O₂	C₂H₄O₂	C₃H₆O₂
∞	0.00	−25.5	−32.6	−33.9	−34.0	−29.6	−20.7	−21.0	−1.5	+26.7
500,000	.000111	−23.0	.....	.....	.....	.....	.....	−9.8	+25.8	38.0
100,000	.000555	−18.8	−32.4	−33.8	−33.9	−29.4	−20.6	−1.2	32.6	45.1
50,000	.00111	−16.6	−32.4	−33.7	−33.8	−29.3	−20.5	+3.1	34.0	48.3
20,000	.00278	−12.4	−32.3	−33.6	−33.7	−29.1	−20.4	10.2	35.7	52.2
10,000	.00555	−8.6	−32.2	−33.4	−33.5	−28.5	−20.3	12.7	36.9	54.1
7,000	.00793	−6.7	−32.1	−33.4	−33.4	−28.4	−20.2	13.7	37.4	54.8
5,000	.01110	−4.9	−32.0	−33.3	−33.3	−28.1	−20.1	14.3	37.8	55.3
4,000	.01388	−3.6	−31.9	−33.2	−33.2	−27.7	−20.1	14.7	37.9	55.6
3,000	.01850	−2.2	−31.8	−33.1	−33.1	−27.2	−20.0	15.1	38.1	56.1
2,000	.02775	−0.5	−31.6	−32.9	−32.9	−25.8	−19.8	15.8	38.5	56.7
1,500	.03700	+0.4	−31.4	−32.7	−32.7	−24.9	−19.6	16.4	38.7	57.1
1,000	.05551	1.6	−31.2	−32.5	−32.5	−23.0	−19.3	16.8	39.0	57.7
900	.0617	1.8	−31.2	−32.4	−32.4	−22.3	−19.2	17.0	39.0	57.8
800	.0694	2.0	−31.1	−32.3	−32.3	−21.5	−19.1	17.2	39.1	57.9
700	.0793	2.2	−30.9	−32.2	−32.1	−20.2	−19.0	17.3	39.2	58.0
600	.0925	2.4	−30.8	−32.1	−32.0	−18.7	−18.9	17.5	39.3	58.3
500	.1110	2.7	−30.6	−31.9	−31.7	−16.7	−18.7	17.7	39.4	58.4
400	.1388	2.8	−30.3	−31.6	−31.4	−13.9	−18.4	18.0	39.4	58.6
300	.1850	3.2	−30.0	−31.2	−30.9	−10.1	−17.9	18.3	39.4	58.8
200	.2775	3.3	−29.3	−30.6	−30.2	−4.7	−17.2	18.7	39.3	58.9
150	.3700	3.5	−28.8	−30.1	−29.6	−0.7	−16.4	18.9	39.2	58.8
100	.5551	3.8	−27.8	−29.1	−28.4	+4.8	−15.0	19.0	39.1	58.7
75	.7401	4.1	−27.0	−28.5	−27.5	9.2	−13.7	19.2	38.9	58.6
50	1.1101	4.5	−25.6	−26.8	−25.9	15.7	−11.5	19.8	38.6	58.3
40	1.3877	4.9	−24.8	−25.9	−24.8	19.0	−9.9	19.8	38.4	58.0
30	1.8502	5.3	−23.6	−24.5	−23.3	23.1	−7.3	20.0	38.0	57.1
25	2.2202	5.6	−22.7	−23.6	−22.2	25.7	−5.4	20.1	37.7	56.2
20	2.7753	5.7	−21.5	−22.2	−20.8	.....	−2.7	20.2	37.1	55.0
15	3.7004	6.0	−19.8	−20.3	.....	.....	+1.4	20.4	36.3	53.1
12	4.6255	6.2	−18.2	−18.5	.....	.....	5.0	20.4	35.4	51.3
10	5.5506	6.3	−16.8	−16.8	.....	.....	8.5	20.6	34.8	49.7
9.5	5.8427	6.4	−16.4	−16.3	.....	.....	9.2	20.6	34.7	.....
9.0	6.1674	6.4	−15.8	−15.7	.....	.....	10.3	20.6	34.5	.....
8.5	6.5301	6.5	−15.4	−15.1	.....	.....	11.4	20.7	34.4	.....
8.0	6.9383	6.6	−14.8	−14.4	.....	.....	12.5	20.7	34.2	.....
7.5	7.4008	6.7	−14.2	−13.2	.....	.....	13.7	20.8	34.0	.....
7.0	7.9295	6.9	−13.5	−12.7	.....	.....	14.9	20.8	33.8	.....
6.5	8.5394	7.0	−12.7	−11.9	.....	.....	16.1	20.8	33.5	.....
6.0	9.2510	7.1	−11.8	−10.8	.....	.....	17.1	20.9	33.3	.....
5.5	10.0920	7.2	−10.8	−9.6	.....	.....	18.3	20.9	33.0	.....
5.0	11.1012	7.3	−9.6	−8.2	.....	.....	19.3	21.0	32.8	.....
4.5	12.3346	7.4	−8.7	−6.8	.....	.....	20.4	21.1	32.5	.....
4.0	13.8765	7.5	−6.6	−5.5	.....	.....	21.3	21.2	32.2	.....
3.5	15.8509	7.6	−4.7	−4.0	.....	.....	22.1	21.3	31.8	.....
3.25	17.0788	7.6	.....	−3.2	.....	.....	22.6	21.4	31.7	.....
3.0	18.5020	7.7	.....	−2.3	.....	.....	23.0	21.5	31.5	.....
2.5	22.2024	7.8	.....	−0.4	.....	.....	23.8	21.6	31.2	.....
2.0	27.7530	7.9	.....	.....	.....	.....	24.6	21.7	30.8	.....
1.5	37.0040	.....	.....	.....	.....	.....	25.2	21.8	30.4	.....
1.0	55.506	.....	.....	.....	.....	.....	25.7	22.0	30.1	.....

THERMODYNAMIC FORMULAS

Compiled by Doctor E. A. Coomes

Legend:
- p = Pressure
- V = Volume
- T = Temperature
- n = Number of mols
- S = Entropy
- U = Internal energy (some books use E)
- C_p = Molal specific heat at constant pressure
- β = Coefficient volume expansion
- K = Compressibility
- $H = U + pV$ = Total heat or enthalpy
- $A = U - TS$ = Helmholtz free energy
- $G = H - TS$ = Gibbs' free energy (some books use F).

Use of Table.—Partial derivatives of the first order for the eight fundamental thermodynamic variables, namely, p, V, T, U, S, H, A, G, may be obtained in terms of $(\partial V/\partial T)_p$, $(\partial V/\partial p)_T$, and $(\partial H/\partial T)_p$; the latter three are connected to measurable quantities as follows:

$$\frac{1}{V}\left(\frac{\partial V}{\partial T}\right)_p = \beta; \quad -\frac{1}{V}\left(\frac{\partial V}{\partial p}\right)_T = K; \quad \left(\frac{\partial H}{\partial T}\right)_p = nC_p$$

Computation by the Table.—The method of using the table will become apparent in working several examples. Suppose it is desired to know $(\partial H/\partial p)_S$ in terms of p, V, and T. Under caption "Constant" move horizontally to column marked "S"; across from "H" beside caption "differential" find "$-VnC_p/T$." Across from "p" in column "S" find "$-nC_p/T$"; $(\partial H/\partial p)_S$ is found by taking the ratio of the two:

$$(\partial H/\partial p)_S = (-VnC_p/T)/(-nC_p/T) = V$$

To find $(\partial S/\partial V)_T$ in terms of p, V, T, move to column "T" under "constant." Opposite "S" beside "differential" find "$(\partial V/\partial T)_p$"; opposite "V" find "$-(\partial V/\partial p)_T$."

Taking the ratio:

$$(\partial S/\partial V)_T = (\partial V/\partial T)_p/-(\partial V/\partial p)_T = (\partial p/\partial T)_V.$$

THERMODYNAMIC FORMULAS (Continued)

(First table — Differential vs. Constant T, p, V, S)

Differential	Constant T	Constant p	Constant V	Constant S
T	0	1	$\left(\frac{\partial V}{\partial p}\right)_T$	$-\left(\frac{\partial V}{\partial T}\right)_p$
p	-1	0	$-\left(\frac{\partial V}{\partial T}\right)_p$	$-\dfrac{nC_p}{T}$
V	$-\left(\frac{\partial V}{\partial p}\right)_T$	$\left(\frac{\partial V}{\partial T}\right)_p$	0	$\left(-\frac{1}{T}\right)\left[nC_p\left(\frac{\partial V}{\partial p}\right)_T + T\left(\frac{\partial V}{\partial T}\right)_p^2\right]$
S	$\left(\frac{\partial V}{\partial T}\right)_p$	$\dfrac{nC_p}{T}$	$\left(\frac{1}{T}\right)\left[nC_p\left(\frac{\partial V}{\partial p}\right)_T + T\left(\frac{\partial V}{\partial T}\right)_p^2\right]$	0
U	$T\left(\frac{\partial V}{\partial T}\right)_p + p\left(\frac{\partial V}{\partial p}\right)_T$	$nC_p - p\left(\frac{\partial V}{\partial T}\right)_p$	$nC_p\left(\frac{\partial V}{\partial p}\right)_T + T\left(\frac{\partial V}{\partial T}\right)_p^2$	$\left(\frac{p}{T}\right)\left[nC_p\left(\frac{\partial V}{\partial p}\right)_T + T\left(\frac{\partial V}{\partial T}\right)_p^2\right]$
H	$-V + T\left(\frac{\partial V}{\partial T}\right)_p$	nC_p	$nC_p\left(\frac{\partial V}{\partial p}\right)_T + T\left(\frac{\partial V}{\partial T}\right)_p^2 - V\left(\frac{\partial V}{\partial T}\right)$	$-\dfrac{VnC_p}{T}$
A	$p\left(\frac{\partial V}{\partial p}\right)_T$	$-S - p\left(\frac{\partial V}{\partial T}\right)_p$	$-S\left(\frac{\partial V}{\partial p}\right)_T$	$\left(\frac{1}{T}\right)\left[pnC_p\left(\frac{\partial V}{\partial p}\right)_T + pT\left(\frac{\partial V}{\partial T}\right)_p^2 + TS\left(\frac{\partial V}{\partial T}\right)_p\right]$
G	$-V$	$-S$	$-V\left(\frac{\partial V}{\partial T}\right)_p - S\left(\frac{\partial V}{\partial p}\right)_T$	$\left(-\frac{1}{T}\right)\left[nC_pV - TS\left(\frac{\partial V}{\partial T}\right)_p\right]$

(Second table — Differential vs. Constant U, H, A, G)

Differential	Constant U	Constant H	Constant A	Constant G
T	$-T\left(\frac{\partial V}{\partial T}\right)_p - p\left(\frac{\partial V}{\partial p}\right)_T$	$V - T\left(\frac{\partial V}{\partial T}\right)_p$	$-p\left(\frac{\partial V}{\partial p}\right)_T$	V
p	$-nC_p + p\left(\frac{\partial V}{\partial T}\right)_p$	$-nC_p$	$S + p\left(\frac{\partial V}{\partial T}\right)_p$	S
V	$-nC_p\left(\frac{\partial V}{\partial p}\right)_T - T\left(\frac{\partial V}{\partial T}\right)_p^2$	$-nC_p\left(\frac{\partial V}{\partial p}\right)_T - T\left(\frac{\partial V}{\partial T}\right)_p^2 + V\left(\frac{\partial V}{\partial T}\right)_p$	$S\left(\frac{\partial V}{\partial p}\right)_T$	$V\left(\frac{\partial V}{\partial T}\right)_p + S\left(\frac{\partial V}{\partial p}\right)_T$
S	$\left(-\frac{p}{T}\right)\left[nC_p\left(\frac{\partial V}{\partial p}\right)_T + T\left(\frac{\partial V}{\partial T}\right)_p^2\right]$	$\dfrac{VnC_p}{T}$	$\left(-\frac{1}{T}\right)\left[pnC_p\left(\frac{\partial V}{\partial p}\right)_T + pT\left(\frac{\partial V}{\partial T}\right)_p^2 + TS\left(\frac{\partial V}{\partial T}\right)_p\right]$	$\left(\frac{1}{T}\right)\left[nC_pV - TS\left(\frac{\partial V}{\partial T}\right)_p\right]$
U	0	$V\left[nC_p - p\left(\frac{\partial V}{\partial T}\right)_p\right] + p\left[nC_p\left(\frac{\partial V}{\partial p}\right)_T + T\left(\frac{\partial V}{\partial T}\right)_p^2\right]$	$-p\left[nC_p\left(\frac{\partial V}{\partial p}\right)_T + T\left(\frac{\partial V}{\partial T}\right)_p^2\right] - S\left[T\left(\frac{\partial V}{\partial T}\right)_p + p\left(\frac{\partial V}{\partial p}\right)_T\right]$	$V\left[nC_p - p\left(\frac{\partial V}{\partial T}\right)_p\right] - S\left[T\left(\frac{\partial V}{\partial T}\right)_p + p\left(\frac{\partial V}{\partial p}\right)_T\right]$
H	$-V\left[nC_p - p\left(\frac{\partial V}{\partial T}\right)_p\right] - p\left[nC_p\left(\frac{\partial V}{\partial p}\right)_T + T\left(\frac{\partial V}{\partial T}\right)_p^2\right]$	0	$\left[S + p\left(\frac{\partial V}{\partial T}\right)_p\right] \times \left[V - T\left(\frac{\partial V}{\partial T}\right)_p - pnC_p\left(\frac{\partial V}{\partial p}\right)_T\right]$	$VnC_p + VS - TS\left(\frac{\partial V}{\partial T}\right)_p$
A	$p\left[nC_p\left(\frac{\partial V}{\partial p}\right)_T + T\left(\frac{\partial V}{\partial T}\right)_p^2\right] + S\left[T\left(\frac{\partial V}{\partial T}\right)_p + p\left(\frac{\partial V}{\partial p}\right)_T\right]$	$-\left[S + p\left(\frac{\partial V}{\partial T}\right)_p\right] \times \left[V - T\left(\frac{\partial V}{\partial T}\right)_p - pnC_p\left(\frac{\partial V}{\partial p}\right)_T\right]$	0	$-S\left[V + p\left(\frac{\partial V}{\partial p}\right)_T\right] + pV\left(\frac{\partial V}{\partial T}\right)_p$
G	$-V\left[nC_p - p\left(\frac{\partial V}{\partial T}\right)_p\right] + S\left[T\left(\frac{\partial V}{\partial T}\right)_p + p\left(\frac{\partial V}{\partial p}\right)_T\right]$	$-VnC_p - VS + TS\left(\frac{\partial V}{\partial T}\right)_p$	$S\left[V + p\left(\frac{\partial V}{\partial p}\right)_T\right] + pV\left(\frac{\partial V}{\partial T}\right)_p$	0

LIMITS OF INFLAMMABILITY

Reprinted from "Combustion Flame and Explosions of Gases," B. Lewis and G. von Elbe, authors, Academic Press (1951), publishers, by special permission.

The limits of inflammability given in the following tables were all determined at atmospheric pressure and room* temperature for upward propagation in a tube or bomb 2 inches or more in diameter. Values are on a percentage-by-volume basis.

LIMITS OF INFLAMMABILITY OF GASES AND VAPORS IN AIR

| Compound | Empirical formula | Limits of inflammability | | Compound | Empirical formula | Limits of inflammability | |
		Lower	Upper			Lower	Upper
Paraffin hydrocarbons				**Acids**			
Methane	CH_4	5.00	15.00	Acetic acid	$C_2H_4O_2$	5.40	.....
Ethane	C_2H_6	3.00	12.50	Hydrocyanic acid	HCN	5.60	40.00
Propane	C_3H_8	2.12	9.35	**Esters**			
Butane	C_4H_{10}	1.86	8.41	Methyl formate	$C_2H_4O_2$	5.05	22.70
Isobutane	C_4H_{10}	1.80	8.44	Ethyl formate	$C_3H_6O_2$	2.75	16.40
Pentane	C_5H_{12}	1.40	7.80	Methyl acetate	$C_3H_6O_2$	3.15	15.60
Isopentane	C_5H_{12}	1.32	.....	Ethyl acetate	$C_4H_8O_2$	2.18	11.40
2,2-Dimethylpropane	C_5H_{12}	1.38	7.50	Propyl acetate	$C_5H_{10}O_2$	1.77	8.00
Hexane	C_6H_{14}	1.18	7.40	Isopropyl acetate	$C_5H_{10}O_2$	1.78	7.80
Heptane	C_7H_{16}	1.10	6.70	Butyl acetate	$C_6H_{12}O_2$	1.39	7.55
2,3-Dimethylpentane	C_7H_{16}	1.12	6.75	Amyl acetate	$C_7H_{14}O_2$	1.10	.....
Octane	C_8H_{18}	0.95	.....	**Hydrogen**			
Nonane	C_9H_{20}	0.83	.....	Hydrogen	H_2	4.00	74.20
Decane	$C_{10}H_{22}$	0.77	5.35	**Nitrogen compounds**			
Olefins				Ammonia	NH_3	15.50	27.00
Ethylene	C_2H_4	2.75	28.60	Cyanogen	C_2N_2	6.60	42.60
Propylene	C_3H_6	2.00	11.10	Pyridine	C_5H_5N	1.81	12.40
Butene-1	C_4H_8	1.65	9.95	Ethyl nitrate	$C_2H_5NO_3$	3.80	.....
Butene-2	C_4H_8	1.75	9.70	Ethyl nitrite	$C_2H_5NO_2$	3.01	50.00
Amylene	C_5H_{10}	1.42	8.70	**Oxides**			
Acetylenes				Carbon monoxide	CO	12.50	74.20
Acetylene	C_2H_2	2.50	80.00	Ethylene oxide	C_2H_4O	3.00	80.00
Aromatics				Propylene oxide	C_3H_6O	2.00	22.00
Benzene	C_6H_6	1.40	7.10	Dioxan	$C_4H_8O_2$	1.97	22.25
Toluene	C_7H_8	1.27	6.75	Diethyl peroxide	$C_4H_{10}O_2$	2.34	.....
o-Xylene	C_8H_{10}	1.00	6.00	**Sulfides**			
Cyclic hydrocarbons				Carbon disulfide	CS_2	1.25	50.00
Cyclopropane	C_3H_6	2.40	10.40	Hydrogen sulfide	H_2S	4.30	45.50
Cyclohexane	C_6H_{12}	1.26	7.75	Carbon oxysulfide	COS	11.90	28.50
Methylcyclohexane	C_7H_{14}	1.15	.....	**Chlorides**			
Terpenes				Methyl chloride	CH_3Cl	8.25	18.70
Turpentine	$C_{10}H_{16}$	0.80	.....	Ethyl chloride	C_2H_5Cl	4.00	14.80
Alcohols				Propyl chloride	C_3H_7Cl	2.60	11.10
Methyl alcohol	CH_4O	6.72	36.50	Butyl chloride	C_4H_9Cl	1.85	10.10
Ethyl alcohol	C_2H_6O	3.28	18.95	Isobutyl chloride	C_4H_9Cl	2.05	8.75
Allyl alcohol	C_3H_6O	2.50	18.00	Allyl chloride	C_3H_5Cl	3.28	11.15
n-Propyl alcohol	C_3H_8O	2.15	13.50	Amyl chloride	$C_5H_{11}Cl$	1.60	8.63
Isopropyl alcohol	C_3H_8O	2.02	11.80	Vinyl chloride	C_2H_3Cl	4.00	21.70
n-Butyl alcohol	$C_4H_{10}O$	1.45	11.25	Ethylene dichloride	$C_2H_4Cl_2$	6.20	15.90
Isobutyl alcohol	$C_4H_{10}O$	1.68	.....	Propylene dichloride	$C_3H_6Cl_2$	3.40	14.50
n-Amyl alcohol	$C_5H_{12}O$	1.19	.....	**Bromides**			
Isoamyl alcohol	$C_5H_{12}O$	1.20	.....	Methyl bromide	CH_3Br	13.50	14.50
Aldehydes				Ethyl bromide	C_2H_5Br	6.75	11.25
Acetaldehyde	C_2H_4O	3.97	57.00	Allyl bromide	C_3H_5Br	4.36	7.25
Crotonic aldehyde	C_4H_6O	2.12	15.50	**Amines**			
Furfural	$C_5H_4O_2$	2.10	.....	Methyl amine	CH_5N	4.95	20.75
Paraldehyde	$C_6H_{12}O_3$	1.30	.....	Ethyl amine	C_2H_7N	3.55	13.95
Ethers				Dimethyl amine	C_2H_7N	2.80	14.40
Methylethyl ether	C_3H_8O	2.00	10.00	Propyl amine	C_3H_9N	2.01	10.35
Diethyl ether	$C_4H_{10}O$	1.85	36.50	Diethyl amine	$C_4H_{11}N$	1.77	10.10
Divinyl ether	C_4H_6O	1.70	27.00	Trimethyl amine	C_3H_9N	2.00	11.60
Ketones				Triethyl amine	$C_6H_{15}N$	1.25	7.90
Acetone	C_3H_6O	2.55	12.80				
Methylethyl ketone	C_4H_8O	1.81	9.50				
Methylpropyl ketone	$C_5H_{10}O$	1.55	8.15				
Methylbutyl ketone	$C_6H_{12}O$	1.35	7.60				

* The upper limits of some vapors were determined at somewhat higher temperatures because of their low vapor pressures.

LIMITS OF INFLAMMABILITY OF GASES AND VAPORS IN OXYGEN

Compound	Formula	Limits of inflammability	
		Lower	Upper
Hydrogen	H_2	4.65	93.9
Deuterium	D_2	5.00	95.0
Carbon monoxide	CO	15.50	93.9
Methane	CH_4	5.40	59.2
Ethane	C_2H_6	4.10	50.5
Ethylene	C_2H_4	2.90	79.9
Propylene	C_3H_6	2.10	52.8
Cyclopropane	C_3H_6	2.45	63.1
Ammonia	NH_3	13.50	79.0
Diethyl ether	$C_4H_{10}O$	2.10	82.0
Divinyl ether	C_4H_6O	1.85	85.5

LIMITS FOR HUMAN EXPOSURE TO AIR CONTAMINANTS

From United States Federal Register
Volume 36, Number 105

Exposures by inhalation, ingestion, skin absorption, or contact to any material or substance (1) at a concentration above those specified in the "Threshold Limit Values of Airborne Contaminants for 1970" of the American Conference of Governmental Industrial Hygienists, listed in Table 1, except for the American National Standards listed in Table 2 of this section and except for values of mineral dusts listed in Table 3 of this section, and (2) concentrations above those specified in Table 1, 2, and 3 of this section, shall be avoided, or protective equipment shall be provided and used.

Table 1

Substance	ppm[a]	mg/M³[b]	Substance	ppm[a]	mg/M³[b]
Abate		15	2-Butanone	200	590
Acetaldehyde	200	360	2-Butoxy ethanol (Butyl Cel-		
Acetic acid	10	25	losolve)–Skin	50	240
Acetic anhydride	5	20	Butyl acetate (n -butyl acetate)	150	710
Acetone	1,000	2,400	sec-Butyl acetate	200	950
Acetonitrile	40	70	tert-Butyl acetate	200	950
Acetylene dichloride, see 1,2-			Butyl alcohol	100	300
Dichloroethylene			sec-Butyl alcohol	150	450
Acetylene tetrabromide	1	14	tert-Butyl alcohol	100	300
Acrolein	0.1	0.25	C Butylamine–Skin	5	15
Acrylamide–Skin		0.3	C tert-Butyl chromate (as CrO₃)–		
Acrylonitrile–Skin	20	45	Skin		0.1
Aldrin–Skin		0.25	n-Butyl glycidyl ether (BGE)	50	270
Allyl alcohol–Skin	2	5	*Butyl mercaptan	0.5	1.5
Allyl chloride	1	3	p-tert-Butyltoluene	10	60
**C Allyl glycidyl ether (AGE)	10	45	Calcium arsenate		1
Allyl propyl disulfide	2	12	Calcium oxide		5
2-Aminoethanol, see Ethanol-			**Camphor (Synthetic)	2	
amine			Carbaryl (Sevin®)		5
2-Aminopyridine	0.5	2	Carbon black		3.5
**Ammonia	50	35	Carbon dioxide	5,000	9,000
Ammonium sulfamate (Ammate)		15	Carbon monoxide	50	55
n-Amyl acetate	100	525	Chlordane–Skin		0.5
sec-Amyl acetate	125	650	Chlorinated camphene–Skin		0.5
Aniline–Skin	5	19	Chlorinated diphenyl oxide		0.5
Anisidine (o,p-isomers)–Skin		0.5	*Chlorine	1	3
Antimony and compounds (as Sb)		0.5	Chlorine dioxide	0.1	0.3
ANTU (alpha naphthyl thiourea)		0.3	C Chlorine trifluoride	0.1	0.4
Arsenic and compounds (as As)		0.5	C Chloroacetaldehyde	1	3
Arsine	0.05	0.2	α-Chloroacetophenone (phenacyl-		
Azinphos-methyl–Skin		0.2	chloride)	0.05	0.3
Barium (soluble compounds)		0.5	Chlorobenzene (monochloroben-		
p-Benzoquinone, see Quinone			zene)	75	350
Benzoyl peroxide		5	o-Chlorobenzylidene malononi-		
Benzyl chloride	1	5	trile (OCBM)	0.05	0.4
Biphenyl, see Diphenyl			Chlorobromomethane	200	1,050
Bisphenol A, see Diglycidyl ether			2-Chloro-1,3-butadiene, see		
Boron oxide		15	Chloroprene		
Boron tribromide	1	10	Chlorodiphenyl (42 percent		
C Boron trifluoride	1	3	Chlorine)–Skin		1
Bromine	0.1	0.7	Chlorodiphenyl (54 percent		
*Bromine pentafluoride	0.1	0.7	Chlorine)–Skin		0.5
Bromoform–Skin	0.5	5	1-Chloro-2,3-epoxypropane, see		
Butadiene (1,3-butadiene)	1,000	2,200	Epichlorhydrin		
Butanethiol, see Butyl mercaptan					

Table 1 (continued)

Substance	ppm[a]	mg/M³ [b]
2-Chloroethanol, see Ethylene chlorohydrin		
Chloroethylene, see Vinyl chloride		
C Chloroform (trichloromethane)	50	240
1-Chloro-1-nitropropane	20	100
Chloropicrin	0.1	0.7
Chloroprene (2-chloro-1,3-butadiene)–Skin	25	90
Chromium, sol. chromic, chromous salts as Cr		0.5
Metal and insol. salts		1
Coal tar pitch volatiles (benzene soluble fraction) anthracene, BaP, phenanthrene, acridine, chrysene, pyrene		0.2
Cobalt, metal fume and dust		0.1
Copper fume		0.1
Dusts and Mists		1
Cotton dust (raw)		1
Crag® herbicide		15
Cresol (all isomers)–Skin	5	22
Crotonaldehyde	2	6
Cumene–Skin	50	245
Cyanide (as CN)–Skin		5
*Cyanogen	100	
Cyclohexane	300	1,050
Cyclohexanol	50	200
Cyclohexanone	50	200
Cyclohexene	300	1,015
Cyclopentadiene	75	200
2,4-D		10
DDT–Skin		1
DDVP, see Dichlorvos		
Decaborane–Skin	0.05	0.3
Demeton®–Skin		0.1
Diacetone alcohol (4-hydroxy-4-methyl-2-pentanone)	50	240
1,2-Diaminoethane, see Ethylenediamine		
Diazomethane	0.2	0.4
Diborane	0.1	0.1
Dibutyl phosphate	1	5
Dibutylphthalate		5
*C Dichloroacetylene	0.1	0.4
C o-Dichlorobenzene	50	300
p-Dichlorobenzene	75	450
Dichlorodifluoromethane	1,000	4,950
1,3-Dichloro-5,5-dimethyl hydantoin		0.2
1,1-Dichloroethane	100	400
1,2-Dichloroethylene	200	790
C Dichloroethyl ether–Skin	15	90
Dichloromethane, see Methylenechloride		
Dichloromonofluoromethane	1,000	4,200
C 1,1-Dichloro-1-nitroethane	10	60
1,2-Dichloropropane, see Propylenedichloride		
Dichlorotetrafluoroethane	1,000	7,000
Dichlorvos (DDVP)–Skin		1
Dieldrin–Skin		0.25
Diethylamine	25	75
Diethylamino ethanol–Skin	10	50
**C Diethylene triamine–Skin	10	42
Diethylether, see Ethyl ether		
Difluorodibromomethane	100	860
C Diglycidyl ether (DGE)	0.5	2.8
Dihydroxybenzene, see Hydroquinone		
Diisobutyl ketone	50	290
Diisopropylamine–Skin	5	20
Dimethoxymethane, see Methylal		
Dimethyl acetamide–Skin	10	35
Dimethylamine	10	18
Dimethylaminobenzene, see Xylidene		
Dimethylaniline (N-dimethyl-aniline)–Skin	5	25
Dimethylbenzene, see Xylene		
Dimethyl 1,2-dibromo-2,2-dichloroethyl phosphate, (Dibrom)		3
Dimethylformamide–Skin	10	30
2,6-Dimethylheptanone, see Diisobutyl ketone		
1,1-Dimethylhydrazine–Skin	0.5	1
Dimethylphthalate		5
Dimethylsulfate–Skin	1	5
Dinitrobenzene (all isomers)–Skin		1
Dinitro-o-cresol–Skin		0.2
Dinitrotoluene–Skin		1.5
Dioxane (Diethylene dioxide)–Skin	100	360
Diphenyl	0.2	1
Diphenylamine		10
Diphenylmethane diisocyanate (see Methylene bisphenyl isocyanate (MDI)		
Dipropylene glycol methyl ether–Skin	100	600
Di-sec, octyl phthalate (Di-2-ethylhexylphthalate)		5
*Endosulfan (Thiodan®)–Skin		0.1
Endrin–Skin		0.1
Epichlorhydrin–Skin	5	19
EPN–Skin		0.5
1,2-Epoxypropane, see Propyleneoxide		
2,3-Epoxy-1-propanol, see Glycidol		
Ethanethiol, see Ethylmercaptan		
Ethanolamine	3	6
2-Ethoxyethanol–Skin	200	740
2-Ethoxyethylacetate (Cellosolve acetate)–Skin	100	540
Ethyl acetate	400	1,400
Ethyl acrylate–Skin	25	100
Ethyl alcohol (ethanol)	1,000	1,900
Ethylamine	10	18

Table 1 (continued)

Substance	ppm[a]	mg/M³ [b]	Substance	ppm[a]	mg/M³ [b]
Ethyl sec-amyl ketone (5-methyl-3-heptanone)	25	130	Isoamyl alcohol	100	360
Ethyl benzene	100	435	Isobutyl acetate	150	700
Ethyl bromide	200	890	Isobutyl alcohol	100	300
Ethyl butyl ketone (3-Heptanone)	50	230	Isophorone	25	140
Ethyl chloride	1,000	2,600	Isopropyl acetate	250	950
Ethyl ether	400	1,200	Isopropyl alcohol	400	980
Ethyl formate	100	300	Isopropylamine	5	12
Ethyl mercaptan	0.5	1	Isopropylether	500	2,100
Ethyl silicate	100	850	Isopropyl glycidyl ether (IGE)	50	240
Ethylene chlorohydrin–Skin	5	16	Ketene	0.5	0.9
Ethylenediamine	10	25	Lead arsenate		0.15
Ethylene dibromide, see 1,2-Dibromoethane			Lindane–Skin		0.5
			Lithium hydride		0.025
Ethylene dichloride, see 1,2-Dichloroethane			L.P.G. (liquefied petroleum gas)	1,000	1,800
			Magnesium oxide fume		15
C Ethylene glycol dinitrate and/or Nitroglycerin–Skin	[d]0.2		Malathion–Skin		15
			Maleic anhydride	0.25	1
Ethylene glycol monomethyl ether acetate, see Methyl cellosolve acetate			C Manganese and compounds, as Mn		5
			Mesityl oxide	25	100
Ethylene imine–Skin	0.5	1	Methanethiol, see Methyl mercaptan		
Ethylene oxide	50	90	Methoxychlor		15
Ethylidine chloride, see 1,1-Dichloroethane			2-Methoxyethanol, see Methyl cellosolve		
N-Ethylmorpholine–Skin	20	94	Methyl acetate	200	610
Ferbam		15	Methyl acetylene (propyne)	1,000	1,650
Ferrovanadium dust		1	Methyl acetylene-propadiene mixture (MAPP)	1,000	1,800
Fluoride (as F)		2.5			
Fluorine	0.1	0.2	Methyl acrylate–Skin	10	35
Fluorotrichloromethane	1,000	5,600	Methylal (dimethoxymethane)	1,000	3,100
Formic acid	5	9	Methyl alcohol (methanol)	200	260
Furfural–Skin	5	20	Methylamine	10	12
Furfuryl alcohol	50	200	Methyl amyl alcohol, see Methyl isobutyl carbinol		
Glycidol (2,3-Epoxy-1-propanol)	50	150	*Methyl isoamyl ketone	100	475
Glycol monoethyl ether, see 2-Ethoxyethanol			Methyl (n-amyl) ketone (2-Heptanone)	100	465
Guthion®, see Azinphosmethyl					
Hafnium		0.5	C Methyl bromide–Skin	20	80
Heptachlor–Skin		0.5	Methyl butyl ketone, see 2-Hexanone		
Heptane (n-heptane)	500	2,000			
Hexachloroethane–Skin	1	10	Methyl cellosolve–Skin	25	80
Hexachloronaphthalene–Skin		0.2	Methyl cellosolve acetate–Skin	25	120
Hexane (n-hexane)	500	1,800	Methyl chloroform	350	1,900
2-Hexanone	100	410	Methylcyclohexane	500	2,000
Hexone (Methyl isobutyl ketone)	100	410	Methylcyclohexanol	100	470
sec-Hexyl acetate	50	300	o-Methylcyclohexanone–Skin	100	460
Hydrazine–Skin	1	1.3	Methyl ethyl ketone (MEK), see 2-Butanone		
Hydrogen bromide	3	10			
C Hydrogen chloride	5	7	Methyl formate	100	250
Hydrogen cyanide–Skin	10	11	Methyl iodide–Skin	5	28
Hydrogen peroxide	1	1.4	Methyl isobutyl carbinol–Skin	25	100
Hydrogen selenide	0.05	0.2	Methyl isobutyl ketone, see Hexone		
Hydroquinone		2			
*Indene	10	45	Methyl isocyanate–Skin	0.02	0.05
Indium and compounds, as In		0.1	*Methyl mercaptan	0.5	1
C Iodine	0.1	1	Methyl methacrylate	100	410
Iron oxide fume		10	Methyl propyl ketone, see 2-Pentanone		
Iron salts, soluble, as Fe		1			
Isoamyl acetate	100	525	C Methyl silicate	5	30

Table 1 (continued)

Substance	ppm[a]	mg/M³[b]	Substance	ppm[a]	mg/M³[b]
C α-Methyl styrene	100	480	TEPP–Skin		0.05
C Methylene bisphenyl isocyanate			C Terphenyls	1	9
(MDI)	0.02	0.2	1,1,1,2 Tetrachloro-2,2-difluoro-		
Molybdenum:			ethane	500	4,170
Soluble compounds		5	1,1,2,2-Tetrachloro-1,2-difluoro-		
Insoluble compounds		15	ethane	500	4,170
Monomethyl aniline–Skin	2	9	1,1,2,2-Tetrachloroethane–Skin	5	35
C Monomethyl hydrazine–Skin	0.2	0.35	Tetrachloroethylene, see Per-		
Morpholine–Skin	20	70	chloroethylene		
Naphtha (coaltar)	100	400	Tetrachloromethane, see Carbon		
Naphthalene	10	50	tetrachloride		
Nickel carbonyl	0.001	0.007	Tetrachloronaphthalene–Skin		2
Nickel, metal and soluble cmpds,			Tetraethyl lead (as Pb)–Skin		f0.100
as Ni		1	Tetrahydrofuran	200	590
Nicotine–Skin		0.5	Tetramethyl lead (as Pb)–Skin		f0.150
Nitric acid	2	5	Tetramethyl succinonitrile–Skin	0.5	3
Nitric oxide	25	30	Tetranitromethane	1	8
p-Nitroaniline–Skin	1	6	Tetryl (2,4,6-trinitrophenyl-		
Nitrobenzene–Skin	1	5	methylnitramine)–Skin		1.5
p-Nitrochlorobenzene–Skin		1	Thallium (soluble compounds)–		
Nitroethane	100	310	Skin as T1		0.1
Nitrogen dioxide	5	9	Thiram		5
Nitrogen trifluoride	10	29	Tin (inorganic cmpds, except		
Nitroglycerin–Skin	0.2	2	SnH_4 and SnO_2)		2
Nitromethane	100	250	Tin (organic cmpds)		0.1
1-Nitropropane	25	90	C Toluene-2,4-diisocyanate	0.02	0.14
2-Nitropropane	25	90	o-Toluidine–Skin	5	22
Nitrotoluene–Skin	5	30	Toxaphene, see Chlorinated		
Nitrotrichloromethane, see			camphene		
Chloropicrin			Tributyl phosphate		5
Octachloronaphthalene–Skin		0.1	1,1,1-Trichloroethane (see		
*Octane	400	1,900	Methyl chloroform		
*Oil mist, particulate		5	1,1,2-Trichloroethane–Skin	10	45
Osmium tetroxide		0.002	Parathion–Skin		0.1
Oxalic acid		1	Pentaborane	0.005	0.01
Oxygen difluoride	0.05	0.1	Pentachloronaphthalene–Skin		0.5
Ozone	0.1	0.2	Pentachlorophenol–Skin		0.5
Paraquat–Skin		0.5	*Pentane	500	1,500
Silver, metal and soluble com-			2-Pentanone	200	700
pounds		0.01	Perchloromethyl mercaptan	0.1	0.8
Sodium fluoroacetate (1080)–			Perchloryl fluoride	3	13.5
Skin		0.05	Phenol–Skin	5	19
Sodium hydroxide		2	p-Phenylene diamine–Skin		0.1
Stibine	0.1	0.5	Phenyl ether (vapor)	1	7
*Stoddard solvent	200	1,150	Phenyl ether-biphenyl mixture		
Strychnine		0.15	(vapor)	1	7
Sulfur dioxide	5	13	Phenylethylene, see Styrene		
Sulfur hexafluoride	1,000	6,000	Phenyl glycidyl ether (PGE)	10	60
Sulfuric acid		1	Phenylhydrazine–Skin	5	22
Sulfur monochloride	1	6	Phosdrin (Mevinphos®)–Skin		0.1
Sulfur pentafluoride	0.025	0.25	Phosgene (carbonyl chloride)	0.1	0.4
Sulfuryl fluoride	5	20	Phosphine	0.3	0.4
Systox, see Demeton®			Phosphoric acid		1
2,4,5T		10	Phosphorus (yellow)		0.1
Tantalum		5	Phosphorus pentachloride		1
TEDP–Skin		0.2	Phosphorus pentasulfide		1
Tellurium		0.1	Phosphorus trichloride	0.5	3
Tellurium hexafluoride	0.02	0.2	Phthalic anhydride	2	12

Table 1 (continued)

Substance	ppm[a]	mg/M³ [b]
Picric acid—Skin		0.1
Pival® (2-Pivalyl-1,3-indandione)		0.1
Platinum (Soluble Salts) as Pt		0.002
Propargyl alcohol—Skin	1	
n-Propyl acetate	200	840
Propyl alcohol	200	500
n-Propyl nitrate	25	110
Propylene dichloride	75	350
Propylene imine—Skin	2	5
Propylene oxide	100	240
Propyne, see Methylacetylene		
Pyrethrum		5
Pyridine	5	15
Quinone	0.1	0.4
RDX—Skin		1.5
Rhodium, Metal fume and dusts, as Rh		0.1
Soluble salts		0.001
Ronnel		10
Rotenone (commercial)		5
Selenium compounds (as Se)		0.2
Selenium hexafluoride	0.05	0.4
Trichloromethane, see Chloroform		
Trichloronaphthalene—Skin		5
1,2,3-Trichloropropane	50	300
1,1,2-Trichloro 1,2,2-trifluoroethane	1,000	7,600
Triethylamine	25	100
Trifluoromonobromomethane	1,000	6,100
*Trimethyl benzene	25	120
2,4,6-Trinitrophenol, see Picric acid		
2,4,6-Trinitrophenylmethylnitramine, see Tetryl		
Trinitrotoluene—Skin		1.5
Triorthocresyl phosphate		0.1
Triphenyl phosphate		3
Tungsten and compounds, as W:		
Soluble		1
Insoluble		5
Turpentine	100	560
Uranium (natural) sol. and insol. compounds as U		0.2
C Vanadium:		
V₂O₅ dust		0.5
V₂O₅ fume		0.1
Vinyl benzene, see Styrene		
**C Vinyl chloride	500	1,300
Vinylcyanide, see Acrylonitrile		
Vinyl toluene	100	480
Warfarin		0.1
Xylene (xylol)	100	435
Xylidine—Skin	5	25
Yttrium		1
Zinc chloride fume		1
Zinc oxide fume		5
Zirconium compounds (as Zr)		5

*1970 Addition.

[a]Parts of vapor or gas per million parts of contaminated air by volume at 25°C and 760 mm Hg pressure.

[b]Approximate milligrams of particulate per cubic meter of air.

(No footnote "c" is used to avoid confusion with ceiling value notations.)

[d]An atmospheric concentration of not more than 0.02 ppm, or personal protection may be necessary to avoid headache.

[e]As sampled method that does not collect vapor.

[f]For control of general room air, biologic monitoring is essential for personnel control.

Table 2

	8-hour time weighted average
Benzene (Z37.4—1969)	10 ppm
Beryllium and beryllium compounds (Z37.29—1970)	0.002 mg/M³
Cadmium dust (as Cd) (Z37.5—1970)	0.2 mg/M³
Cadmium fume (as Cd) (Z37.5—1970)	0.1 mg/M³
Carbon disulfide (Z37.3—1968)	20 ppm
Carbon tetrachloride (Z37.17—1967)	10 ppm
Ethylene dibromide (Z37.31—1970)	20 ppm
Ethylene dichloride (Z37.21—1969)	50 ppm
Formaldehyde (Z37.16—1967)	3 ppm
Hydrogen fluoride (Z37.28—1969)	3 ppm
Fluoride as dust (Z37.28—1966)	2.5 mg/M³
Lead and its inorganic compounds (Z37.11—1969)	0.2 mg/M³
Methyl chloride (Z37.18—1969)	100 ppm
Methylene chloride (Z37.23—1969)	500 ppm
Organo (alkyl) mercury (Z37.30—1969)	0.01 mg/M³
Styrene (Z37.12—1969)	100 ppm
Tetrachloroethylene (Z37.22—1967)	100 ppm
Toluene (Z37.12—1967)	200 ppm

	Acceptable ceiling concentration
Hydrogen sulfide (Z37.2—1966)	20 ppm
Chromic acid and chromates (Z37.3—1971)	1 mg/10M³
Mercury (Z37.8—1971)	1 mg/10M³

Table 3

Substance	Mppcf[a]	Mg/M^3		Substance	Mppcf[a]	Mg/M^3
Silica:				Inert or Nuisance Dust:		
Crystalline:				Respirable fraction	15	5mg/M^3
Quartz (respirable)	250[f]	10mg/M$^{3\,m}$		Total dust	50	15mg/M^3
	$\dfrac{\%SiO_2 + 5}{}$	$\dfrac{\%SiO_2 + 2}{}$				
Quartz (total dust)		30mg/M^3				
		$\dfrac{\%SiO_2 + 2}{}$				

NOTE: Conversion factors—
mppcf x 35.3 = million particles per cubic meter
= particles per cc

[a]Millions of particles per cubic foot of air, based on impinger samples counted by light-field technics.

[f]The percentage of crystalline silica in the formula is the amount determined from air-borne samples, except in those instances in which other methods have been shown to be applicable.

[i]As determined by the membrane filter method at 430 x phase contrast magnification.

[m]Both concentration and percent quartz for the application of this limit are to be determined from the fraction passing a size-selector with the following characteristics:

Substance	Mppcf[a]	Mg/M^3
Cristobalite: Use ½ the value calculated from the count or mass formulae for quartz.		
Trioymite: Use ½ the value calculated from the formulae for quartz.		
Amorphous, including natural diatomaceous earth	20	80mg/M^3
Tremolite	5	$\dfrac{\%SiO_2}{20mg/M^3}$ $\dfrac{}{\%SiO_2}$
Silicates (less than 1% crystalline silica):		
Asbestos — 12 fibers per milliliter greater than 5 microns in length,[i] or	2	
Mica	20	
Soapstone	20	
Talc	20	
Portland cement	50	
Graphite (natural)	15	
Coal dust (respirable fraction less than 5% SiO$_2$)		2.4mg/M^3 or
For more than 5% SiO$_2$		10mg/M^3 $\dfrac{}{\%SiO_2 + 2}$

Aerodynamic diameter (unit density sphere)	Percent passing selector
2	90
2.5	75
3.5	50
5.0	25
10	0

The measurements under this note refer to the use of an AEC instrument. If the respirable fraction of coal dust is determined with a MRE the figure corresponding to that of 2.4 Mg/M^3 in the table for coal dust is 4.5 Mg/M^3.

FLAME AND BEAD TESTS

Flame Colorations

VIOLET

Potassium compounds. Purple red through blue glass. Easily obscured by sodium flame. Bluish green through green glass. Rubidium and Caesium compounds impart same flame as potassium compounds

BLUES

Azure.—Copper chloride. Copper bromide gives azure blue followed by green. Other copper compounds give same coloration when moistened with hydrochloric acid.

Light Blue.—Lead, Arsenic, Selenium.

GREENS

Emerald.—Copper compounds except the halides, and when not moistened with hydrochloric acid.

Pure Green.—Compounds of thallium and tellurium.

Yellowish.—Barium compounds. Some molybdenum compounds. Borates, especially when treated with sulphuric acid or when burned with alcohol.

Bluish.—Phosphates with sulphuric acid.

Feeble.—Antimony compounds. Ammonium compounds.

Whitish.—Zinc.

REDS

Carmine.—Lithium compounds. Violet through blue glass. Invisible through green glass. Masked by barium flame.

Scarlet.—Strontium compounds. Violet through blue glass. Yellowish through green glass. Masked by barium flame.

Yellowish.—Calcium compounds. Greenish through blue glass. Green through green glass. Masked by barium flame.

YELLOW

Yellow.—All sodium compounds. Invisible with blue glass.

Borax Beads

Abbreviations employed: s., saturated; s.s., supersaturated; n.s.; not saturated; h., hot; c., cold.

Substance	Oxidizing flame	Reducing flame
Aluminum...	Colorless (h.c., n.s.); opaque (s.s.)	Colorless; opaque (s.)
Antimony....	Colorless; yellow or brownish (h., s.s.)	Gray and opaque
Barium......	Colorless (n.s.)	....
Bismuth.....	Colorless; yellow or brownish (h., s.s.)	Gray and opaque
Cadmium....	Colorless	Gray and opaque
Calcium.....	Colorless (n.s.)	....
Cerium......	Red (h.)	Colorless (h.c.)
Chromium...	Green (c.)	Green
Cobalt.......	Blue (h.c.)	Blue (h.c.)
Copper......	Green (h.); blue (c.)	Red (c.): opaque (s.s.): colorless (h.)
Iron	Yellow or brownish red (h., s.s.)	Green (s.s.)
Lead........	Colorless; yellow or brownish (h., s.s.)	Gray and opaque
Magnesium...	Colorless (n.s.)	....
Manganese...	Violet (h.c.)	Colorless (h.c.)
Molybdenum.	Colorless	Yellow or brown (h.)
Nickel.......	Brown; red (c.)	Gray and opaque
Silicon........	Colorless (h.c.); opaque (s.s.)	Colorless; opaque (s.)
Silver........	Colorless (n.s.)	Gray and opaque
Strontium.....	Colorless (n.s.)	....
Tin..........	Colorless (h.c.); opaque (s.s.)	Colorless; opaque (s.)
Titanium......	Colorless	Yellow (h.); violet (c.)
Tungsten.....	Colorless	Brown
Uranium......	Yellow or brownish (h., n.s.)	Green
Vanadium.....	Colorless	Green

Beads of Microcosmic Salt NaNH₄HPO₄

Substance	Oxidizing flame	Reducing flame
Aluminum...	Colorless; opaque (s.)	Colorless; not clear (s.s.)
Antimony....	Colorless (n.s.)	Gray and opaque
Barium......	Colorless; opaque (s.)	Colorless; not clear (s.s.)
Bismuth....	Colorless (n.s.)	Gray and opaque
Cadmium....	Colorless (n.s.)	Gray and opaque
Calcium.....	Colorless; opaque (s.)	Colorless; not clear (s.s.)
Cerium......	Yellow or brownish red (h., s.)	Colorless
Chromium...	Red (h., s.); green (c.)	Green (c.)
Cobalt......	Blue (h.c.)	Blue (h.c.)
Copper......	Blue (c.); green (h.)	Red and opaque (c.)
Iron.........	Yellow or brown (h., s.)	Colorless; yellow or brownish (h.)
Lead........	Colorless (n.s.)	Gray and opaque
Magnesium...	Colorless; opaque (s.)	Colorless; not clear (s.s.)
Manganese...	Violet (h.c.)	Colorless
Molybdenum.	Colorless; green (h.)	Green (h.)
Nickel......	Yellow (c.); red (h., s.)	Yellow (c.); red (h.); gray and opaque
Silicon......	(Swims undissolved)	(Swims undissolved)
Silver.......	....	Gray and opaque
Strontium...	Colorless; opaque (s.)	Colorless; not clear (s.s.)
Tin.........	Colorless; opaque (s.)	Colorless
Titanium...	Colorless (n.s.)	Violet (c.); yellow or brownish (h.)
Uranium...	Green; yellow or brownish (h., s.)	Green (h.)
Vanadium..	Yellow	Green
Zinc......	Colorless (n.s.)	Gray and opaque

Sodium Carbonate Bead

Substance	Oxidizing flame	Reducing flame
Manganese....	Green	Colorless

PREPARATION OF REAGENTS

The following pages present directions for the preparation of various reagents. The collection has been prepared with the active collaboration of W. D. Bonner, R. K. Carleton, L. L. Carrick, Gilles B. Cooke, E. J. Cragoe, Thos. De Vries, James L. Kassner, Thos. W. Mason, F. C. Mathers, M. G. Mellon, W. C. Pierce, J. H. Reedy, Arthur A. Vernon and S. R. Wood. Many others have contributed valuable suggestions.

Volumes have been stated in milliliters (ml) and liters (l). One milliliter is equivalent to one cubic centimeter (cm³ or cc.). Masses are indicated in grams (g).

The relation to molar solution (M) or normal solution (N) is indicated in many cases.

Distilled water should be used.

LABORATORY REAGENTS FOR GENERAL USE

DILUTE ACIDS, 3 molar. Use the amount of concentrated acid indicated and dilute to one liter.

Acetic acid, 3 N. Use 172 ml of 17.4 M acid (99–100 %).

Hydrochloric acid, 3 N. Use 258 ml of 11.6 M acid (36 % HCl).

Nitric acid, 3 N. Use 195 ml of 15.4 M acid (69 % HNO_3).

Phosphoric acid, 9 N. Use 205 ml of 14.6 M acid (85 % H_3PO_4).

Sulfuric acid, 6 N. Use 168 ml of 17.8 M acid (95 % H_2SO_4).

DILUTE BASES.

Ammonium hydroxide, 3 M, 3 N. Dilute 405 ml of concentrated solution (7.4 M, 28 % NH_3) to 1 liter.

Barium hydroxide, 0.2 M, 0.4 N. Saturated solution, 63 g per liter of $Ba(OH)_2 \cdot 8H_2O$. Use some excess, filter off $BaCO_3$ and protect from CO_2 of the air with soda lime or ascarite in a guard tube.

Calcium hydroxide, 0.02 M, 0.04 N. Saturated solution, 1.5 g per liter of $Ca(OH)_2$. Use some excess, filter off $CaCO_3$ and protect from CO_2 of the air.

Potassium hydroxide, 3 M, 3 N. Dissolve 176 g of the sticks (95 %) in water and dilute to 1 liter.

Sodium hydroxide, 3 M, 3 N. Dissolve 126 g of the sticks (95 %) in water and dilute to 1 liter.

GENERAL REAGENTS. (See also *Decinormal Solutions of Salts and Other Reagents*.)

Aluminum chloride, 0.167 M, 0.5 N. Dissolve 22 g of $AlCl_3$ in 1 liter of water.

Aluminum nitrate, 0.167 M, 0.5 N. Dissolve 58 g of $Al(NO_3)_3 \cdot 7.5H_2O$ in 1 liter of water.

Aluminum sulfate, 0.083 M, 0.5 N. Dissolve 56 g of $Al_2(SO_4)_3 \cdot 18H_2O$ in 1 liter of water.

Ammonium acetate, 3 M, 3 N. Dissolve 230 g of $NH_4C_2H_3O_2$ in water and dilute to 1 liter.

Ammonium carbonate, 1.5 M. Dissolve 144 g of the commercial salt (mixture of $(NH_4)_2CO_3 \cdot H_2O$ and $NH_4CO_2NH_2$) in 500 ml of 3 N NH_4OH and dilute to 1 liter.

Ammonium chloride, 3 M, 3 N. Dissolve 160 g of NH_4Cl in water. Dilute to 1 liter.

Ammonium molybdate.

1. 0.5 M, 1 N. Mix well 72 g of pure MoO_3 (or 81 g of H_2MoO_4) with 200 ml of water, and add 60 ml of conc. ammonium hydroxide. When solution is complete, filter and pour filtrate, *very slowly* and with *rapid stirring*, into a mixture of 270 ml of conc. HNO_3 and 400 ml of water. Allow to stand over night, filter and dilute to 1 liter.

2. The reagent is prepared as two solutions which are mixed as needed, thus always providing fresh reagent of proper strength and composition. Since ammonium molybdate is an expensive reagent, and since an acid solution of this reagent is usually prepared keeps for only a few days, the method proposed will avoid loss of reagent and provide more certain results for quantitative work.

Solution 1. Dissolve 100 g of ammonium molybdate (C.P. grade) in 400 ml of water and 80 ml of 15 M NH_4OH. Filter if necessary, though this seldom has to be done.

Solution 2. Mix 400 ml of 16 M nitric acid with 600 ml of water.

For use, mix the calculated amount of solution 1 with twice its volume of solution 2, adding solution 1 to solution 2 slowly with vigorous stirring. Thus, for amounts of phosphorus up to 20 mg, 10 ml of solution 1 to 20 ml of solution 2 is adequate. Increase amount as needed.

Ammonium nitrate, 1 M, 1 N. Dissolve 80 g of NH_4NO_3 in 1 liter of water.

Ammonium oxalate, 0.25 M, 0.5 N. Dissolve 35.5 g of $(NH_4)_2C_2O_4 \cdot H_2O$ in water. Dilute to 1 liter.

Ammonium sulfate, 0.25 M, 0.5 N. Dissolve 33 g of $(NH_4)_2SO_4$ in 1 liter of water.

Ammonium sulfide, colorless.

1. 3 M. Treat 200 ml of conc. NH_4OH with H_2S until saturated, keeping the solution cold. Add 200 ml of conc. NH_4OH and dilute of 1 liter.

2. 6 N. Saturate 6 N ammonium hydroxide (40 ml conc. ammonia solution + 60 ml H_2O) with washed H_2S gas. The ammonium hydroxide bottle must be completely full and must be kept surrounded by ice while being saturated (about 48 hours for two liters). The reagent is best preserved in brown, completely filled, glass-stoppered bottles.

LABORATORY REAGENTS (Continued)

Ammonium sulfide, yellow. Treat 150 ml of conc. NH_4OH with H_2S until saturated, keeping the solution cool. Add 250 ml of conc. NH_4OH and 10 g of powdered sulfur. Shake the mixture until the sulfur is dissolved and dilute to 1 liter with water. In the solution the concentration of $(NH_4)_2S_2$, $(NH_4)_2S$ and NH_4OH are 0.625, 0.4 and 1.5 normal respectively. On standing, the concentration of $(NH_4)_2S_2$ increases and that of $(NH_4)_2S$ and NH_4OH decreases.

Antimony pentachloride, 0.1 M, 0.5 N. Dissolve 30 g of $SbCl_5$ in 1 liter of water.

Antimony trichloride, 0.167 M, 0.5 N. Dissolve 38 g of $SbCl_3$ in 1 liter of water.

Aqua regia. Mix 1 part concentrated HNO_3 with 3 parts of concentrated HCl. This formula should include one volume of water if the aqua regia is to be stored for any length of time. Without water, objectionable quantities of chlorine and other gases are evolved.

Barium chloride, 0.25 M, 0.5 N. Dissolve 61 g of $BaCl_2.2H_2O$ in water. Dilute to 1 liter.

Barium hydroxide, 0.1 M, about 0.2 N. Dissolve 32 g of $Ba(OH)_2.8H_2O$ in 1 liter of water.

Barium nitrate, 0.25 M, 0.5 N. Dissolve 65 g of $Ba(NO_3)_2$ in 1 liter of water.

Bismuth chloride, 0.167 M, 0.5 N. Dissolve 53 g of $BiCl_3$ in 1 liter of dilute HCl. Use 1 part HCl to 5 parts water.

Bismuth nitrate, 0.083 M, 0.25 N. Dissolve 40 g of $Bi(NO_3)_3.5H_2O$ in 1 liter of dilute HNO_3. Use 1 part of HNO_3 to 5 parts of water.

Cadmium chloride, 0.25 M, 0.5 N. Dissolve 46 g of $CdCl_2$ in 1 liter of water.

Cadmium nitrate, 0.25 M, 0.5 N. Dissolve 77 g of $Cd(NO_3)_2.4H_2O$ in 1 liter of water.

Cadmium sulfate, 0.25 M, 0.5 N. Dissolve 70 g of $CdSO_4.4H_2O$ in 1 liter of water.

Calcium chloride, 0.25 M, 0.5 N. Dissolve 55 g of $CaCl_2.6H_2O$ in water. Dilute to 1 liter.

Calcium nitrate, 0.25 M, 0.5 N. Dissolve 41 g of $Ca(NO_3)_2$ in 1 liter of water.

Chloroplatinic acid.
1. 0.0512 M, 0.102 N. Dissolve 26.53 g of $H_2PtCl_6.6H_2O$ in water. Dilute to 100 ml. Contains 0.100 g Pt per ml.
2. Make a 10% solution by dissolving 1 g of $H_2PtCl_6.6H_2O$ in 9 ml of water. Shake thoroughly to insure complete mixing. Keep in a dropping bottle.

Chromic chloride, 0.167 M, 0.5 N. Dissolve 26 g of $CrCl_3$ in 1 liter of water.

Chromic nitrate, 0.167 M, 0.5 N. Dissolve 40 g of $Cr(NO_3)_3$ in 1 liter of water.

Chromic sulfate, 0.083 M, 0.5 N. Dissolve 60 g of $Cr_2(SO_4)_3.18H_2O$ in 1 liter of water.

Cobaltous nitrate, 0.25 M, 0.5 N. Dissolve 73 g of $Co(NO_3)_2.6H_2O$ in 1 liter of water.

Cobaltous sulfate, 0.25 M, 0.5 N. Dissolve 70 g of $CoSO_4.7H_2O$ in 1 liter of water.

Cupric chloride, 0.25 M, 0.5 N. Dissolve 43 g of $CuCl_2.2H_2O$ in 1 liter of water.

Cupric nitrate, 0.25 M, 0.5 N. Dissolve 74 g of $Cu(NO_3)_2.6H_2O$ in 1 liter of water.

Cupric sulfate, 0.5 M, 1 N. Dissolve 124.8 g of $CuSO_4.5H_2O$ in water to which 5 ml of H_2SO_4 has been added. Dilute to 1 liter.

Ferric chloride, 0.5 M, 1.5 N. Dissolve 135.2 g of $FeCl_3.6H_2O$ in water containing 20 ml of conc. HCl. Dilute to 1 liter.

Ferric nitrate, 0.167 M, 0.5 N. Dissolve 67 g of $Fe(NO_3)_3.9H_2O$ in 1 liter of water.

Ferric sulfate, 0.25 M, 0.5 N. Dissolve 140.5 g of $Fe_2(SO_4)_3.9H_2O$ in water containing 100 ml of conc. H_2SO_4. Dilute to 1 liter.

Ferrous ammonium sulfate, 0.5 M, 1 N. Dissolve 196 g of $Fe(NH_4SO_4)_2.6H_2O$ in water containing 10 ml of conc. H_2SO_4. Dilute to 1 liter. Prepare fresh solutions for best results.

Ferrous sulfate, 0.5 M, 1 N. Dissolve 139 g of $FeSO_4.7H_2O$ in water containing 10 ml of conc. H_2SO_4. Dilute to 1 liter. Solution does not keep well.

Lead acetate, 0.5 M, 1 N. Dissolve 190 g of $Pb(C_2H_3O_2)_2.3H_2O$ in water. Dilute to 1 liter.

Lead nitrate, 0.25 M, 0.5 N. Dissolve 83 g of $Pb(NO_3)_2$ in water. Dilute to one liter.

Lime water. See *Calcium hydroxide*.

Magnesium chloride, 0.25 M, 0.5 N. Dissolve 51 g of $MgCl_2.6H_2O$ in 1 liter of water.

Magnesium chloride reagent. Dissolve 50 g of $MgCl_2.6H_2O$ and 100 g of NH_4Cl in 500 ml of water. Add 10 ml of conc. NH_4OH, allow to stand over night and filter if a precipitate has formed. Make acid to methyl red with dilute HCl. Dilute to 1 liter. Solution contains 0.25 M $MgCl_2$ and 2 M NH_4Cl. Solution may also be diluted with 133 ml of conc. NH_4OH and water to make 1 liter. Such a solution will contain 2 M NH_4OH.

Magnesium nitrate, 0.25 M, 0.5 N. Dissolve 64 g of $Mg(NO_3)_2.6H_2O$ in 1 liter of water.

Magnesium sulfate, 0.25 M, 0.5 N. Dissolve 62 g of $MgSO_4.7H_2O$ in 1 liter of water.

Manganous chloride, 0.25 M, 0.5 N. Dissolve 50 g of $MnCl_2.4H_2O$ in 1 liter of water.

Manganous nitrate, 0.25 M, 0.5 N. Dissolve 72 g of $Mn(NO_3)_2.6H_2O$ in 1 liter of water.

Manganous sulfate, 0.25 M, 0.5 N. Dissolve 69 g of $MnSO_4.7H_2O$ in 1 liter of water.

Mercuric chloride, 0.25 M, 0.5 N. Dissolve 68 g of $HgCl_2$ in water. Dilute to 1 liter.

SPECIAL SOLUTIONS AND REAGENTS

Sodium sulfate, 0.25 M, 0.5 N. Dissolve 36 g of Na_2SO_4 in 1 liter of water.

Sodium sulfide, 0.5 M, 1 N. Dissolve 120 g of $Na_2S.9H_2O$ in water and dilute to 1 liter. Or, saturate 500 ml of 1 M NaOH (21 g of 95% NaOH sticks) with H_2S, keeping the solution cool, and dilute with 500 ml of 1 M NaOH.

Stannic chloride, 0.125 M, 0.5 N. Dissolve 33 g of $SnCl_4$ in 1 liter of water.

Stannous chloride, 0.5 M, 1 N. Dissolve 113 g of $SnCl_2.2H_2O$ in 170 ml of conc. HCl, using heat if necessary. Dilute with water to 1 liter. Add a few pieces of tin foil. Prepare solution fresh at frequent intervals.

Stannous chloride (for Bettendorf test). Dissolve 113 g of $SnCl_2.2H_2O$ in 75 ml of conc. HCl. Add a few pieces of tin foil.

Strontium chloride, 0.25 M, 0.5 N. Dissolve 67 g of $SrCl_2.6H_2O$ in 1 liter of water.

Zinc nitrate, 0.25 M, 0.5 N. Dissolve 74 g of $Zn(NO_3)_2.6H_2O$ in 1 liter of water.

Zinc sulfate, 0.25 M, 0.5 N. Dissolve 72 g of $ZnSO_4.7H_2O$ in 1 liter of water.

SPECIAL SOLUTIONS AND REAGENTS

Aluminon (qualitative test for aluminum). Aluminon is a trade name for the ammonium salt of aurin tricarboxylic acid. Dissolve 1 g of the salt in 1 liter of distilled water. Shake the solution well to insure thorough mixing.

Bang's reagent (for glucose estimation). Dissolve 100 g of K_2CO_3, 66 g of KCl and 160 g of $KHCO_3$ in the order given in about 700 ml of water at 30° C. Add 4.4 g of $CuSO_4$, and dilute to 1 liter after the CO_2 is evolved. This solution should be shaken only in such a manner as not to allow entry of air. After 24 hours 300 ml are diluted to 1 liter with saturated KCl solution, shaken gently and used after 24 hours; 50 ml equivalent to 10 mg glucose.

Barfoed's reagent (test for glucose). See *Cupric acetate.*

Baudisch's reagent. See *Cupferron.*

Benedict's solution (qualitative reagent for glucose). With the aid of heat, dissolve 173 g of sodium citrate and 100 g of Na_2CO_3 in 800 ml of water. Filter, if necessary, and dilute to 850 ml. Dissolve 17.3 g of $CuSO_4.5H_2O$ in 100 ml of water. Pour the latter solution, with constant stirring, into the carbonate-citrate solution, and make up to 1 liter.

Benzidine hydrochloride solution (for sulfate determination). Make a paste of 8 g of benzidine hydrochloride ($C_{12}H_8(NH_2)_2.2HCl$) and 20 ml of water, add 20 ml of HCl (sp. gr. 1.12) and dilute to 1 liter with water. Each ml of this solution is equivalent to 0.00357 g of H_2SO_4.

Bertrand's reagent (glucose estimation). Consists of the following solutions:

LABORATORY REAGENTS (Continued)

Mercuric nitrate, 0.25 M, 0.5 N. Dissolve 81 g of $Hg(NO_3)_2$ in 1 liter of water.

Mercuric sulfate, 0.25 M, 0.5 N. Dissolve 74 g of $HgSO_4$ in 1 liter of water.

Mercurous nitrate. Use 1 part $HgNO_3$, 20 parts water and 1 part HNO_3.

Nickel chloride, 0.25 M, 0.5 N. Dissolve 59 g of $NiCl_2.6H_2O$ in 1 liter of water.

Nickel nitrate, 0.25 M, 0.5 N. Dissolve 73 g of $Ni(NO_3)_2.6H_2O$ in 1 liter of water.

Nickel sulfate, 0.25 M, 0.5 N. Dissolve 66 g of $NiSO_4.6H_2O$ in 1 liter of water.

Potassium bromide, 0.5 M, 0.5 N. Dissolve 60 g of KBr in 1 liter of water.

Potassium carbonate, 1.5 M, 3 N. Dissolve 207 g of K_2CO_3 in 1 liter of water.

Potassium chloride, 0.5 M, 0.5 N. Dissolve 37 g of KCl in 1 liter of water.

Potassium chromate, 0.25 M, 0.5 N. Dissolve 49 g of K_2CrO_4 in 1 liter of water.

Potassium cyanide, 0.5 M, 0.5 N. Dissolve 33 g of KCN in 1 liter of water.

Potassium dichromate, 0.125 M. Dissolve 37 g of $K_2Cr_2O_7$ in 1 liter of water.

Potassium ferricyanide, 0.167 M, 0.5 N. Dissolve 55 g of $K_3Fe(CN)_6$ in 1 liter of water.

Potassium ferrocyanide, 0.5 M, 2 N. Dissolve 211 g of $K_4Fe(CN)_6.3H_2O$ in water. Dilute to 1 liter.

Potassium iodide, 0.5 M, 0.5 N. Dissolve 83 g of KI in 1 liter of water.

Potassium nitrate, 0.5 M, 0.5 N. Dissolve 51 g of KNO_3 in 1 liter of water.

Potassium sulfate, 0.25 M, 0.5 N. Dissolve 44 g of K_2SO_4 in 1 liter of water.

Silver nitrate, 0.5 M, 0.5 N. Dissolve 85 g of $AgNO_3$ in water. Dilute to 1 liter.

Sodium acetate, 3 M, 3 N. Dissolve 408 g of $NaC_2H_3O_2.3H_2O$ in water. Dilute to 1 liter.

Sodium carbonate, 1.5 M, 3 N. Dissolve 159 g of Na_2CO_3, or 430 g of $Na_2CO_3.10H_2O$ in water. Dilute to 1 liter.

Sodium chloride, 0.5 M, 0.5 N. Dissolve 29 g of NaCl in 1 liter of water.

Sodium cobaltinitrite, 0.08 M (reagent for potassium). Dissolve 25 g of $NaNO_2$ in 75 ml of water, add 2 ml of glacial acetic acid and then 2.5 g of $Co(NO_3)_2.6H_2O$. Allow to stand for several days, filter and dilute to 100 ml. Reagent is somewhat unstable.

Sodium hydrogen phosphate, 0.167 M, 0.5 N. Dissolve 60 g of $Na_2HPO_4.12H_2O$ in 1 liter of water.

Sodium nitrate, 0.5 M, 0.5 N. Dissolve 43 g of $NaNO_3$ in 1 liter of water.

SPECIAL SOLUTIONS AND REAGENTS (Continued)

(a) Dissolve 200 g of Rochelle salts and 150 g of NaOH in sufficient water to make 1 liter of solution.

(b) Dissolve 40 g of $CuSO_4$ in enough water to make 1 liter of solution.

(c) Dissolve 50 g of $Fe_2(SO_4)_3$ and 200 g of H_2SO_4 (sp. gr. 1.84) in sufficient water to make 1 liter of solution.

(d) Dissolve 5 g of $KMnO_4$ in sufficient water to make 1 liter of solution.

Bial's reagent (for pentose). Dissolve 1 g of orcinol $(CH_3.C_6H_3(OH)_2)$ in 500 ml of 30 % HCl to which 30 drops of a 10 % solution of $FeCl_3$ has been added.

Boutron-Boudet soap solution.

(a) Dissolve 100 g of pure castile soap in about 2500 ml of 56 % ethyl alcohol.

(b) Dissolve 0.59 g of $Ba(NO_3)_2$ in 1 liter of water.

Adjust the castile soap solution so that 2.4 ml of it will give a permanent lather with 40 ml of solution (b). When adjusted, 2.4 ml of soap solution is equivalent to 220 parts per million of hardness (as $CaCO_3$) for a 40 ml sample.

See also *Soap solution*.

Brucke's reagent (protein precipitation). See *Potassium iodide-mercuric iodide.*

Clarke's soap solution (or A.P.H.A. standard method). Estimation of hardness in water.

(a) Dissolve 100 g of pure powdered castile soap in 1 liter of 80 % ethyl alcohol and allow to stand over night.

(b) Prepare a standard solution of $CaCl_2$ by dissolving 0.5 g of $CaCO_3$ in HCl (sp. gr. 1.19), neutralize with NH_4OH and make slightly alkaline to litmus, and dilute to 500 ml. One ml is equivalent to 1 mg of $CaCO_3$.

Titrate (a) against (b) and dilute (a) with 80 % ethyl alcohol until 1 ml of the resulting solution is equivalent to 1 ml of (b) after making allowance for the lather factor (the amount of standard soap solution required to produce a permanent lather in 50 ml of distilled water). One ml of the adjusted solution after subtracting the lather factor is equivalent to 1 mg of $CaCO_3$.

See also *Soap solution.*

Cobalticyanide paper (Rinmann's test for Zn). Dissolve 4 g of $K_3Co(CN)_6$ and 1 g of $KClO_3$ in 100 ml of water. Soak filter paper in solution and dry at 100° C. Apply drop of zinc solution and burn in an evaporating dish. A green disk is obtained if zinc is present.

Cochineal. Extract 1 g of cochineal for four days with 20 ml of alcohol and 60 ml of distilled water. Filter.

Congo red. Dissolve 0.5 g of congo red in 90 ml of distilled water and 10 ml of alcohol.

Cupferron (Baudisch's reagent for iron analysis). Dissolve 6 g of the ammonium salt of nitroso-phenyl-hydroxyl-amine (cupferron) in 100 ml of H_2O. Reagent good for one week only and must be kept in the dark.

Cupric acetate (Barfoed's reagent for reducing mono-saccharides). Dissolve 66 g of cupric acetate and 10 ml of glacial acetic acid in water and dilute to 1 liter.

Cupric oxide, ammoniacal; Schweitzer's reagent (dissolves cotton, linen and silk; but not wool).

1. Dissolve 5 g of cupric sulfate in 100 ml of boiling water, and add sodium hydroxide until precipitation is complete. Wash the precipitate well, and dissolve it in a minimum quantity of ammonium hydroxide.

2. Bubble a slow stream of air through 300 ml of strong ammonium hydroxide containing 50 g of fine copper turnings. Continue for one hour.

Cupric sulfate in glycerin-potassium hydroxide (reagent for silk). Dissolve 10 g of cupric sulfate, $CuSO_4.5H_2O$, in 100 ml of water and add 5 g of glycerin. Add KOH solution slowly until a deep blue solution is obtained.

Cupron (benzoin oxime). Dissolve 5 g in 100 ml of 95 % alcohol.

Cuprous chloride, acidic (reagent for CO in gas analysis).

1. Cover the bottom of a two-liter flask with a layer of cupric oxide about one-half inch deep, suspend a bunch of copper wire so as to reach from the bottom to the top of the solution, and fill the flask with hydrochloric acid (sp. gr. 1.10). Shake occasionally. When the solution becomes nearly colorless, transfer to reagent bottles, which should also contain copper wire. The stock bottle may be refilled with dilute hydrochloric acid until either the cupric oxide or the copper wire is used up. Copper sulfate may be substituted for copper oxide in the above procedure.

2. Dissolve 340 g of $CuCl_2.2H_2O$ in 600 ml of conc. HCl and reduce the cupric chloride by adding 190 ml of a saturated solution of stannous chloride or until the solution is colorless. The stannous chloride is prepared by treating 300 g of metallic tin in a 500 ml flask with conc. HCl until no more tin goes into solution.

3. (Winkler method). Add a mixture of 86 g of CuO and 17 g of finely divided metallic Cu, made by the reduction of CuO with hydrogen, to a solution of HCl, made by diluting 650 ml of conc. HCl with 325 ml of water. After the mixture has been added slowly and with frequent stirring, a spiral of copper wire is suspended in the bottle, reaching all the way to the bottom. Shake occasionally, and when the solution becomes colorless, it is ready for use.

Cuprous chloride, ammoniacal (reagent for CO in gas analysis).

1. The acid solution of cuprous chloride as prepared above is neutralized with ammonium hydroxide until an ammonia odor persists. An excess of metallic copper must be kept in the solution.

2. Pour 800 ml of acidic cuprous chloride, prepared by the Winkler method, into about 4 liters of water. Transfer the

precipitate to a 250 ml graduate. After several hours, siphon off the liquid above the 50 ml mark and refill with 7.5% NH_4OH solution which may be prepared by diluting 50 ml of conc. NH_4OH with 150 ml of water. The solution is well shaken and allowed to stand for several hours. It should have a faint odor of ammonia.

Dichlorofluorescein Indicator. Dissolve 1 g in 1 liter of 70% alcohol or 1 g of the sodium salt in 1 liter of water.

Dimethylglyoxime (diacetyl dioxime), $(CH_3CNOH)_2$. Dissolve 0.6 g of dimethylglyoxime, $(CH_3CNOH)_2$, in 500 ml of 95% ethyl alcohol. This is an especially sensitive test for nickel, a very definite crimson color being produced.

Diphenylamine (reagent for rayon). Dissolve 0.2 g in 100 ml of concentrated sulfuric acid.

Diphenylamine sulfonate (for titration of iron with $K_2Cr_2O_7$. Dissolve 0.32 g of the barium salt of diphenylamine sulfonic acid in 100 ml of water, add 0.5 g of sodium sulfate and filter off the precipitate of $BaSO_4$.

Diphenylcarbazide. Dissolve 0.2 g of diphenylcarbazide in 10 ml of glacial acetic acid and dilute to 100 ml with 95% ethyl alcohol.

Esbach's reagent (estimation of protein). To a water solution of 10 g of picric acid and 20 g of citric acid, add sufficient water to make one liter of solution.

Eschka's compound. Two parts of calcined ("light") magnesia are thoroughly mixed with one part of anhydrous sodium carbonate.

Fehling's solution (reagent for reducing sugars).
(a) Copper sulfate solution. Dissolve 34.66 g of $CuSO_4\cdot 5H_2O$ in water and dilute to 500 ml.
(b) Alkaline tartrate solution. Dissolve 173 g of potassium sodium tartrate (Rochelle salts, $KNaC_4H_4O_6\cdot4H_2O$) and 50 g of NaOH in water and dilute when cold to 500 ml.
For use, mix equal volumes of the two solutions at the time of using.

Ferric-alum indicator. Dissolve 140 g of ferric-ammonium sulfate crystals in 400 ml of hot water. When cool, filter, and make up to a volume of 500 ml with dilute (6 N) nitric acid.

Folin's mixture (for uric acid). To 650 ml of water add 500 g of $(NH_4)_2SO_4$, 5 g of uranium acetate and 6 g of glacial acetic acid. Dilute to 1 liter.

Formaldehyde-sulfuric acid (Marquis' reagent for alkaloids). Add 10 ml of formaldehyde solution to 50 ml of sulfuric acid.

Froehde's reagent. See *Sulfomolybdic acid.*
Fuchsin (reagent for linen). Dissolve 1 g of fuchsin in 100 ml of alcohol.
Fuchsin-sulfurous acid (Schiff's reagent for aldehydes). Dissolve 1.5 g of fuchsin and 9 g of sodium bisulfite in 500 ml of water, and add 10 ml of HCl. Keep in well-stoppered bottles and protect from light.

Gunzberg's reagent (detection of HCl in gastric juice). Prepare as needed a solution containing 4 g of phloroglucinol and 2 g of vanillin in 100 ml of absolute ethyl alcohol.

Hager's reagent. See *Picric acid.*

Hanus solution (for iodine number). Dissolve 13.2 g of resublimed iodine in one liter of glacial acetic acid which will pass the dichromate test for reducible matter. Add sufficient bromine to double the halogen content, determined by titration (3 ml is about the proper amount). The iodine may be dissolved by the aid of heat, but the solution should be cold when the bromine is added.

Iodine, tincture of. To 50 ml of water add 70 g of I_2 and 50 g of KI. Dilute to 1 liter with alcohol.

Iodo-potassium iodide (Wagner's reagent for alkaloids). Dissolve 2 g of iodine and 6 g of KI in 100 ml of water.

Litmus (indicator). Extract litmus powder three times with boiling alcohol, each treatment consuming an hour. Reject the alcoholic extract. Treat residue with an equal weight of cold water and filter; then exhaust with five times its weight of boiling water, cool and filter. Combine the aqueous extracts.

Magnesia mixture (reagent for phosphates and arsenates). Dissolve 55 g of magnesium chloride and 105 g of ammonium chloride in water, barely acidify with hydrochloric acid, and dilute to 1 liter. The ammonium hydroxide may be omitted until just previous to use. The reagent, if completely mixed and stored for any period of time, becomes turbid.

Magnesium reagent. See *S and O reagent.*

Magnesium uranyl acetate. Dissolve 100 g of $UO_2(C_2H_3O_2)_2\cdot2H_2O$ in 60 ml of glacial acetic acid and dilute to 500 ml. Dissolve 330 g of $Mg(C_2H_3O_2)_2\cdot4H_2O$ in 60 ml of glacial acetic acid and dilute to 200 ml. Heat solutions to the boiling point until clear, pour the magnesium solution into the uranyl solution, cool and dilute to 1 liter. Let stand over night and filter if necessary.

Marme's reagent. See *Potassium-cadmium iodide.*

Marquis' reagent. See *Formaldehyde-sulfuric acid.*

Mayer's reagent (white precipitate with most alkaloids in slightly acid solutions). Dissolve 1.358 g of $HgCl_2$ in 60 ml of water and pour into a solution of 5 g of KI in 10 ml of H_2O. Add sufficient water to make 100 ml.

Methyl orange indicator. Dissolve 1 g of methyl orange in 1 liter of water. Filter, if necessary.

Methyl orange, modified. Dissolve 2 g of methyl orange and 2.8 g of xylene cyanole FF in 1 liter of 50% alcohol.

Methyl red indicator. Dissolve 1 g of methyl red in 600 ml of alcohol and dilute with 400 ml of water.

Methyl red, modified. Dissolve 0.50 g of methyl red and 1.25 g of xylene cyanole FF in 1 liter of 90% alcohol. Or, dissolve 1.25 g of methyl red and 0.825 g of methylene blue in 1 liter of 90% alcohol.

SPECIAL SOLUTIONS AND REAGENTS (Continued)

Millon's reagent (for albumins and phenols). Dissolve 1 part of mercury in 1 part of cold fuming nitric acid. Dilute with twice the volume of water and decant the clear solution after several hours.

Mixed indicator. Prepared by adding about 1.4 g of xylene cyanole FF to 1 g of methyl orange. The dye is seldom pure enough for these proportions to be satisfactory. Each new lot of dye should be tested by adding additional amounts of the dye until a test portion gives the proper color change. The acid color of this indicator is like that of permanganate; the neutral color is gray; and the alkaline color is green. Described by Hickman and Linstead, J. Chem. Soc. (Lon.), **121**, 2502 (1922).

Molisch's reagent. See α-Naphthol.

α-Naphthol (Molisch's reagent for wool). Dissolve 15 g of α-naphthol in 100 ml of alcohol or chloroform.

Nessler's reagent (for ammonia). Dissolve 50 g of KI in the smallest possible quantity of cold water (50 ml). Add a saturated solution of mercuric chloride (about 22 g in 350 ml of water will be needed) until an excess is indicated by the formation of a precipitate. Then add 200 ml of 5 N NaOH and dilute to 1 liter. Let settle, and draw off the clear liquid.

Nickel oxide, ammoniacal (reagent for silk). Dissolve 5 g of nickel sulfate in 100 ml of water, and add sodium hydroxide solution until nickel hydroxide is completely precipitated. Wash the precipitate well and dissolve in 25 ml of concentrated ammonium hydroxide and 25 ml of water.

p-Nitrobenzene-azo-resorcinol (reagent for magnesium). Dissolve 1 g of the dye in 10 ml of N NaOH and dilute to 1 liter.

Nitron (detection of nitrate radical). Dissolve 10 g of nitron ($C_{20}H_{16}N_4$, 4, 5-dihydro-1, 4-diphenyl-3, 5-phenylimino-1, 2, 4-triazole) in 5 ml of glacial acetic acid and 95 ml of water. The solution may be filtered with slight suction through an alundum crucible and kept in a dark bottle.

α-Nitroso-β-naphthol. Make a saturated solution in 50% acetic acid (1 part of glacial acetic acid with 1 part of water). Does not keep well.

Nylander's solution (carbohydrates). Dissolve 20 g of bismuth subnitrate and 40 g of Rochelle salts in 1 liter of 8% NaOH solution. Cool and filter.

Obermayer's reagent (for indoxyl in urine). Dissolve 4 g of FeCl₃ in one liter of HCl (sp. gr. 1.19).

Oxine. Dissolve 14 g of HC_9H_6ON in 30 ml of glacial acetic acid. Warm slightly, if necessary. Dilute to 1 liter.

Oxygen absorbent. Dissolve 300 g of ammonium chloride in one liter of water and add one liter of concentrated ammonium hydroxide solution. Shake the solution thoroughly. For use as an oxygen absorbent, a bottle half full of copper turnings is filled nearly full with the NH₄Cl-NH₄OH solution and the gas passed through.

Pasteur's salt solution. To one liter of distilled water add 2.5 g of potassium phosphate, 0.25 g of calcium phosphate, 0.25 g of magnesium sulfate and 12.00 g of ammonium tartrate.

Pavy's solution (glucose reagent). To 120 ml of Fehling's solution, add 300 ml of NH₄OH (sp. gr. 0.88) and dilute to 1 liter with water.

Phenanthroline ferrous ion indicator. Dissolve 1.485 g of phenanthroline monohydrate in 100 ml of 0.025 M ferrous sulfate solution.

Phenolphthalein. Dissolve 1 g of phenolphthalein in 50 ml of alcohol and add 50 ml of water.

Phenolsulfonic acid (determination of nitrogen as nitrate). Dissolve 25 g of phenol in 150 ml of conc. H_2SO_4, add 75 ml of fuming H_2SO_4 (15% SO_3), stir well and heat for two hours at 100° C.

Phloroglucinol solution (pentosans). Make a 3% phloroglucinol solution in alcohol. Keep in a dark bottle.

Phosphomolybdic acid (Sonnenschein's reagent for alkaloids).

1. Prepare ammonium phosphomolybdate and after washing with water, boil with nitric acid and expel NH₃; evaporate to dryness and dissolve in 2 N nitric acid.

2. Dissolve ammonium molybdate in HNO_3 and treat with phosphoric acid. Filter, wash the precipitate, and boil with aqua regia until the ammonium salt is decomposed. Evaporate to dryness. The residue dissolved in 10% HNO_3 constitutes Sonnenschein's reagent.

Phosphoric acid—sulfuric acid mixture. Dilute 150 ml of conc. H_2SO_4 and 100 ml of conc. H_3PO_4 (85%) with water to a volume of 1 liter.

Phosphotungstic acid (Scheibler's reagent for alkaloids).

1. Dissolve 20 g of sodium tungstate and 15 g of sodium phosphate in 100 ml of water containing a little nitric acid.

2. The reagent is a 10% solution of phosphotungstic acid in water. The phosphotungstic acid is prepared by evaporating a mixture of 10 g of sodium tungstate dissolved in 5 g of phosphoric acid (sp. gr. 1.13) and enough boiling water to effect solution. Crystals of phosphotungstic acid separate.

Picric acid (Hager's reagent for alkaloids, wool and silk). Dissolve 1 g of picric acid in 100 ml of water.

Potassium antimonate (reagent for sodium). Boil 22 g of potassium antimonate with 1 liter of water until nearly all of the salt has dissolved, cool quickly, and add 35 ml of 10% potassium hydroxide. Filter after standing over night.

Potassium-cadmium iodide (Marme's reagent for alkaloids). Add 2 g of CdI₂ to a boiling solution of 4 g of KI in 12 ml of water, and then mix with 12 ml of saturated KI solution.

Potassium hydroxide (for CO₂ absorption). Dissolve 360 g of KOH in water and dilute to 1 liter.

Potassium iodide-mercuric iodide (Brucke's reagent for proteins). Dissolve 50 g of KI in 500 ml of water, and saturate with mercuric iodide (about 120 g). Dilute to 1 liter.

Potassium pyrogallate (for oxygen absorption). For mixtures of gases containing less than 28% oxygen, add 100 ml of KOH solution (50 g of KOH to 100 ml of water) to 5 g of pyrogallol. For mixtures containing more than 28% oxygen the KOH solution should contain 120 g of KOH to 100 ml of water.

Pyrogallol, alkaline.
(a) Dissolve 75 g of pyrogallic acid in 75 ml of water.
(b) Dissolve 500 g of KOH in 250 ml of water. When cool, adjust until sp. gr. is 1.55.
For use, add 270 ml of solution (b) to 30 ml of solution (a).

Rosolic acid (indicator). Dissolve 1 g of rosolic acid in 10 ml of alcohol and add 100-ml of water.

S and O reagent (Suitsu and Okuma's test for Mg). Dissolve 0.5 g of the dye (o-p-dihydroxy-monazo-p-nitrobenzene) in 100 ml of 0.25 N NaOH.

Scheiber's reagent. See Phosphotungstic acid.

Schiff's reagent. See Fuchsin-sulfurous acid.

Schweitzer's reagent. See Cupric oxide, ammoniacal.

Soap solution (reagent for hardness in water). Dissolve 100 g of dry castile soap in 1 liter of 80% alcohol (5 parts alcohol to 1 part water). Allow to stand several days and dilute with 70% to 80% alcohol until 6.4 ml produces a permanent lather with 20 ml of standard calcium solution. The latter solution is made by dissolving 0.2 g of $CaCO_3$ in a small amount of dilute HCl, evaporating to dryness and making up to 1 liter.

Sodium bismuthate (oxidation of manganese). Heat 20 parts of NaOH nearly to redness in an iron or nickel crucible and add slowly 10 parts of basic bismuth nitrate which has been previously dried. Add two parts of sodium peroxide, and pour the brownish-yellow fused mass on an iron plate to cool. When cold, break up in a mortar, extract with water, and collect on an asbestos filter.

Sodium hydroxide (for CO_2 absorption). Dissolve 330 g of NaOH in water and dilute to 1 liter.

Sodium nitroprusside (reagent for hydrogen sulfide and wool). Use a freshly prepared solution of 1 g of sodium nitroprusside in 10 ml of water.

Sodium oxalate, according to Sörensen (primary standard). Dissolve 30 g of the commercial salt in 1 liter of water, make slightly alkaline with sodium hydroxide, and let stand until perfectly clear. Filter and evaporate the filtrate to 100 ml. Cool and filter. Pulverize the residue and wash it several times with small volumes of water. The procedure is repeated until the mother liquor is free from sulfate and is neutral to phenolphthalein.

Sodium plumbite (reagent for wool). Dissolve 5 g of sodium hydroxide in 100 ml of water. Add 5 g of litharge and boil until dissolved.

Sodium polysulfide. Dissolve 480 g of $Na_2S.9H_2O$ in 500 ml of water, add 40 g of NaOH and 18 g of sulfur. Stir thoroughly and dilute to 1 liter with water.

Sonnenschein's reagent. See Phosphomolybdic acid.

Starch solution.

1. Make a paste with 2 g of soluble starch and 0.01 g of HgI_2 with a small amount of water. Add the mixture slowly to 1 liter of boiling water and boil for a few minutes. Keep in a glass stoppered bottle. If other than soluble starch is used, the solution will not clear on boiling; it should be allowed to stand and the clear liquid decanted.

2. A solution of starch which keeps indefinitely is made as follows: Mix 500 ml of saturated NaCl solution (filtered), 80 ml of glacial acetic acid, 20 ml of water and 3 g of starch. Bring slowly to a boil and boil for two minutes.

3. Make a paste with 1 g of soluble starch and 5 mg of HgI_2, using as little cold water as possible. Then pour about 200 ml of boiling water on the paste and stir immediately. This will give a clear solution if the paste is prepared correctly and the water actually boiling. Cool and add 4 g of KI. Starch solution decomposes on standing due to bacterial action, but this solution will keep a long time if stored under a layer of toluene.

Stoke's reagent. Dissolve 30 g of $FeSO_4$ and 20 g of tartaric acid in water and dilute to 1 liter. Just before using, add concentrated NH_4OH until the precipitate first formed is redissolved.

Sulfanilic acid (reagent for nitrites). Dissolve 0.5 g of sulfanilic acid in a mixture of 15 ml of glacial acetic acid and 135 ml of recently boiled water.

Sulfomolybdic acid (Froehde's reagent for alkaloids and glucosides). Dissolve 10 g of molybdic acid or sodium molybdate in 100 ml of conc. H_2SO_4.

Tannic acid (reagent for albumen, alkaloids and gelatin). Dissolve 10 g of tannic acid in 10 ml of alcohol and dilute with water to 100 ml.

Titration mixture. See Zimmermann-Reinhardt reagent.

o-Tolidine solution (residual chlorine in water analysis). Prepare 1 liter of dilute HCl (100 ml of HCl (sp. gr. 1.19) in sufficient water to make 1 liter). Dissolve 1 g of o-tolidine in 100 ml of the dilute HCl and dilute to 1 liter with dilute HCl solution.

Trinitrophenol solution. See Picric acid.

Turmeric paper. Impregnate white, unsized paper with the tincture, and dry.

Turmeric tincture (reagent for borates). Digest ground turmeric root with several quantities of water which are discarded. Dry the residue and digest it several days with six times its weight of alcohol. Filter.

Uffelmann's reagent (turns yellow in presence of a lactic acid). To a 2% solution of pure phenol in water, add a water solution of $FeCl_3$ until the phenol solution becomes violet in color.

SPECIAL SOLUTIONS AND REAGENTS (Continued)

Wagner's reagent. See *Iodo-potassium iodide.*

Wagner's solution (used in phosphate rock analysis to prevent precipitation of iron and aluminum). Dissolve 25 g of citric acid and 1 g of salicylic acid in water and dilute to 1 liter. Use 50 ml of the reagent.

Wij's iodine monochloride solution (for iodine number). Dissolve 13 g of resublimed iodine in 1 liter of glacial acetic acid which will pass the dichromate test for reducible matter. Set aside 25 ml of this solution. Pass into the remainder of the solution dry chlorine gas (dried and washed by passing through H_2SO_4 (sp. gr. 1.84)) until the characteristic color of free iodine has been discharged. Now add the iodine solution which was reserved, until all free chlorine has been destroyed. A slight excess of iodine does little or no harm, but an excess of chlorine must be avoided. Preserve in well stoppered, amber colored bottles. Avoid use of solutions which have been prepared for more than 30 days.

Wij's special solution (for iodine number—Analyst **58,** 523–7, 1933). To 200 ml of glacial acetic acid that will pass the dichromate test for reducible matter, add 12 g of dichloroamine T (paratoluene-sulfonedichloroamide), and 16.6 g of dry KI (in small quantities with continual shaking until all the KI has dissolved). Make up to 1 liter with the same quality of acetic acid used above and preserve in a dark colored bottle.

Zimmermann-Reinhardt reagent (determination of iron). Dissolve 70 g of $MnSO_4.4H_2O$ in 500 ml of water, add 125 ml of conc. H_2SO_4 and 125 ml of 85% H_3PO_4, and dilute to 1 liter.

Zinc chloride solution, basic (reagent for silk). Dissolve 1000 g of zinc chloride in 850 ml of water, and add 40 g of zinc oxide. Heat until solution is complete.

Zinc uranyl acetate (reagent for sodium). Dissolve 10 g of $UO_2(C_2H_3O_2)_2.2H_2O$ in 6 g of 30% acetic acid with heat, if necessary, and dilute to 50 ml. Dissolve 30 g of $Zn(C_2H_3O_2)_2.-2H_2O$ in 3 g of 30% acetic acid and dilute to 50 ml. Mix the two solutions, add 50 mg of NaCl, allow to stand over night and filter.

DECI–NORMAL SOLUTIONS OF SALTS AND OTHER REAGENTS

Atomic and molecular weights in the following table are based upon the 1965 atomic weight scale and the isotope C-12. The weight in grams of the compound in 1 cc of the following deci-normal solutions is found by dividing the H equivalent in the last column by 1000.

Name	Formula	Atomic or molecular weight	Hydrogen equivalent	0.1 Hydrogen equivalent in g
Acetic acid	$HC_2H_3O_2$	60.0530	$HC_2H_3O_2$	6.0053
Ammonia	NH_3	17.0306	NH_3	1.7031
Ammonium ion	NH_4^+	18.0386	NH_4	1.8039
Ammonium chloride	NH_4Cl	53.4916	NH_4Cl	5.3492
Ammonium sulfate	$(NH_4)_2SO_4$	132.1388	$\frac{1}{2}(NH_4)_2SO_4$	6.6069
Ammonium thiocyanate	NH_4CNS	76.1204	NH_4CNS	7.6120
Barium	Ba	137.34	$\frac{1}{2}Ba$	6.867
Barium carbonate	$BaCO_3$	197.3494	$\frac{1}{2}BaCO_3$	9.8675
Barium chloride hydrate	$BaCl_2 \cdot 2H_2O$	244.2767	$\frac{1}{2}BaCl_2 \cdot 2H_2O$	12.2138
Barium hydroxide	$Ba(OH)_2$	171.3547	$\frac{1}{2}Ba(OH)_2$	8.5677
Barium oxide	BaO	153.3394	$\frac{1}{2}BaO$	7.6670
Bromine	Br	79.909	Br	7.9909
Calcium	Ca	40.08	$\frac{1}{2}Ca$	2.004
Calcium carbonate	$CaCO_3$	100.0894	$\frac{1}{2}CaCO_3$	5.0045
Calcium chloride	$CaCl_2$	110.9860	$\frac{1}{2}CaCl_2$	5.5493
Calcium chloride hydrate	$CaCl_2 \cdot 6H_2O$	219.0150	$\frac{1}{2}CaCl_2 \cdot 6H_2O$	10.9508
Calcium hydroxide	$Ca(OH)_2$	74.0947	$\frac{1}{2}Ca(OH)_2$	3.7047
Calcium oxide	CaO	56.0794	$\frac{1}{2}CaO$	2.8040
Chlorine	Cl	35.453	Cl	3.5453
Citric acid	$C_6H_8O_7 \cdot H_2O$	210.1418	$\frac{1}{3}C_6H_8O_7 \cdot H_2O$	7.0047
Cobalt	Co	58.9332	$\frac{1}{2}Co$	2.9466
Copper	Cu	63.54	$\frac{1}{2}Cu$	3.177
Copper oxide (cupric)	CuO	79.5394	$\frac{1}{2}CuO$	3.9770
Copper sulfate hydrate	$CuSO_4 \cdot 5H_2O$	249.6783	$\frac{1}{2}CuSO_4 \cdot 5H_2O$	12.4839
Cyanogen	$(CN)_2$	26.0179	CN	2.6018
Hydrochloric acid	HCl	36.4610	HCl	3.6461
Hydrocyanic acid	HCN	27.0258	HCN	2.7026
Iodine	I	126.9044	I	12.6904
Lactic acid	$C_3H_6O_3$	90.0795	$C_3H_6O_3$	9.0080
Malic acid	$C_4H_6O_5$	134.0894	$\frac{1}{2}C_4H_6O_5$	6.7045
Magnesium	Mg	24.312	$\frac{1}{2}Mg$	1.2156
Magnesium carbonate	$MgCO_3$	84.3214	$\frac{1}{2}MgCO_3$	4.2161
Magnesium chloride	$MgCl_2$	95.2180	$\frac{1}{2}MgCl_2$	4.7609
Magnesium chloride hydrate	$MgCl_2 \cdot 6H_2O$	203.2370	$\frac{1}{2}MgCl_2 \cdot 6H_2O$	10.1623
Magnesium oxide	MgO	40.3114	$\frac{1}{2}MgO$	2.0156
Manganese	Mn	54.938	$\frac{1}{2}Mn$	2.7469
Manganese sulfate	$MnSO_4$	150.9996	$\frac{1}{2}MnSO_4$	7.5500
Mercuric chloride	$HgCl_2$	271.4960	$\frac{1}{2}HgCl_2$	13.5748
Nickel	Ni	58.71	$\frac{1}{2}Ni$	2.9356
Nitric acid	HNO_3	63.0129	HNO_3	6.3013
Nitrogen	N	14.0067	N	1.4007
Nitrogen pentoxide	N_2O_5	108.0104	$\frac{1}{2}N_2O_5$	5.4005
Oxalic acid	$H_2C_2O_4$	90.0358	$\frac{1}{2}H_2C_2O_4$	4.5018
Oxalic acid hydrate	$H_2C_2O_4 \cdot 2H_2O$	126.0665	$\frac{1}{2}H_2C_2O_4 \cdot 2H_2O$	6.3033
Oxalic acid anhydride	C_2O_3	72.0205	$\frac{1}{2}C_2O_3$	3.6010
Phosphoric acid	H_3PO_4	97.9953	$\frac{1}{3}H_3PO_4$	3.2665
Potassium	K	39.102	K	3.9102
Potassium bicarbonate	$KHCO_3$	100.1193	$KHCO_3$	10.0119
Potassium carbonate	K_2CO_3	138.2134	$\frac{1}{2}K_2CO_3$	6.9106
Potassium chloride	KCl	74.5550	KCl	7.4555
Potassium cyanide	KCN	65.1199	KCN	6.5120
Potassium hydroxide	KOH	56.1094	KOH	5.6109
Potassium oxide	K_2O	94.2034	$\frac{1}{2}K_2O$	4.7102

Name	Formula	Atomic or molecular weight	Hydrogen equivalent	0.1 Hydrogen equivalent in g
Potassium permanganate for Co estimation	$KMnO_4$	158.0376	$\frac{1}{6}KMnO_4$	2.6339
Potassium permanganate for Mn estimation	$KMnO_4$	158.0376	$\frac{1}{3}KMnO_4$	5.2678
Potassium tartrate	$K_2H_4C_4O_6$	226.2769	$\frac{1}{2}K_2H_4C_4O_6$	11.3139
Silver	Ag	107.87	Ag	10.787
Silver nitrate	$AgNO_3$	169.8749	$AgNO_3$	16.9875
Sodium	Na	22.9898	Na	2.2990
Sodium bicarbonate	$NaHCO_3$	84.0071	$NaHCO_3$	8.4007
Sodium carbonate	Na_2CO_3	105.9890	$\frac{1}{2}Na_2CO_3$	5.2995
Sodium chloride	$NaCl$	58.4428	$NaCl$	5.8443
Sodium hydroxide	$NaOH$	39.9972	$NaOH$	3.9997
Sodium oxide	Na_2O	61.9790	$\frac{1}{2}Na_2O$	3.0990
Sodium sulfide	Na_2S	78.0436	$\frac{1}{2}Na_2S$	3.9022
Succinic acid	$H_2C_4H_4O_4$	118.0900	$\frac{1}{2}H_2C_4H_4O_4$	5.9045
Sulfuric acid	H_2SO_4	98.0775	$\frac{1}{2}H_2SO_4$	4.9039
Sulfur trioxide	SO_3	80.0622	$\frac{1}{2}SO_3$	4.0031
Tartaric acid	$C_4H_6O_6$	150.0888	$\frac{1}{2}C_4H_6O_6$	7.5044
Zinc	Zn	65.37	$\frac{1}{2}Zn$	3.269
Zinc sulfate	$ZnSO_4 \cdot 7H_2O$	287.5390	$\frac{1}{2}ZnSO_4 7 \cdot H_2O$	14.3769

DECI–NORMAL SOLUTIONS OF OXIDATION AND REDUCTION REAGENTS

Atomic and molecular weights in the following table are based upon the 1965 atomic weight scale and the isotope C-12. The weight in grams of the compound in 1 cc of the following deci-normal solutions is found by dividing the H equivalent in the last column by 1000.

Name	Formula	Atomic or molecular weight	Hydrogen equivalent	0.1 Hydrogen equivalent in g
Antimony	Sb	121.75	$\frac{1}{2}$Sb	6.0875
Arsenic	As	74.9216	$\frac{1}{2}$As	3.7461
Arsenic trisulfide	As_2S_3	246.0352	$\frac{1}{4}As_2S_3$	6.1509
Arsenous oxide	As_2O_3	197.8414	$\frac{1}{4}As_2O_3$	4.9460
Barium peroxide	BaO_2	169.3388	$\frac{1}{2}BaO_2$	8.4669
Barium peroxide hydrate	$BaO_2 \cdot 8H_2O$	313.4615	$\frac{1}{2}BaO_2 \cdot 8H_2O$	15.6730
Calcium	Ca	40.08	$\frac{1}{2}$Ca	2.004
Calcium carbonate	$CaCO_3$	100.0894	$\frac{1}{2}CaCO_3$	5.0045
Calcium hypochlorite	$Ca(OCl)_2$	142.9848	$\frac{1}{4}Ca(OCl)_2$	3.5746
Calcium oxide	CaO	56.0794	$\frac{1}{2}$CaO	2.8040
Chlorine	Cl	35.453	Cl	3.5453
Chromium trioxide	CrO_3	99.9942	$\frac{1}{3}CrO_3$	3.3331
Ferrous ammonium sulfate	$FeSO_4(NH_4)SO_4 \cdot 6H_2O$	392.0764	$FeSO_4(NH_4)_2SO_4 \cdot 6H_2O$	39.2076
Hydroferrocyanic acid	$H_4Fe(CN)_6$	215.9860	$H_4Fe(CN)_6$	21.5986
Hydrogen peroxide	H_2O_2	34.0147	$\frac{1}{2}H_2O_2$	1.7007
Hydrogen sulfide	H_2S	34.0799	$\frac{1}{2}H_2S$	1.7040
Iodine	I	126.9044	I	12.6904
Iron	Fe	55.847	Fe	5.5847
Iron oxide (ferrous)	FeO	71.8464	FeO	7.1846
Iron oxide (ferric)	Fe_2O_3	159.6922	$\frac{1}{2}Fe_2O_3$	7.9846
Lead peroxide	PbO_2	239.1888	$\frac{1}{2}PbO_2$	11.9594
Manganese dioxide	MnO_2	86.9368	$\frac{1}{2}MnO_2$	4.3468
Nitric acid	HNO_3	63.0129	$\frac{1}{3}HNO_3$	2.1004
Nitrogen trioxide	N_2O_3	76.0116	$\frac{1}{4}N_2O_3$	1.9002
Nitrogen pentoxide	N_2O_5	108.0104	$\frac{1}{5}N_2O_5$	1.8001
Oxalic acid	$C_2H_2O_4$	90.0358	$\frac{1}{2}C_2H_2O_4$	4.5018
Oxalic acid hydrate	$C_2H_2O_4 \cdot 2H_2O$	126.0665	$\frac{1}{2}C_2H_2O_4 \cdot 2H_2O$	6.3033
Oxygen	O	15.9994	$\frac{1}{2}$O	0.8000
Potassium dichromate	$K_2Cr_2O_7$	294.1918	$\frac{1}{6}K_2Cr_2O_7$	4.9032
Potassium chlorate	$KClO_3$	122.5532	$\frac{1}{6}KClO_3$	2.0425
Potassium chromate	K_2CrO_4	194.1076	$\frac{1}{3}K_2CrO_4$	6.4733
Potassium ferrocyanide	$K_4Fe(CN)_6$	368.3621	$K_4Fe(CN)_6$	36.8362
Potassium ferrocyanide	$K_4Fe(CN)_6 \cdot 3H_2O$	422.4081	$K_4Fe(CN)_6 \cdot 3H_2O$	42.2408
Potassium iodide	KI	166.0064	KI	16.6006
Potassium nitrate	KNO_3	101.1069	$\frac{1}{3}KNO_3$	3.3702
Potassium perchlorate	$KClO_4$	138.5526	$\frac{1}{8}KClO_4$	1.7319
Potassium permanganate	$KMnO_4$	158.0376	$\frac{1}{5}KMnO_4$	3.1608
Sodium chlorate	$NaClO_3$	106.4410	$\frac{1}{6}NaClO_3$	1.7740
Sodium nitrate	$NaNO_3$	84.9947	$\frac{1}{3}NaNO_3$	2.8332
Sodium thiosulfate	$Na_2S_2O_3 \cdot 5H_2O$	248.1825	$Na_2S_2O_3 \cdot 5H_2O$	24.8183
Stannous chloride	$SnCl_2$	189.5960	$\frac{1}{2}SnCl_2$	9.4798
Stannous oxide	SnO	134.6894	$\frac{1}{2}$SnO	6.7345
Sulfur dioxide	SO_2	64.0628	$\frac{1}{2}SO_2$	3.2031
Tin	Sn	118.69	$\frac{1}{2}$Sn	5.935

ORGANIC ANALYTICAL REAGENTS

Compiled by John H. Yoe

Determination	Reagent	Reference
Acetate......	o-Nitrobenzaldehyde	Feigl, p. 342 (3)
Aldehydes....	Dimethyl-dihydro-resorcin (Dimedon)	Ind. Eng. Chem., Anal. Ed. 3, 365 (1931)
Aluminum...	Alizarin S	J. Am. Chem. Soc. 50, 748 (1928)
	Ammonium salt of aurin tricarboxylic acid ("Aluminon")	J. Am. Chem. Soc. 49, 2395 (1927) J. Am. Chem. Soc. 55, 2437 (1933)
	Ammonium salt of nitrosophenyl hydroxylamine ("Cupferron")	Bull. soc. chim. Belg. 36, 288 (1927)
	Eriochrome cyanine	Z. anal. Chem. 96, 91 (1934)
	Hematoxylin	Ind. Eng. Chem. 16, 233 (1924)
	8-Hydroxyquinoline	J. Am. Chem. Soc. 50, 1900 (1928)
	Morin	Feigl, p. 182 (2) Ind. Eng. Chem., Anal. Ed. 12, 229 (1940)
	Quinalizarine	J. Am. Pharm. Assoc. 17, 260 (1928)
	Sodium or zinc salt of 4-sulfo-2 hydroxy-α-naphthalene-azo-β-naphthol (Pontachrome Blue Black R)	Sandell, p. 241 (6)
	Urea	Ind. Eng. Chem., Anal. Ed. 9, 357 (1937)
Ammonia....	Hematoxylin	Helv. Chim. Acta 12, 730 (1929)
	p-Nitrobenzenediazonium chloride	Feigl, p. 235 (2)
	Phenol and sodium hypochloride	Snell, Vol. II, p. 818 (8)
	Tannin—AgNO₃	Snell, Vol. II, p. 819 (8)
	Thymol	J. Biol. Chem. 131, 309 (1939)
	Zinc oxinate	Feigl, p. 674 (9)
Antimony....	Hexamethylenetetramine	Z. anal. Chem. 67, 298 (1925)
	9-Methyl-2,3,7-tryhydroxyfluorone	Helv. Chim. Acta 20, 1427 (1937)
	Phenylthiohydantoic acid	Compt. rend. 176, 1221 (1923)
	Pyridine	Analyst 53, 373 (1928)
	Pyrogallol	Z. anal. Chem. 64, 44 (1924)
	Rhodamine B	Z. anal. Chem. 70, 400 (1927)
Arsenic......	Cocaine-molybdate	Biochem. Z. 185, 14 (1927)
	N-Ethyl-8-hydroxytetrahydroquinoline hydrochloride	Z. anal. Chem. 99, 180 (1934)
	Quinine arsenomolybdate	Analyst 47, 317 (1922)
	Strychnine-molybdate	Ann. Chim. applicata 23, 517 (1933)
Barium......	Sodium rhodizonate	Feigl, p. 216 (2)
	Tetrahydroxyquinone	Welcher, Vol. I, p. 225 (9)
Beryllium....	1-Amino-4-hydroxyanthraquinone	Ind. Eng. Chem., Anal. 13, 809 (1941)
	Aurin trycarboxylic	J. Am. Chem. Soc. 48, 2125 (1926); ibid., 50, 353 (1928)
	Curcumin	J. Am. Chem. Soc. 50, 393 (1928)
	1,4-Dihydroxyanthraquinone (Quinizarin)	Ind. Eng. Chem. Anal. Ed., 18, 179 (1946)
	1,4-Dihydroxyanthraquinone-2-sulfonic acid (quinizarine-2-sulfonic acid)	Sandell, p. 318 (6)
	8-Hydroxyquinoline	Bur. Standards J. Research 3, 91 (1929)
	Morin	Ind. Eng. Chem., Anal. Ed. 12, 674, 762 (1940)
	Naphthochrome Azurine 2B	Sandell, p. 318 (6)
	Naphthochrome Green G	Sandell, p. 318 (6)
	p-Nitrobenzeneazo-orcinol	Mikrochemie 14, 315 (1934)
	1,2,5,8-Tetrahydroxyanthraquinone (Quinalizarin)	Siemens-Konzerns, Beryllium, p. 25 (1932)
Bismuth....	Caffeine (as sulfate or nitrate)	Ind. Eng. Chem., Anal. Ed. 14, 43 (1942)
	Cinchonine	Scott, p. 158 (7)
	Diethyldithiocarbamate	Sandell, p. 338 (6)
	Dimercaptothiodiazole	Z. anal. Chem. 98, 184 (1934); ibid., 100, 408 (1935)
	Dimethylglyoxime	Z. anal. Chem. 72, 11 (1927)
	Diphenylthiocarbazone	Z. Angew. Chem. 47, 685 (1934); Ind. Eng. Chem., Anal. Ed. 7, 285 (1935)
	8-Hydroxyquinoline	Z. anal. Chem. 72, 177 (1927)
	Phenyldithiobiazolonethiol	J. Indian Chem. Soc., 21, 240, 347 (1944)
	Pyrogallol	Z. anal. Chem. 65, 448 (1925)
	Thiourea	Z. anal. Chem. 94, 161 (1933)

Determination	Reagent	Reference
Boron......	Curcumin	Chem. News 87, 27 (1903)
	1,1-Dianthramide	Boltz, p. 346 (1)
	Diaminochrysazin	Anal. Chem. 29, 1251 (1957)
	Diaminoanthrarufin	Ibid.
	Tribromoanthrarufin	Ibid.
	Mannitol	Scott, p. 168 (7)
	Methyl alcohol	J. Am. Chem. Soc. 50, 1385 (1928)
	p-Nitrobenzeneazochromotropic acid (Chromotrope 2B)	Feigl, p. 341 (2)
	Quinalizarin	Ind. Eng. Chem., Anal. Ed. 11, 540 (1939)
	Titan Yellow (Clayton Yellow)	Compt. rend. 138, 1046 (1904)
	Turmeric	Ind. Eng. Chem., Anal. Ed. 4, 180 (1932)
Bromine...	Fluorescein	Snell, Vol. II, p. 725 (8)
	Fuchsin	Snell, Vol. II, p. 724 (8)
	Phenol red	Snell, Vol. II, p. 725 (8)
Cadmium..	Allythiourea	Helvetica Chim. Acta. 12, 718 (1929)
	Di-β-naphthylthiocarbazone	Ind. Eng. Chem., Anal. Ed., 16, 333, (1944)
	Dinitrodiphenylcarbazide	Feigl, p. 96 (2)
	Diphenylcarbazide	Feigl, p. 99 (2)
	Diphenylthiocarbazone	Z. angew. Chem. 47, 685 (1934); Ind. Eng. Chem., Anal. Ed. 11, 364 (1939)
	Ethylenediamine	Z. anal. Chem. 77, 340 (1929)
	Hexamethylenetetramine alliodide	C. A., 24, 311 (1930)
	β-Naphthoquinoline	Analyst, 58, 667 (1933)
	Nitrophenolarsinic acid	Mikrochemie 8, 277 (1930)
	4-Nitrophthalenediazo-aminobenzene-4-azobenzene (Cadion 2B)	C. A. 32, 2871 (1938)
	Phenyl-trimethyl-ammonium iodide	Analyst 58, 667 (1933)
	Pyridine	Z. Anal. Chem. 73, 279 (1928)
Calcium....	Alizarin	Biochem. J. 16, 494 (1922); Yoe, Vol. I, p. 139 (2)
	1-amino-2-naphthol-4-sulfonic acid	J. Biol. Chem. 81, 1 (1929)
	Ammonium oxalate	Snell, Vol. II, p. 592 (8)
	Ammonium stearate	J. Biol. Chem. 29, 169 (1917); Yoe, Vol. II, p. 119 (3)
	2,5-Dichloro-3,6-dihydroxyquinone (Chloranilic acid)	Anal. Chem., 20, 76 (1948)
	Dihydroxytartaric acid osazone (sodium salt)	Feigl, p. 221 (2)
	Picrolonic acid	Biochem. Z. 265, 85 (1933)
	Potassium oleate	Sandell, p. 377 (6)
	Pyrogallol carboxylic acid	Sandell, p. 380 (6)
	Sodium sulforicinate	Biochem. Z. 137, 157 (1923); Yoe, Vol. II, p. 125 (3)
Cerium.....	Benzidine	Feigl, p. 211 (2)
	Brucine	Sandell, p. 386 (6)
	Gallic acid	Snell, Vol. II, p. 608 (8)
	8-Hydroxyquinoline	Analyst, 75, 275 (1948)
	Malachite Green	C. A. 30, 5143 (1936), 31, 626 (1937)
	Morphine	Sandell, p. 386 (6)
	Sulfanilic acid	Sandell, p. 386 (6)
Cesium.....	Dipicrylamine (Hexanitrodiphenylamine)	Mikrochemie 18, 175 (1935)
Chlorate....	Aniline hydrochloride	Snell, Vol. II, p. 717 (8)
Chlorine....	Benzidine hydrochloride	Ind. Eng. Chem., Anal. Ed. 4, 2 (1932)
	Dimethyl-p-phenylene-diamine	Chem. Weekblad. 23, 203 (1926)
	Oleic acid	J. Soc. Chem. Ind. 42, 427A (1923)
	Sodium sulforicinate	Biochem. Z., 137, 157 (1923); Yoe, Vol. II, p. 125 (3)
	Thymolphthalein	Ind. Eng. Chem. 19, 112 (1927)
	o-Tolidine	Yoe, Vol. I, p. 157 (2)
Columbium..	Benzidine	Feigl, p. 171 (2)
	1,8-Dihydroxynaphthalene-3,6-Disulfonate	Ind. Eng. Chem. 5, 298 (1913)
	s-Diphenylcarbazide	J. Am. Chem. Soc. 50, 2363 (1928)
	Pyrogallol dimethyl ether	C. A. 4, 3178 (1910)
	Serichrome Blue R	Ind. Eng. Chem., Anal. Ed., 4, 245 (1932)

Determination	Reagent	Reference
Cobalt........	Anthranilic acid (*o*-aminobenzoic acid)	Z. anal. Chem. **93**, 241 (1933)
	Cysteine hydrochloride	J. Biol. Chem. **83**, 367 (1929)
	Dimethylglyoxime	J. Am. Chem. Soc. **43**, 482 (1921)
	3,5-Dimethylpyrazole	Ind. Eng. Chem., Anal. Ed. **2**, 38 (1930)
	Dinitrosoresorcinol	J. Am. Chem. Soc. **45**, 1439 (1923)
	Formaldoxime reagent	C. A. **27**, 927 (1933)
	o-Nitrosocresol	Sandell, p. 422 (6)
	α-Nitroso-β-naphthol	Chem. Zeit. **46**, 430 (1922)
	Nitroso-R-salt	J. Am. Chem. Soc. **43**, 746 (1921)
	β-Nitroso-α-naphthol	Ind. Eng. Chem., Anal. Ed. **12**, 405 (1940)
	o-Nitrosoresorcinol	Ind. Eng. Chem., Anal. Ed. **15**, 310 (1943)
	o-Nitrosophenol	Sandell, p. 422 (6)
	Phenylthiohydantoic acid	J. Am. Chem. Soc. **44**, 2219 (1922)
	Rubeanic acid (Dithio-oxamide)	Anal. Chim. Acta **20**, 332, 435 (1959)
	2,2′,2″-Terpyridyl	Ind. Eng. Chem., Anal. Ed., **15**, 74 (1943)
	Niobium	
Columbium ...	See **Niobium**	
Copper.......	Ammonium salt of nitrosophenyl-hydroxylamine ("Cupferron")	Ind. Eng. Chem. **3**, 629 (1911)
	m-Benzamino-semicarbazide	Snell, Vol. II, p. 129 (6)
	Benzidine	Z. anal. Chem. **67**, 31 (1925)
	α-Benzionoxime (Cupron)	Ber. **56**, 2083 (1923)
	Benzotriazole	Ind. Eng. Chem., Anal. Ed. **13**, 349 (1941)
	2-Carboxy-a′-hydroxy-5′ sulfoformazylbenzene (Zincon)	Anal. Chem. **26**, 1345 (1954)
	Diacetyl-dioxime	Analyst **54**, 333 (1929)
	Dibenzyldithiocarbamate	Sandell, p. 443 (6)
	Dihydroxyethyldithiocarbamic acid	Sandell, p. 443 (6)
	p-Dimethylaminobenzalrhodanine	J. Am. Chem. Soc. **52**, 2222 (1930)
	s-Diphenylcarbazide	J. Am. Chem. Soc. **47**, 1268 (1925)
		Chem. Weekblad. **21**, 20 (1924)
	Diphenylthiocarbazone (Dithizone)	J. Assoc. Official Agr. Chem. **18**, 192 (1935)
	Hydroquinone	Bull. soc. chim. **31**, 1176 (1922)
	Isatin	Rec trav chim. **42**, 199 (1923)
	Mercaptobenzothiazole	Z. anal. Chem. **102**, 24, 108 (1935)
	α-Naphthol	Bull. soc. chim. **31**, 1176 (1922)
	β-Naphthol	Am. J. Pharm. **105**, 62 (1933)
	Phenolphthalein	Compt. rend. **173**, 1082 (1921)
	Phenylthiohydantoic acid	J. Am. Chem. Soc. **44**, 225 (1922)
	Piperidinium piperidyl-dithioformate	Analyst **56**, 736 (1931)
	Potassium ethyl xanthate	Yoe, Vol. I, p. 184 (2)
	Pyridine	Z. anal. Chem. **67**, 27 (1925)
	Rubeanic acid (Dithio-oxamide)	Anal. Chim. Acta **20**, 332, 435 (1959)
	Salicylaldoxime	J. Chem. Soc. (1933) 314; Feigl, p. 40 (8)
	Salicylic acid	Yoe, Vol. I, p. 183 (2)
	Sodium diethyldithiocarbamate	Analyst **54**, 650 (1929)
	o-Toluidine	Z. anal. Chem. **67**, 31 (1925)
	Urobilin	Chem. Weekblad. **27**, 552 (1930)
Cyanide......	Benzidine	Feigl, p. 276 (2)
	Phenolphthalin	Analyst **60**, 294 (1935)
	Picric acid	Helv. Chim. Acta **12**, 713 (1929); J. Am. Chem. Soc. **51**, 1171 (1929)
Fluoride......	Acetylacetone	Ind. Eng. Chem., Anal. Ed. **5**, 300 (1933)
	Alizarin sodium sulfonate—Zr(NO₃)₄	Ind. Eng. Chem., Anal. Ed. **7**, 23 (1935)
	p-Dimethylaminoazophenylarsonic acid	Feigl, p. 271 (2)
	Triphenyltin chloride	J. Am. Soc. **54**, 4625 (1932)
	Quinalizarine—Zr(NO₃)₄	Ind. Eng. Chem., Anal. Ed. **6**, 61 (1934)
Gallium......	Camphoric acid	Welcher, Vol. II, p. 31 (9)
	8-Hydroxyquinoline	Ind. Eng. Chem., Anal. Ed. **13**, 844 (1941)
	Morin	Mikrochemie **20**, 194 (1936)
	Quinalizarin	J. Am. Chem. Soc. **59**, 40 (1937)
Germanium ...	Benzidine	Mikrochemie **18**, 66 (1935)
	Quinalizarin	Mikrochemie **18**, 48 (1935)
	Tannin	Welcher, Vol. II, p. 160 (9)

Determination	Reagent	Reference
Gold.......	Benzidine	Bull. Chim. Farm. **52**, 461 (1912)
	o-Dianisidine	Sandell, p. 507 (6)
	Dimethylaminobenzylidene rhodanine	Feigl, p. 127 (2)
	Formaldehyde	Bull. soc. chim. **31**, 717 (1922)
	p-Fuchsine	Ind. Eng. Chem., Anal. Ed., **18**, 400 (1946)
	Malachite Green	Sandell, p. 506 (6)
	m-Phenylenediamine sulfate	Chem. Zeit. **36**, 934 (1912)
	Phenylhydrazine	Ann. chim. anal. **12**, 90 (1907)
	o-Toluidine	Analyst **44**, 94 (1919)
Hafnium...	2-Hydroxy-5-methylazobenzene-4-sulfonic acid	Feigl, p. 288 (4)
Hydrogen .. sulfide	*p*-phenylenedimethyldiamine sulfate	Yoe, Vol. I, p. 375 (2)
Indium.. ...	Diphenylthiocarbazone (Dithizone)	Sandell, p. 516 (6)
	8-Hydroxyquinoline	Z. anorg. allgem. Chem. **209**, 129 (1932)
	Morin	Mikrochim. Acta **2**, 287 (1937)
Iodine......	Starch	Snell, Vol. II, p. 740 (8)
	o-Toluidine	J. Am. Chem. Soc. **47**, 1000 (1925)
Iridium.....	Benzidine	Snell, Vol. II, p. 526 (8)
	Malachite Green, leuco base	C. A. **24**, 2689 (1930)
Iron........	Acetylacetone	J. Am. Chem. Soc. **26**, 967 (1904)
	Alloxantin	Compt. rend. **180**, 519 (1925)
	Ammonium salt of nitrosophenyl hydroxylamine ("Cupferon")	Ind. Eng. Chem. **3**, 629 (1911)
	Bis-*p*-chlorophenylphosphoric acid	Feigl, p. 294 (4)
	Cysteine	Biochem. Z. **187**, 255 (1927)
	Dimethyl glyoxime	Z. anorg. Chemie **89**, 401 (1914)
	Dinitrosoresorcinol	J. Am. Chem. Soc. **47**, 1268 (1925)
	Diisonitrosoacetone	Chem. Listy **23**, 496 (1929); C. A. **24**, 801 (1930)
	Dioximes (various)	Anal. Chem. **19**, 1017 (1947)
	Diphenylamine	J. Am. Chem. Soc. **46**, 263 (1924)
	2,2-Bipyridyl	Snell, Vol. II, p. 316 (8)
	Disodium-1,2-dihydroxybenzene-3,5-disulfonate ("Tiron")	Ind. Eng. Chem., Anal. Ed. **16**, 111 (1944)
	Hexamethylenetetramine	Bull soc. chim. Rom. **2**, 89 (1921)
	4 Hydroxybiphenyl-3-carboxylic acid	J. Am. Chem. Soc. **70**, 648 (1948)
	8-Hydroxyquinoline	Bull. soc. chim. biol., **17**, 432 (1935)
	4-Hydroxybiphenyl-3-carboxylic acid	J. Am. Chem. Soc. **70**, 648 (1948)
	7-Iodo-8-hydroxyquinoline-5-sulfonic acid (Ferron)	J. Am. Chem. Soc. **59**, 872 (1937)
	Isonitrosoacetophenone	Ber. **60**, 527 (1927)
	Isonitrosodimethyldihydroresorcinol	Anal. Chem., **20**, 1205 (1948)
	Kojic acid	Ind. Eng. Chem., Anal. Ed., **13**, 612 (1941)
	α-Nitroso-β-naphthol	Bull. chim. **35**, 641 (1924)
	Nitroso-R salt	Ind. Chem., Anal. Ed., **14**, 756 (1942); **16**, 276 (1944)
	o-Phenanthroline	Ind. Eng. Chem., Anal. Ed. **9**, 67 (1937)
	Protocatechvic acid	J. Biol. Chem., **137**, 417 (1941)
	Pyramidone	Pharm. Weekblad, **63**, 1121 (1926)
	Pyrocatechol	Helv. chim. Acta **9**, 835 (1926)
	Salicylaldoxime	Ind Eng. Chem., Anal. Ed., **12**, 448 (1940)
	Salicylic acid	J. Chem. Soc. **93**, 93 (1908)
	Salicylsulfonic acid	Snell, Vol. II, p. 321 (8)
	Sulfosalicylic acid	Biochem. Z. **181**, 391 (1927)
	Thioglycollic acid	J. Am. Chem. Soc. **49**, 1916 (1927)
Lanthanum	8-Hydroxyquinoline	Z. anal. Chem. **107**, 191 (1936)
	Sodium alizarinesulfonate	J. Am. Chem. Soc., **53**, 1217 (1931)
Lead......	Ammonium thiocyanate and pyridine	Z. anal. Chem. **72**, 289 (1927)
	Aniline	Ind. Eng. Chem. **11**, 1055 (1919); Yoe, Vol. I, p. 257 (2)
	Anthranilic acid	Z. anal. Chem. **101**, 85 (1935)
	Carminic acid	Mikrochemie **7**, 301 (1929)
	s-Diphenylcarbazide	Yoe, Vol. I, p. 255 (2)
	Diphenylthiocarbazone (Dithizone)	Snell, Vol. IIA, p. 10 (8)
	Hematein	Yoe, Vol. I, p. 257 (2)
	Salicylaldoxime	Ind. Eng. Chem., Anal. Ed. **14**, 359 (1942)
	Tetramethyldiamidodiphenylmethane	Snell, Vol. II, p. 43 (8)
	Thiourea	Z. anorg. Chem., **234**, 224 (1937)

Determination	Reagent	Reference	Determination	Reagent	Reference
Lithium......	Ammonium stearate	J. Am. Chem. Soc. **52**, 2754 (1930)	Nitrite......	Antipyrin	Yoe, Vol. I, p. 311 (2)
	Hexamethylenetetr-amine	Welcher, Vol. III, p. 131 (9)		Dimethylaniline	" p. 311 (2)
	Pyridine	Welcher, Vol. III, p. 33 (9)		Dimethyl-α-Naph-thylamine	Ind. Eng. Chem., Anal. Ed. **1**, 28 (1929)
Magnesium..	Brilliant yellow	Sandell, p. 598 (6)		Diphenylamine sulfate	Yoe, Vol. I, p. 654 (2)
	Curcumin	Ind. Eng. Chem., Anal. Ed. **4**, 426 (1932)		α-Naphthylamine and β-Naphthylamine-6, 8-Disulfonic acid	J. Pharmacol. **51**, 398 (1934)
	Dimethylamine	Z. anorg. Chem. **26**, 347 (1901)			
	Hydroquinone	Yoe, Vol. I, p. 264 (2)		α-Naphthylamine hydrochloride	Yoe, Vol. I, p. 309 (2)
	8-Hydroxyquinoline	Z. anal. Chem. **71**, 122 (1927)		m-Phenylenediamine	Yoe, Vol. I, p. 310 (2)
	p-Nitrobenzeneazo-α-naphthol	Feigl, p. 225 (2)		Sulfanilic acid and α-naphthylamine	Yoe, Vol. I, p. 308 (2)
	p-Nitrobenzeneazo-resorcinol	J. Am. Chem. Soc. **51**, 1456 (1929)	Osmium....	s-Diphenylthiourea	Yoe and Sarver, p. 155 (12)
	Oleic acid	Yoe, Vol. I, p. 270 (2)		1-Naphthylamine-4,6,8-trisulfonic acid	Anal. Chim. Acta **20**, 205 (1959)
	Quinalizarin	Feigl, p. 224 (2)		Strychnine	Welcher, Vol. IV, p. 272 (9)
	Sodium 1-azo-2-hydroxy-3-(2,4-dimethylcarbox-aniliodonaphthalene-1'(2-hydroxyben-zene-5-sulfonate)	Anal. Chem. **28**, 202 (1956); cf. Anal. Chim. Acta **16**, 155 (1957)		Thiourea	Compt. rend. **167**, 235 (1918)
			Oxygen.....	Indigo carmine	Snell, Vol. IIA, p. 726 (8)
				Pyrogallol	Dennis, Gas Analysis, p. 174 (1929)
	Thiazole yellow	Sandell, p. 598 (6)	Palladium..	Dimethylglyoxime	J. Am. Chem. Soc. **57**, 2565 (1935)
	Titan yellow	Sandell, p. 591 (6)		p-Fuchsine	Ind. Eng. Chem., Anal. Ed., **18**, 400 (1946)
	Tropeoline OO	Rec. trav. chim., **61**, 849 (1942)		β-Furfuraldoxime	Ind. Eng. Chem., Anal. Ed. **14**, 491 (1942)
Manganese..	Benzidine	Snell, Vol. II, p. 397 (8)		6-Nitroquinoline	J. Am. Chem. Soc. **50**, 3018 (1928)
	Formaldoxime	Ind. Eng. Chem., Anal. Ed. **9**, 445 (1937); **12**, 307 (1940)		p-Nitrosodiphenyl-amine	J. Am. Chem. Soc. **61**, 2058 (1939)
	Tetramethyldiamino-diphenylmethane	Feigl, p. 174 (2); Snell, Vol. IIA, p. 311 (8)		p-Nitrosodimethyl-aniline	J. Am. Chem. Soc. **63**, 3224 (1941)
	4,4-Tetramethyl-diaminotriphenyl-methane	J. Biol. Chem., **168**, 537 (1947)		p-Nitrosodiethyl-aniline	Ibid.
Mercury....	Anthranilic acid	Z. anal. Chem. **101**, 88 (1935)		Thiomalic acid	Talanta **2**, 223 (1959)
	p-Dimethylamino-benzalrhodamine	J. Am. Chem. Soc. **52**, 2222 (1930)	Phosphate..	1,2,4-Aminonaphtho-sulfonic acid	Yoe, Vol. I, p. 348 (2)
	Di-β-naphthylthio-carbazone	Sandell, p. 630 (6)		Hydroquinone	Yoe, Vol. I, pp. 346 and 353 (2)
	s-Diphenylcarbazide	Z. angew. Chem. **39**, 791 (1926)		Quinine-molybdate	Yoe, Vol. I, p. 343 (2)
	Diphenylthiocarba-zone (Dithizone)	Z. anal. Chem. **103**, 241 (1935)		Strychnine-molybdate	Yoe, Vol. II, p. 142 (3)
	Potassium s-diphenyl-carbazone	Snell, Vol. II 78 (8)	Phosphorus.	Hydrazine sulfate	Yoe, Vol. I, p. 341 (2)
	Strychnine	" II 76 (8)	Platinum...	p-Nitrosodimethyl-aniline	Anal. Chem. **26**, 1335, 1340 (1954)
Molybdenum	α-Benzoin-oxime (Cupron)	B. S. J. Research **9**, 1 (1932)	Potassium..	6-Chloro-5-nitrotol-uene-3-sulfonic acid	Mikrochem. **14**, 368 (1934)
	Disodium-1,2-dihy-droxy-benzene-3,5-disulfonate (Tiron)	Anal. Chim. Acta **8**, 546 (1953)		Dipicrylamine	Z. angew. Chem. **49**, 827 (1936)
	4-Methyl-1,2-dimer-captobenzene (Dithiol)	J. Am. Pharm. Assoc., **37**, 255 (1948)		Picric acid	J. Am. Chem. Soc. **53**, 539 (1931)
			Rhodium...	Thiomalic acid	Talanta **2**, 239 (1959)
	Phenylhydrazine	Ber. **36**, 512 (1903)	Ruthenium.	s-Diphenylthiourea	Yoe and Sarver, p. 155 (12)
	Potassium ethyl xan-thate and chloroform	J. Am. Chem. Soc. **44**, 1462 (1922)		5-Hydroxyquinoline-8-carboxylic acid	Canadian J. Research B25, **49**, (1945)
	Tannic acid	Chem. Eng. Mining Rev. **11**, 258 (1919)		1-Naphthylamine-3,5,7-trisulfonic acid	Anal. Chim Acta **20**, 211 (1959)
Nickel......	α-Benzil-dioxime	Analyst **38**, 316 (1913)		Rubianic acid (Dithio-oxamide)	Mikrochemie **15**, 295 (1934)
	Cyclohexanedione-dioxime	Ann. **437**, 148 (1925)		Thioglycolyl-β-amido-naphthalide (Thion-alid)	Ind. Eng. Chem., Anal. Ed. **12**, 5611 (1940)
	Dicyandiamidine sulfate	Chem. Zeit. **31**, 335, 911 (1907)		Thiourea	Sandell, p. 781 (6)
	Diethyldithiocar-bamate	Ind. Eng. Chem., Anal. Ed., **18**, 206 (1946)	Scandium..	Morin	Mikrochem. Acta **2**, 9, 287 (1937)
	Dimethylglyoxime	Chem. Weekblad. **21**, 358 (1924)	Selenium...	Codeine phosphate	Arch Pharm. **252**, 161 (1914)
	Formaldoxime	Snell, Vol. IIA, p. 265 (8)		Hydrazine	Boltz, p. 321 (1)
	α-Furildioxime	J. Am. Chem. Soc. **47**, 918 (1925)		Hydroquinone	Am. J. Sci. **15**, 253 (1928)
	Potassium dithiooxa-late	J. Am. Chem. Soc. **54**, 1866 (1932)		Hydroxylamine hydrochloride	J. Am. Chem. Soc. **47**, 2456 (1925)
	Rubianic acid (Dithio-oxamide)	Anal. Chim. Acta **20**, 332 435 (1959)		Pyrrol	Snell, Vol. II, p. 779 (8)
Niobium (Columbium)	Ammonium salt of ni-trosophenyl hydrox-ylamine ("Cupfer-ron")	Hillebrand et al., p. 120 (5)		Thiourea	Ann. chim. applicata **17**, 357 (1927); Feigl, p. 231 (8)
			Silver......	Chromotropic acid	Helvetica Chim. Acta **12**, 714 (1929)
	8 Hydroxyquinolin	Wechler, Vol. I, p. 302 (2)		Dichlorofluorescein	J. Am. Chem. Soc. **51**, 3273 (1929)
				p-Dimethylamino-benzalrhodamine	J. Am. Chem. Soc. **52**, 2222 (1930)
				Diphenylthiocarba-zone (Dithizone)	Z. anal. Chem. **101**, 1 (1935)
				Formazylcarboxylic acid	J. Anal. Chem. Russ., **2**, 131 (1934); abs. in Analyst, **73**, 352 (1948)
				Methylamine	Mikrochemie **7**, 233 (1929)
Nitrate.....	Brucine	Yoe, Vol. I, p. 318 (2)		2-Thio-5-keto-4-car-bethoxy-1,3-dihydro-pyrimidine	Ind. Eng. Chem., Anal. Ed. **14**, 148 (1942)
	Diphenylamine sulfonic acid	J. Am. Chem. Soc. **55**, 1448 (1933)	Sodium....	6,8-Dichlorobenzoyl-urea	J. Org. Chem. **3**, 414 (1938)
	Diphenylbenzidine	Yoe, Vol. I, p. 316 (2)		Dihydroxy-tartaric acid	J. Russ. Phys. Chem. Soc. **60**, 661 (1928)
	Diphenyl-endo-anilo-hydrotriazole ("Nitron")	Fales and Kenny, Inorg. Quant. Anal., p. 347 (1938)		Uranyl zinc acetate	J. Am. Chem. Soc. **51**, 1664 (1929)
	Phenoldisulfonic acid	Yoe, Vol. I, p. 313 (2)	Strontium.	Sodium rhodizonate	Mikrochemie **2**, 187 (1924)
	Pyrogallol	" p. 319 (2)	Sulfide....	p-Aminodimethyl-aniline	Snell, Vol. IIA, p. 658 (8)
	Strychnine sulfate	" p. 320 (2)	Sulfur....	p-Phenylenedimethyl-diamine-hydro-chloride	Yoe, Vol. I, p. 373 (2)
	2:4-Xylenol	J. Assoc. Off. Agri. Chem. **18**, 459 (1935)			

Determination	Reagent	Reference
Tantalum	Ammonium salt of nitrosophenyl hydroxylamine ("Cupferron")	Hillebrand et. al., p. 120 (5)
Tellurium	Pyrogallol	Sandell, p. 695 (6)
	Hydrazine hydrochloride	J. Am. Chem. Soc. 47, 2456 (1925)
	Hydroquinone	Am. J. Sci. 15, 253 (1928)
	Thiourea	Ann. chim. applicata 17, 359 (1927)
Thallium	Diphenylthiocarbazone (Dithizone)	Analyst 60, 394 (1935)
	Thionalid (Thioglycolyl-β-amidonaphthalide)	Z. angew. Chem. 48, 430, 597 (1935)
Thorium	1-Amino-4-hydroxyanthraquinone	Ind. Eng. Chem., Anal. Ed. 13, 809 (1941)
	Cupferron (Ammonium nitrosophenylhydroxylamine)	Chem. Ztg. 33, 1298 (1908)
	8-Hydroxyquinoline	Z. anal. Chem. 100, 98 (1935)
	Phenylarsonic acid	J. Am. Chem. Soc. 48, 895 (1926)
Tin	Ammonium salt of nitrosophenyl hydroxylamine ("Cupferron")	Hillebrand et al., p. 120 (5)
	Cacotheline	Ind. Eng. Chem., Anal. Ed. 7, 26 (1935)
	4-Chloro-1,2-dimercaptobenzene (1-chloro-benzene-3,4-dithiol)	J. Chem. Soc. 149, 175 (1936)
	Hematoxylin	Sandell, p. 866 (6)
	Quinalizarin	Sandell, p. 866 (6)
	Toluene-3,4-dithiol (4-methyl-1,2-dimercaptobenzene)	Analyst 61, 242 (1936); Ibid., 62, 661 (1937)
Titanium	Ammonium salt of nitrosophenyl hydroxylamine ("Cupferron")	Hillebrand et al., p. 119 (5); Z. anal. Chem. 83, 345 (1931)
	Chromotropic acid	Feigl, p. 197 (2)
	5,7-Dibromo-8-hydroxyquinoline	Z. anorg. Chem. 204, 215 (1932)
	Dihydroxymaleic acid	Snell, Vol. II, p. 445 (8)
	Disodium 1,2-dihydroxybenzene-3,5-disulfonate ("Tiron")	Ind. Eng. Chem., Anal. Ed. 19, 100 (1947)
	Gallic acid	Snell, Vol. II, p. 444 (8)
	p-Hydroxyphenylarsonic acid	Ind. Eng. Chem., Anal. Ed. 10, 642 (1938)
	8-Hydroxyquinoline	Z. anal. Chem. 81, 1 (1930)
	Resoflavine (Color Index 1015)	Anal. Chim. Acta, 1, 244 (1947)
	Tannic acid	Analyst 55, 605 (1930)
	Thymol	Yoe, Vol. I, p. 381 (2)
Tungsten (Wolfram)	Anti-1,5-di-(p-methoxyphenyl)-1-hydroxylamino-3-oximino-4-pentene ("Wolfron")	Ind. Eng. Chem., Anal. Ed. 16, 45 (1944)
	Benzidine	Ber. 38, 783 (1905)
	α-Benzoinoxime ("Cupron")	Bur. Std. J. Research 9, 1 (1932)
	Cinchonine	Hillebrand et al., p. 689 (5)
	Hydroquinone	Z. angew. Chem. 44, 237 (1931)
	Phenylhydrazine	Bull. soc. chim. Belg. 38, 385 (1929)
	Rhodamine B.	Snell, Vol. II, p. 469 (8)
Tungsten (Wolfram) (Cont.)	Toluene-3,4-dithiol	Analyst, 69, 109 (1944); J. Am. Pharm. Assoc., 37, 255 (1948)
	Uric acid	Ann. chim. anal. 9, 371 (1904)
	α-Benzoinoxime ("Cupron")	Bur. Std. J. Research 9, 1 (1932)
	Cinchonine	Hillebrand et al., p. 689 (5)
	Hydroquinone	Z. angew. Chem. 44, 237 (1931)
	Phenylhydrazine	Bull. soc. chim. Belg. 38, 385 (1929)
	Rhodamine B.	Snell, Vol. II, p. 469 (8)
	Toluene-3,4-dithiol	Analyst, 69, 109 (1944); J. Am. Pharm. Assoc., 37, 255 (1948)
Uranium	Uric acid	Ann. chim. anal. 9, 371 (1904)
	Dibenzoylmethane	Anal. Chem. 25, 1200 (1953)
	o-Hydroxybenzoic acid	Snell, Vol. II, p. 492 (8)
	α-Quinaldinic acid	Z. anal. Chem. 95, 400 (1933)
	Sodium diethyldithiocarbamate	Sandell, p. 921 (6)
	Sodium salicylate	Chem. Zeit. 43, 739 (1919)
	Thioglycolic acid (Mercapto acetic acid)	Anl. Chem., 21, 1093 (1949)!
Urea	Xanthydrol	Mikrochem. 14, 132 (1934)
Vanadium	Ammonium benzoate	C. A. 29, 2880 (1935)
	Aniline	C. A. 24, 567 (1930)
	Benzidine	J. Applied Chem. (U.S.S.R.) 17, 83 (1944); C. A. 39, 1115 (1945)
	Diphenylamine	Yoe, Vol. I, p. 715 (2)
	Diphenylbenzidine	Ind. Eng. Chem. 20, 764 (1928)
	8-Hydroxyquinoline	Feigl, p. 125 (2)
	Safranine	Vol. Anal., Vol. II, p. 326 (6)
	Strychnine	Yoe, Vol. I, p. 393 (2)
Wolfram	See Tungsten	
Zinc	Anthranilic acid	Z. anal. Chem. 91, 332 (1933)
	2-Carboxy-2'-hydroxy-5'-sulfoformazylbenzene (Zincon)	Anal. Chem. 26, 1345 (1954)
	Di-β-napthylthiocarbazone	Sandell, pp. 945, 962 (6)
	Diphenylamine	J. Am. Chem. Soc. 49, 2214 (1927)
	Diphenylbenzidine	J. Am. Chem. Soc. 49, 356 (1927)
	Diphenylthiocarbazone (Dithizone)	Ind. Eng. Chem., Anal. Ed. 9, 127 (1937)
	8-Hydroxyquinoline	Z. anal. Chem. 71, 171 (1927)
	5-Nitroquinaldic acid	Ind. Eng. Chem., Anal. Ed. 10, 335 (1938)
	Pyridine	Z. anal. Chem. 73, 356 (1928)
	α-Quinaldinic acid	Z. anal. Chem. 100, 324 (1935)
	Resorcinol	Yoe, Vol. I, p. 396 (2)
	Urobilin	J. Ind. Hyg. 7, 273 (1925)
Zirconium	Ammonium salt of nitrosophenyl hydroxylamine ("Cupferron")	Hillebrand et al., p. 572 (5)
	5-Chlorobromamine acid	Ind. Eng. Chem., Anal. Ed. 15, 73 (1943)
	p-Dimethylaminoazophenylarsenic acid	Ind. Eng. Chem., Anal. Ed., 13, 603 (1941)
	2-Hydroxy-5-methylazobenzene-4-sulfonic acid	Feigl, p. 288 (4)
	Morin	Sandell, p. 971 (6)
	Phenylarsenic acid	J. Am. Chem. Soc. 48, 895 (1926)
	Sodium alizarin sulfonate (Alizarin S)	Chem. Weekblad 20, 404 (1924); Feigl, p. 200 (2)

(1) Colorimetric Determination of Nonmetals, Boltz, Edition 1958.
(2) Feigl, Spot Tests in Inorganic Analysis, 5th English Ed., translated by Oesper, 1958.
(3) Feigl, Spot Tests in Organic Analysis, 5th English Ed., translated by Oesper, 1956.
(4) Feigl, Chemistry of Specific, Selective and Sensitive Reactions translated by Oesper, 1949.
(5) Hillebrand, Lundell, Bright and Hoffman, Applied Inorganic Analysis, 2nd Edition, 1953.
(6) Sandell, Colorimetric Determination of Traces of Metals, 3rd Edition, 1959.
(7) Scott's Standard Methods of Chemical Analysis, Furman, 5th Edition 1939.
(8) Snell, Snell and Snell, Colorimetric Methods of Analysis, Volume II (1949), II A (1959).
(9) Welcher, Organic Analytical Reagents, Vols. I–IV, 1947–1948.
(10) Yoe, Photometric Chemical Analysis, Vol. I, Colorimetry, 1928.
(11) Yoe, Photometric Chemical Analysis Vol. II, Nephelometry, 1929
(12) Yoe and Sarver, Organic Analytical Reagents, 1941

CALIBRATION OF VOLUMETRIC GLASSWARE FROM THE WEIGHT OF THE CONTAINED WATER OR MERCURY WHEN WEIGHED IN AIR WITH BRASS WEIGHTS

D. F. SWINEHART

A borosilicate glass vessel containing g_t grams of water at a temperature of $t°C$ has, at the same temperature, a volume $V_t = W_t \times g_t$ cubic centimeters. Similarly when filled with G_t grams of mercury at a temperature of $t°C$ the volume at the same temperature is given by $V_t = M_t \times G_t$ cubic centimeters.

When filled with g_t grams of water at a temperature of $t°C$ the volume of the vessel at 18°C is given by $V_{18} = W_{18} \times g_t$ cubic centimeters and the true volume at 25°C is given by $V_{25} = W_{25} \times g_t$. The volumes at 18°C and 25°C are given similarly when using mercury by using the values under M_{18} and M_{25}, respectively.

The data on water are adapted from the data of G. S. Kell, *Journal of Chemical and Engineering Data*, 12, 67–68 (1967) (Table on p. F5, 52nd Edition, this handbook) and the data on mercury are adapted from *Smithsonian Tables*, Ninth Revised Edition, Volume 120, Publication No. 4169. The coefficient of linear expansion for borosilicate glass used here is 32.5×10^{-7} deg^{-1} and the volume coefficient of expansion is 97.5×10^{-7} deg^{-1}.

$t°C$	W_t	W_{18}	W_{25}	M_t	M_{18}	M_{25}
0	1.001 220	1.001 396	1.001 466	0.0735 519	0.0735 648	0.0735 698
1	1.001 161	1.001 327	1.001 395	0.0735 653	0.0735 775	0.0735 825
2	1.001 120	1.001 276	1.001 345	0.0735 787	0.0735 902	0.0735 952
3	1.001 096	1.001 242	1.001 311	0.0735 920	0.0736 028	0.0736 078
4	1.001 088	1.001 225	1.001 293	0.0736 054	0.0736 154	0.0736 205
5	1.001 096	1.001 223	1.001 291	0.0736 188	0.0736 281	0.0736 332
6	1.001 120	1.001 237	1.001 306	0.0736 322	0.0736 408	0.0736 458
7	1.001 158	1.001 265	1.001 334	0.0736 456	0.0736 535	0.0736 585
8	1.001 211	1.001 309	1.001 377	0.0736 590	0.0736 662	0.0736 712
9	1.001 279	1.001 367	1.001 435	0.0736 724	0.0736 789	0.0736 839
10	1.001 360	1.001 438	1.001 506	0.0736 858	0.0736 915	0.0736 966
11	1.001 455	1.001 523	1.001 592	0.0736 992	0.0737 042	0.0737 093
12	1.001 563	1.001 622	1.001 690	0.0737 125	0.0737 168	0.0737 218
13	1.001 684	1.001 733	1.001 801	0.0737 259	0.0737 295	0.0737 345
14	1.001 816	1.001 855	1.001 923	0.0737 393	0.0737 422	0.0737 472
15	1.001 961	1.001 990	1.002 059	0.0737 526	0.0737 548	0.0737 598
16	1.002 118	1.002 138	1.002 206	0.0737 660	0.0737 674	0.0737 725
17	1.002 286	1.002 296	1.002 364	0.0737 794	0.0737 801	0.0737 852
18	1.002 466	1.002 466	1.002 534	0.0737 928	0.0737 928	0.0737 978
19	1.002 658	1.002 648	1.002 717	0.0738 062	0.0738 055	0.0738 105
20	1.002 859	1.002 839	1.002 908	0.0738 196	0.0738 182	0.0738 232
21	1.003 072	1.003 043	1.003 111	0.0738 330	0.0738 308	0.0738 359
22	1.003 294	1.003 255	1.003 323	0.0738 463	0.0738 434	0.0738 485
23	1.003 528	1.003 479	1.003 548	0.0738 597	0.0738 561	0.0738 611
24	1.003 771	1.003 712	1.003 781	0.0738 731	0.0738 688	0.0738 738
25	1.004 024	1.003 955	1.004 024	0.0738 864	0.0738 814	0.0738 864
26	1.004 287	1.004 209	1.004 277	0.0738 998	0.0738 940	0.0738 991
27	1.004 560	1.004 472	1.004 540	0.0739 132	0.0739 067	0.0739 118
28	1.004 842	1.004 744	1.004 813	0.0739 266	0.0739 194	0.0739 244
29	1.005 133	1.005 025	1.005 094	0.0739 400	0.0739 321	0.0739 371
30	1.005 434	1.005 316	1.005 385	0.0739 534	0.0739 447	0.0739 498
31	1.005 743	1.005 615	1.005 684	0.0739 669	0.0739 575	0.0739 626
32	1.006 060	1.005 923	1.005 991	0.0739 801	0.0739 700	0.0739 750
33	1.006 388	1.006 241	1.006 310	0.0739 934	0.0739 826	0.0739 876
34	1.006 723	1.006 566	1.006 635	0.0740 068	0.0739 953	0.0740 003
35	1.007 066	1.006 899	1.006 968	0.0740 202	0.0740 079	0.0740 130
36	1.007 418	1.007 242	1.007 311	0.0740 335	0.0740 205	0.0740 256
37	1.007 780	1.007 593	1.007 669	0.0740 469	0.0740 332	0.0740 382
38	1.008 149	1.007 952	1.008 021	0.0740 603	0.0740 459	0.0740 509
39	1.008 525	1.008 318	1.008 387	0.0740 737	0.0740 585	0.0740 636
40	1.008 910	1.008 694	1.008 762	0.0740 871	0.0740 712	0.0740 763
41	1.009 303	1.009 077	1.009 146	0.0741 007	0.0740 841	0.0740 891
42	1.009 703	1.009 467	1.009 536	0.0741 139	0.0740 966	0.0741 016
43	1.010 112	1.009 866	1.009 935	0.0741 273	0.0741 092	0.0741 143
44	1.010 528	1.010 272	1.010 341	0.0741 407	0.0741 219	0.0741 270
45	1.010 951	1.010 685	1.010 754	0.0741 541	0.0741 346	0.0741 396
46	1.011 382	1.011 106	1.011 175	0.0741 675	0.0741 473	0.0741 523
47	1.011 820	1.011 534	1.011 603	0.0741 810	0.0741 600	0.0741 651
48	1.012 266	1.011 970	1.012 039	0.0741 944	0.0741 727	0.0741 778
49	1.012 719	1.012 413	1.012 482	0.0742 078	0.0741 854	0.0741 904
50	1.013 180	1.012 864	1.012 933	0.0742 213	0.0741 981	0.0742 031

SOLUBILITY CHART

Abbreviations: W, soluble in water; A, insoluble in water but soluble in acids; w, sparingly soluble in water but soluble in acids; a, insoluble in water and only sparingly soluble in acids; I, insoluble in both water and acids; d, decomposes in water. * Certain salts occur in two modifications.

No.		Al	NH4	Sb	Ba	Bi	Cd	Ca	Cr	Co	Cu	Au'	Au'''	H	Fe''	Fe'''
1	Acetates —$(C_2H_3O_2)$	W $Al(-)_3$	W $NH_4(-)$	......	W $Ba(-)_2$	W $Bi(-)_3$	W $Cd(-)_2$	W $Ca(-)_2$	W $Cr(-)_3$	W $Co(-)_2$	W $Cu(-)_2$	......	......	W $C_2H_4O_2$	W $Fe(-)_2$	W $Fe_2(-)_6$
2	Arsenate —(AsO_4)	a $Al(-)$	W $(NH_4)_3(-)$	A $Sb(-)$	w $Ba_3(-)_2$	A $Bi(-)$	A $Cd_3(-)_2$	w $Ca_3(-)_2$		A $Co_3(-)_2$	A $Cu_3(-)_2$			W H_3AsO_4	A $Fe_3(-)_2$	A $Fe(-)$
3	Arsenite —(AsO_3)	......	W NH_4AsO_2	A $Sb(-)$				A $Ca_3(-)_2$		A $Co_3H_6(-)_4$	A $CuH(-)$					
4	Benzoate —$(C_7H_5O_2)$	......	W $NH_4(-)$		W $Ba(-)_2$	A $Bi(-)_3$	W $Cd(-)_2$	W $Ca(-)_2$		W $Co(-)_2$	w $Cu(-)_2$			W $C_7H_6O_2$	W $Fe(-)_2$	A $Fe_2(-)_6$
5	Bromide	W $AlBr_3$	W NH_4Br	d $SbBr_3$	W $BaBr_2$	d $BiBr_3$	W $CdBr_2$	W $CaBr_2$	W(I)* $CrBr_3$	W $CoBr_2$	W $CuBr_2$	w $AuBr$	W $AuBr_3$	W HBr	W $FeBr_2$	W $FeBr_3$
6	Carbonate	......	W $(NH_4)_2CO_3$		A $BaCO_3$		A $CdCO_3$	A $CaCO_3$	A $CrCO_3$	A $CoCO_3$					A $FeCO_3$	
7	Chlorate —(ClO_3)	W $Al(-)_3$	W $NH_4(-)$		W $Ba(-)_2$	W $Bi(-)_3$	W $Cd(-)_2$	W $Ca(-)_2$		W $Co(-)_2$	W $Cu(-)_2$			W $HClO_3$	W $Fe(-)_2$	W $Fe(-)_3$
8	Chloride	W $AlCl_3$	W NH_4Cl	W $SbCl_3$	W $BaCl_2$	d $BiCl_3$	W $CdCl_2$	W $CaCl_2$	I $CrCl_3$	W $CoCl_2$	W $CuCl_2$	w $AuCl$	W $AuCl_3$	W HCl	W $FeCl_2$	W $FeCl_3$
9	Chromate —(CrO_4)		W $(NH_4)_2(-)$		A $Ba(-)$		W $Cd(-)$	W $Ca(-)$		A $Co(-)$						W $Fe_2(-)_3$
10	Citrate —$(C_6H_5O_7)$	W $Al(-)$	W $(NH_4)_3(-)$		w $Ba_3(-)_2$	w $Bi(-)$	A $Cd_3(-)_2$	w $Ca_3(-)_2$		W $Co_3(-)_2$	w $Cu_3(-)_2$			W $C_6H_8O_7$		W $Fe(-)$
11	Cyanide		W NH_4CN		W $Ba(CN)_2$	w $Bi(CN)_3$	W $Cd(CN)_2$	W $Ca(CN)_2$	A $Cr(CN)_3$	A $Co(CN)_2$	A $Cu(CN)_2$	w $AuCN$	W $Au(CN)_3$	W HCN	a $Fe(CN)_2$	
12	Ferricy'de —$(Fe(CN)_6)$		W $(NH_4)_3(-)$		w $Ba_3(-)_2$		A $Cd_3(-)_2$	W $Ca_3(-)_2$	I	I $Co_3(-)_2$	A $Cu_3(-)_2$			W $H_3(-)$	I $Fe_3(-)_2$	I
13	Ferrocy'de —$(Fe(CN)_6)$	W $Al_4(-)_3$	W $(NH_4)_4(-)$		A $Ba_2(-)$		A $Cd_2(-)$	A $Ca_2(-)$	I	I $Co_2(-)$	I $Cu_2(-)$			W $H_4(-)$	I $Fe_2(-)$	a $Fe_4(-)_3$
14	Fluoride	W AlF_3	W NH_4F	W SbF_3	w BaF_2	W BiF_3	W CdF_2	w CaF_2	W(a)* CrF_3	W CoF_2	w CuF_2			W HF	W FeF_2	W FeF_3
15	Formate —(CHO_2)	W $Al(-)_3$	W $NH_4(-)$		W $Ba(-)_2$	W $Bi(-)_3$	W $Cd(-)_2$	W $Ca(-)_2$		W $Co(-)_2$	W $Cu(-)_2$			W CH_2O_2	W $Fe(-)_2$	W $Fe(-)_3$
16	Hydroxide	A $Al(OH)_3$	W NH_4OH		W $Ba(OH)_2$	A $Bi(OH)_3$	A $Cd(OH)_2$	W $Ca(OH)_2$	A $Cr(OH)_3$	A $Co(OH)_2$	A $Cu(OH)_2$	W $AuOH$	A $Au(OH)_3$		A $Fe(OH)_2$	A $Fe(OH)_3$
17	Iodide	W AlI_3	W NH_4I	d SbI_3	W BaI_2	A BiI_3	W CdI_2	W CaI_2	W CrI_2	W CoI_2	a CuI	a AuI	a AuI_3	W HI	W FeI_2	W FeI_2
18	Nitrate	W $Al(NO_3)_3$	W NH_4NO_3		W $Ba(NO_3)_2$	d $Bi(NO_3)_3$	W $Cd(NO_3)_2$	W $Ca(NO_3)_2$	W $Cr(NO_3)_3$	W $Co(NO_3)_2$	W $Cu(NO_3)_2$			W HNO_3	W $Fe(NO_3)_2$	W $Fe(NO_3)_3$
19	Oxalate —(C_2O_4)	A $Al_2(-)_3$	W $(NH_4)_2(-)$		w $Ba(-)$	A $Bi_2(-)_3$	A $Cd(-)$	A $Ca(-)$	W $Cr(-)$	A $Co(-)$	A $Cu(-)$			W $C_2H_2O_4$	A $Fe(-)$	W $Fe_2(-)_3$
20	Oxide	a Al_2O_3	......	w Sb_2O_3	W BaO	A Bi_2O_3	A CdO	A CaO	a Cr_2O_3	A CoO	A CuO	A Au_2O	A Au_2O_3	W H_2O_2	A FeO	A Fe_2O_3
21	Phosphate	A $AlPO_4$	W $NH_4H_2PO_4$		A $Ba_3(PO_4)_2$	A $BiPO_4$	A $Cd_3(PO_4)_2$	A $Ca_3(PO_4)_2$	A $Cr_2(PO_4)_2$	A $Co_3(PO_4)_2$	A $Cu_3(PO_4)_2$			W H_3PO_4	A $Fe_3(PO_4)_2$	A $FePO_4$
22	Silicate, —(SiO_3)	I $Al_2(-)_3$	......		W $Ba(-)$		W $Cd(-)$	W $Ca(-)$		A Co_2SiO_4	A $Cu(-)$			I H_2SiO_3		
23	Sulfate	W $Al_2(SO_4)_3$	W $(NH_4)_2SO_4$	A $Sb_2(SO_4)_3$	a $BaSO_4$	d $Bi_2(SO_4)_3$	W $CdSO_4$	W $CaSO_4$	W(I)* $Cr_2(SO_4)_3$	W $CoSO_4$	W $CuSO_4$			W H_2SO_4	W $FeSO_4$	W $Fe_2(SO_4)_3$
24	Sulfide	d Al_2S_3	W $(NH_4)_2S$	A Sb_2S_3	W BaS	A Bi_2S_3	A CdS	W CaS	d Cr_2S_3	A CoS	A CuS	I Au_2S	I Au_2S_3	W H_2S	A FeS	d Fe_2S_3
25	Tartrate —$(C_4H_4O_6)$	w $Al_2(-)_3$	W $(NH_4)_2(-)$	W $Sb_2(-)$	w $Ba(-)$	A $Bi_2(-)$	W $Cd(-)$	w $Ca(-)$		w $Co(-)$	w $Cu(-)$			W $C_4H_6O_6$	w $Fe(-)$	W $Fe_2(-)_3$
26	Thiocy'te	......	W NH_4CNS		W $Ba(CNS)_2$			W $Ca(CNS)$		W $Co(CNS)_2$	d $CuCNS$			W $CNSH$	W $Fe(CNS)_2$	W $Fe(CNS)_3$

No.		Pb	Mg	Mn	Hg'	Hg''	Ni	K	Ag	Na	Sn''''	Sn''	Sr	Zn	Pt
1	Acetate —$(C_2H_3O_2)$	W $Pb(-)_2$	W $Mg(-)_2$	W $Mn(-)_2$	w $Hg(-)$	W $Hg(-)_2$	W $Ni(-)_2$	W $K(-)$	w $Ag(-)$	W $Na(-)$	W $Sn(-)_4$	d $Sn(-)_2$	W $Sr(-)_2$	W $Zn(-)_2$	......
2	Arsenate —(AsO_4)	A $PbH(-)$	A $Mg_3(-)$	A $MnH(-)$	A $Hg_3(-)_2$	A $Hg_3(-)_2$	A $Ni_3(-)_2$	W $K_3(-)$	A $Ag_3(-)$	W $Na_3(-)$	......	w	A $SrH(-)$	A $Zn_3(-)_2$	
3	Arsenite —(AsO_3)	......	W $Mg_3(-)_2$	W $Mn_3H_6(-)_4$	A $Hg_3(-)$	A $Hg_3(-)$	W $Ni_3H_6(-)_4$	W K_3AsO_3	A $Ag_3(-)$	W $Na_2H(-)$		A $Sn_3(-)_2$	w $Sr_3(-)_2$		
4	Benzoate —$(C_7H_5O_2)$	w $Pb(-)_2$	W $Mg(-)_2$	W $Mn(-)_2$	w $Hg_2(-)_2$	W $Hg(-)_2$	W $Ni(-)_2$	W $K(-)$	w $Ag(-)$	W $Na(-)$				W $Zn(-)_2$	
5	Bromide	w $PbBr_2$	W $MgBr_2$	W $MnBr_2$	a $HgBr$	W $HgBr_2$	W $NiBr_2$	W KBr	a $AgBr$	W $NaBr$	W $SnBr_4$	W $SnBr_2$	W $SrBr_2$	W $ZnBr_2$	W $PtBr_4$
6	Carbonate	A $PbCO_3$	w $MgCO_3$	A $MnCO_3$	A Hg_2CO_3	......	A $NiCO_3$	W K_2CO_3	A Ag_2CO_3	W Na_2CO_3	......	......	w $SrCO_3$	w $ZnCO_3$	
7	Chlorate —(ClO_3)	W $Pb(-)_2$	W $Mg(-)_2$	W $Mn(-)_2$	w $Hg(-)$	W $Hg(-)_2$	W $Ni(-)_2$	W $K(-)$	W $Ag(-)$	W $Na(-)$		W $Sn(-)_2$	W $Sr(-)_2$	W $Zn(-)_2$	
8	Chloride	w $PbCl_2$	W $MgCl_2$	W $MnCl_2$	a $HgCl$	W $HgCl_2$	W $NiCl_2$	W KCl	A $AgCl$	W $NaCl$	W $SnCl_4$	W $SnCl_2$	W $SrCl_2$	W $ZnCl_2$	W $PtCl_4$
9	Chromate —(CrO_4)	A $Pb(-)$	W $Mg(-)$	......	A $Hg_2(-)$	w $Hg(-)$	A $Ni(-)$	W $K_2(-)$	A $Ag_2(-)$	W $Na_2(-)$	W $Sn(-)_2$	W $Sn(-)$	w $Sr(-)$	W $Zn(-)$	
10	Citrate —$(C_6H_5O_7)$	W $Pb_3(-)_2$	W $Mg_3(-)_2$	w $MnH(-)$	W $Hg_3(-)$	......	W $Ni_3(-)_2$	W $K_3(-)$	A $Ag_3(-)$	w $Na_3(-)$			A $SrH(-)$	W $Zn_3(-)_2$	

No.		Pb	Mg	Mn	Hg'	Hg''	Ni	K	Ag	Na	Sn''''	Sn''	Sr	Zn	Pt
11	Cyanide	w $Pb(CN)_2$	W $Mg(CN)_2$	……	A $HgCN$	W $Hg(CN)_2$	a $Ni(CN)_2$	W KCN	a $AgCN$	W $NaCN$	……	……	W $Sr(CN)_2$	A $Zn(CN)_2$	I $Pt(CN)_2$
12	Ferricy'de —$Fe(CN)_6$	w $Pb_3(—)_2$	W $Mg_3(—)_2$		……	A $Hg_3(—)_2$	I $Ni_3(—)_2$	W $K_3(—)$	I $Ag_3(—)$	W $Na_3(—)$		A $Sn_3(—)_2$	W $Sr_3(—)_2$	A $Zn_3(—)_2$	……
13	Ferrocy'de —$Fe(CN)_6$	a $Pb_2(—)$	W $Mg_2(—)$	A $Mn_2(—)$	……	I $Hg_2(—)$	I $Ni_2(—)$	W $K_4(—)$	I $Ag_4(—)$	W $Na_4(—)$		a $Sn_2(—)$	W $Sr_2(—)$	I $Zn_2(—)$	……
14	Fluoride	w PbF_2	W MgF_2	A MnF_2	d HgF	d HgF_2	w NiF_2	W KF	W AgF	W NaF	W SnF_4	W SnF_2	W SrF_2	w ZnF_2	W PtF_4
15	Formate —(CHO_2)	W $Pb(—)_2$	W $Mg(—)_2$	w $Mn(—)_2$	w $Hg(—)$	W $Hg(—)_2$	W $Ni(—)_2$	W $K(—)$	W $Ag(—)$	W $Na(—)$	……	……	W $Sr(—)_2$	W $Zn(—)_2$	
16	Hydroxide	w $Pb(OH)_2$	A $Mg(OH)_2$	A $Mn(OH)_2$	……	A $Hg(OH)_2$	A $Ni(OH)_2$	W KOH	……	W $NaOH$	w $Sn(OH)_4$	A $Sn(OH)_2$	W $Sr(OH)_2$	A $Zn(OH)_2$	A $Pt(OH)_4$
17	Iodide	w PbI_2	W MgI_2	W MnI_2	A HgI	w HgI_2	W NiI_2	W KI	I AgI	W NaI	d SnI_4	W SnI_2	W SrI_2	W ZnI_2	I PtI_2
18	Nitrate	W $Pb(NO_3)_2$	W $Mg(NO_3)_2$	W $Mn(NO_3)_2$	W $HgNO_3$	W $Hg(NO_3)_2$	W $Ni(NO_3)_2$	W KNO_3	W $AgNO_3$	W $NaNO_3$		d $Sn(NO_3)_2$	W $Sr(NO_3)_2$	W $Zn(NO_3)_2$	W $Pt(NO_3)_4$
19	Oxalate —(C_2O_4)	A $Pb(—)$	w $Mg(—)$	w $Mn(—)$	a $Hg_2(—)$	A $Hg(—)$	A $Ni(—)$	W $K_2(—)$	a $Ag_2(—)$	W $Na_2(—)$		A $Sn(—)$	w $Sr(—)$	A $Zn(—)$	……
20	Oxide	w PbO	A MgO	A MnO	A Hg_2O	w HgO	A NiO	W K_2O	w Ag_2O	d Na_2O	A SnO_2	A SnO	A SrO	w ZnO	A PtO
21	Phosphate	A $Pb_3(PO_4)_2$	A $Mg_3(PO_4)_2$	A $Mn_3(PO_4)_2$	A Hg_3PO_4	A $Hg_3(PO_4)_2$	A $Ni_3(PO_4)_2$	W K_3PO_4	A Ag_3PO_4	W Na_3PO_4		A $Sn_3(PO_4)_2$	A $Sr_3(PO_4)_2$	A $Zn_3(PO_4)_2$	……
22	Silicate --(SiO_3)	A $Pb(—)$	A $Mg(—)$	I $Mn(—)$				W $K_2(—)$	……	W $Na_2(—)$		A $Sn(—)$	A $Sr(—)$	A $Zn(—)$	……
23	Sulfate	A $PbSO_4$	W $MgSO_4$	W $MnSO_4$	A Hg_2SO_4	d $HgSO_4$	W $NiSO_4$	W K_2SO_4	w Ag_2SO_4	W Na_2SO_4	W $Sn(SO_4)_2$	W $SnSO_4$	W $SrSO_4$	W $ZnSO_4$	W $Pt(SO_4)_2$
24	Sulfide	A PbS	d MgS	A MnS	I Hg_2S	I HgS	A NiS	W K_2S	A Ag_2S	W Na_2S	A SnS_2	A SnS	A SrS	A ZnS	I PtS
25	Tartrate —$(C_4H_4O_6)$	A $Pb(—)$	w $Mg(—)$	w $Mn(—)$	I $Hg_2(—)$	……	w $Ni(—)$	W $K_2(—)$	A $Ag_2(—)$	W $Na_2(—)$	……	W $Sn(—)$	w $Sr(—)$	w $Zn(—)$	……
26	Thiocy'te	w $Pb(CNS)_2$	W $Mg(CNS)_2$	W $Mn(CNS)_2$	A $HgCNS$	w $Hg(CNS)_2$	……	W $KCNS$	I $AgCNS$	W $NaCNS$	……	……	W $Sr(CNS)_2$	W $Zn(CNS)_2$	……

REDUCTIONS OF WEIGHINGS IN AIR TO VACUO

When the weight M in grams of a body is determined in air, a correction is necessary for the buoyancy of the air. The following table is computed for an air density of 0.0012. The corrected weight $= M + kM/1000$, values of k being found in the table.

Density of body weighed	Correction factor, k.			Density of body weighed	Correction factor, k.		
	Pt Ir weights	Brass weights	Quartz or Al weights		Pt Ir weights	Brass weights	Quartz or Al weights
.5	+2.34	+2.26	+1.95	1.6	+ .69	+ .61	+ .30
.6	+1.94	+1.86	+1.55	1.7	+ .65	+ .56	+ .25
.7	+1.66	+1.57	+1.26	1.8	+ .62	+ .52	+ .21
.75	+1.55	+1.46	+1.15	1.9	+ .58	+ .49	+ .18
.80	+1.44	+1.36	+1.05	2.0	+ .54	+ .46	+ .15
.85	+1.36	+1.27	+0.96	2.5	+ .43	+ .34	+ .03
.90	+1.28	+1.19	+ .88	3.0	+ .34	+ .26	— .05
.95	+1.21	+1.12	+ .81	4.0	+ .24	+ .16	— .15
1.00	+1.14	+1.06	+ .75	6.0	+ .14	+ .06	— .25
1.1	+1.04	+0.95	+ .64	8.0	+ .09	+ .01	— .30
1.2	+0.94	+ .86	+ .55	10.0	+ .06	— .02	— .33
1.3	+ .87	+ .78	+ .47	15.0	+ .03	— .06	— .37
1.4	+ .80	+ .71	+ .40	20.0	+ .004	— .08	— .39
1.5	+ .75	+ .66	+ .35	22.0	— .001	— .09	— .40

OPERATIONAL DEFINITIONS OF pH
Prepared by R. A. Robinson

The operational definition of pH is:

$$pH - pH(s) + E/k$$

where E is the e.m.f. of the cell:

$$H_2|Solution, pH|Saturated\ KCl|Solution, pH(s)|H_2$$

the half cell on the left containing the solution whose pH is being measured and that on the right a standard buffer mixture of known pH; $k = 2.303RT/F$, where R is the gas constant, T the temperature in degrees Kelvin and F the value of the faraday.

Alternatively, the cell:

$$Glass\ electrode|Solution, pH|Saturated\ calomel\ electrode$$

can be used, the glass electrode being calibrated using a standard buffer mixture or, if possible, two standard buffer mixtures whose pH values lie on either side of that of the solution which is being measured. Suitable standard buffer mixtures are:

> 0.05 M potassium hydrogen phthalate (pH = 4.008 at 25°C)
> 0.025 M potassium dihydrogen phosphate
> 0.025 M disodium hydrogen phosphate (pH = 6.865 at 25°C)
> 0.01 M borax (pH = 9.180 at 25°C)

For most purposes pH can be equated to $- \log_{10} \gamma_{H^+}m_{H^+}$, i.e., to the negative logarithm of the hydrogen ion activity. There is a small difference between those two quantities if pH > 9.2 or pH < 4.0, given by:

$$- \log \gamma_{H^+}m_{H^+} = pH + 0.014(pH - 9.2) \text{ for } pH > 9.2$$
$$= pH + 0.009(4.0 - pH) \text{ for } pH < 4.0$$

It should be noted that in the table titled "Solutions giving Round Values of pH at 25°C" it is $- \log \gamma_{H^+}m_{H^+}$ and not pH which is quoted when there is a difference between them.

References:

R. G. Bates, "Electrometric pH Determinations: Theory and Practice" Wiley, New York, 1954.
R. A. Robinson and R. H. Stokes, "Electrolyte Solutions," 2nd edition, Butterworths, London; Academic Press, Inc. New York, 1959. R. C. Bates, J. Res. of N.B.S. 66 A, 179 (1962).

National Bureau of Standards
R. G. Bates and S. F. Acree, Res. **34**, 373 (1945); W. J. Hammer, C. D. Pinching and S. F. Acree, ibid. **36**, 47 (1946); G. G. Manor, N. J. DeLollis, P. W. Lindwall and S. F. Acree, ibid., **36**, 543 (1946); R. G. Bates, ibid., **39**, 411 (1947); R. G. Bates, V. E. Bower, R. G. Miller and E. R. Smith, ibid., **47**, 433 (1951); V. E. Bower, R. G. Bates and E. R. Smith, ibid., **51**, 189 (1953); V. E. Bower and R. G. Bates, ibid., **55**, 197 (1955); R. G. Bates, V. E. Bower and E. R. Smith, ibid., **56**, 305 (1956); V. E. Bower and R. G. Bates, ibid., **59**, 261; R. G. Bates and V. E. Bower, Anal. Chem., **28**, 1322 (1956).

PROPERTIES OF STANDARD AQUEOUS BUFFER SOLUTIONS AT 25°C

Solution	Buffer substance	Molality m	Weight of salt in air per liter solution	Density g/ml	Molarity M	Dilution value $\Delta pH_{\frac{1}{2}}$	ΔpH_s[a]	Buffer value, equiv. per pH	Temp coeff., dpH_s/dt. Units per °C
Tetroxalate	$KH_3(C_2O_4)_2 \cdot 2H_2O$	0.05	12.61	1.0032	0.04962	+0.186	−0.0028	0.070	+0.001
Tartrate	$KHC_4H_4O_6$, sat. sol'n. at 25°C	0.0341	......	1.0036	0.034	+0.049	−0.0003	0.027	−0.0014
Phthalate	$KHC_8O_4H_4$	0.05	10.12	1.0017	0.04958	+0.052	−0.0009	0.016	+0.0012
Phosphate	KH_2PO_4 + Na_2HPO_4	0.025[b]	3.39 3.53	1.0028	0.0249[b]	+0.080	−0.0006	0.029	−0.0028
Phosphate	KH_2PO_4 + Na_2HPO_4	0.008695[c] 0.03043[d]	1.179 4.30	1.0020	0.008665[c] 0.03032[d]	+0.07[e]	−0.0005	0.016	−0.0028
Borax	$Na_2B_4O_7 \cdot 10H_2O$	0.01	3.80	0.9996	0.009971	+0.01	−0.0001	0.020	−0.0082
Calcium hydroxide	$Ca(OH)_2$, sat. sol'n. at 25°C	0.0203	......	0.9991	0.02025	−0.28	+0.0014	0.09	−0.033

[a] ΔpH_s = pHs (M Molar solution) − pH$_s$ (m molal solution).
[b] Concentration of each phosphate salt.
[c] KH_2PO_4.
[d] Na_2HPO_4.
[e] Calculated value.

SOLUTIONS GIVING ROUND VALUES OF pH AT 25°C

Reproduced from "Electrolyte Solutions" by permission from Robinson and Stokes, authors, and Butterworth's Scientific Publications.

A*		B*		C*		D*		E*	
pH	x	pH	x	pH	x	pH	x	pH	x
1.00	67.0	2.20	49.5	4.10	1.3	5.80	3.6	7.00	46.6
1.10	52.8	2.30	45.8	4.20	3.0	5.90	4.6	7.10	45.7
1.20	42.5	2.40	42.2	4.30	4.7	6.00	5.6	7.20	44.7
1.30	33.6	2.50	38.8	4.40	6.6	6.10	6.8	7.30	43.4
1.40	26.6	2.60	35.4	4.50	8.7	6.20	8.1	7.40	42.0
1.50	20.7	2.70	32.1	4.60	11.1	6.30	9.7	7.50	40.3
1.60	16.2	2.80	28.9	4.70	13.6	6.40	11.6	7.60	38.5
1.70	13.0	2.90	25.7	4.80	16.5	6.50	13.9	7.70	36.6
1.80	10.2	3.00	22.3	4.90	19.4	6.60	16.4	7.80	34.5
1.90	8.1	3.10	18.8	5.00	22.6	6.70	19.3	7.90	32.0
2.00	6.5	3.20	15.7	5.10	25.5	6.80	22.4	8.00	29.2
2.10	5.1	3.30	12.9	5.20	28.8	6.90	25.9	8.10	26.2
2.20	3.9	3.40	10.4	5.30	31.6	7.00	29.1	8.20	22.9
		3.50	8.2	5.40	34.1	7.10	32.1	8.30	19.9
		3.60	6.3	5.50	36.6	7.20	34.7	8.40	17.2
		3.70	4.5	5.60	38.8	7.30	37.0	8.50	14.7
		3.80	2.9	5.70	40.6	7.40	39.1	8.60	12.2
		3.90	1.4	5.80	42.3	7.50	41.1	8.70	10.3
		4.00	0.1	5.90	43.7	7.60	42.8	8.80	8.5
						7.70	44.2	8.90	7.0
						7.80	45.3	9.00	5.7
						7.90	46.1		
						8.00	46.7		

F*		G*		H*		I*		J*	
pH	x	pH	x	pH	x	pH	x	pH	x
8.00	20.5	9.20	0.9	9.60	5.0	10.90	3.3	12.00	6.0
8.10	19.7	9.30	3.6	9.70	6.2	11.00	4.1	12.10	8.0
8.20	18.8	9.40	6.2	9.80	7.6	11.10	5.1	12.20	10.2
8.30	17.7	9.50	8.8	9.90	9.1	11.20	6.3	12.30	12.8
8.40	16.6	9.60	11.1	10.00	10.7	11.30	7.6	12.40	16.2
8.50	15.2	9.70	13.1	10.10	12.2	11.40	9.1	12.50	20.4
8.60	13.5	9.80	15.0	10.20	13.8	11.50	11.1	12.60	25.6
8.70	11.6	9.90	16.7	10.30	15.2	11.60	13.5	12.70	32.2
8.80	9.6	10.00	18.3	10.40	16.5	11.70	16.2	12.80	41.2
8.90	7.1	10.10	19.5	10.50	17.8	11.80	19.4	12.90	53.0
9.00	4.6	10.20	20.5	10.60	19.1	11.90	23.0	13.00	66.0
9.10	2.0	10.30	21.3	10.70	20.2	12.00	26.9		
		10.40	22.1	10.80	21.2				
		10.50	22.7	10.90	22.0				
		10.60	23.3	11.00	22.7				
		10.70	23.8						
		10.80	24.25						

*A. 25 ml of 0.2 molar KCl + x ml of 0.2 molar HCl.
*B. 50 ml of 0.1 molar potassium hydrogen phthalate + x ml of 0.1 molar HCl.
*C. 50 ml of 0.1 molar potassium hydrogen phthalate + x ml of 0.1 molar NaOH.
*D. 50 ml of 0.1 molar potassium dihydrogen phosphate + x ml 0.1 molar NaOH.
*E. 50 ml of 0.1 molar tris(hydroxymethyl) aminomethane + x ml of 0.1 M HCl.
*F. 50 ml of 0.025 molar borax + x ml of 0.1 molar HCl.
*G. 50 ml of 0.025 molar borax + x ml of 0.1 molar NaOH.
*H. 50 ml of 0.05 molar sodium bicarbonate + x ml of 0.1 molar NaOH.
*I. 50 ml of 0.05 molar disodium hydrogen phosphate + x ml of 0.1 molar NaOH.
*J. 25 ml of 0.2 molar KCl + x ml of 0.2 molar NaOH.
Final Volume of Mixtures = 100 ml

STANDARD VALUES OF pH AT TEMPERATURE 0–95°C

Temper-ature	Tetroxalate 0.05 molal	Tartrate 0.0341 molal (sat'd at 25°C)	Phthalate 0.05 molal	Phosphate[a]	Phosphate[b]	Borax 0.01 molal	Calcium hydroxide (sat'd at 25°C)
0	1.666	.....	4.003	6.984	7.534	9.464	13.423
5	1.668	.....	3.999	6.951	7.500	9.395	13.207
10	1.670	.....	3.998	6.923	7.472	9.332	13.003
15	1.672	.....	3.999	6.900	7.448	9.276	12.810
20	1.675	.....	4.002	6.881	7.429	9.225	12.627
25	1.679	3.557	4.008	6.865	7.413	9.180	12.454
30	1.683	3.552	4.015	6.853	7.400	9.139	12.289
35	1.688	3.549	4.024	6.844	7.389	9.102	12.133
38	1.691	3.548	4.030	6.840	7.384	9.081	12.043
40	1.694	3.547	4.035	6.838	7.380	9.068	11.984
45	1.700	3.547	4.047	6.834	7.373	9.038	11.841
50	1.707	3.549	4.060	6.833	7.367	9.011	11.705
55	1.715	3.554	4.075	6.834	.....	8.985	11.574
60	1.723	3.560	4.091	6.836	.....	8.962	11.449
70	1.743	3.580	4.126	6.845	.....	8.921	.....
80	1.766	3.609	4.164	6.859	.....	8.885	.....
90	1.792	3.650	4.205	6.877	.....	8.850	.....
95	1.806	3.674	4.227	6.886	.....	8.833	.....

[a] Solution 0.025 m KH_2PO_4 and 0.025 m Na_2HPO_4.
[b] Solution 0.008695 m KH_2PO_4 and 0.03043 m Na_2HPO_4.

APPROXIMATE pH VALUES

The following tables give approximate pH values for a number of substances such as acids, bases, foods, biological fluids, etc. All values are rounded off to the nearest tenth and are based on measurements made at 25° C. A few buffer systems with their pH values are also given.

From Modern pH and Chlorine Control, W. A. Taylor & Co., by permission

ACIDS

Hydrochloric, N	0.1	Oxalic, 0.1N	1.6	Acetic, 0.01N	3.4
Hydrochloric, 0.1N	1.1	Tartaric, 0.1N	2.2	Benzoic, 0.01N	3.1
Hydrochloric, 0.01N	2.0	Malic, 0.1N	2.2	Alum, 0.1N	3.2
Sulfuric, N	0.3	Citric, 0.1N	2.2	Carbonic (saturated)	3.8
Sulfuric, 0.1N	1.2	Formic, 0.1N	2.3	Hydrogen sulfide, 0.1N	4.1
Sulfuric, 0.01N	2.1	Lactic, 0.1N	2.4	Arsenious (saturated)	5.0
Orthophosphoric, 0.1N	1.5	Acetic, N	2.4	Hydrocyanic, 0.1N	5.1
Sulfurous, 0.1N	1.5	Acetic, 0.1N	2.9	Boric, 0.1N	5.2

BASES

Sodium hydroxide, N	14.0	Lime (saturated)	12.4	Magnesia (saturated)	10.5
Sodium hydroxide, 0.1N	13.0	Trisodium phosphate, 0.1N	12.0	Sodium sesquicarbonate, 0.1M	10.1
Sodium hydroxide, 0.01N	12.0	Sodium carbonate, 0.1N	11.6	Ferrous hydroxide (saturated)	9.5
Potassium hydroxide, N	14.0	Ammonia, N	11.6	Calcium carbonate (saturated)	9.4
Potassium hydroxide, 0.1N	13.0	Ammonia, 0.1N	11.1	Borax, 0.1N	9.2
Potassium hydroxide, 0.01N	12.0	Ammonia, 0.01N	10.6	Sodium bicarbonate, 0.1N	8.4
Sodium metasilicate, 0.1N	12.6	Potassium cyanide, 0.1N	11.0		

BIOLOGIC MATERIALS

Blood, plasma, human	7.3–7.5	Gastric contents, human	1.0–3.0	Milk, human	6.6–7.6
Spinal fluid, human	7.3–7.5	Duodenal contents, human	4.8–8.2	Bile, human	6.8–7.0
Blood, whole, dog	6.9–7.2	Feces, human	4.6–8.4		
Saliva, human	6.5–7.5	Urine, human	4.8–8.4		

FOODS

Apples	2.9–3.3	Gooseberries	2.8–3.0	Potatoes	5.6–6.0
Apricots	3.6–4.0	Grapefruit	3.0–3.3	Pumpkin	4.8–5.2
Asparagus	5.4–5.8	Grapes	3.5–4.5	Raspberries	3.2–3.6
Bananas	4.5–4.7	Hominy (lye)	6.8–8.0	Rhubarb	3.1–3.2
Beans	5.0–6.0	Jams, fruit	3.5–4.0	Salmon	6.1–6.3
Beers	4.0–5.0	Jellies, fruit	2.8–3.4	Sauerkraut	3.4–3.6
Beets	4.9–5.5	Lemons	2.2–2.4	Shrimp	6.8–7.0
Blackberries	3.2–3.6	Limes	1.8–2.0	Soft drinks	2.0–4.0
Bread, white	5.0–6.0	Maple syrup	6.5–7.0	Spinach	5.1–5.7
Butter	6.1–6.4	Milk, cows	6.3–6.6	Squash	5.0–5.4
Cabbage	5.2–5.4	Olives	3.6–3.8	Strawberries	3.0–3.5
Carrots	4.9–5.3	Oranges	3.0–4.0	Sweet potatoes	5.3–5.6
Cheese	4.8–6.4	Oysters	6.1–6.6	Tomatoes	4.0–4.4
Cherries	3.2–4.0	Peaches	3.4–3.6	Tuna	5.9–6.1
Cider	2.9–3.3	Pears	3.6–4.0	Turnips	5.2–5.6
Corn	6.0–6.5	Peas	5.8–6.4	Vinegar	2.4–3.4
Crackers	6.5–8.5	Pickles, dill	3.2–3.6	Water, drinking	6.5–8.0
Dates	6.2–6.4	Pickles, sour	3.0–3.4	Wines	2.8–3.8
Eggs, fresh white	7.6–8.0	Pimento	4.6–5.2		
Flour, wheat	5.5–6.5	Plums	2.8–3.0		

Indicator	Approximate pH range	Color-change	Preparation
Methyl Violet	0.0–1.6	yel to bl	0.01–0.05% in water
Crystal Violet	0.0–1.8	yel to bl	0.02% in water
Ethyl Violet	0.0–2.4	yel to bl	0.1 g in 50 ml of MeOH + 50 ml of water
Malachite Green	0.2–1.8	yel to bl grn	water
Methyl Green	0.2–1.8	yel to bl	0.1% in water
2-(p-dimethylaminophenylazo)pyridine	0.2–1.8	yel to bl	0.1% in EtOH
	4.4–5.6	red to yel	
o-Cresolsulfonephthalein (Cresol Red)	0.4–1.8	yel to red	0.1 g in 26.2 ml 0.01N NaOH + 223.8 ml water
	7.0–8.8	yel to red	
Quinaldine Red	1.0–2.2	col to red	1% in EtOH
p-(p-dimethylaminophenylazo)-benzoic acid, Na-salt (Paramethyl Red)	1.0–3.0	red to yel	EtOH
m-(p-anilnophenylazo)benzene sulfonic acid, Na-salt (Metanil Yellow)	1.2–2.4	red to yel	0.01% in water
4-Phenylazodiphenylamine	1.2–2.6	red to yel	0.01 g in 1 ml 1N HCl + 50 ml EtOH + 49 ml water
Thymolsulfonephthalein (Thymol Blue)	1.2–2.8	red to yel	0.1 g in 21.5 ml 0.01N NaOH + 229.5 ml water
	8.0–9.6	yel to bl	
m-Cresolsulfonephthalein (Metacresol Purple)	1.2–2.8	red to yel	0.1 g in 26.2 ml 0.01N NaOH + 223.8 ml water
	7.4–9.0	yel to purp	
p-(p-anilinophenylazo)benzenesulfonic acid, Na-salt (Orange IV)	1.4–2.8	red to yel	0.01% in water
4-o-Tolylazo-o-toluidine	1.4–2.8	or to yel	water
Erythrosine, disodium salt	2.2–3.6	or to red	0.1% in water
Benzopurpurine 48	2.2–4.2	vt to red	0.1% in water
N,N-dimethyl-p-(m-tolylazo)aniline	2.6–4.8	red to yel	0.1% in water
4,4'-Bix(2-amino-1-naphthylazo)2,2'-stilbenedisulfonic acid	3.0–4.0	purp to red	0.1 g in 5.9 ml 0.05N NaOH + 94.1 ml water
Tetrabromophenolphthaleinethyl ester, K-salt	3.0–4.2	yel to bl	0.1% in EtOH
3',3'',5',5''-tetrabromophenol-sulfonephthalein (Bromophenol Blue)	3.0–4.6	yel to bl	0.1 g in 14.9 ml 0.01N NaOH + 235.1 ml water
2,4-Dinitrophenol	2.8–4.0	col to yel	saturated water solution
N,N-Dimethyl-p-phenylazoaniline (p-Dimethylaminoazobenzene)	2.8–4.4	red to yel	0.1 g in 90 ml in EtOH + 10 ml water
Congo Red	3.0–5.0	blue to red	0.1% in water
Methyl Orange-Xylene Cyanole solution	3.2–4.2	purp to grn	ready solution
Methyl Orange	3.2–4.4	red to yel	0.01% in water
Ethyl Orange	3.4–4.8	red to yel	0.05–0.2% in water or aqueous EtOH
4-(4-Dimethylamino-1-naphthylazo)-3-methoxybenzenesulfonic acid	3.5–4.8	vt to yel	0.1% in 60% EtOH
3',3'',5',5''-Tetrabromo-m-cresol-sulfonephthalein (Bromocresol Green)	3.8–5.4	yel to blue	0.1 g in 14.3 ml 0.01N NaOH + 235.7 ml water
Resazurin	3.8–6.4	or to vt	water
4-Phenylazo-1-naphthylamine	4.0–5.6	red to yel	0.1% in EtOH
Ethyl Red	4.0–5.8	col to red	0.1 g in 50 ml MeOH + 50 ml water
2-(p-Dimethylaminophenylazo)-pyridine	0.2–1.8	yel to red	0.1% in EtOH
	4.4–5.6	red to yel	
4-(p-ethoxyphenylazo)-m-phenylene-diamine monohydrochloride	4.4–5.8	or to yel	0.1% in water
Lacmoid	4.4–6.2	red to bl	0.2% in EtOH
Alizarin Red S	4.6–6.0	yel to red	dilute solution in water
Methyl Red	4.8–6.0	red to yel	0.02 g in 60 ml EtOH + 40 ml water

Indicator	Approximate pH range	Color-change	Preparation
Propyl Red	4.8–6.6	red to yel	EtOH
5′,5″-Dibromo-o-cresolsulfone-phthalein (Bromocresol Purple)	5.2–6.8	yel to purp	0.1 g in 18.5 ml 0.01N NaOH + 231.5 ml water
3′,3″-Dichlorophenolsulfoncphthalein (Chlorophenol Red)	5.2–6.8	yel to red	0 1 g in 23.6 ml 0.01N NaOH + 226.4 ml water
p-Nitrophenol	5.4–6.6	col to yel	0.1% in water
Alizarin	5.6–7.2	yel to red	0.1% in MeOH
	11.0–12.4	red to purp	
2-(2,4-Dinitrophenylazo)-1-naphthol-3, 6-disulfonic acid, di-Na salt	6.0–7.0	yel to bl	0.1% in water
3′,3″-Dibromothymolsulfonephthalein (Bromothymol Blue)	6.0–7.6	yel to bl	0.1 g in 16 ml 0.01N NaOH + 234 ml water
6,8-Dinitro-2,4-(1H)quinazolinedione (m-Dinitrobenzoylene urea)	6.4–8.0	col to yel	25 g in 115 ml M NaOH + 50 ml boiling water
			0.292 g of NaCl in 100 ml water
Brilliant Yellow	6.6–7.8	yel to or	1% in water
Phenolsulfonephthalein (Phenol Red)	6.6–8.0	yel to red	0.1 g in 28.2 ml 0.01N NaOH + 221.8 ml water
Neutral Red	6.8–8.0	red to amb	0.01 g in 50 ml EtOH + 50 ml water
m-Nitrophenol	6.8–8.6	col to yel	0.3% in water
o-Cresolsulfonephthalein (Cresol Red)	0.0–1.0	red to yel	0.1 g in 26.2 ml 0.01N NaOH + 223.8 ml water
	7.0–8.8	yel to red	
Curcumin	7.4–8.6	yel to red	EtOH
	10.2–11.8		
m-Cresolsulfonephthalein (Metacresol Purple)	1.2–2.8	red to yel	0.1 g in 26.2 ml 0.01N NaOH + 223.8 ml water
	7.4–9.0	yel to purp	
4,4′-Bis(4-amino-1-naphthylazo) 2,2′stilbene disulfonic acid	8.0–9.0	bl to red	0.1 g in 5.9 ml 0.05N NaOH + 94.1 ml water
Thymolsulfonephthalein (Thymol Blue)	1.2–2.8	red to yel	0.1 g in 21.5 ml 0.01N NaOH + 228.5 ml water
	8.0–9.6		
o-Cresolphthalein	8.2–9.8	col to red	0.04% in EtOH
p-Naphtholbenzene	8.2–10.0	or to bl	1% in dil. alkali
Phenolphthalein	8.2–10.0	col to pink	0.05 g in 50 ml EtOH + 50 ml water
Ethyl-bis(2,4-dimethylphenyl)acetate	8.4–9.6	col to bl	saturated solution in 50% acetone alcohol
Thymolphthalein	9.4–10.6	col to bl	0.04 g in 50 ml EtOH + 50 ml water
5-(p-Nitrophenylazo)salicylic acid, Na-salt (Alizarin Yellow R)	10.1–12.0	yel to red	0.01% in water
p-(2,4-Dihydroxyphenylazo)benzene-sulfonic acid, Na-salt	11.4–12.6	yel to or	0.1% in water
5,5′-Indigodisulfonic acid, di-Na-salt	11.4–13.0	bl to yel	water
2,4,6-Trinitrotoluene	11.5–13.0	col to or	0.1–0.5% in EtOH
1,3,5-Trinitrobenzene	12.0–14.0	col to or	0.1–0.5% in EtOH
Clayton Yellow	12.2–13.2	yel to amb	0.1% in water

FLUORESCENT INDICATORS

Jack DeMent

Fluorescent indicators are substances which show definite changes in fluorescence with change in pH. Some fluorescent materials are not suitable for indicators since their change in fluorescence is too gradual. Fluorescent indicators find greatest utility in the titration of opaque, highly turbid or deeply colored solutions. A long wavelength ultraviolet ("black light") lamp in a dimly lighted room provides the best environment for titrations involving fluorescent indicators, although bright daylight is sometimes sufficient to evoke a response in the bright green, yellow and orange fluorescent indicators. Titrations are carried out in non-fluorescent glassware. One should check the glassware prior to use to make certain that it does not fluoresce due to the wavelengths of light involved in the titration. The meniscus of the liquid in the burette can be followed when a few particles of an insoluble fluorescent solid are dropped onto its surface.

In this table the indicators are arranged by approximate pH range covered. In the case of some of the dyestuffs the end point may vary slightly with the source or manufacturer.

pH 0 to 2

Indicator	C.I.	From pH	To pH
Benzoflavine	—	0.3, yellow fl.	1.7, green fl.
3,6-Dioxyphthalimide	—	0, blue fl.	2.4, green fl.
Eosine YS	768	0, yellow colored	3.0, yellow fl.
Erythrosine	772	0, yellow colored	3.6, yellow fl.
Esculin	—	1.5, colorless	2, blue fl.
4-Ethoxyacridone	—	1.2, green fl.	3.2, blue fl.
3,6-Tetramethyldiaminooxanthone	—	1.2, green fl.	3.4, blue fl.

pH 2 to 4

Indicator	C.I.	From pH	To pH
Chromotropic acid	—	3.5, colorless	4.5, blue fl.
Fluorescein	766	4, colorless	4.5, green fl.
Magdala Red	—	3.0, purple colored	4.0, fl.
α-Naphthylamine	—	3.4, colorless	4.8, blue fl.
β-Naphthylamine	—	2.8, colorless	4.4, violet fl.
Phloxine	774	3.4, colorless	5.0, bright yellow fl.
Salicylic acid	—	2.5, colorless	3.5, blue fl.

pH 4 to 6

Indicator	C.I.	From pH	To pH
Acridine	788	4.9, green fl.	5.1, violet colored
Dichlorofluorescein	—	4.0, colorless	5.0, green fl.
3,6-Dioxyxanthone	—	5.4, colorless	7.6, blue-violet fl.
Erythrosine	772	4.0, colorless	4.5, yellow-green fl.
β-Methylesculetin	—	4.0, colorless	6.2, blue fl.
Neville-Winther acid	—	6.0, colorless	6.5, blue fl.
Resorufin	—	4.4, yellow fl.	6.4, weak orange fl.
Quininic acid	—	4.0, yellow colored	5.0, blue fl.
Quinine [first end point]	—	5.0, blue fl.	6.1, violet fl.

pH 6 to 8

Indicator	C.I.	From pH	To pH
Acid R Phosphine	—	(claimed for range pH 6.0–7.0)	
Brilliant Diazol Yellow	—	6.5, colorless	7.5, violet fl.
Cleves acid	—	6.5, colorless	7.5, green fl.
Coumaric acid	—	7.2, colorless	9.0, green fl.
3,6-Dioxyphthalic dinitrile	—	5.8, blue fl.	8.2, green fl.
Magnesium 8-hydroxyquinolinate	—	6.5, colorless	7.5, golden fl.
β-Methylumbelliferone	—	7.0, colorless	7.5, blue fl.
1-Naphthol-4-sulfonic acid	—	6.0, colorless	6.5, blue fl.
Orcinaurine	—	6.5, colorless	8.0, green fl.
Patent Phosphine	789	(for the range pH 6.0–7.0, green-yellow fl.)	
Thioflavine	816	(for the region pH 6.5–7.0, yellow fl.)	
Umbelliferone	—	6.5, colorless	7.6, blue fl.

pH 8 to 10

Indicator	C.I.	From pH	To pH
Acridine Orange	788	8.4, orange colored	10.4, green fl.
Ethoxyphenylnaphthostilbazonium chloride	—	9, green fl.	11, non-fl.
G Salt	—	9.0, dull blue fl.	9.5, bright blue fl.
Naphthazol derivatives	—	8.2, colorless	10.0, yellow or green fl.
α-Naphthionic acid	—	9, blue fl.	11, green fl.
2-Naphthol-3,6-disulfonic acid	—	9.5, dark blue fl.	Light blue fl. at higher pH
β-Naphthol	—	8.6, colorless	Blue fl. at higher pH
α-Naphtholsulfonic acid	—	8.0, dark blue fl.	9.0, bright violet fl.
1,4-Naphtholsulfonic acid	—	8.2, dark blue fl.	Light blue fl. at higher pH
Orcinsulfonphthalein	—	8.6, yellow colored	10.0 fl.
Quinine [second end point]	—	9.5, violet fl.	10.0, colorless
R-Salt	—	9.0, dull blue fl.	9.5, bright blue fl.
Sodium 1-naphthol-2-sulfonate	—	9.0, dark blue fl.	10.0, bright violet fl.

pH 10 to 12

Indicator	C.I.	From pH	To pH
Coumarin	—	9.8, deep green fl.	12, light green fl.
Eosine BN	771	10.5, colorless	14.0, yellow fl.
Papaverine (permanganate oxidized)	—	9.5, yellow fl.	11.0, blue fl.
Schaffers Salt	—	5.0, violet fl.	11.0, green-blue fl.
SS-Acid (sodium salt)	—	10.0, violet fl.	12.0, yellow colored

pH 12 to 14

Indicator	C.I.	From pH	To pH
Cotarnine	—	12.0, yellow fl.	13.0, white fl.
α-Naphthionic acid	—	12, blue fl.	13, green fl.
β-Naphthionic acid	—	12, blue fl.	13, violet fl.

FORMULAS FOR CALCULATING TITRATION DATA, pH VS. ML. OF REAGENT

A — Substance Titrated V_0 ml. of solution M_0 its molarity	B — Initial $[H^+]$ or $[OH^-]$	C — Intermediate Points 10, 50, 99, etc., per cent neutralized, V_1 ml. of reagent of M_1 molarity added	D — Equivalence Point	E — Excess of Reagent V_1 volume reagent M_1 its molarity V_T total volume
(1) Strong Acid	$[H^+] = M_0$	$[H^+] = \dfrac{V_0M_0 - V_1M_1}{V_0 + V_1}$	$\sqrt{K_w}$	$[OH^-] = \dfrac{V_1M_1}{V_T}$
(2) Strong Base	$[OH^-] = M_0$	$[OH^-] = \dfrac{V_0M_0 - V_1M_1}{V_0 + V_1}$	$\sqrt{K_w}$	$[H^+] = \dfrac{V_1M_1}{V_T}$
(3) Weak Acid ($K_a = 10^{-5}$ to 10^{-8})	$[H^+] = \sqrt{M_0 K_a}$	$[H^+] = \dfrac{[Acid]}{[Salt]} K_a$	$[OH^-] = \sqrt{\dfrac{K_w}{K_a} c}$	$[OH^-] = \dfrac{V_1M_1}{V_T}$ (Value in column D to be added)
(4) Weak Base ($K_b = 10^{-5}$ to 10^{-8})	$[OH^-] = \sqrt{M_0 K_b}$	$[OH^-] = \dfrac{[Base]}{[Salt]} K_b$	$[H^+] = \sqrt{\dfrac{K_w}{K_b} c}$	$[H^+] = \dfrac{V_1M_1}{V_T}$ (Value in column D to be added)
(5) Salt of a Very Weak Acid (e.g. KCN)	$[OH^-] = \sqrt{\dfrac{K_w}{K_a} c}$	$[H^+] = \dfrac{[Acid]}{[Salt]} K_a$	$[H^+] = \sqrt{[Acid]K_a}$	$[H^+] = \dfrac{V_1M_1}{V_T}$ (Correct for value in column D)
(6) Salt of a Very Weak Base	$[H^+] = \sqrt{\dfrac{K_w}{K_b} c}$	$[OH^-] = \dfrac{[Base]}{[Salt]} K_b$	$[OH^-] = \sqrt{[Base]K_b}$	$[OH^-] = \dfrac{V_1M_1}{V_T}$ (Add to $[OH^-]$ found in column D)

CONVERSION FORMULAE FOR SOLUTIONS HAVING CONCENTRATIONS EXPRESSED IN VARIOUS WAYS

A = Weight per cent of solute
B = Molecular weight of solvent
E = Molecular weight of solute
F = Grams of solute per liter of solution
G = Molality
M = Molarity
N = Mole fraction
R = Density of solution grams per cc

Concentration of solute— SOUGHT	Concentration of solute—GIVEN A	N	G	M	F
A	—	$\dfrac{100N \times E}{N \times E + (1-N)B}$	$\dfrac{100G \times E}{1000 + G \times E}$	$\dfrac{M \times E}{10R}$	$\dfrac{F}{10R}$
N	$\dfrac{\dfrac{A}{E}}{\dfrac{A}{E} + \dfrac{100-A}{B}}$	—	$\dfrac{B \times G}{B \times G + 1000}$	$\dfrac{B \times M}{M(B-E) + 1000R}$	$\dfrac{B \times F}{F(B-E) + 1000R \times E}$
G	$\dfrac{1000A}{E(100-A)}$	$\dfrac{1000N}{B - N \times B}$	—	$\dfrac{1000M}{1000R - (M \times E)}$	$\dfrac{1000F}{E(1000R - F)}$
M	$\dfrac{10R \times A}{E}$	$\dfrac{1000R \times N}{N \times E + (1-N)B}$	$\dfrac{1000R \times G}{1000 + E \times G}$	—	$\dfrac{F}{E}$
F	$10AR$	$\dfrac{1000R \times N \times E}{N \times E + (1-N)B}$	$\dfrac{1000R \times G \times E}{1000 + G \times E}$	$M \times E$	—

ELECTROCHEMICAL SERIES

Table I
Alphabetical listing
Compiled by J. F. Hunsberger
Values listed are Standard Reduction Potentials

Reaction	Potential, volts
$Ag^+ + e^- \rightleftharpoons Ag$	0.7996
$Ag^{+2} + e^- \rightleftharpoons Ag^{+1}(4f\ HClO_4)$	1.987
$AgAc + e^- \rightleftharpoons Ag + Ac^-$	0.64
$AgBr + e^- \rightleftharpoons Ag + Br^-$	0.0713
$AgBrO_3 + e^- \rightleftharpoons Ag + BrO_3^-$	0.680
$Ag_2C_2O_4 + 2e^- \rightleftharpoons Ag + C_2O_4^{-2}$	0.4776
$AgCl + e^- \rightleftharpoons Ag + Cl^-$	0.2223
$AgCN + e^- \rightleftharpoons Ag + CN^-$	−0.02
$Ag_2CO_3 + 2e^- \rightleftharpoons 2Ag + CO_3^{-2}$	0.4769
$Ag_2CrO_4 + 2e^- \rightleftharpoons 2Ag + CrO_4^{-2}$	0.4463
$Ag_4Fe(CN)_6 + 4e^- \rightleftharpoons 4Ag + Fe(CN)_6^{-4}$	0.1943
$AgI + e^- \rightleftharpoons Ag + I^-$	−0.1519
$AgIO_3 + e^- \rightleftharpoons Ag + IO_3^-$	0.3551
$Ag_2MoO_4 + 2e^- \rightleftharpoons 2Ag + MoO_4^{-2}$	0.49
$AgNO_2 + e^- \rightleftharpoons Ag + NO_2^-$	0.59
$Ag_2O + H_2O + 2e^- \rightleftharpoons 2Ag + 2OH^-$	0.342
$Ag_2O_3 + H_2O + 2e^- \rightleftharpoons 2AgO + 2OH^-$	0.74
$2AgO + H_2O + 2e^- \rightleftharpoons Ag_2O + 2OH^-$	0.599
$AgOCN + e^- \rightleftharpoons Ag + OCN^-$	0.41
$Ag_2S + 2e^- \rightleftharpoons 2Ag + S^{-2}$	−0.7051
$Ag_2S + 2H^+ + 2e^- \rightleftharpoons 2Ag + H_2S$	−0.0366
$AgSCN + e^- \rightleftharpoons Ag + SCN^-$	0.0895
$Ag_2SeO_3 + 2e^- \rightleftharpoons 2Ag + SeO_3^{\,2}$	0.3629
$Ag_2SO_4 + 2e^- \rightleftharpoons 2Ag + SO_4^{-2}$	0.653
$Ag_2(WO_4) + 2e^- \rightleftharpoons 2Ag + WO_4^{-2}$	0.466
$Al^{+3} + 3e^- \rightleftharpoons Al\ (0.1f\ NaOH)$	−1.706
$H_2AlO_3^- + H_2O + 3e^- \rightleftharpoons Al + 4OH^-$	−2.35
$As + 3H^+ + 3e^- \rightleftharpoons AsH_3$	−0.54
$As_2O_3 + 6H^+ + 6e^- \rightleftharpoons 2As + 3H_2O$	0.234
$HAsO_2 + 3H^+ + 3e^- \rightleftharpoons As + 2H_2O$	0.2475
$AsO_2^- + 2H_2O + 3e^- \rightleftharpoons As + 4OH^-$	−0.68
$H_2AsO_4 + 2H^+ + 2e^- \rightleftharpoons HAsO_2 + 2H_2O(1f\ HCl)$	0.58
$AsO_4^{-3} + 2H_2O + 2e^- \rightleftharpoons AsO_2^- + 4OH^-$	−0.71
$AsO_4^{-3} + 2H_2O + 2e^- \rightleftharpoons AsO_2^- + 4OH^-\ (1f\ NaOH)$	−0.08
$Au^+ + e^- \rightleftharpoons Au$	1.68
$Au^{+3} + 2e^- \rightleftharpoons Au^{+1}$	1.29
$Au^{+3} + 3e^- \rightleftharpoons Au$	1.42
$AuBr_2^- + e^- \rightleftharpoons Au + 2Br^-$	0.963
$AuBr_4^- + 3e^- \rightleftharpoons Au + 4Br^-$	0.858
$AuCl_4^- + 3e^- \rightleftharpoons Au + 4Cl^-$	0.994
$Au(OH)_3 + 3H^+ + 3e^- \rightleftharpoons Au + 3H_2O$	1.45
$H_2BO_3^- + 5H_2O + 8e^- \rightleftharpoons BH_4^- + 8OH^-$	−1.24
$H_2BO_3^- + H_2O + 3e^- \rightleftharpoons B + 4OH^-$	−2.5
$H_3BO_3 + 3H^+ + 3e^- \rightleftharpoons B + 3H_2O$	−0.73
$Ba^{+2} + 2e^- \rightleftharpoons Ba$	−2.90
$Ba^{+2} + 2e^- \rightleftharpoons Ba(Hg)$	−1.570
$Ba(OH)_2 \cdot 8H_2O + 2e^- \rightleftharpoons Ba + 2OH^- + 8H_2O$	−2.97
$Be^{+2} + 2e^- \rightleftharpoons Be$	−1.70
	(−1.85)
$Be_2O_3^{-2} + 3H_2O + 4e^- \rightleftharpoons 2Be + 6OH^-$	−2.28
$Bi(Cl)_4^- + 3e^- \rightleftharpoons Bi + 4Cl^-$	0.168
$Bi_2O_3 + 3H_2O + 6e^- \rightleftharpoons 2Bi + 6OH^-$	−0.46
$Bi_2O_4 + 4H^+ + 2e^- \rightleftharpoons 2BiO^+ + 2H_2O$	1.59
$BiO^+ + 2H^+ + 3e^- \rightleftharpoons Bi + H_2O$	0.32
$BiOCl + 2H^+ + 3e^- \rightleftharpoons Bi + Cl^- + H_2O$	0.1583
$BiOOH + H_2O + 3e^- \rightleftharpoons Bi + 3OH^-$	−0.46
$Br_2(aq) + 2e^- \rightleftharpoons 2Br^-$	1.087
$Br_2(l) + 2e^- \rightleftharpoons 2Br^-$	1.065
$HBrO + H^+ + e^- \rightleftharpoons 1/2Br_2 + H_2O$	1.59
$HBrO + H^+ + 2e^- \rightleftharpoons Br^- + H_2O$	1.33
$2HBrO + 2H^+ + 2e^- \rightleftharpoons Br_2(l) + 2H_2O$	1.6
$BrO^- + H_2O + 2e^- \rightleftharpoons Br^- + 2OH^-(1f\ NaOH)$	0.70
$BrO_3^- + 6H^+ + 5e^- \rightleftharpoons 1/2Br_2 + 3H_2O$	1.52
$BrO_3^- + 6H^+ + 6e^- \rightleftharpoons Br^- + 3H_2O$	1.44
$BrO_3^- + 3H_2O + 6e^- \rightleftharpoons Br^- + 6OH^-$	0.61
$C_6H_4O_2 + 2H^+ + 2e^- \rightleftharpoons C_6H_4(OH)_2$	0.6992
$Ca^+ + e^- \rightleftharpoons Ca$	−3.02
$Ca^{+2} + 2e^- \rightleftharpoons Ca$	−2.76
Calomel Electrode, Molal KCl	0.2800
*Calomel Electrode, N KCl	0.2807
*Calomel Electrode 0.1 N KCl	0.3337
*Calomel Electrode, Sat'd. KCl	0.2415
*Calomel Electrode, Sat'd NaCl	0.2360
$Ca(OH)_2 + 2e^- \rightleftharpoons Ca + 2OH^-$	−3.02
$Cb_2O_5 + 10H^+ + 10e^- \rightleftharpoons 2Cb + 5H_2O$	−0.62
$Cd^{+2} + 2e^- \rightleftharpoons Cd$	−0.4026
$Cd^{+2} + 2e^- \rightleftharpoons Cd(Hg)$	−0.3521
$Cd(OH)_2 + 2e^- \rightleftharpoons Cd(Hg) + 2OH$	−0.761
	(−0.81)
$CdSO_4 \cdot 8/3H_2O + 2e^- \rightleftharpoons Cd(Hg) + CdSO_4(sat'd\ aq)$	−0.4346
$Ce^{+3} + 3e^- \rightleftharpoons Ce$	−2.335
$Ce^{+3} + 3e^- \rightleftharpoons Ce(Hg)$	−1.4373
$Ce^{+4} + e^- \rightleftharpoons Ce^{+3}$	1.4430
	(1.61)
$Ce^{+4} + e^- \rightleftharpoons Ce^{+3}(0.5f\ H_2SO_4)$	1.4587
$CeOH^{+3} + H^+ + e^- \rightleftharpoons Ce^{+3} + H_2O$	1.7134
$Cl_2(g) + 2e^- \rightleftharpoons 2Cl^-$	1.3583
$HClO + H^+ + e^- \rightleftharpoons 1/2Cl_2 + H_2O$	1.63
$HClO + H^+ + 2e^- \rightleftharpoons Cl^- + H_2O$	1.49
$ClO^- + H_2O + 2e^- \rightleftharpoons Cl^- + 2OH^-$	0.90
$ClO_2 + e^- \rightleftharpoons ClO_2^-$	1.15
$ClO_2 + H^+ + e^- \rightleftharpoons HClO_2$	1.27
$HClO_2 + 2H^+ + 2e^- \rightleftharpoons HClO + H_2O$	1.64
$HClO_2 + 3H^+ + 3e^- \rightleftharpoons 1/2Cl_2 + 2H_2O$	1.63
$HClO_2 + 3H^+ + 4e^- \rightleftharpoons Cl^- + 2H_2O$	1.56
$ClO_2^- + 2H^+ + 2e^- \rightleftharpoons ClO^- + 2OH^-$	0.59
$ClO_2^- + 2H_2O + 4e^- \rightleftharpoons Cl^- + 4OH^-$	0.76
$ClO_2(aq) + e^- \rightleftharpoons ClO_2^-$	0.954
$ClO_3^- + 2H^+ + e^- \rightleftharpoons ClO_2 + H_2O$	1.15
$ClO_3^- + 3H^+ + 2e^- \rightleftharpoons HClO_2 + H_2O$	1.21
	(1.23)
$ClO_3^- + 6H^+ + 5e^- \rightleftharpoons \tfrac{1}{2}Cl_2 + 3H_2O$	1.47
$ClO_3^- + 6H^+ + 6e^- \rightleftharpoons Cl^- + 3H_2O$	1.45
$ClO_3^- + H_2O + 2e^- \rightleftharpoons ClO_2^- + 2OH^-$	0.35
$ClO_3^- + 3H_2O + 6e^- \rightleftharpoons Cl^- + 6OH^-$	0.62
$ClO_4^- + 2H^+ + 2e^- \rightleftharpoons ClO_3 + H_2O$	1.19
$ClO_4^- + 8H^+ + 7e^- \rightleftharpoons \tfrac{1}{2}Cl_2 + 4H_2O$	1.34
$ClO_4^- + 8H^+ + 8e^- \rightleftharpoons Cl^- + 4H_2O$	1.37
$ClO_4^- + H_2O + 2e^- \rightleftharpoons ClO_3^- + 2OH^-$	0.17
$(CN)_2 + 2H^+ + 2e^- \rightleftharpoons 2HCN$	0.37
$2HCNO + 2H^+ + 2e^- \rightleftharpoons (CN)_2 + 2H_2O$	0.33
$(CNS)_2 + 2e^- \rightleftharpoons 2CNS^-$	0.77
$Co^{+2} + 2e^- \rightleftharpoons Co$	−0.28
$Co^{+3} + e^- \rightleftharpoons Cu^{+2}(3f\ HNO_3)$	1.842
$CO_2 + 2H^+ + 2e^- \rightleftharpoons HCOOH$	−0.2
$2CO_2 + 2H^+ + 2e^- \rightleftharpoons H_2C_2O_4$	−0.49
$Co(NH_3)_6^{+3} + e^- \rightleftharpoons Co(NH_3)_6^{+2}$	0.1
$Co(OH)_2 + 2e^- \rightleftharpoons Co + 2OH^-$	−0.73
$Co(OH)_3 + e^- \rightleftharpoons Co(OH)_2 + OH^-$	0.2 (0.17)
$Cr^{+2} + 2e \rightleftharpoons Cr$	−0.557
$Cr^{+3} + e^- \rightleftharpoons Cr^{+2}$	−0.41
$Cr^{+3} + 3e^- \rightleftharpoons Cr$	−0.74
$Cr^{+6} + 3e^- \rightleftharpoons Cr^{+3}(2f\ H_2SO_4)$	1.10
$Cr^{+6} + 3e^- \rightleftharpoons Cr^{+3}(1f\ NaOH)$	−0.12
$Cr_2O_7^{-2} + 14H^+ + 6e^- \rightleftharpoons 2Cr^{+3} + 7H_2O$	1.33
$CrO_2^- + 2H_2O + 3e^- \rightleftharpoons Cr + 4OH^-$	−1.2
$HCrO_4^- + 7H^+ + 3e^- \rightleftharpoons Cr^{+3} + 4H_2O$	1.195
$CrO_4^{-2} + 4H_2O + 3e^- \rightleftharpoons Cr(OH)_3 + 5OH^-$	−0.12
$Cr(OH)_3 + 3e^- \rightleftharpoons Cr + 3OH^-$	−1.3
$Cs^+ + e^- \rightleftharpoons Cs$	−2.923
$Cu^+ + e^- \rightleftharpoons Cu$	0.522
$Cu^{+2} + 2CN^- + e^- \rightleftharpoons Cu(CN)_2$	1.12
$Cu^{+2} + e \rightleftharpoons Cu^+$	0.158
	(0.167)
$Cu^{+2} + 2e^- \rightleftharpoons Cu$	0.3402
$Cu^{+2} + 2e \rightleftharpoons Cu(Hg)$	0.345
$CuI_2^- + e^- \rightleftharpoons Cu + 2I^-$	0.00
$Cu_2O + H_2O + 2e^- \rightleftharpoons 2Cu + 2OH^-$	−0.361
$Cu(OH)_2 + 2e^- \rightleftharpoons Cu + 2OH^-$	−0.224
$2Cu(OH)_2 + 2e^- \rightleftharpoons Cu_2O + 2OH^- + H_2O$	−0.09
$D^+ + e^- \rightleftharpoons 1/2D_2$	−0.0034
$2D^+ + 2e^- \rightleftharpoons D_2$	−0.044
$Eu^{+3} + e^- \rightleftharpoons Eu^{+2}$	−0.43
$1/2F_2 + e^- \rightleftharpoons F^-$	2.85
$1/2F_2 + H^+ + e^- \rightleftharpoons HF$	3.03
$F_2 + 2e^- \rightleftharpoons 2F^-$	2.87
$F_2O + 2H^+ + 4e^- \rightleftharpoons H_2O + 2F^-$	2.1
$Fe^{+2} + 2e^- \rightleftharpoons Fe$	−0.409
$Fe^{+3} + 3e^- \rightleftharpoons Fe$	−0.036
$Fe^{+3} + e^- \rightleftharpoons Fe^{+2}$	0.770
$Fe^{+3} + e^- \rightleftharpoons Fe^{+2}(1f\ HCl)$	0.770
$Fe^{+3} + e^- \rightleftharpoons Fe^{+2}(1f\ HClO_4)$	0.747
$Fe^{+3} + e^- \rightleftharpoons Fe^{+2}(1f\ H_3PO_4)$	0.438
$Fe^{+3} + e^- \rightleftharpoons Fe^{+2}(0.5f\ H_2SO_4)$	0.679
$Fe(CN)_6^{-3} + e^- \rightleftharpoons Fe(CN)_6^{-4}(0.01f\ NaOH)$	0.46
$Fe(CN)_6^{-3} + e^- \rightleftharpoons Fe(CN)_6^{-4}(1f\ H_2SO_4)$	0.69
$FeO_4^{-2} + 8H^+ + 3e^- \rightleftharpoons Fe^{+3} + 4H_2O$	1.9
$Fe(OH)_3 + e^- \rightleftharpoons Fe(OH)_2 + OH^-$	−0.56
$Fe(phenanthroline)_3^{+3} + e^- \rightleftharpoons Fe(ph)_3^{+2}$	1.14
$Fe(phenanthroline)_3^{+3} + e^- \rightleftharpoons Fe(ph)_3^{+2}(2f\ H_2SO_4)$	1.056
$Ga^{+3} + 3e^- \rightleftharpoons Ga$	−0.560
$H_2GaO_3^- + H_2O + 3e^- \rightleftharpoons Ga + 4OH^-$	−1.22

Reaction	Potential, volts	Reaction	Potential, volts
$GeO_2 + 2H^+ + 2e^- \rightarrow GeO + H_2O$	-0.12	$NO_2^- + H_2O + e^- \rightarrow NO + 2OH^-$	-0.46
$H_2GeO_3 + 4H^+ + 4e^- \rightarrow Ge + 3H_2O$	-0.13	$2NO_2^- + 2H_2O + 4e^- \rightarrow N_2O_2^{-2} + 4OH^-$	-0.18
$2H^+ + 2e^- \rightarrow H_2$	0.0000	$2NO_2^- + 3H_2O + 4e^- \rightarrow N_2O + 6OH^-$	0.15
$1/2H_2 + e^- \rightarrow H^-$	-2.23	$NO_3^- + 3H^+ + 2e^- \rightarrow HNO_2 + H_2O$	0.94
$2H_2O + 2e^- \rightarrow H_2 + 2OH^-$	-0.8277	$NO_3^- + 4H^+ + 3e^- \rightarrow NO + 2H_2O$	0.96
$H_2O_2 + 2H^+ + 2e^- \rightarrow 2H_2O$	1.776	$2NO_3^- + 4H^+ + 2e^- \rightarrow N_2O_4 + 2H_2O$	0.81
$HfO^{+2} + 2H^+ + 4e^- \rightarrow Hf + H_2O$	-1.68	$NO_3^- + H_2O + 2e^- \rightarrow NO_2^- + 2OH^-$	0.01
$HfO_2 + 4H^+ + 4e^- \rightarrow Hf + 2H_2O$	-1.57	$2NO_3^- + 2H_2O + 2e^- \rightarrow N_2O_4 + 4OH^-$	-0.85
$HfO(OH)_2 + H_2O + 4e^- \rightarrow Hf + 4OH^-$	-2.60	$Np^{+3} + 3e^- \rightarrow Np$	-1.9
$Hg^{+2} + 2e^- \rightarrow Hg$	0.851	$Np^{+4} + e^- \rightarrow Np^{+3}(1fHClO_4)$	0.155
$2Hg^{+2} + 2e^- \rightarrow Hg_2^{+2}$	0.905	$Np^{+5} + e^- \rightarrow Np^{+4}(1fHClO_4)$	0.739
$1/2Hg_2^{+2} + e^- \rightarrow Hg$	0.7986	$Np^{+6} + e^- \rightarrow Np^{+5}(1fHClO_4)$	1.137
$Hg_2^{+2} + 2e^- \rightarrow 2Hg$	0.7961	$1/2O_2 + 2H^+(10^{-7}M) + 2e^- \rightarrow H_2O$	0.815
$Hg_2(AcO)_2 + 2e^- \rightarrow 2Hg + 2AcO^-$	0.5113	$O_2 + 2H^+ + 2e^- \rightarrow H_2O_2$	0.682
$Hg_2Br_2 + 2e^- \rightarrow 2Hg + 2Br^-$	0.1396	$O_2 + 4H^+ + 4e^- \rightarrow 2H_2O$	1.229
$Hg_2Cl_2 + 2e^- \rightarrow 2Hg + 2Cl^-$	0.2682	$O_2 + H_2O + 2e^- \rightarrow HO_2^- + OH^-$	-0.076
$Hg_2Cl_2 + 2e \rightarrow 2Hg + 2Cl^-(0.1f\ NaOH)$	0.3419	$O_2 + 2H_2O + 2e^- \rightarrow H_2O_2 + 2OH^-$	-0.146
	(0.268)	$O_2 + 2H_2O + 4e^- \rightarrow 4OH^-$	0.401
$Hg_2HPO_4 + H^+ + 2e^- \rightarrow 2Hg + H_2PO_4^-$	0.639	$O_3 + 2H^+ + 2e^- \rightarrow O_2 + H_2O$	2.07
$Hg_2I_2 + 2e^- \rightarrow 2Hg + 2I^-$	-0.0405	$O_3 + H_2O + 2e^- \rightarrow O_2 + 2OH^-$	1.24
$Hg_2O + H_2O + 2e^- \rightarrow 2Hg + 2OH^-$	0.123	$O_{(g)} + 2H^+ + 2e^- \rightarrow H_2O$	2.42
$HgO + H_2O + 2e^- \rightarrow Hg + 2OH^-$	0.0984	$OH + e^- \rightarrow OH^-$	1.4
$Hg_2SO_4 + 2e^- \rightarrow 2Hg + SO_4^{-2}$	0.6158	$HO_2^- + H_2O + 2e^- \rightarrow 3OH^-$	0.87
$HO_2 + H^+ + e^- \rightarrow H_2O_2$	1.5	$OsO_4 + 8H^+ + 8e^- \rightarrow Os + 4H_2O$	0.85
$I_2 + 2e^- \rightarrow 2I^-$	0.535	$P + 3H^+ + 3e^- \rightarrow PH_3(g)$	-0.04
$I_3^- + 2e^- \rightarrow 3I^-$	0.5338	$P + 3H_2O + 3e^- \rightarrow PH_3(g) + 3OH^-$	-0.87
$In^{+2} + e^- \rightarrow In^{+1}$	-0.40	$Pb^{+2} + 2e^- \rightarrow Pb$	-0.1263
$In^{+3} + e^- \rightarrow In^{+2}$	-0.49		(-0.126)
$In^{+3} + 2e^- \rightarrow In^{+1}$	-0.40	$Pb^{+2} + 2e^- \rightarrow Pb(Hg)$	-0.1205
$In^{+3} + 3e^- \rightarrow In$	-0.338	$PbBr_2 + 2e^- \rightarrow Pb(Hg) + 2Br^-$	-0.275
$H_3IO_6^{-2} + 2e^- \rightarrow IO_3^- + 3OH^-$	~ 0.70	$PbCl_2 + 2e^- \rightarrow Pb(Hg) + 2Cl^-$	-0.262
$H_5IO_6 + H^+ + 2e^- \rightarrow IO_3^- + 3H_2O$	~ 1.7	$PbF_2 + 2e^- \rightarrow Pb(Hg) + 2F^-$	-0.3444
$HIO + H^+ + e^- \rightarrow 1/2I_2 + H_2O$	1.45	$PbHPO_4 + H^+ + 2e^- \rightarrow Pb(Hg) + HPO_4^-$	-0.2448
$HIO + H^+ + 2e^- \rightarrow I^- + H_2O$	0.99	$PbI_2 + 2e^- \rightarrow Pb(Hg) + 2I^-$	-0.358
$IO^- + H_2O + 2e^- \rightarrow I^- + 2OH^-$	0.49	$PbO + H_2O + 2e^- \rightarrow Pb + 2OH^-$	-0.576
$IO_3^- + 6H^+ + 5e^- \rightarrow 1/2I_2 + 3H_2O$	1.195	$PbO_2 + 4H^+ + 2e^- \rightarrow Pb^{+2} + 2H_2O$	1.46
$IO_3^- + 6H^+ + 6e^- \rightarrow I^- + 3H_2O$	1.085	$HPbO_2^- + H_2O + 2e^- \rightarrow Pb + 3OH^-$	-0.54
$2IO_3^- + 12H^+ + 10e^- \rightarrow I_2 + 6H_2O$	1.19	$PbO_2 + H_2O + 2e^- \rightarrow PbO + 2OH^-$	0.28
$IO_3^- + 2H_2O + 4e^- \rightarrow IO^- + 4OH^-$	0.56	$PbO_2 + SO_4^{-2} + 4H^+ + 2e^- \rightarrow PbSO_4 + 2H_2O$	1.685
$IO_3^- + 3H_2O + 6e^- \rightarrow I^- + 6OH^-$	0.26	$PbSO_4 + 2e^- \rightarrow Pb + SO_4^{-2}$	-0.356
$IrCl_6^{-2} + e^- \rightarrow IrCl_6^{-3}$	1.02	$PbSO_4 + 2e^- \rightarrow Pb(Hg) + SO_4^{-2}$	-0.3505
$IrCl_6^{-3} + 3e^- \rightarrow Ir + 6Cl^-$	0.77	$Pd^{+2} + 2e^- \rightarrow Pd$	0.83
$Ir_2O_3 + 3H_2O + 6e^- \rightarrow 2Ir + 6OH^-$	0.1	$Pd^{+2} + 2e^- \rightarrow Pd(1fHCl)$	0.623
$K^+ + e^- \rightarrow K$	-2.924	$Pd^{+2} + 2e^- \rightarrow Pd(4f\ HClO_4)$	0.987
	(-2.923)	$PdCl_4^{-2} + 2e^- \rightarrow Pd + 4Cl^-$	0.623
$La^{+3} + 3e^- \rightarrow La$	-2.37	$PdCl_6^{-2} + 2e^- \rightarrow PdCl_4^{-2} + 2Cl^-$	1.29
$La(OH)_3 + 3e \rightarrow La + 3OH^-$	-2.76	$Pd(OH)_2 + 2e^- \rightarrow Pd + 2OH^-$	0.1
$Li^+ + e^- \rightarrow Li$	-3.045	$H_2PO_2^- + e^- \rightarrow P + 2OH^-$	-1.82
	(-3.02)	$H_3PO_2 + H^+ + e^- \rightarrow P + 2H_2O$	-0.51
$Mg^{++} + 2e^- \rightarrow Mg$	-2.375	$H_3PO_3 + 2H^+ + 2e^- \rightarrow H_3PO_2 + H_2O$	-0.50
$Mg(OH)_2 + 2e^- \rightarrow Mg + 2OH^-$	-2.67		(-0.59)
$Mn^{+2} + 2e^- \rightarrow Mn$	-1.029	$H_3PO_3 + 3H^+ + 3e^- \rightarrow P + 3H_2O$	-0.49
$Mn^{+3} + e^- \rightarrow Mn^{+2}$	1.51	$HPO_3^{-2} + 2H_2O + 2e^- \rightarrow H_2PO_2^- + 3OH^-$	-1.65
$MnO_2 + 4H^+ + 2e^- \rightarrow Mn^{+2} + 2H_2O$	1.208	$HPO_3^{-2} + 2H_2O + 3e^- \rightarrow P + 5OH^-$	-1.71
$MnO_4^- + e^- \rightarrow MnO_4^{-2}$	0.564	$H_3PO_4 + 2H^+ + 2e^- \rightarrow H_3PO_3 + H_2O$	-0.276
$MnO_4^- + 4H^+ + 3e^- \rightarrow MnO_2 + 2H_2O$	$+1.679$		(-0.2)
$MnO_4^- + 8H^+ + 5e^- \rightarrow Mn^{+2} + 4H_2O$	1.491	$PO_4^{-3} + 2H_2O + 2e^- \rightarrow HPO_3^{-2} + 3OH^-$	-1.05
$MnO_4^- + 2H_2O + 3e^- \rightarrow MnO_2 + 4OH^-$	0.588	$Pt^{+2} + 2e^- \rightarrow Pt$	~ 1.2
$MnO_4^{-1} + 2H_2O + 3e^- \rightarrow MnO_2 + 4OH^-$	0.58	$PtCl_4^{-2} + 2e^- \rightarrow Pt + 4Cl^-$	0.73
$Mn(OH)_2 \rightarrow Mn + 2OH^-$	-1.47	$PtCl_6^{-2} + 2e^- \rightarrow PtCl_4^{-2} + 2Cl^-$	0.74
$Mn(OH)_3 + e^- \rightarrow Mn(OH)_2 + OH^-$	-0.40	$Pt(OH)_2 + 2e^- \rightarrow Pt + 2OH^-$	0.16
$H_2MoO_4 + 6H^+ + 6e^- \rightarrow Mo + 4H_2O$	0.0	$Pu^{+4} + e^- \rightarrow Pu^{+3}(1f\ HClO_4)$	0.982
$N_2 + 2H_2O + 4H^+ + 2e^- \rightarrow 2NH_3OH^+$	-1.87	$Pu^{+5} + e^- \rightarrow Pu^{+4}(0.5f\ HCl)$	1.099
$3N_2 + 2H^+ + 2e^- \rightarrow 2HN_3$	-3.1	$Pu^{+6} + e^- \rightarrow Pu^{+5}(1f\ HClO_4)$	0.9184
$N_2H_5^+ + 3H^+ + 2e^- \rightarrow 2NH_4^+$	1.27	$Pu^{+6} + 2e^- \rightarrow Pu^{+4}(1f\ HCl)$	1.052
$N_2O + 2H^+ + 2e^- \rightarrow N_2 + H_2O$	1.77	Quinhydrone Elec. $H^+, a = 1$	0.6995
$H_2N_2O_2 + 2H^+ + 2e^- \rightarrow N_2 + 2H_2O$	2.65	$Rb^+ + e^- \rightarrow Rb$	-2.925
$N_2O_4 + 2e^- \rightarrow 2NO_2^-$	0.88		(-2.99)
$N_2O_4 + 2H^+ + 2e^- \rightarrow 2HNO_2$	1.07	$Re^{+3} + 3e^- \rightarrow Re$	$0.3 \sim$
$N_2O_4 + 4H^+ + 4e^- \rightarrow 2NO + 2H_2O$	1.03	$ReO_4^- + 4H^+ + 3e^- \rightarrow ReO_2 + 2H_2O$	0.51
$Na^+ + e^- \rightarrow Na$	-2.7109	$ReO_2 + 4H^+ + 4e^- \rightarrow Re + 2H_2O$	0.26
	(-2.712)	$ReO_4^- + 2H^+ + e^- \rightarrow ReO_{3(ce)} + 2H_2O$	0.768
$Nb^{+5} + 2e \rightarrow Nb^{+3}(2fHCl)$	0.344	$ReO_4^- + 4H_2O + 7e^- \rightarrow Re + 80H^-$	-0.81
$Nd^{+3} + 3e^- \rightarrow Nd$	-2.246	$ReO_4^- + 8H^+ + 7e^- \rightarrow Re + 4H_2O$	0.367
$2NH_3OH^+ + H^+ + 2e^- \rightarrow N_2H_3^+ + 2H_2O$	1.42	$Rh^{+4} + e^- \rightarrow Rh^{+3}$	1.43
$Ni^{+2} + 2e^- \rightarrow Ni$	-0.23	$Rh(Cl)_6^{-3} + 3e^- \rightarrow Rh + 6Cl^-$	0.44
$Ni(OH)_2 + 2e^- \rightarrow Ni + 2OH^-$	-0.66	$Ru^{+3} + e^- \rightarrow Ru^{+2}(0.1f\ HClO_4)$	-0.11
$NiO_2 + 4H^+ + 2e^- \rightarrow Ni^{+2} + 2H_2O$	1.93	$Ru^{+3} + e^- \rightarrow Ru^{+2}(1-6f\ HCl)$	-0.084
$NiO_2 + 2H_2O + 2e^- \rightarrow Ni(OH)_2 + 2OH^-$	0.49	$Ru^{+4} + e^- \rightarrow Ru^{+3}(0.1f\ HClO_4)$	0.49
$2NO + 2e^- \rightarrow N_2O_2^{-2}$	0.10	$Ru^{+4} + e^- \rightarrow Ru^{+3}(2f\ HCl)$	0.858
$2NO + 2H^+ + 2e^- \rightarrow N_2O + H_2O$	1.59	$RuO_2 + 4H^+ + 4e^- \rightarrow Ru + 2H_2O$	-0.8
$2NO + 2H_2O + 2e^- \rightarrow N_2O + 2OH^-$	0.76	$RuO_4^- + e^- \rightarrow RuO_4^{-2}$	0.59
$HNO_2 + H^+ + e^- \rightarrow NO + H_2O$	0.99	$RuO_{4(c)} + e^- \rightarrow RuO_4^-$	1.00
$2HNO_2 + 4H^+ + 4e^- \rightarrow H_2N_2O_2 + 2H_2O$	0.80	$S + 2e^- \rightarrow S^{-2}$	-0.508
$2HNO_2 + 4H^+ + 4e^- \rightarrow N_2O + 3H_2O$	1.27	$S + 2H^+ + 2e^- \rightarrow H_2S_{(aq)}$	0.141
	(1.29)	$S + H_2O + 2e^- \rightarrow HS^- + OH^-$	-0.478

Reaction	Potential, volts	Reaction	Potential, volts
$S_2O_6^{-2} + 4H^+ + 2e^- \rightarrow 2H_2SO_3$	0.6	$TeO_4^- + 8H^+ + 7e^- \rightarrow Te + 4H_2O$	0.472
$S_2O_8^{2} + 2e^- \rightarrow 2SO_4^{-2}$	2.0	$H_6TeO_{6(s)} + 2H^+ + 2e^- \rightarrow TeO_{2(s)} + 4H_2O$	1.02
	(2.05)	$Th^{+4} + 4e^- \rightarrow Th$	−1.90
$S_4O_6^- + 2e^- \rightarrow 2S_2O_3^{-2}$	0.09	$ThO_2 + 4H^+ + 4e^- \rightarrow Th + 2H_2O$	−1.80
	(0.10)	$ThO_2 + 2H_2O + 4e^- \rightarrow Th + 4OH^-$	−2.64
$Sb + 3H^+ + 3e^- \rightarrow H_3Sb$	−0.51	$Ti^{+2} + 2e^- \rightarrow Ti$	−1.63
$Sb^{+5} + 2e^- \rightarrow Sb^{+3}(3.5f\,HCl)$	0.75	$Ti^{+3} + e^- \rightarrow Ti^{+2}$	−2.0
$Sb_2O_3 + 6H^+ + 6e^- \rightarrow 2Sb + 3H_2O$	0.1445	$TiO_2 + 4H^+ + 4e^- \rightarrow Ti + 2H_2O$	−0.86
	(0.152)	$Ti(OH)^{+3} + H^+ + e^- \rightarrow Ti^{+3} + H_2O$	0.06
$Sb_2O_5 + 4H^+ + 4e^- \rightarrow Sb_2O_3 + 2H_2O$	0.69	$Tl^+ + e^- \rightarrow Tl$	−0.3363
$Sb_2O_{5(s)} + 6H^+ + 4e^- \rightarrow 2SbO^+ + 3H_2O$	0.64	$Tl^+ + e^- \rightarrow Tl(Hg)$	−0.3338
$SbO^+ + 2H^+ + 3e^- \rightarrow Sb + 2H_2O$	0.212	$Tl^{+3} + e^- \rightarrow Tl^{+2}$	−0.37
$SbO_2^- + 2H_2O + 3e^- \rightarrow Sb + 4OH^-$	−0.66	$Tl^{+3} + 2e^- \rightarrow Tl^{+1}$	1.247
$SbO_3^- + H_2O + 2e^- \rightarrow SbO_2^- + 2OH^-$	−0.59	$Tl^{+3} + 2e^- \rightarrow Tl^{+1}(1f\,HCl)$	0.783
$Sc^{+3} + 3e^- \rightarrow Sc$	−2.08	$TlBr + e^- \rightarrow Tl(Hg) + Br^-$	−0.606
$Se + 2e^- \rightarrow Se^{-2}$	−0.78	$TlCl + e^- \rightarrow Tl(Hg) + Cl^-$	−0.555
$Se + 2H^+ + 2e^- \rightarrow H_2Se(aq)$	−0.36	$TlI + e^- \rightarrow Tl(Hg) + I^-$	−0.769
$H_2SeO_3 + 4H^+ + 4e^- \rightarrow Se + 3H_2O$	0.74	$Tl_2O_3 + 3H_2O + 4e^- \rightarrow 2Tl^+ + 6OH^-$	0.02
$SeO_3^{-2} + 3H_2O + 4e^- \rightarrow Se + 6OH^-$	−0.35	$TlOH + e^- \rightarrow Tl + OH^-$	−0.3445
$SeO_4^{-2} + 4H^+ + 2e^- \rightarrow H_2SeO_3 + H_2O$	1.15	$Tl(OH)_3 + 2e^- \rightarrow TlOH + 2OH^-$	−0.05
$SeO_4^{-2} + H_2O + 2e^- \rightarrow SeO_3^{-2} + 2OH^-$	0.03	$Tl_2SO_4 + 2e^- \rightarrow Tl(Hg) + SO_4^{-2}$	−0.4360
$SiF_6^{-2} + 4e^- \rightarrow Si + 6F^-$	−1.2	$U^{+3} + 3e^- \rightarrow U$	−1.8
$SiO_2 + 4H^+ + 4e^- \rightarrow Si + 2H_2O$	−0.84	$U^{+4} + e^- \rightarrow U^{+3}$	−0.61
$SiO_3^{-2} + 3H_2O + 4e^- \rightarrow Si + 6OH^-$	−1.73	$U^{+4} + e^- \rightarrow U^{+3}(1f\,HClO_4)$	−0.631
$Sn^{+2} + 2e^- \rightarrow Sn$	−0.1364	$U^{+5} + e^- \rightarrow U^{+4}(1f\,HCl)$	1.02
$Sn^{+4} + 2e^- \rightarrow Sn^{+2}$	0.15	$U^{+6} + e^- \rightarrow U^{+5}(1f\,HClO_4)$	0.063
$Sn^{+4} + 2e^- \rightarrow Sn^{+2}(0.1f\,HCl)$	0.070	$UO_3^+ + 4H^+ + e^- \rightarrow U^{+4} + 2H_2O$	0.62
$Sn^{+4} + 2e^- \rightarrow Sn^{+2}(1f\,HCl)$	0.139	$UO_2^{+2} + e^- \rightarrow UO_2^+$	0.062
$HSnO_2^- + H_2O + 2e^- \rightarrow Sn + 3OH^-$	−0.79	$UO_2^{+2} + 4H^+ + 2e^- \rightarrow U^{+4} + 2H_2O$	0.334
$Sn(OH)_6^{-2} + 2e^- \rightarrow HSnO_2^- + 3OH^- + H_2O$	−0.96	$UO_2^{+2} + 4H^+ + 6e^- \rightarrow U + 2H_2O$	−0.82
$2H_2SO_3 + H^+ + 2e^- \rightarrow HS_2O_4^- + 2H_2O$	−0.08	$V^{+2} + 2e^- \rightarrow V$	−1.2
$H_2SO_3 + 4H^+ + 4e^- \rightarrow S + 3H_2O$	0.45	$V^{+3} + e^- \rightarrow V^{+2}$	−0.255
$2SO_3^{-2} + 2H_2O + 2e^- \rightarrow S_2O_4^{-2} + 4OH^-$	−1.12	$V^{+5} + e^- \rightarrow V^{+4}(1f\,NaOH)$	−0.74
$2SO_3^{-2} + 3H_2O + 4e^- \rightarrow S_2O_3^{-2} + 6OH^-$	−0.58	$VO^{+2} + 2H^+ + e^- \rightarrow V^{+3} + H_2O$	0.337
$SO_4^{-2} + 4H^+ + 2e^- \rightarrow H_2SO_3 + H_2O$	0.20	$VO_2^+ + 2H^+ + e^- \rightarrow VO^{+2} + H_2O$	1.00
$2SO_4^{-2} + 4H^+ + 2e^- \rightarrow S_2O_6^{-2} + H_2O$	−0.2	$V(OH)_4^+ + 2H^+ + e^- \rightarrow VO^{+2} + 3H_2O$	1.00
$SO_4^{-2} + H_2O + 2e^- \rightarrow SO_3^{-2} + 2OH^-$	−0.92	$V(OH)_4^+ + 4H^+ + 5e^- \rightarrow V + 4H_2O$	−0.25
$Sr^{+2} + 2e^- \rightarrow Sr$	−2.89	$W_2O_5 + 2H^+ + 2e^- \rightarrow 2WO_2 + H_2O$	−0.04
$Sr^{+2} + 2e^- \rightarrow Sr(Hg)$	−1.793	$WO_2 + 4H^+ + 4e^- \rightarrow W + 2H_2O$	−0.12
$Sr(OH)_2 \cdot 8H_2O + 2e^- \rightarrow Sr + 2OH^- + 8H_2O$	−2.99	$WO_3 + 6H^+ + 6e^- \rightarrow W + 3H_2O$	−0.09
$Ta_2O_5 + 10H^+ + 10e^- \rightarrow 2Ta + 5H_2O$	−0.71	$2WO_3 + 2H^+ + 2e^- \rightarrow W_2O_5 + H_2O$	−0.03
$TcO_4^- + 4H^+ + 3e^- \rightarrow TcO_{2(c)} + 2H_2O$	0.738	$Y^{+3} + 3e^- \rightarrow Y$	−2.37
$Te + 2e^- \rightarrow Te^{-2}$	−0.92	$Zn^{+2} + 2e^- \rightarrow Zn$	−0.7628
$Te + 2H^+ + 2e^- \rightarrow H_2Te(Ag)$	−0.69	$Zn^{+2} + 2e^- \rightarrow Zn(Hg)$	−0.7628
	(−0.72)	$ZnO_2^- + 2H_2O + 2e^- \rightarrow Zn + 4OH^-$	−1.216
$Te^{+4} + 4e^- \rightarrow Te(2.5f\,HCl)$	0.63	$ZnSO \cdot 7H_2O + 2e^- \rightarrow Zn(Hg) + SO_4^{-2}(Sat'd\,ZnSO_4)$	−0.7993
$TeO_2 + 4H^+ + 4e^- \rightarrow Te + 2H_2O$	0.593	$ZrO_2 + 4H^+ + 4e^- \rightarrow Zr + 2H_2O$	−1.43
$TeO_3^{-2} + 3H_2O + 4e^- \rightarrow Te + 6OH^-$	−0.02	$ZrO(OH)_2 + H_2O + 4e^- \rightarrow Zr + 4OH^-$	−2.32

ELECTROCHEMICAL SERIES

Table II
Compiled by J. F. Hunsberger
Values listed are Standard Reduction Potentials

This table is divided into two parts. The first part lists reduction reactions which are positive with respect to the potential of the Standard Hydrogen Electrode. In this first part of Table II the reduction reactions are written in increasing order of the positive potential, beginning with 0.00 and ending with +3.03 volts. The second part of this Table II lists reduction reactions having reduction potentials more negative than that of the Standard Hydrogen Electrode. This second part of the table lists reactions in their order of increasing negative potential, beginning with 0.00 and ending with −3.1 volts.

PART 1

Reaction	Potential, volts	Reaction	Potential, volts
$2H^+ + 2e^- \rightarrow H_2$	0.0000	$Pd(OH)_2 + 2e^- \rightarrow Pd + 2OH^-$	0.1
$CuI_2^- + e^- \rightarrow Cu + 2I^-$	0.00	$Co(NH_3)_6^{+3} + e^- \rightarrow Co(NH_3)_6^{+2}$	0.1
$H_2MoO_4 + 6H^+ + 6e^- \rightarrow Mo + 4H_2O$	0.0	$Hg_2O + H_2O + 2e^- \rightarrow 2Hg + 2OH^-$	0.123
$NO_3^- + H_2O + 2e^- \rightarrow NO_2^- + 2OH^-$	0.01	$Sn^{+4} + 2e^- \rightarrow Sn^{+2}(1f\,HCl)$	0.139
$Ti_2O_3 + 6H^+ + 4e^- \rightarrow 2Ti^{+1} + HOH$	0.02	$Hg_2Br_2 + 2e^- \rightarrow 2Hg + 2Br^-$	0.1396
$SeO_4^{-2} + H_2O + 2e^- \rightarrow SeO_3^{-2} + 2OH^-$	0.03	$S + 2H^+ + 2e^- \rightarrow H_2S_{(aq)}$	0.141
$Ti(OH)^{+3} + H^+ + e^- \rightarrow Ti^{+3} + H_2O$	0.06	$Sb_2O_3 + 6H^+ + 6e^- \rightarrow 2Sb + 3H_2O$	0.1445
$UO_2^{+2} + e^- \rightarrow UO_2^+$	0.062		(0.152)
$U^{+6} + e^- \rightarrow U^{+5}(1f\,HClO_4)$	0.063	$2NO_2 + 3H_2O + 4e^- \rightarrow N_2O + 6OH^-$	0.15
$Sn^{+4} + 2e^- \rightarrow Sn^{+2}(0.1f\,HCl)$	0.070	$ReO_4^- + 8H^+ + 7e^- \rightarrow Re + 4H_2O$	0.15
$AgBr + e^- \rightarrow Ag + Br^-$	0.0713	$Sn^{+4} + 2e^- \rightarrow Sn^{+2}$	0.15
$AgSCN + e \rightarrow Ag + SCN^-$	0.0895	$Np^{+4} + e^- \rightarrow Np^{+3}(1f\,HClO_4)$	0.155
$S_4O_6^= + 2e^- \rightarrow 2S_2O_3^-{}^2$	0.09	$Cu^{+2} + e \rightarrow Cu^+$	0.158
	(0.10)		(0.167)
$HgO + H_2O + 2e^- \rightarrow Hg + 2OH^-$	0.0984	$BiOCl + 2H^+ + 3e^- \rightarrow Bi + Cl^- + H_2O$	0.1583
$2NO + 2e^- \rightarrow N_2O_2^{-2}$	0.10	$Pt(OH)_2 + 2e^- \rightarrow Pt + 2OH^-$	0.16
$Ir_2O_3 + 3H_2O + 6e^- \rightarrow 2Ir + 6OH^-$	0.1	$Bi(Cl)_4^- + 3e^- \rightarrow Bi + 4Cl^-$	0.168

Reaction	Potential, volts
$ClO_4^- + H_2O + 2e^- \rightarrow ClO_3^- + 2OH^-$	0.17
$Ag_4Fe(CN)_6 + 4e^- \rightarrow 4Ag + Fe(CN)_6^{-4}$	0.1943
$SO_4^{-2} + 4H^+ + 2e^- \rightarrow H_2SO_3 + H_2O$	0.20
$Co(OH)_3 + e^- \rightarrow Co(OH)_2 + OH^-$	0.2
	(0.17)
$SbO^+ + 2H^+ + 3e^- \rightarrow Sb + 2H_2O$	0.212
$AgCl + e^- \rightarrow Ag + Cl^-$	0.2223
*Calomel Electrode, Sat'd NaCl	0.2360
$As_2O_3 + 6H^+ + 6e^- \rightarrow 2As + 3H_2O$	0.234
*Calomel Electrode, Sat'd. KCl	0.2415
$HAsO_2 + 3H^+ + 3e^- \rightarrow As + 2H_2O$	0.2475
$IO_3^- + 3H_2O + 6e^- \rightarrow I^- + 6OH^-$	0.26
$ReO_2 + 4H^+ + 4e^- \rightarrow Re + 2H_2O$	0.26
$Hg_2Cl_2 + 2e^- \rightarrow 2Hg + 2Cl^-$	0.2682
Calomel Electrode, Molal KCl	0.2800
$PbO_2 + H_2O + 2e^- \rightarrow PbO + 2OH^-$	0.28
*Calomel Electrode, N KCl	0.2807
$Re^{+3} + 3e^- \rightarrow Re$	0.3 ~
$BiO^+ + 2H^+ + 3e^- \rightarrow Bi + H_2O$	0.32
$2HCNO + 2H^+ + 2e \rightarrow (CN)_2 + 2H_2O$	0.33
*Calomel Electrode 0.1 N KCl	0.3337
$UO_2^{+2} + 4H^+ + 2e^- \rightarrow U^{+4} + 2H_2O$	0.334
$VO^{+2} + 2H^+ + e^- \rightarrow V^{+3} + H_2O$	0.337
$Cu^{+2} + 2e^- \rightarrow Cu$	0.3402
$Hg_2Cl_2 + 2e^- \rightarrow 2Hg + 2Cl^-(0.1fNaOH)$	0.3419
	(0.268)
$Ag_2O + H_2O + 2e^- \rightarrow 2Ag + 2OH^-$	0.342
$Nb^{+5} + 2e^- \rightarrow Nb^{+3}(2f HCl)$	0.344
$Cu^{+2} + 2e \rightarrow Cu(Hg)$	0.345
$ClO_3^- + H_2O + 2e^- \rightarrow ClO_2^- + 2OH^-$	0.35
$AgIO_3 + e^- \rightarrow Ag + IO_3$	0.3551
$Ag_2SeO_3 + 2e \rightarrow 2Ag + SeO_3^{-2}$	0.3629
$ReO_4^- + 8H^+ + 7e^- \rightarrow Re + 4H_2O$	0.367
$(CN)_2 + 2H^+ + 2e^- \rightarrow 2HCN$	0.37
$O_2 + 2H_2O + 4e^- \rightarrow 4OH^-$	0.401
$AgOCN + e^- \rightarrow Ag + OCN^-$	0.41
$Fe^{+3} + e^- \rightarrow Fe^{+2}(1f H_3PO_4)$	0.438
$Rh(Cl)_6^{-3} + 3e^- \rightarrow Rh + 6Cl^-$	0.44
$Ag_2CrO_4 + 2e^- \rightarrow 2Ag + CrO_4^{-2}$	0.4463
$H_2SO_3 + 4H^+ + 4e^- \rightarrow S + 3H_2O$	0.45
$Fe(CN)_6^{-3} + e^- \rightarrow Fe(CN)_6^{-4}(0.01f NaOH)$	0.46
$Ag_2(WO_4) + 2e^- \rightarrow 2Ag + WO_4^{-2}$	0.466
$TeO_4^- + 8H^+ + 7e^- \rightarrow Te + 4H_2O$	0.472
$Ag_2CO_3 + 2e^- \rightarrow 2Ag + CO_3^{-2}$	0.4769
$AgC_2O_4 + 2e^- \rightarrow Ag + C_2O_4^{-2}$	0.4776
$Ag_2MoO_4 + 2e^- \rightarrow 2Ag + MoO_4^{-2}$	0.49
$IO^- + H_2O + 2e^- \rightarrow I^- + 2OH^-$	0.49
$NiO_2 + 2H_2O + 2e^- \rightarrow Ni(OH)_2 + 2OH^-$	0.49
$Ru^{+4} + e^- \rightarrow Ru^{+3}(0.1f HClO_4)$	0.49
$ReO_4^- + 4H^+ + 3e^- \rightarrow ReO_2 + 2H_2O$	0.51
$Hg_2(AcO)_2 + 2e^- \rightarrow 2Hg + 2AcO^-$	0.5113
$Cu^+ + e^- \rightarrow Cu$	0.522
$I_3^- + 2e^- \rightarrow 3I^-$	0.5338
$I_2 + 2e^- \rightarrow 2I^-$	0.535
$IO_3^- + 2H_2O + 4e^- \rightarrow IO^- + 4OH^-$	0.56
$MnO_4^- + e^- \rightarrow MnO_4^{-2}$	0.564
$MnO_4^{-1} + 2H_2O + 3e^- \rightarrow MnO_2 + 4OH^-$	0.58
$H_3AsO_4 + 2H^+ + 2e^- \rightarrow HAsO_2 + 2H_2O(1f HCl)$	0.58
$MnO_4^- + 2H_2O + 3e^- \rightarrow MnO_2 + 4OH^-$	0.588
$AgNO_2 + e^- \rightarrow Ag + NO_2^-$	0.59
$ClO_2^- + H_2O + 2e^- \rightarrow ClO^- + 2OH^-$	0.59
$RuO_4^- + e^- \rightarrow RuO_4^{-2}$	0.59
$TeO_2 + 4H_2 + 4e^- \rightarrow Te + 2H_2O$	0.593
$2AgO + H_2O + 2e^- \rightarrow Ag_2O + 2OH^-$	0.599
$S_2O_6^{-2} + 4H^+ + 2e^- \rightarrow 2H_2SO_3$	0.6
$BrO_3^- + 3H_2O + 6e^- \rightarrow Br^- + 6OH^-$	0.61
$Hg_2SO_4 + 2e^- \rightarrow 2Hg + SO_4^{-2}$	0.6158
$ClO_3^- + 3H_2O + 6e^- \rightarrow Cl^- + 6OH^-$	0.62
$UO_2^+ + 4H^+ + e^- \rightarrow U^{+4} + 2H_2O$	0.62
$Pd^{+2} + 2e^- \rightarrow Pd(1f HCl)$	0.623
$PdCl_4^- + 2e^- \rightarrow Pd + 4Cl^-$	0.623
$Te^{+4} + 4e^- \rightarrow Te(2.5f HCl)$	0.63
$Hg_2HPO_4 + H^+ + 2e^- \rightarrow 2Hg + H_2PO_4^-$	0.639
$AgAc + e^- \rightarrow Ag + Ac^-$	0.64
$Sb_2O_{5(s)} + 6H^+ + 4e^- \rightarrow 2SbO^+ + 3H_2O$	0.64
$Ag_2SO_4 + 2e^- \rightarrow 2Ag + SO_4^{-2}$	0.653
$Fe^{+3} + e^- \rightarrow Fe^{+2}(0.5f H_2SO_4)$	0.679
$AgBrO_3 + e^- \rightarrow Ag + BrO_3^-$	0.680
$O_2 + 2H^+ + 2e^- \rightarrow H_2O_2$	0.682
$Fe(CN)_6^{-3} + e^- \rightarrow Fe(CN)_6^{-4}(1f H_2SO_4)$	0.69
$Sb_2O_5 + 4H^+ + 4e^- \rightarrow Sb_2O_3 + 2H_2O$	0.69
$C_6H_4O_2 + 2H^+ + 2e \rightarrow C_6H_4(OH)_2$	0.6992
Quinhydrone Elec. $H^+, a = 1$	0.6995
$BrO^- + H_2O + 2e^- \rightarrow Br^- + 2OH^-(1f NaOH)$	0.70
$H_3IO_6^{-2} + 2e^- \rightarrow IO_3^- + 3OH^-$	~0.70
$PtCl_4^{-2} + 2e^- \rightarrow Pt + 4Cl^-$	0.73
$TcO_4^- + 4H^+ + 3e^- \rightarrow TcO_{2(c)} + 2H_2O$	0.738
$Np^{+5} + e^- \rightarrow Np^{+4}(1f HClO_4)$	0.739
$Ag_2O_3 + H_2O + 2e^- \rightarrow 2AgO + 2OH^-$	0.74
$H_2SeO_3 + 4H^+ + 4e^- \rightarrow Se + 3H_2O$	0.74
$PtCl_6^{-2} + 2e^- \rightarrow PtCl_4^{-2} + 2Cl^-$	0.74
$Fe^{+3} + e^- \rightarrow Fe^{+2}(1f HClO_4)$	0.747
$Sb^{+5} + 2e^- \rightarrow Sb^{+3}(3.5f HCl)$	0.75
$ClO_2^- + 2H_2O + 4e^- \rightarrow Cl^- + 4OH^-$	0.76
$NiO_2 + 2H_2O + 2e^- \rightarrow Ni(OH)_2 + 2OH^-$	0.76
$2NO + H_2O + 2e^- \rightarrow N_2O + 2OH^-$	0.76
$ReO_4^- + 2H^+ + e^- \rightarrow ReO_{3(cc)} + 2H_2O$	0.768
$(CNS)_2 + 2e^- \rightarrow 2CNS^-$	0.77
$Fe^{+3} + e^- \rightarrow Fe^{+2}$	0.770
$Fe^{+3} + e^- \rightarrow Fe^{+2}(1f HCl)$	0.770
$IrCl_6^{-3} + 3e^- \rightarrow Ir + 6Cl^-$	0.77
$Tl^{+3} + 2e^- \rightarrow Tl^{+1}(1f HCl)$	0.783
$Hg_2^{+2} + 2e^- \rightarrow 2Hg$	0.7961
$1/2Hg_2^{+2} + e^- \rightarrow Hg$	0.7986
$Ag^+ + e^- \rightarrow Ag$	0.7996
$2HNO_2 + 4H^+ + 4e^- \rightarrow H_2N_2O_2 + 2H_2O$	0.80
$2NO_3^- + 4H^+ + 2e^- \rightarrow N_2O_4 + 2H_2O$	0.81
$1/2O_2 + 2H^+(10^{-7}M) + 2e^- \rightarrow H_2O$	0.815
$Pd^{+2} + 2e^- \rightarrow Pd$	0.83
$OsO_4 + 8H^+ + 8e^- \rightarrow Os + 4H_2O$	0.85
$Hg^{+2} + 2e^- \rightarrow Hg$	0.851
$AuBr_4^- + 3e^- \rightarrow Au + 4Br^-$	0.858
$Ru^{+4} + e^- \rightarrow Ru^{+3}(2f HCl)$	0.858
$TiO_2 + 4H^+ + 4e^- \rightarrow Ti + 2H_2O$	0.86
$HO_2^- + H_2O + 2e^- \rightarrow 3OH^-$	0.87
$N_2O_4 + 2e^- \rightarrow 2NO_2^-$	0.88
$ClO^- + H_2O + 2e^- \rightarrow Cl^- + 2OH^-$	0.90
$2Hg^{+2} + 2e^- \rightarrow Hg_2^{+2}$	0.905
$Pu^{+6} + e^- \rightarrow Pu^{+5}(1f HClO_4)$	0.9184
$NO_3^- + 3H^+ + 2e^- \rightarrow HNO_2 + H_2O$	0.94
$ClO_2(aq) + e^- \rightarrow ClO_2^-$	0.954
$NO_3^- + 4H^+ + 3e^- \rightarrow NO + 2H_2O$	0.96
$AuBr_2^- + e^- \rightarrow Au + 2Br^-$	0.963
$Pu^{+4} + e^- \rightarrow Pu^{+3}(1f HClO_4)$	0.982
$Pd^{+2} + 2e^- \rightarrow Pd(4f HClO_4)$	0.987
$HIO + H^+ + 2e^- \rightarrow I^- + H_2O$	0.99
$HNO_2 + H^+ + e^- \rightarrow NO + H_2O$	0.99
$AuCl_4^- + 3e^- \rightarrow Au + 4Cl^-$	0.994
$RuO_{4(c)} + e^- \rightarrow RuO_4^-$	1.00
$VO_2^+ + 2H^+ + e^- \rightarrow VO^{+2} + H_2O$	1.00
$V(OH)_4^+ + 2H^+ + e^- \rightarrow VO^{+2} + 3H_2O$	1.00
$H_6TeO_{6(s)} + 2H^+ + 2e^- \rightarrow TeO_{2(s)} + 4H_2O$	1.02
$IrCl_6^{-2} + e^- \rightarrow IrCl_6^{-3}$	1.02
$U^{+5} + e^- \rightarrow U^{+4}(1f HCl)$	1.02
$N_2O_4 + 4H^+ + 4e^- \rightarrow 2NO + 2H_2O$	1.03
$Pu^{+6} + 2e^- \rightarrow Pu^{+4}(1f HCl)$	1.052
$Fe(phenanthroline)_3^{+3} + e^- \rightarrow Fe(ph)_3^{+2}(2f H_2SO_4)$	1.056
$Br_{2(1)} + 2e^- \rightarrow 2Br^-$	1.065
$N_2O_4 + 2H^+ + 2e^- \rightarrow 2HNO_2$	1.07
$IO_3^- + 6H^+ + 6e^- \rightarrow I^- + 3H_2O$	1.085
$Br_{2(aq)} + 2e^- \rightarrow 2Br^-$	1.087
$Pu^{+5} + e^- \rightarrow Pu^{+4}(0.5f HCl)$	1.099
$Cr^{+6} + 3e^- \rightarrow Cr^{+3}(2f H_2SO_4)$	1.10
$Cu^+ + 2CN^- + e^- \rightarrow Cu(CN)_2^-$	1.12
$Np^{+6} + e^- \rightarrow Np^{+5}(1f HClO_4)$	1.137
$Fe(phenanthroline)_3^{+3} + e^- \rightarrow Fe(ph)_3^{+2}$	1.14
$SeO_4^{-2} + 4H^+ + 2e^- \rightarrow H_2SeO_3 + H_2O$	1.15
$ClO_2 \rightarrow ClO_2^-$	1.15
$ClO_3^- + 2H^+ + e^- \rightarrow ClO_2 + H_2O$	1.15
$ClO_4^- + 2H^+ + 2e^- \rightarrow ClO_3^- + H_2O$	1.19
$2IO_3^- + 12H^+ + 10e^- \rightarrow I_2 + 6H_2O$	1.19
$HCrO_4^- + 7H^+ + 3e^- \rightarrow Cr^{+3} + 4H_2O$	1.195
$IO_3^- + 6H^+ + 5e^- \rightarrow 1/2I_2 + 3H_2O$	1.195
$Pt^{+2} + 2e^- \rightarrow Pt$	~1.2
$MnO_2 + 4H^+ + 2e^- \rightarrow Mn^{+2} + 2H_2O$	1.208
$ClO_3^- + 3H^+ + 2e \rightarrow HClO_2 + H_2O$	1.21
	(1.23)
$O_2 + 4H^+ + 4e^- \rightarrow 2H_2O$	1.229
$O_3 + H_2O + 2e^- \rightarrow O_2 + 2OH^-$	1.24
$Tl^{+3} + 2e^- \rightarrow Tl^{+1}$	1.247
$ClO_2 + H^+ + e^- \rightarrow HClO_2$	1.27
$2HNO_2 + 4H^+ + 4e^- \rightarrow N_2O + 3H_2O$	1.27
	(1.29)
$N_2H_5^+ + 3H^+ + 2e^- \rightarrow 2NH_4^+$	1.27
$Au^{+3} + 2e^- \rightarrow Au^{+1}$	~1.29
$PdCl_6^{-2} + 2e^- \rightarrow PdCl_4^{-2} + 2Cl^-$	1.29
$HBrO + H^+ + 2e^- \rightarrow Br^- + H_2O$	1.33
$Cr_2O_7^{-2} + 14H^+ + 6e^- \rightarrow 2Cr^{+3} + 7H_2O$	1.33
$ClO_4^- + 8H^+ + 7e^- \rightarrow 1/2Cl_2 + 4H_2O$	1.34
$Cl_{2(g)} + 2e^- \rightarrow 2Cl^-$	1.3583
$ClO_4^- + 8H^+ + 8e^- \rightarrow Cl^- + 4H_2O$	1.37

ELECTROCHEMICAL SERIES—TABLE II (Continued)

Reaction	Potential, volts	Reaction	Potential, volts
$OH + e^- \rightarrow OH^-$	1.4	$HClO_2 + 3H^+ + 3e^- \rightarrow 1/2Cl_2 + 2H_2O$	1.63
$Au^{+3} + 3e^- \rightarrow Au$	1.42	$HClO + H^+ + e^- \rightarrow 1/2Cl_2 + H_2O$	1.63
$2NH_3OH^+ + H^+ + 2e^- \rightarrow N_2H_3^+ + 2H_2O$	1.42	$HClO_2 + 2H^+ + 2e^- \rightarrow HClO + H_2O$	1.64
$Rh^{+4} + e^- \rightarrow Rh^{+3}$	1.43	$MnO_4^- + 4H^+ + 3e^- \rightarrow MnO_2 + 2H_2O$	1.679
$BrO_3^- + 6H^+ + 6e^- \rightarrow Br^- + 3H_2O$	1.44	$Au^+ + e^- \rightarrow Au$	1.68
$Ce^{+4} + e^- \rightarrow Ce^{+3}$	1.4430 (1.61)	$PbO_2 + SO_4^{-2} + 4H^+ + 2e^- \rightarrow PbSO_4 + 2H_2O$	1.685
		$H_5IO_6 + H^+ + 2e^- \rightarrow IO_3^- + 3H_2O$	~1.7
$Au(OH)_3 + 3H^+ + 3e^- \rightarrow Au + 3H_2O$	1.45	$CeOH^{+3} + H^+ + e^- \rightarrow Ce^{+3} + H_2O$	1.7134
$ClO_3^- + 6H^+ + 6e^- \rightarrow Cl^- + 3H_2O$	1.45	$N_2O + 2H^+ + 2e^- \rightarrow N_2 + H_2O$	1.77
$HIO + H^+ + e^- \rightarrow 1/2I_2 + H_2O$	1.45	$H_2O_2 + 2H^+ + 2e^- \rightarrow 2H_2O$	1.776
$Ce^{+4} + e^- \rightarrow Ce^{+3}(0.5f\ H_2SO_4)$	1.4587	$Co^{+3} + e^- \rightarrow Co^{+2}(3f\ HNO_3)$	1.842
$PbO_2 + 4H^+ + 2e^- \rightarrow Pb^{+2} + 2H_2O$	1.46	$FeO_4^{-2} + 8H^+ + 3e^- \rightarrow Fe^{+3} + 4H_2O$	1.9
$ClO^- + 6H^+ + 5e^- \rightarrow 1/2Cl_2 + 3H_2O$	1.47	$NiO_2 + 4H^+ + 2e^- \rightarrow Ni^{+2} + 2H_2O$	1.93
$HClO + H^+ + 2e^- \rightarrow Cl^- + H_2O$	1.49	$Ag^{+2} + e^- \rightarrow Ag^{+1}(4f\ HClO_4)$	1.987
$MnO_4^- + 8H^+ + 5e^- \rightarrow Mn^{+2} + 4H_2O$	1.491	$S_2O_8^{-2} + 2e^- \rightarrow 2SO_4^{-2}$	2.0 (2.05)
$HO_2 + H^+ + e^- \rightarrow H_2O_2$	1.5		
$Mn^{+3} + e^- \rightarrow Mn^{+2}$	1.51	$O_3 + 2H^+ + 2e^- \rightarrow O_2 + H_2O$	2.07
$BrO_3^- + 6H^+ + 5e^- \rightarrow 1/2Br_2 + 3H_2O$	1.52	$F_2O + 2H^+ + 4e^- \rightarrow H_2O + 2F^-$	2.1
$HClO_2 + 3H^+ + 4e^- \rightarrow Cl^- + 2H_2O$	1.56	$O_{(g)} + 2H^+ + 2e^- \rightarrow H_2O$	2.42
$Bi_2O_4 + 4H^+ + 2e^- \rightarrow 2BiO^+ + 2H_2O$	1.59	$H_2N_2O_2 + 2H^+ + 2e^- \rightarrow N_2 + 2H_2O$	2.65
$HBrO + H^+ + e^- \rightarrow 1/2Br_2 + H_2O$	1.59	$1/2F_2 + e^- \rightarrow F^-$	2.85
$2NO + 2H^+ + 2e^- \rightarrow N_2O + H_2O$	1.59	$F_2 + 2e^- \rightarrow 2F^-$	2.87
$2HBrO + 2H^+ + 2e^- \rightarrow Br_{2(l)} + 2H_2O$	1.6	$1/2F_2 + H^+ + e^- \rightarrow HF$	3.03

PART 2

Reaction	Potential, volts	Reaction	Potential, volts
$2H^+ + 2e^- \rightarrow H_2$	0.0000	$In^{+2} + e^- \rightarrow In^{+1}$	-0.40
$D^+ + e^- \rightarrow 1/2D_2$	-0.0034	$In^{+3} + 2e^- \rightarrow In^{+1}$	-0.40
$AgCN + e^- \rightarrow Ag + CN^-$	-0.02	$Mn(OH)_3 + e^- \rightarrow Mn(OH)_2 + OH^-$	-0.40
$TeO_3^{-2} + 3H_2O + 4e^- \rightarrow Te + 6OH^-$	-0.02	$Cd^{+2} + 2e^- \rightarrow Cd$	-0.4026
$2WO_3 + 2H^+ + 2e^- \rightarrow W_2O_5 + H_2O$	-0.03	$Fe^{+2} + 2e^- \rightarrow Fe$	-0.409
$Fe^{+3} + 3e^- \rightarrow Fe$	-0.036	$Cr^{+3} + e^- \rightarrow Cr^{+2}$	-0.41
$Ag_2S + 2H^+ + 2e^- \rightarrow 2Ag + H_2S$	-0.0366	$Eu^{+3} + e^- \rightarrow Eu^{+2}$	-0.43
$P + 3H^+ + 3e^- \rightarrow PH_3(g)$	-0.04	$CdSO_4 \cdot 8/3H_2O + 2e^- \rightarrow Cd(Hg) + CdSO_4$ (sat'd aq)	-0.4346
$W_2O_5 + 2H^+ + 2e^- \rightarrow 2WO_2 + H_2O$	-0.04	$Tl_2SO_4 + 2e^- \rightarrow Tl(Hg) + SO_4^{-2}$	-0.4360
$Hg_2I_2 + 2e^- \rightarrow 2Hg + 2I^-$	-0.0405	$Bi_2O_3 + 3H_2O + 6e^- \rightarrow 2Bi + 6OH^-$	-0.46
$2D^+ + 2e^- \rightarrow D_2$	-0.044	$BiOOH + H_2O + 3e^- \rightarrow Bi + 3OH^-$	-0.46
$Tl(OH)_3 + 2e^- \rightarrow TlOH + 2OH^-$	-0.05	$NO_2^- + H_2O + e^- \rightarrow NO + 2OH^-$	-0.46
$O_2 + H_2O + 2e^- \rightarrow HO_2^- + OH^-$	-0.076	$S + H_2O + 2e^- \rightarrow HS^- + OH^-$	-0.478
$AsO_4^{-3} + 2H_2O + 2e^- \rightarrow AsO_2^- + 4OH^-$ (1f NaOH)	-0.08	$H_3PO_3 + 3H^+ + 3e^- \rightarrow P + 3H_2O$	-0.49
$2H_2SO_3 + H^+ + 2e^- \rightarrow HS_2O_4^- + 2H_2O$	-0.08	$In^{+3} + e^- \rightarrow In^{+2}$	-0.49
$Ru^{+3} + e^- \rightarrow Ru^{+2}(1-6f\ HCL)$	-0.084	$2CO_2 + 2H^+ + 2e^- \rightarrow H_2C_2O_4$	-0.49
$2Cu(OH)_2 + 2e^- \rightarrow Cu_2O + 2OH^- + H_2O$	-0.09	$H_3PO_3 + 2H^+ + 2e^- \rightarrow H_3PO_2 + H_2O$	-0.50 (-0.59)
$WO_3 + 6H^+ + 6e^- \rightarrow W + 3H_2O$	-0.09	$S + 2e^- \rightarrow S^{-2}$	-0.508
$Ru^{+3} + e^- \rightarrow Ru^{+2}(0.1f\ HClO_4)$	-0.11	$H_3PO_2 + H^+ + e^- \rightarrow P + 2H_2O$	-0.51
$Cr^{+6} + 3e^- \rightarrow Cr^{+3}(1f\ NaOH)$	-0.12	$Sb + 3H^+ + 3e^- \rightarrow H_3Sb$	-0.51
$CrO_4^{-2} + 4H_2O + 3e^- \rightarrow Cr(OH)_3 + 5OH^-$	-0.12	$As + 3H^+ + 3e^- \rightarrow AsH_3$	-0.54
$GeO_2 + 2H^+ + 2e^- \rightarrow GeO + H_2O$	-0.12	$HPbO_2^- + H_2O + 2e^- \rightarrow Pb + 3OH^-$	-0.54
$WO_2 + 4H^+ + 4e^- \rightarrow W + 2H_2O$	-0.12	$TlCl + e^- \rightarrow Tl(Hg) + Cl^-$	-0.555
$Pb^{+2} + 2e^- \rightarrow Pb(Hg)$	-0.1205	$Cr^{+2} + 2e^- \rightarrow Cr$	-0.557
$Pb^{+2} + 2e^- \rightarrow Pb$	-0.1263 (0.126)	$Ga^{+3} + 3e^- \rightarrow Ga$	-0.560
		$Fe(OH)_3 + e^- \rightarrow Fe(OH)_2 + OH^-$	-0.56
$H_2GeO_3 + 4H^+ + 4e^- \rightarrow Ge + 3H_2O$	-0.13	$PbO + H_2O + 2e^- \rightarrow Pb + 2OH^-$	-0.576
$Sn^{+2} + 2e^- \rightarrow Sn$	-0.1364	$2SO_3^{-2} + 3H_2O + 4e^- \rightarrow S_2O_3^{-2} + 6OH^-$	-0.58
$O_2 + 2H_2O + 2e^- \rightarrow H_2O_2 + 2OH^-$	-0.146	$SbO_3^- + H_2O + 2e^- \rightarrow SbO_2^- + 2OH^-$	-0.59
$AgI + e^- \rightarrow Ag + I^-$	-0.1519	$TlBr + e^- \rightarrow Tl(Hg) + Br^-$	-0.606
$2NO_2^- + 2H_2O + 4e^- \rightarrow N_2O_2^{-2} + 4OH^-$	-0.18	$U^{+4} + e^- \rightarrow U^{+3}$	-0.61
$CO_2 + 2H^+ + 2e^- \rightarrow HCOOH$	-0.2	$Cb_2O_5 + 10H^+ + 10e^- \rightarrow 2Cb + 5H_2O$	-0.62
$2SO_4^{-2} + 4H^+ + 2e^- \rightarrow S_2O_6^{-2} + 2H_2O$	-0.2	$U^{+4} + e^- \rightarrow U^{+3}(1f\ HClO_4)$	-0.631
$Cu(OH)_2 + 2e^- \rightarrow Cu + 2OH^-$	-0.224	$Ni(OH)_2 + 2e^- \rightarrow Ni + 2OH^-$	-0.66
$Ni^{+2} + 2e^- \rightarrow Ni$	-0.23	$SbO_2^- + 2H_2O + 3e^- \rightarrow Sb + 4OH^-$	-0.66
$PbHPO_4 + H^+ + 2e^- \rightarrow Pb(Hg) + HPO_4^-$	-0.2448	$AsO_2^- + 2H_2O + 3e^- \rightarrow As + 4OH^-$	-0.68
$V(OH)_4^+ + 4H^+ + 5e^- \rightarrow V + 4H_2O$	-0.25	$*Te + 2H^+ + 2e^- \rightarrow H_2Te(Ag)$	-0.69 (-0.72)
$V^{+3} + e^- \rightarrow V^{+2}$	-0.255	$Ag_2S + 2e \rightarrow 2Ag + S^{-2}$	-0.7051
$PbCl_2 + 2e^- \rightarrow Pb(Hg) + 2Cl^-$	-0.262	$Ta_2O_5 + 10H^+ + 10e^- \rightarrow 2Ta + 5H_2O$	-0.71
$PbBr_2 + 2e^- \rightarrow Pb(Hg) + Br^-$	-0.275	$AsO_4^{-3} + 2H_2O + 2e^- \rightarrow AsO_2^- + 4OH^-$	-0.71
$H_3PO_4 + 2H^+ + 2e^- \rightarrow H_3PO_3 + H_2O$	-0.276 (-0.2)	$Cu(OH)_2 + 2e^- \rightarrow Cu + 2OH^-$	-0.73
$Cu^{+2} + 2e^- \rightarrow Cu$	-0.28	$H_3BO_3 + 3H^+ + 3e^- \rightarrow B + 3H_2O$	-0.73
$Tl^+ + e^- \rightarrow Tl(Hg)$	-0.3338	$Cr^{+3} + 3e^- \rightarrow Cr$	-0.74
$Tl^+ + e^- \rightarrow Tl$	-0.3363	$V^{+5} + e^- \rightarrow V^{+4}(1f\ NaOH)$	-0.74
$In^{+3} + 3e^- \rightarrow In$	-0.338	$Cd(OH)_2 + 2e^- \rightarrow Cd(Hg) + 2OH^-$	-0.761 (-0.81)
$PbF_2 + 2e^- \rightarrow Pb(Hg) + 2F^-$	-0.3444	$Zn^{+2} + 2e^- \rightarrow Zn$	-0.7628
$TlOH + e^- \rightarrow Tl + OH^-$	-0.3445	$Zn^{+2} + 2e^- \rightarrow Zn(Hg)$	-0.7628
$SeO_3^{-2} + 3H_2O + 4e^- \rightarrow Se + 6OH^-$	-0.35	$TlI + e^- \rightarrow Tl(Hg) + I^-$	-0.769
$PbSO_4 + 2e^- \rightarrow Pb(Hg) + SO_4^{-2}$	-0.3505	$Se + 2e^- \rightarrow Se^{-2}$	-0.78
$Cd^{+2} + 2e^- \rightarrow Cd(Hg)$	-0.3521	$HSnO_2^- + H_2O + 2e^- \rightarrow Sn + 3OH^-$	-0.79
$PbSO_4 + 2e^- \rightarrow Pb + SO_4^{-2}$	-0.356	$ZnSO_4 \cdot 7H_2O + 2e^- \rightarrow Zn(Hg) + SO_4^{-2}$ (Sat'd ZnSO₄)	-0.7993
$PbI_2 + 2e^- \rightarrow Pb(Hg) + 2I^-$	-0.358	$RuO_2 + 4H^+ + 4e^- \rightarrow Ru + 2H_2O$	-0.8
$Se + 2H^+ + 2e^- \rightarrow H_2Se(aq)$	-0.36	$ReO_4^- + 4H_2O + 7e^- \rightarrow Re + 8OH^-$	-0.81
$Cu_2O + H_2O + 2e^- \rightarrow 2Cu + 2OH^-$	-0.361		
$Tl^{+3} + e^- \rightarrow Tl^{+2}$	-0.37		

Reaction	Potential, volts	Reaction	Potential, volts
$UO_2^{+2} + 4H^+ + 6e^- \rightarrow U + 2H_2O$	-0.82	$N_2 + 2H_2O + 4H^+ + 2e^- \rightarrow 2NH_3OH^+$	-1.87
$2H_2O + 2e^- \rightarrow H_2 + 2OH^-$	-0.8277	$Th^{+4} + 4e^- \rightarrow Th$	-1.90
$SiO_2 + 4H^+ + 4e^- \rightarrow Si + 2H_2O$	-0.84	$Np^{+3} + 3e^- \rightarrow Np$	-1.9
$2NO_3^- + 2H_2O + 2e^- \rightarrow N_2O_4 + 4OH^-$	-0.85	$Ti^{+3} + e^- \rightarrow Ti^{+2}$	-2.0
$TiO_2 + 4H^+ + 4e^- \rightarrow Ti + 2H_2O$	-0.86	$Sc^{+3} + 3e^- \rightarrow Sc$	-2.08
$P + 3H_2O + 3e^- \rightarrow PH_3(g) + 3OH^-$	-0.87	$1/2H_2 + e^- \rightarrow H^-$	-2.23
$SO_4^{-2} + H_2O + 2e^- \rightarrow SO_3^{-2} + 2OH^-$	-0.92	$Nd^{+3} + 3e^- \rightarrow Nd$	-2.246
$Te + 2e^- \rightarrow Te^{-2}$	-0.92	$Be_2O_3^{-2} + 3H_2O + 4e^- \rightarrow 2Be + 6OH^-$	-2.28
$Sn(OH)_6^{-2} + 2e^- \rightarrow HSnO_2^- + 3OH^- + H_2O$	-0.96	$ZrO(OH)_2 + H_2O + 4e^- \rightarrow Zr + 4OH^-$	-2.32
$Mn^{+2} + 2e^- \rightarrow Mn$	-1.029	$Ce^{+3} + 3e^- \rightarrow Ce$	-2.335
$PO_4^{-3} + 2H_2O + 2e^- \rightarrow HPO_3^{-2} + 3OH^-$	-1.05	$H_2AlO_3^- + H_2O + 3e^- \rightarrow Al + 4OH^-$	-2.35
$2SO_3^{-2} + 2H_2O + 2e^- \rightarrow S_2O_4^{-2} + 4OH^-$	-1.12	$Y^{+3} + 3e^- \rightarrow Y$	-2.37
$CrO_2^- + 2H_2O + 3e^- \rightarrow Cr + 4OH^-$	-1.2	$La^{+3} + 3e^- \rightarrow La$	-2.37
$SiF_6^{-2} + 4e^- \rightarrow Si + 6F^-$	-1.2	$Mg^{++} + 2e^- \rightarrow Mg$	-2.375
$V^{+2} + 2e^- \rightarrow V$	-1.2	$H_2BO_3^- + H_2O + 3e^- \rightarrow B + 4OH^-$	-2.5
$ZnO_2^{-2} + 2H_2O + 2e^- \leftrightharpoons Zn + 4OH^-$	-1.216	$HfO(OH)_2 + H_2O + 4e^- \rightarrow Hf + 4OH^-$	-2.60
$H_2GaO_3^- + H_2O + 3e^- \rightarrow Ga + 4OH^-$	-1.22	$ThO_2 + 2H_2O + 4e^- \rightarrow Th + 4OH^-$	-2.64
$H_2BO_3^- + 5H_2O + 8e^- \rightarrow BH_4^- + 8OH^-$	-1.24	$Mg(OH)_2 + 2e^- \rightarrow Mg + 2OH^-$	-2.67
$Cr(OH)_3 + 3e^- \rightarrow Cr + 3OH^-$	-1.3	$Na^+ + e^- \rightarrow Na$	-2.7109
$ZrO_2 + 4H^+ + 4e^- \rightarrow Zr + 2H_2O$	-1.43		(-2.712)
$Ce^{+3} + 3e^- \rightarrow Ce(Hg)$	-1.4373	$Ca^{+2} + 2e^- \rightarrow Ca$	-2.76
$Mn(OH)_2 \rightarrow Mn + 2OH^-$	-1.47	$La(OH)_3 + 3e \rightarrow La + 3OH^-$	-2.76
$Ba^{+2} + 2e^- \rightarrow Ba(Hg)$	-1.570	$Sr^{+2} + 2e^- \rightarrow Sr$	-2.89
$HfO_2 + 4H^+ + 4e^- \rightarrow Hf + 2H_2O$	-1.57	$Ba^{+2} + 2e^- \rightarrow Ba$	-2.90
$Ti^{+2} + 2e^- \rightarrow Ti$	-1.63	$Cs^+ + e^- \rightarrow Cs$	-2.923
$HPO_3^{-2} + 2H_2O + 2e^- \rightarrow H_2PO_2^- + 3OH^-$	-1.65	$K^+ + e^- \rightarrow K$	-2.924
$HfO^{+2} + 2H^+ + 4e^- \rightarrow Hf + H_2O$	-1.68		(-2.923)
$Be^{+2} + 2e^- \rightarrow Be$	-1.70	$Rb^+ + e^- \rightarrow Rb$	-2.925
	(-1.85)		(-2.99)
$Al^{+3} + 3e^- \rightarrow Al(0.1f\ NaOH)$	-1.706	$Ba(OH)_2 \cdot 8H_2O + 2e^- \rightarrow Ba + 2OH^- + 8H_2O$	-2.97
$HPO_3^{-2} + 2H_2O + 3e^- \rightarrow P + 5OH^-$	-1.71	$Sr(OH)_2 \cdot 8H_2O + 2e^- \rightarrow Sr + 2OH^- + 8H_2O$	-2.99
$SiO_3^{-2} + 3H_2O + 4e^- \rightarrow Si + 6OH^-$	-1.73	$Ca(OH)_2 + 2e^- \rightarrow Ca + 2OH^-$	-3.02
$Sr^{+2} + 2e^- \rightarrow Sr(Hg)$	-1.793	$Ca^+ + e^- \rightarrow Ca$	-3.02
$ThO_2 + 4H^+ + 4e^- \rightarrow Th + 2H_2O$	-1.80	$Li^+ + e^- \rightarrow Li$	-3.045
$U^{+3} + 3e^- \rightarrow U$	-1.8		(-3.02)
$H_2PO_2^- + e^- \rightarrow P + 2OH^-$	-1.82	$3N_2 + 2H^+ + 2e^- \rightarrow 2HN_3$	-3.1

No.	Compound	Temp. °C	Step	pK_a	K_a	No.	Compound	Temp. °C	Step	pK_a	K_a
a1	Acetamide...........	25		0.63	2.34×10^{-1}	b15	Brucine.............	25	1	8.28	5.24×10^{-9}
a2	Acridine............	20		5.58	2.63×10^{-6}	b16	Butane, 1-amino-3-methyl...........	25		10.60	2.51×10^{-11}
a3	α-Alanine...........	25		2.345	4.52×10^{-3}						
a4	Alanine, glycyl-....	25		3.153	7.03×10^{-4}	b17	Butane, 2-amino-2-methyl...........	19		10.85	1.41×10^{-11}
a5	Alanine, methoxy-(DL)..............	25		2.037	9.18×10^{-3}	b18	Butane, 1,4-diamino (Putrescine)........	10	1	11.15	7.08×10^{-12}
a6	Alanine, phenyl......	25	2	9.18	6.61×10^{-10}			10	2	9.71	1.95×10^{-10}
a7	Allothreonine........	25	1	2.108	7.80×10^{-3}	b19	n-Butylamine........	20		10.77	1.69×10^{-11}
	Allothreonine........	25	2	0.006	8.02×10^{-10}	b20	t-Butylamine........	18		10.83	1.48×10^{-11}
a8	n-Amylamine........	25		10.63	2.34×10^{-11}	b21	Butyric acid, 4-amino..	25	1	4.0312	9.31×10^{-5}
a9	Aniline.............	25		4.63	2.34×10^{-5}			25	2	10.5557	2.78×10^{-11}
a10	Aniline, n-allyl......	25		4.17	6.76×10^{-5}	b22	n-Butyric acid, glycyl-2-amino.....	25	1	3.1546	7.01×10^{-4}
a11	Aniline, 4-(p-aminobenzoyl)...	25	1	2.932	1.17×10^{-3}						
a12	Aniline, 4-benzyl......	25		2.17	6.76×10^{-3}	c1	Cacodylic acid......	25	1	1.57	2.69×10^{-2}
a13	Aniline, 2-bromo.....	25		2.53	2.95×10^{-3}				2	6.27	5.37×10^{-7}
a14	Aniline, 3-bromo.....	25		3.58	2.63×10^{-4}	c2	β-Chlortriethyl-ammonium.........	25		8.80	1.59×10^{-9}
a15	Aniline, 4-bromo.....	25		3.86	1.38×10^{-4}	c3	Cinnoline...........	20		2.37	4.27×10^{-3}
a16	Aniline, 4-bromo-N,N-dimethyl.....	25		4.232	5.86×10^{-5}	c4	Codeine.............	25		8.21	6.15×10^{-9}
a17	Aniline, o-chloro.....	25		2.65	2.24×10^{-3}	c5	Cyclohexaneamine, n-butyl.........	25		11.23	5.89×10^{-12}
a18	Aniline, m-chloro.....	25		3.46	3.47×10^{-4}	c6	Cyclohexylamine......	24		10.66	2.19×10^{-11}
a19	Aniline, p-chloro.....	25		4.15	7.08×10^{-5}	c7	Cystine.............	30	1	1.90	1.25×10^{-2}
a20	Aniline, 3-chloro-N,N-dimethyl.....	20		3.837	1.46×10^{-4}			30	2	8.24	5.76×10^{-9}
a21	Aniline, 4-chloro-N,N-dimethyl.....	20		4.395	4.03×10^{-5}	d1	n-Decylamine........	25		10.64	2.29×10^{-11}
a22	Aniline, 3,5-dibromo...	25		2.34	4.57×10^{-3}	d2	Diethylamine........	40		10.489	3.24×10^{-11}
a23	Aniline, 2,4-dichloro...	22		2.05	8.91×10^{-3}	d3	Diisobutylamine.....	21		10.91	1.23×10^{-11}
a24	Aniline, N,N-diethyl..	22		6.61	2.46×10^{-7}	d4	Diisopropylamine.....	28.5		10.96	1.00×10^{-11}
a25	Aniline, N,N-dimethyl.	25		5.15	7.08×10^{-6}	d5	Dimethylamine......	25		10.732	1.85×10^{-11}
a26	Aniline, N,N-dimethyl-3-nitro....	25		2.626	2.37×10^{-3}	d6	n-Diphenylamine....	25		0.79	1.62×10^{-1}
a27	Aniline, N-ethyl......	24		5.12	7.59×10^{-6}	d7	n-Dodecaneamine (Laurylamine)......	25		10.63	2.35×10^{-11}
a28	Aniline, 2-fluoro.....	25		3.20	6.31×10^{-4}						
a29	Aniline, 3-fluoro.....	25		3.50	3.16×10^{-4}	e1	d-Ephedrine........	10		10.139	7.26×10^{-11}
a30	Aniline, 4-fluoro.....	25		4.65	2.24×10^{-5}	e2	l-Ephedrine........	10		9.958	1.10×10^{-10}
a31	Aniline, 2-iodo......	25		2.60	2.51×10^{-2}	e3	Ethane, 1-amino-3-methoxy........	10		9.89	1.29×10^{-10}
a32	Aniline, N-methyl.....	25		4.848	1.41×10^{-5}	e4	Ethane, 1,2-bismethylamino..	25	1	10.40	3.98×10^{-11}
a33	Aniline, 4-methylthio..	25		4.35	4.46×10^{-5}			25	2	8.26	5.50×10^{-9}
a34	Aniline, 3-nitro.....	25		2.466	3.42×10^{-3}	e5	Ethanol, 2-amino....	25		9.50	3.16×10^{-10}
a35	Aniline, 4-nitro.....	25		1.0	1.00×10^{-1}	e6	Ethylamine.........	20		10.807	1.56×10^{-11}
a36	Aniline, 2-sulfonic acid	25	2	2.459	3.47×10^{-3}	e7	Ethylenediamine.....	0	1	10.712	1.94×10^{-11}
a37	Aniline, 3-sulfonic acid	25	2	3.738	1.82×10^{-4}			0	2	7.564	2.73×10^{-8}
a38	Aniline, 4-sulfonic acid	25	2	3.227	5.92×10^{-4}						
a39	o-Anisidine.........	25		4.52	3.02×10^{-5}	g1	l-Glutamic acid......	25	1	2.13	7.41×10^{-3}
a40	m-Anisidine	25		4.23	5.89×10^{-5}			25	2	4.31	4.90×10^{-5}
a41	p-Anisidine.........	25		5.34	4.57×10^{-6}	e2	Glutamic acid, α-monoethyl........	25	1	3.846	1.42×10^{-4}
a42	Arginine	25	1	1.8217	1.51×10^{-2}			25	2	7.838	1.45×10^{-8}
		25	2	8.9936	1.01×10^{-9}	e3	l-Glutamine........	—		9.28	5.25×10^{-10}
a43	Asparagine..........	20	1	2.213	6.12×10^{-3}	e4	l-Glutathione........	25	2	3.59	2.57×10^{-4}
		20	2	8.85	1.41×10^{-9}	e5	Glycine............	25	1	2.3503	4.46×10^{-3}
a44	Asparagine, glycyl.....	25	1	2.942	1.14×10^{-3}			25	2	9.7796	1.68×10^{-10}
		18	2	8.44	3.63×10^{-9}	e6	Glycine, n-acetyl.....	25		3.6698	2.14×10^{-4}
a45	DL-Aspartic acid......	1	1	2.122	7.55×10^{-3}	e7	Glycine, dimethyl....	5		10.3371	4.60×10^{-11}
		1	2	4.006	1.00×10^{-4}	e8	Glycine, glycyl.......	25		3.1397	7.25×10^{-4}
a46	Azetidine (Trimethylimidine)..	25		11.29	5.12×10^{-12}	c9	Glycine, glycylglycyl...	25	1	3.225	5.96×10^{-4}
a47	Aziridine............	25		8.01	9.77×10^{-9}			25	2	8.090	8.13×10^{-9}
						e10	Glycine, leucyl.......	25	1	3.25	5.62×10^{-4}
b1	Benzene, 4-aminoazo...	25		2.82	1.51×10^{-3}			25	2	8.28	5.25×10^{-9}
b2	Benzene, 2-aminoethyl (β-Phenylamine)....	25		9.84	1.45×10^{-10}	e11	Glycine, methyl (Sarcosine).........	25	1	2.21	6.16×10^{-3}
b3	Benzene, 4-dimethylaminoazo.	25		3.226	5.94×10^{-4}			25	2	10.12	7.58×10^{-11}
b4	Benzidine...........	30	1	4.66	2.19×10^{-5}	g12	Glycine, phenyl......	25	1	1.83	1.48×10^{-2}
		30	2	3.57	2.69×10^{-4}			25	2	4.39	4.07×10^{-5}
b5	Benzimidazole........	25		5.532	2.94×10^{-6}	g13	Glycine, N,n-propyl...	25	1	2.35	4.46×10^{-3}
b6	Benzimidazole, 2-ethyl.	25		6.18	6.61×10^{-7}			25	2	10.19	6.46×10^{-11}
b7	Benzimidazole, 2-methyl...........	25		6.19	6.46×10^{-7}	g14	Glycine, tetraglycyl...	20	1	3.10	7.94×10^{-4}
b8	Benzimidazole, 2-phenyl...........	25	1	5.23	5.89×10^{-6}			20	2	8.02	9.55×10^{-9}
		25	2	11.91	1.23×10^{-12}	g15	Glycylserine.........	25	1	2.9808	1.04×10^{-3}
b9	Benzoic acid, 2-amino (Anthranilic acid)...	25	1	2.108	7.80×10^{-3}			25	2	8.38	4.17×10^{-9}
		25	2	4.946	1.13×10^{-5}	h1	Hexadecaneamine.....	25		10.63	2.35×10^{-11}
b10	Benzoic acid, 4-amino..	25	1	2.501	3.15×10^{-3}	h2	Heptane, 1-amino....	25		10.66	2.19×10^{-11}
		25	2	4.874	1.33×10^{-5}	h3	Heptane, 2-amino....	19		10.88	1.58×10^{-11}
b11	Benzylamine........	25		9.33	4.67×10^{-10}	h4	Heptane, 2-methylamino......	17		10.99	1.02×10^{-11}
b12	Betaine............	0		1.83	1.48×10^{-2}	h5	Hexadecaneamine.....	25		10.61	2.46×10^{-11}
b13	Biphenyl, 2-amino.....	22		3.82	1.51×10^{-4}						
b14	Bornylamine(trans-)...	25		10.17	6.76×10^{-11}						

No.	Compound	Temp. °C	Step	pK_a	K_a
h6	Hexamethylene-diamine	0	1	111.857	1.39×10^{-12}
		0	2	0.762	1.73×10^{-11}
h7	Hexanoic acid, 6-amino.	25	1	4.373	4.23×10^{-5}
		25	2	10.804	1.57×10^{-11}
h8	n-Hexylamine	25		10.56	2.75×10^{-11}
h9	dl-Histidine	25	1	1.80	1.58×10^{-2}
		25	2	6.04	9.12×10^{-7}
		25	3	9.33	4.67×10^{-10}
h10	Histidine, β-alanyl (Carnosine)	20	1	2.73	1.86×10^{-3}
		20	2	6.87	1.35×10^{-7}
		20	3	9.73	1.48×10^{-10}
i1	Imidazol	25		6.953	1.11×10^{-7}
i2	Imidazol, 2,4-dimethyl.	25		8.359	5.50×10^{-9}
i3	Imidazol, 1-methyl (Oxalmethyline)	25		6.95	1.12×10^{-7}
i4	Indane, 1-amino (d-1-Hydrindamine	22.5		9.21	6.17×10^{-10}
i5	Isobutyric acid, 2-amino	25	1	2.357	4.30×10^{-3}
		25	2	10.205	6.23×10^{-11}
i6	Isoleucine	25	1	2.318	4.81×10^{-3}
		25	2	9.758	1.74×10^{-10}
i7	Isoquinoline (Leucoline)	20		5.42	3.80×10^{-6}
i8	Isoquinoline, 1-amino	20		7.59	2.57×10^{-8}
i9	Isoquinoline, 7-hydroxy	20	1	5.68	2.09×10^{-6}
		20	2	8.90	1.26×10^{-9}
l1	L-Leucine	25	1	2.328	4.70×10^{-3}
		25	2	9.744	1.80×10^{-10}
l2	Leucine, glycyl	25		3.18	6.61×10^{-4}
m1	Methionine	25	1	2.22	6.02×10^{-3}
		25	2	9.27	5.37×10^{-10}
m2	Methylamine	25		10.657	2.70×10^{-11}
m3	Morphine	25		8.21	6.16×10^{-9}
m4	Morpholine	25		8.33	4.67×10^{-9}
n1	Naphthalene, 1-amino-6-hydroxy	25		3.97	1.07×10^{-4}
n2	Naphthalene, dimethylamino	25		4.566	2.72×10^{-5}
n3	α-Naphthylamine	25		3.92	1.20×10^{-4}
n4	β-Naphthylamine	25		4.16	6.92×10^{-5}
n5	α-Naphthylamine, n-methyl	27		3.67	2.13×10^{-4}
n6	Neobornylamine(cis-)	25		10.01	9.77×10^{-11}
n7	Nicotine	25	1	8.02	9.55×10^{-9}
		25	2	3.12	7.59×10^{-4}
n8	n-Nonylamine	25		10.64	2.29×10^{-11}
n9	Norleucine	25		2.335	4.62×10^{-3}
o1	Octadecaneamine	25		10.60	2.51×10^{-11}
o2	Octylamine	25		10.65	2.24×10^{-11}
o3	Ornithine	25	1	1.705	1.97×10^{-2}
		25	2	8.690	2.04×10^{-9}
p1	Papaverine	25		6.40	3.98×10^{-7}
p2	Pentane, 3-amino	17		10.59	2.57×10^{-11}
p3	Pentane, 3-amino-3-methyl	16		11.01	9.77×10^{-12}
p4	n-Pentadecylamine	25		10.61	2.46×10^{-11}
p5	Pentanoic acid, 5-amino(Valeric acid)	25	1	4.270	5.37×10^{-5}
		25	2	10.766	1.71×10^{-11}
p6	Perimidine	20		6.35	4.47×10^{-7}
p7	Phenanthridine	20		5.58	2.63×10^{-6}
p8	1,10-Phenanthroline	25		4.84	1.44×10^{-5}
p9	o-Phenetidine (2-Ethoxyaniline)	28		4.43	3.72×10^{-5}
p10	m-Phenetidine (3-Ethoxyaniline)	25		4.18	6.60×10^{-5}
p11	p-Phenetidine (4-Ethoxyaniline)	28		5.20	6.31×10^{-6}
p12	α-Picoline	20		5.97	1.07×10^{-6}
p13	β-Picoline	20		5.68	2.09×10^{-6}
p14	γ-Picoline	20		6.02	9.55×10^{-7}
p15	Pilocarpine	30		6.87	1.35×10^{-7}

No.	Compound	Temp. °C	Step	pK_a	K_a
p16	Piperazine	23.5	1	9.83	1.48×10^{-10}
		23.5	2	5.56	2.76×10^{-6}
p17	Piperazine, 2,5-dimethyl(trans-)	25	1	9.66	2.19×10^{-10}
		25	2	5.20	6.31×10^{-6}
p18	Piperidine	25		11.123	7.53×10^{-12}
p19	Piperidine, 3-acetyl	25		3.18	6.61×10^{-4}
p20	Piperidine, 1-n-butyl	23		10.47	3.39×10^{-11}
p21	Piperidine, 1,2-dimethyl	25		10.22	6.03×10^{-11}
p22	Piperidine, 1-ethyl	23		10.45	3.55×10^{-11}
p23	Piperidine, 1-methyl	25		10.08	8.32×10^{-11}
p24	Piperidine, 2,2,6,6-tetramethyl	25		11.07	8.51×10^{-12}
p25	Piperidine, 2,2,4-trimethyl	30		11.04	9.12×10^{-12}
p26	Proline	25	1	1.952	1.11×10^{-2}
		25	2	10.640	2.29×10^{-11}
p27	Proline, hydroxy	25	1	1.818	1.52×10^{-2}
		25	2	9.662	2.18×10^{-10}
p28	Propane, 1-amino-2,2-dimethyl	25		10.15	7.08×10^{-11}
p29	Propane, 1,2-diamino	25	1	9.82	1.52×10^{-10}
		25	2	6.61	2.46×10^{-7}
p30	Propane, 1,3-diamino	10	1	10.94	1.15×10^{-11}
		10	2	9.03	9.33×10^{-10}
p31	Propane, 1,2,3-triamino	20	1	9.59	2.57×10^{-10}
		20	2	7.95	1.12×10^{-8}
p32	Propanoic acid, 3-amino (β-Alanine)	25	1	3.551	2.81×10^{-4}
		25	2	10.238	5.78×10^{-11}
p33	Propylamine	20		10.708	1.96×10^{-11}
p34	Pteridine	20		4.05	8.91×10^{-5}
p35	Pteridine, 2-amino-4, 6-dihydroxy	20	2	6.59	2.57×10^{-7}
		20	3	9.31	4.90×10^{-10}
p36	Pteridine, 2-amino-4-hydroxy	20	1	2.27	5.37×10^{-3}
		20	2	7.96	1.10×10^{-8}
p37	Pteridine, 6-chloro	20		3.68	2.09×10^{-4}
p38	Pteridine, 6-hydroxy-4-methyl	20	1	4.08	8.32×10^{-5}
			2	6.41	3.89×10^{-7}
p39	Purine	20	1	2.30	5.01×10^{-3}
		20	2	8.96	1.10×10^{-9}
p40	Purine, 6-amino (Adenine)	25	1	4.12	7.59×10^{-5}
		25	2	9.83	1.48×10^{-10}
p41	Purine, 2-dimethylamino	20	1	4.00	1.00×10^{-4}
		20	2	10.24	5.75×10^{-11}
p42	Purine, 8-hydroxy	20	1	2.56	2.75×10^{-3}
		20	2	8.26	9.49×10^{-9}
p43	Pyrazine	27		0.65	2.24×10^{-1}
p44	Pyrazine, 2-methyl	27		1.45	3.54×10^{-2}
p45	Pyrazine, methylamino	25		3.39	4.07×10^{-4}
p46	Pyridazine	20		2.24	5.76×10^{-3}
p47	Pyrimidine, 2-amino	20		3.45	3.54×10^{-4}
p48	Pyrimidine, 2-amino-4,6-dimethyl	20		4.82	1.51×10^{-5}
p49	Pyrimidine, 2-amino-5-nitro	20		0.35	4.46×10^{-1}
p50	Pyridine	25		5.25	5.62×10^{-6}
p51	Pyridine, 2-aldoxime	20	1	3.59	2.57×10^{-4}
		20	2	10.18	6.61×10^{-11}
p52	Pyridine, 2-amino	20		6.82	1.51×10^{-7}
p53	Pyridine, 4-amino	25		9.1141	7.69×10^{-10}
p54	Pyridine, 2-benzyl	25		5.13	7.41×10^{-6}
p55	Pyridine, 3-bromo	25		2.84	1.45×10^{-3}
p56	Pyridine, 3-chloro	25		2.84	1.45×10^{-3}
p57	Pyridine, 2,5-diamino	20		6.48	3.31×10^{-7}
p58	Pyridine, 2,3-dimethyl (2,3-Lutidine)	25		6.57	2.69×10^{-7}
p59	Pyridine, 2,4-dimethyl (2,4-Lutidine)	25		6.99	1.02×10^{-7}
p60	Pyridine, 3,5-dimethyl (3,5-Lutidine)	25		6.15	7.08×10^{-7}
p61	Pyridine, 2-ethyl	25		5.89	1.28×10^{-6}
p62	Pyridine, 2-formyl	20		3.80	1.59×10^{-4}
p63	Pyridine, 2-hydroxy (2-Pyridol)	20	1	0.75	9.82×10^{-1}
		20	2	11.65	2.24×10^{-12}

No.	Compound	Temp. °C	Step	pK_a	K_a
p64	Pyridine, 4-hydroxy...	20	1	3.20	6.31×10^{-4}
		20	2	11.12	7.59×10^{-12}
p65	Pyridine, methoxy....	25		6.47	3.30×10^{-7}
p66	Pyridine, 4-methylamino......	20		9.65	2.24×10^{-10}
p67	Pyridine, 2,4,6-trimethyl......	25		7.43	3.72×10^{-8}
p68	Pyrrolidine..........	25		11.27	5.37×10^{-12}
p69	Pyrrolidine, 1,2-dimethyl........	26		10.20	6.31×10^{-11}
p70	Pyrrolidine, n-methyl..	25		10.32	4.79×10^{-11}
q1	Quinazoline..........	20		3.43	3.72×10^{-4}
q2	Quinazoline, 5-hydroxy.	20	1	3.62	2.40×10^{-4}
		20	2	7.41	3.89×10^{-8}
q3	Quinine.............	25	1	8.52	3.02×10^{-9}
		25	2	4.13	7.41×10^{-5}
q4	Quinoline............	20		4.90	1.25×10^{-5}
q5	Quinoline, 3-amino....	20		4.91	1.23×10^{-5}
q6	Quinoline, 3-bromo....	25		2.69	2.04×10^{-3}
q7	Quinoline, 8-carboxy...	25		1.82	1.51×10^{-2}
q8	Quinoline, 3-hydroxy (3-Quinolinol)......	20	1	4.28	5.25×10^{-5}
		20	2	8.08	8.32×10^{-9}
q9	Quinoline, 8-hydroxy (8-Quinolinol)......	20	1	5.017	1.21×10^{-5}
		25	2	9.812	1.54×10^{-10}
q10	Quinoline, 8-hydroxy-5-sulfo........	25	1	4.112	7.73×10^{-5}
		25	2	8.757	1.75×10^{-9}
q11	Quinoline, 6-methoxy..	20		5.03	9.33×10^{-6}
q12	Quinoline, 2-methyl (Quinaldine)........	20		5.83	1.48×10^{-6}
q13	Quinoline, 4-methyl (Lepidine)..........	20		5.67	2.14×10^{-6}
q14	Quinoline, 5-methyl...	20		5.20	6.31×10^{-6}

No.	Compound	Temp. °C	Step	pK_a	K_a
q15	Quinoxaline (Quinazine)........	20		0.56	3.63×10^{-1}
s1	Serine (2-amino-3-hydroxypropanoic acid).............	25	1	2.186	5.49×10^{-3}
		25	2	9.208	6.19×10^{-10}
s2	Strychnine..........	25		8.26	5.49×10^{-9}
t1	Taurine (2-Aminoethane sulfonic acid).......	25	2	9.0614	8.69×10^{-10}
t2	Tetradecaneamine (Myristilamine).....	25		10.62	2.40×10^{-11}
t3	Thiazole..........	20		2.44	3.63×10^{-3}
t4	Thiazole, 2-amino.....	20		5.36	4.36×10^{-5}
t5	Threonine...........	25	1	2.088	8.16×10^{-3}
		25	2	9.10	7.94×10^{-10}
t6	o-Toluidine.........	25		4.44	3.63×10^{-5}
t7	m-Toluidine.........	25		4.73	1.86×10^{-5}
t8	p-Toluidine.........	25		5.08	8.32×10^{-6}
t9	1,3,5-Triazine, 2,4,6-triamino.......	25		5.00	1.00×10^{-5}
t10	Tridecaneamine......	25		10.63	2.35×10^{-11}
t11	Triethylamine........	18		11.01	9.77×10^{-12}
t12	Trimethylamine.......	25		9.81	1.55×10^{-10}
t13	Tryptophan..........	25	1	2.43	3.72×10^{-3}
		25	2	9.44	3.63×10^{-10}
t14	Tyrosine............	25	2	9.11	7.76×10^{-10}
		25	3	10.13	7.41×10^{-11}
t15	Tyrosineamide........	25		7.33	4.68×10^{-8}
u1	Urea...............	21		0.10	7.94×10^{-1}
v1	Valine.............	25	1	2.286	5.17×10^{-3}
		25	2	9.719	1.91×10^{-10}

DISSOCIATION CONSTANTS OF INORGANIC BASES IN AQUEOUS SOLUTIONS

(Approximately 0.1–0.01 N)

Compound	$T°C$	Step	K_b	pK_b
Ammonium hydroxide..............	25		1.79×10^{-5}	4.75
Arsenous oxide....................	25		1.1×10^{-4}	3.96
Beryllium hydroxide...............	25	2	5×10^{-11}	10.30
Calcium hydroxide................	25	1	3.74×10^{-3}	2.43
Calcium hydroxide................	30	2	4.0×10^{-2}	1.40
Deuteroammonium hydroxide.......	25		1.1×10^{-5}	4.96
Hydrazine.......................	20		1.7×10^{-6}	5.77
Hydroxylamine....................	20		1.07×10^{-8}	7.97
Lead Hydroxide..................	25		9.6×10^{-4}	3.02
Silver Hydroxide..................	25		1.1×10^{-4}	3.96
Zinc Hydroxide...................	25		9.6×10^{-4}	3.02

DISSOCIATION CONSTANTS OF ORGANIC ACIDS IN AQUEOUS SOLUTIONS

Compound	T°C	Step	K	pK
Acetic	25		1.76×10^{-5}	4.75
Acetoacetic	18		2.62×10^{-4}	3.58
Acrylic	25		5.6×10^{-5}	4.25
Adipamic	25		2.35×10^{-5}	4.63
Adipic	25	1	3.71×10^{-5}	4.43
Adipic	25	2	3.87×10^{-5}	4.41
d-Alanine	25		1.35×10^{-10}	9.87
Allantoin	25		1.10×10^{-9}	8.96
Alloxanic	25		2.3×10^{-7}	6.64
α-Aminoacetic (glycine)	25		1.67×10^{-10}	9.78
o-Aminobenzoic	25		1.07×10^{-5}	4.97
m-Aminobenzoic	25		1.67×10^{-5}	4.78
p-Aminobenzoic	25		1.2×10^{-5}	4.92
o-Aminobenzosulfonic	25		3.3×10^{-3}	2.48
m-Aminobenzosulfonic	25		1.85×10^{-4}	3.73
p-Aminobenzosulfonic	25		5.81×10^{-4}	3.24
Anisic	25		3.38×10^{-5}	4.47
o-β-Anisylpropionic	25		1.59×10^{-5}	4.80
m-β-Anisylpropionic	25		2.24×10^{-5}	4.65
p-β-Anisylpropionic	25		2.04×10^{-5}	4.69
Ascorbic	24	1	7.94×10^{-5}	4.10
Ascorbic	16	2	1.62×10^{-12}	11.79
DL-Aspartic	25	1	1.38×10^{-4}	3.86
DL-Aspartic	25	2	1.51×10^{-10}	9.82
Barbituric	25		9.8×10^{-5}	4.01
Benzoic	25		6.46×10^{-5}	4.19
Benzosulfonic	25		2×10^{-1}	0.70
Bromoacetic	25		2.05×10^{-3}	2.69
o-Bromobenzoic	25		1.45×10^{-3}	2.84
m-Bromobenzoic	25		1.37×10^{-4}	3.86
n-Butyric	20		1.54×10^{-5}	4.81
iso-Butyric	18		1.44×10^{-5}	4.84
Cacodylic	25		6.4×10^{-7}	6.19
n-Caproic	18		1.43×10^{-5}	4.83
iso-Caproic	18		1.46×10^{-5}	4.84
Chloroacetic	25		1.40×10^{-3}	2.85
o-Chlorobenzoic	25		1.20×10^{-3}	2.92
m-Chlorobenzoic	25		1.51×10^{-4}	3.82
p-Chlorobenzoic	25		1.04×10^{-4}	3.98
α-Chlorobutyric	R.T.		1.39×10^{-3}	2.86
β-Chlorobutyric	R.T.		8.9×10^{-5}	4.05
γ-Chlorobutyric	R.T.		3.0×10^{-5}	4.52
o-Chlorocinnamic	25		5.89×10^{-5}	4.23
m-Chlorocinnamic	25		5.13×10^{-5}	4.29
p-Chlorocinnamic	25		3.89×10^{-5}	4.41
o-Chlorophenoxyacetic	25		8.91×10^{-4}	3.05
m-Chlorophenoxyacetic	25		8.51×10^{-4}	3.07
p-Chlorophenoxyacetic	25		7.94×10^{-4}	3.10
o-Chlorophenylacetic	25		1.18×10^{-5}	4.07
m-Chlorophenylacetic	25		7.25×10^{-5}	4.14
p-Chlorophenylacetic	25		6.46×10^{-5}	4.19
β-(o-Chlorophenyl) propionic	25		2.63×10^{-4}	4.58
β-(m-Chlorophenyl) propionic	25		2.57×10^{-5}	4.59
β-(p-Chlorophenyl) propionic	25		2.46×10^{-5}	4.61
α-Chloropropionic	25		1.47×10^{-3}	2.83
β-Chloropropionic	25		1.04×10^{-4}	3.98
cis-Cinnamic	25		1.3×10^{-4}	3.89
trans-Cinnamic	25		3.65×10^{-5}	4.44
Citric	18	1	7.10×10^{-4}	3.14
Citric	18	2	1.68×10^{-5}	4.77
Citric	18	3	6.4×10^{-6}	6.39
o-Cresol	25		6.3×10^{-11}	10.20
m-Cresol	25		9.8×10^{-11}	10.01
p-Cresol	25		6.7×10^{-11}	10.17
Crotonic (trans-)	25		2.03×10^{-5}	4.69
Cyanoacetic	25		3.65×10^{-3}	2.45
γ-Cyanobutyric	25		3.80×10^{-3}	2.42
o-Cyanophenoxyacetic	25		1.05×10^{-3}	2.98
m-Cyanophenoxyacetic	25		9.33×10^{-4}	3.03
p-Cyanophenoxyacetic	25		1.18×10^{-3}	2.93
Cyanopropionic	25		3.6×10^{-3}	2.44
Cyclohexane-1:1-dicarboxylic	25	1	3.55×10^{-4}	3.45
Cyclohexane-1:1-dicarboxylic	25	2	7.76×10^{-7}	6.11
Cyclopropane-1:1-dicarboxylic	25	1	1.51×10^{-2}	1.82
Cyclopropane-1:1-dicarboxylic	25	2	3.72×10^{-8}	7.43
DL-Cysteine	30	1	7.25×10^{-9}	8.14
DL-Cysteine	30	2	4.6×10^{-11}	10.34
L-Cystine	25	1	1.4×10^{-8}	7.85
L-Cystine	25	2	1.4×10^{-10}	9.85
Deuteroacetic (in D_2O)	25		5.5×10^{-6}	5.25
Dichloroacetic	25		3.32×10^{-2}	1.48
Dichloroacetylacetic	?		7.8×10^{-3}	2.11
Dichlorophenol (2,3-)	25		3.6×10^{-8}	7.44
Dihydroxybenzoic (2,2-)	25		1.14×10^{-3}	2.94
Dihydroxybenzoic (2,5-)	25		1.08×10^{-3}	2.97
Dihydroxybenzoic (3,4-)	25		3.3×10^{-5}	4.48
Dihydroxybenzoic (3,5-)	25		9.1×10^{-5}	4.04
Dihydroxymalic	25		1.2×10^{-2}	1.92
Dihydroxytartaric	25		1.2×10^{-2}	1.92
Dimethylglycine	25		1.3×10^{-10}	9.89
Dimethylmalic	25	1	6.83×10^{-4}	3.17
Dimethylmalic	25	2	8.72×10^{-7}	6.06
Dimethylmalonic	25		7.08×10^{-4}	3.15
Dinicotinic	25		1.6×10^{-3}	2.80
Dinitrophenol (2,4-)	15		1.1×10^{-4}	3.96
Dinitrophenol (3,6-)	15		7.1×10^{-6}	5.15
Diphenylacetic	25		1.15×10^{-4}	3.94
Ethylbenzoic	25		4.47×10^{-5}	4.35
Ethylphenylacetic	25		4.27×10^{-5}	4.37
Fluorobenzoic	17		1.25×10^{-3}	2.90
Formic	20		1.77×10^{-4}	3.75
Fumaric (trans-)	18	1	9.30×10^{-4}	3.03
Fumaric (trans-)	18	2	3.62×10^{-5}	4.44
Furancarboxylic	25		7.1×10^{-4}	3.15
Furoic	25		6.76×10^{-4}	3.17
Gallic	25		3.9×10^{-5}	4.41
Glutaramic	25		3.98×10^{-5}	4.60
Glutaric	25	1	4.58×10^{-5}	4.34
Glutaric	25	2	3.89×10^{-6}	5.41
Glycerol	25		7×10^{-15}	14.15
Glycine	25		1.67×10^{-10}	9.87
Glycol	25		6×10^{-15}	14.22
Glycolic	25		1.48×10^{-4}	3.83
Heptanoic	25		1.28×10^{-5}	4.89
Hexahydrobenzoic	25		1.26×10^{-5}	4.90
Hexanoic	25		1.31×10^{-5}	4.88
Hippuric	25		1.57×10^{-4}	3.80
Histidine	25		6.7×10^{-10}	9.17
Hydroquinone	20		4.5×10^{-11}	10.35
o-Hydroxybenzoic	19	1	1.07×10^{-3}	2.97
o-Hydroxybenzoic	18	2	4×10^{-14}	13.40
m-Hydroxybenzoic	19	1	8.7×10^{-5}	4.06
m-Hydroxybenzoic	19	2	1.2×10^{-10}	9.92
p-Hydroxybenzoic	19	1	3.3×10^{-5}	4.48
p-Hydroxybenzoic	19	2	4.8×10^{-10}	9.32
β-Hydroxybutyric	25		2×10^{-5}	4.70
γ-Hydroxybutyric	25		1.9×10^{-5}	4.72
β-Hydroxypropionic	25		3.1×10^{-5}	4.51
γ-Hydroxyquinoline	20		3.1×10^{-10}	9.51
Iodoacetic	25		7.5×10^{-4}	3.12
o-Iodobenzoic	25		1.4×10^{-3}	2.85
m-Iodobenzoic	25		1.6×10^{-4}	3.80
Itaconic	25	1	1.40×10^{-4}	3.85
Itaconic	25	2	3.56×10^{-6}	5.45
Lactic	100		8.4×10^{-4}	3.08
Lutidinic	25		7.0×10^{-3}	2.15
Lysine	25		2.95×10^{-11}	10.53
Maleic	25	1	1.42×10^{-2}	1.83
Maleic	25	2	8.57×10^{-7}	6.07
Malic	25	1	3.9×10^{-4}	3.40
Malic	25	2	7.8×10^{-6}	5.11
Malonic	25	1	1.49×10^{-3}	2.83
Malonic	25	2	2.03×10^{-6}	5.69
DL-Mandelic	25		1.4×10^{-4}	3.85
Mesaconic	25	1	8.22×10^{-4}	3.09
Mesaconic	25	2	1.78×10^{-5}	4.75
Mesitylenic	25		4.8×10^{-5}	4.32
Methyl-o-aminobenzoic	25		4.6×10^{-6}	5.34
Methyl-m-aminobenzoic	25		8×10^{-6}	5.10
Methyl-p-aminobenzoic	25		9.2×10^{-6}	5.04
o-Methylcinnamic	25		3.16×10^{-5}	4.50
m-Methylcinnamic	25		3.63×10^{-5}	4.44
p-Methylcinnamic	25		2.76×10^{-5}	4.56
β-Methylglutaric	25		5.75×10^{-5}	4.24
n-Methylglycine	18		1.2×10^{-10}	9.92
Methylmalonic	25		1.17×10^{-4}	3.07
Methylsuccinic	25	1	7.4×10^{-5}	4.13
Methylsuccinic	25	2	2.3×10^{-6}	5.64
o-Monochlorophenol	25		3.2×10^{-9}	8.49
m-Monochlorophenol	25		1.4×10^{-9}	8.85
p-Monochlorophenol	25		6.6×10^{-10}	9.18
Naphthalenesulfonic	25		2.7×10^{-1}	0.57
α-Naphthoic	25		2×10^{-4}	3.70
β-Naphthoic	25		6.8×10^{-5}	4.17
α-Naphthol	25		4.6×10^{-10}	9.34
β-Naphthol	25		3.1×10^{-10}	9.51
Nitrobenzene	0		1.05×10^{-4}	3.98
o-Nitrobenzoic	18		6.95×10^{-3}	2.16
m-Nitrobenzoic	25		3.4×10^{-4}	3.47
p-Nitrobenzoic	25		3.93×10^{-4}	3.41
o-Nitrophenol	25		6.8×10^{-8}	7.17
m-Nitrophenol	25		5.3×10^{-9}	8.28
p-Nitrophenol	25		7×10^{-8}	7.15
o-Nitrophenylacetic	25		1.00×10^{-4}	4.00
m-Nitrophenylacetic	25		1.07×10^{-4}	3.97
p-Nitrophenylacetic	25		1.41×10^{-4}	3.85
o-β-Nitrophenylpropionic	25		3.16×10^{-5}	4.50
p-β-Nitrophenylpropionic	25		3.39×10^{-5}	4.47
Nonanic	25		1.09×10^{-5}	4.96
Octanoic	25		1.28×10^{-5}	4.89
Oxalic	25	1	5.90×10^{-2}	1.23
Oxalic	25	2	6.40×10^{-5}	4.19

Compound	T°C	Step	K	pK	Compound	T°C	Step	K	pK
Phenol	20		1.28×10^{-10}	9.89	Sulfanilic	25		5.9×10^{-4}	3.23
Phenylacetic	18		5.2×10^{-5}	4.28	α-Tartaric	25	1	1.04×10^{-3}	2.98
o-Phenylbenzoic	25		3.47×10^{-4}	3.46	α-Tartaric	25	2	4.55×10^{-5}	4.34
γ-Phenylbutyric	25		1.74×10^{-5}	4.76	meso-Tartaric	25	1	6×10^{-4}	3.22
α-Phenylpropionic	25		2.27×10^{-5}	4.64	meso-Tartaric	25	2	1.53×10^{-5}	4.82
β-Phenylpropionic	25		4.25×10^{-5}	4.37	Theobromine	18		1.3×10^{-8}	7.89
o-Phthalic	25	1	1.3×10^{-3}	2.89	Terephthalic	25		3.1×10^{-4}	3.51
o-Phthalic	25	2	3.9×10^{-6}	5.51	Thioacetic	25		4.7×10^{-4}	3.33
m-Phthalic	25	1	2.9×10^{-4}	3.54	Thiophenecarboxylic	25		3.3×10^{-4}	3.48
m-Phthalic	18	2	2.5×10^{-5}	4.60	o-Toluic	25		1.22×10^{-4}	3.91
p-Phthalic	25	1	3.1×10^{-4}	3.51	m-Toluic	25		5.32×10^{-5}	4.27
p-Phthalic	16	2	1.5×10^{-5}	4.82	p-Toluic	25		4.33×10^{-5}	4.36
Picric	25		4.2×10^{-1}	0.38	Trichloroacetic	25		2×10^{-1}	0.70
Pimelic	25		3.09×10^{-5}	4.71	Trichlorophenol	25		1×10^{-6}	6.00
Propionic	25		1.34×10^{-5}	4.87	Trihydroxybenzoic (2,4,6-)	25		2.1×10^{-2}	1.68
iso-Propylbenzoic	25		3.98×10^{-5}	4.40	Trimethylacetic	18		9.4×10^{-6}	5.03
2-Pyridinecarboxylic	25		3×10^{-6}	5.52	Trinitrophenol (2,4,6-)	25		4.2×10^{-1}	0.38
3-Pyridinecarboxylic	25		1.4×10^{-5}	4.85	Tryptophan	25		4.2×10^{-10}	9.38
4-Pyridinecarboxylic	25		1.1×10^{-5}	4.96	Tyrosine	17		3.98×10^{-9}	8.40
Pyrocatechol	20		1.4×10^{-10}	9.85	Uric	12		1.3×10^{-4}	3.89
Quinolinic	25		3×10^{-3}	2.52	n-Valeric	18		1.51×10^{-5}	4.82
					iso-Valeric	25		1.7×10^{-5}	4.77
Resorcinol	25		1.55×10^{-10}	9.81	Veronal	25		3.7×10^{-8}	7.43
					Vinylacetic	25		4.57×10^{-5}	4.34
Saccharin	18		2.1×10^{-12}	11.68					
Suberic	25		2.99×10^{-5}	4.52	Xanthine	40		1.24×10^{-10}	9.91
Succinic	25	1	6.89×10^{-5}	4.16					
Succinic	25	2	2.47×10^{-6}	5.61					

**DISSOCIATION CONSTANTS OF INORGANIC ACIDS
IN AQUEOUS SOLUTIONS**
(Approximately 0.1–0.01 N)

Compound	T°C	Step	K	pK	Compound	T°C	Step	K	pK
Arsenic	18	1	5.62×10^{-3}	2.25	Periodic	25		2.3×10^{-2}	1.64
Arsenic	18	2	1.70×10^{-7}	6.77	o-Phosphoric	25	1	7.52×10^{-3}	2.12
Arsenic	18	3	3.95×10^{-12}	11.60	o-Phosphoric	25	2	6.23×10^{-8}	7.21
Arsenious	25		6×10^{-10}	9.23	o-Phosphoric	18	3	2.2×10^{-13}	12.67
					Phosphorous	18	1	1.0×10^{-2}	2.00
o-Boric	20	1	7.3×10^{-10}	9.14	Phosphorous	18	2	2.6×10^{-7}	6.59
o-Boric	20	2	1.8×10^{-13}	12.74	Pyrophosphoric	18	1	1.4×10^{-1}	0.85
o-Boric	20	3	1.6×10^{-14}	13.80	Pyrophosphoric	18	2	3.2×10^{-2}	1.49
					Pyrophosphoric	18	3	1.7×10^{-6}	5.77
Carbonic	25	1	4.30×10^{-7}	6.37	Pyrophosphoric	18	4	6×10^{-9}	8.22
Carbonic	25	2	5.61×10^{-11}	10.25					
Chromic	25	1	1.8×10^{-1}	0.74	Selenic	25	2	1.2×10^{-2}	1.92
Chromic	25	2	3.20×10^{-7}	6.49	Selenious	25	1	3.5×10^{-3}	2.46
					Selenious	25	2	5×10^{-8}	7.31
Germanic	25	1	2.6×10^{-9}	8.59	m-Silicic	R.T.	1	2×10^{-10}	9.70
Germanic	25	2	1.9×10^{-13}	12.72	m-Silicic	R.T.	2	1×10^{-12}	12.00
					o-Silicic	30	1	2.2×10^{-10}	9.66
Hydrocyanic	25		4.93×10^{-10}	9.31	o-Silicic	30	2	2×10^{-12}	11.70
Hydrofluoric	25		3.53×10^{-4}	3.45	o-Silicic	30	3	1×10^{-12}	12.00
Hydrogen sulfide	18	1	9.1×10^{-8}	7.04	o-Silicic	30	4	1×10^{-12}	12.00
Hydrogen sulfide	18	2	1.1×10^{-12}	11.96	Sulfuric	25	2	1.20×10^{-2}	1.92
Hydrogen peroxide	25		2.4×10^{-12}	11.62	Sulfurous	18	1	1.54×10^{-2}	1.81
Hypobromous	25		2.06×10^{-9}	8.69	Sulfurous	18	2	1.02×10^{-7}	6.91
Hypochlorous	18		2.95×10^{-8}	7.53	Telluric	18	1	2.09×10^{-8}	7.68
Hypoiodous	25		2.3×10^{-11}	10.64	Telluric	18	2	6.46×10^{-12}	11.29
					Tellurous	25	1	3×10^{-3}	2.48
Iodic	25		1.69×10^{-1}	0.77	Tellurous	25	2	2×10^{-8}	7.70
Nitrous	12.5		4.6×10^{-4}	3.37	Tetraboric	25	1	$\sim 10^{-4}$	~ 4.00
					Tetraboric	25	2	$\sim 10^{-9}$	~ 9.00

**DISSOCIATION CONSTANTS (K_b) OF AQUEOUS
AMMONIA FROM 0 TO 50°C.**

Temperature °C.	pK_b	K_b
0	4.862	1.374×10^{-5}
5	4.830	1.479×10^{-5}
10	4.804	1.570×10^{-5}
15	4.782	1.652×10^{-5}
20	4.767	1.710×10^{-5}
25	4.751	1.774×10^{-5}
30	4.740	1.820×10^{-5}
35	4.733	1.849×10^{-5}
40	4.730	1.862×10^{-5}
45	4.726	1.879×10^{-5}
50	4.723	1.892×10^{-5}

Values of K_b accurate to ± 0.005; determined by e.m.f. method by: R. G. Bates and G. D. Pinching, J. Am. Chem. Soc., 1950, **72**, 1393.

IONIZATION CONSTANT FOR WATER (K_w)

$-\log_{10} K_w$	Temperature °C.	$-\log_{10} K_w$	Temperature °C.
14.9435	0	13.8330	30
14.7338	5	13.6801	35
14.5346	10	13.5348	40
14.3463	15	13.3960	45
14.1669	20	13.2617	50
14.0000	24	13.1369	55
13.9965	25	13.0171	60

IONIZATION CONSTANTS OF ACIDS IN WATER AT VARIOUS TEMPERATURES

Acids		0°	5°	10°	15°	20°	25°	30°	35°	40°	45°	50°
Formic	$K_A \cdot 10^4$	1.638	1.691	1.728	1.749	1.765	1.772	1.768	1.747	1.716	1.685	1.650
Acetic	$K_A \cdot 10^5$	1.657	1.700	1.729	1.745	1.753	1.754	1.750	1.728	1.703	1.670	1.633
Propionic	$K_A \cdot 10^5$	1.274	1.305	1.326	1.336	1.338	1.336	1.326	1.310	1.280	1.257	1.229
n-Butyric	$K_A \cdot 10^5$	1.563	1.574	1.576	1.569	1.542	1.515	1.484	1.439	1.395	1.347	1.302
Chloracetic	$K_A \cdot 10^3$	1.528	....	1.488	....	....	1.379	....	....	1.230	....	....
Lactic	$K_A \cdot 10^4$	1.287	....	....	....	....	1.374	....	....	....	....	1.270
Glycollic	$K_A \cdot 10^4$	1.334	....	....	....	....	1.475	....	....	....	....	1.415
Oxalic	$K_{2A} \cdot 10^5$	5.91	5.82	5.70	5.55	5.40	5.18	4.92	4.67	4.41	4.09	3.83
Malonic	$K_{2A} \cdot 10^6$	2.140	2.165	2.152	2.124	2.076	2.014	1.948	1.863	1.768	1.670	1.575
Phosphoric	$K_A \cdot 10^3$	8.968	....	....	....	....	7.516	....	....	....	....	5.495
Phosphoric	$K_{2A} \cdot 10^8$	4.85	5.24	5.57	5.89	6.12	6.34	6.46	6.53	6.58	6.59	6.55
Boric	$K_A \cdot 10^{10}$	....	3.63	4.17	4.72	5.26	5.79	6.34	6.86	7.38	....	8.32
Carbonic	$K_{1A} \cdot 10^7$	2.64	3.04	3.44	3.81	4.16	4.45	4.71	4.90	5.04	5.13	5.19
Phenol-sulfonic	$K_{2A} \cdot 10^{10}$	4.45	5.20	6.03	6.92	7.85	8.85	9.89	10.94	12.00	13.09	14.16
Glycine	$K_{1A} \cdot 10^7$	....	3.82	3.99	4.17	4.32	4.46	4.57	4.66	4.73	4.77	4.79
Citric	$K_{1A} \cdot 10^4$	6.03	6.31	6.69	6.92	7.21	7.45	7.66	7.78	7.96	7.99	8.04
	$K_{2A} \cdot 10^5$	1.45	1.54	1.60	1.65	1.70	1.73	1.76	1.77	1.78	1.76	1.75
	$K_{3A} \cdot 10^7$	4.05	4.11	4.14	4.13	4.09	4.02	3.99	3.78	3.69	3.45	3.28

Reproducibility between various workers is about $\pm (0.01 - 0.02) \cdot 10^5$.
All values are on the m-scale.

COMPOSITION OF SOME INORGANIC ACIDS AND BASES

The following acids and bases are frequently supplied as concentrated aqueous solutions. This table presents certain data concerning these solutions.

	Formula weight	Molarity	Specific gravity	Weight percent	
Acetic acid	60.05	17.5	1.05	99–100	CH_3COOH
Ammonium hydroxide	35.05	14.8	0.90	28–30	NH_3
Hydriodic acid	127.91	5.5	1.5	47–47.5	HI
Hydrobromic acid	80.93	9.0	1.5	47–49	HBr
Hydrochloric acid	36.46	12.0	1.18	36.5–38	HCl
Hydrofluoric acid	20.01	28.9	1.17	48–51	HF
Phosphoric acid	98.00	14.7	1.7	85	H_3PO_4
Sulfuric acid	98.08	18.0	1.84	95–98	H_2SO_4

IONIZATION CONSTANTS FOR DEUTERIUM OXIDE FROM 10 TO 50°C.

From NBS Technical Note 400

The subscript m indicates values on the molal scale, whereas the subscript c indicates values on the molar scale.

t, °C	pK_m	pK_c
10	15.526	15.439
20	15.136	15.049
25	14.955	14.869
30	14.784	14.699
40	14.468	14.385
50	14.182	14.103

EQUIVALENT CONDUCTANCES OF SOME ELECTROLYTES IN AQUEOUS SOLUTIONS AT 25°C

Compound	Infinite dilution	0.0005	0.001	0.005	0.01	0.02	0.05	0.1
AgNO₃	133.36	131.36	130.51	127.20	124.76	121.41	115.24	109.14
BaCl₂	139.98	135.96	134.34	128.02	123.94	119.09	111.48	105.19
CaCl₂	135.84	131.93	130.36	124.25	120.36	115.65	108.47	102.4
Ca(OH)₂	257.9			232.9	225.9	213.9		
CuSO₄	133.6	121.6	115.26	94.07	83.12	72.20	59.05	50.58
HCl	426.16	422.74	421.36	415.80	412.00	407.24	399.09	391.32
KBr	151.9			146.09	143.43	140.48	135.68	131.39
KCl	149.86	147.81	146.95	143.35	141.27	138.34	133.37	128.96
KClO₄	140.04	138.76	137.87	134.16	131.46	127.92	121.62	115.20
K₃Fe(CN)₆	174.5	166.4	163.1	150.7				
K₄Fe(CN)₆	184.5		167.24	146.09	134.83	122.82	107.70	97.87
KHCO₃	118.0	116.10	115.34	112.24	110.08	107.22		
KI	150.38			144.37	142.18	139.45	134.97	131.11
KIO₄	127.92	125.80	124.94	121.24	118.51	114.14	106.72	98.12
KNO₃	144.96	142.77	141.84	138.48	132.82	132.41	126.31	120.40
KReO₄	128.20	126.03	125.12	121.31	118.49	114.49	106.40	97.40

Compound	Infinite dilution	0.0005	0.001	0.005	0.01	0.02	0.05	0.1
LaCl₃	145.8	139.6	137.0	127.5	121.8	115.3	106.2	99.1
LiCl	115.03	113.15	112.40	109.40	107.40	104.65	100.11	95.86
LiClO₄	105.98	104.18	103.44	100.57	98.61	96.18	92.20	88.56
MgCl₂	129.40	125.61	124.11	118.31	114.55	110.04	103.08	97.10
NH₄Cl	149.7		146.8	143.5	141.28	138.33	133.29	128.75
NaCl	126.45	124.50	123.74	120.65	118.51	115.51	111.06	106.74
NaClO₄	117.48	115.64	114.87	111.75	109.59	106.96	102.40	98.43
NaI	126.94	125.36	124.25	121.25	119.24	116.70	112.79	108.78
NaOOCCH₃	91.0	89.2	88.5	85.72	83.76	81.24	76.92	72.80
NaOOCC₂H₅	85.9		83.5	80.9	79.1	76.6		
NaOOCC₃H₇	82.70	81.04	80.31	77.58	75.76	73.39	69.32	65.27
NaOH	247.8	245.6	244.7	240.8	238.0			
Na₂SO₄	129.9	125.74	124.15	117.15	112.44	106.78	97.75	89.98
SrCl₂	135.80	131.90	130.33	124.24	120.24	115.54	108.25	102.19
ZnSO₄	132.8	121.4	114.53	95.49	84.91	74.24	61.20	52.64

THE EQUIVALENT CONDUCTANCE OF THE SEPARATE IONS

(From Smithsonian Physical Tables)

Ion.	0°	18°	25°	50°	75°	100°	128°	156°
K	40.4	64.6	74.5	115	159	206	263	317
Na	26.	43.5	50.0	82	116	155	203	249
NH₄	40.2	64.5	74.5	115	159	207	264	319
Ag	32.9	54.3	63.5	101	143	188	245	299
½Ba	33.	55.	65.	104	149	200	262	322
½Ca	30.	51.	60.	98	142	191	252	312
⅓La	35.	61.	72.	119	173	235	312	388
Cl	41.1	65.5	75.5	116	160	207	264	318
NO₃	40.4	61.7	70.6	104	140	178	222	263
C₂H₃O₂	20.3	34.6	40.8	67	96	130	171	211

Ion.	0°	18°	25°	50°	75°	100°	128°	156°
½SO₄	41.	68.	79.	125	177	234	303	370
½C₂O₄	39.	63.	73.	115	163	213	27 ?	336
⅓C₆H₅O₇	36.	60.	70.	113	161	214		
¼Fe(CN)₆	58.	95.	111.	173	244	321		
H	240.	314.	350.	465	565	644	722	777
OH	105.	172.	192.	284	360	439	525	592

ACTIVITY COEFFICIENTS OF ACIDS, BASES AND SALTS

The following coefficients are valid only at 25°C. The concentrations are expressed as molalities.

Name	0.1	0.2	0.3	0.4	0.5	0.6	0.7	0.8	0.9	1.0
AgNO₃	0.734	0.657	0.606	0.567	0.536	0.509	0.485	0.464	0.446	0.429
AlCl₃	(0.337)	0.305	0.302	0.313	0.331	0.356	0.388	0.429	0.479	0.539
Al₂(SO₄)₃	(0.0350)	0.0225	0.0176	0.0153	0.0143	0.0140	0.0142	0.0149	0.0159	0.0175
CdSO₄	(0.150)	0.102	0.082	0.069	0.061	0.055	0.050	0.046	0.043	0.041
CrCl₃	(0.331)	0.298	0.294	0.300	0.314	0.335	0.362	0.397	0.436	0.481
Cr(NO₃)₃	(0.319)	0.285	0.279	0.281	0.291	0.304	0.322	0.344	0.371	0.401
Cr₂(SO₄)₃	(0.0458)	0.0300	0.0238	0.0207	0.0190	0.0182	0.0181	0.0185	0.0194	0.0208
CsBr	0.754	0.694	0.654	0.626	0.603	0.586	0.571	0.558	0.547	0.538
CsCl	0.756	0.694	0.656	0.628	0.606	0.589	0.575	0.563	0.553	0.544
CsI	0.754	0.692	0.651	0.621	0.599	0.581	0.567	0.554	0.543	0.533
CsNO₃	0.733	0.655	0.602	0.561	0.528	0.501	0.478	0.458	0.439	0.422
CsOAc	0.799	0.771	0.761	0.759	0.762	0.768	0.776	0.783	0.792	0.802
CuSO₄	(0.150)	0.104	0.083	0.071	0.062	0.056	0.052	0.048	0.045	0.043
HBr	0.805	0.782	0.777	0.781	0.789	0.801	0.815	0.832	0.850	0.871
HCl	0.796	0.767	0.756	0.755	0.757	0.763	0.772	0.783	0.795	0.809
HClO₄	0.803	0.778	0.768	0.766	0.769	0.776	0.785	0.795	0.808	0.823
HI	0.818	0.807	0.811	0.823	0.839	0.860	0.883	0.908	0.935	0.963
HNO₃	0.791	0.754	0.735	0.725	0.720	0.717	0.717	0.718	0.721	0.724
KBr	0.772	0.722	0.693	0.673	0.657	0.646	0.636	0.629	0.622	0.617
KCl	0.770	0.718	0.688	0.666	0.649	0.637	0.626	0.618	0.610	0.604
KCNS	0.769	0.716	0.685	0.663	0.646	0.633	0.623	0.614	0.606	0.599
KF	0.775	0.727	0.700	0.682	0.670	0.661	0.654	0.650	0.646	0.645
KI	0.778	0.733	0.707	0.689	0.676	0.667	0.660	0.654	0.649	0.645
KNO₃	0.739	0.663	0.614	0.576	0.545	0.519	0.496	0.476	0.459	0.443
KOAc	0.796	0.766	0.754	0.750	0.751	0.754	0.759	0.766	0.774	0.783

Name	0.1	0.2	0.3	0.4	0.5	0.6	0.7	0.8	0.9	1.0
KOH	0.798	0.760	0.742	0.734	0.732	0.733	0.736	0.742	0.749	0.756
LiBr	0.796	0.766	0.756	0.752	0.753	0.758	0.767	0.777	0.789	0.803
LiCl	0.790	0.757	0.744	0.740	0.739	0.743	0.748	0.755	0.764	0.774
LiClO₄	0.812	0.794	0.792	0.798	0.808	0.820	0.834	0.852	0.869	0.887
LiI	0.815	0.802	0.804	0.813	0.824	0.838	0.852	0.870	0.888	0.910
LiNO₃	0.788	0.752	0.736	0.728	0.726	0.727	0.729	0.733	0.737	0.743
LiOAc	0.784	0.742	0.721	0.709	0.700	0.691	0.689	0.688	0.688	0.689
MgSO₄	(0.150)	0.108	0.088	0.076	0.068	0.062	0.057	0.054	0.051	0.049
MnSO₄	(0.150)	0.106	0.085	0.073	0.064	0.058	0.053	0.049	0.046	0.044
NaBr	0.782	0.741	0.719	0.704	0.697	0.692	0.689	0.687	0.687	0.687
NaCl	0.778	0.735	0.710	0.693	0.681	0.673	0.667	0.662	0.659	0.657
NaClO₄	0.775	0.729	0.701	0.683	0.668	0.656	0.648	0.641	0.635	0.629
NaCNS	0.787	0.750	0.731	0.720	0.715	0.712	0.710	0.710	0.711	0.712
NaF	0.765	0.710	0.676	0.651	0.632	0.616	0.603	0.592	0.582	0.573
NaH₂PO₄	0.744	0.675	0.629	0.593	0.563	0.539	0.517	0.499	0.483	0.468
NaI	0.787	0.751	0.735	0.727	0.723	0.723	0.724	0.727	0.731	0.736
NaNO₂	0.762	0.703	0.666	0.638	0.617	0.599	0.583	0.570	0.558	0.548
NaOAc	0.791	0.757	0.744	0.737	0.735	0.736	0.740	0.745	0.752	0.757
NaOH	0.766	0.727	0.708	0.697	0.690	0.685	0.681	0.679	0.678	0.678
NiSO₄	(0.150)	0.105	0.084	0.071	0.063	0.056	0.052	0.047	0.044	0.042
RbBr	0.763	0.706	0.673	0.650	0.632	0.617	0.605	0.595	0.586	0.578
RbCl	0.764	0.709	0.675	0.652	0.634	0.620	0.608	0.599	0.590	0.583
RbI	0.762	0.705	0.671	0.647	0.629	0.614	0.602	0.591	0.583	0.575
RbNO₃	0.734	0.658	0.606	0.565	0.534	0.508	0.485	0.465	0.446	0.430
RbOAc	0.796	0.767	0.756	0.753	0.759	0.759	0.766	0.773	0.782	0.792
TlNO₃	0.702	0.606	0.545	0.500	....	....	....	....	....	....
ZnSO₄	(0.150)	0.104	0.083	0.071	0.063	0.057	0.052	0.048	0.046	0.043

EQUIVALENT CONDUCTANCES OF AQUEOUS SOLUTIONS OF HYDROHALOGEN ACIDS

From NSRDS-NBS 33
Walter J. Hamer and Harold J. DeWane

One may wish to refer to the above document which defines terms relating to conductance of electrolytic solutions and also discusses some general considerations of the migration of ions under applied potential gradients. In NSRDS-NBS 33 conductance equations are given and some treatment of the Debye–Hückel–Onsager–Fuoss theories is presented.

Equivalent conductances (Ω^{-1} cm^2 equiv^{-1} of aqueous solutions of HF at 0, 16, 18, 20, and 25°C

c	0°C	16°C	18°C	20°C	25°C
mol l^{-1}					
0.004	106.7	—	—	—	140.5
0.005	97.7	—	—	—	128.1
0.006	90.9	112.9	114.6	116.3	118.8
0.007	85.5	105.7	107.3	108.9	111.4
0.008	81.1	99.9	101.3	102.9	105.4
0.009	77.3	95.0	96.4	97.8	100.4
0.01	74.2	90.8	92.1	93.5	96.1
0.02	56.2	67.7	68.8	69.8	72.2
0.05	39.3	46.8	47.6	48.3	50.1
0.07	34.7	41.3	41.9	42.6	44.3
0.10	30.7	36.4	37.0	37.7	39.1
0.20	24.8	29.6	30.1	30.7	31.7
0.50	20.4	—	—	—	26.3
0.70	19.5	—	—	—	25.1
1.0	18.8	—	—	—	24.3

Equivalent conductances (Ω^{-1} cm^2 equiv^{-1}) of aqueous solutions of HCl from -20 to 65°C

c	−20°C	−10°C	0°C	5°C	10°C	15°C	20°C	25°C	30°C	35°C	40°C	45°C	50°C	55°C	65°C
mol l^{-1}															
0.0001	—	—	—	296.4	—	360.8	—	424.5	—	487.0	—	547.9	577.7	606.6	662.9
0.0005	—	—	—	295.2	—	359.2	—	422.6	—	484.7	—	545.2	575.1	603.5	660.0
0.001	—	—	—	294.3	—	358.0	—	421.2	—	483.1	—	543.2	573.1	601.3	657.8
0.005	—	—	—	291.0	—	353.5	—	415.7	—	476.7	—	535.5	564.4	592.6	647.3
0.01	—	—	—	288.6	—	350.3	—	411.9	—	472.2	—	530.3	558.7	586.5	641.2
0.05	—	—	—	280.3	—	339.9	—	398.9	—	456.7	—	512.4		565.6	616.9
0.1	—	—	—	275.0	—	333.3	—	391.1	—	446.8	—	501.1	—	552.8	602.8
0.5	—	—	228.7	254.8	283.0	308.1	336.4	360.7	386.8	411.9	436.9	461.1	482.4	508.0	552.3
1.0	—	—	211.7	235.2	261.6	283.9	312.2	332.2	359.0	379.4	402.9	424.8	445.3	468.1	509.3
1.5	—	—	196.2	216.9	241.5	261.5	287.5	305.8	331.1	349.4	371.6	391.5	410.8	431.7	469.9
2.0	—	—	182.0	199.9	222.7	240.7	262.9	281.4	303.3	321.6	342.4	360.6	378.2	398.0	433.6
2.5	—	131.7	168.5	184.3	205.1	221.4	239.8	258.9	277.0	295.8	315.2	332.0	347.6	366.7	399.9
3.0	—	120.8	154.6	169.5	188.5	203.4	219.3	237.6	253.3	271.5	289.3	304.8	319.0	336.9	368.0
3.5	85.5	111.3	139.6	155.6	172.2	186.5	201.6	218.3	232.9	248.6	263.9	279.4	292.1	308.6	337.2
4.0	79.3	102.7	129.2	143.4	158.1	171.5	185.6	200.0	214.2	228.4	242.2	256.6	268.2	283.6	310.1
4.5	73.7	94.9	119.5	132.0	145.4	157.4	170.6	183.1	196.6	209.5	222.5	235.2	246.7	260.2	284.7
5.0	68.5	87.8	110.3	121.3	133.5	144.4	156.6	167.4	180.2	191.9	204.1	215.4	226.5	238.4	261.0
5.5	63.6	81.1	101.7	111.4	122.5	132.3	143.6	152.9	165.0	175.6	187.1	197.1	207.7	218.3	239.1
6.0	58.9	74.9	93.7	102.2	112.3	121.2	131.5	139.7	151.0	160.6	171.3	180.2	190.3	199.7	218.9
6.5	54.4	69.1	86.2	93.8	103.0	111.0	120.4	127.7	138.2	146.8	156.9	164.8	174.3	182.7	200.4
7.0	50.2	63.7	79.3	86.0	94.4	101.7	110.2	116.9	126.4	134.3	143.3	150.8	159.7	167.2	183.5
7.5	46.3	58.6	73.0	78.9	86.5	93.3	100.9	107.0	115.7	122.9	131.6	138.1	146.2	153.1	168.1
8.0	42.7	54.0	67.1	72.4	79.4	85.6	92.4	98.2	106.1	112.6	120.6	126.7	134.0	140.4	154.1
8.5	39.4	49.8	61.7	66.5	72.9	78.7	84.7	90.3	97.3	103.2	110.7	116.4	123.0	128.8	141.5
9.0	36.4	45.9	56.8	61.2	67.1	72.5	77.8	83.1	89.4	94.8	101.7	107.1	112.9	118.3	130.1
9.5	33.6	42.3	52.3	56.4	61.8	66.8	71.5	76.6	82.3	87.3	93.6	98.7	103.9	108.8	119.7
10.0	31.2	39.1	48.2	52.0	57.0	61.6	65.8	70.7	75.9	80.5	86.3	91.1	95.7	—	—
10.5	28.9	36.1	44.5	48.0	52.7	56.9	60.7	65.3	70.1	74.3	79.6	84.1	88.4	—	—
11.0	26.8	33.4	41.1	44.4	48.8	52.6	56.1	60.2	64.9	68.7	73.6	77.7	81.7	—	—
11.5	24.9	31.0	38.0	41.1	45.3	48.5	51.9	55.3	60.1	63.6	68.0	71.7	75.6	—	—
12.0	23.1	28.7	35.3	38.0	42.0	—	48.0	—	55.6	—	62.8	—	70.0	—	—
12.5	21.4	26.7	32.7	—	39.0	—	44.4	—	51.4	—	57.9		64.8	—	—
13.0	20.0	24.9	—	—	—	—	—	—	—	—	—	—	—	—	—

Equivalent conductances (Ω^{-1} cm^2 equiv^{-1}) of aqueous solutions of HBr at 25°C

c	Λ	c	Λ	c	Λ	c	Λ	c	Λ	c	Λ
mol l^{-1}		mol l^{-1}		mol l^{-1}		mol l^{-1}		mol l^{-1}		mol l^{-1}	
0.0002	425.5	0.003	419.7	0.04	402.7	0.30	374.0	0.80	345.3	4.0	199.4
0.0003	425.0	0.004	418.5	0.05	400.4	0.35	370.8	0.85	342.6	4.5	182.4
0.0004	424.6	0.005	417.6	0.06	398.4	0.40	367.7	0.90	339.9	5.0	166.5
0.0005	424.3	0.006	416.7	0.07	396.5	0.45	364.7	0.95	337.2	5.5	151.8
0.0006	424.0	0.007	415.8	0.08	394.9	0.50	361.9	1.0	334.5	6.0	138.2
0.0007	423.7	0.008	415.1	0.09	393.4	0.55	359.0	1.5	307.6	6.5	125.7
0.0008	423.4	0.009	414.4	0.10	391.9	0.60	356.3	2.0	281.7	7.0	114.2
0.0009	423.2	0.01	413.7	0.15	386.0	0.65	353.5	2.5	257.8	7.5	103.8
0.001	422.9	0.02	408.9	0.20	381.4	0.70	350.8	3.0	236.8	8.0	94.4
0.002	421.1	0.03	405.4	0.25	377.5	0.75	348.0	3.5	217.5	8.5	85.8

Equivalent conductances (Ω^{-1} cm^2 equiv^{-1}) of aqueous solutions of HBr from -20 to $50°C$

c	$-20°C$	$-10°C$	$0°C$	$10°C$	$20°C$	$30°C$	$40°C$	$50°C$
mol l^{-1}								
0.50	—	—	240.9	295.9	347.0	398.9	453.6	496.8
0.75	—	—	234.7	284.9	339.0	387.2	433.8	480.6
1.00	—	—	229.6	276.0	329.0	380.4	418.6	465.2
1.25	—	—	221.7	265.8	314.9	362.8	401.8	442.9
1.50	—	—	209.5	254.9	298.9	340.6	381.8	421.4
1.75	—	—	198.3	243.1	284.6	327.3	366.2	404.8
2.00	—	150.8	188.6	231.3	271.8	314.1	350.5	387.4
2.25	—	143.4	180.1	219.6	258.3	296.9	332.3	367.0
2.50	—	136.8	171.7	208.3	244.8	281.7	316.0	349.1
2.75	—	131.1	164.1	198.3	232.9	267.6	301.2	333.2
3.00	—	125.7	157.2	189.5	222.2	255.0	287.8	318.6
3.25	—	120.6	150.8	181.7	212.4	244.3	275.4	304.9
3.50	—	116.1	144.1	174.6	203.2	234.4	263.7	291.9
3.75	87.1	112.0	137.6	167.4	194.7	224.2	252.2	279.4
4.00	84.0	107.5	132.3	160.2	186.8	214.2	239.7	266.9
4.25	80.9	103.1	127.7	153.2	179.0	204.5	228.8	254.6
4.50	78.0	99.0	123.0	146.4	171.2	195.1	218.8	242.6
4.75	75.1	95.1	117.7	139.9	163.1	186.1	209.3	231.3
5.00	72.3	91.4	112.6	134.0	155.7	178.2	199.6	221.3
5.25	69.6	87.8	107.8	128.3	148.7	170.5	190.0	211.4
5.50	67.0	84.2	103.1	122.7	142.1	162.8	181.4	201.8
5.75	64.4	80.6	98.6	117.3	135.7	155.3	173.2	192.4
6.00	61.8	77.2	94.3	112.0	129.6	148.0	165.4	183.4
6.25	59.3	73.8	90.1	106.9	123.7	140.9	157.8	174.7
6.50	56.8	70.7	86.0	102.0	118.0	134.1	150.5	166.3
6.75	54.4	67.7	82.1	97.2	112.5	127.6	143.3	158.4
7.00	51.9	64.6	78.4	92.6	107.1	121.4	136.3	150.8

Equivalent conductances (Ω^{-1} cm^2 equiv^{-1}) of aqueous solutions of HI at 25°C

c	Λ	c	Λ	c	Λ	c	Λ	c	Λ
mol l^{-1}		mol l^{-1}		mol l^{-1}		mol l^{-1}		mol l^{-1}	
0.00045	423.2								
0.00050	423.0	0.0035	417.9	0.025	406.6	0.10	394.0	0.90	349.2
0.00055	422.9	0.0040	417.3	0.030	405.2	0.15	389.5	0.95	346.6
0.00060	422.7	0.0045	416.8	0.035	403.9	0.20	385.9	1.0	343.9
0.00065	422.6	0.0050	416.4	0.040	402.8	0.25	382.9	1.5	316.4
0.00070	422.4	0.0055	415.9	0.045	401.7	0.30	380.1	2.0	288.9
0.00075	422.3	0.0060	415.5	0.050	400.8	0.40	374.9	2.5	262.5
0.00080	422.2	0.0065	415.1	0.055	399.9	0.45	372.3	3.0	237.9
0.00085	422.0	0.0070	414.8	0.060	399.1	0.50	369.8	3.5	215.4
0.00090	421.9	0.0075	414.4	0.065	398.3	0.55	367.3	4.0	195.1
0.00095	421.8	0.0080	414.1	0.070	397.6	0.60	364.8	4.5	176.8
0.0010	421.7	0.0090	413.4	0.075	396.9	0.65	362.2	5.0	160.4
0.0015	420.7	0.0095	413.1	0.080	396.3	0.70	359.7	5.5	145.5
0.0020	419.8	0.010	412.8	0.085	395.6	0.75	357.1	6.0	131.7
0.0025	419.1	0.015	410.3	0.090	395.1	0.80	354.5	6.5	118.6
0.0030	418.5	0.020	408.3	0.095	394.5	0.85	351.9	7.0	105.7

EQUIVALENT CONDUCTANCES OF AQUEOUS SOLUTIONS OF HYDROHALOGEN ACIDS (Continued)

Equivalent conductances (Ω^{-1} cm^2 equiv^{-1}) of aqueous solutions of HI from -20 to 50°C

c	-20°C	-10°C	0°C	10°C	20°C	30°C	40°C	50°C
mol l^{-1}								
0.4	—	—	253.9	300.7	354.5	411.9	453.6	501.8
0.6	—	—	249.1	293.6	344.6	401.1	441.5	488.4
0.8	—	—	242.4	285.5	333.9	389.1	429.3	474.8
1.0	—	—	234.8	276.9	322.7	376.3	416.5	460.8
1.2	—	—	226.6	267.9	311.4	363.1	403.4	446.3
1.4	—	—	218.2	258.8	300.2	349.8	390.0	431.4
1.6	—	—	209.9	249.7	289.1	336.6	376.5	416.3
1.8	—	—	201.8	240.7	278.4	323.7	363.0	401.2
2.0	—	—	194.0	231.9	268.1	311.1	349.6	386.1
2.2	—	147.7	186.6	223.4	258.2	299.0	336.3	371.2
2.4	—	143.5	179.5	215.1	248.8	287.3	323.3	356.5
2.6	—	138.8	172.8	207.2	239.7	276.1	310.5	342.2
2.8	—	133.9	166.5	199.5	231.0	265.4	298.1	328.2
3.0	99.9	129.0	160.5	192.0	222.7	255.1	286.1	314.7
3.2	97.4	124.1	154.7	184.8	214.6	245.2	274.5	301.7
3.4	94.2	119.5	149.1	177.8	206.7	235.7	263.4	289.2
3.6	90.6	115.0	143.7	171.0	198.9	226.4	252.6	277.3
3.8	86.9	110.9	138.3	164.3	191.2	217.4	242.3	266.0
4.0	83.6	106.9	132.8	157.6	183.5	208.4	232.5	255.3
4.2	80.9	103.0	127.3	151.0	175.6	199.6	223.1	245.3
4.4	79.3	99.2	121.6	144.3	167.5	190.7	214.1	235.9

SPECIFIC HEAT OF WATER

Heat Capacity of Air-free Water 0°–100°C at 1 Atmosphere Pressure

The heat capacity of air-free water is given in international steam table calories per gram and in absolute joules per gram. (1 absolute joule— 0.238846 I.T. Cal.).

The enthalpy or heat content is given for air-free water in I.T. Cal. per gram and in absolute joules per gram.

From Osborne, Stimson and Ginnings; B. of S. Jour. Res. 23. 238, 1939.

Temp. °C.	Thermal Capacity		Enthalpy		Temp. °C	Thermal Capacity		Enthalpy	
	Cal./g/°C	Joules/g/°C	Cal./g	Joules/g		Cal/g/°C	Joules/g/°C	Cal/g	Joules/g
0	1.00738	4.2177	0.0245	0.1026	50	.99854	4.1807	50.0079	209.3729
1	1.00652	4.2141	1.0314	4.3184	51	.99862	4.1810	51.0065	213.5538
2	1.00571	4.2107	2.0376	8.5308	52	.99871	4.1814	52.0051	217.7350
3	1.00499	4.2077	3.0429	12.7400	53	.99878	4.1817	53.0039	221.9166
4	1.00430	4.2048	4.0475	16.9462	54	.99885	4.1820	54.0027	226.0984
5	1.00368	4.2022	5.0515	21.1498	55	.99895	4.1824	55.0016	230.2806
6	1.00313	4.1999	6.0549	25.3508	56	.99905	4.1828	56.0006	234.4632
7	1.00260	4.1977	7.0578	29.5496	57	.99914	4.1832	56.9997	238.6462
8	1.00213	4.1957	8.0602	33.7463	58	.99924	4.1836	57.9989	242.8296
9	1.00170	4.1939	9.0621	37.9410	59	.99933	4.1840	58.9982	247.0134
10	1.00129	4.1922	10.0636	42.1341	60	.99943	4.1844	59.9975	251.1976
11	1.00093	4.1907	11.0647	46.3255	61	.99955	4.1849	60.9970	255.3822
12	1.00060	4.1893	12.0654	50.5155	62	.99964	4.1853	61.9966	259.5673
13	1.00029	4.1880	13.0659	54.7041	63	.99976	4.1858	62.9963	263.7529
14	1.00002	4.1869	14.0660	58.8916	64	.99988	4.1863	63.9962	267.9390
15	.99976	4.1858	15.0659	63.0779	65	1.00000	4.1868	64.9961	272.1256
16	.99955	4.1849	16.0655	67.2632	66	1.00014	4.1874	65.9962	276.3127
17	.99933	4.1840	17.0650	71.4476	67	1.00026	4.1879	66.9964	280.5003
18	.99914	4.1832	18.0642	75.6312	68	1.00041	4.1885	67.9967	284.6885
19	.99897	4.1825	19.0633	79.8141	69	1.00053	4.1890	68.9972	288.8772
20	.99883	4.1819	20.0622	83.9963	70	1.00067	4.1896	69.9977	293.0665
21	.99869	4.1813	21.0609	88.1778	71	1.00081	4.1902	70.9985	297.2564
22	.99857	4.1808	22.0596	92.3589	72	1.00096	4.1908	71.9994	301.4469
23	.99847	4.1804	23.0581	96.5395	73	1.00112	4.1915	73.0004	305.6381
24	.99838	4.1800	24.0565	100.7196	74	1.00127	4.1921	74.0016	309.8299
25	.99828	4.1796	25.0548	104.8994	75	1.00143	4.1928	75.0030	314.0224
26	.99821	4.1793	26.0530	109.0788	76	1.00160	4.1935	76.0045	318.2155
27	.99814	4.1790	27.0512	113.2580	77	1.00177	4.1942	77.0062	322.4094
28	.99809	4.1788	28.0493	117.4369	78	1.00194	4.1949	78.0080	326.6039
29	.99804	4.1786	29.0474	121.6157	79	1.00213	4.1957	79.0101	330.7992
30	.99802	4.1785	30.0455	125.7943	80	1.00229	4.1964	80.0123	334.9952
31	.99799	4.1784	31.0435	129.9727	81	1.00248	4.1972	81.0147	339.1920
32	.99797	4.1783	32.0414	134.1510	82	1.00268	4.1980	82.0172	343.3897
33	.99797	4.1783	33.0394	138.3293	83	1.00287	4.1988	83.0200	347.5881
34	.99795	4.1782	34.0374	142.5076	84	1.00308	4.1997	84.0230	351.7873
35	.99795	4.1782	35.0353	146.6858	85	1.00327	4.2005	85.0262	355.9874
36	.99797	4.1783	36.0333	150.8641	86	1.00349	4.2014	86.0295	360.1883
37	.99797	4.1783	37.0312	155.0423	87	1.00370	4.2023	87.0331	364.3902
38	.99799	4.1784	38.0292	159.2207	88	1.00392	4.2032	88.0369	368.5929
39	.99802	4.1785	39.0272	163.3991	89	1.00416	4.2042	89.0410	372.7966
40	.99804	4.1786	40.0253	167.5777	90	1.00437	4.2051	90.0452	377.0012
41	.99807	4.1787	41.0233	171.7563	91	1.00461	4.2061	91.0497	381.2068
42	.99811	4.1789	42.0214	175.9351	92	1.00485	4.2071	92.0545	385.4135
43	.99816	4.1791	43.0195	180.1141	93	1.00509	4.2081	93.0594	389.6211
44	.99819	4.1792	44.0177	184.2933	94	1.00535	4.2092	94.0647	393.8297
45	.99826	4.1795	45.0159	188.4726	95	1.00561	4.2103	95.0701	398.0395
46	.99830	4.1797	46.0142	192.6522	96	1.00588	4.2114	96.0759	402.2503
47	.99835	4.1799	47.0125	196.8320	97	1.00614	4.2125	97.0819	406.4622
48	.99842	4.1802	48.0109	201.0120	98	1.00640	4.2136	98.0882	410.6753
49	.99847	4.1804	49.0094	205.1923	99	1.00669	4.2148	99.0947	414.8895
					100	1.00697	4.2160	100.1015	419.1049

SPECIFIC HEAT OF WATER (Continued)

Enthalpy of Air-saturated Water
1 Atmosphere Pressure 0–100°C

Temp. °C	Enthalpy Cal/g	Enthalpy Joules/g	Temp. °C	Enthalpy Cal/g	Enthalpy Joules/g
0	0	0	75	74.9907	313.9712
5	5.0276	21.0496	80	80.0019	334.9519
10	10.0402	42.0363	85	85.0180	355.9532
15	15.0431	62.9826	90	90.0395	376.9773
20	20.0400	83.9034	95	95.0671	398.0270
25	25.0332	104.8089	100	100.1016	419.1053
30	30.0244	125.7063			
35	35.0149	146.6003			
40	40.0055	167.4949			
45	44.9968	188.3928			
50	49.9896	209.2964			
55	54.9842	230.2077			
60	59.9811	251.1289			
65	64.9808	272.0619			
70	69.9839	293.0087			

Specific Heat of Water Above 100°C

Mean specific heat of water in 15°C calories between 0°C and the temperature stated.

Heat content (Enthalpy) in joules per gram between 0°C and the temperature stated.

From data by Osborne, Stimson and Fiock, B of S Jour. Res. 5, 411, 1930.

Temp. °C	Specific heat mean 0–t°C	Heat content 0–t joules/g	Temp. °C	Specific heat mean 0–t°C	Heat content 0–t joules/g
100	1.0008	418.75	190	1.0153	807.15
110	1.0015	460.97	200	1.0181	852.02
120	1.0025	503.36	210	1.0212	897.35
130	1.0037	545.93	220	1.0247	943.24
140	1.0050	588.71	230	1.0285	989.75
150	1.0067	631.75	240	1.0326	1036.97
160	1.0083	675.06	250	1.0376	1084.97
170	1.0103	718.66	260	1.0423	1133.87
180	1.0127	762.72	270	1.0483	1184.32

Specific Heat of Ice—Cal./g/°C

Temp. °C	Specific heat	Observer	Temp. °C.	Specific heat	Observer
−252 to −188	.146	Dieterici, 1903	−31.8	.4454	Dickinson-Osborne, 1915
−250	.0361		−23.7	.4599	Dickinson-Osborne, 1915
−200	.162	Mean	−24.5	.4605	Dickinson-Osborne, 1915
−188 to −78	.285	Dieterici, 1903	−20.8	.4668	Dickinson-Osborne, 1915
−180	.199	Nernst, 1910	−14.8	.4782	Dickinson-Osborne, 1915
−160	.230	Nernst, 1910	−14.6	.4779	Dickinson-Osborne, 1915
−150	.246		−11.0	.4861	Dickinson-Osborne, 1915
−140	.262	Nernst, 1910	− 8.1	.4896	Dickinson-Osborne, 1915
−100	.329	Mean	− 4.3	.4989	Dickinson-Osborne, 1915
− 78 to −18	.463	Dieterici, 1903	− 4.5	.4984	Dickinson-Osborne, 1915
− 60	.392		− 4.9	.4932	Dickinson-Osborne, 1915
− 38.3	.4346	Dickinson-Osborne, 1915	− 2.6	.5003	Dickinson-Osborne, 1915
− 34.3	.4411	Dickinson-Osborne, 1915	− 2.2	.5018	Dickinson-Osborne, 1915
− 30.6	.4488	Dickinson-Osborne, 1915			

Water Below 0°C

− 6	1.0119	Martinetti, 1890	− 3	1.0102	Martinetti, 1890
− 5	1.0155	Barnes, 1902	− 2	1.0097	Martinetti, 1890
− 5	1.0113	Martinetti, 1890	− 1	1.0092	Martinetti, 1890
− 4	1.0105	Martinetti, 1890			

Specific Heat of Super-heated Steam

Specific heat of steam under constant pressure given in atmospheres and at temperatures above saturation in Cal./g/°C

Temp. °C	Pressure in atmospheres 1	2	4	6	8	10	12
110	0.481						
120	0.477	0.498					
130	0.475	0.494					
140	0.473	0.489					
150	0.472	0.486	0.519				
160	0.471	0.483	0.512	0.549			
170	0.470	0.481	0.507	0.538			
180	0.469	0.479	0.502	0.528	0.561	0.602	
190	0.469	0.478	0.498	0.522	0.549	0.583	0.625
200	0.469	0.478	0.495	0.515	0.539	0.567	0.601
210	0.470	0.477	0.493	0.510	0.531	0.555	0.584
220	0.470	0.477	0.491	0.506	0.524	0.545	0.569
230	0.471	0.477	0.489	0.504	0.519	0.537	0.557
240	0.472	0.477	0.488	0.501	0.515	0.530	0.548
250	0.473	0.477	0.488	0.499	0.512	0.525	0.540
260	0.474	0.478	0.487	0.498	0.509	0.521	0.534
270	0.474	0.478	0.487	0.497	0.507	0.518	0.529
280	0.475	0.479	0.487	0.496	0.505	0.515	0.525
290	0.476	0.480	0.487	0.495	0.504	0.513	0.523
300	0.477	0.481	0.488	0.495	0.503	0.511	0.519
310	0.478	0.482	0.488	0.495	0.502	0.510	0.518
320	0.480	0.483	0.489	0.496	0.502	0.509	0.516
330	0.482	0.484	0.490	0.496	0.502	0.508	0.515
340	0.483	0.485	0.491	0.496	0.502	0.507	0.513
350	0.484	0.486	0.492	0.497	0.502	0.507	0.512
360	0.485	0.487	0.492	0.497	0.502	0.507	0.511
370	0.486	0.488	0.493	0.498	0.503	0.507	0.511
380	0.488	0.490	0.494	0.498	0.503	0.507	0.511
390	0.489	0.491	0.495	0.499	0.503		
400	0.490	0.492	0.496	0.500	0.504		
410	0.492	0.494	0.497	0.501	0.505		
420	0.494	0.496	0.498	0.502	0.506		
430	0.495	0.497	0.500	0.504	0.507		
440	0.497	0.499	0.501	0.505	0.508		
450	0.498	0.500	0.503	0.506	0.509		
460	0.500	0.501	0.505	0.507	0.510		
470	0.502	0.503	0.506	0.508	0.512		
480	0.504	0.505	0.507	0.509	0.513		
490	0.505	0.506	0.509	0.511	0.514		
500	0.506	0.508	0.510	0.512	0.515		

HEAT CAPACITY OF MERCURY

The specific heat of solid mercury is given in relation to water at 15°C The values are from Carpenter and Stoodley, Phil. Mag. 10, 249, 1930. Heat capacity is given in calories per gram and in calories per gram atom (1 cal = 4.1840 absolute joules and the atomic weight of mercury 200.61). Values for the liquid and vapor are from Douglas, Ball and Ginnings, Jour of Res. Bureau of Standards 46, 334, 1951.

Temp. °C	Specific heat	Heat capacity cal/g-atom	Temp. °C	Heat capacity cal/g	Heat capacity cal/g-atom
	Solid	Solid		Liquid	Liquid
−75.6	.0319	6.3995	200	.032426	6.5050
−72.9	.0324	6.4998	220	.032386	6.4970
−65.4	.0324	6.4998	240	.032356	6.4910
−59.5	.0324	6.4998	260	.032336	6.4869
−44.9	.0336	6.7405	280	.032325	6.4847
−42.2	.0336	6.7405	300	.032322	6.4843
−40.0	.0337	6.7606	320	.032330	6.4858
Temp. °C	Heat capacity cal/g	Heat capacity cal/g-atom	340	.032346	6.4890
			356.58	.032366	6.4930
	Liquid	Liquid	360	.032371	6.4940
−38.88	.033080	6.7676	380	.032404	6.5005
−20	.033534	6.7272	400	.032445	6.5087
0	.033382	6.6967	420	.032494	6.5186
20	.033240	6.6683	440	.032550	6.5298
25	.033206	6.6615	460	.032614	6.5426
40	.033109	6.6419	480	.032684	6.5567
60	.032987	6.6176	500	.032762	6.5723
80	.032877	6.5954		Vapor	Vapor
100	.032776	6.5752	0	.02476	4.968
120	.032686	6.5571	100	.02476	4.968
140	.032606	6.5410	200	.02477	4.969
160	.032535	6.5270	300	.02480	4.975
180	.032476	6.5150	400	.02489	4.993
			500	.02507	5.030

HEAT CAPACITY (C_p) OF ORGANIC LIQUIDS AND VAPORS AT 25C

The values in this table are expressed as cal/(g mole) ($^\circ$K) at 1 atm pressure. Calories, g $\times$ 4.184 = joules.

Robert Shaw

Reproduced from *Chemical and Engineering Data*, *14*, 461 (1969) with permission of the copyright owner, the American Chemical Society.

	$C_p(l)$	$C_p(g)$		$C_p(l)$	$C_p(g)$
Alkanes			Diethyl ether	41.1	25.8
2-Methyl butane	39.4	28.5	Acetone	30.2	18.0
n-Hexane	46.6	34.2	Formic acid	23.6	10.8
2-Methyl pentane	46.2	34.5	Acetic acid	29.4	16.0
3-Methyl pentane	45.6	34.2	Ethyl acetate	40.6	
2,3-Dimethyl butane	45.0	33.6	Benzyl alcohol	52.1	
2,2-Dimethyl butane	45.0	33.9	Diphenyl ether	64.2	
n-Heptane	53.7	39.7	Furan	27.4	
2-Methyl hexane	53.1		**Nitrogen-Containing**		
3-Ethyl pentane	52.5		Hydrogen cyanide	16.9	8.6
2,2-Dimethyl pentane	52.8		Hydrazine	22.2	12.2
2,3-Dimethyl pentane	51.8		Unsym. dimethyl hydrazine	39.2	
2,4-Dimethyl pentane	53.5		Trimethyl hydrazine	44.5	
3,3-Dimethyl pentane	51.4		Aniline	46.2	26.1
2,2,3-Trimethyl butane	51.0	39.3	Quinoline	47.6	
n-Octane	60.7	45.1	Acrylonitrile	26.5	14.9
2,2,4-Trimethyl pentane	56.5		Perfluoro piperidene	71.0	
2,2,3,3-Tetramethyl butane	55.9	46.0	Methyl nitrate	37.5	
n-Nonane	68.0	50.6	Tetrahydropyrole	37.4	
n-Decane	75.2	56.1	Nitromethane	25.4	13.8
2-Methyl nonane	75.6		**Ring Compounds**		
n-Undecane	82.5	61.5	Cyclopentane	30.4	19.8
n-Dodecane	89.7	67.0	Methyl cyclopentane	38.0	26.2
n-Tridecane	97.2	72.5	Ethyl cyclopentane	44.5	31.5
n-Tetradecane	104.8	77.9	1,1-Dimethyl cyclopentane	44.6	31.9
n-Pentadecane	112.2	83.4	*cis*-1,2-Dimethyl cyclopentane	45.1	32.1
n-Hexadecane	119.9	88.9	*trans*-1,2-Dimethyl cyclopentane	45.1	32.1
Olefins			*trans*-1,3-Dimethyl cyclopentane	45.1	32.1
Pentene-1	37.1	26.2	Cyclopentane	29.4	18.0
cis-Pentene-2	36.3	24.3	Cyclohexane	36.4	25.4
trans-Pentene-2	37.6	25.9	Methyl cyclohexane	44.2	32.3
2-Methyl butene-1	37.5	26.7	Ethyl cyclohexane	50.0	38.0
3-Methyl butene-1	37.3	28.4	1,2-Dimethyl cyclohexane	50.4	37.4
2-Methyl butene-2	36.4	25.1	*cis*-1,3-Dimethyl cyclohexane	50.0	37.6
Hexene-1	43.8	31.6	*trans*-1,3-Dimethyl cyclohexane	50.8	37.6
2,3-Dimethyl butene-2	41.7	30.5	*cis*-1,4-Dimethyl cyclohexane	50.5	37.6
Heptene-1	50.5	37.1	*trans*-1,4-Dimethyl cyclohexane	50.3	37.7
Octene-1	57.7	42.6	Cyclohexane	35.6	25.1
Decene-1	71.8	53.5	Cyclooctatetraene	44	
Undecene-1	78.9	59.0			
Dodecene-1	86.2	64.4	Tetralin $C_6H_4(CH_2)_4$	52	
Hexadecene-1	115.9	86.3	*cis*-Decalin	55.4	
Butadiene-1,3	29.5	19.0	*trans*-Decalin	54.5	
Pentadiene-1,4	34.8	25.1	**Halogen-Containing**		
2-Methyl butadiene-1,3	36.7	25.0	Chloroform	27.6	15.7
Butyne-2	29.4	18.6	Carbon tetrachloride	31.7	19.9
Aromatics			1,2-Dibromoethane	32.2	18.2
Benzene	32.4	19.5	1,1,1-Trichloro ethane	34.4	22.4
Toluene	37.3	24.8	1,1-Dichloro ethylene	26.6	16.1
Ethyl benzene	44.5	30.7	Fluoro benzene	35.1	22.7
p-Xylene	43.6	30.3	Chloro benzene	34.9	23.6
1,2,3-Trimethyl benzene	51.8	36.9	Bromo benzene	37.1	24.2
1,2,4-Trimethyl benzene	51.6	37.1	**Sulfur-Containing**		
1,3,5-Trimethyl benzene	50.1	35.9	Carbon disulfide [d]	18.2	10.9
Oxygen-Containing			Dimethyl sulfide	28.3	17.8
Methanol	19.5	10.5	Methylethyl sulfide	34.6	22.8
Ethanol	27.0	15.7	Methyl *n*-propyl sulfide	41.0	28.2
Propanol-1	34.3	20.9	Methyl *n*-butyl sulfide	48.0	33.8
Propanol-2	37.1	21.3	Diethyl sulfide	40.9	28.1
2-Methyl propanol-2	53.2	27.2	Ethyl *n*-propyl sulfide	47.4	33.4
estimated alternative	42.2		Di-*n*-propyl sulfide	54.0	38.7

Sulfur-Containing (Continued)	$C_p(l)$	$C_p(g)$		$C_p(l)$	$C_p(g)$
Di-*n*-butyl sulfide	68.0	49.7			
Methyl isopropyl sulfide	41.2	28.8	Diethyl disulfide	48.7	33.9
Ethyl mercaptan	28.2	17.4	(CH$_2$)$_3$S	27.1	16.7
N-butyl mercaptan	41.3	28.4			
Iso-butyl mercaptan	41.1	28.4	(CH$_2$)$_4$S	33.5	21.9
Amyl mercaptan	48.2	33.9			
Iso-propyl mercaptan	34.7	23.1	(CH$_2$)$_5$S	39.0	26.0
Sec-butyl mercaptan	40.9	28.6	Phenyl mercaptan	39.1	25.2
Cyclo-pentyl mercaptan	39.5	25.9	*Silicon-Containing*		
Tert-butyl mercaptan	41.8	29.0	Tetramethylsilane	49.8	33.5
Dimethyl disulfide	34.9	22.6	Hexamethyldisiloxane	74.4	

HEAT CAPACITY (C_p) OF ORGANIC GASES AT 300 and 800 K

These data are a portion of those contained in "Additivity Rules for the Estimation of Thermochemical Properties", authored by S. W. Benson, F. R. Cruickshank, D. M. Golden, G. R. Haugen, H. E. O'Neal, A. S. Rodgers, R. Shaw and R. Walsh in *Chemical Reviews*, *69*, 279 (1969). These data are reproduced here with permission of the copyright owner, the American Chemical Society.

	C_p			C_p	
	300 K	800 K		300 K	800 K
Alkanes			1,2,4-Trimethylbenzene	36.99	76.93
Ethane	12.65	25.83	1,3,5-Trimethylbenzene	36.10	76.84
Propane	17.66	37.08	1,2,3,4-Tetramethylbenzene	45.50	89.42
n-Butane	23.40	48.23	1,2,3,5-Tetramethylbenzene	44.57	88.79
n-Hexane	34.37	70.36	1,2,4,5-Tetramethylbenzene	44.77	88.41
n-Octane	43.35	92.50	Pentamethylbenzene	51.99	101.29
n-Decane	(56.34)	(114.63)	Hexamethylbenzene	59.73	113.51
n-Dodecane	(67.33)	(136.76)	**Unsaturated Benzenes**		
2-Methylpropane	23.25	48.49	Styrene	29.35	61.40
2-Methylbutane	28.54	59.71	S-Methylstyrene	(34.9)	(71.8)
2,2-Dimethylpropane	29.21	60.78	*cis*-β-Methylstyrene	(34.9)	(71.8)
2,3-Dimethylbutane	33.76	70.7	*trans*-β-Methylstyrene	(35.1)	(72.2)
2,2,3-Trimethylbutane	39.54	82.73	*o*-Methylstyrene	(34.9)	(71.8)
2,2,3,3-Tetramethylbutane	46.29	96.18	*m*-Methylstyrene	(34.9)	(71.8)
Alkenes			*p*-Methylstyrene	(34.9)	(71.8)
Ethene	10.45	20.20	Ethynylbenzene	27.63	55.79
Propene	15.34	30.68			
But-1-ene	20.57	41.80	**Polyaromatics**		
cis-But-2-ene	18.96	40.87	Biphenyl	39.05	86.92
trans-But-2-ene	21.08	41.50			
2-Methylpropene	21.39	41.86	**Nonaromatic Rings: Ring Corrections**		
Pent-1-ene	26.31	52.95	Cyclopropane	13.44	31.44
cis-Pent-2-ene	(24.45)	(52.29)	Cyclobutane	17.37	42.42
trans-Pent-2-ene	(26.04)	(52.45)	Cyclobutene	16.03	32.26
2-Methylbut-1-ene	26.41	53.15	Cyclopentane	19.98	52.44
3-Methylbut-1-ene	(28.47)	(53.85)	Cyclopentene	18.08	45.78
2-Methylbut-2-ene	25.22	52.05	Methylcyclopentane	26.43	63.8
Allenic Dienes			1-Methylcyclopentene	(24.3)	(57.0)
Allene	14.16	25.42	1,1-Dimethylcyclopentane	(32.16)	(76.18)
1,2-Butadiene	19.23	36.01	*cis*-1,2-Dimethylcyclopentane	(32.34)	74.98
1,2-Pentadiene	(25.3)	(47.7)	*trans*-1,2-Dimethylcyclopentane	(32.44)	(75.84)
2,3-Pentadiene	(24.3)	(46.6)	*cis*-1,3-Dimethylcyclopentane	32.72	75.68
3-Methyl-1,2-butadiene	(25.3)	(47.2)	*trans*-1,3-Dimethylcyclopentane	(32.72)	(75.68)
Nonallenic Dienes			Cyclohexane	25.58	66.76
1,3-Butadiene	19.11	36.84	Cyclohexene	25.28	59.49
cis-1,3-Pentadiene	(22.7)	(47.0)	Methylcyclohexane	32.51	78.74
trans-1,3-Pentadiene	(24.9)	(47.7)	Ethylcyclohexane	38.23	90.1
1,4-Pentadiene	(25.2)	(47.6)	1,1-Dimethylcyclohexane	(37.2)	(90.7)
2-Methyl-1,3-butadiene (isoprene)	(25.2)	(48.0)	*cis*-1,2-Dimethylcyclohexane	(37.7)	(90.1)
Alkynes			*trans*-1,2-Dimethylcyclohexane	(38.3)	(90.5)
Ethyne	10.53	14.93	*cis*-1,3-Dimethylcyclohexane	(37.9)	(90.5)
Propyne	14.55	25.14	*trans*-1,3-Dimethylcyclohexane	(37.9)	(89.8)
But-1-yne	19.54	35.95	*cis*-1,4-Dimethylcyclohexane	(37.9)	(89.8)
But-2-yne	18.70	35.14	*trans*-1,4-Dimethylcyclohexane	(38.0)	(90.6)
Pent-1-yne	(25.65)	(47.1)	Spiropentane	21.19	47.91
Pent-2-yne	(23.69)	(45.9)			
Aromatics			**Alcohols and Phenols**		
Benzene	19.65	45.06	Methanol, CH_3OH	10.5	19.0
Toluene	24.94	56.61	Ethanol, C_2H_5OH	15.7	30.3
Ethylbenzene	30.88	67.15	1-Propanol, C_3H_7OH	20.9	41.0
1,2-Dimethylbenzene	32.10	66.50	2-Propanol $(CH_3)_2CHOH$	21.3	42.1
1,3-Dimethylbenzene	30.66	66.41	2-Butanol $(CH_3CH_2)(CH_3)CHOH$	27.2	52.7
1,4-Dimethylbenzene	30.49	66.14	2-Methyl-2-propanol,		
n-Propylbenzene	(36.99)	(78.30)	$(CH_3)_3COH$	27.2	53.3
n-Butylbenzene	(42.09)	(89.37)	Phenol, C_6H_5OH	24.8	50.7
1-Propylbenzene	(36.47)	(78.6)	*o*-Cresol, $CH_3C_6H_4OH$	31.2	61.6
1-Methyl-2-ethylbenzene	(37.94)	(78.1)	*m*-Cresol, $CH_3C_6H_4OH$	29.8	61.3
1-Methyl-3-ethylbenzene	(36.59)	(77.8)	*p*-Cresol, $CH_3C_6H_4OH$	29.8	61.1
1-Methyl-4-ethylbenzene	(36.42)	(77.6)			
1,2,3-Trimethylbenzene	37.82	77.56	**Ethers**		
			Dimethyl ether, CH_3OCH_3	15.8	30.4

	C_p			C_p	
	300 K	800 K		300 K	800 K
Peroxides and Hydroperoxides			$HONO_2$	12.80	20.33
Hydrogen peroxide, HOOH	10.3	14.3	CH_2NO_2	13.76	25.56
			N_2	6.96	7.51
Cyclics			NO	7.13	7.83
Ethylene oxide	11.5	24.6	NO_2	8.85	11.88
Propylene oxide	17.4	35.7	NO_3 sym	11.26	17.51
Trimethylene oxide	14.3	35.1	N_2O	9.25	12.49
Aldehydes and Ketones			N_2O_3	15.72	21.39
Acetaldehyde, CH_3CHO	13.2	24.2	N_2O_4	18.52	27.11
Propionaldehyde, C_2H_5CHO	18.8	35.2	N_2O_5	23.09	32.74
Acetone, CH_3COCH_3	18.0	34.9	$CH_2{=}CHNO_2$	17.43	31.7
Methyl ethyl ketone,					
$\quad CH_3CH_2COCH_3$	24.7	46.1	**Haloalkanes**		
Acids, Esters, and Anhydrides			CF_3CCl_3	28.1	39.6
Formic acid, HCOOH	10.8	18.3	CF_2ClCF_2Cl	28.9	...
Acetic acid, CH_3COOH	16.0	29.1	CF_3CF_3	25.5	38.3
			CCl_3CCl_3	32.7	41.3
Aliphatic and Aromatic Amines			CBr_3CBr_3	33.4	39.9
CH_3NH_2	11.91	22.43	$CF_3CHClBr$	25.1	37.2
$(CH_3)_2NH$	16.58	33.94	CF_3CHCl_2	24.4	37.3
$(CH_3)_3N$	22.05	45.62	CF_3CH_2Cl	21.4	34.8
$C_6H_5NH_2$	26.07	53.79	CF_3CH_2Br	21.8	35.1
			CF_3CH_2I	21.9	35.1
Cyanides			CF_3CH_2F	20.9	34.5
C_2H_5CN	17.30	32.7	CF_3CH_3	18.9	...
C_6H_5CN	26.2	52.1	$CHCl_2CH_2Cl$	21.3	33.3
$c\text{-}C_3H_5CN$	18.95	37.68	CH_3CCl_3	22.4	33.3
$CH_2{=}CHCN$	15.30	26.43	CH_3CHF_2	16.1	...
$trans\text{-}CH_3CH{=}CHCN$	19.71	36.97	CH_3CHCl_2	18.2	30.9
$C_2(CN)_2$	20.58	27.26	CH_3CH_2F	14.1	...
			CH_3CH_2Cl	15.1	28.3
Nitrites			CH_3CH_2Br	15.5	28.6
CH_3ONO	15.36	26.27	$CF_2ClCF_2CF_2Cl$	37.4	...
			$CF_3CF_2CH_3$	28.8	...
Hydrazines, Azo Compounds, and Tetrazines			$CH_3CH_2CH_2Cl$	20.3	39.2
N_2H_4	12.19	21.08	$CH_3CHClCH_3$	21.3	...
CH_3NHNH_2	17.1	31.3	$CH_3CH_2CH_2Br$	20.7	39.4
$NH{=}NH$	8.75	13.55	$(CH_3)_3CCl$	27.9	...
			$CH_2ICH_{22}I$	19.2	
Amides			CH_3CHICH_2I	(24.1)	
$HCONH_2$	11.10	21.12			
CH_3CONH_2	15.63	32.60	**Haloalkenes, Alkynes, and Arenes**		
			$CFCl{=}CCl_2$	21.8	28.8
Heterocyclic N-Atom-Containing Ring Compounds in the Ideal Gas State			$CF_2{=}CClBr$	21.8	28.5
Pyrrole	17.16	...	$CFCl{=}CFCl$	21.0	28.4
Pyridine	18.80	...	$CF_2{=}CBr_2$	22.2	...
Picolines, α	24.05	...	$CF_2{=}CFCl$	20.0	28.0
$\quad \beta$	23.94	...	$CF_2{=}CFBr$	20.5	28.1
			$CF_2{=}CF_2$	19.3	27.6
Unique Groups			$CCl_2{=}CCl_2$	22.7	29.2
NH_3	8.53	12.23	$CBr_2{=}CBr_2$	24.5	29.7
HCN	8.61	11.45	$CHF{=}CCl$	18.3	26.5
CH_3CN	12.55	21.32	$CF_2{=}CHBr$	17.6	26.2
$(CN)_2$	13.59	17.42	$CF_2{=}CHF$	16.5	25.6
$CH_2(CN)_2$	17.38	27.72	$CHCl{=}CCl_2$	19.3	26.9
HNC	9.33	11.49	$CHBr{=}CBr_2$	20.5	...
CH_3NC	12.83	21.34	$CH_2{=}CFCl$	15.3	24.4
HN_3	10.46	15.10	$CH_2{=}CCl_2$	16.1	24.7
CH_2N_2	12.58	18.73	$CHCl{=}CHCl$ (av)	15.8	24.6
$CH_2\!\!\begin{array}{c}N\\|\\N\end{array}$	10.23	18.35	$CHBr{=}CHBr$ cis	16.5	...
			$CH_2{=}CHCl$	12.9	22.4
			$CH_2{=}CHBr$	13.4	22.5
HCNO	10.57	15.19	$CH_2{=}CHI$	13.9	22.7
HNO	8.29	10.77	$CH_3C{\equiv}CCl$	17.2	27.0
			$CH_3C{\equiv}CBr$	17.6	27.1

	C_p				C_p	
	300 K	800 K			300 K	800 K
Haloalkenes, Alkynes, and Arenes (Continued)				[thiirane ring (S)]	12.90	25.61
$CH_3C{\equiv}CI$	17.8	27.2				
C_6H_5F	22.7	47.6		[thietane ring (S)]	16.66	36.40
$o\text{-}C_6H_4F_2$	25.6	49.5				
$m\text{-}C_6H_4F_2$	25.5	49.7				
$p\text{-}C_6H_4F_2$	25.7	49.7		[tetrahydrothiophene ring (S)]	21.85	47.66
$p\text{-}FC_6H_4CH_3$	27.9	58.6				
$C_6H_5CF_3$	31.4	62.8				
C_6H_5Cl	23.6	47.9		[thiane ring (S)]	26.03	64.00
C_6H_5Br	24.0	48.0				
C_6H_5I	24.2	48.0				
Organosulfur Compounds				[thiophene ring (S)]	17.52	36.01
CH_3SH	12.05	20.32				
CH_3CH_2SH	17.44	31.83				
$CH_3(CH_2)_2SH$	22.75	43.60		[2-methylthiophene ring (S, CH_3)]	22.92	46.43
$CH_3(CH_2)_3SH$	28.37	55.68				
$CH_3(CH_2)_4SH$	33.91	66.78				
$((CH_3)_2CH)SH$	23.04	43.26		[3-methylthiophene ring (S, CH_3)]	22.80	45.95
$(CH_3)_2CHCH_2SH$	28.41	53.77				
$(CH_3)(CH_3CH_2)CHSH$	28.64	54.29				
$(CH_3)_3CSH$	29.04	55.53		*Compounds Containing Unique Groups*		
$(CH_3)_2(CH_3CH_2)CSH$	34.46	66.28		SOF	9.97	12.79
				$SOCl_2$	15.94	18.88
				$SOCl$	10.88	13.03
[cyclopentyl]SH	25.94	58.61		S_2F_2	15.33	18.94
				SF_2	10.44	13.14
				SF	7.57	8.68
[cyclohexyl]SH	32.13	75.19		S_2Cl_2	17.44	19.46
				SCl_2	12.19	13.61
				SCl	8.20	8.95
[cyclohexenyl]SH	25.22	51.59		$CSCl_2$	15.34	18.78
				NSF_3	17.23	23.56
				BO_2	10.08	13.45
$(CH_3)_2S$	17.77	31.59		H_3SiBr	12.69	20.02
$CH_3CH_2S_3CH$	22.82	42.93		H_3SiI	12.86	
$CH_3S(CH_2)_2CH_3$	28.17	54.45		H_2SiBr_2	15.68	21.73
$(CH_3)_2CHSCH_3$	28.82	54.89		$SiBr_4$	23.21	25.39
$CH_3S(CH_2)_3CH_3$	33.79	66.53		$ClSiBr_3$	22.78	25.31
$CH_3SC(CH_3)_3$	34.66	66.74		Cl_2SiBr_2	22.39	25.23
$CH_3CH_2SCH_2CH_3$	28.09	54.91		Cl_3SiBr	21.72	25.13
$CH_3CH_2SCH_2CH_2CH_3$	33.40	66.68		$ISiBr_3$	23.39	25.42
$CH_3(CH_2)_2S(CH_2)_2CH_3$	38.71	78.45		$Si(CH_3)_4$	33.52	60.55
$(CH_3)_2CHSCH(CH_3)_2$	40.65	77.12		$(CH_3)_3SiCl$	31.36	52.15
$CH_3(CH_2)_3S(CH_2)_3CH_3$	49.70	100.58		$(CH_3)_2SiCl_2$	26.17	42.54
CH_3SSCH_3	22.61	37.66		$(CH_3)_3SiF$	29.42	51.30
$CH_3CH_2SSCH_2CH_3$	33.91	60.19		$(CH_3)_2SiF_2$	25.26	42.16
$CH_3(CH_2)_2SS(CH_2)_2CH_3$	44.50	83.70		CH_3SiF_3	22.73	
$CH_3(SO)CH_3$	21.26	37.02		$[(CH_3)_3Si]_2O$	57.22	99.95
$CH_3(SO_2)CH_3$	23.9			$(CH_3)_3SiH$	28.36	50.50
NH_2CSNH_2	17.72	29.06		$(CH_3)_2SiH_2$	22.03	39.79
CH_3NCS	15.70	25.87				
S_8	37.25	42.62				

SPECIFIC HEAT OF THE ELEMENTS AT 25°C

$$C_p = cal\ g^{-1}\ {}^{\circ}K^{-1}$$

Element	Kelly: Bureau of Mines Bulletin 592 (1961)	Hultgren: Selected values of Thermodynamic properties of Metals and Alloys (1963)	N.B.S. Circular #500 Part 1 (1952)
Aluminum	0.215	0.215	0.2154
Antimony	0.049	0.0495	0.0501
Argon	0.124	......	0.124
Arsenic	0.0785	......	0.0796
Barium	0.046	0.0362	0.0458
Beryllium	0.436	0.436	0.4733
Bismuth	0.0296	0.0238	0.0292
Boron	0.245	......	0.2463
Bromine (Br₂)	0.113	0.0537	
Cadmium	0.0555	0.0552	0.0554
Calcium	0.156	0.155	0.1566
Carbon (Diamond)	0.124	......	0.120
" (Graphite)	0.170	......	0.172
Cerium	0.049	0.0459	0.0442
Cesium	0.057	0.0575	0.0558
Chlorine (Cl₂)	0.114	......	0.114
Chromium	......	0.107	0.1073
Cobalt	0.109	0.107	0.1037
Columbium	See Niobium		
Copper	0.092	0.0924	0.0920
Dysprosium	0.0414	0.0414	
Erbium	0.0401	0.0401	
Europium	0.0421	0.0326	
Fluorine (F₂)	0.197	0.197	
Gadolinium	0.055	0.056	
Gallium	0.089	0.088	0.0911
Germanium	0.077		
Gold	0.0308	0.0308	0.0305
Hafnium	0.035	0.028	0.0344
Helium	1.24	......	1.242
Holmium	0.0393	0.0394	
Hydrogen (H₂)	3.41	......	3.42
Indium	0.056	0.0556	0.0570
Iodine (I₂)	0.102	......	0.034
Iridium	0.0317	0.0312	0.0305
Iron (α)	0.106	0.1075	0.1078
Krypton	0.059	......	0.059
Lanthanum	0.047	0.0479	0.0475
Lead	0.038	0.0305	0.0308
Lithium	0.85	0.834	0.814
Lutetium	0.037	0.0285	
Magnesium	0.243	0.245	0.235
Manganese (α)	0.114	0.114	0.1147
" (β)	0.119	......	0.1120
Mercury	0.0331	0.0333	0.0331
Molybdenum	0.0599	0.0597	0.0584
Neodymium	0.049	0.0458	0.0499
Neon	0.246	......	0.246
Nickel	0.106	0.1061	0.1057
Niobium	0.064	0.0633	
Nitrogen (N₂)	0.249	......	0.249
Osmium	0.03127	0.0310	0.0310
Oxygen (O₂)	0.219	0.219	
Palladium	0.0584	0.0583	0.0590

Element	Kelly: Bureau of Mines Bulletin 592 (1961)	Hultgren: Selected values of Thermodynamic properties of Metals and Alloys (1963)	N.B.S. Circular #500 Part 1 (1952)
Phosphorus, white	0.181	......	0.178
" red, triclinic	0.160		
Platinum	0.0317	0.0317	0.0325
Polonium	0.030		
Potassium	0.180	0.180	0.1787
Praseodymium	0.046	(0.0467)	0.0482
Promethium	0.0442		
Protactinium	0.029		
Radium	0.0288		
Radon	0.0224	......	0.0224
Rhenium	0.0329	0.0330	0.0327
Rhodium	0.0583	0.0580	0.0592
Rubidium	0.0861	0.0860	0.0850
Ruthenium	0.057	0.0569	
Samarium	0.043	0.0469	
Scandium	0.133	0.1173	
Selenium (Se₂)	0.0767	......	0.0535
Silicon	0.168	......	0.169
Silver	0.0566	0.0562	0.0564
Sodium	0.293	0.292	0.2952
Strontium	0.0719	0.0719	0.0684
Sulfur, yellow	0.175	......	0.177
Tantalum	0.0334	0.0334	0.0335
Technetium	0.058		
Tellurium	0.0481	......	0.482
Terbium	0.0437	0.0435	
Thallium	0.0307	0.0307	0.0310
Thorium	0.0271	0.0281	0.0331
Thulium	0.0382		
Tin (α)	0.0510	0.0519	0.0518
Tin (β)	0.0530	0.0543	0.0530
Titanium	0.125	0.1248	0.1231
Tungsten	0.0317	0.0322	0.0324
Uranium	0.0276	0.0278	0.0276
Vanadium	0.116	0.116	0.1147
Xenon	0.0378	......	0.0379
Ytterbium	0.0346	0.0287	
Yttrium	0.068	0.0713	
Zinc	0.0928	0.0922	0.0916
Zirconium	0.0671	0.0660	

SPECIFIC HEAT AND ENTHALPY OF SOME SOLIDS AT LOW TEMPERATURES

R. J. Corruccini and J. J. Gniewek

For a more extensive listing of data one is referred to N.B.S. Monograph 21 (1960)

Joules/gm × 453.6 = joules/lb × 0.239 = cal/gm × 0.4299 = Btu/lb

METALS

T	Aluminum C_p	Aluminum $H - H_0$	Beryllium C_p	Beryllium $H - H_0$	Bismuth C_p	Bismuth $H - H_0$	Cadmium C_p	Cadmium $H - H_0$
°K	$jg^{-1} deg^{-1} K$	jg^{-1}	$jg^{-1} deg^{-1} K$	jg^{-1}	$jg^{-1} deg^{-1} K$	jg^{-1}	$jg^{-1} deg^{-1} K$	jg^{-1}
1	0.000 10[a]	....						
1	.000 051	0.000 025	0.000 025	0.000 013	0.000 00598	0.000 00158	0.000 008	0.000 003
2	.000 108	.000 105	.000 051	.000 051	.000 0461	.000 0233	.000 033	.000 022
3	.000 176	.000 246	.000 079	.000 116	.000 170	.000 123	.000 090	.000 082
4	.000 261	.000 463	.000 109	.000 209	.000 493	.000 432	.000 21	.000 22
6	.000 50	.001 21	.000 180	.000 496	.002 14	.002 88	.001 30	.001 5
8	.000 88	.002 6	.000 271	.000 944	.005 47	.010 2	.004 3	.007 0
10	.001 4	.004 9	.000 389	.001 60	.010 4	.025 9	.008 0	.019
15	.004 0	.018	.000 842	.004 57	.023 8	.111	.025	.102
20	.008 9	.048	.001 61	.010 5	.036 3	.262	.046	.28
25	.017 5	.112	.002 79	.021 2	.047 7	.472	.066	.56
30	.031 5	.232	.004 50	.039 2	.057 2	.734	.086	.94
35	.051 5	.436	....	....				
40	.077 5	.755	.009 96	.109	.072 7	1.38	.117	1.96
50	.142	1.85	.019 2	.253	.084 6	2.17	.141	3.26
60	.214	3.64	.034 1	.523	.093 5	3.06	.159	4.76
70	.287	6.15	.056 2	.971	.100	4.03	.172	6.43
80	.357	9.37	.090 6	1.69	.105	5.05	.182	8.20
90	.422	13.25	.139	2.82	.108	6.12	.190	10.1
100	.481	17.76	.100	4.51	.111	7.21	.196	12.0

T	Chromium C_v	Chromium $H - H_0$	Copper C_p	Copper $H - H_0$	Germanium[b] C_p	Germanium[b] $H - H_0$	Gold C_p	Gold $H - H_0$
°K	$jg^{-1} deg^{-1} K$	jg^{-1}	$jg^{-1} deg^{-1} K$	jg^{-1}	$g^{-1} deg^{-1} K$	jg^{-1}	$jg^{-1} deg^{-1} K$	jg^{-1}
1	0.000 0285	0.000 0142	0.000 012	0.000 006	0.000 000 528	0.000 000 132	0.000 006	0.000 002
2	.000 058	.000 0573	.000 028	.000 025	.000 004 23	.000 002 11	.000 025	.000 016
3	.000 089	.000 131	.000 053	.000 064	.000 014 4	.000 010 7	.000 070	.000 061
4	.000 121	.000 237	.000 091	.000 13	.000 034 4	.000 034 3	.000 16	.000 17
6	.000 206	.000 567	.000 23	.000 44	.000 125	.000 179	.000 50	.000 78
8	.000 312	.001 07	.000 47	.001 12	.000 335	.000 612	.001 2	.002 4
10	.000 451	.001 82	.000 86	.002 4	.000 813	.001 69	.002 2	.005 6
15	.001 02	.005 28	.002 7	.010 7	.004 45	.013 6	.007 4	.028
20	.002 10	.012 8	.007 7	.034	.012 5	.054 0	.015 9	.086
25	.003 92	.027 4	.016	.090	.024 0	.145	.026 3	.191
30	.006 83	.053 2	.027	.195	.036 6	.296	.037 1	.349
40	.017 1	.163	.060	.61	.061 7	.786	.057 2	.821
50	.035 8	.421	.099	1.40	.085 8	1.52	.072 6	1.47
60	.062 1	.904	.137	2.58	.108	2.50	.084 2	2.25
70	.093	1.68	.173	4.13	.131	3.70	.092 8	3.14
80	.127	2.77	.205	6.02	.153	5.12	.099 2	4.10
90	.161	4.21	.232	8.22	.173	6.74	.104 3	5.12
100	.193	5.98	.254	10.6	.191	8.55	.108 3	6.18

T	Indium C_p	Indium $H - H_0$	α-Iron[c] C_p	α-Iron[c] $H - H_0$	γ-Iron[d] C_p	γ-Iron[d] $H - H_0$	Lead C_p	Lead $H - H_0$
°K	$jg^{-1} deg^{-1} K$	jg^{-1}	$jg^{-1} deg^{-1} K$	jg^{-1}	$jg^{-1} deg^{-1} K$	jg^{-1}	$jg^{-1} deg^{-1} K$	jg^{-1}
1	0.000 029	0.000 011	0.000 090	0.000 045	....	....	0.000 026	0.000 010
1	[a].000 019	[a].000 006	....	....	....	....	[a].000 012	[a].000 003
2	.000 138	.000 085	.000 183	.000 181	....	....	.000 12	.000 07
2	[a].000 141	[a].000 073	....	....	....	....	[a].000 09	[a].000 05
								.000 28
3	.000 410	.000 341	.000 279	.000 412	....	....	.000 33	[a].000 23
3	[a].000 464	[a].000 357	....	....	....	....	[a].000 31	
e3.40	.000 584	.000 537	....	....	....	....	....	....
3.40	[a].000 669	[a].000 581	....	....	....	....	....	....
4	.000 95	.000 99	.000 382	.000 742	....	....	.000 7	.000 8
4	....	....	....	....	....	....	[a].000 7	[a].000 7
5	....	....	....	....	....	....	.001 5	.001 8
5	....	....	....	....	....	....	[a].001 5	[a].001 8
6	.003 59	.005 20	.000 615	.001 73	....	....	.002 9	.003 9
6	....	....	....	....	....	....	[a].003 0	[a].004 0
7	....	....	....	....	....	....	.004 8	.008
7	....	....	....	....	....	....	[a].005 0	[a].008
8	.008 55	.017 0	.000 90	.003 29	....	....	.007 3	.014
10	.015 8	.040 8	.001 31	.005 87	....	....	.013 7	.034
15	.036 7	.170	.002 49	.014 5	....	....	.033 5	.150
20	.060 8	.413	.004 5	.031 6	0.007	0	.053 1	.368
25	.085 7	.778	.007 5	.061	....	....	.068 1	.672
30	.108	1.265	.012 4	.110	.016	.11	.079 6	1.042
40	.141	2.52	.029	.31	.041	.39	.094 4	1.920
50	.162	4.04	.055	.73	.090	1.0₂	.103	2.91
60	.176	5.73	.087	1.43	.13₇	2.1₆	.108	3.97
70	.186	7.53	.121	2.46	.18₀	3.7₅	.112	5.07
80	.193	9.42	.154	3.84	.21₈	5.7₄	.114	6.20
90	.198	11.38	.180	5.55	.25₅	8.1₁	.116	7.35
100	.203	13.39	.216	7.56	.28₅	10.₈	.118	8.53

T	Molybdenum C_p	Molybdenum $H - H_0$	Nickel C_p	Nickel $H - H_0$	Palladium C_p	Palladium $H - H_0$
°K	$jg^{-1} deg^{-1} K$	jg^{-1}	$jg^{-1} deg^{-1} K$	jg^{-1}	$jg^{-1} deg^{-1} K$	jg^{-1}
1	0.000 0229	0.000 0105	0.000 120	0.000 060	0.000 099	0.000 0493
2	.000 0472	.000 0445	.000 242	.000 241	.000 203	.000 200
3	.000 0745	.000 105	.000 369	.000 546	.000 318	.000 459
4	.000 106	.000 194	.000 503	.000 98	.000 447	.000 840
6	.000 191	.000 484	.000 82	.002 28	.000 891	.002 31
8	.000 317	.000 981	.001 19	.004 28	.001 41	.004 60
10	.000 498	.001 78	.001 62	.007 1	.002 10	.008 07
15	.001 31	.006 10	.003 1	.018 5	.004 71	.024 5
20	.002 87	.016 1	.005 8	.041	.009 22	.058 6
25	.005 77	.037 4	.010 1	.079	.016 0	.120
30	.009 60	.072 9	.016 7	.145	.025 8	.223
40	.023 6	.232	.038 1	.413	.050 7	.600
50	.041 0	.554	.068 2	.937	.077 7	1.24
60	.061 9	1.07	.103	1.79	.101	2.14
70	.083 8	1.80	.139	3.00	.122	3.26
80	.104	2.74	.173	4.56	.139	4.56
90	.123	3.88	.204	6.45	.154	6.03
100	.139	5.20	.232	8.63	.167	7.63

T	Platinum C_p	Platinum $H - H_0$	Rhodium C_p	Rhodium $H - H_0$	Silicon[1] C_p	Silicon[1] $H - H_0$	Silver C_p	Silver $H - H_0$
°K	$jg^{-1} deg^{-1} K$	jg^{-1}	$jg^{-1} deg^{-1} K$	jg^{-1}	$jg^{-1} deg^{-1} K$	jg^{-1}	$jg^{-1} deg^{-1} K$	jg^{-1}
1	0.000 035	0.000 0175	0.000 048	0.000 024	0.000 000 263	0.000 000 0658	0.000 0072	0.000 0032
2	.000 074	.000 097	.000 096	.000 096	.000 002 10	.000 001 05	.000 0239	.000 0176
3	.000 122	.000 168	.000 147	.000 218	.000 007 09	.000 005 32	.000 0595	.000 0574
4	.000 186	.000 320	.000 201	.000 392	.000 016 8	.000 016 8	.000 124	.000 146
6	.000 37	.000 85	.000 32	.000 91	.000 059 6	.000 085 3	.000 39	.000 62
8	.000 67	.001 88	.000 47	.001 70	.000 140	.000 279	.000 91	.001 87
10	.001 12	.003 65	.000 65	.002 81	.000 275	.000 679	.001 8	.004 52
15	.003 3	.013 5	.001 35	.007 65	.001 09	.003 74	.006 4	.023 3
20	.007 4	.039 5	.002 71	.017 4	.003 37	.013 8	.015 5	.076
25	.013 7	.092	.005 61	.037 3	.008 49	.042 3	.028 7	.185
30	.021 2	.182	.010 6	.077 1	.017 1	.105	.044 2	.368
40	.038	.48	.026 6	.256	.044 0	.400	.078	.979
50	.055	.95	.048 9	.633	.078 5	1.00	.108	1.91
60	.068	1.56	.072 4	1.238	.115	1.97	.133	3.12
70	.079	2.29	.094	2.07	.152	3.31	.151	4.54
80	.088	3.12	.114	3.11	.188	5.01	.166	6.13
90	.094	4.02	.132	4.34	.224	7.06	.177	7.85
100	.100	5.01	.147	5.74	.259	9.47	.187	9.67

T	Sodium[m] C_p	Sodium[m] $H - H_0$	Tantalum C_p	Tantalum $H - H_0$	Tin (white) C_p	Tin (white) $H - H_0$	Titanium C_p	Titanium $H - H_0$
°K	$jg^{-1} deg^{-1} K$	jg^{-1}	$jg^{-1} deg^{-1} K$	jg^{-1}	$jg^{-1} deg^{-1} K$	jg^{-1}	$jg^{-1} deg^{-1} K$	jg^{-1}
1	0.000 081	0.000 035	0.000 032	0.000 016	0.000 0170	0.000 0079	0.000 071	0.000 035
1			[a].000 0063	[a].000 0021	[a].000 0041	[a].000 0009		
2	.000 289	.000 204	.000 068	.000 065	.000 047	.000 0383	.000 146	.000 143
2			[a].000 054	[a].000 026	[a].000 048	[a].000 0228		
3	.000 76	.000 70	.000 112	.000 155	.000 109	.000 113	.000 226	.000 329
3			[a].000 178	[a].000 138	[a].000 151	[a].000 116		
[n]3.72					.000 198	.000 221		
3.72					[a].000 285	[a].000 270		
4	.001 60	.001 84	.000 171	.000 295	.000 245	.000 283	.000 317	.000 599
4			[a].000 352	[a].000 400				
[o]4.39			.000 201	.000 368				
4.39			[a].000 433	[a].000 553				
5	.002 98	.004 08			.000 54	.000 65		
6	.005 1	.008 1	.000 333	.000 776	.001 27	.001 51	.000 54	.001 45
8	.012 2	.024 7	.000 648	.001 73	.004 2	.006 8	.000 84	.002 81
10	.023 8	.060 2	.001 17	.003 52	.008 1	.019 0	.001 26	.004 89
12	.039 7	.123						
14	.063	.225						
15			.003 60	.014 5	.022 6	.093	.003 3	.015 6
16	.093	.380						
18	.124	.597						
20	.155	.875	.008 23	.043 2	.040	.251	.007 0	.040
25	.259	1.90	.015 3	.102	.058	.498	.013 4	.090
30	.364	3.45	.024 0	.202	.076	.834	.024 5	.182
40	.544	8.03	.043 0	.540	.106	1.75	.057 1	.581
50	.695	14.2	.060 4	1.06	.130	2.93	.099 2	1.358
60	.793	21.7	.075 4	1.74	.148	4.33	.146 7	2.592
70	.86	30.0	.087 9	2.56	.162	5.88	.189	4.27
80	.91	38.9	.097 6	3.49	.173	7.55	.230	6.37
90	.95	48.2	.105	4.50	.182	9.33	.267	8.86
100	.98	57.9	.111	5.58	.189	11.18	.300	11.69

Metals (*Continued*)

T	Tungsten		Zinc	
	C_p	$H - H_0$	C_p	$H - H_0$
°K	$jg^{-1} deg^{-1} K$	jg^{-1}	$jg^{-1} deg^{-1} K$	jg^{-1}
1	0.000 0074	0.000 0037	0.000 011	0.000 005
2	.000 0158	.000 0152	.000 028	.000 023
3	.000 0262	.000 0360	.000 058	.000 065
4	.000 0393	.000 0685	.000 11	.000 14
6	.000 0783	.000 182	.000 29	.000 53
8	.000 141	.000 396	.000 96	.001 6
10	.000 234	.000 765	.002 5	.005 0
15	.000 725	.002 97	.011	.034
20	.001 89	.009 27	.026	.125
25	.004 21	.023 7	.049	.31
30	.007 83	.053 4	.076	.62
40	.018 4	.181	.125	1.62
50	.033 2	.436	.171	3.11
60	.048 3	.843	.208	5.01
70	.060 5	1.39	.236	7.23
80	.071 5	2.05	.258	9.70
90	.081 0	2.81	.277	12.38
100	.088 8	3.66	.293	15.24

a Superconducting.

b In germanium the electronic specific heat is markedly dependent on impurities. The values given are for pure germanium (negligible electronic specific heat).

c α-Iron is the form that is thermodynamically stable at low temperatures. It has the body-centered cubic lattice which is the basis of the ferritic steels.

d γ-Iron is stable between 910° and 1,400°C. It has the face-centered cubic structure which is the basis of the austenitic steels. Since pure γ-iron is not stable at low temperatures the above values were calculated by application of the Kopp-Neumann rule to experimental data on two austenitic Fe-Mn alloys and are of uncertain accuracy.

e Superconducting transition temperature.

i Superconducting transition temperature of mercury.

j Melting temperature of mercury.

l In silicon the electronic specific heat, γT, is markedly dependent on impurities. Values of the coefficient, γ, from zero to 2.4×10^{-6} jg^{-1} deg^{-2} K have been reported. The values in the above table are for pure silicon ($\gamma = 0$).

m It has been shown (Barrett 1956, Hull & Rosenberg 1959) that sodium partially transforms at low temperatures from the normal body-centered cubic structure to close-packed hexagonal. The transformation is of the martensitic type and is promoted by cold-working at the low temperatures. Inasmuch as none of the calorimetric measurements on sodium were accompanied by crystallographic analysis, the tabulated data below 100°K are to some degree ambiguous.

n Superconducting transition temperature of tin.

o Superconducting transition temperature of tantalum.

CONSTANTS OF DEBYE-SOMMERFELD EQUATION

$C_v = \gamma T + \alpha T^3$; $\alpha = 12\pi^4 R/5\theta_0^3$; $0 \lesssim T \lesssim T_{max}$; T_{max} = maximum temperature to which the equation can be used with the limiting value of θ.

Substance	$10^6 \gamma$	γ	$10^6 \alpha$	θ_0	T_{max}
	$jg^{-1} deg^{-2} K$	mjg-$atom^{-1} deg^{-2} K$	$jg^{-1} deg^{-4} K$	$deg K$	$deg K$
Metals:					
Aluminum.........	50.4	1.36	0.93	426	4
Beryllium.........	25	0.226	.138	1160	20
Bismuth.........	0.32	.067	5.66	118	2
Cadmium.........	5.6	.63	2.69	186	3
Chromium........	28.3	1.47	0.165	610	4
Copper.........	10.81	0.687	.746	344.5	10
Germanium.......	(a)	(a)	.528	370	2
Gold...........	3.75	0.74	2.19	165	15
Indium.........	15.8	1.81	13.1	109	2
α-Iron..........,	00	5.0	0.349	464	10
Lead...........	15.1	3.1	10.6	96	4
Magnesium.......	54	1.32	1.19	406	4
α-Manganese.....	251	13.8	0.328	476	12
Molybdenum.....	23	2.18	.238	440	4
Nickel..........	120	7.0	.39	440	4
Niobium.........	85	7.9	.64	320	1
Palladium........	98	10.5	.89	274	4
Platinum........	34.1	6.7	.72	240	3
Rhodium........	48	4.9	.173	478	4
Silicon.........	(a)	(a)	.263	640	4
Silver..........	5.65	0.610	1.58	225	4
Sodium[a]........	60	1.37	21.4	158	4
Tantalum........	31.5	5.7	0.69	250	4
Tin (white)......	14.7	1.75	2.21	195	2
Titanium........	71	3.4	0.54	420	10
Tungsten........	7	1.3	.16	405	4
Zinc...........	9.6	0.63	1.10	300	4
Alloys:					
Constantan[a]......	113	6.9	0.56	384	15
Monel[a].........	108	6.5	.62	374	20
Other Inorg. subs.:					
Diamond........	....	....	0.0152	2200	50
Ice............	....	....	15.2	192	10
Pyrex.........	....	....	3.14	......	5
Organic subs.:					
Glyptal.........	....	....	27	......	4
Lucite.........	....	....	35	......	4
Polystyrene......	....	....	63	......	4

(a) Superconducting.

BOILING POINT OF WATER
(Hydrogen Scale)

Pressure mm	.0	.1	.2	.3	.4	.5	.6	.7	.8	.9
700	97.714	718	722	725	729	733	737	741	745	749
701	753	757	761	765	769	773	777	781	785	789
702	792	796	800	804	808	812	816	820	824	828
703	832	836	840	844	847	851	855	859	863	867
704	871	875	879	883	887	891	895	899	902	906
705	97.910	914	918	922	926	930	934	938	942	946
706	949	953	957	961	965	969	973	977	981	985
707	989	993	996	*000	*004	*008	*012	*016	*020	*024
708	98.028	032	036	040	043	047	051	055	059	063
709	067	071	075	079	082	086	090	094	098	102
710	98.106	110	114	118	121	125	129	133	137	141
711	145	149	153	157	160	164	168	172	176	180
712	184	188	192	195	199	203	207	211	215	219
713	223	227	230	234	238	242	246	250	254	258
714	261	265	269	273	277	281	285	289	292	296
715	98.300	304	308	312	316	320	323	327	331	335
716	339	343	347	351	355	358	362	366	370	374
717	378	382	385	389	393	397	401	405	409	412
718	416	420	424	428	432	436	440	443	447	451
719	455	459	463	467	470	474	478	482	486	490
720	98.493	497	501	505	509	513	517	520	524	528
721	532	536	540	544	547	551	555	559	563	567
722	570	574	578	582	586	590	593	597	601	605
723	609	613	617	620	624	628	632	636	640	643
724	647	651	655	659	662	666	670	674	678	682
725	98.686	689	693	697	701	705	709	712	716	720
726	724	728	732	735	739	743	747	751	755	758
727	762	766	770	774	777	781	785	789	793	797
728	800	804	808	812	816	819	823	827	831	835
729	838	842	846	850	854	858	861	865	869	873
730	98.877	880	884	888	892	896	899	903	907	911
731	915	918	922	926	930	934	937	941	945	949
732	953	956	960	964	968	972	975	979	983	987
733	991	994	998	*002	*006	*010	*013	*017	*021	*025
734	99.029	032	036	040	044	048	051	055	059	063
735	99.067	070	074	078	082	085	089	093	097	101
736	104	108	112	116	119	123	127	131	135	138
737	142	146	150	153	157	161	165	169	172	176
738	180	184	187	191	195	199	203	206	210	214
739	218	221	225	229	233	236	240	244	248	252
740	99.255	259	263	267	270	274	278	282	285	289
741	293	297	300	304	308	312	316	319	323	327
742	331	334	338	342	346	349	353	357	361	364
743	368	372	376	379	383	387	391	394	398	402
744	406	409	413	417	421	424	428	432	436	439
745	99.443	447	451	454	458	462	466	469	473	477
746	481	484	488	492	495	499	503	507	510	514
747	518	522	525	529	533	537	540	544	548	551
748	555	559	563	566	570	574	578	581	585	589
749	592	596	600	604	607	611	615	619	622	626

Pressure mm	.0	.1	.2	.3	.4	.5	.6	.7	.8	.9
750	99.630	633	637	641	645	648	652	656	659	663
751	667	671	674	678	682	686	689	693	697	700
752	704	708	712	715	719	723	726	730	734	738
753	741	745	749	752	756	760	764	767	771	775
754	778	782	786	790	793	797	801	804	808	812
755	99.815	819	823	827	830	834	838	841	845	849
756	852	856	860	863	867	871	875	878	882	886
757	889	893	897	900	904	908	911	915	919	923
758	926	930	934	937	941	945	948	952	956	959
759	963	967	970	974	978	982	985	989	993	996
760	100.000	004	007	011	015	018	022	026	029	033
761	037	040	044	048	052	055	059	063	066	070
762	074	077	081	085	088	092	096	099	103	107
763	110	114	118	121	125	129	132	136	140	143
764	147	151	154	158	162	165	169	173	176	180
765	100.184	187	191	195	198	202	206	209	213	216
766	220	224	227	231	235	238	242	246	249	253
767	257	260	264	268	271	275	279	283	286	290
768	293	297	300	304	308	311	315	319	322	326
769	330	333	337	341	344	348	352	355	359	363
770	100.366	370	373	377	381	384	388	392	395	399
771	403	406	410	414	417	421	424	428	432	435
772	439	442	446	450	453	457	461	464	468	472
773	475	479	483	486	490	493	497	501	504	508
774	511	515	519	522	526	530	533	537	540	544
775	100.548	551	555	559	562	566	569	573	577	580
776	584	588	591	595	598	602	606	609	613	616
777	620	624	627	631	634	638	642	645	649	653
778	656	660	663	667	671	674	678	681	685	689
779	692	696	699	703	707	710	714	718	721	725
780	100.728	732	735	739	743	746	750	753	757	761
781	764	768	772	775	779	782	786	789	793	797
782	800	804	807	811	815	818	822	825	829	833
783	836	840	843	847	851	854	858	861	865	869
784	872	876	879	883	886	890	894	897	901	904
785	100.908	912	915	919	922	926	929	933	937	940
786	944	947	951	954	958	962	965	969	972	976
787	979	983	987	990	994	997	*001	*005	*008	*012
788	101.015	019	022	026	029	033	037	040	044	047
789	051	054	058	062	065	069	072	076	079	083
790	101.087	090	094	097	101	104	108	112	115	119
791	122	126	129	133	136	140	144	147	151	154
792	158	161	165	168	172	176	179	183	186	190
793	193	197	200	204	207	211	215	218	222	225
794	229	232	236	239	243	246	250	254	257	261
795	101.264	268	271	275	278	282	286	289	293	296
796	300	303	307	310	314	317	321	324	328	332
797	335	339	342	346	349	353	356	360	363	367
798	370	374	377	381	385	388	392	395	399	402
799	406	409	413	416	420	423	427	430	434	437
800	101.441	....	....	....	....	....	....	....	....	....

For lower pressures see under Vapor Tension of Water

MELTING POINTS OF MIXTURES OF METALS
(Smithsonian Physical Tables)
Melting-points, °C.

Metals		Percentage of metal in second column.									
		0%	10%	20%	30%	40%	50%	60%	70%	80%	90%	100%
Pb.	Sn.	*326	295	276	262	240	220	190	185	200	216	232
	Bi.	322	290	...	...	179	145	126	168	205	...	268
	Te.	322	710	790	880	917	760	600	480	410	425	446
	Ag.	328	460	545	590	620	650	705	775	840	905	959
	Na.	...	360	420	400	370	330	290	250	200	130	96
	Cu.	326	870	920	925	945	950	955	985	1005	1020	1084
	Sb.	326	250	275	330	395	440	490	525	560	600	632
Al.	Sb.	650	750	840	925	945	950	970	1000	1040	1010	632
	Cu.	650	630	600	560	540	580	610	755	930	1055	1084
	Au.	655	675	740	800	855	915	970	1025	1055	675	1062
	Ag.	650	625	615	600	590	580	575	570	650	750	954
	Zn.	654	640	620	600	580	560	530	510	475	425	419
	Fe.	653	860	1015	1110	1145	1145	1220	1315	1425	1500	1515
	Sn.	650	645	635	625	620	605	590	570	560	540	232
Sb.	Bi.	632	610	590	575	555	540	520	470	405	330	268
	Ag.	630	595	570	545	520	500	505	545	680	850	959
	Sn.	622	600	570	525	480	430	395	350	310	255	232
	Zn.	632	555	510	540	570	565	540	540	525	510	419

Metals		Percentage of metal in second column.									
		0%	10%	20%	30%	40%	50%	60%	70%	80%	90%	100%
Ni.	Sn.	*1455	1380	1290	1200	1235	1290	1305	1230	1060	800	232
Na.	Bi.	96	425	520	590	645	690	720	730	715	570	268
	Cd.	96	125	185	245	285	325	330	340	360	390	322
Cd.	Ag.	322	420	520	610	700	760	805	850	895	940	954
	Tl.	321	300	285	270	262	258	245	230	210	235	302
	Zn.	322	280	270	295	313	327	340	355	370	390	419
Au.	Cu.	1063	910	890	895	905	925	975	1000	1025	1060	1084
	Ag.	1064	1062	1061	1058	1054	1049	1039	1025	1006	982	963
	Pt.	1075	1125	1190	1250	1320	1380	1455	1530	1610	1685	1775
K.	Na.	62	17.5	−10	−3.5	5	11	26	41	58	77	97.5
	Hg.	...	...	...	...	...	90	110	135	162	265	...
	Tl.	62.5	133	165	188	205	215	220	240	280	305	301
Cu.	Ni.	1080	1180	1240	1290	1320	1355	1380	1410	1430	1440	1455
	Ag.	1082	1035	990	945	910	870	830	788	814	875	960
	Sn.	1084	1005	890	755	725	680	630	580	530	440	232
	Zn.	1084	1040	995	930	900	880	820	780	700	580	419
Ag.	Zn.	959	850	755	705	690	660	630	610	570	505	419
	Sn.	959	870	750	630	550	495	450	420	375	300	232
Na.	Hg.	96.5	90	80	70	60	45	22	55	95	215	...

* The data in this table are compiled from various sources,— hence variations in the melting point of the metals as shown in this column.

The triple point of water, 0.01°C (273.16°K) is the thermodynamic point for temperature measurements.

COMMERCIAL METALS AND ALLOYS

Miscellaneous Properties

Properties (Typical Only)

Common name and classification	Thermal conductivity, Btu/hr ft °F	Thermal conductivity, Kcal/sec m °C	Specific gravity	Coeff. of linear expansion, μ in./in. °F	Electrical resistivity, microhm-cm	Modulus of elasticity, millions of psi	Approximate melting point, °F	Approximate melting point, °C
Ingot iron (included for comparison)	42.	0.32	7.86	6.8	9.	30	2800	1538
Plain carbon steel AISI–SAE 1020	30.	0.23	7.86	6.7	10.	30	2760	1515
Stainless steel type 304	10.	0.08	8.02	9.6	72.	28	2600	1427
Cast gray iron ASTM A48–48. Class 25	26.	0.20	7.2	6.7	67.	13	2150	1177
Malleable iron ASTM A47	—		7.32	6.6	30.	25	2250	1232
Ductile cast iron ASTM A339, A395	19	0.14	7.2	7.5	60.	25	2100	1149
Ni-resist cast iron, type 2	23	0.17	7.3	9.6	170.	15.6	2250	1232
Cast 28-7 alloy (IID) ASTM A297–63T	1.5	0.01	7.6	9.2	41.	27	2700	1482
Hastelloy C	5	0.04	3.94	6.3	139.	30	2350	1288
Inconel X, annealed	9	0.07	8.25	6.7	122.	31	2550	1399
Haynes Stellite alloy 25 (L605)	5.5	0.04	9.15	7.61	88.	34	2500	1371
Aluminum alloy 3003, rolled ASTM B221	90	0.68	2.73	12.9	4.	10	1200	649
Aluminum alloy 2017, annealed ASTM B221	95	0.72	2.8	12.7	4.	10.5	1185	641
Aluminum alloy 380 ASTM SC84B	56	0.42	2.7	11.6	7.5	10.3	1050	566
Copper ASTM B152, B124, B133, B1, B2, B3	225	1.70	8.91	9.3	1.7	17	1980	1082
Yellow brass (high brass) ASTM B36, B134, B135	69	0.52	8.47	10.5	7.	15	1710	932
Aluminum bronze ASTM B169, alloy A; ASTM B124, B150	41	0.31	7.8	9.2	12.	17	1900	1038

COMMERCIAL METALS AND ALLOYS (*Continued*)

Common name and classification	Btu/hr ft°F	Kcal/sec m °C	Specific gravity	Coeff. of linear expansion, μ in./in. °F	Electrical resistivity, microhm-cm	Modulus of elasticity, millions of psi	Approximate melting point, °F	°C
Beryllium copper 25 ASTM B194	7	0.05	8.25	9.3	–	19	1700	927
Nickel silver 18% alloy A (wrought) ASTM B122, No. 2	19	0.14	8.8	9.0	29.	18	2030	1110
Cupronickel 30%	17	0.13	8.95	8.5	35.	22	2240	1227
Red brass (cast) ASTM B30, No. 4A	42	0.32	8.7	10.	11.	13	1825	996
Chemical lead	20	0.15	11.35	16.4	21.	2	621	327
Antimonial lead (hard lead)	17	0.13	10.9	15.1	23.	3	554	290
Solder 50–50	26	0.20	8.89	13.1	15.	–	420	216
Magnesium alloy AZ31B	45	0.34	1.77	14.5	9.	6.5	1160	627
K Monel	11	0.08	8.47	7.4	58.	26	2430	1332
Nickel ASTM B160, B161, B162	35	0.26	8.89	6.6	10.	30	2625	1441
Cupronickel 55–45 (Constantan)	13	0.10	8.9	8.1	49.	24	2300	1260
Commercial titanium	10	0.08	5.	4.9	80.	16.5	3300	1816
Zinc ASTM B69	62	0.47	7.14	18	6.	–	785	418
Zirconium, commercial	10	0.08	6.5	2.9	41.	12	3350	1843

THERMAL PROPERTIES OF PURE METALS

From Handbook of Tables for Applied Engineering Science by R. E. Bolz and G. L. Tuve, The Chemical Rubber Co., 1970

	At Atmospheric Pressure							Liquid Metal		
	At 100°K			At 25°C (77°F)				Vapor pressure		
Metal	Latent heat of fusion, cal/g	Thermal conductivity, watts cm°C	Specific heat, cal/g°C	Specific heat, cal/g°C	Coeff. of linear expansion, ($\times 10^6$) ($°C)^{-1}$	Thermal conductivity, watts/cm°C*	Specific heat (liquid) at 2000°K cal/g°C	10^{-3} atm	10^{-6} atm	10^{-9} atm
								Boiling point temperatures, °K		
Aluminum	95	3.00	0.115	0.215	25	2.37	0.26	1,782	1,333	1,063
Antimony	38.5	—	0.040	0.050	9	0.185	0.062	1,007	741	612
Beryllium	324	—	0.049	0.436	12	2.18	0.78	1,793	1,347	1,085
Bismuth	12.4	—	0.026	0.030	13	0.084	0.036	1,155	851	677
Cadmium	13.2	1.03	0.047	0.055	30	0.93	0.063	655	486	388
Chromium	79	1.58	0.046	0.110	6	0.91	0.224	1,992	1,530	1,247
Cobalt	66	—	0.057	0.10	12	0.69	0.164	2,167	1,652	1,345
Copper	49	4.83	0.061	0.092	16.6	3.98	0.118	1,862	1,391	1,120
Gold	15	3.45	0.026	0.031	14.2	3.15	0.0355	2,023	1,510	1,211
Iridium	33	—	0.022	0.031	6	1.47	0.0434	3,253	2,515	2,062
Iron	65	1.32	0.052	0.108	12	0.803	0.197	2,093	1,594	1,297
Lead	5.5	0.396	0.028	0.031	29	0.346	0.033	1,230	889	698
Magnesium	88.0	1.69	0.016	0.243	25	1.59	0.32	857	638	509
Manganese	64	—	0.064	0.114	22	—	0.20	1,495	1,131	913
Mercury	2.7	—	0.029	0.033	—	0.0839	—	393	287	227
Molybdenum	69	1.79	0.033	0.060	5	1.4	0.089	3,344	2,558	2,079
Nickel	71	1.58	0.055	0.106	13	0.899	0.175	2,156	1,646	1,343
Niobium (Columbium)	68	0.552	0.045	0.064	7	0.52	0.083	3,523	2,721	2,232
Osmium	34	—	—	0.031	5	0.61	0.039	—	—	—
Platinum	24	0.79	0.024	0.032	9	0.73	0.043	2,817	2,155	1,757
Plutonium	3	—	0.019	0.032	54	0.08	0.041	2,200	1,596	1,252
Potassium	14.5	—	0.150	0.180	83	0.99	—	606	430	335
Rhodium	50	—	—	0.058	8	1.50	0.092	—	—	—
Selenium	16	—	—	0.077	37	0.005	—	—	—	—
Silicon	430	—	0.062	0.17	3	0.835	0.217	2,340	1,749	1,427
Silver	26.5	4.50	0.045	0.057	19	4.27	0.068	1,582	1,179	952
Sodium	27	—	0.234	0.293	70	1.34	—	701	504	394
Tantalum	41	0.592	0.026	0.034	6.5	0.54	0.040	3,959	3,052	2,495
Thorium	17	—	0.024	0.03	12	0.41	0.047	3,251	2,407	1,919
Tin	14.1	0.85	0.039	0.054	20	0.64	0.058	1,857	1,366	1,080
Titanium	100	0.312	0.072	0.125	8.5	0.2	0.188	2,405	1,827	1,484
Tungsten	46	2.35	0.021	0.032	4.5	1.78	0.040	4,139	3,228	2,656
Uranium	12	—	0.022	0.028	13.4	0.25	0.048	2,861	2,128	1,699
Vanadium	98	—	0.061	0.116	8	0.60	0.207	2,525	1,948	1,591
Zinc	27	1.32	0.063	0.093	35	1.15	—	752	559	449

* (watts/cm°C) $\times$ 860.421 = Cal(gm)hr^{-1}cm^{-1}°C^{-1}
  (watts/cm°C) $\times$ 57.818 = Btu hr^{-1} ft^{-1} °F.

MELTING AND BOILING POINTS OF THE ELEMENTS

Element	Melting Point °C	Boiling Point °C	Element	Melting Point °C	Boiling Point °C
Actinium	1050	3200 ± 300	Manganese	1244 ± 3	1962
Aluminum	660.37	2467	Mendelevium	—	
Americium	994 ± 4	2607	Mercury	−38.87	356.58
Antimony	630.74	1750	Molybdenum	2617	4612
Argon	−189.2	−185.7	Neodymium	1021	3068
Arsenic (gray)	817 (28 atm.)	613 (sub.)	Neon	−248.67	−246.048
Astatine	302	337	Neptunium	640 ± 1	3902
Barium	725	1640	Nickel	1453	2732
Berkelium	—	—	Niobium	2468 ± 10	4742
Beryllium	1278 ± 5	2970 (5 mm)	Nitrogen	−209.86	−195.8
Bismuth	271.3	1560 ± 5	Nobelium	—	
Boron	2300	2550 (sub.)	Osmium	3045 ± 30	5027 ± 100
Bromine	−7.2	58.78	Oxygen	−218.4	−182.962
Cadmium	320.9	765	Ozone	−192.7 ± 2	−111.9
Calcium	839 ± 2	1484	Palladium	1552	3140
Californium	—	—	Phosphorus (white)	44.1	280
Carbon	~3550	4827	Platinum	1772	3827 ± 100
Cerium	799 ± 3	3426	Plutonium	641	3232
Cesium	28.40 ± 0.01	678.4	Polonium	254	962
Chlorine	−100.98	−34.6	Potassium	63.65	774
Chromium	1857 ± 20	2672	Praseodymium	931	3512
Cobalt	1495	2870	Promethium	~1080	2460 (?)
Columbium			Protactinium	<1600	
(See *Niobium*)			Radium	700	1140
Copper	1083.4 ± 0.2	2567	Radon	−71	−61.8
Curium	1340 ± 40	—	Rhenium	3180	5627 (est.)
Deuterium			Rhodium	1966 ± 3	3727 ± 100
(See *Hydrogen*)			Rubidium	38.89	688
Dysprosium	1412	2562	Ruthenium	2310	3900
Einsteinium	—	—	Samarium	1077 ± 5	1791
Element 104	—	—	Scandium	1541	2831
Element 105	—	—	Selenium (gray)	217	684.9 ± 1.0
Erbium	1529	2863	Silicon	1410	2355
Europium	822	1597	Silver	961.93	2212
Fermium	—		Sodium	97.81 ± 0.03	882.9
Fluorine	−219.62	−188.14	Strontium	769	1384
Francium	(27)	(677)	Sulfur (rhombic)	112.8	444.674
Gadolinium	1313 ± 1	3266	(monoclinic)	119.0	444.674
Gallium	29.78	2403	Tantalum	2996	5425 ± 100
Germanium	937.4	2830	Technetium	2172	4877
Gold (Aurum)	1064.43	2807	Tellurium	449.5 ± 0.3	989.8 ± 3.8
Hafnium	2227 ± 20	4602	Terbium	1356 ± 4	3123
Helium	−272.2 26 atm.	−268.934	Thallium	303.5	1457 ± 10
Holmium	1474	2695	Thorium	1750	~4790
Hydrogen	−259.14	−252.87	Thulium	1545	1947
Indium	156.61	2080	Tin	231.9681	2270
Iodine	113.5	184.35	Titanium	1660 ± 10	3287
Iridium	2410	4130	Tungsten	3410 ± 20	5660
Iron (ferrum)	1535	2750	Uranium	1132.3 ± 0.8	3818
Krypton	−156.6	−152.30 ± 0.10	Vanadium	1890 ± 10	3380
Lanthanum	921 ± 5	3457	Wolfram (See *Tungsten*)		
Lawrencium	—	—	Xenon	−111.9	−107.1 ± 3
Lead	327.502	1740	Ytterbium	819 ± 5	1194
Lithium	180.54	1347	Yttrium	1522 ± 8	3338
Lutetium	1663 ± 5	3395	Zinc	419.58	907
Magnesium	648.8 ± 0.5	1090	Zirconium	1852 ± 2	4377

BOILING POINTS AND TRIPLE POINTS OF SOME LOW BOILING ELEMENTS

Element	Boiling point °K	Triple point °K	λ point °K
He	4.216		2.174
p-H₂	20.27	13.81	
n-H₂	20.379	13.95	
N₂	77.35		
O₂	90.188	54.34	
A	87.45		

MOLECULAR ELEVATION OF THE BOILING POINT

(Most values from Hoyt, C.S. and Fink, C.K., Journal of Physical Chemistry, Vol. 41. No. 3., March, 1937.)

Molecular elevation of the boiling point showing the elevation of the boiling point in degrees C due to the addition of one gram molecular weight of the dissolved substance to 1000 grams of any one of the solvents below. The correction in the last column gives the number of degrees to be subtracted for each mm. of difference between the barometric reading and 760 mm.

Solvent	K_B	Barometric Correction per mm.
Acetic acid	3.07	0.0008
Acetone	1.71	0.0004
Aniline	3.52	0.0009
Benzene	2.53	0.0007
Bromobenzene	6.26	0.0016
Carbon bisulfide	2.34	0.0006
Carbon tetrachloride	5.03	0.0013
Chloroform	3.63	0.0009
Cyclohexane	2.79	0.0007
Ethanol (ethyl alcohol)	1.22	0.0003
Ethyl acetate	2.77	0.0007
Ethyl ether	2.02	0.0005
n-Hexane	2.75	0.0007
Methanol (methyl alcohol)	0.83	0.0002
Methyl acetate	2.15	0.0005
Nitrobenzene	5.24	0.0013
n-Octane	4.02	0.0010
Phenol	3.56	0.0009
Toluene	3.33	0.0008
Water	0.512	0.0001

MOLECULAR DEPRESSION OF THE FREEZING POINT

Showing the depression of the freezing point due to the addition of one gram molecular weight of dissolved substance, for various solvents.

Solvent	Depression for one gram molecular weight dissolved in 100 gms. °C
Acetic acid	39.0
Benzene	49.0
Benzophenone	98.0
Diphenyl	80.0
Diphenylamine	86.0
Ethylene dibromide	118.0
Formic acid	27.7
Naphthalene	68–69
Nitrobenzene	70.0
Phenol	74.0
Stearic acid	45.0
Triphenyl methane	124.5
Urethane	51.4
Water	18.5–18.7

CORRECTION OF BOILING POINTS TO STANDARD PRESSURE

By H. B. Hass and R. F. Newton

This correction may be made by using the equation:

$$\Delta t = \frac{(273.1 + t)(2.8808 - \log p)}{\phi + .15(2.8808 - \log p)} \tag{1}$$

where Δt = degrees C to be added to the observed boiling point.

t = the observed boiling point.

$\log p$ = the logarithm of the observed pressure in millimeters of mercury.

ϕ = the entropy of vaporization at 760 mm.

The value of ϕ may be estimated from the graph and the table. Substances not included in the table may be classified by grouping them with compounds which bear a close physical or structural resemblance to them.

Example 1. Benzene boils at 20°C. at 75 mm pressure. What is its normal boiling point? We do not find benzene in the table but we find hydrocarbons in group 2, and a group 2 compound with a boiling point of 20° has a ϕ of 4.6.

Substituting in the equation

$$\Delta t = \frac{(273.1 + 20)(2.8808 - 1.8751)}{4.60 + .15(2.8808 - 1.8751)} = 62°$$

Adding this to 20° gives 82° as a first approximation.

The graph shows that the ϕ for a compound of group 2 boiling at 82° is 4.72 instead of 4.60 which we originally used. Since ϕ is in the denominator, this increase will lower our Δt by the ratio, 4.60/4.72, or the corrected Δt is $62 \times 4.60/4.72 = 60.4$. Adding Δt to t, gives 80.4° as a second approximation.

The formula can best be used in a slightly different form when the reverse calculation is desired, i.e., when one calculates the vapor pressure at a given temperature, lower than the normal boiling point.

$$2.8808 - \log p = \frac{\phi \Delta t}{273.1 + t - .15\Delta t} \tag{2}$$

Example 2. Alcohol boils at 78.4°C. What is its vapor pressure at 20°C.? Substituting in equation 2:

$$2.8808 - \log p = \frac{6.06 \times 58.4}{293.1 - (.15 \times 58.4)} = 1.245$$

$$\log p = 2.8808 - 1.245 = 1.6358$$

$$p = 43.2 \text{ mm.}$$

Here no second approximation is necessary, since the correct value of ϕ was taken immediately, the normal boiling point having been known.

Compound	Group	Compound	Group
Acetaldehyde...............	3	Amines.....................	3
Acetic acid..................	4	n-Amyl alcohol.............	8
Acetic anhydride...........	6	Anthracene.................	1
Acetone....................	3	Anthraquinone.............	1
Acetophenone..............	4	Benzaldehyde..............	2

CORRECTION OF BOILING POINTS TO STANDARD PRESSURE(Continued)

Compound	Group	Compound	Group
Benzoic acid	5	Hydrogen cyanide	3
Benzonitrile	2	Isoamyl alcohol	7
Benzophenone	2	Isobutyl alcohol	8
Benzyl alcohol	5	Isobutyric acid	6
Butylethylene	1	Isocaproic acid	7
Butyric acid	7	Methane	1
Camphor	2	Methanol	7
Carbon monoxide	1	Methyl amine	5
Carbon oxysulfide	2	Methyl benzoate	3
Carbon suboxide	2	Methyl ether	3
Carbon sulfoselenide	2	Methyl ethyl ether	3
m.p. Chloroanilines	3	Methyl ethyl ketone	2
Chlorinated derivatives	Same group as though Cl were H	Methyl fluoride	3
		Methyl formate	4
o.m.p. Cresols	4	Methyl salicylate	2
Cyanogen	4	Methyl silicane	1
Cyanogen chloride	3	α, β Naphthols	3
Dibenzyl ketone	2	Nitrobenzene	3
Dimethyl amine	4	Nitromethane	3
Dimethyl oxalate	4	o.m.p. Nitrotoluenes	2
Dimethyl silicane	2	o.m.p. Nitrotoluidines	2
Esters	3	Phenanthrene	1
Ethanol	8	Phenol	5
Ethers	2	Phosgene	2
Ethylamine	4	Phthalic anhydride	2
Ethylene glycol	7	Propionic acid	5
Ethylene oxide	3	n-Propyl alcohol	8
Formic acid	3	Quinoline	2
Glycol diacetate	4	Sulfides	2
Halogen derivatives	Same group as though halogen were hydrogen.	Tetranitromethane	3
		Trichloroethylene	1
		Valeric acid	7
Heptylic acid	7	Water	6
Hydrocarbons	2		

BOILING POINT AT STANDARD PRESSURE

VAN DER WAALS' CONSTANTS FOR GASES

(Calculated from Amagat units in Landolt-Bornstein Physical Chemical Tables)

Van der Waals' equation is an equation of state for real gases. It may be written

$$\left(P + \frac{a}{V^2}\right)(V - b) = RT \text{ for one mole.} \qquad \text{or} \qquad \left(P + \frac{n^2a}{V^2}\right)(V - nb) = nRT \text{ for } n \text{ moles.}$$

The term a is a measure of the attractive force between the molecules. The term b is due to the finite volume of the molecules and to their general incompressibility. It is known that a and b vary to some extent with temperature.

The values for a and b in the following table are those to be used when the pressure is in atmospheres and the volume is in liters. Thus R in the above equation will be 0.08206 liter atmospheres per mole per degree. T is degrees Kelvin.

Name	Formula	a $\frac{(\text{liters})^2 \times \text{atm.}}{(\text{mole})^2}$	b $\frac{\text{liters}}{\text{mole}}$	Name	Formula	a $\frac{(\text{liters})^2 \times \text{atm.}}{(\text{mole})^2}$	b $\frac{\text{liters}}{\text{mole}}$
Acetic acid	CH_3CO_2H	17.59	0.1068	n-Hexane	C_6H_{14}	24.39	0.1735
Acetic anhydride	$(CH_3CO)_2O$	19.90	0.1263	Hydrogen	H_2	0.2444	0.02661
Acetone	$(CH_3)_2CO$	13.91	0.0994	Hydrogen bromide	HBr	4.451	0.04431
Acetonitrile	CH_3CN	17.58	0.1168	Hydrogen chloride	HCl	3.667	0.04081
Acetylene	C_2H_2	4.390	0.05136	Hydrogen selenide	H_2Se	5.268	0.04637
Ammonia	NH_3	4.170	0.03707	Hydrogen sulfide	H_2S	4.431	0.04287
Amyl formate	$HCO_2C_5H_{11}$	27.58	0.1730	Iodobenzene	C_6H_5I	33.08	0.1656
Amylene	C_5H_{10}	15.90	0.1207	Krypton	Kr	2.318	0.03978
Isoamylene	C_5H_{10}	18.08	0.1405	Mercury	Hg	8.093	0.01696
Aniline	$C_6H_5NH_2$	26.50	0.1369	Mesitylene	$(CH_3)_3C_6H_3$	34.32	0.1979
Argon	A	1.345	0.03219	Methane	CH_4	2.253	0.04278
Benzene	C_6H_6	18.00	0.1154	Methyl acetate	$CH_3CO_2CH_3$	15.29	0.1091
Benzonitrile	C_6H_5CN	33.39	0.1724	Methyl alcohol	CH_3OH	9.523	0.06702
Bromobenzene	C_6H_5Br	28.56	0.1539	Methylamine	CH_3NH_2	7.130	0.05992
n-Butane	C_4H_{10}	14.47	0.1226	Methyl butyrate	$C_3H_7CO_2CH_3$	23.94	0.1569
iso-Butane	C_4H_{10}	12.87	0.1142	Methyl isobutyrate	$C_3H_7CO_2CH_3$	24.50	0.1637
iso-Butyl acetate	$CH_3CO_2C_4H_9$	28.50	0.1833	Methyl chloride	CH_3Cl	7.471	0.06483
iso-Butyl alcohol	C_4H_9OH	17.03	0.1143	Methyl ether	$(CH_3)_2O$	8.073	0.07246
iso-Butyl benzene	$C_6H_5C_4H_9$	38.59	0.2144	Methyl ethyl ether	$CH_3OC_2H_5$	11.95	0.09775
iso-Butyl formate	$HCO_2C_4H_9$	22.54	0.1476	Methyl ethyl sulfide	$CH_3SC_2H_5$	19.23	0.1304
Butyronitrile	C_3H_7CN	25.72	0.1596	Methyl fluoride	CH_3F	4.631	0.05264
Capronitrile	$C_5H_{11}CN$	34.16	0.1984	Methyl formate	HCO_2CH_3	10.84	0.08068
Carbon dioxide	CO_2	3.592	0.04267	Methyl propionate	$C_2H_5CO_2CH_3$	19.91	0.1360
Carbon disulfide	CS_2	11.62	0.07685	Methyl sulfide	$(CH_3)_2S$	12.87	0.09213
Carbon monoxide	CO	1.485	0.03985	Methyl valerate	$C_4H_9CO_2CH_3$	28.96	0.1845
Carbon oxysulfide	COS	3.933	0.05817	Naphthalene	$C_{10}H_8$	39.74	0.1937
Carbon tetrachloride	CCl_4	20.39	0.1383	Neon	Ne	0.2107	0.01709
Chlorine	Cl_2	6.493	0.05622	Nitric oxide	NO	1.340	0.02789
Chlorobenzene	C_6H_5Cl	25.43	0.1453	Nitrogen	N_2	1.390	0.03913
Chloroform	$CHCl_3$	15.17	0.1022	Nitrogen dioxide	NO_2	5.284	0.04424
m-Cresol	$CH_3C_6H_4OH$	31.38	0.1607	Nitrous oxide	N_2O	3.782	0.04415
Cyanogen	C_2N_2	7.667	0.06901	n-Octane	C_8H_{18}	37.32	0.2368
Cyclohexane	C_6H_{12}	22.81	0.1424	Oxygen	O_2	1.360	0.03183
Cymene	$C_{10}H_{14}$	42.16	0.2336	n-Pentane	C_5H_{12}	19.01	0.1460
Decane	$C_{10}H_{12}$	48.55	0.2905	iso-Pentane	C_5H_{12}	18.05	0.1417
Di-isobutyl	C_8H_{18}	34.97	0.2296	Phenetole	$C_6H_5OC_2H_5$	35.16	0.1963
Diethylamine	$(C_2H_5)_2NH$	19.15	0.1392	Phosphine	PH_3	4.631	0.05156
Dimethylamine	$(CH_3)_2NH$	10.38	0.08570	Phosphonium chloride	PH_4Cl	4.054	0.04545
Dimethylaniline	$C_6H_5N(CH_3)_2$	37.49	0.1970	Phosphorus	P	52.94	0.1566
Diphenyl	$(C_6H_5)_2$	52.79	0.2480	Propane	C_3H_8	8.664	0.08445
Diphenyl methane	$(C_6H_5)_2CH_2$	38.20	0.2240	Propionic acid	$C_2H_5CO_2H$	20.11	0.1187
Dipropylamine	$(C_2H_7)_2NH$	27.72	0.1820	Propionitrile	C_2H_5CN	16.44	0.1064
Di-isopropyl	$(C_3H_7)_2$	23.13	0.1669	Propyl acetate	$CH_3CO_2C_3H_7$	24.63	0.1619
Durene	$C_{10}H_{14}$	45.32	0.2424	Propyl alcohol	C_3H_7OH	14.92	0.1019
Ethane	C_2H_6	5.489	0.06380	Propylamine	$C_3H_7NH_2$	14.99	0.1090
Ethyl acetate	$CH_3CO_2C_2H_5$	20.45	0.1412	Propyl benzene	$C_6H_5C_3H_7$	35.85	0.2028
Ethyl alcohol	C_2H_5OH	12.02	0.08407	iso-Propyl benzene	$C_6H_5C_3H_7$	35.64	0.2025
Ethylamine	$C_2H_5NH_2$	10.60	0.08409	Propyl chloride	C_3H_7Cl	15.91	0.1141
Ethyl benzene	$C_2H_5C_6H_5$	28.60	0.1667	Propyl formate	$HCO_2C_3H_7$	18.95	0.1280
Ethyl butyrate	$C_3H_7CO_2C_2H_5$	30.07	0.1919	Propylene	C_3H_6	8.379	0.08272
Ethyl isobutyrate	$C_3H_7CO_2C_2H_5$	28.87	0.1994	Pseudo-cumene	$C_6H_3(CH_3)_3$	36.61	0.2021
Ethyl chloride	C_2H_5Cl	10.91	0.08651	Silicon fluoride	SiF_4	4.195	0.05771
Ethyl ether	$(C_2H_5)_2O$	17.38	0.1344	Silicon tetrahydride	SiH_4	4.320	0.05786
Ethyl formate	$HCO_2C_2H_5$	14.80	0.1056	Stannic chloride	$SnCl_4$	26.91	0.1642
Ethyl mercaptan	C_2H_5SH	11.24	0.08098	Sulfur dioxide	SO_2	6.714	0.05636
Ethyl propionate	$C_2H_5CO_2C_2H_5$	24.39	0.1615	Thiophene	C_4H_4S	20.72	0.1270
Ethyl sulfide	$(C_2H_5)_2S$	18.75	0.1214	Toluene	$C_6H_5CH_3$	24.06	0.1463
Ethylene	C_2H_4	4.471	0.05714	Triethylamine	$(C_2H_5)_3N$	27.17	0.1831
Ethylene bromide	$(CH_2Br)_2$	13.98	0.08664	Trimethylamine	$(CH_3)_3N$	13.02	0.1084
Ethylene chloride	$(CH_2Cl)_2$	16.91	0.1086	Xenon	Xe	4.194	0.05105
Ethylidene chloride	CH_3CHCl_2	15.50	0.1073	m-Xylene	$C_6H_4(CH_3)_2$	30.36	0.1772
Fluorobenzene	C_6H_5F	19.93	0.1286	o-Xylene	$C_6H_4(CH_3)_2$	29.98	0.1755
Germanium tetrachloride	$GeCl_4$	22.60	0.1485	p-Xylene	$C_6H_4(CH_3)_2$	30.93	0.1809
Helium	He	0.03412	0.02370	Water	H_2O	5.464	0.03049
n-Heptane	C_7H_{16}	31.51	0.2065				

VAN DER WAALS' RADII IN Å

		H 1.2
N 1.5	O 1.40	F 1.35
P 1.9	S 1.85	Cl 1.80
As 2.0	Se 2.00	Br 1.95
Sb 2.2	Te 2.20	I 2.15

Methyl group CH_3 and methylene CH_2: 2.0. Half thickness of aromatic nucleus 1.85.

EMERGENT STEM CORRECTION FOR LIQUID-IN-GLASS THERMOMETERS

Accurate thermometers are calibrated with the entire stem immersed in the bath which determines the temperature of the thermometer bulb. However, for reasons of convenience it is common practice when using a thermometer to permit its stem to extend out of the apparatus. Under these conditions both the stem and the mercury in the exposed stem are at a temperature different from that of the bulb. This introduces an error into the observed temperature. Since the coefficient of thermal expansion of glass is less than that of mercury, the observed temperature will be less than the true temperature if the bulb is hotter than the stem and greater than the true temperature, providing the thermal gradient is reversed. For exact work the magnitude of this error can only be determined by experiment. However, for most purposes it is sufficiently accurate to apply the following equation which takes into account the difference of the thermal expansion of glass and mercury:

$$T_c = T_o + F \times L(T_o - T_m)$$

Where

T_c = corrected temperature

T_o = observed temperature

T_m = mean temperature of exposed stem. The mean temperature of the exposed stem may be determined by fastening the bulb of a second thermometer against the midpoint of the exposed liquid column.

L = the length of the exposed column in degrees above the surface of the substance whose temperature is being determined.

F = correction factor. For approximate work and when the liquid in the thermometer is mercury a value for F of 0.00016 is generally used. For more accurate work with mercury filled thermometers values as given in the following table are used. For thermometers filled with organic liquids it is customary to use 0.001 for the value of F.

Values of F for various glasses

T_m°C.	Corning 0041	Corning 8800	Corning 8810	Jena 16 III	Jena 59 III
50	0.000157	0.000166	0.000156	0.000158	0.000164
150	0.000159	0.000167	0.000157	0.000158	0.000165
250	0.000163	0.000168	0.000161	0.000161	0.000170
350	0.000168	0.000173	0.000166	....	0.000177

PRESSURE OF AQUEOUS VAPOR
VAPOR PRESSURE OF ICE

Pressure of aqueous vapor over ice in mm of Hg for temperatures from −98 to 0°C.

Temp. °C	0	2	4	6	8
−90	.000070	.000048	.000033	.000022	.000015
−80	.00040	.00029	.00020	.00014	.00010
−70	.00194	.00143	.00105	.00077	.00056
−60	.00808	.00614	.00464	.00349	.00261
−50	.02955	.0230	.0178	.0138	.0106
−40	.0966	.0768	.0609	.0481	.0378
−30	.2859	.2318	.1873	.1507	.1209

Temp. °C	0.0	0.2	0.4	0.6	0.8
−29	0.317	0.311	0.304	0.298	0.292
−28	0.351	0.344	0.337	0.330	0.324
−27	0.389	0.381	0.374	0.366	0.359
−26	0.430	0.422	0.414	0.405	0.397
−25	0.476	0.467	0.457	0.448	0.439
−24	0.526	0.515	0.505	0.495	0.486
−23	0.580	0.569	0.558	0.547	0.536
−22	0.640	0.627	0.615	0.603	0.592
−21	0.705	0.691	0.678	0.665	0.652
−20	0.776	0.761	0.747	0.733	0.719

Temp. °C	0.0	0.2	0.4	0.6	0.8
−19	0.854	0.838	0.822	0.806	0.791
−18	0.939	0.921	0.904	0.887	0.870
−17	1.031	1.012	0.993	0.975	0.956
−16	1.132	1.111	1.091	1.070	1.051
−15	1.241	1.219	1.196	1.175	1.153
−14	1.361	1.336	1.312	1.288	1.264
−13	1.490	1.464	1.437	1.411	1.386
−12	1.632	1.602	1.574	1.546	1.518
−11	1.785	1.753	1.722	1.691	1.661
−10	1.950	1.916	1.883	1.849	1.817
−9	2.131	2.093	2.057	2.021	1.985
−8	2.326	2.285	2.246	2.207	2.168
−7	2.537	2.493	2.450	2.408	2.367
−6	2.765	2.718	2.672	2.626	2.581
−5	3.013	2.962	2.912	2.862	2.813
−4	3.280	3.225	3.171	3.117	3.065
−3	3.568	3.509	3.451	3.393	3.336
−2	3.880	3.816	3.753	3.691	3.630
−1	4.217	4.147	4.079	4.012	3.946
−0	4.579	4.504	4.431	4.359	4.287

VAPOR PRESSURE OF WATER BELOW 100°C

Pressure of aqueous vapor over water in mm of Hg for temperatures from −15.8 to 100°C. Values for fractional degrees between 50 and 89 were obtained by interpolation.

Temp. °C	0.0	0.2	0.4	0.6	0.8
−15	1.436	1.414	1.390	1.368	1.345
−14	1.560	1.534	1.511	1.485	1.460
−13	1.691	1.665	1.637	1.611	1.585
−12	1.834	1.804	1.776	1.748	1.720
−11	1.987	1.955	1.924	1.893	1.863
−10	2.149	2.116	2.084	2.050	2.018
− 9	2.326	2.289	2.254	2.219	2.184
− 8	2.514	2.475	2.437	2.399	2.362
− 7	2.715	2.674	2.633	2.593	2.553
− 6	2.931	2.887	2.843	2.800	2.757
− 5	3.163	3.115	3.069	3.022	2.976
− 4	3.410	3.359	3.309	3.259	3.211
− 3	3.673	3.620	3.567	3.514	3.461
− 2	3.956	3.898	3.841	3.785	3.730
− 1	4.258	4.196	4.135	4.075	4.016
− 0	4.579	4.513	4.448	4.385	4.320
0	4.579	4.647	4.715	4.785	4.855
1	4.926	4.998	5.070	5.144	5.219
2	5.294	5.370	5.447	5.525	5.605
3	5.685	5.766	5.848	5.931	6.015
4	6.101	6.187	6.274	6.363	6.453
5	6.543	6.635	6.728	6.822	6.917
6	7.013	7.111	7.209	7.309	7.411
7	7.513	7.617	7.722	7.828	7.936
8	8.045	8.155	8.267	8.380	8.494
9	8.609	8.727	8.845	8.965	9.086
10	9.209	9.333	9.458	9.585	9.714
11	9.844	9.976	10.109	10.244	10.380
12	10.518	10.658	10.799	10.941	11.085
13	11.231	11.379	11.528	11.680	11.833
14	11.987	12.144	12.302	12.462	12.624
15	12.788	12.953	13.121	13.290	13.461
16	13.634	13.809	13.987	14.166	14.347
17	14.530	14.715	14.903	15.092	15.284
18	15.477	15.673	15.871	16.071	16.272
19	16.477	16.685	16.894	17.105	17.319
20	17.535	17.753	17.974	18.197	18.422
21	18.650	18.880	19.113	19.349	19.587
22	19.827	20.070	20.316	20.565	20.815
23	21.068	21.324	21.583	21.845	22.110
24	22.377	22.648	22.922	23.198	23.476
25	23.756	24.039	24.326	24.617	24.912
26	25.209	25.509	25.812	26.117	26.426
27	26.739	27.055	27.374	27.696	28.021
28	28.349	28.680	29.015	29.354	29.697
29	30.043	30.392	30.745	31.102	31.461
30	31.824	32.191	32.561	32.934	33.312
31	33.695	34.082	34.471	34.864	35.261
32	35.663	36.068	36.477	36.891	37.308
33	37.729	38.155	38.584	39.018	39.457
34	39.898	40.344	40.796	41.251	41.710
35	42.175	42.644	43.117	43.595	44.078
36	44.563	45.054	45.549	46.050	46.556
37	47.067	47.582	48.102	48.627	49.157
38	49.692	50.231	50.774	51.323	51.879
39	52.442	53.009	53.580	54.156	54.737
40	55.324	55.91	56.51	57.11	57.72
41	58.34	58.96	59.58	60.22	60.86

Temp. °C	0.0	0.2	0.4	0.6	0.8
42	61.50	62.14	62.80	63.46	64.12
43	64.80	65.48	66.16	66.86	67.56
44	68.26	68.97	69.69	70.41	71.14
45	71.88	72.62	73.36	74.12	74.88
46	75.65	76.43	77.21	78.00	78.80
47	79.60	80.41	81.23	82.05	82.87
48	83.71	84.56	85.42	86.28	87.14
49	88.02	38.90	89.79	90.69	91.59
50	92.51	93.5	94.4	95.3	96.3
51	97.20	98.2	99.1	100.1	101.1
52	102.09	103.1	104.1	105.1	106.2
53	107.20	108.2	109.3	110.4	111.4
54	112.51	113.6	114.7	115.8	116.9
55	118.04	119.1	120.3	121.5	122.6
56	123.80	125.0	126.2	127.4	128.6
57	129.82	131.0	132.3	133.5	134.7
58	136.08	137.3	138.5	139.9	141.2
59	142.60	143.9	145.2	146.6	148.0
60	149.38	150.7	152.1	153.5	155.0
61	156.43	157.8	159.3	160.8	162.3
62	163.77	165.2	166.8	168.3	169.8
63	171.38	172.9	174.5	176.1	177.7
64	179.31	180.9	182.5	184.2	185.8
65	187.54	189.2	190.9	192.6	194.3
66	196.09	197.8	199.5	201.3	203.1
67	204.96	206.8	208.6	210.5	212.3
68	214.17	216.0	218.0	219.9	221.8
69	223.73	225.7	227.7	229.7	231.7
70	233.7	235.7	237.7	239.7	241.8
71	243.9	246.0	248.2	250.3	252.4
72	254.6	256.8	259.0	261.2	263.4
73	265.7	268.0	270.2	272.6	274.8
74	277.2	279.4	281.8	284.2	286.6
75	289.1	291.5	294.0	296.4	298.8
76	301.4	303.8	306.4	308.9	311.4
77	314.1	316.6	319.2	322.0	324.6
78	327.3	330.0	332.8	335.6	338.2
79	341.0	343.8	346.6	349.4	352.2
80	355.1	358.0	361.0	363.8	366.8
81	369.7	372.6	375.6	378.8	381.8
82	384.9	388.0	391.2	394.4	397.4
83	400.6	403.8	407.0	410.2	413.6
84	416.8	420.2	423.6	426.8	430.2
85	433.6	437.0	440.4	444.0	447.5
86	450.9	454.4	458.0	461.6	465.2
87	468.7	472.4	476.0	479.8	483.4
88	487.1	491.0	494.7	498.5	502.2
89	506.1	510.0	513.9	517.8	521.8
90	525.76	529.77	533.80	537.86	541.95
91	546.05	550.18	554.35	558.53	562.75
92	566.99	571.26	575.55	579.87	584.22
93	588.60	593.00	597.43	601.89	606.38
94	610.90	615.44	620.01	624.61	629.24
95	633.90	638.59	643.30	648.05	652.82
96	657.62	662.45	667.31	672.20	677.12
97	682.07	687.04	692.05	697.10	702.17
98	707.27	712.40	717.56	722.75	727.98
99	733.24	738.53	743.85	749.20	754.58
100	760.00	765.45	770.93	776.44	782.00
101	787.57	793.18	798.82	804.50	810.21

VAPOR PRESSURE OF WATER ABOVE 100° C.

Based on values given by Keyes in the International Critical Tables.

Temp. °C	mm	Pounds per sq. in.	Temp. °F	Temp. °C	mm	Pounds per sq. in.	Temp. °F	Temp. °C	mm	Pounds per sq. in.	Temp. °F	Temp. °C	mm	Pounds per sq. in.	Temp. °F
100	760.	14.696	212.0	170	5940.02	114.879	338.0	240	25100.52	485.365	464.0	310	74024.00	1431.390	590.0
101	787.51	15.228	213.8	171	6085.32	117.671	339.8	241	25543.60	493.933	465.8	311	75042.40	1451.083	591.8
102	815.86	15.776	215.6	172	6233.52	120.537	341.6	242	25994.28	502.647	467.6	312	76076.00	1471.070	593.6
103	845.12	16.342	217.4	173	6383.24	123.432	343.4	243	26449.52	511.450	469.4	313	77117.20	1491.203	595.4
104	875.06	16.921	219.2	174	6538.28	126.430	345.2	244	26912.36	520.400	471.2	314	78166.00	1511.484	597.2
105	906.07	17.521	221.0	175	6694.08	129.442	347.0	245	27381.28	529.467	473.0	315	79230.00	1532.058	599.0
106	937.92	18.136	222.8	176	6852.92	132.514	348.8	246	27855.52	538.638	474.8	316	80294.00	1552.632	600.8
107	970.60	18.768	224.6	177	7015.56	135.659	350.6	247	28335.84	547.926	476.6	317	81373.20	1573.501	602.6
108	1004.42	19.422	226.4	178	7180.48	138.848	352.4	248	28823.76	557.360	478.4	318	82467.60	1594.663	604.4
109	1038.92	20.089	228.2	179	7349.20	142.110	354.2	249	29317.00	566.898	480.2	319	83569.60	1615.972	606.2
110	1074.56	20.779	230.0	180	7520.20	145.417	356.0	250	29817.84	576.583	482.0	320	84686.80	1637.575	608.0
111	1111.20	21.487	231.8	181	7694.24	148.782	357.8	251	30324.00	586.370	483.8	321	85819.20	1659.472	609.8
112	1148.74	22.213	233.6	182	7872.08	152.221	359.6	252	30837.76	596.305	485.6	322	86959.20	1681.516	611.6
113	1187.42	22.961	235.4	183	8052.96	155.719	361.4	253	31356.84	606.342	487.4	323	88114.40	1703.854	613.4
114	1227.25	23.731	237.2	184	8236.88	159.275	363.2	254	31885.04	616.556	489.2	324	89277.20	1726.339	615.2
115	1267.98	24.519	239.0	185	8423.84	162.890	365.0	255	32417.80	626.858	491.0	325	90447.60	1748.971	617.0
116	1309.94	25.330	240.8	186	8616.12	166.600	366.8	256	32957.40	637.292	492.8	326	91633.20	1771.897	618.8
117	1352.95	26.162	242.6	187	8809.92	170.356	368.6	257	33505.36	647.888	494.6	327	92826.40	1794.969	620.6
118	1397.18	27.017	244.4	188	9007.52	174.177	370.4	258	34059.40	658.601	496.4	328	94042.40	1818.483	622.4
119	1442.63	27.896	246.2	189	9208.16	178.057	372.2	259	34618.76	669.417	498.2	329	95273.60	1842.291	624.2
120	1489.14	28.795	248.0	190	9413.36	182.025	374.0	260	35188.00	680.425	500.0	330	96512.40	1866.245	626.0
121	1536.80	29.717	249.8	191	9620.08	186.022	375.8	261	35761.80	691.520	501.8	331	97758.80	1890.346	627.8
122	1586.04	30.669	251.6	192	9831.36	190.107	377.6	262	36343.20	702.763	503.6	332	99020.40	1914.742	629.6
123	1636.36	31.642	253.4	193	10047.20	194.281	379.4	263	36932.20	714.152	505.4	333	100297.20	1939.431	631.4
124	1687.81	32.637	255.2	194	10265.32	198.499	381.2	264	37529.56	725.703	507.2	334	101581.60	1964.267	633.2
125	1740.93	33.664	257.0	195	10488.76	202.819	383.0	265	38133.00	737.372	509.0	335	102881.20	1989.398	635.0
126	1795.12	34.712	258.8	196	10715.24	207.199	384.8	266	38742.52	749.158	510.8	336	104196.00	2014.822	636.8
127	1850.83	35.789	260.6	197	10944.76	211.637	386.6	267	39361.92	761.135	512.6	337	105526.00	2040.540	638.6
128	1907.83	36.891	262.4	198	11179.60	216.178	388.4	268	39986.64	773.215	514.4	338	106871.20	2066.552	640.4
129	1966.35	38.023	264.2	199	11417.48	220.778	390.2	269	40619.72	785.457	516.2	339	108224.00	2092.710	642.2
130	2026.16	39.180	266.0	200	11659.16	225.451	392.0	270	41261.16	797.861	518.0	340	109592.00	2119.163	644.0
131	2087.42	40.364	267.8	201	11905.40	230.213	393.8	271	41910.20	810.411	519.8	341	110967.60	2145.763	645.8
132	2150.42	41.582	269.6	202	12155.44	235.048	395.6	272	42566.08	823.094	521.6	342	112358.40	2172.657	647.6
133	2214.64	42.824	271.4	203	12408.52	239.942	397.4	273	43229.56	835.923	523.4	343	113749.20	2199.550	649.4
134	2280.76	44.103	273.2	204	12666.16	244.924	399.2	274	43902.16	848.929	525.2	344	115178.00	2227.179	651.2
135	2347.26	45.389	275.0	205	12929.12	250.008	401.0	275	44580.84	862.053	527.0	345	116614.40	2254.954	653.0
136	2416.34	46.724	276.8	206	13197.40	255.196	402.8	276	45269.40	875.367	528.8	346	118073.60	2283.171	654.8
137	2488.16	48.113	278.6	207	13467.96	260.428	404.6	277	45964.04	888.799	530.6	347	119532.80	2311.387	656.6
138	2560.67	49.515	280.4	208	13742.32	265.733	406.4	278	46669.32	902.437	532.4	348	121014.80	2340.044	658.4
139	2634.84	50.950	282.2	209	14022.76	271.156	408.2	279	47382.20	916.222	534.2	349	122504.40	2368.848	660.2
140	2710.92	52.421	284.0	210	14305.48	276.623	410.0	280	48104.20	930.183	536.0	350	124001.60	2397.799	662.0
141	2788.44	53.920	285.8	211	14595.04	282.222	411.8	281	48833.80	944.291	537.8	351	125521.60	2427.191	663.8
142	2867.48	55.448	287.6	212	14888.10	287.895	413.6	282	49570.24	958.532	539.6	352	127049.20	2456.730	665.6
143	2948.80	57.030	289.4	213	15184.80	293.626	415.4	283	50316.56	972.963	541.4	353	128599.60	2486.710	667.4
144	3031.64	58.622	291.2	214	15488.04	299.490	417.2	284	51072.76	987.586	543.2	354	130157.60	2516.837	669.2
145	3116.76	60.268	293.0	215	15792.80	305.383	419.0	285	51838.08	1002.385	545.0	355	131730.80	2547.258	671.0
146	3203.40	61.944	294.8	216	16104.40	311.408	420.8	286	52611.76	1017.345	546.8	356	133326.80	2578.119	672.8
147	3292.32	63.663	296.6	217	16420.56	317.522	422.6	287	53395.32	1032.497	548.6	357	134945.60	2609.422	674.6
148	3382.76	65.412	298.4	218	16742.04	323.738	424.4	288	54187.24	1047.810	550.4	358	136579.60	2641.018	676.4
149	3476.24	67.220	300.2	219	17067.32	330.028	426.2	289	54989.04	1063.314	552.2	359	138228.80	2672.908	678.2
150	3570.48	69.042	302.0	220	17395.64	336.377	428.0	290	55799.20	1078.980	554.0	360	139893.20	2705.093	680.0
151	3667.00	70.908	303.8	221	17731.56	342.872	429.8	291	56612.40	1094.705	555.8	361	141572.80	2737.571	681.8
152	3766.56	72.833	305.6	222	18072.80	349.471	431.6	292	57448.40	1110.871	557.6	362	143275.20	2770.490	683.6
153	3866.88	74.773	307.4	223	18417.84	356.143	433.4	293	58284.40	1127.036	559.4	363	144992.80	2803.703	685.4
154	3970.24	76.772	309.2	224	18766.68	362.888	435.2	294	59135.60	1143.496	561.2	364	146733.20	2837.357	687.2
155	4075.88	78.815	311.0	225	19123.12	369.781	437.0	295	59994.40	1160.102	563.0	365	148519.20	2871.892	689.0
156	4183.80	80.901	312.8	226	19482.60	376.732	438.8	296	60860.80	1176.856	564.8	366	150320.40	2906.722	690.8
157	4293.24	83.018	314.6	227	19848.92	383.815	440.6	297	61742.40	1193.903	566.6	367	152129.20	2941.698	692.6
158	4404.96	85.178	316.4	228	20219.80	390.087	442.4	298	62624.00	1210.950	568.4	368	153960.80	2977.116	694.4
159	4519.72	87.397	318.2	229	20596.76	398.276	444.2	299	63528.40	1228.439	570.2	369	155815.20	3012.974	696.2
160	4636.00	89.646	320.0	230	20978.28	405.654	446.0	300	64432.80	1245.927	572.0	370	157692.40	3049.273	698.0
161	4755.32	91.953	321.8	231	21368.12	413.134	447.8	301	65352.40	1263.709	573.8	371	159604.80	3086.090	699.8
162	4878.92	94.344	323.6	232	21757.28	420.717	449.6	302	66279.00	1281.638	575.6	372	161507.60	3123.047	701.6
163	5000.04	96.685	325.4	233	22154.00	428.388	451.4	303	67214.40	1299.714	577.4	373	163468.40	3160.963	703.4
164	5126.96	99.139	327.2	234	22558.32	436.207	453.2	304	68156.80	1317.937	579.2	374	165467.20	3199.613	705.2
165	5256.16	101.638	329.0	235	22967.96	444.146	455.0	305	69114.40	1336.454	581.0				
166	5386.88	104.165	330.8	236	23382.92	452.152	456.8	306	70072.00	1354.971	582.8				
167	5521.40	106.766	332.6	237	23802.44	460.264	458.6	307	71052.40	1373.929	584.6				
168	5658.20	109.412	334.4	238	24229.56	468.523	460.4	308	72048.00	1393.181	586.4				
169	5798.04	112.116	336.2	239	24661.24	476.871	462.2	309	73028.40	1412.130	588.2				

VAPOR PRESSURE OF MERCURY

Vapor pressure of mercury in mm. of Hg for temperatures from −38 to 400°C. Note that the values for the first four lines only, are to be multiplied by 10^{-6}.

Temp. °C	0	2	4	6	8	Temp. °C	0	2	4	6	8
	10^{-6}	10^{-6}	10^{-6}	10^{-6}	10^{-6}						
−30	4.78	3.59	2.66	1.97	1.45	200	17.287	18.437	19.652	20.936	22.292
−20	18.1	14.0	10.8	8.28	6.30	210	23.723	25.233	26.826	28.504	30.271
−10	60.6	48.1	38.0	29.8	23.2	220	32.133	34.092	36.153	38.318	40.595
− 0	185.	149.	119.	95.4	76.2	230	42.989	45.503	48.141	50.909	53.812
						240	56.855	60.044	63.384	66.882	70.543
+ 0	.000185	.000228	.000276	.000335	.000406						
+10	.000490	.000588	.000706	.000846	.001009	250	74.375	78.381	82.568	86.944	91.518
20	.001201	.001426	.001691	.002000	.002359	260	96.296	101.28	106.48	111.91	117.57
30	.002777	.003261	.003823	.004471	.005219	270	123.47	129.62	136.02	142.69	149.64
40	.006079	.007067	.008200	.009497	.01098	280	156.87	164.39	172.21	180.34	188.79
						290	197.57	206.70	216.17	226.00	236.21
50	.01267	.01459	.01677	.01925	.02206						
60	.02524	.02883	.03287	.03740	.04251	300	246.80	257.78	269.17	280.98	293.21
70	.04825	.05469	.06189	.06993	.07889	310	305.89	319.02	332.62	346.70	361.26
80	.08880	.1000	.1124	.1261	.1413	320	376.33	391.92	408.04	424.71	441.94
90	.1582	.1769	.1976	.2202	.2453	330	459.74	478.13	497.12	516.74	537.00
						340	557.90	579.45	601.69	624.64	648.30
100	.2729	.3032	.3366	.3731	.4132						
110	.4572	.5052	.5576	.6150	.6776	350	672.69	697.83	723.73	750.43	777.92
120	.7457	.8198	.9004	.9882	1.084	360	806.23	835.38	865.36	896.23	928.02
130	1.186	1.298	1.419	1.551	1.692	370	960.66	994.34	1028.9	1064.4	1100.9
140	1.845	2.010	2.188	2.379	2.585	380	1138.4	1177.0	1216.6	1257.3	1299.1
						390	1341.9	1386.1	1431.3	1477.7	1525.2
150	2.807	3.046	3.303	3.578	3.873						
160	4.189	4.528	4.890	5.277	5.689	400	1574.1	......	......	......	......
170	6.128	6.596	7.095	7.626	8.193						
180	8.796	9.436	10.116	10.839	11.607						
190	12.423	13.287	14.203	15.173	16.200						

VAPOR PRESSURES OF SOME OF THE ELEMENTS* AT VARIOUS TEMPERATURES °C

Element	Melting point (°C)	Pressure (mm Hg)						Element	Melting point (°C)	Pressure (mm Hg)					
		10^{-5}	10^{-4}	10^{-3}	10^{-2}	10^{-1}	1			10^{-5}	10^{-4}	10^{-3}	10^{-2}	10^{-1}	1
Ag	961	767	848	936	1047	1184	1353	Mg	651	287	331	383	443	515	605
Al	660	724	808	889	996	1123	1279	Mn	1244	717	791	878	980	1103	1251
Au	1063	1083	1190	1316	1465	1646	1867	Mo	2622	1923	2095	2295	2533	....	....
Ba	717	418	476	546	629	730	858	Ni	1455	1157	1257	1371	1510	1679	1884
Be	1284	942	1029	1130	1246	1395	1582	Os	2697	2101	2264	2451	2667	2920	3221
Bi	271	474	536	609	698	802	934	Pb	328	483	548	625	718	832	975
C	....	2129	2288	2471	2681	2926	3214	Pd	1555	1156	1271	1405	1566	1759	2000
Cd	321	148	180	220	264	321	....	Pt	1774	1606	1744	1904	2090	2313	2582
Co	1478	1249	1362	1494	1649	1833	2056	Sb	630	466	525	595	678	779	904
Cr	1900	907	992	1090	1205	1342	1504	Si	1410	1024	1116	1223	1343	1485	1670
Cu	1083	946	1035	1141	1273	1432	1628	Sn	232	823	922	1042	1189	1373	1609
Fe	1535	1094	1195	1310	1447	1602	1783	Ta	2996	2407	2599	2820	....	....	....
Hg	−38.9	−23.9	−5.5	18.0	48.0	82.0	126	W	3382	2554	2767	3016	3309	....	....
In	157	667	746	840	952	1088	1260	Zn	419	211	248	292	343	405	....
Ir	2454	1993	2154	2340	2556	2811	3118	Zr	2127	1527	1660	1816	2001	2212	2459

Reprinted with permission from Saul Dushman, "Scientific Foundations of Vacuum Technique," 1949, John Wiley and Sons, Inc., New York. * The values given in this table are from a variety of sources, not all of which are in agreement. The table is to be used, therefore, only as a general guide. For a detailed discussion of vapor pressure data, see Dr. Dushman's book, pages 752–754.

VAPOR PRESSURE OF CARBON DIOXIDE

SOLID

From Bureau of Standards Journal of Research

(Mercury column, density = 13.5951 g/cm³, g = 980.665)

Pressure in microns of mercury

°C	0	1	2	3	4	5	6	7	8	9
−180	0.013	0.008	0.006	0.004	0.003	0.0017	0.0011	0.0007	0.0005	0.0003
−170	.37	.27	.20	.14	.10	.074	.052	.037	.026	.018
−160	5.9	4.6	3.6	2.7	2.1	1.58	1.19	.90	.67	.50
−150	60.5	48.8	39.2	31.4	25.1	19.9	15.8	12.4	9.8	7.6
−140	431	359	298	247	204	168	138	113	92	75

Pressure in mm of mercury

°C	0	1	2	3	4	5	6	7	8	9
−130	2.31	1.97	1.68	1.43	1.22	1.03	0.87	0.73	0.61	0.51
−120	9.81	8.57	7.46	6.49	5.63	4.88	4.22	3.64	3.13	2.69
−110	34.63	30.76	27.27	24.14	21.34	18.83	16.58	14.58	12.80	11.22
−100	104.81	94.40	84.91	76.27	68.43	61.30	54.84	48.99	43.71	38.94
− 90	279.5	254.7	231.8	210.8	191.4	173.6	157.3	142.4	128.7	116.2
− 80	672.2	618.3	568.2	521.7	478.5	438.6	401.6	367.4	335.7	306.5
− 70	1486.1	1377.3	1275.6	1180.5	1091.7	1008.9	931.7	859.7	792.7	730.3
− 60	3073.1	2865.1	2669.7	2486.3	2314.2	2152.8	2001.5	1859.7	1726.9	1602.5
− 50	......							3780.9	3530.2	3294.6

LIQUID

°C	0	1	2	3	4	5	6	7	8	9
−50	5127.8	4922.7	4723.9	4531.1	4344.3	4163.2	3987.9	3818.2*	3653.9*	3495.0*
−40	7545	7271	7005	6746	6494	6250	6012	5781	5557	5339
−30	10718	10363	10017	9679	9350	9029	8716	8412	8115	7826
−20	14781	14331	13891	13461	13040	12630	12229	11838	11455	11082
−10	19872	19312	18764	18228	17703	17189	16686	16194	15712	15241
− 0	26142	25457	24786	24127	23482	22849	22229	21622	21026	20443
0	26142	26840	27552	28277	29017	29771	30539	31323	32121	32934
10	33763	34607	35467	36343	37236	38146	39073	40017	40980	41960
20	42959	43977	45014	46072	47150	48250	49370	50514	51680	52871
30	54086	55327								

* Undercooled liquid.

Critical temperature = 31.0°C. Triple point, −56.602 ± 0.005°C; 3885.2 ± 0.4 mm.

VAPOR PRESSURE

The following table is an abridged form of the very extensive compilation by Daniel R. Stull and published in Industrial and Engineering Chemistry **39**, 517 (1947).

The table gives the temperatures in degrees centigrade at which the vapor of the compound listed at the left has the pressure indicated at the top of the column. Organic compounds are listed in the order of their empirical formulae and inorganic compounds in the alphabetic order of their names. Pressures greater than one atmosphere are listed in separate tables.

Abbreviations:
d = decomposes
d = dextrorotatory
dl = inactive (50% d and 50% l)
e = explodes
l = levorotatory
M.P. = melting point
p = polymerizes
s = solid

INORGANIC COMPOUNDS
Pressures Less than One Atmosphere

Name	Formula	Temperature, °C						M.P.	Citation No.
		1 mm	10 mm	40 mm	100 mm	400 mm	760 mm		
Aluminum	Al	1284	1487	1635	1749	1947	2056	660	(153, 229, 469)
Aluminum borohydride	AlB₃H₁₂	$-$ 42.9$_s$	$-$ 20.9	$-$ 3.9	$+$ 28.1	45.9	$-$ 64.5	(386)
Aluminum bromide	AlBr₃	81.3$_s$	118.0	150.6	176.1	227.0	256.3	97.5	(9, 127, 229)
Aluminum chloride	AlCl₃	100.0$_s$	123.8$_s$	139.9$_s$	152.0$_s$	171.6$_s$	180.2$_s$	192.4	(127, 130, 229, 264, 409, 410, 457)
Aluminum fluoride	AlF₃	1238	1324	1378	1422	1496	1537	1040	(362)
Aluminum iodide	AlI₃	178.0$_s$	225.8	265.0	294.5	354.0	385.5		(127, 229)
Aluminum oxide	Al₂O₃	2148	2385	2549	2665	2874	2977	2050	(229, 359, 369)
Ammonia	NH₃	$-$109.1$_s$	$-$ 91.9$_s$	$-$ 79.2$_s$	$-$ 68.4	$-$ 45.4	$-$ 33.6	$-$ 77.7	(23, 25, 33, 49, 62, 82, 142, 175, 192, 223, 231, 279, 305, 334, 420)
Deutero ammonia	ND₃				$-$ 67.4	$-$ 45.4	$-$ 33.4	$-$ 74.0	(443)
Ammonium azide	NH₄N₃	29.2$_s$	59.2$_s$	80.1$_s$	95.2$_s$	120.4$_s$	133.8$_s$		(131)
Ammonium bromide	NH₄Br	198.3$_s$	252.0$_s$	290.0$_s$	320.0$_s$	370.9$_s$	390.0$_s$		(403)
Ammonium carbamate	NH₂CO₂NH₂	$-$ 26.1$_s$	$-$ 2.9$_s$	$+$ 14.0$_s$	26.7	48.0$_s$	58.3$_s$		(48, 107)
Ammonium chloride	NH₄Cl	160.4$_s$	209.8$_s$	245.0$_s$	271.5$_s$	316.5$_s$	337.8$_s$	520	(333, 403)
Ammonium hydrogen sulfide	NH₄HS	$-$ 51.1	$-$ 28.7	$-$ 12.3	0.0	$+$ 21.8	33.3		(200)
Ammonium iodide	NH₄I	210.9$_s$	263.5$_s$	302.8$_s$	331.8$_s$	381.0$_s$	404.9$_s$		(403)
Ammonium cyanide	NH₄CN	$-$ 50.6$_s$	$-$ 28.6$_s$	$-$ 12.6$_s$	$-$ 0.5$_s$	$+$ 20.5$_s$	31.7$_s$	36	(201)
Antimony	Sb	886	1033	1141	1223	1364	1440	630.5	(153, 229, 255, 348, 485)
Antimony tribromide	SbBr₃	93.9	142.7	177.4	203.5	250.2	275.0	96.6	(9, 102)
Antimony trichloride	SbCl₃	49.2$_s$	85.2	117.8	143.3	192.2	219.0	73.4	(8, 9, 43, 102, 229, 264)
Antimony pentachloride	SbCl₅	22.7	61.8	91.0	114.1			2.8	(8, 9, 43, 229)
Antimony triiodide	SbI₃	163.6$_s$	223.5	267.8	303.5	368.5	401.0	167	(9, 102)
Antimony trioxide	Sb₂O₃	574$_s$	666	812	957	1242	1425	656	(183, 229)
Argon	A	$-$218.2$_s$	$-$210.9$_s$	$-$204.9$_s$	$-$200.5$_s$	$-$190.6$_s$	$-$185.6	$-$189.2	(41, 83, 84, 85, 193, 229, 295, 329, 466)
Arsenic (metallic)	As	372$_s$	437$_s$	483$_s$	518$_s$	579$_s$	610$_s$	814	(143, 194, 229, 322, 348, 367)
Arsenic tribromide	AsBr₃	41.8	85.2	118.7	145.2	193.6	220.0		(9)
Arsenic trichloride	AsCl₃	$-$ 11.4	$+$ 23.5	50.0	70.9	109.7	130.4	$-$ 18	(9, 20, 229, 264)
Arsenic trifluoride	AsF₃			$-$ 2.5	$+$ 13.2	41.5	56.3	$-$ 5.9	(376)
Arsenic pentafluoride	AsF₅	$-$117.9$_s$	$-$103.1$_s$	$-$ 92.4$_s$	$-$ 84.3$_s$	$-$ 64.0	$-$ 52.8	$-$ 79.8	(229, 352)
Arsenic hydride (arsine)	AsH₃	$-$142.6$_s$	$-$124.7$_s$	$-$110.2	$-$ 98.0	$-$ 75.2	$-$ 62.1	$-$116.3	(215)
Arsenic trioxide	As₂O₃	212.5$_s$	259.7$_s$	299.2$_s$	332.5	412.2	457.2	312.8	(229, 287, 373, 402, 405, 418, 479)
Barium	Ba	$_s$	1049	1195	1301	1518	1638	850	(167, 229, 355)
Beryllium borohydride	BeB₂H₈	$+$ 1.0$_s$	28.1$_s$	46.2$_s$	58.6$_s$	79.7$_s$	90.0$_s$	123	(60)
Beryllium bromide	BeBr₂	289$_s$	342$_s$	379$_s$	405$_s$	451$_s$	474$_s$	490	(229, 326)
Beryllium chloride	BeCl₂	291$_s$	346$_s$	384$_s$	411	461	487	405	(229, 326)
Beryllium iodide	BeI₂	283$_s$	341$_s$	382$_s$	411$_s$	461$_s$	487$_s$	488	(229, 326)
Bismuth	Bi	1021	1136	1217	1271	1370	1420	271	(17, 153, 154, 155, 229, 255, 348)
Bismuth tribromide	BiBr₃	$_s$	282	327	360	425	461	218	(116, 229)
Bismuth trichloride	BiCl₃		264	311	343	405	441	230	(116, 229, 264)
Borine carbonyl	BH₂CO	$-$139.2	$-$121.1	$-$106.6	$-$ 95.3	$-$ 74.8	$-$ 64.0	$-$137.0	(59)
Boron tribromide	BBr₃	$-$ 41.4	$-$ 10.1	$+$ 14.0	33.5	70.0	91.7	$-$ 45	(229, 421)
Boron trichloride	BCl₃	$-$ 91.5	$-$ 66.9	$-$ 47.8	$-$ 32.4	$-$ 3.6	$+$ 12.7	$-$107	(229, 308, 334, 430)
Boron trifluoride	BF₃	$-$154.6	$-$141.3$_s$	$-$131.0$_s$	$-$123.0	$-$108.3	$-$110.7	$-$126.8	(30, 118, 229, 319, 352)
Dihydrodiborane	B₂H₆	$-$159.7	$-$144.3	$-$131.6	$-$120.9	$-$ 99.6	$-$ 86.5	$-$169	(229, 419, 423)
Diborane hydrobromide	B₂BrH₅	$-$ 93.3	$-$ 66.3	$-$ 45.4	$-$ 29.0	0.0	$+$ 16.3	$-$104.2	(229, 424)
Triborine triamine	B₃H₆N₃	$-$ 63.0$_s$	$-$ 35.3	$-$ 13.2	$+$ 4.0	34.3	50.6	$-$ 58.2	(229, 427)
Tetrahydrotetraborane	B₄H₁₀	$-$ 90.9	$-$ 64.0	$-$ 44.0	$-$ 28.1	$+$ 0.8	10.1	$-$119.5	(229, 423, 425, 426)
Dihydropentaborane	B₅H₉	$_s$	$-$ 30.7	$-$ 8.0	$+$ 9.6	40.8	58.1	$-$ 47.0	(229, 423)
Tetrahydropentaborane	B₅H₁₁	$-$ 50.2	$-$ 19.9	$+$ 2.7	20.1	51.2	67.0		(229, 426)
Dihydrodecaborane	B₁₀H₁₄	60.0$_s$	90.2$_s$	117.4	142.3	d		99.6	(229, 428)
Bromine	Br₂	$-$ 48.7$_s$	$-$ 25.0$_s$	$-$ 8.0$_s$	$+$ 9.3	41.0	58.2	$-$ 7.3	(88, 102, 171, 203, 217, 229, 281, 331, 345, 381, 458, 487)
Bromine pentafluoride	BrF₅	$-$ 69.3$_s$	$-$ 41.9	$-$ 21.0	$-$ 4.5	$+$ 25.7	40.0	$-$ 61.4	(229, 365)
Cadmium	Cd	394	484	553	611	711	765	320.9	(17, 42, 61, 109, 111, 129, 163, 181, 210, 229, 243, 348)

VAPOR PRESSURE (Continued)
INORGANIC COMPOUNDS (Continued)
Pressures Less than One Atmosphere (Continued)

Name	Formula	Temperature, °C						M.P.	Citation No.
		1 mm	10 mm	40 mm	100 mm	400 mm	760 mm		
Cadmium chloride	$CdCl_2$	s	656	736	797	908	967	568	(156, 229, 264)
Cadmium fluoride	CdF_2	1112	1286	1400	1486	1651	1751	520	(362)
Cadmium iodide	CdI_2	416	512	584	640	742	796	385	(229, 387)
Cadmium oxide	CdO	1000_s	1149_s	1257_s	1341_s	1484_s	1559_s	......	(119, 184, 229)
Calcium	Ca	s	983	1111	1207	1388	1487	851	(167, 229, 318, 346, 355)
Carbon	C	3586_s	3946_s	4196_s	4373_s	4660_s	4827_s	......	(4, 176, 177, 229, 241, 242, 266, 377, 445, 480)
Carbon tetrabromide	CBr_4	s	s	96.3	119.7	163.5	189.5	90.1	(38)
Carbon tetrachloride	CCl_4	-50.0_s	-19.6	$+4.3$	23.0	57.8	76.7	-22.6	(104, 179, 279, 334, 335, 413, 495)
Carbon tetrafluoride	CF_4	-184.6_s	-169.3	-158.8	-150.7	-135.5	-127.7	-183.7	(229, 270)
Carbon dioxide	CO_2	-134.3_s	-119.5_s	-108.6_s	-100.2_s	-85.7_s	-78.2_s	-57.5	(5, 46, 117, 172, 175, 211, 229, 272, 292, 302, 334, 420, 464, 467, 477, 497)
Carbon suboxide	C_3O_2	-94.8	-71.0	-52.0	-36.9	-8.9	$+6.3$	-107	(237, 435)
Carbon disulfide	CS_2	-73.8	-44.7	-22.5	-5.1	$+28.0$	46.5	-110.8	(175, 229, 265, 328, 334, 335, 420, 467, 490)
Carbon subsulfide	C_3S_2	14.0	54.9	85.6	109.9	p	......	$+0.4$	(229, 429)
Carbon selenosulfide	$CSSe$	-47.3	-16.0	$+8.6$	28.3	65.2	85.6	-75.2	(229, 436)
Carbon monoxide	CO	-222.0_s	-215.0_s	-210.0_s	-205.7_s	-196.3	-191.3	-205.0	(16, 67, 77, 78, 87, 229, 293, 463)
Carbonyl chloride	$COCl_2$	-92.9	-69.3	-50.3	-35.6	-7.6	$+8.3$	-104	(14, 135, 229, 288, 309)
Carbonyl selenide	$COSe$	-117.1	-95.0	-76.4	-61.7	-35.6	-21.9	......	(325)
Carbonyl sulfide	COS	-132.4	-113.3	-98.3	-85.9	-62.7	-49.9	-138.8	(196, 229, 230, 422)
Chloropicrin	CCl_3NO_2	-25.5	$+7.8$	33.8	53.8	91.8	111.9	-64	(20, 31)
Chlorotrifluoromethane	$CClF_3$	-149.5	-134.1	-121.9	-111.7	-92.7	-81.2		(102, 447)
Cyanogen	C_2N_2	-95.8_s	-76.8_s	-62.7_s	-51.8_s	-33.0	-21.0	-34.4	(74, 83, 102, 118, 313, 444)
Cyanogen bromide	$CBrN$	-35.7_s	-10.0_s	$+8.6_s$	22.6_s	46.0_s	61.5	58	(20, 229)
Cyanogen chloride	$CClN$	-76.7_s	-53.8_s	-37.5_s	-24.9_s	-2.3	$+13.1$	-6.5	(229, 334)
Cyanogen fluoride	CFN	-134.4_s	-118.5_s	-106.4_s	-97.0_s	-80.5_s	-72.6_s		(80, 229)
Cyanogen iodide	CIN	25.2_s	57.7_s	80.3_s	97.6_s	126.1_s	141.1_s	......	(229, 493)
Deuterocyanic acid	CDN	-68.9_s	-46.7_s	-30.1_s	-17.5_s	$+10.0$	26.2	-12	(258)
Dichlorodifluoromethane	CCl_2F_2	-118.5	-97.8	-81.6	-68.6	-43.9	-29.8		(102, 144)
Dichlorofluoromethane	$CHCl_2F$	-91.3	-67.5	-48.8	-33.9	-6.2	$+8.9$	-135	(233)
Chlorodifluoromethane	$CHClF_2$	-122.8	-103.7	-88.6	-76.4	-53.6	-40.8	-160	(40, 233)
Trichlorofluoromethane	CCl_3F	-84.3	-59.0	-39.0	-23.0	$+6.8$	23.7		(233)
Cesium	Cs	279	375	449	509	624	690	28.5	(35, 132, 161, 229, 246, 251, 357, 394, 462)
Cesium bromide	$CsBr$	748	887	993	1072	1221	1300	636	(229, 367, 475)
Cesium chloride	$CsCl$	744	884	989	1069	1217	1300	646	(122, 229, 367, 475)
Cesium fluoride	CsF	712	844	947	1025	1170	1251	683	(229, 370, 371, 475)
Cesium iodide	CsI	738	873	976	1055	1200	1280	621	(229, 367, 475)
Chlorine	Cl_2	-118.0_s	-101.6_s	-84.5	-71.7	-47.3	-33.8	-100.7	(139, 166, 171, 214, 229, 239, 312, 452)
Chlorine fluoride	ClF	s	-139.0	-128.8	-120.8	-107.0	-100.5	-145	(229, 361)
Chlorine trifluoride	ClF_3	s	-71.8	-51.3	-34.7	$+4.9$	$+11.5$	-83	(229, 360)
Chlorine monoxide	Cl_2O	-98.5	-73.1	-54.3	-39.4	-12.5	$+2.2$	-116	(147, 229)
Chlorine dioxide	ClO_2	s	-59.0	-42.8	-29.4	-4.0	$+11.1$	-59	(229, 234)
Dichlorine hexoxide	Cl_2O_6	$+7.5$	42.0	68.0	87.7	123.8	142.0	3.5	(149)
Chlorine heptoxide	Cl_2O_7	-45.3	-13.2	$+10.3$	29.1	62.2	78.8	-91	(148, 229)
Chlorosulfonic acid	HSO_3Cl	32.0	64.0	87.6	105.3	136.1	151.0d	-80	(9)
Chromium	Cr	1616	1845	2013	2139	2361	2482	1615	(153, 229)
Chromium carbonyl	$Cr(CO)_6$	36.0	68.3	91.2	108.0	137.2	151.0		(484)
Chromyl chloride	CrO_2Cl_2	-18.4	$+13.8$	38.5	58.0	95.2	117.1		(229, 276)
Cobaltous chloride	$COCl_2$	s	s	770	843	974	1050	735	(229, 264)
Cobalt nitrosyl tricarbonyl	$Co(CO)_2NO$	s	s	$+11.0$	29.0	62.0	80.0	-11	(30)
Columbium pentafluoride	CbF_5	s	86.3	121.5	148.5	198.0	225.0	75.5	(229, 368)
Copper	Cu	1628	1879	2067	2207	2465	2595	1083	(153, 154, 155, 165, 218, 229, 262, 348, 359, 469)
Cuprous bromide	Cu_2Br_2	572	718	844	951	1189	1355	504	(209, 229, 474)
Cuprous chloride	Cu_2Cl_2	546	702	838	960	1249	1490	422	(229, 264, 474)
Cuprous iodide	Cu_2I_2	s	656	786	907	1158	1336	605	(156, 209, 229, 474)
Ferric chloride	$FeCl_3$	194.0_s	235.5_s	256.8_s	272.5_s	298.0_s	319.0	304	(208, 229, 264)
Ferrous chloride	$FeCl_2$	....	700	779	842	961	1026	......	(229, 264)
Fluorine	F_2	-223.0	-214.1	-207.7	-202.7	-193.2	-187.9	-223	(65, 229)
Fluorine monoxide	F_2O	-196.1	-182.3	-173.0	-165.8	-151.9	-144.6	-223.9	(229, 363, 364)
Gallium	Ga	1349	1541	1680	1784	1974	2071	30	(165, 229)
Gallium trichloride	$GaCl_3$	48.0_s	76.5_s	107.5	132.0	176.3	200.0	77.0	(126, 253)
Germanium hydride	GeH_4	-163.0	-145.3	-131.6	-120.3	-100.2	-88.9	-165	(79, 229, 307, 383)
Germanium bromide	$GeBr_4$	s	56.8	88.1	113.2	161.6	189.0	26.1	(45, 229)
Germanium chloride	$GeCl_4$	-45.0	-15.0	$+8.0$	27.5	63.8	84.0	-49.5	(229, 254, 289)
Trichlorogermane	$GeHCl_3$	-41.3	-13.0	$+8.8$	26.5	58.3d	75.0d	-71.1	(94, 229)
Tetramethylgermanium	$Ge(CH_3)_4$	-73.2	-45.2	-23.4	$+2.6$	$+26.0$	44.0	-88	(93, 229)
Digermane	Ge_2H_6	-88.7	-60.1	-38.2	-20.3	$+13.3$	31.5	-109	(92, 229)
Trigermane	Ge_3H_8	-36.9	-0.9	$+26.3$	47.9	88.6	110.8	-105.6	(92, 229)

Name	Formula	Temperature, °C						M.P.	Citation No.
		1 mm	10 mm	40 mm	100 mm	400 mm	760 mm		
Gold....................	Au	1869	2154	2363	2521	2807	2966	1063	(165, 229, 348, 359, 469)
Helium...	He	−271.7	−271.3	−270 7	−270.3	−269.3	−268.6	......	(227, 228, 229, 300, 301)
Hydrogen................	H₂	−263.3ₛ	−261.3ₛ	−259.6ₛ	−257.9	−254.5	−252.5	−259.1	(58, 71, 173, 225, 229, 298, 299, 396, 454, 455)
Hydrogen deuteride.........	HD	......	−259.8	−258 2	−256.6	−253.0	−251.0	......	(395)
Hydrogen bromide............	HBr	−138.8ₛ	−121.8ₛ	−108.3ₛ	− 97.7ₛ	− 78.0	− 66.5	− 87.0	(18, 103, 169, 229, 415, 416)
Hydrogen chloride.........	HCl	−150.8ₛ	−135.6ₛ	−123.8ₛ	−114.0	− 95.3	− 84.8	−114.3	(50, 69, 103, 118, 141, 169, 175, 223, 229, 416, 420)
Hydrogen cyanide................	HCN	− 71.0ₛ	− 47.7ₛ	− 30.9ₛ	− 17.8ₛ	+ 10.2	25.9	− 13.2	(44, 164, 229, 258, 314, 397, 401)
Hydrogen fluoride..............	HF	ₛ	− 65.8	− 45.0	− 28.2	+ 2.5	19.7	− 83.7	(76, 229, 398, 400)
Hydrogen iodide.................	HI	−123.3ₛ	−102.3ₛ	− 85 6ₛ	− 72.1ₛ	− 48.3	− 35.1	− 50.9	(103, 169, 229, 415, 416)
Hydrogen peroxide............	H₂O₂	15.3	50.4	77.0	97.9	137.4d	158.0d	− 0.9	(229, 260)
Hydrogen selenide............	H₂Se	−115.3ₛ	− 97.9ₛ	− 84.7ₛ	− 74.2ₛ	− 53.6	− 41.1	− 64	(57, 90, 91, 229, 292, 417)
Hydrogen sulfide.......	H₂S	−134.3ₛ	−116.3ₛ	−102.3ₛ	− 91.6ₛ	− 71.8	− 60.4	− 85.5	(118, 137, 229, 235, 236, 292, 334, 415, 416)
Hydrogen disulfide............	H₂S₂	− 43.2	− 15.2	+ 6.0	22.0	49.6	64.0	− 89.7	(64, 229)
Hydrogen teluride............	H₂Te	− 96.4ₛ	− 75.4ₛ	− 59.1ₛ	− 45.7	− 17.2	− 2.0	− 49.0	(56, 229, 417)
Hydroxylamine..........	NH₂OH	ₛ	47.2	64.6	77.5	99.2	110.0	34.0	(9, 55, 259)
Iodine.........................	I₂	38.7ₛ	73.2ₛ	97.5ₛ	116.5	159.8	183.0	112.9	(10, 21, 22, 96, 136, 145, 159, 229, 282, 331, 336, 440, 483, 486)
Iodine pentafluoride...........	IF₅	− 15.2	+ 8.5	32.2	50.0	81.2	97.0	8.0	(351)
Iodine heptafluoride...........	IF₇	− 87.0ₛ	− 63.0ₛ	− 45.3ₛ	− 31.9ₛ	− 8 3ₛ	+ 4.0ₛ	5.5	(229, 358)
Iron..........................	Fe	1787	2039	2224	2360	2605	2735	1535	(153, 218, 229, 350)
Iron pentacarbonyl..............	Fe(CO)₅	ₛ	+ 4.6	30.3	50.3	86.1	105.0	− 21	(229, 450)
Krypton......................	Kr	−199.3ₛ	−187.2ₛ	−178.4ₛ	−171.8ₛ	−159.0ₛ	−152.0	−156.7	(3, 221, 229, 315, 317, 329)
Lead.........................	Pb	973	1162	1309	1421	1630	1744	327.5	(110, 153, 154, 155, 165, 197, 229, 255, 341, 342, 348, 469, 471)
Lead bromide...................	PbBr₂	513	610	686	745	856	914	373	(156, 229, 465, 474)
Lead chloride..................	PbCl₂	547	648	725	784	893	954	501	(105, 156, 207, 229, 465, 474)
Lead fluoride..................	PbF₂	ₛ	904	1003	1080	1219	1293	855	(229, 474)
Lead iodide...................	PbI	479	571	644	701	807	872	402	(156, 209, 229)
Lead oxide....................	PbO	943	1085	1189	1265	1402	1472	890	(119, 229)
Lead sulfide..................	PbS	852ₛ	975ₛ	1048ₛ	1108ₛ	1221	1281	1114	(229, 382)
Lithium.......................	Li	723	881	1003	1097	1273	1372	186	(36, 37, 167, 229, 257)
Lithium bromide...............	LiBr	748	888	994	1076	1226	1310	547	(229, 367, 475)
Lithium chloride..............	LiCl	783	932	1045	1129	1290	1382	614	(229, 264, 367, 475)
Lithium fluoride..............	LiF	1047	1211	1333	1425	1591	1681	870	(229, 371, 475)
Lithium iodide................	LiI	723	841	927	993	1110	1171	446	(229, 367, 475)
Magnesium...................	Mg	621ₛ	743	838	909	1034	1107	651	(153, 167, 229, 355, 469)
Magnesium chloride............	MgCl₂	778	930	1050	1142	1316	1418	712	(229, 264)
Manganese....................	Mn	1292	1505	1666	1792	2029	2151	1260	(133, 153, 229, 349)
Manganous chloride............	MnCl₂	ₛ	778	879	960	1108	1190	650	(229, 264)
Mercury.....................	Hg	126.2	184.0	228.8	261.7	323.0	357.0	− 38.9	(26, 34, 109, 134, 159, 178, 181, 182, 185, 210, 222, 229, 240, 243, 271, 273, 277, 285, 316, 320, 330, 334, 342, 348, 439, 460, 494)
Mercuric bromide.............	HgBr₂	136.5ₛ	179.8ₛ	211.5ₛ	237 8	290.0	319.0	237	(212, 220, 229, 324, 405, 406)
Mercuric chloride..............	HgCl₂	136.2ₛ	180.2ₛ	212.5ₛ	237.0ₛ	275.5ᵦ	304.0	277	(124, 212, 229, 324, 336, 387, 438, 483)
Mercuric iodide..............	HgI₂	157.5ₛ	204.5ₛ	238.2ₛ	261.8	324.2	354.0	259	(98, 212, 229, 324, 339, 438, 483)
Molybdenum.................	Mo	3102	3535	3859	4109	4553	5560	2622	(218, 229, 252)
Molybdenum hexafluoride.........	MoF₆	− 65.5ₛ	− 40.8ₛ	− 22.1ₛ	− 8.0ₛ	+ 17.2	36.0	17	(229, 347)
Molybdenum trioxide...........	MoO₃	734ₛ	814	892	955	1082	1151	795	(120, 205, 229)
Neon.......................	Ne	−257.3ₛ	−254.6ₛ	−252.6ₛ	−251.0ₛ	−248.1	−246.0	−248.7	(71, 229, 297, 455)
Nickel......................	Ni	1810	2057	2234	2364	2603	2732	1452	(218, 229, 349)
Nickel chloride..............	NiCl₂	671ₛ	759ₛ	821ₛ	866ₛ	945ₛ	987ₛ	1001	(125, 229, 264)

Name	Formula	Temperature, °C						M.P.	Citation No.
		1 mm	10 mm	40 mm	100 mm	400 mm	760 mm		
Nickel carbonyl	Ni(CO)₄	s	s	− 23.0	− 6.0	+ 25.8	42.5	− 25	(7, 96, 97, 229, 274)
Nitrogen	N₂	−226.1s	−219.1s	−214.0s	−209.7	−200.9	−195.8	−210.0	(15, 70, 86, 100, 123, 138, 173, 174, 193, 229, 292, 321, 463, 467, 489)
Nitrogen trifluoride	NF₃	s	−170.7	−160.2	−152.3	−137.4	−129.0	−183.7	(229, 270)
Nitric oxide	NO	−184.5s	−178.2s	−171.7s	−166.0s	−156.8s	−151.7	−161	(1, 146, 170, 216, 229, 279, 292, 294)
Nitrous oxide	N₂O	−143.4s	−128.7s	−118.3s	−110.3s	− 96.2s	− 88.5	− 90.9	(29, 32, 53, 62, 115, 188, 229, 247, 327, 464)
Nitrogen tetroxide	N₂O₄	− 55.6s	− 36.7s	− 23.9s	− 14.7s	+ 8.0	21.0	− 9.3	(19, 108, 158, 229, 275, 317, 332, 374, 380, 385)
Nitrogen pentoxide	N₂O₅	− 36.8s	− 16.7s	− 2.9s	+ 7.4s	24.4s	32.4	30	(89, 229, 375)
Nitrosyl chloride	NOCl	s	s	− 60.2	− 46.3	− 20.3	− 6.4	− 64.5	(52, 229, 451)
Nitrosyl fluoride	NOF	−132.0	−114.3	−100.3	− 88.8	− 68.2	− 56.0	−134	(366)
Nitroxyl fluoride	NO₂F	−143.7s	−126.2	−112.8	−102.3	− 83.2	− 72.0	−139	(366)
Osmium tetroxide (white)	OsO₄	− 5.6s	+ 26.0s	50.5	71.5	109.3	130.0	42	(229, 245, 290, 372, 468)
Osmium tetroxide (yellow)	OsO₄	3.2s	31.3s	51.7s	71.5	109.3	130.0	56	(229, 245, 290, 372, 468)
Oxygen	O₂	−219.1s	−210.6	−204.1	−198.8	−188.8	−182.96	−218.4	(15, 28, 58, 70, 86, 100, 114, 172, 174, 226, 229, 292, 296, 420, 456, 467, 488)
Ozone	O₃	−180.4	−163.2	−150.7	−141.0	−122.5	−111.9	−192.1 ±.1	(229, 337, 338, 414)
Phosphorus (yellow)	P	76.6	128.0	166.7	197.3	251.0	280.0	44.1	(72, 186, 219, 229, 263, 322)
Phosphorus (violet)	P	237s	287s	323s	349s	391s	417s	590	(186, 229, 286, 406, 408)
Phosphorus (black)	P	290s	338s	371s	393s	432s	453s	....	(47, 186, 229, 286, 408)
Phosphorus tribromide	PBr₃	7.8	47.8	79.0	103.6	149.7	175.3	− 40	(9)
Phosphorus trichloride	PCl₃	− 51.6	− 21.3	+ 2.3	21.0	56.9	74.2	−111.8	(229, 334)
Phosphorus pentachloride	PCl₅	55.5s	83.2s	102.5s	117.0s	147.2s	162.0s		(403)
Phosphorus hydride (Phosphene)	PH₃	s	s	−129.4	−118.8	− 98.3	− 87.5	−132.5	(50, 175, 229, 416, 420)
Phosphonium bromide	PH₄Br	− 43.7s	− 21.2s	− 5.0s	+ 7.4s	28.0s	38.3d		(202, 213)
Phosphonium chloride	PH₄Cl	− 91.0s	− 74.0s	− 61.5s	− 52.0s	− 35.4s	− 27.0s	− 28.5	(50, 442)
Phosphonium iodide	PH₄I	− 25.2s	− 1.1s	16.1s	29.3s	51.6s	62.3s		(213, 403)
Phosphorus trioxide	P₂O₃	s	53.0	84.0	108.3	150.3	173.1	22.5	(229, 384, 461)
Phosphorus oxychloride	POCl₃		2.0	27.3	47.4	84.3	105.1	2	(12, 13, 229)
Phosphorus pentoxide (stable form)	P₂O₅	384s	442s	481s	510s	556s	591	569	(187, 229, 407)
Phosphorus pentoxide (Metastable form)	P₂O₅	189	236	270	294	336	358		(187, 229, 407)
Phosphorus thiobromide	PSBr₃	50.0	83.6	108.0	126.3	157.8	175.0d	38	(9)
Phosphorus thiochloride	PSCl₃	− 18.3	+ 16.1	42.7	63.8	102.3	124.0	− 36.2	(9)
Platinum	Pt	2730	3146	3469	3714	4169	4407	1755	(218, 229, 252)
Potassium	K	341	443	524	586	708	774	62.3	(106, 122, 161, 163, 181, 229, 246, 257, 285, 357, 478)
Potassium bromide	KBr	795	982	1050	1137	1297	1383	730	(122, 229, 367, 473)
Potassium chloride	KCl	821	968	1078	1164	1322	1407	790	(122, 156, 162, 195, 204, 229, 243, 367, 473)
Potassium fluoride	KF	885	1039	1156	1245	1411	1502	880	(229, 371, 475)
Potassium hydroxide	KOH	719	863	976	1064	1233	1327	380	(204, 229, 475)
Potassium iodide	KI	745	887	995	1080	1238	1324	723	(122, 156, 229, 365, 475)
Radon	Rn	−144.2s	−126.3s	−111.3s	− 99.0s	− 75.0s	− 61.8	− 71	(152, 229, 244)
Rhenium heptoxide	Re₂O₇	212.5s	248.0s	272.0s	289.0s	336.0	362.4	296	(229, 291)
Rubidium	Rb	297	389	459	514	620	679	38.5	(161, 229, 357, 394)
Rubidium bromide	RbBr	781	923	1031	1114	1267	1352	682	(229, 367, 475)
Rubidium chloride	RbCl	792	937	1047	1133	1294	1381	715	(229, 367, 475)
Rubidium fluoride	RbF	921	1016	1096	1168	1322	1408	760	(229, 371, 475)
Rubidium iodide	RbI	748	884	991	1072	1223	1304	642	(229, 367, 475)
Selenium	Se	356	442	506	554	637	680	217	(99, 206, 229, 322)
Selenium dioxide	SeO₂	157.0s	202.5s	234.1s	258.0s	297.7s	317.0s	340	(6, 206, 229)
Selenium hexafluoride	SeF₆	−118.6s	− 98.9s	− 84.7s	− 73.9s	− 55.2s	− 45.8s	− 34.7	(229, 238, 491)
Selenium oxychloride	SeOCl₂	34.8	71.9	98.0	118.0	151.7	168.0	8.5	(229, 256)
Selenium tetrachloride	SeCl₄	74.0s	107.4s	130.1s	147.5s	176.4s	191.5d		(492)
Silane	SiH₄	−179.3	−163.0	−150.3	−140.5	−122.0	−111.5	−185	(2, 229, 470)
Silicon	Si	1724	1888	2000	2083	2220	2287	1420	(229, 359, 470)
Silicon dioxide	SiO₂		1732	1867	1969	2141	2227	1710	(229, 369)
Silicon tetrachloride	SiCl₄	− 63.4	− 34.4	− 12.1	+ 5.4	38.4	56.8	− 68.8	(24, 224, 229, 334, 434)
Silicon tetrafluoride	SiF₄	−144.0s	−130.4s	−120.8s	−113.3s	−100.7s	− 94.8s	− 90	(40, 229, 310, 347)
Bromosilane	SiH₃Br		− 77.3	− 57.8	− 42.3	− 13.3	+ 2.4	− 93.9	(229, 431)
Chlorosilane	SiH₃Cl	−117.8	− 97.7	− 81.8	− 68.5	− 44.5	− 30.4		(431)
Fluorosilane	SiH₃F	−153.0	−141.2	−130.8	−122.4	−106.8	− 98.0		(112)
Iodosilane	SiH₃I	s	− 43.7	− 21.8	− 4.4	+ 27.9	45.4	− 57.0	(112)

Name	Formula	Temperature, °C						M.P.	Citation No.
		1 mm	10 mm	40 mm	100 mm	400 mm	760 mm		
Bromodichlorofluorosilane.........	SiBrCl₂F	− 86.5	− 59.0	− 37.0	− 19.5	+ 15.4	35.4	−112.3	(389)
Bromotrifluorosilane.............	SiBrF₃			s	s	− 55.9	− 41.7	− 70.5	(388)
Chlorotrifluorosilane............	SiClF₃	−144.0₈	−127.0	−112.8	−101.7	− 81.0	− 70.0	−142	(40, 229, 392)
Dibromochlorofluorosilane........	SiBr₂ClF	− 65.2	− 35.6	− 12.0	+ 6.3	43.0	59.5	− 99.3	(389)
Dibromodifluorosilane...........	SiBr₂F₂		− 66.8	− 47.4	− 31.9	− 2.6	+ 13.7	− 66.9	(389)
Dibromosilane.................	SiH₂Br₂	− 60.9	− 29.4	− 5.2	+ 14.1	50.7	70.5	− 70.2	(229, 432)
Dichlorodifluorosilane..........	SiCl₂F₂	−124.7	−102.9	− 85.0	− 70.3	45.0	− 31.8	−139.7	(40, 229, 392)
Difluorosilane................	SiH₂F₂	−146.7	−130.4	−117.6	−107.3	− 87.6	− 77.8	....	(112)
Diiodosilane.................	SiH₂I₂	s	18.0	52.6	79.4	125.5	149.5	− 1.0	(113)
Disilane....................	Si₂H₆	−114.8	− 91.4	− 72.8	− 57.5	− 29.0	− 14.3	−132.6	(229, 431, 434)
Disiloxane...................	(SiH₃)₂O	−112.5	− 88.2	− 70.4	− 55.9	− 29.3	− 15.4	−144.2	(229, 434)
Fluorotrichlorosilane...........	SiCl₃F	− 92.6	− 68.3	− 48.8	− 33.2	− 4.0	+ 12.2	−120.8	(40)
Hexachlorodisilane............	Si₂Cl₆	+ 4.0	38.8	65.3	85.4	120.6	139.0	− 1.2	(229, 267)
Hexachlorodisiloxane..........	(SiCl₃)₂O	5.0	+ 29.4	55.2	75.4	113.6	135.6	− 33.2	(229, 434)
Hexafluorodisilane............	Si₂F₆	− 81.0₈	− 63.1₈	− 50.6₈	− 41.7₈	− 26.4₈	− 18.9₈	− 18.6	(229, 391, 392)
Octachlorotrisilane...........	Si₃Cl₈	46.3	89.3	121.5	146.0	189.5	211.4	....	(229, 267)
Tetrasilane.................	Si₄H₁₀	− 27.7	+ 4.3	28.4	47.4	81.7	100.0	− 93.6	(229, 431)
Tribromofluorosilane..........	SiBr₃F	− 46.1	− 15.1	+ 9.2	28.6	64.6	83.8	− 82.5	(388)
Tribromosilane..............	SiHBr₃	− 30.5	+ 3.4	30.0	51.6	90.2	111.8	− 73.5	(390)
Trichlorosilane..............	SiHCl₃	− 80.7	− 53.4	− 32.9	− 16.4	+ 14.5	31.8	−126.6	(229, 437)
Trifluorosilane..............	SiHF₃	−152.0₈	−138.2ₓ	−127.3	−118.7	−102.8	− 95.0	−131.4	(112)
Trisilane...................	Si₃H₈	− 68.9	− 40.0	− 16.9	+ 1.6	35.5	53.1	−117.2	(229, 431)
Disilazane..................	(SiH₃)₂N	− 68.7	− 40.4	− 18.5	− 1.1	+ 31.0	48.7	−105.7	(229, 433)
Silver.....................	Ag	1357	1575	1743	1865	2090	2212	960.5	(153, 154, 155, 163, 165, 218, 229, 348, 469, 471)
Silver chloride..............	AgCl	912	1074	1200	1297	1467	1564	455	(229, 264, 474)
Silver iodide...............	AgI	820	983	1111	1210	1400	1506	552	(209, 229)
Sodium....................	Na	439	549	633	701	823	892	97.5	(106, 134, 150, 160, 161, 163, 181, 229, 248, 257, 340, 343, 344, 357, 446, 472, 478)
Sodium bromide.............	NaBr	806	952	1063	1148	1304	1392	755	(229, 367, 473)
Sodium chloride.............	NaCl	865	1017	1131	1220	1379	1465	800	(122, 156, 162, 195, 229, 243, 264, 362, 367, 473)
Sodium cyanide.............	NaCN	817	983	1115	1214	1401	1497	564	(198, 229)
Sodium fluoride.............	NaF	1077	1240	1363	1455	1617	1704	992	(229, 371, 475)
Sodium hydroxide...........	NaOH	739	897	1017	1111	1286	1378	318	(229, 473)
Sodium iodide..............	NaI	767	903	1005	1083	1225	1304	651	(156, 229, 367, 475)
Stannic bromide............	SnBr₄	s	72.7	105.5	131.0	177.7	204.7	31.0	(9)
Stannic chloride............	SnCl₄	− 22.7	+ 10.0	35.2	54.7	92.1	113.0	− 30.2	(229, 279, 481, 494, 496)
Stannic hydride............	SnH₄	−140.0	−118.5	−102.3	− 89.2	− 65.2	− 52.3	−149.9	(229, 306)
Stannic iodide.............	SnI₄	s	175.8	218.8	254.2	315.5	348.0	144.5	(283)
Stannous chloride..........	SnCl₂	316	391	450	493	577	623	246.8	(229, 264)
Strontium.................	Sr	s	898	1018	1111	1285	1384	800	(167, 229, 355)
Strontium oxide...........	SrO	2068₈	2262₈	2410₈	....	....	....	2430	(75, 229)
Sulfur....................	S	183.8	243.8	288.3	327.2	399.6	444.6	112.8	(17, 34, 54, 66, 73, 157, 191, 229, 268, 278, 284, 323, 334, 353, 354, 482)
Sulfur hexafluoride.........	SF₆	−132.7₈	−114.7₈	−101.5₈	− 90.9₈	− 72.6₈	− 63.5₈	− 50.2	(229, 238)
Sulfur dioxide.............	SO₂	− 95.5₈	− 76.8₈	− 60.5	− 46.9	− 23.0	− 10.0	− 73.2	(25, 33, 51, 63, 68, 140, 142, 175, 229, 261, 280, 334, 385, 415, 420)
Sulfur monochloride........	S₂Cl₂	− 7.4	+ 27.5	54.1	75.3	115.4	138.0	− 80	(168, 229, 453)
Sulfuryl chloride..........	SO₂Cl₂	s	− 24.8	− 1.0	+ 17.8	51.3	69.2	− 54.1	(229, 448, 449)
Sulfur trioxide (α).........	SO₃	− 39.0₈	− 16.5₈	− 1.0₈	+ 10.5₈	32.6	44.8	16.8	(27, 151, 229, 411, 412)
Sulfur trioxide (β).........	SO₃	− 34.0₈	− 12.3₈	+ 3.2₈	14.3₈	32.6	44.8	32.3	(27, 151, 229, 411, 412)
Sulfur trioxide (γ).........	SO₃	− 15.3₈	+ 4.3₈	17.9₈	28.0₈	44.0₈	51.6₈	62.1	(27, 151, 229, 411, 412)
Sulfuric acid.............	H₂SO₄	145.8	194.2	229.7	257.0	305.0	330.0d	10.5	(9)
Thionyl bromide...........	SOBr₂	− 6.7	+ 31.0	58.8	80.6	119.2	139.5	− 52.2	(229, 269)
Thionyl chloride..........	SOCl₂	− 52.9	− 21.9	+ 2.2	21.4	56.5	75.4	−104.5	(11, 13, 229)
Tantalum pentafluoride.....	TaF₅				130.0	194.0	230.0	96.8	(229, 368)
Tellurium................	Te	520	650	753	838	997	1087	452	(101, 229)
Tellurium tetrachloride.....	TeCl₄	s	233	273	304	360	392	224	(229, 399)
Tellurium hexafluoride.....	TeF₆	−111.3₈	− 92.4₈	− 78.4₈	− 67.9₈	− 48.2₈	− 38.6₈	− 37.8	(229, 238, 491)
Thallium.................	Tl	825	983	1103	1196	1364	1457	303.5	(143, 229, 255, 466)
Thallium bromide..........	TlBr	s	522	598	653	759	819	460	(229, 405, 474)
Thallium chloride..........	TlCl	s	517	589	645	748	807	430	(229, 465, 474)
Thallium iodide...........	TlI	440	531	607	663	763	823	440	(229, 465, 474)
Tin......................	Sn	1492	1703	1855	1968	2169	2270	231.9	(153, 154, 155, 165, 229, 348, 469, 471)
Titanium tetrachloride......	TiCl₄	− 13.9	+ 21.3	48.4	71.0	112.7	136.0	− 30	(11, 229)
Tungsten.................	W	3990	4507	4886	5168	5666	5927	3370	(218, 229, 250, 498, 499)
Tungsten hexafluoride......	WF₆	− 71.4₈	− 49.2₈	− 33.0₈	− 20.3₈	+ 1.2	17.3	− 0.5	(229, 347)
Uranium hexafluoride.......	UF₆	− 38.8₈	− 13.8₈	+ 4.4₈	18.2₈	42.7₈	55.7₈	69.2	(229, 356)
Vanadyl trichloride........	VOCl₃	− 23.2	+ 12.2	40.0	62.5	103.5	127.2	....	(128)

INORGANIC COMPOUNDS (Continued)
Pressures Less than One Atmosphere (Continued)

Name	Formula	Temperature, °C						M.P.	Citation No.
		1 mm	10 mm	40 mm	100 mm	400 mm	760 mm		
Water..............	H_2O	− 17.3₃	+ 11.3	34.1	51.6	83.0	100.0	0.0	(81, 95, 104, 121, 189, 190, 217, 222, 229, 232, 303, 304, 378, 379, 404, 476, 481)
Xenon.............	Xe	− 168.5₃	− 152.8₃	− 141.2₃	− 132.8₃	− 117.1₃	− 108.0	−111.6	(3, 180, 229, 311, 315, 329)
Zinc...............	Zn	487	593	673	736	844	907	419.4	(17, 42, 61, 109, 154, 155, 163, 181, 210, 229, 255, 342, 348)
Zinc chloride........	$ZnCl_2$	428	508	566	610	689	732	365	(208, 229, 264)
Zinc fluoride........	ZnF_2	970	1086	1175	1254	1417	1497	872	(362)
Zirconium tetrabromide........	$ZrBr_4$	207₃	250₃	281₃	301₃	337₃	357₃	450	(229, 326)
Zirconium tetrachloride........	$ZrCl_4$	190₃	230₃	259₃	279₃	312₃	331₃	437	(229, 326)
Zirconium tetraiodide........	ZrI_4	264₃	311₃	344₃	369₃	409₃	431₃	499	(229, 326)

Pressures Greater than One Atmosphere

Name	Formula	Temperature, °C							Citation No.
		1 atm.	2 atm.	5 atm.	10 atm.	20 atm.	40 atm.	60 atm.	
Ammonia................	NH_3	− 33.6	− 18.7	+ 4.7	25.7	50.1	78.9	98.3	(23, 25, 33, 49, 62, 82, 142, 175, 192, 223, 231, 279, 305, 334, 420)
Argon...................	A	− 185.6	− 179.0	− 166.7	− 154.9	− 141.3	− 124.9	......	(41, 83, 193, 229, 295, 329, 466)
Boron trichloride........	BCl_3	12.7	33.2	66.0	96.7	135.4	......	......	(229, 308, 334, 430)
Boron trifluoride........	BF_3	−100.7	− 89.4	− 72.6	− 57.7	− 40.0	− 19.0	......	(39, 118, 229, 319, 352)
Bromine...............	Br_2	58.2	78.8	110.3	139.8	174.0	216.0	243.5	(88, 102, 171, 203, 217, 229, 281, 331, 345, 381, 458, 487)
Carbontetrachloride........	CCl_4	76.7	102.0	141.7	178.0	222.0	276.0	......	(104, 179, 279, 334, 335, 413, 495)
Carbon dioxide...........	CO_2	− 78.2₃	− 69.1₃	− 56.7	− 39.5	− 18.9	+ 5.9	22.4	(5, 46, 117, 172, 175, 211, 229, 272, 292, 302, 334, 420, 464, 467, 477, 497)
Carbon disulfide..........	CS_2	46.5	69.1	104.8	136.3	175.5	222.8	256.0	(175, 229, 265, 328, 334, 335, 420, 467, 490)
Carbon monoxide..........	CO	− 191.3	− 183.5	− 170.7	− 161.0	− 149.7	......	......	(16, 67, 77, 78, 87, 229, 293, 463)
Carbonyl chloride..........	$COCl_2$	+ 8.3	27.3	57.2	85.0	119.0	159.8	......	(14, 135, 229, 288, 309)
Chlorotrifluoromethane......	$CClF_3$	− 81.2	− 66.7	− 42.7	− 18.5	+ 12.0	52.8	......	(102, 447)
Cyanogen................	C_2N_2	− 21.0	− 4.4	+ 21.4	44.6	72.6	106.5	......	(74, 83, 102, 118, 313, 444)
Dichlorodifluoromethane....	CCl_2F_2	− 29.8	− 12.2	+ 16.1	42.4	74.0	......	......	(102, 144)
Dichlorofluoromethane......	$CHCl_2F$	8.9	28.4	59.0	87.0	121.2	162.6	......	(233)
Chlorodifluoromethane......	$CHClF_2$	− 40.8	− 24.7	+ 0.3	24.0	52.0	85.3	......	(40, 233)
Trichlorofluoromethane......	CCl_3F	23.7	44.1	77.3	108.2	146.7	194.0	......	(233)
Chlorine...............	Cl_2	− 33.8	− 16.9	+ 10.3	35.6	65.0	101.6	127.1	(139, 166, 171, 214, 229, 239, 312, 452)
Helium.................	He	−268.6	−268.0	......	......	......	......	......	(227, 228, 229, 300, 301)
Hydrogen...............	H_2	−252.5	−250.2	−246.0	−241.8	......	......	......	(58, 71, 173, 225, 229, 298, 299, 396, 454, 455)
Hydrogen bromide........	HBr	− 66.5	− 51.5	− 29.1	− 8.4	+ 16.8	48.1	70.6	(18, 103, 169, 229, 415, 416)
Hydrogen chloride........	HCl	− 84.8	− 71.4	− 50.5	− 31.7	− 8.8	+ 17.8	36.2	(50, 69, 103, 118, 141, 169, 175, 223, 229, 416, 420)
Hydrogen cyanide....	HCN	25.9	45.8	75.8	102.7	135.0	169.9	......	(44, 164, 229, 258, 314, 397, 401)
Hydrogen iodide..........	HI	− 35.1	− 18.9	+ 7.3	32.0	62.2	100.7	127.5	(103, 169, 229, 415, 416)
Hydrogen sulfide..........	H_2S	− 60.4	− 45.9	− 22.3	− 0.4	+ 25.5	55.8	76.3	(118, 137, 229, 235, 236, 292, 334, 415, 416)
Hydrogen selenide.........	H_2Se	− 41.1	− 25.2	0.0	+ 23.4	50.8	84.6	108.7	(57, 90, 91, 229, 292, 417)
Krypton.................	Kr	− 152.0	−143.5	−130.0	−118.0	−101.7	− 78.4	......	(3, 221, 229, 315, 317, 329)
Neon...................	Ne	−246.0	−243.8	−239.9	−236.0	−230.8	......	......	(71, 229, 297, 455)
Nitrogen...............	N_2	−195.8	−189.2	−179.1	−169.8	−157.6	......	......	(15, 70, 86, 100, 123, 138, 173, 174, 193, 229, 292, 321, 463, 467, 489)
Nitric oxide...........	NO	−151.7	−145.1	−135.7	−127.3	−116.8	− 103.2	− 94.8	(1, 146, 170, 216, 229, 279, 292, 294)
Nitrous oxide...........	N_2O	− 88.5	− 76.8	− 58.0	− 40.7	− 18.8	+ 8.0	27.4	(29, 33, 53, 62, 115, 188, 229, 247, 327, 464)
Nitrogen tetroxide..........	N_2O_4	21.0	37.3	59.8	79.4	100.3	121.4	132.2	(19, 108, 158, 229, 275, 317, 332, 374, 380, 385)
Oxygen.................	O_2	−183.1	−176.0	−164.5	−153.2	−140.0	−124.1	... ...	(15, 28, 58, 70, 86, 100, 114, 172, 174, 226, 229, 292, 296, 420, 456, 467, 488)
Silicon tetrafluoride........	SiF_4	− 94.8₃	− 84.4	− 67.9	− 52.6	− 33.4	......	......	(40, 229, 310, 347)
Chlorotrifluorosilane........	$SiClF_3$	− 70.0	− 57.3	− 37.2	− 18.6	+ 4.1	......	......	(40, 229, 392)
Dichlorodifluorosilane........	$SiCl_2F_2$	− 31.8	− 15.1	+ 11.6	36.6	66.2	......	......	(40, 229, 392)
Fluorotrichlorosilane........	$SiCl_3F$	12.2	32.4	64.6	94.2	131.8	......	......	(40)
Stannic chloride...........	$SnCl_4$	113.0	141.3	184.3	223.0	270.0	......	......	(229, 279, 481, 494, 496)
Sulfur dioxide............	SO_2	− 10.0	+ 6.3	32.1	55.5	83.8	118.0	141.7	(25, 33, 51, 63, 68, 140, 142, 175, 229, 261, 280, 334, 385, 415, 420)
Sulfur trioxide.............	SO_3	44.8	60.0	82.5	104.0	138.0	175.0	198.0	(27, 151, 229, 411, 412)
Water.................	H_2O	100.0	120.1	152.4	180.5	213.1	251.1	276.5	(81, 95, 104, 121, 189, 190, 217, 222, 229, 232, 303, 304, 378, 379, 404, 476, 481)

(1) Adwentowski, Bull. intern. acad. sci., Cracovie, [II] **1909, 742.**
(2) Adwentowski and Drozdowski, Ibid., [A] **1911,** 330–44.
(3) Allen and Moore, J. Am. Chem. Soc., **53,** 2522–7 (1931).
(4) Alterthum and Koref, Z. Elektrochem., **31,** 658–62 (1925).
(5) Amagat, Compt. rend., **114,** 1093–8 (1892).
(6) Amelin and Belyakov, J. Phys. Chem. (U.S.S.R.), **18,** 446–8, (1944).
(7) Anderson, J. Chem. Soc., **1930,** 1653–6.
(8) Anschütz and Evans, Ber., **19,** 1994–5 (1886).
(9) Anschütz and Reitter, "Die Destillation unter vermindertem Druck im Laboratorium," 2nd ed., Bonn, Cohen, 1895.
(10) Arctowski, Z. anorg. allgem. Chem., **12,** 427–30 (1896).
(11) Arii, Bull. Inst. Phys. Chem. Research (Tokyo), **8,** 714 (1929).
(12) Ibid., **8,** 545–51 (1929).
(13) Arii, Science Reports Tôhoku Imp. Univ., First Ser., **22,** 182–99 (1933).
(14) Atkinson, Heycock, and Pope, J. Chem. Soc., **117,** 1410–26 (1920).
(15) Baly, Phil. Mag., [5] **49,** 517 (1900).
(16) Baly and Donnan, J. Chem. Soc., **81,** 907–23 (1902).
(17) Barus, Phil. Mag., [5] **29,** 141–57 (1890).
(18) Bates, Halford, and Anderson, J. Chem. Phys., **3,** 531–4 (1935).
(19) Baume and Robert, Compt. rend., **168,** 1199–201 (1919).
(20) Baxter. Bezzenberger, and Wilson, J. Am. Chem. Soc., **42,** 1386–93 (1920).
(21) Baxter and Grose, Ibid., **37,** 1061–72 (1915).
(22) Baxter, Hickey and Holmes, Ibid., **29,** 127–36 (1907).
(23) Beattie and Lawrence, Ibid., **52,** 6–14 (1930).
(24) Becker and Meyer, Z. anorg. allgem. Chem., **43,** 251–66 (1907).
(25) Bergstrom, J. Phys. Chem., **26,** 358–76 (1922).
(26) Bernhardt, Physik Z., **26,** 265–75 (1925).
(27) Berthoud, Helv. Chim. Acta, **5,** 513–32 (1922).
(28) Bestelmeyer, Ann. Physik., [4] **14,** 87–98 (1904).
(29) Black, Van Praagh, and Topley, Trans. Faraday Soc., **26,** 196–7 (1930).
(30) Blanchard, Rafter, and Adams, J. Am. Chem. Soc., **56,** 16–7 (1934).
(31) Blaszkowska and Zakrzewska, Roczniki Chem., **8,** 210–8 (1928).
(32) Blue and Giauque, J. Am. Chem. Soc., **57,** 991–7 (1935).
(33) Blümcke, Ann. [2] **34,** 10–21 (1888).
(34) Bodenstein. Z. physik. Chem., **30,** 113–39 (1899).
(35) Boer and Dippel, Z. Physik., **B21,** 273–7 (1933).
(36) Bogros, Ann. phys., [10] **17,** 199–282 (1932).
(37) Bogros, Compt. rend., **191,** 560–2 (1930).
(38) Bolas, J. Chem. Soc., **24,** 780 (1871).
(39) Booth and Carter, J. Phys. Chem., **36,** 1359–63 (1932).
(40) Booth and Swinehart, J. Am. Chem. Soc., **57,** 1337–42 (1935).
(41) Born, Ann. Physik., [4] **69,** 473–504 (1922).
(42) Braune, Z. Anorg. allgem. Chem., **111,** 109–47 (1920).
(43) Braune and Tiedje, Ibid., **152,** 39–51 (1926).
(44) Bredig and Teichmann, Z. Electrochem., **31,** 449–54 (1925).
(45) Brewer and Dennis, J. Phys. Chem., **31,** 1101–5 (1927).
(46) Bridgman, J. Am. Chem. Soc., **49,** 1174–83 (1927).
(47) Bridgman, Ibid., **36,** 1344–63 (1914).
(48) Briggs and Migrdichian, J. Phys. Chem., **28,** 1121–35 (1924).
(49) Brill, Ann. Physik., [4] **21,** 170–180 (1906).
(50) Briner, J. chim. phys., **4,** 476 (1906).
(51) Briner and Cardoso, Ibid., **6,** 665 (1908).
(52) Briner and Pylkoff, Ibid., **10,** 640–79 (1912).
(53) Britton, Trans. Faraday Soc., **25,** 520–25 (1929).
(54) Brown and Muir, Phys. Rev., **41,** 111 (1932).
(55) Brühl, Ber., **26,** 2508–20 (1893).
(56) Bruylants, Bull. sci. acad. roy. belg., **1920,** 472–8.
(57) Bruylants, and Dondeyne, Ibid., [V] **8,** 387–405 (1922).
(58) Bulle, Physik. Z., **14,** 860–2 (1913).
(59) Burg and Schlesinger, J. Am. Chem. Soc., **59,** 780–7 (1937).
(60) Ibid., **62,** 3425–9 (1940).
(61) Burmeister and Jellinek, Z. physik. Chem., **A165,** 121–32 (1933).
(62) Burrell and Robertson, J. Am. Chem. Soc., **37,** 2482–6 (1915).
(63) Burrell and Robertson, U. S. Bur. Mine, Tech. Paper **142** (1916).
(64) Butler and Maass, J. Am. Chem. Soc., **52,** 2184–98 (1930).
(65) Cady and Hildebrand, Ibid., **52,** 3839–43 (1930).
(66) Callender and Griffiths, Chem. News, **63,** 1–2 (1891).
(67) Cardoso, J. chim. phys., **13,** 312–50 (1915).
(68) Cardoso and Fiorentino, Ibid., **23,** 841–7 (1926).
(69) Cardoso and Germann, Ibid., **11,** 632 (1913).
(70) Cath, Verslag. Akad. Wetenschappen, **27,** 553–60 (1918).
(71) Cath and Onnes, Ibid., **26,** 490 (1917).
(72) Centnerszwer, Z. physik. Chem., **85,** 99–112 (1913).
(73) Chappuis, Trav. bur. intern. poids measures, **16,** (1914).
(74) Chappuis and Rivière, Compt. rend., **104,** 1504–5 (1887).
(75) Claassen and Veenemans, Z. Physik., **80,** 342–51 (1933).
(76) Claussen and Hildebrand, J. Am. Chem. Soc., **56,** 1820 (1934).
(77) Clayton and Giauque, Ibid., **54,** 2610–26 (1932).
(78) Clusius and Teske, Z. physik. Chem., **6B,** 135–51 (1929).
(79) Corey, Laubengayer, and Dennis, J. Am. Chem. Soc., **47,** 112–7 (1925).
(80) Cosslett, Z. anorg. allgem. Chem., **201,** 75–80 (1931).
(81) Crafts, J. chim. phys., **13,** 105–61 (1915).
(82) Cragoe, Refrig. Eng., **12,** 131–42 (1925).
(83) Crommelin, Verslag. Akad. Wetenschappen, **22,** 510–20 (1913).
(84) Ibid., **16,** 477–85 (1913).
(85) Ibid., **22,** 1212–5 (1913).
(86) Ibid., **23,** 601–4 (1914).
(87) Crommelin, Bijleved, and Brown, Proc. Acad. Sci. Amsterdam, **34,** 1314–7 (1931).
(88) Cuthbertson and Cuthbertson, Proc. Roy. Soc. (London), **85,** 306–8 (1911).
(89) Daniels and Bright, J. Am. Chem. Soc., **42,** 1131–41 (1920).
(90) De Forcrand and Fonezes-Diacon, Compt. rend., **134,** 171–3 (1902).
(91) Ibid., **134,** 229–31 (1902).
(92) Dennis, Corey, and Moore, J. Am. Chem. Soc., **46,** 657–74 (1924).
(93) Dennis and Hance, J. Phys. Chem. **30,** 1055–9 (1926).
(94) Dennis, Orndorff, and Tabern, J. Phys. Chem., **30,** 1049–54 (1926).
(95) Derby, Daniels and Gutsche, J. Am. Chem. Soc., **36,** 793–804 (1914).
(96) Dewer, Proc. Chem. Soc. (London), **14,** 241–8 (1898).
(97) Dewer and Jones, Proc. Roy. Soc. (London), **A71,** 427–39 (1903).

(98) Ditte, Compt. rend., **140,** 1162–7 (1905).
(99) Dodd, J. Am. Chem. Soc., **42,** 1579–94 (1920).
(100) Dodge and Davis, Ibid., **49,** 610–20 (1927).
(101) Doolan and Partington, Trans. Faraday Soc., **20,** 342–4 (1924).
(102) Dow Chemical Co. files.
(103) Drozdowski and Pietrzak, Bull. intern. acad. sci. Cracovie, **A1913,** 219–40.
(104) Drucker, Jimeno, and Kangro, Z. physik. Chem., **90,** 513–52 (1915).
(105) Eastman and Duschak, U. S. Bur. Mines, Tech. Paper **225,** (1919).
(106) Edmondson and Egerton, Proc. Roy. Soc. (London), **A113,** 520–42 (1927).
(107) Egan, Potts, and Potts, Ind. Eng. Chem., **38,** 454–6 (1946).
(108) Egerton, J. Chem. Soc., **105,** 647–57 (1914).
(109) Egerton, Phil. Mag., [6] **33,** 33 (1917).
(110) Egerton, Proc. Roy. Soc. (London), **103A,** 469–86 (1923).
(111) Egerton and Raleigh, J. Chem. Soc., **123,** 3024–32 (1923).
(112) Emeléus and Maddock, Ibid., **1944,** 293–6.
(113) Emeléus, Maddock, and Reid, Ibid., **1941,** 353–8.
(114) Estreicher and Olszewski, Phil. Mag., [5] **40,** 454 (1895).
(115) Eucken and Donath, Z. physik. Chem., **124,** 181–203 (1926).
(116) Evnevitsch and Suchodski, J. Russ. Phys.-Chem. Soc., **61,** 1503–12 (1929).
(117) Falck, Physik Z., **9,** 433–40 (1908).
(118) Faraday, Phil. Trans., **135A,** 155 (1845).
(119) Feiser, Metall u. Erz, **26,** 269–84 (1929).
(120) Ibid., **28,** 297–302 (1931).
(121) Fenby, Chem. Age (London), **2,** 434–5 (1920).
(122) Fiock and Rodebush, J. Am. Chem. Soc., **48,** 2522–8 (1926).
(123) Fischer and Alt, Ann. Physik., [4] **9,** 1149 (1902).
(124) Fischer and Biltz, Z. anorg. allgem. Chem., **176,** 81–111 (1928).
(125) Fischer and Gewehr, Ibid., **222,** 303–11 (1935).
(126) Fischer and Jübermann, Ibid., **227,** 227–36 (1936).
(127) Fischer, Rahlfs, and Benze, Ibid., **205,** 1–41 (1932).
(128) Flood, Gorrissen, and Veimo, J. Am. Chem. Soc., **59,** 2494–5 (1937).
(129) Folger and Rodebush, Ibid., **45,** 2080 90 (1923).
(130) Friedel and Crafts, Compt. rend., **106,** 1764–70 (1888).
(131) Frost, Cothran, and Browne, J. Am. Chem. Soc., **55,** 3516–8 (1933).
(132) Füchtbauer and Bartels, Z. Physik., **4,** 337–42 (1921).
(133) Gayler, Metallwirtschaft, **9,** 677–9 (1930).
(134) Gebhardt, Ber. physik. Ges., **3,** 184–8 (1905).
(135) German and Taylor, J. Am. Chem. Soc., **48,** 1154–9 (1926).
(136) Gerry and Gillespie, Phys. Rev., [2] **40,** 269–80 (1932).
(137) Giauque and Blue, J. Am. Chem. Soc., **58,** 831–7 (1936).
(138) Giauque and Clayton, Ibid., **55,** 4875–89 (1933).
(139) Giauque and Powell, Ibid., **61,** 1970–4 (1939).
(140) Giauque and Stephenson, Ibid., **60,** 1389–94 (1938).
(141) Giauque and Wiebe, Ibid., **50,** 101–22 (1928).
(142) Gibbs, Ibid., **27,** 851–65 (1905).
(143) Gibson, dissertation, Breslau (1911).
(144) Gilkey, Gerard, and Bixler, Ind. Eng. Chem., **23,** 364–7 (1931).
(145) Gillespie and Fraser, J. Am. Chem. Soc., **58,** 2260–3 (1936).
(146) Goldschmidt, Z. Physik., **20,** 159–65 (1923).
(147) Goodeve, J. Chem. Soc., **1930,** 2733–7).
(148) Goodeve and Powney, Ibid., **1932,** 2078–81.
(149) Goodeve and Richardson, Ibid., **1937,** 294–300.
(150) Gordon, J. Chem. Phys., **4,** 100–2 (1936).
(151) Grau and Roth, Z. anorg. allgem. Chem. **188,** 173–185 (1930).
(152) Gray and Ramsay, J. Chem. Soc., **95,** 1073–85 (1909).
(153) Greenwood, Proc. Roy. Soc. (London), **A82,** 396–408 (1909).
(154) Ibid., **A83,** 483–91 (1910).
(155) Greenwood, Z. physik. Chem., **76,** 484–90 (1911).
(156) Greiner and Jellinck, Ibid., **A165,** 97–120 (1933).
(157) Gruener, J. Am. Chem. Soc., **29,** 1396–402 (1907).
(158) Guye and Drouguinine, J. chim. phys., **8,** 473 (1910).
(159) Haber and Kirschbaum, Z. Elektrochem., **20,** 296–305 (1914).
(160) Haber and Zisch, Z. Physik., **9,** 302–26 (1922).
(161) Hackspill, Ann. chim. phys., [8] **28,** 613–96 (1913).
(162) Hackspill and Grandadam, Ann. chimie, [10] **5,** 218–50 (1926).
(163) Hansen, Ber., **42,** 210–4 (1909).
(164) Hara and Shinozaki, Tech. Reports. Tôhoku Imp. Univ., **4,** 145–52 (1924).
(165) Harteck, Z. physik. Chem., **134,** 1–20 (1928).
(166) Ibid., **134,** 21–5 (1928).
(167) Hartman and Schneider, Z. Anorg. allgem. Chem., **180,** 275–83 (1929).
(168) Harvey and Schuette, J. Am. Chem. Soc., **48,** 2065–8 (1926).
(169) Henglein, Z. Physik., **18,** 64–9 (1923).
(170) Henglein and Krüger, Z. anorg. allgem. Chem., **130,** 181–7 (1923).
(171) Henglein, Von Rosenberg, and Muchlinski, Z. Physik., **11,** 1–11 (1922).
(172) Henning, Ann. Physik., [4] **43,** 282–94 (1914).
(173) Henning, Z. Physik., **40,** 775–85 (1927).
(174) Henning and Hense, Ibid., **23,** 105–16 (1924).
(175) Henning and Stock, Ibid., **4,** 226–40 (1921).
(176) Herbst, Physik. Z., **27,** 366–71 (1926).
(177) Herbst, Z. tech., Physik., **7,** 467–8 (1926).
(178) Hertz, Ann., [2] **17,** 177–200 (1882).
(179) Herz and Rathmann, Chem.-Ztg., **36,** 1417–8 (1912).
(180) Heuse and Otto, Z. tech. Physik., **13,** 277–8 (1932).
(181) Heycock and Lamplough, Proc. Chem. Soc. (London), **28,** 3–4 (1912).
(182) Hill, Phys. Rev. **20,** 259–60 (1922).
(183) Hincke, J. Am. Chem. Soc., **52,** 3869–77 (1930).
(184) Ibid., **55,** 1751–3 (1933).
(185) Hirst and Olson, J. Am. Chem. Soc., **51,** 2398–403 (1929).
(186) Hittorf, Ann., [2] **126,** 193–228 (1865).
(187) Hoeflake and Scheffer, Rec. trav. chim., **45,** 191–200 (1926).
(188) Hoge, J. Research Natl. Bur. Standards, **34,** 281–93 (1945).
(189) Holborn and Baumann, Ann. Physik., [4] **31,** 945–70 (1910).
(190) Holborn and Henning, Ibid., **26,** 833–83 (1908).
(191) Ibid., **35,** 761–4 (1911).
(192) Holst, thesis, Zurich, 1914.
(193) Holst and Hamburger, Z. physik. Chem., **91,** 513–47 (1916).
(194) Horiba, Proc. Acad. Sci. Amsterdam **25,** 387 (1923).
(195) Horiba and Baba, Bull. Chem. Soc. Japan, **3,** 11–7 (1928).

Inorganic Compounds

(196)Ilosvay, Bull. Soc. Chem., [2] **37**, 294 (1882).
(197)Ingold, J. Chem. Soc., **121**, 2419–32 (1922).
(198)Ibid., **123**, 885–91 (1923).
(199)International Critical Tables, **III**, 201–49 New York, McGraw-Hill Book Co., Inc., 1928.
(200)Isambert, Compt. rend., **92**, 919–22 (1881).
(201)Ibid., **94**, 958–60 (1882).
(202)Ibid., **96**, 643–8 (1883).
(203)Isnardi, Ann. Physik, [4] **61**, 264–72 (1920).
(204)Jackson and Morgan, Ind. Eng. Chem., **13**, 110–8 (1921).
(205)Jaeger and Germs, Z. anorg. allgem. Chem., **119**, 145–73 (1921).
(206)Jannek and Meyer, Ibid., **83**, 51–96 (1913).
(207)Jellinek and Golubowski, Z. physik. Chem., **A147**, 461–9 (1930).
(208)Jellinek and Koop, Ibid., **145A**, 305–29 (1929).
(209)Jellinek and Rudat, Ibid., **A143**, 55–61 (1929).
(210)Jenkens, Proc. Roy. Soc. (London), **110A**, 456–63 (1926).
(211)Jenkins and Pye, Phil. Trans. Roy. Soc., **A213**, 67 (1913).
(212)Johnson, J. Am. Chem. Soc., **33**, 777–81 (1911).
(213)Ibid., **34**, 877–80 (1912).
(214)Johnson and McIntosh, J. Am. Chem. Soc., **31**, 1138–44 (1909).
(215)Johnson and Pechukas, Ibid., **59**, 2065–8 (1937).
(216)Johnston and Giauque, Ibid., **51**, 3194–214 (1929).
(217)Jolly and Briscoe, J. Chem. Soc., **129**, 2154–9 (1926).
(218)Jones, Langmuir, and MacKay, Phys. Rev., [2] **30**, 201–214 (1927).
(219)Joubert, Compt. rend., **78**, 1853–5 (1874).
(220)Jung and Ziegler, Z. physik. Chem., **150**, 139–44 (1930).
(221)Justi, Physik. Z., **36**, 571–4 (1935).
(222)Kahlbaum, Z. physik. Chem., **13**, 14–55 (1894).
(223)Karwat, Ibid., **112**, 486–90 (1924).
(224)Kearby, J. Am. Chem. Soc., **58**, 374–5 (1936).
(225)Keesom, Byl, and Van der Horst, Proc. Acad. Sci., Amsterdam, **34**, 1223 (1931).
(226)Keesom, Van der Horst, and Jansen, Ibid., **32**, 1167–70 (1929).
(227)Keesom, Weber, and Norgaard, Ibid., **32**, 864 (1929).
(228)Keesom, Weber, and Schmidt, Ibid., **32**, 1314 (1929).
(229)Kelley, U. S. Bur. Mines, Bull. **383** (1935).
(230)Kemp and Giauque, J. Am. Chem. Soc., **59**, 79–84 (1937).
(231)Keyes and Brownlee, Ibid., **40**, 25–45 (1918).
(232)Keyes and Smith, Mech. Eng., **53**, 132–5 (1931).
(233)Kinetic Chemical Corporation bulletins.
(234)King and Partington, J. Chem. Soc., **129**, 925–9 (1926).
(235)Klemenc, Z. Elektrochem., **38**, 592–5 (1932).
(236)Klemenc and Bankowski, Z. anorg. allgem. Chem., **208**, 348–66 (1932).
(237)Klemens and Wagner, Ber., **70B**, 1880–2 (1937).
(238)Klemm and Henkel, Z. anorg. allgem. Chem., **207**, 73–86 (1932).
(239)Knietsch, Ann., [2] **259**, 100–24 (1890).
(240)Knudsen, Ann. Physik, [4] **29**, 179–93 (1909).
(241)Kohn, Z. Physik., **3**, 143–56 (1920).
(242)Kohn and Guckel, Ibid, **27**, 305–57 (1924).
(243)Kordes and Raaz, Z. anorg. allgem. Chem., **181**, 225–36 (1929).
(244)Kovarik, Phil. Mag., [VII] **4**, 1262–75 (1927).
(245)Krauss and Wilken, Z. anorg. allgem. Chem., **145**, 151–68 (1925).
(246)Kröner, Ann. Physik, [4] **40**, 438–52 (1913).
(247)Kuenen, Phil. Mag., [5] **40**, 173 (1895).
(248)Landenberg and Thiele, Z. physik. Chem., **B7**, 161–87 (1930).
(249)Landolt-Börnstein, "Physikalisch-Chemische Tabellen," Hauptwerk, 1332–77; I Ergänzungsband, 721–42; II Ergänzungsband, 1290–1310; III Ergänzungsband, 2430–62; Berlin, Julius Springer, 1923–36.
(250)Langmuir, Phys. Rev., [2] **2**, 329–42 (1913).
(251)Langmuir and Kingdon, Science, **57**, 58–60 (1923).
(252)Langmuir and MacKay, Phys. Rev., [2] **4**, 377–86 (1914).
(253)Laubengayer and Schirmer, J. Am. Chem. Soc., **62**, 1578–83 (1940).
(254)Laubengayer and Tabern, J. Phys. Chem., **30**, 1947–8 (1926).
(255)Leitgebel, Z. anorg. allgem. Chem., **202**, 305–24 (1931).
(256)Lenher, Smith, and Town, J. Phys. Chem., **26**, 156–60 (1922).
(257)Lewis, Z. Physik, **69**, 786–809 (1931).
(258)Lewis and Schutz, J. Am. Chem. Soc., **56**, 1002 (1934).
(259)Lobry de Bruyn, Rec. trav. chim., **10**, 100–12 (1891).
(260)Maass and Hiebert, J. Am. Chem. Soc., **46**, 2693–700 (1924).
(261)Maass and Maass, Ibid., **50**, 1352–68 (1928).
(262)Mack, Osterhof, and Kraner, Ibid., **45**, 617–23 (1923).
(263)Mac Rae and Van Voorhis, Ibid., **43**, 547–53 (1921).
(264)Maier, U. S. Bur. Mines, Tech. Paper **360**, (1925).
(265)Mali, Z. Anorg. Chem., **149**, 150–6 (1925).
(266)Marshall and Norton, J. Am. Chem. Soc., **55**, 431–2 (1933).
(267)Martin, J. Chem. Soc., **105**, 2836–60 (1914).
(268)Matthies, Physik. Z., **7**, 395–7 (1906).
(269)Mayes and Partington, J. Chem. Soc., **129**, 2594–605 (1926).
(270)Menzel and Mohry, Z. anorg. allgem. Chem. **210**, 257–63 (1933).
(271)Menzies, Z. physik. Chem., **130**, 90–8 (1927).
(272)Meyers and Van Dusen, J. Research Natl. Bur. Standards, **10**, 381–412 (1933).
(273)Millar, J. Am. Chem. Soc., **49**, 3003–10 (1927).
(274)Mittasch, Z. physik. Chem., **40**, 1–83 (1902).
(275)Mittasch, Kusz, and Schlenter, Z. Anorg. allgem. Chem., **159**, 1–36 (1926).
(276)Moles and Gómez, Z. physik. Chem., **80**, 513–30 (1912).
(277)Morley, Ibid., **49**, 95–100 (1904).
(278)Mueller and Burgess, J. Franklin Inst., **188**, 264–5 (1919).
(279)Mündel, Z. phys. Chem., **85**, 435–65 (1913).
(280)Mund, Bull. sci. acad. roy. belg., [V] **5**, 529 (1919).
(281)Nadejdine, Bull. Acad. imp. Sci. St. Petersburg, **30**, 327–30 (1886).
(282)Naumann, dissertation, Berlin (1907).
(283)Negishi, J. Am. Chem. Soc., **58**, 2293–6 (1936).
(284)Neumann, Z. physik. Chem., **A171**, 416–20 (1934).
(285)Neumann and Völker, Ibid., **161A**, 33–45 (1932).
(286)Nicolaieff, Compt. rend., **186**, 1621–4 (1928).
(287)Niederschulte, dissertation, Erlangen (1903).
(288)Nikitin, J. Russ. Phys. Chem. Soc., **52**, 235–49 (1920).
(289)Nilson and Pettersson, Z. physik. Chem., **1**, 27–38 (1887).
(290)Ogawa, Bull. Chem. Soc. Japan, **6**, 302–17 (1931).

(291)Ibid., **7**, 265–73 (1932.)
(292)Olszewski, Ann., [2] **31**, 58–74 (1887).
(293)Olszewski, Compt. rend., **99**, 706–7 (1884).
(294)Ibid., **100**, 940–3 (1885).
(295)Olszewski, Z. physik. Chem., **16**, 380–4 (1895).
(296)Onnes and Braak, Commun. Kamerlingh Onnes Lab. Univ. Leiden, No. **107a** (1908).
(297)Onnes, Crommelin, and Cath, Ibid., No. **151**, 15 (1917).
(298)Onnes, Crommelin, and Cath, Verslag. Akad. Wetenschappen, **26**, 124 (1917).
(299)Onnes and Keesom, Ibid., **22**, 389 (1913).
(300)Onnes and Weber, Comm. Phys. Lab. Leiden, No. **147b** (1915).
(301)Onnes and Weber, Proc. Acad. Sci. Amsterdam. **18**, 493 (1915).
(302)Onnes and Weber, Verslag. Akad. Wetenschappen, **22**, 226 (1913).
(303)Osborne, Stimson, Fiock, and Ginnings, J. Research Natl. Bur. Standards, **10**, 155–88 (1933).
(304)Osborne, Stimson, and Ginnings, Ibid., **23**, 197–270 (1939).
(305)Overstreet and Giauque, J. Am. Chem. Soc., 254–9 (1937).
(306)Paneth, Haken, and Rabinowitsch, Ber., **57**, 1891–903 (1924).
(307)Paneth and Rabinowitsch, Ber., **58**, 1138–63 (1925).
(308)Parker and Robinson, J. Chem. Soc., **130**, 2977–81 (1927).
(309)Paterno and Mazzuchelli, Gazz. chim. ital., **50, I**, 3052 (1920).
(310)Patnode and Papish, J. Phys. Chem., **34**, 1494–6 (1930).
(311)Patterson, Cripps, and Whytlow-Gray, Proc. Roy. Soc. (London), **86**, 579–90 (1912).
(312)Pellaton, J. chim. phys., **13**, 426–64 (1915).
(313)Perry and Bardwell, J. Am. Chem. Soc., **47**, 2629–32 (1925).
(314)Perry and Porter, Ibid., **48**, 299–302 (1926).
(315)Peters and Weil, Z. physik. Chem., **148A**, 27–35 (1930).
(316)Pfaundler, Ann., [2] **63**, 36–43 (1897).
(317)Pickering, U. S. Natl. Bur. Standards, Sci. Tech. Papers, **21**, 597–629 (1926).
(318)Pilling, Phys. Rev., [2] **18**, 362–8 (1921).
(319)Pohland and Harlos, Z. anorg. allgem. Chem., **207**, 242–5 (1932).
(320)Poindexter, Phys. Rev., **26**, 859–68 (1925).
(321)Porter and Perry, J. Am. Chem. Soc., **48**, 2059–60 (1926).
(322)Preuner and Brockmöller, Z. physik. Chem., **81**, 129–70 (1913).
(323)Preuner and Schupp, Ibid., **68**, 129–68 (1910).
(324)Prideaux, J. Chem. Soc., **97**, 2032–44 (1910).
(325)Purcell and Zahoorbux, J. Chem. Soc., **140**, 1029–35 (1937).
(326)Rahlfs and Fisher, Z. anorg. allgem. Chem., **211**, 349–67 (1933).
(327)Ramsay and Shields, J. Chem. Soc., **63**, 833–7 (1893).
(328)Ramsay and Shields, Z. physik. Chem., **12**, 433–76 (1893).
(329)Ramsay and Travers, Ibid., **38**, 641–89 (1901).
(330)Ramsay and Young, J. Chem. Soc., **49**, 37–50 (1886).
(331)Ibid., **49**, 453–62 (1886).
(332)Ramsay and Young, Trans. Roy. Soc. (London), **A177**, 86 (1886).
(333)Rassow, Z. anorg. allgem. Chem., **114**, 117–50 (1920).
(334)Regnault, Mém. Paris, **26**, 339 (1862).
(335)Rex, Z. physik. Chem., **55**, 355–70 (1916).
(336)Richter, Ber., **19**, 1057–60 (1886).
(337)Riesenfeld and Beja, Z. anorg. allgem. Chem., **132**, 179–200 (1923).
(338)Riesenfeld and Schwab, Z. Physik, **11**, 12–21 (1922).
(339)Rinse, Rec. trav. chim., **47**, 33–6 (1928).
(340)Rodebush and DeVries, J. Am. Chem. Soc., **47**, 2488–93 (1925).
(341)Rodebush and Dixon, Ibid., **47**, 1036–43 (1925).
(342)Rodebush and Dixon, Phys. Rev., [2] **26**, 851–8 (1925).
(343)Rodebush and Henry, J. Am. Chem. Soc., **52**, 3159–61 (1930).
(344)Rodebush and Walters, Ibid., **52**, 2654–65 (1930).
(345)Roozeboom, Rec. trav. chim., **3**, 67–76 (1884).
(346)Rudeberg, Phys. Rev., **46**, 763–7 (1934).
(347)Ruff and Ascher, Z. anorg. allgem. Chem., **196**, 413–20 (1931).
(348)Ruff and Bergdahl, Ibid., **106**, 76–94 (1919).
(349)Ruff and Bormann, Ibid., **88**, 365–85 (1914).
(350)Ibid., **88**, 397–409 (1914).
(351)Ruff and Braida, Ibid., **220**, 43–8 (1934).
(352)Ruff, Braida, Bretschneider, Menzel and Plaut, Ibid., **206**, 59–64 (1932).
(353)Ruff and Graf, Ber., **40**, 4199–205 (1907).
(354)Ruff and Graf, Z. anorg. allgem. Chem., **58**, 209–12 (1908).
(355)Ruff and Hartmann, Ibid., **133**, 29–45 (1924).
(356)Ruff and Heinzelmann, Ibid., **72**, 63–84 (1911).
(357)Ruff and Johannsen, Ber., **38**, 3601–4 (1905).
(358)Ruff and Keim, Z. anorg. allgem. Chem., **193**, 176–86 (1930).
(359)Ruff and Konschak, Z. Elektrochem., **32**, 515–25 (1926).
(360)Ruff and Krug, Z. anorg. allgem. Chem., **190**, 270–6 (1930).
(361)Ruff and Laass, Ibid., **183**, 214–22 (1929).
(362)Ruff and LeBoucher, Ibid., **219**, 376–81 (1934).
(363)Ruff and Menzel, Ibid., **190**, 257–66 (1930).
(364)Ibid., **198**, 39–52 (1931).
(365)Ibid., **202**, 49–61 (1931).
(366)Ruff, Menzel, and Neumann, Z. Anorg. allgem. Chem., **208**, 293–303 (1932).
(367)Ruff and Mugdan, Ibid., **117**, 147–71 (1921).
(368)Ruff and Schiller, Ibid., **72**, 329–57 (1911).
(369)Ruff and Schmidt, Ibid., **117**, 172–90 (1921).
(370)Ibid., **123**, 83–8 (1922).
(371)Ruff, Schmidt, and Mugdan, Z. anorg. allgem. Chem., **123**, 83–8 (1922).
(372)Ruff and Tschirch, Ber., **46**, 929–49 (1913).
(373)Rushton and Daniels, J. Am. Chem. Soc., **48**, 384–9 (1926).
(374)Russ, Z. physik. Chem., **82**, 217–22 (1913).
(375)Russ and Pokorny, Monatsh., **34**, 1027–60 (1913).
(376)Russell, Rundle, and Yost, J. Am. Chem. Soc., **63**, 2825–8 (1941).
(377)Ryschkewitsch, Z. Elektrochem., **31**, 54–63 (1925).
(378)Scheel and Heuse, Ann. Physik, [4] **29**, 723–37 (1909).
(379)Ibid., [4] **31**, 715–36 (1910).
(380)Scheffer and Treub, Z. physik. Chem., **81**, 308–32 (1913).
(381)Scheffer and Voogd, Rec. trav. chim., **45**, 214–23 (1926).
(382)Schenck and Albers, Z. anorg. allgem. Chem., **105**, 145–66 (1919).
(383)Schenck and Imker, Ber., **58B**, 271–2 (1925).
(384)Schenck, Mihr, and Banthien, Ibid., **39**, 1506–21 (1906).

(385)Scheuer, Anz. Akad. Wiss. Wien, **48**, 304 (1911).
(386)Schlesinger, Sanderson and Burg, J. Am. Chem. Soc., **62**, 3421–5 (1940).
(387)Schmidt and Walter, Ann. Physik, **72**, 565 (1923).
(388)Schumb and Anderson, J. Am. Chem. Soc., **58**, 994–6 (1936).
(389)Ibid., **59**, 651–3 (1937).
(390)Schumb and Bickford, Ibid., **56**, 852–4 (1934).
(391)Schumb and Gamble, Ibid., **53**, 3191–2 (1931).
(392)Ibid., **54**, 583–90 (1932).
(393)Ibid., **54**, 3943–9 (1932).
(394)Scott, Phil. Mag., [6] **47**, 32–50 (1924).
(395)Scott and Brickwedde, Phys. Rev., [2] **48**, 483 (1935).
(396)Scott et al., J. Chem. Phys., **2**, 454–64 (1934).
(397)Shirado, Bull. Chem. Soc. Japan, **2**, 85–95 (1927).
(398)Simons, J. Am. Chem. Soc., **46**, 2179–83 (1924).
(399)Ibid., **52**, 3488–93 (1930).
(400)Simons and Hildebrand, Ibid., **46**, 2183–91 (1924).
(401)Sinozaki, Hara, and Mitsukuri, Tech. Repts. Tôhoku Imp. Univ., **6**, 157 (1926).
(402)Smellie, J. Soc. Chem. Ind., **42**, 466–8 (1923).
(403)Smith and Calvert, J. Am. Chem. Soc., **36**, 1363–82 (1914).
(404)Smith and Menzies, Ibid., **32**, 907–14 (1910).
(405)Smits and Beljaars, Proc. Acad. Sci. Amsterdam, **34**, 1141 (1931).
(406)Smits and Bokhorst, Z. physik. Chem., **91**, 249–312 (1916).
(407)Smits and Dienum, Proc. Acad. Sci. Amsterdam, **33**, 514–25 (1930).
(408)Smits, Meyer, and Beck, Verslag Akad. Wetenschappen, **24**, 939 (1915).
(409)Smits, Meyering, and Kamermans, Proc. Acad. Sci. Amsterdam, **34**, 1327–39 (1931).
(410)Ibid., **35**, 193–6 (1932).
(411)Smits and Moerman, Z. physik. Chem., **B35**, 69–81 (1937).
(412)Smits and Shoenmaker, J. Chem. Soc., **125**, 2554–73 (1924).
(413)Smyth and Engel, J. Am. Chem. Soc., **51**, 2646–70 (1929).
(414)Spangenberg, Z. physik. Chem., **119**, 419–38 (1926).
(415)Steele and Bagster, J. Chem. Soc., **97**, 2607–20 (1911).
(416)Steele, McIntosh, and Archibald, Z. physik. Chem., **55**, 129–99 (1906).
(417)Stein, J. Chem. Soc., **134**, 2134–8 (1931).
(418)Stelzner, dissertation, Erlangen (1901).
(419)Stock and Friederici, Ber., **46**, 1959–71 (1913).
(420)Stock, Henning and Kuss, Ibid., **54**, 1119–29 (1921).
(421)Stock and Kuss, Ibid., **47**, 3113–5 (1914).
(422)Ibid., **50**, 159–64 (1917).
(423)Ibid., **56B**, 789–808 (1923).
(424)Stock, Kuss, and Priess, Ibid., **47**, 3115–49 (1914).
(425)Stock and Massenez, Ibid., **45**, 3539–68 (1912).
(426)Ibid., **59**, 2210–5 (1926).
(427)Ibid., **59**, 2215–23 (1926).
(428)Ibid., **62**, 90–9 (1929).
(429)Stock and Praetorius, Ibid., **45**, 3568 (1912).
(430)Stock and Priess, Ibid., **47**, 3109–13 (1914).
(431)Stock and Somieski, Ibid., **49**, 111–57 (1916).
(432)Ibid., **50**, 1739–54 (1917).
(433)Ibid., **54**, 740–58 (1921).
(434)Stock, Somieski, and Wintgen, Ibid., **50**, 1754–64 (1917).
(435)Stock and Stoltzenberg, Ibid., **50**, 498–502 (1917).
(436)Stock and Willfroth, Ibid., **47**, 144–54 (1914).
(437)Stock and Zeidler, Ibid., **56**, 986–97 (1923).
(438)Stock and Zimmermann, Monatsh., **53–54**, 786–90 (1929).
(439)Ibid., **55**, 1–2 (1930).
(440)Strassmann, dissertation, Hanover (1929).
(441)Stull, Ind. Eng. Chem. **39**, 517 (1947).
(442)Tamman, "Kristallisieren und Schmelzen; ein Bertrag zur Lehre der Anderungen des Aggregatzustandes", p. 289, Leipzig, Barth, 1903.

(443)Taylor and Jungers, J. Am. Chem. Soc., **55**, 5057–8 (1933).
(444)Terwen, Z. physik. Chem., **91**, 469–99 (1916).
(445)Thiel and Ritter, Z. anorg. allgem. Chem., **132**, 125–52 (1923).
(446)Thiele, Ann. Physik., [5] **14**, 957–70 (1932).
(447)Thornton, Burg, and Schlesinger, J. Am. Chem. Soc., **55**, 3177–82 (1933).
(448)Trautz, Z. Elektrochem., **14**, 271–2 (1908).
(449)Ibid., **14**, 534–44 (1908).
(450)Trautz and Badstübner, Ibid., **35**, 799–802 (1929).
(451)Trautz and Gerwig, Z. anorg. allgem. Chem., **134**, 409–16 (1924).
(452)Ibid., **134**, 417–20 (1924).
(153)Trautz, Rick, and Acker, Z. Elektrochem., **35**, 122–4 (1929).
(454)Travers and Jacquerod, Trans. Roy. Soc. (London), **200A**, 155 (1903).
(455)Travers and Jacquerod, Z. physik. Chem., **45**, 435–60 (1903).
(456)Travers, Senter, and Jacquerod, Ibid., **45**, 416–34 (1903).
(457)Treadwell and Terebesi, Helv. Chim. Acta, **15**, 1053–66 (1932).
(458)Tsuruta, Physik. Z., **1**, 417–9 (1900).
(459)Ultee, Ber., **39**, 1856–8 (1906).
(460)Van der Plaats, Rec. trav. chim., **5**, 149–83 (1886).
(461)Van Doormaal and Scheffer, Ibid., **50**, 1100–4 (1931).
(462)Van Leimpt, Ibid., **55**, 157–60 (1936).
(463)Verschoyle, Trans. Roy. Soc. (London), **A230**, 189 (1931).
(464)Villard, Ann. chim. phys., [7] **10**, 387 (1897).
(465)Volmer, Physik. Z., **30**, 590–6 (1929).
(466)Von Rechenberg, "Destillation," Leipzig (1923).
(467)Von Siemens, Ann. Physik, [4] **42**, 871–88 (1913).
(468)Von Wartenberg, Ann., [2] **440**, 97–110 (1924).
(469)Von Wartenberg, Z. anorg. allgem. Chem., **56**, 320–36 (1908).
(470)Ibid., **79**, 71–87 (1913).
(471)Von Wartenberg, Z. Elektrochem., **19**, 482–9 (1913).
(472)Ibid., **20**, 443–9 (1914).
(473)Von Wartenberg and Albrecht, Ibid., **27**, 162–7 (1921).
(474)Von Wartenberg and Bosse, Ibid., **28**, 384–7 (1922).
(475)Von Wartenberg and Schulz, Ibid., **27**, 568–73 (1921).
(476)Washburn, Monthly Weather Rev., **52**, 488–90 (1924).
(477)Weber, Verslag. Akad. Wetenschappen, **22**, 380 (1914).
(478)Weiler, Ann. Physik., [5] **1**, 361–99 (1929).
(479)Welch and Duschak, U. S. Bur. Mines, Tech. Paper **81**, (1915).
(480)Wertenstein and Jedrzejewski, Compt. rend., **177**, 316–22 (1923).
(481)Wertheimer, Ber. deut. physik. Ges., **21**, 435–53 (1919).
(482)West and Menzies, J. Phys. Chem., **33**, 1880–92 (1929).
(483)Wiedmann, Stelzner, and Niederschulte, Ber. deut. physik. Ges., **3**, 159–62 (1905).
(484)Windsor and Blanchard, J. Am. Chem. Soc., **56**, 823–5 (1934).
(485)Winkler, dissertation, Müchen (1917).
(486)Wright, J. Chem. Soc., **107**, 1527–31 (1915).
(487)Ibid., **109**, 1134–9 (1916).
(488)Wroblewski, Compt. rend., **98**, 982–5 (1884).
(489)Ibid., **102**, 1010–2 (1886).
(490)Wüllener and Grotrain, Ann., [2] **11**, 545–604 (1880).
(491)Yost and Claussen, J. Am. Chem. Soc., **55**, 885–91 (1933).
(492)Yost and Kircher, Ibid., **52**, 4680–5 (1930).
(493)Yost and Stone, Ibid., **55**, 1889–95 (1933).
(494)Young, J. Chem. Soc., **59**, 626–34 (1891).
(495)Ibid., **59**, 911–36 (1891).
(496)Young, Sci. Proc. Roy. Dublin Soc., **12**, 374–443 (1909–1910).
(497)Zeleny and Smith, Physik. Z., **7**, 667–71 (1906).
(498)Zwikker, Physica, **5**, 249–60 (1925).
(499)Ibid., **5**, 319 (1925).

VAPOR PRESSURE (Continued) ORGANIC COMPOUNDS Pressures Less than One Atmosphere

Name	Formula	Temperature °C						M.P.	Citation No.
		1 mm	10 mm	40 mm	100 mm	400 mm	760 mm		
Cyanogen bromide	CBrN	− 35.7s	− 10.0s	+ 8.6s	22.6s	46.0s	61.5	58	(26, 208)
Carbon tetrabromide	CBr4	s	s	96.3	119.7	163.5	189.5	90.1	(48)
Chlorotrifluoromethane	CClF3	−149.5	−134.1	−121.9	−111.7	− 92.7	− 81.2		(113, 430)
Cyanogen chloride	CClN	− 76.7s	− 53.8s	− 37.5s	− 24.9s	− 2.3	+ 13.1	− 6.5	(208, 344)
Dichlorodifluoromethane	CCl2F2	−118.5	− 97.8	− 81.6	− 68.6	− 43.9	− 29.8		(113, 146)
Carbonyl chloride	CCl2O	− 92.9	− 69.3	− 50.3	− 35.6	− 7.6	+ 8.3	−104	(20, 145, 208, 305, 311)
Trichlorofluoromethane	CCl3F	− 84.3	− 59.0	− 39.0	− 23.0	+ 6.8	23.7	......	(212)
Trichloronitromethane	CCl3NO2	− 25.5	+ 7.8	33.8	53.8	91.8	111.9	− 64	(26, 46, 47)
Carbontetrachloride	CCl4	− 50.0s	− 19.6	+ 4.3	23.0	57.8	76.7	− 22.6	(115, 175, 289, 343, 352, 394, 481)
Cyanogen fluoride	CFN	−134.4s	−118.5s	−106.4s	− 97.0s	− 80.5s	− 72.6s		(94, 208)
Carbontetrafluoride	CF4	−184.6s	−169.3	−158.8	−150.7	−135.5	−127.7		(208, 271)
Tribromomethane	CHBr3	s	34.0	63.6	85.9	127.9	150.5	8.5	(113, 201)
Chlorodifluoromethane	CHClF2	−122.8	−109.7	− 90.6	− 76.4	− 64.8	− 40.8	−160	(50, 010)
Dichlorofluoromethane	CHCl2F	− 91.3	− 67.5	− 48.8	− 33.9	− 6.2	+ 8.9	−135	(212)
Trichloromethane	CHCl3	− 58.0	− 29.7	− 7.1	+ 10.4	42.7	61.3	− 63.5	(32, 115, 175, 345, 352, 365)
Hydrocyanic acid	CHN	− 70.8s	− 48.2s	− 31.3s	− 18.8s	+ 9.8	25.8	− 14	(252)
Dibromomethane	CH2Br2	− 35.1	− 2.4	+ 23.3	42.3	79.0	98.6	− 52.8	(113, 352)
Dichloromethane	CH2Cl2	− 70.0	− 43.3	− 22.3	− 6.3	24.1	40.7	− 96.7	(317, 352)
Formaldehyde	CH2O	s	− 88.0	− 70.6	− 57.3	− 33.0	− 19.5	− 92	(264, 399)
Formic acid	CH2O2	− 20.0s	+ 2.1s	24.0	43.8	80.3	100.6	8.2	(7, 91, 203, 219, 246, 353, 373)
Dichloromethylarsine	CH3AsCl2	− 11.1	+ 24.3	51.5	73.0	112.7	134.5	− 59	(26)
Borine carbonyl	CH3BO	−139.2	−121.1	−106.6	− 95.3	− 74.8	− 64.0		(64)
Methyl bromide	CH3Br	− 96.3s	− 72.8	− 54.2	− 39.4	− 11.9	+ 3.6	− 93	(117, 323)
Methyl chloride	CH3Cl	s	− 92.4	− 76.0	− 63.0	− 38.0	− 24.0	− 97.7	(54, 182, 241, 350, 451)

Name	Formula	Temperature °C						M.P.	Citation No.
		1 mm	10 mm	40 mm	100 mm	400 mm	760 mm		
Trichloromethylsilane	CH_3Cl_3Si	− 60.8	− 30.7	− 7.0	+ 12.1	47.0	66.4	− 90	(113)
Methyl fluoride	CH_3F	−147.3	−131.6	−119.1	−109.0	− 89.5	78.2	......	(89, 113, 281)
Methyl iodide	CH_3I	s	− 45.8	− 24.2	− 7.0	+ 25.3	42.4	− 64.4	(351, 352, 363)
Formamide	CH_3NO	70.5	109.5	137.5	157.5	193.5	210.5d	......	(11, 113)
Nitromethane	CH_3NO_2	− 29.0	+ 2.8	27.5	46.6	82.0	101.2	− 29	(154, 470)
Methane	CH_4	−205.9s	−195.5s	−187.7s	−181.4	−168.8	−161.5	−182.5	(6, 72, 73, 93, 123, 206, 359, 407)
Dichloromethylsilane	CH_4Cl_2Si	− 75.0	− 47.8	− 26.2	− 9.0	+ 23.7	41.9	......	(113, 114, 410)
Methanol	CH_4O	− 44.0	− 16.2	+ 5.0	21.2	49.9	64.7	− 97.8	(111, 289, 319, 338, 353)
Methanethiol	CH_4S	− 90.7	− 67.5	− 49.2	− 34.8	− 7.9	+ 6.8	−121	(39)
Chloromethylsilane	CH_5ClSi	− 95.0	− 71.0	− 51.7	− 36.4	− 7.8	+ 8.7	......	(410)
Methylamine	CH_5N	− 95.8s	− 73.8	− 56.9	− 43.7	− 19.7	− 6.3	− 93.5	(19, 38, 130, 186, 324)
Methylsilane	CH_6Si	−138.5	−120.0	−104.8	− 93.0	− 70.3	− 56.9	......	(410)
2-Methyldisilazane	CH_9NSi_2	− 76.3	− 50.1	− 29.6	− 13.1	+ 17.2	34.0	......	(118)
Cyanogen iodide	CIN	25.2s	57.7s	80.3s	97.6s	126.1s	141.1s	......	(208, 476)
Tetranitromethane	CN_4O_8	s	22.7	48.4	68.9	105.9	125.7d	13	(272)
Carbon monoxide	CO	−222.0s	−215.0s	−210.0s	−205.7s	−196.3	−191.3	−205.0	(23, 72, 73, 82, 83, 102, 208, 306, 447)
Carbonyl sulfide	COS	−132.4	−113.3	− 98.3	− 85.9	− 62.7	− 49.9	−138.8	(190, 208, 209, 408)
Carbonyl selenide	COSe	−117.1	− 95.0	− 76.4	− 61.7	− 35.6	− 21.9	......	(330)
Carbon dioxide	CO_2	−134.3s	−119.5s	−108.6s	−100.2s	− 85.7s	− 78.2s	− 57.5	(4, 5, 53, 124, 167, 168, 196, 208, 242, 275, 307, 308, 343, 407, 448, 454, 463, 493)
Carbon Selenosulfide	CSSe	− 47.3	− 16.0	+ 8.6	28.3	65.2	85.6	− 75.2	(208, 412)
Carbon disulfide	CS_2	− 73.8	− 44.7	− 22.5	− 5.1	+ 28.0	46.5	−110.8	(168, 208, 263, 331, 343, 352, 407, 454, 475)
Trichloroacetyl bromide	C_2BrCl_3O	− 7.4	+ 29.3	57.2	79.5	120.2	143.0	......	(11)
1-Chloro-1,2,2-trifluoroethylene	C_2ClF_3	−116.0	− 95.9	− 79.7	− 66.7	− 41.7	− 27.9	−157.5	(49, 50, 113)
1,2-Dichloro-1,2-difluoroethylene	$C_2Cl_2F_2$	− 82.0	− 57.3	− 38.2	− 23.0	+ 5.0	20.9	−112	(49, 113)
1,2-Dichloro-1,1,2,2-tetrafluoroethane	$C_2Cl_2F_4$	− 95.4	− 72.3	− 53.7	− 39.1	− 12.0	+ 3.5	− 94	(212)
1,1,2-Trichloro-1,2,2-trifluoroethane	$C_2Cl_3F_3$	− 68.0s	− 40.3s	− 18.5	− 1.7	+ 30.2	47.6	− 35	(212)
Tetrachloroethylene	C_2Cl_4	− 20.6s	+ 13.8	40.1	61.3	100.0	120.8	− 19.0	(113, 175, 176)
1,1,2,2-Tetrachloro-1,2-difluoroethane	$C_2Cl_4F_2$	− 37.5s	− 5.0s	+ 19.8s	38.6	73.1	92.0	26.5	(113, 184)
Hexachloroethane	C_2Cl_6	32.7s	73.5s	102.3s	124.2s	163.8s	185.6s	186.6	(296, 402)
Tribromoacetaldehyde	C_2HBr_3O	18.5	58.0	87.8	110.2	151.6	174.0d	......	(113, 201)
Trichloroethylene	C_2HCl_3	− 43.8	− 12.4	+ 11.9	31.4	67.0	86.7	− 73	(113, 175)
Trichloroacetaldehyde	C_2HCl_3O	− 37.8	− 5.0	20.2	40.2	77.5	97.7	− 57	(113, 280)
Trichloroacetic acid	$C_2HCl_3O_2$	51.0s	88.2	116.3	137.8	175.2	195.6	57	(11)
Pentachloroethane	C_2HCl_5	+ 1.0	39.8	69.9	93.5	137.2	160.5	− 22	(175, 296, 402)
Acetylene	C_2H_2	−142.9s	−128.2s	−116.7s	−107.9s	− 92.0s	− 84.0s	− 81.5	(12, 66, 67, 69, 217, 449)
1,1,1,2-Tetrabromoethane	$C_2H_2Br_4$	58.0	95.7	123.2	144.0	181.0	200.0d	......	(11)
1,1,2,2-Tetrabromoethane	$C_2H_2Br_4$	65.0	110.0	144.0	170.0	217.5	243.5	......	(11, 113)
cis-1,2-Dichloroethylene	$C_2H_2Cl_2$	− 58.4	− 29.9	− 7.9	+ 9.5	41.0	59.0	− 80.5	(113, 175, 176)
trans-1,2-Dichloroethylene	$C_2H_2Cl_2$	− 65.4s	− 38.0	− 17.0	− 0.2	+ 30.8	47.8	− 50.0	(113, 175, 176)
1,1-Dichloroethene	$C_2H_2Cl_2$	− 77.2	− 51.2	− 31.1	− 15.0	+ 14.8	31.7	−122.5	(113)
Dichloroacetic acid	$C_2H_2Cl_2O_2$	44.0	82.6	111.8	134.0	173.7	194.4	9.7	(11, 313)
1,1,1,2-Tetrachloroethane	$C_2H_2Cl_4$	− 16.3	+ 19.3	46.7	68.0	108.2	130.5	− 68.7	(113, 402)
1,1,2,2-Tetrachloroethane	$C_2H_2Cl_4$	− 3.8	+ 33.0	60.8	83.2	124.0	145.9	− 36	(113, 175, 296, 402)
1-Bromoethylene	C_2H_3Br	− 95.4	− 68.8	− 48.1	− 31.9	− 1.1	+ 15.8	−138	(378)
Bromoacetic acid	$C_2H_3BrO_2$	54.7	94.1	124.0	146.3	186.7	208.0	49.5	(11)
1,1,2-Tribromoethane	$C_2H_3Br_3$	32.6	70.6	100.0	123.5	165.4	188.4	− 26	(9, 11)
1-Chloroethylene	C_2H_3Cl	−105.6	− 83.7	− 66.8	− 53.2	− 28.0	− 13.8	−153.7	(104, 113)
Chloroacetic acid	$C_2H_3ClO_2$	43.0s	81.0	109.2	130.7	169.0	189.5	61.2	(203, 204, 313)
1,1,1-Trichloroethane	$C_2H_3Cl_3$	− 52.0	− 21.9	+ 1.6	20.0	54.6	74.1	− 30.6	(113, 361, 402)
1,1,2-Trichloroethane	$C_2H_3Cl_3$	− 24.0	+ 8.3	35.2	55.7	93.0	113.9	− 36.7	(113, 402)
Trichloroacetaldehyde hydrate	$C_2H_3Cl_3O_2$	− 9.8s	+ 19.5s	39.7s	55.0	82.1	96.2d	51.7	(113)
1-Fluoroethylene	C_2H_3F	−149.3	−132.2	−118.0	−106.2	− 84.0	− 72.2	−160.5	(75)
Acetonitrile	C_2H_3N	− 47.0s	− 16 3	+ 7.7	27.0	62.5	81.8	− 41	(159)
Methyl thiocyanate	C_2H_3NS	− 14.0	+ 21.6	49.0	70.4	110.8	132.9	− 51	(11)
Methyl isothiocyanate	C_2H_3NS	− 34.7s	+ 5.4s	38.2	59.3	97.8	119.0	35.5	(25)
Ethylene	C_2H_4	−168.3	−153.2	−141.3	−131.8	−113.9	−103.7	−169	(6, 57, 66, 93, 116, 244, 359, 407, 448, 453)
1-Bromo-1-chloroethane	C_2H_4BrCl	− 36.0s	− 9.4s	+ 10.4s	28.0	63.4	82.7	16.6	(113, 402)
1-Bromo-2-chloroethane	C_2H_4BrCl	− 28.8s	+ 4.1	29.7	49.5	86.0	106.7	− 16.6	(113, 402)
1,2-Dibromoethane	$C_2H_4Br_2$	− 27.0s	+ 18.6	48.0	70.4	110.1	131.5	10	(11, 31, 113, 349, 351, 438)
1,1-Dichloroethane	$C_2H_4Cl_2$	− 60.7	− 32.3	− 10.2	+ 7.2	39.8	57.4	− 96.7	(113, 352, 402)
1,2-Dichloroethane	$C_2H_4Cl_2$	− 44.5s	− 13.6	+ 10.0	29.4	64.0	82.4	− 35.3	(113, 133, 315, 352, 402)
1,1-Difluoroethane	$C_2H_4F_2$	−112.5	− 91.7	− 75.8	− 63.2	− 39.5	− 26.5	−117	(75)
Acetaldehyde	C_2H_4O	− 81.5	− 56.8	− 37.8	− 22.6	+ 4.9	20.2	−123.5	(113, 147, 248)
Ethylene oxide	C_2H_4O	− 89.7	− 65.7	− 46.9	− 32.1	− 4.9	+ 10.7	−111.3	(260)
Acetic acid	$C_2H_4O_2$	− 17.2s	+ 17.5	43.0	63.0	99.0	118.1	16.7	(113, 203, 246, 258, 289, 335, 353, 373, 480)
Methyl formate	$C_2H_4O_2$	− 74.2	− 48.6	− 28.7	− 12.9	16.0	32.0	− 99.8	(297, 491)
Mercaptoacetic acid	$C_2H_4O_2S$	60.0	101.5	131.8	154.0d	......	......	− 16.5	(113)
Ethyl bromide	C_2H_5Br	− 74.3	− 47.5	− 26.7	− 10.0	+ 21.0	38.4	−117.8	(113, 347, 391, 438)

Name	Formula	Temperature °C						M.P.	Citation No.
		1 mm	10 mm	40 mm	100 mm	400 mm	760 mm		
Ethyl chloride	C_2H_5Cl	− 89.8	− 65.8	− 47.0	− 32.0	− 3.9	+ 12.3	−139	(38, 113, 195, 346, 402)
2-Chloroethanol	C_2H_5ClO	− 4.0	+ 30.3	56.0	75.0	110.0	128.8	− 69	(11, 113)
Trichloroethylsilane	$C_2H_5Cl_3Si$	− 27.9	+ 3.6	27.9	46.3	80.3	99.5	− 40	(114)
Trichloroethoxysilane	$C_2H_5Cl_3OSi$	− 32.4	0.0	+ 25.3	45.2	82.2	102.4	......	(114)
Ethyl fluoride	C_2H_5F	−117.0	− 97.7	− 81.8	− 69.3	45.5	− 32.0	......	(50)
Ethyltrifluorosilane	$C_2H_5F_3Si$	− 95.4	− 73.7	− 56.8	− 43.6	− 19.1	− 5.4	......	(119)
Ethyl Iodide	C_2H_5I	− 54.4	− 24.3	− 0.9	+ 18.0	52.3	72.4	−105	(113, 348, 351, 352, 394)
Acetamide	C_2H_5NO	65.0s	105.0	135.8	158.0	200.0	222.0	81	(11)
Acetaldoxime	C_2H_5NO	− 5.8s	+ 25.8	48.6	66.2	98.0	115.0	47	(11)
Nitroethane	$C_2H_5NO_2$	− 21.0	+ 12.5	38.0	57.8	94.0	114.0	− 90	(31, 90)
Di(nitrosomethyl)amine	$C_2H_5N_3O_2$	+ 3.2	40.0	68.2	90.3	131.3	153.0	......	(11)
Ethane	C_2H_6	−159.5	−142.9	−129.8	−119.3	− 99.7	− 88.6	−183.2	(6, 30, 65, 84, 93, 153, 261, 262, 359, 453)
Dichlorodimethylsilane	$C_2H_6Cl_2Si$	− 53.5	− 23.8	− 0.4	+ 17.5	51.9	70.3	− 86.0	(113)
Ethanol	C_2H_6O	− 31.3	− 2.3	+ 19.0	34.9	63.5	78.4	−112	(32, 113, 115, 202, 273, 289, 329, 337, 343, 365, 374, 394)
Dimethyl ether	C_2H_6O	−115.7	− 93.3	− 76.2	− 62.7	− 37.8	− 23.7	−138.5	(55, 74, 211, 260, 350)
1,2-Ethanediol	$C_2H_6O_2$	53.0	92.1	120.0	141.8	178.5	197.3	− 15.6	(11, 71, 113, 136, 141)
Dimethyl sulfide	C_2H_6S	− 75.6	− 49.2	− 28.4	− 12.0	+ 18.7	36.0	− 83.2	(39)
Ethanethiol	C_2H_6S	− 76.7	− 50.2	− 29.8	− 13.0	17.7	35.5	−121	(39)
Dimethylantimony	C_2H_6Sb	44.0	86.0	118.3	143.5	187.2	211.0	......	(309)
Ethylamine	C_2H_7N	− 82.3s	− 58.3	− 39.8	− 25.1	+ 2.0	16.6	− 80.6	(38)
Dimethylamine	C_2H_7N	− 87.7	− 64.6	− 46.7	− 32.6	− 7.1	+ 7.4	− 96	(38, 390, 467)
1,2-Ethanediamine	$C_2H_8N_2$	− 11.0s	+ 21.5	45.8	62.5	99.0	117.2	8.5	(181)
Dimethylsilane	C_2H_8Si	−115.0	− 93.1	− 75.7	− 61.4	− 35.0	− 20.1	......	(410)
Dimethyldiborane	$C_2H_{10}B_2$	−106.5	− 82.1	− 62.4	− 47.0	− 18.8	− 2.6	−150.2	(371)
2-Ethyldisilazane	$C_2H_{11}NSi_2$	− 62.0	− 32.2	− 8.3	+ 10.4	45.9	65.9	−127	(118)
Cyanogen	C_2N_2	− 95.8s	− 76.8s	− 62.7s	− 51.8s	− 33.0	− 21.0	− 34.4	(79, 101, 113, 125, 318, 426)
Acrylonitrile	C_3H_3N	− 51.0	− 20.3	+ 3.8	22.8	58.3	78.5	− 82	(113)
Propadiene	C_3H_4	−120.6	101.0	− 85.2	− 72.5	− 48.5	− 35.0	−136	(113, 244, 255)
Propyne	C_3H_4	−111.0s	− 90.5	− 74.3	− 61.3	− 37.2	− 23.3	−102.7	(113, 165, 262, 286)
2,3-Dibromopropene	$C_3H_4Br_2$	− 6.0	+ 30.0	57.8	79.5	119.5	141.2	......	(113, 204)
Methyl dichloroacetate	$C_3H_4Cl_2O_2$	3.2	38.1	64.7	85.4	122.6	143.0	......	(11)
2-Propenal	C_3H_4O	− 64.5	− 36.7	− 15.0	+ 2.5	34.5	52.5	− 87.7	(283)
Acrylic acid	$C_3H_4O_2$	+ 3.5s	39.0	66.2	86.1	122.0	141.0	14	(342)
Pyruvic acid	$C_3H_4O_3$	21.4	57.9	85.3	106.5	144.7	165.0d	13.6	(11)
1,2,3-Tribromopropene	$C_3H_5Br_3$	47.5	90.0	122.8	148.0	195.0	220.0	16.5	(113)
1-Chloropropene	C_3H_5Cl	− 81.3	− 54.1	− 32.7	− 15.1	+ 18.0	37.0	− 99.0	(113)
3-Chloropropene	C_3H_5Cl	− 70.0	− 42.9	− 21.2	− 4.5	+ 27.5	44.6	−136.4	(113, 192)
Epichlorohydrine	C_3H_5ClO	− 16.5	+ 16.6	42.0	62.0	98.0	117.9	25.6	(11)
Methyl chloroacetate	$C_3H_5ClO_2$	− 2.9	+ 30.0	54.5	73.5	109.5	130.3	− 31.9	(113, 297)
1,1,1-Trichloropropane	$C_3H_5Cl_3$	− 28.8	+ 4.2	29.9	50.0	87.5	108.2	− 77.7	(113)
1,2,3-Trichloropropane	$C_3H_5Cl_3$	+ 9.0	46.0	74.0	96.1	137.0	158.0	− 14.7	(11)
Allyltrichlorosilane	$C_3H_5Cl_3Si$	− 20.7	+ 13.2	39.2	59.3	97.1	118.0	......	(114)
Propionitrile	C_3H_5N	− 35.0	− 3.0	+ 22.0	41.4	77.7	97.1	− 91.9	(159)
3-Hydroxypropionitrile	C_3H_5NO	58.7	102.0	134.1	157.7	200.0	221.0	......	(113, 210)
Ethylisothiocyanate	C_3H_5NS	− 13.2s	+ 22.8	50.8	71.9	110.1	131.0	− 5.9	(25)
Nitroglycerine	$C_3H_5N_3O_9$	127	188	235	e	....	....	11	(100, 268)
Propylene	C_3H_6	−131.9	−112.1	− 96.5	− 84.1	− 60.9	− 47.7	−185	(6, 66, 67, 137, 244, 262, 359, 382)
Cyclopropane	C_3H_6	−116.8	− 97.5	− 82.3	− 70.0	− 46.9	− 33.5	−126.6	(113)
2-Bromo-2-nitrosopropane	C_3H_6BrNO	− 33.5	− 4.3	+ 17.9	35.2	66.2	83.0	......	(321)
1,2-Dibromopropane	$C_3H_6Br_2$	− 7.0	+ 29.4	57.2	78.7	118.5	141.6	− 55.5	(11, 113, 204)
1,3-Dibromopropane	$C_3H_6Br_2$	+ 9.7	48.0	77.8	101.3	144.1	167.5	− 34.4	(113, 204)
2,3-Dibromo-1-propanol	$C_3H_6Br_2O$	57.0	98.2	129.8	153.0	196.0	219.0	......	(11)
1,2-Dichloropropane	$C_3H_6Cl_2$	− 38.5	− 6.1	+ 19.4	39.4	76.0	96.8	......	(301)
1,3-Dichloro-2-propanol	$C_3H_6Cl_2O$	28.0	64.7	93.0	114.8	153.5	174.3	......	(11, 199, 201)
Acetone	C_3H_6O	− 59.4	− 31.1	− 9.4	+ 7.7	39.5	56.5	− 94.6	(29, 115, 129, 343, 364)
Allyl alcohol	C_3H_6O	− 20.0	+ 10.5	33.4	50.0	80.2	96.6	−129	(25, 291)
Propylene oxide	C_3H_6O	− 75.0	− 49.0	− 28.4	− 12.0	+ 17.8	34.5	−112.1	(113)
Propionic acid	$C_3H_6O_2$	4.6	39.7	65.8	85.8	122.0	141.1	− 22	(203, 204, 353, 373)
Methyl acetate	$C_3H_6O_2$	− 57.2	− 29.3	− 7.9	+ 9.4	40.0	57.8	− 98.7	(113, 491)
Ethyl formate	$C_3H_6O_2$	− 60.5	− 33.0	− 11.5	+ 5.4	37.1	54.3	− 79	(297, 491)
Methyl glycolate	$C_3H_6O_3$	+ 9.6	45.3	72.3	93.7	131.7	151.5	......	(113)
Methoxyacetic acid	$C_3H_6O_3$	52.5	92.0	122.0	144.5	184.2	204.0	......	(113)
1-Bromopropane	C_3H_7Br	− 53.0	− 23.3	− 0.3	+ 18.0	52.0	71.0	−109.9	(113, 352)
2-Bromopropane	C_3H_7Br	− 61.8	− 32.8	− 10.1	+ 8.0	41.5	60.0	− 89.0	(113, 352)
1-Chloropropane	C_3H_7Cl	− 68.1	− 41.0	19.6	2.5	+ 29.4	46.4	−122.8	(38, 113, 160, 757)
2-Chloropropane	C_3H_7Cl	− 78.8	− 52.0	− 31.0	− 13.7	+ 18.0	36.5	−117	(113, 352)
Trichloroisopropylsilane	$C_3H_7Cl_3Si$	− 24.3	+ 9.9	36.5	57.8	96.8	118.5	....	(114)
1-Iodopropane	C_3H_7I	− 36.0	− 2.4	+ 23.6	43.8	81.8	102.5	− 98.8	(352)
2-Iodopropane	C_3H_7I	− 43.3	− 11.7	+ 13.2	32.8	69.5	89.5	− 90	(352)
Propionamide	C_3H_7NO	65.0s	105.0	134.8	156.0	194.0	213.0	79	(11, 113)
1-Nitropropane	$C_3H_7NO_2$	− 9.6	+ 25.3	51.8	72.3	110.6	131.6	−108	(90)
2-Nitropropane	$C_3H_7NO_2$	− 18.8	+ 15.8	41.8	62.0	99.8	120.3	− 93	(90)
Ethyl Carbamate	$C_3H_7NO_2$		77.8	105.6	126.2	164.0	184.0	49	(11)
Propane	C_3H_8	−128.9	−108.5	− 92.4	− 79.6	− 55.6	42.1	−187.1	(6, 30, 66, 93, 137, 153, 262, 359)
Dichloroethoxymethylsilane	$C_3H_8Cl_2OSi$	− 33.8	− 1.3	+ 24.4	44.1	80.3	100.6	......	(114)
1-Propanol	C_3H_8O	− 15.0	+ 14.7	36.4	52.8	82.0	97.8	−127	(113, 289, 340, 374)

Name	Formula	Temperature °C 1 mm	10 mm	40 mm	100 mm	400 mm	760 mm	M.P.	Citation No.
2-Propanol	C₃H₈O	− 26.1	+ 2.4	23 8	39.5	67.8	82 5	− 85.8	(310)
Ethyl methyl ether	C₃H₈O	− 91.0	− 67 8	− 49.4	− 34.8	− 7.8	+ 7.5	......	(39)
1,2-Propanediol	C₃H₈O₂	45.5	83.2	111.2	132.0	168.1	188.2	......	(71, 113, 368)
1,3-Propanediol	C₃H₈O₂	59.4	100.6	131.0	153.4	193.8	214 2	......	(113, 141, 368)
2-Methoxyethanol	C₃H₈O₂	− 13.5	+ 22.0	47.8	68.0	104 3	124 4	....	(141)
Glycerol	C₃H₈O₃	125.5	167.2	198.0	220.1	263.0	290.0	17 9	(11, 71, 134, 205, 353, 403)
1-Propanethiol	C₃H₈S	− 56.0	− 26.3	− 3.2	+ 15 3	49.2	67.4	−112	(422)
Trimethylborine	C₃H₉B	−118.0	− 92.4	− 74.7	− 60.8	− 34.7	− 20 1	......	(413)
Chlorotrimethylsilane	C₃H₉ClSi	− 62.8	− 34.0	− 11.4	+ 6.0	39 4	57.9	.....	(113, 424)
Trimethylgallium	C₃H₉Ga	− 62.3ₛ	− 31.7ₛ	− 9.0	+ 8.0	39.0	55.6	− 19	(240)
Propylamine	C₃H₉N	− 64.4	− 37.2	− 16.0	+ 0.5	31.5	48.5	− 83	(38)
Trimethylamine	C₃H₉N	− 97.1	− 73.8	− 55.2	− 40.3	− 12.5	+ 2.9	−117.1	(18, 390, 418, 467)
Trimethyl phosphate	C₃H₉O₄P	26.0	67.8	100.0	124.0	167.8	192.7	−122.9	(77)
Trimethyldiborane	C₃H₁₂B₂	− 74.0	− 44.8	− 22.0	− 4.4	+ 27.8	45.5	−122.9	(371)
Carbon suboxide	C₃O₂	− 94.8	− 71.0	− 52.0	− 36.9	− 8.9	+ 6.3	−107	(411)
Carbon subsulfide	C₃S₂	14.0	54.9	85.6	109 9	......	+ 0.4	...	(208, 409)
Trichloroacetic anhydride	C₄Cl₆O₃	56.2	99.6	131.2	155 2	199.8	223.0	......	(11)
1,3-Butadiyne	C₄H₂	− 82.5ₛ	− 61.2ₛ	− 45.9ₛ	− 34.0	− 6.1	+ 9.7	− 34.9	(414, 421)
α,β-Dibromomaleic anhydride	C₄H₂Br₂O₃	50.0	92.0	123.5	147.7	192.0	215.0	......	(11)
trans-Fumaryl chloride	C₄H₂Cl₂O₂	+ 15.0	51.8	79.5	101.0	140.0	160.0	......	(11)
Maleic anhydride	C₄H₂O₃	44 0	78 7	111.8	135.8	179.5	202.0	58	(11, 189)
2-Nitrothiophene	C₄H₃NO₂S	48.2	92.0	125.8	151.5	199.6	224.5	46	(22)
Butenyne	C₄H₄	− 93 2	− 70.0	− 51.7	− 37.1	− 10.1	+ 5 3	......	(304)
Succinyl chloride	C₄H₄Cl₂O₂	39 0	78 0	107.5	130.0	170.0	192.5	17	(11)
Chloroacetic anhydride	C₄H₄Cl₂O₃	67.2	108.0	138.2	159.8	197.0	217.0	46	(313)
Succinic anhydride	C₄H₄O₃	92.0ₛ	128 2	163.0	189.0	237.0	261.0	119.6	(11, 234)
1,4-Dioxane-2,6-dione	C₄H₄O₄	ₛ	116 6	148.6	173.2	217 0	240.0	97	(11)
Thiophene	C₄H₄S	− 40.7ₛ	− 10.9	+ 12 5	30.5	64.7	84 4	− 38.3	(113, 127)
Selenophene	C₄H₄Se	− 39.0	− 4.0	+ 24.1	47 0	89 8	114.3	......	(56)
α-Chlorocrotonic acid	C₄H₅ClO₂	70.0	108.0	135.6	155.9	193.2	212.0	......	(11)
Ethyl chloroglyoxylate	C₄H₅ClO₃	− 5.1	+ 29.9	56.0	76.6	114.7	135.0	......	(11)
Ethyl trichloroacetate	C₄H₅Cl₃O₂	20.7	57.7	85.5	107 4	146.0	167.0	......	(11)
3-Butenenitrile	C₄H₅N	− 19.6	+ 14.1	40.0	60.2	98.0	119.0	......	(159)
Methacrylonitrile	C₄H₅N	− 44.5	− 12.5	+ 12.8	32.8	32.8	90 3	......	(113)
cis-Crotononitrile	C₄H₅N	− 29.0	+ 4.0	30.0	50.1	88.0	108.0	......	(159)
trans-Crotononitrile	C₄H₅N	− 19.5	+ 15 0	41.8	62.8	101.5	122.8	......	(159)
Succinimide	C₄H₅NO₂	115.0ₛ	157.0	192.0	217.4	263.5	287.5	125.5	(11)
Allylisothiocyanate	C₄H₅NS	− 2.0	+ 38.3	67.4	89.5	129.8	156.7	− 80	(11, 25, 299, 201)
1,2-Butadiene	C₄H₆	− 89.0	− 64.2	− 44.3	− 28.3	+ 1.8	18.5	......	(113)
1,3-Butadiene	C₄H₆	−102.8	− 79.7	− 61.3	− 46.8	− 19.3	− 4.5	−108.9	(52, 162, 189, 445)
Cyclobutene	C₄H₆	− 99.1	− 75.4	− 56.4	− 41.2	− 12.2	+ 2.4	......	(163)
1 Butyne	C₄H₆	− 92.5	− 68.7	− 50.0	− 34.9	− 6.9	+ 8.7	−130	(286)
2-Butyne	C₄H₆	− 73.0ₛ	− 50.5ₛ	− 33.9ₛ	− 18.8	+ 10.6	27.2	− 32.5	(164, 287)
Ethyl dichloroacetate	C₄H₆Cl₂O₂	9.6	46.3	74.0	96.1	135.9	156 5	......	(11)
2-Chloroethyl chloroacetate	C₄H₆Cl₂O₂	46.0	86.0	116.0	140.0	182.2	205.0	......	(113)
cis-Crotonic acid	C₄H₆O₂	33.5	69.0	96 0	116.3	152.2	171.9d	15.5	(11)
trans-Crotonic acid	C₄H₆O₂	ₛ	80.0	107.8	128.0	165 5	185.0	72	(11)
Methyl acrylate	C₄H₆O₂	− 43.7	− 13.5	+ 9.2	28.0	61.8	80.2p	......	(113)
Methacrylic acid	C₄H₆O₂	25.5	60.0	86.4	106.6	142.5	161.0	15	(342)
Vinyl acetate	C₄H₆O₂	− 48.0	− 18.0	+ 5.3	23 3	55.5	72.5	......	(267)
Acetic anhydride	C₄H₆O₃	1.7	36.0	62.1	82.2	119 8	139.6	− 73	(33, 113, 201)
Dimethyl oxalate	C₄H₆O₄	20.0	56.0	83 6	104.8	143 3	163.3	......	(11, 97, 144)
cis-1 Bromo-1-butene	C₄H₇Br	− 44.0	− 12.8	+ 11.5	30 8	66 8	86 2	......	(250)
trans-1-Bromo-1-butene	C₄H₇Br	− 38.4	− 6 4	+ 18.4	38 1	75 0	94.7	−100.3	(250)
2-Bromo-1-butene	C₄H₇Br	− 47.3	− 16.8	+ 7 2	26.3	61.9	81 0	−133 4	(250)
cis-2-Bromo-2-butene	C₄H₇Br	− 39.0	− 7.2	+ 17 7	37.5	74.0	93.0	−111.2	(250)
trans-2-Bromo-2-butene	C₄H₇Br	− 45.0	− 13.8	+ 10.5	29.9	66.0	85.5	−114.6	(250)
1-Bromo-2-Butanone	C₄H₇BrO	+ 6.2	41.8	68 2	89.2	126.3	147.0	......	(285)
2-Methylpropionyl bromide	C₄H₇BrO	13.5	50.6	79.4	101.6	141.7	163.0	......	(11)
1,1,2-Tribromobutane	C₄H₇Br₃	45.0	87.8	120.2	146.0	192 0	216 2	......	(250)
1,2,2-Tribromobutane	C₄H₇Br₃	41.0	83.2	116.0	141.8	188 0	213 8	......	(250)
2,2,3-Tribromobutane	C₄H₇Br₃	38.2	79.8	111.8	136.3	182.2	206.5	......	(250)
Ethyl chloroacetate	C₄H₇ClO₂	+ 1.0	37.5	65.2	86.0	123.8	144.2	− 26	(11, 298)
1,2,3-Trichlorobutane	C₄H₇Cl₃	+ 0.5	41.0	71.5	96.2	143.0	169.0	......	(285)
Butyronitrile	C₄H₇N	− 20.0	+ 13.4	38.4	59.0	96.8	117.5	......	(159)
Diacetamide	C₄H₇NO₂	70.0ₛ	108.0	138.2	160.6	202.0	223.0	78.5	(11, 171)
1-Butene	C₄H₈	−104.8	− 81.6	− 63.4	− 48.9	− 21.7	− 6.3	−130	(6, 84, 112, 244, 359)
cis-2-Butene	C₄H₈	− 96.4	− 73.4	− 54.7	− 39.8	− 12.0	+ 3.7	−138.9	(6, 84, 213, 244, 359)
trans-2-Butene	C₄H₈	− 99.4	− 76.3	− 57.6	− 42.7	− 14.8	+ 0.9	−105.4	(6, 213, 244, 359)
2-Methylpropene	C₄H₈	−105.1	− 81.9	− 63.8	− 49.3	− 22.2	− 6.9	−140.3	(6, 84, 85, 86, 113, 244, 359)
Cyclobutane	C₄H₈	− 92.0ₛ	− 67.9ₛ	− 48.4	− 32.8	− 3.4	+ 12.9	− 50	(113, 163)
Methylcyclopropane	C₄H₈	− 96.0	− 72.8	− 54.2	− 39.3	− 11.3	+ 4.5	−110	(110)
2-Bromoethyl 2-chloroethyl ether	C₄H₈BrClO	36.5	76.3	106.6	129.8	172.3	195.8	......	(113)
1,2-Dibromobutane	C₄H₈Br₂	7.5	46.1	76.0	99.8	143.5	166.3	− 64.5	(250)
dl-2,3-Dibromobutane	C₄H₈Br₂	+ 5.0	41.6	72.0	95.3	138.0	160.5	......	(250)
meso-2,3-Dibromobutane	C₄H₈Br₂	+ 1.5	39.3	68.2	91.7	134.2	157.3	− 34.5	(250)
1,4-Dibromobutane	C₄H₈Br₂	32.0	72.4	104.0	128.7	173.8	197.5	− 20	(113)
1,2-Dibromo-2-methylpropane	C₄H₈Br₂	− 28.8	+ 10.5	42.3	68.8	119.8	149.0	− 70.3	(11, 86)
1,3-Dibromo-2-methylpropane	C₄H₈Br₂	14.0	53.0	83.5	107.4	150.6	174.6	......	(113)
Di(2-bromoethyl) ether	C₄H₈Br₂O	47.7	88.5	119.8	144.0	188.0	212.5	......	(113)
1,2-Dichlorobutane	C₄H₈Cl₂	− 23.6	+ 11.5	37.7	60.2	100.8	123.5	......	(285)
2,3-Dichlorobutane	C₄H₈Cl₂	− 25.2	+ 8.5	35.0	56.0	94.2	116.0	− 80.4	(437)
1,1-Dichloro-2-methylpropane	C₄H₈Cl₂	− 31.0	+ 2.6	28.2	48.2	85.4	−106.0d		(113)
1,2-Dichloro-2-methylpropane	C₄H₈Cl₂	− 25.8	+ 6.7	32.0	51.7	87.8	108.0	......	(113)
1,3-Dichloro-2-methylpropane	C₄H₈Cl₂	− 3.0	+ 32.0	58.6	78.8	115.4	135.0	......	(113)
di(2-chloroethyl) ether	C₄H₈Cl₂O	23.5	62.0	91.5	114.5	155.4	178.5	......	(113, 133, 141)

Name	Formula	Temperature °C						M.P	Citation No.
		1 mm	10 mm	40 mm	100 mm	400 mm	760 mm		
1,2-Epoxy-2-methylpropane	C_4H_8O	− 69.0	− 40.3	− 17.3	+ 1.2	36.0	55.5	......	(113)
2-Butanone	C_4H_8O	− 48.3	− 17.7	+ 6.0	25.0	60.0	79.6	− 85.9	(113)
1,4-Dioxane	$C_4H_8O_2$	− 35.8_s	− 1.2_s	+ 25.2	45.1	81.8	101.1	10	(141, 173)
Butyric acid	$C_4H_8O_2$	25.5	61.5	88.0	108.0	144.5	163.5	− 4.7	(204, 332, 373, 374)
Isobutyric acid	$C_4H_8O_2$	14.7	51.2	77.8	98.0	134.5	154.5	− 47	(203, 204, 353, 373, 374)
Ethyl acetate	$C_4H_8O_2$	− 43.4	− 13.5	+ 9.1	27.0	59.3	77.1	− 82.4	(113, 455, 491)
Methyl propionate	$C_4H_8O_2$	− 42.0	− 11.8	+ 11.0	29.0	61.8	79.8	− 87.5	(491)
Propyl formate	$C_4H_8O_2$	− 43.0	− 12.6	+ 10.8	29.5	62.6	81.3	− 92.9	(297, 491)
Isopropyl formate	$C_4H_8O_2$	− 52.0	− 22.7	− 0.2	+ 17.8	50.5	68.3	......	(113, 297, 491)
α-Hydroxyisobutyric acid	$C_4H_8O_3$	73.5_s	110.5	138.0	157.7	193 8	212.0	79	(11)
Ethyl glycolate	$C_4H_8O_3$	14.3	50.5	78.1	99.8	138.0	158.2	......	(113)
1-Bromobutane	C_4H_9Br	− 33.0	− 0.3	+ 24.8	44.7	81.7	101.6	− 112.4	(113)
1-Bromo-2-butanol	C_4H_9BrO	23.7	55.8	79.5	97.6	128.3	145.0	......	(285)
1-Chlorobutane	C_4H_9Cl	− 49.0	− 18.6	+ 5.0	24.0	58.8	77.8	− 123.1	(113, 249, 333, 394)
sec-Butyl chloride	C_4H_9Cl	− 60.2	− 29.2	− 5.0	+ 14.2	50.0	68.0	− 131.3	(113, 439)
Isobutyl chloride	C_4H_9Cl	− 53.8	− 24.5	− 1.9	+ 16.0	50.0	68.9	− 131.2	(113, 438)
tert-Butyl chloride	C_4H_9Cl	_s	− 19.0	− 1.0	+ 32.6	51.0	− 26.5	(87, 113)
2-(2-Chloroethoxy) ethanol	$C_4H_9ClO_2$	53.0	90.7	118.4	139.5	176.5	196.0	......	(113)
1-Iodo-2-methylpropane	C_4H_9I	− 17.0	+ 17.0	42.8	63 5	100.3	120.4	− 90.7	(11)
Ethyl methylcarbamate	$C_4H_9NO_2$	26.5	63.2	91.0	112.0	149.8	170.0	......	(375)
Propyl carbamate	$C_4H_9NO_2$	52.4	90.0	117 7	138.3	175.8	195.0	......	(11)
Di(nitrosoethyl)amine	$C_4H_9N_2O_2$	18.5	57.7	87 6	111.0	153.5	176.9	......	(11)
Butane	C_4H_{10}	− 101.5	− 77.8	− 59.1	− 44.2	− 16 3	− 0.5	− 135	(6, 66, 93, 359, 382)
2-Methylpropane	C_4H_{10}	− 109.2	− 86.4	− 68.4	− 54.1	− 27.1	− 11.7	− 145	(6, 16, 93, 187, 359, 382)
Dichlorodiethylsilane	$C_4H_{10}Cl_2Si$	− 9.2	+ 25.4	51.6	71.8	110.0	130.4	......	(114)
Diethyldifluorosilane	$C_4H_{10}F_2Si$	− 56.8	− 28.8	− 7.3	+ 9.8	40.5	58.0	......	(119)
Butyl alcohol	$C_4H_{10}O$	− 1.2	+ 30.2	53.4	70.1	100.8	117.5	− 79.9	(68, 174, 203, 204, 314)
sec-Butyl alcohol	$C_4H_{10}O$	− 12.2	+ 16.9	38.1	54.1	83.9	99.5	− 114.7	(68)
Isobutyl alcohol	$C_4H_{10}O$	− 9.0	+ 21.7	44.1	61.5	91.4	108.0	− 108	(68, 203, 219, 291, 374)
tert-Butyl alcohol	$C_4H_{10}O$	− 20.4_s	+ 5.5_s	24.5_s	39.8	68.0	82.9	25.3	(68, 310)
Diethyl ether	$C_4H_{10}O$	− 74.3	− 48.1	− 27.7	− 11.5	+ 17.9	34.6	116.3	(31, 113, 115, 289, 338, 423a)
Methyl propyl ether	$C_4H_{10}O$	− 72.2	− 45.4	− 24.3	− 8.1	+ 22.5	39.1	......	(113)
1,3-Butanediol	$C_4H_{10}O_2$	22.2_s	85.3	117.4	141.2	183.8	206.5	77	(189)
2,3-Butanediol	$C_4H_{10}O_2$	44.0	80.3	107.8	127.8	164.0	182.0	22.5	(368)
1,2-Dimethoxyethane	$C_4H_{10}O_2$	− 48.0	− 15.3	+ 10.7	31 8	70.8	93.0	......	(254)
2,2'-Thiodiethanol	$C_4H_{10}O_2S$	42.0	128.0	210.0_d	285_d	......	......	......	(25)
Diethylene glycol	$C_4H_{10}O_3$	91.8	133 8	164.3	187.5	226 5	244.8	......	(71, 141, 355)
1,2,3-Butanetriol	$C_4H_{10}O_3$	102.0	146.0	178.0	202.5	243.5	264.0	......	(113)
Diethyl sulfite	$C_4H_{10}O_4S$	10 0	46.4	74 2	96.3	137.0	159.0	......	(11, 13, 14)
Diethyl sulfate	$C_4H_{10}O_4S$	47.0	87.7	118.0	142.5	185 5	209.5_d	− 25.0	(11, 450)
Diethyl sulfide	$C_4H_{10}S$	− 39.6	− 8.0	+ 16.1	35.0	69.7	88.0	− 99.5	(25, 39)
Diethyl selenide	$C_4H_{10}Se$	− 25.7	+ 7.0	31.2	51.8	88.0	108.0	......	(420)
Diethylzinc	$C_4H_{10}Zn$	− 22.4	+ 11 7	38.0	59.1	97.3	118.0	− 28	(161)
Diethylamine	$C_4H_{11}N$	_s	− 33.0	− 11.3	+ 6.0	38.0	55.5	− 38.9	(38)
Isobutylamine	$C_4H_{11}N$	− 50.0	− 21.0	+ 1.3	18.9	50.7	68.6	− 85.0	(390)
1,3-Dichlorotetramethyldisiloxane	$C_4H_{12}Cl_2Si_2$	− 7 4	+ 28.3	55.7	76.9	116.3	138.0	− 37	(312)
Tetramethyllead	$C_4H_{12}Pb$	− 29.0_s	+ 4.4	30.3	50.8	89.0	110.0	− 27.5	(420)
Tetramethylsilane	$C_4H_{12}Si$	− 83.8	− 58.0	− 37.4	− 20.9	+ 10.0	27.0	− 102.1	(15, 114)
Tetramethyltin	$C_4H_{12}Sn$	− 51.3	− 20.6	+ 3.5	22.8	58.5	78.0	......	(62, 420)
Tetramethyldiborane	$C_4H_{14}B_2$	− 59.6	− 27.4	− 3.4	+ 15.3	49.8	68.6	− 72.5	(371)
3-Bromopyridine	C_5H_4BrN	16.8	55.2	84.1	107.8	150.0	173.4	......	(113)
2-Chloropyridine	C_5H_4ClN	13.3	51.7	81.7	104.6	147.7	170.2	......	(113)
2-Furaldehyde	$C_5H_4O_2$	18.5	54.8	82.1	103.4	141.8	161.8	− 36.5	(193, 369, 459)
Citraconic anhydride	$C_5H_4O_3$	47.1	88.9	120.3	145.4	189.8	213.5	......	(11)
Pyridine	C_5H_5N	− 18.9	+ 13.2	38.0	57.8	95.6	115.4	− 42	(11, 181, 199, 203, 204, 443)
Glutaryl chloride	$C_5H_6Cl_2O_2$	56.1	97.8	128.3	151.8	195.3	217.0	......	(11)
Glutaronitrile	$C_5H_6N_2$	91.3	140.0	176.4	205.5	257.3	286.2	......	(11, 234)
Furfuryl alcohol	$C_5H_6O_2$	31.8	68.0	95.7	115.9	151.8	170.0	......	(113, 121)
Glutaric anhydride	$C_5H_6O_3$	100.8	149.5	185.5	212.5	261.0	287.0	......	(11, 234)
Pyrotartaric anhydride	$C_5H_6O_3$	69.7	114.2	147.8	173.8	221.0	247.4	......	(11)
2-Methylthiophene	C_5H_6S	− 27.4	+ 6.0	32.3	53.1	91.8	112.5	− 63.5	(126)
3-Methylthiophene	C_5H_6S	− 24.5	+ 9.1	35.4	55.8	93.8	115.4	− 68.9	(126)
Propyl chloroglyoxylate	$C_5H_7ClO_3$	9.7	43.5	68.8	88.0	123.0	150.0	......	(11)
Tiglonitrile	C_5H_7N	− 25.5	+ 9.2	36.7	58.2	99.7	122.0	......	(113)
Angelonitrile	C_5H_7N	− 8.0	+ 28.0	55.8	77.5	117.7	140.0	......	(113)
α-Ethylacrylonitrile	C_5H_7N	− 29.0	+ 5.0	31.8	53.0	92.2	114.0	......	(113)
Ethyl cyanoacetate	$C_5H_7NO_2$	67.8	106.0	133.8	152 8	187.8	206.0	......	(113)
Isoprene	C_5H_8	− 79.8	− 53.3	− 32.6	− 16.0	+ 15.4	32.6	− 146.7	(113, 189)
1,3-Pentadiene	C_5H_8	− 71.8	− 45.0	− 23.4	− 6.7	+ 24 7	42 1	......	(113)
1,4-Pentadiene	C_5H_8	− 83 5	− 57.1	− 37.0	− 20.6	+ 8.3	26.1	......	(244)
Tiglaldehyde	C_5H_8O	− 25.0	+ 10.0	47.0	77.7	95.5	116.4	......	(113)
Levulinaldehyde	$C_5H_8O_2$	28 1	68.0	98.3	121.8	164 0	107.0	......	(158)
Tiglic acid	$C_5H_8O_2$	52.0_s	90.2	119.0	140.5	179.2	198.5	64.5	(11, 113, 220, 257)
α-Valerolactone	$C_5H_8O_2$	37.5	79 8	101.9	136.5	182.3	207.5	......	(11, 377)
α-Ethylacrylic acid	$C_5H_8O_2$	47.0	82.0	108.1	127.5	160.7	179 2	......	(45, 113, 401)
Ethyl acrylate	$C_5H_8O_2$	− 29.5	+ 2.0	26.0	44.5	80.0	99.5	− 71.2	(113)
Methyl methacrylate	$C_5H_8O_2$	− 30.5	+ 1.0	25.5	47.0	82.0	101.0	......	(113)
Levulinic acid	$C_5H_8O_3$	102.0	141.8	169 5	190.2	227.4	245.8_d	33.5	(11)
Glutaric acid	$C_5H_8O_4$	155.5	196.0	226.3	247.0	283.5	303.0	97 5	(11, 234)
Dimethyl malonate	$C_5H_8O_4$	35.0	72.0	100.0	121.9	159.8	180.7	62	(11)
Ethyl α-chloropropionate	$C_5H_9ClO_2$	+ 6.6	41.9	68.2	89.3	126.2	146.5	......	(11)
Isopropyl chloroacetate	$C_5H_9ClO_2$	+ 3.8	40.2	68.8	90.3	128.0	148.6	......	(297)
Valeronitrile	C_5H_9N	− 6.0	+ 30.0	57.8	78.6	118.7	140.8	......	(159)
α-Hydroxybutyronitrile	C_5H_9NO	41.0	77.8	104.8	125.0	159.8	178.8	......	(113, 169, 170, 442)

Name	Formula	Temperature °C						M.P	Citation No.
		1 mm	10 mm	40 mm	100 mm	400 mm	760 mm		
1-Pentene	C_5H_{10}	− 80.4	− 54.5	− 34.1	− 17.7	+ 12.8	30.1	......	(6, 113, 359)
2-Methyl-2-butene	C_5H_{10}	− 75.4	− 47.9	− 26.7	− 9.9	+ 21.6	38.5	− 133	(244)
2-Methyl-1-butene	C_5H_{10}	− 89.1	− 64.3	− 44.1	− 28.0	+ 2.5	20.2	− 135	(290)
Cyclopentane	C_5H_{10}	− 68.0	− 40.4	− 18.6	− 1.3	+ 31.0	49.3	− 93.7	(6, 359, 472)
1,2-Dibromopentane	$C_5H_{10}Br_2$	19.8	58.0	87.4	110.1	151.8	175.0	......	(11)
2-Chloroethyl 2-chloroisopropyl ether	$C_5H_{10}Cl_2O$	24.7	63.0	92.4	115.8	156.5	180.0	......	(113)
2-Chloroethyl 2-chloropropyl ether	$C_5H_{10}Cl_2O$	29.8	70.0	101.5	125.6	169.8	194.1	......	(113)
Di(2-chloroethoxy)methane	$C_5H_{10}Cl_2O_2$	53.0	94.0	125.5	149.6	192.0	215.0	......	(113)
Allyldichloroethylsilane	$C_5H_{10}Cl_2Si$	− 3.0	34.2	62.7	85.2	127.0	150.3	......	(114)
3-Pentanone	$C_5H_{10}O$	− 12.7	+ 17.2	39.4	56.2	86.3	102.7	− 42	(113)
2-Pentanone	$C_5H_{10}O$	− 12.0	+ 17.9	39.8	56.8	86.8	103.3	− 77.8	(113, 491)
3-Methyl-2-butanone	$C_5H_{10}O$	− 19.9	+ 8.3	29.6	45.5	73.8	88.9	− 92	(11, 199, 201)
4-Hydroxy-3-methyl-2-butanone	$C_5H_{10}O_2$	44.6	81.0	108.2	129.0	165.5	185.0	......	(113)
Valeric acid	$C_5H_{10}O_2$	42.2	79.8	107.8	128.3	165.0	184.4	− 34.5	(11, 198, 199, 200, 203, 204)
Isovaleric acid	$C_5H_{10}O_2$	34.5	71.3	98.0	118.9	155.2	175.1	− 37.6	(11, 198, 199, 200, 203)
Ethyl propionate	$C_5H_{10}O_2$	− 28.0	+ 3.4	27.2	45.2	79.8	99.1	− 72.6	(491)
Propyl acetate	$C_5H_{10}O_2$	− 26.7	+ 5.0	28.8	47.8	82.0	101.8	− 92.5	(11, 113, 199, 491)
Isopropyl acetate	$C_5H_{10}O_2$	− 38.3	− 7.2	+ 17.0	35.7	69.8	89.0	......	(152)
Methyl butyrate	$C_5H_{10}O_2$	− 26.8	+ 5.0	29.6	48.0	83.1	102.3	......	(11, 491)
Methyl isobutyrate	$C_5H_{10}O_2$	− 34.1	− 2.9	+ 21.0	39.6	73.6	92.6	− 84.7	(491)
Butyl formate	$C_5H_{10}O_2$	− 26.4	+ 6.1	31.6	51.0	86.2	106.0	......	(297)
Isobutyl formate	$C_5H_{10}O_2$	− 32.7	− 0.8	+ 24.1	43.4	79.0	98.2	......	(292, 380)
sec-Butyl formate	$C_5H_{10}O_2$	− 34.4	− 3.1	+ 21.3	40.2	75.2	93.6	− 95.3	(297)
Diethyl carbonate	$C_5H_{10}O_3$	− 10.1	+ 23.8	49.5	69.7	105.8	125.8	− 43	(11)
1-Bromo-3-methylbutane	$C_5H_{11}Br$	− 20.4	+ 13.6	39.8	60.4	99.4	120.4	......	(199, 201)
1-Iodo-3-methylbutane	$C_5H_{11}I$	− 2.5	+ 34.1	62.3	84.4	125.8	148.2	......	(11)
Piperidine	$C_5H_{11}N$	s	+ 3.9	29.2	49.0	85.7	106.0	− 9	(11, 199, 201)
Isobutyl carbamate	$C_5H_{11}NO_2$		96.4	125.3	147.2	186.0	206.5	65	(11)
Isoamyl nitrate	$C_5H_{11}NO_3$	+ 5.2	40.3	67.6	88.6	126.5	147.5	......	(11)
Pentane	C_5H_{12}	− 76.6	− 50.1	− 29.2	− 12.6	+ 18.5	36.1	− 129.7	(6, 28, 93, 274, 359, 482, 485)
2-Methylbutane	C_5H_{12}	− 82.9	− 57.0	− 36.5	− 20.2	+ 10.5	27.8	− 159.7	(6, 93, 359, 485, 486, 492)
2,2-Dimethylpropane	C_5H_{12}	−102.0	− 76.7s	− 56.1s	− 39.1s	− 7.1	+ 9.5	− 16.6	(6, 17, 113, 253, 359, 465)
Amyl alcohol	$C_5H_{12}O$	+ 13.6	44.9	68.0	85.8	119.8	137.8		(68, 148)
Isoamyl alcohol	$C_5H_{12}O$	+ 10.0	40.8	63.4	80.7	113.7	130.6	− 117.2	(11, 68, 199, 3)
2-Pentanol	$C_5H_{12}O$	+ 1.5	32.2	54.1	70.7	102.3	119.7	......	(68)
tert-Amyl alcohol	$C_5H_{12}O$	− 12.9s	+ 17.2	38.8	55.3	85.7	101.7	− 11.9	(11, 68)
Ethyl propyl ether	$C_5H_{12}O$	− 64.3	− 35.0	− 12.0	+ 6.8	41.6	61.7	......	(39)
2,3,4-Pentanetriol	$C_5H_{12}O_3$	155.0	204.5	239.6	263.5	307.0	327.2	......	(113)
Ethoxytrimethylsilane	$C_5H_{14}OSi$	− 50.9	− 20.7	+ 3.7	22.1	56.3	75.7	......	(114)
Ethyltrimethylsilane	$C_5H_{14}Si$	− 60.6	− 31.8	− 9.0	+ 9.2	42.8	62.0	......	(466)
Ethyltrimethyltin	$C_5H_{14}Sn$	− 30.0	+ 3.8	30.0	50.0	87.6	108.8	......	(62)
Chloranil	$C_6Cl_4O_2$	70.7s	97.8s	116.1s	129.5s	151.3s	162.6s	290	(92)
Hexachlorobenzene	C_6Cl_6	114.4s	166.4s	206.0s	235.5	283.5	309.4	230	(113)
Pentachlorobenzene	C_6HCl_5	98.6	144.3	178.5	205.5	251.6	276.0	85.5	(113)
Pentachlorophenol	C_6HCl_5O	s	s	211.2	239.6	285.0	309.3d	188.5	(113)
3-Bromo-2,4,6-trichlorophenol	$C_6H_2BrCl_3O$	112.4	163.2	200.5	229.3	278.0	305.8	......	(113)
1,2,3,4-Tetrachlorobenzene	$C_6H_2Cl_4$	68.5	114.7	149.2	175.7	225.5	254.0	46.5	(113)
1,2,3,5-Tetrachlorobenzene	$C_6H_2Cl_4$	58.2	104.1	140.0	168.0	220.0	246.0	54.5	(113)
1,2,4,5-Tetrachlorobenzene	$C_6H_2Cl_4$	s	s	146.0	173.5	220.5	245.0	139	(113)
2,3,4,6-Tetrachlorophenol	$C_6H_2Cl_4O$	100.0	145.3	179.1	205.2	250.4	275.0	69.5	(113)
2-Bromo-4,6-dichlorophenol	$C_6H_3BrCl_2O$	84.0	130.8	165.8	193.2	242.0	268.0	68	(113)
1,2,3-Trichlorobenzene	$C_6H_3Cl_3$	40.0s	85.6	119.8	146.0	193.5	218.5	52.5	(113)
1,2,4-Trichlorobenzene	$C_6H_3Cl_3$	38.4	81.7	114.8	140.0	187.7	213.0	17	(113)
1,3,5-Trichlorobenzene	$C_6H_3Cl_3$	s	78.0	110.8	136.0	183.0	208.4	63.5	(113)
2,4,5-Trichlorophenol	$C_6H_3Cl_3O$	72.0	117.3	151.5	178.0	226.5	251.8	62	(113)
2,4,6-Trichlorophenol	$C_6H_3Cl_3O$	76.5	120.2	152.2	177.8	222.5	246.0	68.5	(113)
1,4-Dibromobenzene	$C_6H_4Br_2$	61.0s	87.7	120.8	146.5	192.5	218.6	87.5	(11, 113, 243)
1,4-Bromochlorobenzene	C_6H_4BrCl	32.0	72.7	103.8	128.0	172.6	196.9	......	(113)
1,2-Dichlorobenzene	$C_6H_4Cl_2$	20.0	59.1	89.4	112.9	155.8	179.0	− 17.6	(113)
1,3-Dichlorobenzene	$C_6H_4Cl_2$	12.1	52.0	82.0	105.0	149.0	173.0	− 24.2	(113)
1,4-Dichlorobenzene	$C_6H_4Cl_2$	s	54.8	84.8	108.4	150.2	173.9	53.0	(113)
2,4-Dichlorophenol	$C_6H_4Cl_2O$	53.0	92.8	123.4	146.0	187.5	210.0	45.0	(113)
2,6-Dichlorophenol	$C_6H_4Cl_2O$	59.5	101.0	131.6	154.6	197.7	220.0	......	(113)
2,4,6-Trichloroaniline	$C_6H_4Cl_3N$	134.0	170.0	195.8	214.6	246.4	262.0	78	(11)
Dichlorophenylarsine	$C_6H_5AsCl_2$	61.8	116.0	151.0	178.9	228.8	256.5	......	(11)
Bromobenzene	C_6H_5Br	+ 2.9	40.0	68.6	90.8	132.3	156.2	− 30.7	(11, 199, 204, 289, 358, 478)
Chlorobenzene	C_6H_5Cl	− 13.0	+ 22.2	49.7	70.7	110.0	132.2	− 45.2	(11, 199, 289, 478)
2-Chlorophenol	C_6H_5ClO	12.1	51.2	82.0	106.0	149.8	174.5	7.0	(113)
3-Chlorophenol	C_6H_5ClO	44.2	86.1	118.0	143.0	188.7	214.0	32.5	(113)
4-Chlorophenol	C_6H_5ClO	49.8	92.2	125.0	150.0	196.0	220.0	42	(113)
Benzenesulfonylchloride	$C_6H_5ClO_2S$	65.9	112.0	147.7	174.5	224.0	251.5d	14.5	(11, 235)
Phenyl dichlorophosphate	$C_6H_5Cl_2O_2P$	66.7	110.0	143.4	168.0	213.0	239.5	......	(11, 113)
Trichlorophenylsilane	$C_6H_5Cl_3Si$	33.0	74.2	105.8	130.5	175.7	201.0	......	(114)
Fluorobenzene	C_6H_5F	− 43.4s	− 12.4	+ 11.5	30.4	65.7	84.7	− 42.1	(113, 416, 478)
Trifluorophenylsilane	$C_6H_5F_3Si$	− 31.0	+ 0.8	25.4	44.2	78.7	98.3	......	(119)
Iodobenzene	C_6H_5I	24.1	64.0	94.4	118.3	163.9	188.6	− 28.5	(115, 289, 358, 478)
Nitrobenzene	$C_6H_5NO_2$	44.4	84.9	115.4	139.9	185.8	210.6	+ 5.7	(11, 58, 199, 204)
2-Nitrophenol	$C_6H_5NO_3$	49.3	90.4	122.1	146.4	191.0	214.5	45	(11)
1,5-Hexadiene-3-yne	C_6H_6	− 45.1	− 14.0	+ 10.0	29.5	64.4	84.0	......	(304)
Benzene	C_6H_6	− 36.7	− 11.5s	+ 7.6	26.1	60.6	80.1	+ 5.5	(3, 6, 11, 32, 109, 131, 197, 204, 289, 343, 359, 366, 367, 392, 415, 478)

Name	Formula	Temperature °C						M.P.	Citation No.
		1 mm	10 mm	40 mm	100 mm	400 mm	760 mm		
2-Chloroaniline	C_6H_6ClN	46.3	84.8	115.6	139.5	183.7	208.8	......	(204)
3-Chloroaniline	C_6H_6ClN	63.5	102.0	133.6	158.0	203.5	228.5	− 10.4	(204)
4-Chloroaniline	C_6H_6ClN	59.3s	102.1	135.0	159.9	206.6	230.5	70.5	(11)
4-Chlorophenol	C_6H_6ClO	54.3	95.8	126.8	150 6	194.3	217.0	42	(11)
2-Nitroaniline	$C_6H_6N_2O_2$	104.0	150.4	186.0	213 0	260.0	284.5d	71.5	(35)
3-Nitroaniline	$C_6H_6N_2O_2$	119.3	167 8	204.2	232.1	280.2	305.7d	114	(35)
4-Nitroaniline	$C_6H_6N_2O_2$	142.4s	194.4	234.2	261.8	310.2d	336.0d	146.5	(35)
Phenol	C_6H_6O	40.1s	73.8	100.1	121.4	160.0	181.9	40.6	(11, 34, 113, 151, 174, 203, 204)
Pyrocatechol	$C_6H_6O_2$	s	118.3	150.6	176.0	221.5	245.5	105	(11)
Resorcinol	$C_6H_6O_2$	108.4s	152.1	185.3	209.8	253.4	276.5	110.7	(11)
Hydroquinone	$C_6H_6O_2$	132.4s	163.5s	192.0	216.5	262.5	286.2	170.3	(404)
Pyrogallol	$C_6H_6O_3$	s	167.7	204 2	232.0	281.5	309.0d	133	(11)
Benzenethiol	C_6H_6S	18.6	56.0	84.2	106.6	146.7	168.0	......	(11)
Aniline	C_6H_7N	34.8	69.4	96.7	119.9	161.9	184.4	− 6.2	(11, 34, 143, 151, 204, 341)
2-Picoline	C_6H_7N	− 11.1	+ 24.4	51.2	71.4	108.4	128.8	− 70	(11, 199)
Ethylene-bis-(chloroacetate)	$C_6H_8Cl_2O_4$	112.0	158.0	191.0	215.0	259.5	283.5	......	(113)
1,3-Phenylenediamine	$C_6H_8N_2$	99.8	147.0	182.5	209.9	259.0	285.5	62.8	(11)
Phenylhydrazine	$C_6H_8N_2$	71.8	115.8	148.2	173.5	218.2	243.5d	19.5	(11, 113)
α-Methylglutaric anhydride	$C_6H_8O_3$	93.8	141.8	177.5	205.0	255.5	282.5	......	(11)
α,α-Dimethylsuccinic anhydride	$C_6H_8O_3$	61.4	102.0	132.3	155.3	197.5	219.5	......	(11)
Dimethyl maleate	$C_6H_8O_4$	45.7	86.4	117.7	140.3	182.2	205.0	......	(11)
Isobutyl dichloroacetate	$C_6H_{10}Cl_2O_2$	28.6	67 5	96.7	119.8	160.0	183.0	......	(11)
Diallyldichlorosilane	$C_6H_{10}Cl_2Si$	+ 9.5	47.4	76.4	99.7	142.0	165.3	......	(114)
Cyclohexanone	$C_6H_{10}O$	+ 1.4	38.7	67 8	90.4	132.5	155.6	− 45.0	(440)
Mesityl oxide	$C_6H_{10}O$	− 8.7	+ 26.0	51.7	72.1	109.8	130.0	− 59	(11, 199)
Isocaprolactone	$C_6H_{10}O_2$	38.3	80.3	112 3	137.2	182 1	207 0	......	(11)
Propionic anhydride	$C_6H_{10}O_3$	20.6	57.7	85.6	107.2	146.0	167.0	− 45	(11, 198, 199)
Ethyl acetoacetate	$C_6H_{10}O_3$	28.5	67.3	96.2	118.5	158.2	180.8	− 45	(11, 199)
Methyl levulinate	$C_6H_{10}O_3$	39 8	79.7	109.5	133 0	175 8	197.7	......	(376)
Adipic acid	$C_6H_{10}O_4$	159.5	205.5	240 5	265 0	312.5	337.5	152	(11, 234)
Diethyl oxalate	$C_6H_{10}O_4$	47.4	83 8	110.6	130 8	166.2	185.7	− 40.6	(11, 199, 201)
Glycol diacetate	$C_6H_{10}O_4$	38.3	77.1	106.1	128.0	168.3	190.5	− 31	(423)
Dimethyl-l-malate	$C_6H_{10}O_5$	75.4	118.3	150.1	175.1	219.5	242.6	......	(11)
Dimethyl-d-tartrate	$C_6H_{10}O_6$	102.1	148.2	182.4	208.8	255.0	280.0	61.5	(11, 149)
Dimethyl-dl-tartrate	$C_6H_{10}O_6$	100.4	147.5	182.4	209.5	257.4	282.0	89	(11, 149)
Diallyl sulfide	$C_6H_{10}S$	− 9.5	+ 26.6	54.2	75.8	116.1	138.6	− 83	(11, 25)
Ethyl α-bromoisobutyrate	$C_6H_{11}BrO_2$	10.6	48.0	77.0	99.8	141.2	163.6	......	(11)
sec-Butyl chloroacetate	$C_6H_{11}ClO_2$	17.0	54.6	83.6	105.5	146.0	167.8	......	(297)
Capronitrile	$C_6H_{11}N$	+ 9.2	47.5	76.9	99.8	141.0	163.7	......	(159)
1-Hexene	C_6H_{12}	− 57.5	− 28.1	− 5.0	+ 13.0	46.8	66.0	− 98.5	(474)
Cyclohexane	C_6H_{12}	− 45.3s	− 15.9s	+ 6.7	25.5	60.8	80.7	+ 6.6	(6, 109, 293, 359, 367, 487)
Methylcyclopentane	C_6H_{12}	− 53.7	− 23.7	− 0.6	+ 17.9	52.3	71.8	− 142.4	(6, 359, 471)
Dichlorodiisopropyl ether	$C_6H_{12}Cl_2O$	29.6	68.2	97.3	119.7	159.8	182.7	......	(113)
Bis-2-chloroethyl acetal	$C_6H_{12}Cl_2O_2$	56.2	97.6	127 8	150.7	190.5	212.6	......	(113)
2-Hexanone	$C_6H_{12}O$	+ 7.7	38.8	62.0	79.8	111.0	127.5	− 56.9	(113)
4-Methyl-2-pentanone	$C_6H_{12}O$	− 1.4	+ 30.0	52.8	70.4	102.0	119.0	− 84.7	(113)
Allyl propyl ether	$C_6H_{12}O$	− 39.0	− 7.9	+ 16.4	35.8	71.4	90.5	......	(254)
Allyl isopropyl ether	$C_6H_{12}O$	− 43.7	− 12.9	+ 10.9	29.0	61.7	79.5	......	(254)
Cyclohexanol	$C_6H_{12}O$	21.0s	56.0	83.0	103.7	141.4	161.0	23.9	(113)
Caproic acid	$C_6H_{12}O_2$	71.4	99.5	125.0	144.0	181.0	202.0	− 1.5	(11, 203)
Isocaproic acid	$C_6H_{12}O_2$	66.2	94.0	120.4	141.4	181.0	207.7	− 35	(11, 203, 204)
4-Hydroxy-4-methyl-2-pentanone	$C_6H_{12}O_2$	22.0	58 8	86.7	108.2	147.5	167.9	− 47	(113)
Methyl isovalerate	$C_6H_{12}O_2$	− 19.2	+ 14.0	39.8	59.8	96.7	116.7	......	(380)
Ethyl butyrate	$C_6H_{12}O_2$	− 18.4	+ 15.3	41.5	62.0	100.0	121.0	− 93.3	(380)
Ethyl isobutyrate	$C_6H_{12}O_2$	− 24.3	+ 8.4	33.8	53.5	90.0	110.1	− 88.2	(292, 380)
Propyl propionate	$C_6H_{12}O_2$	− 14.2	+ 19.4	45.0	65.2	102.0	122.4	− 76	(11, 380)
Isobutyl acetate	$C_6H_{12}O_2$	− 21.2	+ 12.8	39.2	59.7	97.5	118.0	− 98.9	(11, 199, 292, 380)
Isoamyl formate	$C_6H_{12}O_2$	− 17.5	+ 17.1	44.0	65.4	102.7	123.3	......	(380)
Paraformaldehyde	$C_6H_{12}O_3$	− 9.4s	+ 24.1s	49.5s	69.0s	104.3s	124.0s	155 ± 5	(11)
sec-Butyl glycolate	$C_6H_{12}O_3$	28.3	66.0	94.2	116.4	155.6	177.5	......	(113)
Hexane	C_6H_{14}	− 53.9	− 25.0	− 2.3	+ 15.8	49.6	68.7	− 95.3	(6, 115, 251, 289, 359, 394, 427, 474)
2-Methylpentane	C_6H_{14}	− 60.9	− 32.1	− 9.7	+ 8.1	41.6	60.3	− 154	(6, 21, 359, 471)
3-Methylpentane	C_6H_{14}	− 59.0	− 30.1	− 7.3	+ 10.5	44.2	63.3	− 118	(6, 359, 471)
2,2-Dimethylbutane	C_6H_{14}	− 69.3	− 41.5	− 19.5	− 2.0	+ 31.0	49.7	− 99.8	(6, 21, 359, 471)
2,3-Dimethylbutane	C_6H_{14}	− 63.6	− 34.9	− 12.4	+ 5.4	39.0	58.0	− 128.2	(6, 359, 471, 488)
1-Hexanol	$C_6H_{14}O$	24.4	58.2	83.7	102.8	138.8	157 0	− 51 6	(68, 185, 380)
2-Hexanol	$C_6H_{14}O$	14.6	45.0	67.9	87.3	121.8	139.9	......	(185)
3-Hexanol	$C_6H_{14}O$	+ 2.5	36.7	62.2	81.8	117.0	135.5	......	(185)
2-Methyl-1-pentanol	$C_6H_{14}O$	15.4	49 6	74.7	94 2	129.8	147.9	......	(184a, 185)
2-Methyl-2-pentanol	$C_6H_{14}O$	− 4.5	+ 27.6	51.3	100.8	121 1	103	(185)
2-Methyl-4-pentanol	$C_6H_{14}O$	− 0.3	+ 33.3	58.2	78.0	113.5	131.7	......	(185)
Dipropyl ether	$C_6H_{14}O$	− 43.3	− 11 8	+ 13.2	33.0	69.5	89.5	− 122	(113)
Diisopropyl ether	$C_6H_{14}O$	− 57 0	− 27.4	− 4.5	+ 13.7	48.2	67.5	− 60	(133)
Acetal	$C_6H_{14}O_2$	− 23.0	+ 8.0	31.9	50.1	84.0	102.0	......	(11, 199)
1,2-Diethoxyethane	$C_6H_{14}O_2$	− 33.5	+ 1.6	29.7	51.8	94.1	119.5	......	(254)
Di(2-methoxyethyl) ether	$C_6H_{14}O_3$	13.0	50.0	77.5	99.5	138.5	159.8	......	(141)
Diethylene glycol, ethyl ether	$C_6H_{14}O_3$	45.3	85.8	116.7	140.3	180.3	201.9	......	(113)
Dipropyleneglycol	$C_6H_{14}O_3$	73.8	116 2	147.4	169.9	210.5	231.8	......	(71, 113)
Triethyleneglycol	$C_6H_{14}O_4$	114.0	158.1	191.3	214.6	256.6	278.3	......	(71, 141)
Triethylboron	$C_6H_{15}B$	−	− 148.0	− 131.4	− 116.0	− 81.0	− 56.2	......	(413)
Chlorotriethylsilane	$C_6H_{15}ClSi$	− 4.9	+ 32.0	60.2	82.3	123.6	146.3	......	(114)
Triethyl phosphate	$C_6H_{15}O_4P$	39.6	82.1	115.7	141.6	187.0	211.0	......	(76)
Triethylthallium	$C_6H_{15}Tl$	+ 9.3	51.7	85.4	112.1	163.5	192.1d	− 63.0	(357)

Name	Formula	Temperature °C						M.P.	Citation No.
		1 mm	10 mm	40 mm	100 mm	400 mm	760 mm		
Diethoxydimethylsilane	$C_6H_{16}O_2Si$	− 19.1	+ 13.3	38.0	57.6	93.2	113.5	......	(114)
Trimethylpropylsilane	$C_6H_{16}Si$	− 46.0	− 13.9	+ 11.3	31.6	69.2	90.0	......	(466)
Trimethylpropyltin	$C_6H_{16}Sn$	− 12.0	+ 21.8	48.5	69.8	109.6	131.7	......	(62)
1,5-Dichlorohexamethyltrisiloxane	$C_6H_{18}Cl_2O_2Si_3$	26.0	65.1	94.8	118.2	160.2	184.0	− 53	(312)
Hexamethylcyclotrisiloxane	$C_6H_{18}O_3Si_3$				78.7	114.7	134.0	64	(188, 312)
Hexamethyldisiloxane	$C_6H_{18}OSi_2$	− 29.0	+ 2.8	26.7	45.6	80.0	99.2	......	(114)
3,4-Dichloro-α,α,α-trifluorotoluene	$C_7H_3Cl_2F_3$	11.0	52.2	84.0	109.2	150.5	172.8	− 12.1	(113)
2-Chloro-α,α,α-trifluorotoluene	$C_7H_4ClF_3$	0.0	37.1	65.9	88.3	130.0	152.2	− 6.0	(113)
2-α,α,α-tetrachlorotoluene	$C_7H_4Cl_4$	69.0	117.9	155.0	185.0	233.0	262.1	28.7	(113)
Benzoyl bromide	C_7H_5BrO	47.0	89.8	122.6	147.7	193.7	218.5	0	(11)
Benzoyl chloride	C_7H_5ClO	32.1	73.0	103.8	128.0	172.8	197.2	− 0.5	(11, 203, 204)
α,α,α-Trichlorotoluene	$C_7H_5Cl_3$	45.8	87.6	119.8	144.3	189.2	213.5	− 21.2	(11)
α,α,α-Trifluorotoluene	$C_7H_5F_3$	− 32.0	+ 0.4	25.7	45.3	82.0	102.2	− 29.3	(113)
Benzonitrile	C_7H_5N	28.2	69.2	99.6	123.5	166.7	190.6	− 12.9	(113, 204)
Phenyl isocyanide	C_7H_5N	12.0	49.7	78.3	101.0	142.3	165.0d	......	(11, 235)
Phenyl isocyanate	C_7H_5NO	10.6	48.5	77.7	100.6	142.7	165.6	......	(113)
2-Nitrobenzaldehyde	$C_7H_5NO_3$	85.8	133.4	168.8	196.2	246.8	273.5	40.9	(11)
3-Nitrobenzaldehyde	$C_7H_5NO_3$	96.2	142.8	177.7	204.3	252.1	278.3	58	(11)
Phenyl isothiocyanate	C_7H_5NS	47.2	89.8	122.5	147.7	194.0	218.5	− 21.0	(11, 25, 198, 199)
α,α-dichlorotoluene	$C_7H_6Cl_2$	35.4	78.7	112.1	138.3	187.0	214.0	− 16.1	(11)
Benzaldehyde	C_7H_6O	26.2	62.0	90.1	112.5	154.1	179.0	− 26	(11, 199, 204)
Benzoic acid	$C_7H_6O_2$	96.0s	132.1	162.6	186.2	227.0	249.2	121.7	(11, 189, 204, 218, 303)
Salicylaldehyde	$C_7H_6O_2$	33.0	73.8	105.2	129.4	173.7	196.5	− 7	(113)
4-Hydroxybenzaldehyde	$C_7H_6O_2$	121.2	169.7	206.0	233.5	282.6	310.0	115.5	(11)
Salicylic acid	$C_7H_6O_3$	113.7s	146.2s	172.2	193.4	230.5	256.0	159	(404)
α-Bromotoluene	C_7H_7Br	32.2	73.4	104.8	129.8	175.2	198.5	− 4	(11)
2-Bromotoluene	C_7H_7Br	24.4	62.3	91.0	112.0	157.3	181.8	− 28	(128, 201, 415)
3-Bromotoluene	C_7H_7Br	14.8	64.0	93.9	117.8	160.0	183.7	− 39.8	(128, 415)
4-Bromotoluene	C_7H_7Br	10.3	61.1	91.8	116.4	160.2	184.5	28.5	(11, 113, 199, 128)
4-Bromoanisole	C_7H_7BrO	48.8	91.9	125.0	150.1	197.5	223.0	12.5	(11)
α-Chlorotoluene	C_7H_7Cl	22.0	60.8	90.7	114.2	155.8	179.4	− 39	(11, 199, 201)
2-Chlorotoluene	C_7H_7Cl	+ 5.4	43.2	72.0	94.7	137.1	159.3	......	(11, 113, 128, 415)
3-Chlorotoluene	C_7H_7Cl	+ 4.8	43.2	73.0	96.3	139.7	162.3	......	(128, 415)
4-Chlorotoluene	C_7H_7Cl	+ 5.5	43.8	73.5	96.6	139.8	162.3	+ 7.3	(11, 113, 128, 199, 415)
2-Fluorotoluene	C_7H_7F	− 24.2	+ 8.9	34.7	55.3	92.8	114.0	− 80	(113)
3-Fluorotoluene	C_7H_7F	− 22.4	+ 11.0	37.0	57.5	95.4	116.0	− 110.8	(113)
4-Fluorotoluene	C_7H_7F	− 21.8	+ 11.8	37.8	58.1	96.1	117.0	......	(113)
2-Iodotoluene	C_7H_7I	37.2	79.8	112.4	138.1	185.7	211.0	......	(11)
2-Nitrotoluene	$C_7H_7NO_2$	50.0	93.8	126.3	151.5	197.7	222.3	− 4.1	(11, 36, 204, 302)
3-Nitrotoluene	$C_7H_7NO_2$	50.2	96.0	130.7	156.9	206.8	231.9	15.1	(36, 302)
4-Nitrotoluene	$C_7H_7NO_2$	53.7	100.5	136.0	163.0	212.5	238.3	51.9	(11, 36, 204)
Toluene	C_7H_8	− 26.7	+ 6.4	31.8	51.9	89.5	110.6	− 95.0	(6, 11, 24, 107, 115, 199, 204, 239, 253, 359)
Benzyldichlorosilane	$C_7H_8Cl_2Si$	45.3	83.2	111.8	133.5	173.0	194.3	......	(114)
Dichloromethylphenylsilane	$C_7H_8Cl_2Si$	35.7	77.4	109.5	134.2	180.2	205.5	......	(114)
Dichloro-4-tolysilane	$C_7H_8Cl_2Si$	46.2	84.2	113.2	135.5	175.2	196.3	......	(114)
Anisole	C_7H_8O	+ 5.4	42.2	70.7	93.0	133.8	155.5	− 37.3	(11)
Benzyl alcohol	C_7H_8O	58.0	92.6	119.8	141.7	183.0	204.7	− 15.3	(11, 204)
2-Cresol	C_7H_8O	38.2	76.7	105.8	127.4	168.4	190.8	30.8	(11, 204, 406)
3-Cresol	C_7H_8O	52.0	87.8	116.0	138.0	179.0	202.8	10.9	(11, 204, 406)
4-Cresol	C_7H_8O	53.0	88.6	117.7	140.0	179.4	201.8	35.5	(11, 204, 406)
3,5-Dimethyl-1,2-pyrone	$C_7H_8O_2$	78.6	122.0	152.7	177.5	221.0	245.0	51.5	(11)
2-Methoxyphenol	$C_7H_8O_2$	52.4	92.0	121.6	144.0	184.1	205.0	28.3	(11)
Ethyl 2-furoate	$C_7H_8O_3$	37.6	77.1	107.5	130.4	172.5	195.0	34	(11)
Benzylamine	C_7H_9N	29.0	67.7	97.3	120.0	161.3	184.5	......	(11)
N-Methylaniline	C_7H_9N	36.0	76.2	106.0	129.8	172.0	195.5	− 57	(11, 204, 300)
2-Toluidine	C_7H_9N	44.0	81.4	110.0	133.0	176.2	199.7	− 16.3	(11, 37, 204)
3-Toluidine	C_7H_9N	41.0	82.0	113.5	136.7	180.6	203.3	− 31.5	(11, 37, 204)
4-Toluidine	C_7H_9N	42.0	81.8	111.5	133.7	176.9	200.4	44.5	(11, 37, 204)
2-Methoxyaniline	C_7H_9NO	61.0	101.7	132.0	155.2	197.3	218.5	5.2	(11)
Toluene-2,4-diamine	$C_7H_{10}N_2$	106.5	151.7	185.7	211.5	256.0	280.0	99	(11)
4-Tolylhydrazine	$C_7H_{10}N_2$	82.0	123.8	154.1	178.0	219.5	242.0d	65.5	(11)
Trimethysuccinic anhydride	$C_7H_{10}O_3$	53.5	97.4	131.0	156.5	205.5	231.0	......	(11)
Dimethyl citraconate	$C_7H_{10}O_4$	50.8	91.8	122.6	145.8	188.0	210.5	......	(11)
Dimethyl itaconate	$C_7H_{10}O_4$	69.3	106.6	133.7	153.7	189.8	208.0	38	(11)
trans-Dimethyl mesaconate	$C_7H_{10}O_4$	46.8	87.8	118.0	141.5	183.5	206.0	......	(11)
2-Cyano-2-butyl acetate	$C_7H_{11}NO_2$	42.0	82.0	111.8	133.8	173.4	195.2	......	(113, 170)
Butyl acrylate	$C_7H_{12}O_2$	− 0.5	+ 35.5	63.4	85.1	125.2	147.4	− 64.6	(113)
Ethyl levulinate	$C_7H_{12}O_3$	47.3	87.3	117.7	141.3	183.0	206.2	...	(376)
Pimelic acid	$C_7H_{12}O_4$	163.4	212.0	247.0	272.0	318.5	342.1	103	(11, 415)
Diethyl malonate	$C_7H_{12}O_4$	40.0	81.3	113.3	136.2	176.8	198.9	− 49.8	(11, 180)
Enanthyl chloride	$C_7H_{13}ClO$	34.2	64.6	86.4	102.7	130.7	145.0	......	(11, 229)
Enanthonitrile	$C_7H_{13}N$	21.0	61.6	92.6	116.8	160.0	184.6	......	(159)
Ethylcyclopentane	C_7H_{14}	− 32.2	− 0.1	+ 25.0	45.0	82.3	103.4	− 138.6	(6, 359, 471)
Methylcyclohexane	C_7H_{14}	− 35.9	− 3.2	+ 22.0	42.1	79.6	100.9	− 126.4	(6, 253, 359, 415, 471)
2-Heptene	C_7H_{14}	− 35.8	− 3.5	+ 21.5	41.3	78.1	98.5	......	(446)
Enanthaldehyde	$C_7H_{14}O$	12.0	43.0	66.3	84.0	125.5	155.0	− 42	(11, 199, 203, 415)
2-Heptanone	$C_7H_{14}O$	19.3	55.5	81.2	100.0	133.2	150.2	......	(11)
4-Heptanone	$C_7H_{14}O$	23.0	55.0	78.1	96.0	127.3	143.7	− 32.6	(11)
2,4-Dimethyl-3-pentanone	$C_7H_{14}O$	+ 5.2	36.7	59.6	77.0	108.0	123.7	......	(113)
Enanthic acid	$C_7H_{14}O_2$	78.0	113.2	139.5	160.0	199.6	221.5	− 10	(11, 203, 204)
Methyl caproate	$C_7H_{14}O_2$	+ 5.0	42.0	70.0	91.4	129.8	150.0d	......	(2)
Ethyl isovalerate	$C_7H_{14}O_2$	− 6.1	+ 28.7	55.2	75.9	114.0	134.3	− 99.3	(11, 380)
Propyl butyrate	$C_7H_{14}O_2$	− 1.6	+ 34.0	61.5	82.6	121.7	142.7	− 95.2	(11, 380)
Propyl isobutyrate	$C_7H_{14}O_2$	− 6.2	+ 28.3	54.3	73.9	112.0	133.9	......	(380)
Isopropyl isobutyrate	$C_7H_{14}O_2$	− 16.3	+ 17.0	42.4	62.3	100.0	120.5	......	(489)
Isobutyl propionate	$C_7H_{14}O_2$	− 2.3	+ 32.3	58.5	79.5	116.4	136.8	− 71	(380)

Name	Formula	Temperature °C						M.P.	Citation No.
		1 mm	10 mm	40 mm	100 mm	400 mm	760 mm		
Isoamyl acetate	$C_7H_{14}O_2$	0.0	+ 35.2	62.1	83.2	121.5	142.0	......	(11)
Heptane	C_7H_{16}	− 34.0	− 2.1	+ 22.3	41.8	78.0	98.4	− 90.6	(6, 251, 269, 289, 359, 394, 483)
2-Methylhexane	C_7H_{16}	− 40.4	− 9.1	+ 14.9	34.1	69.8	90.0	−118.2	(6, 359, 471)
3-Methylhexane	C_7H_{16}	− 39.0	− 7.8	+ 16.4	35.6	71.6	91.9	−119.4	(6, 359, 471)
3-Ethylpentane	C_7H_{16}	− 37.8	− 6.8	+ 17.5	36.9	73.0	93.5	−118.6	(6, 359, 471)
2,2-Dimethylpentane	C_7H_{16}	− 49.0	− 18.7	+ 5.0	23.9	59.2	79.2	−123.7	(6, 359, 471)
2,3-Dimethylpentane	C_7H_{16}	− 42.0	− 10.3	+ 13.9	33.3	69.4	89.8	−135	(6, 359, 471)
2,4-Dimethylpentane	C_7H_{16}	− 48.0	− 17.1	+ 6.5	25.4	60.6	80.5	−119.5	(6, 359, 471)
3,3-Dimethylpentane	C_7H_{16}	− 45.9	− 14.4	+ 9.9	29.3	65.5	86.1	−135.0	(6, 359, 471)
2,2,3-Trimethylbutane	C_7H_{16}	8	− 18.8	+ 5.2	24.4	60.4	80.9	− 25.0	(6, 359, 471)
1-Heptanol	$C_7H_{16}O$	42.4	74.7	99.8	119.5	155.6	175.8	34.6	(11, 68)
Triethyl orthoformate	$C_7H_{16}O_3$	+ 5.5	40.5	67.5	88.0	125.7	146.0	......	(11)
Triethoxymethylsilane	$C_7H_{18}O_3Si$	− 1.5	+ 34.6	61.7	82.7	121.8	143.5	......	(114)
Butyltrimethylsilane	$C_7H_{18}Si$	− 23.4	+ 9.9	35.9	56.3	93.8	115.0	......	(466)
Triethylmethylsilane	$C_7H_{18}Si$	− 18.2	+ 16.6	44.0	65.6	105.3	127.0	......	(466)
Phthaloyl chloride	$C_8H_4Cl_2O_2$	86.3₈	134.2	170.0	197.8	248.3	275.8	88.5	(11)
Phthalic anhydride	$C_8H_4O_3$	96.5₈	134.0	172.0	202.3	256.8	284.5	130.8	(97, 189, 284)
α,α-Dichlorophenylacetonitrile	$C_8H_5Cl_2N$	56.0	98.1	130.0	154.5	199.5	223.5	......	(11)
Pentachloroethylbenzene	$C_8H_5Cl_5$	96.2	148.0	186.2	216.0	269.3	299.0	......	(113)
Phenylglyoxylonitrile	C_8H_5NO	44.5	85.5	116.6	141.0	185.0	208.0	33.5	(11)
2,3-Dichlorostyrene	$C_8H_6Cl_2$	61.0	104.6	137.8	163.5	210.0ₚ	235.0ₚ		(113, 276)
2,4-Dichlorostyrene	$C_8H_6Cl_2$	53.5	97.4	129.2	153.8	200.0ₚ	225.0ₚ		(113, 276)
2,5-Dichlorostyrene	$C_8H_6Cl_2$	55.5	98.2	131.0	155.8	202.5ₚ	227.0ₚ		(113, 276)
2,6-Dichlorostyrene	$C_8H_6Cl_2$	47.8	90.0	122.4	147.6	193.5ₚ	217.0ₚ		(113, 276)
3,4-Dichlorostyrene	$C_8H_6Cl_2$	57.2	100.4	133.7	158.2	205.7ₚ	230.0ₚ		(113, 276)
3,5-Dichlorostyrene	$C_8H_6Cl_2$	53.5	97.4	129.2	153.8	200.0ₚ	225.0ₚ		(113, 276)
3,4,5,6-Tetrachloro-1,2-xylene	$C_8H_6Cl_4$	94.4	140.3	174.2	200.5	248.3	273.5		(11)
1,2,3,5-Tetrachloro-4-ethylbenzene	$C_8H_6Cl_4$	77.0	126.0	162.1	191.6	243.0	270.0		(113)
Phenylglyoxal	$C_8H_6O_2$	8	87.8	115.5	136.2	173.5	193.5	73	(354)
Phthalide	$C_8H_6O_2$	95.5	144.0	181.0	210.0	261.8	290.0	73	(11)
Piperonal	$C_8H_6O_3$	87.0	132.0	165.7	191.7	238.5	263.0	37	(11)
3-Chlorostyrene	C_8H_7Cl	25.3	65.2	96.5	121.2	165.7ₚ	190.0ₚ		(113)
4-Chlorostyrene	C_8H_7Cl	28.0	67.5	98.0	122.0	166.0ₚ	191.0ₚ	− 15.0	(113)
Phenylacetyl chloride	C_8H_7ClO	48.0	89.0	119.8	143.5	186.0	210.0	......	(11)
2-Tolunitrile	C_8H_7N	36.7	77.9	110.0	135.0	180.0	205.2	− 13	(11)
4-Tolunitrile	C_8H_7N	42.5	85.8	109.5	145.2	193.0	217.6	29.5	(11)
Phenylacetonitrile	C_8H_7N	60.0	103.5	136.3	161.8	208.5	233.5	− 23.8	(11)
2-Tolyl isocyanide	C_8H_7N	25.2	64.0	94.0	117.7	159.9	183.5		(11, 294)
2-Nitrophenyl acetate	$C_8H_7NO_4$	100.0	142.0	172.8	194.1	233.5	253.0d		(11)
2-Methylbenzothiazole	C_8H_7NS	70.0	111.2	141.2	163.9	204.5	225.5	15.4	(95)
Benzylisothiocyanate	C_8H_7NS	79.5	121.8	153.0	177.7	220.4	243.0		(277)
Styrene	C_8H_8	− 7.0	+ 30.8	59.8	82.0ₚ	122.5ₚ	145.2ₚ	− 30.6	(11, 44, 63, 113, 253)
(1,2-Dibromoethyl) benzene	$C_8H_8Br_2$	86.0	129.8	161.8	186.3	230.0	254.0		(11)
1,2-Dichloro-3-ethylbenzene	$C_8H_8Cl_2$	46.0	90.0	123.8	149.8	197.0	222.1	− 40.8	(113)
1,2-Dichloro-4-ethylbenzene	$C_8H_8Cl_2$	47.0	92.3	127.5	153.3	201.7	226.6	− 76.4	(113)
1,4-Dichloro-2-ethylbenzene	$C_8H_8Cl_2$	38.5	83.2	118.0	144.0	191.5	216.3	− 61.2	(113)
Acetophenone	C_8H_8O	37.1	78.0	109.4	133.6	178.0	202.4	20.5	(11, 156, 203, 204)
Phenyl acetate	$C_8H_8O_2$	38.2	78.0	108.1	131.6	173.5	195.9	......	(11)
Phenylacetic acid	$C_8H_8O_2$	97.0	141.3	173.6	198.2	243.0	265.5	76.5	(11)
Anisaldehyde	$C_8H_8O_2$	73.2	117.8	150.5	176.7	223.0	248.0	2.5	(11, 316)
Methyl benzoate	$C_8H_8O_2$	39.0	77.3	107.8	130.8	174.7	199.5	− 12.5	(11, 203, 204)
Methyl salicylate	$C_8H_8O_3$	54.0	95.3	126.2	150.0	197.5	223.2	− 8.3	(11, 334, 341)
Vanillin	$C_8H_8O_3$	107.0	154.0	188.7	214.5	260.0	285.0	81.5	(11)
Dehydroacetic acid	$C_8H_8O_4$	91.7	137.3	171.0	197.5	244.5	269.0	......	(11)
2-Bromo-1,4-xylene	C_8H_9Br	37.5	78.8	110.6	135.7	181.0	206.7	+ 9.5	(113, 166)
1-Bromo-4-ethylbenzene	C_8H_9Br	30.4	74.0	108.5	135.5	182.0	206.0	− 45.0	(11, 113)
(2-Bromoethyl) benzene	C_8H_9Br	48.0	90.5	123.2	148.2	194.0	219.0		(113)
1-Chloro-2-ethylbenzene	C_8H_9Cl	17.2	56.1	86.2	110.0	152.2	177.6	− 80.2	(113)
1-Chloro-3-ethylbenzene	C_8H_9Cl	18.6	58.2	89.2	113.6	156.7	181.1	− 53.3	(113)
1-Chloro-4-ethylbenzene	C_8H_9Cl	19.2	60.0	91.8	116.0	159.8	184.3	− 62.6	(113)
1-Chloro-2-ethoxybenzene	C_8H_9ClO	45.8	86.5	117.8	141.8	185.5	208.0	......	(11)
4-Chlorophenethyl alcohol	C_8H_9ClO	84.0	129.0	162.0	188.1	234.5	259.3	......	(113)
Acetanilide	C_8H_9NO	114.0	162.0	199.6	227.2	277.0	303.8	113.5	(11)
Methyl anthranilate	$C_8H_9NO_2$	77.6	124.2	159.7	187.8	238.5	266.5	24	(383)
4-Nitro-1,3-xylene	$C_8H_9NO_2$	65.6	109.8	143.3	168.5	217.5	244.0	+ 2	(302)
Ethylbenzene	C_8H_{10}	− 9.8	+ 25.9	52.8	74.1	113.8	136.2	− 94.9	(6, 11, 265, 359, 415, 471, 474)
2-Xylene	C_8H_{10}	− 3.8	+ 32.1	59.5	81.3	121.7	144.4	− 25.2	(6, 207, 253, 265, 302, 359, 415, 474)
3-Xylene	C_8H_{10}	− 6.9	+ 28.3	55.3	76.8	116.7	139.1	− 47.9	(6, 11, 207, 253, 265, 302, 359, 415, 474)
4-Xylene	C_8H_{10}	− 8.1	+ 27.3	54.4	75.9	115.9	138.3	+ 13.3	(6, 207, 253, 265, 302, 359, 415, 474)
Dichloroethoxyphenylsilane	$C_8H_{10}Cl_2OSi$	52.4	94.6	126.2	151.4	197.2	220.0	....	(114)
Dichloroethylphenylsilane	$C_8H_{10}Cl_2Si$	48.5	92.4	126.7	153.3	203.5	230.0	....	(114)
2-Ethylphenol	$C_8H_{10}O$	46.2	87.0	117.9	141.8	184.5	207.5	− 45	(406)
3-Ethylphenol	$C_8H_{10}O$	60.0	100.2	130.0	152.0	193.3	214.0	− 4	(406)
4-Ethylphenol	$C_8H_{10}O$	59.3	100.2	131.3	154.2	197.4	219.0	46.5	(406)
2,3-Xylenol	$C_8H_{10}O$	56.0₈	97.6	129.2	152.2	196.0	218.0	75	(406)
2,4-Xylenol	$C_8H_{10}O$	51.8	91.3	121.5	143.0	184.2	211.5	25.5	(406)
2,5-Xylenol	$C_8H_{10}O$	51.8₈	91.3	121.5	143.0	184.2	211.5	74.5	(406)
3,4-Xylenol	$C_8H_{10}O$	66.2	107.7	138.0	161.0	203.6	225.2	62.5	(406)
3,5-Xylenol	$C_8H_{10}O$	62.0₈	102.4	133.3	156.0	197.8	210.5	68	(406)
Phenetole	$C_8H_{10}O$	18.1	56.4	86.6	108.4	149.8	172.0	− 30.2	(11, 199)
α-Methyl benzyl alcohol	$C_8H_{10}O$	49.0	88.0	117.8	140.3	180.7	204.0	......	(113)
Phenethylalcohol	$C_8H_{10}O$	58.2	100.0	130.5	154.0	197.5	219.5	......	(113, 395, 396, 456)
4,6-Dimethylresorcinol	$C_8H_{10}O_2$	49.0	90.7	122.5	147.3	192.0	215.0	......	(11)

Name	Formula	Temperature °C						M.P.	Citation No.
		1 mm	10 mm	40 mm	100 mm	400 mm	760 mm		
2-Phenoxyethanol	$C_8H_{10}O_2$	78.0	121.2	152.2	176.5	221.0	245.3	11.6	(113)
Diethyl dioxosuccinate	$C_8H_{10}O_6$	70.0	112.0	143.8	167.7	210.8	233.5		(11)
Chlorodimethylphenylsilane	$C_8H_{11}ClSi$	29.8	70.0	101.2	124.7	168.6	193.5		(114)
N-Ethylaniline	$C_8H_{11}N$	38.5	80.6	113.2	137.3	180.8	204.0	− 63.5	(11, 203, 204, 300)
N,N-Dimethylaniline	$C_8H_{11}N$	29.5	70.0	101.6	125.8	169.2	193.1	+ 2.5	(11, 203, 204, 300)
4-Ethylaniline	$C_8H_{11}N$	52.0	93.8	125.7	149.8	194.2	217.4	− 4	(113)
2,4-Xylidine	$C_8H_{11}N$	52.6	93.0	123.8	146.8	188.3	211.5		(113)
2,6-Xylidine	$C_8H_{11}N$	44.0	87.0	120.2	146.0	193.7	217.9		(11, 199)
2-Phenetidine	$C_8H_{11}NO$	67.0	108.6	139.9	163.5	207.0	228.0		(302)
2-Anilinoethanol	$C_8H_{11}NO$	104.0	149.6	183.7	209.5	254.5	279.6		(11)
Dimethyl arsanilate	$C_8H_{12}AsNO_2$	15.0	51.8	79.7	101.0	140.3	160.5		(113)
Diethyleneglycol-bis-chloroacetate	$C_8H_{12}Cl_2O_5$	148.3	195.8	229.0	252.0	291.8	313.0		(11)
Diethyl maleate	$C_8H_{12}O_4$	57.3	100.0	131.8	156.0	201.7	225.0		(113)
Diethyl fumarate	$C_8H_{12}O_4$	53.2	95.3	126.7	151.1	195.8	218.5	+ 0.6	(11)
Dimethylphenylsilane	$C_8H_{12}Si$	+ 5.3	42.6	71.4	94.2	136.4	159.3		(114)
Ethyl-α-ethylacetoacetate	$C_8H_{14}O_3$	40.5	80.2	110.3	133.8	175.6	198.0		(11)
Propyl levulinate	$C_8H_{14}O_3$	59.7	99.9	130.1	154.0	198.0	221.2		(376)
Isopropyl levulinate	$C_8H_{14}O_3$	48.0	88.0	118.1	141.8	185.2	208.2		(376)
Dipropyl oxalate	$C_8H_{14}O_4$	53.4	93.9	124.6	148.1	190.3	213.5		(11)
Diisopropyl oxalate	$C_8H_{14}O_4$	43.2	81.9	110.5	132.6	171.8	193.5		(11)
Diethyl succinate	$C_8H_{14}O_4$	54.6	96.6	127.8	151.1	193.8	216.5	− 20.8	(11, 180)
Diethyl isosuccinate	$C_8H_{14}O_4$	39.8	80.0	111.0	134.8	177.7	201.3		(11)
Suberic acid	$C_8H_{14}O_4$	172.8	219.5	254.6	279.0	322.8	345.5	142	(234)
Diethyl malate	$C_8H_{14}O_5$	80.7	125.6	157.8	183.9	229.5	253.4		(11)
Diethyl-dl-tartrate	$C_8H_{14}O_6$	100.0	147.2	181.7	208.0	254.3	280.0		(11)
Diethyl-d-tartrate	$C_8H_{14}O_6$	102.0	148.0	182.3	208.5	254.8	280.0		(11)
(2-Bromoethyl) cyclohexane	$C_8H_{15}Br$	38.7	80.5	113.0	138.0	186.2	213.0		(113)
Caprylonitrile	$C_8H_{15}N$	43.0	80.4	110.6	134.8	179.5	204.5		(159)
Ethyl N,N-diethyloxamate	$C_8H_{15}NO_3$	76.0	121.7	154.4	180.3	226.5	252.0		(11)
2-Methyl-2-heptene	C_8H_{16}	− 16.1	+ 17.8	44.0	64.6	102.2	122.5		(11)
1,1-Dimethylcyclohexane	C_8H_{16}	− 24.4	+ 10.3	37.3	57.9	97.2	119.5	− 34	(6, 359, 471)
cis-1,2-Dimethylcyclohexane	C_8H_{16}	− 15.9	+ 18.4	45.3	66.8	107.0	129.7	− 50.0	(6, 359, 471)
trans-1,2-Dimethylcyclohexane	C_8H_{16}	− 21.1	+ 13.0	39.7	61.0	100.9	123.4	− 88.0	(6, 359, 471)
cis-1,3-Dimethylcyclohexane	C_8H_{16}	− 22.7	+ 11.2	37.5	58.5	97.8	120.1	− 76.2	(6, 359, 471)
trans-1,3-Dimethylcyclohexane	C_8H_{16}	− 19.4	+ 14.9	41.4	62.5	102.1	124.4	− 92.0	(6, 359, 471)
cis-1,4-Dimethylcyclohexane	C_8H_{16}	− 20.0	+ 14.5	41.1	62.3	101.9	124.3	− 87.4	(6, 359, 471)
trans-1,4-Dimethylcyclohexane	C_8H_{16}	− 24.3	+ 10.1	36.5	57.6	97.0	119.3	− 36.9	(6, 359, 471)
Ethylcyclohexane	C_8H_{16}	− 14.5	+ 20.6	47.6	69.0	109.1	131.8	−111.3	(6, 359, 471)
Caprylaldehyde	$C_8H_{16}O$	73.4	101.2	120.0	133.9	156.5	168.5		(11, 225)
Cyclohexaneethanol	$C_8H_{16}O$	50.4	90.0	119.8	142.7	183.5	205.4		(113)
6-Methyl-3-hepter-2-ol	$C_8H_{16}O$	41.6	76.7	102.7	122.6	156.6	175.5		(431, 434, 460)
6-Methyl-5-liepten-2-ol	$C_8H_{16}O$	41.9	77.8	104.0	123.8	156.6	174.3		(113)
2-Octanone	$C_8H_{16}O$	23.6	60.9	89.8	111.7	151.0	172.9	− 16	(11)
2,2,4-Trimethyl-3-pentanone	$C_8H_{16}O$	14.7	46.4	69.8	87.6	118.4	135.0		(113)
Caprylic acid	$C_8H_{16}O_2$	92.3	124.0	150.6	172.2	213.9	237.5	16	(11, 203, 204)
Ethyl isocaproate	$C_8H_{16}O_2$	11.0	48.0	76.3	98.4	139.2	160.4		(11)
Propyl isovalerate	$C_8H_{16}O_2$	+ 8.0	45.1	72.8	95.0	135.0	155.9		(380)
Isobutyl butyrate	$C_8H_{16}O$	+ 4.6	42.2	71.7	94.0	135.7	156.9		(11, 380)
Isobutyl isobutyrate	$C_8H_{16}O_2$	+ 4.1	39.9	67.2	88.0	126.3	147.5	− 80.7	(11, 203, 380)
Amyl propionate	$C_8H_{16}O_2$	+ 8.5	46.3	75.5	97.6	138.4	160.2		(380)
Tetraethyleneglycol chlorohydrin	$C_8H_{16}ClO_4$	110.1	156.1	190.0	214.7	258.2	281.5		(11)
1-Iodoöctane	$C_8H_{17}I$	45.8	90.0	123.8	150.0	199.3	225.5	− 45.9	(11, 228)
Ethyl-l-leucinate	$C_8H_{17}NO_2$	27.8	72.1	106.0	131.8	167.3	184.0		(419)
Octane	C_8H_{18}	− 14.0	+ 19.2	45.1	65.7	104.0	125.6	− 56.8	(6, 251, 253, 359, 471, 474, 483a)
2-Methylheptane	C_8H_{18}	− 21.0	+ 12.3	37.9	58.3	96.2	117.6	−109.5	(6, 359, 471)
3-Methylheptane	C_8H_{18}	− 19.8	+ 13.3	38.9	59.4	97.4	118.9	−120.8	(6, 359, 471)
4-Methylheptane	C_8H_{18}	− 20.4	+ 12.4	38.0	58.3	96.3	117.7	−121.1	(6, 359, 471)
2,2-Dimethylhexane	C_8H_{18}	− 29.7	+ 3.1	28.2	48.2	85.6	106.8		(6, 359, 471)
2,3-Dimethylhexane	C_8H_{18}	− 23.0	+ 9.9	35.6	56.0	94.1	115.6		(6, 359, 471)
2,4-Dimethylhexane	C_8H_{18}	− 26.9	+ 5.2	30.5	50.6	88.2	109.4		(6, 359, 471)
2,5-Dimethylhexane	C_8H_{18}	− 26.7	+ 5.3	30.4	50.5	87.9	109.1	− 90.7	(6, 359, 471, 488)
3,3-Dimethylhexane	C_8H_{18}	− 25.8	+ 6.1	31.7	52.5	90.4	112.0		(6, 359, 471)
3,4-Dimethylhexane	C_8H_{18}	− 22.1	+ 11.3	37.1	57.7	96.0	117.7		(6, 359, 471)
3-Ethylhexane	C_8H_{18}	− 20.0	+ 12.8	38.5	58.9	97.0	118.5		(6, 359, 471)
2,2,3-Trimethylpentane	C_8H_{18}	− 29.0	+ 3.9	29.5	49.9	88.2	109.8	−112.3	(6, 359, 471)
2,2,4-Trimethylpentane	C_8H_{18}	− 36.5	− 4.3	+ 20.7	40.7	78.0	99.2	−107.3	(6, 132, 253, 359, 471)
2,3,3-Trimethylpentane	C_8H_{18}	− 25.8	+ 6.9	33.0	53.8	92.7	114.8	−101.5	(6, 359, 471)
2,3,4-Trimethylpentane	C_8H_{18}	− 26.3	+ 7.1	32.9	53.4	91.8	113.5	−109.2	(6, 359, 471)
2-Methyl-3-ethylpentane	C_8H_{18}	− 24.0	+ 9.5	35.2	55.7	94.0	115.6	−114.5	(6, 359, 471)
3-Methyl-3-ethylpentane	C_8H_{18}	− 23.9	+ 9.9	36.2	57.1	96.2	118.3	− 90	(6, 359, 471)
2,2,3,3-Tetramethylbutane	C_8H_{18}	− 17.4	+ 13.5	36.8	54.8	87.4	106.3	+100.7	(6, 132, 253, 359, 471, 495)
Tetramethylpiperazine	$C_8H_{18}N_2$	23.7	61.7	90.0	113.8	157.8	183.5		(113)
1-Octanol	$C_8H_{18}O$	54.0	88.3	115.2	135.2	173.8	195.2	− 15.4	(68, 113, 278, 279, 494)
2-Octanol	$C_8H_{18}O$	32.8	70.0	98.0	119.8	157.5	178.5	− 38.6	(11, 199)
1,2-Dipropoxy ethane	$C_8H_{18}O_2$	− 38.8	+ 5.0	42.3	74.2	140.0	180.0		(254)
Diethylene glycol butyl ether	$C_8H_{18}O_3$	70.0	107.8	135.5	159.8	205.0	231.2		(113)
Tetraethylene glycol	$C_8H_{18}O_5$	153.9	197.1	228.0	250.0	228.0	307.8		(71, 141)
Dibutyl sulfide	$C_8H_{18}S$	+ 21.7	66.4	96.0	118.6	159.0	182.0	− 79.7	(25)
Dibutyl disulfide	$C_8H_{18}S_2$	+ 34.6	94.0	145.1	188.0	275.5	330.5		(25)
Diisobutylamine	$C_8H_{19}N$	− 5.1	+ 30.6	57.8	79.2	118.0	139.5	− 70	(11)
Tetraethoxysilane	$C_8H_{20}O_4Si$	16.0	52.6	81.1	103.6	146.2	168.5		(114, 398)
Tetraethyllead	$C_8H_{20}Pb$	38.4	74.8	102.4	123.8	161.8	183.0	−136	(61)
Amyltrimethylsilane	$C_8H_{20}Si$	− 9.2	+ 26.7	54.4	76.2	116.6	139.0		(466)
Tetraethylsilane	$C_8H_{20}Si$	− 1.0	+ 36.3	65.3	88.0	130.2	153.0		(466)

Name	Formula	Temperature °C						M.P.	Citation No.
		1 mm	10 mm	40 mm	100 mm	400 mm	760 mm		
Tetraethyl bistibine	$C_8H_{20}Sb_2$	97.0	151.2	193.2	225.6	286.2	320.3	......	(309)
1,3-Diethoxytetramethyldisiloxane	$C_8H_{22}O_3Si_2$	14.8	51.2	78.7	100.3	139.8	162.7	......	(114)
1,7-Dichlorooctamethyltetra-siloxane	$C_8H_{24}Cl_2O_3Si_4$	53.3	95.8	127.8	152.7	197.8	222.0	− 62	(312)
Octamethyltrisiloxane	$C_8H_{24}O_2Si_3$	7.4	43.1	70.0	91.1	129.4	150.2	......	(114, 469)
Octamethylcyclotetrasiloxane	$C_8H_{24}O_4Si_4$	21.7	59.0	87.4	110.0	149.6	171.2	17.4	(188, 312, 469)
Coumarin	$C_9H_6O_2$	106.0	153.4	189.0	216.5	264.7	291.0	70	(11)
Quinoline	C_9H_7N	59.7	103.8	136.7	163.2	212.3	237.7	− 15	(11, 199, 477)
Isoquinoline	C_9H_7N	63.5	107.8	141.6	167.6	214.5	240.5	24.6	(11)
Indene	C_9H_8	16.4	58.5	90.7	114.7	157.8	181.6	− 2	(63)
Cinnamylaldehyde	C_9H_8O	76.1	120.0	152.2	177.7	222.4	246.0	− 7.5	(11)
trans-Cinnamic acid	$C_9H_8O_2$	127.5s	173.0	207.1	232.4	276.7	300.0	133	(11)
Skatole	C_9H_9N	95.0	139.6	171.9	197.4	242.5	266.2	95	(78)
Ethyl 3-nitrobenzoate	$C_9H_9NO_4$	108.1	155.0	192.6	220.3	270.6	298.0	47	(11)
α-Methyl styrene	C_9H_{10}	7.4	47.1	77.8	102.2	143.0	165.4p	− 23.2	(113)
β-Methyl styrene	C_9H_{10}	17.5	57.0	87.7	111.7	154.7	179.0	− 30.1	(113, 436)
4-Methyl styrene	C_9H_{10}	16.0	55.1	85.0	108.6	151.2	175.0p	......	(216)
Propenylbenzene	C_9H_{10}	17.5	57.0	87.7	111.7	154.7	179.0	− 30.1	(113)
2,4-Xylaldehyde	$C_9H_{10}O$	59.0s	99.0	129.7	152.2	194.1	215.5	75	(51, 138, 139)
Cinnamyl alcohol	$C_9H_{10}O$	72.6	117.8	151.0	177.8	224.6	250.0	33	(11)
Propiophenone	$C_9H_{10}O$	50.0	92.2	124.3	149.3	194.2	218.0	21	(11)
2-Vinylanisole	$C_9H_{10}O$	41.9	81.0	110.0	132.3	172.1	194.0p	......	(215)
3-Vinylanisole	$C_9H_{10}O$	43.4	83.0	112.5	135.3	175.8	197.5p	......	(215)
4-Vinylanisole	$C_9H_{10}O$	45.2	85.7	116.0	139.7	182.0	204.5p	......	(215)
Benzyl acetate	$C_9H_{10}O_2$	45.0	87.6	119.6	144.0	189.0	213.5	− 51.5	(179)
Ethyl Benzoate	$C_9H_{10}O_2$	44.0	86.0	118.2	143.2	188.4	213.4	− 34.6	(11)
Hydrocinnamic acid	$C_9H_{10}O_2$	102.2	148.7	183.3	200.0	255.0	279.8	48.5	(11)
Ethyl salicylate	$C_9H_{10}O_3$	61.2	104.2	136.7	161.5	207.0	231.5	1.3	(11, 199)
N-Methylacetanilide	$C_9H_{11}NO$	s	118.6	152.2	179.8	227.4	253.0	102	(11)
Ethyl carbanilate	$C_9H_{11}NO_2$	107.8	143.7	168.8	187.9	220.0	237.0	52.5	(11)
1,2,3-Trimethylbenzene	C_9H_{12}	16.8	55.9	85.4	108.8	152.0	176.1	− 25.5	(6, 359, 471)
1,2,4-Trimethylbenzene	C_9H_{12}	13.6	50.7	79.8	102.8	145.4	169.2	− 44.1	(6, 359, 471, 474)
1,3,5-Trimethylbenzene	C_9H_{12}	9.6	47.4	76.1	98.9	141.0	164.7	− 44.8	(6, 11, 207, 253, 415, 471, 474)
2-Ethyltoluene	C_9H_{12}	9.4	47.6	76.4	99.0	141.4	165.1	......	(6,113,359,471)
3-Ethyltoluene	C_9H_{12}	7.2	44.7	73.3	95.9	137.8	161.3	− 95.5	(6,113,359,471, 495)
4-Ethyltoluene	C_9H_{12}	7.6	44.9	73.6	96.3	136.4	162.0	......	(6, 216, 359, 471)
Cumene	C_9H_{12}	2.9	38.3	66.1	88.1	129.2	152.4	− 96.0	(6, 253, 359, 471, 474)
Propylbenzene	C_9H_{12}	6.3	43.4	71.6	94.0	135.7	159.2	− 99.5	(6, 359, 471)
2-Ethylanisole	$C_9H_{12}O$	29.7	69.0	98.8	122.3	164.2	187.1	......	(215)
3-Ethylanisole	$C_9H_{12}O$	33.7	73.9	104.8	129.2	172.8	196.5	......	(215)
4-Ethylanisole	$C_9H_{12}O$	33.5	73.9	104.7	128.4	172.3	196.5	......	(215)
3-Phenyl-1-propanol	$C_9H_{12}O$	74.7	116.0	147.4	170.3	212.8	235.0	......	(429)
2-Isopropylphenol	$C_9H_{12}O$	56.6	97.0	127.5	150.3	192.6	214.5	15.5	(113)
3-Isopropylphenol	$C_9H_{12}O$	62.0	104.1	136.2	160.2	205.0	228.0	26	(113)
4-Isopropylphenol	$C_9H_{12}O$	67.0	108.0	139.8	163.3	206.1	228.2	61	(113)
Benzyl ethyl ether	$C_9H_{12}O$	26.0	65.0	95.4	118.9	161.5	185.0	......	(11)
Chloroethoxymethylphenylsilane	$C_9H_{13}ClOSi$	44.8	94.6	117.8	142.6	187.7	212.0	......	(114)
2,4,5-Trimethylaniline	$C_9H_{13}N$	68.4	109.0	139.8	162.0	203.7	234.5	67	(11)
N,N-Dimethyl-2-toluidine	$C_9H_{13}N$	28.8	66.2	95.0	118.1	161.5	184.8	− 61	(11, 204)
N,N-Dimethyl-4-toluidine	$C_9H_{13}N$	50.1	86.7	116.3	140.3	185.4	209.5	......	(11, 204)
4-Cumidine	$C_9H_{13}N$	60.0	102.2	134.2	158.0	203.2	227.0	......	(113)
Phorone	$C_9H_{14}O$	42.0	81.5	111.3	134.0	175.3	197.2	28	(11)
Isophorone	$C_9H_{14}O$	38.0	81.2	114.5	140.6	188.7	215.2	......	(393)
cis-Diethyl citraconate	$C_9H_{14}O_4$	59.8	103.0	135.7	160.0	206.5	230.3	......	(11)
Diethyl itaconate	$C_9H_{14}O_4$	51.3	95.2	128.2	154.3	203.1	227.9	......	(11)
Diethyl mesaconate	$C_9H_{14}O_4$	62.8	105.3	137.3	161.6	205.8	229.0	......	(11)
Trimethyl citrate	$C_9H_{14}O_7$	106.2	160.4	194.2	219.6	264.2	287.0d	78.5	(11)
Isobutyl levulinate	$C_9H_{16}O_3$	65.0	103.9	136.2	160.2	205.5	229.9	......	(376)
Azelaic acid	$C_9H_{16}O_4$	178.3	225.5	260.0	286.5	332.8	356.5d	106.5	(234)
Diethyl ethylmalonate	$C_9H_{16}O_4$	50.8	91.6	122.4	146.0	188.7	211.5	......	(11)
Diethyl glutarate	$C_9H_{16}O_4$	65.6	109.7	142.8	167.8	212.8	237.0	......	(180)
2-Nonanone	$C_9H_{18}O$	32.1	72.3	103.4	127.4	171.2	195.0	− 19	(183)
Azelaldehyde	$C_9H_{18}O$	33.3	71.6	100.2	123.0	163.4	185.0	......	(458)
Pelargonic acid	$C_9H_{18}O_2$	108.2	137.4	163.7	184.4	227.5	253.5	12.5	(11, 203, 223)
Methyl caprylate	$C_9H_{18}O_2$	34.2	74.9	105.3	128.0	170.0	193.0d	− 40	(2)
Isobutyl isovalerate	$C_9H_{18}O_2$	16.0	53.8	82.7	105.2	146.4	168.7	......	(380)
Isoamyl butyrate	$C_9H_{18}O_2$	21.2	59.9	90.0	113.1	155.3	178.6	......	(380)
Isoamyl isobutyrate	$C_9H_{18}O_2$	14.8	52.8	81.8	104.4	146.0	168.8	......	(380)
Iodononane	$C_9H_{19}I$	70.0	109.0	138.1	159.8	199.3	219.5	......	(225, 228)
Nonane	C_9H_{20}	+ 1.4	38.0	66.0	88.1	128.2	150.8	− 53.7	(11, 223, 484, 495)
1-Nonanol	$C_9H_{20}O$	59.5	99.7	129.0	151.3	192.1	213.5	− 5	(11, 228)
Dipropyleneglycol, isopropyl ether	$C_9H_{20}O_3$	46.0	86.2	117.0	140.3	183.1	205.6	......	(113)
Tripropyleneglycol	$C_9H_{20}O_4$	96.0	140.5	173.7	199.0	244.3	267.2	......	(113)
Heptyltrimethylsilane	$C_9H_{22}Si$	+ 6.7	44.8	74.0	97.2	139.9	163.0	......	(466)
Triethylpropylsilane	$C_9H_{22}Si$	15.2	51.0	80.0	107.1	148.8	173.0	......	(466)
1-Bromonaphthalene	$C_{10}H_7Br$	84.2	133.6	170.2	198.8	252.0	281.1	6.5	(11, 203, 204, 334)
1-Chloronaphthalene	$C_{10}H_7Cl$	80.6	118.6	153.2	180.4	230.8	259.3	− 20	(203, 204)
Dicyclopentadiene	$C_{10}H_{12}$	s	17.6	77.9	101.7	144.2	166.6d	32.9	(63)
Naphthalene	$C_{10}H_8$	52.6s	85.8	119.3	145.5	193.2	217.9	80.2	(1, 8, 11, 24, 34, 98, 140, 194, 288, 299, 303, 372, 400, 404, 417)
Dichloro-1-naphthylsilane	$C_{10}H_8Cl_2Si$	106.2	149.2	181.7	205.9	249.7	273.3	......	(114)
1-Naphthol	$C_{10}H_8O$	94.0s	142.0	177.8	206.0	255.8	282.5	96	(11, 270)
2-Naphthol	$C_{10}H_8O$	s	145.5	181.7	209.8	260.6	288.0	122.5	(11, 270, 400)
1-Naphthylamine	$C_{10}H_9N$	104.3	153.8	191.5	220.0	272.2	300.8	50	(11)

Name	Formula	\multicolumn{6}{c}{Temperature °C}			M.P.	Citation No.
		1 mm	10 mm	40 mm	100 mm	400 mm	760 mm		
2-Naphthylamine	$C_{10}H_9N$	108.0	157.6	195 7	224.3	277.4	306.1	111.5	(11)
2-Methylquinoline	$C_{10}H_9N$	75.3	119.0	150.8	176.2	211.7	246.5	− 1	(11)
1,3-Divinylbenzene	$C_{10}H_{10}$	32.7	73.8	105.5	130.0	175.2	199.5p	− 66.9	(113)
4-Phenyl-3-buten-2-one	$C_{10}H_{10}O$	81.7	127.4	161.3	187.8	235.4	261.0	41.5	(11)
α-Methylcinnamic acid	$C_{10}H_{10}O_2$	125.7	169.8	201 8	224.8	266.8	288.0		(11)
Methyl cinnamate	$C_{10}H_{10}O_2$	77.4	123.0	157.9	185.8	235.0	263.0	33.4	(370)
Safrole	$C_{10}H_{10}O_2$	63.8	107.6	140.1	165.1	210.0	233.0	11.2	(383)
1,2-Phenylene diacetate	$C_{10}H_{10}O_4$	98.0	145.7	179.8	206.5	253.3	278.0		(11)
Dimethyl phthalate	$C_{10}H_{10}O_4$	100.3	147.6	182.8	210.0	257 8	283.7		(142)
2,4-Dimethylstyrene	$C_{10}H_{12}$	34.2	75.8	107.7	132.3	177.5	202.0p		(216)
2,5-Dimethylstyrene	$C_{10}H_{12}$	29.0	69.0	100.2	124.7	168.7	193.0p		(216)
3-Ethylstyrene	$C_{10}H_{12}$	28.3	68.3	99 2	123.2	167.2	191.5p		(113)
4-Ethylstyrene	$C_{10}H_{12}$	26.0	66.3	97 3	121 5	165 0	189.0p		(216)
Tetralin	$C_{10}H_{12}$	38.0	79.0	110.4	135.3	181.8	207.2	− 31.0	(177, 253)
Anethole	$C_{10}H_{12}O$	62.6	106.0	139.3	164.2	210.5	235.3	22.5	(11)
4-Methylpropiophenone	$C_{10}H_{12}O$	59.6	103.8	138.0	164.2	212.7	238.5		(214)
Estragole	$C_{10}H_{12}O$	52.6	93.7	124.6	148.5	192.0	215.0		(436)
Cuminal	$C_{10}H_{12}O$	58.0	102.0	135.2	160.0	206.7	232.0		(11, 199, 203, 204)
4-Vinylphenetole	$C_{10}H_{12}O$	64.0	105.6	136.3	159.8	202.8	225.0p		(215)
Eugenol	$C_{10}H_{12}O_2$	78.4	123.0	155.8	182.2	228.3	253.5		(11, 40)
Isoeugenol	$C_{10}H_{12}O_2$	86.3	132.4	167.0	194.0	242.3	267.5	− 10	(383)
Chavibetol	$C_{10}H_{12}O_2$	83.6	127.0	159.8	185.5	229.8	254.0		(113)
Propyl benzoate	$C_{10}H_{12}O_2$	54.6	98.0	131.8	157.4	205.2	231.0	− 51.6	(11)
2-Phenoxyethyl acetate	$C_{10}H_{12}O_3$	82.6	128.0	162.3	189.2	235.0	259.7	− 6.7	(113)
2-Chloroethyl α-methylbenzyl ether	$C_{10}H_{13}ClO$	62.3	106.0	139.6	164.8	210.8	235.0		(113)
4-tert-Butylphenyl dichlorophosphate	$C_{10}H_{13}Cl_2O_2P$	90.0	146.0	184.3	214.3	268.2	299.0		(113)
1,2,3,4-Tetramethylbenzene	$C_{10}H_{14}$	42.6	81.8	111.5	135.7	180.0	204.4	− 6.2	(259, 495)
1,2,3,5-Tetramethylbenzene	$C_{10}H_{14}$	40.6	77.8	105.8	128.3	173.7	197.9	− 24.0	(259)
1,2,4,5-Tetramethylbenzene	$C_{10}H_{14}$	45.0s	74.6s	104.2	128.1	172.1	195.9	79.5	(253, 259)
4-Ethyl-1,3-xylene	$C_{10}H_{14}$	26.3	66.4	97.2	121.2	164.4	188.4		(216, 495)
5-Ethyl-1,3-xylene	$C_{10}H_{14}$	22.1	62.1	92.6	116.5	159.6	183.7		(113, 495)
2-Ethyl-1,4-xylene	$C_{10}H_{14}$	25.7	65.6	96.0	120.0	163 1	186.9		(216, 495)
1,2-Diethylbenzene	$C_{10}H_{14}$	22.3	62.0	92.5	116.2	159.0	183.5	− 31.4	(140, 495, 501)
1,3-Diethylbenzene	$C_{10}H_{14}$	20.7	59.9	90.4	114.4	156.9	181.1	− 83.9	(113, 253, 495)
1,4-Diethylbenzene	$C_{10}H_{14}$	20.7	60.3	91.1	115.3	159.0	183.8	− 43.2	(113, 216, 253, 495)
Cymene	$C_{10}H_{14}$	17.3	57.0	87.0	110.8	153.5	177.2	− 68.2	(11, 253, 474, 498)
Butylbenzene	$C_{10}H_{14}$	22.7	62.0	92.4	116.2	159.2	183.1	− 88.0	(253, 495)
Isobutylbenzene	$C_{10}H_{14}$	14.1	53.7	83.3	107.0	149.6	172.8	− 51.5	(474, 495)
sec-Butylbenzene	$C_{10}H_{14}$	18.6	57.0	86.2	109.5	150.3	173.5	− 75.5	(253, 495)
tert-Butylbenzene	$C_{10}H_{14}$	13.0	51.7	80.8	103.8	145.8	168.5	− 58	(253)
Carvacrol	$C_{10}H_{14}O$	70.0	113.2	145.2	169.7	213.8	237.0	+ 0.5	(11, 59, 113, 385)
Carbone	$C_{10}H_{14}O$	57.4	100.4	133.0	157.3	203.5	227.5		(11, 59, 362)
Cuminyl alcohol	$C_{10}H_{14}O$	74.2	118.0	150.3	176.2	221.7	246.6		(11)
4-Ethylphenetole	$C_{10}H_{14}O$	48.5	89.5	119.8	143.5	185.7	208.0		(215)
Thymol	$C_{10}H_{14}O$	64.3	107.4	139.8	164.1	209.2	231.8	51.5	(11, 113, 322)
4-Isobutylphenol	$C_{10}H_{14}O$	72.1	115.5	147.2	171.2	214.7	237.0		(11)
4-sec-Butylphenol	$C_{10}H_{14}O$	71.4	114.8	147.8	172.4	217.6	242.1		(113)
2-sec-Butylphenol	$C_{10}H_{14}O$	57.4	100.8	133.4	157.3	203.8	228.0		(113)
2-tert-Butylphenol	$C_{10}H_{14}O$	56.6	98.1	129.2	153.5	196.3	219.5		(113)
4-tert-Butylphenol	$C_{10}H_{14}O$	70.0	114.0	146.0	170.2	214.0	238.0	99	(113, 406)
Nicotine	$C_{10}H_{14}N_2$	61.8	107.2	142.1	169.5	219.8	247.3		(490)
N-Diethylaniline	$C_{10}N_{15}N$	49.7	91.9	123.6	147.3	192.4	215.5	− 34.4	(11, 199, 204, 300)
N-Phenyliminodiethanol	$C_{10}H_{15}NO_2$	145.0	195.8	233.0	260.6	311.3	337.8		(113)
Camphene	$C_{10}H_{16}$	s	47.2s	75.7	97.9	138.7	160.5	50	(383)
Dipentene	$C_{10}H_{16}$	14.0	53.8	84.3	108.3	150.5	174.6		(11, 253, 320)
d-Limonene	$C_{10}H_{16}$	14.0	53.8	84.3	108.3	151.4	175.0		(11, 253)
Myrcene	$C_{10}H_{16}$	14.5	53.2	82.6	106.0	148.3	171.5		(327, 387)
α-Phellandrene	$C_{10}H_{16}$	20.0	58.0	87.8	110.6	152.0	175.0		(461)
α-Pinene	$C_{10}H_{16}$	− 1.0	+ 37.3	66.8	90.1	132.3	155.0	− 55	(253, 320, 351)
β-Pinene	$C_{10}H_{16}$	+ 4.2	42.3	71.5	94.0	136.1	158.3		(320)
Terpenoline	$C_{10}H_{16}$	32.3	70.6	100.0	122.7	163.5	185.0		(320, 383)
Diethyl arsanilate	$C_{10}H_{16}AsNO_3$	38.0	74.8	102.6	123.8	161.0	181.0		(11)
d-Camphor	$C_{10}H_{16}O$	41.5s	82.3s	114.0d	138.0s	182.0	209.2	178.5	(1, 105, 303, 336, 404, 444)
l-Dihydrocarvone	$C_{10}H_{16}O$	46.6	90.0	123.7	149.7	197.0	223.0		(383)
α-Citral	$C_{10}H_{16}O$	61.7	103.9	135.9	160.0	205.0	228.0d		(383)
d-Fenchone	$C_{10}H_{16}O$	28.0	68.3	99.5	123.6	166.8	191.0	5	(42)
Pulegone	$C_{10}H_{16}O$	58.3	94.0	121.7	143.1	189.8	221.0		(383)
α-Thyjone	$C_{10}H_{16}O$	38.3	79.3	110.0	134.0	177.8	201.		(265)
Ethoxydimethylphenylsilane	$C_{10}H_{16}OSi$	36.3	76.2	107.2	131.4	175.0	199.5		(114)
Campholenic acid	$C_{10}H_{16}O_2$	97.6	139.8	170.0	193.7	234.0	256.0		(11)
Diosphenol	$C_{10}H_{16}O_2$	66.7	109.0	141.2	165.6	209.5	232.0		(383)
Fencholic acid	$C_{10}H_{16}O_2$	101.7	142.3	171.8	194.0	237.8	264.1	19	(113)
cis-Decalin	$C_{10}H_{18}$	22.5	64.2	97.2	122.3	169.9	194.6	− 43.3	(389)
trans-Decalin	$C_{10}H_{18}$	− 0.8	+ 47.2	85.7	114.6	160.1	186.7	− 30.7	(389)
d-Citronellal	$C_{10}H_{18}O$	44.0	84.8	116.1	140.1	183.8	206.5		(432)
Cineol	$C_{10}H_{18}O$	15.0	54.1	84.2	108.2	151.6	176.0	− 1	(11)
Dihydrocarveol	$C_{10}H_{18}O$	63.9	105.0	136.1	159.8	202.8	225.0		(362, 441)
dl-Fenchyl alcohol	$C_{10}H_{18}O$	45.8	82.1	110.8	132.3	173.2	201.0	35	(320)
Geraniol	$C_{10}H_{18}O$	69.2	110.0	141.8	165.3	207.8	230.0		(383)
d-Linalool	$C_{10}H_{18}O$	40.0	79.8	109.9	133.3	175.6	198.0		(383)
Nerol	$C_{10}H_{18}O$	61.7	104.0	136.1	159.8	203.5	226.0		(179, 397)
α-Terpineol	$C_{10}H_{18}O$	52.8	94.3	126.0	150.1	194.3	217.5	35	(320)
Citronellic acid	$C_{10}H_{18}O_2$	99.5	141.4	171.9	195.4	236.6	257.0		(386, 432, 433, 435)
Amyl levulinate	$C_{10}H_{18}O_3$	81.3	124.0	155.8	180.5	227.4	253.2		(376)
Isoamyl levulinate	$C_{10}H_{18}O_3$	75.6	118.8	151.7	177.0	222.7	247.9		(376)
Diethyl ethylmethylmalonate	$C_{10}H_{18}O_4$	44.7	85.7	116.7	140.8	184.1	207.5		(11)

Name	Formula	Temperature °C						M.P.	Citation No.
		1 mm	10 mm	40 mm	100 mm	400 mm	760 mm		
Diethyl adipate	$C_{10}H_{18}O_4$	74.0	123.0	154.6	179.0	219.1	240.0	− 21	(180)
Diisobutyl oxalate	$C_{10}H_{18}O_4$	63.2	105.3	137.5	161.8	205.8	229.5	....	(11)
Dipropyl succinate	$C_{10}H_{18}O_4$	77.5	122.2	154.8	180.3	226.5	250.8	....	(11)
Sebacic acid	$C_{10}H_{18}O_4$	183.0	232.0	268.2	294.5	332.8	352.3d	134.5	(11, 234)
Dipropyl-d-tartrate	$C_{10}H_{18}O_6$	115.6	163.5	199.7	227.0	275.6	303.0	....	(11)
Diisopropyl-d-tartrate	$C_{10}H_{18}O_6$	103.7	148.2	181.8	207.3	251.8	275.0	....	(11)
Camphylamine	$C_{10}H_{19}N$	45.3	83.7	112.5	134.6	173.8	195.0	....	(11)
Menthane	$C_{10}H_{20}$	+ 9.7	48.3	78.3	102.1	146.0	169.5	....	(253)
1-Decene	$C_{10}H_{20}$	14.7	53.7	83.3	106.5	149.2	172.0	....	(11, 150)
1,2-Dibromodecane	$C_{10}H_{20}Br_2$	95.7	137.3	167.4	190.2	229.8	250.4	....	(11, 150)
Citronellol	$C_{10}H_{20}O$	66.4	107.0	137.2	159.8	201.0	221.5	....	(432)
Capraldehyde	$C_{10}H_{20}O$	51.9	92.0	122.2	145.3	186.3	208.5	....	(405)
l-Menthol	$C_{10}H_{20}O$	56.0	96.0	126.1	149.4	190.2	212.0	42.5	(11, 31, 325)
Decan-2-one	$C_{10}H_{20}O$	44.2	85.8	117.1	142.0	186.7	211.0	+ 3.5	(11, 183, 224)
Capric acid	$C_{10}H_{20}O_2$	125.0	152.2	179.9	200.0	240.3	268.4	31.5	(11, 203, 223, 224, 225, 231)
Isoamyl isovalerate	$C_{10}H_{20}O_2$	27.0	68.6	100.6	125.1	169.5	194.0	....	(11, 203)
Decane	$C_{10}H_{22}$	16.5	55.7	85.5	108.6	150.6	174.1	− 29.7	(11, 223, 224, 253, 484, 496)
2,7-Dimethyloctane	$C_{10}H_{22}$	+ 6.3	42.3	71.2	93.9	136.0	159.7	− 52.8	(253, 474)
Decyl alcohol	$C_{10}H_{22}O$	69.5	111.3	142.1	165.8	208.8	231.0	+ 7	(11, 225, 228)
Diisoamyl ether	$C_{10}H_{22}O$	18.6	57.0	86.3	109.6	150.3	173.4	....	(11, 247)
2-Butyl-2-ethylbutane-1,3-diol	$C_{10}H_{22}O_2$	94.1	136.8	167.8	191.9	233.5	255.0	....	(11, 150)
Dihydrocitronellol	$C_{10}H_{22}O$	68.0	103.0	127.6	145.9	176.8	193.5	....	(155)
Dipropylene glycol monobutyl ether	$C_{10}H_{22}O_3$	64.7	106.0	136.3	159.8	203.8	227.0	....	(113)
Diisoamyl sulfide	$C_{10}H_{22}S$	43.0	87.6	120.0	145.3	191.0	216.0	....	(25)
Heptyltrimethylsilane	$C_{10}H_{24}Si$	22.3	62.1	92.4	116.5	159.8	184.0	....	(466)
Butyltriethylsilane	$C_{10}H_{24}Si$	27.1	67.5	98.3	123.2	167.5	192.0	....	(466)
1,5-Diethoxyhexamethyltrisiloxane	$C_{10}H_{28}O_4Si_3$	41.8	80.7	110.0	133.2	174.0	196.6	....	(114)
Decamethyltetrasiloxane	$C_{10}H_{30}O_3Si_4$	35.3	74.3	104.0	127.3	169.8	193.5	....	(114, 469)
Decamethylcyclopentasiloxane	$C_{10}H_{30}O_5Si_5$	45.2	86.2	117.7	142.0	186.0	210.0	− 38.0	(188, 312, 469)
1-Naphthoic acid	$C_{11}H_8O_2$	156.0	196.8	225.0	245.8	281.4	300.0	160.5	(11)
2-Naphthoic acid	$C_{11}H_8O_2$	160.8	202.8	231.5	252.7	289.5	308.5	184	(11)
Ethyl-trans-cinnamate	$C_{11}H_{12}O_2$	87.6	134.0	169.2	196.0	245.0	271.0	12	(11)
1-Phenyl-1,3-pentanedione	$C_{11}H_{12}O_2$	98.0	144.0	178.0	204.5	251.2	276.5	....	(43)
Ethyl benzoylacetate	$C_{11}H_{12}O_3$	107.6	150.3	181.8	205.0	244.7	265.0d	....	(11)
Myristicine	$C_{11}H_{12}O_3$	95.2	142.0	177.7	205.0	253.5	280.0	....	(384, 428)
2,4,5-Trimethylstyrene	$C_{11}H_{14}$	48.1	91.6	124.2	149.8	196.1	221.2p	....	(216)
2,4,6-Trimethylstyrene	$C_{11}H_{14}$	37.5	79.7	111.8	136.8	182.3	207.0p	....	(216)
4-Isopropylstyrene	$C_{11}H_{14}$	34.7	76.0	108.0	132.8	178.0	202.5p	....	(216)
Isovalerophenone	$C_{11}H_{14}O$	58.3	101.4	133.8	158.0	204.2	228.0	....	(11)
Pivalophenone	$C_{11}H_{14}O$	57.8	99.0	130.4	154.0	197.7	220.0	....	(295)
2,3,5-Trimethylacetophenone	$C_{11}H_{14}O$	79.0	122.3	154.2	179.7	224.3	247.5	....	(383)
Isobutyl benzoate	$C_{11}H_{14}O_2$	64.0	108.6	141.8	166.4	212.8	237.0	....	(11, 199)
4-Allylveratrole	$C_{11}H_{14}O_2$	85.0	127.0	158.3	183.7	226.2	248.0	....	(40)
3,5-Diethyltoluene	$C_{11}H_{16}$	34.0	75.3	107.0	131.7	176.5	200.7	....	(113, 498)
1,2,4-Trimethyl-5-ethylbenzene	$C_{11}H_{16}$	43.7	84.6	106.0	140.3	184.5	208.1	....	(216)
1,3,5-Trimethyl-2-ethylbenzene	$C_{11}H_{16}$	38.8	80.5	113.2	137.9	183.5	208.0	....	(216)
3-Ethylcumene	$C_{11}H_{16}$	28.3	68.8	99.9	124.3	168.2	193.0	....	(113)
4-Ethylcumene	$C_{11}H_{16}$	31.5	72.0	103.3	127.2	171.8	195.8	....	(216)
sec-Amylbenzene	$C_{11}H_{16}$	29.0	69.2	100.0	124.1	168.0	193.0	....	(11, 503)
4-tert-Butyl-2-cresol	$C_{11}H_{16}O$	74.3	118.0	150.8	176.2	221.8	247.0	....	(113)
2-tert-Butyl-4-cresol	$C_{11}H_{16}O$	70.0	112.0	143.9	167.0	210.0	232.6	....	(406)
4-tert-Amylphenol	$C_{11}H_{16}O$	s	125.5	160.3	189.0	239.5	266.0	93	(11)
Ethylcamphoronic anhydride	$C_{11}H_{16}O_5$	118.2	165.0	199.8	226.6	272.8	298.0	....	(11)
Bornyl formate	$C_{11}H_{18}O_2$	47.0	89.3	121.2	145.8	190.2	214.0	....	(383)
Geranyl formate	$C_{11}H_{18}O_2$	61.8	104.3	136.2	160.7	205.8	230.0	....	(432)
Neryl formate	$C_{11}H_{18}O_2$	57.3	99.7	131.5	155.6	200.0	224.5	....	(178, 397)
Diethoxymethylphenylsilane	$C_{11}H_{18}O_2Si$	56.5	97.2	127.5	151.2	193.8	216.5	....	(114)
Diethyl-γ-oxoazelate	$C_{11}H_{18}O_5$	121.0	165.7	197.7	221.6	264.5	286.0	....	(11)
10-Hendecenoic acid	$C_{11}H_{20}O_2$	114.0	156.3	188.7	213.5	254.0	275.0	24.5	(11, 60)
Menthyl formate	$C_{11}H_{20}O_2$	47.3	90.0	123.0	148.0	194.2	219.0	....	(425)
2-Ethylhexyl acrylate	$C_{11}H_{20}O_2$	50.0	91.8	123.7	147.9	192.2	216.0	....	(113)
Octyl acrylate	$C_{11}H_{20}O_2$	58.5	102.0	135.6	159.1	204.0	227.0	....	(113)
Hexyl levulinate	$C_{11}H_{20}O_3$	90.0	134.7	167.8	193.6	241.0	266.8	....	(376)
Hendecan-2-one	$C_{11}H_{22}O$	68.2	108.9	139.0	161.0	202.3	224.0	15	(11, 223, 224, 328)
Methyl caprate	$C_{11}H_{22}O_2$	63.7	108.0	139.0	161.5	202.9	224.0d	− 18	(2)
Hendecanoic acid	$C_{11}H_{22}O_2$	101.4	149.0	185.6	212.5	262.8	290.0	29.5	(11, 221, 223)
Hendecane	$C_{11}H_{24}$	32.7	73.9	104.4	128.1	171.9	195.8	− 25.6	(11, 223, 224, 484, 504)
Hendecan-2-ol	$C_{11}H_{24}O$	71.1	112.8	143.7	167.2	209.8	232.0	....	(183, 266)
Trimethyloctylsilane	$C_{11}H_{26}Si$	41.8	82.3	113.0	136.5	179.5	202.0	....	(466)
Amyltriethylsilane	$C_{11}H_{26}Si$	41.8	83.8	116.0	141.2	186.3	211.0	....	(466)
1-Bromobiphenyl	$C_{12}H_9Br$	98.0	150.6	190.8	221.8	277.7	310.0	90.5	(113)
2-Bromo-4-Phenylphenol	$C_{12}H_9BrO$	100.0	152.3	193.8	224.5	280.2	311.0	95	(113)
2-Chlorobiphenyl	$C_{12}H_9Cl$	89.3	134.7	169.9	197.0	243.8	267.5	34	(113)
4-Chlorobiphenyl	$C_{12}H_9Cl$	90.4	140.0	180.8	213.5	264.5	292.9	75.5	(113)
2-Chloro-3-phenylphenol	$C_{12}H_9ClO$	118.0	169.7	207.4	237.0	289.4	317.5	+ 6	(113)
2-Chloro-6-phenylphenol	$C_{12}H_9ClO$	119.8	170.7	208.2	237.1	289.5	317.0	....	(113)
2-Xenyl dichlorophosphate	$C_{12}H_9Cl_2PO$	138.2	187.0	223.8	251.5	301.5	328.5	....	(113)
Carbazole	$C_{12}H_9N$	s	s	s	265.0	323.0	354.8	244.8	(388)
Acenaphthene	$C_{12}H_{10}$	s	131.2	168.2	197.5	250.0	277.5	95	(11, 253, 288)
Biphenyl	$C_{12}H_{10}$	70.6	117.0	152.5	180.7	229.4	254.9	69.5	(11, 34, 80, 103, 143, 194, 379)
Diphenyl chlorophosphate	$C_{12}H_{10}ClPO_3$	121.5	182.0	227.9	265.0	337.2	378.0	....	(113)
Dichlorodiphenylsilane	$C_{12}H_{10}Cl_2Si$	109.6	158.0	195.5	223.8	275.5	304.0	....	(114)
Difluorodiphenylsilane	$C_{12}H_{10}F_2Si$	68.4	115.5	149.8	176.3	225.4	252.5	....	(119)
Azobenzene	$C_{12}H_{10}N_2$	103.5	151.5	187.9	216.0	266.1	293.0	68	(11)
1-Acetonaphthone	$C_{12}H_{10}O$	115.6	161.5	196.8	223.8	270.5	295.5	....	(360)
2-Acetonaphthone	$C_{12}H_{10}O$	120.2	168.5	203.8	229.8	275.8	301.0	55.5	(360)
Diphenyl ether	$C_{12}H_{10}O$	66.1	114.0	150.0	178.8	230.7	258.5	27	(113)

Name	Formula	Temperature °C						M.P.	Citation No.
		1 mm	10 mm	40 mm	100 mm	400 mm	760 mm		
2-Phenylphenol	$C_{12}H_{10}O$	100.0	146.2	180.3	205.9	251.8	275.0	56.5	(113)
4-Phenylphenol	$C_{12}H_{10}O$	s	176.2	213.0	240.9	285.5	308.0	164.5	(113)
Diphenyl sulfide	$C_{12}H_{10}S$	96.1	145.0	182.8	211.8	263.9	292.5		(11, 232, 237)
Diphenyl disulfide	$C_{12}H_{10}S$	131.6	180.0	214.8	241.3	285.8	310.0	61	(11, 232, 237)
Diphenyl selenide	$C_{12}H_{10}Se$	105.7	154.4	192.2	220.8	273.2	301.5	+ 2.5	(11, 232, 237)
Diphenylamine	$C_{12}H_{11}N$	108.3	157.0	194.3	222.8	274.1	302.0	52.9	(11, 159)
1-Ethylnaphthalene	$C_{12}H_{12}$	70.0	116.8	152.0	180.0	230.8	258.1d	− 27	(113)
1,1-Diphenylhydrazine	$C_{12}H_{12}N_2$	126.0	176.1	213.5	242.5	294.0	322.2	44	(11)
2-Cyclohexyl-4,6-dinitrophenol	$C_{12}H_{14}N_2O_5$	132.8	175.9	206.7	229.0	269.8	291.5	......	(113)
Eugenyl acetate	$C_{12}H_{14}O_3$	101.6	148.0	183.0	209.7	257.4	282.0	29.5	(122)
Apiole	$C_{12}H_{14}O_4$	116.0	160.2	193.7	218.0	262.1	285.0	30	(81, 88)
Diethyl phthalate	$C_{12}H_{14}O_4$	108.8	156.0	192.1	219.5	267.5	294.0	......	(11)
2,5-Diethylstyrene	$C_{12}H_{16}$	49.7	92.6	125.8	151.0	198.0	223.0p		(216)
Phenylcyclohexane	$C_{12}H_{16}$	67.5	111.3	144.0	169.3	214.6	240.0	+ 7.5	(113, 253)
Isoamyl benzoate	$C_{12}H_{16}O_2$	72.0	121.6	158.3	186.8	235.8	262.0		(11, 199)
1,2,4-Triethylbenzene	$C_{12}H_{18}$	46.0	88.5	121.7	146.8	193.7	218.0	......	(113)
1,4-Diisopropylbenzene	$C_{12}H_{18}$	40.0	81.8	114.0	138.7	184.3	209.0		(113, 500)
1,3-Diisopropylbenzene	$C_{12}H_{18}$	34.7	76.0	107.9	132.3	177.6	202.0	−105	(113)
2-tert-Butyl-4-ethylphenol	$C_{12}H_{18}O$	76.3	121.0	154.0	179.0	223.8	247.8		(406)
4-tert-Butyl-2,5-xylenol	$C_{12}H_{18}O$	88.2	135.0	169.8	195.0	241.3	265.3	......	(406)
4-tert-Butyl-2,6-xylenol	$C_{12}H_{18}O$	74.0	119.0	152.2	176.0	217.8	239.8		(406)
6-tert-Butyl-2,4-xylenol	$C_{12}H_{18}O$	70.3	115.0	148.5	172.0	214.2	236.5		(406)
6-tert-Butyl-3,4-xylenol	$C_{12}H_{18}O$	83.9	127.0	159.7	184.0	226.7	249.5	......	(406)
d-Bornyl acetate	$C_{12}H_{20}O_2$	46.9	90.2	123.7	149.8	197.5	223.0	29	(383)
Geranyl acetate	$C_{12}H_{20}O_2$	73.5	117.9	150.0	175.2	219.8	243.3d	......	(41)
Linalyl acetate	$C_{12}H_{20}O_2$	55.4	96.0	127.7	151.8	196.2	220.0d		(383)
Triethoxyphenylsilane	$C_{12}H_{20}O_3Si$	71.0	112.6	143.5	167.5	210.5	233.5	......	(114)
Triethyl citrate	$C_{12}H_{20}O_7$	107.0	144.0	190.4	217.8	267.5	294.0d		(11)
Trimethallyl phosphate	$C_{12}H_{21}PO_4$	93.7	149.8	192.0	225.7	288.5	324.0		(113)
Citronellyl acetate	$C_{12}H_{22}O_2$	74.7	113.0	140.5	161.0	197.8	217.0	......	(432)
Menthyl acetate	$C_{12}H_{22}O_2$	57.4	100.0	132.1	156.7	202.8	227.0	......	(383)
Dimethyl sebacate	$C_{12}H_{22}O_4$	104.0	156.2	196.0	222.6	269.6	293.5	38	(180)
Diisoamyl oxalate	$C_{12}H_{22}O_4$	85.4	131.4	165.7	192.2	240.0	265.0	......	(11)
Diisobutyl-d-tartrate	$C_{12}H_{22}O_6$	117.8	169.0	208.5	239.5	294.0	324.0	73.5	(11)
1-Dodecene	$C_{12}H_{24}$	47.2	87.8	118.6	142.3	185.5	208.0	− 31.5	(11, 226)
Triisobutylene	$C_{12}H_{24}$	18.0	56.5	86.7	110.0	153.0	179.0	......	(406)
Dodecan-2-one	$C_{12}H_{24}O$	77.1	120.4	152.4	177.5	222.5	246.5	......	(11, 223, 224)
Lauraldehyde	$C_{12}H_{24}O$	77.7	123.7	157.8	184.5	231.8	257.0	44.5	(11, 222, 225, 230)
Lauric acid	$C_{12}H_{24}O_2$	121.0	166.0	201.4	227.5	273.8	299.2	48	(11, 157, 221, 223, 224, 225, 226)
Dodecane	$C_{12}H_{26}$	47.8	90.0	121.7	146.2	191.0	216.2	− 9.6	(11, 27, 223, 224, 225, 497, 502)
Dodecyl alcohol	$C_{12}H_{26}O$	91.0	134.7	167.2	192.0	235.7	259.0	24	(11, 225)
Tripropylene glycol monoisopropyl ether	$C_{12}H_{26}O_4$	82.4	127.3	161.4	187.8	232.8	256.6	......	(113)
Triisobutylamine	$C_{12}H_{27}N$	32.3	69.8	97.8	119.7	157.8	179.0	− 22	(11)
Dodecylamine	$C_{12}H_{27}N$	82.8	127.8	157.4	182.1	225.0	248.0	......	(11, 230)
Triethylhexylsilane	$C_{12}H_{28}Si$	52.4	96.4	130.0	156.0	204.6	230.0		(466)
1,7-Diethoxyoctamethyltetrasiloxane	$C_{12}H_{34}O_5Si_4$	67.7	108.6	319.0	162.0	204.0	227.5		(114)
Dodecamethylpentasiloxane	$C_{12}H_{36}O_4Si_5$	56.6	98.0	128.8	162.8	196.5	220.5	......	(114, 469)
Dodecamethylcyclohexasiloxane	$C_{12}H_{36}O_6Si_6$	67.3	110.0	141.8	166.3	210.6	236.0	− 3.0	(188, 312, 469)
Acridine	$C_{13}H_9N$	129.4	184.0	224.2	256.0	314.3	346.0	110.5	(11)
Fluorene	$C_{13}H_{10}$	s	146.0	185.2	214.7	268.6	295.0	113	(11, 135, 288)
Benzophenone	$C_{13}H_{10}O$	108.2	157.6	195.7	224.4	276.8	305.4	48.5	(11, 70, 194, 452)
Phenyl benzoate	$C_{13}H_{10}O_2$	106.8	157.8	197.6	227.8	283.5	314.0	70.5	(11)
Salol	$C_{13}H_{10}O_3$	117.8	167.0	205.0	233.8	284.8	313.0	42.5	(11)
Diphenylmethane	$C_{13}H_{12}$	76.0	122.8	157.8	186.3	237.5	264.5	26.5	(97, 99)
Benzhydrol	$C_{13}H_{12}O$	110.0	162.0	200.0	227.5	275.6	301.0	68.5	(11)
Benzyl phenyl ether	$C_{13}H_{12}O$	95.4	144.0	180.1	209.2	259.8	287.0	......	(11)
1-Propionaphthone	$C_{13}H_{12}O$	124.0	171.0	206.9	233.5	280.2	306.0		(360)
Chloromethyldiphenylsilane	$C_{13}H_{13}ClSi$	105.0	152.7	189.2	216.0	266.5	295.5	......	(114)
Methyldiphenylamine	$C_{13}H_{13}N$	103.5	149.7	184.0	210.1	257.0	282.0	− 7.6	(11)
2-Isopropylnaphthalene	$C_{13}H_{14}$	76.0	123.4	159.0	187.6	238.5	266.0	......	(113)
Methyldiphenylsilane	$C_{13}H_{14}Si$	88.0	132.8	166.4	193.7	241.5	266.8		(114)
Enanthophenone	$C_{13}H_{18}O$	100.0	145.5	178.9	204.2	248.3	271.3		(11, 229)
Heptylbenzene	$C_{13}H_{20}$	64.0	110.0	144.0	170.2	217.8	244.0	......	(11, 229, 499)
α-Ionone	$C_{13}H_{20}O$	79.5	123.0	155.6	181.2	225.2	250.0	......	(256)
Bornyl propionate	$C_{13}H_{22}O_2$	64.6	108.0	140.4	165.7	211.2	235.0	......	(383)
2-Tridecanone	$C_{13}H_{26}O$	86.8	131.8	165.7	191.5	238.3	262.5	28.5	(11, 223, 224)
Methyl laurate	$C_{13}H_{26}O_2$	87.8	133.2	166.0	190.8	d	d	5	(2)
Tridecanoic acid	$C_{13}H_{26}O_2$	137.8	181.0	212.4	236.0	276.5	299.0	41	(11, 221)
Tridecane	$C_{13}H_{28}$	59.4	104.0	137.7	162.5	209.4	234.0	− 6.2	(11, 223, 484)
Tripropyleneglycol, monobutyl ether	$C_{13}H_{28}O_4$	101.5	147.0	179.8	204.4	247.0	269.5	......	(113)
Decyltrimethylsilane	$C_{13}H_{30}Si$	67.4	111.0	144.0	169.5	215.5	240.0	......	(466)
Triethylheptylsilane	$C_{13}H_{30}Si$	70.0	114.6	148.0	174.0	221.0	247.0		(466)
Anthraquinone	$C_{14}H_8O_2$	190.0s	234.2s	264.3s	285.0s	346.2	379.9	286	(299, 404)
1,4-Dihydroxyanthraquinone	$C_{14}H_8O_4$	196.7	259.8	307.4	345.5	413.0d	450.0d	194	(464)
Anthracene	$C_{14}H_{10}$	145.0s	187.2s	217.5s	250.0	310.2	342.0	217.5	(11, 97, 288, 299, 303, 381)
Phenanthrene	$C_{14}H_{10}$	118.2	173.0	215.8	249.0	308.0	340.2	99.5	(11, 288, 299)
Benzil	$C_{14}H_{10}O_2$	128.4	183.0	224.5	255.8	314.3	347.0	95	(11, 238, 473)
Benzoic anhydride	$C_{14}H_{10}O_3$	143.8	198.0	239.8	270.4	328.8	360.0	42	(11)
1,1-Diphenylethylene	$C_{14}H_{12}$	87.4	135.0	170.8	198.6	249.8	277.0	......	(11)
trans-Diphenylethylene	$C_{14}H_{12}$	113.2	161.0	199.0	227.4	287.3	306.5	124	(10, 11)
Desoxybenzoin	$C_{14}H_{12}O$	123.3	173.5	212.0	241.3	293.0	321.0	60	(11)
Benzoin	$C_{14}H_{12}O$	135.6	188.0	227.6	258.0	313.5	343.0	132	(11)
Dibenzyl	$C_{14}H_{14}$	86.8	136.0	173.7	202.8	255.0	284.0	51.5	(11)
2-Isobutyronaphthone	$C_{14}H_{14}O$	133.2	181.0	215.6	242.3	288.2	313.0	......	(360)
Dibenzylamine	$C_{14}H_{15}O$	118.3	165.6	200.2	227.3	274.3	300.0	− 26	(11)

Name	Formula	1 mm	10 mm	40 mm	100 mm	400 mm	760 mm	M.P.	Citation No.
Ethyldiphenylamine	C₁₄H₁₅N	98.3	146.0	182.0	209.8	258.8	286.0	......	(11)
1,2-Dichlorotetraethylbenzene	C₁₄H₂₀Cl₂	105.6	155.0	192.2	220.7	272.8	302.0	......	(113)
1,4-Dichlorotetraethylbenzene	C₁₄H₂₀Cl₂	91.7	143.8	183.2	212.0	265.8	296.5	......	(113)
2-(4-*tert*-Butylphenoxy) ethyl acetate	C₁₄H₂₀O₃	118.0	165.8	201.5	228.0	277.6	304.4	......	(113)
1,2,4,5-Tetraethylbenzene	C₁₄H₂₂	65.7	111.6	145.8	172.4	221.4	248.0	11.6	(505)
2,4-Di-*tert*-butylphenol	C₁₄H₂₂O	84.5	130.0	164.3	190.0	237.0	260.8	......	(406)
Bornyl butyrate	C₁₄H₂₄O₂	74.0	118.0	150.7	176.4	222.2	247.0	......	(383)
Bornyl isobutyrate	C₁₄H₂₄O₂	70.0	114.0	147.2	172.2	218.2	243.0	......	(277)
Geranyl butyrate	C₁₄H₂₄O₂	96.8	139.0	170.1	193.8	235.0	257.4	......	(120)
Geranyl isobutyrate	C₁₄H₂₄O₂	90.7	133.0	164.0	187.7	228.5	251.0	......	(120)
Diethyl sebacate	C₁₄H₂₆O₄	125.3	172.1	207.5	234.4	280.3	305.5	1.3	(11)
2-Tetradecanone	C₁₄H₂₈O	99.3	145.5	179.8	206.0	253.0	278.0	......	(11, 223)
Myristaldehyde	C₁₄H₂₈O	99.0	148.3	186.0	214.5	267.9	297.8	23.5	(11, 222, 225, 230)
Myristic acid	C₁₄H₂₈O₂	142.0	190.8	223.5	250.5	294.6	318.0	57.5	(11, 157, 221, 223, 225)
1-Chlorotetradecane	C₁₄H₂₉Cl	98.5	148.2	187.0	215.5	267.5	296.0	+ 0.9	(113)
Tetradecane	C₁₄H₃₀	76.4	120.7	152.7	178.5	226.8	252.5	5.5	(11, 223, 224, 253, 484)
Tetradecylamine	C₁₄H₃₁N	102.6	152.0	189.0	215.7	264.6	291.2	......	(11, 230)
Triethyloctylsilane	C₁₄H₃₂Si	73.7	120.6	155.7	184.3	235.0	262.0	......	(466)
1,9-Diethoxydecamethylpentasiloxane	C₁₄H₄₀O₆Si₅	89.0	131.5	162.2	187.0	230.0	253.3	......	(114)
Tetradecamethylhexasiloxane	C₁₄H₄₂O₅Si₆	73.7	117.6	149.8	175.2	220.5	245.5	......	(114, 469)
Tetradecamethylcycloheptasiloxane	C₁₄H₄₂O₇Si₇	86.3	131.5	165.3	191.8	239.2	264.0	− 32	(188, 312, 469)
1,3-Diphenyl-2-propanone	C₁₅H₁₄O	125.5	177.6	216.6	246.6	301.7	330.5	34.5	(479)
1-Biphenyloxy-2,3-epoxypropane	C₁₅H₁₄O₂	135.3	187.2	226.3	255.0	309.8	340.0	......	(113)
1-Isovaleronaphthone	C₁₅H₁₆O	136.0	184.0	219.7	246.7	294.0	320.0	......	(360)
4,4-Isopropylidenebisphenol	C₁₅H₁₆O₂	193.0	240.8	273.0	297.0	339.0	360.5	......	(113)
Ethoxymethyldiphenylsilane	C₁₅H₁₈OSi	109.0	152.7	186.0	211.8	256.8	282.0	......	(114)
Helenin	C₁₅H₂₀O₂	157.7	192.1	215.2	232.6	260.6	275.0	76	(11)
Cadinene	C₁₅H₂₄	101.3	146.0	179.8	205.6	250.7	275.0	......	(383)
2,6-Di-*tert*-butyl-4-cresol	C₁₅H₂₄O	85.8	131.0	164.1	190.0	237.6	262.5	......	(406)
4,6-Di-*tert*-butyl-2-cresol	C₁₅H₂₄O	86.2	132.4	167.4	194.0	243.4	269.3	......	(406)
4,6-Di-*tert*-butyl-3-cresol	C₁₅H₂₄O	103.7	150.0	185.3	211.0	257.1	282.0	......	(406)
Champacol	C₁₅H₂₆O	100.0	148.0	184.0	211.9	261.2	288.0	91	(462)
Triethyl camphoronate	C₁₅H₂₆O₆	s	166.0	201.8	228.6	276.0	301.0	135	(11)
Methyl myristate	C₁₅H₃₀O₂	115.0	160.8	195.8	222.6	269.8	295.8	18.5	(2)
Pentadecane	C₁₅H₃₂	91.6	135.4	167.7	194.0	242.8	270.5	10	(11, 223, 224, 484)
Tetrapropylene glycol monoisopropyl ether	C₁₅H₃₂O₅	116.6	163.0	197.7	223.3	268.3	292.7	......	(113)
Dodecyltrimethylsilane	C₁₅H₃₄Si	91.2	137.7	172.1	199.5	248.0	273.0	......	(466)
Benzyl cinnamate	C₁₆H₁₄O₂	173.8	221.5	255.8	281.5	326.7	350.0	39	(172)
Di(α-methylbenzyl) ether	C₁₆H₁₈O	96.7	144.0	179.6	206.8	254.8	281.0	......	(113)
Diethoxydiphenylsilane	C₁₆H₂₀O₂Si	111.5	157.6	193.2	220.0	259.7	296.0	......	(114)
Dibutyl phthalate	C₁₆H₂₂O₄	148.2	198.2	235.8	263.7	313.5	340.0	......	(142)
Pentaethylchlorobenzene	C₁₆H₂₅Cl	90.0	140.7	178.2	208.0	257.2	285.0	......	(113)
Pentaethylbenzene	C₁₆H₂₆	86.0	135.8	171.9	200.0	250.2	277.0	......	(113)
2,6-Di-*tert*-butyl-4-ethylphenol	C₁₆H₂₆O	89.1	137.0	172.1	198.0	244.0	268.6	......	(406)
4,6-Di-*tert*-butyl-3-ethylphenol	C₁₆H₂₆O	111.5	157.4	192.3	218.0	264.6	290.0	......	(406)
Muscone	C₁₆H₃₀O	118.0	170.0	210.0	241.5	297.2	328.0	......	(457)
Palmitonitrile	C₁₆H₃₁N	134.3	185.8	223.8	251.5	304.5	332.0	31	(11, 233, 236)
1-Hexadecene	C₁₆H₃₂	101.6	146.2	178.8	205.3	250.0	274.0	4	(11, 226)
Tetraisobutylene	C₁₆H₃₂	63.8	108.5	142.2	167.5	214.6	240.0	......	(406)
2-Hexadecanone	C₁₆H₃₂O	109.8	167.3	203.7	230.5	279.8	307.0	......	(11, 223, 224)
Palmitaldehyde	C₁₆H₃₂O	121.6	171.5	210.0	239.5	292.3	321.0	34	(11, 222, 225, 230)
Palmitic acid	C₁₆H₃₂O₂	153.6	205.8	244.4	271.5	326.0	353.8	64.0	(11, 150, 157, 221, 223, 224, 225)
Hexadecane	C₁₆H₃₄	105.3	149.8	181.3	208.5	258.3	287.5	18.5	(11, 223, 224, 228, 484)
Cetyl alcohol	C₁₆H₃₄O	122.7	177.8	219.8	251.7	312.7	344.0	49.3	(11, 225)
Cetylamine	C₁₆H₃₅N	123.6	176.0	215.7	245.8	300.4	330.0	......	(11, 230, 233)
Decyltriethylsilane	C₁₆H₃₆Si	108.5	155.6	191.7	218.3	267.5	293.0	......	(466)
1,1,1-Diethoxydodecamethylhexasiloxane	C₁₆H₄₆O₇Si₆	103.6	147.5	180.0	205.5	250.0	273.5	......	(114)
Hexadecamethylheptasiloxane	C₁₆H₄₈O₆Si₇	93.2	138.5	171.8	198.0	244.7	270.0	......	(114, 469)
Hexadecamethylcyclooctasiloxane	C₁₆H₄₈O₈Si₈	103.5	150.5	186.3	213.8	263.0	290.0	31.5	(188, 469)
Benzanthrone	C₁₇H₁₀O	225.0	297.2	350.0	390.0	......	......	174	(464)
4-*tert*-Butylphenyl salicylate	C₁₇H₁₈O₃	166.2	225.0	270.7	305.8	370.6	404.0d	......	(113)
Menthyl benzoate	C₁₇H₂₄O₂	123.2	170.0	204.3	230.4	277.1	301.0	54.5	(383)
2-Heptadecanone	C₁₇H₃₄O	129.6	178.0	214.3	242.0	291.7	319.5	......	(11, 223, 224)
Methyl palmitate	C₁₇H₃₄O₂	134.3	184.3	d	......	......	......	30	(2)
Heptadecane	C₁₇H₃₆	115.0	160.0	195.8	223.0	274.5	303.0	22.5	(11, 223, 224, 484)
Tetradecyltrimethylsilane	C₁₇H₃₈Si	120.0	166.2	201.5	227.8	275.0	300.0	......	(466)
Tri-2-chlorethylthiophosphate	C₁₈H₁₂Cl₃O₃PS	188.2	231.2	261.7	283.8	322.0	341.3	......	(113)
Triphenyl phosphate	C₁₈H₁₅O₄P	193.5	249.8	290.3	322.5	379.2	413.5	49.4	(113)
Hexaethylbenzene	C₁₈H₃₀	s	150.3	187.7	216.0	268.5	298.3	130	(113)
2,4,6-Tri-*tert*-butylphenol	C₁₈H₃₀O	95.2	142.0	177.4	203.0	250.6	276.3	......	(406)
Oleic Acid	C₁₈H₃₄O₂	176.5	223.0	257.2	286.0	334.7	360.0d	14	(11, 122, 134, 234)
Elaidic acid	C₁₈H₃₄O₂	171.3	223.5	260.8	288.0	337.0	362.0	51.5	(11, 230, 234)
Stearaldehyde	C₁₈H₃₆O	140.0	192.1	230.8	260.0	313.8	342.5	63.5	(11, 222, 225, 230)
Stearic acid	C₁₈H₃₆O₂	173.7	225.0	263.3	291.0	343.0	370.0d	69.3	(11, 150, 221, 222, 225, 227, 230, 234)
Octadecane	C₁₈H₃₈	119.6	169.6	207.4	236.0	288.0	317.0	28	(223, 225, 484)
2-Methylheptadecane	C₁₈H₃₈	119.8	168.7	204.8	231.5	279.8	306.5	......	(245)
1-Octadecanol	C₁₈H₃₈O	150.3	202.0	240.4	269.4	320.3	349.5	58.5	(11, 225)

Name	Formula	Temperature °C						M.P.	Citation No.
		1 mm	10 mm	40 mm	100 mm	400 mm	760 mm		
Ethylcetylamine	$C_{18}H_{39}N$	133.2	186.0	226.5	256.8	313.0	342.0d	......	(11, 233)
1,1,3-Diethoxytetradecamethyl-heptasiloxane	$C_{18}H_{52}O_8Si_7$	119.0	163.5	197.0	223.2	268.3	293.5	......	(114)
Octadecamethyloctasiloxane	$C_{18}H_{54}O_7Si_9$	105.8	152.3	187.5	214.5	263.5	290.0	......	(114, 469)
Triphenylmethane	$C_{19}H_{16}$	169.7	197.0	215.5	228.4	249.8	259.2	93.4	(11, 70, 383)
Diphenyl-2-tolyl thiophosphate	$C_{19}H_{17}O_3PS$	159.7	201.6	230.6	252.5	290.0	310.0	......	(113)
Nonadecane	$C_{19}H_{40}$	133.2	183.5	220.0	248.0	299.8	330.0	32	(11, 223, 224, 484)
Ethoxytriphenylsilane	$C_{20}H_{20}OSi$	167.0	213.5	247.0	273.5	319.5	344.0	......	(114)
Diethylhexadecylamine	$C_{20}H_{43}N$	139.8	194.0	235.0	265.5	324.6	355.0	......	(11, 233)
1,1,5-Diethoxyhexadecamethyl-octasiloxane	$C_{20}H_{58}O_9Si_8$	133.7	179.7	213.8	240.0	286.0	311.5	......	(114)
Eicosamethylnonasiloxane	$C_{20}H_{60}O_8Si_9$	144.0	189.0	220.5	244.3	286.0	307.5	......	(469)
Tritolyl phosphate	$C_{21}H_{21}O_4P$	154.6	198.0	229.7	252.2	292.7	313.0	......	(113)
Heneicosane	$C_{21}H_{44}$	152.6	205.4	243.4	272.0	323.8	350.5	40.4	(11, 223, 224, 484)
Erucic acid	$C_{22}H_{42}O_2$	206.7	254.5	289.1	314.4	358.8	381.5d	33.5	(11, 234)
Brassidic acid	$C_{22}H_{42}O_2$	209.6	256.0	290.0	316.2	359.6	382.5d	61.5	(11, 234)
Docosane	$C_{22}H_{46}$	157.8	213.0	254.5	286.0	343.5	376.0	44.5	(11, 223, 224, 468, 484)
Docosamethyldecasiloxane	$C_{22}H_{56}O_9Si_{10}$	160.3	202.8	233.8	255.0	293.8	314.0	......	(469)
Tricosane	$C_{23}H_{48}$	170.0	223.0	261.3	289.8	339.8	366.5	47.7	(11, 223, 224, 484)
Tetracosane	$C_{24}H_{50}$	183.8	237.6	276.3	305.2	358.0	386.4	51.1	(11, 223, 224, 468, 484)
Tetracosamethylhendecasiloxane	$C_{24}H_{72}O_{10}Si_{11}$	175.2	216.7	246.2	266.3	303.7	322.8	......	(469)
Pentacosane	$C_{25}H_{52}$	194.2	248.2	285.6	314.0	365.4	390.3	53.3	(484)
Hexacosane	$C_{26}H_{54}$	204.0	257.4	295.2	323.2	374.6	399.8	56.6	(11, 468, 484)
Dicarvacryl-2-tolyl phosphate	$C_{27}H_{33}O_4P$	180.2	221.8	251.5	272.5	309.8	330.0	......	(113)
Heptacosane	$C_{27}H_{56}$	211.7	266.8	305.7	333.5	385.0	410.6	59.5	(11, 223, 484)
Octacosane	$C_{28}H_{58}$	226.5	277.4	314.2	341.8	388.9	412.5	61.6	(11, 468, 484)
Nonacosane	$C_{29}H_{60}$	234.2	286.4	323.2	350.0	397.2	421.8	63.8	(484)
Dicarvacryl-mono-(6-chloro-2-xenyl) phosphate	$C_{32}H_{34}ClO_4P$	204.2	249.3	280.5	304.9	342.0	361.0	......	(113)

Pressures Greater than One Atmosphere

Name	Formula	Temperature °C							Citation No.
		1 atm.	2 atm.	5 atm.	10 atm.	20 atm.	40 atm.	60 atm.	
Chlorotrifluoromethane	$CClF_3$	− 81.2	− 66.7	− 42.7	− 18.5	+ 12.0	52.8	......	(113, 430)
Dichlorodifluoromethane	CCl_2F_2	− 29.8	− 12.2	+ 16.1	42.4	74.0	.....	......	(113, 146)
Carbonyl chloride	CCl_2O	8.3	27.3	57.2	85.0	119.0	159.8	.....	(20, 145, 208, 305, 311)
Trichlorofluoromethane	CCl_3F	23.7	44.1	77.3	108.2	146.7	194.0	.....	(212)
Carbontetrachloride	CCl_4	76.7	102.0	141.7	178.0	222.0	276.0	.....	(115, 175, 289, 343, 352, 394, 481)
Chlorodifluoromethane	$CHClF_2$	− 40.8	− 24.7	+ 0.3	24.0	52.0	85.3	.....	(50, 212)
Dichlorofluoromethane	$CHCl_2F$	8.9	28.4	59.0	87.0	121.2	162.6	.....	(212)
Trichloromethane	$CHCl_3$	61.3	83.9	120.0	152.3	191.8	237.5	......	(32, 115, 175, 345, 352, 365)
Hydrocyanic acid	CHN	25.8	45.5	75.5	103.5	134.2	170.2	.....	(252)
Methyl bromide	CH_3Br	3.6	23.3	54.8	84.0	121.7	170.2	.....	(117, 323)
Methyl chloride	CH_3Cl	− 24.0	− 6.4	+ 22.0	47.3	77.3	113.8	137.5	(54, 182, 241, 350, 451)
Methyl fluoride	CH_3F	− 78.2	− 64.5	− 42.0	− 21.0	+ 2.6	26.5	43.5	(89, 113, 281)
Methyl iodide	CH_3I	42.4	65.5	101.8	138.0	176.5	228.5	.....	(351, 352, 363)
Methane	CH_4	−161.5	−152.3	−138.3	−124.8	−108.5	− 86.3	.....	(6, 72, 93, 123, 206, 359, 407)
Methanol	CH_4O	64.7	84.0	112.5	138.0	167.8	203.5	224.0	(111, 289, 319, 338, 353)
Methanethiol	CH_4S	6.8	26.1	55.9	83.4	117.5	157.7	185.0	(39)
Methylamine	CH_5N	− 6.3	+ 10.1	36.0	59.5	87.8	121.8	144.6	(19, 38, 130, 186, 324)
Carbon monoxide	CO	−191.3	−183.5	−170.7	−161.0	−149.7	......	.....	(23, 72, 82, 83, 102, 208, 306, 447)
Carbon dioxide	CO_2	− 78.2s	− 69.1s	− 56.7	− 39.5	− 18.9	+ 5.9	22.4	(4, 5, 53, 124, 167, 168, 196, 208, 242, 275, 307, 308, 343, 407, 448, 454, 463, 493)
Carbon disulfide	CS_2	46.5	69.1	104.8	136.3	175.5	222.8	256.0	(138, 208, 263, 331, 343, 352, 407, 454, 475)
1-Chloro-1,2,2-trifluoroethylene	C_2ClF_3	− 27.9	− 11.1	+ 15.5	40.0	71.1	......	.....	(49, 50, 113)
1,2-Dichloro-1,1,2,2-tetrafluoroethane	$C_2Cl_2F_4$	3.5	22.8	54.0	82.3	117.5	......	.....	(212)
1,1,2-Trichloro-1,2,2-trifluoroethane	$C_2Cl_3F_3$	47.6	70.0	105.5	138.0	177.7	......	.....	(212)
Acetylene	C_2H_2	− 84.0s	− 71.6	− 50.2	− 32.7	− 10.0	+ 16.8	34.8	(12, 66, 67, 69, 217, 449)
cis-1,2-Dichloroethylene	$C_2H_2Cl_2$	59.0	82.1	119.3	152.3	194.0	244.5	.....	(113, 175, 176)
trans-1,2-Dichloroethylene	$C_2H_2Cl_2$	47.8	69.8	104.0	135.7	174.0	220.0	.....	(113, 175, 176)
Ethylene	C_2H_4	−103.7	− 90.8	− 71.1	− 52.8	− 29.1	− 1.5	.....	(6, 66, 93, 57, 116, 244, 359, 407, 448, 453)
1,2-Dibromoethane	$C_2H_4Br_2$	131.5	157.7	200.0	237.0	269.0	295.0	304.5	(11, 31, 113, 349, 351, 438)
1,1-Dichloroethane	$C_2H_4Cl_2$	57.3	80.2	117.3	150.3	192.7	243.0	.....	(113, 352, 402)
1,2-Dichloroethane	$C_2H_4Cl_2$	83.7	108.1	147.8	183.5	226.5	272.0	.....	(113, 133, 315, 352, 402)
Acetic acid	$C_2H_4O_2$	118.1	143.5	180.3	214.0	252.0	297.0	.....	(113, 203, 246, 258, 289, 335, 353, 373, 480)
Methyl formate	$C_2H_4O_2$	32.0	51.9	83.5	112.0	147.2	188.5	.....	(297, 491)
Ethyl bromide	C_2H_5Br	38.4	60.2	95.0	126.8	164.3	206.5	229.5	(113, 347, 391, 438)
Ethyl chloride	C_2H_5Cl	12.3	32.5	64.0	92.6	127.3	167.0	.....	(38, 113, 195, 346, 402)
Ethyl fluoride	C_2H_5F	− 32.0	− 16.7	+ 7.7	30.2	57.5	90.0	.....	(50)
Ethane	C_2H_6	− 88.6	− 75.0	− 52.8	− 32.0	− 6.4	+ 23.6	.....	(6, 30, 65, 84, 93, 153, 261, 262, 359, 453)

Name	Formula	Temperature °C							Citation No.
		1 atm.	2 atm.	5 atm.	10 atm.	20 atm.	40 atm.	60 atm.	
Ethanol	C_2H_6O	78.4	97.5	126.0	151.8	183.0	218.0	242.0	(32, 113, 115, 202, 273, 289, 329, 337, 343, 365, 374, 394)
Dimethyl ether	C_2H_6O	−23.7	−6.4	+20.8	45.5	75.7	112.1	....	(55, 74, 211, 260, 350)
Ethanethiol	C_2H_6S	35.0	56.6	90.7	121.9	159.5	204.7	....	(39)
Dimethyl sulfide	C_2H_6S	36.0	57.8	92.3	124.5	163.8	209.0	....	(39)
Ethylamine	C_2H_7N	16.6	35.7	65.3	91.8	124.0	163.0	....	(38)
Dimethylamine	C_2H_7N	7.4	25.0	53.9	80.0	111.7	149.8	....	(38, 390, 467)
Cyanogen	C_2N_2	−21.0	−4.4	+21.4	44.6	72.6	106.5	....	(79, 101, 113, 125, 318, 426)
Propadiene	C_3H_4	−35.0	−18.4	+8.0	33.2	64.5	103.5	....	(113, 244, 255)
Propyne	C_3H_4	−23.3	−7.1	+19.5	43.8	74.0	111.5	....	(113, 165, 262, 286)
Propylene	C_3H_6	−47.7	−31.4	−4.8	+19.8	49.5	85.0	....	(6, 66, 67, 137, 244, 262, 359, 382)
Acetone	C_3H_6O	56.5	78.6	113.0	144.5	181.0	214.5	....	(29, 115, 129, 343, 364)
Propionic acid	$C_3H_6O_2$	141.1	160.0	186.0	203.5	220.0	233.0	....	(203, 204, 353, 373)
Methyl acetate	$C_3H_6O_2$	57.8	79.5	113.1	144.2	181.0	225.0	....	(113, 491)
Ethyl formate	$C_3H_6O_2$	54.3	76.0	110.5	142.2	180.0	225.0	....	(297, 491)
Propane	C_3H_8	−42.1	−25.6	+1.4	26.9	58.1	94.8	....	(6, 30, 66, 93, 137, 153, 262, 359)
1-Propanol	C_3H_8O	97.8	117.0	149.0	177.0	210.8	250.0	....	(113, 289, 340, 374)
2-Propanol	C_3H_8O	82.5	101.3	130.2	155.7	186.0	220.2	....	(310)
Ethyl methyl ether	C_3H_8O	7.5	26.5	56.4	84.0	108.0	160.0	....	(39)
Propylamine	C_3H_9N	48.5	69.8	102.8	133.4	170.0	214.5	....	(38)
1,3-Butadiene	C_4H_6	−4.5	+15.3	47.0	76.0	114.0	158.0	....	(52, 162, 189, 445)
Acetic anhydride	$C_4H_6O_3$	139.6	162.0	194.0	221.5	253.0	288.5	....	(33, 113, 201)
Dimethyl oxalate	$C_4H_6O_4$	163.3	189.6	228.7	....	....	....	....	(11, 97, 144)
Butyric acid	$C_4H_8O_2$	163.5	188.3	225.0	257.0	295.0	338.0	....	(204, 332, 373, 374)
Isobutyric acid	$C_4H_8O_2$	154.5	179.8	217.0	250.0	289.0	336.0	....	(203, 204, 353, 373, 374)
Ethyl acetate	$C_4H_8O_2$	77.1	100.6	136.6	169.7	209.5	....	....	(113, 455, 491)
Methyl propionate	$C_4H_8O_2$	79.8	103.0	139.8	172.6	212.5	....	....	(491)
Propyl formate	$C_4H_8O_2$	81.3	104.3	142.0	176.4	217.5	....	....	(297, 491)
Butane	C_4H_{10}	−0.5	+18.8	50.0	79.5	116.0	....	....	(6, 66, 93, 359, 382)
2-Methylpropane	C_4H_{10}	−11.7	+7.5	39.0	66.8	99.5	....	....	(6, 16, 93, 187, 359, 382)
Butyl alcohol	$C_4H_{10}O$	117.5	139.8	172.5	203.0	237.0	277.0	....	(68, 174, 203, 204, 314)
sec-Butyl alcohol	$C_4H_{10}O$	99.5	118.2	147.5	172.0	204.0	251.0	....	(68)
Isobutyl alcohol	$C_4H_{10}O$	108.0	127.3	156.2	182.0	212.5	251.0	....	(68, 203, 219, 374)
tert-Butyl alcohol	$C_4H_{10}O$	82.9	102.0	130.0	154.2	184.5	222.5	....	(68, 310)
Diethyl ether	$C_4H_{10}O$	34.6	56.0	90.0	122.0	159.0	....	....	(31, 113, 115, 289, 338, 423a)
Diethyl sulfide	$C_4H_{10}S$	88.0	112.0	153.8	190.2	234.0	....	....	(25, 39)
Diethylamine	$C_4H_{11}N$	55.5	77.8	113.0	145.3	184.5	....	....	(38)
Tetramethylsilane	$C_4H_{12}Si$	27.0	48.0	82.0	113.0	152.0	....	....	(15, 114)
Ethyl propionate	$C_5H_{10}O_2$	99.1	123.8	162.7	197.8	240.0	....	....	(491)
Propyl acetate	$C_5H_{10}O_2$	101.8	126.8	165.7	200.5	242.8	....	....	(11, 113, 199, 491)
Isobutyl formate	$C_5H_{10}O_2$	98.2	121.8	157.8	192.4	234.0	....	....	(292, 380)
Methyl butyrate	$C_5H_{10}O_2$	102.3	127.5	166.7	203.0	244.5	....	....	(11, 491)
Methyl isobutyrate	$C_5H_{10}O_2$	92.6	116.7	155.2	190.2	232.0	....	....	(491)
Pentane	C_5H_{12}	36.1	58.0	92.4	124.7	164.3	....	....	(6, 28, 93, 274, 359, 482, 485)
2-Methylbutane	C_5H_{12}	27.8	48.8	82.8	114.5	154.0	....	....	(6, 93, 359, 485, 486, 492)
2,2-Dimethylpropane	C_5H_{12}	9.5	29.5	61.1	90.7	127.6	....	....	(6, 17, 113, 253, 359, 165)
Ethyl propyl ether	$C_5H_{12}O$	61.7	85.3	123.1	156.2	197.2	....	....	(39)
Bromobenzene	C_6H_5Br	156.2	186.2	232.5	274.5	327.0	387.5	....	(11, 199, 204, 289, 358, 478)
Chlorobenzene	C_6H_5Cl	132.2	160.2	205.0	245.3	292.8	349.8	....	(11, 199, 289, 478)
Fluorobenzene	C_6H_5F	84.7	109.9	148.5	184.4	227.6	279.3	....	(113, 416, 478)
Iodobenzene	C_6H_5I	188.6	220.0	270.0	315.7	371.5	437.2	....	(115, 289, 358, 478)
Benzene	C_6H_6	80.1	103.8	142.5	178.8	221.5	272.3	....	(3, 6, 11, 32, 109, 131, 197, 204, 289, 343, 359, 366, 392, 415, 478)
Phenol	C_6H_6O	181.9	208.0	248.2	283.8	328.7	382.1	418.7	(11, 34, 113, 151, 174, 203, 204)
Aniline	C_6H_7N	184.4	212.8	254.8	292.7	342.0	400.0	....	(11, 34, 143, 151, 204, 341)
Cyclohexane	C_6H_{12}	80.7	106.0	146.4	184.0	228.4	....	....	(6, 109, 293, 359, 487)
Ethyl isobutyrate	$C_6H_{12}O_2$	110.1	135.5	174.2	210.0	253.0	....	....	(292, 380)
Hexane	C_6H_{14}	68.7	93.0	131.7	166.6	209.4	....	....	(6, 115, 251, 289, 359, 394, 427, 474)
2,3-Dimethylbutane	C_6H_{14}	58.0	82.0	120.3	155.7	198.7	....	....	(6, 359, 471, 488)
Toluene	C_7H_8	110.6	136.5	178.0	215.8	262.5	319.0	....	(6, 11, 24, 107, 115, 199, 204, 239, 253, 359)
Heptane	C_7H_{16}	98.4	124.8	165.7	202.8	247.5	....	....	(6, 251, 269, 289, 359, 394, 483)
Ethylbenzene	C_8H_{10}	136.2	163.5	207.5	246.3	294.5	....	....	(6, 11, 265, 359, 415, 471, 474)
Octane	C_8H_{18}	125.6	152.7	196.2	235.8	181.4	....	....	(6, 251, 253, 359, 471, 474, 492)
Dodecane	$C_{12}H_{26}$	216.2	249.2	300.0	345.8	....	....	....	(11, 27, 223, 224, 225)

VAPOR PRESSURE—CITATIONS
Organic Compounds

(1) Allen, J. Chem. Soc., **77**, 400–16 (1900).
(2) Althouse and Triebold, Ind. Eng. Chem. Anal. Ed., **16**, 605–6 (1944).
(3) Altschul, Z. Physik. Chem., **11**, 577–97 (1893).
(4) Amagat, Compt. rend., **114**, 1093–8 (1892).
(5) Amagat, J. Phys., (3) **1**, 297 (1892).
(6) Am. Petroleum Inst. Research Project, **44**, Natl. Bur. Standards, tables ending with letter K (June 30, 1946).
(7) André, Compt. rend., **126**, 1105–7 (1898).
(8) Andrews, J. Phys. Chem., **30**, 1497–1500 (1926).
(9) Anschütz, Ann. **221**, 133–57 (1883).
(10) Anschütz, and Berns, Ber., **20**, 1389–93 (1887).

(11) Anschütz and Reitter, "Die Destillation unter vermindertem Druck im Laboratorium," 2nd ed., Bonn, Cohen, 1895.
(12) Ansdell, Chem. News, **40**, 136–8 (1879).
(13) Arbusow, Chem. Zentr., **1909, II**, 684–5.
(14) Arbusow, J. Russ. Phys.-Chem. Soc., **41**, 429–46 (1909).
(15) Aston, Kennedy, and Messerly, J. Am. Chem. Soc., **63**, 2343–8 (1941)
(16) Aston, Kennedy, and Schumann, Ibid., **62**, 2059–63 (1940).
(17) Aston and Messerly, Ibid., **58**, 2354–61 (1936).
(18) Aston, Sagenkahn, Szasz, Moessen, and Zuhr, Ibid., **66**, 1171–7 (1944).
(19) Aston, Siller, and Messerly, Ibid., **59**, 1743–51, (1937).
(20) Atkinson, Heycock, and Pope, J. Chem. Soc., **117**, 1410–26 (1920)

(21)Auwers and Lange, Ann., **409**, 149–82 (1915).
(22)Babasinian and Jackson, J. Am. Chem Soc., **51**, 2147–51 (1929)
(23)Baly and Donnan, J. Chem. Soc., **81**, 907–23 (1902).
(24)Barker, Z. Physik Chem., **71**, 235–53 (1910).
(25)Bauer and Burschkies, Ber., **68B**, 1238–43 (1935).
(26)Baxter, Bezzenberger, and Wilson, J. Am. Chem. Soc., **42**, 1386–93 (1920).
(27)Beale and Docksey, J. Inst. Petroleum Tech., **21**, 860–70 (1935).
(28)Beall, Refiner Natural Gasoline Mfr., **14**, 588–9 (1935).
(29)Beare, McVicar, and Ferguson, J. Phys. Chem., **34**, 1310–8 (1930).
(30)Beattie, Hadlock, and Poffenberger, J. Chem. Phys., **3**, 93–6 (1935).
(31)Beckman, Fuchs, and Gernhardt, Z. Physik. Chem., **18**, 473–513 (1895).
(32)Beckmann and Liesche, Ibid., **88**, 13–34 (1914).
(33)Ibid., **88**, 419–27 (1914).
(34)Ibid., **89**, 111–24, (1915).
(35)Berliner and May, J. Am. Chem. Soc., **47**, 2350–6 (1925).
(36)Ibid., **48**, 2630–4 (1926).
(37)Ibid., **49**, 1007–11 (1927).
(38)Berthoud, J. chim. phys., **15**, 3–29 (1917).
(39)Berthoud and Brum, Ibid., **21**, 143–60 (1924).
(40)Bertram and Gildemeister, J. prakt. Chem., II, **39**, 349–55 (1889).
(41)Ibid., **49**, 185–96 (1894).
(42)Bertram and Helle, Ibid., II, **61**, 293–306 (1900). .
(43)Beyer and Claisen, Ber., **20**, 2178–88 (1887).
(44)Biltz, Ann., **297**, 263–78 (1897).
(45)Blaise and Luttringer, Bull. soc. chim. Mém., III, **33**, 761–83 (1905).
(46)Blaszkowska and Zakrzewska, Chem. Zentr., **1929**, II, 3076.
(47)Blaszkowska and Zakrzewska, Roczniki Chem., **8**, 210–18 (1928).
(48)Bolas and Groves, J. Chem. Soc., **24**, 773–85 (1871).
(49)Booth, Burchfield, Bixby, and McKelvey, J. Am. Chem. Soc., **55**, 2231–5 (1933).
(50)Booth and Swinehart, Ibid., **57**, 1337–42 (1935).
(51)Bouveault, Bull. soc. chim. III, **17**, 363–72 (1897).
(52)Brickwedde, Bekkedahl, Meyers, Rands, and Scott, J. Research Natl. Bur. Standards, **35**, 39–87 (1945).
(53)Bridgeman, J. Am. Chem. Soc., **49**, 1174–83 (1927).
(54)Brinkman, Thesis, Amsterdam.
(55)Briner and Cardoso, J. chim. physic., **6**, 663 (1908).
(56)Briscoe and Peel, J. Chem. Soc., **131**, 1741–7 (1928).
(57)Britton, Trans. Faraday Soc., **55**, 520–5 (1929).
(58)Brückner, Z. anorg. allgem. Chem., **199**, 91–2 (1931).
(59)Brühl, Ber., **32**, 1222–36 (1899).
(60)Brunner, Ibid., **19**, 2224–8 (1886).
(61)Buckler and Norrish, J. Chem. Soc., **139**, 1567–9 (1936).
(62)Bullard and Haussmann, J. Phys. Chem., **34**, 743–7 (1930).
(63)Burchfield, J. Am. Chem. Soc., **64**, 2501 (1942).
(64)Burg and Schlesinger, Ibid., **59**, 780–7 (1937).
(65)Burrell and Robertson, Ibid., **37**, 1893–1902 (1915).
(66)Ibid., **37**, 2188–93 (1915).
(67)Burrell and Robertson, U S. Bur. Mines, Tech. Paper **142** (1916).
(68)Butler et al., J Chem. Soc., **138**, 280–5 (1935).
(69)Cailletet, Compt. rend., **85**, 851–4 (1877).
(70)Callendar and Griffiths, Chem. News, **63**, 1–2 (1891).
(71)Carbide and Carbon Chemicals Corp. bulletins (1945).
(72)Cardoso, J. chim. phys., **13**, 312–50 (1915).
(73)Ibid., **13**, 332 (1915)
(74)Cardoso and Bruno, Ibid., **20**, 347–51 (1923).
(75)Carpmael, British Patent 469,421 (1937).
(76)Cavalier, Ann. chim. phys., **18**, 449–507 (1899).
(77)Cavalier, Bull. soc. chim., **19**, 883–7 (1898).
(78)Chamuleau and Noyous, Acta Brevia Neerland, Physiol. Pharmacol. Microbiol., **2**, 94–5 (1932).
(79)Chappuis and Rivière, Compt. rend., **104**, 1504–5 (1887).
(80)Chipman and Peltier, Ind. Eng. Chem., **21**, 1106–8 (1929).
(81)Ciamician and Silber, Ber , **29**, 1799–1811 (1896).
(82)Clayton and Giauque, J. Am. Chem. Soc., **54**, 2610–26 (1932).
(83)Clusius and Teske, Z. physik Chem., **6B**, 135–51 (1929).
(84)Coffin and Maass, J. Am. Chem Soc., **50**, 1427–37 (1926).
(85)Coffin and Maass, Chem. Zentr., **1928**, I, 1643.
(86)Coffin and Maass, Trans. Roy. Soc Can., [3] **21**, 33–40 (1927).
(87)Coffin, Sutherland, and Maass, Can. J Research, **2**, 267–78 (1930).
(88)Cole, Philippine J. Sci., **40**, 499–502 (1929).
(89)Collie, J. Chem. Soc., **55**, 110–13 (1889).
(90)Commercial Solvents Corp. bull. (1944).
(91)Coolidge, J. Am. Chem. Soc., **52**, 1874–87 (1930).
(92)Coolidge and Coolidge, Ibid., **49**, 100–4 (1927).
(93)Copson and Frolich, Ind. Eng. Chem., **21**, 1116–7 (1929).
(94)Cosslett, Z. anorg. allgem. Chem., **201**, 75–80 (1931).
(95)Courtot and Metzger, Compt. rend., **219**, 487–90 (1944).
(96)Cox, Ind. Eng. Chem., **15**, 592 (1923).
(97)Crafts, Ber , **20**, 709–16 (1887).
(98)Crafts, J. chim. phys., **11**, 429–77 (1913).
(99)Ibid., **13**, 105–61 (1915).
(100)Crater, Ind. Eng. Chem., **21**, 674–6 (1929).
(101)Crommelin, Proc. "Konink." Akad. Wetenschappen Amsterdam (1913).
(102)Crommelin, Bijleved, and Brown, Proc. Acad. Sci. Amsterdam, **34**, 1314 (1931).
(103)Cunningham, Power, **72**, 374–7 (1930).
(104)Dana, Burdick, and Jenkins, J. Am. Chem. Soc., **49**, 2801–6 (1927).
(105)Datin, Ann. Physik., [9] **5**, 218–40 (1916).
(106)Davis, Ind. Eng. Chem , **17**, 735 (1925).
(107)Ibid., **22**, 380–1 (1930).
(108)Davis and Calingaert, Ibid., **17**, 1287 (1925).
(109)Déjardin, Ann. phys., [9] **11**, 253–5 (1919).
(110)Demjanoff, Ber , **28**, 22–4 (1895).
(111)Dittmar and Fawsitt, Edinburgh Trans., **33**, II, 509 (1886–1887).
(112)Doss, "Physical Constants of Principle Hydrocarbons," 4th ed., p. 20, New York, Texas Co., 1943.
(113)Dow Chemical Co. files.
(114)Dow Corning Corp. files.
(115)Drücker, Jimeno, and Kangro, Z. physik. Chem., **90**, 513–52 (1915).
(116)Egan and Kemp, J. Am. Chem. Soc., **59**, 1264–8 (1937).
(117)Ibid., **60**, 2097–101 (1938).
(118)Emeléus and Miller, J. Chem. Soc., **142**, 819–23 (1939).
(119)Emeléus and Wilkins, Ibid., **146**, 454–6 (1944).
(120)Erdmann, Ber., **31**, 356–60 (1898).
(121)Ibid., **35**, 1855–62 (1902).
(122)Erdmann, J. prakt. Chem., II, **56**, 143–56 (1897).
(123)Eucken and Berger, Z. ges. Kälte-Ind., **41**, 147 (1934).
(124)Falck, Physik. Z., **9**, 433–40 (1908).
(125)Faraday, Phil. Trans., **1351**, 155 (1845).
(126)Fawcett, J. Am. Chem. Soc., **68**, 1420–2 (1946).
(127)Fawcett and Rasmussen, Ibid., **67**, 1705–9 (1945).
(128)Feitler, Z. physik. Chem. **4**, 66–88 (1889).
(129)Felsing and Durban, J. Am. Chem. Soc. **48**, 2885–93 (1926).
(130)Felsing and Thomas, Ind. Eng. Chem., **21**, 1269–72 (1929).
(131)Ferche, Ann. Physik., **44**, 265–87 (1891).
(132)Ferguson, Freed, and Morris, J. Phys. Chem., **37**, 87–91 (1933).
(133)Fife and Reid, Ind. Eng. Chem., **22**, 513–15 (1930).
(134)Fischer and Harries, Ber., **35**, 2158–63 (1902).
(135)Fittig and Schmitz, Ann., **193**, 134–42 (1878).
(136)deForcand, Compt. rend., **132**, 688–92 (1901).
(137)Francis and Robbins, J. Am. Chem. Soc., **55**, 4339–42 (1933).
(138)Friedr. Bayer and Co., Chem. Zentr., **1898**, II, 951–2.
(139)Ibid., **1899**, I, 461–2.
(140)Fries and Bestian, Ber., **69**, 715–22 (1936).
(141)Gallaugher and Hibbert, J. Am. Chem. Soc., **59**, 2521–5 (1937).
(142)Gardner and Brewer, Ind. Eng. Chem., **29**, 179–81 (1937).
(143)Garrick, Trans. Faraday Soc., **23**, 560–3 (1927).
(144)Germann and Pickering, International Critical Tables, **III**, 248 (1928).
(145)Germann and Taylor, J. Am. Chem. Soc., **48**, 1154–9 (1926).
(146)Gilkey, Gerard, Bixler, Ind. Eng. Chem., **23**, 364–7 (1931).
(147)Gilmore, J. Soc. Chem. Ind. (Trans.), **41**, 293–4 (1922).
(148)Grassi, Nuovo cimento, [3] **24**, 109 (1888).
(149)Gróh, Ber., **45**, 1441–7 (1912).
(150)Grosjean, Ibid., **25**, 478–81 (1892).
(151)Guye and Mallet, Arch. sci. phys. nat., **13**, 30, 129, 274, 462 (1902).
(152)Haggerty and Weiler, J. Am. Chem. Soc., **51**, 1621–6 (1929).
(153)Hainlen, Ann. **282**, 229–45 (1894).
(154)Halban, Z. physik. Chem., **84**, 129–59 (1913).
(155)Haller and Martine, Compt. rend., **140**, 1298–1303 (1905).
(156)Ham, Churchill, and Ryder, J. Franklin Inst., **186**, 13–28 (1918).
(157)Hansen, Z. physik. Chem., **74**, 65–114 (1910).
(158)Harries, Ber., **31**, 37–47 (1898).
(159)Heim, Bull. soc. chim. Belg., **42**, 467–82 (1933).
(160)Hein, Z. physik. Chem., **86**, 385–426 (1914).
(161)Hein and Schramm, Ibid., **A149**, 408–16 (1930).
(162)Heisig, J. Am. Chem. Soc., **55**, 2304–11 (1933).
(163)Ibid., **63**, 1698–9 (1941).
(164)Heisig and Davis, Ibid., **57**, 339–40 (1935).
(165)Heisig and Hurd, Ibid., **55**, 3485–7 (1933).
(166)Henglein, Z. Physik, **18**, 64–9 (1923).
(167)Henning, Ann. Physik, [4] **43**, 282–94 (1914).
(168)Henning and Stock, Z. Physik, **4**, 226–40 (1921).
(169)Henry, Bull. acad. roy. méd. Belg., [3] **36**, 241–62 (1898).
(170)Henry, Chem. Zentr., **1899**, I, 194–5.
(171)Hentschel, Ber., **23**, 2394–401 (1890).
(172)Ibid., **31**, 246–9 (1898).
(173)Herz and Lorentz, Z. physik. Chem., **A140**, 406–22 (1929).
(174)Herz and Neukirch, Ibid., **104**, 433–50 (1923).
(175)Herz and Rathmann, Chem.-Ztg., **36**, 1417–8 (1912).
(176)Ibid., **37**, 621–2 (1913).
(177)Herz and Schuftan, Z. physik. Chem., **101**, 269–85 (1922).
(178)Hess and Zeitschel, J. prakt. Chem. II, **66**, 481–516 (1902).
(179)Hess and Muller, Ber., **32**, 565–74 (1899).
(180)Hieber and Reindl, Z. Elektrochem., **46**, 559–70 (1940).
(181)Hieber and Woerner, Ibid., **40**, 252–6 (1934).
(182)Holst, Thesis, Zurich (1914).
(183)Houben, Ber., **35**, 3587–92 (1902).
(184)Hovorka and Geiger, J. Am. Chem. Soc., **55**, 4759–61 (1933).
(184a Hovorka, Lankelma, and Nanjoks, Ibid., **55**, 4820–2 (1933).
(185)Hovorka, Lankelma, and Stanford, Ibid., **60**, 820–7 (1938).
(186)Hsia, Z. tech. Phys., **12**, 550–1 (1931).
(187)Hückel and Rassmann, J. prakt. Chem. [N. F.], **136**, 30–40 (1933).
(188)Hunter, Hyde, Warrick and Fletcher, J. Am. Chem. Soc. **68**, 667–72 (1946).
(189)I. G. Oppau and Ludwigshafen, unpublished report.
(190)Ilosvay, Bull. Soc. Chem., [2] **37**, 294 (1882).
(191)International Critical Tables, **III**, 201–49, New York, McGraw-Hill Book Co., Inc., (1928).
(192)Ioffe and Yampol'skaya, J. Applied Chem. (U.S.S.R.), **17**, 527 8 (1944).
(193)Jaeger, Z. Anorg. allgem. Chem., **101**, 155 (1917).
(194)Jaquerod and Wassmer, Ber., **37**, 2531–4 (1904).
(195)Jenkin and Shorthose, Dept. Sci. Ind. Research (Brit.), Special Report 14 (1923).
(196)Jenkins and Pye, Phil. Trans. Roy. Soc. (London), **A213**, 67 (1913).
(197)Jolly and Birscoe, J. Chem. Soc., **129**, 2154–9 (1926).
(198)Kahlbaum, Ber., **16**, 2476–84 (1883).
(199)Ibid., **17**, 1245–62 (1884).
(200)Ibid., **19**, 2863–5 (1886).
(201)Kahlbaum, "Sedetemperatur und Druck", Leipzig (1885).
(202)Kahlbaum, "Studien uber Dampfspannkraft", p. 116, Basel, **1897**.
(203)Kahlbaum, Z. physik. Chem., **13**, 14–55 (1894).
(204)Ibid., **26**, 577–658 (1898).
(205)Kailan, Z. anal. Chem. **51**, 81–101 (1912).
(206)Karwat, Z. physik, Chem., **112**, 486–90 (1924).
(207)Kassel, J. Am. Chem. Soc., **58**, 670 (1936).
(208)Kelley, U. S. Bur. Mines, Bull. 383 (1935).
(209)Kemp and Giauque, J. Am. Chem. Soc., **59**, 79–84 (1937).
(210)Kendall and McKenzie, "Organic Syntheses", Vol. III, pp. 57–9, New York, John Wiley & Sons, Inc., 1923.

(211) Kennedy, Sagenkahn, and Aston, J. Am. Chem. Soc., 63, 2267-72 (1941).
(212) Kinetic Chemicals Corp. bulletins (1933-1942).
(213) Kistiakowski, Ruoff, Smith, and Vaughan, J. Am. Chem. Soc., 57, 876-82 (1935).
(214) Klages, Ber., 35, 2245-62 (1902).
(215) Ibid., 36, 3584-97 (1903).
(216) Klages and Keil, Ibid., 36, 1632-45 (1903).
(217) Klemenc, Bankowski, and Von Frugnoni, Naturwissenschaften, 22, 465 (1934).
(218) Klosky, Woo, and Flanigan J. Am. Chem. Soc., 49, 1280-4 (1927).
(219) Konowalow, Ann. Physik., 14, 34-52 (1881).
(220) Kopp, Ann., 195, 81-92 (1879).
(221) Krafft, Ber., 12, 1664-8 (1879).
(222) Ibid., 13, 1413-21 (1880).
(223) Ibid., 15, 1687-711 (1882).
(224) Ibid., 15, 1711-28 (1882).
(225) Ibid., 16, 1714-26 (1883).
(226) Ibid., 16, 3018-24 (1883).
(227) Ibid., 17, 1627-31 (1884).
(228) Ibid., 19, 2218-23 (1886).
(229) Ibid., 19, 2982-8 (1886).
(230) Ibid., 23, 2360-4 (1890).
(231) Krafft and Bürger, Ibid., 17, 1378-80 (1884).
(232) Krafft and Lyons, Ibid., 27, 1761-8 (1894).
(233) Krafft and Moye, Ibid., 22, 811-5 (1889).
(234) Krafft and Noerdlinger, Ibid., 22, 816-20 (1889).
(235) Krafft and Roos, Ibid., 25, 2255-62 (1892).
(236) Krafft and Stauffer, Ibid., 15, 1728-31 (1882).
(237) Krafft and Vorster, Ibid., 26, 2813-22 (1893).
(238) Krafft and Weilandt, Ibid., 29, 1316-28 (1896).
(239) Krase and Goodman, Ind. Eng. Chem., 22, 13 (1930).
(240) Kraus and Toonder, Proc. Natl. Acad. Sci. U. S., 19, 292-8 (1933).
(241) Kuenen, Arch. néerland, sci., 26, 354 (1898).
(242) Kuenen and Robson, Phil. Mag., [6] 3, 149 (1902).
(243) Küster, Z. physik. Chem. 51, 222-42 (1905).
(244) Lamb and Roper, J. Am. Chem. Soc., 62, 806-14 (1940).
(245) Landa and Riedl, Collection Czechoslov. Chem. Commun., 2, 520-30 (1930).
(246) Landolt, Ann. Suppl., 6, 129-81 (1868).
(246a) Landolt-Börnstein, "Physikalisch-Chemische Tabellen", Hauptwerk, 1353-77; I Ergänzungsband, 729-42; II Ergänzungsband, 1302-10; III Ergänzungsband, 2450-62, Berlin, Julius Springer, 1023 36.
(247) Lecat, Ann. soc. sci. Bruxelles, 49B, 17-27 (1929).
(248) deLeeuw, Z. phys. Chem., 77, 284-314 (1911).
(249) Lenth, J. Am. Chem. Soc., 55, 3283 (1933).
(250) Lépingle, Bull. soc. chim. Mém., 39, 741-62 (1926).
(251) Leslie and Carr, Ind. Eng. Chem., 17, 810-17 (1925).
(252) Lewis and Schutz, J. Am. Chem. Soc., 56, 1002 (1934).
(253) Linder, J. Phys. Chem. 35, 531-5 (1931).
(254) Lippert, Ann., 276, 148-99 (1893).
(255) Livingston and Heisig, J. Am. Chem. Soc., 52, 2409-10 (1930).
(256) Lobry and Bruyn, Ber., 26, 266-7 (1893).
(257) Lucas and Prater, J. Am. Chem. Soc., 59, 1682-6 (1939).
(258) MacDougall, Ibid., 58, 2585-91 (1936).
(259) MacDougall and Smith, Ibid., 52, 1998-2001 (1930).
(260) Maass and Boomer, Ibid., 44, 1709-28 (1922).
(261) Maass and McIntosh, Ibid., 36, 737-42 (1914).
(262) Maass and Wright, Ibid., 43, 1098-111 (1921).
(263) Mali, Z. anorg. Chem., 149, 150-6 (1925).
(264) Mali and Ghosh, Quart. J. Indian Chem. Soc., 1, 37-43 (1924).
(265) Mangold, Wien, Akad. Ber., 102, IIA, 1071 (1893).
(266) Mannich, Ber., 35, 2144-6 (1902).
(267) Marsden and Cuthberton, Can. J. Research, 9, 419-23 (1933).
(268) Marshall, J. Chem. Soc., 89, 1371-86 (1906).
(269) Mathews, J. Am. Chem. Soc., 48, 562-76 (1926).
(270) May, Berliner, and Lynch, Ibid., 49, 1012-6 (1927).
(271) Menzel and Mohry, Z. Anorg. allgem. Chem., 210, 257-63 (1933).
(272) Menzies, J. Am. Chem. Soc., 41, 1336-7 (1919).
(273) Merriman, J. Chem. Soc., 103, 628-36 (1913).
(274) Messerly and Kennedy, J. Am. Chem. Soc., 62, 2988-91 (1940).
(275) Meyers and Van Dusen, J. Research Natl. Bur. Standards, 10, 381-412 (1933).
(276) Michalek and Clark, Chem. Eng. News, 22, 1559-63 (1944).
(277) Minguin, Gregoire, and Bollemont, Compt. rend., 134, 608-10 (1902).
(278) Möslinger, Ann. 185, 26-74 (1887).
(279) Möslinger, Ber., 9, 998-1008 (1876).
(280) Moitessier and Engel, Jahresber. Chemie, 1880, 142.
(281) Moles and Batuecas, J. chim. phys., 17, 537-88 (1919).
(282) Monhaupt, Chem.-Ztg., 32, 573 (1908).
(283) Monrew, Bontaric, and Dufraisse, J. chim. phys. 18, 333-47 (1920).
(284) Monroe, Ind. Eng. Chem., 12, 969-71 (1920).
(285) Montmollin and Matile, Helv. Chim. Acta, 7, 106-11 (1924).
(286) Moorehouse and Maass, Can. J. Research, 5, 306-12 (1931).
(287) Ibid., 11, 637-43 (1934).
(288) Mortimer and Murphy, Ind. Eng. Chem., 15, 1140-2 (1923).
(289) Mundel, Z. phys. chem., 85, 435-65 (1913).
(290) Nadejdine, J. Russ. Phys. Chem. Soc., 14, 157 (1882).
(291) Ibid., 15, 25 (1883).
(292) Nadejdine, Rep. phys., 23, 759 (1887).
(293) Nagornow and Rolinjanz, Ann. inst. anal. phys. chim. (U.S.S.R.) 2, 371-400 (1924).
(294) Nef, Ann., 270, 267-335 (1892).
(295) Ibid., 310, 316-35 (1900).
(296) Nelson, Ind. Eng. Chem., 22, 971-2 (1930).
(297) Ibid., 20, 1380-2 (1928).
(298) Ibid., 20, 1382-4 (1928).
(299) Nelson and Senseman, Ibid., 14, 58-62 (1922).
(300) Nelson and Wales, J. Am. Chem. Soc., 47, 867-72 (1925).
(301) Nelson and Young, Ibid., 55, 2429-31 (1933).
(302) Neubeck, Z. physik. Chem., 1, 649-66 (1887).

(303) Niederschulte, Dissertation Erlangen, 1903.
(304) Nieuwland, Calcott, Downing, and Carter, J. Am. Chem. Soc., 53, 4197-202 (1931).
(305) Nikitin, J. Russ. Phys.-Chem. Soc., 52, 235-49 (1920).
(306) Olszewski, Compt. rend., 99, 706-7 (1884).
(307) Olszewski, Ann. Physik., 31, 58 74 (1887).
(308) Onnes and Weber, Verslag Akad. Wetenschappen, 22, 226 (1913)
(309) Paneth and Loleit, J. Chem. Soc., 138, 366-71 (1935).
(310) Parks and Barton, J. Am. Chem. Soc., 50, 24-6 (1928).
(311) Paterno and Mazzuchelli, Gazz. chim. ital., 50, I, 30-52 (1920).
(312) Patnode and Wilcock, J. Am. Chem. Soc., 68, 358-63 (1946).
(313) Patterson, Ber., 38, 210-3 (1905).
(314) Pawlewski, Ibid., 16, 2633-6 (1883).
(315) Pearce and Peters, J. Phys. Chem., 33, 871-8 (1929).
(316) Perkin, J. Chem. Soc., 55, 549-51 (1881).
(317) Perry, J. Phys. Chem., 31, 1737-41 (1927).
(318) Perry and Bardwell, J. Am. Chem. Soc., 47, 2629-32 (1925).
(319) Pesce and Evdokimoff, Gazz. chim. ital., 70, 712-6 (1940).
(320) Pickett and Peterson, Ind. Eng. Chem., 21, 325-6 (1929).
(321) Piloty, Ber., 31, 454-7 (1898).
(322) Pinette, Ann. 243, 32-63 (1888).
(323) Plank and Hsia, Z. ges. Kälte-Ind., 38, 97 (1931).
(324) Plank and Vahl, Forch. Gebiete Ingenieurw., Ausgabe 2, 11-8 (1931).
(325) Power and Kleber, Arch. Pharm. 232, 634-48 (1894).
(326) Ibid., 649-59 (1894).
(327) Power and Kleber, Pharm. Rev., 13, 60 (1895).
(328) Power and Lees, J. Chem. Soc., 81, 1585-94 (1902).
(329) Price, Ibid 107, 188-98 (1915).
(330) Purcell and Zahoorbux, Ibid., 140, 1029-35 (1937).
(331) Ramsay and Shields, Z. Physik, Chem., 12, 433-76 (1893).
(332) Ramsay and Young, Ber., 19, 2107-14 (1886).
(333) Ramsay and Young, J. Chem. Soc. 47, 42-5 (1885).
(334) Ibid., 47, 640-57 (1885).
(335) Ibid., 49, 790-812 (1886).
(336) Ramsay and Young, Phil. Trans., A175, 37 (1884).
(337) Ibid., 1771, 123 (1886).
(338) Ibid., A178, 57 (1887).
(339) Ibid., A178, 313 (1887).
(340) Ibid., 180, 137 (1889).
(341) Ramsay and Young, Z. physik. Chem., 1, 237-57 (1887).
(342) Ratchford, Rehberg, and Fisher, J. Am. Chem. Soc., 66, 1864-7 (1944).
(343) Regnault, Mém. Paris. 26, 339 (1862).
(344) Ibid., 26, 375 (1862).
(345) Ibid., 26, 403 (1862).
(346) Ibid., 26, 440 (1862).
(347) Ibid., 26, 448 (1862).
(348) Ibid., 26, 455 (1862).
(349) Ibid., 26, 462 (1862).
(350) Ibid., 26, 535 (1862).
(351) Regnault, Rel. des exp. 2, 440-62.
(352) Rex, Z. physik. Chem. 55, 355-70 (1916).
(353) Richardson, J. Chem. Soc., 49, 761-76 (1886).
(354) Riley and Gray, "Organic Syntheses," Vol. XV, pp. 67-9, New York, John Wiley & Sons, Inc., 1935.
(355) Rinkenbach, Ind. Eng. Chem., 19, 474-6 (1927).
(356) Robinson "Elements of Fractional Distillation", 1st ed., New York, McGraw-Hill Book Co., Inc., 1922.
(357) Rochow and Dennis, J. Am. Chem. Soc. 57, 486-7 (1935).
(358) Rolla, Atti accad Lincei, 18, 365-73 (1909).
(359) Rossini, Am. Petroleum Inst. Research Project 44; Willingham et al., Ibid.
(360) Rousset, Bull. soc. chim. Mém., III, 15, 58-72 (1896).
(361) Rubin, Levedahl, and Yost, J. Am. Chem. Soc., 66, 279-82 (1944).
(362) Rupe and Schlochoff, Ber., 38, 1719-25 (1905).
(363) Sajotschewsky, Beibl. Ann. Physik., 3, 741 (1879).
(364) Sameshima, J. Am. Chem. Soc., 40, 1482-508 (1918).
(365) Scatchard and Raymond, Ibid., 60, 1278-87 (1938).
(366) Scatchard, Wood, and Mochel, Ibid., 61, 3206-10 (1939).
(367) Scatchard, Wood, and Mochel, J. Phys. Chem., 43, 119-130 (1939).
(368) Schierholtz and Staples, J. Am. Chem. Soc., 57, 2709-11 (1935).
(369) Schiff, Ann., 220, 71-113 (1883).
(370) Schimmel and Co., bulletins.
(371) Schlesinger and Walker, J. Am. Chem. Soc., 57, 621-5 (1935).
(372) Schlumberger, J. Gasbeleucht., 55, 1257-60 (1912).
(373) Schmidt, Z. physik. Chem., 7, 433-67 (1891).
(374) Ibid., 8, 628-46 (1891).
(375) Ibid., 58, 513-40 (1907).
(376) Schuette and Cowley, J. Am. Chem. Soc., 53, 3485-9 (1931).
(377) Schuette and Thomas, Ibid., 52, 2028-30 (1930).
(378) Schütze and Widenmann, Helv. Chim. Acta, 20, 936-49 (1937).
(379) Schultz, Ann., 174, 201-35 (1874).
(380) Schumann, Ann. Physik., 12, 40-65 (1881).
(381) Schweitzer, Ann., 264, 193-6 (1891).
(382) Seibert and Burrell, J. Am. Chem. Soc., 37, 2683 94 (1915).
(383) Semmler, "Die Atherischen Öle", Vol. I IV, Leipzig, Veit & Co., 1906-7.
(384) Semmler, Ber., 23, 1803-10 (1890).
(385) Ibid., 25, 3352-4 (1892).
(386) Ibid., 26, 2254-8 (1893).
(387) Ibid., 34, 3122-30 (1901).
(388) Senseman and Nelson, Ind. Eng. Chem., 15, 382-3 (1923).
(389) Seyer and Mann, J. Am. Chem. Soc., 67, 328-9 (1945).
(390) Simon and Huter, Z. Elektrochem., 41, 28-33 (1935).
(391) Smith, J. Chem. Soc. 134 (2), 2573-83 (1931).
(392) Smith and Menzies, J. Am. Chem. Soc., 32, 1448-59 (1910).
(393) Smyth and Seaton, J. Ind. Hyg. Toxicol., 22, 477-83 (1940).
(394) Smythe and Engel, J. Am Chem. Soc., 51, 2646-70 (1929).
(395) Soden and Rojahn, Ber. 33, 1720-4 (1900).
(396) Ibid., 33, 3063-5 (1900).
(397) Soden and Treff, Chem.-Ztg., 27, 807 (1903).
(398) Solana and Moles, Anales soc. españ. fís. quím., 30, 886-917 (1932).

(399)Spence and Wild, J. Chem. Soc., **138**, 506–9 (1935).
(400)Speranski, Z. physik. Chem. **46**, 70–8 (1903).
(401)Ssemenow, J. Russ. Phys.-Chem. Soc., **31**, 115–35 (1889).
(402)Staedel, Ber., **15**, 2559–72 (1882).
(403)Stedman, Trans. Faraday Soc., **24**, 289–98 (1928).
(404)Stelzner, Dissertation Erlangen (1901).
(405)Stephan, J. prakt. Chem., **II, 62**, 523–35 (1900).
(406)Stevens, Ind. Eng. Chem., **35**, 655–60 (1943).
(407)Stock, Henning, and Kuss, Ber., **54**, 1119–29 (1921).
(408)Stock and Kuss, Ibid., **50**, 159–64 (1917).
(409)Stock and Praetorius, Ibid., **45**, 3568 (1912).
(410)Stock and Somieski, Ibid., **52**, 695–724 (1919).
(411)Stock and Stoltzenberg, Ibid., **50**, 498–502 (1917).
(412)Stock and Willfroth, Ibid., **47**, 144–54 (1914).
(413)Stock and Zeidler, Ibid., **54**, 531–41 (1921).
(414)Straus and Kollek, Ibid., **59**, 1664–81 (1926).
(415)Stuckey and Saylor, J. Am. Chem. Soc., **62**, 2922–5 (1940).
(416)Stull, Ibid., **59**, 2726–33 (1937).
(417)Swan and Mack, Ibid., **47**, 2112–6 (1925).
(418)Swift and Hochanadel, Ibid., **67**, 880–1 (1945).
(419)Takahashi and Yaginuma, Jap. J. Chem., **4**, 19 (1920).
(420)Tanaka and Nagai, Proc. Imp. Acad. (Tokyo), **5**, 78–9 (1929).
(421)Tannenberger, Ber., **66**, 484–6 (1933).
(422)Taylor and Layng, J. Chem. Phys., **1**, 798–808 (1933).
(423)Taylor and Rinkenbach, J. Am. Chem. Soc., **48**, 1305–9 (1926).
(423a Taylor and Smith, Ibid., **44**, 2450–63 (1922).
(424)Taylor and Walden, Ibid., **66**, 842–3 (1944).
(425)Tchugaeff, Ber., **31**, 360–8 (1898).
(426)Terwen, Z. physik. Chem., **91**, 469–99 (1916).
(427)Thomas and Young, J. Chem. Soc., **67**, 1071–5 (1895).
(428)Thoms, Ber., **36**, 3446–51 (1903).
(429)Thoms and Biltz, Z. allgem. österr. Apoth-Ver., **42**, 943–7 (1904).
(430)Thornton, Burg, and Schlesinger, J. Am. Chem. Soc., **55, 3177–82** (1933).
(431)Tiemann, Ber., **31**, 2989–92 (1898).
(432)Tiemann and Schmidt, Ibid., **29**, 903–26 (1896).
(433)Ibid., **30**, 33–8 (1897).
(434)Tiemann and Semmler, Ber., **26**, 2708–29 (1893).
(435)Ibid., **31**, 2889–99 (1898).
(436)Tiffeneau, Compt. rend, **139**, 481–6 (1904).
(437)Timmermans, Bull. soc. chim. Belg., **36**, 502–8 (1927).
(438)Timmermans and Martin, J. Chim. phys., **23**, 733–46 (1926).
(439)Ibid., **25**, 411–51 (1928).
(440)Treon, Crutchfield, and Kitzmiller, J. Ind. Hyg. Toxicol., **25**, 199–214 (1943).
(441)Tschugaeff, Ber., **33**, 735–6 (1900).
(442)Ultee, Ibid., **39**, 1856–8 (1906).
(443)Van der Meulen and Mann, J. Am. Chem. Soc., **53**, 451–3 (1931).
(444)Vanstone, J. Chem. Soc., **97**, 429–43 (1910).
(445)Vaughan, J. Am. Chem. Soc., **54**, 3863–76 (1932).
(446)Venable, Ber., **13** (2), 1649–52 (1880).
(447)Verschoyle, Trans. Roy. Soc. (London), **A230**, 189 (1931).
(448)Villard, Ann. chim. phys. [7] **10**, 387 (1897).
(449)Villard, Compt. rend., **120**, 1262–5 (1895).
(450)Villiers, Bull. soc. chim. **34**, 25–7 (1880).
(451)Vincent and Chappuis, Compt. rend., **100**, 1216–8 (1885).
(452)Volmer and Kirchoff, Z. physik. Chem., **115**, 233–8 (1925).

(453)Von Rechenberg, "Destillation", Leipzig, 1923.
(454)Von Siemens, Ann. Physik., [4] **42**, 871–88 (1913).
(455)Wade and Merriman, J. Chem. Soc., **101**, 2438–43 (1912).
(456)Walbaum, Ber., **33**, 2299–302 (1900).
(457)Walbaum, J. prakt. Chem., **II, 73**, 488–93 (1906).
(458)Walbaum and Stephan, Ber., **33**, 2302–8 (1900).
(459)Walden, Z. physik. Chem., **70**, 569–619 (1910).
(460)Wallach, Ann. **275**, 171 (1893).
(461)Ibid., **336**, 1–46 (1904).
(462)Wallach et al., Ibid., **279**, 366–97 (1894).
(463)Weber, Verslag Akad. Wetenschappen, **22**, 380 (1914).
(464)Wenzel and Pirak, Collection Czechoslov. Chem. Commun., **6**, 54–9 (1934).
(465)Whitmore and Fleming, J. Am. Chem. Soc., **55**, 3803–6 (1933).
(466)Whitmore et al., Ibid., **68**, 475–81 (1946).
(467)Wiberg and Sütterlin, Z. Eleketrochem., **41**, 151–3 (1935).
(468)Wilbrand and Beilstein, Z. Chemie, **7**, 153–60 (1864):
(469)Wilcock, J. Am. Chem. Soc., **68**, 691–6 (1946).
(470)Williams, Ibid., **47**, 2644–52 (1925).
(471)Willingham et al., J. Research Natl. Bur. Standards, **35**, 219 (1945).
(472)Wislicenus, Ann., **275**, 309–82 (1893).
(473)Wittenberg and Meyer, Ber., **16**, 500–8 (1883).
(474)Woringer, Z. physik. Chem., **34**, 257–89 (1900).
(475)Wüllener and Grotrian, Wied Ann., **11**, 545–604 (1880).
(476)Yost and Stone, J. Am. Chem. Soc., **55**, 1889–95 (1933).
(477)Young, J. Chem. Soc. **55**, 483–5 (1889).
(478)Ibid., **55**, 486–521 (1889).
(479)Ibid., **59**, 621–6 (1891).
(480)Ibid., **59**, 903–11 (1891).
(481)Ibid., **59**, 911–36 (1891).
(482)Ibid., **71**, 446–57 (1897).
(483)Ibid., **73**, 675–81 (1898).
(483a Ibid., **77**, 1145–51 (1900).
(484)Young, Proc. Roy. Irish Acad., **38B**, 65–92 (1928).
(485)Young, Sci. Proc. Roy. Dublin Soc., **12**, 374–432 (1910).
(486)Young, Z. physik. Chem., **29**, 193–241 (1899).
(487)Young and Fortey, J. Chem. Soc., **75**, 873–83 (1899).
(488)Ibid., **77**, 1126–51 (1900).
(489)Ibid., **81**, 783–6 (1902).
(490)Young and Nelson, Ind. Eng. Chem., **21**, 321–2 (1929).
(491)Young and Thomas, J. Chem. Soc., **63**, 1191–262 (1893).
(492)Ibid., **71**, 440–6 (1897).
(493)Zeleny and Smith, Physik. Z, **7**, 667–71 (1906).
(494)Zincke, Ann. **152**, 1–21 (1869).
(495)American Petroleum Institute Research Project 44, Nat. Bur. Standards, "Selected Values of Properties of Hydrocarbons."
(496)Boord, et al, Ind. Eng. Chem., to be published.
(497)Deanesly and Carleton, J. Phys. Chem., **45**, 1104–23 (1941).
(498)Gibbons and co-workers, J. Am. Chem. Soc. **68**, 1130–1 (1946).
(499)Gilman and Meals, J. Org. Chem., **8**, 126–46 (1943).
(500)Heise and Töhl, Ann., **270**, 155–71 (1892).
(501)Karabinos and co-workers, J Am. Chem. Soc., **68**, 2107–8 (1946).
(502)Mair and Streiff, J. Research Natl. Bur. Standards, **24**, 395–414 (1940).
(503)O'Connor and Sowa, J. Am. Chem. Soc., **60**, 125–7 (1938).
(504)Shephard and co-workers, Ibid., **53**, 1948–58 (1931).
(505)Smith and Guss, Ibid., **62**, 2630–1 (1940).

VAPOR PRESSURE OF THE ELEMENTS

Rudolf Loebel

This table lists the temperature in degrees Celsius at which an element has a vapor pressure indicated by the headings of the columns. For pressures of one atmosphere and lower, the pressures are given in millimeters of mercury; for pressures above one atmosphere, the pressures are given in atmospheres.

Element		mm Hg					atm.				
		1	10	100	400	760	2	5	10	20	40
Aluminum	Al	1540	1780	2080	2320	2467	2610	2850	3050	3270	3530
Antimony	Sb		960	1280	1570	1750	1960	2490			
Arsenic	As	380	440	510	580	610					
Barium	Ba	860	1050	1300	1520	1640	1790	2030	2230		
Beryllium	Be	1520	1860	2300	2770	2970	3240	3730	4110	4720	5610
Bismuth	Bi		1060	1280	1450	1560	1660	1850	2000	2180	
Boron	B	2660	3030	3460	3810	4000					
Bromine	Br	−60	−30	+9	39	59	78	110			
Cadmium	Cd	393	486	610	710	765	830	930	1030	1120	1240
Calcium	Ca	800	970	1200	1390	1490	1630	1850	2020	2290	
Cesium	Cs		373	513	624	690					
Chlorine	Cl	−123	−101	−71	−46	−34	−17	+9	30	55	97
Chromium	Cr	1610	1840	2140	2360	2480	2630	2850	3010	3180	
Cobalt	Co	1910	2170	2500	2760	2870	3040	3270			
Copper	Cu		1870	2190	2440	2600	2760	3010	3500	3460	3740
Fluorine	F			−203	−193	−188	−180.7	−169.1	−159.6		
Gallium	Ga	1350	1570	1850	2060	2180	2320	2560	2730		
Germanium	Ge		2080	2440	2710	2830	2970	3200	3430		
Gold	Au	1880	2160	2520	2800	2940	3120	3490	3630	3890	
Indium	In				1960	2080	2230	2440	2600		
Iridium	Ir	2830	3170	3630	3960	4130	4310	4650			
Iron	Fe	1780	2040	2370	2620	2750	2900	3150	3360	3570	
Iodine	I	40	72	115	160	185	216	265			
Lanthanum	La				3230	3420	3620	3960	4270		
Lead	Pb	970	1160	1420	1630	1740	1880	2140	2320	2620	
Lithium	Li	750	890	1080	1240	1310	1420	1518			
Magnesium	Mg	620	740	900	1040	1110	1190	1330	1430	1560	
Manganese	Mn		1510	1810	2050	2100	2360	2580	2850		
Mercury	Hg			260	330	356.9	398	465	517	581	657
Molybdenum	Mo	3300	3770	4200	4580	4830	5050	5340	5680	5980	
Neodymium	Nd				2870	3100	3300	3680	3990		
Nickel	Ni	1800	2090	2370	2620	2730	2880	3120	3300	3310	
Palladium	Pd	1470	2290	2670	2950	3140	3270	3560	3840		
Phosphorus	P		127	199	253	283	319				
Platinum	Pt	2600	2940	3360	3650	3830	4000	4310	4570	4860	
Polonium	Po	472	587	752	890	960	1060	1200	1340		
Potassium	K			590	710	770	850	950	1110	1240	1420
Rhodium	Rh	2530	2850	3260	3590	3760	3930	4230	4440		
Rubidium	Rb		390	527	640	700					
Selenium	Se		429	547	640	685	750	850	920	1010	1120
Silver	Ag	1310	1540	1850	2060	2210	2360	2600	2850	3050	3300
Sodium	Na	440	546	700	830	890	980	1120	1230	1370	
Strontium	Sr	740	900	1100	1280	1380	1480	1670	1850	2030	
Sulfur	S		246	333	407	445	493	574	640	720	
Tellurium	Te	520	633	792	900	962	1030	1160	1250		
Thallium	Tl		1000	1210	1370	1470	1560	1750	1900	2050	2260
Tin	Sn	1610	1890	2270	2580	2750	2950	3270	3540	3890	
Titanium	Ti	2180	2480	2860	3100	3260	3400	3650	3800		
Tungsten	W	3980	4490	5160	5470	5940	6260	6670	7250	7670	
Uranium	U	2150	2800	3270	3620	3800	4040	4420			
Vanadium	V	2290	2570	2950	3220	3380	3540	3800			
Zinc	Zn		590	730	840	907	970	1090	1180	1290	

VAPOR PRESSURE OF ELEMENTS THAT ARE GASEOUS AT STANDARD CONDITIONS

The following tables contain vapor pressure data for helium, hydrogen, neon, nitrogen, and oxygen.

Vapor Pressure (atm) vs. Temperature (K) for Helium-4

Temperature, K	Pressure atm
2.177	0.04969
2.20	0.05256
2.25	0.05916
2.30	0.06629
2.35	0.07399
2.40	0.08228
2.45	0.09120
2.50	0.1008
2.55	0.1110
2.60	0.1219
2.65	0.1336
2.70	0.1460
2.75	0.1591
2.80	0.1730
2.85	0.1878
2.90	0.2033
2.95	0.2198
3.00	0.2371
3.05	0.2553
3.10	0.2744
3.15	0.2945
3.20	0.3156
3.25	0.3376
3.30	0.3607
3.35	0.3848
3.40	0.4100
3.45	0.4363
3.50	0.4637
3.55	0.4923
3.60	0.5220
3.65	0.5528
3.70	0.5849
3.75	0.6182
3.80	0.6528
3.85	0.6886
3.90	0.7257
3.95	0.7642
4.00	0.8040
4.05	0.8452
4.10	0.8878
4.15	0.9318
4.20	0.9772
4.224	1.000
4.25	1.024
4.30	1.073

Temperature, K	Pressure atm
4.35	1.123
4.40	1.174
4.45	1.227
4.50	1.282
4.55	1.339
4.60	1.397
4.65	1.457
4.70	1.519
4.75	1.582
4.80	1.648
4.85	1.715
4.90	1.784
4.95	1.856
5.00	1.929
5.05	2.004
5.10	2.082
5.201	2.245

Vapor Pressure (atm) vs. Temperature (K) for Equilibrium Hydrogen

Temperature, K	Pressure, atm
13.803	0.069_5
14	0.077_8
15	0.133
16	0.213
17	0.325
18	0.476
19	0.673
20	0.923
20.268	1.000
21	1.233
22	1.613
23	2.069
24	2.611
25	3.245
26	3.982
27	4.829
28	5.794
29	6.887
30	8.118
31	9.501
32	11.051
32.976	12.759

Vapor Pressure (atm) vs. Temperature (K) for Neon

Temperature, K	Pressure, atm
25	0.50366
26	0.70902
27	0.97255
28	1.3037
29	1.7124
30	2.2088
31	2.8031
32	3.5061
33	4.3286
34	5.2818
35	6.3773
36	7.6271
37	9.0439
38	10.641
39	12.432
40	14.434
41	16.661
42	19.133
43	21.867
44	24.887
44.4	26.19

Temperature, K	Pressure, atm
102	8.8083
104	10.041
106	11.392
108	12.870
110	14.481
112	16.233
114	18.133
116	20.190
118	22.411
120	24.806
122	27.386
124	30.174
126	33.227
126.200	33.555

Vapor Pressure (atm) vs. Temperature (K) for Nitrogen

Temperature, K	Pressure, atm
63.148	0.1237
64	0.1443
66	0.2037
68	0.2813
70	0.3807
72	0.5059
74	0.6610
76	0.8506
77.347	1.0000
78	1.0793
80	1.3520
82	1.6739
84	2.0503
86	2.4865
88	2.9882
90	3.5607
92	4.2099
94	4.9415
98	6.6748
100	7.6885

Vapor Pressure (atm) vs. Temperature (K) for Oxygen

Temperature, K	Pressure, atm
54.351	0.001
56	0.002
58	0.004
60	0.007
62	0.012
64	0.018
66	0.028
68	0.042
70	0.061
72	0.087
74	0.122
76	0.167
78	0.224
80	0.297
82	0.387
84	0.497
86	0.631
88	0.791
90	0.981
90.180	1.000
92	1.205
94	1.466
96	1.768
98	2.114
100	2.509
102	2.957
104	3.462
106	4.029
108	4.661
110	5.363

Vapor Pressure (atm) vs. Temperature (K) for Oxygen (Continued)

Temperature, K	Pressure atm	Temperature, K	Pressure, atm
112	6.139	136	22.986
114	6.995	138	25.170
116	7.934	140	27.501
118	8.961		
120	10.082	142	29.986
		144	32.631
122	11.300	146	35.448
124	12.621	148	38.446
126	14.049	150	41.638
128	15.591		
130	17.249	152	45.041
		154	48.675
132	19.031	154.576	49.767
134	20.942		

Data from Sparks, L. L., ASRDI Oxygen Technology Survey, Vol. IV: Low Temperature Measurement, NASA-3073, 1974.

VAPOR PRESSURE OF NITRIC ACID

Temperature °C	Vapor Pressure, mm. of Hg	
	100% HNO_3	90% of HNO_3
0	14.4	5.5
10	26.6	11.
20	47.9	20.
30	81.3	37.3
40	133.	64.4
50	208.	107.
70	467.	242.
80	670.	352.
90	937.	504.
100	1282.	710.

LOW TEMPERATURE LIQUID BATHS

Liquid thermostat baths suitable for many physical measurements can be produced by using a stirred solid–liquid mixture at its melting point. Dry-ice or liquid air can be used to produce the solid. A Dewar flask is preferable as a container and, with adequate insulation or immersion in another somewhat colder bath, good temperature constancy can be maintained over several hours. Such baths are especially useful over the temperature range between dry-ice (−78C) and liquid air (−190). The following table gives the melting and normal boiling points of some readily available organic liquids suitable for this purpose. The compounds are listed in order of their increasing melting points. Temperatures are in degrees Celcius.

Compound	M.P.	B.P.	Compound	M.P.	B.P.
Isopentane (2-Methyl butane)	−159.9	27.85	Ethyl acetate	− 84	77
Methyl cyclopentane	−142.4	71.8	(Dry-ice + acetone)	− 78	——
Allyl chloride	−134.5	45	p-Cymene	− 67.9	177.1
n-Pentane	−129.7	36.1	Chloroform	− 63.5	61.7
Allyl alcohol	−129	97	N-Methyl aniline	− 57	196
Ethyl alcohol	−117.3	78.5	Chlorobenzene	− 45.6	132
Carbon disulfide	−110.8	46.3	Anisole	− 37.5	155
Isobutyl alcohol	−108	108.1	Bromobenzene	− 30.8	156
Acetone	− 95.4	56.2	Carbon tetrachloride	− 23	76.5
Toluene	− 95	110.6	Benzonitrile	− 13	205

FATS AND OILS

These data for fats and oils were compiled originally for the Biology Data Book by H. J. Harwood, and R. P. Geyer. 1964. Data are reproduced here by permission of the copyright owners of the above publication, the Federation of American Societies for Experimental Biology, Washington, D.C. pp. 380–382.

Values are typical rather than average, and frequently were derived from specific analyses for particular samples (especially the constituent fatty acids). Extreme variations may occur, depending on a number

	Fat or Oil	Source	Melting (or Solidification) Point, °C	Specific Gravity (or Density)	Refractive Index $\frac{40°C}{D}$ n	Iodine Value	Saponification Value
	(A)	(B)	(C)	(D)	(E)	(F)	(G)
	Land Animals						
1	Butterfat	*Bos taurus*	32.2	$0.911^{40°/15°}$	1.4548	36.1	227
2	Depot fat	*Homo sapiens*	(15)	$0.918^{15°}$	1.4602	67.6	196.2
3	Lard oil	*Sus scrofa*	(30.5)	$0.919^{15°}$	1.4615	58.6	194.6
4	Neat's-foot oil	*B. taurus*	....	$0.910^{25°}$	$1.464^{25°}$	69–76	190–199
5	Tallow, beef	*B. taurus*	....	....	....	49.5	197
6	Tallow, mutton	*Ovis aries*	(42.0)	$0.945^{15°}$	1.4565	40	194
	Marine Animals						
7	Cod-liver oil	*Gadus morhua*	....	0.925^{25}	$1.481^{25°}$	165	186
8	Herring oil	*Clupea harengus*	....	$0.900^{60°}$	$1.4610^{60°}$	140	192
9	Menhaden oil	*Brevoortia tyrannus*	....	$0.903^{60°}$	$1.4645^{60°}$	170	191
10	Sardine oil	*Sardinops caerulea*	....	$0.905^{60°}$	$1.4660^{60°}$	185	191
11	Sperm oil, body	*Physeter macrocephalus*	....	....	....	76–88	122–130
12	Sperm oil, head	*P. macrocephalus*	....	....	....	70	140–144
13	Whale oil	*Balaena mysticetus*	....	0.892^{60}	$1.460^{60°}$	120	195
	Plants						
14	Babassu oil	*Attalea funifera*	22–26	$(0.893^{60°})$	$1.443^{60°}$	15.5	247
15	Castor oil	*Ricinus communis*	(−18.0)	$0.961^{15°}$	1.4770	85.5	180.3
16	Cocoa butter	*Theobroma cacao*	34.1	$0.964^{15°}$	1.4568	36.5	193.8
17	Coconut oil	*Cocos nucifera*	25.1	$0.924^{15°}$	1.4493	10.4	268
18	Corn oil	*Zea mays*	(−20.0)	$0.922^{15°}$	1.4734	122.6	192.0
19	Cotton seed oil	*Gossypium hirsutum*	(−1.0)	$0.917^{25°}$	1.4735	105.7	194.3
20	Linseed oil	*Linum usitatissimum*	(−24.0)	$0.938^{15°}$	$1.4782^{25°}$	178.7	190.3
21	Mustard oil	*Brassica hirta*	....	$0.9145^{15°}$	1.475	102	174
22	Neem oil	*Melia azadirachta*	−3	$0.917^{15°}$	1.4615	71	194.5
23	Niger-seed oil	*Guizotia abyssinica*	....	$0.925^{15°}$	1.471	128.5	190
24	Oiticica oil	*Licania rigida*	....	$0.974^{25°}$	....	140–180	....
25	Olive oil	*Olea europaea sativa*	(−6.0)	$0.918^{15°}$	1.4690	81.1	189.7
26	Palm oil	*Elaeis guineensis*	35.0	$0.915^{15°}$	1.4578	54.2	199.1
27	Palm-kernel oil	*E. guineensis*	24.1	$0.923^{15°}$	1.4569	37.0	219.9
28	Peanut oil	*Arachis hypogaea*	(3.0)	$0.914^{15°}$	1.4691	93.4	192.1
29	Perilla oil	*Perilla frutescens*	....	$(0.935^{15°})$	$1.481^{25°}$	195	192
30	Poppy-seed oil	*Papaver somniferum*	(−15)	$0.925^{15°}$	1.4685	135	194
31	Rapeseed oil	*Brassica campestris*	(−10)	$0.915^{15°}$	1.4706	98.6	174.7
32	Safflower oil	*Carthamus tinctorius*	....	$(0.900^{60°})$	$1.462^{60°}$	145	192
33	Sesame oil	*Sesamum indicum*	(−6.0)	$0.919^{25°}$	1.4646	106.6	187.9
34	Soybean oil	*Glycine soja*	(−16.0)	$0.927^{15°}$	1.4729	130.0	190.6
35	Sunflower-seed oil	*Helianthus annuus*	(−17.0)	$0.923^{15°}$	1.4694	125.5	188.7
36	Tung oil	*Aleurites fordi*	(−2.5)	$0.934^{15°}$	$1.5174^{25°}$	168.2	193.1
37	Wheat-germ oil	*Triticum aestivum*	....	....	....	125	....

[1] Caproic. [2] Capryli. [3] Capric. [4] Butyric. [5] Decenoic. [6] C_{12} monoethenoic. [7] C_{14} monoethenoic. [8] Gadoleic plus erucic. [9] C_{12} n-pentadecanoic. [10] C_{17} margaric. [11] 12-Methyl tetradecanoic. [12] C_{20} polyethenoic.

of variables such as source, treatment, and age of a fat or oil. **Specific Gravity** (column D) was calculated at the specified temperature (degrees centigrade) and referred to water at the same temperature, unless otherwise specified. **Density,** shown in parentheses (column D), was measured at the specified temperature (degrees centigrade). **Refractive Index** (column E) was measured at 50°C, unless otherwise specified.

Constituent Fatty Acids, g/100 g total fatty acids

	Saturated					Unsaturated				
Lauric	Myristic	Palmitic	Stearic	Arachidic	Other	Palmitoleic	Oleic	Linoleic	Linolenic	Other
(H)	(I)	(J)	(K)	(L)	(M)	(N)	(O)	(P)	(Q)	(R)
2.5	11.1	29.0	9.2	2.4	2.0[1]; 0.5[2]; 2.3[3]	4.6	26.7	3.6	....	3.6[4]; 0.1[5]; 0.1[6]; 0.9[7] 1.4[8]; 1.0[9]; 1.0[10]; 0.4[11]
....	2.7	24.0	8.4			5	46.9	10.2	....	2.5[8]
....	1.3	28.3	11.9			2.7	47.5	6	....	0.2[7]; 2.1[8]
....	....	17–18	2–3			....	74–76		....	....
....	6.3	27.4	14.1			....	49.6	2.5		....
....	4.6	24.6	30.5			....	36.0	4.3		....
....	5.8	8.4	0.6			20.0	←— 29.1 —→		....	25.4[12]; 9.6[13]
....	7.3	13.0	Trace	....		4.9			20.7	30.1[12]; 23.2[13]
....	5.9	16.3	0.6	0.6		15.5	....	....	29.6	19.0[12]; 11.7[13]; 0.8[14]
....	5.1	14.6	3.2			11.8	←— 17.8 —→			18.1[12]; 14.0[13]; trace[7]; 15.4[15]
1	5	6.5	....			26.5	37	19	....	1[13]; 4[7]; 19[16]
16	14	8	2		3.5[3]	15	17	6.5		4[6]; 14[7]; 6.5[16]
0.2	9.3	15.6	2.8			14.4	35.2			13.6[12]; 5.9[13]; 2.5[7]; 0.2[17]
44.1	15.4	8.5	2.7	0.2	0.2[1]; 4.8[2]; 6.6[3]	....	16.1	1.4	....	....
←————— 2.4 —————→						....	7.4	3.1	....	87[18]
....		24.4	35.4	....		....	38.1	2.1	....	....
45.4	18.0	10.5	2.3	0.4[19]	0.8[1]; 5.4[2]; 8.4[3]	0.4	7.5	Trace	....	....
....	1.4	10.2	3.0			1.5	49.6	34.3		....
....	1.4	23.4	1.1	1.3		2.0	22.9	47.8		....
....	....	6.3	2.5	0.5		....	19.0	24.1	47.4	0.2[14]
....	1.3[20]	....	....			....	27.2[20]	16.6[20]	1.8[20]	1.1[14]; 1.0[21]; 51.0[22]
....	2.6[20]	14.1[20]	24.0[20]	0.8[20]			58.5[20]			....
....	3.3[20]	8.2[20]	4.8[20]	0.5[20]			30.3[20]	57.3[20]	....	....
←————— 11.3[23] —————→							6.2			82.5[24]
....	Trace	6.9	2.3	0.1			84.4	4.6		....
....	1.4	40.1	5.5	....			42.7	10.3		....
46.9	14.1	8.8	1.3		2.7[2]; 7.0[3]		18.5	0.7		....
....	....	8.3	3.1	2.4			56.0	26.0		3.1[14]; 1.1[21]
←————— 9.6[23] —————→							17.8	....	17.5	
....	....	4.8[20]	2.9[20]	....			30.1[20]	62.2[20]		....
....	....	1	....				32	15	1	50[22]
←————— 6.8[23] —————→							18.6	70 1	3 4	....
....	....	9.1	4.3	0.8			45.4	40.4		....
0.2	0.1	9.8	2.4	0.9		0.4	28.9	50.7	6.5	0.1[7]
....	....	5.6	2.2	0.9		....	25.1	66.2	....	....
←————— 4.6[23] —————→							4.1	0.6		90.7[25]
←————— 16.0[23] —————→							28.1	52.3	3.6	

[13] C_{22} polyethenoic. [14] Behenic. [15] C_{14} polyethenoic. [16] Gadoleic. [17] C_{24} polyethenoic. [18] Ricinoleic. [19] Includes behenic and lignoceric. [20] Percent by weight. [21] Lignoceric. [22] Erucic. [23] Includes behenic. [24] Licanic. [25] Eleostearic.

CONCENTRATIVE PROPERTIES OF AQUEOUS SOLUTIONS: CONVERSION TABLES

A. V. Wolf, Morden G. Brown and Phoebe G. Prentiss

The table columns are:

$A\%$ = anhydrous solute weight per cent, g solute/100 g solution.

$H\%$ = hydrated solute weight per cent, g solute/100 g solution.

ρ or D_4^{20} = relative density at 20°C, kg/l.

D_{20}^{20} = specific gravity at 20°C.

C_s = anhydrous solute concentration, g/l.

M = molar concentration, g-mol/l.

C_w = total water concentration, g/l.

$(C_0 - C_w)$ = water displaced by anhydrous solute, g/l.

$(n - n_0) \times 10^4$ = index of refraction increment above index of refraction of pure water $\times 10^4$; refraction at 20°C.

n = index of refraction at 20°C relative to air for sodium yellow light.

Δ = freezing point depression, °C.

O = osmolality, Os/kg water.

S = osmosity, molar concentration of NaCl solution having same freezing point or osmotic pressure as given solution, g-mol/l.

η/η_0 = relative viscosity, ratio of the absolute viscosity of a solution at 20°C to the absolute viscosity of water at 20°C.

η/ρ = kinematic viscosity, ratio of absolute viscosity at 20°C (centipoise, cP) to relative density, (centistokes, cS).

ϕ = fluidity, reciprocal of absolute viscosity at 20°C, (poise^{-1}), rhe.

γ = specific conductance (electrical) at 20°C, mmho/cm.

T = condosity, molar concentration of NaCl solution having same specific conductance (electrical) at 20°C as given solution, g-mol/l.

Some related measures are:

Specific gravity, $D_{20}^{20} = D_4^{20}/.99823$

Relative density, $D_4^{20} = (C_s + C_w)/1000$

Molality, g-mol/kg water = $1000 \times M/C_w$

Osmolality, $O = \Delta/1.86$

Absolute viscosity (cP) = kinematic viscosity (cS) $\times D_4^{20}$

Specific viscosity = $\eta/\eta_0 - 1$

Specific refraction = $(n - 1)/\rho$

Specific refractive increment = $1000(n - n_0)/C_w$

Molar conductance (ohm^{-1} cm^2 g-mol^{-1}), $\Lambda_M = \lambda/M$

Relative salinity, $\Sigma = T/S$

Ratios such as S/M, T/M, r/A%, $(D_{20}^{20} - 1)/S$, etc.

G water displaced/g solute = $(C_0 - C_w)/C_s$

Ml water displaced/g solute = $(C_0 - C_w)/(.99823 \times C_s)$

G water displaced/mol solute = $(C_0 - C_w)/M$

Ml water displaced/mol solute = $(C_0 - C_w)/(.99823 \times M)$

Mols water displaced/mol solute = $(C_0 - C_w)/(18.015 \times M)$

Concentration of solute relative to water, g/kg water = $1000 \times C_s/C_w$

Relative specific refractivity = contribution of unit weight of solute relative to unit weight of water to the imaginary concentration of water with same refractive index as solution, equivalent concentration of water (ECW) = $3694.1788 \times n - 300 \times n^2 - 3394.1788$. The refractive index for this equation is relative to a vacuum whereas the tabulated values are relative to air. The above equation for the equivalent concentration of water provides better constancy of relative specific refractivity than Lorentz and Lorenz relation, ECW = $4848.3431 - 14545.029/(n^2 + 2)$.

Tables are based upon *Handbook of Chemistry and Physics,* 51st Edition (1970); G. F. Hewitt, Tables of the resistivity of aqueous chloride solutions, Chem. Eng. Div., U.K.A.E.A. Res. Group, Harwell, Gr. Brit. Oct. 1960, HL 60/5450 (S.C. 2), AERE-R 3497; A. V. Wolf, *Aqueous Solutions and Body Fluids,* Hoeber, 1966; and new data.

LIST OF TABLES

1 ACETIC ACID, CH₃COOH

MOLECULAR WEIGHT = 60.05
RELATIVE SPECIFIC REFRACTIVITY = 1.065

0.00 % by wt. data are the same for all compounds.
For Values of 0.00 wt. % solutions see Table 1, Acetic Acid.

A % by wt.	ρ D_4^{20}	D_{20}^{20}	C_s g/l	M g-mol/l	C_w g/l	$(C_o - C_w)$ g/l	$(n - n_o)$ × 10⁴	n	Δ °C	O Os/kg	S g-mol/l	η/η_o	η/ρ cS	ϕ rhe	γ mmho/cm	T g-mol/l
0.00	0.9982	1.0000	0.0	0.000	998.2	0.0	0	1.3330	0.000	0.000	0.000	1.000	1.004	99.80	0.0	0.000
0.50	0.9989	1.0007	5.0	0.083	993.9	4.3	4	1.3334	0.159	0.086	0.045	1.010	1.013	98.81	0.3	0.003
1.00	0.9996	1.0014	10.0	0.166	989.6	8.6	7	1.3337	0.317	0.170	0.091	1.020	1.022	97.84	0.6	0.006
1.50	1.0003	1.0021	15.0	0.250	985.3	12.9	11	1.3341	0.474	0.255	0.137	1.030	1.032	96.90	0.7	0.007
2.00	1.0011	1.0028	20.0	0.333	981.0	17.2	15	1.3345	0.630	0.339	0.183	1.040	1.041	95.96	0.8	0.008
2.50	1.0018	1.0035	25.0	0.417	976.7	21.5	18	1.3348	0.786	0.423	0.229	1.050	1.051	95.02	0.9	0.009
3.00	1.0025	1.0042	30.1	0.501	972.4	25.9	22	1.3352	0.942	0.507	0.275	1.061	1.060	94.07	1.0	0.010
3.50	1.0031	1.0049	35.1	0.585	968.0	30.2	26	1.3355	1.099	0.591	0.321	1.072	1.070	93.14	1.1	0.010
4.00	1.0038	1.0056	40.2	0.669	963.7	34.5	29	1.3359	1.256	0.675	0.367	1.082	1.080	92.24	1.1	0.011
4.50	1.0045	1.0063	45.2	0.753	959.3	38.9	33	1.3363	1.415	0.761	0.414	1.092	1.090	91.36	1.2	0.011
5.00	1.0052	1.0070	50.3	0.837	955.0	43.3	36	1.3366	1.576	0.847	0.461	1.103	1.099	90.50	1.2	0.012
5.50	1.0059	1.0077	55.3	0.921	950.6	47.6	40	1.3370	1.737	0.934	0.508	1.113	1.109	89.66	1.3	0.012
6.00	1.0066	1.0084	60.4	1.006	946.2	52.0	44	1.3373	1.899	1.021	0.555	1.123	1.118	88.87	1.3	0.013
6.50	1.0073	1.0091	65.5	1.090	941.8	56.4	47	1.3377	2.062	1.108	0.602	1.132	1.126	88.14	1.4	0.013
7.00	1.0080	1.0098	70.6	1.175	937.4	60.8	51	1.3381	2.225	1.196	0.650	1.141	1.134	87.46	1.4	0.013
7.50	1.0087	1.0105	75.7	1.260	933.0	65.2	54	1.3384	2.390	1.285	0.697	1.150	1.142	86.78	1.4	0.014
8.00	1.0093	1.0111	80.7	1.345	928.6	69.6	58	1.3388	2.555	1.374	0.745	1.160	1.152	86.03	1.4	0.014
8.50	1.0100	1.0118	85.9	1.430	924.2	74.1	62	1.3391	2.722	1.463	0.792	1.171	1.162	85.20	1.5	0.014
9.00	1.0107	1.0125	91.0	1.515	919.7	78.5	65	1.3395	2.889	1.553	0.840	1.184	1.173	84.31	1.5	0.014
9.50	1.0114	1.0132	96.1	1.600	915.3	82.9	69	1.3399	3.057	1.644	0.888	1.196	1.185	83.43	1.5	0.015
10.00	1.0121	1.0138	101.2	1.685	910.8	87.4	72	1.3402	3.226	1.734	0.935	1.208	1.196	82.62	1.5	0.015
11.00	1.0134	1.0152	111.5	1.856	901.9	96.3	79	1.3409	3.567	1.918	1.031	1.229	1.215	81.19	1.6	0.015
12.00	1.0147	1.0165	121.8	2.028	893.0	105.3	86	1.3416	3.911	2.103	1.127	1.250	1.234	79.84	1.6	0.016
13.00	1.0161	1.0178	132.1	2.200	884.0	114.3	93	1.3423	4.259	2.290	1.223	1.272	1.255	78.43	1.6	0.016
14.00	1.0174	1.0192	142.4	2.372	874.9	123.3	100	1.3430	4.611	2.479	1.320	1.295	1.275	77.07	1.7	0.016
15.00	1.0187	1.0205	152.8	2.545	865.9	132.4	107	1.3437	4.967	2.670	1.415	1.317	1.295	75.79	1.7	0.016
16.00	1.0200	1.0218	163.2	2.718	856.8	141.5	114	1.3444	5.33	2.86	1.511	1.338	1.314	74.59	1.7	0.016
17.00	1.0213	1.0231	173.6	2.891	847.6	150.6	121	1.3451	5.69	3.06	1.607	1.357	1.331	73.54	1.7	0.017
18.00	1.0225	1.0243	184.1	3.065	838.5	159.8	128	1.3458	6.06	3.26	1.703	1.377	1.349	72.48	1.7	0.017
19.00	1.0238	1.0256	194.5	3.239	829.3	169.0	135	1.3465	6.43	3.46	1.798	1.402	1.372	71.18	1.7	0.017
20.00	1.0250	1.0269	205.0	3.414	820.0	178.2	142	1.3472	6.81	3.66	1.894	1.428	1.396	69.89	1.7	0.017
22.00	1.0275	1.0293	226.1	3.764	801.5	196.8	155	1.3485	7.57	4.07	2.084	1.475	1.438	67.66	1.7	0.017
24.00	1.0299	1.0318	247.2	4.116	782.8	215.5	169	1.3498	8.36	4.49	2.273	1.522	1.481	65.57	1.7	0.016
26.00	1.0323	1.0341	268.4	4.470	763.9	234.3	182	1.3512	9.17	4.93	2.462	1.569	1.523	63.61	1.6	0.015
28.00	1.0346	1.0365	289.7	4.824	744.9	253.3	195	1.3525	10.00	5.38	2.650	1.610	1.559	61.99	1.5	0.015
30.00	1.0369	1.0388	311.1	5.180	725.8	272.4	207	1.3537	10.84	5.83	2.835	1.666	1.610	59.90	1.4	0.014
32.00	1.0391	1.0410	332.5	5.537	706.6	291.6	220	1.3550	11.70	6.29	3.017	1.712	1.651	58.29	1.4	0.013
34.00	1.0413	1.0431	354.0	5.896	687.3	311.0	232	1.3562	12.55	6.75	3.192	1.758	1.692	56.77	1.3	0.012
36.00	1.0434	1.0452	375.6	6.255	667.8	330.5	245	1.3574	13.38	7.20	3.359	1.808	1.736	55.20	1.2	0.011
38.00	1.0454	1.0473	397.3	6.615	648.2	350.1	257	1.3586				1.848	1.771	54.00	1.1	0.011
40.00	1.0474	1.0492	419.0	6.977	628.4	369.8	268	1.3598				1.908	1.825	52.31	1.1	0.010
42.00	1.0493	1.0511	440.7	7.339	608.6	389.7	280	1.3610				1.956	1.868	51.02	1.0	0.010
44.00	1.0510	1.0529	462.5	7.701	588.6	409.7	291	1.3621				2.003	1.910	49.83	1.0	0.009
46.00	1.0528	1.0547	484.3	8.065	568.5	429.7	302	1.3632				2.048	1.949	48.73	0.9	0.009
48.00	1.0545	1.0564	506.2	8.429	548.4	449.9	312	1.3642				2.106	2.001	47.39	0.8	0.008
50.00	1.0562	1.0581	528.1	8.794	528.1	470.1	323	1.3653				2.154	2.043	46.33	0.8	0.007
52.00	1.0577	1.0596	550.0	9.159	507.7	490.5	333	1.3663				2.208	2.092	45.20	0.7	0.007
54.00	1.0592	1.0611	572.0	9.525	487.2	511.0	343	1.3673				2.260	2.138	44.16	0.7	0.006
56.00	1.0605	1.0624	593.9	9.890	466.6	531.6	352	1.3682				2.303	2.176	43.33	0.5	0.005
58.00	1.0618	1.0636	615.8	10.255	445.9	552.3	361	1.3691				2.355	2.222	42.38	0.3	0.003
60.00	1.0629	1.0648	637.7	10.620	425.2	573.1	370	1.3700				2.404	2.266	41.51	0.4	0.004
62.00	1.0640	1.0659	659.7	10.985	404.3	593.9	378	1.3708				2.451	2.308	40.72		
64.00	1.0650	1.0668	681.6	11.350	383.4	614.8	386	1.3716				2.497	2.349	39.97		
66.00	1.0659	1.0678	703.5	11.715	362.4	635.8	394	1.3724				2.548	2.395	39.17		
68.00	1.0668	1.0687	725.4	12.080	341.4	656.9	402	1.3732				2.589	2.432	38.55		
70.00	1.0673	1.0692	747.1	12.441	320.2	678.0	409	1.3738				2.624	2.463	38.03		
72.00	1.0676	1.0695	768.7	12.800	298.9	699.3	415	1.3745				2.657	2.494	37.56		
74.00	1.0678	1.0697	790.2	13.158	277.6	720.6	421	1.3751				2.682	2.517	37.21		
76.00	1.0680	1.0699	811.7	13.516	256.3	741.9	427	1.3757				2.709	2.542	36.84		
78.00	1.0681	1.0700	833.1	13.956	235.0	763.2	432	1.3762				2.715	2.547	36.76		
80.00	1.0680	1.0699	854.4	14.227	213.6	784.6	437	1.3767				2.715	2.547	36.76		
82.00	1.0677	1.0696	875.5	14.579	192.2	806.0	441	1.3770				2.691	2.525	37.09		
84.00	1.0673	1.0692	896.5	14.928	170.8	827.4	443	1.3773				2.653	2.491	37.62		
86.00	1.0666	1.0685	917.3	15.275	149.3	848.9	444	1.3774				2.591	2.434	38.52		
88.00	1.0658	1.0677	937.9	15.618	127.9	870.3	444	1.3774				2.506	2.356	39.82		
90.00	1.0644	1.0663	958.0	15.953	106.4	891.8	441	1.3771				2.381	2.241	41.92		
92.00	1.0629	1.0648	977.9	16.284	85.0	913.2	436	1.3766				2.236	2.108	44.63		
94.00	1.0606	1.0625	997.0	16.602	63.6	934.6	429	1.3759				2.032	1.920	49.11		
96.00	1.0578	1.0597	1015.5	16.912	42.3	955.9	418	1.3748				1.809	1.714	55.11		
98.00	1.0538	1.0557	1032.7	17.196	21.1	977.1	404	1.3734				1.532	1.457	65.14		
100.00	1.0477	1.0496	1047.7	17.446	0.0	998.2	386	1.3716				1.221	1.168	81.73		

2 ACETONE, CH₃COCH₃

MOLECULAR WEIGHT = 58.05
RELATIVE SPECIFIC REFRACTIVITY = 1.349

0.00 % by wt. data are the same for all compounds.
For Values of 0.00 wt. % solutions see Table 1, Acetic Acid.

A % by wt.	ρ D_4^{20}	D_{20}^{20}	C_s g/l	M g-mol/l	C_w g/l	$(C_o - C_w)$ g/l	$(n - n_o)$ × 10⁴	n	Δ °C	O Os/kg	S g-mol/l	η/η_o	η/ρ cS	ϕ rhe	γ mmho/cm	T g-mol/l
0.50	0.9975	0.9993	5.0	0.086	992.5	5.7	4	1.3334	0.160	0.086	0.045	1.011	1.015	98.73		
1.00	0.9968	0.9985	10.0	0.172	986.8	11.4	7	1.3337	0.321	0.173	0.092	1.022	1.027	97.65		
1.50	0.9961	0.9978	14.9	0.257	981.1	17.1	11	1.3341	0.483	0.260	0.140	1.033	1.039	96.58		

2 ACETONE, CH₃COCH₃—(Continued)

A% by wt.	ρ D_4^{20}	D_{20}^{20}	C_s g/l	M g-mol/l	C_w g/l	$(C_o - C_w)$ g/l	$(n - n_o)$ $\times 10^4$	n	Δ °C	O Os/kg	S g-mol/l	η/η_o	η/ρ cS	ϕ rhe	γ mmho/cm	T g-mol/l
2.00	0.9954	0.9971	19.9	0.343	975.5	22.8	15	1.3344	0.645	0.347	0.187	1.045	1.052	95.50		
2.50	0.9947	0.9964	24.9	0.428	969.8	28.4	18	1.3348	0.807	0.434	0.235	1.057	1.065	94.39		
3.00	0.9940	0.9957	29.8	0.514	964.1	34.1	22	1.3352	0.970	0.521	0.283	1.070	1.079	93.25		
3.50	0.9933	0.9950	34.8	0.599	958.5	39.7	25	1.3355	1.133	0.609	0.331	1.083	1.093	92.11		
4.00	0.9926	0.9943	39.7	0.684	952.9	45.4	29	1.3359	1.296	0.697	0.379	1.097	1.107	90.99		
4.50	0.9919	0.9937	44.6	0.769	947.3	51.0	33	1.3363	1.460	0.785	0.427	1.110	1.121	89.90		
5.00	0.9912	0.9930	49.6	0.854	941.7	56.6	36	1.3366	1.625	0.874	0.475	1.123	1.135	88.87		
5.50	0.9906	0.9923	54.5	0.939	936.1	62.1	40	1.3370	1.790	0.962	0.523	1.136	1.149	87.89		
6.00	0.9899	0.9917	59.4	1.023	930.5	67.7	44	1.3373	1.955	1.051	0.571	1.148	1.162	86.94		
6.50	0.9893	0.9910	64.3	1.108	925.0	73.3	47	1.3377	2.120	1.140	0.619	1.160	1.175	86.03		
7.00	0.9886	0.9904	69.2	1.192	919.4	78.8	51	1.3381	2.286	1.229	0.667	1.172	1.188	85.14		
7.50	0.9880	0.9897	74.1	1.276	913.9	84.4	54	1.3384	2.452	1.318	0.715	1.184	1.201	84.28		
8.00	0.9874	0.9891	79.0	1.361	908.4	89.9	58	1.3388	2.619	1.408	0.763	1.196	1.214	83.44		
8.50	0.9867	0.9885	83.9	1.445	902.9	95.4	62	1.3392	2.785	1.498	0.811	1.208	1.226	82.64		
9.00	0.9861	0.9879	88.8	1.529	897.4	100.9	65	1.3395	2.952	1.587	0.858	1.219	1.239	81.85		
9.50	0.9855	0.9873	93.6	1.613	891.9	106.3	69	1.3399	3.119	1.677	0.905	1.231	1.251	81.09		
10.00	0.9849	0.9867	98.5	1.697	886.4	111.8	73	1.3402	3.287	1.767	0.953	1.242	1.264	80.35		

3 AMMONIA, NH₃, AND AMMONIUM HYDROXIDE, NH₄OH

MOLECULAR WEIGHT, NH₃ = 17.03   FORMULA WEIGHT, NH₄OH = 35.05

RELATIVE SPECIFIC REFRACTIVITY = 1.582

0.00 % by wt. data are the same for all compounds.
For Values of 0.00 wt. % solutions see Table 1, Acetic Acid.

NH₃ % by wt.	NH₄OH % by wt.	ρ D_4^{20}	D_{20}^{20}	C_s (NH₃) g/l	M g-mol/l	C_w g/l	$(C_o - C_w)$ g/l	$(n - n_o)$ $\times 10^4$	n	Δ °C	O Os/kg	S g-mol/l	η/η_o	η/ρ cS	ϕ rhe	γ mmho/cm	T g-mol/l
0.50	1.03	0.9960	0.9978	5.0	0.292	991.0	7.2	2	1.3332	0.550	0.296	0.160	1.007	1.013	99.14	0.5	0.005
1.00	2.06	0.9938	0.9956	9.9	0.584	983.9	14.3	5	1.3335	1.135	0.610	0.332	1.013	1.022	98.48	0.7	0.007
1.50	3.09	0.9917	0.9934	14.9	0.873	976.8	21.5	7	1.3337	1.725	0.927	0.504	1.020	1.031	97.82	0.9	0.008
2.00	4.12	0.9895	0.9913	19.8	1.162	969.7	28.5	9	1.3339	2.319	1.247	0.677	1.027	1.040	97.17	1.0	0.009
2.50	5.15	0.9874	0.9891	24.7	1.449	962.7	35.5	12	1.3342	2.921	1.570	0.849	1.034	1.049	96.52	1.0	0.010
3.00	6.17	0.9853	0.9870	29.6	1.736	955.7	42.5	14	1.3344	3.531	1.898	1.021	1.041	1.059	95.88	1.0	0.011
3.50	7.20	0.9832	0.9849	34.4	2.021	948.8	49.5	17	1.3347	4.150	2.231	1.193	1.048	1.068	95.24	1.1	0.011
4.00	8.23	0.9811	0.9828	39.2	2.304	941.8	56.4	19	1.3349	4.781	2.570	1.365	1.055	1.077	94.60	1.1	0.011
4.50	9.26	0.9790	0.9808	44.1	2.587	935.0	63.3	22	1.3352	5.42	2.92	1.537	1.062	1.087	93.98	1.1	0.011
5.00	10.29	0.9770	0.9787	48.8	2.868	928.1	70.1	24	1.3354	6.08	3.27	1.708	1.069	1.096	93.36	1.1	0.011
5.50	11.32	0.9750	0.9767	53.6	3.149	921.3	76.9	27	1.3357	6.75	3.63	1.879	1.076	1.106	92.75	1.1	0.011
6.00	12.35	0.9730	0.9747	58.4	3.428	914.6	83.6	30	1.3359	7.43	4.00	2.049	1.083	1.115	92.15	1.1	0.011
6.50	13.38	0.9710	0.9727	63.1	3.706	907.9	90.4	32	1.3362	8.13	4.37	2.219	1.090	1.125	91.55	1.1	0.011
7.00	14.41	0.9690	0.9707	67.8	3.983	901.2	97.1	35	1.3365	8.85	4.76	2.388	1.097	1.134	90.96	1.1	0.011
7.50	15.44	0.9671	0.9688	72.5	4.259	894.5	103.7	38	1.3367	9.58	5.15	2.557	1.104	1.144	90.38	1.1	0.011
8.00	16.47	0.9651	0.9668	77.2	4.534	887.9	110.3	40	1.3370	10.34	5.56	2.725	1.111	1.154	89.81	1.1	0.011
8.50	17.49	0.9632	0.9649	81.9	4.807	881.3	116.9	43	1.3373	11.11	5.97	2.892	1.118	1.163	89.25	1.1	0.010
9.00	18.52	0.9613	0.9630	86.5	5.080	874.8	123.5	46	1.3376	11.90	6.40	3.059	1.125	1.173	88.70	1.1	0.010
9.50	19.55	0.9594	0.9611	91.1	5.352	868.3	130.0	48	1.3378	12.71	6.84	3.225	1.132	1.182	88.16	1.0	0.010
10.00	20.58	0.9575	0.9592	95.8	5.623	861.8	136.5	51	1.3381	13.55	7.28	3.391	1.139	1.192	87.63	1.0	0.010
11.00	22.64	0.9538	0.9555	104.9	6.161	848.9	149.3	57	1.3387	15.29	8.22	3.719	1.153	1.211	86.57	0.9	0.009
12.00	24.70	0.9502	0.9519	114.0	6.695	836.2	162.1	63	1.3393	17.13	9.21	4.044	1.167	1.230	85.53	0.9	0.009
13.00	26.76	0.9466	0.9483	123.1	7.226	823.5	174.7	68	1.3398	19.07	10.25	4.365	1.180	1.250	84.55	0.8	0.008
14.00	28.81	0.9431	0.9447	132.0	7.753	811.0	187.2	74	1.3404	21.13	11.36		1.193	1.268	83.64	0.8	0.007
15.00	30.87	0.9396	0.9412	140.9	8.276	798.6	199.6	80	1.3410	23.32	12.54		1.205	1.285	82.84	0.7	0.007
16.00	32.93	0.9361	0.9378	149.8	8.795	786.4	211.9	86	1.3416	25.63	13.78		1.216	1.301	82.01	0.7	0.006
17.00	34.99	0.9327	0.9344	158.6	9.311	774.2	224.1	92	1.3422	28.09	15.10		1.226	1.317	81.43	0.6	0.006
18.00	37.05	0.9294	0.9310	167.3	9.823	762.1	236.1	98	1.3428	30.70	16.51		1.235	1.331	80.82	0.6	0.005
19.00	39.10	0.9261	0.9277	176.0	10.332	750.1	248.1	104	1.3434	33.47	18.00		1.243	1.345	80.26	0.5	0.005
20.00	41.16	0.9228	0.9245	184.6	10.838	738.3	260.0	110	1.3440	36.42	19.58		1.251	1.359	79.75	0.5	0.005
22.00	45.28	0.9164	0.9181	201.6	11.839	714.8	283.4	123	1.3453	43.36	23.31		1.265	1.383	78.88	0.4	0.004
24.00	49.40	0.9102	0.9118	218.4	12.827	691.7	306.5	135	1.3465	51.38	27.62		1.277	1.405	78.18	0.4	0.004
26.00	53.51	0.9040	0.9056	235.0	13.802	669.0	329.3	148	1.3477	60.77	32.67		1.285	1.425	77.64	0.4	0.004
28.00	57.63	0.8980	0.8996	251.4	14.764	646.5	351.7	160	1.3490	71.66	38.53						
30.00	61.74	0.8920	0.8936	267.6	15.713	624.4	373.8	172	1.3502	84.06	45.19						

4 AMMONIUM CHLORIDE, NH₄Cl

MOLECULAR WEIGHT = 53.50

RELATIVE SPECIFIC REFRACTIVITY = 1.241

0.00 % by wt. data are the same for all compounds.
For Values of 0.00 wt. % solutions see Table 1, Acetic Acid.

A% by wt.	ρ D_4^{20}	D_{20}^{20}	C_s g/l	M g-mol/l	C_w g/l	$(C_o - C_w)$ g/l	$(n - n_o)$ $\times 10^4$	n	Δ °C	O Os/kg	S g-mol/l	η/η_o	η/ρ cS	ϕ rhe	γ mmho/cm	T g-mol/l
0.50	0.9998	1.0016	5.0	0.093	994.8	3.4	10	1.3340	0.322	0.173	0.092	0.997	0.999	100.13	10.5	0.110
1.00	1.0014	1.0032	10.0	0.187	991.4	6.9	19	1.3349	0.637	0.343	0.185	0.994	0.995	100.40	20.4	0.225
1.50	1.0030	1.0047	15.0	0.281	987.9	10.3	29	1.3359	0.953	0.512	0.278	0.992	0.991	100.62	30.3	0.347
2.00	1.0045	1.0063	20.1	0.376	984.4	13.8	39	1.3369	1.270	0.683	0.371	0.990	0.988	100.81	40.3	0.474
2.50	1.0061	1.0079	25.2	0.470	980.9	17.3	48	1.3378	1.590	0.855	0.465	0.988	0.984	101.00	49.9	0.601
3.00	1.0076	1.0094	30.2	0.565	977.4	20.8	58	1.3388	1.913	1.029	0.559	0.986	0.981	101.18	59.2	0.728
3.50	1.0092	1.0110	35.3	0.660	973.8	24.4	68	1.3397	2.240	1.205	0.654	0.985	0.978	101.35	68.3	0.858
4.00	1.0107	1.0125	40.4	0.756	970.3	28.0	77	1.3407	2.571	1.382	0.749	0.983	0.975	101.52	77.3	0.992
4.50	1.0122	1.0140	45.6	0.851	966.7	31.6	87	1.3417	2.907	1.563	0.845	0.982	0.972	101.68	86.3	1.13
5.00	1.0138	1.0155	50.7	0.947	963.1	35.2	96	1.3426	3.246	1.745	0.941	0.980	0.969	101.84	95.3	1.27
5.50	1.0153	1.0171	55.8	1.044	959.4	38.8	106	1.3436	3.591	1.931	1.038	0.979	0.966	101.99	104.	1.42
6.00	1.0168	1.0186	61.0	1.140	955.8	42.5	115	1.3445	3.941	2.119	1.135	0.977	0.963	102.15	113.	1.58
6.50	1.0183	1.0201	66.2	1.237	952.1	46.1	125	1.3455	4.296	2.310	1.233	0.976	0.960	102.30	122.	1.74

4 AMMONIUM CHLORIDE, NH₄Cl—(Continued)

A% by wt.	ρ D_4^{20}	D_{20}^{20}	C_s g/l	M g-mol/l	C_w g/l	$(C_o - C_w)$ g/l	$(n - n_o)$ × 10⁴	n	Δ °C	O Os/kg	S g-mol/l	η/η_o	η/ρ cS	ϕ rhe	γ mmho/cm	T g-mol/l
7.00	1.0198	1.0216	71.4	1.334	948.4	49.8	135	1.3464	4.657	2.504	1.332	0.974	0.957	102.44	131.	1.91
7.50	1.0213	1.0231	76.6	1.432	944.7	53.6	144	1.3474	5.02	2.70	1.431	0.973	0.955	102.58	139.	2.09
8.00	1.0227	1.0246	81.8	1.529	940.9	57.3	154	1.3483	5.40	2.90	1.530	0.972	0.952	102.71	147.	2.27
8.50	1.0242	1.0260	87.1	1.627	937.2	61.1	163	1.3493	5.77	3.10	1.629	0.971	0.950	102.83	156.	2.46
9.00	1.0257	1.0275	92.3	1.725	933.4	64.9	172	1.3502	6.16	3.31	1.728	0.970	0.947	102.93	164.	2.66
9.50	1.0272	1.0290	97.6	1.824	929.6	68.7	182	1.3512	6.55	3.52	1.828	0.969	0.945	103.02	172.	2.86
10.00	1.0286	1.0304	102.9	1.923	925.8	72.5	191	1.3521	6.95	3.73	1.928	0.968	0.943	103.10	180.	3.07
11.00	1.0315	1.0333	113.5	2.121	918.1	80.2	210	1.3540	7.76	4.17	2.129	0.967	0.939	103.20	200.	3.71
12.00	1.0344	1.0362	124.1	2.320	910.3	88.0	229	1.3559	8.60	4.62	2.330	0.967	0.936	103.23	220.	4.84
13.00	1.0373	1.0391	134.8	2.520	902.4	95.8	248	1.3578	9.47	5.09	2.531	0.967	0.934	103.22		
14.00	1.0401	1.0419	145.6	2.722	894.5	103.8	267	1.3596				0.967	0.932	103.17		
15.00	1.0429	1.0447	156.4	2.924	886.5	111.8	285	1.3615				0.968	0.930	103.10		
16.00	1.0457	1.0475	167.3	3.127	878.4	119.8	304	1.3634				0.969	0.928	103.01		
17.00	1.0485	1.0503	178.2	3.332	870.2	128.0	322	1.3652				0.970	0.927	102.90		
18.00	1.0512	1.0531	189.2	3.537	862.0	136.2	341	1.3671				0.971	0.926	102.75		
19.00	1.0540	1.0558	200.3	3.743	853.7	144.5	360	1.3689				0.973	0.925	102.54		
20.00	1.0567	1.0586	211.3	3.950	845.3	152.9	378	1.3708				0.976	0.925	102.25		
22.00	1.0621	1.0640	233.7	4.367	828.4	169.8	415	1.3745				0.984	0.928	101.46		
24.00	1.0674	1.0693	256.2	4.788	811.2	187.0	452	1.3782				0.994	0.933	100.40		

5 AMMONIUM SULFATE, (NH₄)₂SO₄

MOLECULAR WEIGHT = 132.14
RELATIVE SPECIFIC REFRACTIVITY = 0.886

0.00 % by wt. data are the same for all compounds.
For Values of 0.00 wt. % solutions see Table 1, Acetic Acid.

A% by wt.	ρ D_4^{20}	D_{20}^{20}	C_s g/l	M g-mol/l	C_w g/l	$(C_o - C_w)$ g/l	$(n - n_o)$ × 10⁴	n	Δ °C	O Os/kg	S g-mol/l	η/η_o	η/ρ cS	ϕ rhe	γ mmho/cm	T g-mol/l
0.50	1.0012	1.0030	5.0	0.038	996.2	2.1	8	1.3338	0.173	0.093	0.049	1.006	1.007	99.22	7.4	0.077
1.00	1.0042	1.0059	10.0	0.076	994.1	4.1	16	1.3346	0.331	0.178	0.095	1.012	1.010	98.62	14.2	0.151
2.00	1.0101	1.0119	20.2	0.153	989.9	8.3	33	1.3363	0.631	0.339	0.183	1.025	1.017	97.37	25.7	0.290
3.00	1.0160	1.0178	30.5	0.231	985.6	12.7	49	1.3379	0.921	0.495	0.269	1.039	1.025	96.03	36.7	0.428
4.00	1.0220	1.0238	40.9	0.309	981.1	17.1	65	1.3395	1.208	0.649	0.353	1.055	1.034	94.63	47.2	0.565
5.00	1.0279	1.0297	51.4	0.389	976.5	21.7	82	1.3411	1.489	0.800	0.435	1.071	1.044	93.18	57.4	0.704
6.00	1.0338	1.0356	62.0	0.469	971.8	26.5	98	1.3428	1.768	0.951	0.517	1.088	1.055	91.71	67.4	0.845
7.00	1.0397	1.0416	72.8	0.551	966.9	31.3	114	1.3444	2.047	1.101	0.598	1.106	1.066	90.21	77.0	0.987
8.00	1.0456	1.0475	83.6	0.633	962.0	36.3	130	1.3460	2.327	1.251	0.679	1.125	1.079	88.67	86.3	1.13
9.00	1.0515	1.0534	94.6	0.716	956.9	41.4	146	1.3476	2.608	1.402	0.760	1.145	1.091	87.13	95.5	1.28
10.00	1.0574	1.0593	105.7	0.800	951.6	46.6	162	1.3492	2.892	1.555	0.841	1.166	1.105	85.59	105.	1.43
12.00	1.0691	1.0710	128.3	0.971	940.8	57.4	193	1.3523	3.473	1.867	1.005	1.208	1.133	82.58	122.	1.75
14.00	1.0808	1.0827	151.3	1.145	929.5	68.8	225	1.3555	4.073	2.190	1.171	1.253	1.162	79.63	139.	2.09
16.00	1.0924	1.0943	174.8	1.323	917.6	80.6	256	1.3586	4.689	2.521	1.341	1.302	1.194	76.66	156.	2.44
18.00	1.1039	1.1059	198.7	1.504	905.2	93.0	287	1.3616				1.356	1.231	73.59	171.	2.82
20.00	1.1154	1.1174	223.1	1.688	892.3	105.9	317	1.3647				1.418	1.274	70.38	185.	3.21
22.00	1.1269	1.1289	247.9	1.876	879.0	119.3	347	1.3677				1.487	1.323	67.10	198.	3.67
24.00	1.1383	1.1403	273.2	2.067	865.1	133.2	377	1.3707				1.563	1.376	63.84	210.	4.18
26.00	1.1496	1.1516	298.9	2.262	850.7	147.5	407	1.3737				1.647	1.435	60.60	220.	4.84
28.00	1.1609	1.1629	325.0	2.460	835.8	162.4	436	1.3766				1.740	1.502	57.37		
30.00	1.1721	1.1742	351.6	2.661	820.5	177.7	465	1.3795				1.843	1.576	54.15		
32.00	1.1833	1.1854	378.7	2.866	804.7	193.6	494	1.3824				1.957	1.657	50.99		
34.00	1.1945	1.1966	406.1	3.073	788.3	209.9	523	1.3853				2.082	1.747	47.93		
36.00	1.2056	1.2077	434.0	3.284	771.6	226.7	551	1.3881				2.218	1.844	44.99		
38.00	1.2166	1.2188	462.3	3.499	754.3	243.9	580	1.3909				2.366	1.948	42.19		
40.00	1.2277	1.2298	491.1	3.716	736.6	261.6	608	1.3938				2.525	2.061	39.52		

6 BARIUM CHLORIDE, BaCl₂ · 2H₂O

MOLECULAR WEIGHT = 208.27   FORMULA WEIGHT, HYDRATE = 244.31
RELATIVE SPECIFIC REFRACTIVITY = 0.552

0.00 % by wt. data are the same for all compounds.
For Values of 0.00 wt. % solutions see Table 1, Acetic Acid.

A% by wt.	H% by wt.	ρ D_4^{20}	D_{20}^{20}	C_s g/l	M g-mol/l	C_w g/l	$(C_o - C_w)$ g/l	$(n - n_o)$ × 10⁴	n	Δ °C	O Os/kg	S g-mol/l	η/η_o	η/ρ cS	ϕ rhe	γ mmho/cm	T g-mol/l
0.50	0.59	1.0026	1.0044	5.0	0.024	997.6	0.6	7	1.3337	0.119	0.064	0.033	1.007	1.007	99.06	4.7	0.047
1.00	1.17	1.0070	1.0088	10.1	0.048	996.9	1.3	15	1.3345	0.233	0.125	0.066	1.014	1.009	98.42	9.1	0.094
2.00	2.35	1.0159	1.0177	20.3	0.098	995.6	2.6	30	1.3360	0.461	0.248	0.133	1.024	1.010	97.46	17.4	0.189
3.00	3.52	1.0249	1.0267	30.7	0.148	994.2	4.0	45	1.3375	0.691	0.372	0.201	1.035	1.012	96.41	25.2	0.284
4.00	4.69	1.0341	1.0359	41.4	0.199	992.7	5.5	61	1.3391	0.928	0.499	0.271	1.047	1.015	95.28	32.8	0.379
5.00	5.87	1.0434	1.0452	52.2	0.250	991.2	7.0	76	1.3406	1.177	0.633	0.344	1.060	1.018	94.15	40.4	0.476
6.00	7.04	1.0528	1.0547	63.2	0.303	989.6	8.6	92	1.3422	1.435	0.772	0.420	1.073	1.021	93.05	47.9	0.575
7.00	8.21	1.0624	1.0643	74.4	0.357	988.0	10.2	108	1.3438	1.704	0.916	0.498	1.085	1.024	91.95	55.3	0.675
8.00	9.38	1.0721	1.0740	85.8	0.412	986.3	11.9	124	1.3454	1.984	1.067	0.580	1.099	1.027	90.85	62.6	0.777
9.00	10.56	1.0820	1.0839	97.4	0.468	984.6	13.6	140	1.3470	2.274	1.222	0.664	1.112	1.030	89.72	69.8	0.880
10.00	11.73	1.0921	1.0940	109.2	0.524	982.9	15.4	157	1.3487	2.575	1.385	0.751	1.127	1.034	88.55	76.7	0.983
12.00	14.08	1.1128	1.1148	133.5	0.641	979.3	19.0	191	1.3520	3.218	1.730	0.933	1.159	1.043	86.14	90.1	1.19
14.00	16.42	1.1342	1.1362	158.8	0.762	975.4	22.8	225	1.3555	3.921	2.108	1.129	1.193	1.054	83.63	103.0	1.40
16.00	18.77	1.1564	1.1584	185.0	0.888	971.4	26.9	261	1.3591	4.689	2.521	1.341	1.232	1.067	81.03	115.0	1.61
18.00	21.11	1.1793	1.1814	212.3	1.019	967.0	31.2	297	1.3627				1.274	1.083	78.32	126.0	1.82
20.00	23.46	1.2031	1.2052	240.6	1.155	962.5	35.8	334	1.3664				1.322	1.101	75.49	137.0	2.04
22.00	25.81	1.2277	1.2299	270.1	1.297	957.6	40.6	373	1.3703				1.375	1.122	72.57	147.0	2.26
24.00	28.15	1.2531	1.2553	300.7	1.444	952.4	45.9	411	1.3741				1.434	1.147	69.57	157.0	2.48
26.00	30.50	1.2793	1.2816	332.6	1.597	946.7	51.6	451	1.3781				1.500	1.175	66.53	166.0	2.70

7 CADMIUM CHLORIDE, CdCl₂

MOLECULAR WEIGHT = 183.32

A% by wt.	ρ D_4^{20}	D_{20}^{20}	C_s g/l	M g-mol/l	C_w g/l	$(C_0 - C_w)$ g/l	$(n - n_0)$ $\times 10^4$	n	Δ °C	O Os/kg	S g-mol/l	η/η_0	η/ρ cS	ϕ rhe	γ mmho/cm	T g-mol/l
1.00	1.0062	1.0080	10.1	0.055	996.1	2.1	16.	1.3346	0.186	0.100	0.053	1.012	1.008	98.60	5.3	0.053
2.00	1.0148	1.0166	20.3	0.111	994.5	3.7	31.	1.3361	0.368	0.198	0.106	1.028	1.015	97.09	9.0	0.093
3.00	1.0237	1.0255	30.7	0.168	993.0	5.2	47.	1.3377	0.555	0.299	0.161	1.044	1.022	95.59	11.8	0.124
4.00	1.0325	1.0344	41.3	0.225	991.2	7.0	62.	1.3392	0.715	0.384	0.208	1.059	1.028	94.21	14.1	0.150
5.00	1.0415	1.0434	52.1	0.284	989.4	8.8	78.	1.3408	0.878	0.472	0.256	1.076	1.035	92.77	16.0	0.172
6.00	1.0508	1.0527	63.0	0.344	987.8	10.4	94.	1.3424	1.035	0.557	0.302	1.092	1.041	91.42	17.5	0.190
7.00	1.0600	1.0619	74.2	0.405	985.8	12.4	110.	1.3440	1.191	0.640	0.348	1.109	1.048	90.02	18.9	0.207
8.00	1.0692	1.0711	85.5	0.467	983.7	14.5	127.	1.3457	1.351	0.726	0.395	1.125	1.054	88.74	20.2	0.222
9.00	1.0794	1.0813	97.1	0.530	982.3	15.9	143.	1.3473	1.491	0.802	0.436	1.146	1.064	87.08	21.2	0.235
10.00	1.0897	1.0917	109.0	0.594	980.7	17.5	159.	1.3489	1.634	0.878	0.478	1.166	1.072	85.60	22.1	0.246
12.00	1.1103	1.1123	133.2	0.727	977.1	21.1	193.	1.3523	1.936	1.041	0.566	1.208	1.090	82.63	23.7	0.265
14.00	1.1308	1.1328	158.3	0.864	972.5	25.7	228.	1.3558	2.236	1.203	0.653	1.264	1.120	78.96	24.7	0.278
16.00	1.1531	1.1552	184.5	1.006	968.6	29.6	264.	1.3594	2.564	1.378	0.747	1.322	1.149	75.48	25.5	0.287
18.00	1.1749	1.1770	211.5	1.154	963.4	34.8	301.	1.3631	2.889	1.553	0.840	1.386	1.182	72.01	25.9	0.293
20.00	1.1988	1.2010	239.8	1.308	959.0	39.2	338.	1.3668	3.246	1.745	0.941	1.455	1.216	68.60	26.3	0.297
24.00	1.2476	1.2498	299.4	1.633	948.2	50.0	420.	1.3750	3.984	2.142	1.147	1.596	1.282	62.52	25.8	0.291
28.00	1.3003	1.3026	364.1	1.986	936.2	62.0	506.	1.3836	4.750	2.554	1.357	1.832	1.412	54.47	24.5	0.275
32.00	1.3558	1.3582	433.8	2.367	922.0	76.2	597.	1.3927				2.135	1.578	46.74	22.5	0.251
36.00	1.4178	1.4204	510.4	2.784	907.4	90.8	696.	1.4026				2.556	1.806	39.05	20.2	0.222
40.00	1.4843	1.4870	593.7	3.239	890.6	107.6	803.	1.4133				3.259	2.200	30.62	17.2	0.187
44.00	1.5563	1.5591	684.8	3.735	871.5	126.7	918.	1.4248				4.155	2.675	24.02	14.3	0.152
48.00	1.6345	1.6374	784.5	4.280	850.0	148.2	1044.	1.4374				5.740	3.519	17.39	11.3	0.119
52.00	1.7206	1.7237	894.7	4.881	825.9	172.3	1180.	1.4510				8.811	5.131	11.33	8.4	0.087
56.00	1.8131	1.8164	1015.4	5.539	797.7	200.5	1326.	1.4656				14.67	8.109	6.802	5.9	0.060

8 CADMIUM SULFATE, CdSO₄

MOLECULAR WEIGHT = 208.46

A% by wt.	ρ D_4^{20}	D_{20}^{20}	C_s g/l	M g-mol/l	C_w g/l	$(C_0 - C_w)$ g/l	$(n - n_0)$ $\times 10^4$	n	Δ °C	O Os/kg	S g-mol/l	η/η_0	η/ρ cS	ϕ rhe	γ mmho/cm	T g-mol/l
1.00	1.0078	1.0096	10.1	0.048	997.7	0.5	14.	1.3344	0.135	0.053	0.028	1.029	1.023	97.00	4.2	0.042
2.00	1.0175	1.0193	20.3	0.098	997.2	1.0	28.	1.3358	0.194	0.104	0.055	1.059	1.043	94.23	7.4	0.075
3.00	1.0271	1.0290	30.8	0.148	996.3	1.9	42.	1.3372	0.290	0.156	0.083	1.089	1.062	91.67	10.2	0.105
4.00	1.0375	1.0394	41.5	0.199	996.0	2.2	56.	1.3386	0.382	0.205	0.110	1.125	1.086	88.75	12.6	0.133
5.00	1.0478	1.0497	52.4	0.251	995.4	2.8	69.	1.3399	0.477	0.256	0.138	1.162	1.111	85.90	14.9	0.160
6.00	1.0579	1.0598	63.5	0.304	994.4	3.8	84.	1.3414	0.569	0.306	0.165	1.197	1.134	83.36	17.1	0.186
7.00	1.0684	1.0703	74.8	0.359	993.6	4.6	98.	1.3428	0.657	0.354	0.191	1.238	1.161	80.62	20.1	0.211
8.00	1.0789	1.0808	86.3	0.414	992.6	5.6	114.	1.3444	0.742	0.399	0.216	1.280	1.189	77.96	21.2	0.235
9.00	1.0894	1.0914	98.0	0.470	991.4	6.8	129.	1.3459	0.831	0.447	0.242	1.325	1.219	75.30	23.2	0.259
10.00	1.1004	1.1024	110.0	0.528	990.4	7.8	143.	1.3473	0.933	0.502	0.272	1.375	1.252	72.58	25.1	0.282
12.00	1.1233	1.1253	134.8	0.647	988.5	9.7	173.	1.3503	1.137	0.611	0.332	1.480	1.320	67.44	28.7	0.327
14.00	1.1470	1.1491	160.6	0.770	986.4	11.8	203.	1.3533	1.354	0.728	0.396	1.603	1.400	62.27	32.0	0.369
16.00	1.1715	1.1736	187.4	0.899	984.1	14.1	234.	1.3564	1.604	0.862	0.469	1.742	1.490	57.29	35.6	0.405
18.00	1.1967	1.1989	215.4	1.033	981.3	16.9	266.	1.3596	1.854	0.997	0.542	1.909	1.598	52.29	37.5	0.439
20.00	1.2229	1.2251	244.6	1.173	978.3	19.9	299.	1.3629	2.140	1.150	0.625	2.081	1.705	47.96	39.8	0.469
24.00	1.2784	1.2807	306.8	1.472	971.6	26.6	369.	1.3699	2.864	1.540	0.833	2.515	1.971	39.69	43.2	0.513
28.00	1.3385	1.3409	374.8	1.798	963.7	34.5	445.	1.3775	3.959	2.129	1.140	3.150	2.358	31.68	45.2	0.539
32.00	1.3996	1.4021	447.9	2.148	951.7	46.5	520.	1.3850				4.083	2.923	24.44	45.5	0.542
36.00	1.4655	1.4681	527.6	2.531	937.9	60.3	597.	1.3927				5.334	3.647	18.71	44.1	0.524
40.00	1.5456	1.5484	618.2	2.966	927.4	70.8	676.	1.4006				7.381	4.785	13.52	40.3	0.475

9 CALCIUM CHLORIDE, CaCl$_2$ · 2H$_2$O

MOLECULAR WEIGHT = 110.99   FORMULA WEIGHT, HYDRATE = 147.03

RELATIVE SPECIFIC REFRACTIVITY = 0.863

0.00 % by wt. data are the same for all compounds.
For Values of 0.00 wt. % solutions see Table 1, Acetic Acid.

A% by wt.	H% by wt.	ρ D_4^{20}	D_{20}^{20}	C_s g/l	M g-mol/l	C_w g/l	$(C_o - C_w)$ g/l	$(n - n_o) \times 10^4$	n	Δ °C	O Os/kg	S g-mol/l	η/η_o	η/ρ cS	φ rhe	γ mmho/cm	T g-mol/l
0.50	0.66	1.0024	1.0041	5.0	0.045	997.3	0.9	12	1.3342	0.222	0.119	0.063	1.013	1.013	98.47	8.1	0.083
1.00	1.32	1.0065	1.0083	10.1	0.091	996.4	1.8	24	1.3354	0.440	0.237	0.127	1.026	1.021	97.27	15.7	0.169
1.50	1.99	1.0106	1.0124	15.2	0.137	995.5	2.7	36	1.3366	0.661	0.355	0.192	1.037	1.028	96.24	22.7	0.254
2.00	2.65	1.0148	1.0166	20.3	0.183	994.5	3.7	48	1.3378	0.880	0.473	0.257	1.048	1.035	95.23	29.4	0.337
2.50	3.31	1.0190	1.0208	25.5	0.230	993.5	4.7	60	1.3390	1.102	0.593	0.322	1.061	1.043	94.06	36.1	0.421
3.00	3.97	1.0232	1.0250	30.7	0.277	992.5	5.8	72	1.3402	1.330	0.715	0.389	1.076	1.053	92.79	42.6	0.504
3.50	4.64	1.0274	1.0292	36.0	0.324	991.4	6.8	84	1.3414	1.567	0.843	0.458	1.091	1.064	91.45	48.9	0.588
4.00	5.30	1.0316	1.0334	41.3	0.372	990.3	7.9	96	1.3426	1.815	0.976	0.531	1.108	1.076	90.09	55.1	0.672
4.50	5.96	1.0358	1.0377	46.6	0.420	989.2	9.0	109	1.3438	2.074	1.115	0.606	1.125	1.088	88.75	61.1	0.756
5.00	6.62	1.0401	1.0419	52.0	0.469	988.1	10.2	121	1.3451	2.345	1.261	0.684	1.141	1.099	87.47	67.0	0.840
5.50	7.29	1.0443	1.0462	57.4	0.518	986.9	11.3	133	1.3463	2.630	1.414	0.766	1.157	1.110	86.25	72.8	0.924
6.00	7.95	1.0486	1.0505	62.9	0.567	985.7	12.5	145	1.3475	2.930	1.575	0.852	1.173	1.121	85.07	78.3	1.01
6.50	8.61	1.0529	1.0548	68.4	0.617	984.5	13.8	158	1.3487	3.244	1.744	0.941	1.189	1.132	83.91	83.6	1.09
7.00	9.27	1.0572	1.0591	74.0	0.667	983.2	15.0	170	1.3500	3.573	1.921	1.033	1.206	1.143	82.77	88.7	1.17
7.50	9.94	1.0615	1.0634	79.6	0.717	981.9	16.3	182	1.3512	3.917	2.106	1.128	1.222	1.154	81.64	93.6	1.25
8.00	10.60	1.0659	1.0678	85.3	0.768	980.6	17.6	195	1.3525	4.275	2.299	1.227	1.240	1.165	80.51	98.4	1.33
8.50	11.26	1.0703	1.0722	91.0	0.820	979.3	18.9	207	1.3537	4.649	2.499	1.330	1.257	1.177	79.38	103.	1.41
9.00	11.92	1.0747	1.0766	96.7	0.871	977.9	20.3	220	1.3549	5.04	2.71	1.434	1.276	1.190	78.22	108.	1.49
9.50	12.58	1.0791	1.0810	102.5	0.924	976.6	21.7	232	1.3562	5.44	2.92	1.541	1.295	1.203	77.04	112.	1.57
10.00	13.25	1.0835	1.0854	108.3	0.976	975.1	23.1	245	1.3575	5.86	3.15	1.651	1.316	1.217	75.84	117.	1.65
11.00	14.57	1.0923	1.0943	120.2	1.083	972.2	26.1	270	1.3600	6.74	3.63	1.877	1.359	1.247	73.41	125.	1.81
12.00	15.90	1.1014	1.1033	132.2	1.191	969.2	29.0	295	1.3625	7.70	4.14	2.113	1.405	1.278	71.03	133.	1.97
13.00	17.22	1.1105	1.1125	144.4	1.301	966.2	32.1	321	1.3651	8.72	4.69	2.358	1.454	1.311	68.66	141.	2.13
14.00	18.55	1.1198	1.1218	156.8	1.412	963.0	35.2	347	1.3677	9.83	5.28	2.611	1.505	1.347	66.30	148.	2.28
15.00	19.87	1.1292	1.1312	169.4	1.526	959.8	38.4	374	1.3704	11.01	5.92	2.872	1.561	1.385	63.93	154.	2.42
16.00	21.20	1.1386	1.1407	182.2	1.641	956.5	41.8	400	1.3730	12.28	6.60	3.138	1.622	1.427	61.54	160.	2.55
17.00	22.52	1.1482	1.1502	195.2	1.759	953.0	45.2	427	1.3757	13.65	7.34	3.410	1.688	1.473	59.14	165.	2.67
18.00	23.84	1.1579	1.1599	208.4	1.878	949.5	48.8	454	1.3784	15.11	8.12	3.686	1.760	1.523	56.72	169.	2.78
19.00	25.17	1.1677	1.1697	221.9	1.999	945.8	52.4	482	1.3812	16.7	8.98	3.97	1.839	1.578	54.27	173.	2.88
20.00	26.49	1.1775	1.1796	235.5	2.122	942.0	56.2	509	1.3839	18.3	9.84	4.24	1.926	1.639	51.82	177.	2.97
22.00	29.14	1.1976	1.1997	263.5	2.374	934.1	64.1	565	1.3895	21.7	11.67		2.123	1.777	47.00	182.	3.11
24.00	31.79	1.2180	1.2201	292.3	2.634	925.7	72.6	621	1.3951	25.3	13.60		2.351	1.934	42.45	183.	3.16
26.00	34.44	1.2388	1.2410	322.1	2.902	916.7	81.5	678	1.4008	29.7	15.97		2.640	2.135	32.81	182.	3.12
28.00	37.09	1.2600	1.2622	352.8	3.179	907.2	91.0	736	1.4066	34.7	18.66		2.994	2.381	33.33	179.	3.03
30.00	39.74	1.2816	1.2838	384.5	3.464	897.1	101.1	794	1.4124	41.0	22.04		3.460	2.705	28.85	172.	2.85
32.00	42.39	1.3036	1.3059	417.1	3.758	886.4	111.8	853	1.4183	49.7	26.72		4.027	3.095	24.79	162.	2.61
34.00	45.04	1.3260	1.3283	450.8	4.062	875.1	123.1	912	1.4242				4.810	3.635	20.75	150.	2.34
36.00	47.69	1.3488	1.3512	485.6	4.375	863.2	135.0	971	1.4301				5.795	4.305	17.22	137.	2.05
38.00	50.34	1.3720	1.3745	521.4	4.697	850.7	147.6	1031	1.4361				7.306	5.336	13.66	123.	1.76
40.00	52.99	1.3957	1.3982	558.3	5.030	837.4	160.8	1090	1.4420				8.979	6.446	11.12	106.	1.45

10 CESIUM CHLORIDE, CsCl

MOLECULAR WEIGHT = 168.37

RELATIVE SPECIFIC REFRACTIVITY = 0.464

0.00 % by wt. data are the same for all compounds.
For Values of 0.00 wt. % solutions see Table 1, Acetic Acid.

A% by wt.	ρ D_4^{20}	D_{20}^{20}	C_s g/l	M g-mol/l	C_w g/l	$(C_o - C_w)$ g/l	$(n - n_o) \times 10^4$	n	Δ °C	O Os/kg	S g-mol/l	η/η_o	η/ρ cS	φ rhe	γ mmho/cm	T g-mol/l
0.50	1.0020	1.0038	5.0	0.030	997.0	1.2	4	1.3334	0.100	0.054	0.028	0.998	0.997	100.05	3.8	0.038
1.00	1.0058	1.0076	10.1	0.060	995.8	2.5	8	1.3337	0.201	0.108	0.057	0.995	0.991	100.30	7.4	0.075
1.50	1.0097	1.0114	15.1	0.090	994.5	3.7	11	1.3341	0.302	0.162	0.087	0.992	0.985	100.56	10.6	0.111
2.00	1.0135	1.0153	20.3	0.120	993.3	5.0	15	1.3345	0.403	0.217	0.116	0.990	0.979	100.81	13.8	0.147
2.50	1.0174	1.0192	25.4	0.151	992.0	6.2	19	1.3349	0.505	0.272	0.146	0.988	0.973	101.04	17.0	0.184
3.00	1.0214	1.0232	30.6	0.182	990.7	7.5	23	1.3353	0.607	0.326	0.176	0.986	0.967	101.26	20.2	0.222
3.50	1.0253	1.0271	35.9	0.213	989.4	8.8	27	1.3357	0.709	0.381	0.206	0.984	0.961	101.46	23.3	0.260
4.00	1.0293	1.0311	41.2	0.245	988.2	10.1	31	1.3361	0.812	0.436	0.236	0.982	0.956	101.65	26.5	0.300
4.50	1.0334	1.0352	46.5	0.276	986.9	11.4	35	1.3365	0.915	0.492	0.267	0.980	0.950	101.84	29.7	0.340
5.00	1.0374	1.0392	51.9	0.308	985.5	12.7	39	1.3369	1.018	0.547	0.297	0.978	0.945	102.02	32.9	0.380
5.50	1.0415	1.0433	57.3	0.340	984.2	14.0	43	1.3373	1.121	0.602	0.327	0.976	0.939	102.20	36.1	0.421
6.00	1.0456	1.0475	62.7	0.373	982.9	15.3	47	1.3377	1.223	0.658	0.358	0.975	0.934	102.37	39.3	0.462
6.50	1.0498	1.0516	68.2	0.405	981.6	16.7	52	1.3382	1.326	0.713	0.388	0.973	0.929	102.53	42.5	0.504
7.00	1.0540	1.0558	73.8	0.438	980.2	18.0	56	1.3386	1.428	0.768	0.418	0.972	0.924	102.67	45.8	0.546
7.50	1.0582	1.0601	79.4	0.471	978.8	19.4	60	1.3390	1.531	0.823	0.448	0.971	0.919	102.82	49.0	0.589
8.00	1.0625	1.0643	85.0	0.505	977.5	20.8	64	1.3394	1.635	0.879	0.478	0.969	0.914	102.95	52.3	0.633
8.50	1.0668	1.0686	90.7	0.539	976.1	22.2	69	1.3399	1.739	0.935	0.509	0.968	0.909	103.09	55.6	0.678
9.00	1.0711	1.0730	96.4	0.573	974.7	23.5	73	1.3403	1.845	0.992	0.539	0.967	0.904	103.22	59.0	0.724
9.50	1.0754	1.0773	102.2	0.607	973.3	25.0	77	1.3407	1.952	1.049	0.571	0.966	0.900	103.36	62.4	0.772
10.00	1.0798	1.0818	108.0	0.641	971.9	26.4	82	1.3412	2.060	1.108	0.602	0.964	0.895	103.51	65.8	0.822
11.00	1.0887	1.0907	119.8	0.711	969.0	29.3	91	1.3421	2.281	1.227	0.666	0.961	0.885	103.80	72.8	0.926
12.00	1.0978	1.0997	131.7	0.782	966.1	32.2	100	1.3430	2.507	1.348	0.731	0.959	0.875	104.09	80.0	1.03
13.00	1.1070	1.1089	143.9	0.855	963.1	35.2	109	1.3439	2.737	1.472	0.797	0.956	0.865	104.38	87.3	1.15
14.00	1.1163	1.1183	156.3	0.928	960.0	38.2	118	1.3448	2.972	1.598	0.864	0.953	0.856	104.67	94.8	1.27
15.00	1.1258	1.1278	168.9	1.003	956.9	41.3	128	1.3458	3.212	1.727	0.932	0.951	0.846	104.96	102.	1.40
16.00	1.1355	1.1375	181.7	1.079	953.8	44.5	138	1.3468	3.457	1.859	1.000	0.948	0.837	105.27	110.	1.54
17.00	1.1453	1.1473	194.7	1.156	950.6	47.7	147	1.3477	3.708	1.993	1.070	0.945	0.827	105.58	118.	1.68
18.00	1.1552	1.1573	207.9	1.235	947.3	51.0	157	1.3487	3.963	2.131	1.141	0.943	0.817	105.89	126.	1.83
19.00	1.1653	1.1674	221.4	1.315	943.9	54.3	167	1.3497	4.224	2.271	1.213	0.940	0.808	106.19	134.	1.99
20.00	1.1756	1.1777	235.1	1.396	940.5	57.7	178	1.3507	4.491	2.415	1.287	0.937	0.799	106.49	142.	2.17
22.00	1.1967	1.1989	263.3	1.564	933.5	64.8	198	1.3528				0.932	0.781	107.05	159.	2.53
24.00	1.2185	1.2207	292.4	1.737	926.1	72.1	220	1.3550				0.928	0.763	107.56	176.	2.95
26.00	1.2411	1.2433	322.7	1.916	918.4	79.8	242	1.3572				0.924	0.746	107.97	192.	3.48

10 CESIUM CHLORIDE, CsCl—(Continued)

Λ% by wt.	ρ D₄²⁰	D₂₀²⁰	Cs g/l	M g-mol/l	Cw g/l	(Co - Cw) g/l	(n-no) ×10⁴	n	Λ °C	O Os/kg	S g-mol/l	η/ηo	η/ρ cS	φ rhe	γ mmho/cm	T g-mol/l
28.00	1.2644	1.2666	354.0	2.103	910.4	87.9	264	1.3594				0.922	0.730	108.27	207.	4.15
30.00	1.2885	1.2908	386.6	2.296	902.0	96.3	288	1.3617				0.920	0.716	108.44	221.	4.95
32.00	1.3135	1.3158	420.3	2.496	893.1	105.1	311	1.3641				0.920	0.702	108.43		
34.00	1.3393	1.3417	455.4	2.705	883.9	114.3	336	1.3666				0.922	0.690	108.25		
36.00	1.3661	1.3685	491.8	2.921	874.3	124.0	361	1.3691				0.924	0.678	107.97		
38.00	1.3938	1.3963	529.6	3.146	864.2	134.1	387	1.3717				0.928	0.667	107.56		
40.00	1.4226	1.4251	569.0	3.380	853.5	144.7	414	1.3744				0.932	0.657	107.02		
42.00	1.4525	1.4550	610.0	3.623	842.4	155.8	442	1.3771				0.938	0.647	106.40		
44.00	1.4835	1.4861	652.7	3.877	830.8	167.5	470	1.3800				0.945	0.638	105.63		
46.00	1.5158	1.5185	697.3	4.141	818.5	179.7	500	1.3829				0.954	0.630	104.64		
48.00	1.5495	1.5522	743.7	4.417	805.7	192.5	530	1.3860				0.965	0.624	103.45		
50.00	1.5846	1.5874	792.3	4.706	792.3	206.0	562	1.3892				0.979	0.619	101.94		
52.00	1.6212	1.6241	843.0	5.007	778.2	220.0	595	1.3925				0.998	0.617	100.02		
54.00	1.6596	1.6625	896.2	5.323	763.4	234.8	630	1.3960				1.021	0.616	97.76		
56.00	1.6999	1.7029	951.9	5.654	747.9	250.3	666	1.3996				1.048	0.618	95.25		
58.00	1.7422	1.7453	1010.5	6.001	731.7	266.5	705	1.4035				1.078	0.620	92.54		
60.00	1.7868	1.7900	1072.1	6.367	714.7	283.5	746	1.4076				1.118	0.627	89.27		
62.00	1.8340	1.8373	1137.1	6.754	696.9	301.3	790	1.4120				1.170	0.639	85.28		
64.00	1.8842	1.8875	1205.9	7.162	678.3	319.9	837	1.4167				1.236	0.657	80.74		

11 CITRIC ACID, (COOH)CH₂C(OH)(COOH)CH₂COOH · 1H₂O

MOLECULAR WEIGHT = 192.12   FORMULA WEIGHT, HYDRATE = 210.14
RELATIVE SPECIFIC REFRACTIVITY = 0.951

0.00 % by wt. data are the same for all compounds.
For Values of 0.00 wt. % solutions see Table 1, Acetic Acid.

A% by wt.	H% by wt.	ρ D₄²⁰	D₂₀²⁰	Cs g/l	M g-mol/l	Cw g/l	(Co - Cw) g/l	(n-no) ×10⁴	n	Δ °C	O Os/kg	S g-mol/l	η/ηo	η/ρ cS	φ rhe	γ mmho/cm	T g-mol/l
0.50	0.55	1.0002	1.0020	5.0	0.026	995.2	3.0	7	1.3336	0.052	0.028	0.014	1.011	1.013	98.74	1.2	0.012
1.00	1.09	1.0022	1.0040	10.0	0.052	992.2	6.0	13	1.3343	0.105	0.056	0.029	1.022	1.022	97.65	2.1	0.021
2.00	2.19	1.0063	1.0081	20.1	0.105	986.2	12.0	26	1.3356	0.211	0.113	0.060	1.046	1.041	95.41	3.0	0.030
3.00	3.28	1.0105	1.0123	30.3	0.158	980.2	18.1	38	1.3368	0.318	0.171	0.091	1.071	1.062	93.21	3.7	0.037
4.00	4.38	1.0147	1.0165	40.6	0.211	974.1	24.1	51	1.3381	0.428	0.230	0.123	1.096	1.082	91.05	4.2	0.042
5.00	5.47	1.0189	1.0207	50.9	0.265	968.0	30.3	64	1.3394	0.539	0.290	0.156	1.123	1.104	88.87	4.7	0.047
6.00	6.56	1.0232	1.0250	61.4	0.320	961.8	36.5	77	1.3407	0.651	0.350	0.189	1.151	1.128	86.68	5.1	0.051
7.00	7.66	1.0274	1.0292	71.9	0.374	955.5	42.8	90	1.3420	0.764	0.411	0.222	1.181	1.152	84.50	5.5	0.055
8.00	8.75	1.0316	1.0335	82.5	0.430	949.1	49.1	103	1.3433	0.879	0.473	0.256	1.212	1.177	82.32	5.7	0.058
9.00	9.84	1.0359	1.0377	93.2	0.485	942.7	55.6	116	1.3446	0.997	0.536	0.291	1.245	1.204	80.15	6.0	0.060
10.00	10.94	1.0402	1.0420	104.0	0.541	936.1	62.1	129	1.3459	1.120	0.602	0.327	1.280	1.233	77.97	6.2	0.063
12.00	13.13	1.0490	1.0509	125.9	0.655	923.2	75.1	156	1.3486	1.379	0.741	0.403	1.354	1.293	73.72	6.6	0.067
14.00	15.31	1.0580	1.0599	148.1	0.771	909.9	88.3	184	1.3514	1.656	0.890	0.484	1.433	1.358	69.62	6.9	0.070
16.00	17.50	1.0672	1.0690	170.7	0.889	896.4	101.8	211	1.3541	1.950	1.048	0.570	1.522	1.429	65.58	7.1	0.072
18.00	19.69	1.0764	1.0783	193.8	1.009	882.7	115.6	239	1.3569	2.255	1.213	0.658	1.622	1.510	61.53	7.1	0.072
20.00	21.88	1.0858	1.0877	217.2	1.130	868.6	129.6	268	1.3598	2.567	1.380	0.748	1.737	1.603	57.46	7.2	0.073
22.00	24.06	1.0953	1.0972	241.0	1.254	854.3	143.9	296	1.3626	2.884	1.550	0.839	1.868	1.709	53.43	7.2	0.073
24.00	26.25	1.1049	1.1069	265.2	1.380	839.8	158.5	325	1.3655	3.210	1.726	0.931	2.013	1.826	49.57	7.2	0.073
26.00	28.44	1.1147	1.1167	289.8	1.509	824.9	173.4	355	1.3684	3.547	1.907	1.025	2.174	1.954	45.91	7.1	0.072
28.00	30.63	1.1246	1.1266	314.9	1.639	809.7	188.5	384	1.3714	3.893	2.093	1.122	2.351	2.094	42.46	6.8	0.069
30.00	32.81	1.1346	1.1366	340.4	1.772	794.2	204.0	414	1.3744	4.250	2.285	1.220	2.544	2.247	39.23	6.5	0.066

12 COBALTOUS CHLORIDE, CoCl₂ · 6H₂O

MOLECULAR WEIGHT = 129.85   FORMULA WEIGHT, HYDRATE = 237.95
RELATIVE SPECIFIC REFRACTIVITY = 0.733

0.00 % by wt. data are the same for all compounds.
For Values of 0.00 wt. % solutions see Table 1, Acetic Acid.

A% by wt.	H% by wt.	ρ D₄²⁰	D₂₀²⁰	Cs g/l	M g-mol/l	Cw g/l	(Co - Cw) g/l	(n-no) ×10⁴	n	Δ °C	O Os/kg	S g-mol/l	η/ηo	η/ρ cS	φ rhe	γ mmho/cm	T g-mol/l
0.50	0.92	1.0027	1.0045	5.0	0.039	997.7	0.5	11	1.3341	0.191	0.103	0.054	1.017	1.017	98.09	6.7	0.068
1.00	1.83	1.0073	1.0090	10.1	0.078	997.2	1.1	23	1.3352	0.380	0.204	0.110	1.034	1.029	96.52	12.7	0.134
2.00	3.66	1.0104	1.0182	20.3	0.157	996.0	2.2	45	1.3375	0.771	0.415	0.224	1.064	1.049	93.80	22.4	0.267
3.00	5.50	1.0256	1.0274	30.8	0.237	994.8	3.4	68	1.3398	1.187	0.638	0.347	1.096	1.071	91.05	33.6	0.389
4.00	7.33	1.0349	1.0368	41.4	0.319	993.5	4.7	91	1.3421	1.627	0.875	0.476	1.130	1.094	88.30	43.3	0.514
5.00	9.16	1.0444	1.0462	52.2	0.402	992.2	6.1	114	1.3444	2.099	1.128	0.613	1.166	1.119	85.59	52.5	0.636
6.00	10.99	1.0540	1.0559	63.2	0.487	990.8	7.5	137	1.3467	2.611	1.404	0.761	1.203	1.143	82.97	61.0	0.754
7.00	12.83	1.0637	1.0656	74.5	0.573	989.3	9.0	161	1.3491	3.164	1.701	0.918	1.241	1.169	80.43	69.0	0.868
8.00	14.66	1.0736	1.0755	85.9	0.661	987.7	10.5	185	1.3515	3.761	2.022	1.085	1.281	1.195	77.91	76.4	0.979
9.00	16.49	1.0837	1.0856	97.5	0.751	986.2	12.1	209	1.3539				1.324	1.224	75.40	83.4	1.08
10.00	18.32	1.0939	1.0958	109.4	0.842	984.5	13.7	234	1.3563				1.370	1.255	72.85	89.9	1.18
12.00	21.99	1.1148	1.1168	133.8	1.030	981.0	17.2	283	1.3613				1.474	1.324	67.73	102.	1.38
14.00	25.65	1.1364	1.1384	159.1	1.225	977.3	20.9	334	1.3664				1.592	1.403	62.71	112.	1.55
16.00	29.32	1.1587	1.1607	185.4	1.428	973.3	24.9	386	1.3716				1.725	1.492	57.85	120.	1.70
18.00	32.98	1.1816	1.1836	212.7	1.638	968.9	29.4	439	1.3769				1.876	1.591	53.19	126.	1.82
20.00	36.65	1.2050	1.2071	241.0	1.856	964.0	34.3	493	1.3822				2.046	1.701	48.78	130.	1.90

13 CREATININE, $CH_3NC(:NH)NHCOCH_2$

MOLECULAR WEIGHT = 113.12
RELATIVE SPECIFIC REFRACTIVITY = 1.301

A % by wt.	D_4^{20}	D_{20}^{20}	C_s g/l	M g-mol/l	C_w g/l	$(C_o - C_w)$ g/l	$(n - n_o)$ × 10^4	n	Δ °C	O Os/kg	S g-mol/l	η/η_o	η/ρ cS	φ rhe	γ mmho/cm	T g-mol/l
0.50	0.9995	1.0012	5.0	0.044	994.5	3.8	9	1.3339	0.080	0.043	0.022	1.009	1.011	98.95		
1.00	1.0007	1.0025	10.0	0.088	990.7	7.5	19	1.3349	0.150	0.081	0.042	1.019	1.020	97.97		
1.50	1.0019	1.0037	15.0	0.133	986.9	11.3	28	1.3358	0.220	0.118	0.063	1.030	1.030	96.89		
2.00	1.0032	1.0050	20.1	0.177	983.1	15.1	38	1.3368	0.300	0.161	0.086	1.043	1.041	95.73		
2.50	1.0045	1.0063	25.1	0.222	979.4	18.9	48	1.3378	0.380	0.204	0.110	1.056	1.053	94.52		
3.00	1.0058	1.0075	30.2	0.267	975.6	22.6	57	1.3387	0.460	0.247	0.133	1.070	1.066	93.29		
3.50	1.0071	1.0088	35.2	0.312	971.8	26.4	67	1.3397				1.084	1.079	92.05		
4.00	1.0084	1.0102	40.3	0.357	968.0	30.2	77	1.3407				1.099	1.092	90.83		
4.50	1.0097	1.0115	45.4	0.402	964.3	34.0	87	1.3417				1.113	1.105	89.65		
5.00	1.0110	1.0128	50.6	0.447	960.5	37.7	97	1.3427				1.128	1.117	88.51		
5.50	1.0124	1.0142	55.7	0.492	956.7	41.5	107	1.3437				1.141	1.130	87.45		
6.00	1.0138	1.0156	60.8	0.538	952.9	45.3	117	1.3447				1.154	1.141	86.46		
6.50	1.0151	1.0169	66.0	0.583	949.2	49.1	127	1.3457				1.166	1.151	85.57		
7.00	1.0165	1.0183	71.2	0.629	945.4	52.8	137	1.3467				1.177	1.160	84.78		
7.50	1.0180	1.0198	76.3	0.675	941.6	56.6	148	1.3478				1.186	1.168	84.11		
8.00	1.0194	1.0212	81.6	0.721	937.8	60.4	158	1.3488				1.194	1.174	83.58		

14 CUPRIC SULFATE, $CuSO_4 \cdot 5H_2O$

MOLECULAR WEIGHT = 159.61   FORMULA WEIGHT, HYDRATE = 249.69
RELATIVE SPECIFIC REFRACTIVITY = 0.517

A % by wt.	H % by wt.	ρ D_4^{20}	D_{20}^{20}	C_s g/l	M g-mol/l	C_w g/l	$(C_o - C_w)$ g/l	$(n - n_o)$ × 10^4	n	Δ °C	O Os/kg	S g-mol/l	η/η_o	η/ρ cS	φ rhe	γ mmho/cm	T g-mol/l
0.50	0.78	1.0033	1.0051	5.0	0.031	998.3	-0.1	9	1.3339	0.075	0.040	0.021	1.015	1.014	98.30	2.9	0.028
1.00	1.56	1.0085	1.0103	10.1	0.063	998.4	-0.2	18	1.3348	0.140	0.075	0.039	1.034	1.027	96.52	5.4	0.054
1.50	2.35	1.0137	1.0155	15.2	0.095	998.5	-0.3	28	1.3358	0.200	0.108	0.057	1.057	1.045	94.40	7.4	0.076
2.00	3.13	1.0190	1.0208	20.4	0.128	998.6	-0.4	37	1.3367	0.259	0.139	0.074	1.082	1.064	92.24	9.3	0.096
2.50	3.91	1.0243	1.0261	25.6	0.160	998.7	-0.4	47	1.3377	0.316	0.170	0.091	1.105	1.081	90.31	11.1	0.116
3.00	4.69	1.0296	1.0314	30.9	0.194	998.7	-0.5	56	1.3386	0.372	0.200	0.107	1.127	1.097	88.54	12.8	0.135
3.50	5.48	1.0349	1.0368	36.2	0.227	998.7	-0.5	66	1.3396	0.428	0.230	0.124	1.149	1.112	86.86	14.4	0.154
4.00	6.26	1.0403	1.0421	41.6	0.261	998.7	-0.5	75	1.3405	0.484	0.260	0.140	1.171	1.128	85.23	16.0	0.172
4.50	7.04	1.0457	1.0475	47.1	0.295	998.6	-0.4	85	1.3414	0.539	0.290	0.156	1.194	1.144	83.58	17.5	0.190
5.00	7.82	1.0511	1.0530	52.6	0.329	998.6	-0.3	94	1.3424	0.594	0.319	0.172	1.219	1.162	81.87	19.0	0.208
5.50	8.60	1.0565	1.0584	58.1	0.364	998.4	-0.2	104	1.3433	0.648	0.349	0.188	1.246	1.181	80.12	20.5	0.226
6.00	9.39	1.0620	1.0639	63.7	0.399	998.3	0.0	113	1.3443	0.703	0.378	0.205	1.273	1.201	78.37	21.9	0.243
6.50	10.17	1.0675	1.0694	69.4	0.435	998.1	0.1	123	1.3452	0.759	0.408	0.221	1.302	1.222	76.63	23.3	0.260
7.00	10.95	1.0730	1.0749	75.1	0.471	997.9	0.3	132	1.3462	0.816	0.439	0.238	1.333	1.244	74.90	24.6	0.277
7.50	11.73	1.0786	1.0805	80.9	0.507	997.7	0.5	142	1.3472	0.874	0.470	0.255	1.364	1.267	73.17	26.0	0.293
8.00	12.52	1.0842	1.0861	86.7	0.543	997.5	0.8	151	1.3481	0.933	0.501	0.272	1.397	1.291	71.46	27.2	0.309
8.50	13.30	1.0898	1.0918	92.6	0.580	997.2	1.0	161	1.3491	0.992	0.533	0.289	1.431	1.315	69.77	28.5	0.325
9.00	14.08	1.0955	1.0975	98.6	0.618	996.9	1.3	171	1.3501	1.052	0.566	0.307	1.466	1.341	68.09	29.7	0.341
9.50	14.86	1.1012	1.1032	104.6	0.655	996.6	1.6	181	1.3511	1.113	0.599	0.325	1.502	1.367	66.44	31.0	0.356
10.00	15.64	1.1070	1.1090	110.7	0.694	996.3	1.9	191	1.3520	1.177	0.633	0.344	1.540	1.394	64.81	32.2	0.371
11.00	17.21	1.1186	1.1206	123.0	0.771	995.6	2.7	210	1.3540	1.308	0.703	0.382	1.617	1.449	61.70	34.4	0.400
12.00	18.77	1.1304	1.1324	135.6	0.850	994.7	3.5	230	1.3560	1.447	0.778	0.423	1.698	1.505	58.77	36.6	0.427
13.00	20.34	1.1424	1.1444	148.5	0.930	993.8	4.4	251	1.3581	1.596	0.858	0.467	1.786	1.566	55.88	38.6	0.453
14.00	21.90	1.1545	1.1566	161.6	1.013	992.9	5.3	271	1.3601	1.753	0.942	0.513	1.885	1.636	52.95	40.5	0.478
15.00	23.47	1.1669	1.1690	175.0	1.097	991.9	6.4	292	1.3622				2.000	1.717	49.90	42.3	0.501
16.00	25.03	1.1796	1.1817	188.7	1.182	990.9	7.4	314	1.3644				2.132	1.811	46.81	44.0	0.523
17.00	26.59	1.1926	1.1947	202.7	1.270	989.8	8.4	336	1.3666				2.280	1.916	43.77	45.6	0.543
18.00	28.16	1.2059	1.2080	217.1	1.360	988.8	9.4	359	1.3689				2.444	2.031	40.83	47.0	0.562

15 DEXTRAN, $(C_6H_{10}O_5)_x$

MOLECULAR WEIGHT, AVERAGE = 72,000
RELATIVE SPECIFIC REFRACTIVITY = 1.045

A % by wt.	ρ D_4^{20}	d D_{20}^{20}	C_s g/l	M g-mol/l	C_w g/l	$(C_o - C_w)$ g/l	$(n - n_o)$ × 10^4	n	Δ °C	O Os/kg	S g-mol/l	η/η_o	η/ρ cS	φ rhe	γ mmho/cm	T g-mol/l
0.50	1.0001	1.0019	5.0		995.1	3.1	7	1.3337				1.129	1.131	88.38		
1.00	1.0020	1.0037	10.0		992.0	6.3	15	1.3345				1.280	1.280	77.97		
1.50	1.0039	1.0056	15.1		988.8	9.4	22	1.3352				1.453	1.450	68.69		
2.00	1.0057	1.0075	20.1		985.6	12.6	29	1.3359				1.647	1.641	60.60		
2.50	1.0076	1.0094	25.2		982.5	15.8	37	1.3367				1.858	1.848	53.71		
3.00	1.0096	1.0113	30.3		979.3	19.0	44	1.3374				2.086	2.071	47.83		
3.50	1.0115	1.0133	35.4		976.1	22.2	52	1.3382				2.336	2.314	42.73		
4.00	1.0134	1.0152	40.5		972.9	25.4	59	1.3389				2.611	2.581	38.23		
4.50	1.0153	1.0171	45.7		969.6	28.6	67	1.3397				2.915	2.877	34.24		
5.00	1.0173	1.0191	50.9		966.4	31.8	74	1.3404				3.254	3.205	30.67		
5.50	1.0192	1.0210	56.1		963.2	35.1	82	1.3412				3.627	3.566	27.52		
6.00	1.0212	1.0230	61.3		959.9	38.3	89	1.3419				4.031	3.955	24.76		
6.50	1.0232	1.0250	66.5		956.7	41.6	97	1.3427				4.466	4.373	22.35		
7.00	1.0251	1.0270	71.8		953.4	44.8	105	1.3435				4.933	4.821	20.23		
7.50	1.0271	1.0290	77.0		950.1	48.1	112	1.3442				5.431	5.299	18.37		
8.00	1.0291	1.0310	82.3		946.8	51.4	120	1.3450				5.963	5.805	16.74		
8.50	1.0312	1.0330	87.6		943.5	54.7	128	1.3458				6.527	6.342	15.29		
9.00	1.0332	1.0350	93.0		940.2	58.0	135	1.3465				7.124	6.909	14.01		
9.50	1.0352	1.0371	98.3		936.9	61.4	143	1.3473				7.754	7.506	12.87		
10.00	1.0373	1.0391	103.7		933.5	64.7	151	1.3481				8.419	8.133	11.85		

16 ETHANOL, CH₃CH₂OH

MOLECULAR WEIGHT = 46.07
RELATIVE SPECIFIC REFRACTIVITY = 1.363

0.00 % by wt. data are the same for all compounds.
For Values of 0.00 wt. % solutions see Table 1, Acetic Acid.

A % by wt.	ρ D_4^{20}	D_{20}^{20}	C_s g/l	M g-mol/l	C_w g/l	$(C_o - C_w)$ g/l	$(n - n_o)$ × 10⁴	n	Δ °C	O Os/kg	S g-mol/l	η/η_o	η/ρ cS	ϕ rhe	γ mmho/cm	T g-mol/l
0.50	0.9973	0.9991	5.0	0.108	992.3	5.9	3	1.3333	0.20	0.11	0.057	1.021	1.026	97.71		
1.00	0.9963	0.9981	10.0	0.216	986.4	11.8	6	1.3336	0.40	0.22	0.116	1.044	1.050	95.59		
1.50	0.9954	0.9972	14.9	0.324	980.5	17.8	9	1.3339	0.60	0.32	0.175	1.068	1.075	93.42		
2.00	0.9945	0.9962	19.9	0.432	974.6	23.6	12	1.3342	0.81	0.44	0.236	1.093	1.101	91.31		
2.50	0.9936	0.9953	24.8	0.539	968.7	29.5	15	1.3345	1.02	0.55	0.297	1.116	1.126	89.42		
3.00	0.9927	0.9945	29.8	0.646	962.9	35.3	18	1.3348	1.23	0.66	0.359	1.138	1.149	87.70		
3.50	0.9918	0.9936	34.7	0.754	957.1	41.1	21	1.3351	1.44	0.77	0.421	1.159	1.171	86.08		
4.00	0.9910	0.9927	39.6	0.860	951.4	46.9	24	1.3354	1.65	0.89	0.484	1.181	1.194	84.52		
4.50	0.9902	0.9919	44.6	0.967	945.6	52.6	27	1.3357	1.87	1.01	0.547	1.203	1.217	82.98		
5.00	0.9893	0.9911	49.5	1.074	939.9	58.4	31	1.3360	2.09	1.12	0.611	1.226	1.242	81.40		
5.50	0.9885	0.9903	54.4	1.180	934.2	64.1	34	1.3364	2.31	1.24	0.675	1.250	1.267	79.81		
6.00	0.9878	0.9895	59.3	1.286	928.5	69.7	37	1.3367	2.54	1.36	0.739	1.276	1.294	78.24		
6.50	0.9870	0.9887	64.2	1.393	922.8	75.4	41	1.3370	2.76	1.49	0.804	1.301	1.321	76.69		
7.00	0.9862	0.9880	69.0	1.498	917.2	81.0	44	1.3374	2.99	1.61	0.870	1.328	1.349	75.16		
7.50	0.9855	0.9872	73.9	1.604	911.6	86.7	48	1.3377	3.23	1.74	0.936	1.355	1.378	73.66		
8.00	0.9847	0.9865	78.8	1.710	906.0	92.3	51	1.3381	3.47	1.86	1.003	1.382	1.407	72.19		
8.50	0.9840	0.9857	83.6	1.816	900.4	97.9	55	1.3384	3.71	2.00	1.071	1.411	1.436	70.75		
9.00	0.9833	0.9850	88.5	1.921	894.8	103.4	58	1.3388	3.96	2.13	1.140	1.439	1.467	69.34		
9.50	0.9826	0.9843	93.3	2.026	889.2	109.0	62	1.3392	4.21	2.27	1.210	1.468	1.497	67.97		
10.00	0.9819	0.9836	98.2	2.131	883.7	114.5	65	1.3395	4.47	2.40	1.282	1.498	1.529	66.62		
11.00	0.9805	0.9822	107.9	2.341	872.6	125.6	73	1.3403	5.00	2.69	1.426	1.560	1.594	63.99		
12.00	0.9792	0.9809	117.5	2.550	861.7	136.6	80	1.3410	5.56	2.99	1.572	1.624	1.662	61.44		
13.00	0.9778	0.9796	127.1	2.759	850.7	147.5	87	1.3417	6.13	3.30	1.722	1.691	1.732	59.03		
14.00	0.9765	0.9782	136.7	2.967	839.8	158.4	95	1.3425	6.73	3.62	1.874	1.757	1.803	56.80		
15.00	0.9752	0.9769	146.3	3.175	828.8	169.3	102	1.3432	7.36	3.96	2.030	1.822	1.872	54.78		
16.00	0.9739	0.9756	155.8	3.382	818.1	180.2	110	1.3440	8.01	4.31	2.189	1.886	1.941	52.91		
17.00	0.9726	0.9743	165.3	3.589	807.3	191.0	117	1.3447	8.69	4.67	2.351	1.951	2.010	51.16		
18.00	0.9713	0.9730	174.8	3.795	796.5	201.8	125	1.3455	9.40	5.05	2.516	2.015	2.078	49.54		
19.00	0.9700	0.9717	184.3	4.000	785.7	212.5	132	1.3462	10.14	5.45	2.683	2.077	2.146	48.04		
20.00	0.9687	0.9704	193.7	4.205	774.9	223.3	140	1.3469	10.92	5.87	2.853	2.138	2.212	46.68		
22.00	0.9660	0.9677	212.5	4.613	753.5	244.8	154	1.3484	12.60	6.78	3.203	2.254	2.338	44.27		
24.00	0.9632	0.9649	231.2	5.018	732.0	266.2	168	1.3498	14.47	7.78	3.568	2.365	2.460	42.20		
26.00	0.9602	0.9619	249.7	5.419	710.6	287.7	181	1.3511	16.41	8.82	3.920	2.471	2.579	40.39		
28.00	0.9571	0.9588	268.0	5.817	689.1	309.1	194	1.3524	18.43	9.91	4.262	2.576	2.696	38.75		
30.00	0.9539	0.9556	286.2	6.211	667.7	330.5	205	1.3535	20.47	11.01	4.583	2.662	2.796	37.49		
32.00	0.9504	0.9521	304.1	6.601	646.3	352.0	216	1.3546	22.44	12.07		2.721	2.869	36.68		
34.00	0.9468	0.9485	321.9	6.988	624.9	373.3	227	1.3557	24.27	13.05		2.762	2.923	36.13		
36.00	0.9431	0.9447	339.5	7.369	603.6	394.7	236	1.3566	25.98	13.97		2.797	2.971	35.69		
38.00	0.9392	0.9408	356.9	7.747	582.3	415.9	245	1.3575	27.62	14.85		2.823	3.012	35.35		
40.00	0.9352	0.9369	374.1	8.120	561.1	437.1	253	1.3583	29.26	15.73		2.840	3.043	35.14		
42.00	0.9311	0.9328	391.1	8.488	540.0	458.2	260	1.3590	30.98	16.66		2.846	3.063	35.06		
44.00	0.9269	0.9286	407.8	8.853	519.1	479.2	268	1.3598	32.68	17.57		2.844	3.074	35.09		
46.00	0.9227	0.9243	424.4	9.213	498.2	500.0	274	1.3604	34.36	18.47		2.837	3.081	35.18		
48.00	0.9183	0.9199	440.8	9.568	477.5	520.7	280	1.3610	36.04	19.38		2.826	3.083	35.32		
50.00	0.9139	0.9155	457.0	9.919	457.0	541.3	286	1.3616	37.67	20.25		2.807	3.078	35.55		
52.00	0.9095	0.9111	472.9	10.265	436.5	561.7	291	1.3621	39.20	21.08		2.783	3.066	35.87		
54.00	0.9049	0.9065	488.7	10.607	416.3	582.0	296	1.3626	40.65	21.85		2.749	3.044	36.31		
56.00	0.9004	0.9020	504.2	10.944	396.2	602.1	300	1.3630	42.06	22.61		2.696	3.000	37.02		
58.00	0.8958	0.8974	519.5	11.277	376.2	622.0	304	1.3634	43.49	23.38		2.627	2.938	38.00		
60.00	0.8911	0.8927	534.7	11.606	356.5	641.8	308	1.3638	44.93	24.15		2.542	2.858	39.26		
62.00	0.8865	0.8880	549.6	11.930	336.9	661.4	311	1.3641	46.28	24.88		2.474	2.796	40.34		
64.00	0.8818	0.8833	564.3	12.250	317.4	680.8	315	1.3644	47.52	25.55		2.410	2.739	41.41		
66.00	0.8771	0.8786	578.9	12.565	298.2	700.0	317	1.3647	48.64	26.15		2.342	2.676	42.61		
68.00	0.8724	0.8739	593.2	12.876	279.2	719.1	320	1.3650	49.52	26.62		2.276	2.614	43.85		
70.00	0.8676	0.8692	607.3	13.183	260.3	737.9	322	1.3652				2.210	2.552	45.17		
72.00	0.8629	0.8644	621.3	13.486	241.6	756.6	324	1.3654				2.144	2.490	46.55		
74.00	0.8581	0.8596	635.0	13.784	223.1	775.1	325	1.3655				2.078	2.426	48.03		
76.00	0.8533	0.8549	648.5	14.077	204.8	793.4	327	1.3657				2.011	2.361	49.63		
78.00	0.8485	0.8500	661.8	14.366	186.7	811.6	327	1.3657				1.944	2.296	51.33		
80.00	0.8436	0.8451	674.9	14.650	168.7	829.5	328	1.3658				1.877	2.229	53.15		
82.00	0.8387	0.8401	687.7	14.927	151.0	847.3	328	1.3657				1.804	2.155	55.31		
84.00	0.8335	0.8350	700.2	15.198	133.4	864.9	326	1.3656				1.738	2.089	57.42		
86.00	0.8284	0.8299	712.4	15.464	116.0	882.3	325	1.3655				1.671	2.021	59.74		
88.00	0.8232	0.8247	724.4	15.725	98.8	899.4	323	1.3653				1.603	1.951	62.26		
90.00	0.8180	0.8194	736.2	15.979	81.8	916.4	320	1.3650				1.539	1.885	64.85		
92.00	0.8125	0.8140	747.5	16.226	65.0	933.2	316	1.3646				1.472	1.815	67.80		
94.00	0.8070	0.8084	758.6	16.466	48.4	949.8	312	1.3642				1.404	1.743	71.07		
96.00	0.8013	0.8027	769.2	16.697	32.1	966.2	306	1.3636				1.339	1.674	74.53		
98.00	0.7954	0.7968	779.5	16.920	15.9	982.3	300	1.3630				1.270	1.600	78.59		
100.00	0.7893	0.7907	789.3	17.133	0.0	998.2	284	1.3614				1.201	1.525	83.10		

17 (ETHYLENEDINITRILO)TETRAACETIC ACID DISODIUM SALT, EDTA DISODIUM*, $Na_2C_{10}H_{14}O_8N_2 \cdot 2H_2O$

MOLECULAR WEIGHT = 336.21 FORMULA WEIGHT, HYDRATE = 372.24
RELATIVE SPECIFIC REFRACTIVITY = 0.977

0.00 % by wt. data are the same for all compounds.
For Values of 0.00 wt. % solutions see Table 1, Acetic Acid.

A% by wt.	H% by wt.	ρ D_4^{20}	D_{20}^{20}	C_s g/l	M g-mol/l	C_w g/l	$(C_o - C_w)$ g/l	$(n - n_o)$ ×10⁴	n	Δ °C	O Os/kg	S g-mol/l	η/η_o	η/ρ cS	ϕ rhe	γ mmho/cm	T g-mol/l
0.50	0.55	1.0009	1.0027	5.0	0.015	995.9	2.3	9	1.3339	0.07	0.04	0.020	1.015	1.016	98.35	1.9	0.018
1.00	1.11	1.0036	1.0053	10.0	0.030	993.5	4.7	18	1.3348	0.14	0.07	0.039	1.030	1.028	96.94	3.5	0.034
1.50	1.66	1.0062	1.0080	15.1	0.045	991.1	7.1	26	1.3356	0.21	0.11	0.059	1.044	1.040	95.55	5.0	0.049
2.00	2.21	1.0089	1.0107	20.2	0.060	988.7	9.5	35	1.3365	0.27	0.15	0.078	1.060	1.052	94.19	6.3	0.064
2.50	2.77	1.0115	1.0133	25.3	0.075	986.2	12.0	44	1.3374	0.33	0.18	0.096	1.075	1.065	92.84	7.6	0.077
3.00	3.32	1.0142	1.0160	30.4	0.090	983.8	14.5	53	1.3383	0.40	0.21	0.115	1.091	1.078	91.51	8.8	0.091
3.50	3.88	1.0169	1.0187	35.6	0.106	981.3	16.9	62	1.3392	0.46	0.25	0.133	1.107	1.091	90.18	10.1	0.105
4.00	4.43	1.0196	1.0214	40.8	0.121	978.8	19.5	70	1.3400	0.52	0.28	0.151	1.123	1.104	88.85	11.3	0.119
4.50	4.98	1.0223	1.0241	46.0	0.137	976.3	22.0	79	1.3409	0.58	0.31	0.169	1.140	1.118	87.53	12.5	0.133
5.00	5.54	1.0250	1.0268	51.2	0.152	973.7	24.5	88	1.3418	0.65	0.35	0.187	1.158	1.132	86.20	13.7	0.145
5.50	6.09	1.0277	1.0295	56.5	0.168	971.2	27.0	97	1.3427	0.71	0.38	0.206	1.176	1.147	84.86	14.6	0.156
6.00	6.64	1.0305	1.0323	61.8	0.184	968.6	29.6	106	1.3436	0.77	0.42	0.225	1.195	1.162	83.51	15.3	0.164

* Sodium(Di)Ethylenediamine Tetraacetate.

18 ETHYLENE GLYCOL, CH_2OHCH_2OH

MOLECULAR WEIGHT = 62.07
RELATIVE SPECIFIC REFRACTIVITY = 1.147

0.00 % by wt. data are the same for all compounds.
For Values of 0.00 wt. % solutions see Table 1, Acetic Acid.

A% by wt.	ρ D_4^{20}	D_{20}^{20}	C_s g/l	M g-mol/l	C_w g/l	$(C_o - C_w)$ g/l	$(n - n_o)$ ×10⁴	n	Δ °C	O Os/kg	S g-mol/l	η/η_o	η/ρ cS	ϕ rhe	γ mmho/cm	T g-mol/l
0.50	0.9988	1.0006	5.0	0.080	993.8	4.4	5	1.3335	0.15	0.08	0.042	1.008	1.011	99.03		
1.00	0.9995	1.0012	10.0	0.161	989.5	8.8	9	1.3339	0.30	0.16	0.086	1.018	1.021	98.04		
2.00	1.0007	1.0025	20.0	0.322	980.7	17.6	19	1.3348	0.61	0.33	0.176	1.046	1.047	95.41		
3.00	1.0019	1.0037	30.1	0.484	971.9	26.4	28	1.3358	0.92	0.50	0.269	1.072	1.072	93.09		
4.00	1.0032	1.0049	40.1	0.646	963.0	35.2	37	1.3367	1.24	0.67	0.364	1.097	1.096	90.98		
5.00	1.0044	1.0062	50.2	0.809	954.2	44.0	47	1.3377	1.58	0.85	0.461	1.123	1.120	88.87		
6.00	1.0057	1.0075	60.3	0.972	945.3	52.9	56	1.3386	1.91	1.03	0.560	1.151	1.147	86.72		
7.00	1.0070	1.0087	70.5	1.136	936.5	61.8	66	1.3396	2.26	1.22	0.660	1.180	1.174	84.60		
8.00	1.0082	1.0100	80.7	1.299	927.6	70.6	75	1.3405	2.62	1.41	0.763	1.210	1.202	82.49		
9.00	1.0095	1.0113	90.9	1.464	918.7	79.6	85	1.3415	2.99	1.61	0.868	1.241	1.232	80.41		
10.00	1.0108	1.0126	101.1	1.629	909.8	88.5	95	1.3425	3.37	1.81	0.975	1.274	1.263	78.34		
12.00	1.0134	1.0152	121.6	1.959	891.8	106.4	114	1.3444	4.16	2.24	1.196	1.345	1.330	74.21		
14.00	1.0161	1.0179	142.3	2.292	873.8	124.4	134	1.3464	5.01	2.69	1.426	1.421	1.401	70.25		
16.00	1.0188	1.0206	163.0	2.626	855.8	142.5	154	1.3484	5.91	3.18	1.665	1.497	1.473	66.65		
18.00	1.0214	1.0232	183.9	2.962	837.6	160.7	174	1.3503	6.89	3.70	1.913	1.575	1.545	63.35		
20.00	1.0241	1.0259	204.8	3.300	819.3	178.9	194	1.3523	7.93	4.27	2.171	1.658	1.622	60.19		
24.00	1.0296	1.0314	247.1	3.981	782.5	215.8	234	1.3564	10.28	5.53	2.714	1.839	1.790	54.26		
28.00	1.0350	1.0369	289.8	4.669	745.2	253.0	275	1.3605	13.03	7.01	3.289	2.043	1.978	48.84		
32.00	1.0405	1.0424	333.0	5.364	707.6	290.7	316	1.3646	16.23	8.73	3.889	2.275	2.191	43.87		
36.00	1.0460	1.0478	376.6	6.067	669.4	328.8	357	1.3687	19.82	10.66	4.483	2.532	2.425	39.42		
40.00	1.0514	1.0532	420.6	6.775	630.8	367.4	398	1.3728	23.84	12.82		2.826	2.693	35.32		
44.00	1.0567	1.0586	465.0	7.491	591.8	406.5	440	1.3769	28.32	15.23		3.160	2.996	31.59		
48.00	1.0619	1.0638	509.7	8.212	552.2	446.0	481	1.3811	33.30	17.90		3.537	3.337	28.22		
52.00	1.0670	1.0689	554.8	8.939	512.2	486.1	521	1.3851	38.81	20.87		3.973	3.731	25.12		
56.00	1.0719	1.0738	600.3	9.671	471.6	526.6	562	1.3892	44.83	24.10		4.466	4.175	22.35		
60.00	1.0765	1.0784	645.9	10.406	430.6	567.6	602	1.3931	51.23	27.54		5.016	4.669	19.90		

19 FERRIC CHLORIDE, $FeCl_3 \cdot 6H_2O$

MOLECULAR WEIGHT = 162.22 FORMULA WEIGHT, HYDRATE = 270.32
RELATIVE SPECIFIC REFRACTIVITY = 0.946

0.00 % by wt. data are the same for all compounds.
For Values of 0.00 wt. % solutions see Table 1, Acetic Acid.

A% by wt.	H% by wt.	ρ D_4^{20}	D_{20}^{20}	C_s g/l	M g-mol/l	C_w g/l	$(C_o - C_w)$ g/l	$(n - n_o)$ ×10⁴	n	Δ °C	O Os/kg	S g-mol/l	η/η_o	η/ρ cS	ϕ rhe	γ mmho/cm	T g-mol/l
0.50	0.83	1.0025	1.0043	5.0	0.031	997.5	0.7	14	1.3344	0.206	0.111	0.059	1.022	1.022	97.61		
1.00	1.67	1.0068	1.0086	10.1	0.062	996.7	1.5	28	1.3358	0.385	0.207	0.111	1.045	1.040	95.49		
2.00	3.33	1.0153	1.0171	20.3	0.125	995.0	3.3	56	1.3386	0.753	0.405	0.219	1.091	1.077	91.48		
3.00	5.00	1.0238	1.0256	30.7	0.189	993.1	5.2	83	1.3413	1.146	0.616	0.335	1.137	1.113	87.79		
4.00	6.67	1.0323	1.0341	41.3	0.255	991.0	7.3	111	1.3441	1.562	0.840	0.457	1.185	1.150	84.22		
5.00	8.33	1.0408	1.0426	52.0	0.321	988.7	9.5	138	1.3468	2.002	1.076	0.585	1.236	1.190	80.76		
6.00	10.00	1.0493	1.0512	63.0	0.388	986.4	11.9	166	1.3496	2.475	1.331	0.722	1.289	1.231	77.41		
7.00	11.66	1.0580	1.0599	74.1	0.457	984.0	14.3	194	1.3524	2.994	1.609	0.870	1.347	1.275	74.11		
8.00	13.33	1.0668	1.0687	85.3	0.526	981.5	16.7	222	1.3552	3.566	1.917	1.031	1.409	1.324	70.82		
9.00	15.00	1.0760	1.0779	96.8	0.597	979.2	19.0	251	1.3581	4.185	2.250	1.202	1.477	1.376	67.55		
10.00	16.66	1.0853	1.0872	108.5	0.669	976.8	21.5	281	1.3611	4.854	2.610	1.385	1.550	1.431	64.39		
12.00	20.00	1.1040	1.1059	132.5	0.817	971.5	26.8	340	1.3670	6.38	3.43	1.785	1.704	1.547	58.57		
14.00	23.33	1.1228	1.1248	157.2	0.969	965.6	32.4	400	1.3730	8.22	4.42	2.240	1.875	1.673	53.22		
16.00	26.66	1.1420	1.1440	182.7	1.126	959.3	39.0			10.45	5.62	2.750	2.076	1.822	48.07		
18.00	29.99	1.1615	1.1636	209.1	1.289	952.5	45.8			13.08	7.03	3.299	2.306	1.990	43.27		
20.00	33.33	1.1816	1.1837	236.3	1.457	945.3	53.0			16.14	8.68	3.873	2.565	2.175	38.91		
24.00	39.99	1.2234	1.2256	293.6	1.810	929.8	68.4			23.79	12.79		3.172	2.598	31.47		
28.00	46.66	1.2679	1.2702	355.0	2.189	912.9	85.3			33.61	18.07		4.030	3.185	24.76		
32.00	53.32	1.3153	1.3176	420.9	2.595	894.4	103.8			49.16	26.43		5.263	4.010	18.96		
36.00	59.99	1.3654	1.3678	491.5	3.030	873.9	124.4						7.116	5.222	14.03		
40.00	66.66	1.4176	1.4201	567.0	3.496	850.6	147.7						9.655	6.824	10.34		

20 FORMIC ACID, HCOOH

MOLECULAR WEIGHT = 46.03
RELATIVE SPECIFIC REFRACTIVITY = 0.916

A % by wt.	ρ D_4^{20}	D_{20}^{20}	C_s g/l	M g-mol/l	C_w g/l	$(C_0 - C_w)$ g/l	$(n - n_0)$ $\times 10^4$	n	Δ °C	O Os/kg	S g-mol/l	η/η_0	η/ρ cS	ϕ rhe	γ mmho/cm	T g-mol/l
0.50	0.9994	1.0012	5.0	0.109	994.4	3.8	3	1.3333	0.210	0.113	0.060	1.004	1.007	99.36	1.4	0.013
1.00	1.0006	1.0023	10.0	0.217	990.6	7.7	6	1.3336	0.418	0.225	0.121	1.009	1.010	98.96	2.4	0.024
2.00	1.0029	1.0047	20.1	0.436	982.9	15.3	12	1.3342	0.824	0.443	0.240	1.015	1.015	98.28	3.5	0.034
3.00	1.0053	1.0071	30.2	0.655	975.2	23.1	18	1.3348	1.243	0.668	0.363	1.023	1.019	97.59	4.3	0.043
4.00	1.0077	1.0095	40.3	0.876	967.4	30.8	24	1.3354	1.672	0.899	0.489	1.030	1.024	96.90	5.0	0.050
5.00	1.0102	1.0119	50.5	1.097	959.6	38.6	29	1.3359	2.103	1.131	0.615	1.037	1.029	96.24	5.6	0.056
6.00	1.0126	1.0144	60.8	1.320	951.8	46.4	35	1.3365	2.534	1.363	0.739	1.044	1.033	95.63	6.1	0.062
7.00	1.0150	1.0168	71.1	1.544	944.0	54.3	41	1.3371	2.967	1.595	0.862	1.050	1.036	95.06	6.6	0.067
8.00	1.0175	1.0193	81.4	1.768	936.1	62.2	46	1.3376	3.402	1.829	0.985	1.056	1.040	94.51	7.0	0.071
9.00	1.0199	1.0217	91.8	1.994	928.1	70.1	52	1.3382	3.838	2.063	1.106	1.062	1.043	93.98	7.4	0.075
10.00	1.0224	1.0242	102.2	2.221	920.1	78.1	57	1.3387	4.267	2.294	1.225	1.068	1.047	93.45	7.8	0.079
12.00	1.0273	1.0291	123.3	2.678	904.0	94.2	67	1.3397	5.19	2.79	1.475	1.080	1.053	92.41	8.4	0.086
14.00	1.0322	1.0340	144.5	3.139	887.7	110.5	78	1.3408	6.11	3.28	1.715	1.092	1.060	91.40	8.8	0.091
16.00	1.0371	1.0389	165.9	3.605	871.1	127.1	88	1.3418	7.06	3.80	1.957	1.104	1.067	90.38	9.3	0.096
18.00	1.0419	1.0438	187.5	4.074	854.4	143.9	98	1.3428	8.08	4.35	2.207	1.117	1.074	89.35	9.6	0.100
20.00	1.0467	1.0486	209.3	4.548	837.4	160.9	107	1.3437	9.11	4.90	2.448	1.130	1.081	88.36	9.9	0.103
24.00	1.0562	1.0580	253.5	5.507	802.7	195.5	126	1.3456	11.10	5.97	2.891	1.154	1.094	86.52	10.3	0.108
28.00	1.0654	1.0673	298.3	6.481	767.1	231.1	145	1.3475	13.10	7.04	3.303	1.177	1.107	84.79	10.5	0.109
32.00	1.0746	1.0765	343.9	7.471	730.7	267.5	163	1.3493	15.28	8.21	3.717	1.201	1.120	83.09	10.5	0.109
36.00	1.0839	1.0858	390.2	8.477	693.7	304.6	181	1.3511	17.65	9.49	4.132	1.225	1.133	81.44	10.3	0.107
40.00	1.0935	1.0955	437.4	9.503	656.1	342.1	199	1.3529	20.18	10.85	4.539	1.251	1.146	79.78	9.9	0.103
44.00	1.1015	1.1035	484.7	10.529	616.9	381.4	217	1.3547	22.93	12.33		1.278	1.162	78.11	9.5	0.098
48.00	1.1097	1.1117	532.7	11.572	577.1	421.2	235	1.3565	26.06	14.01		1.306	1.179	76.42	8.9	0.092
52.00	1.1183	1.1203	581.5	12.634	536.8	461.4	251	1.3581	29.69	15.96		1.337	1.198	74.65	8.3	0.085
56.00	1.1273	1.1293	631.3	13.714	496.0	502.2	267	1.3597	33.81	18.18		1.371	1.218	72.81	7.6	0.078
60.00	1.1364	1.1385	681.9	14.813	454.6	543.7	282	1.3612	38.26	20.57		1.407	1.241	70.93	6.9	0.070
64.00	1.1456	1.1476	733.2	15.928	412.4	585.8	296	1.3626	43.02	23.13		1.446	1.265	69.03	6.2	0.062
68.00	1.1544	1.1565	785.0	17.055	369.4	628.8	311	1.3641				1.487	1.291	67.11	5.4	0.054
70.00	1.1586	1.1607	811.1	17.620	347.6	650.6	318	1.3648				1.508	1.305	66.16	5.1	0.051

21 D-FRUCTOSE (LEVULOSE), $C_6H_{12}O_6$

MOLECULAR WEIGHT = 180.16
RELATIVE SPECIFIC REFRACTIVITY = 1.021

A % by wt.	ρ D_4^{20}	D_{20}^{20}	C_s g/l	M g-mol/l	C_w g/l	$(C_0 - C_w)$ g/l	$(n - n_0)$ $\times 10^4$	n	Δ °C	O Os/kg	S g-mol/l	η/η_0	η/ρ cS	ϕ rhe	γ mmho/cm	T g-mol/l
0.50	1.0002	1.0020	5.0	0.028	995.2	3.0	7	1.3337	0.052	0.028	0.014	1.013	1.015	98.53		
1.00	1.0021	1.0039	10.0	0.056	992.1	6.1	14	1.3344	0.104	0.056	0.029	1.026	1.026	97.28		
1.50	1.0041	1.0059	15.1	0.084	989.1	9.2	21	1.3351	0.157	0.085	0.045	1.039	1.037	96.06		
2.00	1.0061	1.0079	20.1	0.112	986.0	12.3	28	1.3358	0.211	0.113	0.060	1.052	1.048	94.87		
2.50	1.0081	1.0098	25.2	0.140	982.9	15.4	36	1.3366	0.265	0.142	0.076	1.065	1.059	93.71		
3.00	1.0101	1.0118	30.3	0.168	979.7	18.5	43	1.3373	0.319	0.172	0.092	1.078	1.069	92.59		
3.50	1.0120	1.0138	35.4	0.197	976.6	21.6	50	1.3380	0.374	0.201	0.108	1.091	1.080	91.50		
4.00	1.0140	1.0158	40.6	0.225	973.5	24.8	57	1.3387	0.430	0.231	0.124	1.104	1.091	90.40		
4.50	1.0160	1.0178	45.7	0.254	970.3	27.9	65	1.3395	0.487	0.262	0.141	1.118	1.102	89.30		
5.00	1.0181	1.0199	50.9	0.283	967.2	31.1	72	1.3402	0.544	0.292	0.158	1.132	1.114	88.16		
5.50	1.0201	1.0219	56.1	0.311	964.0	34.3	79	1.3409	0.602	0.324	0.175	1.147	1.127	87.00		
6.00	1.0221	1.0239	61.3	0.340	960.8	37.5	87	1.3417	0.660	0.355	0.192	1.163	1.140	85.83		
6.50	1.0241	1.0259	66.6	0.369	957.6	40.7	94	1.3424	0.720	0.387	0.209	1.179	1.153	84.66		
7.00	1.0262	1.0280	71.8	0.399	954.3	43.9	101	1.3431	0.780	0.419	0.227	1.196	1.167	83.48		
7.50	1.0282	1.0300	77.1	0.428	951.0	47.1	109	1.3439	0.841	0.452	0.245	1.213	1.182	82.29		
8.00	1.0303	1.0321	82.4	0.457	947.8	50.4	116	1.3446	0.902	0.485	0.263	1.230	1.197	81.11		
8.50	1.0323	1.0342	87.7	0.487	944.6	53.7	124	1.3454	0.965	0.519	0.282	1.249	1.212	79.93		
9.00	1.0344	1.0362	93.1	0.517	941.3	56.9	131	1.3461	1.028	0.553	0.300	1.267	1.228	78.75		
9.50	1.0365	1.0383	98.5	0.547	938.0	60.2	139	1.3469	1.092	0.587	0.319	1.286	1.244	77.58		
10.00	1.0385	1.0404	103.9	0.576	934.7	63.5	147	1.3476	1.158	0.622	0.338	1.306	1.260	76.42		
11.00	1.0427	1.0446	114.7	0.637	928.0	70.2	162	1.3492	1.290	0.694	0.377	1.346	1.294	74.13		
12.00	1.0469	1.0488	125.6	0.697	921.3	76.9	177	1.3507	1.427	0.767	0.417	1.388	1.329	71.89		
13.00	1.0512	1.0530	136.7	0.758	914.5	83.7	193	1.3522	1.567	0.842	0.458	1.432	1.365	69.67		
14.00	1.0554	1.0573	147.8	0.820	907.7	90.6	208	1.3538	1.710	0.920	0.500	1.480	1.405	67.45		
15.00	1.0597	1.0616	159.0	0.882	900.8	97.5	224	1.3554	1.858	0.999	0.543	1.530	1.447	65.23		
16.00	1.0640	1.0659	170.2	0.945	893.8	104.5	240	1.3569	2.009	1.080	0.587	1.584	1.491	63.02		
17.00	1.0684	1.0703	181.6	1.008	886.8	111.5	255	1.3585	2.162	1.163	0.632	1.640	1.538	60.84		
18.00	1.0728	1.0747	193.1	1.072	879.7	118.6	272	1.3601	2.319	1.247	0.677	1.700	1.588	58.69		
19.00	1.0772	1.0791	204.7	1.136	872.5	125.7	288	1.3618	2.479	1.333	0.723	1.764	1.641	56.56		
20.00	1.0816	1.0835	216.3	1.201	865.3	133.0	304	1.3634	2.640	1.419	0.769	1.833	1.698	54.45		
22.00	1.0906	1.0925	239.9	1.332	810.6	147.6	337	1.3667	3.054	1.642	0.887	1.982	1.821	50.35		
24.00	1.0996	1.1016	263.9	1.465	835.7	162.5	370	1.3700	3.431	1.845	0.993	2.151	1.959	46.41		
26.00	1.1089	1.1108	288.3	1.600	820.5	177.7	404	1.3734	3.815	2.051	1.100	2.343	2.117	42.60		
28.00	1.1182	1.1202	313.1	1.738	805.1	193.1	438	1.3768	4.196	2.256	1.205	2.557	2.291	39.03		
30.00	1.1276	1.1296	338.3	1.878	789.3	208.9	473	1.3803				2.811	2.498	35.50		
32.00	1.1372	1.1392	363.9	2.020	773.3	224.9	509	1.3839				3.106	2.737	32.13		
34.00	1.1469	1.1490	390.0	2.165	757.0	241.3	545	1.3874				3.455	3.018	28.89		
36.00	1.1568	1.1588	416.4	2.312	740.3	257.9	581	1.3911				3.891	3.370	25.65		
38.00	1.1668	1.1688	443.4	2.461	723.4	274.8	618	1.3948				4.409	3.786	22.64		
40.00	1.1769	1.1790	470.8	2.613	706.1	292.1	655	1.3985				5.036	4.288	19.82		
42.00	1.1871	1.1892	498.6	2.767	688.5	309.7	694	1.4023				5.761	4.863	17.32		
44.00	1.1975	1.1996	526.9	2.925	670.6	327.6	732	1.4062				6.631	5.548	15.05		
46.00	1.2080	1.2102	555.7	3.084	652.3	345.9	771	1.4101				7.738	6.419	12.90		
48.00	1.2187	1.2208	585.0	3.247	633.7	364.5	811	1.4141				9.042	7.434	11.04		

21 D-FRUCTOSE (LEVULOSE), $C_6H_{12}O_6$—(Continued)

A% by wt.	ρ D_4^{20}	D_{20}^{20}	C_s g/l	M g-mol/l	C_w g/l	$(C_o - C_w)$ g/l	$(n - n_o)$ $\times 10^4$	n	Δ °C	O Os/kg	S g-mol/l	η/η_o	η/ρ cS	ϕ rhe	γ mmho/cm	T g-mol/l
50.00	1.2295	1.2316	614.7	3.412	614.7	383.5	851	1.4181				10.80	8.80	9.24		
52.00	1.2404	1.2426	645.0	3.580	595.4	402.9	892	1.4222				12.99	10.49	7.69		
54.00	1.2514	1.2536	675.8	3.751	575.7	422.6	934	1.4264				15.84	12.68	6.30		
56.00	1.2626	1.2649	707.1	3.925	555.6	442.7	976	1.4306				20.05	15.91	4.98		
58.00	1.2739	1.2762	738.9	4.101	535.1	463.2	1019	1.4348				25.60	20.13	3.90		
60.00	1.2854	1.2877	771.2	4.281	514.2	484.1	1062	1.4392				32.47	25.31	3.07		
62.00	1.2970	1.2992	804.1	4.463	492.8	505.4	1105	1.4435				42.97	33.20	2.32		
64.00	1.3086	1.3110	837.5	4.649	471.1	527.1	1150	1.4480				58.17	44.54	1.72		
66.00	1.3204	1.3228	871.5	4.837	448.9	549.3	1194	1.4524				82.19	62.37	1.21		
68.00	1.3323	1.3347	906.0	5.029	426.3	571.9	1240	1.4570				118.4	89.08	0.84		
70.00	1.3443	1.3467	941.0	5.223	403.3	594.9	1285	1.4615				177.8	132.5	0.56		

22 D-GLUCOSE (DEXTROSE), $C_6H_{12}O_6 \cdot 1H_2O$

MOLECULAR WEIGHT = 180.16   FORMULA WEIGHT, HYDRATE = 198.17

RELATIVE SPECIFIC REFRACTIVITY = 1.031

0.00 % by wt. data are the same for all compounds.
For Values of 0.00 wt. % solutions see Table 1, Acetic Acid.

A% by wt.	H% by wt.	ρ D_4^{20}	D_{20}^{20}	C_s g/l	M g-mol/l	C_w g/l	$(C_o - C_w)$ g/l	$(n - n_o)$ $\times 10^4$	n	Δ °C	O Os/kg	S g-mol/l	η/η_o	η/ρ cS	ϕ rhe	γ mmho/cm	T g-mol/l
0.50	0.55	1.0001	1.0019	5.0	0.028	995.1	3.1	7	1.3337	0.047	0.025	0.013	1.008	1.010	99.01		
1.00	1.10	1.0020	1.0038	10.0	0.056	992.0	6.2	14	1.3344	0.107	0.057	0.030	1.019	1.019	97.94		
1.50	1.65	1.0039	1.0057	15.1	0.084	988.9	9.4	21	1.3351	0.158	0.085	0.045	1.034	1.032	96.54		
2.00	2.20	1.0058	1.0076	20.1	0.112	985.7	12.5	28	1.3358	0.214	0.115	0.061	1.050	1.046	95.05		
2.50	2.75	1.0078	1.0095	25.2	0.140	982.6	15.7	36	1.3366	0.270	0.145	0.077	1.065	1.059	93.68		
3.00	3.30	1.0097	1.0115	30.3	0.168	979.4	18.8	43	1.3373	0.323	0.174	0.093	1.081	1.072	92.36		
3.50	3.85	1.0116	1.0134	35.4	0.197	976.2	22.0	50	1.3380	0.377	0.202	0.108	1.096	1.085	91.08		
4.00	4.40	1.0136	1.0154	40.5	0.225	973.0	25.2	57	1.3387	0.433	0.233	0.125	1.111	1.098	89.82		
4.50	4.95	1.0155	1.0173	45.7	0.254	969.8	28.4	65	1.3395	0.490	0.264	0.142	1.127	1.112	88.57		
5.00	5.50	1.0175	1.0193	50.9	0.282	966.6	31.6	72	1.3402	0.549	0.295	0.159	1.143	1.126	87.31		
5.50	6.05	1.0194	1.0212	56.1	0.311	963.4	34.9	79	1.3409	0.608	0.327	0.176	1.160	1.140	86.06		
6.00	6.60	1.0214	1.0232	61.3	0.340	960.1	38.1	87	1.3417	0.668	0.359	0.194	1.177	1.154	84.82		
6.50	7.15	1.0234	1.0252	66.5	0.369	956.9	41.4	94	1.3424	0.729	0.392	0.212	1.194	1.169	83.59		
7.00	7.70	1.0254	1.0272	71.8	0.398	953.6	44.6	102	1.3432	0.790	0.425	0.230	1.212	1.184	82.37		
7.50	8.25	1.0274	1.0292	77.1	0.428	950.3	47.9	109	1.3439	0.851	0.458	0.248	1.230	1.199	81.17		
8.00	8.80	1.0294	1.0312	82.4	0.457	947.0	51.2	117	1.3447	0.913	0.491	0.266	1.248	1.215	79.97		
8.50	9.35	1.0314	1.0332	87.7	0.487	943.7	54.5	124	1.3454	0.975	0.524	0.284	1.267	1.231	78.77		
9.00	9.90	1.0334	1.0352	93.0	0.516	940.4	57.8	132	1.3462	1.038	0.558	0.303	1.286	1.247	77.58		
9.50	10.45	1.0354	1.0373	98.4	0.546	937.1	61.2	139	1.3469	1.102	0.592	0.322	1.306	1.264	76.39		
10.00	11.00	1.0375	1.0393	103.7	0.576	933.7	64.5	147	1.3477	1.167	0.627	0.341	1.327	1.282	75.21		
11.00	12.10	1.0416	1.0434	114.6	0.636	927.0	71.2	162	1.3492	1.303	0.700	0.381	1.369	1.317	72.89		
12.00	13.20	1.0457	1.0475	125.5	0.697	920.2	78.0	178	1.3508	1.443	0.776	0.422	1.413	1.354	70.63		
13.00	14.30	1.0498	1.0517	136.5	0.758	913.4	84.9	193	1.3523	1.586	0.853	0.464	1.459	1.393	68.40		
14.00	15.40	1.0540	1.0559	147.6	0.819	906.4	91.8	209	1.3539	1.731	0.931	0.506	1.509	1.434	66.15		
15.00	16.50	1.0582	1.0601	158.7	0.881	899.5	98.8	225	1.3555	1.880	1.011	0.550	1.563	1.480	63.85		
16.00	17.60	1.0624	1.0643	170.0	0.944	892.5	105.8	241	1.3571	2.033	1.093	0.594	1.622	1.530	61.53		
17.00	18.70	1.0667	1.0686	181.3	1.007	885.4	112.9	257	1.3587	2.190	1.178	0.640	1.685	1.583	59.21		
18.00	19.80	1.0710	1.0729	192.8	1.070	878.2	120.0	273	1.3603	2.353	1.265	0.687	1.753	1.640	56.93		
19.00	20.90	1.0753	1.0772	204.3	1.134	871.0	127.2	289	1.3619	2.521	1.355	0.735	1.825	1.700	54.70		
20.00	22.00	1.0797	1.0816	215.9	1.199	863.7	134.5	306	1.3635	2.696	1.449	0.785	1.900	1.763	52.53		
22.00	24.20	1.0884	1.0904	239.5	1.329	849.0	149.3	339	1.3668	3.073	1.652	0.892	2.059	1.896	48.47		
24.00	26.40	1.0973	1.0993	263.4	1.462	834.0	164.3	372	1.3702	3.480	1.871	1.007	2.238	2.044	44.59		
26.00	28.60	1.1063	1.1083	287.6	1.597	818.7	179.6	406	1.3736	3.900	2.097	1.124	2.453	2.222	40.69		
28.00	30.80	1.1154	1.1174	312.3	1.734	803.1	195.1	440	1.3770	4.337	2.332	1.244	2.702	2.427	36.94		
30.00	33.00	1.1246	1.1266	337.4	1.873	787.2	211.0	475	1.3805	4.794	2.577	1.369	2.992	2.666	33.36		
32.00	35.20	1.1340	1.1360	362.9	2.014	771.1	227.1	511	1.3840				3.317	2.931	30.09		
34.00	37.40	1.1434	1.1454	388.8	2.158	754.6	243.6	546	1.3876				3.697	3.240	26.99		
36.00	39.60	1.1529	1.1550	415.1	2.304	737.9	260.3	582	1.3912				4.185	3.637	23.85		
38.00	41.80	1.1626	1.1647	441.8	2.452	720.8	277.4	619	1.3949				4.776	4.116	20.96		
40.00	44.00	1.1724	1.1745	469.0	2.603	703.5	294.8	656	1.3986				5.482	4.685	18.21		
42.00	46.20	1.1823	1.1844	496.6	2.756	685.8	312.5	694	1.4024				6.275	5.318	15.90		
44.00	48.40	1.1924	1.1945	524.7	2.912	667.7	330.5	732	1.4062				7.221	6.068	13.82		
46.00	50.60	1.2026	1.2047	553.2	3.071	649.4	348.8	771	1.4101				8.437	7.029	11.83		
48.00	52.80	1.2130	1.2151	582.2	3.232	630.7	367.5	811	1.4141				9.863	8.148	10.12		
50.00	55.00	1.2235	1.2257	611.7	3.396	611.7	386.5	851	1.4181				11.86	9.713	8.41		
52.00	57.20	1.2342	1.2364	641.8	3.562	592.4	405.8	892	1.4222				14.46	11.74	6.90		
54.00	59.40	1.2451	1.2473	672.4	3.732	572.8	425.5	933	1.4263				17.88	14.39	5.58		
56.00	61.60	1.2562	1.2585	703.5	3.905	552.7	445.5	976	1.4306				22.84	18.22	4.37		
58.00	63.80	1.2676	1.2699	735.2	4.081	532.4	465.8	1020	1.4349				29.33	23.18	3.40		
60.00	66.00	1.2793	1.2816	767.6	4.261	511.7	486.5	1064	1.4394				37.37	29.27	2.67		

23 GLYCEROL, $CH_2OHCHOHCH_2OH$

MOLECULAR WEIGHT = 92.09

RELATIVE SPECIFIC REFRACTIVITY = 1.109

0.00 % by wt. data are the same for all compounds.
For Values of 0.00 wt. % solutions see Table 1, Acetic Acid.

A% by wt.	ρ D_4^{20}	D_{20}^{20}	C_s g/l	M g-mol/l	C_w g/l	$(C_o - C_w)$ g/l	$(n - n_o)$ $\times 10^4$	n	Δ °C	O Os/kg	S g-mol/l	η/η_o	η/ρ cS	ϕ rhe	γ mmho/cm	T g-mol/l
0.50	0.9994	1.0011	5.0	0.054	994.4	3.9	6	1.3336	0.072	0.039	0.020	1.009	1.012	98.89		
1.00	1.0005	1.0023	10.0	0.109	990.5	7.7	12	1.3342	0.180	0.097	0.051	1.020	1.022	97.84		
2.00	1.0028	1.0046	20.1	0.218	982.7	15.5	23	1.3353	0.411	0.221	0.119	1.046	1.045	95.41		
3.00	1.0051	1.0069	30.2	0.327	974.9	23.3	35	1.3365	0.627	0.337	0.182	1.072	1.068	93.12		
4.00	1.0074	1.0092	40.3	0.438	967.1	31.2	46	1.3376	0.849	0.456	0.247	1.098	1.092	90.93		

23 GLYCEROL, CH₂OHCHOHCH₂OH—(Continued)

A% by wt.	D_4^{20}	D_{20}^{20}	C_s g/l	M g-mol/l	C_w g/l	$(C_o - C_w)$ g/l	$(n - n_o)$ × 10^4	n	Δ °C	O Os/kg	S g-mol/l	η/η_o	η/ρ cS	φ rhe	γ mmho/cm	T g-mol/l
5.00	1.0097	1.0115	50.5	0.548	959.2	39.0	58	1.3388	1.078	0.580	0.315	1.125	1.116	88.71		
6.00	1.0120	1.0138	60.7	0.659	951.3	46.9	70	1.3400	1.316	0.708	0.385	1.155	1.143	86.44		
7.00	1.0144	1.0162	71.0	0.771	943.4	54.9	82	1.3412	1.561	0.839	0.457	1.186	1.171	84.17		
8.00	1.0167	1.0185	81.3	0.883	935.4	62.9	94	1.3424	1.811	0.974	0.530	1.218	1.201	81.90		
9.00	1.0191	1.0209	91.7	0.996	927.4	70.9	106	1.3436	2.064	1.110	0.603	1.253	1.232	79.67		
10.00	1.0215	1.0233	102.1	1.109	919.3	78.9	118	1.3448	2.323	1.249	0.678	1.288	1.263	77.48		
12.00	1.0262	1.0281	123.1	1.337	903.1	95.1	142	1.3472	2.880	1.548	0.837	1.362	1.330	73.28		
14.00	1.0311	1.0329	144.4	1.568	886.7	111.5	167	1.3496	3.469	1.865	1.004	1.442	1.401	69.22		
16.00	1.0360	1.0378	165.8	1.800	870.2	128.0	191	1.3521	4.094	2.201	1.177	1.530	1.480	65.22		
18.00	1.0409	1.0428	187.4	2.035	853.6	144.7	217	1.3547	4.756	2.557	1.359	1.627	1.566	61.34		
20.00	1.0459	1.0478	209.2	2.272	836.8	161.5	242	1.3572	5.46	2.93	1.546	1.734	1.661	57.56		
24.00	1.0561	1.0580	253.5	2.752	802.6	195.6	294	1.3624	7.01	3.77	1.944	1.984	1.882	50.31		
28.00	1.0664	1.0683	298.6	3.243	767.8	230.4	347	1.3676	8.77	4.71	2.370	2.274	2.136	43.89		
32.00	1.0770	1.0789	344.6	3.742	732.3	265.9	400	1.3730	10.74	5.78	2.814	2.632	2.449	37.91		
36.00	1.0876	1.0896	391.5	4.252	696.1	302.2	455	1.3785	12.96	6.97	3.276	3.082	2.839	32.38		
40.00	1.0984	1.1003	439.4	4.771	659.0	339.2	511	1.3841	15.50	8.33	3.757	3.646	3.326	27.37		
44.00	1.1092	1.1112	488.1	5.300	621.2	377.1	567	1.3897				4.434	4.005	22.51		
48.00	1.1200	1.1220	537.6	5.838	582.4	415.8	624	1.3954				5.402	4.833	18.47		
52.00	1.1308	1.1328	588.0	6.385	542.8	455.4	681	1.4011				6.653	5.895	15.00		
56.00	1.1419	1.1439	639.4	6.944	502.4	495.8	739	1.4069				8.332	7.311	11.98		
60.00	1.1530	1.1551	691.8	7.513	461.2	537.0	799	1.4129				10.66	9.264	9.36		
64.00	1.1643	1.1663	745.1	8.091	419.1	579.1	859	1.4189				13.63	11.73	7.32		
68.00	1.1755	1.1775	799.3	8.680	376.1	622.1	919	1.4249				18.42	15.70	5.42		
72.00	1.1866	1.1887	854.3	9.277	332.2	666.0	980	1.4310				27.57	23.28	3.62		
76.00	1.1976	1.1997	910.2	9.883	287.4	710.8	1040	1.4370				40.49	33.88	2.46		
80.00	1.2085	1.2106	966.8	10.498	241.7	756.5	1101	1.4431				59.78	49.57	1.67		
84.00	1.2192	1.2214	1024.2	11.121	195.1	803.2	1162	1.4492				84.17	69.18	1.19		
88.00	1.2299	1.2320	1082.3	11.752	147.6	850.7	1223	1.4553				147.2	119.9	0.68		
92.00	1.2404	1.2426	1141.1	12.392	99.2	899.0	1284	1.4613				383.7	310.0	0.26		
96.00	1.2508	1.2530	1200.7	13.039	50.0	948.2	1344	1.4674				778.9	624.0	0.13		
100.00	1.2611	1.2633	1261.1	13.694	0.0	998.2	1405	1.4735				1759.6	1398.1	0.06		

24 HYDROCHLORIC ACID, HCl

MOLECULAR WEIGHT = 36.47
RELATIVE SPECIFIC REFRACTIVITY = 1.152

0.00 % by wt. data are the same for all compounds.
For Values of 0.00 wt. % solutions see Table 1, Acetic Acid.

A% by wt.	D_4^{20}	D_{20}^{20}	C_s g/l	M g-mol/l	C_w g/l	$(C_o - C_w)$ g/l	$(n - n_o)$ × 10^4	n	Δ °C	O Os/kg	S g-mol/l	η/η_o	η/ρ cS	φ rhe	γ mmho/cm	T g-mol/l
0.50	1.0007	1.0025	5.0	0.137	995.7	2.5	12	1.3341	0.486	0.261	0.141	1.006	1.008	99.16	45.1	0.537
1.00	1.0031	1.0049	10.0	0.275	993.1	5.1	23	1.3353	0.989	0.532	0.289	1.013	1.012	98.50	92.9	1.23
1.50	1.0056	1.0074	15.1	0.414	990.5	7.7	35	1.3365	1.519	0.817	0.444	1.020	1.016	97.84	140.	2.10
2.00	1.0081	1.0098	20.2	0.553	987.9	10.3	46	1.3376	2.076	1.116	0.607	1.027	1.021	97.17	183.	3.14
2.50	1.0105	1.0123	25.3	0.693	985.3	13.0	58	1.3388	2.662	1.431	0.775	1.034	1.026	96.49	220.	4.85
3.00	1.0130	1.0148	30.4	0.833	982.6	15.6	69	1.3399	3.276	1.761	0.949	1.042	1.030	95.81		
3.50	1.0154	1.0172	35.5	0.975	979.9	18.3	81	1.3411	3.916	2.105	1.128	1.049	1.035	95.12		
4.00	1.0179	1.0197	40.7	1.116	977.2	21.0	92	1.3422	4.579	2.462	1.311	1.057	1.040	94.43		
4.50	1.0204	1.0222	45.9	1.259	974.4	23.8	104	1.3434	5.27	2.83	1.496	1.065	1.046	93.73		
5.00	1.0228	1.0246	51.1	1.402	971.7	26.5	115	1.3445	5.98	3.22	1.683	1.073	1.051	93.04		
5.50	1.0253	1.0271	56.4	1.546	968.9	29.3	127	1.3457	6.73	3.62	1.874	1.081	1.056	92.34		
6.00	1.0278	1.0296	61.7	1.691	966.1	32.1	138	1.3468	7.52	4.04	2.070	1.089	1.062	91.64		
6.50	1.0302	1.0321	67.0	1.836	963.3	35.0	150	1.3480	8.34	4.49	2.269	1.097	1.067	90.94		
7.00	1.0327	1.0345	72.3	1.982	960.4	37.8	162	1.3491	9.22	4.96	2.474	1.106	1.073	90.24		
7.50	1.0352	1.0370	77.6	2.129	957.5	40.7	173	1.3503	10.14	5.45	2.681	1.115	1.079	89.54		
8.00	1.0377	1.0395	83.0	2.276	954.6	43.6	185	1.3515	11.10	5.97	2.890	1.123	1.085	88.85		
8.50	1.0401	1.0420	88.4	2.424	951.7	46.5	196	1.3526	12.10	6.51	3.101	1.132	1.091	88.15		
9.00	1.0426	1.0445	93.8	2.573	948.8	49.5	208	1.3538	13.15	7.07	3.313	1.141	1.097	87.46		
9.50	1.0451	1.0469	99.3	2.722	945.8	52.4	219	1.3549	14.25	7.66	3.526	1.150	1.103	86.77		
10.00	1.0476	1.0494	104.8	2.872	942.8	55.4	231	1.3561	15.40	8.28	3.740	1.159	1.109	86.08		
11.00	1.0526	1.0544	115.8	3.175	936.8	61.4	254	1.3584	17.85	9.60	4.166	1.178	1.122	84.71		
12.00	1.0576	1.0594	126.9	3.480	930.7	67.6	277	1.3607	20.51	11.03	4.590	1.197	1.134	83.36		
13.00	1.0626	1.0645	138.1	3.788	924.4	73.8	300	1.3630				1.217	1.148	82.01		
14.00	1.0676	1.0695	149.5	4.098	918.1	80.1	323	1.3653				1.237	1.161	80.68		
15.00	1.0726	1.0745	160.9	4.412	911.8	86.5	347	1.3676				1.258	1.175	79.35		
16.00	1.0777	1.0796	172.4	4.728	905.3	93.0	370	1.3700				1.279	1.189	78.03		
17.00	1.0828	1.0847	184.1	5.047	898.7	99.5	393	1.3723				1.301	1.204	76.72		
18.00	1.0878	1.0898	195.8	5.369	892.0	106.2	416	1.3746				1.323	1.219	75.42		
19.00	1.0929	1.0949	207.7	5.694	885.3	113.0	439	1.3769				1.347	1.235	74.11		
20.00	1.0980	1.1000	219.6	6.022	878.4	119.8	462	1.3792				1.371	1.251	72.80		
22.00	1.1083	1.1102	243.8	6.686	864.5	133.8	509	1.3838				1.423	1.286	70.15		
24.00	1.1185	1.1205	268.4	7.361	850.1	148.1	555	1.3884				1.480	1.326	67.44		
26.00	1.1288	1.1308	293.5	8.047	835.3	162.9	600	1.3930				1.544	1.371	64.63		
28.00	1.1391	1.1411	318.9	8.745	820.1	178.1	646	1.3976				1.617	1.423	61.71		
30.00	1.1492	1.1513	344.8	9.454	804.5	193.8	691	1.4020				1.702	1.484	58.64		
32.00	1.1594	1.1614	371.0	10.173	788.4	209.9	736	1.4066				1.795	1.551	55.61		
34.00	1.1693	1.1714	397.6	10.901	771.8	226.5	782	1.4112				1.896	1.625	52.63		
36.00	1.1791	1.1812	424.5	11.639	754.6	243.6	828	1.4158				1.998	1.698	49.95		
38.00	1.1886	1.1907	451.7	12.385	736.9	261.3	874	1.4204				2.101	1.771	47.51		
40.00	1.1977	1.1999	479.1	13.137	718.6	279.6	920	1.4250								

25 INULIN, $(C_6H_{10}O_5)_x$*

MOLECULAR WEIGHT, AVERAGE = 5200
RELATIVE SPECIFIC REFRACTIVITY = 1.034

0.00 % by wt. data are the same for all compounds.
For Values of 0.00 wt. % solutions see Table 1, Acetic Acid.

A % by wt.	ρ D_4^{20}	D_{20}^{20}	C_s g/l	M g-mol/l	C_w g/l	$(C_o - C_w)$ g/l	$(n - n_o)$ $\times 10^4$	n	Δ °C	O Os/kg	S g-mol/l	η/η_o	η/ρ cS	ϕ rhe	γ mmho/cm	T g-mol/l
0.50	1.0001	1.0019	5.0	0.001	995.1	3.1	7	1.3337	0.003	0.001	0.001	1.030	1.032	96.93		
1.00	1.0020	1.0038	10.0	0.002	992.0	6.3	14	1.3344	0.005	0.003	0.001	1.059	1.059	94.24		
1.50	1.0038	1.0056	15.1	0.003	988.8	9.5	22	1.3351	0.007	0.004	0.002	1.088	1.086	91.74		
2.00	1.0057	1.0074	20.1	0.004	985.6	12.7	29	1.3359	0.010	0.005	0.003	1.117	1.113	89.35		
2.50	1.0075	1.0093	25.2	0.005	982.3	15.9	36	1.3366	0.012	0.007	0.003	1.147	1.140	87.03		
3.00	1.0093	1.0111	30.3	0.006	979.0	19.2	43	1.3373	0.015	0.008	0.004	1.177	1.168	84.81		
3.50	1.0112	1.0129	35.4	0.007	975.8	22.5	51	1.3381	0.017	0.009	0.005	1.208	1.197	82.65		
4.00	1.0130	1.0148	40.5	0.008	972.5	25.8	58	1.3388	0.019	0.010	0.005	1.240	1.226	80.51		
4.50	1.0148	1.0166	45.7	0.009	969.2	29.1	65	1.3395	0.022	0.012	0.006	1.274	1.258	78.36		
5.00	1.0167	1.0185	50.8	0.010	965.9	32.4	73	1.3403	0.024	0.013	0.007	1.310	1.291	76.18		
5.50	1.0186	1.0204	56.0	0.011	962.6	35.7	80	1.3410	0.027	0.015	0.007	1.349	1.327	74.00		
6.00	1.0205	1.0223	61.2	0.012	959.3	38.9	88	1.3418	0.030	0.016	0.008	1.389	1.364	71.83		
6.50	1.0225	1.0243	66.5	0.013	956.0	42.2	95	1.3425	0.033	0.018	0.009	1.432	1.403	69.69		
7.00	1.0245	1.0263	71.7	0.014	952.7	45.5	103	1.3433	0.036	0.019	0.010	1.477	1.444	67.59		
7.50	1.0265	1.0283	77.0	0.015	949.5	48.7	110	1.3440	0.039	0.021	0.011	1.523	1.487	65.52		
8.00	1.0286	1.0304	82.3	0.016	946.3	52.0	118	1.3448	0.043	0.023	0.012	1.572	1.531	63.49		
8.50	1.0307	1.0325	87.6	0.017	943.1	55.2	125	1.3455	0.047	0.025	0.013	1.623	1.578	61.50		
9.00	1.0329	1.0347	93.0	0.018	939.9	58.3	133	1.3463	0.051	0.027	0.014	1.676	1.626	59.56		
9.50	1.0351	1.0370	98.3	0.019	936.8	61.4	141	1.3471	0.055	0.030	0.015	1.731	1.675	57.67		
10.00	1.0374	1.0393	103.7	0.020	933.7	64.5	148	1.3478	0.060	0.032	0.017	1.788	1.727	55.82		

* Supersaturated solutions.

26 LACTIC ACID, $CH_3CHOHCOOH$, (D-PROPANOIC ACID, 2-HYDROXY)

MOLECULAR WEIGHT = 90.08
RELATIVE SPECIFIC REFRACTIVITY = 1.058

0.00 % by wt. data are the same for all compounds.
For Values of 0.00 wt. % solutions see Table 1, Acetic Acid.

A % by wt.	ρ D_4^{20}	D_{20}^{20}	C_s g/l	M g-mol/l	C_w g/l	$(C_o - C_w)$ g/l	$(n - n_o)$ $\times 10^4$	n	Δ °C	O Os/kg	S g-mol/l	η/η_o	η/ρ cS	ϕ rhe	γ mmho/cm	T g-mol/l
0.50	0.9992	1.0010	05.0	0.055	994.2	4.0	5	1.3335	0.095	0.051	0.027	1.012	1.015	98.62	1.0	0.010
1.00	1.0002	1.0020	10.0	0.111	990.2	8.0	10	1.3340	0.190	0.102	0.054	1.025	1.027	97.37	1.8	0.018
2.00	1.0023	1.0040	20.0	0.223	982.2	16.0	20	1.3350	0.378	0.203	0.109	1.054	1.053	94.69	2.6	0.026
3.00	1.0043	1.0061	30.1	0.334	974.2	24.0	30	1.3360	0.567	0.305	0.165	1.082	1.078	92.27	3.2	0.031
4.00	1.0065	1.0083	40.3	0.447	966.2	32.0	40	1.3370	0.758	0.407	0.221	1.108	1.102	90.05	3.5	0.035
5.00	1.0086	1.0104	50.4	0.560	958.2	40.0	50	1.3380	0.953	0.512	0.278	1.136	1.127	87.85	3.8	0.038
6.00	1.0108	1.0126	60.6	0.673	950.2	48.1	60	1.3390	1.155	0.621	0.337	1.165	1.154	85.64	4.1	0.041
7.00	1.0131	1.0149	70.9	0.787	942.1	56.1	70	1.3400	1.361	0.732	0.398	1.196	1.181	83.47	4.4	0.043
8.00	1.0153	1.0171	81.2	0.902	934.1	64.1	80	1.3410	1.573	0.846	0.460	1.227	1.210	81.34	4.6	0.045
9.00	1.0176	1.0194	91.6	1.017	926.0	72.2	90	1.3420	1.791	0.963	0.524	1.259	1.239	79.24	4.7	0.047
10.00	1.0199	1.0217	102.0	1.132	917.9	80.3	100	1.3430	2.015	1.084	0.589	1.293	1.269	77.19	4.9	0.049
12.00	1.0246	1.0264	123.0	1.365	901.6	96.6	120	1.3450	2.491	1.339	0.726	1.363	1.332	73.20	5.1	0.051
14.00	1.0294	1.0312	144.1	1.600	885.2	113.0	140	1.3470	2.988	1.607	0.868	1.438	1.399	69.38	5.2	0.052
16.00	1.0342	1.0360	165.5	1.837	868.7	129.5	161	1.3491	3.478	1.870	1.006	1.519	1.471	65.71	5.2	0.052
18.00	1.0390	1.0408	187.0	2.076	852.0	146.3	181	1.3511	3.962	2.130	1.141	1.604	1.546	62.22	5.2	0.052
20.00	1.0439	1.0457	208.8	2.318	835.1	163.1	202	1.3532	4.440	2.387	1.273	1.696	1.628	58.84	5.1	0.051
24.00	1.0536	1.0554	252.9	2.807	800.7	197.5	243	1.3573				1.898	1.806	52.57	4.9	0.048
28.00	1.0632	1.0651	297.7	3.305	765.5	232.7	285	1.3615				2.132	2.010	46.80	4.5	0.045
32.00	1.0728	1.0747	343.3	3.811	729.5	268.8	327	1.3657				2.409	2.251	41.43	4.1	0.041
36.00	1.0822	1.0841	389.6	4.325	692.6	305.7	370	1.3700				2.725	2.524	36.63	3.7	0.036
40.00	1.0915	1.0934	436.6	4.847	654.9	343.4	413	1.3743				3.108	2.853	32.11	3.2	0.032
44.00	1.1008	1.1028	484.4	5.377	616.5	381.8	456	1.3786				3.559	3.239	28.04	2.8	0.027
48.00	1.1105	1.1125	533.0	5.917	577.5	420.8	498	1.3828				4.098	3.699	24.35	2.3	0.022
52.00	1.1201	1.1221	582.4	6.466	537.5	460.6	541	1.3871				4.779	4.276	20.89	1.8	0.018
56.00	1.1297	1.1317	632.6	7.023	497.0	501.2	584	1.3914				5.568	4.940	17.93	1.5	0.014
60.00	1.1392	1.1412	683.5	7.588	455.7	542.6	628	1.3958				6.666	5.865	14.97	1.1	0.011
64.00	1.1486	1.1506	735.1	8.160	413.5	584.7	671	1.4001				8.008	6.988	12.46	0.8	0.008
68.00	1.1579	1.1599	787.4	8.741	370.5	627.7	715	1.4045				9.843	8.519	10.14	0.5	0.005
72.00	1.1670	1.1691	840.3	9.328	326.8	671.5	758	1.4088				12.84	11.02	7.77	0.3	0.003
76.00	1.1760	1.1781	893.8	9.922	282.2	716.0	801	1.4131				16.94	14.43	5.89	0.1	0.001
80.00	1.1848	1.1869	947.9	10.523	237.0	761.3	843	1.4173				22.12	18.70	4.51	0.1	0.001

27 LACTOSE, $C_{12}H_{22}O_{11} \cdot 1H_2O$

MOLECULAR WEIGHT = 342.30   FORMULA WEIGHT, HYDRATE = 360.31
RELATIVE SPECIFIC REFRACTIVITY = 1.036

0.00 % by wt. data are the same for all compounds.
For Values of 0.00 wt. % solutions see Table 1, Acetic Acid.

A % by wt.	H % by wt.	ρ D_4^{20}	D_{20}^{20}	C_s g/l	M g-mol/l	C_w g/l	$(C_o - C_w)$ g/l	$(n - n_o)$ $\times 10^4$	n	Δ °C	O Os/kg	S g-mol/l	η/η_o	η/ρ cS	ϕ rhe	γ mmho/cm	T g-mol/l
0.50	0.53	1.0002	1.0019	5.0	0.015	995.2	3.1	7	1.3337	0.027	0.015	0.007	1.011	1.013	98.71		
1.00	1.05	1.0021	1.0039	10.0	0.029	992.1	6.1	15	1.3345	0.055	0.030	0.015	1.024	1.024	97.46		
1.50	1.58	1.0041	1.0059	15.1	0.044	989.0	9.2	22	1.3352	0.083	0.045	0.023	1.039	1.037	96.01		
2.00	2.11	1.0061	1.0079	20.1	0.059	986.0	12.3	30	1.3359	0.112	0.060	0.031	1.056	1.052	94.51		
2.50	2.63	1.0081	1.0099	25.2	0.074	982.9	15.3	37	1.3367	0.140	0.075	0.040	1.072	1.065	93.12		
3.00	3.16	1.0102	1.0119	30.3	0.089	979.8	18.4	45	1.3375	0.169	0.091	0.048	1.087	1.078	91.80		
3.50	3.68	1.0122	1.0140	35.4	0.103	976.8	21.5	53	1.3382	0.198	0.107	0.056	1.103	1.091	90.52		
4.00	4.21	1.0143	1.0160	40.6	0.119	973.7	24.6	60	1.3390	0.228	0.122	0.065	1.118	1.105	89.25		
4.50	4.74	1.0163	1.0181	45.7	0.134	970.6	27.7	68	1.3398	0.258	0.139	0.074	1.135	1.119	87.96		
5.00	5.26	1.0184	1.0202	50.9	0.149	967.5	30.8	76	1.3406	0.288	0.155	0.083	1.152	1.133	86.63		
5.50	5.79	1.0204	1.0223	56.1	0.164	964.3	33.9	84	1.3413	0.319	0.172	0.092	1.170	1.149	85.27		

A% by wt.	H% by wt.	ρ D_4^{20}	D_{20}^{20}	C_n g/l	M g-mol/l	C_w g/l	$(C_0 - C_w)$ g/l	$(n - n_0)$ $\times 10^4$	n	Δ °C	O Os/kg	S g-mol/l	η/η_0	η/ρ cS	ϕ rhe	γ mmho/cm	T g-mol/l
6.00	6.32	1.0225	1.0243	61.4	0.179	961.2	37.1	91	1.3421	0.351	0.189	0.101	1.189	1.166	83.91		
6.50	6.84	1.0246	1.0264	66.6	0.195	958.0	40.2	99	1.3429	0.385	0.207	0.111	1.209	1.183	82.54		
7.00	7.37	1.0267	1.0285	71.9	0.210	954.8	43.4	107	1.3437	0.420	0.226	0.121	1.230	1.200	81.16		
7.50	7.89	1.0287	1.0305	77.2	0.225	951.6	46.7	115	1.3445	0.456	0.245	0.132	1.251	1.218	79.79		
8.00	8.42	1.0308	1.0326	82.5	0.241	948.3	49.9	123	1.3453	0.495	0.266	0.143	1.273	1.237	78 42		
8.50	8.95	1.0329	1.0347	87.8	0.256	945.1	53.2	130	1.3460				1.295	1.257	77.05		
9.00	9.47	1.0349	1.0367	93.1	0.272	941.8	56.5	138	1.3468				1.318	1.277	75.69		
9.50	10.00	1.0370	1.0388	98.5	0.288	938.5	59.8	146	1.3476				1.342	1.297	74.34		
10.00	10.53	1.0390	1.0409	103.9	0.304	935.1	63.1	154	1.3484				1.367	1.318	73.01		
11.00	11.58	1.0432	1.0450	114.7	0.335	928.4	69.8	170	1.3500				1.418	1.362	70.37		
12.00	12.63	1.0473	1.0492	125.7	0.367	921.7	76.6	185	1.3515				1.473	1.409	67.77		
13.00	13.68	1.0515	1.0534	136.7	0.399	914.8	83.4	201	1.3531				1.530	1.458	65.24		
14.00	14.74	1.0558	1.0577	147.8	0.432	908.0	90.2	218	1.3548				1.590	1.509	62.76		
15.00	15.79	1.0602	1.0621	159.0	0.465	901.2	97.0	234	1.3564				1.654	1.563	60.35		
16.00	16.84	1.0648	1.0667	170.4	0.498	894.4	103.8	252	1.3582				1.721	1.619	58.01		
17.00	17.89	1.0696	1.0714	181.8	0.531	887.7	110.5	270	1.3600				1.791	1.678	55.73		
18.00	18.95	1.0746	1.0765	193.4	0.565	881.2	117.1	289	1.3619				1.865	1.739	53.51		

28 LANTHANUM NITRATE, $La(NO_3)_3 \cdot 6H_2O$

MOLECULAR WEIGHT = 324.93   FORMULA WEIGHT, HYDRATE = 433.02

A% by wt.	H% by wt.	ρ D_4^{20}	D_{20}^{20}	C_S g/l	M g-mol/l	C_W g/l	$(C_0 - C_W)$ g/l	$(n - n_0)$ $\times 10^4$	n	Δ °C	O Os/kg	S g-mol/l	η/η_0	η/ρ cS	ϕ rhe	γ mmho/cm	T g-mol/l
1.00	1.33	1.0062	1.0080	10.1	0.031	996.1	2.1	14.	1.3344	0.180	0.097	0.051	1.013	1.009	98.50	7.8	0.080
2.00	2.67	1.0142	1.0160	20.3	0.062	993.9	4.3	28.	1.3358	0.358	0.192	0.103	1.025	1.013	97.33	14.2	0.151
3.00	4.00	1.0226	1.0244	30.7	0.094	991.9	6.3	42.	1.3372	0.525	0.283	0.152	1.040	1.019	95.97	20.1	0.221
4.00	5.33	1.0309	1.0328	41.2	0.127	989.7	8.5	57.	1.3387	0.698	0.375	0.203	1.056	1.026	94.54	25.6	0.289
5.00	6.66	1.0394	1.0413	52.0	0.160	987.4	10.8	71.	1.3401	0.889	0.478	0.259	1.074	1.035	92.96	31.1	0.358
6.00	8.00	1.0483	1.0502	62.9	0.194	985.4	12.8	86.	1.3416	1.079	0.580	0.315	1.091	1.043	91.46	36.0	0.420
7.00	9.33	1.0575	1.0594	74.0	0.228	983.5	14.7	101.	1.3431	1.266	0.681	0.370	1.110	1.052	89.89	40.6	0.479
8.00	10.66	1.0667	1.0686	85.3	0.263	981.4	16.8	115.	1.3445	1.463	0.787	0.428	1.130	1.061	88.36	45.0	0.535
9.00	11.99	1.0761	1.0780	96.8	0.298	979.3	18.9	130.	1.3460	1.676	0.901	0.490	1.149	1.070	86.85	49.5	0.596
10.00	13.33	1.0853	1.0873	108.5	0.334	976.8	21.4	145.	1.3475	1.874	1.007	0.548	1.170	1.080	85.32	53.4	0.648
12.00	15.99	1.1055	1.1075	132.7	0.408	972.8	25.4	176.	1.3506	2.340	1.258	0.683	1.214	1.100	82.23	60.7	0.750
14.00	18.66	1.1251	1.1271	157.5	0.485	967.6	30.6	208.	1.3538	2.822	1.517	0.821	1.262	1.124	79.08	67.4	0.845
16.00	21.32	1.1456	1.1477	183.3	0.564	962.3	35.9	241.	1.3571	3.331	1.791	0.965	1.322	1.156	75.51	73.2	0.930
18.00	23.99	1.1667	1.1688	210.0	0.646	956.7	41.5	274.	1.3604	3.869	2.080	1.115	1.390	1.194	71.79	77.7	0.999
20.00	26.65	1.1892	1.1914	237.9	0.732	951.3	46.9	308.	1.3638	4.418	2.375	1.267	1.463	1.233	68.20	81.4	1.055
24.00	31.98	1.2337	1.2359	296.1	0.911	937.6	60.6	379.	1.3709				1.641	1.333	60.81	86.7	1.137
28.00	37.31	1.2829	1.2852	359.2	1.105	923.7	74.5	453.	1.3783				1.854	1.448	53.83	86.8	1.138
32.00	42.64	1.3319	1.3343	426.2	1.312	905.7	92.5	530.	1.3860				2.156	1.622	46.29	84.0	1.095
36.00	47.98	1.3874	1.3899	499.5	1.537	887.9	110.3	613.	1.3943				2.580	1.863	38.69	81.4	1.055
40.00	53.31	1.4477	1.4503	579.1	1.782	868.6	129.6	700.	1.4030				3.205	2.218	31.14	71.9	0.911
44.00	58.64	1.5084	1.5111	663.7	2.043	844.7	153.5	788.	1.4118				4.105	2.727	24.31	61.9	0.767

29 LEAD NITRATE, Pb(NO₃)₂

MOLECULAR WEIGHT = 331.23
RELATIVE SPECIFIC REFRACTIVITY = 0.479

0.00 % by wt. data are the same for all compounds.
For Values of 0.00 wt. % solutions see Table 1, Acetic Acid.

A % by wt.	ρ D_4^{20}	D_{20}^{20}	C_s g/l	M g-mol/l	C_w g/l	$(C_o - C_w)$ g/l	$(n - n_o)$ × 10⁴	n	Δ °C	O Os/kg	S g-mol/l	η/η_o	η/ρ cS	ϕ rhe	γ mmho/cm	T g-mol/l
0.50	1.0025	1.0043	5.0	0.015	997.5	0.8	6	1.3336	0.072	0.039	0.020	1.003	1.003	99.49	2.8	0.028
1.00	1.0068	1.0086	10.1	0.030	996.7	1.5	12	1.3342	0.137	0.074	0.039	1.006	1.001	99.21	5.4	0.054
2.00	1.0155	1.0173	20.3	0.061	995.2	3.1	24	1.3354	0.258	0.139	0.074	1.011	0.998	98.71	9.6	0.099
3.00	1.0243	1.0261	30.7	0.093	993.6	4.6	36	1.3366	0.372	0.200	0.107	1.016	0.993	98.27	13.3	0.141
4.00	1.0333	1.0352	41.3	0.125	992.0	6.2	49	1.3379	0.482	0.259	0.140	1.020	0.989	97.85	16.7	0.181
5.00	1.0425	1.0444	52.1	0.157	990.4	7.8	61	1.3391	0.587	0.316	0.170	1.025	0.985	97.37	19.9	0.219
6.00	1.0519	1.0537	63.1	0.191	988.7	9.5	73	1.3403	0.690	0.371	0.201	1.031	0.982	96.78	23.0	0.256
7.00	1.0614	1.0632	74.3	0.224	987.1	11.2	86	1.3415	0.792	0.426	0.231	1.038	0.980	96.12	25.9	0.292
8.00	1.0710	1.0729	85.7	0.259	985.4	12.9	98	1.3428	0.891	0.479	0.260	1.046	0.979	95.40	28.6	0.326
9.00	1.0809	1.0828	97.3	0.294	983.6	14.6	110	1.3440	0.987	0.531	0.288	1.054	0.978	94.64	31.3	0.360
10.00	1.0909	1.0929	109.1	0.329	981.8	16.4	124	1.3454	1.081	0.581	0.316	1.063	0.976	93.89	33.9	0.393
12.00	1.1115	1.1135	133.4	0.403	978.1	20.1	151	1.3481	1.265	0.680	0.370	1.081	0.974	92.33	38.9	0.457
14.00	1.1329	1.1349	158.6	0.479	974.3	24.0	180	1.3510	1.450	0.780	0.424	1.101	0.973	90.69	43.4	0.515
16.00	1.1550	1.1571	184.8	0.558	970.2	28.0	209	1.3539	1.639	0.881	0.479	1.122	0.973	88.94	47.5	0.570
18.00	1.1779	1.1800	212.0	0.640	965.9	32.3	239	1.3569	1.825	0.981	0.534	1.146	0.975	87.10	51.4	0.621
20.00	1.2017	1.2038	240.3	0.726	961.4	36.9	271	1.3601	2.008	1.080	0.587	1.172	0.977	85.15	55.2	0.673
24.00	1.2519	1.2541	300.5	0.907	951.5	46.8	337	1.3667	2.361	1.269	0.689	1.233	0.987	80.97	62.5	0.772
28.00	1.3059	1.3082	365.7	1.104	940.3	58.0	407	1.3737	2.714	1.459	0.790	1.306	1.002	76.43	68.4	0.858
32.00	1.3640	1.3664	436.5	1.318	927.5	70.7	481	1.3811				1.398	1.027	71.39	72.5	0.920
34.00	1.3947	1.3972	474.2	1.432	920.5	77.7	520	1.3850				1.459	1.048	68.42	74.8	0.954

30 LITHIUM CHLORIDE, LiCl

MOLECULAR WEIGHT = 42.40
RELATIVE SPECIFIC REFRACTIVITY = 1.023

0.00 % by wt. data are the same for all compounds.
For Values of 0.00 wt. % solutions see Table 1, Acetic Acid.

A % by wt.	ρ D_4^{20}	D_{20}^{20}	C_s g/l	M g-mol/l	C_w g/l	$(C_o - C_w)$ g/l	$(n - n_o)$ × 10⁴	n	Δ °C	O Os/kg	S g-mol/l	η/η_o	η/ρ cS	ϕ rhe	γ mmho/cm	T g-mol/l
0.50	1.0012	1.0029	5.0	0.118	996.2	2.1	11	1.3341	0.415	0.223	0.120	1.017	1.018	98.08	10.1	0.105
1.00	1.0041	1.0059	10.0	0.237	994.0	4.2	21	1.3351	0.836	0.450	0.244	1.035	1.033	96.43	19.0	0.208
2.00	1.0099	1.0117	20.2	0.476	989.7	8.5	43	1.3373	1.724	0.927	0.504	1.070	1.062	93.27	34.9	0.406
3.00	1.0157	1.0175	30.5	0.719	985.2	13.0	64	1.3394	2.684	1.443	0.782	1.106	1.091	90.22	49.8	0.600
4.00	1.0215	1.0233	40.9	0.964	980.6	17.6	85	1.3415	3.727	2.004	1.075	1.144	1.122	87.26	63.6	0.791
5.00	1.0272	1.0290	51.4	1.211	975.9	22.4	106	1.3436	4.859	2.612	1.386	1.183	1.154	84.36	76.4	0.978
6.00	1.0330	1.0348	62.0	1.462	971.0	27.2	127	1.3457	6.14	3.30	1.723	1.224	1.187	81.55	88.3	1.16
7.00	1.0387	1.0405	72.7	1.715	966.0	32.2	148	1.3478	7.56	4.07	2.081	1.266	1.221	78.83	99.5	1.34
8.00	1.0444	1.0463	83.6	1.971	960.9	37.3	169	1.3499	9.11	4.90	2.449	1.310	1.257	76.16	110.	1.52
9.00	1.0502	1.0521	94.5	2.229	955.7	42.6	190	1.3520	10.79	5.80	2.825	1.357	1.295	73.52	119.	1.69
10.00	1.0560	1.0578	105.6	2.490	950.4	47.9	211	1.3541	12.61	6.78	3.205	1.408	1.336	70.88	127.	1.84
12.00	1.0675	1.0694	128.1	3.021	939.4	58.8	253	1.3583	16.59	8.92	3.951	1.519	1.426	65.68	140.	2.12
14.00	1.0792	1.0811	151.1	3.563	928.1	70.1	295	1.3625	21.04	11.31	4.670	1.644	1.527	60.70	151.	2.34
16.00	1.0910	1.0929	174.6	4.117	916.4	81.8	338	1.3668				1.783	1.637	55.99	160.	2.56
18.00	1.1029	1.1048	198.5	4.682	904.4	93.9	381	1.3711				1.938	1.761	51.50	167.	2.73
20.00	1.1150	1.1170	223.0	5.260	892.0	106.2	425	1.3755				2.124	1.909	46.99	170.	2.80
22.00	1.1274	1.1294	248.0	5.850	879.3	118.9	469	1.3799				2.336	2.076	42.72	170.	2.79
24.00	1.1399	1.1419	273.6	6.452	866.3	131.9	514	1.3844				2.595	2.281	38.46	167.	2.73
26.00	1.1527	1.1548	299.7	7.069	853.0	145.2	560	1.3890				2.919	2.537	34.19	163.	2.63
28.00	1.1658	1.1678	326.4	7.699	839.4	158.9	606	1.3936				3.311	2.846	30.14	156.	2.47
30.00	1.1791	1.1812	353.7	8.343	825.4	172.9	653	1.3983				3.777	3.210	26.42	146.	2.25

31 MAGNESIUM CHLORIDE, MgCl₂ · 6H₂O

MOLECULAR WEIGHT = 95.23   FORMULA WEIGHT, HYDRATE = 203.33
RELATIVE SPECIFIC REFRACTIVITY = 0.893

0.00 % by wt. data are the same for all compounds.
For Values of 0.00 wt. % solutions see Table 1, Acetic Acid.

A% by wt.	H% by wt.	ρ D_4^{20}	D_{20}^{20}	C_s g/l	M g-mol/l	C_w g/l	$(C_o - C_w)$ g/l	$(n - n_o)$ $\times 10^4$	n	Δ °C	O Os/kg	S g-mol/l	η/η_o	η/ρ cS	ϕ rhe	γ mmho/cm	T g-mol/l
0.50	1.07	1.0022	1.0040	5.0	0.053	997.2	1.0	13	1.3343	0.255	0.137	0.073	1.022	1.022	97.66	8.6	0.092
1.00	2.14	1.0062	1.0080	10.1	0.106	996.2	2.0	26	1.3356	0.517	0.278	0.150	1.044	1.040	95.59	16.6	0.183
2.00	4.27	1.0144	1.0162	20.3	0.213	994.1	4.1	51	1.3381	1.063	0.572	0.311	1.089	1.076	91.60	31.2	0.356
3.00	6.41	1.0226	1.0244	30.7	0.322	991.9	6.3	76	1.3406	1.653	0.889	0.483	1.137	1.114	87.80	44.5	0.530
4.00	8.54	1.0309	1.0328	41.2	0.433	989.7	8.5	102	1.3432	2.297	1.235	0.671	1.186	1.153	84.13	56.4	0.690
5.00	10.68	1.0394	1.0412	52.0	0.546	987.4	10.8	127	1.3457	3.012	1.619	0.875	1.239	1.194	80.57	66.9	0.840
6.00	12.81	1.0479	1.0497	62.9	0.660	985.0	13.2	153	1.3483				1.295	1.238	77.09	77.2	0.990
7.00	14.95	1.0564	1.0583	74.0	0.777	982.5	15.7	178	1.3508				1.355	1.285	73.67	86.4	1.13
8.00	17.08	1.0651	1.0670	85.2	0.895	979.9	18.3	204	1.3534				1.420	1.336	70.30	94.5	1.26
9.00	19.22	1.0738	1.0757	96.6	1.015	977.2	21.1	231	1.3560				1.490	1.390	66.98	102.0	1.38
10.00	21.35	1.0826	1.0845	108.3	1.137	974.4	23.9	257	1.3587				1.567	1.450	63.70	108.0	1.49
12.00	25.62	1.1005	1.1025	132.1	1.387	968.5	29.8	311	1.3641				1.742	1.586	57.30	119.0	1.69
14.00	29.89	1.1189	1.1209	156.6	1.645	962.3	36.0	365	1.3695				1.952	1.748	51.13	127.0	1.84
16.00	34.16	1.1372	1.1392	181.9	1.911	955.2	43.0	419	1.3749				2.203	1.941	45.30	132.0	1.94
18.00	38.43	1.1553	1.1574	208.0	2.184	947.4	50.8	474	1.3804				2.502	2.170	39.89	134.0	1.99
20.00	42.70	1.1742	1.1763	234.8	2.466	939.4	58.9	529	1.3859				2.861	2.441	34.89	134.0	1.99
22.00	46.97	1.1938	1.1959	262.6	2.758	931.2	67.1	585	1.3915				3.316	2.783	30.10	131.0	1.93
24.00	51.24	1.2140	1.2162	291.4	3.060	922.6	75.6	642	1.3972				3.909	3.226	25.53	126.0	1.81
26.00	55.51	1.2346	1.2368	321.0	3.371	913.6	84.6	700	1.4030				4.685	3.802	21.30	118.0	1.67
28.00	59.78	1.2555	1.2577	351.5	3.691	903.9	94.3	759	1.4089				5.698	4.547	17.52	109.0	1.50
30.00	64.05	1.2763	1.2786	382.9	4.021	893.4	104.8	818	1.4148				7.003	5.498	14.25	97.9	1.32

32 MAGNESIUM SULFATE, MgSO₄ · 7H₂O

MOLECULAR WEIGHT = 120.37   FORMULA WEIGHT, HYDRATE = 246.48
RELATIVE SPECIFIC REFRACTIVITY = 0.572

0.00 % by wt. data are the same for all compounds.
For Values of 0.00 wt. % solutions see Table 1, Acetic Acid.

A% by wt.	H% by wt.	ρ D_4^{20}	D_{20}^{20}	C_s g/l	M g-mol/l	C_w g/l	$(C_o - C_w)$ g/l	$(n - n_o)$ $\times 10^4$	n	Δ °C	O Os/kg	S g-mol/l	η/η_o	η/ρ cS	ϕ rhe	γ mmho/cm	T g-mol/l
0.50	1.02	1.0033	1.0051	5.0	0.042	998.3	0.0	10	1.3340	0.103	0.055	0.029	1.025	1.024	97.35	4.1	0.041
1.00	2.05	1.0084	1.0102	10.1	0.084	998.3	−0.1	20	1.3350	0.192	0.103	0.055	1.052	1.045	94.88	7.6	0.078
2.00	4.10	1.0186	1.0204	20.4	0.169	998.2	0.0	41	1.3371	0.361	0.194	0.104	1.110	1.092	89.91	13.3	0.141
3.00	6.15	1.0289	1.0307	30.9	0.256	998.0	0.2	61	1.3391	0.522	0.281	0.151	1.175	1.144	84.94	18.4	0.201
4.00	8.19	1.0392	1.0411	41.6	0.345	997.6	0.6	81	1.3411	0.692	0.372	0.201	1.247	1.202	80.05	23.1	0.258
5.00	10.24	1.0497	1.0515	52.5	0.436	997.2	1.1	101	1.3431	0.868	0.467	0.253	1.325	1.265	75.32	27.4	0.311
6.00	12.29	1.0602	1.0621	63.6	0.528	996.6	1.6	121	1.3451	1.048	0.564	0.306	1.408	1.330	70.90	31.1	0.358
7.00	14.34	1.0708	1.0727	75.0	0.623	995.9	2.3	142	1.3471	1.235	0.664	0.361	1.495	1.399	66.77	34.4	0.399
8.00	16.39	1.0816	1.0835	86.5	0.719	995.1	3.2	162	1.3492	1.431	0.770	0.419	1.590	1.473	62.75	37.3	0.436
9.00	18.44	1.0924	1.0944	98.3	0.817	994.1	4.1	182	1.3512	1.635	0.879	0.478	1.699	1.558	58.75	40.0	0.471
10.00	20.48	1.1034	1.1053	110.3	0.917	993.0	5.2	202	1.3532	1.849	0.994	0.541	1.825	1.657	54.69	42.7	0.506
12.00	24.57	1.1257	1.1276	135.1	1.122	990.6	7.7	242	1.3572	2.313	1.243	0.675	2.100	1.869	47.53	48.4	0.581
14.00	28.67	1.1484	1.1504	160.8	1.335	987.6	10.6	283	1.3613	2.861	1.538	0.832	2.407	2.100	41.46	53.3	0.647
16.00	32.76	1.1717	1.1737	187.5	1.557	984.2	14.0	324	1.3654	3.673	1.974	1.061	2.803	2.397	35.61	55.2	0.673
18.00	36.86	1.1955	1.1976	215.2	1.787	980.3	17.9	364	1.3694				3.353	2.810	29.77	53.7	0.652
20.00	40.95	1.2198	1.2220	244.0	2.026	975.9	22.4	405	1.3735				4.139	3.400	24.11	51.1	0.617
22.00	45.05	1.2447	1.2469	273.8	2.275	970.9	27.4	446	1.3776				5.189	4.177	19.23	48.8	0.586
24.00	49.14	1.2701	1.2724	304.8	2.532	965.3	32.9	487	1.3817				6.485	5.116	15.39	45.9	0.547
26.00	53.24	1.2961	1.2984	337.0	2.799	959.1	39.1	528	1.3858				8.050	6.223	12.40	42.3	0.500

33 MALTOSE, C₁₂H₂₂O₁₁ · 1H₂O

MOLECULAR WEIGHT = 342.29   FORMULA WEIGHT, HYDRATE = 360.31
RELATIVE SPECIFIC REFRACTIVITY = 1.038

0.00 % by wt. data are the same for all compounds.
For Values of 0.00 wt. % solutions see Table 1, Acetic Acid.

A% by wt.	H% by wt.	ρ D_4^{20}	D_{20}^{20}	C_s g/l	M g-mol/l	C_w g/l	$(C_o - C_w)$ g/l	$(n - n_o)$ $\times 10^4$	n	Δ °C	O Os/kg	S g-mol/l	η/η_o	η/ρ cS	ϕ rhe	γ mmho/cm	T g-mol/l
0.50	0.53	1.0003	1.0020	5.0	0.015	995.3	3.0	7	1.3337	0.027	0.015	0.007	1.014	1.016	98.45		
1.00	1.05	1.0023	1.0041	10.0	0.029	992.3	6.0	15	1.3345	0.055	0.030	0.015	1.028	1.028	97.08		
1.50	1.58	1.0043	1.0061	15.1	0.044	989.2	9.0	22	1.3352	0.083	0.045	0.023	1.043	1.040	95.71		
2.00	2.11	1.0063	1.0081	20.1	0.059	986.2	12.0	29	1.3359	0.112	0.060	0.031	1.058	1.053	94.33		
2.50	2.63	1.0083	1.0101	25.2	0.074	983.1	15.1	37	1.3367	0.140	0.075	0.040	1.074	1.067	92.95		
3.00	3.16	1.0104	1.0121	30.3	0.089	980.0	18.2	44	1.3374	0.169	0.091	0.048	1.090	1.081	91.56		
3.50	3.68	1.0124	1.0142	35.4	0.104	976.9	21.3	52	1.3382	0.199	0.107	0.057	1.107	1.095	90.17		
4.00	4.21	1.0144	1.0162	40.6	0.119	973.8	24.4	59	1.3389	0.229	0.123	0.065	1.124	1.110	88.78		
4.50	4.74	1.0164	1.0182	45.7	0.134	970.7	27.0	67	1.3397	0.259	0.139	0.074	1.142	1.126	87.41		
5.00	5.26	1.0184	1.0202	50.9	0.149	967.5	30.7	74	1.3404	0.290	0.156	0.082	1.160	1.141	86.03		
5.50	5.79	1.0204	1.0222	56.1	0.164	964.3	33.9	82	1.3412	0.321	0.172	0.092	1.179	1.157	84.68		
6.00	6.32	1.0224	1.0243	61.3	0.179	961.1	37.1	90	1.3420	0.352	0.189	0.101	1.198	1.174	83.34		
6.50	6.84	1.0245	1.0263	66.6	0.195	957.9	40.4	97	1.3427	0.384	0.206	0.111	1.217	1.190	82.01		
7.00	7.37	1.0265	1.0283	71.9	0.210	954.6	43.6	105	1.3435	0.416	0.224	0.120	1.237	1.207	80.69		
7.50	7.89	1.0285	1.0303	77.1	0.225	951.3	46.9	113	1.3443	0.449	0.241	0.130	1.257	1.225	79.38		
8.00	8.42	1.0305	1.0323	82.4	0.241	948.0	50.2	120	1.3450	0.482	0.259	0.139	1.278	1.243	78.07		
8.50	8.95	1.0325	1.0343	87.8	0.256	944.7	53.5	128	1.3458	0.516	0.277	0.149	1.300	1.262	76.77		
9.00	9.47	1.0345	1.0363	93.1	0.272	941.4	56.8	136	1.3466	0.550	0.296	0.159	1.322	1.281	75.48		
9.50	10.00	1.0365	1.0383	98.5	0.288	938.0	60.2	144	1.3474	0.584	0.314	0.169	1.345	1.300	74.19		
10.00	10.53	1.0385	1.0403	103.8	0.303	934.6	63.6	152	1.3482	0.619	0.333	0.180	1.369	1.321	72.90		
11.00	11.58	1.0425	1.0443	114.7	0.335	927.8	70.4	167	1.3497	0.691	0.371	0.201	1.419	1.364	70.34		
12.00	12.63	1.0465	1.0483	125.6	0.367	920.9	77.3	183	1.3513	0.765	0.411	0.223	1.471	1.409	67.83		

33 MALTOSE, $C_{12}H_{22}O_{11} \cdot 1H_2O$—(Continued)

A% by wt.	H% by wt.	ρ D_4^{20}	D_{20}^{20}	C_s g/l	M g-mol/l	C_w g/l	$(C_o - C_w)$ g/l	$(n - n_o)$ $\times 10^4$	n	Δ °C	O Os/kg	S g-mol/l	η/η_o	η/ρ cS	ϕ rhe	γ mmho/cm	T g-mol/l
13.00	13.68	1.0505	1.0523	136.6	0.399	913.9	84.3	199	1.3529	0.841	0.452	0.245	1.527	1.456	65.37		
14.00	14.74	1.0545	1.0563	147.6	0.431	906.8	91.4	216	1.3546	0.919	0.494	0.268	1.585	1.506	62.97		
15.00	15.79	1.0585	1.0603	158.8	0.464	899.7	98.6	232	1.3562	1.000	0.538	0.292	1.646	1.558	60.63		
16.00	16.84	1.0629	1.0648	170.1	0.497	892.8	105.4	248	1.3578	1.080	0.581	0.315	1.712	1.614	58.31		
17.00	17.89	1.0672	1.0691	181.4	0.530	885.8	112.4	265	1.3595	1.165	0.626	0.340	1.780	1.672	56.05		
18.00	18.95	1.0716	1.0735	192.9	0.563	878.7	119.5	282	1.3612	1.250	0.672	0.365	1.855	1.735	53.79		
19.00	20.00	1.0759	1.0778	204.4	0.597	871.5	126.7	298	1.3628	1.338	0.719	0.391	1.936	1.803	51.55		
20.00	21.05	1.0801	1.0820	216.0	0.631	864.1	134.1	314	1.3644	1.430	0.769	0.418	2.017	1.871	49.48		
22.00	23.16	1.0894	1.0913	239.7	0.700	849.7	148.5	348	1.3678	1.635	0.879	0.478	2.212	2.034	45.13		
24.00	25.26	1.0984	1.1004	263.6	0.770	834.8	163.4	384	1.3714	1.848	0.993	0.540	2.458	2.242	40.60		
26.00	27.37	1.1080	1.1100	288.1	0.841	819.9	178.3	419	1.3749	2.080	1.118	0.608	2.748	2.485	36.32		
28.00	29.47	1.1171	1.1191	312.8	0.913	804.3	193.9	455	1.3785	2.335	1.255	0.681	3.060	2.745	32.62		
30.00	31.58	1.1269	1.1289	338.1	0.987	788.8	209.4	491	1.3821	2.615	1.406	0.762	3.420	3.041	29.18		
32.00	33.68	1.1367	1.1387	363.7	1.062	773.0	225.2	528	1.3858	2.925	1.572	0.850	3.910	3.447	25.52		
34.00	35.79	1.1463	1.1483	389.7	1.138	756.6	241.6	566	1.3896	3.252	1.748	0.943	4.438	3.879	22.49		
36.00	37.89	1.1561	1.1582	416.2	1.215	739.9	258.3	605	1.3935	3.600	1.935	1.040	5.040	4.368	19.80		
38.00	40.00	1.1663	1.1684	443.2	1.294	723.1	275.1	644	1.3974	3.990	2.145	1.148	5.820	5.000	17.15		
40.00	42.10	1.1769	1.1790	470.8	1.375	706.1	292.1	683	1.4013	4.408	2.370	1.264	6.912	5.885	14.44		
42.00	44.21	1.1878	1.1899	498.9	1.457	688.9	309.3	721	1.4051	4.878	2.622	1.390	8.175	6.896	12.21		
44.00	46.31	1.1979	1.2000	527.1	1.539	670.8	327.4	764	1.4094	5.352	2.877	1.518	9.630	8.055	10.36		
46.00	48.42	1.2084	1.2105	555.9	1.623	652.5	345.7	806	1.4136				11.45	9.492	8.72		
48.00	50.52	1.2194	1.2216	585.3	1.709	634.1	364.1	847	1.4177				14.12	11.60	7.07		
50.00	52.63	1.2304	1.2326	615.2	1.796	615.2	383.0	887	1.4217				17.75	14.46	5.62		
52.00	54.74	1.2416	1.2438	645.6	1.885	596.0	402.2	930	1.4260				21.99	17.74	4.54		
54.00	56.84	1.2528	1.2550	676.5	1.975	576.3	421.9	978	1.4308				28.70	22.96	3.48		
56.00	58.94	1.2638	1.2660	707.7	2.066	556.1	442.1	1020	1.4350				38.15	30.25	2.62		
58.00	61.05	1.2746	1.2769	739.3	2.159	535.3	462.9	1064	1.4394				49.20	38.68	2.03		
60.00	63.16	1.2855	1.2878	771.3	2.252	514.2	484.0	1110	1.4440								

34 MANGANOUS SULFATE, $MnSO_4 \cdot 1H_2O$

MOLECULAR WEIGHT = 151.00   FORMULA WEIGHT, HYDRATE = 169.01
RELATIVE SPECIFIC REFRACTIVITY = 0.541

0.00 % by wt. data are the same for all compounds.
For Values of 0.00 wt. % solutions see Table 1, Acetic Acid.

A% by wt.	H% by wt.	ρ D_4^{20}	D_{20}^{20}	C_s g/l	M g-mol/l	C_w g/l	$(C_o - C_w)$ g/l	$(n - n_o)$ $\times 10^4$	n	Δ °C	O Os/kg	S g-mol/l	η/η_o	η/ρ cS	ϕ rhe	γ mmho/cm	T g-mol/l
1.00	1.12	1.0080	1.0098	10.1	0.067	997.9	0.3	18	1.3348	0.160	0.086	0.045	1.044	1.038	95.59	6.2	0.063
2.00	2.24	1.0178	1.0196	20.4	0.135	997.5	0.8	36	1.3366	0.306	0.164	0.088	1.088	1.071	91.73	10.6	0.111
3.00	3.36	1.0277	1.0296	30.8	0.204	996.9	1.3	54	1.3384	0.437	0.235	0.126	1.135	1.107	87.93	14.6	0.157
4.00	4.48	1.0378	1.0396	41.5	0.275	996.3	2.0	72	1.3402	0.569	0.306	0.165	1.185	1.145	84.19	18.3	0.199
5.00	5.60	1.0480	1.0498	52.4	0.347	995.6	2.7	90	1.3420	0.701	0.377	0.204	1.240	1.186	80.48	21.6	0.240
6.00	6.72	1.0583	1.0602	63.5	0.421	994.8	3.4	108	1.3438	0.838	0.451	0.244	1.298	1.229	76.87	24.7	0.278
7.00	7.83	1.0688	1.0707	74.8	0.495	994.0	4.3	127	1.3457	0.978	0.526	0.285	1.360	1.275	73.36	27.4	0.312
8.00	8.95	1.0794	1.0813	86.4	0.572	993.1	5.2	145	1.3475	1.122	0.603	0.328	1.428	1.325	69.90	29.9	0.343
9.00	10.07	1.0902	1.0921	98.1	0.650	992.1	6.1	164	1.3494	1.275	0.685	0.373	1.502	1.380	66.46	32.3	0.372
10.00	11.19	1.1012	1.1031	110.1	0.729	991.1	7.2	183	1.3513	1.439	0.773	0.421	1.584	1.441	63.01	34.5	0.401
11.00	12.31	1.1123	1.1143	122.4	0.810	990.0	8.3	202	1.3532	1.612	0.867	0.472	1.675	1.509	59.57	36.7	0.428
12.00	13.43	1.1236	1.1256	134.8	0.893	988.8	9.5	221	1.3551	1.797	0.966	0.526	1.775	1.583	56.23	38.7	0.454
13.00	14.55	1.1351	1.1371	147.6	0.977	987.5	10.7	240	1.3570	1.995	1.073	0.583	1.883	1.663	52.99	40.5	0.478
14.00	15.67	1.1467	1.1487	160.5	1.063	986.2	12.1	259	1.3589	2.207	1.187	0.645	2.001	1.749	49.87	42.2	0.499
15.00	16.79	1.1585	1.1606	173.8	1.151	984.7	13.5	279	1.3609	2.431	1.307	0.709	2.129	1.841	46.88	43.7	0.518
16.00	17.91	1.1705	1.1726	187.3	1.240	983.2	15.0	299	1.3629	2.669	1.435	0.777	2.267	1.940	44.03	44.9	0.534
17.00	19.03	1.1827	1.1847	201.1	1.331	981.6	16.6	318	1.3648	2.922	1.571	0.850	2.415	2.046	41.32	45.9	0.548
18.00	20.15	1.1950	1.1971	215.1	1.425	979.9	18.3	338	1.3668	3.194	1.717	0.926	2.575	2.160	38.75	46.7	0.559
19.00	21.27	1.2075	1.2097	229.4	1.519	978.1	20.1	358	1.3688	3.486	1.874	1.008	2.747	2.280	36.32	47.3	0.566
20.00	22.39	1.2203	1.2224	244.1	1.616	976.2	22.0	378	1.3708	3.801	2.043	1.096	2.932	2.408	34.04	47.6	0.570

35 D-MANNITOL, $CH_2OH(CHOH)_4CH_2OH$

MOLECULAR WEIGHT = 182.17
RELATIVE SPECIFIC REFRACTIVITY = 1.063

0.00 % by wt. data are the same for all compounds.
For Values of 0.00 wt. % solutions see Table 1, Acetic Acid.

A% by wt.	ρ D_4^{20}	D_{20}^{20}	C_s g/l	M g-mol/l	C_w g/l	$(C_o - C_w)$ g/l	$(n - n_o)$ $\times 10^4$	n	Δ °C	O Os/kg	S g-mol/l	η/η_o	η/ρ cS	ϕ rhe	γ mmho/cm	T g-mol/l
0.50	1.0000	1.0018	5.0	0.027	995.0	3.2	7	1.3337	0.051	0.028	0.014	1.015	1.017	98.30		
1.00	1.0017	1.0035	10.0	0.055	991.7	6.5	15	1.3345	0.103	0.055	0.029	1.030	1.030	96.89		
1.50	1.0035	1.0053	15.1	0.083	988.5	9.8	22	1.3352	0.156	0.084	0.044	1.044	1.042	95.59		
2.00	1.0053	1.0071	20.1	0.110	985.2	13.1	29	1.3359	0.209	0.112	0.059	1.058	1.055	94.33		
2.50	1.0070	1.0088	25.2	0.138	981.9	16.4	37	1.3367	0.262	0.141	0.075	1.072	1.067	93.07		
3.00	1.0088	1.0106	30.3	0.166	978.5	19.7	44	1.3374	0.317	0.170	0.091	1.087	1.079	91.84		
3.50	1.0106	1.0124	35.4	0.194	975.2	23.0	52	1.3381	0.371	0.200	0.107	1.101	1.092	90.61		
4.00	1.0124	1.0141	40.5	0.222	971.9	26.4	59	1.3389	0.427	0.230	0.123	1.117	1.105	89.38		
4.50	1.0141	1.0159	45.6	0.251	968.5	29.7	66	1.3396	0.483	0.260	0.140	1.132	1.119	88.13		
5.00	1.0159	1.0177	50.8	0.279	965.1	33.1	73	1.3403	0.540	0.290	0.156	1.149	1.133	86.86		
5.50	1.0177	1.0195	56.0	0.307	961.7	36.5	81	1.3411	0.598	0.321	0.173	1.166	1.148	85.56		
6.00	1.0195	1.0213	61.2	0.336	958.3	39.9	88	1.3418	0.656	0.353	0.191	1.185	1.164	84.24		
6.50	1.0212	1.0230	66.4	0.364	954.9	43.4	95	1.3425	0.715	0.384	0.208	1.204	1.181	82.92		
7.00	1.0230	1.0248	71.6	0.393	951.4	46.8	103	1.3433	0.774	0.416	0.225	1.223	1.198	81.59		
7.50	1.0248	1.0266	76.9	0.422	947.9	50.3	110	1.3440	0.835	0.449	0.243	1.244	1.216	80.26		
8.00	1.0266	1.0284	82.1	0.451	944.5	53.8	117	1.3447	0.896	0.482	0.261	1.264	1.234	78.93		
8.50	1.0284	1.0302	87.4	0.480	941.0	57.2	125	1.3455	0.958	0.515	0.279	1.286	1.253	77.62		
9.00	1.0302	1.0320	92.7	0.509	937.5	60.7	132	1.3462	1.020	0.549	0.298	1.308	1.272	76.31		

35 D-MANNITOL, CH₂OH(CHOH)₄CH₂OH—(Continued)

A% by wt.	ρ D_4^{20}	D_{20}^{20}	C_s g/l	M g-mol/l	C_w g/l	$(C_0 - C_w)$ g/l	$(n - n_0)$ ×10⁴	n	Δ °C	O Os/kg	S g-mol/l	η/η_0	η/ρ cS	ϕ rhe	γ mmho/cm	T g-mol/l
9.50	1.0320	1.0338	98.0	0.538	934.0	64.3	139	1.3469	1.084	0.583	0.316	1.330	1.291	75.03		
10.00	1.0338	1.0357	103.4	0.568	930.5	67.8	147	1.3477	1.148	0.617	0.335	1.353	1.311	73.76		
11.00	1.0375	1.0393	114.1	0.626	923.4	74.8	161	1.3491	1.279	0.688	0.374	1.400	1.352	71.28		
12.00	1.0412	1.0431	124.9	0.686	916.3	81.9	176	1.3506	1.413	0.760	0.413	1.450	1.395	68.85		
13.00	1.0450	1.0469	135.9	0.746	909.2	89.0	191	1.3521	1.551	0.834	0.454	1.501	1.440	66.47		
14.00	1.0489	1.0508	146.9	0.806	902.1	96.1	207	1.3536	1.692	0.910	0.495	1.555	1.486	64.16		
15.00	1.0529	1.0548	157.9	0.867	895.0	103.2	222	1.3552	1.837	0.988	0.537	1.612	1.534	61.91		

36 METHANOL, CH₃OH

MOLECULAR WEIGHT = 32.03
RELATIVE SPECIFIC REFRACTIVITY = 1.247

0.00 % by wt. data are the same for all compounds.
For Values of 0.00 wt. % solutions see Table 1, Acetic Acid.

A% by wt.	ρ D_4^{20}	D_{20}^{20}	C_s g/l	M g-mol/l	C_w g/l	$(C_0 - C_w)$ g/l	$(n - n_0)$ ×10⁴	n	Δ °C	O Os/kg	S g-mol/l	η/η_0	η/ρ cS	ϕ rhe	γ mmho/cm	T g-mol/l
0.50	0.9973	0.9991	5.0	0.156	992.4	5.9	1	1.3331	0.278	0.149	0.080	1.020	1.025	97.84		
1.00	0.9964	0.9982	10.0	0.311	986.5	11.7	2	1.3332	0.560	0.301	0.162	1.038	1.044	96.15		
1.50	0.9956	0.9973	14.9	0.466	980.6	17.6	3	1.3333	0.847	0.455	0.247	1.053	1.060	94.74		
2.00	0.9947	0.9965	19.9	0.621	974.8	23.4	4	1.3334	1.140	0.613	0.333	1.068	1.076	93.45		
2.50	0.9938	0.9956	24.8	0.776	969.0	29.2	5	1.3335	1.442	0.776	0.422	1.083	1.092	92.14		
3.00	0.9930	0.9947	29.8	0.930	963.2	35.0	6	1.3336	1.750	0.941	0.512	1.098	1.108	90.85		
3.50	0.9921	0.9939	34.7	1.084	957.4	40.8	8	1.3337	2.058	1.106	0.601	1.114	1.125	89.59		
4.00	0.9913	0.9930	39.7	1.238	951.6	46.6	9	1.3339	2.370	1.274	0.692	1.129	1.142	88.36		
4.50	0.9904	0.9922	44.6	1.392	945.9	52.4	10	1.3340	2.691	1.447	0.784	1.145	1.159	87.15		
5.00	0.9896	0.9914	49.5	1.545	940.1	58.1	11	1.3341	3.020	1.624	0.877	1.161	1.176	85.96		
5.50	0.9888	0.9905	54.4	1.698	934.4	63.8	12	1.3342	3.362	1.807	0.974	1.177	1.193	84.79		
6.00	0.9880	0.9897	59.3	1.851	928.7	69.5	14	1.3343	3.710	1.995	1.071	1.194	1.210	83.62		
6.50	0.9872	0.9889	64.2	2.003	923.0	75.2	15	1.3345	4.058	2.182	1.167	1.210	1.228	82.46		
7.00	0.9864	0.9881	69.0	2.156	917.3	80.9	16	1.3346	4.410	2.371	1.265	1.227	1.247	81.33		
7.50	0.9855	0.9873	73.9	2.308	911.6	86.6	17	1.3347	4.769	2.564	1.362	1.244	1.265	80.22		
8.00	0.9848	0.9865	78.8	2.460	906.0	92.3	19	1.3348	5.13	2.76	1.459	1.261	1.283	79.15		
8.50	0.9840	0.9857	83.6	2.611	900.3	97.9	20	1.3350	5.49	2.95	1.554	1.278	1.301	78.11		
9.00	0.9832	0.9849	88.5	2.763	894.7	103.5	21	1.3351	5.85	3.15	1.649	1.294	1.319	77.12		
9.50	0.9824	0.9841	93.3	2.914	889.1	109.2	23	1.3352	6.22	3.35	1.745	1.310	1.336	76.17		
10.00	0.9816	0.9833	98.2	3.065	883.5	114.8	24	1.3354	6.60	3.55	1.841	1.326	1.354	75.26		
11.00	0.9801	0.9818	107.8	3.366	872.3	126.0	27	1.3356	7.36	3.96	2.032	1.357	1.387	73.57		
12.00	0.9785	0.9803	117.4	3.666	861.1	137.1	29	1.3359	8.14	4.38	2.221	1.386	1.419	72.00		
13.00	0.9770	0.9787	127.0	3.965	850.0	148.2	32	1.3362	8.93	4.80	2.407	1.415	1.451	70.53		
14.00	0.9755	0.9772	136.6	4.264	838.9	159.3	35	1.3365	9.72	5.23	2.588	1.443	1.482	69.15		
15.00	0.9740	0.9757	146.1	4.561	827.9	170.3	38	1.3367	10.53	5.66	2.767	1.471	1.513	67.85		
16.00	0.9725	0.9742	155.6	4.858	816.9	181.3	40	1.3370	11.36	6.11	2.946	1.498	1.544	66.61		
17.00	0.9710	0.9727	165.1	5.154	805.9	192.3	43	1.3373	12.23	6.57	3.126	1.525	1.574	65.45		
18.00	0.9695	0.9712	174.5	5.449	795.0	203.2	46	1.3376	13.13	7.06	3.308	1.551	1.603	64.35		
19.00	0.9680	0.9698	183.9	5.742	784.1	214.1	49	1.3379	14.06	7.56	3.490	1.576	1.632	63.31		
20.00	0.9666	0.9683	193.3	6.035	773.2	225.0	51	1.3381	15.02	8.07	3.669	1.601	1.660	62.34		
22.00	0.9636	0.9653	212.0	6.618	751.6	246.6	57	1.3387	16.98	9.13	4.019	1.649	1.715	60.52		
24.00	0.9606	0.9623	230.5	7.198	730.1	268.2	62	1.3392	19.04	10.23	4.359	1.694	1.767	58.91		
26.00	0.9576	0.9593	249.0	7.773	708.6	289.6	67	1.3397	21.23	11.42		1.732	1.813	57.61		
28.00	0.9545	0.9562	267.3	8.344	687.2	311.0	72	1.3402	23.59	12.68		1.765	1.853	56.55		
30.00	0.9514	0.9531	285.4	8.911	666.0	332.3	77	1.3407	25.91	13.93		1.791	1.886	55.72		
32.00	0.9482	0.9499	303.4	9.473	644.8	353.5	81	1.3411	28.15	15.13		1.810	1.913	55.13		
34.00	0.9450	0.9466	321.3	10.031	623.7	374.6	85	1.3415	30.48	16.39		1.823	1.933	54.74		
36.00	0.9416	0.9433	339.0	10.583	602.6	395.6	89	1.3419	32.97	17.73		1.831	1.949	54.49		
38.00	0.9382	0.9399	356.5	11.131	581.7	416.6	92	1.3422	35.60	19.14		1.835	1.959	54.40		
40.00	0.9347	0.9363	373.9	11.672	560.8	437.4	95	1.3425	38.6	20.8		1.833	1.965	54.45		
42.00	0.9311	0.9327	391.0	12.209	540.0	458.2	97	1.3427	41.5	22.3		1.827	1.966	54.62		
44.00	0.9273	0.9290	408.0	12.739	519.3	478.9	99	1.3429	44.5	23.9		1.817	1.963	54.93		
46.00	0.9235	0.9251	424.8	13.263	498.7	499.5	100	1.3430	47.8	25.7		1.801	1.955	55.40		
48.00	0.9196	0.9212	441.4	13.781	478.2	520.1	101	1.3431	51.2	27.5		1.781	1.940	56.05		
50.00	0.9156	0.9172	457.8	14.292	457.8	540.5	101	1.3431	54.5	29.3		1.757	1.923	56.80		
52.00	0.9114	0.9130	473.9	14.797	437.5	560.7	101	1.3431	58.1	31.2		1.732	1.905	57.61		
54.00	0.9072	0.9088	489.9	15.295	417.3	580.9	100	1.3430	62.0	33.3		1.705	1.883	58.52		
56.00	0.9030	0.9046	505.7	15.787	397.3	600.9	99	1.3429	66.0	35.5		1.673	1.857	59.64		
58.00	0.8987	0.9003	521.2	16.274	377.5	620.8	98	1.3428	70.0	37.6		1.638	1.826	60.94		
60.00	0.8944	0.8960	536.6	16.754	357.8	640.5	96	1.3426	74.5	40.0		1.597	1.789	62.49		
62.00	0.8901	0.8917	551.9	17.230	338.3	660.0	95	1.3425	79.3	42.6		1.550	1.744	64.40		
64.00	0.8856	0.8872	566.8	17.695	318.8	679.4	92	1.3422	84.4	45.4		1.500	1.697	66.54		
66.00	0.8810	0.8825	581.4	18.153	299.5	698.7	89	1.3419	89.6	48.2		1.453	1.653	68.66		
68.00	0.8763	0.8778	595.9	18.603	280.4	717.8	85	1.3415	96.3	51.8		1.410	1.612	70.78		
70.00	0.8715	0.8730	610.0	19.046	261.4	736.8	81	1.3411				1.365	1.569	73.11		
72.00	0.8667	0.8682	624.0	19.482	242.7	755.6	77	1.3407				1.315	1.521	75.87		
74.00	0.8618	0.8633	637.7	19.910	224.1	774.2	72	1.3402				1.264	1.470	78.93		
76.00	0.8568	0.8583	651.2	20.331	205.6	792.6	67	1.3397				1.216	1.422	82.05		
78.00	0.8518	0.8533	664.4	20.744	187.4	810.8	61	1.3391				1.170	1.377	85.20		
80.00	0.8468	0.8483	677.4	21.149	169.4	828.9	55	1.3385				1.126	1.332	88.63		
82.00	0.8416	0.8431	690.2	21.547	151.5	846.7	49	1.3379				1.072	1.276	93.11		
84.00	0.8365	0.8380	702.6	21.937	133.8	864.4	42	1.3372				1.021	1.223	97.75		
86.00	0.8312	0.8327	714.9	22.318	116.4	881.9	35	1.3365				0.968	1.167	103.1		
88.00	0.8259	0.8274	726.8	22.691	99.1	899.1	27	1.3357				0.914	1.109	109.2		
90.00	0.8204	0.8219	738.4	23.053	82.0	916.2	19	1.3348				0.859	1.049	116.2		
92.00	0.8148	0.8163	749.6	23.404	65.2	933.0	9	1.3339				0.804	0.989	124.1		
94.00	0.8089	0.8103	760.3	23.738	48.5	949.7	−2	1.3328				0.748	0.927	133.4		
96.00	0.8034	0.8048	771.3	24.081	32.1	966.1	−14	1.3316				0.694	0.866	143.8		
98.00	0.7976	0.7990	781.6	24.402	16.0	982.2	−26	1.3304				0.638	0.801	156.4		
100.0	0.7917	0.7931	791.7	24.717	0.0	998.2	−40	1.3290				0.585	0.740	170.6		

37 NICKEL SULFATE, NiSO$_4$ · 6H$_2$O

MOLECULAR WEIGHT = 154.75 **FORMULA WEIGHT, HYDRATE** = 262.85
RELATIVE SPECIFIC REFRACTIVITY = 0.524

0.00 % by wt. data are the same for all compounds.
For Values of 0.00 wt. % solutions see Table 1, Acetic Acid.

A % by wt.	H % by wt.	D_4^{20}	D_{20}^{20}	C_s g/l	M g-mol/l	C_w g/l	$(C_o - C_w)$ g/l	$(n - n_o)$ × 10^4	n	Δ °C	O Os/kg	S g-mol/l	η/η_o	η/ρ cS	ϕ rhe	γ mmho/cm	T g-mol/l
0.50	0.85	1.0035	1.0053	5.0	0.032	998.5	− 0.3	10	1.3340	0.081	0.044	0.023	1.022	1.020	97.66	3.1	0.031
1.00	1.70	1.0089	1.0107	10.1	0.065	998.8	− 0.6	20	1.3349	0.150	0.081	0.043	1.044	1.037	95.59	5.8	0.058
1.50	2.55	1.0142	1.0160	15.2	0.098	999.0	− 0.8	29	1.3359	0.217	0.117	0.062	1.066	1.053	93.60	8.0	0.081
2.00	3.40	1.0196	1.0214	20.4	0.132	999.2	− 1.0	39	1.3369	0.282	0.152	0.081	1.089	1.070	91.64	9.9	0.103
2.50	4.25	1.0250	1.0268	25.6	0.166	999.4	− 1.2	49	1.3379	0.346	0.186	0.099	1.113	1.088	89.67	11.9	0.125
3.00	5.10	1.0304	1.0323	30.9	0.200	999.5	− 1.3	60	1.3389	0.410	0.220	0.118	1.138	1.107	87.70	13.7	0.146
3.50	5.94	1.0359	1.0377	36.3	0.234	999.6	− 1.4	70	1.3400	0.475	0.255	0.137	1.164	1.126	85.75	15.5	0.167
4.00	6.79	1.0413	1.0431	41.7	0.269	999.6	− 1.4	80	1.3410	0.540	0.290	0.156	1.191	1.146	83.80	17.3	0.187
4.50	7.64	1.0467	1.0486	47.1	0.304	999.6	− 1.4	90	1.3420	0.605	0.325	0.176	1.219	1.167	81.87	18.9	0.207
5.00	8.49	1.0521	1.0540	52.6	0.340	999.5	− 1.3	100	1.3430	0.671	0.361	0.195	1.248	1.189	79.95	20.5	0.226
5.50	9.34	1.0575	1.0594	58.2	0.376	999.4	− 1.1	110	1.3440	0.736	0.396	0.214	1.279	1.211	78.06	22.0	0.245
6.00	10.19	1.0629	1.0648	63.8	0.412	999.1	− 0.9	120	1.3450	0.803	0.432	0.234	1.310	1.235	76.18	23.5	0.263

38 NITRIC ACID, HNO$_3$

MOLECULAR WEIGHT = 63.02
RELATIVE SPECIFIC REFRACTIVITY = 0.818

0.00 % by wt. data are the same for all compounds.
For Values of 0.00 wt. % solutions see Table 1, Acetic Acid.

A % by wt.	ρ D_4^{20}	d D_{20}^{20}	C_s g/l	M g-mol/l	C_w g/l	$(C_o - C_w)$ g/l	$(n - n_o)$ × 10^4	n	Δ °C	O Os/kg	S g-mol/l	η/η_o	η/ρ cS	ϕ rhe	γ mmho/cm	T g-mol/l
0.50	1.0009	1.0027	5.0	0.079	995.9	2.3	6	1.3336	0.281	0.151	0.080	1.002	1.003	99.64	28.4	0.323
1.00	1.0037	1.0054	10.0	0.159	993.6	4.6	13	1.3343	0.558	0.300	0.162	1.003	1.001	99.50	56.1	0.686
1.50	1.0064	1.0082	15.1	0.240	991.3	6.9	19	1.3349	0.837	0.450	0.244	1.004	1.000	99.40	84.7	1.10
2.00	1.0091	1.0109	20.2	0.320	988.9	9.3	26	1.3356	1.120	0.602	0.327	1.005	0.998	99.30	108.	1.50
2.50	1.0119	1.0137	25.3	0.401	986.6	11.7	32	1.3362	1.408	0.757	0.412	1.006	0.997	99·17	138.	1.97
3.00	1.0146	1.0164	30.4	0.483	984.2	14.0	39	1.3368	1.704	0.916	0.498	1.008	0.995	99.01	160.	2.57
3.50	1.0174	1.0192	35.6	0.565	981.8	16.5	45	1.3375	2.006	1.078	0.586	1.010	0.995	98.83	184.	3.18
4.00	1.0202	1.0220	40.8	0.648	979.4	18.9	51	1.3381	2.315	1.245	0.676	1.012	0.994	98.64	213.	4.31
4.50	1.0230	1.0248	46.0	0.730	976.9	21.3	58	1.3388	2.632	1.415	0.767	1.014	0.993	98.43		
5.00	1.0257	1.0276	51.3	0.814	974.5	23.8	64	1.3394	2.958	1.590	0.859	1.016	0.992	98.23		
5.50	1.0286	1.0304	56.6	0.898	972.0	26.3	71	1.3401	3.290	1.769	0.953	1.018	0.992	98.02		
6.00	1.0314	1.0332	61.9	0.982	969.5	28.7	78	1.3407	3.629	1.951	1.048	1.020	0.991	97.81		
6.50	1.0342	1.0360	67.2	1.067	967.0	31.3	84	1.3414	3.974	2.137	1.144	1.023	0.991	97.59		
7.00	1.0370	1.0389	72.6	1.152	964.4	33.8	91	1.3421	4.327	2.326	1.241	1.025	0.990	97.36		
7.50	1.0399	1.0417	78.0	1.238	961.9	36.3	97	1.3427	4.687	2.520	1.340	1.028	0.990	97.12		
8.00	1.0427	1.0446	83.4	1.324	959.3	38.9	104	1.3434	5.05	2.72	1.439	1.030	0.990	96.88		
8.50	1.0456	1.0475	88.9	1.410	956.7	41.5	110	1.3440	5.43	2.92	1.538	1.033	0.990	96.62		
9.00	1.0485	1.0504	94.4	1.497	954.1	44.1	117	1.3447	5.81	3.12	1.639	1.036	0.990	96.35		
9.50	1.0514	1.0533	99.9	1.585	951.5	46.7	124	1.3454	6.20	3.33	1.740	1.039	0.990	96.07		
10.00	1.0543	1.0562	105.4	1.673	948.9	49.4	130	1.3460	6.60	3.55	1.841	1.042	0.990	95.78		
11.00	1.0602	1.0620	116.6	1.850	943.5	54.7	144	1.3474	7.42	3.99	2.045	1.049	0.991	95.15		
12.00	1.0660	1.0679	127.9	2.030	938.1	60.1	157	1.3487	8.27	4.45	2.251	1.056	0.993	94.48		
13.00	1.0720	1.0739	139.4	2.211	932.6	65.6	170	1.3500	9.15	4.92	2.459	1.064	0.995	93.76		
14.00	1.0780	1.0799	150.9	2.395	927.1	71.2	184	1.3514	10.08	5.42	2.667	1.073	0.997	93.00		
15.00	1.0840	1.0859	162.6	2.580	921.4	76.8	198	1.3527	11.04	5.93	2.877	1.082	1.001	92.20		
16.00	1.0901	1.0921	174.4	2.768	915.7	82.5	211	1.3541	12.04	6.47	3.087	1.092	1.004	91.35		
17.00	1.0963	1.0982	186.4	2.957	909.9	88.3	225	1.3555	13.08	7.03	3.298	1.103	1.008	90.47		
18.00	1.1025	1.1044	198.4	3.149	904·0	94.2	239	1.3569	14.16	7.61	3.509	1.114	1.013	89.55		
19.00	1.1087	1.1107	210.7	3.343	898.0	100.2	253	1.3582	15.30	8.22	3.720	1.126	1.018	88.60		
20.00	1.1150	1.1170	223.0	3.538	892.0	106.2	266	1.3596				1.139	1.024	87.62		
22.00	1.1277	1.1297	248.1	3.937	879.6	118.6	294	1.3624				1.167	1.037	85.55		
24.00	1.1406	1.1426	273.7	4.344	866.8	131.4	322	1.3652				1.197	1.052	83.36		
26.00	1.1536	1.1557	299.9	4.759	853.7	144.6	350	1.3680				1.231	1.069	81.06		
28.00	1.1668	1.1688	326.7	5.184	840.1	158.1	378	1.3708				1.268	1.089	78.70		
30.00	1.1801	1.1822	354.0	5.618	826.0	172.2	406	1.3736				1.308	1.111	76.30		
32.00	1.1934	1.1955	381.9	6.060	811.5	186.7	433	1.3763				1.351	1.134	73.87		
34.00	1.2068	1.2090	410.3	6.511	796.5	201.7	460	1.3790				1.397	1.160	71.42		
36.00	1.2202	1.2224	439.3	6.970	780.9	217.3	487	1.3817				1.447	1.188	68.96		
38.00	1.2335	1.2357	468.7	7.438	764.8	233.5	513	1.3842				1.501	1.219	66.50		
40.00	1.2466	1.2489	498.7	7.913	748.0	250.2	537	1.3867				1.558	1.252	64.06		

39 OXALIC ACID, HO_2CCO_2H

MOLECULAR WEIGHT = 90.04

A% by wt.	ρ D_4^{20}	D_{20}^{20}	C_s g/l	M g-mol/l	C_w g/l	$(C_0 - C_w)$ g/l	$(n - n_0)$ ×10⁴	n	Δ °C	O Os/kg	S g-mol/l	η/η_0	η/ρ cS	φ rhe	γ mmho/cm	T g-mol/l
0.50	1.0006	1.0024	5.0	0.056	995.6	2.6	6.	1.3336	0.159	0.086	0.045	1.011	1.012	98.76	14.0	0.149
1.00	1.0030	1.0048	10.0	0.111	993.0	5.2	12.	1.3342	0.304	0.163	0.087	1.021	1.020	97.75	21.8	0.242
1.50	1.0054	1.0072	15.1	0.167	990.3	7.9	17.	1.3347	0.440	0.237	0.127	1.031	1.028	96.75	29.3	0.335
2.00	1.0079	1.0097	20.2	0.224	987.7	10.5	23.	1.3353	0.572	0.308	0.166	1.042	1.036	95.77	35.3	0.411
2.50	1.0103	1.0121	25.3	0.281	985.0	13.2	29.	1.3359	0.705	0.379	0.205	1.053	1.044	94.81	41.2	0.486
3.00	1.0126	1.0144	30.4	0.337	982.2	16.0	34.	1.3364	0.838	0.450	0.244	1.063	1.052	93.87	46.9	0.561
3.50	1.0150	1.0168	35.5	0.395	979.5	18.7	40.	1.3370	0.967	0.520	0.282	1.074	1.060	92.95	51.7	0.626
4.00	1.0174	1.0192	40.7	0.452	976.7	21.5	45.	1.3375	1.093	0.587	0.319	1.084	1.068	92.03	57.1	0.700
4.50	1.0197	1.0215	45.9	0.510	973.8	24.4	51.	1.3381				1.095	1.076	91.14	61.2	0.757
5.00	1.0220	1.0238	51.1	0.568	970.9	27.3	56.	1.3386				1.106	1.084	90.27	65.6	0.819
5.50	1.0244	1.0262	56.3	0.626	968.1	30.1	62.	1.3392				1.116	1.092	89.39	69.7	0.879
6.00	1.0265	1.0284	61.6	0.684	964.9	33.3	67.	1.3397				1.127	1.100	88.56	73.7	0.937
6.50	1.0288	1.0307	66.9	0.743	961.8	36.3	72.	1.3402				1.138	1.108	87.73	77.2	0.990
7.00	1.0310	1.0329	72.2	0.802	958.8	39.4	77.	1.3407				1.148	1.116	86.91	80.4	1.038
7.50	1.0332	1.0351	77.5	0.861	955.7	42.5	83.	1.3413				1.159	1.124	86.11	83.4	1.085
8.00	1.0355	1.0374	82.8	0.920	952.7	45.5	88.	1.3418				1.170	1.132	85.31	86.1	1.128

40 PHOSPHORIC ACID, H_3PO_4

MOLECULAR WEIGHT = 98.00
RELATIVE SPECIFIC REFRACTIVITY = 0.727

0.00 % by wt. data are the same for all compounds.
For Values of 0.00 wt. % solutions see Table 1, Acetic Acid.

A% by wt.	ρ D_4^{20}	D_{20}^{20}	C_s g/l	M g-mol/l	C_w g/l	$(C_0 - C_w)$ g/l	$(n - n_0)$ ×10⁴	n	Δ °C	O Os/kg	S g-mol/l	η/η_0	η/ρ cS	φ rhe	γ mmho/cm	T g-mol/l
0.50	1.0010	1.0028	5.0	0.051	996.0	2.2	5	1.3335	0.124	0.067	0.035	1.008	1.009	99.06	5.5	0.057
1.00	1.0038	1.0056	10.0	0.102	993.7	4.5	10	1.3340	0.243	0.131	0.069	1.018	1.016	98.04	10.1	0.105
1.50	1.0065	1.0083	15.1	0.154	991.4	6.8	15	1.3345	0.354	0.190	0.102	1.032	1.028	96.68	13.4	0.142
2.00	1.0092	1.0110	20.2	0.206	989.0	9.2	19	1.3349	0.464	0.249	0.134	1.048	1.041	95.23	16.2	0.175
2.50	1.0119	1.0137	25.3	0.258	986.6	11.6	24	1.3354	0.578	0.311	0.168	1.063	1.052	93.91	19.0	0.208
3.00	1.0146	1.0164	30.4	0.311	984.2	14.1	28	1.3358	0.694	0.373	0.202	1.077	1.064	92.64	21.6	0.239
3.50	1.0173	1.0191	35.6	0.363	981.7	16.5	33	1.3363	0.811	0.436	0.236	1.092	1.075	91.41	24.1	0.270
4.00	1.0200	1.0218	40.8	0.416	979.2	19.0	37	1.3367	0.929	0.499	0.271	1.106	1.087	90.22	26.5	0.300
4.50	1.0227	1.0245	46.0	0.470	976.7	21.6	42	1.3372	1.045	0.562	0.305	1.121	1.098	89.03	29.0	0.331
5.00	1.0254	1.0272	51.3	0.523	974.1	24.1	46	1.3376	1.160	0.624	0.339	1.136	1.110	87.85	31.5	0.363
5.50	1.0281	1.0299	56.5	0.577	971.6	26.7	51	1.3381	1.271	0.683	0.372	1.151	1.122	86.69	34.2	0.397

40 PHOSPHORIC ACID, H_3PO_4—(Continued)

A% by wt.	ρ D_4^{20}	D_{20}^{20}	C_s g/l	M g-mol/l	C_w g/l	$(C_o - C_w)$ g/l	$(n - n_o)$ $\times 10^4$	n	Δ °C	O Os/kg	S g-mol/l	η/η_o	η/ρ cS	ϕ rhe	γ mmho/cm	T g-mol/l
6.00	1.0309	1.0327	61.9	0.631	969.0	29.2	55	1.3385	1.381	0.742	0.404	1.167	1.134	85.54	36.9	0.431
6.50	1.0336	1.0354	67.2	0.686	966.4	31.9	60	1.3390	1.496	0.804	0.438	1.182	1.146	84.42	39.6	0.466
7.00	1.0363	1.0381	72.5	0.740	963.8	34.5	64	1.3394	1.619	0.871	0.474	1.198	1.158	83.32	42.4	0.502
7.50	1.0391	1.0409	77.9	0.795	961.1	37.1	69	1.3399	1.748	0.940	0.511	1.214	1.170	82.23	45.2	0.539
8.00	1.0418	1.0437	83.3	0.850	958.5	39.7	73	1.3403	1.882	1.012	0.550	1.230	1.183	81.14	48.0	0.576
8.50	1.0446	1.0465	88.8	0.906	955.8	42.4	78	1.3408	2.020	1.086	0.590	1.247	1.196	80.05	50.8	0.614
9.00	1.0474	1.0493	94.3	0.962	953.2	45.1	83	1.3413	2.160	1.161	0.631	1.264	1.209	78.96	53.7	0.653
9.50	1.0503	1.0521	99.8	1.018	950.5	47.7	87	1.3417	2.305	1.239	0.673	1.282	1.223	77.87	56.5	0.692
10.00	1.0531	1.0550	105.3	1.075	947.8	50.4	92	1.3422	2.450	1.317	0.715	1.300	1.237	76.77	59.4	0.731
11.00	1.0589	1.0607	116.5	1.189	942.4	55.9	101	1.3431	2.721	1.463	0.792	1.338	1.267	74.56	65.1	0.812
12.00	1.0647	1.0665	127.8	1.304	936.9	61.3	111	1.3441	3.010	1.618	0.874	1.379	1.298	72.38	70.9	0.896
13.00	1.0705	1.0724	139.2	1.420	931.4	66.9	120	1.3450	3.382	1.818	0.979	1.421	1.330	70.22	76.7	0.983
14.00	1.0765	1.0784	150.7	1.538	925.8	72.5	130	1.3460	3.760	2.022	1.085	1.466	1.364	68.08	82.5	1.07
15.00	1.0825	1.0844	162.4	1.657	920.1	78.1	140	1.3470	4.075	2.191	1.172	1.513	1.400	65.98	88.4	1.17
16.00	1.0885	1.0905	174.2	1.777	914.4	83.9	150	1.3480	4.450	2.392	1.276	1.562	1.438	63.90	94.3	1.26
17.00	1.0947	1.0966	186.1	1.899	908.6	89.7	160	1.3489	4.820	2.591	1.376	1.613	1.477	61.86	100.	1.36
18.00	1.1009	1.1028	198.2	2.022	902.7	95.5	170	1.3500	5.25	2.82	1.491	1.668	1.518	59.85	106.	1.46
19.00	1.1071	1.1091	210.4	2.146	896.8	101.5	180	1.3510	5.72	3.07	1.614	1.724	1.561	57.88	112.	1.56
20.00	1.1135	1.1154	222.7	2.272	890.8	107.5	190	1.3520	6.23	3.35	1.747	1.784	1.605	55.94	118.	1.67
22.00	1.1263	1.1283	247.8	2.528	878.5	119.7	211	1.3540	7.38	3.97	2.037	1.910	1.699	52.26	129.	1.89
24.00	1.1395	1.1415	273.5	2.790	866.0	132.2	231	1.3561	8.69	4.67	2.350	2.045	1.798	48.80	141.	2.12
26.00	1.1528	1.1549	299.7	3.059	853.1	145.1	253	1.3582	10.12	5.44	2.677	2.194	1.907	45.50	152.	2.37
28.00	1.1665	1.1685	326.6	3.333	839.9	158.4	274	1.3604	11.64	6.26	3.004	2.360	2.027	42.29	163.	2.63
30.00	1.1804	1.1825	354.1	3.613	826.3	172.0	295	1.3625	13.23	7.11	3.328	2.548	2.163	39.17	173.	2.88
32.00	1.1945	1.1966	382.2	3.900	812.3	186.0	317	1.3647	14.94	8.03	3.656	2.760	2.315	36.16	183.	3.13
34.00	1.2089	1.2111	411.0	4.194	797.9	200.3	339	1.3669	16.81	9.04	3.989	2.995	2.482	33.33	191.	3.38
36.00	1.2236	1.2257	440.5	4.495	783.1	215.1	361	1.3691	18.85	10.13	4.329	3.253	2.664	30.68	199.	3.63
38.00	1.2385	1.2407	470.6	4.802	767.8	230.4	383	1.3713	21.09	11.34	4.677	3.537	2.862	28.21	205.	3.88
40.00	1.2536	1.2558	501.4	5.117	752.2	246.1	405	1.3735	23.58	12.68		3.848	3.076	25.94	209.	4.13

41 POTASSIUM BICARBONATE, $KHCO_3$

MOLECULAR WEIGHT = 100.12
RELATIVE SPECIFIC REFRACTIVITY = 0.667

0.00 % by wt. data are the same for all compounds.
For Values of 0.00 wt. % solutions see Table 1, Acetic Acid.

A% by wt.	ρ D_4^{20}	D_{20}^{20}	C_s g/l	M g-mol/l	C_w g/l	$(C_o - C_w)$ g/l	$(n - n_o)$ $\times 10^4$	n	Δ °C	O Os/kg	S g-mol/l	η/η_o	η/ρ cS	ϕ rhe	γ mmho/cm	T g-mol/l
0.50	1.0014	1.0031	5.0	0.050	996.4	1.9	5	1.3335	0.175	0.094	0.050	1.007	1.007	99.14	4.6	0.046
1.00	1.0046	1.0064	10.0	0.100	994.6	3.7	11	1.3341	0.344	0.185	0.099	1.013	1.010	98.52	8.9	0.092
2.00	1.0114	1.0132	20.2	0.202	991.1	7.1	23	1.3353	0.668	0.359	0.194	1.025	1.016	97.37	17.0	0.184
3.00	1.0181	1.0199	30.5	0.305	987.6	10.6	35	1.3365	0.983	0.528	0.287	1.038	1.021	96.17	24.6	0.275
4.00	1.0247	1.0265	41.0	0.409	983.7	14.5	46	1.3376	1.291	0.694	0.378	1.051	1.028	94.95	31.7	0.365
5.00	1.0310	1.0329	51.6	0.515	979.5	18.8	56	1.3386	1.600	0.860	0.468	1.065	1.035	93.71	38.8	0.455
6.00	1.0379	1.0397	62.3	0.622	975.6	22.6	68	1.3397	1.911	1.028	0.559	1.079	1.042	92.46	45.8	0.547
7.00	1.0446	1.0465	73.1	0.730	971.5	26.7	79	1.3409	2.222	1.195	0.649	1.094	1.049	91.21	52.7	0.639
8.00	1.0514	1.0532	84.1	0.840	967.3	31.0	90	1.3419	2.533	1.362	0.738	1.110	1.057	89.95	59.4	0.732
9.00	1.0581	1.0600	95.2	0.951	962.9	35.3	100	1.3430	2.844	1.529	0.827	1.126	1.066	88.65	65.9	0.825
10.00	1.0650	1.0668	106.5	1.064	958.5	39.8	111	1.3441	3.157	1.697	0.916	1.143	1.075	87.31	72.4	0.918
12.00	1.0788	1.0807	129.5	1.293	949.3	48.9	132	1.3462	3.785	2.035	1.092	1.181	1.097	84.54	84.5	1.10
14.00	1.0929	1.0948	153.0	1.528	939.9	58.4	154	1.3484	4.414	2.373	1.266	1.222	1.120	81.68	95.9	1.29
16.00	1.1073	1.1093	177.2	1.770	930.1	68.1	176	1.3506				1.267	1.147	78.77	107.0	1.47
18.00	1.1221	1.1241	202.0	2.017	920.1	78.1	198	1.3528				1.316	1.175	75.83	118.0	1.67
20.00	1.1372	1.1392	227.4	2.272	909.7	88.5	220	1.3550				1.370	1.207	72.85	128.0	1.86
22.00	1.1527	1.1547	253.6	2.533	899.1	99.2	242	1.3572				1.429	1.242	69.83	137.0	2.05
24.00	1.1685	1.1706	280.4	2.801	888.1	110.2	265	1.3595				1.494	1.281	66.80	145.0	2.23

42 POTASSIUM BIPHTHALATE, $KHC_8H_4O_4$

MOLECULAR WEIGHT = 204.23
RELATIVE SPECIFIC REFRACTIVITY = 1.097

0.00 % by wt. data are the same for all compounds.
For Values of 0.00 wt. % solutions see Table 1, Acetic Acid.

A% by wt.	ρ D_4^{20}	D_{20}^{20}	C_s g/l	M g-mol/l	C_w g/l	$(C_o - C_w)$ g/l	$(n - n_o)$ $\times 10^4$	n	Δ °C	O Os/kg	S g-mol/l	η/η_o	η/ρ cS	ϕ rhe	γ mmho/cm	T g-mol/l
0.50	1.0004	1.0021	5.0	0.024	995.4	2.9	9	1.3339	0.085	0.046	0.024	1.012	1.013	98.67	2.0	0.020
1.00	1.0025	1.0043	10.0	0.049	992.5	5.7	19	1.3349	0.169	0.091	0.048	1.023	1.022	97.56	4.0	0.040
1.50	1.0047	1.0065	15.1	0.074	989.6	8.6	28	1.3358	0.254	0.136	0.073	1.034	1.032	96.48	5.9	0.059
2.00	1.0069	1.0087	20.1	0.099	986.8	11.5	38	1.3368	0.337	0.181	0.097	1.046	1.041	95.41	7.7	0.079
2.50	1.0092	1.0109	25.2	0.124	983.9	14.3	47	1.3377	0.421	0.226	0.121	1.058	1.050	94.35	9.4	0.098
3.00	1.0114	1.0132	30.3	0.149	981.1	17.2	57	1.3387	0.503	0.271	0.146	1.070	1.060	93.29	11.0	0.115
3.50	1.0137	1.0155	35.5	0.174	978.2	20.0	66	1.3396	0.585	0.315	0.170	1.082	1.070	92.24	12.5	0.132
4.00	1.0160	1.0178	40.6	0.199	975.3	22.9	76	1.3406	0.667	0.359	0.194	1.094	1.079	91.19	14.0	0.149
4.50	1.0183	1.0201	45.8	0.224	972.5	25.8	86	1.3416	0.749	0.403	0.218	1.107	1.089	90.15	15.3	0.165
5.00	1.0206	1.0224	51.0	0.250	969.6	28.7	95	1.3425	0.831	0.447	0.242	1.120	1.100	89.11	16.7	0.181
5.50	1.0229	1.0247	56.3	0.275	966.7	31.6	105	1.3435	0.913	0.491	0.266	1.133	1.110	88.07	18.1	0.197
6.00	1.0252	1.0270	61.5	0.301	963.7	34.5	115	1.3444	0.995	0.535	0.290	1.147	1.121	87.04	19.4	0.213
6.50	1.0275	1.0294	66.8	0.327	960.8	37.5	124	1.3454	1.076	0.579	0.314	1.160	1.132	86.01	20.7	0.229
7.00	1.0298	1.0317	72.1	0.353	957.8	40.5	133	1.3463	1.158	0.622	0.338	1.174	1.143	84.99	21.9	0.244
7.50	1.0321	1.0339	77.4	0.379	954.7	43.5	143	1.3473	1.239	0.666	0.362	1.189	1.154	83.97	23.1	0.258
8.00	1.0344	1.0362	82.7	0.405	951.6	46.6	152	1.3482	1.320	0.710	0.386	1.203	1.165	82.96	24.2	0.272

43 POTASSIUM BROMIDE, KBr

MOLECULAR WEIGHT = 119.01
RELATIVE SPECIFIC REFRACTIVITY = 0.627

0.00 % by wt. data are the same for all compounds.
For Values of 0.00 wt. % solutions see Table 1, Acetic Acid.

A% by wt.	ρ D_4^{20}	D_{20}^{20}	C_s g/l	M g-mol/l	C_w g/l	$(C_o \quad C_w)$ g/l	$(n-n_o)$ ×10⁴	n	Δ °C	O Os/kg	S g-mol/l	η/η_o	η/ρ cS	ϕ rhe	γ mmho/cm	T g-mol/l
0.50	1.0018	1.0036	5.0	0.042	996.8	1.4	6	1.3336	0.148	0.080	0.042	0.998	0.998	100.00	5.2	0.053
1.00	1.0054	1.0072	10.1	0.084	995.4	2.9	12	1.3342	0.294	0.158	0.084	0.996	0.993	100.20	10.2	0.106
1.50	1.0090	1.0108	15.1	0.127	993.9	4.3	18	1.3348	0.439	0.236	0.127	0.994	0.987	100.40	14.9	0.160
2.00	1.0127	1.0145	20.3	0.170	992.4	5.8	24	1.3354	0.585	0.315	0.170	0.992	0.982	100.61	19.5	0.214
2.50	1.0164	1.0182	25.4	0.214	990.9	7.3	30	1.3360	0.731	0.393	0.213	0.990	0.976	100.82	24.2	0.270
3.00	1.0200	1.0218	30.6	0.257	989.4	8.8	36	1.3366	0.878	0.472	0.256	0.988	0.970	101.04	28.8	0.328
3.50	1.0238	1.0256	35.8	0.301	987.9	10.3	42	1.3372	1.026	0.552	0.300	0.985	0.965	101.27	33.5	0.387
4.00	1.0275	1.0293	41.1	0.345	986.4	11.9	49	1.3379	1.175	0.632	0.343	0.983	0.959	101.50	38.3	0.447
4.50	1.0312	1.0331	46.4	0.390	984.8	13.4	55	1.3385	1.325	0.712	0.387	0.981	0.953	101.73	43.0	0.509
5.00	1.0350	1.0368	51.8	0.435	983.3	15.0	61	1.3391	1.476	0.794	0.432	0.979	0.948	101.94	47.7	0.572
5.50	1.0388	1.0406	57.2	0.480	981.7	16.6	67	1.3397	1.629	0.876	0.477	0.977	0.942	102.15	52.5	0.636
6.00	1.0426	1.0445	62.6	0.526	980.1	18.2	74	1.3403	1.784	0.959	0.522	0.975	0.937	102.34	57.2	0.701
6.50	1.0465	1.0483	68.0	0.572	978.4	19.8	80	1.3410	1.939	1.043	0.567	0.973	0.932	102.54	62.0	0.767
7.00	1.0503	1.0522	73.5	0.618	976.8	21.4	86	1.3416	2.097	1.127	0.613	0.972	0.927	102.72	66.7	0.834
7.50	1.0542	1.0561	79.1	0.664	975.1	23.1	92	1.3422	2.255	1.213	0.658	0.970	0.922	102.90	71.5	0.903
8.00	1.0581	1.0600	84.6	0.711	973.5	24.8	99	1.3429	2.416	1.299	0.705	0.968	0.917	103.08	76.3	0.974
8.50	1.0620	1.0639	90.3	0.759	971.8	26.5	105	1.3435	2.578	1.386	0.751	0.967	0.912	103.25	81.1	1.05
9.00	1.0660	1.0679	95.9	0.806	970.1	28.2	112	1.3441	2.741	1.474	0.798	0.965	0.907	103.41	85.9	1.12
9.50	1.0700	1.0719	101.6	0.854	968.3	29.9	118	1.3448	2.907	1.563	0.845	0.964	0.902	103.58	90.7	1.20
10.00	1.0740	1.0759	107.4	0.902	966.6	31.6	124	1.3454	3.074	1.653	0.893	0.962	0.898	103.74	95.6	1.28
11.00	1.0821	1.0840	119.0	1.000	963.1	35.2	137	1.3467	3.415	1.836	0.989	0.959	0.888	104.06	105.	1.45
12.00	1.0903	1.0922	130.8	1.099	959.5	38.8	151	1.3481	3.764	2.024	1.086	0.956	0.879	104.36	115.	1.63
13.00	1.0986	1.1005	142.8	1.200	955.8	42.5	164	1.3494	4.122	2.216	1.185	0.954	0.870	104.64	125.	1.82
14.00	1.1070	1.1090	155.0	1.302	952.0	46.2	177	1.3507	4.487	2.412	1.286	0.951	0.861	104.90	134.	2.02
15.00	1.1155	1.1175	167.3	1.406	948.2	50.0	191	1.3521	4.862	2.614	1.387	0.949	0.853	105.13	144.	2.23
16.00	1.1242	1.1262	179.9	1.511	944.3	53.9	205	1.3535	5.25	2.82	1.490	0.947	0.844	105.35	154.	2.46
17.00	1.1330	1.1350	192.6	1.618	940.4	57.9	218	1.3548	5.64	3.03	1.593	0.946	0.836	105.54	164.	2.69
18.00	1.1419	1.1439	205.5	1.727	936.4	61.9	232	1.3562	6.04	3.25	1.698	0.944	0.829	105.70	174.	2.95
19.00	1.1509	1.1530	218.7	1.837	932.2	66.0	247	1.3577	6.46	3.47	1.804	0.943	0.821	105.84	184.	3.22
20.00	1.1601	1.1621	232.0	1.950	928.1	70.2	261	1.3591	6.88	3.70	1.912	0.942	0.814	105.95	194.	3.50
22.00	1.1788	1.1809	259.3	2.179	919.4	78.8	290	1.3620	7.76	4.17	2.130	0.941	0.800	106.07	216.	4.55
24.00	1.1980	1.2002	287.5	2.416	910.5	87.7	320	1.3650	8.70	4.68	2.352	0.941	0.787	106.07		
26.00	1.2179	1.2200	316.6	2.661	901.2	97.0	350	1.3680	9.68	5.20	2.579	0.942	0.775	105.92		
28.00	1.2383	1.2405	346.7	2.913	891.5	106.7	382	1.3711	10.72	5.76	2.809	0.945	0.765	105.59		
30.00	1.2593	1.2615	377.8	3.174	881.5	116.7	413	1.3743	11.82	6.35	3.042	0.950	0.756	105.05		
32.00	1.2810	1.2832	409.9	3.444	871.0	127.2	446	1.3776	12.98	6.98	3.279	0.957	0.748	104.30		
34.00	1.3033	1.3056	443.1	3.723	860.2	138.1	479	1.3809				0.966	0.743	103.33		
36.00	1.3263	1.3287	477.5	4.012	848.8	149.4	513	1.3843				0.977	0.738	102.13		
38.00	1.3501	1.3525	513.0	4.311	837.0	161.2	548	1.3878				0.991	0.736	100.69		
40.00	1.3746	1.3770	549.8	4.620	824.8	173.5	584	1.3914				1.008	0.735	99.01		

44 POTASSIUM CARBONATE, $K_2CO_3 \cdot 1\frac{1}{2}H_2O$

MOLECULAR WEIGHT = 138.20   FORMULA WEIGHT, HYDRATE = 165.23
RELATIVE SPECIFIC REFRACTIVITY = 0.608

0.00 % by wt. data are the same for all compounds.
For Values of 0.00 wt. % solutions see Table 1, Acetic Acid.

A% by wt.	H% by wt.	ρ D_4^{20}	D_{20}^{20}	C_s g/l	M g-mol/l	C_w g/l	$(C_o - C_w)$ g/l	$(n-n_o)$ ×10⁴	n	Δ °C	O Os/kg	S g-mol/l	η/η_o	η/ρ cS	ϕ rhe	γ mmho/cm	T g-mol/l
0.50	0.60	1.0027	1.0045	5.0	0.036	997.7	0.5	9	1.3339	0.176	0.095	0.050	1.011	1.011	98.68	7.0	0.072
1.00	1.20	1.0072	1.0090	10.1	0.073	997.2	1.1	17	1.3347	0.339	0.182	0.097	1.023	1.018	97.	13.6	0.144
2.00	2.39	1.0163	1.0181	20.3	0.147	995.9	2.3	35	1.3365	0.661	0.355	0.192	1.046	1.031	95.1	25.4	0.287
3.00	3.59	1.0254	1.0272	30.8	0.223	994.6	3.6	52	1.3382	0.986	0.530	0.288	1.069	1.045	93.36	36.7	0.428
4.00	4.78	1.0345	1.0363	41.4	0.299	993.1	5.1	69	1.3399	1.322	0.711	0.387	1.092	1.058	91.37	47.4	0.568
5.00	5.98	1.0437	1.0455	52.2	0.378	991.5	6.7	86	1.3416	1.668	0.897	0.488	1.117	1.072	89.35	58.0	0.712
6.00	7.17	1.0529	1.0548	63.2	0.457	989.7	8.5	103	1.3433	2.025	1.089	0.592	1.144	1.088	87.27	68.5	0.862
7.00	8.37	1.0622	1.0640	74.4	0.538	987.8	10.4	120	1.3450	2.395	1.287	0.699	1.172	1.105	85.17	78.8	1.02
8.00	9.56	1.0715	1.0734	85.7	0.620	985.8	12.5	137	1.3467	2.774	1.492	0.807	1.202	1.124	83.06	88.9	1.17
9.00	10.76	1.0809	1.0828	97.3	0.704	983.6	14.6	154	1.3484	3.167	1.702	0.919	1.233	1.143	80.94	98.8	1.34
10.00	11.96	1.0904	1.0923	109.0	0.789	981.3	16.9	171	1.3501	3.574	1.921	1.033	1.266	1.163	78.83	109.	1.50
12.00	14.35	1.1095	1.1115	133.1	0.963	976.4	21.8	205	1.3535	4.445	2.390	1.274	1.336	1.206	74.73	127.	1.83
14.00	16.74	1.1291	1.1311	158.1	1.144	971.0	27.2	239	1.3569	5.39	2.90	1.529	1.411	1.252	70.75	144.	2.17
16.00	19.13	1.1490	1.1510	183.8	1.330	965.2	33.1	273	1.3603	6.42	3.45	1.794	1.494	1.303	66.79	160.	2.53
18.00	21.52	1.1692	1.1713	210.5	1.523	958.8	39.5	307	1.3637	7.55	4.06	2.077	1.591	1.363	62.74	175.	2.90
20.00	23.91	1.1898	1.1919	238.0	1.722	951.9	46.4	341	1.3671	8.82	4.74	2.381	1.704	1.435	58.57	188.	3.31
24.00	28.69	1.2320	1.2342	295.7	2.140	936.3	61.9	409	1.3739	11.96	6.43	3.071	1.974	1.605	50.57	211.	4.24
28.00	33.48	1.2755	1.2778	357.1	2.584	918.4	79.9	477	1.3807	16.01	8.61	3.849	2.326	1.828	42.90		
32.00	38.26	1.3204	1.3227	422.5	3.057	897.8	100.4	544	1.3874	21.46	11.54		2.828	2.146	35.29		
36.00	43.04	1.3665	1.3690	492.0	3.560	874.6	123.6	610	1.3940	28.58	15.37		3.496	2.563	28.55		
40.00	47.82	1.4142	1.4167	565.7	4.093	848.5	149.7	676	1.4006	37.55	20.19		4.351	3.083	22.94		
44.00	52.61	1.4633	1.4659	643.9	4.659	819.5	178.8	741	1.4071				5.709	3.909	17.48		
48.00	57.39	1.5142	1.5169	726.8	5.259	787.4	210.8	806	1.4136				7.749	5.128	12.88		
50.00	59.78	1.5404	1.5431	770.2	5.573	770.2	228.0	838	1.4168				9.350	6.082	10.67		

45 POTASSIUM CHLORIDE, KCl

MOLECULAR WEIGHT = 74.55
RELATIVE SPECIFIC REFRACTIVITY = 0.758

0.00 % by wt. data are the same for all compounds.
For Values of 0.00 wt. % solutions see Table 1, Acetic Acid.

A% by wt.	D_4^{20}	D_{20}^{20}	C_s g/l	M g-mol/l	C_w g/l	$(C_o - C_w)$ g/l	$(n - n_o)$ × 10⁴	n	Δ °C	O Os/kg	S g-mol/l	η/η_o	η/ρ cS	ϕ rhe	γ mmho/cm	T g-mol/l
0.50	1.0014	1.0032	5.0	0.067	996.4	1.8	7	1.3337	0.234	0.126	0.067	0.998	0.999	99.97	8.2	0.084
1.00	1.0046	1.0064	10.0	0.135	994.6	3.7	14	1.3343	0.463	0.249	0.134	0.997	0.995	100.08	15.7	0.169
1.50	1.0078	1.0096	15.1	0.203	992.7	5.5	20	1.3350	0.691	0.372	0.201	0.997	0.991	100.11	22.7	0.253
2.00	1.0110	1.0128	20.2	0.271	990.8	7.4	27	1.3357	0.920	0.495	0.268	0.997	0.988	100.12	29.5	0.338
2.50	1.0142	1.0160	25.4	0.340	988.9	9.4	34	1.3364	1.149	0.618	0.336	0.996	0.984	100.16	36.5	0.426
3.00	1.0174	1.0192	30.5	0.409	986.9	11.3	41	1.3371	1.380	0.742	0.404	0.996	0.981	100.20	43.6	0.517
3.50	1.0207	1.0225	35.7	0.479	984.9	13.3	47	1.3377	1.613	0.867	0.472	0.995	0.977	100.26	50.6	0.610
4.00	1.0239	1.0257	41.0	0.549	982.9	15.3	54	1.3384	1.847	0.993	0.540	0.995	0.974	100.32	57.6	0.707
4.50	1.0271	1.0289	46.2	0.620	980.9	17.3	61	1.3391	2.083	1.120	0.609	0.994	0.970	100.38	64.8	0.807
5.00	1.0304	1.0322	51.5	0.691	978.8	19.4	68	1.3398	2.322	1.248	0.678	0.994	0.966	100.44	71.9	0.911
5.50	1.0336	1.0354	56.8	0.763	976.8	21.5	74	1.3404	2.561	1.377	0.747	0.993	0.963	100.51	79.1	1.01
6.00	1.0369	1.0387	62.2	0.835	974.7	23.6	81	1.3411	2.803	1.507	0.816	0.992	0.959	100.60	86.2	1.12
6.50	1.0402	1.0420	67.6	0.907	972.5	25.7	88	1.3418	3.047	1.638	0.885	0.991	0.955	100.69	93.3	1.24
7.00	1.0434	1.0453	73.0	0.980	970.4	27.8	95	1.3425	3.294	1.771	0.955	0.990	0.951	100.79	100.	1.36
7.50	1.0467	1.0486	78.5	1.053	968.2	30.0	102	1.3431	3.544	1.905	1.025	0.989	0.947	100.89	108.	1.48
8.00	1.0500	1.0519	84.0	1.127	966.0	32.2	108	1.3438	3.797	2.041	1.095	0.988	0.943	100.99	115.	1.61
8.50	1.0533	1.0552	89.5	1.201	963.8	34.4	115	1.3445	4.050	2.177	1.165	0.987	0.939	101.07	122.	1.74
9.00	1.0566	1.0585	95.1	1.276	961.6	36.7	122	1.3452	4.300	2.312	1.234	0.987	0.936	101.14	129.	1.88
9.50	1.0600	1.0619	100.7	1.351	959.3	39.0	129	1.3459	4.550	2.446	1.303	0.986	0.932	101.18	136.	2.02
10.00	1.0633	1.0652	106.3	1.426	957.0	41.2	136	1.3466	4.805	2.583	1.372	0.986	0.929	101.20	143.	2.17
11.00	1.0700	1.0719	117.7	1.579	952.3	45.9	149	1.3479	5.33	2.87	1.513	0.987	0.924	101.15	157.	2.49
12.00	1.0768	1.0787	129.2	1.733	947.6	50.7	163	1.3493	5.88	3.16	1.657	0.988	0.919	101.01	172.	2.84
13.00	1.0836	1.0855	140.9	1.890	942.7	55.5	177	1.3507	6.45	3.47	1.804	0.990	0.915	100.82	185.	3.21
14.00	1.0905	1.0924	152.7	2.048	937.8	60.4	191	1.3521				0.992	0.912	100.58	197.	3.61
15.00	1.0974	1.0993	164.6	2.208	932.8	65.5	205	1.3535				0.995	0.908	100.34	208.	4.05
16.00	1.1043	1.1063	176.7	2.370	927.7	70.6	219	1.3549				0.997	0.905	100.11	220.	4.85
17.00	1.1114	1.1133	188.9	2.534	922.4	75.8	233	1.3563				0.999	0.901	99.87		
18.00	1.1185	1.1204	201.3	2.701	917.1	81.1	247	1.3577				1.002	0.898	99.60		
19.00	1.1256	1.1276	213.9	2.869	911.7	86.5	262	1.3592				1.005	0.895	99.26		
20.00	1.1328	1.1348	226.6	3.039	906.2	92.0	276	1.3606				1.010	0.893	98.81		
22.00	1.1474	1.1494	252.4	3.386	895.0	103.2	305	1.3635				1.022	0.893	97.64		
24.00	1.1623	1.1643	278.9	3.742	883.3	114.9	335	1.3665				1.038	0.895	96.15		

46 POTASSIUM CHROMATE, K₂CrO₄

MOLECULAR WEIGHT = 194.20
RELATIVE SPECIFIC REFRACTIVITY = 0.820

0.00 % by wt. data are the same for all compounds.
For Values of 0.00 wt. % solutions see Table 1, Acetic Acid.

A% by wt.	ρ D_4^{20}	D_{20}^{20}	C_s g/l	M g-mol/l	C_w g/l	$(C_o - C_w)$ g/l	$(n - n_o)$ × 10⁴	n	Δ °C	O Os/kg	S g-mol/l	η/η_o	η/ρ cS	ϕ rhe	γ mmho/cm	T g-mol/l
0.50	1.0023	1.0040	5.0	0.026	997.3	1.0	11	1.3341	0.118	0.063	0.033	1.004	1.004	99.35	5.6	0.056
1.00	1.0063	1.0081	10.1	0.052	996.2	2.0	22	1.3352	0.235	0.126	0.067	1.009	1.005	98.91	10.8	0.113
2.00	1.0144	1.0162	20.3	0.104	994.1	4.2	44	1.3374	0.464	0.249	0.134	1.018	1.006	98.04	20.5	0.226
3.00	1.0224	1.0242	30.7	0.158	991.7	6.5	66	1.3396	0.682	0.367	0.198	1.027	1.006	97.21	29.8	0.340
4.00	1.0305	1.0323	41.2	0.212	989.2	9.0	87	1.3417	0.892	0.480	0.260	1.035	1.007	96.41	38.8	0.455
5.00	1.0386	1.0404	51.9	0.267	986.6	11.6	109	1.3439	1.103	0.593	0.322	1.044	1.007	95.59	47.8	0.573
6.00	1.0467	1.0486	62.8	0.323	983.9	14.3	131	1.3461	1.314	0.707	0.384	1.053	1.008	94.73	56.7	0.695
7.00	1.0550	1.0568	73.8	0.380	981.1	17.1	153	1.3483	1.524	0.819	0.446	1.063	1.010	93.85	65.6	0.819
8.00	1.0633	1.0652	85.1	0.438	978.2	20.0	175	1.3505	1.734	0.932	0.507	1.074	1.012	92.95	74.3	0.947
9.00	1.0718	1.0736	96.5	0.497	975.3	22.9	197	1.3527	1.946	1.047	0.569	1.085	1.014	92.02	83.0	1.08
10.00	1.0803	1.0823	108.0	0.556	972.3	25.9	220	1.3550	2.164	1.163	0.632	1.096	1.017	91.06	91.6	1.22
12.00	1.0980	1.0999	131.8	0.678	966.2	32.0	267	1.3597	2.613	1.405	0.761	1.120	1.022	89.07	109.	1.50
14.00	1.1163	1.1183	156.3	0.805	960.0	38.2	315	1.3645	3.076	1.654	0.893	1.147	1.030	87.00	125.	1.81
16.00	1.1344	1.1364	181.5	0.935	952.9	45.3	363	1.3693	3.555	1.911	1.028	1.176	1.039	84.84	141.	2.14
18.00	1.1527	1.1547	207.5	1.068	945.2	53.0	410	1.3740	4.050	2.177	1.165	1.209	1.051	82.56	157.	2.49
20.00	1.1720	1.1740	234.4	1.207	937.6	60.7	459	1.3789	4.561	2.452	1.306	1.245	1.064	80.16	172.	2.86
22.00	1.1920	1.1941	262.2	1.350	929.7	68.5	509	1.3839				1.285	1.081	77.64	189.	3.32
24.00	1.2125	1.2146	291.0	1.498	921.5	76.7	561	1.3891				1.330	1.099	75.04	201.	3.78
26.00	1.2335	1.2356	320.7	1.651	912.8	85.5	614	1.3944				1.379	1.120	72.37	214.	4.40
28.00	1.2547	1.2570	351.3	1.809	903.4	94.8	668	1.3998				1.433	1.144	69.64		
30.00	1.2763	1.2785	382.9	1.972	893.4	104.8	724	1.4054				1.492	1.171	66.89		

47 POTASSIUM DICHROMATE, K₂Cr₂O₇

MOLECULAR WEIGHT = 294.21
RELATIVE SPECIFIC REFRACTIVITY = 0.835

0.00 % by wt. data are the same for all compounds.
For Values of 0.00 wt. % solutions see Table 1, Acetic Acid.

A% by wt.	ρ D_4^{20}	D_{20}^{20}	C_s g/l	M g-mol/l	C_w g/l	$(C_o - C_w)$ g/l	$(n - n_o)$ × 10⁴	n	Δ °C	O Os/kg	S g-mol/l	η/η_o	η/ρ cS	ϕ rhe	γ mmho/cm	T g-mol/l
0.50	1.0017	1.0035	5.0	0.017	996.7	1.5	9	1.3339	0.101	0.054	0.028	1.000	1.001	99.75	3.7	0.037
1.00	1.0052	1.0070	10.1	0.034	995.1	3.1	18	1.3348	0.192	0.103	0.055	1.001	0.998	99.70	7.3	0.074
1.50	1.0087	1.0105	15.1	0.051	993.6	4.7	27	1.3357	0.278	0.149	0.080	1.001	0.995	99.65	10.6	0.111
2.00	1.0122	1.0140	20.2	0.069	992.0	6.3	36	1.3366	0.359	0.193	0.103	1.002	0.992	99.60	13.8	0.147
2.50	1.0157	1.0175	25.4	0.086	990.3	7.9	46	1.3375	0.435	0.234	0.126	1.003	0.989	99.55	17.0	0.184
3.00	1.0193	1.0211	30.6	0.104	988.7	9.5	55	1.3385				1.003	0.986	99.50	20.1	0.221
3.50	1.0228	1.0246	35.8	0.122	987.0	11.2	64	1.3394				1.003	0.983	99.45	23.1	0.258
4.00	1.0264	1.0282	41.1	0.140	985.3	12.9	73	1.3403				1.004	0.980	99.40	26.2	0.296
4.50	1.0300	1.0318	46.3	0.158	983.6	14.6	83	1.3413				1.004	0.977	99.35	29.2	0.334
5.00	1.0336	1.0354	51.7	0.176	981.9	16.3	92	1.3422				1.005	0.974	99.30	32.2	0.372

47 POTASSIUM DICHROMATE, $K_2Cr_2O_7$—(Continued)

A% by wt.	ρ D_4^{20}	D_{20}^{20}	C_s g/l	M g-mol/l	C_w g/l	(C_o-C_w) g/l	$(n-n_o)$ ×10⁴	n	Δ °C	O Os/kg	S g-mol/l	η/η_o	η/ρ cS	ϕ rhe	γ mmho/cm	T g-mol/l
5.50	1.0372	1.0390	57.0	0.194	980.1	18.1	102	1.3431				1.006	0.971	99.25	35.3	0.410
6.00	1.0408	1.0426	62.4	0.212	978.3	19.9	111	1.3441				1.006	0.969	99.21	38.3	0.449
6.50	1.0444	1.0463	67.9	0.231	976.5	21.7	121	1.3450				1.007	0.966	99.16	41.4	0.488
7.00	1.0481	1.0499	73.4	0.249	974.7	23.5	130	1.3460				1.007	0.963	99.11	44.4	0.528
7.50	1.0517	1.0536	78.9	0.268	972.8	25.4	140	1.3470				1.008	0.960	99.06	47.4	0.567
8.00	1.0554	1.0573	84.4	0.287	971.0	27.3	149	1.3479				1.008	0.957	99.01	50.3	0.607
8.50	1.0591	1.0610	90.0	0.306	969.1	29.2	159	1.3489				1.009	0.954	98.96	53.3	0.647
9.00	1.0628	1.0647	95.7	0.325	967.2	31.1	169	1.3499				1.009	0.951	98.91	56.3	0.688
9.50	1.0665	1.0684	101.3	0.344	965.2	33.0	179	1.3509				1.010	0.948	98.86	59.2	0.729
10.00	1.0703	1.0722	107.0	0.364	963.3	35.0	189	1.3519				1.010	0.946	98.81	62.1	0.770

48 POTASSIUM FERRICYANIDE, $K_3Fe(CN)_6$

MOLECULAR WEIGHT = 329.26
RELATIVE SPECIFIC REFRACTIVITY = 0.929

0.00 % by wt. data are the same for all compounds.
For Values of 0.00 wt. % solutions see Table 1, Acetic Acid.

A% by wt.	ρ D_4^{20}	D_{20}^{20}	C_s g/l	M g-mol/l	C_w g/l	(C_o-C_w) g/l	$(n-n_o)$ ×10⁴	n	Δ °C	O Os/kg	S g-mol/l	η/η_o	η/ρ cS	ϕ rhe	γ mmho/cm	T g-mol/l
0.50	1.0008	1.0026	5.0	0.015	995.8	2.4	8	1.3338	0.093	0.050	0.026	1.003	1.004	99.49	5.0	0.050
1.00	1.0034	1.0052	10.0	0.030	993.4	4.8	17	1.3347	0.180	0.097	0.051	1.006	1.005	99.21	9.7	0.100
1.50	1.0061	1.0079	15.1	0.046	991.0	7.3	25	1.3355	0.258	0.139	0.074	1.009	1.005	98.95	14.0	0.150
2.00	1.0087	1.0105	20.2	0.061	988.5	9.7	34	1.3364	0.334	0.180	0.096	1.011	1.004	98.71	18.2	0.199
2.50	1.0114	1.0132	25.3	0.077	986.1	12.1	42	1.3372	0.412	0.222	0.119	1.013	1.004	98.51	22.4	0.249
3.00	1.0140	1.0158	30.4	0.092	983.6	14.6	50	1.3380	0.491	0.264	0.142	1.015	1.003	98.33	26.5	0.298
3.50	1.0167	1.0185	35.6	0.108	981.1	17.1	59	1.3389	0.570	0.306	0.165	1.017	1.002	98.17	30.5	0.348
4.00	1.0194	1.0212	40.8	0.124	978.6	19.6	67	1.3397	0.649	0.349	0.189	1.018	1.001	98.02	34.5	0.399
4.50	1.0221	1.0239	46.0	0.140	976.1	22.1	75	1.3405	0.728	0.392	0.212	1.020	1.000	97.85	38.4	0.450
5.00	1.0249	1.0267	51.2	0.156	973.6	24.6	84	1.3414	0.807	0.434	0.235	1.022	0.999	97.65	42.4	0.502
5.50	1.0276	1.0294	56.5	0.172	971.1	27.2	92	1.3422	0.885	0.476	0.258	1.024	0.999	97.43	46.4	0.555
6.00	1.0304	1.0322	61.8	0.188	968.5	29.7	100	1.3430	0.962	0.517	0.281	1.027	0.999	97.19	50.5	0.609
6.50	1.0331	1.0350	67.2	0.204	966.0	32.3	109	1.3438	1.039	0.559	0.303	1.030	0.999	96.94	54.5	0.663
7.00	1.0359	1.0377	72.5	0.220	963.4	34.8	117	1.3447	1.115	0.600	0.326	1.032	0.999	96.67	58.5	0.719
7.50	1.0387	1.0406	77.9	0.237	960.8	37.4	125	1.3455	1.192	0.641	0.348	1.035	0.999	96.39	62.5	0.775
8.00	1.0415	1.0434	83.3	0.253	958.2	40.0	134	1.3464	1.268	0.682	0.371	1.039	0.999	96.10	66.5	0.832
8.50	1.0444	1.0462	88.8	0.270	955.6	42.6	142	1.3472	1.345	0.723	0.393	1.042	0.999	95.80	70.4	0.890
9.00	1.0472	1.0491	94.2	0.286	953.0	45.3	150	1.3480	1.422	0.764	0.416	1.045	1.000	95.49	74.4	0.949
9.50	1.0501	1.0519	99.8	0.303	950.3	47.9	159	1.3489	1.500	0.807	0.439	1.049	1.000	95.18	78.4	1.01
10.00	1.0530	1.0548	105.3	0.320	947.7	50.6	167	1.3497	1.580	0.849	0.462	1.052	1.001	94.87	82.4	1.07
11.00	1.0588	1.0607	116.5	0.354	942.3	55.9	184	1.3514	1.740	0.935	0.509	1.059	1.002	94.22	90.4	1.20
12.00	1.0647	1.0665	127.8	0.388	936.9	61.3	201	1.3531	1.901	1.022	0.556	1.067	1.004	93.55	98.4	1.33
13.00	1.0706	1.0725	139.2	0.423	931.4	66.8	219	1.3549	2.066	1.110	0.604	1.075	1.006	92.85	106.0	1.46
14.00	1.0766	1.0785	150.7	0.458	925.9	72.4	236	1.3566	2.235	1.202	0.653	1.084	1.008	92.11	114.0	1.60
15.00	1.0826	1.0845	162.4	0.493	920.2	78.0	254	1.3583	2.413	1.298	0.704	1.093	1.012	91.31	122.0	1.74
16.00	1.0887	1.0907	174.2	0.529	914.5	83.7	271	1.3601	2.600	1.398	0.758	1.103	1.015	90.46	129.0	1.88
17.00	1.0949	1.0968	186.1	0.565	908.8	89.5	289	1.3619	2.795	1.503	0.813	1.114	1.020	89.58	136.0	2.03
18.00	1.1011	1.1031	198.2	0.602	902.9	95.3	307	1.3637	2.997	1.611	0.871	1.126	1.024	88.65	143.0	2.17
19.00	1.1074	1.1093	210.4	0.639	897.0	101.3	325	1.3655	3.208	1.725	0.930	1.138	1.030	87.67	150.0	2.33
20.00	1.1137	1.1156	222.7	0.676	890.9	107.3	344	1.3674	3.427	1.843	0.992	1.152	1.036	86.63	157.0	2.50
22.00	1.1263	1.1283	247.8	0.753	878.6	119.7	381	1.3711				1.182	1.052	84.41	171.0	2.88
24.00	1.1391	1.1411	273.4	0.830	865.7	132.5	419	1.3749				1.217	1.070	82.02	185.0	3.31
26.00	1.1519	1.1540	299.5	0.910	852.4	145.8	457	1.3787				1.256	1.092	79.49	198.0	3.79
28.00	1.1647	1.1668	326.1	0.990	838.6	159.6	495	1.3825				1.299	1.117	76.83	210.0	4.34
30.00	1.1773	1.1794	353.2	1.073	824.1	174.1	533	1.3863				1.347	1.146	74.09	222.0	4.96

49 POTASSIUM FERROCYANIDE, $K_4Fe(CN)_6 \cdot 3H_2O$

MOLECULAR WEIGHT = 368.36 FORMULA WEIGHT, HYDRATE = 422.41
RELATIVE SPECIFIC REFRACTIVITY = 0.921

0.00 % by wt. data are the same for all compounds.
For Values of 0.00 wt. % solutions see Table 1, Acetic Acid.

A% by wt.	H% by wt.	ρ D_4^{20}	D_{20}^{20}	C_s g/l	M g-mol/l	C_w g/l	(C_o-C_w) g/l	$(n-n_o)$ ×10⁴	n	Δ °C	O Os/kg	S g-mol/l	η/η_o	η/ρ cS	ϕ rhe	γ mmho/cm	T g-mol/l
0.50	0.57	1.0016	1.0034	5.0	0.014	996.6	1.6	10	1.3340	0.083	0.044	0.023	1.007	1.008	99.07	4.8	0.048
1.00	1.15	1.0049	1.0067	10.0	0.027	994.9	3.3	21	1.3351	0.162	0.087	0.046	1.014	1.011	98.42	9.3	0.096
1.50	1.72	1.0083	1.0101	15.1	0.041	993.1	5.1	31	1.3361	0.239	0.129	0.068	1.020	1.013	97.87	13.4	0.142
2.00	2.29	1.0116	1.0134	20.2	0.055	991.4	6.9	41	1.3371	0.314	0.169	0.090	1.025	1.015	97.37	17.3	0.188
2.50	2.87	1.0149	1.0167	25.4	0.069	989.5	8.7	51	1.3381	0.385	0.207	0.111	1.031	1.017	96.84	21.3	0.235
3.00	3.44	1.0182	1.0200	30.5	0.083	987.7	10.6	62	1.3391	0.453	0.243	0.131	1.036	1.020	96.33	25.2	0.282
3.50	4.01	1.0215	1.0233	35.8	0.097	985.8	12.5	72	1.3402	0.518	0.278	0.150	1.042	1.022	95.81	29.0	0.331
4.00	4.59	1.0248	1.0266	41.0	0.111	983.8	14.4	82	1.3412	0.582	0.313	0.169	1.047	1.024	95.30	32.9	0.379
4.50	5.16	1.0281	1.0300	46.3	0.126	981.9	16.4	92	1.3422	0.645	0.347	0.187	1.053	1.026	94.77	36.7	0.428
5.00	5.73	1.0315	1.0333	51.6	0.140	979.9	18.4	102	1.3432	0.709	0.381	0.206	1.059	1.029	94.24	40.6	0.478
5.50	6.31	1.0348	1.0366	56.9	0.155	977.9	20.4	112	1.3442	0.771	0.415	0.225	1.065	1.031	93.70	44.4	0.528
6.00	6.88	1.0381	1.0400	62.3	0.169	975.8	22.4	122	1.3452	0.836	0.450	0.244	1.071	1.034	93.15	48.2	0.578
6.50	7.45	1.0415	1.0433	67.7	0.184	973.8	24.5	132	1.3462	0.899	0.483	0.262	1.078	1.037	92.60	51.9	0.629
7.00	8.03	1.0449	1.0467	73.1	0.199	971.7	26.5	143	1.3473	0.961	0.517	0.281	1.084	1.040	92.04	55.7	0.680
7.50	8.60	1.0483	1.0501	78.6	0.213	969.6	28.6	153	1.3483	1.023	0.550	0.299	1.091	1.043	91.47	59.4	0.731
8.00	9.17	1.0517	1.0535	84.1	0.228	967.5	30.7	164	1.3493	1.084	0.583	0.317	1.098	1.046	90.90	63.1	0.784
8.50	9.75	1.0553	1.0572	89.7	0.244	965.6	32.6	175	1.3505	1.144	0.615	0.334	1.105	1.049	90.32	66.8	0.837
9.00	10.32	1.0588	1.0607	95.3	0.259	963.5	34.7	185	1.3515	1.204	0.647	0.352	1.112	1.052	89.74	70.6	0.891
9.50	10.89	1.0623	1.0641	100.9	0.274	961.3	36.9	196	1.3525	1.262	0.679	0.369	1.119	1.056	89.15	74.3	0.947
10.00	11.47	1.0657	1.0676	106.6	0.289	959.2	39.1	206	1.3536	1.320	0.710	0.386	1.127	1.060	88.55	78.1	1.00
11.00	12.61	1.0727	1.0746	118.0	0.320	954.7	43.5	227	1.3557	1.433	0.771	0.419	1.143	1.067	87.35	85.8	1.12

49 POTASSIUM FERROCYANIDE, $K_4Fe(CN)_6 \cdot 3H_2O$—(Continued)

A % by wt.	H % by wt.	ρ D_4^{20}	D_{20}^{20}	C_s g/l	M g-mol/l	C_w g/l	$(C_o - C_w)$ g/l	$(n - n_o)$ × 10⁴	n	Δ °C	O Os/kg	S g-mol/l	η/η_o	η/ρ cS	ϕ rhe	γ mmho/cm	T g-mol/l
12.00	13.76	1.0798	1.0817	129.6	0.352	950.2	48.0	248	1.3578				1.159	1.075	86.13	93.7	1.25
13.00	14.91	1.0869	1.0889	141.3	0.384	945.6	52.6	270	1.3600				1.176	1.084	84.89	101.	1.38
14.00	16.05	1.0941	1.0961	153.2	0.416	941.0	57.3	291	1.3621				1.193	1.093	83.63	109.	1.51
15.00	17.20	1.1014	1.1034	165.2	0.449	936.2	62.0	313	1.3643				1.212	1.103	82.34	117.	1.64
16.00	18.35	1.1088	1.1107	177.4	0.482	931.4	66.9	335	1.3665				1.232	1.113	81.03	124.	1.78
17.00	19.49	1.1162	1.1182	189.8	0.515	926.4	71.8	357	1.3687				1.252	1.124	79.70	131.	1.91
18.00	20.64	1.1237	1.1257	202.3	0.549	921.4	76.8	379	1.3709				1.274	1.136	78.35	137.	2.05
19.00	21.79	1.1312	1.1332	214.9	0.583	916.3	81.9	401	1.3731				1.296	1.148	76.98	143.	2.18
20.00	22.93	1.1389	1.1409	227.8	0.618	911.1	87.1	424	1.3754				1.320	1.161	75.61	149.	2.32

50 POTASSIUM HYDROXIDE, KOH

MOLECULAR WEIGHT = 56.11
RELATIVE SPECIFIC REFRACTIVITY = 0.680

0.00 % by wt. data are the same for all compounds.
For Values of 0.00 wt. % solutions see Table 1, Acetic Acid.

A % by wt.	ρ D_4^{20}	D_{20}^{20}	C_s g/l	M g-mol/l	C_w g/l	$(C_o - C_w)$ g/l	$(n - n_o)$ × 10⁴	n	Δ °C	O Os/kg	S g-mol/l	η/η_o	η/ρ cS	ϕ rhe	γ mmho/cm	T g-mol/l
0.50	1.0025	1.0043	5.0	0.089	997.5	0.7	10	1.3340	0.299	0.161	0.086	1.008	1.008	98.98	20.0	0.220
1.00	1.0068	1.0086	10.1	0.179	996.7	1.5	20	1.3350	0.609	0.327	0.177	1.017	1.012	98.13	38.5	0.452
1.50	1.0111	1.0129	15.2	0.270	995.9	2.3	29	1.3359	0.924	0.497	0.269	1.026	1.017	97.25	56.9	0.697
2.00	1.0155	1.0172	20.3	0.362	995.1	3.1	39	1.3369	1.242	0.668	0.363	1.036	1.022	96.36	75.0	0.957
2.50	1.0198	1.0216	25.5	0.454	994.3	3.9	49	1.3379	1.562	0.840	0.457	1.046	1.027	95.45	92.8	1.23
3.00	1.0242	1.0260	30.7	0.548	993.5	4.8	58	1.3388	1.886	1.014	0.551	1.056	1.033	94.52	110.	1.53
3.50	1.0286	1.0304	36.0	0.642	992.6	5.6	68	1.3398	2.217	1.192	0.648	1.066	1.039	93.58	128.	1.85
4.00	1.0330	1.0348	41.3	0.736	991.7	6.5	78	1.3408	2.565	1.379	0.748	1.077	1.045	92.63	144.	2.20
4.50	1.0374	1.0393	46.7	0.832	990.8	7.5	87	1.3417	2.940	1.581	0.854	1.089	1.051	91.68	161.	2.58
5.00	1.0419	1.0437	52.1	0.928	989.8	8.4	97	1.3427	3.356	1.804	0.972	1.100	1.058	90.71	178.	3.00
5.50	1.0464	1.0482	57.6	1.026	988.8	9.4	106	1.3436	3.747	2.014	1.081	1.112	1.065	89.75	193.	3.47
6.00	1.0509	1.0527	63.1	1.124	987.8	10.4	116	1.3445	4.144	2.228	1.191	1.124	1.072	88.78	206.	3.97
6.50	1.0554	1.0572	68.6	1.223	986.8	11.5	125	1.3455	4.521	2.431	1.295	1.137	1.079	87.81	216.	4.52
7.00	1.0599	1.0618	74.2	1.322	985.7	12.5	134	1.3464	4.921	2.649	1.403	1.149	1.086	86.84		
7.50	1.0644	1.0663	79.8	1.423	984.6	13.6	144	1.3474				1.162	1.094	85.87		
8.00	1.0690	1.0709	85.5	1.524	983.5	14.8	153	1.3483				1.175	1.102	84.91		
8.50	1.0736	1.0755	91.3	1.626	982.3	15.9	162	1.3492				1.189	1.110	83.95		
9.00	1.0781	1.0801	97.0	1.729	981.1	17.1	172	1.3502				1.203	1.118	82.98		
9.50	1.0827	1.0847	102.9	1.833	979.9	18.4	181	1.3511				1.217	1.126	82.03		
10.00	1.0873	1.0893	108.7	1.938	978.6	19.6	190	1.3520				1.231	1.134	81.07		
11.00	1.0966	1.0985	120.6	2.150	976.0	22.3	209	1.3539				1.261	1.152	79.17		
12.00	1.1059	1.1079	132.7	2.365	973.3	25.0	228	1.3558				1.291	1.170	77.28		
13.00	1.1153	1.1172	145.0	2.584	970.3	28.0	246	1.3576				1.324	1.189	75.39		
14.00	1.1246	1.1266	157.5	2.806	967.2	31.0	265	1.3595				1.358	1.210	73.50		
15.00	1.1341	1.1361	170.1	3.032	964.0	34.3	284	1.3614				1.394	1.232	71.59		
16.00	1.1435	1.1456	183.0	3.261	960.6	37.7	302	1.3632				1.433	1.255	69.66		
17.00	1.1531	1.1551	196.0	3.493	957.0	41.2	321	1.3651				1.474	1.281	67.69		
18.00	1.1626	1.1647	209.3	3.730	953.3	44.9	340	1.3670				1.518	1.308	65.75		
19.00	1.1722	1.1743	222.7	3.969	949.5	48.8	358	1.3688				1.565	1.338	63.77		
20.00	1.1818	1.1839	236.4	4.212	945.4	52.8	377	1.3707				1.616	1.370	61.76		
22.00	1.2014	1.2035	264.3	4.710	937.1	61.2	414	1.3744				1.729	1.442	57.72		
24.00	1.2210	1.2231	293.0	5.223	927.9	70.3	451	1.3781				1.857	1.524	53.74		
26.00	1.2408	1.2430	322.6	5.750	918.2	80.0	488	1.3818				2.002	1.617	49.85		
28.00	1.2609	1.2632	353.1	6.292	907.9	90.4	524	1.3854				2.166	1.721	46.09		
30.00	1.2813	1.2836	384.4	6.851	896.9	101.3	559	1.3889				2.352	1.839	42.44		
32.00	1.3020	1.3043	416.6	7.425	885.4	112.9	593	1.3923				2.565	1.974	38.90		
34.00	1.3230	1.3254	449.8	8.017	873.2	125.0	628	1.3957				2.814	2.131	35.47		
36.00	1.3444	1.3468	484.0	8.626	860.4	137.8	664	1.3993				3.105	2.315	32.14		
38.00	1.3661	1.3685	519.1	9.252	847.0	151.3	700	1.4030				3.453	2.533	28.90		
40.00	1.3881	1.3906	555.2	9.896	832.9	165.4	738	1.4068				3.871	2.795	25.78		
42.00	1.4104	1.4129	592.4	10.558	818.1	180.2	776	1.4106				4.380	3.112	22.78		
44.00	1.4331	1.4356	630.6	11.238	802.5	195.7	813	1.4143				5.003	3.498	19.95		
46.00	1.4560	1.4586	669.8	11.936	786.2	212.0	849	1.4179				5.769	3.970	17.30		
48.00	1.4791	1.4817	710.0	12.653	769.1	229.1	884	1.4214				6.713	4.547	14.87		
50.00	1.5024	1.5050	751.2	13.388	751.2	247.0	917	1.4247				7.876	5.253	12.67		

51 POTASSIUM IODIDE, KI

MOLECULAR WEIGHT = 166.03
RELATIVE SPECIFIC REFRACTIVITY = 0.647

0.00 % by wt. data are the same for all compounds.
For Values of 0.00 wt. % solutions see Table 1, Acetic Acid.

A % by wt.	ρ D_4^{20}	D_{20}^{20}	C_s g/l	M g-mol/l	C_w g/l	$(C_o - C_w)$ g/l	$(n - n_o)$ × 10⁴	n	Δ °C	O Os/kg	S g-mol/l	η/η_o	η/ρ cS	ϕ rhe	γ mmho/cm	T g-mol/l
0.50	1.0019	1.0037	5.0	0.030	996.9	1.3	7	1.3337	0.111	0.060	0.031	0.9972	0.9973	100.1	3.8	0.038
1.00	1.0056	1.0074	10.1	0.061	995.5	2.7	13	1.3343	0.220	0.118	0.063	0.9945	0.9910	100.3	7.5	0.076
2.00	1.0131	1.0149	20.3	0.122	992.8	5.4	27	1.3357	0.431	0.232	0.124	0.9892	0.9784	100.9	14.2	0.152
3.00	1.0206	1.0224	30.6	0.184	990.0	8.2	40	1.3370	0.642	0.345	0.187	0.9840	0.9661	101.4	21.1	0.233
4.00	1.0282	1.0301	41.1	0.248	987.1	11.1	54	1.3384	0.858	0.461	0.250	0.9788	0.9538	102.0	28.1	0.320
5.00	1.0360	1.0378	51.8	0.312	984.2	14.1	67	1.3397	1.079	0.580	0.315	0.9736	0.9417	102.5	35.2	0.409
6.00	1.0438	1.0457	62.6	0.377	981.2	17.1	81	1.3411	1.304	0.701	0.381	0.9670	0.9283	103.2	42.3	0.501
7.00	1.0517	1.0536	73.6	0.443	978.1	20.1	95	1.3425	1.534	0.825	0.449	0.9608	0.9153	103.9	49.6	0.597
8.00	1.0598	1.0617	84.8	0.511	975.0	23.2	110	1.3440	1.769	0.951	0.517	0.9549	0.9028	104.5	56.9	0.697
9.00	1.0679	1.0698	96.1	0.579	971.8	26.4	124	1.3454	2.010	1.081	0.588	0.9494	0.8908	105.1	64.3	0.801
10.00	1.0762	1.0781	107.6	0.648	968.6	29.6	139	1.3469	2.257	1.213	0.659	0.9442	0.8791	105.7	71.8	0.909
12.00	1.0931	1.0950	131.2	0.790	961.9	36.3	168	1.3498	2.767	1.488	0.805	0.9348	0.8569	106.8	86.8	1.14

A % by wt.	ρ D_4^{20}	D_{20}^{20}	C_s g/l	M g-mol/l	C_w g/l	$(C_o - C_w)$ g/l	$(n - n_o)$ $\times 10^4$	n	Δ °C	O Os/kg	S g-mol/l	η/η_o	η/ρ cS	ϕ rhe	γ mmho/cm	T g-mol/l
14.00	1.1105	1.1125	155.5	0.936	955.0	43.2	199	1.3529	3.304	1.776	0.957	0.9265	0.8360	107.7	102.	1.39
16.00	1.1284	1.1304	180.5	1.087	947.9	50.4	231	1.3560	3.869	2.080	1.115	0.9193	0.8163	108.6	118.	1.66
18.00	1.1469	1.1489	206.4	1.243	940.4	57.8	263	1.3593	4.464	2.400	1.279	0.9131	0.7977	109.3	133.	1.96
20.00	1.1659	1.1680	233.2	1.405	932.8	65.5	296	1.3626	5.09	2.74	1.449	0.9077	0.7801	109.9	149.	2.30
22.00	1.1856	1.1877	260.8	1.571	924.8	73.4	331	1.3661	5.76	3.09	1.624	0.9031	0.7632	110.5	164.	2.66
24.00	1.2060	1.2081	289.4	1.743	916.5	81.7	366	1.3696	6.46	3.47	1.805	0.8991	0.7470	111.0	180.	3.05
26.00	1.2270	1.2291	319.0	1.921	908.0	90.3	403	1.3733	7.21	3.87	1.993	0.8956	0.7314	111.4	195.	3.53
28.00	1.2487	1.2509	349.6	2.106	899.1	99.2	441	1.3771	8.01	4.30	2.188	0.8928	0.7164	111.8	210.	4.16
30.00	1.2712	1.2734	381.4	2.297	889.8	108.4	480	1.3810	8.86	4.76	2.390	0.8904	0.7019	112.1	224.	5.20
32.00	1.2944	1.2967	414.2	2.495	880.2	118.0	521	1.3851	9.76	5.25	2.597	0.8888	0.6880	112.3		
34.00	1.3185	1.3208	448.3	2.700	870.2	128.0	563	1.3893	10.72	5.76	2.808	0.8880	0.6748	112.4		
36.00	1.3434	1.3458	483.6	2.913	859.8	138.5	606	1.3936	11.73	6.31	3.024	0.8884	0.6626	112.3		
38.00	1.3692	1.3716	520.3	3.134	848.9	149.3	651	1.3981	12.81	6.89	3.246	0.8905	0.6517	112.1		
40.00	1.3959	1.3984	558.4	3.363	837.6	160.7	697	1.4027	13.97	7.51	3.472	0.8952	0.6426	111.5		

52 POTASSIUM NITRATE, KNO$_3$

MOLECULAR WEIGHT = 101.10
RELATIVE SPECIFIC REFRACTIVITY = 0.651

0.00 % by wt. data are the same for all compounds.
For Values of 0.00 wt. % solutions see Table 1, Acetic Acid.

A % by wt.	ρ D_4^{20}	D_{20}^{20}	C_s g/l	M g-mol/l	C_w g/l	$(C_o - C_w)$ g/l	$(n - n_o)$ $\times 10^4$	n	Δ °C	O Os/kg	S g-mol/l	η/η_o	η/ρ cS	ϕ rhe	γ mmho/cm	T g-mol/l
0.50	1.0014	1.0031	5.0	0.050	996.4	1.9	5	1.3335	0.171	0.092	0.049	0.997	0.998	100.10	5.5	0.056
1.00	1.0045	1.0063	10.0	0.099	994.5	3.8	10	1.3339	0.333	0.179	0.096	0.994	0.992	100.40	10.7	0.112
2.00	1.0108	1.0126	20.2	0.200	990.6	7.7	19	1.3349	0.642	0.345	0.187	0.988	0.979	101.01	20.1	0.222
3.00	1.0171	1.0189	30.5	0.302	986.6	11.7	28	1.3358	0.938	0.504	0.274	0.984	0.969	101.46	29.3	0.334
4.00	1.0234	1.0252	40.9	0.405	982.5	15.7	38	1.3368	1.223	0.657	0.357	0.981	0.960	101.77	38.3	0.448
5.00	1.0298	1.0317	51.5	0.509	978.3	19.9	47	1.3377	1.498	0.805	0.438	0.978	0.952	102.05	47.0	0.563
6.00	1.0363	1.0381	62.2	0.615	974.1	24.1	57	1.3386	1.763	0.948	0.516	0.975	0.943	102.33	55.5	0.678
7.00	1.0428	1.0447	73.0	0.722	969.8	28.4	66	1.3396	2.022	1.087	0.591	0.973	0.935	102.59	63.7	0.793
8.00	1.0494	1.0512	84.0	0.830	965.4	32.8	76	1.3405	2.273	1.222	0.664	0.971	0.927	102.81	71.7	0.908
9.00	1.0560	1.0579	95.0	0.940	961.0	37.3	85	1.3415	2.517	1.353	0.734	0.969	0.920	102.98	79.5	1.03
10.00	1.0627	1.0646	106.3	1.051	956.4	41.8	95	1.3425	2.754	1.481	0.802	0.968	0.913	103.10	87.3	1.15
12.00	1.0762	1.0781	129.1	1.277	947.0	51.2	114	1.3444				0.968	0.901	103.13	103.	1.40
14.00	1.0899	1.0918	152.6	1.509	937.3	60.9	133	1.3463				0.970	0.892	102.90	117.	1.66
16.00	1.1039	1.1058	176.6	1.747	927.3	71.0	152	1.3482				0.974	0.884	102.44	131.	1.94
18.00	1.1181	1.1201	201.3	1.991	916.9	81.4	172	1.3502				0.980	0.879	101.79	145.	2.22
20.00	1.1326	1.1346	226.5	2.241	906.1	92.2	191	1.3521				0.988	0.874	101.01	157.	2.49
22.00	1.1473	1.1493	252.4	2.497	894.9	103.3	211	1.3541				0.997	0.871	100.10	168.	2.75
24.00	1.1623	1.1644	279.0	2.759	883.3	114.9	231	1.3561				1.008	0.869	99.01	178.	3.00

53 POTASSIUM OXALATE, K$_2$C$_2$O$_4$ · 1H$_2$O

MOLECULAR WEIGHT = 166.21   FORMULA WEIGHT, HYDRATE = 184.23
RELATIVE SPECIFIC REFRACTIVITY = 0.676

0.00 % by wt. data are the same for all compounds.
For Values of 0.00 wt. % solutions see Table 1, Acetic Acid.

A % by wt.	H % by wt.	ρ D_4^{20}	D_{20}^{20}	C_s g/l	M g-mol/l	C_w g/l	$(C_o - C_w)$ g/l	$(n - n_o)$ $\times 10^4$	n	Δ °C	O Os/kg	S g-mol/l	η/η_o	η/ρ cS	ϕ rhe	γ mmho/cm	T g-mol/l
0.50	0.55	1.0018	1.0035	5.0	0.030	996.6	1.5	8	1.3337	0.137	0.074	0.039	1.005	1.005	99.33	5.8	0.059
1.00	1.11	1.0053	1.0071	10.1	0.060	995.3	3.0	15	1.3345	0.273	0.147	0.078	1.010	1.007	98.81	11.4	0.119
1.50	1.66	1.0089	1.0107	15.1	0.091	993.8	4.5	22	1.3352	0.407	0.219	0.118	1.016	1.009	98.25	16.6	0.180
2.00	2.22	1.0125	1.0143	20.3	0.122	992.3	6.0	29	1.3359	0.540	0.290	0.156	1.022	1.011	97.65	21.7	0.241
2.50	2.77	1.0161	1.0179	25.4	0.153	990.7	7.5	36	1.3366	0.669	0.360	0.194	1.028	1.014	97.04	26.8	0.302
3.00	3.33	1.0198	1.0216	30.6	0.184	989.2	9.0	43	1.3373	0.797	0.429	0.232	1.035	1.017	96.41	31.7	0.364
3.50	3.88	1.0235	1.0253	35.8	0.216	987.6	10.6	50	1.3380	0.925	0.497	0.270	1.042	1.020	95.77	36.6	0.426
4.00	4.43	1.0272	1.0290	41.1	0.247	986.1	12.2	56	1.3386	1.055	0.567	0.308	1.049	1.024	95.11	41.4	0.489
4.50	4.99	1.0309	1.0327	46.4	0.279	984.5	13.8	63	1.3393	1.186	0.638	0.347	1.057	1.027	94.45	46.2	0.552
5.00	5.54	1.0346	1.0364	51.7	0.311	982.9	15.4	70	1.3400	1.318	0.709	0.385	1.064	1.030	93.80	50.9	0.615
5.50	6.10	1.0383	1.0402	57.1	0.344	981.2	17.0	77	1.3407	1.451	0.780	0.425	1.071	1.034	93.14	55.6	0.679
6.00	6.65	1.0421	1.0439	62.5	0.376	979.6	18.7	84	1.3414	1.585	0.852	0.464	1.079	1.038	92.48	60.3	0.743
6.50	7.20	1.0459	1.0477	68.0	0.409	977.9	20.3	90	1.3420	1.720	0.925	0.503	1.087	1.041	91.82	64.8	0.807
7.00	7.76	1.0497	1.0516	73.5	0.442	976.2	22.0	97	1.3427	1.856	0.998	0.543	1.095	1.045	91.15	69.3	0.872
7.50	8.31	1.0535	1.0554	79.0	0.475	974.5	23.7	104	1.3434	1.994	1.072	0.583	1.103	1.049	90.48	73.8	0.937
8.00	8.87	1.0574	1.0592	84.6	0.509	972.8	25.5	111	1.3441	2.132	1.146	0.623	1.111	1.053	89.81	78.1	1.00
8.50	9.42	1.0612	1.0631	90.2	0.543	971.0	27.2	118	1.3448	2.273	1.222	0.663	1.120	1.057	89.13	82.4	1.07
9.00	9.98	1.0651	1.0670	95.9	0.577	969.3	29.0	126	1.3456	2.414	1.298	0.704	1.128	1.061	88.45	86.6	1.13
9.50	10.53	1.0691	1.0709	101.6	0.611	967.5	30.7	133	1.3463	2.557	1.375	0.745	1.137	1.066	87.77	90.8	1.20
10.00	11.08	1.0730	1.0749	107.3	0.646	965.7	32.5	140	1.3470	2.701	1.452	0.786	1.146	1.070	87.09	94.8	1.27
11.00	12.19	1.0810	1.0829	118.9	0.715	962.1	36.2	154	1.3484	2.993	1.609	0.870	1.166	1.081	85.58	104.	1.42
12.00	13.30	1.0891	1.0910	130.7	0.786	958.4	39.8	168	1.3498	3.291	1.769	0.954	1.188	1.093	84.01	112.	1.57
13.00	14.41	1.0973	1.0993	142.7	0.858	954.7	43.6	182	1.3512	3.594	1.932	1.039	1.211	1.106	82.40	121.	1.72
14.00	15.52	1.1057	1.1077	154.8	0.931	950.9	47.3	196	1.3526	3.903	2.098	1.125	1.234	1.118	80.89	129.	1.87

54 POTASSIUM PERMANGANATE, $KMnO_4$

MOLECULAR WEIGHT = 158.04
RELATIVE SPECIFIC REFRACTIVITY = 0.811

0.00 % by wt. data are the same for all compounds.
For Values of 0.00 wt. % solutions see Table 1, Acetic Acid.

A% by wt.	ρ D_4^{20}	D_{20}^{20}	C_s g/l	M g-mol/l	C_w g/l	$(C_o - C_w)$ g/l	$(n-n_o)$ $\times 10^4$	n	Δ °C	O Os/kg	S g-mol/l	$\dot{\eta}/\eta_o$	η/ρ cS	ϕ rhe	γ mmho/cm	T g-mol/l
0.50	1.0017	1.0034		0.032	996.7	1.6			0.110	0.059	0.031	0.999	0.999	99.93	3.5	0.035
1.00	1.0051	1.0068	10.1	0.064	995.0	3.2			0.217	0.117	0.062	0.998	0.995	100.04	6.9	0.070
1.50	1.0085	1.0102	15.1	0.096	993.3	4.9			0.323	0.174	0.093	0.997	0.990	100.14	10.0	0.104
2.00	1.0118	1.0136	20.2	0.128	991.6	6.6			0.426	0.229	0.123	0.996	0.986	100.24	13.0	0.138
2.50	1.0152	1.0170	25.4	0.161	989.9	8.4						0.994	0.981	100.36	16.0	0.173
3.00	1.0186	1.0204	30.6	0.193	988.1	10.2						0.993	0.977	100.49	19.0	0.209
3.50	1.0220	1.0238	35.8	0.226	986.3	12.0						0.992	0.972	100.63	22.0	0.244
4.00	1.0254	1.0272	41.0	0.260	984.4	13.8						0.990	0.968	100.78	24.9	0.280
4.50	1.0288	1.0306	46.3	0.293	982.5	15.7						0.989	0.963	100.94	27.7	0.315
5.00	1.0322	1.0340	51.6	0.327	980.6	17.7						0.987	0.958	101.12	30.5	0.350
5.50	1.0356	1.0374	57.0	0.360	978.6	19.6						0.985	0.953	101.30	33.3	0.385
6.00	1.0390	1.0408	62.3	0.394	976.6	21.6						0.983	0.948	101.51	36.0	0.420

55 POTASSIUM PHOSPHATE, DIHYDROGEN (MONOBASIC), KH_2PO_4

MOLECULAR WEIGHT = 136.13
RELATIVE SPECIFIC REFRACTIVITY = 0.632

0.00 % by wt. data are the same for all compounds.
For Values of 0.00 wt. % solutions see Table 1, Acetic Acid.

A% by wt.	ρ D_4^{20}	D_{20}^{20}	C_s g/l	M g-mol/l	C_w g/l	$(C_o - C_w)$ g/l	$(n-n_o)$ $\times 10^4$	n	Δ °C	O Os/kg	S g-mol/l	η/η_o	η/ρ cS	ϕ rhe	γ mmho/cm	T g-mol/l
0.50	1.0018	1.0035	5.0	0.037	996.8	1.5	6	1.3336	0.130	0.070	0.037	1.008	1.008	98.98	3.0	0.030
1.00	1.0053	1.0071	10.1	0.074	995.3	3.0	12	1.3342	0.252	0.136	0.072	1.017	1.014	98.13	5.9	0.059
1.50	1.0089	1.0107	15.1	0.111	993.8	4.5	18	1.3348	0.371	0.200	0.107	1.026	1.019	97.25	8.5	0.087
2.00	1.0125	1.0143	20.2	0.149	992.2	6.0	24	1.3354	0.488	0.262	0.141	1.036	1.025	96.33	11.0	0.115
2.50	1.0161	1.0179	25.4	0.187	990.7	7.5	29	1.3359	0.603	0.324	0.175	1.046	1.032	95.37	13.5	0.143
3.00	1.0197	1.0215	30.6	0.225	989.1	9.1	35	1.3365	0.720	0.387	0.209	1.058	1.039	94.37	15.9	0.171
3.50	1.0233	1.0251	35.8	0.263	987.5	10.7	41	1.3371	0.838	0.451	0.244	1.069	1.047	93.34	18.3	0.199
4.00	1.0269	1.0288	41.1	0.302	985.9	12.4	47	1.3377	0.957	0.515	0.279	1.081	1.055	92.30	20.6	0.227
4.50	1.0306	1.0324	46.4	0.341	984.2	14.0	52	1.3382	1.075	0.578	0.314	1.094	1.063	91.26	22.8	0.255
5.00	1.0342	1.0360	51.7	0.380	982.5	15.8	58	1.3388	1.190	0.640	0.348	1.106	1.072	90.24	25.0	0.282
5.50	1.0378	1.0396	57.1	0.419	980.7	17.5	64	1.3394	1.303	0.700	0.381	1.119	1.080	89.23	27.2	0.309
6.00	1.0414	1.0432	62.5	0.459	978.9	19.3	70	1.3400	1.414	0.760	0.414	1.131	1.088	88.22	29.4	0.335
6.50	1.0450	1.0469	67.9	0.499	977.1	21.2	75	1.3405	1.523	0.819	0.446	1.144	1.097	87.21	31.5	0.361
7.00	1.0486	1.0505	73.4	0.539	975.2	23.0	81	1.3411	1.631	0.877	0.477	1.158	1.106	86.21	33.5	0.387
7.50	1.0522	1.0541	78.9	0.580	973.3	24.9	87	1.3417	1.736	0.933	0.508	1.171	1.115	85.21	35.5	0.412
8.00	1.0558	1.0577	84.5	0.620	971.4	26.9	92	1.3422	1.839	0.989	0.538	1.185	1.125	84.22	37.5	0.437
8.50	1.0594	1.0613	90.1	0.662	969.4	28.9	98	1.3428	1.941	1.043	0.567	1.199	1.134	83.23	39.3	0.461
9.00	1.0630	1.0649	95.7	0.703	967.4	30.9	104	1.3434	2.039	1.096	0.596	1.213	1.144	82.25	41.2	0.485
9.50	1.0667	1.0686	101.3	0.744	965.3	32.9	109	1.3439	2.136	1.148	0.624	1.228	1.154	81.27	42.9	0.508
10.00	1.0703	1.0722	107.0	0.786	963.3	35.0	115	1.3445	2.230	1.199	0.651	1.243	1.164	80.29	44.6	0.531

56 POTASSIUM PHOSPHATE, MONOHYDROGEN (DIBASIC), $K_2HPO_4 \cdot 3H_2O$

MOLECULAR WEIGHT = 174.18   FORMULA WEIGHT, HYDRATE = 228.23
RELATIVE SPECIFIC REFRACTIVITY = 0.589

0.00 % by wt. data are the same for all compounds.
For Values of 0.00 wt. % solutions see Table 1, Acetic Acid.

A% by wt.	H% by wt.	ρ D_4^{20}	D_{20}^{20}	C_s g/l	M g.mol/l	C_w g/l	$(C_o - C_w)$ g/l	$(n-n_o)$ $\times 10^4$	n	Δ °C	O Os/kg	S g-mol/l	η/η_o	η/ρ cS	ϕ rhe	γ mmho/cm	T g-mol/l
0.50	0.66	1.0025	1.0043	5.0	0.029	997.5	0.7	8.	1.3338	0.126	0.068	0.036	1.011	1.010	98.76	5.2	0.052
1.00	1.31	1.0068	1.0086	10.1	0.058	996.7	1.5	15.	1.3345	0.250	0.134	0.071	1.021	1.016	97.76	9.9	0.102
1.50	1.97	1.0110	1.0128	15.2	0.087	995.8	2.4	23.	1.3353	0.371	0.199	0.107	1.032	1.023	96.69	14.2	0.151
2.00	2.62	1.0153	1.0171	20.3	0.117	994.9	3.3	31.	1.3361	0.490	0.263	0.142	1.044	1.030	95.62	18.3	0.200
2.50	3.28	1.0195	1.0213	25.5	0.146	994.0	4.2	38.	1.3368	0.613	0.329	0.178	1.055	1.037	94.59	23.0	0.248
3.00	3.93	1.0238	1.0256	30.7	0.176	993.1	5.2	46.	1.3376	0.732	0.394	0.213	1.067	1.044	93.56	26.8	0.294
3.50	4.59	1.0281	1.0299	36.0	0.207	992.1	6.1	54.	1.3384	0.855	0.457	0.249	1.079	1.052	92.46	29.7	0.340
4.00	5.24	1.0324	1.0342	41.3	0.237	991.1	7.1	62.	1.3392	0.974	0.523	0.284	1.092	1.060	92.18	33.3	0.385
4.50	5.90	1.0368	1.0386	46.7	0.268	990.1	8.1	69.	1.3399	1.096	0.589	0.320	1.105	1.068	90.31	36.8	0.430
5.00	6.55	1.0412	1.0430	52.1	0.299	989.1	9.1	77.	1.3407	1.218	0.655	0.356	1.118	1.076	89.26	40.3	0.475
5.50	7.21	1.0456	1.0474	57.5	0.330	988.1	10.2	85.	1.3415	1.337	0.719	0.391	1.131	1.084	88.23	43.8	0.520
6.00	7.86	1.0500	1.0519	63.0	0.362	987.0	11.2	92.	1.3422	1.460	0.785	0.427	1.145	1.093	87.13	47.2	0.565
6.50	8.52	1.0545	1.0564	68.5	0.394	986.0	12.3	100.	1.3430	1.580	0.850	0.462	1.160	1.102	86.05	50.6	0.610
7.00	9.17	1.0590	1.0609	74.1	0.426	984.9	13.3	108.	1.3438	1.703	0.915	0.498	1.175	1.112	84.92	53.8	0.654
7.50	9.83	1.0635	1.0654	79.8	0.458	983.8	14.5	115.	1.3445	1.823	0.980	0.533	1.191	1.122	83.80	57.0	0.698
8.00	10.48	1.0680	1.0699	85.4	0.491	982.6	15.7	123.	1.3453	1.947	1.046	0.569	1.207	1.132	82.71	60.0	0.740

57 POTASSIUM SULFATE, K_2SO_4

MOLECULAR WEIGHT = 174.26
RELATIVE SPECIFIC REFRACTIVITY = 0.565

0.00 % by wt. data are the same for all compounds.
For Values of 0.00 wt. % solutions see Table 1, Acetic Acid.

A% by wt.	ρ D_4^{20}	D_{20}^{20}	C_s g/l	M g-mol/l	C_w g/l	$(C_o - C_w)$ g/l	$(n-n_o)$ $\times 10^4$	n	Δ °C	O Os/kg	S g-mol/l	η/η_o	η/ρ cS	ϕ rhe	γ mmho/cm	T g-mol/l
0.50	1.0022	1.0040	5.0	0.029	997.2	1.0	6	1.3336	0.136	0.073	0.039	1.004	1.004	99.37	5.8	0.059
1.00	1.0062	1.0080	10.1	0.058	996.2	2.1	13	1.3343	0.262	0.141	0.075	1.009	1.005	98.91	11.2	0.117
1.50	1.0102	1.0120	15.2	0.087	995.1	3.1	19	1.3349	0.382	0.205	0.110	1.014	1.006	98.42	16.2	0.175
2.00	1.0143	1.0161	20.3	0.116	994.0	4.2	25	1.3355	0.499	0.268	0.144	1.019	1.007	97.92	21.0	0.232
2.50	1.0183	1.0201	25.5	0.146	992.9	5.4	32	1.3362	0.614	0.330	0.178	1.025	1.008	97.39	25.6	0.289
3.00	1.0224	1.0242	30.7	0.176	991.7	6.5	38	1.3368	0.726	0.390	0.211	1.031	1.010	96.84	30.2	0.347

57 POTASSIUM SULFATE, K₂SO₄—(Continued)

A % by wt.	D_4^{20}	D_{20}^{20}	C_s g/l	M g-mol/l	C_w g/l	$(C_o - C_w)$ g/l	$(n - n_o) \times 10^4$	n	Δ °C	O Os/kg	S g-mol/l	η/η_o	η/ρ cS	ϕ rhe	γ mmho/cm	T g-mol/l
3.50	1.0265	1.0283	35.9	0.206	990.6	7.7	44	1.3374	0.839	0.451	0.244	1.037	1.012	96.27	34.7	0.404
4.00	1.0306	1.0324	41.2	0.237	989.4	8.9	50	1.3380	0.950	0.511	0.277	1.043	1.014	95.69	39.2	0.461
4.50	1.0347	1.0365	46.6	0.267	988.1	10.1	57	1.3386	1.061	0.571	0.310	1.049	1.016	95.10	43.7	0.518
5.00	1.0388	1.0406	51.9	0.298	986.8	11.4	63	1.3393	1.172	0.630	0.342	1.056	1.019	94.50	48.0	0.576
5.50	1.0429	1.0447	57.4	0.329	985.5	12.7	69	1.3399				1.063	1.021	93.89	52.3	0.634
6.00	1.0470	1.0489	62.8	0.361	984.2	14.0	75	1.3405				1.070	1.024	93.27	56.6	0.692
6.50	1.0512	1.0530	68.3	0.392	982.8	15.4	81	1.3411				1.077	1.027	92.64	60.8	0.751
7.00	1.0553	1.0572	73.9	0.424	981.4	16.8	87	1.3417				1.085	1.030	92.02	64.9	0.810
7.50	1.0595	1.0614	79.5	0.456	980.0	18.2	93	1.3422				1.092	1.033	91.39	69.0	0.869
8.00	1.0637	1.0655	85.1	0.488	978.6	19.7	98	1.3428				1.100	1.036	90.77	73.1	0.928
8.50	1.0679	1.0697	90.8	0.521	977.1	21.1	104	1.3434				1.107	1.039	90.14	77.0	0.988
9.00	1.0721	1.0740	96.5	0.554	975.6	22.6	110	1.3440				1.115	1.042	89.53	80.9	1.04
9.50	1.0763	1.0782	102.3	0.587	974.1	24.2	116	1.3446				1.122	1.045	88.92	84.8	1.10
10.00	1.0806	1.0825	108.1	0.620	972.5	25.7	122	1.3452				1.130	1.048	88.32	88.6	1.16

58 POTASSIUM THIOCYANATE, KSCN

MOLECULAR WEIGHT = 97.18
RELATIVE SPECIFIC REFRACTIVITY = 1.025

0.00 % by wt. data are the same for all compounds.
For Values of 0.00 wt. % solutions see Table 1, Acetic Acid.

A % by wt.	ρ D_4^{20}	D_{20}^{20}	C_s g/l	M g-mol/l	C_w g/l	$(C_o - C_w)$ g/l	$(n - n_o) \times 10^4$	n	Δ °C	O Os/kg	S g-mol/l	η/η_o	η/ρ cS	ϕ rhe	γ mmho/cm	T g-mol/l
0.50	1.0007	1.0025	5.0	0.051	995.7	2.5	9	1.3339	0.177	0.095	0.050	0.9974	0.9987	100.1	5.8	0.058
1.00	1.0032	1.0049	10.0	0.103	993.1	5.1	19	1.3349	0.355	0.191	0.102	0.9947	0.9936	100.3	11.4	0.119
2.00	1.0081	1.0099	20.2	0.207	987.9	10.3	37	1.3367	0.709	0.381	0.206	0.9887	0.9827	100.9	21.9	0.243
3.00	1.0130	1.0148	30.4	0.313	982.6	15.6	55	1.3385	1.061	0.570	0.310	0.9833	0.9726	101.5	32.1	0.370
4.00	1.0180	1.0198	40.7	0.419	977.3	21.0	74	1.3404	1.414	0.760	0.413	0.9785	0.9632	102.0	42.1	0.499
5.00	1.0229	1.0248	51.1	0.526	971.8	26.4	93	1.3423	1.771	0.952	0.518	0.9741	0.9542	102.5	52.2	0.632
6.00	1.0279	1.0298	61.7	0.635	966.3	32.0	111	1.3441	2.136	1.148	0.624	0.9700	0.9456	102.9	62.4	0.773
7.00	1.0330	1.0348	72.3	0.744	960.7	37.6	130	1.3460	2.506	1.347	0.731	0.9664	0.9374	103.3	72.7	0.922
8.00	1.0380	1.0398	83.0	0.854	955.0	43.3	149	1.3479	2.882	1.549	0.838	0.9632	0.9298	103.6	82.9	1.08
9.00	1.0431	1.0449	93.9	0.966	949.2	49.0	168	1.3498	3.264	1.755	0.946	0.9604	0.9225	103.9	93.	1.24
10.00	1.0482	1.0500	104.8	1.079	943.3	54.9	187	1.3517	3.653	1.964	1.055	0.9579	0.9157	104.2	103.	1.40
12.00	1.0585	1.0603	127.0	1.307	931.4	66.8	226	1.3556	4.451	2.393	1.276	0.9541	0.9032	104.6	121.	1.72
14.00	1.0689	1.0708	149.6	1.540	919.2	79.0	265	1.3595	5.28	2.84	1.498	0.9521	0.8925	104.8	138.	2.06
16.00	1.0795	1.0814	172.7	1.777	906.8	91.5	304	1.3634				0.9523	0.8840	104.8	156.	2.47
18.00	1.0902	1.0922	196.2	2.019	894.0	104.3	345	1.3674				0.9550	0.8777	104.5	176.	2.95
20.00	1.1011	1.1031	220.2	2.266	880.9	117.3	385	1.3715				0.9597	0.8733	104.0	197.	3.60
24.00	1.1236	1.1255	269.7	2.775	853.9	144.3	469	1.3798				0.9755	0.8700	102.3		
28.00	1.1467	1.1488	321.1	3.304	825.6	172.6	554	1.3884				1.001	0.8747	99.69		
32.00	1.1706	1.1727	374.6	3.855	796.0	202.2	643	1.3972				1.037	0.8874	96.27		
36.00	1.1949	1.1970	430.2	4.427	764.7	233.5	732	1.4062				1.081	0.9069	92.28		
40.00	1.2199	1.2220	488.0	5.021	731.9	266.3	824	1.4154				1.150	0.9446	86.78		
44.00	1.2455	1.2477	548.0	5.639	697.5	300.7	918	1.4248				1.253	1.008	79.65		
48.00	1.2719	1.2741	610.5	6.282	661.4	336.9	1014	1.4343				1.389	1.094	71.86		
52.00	1.2990	1.3013	675.5	6.951	623.5	374.7	1112	1.4442				1.552	1.197	64.31		
56.00	1.3269	1.3292	743.1	7.646	583.8	414.4	1212	1.4542				1.735	1.310	57.52		
60.00	1.3556	1.3580	813.4	8.370	542.2	456.0	1315	1.4645				2.013	1.488	49.58		
64.00	1.3853	1.3877	886.6	9.123	498.7	499.5	1420	1.4750				2.434	1.761	41.00		

59 PROCAINE HYDROCHLORIDE, C₆H₄[COOCH₂CH₂N(C₂H₅)₂][NH₂] · HCl-1,4

MOLECULAR WEIGHT = 272.78
RELATIVE SPECIFIC REFRACTIVITY = 1.460

0.00 % by wt. data are the same for all compounds.
For Values of 0.00 wt. % solutions see Table 1, Acetic Acid.

A % by wt.	ρ D_4^{20}	D_{20}^{20}	C_s g/l	M g-mol/l	C_w g/l	$(C_o - C_w)$ g/l	$(n - n_o) \times 10^4$	n	Δ °C	O Os/kg	S g-mol/l	η/η_o	η/ρ cS	ϕ rhe	γ mmho/cm	T g-mol/l
0.50	0.9991	1.0008	5.0	0.018	994.1	4.2	11	1.3341	0.062	0.033	0.017	1.014	1.017	98.42	1.4	0.014
1.00	0.9999	1.0017	10.0	0.037	989.9	8.3	22	1.3352	0.126	0.068	0.035	1.028	1.030	97.08	2.7	0.027
2.00	1.0016	1.0034	20.0	0.073	981.6	16.7	44	1.3374	0.237	0.127	0.068	1.056	1.056	94.51	5.2	0.052
3.00	1.0033	1.0051	30.1	0.110	973.2	25.0	66	1.3396	0.343	0.184	0.099	1.083	1.082	92.16	7.4	0.076
4.00	1.0050	1.0068	40.2	0.147	964.8	33.4	89	1.3419	0.433	0.233	0.125	1.110	1.106	89.95	9.4	0.098
5.00	1.0067	1.0085	50.3	0.185	956.4	41.8	111	1.3441	0.519	0.279	0.150	1.138	1.133	87.70	11.4	0.119
6.00	1.0085	1.0103	60.5	0.222	948.0	50.2	133	1.3463	0.593	0.319	0.172	1.169	1.161	85.38	13.1	0.139
7.00	1.0103	1.0120	70.7	0.259	939.5	58.7	156	1.3486	0.675	0.363	0.196	1.202	1.192	83.06	14.7	0.157
8.00	1.0120	1.0138	81.0	0.297	931.1	67.2	179	1.3508	0.756	0.406	0.220	1.236	1.224	80.73	16.2	0.174
9.00	1.0138	1.0156	91.2	0.334	922.6	75.6	201	1.3531	0.824	0.443	0.240	1.273	1.258	78.40	17.5	0.191
10.00	1.0156	1.0174	101.6	0.372	914.1	84.2	224	1.3554	0.889	0.478	0.259	1.312	1.294	76.07	18.8	0.206
12.00	1.0193	1.0211	122.3	0.448	897.0	101.3	270	1.3600	1.026	0.552	0.300	1.397	1.373	71.45	21.1	0.233
14.00	1.0230	1.0248	143.2	0.525	879.8	118.5	316	1.3646	1.164	0.626	0.340	1.491	1.460	66.84	23.0	0.256
16.00	1.0267	1.0285	164.3	0.602	862.4	135.8	362	1.3692	1.297	0.698	0.379	1.595	1.557	62.57	24.6	0.277
18.00	1.0305	1.0323	185.5	0.680	844.9	153.2	409	1.3739	1.421	0.766	0.417	1.700	1.661	58.44	26.0	0.294
20.00	1.0343	1.0361	206.9	0.758	827.4	170.8	456	1.3786	1.543	0.831	0.432	1.838	1.781	54.30	27.2	0.309
24.00	1.0420	1.0439	250.1	0.917	791.9	206.3	552	1.3881				2.143	2.061	46.57	29.0	0.331
28.00	1.0499	1.0517	294.0	1.078	755.9	242.3	649	1.3978				2.542	2.426	39.26	29.8	0.342
32.00	1.0578	1.0596	338.5	1.241	719.3	278.9	747	1.4077				3.089	2.927	32.30	30.2	0.346
36.00	1.0658	1.0676	383.7	1.407	682.1	316.2	848	1.4178				3.746	3.522	26.64	29.5	0.338
40.00	1.0738	1.0757	429.5	1.575	644.3	354.0	951	1.4280				4.757	4.439	20.98	28.3	0.323
44.00	1.0819	1.0838	476.0	1.745	605.9	392.4	1055	1.4385				6.028	5.583	16.56	26.8	0.304
48.00	1.0900	1.0920	523.2	1.918	566.8	431.4	1162	1.4491				7.888	7.251	12.65	24.7	0.278
52.00	1.0982	1.1002	571.1	2.094	527.2	471.1	1270	1.4600				11.22	10.24	8.89	22.3	0.248
56.00	1.1066	1.1085	619.7	2.272	486.9	511.3	1381	1.4711				15.97	14.46	6.25	19.5	0.214
60.00	1.1151	1.1171	669.1	2.453	446.0	552.2	1493	1.4823				22.12	19.88	4.51	16.1	0.174

61 2-PROPANOL, CH$_3$CHOHCH$_3$

MOLECULAR WEIGHT = 60.09

A% by wt.	ρ D_4^{20}	D_{20}^{20}	C_S g/l	M g·mol/l	C_W g/l	(C_0-C_W) g/l	$(n-n_0)$ ×10⁴	n	Δ °C	O Os/kg	S g·mol/l	η/η_0	η/ρ cS	ϕ rhe	γ mmho/cm	T g·mol/l
1.00	0.9960	0.9978	10.0	0.166	986.0	12.2	8.	1.3338	0.304	0.163	0.087	1.054	1.060	94.72	0.0	0.000
2.00	0.9939	0.9957	19.9	0.331	974.0	24.2	16.	1.3346	0.603	0.324	0.175	1.110	1.119	89.91		
3.00	0.9920	0.9938	29.8	0.495	962.2	36.0	25.	1.3355	0.926	0.498	0.270	1.164	1.176	85.72		
4.00	0.9902	0.9920	39.6	0.659	950.6	47.6	34.	1.3364	1.259	0.677	0.368	1.223	1.238	81.57		
5.00	0.9884	0.9902	49.4	0.822	939.0	59.2	43.	1.3373	1.610	0.866	0.471	1.284	1.302	77.71		
6.00	0.9871	0.9889	59.2	0.986	927.9	70.3	52.	1.3382	1.960	1.054	0.573	1.349	1.369	74.00		
7.00	0.9855	0.9873	69.0	1.148	916.5	81.7	62.	1.3392	2.320	1.247	0.677	1.414	1.438	70.56		
8.00	0.9843	0.9861	78.7	1.310	905.6	92.6	71.	1.3401	2.679	1.440	0.780	1.482	1.509	67.33		
9.00	0.9831	0.9849	88.5	1.472	894.6	103.6	80.	1.3410	3.062	1.646	0.889	1.550	1.580	64.38		
10.00	0.9816	0.9834	98.2	1.634	883.4	114.8	90.	1.3420	3.481	1.871	1.007	1.626	1.660	61.37		
12.00	0.9793	0.9811	117.5	1.956	861.8	136.4	109.	1.3439	4.433	2.383	1.271	1.790	1.831	55.77		
14.00	0.9772	0.9790	136.8	2.277	840.4	157.8	129.	1.3459	5.29	2.85	1.503	1.966	2.016	50.76		
16.00	0.9751	0.9769	156.0	2.596	819.1	179.1	148.	1.3478	6.36	3.42	1.78	2.156	2.215	46.30		
18.00	0.9725	0.9743	175.1	2.913	797.4	200.8	166.	1.3496	7.40	3.98	2.04	2.347	2.418	42.53		
20.00	0.9696	0.9713	193.9	3.227	775.7	222.5	184.	1.3514	8.52	4.58	2.31	2.545	2.630	39.21		
24.00	0.9630	0.9647	231.1	3.846	731.9	266.3	217.	1.3547	10.91	5.87	2.85	2.851	2.966	35.01		
28.00	0.9555	0.9572	267.5	4.452	688.0	310.2	245.	1.3575				3.115	3.267	32.03		
32.00	0.9478	0.9495	303.3	5.047	644.5	353.7	270.	1.3600				3.330	3.520	29.97		
36.00	0.9393	0.9410	338.2	5.627	601.1	397.1	292.	1.3622				3.499	3.733	28.52		
40.00	0.9302	0.9319	372.1	6.192	558.1	440.1	312.	1.3642				3.630	3.910	27.49		
44.00	0.9207	0.9224	405.1	6.742	515.6	482.6	330.	1.3660				3.732	4.061	26.75		
48.00	0.9113	0.9129	437.4	7.279	473.9	524.3	346.	1.3676				3.772	4.147	26.46		
52.00	0.9019	0.9035	469.0	7.805	432.9	565.3	362.	1.3692				3.789	4.210	26.34		
56.00	0.8920	0.8936	499.5	8.313	392.5	605.7	375.	1.3705				3.781	4.247	26.40		
60.00	0.8824	0.8840	529.4	8.811	353.0	645.2	387.	1.3717				3.719	4.223	26.84		
64.00	0.8729	0.8745	558.7	9.297	314.2	684.0	400.	1.3730				3.636	4.174	27.45		
68.00	0.8632	0.8648	587.0	9.769	276.2	722.0	411.	1.3741				3.528	4.095	28.29		
72.00	0.8535	0.8550	614.5	10.226	239.0	759.2	421.	1.3751				3.391	3.981	29.43		
76.00	0.8438	0.8453	641.3	10.672	202.5	795.7	428.	1.3758				3.235	3.841	30.85		
80.00	0.8341	0.8356	667.3	11.105	166.8	831.4	435.	1.3765				3.072	3.690	32.49		
84.00	0.8243	0.8258	692.4	11.523	131.9	866.3	440.	1.3770				2.886	3.508	34.58		
88.00	0.8145	0.8160	716.8	11.929	97.7	900.5	445.	1.3775				2.684	3.302	37.18		
92.00	0.8046	0.8061	740.3	12.319	64.3	933.9	447.	1.3777				2.530	3.151	39.44		
96.00	0.7949	0.7963	763.1	12.699	31.8	966.4	446.	1.3776				2.424	3.055	41.18		
100.00	0.7848	0.7862	784.8	13.060	0.0	998.2	442.	1.3742				2.428	3.100	41.10		

60 1-PROPANOL, CH$_3$CH$_2$CH$_2$OH

MOLECULAR WEIGHT = 60.09

A% by wt.	ρ D_4^{20}	D_{20}^{20}	C_S g/l	M g·mol/l	C_W g/l	(C_0-C_W) g/l	$(n-n_0)$ ×10⁴	n	Δ °C	O Os/kg	S g·mol/l	η/η_0	η/ρ cS	ϕ rhe	γ mmho/cm	T g·mol/l
1.00	0.9963	0.9981	10.0	0.166	986.3	11.9	9.	1.3339	0.307	0.165	0.088	1.049	1.055	95.14	0.0	0.000
2.00	0.9946	0.9964	19.9	0.331	974.7	23.5	18.	1.3348	0.613	0.329	0.178	1.098	1.106	90.91		
3.00	0.9928	0.9946	29.8	0.496	963.0	35.2	27.	1.3357	0.933	0.502	0.272	1.150	1.161	86.76		
4.00	0.9911	0.9929	39.6	0.660	951.5	46.7	36.	1.3366	1.239	0.666	0.362	1.206	1.219	82.77		
5.00	0.9896	0.9914	49.5	0.823	940.1	58.1	46.	1.3376	1.573	0.846	0.460	1.264	1.280	78.94		
6.00	0.9882	0.9900	59.3	0.987	928.9	69.3	55.	1.3385	1.906	1.024	0.557	1.322	1.340	75.52		
7.00	0.9868	0.9886	69.1	1.150	917.7	80.5	64.	1.3394	2.258	1.214	0.659	1.384	1.405	72.12		
8.00	0.9855	0.9873	78.8	1.312	906.7	91.5	74.	1.3404	2.609	1.403	0.760	1.446	1.470	69.03		
9.00	0.9842	0.9860	88.6	1.474	895.6	102.6	84.	1.3414	2.988	1.606	0.868	1.511	1.538	66.06		
10.00	0.9829	0.9847	98.3	1.636	884.6	113.6	93.	1.3423	3.356	1.805	0.972	1.574	1.605	63.39		
12.00	0.9804	0.9822	117.6	1.958	862.8	135.4	112.	1.3442	3.477	2.014	1.181	1.707	1.745	58.45		
14.00	0.9779	0.9797	136.9	2.278	841.0	157.2	130.	1.3460	4.914	2.642	1.401	1.845	1.890	54.10		
16.00	0.9749	0.9767	156.0	2.596	818.9	179.3	147.	1.3477	5.776	3.108	1.629	1.982	2.037	50.35		
18.00	0.9719	0.9737	174.9	2.911	797.0	201.2	164.	1.3494	6.667	3.588	1.859	2.102	2.167	47.48		
20.00	0.9686	0.9703	193.7	3.224	774.9	223.3	180.	1.3510	7.555	4.062	2.079	2.214	2.290	45.09		
24.00	0.9612	0.9629	230.7	3.839	730.5	267.7	209.	1.3539	9.115	4.901	2.450	2.427	2.530	41.12		
28.00	0.9533	0.9550	266.9	4.442	686.4	311.8	236.	1.3566	10.17	5.47	2.688	2.607	2.740	38.28		
32.00	0.9452	0.9469	302.5	5.034	642.7	355.5	262.	1.3592	10.66	5.73	2.797	2.759	2.925	36.17		
36.00	0.9370	0.9387	337.3	5.614	599.7	398.5	284.	1.3614				2.894	3.095	34.48		
40.00	0.9288	0.9305	371.5	6.183	557.3	440.9	305.	1.3635				3.004	3.241	33.22		
44.00	0.9206	0.9223	405.1	6.741	515.5	482.7	328.	1.3658				3.096	3.370	32.23		
48.00	0.9127	0.9143	438.1	7.291	483.6	514.6	348.	1.3678				3.162	3.472	31.56		
52.00	0.9043	0.9059	470.2	7.826	434.1	564.1	367.	1.3697				3.195	3.540	31.24		
56.00	0.8959	0.8975	501.7	8.349	394.2	604.0	385.	1.3715				3.197	3.576	31.21		
60.00	0.8875	0.8891	532.5	8.862	355.0	643.2	404.	1.3734				3.180	3.590	31.39		
64.00	0.8790	0.8806	562.6	9.362	316.4	681.8	422.	1.3752				3.135	3.574	31.83		
68.00	0.8706	0.8722	592.0	9.852	278.6	719.6	437.	1.3767				3.075	3.539	32.46		
72.00	0.8623	0.8639	620.9	10.332	241.4	756.8	453.	1.3783				2.997	3.482	33.30		
76.00	0.8549	0.8564	649.7	10.813	205.2	793.0	467.	1.3797				2.909	3.410	34.30		
80.00	0.8470	0.8485	677.6	11.276	169.4	828.8	482.	1.3812				2.816	3.332	35.43		
84.00	0.8390	0.8405	704.8	11.728	134.2	864.0	495.	1.3825				2.720	3.249	36.69		
88.00	0.8306	0.8321	730.9	12.164	99.7	898.5	505.	1.3835				2.590	3.125	38.53		
92.00	0.8218	0.8233	756.1	12.582	65.7	932.5	513.	1.3843				2.467	3.008	40.45		
96.00	0.8130	0.8145	780.5	12.989	32.5	965.7	518.	1.3848				2.345	2.890	42.56		
100.00	0.8034	0.8048	803.4	13.370	0.0	998.2	522.	1.3852				2.223	2.773	44.89		

62 PROPYLENE GLYCOL, CH₃OHCHOHCH₃

MOLECULAR WEIGHT = 76.09
RELATIVE SPECIFIC REFRACTIVITY = 1.236

0.00 % by wt. data are the same for all compounds.
For Values of 0.00 wt. % solutions see Table 1, Acetic Acid.

A % by wt.	ρ D_4^{20}	D_{20}^{20}	C_s g/l	M g-mol/l	C_w g/l	$(C_o - C_w)$ g/l	$(n - n_o)$ ×10⁴	n	Δ °C	O Os/kg	S g-mol/l	η/η_o	η/η_o cS	ϕ rhe	γ mmho/cm	T g-mol/l
0.50	0.9985	1.0003	5.0	0.066	993.5	4.7	5	1.3335	0.131	0.071	0.037	1.013	1.017	98.52		
1.00	0.9988	1.0006	10.0	0.131	988.8	9.4	10	1.3340	0.259	0.139	0.074	1.028	1.031	97.08		
2.00	0.9994	1.0012	20.0	0.263	979.4	18.8	20	1.3350	0.501	0.269	0.145	1.064	1.067	93.80		
3.00	1.0001	1.0019	30.0	0.394	970.1	28.2	31	1.3361	0.758	0.407	0.221	1.101	1.104	90.61		
4.00	1.0008	1.0025	40.0	0.526	960.7	37.5	41	1.3371	1.027	0.552	0.300	1.140	1.142	87.52		
5.00	1.0015	1.0032	50.1	0.658	951.4	46.8	52	1.3382	1.303	0.701	0.381	1.181	1.182	84.50		
6.00	1.0022	1.0040	60.1	0.790	942.1	56.2	63	1.3393	1.583	0.851	0.463	1.223	1.223	81.59		
7.00	1.0030	1.0047	70.2	0.923	932.8	65.5	74	1.3403	1.870	1.005	0.547	1.267	1.266	78.77		
8.00	1.0037	1.0055	80.3	1.055	923.4	74.8	84	1.3414	2.164	1.163	0.632	1.313	1.310	76.03		
9.00	1.0045	1.0063	90.4	1.188	914.1	84.1	95	1.3425	2.465	1.325	0.719	1.361	1.357	73.34		
10.00	1.0054	1.0071	100.5	1.321	904.8	93.4	107	1.3436	2.773	1.491	0.807	1.412	1.407	70.68		
12.00	1.0070	1.0088	120.8	1.588	886.2	112.0	129	1.3459	3.534	1.900	1.022	1.524	1.516	65.50		
14.00	1.0088	1.0106	141.2	1.856	867.6	130.7	152	1.3482	4.393	2.362	1.260	1.646	1.635	60.65		
16.00	1.0106	1.0124	161.7	2.125	848.9	149.4	175	1.3504	5.44	2.92	1.540	1.776	1.761	56.19		
18.00	1.0124	1.0142	182.2	2.395	830.2	168.1	198	1.3528				1.915	1.895	52.12		
20.00	1.0142	1.0160	202.8	2.666	811.4	186.9	221	1.3551				2.066	2.041	48.31		
24.00	1.0178	1.0196	244.3	3.210	773.6	224.7	267	1.3597				2.410	2.372	41.42		
28.00	1.0214	1.0232	286.0	3.759	735.4	262.8	314	1.3644				2.811	2.758	35.50		
32.00	1.0248	1.0266	327.9	4.310	696.8	301.4	360	1.3690				3.280	3.207	30.43		
36.00	1.0279	1.0297	370.1	4.863	657.9	340.4	406	1.3736				3.811	3.715	26.19		
40.00	1.0308	1.0326	412.3	5.419	618.5	379.8	451	1.3780				4.432	4.308	22.52		
44.00	1.0333	1.0352	454.7	5.975	578.7	419.6	494	1.3824				5.144	4.988	19.40		
48.00	1.0356	1.0374	497.1	6.533	538.5	459.7	537	1.3867				5.963	5.769	16.74		
52.00	1.0377	1.0395	539.6	7.091	498.1	500.2	580	1.3910				6.939	6.700	14.38		
56.00	1.0396	1.0415	582.2	7.651	457.4	540.8	622	1.3952				8.067	7.775	12.37		
60.00	1.0418	1.0436	625.1	8.215	416.7	581.5	665	1.3995				9.348	8.991	10.68		

63 SEA WATER*

RELATIVE SPECIFIC REFRACTIVITY = 0.789

0.00 % by wt. data are the same for all compounds.
For Values of 0.00 wt. % solutions see Table 1, Acetic Acid.

A % by wt.	Salinity ‰	Chlorinity ‰	ρ D_4^{20}	D_{20}^{20}	C_s g/l	C_w g/l	$(C_o - C_w)$ g/l	$(n - n_o)$ ×10⁴	n	Δ °C	O Os/kg	S g-mol/l	η/η_o	η/ρ cS	ϕ rhe	γ mmho/cm	T g-mol/l
0.50	4.94	2.72	1.0019	1.0037	5.0	996.9	1.3	9	1.3339	0.269	0.144	0.077	1.008	1.008	99.02	7.8	0.082
1.00	9.92	5.48	1.0057	1.0075	10.1	995.5	2.7	18	1.3348	0.537	0.289	0.156	1.016	1.012	98.23	15.2	0.163
1.50	14.91	8.24	1.0094	1.0112	15.1	994.1	4.1	27	1.3357	0.806	0.433	0.235	1.024	1.017	97.45	22.0	0.244
2.00	19.89	11.00	1.0132	1.0150	20.3	992.7	5.6	36	1.3366	1.075	0.578	0.314	1.033	1.022	96.61	28.4	0.324
2.50	24.87	13.76	1.0170	1.0188	25.4	991.2	7.0	45	1.3375	1.346	0.724	0.394	1.044	1.029	95.64	34.5	0.401
3.00	29.86	16.53	1.0207	1.0225	30.6	989.7	8.5	54	1.3384	1.616	0.869	0.473	1.055	1.036	94.58	40.4	0.476
3.50	34.84	19.29	1.0245	1.0263	35.8	988.1	10.1	63	1.3393	1.877	1.009	0.549	1.067	1.044	93.55	46.3	0.552
4.00	39.82	22.05	1.0283	1.0301	41.1	986.6	11.7	72	1.3402	2.129	1.145	0.622	1.077	1.050	92.67	52.4	0.635
4.50	44.81	24.81	1.0320	1.0339	46.4	985.0	13.3	81	1.3411	2.374	1.277	0.693	1.087	1.056	91.83	58.6	0.721
5.00	49.79	27.57	1.0358	1.0376	51.8	983.3	14.9	90	1.3420	2.612	1.404	0.761	1.100	1.065	90.75	64.2	0.799
5.50	54.78	30.33	1.0396	1.0414	57.1	981.6	16.6	99	1.3429	2.842	1.528	0.827	1.117	1.077	89.38	68.7	0.865
6.00	59.76	33.09	1.0434	1.0452	62.5	979.9	18.3	108	1.3438	3.064	1.647	0.890	1.137	1.093	87.80	72.6	0.922
6.50	64.74	35.85	1.0472	1.0490	68.0	978.1	20.1	118	1.3448								
7.00	69.73	38.61	1.0509	1.0528	73.5	976.3	21.9	127	1.3457								
7.50	74.71	41.37	1.0547	1.0566	79.0	974.6	23.6	136	1.3466								
8.00	79.69	44.13	1.0585	1.0604	84.6	972.9	25.3	146	1.3476								
8.50	84.68	46.90	1.0623	1.0642	90.2	971.2	27.1	155	1.3485								
9.00	89.66	49.66	1.0662	1.0680	95.9	969.3	28.9	164	1.3494								
9.50	94.64	52.42	1.0700	1.0719	101.6	967.5	30.8	173	1.3503								
10.00	99.63	55.18	1.0738	1.0757	107.3	965.6	32.6	182	1.3512								
11.00	109.6	60.70	1.0814	1.0833	118.9	961.7	36.5	200	1.3530								
12.00	119.6	66.22	1.0891	1.0910	130.6	957.8	40.5	219	1.3548								
13.00	129.5	71.74	1.0968	1.0987	142.5	953.7	44.5	237	1.3567								
14.00	139.5	77.27	1.1045	1.1065	154.6	949.5	48.7	255	1.3585								
15.00	149.5	82.79	1.1122	1.1142	166.8	945.2	53.0	273	1.3602								

* Values corresponding to A ‰ from 0.00–6.00 are based upon measurements of artificial sea water as formulated by Lyman and Fleming, *J. Marine Res.* **3**, 134, 1940. Values corresponding to A ‰ above 6.00 are based upon natural sea water from the Gulf of Mexico at Aransas Pass, Texas, concentrated by evaporation, according to Behrens, ibid. **23**: 165, 1965.

64 SERUM OR PLASMA, HUMAN

0.00 % by wt. data are the same for all compounds.
For Values of 0.00 wt. % solutions see Table 1, Acetic Acid.

A % by wt.	ρ D_4^{20}	D_{20}^{20}	C_s g/l	C_{Pr} g/100 ml	C_{NPr} g/100 ml	C_w g/l	$(C_o - C_w)$ g/l	$(n - n_o)$ ×10⁴	n
1.00	1.0029	1.0047	10.0	0.0	1.00	993.	5.0	16	1.3346
1.50	1.0051	1.0069	15.0	0.0	1.50	990.	8.0	24	1.3354
2.00	1.0069	1.0087	20.0	0.3	1.69	987.	11.0	33	1.3363
2.50	1.0082	1.0100	25.0	0.8	1.68	983.	15.0	42	1.3372
3.00	1.0096	1.0114	30.0	1.4	1.68	979.	19.0	52	1.3382
3.50	1.0110	1.0128	35.0	1.9	1.67	976.	22.0	61	1.3391
4.00	1.0123	1.0141	40.0	2.4	1.66	972.	26.0	71	1.3401
4.50	1.0137	1.0155	46.0	2.9	1.66	968.	30.0	80	1.3410
5.00	1.0150	1.0168	51.0	3.4	1.65	964.	34.0	90	1.3420
5.50	1.0164	1.0182	56.0	3.9	1.64	960.	38.0	99	1.3429

A % by wt.	ρ D_4^{20}	D_{20}^{20}	C_s g/l	C_{Pr} g/100 ml	C_{NPr} g/100 ml	C_w g/l	$(C_o - C_w)$ g/l	$(n - n_o)$ $\times 10^4$	n
6.00	1.0177	1.0195	61.	4.5	1.64	957.	41.	108	1.3438
6.50	1.0190	1.0208	66.	5.0	1.63	953.	45.	118	1.3448
7.00	1.0203	1.0221	71.	5.5	1.62	949.	49.	127	1.3457
7.50	1.0216	1.0234	77.	6.0	1.62	945.	53.	137	1.3467
8.00	1.0229	1.0247	82.	6.6	1.61	941.	57.	146	1.3476
8.50	1.0242	1.0260	87.	7.1	1.60	937.	61.	156	1.3486
9.00	1.0255	1.0273	92.	7.6	1.60	933.	65.	165	1.3495
9.50	1.0267	1.0286	98.	8.2	1.59	929.	69.	175	1.3505
10.00	1.0279	1.0298	103.	8.7	1.58	925.	73.	184	1.3514
11.00	1.0305	1.0324	113.	9.8	1.57	917.	81.	203	1.3533
12.00	1.0329	1.0348	124.	10.8	1.55	909.	89.	222	1.3552
13.00	1.0354	1.0373	135.	11.9	1.54	901.	97.	241	1.3571
14.00	1.0378	1.0397	145.	13.0	1.53	893.	105.	260	1.3590
15.00	1.0401	1.0420	156.	14.1	1.51	884.	114.	279	1.3609

Notes: C_{Pr} = g protein/100 ml; C_{NPr} = g nonprotein solute/100 ml.

65 SERUM OR PLASMA, RABBIT OR GUINEA PIG

0.00 % by wt. data are the same for all compounds.
For Values of 0.00 wt. % solutions see Table 1, Acetic Acid.

A % by wt.	ρ D_4^{20}	D_{20}^{20}	C_s g/l	C_{Pr} g/100 ml	C_w g/l	$(C_o - C_w)$ g/l	$(n - n_o)$ $\times 10^4$	n
4.0	1.0125	1.0143	41.	3.3	972.	28.	71	1.3401
4.5	1.0139	1.0156	46.	3.8	968.	30.	80	1.3410
5.0	1.0152	1.0170	51.	4.2	964.	34.	89	1.3419
5.5	1.0165	1.0183	56.	4.6	961.	38.	98	1.3428
6.0	1.0179	1.0197	61.	5.0	957.	41.	107	1.3437
6.5	1.0192	1.0210	66.	5.4	953.	45.	116	1.3446
7.0	1.0206	1.0224	71.	5.8	949.	49.	125	1.3455
7.5	1.0219	1.0238	77.	6.2	945.	53.	134	1.3464
8.0	1.0233	1.0251	82.	6.6	941.	57.	143	1.3473
8.5	1.0247	1.0265	87.	7.0	938.	61.	152	1.3482
9.0	1.0260	1.0278	92.	7.4	934.	65.	161	1.3491
9.5	1.0274	1.0292	98.	7.8	930.	68.	170	1.3500
10.0	1.0287	1.0306	103.	8.2	926.	72.	179	1.3509
11.0	1.0315	1.0333	113.	9.0	918.	80.	197	1.3527
12.0	1.0342	1.0360	124.	9.8	910.	88.	215	1.3545

Note: C_{Pr} = g protein/100 ml.

66 SILVER NITRATE, AgNO₃

MOLECULAR WEIGHT = 169.89
RELATIVE SPECIFIC REFRACTIVITY = 0.475

0.00 % by wt. data are the same for all compounds.
For Values of 0.00 wt. % solutions see Table 1, Acetic Acid.

A % by wt.	ρ D_4^{20}	D_{20}^{20}	C_s g/l	M g-mol/l	C_w g/l	$(C_o - C_w)$ g/l	$(n - n_o)$ $\times 10^4$	n	Δ °C	O Os/kg	S g-mol/l	η/η_o	η/ρ cS	ϕ rhe	γ mmho/cm	T g-mol/l
0.50	1.0027	1.0045	5.0	0.030	997.7	0.5	6	1.3336	0.103	0.056	0.029	1.001	1.001	99.66	3.1	0.031
1.00	1.0070	1.0088	10.1	0.059	996.9	1.3	12	1.3342	0.202	0.109	0.058	1.003	0.998	99.50	6.1	0.062
2.00	1.0154	1.0172	20.3	0.120	995.1	3.1	22	1.3352	0.395	0.213	0.114	1.007	0.994	99.11	12.0	0.126
3.00	1.0239	1.0257	30.7	0.181	993.2	5.1	33	1.3363	0.586	0.315	0.170	1.011	0.989	98.74	17.2	0.187
4.00	1.0327	1.0345	41.3	0.243	991.4	6.8	44	1.3374	0.775	0.416	0.226	1.014	0.984	98.39	22.0	0.245
5.00	1.0417	1.0436	52.1	0.307	989.6	8.6	55	1.3385	0.961	0.517	0.281	1.018	0.979	98.04	26.7	0.303
6.00	1.0506	1.0524	63.0	0.371	987.5	10.7	66	1.3396	1.146	0.616	0.335	1.022	0.974	97.69	31.4	0.362
7.00	1.0597	1.0616	74.2	0.437	985.5	12.7	78	1.3407	1.329	0.715	0.389	1.025	0.969	97.34	36.1	0.421
8.00	1.0690	1.0709	85.5	0.503	983.5	14.7	89	1.3419	1.511	0.812	0.442	1.029	0.964	97.00	40.7	0.480
9.00	1.0785	1.0804	97.1	0.571	981.4	16.8	101	1.3431	1.690	0.909	0.494	1.033	0.959	96.63	45.3	0.540
10.00	1.0882	1.0901	108.8	0.641	979.3	18.9	113	1.3443	1.868	1.004	0.546	1.037	0.955	96.24	49.8	0.600
12.00	1.1079	1.1099	133.0	0.783	975.0	23.2	138	1.3467	2.213	1.190	0.646	1.047	0.947	95.35	58.8	0.723
14.00	1.1284	1.1304	158.0	0.930	970.4	27.8	163	1.3493	2.546	1.369	0.742	1.058	0.939	94.35	67.6	0.849
16.00	1.1496	1.1516	183.9	1.083	965.7	32.6	189	1.3519	2.862	1.539	0.832	1.070	0.933	93.25	76.3	0.976
18.00	1.1715	1.1736	210.9	1.241	960.6	37.6	216	1.3546				1.084	0.927	92.07	84.7	1.10
20.00	1.1942	1.1963	238.8	1.406	955.4	42.9	244	1.3574				1.099	0.922	90.81	92.8	1.23
22.00	1.2177	1.2198	267.9	1.577	949.8	48.5	273	1.3602				1.115	0.918	89.49	101.0	1.36
24.00	1.2420	1.2442	298.1	1.755	943.9	54.3	302	1.3632				1.133	0.914	88.09	108.0	1.49
26.00	1.2672	1.2694	329.5	1.939	937.7	60.5	332	1.3662				1.152	0.911	86.60	115.0	1.61
28.00	1.2933	1.2956	362.1	2.132	931.2	67.1	364	1.3694				1.174	0.910	85.01	122.0	1.74
30.00	1.3204	1.3228	396.1	2.332	924.3	73.9	397	1.3726				1.198	0.909	83.31	129.0	1.88
32.00	1.3487	1.3510	431.6	2.540	917.1	81.1	430	1.3760				1.225	0.910	81.49	136.0	2.02
34.00	1.3780	1.3805	468.5	2.758	909.5	88.7	465	1.3795				1.254	0.912	79.58	142.0	2.16
36.00	1.4087	1.4112	507.1	2.985	901.6	96.7	502	1.3832				1.287	0.915	77.56	149.0	2.31
38.00	1.4407	1.4433	547.5	3.223	893.2	105.0	541	1.3871				1.323	0.920	75.44	156.0	2.46
40.00	1.4743	1.4769	589.7	3.471	884.6	113.7	581	1.3911				1.363	0.926	73.22	162.0	2.61

67 SODIUM ACETATE, CH₃COONa

MOLECULAR WEIGHT = 82.04
RELATIVE SPECIFIC REFRACTIVITY = 0.884

0.00 % by wt. data are the same for all compounds.
For Values of 0.00 wt. % solutions see Table 1, Acetic Acid.

A % by wt.	ρ D_4^{20}	D_{20}^{20}	C_s g/l	M g-mol/l	C_w g/l	$(C_o - C_w)$ g/l	$(n - n_o)$ × 10⁴	n	Δ °C	O Os/kg	S g-mol/l	η/η_o	η/ρ cS	ϕ rhe	γ mmho/cm	T g-mol/l
0.50	1.0008	1.0026	5.0	0.061	995.8	2.4	7	1.3337	0.217	0.116	0.062	1.019	1.020	97.96	3.9	0.039
1.00	1.0034	1.0052	10.0	0.122	993.4	4.9	14	1.3344	0.433	0.233	0.125	1.038	1.037	96.15	7.6	0.078
2.00	1.0085	1.0103	20.2	0.246	988.3	9.9	28	1.3358	0.877	0.471	0.256	1.078	1.071	92.58	14.4	0.154
3.00	1.0135	1.0153	30.4	0.371	983.1	15.2	42	1.3372	1.339	0.720	0.391	1.122	1.109	88.98	20.4	0.225
4.00	1.0184	1.0202	40.7	0.497	977.7	20.6	56	1.3386	1.820	0.978	0.532	1.169	1.150	85.38	25.7	0.291
5.00	1.0234	1.0252	51.2	0.624	972.2	26.0	70	1.3400	2.323	1.249	0.678	1.220	1.195	81.80	30.9	0.355
6.00	1.0283	1.0302	61.7	0.752	966.6	31.6	85	1.3414	2.848	1.531	0.828	1.275	1.242	78.27	35.9	0.419
7.00	1.0334	1.0352	72.3	0.882	961.1	37.2	99	1.3428	3.398	1.827	0.984	1.334	1.294	74.79	40.8	0.482
8.00	1.0386	1.0404	83.1	1.013	955.5	42.7	112	1.3442	3.975	2.137	1.144	1.398	1.348	71.41	45.4	0.542
9.00	1.0440	1.0458	94.0	1.145	950.0	48.2	126	1.3456	4.566	2.455	1.307	1.465	1.406	68.13	49.6	0.598
10.00	1.0495	1.0514	105.0	1.279	944.6	53.6	140	1.3470				1.536	1.466	64.97	53.4	0.648
12.00	1.0607	1.0625	127.3	1.551	933.4	64.9	168	1.3498				1.685	1.592	59.22	59.0	0.725
14.00	1.0718	1.0737	150.1	1.829	921.8	76.5	196	1.3526				1.851	1.731	53.90	62.7	0.777
16.00	1.0830	1.0849	173.3	2.112	909.7	88.5	224	1.3554				2.050	1.897	48.68	65.5	0.818
18.00	1.0940	1.0960	196.9	2.400	897.1	101.1	253	1.3583				2.279	2.087	43.79	67.8	0.852
20.00	1.1050	1.1070	221.0	2.694	884.0	114.2	281	1.3611				2.562	2.323	38.95	69.3	0.873
22.00	1.1159	1.1179	245.5	2.993	870.4	127.8	309	1.3639				2.942	2.642	33.92	69.9	0.882
24.00	1.1268	1.1288	270.4	3.296	856.4	141.9	336	1.3666				3.393	3.017	29.41	69.7	0.878
26.00	1.1377	1.1397	295.8	3.606	841.9	156.3	363	1.3693				3.869	3.408	25.79	68.8	0.865
28.00	1.1488	1.1508	321.7	3.921	827.1	171.1	390	1.3720				4.379	3.819	22.79	67.0	0.840
30.00	1.1602	1.1623	348.1	4.243	812.2	186.1	418	1.3748				4.930	4.258	20.24	64.3	0.800

68 SODIUM BICARBONATE, NaHCO₃

MOLECULAR WEIGHT = 84.01
RELATIVE SPECIFIC REFRACTIVITY = 0.687

0.00 % by wt. data are the same for all compounds.
For Values of 0.00 wt. % solutions see Table 1, Acetic Acid.

A % by wt.	ρ D_4^{20}	D_{20}^{20}	C_s g/l	M g-mol/l	C_w g/l	$(C_o - C_w)$ g/l	$(n - n_o)$ × 10⁴	n	Δ °C	O Os/kg	S g-mol/l	η/η_o	η/ρ cS	ϕ rhe	γ mmho/cm	T g-mol/l
0.50	1.0018	1.0036	5.0	0.060	996.8	1.4	7	1.3337	0.199	0.107	0.057	1.013	1.013	98.52	4.2	0.041
1.00	1.0054	1.0072	10.1	0.120	995.3	2.9	14	1.3344	0.396	0.213	0.114	1.026	1.023	97.23	8.2	0.083
1.50	1.0089	1.0107	15.1	0.180	993.8	4.4	21	1.3351	0.591	0.318	0.172	1.040	1.033	95.94	11.7	0.123
2.00	1.0125	1.0143	20.2	0.241	992.2	6.0	27	1.3357	0.784	0.422	0.228	1.055	1.044	94.64	15.0	0.161
2.50	1.0160	1.0178	25.4	0.302	990.6	7.6	34	1.3364	0.975	0.524	0.284	1.069	1.055	93.33	18.0	0.197
3.00	1.0196	1.0214	30.6	0.364	989.0	9.3	41	1.3370	1.164	0.626	0.340	1.084	1.066	92.03	20.8	0.230
3.50	1.0231	1.0249	35.8	0.426	987.3	11.0	47	1.3377	1.350	0.726	0.395	1.100	1.077	90.73	23.5	0.263
4.00	1.0266	1.0284	41.1	0.489	985.5	12.7	54	1.3383	1.535	0.825	0.449	1.116	1.089	89.44	26.1	0.295
4.50	1.0301	1.0320	46.4	0.552	983.8	14.5	60	1.3390	1.718	0.924	0.502	1.132	1.101	88.16	28.7	0.327
5.00	1.0337	1.0355	51.7	0.615	982.0	16.2	67	1.3396	1.899	1.021	0.555	1.149	1.114	86.88	31.4	0.361
5.50	1.0372	1.0391	57.0	0.679	980.2	18.1	73	1.3403	2.078	1.117	0.607	1.166	1.126	85.61	34.2	0.397
6.00	1.0408	1.0426	62.4	0.743	978.4	19.9	79	1.3409	2.256	1.213	0.659	1.183	1.139	84.36	37.3	0.437

69 SODIUM BROMIDE, NaBr

MOLECULAR WEIGHT = 102.91
RELATIVE SPECIFIC REFRACTIVITY = 0.626

0.00 % by wt. data are the same for all compounds.
For Values of 0.00 wt. % solutions see Table 1, Acetic Acid.

A % by wt.	ρ D_4^{20}	D_{20}^{20}	C_s g/l	M g-mol/l	C_w g/l	$(C_o - C_w)$ g/l	$(n - n_o)$ × 10⁴	n	Δ °C	O Os/kg	S g-mol/l	η/η_o	η/ρ cS	ϕ rhe	γ mmho/cm	T g-mol/l
0.50	1.0021	1.0039	5.0	0.049	997.1	1.1	7	1.3337	0.173	0.093	0.049	1.002	1.002	99.55	5.0	0.050
1.00	1.0060	1.0078	10.1	0.098	995.9	2.3	14	1.3344	0.344	0.185	0.099	1.005	1.001	99.30	9.7	0.100
1.50	1.0099	1.0117	15.1	0.147	994.8	3.5	21	1.3351	0.515	0.277	0.149	1.007	1.000	99.06	14.1	0.150
2.00	1.0139	1.0157	20.3	0.197	993.6	4.7	28	1.3358	0.687	0.369	0.200	1.010	0.998	98.81	18.4	0.201
2.50	1.0178	1.0196	25.4	0.247	992.4	5.9	35	1.3365	0.860	0.463	0.251	1.013	0.997	98.56	22.7	0.253
3.00	1.0218	1.0236	30.7	0.298	991.1	7.1	42	1.3372	1.036	0.557	0.303	1.015	0.995	98.31	26.9	0.305
3.50	1.0258	1.0276	35.9	0.349	989.9	8.3	49	1.3379	1.214	0.653	0.355	1.018	0.994	98.06	31.2	0.359
4.00	1.0298	1.0317	41.2	0.400	988.6	9.6	57	1.3386	1.394	0.750	0.408	1.020	0.993	97.80	35.5	0.413
4.50	1.0339	1.0357	46.5	0.452	987.4	10.9	64	1.3394	1.577	0.848	0.461	1.023	0.992	97.54	39.8	0.468
5.00	1.0380	1.0398	51.9	0.504	986.1	12.2	71	1.3401	1.761	0.947	0.515	1.026	0.990	97.27	44.0	0.523
5.50	1.0421	1.0439	57.3	0.557	984.8	13.5	78	1.3408	1.949	1.048	0.570	1.029	0.989	97.00	48.2	0.578
6.00	1.0462	1.0481	62.8	0.610	983.5	14.8	86	1.3415	2.139	1.150	0.625	1.032	0.988	96.73	52.4	0.634
6.50	1.0504	1.0522	68.3	0.663	982.1	16.1	93	1.3423	2.332	1.254	0.681	1.035	0.987	96.46	56.5	0.691
7.00	1.0546	1.0564	73.8	0.717	980.8	17.5	100	1.3430	2.528	1.359	0.737	1.038	0.986	96.18	60.6	0.748
7.50	1.0588	1.0607	79.4	0.772	979.4	18.8	108	1.3438	2.728	1.466	0.794	1.041	0.985	95.90	64.7	0.806
8.00	1.0630	1.0649	85.0	0.826	978.0	20.2	115	1.3445	2.929	1.575	0.851	1.044	0.984	95.61	68.7	0.864
8.50	1.0673	1.0692	90.7	0.882	976.6	21.6	123	1.3453	3.133	1.685	0.909	1.047	0.983	95.31	72.7	0.923
9.00	1.0716	1.0735	96.4	0.937	975.2	23.1	130	1.3460	3.342	1.797	0.968	1.051	0.982	95.00	76.7	0.983
9.50	1.0760	1.0779	102.2	0.993	973.7	24.5	138	1.3468	3.554	1.911	1.027	1.054	0.982	94.67	80.6	1.04
10.00	1.0803	1.0822	108.0	1.050	972.3	25.9	145	1.3475	3.768	2.026	1.087	1.058	0.981	94.33	84.6	1.10
11.00	1.0892	1.0911	119.8	1.164	969.3	28.9	161	1.3491	4.206	2.261	1.208	1.066	0.981	93.61	92.4	1.22
12.00	1.0981	1.1000	131.8	1.280	966.3	31.9	176	1.3506	4.665	2.508	1.334	1.075	0.981	92.85	100.	1.35
13.00	1.1072	1.1091	143.9	1.399	963.2	35.0	192	1.3522	5.150	2.770	1.463	1.084	0.981	92.05	108.	1.48
14.00	1.1164	1.1184	156.3	1.519	960.1	38.1	208	1.3538	5.650	3.040	1.597	1.094	0.982	91.21	115.	1.61
15.00	1.1257	1.1277	168.9	1.641	956.9	41.4	224	1.3554	6.180	3.320	1.734	1.105	0.984	90.32	122.	1.75
16.00	1.1352	1.1372	181.6	1.765	953.6	44.7	241	1.3570	6.740	3.620	1.875	1.117	0.986	89.38	129.	1.89
17.00	1.1448	1.1469	194.6	1.891	950.2	48.0	257	1.3587	7.320	3.930	2.021	1.129	0.988	88.40	136.	2.03
18.00	1.1546	1.1566	207.8	2.019	946.8	51.5	274	1.3604				1.142	0.991	87.37	143.	2.18
19.00	1.1645	1.1665	221.3	2.150	943.2	55.0	291	1.3621				1.157	0.995	86.29	150.	2.33
20.00	1.1745	1.1766	234.9	2.283	939.6	58.6	308	1.3638				1.172	1.000	85.15	157.	2.50
22.00	1.1951	1.1972	262.9	2.555	932.2	66.1	343	1.3673				1.205	1.010	82.81	172.	2.84

69 SODIUM BROMIDE, NaBr—(Continued)

A% by wt.	ρ D²⁰₄	D²⁰₂₀	C_s g/l	M g-mol/l	C_w g/l	(C_o − C_w) g/l	(n − n_o) × 10⁴	n	Δ °C	O Os/kg	S g-mol/l	η/η_o	η/ρ cS	φ rhe	γ mmho/cm	T g-mol/l
24.00	1.2163	1.2184	291.9	2.837	924.4	73.9	378	1.3708				1.242	1.023	80.37	185.0	3.21
26.00	1.2382	1.2404	321.9	3.128	916.2	82.0	415	1.3745				1.284	1.039	77.75	197.0	3.60
28.00	1.2608	1.2630	353.0	3.430	907.8	90.5	453	1.3783				1.333	1.059	74.88	207.0	4.03
30.00	1.2842	1.2864	385.2	3.744	889.9	99.3	492	1.3822				1.392	1.086	71.70	216.0	4.50
32.00	1.3083	1.3106	418.7	4.068	889.7	108.6	532	1.3862				1.462	1.120	68.26		
34.00	1.3333	1.3357	453.3	4.405	880.0	118.2	573	1.3903				1.543	1.160	64.68		
36.00	1.3592	1.3616	489.3	4.755	869.9	128.3	616	1.3946				1.636	1.206	61.01		
38.00	1.3860	1.3885	526.7	5.118	859.3	138.9	660	1.3990				1.742	1.259	57.30		
40.00	1.4138	1.4163	565.5	5.495	848.3	150.0	705	1.4035				1.862	1.320	53.60		

70 SODIUM CARBONATE, Na₂CO₃ · 10H₂O

MOLECULAR WEIGHT = 106.00   FORMULA WEIGHT, HYDRATE = 286.16

RELATIVE SPECIFIC REFRACTIVITY = 0.619

0.00 % by wt. data are the same for all compounds.
For Values of 0.00 wt. % solutions see Table 1, Acetic Acid.

A% by wt.	H% by wt.	ρ D²⁰₄	D²⁰₂₀	C_s g/l	M g-mol/l	C_w g/l	(C_o − C_w) g/l	(n − n_o) × 10⁴	n	Δ °C	O Os/kg	S g-mol/l	η/η_o	η/ρ cS	φ rhe	γ mmho/cm	T g-mol/l
0.50	1.35	1.0034	1.0052	5.0	0.047	998.4	−0.2	11	1.3341	0.222	0.119	0.063	1.023	1.021	97.58	7.0	0.072
1.00	2.70	1.0086	1.0104	10.1	0.095	998.5	−0.3	23	1.3352	0.425	0.229	0.123	1.047	1.040	95.32	13.1	0.139
1.50	4.05	1.0138	1.0156	15.2	0.143	998.6	−0.4	34	1.3364	0.598	0.322	0.174	1.073	1.060	93.03	18.4	0.201
2.00	5.40	1.0190	1.0208	20.4	0.192	998.6	−0.4	45	1.3375	0.751	0.404	0.219	1.100	1.082	90.73	23.3	0.260
2.50	6.75	1.0242	1.0260	25.6	0.242	998.6	−0.4	56	1.3386	0.915	0.492	0.267	1.128	1.104	88.46	27.8	0.316
3.00	8.10	1.0294	1.0312	30.9	0.291	998.5	−0.3	67	1.3397	1.082	0.582	0.316	1.157	1.127	86.23	32.0	0.369
3.50	9.45	1.0346	1.0364	36.2	0.342	998.4	−0.2	78	1.3408	1.250	0.672	0.365	1.188	1.150	84.01	36.0	0.420
4.00	10.80	1.0398	1.0416	41.6	0.392	998.2	0.0	89	1.3419	1.421	0.764	0.416	1.220	1.176	81.81	39.8	0.468
4.50	12.15	1.0450	1.0468	47.0	0.444	998.0	0.3	100	1.3430	1.593	0.857	0.466	1.253	1.202	79.62	43.5	0.515
5.00	13.50	1.0502	1.0521	52.5	0.495	997.7	0.5	110	1.3440	1.768	0.951	0.517	1.289	1.230	77.42	47.0	0.562
5.50	14.85	1.0554	1.0573	58.0	0.548	997.3	0.9	121	1.3451	1.945	1.046	0.569	1.326	1.259	75.26	50.4	0.608
6.00	16.20	1.0606	1.0625	63.6	0.600	997.0	1.3	132	1.3462	2.125	1.142	0.621	1.364	1.289	73.16	53.6	0.652
6.50	17.55	1.0658	1.0677	69.3	0.654	996.5	1.7	142	1.3472				1.404	1.320	71.09	56.7	0.694
7.00	18.90	1.0711	1.0730	75.0	0.707	996.1	2.1	153	1.3483				1.445	1.352	69.05	59.7	0.735
7.50	20.25	1.0763	1.0782	80.7	0.762	995.6	2.6	164	1.3494				1.489	1.386	67.04	62.4	0.774
8.00	21.60	1.0816	1.0835	86.5	0.816	995.1	3.1	174	1.3504				1.535	1.422	65.03	65.1	0.812
8.50	22.95	1.0869	1.0888	92.4	0.872	994.5	3.7	185	1.3515				1.583	1.460	63.03	67.6	0.848
9.00	24.30	1.0922	1.0942	98.3	0.927	993.9	4.3	196	1.3525				1.635	1.500	61.03	70.0	0.883
9.50	25.65	1.0975	1.0995	104.3	0.984	993.3	5.0	206	1.3536				1.691	1.543	59.03	72.2	0.916
10.00	27.00	1.1029	1.1048	110.3	1.040	992.6	5.6	217	1.3547				1.750	1.590	57.03	74.4	0.948
11.00	29.70	1.1136	1.1156	122.5	1.156	991.1	7.1	238	1.3568				1.880	1.691	53.09	78.3	1.00
12.00	32.40	1.1244	1.1264	134.9	1.273	989.5	8.8	259	1.3589				2.024	1.803	49.32	81.7	1.05
13.00	35.10	1.1353	1.1373	147.6	1.392	987.7	10.5	280	1.3610				2.182	1.926	45.74	84.6	1.10
14.00	37.79	1.1463	1.1483	160.5	1.514	985.8	12.4	301	1.3631				2.356	2.059	42.36	86.9	1.14
15.00	40.49	1.1574	1.1595	173.6	1.638	983.8	14.4	322	1.3652				2.546	2.204	39.20	88.6	1.16

71 SODIUM CHLORIDE, NaCl

MOLECULAR WEIGHT = 58.44

RELATIVE SPECIFIC REFRACTIVITY = 0.794

0.00 % by wt. data are the same for all compounds.
For Values of 0.00 wt. % solutions see Table 1, Acetic Acid.

A% by wt.	ρ D²⁰₄	D²⁰₂₀	C_s g/l	M g-mol/l	C_w g/l	(C_o − C_w) g/l	(n − n_o) × 10⁴	n	Δ °C	O Os/kg	S g-mol/l	η/η_o	η/ρ cS	φ rhe	γ mmho/cm	T g-mol/l
0.10	0.9989	1.0007	1.0	0.017	997.9	0.3	2	1.3332	0.062	0.033	0.017	1.002	1.005	99.61	1.7	0.017
0.20	0.9997	1.0014	2.0	0.034	997.7	0.6	4	1.3333	0.121	0.065	0.034	1.004	1.006	99.43	3.3	0.034
0.30	1.0004	1.0021	3.0	0.051	997.4	0.9	5	1.3335	0.181	0.097	0.051	1.006	1.007	99.24	5.0	0.051
0.40	1.0011	1.0028	4.0	0.069	997.1	1.2	7	1.3337	0.240	0.129	0.069	1.007	1.008	99.06	6.6	0.069
0.50	1.0018	1.0036	5.0	0.086	996.8	1.5	9	1.3339	0.299	0.161	0.086	1.009	1.009	98.89	8.2	0.086
0.60	1.0025	1.0043	6.0	0.103	996.5	1.8	11	1.3340	0.358	0.192	0.103	1.011	1.011	98.71	9.8	0.103
0.70	1.0032	1.0050	7.0	0.120	996.2	2.1	12	1.3342	0.417	0.224	0.120	1.013	1.012	98.54	11.4	0.120
0.80	1.0039	1.0057	8.0	0.137	995.9	2.4	14	1.3344	0.475	0.256	0.137	1.015	1.013	98.37	12.9	0.137
0.90	1.0046	1.0064	9.0	0.155	995.6	2.7	16	1.3346	0.534	0.287	0.155	1.016	1.014	98.20	14.4	0.155
1.00	1.0053	1.0071	10.1	0.172	995.3	3.0	18	1.3347	0.593	0.319	0.172	1.018	1.015	98.04	16.0	0.172
1.10	1.0060	1.0078	11.1	0.189	995.0	3.3	19	1.3349	0.652	0.351	0.189	1.020	1.016	97.87	17.5	0.189
1.20	1.0068	1.0085	12.1	0.207	994.7	3.6	21	1.3351	0.711	0.382	0.207	1.021	1.017	97.72	18.9	0.207
1.30	1.0075	1.0093	13.1	0.224	994.4	3.9	23	1.3353	0.770	0.414	0.224	1.023	1.017	97.56	20.4	0.224
1.40	1.0082	1.0100	14.1	0.241	994.1	4.2	25	1.3354	0.829	0.446	0.241	1.025	1.018	97.41	21.8	0.241
1.50	1.0089	1.0107	15.1	0.259	993.8	4.5	26	1.3356	0.888	0.478	0.259	1.026	1.019	97.26	23.2	0.259
1.60	1.0096	1.0114	16.2	0.276	993.5	4.8	28	1.3358	0.948	0.509	0.276	1.028	1.020	97.11	24.6	0.276
1.70	1.0103	1.0121	17.2	0.294	993.1	5.1	30	1.3360	1.007	0.541	0.294	1.029	1.021	96.96	26.0	0.294
1.80	1.0110	1.0128	18.2	0.311	992.8	5.4	32	1.3362	1.067	0.573	0.311	1.031	1.022	96.82	27.4	0.311
1.90	1.0117	1.0135	19.2	0.329	992.5	5.7	33	1.3363	1.126	0.605	0.329	1.032	1.022	96.67	28.8	0.329
2.00	1.0125	1.0143	20.2	0.346	992.2	6.0	35	1.3365	1.186	0.638	0.346	1.034	1.023	96.52	30.2	0.346
2.10	1.0132	1.0150	21.3	0.364	991.9	6.3	37	1.3367	1.246	0.670	0.364	1.036	1.024	96.37	31.6	0.364
2.20	1.0139	1.0157	22.3	0.382	991.6	6.6	39	1.3369	1.306	0.702	0.382	1.037	1.025	96.22	33.0	0.382
2.30	1.0146	1.0164	23.3	0.399	991.3	7.0	40	1.3370	1.366	0.734	0.399	1.039	1.026	96.07	34.3	0.399
2.40	1.0153	1.0171	24.4	0.418	991.0	7.3	42	1.3372	1.426	0.767	0.418	1.040	1.027	95.93	35.7	0.418
2.50	1.0160	1.0178	25.4	0.435	990.6	7.6	44	1.3374	1.486	0.799	0.435	1.042	1.028	95.78	37.1	0.435
2.60	1.0168	1.0185	26.4	0.452	990.3	7.9	46	1.3376	1.547	0.832	0.452	1.044	1.028	95.64	38.5	0.452
2.70	1.0175	1.0193	27.5	0.470	990.0	8.2	47	1.3377	1.607	0.864	0.470	1.045	1.029	95.49	39.9	0.470
2.80	1.0182	1.0200	28.5	0.488	989.7	8.6	49	1.3379	1.668	0.897	0.488	1.047	1.030	95.35	41.2	0.488
2.90	1.0189	1.0207	29.5	0.505	989.4	8.9	51	1.3381	1.729	0.930	0.505	1.048	1.031	95.21	42.6	0.505
3.00	1.0196	1.0214	30.6	0.523	989.0	9.2	53	1.3383	1.790	0.962	0.523	1.050	1.032	95.06	44.0	0.523
3.10	1.0203	1.0221	31.6	0.541	988.7	9.5	54	1.3384	1.851	0.995	0.541	1.051	1.033	94.92	45.3	0.541
3.20	1.0211	1.0229	32.7	0.559	988.4	9.9	56	1.3386	1.913	1.028	0.559	1.053	1.033	94.78	46.7	0.559

A % by wt.	ρ D_4^{20}	D_{20}^{20}	C, g/l	M g-mol/l	C_w g/l	$(C_o - C_w)$ g/l	$(n - n_o)$ × 10⁴	n	Δ °C	O Os/kg	S g-mol/l	η/η_o	η/ρ cS	ϕ rhe	γ mmho/cm	T g-mol/l
3.30	1.0218	1.0236	33.7	0.577	988.0	10.2	58	1.3388	1.974	1.061	0.577	1.055	1.034	94.64	48.0	0.577
3.40	1.0225	1.0243	34.8	0.595	987.7	10.5	60	1.3390	2.036	1.094	0.595	1.056	1.035	94.50	49.4	0.595
3.50	1.0232	1.0250	35.8	0.613	987.4	10.8	61	1.3391	2.098	1.128	0.613	1.058	1.036	94.35	50.7	0.613
3.60	1.0239	1.0257	36.9	0.631	987.1	11.2	63	1.3393	2.160	1.161	0.631	1.059	1.037	94.21	52.0	0.631
3.70	1.0246	1.0265	37.9	0.649	986.7	11.5	65	1.3395	2.222	1.194	0.649	1.061	1.037	94.07	53.3	0.649
3.80	1.0254	1.0272	39.0	0.667	986.4	11.8	67	1.3397	2.284	1.228	0.667	1.063	1.038	93.93	54.7	0.667
3.90	1.0261	1.0279	40.0	0.685	986.1	12.2	68	1.3398	2.347	1.262	0.685	1.064	1.039	93.78	56.0	0.685
4.00	1.0268	1.0286	41.1	0.703	985.7	12.5	70	1.3400	2.409	1.295	0.703	1.066	1.040	93.64	57.3	0.703
4.10	1.0275	1.0293	42.1	0.721	985.4	12.8	72	1.3402	2.472	1.329	0.721	1.067	1.041	93.49	58.6	0.721
4.20	1.0282	1.0301	43.2	0.739	985.1	13.2	74	1.3404	2.535	1.363	0.739	1.069	1.042	93.35	59.9	0.739
4.30	1.0290	1.0308	44.2	0.757	984.7	13.5	75	1.3405	2.598	1.397	0.757	1.071	1.043	93.20	61.2	0.757
4.40	1.0297	1.0315	45.3	0.775	984.4	13.9	77	1.3407	2.662	1.431	0.775	1.072	1.044	93.06	62.5	0.775
4.50	1.0304	1.0322	46.4	0.794	984.0	14.2	79	1.3409	2.725	1.465	0.794	1.074	1.045	92.91	63.8	0.794
4.60	1.0311	1.0330	47.4	0.812	983.7	14.5	81	1.3411	2.789	1.500	0.812	1.076	1.046	92.76	65.1	0.812
4.70	1.0318	1.0337	48.5	0.830	983.4	14.9	82	1.3412	2.853	1.534	0.830	1.078	1.046	92.61	66.3	0.830
4.80	1.0326	1.0344	49.6	0.848	983.0	15.2	84	1.3414	2.917	1.569	0.848	1.079	1.047	92.46	67.6	0.848
4.90	1.0333	1.0351	50.6	0.866	982.7	15.6	86	1.3416	2.982	1.603	0.866	1.081	1.048	92.31	68.9	0.866
5.00	1.0340	1.0358	51.7	0.885	982.3	15.9	88	1.3418	3.046	1.638	0.885	1.083	1.049	92.15	70.1	0.885
5.20	1.0355	1.0373	53.8	0.921	981.6	16.6	91	1.3421	3.176	1.708	0.921	1.087	1.052	91.84	72.6	0.921
5.40	1.0369	1.0387	56.0	0.958	980.9	17.3	95	1.3425	3.307	1.778	0.958	1.090	1.054	91.53	75.1	0.958
5.60	1.0384	1.0402	58.1	0.995	980.2	18.0	98	1.3428	3.438	1.848	0.995	1.094	1.056	91.21	77.5	0.995
5.80	1.0398	1.0417	60.3	1.032	979.5	18.7	102	1.3432	3.570	1.919	1.032	1.098	1.058	90.90	80.0	1.032
6.00	1.0413	1.0431	62.5	1.069	978.8	19.4	105	1.3435	3.703	1.991	1.069	1.102	1.060	90.59	82.4	1.069
6.20	1.0427	1.0446	64.6	1.106	978.1	20.2	109	1.3439	3.837	2.063	1.106	1.106	1.062	90.27	84.7	1.106
6.40	1.0442	1.0460	66.8	1.144	977.4	20.9	112	1.3442	3.972	2.135	1.144	1.109	1.065	89.95	87.1	1.144
6.60	1.0456	1.0475	69.0	1.181	976.6	21.6	116	1.3446	4.107	2.208	1.181	1.113	1.067	89.63	89.4	1.181
6.80	1.0471	1.0490	71.2	1.218	975.9	22.3	119	1.3449	4.244	2.282	1.218	1.117	1.069	89.31	91.8	1.218
7.00	1.0486	1.0504	73.4	1.256	975.2	23.1	123	1.3453	4.378	2.354	1.256	1.122	1.072	88.99	94.1	1.256
7.20	1.0500	1.0519	75.6	1.294	974.4	23.8	126	1.3456	4.516	2.428	1.294	1.126	1.074	88.66	96.4	1.294
7.40	1.0515	1.0533	77.8	1.331	973.7	24.6	130	1.3460	4.655	2.503	1.331	1.130	1.077	88.33	98.7	1.331
7.60	1.0530	1.0548	80.0	1.369	972.9	25.3	133	1.3463	4.795	2.578	1.369	1.134	1.079	88.00	101.	1.369
7.80	1.0544	1.0563	82.2	1.407	972.2	26.1	137	1.3467	4.937	2.654	1.407	1.138	1.082	87.67	103.	1.407
8.00	1.0559	1.0578	84.5	1.445	971.4	26.8	140	1.3470	5.079	2.731	1.445	1.143	1.084	87.33	105.	1.445
8.20	1.0574	1.0592	86.7	1.484	970.7	27.6	144	1.3474	5.222	2.808	1.484	1.147	1.087	86.99	107.	1.484
8.40	1.0588	1.0607	88.9	1.522	969.9	28.3	147	1.3477	5.367	2.885	1.522	1.152	1.090	86.65	109	1.522
8.60	1.0603	1.0622	91.2	1.560	969.1	29.1	151	1.3481	5.512	2.964	1.560	1.156	1.093	86.30	112.	1.560
8.80	1.0618	1.0637	93.4	1.599	968.3	29.9	154	1.3484	5.659	3.043	1.599	1.161	1.096	85.95	114.	1.599
9.00	1.0633	1.0651	95.7	1.637	967.6	30.7	158	1.3488	5.807	3.122	1.637	1.166	1.099	85.60	116.	1.637
9.20	1.0647	1.0666	98.0	1.676	966.8	31.4	161	1.3491	5.956	3.202	1.676	1.171	1.102	85.25	118.	1.676
9.40	1.0662	1.0681	100.2	1.715	966.0	32.2	165	1.3495	6.106	3.283	1.715	1.176	1.105	84.89	120.	1.715
9.60	1.0677	1.0696	102.5	1.754	965.2	33.0	168	1.3498	6.258	3.364	1.754	1.181	1.108	84.53	122.	1.754
9.80	1.0692	1.0711	104.8	1.793	964.4	33.8	172	1.3502	6.410	3.446	1.793	1.186	1.111	84.16	124.	1.793
10.00	1.0707	1.0726	107.1	1.832	963.6	34.6	175	1.3505	6.564	3.529	1.832	1.191	1.115	83.80	126.	1.832
10.50	1.0744	1.0763	112.8	1.930	961.6	36.6	184	1.3514	6.954	3.739	1.930	1.204	1.123	82.86	131.	1.930
11.00	1.0781	1.0801	118.6	2.029	959.5	38.7	193	1.3523	7.353	3.953	2.029	1.218	1.132	81.90	136.	2.029
11.50	1.0819	1.0838	124.4	2.129	957.5	40.8	202	1.3532	7.760	4.172	2.129	1.233	1.142	80.94	140.	2.129
12.00	1.0857	1.0876	130.3	2.229	955.4	42.9	211	1.3541	8.176	4.396	2.229	1.248	1.152	79.95	145.	2.229
12.50	1.0894	1.0914	136.2	2.330	953.3	45.0	220	1.3549	8.602	4.625	2.330	1.264	1.162	78.96	149.	2.330
13.00	1.0932	1.0952	142.1	2.432	951.1	47.1	228	1.3558	9.038	4.859	2.432	1.280	1.173	77.97	154.	2.432
13.50	1.0970	1.0990	148.1	2.534	948.9	49.3	237	1.3567	9.484	5.099	2.534	1.297	1.184	76.97	158.	2.534
14.00	1.1008	1.1028	154.1	2.637	946.7	51.5	246	1.3576	9.940	5.344	2.637	1.314	1.196	75.97	163.	2.637
14.50	1.1047	1.1066	160.2	2.741	944.5	53.7	255	1.3585	10.408	5.596	2.741	1.331	1.207	74.97	167.	2.741
15.00	1.1085	1.1105	166.3	2.845	942.2	56.0	264	1.3594	10.888	5.854	2.845	1.349	1.219	73.98	171.	2.845
16.00	1.1162	1.1182	178.6	3.056	937.6	60.6	282	1.3612	11.885	6.390	3.056	1.385	1.243	72.07	179.	3.056
17.00	1.1240	1.1260	191.1	3.270	932.9	65.3	300	1.3630	12.935	6.954	3.270	1.421	1.267	70.21	186.	3.270
18.00	1.1319	1.1339	203.7	3.486	928.1	70.1	318	1.3648	14.044	7.550	3.486	1.460	1.293	68.34	193.	3.486
19.00	1.1398	1.1418	216.6	3.706	923.2	75.0	336	1.3666	15.216	8.181	3.706	1.504	1.322	66.36	199.	3.705
20.00	1.1478	1.1498	229.6	3.928	918.2	80.0	354	1.3684	16.458	8.849	3.928	1.554	1.357	64.22	204.	3.928
21.00	1.1558	1.1579	242.7	4.153	913.1	85.1	372	1.3702	17.776	9.557	4.153	1.611	1.396	61.95	209.	4.153
22.00	1.1640	1.1660	256.1	4.382	907.9	90.4	391	1.3721	19.176	10.310	4.382	1.673	1.441	59.64	213.	4.382
23.00	1.1721	1.1742	269.6	4.613	902.6	95.7	409	1.3739	20.667	11.111	4.613	1.742	1.489	57.29	217.	4.613
24.00	1.1804	1.1825	283.3	4.848	897.1	101.1	428	1.3757			4.848	1.817	1.542	54.93	220.	4.848
25.00	1.1887	1.1909	297.2	5.085	891.6	106.7	446	1.3776			5.085	1.898	1.600	52.58	222.	5.085
26.00	1.1972	1.1993	311.3	5.326	885.9	112.3	465	1.3795			5.326	1.986	1.662	50.26	225.	5.326

72 SODIUM CITRATE, $Na_3 C_6 H_5 O_7 \cdot 2H_2 O$

MOLECULAR WEIGHT = 258.068   FORMULA WEIGHT, HYDRATE = 294.10

A% by wt.	H% by wt.	ρ D_4^{20}	D_{20}^{20}	C_s g/l	M g·mol/l	C_w g/l	$(C_0 - C_w)$ g/l	$(n - n_0)$ × 10^4	n	Δ °C	O Os/kg	S g·mol/l	η/η_0	η/ρ cS	ϕ rhe	γ mmho/cm	T g·mol/l
1.00	1.14	1.0049	1.0067	10.0	0.039	994.9	3.3	18.	1.3348	0.197	0.106	0.056	1.041	1.038	95.87	7.4	0.075
2.00	2.28	1.0120	1.0138	20.2	0.078	991.8	6.4	36.	1.3366	0.389	0.209	0.112	1.079	1.068	92.52	12.8	0.136
3.00	3.42	1.0186	1.0204	30.6	0.118	988.0	10.2	53.	1.3383	0.586	0.315	0.170	1.120	1.102	89.09	17.9	0.195
4.00	4.56	1.0260	1.0278	41.0	0.159	985.0	13.2	71.	1.3401	0.787	0.423	0.229	1.164	1.137	85.72	22.1	0.246
5.00	5.70	1.0331	1.0350	51.7	0.200	981.4	16.8	89.	1.3419	0.974	0.523	0.284	1.208	1.172	82.59	26.2	0.296
6.00	6.84	1.0405	1.0424	62.4	0.242	978.1	20.1	107.	1.3437	1.171	0.630	0.342	1.260	1.213	79.23	29.9	0.343
7.00	7.98	1.0482	1.0501	73.4	0.284	974.8	23.4	125.	1.3455	1.361	0.732	0.398	1.311	1.253	76.14	33.2	0.384
8.00	9.12	1.0557	1.0576	84.5	0.327	971.2	27.0	143.	1.3473	1.566	0.842	0.458	1.368	1.298	72.98	36.5	0.426
9.00	10.26	1.0632	1.0651	95.7	0.371	967.5	30.7	161.	1.3491	1.768	0.951	0.517	1.424	1.342	70.09	39.4	0.463
10.00	11.40	1.0708	1.0727	107.1	0.415	963.7	34.5	179.	1.3509	1.957	1.052	0.572	1.496	1.400	66.71	42.1	0.497
12.00	13.68	1.0861	1.0881	130.3	0.505	955.8	42.4	216.	1.3546	2.376	1.277	0.693	1.646	1.519	60.61	48.9	0.588
14.00	15.95	1.1019	1.1039	154.3	0.598	947.6	50.6	253.	1.3583	2.819	1.515	0.820	1.828	1.662	54.60	50.4	0.608
16.00	18.23	1.1173	1.1193	178.8	0.693	938.5	59.7	288.	1.3618	3.274	1.760	0.949	2.041	1.830	48.91	53.5	0.650
18.00	20.51	1.1327	1.1347	203.9	0.790	928.8	69.4	326.	1.3656	3.815	2.051	1.100	2.285	2.021	43.68	55.7	0.680
20.00	22.79	1.1492	1.1513	229.8	0.891	919.4	78.8	363.	1.3693	4.393	2.362	1.260	2.591	2.259	38.52	57.1	0.700
24.00	27.35	1.1813	1.1834	283.5	1.099	897.8	100.4	437.	1.3767				3.402	2.886	29.33	57.7	0.708
28.00	31.91	1.2151	1.2173	340.2	1.318	874.9	123.3	515.	1.3845				4.577	3.774	21.81	55.9	0.683
32.00	36.47	1.2487	1.2510	399.6	1.548	849.1	149.1	593.	1.3923				6.528	5.238	15.29	51.0	0.616
36.00	41.03	1.2843	1.2866	462.3	1.792	822.0	176.2	671.	1.4001				9.768	7.621	10.22	44.5	0.529

73 SODIUM DIATRIZOATE, $(CH_3CONH)_2 C_6 I_3 COONa$, HYPAQUE®

MOLECULAR WEIGHT = 635.92
RELATIVE SPECIFIC REFRACTIVITY = 0.823

0.00 % by wt. data are the same for all compounds.
For Values of 0.00 wt. % solutions see Table 1, Acetic Acid.

A% by wt.	ρ D_4^{20}	D_{20}^{20}	C_s g/l	M g·mol/l	C_w g/l	$(C_0 - C_w)$ g/l	$(n - n_0)$ × 10^4	n	Δ °C	O Os/kg	S g·mol/l	η/η_0	η/ρ cS	ϕ rhe	γ mmho/cm	T g·mol/l
1.00	1.0041	1.0059	10.0	0.016	994.1	4.1	16	1.3346	0.058	0.031	0.016	1.021	1.019	97.75	0.8	0.008
2.00	1.0102	1.0120	20.2	0.032	990.0	8.2	31	1.3361	0.110	0.059	0.031	1.041	1.033	95.87	1.6	0.016
3.00	1.0164	1.0182	30.5	0.048	985.9	12.3	48	1.3377	0.164	0.088	0.047	1.061	1.046	94.05	2.4	0.024
4.00	1.0227	1.0245	40.9	0.064	981.8	16.4	64	1.3394	0.220	0.118	0.063	1.082	1.060	92.26	3.1	0.031
5.00	1.0292	1.0310	51.5	0.081	977.7	20.5	80	1.3410	0.276	0.148	0.079	1.104	1.075	90.40	3.8	0.038
6.00	1.0357	1.0376	62.1	0.098	973.6	24.6	97	1.3427	0.332	0.178	0.095	1.128	1.092	88.44	4.5	0.045
7.00	1.0424	1.0443	73.0	0.115	969.5	28.8	114	1.3444	0.389	0.209	0.112	1.155	1.110	86.42	5.2	0.052
8.00	1.0493	1.0511	83.9	0.132	965.3	32.9	131	1.3461	0.446	0.240	0.129	1.183	1.130	84.38	5.9	0.059
9.00	1.0562	1.0581	95.1	0.150	961.1	37.1	148	1.3478	0.504	0.271	0.146	1.212	1.150	82.32	6.5	0.066
10.00	1.0632	1.0651	106.3	0.167	956.9	41.3	165	1.3495	0.562	0.302	0.163	1.243	1.171	80.29	7.2	0.073

®Registered trademark, sodium 3,5-diacetamido-2,4,6 tri-iodo benzoate.

73 SODIUM DIATRIZOATE, $(CH_3CONH)_2C_6I_3COONa$, HYPAQUE®—(Continued)

A% by wt.	ρ D_4^{20}	D_{20}^{20}	C_s g/l	M g-mol/l	C_w g/l	$(C_o - C_w)$ g/l	$(n - n_o)$ × 10^4	n	Δ °C	O Os/kg	S g-mol/l	η/η_o	η/ρ cS	ϕ rhe	γ mmho/cm	T g-mol/l
12.00	1.0776	1.0796	129.3	0.203	948.3	49.9	201	1.3530	0.683	0.367	0.199	1.305	1.213	76.50	8.4	0.086
14.00	1.0925	1.0944	152.9	0.240	939.5	58.7	237	1.3567	0.808	0.434	0.235	1.375	1.261	72.60	9.6	0.099
16.00	1.1077	1.1097	177.2	0.279	930.5	67.7	274	1.3603	0.936	0.503	0.273	1.470	1.329	67.91	10.6	0.110
18.00	1.1234	1.1254	202.2	0.318	921.2	77.0	313	1.3643	1.067	0.574	0.312	1.592	1.420	62.70	11.5	0.120
20.00	1.1395	1.1415	227.9	0.358	911.6	86.6	353	1.3683	1.205	0.648	0.352	1.724	1.516	57.89	12.2	0.129
22.00	1.1560	1.1581	254.3	0.400	901.7	96.5	394	1.3724	1.351	0.726	0.395	1.847	1.601	54.03	13.0	0.138
24.00	1.1730	1.1751	281.5	0.443	891.5	106.7	436	1.3766	1.506	0.810	0.441	1.965	1.678	50.79	13.7	0.146
26.00	1.1906	1.1927	309.5	0.487	881.0	117.2	480	1.3810	1.671	0.898	0.489	2.094	1.762	47.66	14.4	0.153
28.00	1.2086	1.2108	338.4	0.532	870.2	128.0	525	1.3854	1.846	0.993	0.540	2.254	1.869	44.27	15.0	0.160
30.00	1.2273	1.2295	368.2	0.579	859.1	139.1	571	1.3901	2.033	1.093	0.594	2.469	2.016	40.42	15.5	0.167
32.00	1.2467	1.2489	399.0	0.627	847.8	150.5	619	1.3949	2.232	1.200	0.652	2.742	2.204	36.39	16.2	0.174
34.00	1.2670	1.2692	430.8	0.677	836.2	162.0	669	1.3999	2.444	1.314	0.713	3.066	2.425	32.55	16.8	0.182
36.00	1.2882	1.2904	463.7	0.729	824.4	173.8	722	1.4052	2.672	1.437	0.778	3.449	2.683	28.93	17.2	0.187
38.00	1.3105	1.3128	498.0	0.783	812.5	185.8	778	1.4108	2.917	1.568	0.848	3.902	2.984	25.58	17.2	0.187
40.00	1.3286	1.3310	531.5	0.836	797.2	201.0	834	1.4164				4.400	3.318	22.68	16.6	0.180

®Registered trademark, sodium 3,5-diacetamido-2,4,6 tri-iodo benzoate.

74 SODIUM DICHROMATE, $Na_2Cr_2O_7 \cdot 2H_2O$

MOLECULAR WEIGHT = 261.97   FORMULA WEIGHT, HYDRATE = 298.00
RELATIVE SPECIFIC REFRACTIVITY = 0.859

0.00 % by wt. data are the same for all compounds.
For Values of 0.00 wt. % solutions see Table 1, Acetic Acid.

A% by wt.	H% by wt.	ρ D_4^{20}	D_{20}^{20}	C_s g/l	M g-mol/l	C_w g/l	$(C_o - C_w)$ g/l	$(n - n_o)$ × 10^4	C_s n	Δ °C	O Os/kg	S g-mol/l	η/η_o	η/ρ cS	ϕ rhe	γ mmho/cm	T g-mol/l
0.50	0.57	1.0019	1.0037	5.0	0.019	996.9	1.4	10	1.3340	0.103	0.056	0.029	1.005	1.005	99.33	3.5	0.035
1.00	1.14	1.0056	1.0073	10.1	0.038	995.5	2.7	21	1.3351	0.204	0.110	0.058	1.009	1.005	98.91	6.9	0.070
2.00	2.28	1.0130	1.0148	20.3	0.077	992.7	5.5	42	1.3371	0.396	0.213	0.114	1.016	1.005	98.23	13.1	0.139
3.00	3.41	1.0204	1.0222	30.6	0.117	989.8	8.4	63	1.3392	0.581	0.312	0.169	1.024	1.005	97.47	19.1	0.209
4.00	4.55	1.0280	1.0298	41.1	0.157	986.9	11.4	84	1.3414	0.762	0.410	0.222	1.033	1.007	96.64	24.9	0.280
5.00	5.69	1.0356	1.0374	51.8	0.198	983.8	14.4	105	1.3435	0.946	0.509	0.276	1.042	1.008	95.78	30.5	0.350
6.00	6.83	1.0433	1.0452	62.6	0.239	980.7	17.5	127	1.3457	1.135	0.610	0.331	1.052	1.010	94.91	36.0	0.419
7.00	7.96	1.0511	1.0530	73.6	0.281	977.5	20.7	149	1.3479	1.325	0.712	0.387	1.061	1.012	94.02	41.2	0.486
8.00	9.10	1.0590	1.0609	84.7	0.323	974.3	23.9	171	1.3501	1.519	0.817	0.444	1.072	1.014	93.10	46.3	0.553
9.00	10.24	1.0670	1.0689	96.0	0.367	971.0	27.2	193	1.3523	1.720	0.924	0.503	1.083	1.017	92.15	51.5	0.622
10.00	11.38	1.0751	1.0770	107.5	0.410	967.6	30.6	216	1.3546	1.929	1.037	0.564	1.095	1.021	91.14	56.7	0.694
12.00	13.65	1.0916	1.0936	131.0	0.500	960.6	37.6	262	1.3592	2.388	1.284	0.697	1.121	1.029	89.01	67.8	0.851
14.00	15.93	1.1086	1.1105	155.2	0.592	953.4	44.8	310	1.3640	2.876	1.546	0.836	1.151	1.040	86.72	78.9	1.02
16.00	18.20	1.1260	1.1280	180.2	0.688	945.9	52.4	358	1.3688	3.356	1.804	0.972	1.184	1.054	84.28	89.2	1.18
18.00	20.48	1.1439	1.1460	205.9	0.786	938.0	60.2	408	1.3738	3.830	2.059	1.104	1.221	1.070	81.71	98.6	1.33
20.00	22.75	1.1624	1.1644	232.5	0.887	929.9	68.3	460	1.3790	4.301	2.312	1.234	1.264	1.090	78.96	107.	1.48
24.00	27.30	1.2009	1.2031	288.2	1.100	912.7	85.5	567	1.3897				1.364	1.138	73.18	121.	1.73
28.00	31.85	1.2418	1.2440	347.7	1.327	894.1	104.1	681	1.4011				1.494	1.206	66.79	131.	1.93
32.00	36.40	1.2851	1.2874	411.2	1.570	873.9	124.4	801	1.4131				1.677	1.308	59.51	140.	2.10
36.00	40.95	1.3302	1.3326	478.9	1.828	851.4	146.9	925	1.4255				1.914	1.442	52.13	145.	2.22
40.00	45.50	1.3786	1.3810	551.4	2.105	827.1	171.1	1058	1.4388				2.246	1.632	44.43	148.	2.29
44.00	50.05	1.4304	1.4330	629.4	2.403	801.0	197.2	1200	1.4530				2.646	1.853	37.72	147.	2.26
48.00	54.60	1.4860	1.4886	713.3	2.723	772.7	225.5	1353	1.4683				3.225	2.174	30.95	141.	2.12
52.00	59.15	1.5454	1.5482	803.6	3.068	741.8	256.4						4.297	2.786	23.23	131.	1.94
56.00	63.70	1.6088	1.6117	900.9	3.439	707.9	290.3						5.933	3.695	16.82	117.	1.67
60.00	68.25	1.6763	1.6793	1005.8	3.839	670.5	327.7						8.221	4.914	12.14	93.9	1.25

75 SODIUM FERROCYANIDE, $Na_4Fe(CN)_6 \cdot 10H_2O$

MOLECULAR WEIGHT = 303.91   FORMULA WEIGHT, HYDRATE = 484.07
RELATIVE SPECIFIC REFRACTIVITY = 0.991

0.00 % by wt. data are the same for all compounds.
For Values of 0.00 wt. % solutions see Table 1, Acetic Acid.

A% by wt.	H% by wt.	ρ D_4^{20}	D_{20}^{20}	C_s g/l	M g-mol/l	C_w g/l	$(C_o - C_w)$ g/l	$(n - n_o)$ × 10^4	n	Δ °C	O Os/kg	S g-mol/l	η/η_o	η/ρ cS	ϕ rhe	γ mmho/cm	T g-mol/l
0.50	0.80	1.0018	1.0036	5.0	0.016	996.8	1.4	13	1.3342	0.091	0.049	0.026	1.016	1.016	98.23	5.0	0.050
1.00	1.59	1.0055	1.0073	10.1	0.033	995.4	2.8	25	1.3355	0.192	0.103	0.055	1.032	1.028	97.59	9.8	0.102
1.50	2.39	1.0092	1.0110	15.1	0.050	994.0	4.2	38	1.3368	0.302	0.162	0.087	1.047	1.040	95.28	14.3	0.153
2.00	3.19	1.0129	1.0147	20.3	0.067	992.6	5.6	51	1.3381	0.394	0.212	0.114	1.063	1.052	93.87	18.7	0.204
2.50	3.98	1.0166	1.0184	25.4	0.084	991.2	7.0	64	1.3394	0.486	0.261	0.141	1.079	1.063	92.50	22.8	0.254
3.00	4.78	1.0204	1.0222	30.6	0.101	989.8	8.5	77	1.3407	0.576	0.310	0.167	1.095	1.075	91.16	26.7	0.303
3.50	5.57	1.0239	1.0258	35.8	0.118	988.1	10.1	89	1.3419	0.666	0.358	0.194	1.111	1.087	89.83	30.5	0.350
4.00	6.37	1.0276	1.0294	41.1	0.135	986.5	11.7	102	1.3432	0.755	0.406	0.220	1.127	1.099	88.52	34.1	0.396
4.50	7.17	1.0313	1.0331	46.4	0.153	984.9	13.3	115	1.3445	0.842	0.453	0.245	1.144	1.112	87.22	37.7	0.441
5.00	7.96	1.0350	1.0368	51.8	0.170	983.3	15.0	128	1.3457	0.929	0.499	0.271	1.161	1.124	85.93	41.1	0.485
5.50	8.76	1.0387	1.0406	57.1	0.188	981.6	16.6	140	1.3470	1.014	0.545	0.296	1.179	1.138	84.63	44.5	0.529
6.00	9.56	1.0425	1.0443	62.5	0.206	979.9	18.3	153	1.3483	1.098	0.590	0.321	1.198	1.131	83.33	47.7	0.572
6.50	10.35	1.0462	1.0481	68.0	0.224	978.2	20.0	166	1.3496	1.181	0.635	0.345	1.217	1.165	82.02	51.0	0.616
7.00	11.15	1.0500	1.0519	73.5	0.242	976.5	21.7	179	1.3509	1.262	0.679	0.369	1.237	1.180	80.70	54.2	0.659
7.50	11.95	1.0539	1.0557	79.0	0.260	974.8	23.4	192	1.3522	1.342	0.722	0.393	1.257	1.195	79.38	57.3	0.702
8.00	12.74	1.0577	1.0596	84.6	0.278	973.1	25.1	205	1.3535	1.421	0.764	0.416	1.279	1.211	78.04	60.5	0.746
8.50	13.54	1.0616	1.0634	90.2	0.297	971.3	26.9	218	1.3548	1.498	0.806	0.438	1.301	1.228	76.70	63.6	0.790
9.00	14.34	1.0655	1.0673	95.9	0.316	969.6	28.7	232	1.3562	1.574	0.846	0.460	1.325	1.246	75.34	66.7	0.835
9.50	15.13	1.0694	1.0713	101.6	0.334	967.8	30.4	245	1.3575	1.648	0.886	0.482	1.349	1.264	73.98	69.7	0.879
10.00	15.93	1.0733	1.0752	107.3	0.353	966.0	32.2	258	1.3588	1.720	0.925	0.503	1.375	1.283	72.61	72.8	0.925
11.00	17.52	1.0813	1.0832	118.9	0.391	962.4	35.9	285	1.3615				1.429	1.324	69.85	78.8	1.02
12.00	19.11	1.0894	1.0913	130.7	0.430	958.6	39.6	312	1.3642				1.488	1.368	67.09	84.7	1.10
13.00	20.71	1.0976	1.0995	142.7	0.469	954.9	43.4	340	1.3670				1.551	1.416	64.39	90.0	1.19
14.00	22.30	1.1058	1.1078	154.8	0.509	951.0	47.2	367	1.3697				1.619	1.467	61.63	94.7	1.27
15.00	23.89	1.1142	1.1162	167.1	0.550	947.1	51.1	395	1.3725				1.692	1.522	58.98	98.1	1.32

76 SODIUM HYDROXIDE, NaOH

MOLECULAR WEIGHT = 40.01
RELATIVE SPECIFIC REFRACTIVITY = 0.692

0.00 % by wt. data are the same for all compounds.
For Values of 0.00 wt. % solutions see Table 1, Acetic Acid.

A % by wt.	ρ D_4^{20}	D_{20}^{20}	C_s g/l	M g-mol/l	C_w g/l	$(C_o - C_w)$ g/l	$(n - n_o)$ × 10⁴	n	Δ °C	O Os/kg	S g-mol/l	η/η_o	η/ρ cS	ϕ rhe	γ mmho/cm	T g-mol/l
0.50	1.0039	1.0057	5.0	0.125	998.9	− 0.6	14	1.3344	0.429	0.231	0.124	1.025	1.023	97.34	24.8	0.283
1.00	1.0095	1.0113	10.1	0.252	999.4	− 1.2	29	1.3358	0.860	0.462	0.251	1.052	1.044	94.87	48.6	0.584
1.50	1.0151	1.0169	15.2	0.381	999.9	− 1.7	43	1.3373	1.294	0.695	0.378	1.080	1.066	92.39	71.3	0.900
2.00	1.0207	1.0225	20.4	0.510	1000.3	− 2.0	56	1.3386	1.735	0.933	0.507	1.110	1.090	89.91	93.1	1.24
2.50	1.0262	1.0281	25.7	0.641	1000.6	− 2.4	70	1.3400	2.184	1.174	0.638	1.141	1.114	87.44	114.	1.61
3.00	1.0318	1.0336	31.0	0.774	1000.8	− 2.6	84	1.3414	2.642	1.420	0.770	1.174	1.140	84.98	134.	2.02
3.50	1.0373	1.0391	36.3	0.907	1001.0	− 2.8	97	1.3427	3.109	1.671	0.902	1.209	1.168	82.54	153.	2.45
4.00	1.0428	1.0446	41.7	1.043	1001.1	− 2.9	111	1.3441	3.587	1.929	1.037	1.246	1.197	80.11	171.	2.92
4.50	1.0483	1.0502	47.2	1.179	1001.1	− 2.9	124	1.3454	4.074	2.190	1.172	1.285	1.228	77.69	189.	3.42
5.00	1.0538	1.0557	52.7	1.317	1001.1	− 2.9	138	1.3467	4.569	2.457	1.308	1.326	1.261	75.26	206.	3.96
5.50	1.0593	1.0612	58.3	1.456	1001.0	− 2.8	151	1.3481	5.08	2.73	1.445	1.369	1.295	72.90	222.	4.54
6.00	1.0648	1.0667	63.9	1.597	1000.9	− 2.7	164	1.3494	5.60	3.01	1.582	1.413	1.330	70.62		
6.50	1.0703	1.0722	69.6	1.739	1000.7	− 2.5	177	1.3507	6.13	3.30	1.722	1.459	1.366	68.40		
7.00	1.0758	1.0777	75.3	1.882	1000.5	− 2.3	190	1.3520	6.69	3.60	1.864	1.507	1.404	66.21		
7.50	1.0813	1.0833	81.1	2.027	1000.2	− 2.0	203	1.3533	7.27	3.91	2.008	1.558	1.444	64.05		
8.00	1.0869	1.0888	86.9	2.173	999.9	− 1.7	216	1.3546	7.87	4.23	2.155	1.613	1.487	61.89		
8.50	1.0924	1.0943	92.9	2.321	999.5	− 1.3	229	1.3559	8.48	4.56	2.303	1.671	1.533	59.72		
9.00	1.0979	1.0998	98.8	2.470	999.1	− 0.9	242	1.3572	9.12	4.91	2.452	1.734	1.583	57.54		
9.50	1.1034	1.1054	104.8	2.620	998.6	− 0.3	255	1.3585	9.78	5.26	2.602	1.803	1.637	55.35		
10.00	1.1089	1.1109	110.9	2.772	998.0	0.2	268	1.3597	10.47	5.63	2.753	1.878	1.697	53.14		
11.00	1.1199	1.1219	123.2	3.079	996.7	1.5	293	1.3623	11.89	6.39	3.058	2.035	1.821	49.04		
12.00	1.1309	1.1329	135.7	3.392	995.2	3.0	318	1.3648	13.42	7.21	3.365	2.197	1.947	45.42		
13.00	1.1419	1.1440	148.5	3.710	993.5	4.8	343	1.3673	15.04	8.08	3.673	2.371	2.080	42.09		
14.00	1.1530	1.1550	161.4	4.034	991.6	6.7	367	1.3697	16.76	9.01	3.981	2.563	2.228	38.93		
15.00	1.1640	1.1661	174.6	4.364	989.4	8.8	392	1.3722				2.783	2.395	35.87		
16.00	1.1751	1.1771	188.0	4.699	987.0	11.2	416	1.3746				3.037	2.590	32.86		
17.00	1.1861	1.1882	201.6	5.040	984.5	13.8	440	1.3770				3.337	2.819	29.91		
18.00	1.1971	1.1993	215.5	5.386	981.7	16.6	463	1.3793				3.691	3.089	27.04		
19.00	1.2082	1.2103	229.6	5.737	978.6	19.6	487	1.3817				4.111	3.410	24.27		
20.00	1.2192	1.2214	243.8	6.094	975.4	22.9	510	1.3840				4.610	3.789	21.65		
22.00	1.2412	1.2434	273.1	6.825	968.1	30.1	555	1.3885				5.753	4.644	17.35		
24.00	1.2631	1.2653	303.1	7.576	959.9	38.3	599	1.3929				7.086	5.621	14.08		
26.00	1.2848	1.2871	334.0	8.349	950.8	47.5	641	1.3971				8.727	6.806	11.44		
28.00	1.3064	1.3087	365.8	9.142	940.6	57.6	682	1.4012				10.81	8.29	9.23		
30.00	1.3277	1.3301	398.3	9.956	929.4	68.8	721	1.4051				13.49	10.18	7.40		
32.00	1.3488	1.3512	431.6	10.788	917.2	81.0	758	1.4088				16.81	12.49	5.94		
34.00	1.3697	1.3721	465.7	11.639	904.0	94.3	793	1.4123				20.71	15.15	4.82		
36.00	1.3901	1.3926	500.5	12.508	889.7	108.5	826	1.4156				25.24	18.19	3.95		
38.00	1.4102	1.4127	535.9	13.394	874.3	123.9	856	1.4186				30.40	21.60	3.28		
40.00	1.4299	1.4324	571.9	14.295	857.9	140.3	885	1.4215				36.24	25.40	2.75		

77 SODIUM MOLYBDATE, Na₂MoO₄ · 2H₂O

MOLECULAR WEIGHT = 205.94 FORMULA WEIGHT, HYDRATE = 241.98
RELATIVE SPECIFIC REFRACTIVITY = 0.642

0.00 % by wt. data are the same for all compounds.
For Values of 0.00 wt. % solutions see Table 1, Acetic Acid.

A % by wt.	H % by wt.	ρ D_4^{20}	D_{20}^{20}	C_s g/l	M g-mol/l	C_w g/l	$(C_o - C_w)$ g/l	$(n - n_o)$ × 10⁴	n	Δ °C	O Os/kg	S g-mol/l	η/η_o	η/ρ cS	ϕ rhe	γ mmho/cm	T g-mol/l
0.50	0.59	1.0024	1.0042	5.0	0.024	997.4	0.8	8	1.3338	0.096	0.052	0.027	1.013	1.012	98.56	4.1	0.041
1.00	1.18	1.0067	1.0084	10.1	0.049	996.6	1.6	17	1.3347	0.203	0.109	0.058	1.025	1.020	97.37	7.8	0.080
1.50	1.76	1.0110	1.0128	15.2	0.074	995.8	2.4	25	1.3355	0.322	0.173	0.092	1.037	1.028	96.24	11.2	0.118
2.00	2.35	1.0153	1.0171	20.3	0.099	995.0	3.2	34	1.3364	0.440	0.237	0.127	1.049	1.035	95.14	14.4	0.154
2.50	2.94	1.0197	1.0215	25.5	0.124	994.2	4.0	43	1.3373	0.558	0.300	0.162	1.061	1.043	94.05	17.5	0.190
3.00	3.53	1.0242	1.0260	30.7	0.149	993.4	4.8	52	1.3382	0.670	0.360	0.195	1.073	1.050	92.98	20.5	0.226
3.50	4.11	1.0286	1.0305	36.0	0.175	992.6	5.6	61	1.3391	0.782	0.420	0.228	1.086	1.058	91.91	23.3	0.261
4.00	4.70	1.0332	1.0350	41.3	0.201	991.8	6.4	70	1.3400	0.900	0.484	0.263	1.098	1.065	90.85	26.1	0.296
4.50	5.29	1.0377	1.0395	46.7	0.227	991.0	7.2	79	1.3409	1.015	0.546	0.296	1.112	1.073	89.79	28.9	0.330
5.00	5.88	1.0423	1.0441	52.1	0.253	990.1	8.1	88	1.3418	1.126	0.606	0.329	1.125	1.082	88.71	31.6	0.364
5.50	6.46	1.0468	1.0487	57.6	0.280	989.3	9.0	97	1.3427	1.238	0.666	0.362	1.139	1.090	87.62	34.3	0.398
6.00	7.05	1.0514	1.0533	63.1	0.306	988.4	9.9	106	1.3436	1.350	0.726	0.395	1.153	1.099	86.53	36.9	0.431
6.50	7.64	1.0561	1.0579	68.6	0.333	987.4	10.8	115	1.3445				1.168	1.108	85.44	39.5	0.465
7.00	8.23	1.0607	1.0626	74.2	0.361	986.4	11.8	124	1.3454				1.183	1.118	84.35	42.1	0.497
7.50	8.81	1.0653	1.0672	79.9	0.388	985.4	12.8	133	1.3463				1.199	1.127	83.25	44.5	0.530
8.00	9.40	1.0700	1.0719	85.6	0.416	984.3	13.8	142	1.3472				1.215	1.138	82.16	46.9	0.562
8.50	9.99	1.0747	1.0766	91.3	0.444	983.3	14.9	151	1.3481				1.231	1.148	81.06	49.3	0.593
9.00	10.58	1.0794	1.0813	97.1	0.472	982.2	16.0	160	1.3490				1.248	1.159	79.97	51.6	0.624

78 SODIUM NITRATE, NaNO₃

MOLECULAR WEIGHT = 85.01
RELATIVE SPECIFIC REFRACTIVITY = 0.657

0.00 % by wt. data are the same for all compounds.
For Values of 0.00 wt. % solutions see Table 1, Acetic Acid.

A % by wt.	ρ D_4^{20}	D_{20}^{20}	C_s g/l	M g-mol/l	C_w g/l	$(C_o - C_w)$ g/l	$(n - n_o)$ × 10⁴	n	Δ °C	O Os/kg	S g-mol/l	η/η_o	η/ρ cS	ϕ rhe	γ mmho/cm	T g-mol/l
0.50	1.0016	1.0034	5.0	0.059	996.6	1.6	6	1.3336	0.204	0.110	0.058	1.002	1.003	99.55	5.4	0.055
1.00	1.0050	1.0067	10.0	0.118	994.9	3.3	11	1.3341	0.403	0.216	0.116	1.005	1.002	99.30	10.6	0.111
2.00	1.0117	1.0135	20.2	0.238	991.5	6.7	23	1.3353	0.793	0.426	0.231	1.010	1.000	98.81	20.4	0.225
3.00	1.0185	1.0203	30.6	0.359	988.0	10.3	34	1.3364	1.177	0.633	0.344	1.016	0.999	98.24	29.5	0.336
4.00	1.0254	1.0272	41.0	0.482	984.4	13.9	46	1.3375	1.561	0.839	0.456	1.023	0.999	97.60	38.0	0.445
5.00	1.0322	1.0341	51.6	0.607	980.6	17.6	57	1.3387	1.942	1.044	0.568	1.030	1.000	96.89	46.2	0.552
6.00	1.0392	1.0410	62.4	0.733	976.8	21.4	68	1.3398	2.323	1.249	0.678	1.038	1.001	96.14	54.2	0.659
7.00	1.0462	1.0480	73.2	0.861	972.9	25.3	79	1.3409	2.703	1.453	0.787	1.047	1.003	95.32	61.7	0.764

78 SODIUM NITRATE, NaNO$_3$—(Continued)

A% by wt.	D_4^{20}	D_{20}^{20}	C_s g/l	M g-mol/l	C_w g/l	$(C_o - C_w)$ g/l	$(n - n_o) \times 10^4$	n	Δ °C	O Os/kg	S g-mol/l	η/η_o	η/ρ cS	φ rhe	γ mmho/cm	T g-mol/l
8.00	1.0532	1.0550	84.3	0.991	968.9	29.3	91	1.3421	3.083	1.657	0.895	1.057	1.005	94.45	68.9	0.868
9.00	1.0603	1.0622	95.4	1.123	964.8	33.4	102	1.3432	3.462	1.862	1.002	1.067	1.009	93.51	75.8	0.971
10.00	1.0674	1.0693	106.7	1.256	960.7	37.6	113	1.3443	3.841	2.065	1.107	1.079	1.013	92.49	82.6	1.07
12.00	1.0819	1.0838	129.8	1.527	952.1	46.1	136	1.3466	4.599	2.472	1.316	1.105	1.024	90.28	95.3	1.27
14.00	1.0967	1.0986	153.5	1.806	943.2	55.1	159	1.3489	5.37	2.89	1.523	1.136	1.038	87.85	106.	1.46
18.00	1.1272	1.1292	202.9	2.387	924.3	73.9	206	1.3536	6.98	3.75	1.937	1.213	1.078	82.30	125.	1.82
20.00	1.1429	1.1449	228.6	2.689	914.3	83.9	230	1.3559	7.81	4.20	2.142	1.260	1.105	79.21	134.	1.99
24.00	1.1752	1.1772	282.0	3.318	893.1	105.1	277	1.3607	9.52	5.12	2.542	1.374	1.172	72.64	149.	2.30
28.00	1.2085	1.2106	338.4	3.981	870.1	128.1	325	1.3654	11.28	6.07	2.929	1.519	1.259	65.71	160.	2.56
30.00	1.2256	1.2278	367.7	4.325	858.0	140.3	348	1.3678				1.606	1.313	62.14	165.	2.68
34.00	1.2610	1.2632	428.7	5.043	832.2	166.0	397	1.3726				1.814	1.442	55.01	173.	2.87
40.00	1.3175	1.3198	527.0	6.199	790.5	207.7	472	1.3802				2.222	1.690	44.91	178.	3.00

79 SODIUM PHOSPHATE (TRIBASIC), Na$_3$PO$_4$ · 12H$_2$O

MOLECULAR WEIGHT = 163.96   FORMULA WEIGHT, HYDRATE = 380.14   0.00% by wt. data are the same for all compounds.
RELATIVE SPECIFIC REFRACTIVITY = 0.555   For Values of 0.00 wt.% solutions see Table 1, Acetic Acid.

A% by wt.	H% by wt.	D_4^{20}	D_{20}^{20}	C_s g/l	M g-mol/l	C_w g/l	$(C_o - C_w)$ g/l	$(n - n_o) \times 10^4$	n	Δ °C	O Os/kg	S g-mol/l	η/η_o	η/ρ cS	φ rhe	γ mmho/cm	T g-mol/l
0.50	1.16	1.0042	1.0059	5.0	0.031	999.1	−0.9	13	1.3343	0.192	0.103	0.055	1.031	1.029	96.80	7.3	0.075
1.00	2.32	1.0100	1.0118	10.1	0.062	999.9	−1.7	26	1.3356	0.368	0.198	0.106	1.062	1.054	93.97	14.1	0.150
1.50	3.48	1.0158	1.0176	15.2	0.093	1000.6	−2.3	39	1.3369	0.527	0.283	0.153	1.092	1.078	91.36	18.8	0.206
2.00	4.64	1.0216	1.0234	20.4	0.125	1001.2	−2.9	51	1.3381	0.668	0.359	0.194	1.124	1.102	88.79	22.7	0.253
2.50	5.80	1.0275	1.0293	25.7	0.157	1001.8	−3.6	64	1.3394	0.790	0.425	0.230	1.159	1.130	86.13	26.7	0.302
3.00	6.96	1.0335	1.0353	31.0	0.189	1002.5	−4.2	76	1.3406				1.196	1.160	83.45	30.4	0.349
3.50	8.11	1.0395	1.0413	36.4	0.222	1003.1	−4.9	89	1.3419				1.236	1.191	80.76	34.0	0.394
4.00	9.27	1.0456	1.0474	41.8	0.255	1003.8	−5.5	102	1.3432				1.278	1.225	78.06	37.3	0.436
4.50	10.43	1.0517	1.0536	47.3	0.289	1004.4	−6.2	114	1.3444				1.324	1.261	75.39	40.5	0.477
5.00	11.59	1.0579	1.0598	52.9	0.323	1005.0	−6.8	127	1.3457				1.372	1.299	72.74	43.5	0.516
5.50	12.75	1.0642	1.0661	58.5	0.357	1005.7	−7.4	140	1.3470				1.423	1.340	70.13	46.4	0.554
6.00	13.91	1.0705	1.0724	64.2	0.392	1006.3	−8.0	152	1.3482				1.477	1.383	67.56	49.0	0.589
6.50	15.07	1.0768	1.0787	70.0	0.427	1006.8	−8.6	165	1.3495				1.535	1.428	65.03	51.5	0.622
7.00	16.23	1.0832	1.0851	75.8	0.462	1007.4	−9.1	177	1.3507				1.595	1.475	62.57	53.7	0.653
7.50	17.39	1.0896	1.0915	81.7	0.498	1007.9	−9.7	189	1.3519				1.659	1.525	60.16	55.8	0.681
8.00	18.55	1.0961	1.0980	87.7	0.535	1008.4	−10.1	202	1.3532				1.726	1.578	57.82	57.6	0.706

80 SODIUM PHOSPHATE, DIHYDROGEN (MONOBASIC), NaH$_2$PO$_4$ · 1H$_2$O

MOLECULAR WEIGHT = 119.97   FORMULA WEIGHT, HYDRATE = 137.99   0.00% by wt. data are the same for all compounds.
RELATIVE SPECIFIC REFRACTIVITY = 0.637   For Values of 0.00 wt.% solutions see Table 1, Acetic Acid.

A% by wt.	H% by wt.	D_4^{20}	D_{20}^{20}	C_s g/l	M g-mol/l	C_w g/l	$(C_o - C_w)$ g/l	$(n - n_o) \times 10^4$	n	Δ °C	O Os/kg	S g-mol/l	η/η_o	η/ρ cS	φ rhe	γ mmho/cm	T g-mol/l
0.50	0.58	1.0019	1.0037	5.0	0.042	996.9	1.3	7	1.3336	0.140	0.075	0.040	1.016	1.017	98.18	2.2	0.021
1.00	1.15	1.0056	1.0074	10.1	0.084	995.6	2.7	13	1.3343	0.279	0.150	0.080	1.033	1.029	96.61	4.4	0.044
1.50	1.73	1.0094	1.0111	15.1	0.126	994.2	4.0	20	1.3349	0.418	0.225	0.120	1.049	1.042	95.10	6.8	0.068
2.00	2.30	1.0131	1.0149	20.3	0.169	992.8	5.4	26	1.3356	0.556	0.299	0.161	1.066	1.054	93.62	9.1	0.094
2.50	2.88	1.0168	1.0186	25.4	0.212	991.4	6.8	33	1.3362	0.695	0.374	0.202	1.083	1.067	92.13	11.3	0.119
3.00	3.45	1.0206	1.0224	30.6	0.255	990.0	8.3	39	1.3369	0.835	0.449	0.243	1.101	1.081	90.65	13.4	0.143
3.50	4.03	1.0244	1.0262	35.9	0.299	988.5	9.7	45	1.3375	0.976	0.525	0.285	1.119	1.095	89.17	15.4	0.166
4.00	4.60	1.0281	1.0300	41.1	0.343	987.0	11.2	52	1.3382	1.116	0.600	0.326	1.138	1.109	87.69	17.4	0.189
4.50	5.18	1.0319	1.0338	46.4	0.387	985.5	12.7	58	1.3388	1.254	0.674	0.367	1.158	1.124	86.21	19.2	0.211
5.00	5.75	1.0358	1.0376	51.8	0.432	984.0	14.3	65	1.3395	1.388	0.746	0.406	1.178	1.140	84.72	21.0	0.232
5.50	6.33	1.0396	1.0414	57.2	0.477	982.4	15.8	71	1.3401	1.519	0.817	0.444	1.199	1.156	83.23	22.6	0.252
6.00	6.90	1.0434	1.0453	62.6	0.522	980.8	17.4	78	1.3408	1.645	0.884	0.481	1.221	1.172	81.74	24.1	0.270
6.50	7.48	1.0473	1.0491	68.1	0.567	979.2	19.0	84	1.3414	1.767	0.950	0.517	1.243	1.190	80.26	25.5	0.287
7.00	8.05	1.0511	1.0530	73.6	0.613	977.6	20.7	91	1.3421	1.887	1.014	0.552	1.267	1.208	78.78	26.7	0.303
7.50	8.63	1.0550	1.0569	79.1	0.660	975.9	22.3	97	1.3427	2.004	1.077	0.586	1.291	1.226	77.31	27.9	0.317
8.00	9.20	1.0589	1.0608	84.7	0.706	974.2	24.0	104	1.3434	2.119	1.139	0.619	1.316	1.245	75.85	29.0	0.330
8.50	9.78	1.0628	1.0647	90.3	0.753	972.5	25.7	110	1.3440	2.234	1.201	0.652	1.342	1.265	74.39	30.0	0.344
9.00	10.35	1.0668	1.0686	96.0	0.800	970.8	27.5	117	1.3447	2.350	1.263	0.686	1.368	1.285	72.93	31.0	0.357
9.50	10.93	1.0707	1.0726	101.7	0.848	969.0	29.2	123	1.3453	2.466	1.326	0.719	1.396	1.307	71.48	32.1	0.370
10.00	11.50	1.0747	1.0766	107.5	0.896	967.2	31.0	130	1.3460	2.584	1.389	0.753	1.425	1.329	70.04	33.2	0.384
11.00	12.65	1.0826	1.0846	119.1	0.993	963.6	34.7	143	1.3473	2.821	1.517	0.821	1.485	1.374	67.20	35.4	0.412
12.00	13.80	1.0907	1.0926	130.9	1.091	959.8	38.4	156	1.3486	3.056	1.643	0.887	1.549	1.423	64.44	37.5	0.439
13.00	14.95	1.0988	1.1007	142.8	1.191	955.9	42.3	169	1.3499	3.291	1.769	0.954	1.617	1.474	61.73	39.6	0.465
14.00	16.10	1.1070	1.1089	155.0	1.292	952.0	46.2	182	1.3512	3.529	1.897	1.021	1.691	1.530	59.04	41.5	0.490
15.00	17.25	1.1152	1.1172	167.3	1.394	947.9	50.3	195	1.3525	3.775	2.029	1.089	1.771	1.591	56.35	43.3	0.513
16.00	18.40	1.1236	1.1255	179.8	1.498	943.8	54.4	209	1.3538	4.028	2.166	1.159	1.857	1.656	53.74	44.8	0.534
17.00	19.55	1.1320	1.1340	192.4	1.604	939.5	58.7	222	1.3552	4.287	2.305	1.230	1.948	1.724	51.24	46.2	0.552
18.00	20.70	1.1404	1.1425	205.3	1.711	935.2	63.1	235	1.3565	4.551	2.447	1.303	2.046	1.798	48.77	47.4	0.568
19.00	21.85	1.1491	1.1511	218.5	1.820	930.7	67.5	248	1.3578	4.820	2.592	1.376	2.153	1.880	46.30	48.5	0.583
20.00	23.00	1.1576	1.1597	231.5	1.930	926.1	72.1	262	1.3592	5.10	2.74	1.450	2.278	1.972	43.81	49.6	0.597
22.00	25.30	1.1752	1.1773	258.5	2.155	916.6	81.6	289	1.3618				2.545	2.170	39.21	51.4	0.622
24.00	27.60	1.1931	1.1952	286.3	2.387	906.7	91.5	316	1.3646				2.844	2.389	35.09	52.7	0.639
26.00	29.91	1.2113	1.2134	314.9	2.625	896.3	101.9	343	1.3673				3.208	2.654	31.11	53.5	0.650
28.00	32.21	1.2299	1.2320	344.4	2.870	885.5	112.7	370	1.3700				3.675	2.994	27.16	53.9	0.655
30.00	34.51	1.2488	1.2510	374.6	3.123	874.2	124.1	398	1.3728				4.291	3.443	23.26	54.0	0.656
32.00	36.81	1.2682	1.2704	405.8	3.383	862.4	135.9	426	1.3756				5.069	4.005	19.69	53.7	0.653
34.00	39.11	1.2879	1.2902	437.9	3.650	850.0	148.2	454	1.3784				5.996	4.665	16.64	52.9	0.642
36.00	41.41	1.3080	1.3103	470.9	3.925	837.1	161.1	482	1.3812				7.084	5.427	14.09	51.5	0.622
38.00	43.71	1.3285	1.3308	504.8	4.208	823.6	174.6	511	1.3840				8.346	6.295	11.96	49.3	0.593
40.00	46.01	1.3493	1.3517	539.7	4.499	809.6	188.6	539	1.3869				9.794	7.273	10.19	46.1	0.551

81 SODIUM PHOSPHATE, MONOHYDROGEN (DIBASIC), Na$_2$HPO$_4 \cdot$ 7H$_2$O

MOLECULAR WEIGHT = 141.97   FORMULA WEIGHT, HYDRATE = 268.09
RELATIVE SPECIFIC REFRACTIVITY = 0.576

0.00 % by wt. data are the same for all compounds.
For Values of 0.00 wt. % solutions see Table 1, Acetic Acid.

A% by wt.	H% by wt.	ρ D$_4^{20}$	D$_{20}^{20}$	C$_s$ g/l	M g-mol/l	C$_w$ g/l	(C$_o$ − C$_w$) g/l	(n − n$_o$) × 10^4	n	Δ °C	O Os/kg	S g-mol/l	η/η$_o$	η/ρ cS	φ rhe	γ mmho/cm	T g-mol/l
0.50	0.94	1.0032	1.0050	5.0	0.035	998.2	0.0	10	1.3340	0.167	0.090	0.047	1.019	1.018	97.91	4.6	0.046
1.00	1.89	1.0082	1.0100	10.1	0.071	998.1	0.1	19	1.3349	0.319	0.172	0.092	1.040	1.034	95.96	8.7	0.090
1.50	2.83	1.0131	1.0149	15.2	0.107	997.9	0.3	28	1.3358	0.462	0.248	0.133	1.062	1.051	93.94	12.3	0.130
2.00	3.78	1.0180	1.0198	20.4	0.143	997.7	0.6	38	1.3368				1.086	1.069	91.90	15.6	0.168
2.50	4.72	1.0229	1.0247	25.6	0.180	997.4	0.9	47	1.3377				1.111	1.088	89.86	18.7	0.205
3.00	5.67	1.0279	1.0297	30.8	0.217	997.0	1.2	56	1.3386				1.136	1.108	87.82	21.6	0.240
3.50	6.61	1.0328	1.0346	36.1	0.255	996.7	1.6	66	1.3396				1.163	1.129	85.80	24.3	0.273
4.00	7.55	1.0378	1.0396	41.5	0.292	996.3	1.9	75	1.3405				1.191	1.150	83.78	26.8	0.304
4.50	8.50	1.0428	1.0446	46.9	0.331	995.9	2.4	84	1.3414				1.221	1.173	81.77	29.2	0.334
5.00	9.44	1.0478	1.0496	52.4	0.369	995.4	2.8	94	1.3424				1.251	1.196	79.78	31.4	0.362
5.50	10.39	1.0528	1.0546	57.9	0.408	994.9	3.4	103	1.3433				1.283	1.221	77.80	33.5	0.388

82 SODIUM SULFATE, Na$_2$SO$_4 \cdot$ 10H$_2$O

MOLECULAR WEIGHT = 142.06   FORMULA WEIGHT, HYDRATE = 322.22
RELATIVE SPECIFIC REFRACTIVITY = 0.548

0.00 % by wt. data are the same for all compounds.
For Values of 0.00 wt. % solutions see Table 1, Acetic Acid.

A% by wt.	H% by wt.	ρ D$_4^{20}$	D$_{20}^{20}$	C$_s$ g/l	M g-mol/l	C$_w$ g/l	(C$_o$ − C$_w$) g/l	(n − n$_o$) × 10^4	n	Δ °C	O Os/kg	S g-mol/l	η/η$_o$	η/ρ cS	φ rhe	γ mmho/cm	T g-mol/l
0.50	1.13	1.0027	1.0044	5.0	0.035	997.7	0.6	8	1.3338	0.165	0.089	0.047	1.011	1.010	98.71	5.9	0.060
1.00	2.27	1.0071	1.0089	10.1	0.071	997.1	1.2	15	1.3345	0.320	0.172	0.092	1.024	1.019	97.46	11.2	0.117
1.50	3.40	1.0116	1.0134	15.2	0.107	996.4	1.8	23	1.3353	0.466	0.251	0.135	1.039	1.030	96.02	15.7	0.169
2.00	4.54	1.0161	1.0179	20.3	0.143	995.8	2.4	30	1.3360	0.606	0.326	0.176	1.056	1.041	94.51	19.8	0.218
2.50	5.67	1.0206	1.0225	25.5	0.180	995.1	3.1	38	1.3368	0.742	0.399	0.216	1.072	1.053	93.06	23.9	0.268
3.00	6.80	1.0252	1.0270	30.8	0.216	994.4	3.8	46	1.3376	0.873	0.469	0.254	1.089	1.065	91.63	27.9	0.317
3.50	7.94	1.0298	1.0316	36.0	0.254	993.7	4.5	53	1.3383	1.001	0.538	0.292	1.106	1.077	90.21	31.8	0.365
4.00	9.07	1.0343	1.0362	41.4	0.291	993.0	5.3	61	1.3391	1.125	0.605	0.329	1.124	1.089	88.80	35.5	0.413
4.50	10.21	1.0389	1.0408	46.8	0.329	992.2	6.0	68	1.3398	1.245	0.669	0.364	1.142	1.101	87.38	39.2	0.460
5.00	11.34	1.0436	1.0454	52.2	0.367	991.4	6.8	76	1.3406	1.359	0.731	0.397	1.161	1.115	85.96	42.7	0.506
5.50	12.48	1.0481	1.0499	57.6	0.406	990.4	7.8	83	1.3413	1.465	0.788	0.429	1.180	1.129	84.54	46.1	0.551
6.00	13.61	1.0526	1.0545	63.2	0.445	989.5	8.8	90	1.3420	1.560	0.839	0.456	1.200	1.143	83.14	49.4	0.594
6.50	14.74	1.0572	1.0591	68.7	0.484	988.5	9.7	97	1.3427				1.221	1.157	81.75	52.5	0.636
7.00	15.88	1.0619	1.0638	74.3	0.523	987.5	10.7	105	1.3435				1.242	1.172	80.36	55.5	0.676
7.50	17.01	1.0666	1.0684	80.0	0.563	986.6	11.7	112	1.3442				1.264	1.187	78.98	58.3	0.716
8.00	18.15	1.0713	1.0732	85.7	0.603	985.6	12.7	120	1.3449				1.286	1.203	77.59	61.1	0.755
8.50	19.28	1.0760	1.0779	91.5	0.644	984.6	13.7	127	1.3457				1.310	1.220	76.20	63.7	0.793
9.00	20.41	1.0808	1.0827	97.3	0.685	983.5	14.7	134	1.3464				1.334	1.237	74.80	66.3	0.830
9.50	21.55	1.0856	1.0875	103.1	0.726	982.5	15.7	142	1.3472				1.360	1.255	73.38	68.8	0.866
10.00	22.68	1.0905	1.0924	109.0	0.768	981.4	16.8	149	1.3479				1.387	1.274	71.95	71.3	0.902
11.00	24.95	1.1002	1.1022	121.0	0.852	979.2	19.0	164	1.3494				1.444	1.315	69.11	75.9	0.970
12.00	27.22	1.1101	1.1121	133.2	0.938	976.9	21.3	179	1.3509				1.505	1.359	66.30	80.1	1.03
13.00	29.49	1.1201	1.1221	145.6	1.025	974.5	23.8	194	1.3524				1.571	1.406	63.52	83.9	1.09
14.00	31.75	1.1301	1.1321	158.2	1.114	971.9	26.3	209	1.3539				1.643	1.457	60.74	87.5	1.15
15.00	34.02	1.1402	1.1422	171.0	1.204	969.2	29.1	223	1.3553				1.722	1.513	57.96	91.1	1.21
16.00	36.29	1.1503	1.1523	184.0	1.296	966.2	32.0	237	1.3567				1.808	1.575	55.20	94.9	1.27
17.00	38.56	1.1604	1.1625	197.3	1.389	963.1	35.1	251	1.3581				1.901	1.641	52.50	98.5	1.33
18.00	40.83	1.1705	1.1726	210.7	1.483	959.8	38.4	265	1.3595				2.001	1.713	49.88	102.0	1.39
19.00	43.10	1.1806	1.1827	224.3	1.579	956.3	41.9	278	1.3608				2.108	1.789	47.34	105.0	1.44
20.00	45.36	1.1907	1.1928	238.1	1.676	952.6	45.7	290	1.3620				2.223	1.871	44.89	109.0	1.50
22.00	49.90	1.2106	1.2127	266.3	1.875	944.2	54.0	313	1.3643				2.476	2.050	40.30	114.0	1.61

83 SODIUM TARTRATE, NaOOC(CHOH)$_2$COONa $\cdot$ 2H$_2$O

MOLECULAR WEIGHT = 194.06   FORMULA WEIGHT, HYDRATE = 230.10
RELATIVE SPECIFIC REFRACTIVITY = 0.781

0.00 % by wt. data are the same for all compounds.
For Values of 0.00 wt. % solutions see Table 1, Acetic Acid.

A% by wt.	H% by wt.	ρ D$_4^{20}$	D$_{20}^{20}$	C$_s$ g/l	M g-mol/l	C$_w$ g/l	(C$_o$ − C$_w$) g/l	(n − n$_o$) × 10^4	n	Δ °C	O Os/kg	S g-mol/l	η/η$_o$	η/ρ cS	φ rhe	γ mmho/cm	T g-mol/l
0.50	0.59	1.0017	1.0035	5.0	0.026	996.7	1.5	8	1.3338	0.111	0.060	0.031	1.015	1.016	98.28	3.8	0.037
1.00	1.19	1.0052	1.0070	10.1	0.052	995.2	3.1	17	1.3347	0.224	0.121	0.064	1.031	1.028	96.80	7.1	0.072
2.00	2.37	1.0123	1.0141	20.2	0.104	992.0	6.2	33	1.3363	0.457	0.246	0.132	1.062	1.051	93.97	12.6	0.133
3.00	3.56	1.0194	1.0212	30.6	0.158	988.8	9.4	50	1.3380	0.678	0.365	0.197	1.094	1.075	91.21	17.5	0.191
4.00	4.74	1.0266	1.0284	41.1	0.212	985.5	12.7	67	1.3397	0.891	0.479	0.260	1.128	1.101	88.49	22.1	0.245
5.00	5.93	1.0338	1.0356	51.7	0.266	982.1	16.1	84	1.3414	1.103	0.593	0.322	1.164	1.128	85.74	26.2	0.297
6.00	7.11	1.0410	1.0428	62.5	0.322	978.5	19.7	101	1.3431	1.317	0.708	0.385	1.203	1.157	82.99	30.1	0.346
7.00	8.30	1.0482	1.0501	73.4	0.378	974.9	23.4	118	1.3448	1.529	0.822	0.447	1.243	1.188	80.28	33.7	0.390
8.00	9.49	1.0555	1.0574	84.4	0.435	971.1	27.2	135	1.3465	1.742	0.937	0.509	1.287	1.222	77.56	37.0	0.432
9.00	10.67	1.0628	1.0647	95.7	0.493	967.2	31.1	152	1.3482	1.955	1.051	0.572	1.334	1.258	74.81	40.0	0.471
10.00	11.86	1.0702	1.0721	107.0	0.551	963.2	35.1	169	1.3499	2.171	1.167	0.634	1.386	1.298	72.01	43.0	0.509
12.00	14.23	1.0851	1.0870	130.2	0.671	954.9	43.4	203	1.3533	2.607	1.402	0.760	1.499	1.384	66.58	48.1	0.577
14.00	16.60	1.1002	1.1022	154.0	0.794	946.2	52.0	237	1.3567	3.048	1.639	0.885	1.625	1.480	61.43	52.2	0.632
15.00	17.79	1.1079	1.1098	166.2	0.856	941.7	56.5	254	1.3584	3.269	1.758	0.948	1.695	1.533	58.88	53.9	0.655
18.00	21.34	1.1313	1.1333	203.6	1.049	927.6	70.6	307	1.3637	3.938	2.117	1.134	1.951	1.728	51.14	57.9	0.710
20.00	23.71	1.1471	1.1492	229.4	1.182	917.7	80.5	342	1.3672	4.385	2.358	1.258	2.174	1.899	45.91	59.9	0.738
22.00	26.09	1.1633	1.1653	255.9	1.319	907.4	90.9	378	1.3708				2.444	2.105	40.84	61.4	0.759
24.00	28.46	1.1797	1.1818	283.1	1.459	896.6	101.7	414	1.3744				2.757	2.342	36.20	62.0	0.768
26.00	30.83	1.1963	1.1984	311.0	1.603	885.3	113.0	450	1.3780				3.117	2.611	32.01	61.6	0.762
28.00	33.20	1.2132	1.2153	339.7	1.750	873.5	124.7	487	1.3817				3.528	2.914	28.29	60.1	0.741

84 SODIUM THIOCYANATE, NaCNS

MOLECULAR WEIGHT = 81.07

A% by wt.	ρ D_4^{20}	D_{20}^{20}	C_s g/l	M g-mol/l	C_w g/l	$(C_0 - C_w)$ g/l	$(n - n_0)$ $\times 10^4$	n	Δ °C	O Os/kg	S g-mol/l	η/η_0	η/ρ cS	ϕ rhe	γ mmho/cm	T g-mol/l
1.00	1.0030	1.0048	10.0	0.124	993.0	5.2	22.	1.3352	0.426	0.229	0.123	1.006	1.005	99.21	10.0	0.113
2.00	1.0078	1.0096	20.2	0.249	987.6	10.6	44.	1.3374	0.848	0.456	0.247	1.012	1.006	98.64	20.5	0.226
3.00	1.0127	1.0145	30.4	0.375	982.3	15.9	66.	1.3396	1.280	0.688	0.374	1.019	1.008	97.96	29.8	0.341
4.00	1.0176	1.0194	40.7	0.502	976.9	21.3	88.	1.3418	1.734	0.932	0.507	1.025	1.009	97.40	39.0	0.458
5.00	1.0226	1.0244	51.1	0.631	971.5	26.7	110.	1.3440	2.202	1.184	0.643	1.032	1.011	96.73	48.0	0.576
6.00	1.0275	1.0294	61.7	0.760	965.8	32.4	132.	1.3462	2.679	1.440	0.780	1.039	1.013	96.07	56.7	0.694
7.00	1.0327	1.0346	72.3	0.892	960.4	37.8	155.	1.3485	3.168	1.703	0.919	1.047	1.016	95.31	65.1	0.812
8.00	1.0381	1.0400	83.1	1.024	955.0	43.2	178.	1.3508	3.671	1.974	1.060	1.057	1.020	94.44	73.3	0.932
9.00	1.0435	1.0454	93.9	1.158	949.6	48.6	201.	1.3531	4.184	2.250	1.202	1.067	1.025	93.49	81.2	1.052
10.00	1.0491	1.0510	104.9	1.294	944.2	54.0	224.	1.3554	4.706	2.530	1.345	1.079	1.031	92.45	89.0	1.174
12.00	1.0603	1.0622	127.2	1.569	933.1	65.1	270.	1.3600				1.106	1.045	90.25	104.	1.418
14.00	1.0715	1.0734	150.0	1.850	921.5	76.7	318.	1.3648				1.138	1.064	87.72	118.	1.664
16.00	1.0828	1.0848	173.3	2.137	909.5	88.7	366.	1.3696				1.175	1.087	84.96	130.	1.912
18.00	1.0942	1.0962	197.0	2.430	897.2	101.0	414.	1.3744				1.217	1.114	82.04	142.	2.162
20.00	1.1056	1.1076	221.1	2.728	884.5	113.7	464.	1.3794				1.268	1.149	78.72	154.	2.412
24.00	1.1284	1.1304	270.8	3.340	857.6	140.6	564.	1.3894				1.396	1.240	71.47	170.	2.786
28.00	1.1515	1.1536	322.4	3.977	829.1	169.1	666.	1.3996				1.546	1.345	64.57	178.	3.016
32.00	1.1763	1.1784	376.4	4.643	799.9	198.3	774.	1.4104				1.764	1.503	56.56	184.	3.194
36.00	1.2018	1.2040	432.7	5.337	769.1	229.1	882.	1.4212				2.101	1.752	47.49	185.	3.227
40.00	1.2282	1.2304	491.3	6.060	736.9	261.3	990.	1.4320				2.483	2.026	40.19	177.	2.986
44.00	1.2549	1.2572	552.2	6.811	702.7	295.5	1105.	1.4435				3.151	2.516	31.67	165.	2.678
48.00	1.2821	1.2844	615.4	7.591	666.7	331.5	1223.	1.4553				3.936	3.076	25.36	148.	2.290
52.00	1.3100	1.3124	681.2	8.403	628.8	369.4	1342.	1.4672				5.279	4.038	18.90	130.	1.900
56.00	1.3388	1.3412	749.7	9.248	589.1	409.1	1461.	1.4791				7.554	5.654	13.21	108.	1.493

85 SODIUM THIOSULFATE, $Na_2S_2O_3 \cdot 5H_2O$

MOLECULAR WEIGHT = 158.13   FORMULA WEIGHT, HYDRATE = 248.21
RELATIVE SPECIFIC REFRACTIVITY = 0.773

0.00 % by wt. data are the same for all compounds.
For Values of 0.00 wt. % solutions see Table 1, Acetic Acid.

A% by wt.	H% by wt.	ρ D_4^{20}	D_{20}^{20}	C_s g/l	M g-mol/l	C_w g/l	$(C_0 - C_w)$ g/l	$(n - n_0)$ $\times 10^4$	n	Δ °C	O Os/kg	S g-mol/l	η/η_0	η/ρ cS	ϕ rhe	γ mmho/cm	T g-mol/l
0.50	0.78	1.0024	1.0041	5.0	0.032	997.4	0.9	10	1.3340	0.139	0.075	0.039	1.010	1.010	98.76	5.7	0.057
1.00	1.57	1.0065	1.0083	10.1	0.064	996.4	1.8	21	1.3351	0.279	0.150	0.080	1.021	1.016	97.75	10.7	0.112
2.00	3.14	1.0148	1.0166	20.3	0.128	994.5	3.7	42	1.3371	0.566	0.304	0.164	1.042	1.029	95.78	19.5	0.214
3.00	4.71	1.0231	1.0249	30.7	0.194	992.4	5.8	62	1.3392	0.835	0.449	0.243	1.064	1.042	93.77	27.7	0.315
4.00	6.28	1.0315	1.0333	41.3	0.261	990.2	8.0	83	1.3413	1.090	0.586	0.318	1.088	1.057	91.74	35.6	0.415
5.00	7.85	1.0399	1.0417	52.0	0.329	987.9	10.3	104	1.3434	1.341	0.721	0.392	1.113	1.072	89.67	43.3	0.513
6.00	9.42	1.0483	1.0502	62.9	0.398	985.4	12.8	124	1.3454	1.588	0.854	0.464	1.139	1.089	87.59	50.6	0.610
7.00	10.99	1.0568	1.0587	74.0	0.468	982.8	15.4	145	1.3475	1.826	0.982	0.534	1.167	1.107	85.5	57.5	0.705
8.00	12.56	1.0654	1.0673	85.2	0.539	980.1	18.1	166	1.3496	2.062	1.108	0.602	1.197	1.126	83.38	64.2	0.799
9.00	14.13	1.0740	1.0759	96.7	0.611	977.3	20.9	187	1.3517	2.299	1.236	0.671	1.229	1.147	81.21	70.5	0.891
10.00	15.70	1.0827	1.0846	108.3	0.685	974.4	23.8	208	1.3538	2.546	1.369	0.742	1.264	1.170	76.7	76.7	0.982
12.00	18.84	1.1003	1.1023	132.0	0.835	968.3	29.9	251	1.3581	3.064	1.647	0.890	1.342	1.222	74.35	88.2	1.16
14.00	21.98	1.1182	1.1202	156.6	0.990	961.7	36.5	294	1.3624	3.604	1.938	1.041	1.432	1.283	69.71	98.8	1.33
16.00	25.11	1.1365	1.1385	181.8	1.150	954.6	43.6	337	1.3667	4.168	2.241	1.197	1.534	1.353	65.04	108.	1.49
18.00	28.25	1.1551	1.1571	207.9	1.315	947.1	51.1	381	1.3711	4.758	2.558	1.359	1.654	1.435	60.34	117.	1.64
20.00	31.39	1.1740	1.1760	234.8	1.485	939.2	59.1	426	1.3756	5.37	2.89	1.524	1.794	1.531	55.63	123.	1.77
22.00	34.53	1.1932	1.1953	262.5	1.660	930.7	67.5	471	1.3801				1.954	1.641	51.08	129.	1.87
24.00	37.67	1.2128	1.2150	291.1	1.841	921.8	76.5	517	1.3847				2.137	1.765	46.70	132.	1.94
26.00	40.81	1.2328	1.2350	320.5	2.027	912.3	85.9	563	1.3893				2.351	1.911	42.45	135.	2.00
28.00	43.95	1.2532	1.2554	350.9	2.219	902.3	95.9	610	1.3940				2.591	2.072	38.52	136.	2.02
30.00	47.09	1.2739	1.2762	382.2	2.417	891.7	106.5	657	1.3987				2.897	2.279	34.45	136.	2.03
32.00	50.23	1.2950	1.2973	414.4	2.621	880.6	117.6	705	1.4035				3.298	2.552	30.26	135.	1.99
34.00	53.37	1.3164	1.3188	447.6	2.831	868.8	129.4	754	1.4084				3.784	2.881	26.37	132.	1.93
36.00	56.51	1.3382	1.3406	481.8	3.047	856.5	141.8	802	1.4132				4.350	3.257	22.95	128.	1.86
38.00	59.65	1.3603	1.3627	516.9	3.269	843.4	154.8	851	1.4181				5.001	3.684	19.96	124.	1.77
40.00	62.79	1.3827	1.3852	553.1	3.498	829.6	168.6	899	1.4229				5.747	4.165	17.37	118.	1.66

86 SODIUM TUNGSTATE, Na$_2$WO$_4 \cdot$ 2H$_2$O

MOLECULAR WEIGHT = 293.91 FORMULA WEIGHT, HYDRATE = 329.95
RELATIVE SPECIFIC REFRACTIVITY = 0.414

0.00 % by wt. data are the same for all compounds.
For Values of 0.00 wt. % solutions see Table 1, Acetic Acid.

A% by wt.	H% by wt.	ρ D$_4^{20}$	D$_{20}^{20}$	C$_s$ g/l	M g-mol/l	C$_w$ g/l	(C$_o$ − C$_w$) g/l	(n − n$_o$) × 10^4	n	Δ °C	O Os/kg	S g-mol/l	η/η$_o$	η/ρ cS	φ rhe	γ mmho/cm	T g-mol/l
0.50	0.56	1.0028	1.0046	5.0	0.017	997.8	0.4	5	1.3335	0.081	0.044	0.023	1.007	1.006	99.13	2.8	0.028
1.00	1.12	1.0074	1.0091	10.1	0.034	997.3	0.9	11	1.3341	0.161	0.086	0.046	1.014	1.009	98.42	5.5	0.055
1.50	1.68	1.0119	1.0137	15.2	0.052	996.8	1.5	16	1.3346	0.239	0.129	0.068	1.022	1.012	97.67	7.9	0.081
2.00	2.25	1.0166	1.0184	20.3	0.069	996.2	2.0	21	1.3351	0.317	0.171	0.091	1.030	1.015	96.89	10.3	0.107
2.50	2.81	1.0212	1.0230	25.5	0.087	995.7	2.5	27	1.3357	0.396	0.213	0.114	1.039	1.019	96.08	12.5	0.132
3.00	3.37	1.0259	1.0278	30.8	0.105	995.2	3.1	33	1.3362	0.474	0.255	0.137	1.048	1.024	95.23	14.7	0.157
3.50	3.93	1.0307	1.0326	36.1	0.123	994.7	3.6	38	1.3368	0.553	0.297	0.160	1.058	1.028	94.35	16.8	0.182
4.00	4.49	1.0356	1.0374	41.4	0.141	994.1	4.1	44	1.3374	0.633	0.340	0.184	1.068	1.033	93.46	18.8	0.206
4.50	5.05	1.0405	1.0423	46.8	0.159	993.6	4.6	50	1.3380	0.714	0.384	0.208	1.078	1.038	92.58	20.8	0.230
5.00	5.61	1.0453	1.0472	52.3	0.178	993.1	5.2	56	1.3386	0.796	0.428	0.232	1.088	1.043	91.73	22.8	0.254
5.50	6.17	1.0502	1.0520	57.8	0.197	992.4	5.8	62	1.3392	0.879	0.472	0.256	1.098	1.048	90.89	24.7	0.278
6.00	6.74	1.0550	1.0569	63.3	0.215	991.7	6.5	67	1.3397	0.962	0.517	0.281	1.108	1.052	90.06	26.7	0.302
6.50	7.30	1.0599	1.0618	68.9	0.234	991.0	7.2	73	1.3403	1.046	0.562	0.305	1.118	1.057	89.24	28.6	0.326
7.00	7.86	1.0648	1.0667	74.5	0.254	990.3	8.0	79	1.3409	1.130	0.607	0.330	1.129	1.062	88.43	30.5	0.350
7.50	8.42	1.0698	1.0717	80.2	0.273	989.5	8.7	85	1.3414	1.212	0.652	0.354	1.139	1.067	87.62	32.4	0.374
8.00	8.98	1.0748	1.0767	86.0	0.293	988.8	9.4	91	1.3420	1.293	0.695	0.378	1.150	1.072	86.81	34.3	0.398
8.50	9.54	1.0799	1.0818	91.8	0.312	988.1	10.1	97	1.3427	1.371	0.737	0.401	1.160	1.077	86.02	36.1	0.422
9.00	10.10	1.0852	1.0871	97.7	0.332	987.5	10.7	103	1.3433	1.445	0.777	0.423	1.171	1.081	85.23	38.0	0.445

87 STRONTIUM CHLORIDE, SrCl$_2 \cdot$ 6H$_2$O

MOLECULAR WEIGHT = 158.54 FORMULA WEIGHT, HYDRATE = 266.64
RELATIVE SPECIFIC REFRACTIVITY = 0.635

0.00 % by wt. data are the same for all compounds.
For Values of 0.00 wt. % solutions see Table 1, Acetic Acid.

A% by wt.	H% by wt.	ρ D$_4^{20}$	D$_{20}^{20}$	C$_s$ g/l	M g-mol/l	C$_w$ g/l	(C$_o$ − C$_w$) g/l	(n − n$_o$) × 10^4	n	Δ °C	O Os/kg	S g-mol/l	η/η$_o$	η/ρ cS	φ rhe	γ mmho/cm	T g-mol/l
0.50	0.84	1.0027	1.0044	5.0	0.032	997.6	0.6	9	1.3339	0.158	0.085	0.045	1.010	1.009	98.85	5.9	0.060
1.00	1.68	1.0071	1.0089	10.1	0.064	997.0	1.2	18	1.3348	0.310	0.167	0.089	1.019	1.014	97.94	11.4	0.120
2.00	3.36	1.0161	1.0179	20.3	0.128	995.8	2.5	36	1.3366	0.619	0.333	0.180	1.037	1.023	96.24	22.0	0.244
3.00	5.05	1.0252	1.0270	30.8	0.194	994.4	3.8	54	1.3384	0.934	0.502	0.272	1.055	1.032	94.56	31.4	0.362
4.00	6.73	1.0344	1.0362	41.4	0.261	993.0	5.2	73	1.3402	1.261	0.678	0.369	1.074	1.041	92.89	40.4	0.475
5.00	8.41	1.0437	1.0456	52.2	0.329	991.5	6.7	91	1.3421	1.607	0.864	0.470	1.094	1.050	91.23	49.1	0.591
6.00	10.09	1.0532	1.0551	63.2	0.399	990.0	8.2	110	1.3440	1.978	1.064	0.578	1.114	1.060	89.59	58.0	0.712
7.00	11.77	1.0628	1.0647	74.4	0.469	988.4	9.8	129	1.3459	2.377	1.278	0.693	1.134	1.069	87.98	66.8	0.836
8.00	13.45	1.0726	1.0745	85.8	0.541	986.8	11.4	148	1.3478	2.800	1.505	0.815	1.155	1.079	86.37	75.3	0.962
9.00	15.14	1.0825	1.0844	97.4	0.614	985.0	13.2	168	1.3498	3.252	1.748	0.943	1.178	1.090	84.73	83.6	1.08
10.00	16.82	1.0925	1.0944	109.3	0.689	983.3	15.0	188	1.3518	3.736	2.009	1.078	1.202	1.102	83.03	91.5	1.21
12.00	20.18	1.1131	1.1150	133.6	0.842	979.5	18.7	228	1.3558	4.811	2.587	1.374	1.255	1.130	79.53	107.	1.46
14.00	23.55	1.1342	1.1362	158.8	1.002	975.4	22.9	269	1.3599	6.03	3.24	1.696	1.314	1.160	75.98	120.	1.71
16.00	26.91	1.1558	1.1579	184.9	1.166	970.9	27.3	311	1.3641	7.41	3.99	2.044	1.380	1.196	72.32	133.	1.96
18.00	30.27	1.1780	1.1801	212.0	1.337	966.0	32.3	354	1.3684	8.98	4.83	2.418	1.457	1.239	68.52	144.	2.19
20.00	33.64	1.2008	1.2029	240.2	1.515	960.6	37.6	398	1.3728	10.74	5.78	2.814	1.546	1.290	64.55	153.	2.40
22.00	37.00	1.2241	1.2263	269.3	1.699	954.8	43.4	442	1.3772	12.74	6.85	3.230	1.647	1.348	60.58	160.	2.56
24.00	40.36	1.2481	1.2503	299.5	1.889	948.6	49.7	487	1.3817	14.99	8.06	3.664	1.761	1.414	56.67	165.	2.68
26.00	43.73	1.2728	1.2751	330.9	2.087	941.9	56.3	534	1.3864				1.893	1.491	52.71	170.	2.79
28.00	47.09	1.2983	1.3006	363.5	2.293	934.8	63.4	582	1.3911				2.052	1.584	48.64	174.	2.90

A% by wt.	H% by wt.	ρ D_4^{20}	D_{20}^{20}	C_s g/l	M g-mol/l	C_w g/l	$(C_o - C_w)$ g/l	$(n - n_o)$ ×10⁴	n	Δ °C	O Os/kg	S g-mol/l	η/η_o	η/ρ cS	ϕ rhe	γ mmho/cm	T g-mol/l
30.00	50.46	1.3248	1.3271	397.4	2.507	927.3	70.9	631	1.3961					2.241	1.695	44.53	178.0	3.02
32.00	53.82	1.3523	1.3547	432.7	2.729	919.6	78.7	683	1.4013					2.522	1.869	39.57	178.0	3.02
34.00	57.18	1.3811	1.3835	469.6	2.962	911.5	86.7	737	1.4067					2.840	2.060	35.14	175.0	2.92
36.00	60.55	1.4114	1.4139	508.1	3.205	903.3	94.9	794	1.4124					3.200	2.272	31.19	166.0	2.70

88 SUCROSE, C₁₂H₂₂O₁₁

MOLECULAR WEIGHT = 342.30
RELATIVE SPECIFIC REFRACTIVITY = 1.031

0.00 % by wt. data are the same for all compounds.
For Values of 0.00 wt. % solutions see Table 1, Acetic Acid.

A% by wt.	ρ D_4^{20}	D_{20}^{20}	C_s g/l	M g-mol/l	C_w g/l	$(C_o - C_w)$ g/l	$(n - n_o)$ ×10⁴	n	Δ °C	O Os/kg	S g-mol/l	η/η_o	η/ρ cS	ϕ rhe	γ mmho/cm	T g-mol/l
0.50	1.0002	1.0019	5.0	0.015	995.2	3.1	7	1.3337	0.027	0.015	0.007	1.013	1.015	98.53		
1.00	1.0021	1.0039	10.0	0.029	992.1	6.2	14	1.3344	0.055	0.030	0.015	1.026	1.026	97.27		
1.50	1.0040	1.0058	15.1	0.044	989.0	9.3	22	1.3351	0.083	0.045	0.023	1.039	1.037	96.03		
2.00	1.0060	1.0078	20.1	0.059	985.9	12.4	29	1.3359	0.112	0.060	0.031	1.053	1.049	94.78		
2.50	1.0079	1.0097	25.2	0.074	982.7	15.5	36	1.3366	0.140	0.076	0.040	1.067	1.061	93.51		
3.00	1.0099	1.0117	30.3	0.089	979.6	18.6	43	1.3373	0.170	0.091	0.048	1.082	1.074	92.24		
3.50	1.0119	1.0137	35.4	0.103	976.5	21.8	51	1.3381	0.199	0.107	0.057	1.097	1.086	90.99		
4.00	1.0139	1.0156	40.6	0.118	973.3	24.9	58	1.3388	0.229	0.123	0.066	1.112	1.099	89.75		
4.50	1.0158	1.0176	45.7	0.134	970.1	28.1	65	1.3395	0.260	0.140	0.074	1.128	1.112	88.49		
5.00	1.0178	1.0196	50.9	0.149	966.9	31.3	73	1.3403	0.291	0.156	0.083	1.144	1.126	87.24		
5.50	1.0198	1.0216	56.1	0.164	963.7	34.5	80	1.3410	0.322	0.173	0.093	1.160	1.140	86.02		
6.00	1.0218	1.0236	61.3	0.179	960.5	37.7	88	1.3418	0.354	0.190	0.102	1.177	1.154	84.79		
6.50	1.0238	1.0257	66.5	0.194	957.3	40.9	95	1.3425	0.386	0.208	0.111	1.195	1.169	83.54		
7.00	1.0259	1.0277	71.8	0.210	954.1	44.2	103	1.3433	0.419	0.225	0.121	1.213	1.185	82.28		
7.50	1.0279	1.0297	77.1	0.225	950.8	47.4	110	1.3440	0.452	0.243	0.131	1.232	1.201	81.02		
8.00	1.0299	1.0317	82.4	0.241	947.5	50.7	118	1.3448	0.485	0.261	0.140	1.251	1.217	79.78		
8.50	1.0320	1.0338	87.7	0.256	944.2	54.0	125	1.3455	0.520	0.279	0.150	1.271	1.234	78.54		
9.00	1.0340	1.0358	93.1	0.272	940.9	57.3	133	1.3463	0.554	0.298	0.161	1.291	1.251	77.30		
9.50	1.0361	1.0379	98.4	0.288	937.6	60.6	141	1.3471	0.589	0.317	0.171	1.312	1.269	76.09		
10.00	1.0381	1.0400	103.8	0.303	934.3	63.9	148	1.3478	0.625	0.336	0.181	1.333	1.287	74.87		
11.00	1.0423	1.0441	114.7	0.335	927.6	70.6	164	1.3494	0.698	0.375	0.203	1.378	1.325	72.42		
12.00	1.0465	1.0483	125.6	0.367	920.9	77.4	180	1.3509	0.773	0.415	0.225	1.426	1.365	69.99		
13.00	1.0507	1.0525	136.6	0.399	914.1	84.2	195	1.3525	0.850	0.457	0.248	1.477	1.409	67.57		
14.00	1.0549	1.0568	147.7	0.431	907.2	91.0	211	1.3541	0.930	0.500	0.271	1.531	1.454	65.19		
15.00	1.0592	1.0610	158.9	0.464	900.3	97.9	227	1.3557	1.012	0.544	0.295	1.589	1.503	62.81		
16.00	1.0635	1.0653	170.2	0.497	893.3	104.9	243	1.3573	1.097	0.590	0.320	1.650	1.555	60.49		
17.00	1.0678	1.0697	181.5	0.530	886.3	112.0	259	1.3589	1.185	0.637	0.346	1.716	1.610	58.16		
18.00	1.0722	1.0741	193.0	0.564	879.2	119.1	276	1.3606	1.275	0.686	0.373	1.786	1.669	55.88		
19.00	1.0766	1.0785	204.5	0.598	872.0	126.2	292	1.3622	1.369	0.736	0.400	1.861	1.732	53.63		
20.00	1.0810	1.0829	216.2	0.632	864.8	133.5	309	1.3639	1.465	0.788	0.429	1.941	1.799	51.42		
22.00	1.0899	1.0918	239.8	0.701	850.1	148.1	342	1.3672	1.668	0.897	0.488	2.120	1.949	47.08		
24.00	1.0990	1.1009	263.8	0.771	835.2	163.0	376	1.3706	1.886	1.014	0.551	2.326	2.121	42.91		
26.00	1.1082	1.1102	288.1	0.842	820.1	178.2	411	1.3741	2.120	1.140	0.619	2.568	2.322	38.86		
28.00	1.1175	1.1195	312.9	0.914	804.6	193.6	446	1.3776	2.371	1.275	0.692	2.849	2.554	35.03		
30.00	1.1270	1.1290	338.1	0.988	788.9	209.3	482	1.3812	2.644	1.421	0.770	3.181	2.828	31.37		
32.00	1.1366	1.1386	363.7	1.063	772.9	225.3	518	1.3848	2.942	1.582	0.855	3.754	3.309	26.59		
34.00	1.1464	1.1484	389.8	1.139	756.6	241.6	555	1.3885	3.268	1.757	0.947	4.044	3.535	24.68		
36.00	1.1562	1.1583	416.2	1.216	740.0	258.2	592	1.3922	3.625	1.949	1.047	4.612	3.997	21.64		
38.00	1.1663	1.1683	443.2	1.295	723.1	275.1	630	1.3960	4.018	2.160	1.156	5.304	4.557	18.82		
40.00	1.1765	1.1785	470.6	1.375	705.9	292.4	669	1.3999	4.452	2.394	1.276	6.150	5.238	16.23		
42.00	1.1868	1.1889	498.4	1.456	688.3	309.9	708	1.4038	4.932	2.652	1.406	7.220	6.096	13.82		
44.00	1.1972	1.1994	526.8	1.539	670.5	327.8	748	1.4078				8.579	7.180	11.63		
46.00	1.2079	1.2100	555.6	1.623	652.2	346.0	788	1.4118				10.28	8.53	9.71		
48.00	1.2186	1.2208	584.9	1.709	633.7	364.6	829	1.4159				12.49	10.27	7.99		
50.00	1.2295	1.2317	614.8	1.796	614.8	383.5	871	1.4201				15.40	12.55	6.48		
52.00	1.2406	1.2428	645.1	1.885	595.5	402.7	913	1.4243				19.30	15.59	5.17		
54.00	1.2518	1.2540	676.0	1.975	575.8	422.4	956	1.4286				24.63	19.71	4.05		
56.00	1.2632	1.2654	707.4	2.067	555.8	442.4	1000	1.4330				32.06	25.43	3.11		
58.00	1.2747	1.2770	739.3	2.160	535.4	462.8	1044	1.4374				42.69	33.56	2.34		
60.00	1.2864	1.2887	771.9	2.255	514.6	483.7	1089	1.4419				58.37	45.46	1.71		
62.00	1.2983	1.3006	804.9	2.352	493.3	504.9	1135	1.4465				82.26	63.49	1.21		
64.00	1.3103	1.3126	838.6	2.450	471.7	526.5	1181	1.4511				119.9	91.69	0.83		
66.00	1.3224	1.3248	872.8	2.550	449.6	548.6	1228	1.4558				181.7	137.6	0.55		
68.00	1.3348	1.3371	907.6	2.652	427.1	571.1	1276	1.4606				287.9	216.1	0.35		
70.00	1.3472	1.3496	943.1	2.755	404.2	594.1	1324	1.4654				480.6	357.4	0.21		
72.00	1.3599	1.3623	979.1	2.860	380.8	617.5	1373	1.4703				853.2	628.6	0.12		
74.00	1.3726	1.3751	1015.7	2.967	356.9	641.4	1423	1.4753				1628.	1188.	0.06		
76.00	1.3855	1.3880	1053.0	3.076	332.5	665.7	1473	1.4803								
78.00	1.3986	1.4011	1090.9	3.187	307.7	690.5	1524	1.4854								
80.00	1.4117	1.4142	1129.4	3.299	282.3	715.9	1576	1.4906								
82.00	1.4250	1.4275	1168.5	3.414	256.5	741.7	1628	1.4958								
84.00	1.4383	1.4409	1208.2	3.530	230.1	768.1	1681	1.5010								

89 SULFURIC ACID, H₂SO₄

MOLECULAR WEIGHT = 98.08
RELATIVE SPECIFIC REFRACTIVITY = 0.685

0.00 % by wt. data are the same for all compounds.
For Values of 0.00 wt. % solutions see Table 1, Acetic Acid.

A% by wt.	ρ D_4^{20}	D_{20}^{20}	C_s g/l	M g-mol/l	C_w g/l	$(C_o - C_w)$ g/l	$(n - n_o)$ × 10⁴	n	Δ °C	O Os/kg	S g-mol/l	η/η_o	η/ρ cS	φ rhe	γ mmho/cm	T g-mol/l
0.50	1.0016	1.0034	5.0	0.051	996.6	1.7	6	1.3336	0.210	0.113	0.060	1.008	1.009	98.96	24.3	0.277
1.00	1.0049	1.0067	10.0	0.102	994.9	3.3	13	1.3342	0.423	0.227	0.122	1.017	1.014	98.13	47.8	0.573
1.50	1.0083	1.0101	15.1	0.154	993.2	5.1	19	1.3349	0.662	0.356	0.192	1.025	1.019	97.34	70.3	0.886
2.00	1.0116	1.0134	20.2	0.206	991.4	6.8	25	1.3355	0.796	0.428	0.232	1.034	1.024	96.52	92.	1.22
2.50	1.0150	1.0168	25.4	0.259	989.6	8.6	31	1.3361	1.004	0.540	0.293	1.044	1.031	95.55	113.	1.58
3.00	1.0183	1.0201	30.6	0.311	987.8	10.4	37	1.3367	1.172	0.630	0.343	1.057	1.040	94.45	134.	1.98
3.50	1.0217	1.0235	35.8	0.365	985.9	12.3	43	1.3373	1.354	0.728	0.396	1.070	1.049	93.29	155.	2.42
4.00	1.0250	1.0269	41.0	0.418	984.0	14.2	49	1.3379	1.599	0.860	0.468	1.083	1.059	92.11	175.	2.93
4.50	1.0284	1.0302	46.3	0.472	982.1	16.1	55	1.3385	1.855	0.998	0.543	1.097	1.069	90.97	194.	3.57
5.00	1.0318	1.0336	51.6	0.526	980.2	18.0	61	1.3391	2.047	1.101	0.598	1.110	1.078	89.91	211.	4.25
5.50	1.0352	1.0370	56.9	0.580	978.2	20.0	67	1.3397	2.259	1.214	0.659	1.122	1.086	88.93		
6.00	1.0385	1.0404	62.3	0.635	976.2	22.0	73	1.3403	2.495	1.341	0.727	1.134	1.094	88.00		
6.50	1.0419	1.0438	67.7	0.691	974.2	24.0	79	1.3409	2.730	1.468	0.795	1.146	1.102	87.10		
7.00	1.0453	1.0472	73.2	0.746	972.2	26.1	85	1.3415	2.952	1.587	0.858	1.157	1.109	86.24		
7.50	1.0488	1.0506	78.7	0.802	970.1	28.1	91	1.3421	3.197	1.719	0.927	1.169	1.117	85.39		
8.00	1.0522	1.0541	84.2	0.858	968.0	30.2	97	1.3427	3.493	1.878	1.010	1.180	1.124	84.56		
8.50	1.0556	1.0575	89.7	0.915	965.9	32.3	103	1.3433	3.801	2.043	1.096	1.192	1.131	83.74		
9.00	1.0591	1.0610	95.3	0.972	963.8	34.4	109	1.3439	4.083	2.195	1.174	1.204	1.139	82.92		
9.50	1.0626	1.0645	100.9	1.029	961.6	36.6	115	1.3445	4.360	2.344	1.250	1.216	1.146	82.10		
10.00	1.0661	1.0680	106.6	1.087	959.5	38.8	121	1.3451	4.644	2.497	1.328	1.228	1.154	81.27		
11.00	1.0731	1.0750	118.0	1.204	955.1	43.2	133	1.3463	5.25	2.82	1.490	1.253	1.170	79.63		
12.00	1.0802	1.0821	129.6	1.322	950.6	47.6	145	1.3475	5.93	3.19	1.669	1.279	1.187	78.02		
13.00	1.0874	1.0893	141.4	1.441	946.0	52.2	158	1.3488	6.67	3.59	1.859	1.306	1.203	76.43		
14.00	1.0947	1.0966	153.3	1.563	941.4	56.8	170	1.3500	7.49	4.03	2.063	1.334	1.221	74.82		
15.00	1.1020	1.1039	165.3	1.685	936.7	61.5	183	1.3513	8.35	4.49	2.270	1.364	1.240	73.17		
16.00	1.1094	1.1114	177.5	1.810	931.9	66.3	195	1.3525	9.26	4.98	2.483	1.396	1.261	71.47		
17.00	1.1169	1.1189	189.9	1.936	927.0	71.2	208	1.3538	10.23	5.50	2.702	1.431	1.284	69.74		
18.00	1.1245	1.1265	202.4	2.064	922.1	76.2	221	1.3551	11.29	6.07	2.932	1.467	1.308	68.01		
19.00	1.1321	1.1341	215.1	2.193	917.0	81.2	233	1.3563	12.43	6.68	3.169	1.505	1.332	66.32		
20.00	1.1398	1.1418	228.0	2.324	911.9	86.4	246	1.3576	13.64	7.33	3.409	1.543	1.356	64.68		
22.00	1.1554	1.1575	254.2	2.592	901.2	97.0	272	1.3602	16.48	8.86	3.932	1.621	1.405	61.58		
24.00	1.1714	1.1735	281.1	2.866	890.3	108.0	298	1.3628	19.85	10.67	4.488	1.703	1.457	58.60		
26.00	1.1872	1.1893	308.7	3.147	878.5	119.7	323	1.3653	24.29	13.06		1.793	1.513	55.67		
28.00	1.2031	1.2052	336.9	3.435	866.2	132.0	347	1.3677	29.65	15.94		1.890	1.574	52.81		
30.00	1.2191	1.2213	365.7	3.729	853.4	144.9	371	1.3701	36.21	19.47		1.997	1.641	49.98		
32.00	1.2353	1.2375	395.3	4.030	840.0	158.2	395	1.3725	44.76	24.07		2.118	1.718	47.12		
34.00	1.2518	1.2540	425.6	4.339	826.2	172.1	419	1.3749	55.28	29.72		2.250	1.801	44.36		
36.00	1.2685	1.2707	456.7	4.656	811.8	186.4	443	1.3773				2.387	1.885	41.82		
38.00	1.2855	1.2878	488.5	4.981	797.0	201.2	467	1.3797				2.528	1.970	39.48		
40.00	1.3028	1.3051	521.1	5.313	781.7	216.5	491	1.3821				2.685	2.065	37.17		
42.00	1.3205	1.3229	554.6	5.655	765.9	232.3	516	1.3846				2.866	2.174	34.83		
44.00	1.3386	1.3410	589.0	6.005	749.6	248.6	540	1.3870				3.067	2.296	32.53		
46.00	1.3570	1.3594	624.2	6.365	732.8	265.4	565	1.3895				3.292	2.431	30.32		
48.00	1.3759	1.3783	660.4	6.734	715.5	282.8	590	1.3920				3.539	2.577	28.20		
50.00	1.3952	1.3977	697.6	7.113	697.6	300.6	616	1.3945				3.818	2.742	26.14		
52.00	1.4149	1.4174	735.8	7.502	679.2	319.1	641	1.3971				4.134	2.927	24.14		
54.00	1.4351	1.4377	775.0	7.901	660.2	338.1	667	1.3997				4.490	3.135	22.23		
56.00	1.4558	1.4584	815.3	8.312	640.6	357.7	694	1.4024				4.896	3.370	20.38		
58.00	1.4770	1.4796	856.7	8.734	620.3	377.9	720	1.4050				5.343	3.625	18.68		
60.00	1.4987	1.5013	899.2	9.168	599.5	398.8	747	1.4077				5.905	3.948	16.90		
62.00	1.5200	1.5227	942.4	9.608	577.6	420.6										
64.00	1.5421	1.5448	986.9	10.062	555.2	443.0										
66.00	1.5646	1.5674	1032.6	10.528	532.0	466.2										
68.00	1.5874	1.5902	1079.4	11.005	508.0	490.2										
70.00	1.6105	1.6134	1127.4	11.495	483.1	515.1										
72.00	1.6338	1.6367	1176.3	11.993	457.5	540.7										
74.00	1.6574	1.6603	1226.5	12.505	430.9	567.3										
76.00	1.6810	1.6840	1277.6	13.026	403.4	594.8										
78.00	1.7043	1.7073	1329.4	13.554	374.9	623.3										
80.00	1.7272	1.7303	1381.8	14.088	345.4	652.8										
82.00	1.7491	1.7522	1434.3	14.624	314.8	683.4										
84.00	1.7693	1.7724	1486.2	15.153	283.1	715.1										
86.00	1.7872	1.7904	1537.0	15.671	250.2	748.0										
88.00	1.8022	1.8054	1585.9	16.169	216.3	781.9										
90.00	1.8144	1.8176	1633.0	16.650	181.4	816.8										
92.00	1.8240	1.8272	1678.1	17.110	145.9	852.3										
94.00	1.8312	1.8344	1721.3	17.550	109.9	888.3										
96.00	1.8355	1.8388	1762.1	17.966	73.4	924.8										
98.00	1.8361	1.8394	1799.4	18.346	36.7	961.5										
100.00	1.8305	1.8337	1830.5	18.663	0.0	998.2										

90 TARTARIC ACID, HO$_2$C(CHOH)$_2$CO$_2$H

MOLECULAR WEIGHT = 150.09

A% by wt.	ρ D_4^{20}	D_{20}^{20}	C_s g/l	M g-mol/l	C_w g/l	$(C_0 - C_w)$ g/l	$(n - n_0)$ $\times 10^4$	n	Δ °C	O Os/kg	S g-mol/l	η/η_0	η/ρ cS	ϕ rhe	γ mmho/cm	T g-mol/l
1.00	1.0029	1.0047	10.0	0.067	992.9	5.3	12.	1.3342	0.132	0.070	0.037	1.021	1.020	97.76	2.5	0.025
2.00	1.0072	1.0090	20.1	0.134	987.1	11.1	25.	1.3355	0.262	0.141	0.075	1.044	1.039	95.56	3.9	0.039
3.00	1.0121	1.0139	30.4	0.202	981.7	16.5	37.	1.3367	0.402	0.216	0.116	1.069	1.058	93.39	4.9	0.049
4.00	1.0163	1.0181	40.7	0.271	975.6	22.6	49.	1.3379	0.538	0.290	0.156	1.092	1.077	91.36	5.5	0.056
5.00	1.0208	1.0226	51.0	0.340	969.8	28.4	62.	1.3392	0.681	0.366	0.198	1.119	1.098	89.22	6.2	0.063
6.00	1.0255	1.0273	61.5	0.410	964.0	34.2	73.	1.3403	0.824	0.443	0.240	1.147	1.121	86.99	6.9	0.070
7.00	1.0310	1.0329	72.2	0.481	958.8	39.4	88.	1.3418	0.974	0.523	0.284	1.176	1.143	84.86	7.3	0.075
8.00	1.0348	1.0367	82.8	0.552	952.0	46.2	99.	1.3429	1.130	0.607	0.330	1.207	1.169	82.67	7.8	0.080
9.00	1.0393	1.0412	93.5	0.623	945.8	52.4	111.	1.3441	1.283	0.690	0.375	1.236	1.192	80.72	8.2	0.084
10.00	1.0443	1.0462	104.4	0.696	939.9	58.3	124.	1.3454	1.443	0.776	0.422	1.272	1.220	78.49	8.5	0.088
12.00	1.0540	1.0559	126.5	0.843	927.5	70.7	151.	1.3481	1.768	0.951	0.517	1.343	1.277	74.30	9.2	0.095
14.00	1.0639	1.0658	148.9	0.992	915.0	83.2	178.	1.3508	2.130	1.145	0.622	1.413	1.331	70.62	9.7	0.100
16.00	1.0738	1.0757	171.8	1.145	902.0	96.2	205.	1.3535	2.504	1.346	0.730	1.498	1.398	66.61	10.1	0.104
18.00	1.0839	1.0859	195.1	1.300	888.8	109.4	231.	1.3561	2.917	1.568	0.848	1.591	1.471	62.72	10.3	0.107
20.00	1.0942	1.0962	218.8	1.458	875.4	122.8	260.	1.3590	3.360	1.807	0.973	1.701	1.558	58.66	10.5	0.109
24.00	1.1152	1.1172	267.6	1.783	847.6	150.6	316.	1.3646	4.309	2.316	1.236	1.957	1.758	51.01	10.6	0.110
28.00	1.1366	1.1387	318.3	2.120	818.3	179.9	375.	1.3705	5.46	2.93	1.546	2.296	2.024	43.47	10.4	0.108
32.00	1.1588	1.1609	370.8	2.471	788.0	210.2	436.	1.3766	6.73	3.62	1.874	2.695	2.330	37.04	10.1	0.104
36.00	1.1813	1.1834	425.3	2.833	756.0	242.2	499.	1.3829	8.30	4.47	2.259	3.242	2.750	30.78	9.3	0.096
40.00	1.2049	1.2071	482.0	3.211	722.9	275.3	561.	1.3891	10.20	5.48	2.695	4.002	3.328	24.94	8.2	0.085
44.00	1.2290	1.2312	540.8	3.603	688.2	310.0	627.	1.3957				5.088	4.148	19.62	7.3	0.074
48.00	1.2535	1.2558	601.7	4.009	651.8	346.4	692.	1.4022				6.605	5.280	15.11	6.2	0.063
52.00	1.2787	1.2810	664.9	4.430	613.8	384.4	762.	1.4092				8.961	7.022	11.14	5.0	0.050
56.00	1.3058	1.3082	731.3	4.872	574.5	423.7	834.	1.4164				12.60	9.670	7.92	3.7	0.037
58.00	1.3196	1.3220	765.4	5.099	554.2	444.0	869.	1.4199				15.64	11.87	6.38	3.0	0.030

91 TETRACAINE HYDROCHLORIDE, C$_{15}$H$_{24}$N$_2$O$_2$ · HCl

MOLECULAR WEIGHT = 300.84

A% by wt.	ρ D_4^{20}	D_{20}^{20}	C_s g/l	M g-mol/l	C_w g/l	$(C_0 - C_w)$ g/l	$(n - n_0)$ $\times 10^4$	n	Δ °C	O Os/kg	S g-mol/l	η/η_0	η/ρ cS	ϕ rhe	γ mmho/cm	T g-mol/l
0.50	0.9988	1.0006	5.0	0.017	993.8	4.4	11.	1.3341	0.058	0.031	0.016	1.013	1.016	98.54	1.2	0.012
1.00	0.9995	1.0013	10.0	0.033	989.5	8.7	23.	1.3353	0.110	0.059	0.031	1.029	1.032	96.95	2.4	0.024
1.50	1.0001	1.0019	15.0	0.050	985.1	13.1	34.	1.3364	0.159	0.086	0.045	1.045	1.047	95.50	3.6	0.036
2.00	1.0008	1.0026	20.0	0.067	980.8	17.4	46.	1.3376	0.204	0.109	0.058	1.063	1.064	93.91	4.7	0.047
2.50	1.0014	1.0032	25.0	0.083	976.4	21.8	57.	1.3387				1.081	1.082	92.29	5.6	0.057
3.00	1.0021	1.0039	30.1	0.100	972.0	26.2	69.	1.3399				1.100	1.100	90.72	6.6	0.067
3.50	1.0027	1.0045	35.1	0.117	967.6	30.6	80.	1.3410				1.121	1.120	89.05	7.4	0.076
4.00	1.0034	1.0057	40.1	0.133	963.3	34.9	92.	1.3422				1.142	1.140	87.42	8.2	0.084
4.50	1.0040	1.0058	45.2	0.150	958.8	39.4	103.	1.3433				1.163	1.161	85.79	8.9	0.092
5.00	1.0046	1.0064	50.2	0.167	954.4	43.8	115.	1.3445				1.187	1.184	84.07	9.6	0.099
5.50	1.0053	1.0071	55.3	0.184	950.0	48.2	126.	1.3456				1.211	1.207	82.41	10.2	0.106
6.00	1.0059	1.0077	60.4	0.201	945.5	52.7	138.	1.3468				1.237	1.232	80.69	10.8	0.113
6.50	1.0066	1.0084	65.4	0.217	941.2	57.0	149.	1.3479				1.263	1.257	79.03	11.4	0.120
7.00	1.0072	1.0090	70.5	0.234	936.7	61.5	160.	1.3490				1.291	1.284	77.33	11.9	0.126
7.50	1.0079	1.0097	75.6	0.251	932.3	65.9	172.	1.3502				1.319	1.311	75.68	12.5	0.132
8.00	1.0085	1.0103	80.7	0.268	927.8	70.4	183.	1.3513				1.348	1.339	74.05	13.0	0.138
8.50	1.0092	1.0110	85.8	0.285	923.4	74.8	195.	1.3525				1.379	1.369	72.38	13.6	0.144
9.00	1.0098	1.0116	90.9	0.302	918.9	79.3	206.	1.3536				1.410	1.399	70.79	14.0	0.149
9.50	1.0105	1.0123	96.0	0.319	914.5	83.7	218.	1.3548				1.441	1.429	69.25	14.4	0.154
10.00	1.0111	1.0129	101.1	0.336	910.0	88.2	229.	1.3559				1.477	1.464	67.56	14.7	0.158
11.00	1.0124	1.0142	111.4	0.370	901.0	97.2	252.	1.3582				1.548	1.532	64.48	15.8	0.170
12.00	1.0137	1.0155	121.6	0.404	892.1	106.1	275.	1.3605				1.623	1.604	61.50	16.8	0.182

92 TRICHLOROACETIC ACID, CCl$_3$COOH

MOLECULAR WEIGHT = 163.38
RELATIVE SPECIFIC REFRACTIVITY = 0.865

0.00 % by wt. data are the same for all compounds.
For Values of 0.00 wt. % solutions see Table 1, Acetic Acid.

A% by wt.	ρ D_4^{20}	D_{20}^{20}	C_s g/l	M g-mol/l	C_w g/l	$(C_0 - C_w)$ g/l	$(n - n_0)$ $\times 10^4$	n	Δ °C	O Os/kg	S g-mol/l	η/η_0	η/ρ cS	ϕ rhe	γ mmho/cm	T g-mol/l
0.50	1.0008	1.0026	5.0	0.031	995.8	2.4	7	1.3337	0.105	0.057	0.030	1.009	1.010	98.91	10.3	0.107
1.00	1.0034	1.0051	10.0	0.061	993.3	4.9	13	1.3343	0.211	0.113	0.060	1.019	1.018	97.94	19.6	0.215
2.00	1.0083	1.0101	20.2	0.123	988.2	10.1	26	1.3356	0.423	0.227	0.122	1.042	1.035	95.78	37.2	0.435
3.00	1.0133	1.0151	30.4	0.186	982.9	15.4	39	1.3369	0.638	0.343	0.185	1.067	1.055	93.53	54.0	0.656

92 TRICHLOROACETIC ACID, CCl₃COOH—(Continued)

A% by wt.	ρ D₄²⁰	D₂₀²⁰	C_s g/l	M g-mol/l	C_w g/l	(C_o − C_w) g/l	(n − n_o) × 10⁴	n	Δ °C	O Os/kg	S g-mol/l	η/η_o	η/ρ cS	φ rhe	γ mmho/cm	T g-mol/l
4.00	1.0182	1.0200	40.7	0.249	977.4	20.8	52	1.3381	0.857	0.461	0.250	1.094	1.077	91.24	69.8	0.880
5.00	1.0230	1.0248	51.2	0.313	971.9	26.4	64	1.3394	1.079	0.580	0.315	1.121	1.098	89.03	84.7	1.10
6.00	1.0279	1.0297	61.7	0.377	966.2	32.0	76	1.3406	1.303	0.700	0.381	1.148	1.119	86.95	99.	1.33
7.00	1.0328	1.0346	72.3	0.443	960.5	37.7	89	1.3418	1.529	0.822	0.447	1.175	1.140	84.95	113.	1.57
8.00	1.0378	1.0396	83.0	0.508	954.8	43.5	101	1.3431	1.758	0.945	0.514	1.202	1.161	83.01	125.	1.80
9.00	1.0428	1.0446	93.9	0.574	948.9	49.3	114	1.3444	1.992	1.071	0.582	1.231	1.182	81.10	137.	2.04
10.00	1.0479	1.0497	104.8	0.641	943.1	55.1	126	1.3456	2.233	1.201	0.652	1.260	1.205	79.21	148.	2.28
12.00	1.0583	1.0602	127.0	0.777	931.3	66.9	153	1.3483	2.734	1.470	0.796	1.323	1.252	75.44	169.	2.76
14.00	1.0692	1.0710	149.7	0.916	919.5	78.8	180	1.3510	3.261	1.753	0.945	1.390	1.302	71.81	186.	3.24
16.00	1.0806	1.0825	172.9	1.058	907.7	90.6	209	1.3539	3.815	2.051	1.100	1.459	1.353	68.41	200.	3.73
18.00	1.0921	1.0941	196.6	1.203	895.5	102.7	239	1.3568				1.530	1.404	65.21	211.	4.22
20.00	1.1035	1.1055	220.7	1.351	882.8	115.4	267	1.3597				1.605	1.457	62.18	221.	4.90
24.00	1.1260	1.1280	270.2	1.654	855.8	142.5	322	1.3652				1.764	1.570	56.58		
28.00	1.1485	1.1505	321.6	1.968	826.9	171.3	376	1.3705				1.931	1.685	51.68		
32.00	1.1713	1.1734	374.8	2.294	796.5	201.8	429	1.3759				2.114	1.808	47.22		
36.00	1.1947	1.1968	430.1	2.633	764.6	233.6	483	1.3813				2.315	1.942	43.11		
40.00	1.2188	1.2210	487.5	2.984	731.3	266.9	538	1.3868				2.540	2.088	39.29		
44.00	1.2435	1.2457	547.1	3.349	696.3	301.9	593	1.3923				2.791	2.249	35.75		
48.00	1.2682	1.2704	608.7	3.726	659.5	338.8	647	1.3977				3.070	2.425	32.51		
50.00	1.2803	1.2826	640.2	3.918	640.2	358.1	673	1.4003				3.219	2.519	31.00		

93 TRIS(HYDROXYMETHYL)AMINOMETHANE,* THAM,® H₂NC(CH₂OH)₃

MOLECULAR WEIGHT = 121.14
RELATIVE SPECIFIC REFRACTIVITY = 1.169

0.00 % by wt. data are the same for all compounds.
For Values of 0.00 wt. % solutions see Table 1, Acetic Acid.

A% by wt.	ρ D₄²⁰	D₂₀²⁰	C_s g/l	M g-mol/l	C_w g/l	(C_o − C_w) g/l	(n − n_o) × 10⁴	n	Δ °C	O Os/kg	S g-mol/l	η/η_o	η/ρ cS	φ rhe	γ mmho/cm	T g-mol/l
0.50	0.9994	1.0012	5.0	0.041	994.4	3.8	7	1.3337	0.080	0.043	0.022	1.012	1.015	98.59		
1.00	1.0006	1.0024	10.0	0.083	990.6	7.6	15	1.3344	0.159	0.085	0.045	1.025	1.026	97.37		
2.00	1.0030	1.0048	20.1	0.166	982.9	15.3	29	1.3359	0.314	0.169	0.090	1.052	1.051	94.87		
3.00	1.0054	1.0072	30.2	0.249	975.2	23.0	44	1.3374	0.473	0.254	0.137	1.081	1.078	92.29		
4.00	1.0078	1.0096	40.3	0.333	967.5	30.7	58	1.3388	0.636	0.342	0.185	1.113	1.106	89.67		
5.00	1.0103	1.0121	50.5	0.417	959.8	38.4	73	1.3403	0.804	0.432	0.234	1.146	1.137	87.09		
6.00	1.0128	1.0146	60.8	0.502	952.0	46.2	88	1.3418	0.974	0.524	0.284	1.180	1.168	84.57		
7.00	1.0153	1.0171	71.1	0.587	944.3	54.0	103	1.3433	1.149	0.618	0.336	1.216	1.200	82.10		
8.00	1.0179	1.0197	81.4	0.672	936.4	61.8	118	1.3448	1.328	0.714	0.388	1.253	1.233	79.66		
9.00	1.0204	1.0222	91.8	0.758	928.6	69.6	133	1.3463	1.510	0.812	0.442	1.292	1.269	77.24		
10.00	1.0230	1.0248	102.3	0.844	920.7	77.5	148	1.3478	1.696	0.912	0.496	1.334	1.307	74.81		
12.00	1.0282	1.0301	123.4	1.019	904.8	93.4	178	1.3508	2.076	1.116	0.606	1.424	1.388	70.09		
14.00	1.0335	1.0354	144.7	1.194	888.8	109.4	209	1.3539	2.473	1.329	0.721	1.524	1.478	65.48		
16.00	1.0389	1.0407	166.2	1.372	872.7	125.6	240	1.3570	2.899	1.559	0.843	1.639	1.581	60.88		
18.00	1.0443	1.0462	188.0	1.552	856.4	141.9	271	1.3601	3.357	1.805	0.972	1.768	1.696	56.45		
20.00	1.0498	1.0517	210.0	1.733	839.9	158.4	303	1.3633	3.847	2.068	1.109	1.916	1.829	52.09		
22.00	1.0554	1.0572	232.2	1.917	823.2	175.0	335	1.3665				2.079	1.974	48.00		
24.00	1.0610	1.0628	254.6	2.102	806.3	191.9	367	1.3697				2.256	2.131	44.23		
26.00	1.0666	1.0685	277.3	2.289	789.3	208.9	400	1.3730				2.459	2.310	40.59		
28.00	1.0723	1.0742	300.2	2.479	772.1	226.2	433	1.3763				2.700	2.523	36.97		
30.00	1.0781	1.0800	323.4	2.670	754.6	243.6	467	1.3797				2.992	2.781	33.36		
32.00	1.0839	1.0858	346.8	2.863	737.0	261.2	501	1.3831				3.337	3.085	29.91		
34.00	1.0897	1.0916	370.5	3.058	719.2	279.0	535	1.3865				3.729	3.429	26.76		
36.00	1.0956	1.0976	394.4	3.256	701.2	297.0	570	1.3900				4.169	3.812	23.94		
38.00	1.1016	1.1035	418.6	3.456	683.0	315.2	605	1.3935				4.658	4.237	21.43		
40.00	1.1076	1.1096	443.1	3.657	664.6	333.6	640	1.3970				5.198	4.702	19.20		

* 1,2-Propanediol, 2-amino-2(hydroxymethyl).   ®Registered trademark.

94 UREA, NH₂CONH₂

MOLECULAR WEIGHT = 60.06
RELATIVE SPECIFIC REFRACTIVITY = 1.147

0.00 % by wt. data are the same for all compounds.
For Values of 0.00 wt. % solutions see Table 1, Acetic Acid.

A% by wt.	ρ D₄²⁰	D₂₀²⁰	C_s g/l	M g-mol/l	C_w g/l	(C_o − C_w) g/l	(n − n_o) × 10⁴	n	Δ °C	O Os/kg	S g-mol/l	η/η_o	η/ρ cS	φ rhe	γ mmho/cm	T g-mol/l
0.50	0.9995	1.0012	5.0	0.083	994.5	3.8	7	1.3337	0.155	0.083	0.044	1.005	1.007	99.33		
1.00	1.0007	1.0025	10.0	0.167	990.7	7.5	14	1.3344	0.310	0.167	0.089	1.008	1.009	99.01		
1.50	1.0020	1.0038	15.0	0.250	987.0	11.3	21	1.3351	0.465	0.250	0.134	1.009	1.009	98.89		
2.00	1.0033	1.0050	20.1	0.334	983.2	15.0	28	1.3358	0.620	0.333	0.180	1.010	1.009	98.81		
2.50	1.0045	1.0063	25.1	0.418	979.4	18.8	35	1.3365	0.775	0.417	0.226	1.012	1.010	98.60		
3.00	1.0058	1.0076	30.2	0.502	975.7	22.6	42	1.3372	0.928	0.499	0.271	1.015	1.011	98.30		
3.50	1.0071	1.0089	35.3	0.587	971.9	26.3	50	1.3379	1.082	0.582	0.316	1.019	1.014	97.95		
4.00	1.0085	1.0102	40.3	0.672	968.1	30.1	57	1.3387	1.237	0.665	0.362	1.023	1.016	97.56		
4.50	1.0098	1.0116	45.4	0.757	964.3	33.9	64	1.3394	1.393	0.749	0.407	1.027	1.019	97.17		
5.00	1.0111	1.0129	50.6	0.842	960.6	37.7	71	1.3401	1.552	0.835	0.454	1.031	1.022	96.80		
5.50	1.0125	1.0142	55.7	0.927	956.8	41.5	79	1.3409	1.715	0.922	0.501	1.035	1.024	96.45		
6.00	1.0138	1.0156	60.8	1.013	953.0	45.3	86	1.3416	1.880	1.011	0.550	1.039	1.027	96.09		
6.50	1.0151	1.0169	66.0	1.099	949.2	49.1	93	1.3423	2.048	1.101	0.598	1.043	1.029	95.72		
7.00	1.0165	1.0183	71.2	1.185	945.4	52.9	101	1.3431	2.218	1.192	0.648	1.047	1.032	95.35		
7.50	1.0179	1.0197	76.3	1.271	941.5	56.7	108	1.3438	2.389	1.285	0.697	1.051	1.034	94.98		
8.00	1.0192	1.0210	81.5	1.358	937.7	60.5	116	1.3446	2.562	1.378	0.747	1.055	1.037	94.60		
8.50	1.0206	1.0224	86.8	1.444	933.9	64.4	123	1.3453	2.737	1.471	0.797	1.059	1.040	94.23		

94 UREA, NH$_2$CONH$_2$—(Continued)

A% by wt.	ρ D_4^{20}	D_{20}^{20}	C_s g/l	M g-mol/l	C_w g/l	$(C_o - C_w)$ g/l	$(n - n_o)$ × 10⁴	n	Δ °C	O Os/kg	S g-mol/l	η/η_u	η/ρ cS	ϕ rhe	γ mmho/cm	T g-mol/l
9.00	1.0220	1.0238	92.0	1.531	930.0	68.2	131	1.3461	2.911	1.565	0.846	1.063	1.043	93.85		
9.50	1.0234	1.0252	97.2	1.619	926.2	72.1	138	1.3468	3.086	1.659	0.896	1.068	1.045	93.47		
10.00	1.0248	1.0266	102.5	1.706	922.3	75.9	146	1.3476	3.260	1.753	0.945	1.072	1.048	93.10		
11.00	1.0276	1.0294	113.0	1.882	914.5	83.7	161	1.3491	3.606	1.939	1.042	1.081	1.054	92.36		
12.00	1.0304	1.0322	123.6	2.059	906.7	91.5	176	1.3506	3.952	2.125	1.138	1.089	1.059	91.64		
13.00	1.0332	1.0350	134.3	2.236	898.9	99.4	192	1.3521	4.301	2.312	1.234	1.098	1.065	90.91		
14.00	1.0360	1.0378	145.0	2.415	891.0	107.3	207	1.3537	4.656	2.503	1.332	1.107	1.071	90.15		
15.00	1.0388	1.0407	155.8	2.594	883.0	115.2	222	1.3552	5.02	2.70	1.430	1.117	1.077	89.35		
16.00	1.0417	1.0435	166.7	2.775	875.0	123.2	238	1.3568	5.40	2.90	1.531	1.128	1.085	88.50		
17.00	1.0445	1.0463	177.6	2.956	866.9	131.3	253	1.3583	5.79	3.11	1.633	1.139	1.093	87.62		
18.00	1.0473	1.0492	188.5	3.139	858.8	139.4	269	1.3599	6.19	3.33	1.736	1.151	1.101	86.72		
19.00	1.0502	1.0520	199.5	3.322	850.6	147.6	284	1.3614	6.59	3.54	1.839	1.163	1.110	85.80		
20.00	1.0530	1.0549	210.6	3.506	842.4	155.8	300	1.3629	7.00	3.76	1.941	1.176	1.119	84.86		
22.00	1.0586	1.0605	232.9	3.878	825.7	172.5	331	1.3661	7.81	4.20	2.141	1.203	1.139	82.93		
24.00	1.0643	1.0662	255.4	4.253	808.9	189.4	362	1.3692	8.64	4.65	2.339	1.233	1.161	80.95		
26.00	1.0699	1.0718	278.2	4.632	791.7	206.5	393	1.3723	9.52	5.12	2.543	1.263	1.183	79.00		
28.00	1.0756	1.0775	301.2	5.014	774.4	223.8	424	1.3754	10.45	5.62	2.751	1.295	1.206	77.09		
30.00	1.0812	1.0831	324.4	5.401	756.8	241.4	455	1.3785	11.40	6.13	2.955	1.329	1.232	75.09		
32.00	1.0869	1.0888	347.8	5.791	739.1	259.2	487	1.3817	12.34	6.63	3.150	1.368	1.261	72.97		
34.00	1.0926	1.0945	371.5	6.185	721.1	277.1	518	1.3848	13.27	7.14	3.337	1.410	1.293	70.77		
36.00	1.0984	1.1004	395.4	6.584	703.0	295.2	551	1.3881	14.20	7.63	3.516	1.456	1.329	68.52		
38.00	1.1044	1.1064	419.7	6.988	684.7	313.5	583	1.3913	15.11	8.12	3.686	1.506	1.367	66.26		
40.00	1.1106	1.1126	444.2	7.397	666.4	331.9	617	1.3947	15.99	8.60	3.845	1.562	1.409	63.89		
42.00	1.1171	1.1191	469.2	7.812	647.9	350.3	652	1.3982	16.83	9.05	3.993	1.626	1.458	61.40		
44.00	1.1239	1.1259	494.5	8.234	629.4	368.8	688	1.4018	17.62	9.47	4.127	1.697	1.512	58.83		
46.00	1.1313	1.1333	520.4	8.665	610.9	387.3	726	1.4056				1.776	1.573	56.21		

95 URINE, CAT

RELATIVE SPECIFIC REFRACTIVITY = 1.08

0.00 % by wt. data are the same for all compounds.
For Values of 0.00 wt. % solutions see Table 1, Acetic Acid.

A% by wt.	ρ D_4^{20}	D_{20}^{20}	C_s g/l	C_w g/l	$(C_o - C_w)$ g/l	$(n - n_o)$ × 10⁴	n
0.50	1.000	1.002	5	995	3	8	1.3338
1.00	1.002	1.004	10	992	6	16	1.3346
1.50	1.004	1.006	15	989	9	24	1.3354
2.00	1.006	1.008	20	986	12	33	1.3363
2.50	1.008	1.010	25	983	15	41	1.3371
3.00	1.010	1.012	30	979	19	49	1.3379
3.50	1.011	1.013	35	976	22	57	1.3387
4.00	1.013	1.015	41	973	25	65	1.3395
4.50	1.015	1.017	46	970	28	73	1.3403
5.00	1.017	1.019	51	966	32	81	1.3411
5.50	1.019	1.021	56	963	35	89	1.3419
6.00	1.021	1.023	61	960	38	97	1.3427
6.50	1.023	1.025	67	956	42	105	1.3435
7.00	1.025	1.027	72	953	45	113	1.3443
7.50	1.026	1.028	77	950	48	121	1.3451
8.00	1.028	1.030	82	946	52	129	1.3459
8.50	1.030	1.032	88	943	55	136	1.3466
9.00	1.032	1.034	93	939	59	144	1.3474
9.50	1.034	1.036	98	936	62	152	1.3482
10.00	1.036	1.038	104	932	66	160	1.3490
11.00	1.039	1.041	114	925	73	175	1.3505
12.00	1.043	1.045	125	918	80	191	1.3521
13.00	1.047	1.049	136	911	87	206	1.3536
14.00	1.050	1.052	147	903	95	222	1.3552
15.00	1.054	1.056	158	896	102	237	1.3567
16.00	1.058	1.060	169	888	110	252	1.3582
17.00	1.061	1.063	180	881	117	267	1.3597
18.00	1.065	1.067	192	873	125	282	1.3612
19.00	1.068	1.070	203	865	133	296	1.3626
20.00	1.072	1.074	214	857	141	311	1.3641

96 URINE, GUINEA PIG

RELATIVE SPECIFIC REFRACTIVITIES: CLEAR* = 0.984, TURBID = 0.955

0.00 % by wt. data are the same for all compounds.
For Values of 0.00 wt. % solutions see Table 1, Acetic Acid.

	CLEAR								TURBID				
A% by wt.	ρ D_4^{20}	D_{20}^{20}	C_s g/l	C_w g/l	$(C_o - C_w)$ g/l	$(n - n_o)$ × 10⁴	n	A% by wt.	ρ D_4^{20}	D_{20}^{20}	C_s g/l	C_w g/l	$(C_o - C_w)$ g/l
0.5	1.001	1.002	5	996	2	8	1.3338	0.5	1.001	1.002	5	996	2
1.0	1.003	1.005	10	993	5	16	1.3346	1.0	1.003	1.005	10	993	5
1.5	1.005	1.007	15	990	8	23	1.3353	1.5	1.005	1.007	15	990	8
2.0	1.008	1.009	20	988	10	31	1.3361	2.1	1.008	1.010	21	987	11
2.5	1.010	1.012	25	985	13	39	1.3369	2.6	1.010	1.012	26	984	14
3.0	1.012	1.014	30	982	16	47	1.3377	3.1	1.013	1.015	31	982	16

* Cleared by centrifuging 15 minutes at 25,000 G.

	CLEAR								TURBID				
A % by wt.	$\rho\ D_4^{20}$	D_{20}^{20}	C_s g/l	C_w g/l	$(C_o - C_w)$ g/l	$(n - n_o)$ $\times 10^4$	n	A % by wt.	$\rho\ D_4^{20}$	D_{20}^{20}	C_s g/l	C_w g/l	$(C_o - C_w)$ g/l
3.5	1.015	1.016	36	979	19	55	1.3385	3.6	1.015	1.017	37	978	20
4.0	1.017	1.019	41	976	22	63	1.3393	4.1	1.018	1.020	42	976	22
4.5	1.019	1.021	46	973	25	70	1.3400	4.6	1.020	1.022	47	973	25
5.0	1.022	1.024	51	971	27	78	1.3408	5.2	1.023	1.025	53	970	28
5.5	1.024	1.026	56	968	30	86	1.3416	5.7	1.026	1.027	58	968	30
6.0	1.026	1.028	62	964	34	94	1.3424	6.2	1.029	1.030	64	965	33
6.5	1.029	1.031	67	962	36	102	1.3432	6.7	1.031	1.032	69	962	36
7.0	1.031	1.033	72	959	39	110	1.3440	7.2	1.034	1.035	74	960	38
7.5	1.033	1.035	77	956	42	117	1.3447	7.8	1.036	1.038	81	955	43
8.0	1.036	1.038	83	953	45	125	1.3455	8.3	1.038	1.040	86	952	46
8.5	1.038	1.040	88	950	48	133	1.3463	8.8	1.040	1.042	92	948	50
9.0	1.040	1.042	94	946	52	141	1.3471	9.3	1.043	1.045	97	946	52
9.5	1.043	1.045	99	944	54	149	1.3479	9.8	1.046	1.047	103	943	55
10.0	1.045	1.047	104	941	57	157	1.3487	10.3	1.049	1.050	108	941	57
11.0	1.050	1.052	116	934	64	172	1.3502	11.4	1.054	1.055	120	934	64
12.0	1.054	1.056	126	928	70	188	1.3518	12.4	1.058	1.060	131	927	71
13.0	1.059	1.061	138	921	77	204	1.3534	13.4	1.064	1.066	143	921	77
14.0	1.064	1.066	149	915	83	220	1.3550	14.5	1.069	1.071	155	914	84
15.0	1.069	1.070	160	909	89	235	1.3565	15.5	1.074	1.076	166	908	90
16.0	1.073	1.075	172	901	97	251	1.3581	16.5	1.078	1.080	178	900	98
17.0	1.078	1.080	183	895	103	266	1.3596	17.6	1.084	1.086	191	893	105
18.0	1.083	1.085	195	888	110	282	1.3612	18.6	1.089	1.091	203	886	112
19.0	1.087	1.089	207	880	118	298	1.3628	19.6	1.094	1.096	214	880	118
20.0	1.092	1.094	218	874	124	314	1.3644	20.7	1.099	1.101	227	872	126

97 URINE, HUMAN

RELATIVE SPECIFIC REFRACTIVITY = 1.02

0.00 % by wt. data are the same for all compounds.
For Values of 0.00 wt. % solutions see Table 1, Acetic Acid.

A % by wt.	$\rho\ D_4^{20}$	D_{20}^{20}	C_s g/l	C_w g/l	$(C_o - C_w)$ g/l	$(n - n_o)$ $\times 10^4$	n
0.50	1.000	1.002	5	996	2	8	1.3338
1.00	1.003	1.005	10	993	5	16	1.3346
1.50	1.005	1.007	15	990	8	24	1.3354
2.00	1.007	1.009	20	987	11	32	1.3362
2.50	1.009	1.011	24	984	14	40	1.3370
3.00	1.012	1.014	31	981	17	47	1.3377
3.50	1.014	1.016	36	978	20	55	1.3385
4.00	1.016	1.018	41	975	23	63	1.3393
4.50	1.018	1.020	46	972	26	71	1.3401
5.00	1.020	1.022	51	969	29	78	1.3408
5.50	1.022	1.024	56	966	32	86	1.3416
6.00	1.024	1.026	61	962	36	94	1.3424
6.50	1.026	1.028	67	959	39	101	1.3431
7.00	1.027	1.029	72	956	42	109	1.3439
7.50	1.029	1.031	77	952	46	116	1.3446
8.00	1.031	1.033	83	949	49	123	1.3453
8.50	1.033	1.035	88	945	53	131	1.3461
9.00	1.034	1.036	93	941	57	138	1.3468
9.50	1.036	1.038	98	937	61	145	1.3475
10.00	1.037	1.039	104	934	64	152	1.3482

98 URINE, RABBIT

RELATIVE SPECIFIC REFRACTIVITIES: CLEAR* = 0.997; TURBID = 0.958

0.00 % by wt. data are the same for all compounds.
For Values of 0.00 wt. % solutions see Table 1, Acetic Acid.

	CLEAR								TURBID				
A % by wt.	$\rho\ D_4^{20}$	D_{20}^{20}	C_s g/l	C_w g/l	$(C_o - C_w)$ g/l	$(n - n_o)$ $\times 10^4$	n	A % by wt.	$\rho\ D_4^{20}$	D_{20}^{20}	C_s g/l	C_w g/l	$(C_o - C_w)$ g/l
0.5	1.000	1.002	5	995	3	7	1.3337	0.6	1.002	1.003	6	996	2
1.0	1.003	1.004	10	993	5	15	1.3345	1.1	1.003	1.005	11	992	6
1.5	1.005	1.007	15	990	8	22	1.3352	1.7	1.006	1.008	17	989	9
2.0	1.007	1.009	20	987	11	30	1.3360	2.2	1.008	1.010	22	986	12
2.5	1.009	1.011	25	984	14	38	1.3368	2.7	1.011	1.012	27	984	14
3.0	1.011	1.013	30	981	17	45	1.3375	3.2	1.013	1.014	32	981	17
3.5	1.014	1.015	35	979	19	53	1.3383	3.8	1.016	1.017	39	977	21
4.0	1.016	1.018	41	975	23	60	1.3390	4.3	1.018	1.019	44	974	24
4.5	1.018	1.020	46	972	26	68	1.3398	4.9	1.020	1.021	50	970	28
5.0	1.020	1.022	51	969	29	76	1.3406	5.4	1.022	1.024	55	967	31
5.5	1.022	1.024	56	966	32	83	1.3413	5.9	1.024	1.026	60	964	34
6.0	1.025	1.026	62	963	35	91	1.3421	6.5	1.027	1.029	67	960	38
6.5	1.027	1.029	67	960	38	98	1.3428	7.0	1.029	1.031	72	957	41

* Cleared by centrifuging 15 minutes at 25,000 G.

	CLEAR								TURBID				
A% by wt.	ρ D_4^{20}	D_{20}^{20}	C_s g/l	C_w g/l	$(C_o - C_w)$ g/l	$(n - n_o) \times 10^4$	n	A% by wt.	ρ D_4^{20}	D_{20}^{20}	C_s g/l	C_w g/l	$(C_o - C_w)$ g/l
7.0	1.029	1.031	72	957	41	106	1.3436	7.5	1.032	1.034	77	955	43
7.5	1.031	1.033	77	954	44	113	1.3443	8.0	1.034	1.036	83	951	47
8.0	1.033	1.035	83	950	48	121	1.3451	8.6	1.037	1.039	89	948	50
8.5	1.036	1.037	88	948	50	128	1.3458	9.1	1.039	1.041	95	944	54
9.0	1.038	1.040	93	945	53	136	1.3466	9.7	1.042	1.044	101	941	57
9.5	1.040	1.042	99	941	57	143	1.3473	10.2	1.044	1.046	106	938	60
10.0	1.042	1.044	104	938	60	151	1.3481	10.8	1.047	1.049	113	934	64
11.0	1.046	1.048	115	931	67	166	1.3496	11.8	1.051	1.053	124	927	71
12.0	1.051	1.053	126	925	73	181	1.3511	12.9	1.056	1.058	136	920	78
13.0	1.055	1.057	137	918	80	196	1.3526	14.0	1.061	1.063	149	912	86
14.0	1.060	1.062	148	912	86	211	1.3541	15.1	1.066	1.068	161	905	93
15.0	1.064	1.066	160	904	94	226	1.3556	16.2	1.071	1.073	174	897	101
16.0	1.068	1.070	171	897	101	242	1.3572	17.2	1.076	1.077	185	891	107
17.0	1.073	1.075	182	891	107	257	1.3587	18.3	1.080	1.082	198	882	116

99 ZINC SULFATE, $ZnSO_4 \cdot 7H_2O$

MOLECULAR WEIGHT = 161.44   FORMULA WEIGHT, HYDRATE = 287.56

RELATIVE SPECIFIC REFRACTIVITY = 0.493

0.00 % by wt. data are the same for all compounds.
For Values of 0.00 wt. % solutions see Table 1, Acetic Acid.

A% by wt.	H% by wt.	ρ D_4^{20}	D_{20}^{20}	C_s g/l	M g-mol/l	C_w g/l	$(C_o - C_w)$ g/l	$(n - n_o) \times 10^4$	n	Δ °C	O Os/kg	S g-mol/l	η/η_o	η/ρ cS	ϕ rhe	γ mmho/cm	T g-mol/l
0.50	0.89	1.0034	1.0051	5.0	0.031	998.3	-0.1	9	1.3339	0.079	0.043	0.022	1.019	1.017	97.97	2.8	0.028
1.00	1.78	1.0085	1.0103	10.1	0.062	998.4	-0.2	18	1.3348	0.150	0.081	0.042	1.038	1.031	96.15	5.4	0.054
1.50	2.67	1.0137	1.0155	15.2	0.094	998.5	-0.3	27	1.3357	0.217	0.117	0.062	1.058	1.046	94.32	7.8	0.080
2.00	3.56	1.0190	1.0208	20.4	0.126	998.6	-0.4	36	1.3366	0.282	0.152	0.081	1.079	1.061	92.49	10.0	0.104
2.50	4.45	1.0243	1.0261	25.6	0.159	998.7	-0.4	45	1.3375	0.346	0.186	0.099	1.101	1.077	90.65	12.1	0.127
3.00	5.34	1.0296	1.0314	30.9	0.191	998.7	-0.5	54	1.3384	0.408	0.219	0.118	1.124	1.094	88.80	13.9	0.148
3.50	6.23	1.0349	1.0368	36.2	0.224	998.7	-0.5	64	1.3393	0.470	0.253	0.136	1.148	1.111	86.94	15.7	0.169
4.00	7.12	1.0403	1.0421	41.6	0.258	998.7	-0.5	73	1.3403	0.531	0.286	0.154	1.173	1.130	85.10	17.3	0.188
4.50	8.02	1.0457	1.0475	47.1	0.291	998.6	-0.4	82	1.3412	0.591	0.318	0.172	1.198	1.148	83.27	18.9	0.207
5.00	8.91	1.0511	1.0530	52.6	0.326	998.5	0.3	91	1.3421	0.651	0.350	0.189	1.225	1.168	81.47	20.5	0.226
5.50	9.80	1.0565	1.0584	58.1	0.360	998.4	-0.2	100	1.3430	0.711	0.382	0.207	1.252	1.188	79.70	22.0	0.245
6.00	10.69	1.0620	1.0639	63.7	0.395	998.3	0.0	109	1.3439	0.772	0.415	0.225	1.280	1.208	77.98	23.5	0.263
6.50	11.58	1.0675	1.0694	69.4	0.430	998.1	0.1	118	1.3448	0.833	0.448	0.243	1.308	1.228	76.28	24.9	0.280
7.00	12.47	1.0730	1.0749	75.1	0.465	997.9	0.3	127	1.3457	0.893	0.480	0.260	1.338	1.249	74.60	26.3	0.297
7.50	13.36	1.0786	1.0805	80.9	0.501	997.7	0.5	136	1.3466	0.953	0.512	0.278	1.368	1.271	72.95	27.6	0.314
8.00	14.25	1.0842	1.0861	86.7	0.537	997.5	0.8	146	1.3475	1.013	0.544	0.296	1.400	1.294	71.30	28.9	0.330
8.50	15.14	1.0899	1.0918	92.6	0.574	997.2	1.0	155	1.3485	1.073	0.577	0.313	1.433	1.317	69.65	30.1	0.345
9.00	16.03	1.0956	1.0975	98.6	0.611	997.0	1.3	164	1.3494	1.136	0.611	0.332	1.467	1.342	68.01	31.3	0.360
9.50	16.92	1.1013	1.1032	104.6	0.648	996.7	1.6	173	1.3503	1.200	0.645	0.351	1.504	1.368	66.37	32.5	0.375
10.00	17.81	1.1071	1.1091	110.7	0.686	996.4	1.8	183	1.3513	1.267	0.681	0.370	1.542	1.396	64.72	33.7	0.390
11.00	19.59	1.1188	1.1208	123.1	0.762	995.8	2.5	202	1.3532	1.407	0.756	0.411	1.624	1.454	61.45	35.9	0.418
12.00	21.37	1.1308	1.1328	135.7	0.841	995.1	3.1	221	1.3551	1.553	0.835	0.454	1.713	1.518	58.25	38.0	0.445
13.00	23.16	1.1429	1.1450	148.6	0.920	994.4	3.9	241	1.3570	1.711	0.920	0.500	1.810	1.587	55.14	39.9	0.470
14.00	24.94	1.1553	1.1573	161.7	1.002	993.6	4.7	260	1.3590	1.889	1.015	0.552	1.914	1.660	52.14	41.7	0.492
15.00	26.72	1.1679	1.1699	175.2	1.085	992.7	5.6	280	1.3610	2.087	1.122	0.610	2.027	1.739	49.24	43.3	0.513
16.00	28.50	1.1806	1.1827	188.9	1.170	991.7	6.5	300	1.3630	2.306	1.240	0.673	2.148	1.823	46.46	44.6	0.531

OSMOTIC PARAMETERS AND ELECTRICAL CONDUCTIVITIES OF AQUEOUS SOLUTIONS

For any aqueous solutions within the range, the two right hand columns provide values for either condosity (T) or specific conductance (γ) where the other value is given; the three left hand columns provide values for freezing point depression (Δ), osmolality (O) or osmosity (S) where any one of these values is given. Values in all four columns are interconvertible *only* for solutions of sodium chloride, in which case, by definition, osmosity, molarity (M) and condosity are always equal. Other concentrative properties of specific solutions may be found in conversion tables on preceding pages.

Table columns are:

Δ = freezing point depression, °C

O = osmolality ($= \Delta/1.86$, Os/kg

S = osmosity, molar concentration of NaCl solution having same freezing point or osmotic pressure as given solution, g-mol/1

M = molarity of NaCl solution, g-mol/1

T = condosity, molar concentration of NaCl solution having same specific conductance at 20°C as given solution, g-mol/1

γ = specific conductance (electrical) at 20°C, mmho/cm.

Δ °C	O Os/Kg	S,M,T, g-mol/l	γ mmho/cm	Δ °C	O Os/Kg	S,M,T, g-mol/l	γ mmho/cm
0.000	0.000	0.000	0.0	1.881	1.011	0.550	46.1
0.037	0.020	0.010	1.0	1.916	1.030	0.560	46.8
0.072	0.039	0.020	2.0	1.950	1.048	0.570	47.6
0.107	0.057	0.030	3.0	1.985	1.067	0.580	48.3
0.142	0.076	0.040	4.0	2.019	1.086	0.590	49.1
0.176	0.095	0.050	5.0	2.054	1.104	0.600	49.8
0.211	0.113	0.060	5.9	2.088	1.123	0.610	50.6
0.245	0.132	0.070	6.9	2.123	1.141	0.620	51.3
0.279	0.150	0.080	7.8	2.157	1.160	0.630	52.0
0.314	0.169	0.090	8.7	2.192	1.178	0.640	52.8
0.348	0.187	0.100	9.7	2.226	1.197	0.650	53.5
0.382	0.205	0.110	10.6	2.261	1.216	0.660	54.2
0.416	0.224	0.120	11.4	2.296	1.234	0.670	55.0
0.450	0.242	0.130	12.3	2.330	1.253	0.680	55.7
0.484	0.260	0.140	13.2	2.365	1.271	0.690	56.4
0.518	0.279	0.150	14.1	2.400	1.290	0.700	57.1
0.552	0.297	0.160	14.9	2.434	1.309	0.710	57.9
0.586	0.315	0.170	15.8	2.469	1.328	0.720	58.6
0.620	0.333	0.180	16.6	2.504	1.346	0.730	59.3
0.654	0.352	0.190	17.5	2.539	1.365	0.740	60.0
0.688	0.370	0.200	18.3	2.574	1.384	0.750	60.7
0.722	0.388	0.210	19.2	2.609	1.403	0.760	61.4
0.756	0.407	0.220	20.0	2.644	1.421	0.770	62.1
0.790	0.425	0.230	20.8	2.679	1.440	0.780	62.9
0.824	0.443	0.240	21.6	2.714	1.459	0.790	63.6
0.858	0.461	0.250	22.4	2.749	1.478	0.800	64.3
0.892	0.480	0.260	23.3	2.784	1.497	0.810	65.0
0.926	0.498	0.270	24.1	2.819	1.515	0.820	65.7
0.960	0.516	0.280	24.9	2.854	1.534	0.830	66.3
0.994	0.534	0.290	25.7	2.889	1.553	0.840	67.0
1.028	0.553	0.300	26.5	2.924	1.572	0.850	67.7
1.062	0.571	0.310	27.3	2.959	1.591	0.860	68.4
1.096	0.589	0.320	28.1	2.995	1.610	0.870	69.1
1.130	0.607	0.330	28.9	3.030	1.629	0.880	69.8
1.164	0.626	0.340	29.7	3.065	1.648	0.890	70.5
1.198	0.644	0.350	30.5	3.101	1.667	0.900	71.2
1.232	0.662	0.360	31.3	3.136	1.686	0.910	71.8
1.266	0.681	0.370	32.1	3.171	1.705	0.920	72.5
1.300	0.699	0.380	32.9	3.207	1.724	0.930	73.2
1.334	0.717	0.390	33.7	3.242	1.743	0.940	73.9
1.368	0.736	0.400	34.4	3.278	1.762	0.950	74.5
1.402	0.754	0.410	35.2	3.313	1.781	0.960	75.2
1.436	0.772	0.420	36.0	3.349	1.801	0.970	75.9
1.470	0.791	0.430	36.8	3.385	1.820	0.980	76.5
1.505	0.809	0.440	37.6	3.420	1.839	0.990	77.2
1.539	0.827	0.450	38.4	3.456	1.858	1.000	77.8
1.573	0.846	0.460	39.2	3.492	1.877	1.010	78.5
1.607	0.864	0.470	39.9	3.527	1.896	1.020	79.2
1.641	0.882	0.480	40.7	3.563	1.916	1.030	79.8
1.676	0.901	0.490	41.5	3.599	1.935	1.040	80.5
1.710	0.919	0.500	42.3	3.635	1.954	1.050	81.1
1.744	0.938	0.510	43.0	3.671	1.974	1.060	81.8
1.778	0.956	0.520	43.8	3.707	1.993	1.070	82.4
1.813	0.975	0.530	44.6	3.743	2.012	1.080	83.1
1.847	0.993	0.540	45.3	3.779	2.032	1.090	83.7

Δ °C	O Os/Kg	S,M,T, g-mol/l	γ mmho/cm	Δ °C	O Os/Kg	S,M,T, g-mol/l	γ mmho/cm
3.815	2.051	1.100	84.3	5.86	3.15	1.650	117
3.851	2.070	1.110	85.0	5.89	3.17	1.660	117
3.887	2.090	1.120	85.6	5.93	3.19	1.670	118
3.923	2.109	1.130	86.2	5.97	3.21	1.680	119
3.959	2.129	1.140	86.9	6.01	3.23	1.690	119
3.995	2.148	1.150	87.5	6.05	3.25	1.700	120
4.032	2.168	1.160	88.1	6.09	3.27	1.710	120
4.068	2.187	1.170	88.8	6.13	3.29	1.720	121
4.104	2.207	1.180	89.4	6.16	3.31	1.730	121
4.141	2.226	1.190	90.0	6.20	3.34	1.740	122
4.177	2.246	1.200	90.6	6.24	3.36	1.750	122
4.214	2.265	1.210	91.3	6.28	3.38	1.760	123
4.250	2.285	1.220	91.9	6.32	3.40	1.770	123
4.287	2.305	1.230	92.5	6.36	3.42	1.780	124
4.323	2.324	1.240	93.1	6.40	3.44	1.790	125
4.360	2.344	1.250	93.7	6.44	3.46	1.800	125
4.393	2.362	1.260	94.3	6.48	3.48	1.810	126
4.429	2.381	1.270	94.9	6.52	3.50	1.820	126
4.466	2.401	1.280	95.6	6.56	3.52	1.830	127
4.503	2.421	1.290	96.2	6.60	3.55	1.840	127
4.539	2.441	1.300	96.8	6.64	3.57	1.850	128
4.576	2.460	1.310	97.4	6.67	3.59	1.860	128
4.613	2.480	1.320	98.0	6.71	3.61	1.870	129
4.650	2.500	1.330	98.6	6.75	3.63	1.880	129
4.687	2.520	1.340	99.2	6.79	3.65	1.890	129
4.724	2.540	1.350	99.8	6.83	3.67	1.900	130
4.761	2.560	1.360	100	6.87	3.70	1.910	130
4.798	2.580	1.370	101	6.91	3.72	1.920	131
4.835	2.600	1.380	102	6.95	3.74	1.930	131
4.872	2.620	1.390	102	6.99	3.76	1.940	132
4.910	2.640	1.400	103	7.03	3.78	1.950	132
4.947	2.660	1.410	103	7.07	3.80	1.960	133
4.984	2.680	1.420	104	7.11	3.82	1.970	133
5.02	2.70	1.430	104	7.15	3.85	1.980	134
5.06	2.72	1.440	105	7.19	3.87	1.990	134
5.10	2.74	1.450	106	7.23	3.89	2.000	135
5.13	2.76	1.460	106	7.27	3.91	2.010	135
5.17	2.78	1.470	107	7.32	3.93	2.020	136
5.21	2.80	1.480	107	7.36	3.95	2.030	136
5.25	2.82	1.490	108	7.40	3.98	2.040	137
5.28	2.84	1.500	109	7.44	4.00	2.050	137
5.32	2.86	1.510	109	7.48	4.02	2.060	137
5.36	2.88	1.520	110	7.52	4.04	2.070	138
5.40	2.90	1.530	110	7.56	4.06	2.080	138
5.44	2.92	1.540	111	7.60	4.09	2.090	139
5.47	2.94	1.550	111	7.64	4.11	2.100	139
5.51	2.96	1.560	112	7.68	4.13	2.110	140
5.55	2.98	1.570	112	7.72	4.15	2.120	140
5.59	3.00	1.580	113	7.76	4.17	2.130	141
5.63	3.02	1.590	114	7.81	4.20	2.140	141
5.66	3.05	1.600	114	7.85	4.22	2.150	142
5.70	3.07	1.610	115	7.89	4.24	2.160	142
5.74	3.09	1.620	115	7.93	4.26	2.170	142
5.78	3.11	1.630	116	7.97	4.29	2.180	143
5.82	3.13	1.640	116	8.01	4.31	2.190	143

Δ °C	O Os/Kg	S,M,T, g-mol/l	γ mmho/cm	Δ °C	O Os/Kg	S,M,T, g-mol/l	γ mmho/cm
8.05	4.33	2.200	144	10.45	5.62	2.750	168
8.10	4.35	2.210	144	10.50	5.64	2.760	168
8.14	4.38	2.220	145	10.54	5.67	2.770	169
8.18	4.40	2.230	145	10.59	5.69	2.780	169
8.22	4.42	2.240	146	10.63	5.72	2.790	170
8.26	4.44	2.250	146	10.68	5.74	2.800	170
8.31	4.47	2.260	147	10.73	5.77	2.810	170
8.35	4.49	2.270	147	10.77	5.79	2.820	171
8.39	4.51	2.280	148	10.82	5.82	2.830	171
8.43	4.53	2.290	148	10.86	5.84	2.840	172
8.47	4.56	2.300	148	10.91	5.87	2.850	172
8.52	4.58	2.310	149	10.96	5.89	2.860	172
8.56	4.60	2.320	149	11.00	5.92	2.870	173
8.60	4.62	2.330	150	11.05	5.94	2.880	173
8.64	4.65	2.340	150	11.10	5.97	2.890	173
8.69	4.67	2.350	151	11.14	5.99	2.900	174
8.73	4.69	2.360	151	11.19	6.02	2.910	174
8.77	4.72	2.370	152	11.24	6.04	2.920	175
8.82	4.74	2.380	152	11.28	6.07	2.930	175
8.86	4.76	2.390	153	11.33	6.09	2.940	175
8.90	4.79	2.400	153	11.38	6.12	2.950	176
8.94	4.81	2.410	153	11.43	6.14	2.960	176
8.99	4.83	2.420	154	11.47	6.17	2.970	176
9.03	4.85	2.430	154	11.52	6.19	2.980	177
9.07	4.88	2.440	155	11.57	6.22	2.990	177
9.12	4.90	2.450	155	11.62	6.25	3.000	178
9.16	4.92	2.460	156	11.71	6.30	3.020	178
9.20	4.95	2.470	156	11.81	6.35	3.040	179
9.25	4.97	2.480	156	11.90	6.40	3.060	180
9.29	5.00	2.490	157	12.00	6.45	3.080	181
9.33	5.02	2.500	157	12.10	6.50	3.100	181
9.38	5.04	2.510	158	12.20	6.56	3.120	182
9.42	5.07	2.520	158	12.29	6.61	3.140	183
9.47	5.09	2.530	159	12.39	6.66	3.160	183
9.51	5.11	2.540	159	12.49	6.71	3.180	184
9.55	5.14	2.550	160	12.59	6.77	3.200	185
9.60	5.16	2.560	160	12.69	6.82	3.220	185
9.64	5.18	2.570	160	12.79	6.87	3.240	186
9.69	5.21	2.580	161	12.89	6.93	3.260	187
9.73	5.23	2.590	161	12.99	6.98	3.280	187
9.78	5.26	2.600	162	13.09	7.04	3.300	188
9.82	5.28	2.610	162	13.19	7.09	3.320	189
9.86	5.30	2.620	163	13.29	7.15	3.340	189
9.91	5.33	2.630	163	13.39	7.20	3.360	190
9.95	5.35	2.640	163	13.49	7.26	3.380	190
10.00	5.38	2.650	164	13.60	7.31	3.400	191
10.04	5.40	2.660	164	13.70	7.37	3.420	192
10.09	5.42	2.670	165	13.80	7.42	3.440	192
10.13	5.45	2.680	165	13.91	7.48	3.460	193
10.18	5.47	2.690	165	14.01	7.53	3.480	193
10.22	5.50	2.700	166	14.12	7.59	3.500	194
10.27	5.52	2.710	166	14.22	7.65	3.520	195
10.31	5.55	2.720	167	14.33	7.70	3.540	195
10.36	5.57	2.730	167	14.43	7.76	3.560	196
10.41	5.59	2.740	168	14.54	7.82	3.580	196

Δ °C	O Os/Kg	S,M,T, g-mol/l	γ mmho/cm	Δ °C	O Os/Kg	S,M,T, g-mol/l	γ mmho/cm
14.65	7.87	3.600	197	18.67	10.04	4.300	212
14.75	7.93	3.620	197	18.79	10.10	4.320	213
14.86	7.99	3.640	198	18.92	10.17	4.340	213
14.97	8.05	3.660	198	19.04	10.24	4.360	213
15.08	8.11	3.680	199	19.17	10.30	4.380	214
15.19	8.16	3.700	199	19.29	10.37	4.400	214
15.30	8.22	3.720	200	19.42	10.44	4.420	214
15.41	8.28	3.740	200	19.55	10.51	4.440	215
15.52	8.34	3.760	201	19.67	10.58	4.460	215
15.63	8.40	3.780	201	19.80	10.65	4.480	215
15.74	8.46	3.800	202	19.93	10.72	4.500	216
15.85	8.52	3.820	202	20.06	10.78	4.520	216
15.96	8.58	3.840	203	20.19	10.85	4.540	216
16.07	8.64	3.860	203	20.32	10.92	4.560	216
16.19	8.70	3.880	204	20.45	10.99	4.580	217
16.30	8.76	3.900	204	20.58	11.07	4.600	217
16.41	8.82	3.920	205	20.71	11.14	4.620	217
16.53	8.89	3.940	205	20.85	11.21	4.640	218
16.64	8.95	3.960	206	20.98	11.28	4.660	218
16.76	9.01	3.980	206	21.11	11.35	4.680	218
16.87	9.07	4.000	206			4.700	218
16.99	9.13	4.020	207			4.750	219
17.11	9.20	4.040	207			4.800	220
17.22	9.26	4.060	208			4.850	220
17.34	9.32	4.080	208			4.900	221
17.46	9.39	4.100	209			4.950	221
17.58	9.45	4.120	209			5.000	222
17.70	9.51	4.140	209			5.050	222
17.82	9.58	4.160	210			5.100	223
17.94	9.64	4.180	210			5.150	223
18.06	9.71	4.200	210			5.200	224
18.18	9.77	4.220	211			5.250	224
18.30	9.84	4.240	211			5.300	225
18.42	9.90	4.260	212				
18.55	9.97	4.280	212				

SPECIFIC GRAVITY OF AQUEOUS INVERT SUGAR SOLUTIONS

t = 20 C

Invert sugar is the equimolar mixture of fructose and glucose obtained by hydrolyzing sucrose.

Wt % (Vacuum)	Specific Gravity	G solute per liter of solution	lb solute per cu ft of solution	lb solute per gallon (U.S.) of solution
1	1.00211	10.021	0.62561	0.08363
2	1.00611	20.120	1.25609	0.16790
3	1.00934	30.298	1.89150	0.25284
4	1.01359	40.556	2.53191	0.33844
5	1.01756	50.893	3.17725	0.42470
6	1.02156	61.312	3.82771	0.51165
7	1.02559	71.812	4.48322	0.59927
8	1.02965	82.396	5.14398	0.68759
9	1.03403	93.063	5.80992	0.77661
10	1.03814	103.814	6.48111	0.86633
11	1.04227	114.649	7.15754	0.95675
12	1.04644	125.573	7.83952	1.04791
13	1.05143	136.582	8.52681	1.13978
14	1.05484	147.678	9.21954	1.23237
15	1.05909	158.864	9.91788	1.32572
16	1.06337	170.139	10.62178	1.41981
17	1.06767	181.504	11.33129	1.51465
18	1.07200	192.960	12.04649	1.61025
19	1.07637	204.510	12.76756	1.70664
20	1.08076	216.152	13.49437	1.80379
21	1.08518	227.888	14.22705	1.90173
22	1.08963	239.719	14.96566	2.00046
23	1.09411	251.645	15.71020	2.09998
24	1.09862	263.669	16.46086	2.20032
25	1.10316	275.790	17.21757	2.30147
26	1.10773	288.010	17.98046	2.40344
27	1.11233	300.329	18.74954	2.50625
28	1.11697	312.752	19.52511	2.60992
29	1.12163	325.273	20.30679	2.71440
30	1.12633	337.899	21.09503	2.81977
31	1.13105	350.626	21.88958	2.92597
32	1.13581	363.459	22.69075	3.03307
33	1.14060	376.398	23.49853	3.14104
34	1.14542	389.443	24.31293	3.24990
35	1.15027	402.595	25.13401	3.35966
36	1.15516	415.858	25.96201	3.47034
37	1.16007	429.226	26.79658	3.58199
38	1.16502	442.708	27.63826	3.69440
39	1.17000	456.300	28.48681	3.80728
40	1.17502	470.008	29.34260	3.92222
41	1.18006	483.825	30.20519	4.03752
42	1.18514	497.759	31.07509	4.15380
43	1.19025	511.808	31.95217	4.27104
44	1.19539	525.972	32.83643	4.38924
45	1.20057	540.257	33.72824	4.50844
46	1.20577	554.654	34.62705	4.62859
47	1.21101	569.175	35.53360	4.74977
48	1.21629	583.819	36.44782	4.87197
49	1.22159	598.579	37.36929	4.99514
50	1.22693	613.465	38.29862	5.11937
51	1.23230	628.473	39.23557	5.24461
52	1.23771	643.609	40.18051	5.37092
53	1.24315	658.870	41.13325	5.49827
54	1.24861	674.249	42.09337	5.62661
55	1.25412	689.766	43.06209	5.75610
56	1.25965	705.404	44.03837	5.88660
57	1.26522	721.175	45.02296	6.01821
58	1.27082	737.076	46.01565	6.15090
59	1.27646	753.111	47.01672	6.28471
60	1.28112	768.672	47.98819	6.41457
61	1.28782	785.570	49.04310	6.55558
62	1.29355	802.001	50.06892	6.69270
63	1.29932	818.572	51.10345	6.83098
64	1.30511	835.270	52.14591	6.97033
65	1.31094	852.111	53.19729	7.11087
66	1.31680	869.088	54.25716	7.25254
67	1.32269	886.202	55.32559	7.39536
68	1.32862	903.462	56.40313	7.53939
69	1.33458	920.860	57.48929	7.68458
70	1.34057	938.399	58.58425	7.83094
71	1.34659	956.079	59.68801	7.97848
72	1.35264	973.901	60.80064	8.12720
73	1.35872	991.866	61.92219	8.27712
74	1.36484	1009.982	63.05318	8.42830
75	1.37099	1028.243	64.19321	8.58069
76	1.37717	1046.649	65.34230	8.73429
77	1.38337	1065.195	66.50012	8.88905
78	1.38962	1083.904	67.66813	9.04518
79	1.39589	1102.753	68.84487	9.20247
80	1.40219	1121.752	70.03093	9.36102
81	1.40852	1140.901	71.22645	9.52082
82	1.41488	1160.202	72.43141	9.68189
83	1.42128	1179.662	73.64630	9.84428
84	1.42770	1199.268	74.87030	10.00790
85	1.43415	1219.028	76.10392	10.17279

HEATS OF COMBUSTION
For Organic Compounds

The heat of combustion is given in kilogram calories per gram molecular weight of the substance when combustion takes place at atmospheric pressure and at either 20°C or 25°C. If the data are for 20°C there is no asterisk for the numerical value of the heat of combustion. If the numerical value is for 25°C there is an asterisk marking the numerical value of the heat of combustion. The final products of combustion are gaseous carbon dioxide, liquid water and nitrogen gas for C, H, N compounds. For method of computing heats of formation see statement following this table.

Name	Formula	Physical state	Heat of combustion, kg. calories
Acetaldehyde	CH_3CHO	liquid	278.77*
Acetamide	CH_3CONH_2	solid	282.6
Acetanilide	$CH_3CONHC_6H_5$	solid	1,010.4
Acetic acid	CH_3CO_2H	liquid	209.02*
Acetic anhydride	$(CH_3CO)_2O$	liquid	431.70*
Acetone	$(CH_3)_2CO$	liquid	427.92*
Acetonitrile	CH_3CN	liquid	302.4
Acetophenone	$C_6H_5COCH_3$	liquid	991.60*
Acetylacetone	$CH_3COCH_2COCH_3$	liquid	615.9
Acetylene	$(CH)_2$	gas	310.61*
Acrolein	$CH_2:CHCHO$	liquid	389.6
Acrylic acid	$CH_2:CHCO_2H$	liquid	327.0*
Adipic acid	$(CH_2)_4(CO_2H)_2$	solid	668.29*
Alanine	$CH_3CH(NH_2)CO_2H$	solid	387.7
Aldol, *see β-hydroxybutyr-aldehyde*			
Alizarin, *see Dihydroxyanthraquinone*			
Allyl alcohol	$CH_2:CHCH_2OH$	liquid	442.4
Allylene	$CH_3C:CH$	gas	465.1
p-Aminoazobenzene	$H_2NC_6H_4N_2C_6H_5$	solid	1,574.0
p-Aminophenol	$HOC_6H_4NH_2$	solid	760.0
Amygdalin	$C_{20}H_{27}O_{11}N$	solid	2,348.4
Amyl acetate	$C_4H_9CO_2C_2H_5$	liquid	1,042.5
Amyl alcohol	$(CH_3)_2CHCH_2CH_2OH$	liquid	793.7
Amylene	C_5H_{10}	liquid	803.4
Anethole	$C_{10}H_{12}O$	solid	1,324.4
Aniline	$C_6H_5NH_2$	liquid	811.7
p-Anisidine	$CH_3OC_6H_4NH_2$	solid	924.0
Anisole	$C_6H_5OCH_3$	liquid	905.1
Anthracene	$C_{14}H_{10}$	solid	1,712.0*
Anthraquinone	$C_{14}H_8O_2$	solid	1,544.5
Arabinose	$C_5H_{10}O_5$	solid	559.9
Arabitol	$C_5H_{12}O_5$	solid	661.2
Arachidic acid	$C_{20}H_{40}O_2$	solid	3,025.9
Azelaic acid	$(CH_2)_7(CO_2H)_2$	solid	1,141.7
Azobenzene	$(C_6H_5N)_2$	solid	1,545.9
Azoxybenzene	$(C_6H_5N)_2O$	solid	1,534.5
Behenic acid	$C_{22}H_{44}O_2$	solid	3,338.4
Benzalacetone	$C_6H_5CH:CHCOCH_3$	solid	1,257.4
Benzaldehyde	C_6H_5CHO	liquid	843.2*
Benzamide	$C_6H_5CONH_2$	solid	847.6
Benzanilide	$C_6H_5CONHC_6H_5$	solid	1,575.5
Benzene	C_6H_6	liquid	780.96*
Benzenediazonium nitrate	$C_6H_5N_2NO_3$	solid	782.6
Benzidine	$(C_6H_4NH_2)_2$	solid	1,560.9
Benzil	$(C_6H_5CO)_2$	solid	1,624.6
* Benzoic acid	$C_6H_5CO_2H$	solid	771.24*
Benzoic anhydride	$(C_6H_5CO)_2O$	solid	1,555.1
Benzoin	$C_6H_5.CHOH.COC_6H_5$	solid	1,671.4
Benzonitrile	C_6H_5CN	liquid	865.5
Benzophenone	$(C_6H_5)_2CO$	solid	1,556.5
Benzoyl chloride	C_6H_5COCl	liquid	782.8
Benzoyl peroxide	$(C_6H_5CO)_2O_2$	solid	1,551.7
Benzyl alcohol	$C_6H_5CH_2OH$	liquid	894.3
Benzylamine	$C_6H_5CH_2NH_2$	liquid	969.4
Benzyl carbylamine	$C_6H_5CH_2NC$	liquid	1,046.5
Benzyl chloride	$C_6H_5CH_2Cl$	liquid	886.4
Benzyl cyanide	$C_6H_5CH_2CN$	liquid	1,023.5
Borneol	$C_{10}H_{18}O$	liquid	1,469.6
Brucine	$C_{23}H_{26}O_4N_2$	gas	687.68*
n-Butyl alcohol	C_4H_9OH	liquid	639.53*
tert.-Butyl alcohol, *see Trimethyl carbinol*			
n-Butylamine	$C_4H_9NH_2$	liquid	710.6
sec.-Butylamine	$(CH_3)(C_2H_5):CHNH_2$	liquid	713.0
tert.-Butylamine	$(CH_3)_3CNH_2$	liquid	716.0
tert.-Butylbenzene	$C_6H_5C(CH_3)_3$	liquid	1,400.4
n-Butyramide	$C_3H_7CONH_2$	solid	596.0
n-Butyric acid	$C_3H_7CO_2H$	liquid	521.87*
n-Butyronitrile	C_3H_7CN	liquid	613.3
Caffeine	$C_8H_{10}O_2N_4$	solid	1,014.2
Camphene	$C_{10}H_{16}$	solid	1,468.8
Camphor	$C_{10}H_{16}O$	solid	1,411.0
Cane sugar, *see Sucrose*			
Capric acid	$C_9H_{18}O_2$	solid	1,453.07*
Caproic acid	$C_5H_{11}CO_2H$	liquid	834.49*
Carbon disulfide	CS_2	liquid	246.6
Carbon subnitride	$(C.CN)_2$	solid	514.8
Carbon tetrachloride	CCl_4	liquid	37.3
Carbonyl sulfide	COS	gas	130.5
Carvacrol	$C_{10}H_{14}O$	liquid	1,354.5
Cetyl alcohol	$C_{16}H_{34}O$	solid	2,504.4
Cetyl palmitate	$C_{32}H_{64}O_2$	solid	4,872.8
Chloracetic acid	$ClCH_2CO_2H$	solid	171.0
o-Chlorobenzoic acid	$ClC_6H_4CO_2H$	solid	734.5
Chloroform	$CHCl_3$	liquid	89.2
Chrysene	$C_{18}H_{12}$	solid	2,139.1
Cinnamic acid (*trans*)	$C_6H_5CH:CHCO_2H$	solid	1,040.2
Cinnamic aldehyde	$C_6H_5CH:CHCHO$	liquid	1,112.3

*25 C

Name	Formula	Physical state	Heat of combustion, kg. calories
Cinnamic anhydride	$C_{18}H_{14}O_3$	solid	2,091.3
d-Citrene	$C_{10}H_{16}$	liquid	1,473.0
Citric acid (anhydr.)	$C_6H_8O_7$	solid	468.6*
Codeine	$C_{18}H_{21}O_2N.H_2O$	solid	2,327.6
Coniine	$C_8H_{17}N$	liquid	1,275.5
Creatine (anhydr.)	$C_4H_9O_2N_3$	solid	559.8
Creatinine	$C_4H_7ON_3$	solid	563.4
o-Cresol	$CH_3C_6H_4OH$	liquid	882.6
o-Cresol	$CH_3C_6H_4OH$	solid	882.72*
m-Cresol	$CH_3C_6H_4OH$	liquid	880.5
p-Cresol	$CH_3C_6H_4OH$	liquid	882.5
p-Cresol	$CH_3C_6H_4OH$	solid	883.99*
m-Cresolmethyl ether	$CH_3C_6H_4OCH_3$	liquid	1,057.0
Crotonaldehyde	C_3H_5CHO	liquid	542.1
Cyanoacetic acid	$NC\ CH_2CO_2H$	solid	298.8
Cyanogen	$(CN)_2$	gas	258.3
Cyclobutane	C_4H_8	liquid	650.22*
Cycloheptane	$(CH_2)_7$	liquid	1,087.3
Cycloheptanol	$CH_2(CH_2)_5CHOH$	liquid	1,050.2
Cycloheptene	C_7H_{12}	liquid	1,099.09*
Cyclohexane	$(CH_2)_6$	liquid	936.87*
Cyclohexanol	$CH_2(CH_2)_4CHOH$	liquid	890.7
Cyclohexene, see Tetrahydrobenzene			
Cyclopentane	$(CH_2)_5$	liquid	786.55*
Cyclopropane, see Trimethylene			
Cymene	$C_6H_4(CH_3)(CH_3CHCH_3)$—(1, 4)	liquid	1,402.8
Decahydronaphthalene (cis)	$C_{10}H_{18}$	liquid	1,502.5
Decahydronaphthalene (trons)	$C_{10}H_{18}$	liquid	1,499.5
Decane	$C_{10}H_{22}$	liquid	1,610.2
Dextrose, see Glucose			
Diallyl	$(CH_2:CHCH_2)_2$	vapor	903.4
Diamyl ether	$(C_5H_{11})_2O$	liquid	1,609.3
Diamylene	$C_{10}H_{20}$	liquid	1,582.2
Dibenzyl	$(C_6H_5CH_2)_2$	solid	1,810.6
Dibenzyl amine	$(C_6H_5CH_2)_2NH$	solid	1,853.0
o-Dichlorobenzene	$C_6H_4Cl_2$	liquid	671.8
Diethylacetic acid	$(C_2H_5)_2CHCO_2H$	liquid	830.8
Diethyl amine	$(C_2H_5)_2NH$	liquid	716.9
Diethylaniline	$C_6H_5N(C_2H_5)_2$	liquid	1,451.6
Diethyl carbonate	$CO(OC_2H_5)_2$	liquid	647.9
Diethyl ether	$(C_2H_5)_2O$	liquid	657.52*
Diethyl ketone	$(C_2H_5)_2CO$	liquid	735.6
Diethyl malonate	$CH_2(CO_2C_2H_5)_2$	liquid	860.4
Diethyl oxalate	$(CO_2C_2H_5)_2$	liquid	716.0
Diethyl succinate	$(CH_2CO_2C_2H_5)_2$	liquid	1,007.3
Dihydrobenzene	C_6H_8	liquid	847.8
Δ_1-Dihydronaphthalene	$C_{10}H_{10}$	liquid	1,296.3
Δ_1-Dihydronaphthalene	$C_{10}H_{10}$	solid	1,298.3
Dihydroxyanthraquinone	$C_{14}H_6O_2(OH)_2$—(1, 2)	solid	1,448.9
Diisoamyl	$[(CH_3)_2CHCH_2CH_2]_2$	liquid	1,615.8
Diisobutylene	$[(CH_3)_2CHCH_2]_2$	liquid	1,252.4
Diisopropyl	$[(CH_3)_2CH]_2$	vapor	993.9
Diisopropyl ketone	$[(CH_3)_2CH]_2CO$	liquid	1,045.5
Dimethyl amine	$(CH_3)_2NH$	liquid	416.7
Dimethylaniline	$C_6H_5N(CH_3)_2$	liquid	1,142.7
Dimethyl carbonate	$CO(OCH_3)_2$	liquid	340.8
Dimethyl ether	$(CH_3)_2O$	gas	
Dimethylethyl carbinol	$C_2H_5(CH_3)_2CHOH$	liquid	784.6
Dimethyl fumarate	$(CHCO_2CH_3)_2$	solid	663.3*
2, 5-Dimethylhexane	$(CH_3)_2CH.C_2H_4CH(CH_3)_2$	liquid	1,303.3
3, 4-Dimethylhexane	$[(C_2H_5)_2CH]_2$	liquid	1,303.7
Dimethyl maleate	$(CHCO_2CH_3)_2$	liquid	669.4*
Dimethyl oxalate	$(CO_2CH_3)_2$	liquid	400.2*
2, 2-Dimethylpentane	$(CH_3)_3C.C_3H_7$	liquid	1,148.9
2, 3-Dimethylpentane	$(CH_3)_2CHCH(CH_3)C_2H_5$	liquid	1,148.9
2, 4-Dimethylpentane	$(CH_3)_2CHCH_2CH(CH_3)_2$	liquid	1,148.9
3, 3-Dimethylpentane	$(CH_3)_2C(C_2H_5)_2$	liquid	1,147.9
Dimethyl phthalate	$C_6H_4(CO_2CH_3)_2$	liquid	1,119.7
Dimethyl succinate	$(CH_2CO_2CH_3)_2$	solid	706.3*
m-Dinitrobenzene	$C_6H_4(NO_2)_2$	solid	696.8
Dinitrophenol	$C_6H_3(OH)(NO_2)_2$—(1, 2, 4)	solid	648.0
Dinitrotoluene	$C_6H_3(CH_3)(NO_2)_2$—(1, 2, 4)	solid	852.8
Diphenyl	$(C_6H_5)_2$	solid	1,493.6
Diphenyl amine	$(C_6H_5)_2NH$	solid	1,536.2
Diphenyl carbinol	$(C_6H_5)_2CHOH$	solid	1,615.4
Diphenylmethane	$(C_6H_5)_2CH_2$	solid	1,655.0
Diphenylnitrosamine	$(C_6H_5)_2N.NO$	solid	1,532.6
Dipropargyl	$(CH:C.CH_2)_2$	vapor	882.9
Dipropyl ketone	$(C_3H_7)_2CO$	liquid	1,050.5
Dulcitol	$C_6H_{14}O_6$	solid	729.1
Durene	$C_6H_2(CH_3)_4$—(1, 2, 4, 5)	solid	1,393.6
Eicosane	$C_{20}H_{42}$	solid	3,183.1
Erythritol	$C_4H_{10}O_4$	solid	504.1
Ethane	C_2H_6	gas	372.81*
Ethine, see Acetylene			
Ethyl acetate	$CH_3CO_2C_2H_5$	liquid	536.9
Ethyl acetoacetate	$CH_3COCH_2CO_2C_2H_5$	liquid	690.8
Ethyl alcohol	C_2H_5OH	liquid	326.68*
Ethyl amine	$C_2H_5NH_2$	liquid	409.5*
Ethylaniline	$C_6H_5NHC_2H_5$	liquid	1,121.5
Ethylbenzene	$C_2H_5C_6H_5$	liquid	1,091.2

*25 C

Name	Formula	Physical state	Heat of combustion, kg. calories
Ethyl benzoate	$C_6H_5CO_2C_2H_5$	liquid	1,098.7
Ethyl bromide	C_2H_5Br	vapor	340.5
Ethyl n-butyrate	$C_3H_7CO_2C_2H_5$	liquid	851.2
Ethyl carbylamine	C_2H_5NC	liquid	477.1
Ethyl chloride	C_2H_5Cl	vapor	316.7
Ethylcycloheptane	$C_2H_5C_7H_{13}$	liquid	1,406.8
Ethyl formate	$HCO_2C_2H_5$	liquid	391.7
3-Ethylhexane	$(C_2H_5)_2CH.C_3H_7$	liquid	1,302.3
Ethyl iodide	C_2H_5I	liquid	356.0
Ethyl isobutyrate	$(CH_3)_2CHCH_2CO_2C_2H_5$	liquid	845.7
Ethyl isocyanate	C_2H_5NCO	liquid	424.5
Ethyl nitrate	$C_2H_5ONO_2$	vapor	322.4
Ethyl nitrite	C_2H_5ONO	vapor	332.6
3-Ethylpentane	$(C_2H_5)_3CH$	liquid	1,149.9
Ethyl propionate	$C_2H_5CO_2C_2H_5$	liquid	690.8
Ethyl salicylate	$HOC_6H_4CO_2C_2H_5$	liquid	1,051.2
Ethyl valerate	$C_4H_9CO_2C_2H_5$	liquid	1,017.5
Ethylene	$CH_2:CH_2$	gas	337.23*
Ethylene chloride	$(CH_2Cl)_2$	vapor	271.0
Ethylene diamine	$(CH_2NH_2)_2$	liquid	452.6
Ethylene glycol	$(CH_2OH)_2$	liquid	281.9
Ethylene iodide	$(CH_2I)_2$	solid	324.8
Ethylene oxide	CH_2CH_2O	liquid	302.1
Ethylidene chloride	CH_3CHCl_2	liquid	267.1
Eugenol	$C_{10}H_{12}O_2$	liquid	1,286.6
Fenchane	$C_{10}H_{18}$	liquid	1,502.6
Fluorene	$(C_6H_4)_2:CH_2$	solid	1,584.9
Fluorobenzene	C_6H_5F	liquid	747.2
Formaldehyde	CH_2O	gas	136.42*
Formamide	$HCONH_2$	solid	134.9
Formic acid	HCO_2H	liquid	60.86*
β-D-Fructose	$C_6H_{12}O_6$	solid	672.0*
Fumaric acid (trans)	$(CHCO_2H)_2$	solid	318.99*
Furfural	C_4H_3OCHO	liquid	559.5
α-D-Galactose	$C_6H_{12}O_6$	solid	670.1*
Gallic acid	$C_6H_2(OH)_3CO_2H—(1, 3, 5, 6)$	solid	633.7
α-D-Glucose	$C_6H_{12}O_6$	solid	669.94*
Glutaric acid	$(CH_2)_3(CO_2H)_2$	solid	514.08*
Glycerol	$(CH_2OH)_2CHOH$	liquid	397.0
Glyceryl tributyrate	$C_{15}H_{26}O_6$	liquid	1,941.1
Glycine	$H_2NCH_2CO_2H$	solid	232.67*
Glycogen	$(C_6H_{10}O_5)x$ per kg.	solid	4,186.8
Glycollic acid	CH_2OHCO_2H	solid	166.1*
Glycylglycine	$C_4H_8O_3N_2$	solid	470.7
n-Heptaldehyde	$CH_3(CH_2)_5CHO$	liquid	1,062.2*
n-Heptane	C_7H_{16}	liquid	1,149.9
Heptine-1	$CH:C(CH_2)_4CH_3$	liquid	1,091.2
n-Heptyl alcohol	$CH_3(CH_2)_5CH_2OH$	liquid	1,104.9
Heptyl amine	$C_7H_{15}NH_2$	liquid	1,178.9
Heptylic acid	$C_7H_{14}O_2$	liquid	986.1
n-Hexane	C_6H_{14}	liquid	995.01*
Hexachlorbenzene	C_6Cl_6	solid	509.0
Hexachlorethane	C_2Cl_6	solid	110.0
Hexadecane	$C_{16}H_{34}$	solid	2,559.1
Hexahydronaphthalene	$C_{10}H_{14}$	liquid	1,419.3
Hexamethylbenzene	$C_6(CH_3)_6$	solid	1,711.9
Hexamethylenetetramine	$(CH_2)_6N_4$	solid	1,006.7
Hexamethylethane	$[(CH_3)_3C]_2$	solid	1,301.8
Hexyl amine	$C_6H_{13}NH_2$	liquid	1,022.2
Hexylene	C_6H_{12}	liquid	952.6
Hippuric acid	$C_6H_5CONHCH_2CO_2H$	solid	1,012.4
Hydantoic acid	$C_3H_6O_3N_2$	solid	308.6
Hydrazobenzene	$(C_6H_5NH)_2$	solid	1,597.3
Hydroquinol	$C_6H_4(OH)_2$	solid	681.78*
Hydroquinoldimethyl ether	$(CH_3O)_2C_6H_4$	solid	1,014.7
p-Hydroxyazobenzene	$HOC_6H_4N_2C_6H_5$	solid	1,502.0
o-Hydroxybenzaldehyde	$C_6H_4(OH)CHO$	liquid	796.4*
m-Hydroxybenzaldehyde	$C_6H_4(OH)CHO$	solid	788.7
p-Hydroxybenzaldehyde	$C_6H_4(OH)CHO$	solid	792.7
m-Hydroxybenzoic acid	$HOC_6H_4CO_2H$	solid	726.1
p-Hydroxybenzoic acid	$HOC_6H_4CO_2H$	solid	725.4
β-Hydroxybutyraldehyde	$CH_3CHOHCH_2CHO$	liquid	546.6
Indigo	$C_{16}H_{10}O_2N_2$	solid	1,815.0
Indole	C_8H_7N	solid	1,022.2
Inositol	$C_6H_{12}O_6$	solid	662.1
Iodoform	CHI_3	solid	161.9
Isoamyl amine	$(CH_3)_2CH.C_2H_4NH_2$	liquid	866.8
Isobutane	$(CH_3)_3CH$	gas	683.4
Isobutyl alcohol	$(CH_3)_2CHCH_2OH$	liquid	638.2
Isobutyl amine	$C_4H_9NH_2$	liquid	713.6
Isobutylene	$(CH_3)_2C:CH_2$	gas	647.2
Isobutyraldehyde	$(CH_3)_2CHCHO$	vapor	596.8
Isobutyramide	$(CH_3)_2CHCONH_2$	solid	595.9
Isobutyric acid	$(CH_3)_2CHCO_2H$	liquid	517.4
Isoeugenol	$C_{10}H_{12}O_2$	liquid	1,277.6
Isopentane	C_5H_{12}	gas	843.5(?)
Isopentane	C_5H_{12}	liquid	838.3(?)
Isophthalic acid	$C_6H_4(CO_2H)_2$	solid	768.3
Isopropyl alcohol	$(CH_3)_2CHOH$	liquid	474.8
Isopropylbenzene	$(CH_3)_2CHC_6H_5$	liquid	1,247.3
Isopropyltoluene	$C_6H_4(CH_3)(CH_3CHC_2)—(1, 3)$	liquid	1,409.5

Isopropyltoluene, *see Cymene*

*25 C

Name	Formula	Physical state	Heat of combustion, kg. calories
Isosafrole	$C_{10}H_{10}O_2$	liquid	1,233.9
Lactic acid, DL	$CH_3CHOHCO_2H$	liquid	326.8*
Lactose (anhydr.)	$C_{12}H_{22}O_{11}$	solid	1,350.0*
Lauric acid	$C_{12}H_{24}O_2$	solid	1,763.25*
Leucine	$C_6H_{13}O_2N$	solid	855.6
d-Limonene	$C_{10}H_{16}$	liquid	1,471.2
Maleic acid (cis)	$(CHCO_2H)_2$	solid	323.89*
Maleic anhydride	$(CHCO)_2O$	solid	332.10*
l-Malic acid	$(CHOHCH_2).(CO_2H)_2$	solid	317.37*
Malonic acid	$CH_2(CO_2H)_2$	solid	205.82*
Maltose	$C_{12}H_{22}O_{11}$	solid	1,349.3*
Mandelic acid	$C_6H_5CHOHCO_2H$	solid	890.3
d-Mannitol	$C_6H_{14}O_6$	solid	727.6
Menthene	$C_{10}H_{18}$	liquid	1,523.2
Menthol	$C_{10}H_{20}O$	solid	1,508.8
Mesitylene	$(CH_3)_3C_6H_3—(1, 3, 5)$	liquid	1,243.6
Mesityl oxide	$(CH_3)_2C:CHCOCH_3$	liquid	846.7
Mesotartaric acid	$(CHOH)_2(CO_2H)_2$	solid	276.0
Methane	CH_4	gas	212.79*
Methyl acetate	$CH_3CO_2CH_3$	liquid	381.2
Methyl alcohol	CH_3OH	liquid	173.64*
Methyl amine	CH_3NH_2	liquid	253.5*
Methylaniline	$C_6H_5NHCH_3$	liquid	973.5
Methyl benzoate	$C_6H_5CO_2CH_3$	liquid	945.9*
Methyl bromide	CH_3Br	vapor	184.0
Methyl butyl ketone	$CH_3COC_4H_9$	liquid	895.2
Methyl tert-butyl ketone, see Pinacoline			
Methyl butyrate	$C_3H_7COOCH_3$	liquid	692.8
Methyl carbylamine	CH_3NC	liquid	320.1
Methyl chloride	CH_3Cl	gas	164.2
Methyl cinnamate	$C_{10}H_{10}O_2$	solid	1,213.0
Methylcyclobutane	$CH_3CHCH_2CH_2CH_2$	liquid	784.2
Methylcycloheptane	$CH_3C_7H_{13}$	liquid	1,244.5
Methylcyclohexane	$CH_3C_6H_{11}$	liquid	1,091.8
Methylcyclopentane	$CH_3CH.C_3H_8CH_2$	liquid	937.9
Methyldiethyl carbinol	$CH_3(C_2H_5)_2CHOH$	liquid	927.0
Methylene chloride	CH_2Cl_2	vapor	106.8
Methylene iodide	CH_2I_2	liquid	178.4
Methylethyl ether	$CH_3OC_2H_5$	vapor	503.69*
Methylethyl ketone	$CH_3COC_2H_5$	liquid	584.17*
Methyl formate	HCO_2CH_3	liquid	234.1*
2-Methylheptane	$(CH_3)_2CH.C_5H_{11}$	liquid	1,306.1
2-Methylhexane	$(CH_3)_2CHC_4H_9$	liquid	1,148.9
3-Methylhexane	$(C_2H_5)(CH_3)CHC_3H_7$	liquid	1,148.9
Methylhexyl ketone	$CH_3COC_6H_{13}$	liquid	1,205.1
Methyl iodide	CH_3I	liquid	194.7
Methyl isobutyrate	$(CH_3)_2CHCO_2CH_3$	liquid	694.2
Methyl isocyanate	CH_3NCO	liquid	269.4
Methylisopropyl ketone	$CH_3COCH(CH_3)_2$	liquid	733.9
Methyl lactate	$CH_3CHOHCO_2CH_3$	liquid	497.2
Methyl propionate	$C_2H_5CO_2CH_3$	vapor	552.3
Methylpropyl ketone	$CH_3COC_3H_7$	liquid	740.78*
Methyl salicylate	$HOC_6H_4CO_2CH_3$	liquid	898.6*
Milk sugar, see Lactose			
Morphine	$C_{17}H_{19}O_3N.H_2O$	solid	2,146.3
Mucic acid	$C_6H_{10}O_8$	solid	483.0*
Myristic acid	$C_{14}H_{28}O_2$	solid	2,073.91*
Naphthalene	$C_{10}H_8$	solid	1,231.8*
α-Naphthoic acid	$C_{10}H_7CO_2H$	solid	1,231.8
β-Naphthoic acid	$C_{10}H_7CO_2H$	solid	1,227.6
α-Naphthol	$C_{10}H_7OH$	solid	1,185.4
β-Naphthol	$C_{10}H_7OH$	solid	1,187.2
α-Naphthonitrile	$C_{10}H_7CN$	solid	1,326.2
β-Naphthonitrile	$C_{10}H_7CN$	solid	1,321.0
α-Naphthoquinone	$C_{10}H_6O_2$	solid	1,100.8
β-Naphthoquinone	$C_{10}H_6O_2$	solid	1,106.4
α-Naphthyl amine	$C_{10}H_7NH_2$	solid	1,263.5
β-Naphthyl amine	$C_{10}H_7NH_2$	solid	1,261.0
Narceine	$C_{23}H_{27}O_8N.2H_2O$	solid	2,802.9
Narcotine	$C_{22}H_{23}O_7N$	solid	2,644.5
Nicotine	$C_{10}H_{14}N_2$	liquid	1,427.7
o-Nitraniline	$C_6H_4(NH_2)(NO_2)$	solid	765.8
m-Nitraniline	$C_6H_4(NH_2)(NO_2)$	solid	765.2
p-Nitraniline	$C_6H_4(NH_2)(NO_2)$	solid	761.0
m-Nitrobenzaldehyde	$O_2NC_6H_4CHO$	solid	800.4
Nitrobenzene	$C_6H_5NO_2$	liquid	739.2
m-Nitrobenzoic acid	$O_2NC_6H_4CO_2H$	solid	729.1
Nitroethane	$C_2H_5NO_2$	liquid	322.2
Nitroglycerine, see Trinitroglycerol			
Nitromethane	CH_3NO_2	liquid	169.4
o-Nitrophenol	$HOC_6H_4NO_2$	solid	689.1
m-Nitrophenol	$HOC_6H_4NO_2$	solid	684.4
p-Nitrophenol	$HOC_6H_4NO_2$	solid	688.8
Nitropropane	$C_3H_7NO_2$	liquid	477.9
o-Nitrotoluene	$CH_3C_6H_4NO_2$	liquid	897.0
p-Nitrotoluene	$CH_2C_6H_5NO_2$	solid	888.6
Octahydronaphthalene	$C_{10}H_{16}$	liquid	1,461.7
n-Octane	C_8H_{18}	liquid	1,302.7
Octyl alcohol	$C_8H_{18}O$	liquid	1,262.0
Oleic acid	$C_{18}H_{34}O_2$	liquid	2,657.4*
Oxalic acid, a	$(CO_2H)_2$	solid	58.7*
Oxamide	$(CONH_2)_2$	solid	203.2
Palmitic acid	$C_{16}H_{32}O_2$	solid	2,384.76*

*25C

Name	Formula	Physical state	Heat of combustion, kg. calories
Papaverine	$C_{20}H_{21}O_4N$	solid	2,478.1
Pentamethylbenzene	$C_6H(CH_3)_5$	solid	1,554.0
n-Pentane	C_5H_{12}	gas	845.16*
n-Pentane	C_5H_{12}	liquid	838.78*
Phenacetin	$C_{10}H_{13}O_2N$	solid	1,285.2
Phenanthraquinone	$C_{14}H_8O_2$	solid	1,544.0
Phenanthrene	$C_{14}H_{10}$	solid	1,685.6*
Phenetole	$C_6H_5OC_2H_5$	liquid	1,060.3
Phenol	C_6H_5OH	solid	729.80*
Phenylacetic acid	$C_6H_5CH_2CO_2H$	solid	930.4*
Phenylacetylene	$C_6H_5C{:}CH$	liquid	1,024.2
Phenylalanine	$C_9H_{11}O_2N$	solid	1,111.3
p-Phenylenediamine	$C_6H_4(NH_2)_2$	solid	843.4
Phenylethylene, see Styrene			
Phenylglycine	$C_2H_5NHCH_2CO_2H$	solid	955.1
Phenylhydrazine	$C_6H_5N_2H_3$	solid	875.4
Phenylhydroxylamine	C_6H_5NHOH	liquid	803.7
Phenyl iodide	C_6H_5I	liquid	770.7
Phloroglucinol	$C_6H_3(OH)_3$	solid	635.7
o-Phthalic acid	$C_6H_4(CO_2H)_2$	solid	770.44*
Phthalic anhydride	$C_6H_4(CO)_2O$	solid	783.4
Phthalimide	$C_8H_5O_2N$	solid	849.5
Picric acid	$C_6H_2(OH)(NO_2)_3{-}(1, 2, 4, 6)$	solid	611.8
Pinacoline	$CH_3COC(CH_3)_3$	solid	891.8
Piperidine	$C_5H_{11}N$	liquid	826.6
Piperonal	$C_8H_6O_3$	solid	870.7
Propane	C_3H_8	gas	530.57*
Propine, see Allylene			
Propionaldehyde	C_2H_5CHO	liquid	434.1*
Propionamide	$C_2H_5CONH_2$	solid	439.9
Propionic acid	$C_2H_5CO_2H$	liquid	365.03*
Propionic anhydride	$(C_2H_5CO)_2O$	liquid	746.6
Propionitrile	C_2H_5CN	liquid	456.4
n-Propyl alcohol	C_3H_7OH	liquid	482.75*
Propyl amine	$C_3H_7NH_2$	liquid	565.31*
n-Propylbenzene	$C_3H_7C_6H_5$	liquid	1,246.4
Propyl bromide	C_3H_7Br	vapor	497.3
Propyl carbylamine	C_3H_7NC	liquid	639.6
Propyl chloride	C_3H_7Cl	vapor	478.3
Propylene	$CH_3CH{:}CH_2$	gas	490.2
Propylene glycol	$CH_3CHOHCH_2OH$	liquid	431.0
n-Propyl iodide	C_3H_7I	liquid	514.3
n-Propyltoluene	$C_6H_4(CH_3)(C_3H_7){-}(1, 3)$	liquid	1,405.4
Pseudocumene	$C_6H_3(CH_3)_3{-}(1, 2, 4)$	liquid	1,241.7
Pyridine	C_5H_5N	liquid	665.0*
Pyrocatechol	$C_6H_4(OH)_2$	solid	683.0*
Pyrogallol	$C_6H_3(OH)_3$	solid	638.7
Pyrrole	C_4H_5N	liquid	567.7
Quercitol	$C_6H_{12}O_5$	solid	704.2
Quinoline	C_9H_7N	liquid	1,123.5
Quinone	$O{:}C_6H_4{:}O$	solid	656.6
Raffinose	$C_{18}H_{32}O_{16}$	solid	2,025.5
Retene	$C_{18}H_{18}$	solid	2,306.8
Resorcinol	$C_6H_4(OH)_2$	solid	681.30*
Resorcinoldimethyl ether	$(CH_3O)_2C_6H_4$	liquid	1,022.6
Rhamnose	$C_6H_{12}O_6$	solid	718.3
Safrole	$C_{10}H_{10}O_2$	liquid	1,244.1
Salicylaldehyde, see o-Hydroxybenzaldehyde			
*Salicylic acid	$HOC_6H_4CO_2H{-}(1, 2)$	solid	722.4**
Sarcosine	$CH_3NHCH_2CO_2H$	solid	401.1
Sebacic acid	$(CH_2)_8(CO_2H)_2$	solid	1,297.3
Skatole	C_9H_9N	liquid	1,170.5
d-Sorbose	$C_6H_{12}O_6$	solid	668.3
Starch	$(C_6H_{10}O_5)x$ per kg	solid	4,178.8
Stearic acid	$C_{18}H_{36}O_2$	solid	2,696.12*
Strychnine	$C_{21}H_{22}O_2N_2$	solid	2,685.7
Styrene	$C_6H_5CH{:}CH_2$	liquid	1,047.1
Suberic acid	$(CH_2)_6(CO_2H)_2$	solid	985.2
Succinic acid	$(CH_2CO_2H)_2$	solid	356.36*
Succinic acid nitrile	$(CH_2CN)_2$	liquid	545.7
Succinic anhydride	$(CH_2CO)_2O$	solid	369.0*
Succinimide	$C_4H_5O_2N$	solid	437.9
Sucrose	$C_{12}H_{22}O_{11}$	solid	1,348.2*
Sylvestrene	$C_{10}H_{16}$	liquid	1,464.7
l-Tartaric acid	$(CHOH)_2(CO_2H)_2$	solid	274.7*
d, l-Tartaric acid (anhydr.)	$(CHOH)_2(CO_2H)_2$	solid	272.6*
Terephthalic acid	$C_6H_4(CO_2H)_2$	solid	770.4
Terpin hydrate	$C_{10}H_{22}O_3$	solid	1,451.0
Terpineol	$C_{10}H_{18}O$	solid	1,469.5
Tetrahydrobenzene	C_6H_{10}	liquid	891.9
Tetrahydronaphthalene	$C_{10}H_{12}$	liquid	1,352.4
Tetramethylmethane	$(CH_3)_4C$	gas	842.6
Tetraphenylmethane	$(C_6H_5)_4C$	solid	3,102.4
Tetryl	$C_7H_5N_5O_8$	solid	842.3
Thebaine	$C_{19}H_{21}O_3N$	solid	2,441.3
Thiophene	C_4H_4S	liquid	670.5
Thujane	$C_{10}H_{18}$	liquid	1,506.4
Thymol	$C_{10}H_{14}O$	liquid	1,353.4
Thymol	$C_{10}H_{14}O$	solid	1,349.7
Thymoquinone	$C_{10}H_{12}O_2$	solid	1,271.3
Toluene	$CH_3C_6H_5$	liquid	934.2
o-Toluic acid	$CH_3C_6H_4CO_2H$	solid	928.9

*25 C

**Recommended as a secondary thermochemical standard.

FOR ORGANIC COMPOUNDS

Name	Formula	Physical state	Heat of combustion, kg. calories
m-Toluic acid	$CH_3C_6H_4CO_2H$	solid	928.6
p-Toluic acid	$CH_3C_6H_4CO_2H$	solid	926.9
o-Toluidine	$CH_3C_6H_4NH_2$	liquid	964.3
m-Toluidine	$CH_3C_6H_4NH_2$	liquid	965.3
p-Toluidine	$CH_3C_6H_4NH_2$	solid	958.4
o-Tolunitrile	$CH_3C_6H_4CN$	liquid	1,030.3
Toluquinone	$C_7H_6O_2$	solid	803.2
Triaminotriphenyl carbinol	$(C_6H_4NH_2)_3COH$	solid	2,483.5
Tribenzyl amine	$(C_6H_5CH_2)_3N$	solid	2,762.1
Trichloracetic acid	$Cl_3C.CO_2H$	solid	92.8
Triethyl amine	$(C_2H_5)_3N$	liquid	1,036.8
Triethyl carbinol	$(C_2H_5)_3CHOH$	liquid	1,080.0
Triisoamyl amine	$[(CH_3)_2CHCH_2CH_2]_3N$	liquid	2,459.3
Triisobutyl amine	$[(CH_3)_2CHCH_2]_3N$	liquid	1,973.6
Trimethyl amine	$(CH_3)_3N$	liquid	578.6
2, 2, 3-Trimethylbutane	$(CH_3)_3C.CH(CH_3)_2$	liquid	1,147.9
Trimethyl carbinol	$(CH_3)_3COH$	liquid	629.3
Trimethylene	$CH_2CH_2CH_2$	gas	499.89*
Trimethylethylene	$(CH_3)_2C:CHCH_3$	liquid	796.0
Trimethylethylene	$(CH_3)_2C:CHCH_3$	vapor	803.6
2, 2, 4-Trimethylpentane	$(CH_3)_3C.CH_2CH(CH_3)_2$	liquid	1,303.9
Trinitrobenzene	$C_6H_3(NO_2)_3—(1, 3, 5)$	solid	663.7
Trinitroglycerol	$C_3H_5(NO_3)_3$	liquid	368.4
Trinitrotoluene	$C_6H_2(CH_3)(NO_2)_3—$ $(1, 2, 4, 6)$	solid	820.7
Triphenyl amine	$(C_6H_5)_3N$	solid	2,267.8
Triphenylbenzene	$C_6H_3(C_6H_5)_3—(1, 3, 5)$	solid	2,936.7
Triphenyl carbinol	$(C_6H_5)_3CHOH$	solid	2,340.8
Triphenylmethane	$(C_6H_5)_3CH$	solid	2,388.7
Triphenyl methyl	$(C_6H_5)_3C$	solid	2,378.5
Tyrosine	$C_9H_{11}O_3N$	solid	1,070.2
Undecylic acid	$C_{11}H_{22}O_2$	solid	1,615.9
Urea	$(NH_2)_2CO$	solid	150.97*
Urethane	$NH_2CO_2C_2H_5$	solid	397.2
Uric acid	$C_5H_4O_3N_4$	solid	460.2
n-Valeric acid	$C_4H_9CO_2H$	liquid	678.12*
Vanillin	$C_6H_3(OH)(OCH_3)CHO—$ $(1, 2, 4)$	solid	914.1
o-Xylene	$(CH_3)_2C_6H_4$	liquid	1,091.7
m-Xylene	$(CH_3)_2C_6H_4$	liquid	1,088.4
p-Xylene	$(CH_3)_2C_6H_4$	liquid	1,089.1
Xylose	$C_5H_{10}O_5$	solid	559.0*

*25 C

HEAT OF FORMATION

FOR ORGANIC COMPOUNDS

The heat of formation of a compound "A" is equal to the sum of the heats of formation of the products of combustion minus the heat of combustion (see preceding table) of the compound "A." The heat of formation of:

Free elements	0	kg-cal
CO_2 (gas)	94.38	"
$\frac{1}{2}H_2O$ (liquid from 1 H)	34.19	"
HF (dilute aqueous solution)	75.6	"
SO_2 (gas)	69.3	"
HBr (aqueous solution)	28.54	"
HCl (aqueous solution)	39.46	"
HNO_3 (aqueous solution)	49.80	"
H_2SO_4 (aqueous solution)	207.5	"

Example I

To calculate the heat of formation of methane (CH_4) where

Heat of combustion of methane = 210.8
Heat of formation of CO_2 = 94.38
Heat of formation of $\frac{1}{2}H_2O$ = 34.19

and where the combustion occurs according to the equation:

$$CH_4 + 2O_2 = CO_2 \text{ (gas)} + 2H_2O \text{ (liquid)}$$

Then the heat of formation of $CH_4 = 94.38 + 4(34.19) - 210.8 = +20.34$ kg-cal. per gram molecular weight.

Example II

To calculate the heat of formation of ethylene (C_2H_4) where

Heat of combustion of ethylene = 337.23

and the combustion occurs according to the equation:

$$C_2H_4 + 3O_2 = 2CO_2 + 2H_2O$$

The heat of formation of $C_2H_4 = 2(94.38) + 4(34.19) - 337.23 = -11.71$ kg-cal. per gram molecular weight.

Example III

To calculate the heat of formation of ethylamine ($C_2H_5NH_2$) where

Heat of combustion of ethylamine = 409.5

and the combustion occurs according to the equation:

$$C_2H_5NH_2 + 3.75O_2 = 2CO_2 + 3.5(H_2O) + 0.5N_2$$

The heat of formation of $C_2H_5NH_2 = 2(94.38) + 7(34.19) + O(N_2) - 409.5 = +18.59$ kg-cal. per gram molecular weight.

LOWERING OF VAPOR PRESSURE BY SALTS IN AQUEOUS SOLUTIONS

The table gives the reduction of the vapor pressure in millimeters due to the presence of the number of grammolecules of salt per liter of water given at the head of the columns, at the temperature 100° C, at which temperature the vapor pressure of pure water is 760 millimeters.
(From Smithsonian Tables.)

Substance	0.5	1.0	2.0	3.0	4.0	5.0	6.0	8.0	10.0
$Al_2(SO_4)_3$	12.8	36.5							
$AlCl_3$	22.5	61.0	179.0	318.0					
BaS_2O_6	6.6	15.4	34.4						
$Ba(OH)_2$	12.3	22.5	39.0						
$Ba(NO_3)_2$	13.5	27.0							
$Ba(ClO_3)_2$	15.8	33.3	70.5	108.2					
$BaCl_2$	16.4	36.7	77.6						
$BaBr_2$	16.8	38.8	91.4	150.0	204.7				
CaS_2O_8	9.9	23.0	56.0	106.0					
$Ca(NO_3)_2$	16.4	34.8	74.6	139.3	161.7	205.4			
$CaCl_2$	17.0	39.8	95.3	166.6	241.5	319.5			
$CaBr_2$	17.7	44.2	105.8	191.0	283.3	368.5			
$CdSO_4$	4.1	8.9	18.1						
CdI_2	7.6	14.8	33.5	52.7					
$CdBr_2$	8.6	17.8	36.7	55.7	80.0				
$CdCl_2$	9.6	18.8	36.7	57.0	77.3	99.0			
$Cd(NO_3)_2$	15.9	36.1	78.0	122.2					
$Cd(ClO_3)_2$	17.5								
$CoSO_4$	5.5	10.7	22.9	45.5					
$CoCl_2$	15.0	34.8	83.0	136.0	186.4				
$Co(NO_3)_2$	17.3	39.2	89.0	152.0	218.7	282.0	332.0		
$FeSO_4$	5.8	10.7	24.0	42.4					
H_3BO_3	6.0	12.3	25.1	38.0	51.0				
H_3PO_4	6.6	14.0	28.6	45.2	62.0	81.5	103.0	146.9	189.5
H_3AsO_4	7.3	15.0	30.2	46.4	64.9				
H_2SO_4	12.9	26.5	62.8	104.0	148.0	198.4	247.0	343.2	
KH_2PO_4	10.2	19.5	33.3	47.8	60.5	73.1	85.2		
KNO_3	10.3	21.1	40.1	57.6	74.5	88.2	102.1	126.3	148.0
$KClO_3$	10.6	21.6	42.8	62.1	80.0				
$KBrO_3$	10.9	22.4	45.0						
$KHSO_4$	10.9	21.9	43.3	65.3	85.5	107.8	129.9	170.0	
KNO_2	11.1	22.8	44.8	67.0	90.0	110.5	130.7	167.0	198.8
$KClO_4$	11.5	22.3							
KCl	12.2	24.4	48.8	74.1	100.9	128.5	152.2		
$KHCO_3$	11.6	23.6	59.0	77.6	104.2	132.0	160.0	210.0	255.0
KI	12.5	25.3	52.2	82.6	112.2	141.5	171.8	225.5	278.5
$K_2C_2O_4$	13.9	28.3	59.8	94.2	131.0				
K_2WO_4	13.9	33.0	75.0	123.8	175.4	226.4			
K_2CO_3	14.4	31.0	68.3	105.5	152.0	209.0	258.5	350.0	
KOH	15.0	29.5	64.0	99.2	140.0	181.8	223.0	309.5	387.8
K_2CrO_4	16.2	29.5	60.0						
$LiNO_3$	12.2	25.9	55.7	88.9	122.2	155.1	188.0	253.4	309.2
$LiCl$	12.1	25.5	57.1	95.0	132.5	175.5	219.5	311.5	393.5
$LiBr$	12.2	26.2	60.0	97.0	140.0	186.3	241.5	341.5	438.0
Li_2SO_4	13.3	28.1	56.8	89.0					
$LiHSO_4$	12.8	27.0	57.0	93.0	130.0	168.0			
LiI	13.6	28.6	64.7	105.2	154.5	206.0	264.0	357.0	445.0
Li_2SiFl_6	15.4	34.0	70.0	106.0					
$LiOH$	15.9	37.4	78.1						
Li_2CrO_4	16.4	32.6	74.0	120.0	171.0				
$MgSO_4$	6.5	12.0	24.5	47.5					
$MgCl_2$	16.8	39.0	100.5	183.3	277.0	377.0			
$Mg(NO_3)_2$	17.6	42.0	101.0	174.8					
$MgBr_2$	17.9	44.0	115.8	205.3	298.5				
$MgH_2(SO_4)_2$	18.3	46.0	116.0						
$MnSO_4$	6.0	10.5	21.0						
$MnCl_2$	15.0	34.0	76.0	122.3	167.0	209.0			
NaH_2PO_4	10.5	20.0	36.5	51.7	66.8	82.0	96.5	126.7	157.1
$NaHSO_4$	10.9	22.1	47.3	75.0	100.2	126.1	148.5	189.7	231.4
$NaNO_3$	10.6	22.5	46.2	68.1	90.3	111.5	131.7	167.8	198.8
$NaClO_3$	10.5	23.0	48.4	73.5	98.5	123.3	147.5	196.5	223.5
$(NaPO_3)_6$	11.6								
$NaOH$	11.8	22.8	48.2	77.3	107.5	139.1	172.5	243.3	314.0
$NaNO_2$	11.6	24.4	50.0	75.0	98.2	122.5	146.5	189.0	226.2
Na_2HPO_4	12.1	23.5	43.0	60.0	78.7	99.8	122.1		
$NaHCO_3$	12.9	24.1	48.2	77.6	102.2	127.8	152.0	198.0	239.4
Na_2SO_4	12.6	25.0	48.9	74.2					
$NaCl$	12.3	25.2	52.1	80.0	111.0	143.0	176.5		
$NaBrO_3$	12.1	25.0	54.1	81.3	108.8	136.0			
$NaBr$	12.6	25.9	57.0	89.2	124.2	159.5	197.5	268.0	
NaI	12.1	25.6	60.2	99.5	136.7	177.5	221.0	301.5	370.0
$Na_4P_2O_7$	13.2	22.0							
Na_2CO_3	14.3	27.3	53.5	80.2	111.0				
$Na_2C_2O_4$	14.5	30.0	65.8	105.8	146.0				
Na_2WO_4	14.8	33.6	71.6	115.7	162.6				
Na_3PO_4	16.5	30.0	52.5						
$(NaPO_3)_3$	17.1	36.5							
NH_4NO_3	12.8	22.0	42.1	62.7	82.9	103.8	121.0	152.2	180.0
$(NH_4)_2SiF_6$	11.5	25.0	44.5						
NH_4Cl	12.0	23.7	45.1	69.3	94.2	118.5	138.2	179.0	213.8
NH_4HSO_4	11.5	22.0	46.8	71.0	94.5	118.	139.0	181.2	218.0
$(NH_4)_2SO_4$	11.0	24.0	46.5	69.5	93.0	117.0	141.8		
NH_4Br	11.9	23.9	48.8	74.1	99.4	121.5	145.5	190.2	228.5
NH_4I	12.9	25.1	49.8	78.5	104.5	132.3	156.0	200.0	243.5
$NiSO_4$	5.0	10.2	21.5						
$NiCl_2$	16.1	37.0	86.7	147.0	212.8				
$Ni(NO_3)_2$	16.1	37.3	91.3	156.2	235.0				
$Pb(NO_3)_2$	12.3	23.5	45.0	63.0					
$Sr(SO_3)_2$	7.2	20.3	47.0						
$Sr(NO_3)_2$	15.8	31.0	64.0	97.4	131.4				
$SrCl_2$	16.8	38.8	91.4	156.8	223.3	281.5			
$SrBr_2$	17.8	42.0	101.1	179.0	267.0				
$ZnSO_4$	4.9	10.4	21.5	42.1	66.2				
$ZnCl_2$	9.2	18.7	46.2	75.0	107.0	153.0	195.0		
$Zn(NO_3)_2$	16.6	39.0	93.5	157.5	223.8				

THERMAL CONDUCTIVITY OF GASES

The values in this table are given as cal/(sec)(cm²)(°C/cm) × 10⁻⁶. To convert these values to Btu/(hr)(ft²)(°F/ft) × 10⁻⁶ multiply by 241,909.

Gas	°F / °C	-400 / -240	-300 / -184.4	-200 / -128.9	-100 / -73.3	-40 / -40	-20 / -28.9	0 / -17.8	20 / -6.7	40 / 4.4	60 / 15.6	80 / 26.7	100 / 37.8	120 / 48.9	200 / 93.3
Acetylene					28.10	34.71	37.19	39.67	42.15	45.04	47.94	50.83	53.72	56.62	69.43
Air						50.09	52.15	54.22	56.24	58.31	60.34	62.20	64.22	66.04	
Ammonia						43.39	45.87	48.35	50.83	53.31	55.79	58.68	61.58	64.47	
Argon						34.30	35.95	37.19	38.85	40.09	41.33	42.57	44.22	45.46	
Bromine								9.09					11.57		
n-Butane									30.99	33.06	35.54	38.02	40.91	43.39	54.14
i-Butane									32.65	33.89	36.37	38.85	41.74	44.22	55.79
Carbon dioxide						27.90	29.75	31.70	33.68	35.62	37.61	39.67	41.74	43.81	
Carbon disulfide								14.05	15.29	16.53	17.77	19.01	19.84		
Carbon monoxide						47.94	50.00	51.95	53.85	55.87	57.86	59.92		63.89	
Chlorine						15.29	16.53	17.36	18.18	19.01	20.25	21.08	21.90	23.14	
Deuterium						274.82	285.15	295.07	305.81	309.95	322.34	334.74	343.01	355.40	
Ethane					23.97	32.65	35.54	38.43	41.33	44.63	47.94	51.24	54.55	58.27	74.39
Ethanol									29.34	30.99	32.65	34.71	36.78		
Ethylamine									31.41	33.47	35.54	37.61	39.67	42.15	
Ethylene					26.86	33.06	35.54	38.02	40.50	43.39	46.29	49.18	52.07	54.96	68.19
Fluorine			18.18	30.58	13.39	50.83	52.90	55.38	57.86	59.92	61.99	64.06	66.12	68.19	76.04
Helium		84.31	163.24	221.51	274.8	304.99	314.49	324.00	333.50	343.42	352.10	360.36	368.63	376.07	
Hydrogen		59.92	142.57	227.29	308.7	357.47	371.93	388.46	405.00	417.39	433.92	446.32	458.72	471.11	
Hydrogen bromide						15.29	16.11	16.49	17.77	18.60	19.84	20.66	21.49		
Hydrogen chloride						25.62	26.86	28.51	29.75	30.99	32.23	33.89	35.12		
Hydrogen cyanide								23.97	25.62	26.86	28.10	29.75	30.99	32.65	
Hydrogen sulfide								28.10	29.75	31.41	33.47		36.78		
Krypton								19.84					23.56		
Methane			22.32	36.86	52.07	61.37	64.55	67.86	71.08	74.39	78.11	81.83	85.54	89.26	106.62
Neon						97.94	100.84	104.14	107.03	109.93	112.82	115.71	118.19	121.09	
Nitric oxide				30.91	42.40	49.01	51.24	53.39	55.54	57.65	59.76	61.99	64.06	66.12	74.39
Nitrogen			20.25	33.06	44.22	50.42	52.48	54.55	56.20	58.27	60.34	62.40	64.06	65.71	
Nitrous oxide						28.93	30.91	32.90	35.04	37.15	39.30	41.45	43.81	46.08	
Oxygen			18.84	31.66	43.72	50.54	52.81	54.96	57.24	59.43	61.58	63.64	65.91	68.19	76.87
n-Propane						27.69	29.75	32.23	34.71	37.19	39.67	42.47	45.46	48.35	60.75
R-11(CCl₃F)							12.81	13.64	14.88	15.70	16.53	17.77	18.60		
R-12(CCl₂F₂)							17.36	18.60	19.42	20.66	21.49	22.73	23.56		
R-21(CHCl₂F)								21.90	22.32	22.73	23.14	23.56	23.97		
R-22(CHClF₂)								24.80	25.62	26.45	27.28	28.10	28.93		
Water								34.71	36.78	38.85	40.50	42.57	44.63	46.70	54.96

THERMAL CONDUCTIVITY OF GASEOUS HELIUM, NITROGEN AND WATER

From NSRDS-NBS 8
R. W. Powell, C. Y. Ho, and P. E. Liley

The thermal conductivity, k, is given in the units Milliwatt cm^{-1} °K^{-1}. To convert to Cal(*gm*) hr^{-1} cm^{-1} °K^{-1} multiply the values listed in the table by 0.860421

	k			k				k				k	
T (K)	He	N$_2$	T (K)	He	N$_2$	H$_2$O	T (K)	He	N$_2$	H$_2$O	T (K)	He	N$_2$
0.08	0.00044		150	0.950	0.1385		650	2.64	0.467	0.518	1750	5.57	0.981
0.09	0.00053		160	0.992	0.1474		660	2.67	0.472	0.529	1800	5.70	1.013
0.10	0.00064		170	1.033	0.1562		670	2.69	0.478	0.540	1850	5.83	1.046
0.15	0.00130		180	1.072	0.1651		680	2.72	0.483	0.551	1900	5.96	1.080
0.20	0.00231		190	1.112	0.1739		690	2.75	0.488	0.562	1950	6.08	1.113
0.25	0.0039		200	1.151	0.1826		700	2.78	0.493	0.572	2000	6.20	1.146
0.30	0.0062		210	1.190	0.1908		710	2.81	0.498	0.58	2100	6.44	1.207
0.35	0.0089		220	1.228	0.1989		720	2.84	0.503	0.59	2200	6.69	1.263
0.40	0.0120		230	1.266	0.2067		730	2.87	0.508	0.60	2300	6.93	1.314
0.45	0.0154		240	1.304	0.2145		740	2.90	0.513	0.62	2400	7.16	1.361
0.5	0.0187		250	1.338	0.2222	(0.140)*	750	2.92	0.517	0.63	2500	7.39	1.406
0.6	0.0231		260	1.372	0.2298	(0.148)*	760	2.95	0.522	0.64	2600	7.62	1.449
0.7	0.0252		270	1.405	0.2374	(0.156)*	770	2.98	0.526	0.65	2700	7.85	1.494
0.8	0.0262		280	1.437	0.2449	0.164	780	3.01	0.531	0.66	2800	8.07	1.542
0.9	0.0266		290	1.468	0.2524	0.172	790	3.04	0.536	0.67	2900	8.29	1.590
1.0	0.0269		300	1.499	0.2598	0.181	800	3.07	0.541	0.68	3000	8.51	1.640
1.25	0.0281		310	1.530	0.2671	0.189	810	3.09	0.546	0.69	3100	8.72	1.691
1.5	0.0306		320	1.560	0.2741	0.197	820	3.12	0.551	0.70	3200	8.95	1.743
2.0	0.0393		330	1.590	0.2808	0.205	830	3.15	0.555	0.71	3300	9.16	1.795
2.5	0.0502		340	1.619	0.2874	0.214	840	3.18	0.559	0.72	3400	9.37	1.853
3.0	0.0607		350	1.649	0.2939	0.222	850	3.21	0.564	0.73	3500	9.58	1.915
3.5	0.0732		360	1.678	0.3002	0.231	860	3.23	0.569	0.74	3600	9.79	
4.0	0.0803		370	1.708	0.3065	0.239	870	3.26	0.574	0.75	3700	10.00	
4.5	0.0879		380	1.737	0.3127	0.248	880	3.29	0.578	0.76	3800	10.22	
5.0	0.0962		390	1.766	0.3189	0.256	890	3.32	0.583	0.77	3900	10.43	
6	0.1113		400	1.795	0.3252	0.264	900	3.35	0.587	0.78	4000	10.64	
7	0.1247		410	1.824	0.3314	0.273	910	3.37	0.592		4100	10.85	
8	0.1393		420	1.853	0.3376	0.282	920	3.40	0.596		4200	11.06	
9	0.1523		430	1.882	0.3438	0.291	930	3.43	0.600		4300	11.27	
10	0.1640		440	1.914	0.3501	0.300	940	3.46	0.605		4400	11.48	
12	0.1866		450	1.947	0.3564	0.307	950	3.49	0.609		4500	11.69	
14	0.2067		460	1.980	0.3626	0.317	960	3.52	0.613		4600	11.90	
16	0.2259		470	2.013	0.3688	0.327	970	3.54	0.618		4700	12.11	
18	0.2435		480	2.046	0.3749	0.337	980	3.57	0.622		4800	12.31	
20	0.2582		490	2.080	0.3808	0.347	990	3.60	0.626		4900	12.51	
25	0.2962		500	2.114	0.3864	0.357	1000	3.63	0.631		5000	12.71	
30	0.3330		510	2.15	0.392	0.368	1050	3.76	0.651				
35	0.3669		520	2.18	0.398	0.378	1100	3.89	0.672				
40	0.4000		530	2.22	0.403	0.389	1150	4.03	0.693				
45	0.4314		540	2.25	0.408	0.400	1200	4.16	0.713				
50	0.4623	(0.0485)*	550	2.29	0.414	0.411	1250	4.29	0.733				
60	0.521	(0.0578)*	560	2.33	0.420	0.422	1300	4.43	0.754				
70	0.578	(0.0670)*	570	2.36	0.425	0.432	1350	4.55	0.775				
80	0.631	0.0762	580	2.40	0.431	0.443	1400	4.69	0.797				
90	0.679	0.0852	590	2.43	0.436	0.454	1450	4.82	0.819				
100	0.730	0.0941	600	2.47	0.441	0.464	1500	4.94	0.842				
110	0.776	0.1030	610	2.51	0.446	0.475	1550	5.07	0.867				
120	0.819	0.1119	620	2.54	0.452	0.486	1600	5.21	0.893				
130	0.863	0.1208	630	2.58	0.457	0.497	1650	5.33	0.921				
140	0.907	0.1296	640	2.61	0.462	0.508	1700	5.45	0.950				

THERMAL CONDUCTIVITY OF DIELECTRIC CRYSTALS

Name	Remarks	Conductivity mw/cm deg K	
		83° K	273° K
Marble	Small crystals, 99.9 % CaCO₃	42	33
Do	99.99 % CaCO₃	54	38
Do	Large crystals	50	33
Calcite	Main crystal axis perpendicular to rod axis.	180	46
Do	Main crystal axis parallel to rod axis.	293	54
Sylvite	Natural crystal	159	75
KCl	Pressed at 8,000 atm	314	88
KCl	From a melt	402	92
NaCl	do	343	92
NaCl	Pressed at 8,000 atm	251	71
Rock salt	do	180	63
Sylvite	do	343	84
KCl	Pressed at 1,250 atm	243	75
KCl	Pressed at 2,500 atm	368	92
KCl	Pressed at 8,900 atm	402	96
KBr	Pressed at 8,000 atm	92	38
NaBr	do	50	25
KI	do	121	29
KF	do	234	71
NaF	do	519	105
RbI	do	59	33
RbCl	do	29	21
90 % KBr, 10 % KCl	do	50	29
75 % KBr, 25 % KCl	do	29	21
50 % KBr, 50 % KCl	do	25	25
25 % KBr, 75 % KCl	Pressed at 8,000 atm	46	33
10 % KBr, 90 % KCl	do	80	50
50 % KCl, 50 % NaCl	do	188	71
KNO₃	do	17	21
Mercuric chloride	do	17	13
NH₄Cl	do	109	25
NH₄Br	do	67	25
Ba(NO₃)₂	do	33	13
Copper sulfate		29	21
Magnesium sulfate		25	25
K₄Fe(CN)₆		17	17
Chrom alum		13	21
Potassium alum		13	21
Potassium bichromate	Main crystal axis perpendicular to rod axis.	17	21
Do	Main crystal axis parallel to rod axis.	17	17
Topaz	Mineral		234
Zincblend	do	63	264
Beryll	do	88	84
Tourmaline	do	38	46

THERMAL CONDUCTIVITY OF ORGANIC COMPOUNDS

The values in this table are given as cal/(sec)(cm²)(°C/cm). To convert these values to Btu/(hr)(ft²)(°F/ft) multiply by 242.08.

Substance	k	t, °C	t, °F
Acetaldehyde	0.0004089	21	69.8
Acetic acid	0.0004109	20	68
Acetic anhydride	0.0005286	21	69.8
Acetone	0.0004750	−80	−112
	0.0004543	16	61
	0.0004031	75	167
Allyl alcohol	0.0004295	30	86
Amyl acetate (n)	0.0003085	20	68
(iso)	0.000310	20	68
Amyl alcohol (n)	0.0003874	30–100	86–212
(iso)	0.0003531	30	86
Amyl bromide (n)	0.0002350	18	64.4
Aniline	0.0004237	16.5	61.5
Benzene	0.0003780	22.5	72.5
	0.0003275	60	122
	0.0003630	60	140
	0.0002870	140	284
Bromobenzene	0.0002664	20	68
Butyl acetate (n)	0.000327	20	68
Butyl alcohol (n)	0.0003663	20	68
Carbon tetrachloride	0.0002470	20	68
	0.0002333	50	122
Chlorobenzene	0.0003457	30–100	86–212
Chlorotoluene (p)	0.000310	20	68
Chloroform	0.0002891	16	61
	0.000246	20	68
Cresol (m)	0.0003581	20	68
(p)	0.000345	20.1	68.2
Cumene	0.000298	20	68
Cymene (p)	0.0000217	30	86
Decane	0.0003349	30	86

THERMAL CONDUCTIVITY OF ORGANIC COMPOUNDS (Continued)

Substance	k	t, °C	t, °F
Diethyl ether	0.0003283	30	86
Dichloroethane, 1–2	0.000302	20	68
Di-isopropyl ether	0.000262	20	68
Ethyl acetate	0.0003560	16	60.8
Ethyl alcohol	0.0003995	20	68
Ethyl benzene	0.0003160	20	68
Ethyl bromide	0.0002862	30	86
Ethyl ether	0.0003283	30	86
Ethyl iodide	0.0002651	30	86
Ethylene glycol	0.0006236	20	68
	0.0006323	15	122
	0.0006443	80	176
Freon-12 (CCl₂F₂)	0.0002310	0–75	32–167
Freon-21 (CHCl₂F)	0.0003180	0–75	32–167
Freon-22 (CHClF₂)	0.0002309	40	104
Freon-113 (CCl₂FCCl₂F)	0.0002379	0–80	32–176
Freon-114 (C₂H₂F₄)	0.0002127	0–75	32–167
Glycerol	0.000703	20	68
Heptane (n)	0.0003354	30	86
Heptyl alcohol	0.0003882	70–100	86–212
Hexane (n)	0.0003287	30–100	86–212
Hexyl alcohol (n)	0.0003857	30–100	86–212
Iodobenzene	0.0002874	30–100	86–212
Mesitylene	0.0003246	20	68
Methyl alcohol	0.0004832	20	68
Methyl aniline	0.0004419	21.5	70.5
Methyl chloride	0.0004597	−15 (−) +30	5–86
Methyl cyclohexane	0.0003052	30	86
Methylene chloride	0.0002908	0	32
Nitrobenzene	0.0003907	30–100	86–212
Nitromethane	0.0005142	30	86
Nonane (n)	0.0003374	30–100	86–212
Nonyl alcohol (n)	0.0004014	30–100	86–212
Octane (n)	0.0003469	30	86
Octyl alcohol (n)	0.0003973	30–100	86–212
Oleic acid	0.0005514	26.5	79.7
Palmitic acid	0.0004097	72.5	162.5
Pentachloroethane	0.0002994	20	68
Pentane (n)	0.0003221	30	86
Phenetole	0.0003577	−20	−4
Phenyl hydrazine	0.0004121	25	69.8
Propyl acetate (iso)	0.000321	20	68
Propyl alcohol (iso)	0.0003362	20	68
Propylene chloride	0.0002994	20–50	68–122
Propylene glycol (1–2)	0.0004799	20–80	68–176
Stearic acid	0.0003824	72.5	162.5
Tetrachloroethane (sym)	0.000272	20	68
Tetrachloroethylene	0.0003366	20	68
Toluene	0.0003804	−80	−112
	0.0003221	20	68
	0.0002808	80	176
Trichloroethylene	0.0003246	−60	−76
	0.0002775	20	68
Triethylamine	0.0003498	−80	−112
	0.0002891	20	68
	0.0002664	44.4	112
Xylene (o)	0.0003411	−20 (−) +80	(−4)–176
Xylene (m)	0.0003767	25	77

THERMAL CONDUCTIVITY OF INORGANIC COMPOUNDS

Substance	k	t, °C	t, °F
Ammonia	0.0001198	−15 (−) +30	5–86
Argon	0.0002895	−183	−297
	0.0001677	−133	−207
	0.0000553	−105	−157.5
	0.0000409	−75	−102.5
Carbon dioxide	0.0002040	−50	−58
	0.0002412	−40	−40
	0.0002664	−30	−22
	0.0002746	−20	−4
	0.0002495	0	32
	0.0001677	30	86
Nitrogen	0.0003400	−196	−321.5
	0.0002961	−189	−308
	0.0002028	−158	−253
	0.0000640	−105	155
Oxygen	0.0000300	(−207)–(−191)	(−340)–(−312)
	0.0000504	(−178)–(−182)	(−288)–(−295)
Water	0.001348	0	72
	0.001429	20	68
	0.001499	40	104
	0.001557	60	140
	0.001598	100	212
	0.001631	149	300
	0.001553	216	420
	0.001404	271	520
	0.001136	327	620

THERMAL CONDUCTIVITY OF MISCELLANEOUS SUBSTANCES

Chlorinated diphenyl 1242....	0.0002936	30–100	86–212
Chlorinated diphenyl 1248....	0.0002808	30–100	86–212
Kerosene........................	0.0003572	30	86
Light heat transfer oil........	0.0003159	30–100	86–212
Petroleum ether...............	0.0003118	30	86
Red oil........................	0.0003366	30	86
Transformer oil	0.0004242	70–100	86–212

THERMAL CONDUCTIVITY OF MATERIALS
(Bureau of Standards Letter Circular No. 227)

D = Density in pounds per cubic foot.

K = Thermal conductivity in B.T.U. per hour, square foot, and temperature gradient of 1 degree Fahrenheit per inch thickness. The lower the conductivity, the greater the insulating values.

SOFT FLEXIBLE MATERIALS IN SHEET FORM

		D	K
Dry Zero	Kapok between burlap or paper..	1.0	0.24
		2.0	0.25
Cabots Quilt	Eel grass between kraft paper....	3.4	0.25
		4.6	0.26
Hair Felt	Felted cattle hair...............	11.0	0.26
		13.0	0.26
Balsam Wool	Chemically treated wood fibre....	2.2	0.27
Hairinsul	75% hair 25% jute............	6.3	0.27
	50% hair 50% jute............	6.1	0.26
Linofelt	Flax fibres between paper........	4.9	0.28
Thermofelt	Jute and asbestos fibres. felted...	10.0	0.37
	Hair and asbestos fibres. felted...	7.8	0.28

LOOSE MATERIALS

Rock Wool	Fibrous material made from rock,	6.0	0.26
	also made in sheet form, felted and	10.0	0.27
	confined with wire netting.......	14.0	0.28
		18.0	0.29
Glass Wool	Pyrex glass, curled..............	4.0	0.29
		10.0	0.29
Sil-O-Cel	Powdered diatomaceous earth....	10.6	0.31
Regranulated	Fine particles..................	9.4	0.30
Cork	about 3/16 inch particles.........	8.1	0.31
Thermofill	Gypsum in powdered form......	26.	0.52
		34.	0.60
Sawdust	Various.......................	12.0	0.41
	redwood......................	10.9	0.42
Shavings	Various, from planer............	8.8	0.41
Charcoal	From maple, beech and birch,		
	coarse.....................	13.2	0.36
	6 mesh.....................	15.2	0.37
	20 mesh....................	19.2	0.39

SEMI-FLEXIBLE MATERIALS IN SHEET FORM

Flaxlinum	Flax fibre...............	13.0	0.31
Fibrofelt	Flax and rye fibre..............	13.6	0.32

SEMI-RIGID MATERIALS IN BOARD FORM

Corkboard	No added binder; very low density	5.4	0.25
Corkboard	No added binder; low density....	7.0	0.27
Corkboard	No added binder; medium density	10.6	0.30
Corkboard	No added binder; high density .	14.0	0.34
Eureka	Corkboard with asphaltic binder .	14.5	0.32
Rock Cork	Rock wool block with binder.....	14.5	0.326
	Also called "Tucork"		
Lith	Board containing rock wool, flax		
	and straw pulp.................	14.3	0.40

STIFF FIBROUS MATERIALS IN SHEET FORM

Insulite	Wood pulp...................	16.2	0.34
		16.9	0.34
Celotex	Sugar cane fibre.............	13.2	0.34
		14.8	0.34
*Masonite.....................		K =	0.33
*Inso-board			0.33
*Maizewood................			0.33 to 0.39
*Cornstalk Pith Board			0.24 to 0.30
*Maftex.......................			0.34

THERMAL CONDUCTIVITY OF MATERIALS
(Continued)

CELLULAR GYPSUM

Insulex or Pyrocell...................	8	0.35
	12	0.44
	18	0.59
	24	0.77
	30	1.00

WOODS (Across Grain)

Balsa	7.3	0.33
	8.8	0.38
	20	0.58
Cypress.......................	29	0.67
White pine....................	32	0.78
Mahogany.....................	34	0.90
Virginia pine..................	34	0.98
Oak...........................	38	1.02
Maple.........................	44	1.10

MISCELLANEOUS BUILDING MATERIALS
(Data taken from various sources)

	K		K
Cinder concrete....	2 to 3	Limestone......	4 to 9
Building gypsum....	About 3	Concrete.......	6 to 9
Plaster............	2 to 5	Sandstone......	8 to 16
Building brick......	3 to 6	Marble.......	14 to 20
Glass.............	5 to 6	Granite........	13 to 28

* From various commercial laboratories and the work of O. R. Sweeney at Iowa State College.

THERMAL CONDUCTIVITY DATA ON CERAMIC MATERIALS

Description[a]	Class.[b]	Water Abs. %	Bulk Density gms/cc	Thermal Conductivity[c]		
				100°F	200°F	300°F
Single Crystals						
Silicon carbide	5	—	—	52.0	50.0	49.0
Periclase	5	—	—	26.7	22.5	19.5
Sapphire, c-axis	5	—	—	20.2	16.0	14.0
Sapphire, a-axis	5	—	—	18.7	15.0	12.9
Topaz, a-axis	5	—	—	10.8	9.4	7.9
Kyanite, a-axis	5	—	—	10.00	8.6	7.4
Kyanite, b-axis	5	—	—	9.6	8.3	7.1
Spinel, MgO·Al₂O₃	5	—	—	6.80	6.20	5.50
Quartz, c-axis	4	—	—	6.40	5.40	5.02
Quartz, a-axis	4	—	—	3.40	3.00	2.60
Rutile, c-axis	5	—	—	5.60	4.80	4.40
Rutile, a-axis	5	—	—	3.20	3.20	3.20
Fluorite	5	—	—	5.30	4.37	3.45
Beryl, aquamarine, c-axis	4	—	—	3.18	3.15	3.12
Beryl, aquamarine, a-axis	4	—	—	2.52	2.52	2.52
Zircon, a-axis	4	—	—	2.45	2.45	2.45
Zircon, c-axis	4	—	—	2.34	2.34	2.35
Polycrystalline Single Oxide Ceramics						
Pure BeO, hot pressed	2	0.03	2.97	125.0	104.0	92.0
MgO (spec. pure)	1	0.83	3.21	21.2	18.4	16.0
SnO₂ 98 %	1	0.03	6.62	17.5	15.0	12.7
ZnO (yellow)	1	0.00	5.28	16.8	14.6	12.5
ZnO (gray)	1	0.03	5.20	13.6	11.8	10.2
CuO (100 %)	1	0.04	6.70	10.2	9.00	7.80
ThO₂, hot pressed	2	—	9.58	8.00	7.02	6.50
CeO₂	1	0.00	6.20	6.63	6.29	5.20
Mn₃O₄	1	0.02	4.21	4.18	3.80	3.41
PbO (100 %)	1	0.38	7.98	1.6	1.25	0.98

[a] Composition: 90 % MgO, 10 % Al₂O₃ designates weight percent. Li₂O:4B₂O₃ designates mole composition, does not indicate compound formation.

[b] Classification: 1 = research body; 2 = industrial research body; 3 = commercial body; 4 = natural mineral; 5 = synthetic mineral.

[c] Thermal conductivity: Units in Btu/(hr) (sq ft)(°F/ft); to convert to cal/(sec) (sq cm)(°C/cm) multiply by 0.00413. (I) = determination made with high vacuum apparatus, inconel thermodes. No letters following value, determination made with high vacuum thermal conductivity apparatus, copper thermodes.

By permission from Engineering Research Bulletin No. 40 Rutgers University (1958).

THERMAL CONDUCTIVITIES OF GLASSES BETWEEN −150 AND +100°C
E. H. Ratcliffe

Type of glass	Approximate silica contents (wt. %)	Approximate contents other oxides normally present in quantity (wt. %)		Estimated approximate thermal conductivity at various temperatures	
				Temperature (°C)	Thermal conductivity $\left(\dfrac{\text{cal cm}}{\text{cm}^2\,\text{s deg C}}\right) \times 10^4$
(a) Vitreous silica	100	. . . .		−150	20.0
				−100	25.0
				− 50	28.8
				0	31.5
				50	33.7
				100	35.4
(b) 'Vycor' glass	96	B_2O_3	3	−100	24
				0	30
				100	34
(c) General information					
'Crown' glasses	50–75	Various		−100	12–20.5
				30	19–26
				100	21–29
'Flint' glasses	20–55	Various		−100	9–15
				30	13–21
				100	15–23
(d) Pyrex type chemically-resistant borosilicate glasses	80–81	B_2O_3	12–13	−100	21
		Na_2O	4	0	26
		Al	2	100	30
(e) Borosilicate crown glasses	60–65	B_2O_3	15–20	−100	16–17.5
				0	21–22.5
				100	24–25.5
	65–70	B_2O_3	10–15	−100	17.5–19
				0	22.5–24
				100	25.5–27
	70–75	B_2O_3	5–10	−100	19–20.5
				0	24.5–26
				100	27.5–29
(f) (i) Zinc crown glasses	55–65	ZnO	5–15	−100	21–22
		Remainder		0	26–27
		B_2O_3, Al_2O_3		100	28–30
		ZnO	5–15	−100	14–17
		Remainder		0	17–21
		Na_2O, K_2O		100	20–23
		ZnO	15–25	−100	21–22
		Remainder		0	26–27
		B_2O_3, Al_2O_3		100	27–29
		ZnO	15–25	−100	16–19
		Remainder		0	20–23
		Na_2O, K_2O		100	22–25
(f) (ii) Zinc crown glasses	65–75	ZnO	5–15	−100	21–22
		Remainder		0	27–28
		B_2O_3, Al_2O_3		100	29–31
		ZnO	5–15	−100	17–20
		Remainder		0	21–25
		Na_2O, K_2O		100	24–27
		ZnO	15–25	−100	21–23
		Remainder		0	27–28
		B_2O_3, Al_2O_3		100	29–30
		ZnO	15–25	−100	16–20
		Remainder		0	20–24
		Na_2O, K_2O		100	25–29

Type of glass	Approximate silica contents (wt. %)	Approximate contents other oxides normally present in quantity (wt. %)		Estimated approximate thermal conductivity at various temperatures	
				Temperature (°C)	Thermal conductivity $\left(\dfrac{\text{cal cm}}{\text{cm}^2 \text{ s deg C}}\right) \times 10^4$
(g) Barium crown glasses	31	B_2O_3	12	−100	13
		Al_2O_3	8	0	17
		BaO	48	100	19
	41	B_2O_3	6	−100	14
		Al_2O_3	2	0	18
		ZnO	8	100	20
		BaO	43		
	47	B_2O_3	4	−100	15
		Na_2O	1	0	18
		K_2O	7	100	21
		ZnO	8		
		BaO	32		
	65	B_2O_3	2	−100	17
		Na_2O	5	0	21
		K_2O	15	100	24
		ZnO	2		
		BaO	10		
(h) Borate glasses					
Borate flint glass	9	B_2O_3	36	−100	13
		Na_2O	1	0	16
		K_2O	2	100	19
		PbO	36		
		Al_2O_3	10		
		ZnO	6		
Borate flint glass	. . . .	B_2O_3	56	−100	12
		Al_2O_3	12	0	16
		PbO	32	100	20
Borate flint glass	. . . . .	B_2O_3	43	−100	9
		Al_2O_3	5	0	13
		PbO	52	100	17
Borate glass	4	B_2O_3	55	−100	15
		Al_2O_3	14	0	19
		PbO	11	100	21
		K_2O	4		
		ZnO	12		
Borate crown glass	. . . . .	B_2O_3	64	−100	12
		Na_2O	8	0	16
		K_2O	3	100	20
		BaO	4		
		PbO	3		
		Al_2O_3	18		
Light borate crown glass	. . . . .	B_2O_3	69	−100	13
		Na_2O	8	0	17
		BaO	5	100	21
		Al_2O_3	18		
Zinc borate glass	. . . . .	B_2O_3	40	−100	16
		ZnO	60	0	18
				100	20
(i) Phosphate crown glasses					
Potash phosphate glass	. . . . .	P_2O_5	70	0	18
		B_2O_3	3	100	20
		K_2O	12		

Type of glass	Approximate silica contents (wt. %)	Approximate contents other oxides normally present in quantity (wt. %)		Estimated approximate thermal conductivity at various temperatures	
				Temperature (°C)	Thermal conductivity $\left(\dfrac{\text{cal cm}}{\text{cm}^2\,\text{s deg C}}\right) \times 10^4$
(i) Potash phosphate glass (*Continued*)	. . . . .	Al_2O_3 MgO	10 4		
Baryta phosphate glass	. . . . .	P_2O_5 B_2O_3 Al_2O_3 BaO	60 3 8 28	45	18
(j) Soda-lime glasses	75	Na_2O CaO	17 8	−100 0 100	18 23 26
	75	Na_2O CaO	12 13	−100 0 100	21 26 28
	72	Na_2O CaO Al_2O_3	15 11 2	−100 0 100	19 24 27
	65	Na_2O CaO	25 10	−100 0 100	16 20 23
	65	Na_2O CaO	15 20	−100 0 100	20 24 26
	60	Na_2O CaO	20 20	−100 0 100	18 22 24
(k) Other crown glasses Crown glass	75	Na_2O K_2O CaO	9 11 5	−100 0 100	19 24 26
High dispersion crown glass	68	Na_2O ZnO PbO	16 3 13	−100 0 100	16 20 24
(l) Miscellaneous flint glasses (i) Silicate flint glasses Light flint glasses	65	PbO Others	25 10	−100 0 100	16–17 21–22 24–25
	55	PbO Others	35 10	−100 0 100	14–16 18–20 21–22
Ordinary flint glass	45	PbO Others	45 10	−100 0 100	12–14 16–18 19–20
Heavy flint glass	35	PbO Others	60 5	−100 0 100	11–12 14–15 17–18
Very heavy flint glasses	25	PbO Others	73 2	−100 0 100	10–11 13–14 15–16
	20	PbO	80	−100 0 100	10 12 14

Type of glass	Approximate silica contents (wt. %)	Approximate contents other oxides normally present in quantity (wt. %)		Estimated approximate thermal conductivity at various temperatures	
				Temperature (°C)	Thermal conductivity $\left(\dfrac{cal\ cm}{cm^2\ s\ deg\ C} \right) \times 10^4$
(ii) Borosilicate flint glass	33	B_2O_3	31	−100	15
		PbO	25	0	20
		Al_2O_3	7	100	23
		K_2O	3		
		Na_2O	1		
(iii) Barium flint glass	50	BaO	24	−100	14
		PbO	6	0	17
		K_2O	8	100	20
		Na_2O	3		
		ZnO	8		
		Sb_2O_3	1		
(m) Other glasses					
(i) Potassium glass	59	K_2O	33	50	21–22
		CaO	8		
(ii) Iron glasses	63	Fe_2O_3	10	−100	19
		Na_2O	17	0	23
		MgO	4	100	25
		CaO	3		
		Al_2O_3	2		
	67	Fe_2O_3	15	0	21–22
		Na_2O_3	18	100	24–25
	62	Fe_2O_3	20	0	20.5–21.5
		Na_2O	18	100	23–24
(ii) Rock glasses					
Obsidian				0	32
				100	35
Artificial diabase				0	27
				100	30

THERMAL CONDUCTIVITY OF CERTAIN METALS

From NSRDS-NBS 8
R. W. Powell, C. Y. Ho, and P. E. Liley

The thermal conductivity, k, is given in the units Watt cm^{-1} °K^{-1}.
To convert to Cal(gm) hr^{-1} cm^{-1} °C^{-1} multiply the values listed in the tables by 860.421
To convert to Btu hr^{-1} ft^{-1} °F^{-1} multiply the values listed in the tables by 57.818.
ρ_0 is the residual electrical resistivity and the value of ρ at 4.2°K is used approximately as ρ_0.

T,K	Aluminum 99.996+% $\rho_0 = 0.00315$ μohm cm	Copper 99.999+% $\rho_0 = 0.000851$ μohm cm	Gold 99.999+% $\rho_0 = 0.0055$ μohm cm	Iron 99.998+% $\rho_0 = 0.0327$ μohm cm	Manganin	Platinum 99.999% $\rho_0 = 0.0106$ μohm cm	Silver 99.999+% $\rho_0 = 0.00062$ μohm cm	Tungsten 99.99+% $\rho_0 = 0.0017$ μohm cm
0	0	0	0	0	0	0	0	0
1	7.8	28.7	4.4	0.75	0.0007	2.31	39.4	14.4
2	15.5	57.3	8.9	1.49	0.0018	4.60	78.3	28.7
3	23.2	85.5	13.1	2.24	0.0031	6.79	115	42.6
4	30.8	113	17.1	2.97	0.0046	8.8	147	55.6
5	38.1	138	20.7	3.71	0.0062	10.5	172	67.1
6	45.1	159	23.7	4.42	0.0078	11.8	187	76.2
7	51.5	177	26.0	5.13	0.0095	12.6	193	82.4
8	57.3	189	27.5	5.80	0.0111	12.9	190	85.3
9	62.2	195	28.2	6.45	0.0128	12.8	181	85.1
10	66.1	196	28.2	7.05	0.0145	12.3	168	82.4
11	69.0	193	27.7	7.62	0.0162	11.7	154	77.9
12	70.8	185	26.7	8.13	0.0180	10.9	139	72.4
13	71.5	176	25.5	8.58	0.0197	10.1	124	66.4
14	71.3	166	24.1	8.97	0.0215	9.3	109	60.4
15	70.2	156	22.6	9.30	0.0232	8.4	96	54.8
16	68.4	145	20.9	9.56	0.0250	7.6	85	49.3
18	63.5	124	17.7	9.88	0.0285	6.1	66	40.0
20	56.5	105	15.0	9.97	0.0322	4.9	51	32.6
25	40.0	68	10.2	9.30	0.0410	3.15	29.5	20.4
30	28.5	43	7.6	8.14	0.0497	2.28	19.3	13.1
35	21.0	29	6.1	6.81	0.0583	1.80	13.7	8.9
40	16.0	20.5	5.2	5.55	0.067	1.51	10.5	6.5
45	12.5	15.3	4.6	4.50	0.075	1.32	8.4	5.07
50	10.0	12.2	4.2	3.72	0.082	1.18	7.0	4.17
60	6.7	8.5	3.8	2.65	0.097	1.01	5.5	3.18
70	5.0	6.7	3.58	2.04	0.110	0.90	4.97	2.76
80	4.0	5.7	3.52	1.68	0.120	0.84	4.71	2.56
90	3.4	5.14	3.48	1.46	0.127	0.81	4.60	2.44
100	3.0	4.83	3.45	1.32	0.133	0.79	4.50	2.35
150	2.47	4.28	3.35	1.04	0.156	0.762	4.32	2.10
200	2.37	4.13	3.27	0.94	0.172	0.748	4.30	1.97
250	2.35	4.04	3.20	0.865	0.193	0.737	4.28	1.86
273	2.36	4.01	3.18	0.835	0.206	0.734	4.28	1.82
300	2.37	3.98	3.15	0.803	0.222	0.730	4.27	1.78
350	2.40	3.94	3.13	0.744	0.250	0.726	4.24	1.70
400	2.40	3.92	3.12	0.694	(0.279)	0.722	4.20	1.62
500	2.37	3.88	3.09	0.613	(0.338)	0.719	4.13	1.49
600	2.32	3.83	3.04	0.547	(0.397)	0.720	4.05	1.39
700	2.26	3.77	2.98	0.487		0.723	3.97	1.33
800	2.20	3.71	2.92	0.433		0.729	3.89	1.28
900	2.13	3.64	2.85	0.380		0.737	3.82	1.24
1000	[0.93]**	3.57	(2.78)	0.326		0.748	(3.74)	1.21
1100	[0.96]	3.50	(2.71)	0.297		0.760	(3.66)	1.18
1200	[0.99]	3.42	(2.62)	0.282		0.775	(3.58)	1.15
1300	[1.02]	(3.34)†	(2.51)	0.299		0.791		1.13
1400				0.309		0.807		1.11
1500				0.318		0.824		1.09
1600				(0.327)		0.842		1.07
						0.860		1.05
						0.877		1.03
						(0.895)		1.02
								1.00
						(0.913)		0.98
								0.96
								0.94
								0.925
								0.915
								0.905
								0.900
								(0.895)

* In the table the third significant figure is given only for the purpose of comparison and for smoothness and is not indicative of the degree of accuracy.

** Values in square brackets are for liquid state.

† Values in parentheses are extrapolated.

‡ Estimated.

THERMAL CONDUCTIVITY OF CERTAIN LIQUIDS

From NSRDS-NBS 8
R. W. Powell, C. Y. Ho, and P. E. Liley

The thermal conductivity, k, is given in the units Milliwatt cm^{-1} °K^{-1}. To convert to Cal(gm) hr^{-1} cm^{-1} °K^{-1} multiply the values listed in the table by 0.860421

T (K)	Helium	Nitrogen	Argon	Carbon tetra-chloride	Diphenyl	m-Terphenyl	Toluene	Water
2.4	0.192							
2.6	0.193							
2.8	0.197							
3.0	0.204							
3.2	0.214							
3.4	0.227							
3.6	0.241							
3.8	0.260							
4.0	0.282							
4.2	0.307							
4.4	(0.335)‡							
4.6	(0.366)‡							
4.8	(0.400)‡							
5.0	(0.437)‡							
5.2	(0.477)‡							
60		1.692†						
65		1.598						
70		1.504						
75		1.411						
80		1.320‡	1.315†					
85		1.229‡	1.258					
90		1.140‡	1.200‡					
95		1.051‡	1.141‡					
100		0.965‡	1.082‡					
105		0.879‡	1.023‡					
110		0.794‡	0.963‡					
115		0.710‡	0.903‡					
120		0.627‡	0.842‡					
125		0.544‡	0.780‡					
130			0.717‡					
135			0.654‡					
140			0.591‡					
145			0.527‡					
150			0.463‡				(1.719)†	
160							(1.694)†	
170							(1.669)†	
180							1.644	
190							1.619	
200							1.594	
210							1.569	
220							1.543	
230				(1.169)†			1.518	
240				(1.150)†			1.492	
250				1.131			1.467	5.22†
260				1.112			1.442	5.39†
270				1.093			1.416	5.55†
280				1.074			1.391	5.74
290				1.055			1.365	5.92
300				1.036			1.340	6.09
310				1.017			1.315	6.23
320				0.997			1.289	6.37
330				0.978	(1.402)†		1.264	6.48
340				0.959	(1.387)†		1.238	6.59
350				0.940	1.373	(1.361)†	1.213	6.68
360				(0.921)	1.359	(1.356)†	1.188	6.75
370				(0.902)	1.345	1.351	1.162	6.80
380				(0.882)	1.331	1.346	1.137	6.84‡
390				(0.863)	1.316	1.341	(1.112)‡	6.86‡
400				(0.844)	1.302	1.335	(1.086)‡	6.86‡
410				(0.825)	1.288	1.329	(1.061)‡	6.86‡
420				(0.806)	1.274	1.323	(1.036)‡	6.84‡
430				(0.787)	1.259	1.317	(1.013)‡	6.81‡
440				(0.768)	1.245	1.310	(0.985)‡	6.78‡
450				(0.749)	1.231	1.304	(0.959)‡	6.73‡
460					1.217	1.297	(0.933)‡	6.67‡
470					1.202	1.290	(0.908)‡	6.61‡
480					1.188	1.283	(0.885)‡	6.53‡
490					1.174	1.276	(0.862)‡	6.45‡
500					1.160	1.268	(0.839)‡	6.35‡
510					1.146	1.261		6.24‡
520					1.131	1.254		6.12‡
530					1.117‡	1.246		5.99‡
540					1.103‡	1.238		5.86‡
550					1.089‡	1.230		5.71‡
560					1.074‡	1.222		5.55‡
570					1.060‡	1.213		5.39‡
580					1.046‡	1.205		5.20‡
590					1.032‡	1.197		5.01‡
600					1.018‡	1.188		4.81‡
610						1.180		4.60‡
620						1.172		4.40‡
630						1.163		(4.20)‡
640						1.155‡		(4.01)‡
650						1.146‡		

† Extrapolated for the supercooled liquid. [Approximate n.m.p. in K: N₂, 63; A, 84; CCl₄, 250; C₁₂H₁₀, 342; m-C₁₈H₁₄, 361; p-C₁₈H₁₄, 486; C₇H₁₀, 178; H₂O, 273.1].

‡ Under saturation vapor pressure [Approximate n.b.p. in K: He, 4.3; N₂, 77; A, 88; CCl₄, 350; C₁₂H₁₀, 528; m-C₁₈H₁₄, 637; p-C₁₈H₁₄, 658; C₇H₁₀, 384; H₂O, 373].

THERMAL CONDUCTIVITY OF THE ELEMENTS

Data contained in the following table were extracted from the extensive compilation prepared by C. Y. Ho, R. W. Powell, and P. E. Lilcy under the National Standard Reference Data System (NSRDS) of the National Bureau of Standards project at the Thermophysical Properties Research Center (TPRC) at Purdue University and published in the Journal of Physical and Chemical Reference Data, *1*, 279-421 (1972). The data in the table below are used with the permission of the authors and the copyright owners, the American Institute of Physics and the American Chemical Society. Users are referred to their more extensive compilation for conductivities at temperatures other than those listed in the table below, and also to obtain an understanding of the basis of selection of recommended and provisional values. Temperatures are in kelvins (K) and conductivities, k, in watt per centimeter kelvin (W cm^{-1} K^{-1}), except as noted. If the numerical value of k has a superscript m, the units of k are milliwatt per centimeter kelvin (mW cm^{-1} K^{-1}). To convert the listed conductivities to units other than those in the tables, one should make use of the conversion factors listed in the table "Conversion Factors for Units of Thermal Conductivity", which follows this table. Conductivity values listed with an asterisk*, are provisional values.

Element	State or Condition	Conductivity at 273.2K	Conductivity at 298.2K	Conductivity at 373.2K
Aluminum	Solid	2.36	2.37	2.40
Antimony	Polycrystalline	0.255	0.244	0.219
Argon	Gas at 1 atm.	0.1619^{m} (270K)	0.1772^{m} (300K)	0.2103^{m} (370K)
Arsenic	Solid, Gray, Polycrystalline	0.539*	0.502*	0.427*
Barium	Solid	0.185*	0.184* (295K)	
Beryllium	Polycrystalline	2.18*	2.01	1.68
Bismuth	Solid			
	// to triagonal axis	0.0554	0.0530	0.0481
	⊥ to triagonal axis	0.0953	0.0919	0.0844
	Polycrystalline	0.0822	0.0792	0.0722
Boron	Solid	0.318	0.274	0.188
Bromine	Saturated liquid	1.30^{m}* (270K)	1.22^{m}* (300K)	1.06^{m}* (370K)
	Saturated vapor		0.048^{m} (300K)	
	Gas	0.042^{m}* (270K)	0.048^{m}* (300K)	0.057^{m}* (350K)
Cadmium	Solid			
	// to c-axis	0.835	0.830	0.816
	⊥ to c-axis	1.04	1.04	1.02
	Polycrystalline	0.975	0.969	0.953
Calcium	Solid	2.06*	2.01*	1.92*
Carbon	Solid, Amorphous	0.0150	0.0159	0.0182
	Solid, Type I	9.94	9.90	7.03*
	Solid, Type IIa	26.2	23.2	17.0*
	Solid, Type IIb	15.2	13.6	10.2*
	Solid, Acheson graphite			
	// to axis of extrusion	1.69	1.65	1.50
	⊥ to axis of extrusion	1.21	1.19	1.11
	Solid, AGOT graphite			
	// to axis of extrusion	2.28	2.21	1.95
	⊥ to axis of extrusion	1.41	1.38	1.22
	Solid, ATJ graphite			
	// to molding pressure	0.984	0.982	0.933
	⊥ to molding pressure	1.31	1.29	1.21
	Solid, AWG graphite			
	// to molding pressure	0.807	0.796	0.733
	⊥ to molding pressure	1.32	1.28	1.16
	Solid, Pyrolytic graphite			
	// to layer planes	21.3	19.6	15.1
	⊥ to layer planes	0.0636	0.0573	0.0442

Element	State or Condition	Conductivity at		
		273.2K	298.2K	373.2K
	Solid, 875S graphite			
	// to axis of extrusion	1.97*	1.92*	1.75*
	⊥ to axis of extrusion	1.49*	1.46*	1.34*
	Solid, 890S graphite			
	// to axis of extrusion	1.87*	1.83*	1.66*
	⊥ to axis of extrusion	1.51*	1.48*	1.36*
Cerium	Solid, Polycrystalline	0.108*	0.113	0.128*
Cesium	Solid	0.361*	0.359 (301.9K)	
	Liquid		0.197 (301.9K)	0.201
Chlorine	Saturated liquid	1.49^{m}* (270K)	1.34^{m}* (300K)	0.95^{m}* (370K)
	Saturated vapor	0.082^{m}* (270K)	0.097^{m}* (300K)	0.155^{m}* (370K)
	Gas, 1 atm.	0.078^{m} (270K)	0.089^{m} (300K)	0.114^{m} (370K)
Chromium	Solid, Polycrystalline	0.965	0.939	0.921
Cobalt	Solid, Polycrystalline	1.05	1.00	0.890
Copper	Solid	4.03	4.01	3.95
Dysprosium	Solid			
	// to c-axis	0.114*	0.117*	
	⊥ to c-axis	0.101*	0.103*	
	Polycrystalline	0.105*	0.107*	0.108*
Erbium	Solid			
	// to c-axis	0.187*	0.184*	
	⊥ to c-axis	0.127*	0.126*	
	Polycrystalline	0.147*	0.145*	0.140*
Europium	Solid	0.140*	0.139*	
Fluorine	Gas, 1 atm.	0.251^{m} (270K)	0.279^{m} (300K)	0.344^{m} (370K)
Gadolinium	Solid			
	// to c-axis	0.104*	0.108*	
	⊥ to c-axis	0.103*	0.103*	
	Polycrystalline	0.103*	0.105*	
Gallium	Solid			
	// to a-axis	0.410	0.408	
	// to b-axis	0.884	0.883	
	// to c-axis	0.160	0.159	
	Liquid		0.281 (302.93K)	0.328
Germanium	Solid	0.667	0.602	0.465
Gold	Solid	3.19	3.18	3.13
Hafnium	Solid, Polycrystalline	0.233*	0.230	0.224
Helium	Solid, ³He	0.033 (0.9K)	0.020 (1K)	0.0021 (2K)
	Solid, ⁴He	0.650 (0.9K)	0.245 (1K)	0.0018 (2K)
	Liquid, saturated; He-I	0.191^{m} (2.5K)	0.232^{m} (3.5K)	0.434^{m} (5K)
	Gas, 1 atm.	1.411^{m}	1.520^{m}	1.766^{m}
Holmium	Solid			
	// to c-axis	0.215*	0.222*	
	⊥ to c-axis	0.136*	0.138*	
	Polycrystalline	0.159*	0.162*	0.170*
Hydrogen	Solid, Normal Hydrogen	2.30 (4K)	0.0158 (10K)	0.0090 (15K)
	Liquid, saturated; Normal Hydrogen	1.022^{m} (15K)	1.269^{m} (25K)	0.60^{m}* (33K)

Element	State or Condition	Conductivity at		
		273.2K	298.2K	373.2K
	Gas, 1 atm. Normal Hydrogen	1.665^m	1.815^m	2.106^m
	Liquid, saturated; para-Hydrogen	0.824^m (14K)	0.998^m (25K)	0.58^m (32K)
	Vapor, saturated; para-Hydrogen	0.081^{m*} (10K)	0.242^{m*} (25K)	0.58^{m*} (32K)
	Gas, 1 atm.; para-Hydrogen	1.768^{m*}	1.880^{m*}	2.126^{m*}
	Deuterium:			
	Liquid, saturated	1.26^m (20K)	1.37^m (30K)	0.83^{m*} (38K)
	Vapor, saturated	0.084^{m*} (20K)	0.26^{m*} (30K)	0.83^{m*} (38K)
	Gas, 1 atm.	1.294^{m*} (270K)	1.406^{m*} (300K)	1.66^{m*} (370K)
	Tritium:			
	Liquid, saturated	1.25 (21K)	1.34 (30K)	0.68 (44K)
Indium	Solid, Polycrystalline	0.837	0.818	0.762
Iodine	Solid	4.81^{m*}	4.49^{m*} (300K)	3.75^{m*} (386.8K)
	Liquid, saturated			1.16^{m*} (386.8K)
Iridium	Solid	1.48	1.47	1.45
Iron	Solid	0.865	0.804	0.720
	Armco Iron	0.747	0.728	0.676
Krypton	Solid	0.4^{m*} (1K)	17^m (10K)	2.5^m (116K)
	Liquid, saturated			0.931^m (116K)
	Vapor, saturated	0.0406^{m*} (120K)	0.0554^{m*} (150K)	0.21^{m*} (210K)
	Gas	0.0860^m (270K)	0.0949^m (300K)	0.1145^m (370K)
Lanthanum	Solid, Polycrystalline	0.131	0.134	0.145
Lead	Solid	0.356	0.353	0.344
Lithium	Solid	0.859	0.848	0.818
Lutetium	Solid			
	∥ to c-axis	0.236*	0.232*	
	⊥ to c-axis	0.140*	0.138*	
	Polycrystalline	0.167*	0.164*	
Magnesium	Solid, Polycrystalline	1.57	1.56	1.54
Manganese	Solid	0.0768*	0.0781*	
Mercury	Liquid	0.0782	0.0830	0.0947
Molybdenum	Solid	1.39*	1.38*	1.35*
Neodymium	Solid, Polycrystalline	0.165*	0.165*	0.167*
Neon	Gas	0.461^{m*} (270K)	0.493^{m*} (300K)	0.563^{m*} (370K)
Neptunium	Solid		0.063* (300K)	
Nickel	Solid	0.941	0.909	0.827
Niobium	Solid	0.533	0.537	0.548
Nitrogen	Solid	56^m (4K)	17^m (10K)	3.2^m (25K)
	Liquid, saturated	1.60^m (65K)	0.966^m (100K)	0.37^{m*} (126K)
	Vapor, saturated	0.061^{m*} (65K)	0.111^{m*} (100K)	0.37^{m*} (126K)
	Gas, 1 atm.	0.2374^m (270K)	0.2598^m (300K)	0.3065^m (370K)

Element	State or Condition	Conductivity at		
		273.2K	298.2K	373.2K
Cesium	Solid			
	// to c-axis	2.93	14.3	15.4
		(2K)	(10K)	(30K)
	⊥ to c-axis	1.76	8.65	11.1
		(2K)	(10K)	(30K)
	Polycrystalline	2.09	10.2	12.4
		(2K)	(10K)	(30K)
	Polycrystalline	0.880*	0.876*	0.870*
Oxygen	Liquid, saturated	1.501^m	1.023^m	0.41^m
		(90K)	(125K)	(155K)
	Vapor, saturated	0.081^m*	0.135^m*	0.41^m*
		(90K)	(125K)	(155K)
	Gas, 1 atm.	0.2424	0.2674	0.3204
		(270K)	(300K)	(370K)
Palladium	Solid	0.716*	0.718	0.730
Phosphorus	Solid			
	Black (Polycrystalline)	0.132	0.121	
	White	0.00250*	0.00236*	
	Liquid, White			0.00181
Platinum	Solid	0.717	0.716	0.717
Plutonium	Solid, polycrystalline	0.0616*	0.0670*	0.0790*
				(350K)
Potassium	Solid	1.036*	1.025	
	Liquid			0.532
Praeseodymium	Solid, polycrystalline	0.120	0.125	0.134
Promethium	Solid, polycrystalline		0.179*	0.184*
Radium	Solid		0.186	
			(293.2K)	
Radon	Gas, 1 atm.	0.0327^m*	0.0364^m*	0.0445^m*
		(270K)	(300K)	(370K)
Rhenium	Solid, polycrystalline	0.486	0.480	0.466
Rhodium	Solid	1.51	1.50	1.47
Rubidium	Solid	0.583*	0.582	0.581
				(312.04K)
	Liquid			0.333
				(312.04K)
Ruthenium	Solid, polycrystalline	1.17	1.17	1.15
Samarium	Solid, polycrystalline	0.133*	0.133*	0.133*
Scandium	Solid, polycrystalline	0.157	0.158	
Selenium	Solid			
	// to c-axis	0.0481	0.0452	0.0483
	⊥ to c-axis	0.0137	0.0131	0.0139
	Amorphous	0.00428	0.00519	0.00818
				(323.2K)
Silicon	Solid	1.68	1.49	1.08
Silver	Solid	4.29	4.29	4.26
Sodium	Solid	1.42	1.42	1.32
				(371K)
Strontium	Solid, polycrystalline	0.364*	0.354*	0.325*
Sulfur	Solid, polycrystalline	0.00287	0.00270	0.00154
	Solid, amorphous	0.00200	0.00205	0.00216*
				(350K)
	Liquid			0.00129
				(392.2K)
Tantalum	Solid	0.574	0.575	0.577
Technetium	Solid, polycrystalline	0.509*	0.506	0.501
Tellurium	Solid			
	// to c-axis	0.0360	0.0338	0.0292
	⊥ to c-axis	0.0208	0.197	0.173

THERMAL CONDUCTIVITY OF THE ELEMENTS (*Continued*)

Element	State or Condition	Conductivity at		
		273.2K	298.2K	373.2K
Terbium	Solid			
	∥ to c-axis	0.138*	0.147*	
	⊥ to c-axis	0.0900*	0.0956*	
	Polycrystalline	0.104*	0.111*	
Thallium	Solid, polycrystalline	0.469	0.461	0.443
Thorium	Solid	0.540*	0.540*	0.543*
Thulium	Solid			
	∥ to c-axis	0.242*	0.242*	
	⊥ to c-axis	0.140*	0.141*	
	Polycrystalline	0.168*	0.169*	
Tin	Solid			
	∥ to c-axis	0.527	0.516	0.489
	⊥ to c-axis	0.759	0.743	0.704
	Polycrystalline	0.682	0.668	0.632
Titanium	Solid, polycrystalline	0.224	0.219	0.207
Tungsten	Solid	1.77	1.73	1.63
Uranium	Solid, polycrystalline	0.270	0.275	0.291
Vanadium	Solid	0.307*	0.307	0.310
Xenon	Liquid, saturated	0.31^m	0.16^{m*}	
		(270K)	(290K)	
	Vapor, saturated	0.084^{m*}	0.16^{m*}	
	Gas, 1 atm.	0.0514^m	0.0569^m	0.0695^m
		(270K)	(300K)	(370K)
Ytterbium	Solid	0.354*	0.349*	0.343*
Yttrium	Solid, polycrystalline	0.170*	0.172*	0.177*
Zinc	Solid, polycrystalline	1.17	1.16	1.12
Zirconium	Solid, polycrystalline	0.232*	0.227	0.218
			(300K)	

THERMAL CONDUCTIVITY OF ROCKS

Rock	Temperature, °C	Conductivity, cal m^{-1} hr^{-1} deg^{-1}	Heat Capacity, cal kg^{-1} deg^{-1}
Granite	0	3.02	0.192
	50	2.81	—
	100	2.59	—
	200	2.34	0.228
	300	2.12	—
	400	—	0.258
Marble	118	1.44	0.21
	196	1.29	0.24
	245	1.19	—
	360	0.95	0.271
Dolomitic	130	1.41	—
limestone	181	1.37	—
	268	1.29	—
	377	1.15	
	0	1.65	0.17
Shale	100	1.31	
	120	1.33	—
	188	1.41	0.24
	304	1.26	0.245
	0	4.9	—
Sandstone	100	3.82	0.26
(quartzitic)	200	3.24	—

CONVERSION FACTORS FOR UNITS OF THERMAL CONDUCTIVITY

MULTIPLY

by appropriate factor to	OBTAIN→					
	Btu_{IT} h^{-1} ft^{-1} F^{-1}	Btu_{IT} in. h^{-1} ft^{-2} F^{-1}	Btu_{th} h^{-1} ft^{-1} F^{-1}	Btu_{th} in. h^{-1} ft^{-2} F^{-1}	cal_{IT} s^{-1} cm^{-1} C^{-1}	cal_{th} s^{-1} cm^{-1} C^{-1}
Btu_{IT} h^{-1} ft^{-1} F^{-1}	1	12	1.00067	12.0080	4.13379×10^{-3}	4.13656×10^{-3}
Btu_{IT} in. h^{-1} ft^{-2} F^{-1}	8.33333×10^{-2}	1	8.33891×10^{-2}	1.00067	3.44482×10^{-4}	3.44713×10^{-4}
Btu_{th} h^{-1} ft^{-1} F^{-1}	0.999331	11.9920	1	12	4.13102×10^{-3}	4.13379×10^{-3}
Btu_{th} in. h^{-1} ft^{-2} F^{-1}	8.32776×10^{-2}	0.999331	8.33333×10^{-2}	1	3.44252×10^{-4}	3.44482×10^{-4}
cal_{IT} s^{-1} cm^{-1} C^{-1}	2.41909×10^{2}	2.90291×10^{3}	2.42071×10^{2}	2.90485×10^{3}	1	1.00067
cal_{th} s^{-1} cm^{-1} C^{-1}	2.41747×10^{2}	2.90096×10^{3}	2.41909×10^{2}	2.90291×10^{3}	0.999331	1
$kcal_{th}$ h^{-1} m^{-1} C^{-1}	0.671520	8.05824	0.671969	8.06363	2.77592×10^{-3}	2.77778×10^{-3}
J s^{-1} cm^{-1} K^{-1}	57.7789	6.93347×10^{2}	57.8176	6.93811×10^{2}	0.238846	0.239006
W cm^{-1} K^{-1}	57.7789	6.93347×10^{2}	57.8176	6.93811×10^{2}	0.238846	0.239006
W m^{-1} K^{-1}	0.577789	6.93347	0.578176	6.93811	2.38846×10^{-3}	2.39006×10^{-3}
mW cm^{-1} K^{-1}	5.77789×10^{-2}	0.693347	5.78176×10^{-2}	0.693811	2.38846×10^{-4}	2.39006×10^{-4}

MULTIPLY

by appropriate factor to	OBTAIN→				
	$kcal_{th}$ h^{-1} m^{-1} C^{-1}	J s^{-1} cm^{-1} K^{-1}	W cm^{-1} K^{-1}	W m^{-1} K^{-1}	mW cm^{-1} K^{-1}
Btu_{IT} h^{-1} ft^{-1} F^{-1}	1.48916	1.73073×10^{-2}	1.73073×10^{-2}	1.73073	17.3073
Btu_{IT} in. h^{-1} ft^{-2} F^{-1}	0.124097	1.44228×10^{-3}	1.44228×10^{-3}	0.144228	1.44228
Btu_{th} h^{-1} ft^{-1} F^{-1}	1.48816	1.72958×10^{-2}	1.72958×10^{-2}	1.72958	17.2958
Btu_{th} in. h^{-1} ft^{-2} F^{-1}	0.124014	1.44131×10^{-3}	1.44131×10^{-3}	0.144131	1.44131
cal_{IT} s^{-1} cm^{-1} C^{-1}	3.60241×10^{2}	4.1868	4.1868	4.1868×10^{2}	4.1868×10^{3}
cal_{th} s^{-1} cm^{-1} C^{-1}	3.6×10^{2}	4.184	4.184	4.184×10^{2}	4.184×10^{3}
$kcal_{th}$ h^{-1} m^{-1} C^{-1}	1	1.16222×10^{-2}	1.16222×10^{-2}	1.16222	11.6222
J s^{-1} cm^{-1} K^{-1}	86.0421	1	1	1×10^{2}	1×10^{3}
W cm^{-1} K^{-1}	86.0421	1	1	1×10^{2}	1×10^{3}
W m^{-1} K^{-1}	0.860421	1×10^{-2}	1×10^{-2}	1	10
mW cm^{-1} K^{-1}	8.60421×10^{-2}	1×10^{-3}	1×10^{-3}	0.1	1

STEAM TABLES

Reproduced by permission of the publishers and copyright owners of the 1967 ASME Steam Tables. Further data and information on the thermodynamic and transport properties of steam and water are contained in the above ASME publication. It is obtainable from The American Society of Mechanical Engineers, United Engineering Center, 345 East 47th Street, New York, New York 10017.

Properties of Saturated Steam and Saturated Water

Temp. F	Press. psia	Volume, ft³/lbm			Enthalpy, Btu/lbm			Entropy, Btu/lbm × F			Temp. F
		Water v_f	Evap. v_{fg}	Steam v_g	Water h_f	Evap. h_{fg}	Steam h_g	Water s_f	Evap. s_{fg}	Steam s_g	
705.47	3208.2	0.05078	0.00000	0.05078	906.0	0.0	906.0	1.0612	0.0000	1.0612	705.47
705.0	3198.3	0.04427	0.01304	0.05730	873.0	61.4	934.4	1.0329	0.0527	1.0856	705.0
704.5	3187.8	0.04233	0.01822	0.06055	861.9	85.3	947.2	1.0234	0.0732	1.0967	704.5
704.0	3177.2	0.04108	0.02192	0.06300	854.2	102.0	956.2	1.0169	0.0876	1.1046	704.0
703.5	3166.8	0.04015	0.02489	0.06504	848.2	115.2	963.5	1.0118	0.0991	1.1109	703.5
703.0	3156.3	0.03940	0.02744	0.06684	843.2	126.4	969.6	1.0076	0.1087	1.1163	703.0
702.5	3145.9	0.03878	0.02969	0.06847	838.9	136.1	974.9	1.0039	0.1171	1.1210	702.5
702.0	3135.5	0.03824	0.03173	0.06997	835.0	144.7	979.7	1.0006	0.1246	1.1252	702.0
701.5	3125.2	0.03777	0.03361	0.07138	831.5	152.6	984.0	0.9977	0.1314	1.1291	701.5
701.0	3114.9	0.03735	0.03536	0.07271	828.2	159.8	988.0	0.9949	0.1377	1.1326	701.0
700.5	3104.6	0.03697	0.03701	0.07397	825.2	166.5	991.7	0.9924	0.1435	1.1359	700.5
700.0	3094.3	0.03662	0.03857	0.07519	822.4	172.7	995.2	0.9901	0.1490	1.1390	700.0
699.0	3073.9	0.03600	0.04149	0.07749	817.3	184.2	1001.5	0.9858	0.1590	1.1447	699.0
698.0	3053.6	0.03546	0.04420	0.07966	812.6	194.6	1007.2	0.9818	0.1681	1.1499	698.0
697.0	3033.5	0.03498	0.04674	0.08172	808.4	204.0	1012.4	0.9783	0.1764	1.1547	697.0
696.0	3013.4	0.03455	0.04916	0.08371	804.4	212.8	1017.2	0.9749	0.1841	1.1591	696.0
695.0	2993.5	0.03415	0.05147	0.08563	800.6	221.0	1021.7	0.9718	0.1914	1.1632	695.0
694.0	2973.7	0.03379	0.05370	0.08749	797.1	228.8	1025.9	0.9689	0.1983	1.1671	694.0
693.0	2954.0	0.03345	0.05587	0.08931	793.8	236.1	1029.9	0.9660	0.2048	1.1708	693.0
692.0	2934.5	0.03313	0.05797	0.09110	790.5	243.1	1033.6	0.9634	0.2110	1.1744	692.0
690.0	2895.7	0.03256	0.06203	0.09459	784.5	256.1	1040.6	0.9583	0.2227	1.1810	690.0
688.0	2857.4	0.03204	0.06595	0.09799	778.8	268.2	1047.0	0.9535	0.2337	1.1872	688.0
686.0	2819.5	0.03157	0.06976	0.10133	773.4	279.5	1052.9	0.9490	0.2439	1.1930	686.0
684.0	2782.1	0.03114	0.07349	0.10463	768.2	290.2	1058.4	0.9447	0.2537	1.1984	684.0
682.0	2745.1	0.03074	0.07716	0.10790	763.3	300.4	1063.6	0.9406	0.2631	1.2036	682.0
680.0	2708.6	0.03037	0.08080	0.11117	758.5	310.1	1068.5	0.9365	0.2720	1.2086	680.0
678.0	2672.5	0.03002	0.08440	0.11442	753.8	319.4	1073.2	0.9326	0.2807	1.2133	678.0
676.0	2636.8	0.02970	0.08799	0.11769	749.2	328.5	1077.6	0.9287	0.2892	1.2179	676.0
674.0	2601.5	0.02939	0.09156	0.12096	744.7	337.2	1081.9	0.9249	0.2974	1.2223	674.0
672.0	2566.6	0.02911	0.09514	0.12424	740.2	345.7	1085.9	0.9212	0.3054	1.2266	672.0
670.0	2532.2	0.02884	0.09871	0.12755	735.8	354.0	1089.8	0.9174	0.3133	1.2307	670.0
668.0	2498.1	0.02858	0.10229	0.13087	731.5	362.1	1093.5	0.9137	0.3210	1.2347	668.0
666.0	2464.4	0.02834	0.10588	0.13421	727.1	370.0	1097.1	0.9100	0.3286	1.2387	666.0
664.0	2431.1	0.02811	0.10947	0.13757	722.9	377.7	1100.6	0.9064	0.3361	1.2425	664.0
662.0	2398.2	0.02789	0.11306	0.14095	718.8	385.1	1103.9	0.9028	0.3434	1.2462	662.0
660.0	2365.7	0.02768	0.11663	0.14431	714.9	392.1	1107.0	0.8995	0.3502	1.2498	660.0
658.0	2333.5	0.02748	0.12023	0.14771	711.1	399.0	1110.1	0.8963	0.3570	1.2533	658.0
656.0	2301.7	0.02728	0.12387	0.15115	707.4	405.7	1113.1	0.8931	0.3637	1.2567	656.0
654.0	2270.3	0.02709	0.12754	0.15463	703.7	412.2	1115.9	0.8899	0.3702	1.2601	654.0
652.0	2239.2	0.02691	0.13124	0.15816	700.0	418.7	1118.7	0.8868	0.3767	1.2634	652.0
650.0	2208.4	0.02674	0.13499	0.16173	696.4	425.0	1121.4	0.8837	0.3830	1.2667	650.0
648.0	2178.1	0.02657	0.13876	0.16534	692.9	431.1	1124.0	0.8806	0.3893	1.2699	648.0
646.0	2148.0	0.02641	0.14258	0.16899	689.4	437.2	1126.6	0.8776	0.3954	1.2730	646.0
644.0	2118.3	0.02625	0.14644	0.17269	685.9	443.1	1129.0	0.8746	0.4015	1.2761	644.0
642.0	2088.9	0.02610	0.15033	0.17643	682.5	448.9	1131.4	0.8716	0.4075	1.2791	642.0
640.0	2059.9	0.02595	0.15427	0.18021	679.1	454.6	1133.7	0.8686	0.4134	1.2821	640.0
638.0	2031.2	0.02580	0.15824	0.18405	675.8	460.2	1136.0	0.8657	0.4193	1.2850	638.0
636.0	2002.8	0.02566	0.16226	0.18792	672.4	465.7	1138.1	0.8628	0.4251	1.2879	636.0
634.0	1974.7	0.02553	0.16633	0.19185	669.1	471.1	1140.2	0.8599	0.4307	1.2907	634.0
632.0	1947.0	0.02539	0.17044	0.19583	665.9	476.4	1142.2	0.8571	0.4364	1.2934	632.0
630.0	1919.5	0.02526	0.17459	0.19986	662.7	481.6	1144.2	0.8542	0.4419	1.2962	630.0
628.0	1892.4	0.02514	0.17880	0.20394	659.5	486.7	1146.1	0.8514	0.4474	1.2988	628.0
626.0	1865.6	0.02501	0.18306	0.20807	656.3	491.7	1148.0	0.8486	0.4529	1.3015	626.0
624.0	1839.0	0.02489	0.18737	0.21226	653.1	496.6	1149.8	0.8458	0.4583	1.3041	624.0
622.0	1812.8	0.02477	0.19173	0.21650	650.0	501.5	1151.5	0.8430	0.4636	1.3066	622.0
620.0	1786.9	0.02466	0.19615	0.22081	646.9	506.3	1153.2	0.8403	0.4689	1.3092	620.0
618.0	1761.2	0.02455	0.20063	0.22517	643.8	511.0	1154.8	0.8375	0.4742	1.3117	618.0
616.0	1735.9	0.02444	0.20516	0.22960	640.8	515.6	1156.4	0.8348	0.4794	1.3141	616.0
614.0	1710.8	0.02433	0.20976	0.23409	637.8	520.2	1158.0	0.8321	0.4845	1.3166	614.0
612.0	1686.1	0.02422	0.21442	0.23865	634.8	524.7	1159.5	0.8294	0.4896	1.3190	612.0
610.0	1661.6	0.02412	0.21915	0.24327	631.8	529.2	1160.9	0.8267	0.4947	1.3214	610.0
608.0	1637.3	0.02402	0.22394	0.24796	628.8	533.6	1162.4	0.8240	0.4997	1.3238	608.0
606.0	1613.4	0.02392	0.22881	0.25273	625.9	537.9	1163.8	0.8214	0.5048	1.3261	606.0
604.0	1589.7	0.02382	0.23374	0.25757	622.9	542.2	1165.1	0.8187	0.5097	1.3284	604.0
602.0	1566.3	0.02373	0.23875	0.26248	620.0	546.4	1166.4	0.8161	0.5147	1.3307	602.0
600.0	1543.2	0.02364	0.24384	0.26747	617.1	550.6	1167.7	0.8134	0.5196	1.3330	600.0
598.0	1520.4	0.02354	0.24900	0.27255	614.3	554.7	1169.0	0.8108	0.5245	1.3353	598.0
596.0	1497.8	0.02345	0.25425	0.27770	611.4	558.8	1170.2	0.8082	0.5293	1.3375	596.0
594.0	1475.4	0.02337	0.25958	0.28294	608.6	562.8	1171.4	0.8056	0.5342	1.3398	594.0
592.0	1453.3	0.02328	0.26499	0.28827	605.7	566.8	1172.6	0.8030	0.5390	1.3420	592.0
590.0	1431.5	0.02319	0.27049	0.29368	602.9	570.8	1173.7	0.8004	0.5437	1.3442	590.0
588.0	1410.0	0.02311	0.27608	0.29919	600.1	574.7	1174.8	0.7978	0.5485	1.3464	588.0
586.0	1388.6	0.02303	0.28176	0.30478	597.3	578.5	1175.9	0.7953	0.5532	1.3485	586.0
584.0	1367.6	0.02295	0.28753	0.31048	594.6	582.4	1176.9	0.7927	0.5580	1.3507	584.0
582.0	1346.7	0.02287	0.29340	0.31627	591.8	586.1	1178.0	0.7902	0.5627	1.3528	582.0
580.0	1326.2	0.02279	0.29937	0.32216	589.1	589.9	1179.0	0.7876	0.5673	1.3550	580.0

Quantities for saturated liquid v_f h_f s_f

Quantities for saturated vapor v_g h_g s_g

Increment for evaporation v_{fg} h_{fg} s_{fg}

STEAM TABLES (Continued)

Properties of Saturated Steam and Saturated Water

Temp. F	Press. psia	Volume, ft³/lbm			Enthalpy, Btu/lbm			Entropy, Btu/lbm ×F			Temp. F
		Water v_f	Evap. v_{fg}	Steam v_g	Water h_f	Evap. h_{fg}	Steam h_g	Water s_f	Evap. s_{fg}	Steam s_g	
580.0	1326.17	0.02279	0.29937	0.32216	589.1	589.9	1179.0	0.7876	0.5673	1.3550	580.0
578.0	1305.84	0.02271	0.30544	0.32816	586.4	593.6	1179.9	0.7851	0.5720	1.3571	578.0
576.0	1285.74	0.02264	0.31162	0.33426	583.7	597.2	1180.9	0.7825	0.5766	1.3592	576.0
574.0	1265.89	0.02256	0.31790	0.34046	581.0	600.9	1181.8	0.7800	0.5813	1.3613	574.0
572.0	1246.26	0.02249	0.32429	0.34678	578.3	604.5	1182.7	0.7775	0.5859	1.3634	572.0
570.0	1226.88	0.02242	0.33079	0.35321	575.6	608.0	1183.6	0.7750	0.5905	1.3654	570.0
568.0	1207.72	0.02235	0.33741	0.35975	572.9	611.5	1184.5	0.7725	0.5950	1.3675	568.0
566.0	1188.80	0.02228	0.34414	0.36642	570.3	615.0	1185.3	0.7699	0.5996	1.3696	566.0
564.0	1170.10	0.02221	0.35099	0.37320	567.6	618.5	1186.1	0.7674	0.6041	1.3716	564.0
562.0	1151.63	0.02214	0.35797	0.38011	565.0	621.9	1186.9	0.7650	0.6087	1.3736	562.0
560.0	1133.38	0.02207	0.36507	0.38714	562.4	625.3	1187.7	0.7625	0.6132	1.3757	560.0
558.0	1115.36	0.02201	0.37230	0.39431	559.8	628.6	1188.4	0.7600	0.6177	1.3777	558.0
556.0	1097.55	0.02194	0.37966	0.40160	557.2	632.0	1189.2	0.7575	0.6222	1.3797	556.0
554.0	1079.96	0.02188	0.38715	0.40903	554.6	635.3	1189.9	0.7550	0.6267	1.3817	554.0
552.0	1062.59	0.02182	0.39479	0.41660	552.0	638.5	1190.6	0.7525	0.6311	1.3837	552.0
550.0	1045.43	0.02176	0.40256	0.42432	549.5	641.8	1191.2	0.7501	0.6356	1.3856	550.0
548.0	1028.49	0.02169	0.41048	0.43217	546.9	645.0	1191.9	0.7476	0.6400	1.3876	548.0
546.0	1011.75	0.02163	0.41855	0.44018	544.4	648.1	1192.5	0.7451	0.6445	1.3896	546.0
544.0	995.22	0.02157	0.42677	0.44834	541.8	651.3	1193.1	0.7427	0.6489	1.3915	544.0
542.0	978.90	0.02151	0.43514	0.45665	539.3	654.4	1193.7	0.7402	0.6533	1.3935	542.0
540.0	962.79	0.02146	0.44367	0.46513	536.8	657.5	1194.3	0.7378	0.6577	1.3954	540.0
538.0	946.88	0.02140	0.45237	0.47377	534.2	660.6	1194.8	0.7353	0.6621	1.3974	538.0
536.0	931.17	0.02134	0.46123	0.48257	531.7	663.6	1195.3	0.7329	0.6665	1.3993	536.0
534.0	915.66	0.02129	0.47026	0.49155	529.2	666.6	1195.9	0.7304	0.6708	1.4012	534.0
532.0	900.34	0.02123	0.47947	0.50070	526.8	669.6	1196.4	0.7280	0.6752	1.4032	532.0
530.0	885.23	0.02118	0.48886	0.51004	524.3	672.6	1196.9	0.7255	0.6796	1.4051	530.0
528.0	870.31	0.02112	0.49843	0.51955	521.8	675.5	1197.3	0.7231	0.6839	1.4070	528.0
526.0	855.58	0.02107	0.50819	0.52926	519.3	678.4	1197.8	0.7206	0.6883	1.4089	526.0
524.0	841.04	0.02102	0.51814	0.53916	516.9	681.3	1198.2	0.7182	0.6926	1.4108	524.0
522.0	826.69	0.02097	0.52829	0.54926	514.4	684.2	1198.6	0.7158	0.6969	1.4127	522.0
520.0	812.53	0.02091	0.53864	0.55956	512.0	687.0	1199.0	0.7133	0.7013	1.4146	520.0
518.0	798.55	0.02086	0.54920	0.57006	509.6	689.9	1199.4	0.7109	0.7056	1.4165	518.0
516.0	784.76	0.02081	0.55997	0.58079	507.1	692.7	1199.8	0.7085	0.7099	1.4183	516.0
514.0	771.15	0.02076	0.57096	0.59173	504.7	695.4	1200.2	0.7060	0.7142	1.4202	514.0
512.0	757.72	0.02072	0.58218	0.60289	502.3	698.2	1200.5	0.7036	0.7185	1.4221	512.0
510.0	744.47	0.02067	0.59362	0.61429	499.9	700.9	1200.8	0.7012	0.7228	1.4240	510.0
508.0	731.40	0.02062	0.60530	0.62592	497.5	703.7	1201.1	0.6987	0.7271	1.4258	508.0
506.0	718.50	0.02057	0.61722	0.63779	495.1	706.3	1201.4	0.6963	0.7314	1.4277	506.0
504.0	705.78	0.02053	0.62938	0.64991	492.7	709.0	1201.7	0.6939	0.7357	1.4296	504.0
502.0	693.23	0.02048	0.64180	0.66228	490.3	711.7	1202.0	0.6915	0.7400	1.4314	502.0
500.0	680.86	0.02043	0.65448	0.67492	487.9	714.3	1202.2	0.6890	0.7443	1.4333	500.0
498.0	668.65	0.02039	0.66743	0.68782	485.6	716.9	1202.5	0.6866	0.7486	1.4352	498.0
496.0	656.61	0.02034	0.68065	0.70100	483.2	719.5	1202.7	0.6842	0.7528	1.4370	496.0
494.0	644.73	0.02030	0.69415	0.71445	480.8	722.1	1202.9	0.6818	0.7571	1.4389	494.0
492.0	633.03	0.02026	0.70794	0.72820	478.5	724.6	1203.1	0.6793	0.7614	1.4407	492.0
490.0	621.48	0.02021	0.72203	0.74224	476.1	727.2	1203.3	0.6769	0.7657	1.4426	490.0
488.0	610.10	0.02017	0.73641	0.75658	473.8	729.7	1203.5	0.6745	0.7700	1.4444	488.0
486.0	598.87	0.02013	0.75111	0.77124	471.5	732.2	1203.7	0.6721	0.7742	1.4463	486.0
484.0	587.81	0.02009	0.76613	0.78622	469.1	734.7	1203.8	0.6696	0.7785	1.4481	484.0
482.0	576.90	0.02004	0.78148	0.80152	466.8	737.2	1204.0	0.6672	0.7828	1.4500	482.0
480.0	566.15	0.02000	0.79716	0.81717	464.5	739.6	1204.1	0.6648	0.7871	1.4518	480.0
478.0	555.55	0.01996	0.81319	0.83315	462.2	742.1	1204.2	0.6624	0.7913	1.4537	478.0
476.0	545.11	0.01992	0.82958	0.84950	459.9	744.5	1204.4	0.6599	0.7956	1.4555	476.0
474.0	534.81	0.01988	0.84632	0.86621	457.5	746.9	1204.4	0.6575	0.7999	1.4574	474.0
472.0	524.67	0.01984	0.86345	0.88329	455.2	749.3	1204.5	0.6551	0.8042	1.4592	472.0
470.0	514.67	0.01980	0.88095	0.90076	452.9	751.6	1204.6	0.6527	0.8084	1.4611	470.0
468.0	504.83	0.01976	0.89885	0.91862	450.7	754.0	1204.6	0.6502	0.8127	1.4629	468.0
466.0	495.12	0.01973	0.91716	0.93689	448.4	756.3	1204.7	0.6478	0.8170	1.4648	466.0
464.0	485.56	0.01969	0.93588	0.95557	446.1	758.6	1204.7	0.6454	0.8213	1.4667	464.0
462.0	476.14	0.01965	0.95504	0.97469	443.8	761.0	1204.8	0.6429	0.8256	1.4685	462.0
460.0	466.87	0.01961	0.97463	0.99424	441.5	763.2	1204.8	0.6405	0.8299	1.4704	460.0
458.0	457.73	0.01958	0.99467	1.01425	439.3	765.5	1204.8	0.6381	0.8342	1.4722	458.0
456.0	448.73	0.01954	1.01518	1.03472	437.0	767.8	1204.8	0.6356	0.8385	1.4741	456.0
454.0	439.87	0.01950	1.03616	1.05567	434.7	770.0	1204.8	0.6332	0.8428	1.4759	454.0
452.0	431.14	0.01947	1.05764	1.07711	432.5	772.3	1204.8	0.6308	0.8471	1.4778	452.0
450.0	422.55	0.01943	1.07962	1.09905	430.2	774.5	1204.7	0.6283	0.8514	1.4797	450.0
448.0	414.09	0.01940	1.10212	1.12152	428.0	776.7	1204.7	0.6259	0.8557	1.4815	448.0
446.0	405.76	0.01936	1.12515	1.14452	425.7	778.9	1204.6	0.6234	0.8600	1.4834	446.0
444.0	397.56	0.01933	1.14874	1.16806	423.5	781.1	1204.6	0.6210	0.8643	1.4853	444.0
442.0	389.49	0.01929	1.17288	1.19217	421.3	783.2	1204.5	0.6185	0.8686	1.4872	442.0
440.0	381.54	0.01926	1.19761	1.21687	419.0	785.4	1204.4	0.6161	0.8729	1.4890	440.0
438.0	373.72	0.01923	1.22293	1.24216	416.8	787.5	1204.3	0.6136	0.8773	1.4909	438.0
436.0	366.03	0.01919	1.24887	1.26806	414.6	789.7	1204.2	0.6112	0.8816	1.4928	436.0
434.0	358.46	0.01916	1.27544	1.29460	412.4	791.8	1204.1	0.6087	0.8859	1.4947	434.0
432.0	351.00	0.01913	1.30266	1.32179	410.1	793.9	1204.0	0.6063	0.8903	1.4966	432.0
430.0	343.67	0.01909	1.33055	1.34965	407.9	796.0	1203.9	0.6038	0.8946	1.4985	430.0

Properties of Saturated Steam and Saturated Water

Temp. F	Press. psia	Volume, ft³/lbm			Enthalpy, Btu/lbm			Entropy, Btu/lbm×F			Temp. F
		Water v_f	Evap. v_{fg}	Steam v_g	Water h_f	Evap. h_{fg}	Steam h_g	Water s_f	Evap. s_{fg}	Steam s_g	
430.0	343.674	0.01909	1.3306	1.3496	407.9	790.0	1203.9	0.6038	0.8946	1.4985	430.0
428.0	336.463	0.01906	1.3591	1.3782	405.7	798.0	1203.7	0.6014	0.8990	1.5004	428.0
426.0	329.369	0.01903	1.3884	1.4075	403.5	800.1	1203.6	0.5989	0.9034	1.5023	426.0
424.0	322.391	0.01900	1.4184	1.4374	401.3	802.2	1203.5	0.5964	0.9077	1.5042	424.0
422.0	315.529	0.01897	1.4492	1.4682	399.1	804.2	1203.3	0.5940	0.9121	1.5061	422.0
420.0	308.780	0.01894	1.4808	1.4997	396.9	806.2	1203.1	0.5915	0.9165	1.5080	420.0
418.0	302.143	0.01890	1.5131	1.5320	394.7	808.2	1202.9	0.5890	0.9209	1.5099	418.0
416.0	295.617	0.01887	1.5463	1.5651	392.5	810.2	1202.8	0.5866	0.9253	1.5118	416.0
414.0	289.201	0.01884	1.5803	1.5991	390.3	812.2	1202.6	0.5841	0.9297	1.5137	414.0
412.0	282.894	0.01881	1.6152	1.6340	388.1	814.2	1202.4	0.5816	0.9341	1.5157	412.0
410.0	276.694	0.01878	1.6510	1.6697	386.0	816.2	1202.1	0.5791	0.9385	1.5176	410.0
408.0	270.600	0.01875	1.6877	1.7064	383.8	818.2	1201.9	0.5766	0.9429	1.5195	408.0
406.0	264.611	0.01872	1.7253	1.7441	381.6	820.1	1201.7	0.5742	0.9473	1.5215	406.0
404.0	258.725	0.01870	1.7640	1.7827	379.4	822.0	1201.5	0.5717	0.9518	1.5234	404.0
402.0	252.942	0.01867	1.8037	1.8223	377.3	824.0	1201.2	0.5692	0.9562	1.5254	402.0
400.0	247.259	0.01864	1.8444	1.8630	375.1	825.9	1201.0	0.5667	0.9607	1.5274	400.0
398.0	241.677	0.01861	1.8862	1.9048	372.9	827.8	1200.7	0.5642	0.9651	1.5293	398.0
396.0	236.193	0.01858	1.9291	1.9477	370.8	829.7	1200.4	0.5617	0.9696	1.5313	396.0
394.0	230.807	0.01855	1.9731	1.9917	368.6	831.6	1200.2	0.5592	0.9741	1.5333	394.0
392.0	225.516	0.01853	2.0184	2.0369	366.5	833.4	1199.9	0.5567	0.9786	1.5352	392.0
390.0	220.321	0.01850	2.0649	2.0833	364.3	835.3	1199.6	0.5542	0.9831	1.5372	390.0
388.0	215.220	0.01847	2.1126	2.1311	362.2	837.2	1199.3	0.5516	0.9876	1.5392	388.0
386.0	210.211	0.01844	2.1616	2.1801	360.0	839.0	1199.0	0.5491	0.9921	1.5412	386.0
384.0	205.294	0.01842	2.2120	2.2304	357.9	840.8	1198.7	0.5466	0.9966	1.5432	384.0
382.0	200.467	0.01839	2.2638	2.2821	355.7	842.7	1198.4	0.5441	1.0012	1.5452	382.0
380.0	195.729	0.01836	2.3170	2.3353	353.6	844.5	1198.0	0.5416	1.0057	1.5473	380.0
378.0	191.080	0.01834	2.3716	2.3900	351.4	846.3	1197.7	0.5390	1.0103	1.5493	378.0
376.0	186.517	0.01831	2.4279	2.4462	349.3	848.1	1197.4	0.5365	1.0148	1.5513	376.0
374.0	182.040	0.01829	2.4857	2.5039	347.2	849.8	1197.0	0.5340	1.0194	1.5534	374.0
372.0	177.648	0.01826	2.5451	2.5633	345.0	851.6	1196.7	0.5314	1.0240	1.5554	372.0
370.0	173.339	0.01823	2.6062	2.6244	342.9	853.4	1196.3	0.5289	1.0286	1.5575	370.0
368.0	169.113	0.01821	2.6691	2.6873	340.8	855.1	1195.9	0.5263	1.0332	1.5595	368.0
366.0	164.968	0.01818	2.7337	2.7519	338.7	856.9	1195.6	0.5238	1.0378	1.5616	366.0
364.0	160.903	0.01816	2.8002	2.8184	336.5	858.6	1195.2	0.5212	1.0424	1.5637	364.0
362.0	156.917	0.01813	2.8687	2.8868	334.4	860.4	1194.8	0.5187	1.0471	1.5658	362.0
360.0	153.010	0.01811	2.9392	2.9573	332.3	862.1	1194.4	0.5161	1.0517	1.5678	360.0
358.0	149.179	0.01809	3.0117	3.0298	330.2	863.8	1194.0	0.5135	1.0564	1.5699	358.0
356.0	145.424	0.01806	3.0863	3.1044	328.1	865.5	1193.6	0.5110	1.0611	1.5721	356.0
354.0	141.744	0.01804	3.1632	3.1812	326.0	867.2	1193.2	0.5084	1.0658	1.5742	354.0
352.0	138.138	0.01801	3.2423	3.2603	323.9	868.9	1192.7	0.5058	1.0705	1.5763	352.0
350.0	134.604	0.01799	3.3238	3.3418	321.8	870.6	1192.3	0.5032	1.0752	1.5784	350.0
348.0	131.142	0.01797	3.4078	3.4258	319.7	872.2	1191.9	0.5006	1.0799	1.5806	348.0
346.0	127.751	0.01794	3.4943	3.5122	317.6	873.9	1191.4	0.4980	1.0847	1.5827	346.0
344.0	124.430	0.01792	3.5834	3.6013	315.5	875.5	1191.0	0.4954	1.0894	1.5849	344.0
342.0	121.177	0.01790	3.6752	3.6931	313.4	877.2	1190.5	0.4928	1.0942	1.5871	342.0
340.0	117.992	0.01787	3.7699	3.7878	311.3	878.8	1190.1	0.4902	1.0990	1.5892	340.0
338.0	114.873	0.01785	3.8675	3.8853	309.2	880.5	1189.6	0.4876	1.1038	1.5914	338.0
336.0	111.820	0.01783	3.9681	3.9859	307.1	882.1	1189.1	0.4850	1.1086	1.5936	336.0
334.0	108.832	0.01781	4.0718	4.0896	305.0	883.7	1188.7	0.4824	1.1134	1.5958	334.0
332.0	105.907	0.01779	4.1788	4.1966	302.9	885.3	1188.2	0.4798	1.1183	1.5981	332.0
330.0	103.045	0.01776	4.2892	4.3069	300.8	886.9	1187.7	0.4772	1.1231	1.6003	330.0
328.0	100.245	0.01774	4.4030	4.4208	298.7	888.5	1187.2	0.4745	1.1280	1.6025	328.0
326.0	97.506	0.01772	4.5205	4.5382	296.6	890.1	1186.7	0.4719	1.1329	1.6048	326.0
324.0	94.826	0.01770	4.6418	4.6595	294.6	891.6	1186.2	0.4692	1.1378	1.6071	324.0
322.0	92.205	0.01768	4.7669	4.7846	292.5	893.2	1185.7	0.4666	1.1427	1.6093	322.0
320.0	89.643	0.01766	4.8961	4.9138	290.4	894.8	1185.2	0.4640	1.1477	1.6116	320.0
318.0	87.137	0.01764	5.0295	5.0471	288.3	896.3	1184.7	0.4613	1.1526	1.6139	318.0
316.0	84.688	0.01761	5.1673	5.1849	286.3	897.9	1184.1	0.4586	1.1576	1.6162	316.0
314.0	82.293	0.01759	5.3096	5.3272	284.2	899.4	1183.6	0.4560	1.1626	1.6185	314.0
312.0	79.953	0.01757	5.4566	5.4742	282.1	901.0	1183.1	0.4533	1.1676	1.6209	312.0
310.0	77.667	0.01755	5.6085	5.6260	280.0	902.5	1182.5	0.4506	1.1726	1.6232	310.0
308.0	75.433	0.01753	5.7655	5.7830	278.0	904.0	1182.0	0.4479	1.1776	1.6256	308.0
306.0	73.251	0.01751	5.9277	5.9452	275.9	905.5	1181.4	0.4453	1.1827	1.6279	306.0
304.0	71.119	0.01749	6.0955	6.1130	273.8	907.0	1180.9	0.4426	1.1877	1.6303	304.0
302.0	69.038	0.01747	6.2689	6.2864	271.8	908.5	1180.3	0.4399	1.1928	1.6327	302.0
300.0	67.005	0.01745	6.4483	6.4658	269.7	910.0	1179.7	0.4372	1.1979	1.6351	300.0
298.0	65.020	0.01743	6.6339	6.6513	267.7	911.5	1179.2	0.4345	1.2031	1.6375	298.0
296.0	63.084	0.01741	6.8259	6.8433	265.6	913.0	1178.6	0.4317	1.2083	1.6400	296.0
294.0	61.194	0.01739	7.0245	7.0419	263.5	914.5	1178.0	0.4290	1.2134	1.6424	294.0
292.0	59.350	0.01738	7.2301	7.2475	261.5	915.9	1177.4	0.4263	1.2186	1.6449	292.0
290.0	57.550	0.01736	7.4430	7.4603	259.4	917.4	1176.8	0.4236	1.2238	1.6473	290.0
288.0	55.795	0.01734	7.6634	7.6807	257.4	918.8	1176.2	0.4208	1.2290	1.6498	288.0
286.0	54.083	0.01732	7.8916	7.9089	255.3	920.3	1175.6	0.4181	1.2342	1.6523	286.0
284.0	52.414	0.01730	8.1280	8.1453	253.3	921.7	1175.0	0.4154	1.2395	1.6548	284.0
282.0	50.786	0.01728	8.3729	8.3902	251.2	923.2	1174.4	0.4126	1.2448	1.6574	282.0
280.0	49.200	0.01726	8.6267	8.6439	249.2	924.6	1173.8	0.4098	1.2501	1.6599	280.0

Properties of Saturated Steam and Saturated Water

Temp. F	Press. psia	Volume, ft³/lbm			Enthalpy, Btu/lbm			Entropy, Btu/lbm × F			Temp. F
		Water v_f	Evap. v_{fg}	Steam v_g	Water h_f	Evap. h_{fg}	Steam h_g	Water s_f	Evap. s_{fg}	Steam s_g	
280.0	49.200	0.017264	8.627	8.644	249.17	924.6	1173.8	0.4098	1.2501	1.6599	280.0
278.0	47.653	0.017246	8.890	8.907	247.13	926.0	1173.2	0.4071	1.2554	1.6625	278.0
276.0	46.147	0.017228	9.162	9.180	245.08	927.5	1172.5	0.4043	1.2607	1.6650	276.0
274.0	44.678	0.017210	9.445	9.462	243.03	928.9	1171.9	0.4015	1.2661	1.6676	274.0
272.0	43.249	0.017193	9.738	9.755	240.99	930.3	1171.3	0.3987	1.2715	1.6702	272.0
270.0	41.856	0.017175	10.042	10.060	238.95	931.7	1170.6	0.3960	1.2769	1.6729	270.0
268.0	40.500	0.017157	10.358	10.375	236.91	933.1	1170.0	0.3932	1.2823	1.6755	268.0
266.0	39.179	0.017140	10.685	10.703	234.87	934.5	1169.3	0.3904	1.2878	1.6781	266.0
264.0	37.894	0.017123	11.025	11.042	232.83	935.9	1168.7	0.3876	1.2933	1.6808	264.0
262.0	36.644	0.017106	11.378	11.395	230.79	937.3	1168.0	0.3847	1.2988	1.6835	262.0
260.0	35.427	0.017089	11.745	11.762	228.76	938.6	1167.4	0.3819	1.3043	1.6862	260.0
258.0	34.243	0.017072	12.125	12.142	226.72	940.0	1166.7	0.3791	1.3098	1.6889	258.0
256.0	33.091	0.017055	12.520	12.538	224.69	941.4	1166.1	0.3763	1.3154	1.6917	256.0
254.0	31.972	0.017039	12.931	12.948	222.65	942.7	1165.4	0.3734	1.3210	1.6944	254.0
252.0	30.883	0.017022	13.358	13.375	220.62	944.1	1164.7	0.3706	1.3266	1.6972	252.0
250.0	29.825	0.017006	13.802	13.819	218.59	945.4	1164.0	0.3677	1.3323	1.7000	250.0
248.0	28.796	0.016990	14.264	14.281	216.56	946.8	1163.4	0.3649	1.3379	1.7028	248.0
246.0	27.797	0.016974	14.744	14.761	214.53	948.1	1162.7	0.3620	1.3436	1.7056	246.0
244.0	26.826	0.016958	15.243	15.260	212.50	949.5	1162.0	0.3591	1.3494	1.7085	244.0
242.0	25.883	0.016942	15.763	15.780	210.48	950.8	1161.3	0.3562	1.3551	1.7113	242.0
240.0	24.968	0.016926	16.304	16.321	208.45	952.1	1160.6	0.3533	1.3609	1.7142	240.0
238.0	24.079	0.016910	16.867	16.884	206.42	953.5	1159.9	0.3505	1.3667	1.7171	238.0
236.0	23.216	0.016895	17.454	17.471	204.40	954.8	1159.2	0.3476	1.3725	1.7201	236.0
234.0	22.379	0.016880	18.065	18.082	202.38	956.1	1158.5	0.3446	1.3784	1.7230	234.0
232.0	21.567	0.016864	18.701	18.718	200.35	957.4	1157.8	0.3417	1.3842	1.7260	232.0
230.0	20.779	0.016849	19.364	19.381	198.33	958.7	1157.1	0.3388	1.3902	1.7290	230.0
229.0	20.394	0.016842	19.707	19.723	197.32	959.4	1156.7	0.3373	1.3931	1.7305	229.0
228.0	20.015	0.016834	20.056	20.073	196.31	960.0	1156.3	0.3359	1.3961	1.7320	228.0
227.0	19.642	0.016827	20.413	20.429	195.30	960.7	1156.0	0.3344	1.3991	1.7335	227.0
226.0	19.274	0.016819	20.777	20.794	194.29	961.3	1155.6	0.3329	1.4021	1.7350	226.0
225.0	18.912	0.016812	21.149	21.166	193.28	962.0	1155.3	0.3315	1.4051	1.7365	225.0
224.0	18.556	0.016805	21.529	21.545	192.27	962.6	1154.9	0.3300	1.4081	1.7380	224.0
223.0	18.206	0.016797	21.917	21.933	191.26	963.3	1154.5	0.3285	1.4111	1.7396	223.0
222.0	17.860	0.016790	22.313	22.330	190.25	963.9	1154.2	0.3270	1.4141	1.7411	222.0
221.0	17.521	0.016783	22.718	22.735	189.24	964.6	1153.8	0.3255	1.4171	1.7427	221.0
220.0	17.186	0.016775	23.131	23.148	188.23	965.2	1153.4	0.3241	1.4201	1.7442	220.0
219.0	16.857	0.016768	23.554	23.571	187.22	965.8	1153.1	0.3226	1.4232	1.7458	219.0
218.0	16.533	0.016761	23.986	24.002	186.21	966.5	1152.7	0.3211	1.4262	1.7473	218.0
217.0	16.214	0.016754	24.427	24.444	185.21	967.1	1152.3	0.3196	1.4293	1.7489	217.0
216.0	15.901	0.016747	24.878	24.894	184.20	967.8	1152.0	0.3181	1.4323	1.7505	216.0
215.0	15.592	0.016740	25.338	25.355	183.19	968.4	1151.6	0.3166	1.4354	1.7520	215.0
214.0	15.289	0.016733	25.809	25.826	182.18	969.0	1151.2	0.3151	1.4385	1.7536	214.0
213.0	14.990	0.016726	26.290	26.307	181.17	969.7	1150.8	0.3136	1.4416	1.7552	213.0
212.0	14.696	0.016719	26.782	26.799	180.17	970.3	1150.5	0.3121	1.4447	1.7568	212.0
211.0	14.407	0.016712	27.285	27.302	179.16	970.9	1150.1	0.3106	1.4478	1.7584	211.0
210.0	14.123	0.016705	27.799	27.816	178.15	971.6	1149.7	0.3091	1.4509	1.7600	210.0
209.0	13.843	0.016698	28.324	28.341	177.14	972.2	1149.4	0.3076	1.4540	1.7616	209.0
208.0	13.568	0.016691	28.862	28.878	176.14	972.8	1149.0	0.3061	1.4571	1.7632	208.0
207.0	13.297	0.016684	29.411	29.428	175.13	973.5	1148.6	0.3046	1.4602	1.7649	207.0
206.0	13.031	0.016677	29.973	29.989	174.12	974.1	1148.2	0.3031	1.4634	1.7665	206.0
205.0	12.770	0.016670	30.547	30.564	173.12	974.7	1147.9	0.3016	1.4665	1.7681	205.0
204.0	12.512	0.016664	31.135	31.151	172.11	975.4	1147.5	0.3001	1.4697	1.7698	204.0
203.0	12.259	0.016657	31.736	31.752	171.10	976.0	1147.1	0.2986	1.4728	1.7714	203.0
202.0	12.011	0.016650	32.350	32.367	170.10	976.6	1146.7	0.2971	1.4760	1.7731	202.0
201.0	11.766	0.016643	32.979	32.996	169.09	977.2	1146.3	0.2955	1.4792	1.7747	201.0
200.0	11.526	0.016637	33.622	33.639	168.09	977.9	1146.0	0.2940	1.4824	1.7764	200.0
199.0	11.290	0.016630	34.280	34.297	167.08	978.5	1145.6	0.2925	1.4856	1.7781	199.0
198.0	11.058	0.016624	34.954	34.970	166.08	979.1	1145.2	0.2910	1.4888	1.7798	198.0
197.0	10.830	0.016617	35.643	35.659	165.07	979.7	1144.8	0.2894	1.4920	1.7814	197.0
196.0	10.605	0.016611	36.348	36.364	164.06	980.4	1144.4	0.2879	1.4952	1.7831	196.0
195.0	10.385	0.016604	37.069	37.086	163.06	981.0	1144.0	0.2864	1.4985	1.7848	195.0
194.0	10.168	0.016598	37.808	37.824	162.05	981.6	1143.7	0.2848	1.5017	1.7865	194.0
193.0	9.956	0.016591	38.564	38.580	161.05	982.2	1143.3	0.2833	1.5050	1.7882	193.0
192.0	9.747	0.016585	39.337	39.354	160.05	982.8	1142.9	0.2818	1.5082	1.7900	192.0
191.0	9.541	0.016578	40.130	40.146	159.04	983.5	1142.5	0.2802	1.5115	1.7917	191.0
190.0	9.340	0.016572	40.941	40.957	158.04	984.1	1142.1	0.2787	1.5148	1.7934	190.0
189.0	9.141	0.016566	41.771	41.787	157.03	984.7	1141.7	0.2771	1.5180	1.7952	189.0
188.0	8.947	0.016559	42.621	42.638	156.03	985.3	1141.3	0.2756	1.5213	1.7969	188.0
187.0	8.756	0.016553	43.492	43.508	155.02	985.9	1140.9	0.2740	1.5246	1.7987	187.0
186.0	8.568	0.016547	44.383	44.400	154.02	986.5	1140.5	0.2725	1.5279	1.8004	186.0
185.0	8.384	0.016541	45.297	45.313	153.02	987.1	1140.2	0.2709	1.5313	1.8022	185.0
184.0	8.203	0.016534	46.232	46.249	152.01	987.8	1139.8	0.2694	1.5346	1.8040	184.0
183.0	8.025	0.016528	47.190	47.207	151.01	988.4	1139.4	0.2678	1.5379	1.8057	183.0
182.0	7.850	0.016522	48.172	48.189	150.01	989.0	1139.0	0.2662	1.5413	1.8075	182.0
181.0	7.679	0.016516	49.178	49.194	149.00	989.6	1138.6	0.2647	1.5446	1.8093	181.0
180.0	7.511	0.016510	50.208	50.225	148.00	990.2	1138.2	0.2631	1.5480	1.8111	180.0

Properties of Saturated Steam and Saturated Water

Temp. F	Press. psia	Volume, ft³/lbm			Enthalpy, Btu/lbm			Entropy, Btu/lbm×F			Temp. F
		Water v_f	Evap. v_{fg}	Steam v_g	Water h_f	Evap. h_{fg}	Steam h_g	Water s_f	Evap. s_{fg}	Steam s_g	
180.0	7.5110	0.016510	50.21	50.22	148.00	990.2	1138.2	0.2631	1.5480	1.8111	180.0
179.0	7.3460	0.016504	51.26	51.28	147.00	990.8	1137.8	0.2615	1.5514	1.8129	179.0
178.0	7.1840	0.016498	52.35	52.36	145.99	991.4	1137.4	0.2600	1.5548	1.8147	178.0
177.0	7.0250	0.016492	53.46	53.47	144.99	992.0	1137.0	0.2584	1.5582	1.8166	177.0
176.0	6.8690	0.016486	54.59	54.61	143.99	992.6	1136.6	0.2568	1.5616	1.8184	176.0
175.0	6.7159	0.016480	55.76	55.77	142.99	993.2	1136.2	0.2552	1.5650	1.8202	175.0
174.0	6.5656	0.016474	56.95	56.97	141.98	993.8	1135.8	0.2537	1.5684	1.8221	174.0
173.0	6.4182	0.016468	58.18	58.19	140.98	994.4	1135.4	0.2521	1.5718	1.8239	173.0
172.0	6.2736	0.016463	59.43	59.45	139.98	995.0	1135.0	0.2505	1.5753	1.8258	172.0
171.0	6.1318	0.016457	60.72	60.74	138.98	995.6	1134.6	0.2489	1.5787	1.8276	171.0
170.0	5.9926	0.016451	62.04	62.06	137.97	996.2	1134.2	0.2473	1.5822	1.8295	170.0
169.0	5.8562	0.016445	63.39	63.41	136.97	996.8	1133.8	0.2457	1.5857	1.8314	169.0
168.0	5.7223	0.016440	64.78	64.80	135.97	997.4	1133.4	0.2441	1.5892	1.8333	168.0
167.0	5.5911	0.016434	66.21	66.22	134.97	998.0	1133.0	0.2425	1.5926	1.8352	167.0
166.0	5.4623	0.016428	67.67	67.68	133.97	998.6	1132.6	0.2409	1.5961	1.8371	166.0
165.0	5.3361	0.016423	69.17	69.18	132.96	999.2	1132.2	0.2393	1.5997	1.8390	165.0
164.0	5.2124	0.016417	70.70	70.72	131.96	999.8	1131.8	0.2377	1.6032	1.8409	164.0
163.0	5.0911	0.016412	72.28	72.30	130.96	1000.4	1131.4	0.2361	1.6067	1.8428	163.0
162.0	4.9722	0.016406	73.90	73.92	129.96	1001.0	1131.0	0.2345	1.6103	1.8448	162.0
161.0	4.8556	0.016401	75.56	75.58	128.96	1001.6	1130.6	0.2329	1.6138	1.8467	161.0
160.0	4.7414	0.016395	77.27	77.29	127.96	1002.2	1130.2	0.2313	1.6174	1.8487	160.0
159.0	4.6294	0.016390	79.02	79.04	126.96	1002.8	1129.8	0.2297	1.6210	1.8506	159.0
158.0	4.5197	0.016384	80.82	80.83	125.96	1003.4	1129.4	0.2281	1.6245	1.8526	158.0
157.0	4.4122	0.016379	82.66	82.68	124.95	1004.0	1129.0	0.2264	1.6281	1.8546	157.0
156.0	4.3068	0.016374	84.56	84.57	123.95	1004.6	1128.6	0.2248	1.6318	1.8566	156.0
155.0	4.2036	0.016369	86.50	86.52	122.95	1005.2	1128.2	0.2232	1.6354	1.8586	155.0
154.0	4.1025	0.016363	88.50	88.52	121.95	1005.8	1127.7	0.2216	1.6390	1.8606	154.0
153.0	4.0035	0.016358	90.55	90.57	120.95	1006.4	1127.3	0.2199	1.6426	1.8626	153.0
152.0	3.9065	0.016353	92.66	92.68	119.95	1007.0	1126.9	0.2183	1.6463	1.8646	152.0
151.0	3.8114	0.016348	94.83	94.84	118.95	1007.6	1126.5	0.2167	1.6500	1.8666	151.0
150.0	3.7184	0.016343	97.05	97.07	117.95	1008.2	1126.1	0.2150	1.6536	1.8686	150.0
149.0	3.6273	0.016337	99.33	99.35	116.95	1008.7	1125.7	0.2134	1.6573	1.8707	149.0
148.0	3.5381	0.016332	101.68	101.70	115.95	1009.3	1125.3	0.2117	1.6610	1.8727	148.0
147.0	3.4508	0.016327	104.10	104.11	114.95	1009.9	1124.9	0.2101	1.6647	1.8748	147.0
146.0	3.3653	0.016322	106.58	106.59	113.95	1010.5	1124.5	0.2084	1.6684	1.8769	146.0
145.0	3.2816	0.016317	109.12	109.14	112.95	1011.1	1124.0	0.2068	1.6722	1.8789	145.0
144.0	3.1997	0.016312	111.74	111.76	111.95	1011.7	1123.6	0.2051	1.6759	1.8810	144.0
143.0	3.1195	0.016308	114.44	114.45	110.95	1012.3	1123.2	0.2035	1.6797	1.8831	143.0
142.0	3.0411	0.016303	117.21	117.22	109.95	1012.9	1122.8	0.2018	1.6834	1.8852	142.0
141.0	2.9643	0.016298	120.05	120.07	108.95	1013.4	1122.4	0.2001	1.6872	1.8873	141.0
140.0	2.8892	0.016293	122.98	123.00	107.95	1014.0	1122.0	0.1985	1.6910	1.8895	140.0
139.0	2.8157	0.016288	125.99	126.01	106.95	1014.6	1121.6	0.1968	1.6948	1.8916	139.0
138.0	2.7438	0.016284	129.09	129.11	105.95	1015.2	1121.1	0.1951	1.6986	1.8937	138.0
137.0	2.6735	0.016279	132.28	132.29	104.95	1015.8	1120.7	0.1935	1.7024	1.8959	137.0
136.0	2.6047	0.016274	135.55	135.57	103.95	1016.4	1120.3	0.1918	1.7063	1.8980	136.0
135.0	2.5375	0.016270	138.93	138.94	102.95	1016.9	1119.9	0.1901	1.7101	1.9002	135.0
134.0	2.4717	0.016265	142.40	142.41	101.95	1017.5	1119.5	0.1884	1.7140	1.9024	134.0
133.0	2.4074	0.016260	145.97	145.98	100.95	1018.1	1119.1	0.1867	1.7178	1.9046	133.0
132.0	2.3445	0.016256	149.64	149.66	99.95	1018.7	1118.6	0.1851	1.7217	1.9068	132.0
131.0	2.2830	0.016251	153.42	153.44	98.95	1019.3	1118.2	0.1834	1.7256	1.9090	131.0
130.0	2.2230	0.016247	157.32	157.33	97.96	1019.8	1117.8	0.1817	1.7295	1.9112	130.0
129.0	2.1642	0.016243	161.32	161.34	96.96	1020.4	1117.4	0.1800	1.7335	1.9134	129.0
128.0	2.1068	0.016238	165.45	165.47	95.96	1021.0	1117.0	0.1783	1.7374	1.9157	128.0
127.0	2.0507	0.016234	169.70	169.72	94.96	1021.6	1116.5	0.1766	1.7413	1.9179	127.0
126.0	1.9959	0.016229	174.08	174.09	93.96	1022.2	1116.1	0.1749	1.7453	1.9202	126.0
125.0	1.9424	0.016225	178.58	178.60	92.96	1022.7	1115.7	0.1732	1.7493	1.9224	125.0
124.0	1.8901	0.016221	183.23	183.24	91.96	1023.3	1115.3	0.1715	1.7533	1.9247	124.0
123.0	1.8390	0.016217	188.01	188.03	90.96	1023.9	1114.9	0.1697	1.7573	1.9270	123.0
122.0	1.7891	0.016213	192.94	192.95	89.96	1024.5	1114.4	0.1680	1.7613	1.9293	122.0
121.0	1.7403	0.016208	198.01	198.03	88.96	1025.0	1114.0	0.1663	1.7653	1.9316	121.0
120.0	1.6927	0.016204	203.25	203.26	87.97	1025.6	1113.6	0.1646	1.7693	1.9339	120.0
119.0	1.6463	0.016200	208.64	208.66	86.97	1026.2	1113.2	0.1629	1.7734	1.9362	119.0
118.0	1.6009	0.016196	214.20	214.21	85.97	1026.8	1112.7	0.1611	1.7774	1.9386	118.0
117.0	1.5566	0.016192	219.93	219.94	84.97	1027.3	1112.3	0.1594	1.7815	1.9409	117.0
116.0	1.5133	0.016188	225.84	225.85	83.97	1027.9	1111.9	0.1577	1.7856	1.9433	116.0
115.0	1.4711	0.016184	231.03	231.04	82.97	1028.5	1111.5	0.1559	1.7897	1.9457	115.0
114.0	1.4300	0.016180	238.21	238.22	81.97	1029.1	1111.0	0.1542	1.7938	1.9480	114.0
113.0	1.3898	0.016177	244.69	244.70	80.98	1029.6	1110.6	0.1525	1.7980	1.9504	113.0
112.0	1.3505	0.016173	251.37	251.38	79.98	1030.2	1110.2	0.1507	1.8021	1.9528	112.0
111.0	1.3123	0.016169	258.26	258.28	78.98	1030.8	1109.8	0.1490	1.8063	1.9552	111.0
110.0	1.2750	0.016165	265.37	265.39	77.98	1031.4	1109.3	0.1472	1.8105	1.9577	110.0
109.0	1.2385	0.016162	272.71	272.72	76.98	1031.9	1108.9	0.1455	1.8146	1.9601	109.0
108.0	1.2030	0.016158	280.28	280.30	75.98	1032.5	1108.5	0.1437	1.8188	1.9626	108.0
107.0	1.1684	0.016154	288.09	288.11	74.99	1033.1	1108.1	0.1419	1.8231	1.9650	107.0
106.0	1.1347	0.016151	296.16	296.18	73.99	1033.6	1107.6	0.1402	1.8273	1.9675	106.0
105.0	**1.1017**	0.016147	304.49	304.50	72.99	1034.2	1107.2	0.1384	1.8315	1.9700	105.0

STEAM TABLES (Continued)

Properties of Saturated Steam and Saturated Water

Temp. F	Press. psia	Volume, ft³/lbm Water v_f	Evap. v_{fg}	Steam v_g	Enthalpy, Btu/lbm Water h_f	Evap. h_{fg}	Steam h_g	Entropy, Btu/lbm×F Water s_f	Evap. s_{fg}	Steam s_g	Temp. F
105.0	1.10174	0.016147	304.5	304.5	72.990	1034.2	1107.2	0.1384	1.8315	1.9700	105.0
104.0	1.06965	0.016144	313.1	313.1	71.992	1034.8	1106.8	0.1366	1.8358	1.9725	104.0
103.0	1.03838	0.016140	322.0	322.0	70.993	1035.4	1106.3	0.1349	1.8401	1.9750	103.0
102.0	1.00789	0.016137	331.1	331.1	69.995	1035.9	1105.9	0.1331	1.8444	1.9775	102.0
101.0	0.97818	0.016133	340.6	340.6	68.997	1036.5	1105.5	0.1313	1.8487	1.9800	101.0
100.0	0.94924	0.016130	350.4	350.4	67.999	1037.1	1105.1	0.1295	1.8530	1.9825	100.0
99.0	0.92103	0.016127	360.5	360.5	67.001	1037.6	1104.6	0.1278	1.8573	1.9851	99.0
98.0	0.89356	0.016123	370.9	370.9	66.003	1038.2	1104.2	0.1260	1.8617	1.9876	98.0
97.0	0.86679	0.016120	381.7	381.7	65.005	1038.8	1103.8	0.1242	1.8660	1.9902	97.0
96.0	0.84072	0.016117	392.8	392.9	64.006	1039.3	1103.3	0.1224	1.8704	1.9928	96.0
95.0	0.81534	0.016114	404.4	404.4	63.008	1039.9	1102.9	0.1206	1.8748	1.9954	95.0
94.0	0.79062	0.016111	416.3	416.3	62.010	1040.5	1102.5	0.1188	1.8792	1.9980	94.0
93.0	0.76655	0.016108	428.6	428.6	61.012	1041.0	1102.1	0.1170	1.8837	2.0006	93.0
92.0	0.74313	0.016105	441.3	441.3	60.014	1041.6	1101.6	0.1152	1.8881	2.0033	92.0
91.0	0.72032	0.016102	454.5	454.5	59.016	1042.2	1101.2	0.1134	1.8926	2.0059	91.0
90.0	0.69813	0.016099	468.1	468.1	58.018	1042.7	1100.8	0.1115	1.8970	2.0086	90.0
89.0	0.67653	0.016096	482.2	482.2	57.020	1043.3	1100.3	0.1097	1.9015	2.0112	89.0
88.0	0.65551	0.016093	496.8	496.8	56.022	1043.9	1099.9	0.1079	1.9060	2.0139	88.0
87.0	0.63507	0.016090	511.9	511.9	55.024	1044.4	1099.5	0.1061	1.9105	2.0166	87.0
86.0	0.61518	0.016087	527.5	527.5	54.026	1045.0	1099.0	0.1043	1.9151	2.0193	86.0
85.0	0.59583	0.016085	543.6	543.6	53.027	1045.6	1098.6	0.1024	1.9196	2.0221	85.0
84.0	0.57702	0.016082	560.3	560.3	52.029	1046.1	1098.2	0.1006	1.9242	2.0248	84.0
83.0	0.55872	0.016079	577.6	577.6	51.031	1046.7	1097.7	0.0988	1.9288	2.0275	83.0
82.0	0.54093	0.016077	595.5	595.6	50.033	1047.3	1097.3	0.0969	1.9334	2.0303	82.0
81.0	0.52364	0.016074	614.1	614.1	49.035	1047.8	1096.9	0.0951	1.9380	2.0331	81.0
80.0	0.050683	0.016072	633.3	633.3	48.037	1048.4	1096.4	0.0932	1.9426	2.0359	80.0
79.0	0.49049	0.016070	653.2	653.2	47.038	1049.0	1096.0	0.0914	1.9473	2.0387	79.0
78.0	0.47461	0.016067	673.8	673.9	46.040	1049.5	1095.6	0.0895	1.9520	2.0415	78.0
77.0	0.45919	0.016065	695.2	695.2	45.042	1050.1	1095.1	0.0877	1.9567	2.0443	77.0
76.0	0.44420	0.016063	717.4	717.4	44.043	1050.7	1094.7	0.0858	1.9614	2.0472	76.0
75.0	0.42964	0.016060	740.3	740.3	43.045	1051.2	1094.3	0.0839	1.9661	2.0500	75.0
74.0	0.41550	0.016058	764.1	764.1	42.046	1051.8	1093.8	0.0821	1.9708	2.0529	74.0
73.0	0.40177	0.016056	788.8	788.8	41.048	1052.4	1093.4	0.0802	1.9756	2.0558	73.0
72.0	0.38844	0.016054	814.3	814.3	40.049	1052.9	1093.0	0.0783	1.9804	2.0587	72.0
71.0	0.37549	0.016052	840.8	840.9	39.050	1053.5	1092.5	0.0764	1.9852	2.0616	71.0
70.0	0.36292	0.016050	868.3	868.4	38.052	1054.0	1092.1	0.0745	1.9900	2.0645	70.0
69.0	0.35073	0.016048	896.9	896.9	37.053	1054.6	1091.7	0.0727	1.9948	2.0675	69.0
68.0	0.33889	0.016046	926.5	926.5	36.054	1055.2	1091.2	0.0708	1.9996	2.0704	68.0
67.0	0.32740	0.016044	957.2	957.2	35.055	1055.7	1090.8	0.0689	2.0045	2.0734	67.0
66.0	0.31626	0.016043	989.0	989.1	34.056	1056.3	1090.4	0.0670	2.0094	2.0764	66.0
65.0	0.30545	0.016041	1022.1	1022.1	33.057	1056.9	1089.9	0.0651	2.0143	2.0794	65.0
64.0	0.29497	0.016039	1056.5	1056.5	32.058	1057.4	1089.5	0.0632	2.0192	2.0824	64.0
63.0	0.28480	0.016038	1092.1	1092.1	31.058	1058.0	1089.0	0.0613	2.0242	2.0854	63.0
62.0	0.27494	0.016036	1129.2	1129.2	30.059	1058.5	1088.6	0.0593	2.0291	2.0885	62.0
61.0	0.26538	0.016035	1167.6	1167.6	29.059	1059.1	1088.2	0.0574	2.0341	2.0915	61.0
60.0	0.25611	0.016033	1207.6	1207.6	28.060	1059.7	1087.7	0.0555	2.0391	2.0946	60.0
59.0	0.24713	0.016032	1249.1	1249.1	27.060	1060.2	1087.3	0.0536	2.0441	2.0977	59.0
58.0	0.23843	0.016031	1292.2	1292.2	26.060	1060.8	1086.9	0.0516	2.0491	2.1008	58.0
57.0	0.23000	0.016029	1337.0	1337.0	25.060	1061.4	1086.4	0.0497	2.0542	2.1039	57.0
56.0	0.22183	0.016028	1383.6	1383.6	24.059	1061.9	1086.0	0.0478	2.0593	2.1070	56.0
55.0	0.21392	0.016027	1432.0	1432.0	23.059	1062.5	1085.6	0.0458	2.0644	2.1102	55.0
54.0	0.20625	0.016026	1482.4	1482.4	22.058	1063.1	1085.1	0.0439	2.0695	2.1134	54.0
53.0	0.19883	0.016025	1534.7	1534.8	21.058	1063.6	1084.7	0.0419	2.0746	2.1165	53.0
52.0	0.19165	0.016024	1589.2	1589.2	20.057	1064.2	1084.2	0.0400	2.0798	2.1197	52.0
51.0	0.18469	0.016023	1645.9	1645.9	19.056	1064.7	1083.8	0.0380	2.0849	2.1230	51.0
50.0	0.17796	0.016023	1704.8	1704.8	18.054	1065.3	1083.4	0.0361	2.0901	2.1262	50.0
49.0	0.17144	0.016022	1766.2	1766.2	17.053	1065.9	1082.9	0.0341	2.0953	2.1294	49.0
48.0	0.16514	0.016021	1830.0	1830.0	16.051	1066.4	1082.5	0.0321	2.1006	2.1327	48.0
47.0	0.15904	0.016021	1896.5	1896.5	15.049	1067.0	1082.1	0.0301	2.1058	2.1360	47.0
46.0	0.15314	0.016020	1965.7	1965.7	14.047	1067.6	1081.6	0.0282	2.1111	2.1393	46.0
45.0	0.14744	0.016020	2037.7	2037.8	13.044	1068.1	1081.2	0.0262	2.1164	2.1426	45.0
44.0	0.14192	0.016019	2112.8	2112.8	12.041	1068.7	1080.7	0.0242	2.1217	2.1459	44.0
43.0	0.13659	0.016019	2191.0	2191.0	11.038	1069.3	1080.3	0.0222	2.1271	2.1493	43.0
42.0	0.13143	0.016019	2272.4	2272.4	10.035	1069.8	1079.9	0.0202	2.1325	2.1527	42.0
41.0	0.12645	0.016019	2357.3	2357.3	9.031	1070.4	1079.4	0.0182	2.1378	2.1560	41.0
40.0	0.12163	0.016019	2445.8	2445.8	8.027	1071.0	1079.0	0.0162	2.1432	2.1594	40.0
39.0	0.11698	0.016019	2538.0	2538.0	7.023	1071.5	1078.5	0.0142	2.1487	2.1629	39.0
38.0	0.11249	0.016019	2634.1	2634.2	6.018	1072.1	1078.1	0.0122	2.1541	2.1663	38.0
37.0	0.10815	0.016019	2734.4	2734.4	5.013	1072.7	1077.7	0.0101	2.1596	2.1697	37.0
36.0	0.10395	0.016020	2839.0	2839.0	4.008	1073.2	1077.2	0.0081	2.1651	2.1732	36.0
35.0	0.09991	0.016020	2948.1	2948.1	3.002	1073.8	1076.8	0.0061	2.1706	2.1767	35.0
34.0	0.09600	0.016021	3061.9	3061.9	1.996	1074.4	1076.4	0.0041	2.1762	2.1802	34.0
33.0	0.09223	0.016021	3180.7	3180.7	0.989	1074.9	1075.9	0.0020	2.1817	2.1837	33.0
32.018	0.08865	0.016022	3302.4	3302.4	0.0003	1075.5	1075.5	0.0000	2.1872	2.1872	32.018
*32.0	0.08859	0.016022	3304.7	3304.7	−0.0179	1075.5	1075.5	−0.0000	2.1873	2.1873	32.0

*The states here shown are metastable

STEAM TABLES (Continued)

Specific Heat at constant pressure of Steam and of Water

Temp. F	c_p, Btu/lbm × F															Temp. F
Press., psia	1	1.5	2	3	4	6	8	10	15	20	30	40	60	80	100	Press., psia
Sat. Water	0.998	0.998	0.999	1.000	1.000	1.002	1.003	1.004	1.007	1.010	1.014	1.019	1.026	1.033	1.039	Sat. Water
Sat. Steam	0.450	0.452	0.454	0.458	0.461	0.466	0.471	0.475	0.485	0.493	0.508	0.521	0.543	0.564	0.582	Sat. Steam
1500	0.559	0.559	0.559	0.559	0.559	0.559	0.559	0.559	0.559	0.559	0.560	0.560	0.560	0.561	0.561	1500
1480	0.557	0.557	0.557	0.557	0.557	0.557	0.557	0.558	0.558	0.558	0.558	0.558	0.559	0.559	0.559	1480
1460	0.556	0.556	0.556	0.556	0.556	0.556	0.556	0.556	0.556	0.556	0.556	0.557	0.557	0.557	0.558	1460
1440	0.554	0.554	0.554	0.554	0.554	0.554	0.554	0.554	0.554	0.554	0.555	0.555	0.555	0.556	0.556	1440
1420	0.552	0.552	0.552	0.552	0.552	0.552	0.553	0.553	0.553	0.553	0.553	0.553	0.554	0.554	0.555	1420
1400	0.551	0.551	0.551	0.551	0.551	0.551	0.551	0.551	0.551	0.551	0.551	0.552	0.552	0.553	0.553	1400
1380	0.549	0.549	0.549	0.549	0.549	0.549	0.549	0.549	0.549	0.549	0.550	0.550	0.550	0.551	0.551	1380
1360	0.547	0.547	0.547	0.547	0.547	0.547	0.547	0.547	0.548	0.548	0.548	0.548	0.549	0.549	0.550	1360
1340	0.546	0.546	0.546	0.546	0.546	0.546	0.546	0.546	0.546	0.546	0.546	0.547	0.547	0.548	0.548	1340
1320	0.544	0.544	0.544	0.544	0.544	0.544	0.544	0.544	0.544	0.544	0.545	0.545	0.545	0.546	0.546	1320
1300	0.542	0.542	0.542	0.542	0.542	0.542	0.542	0.542	0.542	0.543	0.543	0.543	0.544	0.544	0.545	1300
1280	0.540	0.540	0.540	0.540	0.540	0.540	0.540	0.541	0.541	0.541	0.541	0.541	0.542	0.543	0.543	1280
1260	0.538	0.539	0.539	0.539	0.539	0.539	0.539	0.539	0.539	0.539	0.539	0.540	0.540	0.541	0.541	1260
1240	0.537	0.537	0.537	0.537	0.537	0.537	0.537	0.537	0.537	0.537	0.537	0.538	0.538	0.539	0.540	1240
1220	0.535	0.535	0.535	0.535	0.535	0.535	0.535	0.535	0.535	0.535	0.536	0.536	0.536	0.537	0.538	1220
1200	0.533	0.533	0.533	0.533	0.533	0.533	0.533	0.533	0.534	0.534	0.534	0.534	0.535	0.536	0.536	1200
1180	0.531	0.531	0.531	0.531	0.531	0.531	0.532	0.532	0.532	0.532	0.532	0.533	0.533	0.534	0.535	1180
1160	0.529	0.529	0.530	0.530	0.530	0.530	0.530	0.530	0.530	0.530	0.530	0.531	0.532	0.532	0.533	1160
1140	0.528	0.528	0.528	0.528	0.528	0.528	0.528	0.528	0.528	0.528	0.529	0.529	0.530	0.531	0.531	1110
1120	0.526	0.526	0.526	0.526	0.526	0.526	0.526	0.526	0.526	0.527	0.527	0.527	0.528	0.529	0.530	1120
1100	0.524	0.524	0.524	0.524	0.524	0.524	0.524	0.524	0.525	0.525	0.525	0.526	0.526	0.527	0.528	1100
1080	0.522	0.522	0.522	0.522	0.522	0.522	0.522	0.523	0.523	0.523	0.523	0.524	0.525	0.525	0.526	1080
1060	0.520	0.520	0.520	0.520	0.520	0.521	0.521	0.521	0.521	0.521	0.522	0.522	0.523	0.524	0.524	1060
1040	0.518	0.519	0.519	0.519	0.519	0.519	0.519	0.519	0.519	0.519	0.520	0.520	0.521	0.522	0.523	1040
1020	0.517	0.517	0.517	0.517	0.517	0.517	0.517	0.517	0.517	0.517	0.518	0.518	0.519	0.520	0.521	1020
1000	0.515	0.515	0.515	0.515	0.515	0.515	0.515	0.515	0.515	0.516	0.516	0.517	0.518	0.519	0.519	1000
980	0.513	0.513	0.513	0.513	0.513	0.513	0.513	0.513	0.514	0.514	0.514	0.515	0.516	0.517	0.518	980
960	0.511	0.511	0.511	0.511	0.511	0.511	0.512	0.512	0.512	0.512	0.513	0.513	0.514	0.515	0.516	960
940	0.509	0.509	0.509	0.509	0.509	0.510	0.510	0.510	0.510	0.510	0.511	0.511	0.512	0.514	0.515	940
920	0.507	0.508	0.508	0.508	0.508	0.508	0.508	0.508	0.508	0.509	0.509	0.510	0.511	0.512	0.513	920
900	0.506	0.506	0.506	0.506	0.506	0.506	0.506	0.506	0.506	0.506	0.507	0.508	0.509	0.510	0.512	900
880	0.504	0.504	0.504	0.504	0.504	0.504	0.504	0.504	0.504	0.505	0.505	0.506	0.508	0.509	0.510	880
860	0.502	0.502	0.502	0.502	0.502	0.502	0.503	0.503	0.503	0.503	0.504	0.505	0.506	0.507	0.509	860
840	0.500	0.500	0.500	0.500	0.500	0.501	0.501	0.501	0.501	0.502	0.502	0.503	0.504	0.506	0.507	840
820	0.498	0.498	0.499	0.499	0.499	0.499	0.499	0.499	0.499	0.500	0.501	0.501	0.503	0.504	0.506	820
800	0.497	0.497	0.497	0.497	0.497	0.497	0.497	0.497	0.498	0.498	0.499	0.500	0.501	0.503	0.505	800
780	0.495	0.495	0.495	0.495	0.495	0.495	0.495	0.496	0.496	0.496	0.497	0.498	0.500	0.502	0.503	780
760	0.493	0.493	0.493	0.493	0.493	0.494	0.494	0.494	0.494	0.495	0.496	0.497	0.499	0.500	0.502	760
740	0.491	0.491	0.491	0.492	0.492	0.492	0.492	0.492	0.493	0.493	0.494	0.495	0.497	0.499	0.501	740
720	0.490	0.490	0.490	0.490	0.490	0.492	0.490	0.491	0.491	0.492	0.493	0.494	0.496	0.498	0.500	720
700	0.488	0.488	0.488	0.488	0.488	0.488	0.489	0.489	0.490	0.490	0.491	0.492	0.495	0.497	0.500	700
680	0.486	0.486	0.486	0.486	0.487	0.487	0.487	0.487	0.488	0.489	0.490	0.491	0.494	0.496	0.499	680
660	0.484	0.485	0.485	0.485	0.485	0.485	0.485	0.486	0.486	0.487	0.489	0.490	0.493	0.496	0.499	660
640	0.483	0.483	0.483	0.483	0.483	0.484	0.484	0.484	0.485	0.486	0.487	0.489	0.492	0.495	0.499	640
620	0.481	0.481	0.481	0.481	0.482	0.482	0.482	0.483	0.483	0.484	0.486	0.488	0.491	0.495	0.499	620
600	0.479	0.480	0.480	0.480	0.480	0.480	0.481	0.481	0.482	0.483	0.485	0.487	0.491	0.495	0.499	600
580	0.478	0.478	0.478	0.478	0.478	0.479	0.479	0.480	0.481	0.482	0.484	0.486	0.491	0.495	0.500	580
560	0.476	0.476	0.476	0.477	0.477	0.477	0.478	0.478	0.479	0.481	0.483	0.485	0.490	0.496	0.501	560
540	0.475	0.475	0.475	0.475	0.475	0.476	0.476	0.477	0.478	0.480	0.482	0.485	0.491	0.497	0.503	540
520	0.473	0.473	0.473	0.474	0.474	0.475	0.475	0.476	0.477	0.479	0.482	0.485	0.491	0.498	0.505	520
500	0.472	0.472	0.472	0.472	0.473	0.473	0.474	0.475	0.476	0.478	0.481	0.485	0.492	0.500	0.508	500
480	0.470	0.470	0.470	0.471	0.471	0.472	0.473	0.473	0.475	0.477	0.481	0.485	0.493	0.502	0.511	480
460	0.469	0.469	0.469	0.469	0.470	0.471	0.472	0.472	0.475	0.477	0.481	0.486	0.495	0.505	0.516	460
440	0.467	0.467	0.468	0.468	0.469	0.470	0.470	0.471	0.474	0.476	0.481	0.487	0.498	0.509	0.522	440
420	0.466	0.466	0.466	0.467	0.467	0.468	0.470	0.471	0.473	0.476	0.482	0.488	0.501	0.514	0.528	420
400	0.464	0.465	0.465	0.466	0.466	0.467	0.469	0.470	0.473	0.476	0.483	0.490	0.504	0.520	0.536	400
380	0.463	0.463	0.464	0.464	0.465	0.466	0.468	0.469	0.473	0.477	0.484	0.492	0.509	0.527	0.546	380
360	0.462	0.462	0.462	0.463	0.464	0.466	0.467	0.469	0.473	0.477	0.486	0.495	0.515	0.536	0.558	360
340	0.460	0.461	0.461	0.462	0.463	0.465	0.467	0.469	0.473	0.478	0.488	0.499	0.521	0.546	0.572	340
320	0.459	0.460	0.460	0.461	0.462	0.464	0.467	0.469	0.474	0.480	0.491	0.504	0.530	0.558	1.036	320
300	0.458	0.459	0.459	0.460	0.462	0.464	0.466	0.469	0.475	0.482	0.495	0.509	0.539	1.029	1.029	300
280	0.457	0.458	0.458	0.460	0.461	0.464	0.467	0.469	0.477	0.484	0.500	0.516	1.022	1.022	1.022	280
260	0.456	0.457	0.457	0.459	0.461	0.464	0.467	0.470	0.478	0.487	0.505	1.017	1.017	1.017	1.017	260
240	0.455	0.456	0.457	0.458	0.460	0.464	0.468	0.471	0.481	0.491	1.012	1.012	1.012	1.012	1.012	240
220	0.454	0.455	0.456	0.458	0.460	0.464	0.468	0.473	0.484	1.008	1.008	1.008	1.008	1.008	1.008	220
200	0.453	0.454	0.455	0.458	0.460	0.465	0.470	0.475	1.005	1.005	1.005	1.005	1.005	1.005	1.005	200
180	0.452	0.454	0.455	0.458	0.460	0.466	1.003	1.003	1.003	1.003	1.003	1.003	1.003	1.002	1.002	180
160	0.451	0.453	0.455	0.458	0.461	1.001	1.001	1.001	1.001	1.001	1.001	1.001	1.001	1.001	1.001	160
140	0.451	0.453	0.454	1.000	1.000	1.000	1.000	1.000	0.999	0.999	0.999	0.999	0.999	0.999	0.999	140
120	0.450	0.452	0.999	0.999	0.999	0.999	0.999	0.999	0.999	0.999	0.998	0.998	0.998	0.998	0.998	120
100	0.998	0.998	0.998	0.998	0.998	0.998	0.998	0.998	0.998	0.998	0.998	0.998	0.998	0.998	0.998	100
80	0.998	0.998	0.998	0.998	0.998	0.998	0.998	0.998	0.998	0.998	0.998	0.998	0.998	0.998	0.998	80
60	1.000	1.000	1.000	1.000	1.000	1.000	1.000	1.000	1.000	1.000	1.000	1.000	0.999	0.999	0.999	60
40	1.004	1.004	1.004	1.004	1.004	1.004	1.004	1.004	1.004	1.004	1.004	1.004	1.004	1.004	1.003	40
32	1.007	1.007	1.007	1.007	1.007	1.007	1.007	1.007	1.007	1.007	1.007	1.007	1.007	1.007	1.006	32

Specific Heat at constant pressure of Steam and of Water

Temp. F	150	200	300	400	600	800	1000	1500	2000	3000	4000	6000	8000	10000	15000	Temp. F
Press., psia	150	200	300	400	600	800	1000	1500	2000	3000	4000	6000	8000	10000	15000	Press., psia
Sat. Water	1.054	1.067	1.093	1.118	1.168	1.224	1.286	1.492	1.841	7.646	—	—	—	—	—	Sat. Water
Sat. Steam	0.624	0.661	0.729	0.792	0.915	1.046	1.191	1.667	2.557	13.66	—	—	—	—	—	Sat. Steam
1500	0.562	0.563	0.565	0.567	0.571	0.576	0.580	0.590	0.601	0.623	0.645	0.691	0.737	0.780	0.868	1500
1480	0.561	0.562	0.564	0.566	0.570	0.575	0.579	0.590	0.601	0.623	0.647	0.694	0.742	0.786	0.878	1480
1460	0.559	0.560	0.562	0.565	0.569	0.573	0.578	0.589	0.601	0.624	0.648	0.698	0.747	0.793	0.888	1460
1440	0.557	0.559	0.561	0.563	0.568	0.572	0.577	0.589	0.600	0.625	0.650	0.701	0.753	0.800	0.900	1440
1420	0.556	0.557	0.559	0.562	0.566	0.571	0.576	0.588	0.600	0.625	0.651	0.705	0.759	0.808	0.909	1420
1400	0.554	0.555	0.558	0.560	0.565	0.570	0.575	0.587	0.600	0.626	0.653	0.709	0.765	0.817	0.926	1400
1380	0.553	0.554	0.556	0.559	0.564	0.569	0.574	0.587	0.600	0.627	0.655	0.714	0.773	0.827	0.939	1380
1360	0.551	0.552	0.555	0.558	0.563	0.568	0.573	0.586	0.600	0.628	0.657	0.719	0.781	0.838	0.953	1360
1340	0.549	0.551	0.553	0.556	0.561	0.567	0.572	0.586	0.600	0.629	0.660	0.725	0.790	0.850	0.968	1340
1320	0.548	0.549	0.552	0.555	0.560	0.566	0.571	0.585	0.600	0.630	0.663	0.731	0.800	0.864	0.983	1320
1300	0.546	0.548	0.550	0.553	0.559	0.565	0.570	0.585	0.600	0.632	0.666	0.738	0.811	0.879	0.998	1300
1280	0.545	0.546	0.549	0.552	0.558	0.564	0.570	0.585	0.600	0.634	0.669	0.746	0.824	0.897	1.014	1280
1260	0.543	0.544	0.547	0.550	0.556	0.563	0.569	0.585	0.601	0.636	0.673	0.755	0.838	0.918	1.033	1260
1240	0.541	0.543	0.546	0.549	0.555	0.562	0.568	0.584	0.601	0.638	0.678	0.765	0.855	0.942	1.053	1240
1220	0.540	0.541	0.544	0.548	0.554	0.561	0.567	0.584	0.602	0.641	0.683	0.777	0.875	0.969	1.072	1220
1200	0.538	0.540	0.543	0.546	0.553	0.560	0.567	0.584	0.603	0.644	0.689	0.790	0.897	1.000	1.095	1200
1180	0.536	0.538	0.541	0.545	0.552	0.559	0.566	0.584	0.604	0.647	0.696	0.805	0.922	1.033	1.117	1180
1160	0.535	0.536	0.540	0.544	0.551	0.558	0.565	0.585	0.606	0.652	0.704	0.823	0.952	1.070	1.143	1160
1140	0.533	0.535	0.539	0.542	0.550	0.557	0.565	0.585	0.607	0.656	0.713	0.843	0.986	1.107	1.167	1140
1120	0.531	0.533	0.537	0.541	0.549	0.557	0.565	0.586	0.609	0.662	0.723	0.866	1.025	1.149	1.190	1120
1100	0.530	0.532	0.536	0.540	0.548	0.556	0.564	0.587	0.612	0.668	0.735	0.893	1.070	1.193	1.220	1100
1080	0.528	0.530	0.534	0.538	0.547	0.555	0.564	0.588	0.615	0.676	0.749	0.924	1.120	1.242	1.240	1080
1060	0.527	0.529	0.533	0.537	0.546	0.555	0.564	0.590	0.618	0.685	0.765	0.960	1.176	1.295	1.260	1060
1040	0.525	0.527	0.532	0.536	0.545	0.555	0.565	0.592	0.622	0.695	0.783	1.002	1.238	1.351	1.282	1040
1020	0.523	0.526	0.530	0.535	0.545	0.555	0.565	0.594	0.627	0.707	0.804	1.051	1.306	1.399	1.298	1020
1000	0.522	0.524	0.529	0.534	0.544	0.555	0.566	0.597	0.633	0.721	0.829	1.110	1.382	1.471	1.306	1000
980	0.520	0.523	0.528	0.533	0.544	0.555	0.567	0.601	0.640	0.737	0.858	1.180	1.475	1.531	1.312	980
960	0.519	0.521	0.527	0.532	0.543	0.556	0.568	0.605	0.648	0.756	0.893	1.267	1.598	1.595	1.310	960
940	0.517	0.520	0.526	0.531	0.543	0.556	0.570	0.610	0.658	0.778	0.934	1.376	1.708	1.639	1.299	940
920	0.516	0.519	0.525	0.531	0.544	0.558	0.573	0.617	0.669	0.803	0.984	1.520	1.819	1.667	1.281	920
900	0.515	0.518	0.524	0.530	0.544	0.559	0.576	0.624	0.683	0.834	1.048	1.716	1.932	1.660	1.259	900
880	0.513	0.516	0.523	0.530	0.545	0.561	0.580	0.633	0.699	0.872	1.130	1.993	2.000	1.633	1.232	880
860	0.512	0.515	0.523	0.530	0.546	0.564	0.584	0.644	0.718	0.918	1.240	2.316	2.019	1.593	1.212	860
840	0.511	0.514	0.522	0.530	0.548	0.568	0.590	0.657	0.740	0.977	1.395	2.653	1.978	1.547	1.192	840
820	0.510	0.514	0.522	0.531	0.550	0.572	0.597	0.672	0.767	1.054	1.620	2.886	1.888	1.503	1.175	820
800	0.509	0.513	0.522	0.532	0.553	0.577	0.605	0.690	0.800	1.160	1.967	2.872	1.768	1.459	1.157	800
780	0.508	0.513	0.522	0.533	0.557	0.584	0.615	0.712	0.840	1.312	2.550	2.547	1.670	1.416	1.142	780
760	0.507	0.512	0.523	0.535	0.561	0.592	0.628	0.738	0.892	1.542	4.462	2.156	1.576	1.370	1.126	760
740	0.507	0.512	0.524	0.537	0.567	0.602	0.642	0.770	0.960	1.913	8.119	1.886	1.493	1.332	1.114	740
720	0.506	0.512	0.525	0.540	0.574	0.613	0.660	0.811	1.052	2.584	3.458	1.696	1.421	1.290	1.100	720
700	0.506	0.513	0.528	0.544	0.582	0.627	0.681	0.861	1.181	6.145⊕	2.237	1.557	1.358	1.250	1.089	700
680	0.506	0.514	0.530	0.549	0.592	0.644	0.707	0.927	1.365	2.469	1.789	1.450	1.303	1.217	1.079	680
660	0.507	0.515	0.534	0.555	0.604	0.665	0.738	1.015	1.639	1.851	1.587	1.369	1.256	1.187	1.071	660
640	0.507	0.517	0.538	0.562	0.619	0.690	0.777	1.135	2.219	1.601	1.454	1.303	1.216	1.157	1.063	640
620	0.509	0.519	0.543	0.571	0.637	0.720	0.826	1.308	1.614	1.455	1.362	1.252	1.184	1.136	1.056	620
600	0.510	0.522	0.550	0.582	0.659	0.757	0.888	1.586	1.453	1.358	1.295	1.211	1.157	1.118	1.052	600
580	0.513	0.526	0.558	0.595	0.685	0.804	0.969	1.393	1.351	1.289	1.243	1.178	1.134	1.102	1.046	580
560	0.516	0.531	0.568	0.611	0.717	0.862	1.079	1.309	1.281	1.237	1.202	1.151	1.115	1.087	1.039	560
540	0.519	0.538	0.580	0.630	0.756	0.937	1.272	1.249	1.229	1.196	1.169	1.128	1.098	1.074	1.031	540
520	0.524	0.545	0.594	0.653	0.804	1.035	1.221	1.204	1.189	1.164	1.142	1.109	1.083	1.062	1.024	520
500	0.530	0.554	0.611	0.680	0.865	1.187	1.181	1.169	1.157	1.137	1.120	1.092	1.069	1.051	1.017	500
480	0.537	0.565	0.632	0.714	1.159	1.154	1.150	1.140	1.131	1.115	1.101	1.077	1.057	1.041	1.010	480
460	0.545	0.578	0.657	0.755	1.128	1.128	1.125	1.117	1.110	1.096	1.084	1.064	1.047	1.033	1.004	460
440	0.556	0.594	0.687	1.113	1.110	1.107	1.104	1.098	1.092	1.080	1.070	1.052	1.038	1.025	0.999	440
420	0.568	0.614	0.724	1.094	1.091	1.089	1.087	1.081	1.076	1.067	1.058	1.042	1.029	1.018	0.994	420
400	0.583	0.636	1.079	1.078	1.076	1.074	1.072	1.067	1.063	1.055	1.047	1.034	1.022	1.011	0.990	400
380	0.601	1.066	1.065	1.065	1.063	1.061	1.059	1.056	1.052	1.044	1.038	1.026	1.015	1.006	0.986	380
360	0.622	1.054	1.054	1.053	1.052	1.050	1.049	1.045	1.042	1.036	1.030	1.019	1.009	1.001	0.982	360
340	1.045	1.044	1.044	1.043	1.042	1.040	1.039	1.036	1.033	1.028	1.022	1.013	1.004	0.996	0.979	340
320	1.036	1.036	1.035	1.034	1.033	1.032	1.031	1.028	1.026	1.021	1.016	1.007	0.999	0.992	0.976	320
300	1.028	1.028	1.028	1.027	1.026	1.025	1.024	1.022	1.019	1.015	1.010	1.002	0.995	0.988	0.973	300
280	1.022	1.022	1.021	1.021	1.020	1.019	1.018	1.016	1.014	1.009	1.005	0.998	0.991	0.985	0.971	280
260	1.016	1.016	1.016	1.015	1.014	1.013	1.013	1.011	1.009	1.005	1.001	0.994	0.988	0.982	0.968	260
240	1.012	1.011	1.011	1.011	1.010	1.009	1.008	1.006	1.004	1.001	0.997	0.991	0.985	0.979	0.966	240
220	1.008	1.008	1.007	1.007	1.006	1.005	1.005	1.003	1.001	0.998	0.994	0.988	0.982	0.977	0.964	220
200	1.005	1.004	1.004	1.004	1.003	1.002	1.002	1.000	0.998	0.995	0.992	0.986	0.980	0.975	0.963	200
180	1.002	1.002	1.002	1.001	1.001	1.000	0.999	0.998	0.996	0.993	0.989	0.983	0.978	0.973	0.961	180
160	1.000	1.000	1.000	0.999	0.999	0.998	0.997	0.996	0.994	0.991	0.987	0.981	0.976	0.971	0.959	160
140	0.999	0.999	0.998	0.998	0.997	0.997	0.996	0.994	0.992	0.989	0.986	0.980	0.974	0.969	0.958	140
120	0.998	0.998	0.997	0.997	0.996	0.996	0.995	0.993	0.991	0.988	0.984	0.978	0.972	0.967	0.957	120
100	0.997	0.997	0.997	0.996	0.996	0.995	0.994	0.992	0.990	0.986	0.983	0.976	0.970	0.965	0.955	100
80	0.998	0.997	0.997	0.996	0.995	0.994	0.994	0.991	0.989	0.985	0.981	0.974	0.968	0.962	0.951	80
60	0.999	0.999	0.998	0.997	0.996	0.995	0.994	0.991	0.989	0.984	0.979	0.970	0.963	0.956	0.942	60
40	1.003	1.003	1.002	1.001	1.000	0.998	0.997	0.993	0.989	0.983	0.976	0.965	0.954	0.945	0.920	40
32	1.006	1.006	1.005	1.004	1.002	1.000	0.999	0.994	0.990	0.983	0.975	0.962	0.949	0.937	0.904	32

⊕Critical point.

Thermal Conductivity of Steam and Water

Temp. F Press., psia	1	2	5	10	20	50	100	200	500	1000	2000	5000	7500
Sat. Water	364.0	373.1	383.8	390.4	395.2	397.4	394.7	386.2	361.7	327.6	271.8	—	—
Sat. Steam	11.6	12.2	13.0	13.8	14.8	16.6	18.4	21.1	27.2	36.5	61.3	—	—
1500	63.7	63.7	63.7	63.7	63.7	63.8	64.0	64.3	65.4	67.1	70.7	82.0	92.2
1450	61.4	61.4	61.5	61.5	61.5	61.6	61.8	62.1	63.2	64.9	68.5	80.1	90.6
1400	59.2	59.2	59.2	59.2	59.3	59.4	59.6	59.9	60.9	62.7	66.3	78.2	89.2
1350	57.0	57.0	57.0	57.0	57.1	57.2	57.3	57.7	58.7	60.5	64.2	76.3	87.9
1300	54.8	54.8	54.8	54.8	54.8	54.9	55.1	55.5	56.5	58.3	62.0	74.6	86.9
1250	52.6	52.6	52.6	52.6	52.6	52.7	52.9	53.2	54.3	56.1	59.9	73.0	86.3
1200	50.4	50.4	50.4	50.4	50.4	50.5	50.7	51.0	52.1	53.9	57.8	71.6	86.2
1150	48.2	48.2	48.2	48.2	48.2	48.3	48.5	48.9	49.9	51.8	55.7	70.5	87.0
1100	46.0	46.0	46.0	46.0	46.1	46.2	46.3	46.7	47.8	49.6	53.7	69.8	89.0
1050	43.9	43.9	43.9	43.9	43.9	44.0	44.2	44.6	45.6	47.5	51.8	69.7	93.4
1000	41.7	41.7	41.8	41.8	41.8	41.9	42.1	42.4	43.5	45.5	50.0	70.7	102.9
950	39.6	39.6	39.7	39.7	39.7	39.8	40.0	40.3	41.4	43.5	48.3	73.5	115.5
900	37.6	37.6	37.6	37.6	37.6	37.7	37.9	38.3	39.4	41.5	46.8	80.2	138.7
850	35.5	35.6	35.6	35.6	35.6	35.7	35.9	36.3	37.4	39.7	45.6	96.7	178.8
800	33.6	33.6	33.6	33.6	33.6	33.7	33.9	34.3	35.5	37.9	44.9	129.6	223.2
750	31.6	31.6	31.6	31.6	31.7	31.8	32.0	32.3	33.6	36.3	45.2	202.5	258.3
700	29.7	29.7	29.7	29.7	29.8	29.9	30.1	30.4	31.8	35.0	47.5⊚	262.8	295.1
650	27.8	27.8	27.9	27.9	27.9	28.0	28.2	28.6	30.1	34.1	55.7	304.3	326.7
600	26.0	26.0	26.1	26.1	26.1	26.2	26.4	26.9	28.7	34.1	301.9	333.7	349.3
550	24.3	24.3	24.3	24.3	24.4	24.5	24.7	25.2	27.5	36.1	333.7	356.1	368.0
500	22.6	22.6	22.6	22.6	22.7	22.8	23.0	23.6	26.9	350.8	357.4	373.8	383.6
450	21.0	21.0	21.0	21.0	21.0	21.2	21.4	22.3	368.1	370.6	375.3	387.9	396.5
400	19.4	19.4	19.4	19.4	19.5	19.6	20.0	21.3	383.0	384.9	388.5	398.6	406.4
350	17.9	17.9	17.9	17.9	18.0	18.2	18.8	392.0	392.9	394.4	397.4	406.1	413.2
300	16.5	16.5	16.5	16.5	16.6	16.9	396.9	397.2	398.0	399.3	402.0	409.9	416.4
250	15.1	15.1	15.1	15.2	15.3	396.9	397.0	397.3	398.1	399.4	402.1	409.7	415.8
200	13.8	13.8	13.9	14.0	391.6	391.6	391.8	392.1	393.0	394.4	397.2	404.9	410.6
150	12.7	12.7	380.5	380.5	380.6	380.7	380.8	381.1	382.1	383.7	386.7	394.7	400.3
100	363.3	363.3	363.3	363.3	363.3	363.4	363.6	363.9	365.0	366.6	369.8	378.3	384.1
50	339.1	339.1	339.1	339.1	339.2	339.3	339.4	339.8	340.8	342.5	345.7	354.6	361.0
32	328.6	328.6	328.6	328.6	328.6	328.7	328.9	329.2	330.3	331.9	335.1	344.1	350.8

⊚ Critical point.

Ammonia, NH₃

Temp. °F	Abs. press. sat. vap. lb./in.²	Abs. press. sat. vap. kg/cm²	Heat content abv. −40°F BTU/lb. Liq.	Heat content abv. −40°F BTU/lb. Vap.	Ht. of vaporiz BTU/lb.	Heat content abv. −40°C g-cal./g Liq.	Heat content abv. −40°C g-cal./g Vap.	Ht. of vaporiz. g-cal./g	Temp. °C
−60	5.55	0.390	−21.2	589.6	610.8	−11.8	327.6	339.3	−51.11
−58	5.93	.417	−19.1	590.4	609.5	−10.6	328.0	338.6	−50.00
−56	6.33	.445	−17.0	591.1	608.2	−9.44	328.3	337.9	−48.89
−54	6.75	.475	−14.8	592.1	606.9	−8.22	328.9	337.2	−47.78
−52	7.20	.506	−12.7	592.9	605.6	−7.06	329.4	336.4	−46.67
−50	7.67	0.539	−10.6	593.7	604.3	−5.89	329.8	335.7	−45.56
−48	8.16	.574	−8.5	594.4	602.9	−4.7	330.2	334.9	−44.44
−46	8.68	.610	−6.4	595.0	601.6	−3.6	330.7	334.3	−43.33
−44	9.23	.649	−4.3	596.0	600.3	−2.4	331.1	333.5	−42.22
−42	9.81	.690	−2.1	596.8	598.9	−1.2	331.6	332.7	−41.11
−40	10.41	0.7319	0.0 +	597.6	597.6	0.0 +	332.0	332.0	−40.00
−38	11.04	.7762	2.1	598.3	596.2	1.2	332.4	331.2	−38.89
−36	11.71	.8233	4.3	599.1	594.8	2.4	332.8	330.4	−37.78
−34	12.41	.8725	6.4	599.9	593.5	3.6	333.3	329.7	−36.67
−32	13.14	.9238	8.5	600.6	592.1	4.7	333.7	328.9	−35.56
−30	13.90	0.9773	10.7	601.4	590.7	5.94	334.1	328.2	−34.44
−28	14.71	1.034	12.8	602.1	589.3	7.11	334.5	327.4	−33.33
−26	15.55	1.093	14.9	602.8	587.9	8.28	334.9	326.6	−32.22
−24	16.42	1.154	17.1	603.6	586.5	9.50	335.3	325.8	−31.11
−22	17.34	1.219	19.2	604.3	585.1	10.7	335.7	325.1	−30.00
−20	18.30	1.287	21.4	605.0	583.6	11.9	336.1	324.2	−28.89
−18	19.30	1.357	23.5	605.7	582.2	13.1	336.5	323.4	−27.78
−16	20.34	1.430	25.6	606.4	580.8	14.2	336.9	322.7	−26.67
−14	21.43	1.507	27.8	607.1	579.3	15.4	337.3	321.8	−25.56
−12	22.56	1.586	30.0	607.8	577.8	16.7	337.7	321.0	−24.44
−10	23.74	1.669	32.1	608.5	576.4	17.8	338.1	320.2	−23.33
−8	24.97	1.756	34.3	609.2	574.9	19.1	338.4	319.4	−22.22
−6	26.26	1.846	36.6	609.8	573.4	20.2	338.8	318.6	−21.11
−4	27.59	1.940	38.6	610.5	571.9	21.4	339.2	317.7	−20.00
−2	28.98	2.037	40.7	611.1	570.4	22.6	339.5	316.9	−18.89
0	30.42	2.139	42.9	611.8	568.9	23.8	339.9	316.1	−17.78
2	31.92	2.244	45.1	612.4	567.3	25.1	340.2	315.2	−16.67
4	33.47	2.353	47.2	613.0	565.8	26.2	340.6	314.3	−15.56
6	35.09	2.467	49.4	613.6	564.2	27.4	340.9	313.4	−14.44
8	36.77	2.585	51.6	614.3	562.7	28.7	341.3	312.6	−13.33
10	38.51	2.708	53.8	614.9	561.1	29.9	341.6	311.7	−12.22
12	40.31	2.834	56.0	615.5	559.5	31.1	341.9	310.8	−11.11
14	42.18	2.966	58.2	616.0	557.7	32.3	342.2	309.9	−10.00
16	44.12	3.102	60.3	616.6	556.3	33.5	342.6	309.1	−8.89
18	46.13	3.243	62.5	617.2	554.7	34.7	342.9	308.2	−7.78
20	48.21	3.390	64.7	617.8	553.1	35.9	343.2	307.3	−6.67
22	50.36	3.541	66.9	618.3	551.4	37.2	343.5	306.3	−5.56
24	52.59	3.697	69.1	618.9	549.8	38.4	343.8	305.4	−4.44
26	54.90	3.860	71.3	619.4	548.1	39.6	344.1	304.5	−3.33
28	57.28	4.027	73.5	619.9	546.4	40.8	344.4	303.6	−2.22

Ammonia, NH₃

Temp. °C	Entropy from −40°F BTU/lb./°F Vap.	Entropy from −40°F BTU/lb./°F Liq.	Dens. liq. lb./ft.³	Density sat. vap. kg/m³	Density sat. vap. lb./ft.³	Spec. vol. sat. vap. m³/kg	Spec. vol. sat. vap. ft.³/lb.	Temp. °F
−51.11	1.4769	−0.0517	43.91	0.3580	0.02235	2.792	44.73	−60
−50.00	1.4713	−.0464		.3809	.02378	2.625	42.05	−58
−48.89	1.4658	−.0412		.4049	.02528	2.470	39.56	−56
−47.78	1.4604	−.0360		.4301	.02685	2.325	37.24	−54
−46.67	1.4551	−.0307		.4565	.02850	2.191	35.09	−52
−45.56	1.4497	−0.0256	43.49	0.4842	0.03023	2.065	33.08	−50
−44.44	1.4445	−.0204		.5134	.03205	1.948	31.20	−48
−43.33	1.4393	−.0153		.5438	.03395	1.839	29.45	−46
−42.22	1.4342	−.0102		.5758	.03595	1.737	27.82	−44
−41.11	1.4292	−.0051		.6093	.03804	1.641	26.29	−42
−40.00	1.4242	0.0000	43.08	0.6442	0.04022	1.552	24.86	−40
−38.89	1.4193	.0051		.6809	.04251	1.469	23.53	−38
−37.78	1.4144	.0101		.7190	.04489	1.390	22.27	−36
−36.67	1.4096	.0151		.7591	.04739	1.317	21.10	−34
−35.56	1.4048	.0201		.8007	.04999	1.249	20.00	−32
−34.44	1.4001	0.0250	42.65	0.8443	0.05271	1.184	18.97	−30
−33.33	1.3955	.0300		.8898	.05555	1.124	18.00	−28
−32.22	1.3909	.0350		.9371	.05850	1.067	17.09	−26
−31.11	1.3863	.0399		.9864	.06158	1.014	16.24	−24
−30.00	1.3818	.0448		1.038	.06479	0.9633	15.43	−22
−28.89	1.3774	0.0497	42.22	1.091	0.06813	0.9164	14.68	−20
−27.78	1.3729	.0545		1.147	.07161	.8721	13.97	−18
−26.67	1.3686	.0594		1.205	.07522	.8297	13.29	−16
−25.56	1.3643	.0642		1.265	.07898	.7903	12.66	−14
−24.44	1.3600	.0690		1.328	.08289	.7529	12.06	−12
−23.33	1.3558	0.0738	41.78	1.393	0.08695	0.7179	11.50	−10
−22.22	1.3516	.0786		1.460	.09117	.6848	10.97	−8
−21.11	1.3474	.0833		1.531	.09555	.6536	10.47	−6
−20.00	1.3433	.0880		1.603	.1001	.6237	9.991	−4
−18.89	1.3393	.0928		1.679	.1048	.5956	9.541	−2
−17.78	1.3352	0.0975	41.34	1.757	0.1097	0.5691	9.116	0
−16.67	1.3312	.1022		1.839	.1148	.5440	8.714	2
−15.56	1.3273	.1069		1.922	.1200	.5202	8.333	4
−14.44	1.3234	.1115		2.009	.1254	.4976	7.971	6
−13.33	1.3195	.1162		2.100	.1311	.4763	7.629	8
−12.22	1.3157	0.1208	40.89	2.193	0.1369	0.4560	7.304	10
−11.11	1.3118	.1254		2.289	.1429	.4367	6.996	12
−10.00	1.3081	.1300		2.390	.1492	.4185	6.703	14
−8.89	1.3043	.1346		2.492	.1556	.4011	6.425	16
−7.78	1.3006	.1392		2.600	.1623	.3846	6.161	18
−6.67	1.2969	0.1437	40.43	2.710	0.1692	0.3690	5.910	20
−5.56	1.2933	.1483		2.824	.1763	.3540	5.671	22
−4.44	1.2897	.1528		2.943	.1837	.3398	5.443	24
−3.33	1.2861	.1573		3.064	.1913	.3263	5.227	26
−2.22	1.2825	.1618		3.191	.1992	.3135	5.021	28

THERMODYNAMIC PROPERTIES (Continued)

Ammonia, NH₃ (Continued)

Temp. °C	Entropy from -40°F BTU/lb./°F Vap.	Entropy from -40°F BTU/lb./°F Liq.	Dens. liq. lb./ft.³	Density sat. vap. kg/m³	Density sat. vap. lb./ft.³	Spec. vol. sat. vap. m³/kg	Spec. vol. sat. vap. ft.³/lb.	Temp. °F
- 1.11	1.2790	0.1663	39.96	3.321	0.2073	0.3012	4.825	30
0.00	1.2755	.1708		3.453	.2156	.2895	4.637	32
+ 1.11	1.2721	.1753		3.593	.2243	.2784	4.459	34
2.22	1.2686	.1797		3.735	.2332	.2678	4.289	36
3.33	1.2652	.1841		3.881	.2423	.2576	4.126	38
4.44	1.2618	0.1885	39.49	4.033	0.2518	0.2479	3.971	40
5.56	1.2585	.1930		4.190	.2616	.2387	3.823	42
6.67	1.2552	.1974		4.350	.2716	.2299	3.682	44
7.78	1.2519	.2018		4.515	.2819	.2214	3.547	46
8.89	1.2486	.2062		4.687	.2926	.2134	3.418	48
10.00	1.2453	0.2105	39.00	4.863	0.3036	0.2056	3.294	50
11.11	1.2421	.2149		5.044	.3149	.1983	3.176	52
12.22	1.2389	.2192		5.230	.3265	.1912	3.063	54
13.33	1.2357	.2236		5.422	.3385	.1844	2.954	56
14.44	1.2325	.2279		5.619	.3508	.1780	2.851	58
15.56	1.2294	0.2322	38.50	5.823	0.3635	0.1717	2.751	60
16.67	1.2262	.2365		6.031	.3765	.1658	2.656	62
17.78	1.2231	.2408		6.245	.3899	.1601	2.565	64
18.89	1.2201	.2451		6.466	.4037	.1546	2.477	66
20.00	1.2170	.2494		6.694	.4179	.1494	2.393	68
21.11	1.2140	0.2537	38.00	6.928	0.4325	0.1443	2.312	70
22.22	1.2110	.2579		7.166	.4474	.1395	2.235	72
23.33	1.2080	.2622		7.413	.4628	.1349	2.161	74
24.44	1.2050	.2664		7.666	.4786	.1304	2.089	76
25.56	1.2020	.2706		7.927	.4949	.1262	2.021	78
26.67	1.1991	0.2749	37.48	8.193	0.5115	0.1220	1.955	80
27.78	1.1962	.2791		8.469	.5287	.1181	1.892	82
28.89	1.1933	.2833		8.749	.5462	.1143	1.831	84
30.00	1.1904	.2875		9.039	.5643	.1106	1.772	86
31.11	1.1875	.2917		9.335	.5828	.1071	1.716	88
32.22	1.1846	0.2958	36.95	9.641	0.6019	0.1037	1.661	90
33.33	1.1818	.3000		9.954	.6214	.1004	1.609	92
34.44	1.1789	.3041		10.28	.6415	.09733	1.559	94
35.56	1.1761	.3083		10.60	.6620	.09427	1.510	96
36.67	1.1733	.3125		10.94	.6832	.09140	1.464	98
37.78	1.1705	0.3166	36.40	11.29	0.7048	0.08859	1.419	100
38.89	1.1677	.3207		11.65	.7270	.08584	1.375	102
40.00	1.1649	.3248		12.01	.7498	.08328	1.334	104
41.11	1.1621	.3289		12.39	.7732	.08072	1.293	106
42.22	1.1593	.3330		12.77	.7972	.07829	1.254	108
43.33	1.1566	0.3372	35.84	13.17	0.8219	0.07598	1.217	110
44.44	1.1538	.3413		13.57	.8471	.07367	1.180	112
45.56	1.1510	.3453		13.98	.8730	.07148	1.145	114
46.67	1.1483	.3495		14.41	.8996	.06942	1.112	116
47.78	1.1455	.3535		14.85	.9269	.06736	1.079	118
48.89	1.1427	0.3576	35.26	15.30	0.9549	0.06536	1.047	120
50.00	1.1400	.3618		15.76	.9837	.06349	1.017	122
51.11	1.1372	.3659		16.229	1.0132	.0615	0.987	124

Ammonia, NH₃ (Continued)

Temp. °F	Abs. press. sat. lb./in.²	Abs. press. sat. kg/cm²	Heat content abv. -40°F BTU Liq.	Heat content abv. -40°F BTU Vap.	Ht. of vaporiz. BTU/lb.	Heat content abv. -40°C g-cal./g Liq.	Heat content abv. -40°C g-cal./g Vap.	Ht. of vaporiz. g-cal./g	Temp. °C
30	59.74	4.200	75.7	620.5	544.8	42.1	344.7	302.7	- 1.11
32	62.29	4.379	77.9	621.0	543.1	43.3	345.0	301.7	0.00
34	64.91	4.564	80.1	621.5	541.4	44.5	345.3	300.8	+ 1.11
36	67.63	4.755	82.3	622.0	539.7	45.7	345.6	299.8	2.22
38	70.43	4.952	84.6	622.5	537.9	47.0	345.8	298.8	3.33
40	73.32	5.155	86.8	623.0	536.2	48.2	346.1	297.9	4.44
42	76.31	5.365	89.0	623.4	534.4	49.4	346.3	296.9	5.56
44	79.38	5.581	91.2	623.9	532.7	50.7	346.6	295.9	6.67
46	82.55	5.804	93.5	624.3	530.9	51.9	346.9	294.9	7.78
48	85.82	6.034	95.7	624.8	529.1	53.2	347.1	293.9	8.89
50	89.19	6.271	97.9	625.2	527.3	54.4	347.3	292.9	10.00
52	92.66	6.515	100.2	625.7	525.5	55.67	347.6	291.9	11.11
54	96.23	6.766	102.4	626.1	523.7	56.89	347.8	290.9	12.22
56	99.91	7.024	104.7	626.5	521.8	58.17	348.1	289.9	13.33
58	103.7	7.291	106.9	626.9	520.0	59.39	348.3	288.9	14.44
60	107.6	7.565	109.2	627.3	518.1	60.67	348.6	287.8	15.56
62	111.6	7.846	111.5	627.7	516.2	61.94	348.7	286.7	16.67
64	115.7	8.135	113.7	628.0	514.3	63.17	348.9	285.7	17.78
66	120.0	8.437	116.0	628.4	512.4	64.44	349.1	284.7	18.89
68	124.3	8.739	118.3	628.8	510.5	65.72	349.3	283.6	20.00
70	128.8	9.056	120.5	629.1	508.6	66.94	349.5	282.6	21.11
72	133.4	9.379	122.8	629.4	506.6	68.22	349.7	281.4	22.22
74	138.1	9.709	125.1	629.8	504.7	69.50	349.9	280.4	23.33
76	143.0	10.05	127.4	630.1	502.7	70.78	350.1	279.3	24.44
78	147.9	10.40	129.7	630.4	500.7	72.06	350.2	278.2	25.56
80	153.0	10.76	132.0	630.7	498.7	73.33	350.4	277.1	26.67
82	158.3	11.13	134.3	631.0	496.7	74.61	350.6	275.9	27.78
84	163.7	11.51	136.6	631.3	494.7	75.89	350.7	274.8	28.89
86	169.2	11.90	138.9	631.5	492.6	77.17	350.8	273.7	30.00
88	174.8	12.29	141.2	631.8	490.6	78.44	351.0	272.6	31.11
90	180.6	12.70	143.5	632.0	488.5	79.72	351.1	271.4	32.22
92	186.6	13.12	145.8	632.2	486.4	81.00	351.2	270.2	33.33
94	192.7	13.55	148.2	632.5	484.3	82.33	351.4	269.1	34.44
96	198.9	13.98	150.5	632.6	482.1	83.61	351.4	267.8	35.56
98	205.3	14.43	152.9	632.9	480.0	84.94	351.6	266.7	36.67
100	211.9	14.90	155.2	633.1	477.6	86.20	351.7	265.4	37.78
102	218.6	15.37	157.6	633.3	475.5	87.56	351.8	264.2	38.89
104	225.4	15.85	159.9	633.5	473.5	88.83	351.9	263.1	40.00
106	232.5	16.35	162.3	633.5	471.2	90.17	351.9	261.8	41.11
108	239.7	16.85	164.6	633.6	469.0	91.44	352.0	260.6	42.22
110	247.0	17.37	167.0	633.7	466.7	92.78	352.1	259.3	43.33
112	254.5	17.89	169.4	633.8	464.4	94.11	352.1	258.0	44.44
114	262.2	18.43	171.8	633.9	462.1	95.44	352.2	256.7	45.56
116	270.1	18.99	174.2	634.0	459.8	96.78	352.2	255.4	46.67
118	278.2	19.56	176.6	634.0	457.4	98.11	352.2	254.1	47.78
120	286.4	20.14	179.0	634.0	455.0	99.45	352.2	252.8	48.89
122	294.8	20.73	181.4	634.0	452.6	100.8	352.2	251.4	50.00
124	303.4	21.33	183.9	634.0	450.1	102.2	352.2	250.1	51.11

THERMODYNAMIC PROPERTIES (Continued)

Carbon Dioxide, CO₂

Temp. °F	Abs. press sat. vap lb./in.²	Abs. press sat. vap kg/cm²	Heat content abv. 32°F BTU/lb. Liq.	Heat content abv. 32°F BTU/lb. Vap.	Heat of vaporiz. BTU/lb	Heat content abv 0°C g-cal./g Liq.	Heat content abv 0°C g-cal./g Vap.	Heat of vaporiz. g-cal./g	Temp. °C
-20	220.6	15.51	-23.96	102.0	126.0	-13.31	56.67	70.00	-28.89
-18	228.4	16.06	-23.13	102.1	125.2	-12.85	56.72	69.56	-27.78
-16	236.4	16.62	-22.30	102.2	124.5	-12.39	56.78	69.17	-26.67
-14	244.6	17.20	-21.46	102.3	123.7	-11.92	56.78	68.72	-25.56
-12	253.0	17.79	-20.61	102.3	122.9	-11.45	56.83	68.28	-24.44
-10	261.7	18.40	-19.76	102.3	122.0	-10.98	56.78	67.78	-23.33
-8	270.6	19.03	-18.90	102.3	121.2	-10.50	56.83	67.33	-22.22
-6	279.7	19.66	-18.04	102.3	120.3	-10.02	56.83	66.83	-21.11
-4	289.1	20.33	-17.17	102.3	119.5	-9.539	56.83	66.39	-20.00
-2	298.7	21.00	-16.29	102.3	118.6	-9.030	56.83	65.89	-18.89
0	308.6	21.70	-15.41	102.2	117.7	-8.561	56.78	65.39	-17.78
2	318.7	22.41	-14.51	102.1	116.7	-8.061	56.78	64.83	-16.67
4	329.1	23.14	-13.61	102.1	115.8	-7.561	56.72	64.33	-15.56
6	339.8	23.89	-12.71	102.0	114.8	-7.061	56.72	63.78	-14.44
8	350.7	24.66	-11.79	102.0	113.8	-6.550	56.67	63.22	-13.33
10	361.8	25.44	-10.87	101.9	112.8	-6.039	56.61	62.67	-12.22
12	373.3	26.25	-9.934	101.7	111.7	-5.519	56.56	62.06	-11.11
14	385.0	27.07	-8.992	101.6	110.7	-4.996	56.50	61.50	-10.00
16	397.1	27.92	-8.038	101.5	109.6	-4.466	56.44	60.91	-8.89
18	409.4	28.78	-7.076	101.4	108.5	-3.931	56.33	60.28	-7.78
20	422.0	29.67	-6.102	101.2	107.3	-3.390	56.22	59.61	-6.67
22	434.9	30.58	-5.117	101.0	106.1	-2.843	56.11	58.94	-5.56
24	448.1	31.50	-4.121	100.8	104.9	-2.289	56.00	58.28	-4.44
25	454.8	31.98	-3.618	100.7	104.3	-2.010	55.94	57.94	-3.89
27	468.5	32.94	-2.601	100.5	103.1	-1.445	55.83	57.28	-2.78
29	482.5	33.92	-1.570	100.2	101.8	-0.8722	55.67	56.56	-1.67
31	496.8	34.93	-0.525	100.5	100.5	-0.292	55.54	55.84	-0.56
33	511.4	35.95	+0.531	99.98	99.16	+0.295	55.38	55.09	+0.56
35	526.4	37.01	1.604	99.69	97.77	0.8911	55.21	54.32	1.67
37	541.7	38.09	2.697	99.38	96.35	1.498	55.03	53.53	2.78
39	557.4	39.19	3.806	99.05	94.88	2.114	54.83	52.71	3.89
41	573.4	40.31	4.932	98.69	93.32	2.733	54.62	51.87	5.00
43	589.8	41.47	6.080	98.31	91.82	3.378	54.39	51.01	6.11
45	606.5	42.64	7.251	97.90	90.21	4.028	54.14	50.12	7.22
47	623.6	43.84	8.443	97.46	88.55	4.691	53.88	49.19	8.33
49	641.1	45.07	9.664	96.99	86.83	5.369	53.61	48.24	9.44
51	659.0	46.33	10.91	96.50	85.06	6.061	53.32	47.26	10.56
53	677.3	47.62	12.19	95.97	83.21	6.772	53.02	46.23	11.67
55	695.9	48.93	13.49	95.40	81.29	7.494	52.66	45.16	12.78
57	714.9	50.26	14.84	94.78	79.30	8.244	52.29	44.06	13.89
59	734.3	51.63	16.22	94.13	77.22	9.011	51.91	42.90	15.00
61	754.2	53.03	17.65	93.44	75.04	9.806	51.49	41.69	16.11
63	774.5	54.45	19.13	92.69	72.75	10.63	51.04	40.42	17.22
65	795.1	55.90	20.66	91.88	70.35	11.48	50.56	39.08	18.33
67	816.2	57.38	22.25	91.04	67.81	12.36	50.04	37.67	19.44
69	837.8	58.90	23.92	90.07	65.12	13.29	49.47	36.18	20.56
71	859.8	60.45	25.67	89.04	62.25	14.26	48.84	34.58	21.67
73	882.2	62.02	27.52	87.92	59.17	15.29	48.16	32.87	22.78
75	905.1	63.63	29.50	86.69	55.83	16.39	47.41	31.02	23.89
77	928.4	65.27	31.62	85.33	52.17	17.57	46.56	28.98	25.00
79	952.5	66.95	33.95	83.80	48.11	18.86	45.59	26.73	26.11
81	976.5	68.65	36.54	82.06	43.49	20.30	44.46	24.16	27.22
83	1001.0	70.377	39.53	80.05	38.07	21.96	43.07	21.15	28.33
85	1027.0	72.205	43.18	77.60	31.29	23.99	41.37	17.38	29.44
86	1039.0	73.049	45.45	74.47	27.00	25.35	40.26	15.00	30.00
87	1052.0	73.963	48.32	72.46	21.52	26.84	38.80	11.96	30.56
88	1065.0	74.877	52.78	69.84	65.62	12.84	29.32	36.46	7.133	31.11

THERMODYNAMIC PROPERTIES (Continued)

Carbon Dioxide, CO₂

Temp. °F	Spec. vol. sat. vap. ft.³/lb.	Spec. vol. sat. vap. m³/kg	Density sat. vap. lb./ft.³	Density sat. vap. kg/m³	Dens. liq. lb./ft.³	Entropy from 32°F BTU/lb./°F Liq.	Entropy from 32°F BTU/lb./°F Vap.	Temp. °C
-20	0.4166	0.02601	2.401	38.46	64.34	-0.0514	0.2353	-28.89
-18	0.4018	0.02508	2.489	39.87	64.15	-0.0495	0.2342	-27.78
-16	0.3876	0.02420	2.580	41.33	63.94	-0.0476	0.2331	-26.67
-14	0.3739	0.02334	2.674	42.83	63.73	-0.0458	0.2319	-25.56
-12	0.3608	0.02252	2.772	44.40	63.49	-0.0439	0.2307	-24.44
-10	0.3482	0.02174	2.872	46.00	63.25	-0.0420	0.2296	-23.33
-8	0.3360	0.02098	2.976	47.67	63.01	-0.0401	0.2284	-22.22
-6	0.3243	0.02025	3.083	49.38	62.76	-0.0382	0.2273	-21.11
-4	0.3131	0.01955	3.194	51.16	62.50	-0.0362	0.2261	-20.00
-2	0.3022	0.01887	3.309	53.00	62.23	-0.0343	0.2249	-18.89
0	0.2918	0.01822	3.427	54.86	61.95	-0.0324	0.2237	-17.78
2	0.2817	0.01759	3.550	56.86	61.65	-0.0304	0.2225	-16.67
4	0.2720	0.01698	3.676	58.88	61.36	-0.0285	0.2213	-15.56
6	0.2627	0.01640	3.807	60.98	61.07	-0.0266	0.2201	-14.44
8	0.2537	0.01584	3.942	63.14	60.77	-0.0246	0.2189	-13.33
10	0.2450	0.01529	4.082	65.39	60.48	-0.0226	0.2176	-12.22
12	0.2366	0.01477	4.227	67.71	60.18	-0.0206	0.2164	-11.11
14	0.2285	0.01426	4.377	70.11	59.88	-0.0186	0.2151	-10.00
16	0.2207	0.01378	4.532	72.59	59.58	-0.0166	0.2139	-8.89
18	0.2131	0.01330	4.692	75.16	59.27	-0.0146	0.2126	-7.78
20	0.2058	0.01285	4.859	77.83	58.95	-0.0126	0.2113	-6.67
22	0.1987	0.01240	5.031	80.59	58.64	-0.0105	0.2100	-5.56
24	0.1919	0.01198	5.211	83.47	58.31	-0.0074	0.2087	-4.44
25	0.1886	0.01177	5.303	84.94	58.14	-0.0053	0.2080	-3.89
27	0.1821	0.01137	5.492	87.97	57.81	-0.0032	0.2066	-2.78
29	0.1758	0.01097	5.688	91.11	57.47	-0.0011	0.2053	-1.67
31	0.1697	0.01059	5.892	94.38	57.12	+	0.2039	-0.56
33	0.1639	0.01023	6.103	97.76	56.77	0.0011	0.2025	+0.56
35	0.1581	0.009870	6.323	101.3	56.41	0.0033	0.2010	1.67
37	0.1526	0.009527	6.553	105.0	56.03	0.0055	0.1996	2.78
39	0.1472	0.009189	6.792	108.8	55.65	0.0077	0.1981	3.89
41	0.1420	0.008865	7.040	112.8	55.35	0.0099	0.1965	5.00
43	0.1370	0.008553	7.300	116.9	54.84	0.0122	0.1950	6.11
45	0.1321	0.008247	7.571	121.3	54.41	0.0146	0.1934	7.22
47	0.1273	0.007947	7.854	125.8	53.97	0.0169	0.1918	8.33
49	0.1227	0.007660	8.151	130.6	53.51	0.0193	0.1901	9.44
51	0.1182	0.007379	8.461	135.5	53.04	0.0218	0.1884	10.56
53	0.1138	0.007104	8.787	140.8	52.55	0.0243	0.1867	11.67
55	0.1095	0.006836	9.132	146.3	52.05	0.0268	0.1849	12.78
57	0.1053	0.006574	9.497	152.1	51.53	0.0294	0.1830	13.89
59	0.1012	0.006318	9.880	158.3	50.99	0.0321	0.1811	15.00
61	0.0972	0.00607	10.29	164.8	50.42	0.0348	0.1790	16.11
63	0.0933	0.00582	10.72	171.7	49.80	0.0377	0.1770	17.22
65	0.0894	0.00558	11.18	179.1	49.14	0.0406	0.1748	18.33
67	0.0856	0.00534	11.67	186.9	48.44	0.0436	0.1725	19.44
69	0.0819	0.00511	12.21	195.6	47.69	0.0468	0.1701	20.56
71	0.0782	0.00488	12.82	205.4	46.87	0.0501	0.1675	21.67
73	0.0745	0.00465	13.43	215.1	45.95	0.0536	0.1647	22.78
75	0.0708	0.00442	14.13	226.3	45.05	0.0573	0.1618	23.89
77	0.0671	0.00419	14.90	238.7	44.06	0.0613	0.1585	25.00
79	0.0633	0.00395	15.81	253.2	43.04	0.0656	0.1550	26.11
81	0.0592	0.00370	16.90	270.7	41.95	0.0704	0.1509	27.22
83	0.0548	0.00342	18.25	292.3	40.62	0.0759	0.1461	28.33
85	0.0500	0.00312	20.00	320.4	38.76	0.0826	0.1401	29.44
86	0.0474	0.00296	21.09	337.8	37.41	0.0868	0.1363	30.00
87	0.0446	0.00278	22.42	359.1	35.34	0.0921	0.1314	30.56
88	0.0401	0.00250	24.95	399.6	32.79	0.1002	0.1237	31.11

THERMODYNAMIC PROPERTIES (Continued)

Sulfur Dioxide, SO₂

Temp. °F	Spec. vol. sat. vap. ft³/lb.	Spec. vol. sat. vap. m³/kg	Density sat. vap. lb./ft³	Density sat. vap. kg/m³	Dens. liq. lb./ft³	Entropy from -40°F BTU/lb./°F Liq.	Entropy from -40°F BTU/lb./°F Vap.	Temp. °C
-40	22.42	1.400	0.04460	0.7144	95.79	0.00000	0.42562	-40.00
-30	16.56	1.034	.06039	.9673	94.94	.00674	.41864	-34.44
-20	12.42	.7754	.08119	1.301	94.10	.01366	.41192	-28.89
-10	9.44	.5893	.1025	1.642	93.27	.02075	.40544	-23.33
0	7.280	.4545	.1374	2.201	92.42	.02795	.39917	-17.78
2	6.923	.4322	.1444	2.313	92.25	.02941	.39794	-16.67
4	6.584	.4110	.1501	2.404	92.08	.03084	.39670	-15.56
5	6.421	.4009	.1558	2.496	92.00	.03155	.39609	-15.00
6	6.266	.3912	.1596	2.556	91.91	.03228	.39547	-14.44
8	5.967	.3725	.1676	2.685	91.74	.03373	.39426	-13.33
10	5.682	.3547	.1760	2.819	91.58	.03519	.39306	-12.22
12	5.417	.3382	.1846	2.957	91.41	.03664	.39185	-11.11
14	5.164	.3224	.1936	3.101	91.24	.03808	.39065	-10.00
16	4.926	.3075	.2030	3.252	91.07	.03953	.38946	-8.89
18	4.701	.2935	.2127	3.407	90.89	.04098	.38827	-7.78
20	4.487	.2801	.2228	3.569	90.71	.04241	.38707	-6.67
22	4.287	.2676	.2332	3.735	90.53	.04385	.38589	-5.56
24	4.096	.2557	.2441	3.910	90.33	.04528	.38471	-4.44
26	3.915	.2444	.2559	4.099	90.15	.04671	.38354	-3.33
28	3.744	.2337	.2671	4.278	89.96	.04814	.38237	-2.22
30	3.581	.2236	.2800	4.485	89.76	.04956	.38119	-1.11
32	3.437	.2146	.2909	4.660	89.58	.05099	.38003	0.00
34	3.283	.2050	.3046	4.879	89.39	.05242	.37887	+1.11
36	3.144	.1963	.3181	5.095	89.18	.05384	.37772	2.22
38	3.013	.1881	.3319	5.316	89.00	.05527	.37657	3.33
40	2.887	.1802	.3464	5.549	88.81	.05663	.37541	4.44
42	2.769	.1729	.3611	5.784	88.62	.05809	.37425	5.56
44	2.656	.1658	.3765	6.031	88.43	.05949	.37311	6.67
46	2.548	.1591	.3925	6.287	88.24	.06090	.37197	7.78
48	2.446	.1527	.4088	6.548	88.05	.06231	.37083	8.89
50	2.348	.1466	.4259	6.822	87.87	.06370	.36969	10.00
52	2.256	.1408	.4433	7.101	87.67	.06509	.36857	11.11
54	2.167	.1353	.4615	7.392	87.51	.06646	.36743	12.22
56	2.083	.1330	.4801	7.690	87.31	.06785	.36629	13.33
58	2.003	.1250	.4992	7.996	87.13	.06923	.36517	14.44
60	1.926	.1202	.5194	8.320	86.95	.07066	.36405	15.56
62	1.853	.1157	.5396	8.643	86.77	.07196	.36293	16.67
64	1.783	.1113	.5609	8.984	86.59	.07333	.36181	17.78
66	1.716	.1071	.5827	9.334	86.41	.07469	.36070	18.89
68	1.652	.1031	.6054	9.697	86.22	.07602	.35958	20.00
70	1.590	.09926	.6290	10.08	86.02	.07736	.35846	21.11
72	1.532	.09564	.6527	10.45	85.82	.07871	.35736	22.22
74	1.476	.09214	.6777	10.86	85.62	.08003	.35624	23.33
76	1.422	.08877	.7030	11.26	85.42	.08135	.35512	24.44
78	1.371	.08559	.7295	11.69	85.23	.08268	.35401	25.56
80	1.321	.08247	.7570	12.13	85.03	.08399	.35291	26.67
82	1.274	.07953	.7850	12.57	84.84	.08525	.35177	27.78
84	1.229	.07672	.8140	13.04	84.64	.08653	.35065	28.89
86	1.185	.07398	.8440	13.52	84.44	.08783	.34954	30.00
88	1.144	.07142	.8740	14.00	84.25	.08910	.34843	31.11
90	1.104	.06892	.9058	14.51	84.05	.09038	.34731	32.22
92	1.065	.06649	.9390	15.04	83.86	.09165	.34620	33.33
94	1.028	.06418	.9730	15.59	83.67	.09389	.34508	34.44
96	.9931	.06200	1.007	16.16	83.47	.09411	.34397	35.56
98	.9591	.05987	1.043	16.71	83.27	.09532	.34285	36.67
100	0.9262	0.05782	1.080	17.30	83.07	0.09657	0.34173	37.78

Sulfur Dioxide, SO₂

Temp. °F	Abs. press sat. vap. lb./in.²	Abs. press sat. vap. kg/cm²	Heat content abv. -40°F BTU/lb. Liq.	Heat content abv. -40°F BTU/lb. Vap.	Ht. of vaporiz. BTU/lb.	Heat content abv. -40°C g-cal./g Liq.	Heat content abv. -40°C g-cal./g Vap.	Ht. of vaporiz. g-cal./g	Temp. °C
-40	3.136	0.2205	0.00	178.61	178.61	0.00	99.228	99.228	-40.00
-30	4.331	.3045	2.93	179.90	176.97	1.63	99.945	98.317	-34.44
-20	5.883	.4136	5.98	181.07	175.09	3.32	100.59	97.272	-28.89
-10	7.863	.5528	9.16	182.13	172.97	5.09	101.18	96.095	-23.33
0	10.35	.7277	12.44	183.07	170.63	6.911	101.71	94.795	-17.78
2	10.91	.7670	13.12	183.25	170.13	7.289	101.81	94.517	-16.67
4	11.50	.8085	13.78	183.41	169.63	7.656	101.89	94.239	-15.56
5	11.81	.8303	14.45	183.49	169.38	7.839	101.94	94.100	-15.00
6	12.12	.8521	14.45	183.57	169.12	8.028	101.98	93.956	-14.44
8	12.75	.8964	15.23	183.73	168.60	8.406	102.07	93.667	-13.33
10	13.42	.9435	15.80	183.87	168.07	8.778	102.15	93.372	-12.22
12	14.12	.9927	16.48	184.01	167.53	9.156	102.23	93.072	-11.11
14	14.84	1.043	17.15	184.14	166.97	9.528	102.30	92.761	-10.00
16	15.59	1.096	17.84	184.28	166.44	9.911	102.38	92.467	-8.89
18	16.37	1.1509	18.52	184.40	165.88	10.29	102.44	92.156	-7.78
20	17.18	1.208	19.20	184.52	165.32	10.67	102.51	91.845	-6.67
22	18.03	1.268	19.90	184.64	164.74	11.06	102.58	91.522	-5.56
24	18.89	1.328	20.58	184.74	164.16	11.43	102.63	91.201	-4.44
26	19.80	1.392	21.26	184.84	163.58	11.81	102.69	90.878	-3.33
28	20.73	1.457	21.96	184.94	162.98	12.20	102.74	90.545	-2.22
30	21.70	1.526	22.64	185.02	162.38	12.58	102.79	90.211	-1.11
32	22.71	1.597	23.33	185.10	161.77	12.96	102.83	89.872	0.00
34	23.75	1.670	24.03	185.18	161.15	13.35	102.88	89.528	+1.11
36	24.82	.745	24.72	185.25	160.53	13.73	102.92	89.183	2.22
38	25.95	.824	25.42	185.31	159.89	14.12	102.95	88.828	3.33
40	27.10	.905	26.12	185.37	159.25	14.51	102.98	88.472	4.44
42	28.29	.989	26.81	185.42	158.61	14.89	103.01	88.117	5.56
44	29.52	.075	27.51	185.46	157.95	15.28	103.03	87.750	6.67
46	30.79	.165	28.21	185.50	157.29	15.67	103.06	87.383	7.78
48	32.10	.257	28.92	185.54	156.62	16.07	103.08	87.011	8.89
50	33.45	.352	29.61	185.56	155.95	16.45	103.09	86.639	10.00
52	34.86	.451	30.31	185.58	155.27	16.84	103.10	86.261	11.11
54	36.31	.553	31.00	185.59	154.59	17.22	103.11	85.883	12.22
56	37.80	.658	31.72	185.61	153.89	17.62	103.12	85.495	13.33
58	39.33	.765	32.42	185.61	153.19	18.01	103.12	85.106	14.44
60	40.93	.878	33.10	185.59	152.49	18.39	103.11	84.717	15.56
62	42.58	.994	33.79	185.57	151.78	18.77	103.09	84.322	16.67
64	44.27	.112	34.49	185.55	151.06	19.09	103.08	83.922	17.78
66	46.00	.234	35.19	185.53	150.34	19.55	103.06	83.522	18.89
68	47.78	.359	35.88	185.50	149.62	19.93	103.03	83.122	20.00
70	49.62	.489	36.58	185.46	148.88	20.32	103.01	82.711	21.11
72	51.54	.624	37.28	185.42	148.14	20.71	102.98	82.300	22.22
74	53.48	.760	37.97	185.37	147.40	21.09	102.95	81.889	23.33
76	55.48	.901	38.67	185.31	146.64	21.48	102.91	81.467	24.44
78	57.56	.047	39.36	185.24	145.88	21.87	102.87	81.045	25.56
80	59.68	.196	40.05	185.17	145.12	22.25	102.83	80.622	26.67
82	61.88	.351	40.73	185.09	144.36	22.63	102.77	80.200	27.78
84	64.15	.509	41.43	185.01	143.58	23.02	102.73	79.767	28.89
86	66.45	.672	42.12	184.92	142.80	23.40	102.68	79.333	30.00
88	68.84	.840	42.80	184.82	142.02	23.78	102.62	78.900	31.11
90	71.25	5.009	43.50	184.72	141.22	24.17	102.56	78.456	32.22
92	73.70	5.182	44.19	184.61	140.42	24.55	102.49	78.011	33.33
94	76.30	5.364	44.86	184.49	139.62	24.92	102.43	77.567	34.44
96	79.03	5.556	45.54	184.37	138.83	25.29	102.36	77.128	35.56
98	81.77	.749	46.22	184.25	138.03	25.68	102.28	76.683	36.67
100	84.52	.942	46.90	184.10	137.20	26.06	102.28	76.222	37.78

THERMODYNAMIC PROPERTIES (Continued)

Butane, CH₃(CH₂)₂CH₃

Temp. °F	Spec. vol. sat. vap. ft³/lb	Spec. vol. sat. vap. m³/kg	Density of sat. vap. lb/ft³	Density of sat. vap. kg/m³	Density of liq. lb/ft³	Density of liq. kg/m³	Temp. °C
0	11.1	0.693	0.0901	1.44	38.59	618.1	−17.78
10	8.95	.559	.112	1.79	38.24	612.5	−12.22
20	7.23	.451	.138	2.21	37.89	606.9	−6.67
30	5.90	.368	.169	2.71	37.54	601.3	−1.11
40	4.88	.305	.205	3.28	37.19	595.7	+4.44
50	4.07	.254	.246	3.94	36.82	589.8	10.00
60	3.40	.212	.294	4.71	36.45	583.9	15.56
70	2.88	.180	.347	5.56	36.06	577.6	21.11
80	2.46	.154	.407	6.52	35.65	571.0	26.67
90	2.10	.131	.476	7.62	35.24	564.5	32.22
100	1.81	.113	.552	8.84	34.84	558.1	37.78
110	1.58	.0986	.633	10.1	34.41	551.2	43.33
120	1.38	.0862	.725	11.6	33.96	544.0	48.89
130	1.21	.0755	.826	13.2	33.49	536.4	54.44
140	1.07	.0668	.934	15.0	32.98	528.3	60.00

Isobutane, (CH₃)₃CH

Temp. °F	Spec. vol. sat. vap. ft³/lb	Spec. vol. sat. vap. m³/kg	Density of sat. vap. lb/ft³	Density of sat. vap. kg/m³	Density of liq. lb/ft³	Density of liq. kg/m³	Temp. °C
−20	10.5	0.655	0.0952	1.52	38.35	614.3	−28.89
−10	8.91	.556	.112	1.79	37.95	607.9	−23.33
0	7.17	.448	.139	2.23	37.60	602.3	−17.78
+10	5.75	.359	.174	2.79	37.20	595.9	−12.22
20	4.68	.292	.214	3.43	36.80	589.5	−6.67
30	3.86	.241	.259	4.15	36.40	583.1	−1.11
40	3.22	.201	.311	4.98	36.00	576.6	+4.44
50	2.71	.169	.369	5.91	35.60	570.2	10.00
60	2.28	.142	.439	7.03	35.20	563.8	15.56
70	1.94	.121	.515	8.25	34.80	557.4	21.11
80	1.66	.104	.602	9.64	34.35	550.2	26.67
90	1.42	.0886	.704	11.3	33.90	543.0	32.22
100	1.23	.0768	.813	13.0	33.45	535.8	37.78
110	1.07	.0668	.935	15.0	33.00	528.6	43.33
120	0.926	.0578	1.08	17.3	32.50	520.6	48.89
130	0.811	.0506	1.23	19.7	32.00	512.6	54.44
140	0.716	.0447	1.32	21.1	31.80	509.4	60.00

Propane, C₃H₈

Temp. °F	Spec. vol. sat. vap. ft³/lb	Spec. vol. sat. vap. m³/kg	Density of sat. vap. lb/ft³	Density of sat. vap. kg/m³	Density of liq. lb/ft³	Density of liq. kg/m³	Temp. °C
−70	12.9	0.805	0.0775	1.24	37.40	599.1	−56.67
−60	9.93	.620	.111	1.78	37.00	592.7	−51.11
−50	7.74	.483	.129	2.07	36.60	586.3	−45.56
−40	6.13	.383	.163	2.61	36.19	579.7	−40.00
−30	4.93	.308	.203	3.25	35.78	573.1	−34.44
−20	4.00	.250	.250	4.00	35.37	566.6	−28.89
−10	3.26	.204	.307	4.92	34.96	560.0	−23.33
0	2.71	.169	.369	5.91	34.54	553.3	−17.78
+10	2.27	.142	.441	7.06	34.12	546.5	−12.22
20	1.90	.119	.526	8.43	33.73	539.3	−6.67
30	1.60	.0999	.625	10.0	33.20	531.8	−1.11
40	1.37	.0855	.730	11.7	33.24	524.3	+4.44
50	1.18	.0737	.847	13.6	32.24	516.4	10.00
60	1.01	.0631	.990	15.9	31.75	508.6	15.56
70	0.883	.0551	1.13	18.1	31.24	500.4	21.11
80	0.770	.0481	1.30	20.9	30.70	491.8	26.67
90	0.673	.0420	1.49	23.9	30.15	482.3	32.22
100	0.591	.0369	1.69	27.1	29.58	473.8	37.78
110	0.519	.0324	1.96	31.4	28.85	462.1	43.33
120	0.459	.0287	2.18	34.9	28.30	453.3	48.89

Butane, CH₃(CH₂)₂CH₃

Temp. °F	Abs. press. sat. vap. lb/in²	kg/cm²	Heat content abv. 32°F Liq. BTU/lb	Heat content abv. 32°F Vap. BTU/lb	Ht. of vaporiz. BTU/lb	Heat content abv. 0°C Liq. g-cal/g	Heat content abv. 0°C Vap. g-cal/g	Ht. of vaporiz. g-cal/g	Temp. °C
0	7.3	0.51	−17.2	153.3	170.5	−9.56	85.17	94.72	−17.78
10	9.2	0.65	−11.7	156.8	168.5	−6.50	87.11	93.61	−12.22
20	11.6	0.816	−6.7	160.3	167.0	−3.7	89.06	92.78	−6.67
30	14.4	1.01	−1.2	164.3	165.5	−0.67	91.28	91.94	−1.11
40	17.7	1.24	4.3	167.8	163.5	2.4	93.22	90.83	+4.44
50	21.6	1.52	9.8	171.3	161.5	5.4	95.17	89.72	10.00
60	26.3	1.85	15.8	175.3	159.5	8.78	97.39	88.61	15.56
70	31.6	2.22	21.3	178.5	157.5	11.8	99.3	87.50	21.11
80	37.6	2.64	27.3	182.3	155.0	15.2	101.3	86.11	26.67
90	44.5	3.13	33.8	185.8	152.0	18.8	103.2	84.44	32.22
100	52.2	3.67	39.8	189.3	149.5	22.1	105.2	83.06	37.78
110	60.8	4.27	46.3	193.3	147.0	25.7	107.4	81.67	43.33
120	70.8	4.98	52.8	196.3	143.5	29.3	109.1	79.72	48.89
130	81.4	5.72	59.3	199.8	140.5	32.9	111.0	78.06	54.44
140	92.6	6.51	66.3	203.8	137.5	36.8	113.2	76.39	60.00

Isobutane, (CH₃)₃CH

Temp. °F	Abs. press. sat. vap. lb/in²	kg/cm²	Heat content abv. 32°F Liq. BTU/lb	Heat content abv. 32°F Vap. BTU/lb	Ht. of vaporiz. BTU/lb	Heat content abv. 0°C Liq. g-cal/g	Heat content abv. 0°C Vap. g-cal/g	Ht. of vaporiz. g-cal/g	Temp. °C
−20	7.50	0.527	−25.5	140.0	165.5	−14.2	77.78	91.94	−28.89
−10	9.28	0.652	−21.0	142.0	163.0	−11.7	78.89	90.56	−23.33
0	11.6	0.816	−16.5	144.0	160.5	−9.17	80.00	89.17	−17.78
+10	14.6	1.03	−11.5	147.0	158.5	−6.39	81.67	88.06	−12.22
20	18.3	1.28	−6.5	149.5	156.0	−3.6	83.06	86.67	−6.67
30	22.3	1.57	−1.0	152.5	153.5	−0.56	84.72	85.28	−1.11
40	26.9	1.89	4.5	155.5	151.0	2.5	86.39	83.89	+4.44
50	32.1	2.28	10.5	158.5	148.5	5.83	88.33	82.50	10.00
60	38.7	2.72	16.5	162.5	146.0	9.17	90.28	81.11	15.56
70	45.8	3.22	23.0	166.5	143.5	12.8	92.50	79.72	21.11
80	53.3	3.79	30.0	170.5	140.5	16.7	94.72	78.06	26.67
90	63.3	4.45	37.0	174.5	137.5	20.6	96.94	76.33	32.22
100	73.7	5.18	44.5	179.0	134.5	24.7	99.44	74.72	37.78
110	85.1	5.98	52.5	183.5	131.0	29.2	101.9	72.78	43.33
120	98.0	6.89	60.5	188.0	127.5	33.6	104.4	70.83	48.89
130	112.0	7.87	69.5	193.5	124.0	38.6	107.5	68.89	54.44
140	126.8	8.915	78.5	199.0	120.5	43.6	110.6	66.94	60.00

Propane, C₃H₈

Temp. °F	Abs. press. sat. vap. lb/in²	kg/cm²	Heat content abv. 32°F Liq. BTU/lb	Heat content abv. 32°F Vap. BTU/lb	Ht. of vaporiz. BTU/lb	Heat content abv. 0°C Liq. g-cal/g	Heat content abv. 0°C Vap. g-cal/g	Ht. of vaporiz. g-cal/g	Temp. °C
−70	7.37	0.518	−55.2	134.3	189.5	−30.7	74.61	105.3	−56.67
−60	9.72	0.683	−50.2	136.8	187.0	−27.9	76.00	103.9	−51.11
−50	12.6	0.886	−44.7	139.8	184.5	−24.8	77.67	102.5	−45.56
−40	16.2	1.14	−39.7	141.8	181.5	−22.1	78.78	100.8	−40.00
−30	20.3	1.43	−34.2	144.8	179.0	−19.0	80.44	99.44	−34.44
−20	25.4	1.79	−29.2	146.8	176.0	−16.2	81.56	97.78	−28.89
−10	31.4	2.21	−23.7	149.8	173.5	−13.2	83.22	96.39	−23.33
0	38.2	2.69	−18.2	152.3	170.5	−10.1	84.61	95.00	−17.78
+10	46.0	3.23	−12.7	155.3	168.0	−7.06	86.28	93.33	−12.22
20	55.5	3.90	−7.2	157.8	165.0	−4.0	87.67	91.67	−6.67
30	66.3	4.66	−1.2	160.8	162.0	−0.67	89.33	90.00	−1.11
40	78.0	5.48	4.8	163.8	159.0	2.7	91.00	88.33	+4.44
50	91.8	6.45	10.8	166.8	156.0	6.00	92.67	86.67	10.00
60	107.1	7.530	16.8	169.8	153.0	9.33	94.33	85.00	15.56
70	124.0	8.718	22.8	172.3	149.5	12.7	95.72	83.00	21.11
80	142.8	10.04	29.3	175.3	146.0	16.3	97.39	81.11	26.67
90	164.0	11.52	35.3	178.3	143.0	19.9	99.06	79.17	32.22
100	187.0	13.15	42.3	180.8	138.5	23.5	100.4	76.94	37.78
110	213.0	14.98	48.8	182.8	134.0	27.1	101.6	74.44	43.33
120	240.0	16.87	55.3	184.3	129.0	30.7	102.4	71.67	48.89

Difluorodichloromethane, CCl₂F₂ ("F-12")

Temp. °F	Spec. vol sat. vap. ft.³/lb.	Spec. vol sat. vap. m³/kg	Density of vap. lb./ft.³	Density of vap. kg/m³	Dens. liq. lb./ft.³	Entropy from −40°F BTU/lb./°F Liq.	Entropy from −40°F BTU/lb./°F Vap.	Temp. °C
−40	3.911	0.2442	0.2557	4.096	94.58		0.17517	−40.00
−30	3.088	.1928	.3238	5.187	93.59	0.00471	.17337	−34.44
−20	2.474	.1544	.4042	6.474	92.58	.00940	.17275	−28.89
−10	2.003	.1250	.4993	7.998	91.57	.01403	.17175	−23.33
0	1.637	.1022	.6109	9.785	90.52	.01869	.17091	−17.78
+10	1.351	.08434	.7402	11.86	89.45	.02328	.17015	−12.22
20	1.121	.06998	.8921	14.29	88.37	.02783	.16949	−6.67
30	0.939	.0586	1.065	17.06	87.24	.03233	.16837	−1.11
40	.792	.0494	1.263	20.23	86.10	.03680	.16833	+1.11
50	.673	.0420	1.485	23.79	84.94	.04126	.16785	10.00
60	.575	.0359	1.740	27.88	83.78	.04568	.16741	15.56
70	.493	.0308	2.028	32.48	82.60	.05009	.16701	21.11
80	.425	.0265	2.353	37.69	81.39	.05446	.16662	26.67
90	.368	.0230	2.721	43.58	80.11	.05882	.16624	32.22
100	.319	.0199	3.135	50.22	78.80	.06316	.16584	37.78
110	.277	.0173	3.610	57.82	77.46	.06749	.16542	43.33
120	.240	.0150	4.167	66.75	76.02	.07180	.16495	48.89

Temp. °F	Abs. press. sat. vap. lb./in.²	Abs. press. sat. vap. kg/cm²	Heat content abv. −40°F BTU/lb. Liq.	Heat content abv. −40°F BTU/lb. Vap.	Ht. of vaporiz. BTU/lb.	Heat content abv. −40°C g-cal./g Liq.	Heat content abv. −40°C g-cal./g Vap.	Ht. of vaporiz. g-cal./g	Temp. °C
−40	9.33	0.655	0	73.50	73.50	0	40.83	40.83	−40.00
−30	12.02	.845	2.03	74.70	72.67	1.13	41.50	40.37	−34.44
−20	15.28	1.074	4.07	75.87	71.80	2.26	42.15	39.89	−28.89
−10	19.20	1.350	6.14	77.05	70.91	3.41	42.81	39.39	−23.33
0	23.87	1.678	8.25	78.21	69.96	4.58	43.45	38.87	−17.78
+10	29.35	2.064	10.39	79.36	68.97	5.772	44.09	38.32	−12.22
20	35.75	2.513	12.55	80.49	67.94	6.972	44.72	37.74	−6.67
30	43.16	3.034	14.76	81.61	66.85	8.200	45.34	37.14	−1.11
40	51.68	3.633	17.00	82.71	65.71	9.444	45.95	36.51	+1.11
50	61.39	4.316	19.27	83.78	64.51	10.71	46.54	35.84	10.00
60	72.4	5.091	21.57	84.82	63.25	11.98	47.12	35.14	15.56
70	84.82	5.963	23.90	85.82	61.92	13.28	47.68	34.40	21.11
80	98.76	6.944	26.28	86.80	60.52	14.60	48.22	33.62	26.67
90	114.5	8.036	28.70	87.74	59.04	15.94	48.74	32.80	32.22
100	131.6	9.252	31.16	88.62	57.46	17.31	49.23	31.92	37.78
110	150.7	10.60	33.65	89.43	55.78	18.69	49.68	30.99	43.33
120	171.8	12.08	36.16	90.15	53.99	20.09	50.08	29.99	48.89

Carbon Disulfide, CS₂

Temp. °F	Spec. vol sat. vap. ft.³/lb.	Spec. vol sat. vap. m³/kg	Density sat. vap. lb./ft.³	Density sat. vap. kg/m³	Temp. °C
0	53.76	3.356	0.0186	0.2979	−17.78
10	43.47	2.714	.0230	.3684	−12.22
20	34.84	2.175	.0287	.4597	−6.67
30	29.49	1.841	.0339	.5430	−1.11
40	23.52	1.468	.0425	.6808	+4.44
50	20.60	1.286	.0482	.7721	10.00
60	18.00	1.124	.0555	.8890	15.56
70	13.20	0.824	.0758	1.214	21.11
80	10.40	0.649	.0961	1.539	26.67
90	8.30	0.518	.1204	1.929	32.22
100	7.03	0.439	.1369	2.193	37.78
110	5.80	0.362	.1724	2.762	43.33
120	5.10	0.318	.1960	3.140	48.89

Temp. °F	Abs. press. sat. vap. lb./in.²	Abs. press. sat. vap. kg/cm²	Heat content abv. 32°F BTU/lb. Liq.	Heat content abv. 32°F BTU/lb. Vap.	Ht. of vaporiz. BTU/lb.	Heat content abv. 0°C g-cal./g Liq.	Heat content abv. 0°C g-cal./g Vap.	Ht. of vaporiz. g-cal./g	Temp. °C
0	1.10	0.0773	− 8.60	156.90	165.5	− 4.78	87.167	91.94	−17.78
10	1.46	.103	− 5.60	158.90	164.5	− 3.11	88.278	91.39	−12.22
20	1.91	.133	− 3.00	160.70	163.2	− 1.67	89.040	90.67	−6.67
30	2.36	.166	− 0.50	162.70	162.2	− 0.28	89.833	90.11	−1.11
40	3.05	.213	+ 2.05	163.25	161.2	+ 1.14	90.655	89.56	+4.44
50	3.90	.274	4.24	164.24	160.0	2.36	91.245	88.89	10.00
60	4.95	.348	7.20	166.40	159.2	4.00	92.445	88.44	15.56
70	5.85	.411	9.80	167.90	158.1	5.44	93.278	87.83	21.11
80	7.30	.513	11.70	168.60	156.9	6.500	93.867	87.17	26.67
90	9.15	.643	13.80	169.40	155.6	7.667	94.111	86.44	32.22
100	11.05	.7790	16.15	170.55	154.4	8.972	94.750	85.78	37.78
110	13.50	.9491	18.30	171.50	153.2	10.17	95.278	85.11	43.33
120	16.10	1.132	20.01	172.50	152.0	11.12	95.561	84.44	48.89

Carbon Tetrachloride, CCl₄

Temp. °F	Spec. vol sat. vap. ft.³/lb.	Spec. vol sat. vap. m³/kg	Density sat. vap. lb./ft.³	Density sat. vap. kg/m³	Temp. °C
20	69.5	4.34	0.01438	0.2303	− 6.67
30	53.0	3.31	.01886	.3021	− 1.11
40	40.0	2.50	.02500	.4005	+ 4.44
60	24.0	1.50	.04166	.6673	15.56
70	19.5	1.22	.05128	.8214	21.11
80	16.0	0.999	.06345	1.016	26.67
90	13.0	0.812	.07692	1.232	32.22
100	10.0	0.624	.1000	1.602	37.78
110	8.5	0.53	.1176	1.884	43.33
120	7.5	0.47	.1333	2.135	48.89

Temp. °F	Abs. press. sat. vap. lb./in.²	Abs. press. sat. vap. kg/cm²	Heat content abv. 0°F BTU/lb. Liq.	Heat content abv. 0°F BTU/lb. Vap.	Ht. of vaporiz. BTU/lb.	Heat content abv. 0°C g-cal./g Liq.	Heat content abv. 0°C g-cal./g Vap.	Ht. of vaporiz. g-cal./g	Temp. °C
20	0.40	0.028	− 2.00	92.45	94.45	− 1.11	51.36	52.47	− 6.67
30	0.60	.042	− 0.25	93.45	93.70	− 0.14	51.92	52.06	− 1.11
40	0.92	.059	+ 1.60	94.80	93.20	+ 0.889	52.67	51.78	+ 4.44
60	1.42	.100	5.95	97.35	91.40	3.31	54.53	51.22	15.56
70	1.85	.130	8.20	98.53	90.33	4.56	55.29	50.78	21.11
80	2.40	.169	9.80	99.87	90.07	5.44	55.48	50.04	26.67
90	3.12	.219	11.60	101.62	90.02	6.44	56.46	49.67	32.22
100	4.00	.281	13.40	102.80	89.40	7.444	57.11	49.28	37.78
110	4.89	.344	15.80	104.50	88.70	8.778	58.06	48.83	43.33
120	5.95	.418	18.06	105.90	87.90	10.03	58.83	48.44	48.89

Ethyl Ether, (C₂H₅)₂O

Temp. °F	Spec. vol sat. vap. ft.³/lb.	Spec. vol sat. vap. m³/kg	Density sat. vap. lb./ft.³	Density sat. vap. kg/m³	Temp. °C
0	38.0	2.37	0.0263	0.4213	−17.78
10	32.5	2.03	.0332	.5318	−12.22
20	27.0	1.69	.0372	.5959	− 6.67
30	21.4	1.34	.0468	.7496	− 1.11
40	17.0	1.06	.0588	.9419	+ 4.44
50	13.2	0.824	.0757	1.213	10.00
70	7.8	0.49	.1280	2.050	21.11
80	6.2	0.39	.1620	2.595	26.67
90	5.1	0.32	.1960	3.140	37.78
100	4.5	0.28	.2220	3.556	

Temp. °F	Abs. press. sat. vap. lb./in.²	Abs. press. sat. vap. kg/cm²	Heat content abv. −18°F BTU/lb. Liq.	Heat content abv. −18°F BTU/lb. Vap.	Ht. of vaporiz. BTU/lb.	Heat content g-cal./g Liq.	Heat content g-cal./g Vap.	Ht. of vaporiz. g-cal./g	Temp. °C
0	1.3	0.091	−18.00	153.00	171.00	−10.00	85.000	95.00	−17.78
10	1.8	.13	−12.0	158.43	170.4	− 6.67	88.017	94.67	−12.22
20	2.5	.18	− 6.50	163.50	170.0	− 3.61	90.833	94.44	− 6.67
30	3.4	.24	− 1.50	167.90	169.4	− 0.833	93.278	94.11	− 1.11
40	4.4	.31	+ 4.00	172.40	168.4	+ 2.22	95.778	93.56	+ 4.44
50	5.5	.39	9.57	177.17	167.6	5.32	98.428	93.11	10.00
70	8.8	.62	20.04	185.44	165.4	11.13	103.02	91.89	21.11
80	10.9	.766	26.40	190.60	164.2	14.67	105.89	91.22	26.67
90	13.4	.942	31.50	194.50	163.0	17.50	108.06	90.56	32.22
100	16.0	1.12	36.50	197.50	161.5	20.28	109.72	89.72	37.78

THERMODYNAMIC PROPERTIES (Concluded)

Methyl Chloride, CH₃Cl

Temp. °F	Spec. vol. sat. vap. ft³/lb.	Spec. vol. sat. vap. m³/kg	Spec. vol. sat. liq. ft³/lb.	Spec. vol. sat. liq. m³/kg	Density sat. vap. lb./ft³	Density sat. vap. kg/m³	Density of liq. lb./ft³	Density of liq. kg/m³	Temp. °C
-20	8.09	.505	.015827	.0009880	0.124	1.98	63.185	1012.1	-28.89
-10	6.46	.403	.015985	.0009979	.155	2.48	62.560	1002.1	-23.33
-5	5.80	.362	.016013	.0009997	.172	2.76	62.450	1000.3	-20.56
0	5.18	.323	.016146	.001008	.193	3.09	61.936	992.09	-17.78
+5	4.68	.292	.016228	.001013	.214	3.42	61.623	987.08	-15.00
10	4.18	.261	.016310	.001018	.239	3.83	61.311	982.08	-12.22
15	3.88	.242	.016388	.001023	.258	4.13	61.022	977.45	-9.44
20	3.41	.213	.016474	.001028	.293	4.70	60.702	972.32	-6.67
25	3.09	.193	.016552	.001033	.324	5.18	60.415	967.73	-3.89
30	2.81	.175	.016645	.001039	.356	5.70	60.077	962.31	-1.11
35	2.50	.156	.016746	.001045	.400	6.41	59.715	956.51	+1.67
40	2.31	.144	.016809	.001049	.433	6.93	59.492	952.94	4.44
45	2.10	.131	.016929	.001057	.476	7.63	59.069	946.17	7.22
50	1.93	.120	.017023	.001063	.518	8.30	58.745	940.98	10.00
55	1.75	.109	.017118	.001069	.571	9.16	58.419	935.76	12.78
60	1.61	.101	.017219	.001075	.621	9.95	58.077	930.28	15.56
65	1.47	.0918	.017318	.001081	.680	10.9	57.742	924.91	18.33
70	1.34	.0837	.017421	.001088	.746	11.9	57.403	919.48	21.11
75	1.24	.0774	.017526	.001094	.806	12.9	57.058	913.96	23.89
80	1.14	.0712	.017632	.001101	.877	14.1	56.714	908.44	26.67
85	1.05	.0655	.017740	.001108	.952	15.3	56.369	902.92	29.44
90	0.98	.061	.017850	.001114	1.02	16.3	56.022	897.80	32.22
95	0.91	.057	.017961	.001121	1.10	17.6	55.675	891.80	35.00
100	0.85	.053	.018074	.001128	1.18	18.8	55.327	886.23	37.78

Methyl Chloride, CH₃Cl

Temp. °F	Abs. press. sat. vap. lb./in.²	Abs. press. sat. vap. kg/cm²	Heat content abv. 32°F BTU/lb. Liq.	Heat content abv. 32°F BTU/lb. Vap.	Ht. of vaporiz. BTU/lb.	Heat content abv. 0°C g-cal/g Liq.	Heat content abv. 0°C g-cal/g Vap.	Ht. of vaporiz. g-cal/g	Temp. °C
-20	11.75	0.8261	-19.0	167.36	186.36	-10.6	92.978	103.53	-28.89
-10	15.0	1.055	-15.38	168.83	184.21	-8.544	93.795	102.34	-23.33
-5	16.79	1.180	-13.58	169.54	183.12	-7.544	94.189	101.73	-20.56
0	18.8	1.32	-11.75	170.23	181.98	-6.528	94.572	101.10	-17.78
+5	21.0	1.48	-9.93	170.96	180.84	-5.517	94.978	100.47	-15.00
10	23.3	1.64	-8.06	171.58	179.65	-4.478	95.322	99.806	-12.22
15	25.9	1.82	-6.74	172.24	178.47	-3.744	95.689	99.150	-9.44
20	28.8	2.02	-4.32	172.95	177.27	-2.400	96.083	98.483	-6.67
25	31.8	2.24	-2.48	173.63	176.10	-1.378	96.461	97.833	-3.89
30	35.2	2.47	-0.62	174.28	174.90	-0.344	96.822	97.167	-1.11
35	38.7	2.72	+1.75	174.92	173.77	+0.972	97.167	96.539	+1.67
40	42.6	3.00	3.15	175.57	172.42	1.75	97.539	95.789	4.44
45	46.9	3.30	5.04	176.20	171.16	2.80	97.889	95.089	7.22
50	51.5	3.62	6.88	176.78	169.90	3.82	98.211	94.389	10.00
55	56.4	3.97	8.80	177.45	168.65	4.89	98.583	93.695	12.78
60	61.6	4.33	10.70	178.05	167.35	5.944	98.917	92.972	15.56
65	67.3	4.73	12.62	178.64	166.02	7.011	99.245	92.233	18.33
70	73.3	5.15	14.52	179.17	164.65	8.067	99.539	91.472	21.11
75	79.2	5.57	16.46	179.78	163.28	9.144	99.878	90.711	23.89
80	85.3	6.02	18.36	180.24	161.88	10.20	100.13	89.933	26.67
85	94.1	6.62	20.12	180.74	160.48	11.18	100.41	89.156	29.44
90	102.1	7.178	22.13	181.26	159.09	12.29	100.68	88.383	32.22
95	110.3	7.755	24.07	181.76	157.70	13.37	100.98	87.611	35.00
100	118.8	8.352	26.06	182.36	156.30	14.48	101.31	86.833	37.78

Mercury, Hg

Temp. °F	Spec. vol. sat. vap. ft³/lb.	Spec. vol. sat. vap. m³/kg	Density of sat. vap. lb./ft³	Density of sat. vap. kg/m³	Entropy above 32°F BTU/lb./°F Liq.	Entropy Vap.	Entropy Evap.	Temp. °C
402	114.50	7.1480	.008733	.1399	.0209	.1696	.1487	205.56
444	59.72	3.728	.016745	.26822	.0227	.1635	.1408	228.89
458	48.45	3.025	.02064	.3306	.0233	.1616	.1383	236.67
485	33.14	2.069	.03017	.4833	.0244	.1581	.1337	251.67
505	25.32	1.581	.03948	.6324	.0251	.1556	.1305	262.78
558	13.26	0.8278	.07540	1.208	.0271	.1497	.1226	292.22
591	9.096	.5678	.10993	1.7009	.0283	.1462	.1179	310.56
617	6.9630	.43469	.14361	2.3003	.0292	.1439	.1147	325.00
637	5.5610	.35341	.17664	2.8294	.0299	.1420	.1121	336.11
676	3.8923	.24299	.25691	4.1152	.0312	.1387	.1075	357.78
706	2.983	.1862	.3352	5.369	.0322	.1364	.1042	374.44
730	2.429	.1516	.4117	6.595	.0330	.1346	.1016	387.78
751	2.053	.1282	.4871	7.802	.0336	.1331	.0995	399.44
769	1.7815	.11122	.5613	8.991	.0342	.1319	.0977	409.44
785	1.5762	.098399	.6344	10.16	.0346	.1308	.0962	418.33
799	1.4147	.083317	.7069	11.32	.0351	.1300	.0949	426.11
812	1.284	.08016	.7788	12.47	.0355	.1291	.0936	433.33
836	1.086	.06780	.9204	14.74	.0361	.1276	.0915	446.67
857	0.9436	.05912	1.0597	16.974	.0367	.1265	.0898	458.33
875	.8349	.05212	1.1977	19.185	.0372	.1254	.0882	468.33
892	.7497	.04680	1.3338	21.365	.0377	.1247	.0870	477.78
907	.6811	.04252	1.4682	23.518	.0381	.1237	.0856	486.11
921	.6242	.03897	1.6020	25.661	.0385	.1230	.0845	493.89
934	.5767	.03600	1.7340	27.775	.0389	.1224	.0835	501.11
947	.5360	.03346	1.8656	29.883	.0392	.1218	.0826	508.33
958	.5012	.03129	1.9952	31.959	.0395	.1213	.0818	514.44
969	.4706	.02938	2.125	34.04	.0398	.1207	.0809	520.56
1000	.3990	.02491	2.506	40.14	.0406	.1194	.0788	537.78

Mercury, Hg

Temp. °F	Abs. press. sat. vap. lb./in.²	Abs. press. sat. vap. kg/cm²	Heat content abv. 32°F BTU/lb. Liq.	Heat content abv. 32°F BTU/lb. Vap.	Ht. of vaporiz. BTU/lb.	Heat content abv. 0°C g-cal/g Liq.	Heat content abv. 0°C g-cal/g Vap.	Ht. of vaporiz. g-cal/g	Temp. °C
402	0.4	0.03	13.81	141.96	128.15	7.672	78.867	71.195	205.56
444	0.8	0.06	15.36	142.60	127.24	8.533	79.222	70.689	228.89
458	1.0	0.07	15.89	142.81	126.92	8.828	79.339	70.511	236.67
485	1.5	0.11	16.90	143.28	126.33	9.389	79.572	70.183	251.67
505	2.0	0.14	17.65	143.54	125.89	9.806	79.745	69.939	262.78
558	4.0	0.28	19.62	144.34	124.72	10.90	80.189	69.289	292.22
591	6.0	0.42	20.87	144.86	123.99	11.59	80.478	68.883	310.56
617	8.0	0.56	21.81	145.24	123.43	12.12	80.689	68.572	325.00
637	10.0	0.703	22.58	145.56	122.98	12.54	80.867	68.322	336.11
676	15.0	1.05	24.04	146.16	122.12	13.36	81.200	67.844	357.78
706	20.0	1.41	25.15	146.61	121.46	13.97	81.450	67.478	374.44
730	25.0	1.76	26.05	146.98	120.93	14.47	81.656	67.183	387.78
751	30.0	2.11	26.81	147.29	120.48	14.89	81.828	66.933	399.44
769	35.0	2.46	27.49	147.57	120.08	15.27	81.983	66.711	409.44
785	40.0	2.81	28.08	147.81	119.73	15.60	82.117	66.517	418.33
799	45.0	3.16	28.62	148.04	119.42	15.90	82.245	66.355	426.11
812	50	3.5	29.11	148.24	119.13	16.17	82.356	66.183	433.33
836	60	4.2	29.99	148.60	118.61	16.66	82.556	65.894	446.67
857	70	4.9	30.75	148.90	118.15	17.08	82.722	65.639	458.33
875	80	5.6	31.44	149.19	117.75	17.47	82.883	65.417	468.33
892	90	6.3	32.06	149.44	117.38	17.81	83.022	65.211	477.78
907	100	7.03	32.63	149.68	117.05	18.13	83.156	65.028	486.11
921	110	7.73	33.16	149.90	116.74	18.42	83.278	64.856	493.89
934	120	8.44	33.66	150.10	116.44	18.70	83.389	64.689	501.11
947	130	9.14	34.12	150.29	116.17	18.96	83.495	64.539	508.33
958	140	9.84	34.55	150.47	115.92	19.19	83.595	64.400	514.44
969	150	10.5	34.96	150.63	115.67	19.42	83.663	64.261	520.56
1000	180	12.7	36.09	151.10	115.01	20.05	83.945	63.894	537.78

PHYSICAL PROPERTIES OF FLUOROCARBON REFRIGERANTS

Property No.	Refrigerant name		11	12	13	13B1	14	21
1	Formula		CCl_3F	CCl_2F_2	$CClF_3$	$CBrF_3$	CF_4	$CHCl_2F$
2	Molecular weight		137.37	120.91	104.46	148.92	88.01	102.92
3	Normal boiling point; °C		23.82	−29.79	−81.4	−57.75	−127.96	8.92
4	Normal freezing point; °C		−111	−158	−181	−168	−184	−135
5	Critical temperature; °C		198	112	28.9	67	−45.67	178.5
6	Critical pressure; atm		43.5	40.6	38.2	39.1	36.96	51
7	Critical volume; cm/mol		247	217	181	200	141	197
8	Critical density; g/cm		0.554	0.558	0.578	0.745	0.626	0.522
9	Density of liquid at 25°C; g/cm		1.467	1.311	$1.298^{-30°C}$	1.538	$1.317^{-80°C}$	1.366
10	Density of saturated vapor at B.P.; g/liter		5.86	6.33	7.01	8.71	7.62	4.57
11	Specific heat of liquid at 25°C; cal/g		0.208	0.232	$0.247^{-30°C}$	0.208	$0.294^{-80°C}$	0.256
12	Specific heat of vapor at 25°C and 1 atm; cal/g		$0.142^{38°C}$	0.145	0.158	0.112	0.169	0.140
13	Heat of vaporization at B.P.; cal/g		43.10	39.47	35.47	28.38	32.49	57.86
14	Thermal conductivity at 25°C; Btu/(hr)(ft)(°F)	liquid	0.050	0.041	0.020	0.025	$0.040^{-100°F}$	0.063
		vapor; 1 atm	0.00484	0.00557	—	—	—	0.0569
15	Viscosity at 25°C; centipoise	liquid	0.42	0.26	0.016	0.15	0.020	0.34
		vapor; 1 atm	0.011	0.013	—	0.016	—	0.011
16	Surface tension at 25°C; dyne cm		18	9	$14^{-73.3°C}$	4	$14^{-73.3°C}$	18
17	Refractive index of liquid at 25°C		1.374	1.287	$1.199^{-73.3°C}$	1.238	$1.151^{-73.3°C}$	1.354
18	Dielectric constant	liquid	$2.28^{29°C}$	$2.13^{29°C}$	—	—		$5.34^{28°C}$
		vapor at 0.5 atm	$1.10019^{29°C}$	$1.0016^{29°C}$	$1.0013^{29°C}$	—	$1.0006^{24.5°C}$	$1.0035^{30°C}$
19	Solubility in water at 25°C and 1 atm; wt %		0.011	0.028	0.009	0.03	0.0015	0.95
20	Solubility of water in compound at 25°C; wt %		0.011	0.009	—	$0.0095^{21.1°C}$	—	0.13
21	Toxicity; Group number (See separate table for definition of group number.)		5a	6	probably 6	6	probably 6	<4 >5

PHYSICAL PROPERTIES OF FLUOROCARBON REFRIGERANTS (Continued)

Property No.	22	23	112	113	114	114B2	115	116	500	502
1	$CHClF_2$	CHF_3	$C_2Cl_4F_2$	$C_2Cl_3F_3$	$C_2Cl_2F_4$	$C_2Br_2F_4$	C_2ClF_5	C_2F_6	*	**
2	80.47	70.01	203.83	187.38	170.91	259.83	154.47	138.01	105.5	120.7
3	−40.75	−82.03	92.8	47.57	3.77	47.26	−38.7	−78.2	−33.5	−45.6
4	−160	−155.2	26	−35	−94	−110.5	−106	−100.6	−158.9	—
5	96	25.9	278	214.1	145.7	214.5	80	19.7	105.4	179.89
6	49.12	47.7	34	33.7	32.2	34	30.8	29.4	43.7	590.3
7	165	133	370	325	293	329	259	225	—	290
8	0.525	0.525	0.55	0.576	0.582	0.790	0.596	0.612	0.497	0.56
9	1.194	0.670	$1.634^{30°C}$	1.565	1.456	2.163	1.291	$1.587^{-73.3°C}$	$1.138^{30°C}$	1.242
10	4.72	4.66	7.02	7.38	7.83	—	8.37	9.01	—	6.05
11	0.300	1.553	—	0.218	0.243	0.166	0.285	$0.232^{-73.3°C}$	$0.161^{30°C}$	—
12	0.157	0.176	—	$0.161^{60°C}$	0.170	—	0.164	0.182^{0mm}	—	—
13	55.81	57.23	37 (est)	35.07	32.51	25 (est)	30.11	27.97	—	42.48
14	0.052	0.008	0.040	0.038	0.034	0.027	0.026	$0.045^{-100°F}$	—	0.038
	0.00678	—	—	$0.0045^{0.5\ atm}$	0.00646	—	0.00803	0.0098 (est)	—	—
15	0.23	0.016 (est)	1.21	0.68	0.38	0.72	0.26	—	$0.292^{-15°C}$	0.25
	0.013	—	—	$0.01^{0.1\ atm}$	0.011	—	0.013	—	—	—
16	8	$15^{-73.3°C}$	$23^{30°C}$	19	12	18	5	$16^{-73.3°C}$	—	8
17	1.256	$1.251^{-73.3°C}$	1.413	1.354	1.288	1.367	1.214	$1.206^{-73.3°C}$	—	1.235
18	$6.11^{24°C}$	—	$2.52^{25°C}$	$2.41^{25°C}$	$2.26^{25°C}$	$2.34^{25°C}$	—	—	—	—
	$1.0035^{25.4°C}$	—	—	—	$1.0021^{26.5°C}$	—	$1.0018^{27.4°C}$	—	—	—
19	0.30	0.10	0.12 (sat. pr)	0.017 (sat. pr)	0.013	—	0.006	—	—	—
20	0.13	—	—	0.011	0.009	—	—	—	—	0.560
21	5a	probably 6	<4 >5	<4 >5	6	5a	6	probably 6	5a	5a

* Azeotrope of CCl_2F_2 (73.8 wt %) and $C_2H_4F_2$ (26.2 wt %) ** Azeotrope of $CHClF_2$ (48.8 wt %) and C_2ClF_5 (51.2 wt %).

UNDERWRITERS' LABORATORIES' CLASSIFICATION OF COMPARATIVE LIFE HAZARD OF GASES AND VAPORS

(Group number definition)

Group	Definition	Examples
1	Gases or vapors which in concentrations of the order of $\frac{1}{2}$ to 1 percent for durations of exposure of the order of 5 minutes are lethal or produce serious injury.	Sulfur dioxide
2	Gases or vapors which in concentrations of the order of $\frac{1}{2}$ to 1 percent for durations of exposure of the order of $\frac{1}{2}$ hour are lethal or produce serious injury.	Ammonia, Methyl bromide
3	Gases or vapors which in concentrations of the order of 2 to $2\frac{1}{2}$ percent for durations of exposure of the order of 1 hour are lethal or produce serious injury.	Bromochloromethane, Carbon tetrachloride, Chloroform, Methyl formate
4	Gases or vapors which in concentrations of the order of 2 to $2\frac{1}{2}$ percent for durations of exposure of the order of 2 hours are lethal or produce serious injury.	Dichloroethylene, Methyl chloride, Ethyl bromide
Between 4 and 5	Appear to classify as somewhat less toxic than group 4.	Methylene chloride, Ethyl chloride, Refrigerant 112* Refrigerant 113 Refrigerant 21
	Much less toxic than group 4 but somewhat more toxic than group 5.	
5a	Gases or vapors much less toxic than group 4 but more toxic than group 6.	Refrigerant 11 Refrigerant 22 Refrigerant 114B2 Refrigerant 502 Carbon dioxide
5b	Gases or vapors which available data indicate would classify as either group 5a or group 6.	Ethane, Propane, Butane
6	Gases or vapors which in concentrations up to at least about 20 percent by volume for durations of exposure of the order of 2 hours do not appear to produce injury.	Refrigerant 13B1 Refrigerant 12 Refrigerant 114 Refrigerant 115 Refrigerant 13* Refrigerant 14* Refrigerant 23* Refrigerant 116* Refrigerant C318*

* Not tested by U.L. but estimated to belong in group indicated.

MISCELLANEOUS PROPERTIES OF COMMON REFRIGERANTS

Refrigerant	Formula	Flash Point °F.	Ignition Temp. °F.	Explosive Limits % by Volume Lower	Upper	Vapor Density (Air = 1)	Boiling Point °F.	Threshold Limit Value* Parts per Million in Air	Water Soluble	Odor
Ammonia	NH₃	....	1204	16	25	0.59	−28	100	yes	yes
Bromotrifluoromethane (Kulene-131)	CF₃Br	−76	nonflammable			5.25	−73.6	....	no	yes
Butane	C₄H₁₀		806	1.8	8.4	2.04	33	....	no	no
Carbon dioxide	CO₂		nonflammable			1.53	−108	5000	yes	no
Carbon tetrachloride	CCl₄		nonflammable			5.32	170	25	no	yes
Dichlorodifluoromethane (Freon-12)	CCl₂F₂		nonflammable			4.17	−21.6	....	no	no
Dichlorodifluoromethane, 73.8% / Ethylidene fluoride, 26.2% (Carrene-7)	CCl₂F₂ / CH₃CHF₂					3.24	−28.0	....	no	yes
Dichloromonofluoromethane (Freon-21)	CHCl₂F		practically nonflammable			3.55	48	....	no	yes
Dichlorotetrafluoroethane (Freon-114)	C₂Cl₂F₄		practically nonflammable			5.89	38	....	no	no
Ethane	C₂H₆	<20	950	3.0	12.5	1.04	−128	....	no	no
Ethylene	C₂H₄	<20	842	3.1	32	0.972	−155	....	yes	yes
Isobutane	(CH₃)₃CH		1010	1.8	8.4	2.01	14	....	no	no
Methyl chloride	CH₃Cl	632	1170	10.7	11.4	1.78	−11	100	yes	yes
Monochlorodifluoromethane (Freon-22)	CHClF₂		practically nonflammable			2.9	−41	....	yes	no
Monochlorotrifluoromethane (Freon-13)	CClF₃		nonflammable			3.6	−112	....	....	no
Propane	C₃H₈	<20	871	2.2	9.5	1.56	−45	....	no	no
Propylene	C₃H₆	<20	927	2.4	10.3	1.49	−53	....	yes	yes
Sulfur dioxide	SO₂		nonflammable			2.2	14	10	yes	yes
Tetrafluoromethane (Freon-14)	CF₄		nonflammable			3.0	−198	....	no	no
Trichloroethylene	C₂HCl₃		nonflammable at normal temperature			4.53	189	200	no	yes
Trichloromonofluoromethane (Freon-11) (Carrene-2)	CCl₃F		nonflammable			4.7	75.3	....	no	no
Trichlorotrifluoroethane (Freon-113)	C₂Cl₃F₃		practically nonflammable			6.4	118	....	no	no

* Maximum average atmospheric concentration of contaminants to which workers may be exposed for an eight-hour work day without injury to health. (American Conference of Governmental Industrial Hygienists': "Threshold Limit Values for 1954.) Where blanks appear in this column no published information was available on threshold limit values.

HYGROMETRIC AND BAROMETRIC TABLES

CONVERSION TABLE FOR BAROMETRIC READINGS

U. S. inches to cm.

Inches.	.00	.01	.02	.03	.04	.05	.06	.07	.08	.09
27.0	68.580	.606	.631	.656	.682	.707	.733	.758	.783	.809
27.1	.834	.860	.885	.910	.936	.961	.987	*.012	*.037	*.063
27.2	69.088	.114	.139	.164	.190	.215	.241	.266	.291	.317
27.3	.342	.368	.393	.418	.444	.469	.495	.520	.545	.571
27.4	.596	.622	.647	.672	.698	.723	.749	.774	.799	.825
27.5	.850	.876	.901	.926	.952	.977	*.002	*.028	*.053	*.079
27.6	70.104	.130	.155	.180	.206	.231	.257	.282	.307	.333
27.7	.358	.384	.409	.434	.460	.485	.511	.536	.561	.587
27.8	.612	.638	.663	.688	.714	.739	.765	.790	.815	.841
27.9	.866	.892	.917	.942	.968	.993	*.018	*.044	*.069	*.095
28.0	71.120	.146	.171	.196	.222	.247	.273	.298	.323	.349
28.1	.374	.400	.425	.450	.476	.501	.527	.552	.577	.603
28.2	.628	.654	.679	.704	.730	.755	.781	.806	.831	.857
28.3	.882	.908	.933	.958	.984	*.009	*.035	*.060	*.085	*.111
28.4	72.136	.162	.187	.212	.238	.263	.289	.314	.339	.365
28.5	.390	.416	.441	.466	.492	.517	.543	.568	.593	.619
28.6	.644	.670	.695	.720	.746	.771	.797	.822	.847	.873
28.7	.898	.924	.949	.974	*.000	*.025	*.051	*.076	*.101	*.127
28.8	73.152	.178	.203	.228	.254	.279	.305	.330	.355	.381
28.9	.406	.432	.457	.482	.508	.533	.559	.584	.609	.635
29.0	.660	.686	.711	.736	.762	.787	.813	.838	.863	.889
29.1	.914	.940	.965	.990	*.016	*.041	*.067	*.092	*.117	*.143
29.2	74.168	.194	.219	.244	.270	.295	.321	.346	.371	.397
29.3	.422	.448	.473	.498	.524	.549	.575	.600	.625	.651
29.4	.676	.702	.727	.752	.778	.803	.829	.854	.879	.905
29.5	.930	.956	.981	*.006	*.032	*.057	*.083	*.108	*.133	*.159
29.6	75.184	.210	.235	.260	.286	.311	.337	.362	.387	.413
29.7	.438	.464	.489	.514	.540	.565	.591	.616	.641	.667
29.8	.692	.718	.743	.768	.794	.819	.845	.870	.895	.921
29.9	.946	.972	.997	*.022	*.048	*.073	*.099	*.124	*.149	*.175
30.0	76.200	.226	.251	.277	.302	.327	.353	.378	.404	.429
30.1	.454	.480	.505	.531	.556	.581	.607	.632	.658	.683
30.2	.708	.734	.759	.785	.810	.835	.861	.886	.912	.937
30.3	.962	.988	*.013	*.039	*.064	*.089	*.115	*.140	*.166	*.191
30.4	77.216	.242	.267	.293	.318	.343	.369	.394	.420	.445
30.5	.470	.496	.521	.547	.572	.597	.623	.648	.674	.699
30.6	.724	.750	.775	.801	.826	.851	.877	.902	.928	.953
30.7	.978	*.004	*.029	*.055	*.080	*.105	*.131	*.156	*.182	*.207
30.8	78.232	.258	.283	.309	.334	.359	.385	410	.436	.461
30.9	.486	.512	.537	.563	.588	.613	.639	.664	.690	.715

U. S. Inches to Millibars

Based on the relation 1 inch of mercury at 32°F represents a pressure of 33.8639 millibars.

Note:
Figures in last nine columns to be preceded by 7, 8, 9 or 10 as indicated in column 2.

Inches	.00	.01	.02	.03	.04	.05	.06	.07	.08	.09
23.0	7 78.87	79.21	79.55	79.89	80.22	80.56	80.90	81.24	81.58	81.92
23.1	7 82.26	82.59	82.93	83.27	83.61	83.95	84.29	84.63	84.97	85.30
23.2	7 85.64	85.98	86.32	86.66	87.00	87.34	87.67	88.01	88.35	88.69
23.3	7 89.03	89.37	89.71	90.04	90.38	90.72	91.06	91.40	91.74	92.08
23.4	7 92.42	92.75	93.09	93.43	93.77	94.11	94.45	94.79	95.12	95.46
23.5	7 95.80	96.14	96.48	96.82	97.16	97.49	97.83	98.17	98.51	98.85
23.6	7 99.19	99.53	99.87	*00.20	*00.54	*00.88	*01.22	*01.56	*01.90	*02.24
23.7	8 02.57	02.91	03.25	03.59	03.93	04.27	04.61	04.94	05.28	05.62
23.8	8 05.96	06.30	06.64	06.98	07.32	07.65	07.99	08.33	08.67	09.01
23.9	8 09.35	09.69	10.02	10.36	10.70	11.04	11.38	11.72	12.06	12.39
24.0	8 12.73	13.07	13.41	13.75	14.09	14.43	14.77	15.10	15.44	15.78
24.1	8 16.12	16.46	16.80	17.14	17.47	17.81	18.15	18.49	18.83	19.17
24.2	8 19.51	19.85	20.18	20.52	20.86	21.20	21.54	21.88	22.22	22.55
24.3	8 22.89	23.23	23.57	23.91	24.25	24.59	24.92	25.26	25.60	25.94
24.4	8 26.28	26.62	26.96	27.30	27.63	27.97	28.31	28.65	28.99	29.33
24.5	8 29.67	30.00	30.34	30.68	31.02	31.36	31.70	32.04	32.37	32.71
24.6	8 33.05	33.39	33.73	34.07	34.41	34.75	35.08	35.42	35.76	36.10
24.7	8 36.44	36.78	37.12	37.45	37.79	38.13	38.47	38.81	39.15	39.49
24.8	8 39.82	40.16	40.50	40.84	41.18	41.52	41.86	42.20	42.53	42.87
24.9	8 43.21	43.55	43.89	44.23	44.57	44.90	45.24	45.58	45.92	46.26
25.0	8 46.60	46.94	47.27	47.61	47.95	48.29	48.63	48.97	49.31	49.65
25.1	8 49.99	50.32	50.66	51.00	51.34	51.68	52.02	52.35	52.69	53.03
25.2	8 53.37	53.71	54.05	54.39	54.72	55.06	55.40	55.74	56.08	56.42
25.3	8 56.76	57.10	57.43	57.77	58.11	58.45	58.79	59.13	59.47	59.80
25.4	8 60.14	60.48	60.82	61.16	61.50	61.84	62.17	62.51	62.85	63.19

U. S. Inches to Millibars (Continued)

Inches	.00	.01	.02	.03	.04	.05	.06	.07	.08	.09
25.5	8 63.53	63.87	64.21	64.55	64.88	65.22	65.56	65.90	66.24	66.58
25.6	8 66.92	67.25	67.59	67.93	68.27	68.61	68.95	69.29	69.62	69.96
25.7	8 70.30	70.64	70.98	71.32	71.66	72.00	72.33	72.67	73.01	73.35
25.8	8 73.69	74.03	74.37	74.70	75.04	75.38	75.72	76.06	76.40	76.74
25.9	8 77.08	77.41	77.75	78.09	78.43	78.77	79.11	79.45	79.78	80.12
26.0	8 80.46	80.80	81.14	81.48	81.82	82.15	82.49	82.83	83.17	83.51
26.1	8 83.85	84.19	84.53	84.86	85.20	85.54	85.88	86.22	86.56	86.90
26.2	8 87.23	87.57	87.91	88.25	88.59	88.93	89.27	89.60	89.94	90.28
26.3	8 90.62	90.96	91.30	91.64	91.98	92.31	92.65	92.99	93.33	93.67
26.4	8 94.01	94.35	94.68	95.02	95.36	95.70	96.04	96.38	96.72	97.05
26.5	8 97.39	97.73	98.07	98.41	98.75	99.09	99.43	99.76	*00.10	*00.44
26.6	9 00.78	01.12	01.46	01.80	02.13	02.47	02.81	03.15	03.49	03.83
26.7	9 04.17	04.50	04.84	05.18	05.52	05.86	06.20	06.54	06.88	07.21
26.8	9 07.55	07.89	08.23	08.57	08.91	09.25	09.58	09.92	10.26	10.60
26.9	9 10.94	11.28	11.62	11.95	12.29	12.63	12.97	13.31	13.65	13.99
27.0	9 14.33	14.66	15.00	15.34	15.68	16.02	16.36	16.70	17.03	17.37
27.1	9 17.71	18.05	18.39	18.73	19.07	19.40	19.74	20.08	20.42	20.76
27.2	9 21.10	21.44	21.78	22.11	22.45	22.79	23.13	23.47	23.81	24.15
27.3	9 24.48	24.82	25.16	25.50	25.84	26.18	26.52	26.85	27.19	27.53
27.4	9 27.87	28.21	28.55	28.89	29.23	29.56	29.90	30.24	30.58	30.92
27.5	9 31.26	31.60	31.93	32.27	32.61	32.95	33.29	33.63	33.97	34.31
27.6	9 34.64	34.98	35.32	35.66	36.00	36.34	36.68	37.01	37.35	37.69
27.7	9 38.03	38.37	38.71	39.05	39.38	39.72	40.06	40.40	40.74	41.08
27.8	9 41.42	41.76	42.09	42.43	42.77	43.11	43.45	43.79	44.13	44.46
27.9	9 44.80	45.14	45.48	45.82	46.16	46.50	46.83	47.17	47.51	47.85
28.0	9 48.19	48.53	48.87	49.21	49.54	49.88	50.22	50.56	50.90	51.24
28.1	9 51.58	51.91	52.25	52.59	52.93	53.27	53.61	53.95	54.28	54.62
28.2	9 54.96	55.30	55.64	55.98	56.32	56.66	56.99	57.33	57.67	58.01
28.3	9 58.35	58.69	59.03	59.30	59.70	60.04	60.38	60.72	61.06	61.40
28.4	9 61.73	62.07	62.41	62.75	63.09	63.43	63.77	64.11	64.44	64.78
28.5	9 65.12	65.46	65.80	66.14	66.48	66.81	67.15	67.49	67.83	68.17
28.6	9 68.51	68.85	69.18	69.52	69.86	70.20	70.54	70.88	71.22	71.56
28.7	9 71.89	72.23	72.57	72.91	73.25	73.59	73.93	74.26	74.60	74.94
28.8	9 75.28	75.62	75.96	76.30	76.63	76.97	77.31	77.65	77.99	78.33
28.9	9 78.67	79.01	79.34	79.68	80.02	80.36	80.70	81.04	81.38	81.71
29.0	9 82.05	82.39	82.73	83.07	83.41	83.75	84.08	84.42	84.76	85.10
29.1	9 85.44	85.78	86.12	86.46	86.79	87.13	87.47	87.81	88.15	88.49
29.2	9 88.83	89.16	89.50	89.84	90.18	90.52	90.86	91.20	91.53	91.87
29.3	9 92.21	92.55	92.89	93.23	93.57	93.91	94.24	94.58	94.92	95.26
29.4	9 95.60	95.94	96.28	96.61	96.95	97.29	97.63	97.97	98.31	98.65
29.5	9 98.99	99.32	99.66	*00.00	*00.34	*00.68	*01.02	*01.36	*01.69	*02.03
29.6	10 02.37	02.71	03.05	03.39	03.73	04.06	04.40	04.74	05.08	05.42
29.7	10 05.76	06.10	06.44	06.77	07.11	07.45	07.79	08.13	08.47	08.81
29.8	10 09.14	09.48	09.82	10.16	10.50	10.84	11.18	11.51	11.85	12.19
29.9	10 12.53	12.87	13.21	13.55	13.89	14.22	14.56	14.90	15.24	15.58
30.0	10 15.92	16.26	16.59	16.93	17.27	17.61	17.95	18.29	18.63	18.96
30.1	10 19.30	19.64	19.98	20.32	20.66	21.00	21.34	21.67	22.01	22.35
30.2	10 22.69	23.03	23.37	23.71	24.04	24.38	24.72	25.06	25.40	25.74
30.3	10 26.08	26.41	26.75	27.09	27.43	27.77	28.11	28.45	28.79	29.12
30.4	10 29.46	29.80	30.14	30.48	30.82	31.16	31.49	31.83	32.17	32.51
30.5	10 32.85	33.19	33.53	33.86	34.20	34.54	34.88	35.22	35.56	35.90
30.6	10 36.24	36.57	36.91	37.25	37.59	37.93	38.27	38.61	38.94	39.28
30.7	10 39.62	39.96	40.30	40.64	40.98	41.31	41.65	41.99	42.33	42.67
30.8	10 43.01	43.35	43.69	44.02	44.36	44.70	45.04	45.38	45.72	46.06
30.9	10 46.39	46.73	47.07	47.41	47.75	48.09	48.43	48.76	49.10	49.44
31.0	10 49.78	50.12	50.46	50.80	51.14	51.47	51.81	52.15	52.49	52.83
31.1	10 53.17	53.51	53.84	54.18	54.52	54.86	55.20	55.54	55.88	56.22
31.2	10 56.55	56.89	57.23	57.57	57.91	58.25	58.59	58.92	59.26	59.60
31.3	10 59.94	60.28	60.62	60.96	61.29	61.63	61.97	62.31	62.65	62.99
31.4	10 63.33	63.67	64.00	64.34	64.68	65.02	65.36	65.70	66.04	66.37
31.5	10 66.71	67.05	67.39	67.73	68.07	68.41	68.74	69.08	69.42	69.76
31.6	10 70.10	70.44	70.78	71.12	71.45	71.79	72.13	72.47	72.81	73.15
31.7	10 73.49	73.82	74.16	74.50	74.84	75.18	75.52	75.86	76.19	76.53
31.8	10 76.87	77.21	77.55	77.89	78.23	78.57	78.90	79.24	79.58	79.92
31.9	10 80.26	80.60	80.94	81.27	81.61	81.95	82.29	82.63	82.97	83.31

Note: Figures in last nine columns to be preceded by 9 or 10 as indicated.

Centimeters to Millibars
Based on the relation 1 centimeter of mercury at 0°C represents a pressure of 13.3322 millibars. Note: Figures in last nine columns to be preceded by 9.

Centimeters to Millibars (Continued)
Note: Figures in last nine columns to be preceded by 9 or 10.

Centimeters	.00	.01	.02	.03	.04	.05	.06	.07	.08	.09
68.0	9 06.59	06.72	06.86	06.99	07.12	07.26	07.39	07.52	07.66	07.79
68.1	9 07.92	08.06	08.19	08.32	08.46	08.59	08.72	08.86	08.99	09.12
68.2	9 09.26	09.39	09.52	09.66	09.79	09.92	10.06	10.19	10.32	10.46
68.3	9 10.59	10.72	10.86	10.99	11.12	11.26	11.39	11.52	11.66	11.79
68.4	9 11.92	12.06	12.19	12.32	12.46	12.59	12.72	12.86	12.99	13.12
68.5	9 13.26	13.39	13.52	13.66	13.79	13.92	14.06	14.19	14.32	14.46
68.6	9 14.59	14.72	14.86	14.99	15.12	15.26	15.39	15.52	15.66	15.79
68.7	9 15.92	16.06	16.19	16.32	16.46	16.59	16.72	16.86	16.99	17.12
68.8	9 17.26	17.39	17.52	17.66	17.79	17.92	18.06	18.19	18.32	18.46
68.9	9 18.59	18.72	18.86	18.99	19.12	19.26	19.39	19.52	19.66	19.79
69.0	9 19.92	20.06	20.19	20.32	20.46	20.59	20.72	20.86	20.99	21.12
69.1	9 21.26	21.39	21.52	21.65	21.79	21.92	22.05	22.19	22.32	22.45
69.2	9 22.59	22.72	22.85	22.99	23.12	23.25	23.39	23.52	23.65	23.79
69.3	9 23.92	24.05	24.19	24.32	24.45	24.59	24.72	24.85	24.99	25.12
69.4	9 25.25	25.39	25.52	25.65	25.79	25.92	26.05	26.19	26.32	26.45
69.5	9 26.59	26.72	26.85	26.99	27.12	27.25	27.39	27.52	27.65	27.79
69.6	9 27.92	28.05	28.19	28.32	28.45	28.59	28.72	28.85	28.99	29.12
69.7	9 29.25	29.39	29.52	29.65	29.79	29.92	30.05	30.19	30.32	30.45
69.8	9 30.59	30.72	30.85	30.99	31.12	31.25	31.39	31.52	31.65	31.79
69.9	9 31.92	32.05	32.19	32.32	32.45	32.59	32.72	32.85	32.99	33.12
70.0	9 33.25	33.39	33.52	33.65	33.79	33.92	34.05	34.19	34.32	34.45
70.1	9 34.59	34.72	34.85	34.99	35.12	35.25	35.39	35.52	35.65	35.79
70.2	9 35.92	36.05	36.19	36.32	36.45	36.59	36.72	36.85	36.99	37.12
70.3	9 37.25	37.39	37.52	37.65	37.79	37.92	38.05	38.19	38.32	38.45
70.4	9 38.59	38.72	38.85	38.99	39.12	39.25	39.39	39.52	39.65	39.79
70.5	9 39.92	40.05	40.19	40.32	40.45	40.59	40.72	40.85	40.99	41.12
70.6	9 41.25	41.39	41.52	41.65	41.79	41.92	42.05	42.19	42.32	42.45
70.7	9 42.59	42.72	42.85	42.99	43.12	43.25	43.39	43.52	43.65	43.79
70.8	9 43.92	44.05	44.19	44.32	44.45	44.59	44.72	44.85	44.99	45.12
70.9	9 45.25	45.39	45.52	45.65	45.79	45.92	46.05	46.19	46.32	46.45
71.0	9 46.59	46.72	46.85	46.99	47.12	47.25	47.39	47.52	47.65	47.79
71.1	9 47.92	48.05	48.19	48.32	48.45	48.59	48.72	48.85	48.99	49.12
71.2	9 49.25	49.39	49.52	49.65	49.79	49.92	50.05	50.19	50.32	50.45
71.3	9 50.59	50.72	50.85	50.99	51.12	51.25	51.39	51.52	51.65	51.79
71.4	9 51.92	52.05	52.19	52.32	52.45	52.59	52.72	52.85	52.99	53.12
71.5	9 53.25	53.39	53.52	53.65	53.79	53.92	54.05	54.19	54.32	54.45
71.6	9 54.59	54.72	54.85	54.99	55.12	55.25	55.39	55.52	55.65	55.79
71.7	9 55.92	56.05	56.19	56.32	56.45	56.59	56.72	56.85	56.99	57.12
71.8	9 57.25	57.39	57.52	57.65	57.79	57.92	58.05	58.19	58.32	58.45
71.9	9 58.59	58.72	58.85	58.99	59.12	59.25	59.39	59.52	59.65	59.79
72.0	9 59.92	60.05	60.19	60.32	60.45	60.59	60.72	60.85	60.98	61.12
72.1	9 61.25	61.38	61.52	61.65	61.79	61.92	62.05	62.18	62.32	62.45
72.2	9 62.58	62.72	62.85	62.98	63.12	63.25	63.38	63.52	63.65	63.78
72.3	9 63.92	64.05	64.18	64.32	64.45	64.58	64.72	64.85	64.98	65.12
72.4	9 65.25	65.38	65.52	65.65	65.78	65.92	66.05	66.18	66.32	66.45
72.5	9 66.58	66.72	66.85	66.98	67.12	67.25	67.38	67.52	67.65	67.78
72.6	9 67.92	68.05	68.18	68.32	68.45	68.58	68.72	68.85	68.98	69.12
72.7	9 69.25	69.38	69.52	69.65	69.79	69.92	70.05	70.18	70.32	70.45
72.8	9 70.58	70.72	70.85	70.98	71.12	71.25	71.38	71.52	71.65	71.78
72.9	9 71.92	72.05	72.18	72.32	72.45	72.58	72.72	72.85	72.98	73.12

Centimeters	.00	.01	.02	.03	.04	.05	.06	.07	.08	.09
73.0	9 73.25	73.38	73.52	73.65	73.78	73.92	74.05	74.18	74.32	74.45
73.1	9 74.58	74.72	74.85	74.98	75.12	75.25	75.38	75.52	75.65	75.78
73.2	9 75.92	76.05	76.18	76.32	76.45	76.58	76.72	76.85	76.98	77.12
73.3	9 77.25	77.38	77.52	77.65	77.78	77.92	78.05	78.18	78.32	78.45
73.4	9 78.58	78.72	78.85	78.98	79.12	79.25	79.38	79.52	79.65	79.78
73.5	9 79.92	80.05	80.18	80.32	80.45	80.58	80.72	80.85	80.98	81.12
73.6	9 81.25	81.38	81.52	81.65	81.78	81.92	82.05	82.18	82.32	82.45
73.7	9 82.58	82.72	82.85	82.98	83.12	83.25	83.38	83.52	83.65	83.78
73.8	9 83.92	84.05	84.18	84.32	84.45	84.58	84.72	84.85	84.98	85.12
73.9	9 85.25	85.38	85.52	85.65	85.78	85.92	86.05	86.18	86.32	86.45
74.0	9 86.58	86.72	86.85	86.98	87.12	87.25	87.38	87.52	87.65	87.78
74.1	9 87.92	88.05	88.18	88.32	88.45	88.58	88.72	88.85	88.98	89.12
74.2	9 89.25	89.38	89.52	89.65	89.78	89.92	90.05	90.18	90.32	90.45
74.3	9 90.58	90.72	90.85	90.98	91.12	91.25	91.38	91.52	91.65	91.78
74.4	9 91.92	92.05	92.18	92.32	92.45	92.58	92.72	92.85	92.98	93.12
74.5	9 93.25	93.38	93.52	93.65	93.78	93.92	94.05	94.18	94.32	94.45
74.6	9 94.58	94.72	94.85	94.98	95.12	95.25	95.38	95.52	95.65	95.78
74.7	9 95.92	96.05	96.18	96.32	96.45	96.58	96.72	96.85	96.98	97.12
74.8	9 97.25	97.38	97.52	97.65	97.78	97.92	98.05	98.18	98.32	98.45
74.9	9 98.58	98.72	98.85	98.98	99.12	99.25	99.38	99.52	99.65	99.78
75.0	9 99.92	*00.05	*00.18	*00.31	*00.45	*00.58	*00.71	*00.85	*00.98	*01.11
75.1	10 01.25	01.38	01.51	01.65	01.78	01.91	02.05	02.18	02.31	02.45
75.2	10 02.58	02.71	02.85	02.98	03.11	03.25	03.38	03.51	03.65	03.78
75.3	10 03.91	04.05	04.18	04.31	04.45	04.58	04.71	04.85	04.98	05.11
75.4	10 05.25	05.38	05.51	05.65	05.78	05.91	06.05	06.18	06.31	06.45
75.5	10 06.58	06.71	06.85	06.98	07.11	07.25	07.38	07.51	07.65	07.78
75.6	10 07.91	08.05	08.18	08.31	08.45	08.58	08.71	08.85	08.98	09.11
75.7	10 09.25	09.38	09.51	09.65	09.78	09.91	10.05	10.18	10.31	10.45
75.8	10 10.58	10.71	10.85	10.98	11.11	11.25	11.38	11.51	11.65	11.78
75.9	10 11.91	12.05	12.18	12.31	12.45	12.58	12.71	12.85	12.98	13.11
76.0	10 13.25	13.38	13.51	13.65	13.78	13.91	14.05	14.18	14.31	14.45
76.1	10 14.58	14.71	14.85	14.98	15.11	15.25	15.38	15.51	15.65	15.78
76.2	10 15.91	16.05	16.18	16.31	16.45	16.58	16.71	16.85	16.98	17.11
76.3	10 17.25	17.38	17.51	17.65	17.78	17.91	18.05	18.18	18.31	18.45
76.4	10 18.58	18.71	18.85	18.98	19.11	19.25	19.38	19.51	19.65	19.78
76.5	10 19.91	20.05	20.18	20.31	20.45	20.58	20.71	20.85	20.98	21.11
76.6	10 21.25	21.38	21.51	21.65	21.78	21.91	22.05	22.18	22.31	22.45
76.7	10 22.58	22.71	22.85	22.98	23.11	23.25	23.38	23.51	23.65	23.78
76.8	10 23.91	24.05	24.18	24.31	24.45	24.58	24.71	24.85	24.98	25.11
76.9	10 25.25	25.38	25.51	25.65	25.78	25.91	26.05	26.18	26.31	26.45
77.0	10 26.58	26.71	26.85	26.98	27.11	27.25	27.38	27.51	27.65	27.78
77.1	10 27.91	28.05	28.18	28.31	28.45	28.58	28.71	28.85	28.98	29.11
77.2	10 29.25	29.38	29.51	29.65	29.78	29.91	30.05	30.18	30.31	30.45
77.3	10 30.58	30.71	30.85	30.98	31.11	31.25	31.38	31.51	31.65	31.78
77.4	10 31.91	32.05	32.18	32.31	32.45	32.58	32.71	32.85	32.98	33.11
77.5	10 33.25	33.38	33.51	33.65	33.78	33.91	34.05	34.18	34.31	34.45
77.6	10 34.58	34.71	34.85	34.98	35.11	35.25	35.38	35.51	35.65	35.78
77.7	10 35.91	36.05	36.18	36.31	36.45	36.58	36.71	36.85	36.98	37.11
77.8	10 37.25	37.38	37.51	37.65	37.78	37.91	38.05	38.18	38.31	38.45
77.9	10 38.58	38.71	38.85	38.98	39.11	39.24	39.38	39.51	39.64	39.78

TEMPERATURE CORRECTION FOR BAROMETER READINGS
BRASS SCALE—METRIC UNITS

To reduce readings of a mercurial barometer with a brass scale to 0°C subtract the appropriate quantity as found in the table. These values are based on the coefficient of expansion of mercury $(181792 + 0.175t + 0.035116t^2) \times 10^{-9}$, and of brass 0.0000184 per °C. Corrections are in millimeters.

Temp. °C	Observed height in millimeters																	
	620	630	640	650	660	670	680	690	700	710	720	730	740	750	760	770	780	790
0	0.00	0.00	0.00	0.00	0.00	0.00	0.00	0.00	0.00	0.00	0.00	0.00	0.00	0.00	0.00	0.00	0.00	0.00
1	.10	.10	.10	.11	.11	.11	.11	.11	.11	.12	.12	.12	.12	.12	.12	.13	.13	.13
2	.20	.21	.21	.21	.22	.22	.22	.23	.23	.23	.24	.24	.24	.25	.25	.25	.25	.26
3	.30	.31	.31	.32	.32	.33	.33	.34	.34	.35	.35	.36	.36	.37	.37	.38	.38	.39
4	.40	.41	.42	.42	.43	.44	.44	.45	.46	.46	.47	.48	.48	.49	.50	.50	.51	.52
5	0.51	0.51	0.52	0.53	0.54	0.55	0.56	0.56	0.57	0.58	0.59	0.60	0.60	0.61	0.62	0.63	0.64	0.64
6	.61	.62	.63	.64	.65	.66	.67	.68	.69	.70	.71	.71	.72	.73	.74	.75	.76	.77
7	.71	.72	.73	.74	.75	.77	.78	.79	.80	.81	.82	.83	.85	.86	.87	.88	.89	.90
8	.81	.82	.84	.85	.86	.87	.89	.90	.91	.93	.94	.95	.97	.98	.99	1.01	1.02	1.03
9	.91	.92	.94	.95	.97	.98	1.00	1.01	1.03	1.04	1.06	1.07	1.09	1.10	1.12	1.13	1.15	1.16
10	1.01	1.03	1.04	1.06	1.08	1.09	1.11	1.13	1.14	1.16	1.17	1.19	1.21	1.22	1.24	1.26	1.27	1.29
11	1.11	1.13	1.15	1.17	1.18	1.20	1.22	1.24	1.26	1.27	1.29	1.31	1.33	1.35	1.36	1.38	1.40	1.42
12	1.21	1.23	1.25	1.27	1.29	1.31	1.33	1.35	1.37	1.39	1.41	1.43	1.45	1.47	1.49	1.51	1.53	1.55
13	1.31	1.34	1.36	1.38	1.40	1.42	1.44	1.46	1.48	1.50	1.53	1.55	1.57	1.59	1.61	1.63	1.65	1.67
14	1.41	1.44	1.46	1.48	1.51	1.53	1.55	1.57	1.60	1.62	1.64	1.67	1.69	1.71	1.73	1.76	1.78	1.80

BRASS SCALE—METRIC UNITS (Continued)

Temp. °C	Observed height in millimeters																	
	620	630	640	650	660	670	680	690	700	710	720	730	740	750	760	770	780	790
15	1.52	1.54	1.56	1.59	1.61	1.64	1.66	1.69	1.71	1.74	1.76	1.78	1.81	1.83	1.86	1.88	1.91	1.93
16	1.62	1.64	1.67	1.69	1.72	1.75	1.77	1.80	1.82	1.85	1.88	1.90	1.93	1.96	1.98	2.01	2.03	2.06
17	1.72	1.74	1.77	1.80	1.83	1.86	1.88	1.91	1.94	1.97	1.99	2.02	2.05	2.08	2.10	2.13	2.16	2.19
18	1.82	1.85	1.88	1.91	1.93	1.96	1.99	2.02	2.05	2.08	2.11	2.14	2.17	2.20	2.23	2.26	2.29	2.32
19	1.92	1.95	1.98	2.01	2.04	2.07	2.10	2.13	2.17	2.20	2.23	2.26	2.29	2.32	2.35	2.38	2.41	2.44
20	2.02	2.05	2.08	2.12	2.15	2.18	2.21	2.25	2.28	2.31	2.34	2.38	2.41	2.44	2.47	2.51	2.54	2.57
21	2.12	2.15	2.19	2.22	2.26	2.29	2.32	2.36	2.39	2.43	2.46	2.50	2.53	2.56	2.60	2.63	2.67	2.70
22	2.22	2.26	2.29	2.33	2.36	2.40	2.43	2.47	2.51	2.54	2.58	2.61	2.65	2.69	2.72	2.76	2.79	2.83
23	2.32	2.36	2.40	2.43	2.47	2.51	2.54	2.58	2.62	2.66	2.69	2.73	2.77	2.81	2.84	2.88	2.92	2.96
24	2.42	2.46	2.50	2.54	2.58	2.62	2.66	2.69	2.73	2.77	2.81	2.85	2.89	2.93	2.97	3.01	3.05	3.08
25	2.52	2.56	2.60	2.64	2.68	2.72	2.77	2.81	2.85	2.89	2.93	2.97	3.01	3.05	3.09	3.13	3.17	3.21
26	2.62	2.66	2.71	2.75	2.79	2.83	2.88	2.92	2.96	3.00	3.04	3.09	3.13	3.17	3.21	3.26	3.30	3.34
27	2.72	2.77	2.81	2.85	2.90	2.94	2.99	3.03	3.07	3.12	3.16	3.20	3.25	3.29	3.34	3.38	3.42	3.47
28	2.82	2.87	2.91	2.96	3.00	3.05	3.10	3.14	3.19	3.23	3.28	3.32	3.37	3.41	3.46	3.51	3.55	3.60
29	2.92	2.97	3.02	3.06	3.11	3.16	3.21	3.25	3.30	3.35	3.39	3.44	3.49	3.54	3.58	3.63	3.68	3.72
30	3.02	3.07	3.12	3.17	3.22	3.27	3.32	3.36	3.41	3.46	3.51	3.56	3.61	3.66	3.71	3.75	3.80	3.85
31	3.12	3.17	3.22	3.27	3.32	3.37	3.43	3.48	3.53	3.58	3.63	3.68	3.73	3.78	3.83	3.88	3.93	3.98
32	3.22	3.28	3.33	3.38	3.43	3.48	3.54	3.59	3.64	3.69	3.74	3.79	3.85	3.90	3.95	4.00	4.05	4.11
33	3.32	3.38	3.43	3.48	3.54	3.59	3.64	3.70	3.75	3.81	3.86	3.91	3.97	4.02	4.07	4.13	4.18	4.23
34	3.42	3.48	3.53	3.59	3.64	3.70	3.75	3.81	3.87	3.92	3.98	4.03	4.09	4.14	4.20	4.25	4.31	4.36
35	3.52	3.58	3.64	3.69	3.75	3.81	3.86	3.92	3.98	4.03	4.09	4.15	4.21	4.26	4.32	4.38	4.43	4.49

BRASS SCALE—ENGLISH UNITS

Standard Temperature of scale 62° F; of mercury, 32° F. Zero correction at 28.5° F; subtract corrections above, add below. Owing to the difference in the standard temperature of English and metric scales, readings taken in inches to be reduced to centimeters should *first* be corrected for temperature.

Temp. °F	Observed height in inches																	
	23.0 in.	23.5 in.	24.0 in.	24.5 in.	25.0 in.	25.5 in.	26.0 in.	26.5 in.	27.0 in.	27.5 in.	28.0 in.	28.5 in.	29.0 in.	29.5 in.	30.0 in.	30.5 in.	31.0 in.	31.5 in.
0	+.060	+.061	+.063	+.064	+.065	+.067	+.068	+.069	+.070	.072	.073	.075	.076	.077	.078	.080	.081	.082
2	.056	.057	.058	.060	.061	.062	.063	.065	.065	.067	.068	.069	.070	.072	.073	.074	.075	.077
4	.052	.053	.054	.055	.056	.057	.058	.060	.061	.062	.063	.064	.065	.066	.067	.069	.070	.071
6	.047	.048	.049	.051	.052	.053	.054	.055	.056	.057	.058	.059	.060	.061	.062	.063	.064	.065
8	.043	.044	.045	.046	.047	.048	.049	.050	.051	.052	.053	.054	.054	.056	.056	.057	.058	.059
10	.039	.040	.041	.042	.042	.043	.044	.045	.046	.047	.047	.048	.049	.050	.051	.052	.053	.054
12	.035	.036	.036	.037	.038	.039	.039	.040	.041	.042	.042	.043	.044	.045	.045	.046	.047	.048
14	.031	.031	.032	.033	.033	.034	.035	.035	.036	.037	.037	.038	.039	.039	.040	.041	.041	.042
16	.026	.027	.028	.028	.029	.029	.030	.031	.031	.032	.032	.033	.033	.034	.034	.035	.036	.036
18	.022	.023	.023	.024	.024	.025	.025	.026	.026	.027	.027	.028	.028	.029	.029	.030	.030	.031
20	.018	.018	.019	.019	.020	.020	.020	.021	.021	.022	.022	.022	.023	.023	.024	.024	.024	.025
22	.014	.014	.014	.015	.015	.015	.016	.016	.016	.017	.017	.017	.017	.018	.018	.018	.019	.019
24	.010	.010	.010	.010	.011	.011	.011	.011	.011	.012	.012	.012	.012	.013	.013	.013	.013	.013
26	.005	.006	.006	.006	.006	.006	.006	.006	.006	.007	.007	.007	.007	.007	.007	.007	.007	.008
28	+.001	+.001	+.001	+.001	+.001	+.001	+.001	+.002	+.002	+.002	+.002	+.002	+.002	+.002	+.002	+.002	+.002	+.002
30	−.003	−.003	−.003	−.003	−.003	−.003	.003	−.003	−.003	−.003	−.003	−.004	−.004	−.004	−.004	−.004	−.004	−.004
32	.007	.007	.007	.008	.008	.008	.008	.008	.008	.008	.009	.009	.009	.009	.009	.009	.009	.010
34	.011	.011	.012	.012	.012	.012	.013	.013	.013	.013	.014	.014	.014	.014	.015	.015	.015	.015
36	.015	.016	.016	.016	.017	.017	.017	.018	.018	.018	.019	.019	.019	.020	.020	.020	.021	.021
38	.020	.020	.020	.021	.021	.022	.022	.023	.023	.023	.024	.024	.025	.025	.026	.026	.026	.027
40	.024	.024	.025	.025	.026	.026	.027	.027	.028	.028	.029	.030	.030	.031	.031	.032	.032	.033
42	.028	.029	.029	.030	.030	.031	.032	.032	.033	.033	.034	.035	.035	.036	.036	.037	.038	.038
44	.032	.033	.033	.034	.035	.036	.036	.037	.038	.038	.039	.040	.040	.041	.042	.043	.043	.044
46	.036	.037	.038	.039	.039	.040	.041	.042	.043	.043	.044	.045	.046	.047	.047	.048	.049	.050
48	.040	.041	.042	.043	.044	.045	.046	.047	.047	.048	.049	.050	.051	.052	.053	.054	.054	.055
50	.045	.046	.046	.048	.048	.050	.050	.052	.052	.053	.054	.055	.056	.057	.058	.059	.060	.061
52	.049	.050	.051	.052	.053	.054	.055	.056	.057	.058	.059	.061	.061	.063	.064	.065	.066	.067
54	.053	.054	.055	.057	.057	.059	.060	.061	.062	.063	.064	.066	.067	.068	.069	.070	.071	.073
56	.057	.058	.060	.061	.062	.063	.064	.066	.067	.068	.069	.071	.072	.073	.074	.076	.077	.078
58	.061	.063	.064	.065	.066	.068	.069	.071	.072	.073	.074	.076	.077	.079	.080	.081	.082	.084
60	.065	.067	.068	.070	.071	.073	.074	.076	.077	.078	.080	.081	.082	.084	.085	.087	.088	.090
62	.069	.071	.073	.074	.076	.077	.079	.080	.082	.083	.085	.086	.088	.089	.091	.092	.094	.095
64	.074	.075	.077	.079	.080	.082	.083	.085	.086	.088	.090	.092	.093	.095	.096	.098	.099	.101
66	.078	.079	.081	.083	.085	.087	.088	.090	.091	.093	.095	.097	.098	.100	.101	.103	.105	.107
68	.082	.084	.085	.088	.089	.091	.093	.095	.096	.098	.100	.102	.103	.105	.107	.109	.110	.113
70	.086	.088	.090	.092	.094	.096	.097	.100	.101	.103	.105	.107	.109	.111	.112	.115	.116	.118
72	.090	.092	.094	.096	.098	.100	.102	.104	.106	.108	.110	.112	.114	.116	.118	.120	.122	.124
74	.094	.096	.098	.101	.103	.105	.107	.109	.111	.113	.115	.117	.119	.121	.123	.125	.127	.130
76	.098	.101	.103	.105	.107	.110	.111	.114	.116	.118	.120	.122	.124	.127	.128	.131	.133	.135
78	.103	.105	.107	.110	.112	.114	.116	.119	.120	.123	.125	.128	.129	.132	.134	.137	.138	.141
80	.107	.109	.111	.114	.116	.119	.121	.123	.125	.128	.130	.133	.135	.137	.139	.142	.144	.147
82	.111	.113	.116	.119	.121	.123	.125	.128	.130	.133	.135	.138	.140	.143	.145	.148	.149	.152
84	.115	.118	.120	.123	.125	.128	.130	.133	.135	.138	.140	.143	.145	.148	.150	.153	.155	.158
86	.119	.122	.124	.127	.130	.133	.135	.138	.140	.143	.145	.148	.150	.153	.155	.159	.161	.164
88	.123	.126	.129	.132	.134	.137	.139	.143	.145	.148	.150	.153	.155	.159	.161	.164	.166	.169
90	.127	.130	.133	.136	.138	.142	.144	.147	.150	.153	.155	.158	.161	.164	.166	.170	.172	.175
92	.132	.134	.137	.141	.143	.146	.149	.152	.154	.158	.160	.163	.166	.169	.172	.175	.177	.181
94	.136	.139	.142	.145	.147	.151	.153	.157	.159	.163	.165	.169	.171	.175	.177	.180	.183	.186
96	.140	.143	.146	.150	.152	.155	.158	.161	.164	.168	.170	.174	.176	.180	.182	.186	.188	.192
98	.144	.147	.150	.154	.156	.160	.163	.166	.169	.172	.175	.179	.181	.185	.188	.191	.194	.197
100	.148	.151	.154	.158	.161	.164	.167	.171	.174	.177	.180	.184	.187	.190	.193	.197	.200	.203

TEMPERATURE CORRECTION, GLASS SCALE
METRIC
To reduce readings of a mercurial barometer with a glass scale to 0° C.
subtract the appropriate quantity as found in table.

Temp. °C	70 cm.	71 cm.	72 cm.	73 cm.	74 cm.	75 cm.	76 cm.	77 cm.	78 cm.	Temp. °C	70 cm.	71 cm.	72 cm.	73 cm.	74 cm.	75 cm.	76 cm.	77 cm.	78 cm.
	Observed height in centimeters.										Observed height in centimeters.								
0	0.000	0.000	0.000	0.000	0.000	0.000	0.000	0.000	0.000	15	0.181	0.184	0.186	0.189	0.191	0.193	0.196	0.198	0.201
1	.012	.012	.013	.013	.013	.013	.013	.013	.014	16	.194	.196	.199	.201	.204	.207	.209	.212	.214
2	.025	.025	.025	.026	.026	.026	.026	.027	.027	17	.205	.208	.210	.213	.216	.219	.221	.224	.227
3	.036	.036	.037	.037	.038	.038	.039	.039	.040	18	.217	.220	.223	.226	.229	.232	.235	.238	.241
4	.048	.049	.049	.050	.051	.051	.052	.053	.053	19	.230	.233	.236	.239	.242	.245	.248	.251	.254
5	0.060	0.061	0.062	0.063	0.064	0.064	0.065	0.066	0.067	20	0.242	0.245	0.248	0.252	0.255	0.258	0.261	0.264	0.268
6	.073	.074	.074	.076	.077	.077	.078	.079	.080	21	.254	.258	.261	.264	.268	.271	.275	.278	.281
7	.085	.086	.087	.088	.089	.091	.092	.093	.094	22	.266	.269	.273	.276	.280	.283	.287	.290	.294
8	.096	.098	.099	.100	.101	.103	.104	.105	.107	23	.278	.282	.285	.289	.293	.296	.300	.304	.308
9	.109	.110	.111	.113	.114	.116	.117	.119	.120	24	.290	.294	.298	.302	.306	.310	.313	.317	.321
10	0.121	0.122	0.124	0.126	0.127	0.129	0.130	0.132	0.134	25	0.303	0.307	0.311	0.315	0.319	0.323	0.327	0.331	0.335
11	.133	.135	.137	.138	.140	.142	.144	.146	.147	26	.315	.319	.323	.327	.332	.336	.340	.344	.348
12	.144	.146	.148	.150	.152	.154	.156	.158	.160	27	.326	.331	.335	.339	.344	.348	.352	.357	.361
13	.157	.159	.161	.163	.165	.167	.169	.171	.174	28	.339	.343	.348	.352	.357	.361	.366	.370	.375
14	.169	.171	.174	.176	.178	.180	.183	.185	.187	29	.351	.356	.360	.365	.370	.374	.379	.384	.388
										30	0.363	0.368	0.373	0.378	0.383	0.387	0.392	0.397	0.402

WEIGHT IN GRAMS OF A CUBIC METER OF SATURATED AQUEOUS VAPOR
(From Smithsonian Tables)

Mass in grams per cubic meter.

Temp. °C	0.0	1.0	2.0	3.0	4.0	5.0	6.0	7.0	8.0	9.0
−20	1.074	.988	.909	.836	.768	.705	.646	.592	.542	.496
−10	2.358	2.186	2.026	1.876	1.736	1.605	1.483	1.369	1.264	1.165
− 0	4.847	4.523	4.217	3.930	3.660	3.407	3.169	2.946	2.737	2.541
+ 0	4.847	5.192	5.559	5.947	6.360	6.797	7.260	7.750	8.270	8.819
+10	9.399	10.01	10.66	11.35	12.07	12.83	13.63	14.84	15.37	16.21
+20	17.30	18.34	19.43	20.58	21.78	23.05	24.38	25.78	27.24	28.78
+30	30.38	32.07	33.83	35.68	37.61	39.63	41.75	43.96	46.26	48.67

EFFICIENCY OF DRYING AGENTS
Compiled by John H. Yoe

A. Drying agents depending upon chemical action (absorption) for their efficiency:*

Substance	Residual water, mg per liter of dry air**	Reference
P_2O_5	<1 mg in 40,000 l.	Morley, Am. J. Sci., **34**, 199 (1887); J.A.C.S., **26**, 1171 (1904).
$Mg(ClO_4)_2$ anhyd.	"Unweighable" in 210 l.	Willard and Smith, J.A.C.S., **44**, 2255 (1922).
BaO	0.00065	Bower, Bur. Std. J. Res., **12**, 241 (1934).
KOH fused	0.002	Baxter and Starkweather, J.A.C.S., **38**, 2038 (1916).
CaO	0.003	Bower, loc. cit.
H_2SO_4	0.003	Baxter and Starkweather, loc. cit.
$CaSO_4$ anhyd.	0.005	Bower, loc. cit.
Al_2O_3	0.005	Ibid.
KOH sticks	0.014	Ibid.
NaOH fused	0.16	Baxter and Starkweather, loc. cit.
$CaBr_2$	0.18	Baxter and Warren, J.A.C.S., **33**, 340 (1911).
$CaCl_2$ fused	0.34	Baxter and Starkweather, loc. cit.
NaOH sticks	0.80	Bower, loc. cit.
$Ba(ClO_4)_2$	0.82	Ibid.
$ZnCl_2$	0.85	Baxter and Warren, loc. cit.
$ZnBr_2$	1.16	Ibid.
$CaCl_2$ granular	1.5	Bower, loc. cit.
$CuSO_4$ anhyd.	2.8	Ibid.

B. Drying agents depending upon physical action (adsorption) for their efficiency:* Alumina (low temperature fired), asbestos, charcoal, clay and porcelain (low temperature fired), glass wool, kieselguhr, silica gel, refrigeration.

* It should be noted that the efficiency of some drying agents (e.g. Al_2O_3 and anhydrous $CaCl_2$, and probably also BaO, anhydrous $Mg(ClO_4)_2$, $Mg(ClO_4)_2 \cdot 3H_2O$, anhydrous $Ba(ClO_4)_2$, and $CaSO_4$) depends upon both adsorption and absorption.

** 30°C. for Bower's values; others 25°C. or room temp.

REDUCTION OF BAROMETER TO SEA LEVEL

The correction to be added to reduce barometric readings to "sea level" values depends principally on three factors: The temperature of the air column (assumed) from the station to sea level, the altitude of the station, and the value of the reading itself. Two tables are provided. Table I is entered with the altitude and assumed temperature and a factor "2000 m" taken out. Table II is entered with the above factor and the approximate barometer reading and the final correction taken out.

The correction is to be added. If B_0 is the corrected or sea level value; B the barometer reading at the station; C the correction,—

$$C = B_0 - B = B(10^m - 1)$$

The actual barometer reading at the station should be corrected for temperature of the mercury column by the usual methods before entering the tables or applying the sea level correction.

A complete explanation of the theory of the corrections and a more extended set of tables will be found in the Smithsonian Meteorological Tables.

LATITUDE FACTOR

The influence of the latitude on the value of the correction is usually negligible, being overshadowed by uncertainties in the assumed temperature of the air column. For cases where this correction is desirable the table below is provided. The value of the temperature-altitude factor "2000 m" obtained in Table I is corrected for latitude by subtracting for latitudes 0-45° and adding for latitudes from 45-90° the values found. With this corrected value of "2000 m" Table II is entered for the value of the correction.

LATITUDE FACTOR

To be used in connection with Tables I and II, either English or metric units, to obtain latitude corrections to temperature-altitude factor. For latitudes 0-45° subtract the correction. For latitudes 45-90° add the correction.

Temp.—Alt. from Table I	Latitude			
	0°	15°	30°	45°
100	0.3	0.2	0.1	0.0
200	0.5	0.5	0.3	0.0
300	0.8	0.7	0.4	0.0
	90°	75°	60°	45°

METRIC UNITS—TABLE I

Values of the temperature-altitude factor (2000 m.) for entering table II.

Altitude in meters	Assumed temperature of air column °C									
	−16°	−8°	0°	+4°	+8°	+12°	+16°	+20°	+24°	+28°
10	1.2	1.1	1.1	1.1	1.0	1.0	1.0	1.0	1.0	1.0
50	5.8	5.6	5.4	5.3	5.2	5.2	5.1	5.0	4.9	4.9
100	11.5	11.2	10.8	10.7	10.5	10.3	10.2	10.0	9.9	9.7
150	17.3	16.7	16.2	16.0	15.7	15.5	15.3	15.0	14.8	14.6
200	23.0	22.3	21.6	21.3	21.0	20.7	20.3	20.0	19.7	19.5
250	28.8	27.9	27.0	26.6	26.2	25.8	25.4	25.0	24.7	24.3
300	34.5	33.5	32.5	32.0	31.5	31.0	30.5	30.1	29.6	29.2
350	40.3	39.0	37.9	37.3	36.7	36.2	35.6	35.1	34.6	34.0
400	46.0	44.6	43.3	42.6	42.0	41.3	40.7	40.1	39.5	38.9
450	51.8	50.2	48.7	47.9	47.2	46.5	45.8	45.1	44.4	43.8
500	57.5	55.8	54.1	53.3	52.4	51.6	50.9	50.1	49.4	48.6
550	63.3	61.4	59.5	58.6	57.7	56.8	55.9	55.1	54.3	53.5
600	69.0	66.9	64.9	63.9	62.9	62.0	61.0	60.1	59.2	58.3
650	74.8	72.5	70.3	69.2	68.2	67.1	66.1	65.1	64.2	63.2
700	80.6	78.1	75.7	74.6	73.4	72.3	71.2	70.1	69.1	68.1
750	86.3	83.7	81.1	79.9	78.7	77.5	76.3	75.1	74.0	72.9
800	92.1	89.2	86.5	85.2	83.9	82.6	81.4	80.1	79.0	77.8
850	97.8	94.8	91.9	90.5	89.2	87.8	86.5	85.1	83.9	82.7
900	103.6	100.4	97.4	95.9	94.4	93.0	91.5	90.2	88.8	87.5
950	109.3	106.0	102.8	101.2	99.6	98.1	96.6	95.2	93.8	92.4
1000	115.1	111.5	108.2	106.5	104.9	103.3	101.7	100.2	98.7	97.3
1050	120.8	117.1	113.6	111.8	110.1	108.4	106.8	105.2	103.6	102.1
1100	126.6	122.7	119.0	117.2	115.4	113.6	111.9	110.2	108.6	107.0
1150	132.3	128.3	124.4	122.5	120.6	118.8	117.0	115.2	113.5	111.8
1200	138.1	133.8	129.8	127.8	125.9	123.9	122.0	120.2	118.4	116.7
1250	143.8	139.4	135.2	133.1	131.1	129.1	127.1	125.2	123.4	121.6
1300	149.6	145.0	140.6	138.5	136.3	134.3	132.2	130.2	128.3	126.4
1350	155.3	150.6	146.0	143.8	141.6	139.4	137.3	135.2	133.2	131.3
1400	161.1	156.2	151.4	149.1	146.8	144.6	142.4	140.2	138.2	136.2
1450	166.8	161.7	156.8	154.5	152.1	149.7	147.5	145.3	143.1	141.0

METRIC UNITS—TABLE I   (Continued)

Altitude in meters	Assumed temperature of air column °C									
	−16°	−8°	0°	+4°	+8°	+12°	+16°	+20°	+24°	+28°
1500	172.6	167.3	162.3	159.8	157.3	154.9	152.5	150.3	148.0	145.9
1550	178.3	172.9	167.7	165.1	162.6	160.1	157.6	155.3	153.0	150.7
1600	184.1	178.5	173.1	170.4	167.8	165.2	162.7	160.3	157.9	155.6
1650	189.8	184.0	178.5	175.7	173.0	170.4	167.8	165.3	162.8	160.5
1700	195.6	189.6	183.9	181.1	178.3	175.6	172.9	170.3	167.8	165.3
1750	201.4	195.2	189.3	186.4	183.5	180.7	178.0	175.3	172.7	170.2
1800	207.1	200.8	194.7	191.7	188.8	185.9	183.1	180.3	177.6	175.0
1850	212.9	206.3	200.1	197.0	194.0	191.0	188.1	185.3	182.6	179.9
1900	218.6	211.9	205.5	202.4	199.3	196.2	193.2	190.3	187.5	184.8
1950	224.4	217.5	210.9	207.7	204.5	201.4	198.3	195.3	192.4	189.6
2000	230.1	223.0	216.3	213.0	209.7	206.5	203.4	200.3	197.4	194.5
2050	235.9	228.6	221.7	218.3	215.0	211.7	208.5	205.3	202.3	199.3
2100	241.6	234.2	227.1	223.7	220.2	216.8	213.5	210.4	207.2	204.2
2150	247.4	239.8	232.5	229.0	225.5	222.0	218.6	215.4	212.2	209.1
2200	253.1	245.4	237.9	234.3	230.7	227.2	223.7	220.4	217.1	213.9
2250	258.9	250.9	243.4	239.6	225.9	232.3	228.8	225.4	222.0	218.8
2300	264.6	256.5	248.8	245.0	241.2	237.5	233.9	230.4	227.0	223.6
2350	270.4	262.1	254.2	250.3	246.4	242.7	239.0	235.4	231.9	228.5
2400	276.1	267.7	259.6	255.6	251.7	247.8	244.0	240.4	236.8	233.4
2450	281.9	273.2	265.0	260.9	256.9	253.0	249.1	245.4	241.8	238.2
2500	287.6	278.8	270.4	266.2	262.2	258.1	254.2	250.4	246.7	243.1
2550	293.4	284.4	275.8	271.6	267.4	263.3	259.3	255.5	251.6	247.9
2600	299.1	290.0	281.2	276.9	272.6	268.5	264.4	260.4	256.6	252.8
2650	304.9	295.5	286.6	282.2	277.9	273.6	269.5	265.4	261.5	257.7
2700	310.6	301.1	292.0	287.5	283.1	278.8	274.5	270.4	266.4	262.5
2750	316.4	306.7	297.4	292.9	288.4	283.9	279.6	275.4	271.4	267.4
2800	322.1	312.3	302.8	298.2	293.6	289.1	284.7	280.4	276.3	272.2
2850	327.9	317.8	308.2	303.5	298.8	294.3	289.8	285.4	281.2	277.1
2900	333.6	323.4	313.6	308.8	304.1	299.4	294.9	290.4	286.2	282.0
2950	339.4	329.0	319.0	314.2	309.3	304.6	299.9	295.5	291.1	286.8
3000	345.1	334.5	324.4	319.5	314.6	309.7	305.0	300.5	296.0	291.7

METRIC UNITS—TABLE II

Values of Correction to be Added

Temp.—alt. factor	Barometer reading						Temp.—alt. factor	Barometer reading				
	780 mm	760 mm	740 mm	720 mm	700 mm			640 mm	620 mm	600 mm	580 mm	560 mm
1	0.9	0.9	0.9	0.8	0.8		170	138.4	134.0	129.7	125.4	121.1
5	4.5	4.4	4.3	4.2	4.0		175	142.9	138.4	133.9	129.5	125.0
10	9.0	8.8	8.6	8.3	8.1		180	147.4	142.8	138.2	133.6	129.0
15	13.6	13.2	12.9	12.5	12.2		185	151.9	147.2	142.4	137.7	132.9
20	18.2	17.7	17.2	16.8	16.3		190	156.5	151.6	146.7	141.8	136.9
25	22.8	22.1	21.6	21.0	20.4		195	161.1	156.1	151.0	146.0	141.0
30	27.4	26.7	26.0	25.3	24.6		200	165.7	160.5	155.4	150.2	145.0
35	.....	31.2	30.4	29.6	28.8		205	170.4	165.0	159.7	154.4	149.1
							210	.....	169.6	164.1	158.6	153.2
							215	.....	174.1	168.5	162.9	157.3

Temp.—alt. factor	760 mm	740 mm	720 mm	700 mm	680 mm	660 mm	Temp.—alt. factor	620 mm	600 mm	580 mm	560 mm	540 mm
40	35.8	34.9	33.9	33.0	32.0	31.1						
45	40.4	39.3	38.3	37.2	36.2	35.1	215	174.1	168.5	162.9	157.3	151.7
50	45.0	43.8	42.7	41.5	40.3	39.1	220	178.7	172.9	167.2	161.4	155.7
55	49.7	48.4	47.1	45.8	44.5	43.1	225	183.3	177.4	171.5	165.6	159.7
60	.....	52.9	51.5	50.1	48.6	47.2	230	188.0	181.9	175.8	169.8	163.7
65	.....	57.5	55.9	54.4	52.8	51.3	235	192.6	186.4	180.2	174.0	167.8
70	.....	62.1	60.4	58.7	57.1	55.4	240	.....	191.0	184.6	178.2	171.9
75	.....	66.7	64.9	63.1	61.3	59.5	245	.....	195.5	189.0	182.5	176.0
							250	.....	200.1	193.4	186.8	180.1
							255	.....	204.7	197.9	191.1	184.3
							260	.....	209.4	202.4	195.4	188.4

Temp.—alt. factor	720 mm	700 mm	680 mm	660 mm	640 mm	Temp.—alt. factor	580 mm	560 mm	540 mm	520 mm
80	69.5	67.5	65.6	63.7	61.7					
85	74.0	72.0	69.9	67.9	65.8					
90	78.6	76.4	74.2	72.1	69.9	260	202.4	195.4	188.4	181.5
95	83.2	80.9	78.6	76.3	74.0	265	206.9	199.8	192.6	185.5
100	87.9	85.4	83.0	80.5	78.1	270	211.5	204.2	196.9	189.6
105	.....	89.9	87.4	84.8	82.2	275	216.0	208.6	201.1	193.7
110	.....	94.5	91.8	89.1	86.4	280	220.6	213.0	205.4	197.8
115	.....	99.1	96.3	93.4	90.6	285	225.2	217.5	209.7	201.9
120	.....	103.7	100.7	97.8	94.8	290	229.9	222.0	214.0	206.1
125	.....	108.3	105.3	102.2	99.1	295	.....	226.5	218.4	210.3
						300	.....	231.0	222.8	214.5

Temp.—alt. factor	680 mm	660 mm	640 mm	620 mm	600 mm	Temp.—alt. factor	560 mm	540 mm	520 mm	500 mm	480 mm
125	105.3	102.2	99.1	96.0	92.9						
130	109.8	106.6	103.3	100.1	96.9						
135	114.4	111.0	107.6	104.3	100.9	305	235.6	227.2	218.8	210.3	201.9
140	118.9	115.4	111.9	108.4	104.9	310	240.2	231.6	223.0	214.4	205.9
145	123.5	119.9	116.3	112.0	109.0	315	244.8	236.0	227.3	218.6	209.8
150	128.2	124.4	120.6	116.9	113.1	320	249.4	240.5	231.6	222.7	213.8
155	.....	128.9	125.0	121.0	117.2	325	254.1	245.0	236.0	226.9	217.8
160	.....	133.5	129.4	125.4	121.4	330	.....	249.6	240.3	231.1	221.8
165	.....	138.1	133.9	129.7	125.5	335	.....	254.1	244.7	235.3	225.9
170	.....	142.7	138.4	134.0	129.7	340	.....	258.7	249.1	239.6	230.0
						345	.....	263.3	253.5	243.8	234.1

ENGLISH UNITS—TABLE I

Values of the temperature-altitude factor (2000 m.) for entering table II.

Altitude feet	Assumed temperature of air column °F									
	−20	0	+10	+20	+30	+40	+50	+60	+70	+80
200	7.4	7.1	6.9	6.8	6.6	6.5	6.3	6.2	6.1	6.0
400	14.8	14.1	13.8	13.5	13.2	13.0	12.7	12.4	12.2	11.9
600	22.2	21.2	20.7	20.3	19.9	19.5	19.0	18.6	18.2	17.9
800	29.6	28.3	27.7	27.1	26.5	25.9	25.4	24.8	24.3	23.8
1000	37.0	35.3	34.6	33.8	33.1	32.4	31.7	31.1	30.4	29.8
1200	44.3	42.4	41.5	40.6	39.7	38.9	38.1	37.3	36.5	35.8
1400	51.7	49.5	48.4	47.4	46.4	45.4	44.4	43.5	42.6	41.7
1600	59.1	56.5	55.3	54.1	53.0	51.9	50.8	49.7	48.7	47.7
1800	66.5	63.6	62.2	60.9	59.6	58.4	57.1	55.9	54.7	53.6
2000	73.9	70.6	69.1	67.7	66.2	64.8	63.4	62.1	60.8	59.6
2200	81.3	77.7	76.0	74.4	72.9	71.3	69.8	68.3	66.9	65.5
2400	88.7	84.8	82.9	81.2	79.5	77.8	76.1	74.5	73.0	71.5
2600	96.1	91.8	89.9	87.9	86.1	84.3	82.5	80.7	79.1	77.5
2800	103.5	98.9	96.8	94.7	92.7	90.8	88.8	87.0	85.1	83.4
3000	110.9	106.0	103.7	101.5	99.3	97.2	95.2	93.2	91.2	89.4
3200	118.2	113.0	110.6	108.2	106.0	103.7	101.5	99.4	97.3	95.3
3400	125.6	120.1	117.5	115.0	112.6	110.2	107.9	105.6	103.4	101.3
3600	133.0	127.2	124.4	121.8	119.2	116.7	114.2	111.8	109.5	107.2
3800	140.4	134.2	131.3	128.5	125.8	123.2	120.5	118.0	115.5	113.2
4000	147.8	141.3	138.2	135.3	132.4	129.6	126.9	124.2	121.6	119.2
4200	155.2	148.3	145.1	142.1	139.1	136.1	133.2	130.4	127.7	125.1
4400	162.6	155.4	152.0	148.8	145.7	142.6	139.6	136.6	133.8	131.1
4600	170.0	162.5	159.0	155.6	152.3	149.1	145.9	142.8	139.9	137.0
4800	177.3	169.5	165.9	162.3	158.9	155.6	152.2	149.0	145.9	143.0
5000	184.7	176.6	172.8	169.1	165.6	162.0	158.6	155.2	152.0	148.9
5200	192.1	183.7	179.7	175.9	172.2	168.5	164.9	161.5	158.1	154.9
5400	199.5	190.7	186.6	182.6	178.8	175.0	171.3	167.7	164.2	160.8
5600	206.9	197.8	193.5	189.4	185.4	181.5	177.6	173.9	170.3	166.8
5800	214.3	204.8	200.4	196.2	192.0	188.0	184.0	180.1	176.3	172.8
6000	221.7	211.9	207.3	202.9	198.7	194.4	190.3	186.3	182.4	178.7
6200	229.1	219.0	214.2	209.7	205.3	200.9	196.6	192.5	188.5	184.7
6400	236.4	226.0	221.1	216.4	211.9	207.4	203.0	198.7	194.6	190.6
6600	243.8	233.1	228.0	223.2	218.5	213.0	209.3	204.9	200.7	196.6
6800	251.2	240.1	235.0	230.0	225.1	220.4	215.7	211.1	206.7	202.5
7000	258.6	247.2	241.9	236.7	231.8	226.8	222.0	217.3	212.8	208.5
7200	266.0	254.3	248.8	243.5	238.4	233.2	228.3	223.5	218.9	214.4
7400	273.4	261.3	255.7	250.2	245.0	239.8	234.7	229.7	225.0	220.4
7600	280.8	268.4	262.6	257.0	251.6	246.3	241.0	235.9	231.1	226.4
7800	288.1	275.4	269.5	263.8	258.2	252.8	247.4	242.2	237.1	232.3
8000	295.5	282.5	276.4	270.5	264.8	259.2	253.7	248.4	243.2	238.3
8200	302.9	289.6	283.3	277.3	271.5	265.7	260.1	254.6	249.3	244.2
8400	310.3	296.6	290.2	284.0	278.1	272.2	266.4	260.8	255.4	250.2
8600	317.7	303.7	297.1	290.8	284.7	278.7	272.7	267.0	261.4	256.1
8800	325.1	310.7	304.0	297.6	291.3	285.2	279.1	273.2	267.5	262.1
9000	332.5	317.8	310.9	304.3	297.9	291.6	285.4	279.4	273.6	268.0

ENGLISH UNITS—TABLE II

Value of Correction to be Added.

Temp. alt. factor	Barometer reading					Temp. alt. factor	Barometer reading				
	31	30	29	28	27		26	25	24	23	22
	in.	in.	in.	in.	in.		in.	in.	in.	in.	in.
1	0.04	0.03	0.03	....	....	165	5.44	5.23	5.02		
5	0.18	0.17	0.17	....	....	170	5.62	5.40	5.19		
10	0.36	0.35	0.34	0.32	....	175	....	5.58	5.36		
15	0.54	0.52	0.51	0.49	....	180	....	5.76	5.53	5.30	
20	0.72	0.70	0.68	0.65	....	185	....	5.93	5.70	5.46	
25	....	0.88	0.85	0.82	....	190	....	6.11	5.87	5.62	
30	....	1.05	1.02	0.98	....	195	....	6.29	6.04	5.79	
35	....	1.23	1.19	1.15	....	200	....	6.47	6.21	5.96	
40	....	1.41	1.37	1.32	1.27	205			6.39	6.12	
45	....	1.60	1.54	1.49	1.44	210			6.56	6.29	
50	....	....	1.72	1.66	1.60	215			6.74	6.46	
55	....	....	1.90	1.83	1.76	220			6.92	6.63	6.34
60	....	....	2.07	2.00	1.93	225			7.10	6.80	6.51
65	....	....	2.25	2.18	2.10	230			7.28	6.97	6.67
70	....	....	2.43	2.35	2.27	235			7.46	7.15	6.84
75	....	....	....	2.53	2.43	240				7.32	7.00
80	....	....	....	2.70	2.60	245				7.49	7.17

Temp. alt. factor	28	27	26	25	24	Temp. alt. factor	23	22	21	20
	in.	in.	in.	in.	in.		in.	in.	in.	in.
75	2.53	2.43	2.34	....	....	250	7.67	7.34		
80	2.70	2.60	2.51	....	....	255	7.85	7.51		
85	2.88	2.78	2.67	....	....	260	8.03	7.68	7.33	
90	3.06	2.95	2.84	....	....	265	8.21	7.85	7.49	
95	3.24	3.12	3.01	....	....	270	8.39	8.02	7.66	
100	3.42	3.29	3.17	....	....	275	8.57	8.19	7.82	
105	3.60	3.47	3.34	3.21	....	280		8.37	7.99	

ENGLISH UNITS—TABLE II (Cont)

Value of Correction to be Added.

	28	27	26	25	24		23	22	21	20
110	....	3.85	3.51	3.38	....	285	....	8.54	8.16	
115	....	3.82	3.68	3.54	....	290	....	8.72	8.32	
120	....	4.00	3.85	3.70	....	295	....	8.90	8.49	8.09
125	....	4.18	4.02	3.87	....	300	....	9.08	8.66	8.25
130	....	4.36	4.20	4.04	....	305	....	9.26	8.83	8.41
135	....	4.54	4.37	4.20	....	310	....	9.44	9.01	8.58
140	....	4.55	4.37	4.20	....	315	....	9.62	9.48	8.74
145	....	4.72	4.54	4.36	....	320	....	9.80	9.35	8.91
150	....	4.90	4.71	4.52	....	325	....	....	9.53	9.08
155	....	5.08	4.88	4.69	....	330	....	....	9.71	9.24
160	....	5.26	5.06	4.85						

REDUCTION OF BAROMETER TO GRAVITY AT SEA LEVEL

METRIC UNITS

Correction to be subtracted given in millimeters

(From Smithsonian Physical Tables)

Height above sea level in meters	Observed Height of Barometer in Millimeters						
	500	550	600	650	700	750	800
100	....	....	....	....	.02	.02	.02
200	....	....	....	....	.04	.05	.05
300	....	....	....	....	.07	.07	.07
400	....	....	....	....	.09	.10	.10
500	....	....	....	....	.11	.12	.13
600	....	....	....	.12	.13	.14	
700	....	....	....	.14	.15	.16	
800	....	....	....	.16	.18	.19	
900	....	....	....	.18	.20	.22	
1000	....	.18	.19	.20	.22	.24	
1100	....	.19	.21	.22	.24		
1200	....	.21	.23	.24	.26		
1300	....	.22	.24	.26	.29		
1400	....	.24	.26	.28	.31		
1500	.24	.26	.28	.30	.33		
1600	.25	.28	.30	.32			
1700	.27	.30	.32	.34			
1800	.28	.31	.34	.36			
1900	.30	.33	.36	.39			
2000	.31	.34	.38	.41			
2100	.33	.36	.40				
2200	.35	.38	.41				
2300	.36	.40	.43				
2400	.38	.42	.45				
2500	.39	.43	.47				

ENGLISH UNITS

Height above sea level in feet	Observed Height in Inches						
	18	20	22	24	26	28	30
1000	....	....	....	.004	.003	.003	.003
2000	....	....	....	.004	.005	.005	.006
3000	....	....	.007	.007	.008	.008	
4000	....	....	.009	.009	.010		
4500	....	....	.010	.010	.011		
5000	....	.010	.011	.011	.012		
5500	....	.011	.012	.013			
6000	....	.011	.013	.014			
6500	.011	.012	.014	.015			
7000	.012	.013	.015	.016			
7500	.013	.014	.016	.017			
8000	.014	.015	.017				
8500	.015	.016	.018				
9000	.016	.017	.019				
9500	.016	.018	.020				

REDUCTION OF BAROMETER TO LATITUDE 45°

METRIC SCALE

For latitudes below 45°, subtract the correction; for latitudes greater than 45° it is to be added.   Corrections in cm.

(From Smithsonian Meteorological Tables.)

Latitude		Observed Height of Barometer in Centimeters					
		68	70	72	74	76	78
25°	65°	0.116	0.120	0.123	0.127	0.130	0.133
26	64	.111	.115	.118	.121	.125	.128
27	63	.106	.110	.113	.116	.119	.122
28	62	.101	.104	.107	.110	.113	.116
29	61	.096	.099	.102	.104	.107	.110
30	60	0.091	0.094	0.096	0.098	0.101	0.104
31	59	.085	.087	.090	.092	.095	.097
32	58	.079	.082	.084	.086	.089	.091
33	57	.074	.076	.078	.080	.082	.084
34	56	.068	.070	.072	.074	.076	.078
35	55	0.062	0.064	0.066	0.067	0.069	0.071
36	54	.056	.058	.059	.061	.063	.064
37	53	.050	.051	.053	.054	.056	.057
38	52	.044	.045	.046	.048	.049	.050
39	51	.038	.039	.040	.041	.042	.043
40	50	0.031	0.032	0.033	0.034	0.035	0.036
41	49	.025	.026	.027	.027	.028	.029
42	48	.019	.019	.020	.021	.021	.022
43	47	.013	.013	.013	.014	.014	.014
44	46	.006	.007	.007	.007	.007	.007

ENGLISH SCALE

Corrections in inches.

Latitude		Observed Height in Inches					
		25	26	27	28	29	30
25°	65°	0.043	0.044	0.046	0.048	0.050	0.051
26	04	.041	.043	.044	.046	.048	.049
27	63	.039	.041	.042	.044	.045	.047
28	62	.037	.039	.040	.042	.043	.045
29	61	.035	.037	.038	.039	.041	.042
30	60	0.033	0.035	0.036	0.037	0.039	0.040
31	59	.031	.032	.034	.035	.036	.037
32	58	.029	.030	.032	.033	.034	.035
33	57	.027	.028	.029	.030	.031	.032
34	56	.025	.026	.027	.028	.029	.030
35	55	0.023	0.024	0.025	0.025	0.026	0.027
36	54	.021	.021	.022	.023	.024	.025
37	53	.018	.019	.020	.021	.021	.022
38	52	.016	.017	.017	.018	.019	.019
39	51	.014	.014	.015	.015	.016	.017
40	50	0.012	0.012	0.012	0.013	0.013	0.014
41	49	.009	.010	.010	.010	.011	.011
42	48	.007	.007	.008	.008	.008	.008
43	47	.005	.005	.005	.005	.005	.006
44	46	.002	.002	.003	.003	.003	.003

RELATIVE HUMIDITY—DEW-POINT

The table gives the relative humidity of the air for temperature t and dewpoint d.

(From Smithsonian Meteorological Tables.)

Depression of dew-point $t-d$° C.	Dew-point (d).				
	−10	0	+10	+20	+30
0.0	100%	100%	100%	100%	100%
0.2	98	99	99	99	99
0.4	97	97	97	98	98
0.6	95	96	96	96	97
0.8	94	94	95	95	96
1.0	92	93	94	94	94
1.2	91	92	92	93	93
1.4	90	90	91	92	92
1.6	88	89	90	91	91
1.8	87	88	89	90	90
2.0	86	87	88	88	89
2.2	84	85	86	87	88
2.4	83	84	85	86	87
2.6	82	83	84	85	86
2.8	80	82	83	84	85

RELATIVE HUMIDITY—DEW-POINT (Continued)

Depression of dew-point $t-d$° C.	Dew-point (d).				
	−10	0	+10	+20	+30
3.0	79	81	82	83	84
3.2	78	80	81	82	83
3.4	77	79	80	81	82
3.6	76	77	79	80	82
3.8	75	76	78	79	81
4.0	73	75	77	78	80
4.2	72	74	76	77	79
4.4	71	73	75	77	78
4.6	70	72	74	76	77
4.8	69	71	73	75	76
5.0	68	70	72	74	75
5.2	67	69	71	73	75
5.4	66	68	70	72	74
5.6	65	67	69	71	73
5.8	64	66	69	70	72
6.0	63	66	68	70	71
6.2	62	65	67	69	71
6.4	61	64	66	68	70
6.6	60	63	65	67	69
6.8	60	62	64	66	68
7.0	59	61	63	66	68
7.2	58	60	63	65	67
7.4	57	60	62	64	66
7.6	56	59	61	63	65
7.8	55	58	60	63	65
8.0	54	57	60	62	64
8.2	54	56	59	61	63
8.4	53	56	58	60	63
8.6	52	55	57	60	62
8.8	51	54	57	59	61
9.0	51	53	56	58	61
9.2	50	53	55	58	60
9.4	49	52	55	57	59
9.6	48	51	54	56	59
9.8	48	51	53	56	58
10.0	47	50	53	55	57
10.5	45	48	51	54	
11.0	44	47	49	52	
11.5	42	45	48	51	
12.0	41	44	47	49	
12.5	39	42	45	48	
13.0	38	41	44	46	
13.5	37	40	43	45	
14.0	35	38	41	44	
14.5	34	37	40	43	
15.0	33	36	39	42	
15.5	32	35	38	40	
16.0	31	34	37	39	
16.5	30	33	36	38	
17.0	29	32	35	37	
17.5	28	31	34	36	
18.0	27	30	33	35	
18.5	26	29	32	34	
19.0	25	28	31	33	
19.5	24	27	30	33	
20.0	24	26	29	32	
21.0	22	25	27		
22.0	21	23	26		
23.0	19	22	24		
24.0	18	21	23		
25.0	17	19	22		
26.0	16	18	21		
27.0	15	17	20		
28.0	14	16	19		
29.0	13	15	18		
30.0	12	14	17		

RELATIVE HUMIDITY FROM WET AND DRY BULB THERMOMETER (CENT. SCALE)

This table gives the approximate relative humidity directly from the reading of the air temperature (dry bulb) ($t°C$) and the wet bulb ($t'°C$). It is computed for a barometric pressure of 74.27 cm Hg. Errors resulting from the use of this table for air temperatures above −10°C and between 77.5 and 71 cm Hg will usually be within the errors of observation.

Condensed from Bulletin of the U. S. Weather Bureau No. 1071

t \ $t−t'$	0.2	0.4	0.6	0.8	1.0	1.2	1.4	1.6	1.8	2.0	2.2	2.4	2.6	2.8	3.0	3.2	3.4	3.6	3.8	4.0	4.5	5.0	5.5	6.0	6.5	7.0	7.5	8.0	8.5	9.0	9.5	10.0	10.5	11.0
−10	93	87	80	74	67	61	54	48	41	35	28	22	16	9	..	...																		
−9	94	88	81	75	69	63	57	51	45	39	33	27	21	15	9	...																		
−8	94	88	83	77	71	65	60	54	48	43	37	32	26	20	15	10																		
−7	95	89	84	78	73	67	62	57	52	46	41	36	31	25	20	15	10	5	..															
−6	95	90	85	79	74	69	64	59	54	49	45	40	35	30	25	20	15	11	6															
−5	95	90	86	81	76	71	66	62	57	52	48	43	39	34	29	25	20	16	11	7														
−4	95	91	86	82	77	73	68	64	59	55	51	46	42	38	33	29	25	21	17	12														
−3	96	91	87	82	78	74	70	66	62	57	53	49	45	41	37	33	29	25	21	17	8													
−2	96	92	88	84	79	75	71	68	64	60	56	52	48	44	40	37	33	29	25	22	12													
−1	96	92	88	84	81	77	73	69	66	62	58	54	51	47	43	40	36	33	29	26	17	8												
0	96	93	89	85	81	78	74	71	67	64	60	57	53	50	46	43	40	36	33	29	21	13	5											
1	97	93	90	86	83	80	76	73	70	66	63	59	56	53	49	46	43	40	36	33	25	17	10	..										
2	97	93	90	87	84	81	78	74	71	68	65	62	59	55	52	49	46	43	40	37	29	22	14	7										
3	97	94	91	88	84	82	78	76	72	70	67	64	61	58	55	52	49	46	43	40	33	26	19	12	5									
4	97	94	91	88	85	82	79	77	74	71	68	65	62	60	57	54	51	48	45	43	36	29	22	16	9									
5	97	94	91	88	86	83	80	77	75	72	69	67	64	61	58	56	53	51	48	45	39	33	26	20	13	7								
6	97	94	92	89	86	84	81	78	76	73	70	68	65	63	60	58	55	53	50	48	41	35	29	24	17	11	5							
7	97	95	92	89	87	84	82	79	77	74	72	69	67	64	62	59	57	54	52	50	44	38	32	26	21	15	10							
8	97	95	92	90	87	85	82	80	77	75	73	70	68	65	63	61	58	56	54	51	46	40	35	29	24	19	14	8						
9	98	95	93	90	88	85	83	81	78	76	74	71	69	67	64	62	60	58	55	53	48	42	37	32	27	22	17	12	7					
10	98	95	93	90	88	86	83	81	79	77	74	72	70	68	66	63	61	59	57	55	50	44	39	34	29	24	20	15	10	6				
11	98	95	93	91	89	86	84	82	80	78	75	73	71	69	67	65	62	60	58	56	51	46	41	36	32	27	22	18	13	9	5			
12	98	96	93	91	89	87	85	82	80	78	76	74	72	70	68	66	64	62	60	58	53	48	43	39	34	29	25	21	16	12	8			
13	98	96	93	91	89	87	85	83	81	79	77	75	73	71	69	67	65	63	61	59	54	50	45	41	36	32	28	23	19	15	11	7		
14	98	96	94	92	90	88	86	84	82	79	78	76	74	72	70	68	66	64	62	60	56	51	47	42	38	34	30	26	22	18	14	10	6	
15	98	96	94	92	90	88	86	84	82	80	78	76	74	73	71	69	67	65	63	61	57	53	48	44	40	36	32	27	24	20	16	13	9	6

t \ $t−t'$	0.5	1.0	1.5	2.0	2.5	3.0	3.5	4.0	4.5	5.0	5.5	6.0	6.5	7.0	7.5	8.0	8.5	9.0	9.5	10.0	10.5	11.0	11.5	12.0	12.5	13.0	13.5	14.0	14.5	15.0	16.0	17.0	18.0	19.0	20.0
16	95	90	85	81	76	71	67	63	58	54	50	46	42	38	34	30	26	23	19	15	12	8	5												
17	95	90	86	81	76	72	68	64	60	55	51	47	43	40	36	32	28	25	21	18	14	11	8												
18	95	91	86	82	77	73	69	65	61	57	53	49	45	41	38	34	30	27	23	20	17	14	10	7											
19	95	91	87	82	78	74	70	65	62	58	54	50	46	43	39	36	32	29	26	22	19	16	13	10	7										
20	96	91	87	83	78	74	70	66	63	59	55	51	48	44	41	37	34	31	28	24	21	18	15	12	9	6									
21	96	91	87	83	79	75	71	67	64	60	56	53	49	46	42	39	36	32	29	26	23	20	17	14	12	9	6								
22	96	92	87	83	80	76	72	68	64	61	57	54	50	47	44	40	37	34	31	28	25	22	19	17	14	11	8	6							
23	96	92	88	84	80	76	72	69	65	62	58	55	52	48	45	42	39	36	33	30	27	24	21	19	16	13	11	8	6						
24	96	92	88	84	80	77	73	69	66	62	59	56	53	49	46	43	40	37	34	31	29	26	23	20	18	15	13	10	8	5					
25	96	92	88	84	81	77	74	70	67	63	60	57	54	50	47	44	41	38	36	33	30	28	25	22	20	17	15	12	10	8					
26	96	92	88	85	81	78	74	71	67	64	61	58	54	51	49	46	43	40	37	34	32	29	26	24	21	19	17	14	12	10	5				
27	96	92	89	85	82	78	75	71	68	65	62	58	56	52	50	47	44	41	38	36	33	31	28	26	23	21	18	16	14	12	7				
28	96	93	89	86	82	79	75	72	69	65	62	60	57	54	52	49	46	43	41	38	36	33	31	28	26	24	22	19	17	15	11	7			••
29	96	93	89	86	82	79	76	73	70	66	63	60	57	54	52	50	47	44	42	40	38	33	31	28	26	24	22	19	17	15	11	7			
30	96	93	89	86	83	79	76	73	70	67	64	61	58	55	52	50	47	44	42	39	37	35	32	30	28	25	23	21	19	17	13	9	5		
31	96	93	90	86	83	80	77	73	70	67	64	61	59	56	53	51	48	45	43	40	38	36	33	31	29	27	25	22	20	18	14	11	7		••
32	96	93	90	86	83	80	77	74	71	68	65	62	60	57	54	51	49	46	44	41	39	37	35	32	30	28	26	24	22	20	16	12	9	5	
33	97	93	90	87	83	80	77	74	71	68	66	63	60	57	55	52	50	47	45	42	40	38	36	33	31	29	27	25	23	21	17	14	10	7	
34	97	93	90	87	84	81	78	75	72	69	66	63	61	58	56	53	51	48	46	43	41	39	37	35	32	30	28	26	24	23	19	15	12	8	5
35	97	94	90	87	84	81	78	75	72	69	67	64	61	59	56	54	52	49	47	44	42	40	38	36	34	32	30	28	26	24	20	17	13	10	7
36	97	94	90	87	84	81	78	75	73	70	67	64	62	59	57	54	52	50	48	45	43	41	39	37	35	33	31	29	27	25	21	18	15	11	8
37	97	94	91	87	84	82	79	76	73	70	68	65	63	60	58	55	53	51	49	46	44	42	40	38	36	34	32	30	28	26	23	19	16	13	10
38	97	94	91	88	84	82	79	76	74	71	68	66	63	61	58	56	54	51	49	47	45	43	41	39	37	35	33	31	29	27	24	20	17	14	11
39	97	94	91	88	85	82	79	77	74	71	69	66	64	61	59	57	54	52	50	48	46	43	42	39	38	36	34	32	30	28	25	22	18	15	12
40	97	94	91	88	85	82	80	77	74	72	69	67	64	62	59	57	54	53	51	48	46	44	42	40	38	36	35	33	31	29	26	23	20	16	14

REDUCTION OF PSYCHROMETRIC OBSERVATION

For the reduction of observations with the wet and dry bulb thermometer. Assuming the relative velocity of the air to the thermometer bulbs is at least three meters per second; if t is the temperature of the air as indicated by the dry bulb. t_w, the temperature of the wet bulb, B, the barometric pressure, and E_w, the vapor tension of water corresponding to t_w, then the actual vapor tension is

$$E = E_w - 0.00066B(t - t_w)(1 + 0.00115t - t_w)$$

The value of the term

$$0.00066B(t - t_w)(1 + 0.00115t - t_w)$$

is given in the following table.

(From Miller's Laboratory Physics, Ginn & Co., publishers, by permission.)

$t - t_w$	Barometric Pressure B in Centimeters							
	70.0	71.0	72.0	73.0	74.0	75.0	76.0	77.0
°C	mm	mm	mm	mm	mm	mm	mm	mm
1	0.463	0.469	0.476	0.482	0.489	0.496	0.502	0.509
2	0.926	0.939	0.953	0.966	0.979	0.992	1.006	1.019
3	1.391	1.411	1.431	1.450	1.470	1.490	1.510	1.530
4	1.857	1.883	1.910	1.936	1.963	1.989	2.016	2.042
5	2.323	2.356	2.390	2.423	2.456	2.489	2.522	2.556
6	2.791	2.831	2.871	2.911	2.951	2.990	3.030	3.070
7	3.260	3.307	3.353	3.400	3.446	3.493	3.539	3.586
8	3.730	3.783	3.837	3.890	3.943	3.996	4.050	4.103
9	4.201	4.261	4.321	4.381	4.441	4.501	4.561	4.621
10	4.673	4.740	4.807	4.873	4.940	5.007	5.074	5.140
11	5.146	5.220	5.293	5.367	5.440	5.514	5.587	5.661
12	5.621	5.701	5.781	5.861	5.942	6.022	6.102	6.183
13	6.096	6.183	6.270	6.357	6.444	6.531	6.618	6.705
14	6.572	6.666	6.760	6.854	6.948	7.042	7.135	7.229
15	7.050	7.150	7.251	7.352	7.452	7.553	7.654	7.754
16	7.528	7.636	7.743	7.851	7.958	8.066	8.173	8.281
17	8.008	8.122	8.236	8.351	8.465	8.580	8.694	8.808
18	8.488	8.609	8.731	8.852	8.973	9.094	9.216	9.337
19	8.970	9.098	9.226	9.354	9.482	9.610	9.739	9.867
20	9.453	9.588	9.723	9.858	9.993	10.128	10.263	10.398

CONSTANT HUMIDITY

The following table shows the % humidity and the aqueous tension at the given temperature within a closed space when an excess of the substance indicated is in contact with a saturated aqueous solution of the given solid phase.

Solid phase	$t°C.$	% humidity	Aq. tension mm Hg
$H_2PO_4.\frac{1}{2}H_2O$	24	9	1.99
$KC_2H_3O_2$	168	13	738
$LiCl.H_2O$	20	15	2.60
$KC_2H_3O_2$	20	20	3.47
KF	100	22.9	174
$NaBr$	100	22.9	174
$NaCl, KNO_3$ and $NaNO_3$	16.39	30.49	4.23
$CaCl_2.6H_2O$	24.5	31	7.08
$CaCl_2.6H_2O$	20	32.3	5.61
$CaCl_2.6H_2O$	18.5	35	5.54
CrO_3	20	35	6.08
$CaCl_2.6H_2O$	10	38	3.47
$CaCl_2.6H_2O$	5	39.8	2.59
$Zn(NO_3)_2.6H_2O$	20	42	7.29
$K_2CO_3.2H_2O$	24.5	43	9.82
$K_2CO_3.2H_2O$	18.5	44	6.96
KNO_2	20	45	7.81
$KCNS$	20	47	8.16
NaI	100	50.4	383
$Ca(NO_3)_2.4H_2O$	24.5	51	11.6
$NaHSO_4.H_2O$	20	52	9.03
$Na_2Cr_2O_7.2H_2O$	20	52	9.03
$Mg(NO_3)_2.6H_2O$	24.5	52	11.9
$NaClO_3$	100	54	410
$Ca(NO_3)_2.4H_2O$	18.5	56	8.86
$Mg(NO_3)_2.6H_2O$	18.5	50	8.86
KI	100	56.2	427
$NaBr.2H_2O$	20	58	10.1
$Mg(C_2H_3O_2)_2.4H_2O$	20	65	11.3
$NaNO_2$	20	66	11.5
NH_4Cl and KNO_3	30	68.6	21.6
KBr	100	69.2	526
NH_4Cl and KNO_3	25	71.2	16.7
NH_4Cl and KNO_3	20	72.6	12.6
$NaClO_3$	20	75	13.0
$(NH_4)_2SO_4$	108	75	754
$NaC_2H_3O_2.3H_2O$	20	76	13.2
$H_2C_2O_4.2H_2O$	20	76	13.2
$Na_2S_2O_3.5H_2O$	20	78	13.5
NH_4Cl	20	79.5	13.8
NH_4Cl	25	79.3	18.6
NH_4Cl	30	77.5	24.4
$(NH_4)_2SO_4$	20	81	14.1
$(NH_4)_2SO_4$	25	81.1	19.1
$(NH_4)_2SO_4$	30	81.1	25.6
KBr	20	84	14.6
Tl_2SO_4	104.7	84.8	768
$KHSO_4$	20	86	14.9
$Na_2CO_3.10H_2O$	24.5	87	20.9
$BaCl_2.2H_2O$	21.5	88	20.1
K_2CrO_4	20	88	15.3
$Pb(NO_3)_2$	103.5	88.4	760
$ZnSO_4.7H_2O$	20	90	15.6
$Na_2CO_3.10H_2O$	18.5	92	14.6
$NaBrO_3$	20	92	16.0
K_2HPO_4	20	92	16.0
$NH_4H_2PO_4$	30	92.9	29.3
$NH_4H_2PO_4$	25	93	21.9
$Na_2SO_4.10H_2O$	20	93	16.1
$NH_4H_2PO_4$	20	93.1	16.2
$ZnSO_4.7H_2O$	5	94.7	6.10
$Na_2SO_3.7H_2O$	20	95	16.5
$Na_2HPO_4.12H_2O$	20	95	16.5
NaF	100	96.6	734
$Pb(NO_3)_2$	20	98	17.0
$CuSO_4.5H_2O$	20	98	17.0
$TlNO_3$	100.3	98.7	759
$TlCl$	100.1	99.7	761

CONSTANT HUMIDITY WITH SULFURIC ACID SOLUTIONS

The relative humidity and pressure of aqueous vapor of air in equilibrium conditions above aqueous solutions of sulfuric acid are given below.

Density of acid solution	Relative humidity	Vapor pressure at 20°C	Density of acid solution	Relative humidity	Vapor pressure at 20°C
1.00	100.0	17.4	1.30	58.3	10.1
1.05	97.5	17.0	1.35	47.2	8.3
1.10	93.9	16.3	1.40	37.1	6.5
1.15	88.8	15.4	1.50	18.8	3.3
1.20	80.5	14.0	1.60	8.5	1.5
1.25	70.4	12.2	1.70	3.2	0.6

For concentration of sulfuric acid solution refer to tables relating density to percent composition.

VELOCITY OF SOUND

Compiled by Gordon E. Becker, Bell Telephone Laboratories

The data for the Velocity of Sound in Various Materials were compiled from a variety of sources. For more extensive tables one is referred to the following books:

AIP Handbook, Smithsonian Tables.
Mason: Physical Acoustics and the Properties of Solids (1958).
Chalmers and Quarrell: Physical Examination of Metals (1960).
Mason: Piezoelectric Crystals and their Application to Ultrasonics (1950).
Bergmann: Der Ultraschall (Hirzel, 1954).

Definition of Terms: V_l = Velocity of plane longitudinal wave in bulk material
V_s = Velocity of plane transverse (shear) wave
V_{ext} = Velocity of longitudinal wave (extensional wave) in thin rods.

Solids

Substance	Density gm/cc	V_l m/sec	V_s m/sec	V_{ext} m/sec
Metals:				
Aluminum, rolled	2.7	6420	3040	5000
Beryllium	1.87	12890	8880	12870
Brass (70 Cu, 30 Zn)	8.6	4700	2110	3480
Copper, annealed	8.93	4760	2325	3810
Copper, rolled	8.93	5010	2270	3750
Duralumin 17S	2.79	6320	3130	5150
Gold, hard-drawn	19.7	3240	1200	2030
Iron, electrolytic	7.9	5950	3240	5120
Iron, Armco	7.85	5960	3240	5200
Lead, annealed	11.4	2160	700	1190
Lead, rolled	11.4	1960	690	1210
Magnesium, drawn, annealed	1.74	5770	3050	4940
Molybdenum	10.1	6250	3350	5400
Monel metal	8.90	5350	2720	4400
Nickel (unmagnetized)	8.85	5480	2990	4800
Nickel	8.9	6040	3000	4900
Platinum	21.4	3260	1730	2800
Silver	10.4	3650	1610	2680
Steel, mild	7.85	5960	3235	5200
Steel, 347 Stainless	7.9	5790	3100	5000
Steel (1% C)	7.84	5940	3220	5180
Steel (1% C, hardened)	7.84	5854	3150	5070
Tin, rolled	7.3	3320	1670	2730
Titanium	4.5	6070	3125	5080
Tungsten, annealed	19.3	5220	2890	4620
Tungsten, drawn	19.3	5410	2640	4320
Tungsten Carbide	13.8	6655	3980	6220
Zinc, rolled	7.1	4210	2440	3850
Various:				
Fused silica	2.2	5968	3764	5760
Glass, pyrex	2.32	5640	3280	5170
Glass, heavy silicate flint	3.88	3980	2380	3720
Glass, light borate crown	2.24	5100	2840	4540
Lucite	1.18	2680	1100	1840
Nylon 6-6	1.11	2620	1070	1800
Polyethylene	0.90	1950	540	920
Polystyrene	1.06	2350	1120	2240
Rubber, butyl	1.07	1830		
Rubber, gum	0.95	1550		
Rubber, neoprene	1.33	1600		
Brick	1.8			3650
Clay rock	2.2			3480
Cork	0.25			500
Marble	2.6			3810
Paraffin	0.9			1300
Tallow				390
Woods:				
Ash, along the fiber				4670
Ash, across the rings				1390
Ash, along the rings				1260
Beech, along the fiber				3340
Elm, along the fiber				4120
Maple, along the fiber				4110
Oak, along the fiber				3850

Liquids

Substance	Formula	Density gm/cc	Velocity at 25°C m/sec	$-\Delta v/\Delta t$ m/sec °C
Acetone	C_3H_6O	0.79	1174	4.5
Benzene	C_6H_6	0.870	1295	4.65
Carbon disulphide	CS_2	1.26	1149	—
Carbon tetrachloride	CCl_4	1.595	926	2.7
Castor oil	$C_{11}H_{10}O_{10}$	0.969	1477	3.6
Chloroform	$CHCl_3$	1.49	987	3.4
Ethanol	C_2H_6O	0.79	1207	4.0
Ethanol amide	C_2H_7NO	1.018	1724	3.4
Ethyl ether	$C_4H_{10}O$	0.713	985	4.87
Ethylene glycol	$C_2H_6O_2$	1.113	1658	2.1
Glycerol	$C_3H_8O_3$	1.26	1904	2.2
Kerosene		0.81	1324	3.6
Mercury	Hg	13.5	1450	—

Liquids (Continued)

Substance	Formula	Density gm/cc	Velocity at 25°C m/sec	$-\Delta v/\Delta t$ m/sec °C
Methanol	CH_4O	0.791	1103	3.2
Nitrobenzene	$C_6H_5NO_2$	1.20	1463	3.6
Turpentine	—	0.88	1255	—
Water (distilled)	H_2O	0.998	1496.7±.2	−2.4
Water (sea)	—	1.025	1531	−2.4
Xylene hexafluoride	$C_8H_4F_6$	1.37	879	—

Gases and Vapors

Substance	Formula	Density gm/liter	Velocity m/sec	$\Delta v/\Delta t$ m/sec °C
Gases (0°C)				
Air, dry		1.293	331.45	0.59
Ammonia	NH_3	0.771	415	
Argon	Ar	1.783	319	0.56
Carbon monoxide	CO	1.25	338	0.6
Carbon dioxide	CO_2	1.977	259	0.4
Chlorine	Cl_2	3.214	206	
Deuterium	D_2		890	1.6
Ethane (10°C)	C_2H_6	1.356	308	
Ethylene	C_2H_4	1.260	317	
Helium	He	0.178	965	0.8
Hydrogen	H_2	0.0899	1284	2.2
Hydrogen bromide	HBr	3.50	200	
Hydrogen chloride	HCl	1.639	296	
Hydrogen iodide	HI	5.66	157	
Hydrogen sulfide	H_2S	1.539	289	
Illuminating (Coal gas)			453	
Methane	CH_4	0.7168	430	
Neon	Ne	0.900	435	0.8
Nitric oxide (10°C)	NO	1.34	324	
Nitrogen	N_2	1.251	334	0.6
Nitrous oxide	N_2O	1.977	263	0.5
Oxygen	O_2	1.429	316	0.56
Sulfur dioxide	SO_2	2.927	213	0.47
Vapors (97.1°C)				
Acetone	C_3H_6O		239	0.32
Benzene	C_6H_6		202	0.3
Carbon tetrachloride	CCl_4		145	
Chloroform	$CHCl_3$		171	0.24
Ethanol	C_2H_6O		269	0.4
Ethyl ether	$C_4H_{10}O$		206	0.3
Methanol	CH_4O		335	0.46
Water vapor (134°C)	H_2O		494	

SOUND VELOCITY IN WATER ABOVE 212°F

By permission from the Acoustical Society of America, Volume 31 (1959) and J. C. McDade, D. R. Pardue, A. L. Gedrich and F. Vrataric.

Temperature °F	Velocity m/sec.	Velocity ft/sec.
186.8	1552	5092
200	1548	5079
210	1544	5066
220	1538	5046
230	1532	5026
240	1524	5000
250	1516	4974
260	1507	4944
270	1497	4911
280	1487	4879
290	1476	4843
300	1465	4806
310	1453	4767
320	1440	4724
330	1426	4678
340	1412	4633
350	1398	4587
360	1383	4537
370	1368	4488
380	1353	4439
390	1337	4386
400	1320	4331
410	1302	4272
420	1283	4209
430	1264	4147
440	1244	4081
450	1220	4010
460	1200	3940
470	1180	3880

SOUND VELOCITY IN WATER ABOVE 212°F (Continued)

Temperature °F	Velocity m/sec.	Velocity ft/sec.
480	1160	3800
490	1140	3730
500	1110	3650
510	1090	3570
520	1070	3500
530	1040	3410
540	1010	3320
550	980	3230

MUSICAL SCALES

EQUAL TEMPERED CHROMATIC SCALE $A_4 = 440$
American Standard pitch. Adopted by the American Standards Association in 1936

Note	Frequency	Note	Frequency	Note	Frequency	Note	Frequency
C_0	16.35	C_2	65.41	C_4	261.63	C_6	1046.50
$C\#_0$	17.32	$C\#_2$	69.30	$C\#_4$	277.18	$C\#_6$	1108.73
D_0	18.35	D_2	73.42	D_4	293.66	D_6	1174.66
$D\#_0$	19.45	$D\#_2$	77.78	$D\#_4$	311.13	$D\#_6$	1244.51
E_0	20.60	E_2	82.41	E_4	329.63	E_6	1318.51
F_0	21.83	F_2	87.31	F_4	349.23	F_6	1396.91
$F\#_0$	23.12	$F\#_2$	92.50	$F\#_4$	369.99	$F\#_6$	1479.98
G_0	24.50	G_2	98.00	G_4	392.00	G_6	1567.98
$G\#_0$	25.96	$G\#_2$	103.83	$G\#_4$	415.30	$G\#_6$	1661.22
A_0	27.50	A_2	110.00	A_4	440.00	A_6	1760.00
$A\#_0$	29.14	$A\#_2$	116.54	$A\#_4$	466.16	$A\#_6$	1864.66
B_0	30.87	B_2	123.47	B_4	493.88	B_6	1975.53
C_1	32.70	C_3	130.81	C_5	523.25	C_7	2093.00
$C\#_1$	34.65	$C\#_3$	138.59	$C\#_5$	554.37	$C\#_7$	2217.46
D_1	36.71	D_3	146.83	D_5	587.33	D_7	2349.32
$D\#_1$	38.89	$D\#_3$	155.56	$D\#_5$	622.25	$D\#_7$	2489.02
E_1	41.20	E_3	164.81	E_5	659.26	E_7	2637.02
F_1	43.65	F_3	174.61	F_5	698.46	F_7	2793.83
$F\#_1$	46.25	$F\#_3$	185.00	$F\#_5$	739.99	$F\#_7$	2959.96
G_1	49.00	G_3	196.00	G_5	783.99	G_7	3135.96
$G\#_1$	51.91	$G\#_3$	207.65	$G\#_5$	830.61	$G\#_7$	3322.44
A_1	55.00	A_3	220.00	A_5	880.00	A_7	3520.00
$A\#_1$	58.27	$A\#_3$	233.08	$A\#_5$	932.33	$A\#_7$	3729.31
B_1	61.74	B_3	246.94	B_5	987.77	B_7	3951.07
						C_8	4186.01

EQUAL TEMPERED CHROMATIC SCALE $A_4 = 435$
International Pitch, adopted 1891

Note	Frequency	Note	Frequency	Note	Frequency	Note	Frequency
C_0	16.17	C_2	64.66	C_4	258.65	C_6	1034.61
$C\#_0$	17.13	$C\#_2$	68.51	$C\#_4$	274.03	$C\#_6$	1096.13
D_0	18.15	D_2	72.58	D_4	290.33	D_6	1161.31
$D\#_0$	19.22	$D\#_2$	76.90	$D\#_4$	307.59	$D\#_6$	1230.37
E_0	20.37	E_2	81.47	E_4	325.88	E_6	1303.53
F_0	21.58	F_2	86.31	F_4	345.26	F_6	1381.04
$F\#_0$	22.86	$F\#_2$	91.45	$F\#_4$	365.79	$F\#_6$	1463.16
G_0	24.22	G_2	96.89	G_4	387.54	G_6	1550.16
$G\#_0$	25.66	$G\#_2$	102.65	$G\#_4$	410.59	$G\#_6$	1642.34
A_0	27.19	A_2	108.75	A_4	435.00	A_6	1740.00
$A\#_0$	28.80	$A\#_2$	115.22	$A\#_4$	460.87	$A\#_6$	1843.47
B_0	30.52	B_2	122.07	B_4	488.27	B_6	1953.08
C_1	32.33	C_3	129.33	C_5	517.31	C_7	2069.22
$C\#_1$	34.25	$C\#_3$	137.02	$C\#_5$	548.07	$C\#_7$	2192.26
D_1	36.29	D_3	145.16	D_5	580.66	D_7	2322.62
$D\#_1$	38.45	$D\#_3$	153.80	$D\#_5$	615.18	$D\#_7$	2460.73
E_1	40.74	E_3	162.94	E_5	651.76	E_7	2607.05
F_1	43.16	F_3	172.63	F_5	690.52	F_7	2762.08
$F\#_1$	45.72	$F\#_3$	182.89	$F\#_5$	731.58	$F\#_7$	2926.32
G_1	48.44	G_3	193.77	G_5	775.08	G_7	3100.33
$G\#_1$	51.32	$G\#_3$	205.29	$G\#_5$	821.17	$G\#_7$	3284.68
A_1	54.38	A_3	217.50	A_5	870.00	A_7	3480.00
$A\#_1$	57.61	$A\#_3$	230.43	$A\#_5$	921.73	$A\#_7$	3686.93
B_1	61.03	B_3	244.14	B_5	976.54	B_7	3906.17
						C_8	4138.44

SCIENTIFIC OR JUST SCALE $C_4 = 256$

Note	Frequency	Note	Frequency	Note	Frequency	Note	Frequency
C_0	16	C_2	64	C_4	256	C_6	1024
D_0	18	D_2	72	D_4	288	D_6	1152
E_0	20	E_2	80	E_4	320	E_6	1280
F_0	21.33	F_2	85.33	F_4	341.33	F_6	1365.33
G_0	24	G_2	96	G_4	384	G_6	1536
A_0	26.67	A_2	106.67	A_4	426.67	A_6	1706.67
B_0	30	B_2	120	B_4	480	B_6	1920
C_1	32	C_3	128	C_5	512	C_7	2048
D_1	36	D_3	144	D_5	576	D_7	2304
E_1	40	E_3	160	E_5	640	E_7	2560
F_1	42.67	F_3	170.67	F_5	682.67	F_7	2730.67
G_1	48	G_3	192	G_5	768	G_7	3072
A_1	53.33	A_3	213.33	A_5	853.33	A_7	3413.33
B_1	60	B_3	240	B_5	960	B_7	3840
						C_8	4096

ABSORPTION AND VELOCITY OF SOUND IN STILL AIR

The following data refer only to the temperature 20C (68F). They were abstracted from an extensive compilation prepared by L. B. Evans and H. E. Bass. The entire report, Tables of Absorption and Velocity of Sound in Still Air at 68F (20C), AD-738 576 is available from National Technical Information Service, U. S. Department of Commerce, 5285 Port Royal Road, Springfield, Va. 22151.

Frequency (Hz)	Absorption (dB/1000 ft)	Absorption (dB/Km)	Absorption (dB/sec)	Velocity (1000 ft/sec)
Relative Humidity = 0%				
20.	0.154	0.51	0.174	1.126892
40.	0.327	1.07	0.368	1.127013
50.	0.384	1.26	0.433	1.127050
63.	0.436	1.43	0.491	1.127085
100.	0.509	1.67	0.573	1.127131
200.	0.560	1.84	0.631	1.127161
400.	0.596	1.96	0.672	1.127169
630.	0.645	2.11	0.727	1.127171
800.	0.692	2.27	0.780	1.127172
1250.	0.861	2.82	0.970	1.127172
2000.	1.262	4.14	1.423	1.127173
4000.	2.696	8.84	3.039	1.127178
6300.	4.541	14.89	5.118	1.127182
10000.	8.013	26.28	9.032	1.127184
12500.	10.918	35.81	12.306	1.127186
16000.	15.901	52.15	17.923	1.127187
20000.	22.978	75.37	25.901	1.127187
40000.	81.405	267.01	91.759	1.127188
63000.	196.544	644.66	221.542	1.127188
80000.	314.677	1032.14	354.700	1.127188
Relative Humidity = 5%				
20.	0.031	0.10	0.034	1.126973
40.	0.074	0.24	0.083	1.126996
50.	0.092	0.30	0.104	1.127004
63.	0.114	0.37	0.129	1.127009
100.	0.179	0.59	0.202	1.127019
200.	0.449	1.47	0.506	1.127028
400.	1.451	4.76	1.635	1.127043
630.	3.211	10.53	3.619	1.127067
800.	4.774	15.66	5.380	1.127088
1250.	9.164	30.06	10.329	1.127147
2000.	15.175	49.77	17.106	1.127228
4000.	22.685	74.41	25.573	1.127321
6300.	26.245	86.08	29.587	1.127352
10000.	30.781	100.96	34.701	1.127365
12500.	34.306	112.52	38.676	1.127369
16000.	40.263	132.06	45.391	1.127372
20000.	48.653	159.58	54.850	1.127373
40000.	115.903	380.16	130.666	1.127378
63000.	242.070	793.99	272.905	1.127381
80000.	367.063	1203.97	413.821	1.127383
Relative Humidity = 10%				
20.	0.021	0.07	0.024	1.127167
40.	0.064	0.21	0.072	1.127183
50.	0.084	0.28	0.095	1.127191

ABSORPTION AND VELOCITY OF SOUND IN STILL AIR (*Continued*)

Frequency (Hz)	Absorption (dB/1000 ft)	Absorption (dB/Km)	Absorption (dB/sec)	Velocity (1000 ft/sec)
Relative Humidity = 10%				
63.	0.108	0.35	0.122	1.127199
100.	0.161	0.53	0.181	1.127213
200.	0.289	0.95	0.326	1.127225
400.	0.706	2.32	0.796	1.127230
630.	1.501	4.92	1.692	1.127234
800.	2.297	7.54	2.590	1.127238
1250.	5.155	16.91	5.811	1.127254
2000.	11.658	38.24	13.141	1.127287
4000.	31.023	101.76	34.975	1.127386
6300.	47.085	154.44	53.087	1.127462
10000.	61.578	201.98	69.431	1.127522
12500.	68.146	223.52	76.837	1.127540
16000.	76.231	250.04	85.955	1.127555
20000.	85.605	280.78	96.525	1.127563
40000.	151.938	498.36	171.321	1.127576
63000.	277.191	909.19	312.555	1.127581
80000.	403.662	1324.01	455.162	1.127583
Relative Humidity = 20%				
20.	0.013	0.04	0.014	1.127568
40.	0.045	0.15	0.051	1.127577
50.	0.066	0.22	0.074	1.127582
63.	0.093	0.30	0.105	1.127587
100.	0.164	0.54	0.185	1.127603
200.	0.285	0.93	0.321	1.127624
400.	0.476	1.56	0.537	1.127633
630.	0.789	2.59	0.890	1.127636
800.	1.103	3.62	1.244	1.127637
1250.	2.277	7.47	2.568	1.127640
2000.	5.310	17.42	5.987	1.127645
4000.	18.991	62.29	21.416	1.127670
6300.	41.151	134.98	46.406	1.127710
10000.	79.657	261.28	89.836	1.127778
12500.	103.004	337.85	116.170	1.127817
16000.	130.465	427.93	147.146	1.127859
20000.	155.809	511.05	175.736	1.127893
40000.	251.952	826.40	284.192	1.127960
63000.	382.062	1253.16	430.957	1.127977
80000.	508.369	1667.45	573.431	1.127982
Relative Humidity = 30%				
20.	0.009	0.03	0.010	1.127976
40.	0.034	0.11	0.038	1.127980
50.	0.051	0.17	0.057	1.127984
63.	0.075	0.25	0.085	1.127987
100.	0.151	0.50	0.170	1.127999
200.	0.309	1.01	0.349	1.128023
400.	0.484	1.59	0.546	1.128037
630.	0.682	2.24	0.770	1.128041
800.	0.868	2.85	0.979	1.128044
1250.	1.552	5.09	1.751	1.128045
2000.	3.333	10.93	3.760	1.128047
4000.	11.856	38.89	13.374	1.128056

ABSORPTION AND VELOCITY OF SOUND IN STILL AIR (*Continued*)

Frequency (Hz)	Absorption (dB/1000 ft)	Absorption (dB/Km)	Absorption (dB/sec)	Velocity (1000 ft/sec)
Relative Humidity = 30%				
6300.	27.626	90.61	31.164	1.128072
10000.	62.493	204.98	70.498	1.128105
12500.	89.659	294.08	101.148	1.128131
16000.	128.814	422.51	145.324	1.128166
20000.	171.847	563.66	193.879	1.128204
40000.	338.710	1110.97	382.172	1.128316
63000.	499.838	1639.47	563.998	1.128361
80000.	635.085	2083.08	716.614	1.128375
Relative Humidity = 40%				
20.	0.007	0.02	0.008	1.128386
40.	0.027	0.09	0.030	1.128388
50.	0.041	0.13	0.046	1.128390
63.	0.062	0.20	0.070	1.128392
100.	0.134	0.44	0.151	1.128402
200.	0.318	1.04	0.359	1.128424
400.	0.524	1.72	0.592	1.128443
630.	0.692	2.27	0.781	1.128449
800.	0.829	2.72	0.935	1.128451
1250.	1.309	4.29	1.477	1.128453
2000.	2.544	8.34	2.870	1.128456
4000.	8.523	27.96	9.618	1.128460
6300.	19.995	65.58	22.564	1.128467
10000.	47.390	155.44	53.478	1.128484
12500.	70.857	232.41	79.962	1.128499
16000.	108.308	355.25	122.228	1.128521
20000.	154.838	507.87	174.742	1.128549
40000.	380.371	1247.62	429.310	1.128663
63000.	596.091	1955.18	672.827	1.128733
80000.	753.514	2471.53	850.536	1.128758
Relative Humidity = 50%				
20.	0.006	0.02	0.006	1.128795
40.	0.022	0.07	0.025	1.128797
50.	0.034	0.11	0.038	1.128798
63.	0.052	0.17	0.058	1.128800
100.	0.117	0.38	0.132	1.128807
200.	0.313	1.03	0.353	1.128826
400.	0.563	1.85	0.636	1.128849
630.	0.734	2.41	0.828	1.128858
800.	0.851	2.79	0.961	1.128860
1250.	1.231	4.04	1.390	1.128862
2000.	2.176	7.14	2.457	1.128865
4000.	6.752	22.15	7.622	1.128867
6300.	15.643	51.31	17.659	1.128871
10000.	37.521	123.07	42.357	1.128881
12500.	57.009	186.99	64.357	1.128890
16000.	89.594	293.87	101.143	1.128903
20000.	132.719	435.32	149.830	1.128922
40000.	382.722	1255.33	432.101	1.129020
63000.	654.606	2147.11	739.115	1.129099
80000.	844.024	2768.40	953.016	1.129133

Frequency (Hz)	Absorption (dB/1000 ft)	Absorption (dB/Km)	Absorption (dB/sec)	Velocity (1000 ft/sec)
Relative Humidity = 60%				
20.	0.005	0.02	0.005	1.129207
40.	0.018	0.06	0.021	1.129208
50.	0.029	0.09	0.032	1.129209
63.	0.044	0.15	0.050	1.129210
100.	0.103	0.34	0.117	1.129215
200.	0.301	0.99	0.339	1.129232
400.	0.593	1.94	0.669	1.129254
630.	0.782	2.57	0.884	1.129266
800.	0.896	2.94	1.012	1.129269
1250.	1.223	4.01	1.381	1.129273
2000.	1.997	6.55	2.256	1.129275
4000.	5.711	18.73	6.449	1.129277
6300.	12.962	42.51	14.638	1.129279
10000.	31.050	101.84	35.064	1.129286
12500.	47.462	155.67	53.598	1.129292
16000.	75.544	247.78	85.312	1.129300
20000.	113.958	373.78	128.694	1.129313
40000.	364.443	1195.37	411.598	1.129389
63000.	677.023	2220.64	764.675	1.129467
80000.	899.912	2951.71	1016.458	1.129508
Relative Humidity = 70%				
20.	0.004	0.01	0.005	1.129618
40.	0.016	0.05	0.018	1.129619
50.	0.025	0.08	0.028	1.129619
63.	0.039	0.13	0.044	1.129620
100.	0.092	0.30	0.104	1.129623
200.	0.284	0.93	0.321	1.129638
400.	0.611	2.01	0.691	1.129662
630.	0.829	2.72	0.937	1.129673
800.	0.947	3.11	1.070	1.129678
1250.	1.250	4.10	1.412	1.129683
2000.	1.915	6.28	2.163	1.129685
4000.	5.056	16.58	5.712	1.129687
6300.	11.197	36.73	12.649	1.129689
10000.	26.624	87.33	30.077	1.129693
12500.	40.758	133.69	46.044	1.129697
16000.	65.246	214.01	73.708	1.129704
20000.	99.365	325.92	112.254	1.129712
40000.	339.153	1112.42	383.165	1.129770
63000.	673.667	2209.63	761.137	1.129842
80000.	924.481	3032.30	1044.556	1.129884
Relative Humidity = 80%				
20.	0.004	0.01	0.004	1.130030
40.	0.014	0.05	0.016	1.130030
50.	0.022	0.07	0.025	1.130031
63.	0.034	0.11	0.039	1.130032
100.	0.082	0.27	0.093	1.130034
200.	0.267	0.88	0.302	1.130047
400.	0.620	2.03	0.701	1.130069
630.	0.870	2.85	0.983	1.130082
800.	0.998	3.27	1.128	1.130088

ABSORPTION AND VELOCITY OF SOUND IN STILL AIR (*Continued*)

Frequency (Hz)	Absorption (dB/1000 ft)	Absorption (dB/Km)	Absorption (dB/sec)	Velocity (1000 ft/sec)
Relative Humidity = 80%				
1250.	1.293	4.24	1.461	1.130094
2000.	1.887	6.19	2.132	1.130096
4000.	4.626	15.17	5.228	1.130098
6300.	9.976	32.72	11.274	1.130100
10000.	23.466	76.97	26.519	1.130102
12500.	35.896	117.74	40.566	1.130106
16000.	57.588	188.89	65.081	1.130110
20000.	88.144	289.11	99.612	1.130116
40000.	313.525	1028.36	354.334	1.130161
63000.	655.282	2149.33	740.615	1.130223
80000.	925.566	3035.86	1046.134	1.130264
Relative Humidity = 90%				
20.	0.003	0.01	0.004	1.130443
40.	0.013	0.04	0.014	1.130443
50.	0.019	0.06	0.022	1.130444
63.	0.031	0.10	0.035	1.130444
100.	0.074	0.24	0.084	1.130446
200.	0.250	0.82	0.283	1.130457
400.	0.621	2.04	0.702	1.130478
630.	0.903	2.96	1.021	1.130493
800.	1.045	3.43	1.182	1.130498
1250.	1.344	4.41	1.520	1.130505
2000.	1.892	6.21	2.139	1.130508
4000.	4.337	14.22	4.903	1.130511
6300.	9.099	29.84	10.286	1.130512
10000.	21.133	69.32	23.891	1.130514
12500.	32.258	105.81	36.468	1.130516
16000.	51.762	169.78	58.518	1.130520
20000.	79.424	260.51	89.791	1.130526
40000.	290.117	951.58	327.995	1.130561
63000.	629.701	2065.42	711.948	1.130612
80000.	911.286	2989.02	1030.346	1.130651
Relative Humidity = 100%				
20.	0.003	0.01	0.003	1.130856
40.	0.011	0.04	0.013	1.130856
50.	0.018	0.06	0.020	1.130857
63.	0.028	0.09	0.031	1.130857
100.	0.068	0.22	0.076	1.130858
200.	0.234	0.77	0.265	1.130868
400.	0.616	2.02	0.696	1.130888
630.	0.928	3.05	1.050	1.130902
800.	1.087	3.57	1.230	1.130909
1250.	1.399	4.59	1.582	1.130917
2000.	1.917	6.29	2.168	1.130921
4000.	4.140	13.58	4.682	1.130924
6300.	8.451	27.72	9.557	1.130925
10000.	19.357	63.49	21.891	1.130926
12500.	29.461	96.63	33.318	1.130929
16000.	47.227	154.90	53.410	1.130931
20000.	72.538	237.93	82.036	1.130935
40000.	269.598	884.28	304.905	1.130963
63000.	601.714	1973.62	680.543	1.131007
80000.	888.113	2913.01	1004.492	1.131042

VELOCITY OF SOUND IN DRY AIR

Data in this table apply only to dry air. These data have been calculated with air being treated as a perfect gas.

Temp °C	0 m sec⁻¹	1 m sec⁻¹	2 m sec⁻¹	3 m sec⁻¹	4 m sec⁻¹	5 m sec⁻¹	6 m sec⁻¹	7 m sec⁻¹	8 m sec⁻¹	9 m sec⁻¹
60	366.05	366.60	367.14	367.69	368.24	368.78	369.33	369.87	370.42	370.96
50	360.51	361.07	361.62	362.18	362.74	363.29	363.84	364.39	364.95	365.50
40	354.89	355.46	356.02	356.58	357.15	357.71	358.27	358.83	359.39	359.95
30	349.18	349.75	350.33	350.90	351.47	352.04	352.62	353.19	353.75	354.32
20	343.37	343.95	344.54	345.12	345.70	346.29	346.87	347.44	348.02	348.60
10	337.46	338.06	338.65	339.25	339.84	340.43	341.02	341.61	342.20	342.78
0	331.45	332.06	332.66	333.27	333.87	334.47	335.07	335.67	336.27	336.87
−10	325.33	324.71	324.09	323.47	322.84	322.22	321.60	320.97	320.34	319.72
−20	319.09	318.45	317.82	317.19	316.55	315.92	315.28	314.64	314.00	313.36
−30	312.72	312.08	311.43	310.78	310.14	409.49	308.84	308.19	307.53	306.88
−40	306.22	305.56	304.91	304.25	303.58	302.92	302.26	301.59	300.92	300.25
−50	299.58	298.91	298.24	297.56	296.89	296.21	295.53	294.85	294.16	293.48
−60	292.79	292.11	291.42	290.73	290.03	289.34	288.64	287.95	287.25	286.55
−70	285.84	285.14	284.43	283.73	283.02	282.30	281.59	280.88	280.16	279.44
−80	278.72	278.00	277.27	276.55	275.82	275.09	274.36	273.62	272.89	272.15
−90	271.41	270.67	269.92	269.18	268.43	267.68	266.93	266.17	265.42	264.66

SPARK-GAP VOLTAGES

Based on results of the American Institute of Electric Engineers
Air at 760 mm, 25° C.

Peak voltage, kilovolts	Diameter of spherical electrodes, cm				Needle points
	2.5	5	10	25	
	Length of spark gap cm				
5	0.13	0.15	0.15	0.16	0.42
10	0.27	0.29	0.30	0.32	0.85
15	0.42	0.44	0.46	0.48	1.30
20	0.58	0.60	0.62	0.64	1.75
25	0.76	0.77	0.78	0.81	2.20
30	0.95	0.94	0.95	0.98	2.69
35	1.17	1.12	1.12	1.15	3.20
40	1.41	1.30	1.29	1.32	3.81
45	1.68	1.50	1.47	1.49	4.49
50	2.00	1.71	1.65	1.66	5.20
60	2.82	2.17	2.02	2.01	6.81
70	4.05	2.68	2.42	2.37	8.81
80	......	3.26	2.84	2.74	11.1
90	......	3.94	3.28	3.11	13.3
100	......	4.77	3.75	3.49	15.5
110	......	5.79	4.25	3.88	17.7
120	......	7.07	4.78	4.28	19.8
130	......	......	5.35	4.69	22.0
140	......	......	5.97	5.10	24.1
150	......	......	6.64	5.52	26.1
160	......	......	7.37	5.95	28.1
170	......	......	8.16	6.39	30.1
180	......	......	9.03	6.84	32.0
190	......	......	10.0	7.30	33.9
200	......	......	11.1	7.76	35.7
210	......	......	12.3	8.24	37.6
220	......	......	13.7	8.73	39.5
230	......	......	15.3	9.24	41.4
240	......	......	......	9.76	43.3
250	......	......	......	10.3	45.2
300	......	......	......	13.3	54.7

CORRECTIONS FOR TEMPERATURE AND PRESSURE

Values found in the above table may be corrected for temperature and pressure by multiplying the values given by the appropriate correction factor found below:

Temp. °C.	Pressure mm			
	720	740	760	780
0	1.04	1.06	1.09	1.12
10	1.00	1.02	1.05	1.08
20	0.96	0.99	1.02	1.04
30	0.93	0.96	0.98	1.01

DIELECTRIC CONSTANTS
Dielectric Constants of Pure Liquids

The values listed in the following table were obtained from National Bureau of Standards Circular 514
The dielectric constants are intended to be the limiting values at low frequencies. the so-called static values. Temperature is the only variable considered explicitly. Usually pressure is atmospheric or insignificantly different with respect to its effect on the dielectric constant. Where data are listed above the normal boiling point, the pressure corresponds to the vapor pressure of the liquid unless otherwise noted in the footnote.

Symbols

ϵ = dielectric constant ($\epsilon_{vacuum} = 1$)
t = temperature, Centigrade (°C)
T = temperature, Absolute (°K)
$a = -d\epsilon/dt$
$\alpha = -d \log_{10} \epsilon/dt$
t_1, t_2 = the limits of temperature between which a or α is considered applicable
mp = melting point
bp = boiling point
f = frequency of alternating current in cycles per second

STANDARD LIQUIDS

		$\epsilon_{20°C}$	$\epsilon_{25°C}$	a (or α)*
C_6H_{12}	Cyclohexane	2.023	2.015	0.0016
CCl_4	Carbon tetrachloride	2.238	2.228	.0020
C_6H_6	Benzene	2.284	2.274	.0020
C_6H_5Cl	Chlorobenzene	5.708	5.621	.00133(α)
$C_2H_4Cl_2$	1,2-Dichloroethane	10.65	10.36	.00240(α)
CH_4O	Methanol	33.62	32.63	.00260(α)

DIELECTRIC CONSTANTS
Dielectric Constants of Pure Liquids (Continued)

STANDARD LIQUIDS (Continued)

		$\epsilon_{20°C}$	$\epsilon_{25°C}$	a (or α)*
$C_6H_5NO_2$	Nitrobenzene	35.74	34.82	.00225(α)
H_2O	Water	80.37	78.54	.00200(α)
H_2	Hydrogen		1.228 at 20.4°K	.0034
O_2	Oxygen		1.507 at 80.0°K	.0024

* The values of a or α given in this table are derived from data in the vicinity of room temperature and are not necessarily identical with the values listed in the following sections of this table. They may be used to calculate values of dielectric constant between 15° and 30°C without introducing significant error.

INORGANIC LIQUIDS

	Substance	ϵ	t°C	a (or α) $\times 10^2$	Range t_1, t_2
A	Argon	1.53₈	−191	0.34	−191,−184
$AlBr_3$	Aluminum bromide	3.38	100	0.33	100,240
AsH_3	Arsine	2.50	−100	0.43	−116,−72
BBr_3	Boron bromide	2.58	0	0.28	−70,80
Br_2	Bromine	3.09	20	0.7	0,50
CO_2	Carbon dioxide	1.60ᶜ	20		
Cl_2	Chlorine	2.10₁	−50	0.31	−65,−33
		1.91	14	0.32	−22,14
		1.7₃	77		
		1.5₄	142		
D_2	Deuterium	1.277	20°K	0.4	18.8,21.2°K
D_2O	Deuterium oxide	78.25	25	(d)	0.4,98
F_2	Fluorine	1.54	−202	0.19	−216,−190
$GeCl_4$	Germanium tetrachloride	2.43₀	25	0.240	0,55
HBr	Hydrogen bromide	7.00	−85	0.26(α)	−85,−70
HCl	Hydrogen chloride	6.35	−15	0.288(α)	−85,−15
		12.	−113		
		4.6	28		
HF	Hydrogen fluoride	17₅.	−73		
		13₄.	−42		
		11₁.	−27		
		84.	0		
HI	Hydrogen iodide	3.39	−50	0.8	−51,−37
H_2	Hydrogen	1.228	20.4°K	0.34	14,21°K
H_2O	Water	78.54	25	(e)	0,100
		34.5₉	200	(v)	100,370
H_2O_2	Hydrogen peroxide	84.2	0	(z)	−30,20
H_2S	Hydrogen sulfide	9.26	−85.5		
		9.05	−78.5		
He	Helium	1.055₅	2.06°K		
		1.055₉	2.30f		
		1.055₃	2.63		
		1.053₉	3.09		
		1.051₈	3.58		
		1.048	4.19		
I_2	Iodine	6.8	400	....	$\epsilon_r = 13.3 − 0.016$ (± 0.002) T
		11.₇	140		
		13.₀	168		
NH_3	Ammonia	25.	−77.7	....	
		22.4	−33.4	....	
		18.9	5	....	
		17.8	15		
		16.9	25		
		16.3	35		
$NOBr$	Nitrosyl bromide	13.₄	15	....	
$NOCl$	Nitrosyl chloride	18.₂	12	....	
N_2	Nitrogen	1.454	−203	0.29	−210,−195
N_2H_4	Hydrazine	52.₉	20	0.21(α)	0,25
N_2O	Dinitrogen oxide	1.97	−90		
		1.61	0	0.6	−6,14
N_2O_4	Dinitrogen tetroxide	2.5₅ᵇ	15	....	
O_2	Oxygen	1.507	−193	0.24	−218,−183
P	Phosphorus	4.10	34	....	
		4.06	46		
		3.86	85		
PCl_3	Phosphorus trichloride	3.43	25	0.84	17,60
PCl_5	Phosphorus pentachloride	2.8₅	160	....	
$POCl_3$	Phosphoryl chloride	13.₃	22	....	
$PSCl_3$	Thiophosphoryl chloride	5.8	22	....	
$PbCl_4$	Lead tetrachloride	2.78	20	....	
S	Sulfur	3.52	118	(g)	
		3.48	231		
$SOBr_2$	Thionyl bromide	9.06	20	3.0	at 20

ᶜ At pressure of 50 atmospheres.
ᵈ $\epsilon = 78.25[1 − 4.617(10^{-3})(t − 25) + 1.22(10^{-5})(t − 25)^2 − 2.7(10^{-8})(t − 25)^3]$; av. dev. ± 0.04%.
ᵇ $f = 3.6 \times 10^8$ cycles/sec.
ᵉ $\epsilon = 78.54[1 − 4.579(10^{-3})(t − 25) + 1.19(10^{-5})(t − 25)^2 − 2.8(10^{-8})(t − 25)^3]$; av. dev. ± 0.03%.
f Liquid transition and discontinuity in variation of dielectric constant with temperature at 2.295°K.
g Graphical data in the range 118°–350°C show a minimum near 160° and a broad maximum near 200°.
v $\epsilon = 5321/T + 233.76 − 0.9297T + 0.001417T^2 − 0.00000082292T^3$.
z $\epsilon = 84.2 − 0.62t + 0.0032t^2$.

DIELECTRIC CONSTANTS
Dielectric Constants of Pure Liquids (Continued)

INORGANIC LIQUIDS (Continued)						ORGANIC LIQUIDS (Continued)					
	Substance	ϵ	$t°C$	a (or α) $\times 10^2$	Range t_1, t_2		Substance	ϵ	$t°C$	a (or α) $\times 10^2$	Range t_1, t_2
$SOCl_2$	Thionyl chloride	9.25	20	3.9	at 20	$(C_2H_6OSi)_n$					
SO_2	Sulfur dioxide	17.6	−20	0.287(α)	−65,−15	$n = 4$	Octamethylcyclotetra-siloxane	2.39	20		
		15.0$_8$	0			$n = 5$	Decamethylcyclopenta-siloxane	2.50	20		
		14.$_1$	20	7.7	14,140	$n = 6$	Dodecamethylcyclohexa-siloxane	2.59	20		
		2.1$_0$	154^h			$n = 7$	Tetradecamethylcyclo-heptasiloxane	2.68	20		
SO_3	Sulfur trioxide	3.11	18			$n = 8$	Hexadecamethylcyclo-octasiloxane	2.74	20		
S_2Cl_2	Sulfur monochloride	4.79	15	0.146(α)	−41,15	$C_2H_6O_2$	Glycol	37.7	25	0.224(α)	20,100
SO_2Cl_2	Sulfuryl chloride	10.$_0$	22			C_2H_7N	Dimethylamine	6.32	0		
$SbCl_5$	Antimony pentachloride	3.22	20	0.46	2,47			5.26	25		
Se	Selenium	5.40	250	0.25	237,301		C_3				
$SiCl_4$	Silicon tetrachloride	2.4$_0$	16			C_3H_6	Propene	1.87$_5$	20		
$SnCl_4$	Tin tetrachloride	2.87	20	0.30	−30,20			1.79$_5$	45		
$TiCl_4$	Titanium tetrachloride	2.80	20	0.20	−20,20			1.69$_0$	65		
								1.53$_0$	85		
								1.44$_1$	90		
								1.33$_1$	91.9^h		
	ORGANIC LIQUIDS					C_3H_6O	2-Propen-1-ol (Allyl alcohol)	21.$_6$	15		
							Acetone	20.7$_0$	25	0.205(α)	−60,40
								17.7	56		
	C_1						Propionaldehyde	18.$_6$^{a}	17		
CCl_4	Carbon tetrachloride	2.238	20	0.200	−10,60	$C_3H_6O_2$	Propionic acid	3.30	10		
CN_4O_8	Tetranitromethane	2.52$_1$	25					3.44	40		
CO_2	Carbon dioxide	1.60$_4$^{c}	0				Ethyl formate	7.1$_6$	25		
CS_2	Carbon disulfide	2.641	20	0.268	−90,130		Methyl acetate	6.68	25	2.2	25,40
		3.001	−110			$C_3H_6O_3$	dl-Lactic acid	22.	17		
		2.19	180			$C_3H_7NO_2$	Ethyl carbamate (Urethan)	14.2	50	5.2	50,70
$CHBr_3$	Bromoform	4.39	20	0.105(α)	10,70	C_3H_8	Propane	1.61	0	0.20	−90,15
$CHCl_3$	Chloroform	1.806	20	0.160(α)	0,50	C_3H_8O	1-Propanol	20.1	25	0.293(α)	20,90
		6.76	−60					38.	−80		
		6.12	−40					29.	−34		
		5.61	−20				2-Propanol	18.3	25	0.310(α)	20,70
		3.7$_1$	100			$C_3H_8O_2$	1,2-Propanediol	32.$_0$	20	0.27(α)	at 20
		3.3$_2$	140				1,3-Propanediol	35.$_0$	20	0.23(α)	at 20
		2.9$_3$	180			$C_3H_8O_3$	Glycerol	42.5	25	0.208(α)	0,100
CHN	Hydrocyanic acid	158.$_1$	0	(^{i})	−13,18	C_3H_9N	Isopropylamine	5.5^b	20		
		114.$_9$	20	0.63(α)	18,26		Trimethylamine	2.44	25	0.52	0,25
CH_2Br_2	Dibromomethane	7.77	10				C_4				
		6.68	40			$C_4H_2O_3$	Maleic anhydride	50.^{a}	60		
CH_2Cl_2	Dichloromethane	9.08	20	(^{i})	−80,25	C_4H_4O	Furan	2.95	25		
CH_2I_2	Diiodomethane	5.32	25			C_4H_4S	Thiophene	2.76	16		
CH_2O_2	Formic acid	58.$_5$^{a}	16			C_4H_5N	Pyrrole	7.48	18		
CH_3Br	Bromomethane	9.82	0	(^{k})	−80,0	C_4H_5NS	Allyl isothiocyanate	17.$_2$^{b}	18		
CH_3Cl	Chloromethane	12.6	−20	(^{l})	−70,−20	C_4H_6O	Vinyl ether	3.94	20		
CH_3I	Iodomethane	7.00	20	(^{m})	−70,40	$C_4H_6O_3$	Acetic anhydride	22.$_4$	1		
CH_3NO	Formamide	109.	20	72.	18,25			20.$_7$	19		
CH_4	Methane	1.70	−173	0.2	−181,−159	C_4H_8O	2-Butanone	18.5$_1$	20	0.207(α)	−60,60
CH_4O	Methanol	32.63	25	0.264(α)	5,55		Butyraldehyde	13.4	26		
		64.	−113					10.8	77		
		54.	−80			$C_4H_8O_2$	Butyric acid	2.97	20	−0.23	10,70
		40.	−20				Isobutyric acid	2.71	10		
CH_5N	Methylamine	11.4	−10	0.26(α)	−30,−10			2.73	40		
		9.4	25				Propyl formate	7.7$_2$^{a}	19		
	C_2						Ethyl acetate	6.02	25	1.5	at 25
C_2HCl_3	Trichloroethylene	3.4$_2$	ca 16					5.3$_0$	77		
C_2HCl_3O	Chloral	4.9$_4$	20	0.17(α)	15,45		Methyl propionate	5.5^n	19		
		7.6	−40			$C_4H_8O_2$	1,4-Dioxane	2.209	25	0.170	20,50
		4.2	62			C_4H_9NO	Morpholine	7.33	25		
$C_2HCl_3O_2$	Trichloroacetic acid	4.6	60			$C_4H_{10}O$	1-Butanol	17.8	20	0.300(α)	−40,20
$C_2H_2Br_2$	cis-1,2-Dibromoethylene	7.7$_2$	0					17.1	25	0.335(α)	25,70
		7.0$_8$	25					8.2	118		
	$trans$-1,2-Dibromoethylene	2.9$_7$	0				2-Methyl-1-propanol	17.7	25	0.377(α)	20,90
		2.8$_8$	25					34.	−80		
$C_2H_2Br_4$	1,1,2,2-Tetrabromoethane	8.6	3					26.	−34		
		7.0	22				2-Butanol	15.8	25		
$C_2H_2Cl_2$	1,1-Dichloroethylene	4.6$_7$	16				2-Methyl-2-propanol	10.9	30		
	cis-1,2-Dichloroethylene	9.20	25					8.49	50		
	$trans$-1,2-Dichloroethylene	2.14	25					6.89	70		
$C_2H_2Cl_2O_2$	Dichloroacetic acid	8.2	22				Ethyl ether	4.335	20	2.0	at 20
		7.8	61					4.34^z	20	0.217(α)	−40,30
C_2H_3ClO	Acetyl chloride	16.$_9$	2					10.4	−116		
		15.$_8$	22					3.97	40	0.170(α)	40,140
$C_2H_3ClO_2$	Chloroacetic acid	12.3	60	2.	60,80			2.1$_2$	180		
C_2H_4O	Ethylene oxide	13.$_9$	−1					1.8$_9$	190		
	Acetaldehyde	21.$_8$^{a}	10					1.5$_3$	193.3^h		
$C_2H_4O_2$	Acetic acid	6.15	20								
		6.29	40								
		6.62	70								
	Methyl formate	8.5	20	5.	0,20						
C_2H_5ClO	2-Chloroethanol	25.8	25								
	(Ethylene chlorohydrin)	13.$_2$	132								
C_2H_5NO	Acetamide	59.$_a$	83								
$C_2H_5NO_2$	Nitroethane	28.0$_6$	30	11.4	30,35						
C_2H_6O	Ethanol	24.30	25								
		24.3^z	25	0.270(α)	−5,70						
		41.0^z	−60	0.297(α)	−110,−20						
	Methyl ether	5.02	25	2.38	25,100						
		2.97	110								
		2.64	120								
		2.37	125								
		2.26	126.$_1$								
		1.90	127.6^g								

^{a} $f = 4 \times 10^8$ cycles/sec.
^{b} $f = 3.6 \times 10^8$ cycles/sec.
^{c} At pressure of 50 atmospheres.
^{h} Critical temperature.
^{i} $\log_{10} \epsilon = 2.199 - 0.0079t + 0.00005t^2$.
^{j} $\epsilon = (3320/T) - 2.24$.
^{k} $\epsilon = (3320/T) - 2.34$.
^{l} $\epsilon = 12.6 - 0.061(t + 20) + 0.0005(t + 20)^2$.
^{m} $\epsilon = (2160/T) - 0.39$.
^{n} $f = 5 \times 10^8$ cycles/sec.
^{p} Critical temperature = 120.9°C.
^{t} Mixture of cis-$trans$ isomers.
^{z} Value chosen to conform with the remainder of the tabulated data for this substance.

ORGANIC LIQUIDS (Continued)

	Substance	ϵ	$t°C$	a (or α) $\times 10^2$	Range t_1,t_2
$C_6H_{10}Zn$	Diethyl zinc	2.5_5	20		
C_5					
$C_5H_4O_2$	Furfural	$46._9$	1		
		$41._9$	20		
		$34._9$	50		
C_5H_5N	Pyridine	12.3	25		
		9.4	116		
C_5H_8	1,3-Pentadiene[f]	2.32	25		
	2-Methyl-1,3-butadiene (Isoprene)	2.10	25	0.24	$-75,25$
$C_5H_8O_2$	2,4-Pentanedione (Acetylacetone)	25.7^a	20		
C_5H_{10}	1-Pentene	2.100	20		
	2-Methyl-1-butene	2.197	20		
	Cyclopentane	1.965	20		
	Ethylcyclopropane	1.933	20		
$C_5H_{10}O$	2-Pentanone	15.4_5	20	$0.195(\alpha)$	$-40,80$
		22.0	-60		
	3-Pentanone	17.0_0	20	$0.225(\alpha)$	0,80
		19.4	-20		
		19.8	-40		
$C_5H_{10}O_2$	Valeric acid	2.6_6	20		
	Isovaleric acid	2.6_4	20		
	Methyl butyrate	5.6^n	20		
$C_5H_{11}N$	Piperidine	5.8^b	22		
C_5H_{12}	n-Pentane	1.844	20	0.160	$-50,30$
		2.011	-90		
		1.984	-70		
	2-Methylbutane	1.843	20		
$C_5H_{12}O$	1-Pentanol	13.9	25	$0.23(\alpha)$	15,35
	3-Methyl-1-butanol	14.7	25		
		5.8_2	132		
	2-Methyl-2-butanol	5.82	25		
C_6					
$C_6H_4Cl_2$	o-Dichlorobenzene	9.93	25	$0.194(\alpha)$	0,50
	m-Dichlorobenzene	5.04	25	$0.120(\alpha)$	0,50
	p-Dichlorobenzene	2.41	50	0.18	50,80
C_6H_5Br	Bromobenzene	5.40	25	$0.115(\alpha)$	0,70
C_6H_5Cl	Chlorobenzene	5.708	20		
		5.621	25		
		5.71	20	$0.130(\alpha)$	0,80
		7.28	-50		
		6.30	-20		
		4.21	130		
C_6H_5ClO	o-Chlorophenol	6.31	25	2.7	25,58
	p-Chlorophenol	9.47	55	3.7	55,65
C_6H_5I	Iodobenzene	4.63	20		
$C_6H_5NO_2$	Nitrobenzene	34.82	25	$0.225(\alpha)$	10,80
		20.8	130	$0.164(\alpha)$	130,211
		24.9	90		
		22.7	110		
$C_6H_5NO_3$	o-Nitrophenol	$17._5$	50	6.4	50,60
C_6H_6	Benzene	2.284	20	0.200	10,60
		2.073	129		
		1.966	182		
C_6H_6BrN	m-Bromoaniline	13.0^n	19		
C_6H_6ClN	m-Chloroaniline	13.4^n	19		
$C_6H_6N_2O_2$	o-Nitroaniline	$34._5$	90	3.	90,110
	p-Nitroaniline	$56._2$	160	6.	160,180
C_6H_6O	Phenol	9.78	60	$0.32(\alpha)$	40,70
C_6H_7N	Aniline	6.89	20	$0.148(\alpha)$	0,50
		5.93	70		
		4.54	184.6		
	2-Methylpyridine (α-Picoline)	9.8^b	20		
$C_6H_8N_2$	Phenylhydrazine	7.2	23		
C_6H_{10}	Cyclohexene	2.220	25		
		2.6_0	-105		
$C_6H_{10}O$	Cyclohexanone	18.3	20		
		$19._9$	-40		
$C_6H_{10}O_2$	Ethyl acetoacetate	15.7^a	22		
C_6H_{12}	Cyclohexane	2.023	20	0.160	10,60
	Methylcyclopentane	1.985	20		
	Ethylcyclobutane	1.965	20		
$C_6H_{12}O$	Cyclohexanol	15.0	25	$0.437(\alpha)$	20,66
		7.2_4	100		
		4.8_5	150		
$C_6H_{12}O_2$	Butyl acetate	5.01	20	1.4	20,40
		6.8_5	-73		
	Ethyl butyrate	5.10	18	1.0	at 20
$C_6H_{12}O_3$	Paraldehyde	13.9	25		
		6.29	128		
C_6H_{14}	n-Hexane	1.890	20	0.155	$-10,50$
		2.044	-90		
		1.990	-50		
$C_6H_{14}O$	1-Hexanol	13.3	25	$0.35(\alpha)$	15,35
		8.5_5	75		
	Propyl ether	3.3_9	26		
	Isopropyl ether	3.88	25	1.8	0,25
$C_6H_{15}Al$	Triethyl aluminum	2.9	20		
$C_6H_{15}N$	Dipropylamine	2.9^b	21		
	Triethylamine	2.42	25		

ORGANIC LIQUIDS (Continued)

	Substance	ϵ	$t°C$	a (or α) $\times 10^2$	Range t_1,t_2
$C_6H_{15}N$	Dipropylamine	2.9^b	21		
	Triethylamine	2.42	25		
$C_6H_{18}OSi_2$	$(CH_3)_3Si[OSi(CH_3)_2]_nCH_3$				
$n=1$	Hexamethyldisiloxane	2.17	20		
$n=2$	Octamethyltrisiloxane	2.30	20		
$n=3$	Decamethyltetrasiloxane	2.39	20		
$n=4$	Dodecamethylpentasiloxane	2.46	20		
$n=5$	Tetradecamethylhexasiloxane	2.50	20		
$n=66^w$		2.72	20		
C_7					
C_7H_5ClO	Benzoyl chloride	29.	0		
		23.	20		
C_7H_5NO	Phenyl isocyanate	8.8^b	20		
C_7H_5NS	Phenyl isothiocyanate	10.4^a	20		
C_7H_6O	Benzaldehyde	$19._7$	0		
		$17._8$	20		
$C_7H_6O_2$	Salicylaldehyde	$17._1$	30	7.	30,40
C_7H_7Br	o-Bromotoluene	4.28	58		
	m-Bromotoluene	5.36	58		
	p-Bromotoluene	5.49	58		
C_7H_7Cl	o-Chlorotoluene	4.45	20		
		4.16	58		
	m-Chlorotoluene	5.55	20		
		5.04	58		
	p-Chlorotoluene	6.08	20		
		5.55	58		
	α-Chlorotoluene	7.0	13		
$C_7H_7NO_2$	o-Nitrotoluene	27.4	20	15.	at 20
		$21._6$	58		
		11.8	222		
	m-Nitrotoluene	$23._8$	20		
		$21._9$	58		
	p-Nitrotoluene	$22._2$	58	$0.0455(\alpha)$	$-90,0$
C_7H_8	Toluene	2.438	0	0.243	0,90
		2.379	25		
		2.15_7	127		
		2.04_2	181		
C_7H_8O	Benzyl alcohol	13.1	20		
		9.47	70		
		6.6	132	11.	25,30
	o-Cresol	11.5	25	$0.41(\alpha)$	15,50
	m-Cresol	11.8	25		
	p-Cresol	9.9_1	58		
C_7H_9N	o-Toluidine	6.34	18		
		5.71	58		
		4.00	200		
	m-Toluidine	5.95	18		
		5.45	58		
	p-Toluidine	4.98	54		
	N-Methylaniline	5.97	22		
	1-Heptene	2.05	20		
C_8					
C_8H_8	Styrene (Phenylethylene)	2.43	25		
		2.32	75		
	Acetophenone	17.39	25	4.	at 25
		8.64	202		
$C_8H_8O_2$	Phenyl acetate	5.23	20	0.7	at 20
	Methyl benzoate	6.59	20	$0.14(\alpha)$	20,50
$C_8H_8O_3$	Methyl salicylate	9.41	30	3.1	30,40
C_8H_{10}	Ethylbenzene	2.412	20		
	o-Xylene	2.568	20	0.266	$-20,130$
	m-Xylene	2.374	20	0.195	$-40,180$
	p-Xylene	2.270	20	0.160	20,130
C_8H_{18}	n-Octane	1.948	20	0.130	$-50,50$
		1.879	70		
		1.817	110		
	2,2,3-Trimethylpentane	1.96	20		
	2,2,4-Trimethylpentane	1.940	20	0.142	$-100,100$
$C_8H_{18}O$	1-Octanol	10.3_4	20	$0.410(\alpha)$	20,60
$C_8H_{20}O_4Si$	Tetraethyl silicate	4.1^b	ca 20		
C_9					
C_9H_7N	Quinoline	9.00	25		
		5.05	238		
	Isoquinoline	10.7	25		
C_9H_8O	Cinnamaldehyde	16.9	24		
$C_9H_{10}O_2$	Benzyl acetate	5.1^n	21		
	Ethyl benzoate	6.02	20	2.1	20,40
$C_9H_{10}O_3$	Ethyl salicylate	7.99	30	2.	30,40
C_9H_{12}	Isopropylbenzene (Cumene)	2.38_0	20		
	1,3,5-Trimethylbenzene (Mesitylene)	2.27_9	20		

[a] $f = 4 \times 10^8$ cycles/sec.
[b] $f = 3.6 \times 10^8$ cycles/sec.
[h] Critical temperature.
[n] $f = 5 \times 10^8$ cycles/sec.
[f] Mixture of cis-trans isomers.
[z] Value chosen to conform with the remainder of the tabulated data for this substance.
[w] Silicone oil of average molecular weight corresponding to this formula.

Organic Liquids (Continued)

	Substance	ϵ	$t°C$	a (or α) $\times 10^2$	Range t_1,t_2
C_9H_{20}	n-Nonane...............	1.972	20	0.135	−10,90
		2.059	−50		
		1.847	110		
	C_{10}	1.787	150		
$C_{10}H_8$	Naphthalene............	2.54	85		
$C_{10}H_{10}O_4$	Dimethyl phthalate.....	8.5	24		
$C_{10}H_{16}$	d-Camphene............	2.33	ca 40		
	d-Pinene..............	2.64	25		
	l-Pinene..............	2.76	20		
	Terpinene.............	2.7[h]	21		
	d-Limonene...........	2.3₆	20		
	dl-Limonene (Dipentene)..	2.3₀	20		
$C_{10}H_{22}$	n-Decane..............	1.991	20	0.130	10,110
		2.050	−30		
		1.844	130		
		1.783	170		
$C_{10}H_{22}O$	1-Decanol.............	8.1	20		
$C_{11}H_{24}$	n-Undecane............	2.005	20	0.125	10,130
		2.039	−10		
		1.838	150		
	C_{12}	1.781	190		
$C_{12}H_{10}$	Diphenyl..............	2.53	75	0.18	75,155
$C_{12}H_{10}O$	Phenyl ether..........	3.65	30	0.7	30,50
$C_{12}H_{11}N$	Diphenylamine........	3.3	52		
$C_{12}H_{26}$	n-Dodecane...........	2.014	20	0.120	10,150
		2.047	−10		
	C_{13}	1.776	210		
$C_{13}H_{10}O$	Benzophenone..........	11.4	50		
$C_{14}H_{16}N$	C_{14} Dibenzylamine........	3.6[b]	20		
$C_{16}H_{22}O_2$	C_{16} Palmitic acid........	2.30	71		
$C_{18}H_{22}O_2$	C_{18} Linoleic acid..........	2.61	0		
		2.71	20		
		2.70	70		
		2.60	120		
$C_{18}H_{34}O_2$	Oleic acid............	2.46	20		
		2.45	60		
		2.41	100		
$C_{18}H_{36}O_2$	Stearic acid..........	2.29	70		
		2.26	100		
	Ethyl palmitate.......	3.20	20	0.4	20,40
		2.71	104		
		2.46	182		
$C_{19}H_{16}$	C_{19} Triphenylmethane......	2.45	100	0.14	94,175
$C_{19}H_{18}O_4$	Monopalmitin.........	5.34	67		
		5.09	80		
$C_{20}H_{38}O_2$	C_{20} Ethyl Oleate..........	3.17	28	0.48	28,122
$C_{20}H_{40}O_2$	Ethyl Stearate.........	2.98	40	0.6	32,50
		2.69	100		
		2.48	167		
$C_{21}H_{21}O_4P$	C_{21} Tricresyl phosphate....	6.9	40		
$C_{22}H_{42}O_2$	C_{22} Butyl oleate..........	4.0	25		
$C_{22}H_{44}O_2$	Butyl stearate........	3.11₁	30	0.53	30,35

[b] $f = 3.6 \times 10^8$ cycles/sec.
[a] $f = 5 \times 10^8$ cycles/sec.

DIELECTRIC CONSTANTS
Dielectric Constants of Solids
Compiled by Earle C. Gregg, Jr.

Solids* (17 to 22°C)

Material	Frequency	Dielectric constant	Material	Frequency	Dielectric constant
Acetamide............	4×10^8	4.0	Mercuric chloride.....	10^6	3.2
Acetanilide..........		2.9	Mercurous chloride....	10^6	9.4
Acetic acid (2°C)......	4×10^8	4.1	Naphthalene........	4×10^8	2.52
Aluminum oleate......	4×10^8	2.40	Phenanthrene.........	4×10^8	2.80
Ammonium bromide......	10^6	7.1	Phenol (10°C)........	4×10^8	4.3
Ammonium chloride....	10^6	7.0	Phosphorus, red......	10^8	4.1
Antimony trichloride..	10^8	5.34	Phosphorus, yellow...	10^8	3.6
Apatite ⊥ optic axis..	3×10^8	9.50	Potassium aluminum sulfate	10^6	3.8
" ‖ optic axis..	3×10^8	7.41			
Asphalt..............	$<3 \times 10^6$	2.68	Potassium carbonate (15°C)	10^8	5.6
Barium chloride (anhyd.)	6×10^7	11.4	Potassium chlorate...	6×10^7	5.1
" " (2H₂O)	6×10^7	9.4	Potassium chloride....	10^4	5.03
Barium nitrate.......	6×10^7	5.9			

Solids* (17 to 22°C)   (Continued)

Material	Frequency	Dielectric constant	Material	Frequency	Dielectric constant
Barium sulfate (15°C)..	10^8	11.4	Potassium chromate......	6×10^7	7.3
Beryl ⊥ optic axis...	10^4	7.02	Potassium iodide.......	6×10^7	5.6
" ‖ optic axis...	10^4	6.08	Potassium nitrate.......	6×10^7	5.0
Calcite ⊥ optic axis...	10^4	8.5	Potassium sulfate.......	6×10^7	5.9
" ‖ optic axis...	10^4	8.0	Quartz ⊥ optic axis...	3×10^7	4.34
Calcium carbonate.....	10^6	6.14	" ‖ optic axis...	3×10^7	4.27
Calcium fluoride.......	10^4	7.36	Resorcinol............	4×10^8	3.2
Calcium sulfate (2H₂O)..	10^4	5.66	Ruby ⊥ optic axis..	10^4	13.27
Cassiterite ⊥ optic axis	10^{12}	23.4	" ‖ optic axis..	10^4	11.28
Cassiterite ‖ optic axis	10^{12}	24.	Rutile ⊥ optic axis..	10^8	86
d-Cocaine............	5×10^8	3.10	" ‖ optic axis..	10^8	170
Cupric oleate........	4×10^8	2.80	Selenium.............	10^8	6.6
Cupric oxide (15°C)...	10^8	18.1	Silver bromide.......	10^6	12.2
Cupric sulfate (anhyd.)	6×10^7	10.3	Silver chloride......	10^6	11.2
Cupric sulfate (5H₂O)	6×10^7	7.8	Silver cyanide.......	10^6	5.6
Diamond.............			Smithsonite ⊥ optic axis..	10^{12}	9.3
	10^8	5.5	" ‖ optic axis..	10^{10}	9.4
Diphenylmethane......	4×10^8	2.7	Sodium carbonate (anhyd.)	6×10^7	8.4
Dolomite ⊥ optic axis..	10^8	8.0	Sodium carbonate (10H₂O)	6×10^7	5.3
" "	10^8	6.8	Sodium chloride......	10^4	6.12
Ferrous oxide (15°C)...	10^8	14.2	Sodium nitrate.......		5.2
Iodine...............	10^8	4	Sodium oleate........	4×10^8	2.75
Lead acetate..........	10^6	2.6	Sodium perchlorate...	6×10^7	5.4
Lead carbonate (15°C).	10^8	18.6	Sucrose (mean).......	3×10^8	3.32
Lead chloride.........	10^6	4.2	Sulfur (mean)........		4.0
Lead monoxide (15°C)..	10^8	25.9	Thallium chloride....	10^6	46.9
Lead nitrate..........	6×10^7	37.7	p-Toluidine.........	4×10^8	3.0
Lead oleate..........	4×10^8	3.27	Tourmaline ⊥ optic axis..	10^4	7.10
Lead sulfate.........	10^6	14.3	" ‖ optic axis..	10^4	6.3
Lead sulfide (15°)	16^8	17.9	Urea.................	4×10^8	3.5
Malachite (mean).....	10^{12}	7.2	Zircon ⊥, ‖..........	10^8	12

* For plastics and other insulating materials, refer to table on Properties of Dielectrics.

DIELECTRIC CONSTANTS
Table of Dielectric Constants of Reference Gases at 20°C and 1 Atmosphere

The listed values ($\epsilon - 1$) refer to the gas at a temperature of 20°C and pressure of 1 atmosphere. The values can be adjusted to slightly different conditions without introducing more than 0.1% error by use of the following equation:

$$\frac{(\epsilon - 1)_{t,p}}{(\epsilon - 1)_{20°,1\,atm}} = \frac{p}{760[1 + 0.003411(t - 20)]}$$

where p = pressure in mm Hg
t = degrees C

t should be between 10 and 30°C and p between 700 and 800 mm Hg. From National Bureau of Standards Circular 537

Substance	$(\epsilon - 1) \cdot 10^6$	Reference	Substance	$(\epsilon - 1) \cdot 10^6$	Reference
Helium.....	Radio frequency			Radio frequency	
	67.8	Watson		537.₀	Watson
	63.7	Hector			
	64.5	Jelatis		Microwave[a]	
				536.5	Birnbaum
	Microwave			536.6	Essen
	65.6	Birnbaum		536.6	Essen
	65.2	Essen	Air (dry, CO₂ free)......	Optical	
				536.9	Koch
	Optical			535.8	Meggers
	64.6	Koch		536.0	Traub
	64.5	Cuthbertson		536.7	Quarder
Hydrogen...	Radio frequency			536.4	Lowery
	254.₀	Watson		536.5	Tausz
				536.1	Koster
	Microwave			536.3	Perard
	253.4	Essen		535.8	Barrell
	Optical				
	254.1	Cuthbertson	Nitrogen....	Radio frequency	
	253.6	Koch		547.2	Watson
	253.7	Kirn			
	254.3	Tausz		Microwave	
Oxygen....	Radio frequency			547.3	Birnbaum
	494.₈	Watson		548.0	Essen
	490.2	Jelatis		548.0	Essen
	Microwave[a]			Optical	
	494.9	Birnbaum		548.9	Cuthbertson
	495.0	Essen		548.7	Koch
	494.9	Essen		547.2	Tausz
	Optical		Carbon dioxide...	Radio frequency	
	494.5	Cuthbertson		921.₅	Watson
	493.5	Lowery		Microwave	
	494.7	Tausz		922.4	Birnbaum
	494.4	Ladenberg		920.₆	Essen

These values were derived from measurements of the refractive index after making allowance for the magnetic permeability of oxygen.

Table of Dielectric Constants of Reference Gases at 20°C and 1 Atmosphere

Substance	$(\epsilon - 1) \cdot 10^6$	Reference	Substance	$(\epsilon - 1) \cdot 10^6$	Reference
Argon.......	Radio frequency 513.0	Watson			
	516.4	Jelatis			
	Microwave 517.7	Essen			
	Optical 516.8	Cuthbertson			
	517.8	Quarder			
	517.0	Tausz			
	516.7	Damköhler			

a These values were derived from measurements of the refractive index after making allowance for the magnetic permeability of oxygen.

Dielectric Constants of Gases at 760 MM Pressure
Compiled by Earle C. Gregg, Jr.

GASES AT 760 MM PRESSURE

Material	Temperature °C	Frequency cycles/sec.	Dielectric Constant	Material	Temperature °C	Frequency cycles/sec.	Dielectric Constant
Acetaldehyde.....	100	$<3 \times 10^6$		n-Heptane..	20	$<3 \times 10^6$	1.0035
	0	2×10^6	1.0213	Hydrogen..	100	$<3 \times 10^6$	1.000264
Acetone.....			1.0159	Hydrogen bromide..	20	$<3 \times 10^6$	1.00313
Acetyl chloride......	0	$<3 \times 10^6$	1.0217	Hydrogen chloride...	0	$<3 \times 10^6$	1.0046
Acetylene...	0	$<3 \times 10^6$	1.00134	Hydrogen iodide....	0	$<10^6$	
Air........			1.000590		100	$<3 \times 10^6$	1.00234
Ammonia...	0	$<3 \times 10^6$	1.0072	Hydrogen sulfide....	0	$<10^6$	
β-Amylene..			1.0028		100	$<3 \times 10^6$	1.00030
Argon.....	23	10^{10}	1.000545	Mercury....	180	$<3 \times 10^6$	1.00074
Benzene....	400	3×10^8	1.0028	Methane....	0	$<3 \times 10^6$	1.000944
Bromine....	0	$<3 \times 10^6$	1.0128	Methyl alcohol......	0	$<10^6$	1.0057
Butylene....			1.00319	Methyl bromide.....	0	$<3 \times 10^6$	1.00095
Carbon dioxide......	100	$<3 \times 10^6$	1.000985	Methyl chloride.....	0	$<3 \times 10^6$	1.00094
Carbon disulfide....	23	10^{10}	1.0029	Methyl iodide......	110	$<3 \times 10^6$	1.0063
Carbon monoxide.	23	10^{10}	1.00070	Methylamine....	120	$<3 \times 10^6$	1.0038
Carbon tetrachloride.	100	$<3 \times 10^6$	1.0030	Methylene chloride...	23	10^{10}	1.0065
Chloroform .	100	$<3 \times 10^6$	1.0042	Neon.......			1.000127
Dichlorodifluoromethane.....	100	$<3 \times 10^6$		Nitrogen....			1.000580
	0	$<3 \times 10^6$	1.00029	Nitromethane...	23	10^{10}	1.0247
Dichlorofluoromethane.....	0	$<3 \times 10^6$		Nitrous oxide (N_2O).	23	2.5×10^{10}	1.00113
	100	$<3 \times 10^6$	1.00049	Oxygen....	0	$<3 \times 10^6$	1.000523
Dimethylamine.....	0	2×10^6	1.00040	n-Pentane...	100	$<3 \times 10^6$	1.0025
Ethane.....	0	$<3 \times 10^6$	1.00150	n-Propyl chloride...	23	10^{10}	
Ethyl alcohol	100	$<3 \times 10^6$	1.0061	iso-Propyl chloride...	20	$<3 \times 10^6$	1.0143
Ethylamine.			1.00053	Sulfur dioxide.......	20	$<3 \times 10^6$	1.0152
Ethyl bromide.....	20	$<3 \times 10^6$	1.0139	Toluene.....	100	$<3 \times 10^6$	1.00075
Ethyl chloride......	20	$<3 \times 10^6$	1.0132	Vinyl bromide.....	100	$<3 \times 10^6$	1.0043
Ethyl ether.	23	10^{10}	1.0049	Water (steam)...	20	$<3 \times 10^6$	1.0081
Ethyl formate.....	126	$<3 \times 10^6$	1.0083	" ...	0	$<3 \times 10^6$	1.0126
Ethyl iodide.	20	$<3 \times 10^6$	1.0140		100	$<3 \times 10^6$	1.00785
" "			1.0089				
Ethylene....	110	$<3 \times 10^6$	1.00144				
Helium.....	140	$<3 \times 10^6$	1.0000684				

PROPERTIES OF DIELECTRICS

In most cases properties have been determined by A S T M (American Society for Testing Materials) test methods at room temperature under standard conditions. Values will in general change considerably with temperature.

DIELECTRIC CONSTANTS OF SOME PLASTICS AND RUBBERS

Name	°C	Frequency (Hertz)			Name	°C	Frequency (Hertz)		
		1×10^3	1×10^6	1×10^8			1×10^3	1×10^6	1×10^8
Plastics					Polyvinyl chloride............	25	4.55	3.3	—
Phenol-formaldehyde.........	25–27	5.15–8.61	4.45–5.05	4.1–4.5			(1×10^4)		
	57	6.35	4.90	4.5	Polyvinylidene and vinyl chloride	23	4.65	3.18	2.82
	88	8.5	5.2	4.7		84	4.94	4.40	3.2
Phenol-aniline-formaldehyde	25	4.50	4.31	4.11	Polychlorotrifluoroethylene.....	25	2.76	2.48	2.36
	79	4.75	4.51	4.35	Polytetrafluoroethylene (Teflon) .	22	2.1	2.1	2.1
Melamine-formaldehyde.......	24–28	6.0–6.90	5.82–6.20	5.5–5.55		100	2.04	2.04	—
	57	6.95	5.40	4.90	Polyvinylalcohol acetate........	25	7.8	5.2	—
	88	11.8	6.0	5.5		85	100.	10.	—
Urea-formaldehyde...........	24	6.7	6.0	5.2	Polyvinylacetals...............	26–27	3.02–3.12	2.86–2.92	2.67
	80	7.8	6.8	—		88	3.5	3.1	2.85
Polyamide resins:					Polyacrylates:				
Nylon 66.................	25	3.75	3.33	3.16	Lucite....................	−12	2.9	2.63	2.50
Nylon 610...............	25	3.50	3.14	3.0		23	2.84	2.63	2.58
	84	11.2	4.4	3.4		81	3.45	2.72	2.59
Cellulose acetate............	26	3.50–4.48	3.28–3.90	3.05–3.40	Plexiglas.............	27	3.12	2.76	—
Cellulose nitrate............	27	8.4	6.6	5.2	Polystyrene............	25	2.54–2.56	2.54–2.56	2.55
	78	7.5	6.2	5.2		80	2.54	2.54	2.54
Methyl cellulose............	22	6.8	5.7	4.3	Styrene copolymers...........	25	2.55–2.95	2.55–2.80	2.55–2.77
Ethyl cellulose.............	25	3.09	3.01	2.90	Polyesters.................	25	3.22–4.3	3.12–4.0	2.94–2.98
Silicone resins.............	25	3.79–3.91	3.79–3.82	3.82	Alkyd resins:				
Polyethylene...............	−12	2.37	2.35	2.33	Alkyd isocyanate foam.......	25	1.223	1.218	1.20
	23	2.26	2.26	2.26	Plaskon, clay filled.........	25	5.26	4.92	4.77
Polyisobutylene.............	25	2.23	2.23	2.23	Plaskon, glass filled........	25	5.04	4.73	4.50
Vinylite QYNA.............	20	3.10	2.88	2.85	Epoxy resins..............	25	3.63–3.67	3.52–3.62	3.32–3.35
	76	3.83	3.0	2.8	**Rubbers**				
	110	8.6	—	—	Hevea, vulcanized...........	27	2.94	2.74	2.42
Vinylite 5544...............	25	7.20	4.13	3.05	Hevea compound............	27	36.	9.	6.8
Vinylite 5901...............	25	5.5	3.4	3.0	Gutta percha...............	25	2.60	2.53	2.47
Vinylite VU................	24	5.65	3.30	2.80	Balata....................	25	2.50	2.50	2.42
	79	8.15	5.5	3.4	Buna S...................	20	2.66	2.56	2.52
Vinylite VYHW.............	20	3.12	2.91	2.83	Butyl rubber compound.......	25	2.42	2.40	2.39
Vinylite VYNW.............	20	3.15	2.90	2.8	Neoprene..................	24	6.60	6.26	4.5
					Silicon rubber.............	25	3.12–3.30	3.10–3.20	3.06–3.18

DIELECTRIC CONSTANTS OF CERAMICS

Material	Dielectric Constant 10^6 Cycles	Dielectric Strength volts/mil	Volume Resistivity Ohms-cm 23°C	Loss Factor*
Alumina..............	4.5–8.4	40–160	10^{11}–10^{14}	0.0002–0.01
Corderite..............	4.5–5.4	40–250	10^{12}–10^{14}	0.004–0.012
Forsterite.............	6.2	240	10^{14}	0.0004
Porcelain (Dry Process)...	6.0–8.0	40–240	10^{12}–10^{14}	0.003–0.02
Porcelain (Wet Process) ..	6.0–7.0	90–400	10^{12}–10^{14}	0.006–0.01
Porcelain, Zircon........	7.1–10.5	250–400	10^{13}–10^{15}	0.0002–0.008
Steatite..............	5.5–7.5	200–400	10^{13}–10^{15}	0.0002–0.004
Titanates (Ba, Sr, Ca, Mg, and Pb)..........	15–12,000	50–300	10^8–10^{15}	0.0001–0.02
Titanium Dioxide........	14–110	100–210	10^{13}–10^{18}	0.0002–0.005

DIELECTRIC CONSTANTS OF GLASSES

Type	Dielectric Constant at 100 mc 20°C	Volume Resistivity 350°C megohm-cm	Loss Factor*
Corning 0010............	6.32	10	0.015
Corning 0080............	6.75	0.13	0.058
Corning 0120............	6.65	100	0.012
Pyrex 1710.............	6.00	2,500	0.025
Pyrex 3320.............	4.71	....	0.019
Pyrex 7040.............	4.65	80	0.013
Pyrex 7050.............	4.77	16	0.017
Pyrex 7052.............	5.07	25	0.019
Pyrex 7060.............	4.70	13	0.018
Pyrex 7070.............	4.00	1,300	0.0048
Vycor 7230.............	3.83	....	0.0061
Pyrex 7720.............	4.50	16	0.014
Pyrex 7740.............	5.00	4	0.040
Pyrex 7750.............	4.28	50	0.011
Pyrex 7760.............	4.50	50	0.0081
Vycor 7900.............	3.9	130	0.0023
Vycor 7910.............	3.8	1,600	0.00091
Vycor 7911.............	3.8	4,000	0.00072
Corning 8870............	9.5	5,000	0.0085
G. E. Clear (Silica Glass)....	3.81	4,000–30,000	0.00038
Quartz (Fused)............	3.75–4.1 (1 mc)	....	0.0002 (1 mc)

* Power factor × dielectric constant equals loss factor.

DIELECTRIC CONSTANTS OF WAXES

Acrawax C..............	2.4	....	....	0.005
Beeswax, white.........	2.75–3.0	....	5×10^{14}	0.025
Beeswax, yellow........	2.9	....	8×10^{14}	0.029
Candelilla.............	2.25–2.50			
Carnauba.............	2.75–3.0			
Cerese, brown G........	2.27	....	....	0.0025
Ceresine.............	2.25–2.50	....	$> 5 \times 10^{18}$	0.0011
Halowax 1001.........	~4.10	....	2×10^{13}	0.014
Halowax 1013.........	~4.75	....		0.036
Halowax 1014.........	~4.40	.....		0.035
Halowax 11–314.......	2.94	....	....	0.00094
Microcrystalline waxes ..	2.2–2.5			
Opalwax..............	3.1			0.34
Ozokerite wax.........	2.3	100–150	5×10^{14}	0.0018
Paraffin..............	2.0–2.5	250	10^{15}–10^{19}	0.003 (900 cps)
Parawax..............	2.25	....	10^{16}	0.00045
135 A.M.P. wax........	2.25	....	....	0.00023

DIELECTRIC CONSTANT OF WATER

From NSRDS-NBS 24

W. J. Hamer

$t°C$	ε^*	$\varepsilon†$	$t°C$	ε^*	$\varepsilon†$
0	87.74	87.90	50	69.91	69.88
5	85.76	85.90	55	68.34	68.30
10	83.83	83.95	60	66.81	66.76
15	81.95	82.04	65	65.32	65.25
18	80.84	80.93	70	63.86	63.78
20	80.10	80.18	75	62.43	62.34
25	78.30	78.36	80	61.03	60.93
30	76.55	76.58	85	59.66	59.55
35	74.83	74.85	90	58.32	58.20
38	73.82	73.83	95	57.01	56.88
40	73.15	73.15	100	55.72	55.58
45	71.51	71.50			

* From data of Malmberg and Maryott (1956).
† From data of Owen, Miller, Milner and Cogan (1961).

DIELECTRIC CONSTANT OF DEUTERIUM OXIDE

t	ε	$-\dfrac{d\varepsilon}{dt}$	$-\dfrac{1}{\varepsilon}\dfrac{d\varepsilon}{dt}$
°C			
4	85.877	0.3974	4.627×10^{-3}
5	85.480	.3956	4.628
10	83.526	.3862	4.624
15	81.618	.3771	4.620
20	79.755	.3681	4.615
25	77.936	.3594	4.611
30	76.161	.3509	4.607
35	74.427	.3425	4.602
40	72.735	.3344	4.597
45	71.083	.3265	4.593
50	69.470	.3187	4.587
55	67.896	.3112	4.583
60	66.358	.3038	4.578
65	64.857	.2967	4.575
70	63.391	.2898	4.571
75	61.959	.2830	4.567
80	60.561	.2765	4.565
85	59.194	.2701	4.563
90	57.859	.2640	4.563
95	56.554	.2581	4.564
100	55.278	.2523	4.564

DIELECTRIC CONSTANTS (Continued)

Dielectric Constant of Liquid Parahydrogen vs. Temperature (°K) and Pressure (atm)

R. J. Corruccini

P atm \ T °K	20	21	22	23	24	25	26	27	28	29	30	31	32
1	1.2297												
2	1.2302	1.2260	1.2216										
3	1.2306	1.2265	1.2221	1.2174	1.2122								
4	1.2311	1.2270	1.2227	1.2180	1.2129	1.2073	1.2010						
5	1.2315	1.2275	1.2233	1.2186	1.2136	1.2081	1.2020	1.1950					
6	1.2320	1.2280	1.2238	1.2192	1.2143	1.2089	1.2029	1.1962	1.1883				
7	1.2324	1.2285	1.2243	1.2198	1.2150	1.2097	1.2039	1.1973	1.1897	1.1805			
8	1.2329	1.2290	1.2249	1.2204	1.2157	1.2105	1.2048	1.1984	1.1911	1.1824			
9	1.2333	1.2295	1.2254	1.2210	1.2163	1.2112	1.2056	1.1994	1.1924	1.1842	1.1734		
10	1.2337	1.2300	1.2259	1.2216	1.2169	1.2119	1.2065	1.2004	1.1936	1.1857	1.1758	1.1621	
15	1.2358	1.2322	1.2284	1.2243	1.2200	1.2153	1.2103	1.2049	1.1990	1.1924	1.1847	1.1758	1.1645
20	1.2378	1.2343	1.2307	1.2268	1.2227	1.2184	1.2137	1.2088	1.2034	1.1976	1.1913	1.1839	1.1757
25	1.2396	1.2363	1.2328	1.2291	1.2253	1.2211	1.2168	1.2122	1.2073	1.2021	1.1964	1.1903	1.1832
30	1.2414	1.2382	1.2349	1.2313	1.2276	1.2237	1.2196	1.2153	1.2107	1.2059	1.2008	1.1952	1.1891
35	1.2431	1.2400	1.2368	1.2334	1.2298	1.2261	1.2222	1.2181	1.2138	1.2093	1.2046	1.1995	1.1942
40	1.2448	1.2418	1.2386	1.2354	1.2319	1.2284	1.2246	1.2208	1.2167	1.2124	1.2080	1.2033	1.1984
45	1.2464	1.2434	1.2404	1.2372	1.2339	1.2305	1.2269	1.2232	1.2193	1.2153	1.2111	1.2067	1.2021
50	1.2479	1.2450	1.2421	1.2390	1.2358	1.2325	1.2291	1.2255	1.2218	1.2179	1.2139	1.2098	1.2055
60	1.2508	1.2481	1.2453	1.2424	1.2394	1.2363	1.2331	1.2297	1.2263	1.2227	1.2191	1.2153	1.2114
70	1.2535	1.2510	1.2483	1.2455	1.2427	1.2397	1.2367	1.2336	1.2303	1.2270	1.2236	1.2201	1.2165
80	1.2561	1.2536	1.2511	1.2484	1.2457	1.2429	1.2400	1.2371	1.2340	1.2309	1.2277	1.2244	1.2211
90	1.2585	1.2561	1.2537	1.2512	1.2486	1.2459	1.2431	1.2403	1.2374	1.2345	1.2315	1.2284	1.2252
100	1.2608	1.2586	1.2562	1.2538	1.2513	1.2487	1.2461	1.2434	1.2406	1.2378	1.2349	1.2320	1.2290
120	1.2652	1.2631	1.2609	1.2586	1.2563	1.2539	1.2514	1.2489	1.2464	1.2438	1.2412	1.2385	1.2357
140	1.2693	1.2672	1.2651	1.2630	1.2608	1.2586	1.2563	1.2540	1.2516	1.2492	1.2467	1.2442	1.2417
160	1.2730	1.2711	1.2691	1.2671	1.2650	1.2629	1.2607	1.2585	1.2563	1.2540	1.2517	1.2494	1.2470
180	1.2766	1.2747	1.2728	1.2709	1.2689	1.2669	1.2649	1.2628	1.2606	1.2585	1.2563	1.2541	1.2518
200	1.2799	1.2781	1.2763	1.2745	1.2726	1.2707	1.2687	1.2667	1.2647	1.2626	1.2605	1.2584	1.2563
220	1.2831	1.2814	1.2796	1.2779	1.2760	1.2742	1.2723	1.2704	1.2685	1.2665	1.2645	1.2625	1.2605
240		1.2845	1.2828	1.2811	1.2793	1.2775	1.2757	1.2739	1.2720	1.2701	1.2682	1.2663	1.2643
260		1.2874	1.2858	1.2841	1.2824	1.2807	1.2790	1.2772	1.2754	1.2736	1.2717	1.2699	1.2680
280			1.2886	1.2870	1.2853	1.2837	1.2821	1.2803	1.2786	1.2768	1.2751	1.2733	1.2714
300			1.2914	1.2898	1.2882	1.2866	1.2850	1.2833	1.2817	1.2800	1.2782	1.2765	1.2747
320				1.2925	1.2910	1.2894	1.2878	1.2862	1.2846	1.2829	1.2813	1.2796	1.2779
340				1.2951	1.2936	1.2921	1.2905	1.2890	1.2874	1.2858	1.2842	1.2825	1.2809

Note: Values below the stepped line represent an extrapolation of p with density.

Selected Values of Electric Dipole Moments for Molecules in the Gas Phase

Ralph D. Nelson, Jr., David R. Lide, Jr., and Arthur A. Maryott

The following table was abstracted from the publication, "Selected Values of Electric Dipole Moments for Molecules in the Gas Phase" compiled by Nelson, Lide and Maryott and published as part of the National Reference Data Series—National Bureau of Standards (NSRDS—NBS 10). The publication is available from the Superintendent of Documents, U.S. Government Printing Office, Washington, D.C., 20402. Those desiring a complete listing of all compounds in the NSRDS—NBS 10, discussion of the bibliographic procedure and the principal methods of dipole moment measurement should obtain the publication.

Values of the dipole moment, μ, are expressed in the cgs system of units, since this is the system universally used by workers in the field. The numerical values are in debye units, D, ($1\ D = 10^{-18}$ electrostatic units of charge $\times$ centimeters). The conversion factor to the Système International is $1\ D = 3.33564 \times 10^{-30}$ coulomb-meter.

Code symbol	Estimated accuracy of value	Code symbol	Estimated accuracy of value
A	$\pm 1\%$ or, for $\mu < 1.0$ D, ± 0.01 D	i	The significance of these values may involve some ambiguity because of the possibility of different conformations or spatial isomers.
B	$\pm 2\%$ or, for $\mu < 1.0$ D, ± 0.02 D		
C	$\pm 5\%$ or, for $\mu < 1.0$ D, ± 0.05 D		
S	$\mu \cong 0$ on grounds of molecular symmetry		

Compounds not containing carbon

Formula	Compound name	Selected moment (debyes)	
AgCl	Silver chloride	5.73	C
AsCl₃	Arsenic trichloride	1.59	C
AsF₃	Arsenic trifluoride	2.59	B
AsH₃	Arsine	0.20	C
BCl₃	Boron trichloride	0	S
BF₃	Boron trifluoride	0	S
B₂H₆	Diborane	0	S
B₃H₆N₃	Triborotriazine (Borazine)	0	S
B₅H₉	Pentaborane	2.13	B
BaO	Barium oxide	7.95	A
BrH	Hydrogen bromide	0.82	B
BrH₃Si	Bromosilane	1.33	B
BrK	Potassium bromide	10.41	B
BrLi	Lithium bromide	7.27	A
Br₂Hg	Mercury dibromide	0	S
Br₄Sn	Tin tetrabromide	0	S
ClCs	Cesium chloride	10.42	A
ClF	Chlorine fluoride	0.88	C
ClFO₃	Perchloryl fluoride	0.023	A
ClGeH₃	Chlorogermane	2.13	A
ClH	Hydrogen chloride	1.08	B
ClH₃Si	Chlorosilane	1.31	A
ClK	Potassium chloride	10.27	A
ClLi	Lithium chloride	7.13	A
ClNa	Sodium chloride	9.00	A
ClNO₂	Nitryl chloride	0.53	A
ClTl	Thallium chloride	4.44	B
Cl₂F₃P	Dichlorotrifluorophosphorus	0.68	C
Cl₂H₂Si	Dichlorosilane	1.17	B
Cl₂Hg	Mercury dichloride	0	S
Cl₂OS	Thionyl chloride	1.45	B
Cl₂O₂S	Sulfuryl chloride	1.81	B
Cl₃F₂P	Trichlorodifluorophosphorus	0	S
Cl₃HSi	Trichlorosilane	0.86	B
Cl₃P	Phosphorus trichloride	0.78	C
Cl₄FP	Tetrachlorofluorophosphorus	0.21	B
Cl₄Ge	Germanium tetrachloride	0	S
Cl₄Si	Silicon tetrachloride	0	S
Cl₄Sn	Tin tetrachloride	0	S
Cl₄Ti	Titanium tetrachloride	0	S
CsF	Cesium fluoride	7.88	A
FH	Hydrogen fluoride	1.82	A
FH₃Si	Fluorosilane	1.27	B
FH₅Si₂	Fluorodisilane	1.26	A
FK	Potassium fluoride	8.60	A
FLi	Lithium fluoride	6.33	A
FNO	Nitrosyl fluoride	1.81	B
FNa	Sodium fluoride	8.16	A
FRb	Rubidium fluoride	8.55	A
FTl	Thallium fluoride	4.23	A
F₂HN	Difluoramine	1.92	A
F₂H₂Si	Difluorosilane	1.55	A
F₂N₂	cis-Difluorodiazine	0.16	A
F₂O	Oxygen difluoride	0.297	A
F₂OS	Thionyl fluoride	1.63	A
F₂O₂	Dioxygen difluoride	1.44	C
F₂O₂S	Sulfuryl fluoride	1.12	B
F₂S₂	Sulfur monofluoride (S = SF₂ isomer)	1.03	C
F₂S₂	Sulfur monofluoride (FSSF isomer)	1.45	B
F₂Si	Silicon difluoride	1.23	B
F₃HSi	Trifluorosilane	1.27	B
F₃N	Nitrogen trifluoride	0.235	A
F₃NS	Nitridotrifluorosulfur	1.91	B
F₃OP	Phosphoryl fluoride	1.76	B
F₃P	Phosphorus trifluoride	1.03	A
F₃PS	Thiophosphoryl fluoride	0.64	B

Compounds not containing carbon—Continued

Formula	Compound name	Selected moment (debyes)	
F₄N₂	Tetrafluorohydrazine, *gauche* conformation	0.26	B
F₄S	Sulfur tetrafluoride	0.632	A
F₄Si	Silicon tetrafluoride	0	S
F₅P	Phosphorus pentafluoride	0	S
F₅I	Iodine pentafluoride	2.18	C
F₆S	Sulfur hexafluoride	0	S
F₆Se	Selenium hexafluoride	0	S
F₆Te	Tellurium hexafluoride	0	S
F₆U	Uranium hexafluoride	0	S
HI	Hydrogen iodide	0.44	B
HLi	Lithium hydride	5.88	A
HN	Imidyl radical		
HNO₃	Nitric acid	2.17	A
HO	Hydroxyl radical	1.66	A
H₂O	Water	1.85	A
H₂O₂	Hydrogen peroxide	2.2	D
H₂S	Hydrogen sulfide	0.97	A
H₃N	Ammonia	1.47	A
H₃P	Phosphine	0.58	A
H₃Sb	Stibine	0.12	C
H₄N₂	Hydrazine	1.75	A
H₄Si	Silane	0	S
H₆OSi₂	Disilyl ether (disiloxane)	0.24	B
H₆Si₂	Disilane	0	S
HgI₂	Mercury diiodide	0	S
ILi	Lithium iodide	7.43	A
I₄Sn	Tin tetraiodide	0	S
NO	Nitrogen monoxide (nitric oxide)	0.153	A
NO₂	Nitrogen dioxide	0.316	A
N₂O	Dinitrogen oxide (nitrous oxide)	0.167	A
OS	Sulfur monoxide	1.55	A
OS₂	Disulfur monoxide	1.47	B
OSr	Strontium oxide	8.90	A
O₂S	Sulfur dioxide	1.63	A
O₃	Ozone	0.53	B
O₃S	Sulfur trioxide	0	S
O₄Os	Osmium tetroxide	0	S

Compounds containing carbon

Formula	Compound name	Selected moment (debyes)	
CBrF₃	Bromotrifluoromethane	0.65	C
CBr₂F₂	Dibromodifluoromethane	0.66	C
CClF₃	Chlorotrifluoromethane	0.50	A
CClN	Cyanogen chloride	2.82	B
CCl₂F₂	Dichlorodifluoromethane	0.51	A
CCl₂O	Carbonyl chloride (phosgene)	1.17	A
CCl₂S	Thiocarbonyl chloride	0.29	C
CCl₃F	Trichlorofluoromethane	0.45	C
CCl₃NO₂	Trichloronitromethane	1.89	C
CCl₄	Carbon tetrachloride	0	S
CFN	Cyanogen fluoride	2.17	C
CF₂	Carbon difluoride	0.46	B
CF₂O	Carbonyl fluoride	0.95	A
CF₃I	Iodotrifluoromethane	0.92	C
CF₃NO₂	Trifluoronitromethane	1.44	C
CF₄	Carbon tetrafluoride	0	S
CN₄O₈	Tetranitromethane	0	S
CO	Carbon monoxide	0.112	A
COS	Carbonyl sulfide	0.712	A
COSe	Carbonyl selenide	0.73	B
CO₂	Carbon dioxide	0	S
CS	Carbon monosulfide	1.98	A
CSTe	Thiocarbonyl telluride	0.17	A
CS₂	Carbon disulfide	0	S
CHBr₃	Tribromomethane	0.99	B
CHClF₂	Chlorodifluoromethane	1.42	B

Compounds containing carbon—Continued

Formula	Compound name	Selected moment (debyes)	
CHCl2F	Dichlorofluoromethane	1.29	B
CHCl3	Trichloromethane (chloroform)	1.01	B
CHFO	Formyl fluoride	2.02	A
CHF3	Trifluoromethane	1.65	A
CHN	Hydrogen cyanide	2.98	A
CHP	Methylidyne phosphide (methinophosphide)	0.390	A
CH2Br2	Dibromomethane	1.43	B
CH2ClF	Chlorofluoromethane	1.82	B
CH2ClNO2	Chloronitromethane	2.91	B
CH2Cl2	Dichloromethane	1.60	B
CH2F2	Difluoromethane	1.97	A
CH2N2	Cyanogen amide (cyanamide)	4.27	C
CH2N2	Diazomethane	1.50	A
CH2N2	Diazirine	1.59	C
CH2O	Methanal (formaldehyde)	2.33	A
CH2O2	Methanoic acid (formic acid)	1.41	A
CH3BF2	Methyl difluoroborane	1.66	B
CH3BO	Carbonyl borane	1.80	B
CH3Br	Bromomethane	1.81	A
CH3Cl	Chloromethane	1.87	A
CH3F	Fluoromethane	1.85	A
CH3I	Iodomethane	1.62	B
CH3NO	Hydroxyliminomethane (formaldoxime)	0.44	A
CH3NO	Formyl amide (formamide)	3.73	B
CH3NOS	Methyl sulfinylamine	1.70	A
CH3NO2	Nitromethane	3.46	A
CH3NO3	Methyl nitrate	3.12	A
CH3N3	Methyl azide	2.17	B
CH4	Methane	0	S
CH4F2Si	Methyl difluorosilane	2.11	A
CH4O	Methanol	1.70	A
CH4S	Methanethiol (methyl mercaptan)	1.52	C
CH5FSi	Methyl monofluorosilane	1.71	A
CH5N	Methyl amine	1.31	B
CH5P	Methyl phosphine	1.10	A
CH6Ge	Methyl germane	0.643	A
CH6OSi	Methoxysilane	1.17	B
CH6Si	Methyl silane	0.735	A
CH6Sn	Methyl stannane	0.68	C
C2ClF5	Chloropentafluoroethane	0.52	C
C2F6	Hexafluoroethane	0	S
C2N2	Dicyanogen (cyanogen)	0	S
C2N2S	Dicyano sulfide	3.02	A
C2HCl	Chloroacetylene	0.44	B
C2HCl5	Pentachloroethane	0.92	C
C2HF	Fluoroacetylene	0.73	B
C2HF3	Trifluoroethylene	1.40	C
C2HF5	Pentafluoroethane	1.54	C
C2H2	Acetylene	0	S
C2H2Cl2	1,1-Dichloroethylene	1.34	B
C2H2Cl2	cis-1,2-Dichloroethylene	1.90	B
C2H2Cl2O	Chloroacetyl chloride	2.23	Ci
C2H2Cl4	1,1,2,2-Tetrachloroethane	1.32	Ci
C2H2FN	Fluorocyanomethane	3.43	C
C2H2F2	1,1-Difluoroethylene	1.38	A
C2H2F2	cis-1,2-Difluoroethylene	2.42	A
C2H2N2O	1,2,5-Oxadiazole	3.38	A
C2H2N2O	1,3,4-Oxadiazole	3.04	B
C2H2N2S	1,2,5-Thiadiazole	1.56	A
C2H2N2S	1,3,4-Thiadiazole	3.29	B
C2H2O	Methylene carbonyl (ketene)	1.42	B
C2H3Br	Bromoethylene	1.42	B
C2H3Cl	Chloroethylene	1.45	B
C2H3ClF2	1-Chloro-1,1-difluoroethane	2.14	B
C2H3ClO	Acetyl chloride	2.72	C
C2H3Cl3	1,1,1-Trichloroethane	1.78	B
C2H3F	Fluoroethylene	1.43	A
C2H3FO	Acetyl fluoride	2.96	A
C2H3F3	1,1,1-Trifluoroethane	2.32	B
C2H3F3	1,1,2-Trifluoroethane	1.58	B
C2H3N	Cyanomethane (acetonitrile)	3.92	A
C2H3N	Isocyanomethane	3.85	B
C2H4	Ethylene	0	S
C2H4ClF	1-Chloro-2-fluoroethane, gauche conformation	2.72	C
C2H4ClNO2	1-Chloro-1-nitroethane	3.27	B
C2H4Cl2	1,1-Dichloroethane	2.06	B
C2H4F2	1,1-Difluoroethane	2.27	A
C2H4Ge	Germyl acetylene	0.136	A
C2H4O	Oxirane (ethylene oxide)	1.89	A
C2H4O	Ethanal (acetaldehyde)	2.69	A
C2H4O2	Ethanoic acid (acetic acid)	1.74	C
C2H4O2	Methyl methanoate (methyl formate)	1.77	B
C2H4S	Thiirane (ethylene sulfide)	1.85	A
C4H4	Vinyl acetylene	0.310	A
C2H5Br	Bromoethane	2.03	A
C2H5BrO	Bromomethoxymethane	2.05	Ci
C2H5Cl	Chloroethane	2.05	A
C2H5ClO	2-Chloroethanol	1.78	Ci
C2H5F	Fluoroethane	1.94	B
C2H5I	Iodoethane	1.91	B
C2H5N	Iminoethane (ethyleneimine)	1.90	A
C2H5N	Methyliminomethane (CH3N = CH2)	1.53	B

Compounds containing carbon—Continued

Formula	Compound name	Selected moment (debyes)	
C2H5NO	Acetyl amine (acetamide)	3.76	Bi
C2H5NO	Methylaminomethanal (N-methylformamide)	3.83	Bi
C2H5NO2	Nitritoethane (ethyl nitrite)	2.40	Ci
C2H5NO2	Nitroethane	3.65	B
C2H6	Ethane	0	S
C2H6BF	Dimethyl fluoroborane	1.32	C
C2H6O	Ethanol	1.69	Bi
C2H6O	Dimethyl ether	1.30	A
C2H6OS	Dimethylsulfoxide	3.96	A
C2H6O2	1,2-Ethanediol (ethylene glycol)	2.28	Ci
C2H6O2S	Dimethyl sulfoxylate (dimethyl sulfone)	4.49	B
C2H6S	Ethanethiol	1.58	A
C2H6S	Dimethyl sulfide	1.50	A
C2H6Si	Silyl ethylene	0.66	A
C2H7B5	2,4-Dicarbaheptaborane	1.32	B
C2H7N	Aminoethane (ethyl amine)	1.22	Ci
C2H7N	Dimethyl amine	1.03	B
C2H7P	Ethyl phosphine	1.17	Bi
C2H7P	Dimethyl phosphine	1.23	A
C2H8N2	1,2-Diaminoethane	1.99	Ci
C2H8Si	Dimethyl silane	0.75	A
C2H8Si	Ethyl silane	0.81	B
C3O2	Dicarbonyl carbon (carbon suboxide)	0	S
C3HF3	3,3,3-Trifluoropropyne	2.36	B
C3HN	Cyanoacetylene	3.72	A
C3H2N2	Dicyanomethane	3.73	A
C3H2O	Propynal	2.47	B
C3H2O3	Vinylene carbonate	4.55	A
C3H3Br	3-Bromopropyne	1.54	C
C3H3Cl	3-Chloropropyne	1.68	C
C3H3F3	3,3,3-Trifluoropropene	2.45	B
C3H3N	Cyanoethylene	3.87	B
C3H3NO	Acetyl cyanide	3.45	B
C3H3NS	Thiazole	1.62	B
C3H4	Cyclopropene	0.45	A
C3H4	Propyne	0.781	A
C3H4	Propadiene (allene)	0	S
C3H4Cl2	1,1-Dichlorocyclopropane	1.58	B
C3H4O	Ethylidene carbonyl (methyl ketene)	1.79	B
C3H4O	Propenal, trans conformation (acrolein)	3.12	B
C3H4O2	2-Oxooxetane (β-propiolactone)	4.18	A
C3H4O2	Vinyl formate	1.49	A
C3H5Cl	2-Chloropropene	1.66	B
C3H5Cl	cis-1-Chloropropene	1.67	C
C3H5Cl	trans-1-Chloropropene	1.97	C
C3H5Cl	3-Chloropropene	1.94	Ci
C3H5F	cis-1-Fluoropropene	1.46	B
C3H5F	2-Fluoropropene	1.61	B
C3H5F	3-Fluoropropene, cis conformation	1.76	A
C3H5F	3-Fluoropropene, gauche conformation	1.94	A
C3H5N	Cyanoethane (propionitrile)	4.02	A
C3H6	Cyclopropane	0	S
C3H6	Propene	0.366	A
C3H6ClNO2	1-Chloro-1-nitropropane	3.48	Bi
C3H6Cl2	1,2-Dichloropropane		i
C3H6Cl2	1,3-Dichloropropane	2.08	Bi
C3H6Cl2	2,2-Dichloropropane	2.27	C
C3H6O	Oxetane (trimethylene oxide)	1.94	A
C3H6O	Methyl oxirane (propylene oxide)	2.01	A
C3H6O	Propanone (acetone)	2.88	A
C3H6O	2-Propen-1-ol (allyl alcohol)	1.60	C
C3H6O	Propanal, cis conformation (propionaldehyde)	2.52	B
C3H6O2	Propanoic acid	1.75	Ci
C3H6O2	Methyl acetate	1.72	Ci
C3H6O2	Ethyl formate	1.93	Ci
C3H6O3	1,3,5-Trioxane	2.08	A
C3H6S	Thietane (trimethylene sulfide)	1.85	C
C3H6S	Methyl thiirane (propylene sulfide)	1.95	A
C3H7Br	1-Bromopropane	2.18	Ci
C3H7Br	2-Bromopropane	2.21	C
C3H7Cl	1-Chloropropane	2.05	Bi
C3H7Cl	2-Chloropropane	2.17	C
C3H7F	1-Fluoropropane, gauche conformation	1.90	C
C3H7F	1-Fluoropropane, trans conformation	2.05	B
C3H7I	1-Iodopropane	2.04	Ci
C3H7NO	N,N-Dimethylformamide	3.82	Bi
C3H7NO	Acetyl methylamine (N-Methylacetamide)	3.73	Bi
C3H7NO2	1-Nitropropane	3.66	Bi
C3H7NO2	2-Nitropropane	3.73	B
C3H8	Propane	0.084	A
C3H8O	1-Propanol	1.68	Bi
C3H8O	2-Propanol	1.66	Bi
C3H8O	Methoxyethane (methyl ethyl ether)	1.23	Ci
C3H9As	Trimethyl arsine	0.86	B
C3H9N	Trimethyl amine	0.612	A
C3H9N	1-Aminopropane (n-propylamine)	1.17	Ci
C3H9P	Trimethyl phosphine	1.19	A

Compounds containing carbon—Continued

Formula	Compound name	Selected moment (debyes)	
$C_3H_{10}Si$	Trimethyl silane	0.525	A
C_4F_8	Perfluorocyclobutane	0	S
$C_4H_2N_2$	trans-1,2-Dicyanoethylene	0	S
$C_4H_4Cl_2$	1,4-Dichloro-2-butyne	2.-10	Bi
$C_4H_4F_2$	1,1-Difluoro-1,3-butadiene (trans conformation)	1.29	A
C_4H_4O	Furan	0.66	A
$C_4H_4O_2$	Diketene	3.53	B
C_4H_4S	Thiophene	0.55	C
C_4H_5Cl	4-Chloro-1,2-butadiene	2.02	Ci
C_4H_5Cl	1-Chloro-2-butyne	2.19	C
C_4H_5F	2-Fluoro-1,3-butadiene (trans conformation)	1.42	A
C_4H_5N	Pyrrole	1.84	C
C_4H_5N	cis-1-Cyanopropene	4.08	B
C_4H_5N	trans-1-Cyanopropene	4.50	B
C_4H_5N	2-Cyanopropene (methacrylonitrile)	3.69	C
C_4H_6	Cyclobutene	0.132	A
C_4H_6	1-Butyne	0.80	C
C_4H_6	1,2-Butadiene	0.403	A
C_4H_6	1,3-Butadiene	0	S
C_4H_6O	Cyclobutanone	2.99	B
C_4H_6O	trans-2-Butenal (crotonaldehyde)	3.67	Bi
C_4H_6O	2-Methylpropenal (methacrolein)	2.68	Ci
C_4H_6O	3-Butene-2-one	3.16	B
C_4H_7Cl	1-Chloro-2-methylpropene	1.95	Bi
$C_4H_7Cl_3$	1,1,2-Trichloro-2-methylpropane	1.86	Ci
C_4H_7F	Fluorocyclobutane	1.94	A
C_4H_7N	1-Cyanopropane	4.07	Bi
C_4H_8	1-Butene	0.34	Ci
C_4H_8	trans-2-Butene	0	S
C_4H_8	2-Methylpropene	0.50	A
$C_4H_8Cl_2$	1,4-Dichlorobutane	2.22	Ci
C_4H_8O	Tetrahydrofuran	1.63	C
C_4H_8O	cis-2,3-Dimethyloxirane	2.03	A
C_4H_8O	Butanal	2.72	Bi
$C_4H_8O_2$	1,4-Dioxane	0	S
$C_4H_8O_2$	Ethyl acetate	1.78	Ci
C_4H_9Br	1-Bromobutane	2.08	Ci
C_4H_9Br	2-Bromobutane	2.23	Ci
C_4H_9Cl	1-Chlorobutane	2.05	Bi
C_4H_9Cl	2-Chlorobutane	2.04	Ci
C_4H_9Cl	1-Chloro-2-methylpropane	2.00	Ci
C_4H_9Cl	2-Chloro-2-methylpropane	2.13	B
C_4H_9F	2-Fluoro-2-methylpropane	1.96	A
C_4H_9I	1-Iodobutane	2.12	Ci
C_4H_9NO	Propanoyl methylamine (N-methylpropionamide)	3.61	Bi
C_4H_9NO	Acetyl dimethylamine (N,N-dimethylacetamide)	3.81	Bi
$C_4H_9NO_2$	2-Nitrito-2-methylpropane (t-butyl nitrite)	2.74	Ci
$C_4H_9NO_2$	1-Nitrobutane	3.59	Bi
$C_4H_9NO_2$	2-Nitro-2-methylpropane	3.71	B
C_4H_{10}	Butane	⩽0.05	
C_4H_{10}	2-Methylpropane	0.132	A
$C_4H_{10}O$	1-Butanol	1.66	Bi
$C_4H_{10}O$	2-Methylpropan-1-ol (isobutanol)	1.64	C
$C_4H_{10}O$	Diethyl ether	1.15	Bi
$C_4H_{10}S$	Diethyl sulfide	1.54	Ci
$C_4H_{11}N$	Diethyl amine	0.92	Ci
C_5H_5N	Pyridine	2.19	B
C_5H_5N	1-Cyano-1,3-butadiene	3.90	Ci
C_5H_6	1,3-Cyclopentadiene	0.419	A
C_5H_8	Cyclopentene	0.20	B
C_5H_8	1-Pentyne	0.81	Ci
C_5H_8	2-Methyl-1,3-butadiene (trans conformation)	0.25	A
$C_5H_8O_2$	Acetylacetone		Ci
C_5H_9N	1-Cyanobutane	4.12	Bi
C_5H_9N	2-Cyano-2-methylpropane	3.95	A
$C_5H_{10}O_3$	Diethyl carbonate	1.10	Ci
$C_5H_{11}Br$	1-Bromopentane	2.20	Ci
$C_5H_{11}Cl$	1-Chloropentane	2.16	Ci
C_5H_{12}	2-Methylbutane	0.13	C
C_5H_{12}	2,2-Dimethylpropane	0	S
$C_6H_2Cl_2O_2$	2,5-Dichloro-1,4-cyclo-hexadienedione	0	S
$C_6H_4ClNO_2$	o-Chloronitrobenzene	4.64	B
$C_6H_4ClNO_2$	m-Chloronitrobenzene	3.73	B
$C_6H_4ClNO_2$	p-Chloronitrobenzene	2.83	B
$C_6H_4Cl_2$	o-Dichlorobenzene	2.50	B
$C_6H_4Cl_2$	m-Dichlorobenzene	1.72	C
$C_6H_4Cl_2$	p-Dichlorobenzene	0	S
$C_6H_4FNO_2$	p-Fluoronitrobenzene	2.87	B
$C_6H_4F_2$	m-Difluorobenzene	1.58	B
$C_6H_4N_2O_4$	p-Dinitrobenzene	0	S
$C_6H_4O_2$	1,4-Cyclohexadienedione (p-benzoquinone)	0	S
C_6H_5Br	Bromobenzene	1.70	B
C_6H_5Cl	Chlorobenzene	1.69	B
C_6H_5ClO	p-Chlorophenol	2.11	C
C_6H_5F	Fluorobenzene	1.60	C
C_6H_5I	Iodobenzene	1.70	C
$C_6H_5NO_2$	Nitrobenzene	4.22	B
C_6H_6	Benzene	0	S

Compounds containing carbon—Continued

Formula	Compound name	Selected moment (debyes)	
C_6H_6O	Phenol	1.45	C
C_6H_7N	Aminobenzene (aniline)	1.53	C
C_6H_8	1,3-Cyclohexadiene	0.44	B
C_6H_{10}	1-Hexyne	0.83	Ci
C_6H_{10}	3,3-Dimethyl-1-butyne	0.66	A
$C_6H_{10}Cl_2$	cis-le,2a-Dichlorocyclohexane	3.11	C
$C_6H_{12}N_2$	Diisopropylidene hydrazine (dimethyl ketazine)	1.53	Bi
$C_6H_{12}O_2$	Pentyl formate (n-amyl formate)	1.90	Ci
$C_6H_{12}O_3$	2,4,6-Trimethyl-1,3,5-trioxane (paraldehyde)	1.43	C
$C_6H_{14}O$	Dipropyl ether	1.21	Ci
$C_6H_{14}O_2$	1,1-Diethoxyethane		i
$C_6H_{15}N$	Triethyl amine	0.66	Ci
$C_7H_4ClF_3$	o-Chloro(trifluoromethyl)benzene	3.46	B
$C_7H_4ClF_3$	p-Chloro(trifluoromethyl)benzene	1.58	C
$C_7H_5F_3$	(Trifluoromethyl)benzene	2.86	B
C_7H_5N	Cyanobenzene (benzonitrile)	4.18	B
C_7H_7Cl	o-Chlorotoluene	1.56	C
C_7H_7Cl	p-Chlorotoluene	2.21	C
C_7H_7F	o-Fluorotoluene	1.37	C
C_7H_7F	m-Fluorotoluene	1.86	C
C_7H_7F	p-Fluorotoluene	2.00	C
$C_7H_7NO_3$	o-Nitro(methoxy)benzene	4.83	Bi
$C_7H_7NO_3$	m-Nitro(methoxy)benzene	4.55	Bi
$C_7H_7NO_3$	p-Nitro(methoxy)benzene	5.26	B
C_7H_8	1,3,5-Cycloheptatriene	0.25	C
C_7H_8	Toluene	0.36	C
C_7H_8O	Phenylmethanol (benzyl alcohol)	1.71	C
C_7H_8O	Methoxybenzene (anisole)	1.38	C
C_7H_9NO	o-Amino(methoxy)benzene	1.61	Ci
$C_7H_{14}O_2$	Pentyl acetate (n-amyl acetate)	1.75	Ci
$C_7H_{15}Br$	1-Bromoheptane	2.16	Ci
$C_8H_4N_2$	p-Dicyanobenzene	0	S
C_8H_8O	Acetylbenzene (acetophenone)	3.02	B
$C_8H_8O_2$	2,5-Dimethyl-1,4-cyclohexadienedione	0	S
C_8H_{10}	Ethylbenzene	0.59	C
C_8H_{10}	o-Xylene	0.62	C
C_8H_{10}	p-Xylene	0	S
$C_8H_{12}O_2$	Tetramethylcyclobutane-1,3-dione	0	S
$C_8H_{18}O$	Dibutyl ether	1.17	Ci
C_9H_7N	Quinoline	2.29	C
C_9H_7N	Isoquinoline	2.73	C
$C_9H_{10}O_2$	Ethyl phenylformate (ethyl benzoate)	2.00	Ci
$C_{10}H_8$	Azulene	0.80	B
$C_{10}H_{14}BeO_4$	Bis(2,4-pentanedionato) beryllium	0	S
$C_{12}H_9BrO$	p-Bromophenoxybenzene	1.98	C
$C_{12}H_9NO_3$	p-Nitrophenoxybenzene	4.54	B
$C_{12}H_{10}$	Phenylbenzene (diphenyl)	0	S
$C_{13}H_{11}BrO$	p-Bromophenoxy-p-toluene	2.45	C
$C_{14}H_{14}O$	Bis(p-tolyl) ether	1.54	C
$C_{15}H_{21}AlO_6$	Tris(2,4-pentanedionato) aluminum	0	S
$C_{15}H_{21}CrO_6$	Tris(2,4-pentanedionato) chromium (III)	0	S
$C_{15}H_{21}FeO_6$	Tris(2,4-pentanedionato) iron (III)	0	S
$C_{20}H_{28}O_8Th$	Tetrakis(2,4-pentanedionato) thorium	0	S

DIPOLE MOMENTS

The method of measurement of the dipole moments is indicated in the following **two tables** by the symbols:

- B   benzene solution
- C   carbon tetrachloride solution
- D   1,4-dioxane solution
- H   n-heptane solution
- St   measurement of Stark effect in microwave spectrum of gas

Dipole Moments for Some Inorganic Compounds

Compound	Dipole Moment $\times 10^{-18}$ e. s. u.	Method
$AlBr_3$	5.14	B
AlI_3	2.48	B
CsCl	10.42	St
CsF	7.875	St
HF	1.92 ± 0.02	..
HCl	1.084 ± 0.003–0.007	..
NBr	0.78	..
HDSe	0.62	St
HI	0.38	..
DCl	1.084 ± 0.003–0.007	..
HNO_3	2.16	St
$HgBr_2$	0.95	B
$HgCl_2$	1.23	B
H_2O	1.87	..
H_2O_2	2.13 ± 0.05	..
H_2S	1.10	..
SO_2	1.60	..
SO_3	0.00	..
SO_2F_2	1.110	St
NH_3	1.3	..
N_2H_4	1.84	..
NO	0.16	..
NO_2	0.29	..
N_2O_4	0.37	..
NOCl	1.83	..
NOBr	1.87	..
PCl_3	0.90–1.10	..
PCl_5	0.0	..
CO	0.10	..
CO_2	0.0	..
SiD_2F_2	1.53	St
SiH_2F_2	1.54	St
$SnCl_4$	0.95	B
SnI_4	0	B
$TiCl_4$	0	C

Dipole Moments for Some Organo-metallic Compounds

Compound	Dipole Moment $\times 10^{-18}$ e. s. u.	Method
Beryllium diethyl	1.0	H
Cadmium diethyl	0.3	H
Mercury diethyl	0.0	H
Magnesium diethyl	4.8	D
Zinc diethyl	0.0	H
Beryllium diphenyl	1.6	B
Cadmium diphenyl	0.6	B
Mercury diphenyl	0.2	B
Magnesium diphenyl	4.9	D
Zinc diphenyl	0.8	B
Chromium (0), diphenyl	0	B
Chromium, ditolyl	0	B
Cobalt, mononitrosyl tricarbonyl	0.72	B
Cyclopentadienyl, chromium dicarbonyl mono nitrosyl	3.23	B
Cyclopentadienyl, manganese tri-carbonyl	3.30	B
Cyclopentadienyl, cobalt ducarbonyl	2.87	B
Cyclopentadienyl, vanadium tetra-carbonyl	3.17	B
Penta cyclopentadienyl, dicobalt	0	B
Dicyclopentadienyl, iron (II)	0	B
Dicyclopentadienyl, lead (II)	1.63	B
Dicyclopentadienyl, tin (II)	1.02	B
Ethyl lithium	0.87	B
Iron, dinitrosyl dicarbonyl	0.95	B
Iron, tetracarbonyl-diiodide	3.68	B
Iron, tetracarbonyl mono-(methyl isonitrile)	5.07	B
Iron, pentacarbonyl	0.63	B
Iron, bis(p-chlorophenyl cyclo-pentadienyl	3.12	B
Ruthenium (II), di-indenyl	0	B

Dipole Moments

Dipole Moments of Amino Acid Esters

Substance	$\mu \cdot 10^{18}$ e. s. u.
Glycine ethyl ester	2.11
α-Alanine ethyl ester	2.09
α-Aminobutyric acid ethyl ester	2.13
α-Aminovaleric acid ethyl ester	2.13
Valine ethyl ester	2.11
α-Aminocaproic acid ethyl ester	2.13
β-Alanine ethyl ester	2.14
β-Aminobutyric acid ethyl ester	2.11

Accurate to $\pm 0.01 \cdot 10^{-18}$ e. s. u.
J. Wyman, Chem. Rev., 1936, **19**, 213.

Dipole Moments of Amides

Urea	4.56
Thiourea	4.89
Symm.-dimethylurea	4.8
Tetraethylurea	3.3
Propylurea	4.1
Acetamide	3.6
Sulfamide	3.9
Benzamide	3.6
Valeramide	3.7
Caproamide	3.9

For comprehensive list of dipole moments see Trans. Faraday Soc., 1934, **30**, General Discussion.

Dipole Moments of Some Hormones and Related Compounds in Dioxan

Cholestane-3(β) : 7(α)-diol	2.31
Cholestane-3(β) : 7(β)-diol	2.55
Cholestane	2.98
Δ⁵-Cholestane-3(β)ol-7 one	3.79
Androsterone	3.70
β-Androsterone	2.95
Δ⁵-Androstene-3(β) : 17(α)-diol	2.89
Δ⁵-Androstene-3(β) : 17(β)-diol	2.69
Δ⁵-Androstene-3(β)ol-17 one	2.46
Testosterone	4.32
cis-Testosterone	5.17
Δ⁴-Androstene-3 : 17 dione	3.32
Isophorone	3.96

Ethylenic $>C=C<$ in a six membered ring and conjugated with $>C=O$ increases the dipole moment approximately by 1 Debye. Non-conjugated $>C=C<$ in sterols decreases the dipole moment by approximately 0.49. Biological activity is not correlated with dipole moment. W. D. Kumler and G. M. Fohlen, J. Am. Chem. Soc., 1945, **67**, 437

ELECTRON AFFINITIES

F. M. Page

The tabulated values are given in kJ mol^{-1}, eV and kcal mol^{-1} for the convenience of users. All values are experimental observations and refer to the gas phase at 0°K unless otherwise stated. Extended tables of atomic electron affinities are given by L. M. Branscombe in "Atomic and Molecular Processes", Ed. D. R. Bates, Academic Press, New York (1962), and for radical and molecular electron affinities in "Negative Ions and the Magnetron", Wiley —Interscience—London (1969). See also H. O. Pritchard, Chem. Rev. **52**, 529 (1953); F. H. Field and J. L. Franklin, "Electron Impact Phenomena", Academic Press, New York (1957), N. S. Buchel'nikova, Usp, fiz. nauk **65**, 357 (1958), A.E.C. Tr3657, Oak Ridge (1959), V. I. Vedeneyev et al, "Bond Energies, Ionisation Potentials and Electron Affinities", Arnold, London (1966) and C. J. Schexnayder, N.A.S.A. Technical Note D1791, Washington (1963).

Atoms

Ion Formed	Electron Affinity		
	kJ mol^{-1}	eV	kcal mol^{-1}
Br$^-$	324	3.363	77.4
C$^-$	108	1.12	25.8
Cl$^-$	348	3.613	83.2
F$^-$	333	3.448	79.6
H$^-$	77	0.80	18.4
*H$^-$ (1s^2)	72	0.747	17.2
I$^-$	296	3.063	70.8
O$^-$	142	1.466	33.8
S$^-$	200	2.07	47.7

* Quantum mechanical calculation.

Molecules

Ion Formed	Electron Affinity		
	kJ mol^{-1}	eV	kcal mol^{-1}
BF$_3^-$	255	2.65	61.0
(p-Benzoquinone)$^-$	129	1.34	30.9
(Chloranil)$^-$	231	2.40	55.3
(Fluoranil)$^-$	218	2.27	52.2
No$_2^-$	377	3.91	90.0
O$_2^-$	43	0.45	10.1
SF$_6^-$	138	1.43	33.0
(Tetracyanoethylene)$^-$	278	2.88	66.4
WF$_6^-$	264	2.74	63.0
UF$_6^-$	280	2.91	67.0

Radicals

Ion Formed	Electron Affinity		
	kJ mol^{-1}	eV	kcal mol^{-1}
Ch$_3^-$	104	1.08	24.8
C$_2$H$_5^-$	86	0.89	20.5
C$_6$H$_5^-$	210	2.20	49.6
CF$_3^-$	179	1.85	42.7
CCl$_3^-$	117	1.22	28.0
SiF$_3^-$	323	3.35	77.2
NH$_2^-$	108	1.12	25.7
C$_6$H$_5$NH$^-$	149	1.55	35.7
(C$_6$H$_5$)$_2$N$^-$	114	1.19	23.3
PH$_2^-$	154	1.60	36.8
OH$^-$	176	1.83	42.1
CH$_3$O$^-$	36	0.38	8.7
CF$_3$O$^-$	131	1.35	31.2
SH$^-$	211	2.19	50.4
CH$_3$S$^-$	127	1.32	30.4
CN$^-$	305	3.17	7.30
SCN$^-$	209	2.17	49.9
SeCN$^-$	255	2.64	60.9

IONIZATION POTENTIALS
OF THE ELEMENTS

Different methods have been employed to measure ionization potentials. Abbreviations of the methods used for data listed in the following table are:

S; Vacuum ultraviolet spectroscopy
SI; Surface ionization, mass spectrometric
EI; Electron impact with mass analysis

El.	At. No.	Ionization potential in volts								Meth.
		I	II	III	IV	V	VI	VII	VIII	
Ar	18	15.755	27.62	40.9	59.79	75	91.3	124	143.46	S
Ac	89	6.9	12.1	20						S
Ag	47	7.574	21.48	34.82						S
Al	13	5.984	18.823	28.44	119.96	153.77	190.42	241.38	284.53	S
As	33	9.81	18.63	28.34	50.1	62.6	127.5			S
At	85	9.5								S
Au	79	9.22	20.5							S
B	5	8.296	25.149	37.92	259.298	340.127				S
Ba	56	5.21	10.001	35.5						S
Be	4	9.32	18.206	153.85	217.657					S
Bi	83	7.287	16.68	25.56	45.3	56	88.3			S
Br	35	11.84	21.6	35.9	47.3	59.7	88.6	103	193	S
C	6	11.256	24.376	47.871	64.476	391.986	489.84			S
Ca	20	6.111	11.868	51.21	67	84.39	109	128	143.3	S
Cb(Nb)	41	6.88	14.32	25.04	38.3	50	103	125		S
Cd	48	8.991	16.904	37.47						SI
Ce	58	5.6	12.3	20	33.3					S
Cl	17	13.01	23.8	39.9	53.5	67.8	96.7	114.27	348.3	S
Co	27	7.86	17.05	33.49	83.1					S
Cr	24	6.764	16.49	30.95	50	73	91	161	185	S
Cs	55	3.893	25.1	35						S
Cu	29	7.724	20.29	36.83						S
Dy	66	6.8								SI
Er	68	6.08								S
Eu	63	5.67	11.24							S
F	9	17.418	34.98	62.646	87.14	114.214	157.117	185.139	953.6	S
Fe	26	7.87	16.18	30.643	56.8				151	S
Fr	87	4								S
Ga	31	6	20.57	30.7	64.2					S
Gd	64	6.16	12							S
Ge	32	7.88	15.93	34.21	44.7	93.4				S
H	1	13.595								S
He	2	24.481	54.403							S
Hf	72	7	14.9	23.2	33.3					S
Hg	80	10.43	18.751	34.2	49.5**		67**			S
I	53	10.454	19.13						170	S
In	49	5.785	18.86	28.03	54.4					S
Ir	77	9								S
K	19	4.339	31.81	46	60.9	82.6	99.7	118	155	S
Kr	36	13.996	24.56	36.9	43.5**	63**	94**			S
La	57	5.61	11.43	19.17						S
Li	3	5.39	75.619	122.419						S
Lu	71		14.7							S
Mg	12	7.644	15.031	80.14	109.29	141.23	186.49	224.9	265.957	S
Mn	25	7.432	15.636	33.69	52	76		119	196	S
Mo	42	7.10	16.15	27.13	46.4	61.2	68	126	153	S
N	7	14.53	29.593	47.426	77.45	97.863	551.925	666.83		S
Na	11	5.138	47.29	71.715	98.88	138.37	172.09	208.444	264.155	S
Nb(Cb)	41	6.88	14.32	25.04	38.3	50	103	125		SI
Nd	60	5.51								S
Ne	10	21.559	41.07	63.5	97.02	126.3	157.91			S
Ni	28	7.633	18.15	35.16						S
O	8	13.614	35.108	54.886	77.394	113.873	138.08	739.114	871.12	S
Os	76	8.5	17							S
P	15	10.484	19.72	30.156	51.354	65.007	220.414	263.31	309.26	S
Pb	82	7.415	15.028	31.93	42.31	68.8				S
Pd	46	8.33	19.42	32.92						S
Po	84	8.43								S
Pr	59	5.46								SI
Pt	78	9.0	18.56							S
Pu	94	5.1								S
Ra	88	5.277	10.144							S
Rb	37	4.176	27.5	40						S
Re	75	7.87	16.6							S
Rh	45	7.46	18.07	31.05						S
Rn	86	10.746								S
Ru	44	7.364	16.76	28.46						S
S	16	10.357	23.4	35	47.29	72.5	88.029	280.99	328.8	S
Sb	51	8.639	16.5	25.3	44.1	56	108			S
Sc	21	6.54	12.8	24.75	73.9	92	111	139	159	S
Se	34	9.75	21.5	32	43	68	82	155		S
Si	14	8.149	16.34	33.488	45.13	166.73	205.11	246.41	303.07	S
Sm	62	5.6	11.2							S
Sn	50	7.342	14.628	30.49	40.72	72.3				S
Sr	38	5.692	11.027	57						S
Ta	73	7.88	16.2							SI
Tb	65	5.98								S
Tc	43	7.28	15.26	29.54						S
Te	52	9.01	18.6	31	38	60	72	12.7		EI
Th	90	6.95			29.38					S
Ti	22	6.82	13.57	27.47	43.24	99.8	120	141	172	S
Tl	81	6.106	20.42	29.8	50.7					S
Tm	69	5.81								SI
U	92	6.08								S
V	23	6.74	14.65	29.31	48	65	129	151	170	S
W	74	7.98	17.7							S
Xe	54	12.127*	21.2	31.3	42	53	58	135		EI
Y	39	6.38	12.23	20.5	77					S
Yb	70	6.2	12.10							S
Zn	30	9.391	17.96	39.7						S
Zr	40	6.84	13.13	22.98	34.33	99				S

*These steps by S method.   **These steps by EI method.

NUCLEAR SPINS, MOMENTS, AND MAGNETIC RESONANCE FREQUENCIES

Kenneth Lee and Weston A. Anderson
1967

This table contains the published values for the nuclear spins, magnetic moments, and quadrupole moments, and the calculated values for the nuclear magnetic resonance (NMR) frequency and for the relative sensitivities. Only those isotopes with both published spin and magnetic moment values are tabulated. The magnetic and quadrupole moment values were selected from results published during the period from January, 1955 to June, 1967. Earlier references were obtained from H. E. Walchli, A Table of Nuclear Moment Data, U.S. Atomic Energy Commission Report ORNL—1469, Supplement I (1953) and Supplement II (1955), and D. Strominger, J. M. Hollander, and G. T. Seaborg, Table of Isotopes, Rev. Mod. Phys. 30, 585 (1958). A table containing the known (1963) spin and electromagnetic values of nuclear ground and excited states has been compiled by I. Lindgren, Perturbed Angular Correlations; E. Karlsson, E. Mathias, and K. Siegbahn, editors; North-Holland Publishing Co. (1964). The magnetic moments given in this latter table are corrected for the diamagnetic effect. A more complete list of spin and moment results for nuclei in excited states are included in Lindgren's table.

In general, the results chosen for this table were selected with an inclination to NMR measurements and to the precision of the measurement. Only six significant figures are used in this table. Therefore, the number of figures may be less than those published. The experimental methods employed in determining the moments are indicated by the following symbols:

Ab = atomic beam magnetic resonance (hyperfine structure, double or triple resonance or other method)

E = electron spin resonance or electron-nuclear double resonance
M = microwave absorption in gases

Mb = molecular (or diamagnetic) beam magnetic resonance
Mc = miscellaneous
Mo = Mössbauer effect
N = nuclear magnetic resonance
Qr = quadrupole resonance

Other symbols used in the table are:

A = atomic weight (mass number)
El = element
I = nuclear spin in units of $h/2\pi$
μ = magnetic moment in units of the nuclear magneton $eh/4\pi Mc$
m = metastable excited state

No = nuclear orientation
O = optical spectroscopy (hyperfine structure, band structure, double resonance, or optical pumping)
Qr = quadrupole resonance

Q = quadrupole moment in units of barns (10^{-24} cm²)
Z = atomic number
* = radioactive isotope
• = magnetic moment observed by NMR
( ) = assumed or estimated values

Assuming a nuclear magneton value of 5.0505×10^{-24} erg/gauss, the NMR frequency was calculated for a total field of 10 gauss. The sensitivities, relative to the proton, are calculated from the following expressions:

Sensitivity at constant field = $7.652 \times 10^{-3} \mu^3 (I+1)/I^2$
Sensitivity at constant frequency = $0.2387 \mu(I+1)$.

These expressions assume an equal number of nuclei, a constant temperature, and $T_1 = T_2$ (the longitudinal relaxation time equals the transverse relaxation time). These sensitivities represent the ideal induced voltage in the receiver coil at saturation and with a constant noise source. The calculated values are therefore determined under complete optimum conditions and should be regarded as such.

Isotope Z	El	A	Spin I	NMR Frequency in MHz for a 10 kilogauss field	Natural Abundance %	Rel. Sens. At constant field	Rel. Sens. At constant frequency	Magnetic Moment μ (nuclear magneton eh/4πMc)	μ Reference	μ Method	Electric Quadrupole Moment Q (barns 10⁻²⁴cm²)	Q Reference	Q Method
0	n	1*	1/2	29.167	—	0.322	0.685	-1.91315	1	Ab			
1	•H	1	1/2	42.5759	99.985	1.00	1.00	2.79268	2	N			
1	•H	2*	1	6.53566	$1.5{\times}10^{-2}$	$9.65{\times}10^{-3}$	0.409	0.857387	3	N	$2.73{\times}10^{-3}$	4	Ab
1	•H	3*	1/2	45.4129	—	1.21	1.07	2.97877	5	N			
2	He	3	1/2	32.433	$1.3{\times}10^{-4}$	0.442	0.762	-2.1274	6	N			
3	•Li	6	1	6.2653	7.42	$8.50{\times}10^{-3}$	0.392	0.82192	8	N	$6.9{\times}10^{-4}$	9	Ab
3	•Li	7	3/2	16.546	92.58	0.293	1.94	3.2560	8	N	$-3{\times}10^{-2}$	10	O
3	Li	8*	2	6.300	—	$2.59{\times}10^{-2}$	1.184	1.653	11	N			
4	•Be	9	3/2	5.9834	100	$1.39{\times}10^{-2}$	0.703	-1.1774	12	N	$5.2{\times}10^{-2}$	14	Ab
5	•B	10	3	4.5754	19.58	$1.99{\times}10^{-2}$	1.72	1.8007	13	N	$7.4{\times}10^{-2}$	16	Ab
5	•B	11	3/2	13.660	80.42	0.165	1.60	2.6880	15	N	$3.55{\times}10^{-2}$	16	Ab
6	•C	13	1/2	10.7054	1.108	$1.59{\times}10^{-2}$	0.251	0.702199	17	N			
7	N	13*	1/2	4.91	—	$1.53{\times}10^{-3}$	0.115	(-)0.322	19	Ab			
7	•N	14	1	3.0756	99.63	$1.01{\times}10^{-3}$	0.193	0.40347	20	N	$1.6{\times}10^{-2}$	20	Mc
7	•N	15	1/2	4.3142	0.37	$1.04{\times}10^{-3}$	0.101	-0.28298	20	N			
8	O	15*	1/2	11.0	—	$1.70{\times}10^{-2}$	0.257	0.719	23	N			
8	•O	17	5/2	5.772	$3.7{\times}10^{-2}$	$2.91{\times}10^{-2}$	1.58	-1.8930	24	N	$-2.6{\times}10^{-2}$	25	M
9	F	17*	5/2	14.40	—	0.451	3.94	4.720	26	Ab			
9	•F	19	1/2	40.0541	100	0.833	0.941	2.62727	21	N			
9	F	20*	2	7.977	—	$5.26{\times}10^{-2}$	1.50	2.093	27	Ab			
10	Ne	19*	(1/2)	28.75	—	0.308	0.675	-1.886	28	Ab			
10	•Ne	21	3/2	3.3611	0.257	$2.50{\times}10^{-2}$	0.395	-0.66140	29	N			
11	Na	21*	3/2	12.126	—	0.116	1.42	2.3861	30	Ab			
11	Na	22*	3	4.436	—	$1.81{\times}10^{-2}$	1.67	1.746	31	N			
11	•Na	23	3/2	11.262	100	$9.25{\times}10^{-2}$	1.32	2.2161	17	N	0.14-0.15	32	O
11	Na	24*	4	3.221	—	$1.15{\times}10^{-2}$	2.02	1.690	34	Ab		33	
12	•Mg	25	5/2	2.6054	10.13	$2.67{\times}10^{-2}$	0.714	-0.85449	35	N	0.149	36	Ab
13	•Al	27	5/2	11.094	100	0.206	3.04	3.6385		N			

Isotope Z	El	A	Spin I	NMR Frequency in MHz for a 10 kilogauss field	Natural Abundance %	Rel. Sens. At constant field	Rel. Sens. At constant frequency	Magnetic Moment μ (nuclear magneton eh/4πMc)	μ Reference	μ Method	Electric Quadrupole Moment Q (barns 10⁻²⁴cm²)	Q Reference	Q Method
14	•Si	29	1/2	8.4578	4.70	$7.84{\times}10^{-4}$	0.199	-0.55477	37	N	—		—
15	•P	31	1/2	17.235	100	$6.63{\times}10^{-2}$	0.405	1.1305	38	N	—		—
15	P	32*	1	1.923	—	$2.46{\times}10^{-4}$	0.120	-0.2523	39	E			
16	S	33	3/2	3.2654	0.76	$2.26{\times}10^{-4}$	0.383	0.64257	37	N	$-6.4{\times}10^{-2}$	40	M
16	S	35*	3/2	5.08	—	$8.50{\times}10^{-3}$	0.597	1.00	41	M	$4.5{\times}10^{-2}$	40	Ab
17	•Cl	35	3/2	4.1717	75.53	$4.70{\times}10^{-3}$	0.490	0.82091	42	N	$-7.89{\times}10^{-2}$	42	Ab
17	Cl	36*	2	4.8931	—	$1.21{\times}10^{-2}$	0.919	1.2838	43	N	$-1.72{\times}10^{-2}$	44	Ab
17	•Cl	37	3/2	3.472	24.47	$2.71{\times}10^{-3}$	0.408	0.6833	45	N	$-6.21{\times}10^{-2}$	42	Ab
18	Ar	37*	3/2	5.08	—	$8.50{\times}10^{-3}$	0.597	1.0	45	N			
19	K	38*	3	3.491	—	$8.82{\times}10^{-3}$	1.31	1.374	46	Ab			
19	•K	39	3/2	1.9868	93.10	$5.08{\times}10^{-4}$	0.233	0.39097	47	N	0.11	49	O
19	K	40*	4	2.470	$1.18{\times}10^{-2}$	$5.21{\times}10^{-3}$	1.55	-1.296	48	N		50	
19	K	41	3/2	1.0905	6.88	$8.40{\times}10^{-5}$	0.128	0.21459	51	Mb			
19	K	42*	2	4.345	—	$8.50{\times}10^{-3}$	0.816	-1.140	52	Ab			
19	K	43*	3/2	0.828	—	$3.68{\times}10^{-5}$	$9.73{\times}10^{-3}$	-0.163	53	Ab			
20	Ca	41*	7/2	3.4681	—	$1.14{\times}10^{-2}$	1.71	-1.5924	54	N			
20	•Ca	43	7/2	2.8646	0.145	$6.40{\times}10^{-4}$	1.41	-1.3153	55	N			
21	Sc	43*	7/2	10.04	—	0.275	4.95	4.61	56	N	-0.26	56	Ab
21	Sc	44*	2	9.76	—	$9.63{\times}10^{-2}$	1.83	2.56	57	N	0.14	57	Ab
21	Sc	44m*	6	5.03	—	$9.24{\times}10^{-2}$	6.62	3.96	57	N	0.37	57	Ab
21	•Sc	45	7/2	10.343	100	0.301	5.10	4.7492	58	N	-0.22	59	Ab
21	Sc	46*	4	5.77	—	$6.65{\times}10^{-2}$	3.62	3.03	56	Ab	0.12	60	Ab
21	Sc	47*	7/2	11.6	—	0.426	5.73	5.33	56	N	-0.22	56	Ab
22	•Ti	47	5/2	2.4000	7.28	$2.40{\times}10^{-3}$	0.102	-0.78710	61	N			
22	•Ti	49	7/2	2.4005	5.51	$2.09{\times}10^{-3}$	0.658	-1.1022	62	N			
23	V	49*	7/2	9.71	—	1.18		4.46	62	N			
23	V	50*	6	4.4250	0.24	$5.55{\times}10^{-2}$	5.58	3.3413	8	N			
23	•V	51	7/2	11.19	99.76	0.382	5.52	5.139	61	N	$1.5{\times}10^{-1}$	61	Ab
24	•Cr	53	3/2	2.4065	9.55	$9.03{\times}10^{-4}$	0.283	-0.47354	66	N			
25	Mn	52*	6	3.907	—	$4.33{\times}10^{-2}$	5.14	3.075	66	N			
25	Mn	53*	2	0.030	—	$2.9{\times}10^{-9}$	$5.73{\times}10^{-3}$	0.008	67	N			
25	•Mn	55	7/2	11.0	100	0.362	5.42	5.05	69	E	$-4{\times}10^{-2}$	65	O

Upper table (Z = 47–58):

Z	El	A	Spin I	NMR Frequency in MHz for a 10 kilogauss field	Natural Abundance %	Rel. Sens. at constant field	Rel. Sens. at constant frequency	Magnetic Moment μ (eh/4πMc)	μ Reference	μ Method	Electric Quadrupole Moment Q (10⁻²⁴ cm²)	Q Reference	Q Method
47	*Ag	107	1/2	1.7229	51.82	6.62x10⁻⁵	4.05x10⁻²	-0.11301	47	N	—		
47	*Ag	108*	1	32.0	—	1.13	2.01	4.2	119	Ab	—		
47	*Ag	109	1/2	1.9807	48.18	1.01x10⁻⁴	4.66x10⁻²	-0.12992	47	N	—		
47	Ag	110m*	6	4.557	—	6.87x10⁻³	5.99	3.587	120	Ab			
47	Ag	111*	1/2	2.21	—	1.40x10⁻⁴	5.19x10⁻²	-0.145	121	Ab			
47	Ag	112*	2	2.41	—	9.00x10⁻³	3.90x10⁻²	0.0545	122	Ab			
47	Ag	113*	1/2	2.44	—	1.81x10⁻⁴	5.66x10⁻²	0.158	122	Ab			
48	Cd	107*	5/2	1.879	—	1.00x10⁻³	0.515	-0.3162	123	O	0.8	123	O
48	Cd	109*	5/2	2.529	—	2.44x10⁻³	0.693	-0.3293	124	O	0.8	124	O
48	Cd	111	1/2	9.028	12.75	9.54x10⁻³	0.212	-0.5922	125	N			
48	*Cd	113	1/2	9.445	12.26	1.09x10⁻²	0.222	-0.6195	126	N			
48	Cd	113m*	11/2	1.51	—	2.13x10⁻³	1.69	-1.09	239	O	-0.79	239	O
48	Cd	115*	1/2	9.862	—	1.24x10⁻³	0.232	-0.6469	127	N	-0.61	127	O
48	Cd	115m*	11/2	1.447	—	1.87x10⁻²	1.62	-1.044	45	O	1.14	97	Ab
49	*In	113	9/2	9.3099	4.28	4.28x10⁻³	7.22	5.4960	128	N	1.16	97	Ab
49	In	113m*	1/2	3.209	—	7.54x10⁻²	7.54x10⁻²	-0.2105	129	O			
49	In	114*	5	7.2	—	6.64x10⁻³	6.73	4.7	130	Ab			
49	*In	115*	9/2	9.3201	95.72	0.191	7.23	5.5079	131	N	1.16	97	Ab
49	In	115m*	1/2	3.75	—	0.347	6.03	-0.9437	132	Ab			
49	In	116m*	5	6.43	—	0.137	6.30	4.31	129	Ab			
50	Sn	115	1/2	6.7	0.35	3.50x10⁻³	0.327	-0.91320	125	N			
50	Sn	117	1/2	13.922	7.61	4.52x10⁻³	0.356	-0.99490	125	N			
50	Sn	119	1/2	15.148	8.58	5.18x10⁻³	0.373	-1.0409	125	N			
51	Sb	121	5/2	10.189	57.25	0.160	2.79	3.3415	133	N	-0.5	134	O
51	Sb	123	7/2	5.5176	42.75	9.04x10⁻⁴	1.36	2.5334	45	N	-0.7	134	O
52	Te	123	1/2	4.15	0.87	1.8x10⁻³	9.67x10⁻²	0.27	137	N			
52	Te	125*	1/2	11.16	6.99	3.15x10⁻³	0.262	-0.7319	37	N			
52	*Te	127	1/2	13.4	—	0.116	0.316	-0.6824	37	Ab			
53	I	125*	5/2	9.0	—	9.34x10⁻³	2.51	2.7937	138	N	-0.66	138	M
53	I	127	5/2	8.5183	100	4.96x10⁻³	2.33	2.6031	139	N	-0.69	134	O
53	I	129*	7/2	5.963	—	5.77x10⁻³	2.80	2.738	141	Ab	-0.48	140	Qr
53	I	131*	7/2	11.777	—	2.12x10⁻³	2.94	-0.7234	142	N	-0.41	141	Ab
54	*Xe	129	1/2	3.4611	26.44	2.63x10⁻³	0.277	0.8899	142	N	-0.12	143	O
54	*Xe	131	3/2	21.8	21.18	0.134	0.410	1.47	144	N			
55	Cs	129*	1/2	10.7	—	0.146	0.512	1.4	144	Ab			
55	Cs	130*	1	10.72	—	4.20x10⁻³	0.526	2.22	144	Ab			
55	Cs	131*	5/2	8.46	—	6.28x10⁻³	0.668	2.56422	8	N	-3x10⁻³	146	Ab
55	*Cs	133	7/2	5.55469	100	4.74x10⁻³	2.75	2.56422	8	N	0.43	147,149	O
55	Cs	134*	4	5.666	—	6.28x10⁻³	3.55	2.973	148	Ab			
55	Cs	134m*	8	1.0447	—	1.42x10⁻³	2.36	1.0964	150	Ab			
55	Cs	135*	7/2	5.9096	—	5.62x10⁻³	2.91	2.2134	148	Ab			
55	Cs	137*	7/2	6.1459	—	6.32x10⁻³	3.03	2.8219	148	Ab			
56	Ba	135	3/2	4.2296	6.59	4.90x10⁻³	0.497	0.5322	151	N	0.25	153	O
56	*Ba	137	3/2	4.7315	11.32	6.86x10⁻³	0.556	0.5310	152	N	0.2	153	O
57	*La	138*	5*	5.6171	0.089	9.19x10⁻³	5.28	3.8844	154	N	2.7	154	N
57	La	139	7/2	6.0144	99.911	5.92x10⁻³	2.97	2.7615	107	N	0.21	155	Ab
58	Ce	137*	3/2	4.6	—	6.20x10⁻³	0.537	0.9	156	No			
58	Ce	137m*	11/2	0.96	—	5.40x10⁻³	1.07	0.69	157	No			
58	Ce	139*	3/2	5.1	—	8.50x10⁻³	0.597	1.0	156	No			
58	Ce	141*	7/2	2.1	—	2.57x10⁻³	1.04	0.97	158	E			

Lower table (Z = 25–47):

Z	El	A	Spin I	NMR Frequency in MHz for a 10 kilogauss field	Natural Abundance %	Rel. Sens. at constant field	Rel. Sens. at constant frequency	Magnetic Moment μ (eh/4πMc)	μ Reference	μ Method	Electric Quadrupole Moment Q (10⁻²⁴ cm²)	Q Reference	Q Method
25	Mn	54*	(2)	8.4	—	6.11x10⁻²	1.58	(2.2)	70	No			
25	*Mn	55	(3)	6.6	—	5.98x10⁻²	2.48	(2.6)	71	E			
25	*Mn	55*	5/2	10.501	100	0.175	2.88	3.444	72	E	0.55	72	M
26	*Fe	57	1/2	8.233	2.19	0.116	3.09	3.240	73	Ab	—		
27	Co	55*	7/2	1.3758	—	3.37x10⁻⁵	3.23x10⁻²	0.09024	74	No			
27	Co	56*	4	10.0	—	0.274	4.94	4.6	75	No			
27	Co	57*	7/2	7.34	—	0.136	4.60	3.85	76	E	0.40	78	Ab
27	Co	58*	2	10.1	—	0.283	4.99	4.05	77	E			
27	*Co	59	7/2	15.4	100	0.381	2.90	4.6163	241	E			
27	Co	60*	5	10.054	—	0.277	4.96	3.800	242	N	-0.16	82	E
28	*Ni	61	3/2	5.793	1.19	0.101	5.44	-0.74868	79	E			
29	Cu	61*	3/2	3.8047	—	3.57x10⁻²	0.447	2.13	80	Ab			
29	*Cu	63	3/2	10.8	69.09	8.22x10⁻²	1.27	2.2206	81	N	-0.15	82	E
29	*Cu	65	3/2	11.285	30.91	9.31x10⁻²	1.33	0.40	8	N	-2.4x10⁻²	83	O
30	Zn	64*	1	3.1	—	9.79x10⁻³	0.191	-2.3789	83	Ab	0.15	83	O
30	*Zn	65	3/2	12.089	4.11	0.114	1.42	-0.216	37	N	0.178	84	Ab
31	Ga	67*	5/2	1.65	—	1.54x10⁻³	0.103	0.7692	8	Ab	0.112	85	Ab
31	*Ga	69	3/2	2.345	60.4	1.95x10⁻³	0.643	0.8733	86	N	0.72	86	Ab
31	Ga	71	3/2	0.0892	39.6	2.85x10⁻³	0.730	0.0117	87	N			
31	*Ga	72*	3	10.22	—	2.45x10⁻³	1.20	2.011	62	N	-0.2	88	M
32	Ge	73	9/2	10.4	7.76	6.142	1.52	2.5549	15	N	0.3	89	M
33	*As	75	3/2	12.984	100	7.80x10⁻³	0.126	-0.13220	90	N	0.3	40	M
34	Se	77	1/2	0.33591	7.58	7.64x10⁻³	0.197	0.55	8	N			
35	Br	77*	3/2	8.4	—	7.40x10⁻³	1.15	-0.87679	91	M	0.9	92	M
35	Br	78*	1	1.4852	—	1.40x10⁻³	1.15	0.54	92	Ab	0.27	93	Ab
35	*Br	79	3/2	7.2919	50.54	2.51x10⁻²	0.649	-0.905	8	N	0.33	94	Ab
35	Br	80m*	5	3.45	—	4.27x10⁻¹	0.856	1.4349	15	Ab	0.20	93	Ab
35	Br	81	3/2	8.118	49.46	6.93x10⁻³	0.191	-0.5325	90	N	0.76	93	Ab
36	*Kr	83	9/2	2.22	11.55	2.98x10⁻²	1.10	-1.02	8	M	0.28	95	O
37	Rb	82m*	5	4.18	—	2.52x10⁻²	0.262	(-)0.545	91	Ab	(+)0.76	96	O
37	Rb	83*	5/2	10.667	—	7.86x10⁻³	1.25	2.0900	8	Ab	0.15	97	O
37	*Rb	85	5/2	3.92	72.15	2.08x10⁻³	0.245	1.317	94	N	0.25	98	O
37	Rb	87	3/2	2.008	27.85	4.20x10⁻³	1.89	-1.626	94	Ab			
38	*Sr	87	9/2	11.498	7.02	9.85x10⁻³	1.35	-1.30284	95	N	0.27	100	Ab
39	Y	89	1/2	2.479	100	7.90x10⁻³	2.33	-0.9671	96	N			
39	Y	90*	2	1.638	—	1.88x10⁻³	1.27	-1.001	98	O	0.13	101	Ab
39	*Y	91*	1/2	1.6956	—	2.08x10⁻³	1.22	2.05	99	Ab	0.2	104	E
40	*Zr	91	5/2	10.4	11.23	7.32x10⁻³	2.15	1.50	99	Ab	-0.16	105	Ab
41	Nb	93	9/2	2.29	100	6.20x10⁻³	1.19	1.42	99	N	-0.2	108	O
42	*Mo	95	5/2	4.33	15.72	1.23x10⁻²	0.945	-1.32	100	N	0.12	109	N
42	*Mo	97	5/2	5.03	9.46	1.32x10⁻²	1.13	-1.69	102	N	1.1	110	O
43	*Tc	99*	9/2	4.1108	—	1.05x10⁻²	1.21	-2.7414	103	N	0.3	111	O
44	Ru	99	3/2	13.931	12.72	2.77x10⁻²	1.64	-0.0893	66	N			
44	Ru	101	5/2	1.8452	17.07	2.69x10⁻²	1.43	-0.13682	47	N			
45	*Rh	103	1/2	2.0859	100	1.18x10⁻⁴	1.16	-1.62	105	N			
46	*Pd	105	5/2	6.17	22.23	1.99x10⁻³	1.09	0.163	106	N			
47	Ag	104*	5	2.49	—	5.84x10⁻²	8.07	-0.30284	107	N			
47	Ag	104m*	2	10.407	—	9.48x10⁻³	0.482	6.1435	45	N	-0.2	108	O
47	*Ag	105*	1/2	2.774	11.23	3.23x10⁻³	0.760	0.9097	45	N	0.12	109	N
			5/2	2.832	15.72	3.43x10⁻³	0.776	-0.9289	110	Ab	1.1	111	O
			5/2	9.5580	9.46	7.43	7.43	5.6572	112	Mo	0.3		
			3/2	2.1	17.07	0.376	0.576	-0.69	113	N			
			1/2	1.3401	100	1.41x10⁻⁵	3.11x10⁻²	-0.08790	43	N	—		
			5/2	1.95	22.23	1.12x10⁻³	0.534	-0.639	114	N			
			5	6.1	—	0.118	5.73	4.0	115	N			
			1/2	14.0	—	0.291	2.65	3.7	116	Ab			
			1/2	1.54	—	4.73x10⁻⁵	3.62x10⁻²	0.101	117	Ab			

NUCLEAR SPINS, MOMENTS, AND MAGNETIC RESONANCE FREQUENCIES (Continued)

Table (Z = 58 – 75)

Z	El	Isotope A	Spin I	NMR Freq. (MHz, 10 kG)	Natural Abundance %	Rel. Sens. const. field	Rel. Sens. const. freq.	μ (nuclear magneton)	μ Ref.	μ Method	Q (barns, $10^{-24}\,cm^2$)	Q Ref.	Q Method
58	Ce	143*	7/2	2.2	—	2.81×10^{-3}	1.07	1.0	156	No			
59	•Pr	141	5/2	12.5	100	0.293	3.42	4.09	159	Ab	-5.9×10^{-2}	158	Ab
59	Pr	142*	2	1.1		1.55×10^{-4}	0.215	0.30	160				
60	Nd	143	7/2	2.315	12.17	3.38×10^{-3}	1.14	−1.063	161	Ab	4×10^{-2}	161	Ab
60	Nd	145	7/2	1.42	8.30	7.86×10^{-4}	0.703	−0.654	162	Ab	−0.48	162	Ab
60	Nd	147*	5/2	1.77		8.32×10^{-4}	0.484	−0.579	158	E	−0.25	162	Ab
61	Pm	143*	(5/2)	11.6		0.235	3.17	(3.8)	163				
61	Pm	144*		8.5		0.167	2.43	(3.9)					
61	Pm	147*	(7/2)	2.6		9.02×10^{-3}	3.01	(1.7)	164	No	0.7	165	O
61	Pm	148*	(6)	2.3		8.88×10^{-3}	2.77	(1.8)	165	No	0.2	166	Ab
61	Pm	148m	1	5.62		4.83×10^{-3}	1.00	2.58	166				
61	Pm	149*	6	16		0.142	3.54	2.1	163				
61	Pm	151*	5/2	7.2		8.68×10^{-3}	3.01	1.8	167	Ab	1.9	167	Ab
62	Sm	147	7/2	5.5	14.97	2.50×10^{-2}	1.50	−0.807	168	Ab	−0.208	158	Ab
62	•Sm	149	7/2	1.76	13.83	1.48×10^{-3}	0.867	−0.643	163	Ab	6.0×10^{-2}	158	Ab
62	Sm	151*	7/2	1.40	47.82	7.47×10^{-4}	0.691	3.4630	169	Ab	1.16	170	O
63	•Eu	152*	3	10.559		0.178	2.89	1.912	171	O			
63	•Eu	153	5/2	4.858	52.18	2.38×10^{-2}	1.83	1.5292	169	Ab	2.9	170	O
63	Eu	154*	3	4.6627		1.53×10^{-2}	1.28	2.001	172	E			
64	•Gd	155	3/2	5.084	14.73	2.72×10^{-2}	1.91	−0.32	158	O	1.6	173	O
64	•Gd	157	3/2	1.6	15.68	2.79×10^{-4}	0.191	−0.40	173		2	173	O
65	•Tb	156*	3	3.8		5.44×10^{-4}	0.239	1.5	174	No	1.4	175	No
65	Tb	159	3/2	9.66	100	1.15×10^{-2}	1.43	1.90	175	No	1.3	176	No
65	Tb	160*	3	4.1		5.83×10^{-3}	1.13	1.6	177	Ab	1.9	177	No
66	Dy	155*	(3/2)	1.1		1.39×10^{-2}	1.53	0.21	178	No			
66	Dy	157*	5/2	1.6		7.87×10^{-3}	0.125	0.32	178	No			
66	Dy	161	5/2	1.4	18.88	2.79×10^{-3}	0.191	−0.46	158	E	1.4	158	E
66	Dy	163	5/2	2.0	24.97	4.17×10^{-3}	0.384	0.64	158	E	1.6	158	E
67	•Ho	165	7/2	8.73	100	1.12×10^{-3}	0.535	4.01	158	Ab	2.82	158	Ab
68	Er	165*	5/2	2.0		0.181	4.31	−0.565	166	Ab	2.2	166	Ab
68	Er	167	5/2	1.23	22.94	1.18×10^{-3}	0.607	0.51	162	Ab	2.83	162	Ab
68	Er	169*	1/2	7.8		5.07×10^{-4}	0.183	0.70	179	Ab			
68	Er	171*	5/2	2.1		6.09×10^{-3}	0.585	0.05	180	Ab	4.6	181	Ab
69	Tm	166*	2	0.19		1.47×10^{-3}	3.58×10^{-2}	−0.231	181	Ab			
69	•Tm	169	1/2	3.52	100	7.17×10^{-3}	8.27×10^{-2}	−0.26	182	O	0.61	183	Ab
69	Tm	170*	1	2.0		5.66×10^{-3}	0.124	0.227	183				
69	Tm	171*	1/2	3.46		2.69×10^{-3}	8.13×10^{-2}	0.49188	180	Ab			
70	•Yb	171	1/2	7.4990	14.31	5.37×10^{-3}	0.176	−0.67755	184	O	2.8	186	O
70	Yb	173	5/2	2.0659	16.13	5.46×10^{-3}	0.566	−0.15	185	No			
71	•Lu	175	(7/2)	0.33	97.41	1.33×10^{-3}	0.161	2.23	187	Ab	5.68	189	O
71	Lu	175*	7	4.86	2.59	9.40×10^{-6}	2.40	3.1	188		8.0	190	Ab
71	Lu	176*	7/2	3.4		3.12×10^{-3}	5.92	2.22	190	Ab	5.51	191	O
71	Lu	177*	7/2	4.84		3.72×10^{-3}	2.38	0.61	191	Ab	3	192	O
72	Hf	177	7/2	1.3	18.50	6.38×10^{-3}	0.655	−0.47	192	N	3	193	O
73	Hf	179	9/2	0.80	13.75	2.16×10^{-4}	0.617	2.340	193		3	193	O
73	•Ta	181	7/2	5.096	99.988	3.60×10^{-2}	2.51	0.116205	194	Ab	2.8	97	O
74	•W	183	1/2	1.7716	14.40	7.20×10^{-5}	4.16×10^{-2}	3.1437	196	N		241	
75	•Re	185	5/2	9.5855	37.07	0.133	2.63	1.728	13	Ab	2.6	97	O
75	Re	186*	1	13.17		7.90×10^{-2}	0.825	3.1759	197			241	
75	•Re	187*	5/2	9.6837	62.93	0.137	2.65		13	N			O

Table (Z = 75 – 95)

Z	El	Isotope A	Spin I	NMR Freq. (MHz, 10 kG)	Natural Abundance %	Rel. Sens. const. field	Rel. Sens. const. freq.	μ (nuclear magneton)	μ Ref.	μ Method	Q (barns, $10^{-24}\,cm^2$)	Q Ref.	Q Method
75	Re	188*	1	13.55	—	8.59×10^{-2}	0.848	1.777	197	Ab			
76	•Os	187	1/2	0.98059	1.64	1.22×10^{-5}	2.30×10^{-2}	0.06432	198	N		195	O
76	•Os	189	3/2	3.3034	16.1	2.34×10^{-3}	0.388	0.65004	199	N	0.8	202	O
77	•Ir	191	3/2	0.7318	37.3	2.53×10^{-5}	8.59×10^{-2}	0.1440	200	N	1.5	202	O
77	•Ir	193	3/2	0.7968	62.7	3.27×10^{-5}	9.36×10^{-2}	0.1568	201	N	1.5	202	O
78	•Pt	195	1/2	9.153	33.8	9.94×10^{-3}	0.215	0.6004	45				
79	Au	190*	1	0.496		4.20×10^{-3}	3.10×10^{-2}	0.065	203	Ab			
79	Au	194*	1	0.56		5.95×10^{-3}	3.49×10^{-2}	0.073	204	Ab			
79	Au	195*	3/2	0.742		2.65×10^{-3}	8.71×10^{-2}	0.146	204	Ab			
79	Au	196*	2	2.3		1.24×10^{-3}	0.430	0.6	204	Ab			
79	•Au	197	3/2	0.729188	100	2.51×10^{-3}	8.56×10^{-2}	0.143489	205	Ab	0.59	206	Ab
79	Au	198*	2	2.227		1.14×10^{-3}	0.418	0.5842	207	Ab		207	
79	Au	199*	3/2	1.358		1.62×10^{-2}	0.160	0.2673	207	Ab			
80	Hg	193m	13/2	3.1		1.93×10^{-3}	0.364	−0.61	208	O	1.37	209	O
80	Hg	193*	1/2	1.23		1.57×10^{-3}	1.88	−1.05	209	O			
80	•Hg	195m	13/2	8.1		6.84×10^{-3}	0.190	0.53	210				
80	Hg	195*	1/2	1.22		1.53×10^{-3}	1.86	−1.04	211				
80	Hg	197*	13/2	7.9		6.46×10^{-3}	0.186	0.52	209		1.41	209	O
80	•Hg	199	1/2	7.59012	16.84	5.67×10^{-3}	0.178	0.497859	213	No			
80	•Hg	201	3/2	2.8099	13.22	1.44×10^{-3}	0.330	−0.55293	45		0.50	216	Ab
81	Tl	203	1/2	2.5		2.45×10^{-3}	0.693	0.83	214	N	0.5	217	Ab
81	Tl	197*	1/2	23.6		0.171	0.555	1.55	217	O			
81	Tl	199*	1/2	0.57		0.178	0.562	1.57	218	O			
81	•Tl	200*	2	24.1		1.94×10^{-3}	0.107	(0.15)	219	O			
81	Tl	201*	1/2	0.57		0.181	0.566	1.58	219	O			
81	•Tl	202*	2	24.332		1.94×10^{-5}	0.107	(0.15)	219	O			
81	Tl	203	1/2	24.570	29.50	0.187	0.571	1.5960	220	O			
81	•Tl	204*	1/2	8.90771		4.05×10^{-6}	0.577	1.6116	221				
81	•Tl	205	1/2	7.78	70.50	0.192	0.209	0.089	8				
82	•Pb	203*	1/2	5.40	22.6	9.16×10^{-3}	6.03	0.584284	222	Ab	−0.64	223	Ab
83	Bi	204*	6	9.3		0.201	7.10	4.59	223	Ab	−0.41	223	Ab
83	Bi	205*	6	5.79		0.114	7.22	4.25	223	Ab		223	Ab
83	•Bi	206*	9/2	6.84178	100	0.346	(5.5)	(5.5)	224	N	−0.19	223	Ab
83	Bi	209	9/2	0.337		0.141	5.30	4.56	224	N	−0.4	225	Ab
84	Po	210*	1	0.79		1.32×10^{-2}	2.11×10^{-2}	4.03896	225	N	0.13	226	Ab
84	Po	205*	5/2	0.82		7.55×10^{-3}	0.217	0.0442	226	N	0.17	226	Ab
89	Ac	207*	5/2	5.6		8.43×10^{-3}	0.226	0.26	226	N	0.28	227	Ab
90	Th	227*	3/2	1.2		1.13×10^{-3}	0.656	0.27	228		−1.7	228	O
91	Pa	229*	5/2	9.96		2.74×10^{-3}	0.334	1.1	229	E	4.6		E
91	U	231*	3/2	17		6.40×10^{-3}	1.17	0.4	229	E			
92	U	233*	5/2	1.6		6.75×10^{-4}	2.03	1.96	231	E	−3.0	230	Ab
92	•U	235*	7/2	0.76	0.72	1.21×10^{-4}	0.451	0.54	231	E	−3.5	231	E
93	Np	237*	5/2	18		0.926	0.376	0.35	232	E	4.1	231	E
94	Pu	239*	1/2	3.05		3.67×10^{-4}	5.01	(6)	233	E			
94	Pu	241*	5/2	2.09		1.38×10^{-3}	7.16×10^{-2}	−0.200	234	O		236	Ab
95	Am	242*	1	4.82		1.69×10^{-4}	0.573	−0.686	235	Ab	4.9	237	O
95	Am	243*	5/2	2.90		8.46×10^{-4}	1.32	1.58	235	Ab	−2.8	236	O
				4.79	100	1.66×10^{-2}	1.31	0.381	238	O	4.9		
	Free electron with g = 2.00232		1/2	2.80246×10^{4}	—	2.84×10^{-8}	657	−1836.09					

REFERENCES

(1) V. W. Cohen, et al., Phys. Rev. **104**, 283 (1956).
(2) H. Sommer, et al., Phys. Rev. **82**, 697 (1951).
(3) T. F. Wimett, Phys. Rev. **91**, 499A (1953).
(4) H. Kopfermann, et al., Z. Physik **144**, 9 (1956).
(5) F. Bloch, et al., Phys. Rev. **71**, 551 (1947).
(6) H. L. Anderson, Phys. Rev. **76**, 1460 (1949).
(7) M. P. Klein, et al., Phys. Rev. **106**, 837 (1957).
(8) H. E. Walchli, Thesis, M.S., U. of Tenn. (1954). AEC Report ORNL-1775.
(9) N. A. Schuster, et al., Phys. Rev. **81**, 157 (1951).
(10) K. C. Brog, et al., Phys. Rev. **153**, 91 (1967).
(11) D. Connor, Phys. Rev. Letters **3**, 429 (1959).
(12) L. C. Brown, et al., J. Chem. Phys. **24**, 751 (1956).
(13) F. Alder, et al., Phys. Rev. **82**, 105 (1951).
(14) A. G. Blachman, et al., Bull Am. Phys. Soc. **11**, 343 (1966).
(15) Y. Ting, et al., Phys. Rev. **89**, 595 (1954).
(16) G. Wessel, Phys. Rev. **92**, 1581 (1953).
(17) G. Lindström, Arkiv Fysik **4**, 1 (1951).
(18) V. Royden, Phys. Rev. **96**, 543 (1954).
(19) A. M. Bernstein, et al., Phys. Rev. **136**, B27 (1964).
(20) L. W. Anderson, Phys. Rev. **116**, 87 (1959).
(21) M. R. Baker, et al., Phys. Rev. **133**, A1533 (1964).
(22) A. Bassompiere, Compt. Rend. **240**, 285 (1955).
(23) E. D. Commins, et al., Phys. Rev. **131**, 700 (1963).
(24) F. Alder, et al., Phys. Rev. **81**, 1067 (1951).
(25) M. J. Stevenson, et al., Phys. Rev. **107**, 635 (1957).
(26) K. Sugimoto, et al., J. Phys. Soc. Japan **21**, 213 (1966).
(27) T. Tsang, et al., Phys. Rev. **132**, 1141 (1963).
(28) E. D. Commins, et al., Phys. Rev. Letters **10**, 347 (1963).
(29) J. T. LaTourette, et al., Phys. Rev. **107**, 1202 (1957).
(30) O. Ames, et al., Phys. Rev. **137**, B1157 (1965).
(31) L. Davis, et al., Phys. Rev. **76**, 1068 (1949).
(32) H. Ackermann, Z. Physik **194**, 253 (1966).
(33) M. Baumann, et al., Z. Physik **194**, 270 (1966).
(34) Y. W. Chan, et al., Phys. Rev. **150**, 933 (1966).
(35) L. C. Brown, et al., J. Chem. Phys. **24**, 751 (1956).
(36) H. Low, et al., Phys. Rev. **90**, 1 (1953).
(37) H. E. Weaver, Phys. Rev. **89**, 923 (1953).
(38) T. Kanda, et al., Phys. Rev. **85**, 938 (1952).
(39) G. Feher, et al., Phys. Rev. **107**, 1462 (1957).
(40) G. R. Bird, et al., Phys. Rev. **94**, 1203 (1954).
(41) B. F. Burke, et al., Phys. Rev. **93**, 193 (1954).
(42) V. Jaccarino, et al., Phys. Rev. **83**, 471 (1951).
(43) P. B. Sogo, et al., Phys. Rev. **98**, 1316 (1955).
(44) C. H. Townes, et al., Phys. Rev. **76**, 691 (1949).
(45) W. G. Proctor, et al., Phys. Rev. **81**, 20 (1951).
(46) E. A. Phillips, et al., Phys. Rev. **138**, B773 (1965).
(47) E. Brun, et al., Phys. Rev. **93**, 172 (1954).
(48) O. Lutz, et al., Phys. Letters **24A**, 122 (1967).
(49) G. W. Series, Phys. Rev. **105**, 1128 (1957).
(50) G. J. Ritter, et al., Proc. Roy. Soc. (London) **238**, 473 (1957).
(51) J. T. Eisinger, et al., Phys. Rev. **86**, 73 (1952).
(52) J. M. Kahn, et al., Phys. Rev. **134**, A45 (1964).
(53) F. R. Petersen, et al., Phys. Rev. **116**, 734 (1959).
(54) E. Brun, et al., Phys. Rev. Letters **9**, 166 (1962).
(55) C. D. Jeffries, Phys. Rev. **90**, 1130 (1953).
(56) R. G. Cornwall, et al., Phys. Rev. **141**, 1106 (1966).
(57) D. L. Harris, et al., Phys. Rev. **132**, 310 (1963).
(58) D. M. Hunten, Can. J. Phys. **29**, 463 (1951).
(59) G. Fricke, et al., Z. Physik **156**, 416 (1959).
(60) F. R. Petersen, et al., Phys. Rev. **128**, 1740 (1962).
(61) R. G. Cornwall, et al., Phys. Rev. **148**, 1157 (1966).
(62) C. D. Jeffries, Phys. Rev. **92**, 1262 (1953).
(63) M. M. Weiss, et al., Bull. Am. Phys. Soc. **2**, 31 (1957).
(64) H. E. Walchli, et al., Phys. Rev. **87**, 541 (1952).
(65) K. Murakawa, et al., J. Phys. Soc. Japan **21**, 1466 (1966).
(66) C. D. Jeffries, et al., Phys. Rev. **91**, 1286 (1953).
(67) K. E. Adelroth, et al., Arkiv Fysik **31**, 549 (1966).
(68) E. A. Phillips, et al., Phys. Rev. **140**, B555 (1965).
(69) W. Dobrowolski, et al., Phys. Rev. **104**, 1378 (1956).
(70) R. W. Bauer, et al., Phys. Rev. **120**, 946 (1960).
(71) W. B. Mims, et al., Phys. Letters **24A**, 481 (1967).
(72) A. Javan, et al., Phys. Rev. **96**, 649 (1954).
(73) W. J. Childs, et al., Phys. Rev. **122**, 891 (1961).
(74) P. R. Locher, et al., Phys. Rev. **139**, A991 (1965).
(75) R. W. Bauer, et al., Nucl. Phys. **16**, 264 (1960).
(76) J. M. Baker, et al., Proc. Phys. Soc. (London), **A69**, 354 (1956).
(77) W. Dobrov, et al., Phys. Rev. **108**, 60 (1957).
(78) D. V. Ehrenstein, et al., Z. Physik **159**, 230 (1960).
(79) W. Dobrowolski, et al., Phys. Rev. **101**, 1001 (1956).
(80) L. E. Drain, Phys. Letters **11**, 114 (1964).
(81) B. M. Dodsworth, et al., Phys. Rev. **142**, 638 (1966).
(82) B. Bleaney, et al., Proc. Roy. Soc. (London) **228A**, 166 (1955).
(83) A. Lemonick, et al., Phys. Rev. **95**, 1356 (1954).
(84) V. J. Ehlers, et al., Phys. Rev. **127**, 529 (1962).
(85) R. T. Daly, et al., Phys. Rev. **96**, 539 (1954).
(86) W. J. Childs, et al., Phys. Rev. **120**, 2138 (1960).
(87) W. J. Childs, et al., Phys. Rev. **141**, 15 (1966).
(88) J. M. Mays, et al., Phys. Rev. **81**, 940 (1951).
(89) B. P. Dailey, et al., Phys. Rev. **74**, 1245 (1948).
(90) F. M. Pipkin, et al., Phys. Rev. **100**, 1102 (1957).
(91) W. A. Hardy, et al., Phys. Rev. **92**, 1532 (1953).
(92) E. Lipworth, et al., Phys. Rev. **119**, 1053 (1960).
(93) J. G. King, et al., Phys. Rev. **94**, 1610 (1954).
(94) M. B. White, et al., Phys. Rev. **136**, B584 (1964).
(95) H. L. Garvin, et al., Phys. Rev. **116**, 393 (1959).
(96) E. Brun, et al., Helv. Phys. Acta **27**, 173A (1954).
(97) J. E. Mack, Rev. Mod. Phys. **22**, 64 (1950).
(98) E. Rasmussen, et al., Z. Physik **141**, 160 (1955).
(99) J. C. Hubbs, et al., Phys. Rev. **107**, 723 (1957).
(100) H. Walchli, et al., Phys. Rev. **85**, 922 (1952).

(101) B. Senitzky, et al., Phys. Rev. **103**, 315 (1956).
(102) E. H. Bellamy, et al., Phil. Mag. **44**, 33 (1953).
(103) E. Yasaitis, et al., Phys. Rev. **82**, 750 (1951).
(104) J. W. Culvahouse, et al., Phys. Rev. **140**, A1181 (1965).
(105) F. R. Petersen, et al., Phys. Rev. **125**, 284 (1962).
(106) E. Brun, et al., Phys. Rev. **105**, 1929 (1957).
(107) R. E. Sheriff, et al., Phys. Rev. **82**, 651 (1951).
(108) K. Murakawa, Phys. Rev. **98**, 1285 (1955).
(109) A. Narath, et al., Phys. Rev. **143**, 328 (1966).
(110) H. Walchli, et al., Phys. Rev. **85**, 479 (1952).
(111) K. G. Kessler, et al., Phys. Rev. **92**, 303 (1953).
(112) E. Matthias, et al., Phys. Rev. **139**, B532 (1965).
(113) K. Murakawa, J. Phys. Soc. Japan **10**, 919 (1955).
(114) J. A. Seitchik, et al., Phys. Rev. **138**, A148 (1965).
(115) J. A. Seitchik, et al., Phys. Rev. **136**, A1119 (1964).
(116) O. Ames, et al., Phys. Rev. **123**, 1793 (1960).
(117) W. B. Ewbank, et al., Phys. Rev. **129**, 1617 (1963).
(118) P. B. Sogo, et al., Phys. Rev. **93**, 174 (1954).
(119) G. K. Rochester, et al., Phys. Letters **8**, 266 (1964).
(120) S. G. Schmelling, et al., Phys. Rev. **154**, 1142 (1967).
(121) G. K. Woodgate, et al., Proc. Phys. Soc. (London) **69**, 581 (1956).
(122) Y. W. Chan, et al., Phys. Rev. **133**, B1138 (1964).
(123) F. W. Byron, et al., Phys. Rev. **132**, 1181 (1963).
(124) P. Thaddeus, et al., Phys. Rev. **132**, 1186 (1963).
(125) W. G. Proctor, Phys. Rev. **79**, 35 (1950).
(126) M. Leduc, et al., Compt. Rend. **B262**, 736 (1966).
(127) M. N. McDermott, et al., Phys. Rev. **134**, B25 (1964).
(128) W. J. Childs, et al., Phys. Rev. **118**, 1578 (1960).
(129) L. S. Goodman, et al., Phys. Rev. **108**, 1524 (1957).
(130) M. Rice, et al., Phys. Rev. **106**, 953 (1957).
(131) J. A. Cameron, et al., Can. J. Phys. **40**, 931 (1962).
(132) P. B. Nutter, Phil. Mag. **1**, 587 (1956).
(133) V. W. Cohen, Phys. Rev. **79**, 191 (1950).
(134) K. Murakawa, Phys. Rev. **100**, 1369 (1955).
(135) F. M. Pipkin, Bull. Am. Phys. Soc. **3**, 8 (1958).
(136) P. C. B. Fernando, et al., Phil. Mag. **5**, 1309 (1960).
(137) K. E. Adelroth, et al., Arkiv Fysik **30**, 111 (1965).
(138) P. C. Fletcher, et al., Phys. Rev. **110**, 536 (1958).
(139) H. Walchli, et al., Phys. Rev. **82**, 97 (1951).
(140) R. Livingston, et al., Phys. Rev. **90**, 609 (1953).
(141) E. Lipworth, et al., Phys. Rev. **119**, 2022 (1960).
(142) D. Brinkmann, Helv. Phys. Acta **36**, 413 (1963).
(143) A. Bohr, et al., Arkiv Fysik **4**, 455 (1952).
(144) W. A. Nierenberg, et al., Phys. Rev. **112**, 186 (1958).
(145) R. D. Worley, et al., Phys. Rev. **140**, B1483 (1965).
(146) P. Buck, et al., Phys. Rev. **104**, 553 (1956).
(147) K. H. Althoff, et al., Naturwiss. **41**, 368 (1954).
(148) H. H. Stroke, et al., Phys. Rev. **105**, 590 (1957).
(149) G. Heinzelmann, et al., Phys. Letters **21**, 162 (1966).
(150) V. W. Cohen, et al., Phys. Rev. **127**, 517 (1962).
(151) H. E. Walchli, et al., Phys. Rev. **102**, 1334 (1956).
(152) L. Olschewski, et al., Z. Physik **196**, 77 (1966).
(153) N. I. Kaliteevskii, et al., Soviet Physics—JETP **12**, 661 (1961).
(154) P. B. Sogo, et al., Phys. Rev. **99**, 613 (1955).
(155) K. Murakawa, et al., J. Phys. Soc. Japan **16**, 2533 (1961).
(156) J. N. Haag, et al., Phys. Rev. **129**, 1601 (1963).
(157) J. Blok, et al., Phys. Rev. **143**, 78 (1966).
(158) B. Bleaney, Quantum Electronics Conf., Paris, 1963; P. Grivet and N. Bloembergen, editors; Columbia U. Press (1964).
(159) J. Reader, et al., Phys. Rev. **137**, B784 (1965).
(160) E. D. Jones, Phys. Rev. Letters **19**, 432 (1967).
(161) A. Y. Cabezas, et al., Phys. Rev. **126**, 1004 (1962).
(162) K. F. Smith, et al., Proc. Phys. Soc. (London) **86**, 1249 (1965).
(163) R. W. Grant, et al., Phys. Rev. **130**, 1100 (1963).
(164) D. A. Shirley, et al., Phys. Rev. **121**, 558 (1961).
(165) J. Reader, Phys. Rev. **141**, 1123 (1966).
(166) D. Ali, et al., Phys. Rev. **138**, B1356 (1965).
(167) B. Budick, et al., Phys. Rev. **132**, 723 (1963).
(168) G. K. Woodgate, Proc. Roy. Soc. (London) **A293**, 117 (1966).
(169) L. Evans, et al., Proc. Roy. Soc. (London) **A289**, 114 (1965).
(170) W. Müller, et al., Z. Physik **183**, 303 (1965).
(171) S. S. Alpert, Phys. Rev. **129**, 1344 (1963).
(172) E. L. Boyd, Phys. Rev. **145**, 174 (1966).
(173) N. I. Kaliteevskii, et al., Soviet Phys.—JETP **37**, 629 (1960).
(174) E. L. Boyd, et al., Phys. Rev. Letters **12**, 20 (1964).
(175) C. A. Lovejoy, et al., Nucl. Phys. **30**, 452 (1962).
(176) C. Arnoult, et al., J. Opt. Soc. Am. **56**, 177 (1966).
(177) C. E. Johnson, et al., Phys. Rev. **120**, 2108 (1960).
(178) Q. O. Navarro, et al., Phys. Rev. **123**, 186 (1961).
(179) W. M. Doyle, et al., Phys. Rev. **131**, 1586 (1963).
(180) B. Budick, et al., Phys. Rev. **135**, B1281 (1964).
(181) J. C. Walker, Phys. Rev. **127**, 1739 (1962).
(182) D. Giglberger, et al., Z. Physik **199**, 244 (1967).
(183) A. Y. Cabezas, et al., Phys. Rev. **120**, 920 (1960).
(184) L. Olschewski, et al., Z. Physik **200**, 224 (1967).
(185) A. C. Gossard, et al., Phys. Rev. **133**, A881 (1964).
(186) J. S. Ross, et al., Phys. Rev. **128**, 1159 (1962).
(187) M. A. Grace, et al., Phil. Mag. **2**, 1079 (1957).
(188) A. H. Reddoch, et al., Phys. Rev. **126**, 1493 (1962).
(189) G. J. Ritter, Phys. Rev. **126**, 240 (1962).
(190) I. J. Spalding, et al., Proc. Phys. Soc. (London) **79**, 787 (1962).
(191) F. R. Petersen, et al., Phys. Rev. **126**, 252 (1962).
(192) D. R. Speck, Bull. Am. Phys. Soc. **1**, 282 (1956).
(193) D. R. Speck, et al., Phys. Rev. **101**, 1831 (1956).
(194) L. H. Bennett, et al., Phys. Rev. **120**, 1812 (1960).
(195) K. Murakawa, et al., Phys. Rev. **105**, 671 (1957).
(196) M. P. Klein, et al., Bull. Am. Phys. Soc. **6**, 104 (1961).
(197) L. Armstrong, et al., Phys. Rev. **138**, B310 (1965).
(198) J. Kaufmann, et al., Phys. Letters **24A**, 115 (1967).
(199) H. R. Loeliger, et al., Phys. Rev. **95**, 291 (1954).

REFERENCES (Continued)

(200) A. Narath, (to be published in Phys. Rev.).
(201) A. Narath, et al., Bull. Am. Phys. Soc. **12**, 314 (1967).
(202) W. von Siemens, Ann. Physik **13**, 136 (1953).
(203) Y. W. Chan, et al., Phys. Rev. **144**, 1020 (1966).
(204) Y. W. Chan, et al., Phys. Rev. **137**, B1129 (1965).
(205) H. Dahmen, et al., Z. Physik **200**, 456 (1967).
(206) W. J. Childs, et al., Phys. Rev. **141**, 176 (1966).
(207) P. A. Vanden Bout, et al., Phys. Rev. **158**, 1078 (1967).
(208) H. Kleiman, et al., Phys. Letters **13**, 212 (1964).
(209) W. J. Tomlinson, et al., Nucl. Phys. **60**, 614 (1964).
(210) H. Kleiman, et al., J. Opt. Soc. Am. **53**, 822 (1963).
(211) W. J. Tomlinson, et al., J. Opt. Soc. Am. **53**, 828 (1963).
(212) F. Bitter, et al., Phys. Rev. **96**, 1531 (1954).
(213) B. Cagnac, et al., Compt. Rend. **249**, 77 (1959).
(214) B. Cagnac, Ann. Phys. **6**, 467 (1961).
(215) J. C. Lehmann, et al., Compt. Rend. **257**, 3152 (1963).
(216) J. Blaise, et al., J. Phys. Radium **18**, 193 (1957).
(217) O. Redi, et al., Phys. Letters **8**, 257 (1964).
(218) S. P. Davis, et al., J. Opt. Soc. Am. **56**, 1604 (1966).
(219) R. J. Hull, et al., Phys. Rev. **122**, 1574 (1961).
(220) H. L. Poss, Phys. Rev. **75**, 600 (1949).
(221) G. O. Brink, et al., Phys. Rev. **107**, 189 (1957).
(222) E. B. Baker, J. Chem. Phys. **26**, 960 (1957).
(223) I. Lindgren, et al., Arkiv Fysik **15**, 445 (1959).
(224) Y. Ting, et al., Phys. Rev. **89**, 595 (1953).
(225) S. S. Alpert, et al., Phys. Rev. **125**, 256 (1962).
(226) C. M. Olsmats, et al., Arkiv Fysik **19**, 469 (1961).
(227) M. Fred, et al., Phys. Rev. **98**, 1514 (1955).
(228) V. N. Egorov, Opt. Spectry. (USSR) **16**, 301 (1964).
(229) J. D. Axe, et al., Phys. Rev. **121**, 1630 (1961).
(230) R. Marrus, et al., Nucl. Phys. **23**, 90 (1961).
(231) P. B. Dorain, et al., Phys. Rev. **105**, 1307 (1957).
(232) B. Bleaney, et al., Phil. Mag. **45**, 992 (1954).
(233) J. Faust, et al., Phys. Letters **16**, 71 (1965).
(234) R. J. Champeau, et al., Compt. Rend. **257**, 1238 (1963).
(235) L. Armstrong, et al., Phys. Rev. **144**, 994 (1966).
(236) T. E. Manning, et al., Phys. Rev. **102**, 1108 (1956).
(237) R. Marrus, et al., Phys. Rev. **124**, 1904 (1961).
(238) M. Fred, et al., J. Opt. Soc. Am. **47**, 1076 (1957).
(239) B. Perry, et al., Bull. Am. Phys. Soc. **8**, 345 (1963).
(240) M. M. Robertson, et al., Phys. Rev. **140**, B820 (1965).
(241) R. E. Walstedt, et al., Phys. Rev. **162**, 301 (1967).
(242) R. Freeman, et al., Proc. Roy Soc. (London) **242A**, 455 (1957).

IONIZATION POTENTIALS OF MOLECULES

From data published up to July, 1966
Condensed by J. L. Franklin and Pat Haug from a compilation entitled
"Ionization Potentials, Appearance Potentials and Heats of Formation of Positive Ions"
by
J. L. Franklin, J. G. Dillard, H. M. Rosenstock, J. T. Herron, K. Draxl and F. H. Field
Published by National Standard Reference Data System

The following symbols are employed for the principal important methods:

CTS = Charge Transfer Spectra, EI = Electron Impact, PE = Photoelectron
Spectroscopy, PI = Photoionization, S = Optical Spectroscopy.

Molecule	Ionization Potential ev	Method	ΔH_f of Ion Kcal/mole	Reference	Molecule	Ionization Potential ev	Method	ΔH_f of Ion Kcal/mole	Reference
H_2	15.427 ± 0.002	S	356	1	tert-C_5H_{11}	7.12 ± 0.1	EI	164	34, 35
D_2	15.46 ± 0.01	PI	356	2	neo-C_5H_{11}	8.33 ± 0.1	EI	196	34
BH	9.77 ± 0.05	S	333	3	n-C_5H_{12}	10.35	PI	204	24
BH_3	11.4 ± 0.2	EI	279	*	iso-C_5H_{12}	10.32	PI	201	24
B_2H_6	12.0	EI	286	4, 5	neo-C_5H_{12}	10.35	PI	199	24
B_5H_9	10.5	EI	262	*	C_6H_4 (benzyne)	9.6	EI		*
B_6H_{10}	9.3 ± 0.1	EI	237	6	cyclo-C_6H_5	9.2	PI, PE	284	36, 37
C_2	12.0 ± 0.6	EI	475	7	cyclo-C_6H_6	9.24	S, PI	233	*
C_3	12.6	EI	480	7	CH≡CCH=				
CH	11.13 ± 0.22	S	399	8	CHCH=CH_2	9.50	EI	307	38
CH_2	10.396 ± 0.003	EI, S, PI	333	9, 10, 11	C_2H_5C≡CC≡CH	9.25	EI	307	38
CH_3	9.83	S, PI	259	12, 13	CH_3C≡CCH_2C≡CH	9.75	EI	319	38
CD_3	9.832 ± 0.002	S	259	12	CH_3C≡CC≡CCH_3	9.20	EI	301	38
CH_4	12.6	PI	274	*	CH≡CCH_2CH_2C≡CH	10.35	EI	338	38
CD_4	12.888	PI	280	11, 14	C_6H_8 (1-methylcyclo-pentadiene)	8.43 ± 0.05	EI	218	31
C_2H_2	11.4	PI, PE	317	*	C_6H_8 (2-methylcyclo-pentadiene)	8.46 ± 0.05	EI	219	31
C_2D_2	11.416 ± 0.006	PI	317	15	cyclo-C_6H_{10}	8.72	PE	199	17
C_2H_3	9.4	EI	269	*	cyclo-C_6H_{11}	7.7	EI	185	23
C_2H_4	10.5	S, PE	253	16, 17	1-C_6H_{12}	9.45 ± 0.02	PI	208	35, 24
C_2H_5	8.4	PI	219	13	$(CH_3)_2C=C(CH_3)_2$	8.30	PI	175	28
C_2H_6	11.5	PI, PE	245	14, 17	cyclo-C_6H_{12}	9.8	PI, PE	197	17, 24
HC≡C—CH_2	8.25	PI, EI		18	n-C_6H_{14}	10.18	PI	195	24
CH_2=C=CH_2	10.16 ± 0.02	EI	280	19	iso-C_6H_{14}	10.12	PI	192	24
CH_3C≡CH	10.36 ± 0.01	PI	283	20	$(C_2H_5)_2CHCH_3$	10.08	PI	191	24
cyclo-C_3H_4	9.95	EI	296	21	$C_2H_5C(CH_3)_3$	10.06	PI	188	24
C_3H_5 (allyl)	8.15	EI	216	22, 8	$(CH_3)_2CHCH(CH_3)_2$	10.02	PI	189	24
cyclo-C_3H_5	8.05	EI	239	23	cyclo-$C_6H_5CH_2$	7.76 ± 0.08	EI	216	39
C_3H_6	9.73	S, PI	229	*	cyclo-C_7H_7	6.240 ± 0.01	S	209	40
cyclo-C_3H_6	10.09 ± 0.02	PI	245	24	cyclo-$C_6H_5CH_3$	8.82 ± 0.01	PI	215	*
n-C_3H_7	8.1	PI	209	13	cyclo-C_7H_8	8.5	EI	240	32, 41, 42
iso-C_3H_7	7.5	PI	190	13	bicyclo-(2.2.1)C_7H_8	8.67	EI	267	42
C_3H_8	11.1	PI, PE	231	*	bicyclo-(3.2.0)C_7H_8	9.37	EI	246	41
C_4H_7	10.2 ± 0.1	EI		25	C_7H_{10} (1,2-dimethyl-cyclopentadiene)	8.1 ± 0.1	EI	204	31
C_4H_4	9.87	EI	294	25, 26	C_7H_{10} (5,5-dimethyl-cyclopentadiene)	8.22 ± 0.05	EI	206	31
$CH_3CH=C=CH_2$	9.57 ± 0.02	EI	259	19	C_7H_{10} (1,3-cyclo-heptadiene)	8.55	EI	219	41
CH_2=CHCH=CH_2	9.07	PI, PE	236	*	C_7H_{10} (norbornene)	8.95 ± 0.15	EI	237	43
C_2H_5C≡CH	10.18 ± 0.01	PI	274	20	C_7H_{12} (4-methylcyclo-hexane)	8.91 ± 0.01	PI	198	24
CH_3C≡CCH_3	9.9 ± 0.1	EI	263	25	cyclo-$C_6H_{11}CH_3$	9.85 ± 0.03	PI	190	24
cyclo-C_4H_7	7.88 ± 0.05	EI	213	23	n-C_7H_{16}	9.90 ± 0.05	PI	183	37
$CH_3CH=CHCH_2$	7.71 ± 0.05	EI	203	27, 8	cyclo-C_6H_5C≡CH	8.815 ± 0.005	PI	279	24
$CH_2=C(CH_3)CH_2$	8.03 ± 0.05	EI	203	27, 8	C_8H_8 (styrene)	8.47 ± 0.02	PI	232	24
1-C_4H_8	9.6	PI	221	*	C_8H_8 (cyclotatetraene)	8.0	PI, PE	255	17, 24
cis-2-C_4H_8	9.13	PI	209	24, 28	C_8H_8 (cubane)	8.74 ± 0.15	EI	350	44
trans-2-C_4H_8	9.13	PI	208	24, 28	m-$C_6H_4CH_3CH_2$	7.65 ± 0.03	EI	206	39
iso-C_4H_8	9.23 ± 0.02	PI	209	24, 28	p-$C_6H_4CH_3CH_2$	7.46 ± 0.03	EI	202	39
cyclo-C_4H_8	10.58	EI	250	23	cyclo-$C_6H_5C_2H_5$	8.76 ± 0.01	PI	209	24
n-C_4H_9	8.64 ± 0.05	EI	218	29	o-$C_6H_4(CH_3)_2$	8.56	PI	202	*
sec-C_4H_9	7.93 ± 0.05	EI	192	29	m-$C_6H_4(CH_3)_2$	8.58	PI, PE	202	*
iso-C_4H_9	8.35 ± 0.05	EI	205	29	p-$C_6H_4(CH_3)_2$	8.44	PI	199	*
tert-C_4H_9	7.42 ± 0.07	EI	176	29	C_8H_{10} (7-methylcyclo-heptatriene)	8.39 ± 0.1	EI	231	45
n-C_4H_{10}	10.63 ± 0.03	PI	215	30	C_8H_{10} (1-methylspiro-heptadiene)	8.02 ± 0.1	EI	229	45
iso-C_4H_{10}	10.57	PI	212	24	C_8H_{10} (2-methylspiro-heptadiene)	8.07 ± 0.1	EI	230	45
cyclo-C_5H_6	8.97	EI	239	31, 32	C_8H_{10} (6-methylspiro-heptadiene)	8.40 ± 0.1	EI	239	45
$C_2H_5CH=C=CH_2$	9.42	EI	252	21	C_8H_{12} (1,2,3-trimethyl-cyclopentadiene)	7.96 ± 0.05	EI	194	31
$CH_3CH=CHCH=CH_2$	8.68	EI	219	21	C_8H_{12} (1,5,5-trimethyl-cyclopentadiene)	8.00 ± 0.1	EI	193	31
$CH_3CH=C=CHCH_3$	9.26	EI	247	21					
CH_2=CHCH_2CH=CH_2	9.58	EI	246	21					
CH_2=CHC(CH_3)=CH_2	8.845 ± 0.005	PI	235	24					
cyclo-C_5H_8	9.01 ± 0.01	PI	216	24					
cyclo-C_5H_9	7.79 ± 0.02	EI	194	23					
1-C_5H_{10}	9.50 ± 0.02	PI	214	24					
cis-2-C_5H_{10}	9.11	EI	203	21					
trans-2-C_5H_{10}	9.06	EI	201	21					
$(CH_3)_2CHCH=CH_2$	9.51 ± 0.03	PI	212	24					
$C_2H_5C(CH_3)=CH_2$	9.12 ± 0.02	PI	202	24					
$(CH_3)_2C=CHCH_3$	8.67 ± 0.02	PI	189	24					
cyclo-$C_5H_4(CH_3)_2$	9.77 ± 0.02	EI	225	33					
cyclo-C_5H_{10}	10.53 ± 0.05	PI	224	24					

* Average of several values.

Molecule	Ionization Potential ev	Method	ΔH_f of Ion Kcal/mole	Reference
C8H12 (4-vinylcyclohexene)	8.93 ±0.02	PI	224	24
cis-1,2-cyclo-C6H10(CH3)2	10.08 ±0.02	EI	191	46
trans-1,2-cyclo-C6H10(CH3)2	10.08 ±0.03	EI	189	46
C8H18 (2,2,4-trimethylpentane)	9.86	PI	174	24
C8H18 (2,2,3,3-tetramethylbutane)	9.79	EI	184	8
C9H8 (indene)	8.81	EI	246	47
C6H5C(CH3)=CH2	8.35 ±0.01	PI	220	24
cyclo-C6H5(n-C3H7)	8.72 ±0.01	PI	203	24
cyclo-C6H5(iso-C3H7)	8.69 ±0.01	PI	201	24
1,2,3 cyclo-C6H3(CH3)3	8.48	PI	193	28
1,2,4 cyclo-C6H3(CH3)3	8.27	PI	187	28
1,3,5 cyclo-C6H3(CH3)3	8.4	PI	190	*
C10H8 (naphthalene)	8.12	PI	220	24, 48
C10H8 (azulene)	7.42	S	243	49, 50
C6H4C3H7CH2	7.42	EI	188	39
cyclo-C6H5 (n-C4H9)	8.69 ±0.01	PI	197	24
C10H14 (sec-butylbenzene)	8.68 ±0.01	PI	196	24
C10H14 (tert-butylbenzene)	8.68 ±0.01	PI	193	24
C10H14 (1,2,3,5-tetramethylbenzene)	8.47 ±0.05	EI	185	24
C10H14 (1,2,4,5-tetramethylbenzene)	8.03	PI, PE	174	*
C10H18 (cis-decaline)	9.61 ±0.02	EI	181	51
C10H18 (trans-decaline)	9.61 ±0.02	EI	178	51
C11H9 (1-naphthyl methyl)	7.35	EI	208	52
C11H9 (2-naphthyl methyl)	7.56 ±0.05	EI	217	52
C11H10 (methylnaphthalene)	7.96 ±0.01	PI	209	24
C11H10 (2-methylnaphthalene)	7.955 ±0.01	PI	209	24
C6H(CH3)5	7.92 ±0.02	PI	155	53
C11H18 (hexamethylcyclopentadiene)	7.74 ±0.05	EI	165	31
C12H10 (biphenyl)	8.27 ±0.01	PI	230	24
cyclo-C6(CH3)6	7.85 ±0.02	PI	152	28
C13H10 (fluorene)	8.63	EI	243	47
C14H10 (diphenylacetylene)	8.85 ±0.05	EI	303	54
C14H10 (anthracene)	7.55	EI	228	55
C14H10 (phenanthrene)	8.1	EI	233	54, 55
C18H12 (1,2-benzanthracene)	8.01	EI	251	56
C18H30 (1-phenyldodecane)	9.05 ±0.1	EI	165	57
C18H30 (3-phenyldodecane)	8.95 ±0.1	EI	163	57
C19H32 (7-phenyltridecane)	8.91 ±0.1	EI	157	57
C26H46 (1-phenylicosane)	9.34 ±0.1	EI	132	57
C26H46 (2-phenylicosane)	9.22 ±0.1	EI	129	57
C26H46 (3-phenylicosane)	8.95 ±0.1	PI	123	57
C26H46 (4-phenylicosane)	9.01 ±0.1	EI	125	57
C26H46 (5-phenylicosane)	9.04 ±0.1	EI	125	57
C26H46 (7-phenylicosane)	8.97 ±0.1	EI	124	57
C26H46 (9-phenylicosane)	9.06 ±0.1	EI	126	57
(CH3)3B	8.8 ±0.2	EI	173	58
(C2H5)3B	9.0 ±0.2	EI	170	58
N2	15.576	S	359	59
NH	13.10 ±0.05	EI	382	60
NH2	11.4 ±0.1	EI	304	61
NH3	10.2	S, PI, PE	223	*
N2H2	9.85 ±0.1	EI		62
N2H4	8.74 ±0.06	PI	224	63
CN	14.3	EI	430	64, 65
HCN	13.8	EI	351	26, 66
C2N2	13.6	EI	387	8, 64
CH5N	8.97	PI	201	67
C2H2N	10.9	EI	298	68
CH3CN	12.2	PI	302	14, 24
cyclo-C2H5N	9.94 ±0.15	EI	255	69
C2H5NH2	8.86 ±0.02	PI	193	24
(CH3)2NH	8.24 ±0.02	PI	186	24
CH2=CHCN	10.91 ±0.01	PI	296	24
C2H5CN	11.84 ±0.02	PI	289	24
C3H7N	9.1 ±0.15	EI	225	70
(CH2)3NH	9.1 ±0.15	EI	225	70
n-C3H7NH2	8.78 ±0.02	PI	185	24
iso-C3H7NH2	8.72 ±0.03	PI	183	24
(CH3)3N	7.82 ±0.02	PI	175	24
CH2=CHCH2CN	10.39 ±0.01	PI	281	24
C4H5N (pyrrole)	8.20 ±0.01	PI	215	24
(CH3)2CCN	9.15 ±0.1	EI	239	68
n-C3H7CN	11.67 ±0.05	PI	280	24
C4H9N (pyrrolidine)	8.41	PE	192	17
n-C4H9NH2	8.71 ±0.03	PI	179	24
sec-C4H9NH2	8.70	PI	177	24
iso-C4H9NH2	8.70	PI	177	24
tert-C4H9NH2	8.64	PI	173	24
(C2H5)2NH	8.01 ±0.01	PI	163	24
C5H5N (pyridine)	9.3	S, PI	247	24, 71
C6H7N (aniline)	7.7	PI	202	*
C6H7N (2-picoline)	9.02 ±0.03	PI	232	24
C6H7N (3-picoline)	9.04 ±0.03	PI	236	24
C6H7N (4-picoline)	9.04 ±0.03	PI	233	24
C6H13N (cyclohexylamine)	8.86	PE	181	17
(n-C3H7)2NH	7.84 ±0.02	PI	153	24
(iso-C3H7)2NH	7.73 ±0.03	PI	148	24
(C2H5)3N	7.50 ±0.02	PI	147	24
cyclo-C6H5CN	9.705 ±0.01	PI	277	24
C7H9N (n-methylaniline)	7.32	PI	192	72, 73
C7H9N (m-toluidine)	7.50 ±0.02	PI	189	48
C7H9N (2,3-lutidine)	8.85 ±0.02	PI	218	24
C7H9N (2,4-lutidine)	8.85 ±0.03	PI	218	24
C7H9N (2,6-lutidine)	8.85 ±0.02	PI	218	24
C6H5CH2CN	9.40 ±0.5	EI	259	74
m-C6H4CH3CN	9.66 ±0.05	EI	271	74
p-C6H4CH3CN	9.76	EI	273	75
cyclo-C6H5NHC2H5	7.56	CTS	193	76
cyclo-C6H5N(CH3)2	7.12	PI	185	72, 73
(n-C4H9)2NH	7.69 ±0.03	PI	140	24
C9H13N (N-n-propylaniline)	7.54	CTS	188	76
C9H13N (N-ethyl-N-methylaniline)	7.37	CTS	185	76
C9H13N (N,N-dimethyl-o-toluidine)	7.37	CTS	184	76
C9H13N (N,N-dimethyl-m-toluidine)	7.35	CTS	181	76
C9H13N (N,N-dimethyl-p-toluidine)	7.33	CTS	181	76
(n-C3H7)3N	7.23	PI	207	24
C10H15N (N-n-butylaniline)	7.53	CTS	183	76
C10H15N (N,N-diethylaniline)	6.99	CTS	172	76
C10H15N (N,N-dimethyl-p-ethylaniline)	7.38	CTS	177	76
C10H15N (N,N-2,4-tetramethylaniline)	7.17	CTS	171	76
C10H15N (N,N,2,6-tetramethylaniline)	7.22	CTS	173	76
C10H15N (N,N,3,5-tetramethylaniline)	7.25	CTS	172	76
C11H17N (N,N-diethyl-p-toluidene)	6.93	CTS	164	76
C11H17N (N,N-dimethyl-p-isopropylaniline)	7.41	CTS	174	76
(C6H5)2NH	7.25 ±0.03	PI	223	77
C12H19N (N,N-di-n-propylaniline)	6.96	CTS	163	76
C12H19N (N,N-dimethyl-p-tert-butylaniline)	7.43	CTS	165	76
C14H23N (N,N-di-n-butylaniline)	6.95	CTS	153	76

* Average of several values.

Molecule	Ionization Potential ev	Method	ΔH_f of Ion Kcal/mole	Reference	Molecule	Ionization Potential ev	Method	ΔH_f of Ion Kcal/mole	Reference
$(C_6H_5)_3N$	6.86 ±0.03	PI	243	77	C_7H_6O (tropone)	9.68 ±0.02	EI	240	104
CH_2N_2 (diazirine)	10.18 ±0.05	EI	314	78	cyclo-$C_6H_5CH_2OH$	9.14 ±0.05	EI	186	74
CH_2N_2 (diazomethane)	8.999 ±0.001	S	257	79	cyclo-$C_6H_5OCH_3$	8.21 ±0.02	PI	173	24
CH_6N_2 (methyl-hydrazine)	8.00 ±0.06	PI	207	63	C_7H_8O (m-cresol)	8.52 ±0.05	EI	165	74
$CH_3N=NCH_3$	8.65 ±0.1	EI	243	80	n-$C_5H_{11}COCH_3$	9.33 ±0.03	PI	143	24
$C_2H_8N_2$ (1,1-dimethyl-hydrazine)	7.67 ±0.05	PI	197	81	C_8H_8O (acetophenone)	9.27 ±0.03	PI	191	24
$C_2H_8N_2$ (1,2-dimethyl-hydrazine)	7.75 ±0.1	EI	200	82	C_8H_8O (p-methyl-benzaldehyde)	9.33 ±0.05	EI	194	105
$(CH_3)_3N_2H$	7.93 ±0.1	EI	202	82	$C_8H_{10}O$ (benzyl methyl ether)	8.85 ±0.03	PI	184	30
o-$C_4H_4N_2$ (o-diazine)	9.9	EI	275	83	$C_8H_{10}O$ (phenyl ethyl ether)	8.13 ±0.02	PI	167	24
m-$C_4H_4N_2$ (m-diazine)	9.9	EI	277	83	$C_8H_{10}O$ (m-methylanisole)	8.31 ±0.05	EI	169	74
p-$C_4H_4N_2$ (p-diazine)	9.8	EI	274	83	$C_9H_{10}O$ (phenyl ethyl ketone)	9.27 ±0.05	EI	189	74
$1,1(C_2H_5)_2N_2H_2$	7.59 ±0.05	PI	184	63	$C_9H_{10}O$ (m-methyl-acetophenone)	9.15 ±0.05	EI	182	74
$(CH_3)_4N_2$	7.76 ±0.05	EI	196	82	$C_{12}H_{10}O$ (phenyl ether)	8.82 ±0.05	EI	220	106
$C_5H_4NNH_2$	8.97 ±0.05	EI	244	84	$C_{13}H_{10}O$ (benzophenone)	9.4	EI	229	106, 105
$C_5H_{14}N_2$ (1-methyl-1-n-butylhydrazine)	7.62 ±0.05	PI	180	63	$C_{14}H_{12}O$ (p-methyl-benzophenone)	9.13 ±0.05	EI	214	105
$(CH_3)_2NC_6H_4N(CH_3)_2$ [p-bis(dimethylamino)-benzene]	6.9	CTS	180	85	HCOOH	11.05 ±0.01	PI	164	24
CH_3N_3	9.5 ±0.1	EI	276	86	CH_3COOH	10.36	PI	135	24
O_2	12.063 ±0.001	PI	278	*	$HCOOCH_3$	10.815 ±0.005	PI	166	24
O_3	12.3 ±0.1	PE	318	87	C_2H_5COOH	10.24 ±0.03	PI	127	24
OH	13.17 ±0.1	EI	313	88	$HCOOC_2H_5$	10.61 ±0.01	PI	156	24
H_2O	12.6	PI	233	*	CH_3COOCH_3	10.27 ±0.02	PI	138	24
D_2O	12.6	PI	232	37	$(CH_3O)_2CH_2$	10.00 ±0.05	PI	145	24
HO_2	11.53 ±0.02	EI	271	89	$CH_3COCH=CH_2$	9.19 ±0.05	PI	137	24
H_2O_2	11.0	EI	233	90, 91	$CH_3COCOCH_3$	9.24 ±0.03	PI	135	24
Li_2O	6.8		120	92, 93	n-C_3H_7COOH	10.16 ±0.05	PI	121	24
CO	14.013 ±0.004	S	297	94	iso-C_3H_7COOH	10.02 ±0.05	PI	115	24
CO_2	13.769 ±0.03	S	223	96	$HCOOCH_2CH_2CH_3$	10.54 ±0.01	PI	149	24
NO	9.25	PI, S	235	*	$CH_3COOC_2H_5$	10.11 ±0.02	PI	126	24
N_2O	12.894	S	317	95	$C_2H_5COOCH_3$	10.15 ±0.03	PI	127	24
NO_2	9.79	PI	233	97, 98	$C_4H_8O_2$ (p-dioxane)	9.13 ±0.03	PI	126	24
CHO	9.8	EI	221	*	$(CH_3O)_2CHCH_3$	9.65 ±0.03	PI	129	24
CH_2O	10.88	PI	223	24, 48	$C_4H_4O_2$ (2-furfur-aldehyde)	9.21 ±0.01	PI	187	24
CH_3OH	10.84	PI, PE	202	17, 24	$CH_3COCH_2COCH_3$	8.87 ±0.03	PI	122	24
CH_3CO	10.3		152	*	$HCOO(CH_2)_3CH_3$	10.50 ±0.02	PI	144	24
CH_3CHO	10.2	PI	196	*	$HCOOCH_2CH(CH_3)_2$	10.46 ±0.02	PI	139	24
C_2H_4O (ethylene oxide)	10.6	PI, S	231	*	$CH_3COOCH_2CH_2CH_3$	10.04 ±0.03	PI	121	24
C_2H_5OH	10.49		185	24, 30	$CH_3COOCH(CH_3)_2$	9.99 ±0.03	PI	116	24
CH_3OCH_3	9.98	S, PI	186	24, 99	$C_2H_5COOC_2H_5$	10.00 ±0.02	PI	119	24
$CH_2=CHCHO$	10.10 ±0.01	PI	210	24	n-$C_3H_7COOCH_3$	10.07 ±0.03	PI	125	24
C_2H_5CHO	9.98	PI	181	24	iso-$C_3H_7COOCH_3$	9.98 ±0.02	PI	121	24
CH_3COCH_3	9.69	PI	171	*	$(C_2H_5O)_2CH_2$	9.70 ±0.05	PI	134	24
$CH_2=CHCH_2OH$	9.67 ±0.05	PI	191	24	p-$C_6H_4O_2$	9.67 ±0.02	PI	198	48
$CH_2=CHOCH_3$	8.93 ±0.02	PI	178	24	$CH_3COOC_4H_9$	9.56 ±0.03	PI	104	48
C_3H_6O (propyleneoxide)	10.22 ±0.02	PI	214	24	$CH_3COO(CH_2)_3CH_3$	10.01	PI	114	24
C_3H_6O (trimethylene-oxide)	9.667 ±0.005	S	199	100	CH_3COOCH_2-$CH(CH_3)_2$	9.97	PI	111	24
n-C_3H_7OH	10.1	PI	172	24, 101	CH_3COOCH-$(CH_3)C_2H_5$	9.91 ±0.03	PI	110	24
iso-C_3H_7OH	10.15	PI	169	24	C_6H_5COOH	9.73 ±0.09	EI	152	105
C_4H_4O (furan)	8.89	S, PI	197	24, 102	p-HOC_6H_4CHO	9.32 ±0.02	EI	157	105
$CH_3CH=CHCHO$	9.73 ±0.01	PI	194	24	$C_8H_8O_2$ (α-hydroxy-acetophenone)	9.33 ±0.05	EI	159	74
n-C_3H_7CHO	9.86 ±0.02	PI	174	24	$C_6H_5COOCH_3$	9.35 ±0.06	EI	144	105
iso-C_3H_7CHO	9.74 ±0.03	PI	169	24	$C_8H_8O_2$ (p-methoxy-benzaldehyde)	8.60 ±0.03	EI	150	105
$C_2H_5COCH_3$	9.5	PI	161	*	$C_8H_8O_2$ (m-hydroxy-acetophenone)	8.67 ±0.05	EI	134	74
cyclo-C_4H_8O	9.42	S	174	100	$C_8H_8O_2$ (p-hydroxy-acetophenone)	8.70 ±0.03	EI	135	105
n-C_4H_9OH	10.04	PI	165	24	$C_9H_{10}O_2$ (α-methoxy-acetophenone)	8.60 ±0.05	EI	142	74
$C_2H_5OC_2H_5$	9.6	PI	161	24	$C_9H_{10}O_2$ (m-methoxy-acetophenone)	8.53 ±0.05	EI	140	74
C_5H_8O (cyclo-pentanone)	9.26 ±0.01	PI	163	24	$C_9H_{10}O_2$ (p-methoxy-acetophenone)	8.62 ±0.05	EI	142	105
C_5H_8O (dihydropyran)	8.34 ±0.01	PI	164	24	$C_9H_{10}O_2$ (methyl p-toluate)	8.94 ±0.04	EI	130	105
n-C_4H_9CHO	9.82 ±0.05	PI	168	24	$C_{13}H_{10}O_2$ (p-hydroxy-benzophenone)	8.59 ±0.05	EI	165	105
iso-C_4H_9CHO	9.71 ±0.05	PI	164	24	$C_{13}H_{10}O_2$ (phenyl benzoate)	8.98 ±0.05	EI	177	106
n-$C_3H_7COCH_3$	9.37 ±0.02	PI	154	103	$C_{14}H_{10}O_2$ (benzil)	8.78 ±0.05	EI	181	106
iso-$C_3H_7COCH_3$	9.30 ±0.02	PI	151	24, 103					
$(C_2H_5)_2CO$	9.32 ±0.01	PI	153	24					
cyclo-$C_5H_{10}O$	9.25 ±0.01	S	161	100					
C_6H_5O	8.84	EI	226	36					
C_6H_6O (phenol)	8.51	PI	173	24, 48					
$(CH_3)_2C=CHCOCH_3$	9.08 ±0.03	PI	168	24					
$C_6H_{10}O$ (cyclo-hexanone)	9.14 ±0.01	PI	152	24					
n-$C_4H_9COCH_3$	9.35	PI	149	24, 103					
iso-$C_4H_9COCH_3$	9.30	PI	147	24, 103					
tert-$C_4H_9COCH_3$	9.17 ±0.03	PI	140	24					
$(n$-$C_3H_7)_2O$	9.27 ±0.05	PI	147	24					
$(iso$-$C_3H_7)_2O$	9.20 ±0.05	PI	142	24					
C_6H_5CHO	9.52	PI	209	24					

* Average of several values.

Molecule	Ionization Potential ev	Method	ΔH$_f$ of Ion Kcal/mole	Reference
CH$_3$OCH$_2$COOCH$_3$	9.56 ±0.05	EI	88	74
C$_9$H$_{10}$O$_3$ (methyl p-methoxybenzoate)	8.43 ±0.04	EI	90	105
(C$_6$H$_5$)$_2$CO$_3$	9.01 ±0.05	EI	122	106
CH$_3$CONH$_2$	9.77 ±0.02	PI	171	24
HCON(CH$_3$)$_2$	9.12 ±0.02	PI	160	24
CH$_3$CONHCH$_3$	8.90 ±0.02	PI	150	24
CH$_3$CON(CH$_3$)$_2$	8.81 ±0.03	PI	145	24
C$_5$H$_4$NOH	9.70 ±0.05	EI	209	84
HCON(C$_2$H$_5$)$_2$	8.89 ±0.02	PI	145	24
C$_6$H$_5$NO (2-pyridine-carboxaldehyde)	9.75 ±0.05	EI	227	84
C$_6$H$_5$NO (4-pyridine-carboxaldehyde)	10.12 ±0.05	EI	235	84
CH$_3$CON(C$_2$H$_5$)$_2$	8.60 ±0.02	PI	130	24
C$_6$H$_5$NCO	8.77 ±0.02	PI	222	24
C$_7$H$_7$NO (benzamide)	9.4 ±0.2	EI	197	107, 108
C$_7$H$_7$NO (p-amino-benzaldehyde)	8.25 ±0.02	EI	182	105
C$_7$H$_9$NO (p-methoxy-analine)	7.82	EI	169	75
C$_8$H$_9$NO (acetanilide)	8.39 ±0.10	EI	171	108
C$_8$H$_9$NO (m-amino-acetophenone)	8.09 ±0.05	EI	171	74
C$_8$H$_9$NO (p-amino-acetophenone)	8.17 ±0.02	EI	172	105
C$_9$H$_7$NO (α-cyano-acetophenone)	9.56 ±0.05	EI	235	74
CH$_3$NO$_2$	11.1	PI	238	14, 24
C$_2$H$_5$NO$_2$	10.88 ±0.05	PI	226	24
n-C$_3$H$_7$NO$_2$	10.81 ±0.03	PI	221	24
iso-C$_3$H$_7$NO$_2$	10.71 ±0.05	PI	217	24
C$_6$H$_5$NO$_2$	9.92	PI	246	24
C$_7$H$_6$NO$_2$ (m-nitro-benzyl radical)	8.56 ±0.1	EI	227	39
C$_7$H$_7$NO$_2$ (m-nitro-toluene)	9.65 ±0.05	EI	233	74
C$_7$H$_7$NO$_2$ (p-nitro-toluene)	9.82	EI	237	75
C$_8$H$_9$NO$_2$	8.08 ±0.01	EI	122	90
C$_6$H$_6$N$_2$O$_2$ (o-nitro-aniline)	8.66	EI	215	75
C$_6$H$_6$N$_2$O$_2$ (m-nitro-aniline)	8.7	EI	216	75
C$_6$H$_6$N$_2$O$_2$ (p-nitro-aniline)	8.85	EI	219	75
C$_2$H$_5$NO$_3$	11.22	PI	222	24
n-C$_3$H$_7$ONO$_2$	11.07 ±0.02	PI	213	24
C$_6$H$_5$NO$_3$ (p-nitro-phenol)	9.52	EI	187	75
C$_7$H$_5$NO$_3$ (p-nitro-benzaldehyde)	10.27 ±0.01	EI	217	105
C$_8$H$_7$NO$_3$ (m-nitro-acetophenone)	9.89 ±0.05	EI	201	74
C$_8$H$_7$NO$_3$ (p-nitro-acetophenone)	10.07 ±0.02	EI	205	105
C$_8$H$_7$NO$_4$ (methyl-p-nitrobenzoate)	10.20 ±0.03	EI	160	105
F$_2$	15.7	S	362	109
HF	15.77 ±0.02	EI	299	110
BF	11.3	EI	233	111, 112
BF$_3$	15.5	EI	87	*
CF$_2$	11.8	EI	237	113, 114
C$_2$F$_4$	10.12	PI	78	28
C$_6$F$_6$	9.97	PI		28
NF$_2$	11.9	EI	284	115, 116
trans-N$_2$F$_2$	13.1 ±0.1	EI	322	115
NF$_3$	13.2 ±0.2	EI	275	115, 123
N$_2$F$_4$	12.04 ±0.10	EI	276	124
OF$_2$	13.6	EI	309	117, 118
XeF$_2$	11.5 ±0.2	S	239	119
CH$_2$F	9.35	EI	207	29
CH$_3$F	12.85 ±0.01	EI	229	120
C$_2$H$_3$F	10.37	PI	211	28, 121
cyclo-C$_6$H$_5$F	9.2	S, PI	186	*
C$_7$H$_7$F	8.9	PI	172	24
CHF$_2$	9.45	EI	143	29, 122
C$_2$H$_2$F$_2$	10.30	PI	159	28, 121
o-C$_6$H$_4$F$_2$	9.31	PI	147	121
p-C$_6$H$_4$F$_2$	9.15	PI	140	121
C$_2$HF$_3$	10.14	PI	122	28
CH$_2$=CHCF$_3$	10.9	PI	93	28

Molecule	Ionization Potential ev	Method	ΔH$_f$ of Ion Kcal/mole	Reference
C$_7$H$_5$F$_3$	9.68	S, PI	84	24, 125
C$_7$H$_{11}$F$_3$ (trifluoro-methylcyclohexane)	10.46 ±0.02	PI	37	24
C$_6$H$_5$OF (o-fluoro-phenol)	8.66 ±0.01	PI	132	24
Na$_2$	4.90 ±0.01	PI	147	126
AlF	9.8	EI	166	127, 128
(CH$_3$)$_4$Si	9.9	EI	171	129, 130
PH$_3$	9.98	PI	231	131
PF$_3$	9.71	PI	4	131
CH$_3$PH$_2$	9.72 ±0.15	EI	217	132
C$_2$H$_5$PH$_2$	9.47 ±0.5	EI	206	132
(CH$_3$)$_3$P	8.60 ±0.2	EI	175	132
(C$_6$H$_5$)$_3$P	7.36 ±0.05	EI	242	77
S$_6$	9.7	EI	248	133
S$_7$	9.2 ±0.3	EI		133
HS	10.50 ±0.1	EI	276	134
H$_2$S	10.4	S	235	135
CS$_2$	10.080	S	261	95
SO$_2$	12.34 ±0.02	PI	214	30
CH$_3$S	8.06 ±0.1	EI	218	134
CH$_3$SH	9.440 ±0.005	PI	212	24
C$_2$H$_4$S (ethylene sulfide)	8.87 ±0.15	EI	224	69
C$_2$H$_5$SH	9.285 ±0.005	PI	203	24
CH$_3$SCH$_3$	8.685 ±0.005	PI	191	24
C$_3$H$_6$S (propylene sulfide)	8.6 ±0.2	EI	218	136
(CH$_2$)$_3$S	8.9 ±0.15	EI	220	70
n-C$_3$H$_7$SH	9.195 ±0.005	PI	197	24
C$_2$H$_5$SCH$_3$	8.55 ±0.01	PI	183	24
C$_4$H$_4$S (thiophene)	8.860 ±0.005	PI	229	24
CH$_3$SCH$_2$—CH=CH$_2$	8.70 ±0.2	EI	211	137
(CH$_2$)$_4$S	8.57 ±0.75	EI	190	70
n-C$_4$H$_9$SH	9.14 ±0.02	PI	191	24
C$_2$H$_5$SC$_2$H$_5$	8.430 ±0.005	PI	175	24
n-C$_3$H$_7$SCH$_3$	8.8 ±0.15	EI	183	138
iso-C$_3$H$_7$SCH$_3$	8.7 ±0.2	EI	179	137
C$_6$H$_5$S	8.63 ±0.1	EI	250	134
C$_6$H$_5$SH	8.32 ±0.01	PI	217	138
C$_6$H$_8$S (2-ethyl-thiophene)	8.8 ±0.2	EI	215	139
(n-C$_3$H$_7$)$_2$S	8.5	PI, EI	170	24, 143
C$_6$H$_5$S$_2$CH$_3$	8.9	EI	229	137
C$_7$H$_{10}$S (2-propyl-thiophene)	8.6 ±0.2	EI	205	139
C$_8$H$_{12}$S	8.8	EI	221	137
C$_8$H$_{12}$S (2-butyl-thiophene)	8.5 ±0.2	EI	198	139
CH$_3$SSCH$_3$	8.46 ±0.03	PI	189	24
C$_2$H$_5$SSC$_2$H$_5$	8.27 ±0.03	PI	173	24
CH$_3$SSSCH$_3$	8.80 ±0.15	EI	203	140
COS	11.17 ±0.01	PI	224	138
SO$_2$F$_2$	13.3 ±0.1	EI	102	141
CH$_3$NCS	9.25 ±0.03	PI	245	24
CH$_3$SCN	10.065 ±0.01	PI	270	24
C$_2$H$_5$NCS	9.14 ±0.03	PI	237	24
C$_2$H$_5$SCN	9.89 ±0.01	PI	261	24
C$_7$H$_5$NS (phenyl-isothiocyanate)	8.520 ±0.005	PI	260	24
C$_6$H$_5$CH$_2$SCN	9.06 ±0.05	EI	274	74
NH$_2$CSNH$_2$	8.50 ±0.05	EI	194	142
NH$_2$CSNHCH$_3$	8.29 ±0.05	EI	188	142
NH$_2$CSNHCH=CH$_2$	8.29 ±0.05	EI	213	142
NH$_2$CSN(CH$_3$)$_2$	8.34 ±0.05	EI	186	142
CH$_3$NHCSNHCH$_3$	8.17 ±0.05	EI	184	142
CH$_3$NHCSN(CH$_3$)$_2$	7.93 ±0.05	EI	176	142
C$_5$H$_{12}$N$_2$S	7.98 ±0.05	EI	170	142
(CH$_3$)$_2$NCSN(CH$_3$)$_2$	7.95 ±0.05	EI	173	142
CH$_3$COSH	10.00 ±0.02	PI	179	24
Cl$_2$	11.48 ±0.01	PI	265	24
HCl	12.74	PI	272	*
LiCl	10.1	EI	186	144
CCl$_3$	8.78 ±0.05	EI	214	*
CCl$_4$	11.47 ±0.01	PI	240	24
C$_2$Cl$_4$	9.32 ±0.01	PI	212	24, 28
PCl$_3$	9.91	PI	160	131
CH$_2$Cl	9.32	EI	244	29
CH$_3$Cl	11.3	S, PI	239	14, 145
C$_2$H$_3$Cl	9.996	S, PI	239	*
C$_2$H$_5$Cl	10.97	PI	226	24
CH$_3$C≡CCl	9.9 ±0.1	EI	267	25
n-C$_3$H$_7$Cl	10.82 ±0.03	PI	219	24

* Average of several values.

Molecule	Ionization Potential ev	Method	ΔH_f of Ion Kcal/mole	Reference	Molecule	Ionization Potential ev	Method	ΔH_f of Ion Kcal/mole	Reference
iso-C_3H_7Cl	10.78 ± 0.02	PI	211	24	$Fe(CO)_5$	7.95 ± 0.03	PI	8	155
n-C_4H_9Cl	10.67 ± 0.03	PI	210	24	$C_5H_5Co(CO)_2$	8.3 ± 0.2	EI	136	154
sec-C_4H_9Cl	10.65 ± 0.03	PI	210	24	$Ni(CO)_4$	8.28 ± 0.03	PI	47	155
iso-C_4H_9Cl	10.66 ± 0.03	PI	208	24	$(CH_3)_4Ge$	9.2 ± 0.2	EI	177	156
tert-C_4H_9Cl	10.61 ± 0.03	PI	202	24	As_4	9.07 ± 0.07	EI	244	157
C_6H_5Cl	9.07	PI	222	24	AsH_3	10.03	PI	247	131
$C_6H_5CH_2Cl$	9.19 ± 0.05	EI	219	74	$AsCl_3$	11.7 ± 0.1	EI	208	158
o-$C_6H_4ClCH_3$	8.83 ± 0.02	PI	208	24	$(CH_3)_3As$	8.3 ± 0.1	EI	202	158
m-$C_6H_4ClCH_3$	8.83 ± 0.02	PI	207	24	$(C_6H_5)_3As$	7.34 ± 0.07	PI	250	77
p-$C_6H_4ClCH_3$	8.69 ± 0.02	PI	204	24	Br_2	10.54 ± 0.03	PI	250	24, 159
C_7H_9Cl (endo-5-chloro-2-norbornene)	9.1 ± 0.15	EI	233	43	$IIBr$	11.62 ± 0.03	PI	259	24
C_7H_9Cl (exo-5-chloro-2-norbornene)	9.15 ± 0.15	EI	234	43	$MgBr_2$	10.65 ± 0.15	EI	172	160
C_7H_9Cl (3-chloro-nortricyclene)	9.51 ± 0.15	EI	234	43	$BrCl$	11.1 ± 0.2	EI	259	161
					CH_3Br	10.53	S, PI	234	*
$CHCl_2$	9.30	EI	245	29	C_2H_5Br	9.80	PI	243	*
CH_2Cl_2	11.35 ± 0.02	PI	240	24	C_2H_5Br	10.29	S	222	24, 162
cis-$C_2H_2Cl_2$	9.65	PI	223	*	$CH_3C\equiv CBr$	10.1 ± 0.1	EI	283	25
trans-$C_2H_2Cl_2$	9.64	PI	224	*	$CH_3CH=CHBr$	9.30 ± 0.05	PI	224	24
CH_2ClCH_2Cl	11.12 ± 0.05	PI	225	24	n-C_3H_7Br	10.18 ± 0.01	PI	216	24
$CH_2=CClCH_2Cl$	9.82 ± 0.03	PI	218	24	iso-C_3H_7Br	10.075 ± 0.01	PI	208	24
1,2-$C_3H_6Cl_2$	10.87 ± 0.05	PI	215	24	n-C_4H_9Br	10.125 ± 0.01	PI	208	24
1,3-$C_3H_6Cl_2$	10.85 ± 0.05	PI	215	24	sec-C_4H_9Br	9.98 ± 0.01	PI	206	24
o-$C_6H_4Cl_2$	9.06	PI	217	24, 28	iso-C_4H_9Br	10.09 ± 0.02	PI	208	24
m-$C_6H_4Cl_2$	9.12 ± 0.01	PI	217	24	tert-C_4H_9Br	9.89 ± 0.03	PI	201	24
p-$C_6H_4Cl_2$	8.95	PI	212	28	n-$C_5H_{11}Br$	10.10 ± 0.02	PI	205	24
$CHCl_3$	11.42 ± 0.03	PI	239	24	C_6H_5Br	8.98 ± 0.02	PI	231	24
C_2HCl_3	9.45	PI	216	*	σ-$C_6H_4BrCH_3$	8.78 ± 0.01	PI	218	24
$CHCl_2CHCl_2$	11.10 ± 0.05	EI	220	146	m-$C_6H_4BrCH_3$	8.81 ± 0.02	PI	218	24
$CNCl$	12.49 ± 0.04	EI	321	147	p-$C_6H_4BrCH_3$	8.67 ± 0.02	PI	215	24
CF_3Cl	12.91 ± 0.03	PI	132	24	CH_2Br_2	10.49 ± 0.02	PI	241	24
C_2F_5Cl	10.4 ± 0.2	EI	107	148	cis-$C_2H_2Br_2$	9.45	PI	241	*
C_6F_5Cl	10.4 ± 0.1	EI		149	trans-$C_2H_2Br_2$	9.46	PI	240	*
CF_2Cl_2	12.31 ± 0.05	PI	170	24	CH_3CHBr_2	10.19 ± 0.03	PI	240	24
$CF_3CCl=CClCF_3$	10.36 ± 0.1	PI		24	1,3-$C_3H_6Br_2$	10.07 ± 0.02	PI	221	24
$CFCl_3$	11.77 ± 0.02	PI	205	24	$CHBr_3$	10.51 ± 0.02	PI	246	24
CF_3CCl_3	11.78 ± 0.03	PI		24	C_2HBr_3	9.27	PI	240	24, 28
$CFCl_2CF_2Cl$	11.99 ± 0.02	PI	95	24	$CNBr$	11.95 ± 0.08	EI	320	147
ClO_3F	13.6 ± 0.2	EI	308	150	CF_3Br	11.89	EI	121	*
C_5H_4NCl (2-chloro-pyridene)	9.91 ± 0.05	EI	255	84	C_5H_4NBr (2-bromo-pyridine)	9.65 ± 0.05	EI	261	84
C_5H_4NCl (4-chloro-pyridene)	10.15 ± 0.05	EI	260	84	C_5H_4NBr (4-bromo-pyridine)	9.94 ± 0.05	EI	267	84
CH_3COCl	11.02 ± 0.05	PI	196	24	CH_3COBr	10.55 ± 0.05	PI	197	24
CH_3COCH_2Cl	9.99	EI	173	105, 151	C_6H_4BrOH	9.04	EI	187	75
o-$C_6H_4(OH)Cl$	9.28	EI	181	75	$CH_2BrCOOCH_3$	10.37 ± 0.05	EI	146	74
p-$C_6H_4(OH)Cl$	9.07	EI	175	75	C_6H_4FBr	8.99 ± 0.03	PI	187	24
C_6H_5COCl	9.70 ± 0.01	EI	195	105	CF_2BrCH_2Br	10.83 ± 0.01	PI	160	24
ν-C_6H_4ClCHO	9.61 ± 0.01	EI	201	105	C_4H_3BrS	8.63 ± 0.01	PI	228	24
C_8H_7OCl (α-chloro-acetophenone)	9.5	EI	195	74, 105	CH_2ClBr	10.77 ± 0.01	PI	236	24
					CH_2BrCH_2Cl	10.63 ± 0.03	PI	227	24
C_8H_7OCl (p-chloro-acetophenone)	9.47 ± 0.05	EI	190	105	CH_2Br_2Cl	10.88 ± 0.05	EI	237	146
C_8H_7OCl (p-methyl-benzylchloride)	9.37 ± 0.01	EI	187	105	$(CH_3)_3SiBr$	10.24 ± 0.02	EI	171	130
$C_6H_4ClCOC_6H_5$	9.68 ± 0.01	EI	227	105	$Mo(CO)_6$	8.12 ± 0.03	PI	-31	155
$CH_2ClCOOCH_3$	10.53 ± 0.05	EI	138	74	RuO_4	12.33 ± 0.23	EI	240	163
p-$CH_3OC_6H_4COCl$	8.87 ± 0.05	EI	149	105	$(CH_3)_4Sn$	8.25 ± 0.15	EI	186	129
p-ClC_6H_4COCl	9.58 ± 0.03	EI	192	105	SbH_3	9.58	PI	256	131
cis-C_2H_2FCl	9.86	PI	191	24, 121	$(C_6H_5)_3Sb$	7.3 ± 0.1	PI	255	77
trans-C_2H_2FCl	9.87	PI	191	24, 121	I_2	9.28 ± 0.02	PI	229	24
o-C_6H_4FCl	9.155 ± 0.01	PI	180	24	HI	10.39	PI	246	24, 159
m-C_6H_4FCl	9.21 ± 0.01	PI	180	24	ICl	10.31 ± 0.02	EI	242	164
p-C_6H_4FCl	9.43 ± 0.02	EI	185	152	IBr	9.98 ± 0.03	EI	240	164
CHF_2Cl	12.45 ± 0.05	PI	174	24	CH_3I	9.54	S, PI	223	24, 145
cis-C_2HF_2Cl	9.86 ± 0.02	PI	147	121	C_2H_5I	9.33	S, PI	213	24, 162
trans-C_2HF_2Cl	9.83 ± 0.02	PI	147	121	n-C_3H_7I	9.26 ± 0.01	PI	208	24
CH_3CF_2Cl	11.98 ± 0.01	PI		24	iso-C_3H_7I	9.17 ± 0.02	PI	201	24
n-$C_3F_7CH_2Cl$	11.84 ± 0.02	PI		24	n-C_4H_9I	9.21 ± 0.01	PI	202	24
$CHFCl_2$	12.39 ± 0.20	EI	217	153	sec-C_4H_9I	9.09 ± 0.02	PI	198	24
$(CII_3)_3SiCl$	10.58 ± 0.04	EI	160	130	iso-C_4H_9I	9.18 ± 0.02	PI	200	24
CH_3SiCl_3	11.36 ± 0.03	EI	136	153	tert-C_4H_9I	9.02 ± 0.03	PI	193	24
$CH_2=CHSiCl_3$	10.79 ± 0.02	PI	148	24	n-$C_5H_{11}I$	9.19 ± 0.01	PI	197	24
$C_2H_5SiCl_3$	10.74 ± 0.04	EI	117	153	C_6H_5I	8.73 ± 0.03	PI	238	24
iso-$C_3H_7SiCl_3$	10.28 ± 0.1	EI	100	153	o-$C_6H_4ICH_3$	8.62 ± 0.01	PI	228	24
C_4H_3ClS	8.68 ± 0.01	PI	217	24	m-$C_6H_4ICH_3$	8.61 ± 0.03	PI	226	24
$C_6H_4NO_2COCl$	10.66 ± 0.01	EI	219	105	p-$C_6H_4ICH_3$	8.50 ± 0.01	PI	224	24
CaF	5.8	EI	75	*	$W(CO)_6$	8.18 ± 0.03	PI	-20	155
$C_5H_5V(CO)_4$	8.2 ± 0.3	EI	9	154	OsO_4	12.97 ± 0.12	EI	219	163
$Cr(CO)_6$	8.03 ± 0.03	PI	-55	155	$(CH_3)_2Hg$	9.0	EI	233	143, 156
$C_5H_5Mn(CO)_3$	8.3 ± 0.4	EI	83	154	$(C_2H_5)_2Hg$	8.5 ± 0.1	EI	221	143
					$(iso-C_3H_7)_2Hg$	7.6 ± 0.1	EI	188	143
					CH_3HgCl	11.5 ± 0.2	EI	253	143
					$(CH_3)_4Pb$	8.0 ± 0.4	EI	217	129
					$(C_6H_5)_3Bi$	7.3 ± 0.1	PI	288	77

* Average of several values.

REFERENCES

1. Beutler, H. and Junger, H. O. *Zeit. f. Physik* **100**, 80 (1936).
2. Dibeler, V. H., Reese, R. M. and Krauss, M. *Adv. Mass Spectry.* **3**, 471 (1966).
3. Bauer, S. H., Herzberg, G. and Johns, J. W. C. *J. Mol. Spectr.* **13**, 256 (1964).
4. Margrave, J. L. *J. Phys. Chem.* **61**, 38 (1957).
5. Koski, W. S., Kaufman, J. J., Pachucki, C. F. and Shipko, F. J. *J. Am. Chem. Soc.* **80**, 3202 (1958).
6. Fehlner, T. P. and Koski, W. S. *J. Am. Chem. Soc.* **86**, 581 (1964).
7. Drowart, J., DeMaria, G. and Inghram, M. G. *J. Chem. Phys.* **29**, 1015 (1958).
8. Field, F. H. and Franklin, J. L. *Electron Impact Phenomena and the Properties of Gaseous Ions*, Academic Press, Inc., New York, N.Y. (1957).
9. Herzberg, G. *Can. J. Phys.* **39**, 1511 (1961).
10. Waldron, J. D., *Metropolitan Vickers Gazette* **27**, 66 (1956).
11. Dibeler, V. H., Krauss, M., Reese, R. M. and Harllee, F. N. *J. Chem. Phys.* **42**, 3791 (1965).
12. Herzberg, G. and Shoosmith, J., *Can J. Phys.* **34**, 523 (1956).
13. Elder, F. A., Giese, C., Steiner, B. and Inghram, M. *J. Chem. Phys.* **36**, 3292 (1962).
14. Nicholson, A. J. C., *J. Chem. Phys.* **43**, 1171 (1965).
15. Dibeler, V. H. and Reese, R. M. *J. Res. Natl. Bur. Std.* **A68**, 409 (1964).
16. Zelikoff, M. and Watanabe, K., *J. Opt. Soc. Am.* **43**, 756 (1953).
17. Al-Joboury, M. I. and Turner, D. W., *J. Chem. Soc. London* **4434** (1964).
18. Farmer, J. B. and Lossing, F. P., *Can. J. Chem.* **33**, 861 (1955).
19. Collin, J. and Lossing, F. P., *J. Am. Chem. Soc.* **79**, 5848 (1957).
20. Watanabe, K. and Namioka, T., *J. Chem. Phys.* **24**, 915 (1956).
21. Collin, J. and Lossing, F. P., *J. Am. Chem. Soc.* **81**, 2064 (1959).
22. Dorman, F. H. *J. Chem. Phys.* **43**, 3507 (1965).
23. Pottie, R. F., Harrison, A. G. and Lossing, F. P. *J. Am. Chem. Soc.* **83**, 3204 (1961).
24. Watanabe, K., Nakayama, T. and Mottl, J. *J. Quant. Spectrosc. Radiat. Transfer* **2**, 369 (1962).
25. Coats, F. H. and Anderson, R. C. *J. Am. Chem. Soc.* **79**, 1340 (1957).
26. Varsel, C. J., Morrell, F. A., Resnik, F. E. and Powell, W. A. *Anal. Chem.* **32**, 182 (1960).
27. McDowell, C. A., Lossing, F. P., Henderson, I. H. S. and Farmer, J. B. *Can. J. Chem.* **34**, 345 (1956).
28. Bralsford, R., Harris, P. V. and Price, W. C. *Proc. Roy. Soc.* **A258**, 459 (1960).
29. Lossing, F. P., Kebarle, P. and DeSousa, J. B. *Adv. Mass Spectrometry* **431** (1959).
30. Watanabe, K. *J. Chem. Phys.* **26**, 542 (1957).
31. Meyer, F. and Harrison, A. G. *Can. J. Chem.* **42**, 2256 (1964).
32. Harrison, A. G., Honnen, L. R., Dauben, H. J. and Lossing, F. P. *J. Am. Chem. Soc.* **82**, 5593 (1960).
33. Natalis, P. and Laune, J. *Bull. Soc. Chim. Belg.* **73**, 944 (1964).
34. Taubert, R. and Lossing, F. P. *J. Am. Chem. Soc.* **84**, 1523 (1962).
35. Steiner, B., Giese, C. F. and Inghram, M. G. *J. Chem. Phys.* **34**, 189 (1961).
36. Fisher, I. P., Palmer, T. F. and Lossing, F. P. *J. Am. Chem. Soc.* **86**, 2741 (1964).
37. Brehm, B. *Z. Naturforschg.* **21a**, 196 (1966).
38. Momigny, J., Brakier, L. and D Or, L. *Bull. Classe Sci. Acad. Roy. Belg.* **48**, 1002 (1962).
39. Harrison, A. G., Kebarle, P. and Lossing, F. P. *J. Am. Chem. Soc.* **83**, 777 (1961).
40. Thrush, B. A. and Zwolenik, J. J. *Disc. Faraday Soc.* **35**, 196 (1963).
41. Lifshitz, C. and Bauer, S. H. *J. Phys. Chem.* **67**, 1629 (1963).
42. Meyerson, S., McCollum, J. D. and Rylander, P. N. *J. Am. Chem. Soc.* **83**, 1401 (1961).
43. Steele, W. C., Jennings, B. H., Botyos, G. L. and Dudek, G. O. *J. Org. Chem.* **30**, 2886 (1965).
44. Kybett, B. D., Carroll, S., Natalis, P., Bonnell, D. W., Margrave, J. L. and Franklin, J. L. *J. Am. Chem. Soc.* **88**, 626 (1966).
45. Meyer, F., Haynes, P., McLean, S. and Harrison, A. G. *Can. J. Chem.* **43**, 211 (1965).
46. Natalis, P. *Bull. Soc. Chim. Belg.* **73**, 961 (1964).
47. Pottie, R. F. and Lossing, F. P. *J. Am. Chem. Soc.* **85**, 269 (1963).
48. Vilesov, F. I. and Terenin, A. N. *Dokl. Phys. Chem., Proc. Acad. Sci.* **USSR 115**, 539 (1957).
49. Clark, L. B. *J. Chem. Phys.* **43**, 2566 (1965).
50. Kitagawa, T., Harada, Y., Inokuchi, H. and Kodera, K. *J. Mol. Spectr.* **19**, 1 (1966).
51. Natalis, P. *Bull. Soc. Roy. Sci. Liege* **31**, 803 (1962).
52. Harrison, A. G. and Lossing, F. P. *J. Am. Chem. Soc.* **82**, 1052 (1960).
53. Vilesov, F. I. *J. Phys. Chem.* **USSR 35**, 986 (1961).
54. Natalis, P. and Franklin, J. L. *J. Phys. Chem.* **69**, 2935 (1965).
55. Wacks, M. E. and Dibeler, V. H. *J. Chem. Phys.* **31**, 1557 (1959).
56. Wacks, M. E. *J. Chem. Phys.* **41**, 1661 (1964).
57. King, A. B. *J. Chem. Phys.* **42**, 3526 (1965).
58. Law, R. W. and Margrave, J. L. *J. Chem. Phys.* **25**, 1086 (1956).
59. Lofthus, A. *The Molecular Spectrum of Nitrogen* Department of Physics, University of Oslo, Blindern, **Norway, Spectroscopic Report No. 2,** 1 (1960).
60. Reed, R. I. and Snedden, W. *J. Chem. Soc.* **4132** (1959).
61. Foner, S. N. and Hudson, R. L. *J. Chem. Phys.* **29**, 442 (1958).
62. Foner, S. N. and Hudson, R. L. *J. Chem. Phys.* **28**, 719 (1958).
63. Akopyan, M. E. and Vilesov, F. I. *Kinetics and Catalysis*, **4**, 32 (1963).
64. Dibeler, V. H., Reese, R. M. and Franklin, J. L. *J. Am. Chem. Soc.* **83**, 1813 (1961).
65. Berkowitz, J. *J. Chem. Phys.* **36**, 2533 (1962).
66. Morrison, J. D. and Nicholson, A. J. C. *J. Chem. Phys.* **20**, 1021 (1952).
67. Watanabe, K. and Mottl, J. R. *J. Chem. Phys.* **26**, 1773 (1957).
68. Pottie, R. F. and Lossing, F. P. *J. Am. Chem. Soc.* **83**, 4737 (1961)
69. Gallegos, E. and Kiser, R. W. *J. Phys. Chem.* **65**, 1177 (1961).
70. Gallegos, E. J. and Kiser, R. W. *J. Phys. Chem.* **66**, 136 (1962).
71. Amr El-Sayed, M. F., Kasha, M. and Tanaka, Y. *J. Chem. Phys.* **34**, 334 (1961).
72. Akopyan, M. E. and Vilesov, F. I. *Dokl. Phys. Chem., Proc. Acad. Sci.* **USSR 158**, 965 (1964).
73. Kurbatov, B. L., Vilesov, F. I. and Terenin, A. N. *Soviet Physics-Doklady* **6**, 883 (1962).
74. Pignataro, S., Foffani, A., Innorta, G. and Distefano, G. *Z. Phys. Chem. Neue Folge* **49**, 291 (1966).
75. Crable, G. F. and Kearns, G. L. *J. Phys. Chem.* **66**, 436 (1962).
76. Farrell, P. G. and Newton, J. *J. Phys. Chem.* **69**, 3506 (1965).
77. Vilesov, F. I. and Zaitsev, V. M. *Dokl. Phys. Chem., Proc. Acad. Sci.* **USSR 154**, 117 (1964).
78. Paulett, G. S. and Ettinger, R. *J. Chem. Phys.* **39**, 825 (1963).
79. Merer, A. J., *Can. J. Phys.* **42**, 1242 (1964).
80. Gowenlock, B. G., Majer, J. R. and Snelling, D. R. *Trans. Faraday Soc.* **58**, 670 (1962).
81. Akopyan, M. E., Vilesov, F. I. and Terenin, A. N. *Izv. Akad. Nauk USSR, Ser. Fiz.* **27**, 1083 (1963).
82. Dibeler, V. H., Franklin, J. L. and Reese, R. M. *J. Am. Chem. Soc.* **81**, 68 (1959).
83. Momigny, J., Urbain, J. and Wankenne, H. *Bull. Soc. Roy. Sci. Liege* **34**, 337 (1965).
84. Basila, M. R. and Clancy, D. J. *J. Phys. Chem.* **67**, 1551 (1963).
85. Finch, A. C. M. *J. Chem. Soc.* **2272** (1964).
86. Franklin, J. L., Dibeler, V. H., Reese, R. M. and Krauss, M. *J. Am. Chem. Soc.* **80**, 298 (1958).
87. Radwan, T. N. and Turner, D. W. *J. Chem. Soc. Sect.* **A85** (1966).
88. Foner, S. N. and Hudson, R. L. *Advances in Chem. Ser.* **34** (1962).
89. Foner, S. N. and Hudson, R. L. *J. Chem. Phys.* **23**, 1364 (1955).
90. Lindeman, L. P. and Guffy, J. C. *J. Chem. Phys.* **29**, 247 (1958).
91. Foner, S. N. and Hudson, R. L. *J. Chem. Phys.* **36**, 2676 (1962).
92. Berkowitz, J., Chupka, W. A., Blue, G. D. and Margrave, J. L. *J. Phys. Chem.*, **63**, 644 (1959).
93. White, D., Seshadri, K. S., Dever, D. F., Mann, D. E. and Linevski, M. J. *J. Chem. Phys.* **39**, 2463 (1963).
94. Krupenie, P. H. *The Band Spectrum of Carbon Monoxide* Institute for Basic Standards, National Bureau of Standards, Washington, D.C., **NSRDS-NBS 5**, 1 (1966).
95. Tanaka, Y., Jursa, A. S. and LeBlanc, F. J. *J. Chem. Phys.* **32**, 1205 (1960).
96. Tanaka, Y., Jursa, A. S. and LeBlanc, F. J. *J, Chem. Phys.* **32**, 1199 (1960).
97. Nakayama, T., Kitamura, M. Y. and Watanabe, K. *J. Chem. Phys.* **30**, 1180 (1959).
98. Frost, D. C., Mak, D. and McDowell, C. A. *Can. J. Chem.* **40**, 1064 (1962).
99. Hernandez, G. J. *J. Chem. Phys.* **38**, 1644 (1963).
100. Hernandez, G. J. *J. Chem. Phys.* **38**, 2233 (1963).
101. Chupka, W. A. *J. Chem. Phys.* **30**, 191 (1959).
102. Watanabe, K. and Nakayama, T. *J. Chem. Phys.* **29**, 48 (1958).
103. Murad, E. and Inghram, M. G. *J. Chem. Phys.* **40**, 3263 (1964).
104. Higasi, K., Nozoe, T. and Omura, I. *Bull. Chem. Soc. Japan* **30**, 408 (1957).
105. Foffani, A., Pignataro, S., Cantone, B. and Grasso, F. *Z. Phys. Chem. Neue Folge* **42**, 221 (1964).
106. Natalis, P. and Franklin, J. L. *J. Phys. Chem.* **69**, 2943 (1965).
107. Cotter, J. L. *J. Chem. Soc.* **5742** (1965).
108. Cotter, J. L. *J. Chem. Soc.* **5477** (1964).
109. Iczkowski, R. P. and Margrave, J. L. *J. Chem. Phys.* **30**, 403 (1959).
110. Frost, D. C. and McDowell, C. A. *Can. J. Chem.* **36**, 39 (1958).
111. Hildenbrand, D. L. and Muran, E. *J. Chem. Phys.* **43**, 1400 (1965).
112. Marriott, J. and Craggs, J. D. *J. Electronics and Control* **3**, 194 (1957).
113. Fisher, I. P., Homer, J. B. and Lossing, F. P. *J. Am. Chem. Soc.* **87**, 957 (1965).
114. Pottie, R. F. *J. Chem. Phys.* **42**, 2607 (1965).
115. Herron, J. T. and Dibeler, V. H. *J. Res. Natl. Bur. Std.* **65**, 405 (1961).
116. Loughran, E. D. and Mader, C. *J. Chem. Phys.* **32**, 1578 (1960).
117. Frost, D. C. and McDowell, C. A. *The Determination of Ionization and Dissociation Potentials of Molecules by Radiation with Electrons* Department of Chemistry, University of British Columbia, Vancouver 8, B. C., Canada, **AFCRL-TR-60-423 1** (1960).
118. Dibeler, V. H., Reese, R. M. and Franklin, J. L. *J. Chem. Phys.* **27**, 1296 (1957).
119. Wilson, E. G. Jortner, J. and Rice, S. A. *J. Am. Chem. Soc.* **85**, 813 (1963).
120. Frost, D. C. and McDowell, C. A. *Proc. Roy. Soc.* **A241**, 194 (1957).
121. Momigny, J. *Nature* **199**, 1179 (1963).
122. Martin, R. H., Lampe, F. W. and Taft, R. W. *J. Am. Chem. Soc.* **88**, 1353 (1966).
123. Reese, R. M. and Dibeler, V. H. *J. Chem. Phys.* **24**, 1175 (1956).
124. Herron, J. T. and Dibeler, V. H. *J. Chem. Phys.* **33**, 1595 (1960).
125. Hammond, V. J., Price, W. C., Teegan, J. P. and Walsh, A. D. *Disc. Faraday Soc.* **9**, 53 (1950).
126. Hudson, R. D. *J. Chem. Phys.* **43**, 1790 (1965).
127. Margrave, J. L. *J. Chem. Phys.* **41**, 2250 (1964).

REFERENCES (Continued)

128. Ehlert, T. C. and Margrave, J. L. *J. Am. Chem. Soc.* **86**, 3901 (1964).
129. Hobrock, B. G. and Kiser, R. W. *J. Phys. Chem.* **65**, 2186 (1961).
130. Hess, G. G., Lampe, F. W. and Sommer, L. H. *J. Am. Chem. Soc.* **87**, 5327 (1965).
131. Price, W. C. and Passmore, T. R. *Disc. Faraday Soc.* **35**, 232 (1963).
132. Wada, Y. and Kiser, R. W. *J. Phys. Chem.* **68**, 2290 (1964).
133. Berkowitz, J. and Chupka, W. A. *J. Chem. Phys.* **40**, 287 (1964).
134. Palmer, T. F. and Lossing, F. P. *J. Am. Chem. Soc.* **84**, 4661 (1962).
135. Price, W. C. *Bull. Am. Phys. Soc.* **10**, 9 (1935).
136. Hobrock, B. G. and Kiser, R. W. *J. Phys. Chem.* **66**, 1551 (1962).
137. Hobrock, B. G. and Kiser, R. W. *J. Phys. Chem.* **67**, 648 (1963).
138. Hobrock, B. G. and Kiser, R. W. *J. Phys. Chem.* **66**, 1648 (1962).
139. Khvostenko, V. I. *Russ. J. Phys. Chem.* **36**, 197 (1962).
140. Hobrock, B. G. and Kiser, R. W. *J. Phys. Chem.* **67**, 1283 (1963).
141. Reese, R. M., Dibeler, V. H. and Franklin, J. L. *J. Chem. Phys.* **29**, 880 (1958).
142. Baldwin, M., Maccoll, A., Kirkien-Konasiewicz, A. and Saville, B. *Chem. Ind.* **286** (1966).
143. Gowenlock, B. G., Kay, J. and Majer, J. R. *Trans. Faraday Soc.* **59**, 2463 (1963).
144. Berkowitz, J., Tasman, H. A. and Chupka, W. A. *J. Chem. Phys.* **36**, 2170 (1962).
145. Price, W. C. *J. Chem. Phys.* **4**, 539 (1936).
146. Harrison, A. G. and Shannon, T. W. *Can. J. Chem.* **40**, 1730 (1962).
147. Herron, J. T. and Dibeler, V. H. *J. Am. Chem. Soc.* **82**, 1555 (1960).
148. Margrave, J. L. *J. Chem. Phys.* **31**, 1432 (1959).
149. Majer, J. R. and Patrick, C. R. *Trans. Faraday Soc.* **58**, 17 (1962).
150. Dibeler, V. H., Reese, R. M. and Mann, D. E. *J. Chem. Phys.* **27**, 176 (1957).
151. Foffani, A., Pignataro, S., Cantone, B. and Grasso, F. *Nuovo Cimento* **29**, 918 (1963).
152. Momigny, J. and Wirtz-Cordier, A. M. *Ann. Soc. Sci. Bruxelles* **76**, 164 (1962).
153. Hobrock, D. L. and Kiser, R. W. *J. Phys. Chem.* **68**, 575 (1964).
154. Winters, R. E. and Kiser, R. W. *J. Organometal. Chem.* **4**, 190 (1965).
155. Vilesov, F. I. and Kurbatov, B. L. *Dokl. Phys. Chem., Proc. Acad. Sci. USSR* **140**, 792 (1961).
156. Hobrock, B. G. and Kiser, R. W. *J. Phys. Chem.* **66**, 155 (1962).
157. Westmore, J. B., Mann, K. H. and Tickner, A. W. *J. Phys. Chem.* **68**, 606 (1964).
158. Cullen, W. R. and Frost, D. C. *Can. J. Chem.* **40**, 390 (1962).
159. Morrison, J. D., Hurzeler, H., Inghram, M. G. and Stanton, H. E. *J. Chem. Phys.* **33**, 821 (1960).
160. Berkowitz, J. and Marquart, J. R. *J. Chem. Phys.* **37**, 1853 (1962).
161. Irsa, A. P. and Friedman, L. *J. Inorg. Nucl. Chem.* **6**, 77 (1958).
162. Price, W. C. *J. Chem. Phys.* **4**, 547 (1936).
163. Dillard, J. G. and Kiser, R. W. *J. Phys. Chem.* **69**, 3893 (1965).
164. Frost, D. C. and McDowell, C. A. *Can. J. Chem.* **38**, 407 (1960).

ELECTRON WORK FUNCTIONS OF THE ELEMENTS

From data published up to 1954
Compiled by Herbert B. Michaelson

Preferred values for well-outgassed polycrystalline materials are indicated by an asterisk (*). Because of the anisotropy and allotropy of work function, however, the designation "preferred value" has a rather limited meaning.

Values are expressed in electron-volts.

Each value is followed by a reference to the literature.

Element	Thermionic Work Function		Photoelectric Work Function		Work Function by Contact Potential Method	
Ag	3.09	(1)	3.67	(4)	4.21	(116)
	3.56	(2)	4.1 to 4.75	(5)	4.33	(8)
	4.08	(3)	4.50 to 4.52	(117)	4.35	(115)
	4.31	(114)	4.56 (600°)*	(6)	4.44	(9)
			4.73 (20°)*	(6)	4.47	(10)
			4.75 (111) face	(7)		
			4.81 (100) face	(7)		
Al	. . .		2.98	(4)	3.38	(9)
			3.43	(11)	4.25	(115)
			4.08*	(12)		
			4.20	(113)		
			4.36	(13)		
As			4.72	(118)		
			5.11	(14)		
Au	4.0 to 4.58	(2)	4.73 (740°C)*	(15)	4.46	(9)
	4.25	(114)	4.82 (20°C)*	(15)		
	4.32	(3)	4.86 to 4.92	(5)		
B	. . .		4.4 to 4.6	(16)		
Ba	2.11	(17)	2.48*	(19)	1.73	(9)
			2.49	(20)	2.39	(18)
			2.52	(21)		
Be	. . .		3.17	(14)	**3.10**	(9)
			3.30	(22)		
			3.92*	(23)		
Bi	. . .		4.14	(11)	4.17	(9)
			4.22 to 4.25*	(24)		
			4.31	(25)		
			4.34	(118)		
			4.44	(22)		
			4.46	(47)		
C	4.00	(26)	4.81	(29)		
	4.34	(27)				
	4.35	(119)				
	4.39	(28)				
	4.60*	(120)				
	4.83	(121)				
	4.84	(122)				
Ca	2.24	(30)	2.42	(14)	3.33	(9)
			2.706*	(21)		
			2.76	(31)		
			3.20	(32)		
			3.21	(33)		
Cd			3.68	(14)	4.00	(9)
			3.73	(4)	4.49	(123)
			3.94	(11)		
			4.07*	(36)		
			4.099	(113)		
Ce	2.6	(37)	2.84	(32)		
Co	4.40*	(38)	3.90	(31)	4.21	(9)
	4.41	(124)	4.12 to 4.25	(39)		
Cr	4.58	(124)	4.37	(25)	4.38	(9)
	4.60*	(40)				
	4.7	(41)				

Element	Thermionic Work Function		Photoelectric Work Function		Work Function by Contact Potential Method	
Cs	1.81*	(42)	1.9	(43)		
			1.96	(44)		
	3.85	(1)	4.07	(4)	4.46*	(9, 126)
	4.26	(2)	4.18	(31)	4.61	(115)
	4.38	(3)	4.70	(125)	4.86	(123)
	4.50	(114)	4.86 (111) face	(46)		
	4.55 (a)	(45)	5.61 (100) face	(46)		
Fe	4.04	(48)	3.91	(31)	4.40	(9)
	γ4.21	(38)	3.92	(53)		
			β4.62	(128)		
	γ4.31	(124)	γ4.68	(128)		
	4.47	(49)	α4.70	(128)		
	β4.48	(38)	4.72	(50)		
	4.76	(127)	4.77	(51)		
Ga	4.12	(14)	. . .		3.80	(9)
Ge	. . .		4.29	(31)	4.50	(9)
			4.5	(52)		
			4.73	(14)		
			4.80	(16)		
Hf	3.53	(54)				
Hg	. . .		4.50	(55)	4.50	(9)
			4.52	(56)		
			4.53*	(57, 58)		
I	. . .		2.8 (rhombic)	(129)		
			5.4 (monoclinic)	(129)		
			6.8 (amorphous)	(129)		
Ir	5.3	(130)	. . .		4.57	(9)
K	. . .		2.0	(59)	1.60	(9)
			2.12	(22)		
			2.24*	(44, 43)		
			2.26	(60)		
La	3.3	(37)				
Li	. . .		2.28	(43)	1.40	(9)
			2.42	(14)	2.49*	(61)
Mg	. . .		2.74	(14)	3.58	(9)
			<3.0	(62)	3.78	(66)
			3.59	(63)		
			3.62	(64)		
			3.68*	(23)		
			3.79	**(65)**		
Mn	3.83	(124)	3.76	(14)	4.14	(9)
Mo	4.15	(67)	4.15	(67)	4.08	(75)
	4.17	(68)	4.34	(25)	4.48	(9)
	4.19	(69)				
	4.20*	(70)				
	4.23	(121)				
	4.32	(71)				
	4.33	(72)				
	4.38	(73)				
	4.44	(74)				
Na	. . .		2.06	(14)	1.60	(9)
			2.25	(76)	2.26	(77)
			2.28*	(19)		
Nb	3.96	**(34)**	2.29	(23)		
	4.01	**(35)**	2.47	(43)		

(a) By field current method.

Element	Thermionic Work Function	Photoelectric Work Function	Work Function by Contact Potential Method
Nd	3.3 (37)		
Ni	4.50 (124) 4.61 (38) 4.63 (48) 5.03* (78) 5.1 (a) (45) 5.24 (1150°K) (131)	3.67 (4) 4.06 (31) 4.87 (25) 5.01* (51) 5.05 (623°K) (131) 5.20 (1108°K) (131)	4.32 (9) 4.96 (300°K) (79)
Os			4.55 (9)
Pb		3.97 (4) 4.14 (11)	3.94 (9)
Pd	4.99* (80)	4.97* (80)	4.49 (9)
Pr	2.7 (37)		
Pt	4.72 (132) 5.08 (26) 5.29 (81) 5.32* (82) 6.27 (83)	4.09 (4) 6.35 (84)	4.52 (9) 5.36* (85)
Rb		2.09* (44) 2.16 (43)	
Re	4.74 (133) 5.1* (86)	~5.0 (87)	
Rh	4.58 (88) 4.80* (89) 4.9 (130)	4.57 (88)	4.52 (9)
Ru	...	...	4.52 (9)
Sb	...	4.01 (90) 4.60 (118)	4.14 (9)
Se	...	4.62 (11) 5.11 (14)	4.42 (9)
Si	3.59 (28) 4.02 (134)	4.37 to 4.67 (117)	4.2 (91)
Sm	3.2 (37)		
Sn	...	3.62 (4) 3.87 (11) (liq.) 4.21 (92) γ4.38* (92) β4.50* (92)	1.09 (9) 4.64 (123)
Sr		2.06 (93) 2.24 (14) 2.74* (64)	
Ta	4.03 (135) 4.07 (74) 4.10 (94) 4.19* (95)	4.05 (63) 4.12 (32) 4.16 (96)	3.96 (9) 4.25 (97)
Te	...	4.04 (117) 4.76 (16)	4.70 (9)
Th	3.35* (73)	3.38 (32) 3.47 (98) 3.57 (11)	3.46 (9)
Ti	3.95 (124)	3.95 (14) 4.17 (98) 4.45 (136)	4.14 (9)
Tl	...	3.68 (107)	3.84 (9)
U	3.27 (99)	3.63 (32)	4.32 (9)
V	4.12 (124)	3.77 (14)	4.41 (9)
W	4.25 (100) 4.29 (116) face (142) 4.38 (111) face (142) 4.39 (111) face (140) 4.39 (116) face (140) 4.45 (doped) (138) 4.46 (101) 4.52* (001) face (26, 102, 142) 4.53 (103, 138) 4.56 (001) face (140) 4.58 (110) face (71, 73, 142) 4.59 (001) face (139) 4.65 (112) face (142) 4.68 (110) face (140) 4.69 (112) face (140) 5.01 (137)	4.35 (310) face (104) 4.49 (143) 4.50 (211) face (104) 4.54 (105) 4.60 (32)	4.38 (9)
Zn	...	3.08 (4) 3.28 (106) 3.32 and 3.57 (108) 3.60 (11) 3.89 (31) 4.24 (109) 4.26 (0001) face (110) 4.307 (113)	(111) (9) (112) (123)
Zr	4.12 (54) 4.21* (141)	3.73 (32) 4.33 (136)	3.60 (9)

(a) By field current method.

REFERENCES

(1) A. Wehnelt and S. Seliger, Zeits. f. Physik 38, 443 (1926).
(2) I. Ameiser, Zeits. f. Physik 69, 111 (1931).
(3) A. Goetz, Zeits. f. Physik 43, 531 (1927).
(4) P. Lukirsky and S. Prilesaev, Zeits. f. Physik 49, 236 (1928).
(5) R. H. Fowler, Phys. Rev. 38, 45 (1931).
(6) R. P. Winch, Phys. Rev. 37, 1269 (1931).
(7) H. E. Farnsworth and R. P. Winch, Phys. Rev. 58, 812 (1940).
(8) P. A. Anderson, Phys. Rev. 50, 320 (1936).
(9) O. Klein and E. Lange, Zeits. f. Elektrochemie 44, 542 (1938).
(10) P. A. Anderson, Phys. Rev. 59, 1034 (1011).
(11) R. Hamer, Jour. Opt. Soc. Amer. 9, 251 (1924).
(12) J. Brady and P. Jakobsmeyer, Phys. Rev. 49, 670 (1936).
(13) E. Gaviola and J. Strong, Phys. Rev. 49, 441 (1936).
(14) R. Schulze, Zeits. f Physik 92, 212 (1934).
(15) L. W. Morris, Phys. Rev. 37, 1263 (1931).
(16) L. Apker, E. Taft, and J. Dickey, Phys. Rev. 74, 1462 (1948).
(17) A. L. Reimann, Thermionic Emission (Chapman and Hall, London, 1934), p. 37.
(18) P. A. Anderson, Phys. Rev. 47, 958 (1935).
(19) R. J. Maurer, Phys. Rev. 57, 653 (1940).
(20) R. J. Cashman and E. Bassoe, Phys. Rev. 55, 63 (1939).
(21) N. C. Jamison and R. J. Cashman, Phys. Rev. 50, 624 (1936).
(22) R. Suhrmann and A. Schallamach, Zeits. f. Physik 91, 775 (1934).
(23) M. M. Mann, Jr. and L. A. DuBridge, Phys. Rev. 51, 120 (1937).
(24) H. Jupnik, Phys. Rev. 60, 884 (1941).
(25) H. C. Rentschler and D. E. Henry, Jour. Opt. Soc. Amer. 26, 30 (1936).
(26) S. Dushman, "Thermal Emission of Electrons," International Critical Tables (1929) Vol. VI, pp. 53–4.
(27) A. L. Reiman, Proc. Phys. Soc. 50, 496 (1938).
(28) A. Braun and G. Busch, Helv. Phys. Acta 20, #1, 33 (1947).
(29) S. C. Roy, Proc. Roy. Soc. A112, 599 (1926).
(30) S. Dushman, Phys. Rev. 21, 623 (1923).
(31) G. B. Welch, Phys. Rev. 32, 657 (1928).
(32) C. Rentschler, D. E. Henry, and K. O. Smith, Rev. Sci. Instr. 3, 794 (1932).
(33) I. Liben, Phys. Rev. 51, 642 (1937).
(34) H. B. Wahlin and L. O. Sordahl, Phys. Rev. 45, 886 (1934).
(35) A. L. Reimann and C. Kerr Grant, Phil. Mag. 22, 34 (1936).
(36) H. Bomke, Ann. d. Physik 10, 579 (1931).

(37) E. E. Schumaker, J. E. Harris, J. Amer. Chem. Soc. **48**, 3108 (1926).
(38) H. B. Wahlin, Phys. Rev. **61**, 509 (1942).
(39) A. B. Cardwell, Phys. Rev. **38**, 2033 (1931).
(40) H. B. Wahlin, Phys. Rev. **73**, 1458 (1948).
(41) H. Koesters, Zeits f. Physik **66**, 807 (1930).
(42) K. H. Kingdon, Rev. **25**, 892 (1925).
(43) A. R. Olpin, quoted by Hughes and DuBridge, *Photoelectric Phenomena* (1932).
(44) J. J. Brady, Phys. Rev. **41**, 613 (1932).
(45) W. P. Dyke, Thesis, University of Washington, (1946).
(46) N. Underwood, Phys. Rev. **47**, 502 (1935).
(47) A. H. Weber and C. J. Eisele, Phys. Rev. **59**, 473A (1941).
(48) W. Distler and G. Monch, Zeits, f. Physik **84**, 271 (1933).
(49) G. Siljeholm, Ann. d. Physik **10**, 178 (1931).
(50) A. B. Cardwell, Proc. Nat. Acad. Sci. **14**, 439 (1928).
(51) G. N. Glasoe, Phys. Rev. **38**, 1490 (1931).
(52) A. H. Smith, Phys. Rev. **75**, 953 (1949).
(53) G. B. Welch, Phys. Rev. **31**, 709A (1928).
(54) C. Zwikker, Phys. Zeits. **30**, 578 (1929).
(55) H. Cassel and A. Schneider, Naturwiss **22**, 464 (1934).
(56) D. Roller, W. H. Jordan, and C. S. Woodward, Phys. Rev. **38**, (1931).
(57) C. B. Kazda, Phys. Rev. **26**, 643 (1925).
(58) W. B. Hales, Phys. Rev. **32**, 950 (1928).
(59) H. E. Ives, J. Opt. Soc. Am. **8**, 551 (1924).
(60) H. Mayer, Ann. d. Phys. **29**, 129 (1937).
(61) P. A. Anderson, Phys. Rev. **75**, 1205 (1949).
(62) C. Kenty, Phys. Rev. **43**, 776(A), (1933).
(63) J. Cashman and S. Huxford, Phys. Rev. **48**, 734 (1935).
(64) R. J. Cashman and E. Bassoe, Phys. Rev. **53**, 919(A), (1938).
(65) R. J. Cashman, Phys. Rev. **54**, 971 (1938).
(66) P. A. Anderson, Phys. Rev. **54**, 753 (1938).
(67) L. A. DuBridge and W. W. Roehr, Phys. Rev. **42**, 52 (1932).
(68) H. B. Wahlin and J. A. Reynolds, Phys. Rev. **48**, 751 (1935).
(69) H. Grover, Phys. Rev. **52**, 982 (1937).
(70) R. W. Wright, Phys. Rev. **60**, 465 (1941).
(71) A. J. Ahearn, Phys. Rev. **44**, 277 (1933).
(72) H. Freitag and F. Kruger, Ann. d. Physik **21**, 697 (1934).
(73) C. Zwikker, Proc. Roy. Acad. Amsterdam **29**, 792 (1926).
(74) S. Dushman, H. N. Rowe, J. Ewald, C. A. Kidner, Phys. Rev. **25**, 338 (1925).
(75) C. W. Oatley, Proc. Roy. Soc. **A155**, 218 (1936).
(76) Z. Berkes, Math. Phys. Lapok **41**, 131 (1934).
(77) E. Patai, Zeits, f. Physik. **59**, 697 (1930).
(78) G. W. Fox and R. M. Bowie, Phys. Rev. **44**, 345 (1933).
(79) R. C. L. Bosworth, Trans. Far. Soc. **35**, 397 (1939).
(80) L. A. DuBridge and W. W. Roehr, Phys. Rev. **39**, 99 (1932).
(81) H. L. Van Velzer, Phys. Rev. **44**, 831 (1933).
(82) L. V. Whitney, Phys. Rev. **50**, 1154 (1936).
(83) L. A. DuBridge, Phys. Rev. **32**, 961 (1928).
(84) L. A. DuBridge, Phys. Rev. **31**, 236 (1928).
(85) C. W. Oatley, Proc. Phys. Soc. **51**, 318 (1939).
(86) C. Agte, H. Alterthum, K. Becker, G. Heyne, and K. Moers. Naturwiss **19**, 108 (1931).
(87) A. Englemann, Ann. d. Physik **17**, 185 (1933).
(88) E. H. Dixon, Phys. Rev. **37**, 60 (1931).
(89) H. B. Wahlin and L. V. Whitney, J. Chem. Phys. **6**, 594 (1938).
(90) V. Middel, Zeits. f. Physik **105**, 358 (1937).
(91) W. E. Meyerhof, Phys. Rev. **71**, 727 (1947).
(92) A. Goetz, Phys. Rev. **33**, 373 (1929).
(93) R. Doepel, Zeits. f. Physik **33**, 237 (1925).
(94) A. B. Cardwell, Phys. Rev. **47**, 628 (1935).
(95) M. D. Fiske, Phys. Rev. **61**, 513 (1942).
(96) A. B. Cardwell, Phys. Rev. **38**, 2041 (1931).
(97) W. Heinze, Zeits. f. Phys. **109**, 459 (1938).
(98) H. C. Rentschler and D. E. Henry, Trans. Electrochem. Soc. **87**, 289 (1945–6).
(99) W. L. Hole and R. W. Wright, Phys. Rev. **56**, 785 (1939).
(100) A. H. Warner, Proc. Nat. Acad. Sci. **13**, 56 (1927).
(101) G. M. Fleming and J. E. Henderson, Phys. Rev. **58**, 887 (1940).
(102) W. B. Nottingham, Phys. Rev. **47**, 806A (1935).
(103) H. Freitag and F. Krueger, Ann. d. Physik **21**, 697 (1934).
(104) C. E. Mendenhall and C. F. DeVoe, Phys. Rev. **51**, 346 (1937).
(105) A. H. Warner, Phys. Rev. **38**, 1871 (1931).
(106) A. Nitsche, Ann. d. Physik **14**, 463 (1932).
(107) R. Suhrmann and H. Csesch, Zeits. Chem. **B28**, 215 (1935).
(108) J. H. Dillon, Phys. Rev. **38**, 408 (1931).
(109) C. F. DeVoe, Phys. Rev. **50**, 481 (1936).
(110) W. Klug and H. Steyskal, Zeits. f. Physik **116**, 415 (1940).
(111) C. W. Oatley, Proc. Roy. Soc. **A155**, 218 (1936).
(112) P. A. Anderson, Phys. Rev. **57**, 122 (1940).
(113) R. Suhrmann and J. Pietrzyk, Zeits. f. Physik **122**, 600 (1944).
(114) S. C. Jain and K. S. Krishman, Proc. Roy. Soc. **A217**, 451 (1953).
(115) E. W. J. Mitchell and J. W. Mitchell, Proc. Roy. Soc. **A210**, 70 (1952).
(116) G. L. Weissler and T. N. Wilson, J. Appl. Phys. **24**, 472 (1953).
(117) S. M. Fainshtein, Zavodskaya Lab. **14**, 64 (1948).
(118) L. Apker, E. Taft and J. Dickey, Phys. Rev. **76**, 270 (1949).
(119) G. Glockler and J. W. Sausville, J. Electrochem. Soc. **95**, 292 (1949).
(120) H. F. Ivey, Phys. Rev. **76**, 567 (1949).
(121) S. B. L. Mathur, Natl. Inst. Sci. India **19**, 153 (1953).
(122) A. S. Bhatnager, Proc. Nat. Acad. Sci. India **A14**, 5 (1944).
(123) R. Hirschberg and E. Lange, Naturwiss. **39**, 131 (1952).
(124) K. S. Krishman and S. C. Jain, Nature **170**, 759 (1952).
(125) R. Ito, J. Phys. Soc. Japan **6**, 188 (1951).
(126) P. A. Anderson, Phys. Rev. **76**, 388 (1949).
(127) S. B. L. Mathur, Proc. Natl. Inst. Sci. India **19**, 165 (1953).
(128) A. B. Cardwell, Phys. Rev. **92**, 554 (1953).
(129) D. C. West, Can. J. Phys. **31**, 691 (1953).
(130) O. A. Weinreich, Phys. Rev. **82**, 573 (1951).
(131) A. B. Cardwell, Phys. Rev. **76**, 125 (1949).
(132) K. Kondo, Rept. Inst. Sci. Tech., Tokyo Univ. **1**, 24 (1947).
(133) R. Levi and G. A. Espersen, Phys. Rev. **78**, 231 (1950).
(134) L. Esaki, J. Phys. Soc. Japan **8**, 347 (1953).
(135) R. J. Munick, W. B. LaBerge and E. A. Coomes, Phys. Rev. **80**, 887 (1950).
(136) H. Malamud and A. D. Krumbein, J. Appl. Phys. **25**, 591 (1954).
(137) G. M. Fleming and J. E. Henderson, Phys. Rev. **58**, 887 (1940).
(138) M. H. Nichols, Phys. Rev. **78**, 158 (1950).
(139) A. A. Brown, L. J. Neelands and H. E. Farnsworth, J. Appl. Phys. **21**, 1 (1950).
(140) C. Herring and M. H. Nichols, Rev. Mod. Phys. **21**, 185 (1949).
(141) A. Wahl, Phys. Rev. **82**, 574 (1951).
(142) G. F. Smith, Phys. Rev. **94**, 295 (1954).
(143) L. Apker, E. Taft and J. Dickey, Phys. Rev. **73**, 46 (1948).

PROPERTIES OF METALS AS CONDUCTORS

Metal.	Resistivity microhm-centimeters 20° C.	Temp. coefficient 20° C.	Specific gravity.	Tensile strength, lbs./in.	Melting point ° C.
*Advance. See constantan					
Aluminum..........	2.824	0.0039	2.70	30,000	659
Antimony..........	41.7	.0036	6.6	......	630
Arsenic............	33.3	.0042	5.73	......	
Bismuth...........	120	.004	9.8	......	271
Brass.............	7	.002	8.6	70,000	900
Cadmium..........	7.6	.0038	8.6	......	321
*Calido. See nichrome					
Climax............	87	.0007	8.1	150,000	1250
Cobalt............	9.8	.0033	8.71	......	1480
Constantan........	49	.00001	8.9	120,000	1190
Copper: annealed ..	1.7241	.00393	8.89	30,000	1083
hard-drawn.......	1.771	.00382	8.89	60,000	......
Eureka. See constantan					
Excello............	92	.00016	8.9	95,000	1500
Gas Carbon........	5000	−.0005	......	......	3500
German silver, 18 % Ni...............	33	.0004	8.4	150,000	1100
Gold..............	2.44	.0034	19.3	20,000	1063
Ideal. See constantan					
Iron, 99.98 % pure...	10	.005	7.8	......	1530
Lead..............	22	.0039	11.4	3,000	327
Magnesium........	4.6	.004	1.74	33,000	651
Manganin.........	44	.00001	8.4	150,000	910
Mercury...........	95.783	.00089	13.546	0	−38.9
Molybdenum, drawn	5.7	.004	9.0	......	2500
Monel metal.......	42	.0020	8.9	160,000	1300
*Nichrome.........	100	.0004	8.2	150,000	1500
Nickel............	7.8	.006	8.9	120,000	1452
Palladium.........	11	.0033	12.2	39,000	1550
Phosphor bronze....	7.8	.0018	8.9	25,000	750
Platinum..........	10	.003	21.4	50,000	1755
Silver.............	1.59	.0038	10.5	42,000	960
Steel, E. B. B.......	10.4	.005	7.7	53,000	1510
Steel, B. B.........	11.9	.004	7.7	58,000	1510
Steel, Siemens-Martin......	18	.003	7.7	100,000	1510
Steel, manganese....	70	.001	7.5	230,000	1260
Tantalum.........	15.5	.0031	16.6	......	2850
*Therlo...........	47	.00001	8.2	......	
Tin...............	11.5	.0042	7.3	4,000	232
Tungsten, drawn....	5.6	.0045	19	500,000	3400
Zinc..............	5.8	.0037	7.1	10,000	419

* Trade mark.

Superconductivity*

B.W. ROBERTS

General Electric Research Laboratory, Schenectady, New York

The following tables on superconductivity include superconductive properties of chemical elements, thin films, a selected list of compounds and alloys, and high-magnetic-field superconductors.

The historically first observed and most distinctive property of a superconductive body is the near total loss of resistance at a critical temperature (T_c) that is characteristic of each material. Figure 1(a) below illustrates schematically two types of possible transitions. The sharp vertical discontinuity in resistance is indicative of that found for a single crystal of a very pure element or one of a few well annealed alloy compositions. The broad transition, illustrated by broken lines, suggests the transition shape seen for materials that are not homogeneous and contain unusual strain distributions. Careful testing of the resistivity limits for superconductors shows that it is less than 4×10^{-23} ohm-cm, while the lowest resistivity observed in metals is of the order of 10^{-13} ohm-cm. If one compares the resistivity of a superconductive body to that of copper at room temperature, the superconductive body is at least 10^{17} times less resistive.

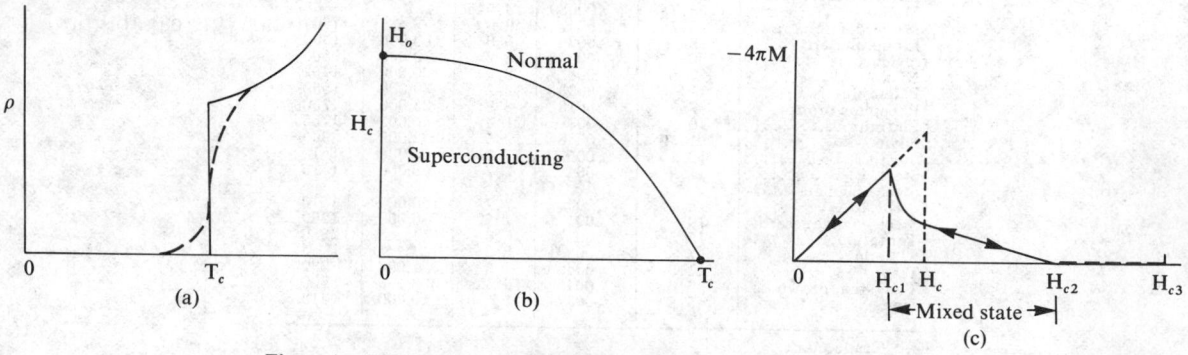

Figure 1. PHYSICAL PROPERTIES OF SUPERCONDUCTORS

(a) Resistivity versus temperature for a pure and perfect lattice (solid line).
   Impure and/or imperfect lattice (broken line).
(b) Magnetic-field temperature dependence for Type-I or "soft" superconductors.
(c) Schematic magnetization curve for "hard" or Type-II superconductors.

The temperature interval ΔT_c, over which the transition between the normal and superconductive states takes place, may be of the order of as little as 2×10^{-5} °K *or* several °K in width, depending on the material state. The narrow transition width was attained in 99.9999 percent pure gallium single crystals.

A Type-I superconductor below T_c, as exemplified by a pure metal, exhibits perfect diamagnetism and excludes a magnetic field up to some critical field H_c, whereupon it reverts to the normal state as shown in the H-T diagram of Figure 1(b).

The difference in entropy near absolute zero between the superconductive and normal states relates directly to the electronic specific heat, γ: $(S_s - S_n)_{T \to 0} = -\gamma T$.

The magnetization of a typical high-field superconductor is shown in Figure 1(c). The discovery of the large current-carrying capability of Nb_3Sn and other similar alloys has led to an extensive study of the physical properties of these alloys. In brief, a high-field superconductor, or Type-II superconductor, passes from the perfect diamagnetic state at low magnetic fields to a mixed state and finally to a sheathed state before attaining the normal resistive state of the metal. The magnetic field values separating the four stages are given as H_{c1}, H_{c2}, and H_{c3}. The superconductive state below H_{c1} is perfectly diamagnetic, identical to the state of most pure metals of the "soft" or Type-I

*Prepared for Office of Standard Reference Data, National Bureau of Standards, by Standard Reference Data Center on Superconductive Materials, Schenectady, N.Y.

superconductor. Between H_{c1} and H_{c2} a "mixed superconductive state" is found in which fluxons (a minimal unit of magnetic flux) create lines of normal superconductor in a superconductive matrix. The volume of the normal state is proportional to $-4\pi M$ in the "mixed state" region. Thus at H_{c2} the fluxon density has become so great as to drive the interior volume of the superconductive body completely normal. Between H_{c2} and H_{c3} the superconductor has a sheath of current-carrying superconductive material at the body surface, and above H_{c3} the normal state exists. With several types of careful measurement, it is possible to determine H_{c1}, H_{c2}, and H_{c3}. Table 2-35 contains some of the available data on high-field superconductive materials.

High-field superconductive phenomena are also related to specimen dimension and configuration. For example, the Type-I superconductor, Hg, has entirely different magnetization behavior in high magnetic fields when contained in the very fine sets of filamentary tunnels found in an unprocessed Vycor glass. The great majority of superconductive materials are Type II. The elements in very pure form and a very few precisely stoichiometric and well annealed compounds are Type-I with the possible exceptions of vanadium and niobium.

Metallurgical Aspects. The sensitivity of superconductive properties to the material state is most pronounced and has been used in a reverse sense to study and specify the detailed state of alloys. The mechanical state, the homogeneity, and the presence of impurity atoms and other electron-scattering centers are all capable of controlling the critical temperature and the current-carrying capabilities in high-magnetic fields. Well annealed specimens tend to show sharper transitions than those that are strained or inhomogeneous. This sensitivity to mechanical state underlines a general problem in the tabulation of properties for superconductive materials. The occasional divergent values of the critical temperature and of the critical fields quoted for a Type-II superconductor may lie in the variation in sample preparation. Critical temperatures of materials studied early in the history of superconductivity must be evaluated in light of the probable metallurgical state of the material, as well as the availability of less pure starting elements. It has been noted that recent work has given extended consideration to the metallurgical aspects of sample preparation.

REFERENCES

References to the data presented in this section, to additional entries of superconductive materials, and to those materials specifically tested and found non-superconductive to some low temperature may be found in the following publications:

"Superconductive Materials and Some of Their Properties", *Progress in Cryogenics*, B.W. Roberts, Vol. IV, Heywood and Co., 1964, pp. 160–231.

"Superconductive Materials and Some of Their Properties", B.W. Roberts, National Bureau of Standards Technical Notes 408 and 482, U.S. Government Printing Office, 1966 and 1969.

SELECTED PROPERTIES OF THE SUPERCONDUCTIVE ELEMENTS

Conversion Factors

Oe $\times$ 79.57 = A/m; katm $\times$ 1.013 $\times$ 10^8 = N/m^2; kb $\times$ 1.0 $\times$ 10^8 = N/m^2

Element	T_c(K)	H_O(oersteds)	θ_D(K)	γ(mJmole^{-1} deg · K^2)
Al	1.175	104.93	420	1.35
Be	0.026			0.21
Cd	0.518, 0.52	29.6	209	0.688
Ga	1.0833	59.3	325	0.60
Ga (β)	5.90 , 6.2	560		
Ga (γ)	7.62	950		
Ga (δ)	7.85	815		
Hg (α)	4.154	411	87, 71.9	1.81
Hg (β)	3.949	339	93	1.37
In	3.405	281.53	109	1.672
Ir	0.14 , 0.11	19	425	3.27
La (α)	4.88	808, 798	142	10.0, 11.3
La (β)	6.00	1,096	139	11.3
Mo	0.916	90, 98	460	1.83
Nb	9.25	1,970	277, 238	7.80
Os	0.655	65	500	2.35
Pa	1.4			
Pb	7.23	803	96.3	3.0
Re	1.697	188, 211	415	2.35
Ru	0.493	66	580	3.0
Sb	2.6–2.7			
Sn	3.721	305	195	1.78
Ta	4.47	831	258	6.15
Tc	7.73 , 7.78	1,410	411	4.84, 6.28
Th	1.39	159.1	165	4.31
Ti	0.39	56, 100	429, 412	3.32
Tl	2.332, 2.39	181	78.5	1.47
V	5.43 , 5.31	1,100, 1,400	382	9.82
W	0.0154	1.15	550	0.90
Zn	0.875	55	319.7	0.633
Zr	0.53	47	290	2.78
Zr (ω)	0.65			

Thin Films Condensed at Various Temperatures

Element	T_c(K)
Al	1.18–~5.7
Be	~03, ~9.6; 6.5–10.6[a]; 10.2[b]
Bi	~2–~5, 6.11, 6.154, 6.173
Cd	0.53–0.91
Ga	6.4–6.8, 7.4–8.4, 8.56
In	3.43–4.5; 3.68–4.17[c]
La	5.0–6.74
Mo	3.3–3.8, 4–6.7
Nb	6.2–10.1
Pb	~2–7.7
Re	~7
Sn	3.6, 3.84–6.0
Ta	<1.7–4.25, 3.16–4.8
Ti	1.3
Tl	2.64
V	5.14–6.02
W	<1.0–4.1
Zn	0.77–1.48

[a]With KCl.
[b]With Zn etioporphyrin.
[c]In glass pores.

Data for Elements Studied Under Pressure

Element	$T_c(K)$	Pressure
As	0.31–0.5	220–140 kb
	0.2–0.25	~140–100 kb
Ba II	~1.3	55 kb
Ba III	3.05	85–88 kb
	~5.2	>140 kb
Bi II	3.916	25 katm
	3.90	25.2 katm
	3.86	26.8 katm
Bi III	6.55	~37 kb
	7.25	27–28.4 katm
Bi IV	7.0	43, 43–62 kb
Bi V	8.3, 8.55	81 kb
Bi VI	8.55	90, 92–101 kb
Ce	1.7	50 kb
Cs	~1.5	>~125 kb
Ga II	6.24, 6.38	⩾35 katm
Ga II'	7.5	⩾35 katm (P → 0)
Ge	4.85–5.4	~120 kb
	5.35	115 kb
La	~5.5–11.93	0–~140 kb
P	4.7	>100 kb
	5.8	170 kb
Pb II	3.55, 3.6	160 kb
Sb	3.55	85 kb
	3.52	93 kb
	3.53	100 kb
	3.40	~150 kb
Se II	6.75, 6.95	~130 kb
Si	6.7, 7.1	120 kb
Sn II	5.2	125 kb
	4.85	160 kb
Sn III	5.30	113 kb
Te II	2.05	43 kb
	3.4	50 kb
Te III	4.28	70 kb
Te IV	4.25	84 kb
Tl, cub.	1.45	35 kb
Tl, hex.	1.95	35 kb
U	2.3	10 kb
Y	~1.2, ~2.7	120–170 kb

From Roberts, B. W., Properties of Selected Superconductive Materials, 1974 Supplement, NBS Technical Note 825, U.S. Government Printing Office, Washington, D.C., 1974, 10.

SELECTED SUPERCONDUCTIVE COMPOUNDS AND ALLOYS

All compositions are denoted on an atomic basis, i.e., AB, AB_2, or AB_3 for compounds, unless noted. Solid solutions or odd compositions may be denoted as A_zB_{1-z} or A_zB. A series of three or more alloys is indicated as A_xB_{1-x} or by actual indication of the atomic fraction range, such as $A_{0-0.6}B_{1-0.4}$. The critical temperature of such a series of alloys is denoted by a range of values or possibly the maximum value.

The selection of the critical temperature from a transition in the effective permeability, or the change in resistance, or possibly the incremental changes in frequency observed by certain techniques is not often obvious from the literature. Most authors choose the mid-point of such curves as the probable critical temperature of the idealized material, while others will choose the highest temperature at which a deviation from the normal state property is observed. In view of the previous discussion concerning the variability of the superconductive properties as a function of purity and other metallurgical aspects, it is recommended that appropriate literature be checked to determine the most probable critical temperature or critical field of a given alloy.

A very limited amount of data on critical fields, H_o, is available for these compounds and alloys; these values are given at the end of the table.

SYMBOLS: n = number of normal carriers per cubic centimeter for semiconductor superconductors.

Substance	T_c, °K	Crystal structure type††	Substance	T_c, °K	Crystal structure type††
$Ag_xAl_yZn_{1-x-y}$	0.5–0.845		$Al_{\sim0.8}Ge_{\sim0.2}Nb_3$	20.7	Al5
$Ag_7BF_4O_8$	0.15	Cubic	$AlLa_3$	5.57	DO_{19}
$AgBi_2$	3.0–2.78		Al_2La	3.23	Cl5
$Ag_7F_{0.25}N_{0.75}O_{10.25}$	0.85–0.90		Al_3Mg_2	0.84	Cubic, f.c.
Ag_7FO_8	0.3	Cubic	$AlMo_3$	0.58	Al5
Ag_2F	0.066		$AlMo_6Pd$	2.1	
$Ag_{0.8-0.3}Ga_{0.2-0.7}$	6.5–8		AlN	1.55	B4
Ag_4Ge	0.85	Hex., c.p.	Al_2NNb_3	1.3	Al3
$Ag_{0.438}Hg_{0.562}$	0.64	$D8_2$	$AlNb_3$	18.0	Al5
$AgIn_2$	~2.4	C16	Al_xNb_{1-x}	<4.2–13.5	$D8_b$
$Ag_{0.1}In_{0.9}Te$			Al_xNb_{1-x}	12–17.5	Al5
(n = 1.40×10^{22})	1.20–1.89	Bl	$Al_{0.27}Nb_{0.73-0.48}V_{0-0.25}$	14.5–17.5	Al5
$Ag_{0.2}In_{0.8}Te$			$AlNb_xV_{1-x}$	<4.2–13.5	
(n = 1.07×10^{22})	0.77–1.00	Bl	AlOs	0.39	B2
AgLa (9.5 kbar)	1.2	B2	Al_3Os	5.90	
Ag_7NO_{11}	1.04	Cubic	AlPb (films)	1.2–7	
Ag_xPb_{1-x}	7.2 max.		Al_2Pt	0.48–0.55	Cl
Ag_xSn_{1-x} (film)	2.0–3.8		Al_5Re_{24}	3.35	Al2
Ag_xSn_{1-x}	1.5–3.7		Al_3Th	0.75	DO_{19}
$AgTe_3$	2.6	Cubic	$Al_xTi_yV_{1-x-y}$	2.05–3.62	Cubic
$AgTh_2$	2.26	C16	$Al_{0.108}V_{0.892}$	1.82	Cubic
$Ag_{0.03}Tl_{0.97}$	2.67		Al_xZn_{1-x}	0.5–0.845	
$Ag_{0.94}Tl_{0.06}$	2.32		$AlZr_3$	0.73	Ll_2
Ag_xZn_{1-x}	0.5–0.845		AsBiPb	9.0	
Al (film)	1.3–2.31		AsBiPbSb	9.0	
Al (1 to 21 katm)	1.170–0.687	Al	$As_{0.33}InTe_{0.67}$		
$AlAu_4$	0.4–0.7	Like Al3	(n = 1.24×10^{22})	0.85–1.15	Bl
Al_2CMo_3	10.0	Al3	$As_{0.5}InTe_{0.5}$		
Al_2CMo_3	9.8–10.2	Al3 + trace 2nd phase	(n = 0.97×10^{22})	0.44–0.62	Bl
			$As_{0.50}Ni_{0.06}Pd_{0.44}$	1.39	C2
Al_2CaSi	5.8		AsPb	8.4	
$Al_{0.131}Cr_{0.088}V_{0.781}$	1.46	Cubic	$AsPd_2$ (low-		
$AlGe_2$	1.75		temperature phase)	0.60	Hexagonal
$Al_{0.5}Ge_{0.5}Nb$	12.6	Al5	$AsPd_2$ (high-temp. phase)	1.70	C22

††See key at end of table.

Substance	T_c, °K	Crystal structure type††	Substance	T_c, °K	Crystal structure type††
$AsPd_5$	0.46	Complex	BW_2	3.1	Cl6
$AsRh$	0.58	B31	B_6Y	6.5–7.1	
$AsRh_{1.4-1.6}$	<0.03–0.56	Hexagonal	$B_{12}Y$	4.7	
$AsSn$	4.10		BZr	3.4	Cubic
$AsSn$			$B_{12}Zr$	5.82	
$\quad (n = 2.14 \times 10^{22})$	3.41–3.65	B1	$BaBi_3$	5.69	Tetragonal
$As_{\sim2}Sn_{\sim3}$	3.5–3.6,		$Ba_xO_3Sr_{1-x}Ti$		
	1.21–1.17		$\quad (n = 4.2-11 \times 10^{19})$	<0.1–0.55	
As_3Sn_4			$Ba_{0.13}O_3W$	1.9	Tetragonal
$\quad (n = 0.56 \times 10^{22})$	1.16–1.19	Rhombohedral	$Ba_{0.14}O_3W$	<1.25–2.2	Hexagonal
Au_5Ba	0.4–0.7	D2$_d$	$BaRh_2$	6.0	Cl5
$AuBe$	2.64	B20	$Be_{22}Mo$	2.51	Cubic,
Au_2Bi	1.80	Cl5			like $Be_{22}Re$
Au_5Ca	0.34–0.38	Cl5$_b$	$Be_8Nb_5Zr_2$	5.2	
$AuGa$	1.2	B31	$Be_{0.98-0.92}Re_{0.02-0.08}$		
$Au_{0.40-0.92}Ge_{0.60-0.08}$	<0.32–1.63	Complex	$\quad$ (quenched)	9.5–9.75	Cubic
$AuIn$	0.4–0.6	Complex	$Be_{0.957}Re_{0.043}$	9.62	Cubic,
$AuLu$	<0.35	B2			like $Be_{22}Re$
$AuNb_3$	11.5	A15	$BeTc$	5.21	Cubic
$AuNb_3$	1.2	A2	$Be_{22}W$	4.12	Cubic,
$Au_{0-0.3}Nb_{1-0.7}$	1.1–11.0				like $Be_{22}Re$
$Au_{0.02-0.98}Nb_3Rh_{0.98-0.02}$	2.53–10.9	A15	$Be_{13}W$	4.1	Tetragonal
$AuNb_{3(1-x)}V_{3x}$	1.5–11.0	A15	Bi_3Ca	2.0	
$AuPb_2$	3.15		$Bi_{0.5}Cd_{0.13}Pb_{0.25}Sn_{0.12}$		
$AuPb_2$ (film)	4.3		$\quad$ (weight fractions)	8.2	
$AuPb_3$	4.40		$BiCo$	0.42–0.49	
$AuPb_3$ (film)	4.25		Bi_2Cs	4.75	Cl5
Au_2Pb	1.18, 6–7	Cl5	Bi_xCu_{1-x}		
$AuSb_2$	0.58	C2	$\quad$ (electrodeposited)	2.2	
$AuSn$	1.25	B8$_1$	$BiCu$	1.33–1.40	
Au_xSn_{1-x} (film)	2.0–3.8		$Bi_{0.019}In_{0.981}$	3.86	
Au_5Sn	0.7–1.1	A3	$Bi_{0.05}In_{0.95}$	4.65	α-phase
Au_3Te_5	1.62	Cubic	$Bi_{0.10}In_{0.90}$	5.05	α-phase
$AuTh_2$	3.08	Cl6	$Bi_{0.15-0.30}In_{0.85-0.70}$	5.3–5.4	α- and β-phases
$AuTl$	1.92		$Bi_{0.34-0.48}In_{0.66-0.52}$	4.0–4.1	
AuV_3	0.74	A15	Bi_3In_5	4.1	
Au_xZn_{1-x}	0.50–0.845		$BiIn_2$	5.65	β-phase
$AuZn_3$	1.21	Cubic	Bi_2Ir	1.7–2.3	
Au_xZr_y	1.7–2.8	A3	Bi_2Ir (quenched)	3.0–3.96	
$AuZr_3$	0.92	A15	BiK	3.6	
$BCMo_2$	5.4	Orthorhombic	Bi_2K	3.58	Cl5
$B_{0.03}C_{0.51}Mo_{0.47}$	12.5		$BiLi$	2.47	Ll$_0$, α-phase
$BCMo_2$	5.3–7.0	Orthorhombic	$Bi_{4-9}Mg$	0.7–~1.0	
BHf	3.1	Cubic	Bi_3Mo	3–3.7	
B_6La	5.7		$BiNa$	2.25	Ll$_0$
$B_{12}Lu$	0.48		$BiNb_3$ (high pressure		
BMo	0.5 (extrap-		$\quad$ and temperature)	3.05	A15
	olated)		$BiNi$	4.25	B8$_1$
BMo_2	4.74	Cl6	Bi_3Ni	4.06	Orthorhombic
BNb	8.25	B$_f$	$Bi_{1-0}Pb_{0-1}$	7.26–9.14	
BRe_2	2.80, 4.6		$Bi_{1-0}Pb_{0-1}$ (film)	7.25–8.67	
$B_{0.3}Ru_{0.7}$	2.58	D10$_2$	$Bi_{0.05-0.40}Pb_{0.95-0.60}$	7.35–8.4	Hexagonal,
$B_{12}Sc$	0.39				c.p., to
BTa	4.0	B$_f$			ε-phase
B_6Th	0.74		$BiPbSb$	8.9	

††See key at end of table.

Substance	T_c, °K	Crystal structure type[††]	Substance	T_c, °K	Crystal structure type[††]
$Bi_{0.5}Pb_{0.31}Sn_{0.19}$			$C_{0.44}Mo_{0.56}$	1.3	B1
(weight fractions)	8.5		$C_{0.5}Mo_xNb_{1-x}$	10.8–12.5	B1
$Bi_{0.5}Pb_{0.25}Sn_{0.25}$	8.5		$C_{0.6}Mo_{4.8}Si_3$	7.6	$D8_8$
$BiPd_2$	4.0		$CMo_{0.2}Ta_{0.8}$	7.5	B1
$Bi_{0.4}Pd_{0.6}$	3.7–4	Hexagonal, ordered	$CMo_{0.5}Ta_{0.5}$	7.7	B1
			$CMo_{0.75}Ta_{0.25}$	8.5	B1
$BiPd$	3.7	Orthorhombic	$CMo_{0.8}Ta_{0.2}$	8.7	B1
Bi_2Pd	1.70	Monoclinic, α-phase	$CMo_{0.85}Ta_{0.15}$	8.9	B1
			CMo_xTi_{1-x}	10.2 max.	B1
Bi_2Pd	4.25	Tetragonal, β-phase	$CMo_{0.83}Ti_{0.17}$	10.2	B1
$BiPdSe$	1.0	C2	CMo_xV_{1-x}	2.9–9.3	B1
$BiPdTe$	1.2	C2	CMo_xZr_{1-x}	3.8–9.5	B1
$BiPt$	1.21	$B8_1$	$C_{0.1-0.9}N_{0.9-0.1}Nb$	8.5–17.9	
$BiPtSe$	1.45	C2	$C_{0-0.38}N_{1-0.62}Ta$	10.0–11.3	
$BiPtTe$	1.15	C2	CNb (whiskers)	7.5–10.5	
Bi_2Pt	0.155	Hexagonal	$C_{0.984}Nb$	9.8	B1
Bi_2Rb	4.25	C15	CNb (extrapolated)	~14	
$BiRe_2$	1.9–2.2		$C_{0.7-1.0}Nb_{0.3-0}$	6–11	B1
$BiRh$	2.06	$B8_1$	CNb_2	9.1	
Bi_3Rh	3.2	Orthorhombic, like NiB_3	CNb_xTa_{1-x}	8.2–13.9	
			CNb_xTi_{1-x}	<4.2–8.8	B1
Bi_4Rh	2.7	Hexagonal	$CNb_{0.6-0.9}W_{0.4-0.1}$	12.5–11.6	B1
Bi_3Sn	3.6–3.8		$CNb_{0.1-0.9}Zr_{0.9-0.1}$	4.2–8.4	B1
$BiSn$	3.8		CRb_x (gold)	0.023–0.151	Hexagonal
Bi_xSn_y	3.85–4.18		$CRe_{0.01-0.08}W$	1.3–5.0	
Bi_3Sr	5.62	$L1_2$	$CRe_{0.06}W$	5.0	
Bi_3Te	0.75–1.0		CTa	~11 (extrapolated)	
Bi_5Tl_3	6.4				
$Bi_{0.26}Tl_{0.74}$	4.4	Cubic, disordered	$C_{0.987}Ta$	9.7	
			$C_{0.848-0.987}Ta$	2.04–9.7	
$Bi_{0.26}Tl_{0.74}$	4.15	$L1_2$, ordered?	CTa (film)	5.09	B1
Bi_2Y_3	2.25		CTa_2	3.26	L'_3
Bi_3Zn	0.8–0.9		$CTa_{0.4}Ti_{0.6}$	4.8	B1
$Bi_{0.3}Zr_{0.7}$	1.51		$CTa_{1-0.4}W_{0-0.6}$	8.5–10.5	B1
$BiZr_3$	2.4–2.8		$CTa_{0.2-0.9}Zr_{0.8-0.1}$	4.6–8.3	B1
CCs_x	0.020–0.135	Hexagonal	CTc (excess C)	3.85	Cubic
C_8K (gold)	0.55		$CTi_{0.5-0.7}W_{0.5-0.3}$	6.7–2.1	B1
$CGaMo_2$	3.7–4.1	Hexagonal, H-phase	CW	1.0	
			CW_2	2.74	L'_3
$CHf_{0.5}Mo_{0.5}$	3.4	B1	CW_2	5.2	Cubic, f.c.
$CHf_{0.3}Mo_{0.7}$	5.5	B1	$CaIr_2$	6.15	C15
$CHf_{0.25}Mo_{0.75}$	6.6	B1	$Ca_xO_3Sr_{1-x}Ti$		
$CHf_{0.7}Nb_{0.3}$	6.1	B1	($n = 3.7–11.0 \times 10^{19}$)	<0.1–0.55	
$CHf_{0.6}Nb_{0.4}$	4.5	B1	$Ca_{0.1}O_3W$	1.4–3.4	Hexagonal
$CHf_{0.5}Nb_{0.5}$	4.8	B1	$CaPb$	7.0	
$CHf_{0.4}Nb_{0.6}$	5.6	B1	$CaRh_2$	6.40	C15
$CHf_{0.25}Nb_{0.75}$	7.0	B1	$Cd_{0.3-0.5}Hg_{0.7-0.5}$	1.70–1.92	
$CHf_{0.2}Nb_{0.8}$	7.8	B1	$CdHg$	1.77, 2.15	Tetragonal
$CHf_{0.9-0.1}Ta_{0.1-0.9}$	5.0–9.0	B1	$Cd_{0.0075-0.05}In_{1-x}$	3.24–3.36	Tetragonal
Ck (excess K)	0.55	Hexagonal	$Cd_{0.97}Pb_{0.03}$	4.2	
C_8K	0.39	Hexagonal	$CdSn$	3.65	
$C_{0.40-0.44}Mo_{0.60-0.56}$	9–13		$Cd_{0.17}Tl_{0.83}$	2.3	
CMo	6.5, 9.26		$Cd_{0.18}Tl_{0.82}$	2.54	
CMo_2	12.2	Orthorhombic	$CeCo_2$	0.84	C15
			$CeCo_{1.67}Ni_{0.33}$	0.46	C15

[††]See key at end of table.

Substance	T_c, °K	Crystal structure type††	Substance	T_c, °K	Crystal structure type††
$CeCo_{1.67}Rh_{0.33}$	0.47	C15	CuSSe	1.5–2.0	C18
$Ce_xGd_{1-x}Ru_2$	3.2–5.2	C15	$CuSe_2$	2.3–2.43	C18
$CeIr_3$	3.34		CuSeTe	1.6–2.0	C18
$CeIr_5$	1.82		Cu_xSn_{1-x}	3.2–3.7	
$Ce_{0.005}La_{0.995}$	4.6		Cu_xSn_{1-x} (film)		
Ce_xLa_{1-x}	1.3–6.3		(made at 10°K)	3.6–7	
$Ce_xPr_{1-x}Ru_2$	1.4–5.3	C15	Cu_xSn_{1-x} (film)		
Ce_xPt_{1-x}	0.7–1.55		(made at 300°K)	2.8–3.7	
$CeRu_2$	6.0	C15	$CuTe_2$	<1.25–1.3	C18
$Co_xFe_{1-x}Si_2$	1.4 max.	C1	$CuTh_2$	3.49	C16
$CoHf_2$	0.56	$E9_3$	$Cu_{0-0.027}V$	3.9–5.3	A2
$CoLa_3$	4.28		Cu_xZn_{1-x}	0.5–0.845	
$CoLu_3$	~0.35		Er_xLa_{1-x}	1.4–6.3	
$Co_{0-0.01}Mo_{0.8}Re_{0.2}$	2–10		$Fe_{0-0.04}Mo_{0.8}Re_{0.2}$	1–10	
$Co_{0.02-0.10}Nb_3Rh_{0.98-0.90}$	2.28–1.90	A15	$Fe_{0.05}Ni_{0.05}Zr_{0.90}$	~3.9	
$Co_xNi_{1-x}Si_2$	1.4 max.	C1	Fe_3Th_7	1.86	D10
$Co_{0.5}Rh_{0.5}Si_2$	2.5		Fe_xTi_{1-x}	3.2 max.	Fe in α-Ti
$Co_xRh_{1-x}Si_2$	3.65 max.		Fe_xTi_{1-x}	3.7 max.	Fe in β-Ti
$Co_{~0.3}Sc_{~0.7}$	~0.35		$Fe_xTi_{0.6}V_{1-x}$	6.8 max.	
$CoSi_2$	1.40, 1.22	C1	FeU_6	3.86	$D2_c$
Co_3Th_7	1.83	$D10_2$	$Fe_{0.1}Zr_{0.9}$	1.0	A3
Co_xTi_{1-x}	2.8 max.	Co in α-Ti	$Ga_{0.5}Ge_{0.5}Nb_3$	7.3	A15
Co_xTi_{1-x}	3.8 max.	Co in β-Ti	$GaLa_3$	5.84	
$CoTi_2$	3.44	$E9_3$	Ga_2Mo	9.5	
CoTi	0.71	A2	$GaMo_3$	0.76	A15
CoU	1.7	B2, distorted	Ga_4Mo	9.8	
CoU_6	2.29	$D2_c$	GaN (black)	5.85	B4
$Co_{0.28}Y_{0.72}$	0.34		$GaNb_3$	14.5	A15
CoY_3	<0.34		$Ga_xNb_3Sn_{1-x}$	14–18.37	A15
$CoZr_2$	6.3	C16	$Ga_{0.7}Pt_{0.3}$	2.9	C1
$Co_{0.1}Zr_{0.9}$	3.9	A3	GaPt	1.74	B20
$Cr_{0.6}Ir_{0.4}$	0.4	Hexagonal, c.p.	GaSb (120 kbar, 77°K,		
$Cr_{0.65}Ir_{0.35}$	0.59	Hexagonal, c.p.	annealed)	4.24	A5
$Cr_{0.7}Ir_{0.3}$	0.76	Hexagonal, c.p.	GaSb (unannealed)	~5.9	
$Cr_{0.72}Ir_{0.28}$	0.83		$Ga_{0.1}Sn_{1-0}$ (quenched)	3.47–4.18	
Cr_3Ir	0.45	A15	$Ga_{0-1}Sn_{1-0}$ (annealed)	2.6–3.85	
$Cr_{0-0.1}Nb_{1-0.9}$	4.6–9.2	A2	Ga_5V_2	3.55	Tetragonal,
$Cr_{0.80}Os_{0.20}$	2.5	Cubic			Mn_2Hg_5 type
Cr_xRe_{1-x}	1.2–5.2		GaV_3	16.8	A15
$Cr_{0.40}Re_{0.60}$	2.15	$D8_b$	$GaV_{2.1-3.5}$	6.3–14.45	A15
$Cr_{0.8-0.6}Rh_{0.2-0.4}$	0.5–1.10	A3	$GaV_{4.5}$	9.15	
Cr_3Ru (annealed)	3.3	A15	Ga_3Zr	1.38	
Cr_2Ru	2.02	$D8_b$	Gd_xLa_{1-x}	<1.0–5.5	
$Cr_{0.1-0.5}Ru_{0.9-0.5}$	0.34–1.65	A3	$Gd_xOs_2Y_{1-x}$	1.4–4.7	
Cr_xTi_{1-x}	3.6 max.	Cr in α-Ti	$Gd_xRu_2Th_{1-x}$	3.6 max.	C15
Cr_xTi_{1-x}	4.2 max.	Cr in β-Ti	GeIr	4.7	B31
$Cr_{0.1}Ti_{0.3}V_{0.6}$	5.6		Ge_2La	1.49, 2.2	Orthorhombic,
$Cr_{0.0175}U_{0.9825}$	0.75	β-phase			distorted
$Cs_{0.32}O_3W$	1.12	Hexagonal			$ThSi_2$-type
$Cu_{0.15}In_{0.85}$ (film)	3.75		$GeMo_3$	1.43	A15
$Cu_{0.04-0.06}In_{1-x}$	4.4		$GeNb_2$	1.9	
CuLa	1.85		$GeNb_3$ (quenched)	6–17	A15
Cu_xPb_{1-x}	5.7–7.7		$Ge_{0.29}Nb_{0.71}$	6	A15
CuS	1.62	B18	$Ge_xNb_3Sn_{1-x}$	17.6–18.0	A15
CuS_2	1.48–1.53	C18	$Ge_{0.5}Nb_3Sn_{0.5}$	11.3	

†† See key at end of table.

Substance	T_c, °K	Crystal structure type††	Substance	T_c, °K	Crystal structure type††
GePt	0.40	B3l	InSb	2.1	
Ge_3Rh_5	2.12	Orthorhombic, related to $InNi_2$	$(InSb)_{0.95-0.10}Sn_{0.05-0.90}$ (various heat treatments)	3.8–5.1	
			$(InSb)_{0-0.07}Sn_{1-0.93}$	3.67–3.74	
Ge_2Sc	1.3		In_3Sn	~5.5	
Ge_3Te_4			In_xSn_{1-x}	3.4–7.3	
($n = 1.06 \times 10^{22}$)	1.55–1.80	Rhombohedral	$In_{0.82-1}Te$		
Ge_xTe_{1-x}			($n = 0.83–1.71 \times 10^{22}$)	1.02–3.45	Bl
($n = 8.5 - 64 \times 10^{20}$)	0.07–0.41	Bl	$In_{1.000}Te_{1.002}$	3.5–3.7	Bl
GeV_3	6.01	A15	In_3Te_4		
Ge_2Y	3.80	C_c	($n = 0.47 \times 10^{22}$)	1.15–1.25	Rhombohedral
$Ge_{1.62}Y$	2.4		In_xTl_{1-x}	2.7–3.374	
$H_{0.33}Nb_{0.67}$	7.28	Cubic, b.c.	$In_{0.8}Tl_{0.2}$	3.223	
$H_{0.1}Nb_{0.9}$	7.38	Cubic, b.c.	$In_{0.62}Tl_{0.38}$	2.760	
$H_{0.05}Nb_{0.95}$	7.83	Cubic, b.c.	$In_{0.78-0.69}Tl_{0.22-0.31}$	3.18–3.32	Tetragonal
$H_{0.12}Ta_{0.88}$	2.81	Cubic, b.c.	$In_{0.69-0.62}Tl_{0.31-0.38}$	2.98–3.3	Cubic, f.c.
$H_{0.08}Ta_{0.92}$	3.26	Cubic, b.c.	Ir_2La	0.48	Cl5
$H_{0.04}Ta_{0.96}$	3.62	Cubic, b.c.	Ir_3La	2.32	Dl0$_2$
$HfN_{0.989}$	6.6	Bl	Ir_3La_7	2.24	Dl0$_2$
$Hf_{0-0.5}Nb_{1-0.5}$	8.3–9.5	A2	Ir_5La	2.13	
$Hf_{0.75}Nb_{0.25}$	>4.2		Ir_2Lu	2.47	Cl5
$HfOs_2$	2.69	Cl4	Ir_3Lu	2.89	Cl5
$HfRe_2$	4.80	Cl4	IrMo	<1.0	A3
$Hf_{0.14}Re_{0.86}$	5.86	Al2	$IrMo_3$	8.8	A15
$Hf_{0.99-0.96}Rh_{0.01-0.04}$	0.85–1.51		$IrMo_3$	6.8	D8$_b$
$Hf_{0-0.55}Ta_{1-0.45}$	4.4–6.5~	A2	$IrNb_3$	1.9	A15
HfV_2	8.9–9.6	Cl5	$Ir_{0.4}Nb_{0.6}$	9.8	D8$_b$
Hg_xIn_{1-x}	3.14–4.55		$Ir_{0.37}Nb_{0.63}$	2.32	D8$_b$
HgIn	3.81		IrNb	7.9	D8$_b$
Hg_2K	1.20	Orthorhombic	$Ir_{0.02}Nb_3Rh_{0.98}$	2.43	A15
Hg_3K	3.18		$Ir_{0.05}Nb_3Rh_{0.95}$	2.38	A15
Hg_4K	3.27		$Ir_{0.287}O_{0.14}Ti_{0.573}$	5.5	E9$_3$
Hg_8K	3.42		$Ir_{0.265}O_{0.035}Ti_{0.65}$	2.30	E9$_3$
Hg_3Li	1.7	Hexagonal	Ir_xOs_{1-x}	0.3–0.98	
Hg_2Na	1.62	Hexagonal		(max.)–0.6	
Hg_4Na	3.05		IrOsY	2.6	Cl5
Hg_xPb_{1-x}	4.14–7.26		$Ir_{1.5}Os_{0.5}$	2.4	Cl4
HgSn	4.2		Ir_2Sc	2.07	Cl5
Hg_xTl_{1-x}	2.30–4.109		$Ir_{2.5}Sc$	2.46	Cl5
Hg_5Tl_2	3.86		$IrSn_2$	0.65–0.78	Cl
Ho_xLa_{1-x}	1.3–6.3		Ir_2Sr	5.70	Cl5
$InLa_3$	9.83, 10.4	Ll2	$Ir_{0.5}Te_{0.5}$	~3	
$InLa_3$ (0–35, kbar)	9.75–10.55		$IrTe_3$	1.18	C2
$In_{1-0.86}Mg_{0-0.14}$	3.395–3.363		IrTh	<0.37	B$_f$
$InNb_3$			Ir_2Th	6.50	Cl5
(high pressure and temp.)	4–8, 9.2	A15	Ir_3Th	4.71	
$In_{0-0.3}Nb_3Sn_{1-0.7}$	18.0–18.19	A15	Ir_3Th_7	1.52	Dl0$_2$
$In_{0.5}Nb_3Zr_{0.5}$	6.4		Ir_5Th	3.93	D2$_d$
$In_{0.11}O_3W$	<1.25–2.8	Hexagonal	$IrTi_3$	5.40	A15
$In_{0.95-0.85}Pb_{0.05-0.15}$	3.6–5.05		IrV_2	1.39	A15
$In_{0.98-0.91}Pb_{0.02-0.09}$	3.45–4.2		IrW_3	3.82	
InPb	6.65		$Ir_{0.28}W_{0.72}$	4.49	
InPd	0.7	B2	Ir_2Y	2.18, 1.38	Cl5
InSb (quenched from			$Ir_{0.69}Y_{0.31}$	1.98, 1.44	Cl5
170 kbar into liquid N_2)	4.8	Like A5	$Ir_{0.70}Y_{0.30}$	2.16	Cl5

††See key at end of table.

Substance	T_c, °K	Crystal structure type††	Substance	T_c, °K	Crystal structure type††
Ir_2Y	1.09	C15	Mo_3Si	1.30	A15
Ir_2Y_3	1.61		$MoSi_{0.7}$	1.34	
Ir_xY_{1-x}	0.3–3.7		Mo_xSiV_{3-x}	4.54–16.0	A15
Ir_2Zr	4.10	C15	Mo_xTc_{1-x}	10.8–15.8	
$Ir_{0.1}Zr_{0.9}$	5.5	A3	$Mo_{0.16}Ti_{0.84}$	4.18, 4.25	
$K_{0.27-0.31}O_3W$	0.50	Hexagonal	$Mo_{0.913}Ti_{0.087}$	2.95	
$K_{0.40-0.57}O_3W$	1.5	Tetragonal	$Mo_{0.04}Ti_{0.96}$	2.0	Cubic
$La_{0.55}Lu_{0.45}$	2.2	Hexagonal, La type	$Mo_{0.025}Ti_{0.975}$	1.8	
$La_{0.8}Lu_{0.2}$	3.4	Hexagonal, La Type	Mo_xU_{1-x}	0.7–2.1	
$LaMg_2$	1.05	C15	Mo_xV_{1-x}	0–~5.3	
LaN	1.35		Mo_2Zr	4.27–4.75	C15
$LaOs_2$	6.5	C15	NNb (whiskers)	10–14.5	
$LaPt_2$	0.46	C15	NNb (diffusion wires)	16.10	
$La_{0.28}Pt_{0.72}$	0.54	C15	NNb (film)	6–9	B1
$LaRh_3$	2.60		$N_{0.988}Nb$	14.9	B1
$LaRh_5$	1.62		$N_{0.824-0.988}Nb$	14.4–15.3	B1
La_7Rh_3	2.58	$Dl0_2$	$N_{0.70-0.795}Nb$	11.3–12.9	Cubic and tetragonal
$LaRu_2$	1.63	C15	NNb_xO_y	13.5 17.0	B1
La_3S_4	6.5	$D7_3$	NNb_xO_y	6.0–11	
La_3Se_4	8.6	$D7_3$	$N_{100-42\ w/o}Nb_{0-58\ w/o}Ti$†	15–16.8	
$LaSi_2$	2.3	C_c	$N_{100-75\ w/o}Nb_{0-25\ w/o}Zr$†	12.5–16.35	
La_xY_{1-x}	1.7–5.4		NNb_xZr_{1-x}	9.8–13.8	B1
$LaZn$	1.04	B2	$N_{0.93}Nb_{0.85}Zr_{0.15}$	13.8	B1
$LiPb$	7.2		$N_xO_yTi_z$	2.9–5.6	Cubic
$LuOs_2$	3.49	C14	$N_xO_yV_z$	5.8–8.2	Cubic
$Lu_{0.275}Rh_{0.725}$	1.27	C15	$N_{0.34}Re$	4–5	Cubic, f.c.
$LuRh_5$	0.49		NTa	12–14	B1
$LuRu_2$	0.86	C14		(extrapolated)	
$Mg_{\sim0.47}Tl_{\sim0.53}$	2.75	B2	NTa (film)	4.84	B1
Mg_2Nb	5.6		$N_{0.6-0.987}Ti$	<1.17–5.8	B1
Mn_xTi_{1-x}	2.3 max.	Mn in α-Ti	$N_{0.82-0.99}V$	2.9–7.9	B1
Mn_xTi_{1-x}	1.1–3.0	Mn in β-Ti	NZr	9.8	B1
MnU_6	2.32	$D2_c$	$N_{0.906-0.984}Zr$	3.0–9.5	B1
MoN	12	Hexagonal	$Na_{0.28-0.35}O_3W$	0.56	Tetragonal
Mo_2N	5.0	Cubic, f.c.	$Na_{0.28}Pb_{0.72}$	7.2	
Mo_xNb_{1-x}	0.016–9.2		NbO	1.25	
Mo_3Os	7.2	A15	$NbOs_2$	2.52	A12
$M_{0.62}Os_{0.38}$	5.65	$D8_b$	Nb_3Os	1.05	A15
Mo_3P	5.31	DO_e	$Nb_{0.6}Os_{0.4}$	1.89, 1.78	$D8_b$
$Mo_{0.5}Pd_{0.5}$	3.52	A3	$Nb_3Os_{0.02-0.10}Rh_{0.98-0.90}$	2.42–2.30	A15
Mo_3Re	10.0		$Nb_{0.6}Pd_{0.4}$	1.60	$D8_f$ plus cubic
Mo_xRe_{1-x}	1.2–12.2		$Nb_3Pd_{0.02-0.10}Rh_{0.98-0.90}$	2.49–2.55	A15
$MoRe_3$	9.25, 9.89	A12	$Nb_{0.62}Pt_{0.38}$	4.21	$D8_b$
$Mo_{0.42}Re_{0.58}$	6.35	$D8_b$	Nb_3Pt	10.9	A15
$Mo_{0.52}Re_{0.48}$	11.1		Nb_5Pt_3	3.73	$D8_b$
$Mo_{0.57}Re_{0.43}$	14.0		$Nb_3Pt_{0.02-0.98}Rh_{0.98-0.02}$	2.52–9.6	A15
$Mo_{\sim0.60}Re_{0.395}$	10.6		$Nb_{0.38-0.18}Re_{0.62-0.82}$	2.43–9.70	A12
$MoRh$	1.97	A3	Nb_3Rh	2.64	A15
Mo_xRh_{1-x}	1.5–8.2	Cubic, b.c.	$Nb_{0.90}Rh_{0.10}$	4.21	$D8_b$ plus other
$MoRu$	9.5–10.5	A3	$Nb_3Rh_{0.98-0.90}Ru_{0.02-0.10}$	2.42–2.44	A15
$Mo_{0.61}Ru_{0.39}$	7.18	$D8_b$	Nb_xRu_{1-x}	1.2–4.8	
$Mo_{0.2}Ru_{0.8}$	1.66	A3	NbS_2	6.1–6.3	Hexagonal, NbSe_2 type
Mo_3Sb_4	2.1				

†*w/o* denotes weight percent. ††See key at end of table.

Substance	T_c, °K	Crystal structure type††	Substance	T_c, °K	Crystal structure type††
NbS_2	5.0–5.5	Hexagonal, three-layer type	Os_2Zr	3.0	C14
			Os_xZr_{1-x}	1.50–5.6	
			PPb	7.8	
$Nb_3Sb_{0-0.7}Sn_{1-0.3}$	6.8–18	A15	$PPd_{3.0-3.2}$	<0.35–0.7	DO_{11}
$NbSe_2$	5.15–5.62	Hexagonal, NbS_2 type	P_3Pd_7 (high temperature)	1.0	Rhombohedral
$Nb_{1-1.05}Se_2$	2.2–7.0	Hexagonal, NbS_2 type	P_3Pd_7 (low temp.)	0.70	Complex
			PRh	1.22	
Nb_3Si	1.5	Ll_2	PRh_2	1.3	C1
Nb_3SiSnV_3	4.0		PW_3	2.26	DO_e
Nb_3Sn	18.05	A15	Pb_2Pd	2.95	C16
$Nb_{0.8}Sn_{0.2}$	18.18, 18.5	A15	Pb_4Pt	2.80	Related to C16
Nb_xSn_{1-x} (film)	2.6–18.5		Pb_2Rh	2.66	C16
$NbSn_2$	2.60	Orthorhombic	PbSb	6.6	
Nb_3Sn_2	16.6	Tetragonal	PbTe (plus 0.1 w/o Pb)†	5.19	
$NbSnTa_2$	10.8	A15	PbTe (plus 0.1 w/o Tl)†	5.24–5.27	
Nb_2SnTa	16.4	A15	$PbTl_{0.27}$	6.43	
$Nb_{2.5}SnTa_{0.5}$	17.6	A15	$PbTl_{0.17}$	6.73	
$Nb_{2.75}SnTa_{0.25}$	17.8	A15	$PbTl_{0.12}$	6.88	
$Nb_{3x}SnTa_{3(1-x)}$	6.0–18.0		$PbTl_{0.075}$	6.98	
NbSnTaV	6.2	A15	$PbTl_{0.04}$	7.06	
$Nb_2SnTa_{0.5}V_{0.5}$	12.2	A15	$Pb_{1-0.26}Tl_{0-0.74}$	7.20–3.68	
$NbSnV_2$	5.5	A15	$PbTl_2$	3.75–4.1	
Nb_2SnV	9.8	A15	Pb_3Zr_5	4.60	$D8_8$
$Nb_{2.5}SnV_{0.5}$	14.2	A15	$PbZr_3$	0.76	A15
Nb_xTa_{1-x}	4.4–9.2	A2	$Pd_{0.9}Pt_{0.1}Te_2$	1.65	C6
$NbTc_3$	10.5	A12	$Pd_{0.05}Ru_{0.05}Zr_{0.9}$	~9	
Nb_xTi_{1-x}	0.6–9.8		$Pd_{2.2}S$ (quenched)	1.63	Cubic
$Nb_{0.6}Ti_{0.4}$	9.8		$PdSb_2$	1.25	C2
Nb_xU_{1-x}	1.95 max.		PdSb	1.50	$B8_1$
$Nb_{0.88}V_{0.12}$	5.7	A2	PdSbSe	1.0	C2
$Nb_{0.75}Zr_{0.25}$	10.8		PdSbTe	1.2	C2
$Nb_{0.66}Zr_{0.33}$	10.8		Pd_4Se	0.42	Tetragonal
$Ni_{0.3}Th_{0.7}$	1.98	$D10_2$	$Pd_{6-7}Se$	0.66	Like Pd_4Te
$NiZr_2$	1.52		$Pd_{2.8}Se$	2.3	
$Ni_{0.1}Zr_{0.9}$	1.5	A3	Pd_xSe_{1-x}	2.5 max.	
$O_3Rb_{0.27-0.29}W$	1.98	Hexagonal	PdSi	0.93	B31
O_3SrTi			PdSn	0.41	B31
$\quad(n = 1.7–12.0 \times 10^{19})$	0.12–0.37		$PdSn_2$	3.34	
O_3SrTi			Pd_2Sn	0.41	C37
$\quad(n = 10^{18}–10^{21})$	0.05–0.47		Pd_3Sn_2	0.47–0.64	$B8_2$
O_3SrTi			PdTe	2.3, 3.85	$B8_1$
$\quad(n = \sim 10^{20})$	0.47		$PdTe_{1.02-1.08}$	2.56–1.88	$B8_1$
OTi	0.58		$PdTe_2$	1.69	C6
$O_3Sr_{0.08}W$	2–4	Hexagonal	$PdTe_{2.1}$	1.89	C6
$O_3Tl_{0.30}W$	2.0–2.14	Hexagonal	$PdTe_{2.3}$	1.85	C6
OV_3Zr_3	7.5	$E9_3$	$Pd_{1.1}Te$	4.07	$B8_1$
OW_3 (film)	3.35, 1.1	A15	$PdTh_2$	0.85	C16
OsReY	2.0	C14	$Pd_{0.1}Zr_{0.9}$	7.5	A3
Os_2Sc	4.6	C14	PtSb	2.1	$B8_1$
OsTa	1.95	A12	PtSi	0.88	B31
Os_3Th_7	1.51	$D10_2$	PtSn	0.37	$B8_1$
Os_xW_{1-x}	0.9–4.1		PtTe	0.59	Orthorhombic
OsW_3	~3		PtTh	0.44	B_f
			Pt_3Th_7	0.98	$D10_2$
Os_2Y	4.7	C14	Pt_5Th	3.13	

†w/o denotes weight percent.   ††See key at end of table.

Substance	T_c, °K	Crystal structure type††	Substance	T_c, °K	Crystal structure type††
$PtTi_3$	0.58	A15	Ru_2Y	1.52	C14
$Pt_{0.02}U_{0.98}$	0.87	β-phase	Ru_2Zr	1.84	C14
$PtV_{2.5}$	1.36	A15	$Ru_{0.1}Zr_{0.9}$	5.7	A3
PtV_3	2.87–3.20	A15	SbSn	1.30–1.42,	Bl or distorted
$PtV_{3.5}$	1.26	A15		1.42–2.37	Bl
$Pt_{0.5}W_{0.5}$	1.45	Al	$SbTi_3$	5.8	A15
Pt_xW_{1-x}	0.4–2.7		Sb_2Tl_7	5.2	
Pt_2Y_3	0.90		$Sb_{0.01-0.03}V_{0.99-0.97}$	3.76–2.63	A2
Pt_2Y	1.57, 1.70	C15	SbV_3	0.80	A15
Pt_3Y_7	0.82	$D10_2$	Si_2Th	3.2	C_c, α-phase
PtZr	3.0	A3	Si_2Th	2.4	C32, β-phase
$Re_{0.64}Ta_{0.36}$	1.46	A12	SiV_3	17.1	A15
$Re_{24}Ti_5$	6.60	A12	$Si_{0.9}V_3Al_{0.1}$	14.05	A15
Re_xTi_{1-x}	6.6 max.		$Si_{0.9}V_3B_{0.1}$	15.8	A15
$Re_{0.76}V_{0.24}$	4.52	$D8_b$	$Si_{0.9}V_3C_{0.1}$	16.4	A15
$Re_{0.92}V_{0.08}$	6.8	A3	$SiV_{2.7}Cr_{0.3}$	11.3	A15
$Re_{0.6}W_{0.4}$	6.0		$Si_{0.9}V_3Ge_{0.1}$	14.0	A15
$Re_{0.5}W_{0.5}$	5.12	$D8_b$	$SiV_{2.7}Mo_{0.3}$	11.7	A15
Re_2Y	1.83	C14	$SiV_{2.7}Nb_{0.3}$	12.8	A15
Re_2Zr	5.9	C14	$SiV_{2.7}Ru_{0.3}$	2.9	A15
Re_6Zr	7.40	A12	$SiV_{2.7}Ti_{0.3}$	10.9	A15
$Rh_{17}S_{15}$	5.8	Cubic	$SiV_{2.7}Zr_{0.3}$	13.2	A15
$Rh_{\sim0.24}Sc_{\sim0.76}$	0.88, 0.92		Si_2W_3	2.8, 2.84	
Rh_xSe_{1-x}	6.0 max.		$Sn_{0.174-0.104}Ta_{0.826-0.896}$	6.5–<4.2	A15
Rh_2Sr	6.2	C15	$SnTa_3$	8.35	A15, highly
$Rh_{0.4}Ta_{0.6}$	2.35	$D8_b$			ordered
$RhTe_2$	1.51	C2	$SnTa_3$	6.2	A15, partially
$Rh_{0.67}Te_{0.33}$	0.49				ordered
Rh_xTe_{1-x}	1.51 max.		$SnTaV_2$	2.8	A15
RhTh	0.36	B_f	$SnTa_2V$	3.7	A15
Rh_3Th_7	2.15	$D10_2$	Sn_xTe_{1-x}		
Rh_5Th	1.07		$(n = 10.5-20 \times 10^{20})$	0.07–0.22	Bl
Rh_xTi_{1-x}	2.25–3.95		Sn_xTl_{1-x}	2.37–5.2	
$Rh_{0.02}U_{0.98}$	0.96		SnV_3	3.8	A15
RhV_3	0.38	A15	$Sn_{0.02-0.057}V_{0.98-0.943}$	2.87–~1.6	A2
RhW	~3.4	A3	$Ta_{0.025}Ti_{0.975}$	1.3	Hexagonal
RhY_3	0.65		$Ta_{0.05}Ti_{0.95}$	2.9	Hexagonal
Rh_2Y_3	1.48		$Ta_{0.05-0.75}V_{0.095-0.25}$	4.30–2.65	A2
Rh_3Y	1.07	C15	$Ta_{0.8-1}W_{0.2-0}$	1.2–4.4	A2
Rh_5Y	0.56		$Tc_{0.1-0.4}W_{0.9-0.6}$	1.25–7.18	Cubic
$RhZr_2$	10.8	C16	$Tc_{0.50}W_{0.50}$	7.52	α plus σ
$Rh_{0.005}Zr$ (annealed)	5.8		$Tc_{0.60}W_{0.40}$	7.88	σ plus α
$Rh_{0-0.45}Zr_{1-0.55}$	2.1–10.8		Tc_6Zr	9.7	A12
$Rh_{0.1}Zr_{0.9}$	9.0	Hexagonal, c.p.	$Th_{0-0.55}Y_{1-0.45}$	1.2–1.8	
Ru_2Sc	1.67	C14	$Ti_{0.70}V_{0.30}$	6.14	Cubic
Ru_2Th	3.56	C15	Ti_xV_{1-x}	0.2–7.5	
RuTi	1.07	B2	$Ti_{0.5}Zr_{0.5}$ (annealed)	1.23	
$Ru_{0.05}Ti_{0.95}$	2.5		$Ti_{0.5}Zr_{0.5}$ (quenched)	2.0	
$Ru_{0.1}Ti_{0.9}$	3.5		V_2Zr	8.80	C15
$Ru_xTi_{0.6}V_y$	6.6 max.		$V_{0.26}Zr_{0.74}$	$\approx$5.9	
$Ru_{0.45}V_{0.55}$	4.0	B2	W_2Zr	2.16	C15
RuW	7.5	A3			

††See key at end of table.

CRITICAL FIELD DATA

Substance	H_o, oersteds	Substance	H_o, oersteds
Ag_2F	2.5	InSb	1,100
Ag_7NO_{11}	57	In_xTl_{1-x}	252–284
Al_2CMo_3	1,700	$In_{0.8}Tl_{0.2}$	252
$BaBi_3$	740	$Mg_{\sim 0.47}Tl_{\sim 0.53}$	220
Bi_2Pt	10	$Mo_{0.16}Ti_{0.84}$	<985
Bi_3Sr	530	$NbSn_2$	620
Bi_5Tl_3	>400	$PbTl_{0.27}$	756
CdSn	>266	$PbTl_{0.17}$	796
$CoSi_2$	105	$PbTl_{0.12}$	849
$Cr_{0.1}Ti_{0.3}V_{0.6}$	1,360	$PbTl_{0.075}$	880
$In_{1-0.86}Mg_{0-0.14}$	272.4–259.2	$PbTl_{0.04}$	864

KEY TO CRYSTAL STRUCTURE TYPES

"Struck-turbericht" type*	Example	Class	"Struck-turbericht" type*	Example	Class
A1	Cu	Cubic, f.c.	$C15_b$	$AuBe_5$	Cubic
A2	W	Cubic, b.c.	C16	$CuAl_2$	Tetragonal, b.c.
A3	Mg	Hexagonal, close packed	C18	FeS_2	Orthorhombic
A4	Diamond	Cubic, f.c.	C22	Fe_2P	Trigonal
A5	White Sn	Tetragonal, b.c.	C23	$PbCl_2$	Orthorhombic
A6	In	Tetragonal, b.c. (f.c. cell usually used)	C32	AlB_2	Hexagonal
			C36	$MgNi_2$	Hexagonal
A7	As	Rhombohedral	C37	Co_2Si	Orthorhombic
A8	Se	Trigonal	C49	$ZrSi_2$	Orthorhombic
A10	Hg	Rhombohedral	C54	$TiSi_2$	Orthorhombic
A12	α-Mn	Cubic, b.c.	C_c	Si_2Th	Tetragonal, b.c.
A13	β-Mn	Cubic	DO_3	BiF_3	Cubic, f.c.
A15	"β-W" (WO_3)	Cubic	DO_{11}	Fe_3C	Orthorhombic
B1	NaCl	Cubic, f.c.	DO_{18}	Na_3As	Hexagonal
B2	CsCl	Cubic	DO_{19}	Ni_3Sn	Hexagonal
B3	ZnS	Cubic	DO_{20}	$NiAl_3$	Orthorhombic
B4	ZnS	Hexagonal	DO_{22}	$TiAl_3$	Tetragonal
$B8_1$	NiAs	Hexagonal	DO_e	Ni_3P	Tetragonal, b.c.
$B8_2$	Ni_2In	Hexagonal	Dl_3	Al_4Ba	Tetragonal, b.c.
B10	PbO	Tetragonal	Dl_c	$PtSn_4$	Orthorhombic
B11	γ-CuTi	Tetragonal	$D2_1$	CaB_6	Cubic
B17	PtS	Tetragonal	$D2_c$	MnU_6	Tetragonal, b.c.
B18	CuS	Hexagonal	$D2_d$	$CaZn_5$	Hexagonal
B20	FeSi	Cubic	$D5_2$	La_2O_3	Trigonal
B27	FeB	Orthorhombic	$D5_8$	Sb_2S_3	Orthorhombic
B31	MnP	Orthorhombic	$D7_3$	Th_3P_4	Cubic, b.c.
B32	NaTl	Cubic, f.c.	$D7_b$	Ta_3B_4	Orthorhombic
B34	PdS	Tetragonal	$D8_1$	Fe_3Zn_{10}	Cubic, b.c.
B_f	δ-CrB	Orthorhombic	$D8_2$	Cu_5Zn_8	Cubic, b.c.
B_g	MoB	Tetragonal, b.c.	$D8_3$	Cu_9Al_4	Cubic
B_h	WC	Hexagonal	$D8_8$	Mn_5Si_3	Hexagonal
B_i	γ-MoC	Hexagonal	$D8_b$	CrFe	Tetragonal
C1	CaF_2	Cubic, f.c.	$D8_i$	Mo_2B_5	Rhombohedral
$C1_b$	MgAgAs	Cubic, f.c.	$D10_2$	Fe_3Th_7	Hexagonal
C2	FeS_2	Cubic	$E2_1$	$CaTiO_3$	Cubic
C6	CdI_2	Trigonal	$E9_3$	Fe_3W_3C	Cubic, f.c.
C11b	$MoSi_2$	Tetragonal, b.c.	$L1_0$	CuAu	Tetragonal
C12	$CaSi_2$	Rhombohedral	$L1_2$	Cu_3Au	Cubic
C14	$MgZn_2$	Hexagonal	L'_{2b}	ThH_2	Tetragonal, b.c.
C15	Cu_2Mg	Cubic, f.c.	L'_3	Fe_2N	Hexagonal

*See "Handbook of Lattice Spacing and Structures of Metals", W.B. Pearson, Vol. I, Pergamon Press, 1958, p. 79, and Vol. II, Pergamon Press, 1967, p. 3.

HIGH CRITICAL MAGNETIC-FIELD SUPERCONDUCTIVE COMPOUNDS AND ALLOYS

With Critical Temperatures, H_{c1}, H_{c2}, H_{c3}, and the Temperature of Field Observations, T_{obs}

Substance	T_c, °K	H_{c1}, kg	H_{c2}, kg	H_{c3}, kg	T_{obs}, °K†
Al_2CMo_3	9.8–10.2	0.091	156		1.2
$AlNb_3$		0.375			
$Ba_xO_3Sr_{1-x}Ti$	<0.1–0.55	0.0039 max.			
$Bi_{0.5}Cd_{0.1}Pb_{0.27}Sn_{0.13}$			>24		3.06
Bi_xPb_{1-x}	7.35–8.4	0.122 max.	~30 max.		4.2
$Bi_{0.56}Pb_{0.44}$	8.8		15		4.2
$Bi_{7.5 w/o}Pb_{92.5 w/o}$‡			2.32		
$Bi_{0.099}Pb_{0.901}$		0.29	2.8		
$Bi_{0.02}Pb_{0.98}$		0.46	0.73		
$Bi_{0.53}Pb_{0.32}Sn_{0.16}$			>25		3.06
$Bi_{1-0.93}Sn_{0-0.07}$			0–0.032		3.7
Bi_5Tl_3	6.4		>5.56		3.35
C_8K (excess K)	0.55		0.160 (H⊥c)		0.32
			0.730 (H‖c)		0.32
C_8K	0.39		0.025 (H⊥c)		0.32
			0.250 (H‖c)		0.32
$C_{0.44}Mo_{0.56}$	12.5–13.5	0.087	98.5		1.2
CNb	8–10	0.12	16.9		4.2
$CNb_{0.4}Ta_{0.6}$	10–13.6	0.19	14.1		1.2
CTa	9–11.4	0.22	4.6		1.2
$Ca_xO_3Sr_{1-x}Ti$	<0.1–0.55	0.002–0.004			
$Cd_{0.1}Hg_{0.9}$ (by weight)		0.23	0.34		2.04
$Cd_{0.05}Hg_{0.95}$		0.28	0.31		2.16
$Cr_{0.10}Ti_{0.30}V_{0.60}$	5.6	0.071	84.4		0
GaN	5.85	0.725			4.2
Ga_xNb_{1-x}			>28		4.2
$GaSb$ (annealed)	4.24		2.64		3.5
$GaV_{1.95}$	5.3		73***		0
$GaV_{2.1-3.5}$	6.3–14.45		230–300**		0
GaV_3		0.4	350***		0
			500**		
$GaV_{4.5}$	9 15		121*		0
Hf_xNb_y			>52–>102		1.2
Hf_xTa_y			>28–>86		1.2
$Hg_{0.05}Pb_{0.95}$		0.235	2.3		
$Hg_{0.101}Pb_{0.899}$		0.23	4.3		4.2
$Hg_{0.15}Pb_{0.85}$	~6.75		>13		2.93
$In_{0.98}Pb_{0.02}$	3.45	0.1		0.12	2.76
$In_{0.96}Pb_{0.04}$	3.68	0.1	0.12	0.25	2.94
$In_{0.94}Pb_{0.06}$	3.90	0.095	0.18	0.35	3.12
$In_{0.913}Pb_{0.087}$	4.2	~0.17	0.55	2.65	
$In_{0.316}Pb_{0.684}$		0.155	3.7		4.2
$In_{0.17}Pb_{0.83}$			2.8	5.5	4.2
$In_{1.000}Te_{1.002}$	3.5–3.7		1.2*		0
$In_{0.95}Tl_{0.05}$		0.263	0.263		3.3
$In_{0.90}Tl_{0.10}$		0.257	0.257		3.25
$In_{0.83}Tl_{0.17}$		0.242	0.39		3.21
$In_{0.75}Tl_{0.25}$		0.216	0.50		3.16
LaN	1.35	0.45			0.76
La_3S_4	6.5	≈0.15	>25		1.3
La_3Se_4	8.6	≈0.2	>25		1.25
$Mo_{0.52}Re_{0.48}$	11.1		14–21	22–33	4.2
			18–28	37–43	1.3
$Mo_{0.6±0.05}Re_{0.395}$	10.6		14–20	20–37	4.2
			19–26	26 37	1.3
$Mo_{~0.5}Tc_{~0.5}$			~75*		0
$Mo_{0.16}Ti_{0.84}$	4.18	0.028	98.7*		0
			36–38		3.0
$Mo_{0.913}Ti_{0.087}$	2.95	0.060	~15		4.2
$Mo_{0.1-0.3}U_{0.9-0.7}$	1.85–2.06		>25		
$Mo_{0.17}Zr_{0.83}$			~30		
$N_{(12.8 w/o)}Nb$	15.2		>9.5		13.2
NNb (wires)	16.1		153*		0
			132		4.2
			95		8
			53		12
NNb_xO_{1-x}	13.5–17.0		· 38		
NNb_xZr_{1-x}	9.8–13.8		4–>130		4.2
$N_{0.93}Nb_{0.85}Zr_{0.15}$	13.8		>130		4.2
$Na_{0.086}Pb_{0.914}$		0.19	6.0		
$Na_{0.016}Pb_{0.984}$		0.28	2.05		

‡w/o denotes weight percent.

Substance	T_c, °K	H_{c1}, kg	H_{c2}, kg	H_{c3}, kg	T_{obs}, °K†
Nb	9.15		2.020		1.4
			1.710		4.2
Nb		0.4–1.1	3–5.5		4.2
Nb (unstrained)		1.1–1.8	3.40	6–9.1	4.2
Nb (strained)		1.25–1.92	3.44	6.0–8.7	4.2
Nb (cold-drawn wire)		2.48	4.10	≈ 10	4.2
Nb (film)			>25		4.2
NbSc			>30		
Nb_3Sn		0.170	221		4.2
			70		14.15
			54		15
			34		16
			17		17
$Nb_{0.1}Ta_{0.9}$		0.084	0.154		4.195
$Nb_{0.2}Ta_{0.8}$			10		4.2
$Nb_{0.65-0.73}Ta_{0.02-0.10}Zr_{0.25}$			>70->90		4.2
Nb_xTi_{1-x}			148 max.		1.2
			120 max.		4.2
$Nb_{0.222}U_{0.778}$		1.98	23		1.2
Nb_xZr_{1-x}			127 max.		1.2
			94 max.		4.2
O_3SrTi	0.43	.0049*	.504*		0
O_3SrTi	0.33	.00195*	.420*		0
$PbSb_{1 \ w/o}$ (quenched)			>1.5		4.2
$PbSb_{1 \ w/o}$ (annealed)			>0.7		4.2
$PbSb_{2.8 \ w/o}$ (quenched)			>2.3		4.2
$PbSb_{2.8 \ w/o}$ (annealed)			>0.7		4.2
$Pb_{0.871}Sn_{0.129}$		0.45	1.1		
$Pb_{0.965}Sn_{0.035}$		0.53	0.56		
$Pb_{1-0.26}Tl_{0-0.74}$	7.20–3.68		2–6.9*		0
$PbTl_{0.17}$	6.73		4.5*		0
$Re_{0.26}W_{0.74}$			>30		
$Sb_{0.93}Sn_{0.07}$			0.12		3.7
SiV_3	17.0	0.55	156***		
Sn_xTe_{1-x}		0.00043–0.00236	0.005–0.0775		0.012–0.079
Ta (99.95%)		0.425	1.850		1.3
		0.325	1.425		2.27
		0.275	1.175		2.66
		0.090	0.375		3.72
$Ta_{0.5}Nb_{0.5}$			3.55		4.2
$Ta_{0.65-0}Ti_{0.35-1}$	4.4–7.8		>14–138		1.2
$Ta_{0.5}Ti_{0.5}$			138		1.2
Te	~3.3	0.25*			0
Tc_xW_{1-x}	5.75–7.88		8–44		4.2
Ti				2.7	4.2
$Ti_{0.75}V_{0.25}$	5.3	0.029*	199*		0
$Ti_{0.775}V_{0.225}$	4.7	0.024*	172*		0
$Ti_{0.615}V_{0.385}$	7.07	0.050	~34		4.2
$Ti_{0.516}V_{0.484}$	7.20	0.062	~28		4.2
$Ti_{0.415}V_{0.585}$	7.49	0.078	~25		4.2
$Ti_{0.12}V_{0.88}$			17.3	28.1	4.2
$Ti_{0.09}V_{0.91}$			14.3	16.4	4.2
$Ti_{0.06}V_{0.94}$			8.2	12.7	4.2
$Ti_{0.03}V_{0.97}$			3.8	6.8	4.2
Ti_xV_{1-x}			108 max.		1.2
V	5.31	~0.8	~3.4		1.79
		~0.75	~3.15		2
		~0.45	~2.2		3
		~0.30	~1.2		4
$V_{0.26}Zr_{0.74}$	≈ 5.9	0 238			1.05
		0.227			1.78
		0.185			3.04
		0.165			3.5
W (film)	1.7–4.1		>34		1

†Temperature of critical field measurement.
*Extrapolated.
**Linear extrapolation.
***Parabolic extrapolation.

TABLES OF PROPERTIES OF SEMICONDUCTORS

Compiled by Dr. Brian Randall Pamplin

The term "semiconductor" is applied to a material in which electric current is carried by electrons or holes and whose electrical conductivity when extremely pure rises exponentially with temperature and may be increased from this low "intrinsic" value by many orders of magnitude by "doping" with electrically active impurities.

Semiconductors are characterised by an energy gap in the allowed energies of electrons in the material which separates the normally filled energy levels of the *valence band* (where "missing" electrons behave like positively charged current carriers "holes") and the *conduction band* (where electrons behave rather like a gas of free negatively charged carriers with an effective mass dependent on the material and the direction of the electrons' motion). This energy gap depends on the nature of the material and varies with direction in anisotropic crystals. It is slightly dependent on temperature and pressure, and this dependence is usually almost linear at normal temperatures and pressures.

The data is presented in three tables. Table I "General Properties of Semiconductors" lists the main crystallographic and semiconducting properties of a large number of semiconducting materials in three main categories; "Tetrahedral Semiconductors" in which every atom is tetrahedrally co-ordinated to four nearest neighbour atoms (or atomic sites) as for example in the diamond structure; "Octahedral Semiconductors" in which every atom is octahedrally co-ordinated to six nearest neighbour atoms—as for example in the halite structure; and "Other Semiconductors".

Table II gives more detailed information about some better known semiconductors, while Table III gives some information about the electronic energy band structure parameters of the best known materials.

TABLE I

GENERAL PROPERTIES OF SEMICONDUCTORS

(listed by Crystal Structure)

Substance	Lattice Parameters (A° Room temperature)	Density (gm/cc)	Melting Point (°K)	Minimum Room Temperature Energy Gap (eV)	Thermal Conductivity	Heat of Formation k cal/mole	Mobility (Room Temperature) Electrons (cm²/V.s)	Holes	Remarks
PART A TETRAHEDRAL SEMICONDUCTORS									
§A1 Diamond Structure Elements (Strukturbericht symbol A4, Space Group Fd3m - 0_h^7)									
C	3.5597	3.51	4300	5.4	2000	161	1800	1400	
Si	5.43072	2.3283	1685	1.107	1240	77.5	1900	500	
Ge	5.65754	5.3234	1231	0.67	640	69.5	3800	1820	
α-Sn	6.4912	5.765	503	0.08		64	2500	2400	
§A2 Sphalerite (Zinc Blende) Structure Compounds (Strukturbericht symbol B3 Space Group F $\overline{4}$ 3m - T_d^2)									
I VII Compounds									
CuF	4.255								
CuCl	5.4057	3.53	695						
CuBr	5.6905	4.72	770	2.94		115			
CuI	6.0427	5.63	878			105			
AgBr						102	4000		
AgI	6.473	5.67				93	30		
II VI Compounds									
BeS	4.865	2.36							
BeSe	5.139	4.315							
BeTe	5.626	5.090							
BePo	8.38	7.3							
ZnO	4.63								see § A3
ZnS	5.4093	4.079	1920	3.54	140	114	180	5(400°C)	see also § A3
ZnSe	5.6676	5.42	1790	2.58	140	101	540	28	
ZnTe	6.101	5.72	1510	2.26	140	90	340	100	
ZnPo									
CdS	5.5818								see also § A3
CdSe	6.05								see § A3
CdTe	6.477	5.86	1370	1.44	55	81	1200	50	
CdPo									
HgS	5.8517	7.73	~2020						
HgSe	6.084	8.25	1070	0.30	10	59	20000		
HgTe	6.429	8.17	943	0.15	20	58	25000	350	
III V Compounds									
BN	3.615	3.49	3000	~4	200	195			
BP(L.T.)	4.538	2.9		~6			500	70	
BAs	4.777								
AlP	5.451	2.85	1770	2.5					
AlAs	5.6622	3.81	1870	2.16		150	1200	420	
AlSb	6.1355	4.218	1330	1.60	600	140	200–400	550	
GaP	5.4505	4.13	1750	2.24	1100	152	300	100	
GaAs	5.65315	5.316	1510	1.35	370	128	8800	400	
GaSb	6.0954	5.619	980	0.67	270	118	4000	1400	
InP	5.86875	4.787	1330	1.27	800	134	4600	150	
InAs	6.05838	5.66	1215	0.36	290	114	33000	460	
InSb	6.47877	5.775	798	0.165	160	107	78000	750	
Other Sphalerite Structure Compounds									
β-SiC	4.348	3.21	3070	2.3			4000		
Ga_2Te_3	5.899	5.75	1063	~1.0	~14	65			
In_2Te_3(H.T.)	6.150	5.8	940	~1.0	~8	47.4	~10		
$MgGeP_2$	5.652								
$ZnSnP_2$	5.65			2.1					
$ZnSnAs_2$(H.T.)	5.851	5.53	1050	~0.7	70				
§ A3 Wurtzite (Zincite) Structure Compounds (Strukturbericht symbol B4, Space Group P 6_3mc - C_{6v}^4)									
I VII Compounds									
CuCl	3.91	6.42	T_c 680°K						
CuBr	4.06	6.66	T_c 658°K						
CuI	4.31	7.09							
AgI	4.580	7.494		2.63					

TABLE 1

GENERAL PROPERTIES OF SEMICONDUCTORS (Continued)

Substance	Lattice Parameters (A° Room temperature)		Density (gm/cc)	Melting Point (°K)	Minimum Room Temperature Energy Gap (eV)	Thermal Conductivity	Heat of Formation k cal/mole	Mobility (Room Temperature) Electrons (cm²/V.s)	Holes	Remarks
II VI Compounds										
BeO	2.698	4.380		2800						
MgTe	4.54	7.39	3.85	~2800						
ZnO	3.24950	5.2069	5.66	2250	3.2	6	154	180		
ZnS	3.8140	6.2576	4.1	2100	3.67		110			
ZnSe	3.996	6.626								
ZnTe	4.27	6.99								
CdS	4.1348	6.7490	4.82	2020	2.42		96	400		
CdSe	4.299	7.010	5.66	1530	1.74		90	650		
CdTe	4.57	7.47			1.50					
III V Compounds										
BP(H.T.)	3.562	5.900								
AlN	3.111	4.978	3.26	~2500	6.02		197			
GaN	3.180	5.166	6.10	1500	3.34		157			
InN	3.533	5.693	6.88	1200	2.0		133			
Other Wurtzite Structure Compounds										
SiC	3.076	5.048								
MnTe	4.078	6.701			~1.0					
Al_2S_3	3.579	5.829	2.55		4.1		426			
Al_2Se_3	3.890	6.30	3.91		3.1		367			

§ A$\overline{4}$ Chalcopyrite Structure Compounds (Strukturbericht symbol E1$_1$, Space Group I $\overline{4}$ 2d $-D_{2d}^{12}$)

Substance	Lattice Parameters (A° Room temperature)		Density (gm/cc)	Melting Point (°K)	Minimum Room Temperature Energy Gap (eV)	Thermal Conductivity	Heat of Formation k cal/mole	Mobility (Room Temperature) Electrons (cm²/V.s)	Holes	Remarks
I III VI₂ Compounds										
$CuAlS_2$	5.323	10.44	3.47		2.5					
$CuAlSe_2$	5.617	10.92	4.70	1270	1.1					
$CuAlTe_2$	5.976	11.80	5.50	1160	0.88					
$CuGaS_2$	5.360	10.49	4.35							
$CuGaSe_2$	5.618	11.01	5.56	1310	0.96, 1.63					
$CuGaTe_2$	6.013	11.93	5.99	1150	0.82, 1.0					
$CuInS_2$	5.528	11.08	4.75		1.2					
$CuInSe_2$	5.785	11.57	5.77	1250	0.86, 0.92	37				
$CuInTe_2$	6.179	12.365	6.10	970	0.95	49				
$CuTlS_2$	5.580	11.17	6.32							
$CuTlSe_2$(L.T.)	5.844	11.65	7.11	680	1.07					
$CuFeS_2$	5.25	10.32		1150	0.53					
$CuFeSe_2$				850	0.16					
$CuLaS_2$	5.65	10.86								
$AgAlS_2$	5.707	10.28	3.94							
$AgAlSe_2$	5.968	10.77	5.07	1220	0.7					
$AgAlTe_2$	6.309	11.85	6.18	1000	0.56					
$AgGaS_2$	5.755	10.28	4.72							
$AgGaSe_2$	5.985	10.90	5.84	1120	1.66					
$AgGaTe_2$	6.301	11.96	6.05	990	1.1	10				
$AgInS_2$(L.T.)	5.828	11.19	5.00		1.9					
$AgInSe_2$	6.102	11.69	5.81	1053	1.18	30				
$AgInTe_2$	6.42	12.59	6.12	965	0.96, 0.52					
$AgFeS_2$	5.66	10.30	4.53							
II IV V₂ Compounds										
$ZnSiP_2$	5.400	10.441	3.39	1640	2.3			1000		
$ZnGeP_2$	5.465	10.771	4.17	1295	2.2					
$CdSiP_2$	5.678	10.431	4.00	~1470	2.2			1000		
$CdGeP_2$	5.741	10.775	4.48	~1060	1.8					
$CdSnP_2$	5.900	11.518			1.5					
$ZnSiAs_2$	5.61	10.88	4.70	~1850	1.7				50	
$ZnGeAs_2$	5.672	11.153	5.32	~1150	0.85	110				
$ZnSnAs_2$	5.8515	11.704	5.53	~910	0.65	150			300	disorders at 910°K
$CdSiAs_2$	5.884	10.882								
$CdGeAs_2$	5.9427	11.2172	5.60	~903	0.53	40		70	25	disorders at 903°K
$CdSnAs_2$	6.0944	11.9182	5.72	880	0.26	70		22000	250	

TABLE I.

GENERAL PROPERTIES OF SEMICONDUCTORS (Continued)

Substance	Lattice Parameters (A° Room temperature)	Density (gm/cc)	Melting Point (°K)	Minimum Room Temperature Energy Gap (eV)	Thermal Conductivity	Heat of Formation k cal/mole	Mobility (Room Temperature) Electrons (cm²/V.s)	Holes	Remarks

§ A5 "Defect Chalcopyrite" Structure Compounds (Strukturbericht symbol E3, Space Group I $\overline{4}$ — S_4^2)

Substance	Lattice Parameters	Density	Melting Point	Energy Gap	Thermal Cond.	Heat of Formation	Electrons	Holes	Remarks
$ZnAl_2Se_4$	5.503 10.90	4.37							
$ZnAl_2Te_4(?)$	5.104 12.05	4.95							
$ZnGa_2S_4(?)$	5.274 10.44	3.80							
$ZnGa_2Se_4(?)$	5.496 10.99	5.21							
$ZnGa_2Te_4(?)$	5.937 11.87	5.67		1.35					
$ZnIn_2Se_4$	5.711 11.42	5.44	1250	2.6					
$ZnIn_2Te_4$	6.122 12.24	5.83	1075	1.2					
$CdAl_2S_4$	5.564 10.32	3.06							
$CdAl_2Se_4$	5.747 10.68	4.54							
$CdAl_2Te_4(?)$	6.011 12.21	5.10							
$CdGa_2S_4$	5.577 10.08	4.03							
$CdGa_2Se_4$	5.743 10.73	5.32							
$CdGa_2Te_4$	6.093 11.81	5.77							
$CdIn_2Te_4$	6.205 12.41	5.9	1060	(1.26 or 0.9)	4000				
$HgAl_2S_4$	5.488 10.26	4.11							
$HgAl_2Se_4$	5.708 10.74	5.05							
$HgAl_2Te_4(?)$	6.004 12.11	5.81							
$HgGa_2S_4$	5.507 10.23	5.00							
$HgGa_2Se_4$	5.715 10.78	6.18							
$HgIn_2Se_4$	5.764 11.80	6.3	1100	0.6					
$HgIn_2Te_4(?)$	6.186 12.37	6.3	980	0.86		200			

§ A6 Other Tetrahedral Compounds

Substance	Lattice Parameters	Density	Melting Point	Energy Gap	Thermal Cond.	Heat of Formation	Electrons	Holes	Remarks
αSiC	3.0817 15.1183	3.21	3070	2.86			400		6H structure
$Hg_5Ga_2Te_8$	6.235								B3 with super lattice
$Hg_5In_2Te_8$	6.328			0.7			2000		B3 with super lattice

PART B OCTAHEDRAL SEMICONDUCTORS

Halite Structure Semiconductors (Strukturbericht symbol B1, Space Group Fm3m — 0_h^5)

Substance	Lattice Parameters	Density	Melting Point	Energy Gap	Thermal Cond.	Heat of Formation	Electrons	Holes	Remarks
$SnSe$	6.020		1133						
$SnTe$	6.313		1080(max)	0.5	91				
PbS	5.9362	7.61	1390	0.37	23	104	600	600	
$PbSe$	6.1243	8.15	1340	0.26	17	94	1000	900	
$PbTe$	6.454	8.16	1180	0.25	23	94	1600	600	

Selected Other Binary Chalcides

Substance	Lattice Parameters	Density	Melting Point	Energy Gap	Thermal Cond.	Heat of Formation	Electrons	Holes	Remarks
$BiSe$	5.99	7.98	880	0.4					
$BiTe$	6.47								
$EuSe$	6.191		2300	1.8	2.4				
$GdSe$	5.771		2400						
NiD	4.1684	6.6	2260	2.0 or 3.7			4	–	
CdO	4.6953		1700	2.5	7	127	100		
SrS	6.0199	3.643	3000	4.1					

Selected Ternary Compounds

Substance	Lattice Parameters	Density	Melting Point	Energy Gap	Thermal Cond.	Heat of Formation	Electrons	Holes	Remarks
$AgSbSe_2$	5.786	6.60	910	0.58	10.5				
$AgSbTe_2$ (or $Ag_{19}Sb_{29}Te_{52}$)	6.078	7.12	830	0.7, 0.27	8.6, 0.3				
$AgBiS_2$(H.T.)	5.648								
$AgBiSe_2$(H.T.)	5.82								
$AgBiTe_2$(H.T.)	6.155								

TABLE II
SEMICONDUCTING PROPERTIES OF SELECTED MATERIALS

Substance	Minimum Energy Gap (eV)		$\frac{dE_g}{dT}$ x 10^4 eV/°C	$\frac{dE_g}{dP}$ x 10^6 eV.cm²/kg	Density of States Electron Effective Mass m_{d_n} (m_o)	Electron Mobility and Temperature Dependence μ_n $-x$ cm²/V.s		Density of States Hole Effective Mass m_{d_p} (m_o)	Hole Mobility and Temperature Dependence μ_p $-x$ cm²/V.s	
	R.T.	0°K								
Si	1.107	1.153	−2.3	−2.0	0.58	1,900	2.6	1.06	500	2.3
Ge	0.67	0.744	−3.7	+7.3	0.35	3,800	1.66	0.56	1,820	2.33
αSn	0.08	0.094	−0.5		0.02	2,500	1.65	0.3	2,400	2.0
Te	0.33				0.68	1,100		0.19	560	
III–V Compounds										
AlAs	2.2	2.3				1,200			420	
AlSb	1.6	1.7	−3.5	−1.6	0.09	200	1.5	0.4	500	1.8
GaP	2.24	2.40	−5.4	−1.7	0.35	300	1.5		150	1.5
GaAs	1.35	1.53	−5.0	+9.4	0.068	9,000	1.0	0.5	500	2.1
GaSb	0.67	0.78	−3.5	+12	0.050	5,000	2.0	0.23	1,400	0.9
InP	1.27	1.41	−4.6	+4.6	0.067	5,000	2.0		200	2.4
InAs	0.36	0.43	−2.8	+8	0.022	33,000	1.2	0.41	460	2.3
InSb	0.165	0.23	−2.8	+15	0.014	78,000	1.6	0.4	750	2.1
II–VI Compounds										
ZnO	3.2		−9.5	+0.6	0.38	180	1.5			
ZnS	3.54		−5.3	+5.7		180			5(400°C)	
ZnSe	2.58	2.80	−7.2	+6		540			28	
ZnTe	2.26			+6		340			100	
CdO	2.5 ± .1		−6		0.1	120				
CdS	2.42		−5	+3.3	0.165	400		0.8		
CdSe	1.74	1.85	−4.6		0.13	650	1.0	0.6		
CdTe	1.44	1.56	−4.1	+8	0.14	1,200		0.35	50	
HgSe	0.30				0.030	20,000	2.0			
HgTe	0.15		−1		0.017	25,000		0.5	350	
Halite Structure Compounds										
PbS	0.37	0.28	+4		0.16	800		0.1	1,000	2.2
PbSe	0.26	0.16	+4		0.3	1,500		0.34	1,500	2.2
PbTe	0.25	0.19	+4	−7	0.21	1,600		0.14	750	2.2
Others										
ZnSb	0.50	0.56			0.15	10				1.5
CdSb	0.45	0.57	−5.4		0.15	300			2,000	1.5
Bi₂S₃	1.3					200			1,100	
Bi₂Se₃	0.27					600			675	
Bi₂Te₃	0.13		−0.95		0.58	1,200	1.68	1.07	510	1.95
Mg₂Si		0.77	−6.4		0.46	400	2.5		70	
Mg₂Ge		0.74	−9			280	2		110	
Mg₂Sn	0.21	0.33	−3.5		0.37	320			260	
Mg₃Sb₂		0.32				20			82	
Zn₃As₂	0.93					10	1.1		10	
Cd₃As₂	0.13				0.046	15,000	0.88			
GaSe	2.05		3.8						20	
GaTe	1.66	1.80	−3.6			14	−5			
InSe	1.8					900				
TlSe	0.57		−3.9		0.3	30		0.6	20	1.5
CdSnAs₂	0.23				0.05	25,000	1.7			
Ga₂Te₃	1.1	1.55	−4.8							
α-In₂Te₃	1.1	1.2			0.7				50	1.1
β-In₂Te₃	1.0								5	
Hg₅In₂Te₈	0.5								11,000	
SnO₂									78	

TABLE III

PART A. DATA ON VALENCE BANDS OF SEMICONDUCTORS (Room Temperature data)

Substance	Heavy Holes	Light Holes	"Split-off" Band Holes	Energy Separation of "Split-off" Band (eV)	Measured (Light) Hole Mobility cm²/V.s
	Band Curvature Effective Mass (Expressed as fraction of free electron mass)				

Semiconductors with Valence Band Maximum at Centre of Brillouin Zone ("Γ")

Substance	Heavy Holes	Light Holes	"Split-off" Band Holes	Energy Separation of "Split-off" Band (eV)	Measured (Light) Hole Mobility cm²/V.s
Si	0.52	0.16	0.25	0.044	500
Ge	0.34	0.043	0.08	0.3	1,820
Sn	0.3				2,400
AlAs					
AlSb	0.4			0.7	550
GaP				0.13	100
GaAs	0.8	0.12	0.20	0.34	400
GaSb	0.23	0.06		0.7	1,400
InP				0.21	150
InAs	0.41	0.025	0.083	0.43	460
InSb	0.4	0.015		0.85	750
CdTe	0.35				50
HgTe	0.5				350

Semiconductors with Multiple Valence Band Maxima

Substance	Number of Equivalent Valleys Direction	Longitudinal m_L	Transverse m_T	Anisotropy $\frac{m_L}{K = m_T}$	Measured (Light) Hole Mobility cm²/V.s
		Curvature Effective Masses			
PbSe	4 "L" [111]	0.095	0.047	2.0	1,500
PbTe	4 "L" [111]	0.27	0.02	10	750
Bi₂Te₃	6	0.207	~0.045	4.5	515

PART B. DATA ON CONDUCTION BANDS OF SEMICONDUCTORS (Room Temperature Data)

Single Valley Semiconductors

Substance	Energy Gap (eV)	Effective Mass (m_o)	Mobility (cm²/V.s)	Comments
GaAs	1.35	0.067	8,500	3(or 6?) equivalent [100] valleys 0.36 eV above this maximum with a mobility of ~50
InP	1.27	0.067	5,000	3(or 6?) equivalent [100] valleys 0.4 eV above this minimum.
InAs	0.36	0.022	33,000	equivalent valleys ~1.0 eV above this minimum.
InSb	0.165	0.014	78,000	
CdTe	1.44	0.11	1,000	4(or 8?) equivalent [111] valleys 0.51 eV above this minimum.

Multivalley Semiconductors

Substance	Energy Gap	Number of Equivalent Valleys and Direction	Longitudinal m_L	Transverse m_T	Anisotropy $\frac{m_L}{K = m_T}$	Comments
			Band Curvature	Effective Mass		
Si	1.107	6 in [100] "△"	0.90	0.192	4.7	
Ge	0.67	4 in [111] at "L"	1.588	0.0815	19.5	
GaSb	0.67	as Ge (?)	~1.0	~0.2	~5	
PbSe	0.26	4 in [111] at "L"	0.085	0.05	1.7	
PbTe	0.25	4 in [111] at "L"	0.21	0.029	5.5	
Bi₂Te₃	0.13	6			~0.05	

STANDARD CALIBRATION TABLES FOR THERMOCOUPLES

The following tables which represent the Temperature-E. M. F. functions of various thermocouples should be used with appropriate correction curves if precise results are desired. These curves must be determined for each individual couple by plotting ΔE, the difference between the observed and the standard E. M. F., against the standard E. M. F. at three or more fixed temperature points. The value ΔE as shown by such a correction curve is then subtracted algebraically from the observed E. M. F. to give the true E. M. F. reading.

In the following tables the fixed or "cold junction" is at 0° C.; when the cold junction is not maintained at 0° C. the readings of the E. M. F. must be corrected as follows: $Et = E(t-tc) + Etc$ where $E(t-tc)$ is the observed reading, Etc is the E. M. F. for the temperature corresponding to the cold junction temperature as read from the standard table and Et is the E. M. F. produced by the hot junction corrected to the value which would be obtained with the cold junction at 0° C. The temperature corresponding to Et is then obtained by reference to the standard table.

Since the E. M. F.-temperature function is not linear the cold junction should be maintained at a temperature very close to that at which the thermocouple was calibrated. Otherwise considerable error will result despite the above correction.

PLATINUM VERSUS PLATINUM-10-PERCENT RHODIUM THERMOCOUPLES

(Electromotive Force in Absolute Millivolts. Temperatures in Degrees C (Int. 1948). Reference Junctions at 0° C.)

°C	0	10	20	30	40	50	60	70	80	90
	Millivolts									
0	0	0.06	0.11	0.17	0.24	0.30	0.36	0.43	0.50	0.57
100	0.64	0.72	0.79	0.87	0.95	1.03	1.11	1.19	1.27	1.35
200	1.44	1.52	1.61	1.69	1.78	1.87	1.96	2.05	2.14	2.23
300	2.32	2.41	2.50	2.59	2.69	2.78	2.87	2.97	3.06	3.16
400	3.25	3.35	3.44	3.54	3.64	3.73	3.83	3.93	4.02	4.12
500	4.22	4.32	4.42	4.52	4.62	4.72	4.82	4.92	5.02	5.12
600	5.22	5.33	5.43	5.53	5.64	5.74	5.84	5.95	6.05	6.16
700	6.26	6.37	6.47	6.58	6.68	6.79	6.90	7.01	7.11	7.22
800	7.33	7.44	7.55	7.66	7.77	7.88	7.99	8.10	8.21	8.32
900	8.43	8.55	8.66	8.77	8.88	9.00	9.11	9.23	9.34	9.46
1000	9.57	9.69	9.80	9.92	10.04	10.15	10.27	10.39	10.51	10.62
1100	10.74	10.86	10.98	11.10	11.22	11.34	11.46	11.58	11.70	11.82
1200	11.94	12.06	12.18	12.30	12.42	12.54	12.66	12.78	12.90	13.02
1300	13.14	13.26	13.38	13.50	13.62	13.74	13.86	13.98	14.10	14.22
1400	14.34	14.46	14.58	14.70	14.82	14.94	15.05	15.17	15.29	15.41
1500	15.53	15.65	15.77	15.89	16.01	16.12	16.24	16.36	16.48	16.60
1600	16.72	16.83	16.95	17.07	17.19	17.31	17.42	17.54	17.66	17.77
1700	17.89	18.01	18.12	18.24	18.36	18.47	18.59	...	...	...

CALIBRATION TABLES FOR THERMOCOUPLES (Continued)
PLATINUM VERSUS PLATINUM-10-PERCENT RHODIUM THERMOCOUPLES

(Electromotive Force in Absolute Millivolts. Temperatures in Degrees F.* Reference Junctions at 32° F.)

°F	0	10	20	30	40	50	60	70	80	90
	Millivolts									
0	...	...	...	...	0.02	0.06	0.09	0.12	0.15	0.19
100	0.22	0.26	0.29	0.33	0.36	0.40	0.44	0.48	0.52	0.56
200	0.60	0.64	0.68	0.72	0.76	0.80	0.84	0.89	0.93	0.97
300	1.02	1.06	1.11	1.15	1.20	1.24	1.29	1.33	1.38	1.43
400	1.47	1.52	1.57	1.62	1.66	1.71	1.76	1.81	1.86	1.91
500	1.96	2.01	2.06	2.11	2.16	2.21	2.26	2.31	2.36	2.41
600	2.46	2.51	2.56	2.61	2.66	2.72	2.77	2.82	2.87	2.92
700	2.98	3.03	3.08	3.14	3.19	3.24	3.29	3.35	3.40	3.45
800	3.51	3.56	3.61	3.67	3.72	3.78	3.83	3.88	3.94	3.99
900	4.05	4.10	4.16	4.21	4.26	4.32	4.37	4.43	4.49	4.54
1000	4.60	4.65	4.71	4.76	4.82	4.87	4.93	4.99	5.04	5.10
1100	5.16	5.21	5.27	5.33	5.38	5.44	5.50	5.56	5.61	5.67
1200	5.73	5.78	5.84	5.90	5.96	6.02	6.07	6.13	6.19	6.25
1300	6.31	6.37	6.42	6.48	6.54	6.60	6.66	6.72	6.78	6.84
1400	6.90	6.96	7.02	7.08	7.14	7.20	7.26	7.32	7.38	7.44
1500	7.50	7.56	7.62	7.68	7.74	7.80	7.86	7.93	7.99	8.05
1600	8.11	8.17	8.23	8.30	8.36	8.42	8.48	8.55	8.61	8.67
1700	8.73	8.80	8.86	8.92	8.98	9.05	9.11	9.17	9.24	9.30
1800	9.37	9.43	9.49	9.56	9.62	9.69	9.75	9.82	9.88	9.94
1900	10.01	10.07	10.14	10.20	10.27	10.33	10.40	10.47	10.53	10.60
2000	10.66	10.73	10.79	10.86	10.93	10.99	11.06	11.12	11.19	11.26
2100	11.32	11.39	11.46	11.52	11.59	11.66	11.72	11.79	11.86	11.92
2200	11.99	12.06	12.12	12.19	12.26	12.32	12.39	12.46	12.52	12.59
2300	12.66	12.72	12.79	12.86	12.92	12.99	13.06	13.12	13.19	13.26
2400	13.33	13.39	13.46	13.53	13.59	13.66	13.73	13.79	13.86	13.92
2500	13.99	14.06	14.12	14.19	14.26	14.32	14.39	14.46	14.52	14.59
2600	14.66	14.72	14.79	14.86	14.92	14.99	15.05	15.12	15.19	15.25
2700	15.32	15.39	15.45	15.52	15.58	15.65	15.72	15.78	15.85	15.91
2800	15.98	16.05	16.11	16.18	16.24	16.31	16.37	16.44	16.51	16.57
2900	16.64	16.70	16.77	16.83	16.90	16.97	17.03	17.10	17.16	17.23
3000	17.29	17.36	17.42	17.49	17.55	17.62	17.68	17.75	17.81	17.88
3100	17.94	18.01	18.07	18.14	18.20	18.27	18.33	18.40	18.46	18.53
3200	18.59	18.66	...	...	...	...	...	...	...	...

* Based on the International Temperature Scale of 1948.

(Electromotive Force in Absolute Millivolts. Temperatures in Degrees C (Int. 1948) Reference Junctions at 0° C.)

°C	0	10	20	30	40	50	60	70	80	90
					Millivolts					
0	0.00	0.06	0.11	0.17	0.23	0.30	0.36	0.43	0.50	0.57
100	0.65	0.72	0.80	0.88	0.96	1.04	1.12	1.21	1.29	1.38
200	1.47	1.55	1.64	1.73	1.83	1.92	2.01	2.11	2.20	2.30
300	2.40	2.49	2.59	2.69	2.79	2.89	2.99	3.09	3.19	3.30
400	3.40	3.50	3.61	3.71	3.82	3.92	4.03	4.13	4.24	4.35
500	4.46	4.56	4.67	4.78	4.89	5.00	5.12	5.23	5.34	5.45
600	5.56	5.68	5.79	5.91	6.02	6.14	6.25	6.37	6.49	6.60
700	6.72	6.84	6.96	7.08	7.20	7.32	7.44	7.56	7.68	7.80
800	7.92	8.05	8.17	8.29	8.42	8.54	8.67	8.80	8.92	9.05
900	9.18	9.30	9.43	9.56	9.69	9.82	9.95	10.08	10.21	10.34
1000	10.47	10.60	10.74	10.87	11.00	11.14	11.27	11.41	11.54	11.68
1100	11.82	11.95	12.09	12.23	12.37	12.50	12.64	12.78	12.92	13.06
1200	13.19	13.33	13.47	13.61	13.75	13.89	14.03	14.17	14.30	14.44
1300	14.58	14.72	14.86	15.00	15.14	15.28	15.42	15.55	15.69	15.83
1400	15.97	16.11	16.25	16.39	16.52	16.66	16.80	16.94	17.08	17.22
1500	17.36	17.49	17.63	17.77	17.91	18.04	18.18	18.32	18.45	18.59
1600	18.73	18.86	19.00	19.14	19.27	19.41	19.55	19.68	19.82	19.95
1700	20.09	...	...	...	...	...	...	...	...	...

(Electromotive Force in Absolute Millivolts. Temperatures in Degrees F.* Reference Junctions at 32° F.)

°F	0	10	20	30	40	50	60	70	80	90
					Millivolts					
0	...	...	...	...	0.02	0.06	0.09	0.12	0.15	0.19
100	0.22	0.26	0.29	0.33	0.36	0.40	0.44	0.48	0.52	0.56
200	0.60	0.64	0.68	0.72	0.76	0.81	0.85	0.89	0.94	0.98
300	1.03	1.08	1.12	1.17	1.21	1.26	1.31	1.36	1.41	1.46
400	1.50	1.55	1.60	1.65	1.70	1.75	1.81	1.86	1.91	1.96
500	2.01	2.07	2.12	2.17	2.22	2.28	2.33	2.38	2.44	2.49
600	2.55	2.60	2.66	2.71	2.77	2.82	2.88	2.94	2.99	3.05
700	3.10	3.16	3.22	3.27	3.33	3.39	3.45	3.50	3.56	3.62
800	3.68	3.74	3.79	3.85	3.91	3.97	4.03	4.09	4.15	4.21
900	4.26	4.32	4.38	4.44	4.50	4.56	4.62	4.69	4.75	4.81
1000	4.87	4.93	4.99	5.05	5.12	5.18	5.24	5.30	5.36	5.43
1100	5.49	5.55	5.61	5.68	5.74	5.81	5.87	5.93	6.00	6.06
1200	6.13	6.19	6.25	6.32	6.38	6.45	6.51	6.58	6.64	6.71
1300	6.77	6.84	6.90	6.97	7.04	7.10	7.17	7.24	7.30	7.37
1400	7.44	7.50	7.57	7.64	7.71	7.77	7.84	7.91	7.98	8.05
1500	8.12	8.18	8.25	8.32	8.39	8.46	8.53	8.60	8.67	8.74
1600	8.81	8.88	8.95	9.02	9.09	9.16	9.23	9.30	9.37	9.45
1700	9.52	9.59	9.66	9.73	9.80	9.87	9.95	10.02	10.09	10.16
1800	10.24	10.31	10.38	10.46	10.53	10.60	10.68	10.75	10.82	10.90
1900	10.97	11.05	11.12	11.20	11.27	11.35	11.42	11.50	11.58	11.65
2000	11.73	11.80	11.88	11.95	12.03	12.11	12.18	12.26	12.34	12.41
2100	12.49	12.56	12.64	12.72	12.80	12.87	12.95	13.03	13.10	13.18
2200	13.26	13.33	13.41	13.49	13.56	13.64	13.72	13.80	13.87	13.95
2300	14.03	14.10	14.18	14.26	14.34	14.41	14.49	14.57	14.64	14.72
2400	14.80	14.88	14.95	15.03	15.11	15.18	15.26	15.34	15.42	15.49
2500	15.57	15.65	15.72	15.80	15.88	15.95	16.03	16.11	16.19	16.26
2600	16.34	16.42	16.49	16.57	16.65	16.73	16.80	16.88	16.96	17.03
2700	17.11	17.19	17.26	17.34	17.42	17.49	17.57	17.65	17.72	17.80
2800	17.88	17.95	18.03	18.10	18.18	18.26	18.33	18.41	18.48	18.56
2900	18.64	18.71	18.79	18.86	18.94	19.02	19.09	19.17	19.24	19.32
3000	19.39	19.47	19.55	19.62	19.70	19.77	19.85	19.92	20.00	20.08
3100	20.15	...	...	...	...	...	...	...	...	...

°C	0	1	2	3	4	5	6	7	8	9
−190	−5.60	−5.62	−5.63	−5.65	−5.67	−5.68	−5.70	−5.71	−5.73	−5.74
−180	−5.43	−5.45	−5.46	−5.48	−5.50	−5.52	−5.53	−5.55	−5.57	−5.58
−170	−5.24	−5.26	−5.28	−5.30	−5.32	−5.34	−5.35	−5.37	−5.39	−5.41
−160	−5.03	−5.05	−5.08	−5.10	−5.12	−5.14	−5.16	−5.18	−5.20	−5.22
−150	−4.81	−4.84	−4.86	−4.88	−4.90	−4.92	−4.95	−4.97	−4.99	−5.01
−140	−4.58	−4.60	−4.62	−4.65	−4.67	−4.70	−4.72	−4.74	−4.77	−4.79
−130	−4.32	−4.35	−4.37	−4.40	−4.42	−4.45	−4.48	−4.50	−4.52	−4.55
−120	−4.06	−4.08	−4.11	−4.14	−4.16	−4.19	−4.22	−4.24	−4.27	−4.30
−110	−3.78	−3.81	−3.84	−3.86	−3.89	−3.92	−3.95	−3.98	−4.00	−4.03
−100	−3.49	−3.52	−3.55	−3.58	−3.61	−3.64	−3.66	−3.69	−3.72	−3.75
−90	−3.19	−3.22	−3.25	−3.28	−3.31	−3.34	−3.37	−3.40	−3.43	−3.46
−80	−2.87	−2.90	−2.93	−2.96	−3.00	−3.03	−3.06	−3.09	−3.12	−3.16
−70	−2.54	−2.57	−2.61	−2.64	−2.67	−2.71	−2.74	−2.77	−2.80	−2.84
−60	−2.20	−2.24	−2.27	−2.30	−2.34	−2.37	−2.41	−2.44	−2.47	−2.51
−50	−1.86	−1.89	−1.93	−1.96	−2.00	−2.03	−2.07	−2.10	−2.13	−2.17
−40	−1.50	−1.54	−1.57	−1.61	−1.64	−1.68	−1.72	−1.75	−1.79	−1.82
−30	−1.14	−1.17	−1.21	−1.25	−1.28	−1.32	−1.36	−1.39	−1.43	−1.47
−20	−0.77	−0.80	−0.84	−0.88	−0.92	−0.95	−0.99	−1.03	−1.06	−1.10
−10	−0.39	−0.42	−0.46	−0.50	−0.54	−0.58	−0.62	−0.66	−0.69	−0.73
(−)0	−0.00	−0.04	−0.08	−0.12	−0.16	−0.19	−0.23	−0.27	−0.31	−0.35
(+)0	0.00	0.04	0.08	0.12	0.16	0.20	0.24	0.28	0.32	0.36
10	0.40	0.44	0.48	0.52	0.56	0.60	0.64	0.68	0.72	0.76
20	0.80	0.84	0.88	0.92	0.96	1.00	1.04	1.08	1.12	1.16
30	1.20	1.24	1.28	1.32	1.36	1.40	1.44	1.49	1.53	1.57
40	1.61	1.65	1.69	1.73	1.77	1.81	1.85	1.90	1.94	1.98
50	2.02	2.06	2.10	2.14	2.18	2.23	2.27	2.31	2.35	2.39
60	2.43	2.47	2.51	2.56	2.60	2.64	2.68	2.72	2.76	2.80
70	2.85	2.89	2.93	2.97	3.01	3.05	3.10	3.14	3.18	3.22
80	3.26	3.30	3.35	3.39	3.43	3.47	3.51	3.56	3.60	3.64
90	3.68	3.72	3.76	3.81	3.85	3.89	3.93	3.97	4.01	4.06
100	4.10	4.14	4.18	4.22	4.26	4.31	4.35	4.39	4.43	4.47
110	4.51	4.55	4.60	4.64	4.68	4.72	4.76	4.80	4.84	4.88
120	4.92	4.96	5.01	5.05	5.09	5.13	5.17	5.21	5.25	5.29
130	5.33	5.37	5.41	5.45	5.49	5.53	5.57	5.61	5.65	5.69
140	5.73	5.77	5.81	5.85	5.89	5.93	5.97	6.01	6.05	6.09
150	6.13	6.17	6.21	6.25	6.29	6.33	6.37	6.41	6.45	6.49
160	6.53	6.57	6.61	6.65	6.69	6.73	6.77	6.81	6.85	6.89
170	6.93	6.97	7.01	7.05	7.09	7.13	7.17	7.21	7.25	7.29
180	7.33	7.37	7.41	7.45	7.49	7.53	7.57	7.61	7.65	7.69
190	7.73	7.77	7.81	7.85	7.89	7.93	7.97	8.01	8.05	8.09
200	8.13	8.17	8.21	8.25	8.29	8.33	8.37	8.41	8.46	8.50
210	8.54	8.58	8.62	8.66	8.70	8.74	8.78	8.82	8.86	8.90
220	8.94	8.98	9.02	9.06	9.10	9.14	9.18	9.22	9.26	9.30
230	9.34	9.38	9.42	9.46	9.50	9.54	9.59	9.63	9.67	9.71
240	9.75	9.79	9.83	9.87	9.91	9.95	9.99	10.03	10.07	10.11
250	10.16	10.20	10.24	10.28	10.32	10.36	10.40	10.44	10.48	10.52
260	10.57	10.61	10.65	10.69	10.73	10.77	10.81	10.85	10.89	10.93
270	10.98	11.02	11.06	11.10	11.14	11.18	11.22	11.26	11.30	11.34
280	11.39	11.43	11.47	11.51	11.55	11.59	11.63	11.67	11.72	11.76
290	11.80	11.84	11.88	11.92	11.96	12.01	12.05	12.09	12.13	12.17
300	12.21	12.25	12.29	12.34	12.38	12.42	12.46	12.50	12.54	12.58
310	12.63	12.67	12.71	12.75	12.79	12.83	12.88	12.92	12.96	13.00
320	13.04	13.08	13.12	13.17	13.21	13.25	13.29	13.33	13.37	13.42
330	13.46	13.50	13.54	13.58	13.62	13.67	13.71	13.75	13.79	13.83
340	13.88	13.92	13.96	14.00	14.04	14.09	14.13	14.17	14.21	14.25
350	14.29	14.34	14.38	14.42	14.46	14.50	14.55	14.59	14.63	14.67
360	14.71	14.76	14.80	14.84	14.88	14.92	14.97	15.01	15.05	15.09
370	15.13	15.18	15.22	15.26	15.30	15.34	15.39	15.43	15.47	15.51
380	15.55	15.60	15.64	15.68	15.72	15.76	15.81	15.85	15.89	15.93
390	15.98	16.02	16.06	16.10	16.14	16.19	16.23	16.27	16.31	16.36
400	16.40	16.44	16.48	16.52	16.57	16.61	16.65	16.69	16.74	16.78
410	16.82	16.86	16.91	16.95	16.99	17.03	17.07	17.12	17.16	17.20
420	17.24	17.29	17.33	17.37	17.41	17.46	17.50	17.54	17.58	17.62
430	17.67	17.71	17.75	17.79	17.84	17.88	17.92	17.96	18.01	18.05
440	18.09	18.13	18.17	18.22	18.26	18.30	18.34	18.39	18.43	18.47
450	18.51	18.56	18.60	18.64	18.68	18.73	18.77	18.81	18.85	18.90
460	18.94	18.98	19.02	19.07	19.11	19.15	19.19	19.24	19.28	19.32
470	19.36	19.41	19.45	19.49	19.54	19.58	19.62	19.66	19.71	19.75
480	19.79	19.84	19.88	19.92	19.96	20.01	20.05	20.09	20.13	20.18
490	20.22	20.26	20.31	20.35	20.39	20.43	20.48	20.52	20.56	20.60
500	20.65	20.69	20.73	20.77	20.82	20.86	20.90	20.94	20.99	21.03
510	21.07	21.11	21.16	21.20	21.24	21.28	21.32	21.37	21.41	21.45
520	21.50	21.54	21.58	21.63	21.67	21.71	21.75	21.80	21.84	21.88
530	21.92	21.97	22.01	22.05	22.09	22.14	22.18	22.22	22.26	22.31
540	22.35	22.39	22.43	22.48	22.52	22.56	22.61	22.65	22.69	22.73
550	22.78	22.82	22.86	22.90	22.95	22.99	23.03	23.07	23.12	23.16

* Based on the International Temperature Scale of 1948.

CALIBRATION TABLES
FOR THERMOCOUPLES (Continued)
CHROMEL-ALUMEL THERMOCOUPLES

Electromotive Force in Absolute Millivolts. Temperatures in Degrees C
(Int. 1948). Reference Junctions at 0° C.

°C	0	1	2	3	4	5	6	7	8	9
					Millivolts					
560	23.20	23.25	23.29	23.33	23.38	23.42	23.46	23.50	23.54	23.59
570	23.63	23.67	23.72	23.76	23.80	23.84	23.89	23.93	23.97	24.01
580	24.06	24.10	24.14	24.18	24.23	24.27	24.31	24.36	24.40	24.44
590	24.49	24.53	24.57	24.61	24.65	24.70	24.74	24.78	24.83	24.87
600	24.91	24.95	25.00	25.04	25.08	25.12	25.17	25.21	25.25	25.29
610	25.34	25.38	25.42	25.47	25.51	25.55	25.59	25.64	25.68	25.72
620	25.76	25.81	25.85	25.89	25.93	25.98	26.02	26.06	26.10	26.15
630	26.19	26.23	26.27	26.32	26.36	26.40	26.44	26.48	26.53	26.57
640	26.61	26.65	26.70	26.74	26.78	26.82	26.86	26.91	26.95	26.99
650	27.03	27.07	27.12	27.16	27.20	27.24	27.28	27.33	27.37	27.41
660	27.45	27.49	27.54	27.58	27.62	27.66	27.71	27.75	27.79	27.83
670	27.87	27.92	27.96	28.00	28.04	28.08	28.13	28.17	28.21	28.25
680	28.29	28.34	28.38	28.42	28.46	28.50	28.55	28.59	28.63	28.67
690	28.72	28.76	28.80	28.84	28.88	28.93	28.97	29.01	29.05	29.10
700	29.14	29.18	29.22	29.26	29.30	29.35	29.39	29.43	29.47	29.52
710	29.56	29.60	29.64	29.68	29.72	29.77	29.81	29.85	29.89	29.93
720	29.97	30.02	30.06	30.10	30.14	30.18	30.23	30.27	30.31	30.35
730	30.39	30.44	30.48	30.52	30.56	30.60	30.65	30.69	30.73	30.77
740	30.81	30.85	30.90	30.94	30.98	31.02	31.06	31.10	31.15	31.19
750	31.23	31.27	31.31	31.35	31.40	31.44	31.48	31.52	31.56	31.60
760	31.65	31.69	31.73	31.77	31.81	31.85	31.90	31.94	31.98	32.02
770	32.06	32.10	32.15	32.19	32.23	32.27	32.31	32.35	32.39	32.43
780	32.48	32.52	32.56	32.60	32.64	32.68	32.72	32.76	32.81	32.85
790	32.89	32.93	32.97	33.01	33.05	33.09	33.13	33.18	33.22	33.26
800	33.30	33.34	33.38	33.42	33.46	33.50	33.54	33.59	33.63	33.67
810	33.71	33.75	33.79	33.83	33.87	33.91	33.95	33.99	34.04	34.08
820	34.12	34.16	34.20	34.24	34.28	34.32	34.36	34.40	34.44	34.48
830	34.53	34.57	34.61	34.65	34.69	34.73	34.77	34.81	34.85	34.89
840	34.93	34.97	35.02	35.06	35.10	35.14	35.18	35.22	35.26	35.30
850	35.34	35.38	35.42	35.46	35.50	35.54	35.58	35.63	35.67	35.71
860	35.75	35.79	35.83	35.87	35.91	35.95	35.99	36.03	36.07	36.11
870	36.15	36.19	36.23	36.27	36.31	36.35	36.39	36.43	36.47	36.51
880	36.55	36.59	36.63	36.67	36.72	36.76	36.80	36.84	36.88	36.92
890	36.96	37.00	37.04	37.08	37.12	37.16	37.20	37.24	37.28	37.32
900	37.36	37.40	37.44	37.48	37.52	37.56	37.60	37.64	37.68	37.72
910	37.76	37.80	37.84	37.88	37.92	37.96	38.00	38.04	38.08	38.12
920	38.16	38.20	38.24	38.28	38.32	38.36	38.40	38.44	38.48	38.52
930	38.56	38.60	38.64	38.68	38.72	38.76	38.80	38.84	38.88	38.92
940	38.95	38.99	39.03	39.07	39.11	39.15	39.19	39.23	39.27	39.31
950	39.35	39.39	39.43	39.47	39.51	39.55	39.59	39.63	39.67	39.71
960	39.75	39.79	39.83	39.86	39.90	39.94	39.98	40.02	40.06	40.10
970	40.14	40.18	40.22	40.26	40.30	40.34	40.38	40.41	40.45	40.49
980	40.53	40.57	40.61	40.65	40.69	40.73	40.77	40.81	40.85	40.89
990	40.92	40.96	41.00	41.04	41.08	41.12	41.16	41.20	41.24	41.28
1000	41.31	41.35	41.39	41.43	41.47	41.51	41.55	41.59	41.63	41.67
1010	41.70	41.74	41.78	41.82	41.86	41.90	41.94	41.98	42.02	42.05
1020	42.09	42.13	42.17	42.21	42.25	42.29	42.33	42.36	42.40	42.44
1030	42.48	42.52	42.56	42.60	42.63	42.67	42.71	42.75	42.79	42.83
1040	42.87	42.90	42.94	42.98	43.02	43.06	43.10	43.14	43.17	43.21
1050	43.25	43.29	43.33	43.37	43.41	43.44	43.48	43.52	43.56	43.60
1060	43.63	43.67	43.71	43.75	43.79	43.83	43.87	43.90	43.94	43.98
1070	44.02	44.06	44.10	44.13	44.17	44.21	44.25	44.29	44.33	44.36
1080	44.40	44.44	44.48	44.52	44.55	44.59	44.63	44.67	44.71	44.74
1090	44.78	44.82	44.86	44.90	44.94	44.97	45.01	45.05	45.09	45.12
1100	45.16	45.20	45.24	45.27	45.31	45.35	45.39	45.43	45.46	45.50
1110	45.54	45.58	45.62	45.65	45.69	45.73	45.77	45.80	45.84	45.88
1120	45.92	45.96	45.99	46.03	46.07	46.11	46.14	46.18	46.22	46.26
1130	46.29	46.33	46.37	46.41	46.44	46.48	46.52	46.56	46.59	46.63
1140	46.67	46.70	46.74	46.78	46.82	46.85	46.89	46.93	46.97	47.00
1150	47.04	47.08	47.12	47.15	47.19	47.23	47.26	47.30	47.34	47.38
1160	47.41	47.45	47.49	47.52	47.56	47.60	47.63	47.67	47.71	47.75
1170	47.78	47.82	47.86	47.89	47.93	47.97	48.00	48.04	48.08	48.12
1180	48.15	48.19	48.23	48.26	48.30	48.34	48.37	48.41	48.45	48.48
1190	48.52	48.56	48.59	48.63	48.67	48.70	48.74	48.78	48.81	48.85
1200	48.89	48.92	48.96	49.00	49.03	49.07	49.11	49.14	49.18	49.22
1210	49.25	49.29	49.32	49.36	49.40	49.43	49.47	49.51	49.54	49.58
1220	49.62	49.65	49.69	49.72	49.76	49.80	49.83	49.87	49.90	49.94
1230	49.98	50.01	50.05	50.08	50.12	50.16	50.19	50.23	50.26	50.30
1240	50.34	50.37	50.41	50.44	50.48	50.52	50.55	50.59	50.62	50.66
1250	50.69	50.73	50.77	50.80	50.84	50.87	50.91	50.94	50.98	51.02
1260	51.05	51.09	51.12	51.16	51.19	51.23	51.27	51.30	51.34	51.37
1270	51.41	51.44	51.48	51.51	51.55	51.58	51.62	51.66	51.69	51.73
1280	51.76	51.80	51.83	51.87	51.90	51.94	51.97	52.01	52.04	52.08
1290	52.11	52.15	52.18	52.22	52.25	52.29	52.32	52.36	52.39	52.43
1300	52.46	52.50	52.53	52.57	52.60	52.64	52.67	52.71	52.74	52.78

* Based on the International Temperature Scale of 1948.

CALIBRATION TABLES
FOR THERMOCOUPLES (Continued)
CHROMEL-ALUMEL THERMOCOUPLES

(Electromotive Force in Absolute Millivolts. Temperatures in Degrees C
(Int. 1948). Reference Junctions at 0° C.)

°C	0	1	2	3	4	5	6	7	8	9
					Millivolts					
1300	52.46	52.50	52.53	52.57	52.60	52.64	52.67	52.71	52.74	52.78
1310	52.81	52.85	52.88	52.92	52.95	52.99	53.02	53.06	53.09	53.13
1320	53.16	53.20	53.23	53.27	53.30	53.34	53.38	53.41	53.44	53.47
1330	53.51	53.54	53.58	53.61	53.65	53.68	53.72	53.75	53.79	53.82
1340	53.85	53.89	53.92	53.96	53.99	54.03	54.06	54.10	54.13	54.16
1350	54.20	54.23	54.27	54.30	54.34	54.37	54.40	54.44	54.47	54.51
1360	54.54	54.57	54.61	54.64	54.68	54.71	54.74	54.78	54.81	54.85
1370	54.88	54.91	....	....	....	....	....	....	....	....

CHROMEL-ALUMEL THERMOCOUPLES

(Electromotive Force in Absolute Millivolts. Temperatures in Degrees F.*
Reference Junctions at 32° F.)

°F	0	1	2	3	4	5	6	7	8	9
					Millivolts					
-300	-5.51	-5.52	-5.53	-5.54	-5.54	=5.55	-5.56	-5.57	-5.58	-5.59
-290	-5.41	-5.42	-5.43	-5.44	-5.45	-5.46	-5.47	-5.48	-5.49	-5.50
-280	-5.30	-5.31	-5.32	-5.34	-5.35	-5.36	-5.37	-5.38	-5.39	-5.40
-270	-5.20	-5.21	-5.22	-5.23	-5.24	-5.25	-5.26	-5.27	-5.28	-5.29
-260	-5.08	-5.09	-5.10	-5.12	-5.13	-5.14	-5.15	-5.16	-5.17	-5.18
-250	-4.96	-4.97	-4.99	-5.00	-5.01	-5.02	-5.03	-5.04	-5.06	-5.07
-240	-4.84	-4.85	-4.86	-4.88	-4.89	-4.90	-4.91	-4.92	-4.94	-4.95
-230	-4.71	-4.72	-4.74	-4.75	-4.76	-4.77	-4.79	-4.80	-4.81	-4.82
-220	-4.58	-4.59	-4.60	-4.62	-4.63	-4.64	-4.66	-4.67	-4.68	-4.70
-210	-4.44	-4.45	-4.46	-4.48	-4.49	-4.51	-4.52	-4.53	-4.55	-4.56
-200	-4.29	-4.31	-4.32	-4.34	-4.35	-4.36	-4.38	-4.39	-4.41	-4.42
-190	-4.15	-4.16	-4.18	-4.19	-4.21	-4.22	-4.24	-4.25	-4.26	-4.28
-180	-4.00	-4.01	-4.03	-4.04	-4.06	-4.07	-4.09	-4.10	-4.12	-4.13
-170	-3.84	-3.86	-3.88	-3.89	-3.91	-3.92	-3.94	-3.95	-3.97	-3.98
-160	-3.69	-3.70	-3.72	-3.73	-3.75	-3.76	-3.78	-3.80	-3.81	-3.83
-150	-3.52	-3.54	-3.56	-3.57	-3.59	-3.60	-3.62	-3.64	-3.65	-3.67
-140	-3.36	-3.38	-3.39	-3.41	-3.42	-3.44	-3.46	-3.47	-3.49	-3.51
-130	-3.19	-3.20	-3.22	-3.24	-3.25	-3.27	-3.29	-3.31	-3.32	-3.34
-120	-3.01	-3.03	-3.05	-3.06	-3.08	-3.10	-3.12	-3.13	-3.15	-3.17
-110	-2.83	-2.85	-2.87	-2.89	-2.90	-2.92	-2.94	-2.96	-2.98	-2.99
-100	-2.65	-2.67	-2.69	-2.71	-2.72	-2.74	-2.76	-2.78	-2.80	-2.82
-90	-2.47	-2.49	-2.50	-2.52	-2.54	-2.56	-2.58	-2.60	-2.62	-2.63
-80	-2.28	-2.30	-2.32	-2.34	-2.36	-2.37	-2.39	-2.41	-2.43	-2.45
-70	-2.09	-2.11	-2.13	-2.15	-2.17	-2.18	-2.20	-2.22	-2.24	-2.26
-60	-1.90	-1.92	-1.94	-1.96	-1.97	-1.99	-2.01	-2.03	-2.05	-2.07
-50	-1.70	-1.72	-1.74	-1.76	-1.78	-1.80	-1.82	-1.84	-1.86	-1.88
-40	-1.50	-1.52	-1.54	-1.56	-1.58	-1.60	-1.62	-1.64	-1.66	-1.68
-30	-1.30	-1.32	-1.34	-1.36	-1.38	-1.40	-1.42	-1.44	-1.46	-1.48
-20	-1.10	-1.12	-1.14	-1.16	-1.18	-1.20	-1.22	-1.24	-1.26	-1.28
-10	-0.89	-0.91	-0.93	-0.95	-0.97	-0.99	-1.01	-1.03	-1.06	-1.08
(-)0	-0.68	-0.70	-0.72	-0.75	-0.77	-0.79	-0.81	-0.83	-0.85	-0.87
(+)0	-0.68	-0.66	-0.64	-0.62	-0.60	-0.58	-0.56	-0.54	-0.52	-0.49
10	-0.47	-0.45	-0.43	-0.41	-0.39	-0.37	-0.34	-0.32	-0.30	-0.28
20	-0.26	-0.24	-0.22	-0.19	-0.17	-0.15	-0.13	-0.11	-0.09	-0.07
30	-0.04	-0.02	0.00	0.02	0.04	0.07	0.09	0.11	0.13	0.15
40	0.18	0.20	0.22	0.24	0.26	0.29	0.31	0.33	0.35	0.37
50	0.40	0.42	0.44	0.46	0.48	0.51	0.53	0.55	0.57	0.60
60	0.62	0.64	0.66	0.68	0.71	0.73	0.75	0.77	0.80	0.82
70	0.84	0.86	0.88	0.91	0.93	0.95	0.97	1.00	1.02	1.04
80	1.06	1.09	1.11	1.13	1.15	1.18	1.20	1.22	1.24	1.27
90	1.29	1.31	1.33	1.36	1.38	1.40	1.43	1.45	1.47	1.49
100	1.52	1.54	1.56	1.58	1.61	1.63	1.65	1.68	1.70	1.72
110	1.74	1.77	1.79	1.81	1.84	1.86	1.88	1.90	1.93	1.95
120	1.97	2.00	2.02	2.04	2.06	2.09	2.11	2.13	2.16	2.18
130	2.20	2.23	2.25	2.27	2.29	2.32	2.34	2.36	2.39	2.41
140	2.43	2.46	2.48	2.50	2.52	2.55	2.57	2.59	2.62	2.64
150	2.66	2.69	2.71	2.73	2.75	2.78	2.80	2.82	2.85	2.87
160	2.89	2.92	2.94	2.96	2.98	3.01	3.03	3.05	3.08	3.10
170	3.12	3.15	3.17	3.19	3.22	3.24	3.26	3.29	3.31	3.33
180	3.36	3.38	3.40	3.43	3.45	3.47	3.49	3.52	3.54	3.56
190	3.59	3.61	3.63	3.66	3.68	3.70	3.73	3.75	3.77	3.80
200	3.82	3.84	3.87	3.89	3.91	3.94	3.96	3.98	4.01	4.03
210	4.05	4.08	4.10	4.12	4.15	4.17	4.19	4.21	4.24	4.26
220	4.28	4.31	4.33	4.35	4.38	4.40	4.42	4.44	4.47	4.49
230	4.51	4.54	4.56	4.58	4.61	4.63	4.65	4.67	4.70	4.72
240	4.74	4.77	4.79	4.81	4.83	4.86	4.88	4.90	4.92	4.95
250	4.97	4.99	5.02	5.04	5.06	5.08	5.11	5.13	5.15	5.17
260	5.20	5.22	5.24	5.26	5.29	5.31	5.33	5.35	5.38	5.40
270	5.42	5.44	5.47	5.49	5.51	5.53	5.56	5.58	5.60	5.62
280	5.65	5.67	5.69	5.71	5.73	5.76	5.78	5.80	5.82	5.85
290	5.87	5.89	5.91	5.93	5.96	5.98	6.00	6.02	6.05	6.07
300	6.09	6.11	6.13	6.16	6.18	6.20	6.22	6.25	6.27	6.29
310	6.31	6.33	6.36	6.38	6.40	6.42	6.45	6.47	6.49	6.51
320	6.53	6.56	6.58	6.60	6.62	6.65	6.67	6.69	6.71	6.73
330	6.76	6.78	6.80	6.82	6.84	6.87	6.89	6.91	6.93	6.96
340	6.98	7.00	7.02	7.04	7.07	7.09	7.11	7.13	7.15	7.18
350	7.20	7.22	7.24	7.26	7.29	7.31	7.33	7.35	7.38	7.40

* Based on the International Temperature Scale of 1948.

CALIBRATION TABLES
FOR THERMOCOUPLES (Continued)
CHROMEL-ALUMEL THERMOCOUPLES

(Electromotive Force in Absolute Millivolts. Temperatures in Degrees F.*
Reference Junctions at 32° F.)

°F	0	1	2	3	4	5	6	7	8	9
					Millivolts					
360	7.42	7.44	7.46	7.49	7.51	7.53	7.55	7.58	7.60	7.62
370	7.64	7.66	7.69	7.71	7.73	7.75	7.78	7.80	7.82	7.84
380	7.87	7.89	7.91	7.93	7.95	7.98	8.00	8.02	8.04	8.07
390	8.09	8.11	8.13	8.16	8.18	8.20	8.22	8.24	8.27	8.29
400	8.31	8.33	8.36	8.38	8.40	8.42	8.45	8.47	8.49	8.51
410	8.54	8.56	8.58	8.60	8.62	8.65	8.67	8.69	8.71	8.74
420	8.76	8.78	8.80	8.82	8.85	8.87	8.89	8.91	8.94	8.96
430	8.98	9.00	9.03	9.05	9.07	9.09	9.12	9.14	9.16	9.18
440	9.21	9.23	9.25	9.27	9.30	9.32	9.34	9.36	9.39	9.41
450	9.43	9.45	9.48	9.50	9.52	9.54	9.57	9.59	9.61	9.63
460	9.66	9.68	9.70	9.73	9.75	9.77	9.79	9.82	9.84	9.86
470	9.88	9.91	9.93	9.95	9.97	10.00	10.02	10.04	10.06	10.09
480	10.11	10.13	10.16	10.18	10.20	10.22	10.25	10.27	10.29	10.31
490	10.34	10.36	10.38	10.40	10.43	10.45	10.47	10.50	10.52	10.54
500	10.57	10.59	10.61	10.63	10.66	10.68	10.70	10.72	10.75	10.77
510	10.79	10.82	10.84	10.86	10.88	10.91	10.93	10.95	10.98	11.00
520	11.02	11.04	11.07	11.09	11.11	11.13	11.16	11.18	11.20	11.23
530	11.25	11.27	11.29	11.32	11.34	11.36	11.39	11.41	11.43	11.45
540	11.48	11.50	11.52	11.55	11.57	11.59	11.61	11.64	11.66	11.68
550	11.71	11.73	11.75	11.78	11.80	11.82	11.84	11.87	11.89	11.91
560	11.94	11.96	11.98	12.01	12.03	12.05	12.07	12.10	12.12	12.14
570	12.17	12.19	12.21	12.24	12.26	12.28	12.30	12.33	12.35	12.37
580	12.40	12.42	12.44	12.47	12.49	12.51	12.53	12.56	12.58	12.60
590	12.63	12.65	12.67	12.70	12.72	12.74	12.76	12.79	12.81	12.83
600	12.86	12.88	12.90	12.93	12.95	12.97	13.00	13.02	13.04	13.06
610	13.09	13.11	13.13	13.16	13.18	13.20	13.23	13.25	13.27	13.30
620	13.32	13.34	13.36	13.39	13.41	13.44	13.46	13.48	13.50	13.53
630	13.55	13.57	13.60	13.62	13.64	13.67	13.69	13.71	13.74	13.76
640	13.78	13.81	13.83	13.85	13.88	13.90	13.92	13.95	13.97	13.99
650	14.02	14.04	14.06	14.09	14.11	14.13	14.15	14.18	14.20	14.22
660	14.25	14.27	14.29	14.32	14.34	14.36	14.39	14.41	14.43	14.46
670	14.48	14.50	14.53	14.55	14.57	14.60	14.62	14.64	14.67	14.69
680	14.71	14.74	14.76	14.78	14.81	14.83	14.85	14.88	14.90	14.92
690	14.95	14.97	14.99	15.02	15.04	15.06	15.09	15.11	15.13	15.16
700	15.18	15.20	15.23	15.25	15.27	15.30	15.32	15.34	15.37	15.39
710	15.41	15.44	15.46	15.48	15.51	15.53	15.55	15.58	15.60	15.62
720	15.65	15.67	15.69	15.72	15.74	15.76	15.79	15.81	15.83	15.86
730	15.88	15.90	15.93	15.95	15.98	16.00	16.02	16.05	16.07	16.09
740	16.12	16.14	16.16	16.19	16.21	16.23	16.26	16.28	16.30	16.33
750	16.35	16.37	16.40	16.42	16.45	16.47	16.49	16.52	16.54	16.56
760	16.59	16.61	16.63	16.66	16.68	16.70	16.73	16.75	16.77	16.80
770	16.82	16.84	16.87	16.89	16.92	16.94	16.96	16.99	17.01	17.03
780	17.06	17.08	17.10	17.13	17.15	17.17	17.20	17.22	17.24	17.27
790	17.29	17.31	17.34	17.36	17.39	17.41	17.43	17.46	17.48	17.50
800	17.53	17.55	17.57	17.60	17.62	17.64	17.67	17.69	17.71	17.74
810	17.76	17.78	17.81	17.83	17.86	17.88	17.90	17.93	17.95	17.97
820	18.00	18.02	18.04	18.07	18.09	18.11	18.14	18.16	18.18	18.21
830	18.23	18.25	18.28	18.30	18.33	18.35	18.37	18.40	18.42	18.44
840	18.47	18.49	18.51	18.54	18.56	18.58	18.61	18.63	18.65	18.68
850	18.70	18.73	18.75	18.77	18.80	18.82	18.84	18.87	18.89	18.91
860	18.94	18.96	18.99	19.01	19.03	19.06	19.08	19.10	19.13	19.15
870	19.18	19.20	19.22	19.25	19.27	19.29	19.32	19.34	19.36	19.39
880	19.41	19.44	19.46	19.48	19.51	19.53	19.55	19.58	19.60	19.63
890	19.65	19.67	19.70	19.72	19.75	19.77	19.79	19.82	19.84	19.86
900	19.89	19.91	19.94	19.96	19.98	20.01	20.03	20.05	20.08	20.10
910	20.13	20.15	20.17	20.20	20.22	20.24	20.27	20.29	20.32	20.34
920	20.36	20.39	20.41	20.43	20.46	20.48	20.50	20.53	20.55	20.58
930	20.60	20.62	20.65	20.67	20.69	20.72	20.74	20.76	20.79	20.81
940	20.84	20.86	20.88	20.91	20.93	20.95	20.98	21.00	21.03	21.05
950	21.07	21.10	21.12	21.14	21.17	21.19	21.21	21.24	21.26	21.28
960	21.31	21.33	21.36	21.38	21.40	21.43	21.45	21.47	21.50	21.52
970	21.54	21.57	21.59	21.62	21.64	21.66	21.69	21.71	21.73	21.76
980	21.78	21.81	21.83	21.85	21.88	21.90	21.92	21.95	21.97	21.99
990	22.02	22.04	22.07	22.09	22.11	22.14	22.16	22.18	22.21	22.23
1000	22.26	22.28	22.30	22.33	22.35	22.37	22.40	22.42	22.44	22.47
1010	22.49	22.52	22.54	22.56	22.59	22.61	22.63	22.66	22.68	22.71
1020	22.73	22.75	22.78	22.80	22.82	22.85	22.87	22.90	22.92	22.94
1030	22.97	22.99	23.01	23.04	23.06	23.08	23.11	23.13	23.16	23.18
1040	23.20	23.23	23.25	23.27	23.30	23.32	23.35	23.37	23.39	23.42
1050	23.44	23.46	23.49	23.51	23.54	23.56	23.58	23.61	23.63	23.65
1060	23.68	23.70	23.72	23.75	23.77	23.80	23.82	23.84	23.87	23.89
1070	23.91	23.94	23.96	23.99	24.01	24.03	24.06	24.08	24.10	24.13
1080	24.15	24.18	24.20	24.22	24.25	24.27	24.29	24.32	24.34	24.36
1090	24.39	24.41	24.44	24.46	24.49	24.51	24.53	24.55	24.58	24.60
1100	24.63	24.65	24.67	24.70	24.72	24.74	24.77	24.79	24.82	24.84

CALIBRATION TABLES
FOR THERMOCOUPLES (Continued)
CHROMEL-ALUMEL THERMOCOUPLES

(Electromotive Force in Absolute Millivolts. Temperatures in Degrees F.*
Reference Junctions at 32° F.)

°F	0	1	2	3	4	5	6	7	8	9
					Millivolts					
1100	24.63	24.65	24.67	24.70	24.72	24.74	24.77	24.79	24.82	24.84
1110	24.86	24.89	24.91	24.93	24.96	24.98	25.01	25.03	25.05	25.08
1120	25.10	25.12	25.15	25.17	25.20	25.22	25.24	25.27	25.29	25.31
1130	25.34	25.36	25.38	25.41	25.43	25.46	25.48	25.50	25.53	25.55
1140	25.57	25.60	25.62	25.65	25.67	25.69	25.72	25.74	25.76	25.79
1150	25.81	25.83	25.86	25.88	25.91	25.93	25.95	25.98	26.00	26.02
1160	26.05	26.07	26.09	26.12	26.14	26.16	26.19	26.21	26.24	26.26
1170	26.28	26.31	26.33	26.35	26.38	26.40	26.42	26.45	26.47	26.49
1180	26.52	26.54	26.56	26.59	26.61	26.63	26.66	26.68	26.70	26.73
1190	26.75	26.77	26.80	26.82	26.85	26.87	26.89	26.91	26.94	26.96
1200	26.98	27.01	27.03	27.06	27.08	27.10	27.12	27.15	27.17	27.20
1210	27.22	27.24	27.27	27.29	27.31	27.34	27.36	27.38	27.40	27.43
1220	27.45	27.48	27.50	27.52	27.55	27.57	27.59	27.62	27.64	27.66
1230	27.69	27.71	27.73	27.76	27.78	27.80	27.83	27.85	27.87	27.90
1240	27.92	27.94	27.97	27.99	28.01	28.04	28.06	28.08	28.11	28.13
1250	28.15	28.18	28.20	28.22	28.25	28.27	28.29	28.32	28.34	28.37
1260	28.39	28.41	28.44	28.46	28.48	28.50	28.53	28.55	28.58	28.60
1270	28.62	28.65	28.67	28.69	28.72	28.74	28.76	28.79	28.81	28.83
1280	28.86	28.88	28.90	28.93	28.95	28.97	29.00	29.02	29.04	29.07
1290	29.09	29.11	29.14	29.16	29.18	29.21	29.23	29.25	29.28	29.30
1300	29.32	29.35	29.37	29.39	29.42	29.44	29.46	29.49	29.51	29.53
1310	29.56	29.58	29.60	29.63	29.65	29.67	29.70	29.72	29.74	29.77
1320	29.79	29.81	29.84	29.86	29.88	29.91	29.93	29.95	29.97	30.00
1330	30.02	30.05	30.07	30.09	30.11	30.14	30.16	30.18	30.21	30.23
1340	30.25	30.28	30.30	30.32	30.35	30.37	30.39	30.42	30.44	30.46
1350	30.49	30.51	30.53	30.56	30.58	30.60	30.63	30.65	30.67	30.70
1360	30.72	30.74	30.77	30.79	30.81	30.83	30.86	30.88	30.90	30.93
1370	30.95	30.97	31.00	31.02	31.04	31.07	31.09	31.11	31.14	31.16
1380	31.18	31.21	31.23	31.25	31.28	31.30	31.32	31.34	31.37	31.39
1390	31.42	31.44	31.46	31.48	31.51	31.53	31.55	31.58	31.60	31.62
1400	31.65	31.67	31.69	31.72	31.74	31.76	31.78	31.81	31.83	31.85
1410	31.88	31.90	31.92	31.95	31.97	31.99	32.02	32.04	32.06	32.08
1420	32.11	32.13	32.15	32.18	32.20	32.22	32.25	32.27	32.29	32.31
1430	32.34	32.36	32.38	32.41	32.43	32.45	32.48	32.50	32.52	32.54
1440	32.57	32.59	32.61	32.64	32.66	32.68	32.70	32.73	32.75	32.77
1450	32.80	32.82	32.84	32.86	32.89	32.91	32.93	32.96	32.98	33.00
1460	33.02	33.05	33.07	33.09	33.12	33.14	33.16	33.18	33.21	33.23
1470	33.25	33.28	33.30	33.32	33.34	33.37	33.39	33.41	33.43	33.46
1480	33.48	33.50	33.53	33.55	33.57	33.59	33.62	33.64	33.66	33.69
1490	33.71	33.73	33.75	33.78	33.80	33.82	33.84	33.87	33.89	33.91
1500	33.93	33.96	33.98	34.00	34.03	34.05	34.07	34.09	34.12	34.14
1510	34.16	34.18	34.21	34.23	34.25	34.28	34.30	34.32	34.34	34.37
1520	34.39	34.41	34.43	34.46	34.48	34.50	34.53	34.55	34.57	34.59
1530	34.62	34.64	34.66	34.68	34.71	34.73	34.75	34.77	34.80	34.82
1540	34.84	34.87	34.89	34.91	34.93	34.96	34.98	35.00	35.02	35.05
1550	35.07	35.09	35.11	35.14	35.16	35.18	35.21	35.23	35.25	35.27
1560	35.29	35.32	35.34	35.36	35.39	35.41	35.43	35.45	35.48	35.50
1570	35.52	35.54	35.57	35.59	35.61	35.63	35.66	35.68	35.70	35.72
1580	35.75	35.77	35.79	35.81	35.84	35.86	35.88	35.90	35.93	35.95
1590	35.97	35.99	36.02	36.04	36.06	36.08	36.11	36.13	36.15	36.17
1600	36.19	36.19	36.22	36.24	36.26	36.31	36.33	36.35	36.37	36.40
1610	36.42	36.44	36.46	36.49	36.51	36.53	36.55	36.58	36.60	36.62
1620	36.64	36.67	36.69	36.71	36.73	36.76	36.78	36.80	36.82	36.84
1630	36.87	36.89	36.91	36.93	36.96	36.98	37.00	37.02	37.05	37.07
1640	37.09	37.11	37.14	37.16	37.18	37.20	37.23	37.25	37.27	37.29
1650	37.31	37.34	37.36	37.38	37.40	37.43	37.45	37.47	37.49	37.52
1660	37.54	37.56	37.58	37.60	37.63	37.65	37.67	37.69	37.72	37.74
1670	37.76	37.78	37.81	37.83	37.85	37.87	37.89	37.92	37.94	37.96
1680	37.98	38.01	38.03	38.05	38.07	38.09	38.12	38.14	38.16	38.18
1690	38.20	38.23	38.25	38.27	38.29	38.32	38.34	38.36	38.38	38.40
1700	38.43	38.45	38.47	38.49	38.51	38.54	38.56	38.58	38.60	38.62
1710	38.65	38.67	38.69	38.71	38.73	38.76	38.78	38.80	38.82	38.84
1720	38.87	38.89	38.91	38.93	38.95	38.98	39.00	39.02	39.04	39.06
1730	39.09	39.11	39.13	39.15	39.17	39.20	39.22	39.24	39.26	39.28
1740	39.31	39.33	39.35	39.37	39.39	39.42	39.44	39.46	39.48	39.50
1750	39.53	39.55	39.57	39.59	39.61	39.64	39.66	39.68	39.70	39.72
1760	39.75	39.77	39.79	39.81	39.83	39.86	39.88	39.90	39.92	39.94
1770	39.96	39.99	40.01	40.03	40.05	40.07	40.10	40.12	40.14	40.16
1780	40.18	40.20	40.23	40.25	40.27	40.29	40.31	40.34	40.36	40.38
1790	40.40	40.42	40.44	40.47	40.49	40.51	40.53	40.55	40.58	40.60
1800	40.62	40.64	40.66	40.68	40.71	40.73	40.75	40.77	40.79	40.82
1810	40.84	40.86	40.88	40.90	40.92	40.95	40.97	40.99	41.01	41.03
1820	41.05	41.08	41.10	41.12	41.14	41.16	41.18	41.21	41.23	41.25
1830	41.27	41.29	41.31	41.34	41.36	41.38	41.40	41.42	41.45	41.47
1840	41.49	41.51	41.53	41.55	41.57	41.60	41.62	41.64	41.66	41.68
1850	41.70	41.73	41.75	41.77	41.79	41.81	41.83	41.85	41.88	41.90

* Based on the International Temperature Scale of 1948.

CALIBRATION TABLES
FOR THERMOCOUPLES (Continued)
CHROMEL-ALUMEL THERMOCOUPLES

(Electromotive Force in Absolute Millivolts. Temperatures in Degrees F.*

Reference Junctions at 32° F.)

°F	0	1	2	3	4	5	6	7	8	9
					Millivolts					
1860	41.92	41.94	41.96	41.99	42.01	42.03	42.05	42.07	42.09	42.11
1870	42.14	42.16	42.18	42.20	42.22	42.24	42.26	42.29	42.31	42.33
1880	42.35	42.37	42.39	42.42	42.44	42.46	42.48	42.50	42.52	42.55
1890	42.57	42.59	42.61	42.63	42.65	42.67	42.69	42.72	42.74	42.76
1900	42.78	42.80	42.82	42.84	42.87	42.89	42.91	42.93	42.95	42.97
1910	42.99	43.01	43.04	43.06	43.08	43.10	43.12	43.14	43.17	43.19
1920	43.21	43.23	43.25	43.27	43.29	43.31	43.34	43.36	43.38	43.40
1930	43.42	43.44	43.47	43.49	43.51	43.53	43.55	43.57	43.59	43.61
1940	43.63	43.66	43.68	43.70	43.72	43.74	43.76	43.78	43.81	43.83
1950	43.85	43.87	43.89	43.91	43.93	43.95	43.98	44.00	44.02	44.04
1960	44.06	44.08	44.10	44.13	44.15	44.17	44.19	44.21	44.23	44.25
1970	44.27	44.30	44.32	44.34	44.36	44.38	44.40	44.42	44.44	44.47
1980	44.49	44.51	44.53	44.55	44.57	44.59	44.61	44.63	44.66	44.68
1990	44.70	44.72	44.74	44.76	44.78	44.80	44.82	44.85	44.87	44.89
2000	44.91	44.93	44.95	44.97	44.99	45.01	45.03	45.06	45.08	45.10
2010	45.12	45.14	45.16	45.18	45.20	45.22	45.24	45.27	45.29	45.31
2020	45.33	45.35	45.37	45.39	45.41	45.43	45.45	45.48	45.50	45.52
2030	45.54	45.56	45.58	45.60	45.62	45.64	45.66	45.69	45.71	45.73
2040	45.75	45.77	45.79	45.81	45.83	45.85	45.87	45.90	45.92	45.94
2050	45.96	45.98	46.00	46.02	46.04	46.06	46.08	46.11	46.13	46.15
2060	46.17	46.19	46.21	46.23	46.25	46.27	46.29	46.31	46.33	46.36
2070	46.38	46.40	46.42	46.44	46.46	46.48	46.50	46.52	46.54	46.56
2080	46.58	46.60	46.63	46.65	46.67	46.69	46.71	46.73	46.75	46.77
2090	46.79	46.81	46.83	46.85	46.87	46.90	46.92	46.94	46.96	46.98
2100	47.00	47.02	47.04	47.06	47.08	47.10	47.12	47.14	47.17	47.19
2110	47.21	47.23	47.25	47.27	47.29	47.31	47.33	47.35	47.37	47.39
2120	47.41	47.43	47.45	47.47	47.49	47.52	47.54	47.56	47.58	47.60
2130	47.62	47.64	47.66	47.68	47.70	47.72	47.74	47.76	47.78	47.80
2140	47.82	47.84	47.86	47.89	47.91	47.93	47.95	47.97	47.99	48.01
2150	48.03	48.05	48.07	48.09	48.11	48.13	48.15	48.17	48.19	48.21
2160	48.23	48.25	48.27	48.29	48.32	48.34	48.36	48.38	48.40	48.42
2170	48.44	48.46	48.48	48.50	48.52	48.54	48.56	48.58	48.60	48.62
2180	48.64	48.66	48.68	48.70	48.72	48.74	48.76	48.79	48.81	48.83
2190	48.85	48.87	48.89	48.91	48.93	48.95	48.97	48.99	49.01	49.03
2200	49.05	49.07	49.09	49.11	49.13	49.15	49.17	49.19	49.21	49.23
2210	49.25	49.27	49.29	49.31	49.33	49.35	49.37	49.39	49.41	49.43
2220	49.45	49.47	49.49	49.51	49.53	49.55	49.57	49.59	49.61	49.63
2230	49.65	49.67	49.69	49.71	49.73	49.76	49.78	49.80	49.82	49.84
2240	49.86	49.88	49.90	49.92	49.94	49.96	49.98	50.00	50.02	50.04
2250	50.06	50.08	50.10	50.12	50.14	50.16	50.18	50.20	50.22	50.24
2260	50.26	50.28	50.30	50.32	50.34	50.36	50.38	50.40	50.42	50.44
2270	50.46	50.48	50.50	50.52	50.54	50.56	50.57	50.59	50.61	50.63
2280	50.65	50.67	50.69	50.71	50.73	50.75	50.77	50.79	50.81	50.83
2290	50.85	50.87	50.89	50.91	50.93	50.95	50.97	50.99	51.01	51.03
2300	51.05	51.07	51.09	51.11	51.13	51.15	51.17	51.19	51.21	51.23
2310	51.25	51.27	51.29	51.31	51.33	51.35	51.37	51.39	51.41	51.43
2320	51.45	51.47	51.48	51.50	51.52	51.54	51.56	51.58	51.60	51.62
2330	51.64	51.66	51.68	51.70	51.72	51.74	51.76	51.78	51.80	51.82
2340	51.84	51.86	51.88	51.90	51.92	51.94	51.96	51.98	52.00	52.01
2350	52.03	52.05	52.07	52.09	52.11	52.13	52.15	52.17	52.19	52.21
2360	52.23	52.25	52.27	52.29	52.31	52.33	52.35	52.37	52.39	52.41
2370	52.42	52.44	52.46	52.48	52.50	52.52	52.54	52.56	52.58	52.60
2380	52.62	52.64	52.66	52.68	52.70	52.72	52.74	52.76	52.77	52.79
2390	52.81	52.83	52.85	52.87	52.89	52.91	52.93	52.95	52.97	52.99
2400	53.01	53.03	53.05	53.07	53.08	53.10	53.12	53.14	53.16	53.18
2410	53.20	53.22	53.24	53.26	53.28	53.30	53.32	53.34	53.35	53.37
2420	53.39	53.41	53.43	53.45	53.47	53.49	53.51	53.53	53.55	53.57
2430	53.59	53.60	53.62	53.64	53.66	53.68	53.70	53.72	53.74	53.76
2440	53.78	53.80	53.82	53.83	53.85	53.87	53.89	53.91	53.93	53.95
2450	53.97	53.99	54.01	54.03	54.04	54.06	54.08	54.10	54.12	54.14
2460	54.16	54.18	54.20	54.22	54.24	54.25	54.27	54.29	54.31	54.33
2470	54.35	54.37	54.39	54.41	54.43	54.44	54.46	54.48	54.50	54.52
2480	54.54	54.56	54.58	54.60	54.62	54.63	54.65	54.67	54.69	54.71
2490	54.73	54.75	54.77	54.79	54.81	54.82	54.84	54.86	54.88	54.90
2500	54.92	....	....	....	....	....	....	....	....	....

* Based on the International Temperature Scale of 1948.

CALIBRATION TABLES
FOR THERMOCOUPLES (Continued)
IRON-CONSTANTAN THERMOCOUPLES
(MODIFIED 1913)

(Electromotive Force in Absolute Millivolts. Temperatures in Degrees C
(Int. 1948). Reference Junctions at 0° C.)

°C	0	1	2	3	4	5	6	7	8	9
					Millivolts					
−190	−7.66	−7.69	−7.71	−7.73	−7.76	−7.78				
−180	−7.40	−7.43	−7.46	−7.49	−7.51	−7.54	−7.56	−7.59	−7.61	−7.64
−170	−7.12	−7.15	−7.18	−7.21	−7.24	−7.27	−7.30	−7.32	−7.35	−7.38
−160	−6.82	−6.85	−6.88	−6.91	−6.94	−6.97	−7.00	−7.03	−7.06	−7.09
−150	−6.50	−6.53	−6.56	−6.60	−6.63	−6.66	−6.69	−6.72	−6.76	−6.79
−140	−6.16	−6.19	−6.22	−6.26	−6.29	−6.33	−6.36	−6.40	−6.43	−6.46
−130	−5.80	−5.84	−5.87	−5.91	−5.94	−5.98	−6.01	−6.05	−6.08	−6.12
−120	−5.42	−5.46	−5.50	−5.54	−5.58	−5.61	−5.65	−5.69	−5.72	−5.76
−110	−5.03	−5.07	−5.11	−5.15	−5.19	−5.23	−5.27	−5.31	−5.35	−5.38
−100	−4.63	−4.67	−4.71	−4.75	−4.79	−4.83	−4.87	−4.91	−4.95	−4.99
−90	−4.21	−4.25	−4.30	−4.34	−4.38	−4.42	−4.46	−4.50	−4.55	−4.59
−80	−3.78	−3.82	−3.87	−3.91	−3.96	−4.00	−4.04	−4.08	−4.13	−4.17
−70	−3.34	−3.38	−3.43	−3.47	−3.52	−3.56	−3.60	−3.65	−3.69	−3.74
−60	−2.89	−2.94	−2.98	−3.03	−3.07	−3.12	−3.16	−3.21	−3.25	−3.30
−50	−2.43	−2.48	−2.52	−2.57	−2.62	−2.66	−2.71	−2.75	−2.80	−2.84
−40	−1.96	−2.01	−2.06	−2.10	−2.15	−2.20	−2.24	−2.29	−2.34	−2.38
−30	−1.48	−1.53	−1.58	−1.63	−1.67	−1.72	−1.77	−1.82	−1.87	−1.91
−20	−1.00	−1.04	−1.09	−1.14	−1.19	−1.24	−1.29	−1.34	−1.39	−1.43
−10	−0.50	−0.55	−0.60	−0.65	−0.70	−0.75	−0.80	−0.85	−0.90	−0.95
(−)0	0.00	−0.05	−0.10	−0.15	−0.20	−0.25	−0.30	−0.35	−0.40	−0.45
(+)0	0.00	0.05	0.10	0.15	0.20	0.25	0.30	0.35	0.40	0.45
10	0.50	0.56	0.61	0.66	0.71	0.76	0.81	0.86	0.91	0.97
20	1.02	1.07	1.12	1.17	1.22	1.28	1.33	1.38	1.43	1.48
30	1.54	1.59	1.64	1.69	1.74	1.80	1.85	1.90	1.95	2.00
40	2.06	2.11	2.16	2.22	2.27	2.32	2.37	2.42	2.48	2.53
50	2.58	2.64	2.69	2.74	2.80	2.85	2.90	2.96	3.01	3.06
60	3.11	3.17	3.22	3.27	3.33	3.38	3.43	3.49	3.54	3.60
70	3.65	3.70	3.76	3.81	3.86	3.92	3.97	4.02	4.08	4.13
80	4.19	4.24	4.29	4.35	4.40	4.46	4.51	4.56	4.62	4.67
90	4.73	4.78	4.83	4.89	4.94	5.00	5.05	5.10	5.16	5.21
100	5.27	5.32	5.38	5.43	5.48	5.54	5.59	5.65	5.70	5.76
110	5.81	5.86	5.92	5.97	6.03	6.08	6.14	6.19	6.25	6.30
120	6.36	6.41	6.47	6.52	6.58	6.63	6.68	6.74	6.79	6.85
130	6.90	6.96	7.01	7.07	7.12	7.18	7.23	7.29	7.34	7.40
140	7.45	7.51	7.56	7.62	7.67	7.73	7.78	7.84	7.89	7.95
150	8.00	8.06	8.12	8.17	8.23	8.28	8.34	8.39	8.45	8.50
160	8.56	8.61	8.67	8.72	8.78	8.84	8.80	8.95	9.00	9.06
170	9.11	9.17	9.22	9.28	9.33	9.39	9.44	9.50	9.56	9.61
180	9.67	9.72	9.78	9.83	9.89	9.95	10.00	10.06	10.11	10.17
190	10.22	10.28	10.34	10.39	10.45	10.50	10.56	10.61	10.67	10.72
200	10.78	10.84	10.89	10.95	11.00	11.06	11.12	11.17	11.23	11.28
210	11.34	11.39	11.45	11.50	11.56	11.62	11.67	11.73	11.78	11.84
220	11.89	11.95	12.00	12.06	12.12	12.17	12.23	12.28	12.34	12.39
230	12.45	12.50	12.56	12.62	12.67	12.73	12.78	12.84	12.89	12.95
240	13.01	13.06	13.12	13.17	13.23	13.28	13.34	13.40	13.45	13.51
250	13.56	13.62	13.67	13.73	13.78	13.84	13.89	13.95	14.00	14.06
260	14.12	14.17	14.23	14.28	14.34	14.39	14.45	14.50	14.56	14.61
270	14.67	14.72	14.78	14.83	14.89	14.94	15.00	15.06	15.11	15.17
280	15.22	15.28	15.33	15.39	15.44	15.50	15.55	15.61	15.66	15.72
290	15.77	15.83	15.88	15.94	16.00	16.05	16.11	16.16	16.22	16.27
300	16.33	16.38	16.44	16.49	16.55	16.60	16.66	16.71	16.77	16.82
310	16.88	16.93	16.99	17.04	17.10	17.15	17.21	17.26	17.32	17.37
320	17.43	17.48	17.54	17.60	17.65	17.71	17.76	17.82	17.87	17.93
330	17.98	18.04	18.09	18.15	18.20	18.26	18.32	18.37	18.43	18.48
340	18.54	18.59	18.65	18.70	18.76	18.81	18.87	18.92	18.98	19.03
350	19.09	19.14	19.20	19.26	19.31	19.37	19.42	19.48	19.53	19.59
360	19.64	19.70	19.75	19.81	19.86	19.92	19.97	20.03	20.08	20.14
370	20.20	20.25	20.31	20.36	20.42	20.47	20.53	20.58	20.64	20.69
380	20.75	20.80	20.86	20.91	20.97	21.02	21.08	21.13	21.19	21.24
390	21.30	21.35	21.41	21.46	21.52	21.57	21.63	21.68	21.74	21.79
400	21.85	21.90	21.96	22.02	22.07	22.13	22.18	22.24	22.29	22.35
410	22.40	22.46	22.51	22.57	22.62	22.68	22.73	22.79	22.84	22.90
420	22.95	23.01	23.06	23.12	23.17	23.23	23.28	23.34	23.39	23.45
430	23.50	23.56	23.61	23.67	23.72	23.78	23.83	23.89	23.94	24.00
440	24.06	24.11	24.17	24.22	24.28	24.33	24.39	24.44	24.50	24.55
450	24.61	24.66	24.72	24.77	24.83	24.88	24.94	25.00	25.05	25.11
460	25.16	25.22	25.27	25.33	25.38	25.44	25.49	25.55	25.60	25.66
470	25.72	25.77	25.83	25.88	25.94	25.99	26.05	26.10	26.16	26.22
480	26.27	26.33	26.38	26.44	26.49	26.55	26.61	26.66	26.72	26.77
490	26.83	26.89	26.94	27.00	27.05	27.11	27.17	27.22	27.28	27.33
500	27.39	27.45	27.50	27.56	27.61	27.67	27.73	27.78	27.84	27.90
510	27.95	28.01	28.07	28.12	28.18	28.23	28.29	28.35	28.40	28.46
520	28.52	28.57	28.63	28.69	28.74	28.80	28.86	28.91	28.97	29.02
530	29.08	29.14	29.20	29.25	29.31	29.37	29.42	29.48	29.54	29.59
540	29.65	29.71	29.76	29.82	29.88	29.94	29.99	30.05	30.11	30.16
550	30.22	30.28	30.34	30.39	30.45	30.51	30.57	30.62	30.68	30.74

* Based on the International Temperature Scale of 1948.

(Electromotive Force in Absolute Millivolts. Temperatures in Degrees C (Int. 1948). Reference Junctions at 0° C.)

°C	0	1	2	3	4	5	6	7	8	9
					Millivolts					
560	30.80	30.85	30.91	30.97	31.02	31.08	31.14	31.20	31.26	31.31
570	31.37	31.43	31.49	31.54	31.60	31.66	31.72	31.78	31.83	31.89
580	31.95	32.01	32.06	32.12	32.18	32.24	32.30	32.36	32.41	32.47
590	32.53	32.59	32.65	32.71	32.76	32.82	32.88	32.94	33.00	33.06
600	33.11	33.17	33.23	33.29	33.35	33.41	33.46	33.52	33.58	33.64
610	33.70	33.76	33.82	33.88	33.94	33.99	34.05	34.11	34.17	34.23
620	34.29	34.35	34.41	34.47	34.53	34.58	34.64	34.70	34.76	34.82
630	34.88	34.94	35.00	35.06	35.12	35.18	35.24	35.30	35.36	35.42
640	35.48	35.54	35.60	36.66	35.72	35.78	35.84	35.90	35.96	36.02
650	36.08	36.14	36.20	36.26	36.32	36.38	36.44	36.50	36.56	36.62
660	36.69	36.75	36.81	36.87	36.93	36.99	37.05	37.11	37.18	37.24
670	37.30	37.36	37.42	37.48	37.54	37.60	37.66	37.73	37.79	37.85
680	37.91	37.97	38.04	38.10	38.16	38.22	38.28	38.34	38.41	38.47
690	38.53	38.59	38.66	38.72	38.78	38.84	38.90	38.97	39.03	39.09
700	39.15	39.22	39.28	39.34	39.40	39.47	39.53	39.59	39.65	39.72
710	39.78	39.84	39.91	39.97	40.03	40.10	40.16	40.22	40.28	40.35
720	40.41	40.48	40.54	40.60	40.66	40.73	40.79	40.86	40.92	40.98
730	41.05	41.11	41.17	41.24	41.30	41.36	41.43	41.49	41.56	41.62
740	41.68	41.75	41.81	41.87	41.94	42.00	42.07	42.13	42.19	42.26
750	42.32	42.38	42.45	42.51	42.58	42.64	42.70	42.77	42.83	42.90
760	42.96	....	....	....	....	....	....	....	....	....

(Electromotive Force in Absolute Millivolts. Temperatures in Degrees F.[*] Reference Junctions at 32° F.)

°F	0	1	2	3	4	5	6	7	8	9
					Millivolts					
−310	−7.66	−7.68	−7.69	−7.70	−7.71	−7.73	−7.74	−7.75	−7.76	−7.78
−300	−7.52	−7.54	−7.55	−7.57	−7.58	−7.59	−7.61	−7.62	−7.64	−7.65
−290	−7.38	−7.39	−7.40	−7.42	−7.44	−7.45	−7.46	−7.48	−7.49	−7.51
−280	−7.22	−7.24	−7.25	−7.27	−7.28	−7.30	−7.31	−7.33	−7.34	−7.36
−270	−7.06	−7.07	−7.09	−7.11	−7.12	−7.14	−7.15	−7.17	−7.19	−7.20
−260	−6.89	−6.90	−6.92	−6.94	−6.96	−6.97	−6.99	−7.01	−7.02	−7.04
−250	−6.71	−6.73	−6.75	−6.77	−6.78	−6.80	−6.82	−6.84	−6.85	−6.87
−240	−6.53	−6.55	−6.57	−6.59	−6.61	−6.62	−6.64	−6.66	−6.68	−6.70
−230	−6.35	−6.37	−6.38	−6.40	−6.42	−6.44	−6.46	−6.48	−6.50	−6.52
−220	−6.16	−6.18	−6.19	−6.21	−6.23	−6.25	−6.27	−6.29	−6.31	−6.33
−210	−5.96	−5.98	−6.00	−6.02	−6.04	−6.06	−6.08	−6.10	−6.12	−6.14
−200	−5.76	−5.78	−5.80	−5.82	−5.84	−5.86	−5.88	−5.90	−5.92	−5.94
−190	−5.55	−5.57	−5.59	−5.61	−5.63	−5.65	−5.67	−5.70	−5.72	−5.74
−180	−5.34	−5.36	−5.38	−5.40	−5.42	−5.44	−5.46	−5.49	−5.51	−5.53
−170	−5.12	−5.14	−5.16	−5.19	−5.21	−5.23	−5.25	−5.27	−5.30	−5.32
−160	−4.90	−4.92	−4.94	−4.97	−4.99	−5.01	−5.03	−5.06	−5.08	−5.10
−150	−4.68	−4.70	−4.72	−4.74	−4.76	−4.79	−4.81	−4.83	−4.86	−4.88
−140	−4.44	−4.47	−4.49	−4.51	−4.54	−4.56	−4.58	−4.61	−4.63	−4.65
−130	−4.21	−4.23	−4.26	−4.28	−4.30	−4.33	−4.35	−4.38	−4.40	−4.42
−120	−3.97	−4.00	−4.02	−4.04	−4.07	−4.09	−4.12	−4.14	−4.16	−4.19
−110	−3.73	−3.76	−3.78	−3.81	−3.83	−3.85	−3.88	−3.90	−3.93	−3.95
−100	−3.49	−3.51	−3.54	−3.56	−3.59	−3.61	−3.64	−3.66	−3.68	−3.71
−90	−3.24	−3.27	−3.29	−3.32	−3.34	−3.36	−3.39	−3.41	−3.44	−3.46
−80	−2.99	−3.02	−3.04	−3.07	−3.09	−3.12	−3.14	−3.17	−3.19	−3.22
−70	−2.74	−2.76	−2.79	−2.81	−2.84	−2.86	−2.89	−2.92	−2.94	−2.97
−60	−2.48	−2.51	−2.53	−2.56	−2.58	−2.61	−2.64	−2.66	−2.69	−2.71
−50	−2.22	−2.25	−2.27	−2.30	−2.33	−2.35	−2.38	−2.40	−2.43	−2.46
−40	−1.96	−1.99	−2.01	−2.04	−2.06	−2.09	−2.12	−2.14	−2.17	−2.20
−30	−1.70	−1.72	−1.75	−1.78	−1.80	−1.83	−1.86	−1.88	−1.91	−1.94
−20	−1.43	−1.46	−1.48	−1.51	−1.54	−1.56	−1.59	−1.62	−1.64	−1.67
−10	−1.16	−1.19	−1.21	−1.24	−1.27	−1.29	−1.32	−1.35	−1.38	−1.40
(−)0	−0.89	−0.91	−0.94	−0.97	−1.00	−1.02	−1.05	−1.08	−1.10	−1.13
+(0)	−0.89	−0.86	−0.83	−0.80	−0.78	−0.75	−0.72	−0.70	−0.67	−0.64
10	−0.61	−0.58	−0.56	−0.53	−0.50	−0.48	−0.45	−0.42	−0.39	−0.36
20	−0.34	−0.31	−0.28	−0.25	−0.22	−0.20	−0.17	−0.14	−0.11	−0.09
30	−0.06	−0.03	0.00	0.03	0.05	0.08	0.11	0.14	0.17	0.19
40	0.22	0.25	0.28	0.31	0.34	0.36	0.39	0.42	0.45	0.48
50	0.50	0.53	0.56	0.59	0.62	0.65	0.67	0.70	0.73	0.76
60	0.79	0.82	0.84	0.87	0.90	0.93	0.96	0.99	1.02	1.04
70	1.07	1.10	1.13	1.16	1.19	1.22	1.25	1.28	1.30	1.33
80	1.36	1.39	1.42	1.45	1.48	1.51	1.54	1.56	1.59	1.62
90	1.65	1.68	1.71	1.74	1.77	1.80	1.83	1.85	1.88	1.91
100	1.94	1.97	2.00	2.03	2.06	2.09	2.12	2.14	2.17	2.20
110	2.23	2.26	2.29	2.32	2.35	2.38	2.41	2.44	2.47	2.50
120	2.52	2.55	2.58	2.61	2.64	2.67	2.70	2.73	2.76	2.79
130	2.82	2.85	2.88	2.91	2.94	2.97	3.00	3.03	3.06	3.08
140	3.11	3.14	3.17	3.20	3.23	3.26	3.29	3.32	3.35	3.38
150	3.41	3.44	3.47	3.50	3.53	3.56	3.59	3.62	3.65	3.68
160	3.71	3.74	3.77	3.80	3.83	3.86	3.89	3.92	3.95	3.98
170	4.01	4.04	4.07	4.10	4.13	4.16	4.19	4.22	4.25	4.28
180	4.31	4.34	4.37	4.40	4.43	4.46	4.49	4.52	4.55	4.58
190	4.61	4.64	4.67	4.70	4.73	4.76	4.79	4.82	4.85	4.88
200	4.91	4.94	4.97	5.00	5.03	5.06	5.09	5.12	5.15	5.18

* Based on the International Temperature Scale of 1948.

CALIBRATION TABLES
FOR THERMOCOUPLES (Continued)
IRON-CONSTANTAN THERMOCOUPLES
(MODIFIED 1913)

(Electromotive Force in Absolute Millivolts. Temperatures in Degrees F.[*] Reference Junctions at 32° F.)

°F	0	1	2	3	4	5	6	7	8	9
					Millivolts					
200	4.91	4.94	4.97	5.00	5.03	5.06	5.09	5.12	5.15	5.18
210	5.21	5.24	5.27	5.30	5.33	5.36	5.39	5.42	5.45	5.48
220	5.51	5.54	5.57	5.60	5.63	5.66	5.69	5.72	5.75	5.78
230	5.81	5.84	5.87	5.90	5.93	5.96	5.99	6.02	6.05	6.08
240	6.11	6.14	6.17	6.20	6.24	6.27	6.30	6.33	6.36	6.39
250	6.42	6.45	6.48	6.51	6.54	6.57	6.60	6.63	6.66	6.69
260	6.72	6.75	6.78	6.81	6.84	6.87	6.90	6.93	6.96	7.00
270	7.03	7.06	7.09	7.12	7.15	7.18	7.21	7.24	7.27	7.30
280	7.33	7.36	7.39	7.42	7.45	7.48	7.51	7.54	7.58	7.61
290	7.64	7.67	7.70	7.73	7.76	7.79	7.82	7.85	7.88	7.91
300	7.94	7.97	8.00	8.04	8.07	8.10	8.13	8.16	8.19	8.22
310	8.25	8.28	8.31	8.34	8.37	8.40	8.44	8.47	8.50	8.53
320	8.56	8.59	8.62	8.65	8.68	8.71	8.74	8.77	8.80	8.84
330	8.87	8.90	8.93	8.96	8.99	9.02	9.05	9.08	9.11	9.14
340	9.17	9.20	9.24	9.27	9.30	9.33	9.36	9.39	9.42	9.45
350	9.48	9.51	9.54	9.58	9.61	9.64	9.67	9.70	9.73	9.76
360	9.79	9.82	9.85	9.88	9.92	9.95	9.98	10.01	10.04	10.07
370	10.10	10.13	10.16	10.19	10.22	10.25	10.28	10.32	10.35	10.38
380	10.41	10.44	10.47	10.50	10.53	10.56	10.60	10.63	10.66	10.69
390	10.72	10.75	10.78	10.81	10.84	10.87	10.90	10.94	10.97	11.00
400	11.03	11.06	11.09	11.12	11.15	11.18	11.21	11.24	11.28	11.31
410	11.34	11.37	11.40	11.43	11.46	11.49	11.52	11.55	11.58	11.62
420	11.65	11.68	11.71	11.74	11.77	11.80	11.83	11.86	11.89	11.92
430	11.96	11.99	12.02	12.05	12.08	12.11	12.14	12.17	12.20	12.23
440	12.26	12.30	12.33	12.36	12.39	12.42	12.45	12.48	12.51	12.54
450	12.57	12.60	12.64	12.67	12.70	12.73	12.76	12.79	12.82	12.85
460	12.88	12.91	12.94	12.98	13.01	13.04	13.07	13.10	13.13	13.16
470	13.19	13.22	13.25	13.28	13.31	13.34	13.38	13.41	13.44	13.47
480	13.50	13.53	13.56	13.59	13.62	13.65	13.68	13.72	13.75	13.78
490	13.81	13.84	13.87	13.90	13.93	13.96	13.99	14.02	14.05	14.08
500	14.12	14.15	14.18	14.21	14.24	14.27	14.30	14.33	14.36	14.39
510	14.42	14.45	14.48	14.52	14.55	14.58	14.61	14.64	14.67	14.70
520	14.73	14.76	14.79	14.82	14.85	14.88	14.91	14.94	14.98	15.01
530	15.04	15.07	15.10	15.13	15.16	15.19	15.22	15.25	15.28	15.31
540	15.34	15.37	15.40	15.44	15.47	15.50	15.53	15.56	15.59	15.62
550	15.65	15.68	15.71	15.74	15.77	15.80	15.84	15.87	15.90	15.93
560	15.96	15.99	16.02	16.05	16.08	16.11	16.14	16.17	16.20	16.23
570	16.26	16.30	16.33	16.36	16.39	16.42	16.45	16.48	16.51	16.54
580	16.57	16.60	16.63	16.66	16.69	16.72	16.75	16.78	16.82	16.85
590	16.88	16.91	16.94	16.97	17.00	17.03	17.06	17.09	17.12	17.15
600	17.18	17.21	17.24	17.28	17.31	17.34	17.37	17.40	17.43	17.46
610	17.49	17.52	17.55	17.58	17.61	17.64	17.68	17.71	17.74	17.77
620	17.80	17.83	17.86	17.89	17.92	17.95	17.98	18.01	18.04	18.08
630	18.11	18.14	18.17	18.20	18.23	18.26	18.29	18.32	18.35	18.38
640	18.41	18.44	18.47	18.50	18.54	18.57	18.60	18.63	18.66	18.69
650	18.72	18.75	18.78	18.81	18.84	18.87	18.90	18.94	18.97	19.00
660	19.03	19.06	19.09	19.12	19.15	19.18	19.21	19.24	19.27	19.30
670	19.34	19.37	19.40	19.43	19.46	19.49	19.52	19.55	19.58	19.61
680	19.64	19.67	19.70	19.74	19.77	19.80	19.83	19.86	19.89	19.92
690	19.95	19.98	20.01	20.04	20.07	20.10	20.13	20.16	20.20	20.23
700	20.26	20.29	20.32	20.35	20.38	20.41	20.44	20.47	20.50	20.53
710	20.56	20.59	20.62	20.66	20.69	20.72	20.75	20.78	20.81	20.84
720	20.87	20.90	20.93	20.96	20.99	21.02	21.05	21.08	21.11	21.14
730	21.18	21.21	21.24	21.27	21.30	21.33	21.36	21.39	21.42	21.45
740	21.48	21.51	21.54	21.57	21.60	21.64	21.67	21.70	21.73	21.76
750	21.79	21.82	21.85	21.88	21.91	21.94	21.97	22.00	22.03	22.06
760	22.10	22.13	22.16	22.19	22.22	22.25	22.28	22.31	22.34	22.37
770	22.40	22.43	22.46	22.49	22.52	22.55	22.58	22.62	22.65	22.68
780	22.71	22.74	22.77	22.80	22.83	22.86	22.89	22.92	22.95	22.98
790	23.01	23.04	23.08	23.11	23.14	23.17	23.20	23.23	23.26	23.29
800	23.32	23.35	23.38	23.41	23.44	23.47	23.50	23.53	23.56	23.60
810	23.63	23.66	23.69	23.72	23.75	23.78	23.81	23.84	23.87	23.90
820	23.93	23.96	23.99	24.02	24.06	24.09	24.12	24.15	24.18	24.21
830	24.24	24.27	24.30	24.33	24.36	24.39	24.42	24.45	24.48	24.52
840	24.55	24.58	24.61	24.64	24.67	24.70	24.73	24.76	24.79	24.82
850	24.85	24.88	24.91	24.94	24.98	25.01	25.04	25.07	25.10	25.13
860	25.16	25.19	25.22	25.25	25.28	25.32	25.35	25.38	25.41	25.44
870	25.47	25.50	25.53	25.56	25.59	25.62	25.65	25.68	25.72	25.75
880	25.78	25.81	25.84	25.87	25.90	25.93	25.96	25.99	26.02	26.06
890	26.09	26.12	26.15	26.18	26.21	26.24	26.27	26.30	26.33	26.36
900	26.40	26.43	26.46	26.49	26.52	26.55	26.58	26.61	26.64	26.67
910	26.70	26.74	26.77	26.80	26.83	26.86	26.89	26.92	26.95	26.98
920	27.02	27.05	27.08	27.11	27.14	27.17	27.20	27.23	27.26	27.30
930	27.33	27.36	27.39	27.42	27.45	27.48	27.51	27.54	27.58	27.61
940	27.64	27.67	27.70	27.73	27.76	27.80	27.83	27.86	27.89	27.92
950	27.95	27.98	28.02	28.05	28.08	28.11	28.14	28.17	28.20	28.23

* Based on the International Temperature Scale of 1948.

CALIBRATION TABLES
FOR THERMOCOUPLES (Continued)
IRON-CONSTANTAN THERMOCOUPLES
(MODIFIED 1913)

(Electromotive Force in Absolute Millivolts. Temperatures in Degrees F.°
Reference Junctions at 32° F.)

°F	0	1	2	3	4	5	6	7	8	9
					Millivolts					
960	28.26	28.30	28.33	28.36	28.39	28.42	28.45	28.48	28.52	28.55
970	28.58	28.61	28.64	28.67	28.70	28.74	28.77	28.80	28.83	28.86
980	28.89	28.92	28.96	28.99	29.02	29.05	29.08	29.11	29.14	29.18
990	29.21	29.24	29.27	29.30	29.33	29.37	29.40	29.43	29.46	29.49
1000	29.52	29.56	29.59	29.62	29.65	29.68	29.71	29.75		29.81
1010	29.84	29.87	29.90	29.94	29.97	30.00	30.03	30.06	30.10	30.13
1020	30.16	30.19	30.22	30.25	30.28	30.32	30.35	30.38	30.41	30.44
1030	30.48	30.51	30.54	30.57	30.60	30.64	30.67	30.70	30.73	30.76
1040	30.80	30.83	30.86	30.89	30.92	30.96	30.99	31.02	31.05	31.08
1050	31.12	31.15	31.18	31.21	31.24	31.28	31.31	31.34	31.37	31.40
1060	31.44	31.47	31.50	31.53	31.56	31.60	31.63	31.66	31.69	31.72
1070	31.76	31.79	31.82	31.85	31.88	31.92	31.95	31.98	32.01	32.05
1080	32.08	32.11	32.14	32.18	32.21	32.24	32.27	32.30	32.34	32.37
1090	32.40	32.43	32.47	32.50	32.53	32.56	32.60	32.63	32.66	32.69
1100	32.72	32.76	32.79	32.82	32.86	32.89	32.92	32.95	32.98	33.02
1110	33.05	33.08	33.11	33.15	33.18	33.21	33.24	33.28	33.31	33.34
1120	33.37	33.41	33.44	33.47	33.50	33.54	33.57	33.60	33.64	33.67
1130	33.70	33.73	33.76	33.80	33.83	33.86	33.90	33.93	33.96	33.99
1140	34.03	34.06	34.09	34.12	34.16	34.19	34.22	34.26	34.29	34.32
1150	34.36	34.39	34.42	34.45	34.49	34.52	34.55	34.58	34.62	34.65
1160	34.68	34.72	34.75	34.78	34.82	34.85	34.88	34.92	34.95	34.98
1170	35.01	35.05	35.08	35.11	35.15	35.18	35.21	35.25	35.28	35.31
1180	35.35	35.38	35.41	35.45	35.48	35.51	35.54	35.58	35.61	35.64
1190	35.68	35.71	35.74	35.78	35.81	35.84	35.88	35.91	35.94	35.98
1200	36.01	36.05	36.08	36.11	36.15	36.18	36.21	36.25	36.28	36.31
1210	36.35	36.38	36.42	36.45	36.48	36.52	36.55	36.58	36.62	36.65
1220	36.69	36.72	36.75	36.79	36.82	36.86	36.89	36.92	36.96	36.99
1230	37.02	37.06	37.09	37.13	37.16	37.20	37.23	37.26	37.30	37.33
1240	37.36	37.40	37.43	37.47	37.50	37.54	37.57	37.60	37.64	37.67
1250	37.71	37.74	37.78	37.81	37.84	37.88	37.91	37.95	37.98	38.02
1260	38.05	38.08	38.12	38.15	38.19	38.22	38.26	38.29	38.32	38.36
1270	38.39	38.43	38.46	38.50	38.53	38.57	38.60	38.64	38.67	38.70
1280	38.74	38.77	38.81	38.84	38.88	38.91	38.95	38.98	39.02	39.05
1290	39.08	39.12	39.15	39.19	39.22	39.26	39.29	39.33	39.36	39.40
1300	39.43	39.47	39.50	39.54	39.57	39.61	39.64	39.68	39.71	39.75
1310	39.78	39.82	39.85	39.89	39.92	39.96	39.99	40.03	40.06	40.10
1320	40.13	40.17	40.20	40.24	40.27	40.31	40.34	40.38	40.41	40.45
1330	40.48	40.52	40.55	40.59	40.62	40.66	40.69	40.73	40.76	40.80
1340	40.83	40.87	40.90	40.94	40.98	41.01	41.05	41.08	41.12	41.15
1350	41.19	41.22	41.26	41.29	41.33	41.36	41.40	41.43	41.47	41.50
1360	41.54	41.58	41.61	41.65	41.68	41.72	41.75	41.79	41.82	41.86
1370	41.90	41.93	41.97	42.00	42.04	42.07	42.11	42.14	42.18	42.22
1380	42.25	42.29	42.32	42.36	42.39	42.43	42.46	42.50	42.53	42.57
1390	42.61	42.64	42.68	42.71	42.75	42.78	42.82	42.85	42.89	42.92
1400	42.96	....	....	....	....	....	....	....	....	....

* Based on the International Temperature Scale of 1948.

CALIBRATION TABLES
FOR THERMOCOUPLES (Continued)
TEMPERATURE-E. M. F. VALUES FOR
COPPER-CONSTANTAN

E. M. F. values are in millivolts; reference junctions at 0°C.; temperatures are in degrees Centigrade
Roeser and Wensel, National Bureau of Standards

°C	0°	10°	20°	30°	40°	50°	60°	70°	80°	90°
−200°	−5.54									
−100°	−3.35	−3.62	−3.89	−4.14	−4.38	−4.60	−4.82	−5.02	−5.20	−5.38
0°	0	−0.38	−0.75	−1.11	−1.47	−1.81	−2.14	−2.46	−2.77	−3.06
0°	0	0.39	0.79	1.19	1.61	2.03	2.47	2.91	3.36	3.81
100°	4.28	4.75	5.23	5.71	6.20	6.70	7.21	7.72	8.23	8.76
200°	9.29	9.82	10.36	10.91	11.46	12.01	12.57	13.14	13.71	14.28
300°	14.86	15.44	16.03	16.62	17.22	17.82	18.42	19.03	19.64	20.25
400°	20.87									

TEMPERATURE-E. M. F. VALUES FOR
COPPER-CONSTANTAN

E. M. F. values are in millivolts; reference junctions at 32°F.; temperatures are in degrees Fahrenheit
Roeser and Wensel, National Bureau of Standards

°F	0°	10°	20°	30°	40°	50°	60°	70°	80°	90°
−300°	−5.28									
−200°	−4.11	−4.25	−4.38	−4.50	−4.63	−4.75	−4.86	−4.97	−5.08	−5.18
−100°	−2.56	−2.73	−2.90	−3.06	−3.22	−3.38	−3.53	−3.68	−3.83	−3.97
0°	−0.67	−0.87	−1.07	−1.27	−1.47	−1.66	−1.84	−2.03	−2.21	−2.39
0°	−0.67	−0.46	−0.26	−0.04	+0.17	0.39	0.61	0.83	1.06	1.29
100°	1.52	1.75	1.99	2.23	2.47	2.71	2.96	3.21	3.46	3.71
200°	3.97	4.22	4.48	4.75	5.01	5.28	5.55	5.82	6.09	6.37
300°	6.64	6.92	7.21	7.49	7.77	8.06	8.35	8.64	8.93	9.23
400°	9.52	9.82	10.12	10.42	10.72	11.03	11.33	11.64	11.95	12.26
500°	12.57	12.89	13.20	13.52	13.83	14.15	14.47	14.79	15.12	15.44
600°	15.77	16.10	16.42	16.75	17.08	17.42	17.75	18.08	18.42	18.75
700°	19.09	19.43	19.77	20.11	20.45	20.80				

REFERENCE TABLE FOR Pt TO Pt—10 PER CENT Rh THERMOCOUPLE

Emfs are expressed in microvolts and temperatures in °C. Cold junctions at 0°C.
ROESER AND WENSEL, NATIONAL BUREAU OF STANDARDS

E(μv)	0	1,000	2,000	3,000	4,000	5,000	6,000	7,000	8,000	E(μv)
0	0	146.9	265.0	373.7	477.7	578.1	675.3	769.5	861.0	0
	17.7	12.5	11.2	10.5	10.2	9.9	9.5	9.3	9.0	
100	17.7	159.4	276.2	384.2	487.9	588.0	684.8	778.8	870.0	100
	16.7	12.3	11.1	10.5	10.2	9.8	9.5	9.2	9.0	
200	34.4	171.7	287.3	394.7	498.1	597.8	694.3	788.0	879.0	200
	15.8	12.1	11.0	10.5	10.1	9.8	9.5	9.2	9.0	
300	50.2	183.8	298.3	405.2	508.2	607.6	703.8	797.2	888.0	300
	15.2	12.0	11.0	10.5	10.1	9.8	9.5	9.2	9.0	
400	65.4	195.8	309.3	415.7	518.3	617.4	713.3	806.4	897.0	400
	14.6	11.8	10.9	10.4	10.1	9.7	9.4	9.2	8.9	
500	80.0	207.6	320.2	426.1	528.4	627.1	722.7	815.6	905.9	500
	14.1	11.7	10.8	10.4	10.0	9.7	9.4	9.1	8.9	
600	94.1	219.3	331.0	436.5	538.4	636.8	732.1	824.7	914.8	600
	13.7	11.6	10.7	10.3	10.0	9.7	9.4	9.1	8.9	
700	107.8	230.9	341.7	446.8	548.4	646.5	741.5	833.8	923.7	700
	13.3	11.5	10.7	10.3	9.9	9.6	9.4	9.1	8.9	
800	121.1	242.4	352.4	457.1	558.3	656.1	750.9	842.9	932.6	800
	13.0	11.3	10.7	10.3	9.9	9.6	9.3	9.1	8.8	
900	134.1	253.7	363.1	467.4	568.2	665.7	760.2	852.0	941.4	900
	12.8	11.3	10.6	10.3	9.9	9.6	9.3	9.0	8.8	
1,000	146.9	265.0	373.7	477.7	578.1	675.3	769.5	861.0	950.2	1,000

Emfs are expressed in microvolts and temperatures in °C. Cold junctions at 0°C.

E(μv)	9,000	10,000	11,000	12,000	13,000	14,000	15,000	16,000	17,000	E(μv)
0	950.2	1,037.2	1,122.3	1,206.4	1,290.0	1,373.8	1,458.0	1,542.6	1,627.8	0
	8.8	8.6	8.5	8.3	8.4	8.4	8.4	8.5	8.6	
100	959.0	1,045.8	1,130.8	1,214.7	1,298.3	1,382.2	1,466.4	1,551.1	1,636.4	100
	8.8	8.6	8.4	8.4	8.4	8.4	8.4	8.5	8.5	
200	967.8	1,054.4	1,139.2	1,223.1	1,306.7	1,390.6	1,474.8	1,559.6	1,644.9	200
	8.7	8.5	8.4	8.3	8.4	8.4	8.5	8.5	8.6	
300	976.5	1,062.9	1,147.6	1,231.4	1,315.1	1,399.0	1,483.3	1,568.1	1,653.5	300
	8.8	8.6	8.4	8.4	8.4	8.4	8.5	8.5	8.6	
400	985.3	1,071.5	1,156.0	1,239.8	1,323.5	1,407.4	1,491.8	1,576.6	1,662.1	400
	8.7	8.5	8.4	8.4	8.3	8.4	8.4	8.5	8.6	
500	994.0	1,080.0	1,164.4	1,248.2	1,331.8	1,415.8	1,500.2	1,585.1	1,670.7	500
	8.7	8.5	8.4	8.3	8.4	8.4	8.5	8.6	8.6	
600	1,002.7	1,088.5	1,172.8	1,256.5	1,340.2	1,424.2	1,508.7	1,593.7	1,679.3	600
	8.6	8.5	8.4	8.4	8.4	8.5	8.5	8.5	8.6	
700	1,011.3	1,097.0	1,181.2	1,264.9	1,348.6	1,432.7	1,517.2	1,602.2	1,687.9	700
	8.7	8.4	8.4	8.4	8.4	8.4	8.4	8.5	8.6	
800	1,020.0	1,105.4	1,189.6	1,273.2	1,357.0	1,441.1	1,525.6	1,610.7	1,696.5	800
	8.6	8.5	8.4	8.4	8.4	8.4	8.5	8.6	8.6	
900	1,028.6	1,113.9	1,198.0	1,281.6	1,365.4	1,449.5	1,534.1	1,619.3	1,705.1	900
	8.6	8.4	8.4	8.4	8.4	8.5	8.5	8.5	8.6	
1,000	1,037.2	1,122.3	1,206.4	1,290.0	1,373.8	1,458.0	1,542.6	1,627.8	1,713.7	1,000

Emfs are expressed in microvolts and temperatures in °F. Cold junctions at 32°F.
ROESER AND WENSEL, NATIONAL BUREAU OF STANDARDS

E(μv)	0	1,000	2,000	3,000	4,000	5,000	6,000	7,000	8,000	E(μv)
0	32.0	296.4	509.0	704.7	891.9	1,072.6	1,247.5	1,417.1	1,581.8	0
	31.9	22.5	20.1	19.0	18.4	17.7	17.1	16.7	16.2	
100	63.9	318.9	529.1	723.7	910.3	1,090.3	1,264.6	1,433.8	1,598.0	100
	30.0	22.1	20.0	18.9	18.3	17.7	17.1	16.6	16.2	
200	93.9	341.0	549.1	742.6	928.6	1,108.0	1,281.7	1,450.4	1,614.2	200
	28.5	21.8	19.9	18.8	18.2	17.7	17.1	16.6	16.2	
300	122.4	362.8	569.0	761.4	946.8	1,125.7	1,298.8	1,467.0	1,630.4	300
	27.3	21.6	19.8	18.8	18.1	17.6	17.1	16.5	16.1	
400	149.7	384.4	588.8	780.2	964.9	1,143.3	1,315.9	1,483.5	1,646.5	400
	26.3	21.3	19.6	18.8	18.1	17.5	17.0	16.5	16.1	
500	176.0	405.7	608.4	799.0	983.0	1,160.8	1,332.9	1,500.0	1,662.6	500
	25.4	21.0	19.4	18.7	18.1	17.5	16.9	16.5	16.0	
600	201.4	426.7	627.8	817.7	1,001.1	1,178.3	1,349.8	1,516.5	1,678.6	600
	24.6	20.9	19.3	18.6	18.0	17.4	16.9	16.4	16.0	
700	226.0	447.6	647.1	836.3	1,019.1	1,195.7	1,366.7	1,532.9	1,694.6	700
	24.0	20.7	19.3	18.5	17.9	17.3	16.9	16.3	16.0	
800	250.0	468.3	666.4	854.8	1,037.0	1,213.0	1,383.6	1,549.2	1,710.6	800
	23.4	20.4	19.2	18.6	17.8	17.3	16.8	16.3	15.9	
900	273.4	488.7	685.6	873.4	1,054.8	1,230.3	1,400.4	1,565.5	1,726.5	900
	23.0	20.3	19.1	18.5	17.8	17.2	16.7	16.3	15.9	
1,000	296.4	509.0	704.7	891.9	1,072.6	1,247.5	1,417.1	1,581.8	1,742.4	1,000

Emfs are expressed in microvolts and temperatures in °F. Cold junctions at 32°F.

E(μv)	9,000	10,000	11,000	12,000	13,000	14,000	15,000	16,000	17,000	E(μv)
0	1,742.4	1,899.0	2,052.1	2,203.5	2,354.0	2,504.8	2,656.4	2,808.7	2,962.0	0
	15.8	15.5	15.2	15.0	15.1	15.1	15.1	15.3	15.4	
100	1,758.2	1,914.5	2,067.3	2,218.5	2,369.0	2,520.0	2,671.5	2,824.0	2,977.4	100
	15.8	15.4	15.2	15.0	15.1	15.1	15.2	15.3	15.4	
200	1,774.0	1,929.9	2,082.5	2,233.5	2,384.1	2,535.1	2,686.7	2,839.3	2,992.8	200
	15.7	15.4	15.2	15.0	15.1	15.1	15.2	15.3	15.5	
300	1,789.7	1,945.3	2,097.7	2,248.5	2,399.2	2,550.2	2,701.9	2,854.6	3,008.3	300
	15.8	15.4	15.1	15.1	15.1	15.1	15.3	15.3	15.5	
400	1,805.5	1,960.7	2,112.8	2,263.6	2,414.3	2,565.3	2,717.2	2,869.9	3,023.8	400
	15.7	15.3	15.1	15.1	15.0	15.1	15.2	15.3	15.5	
500	1,821.2	1,976.0	2,127.9	2,278.7	2,429.3	2,580.4	2,732.4	2,885.2	3,039.3	500
	15.6	15.3	15.1	15.0	15.1	15.2	15.3	15.4	15.4	
600	1,836.8	1,991.3	2,143.0	2,293.7	2,444.4	2,595.6	2,747.7	2,900.6	3,054.7	600
	15.6	15.2	15.2	15.1	15.1	15.2	15.3	15.3	15.5	
700	1,852.4	2,006.5	2,158.2	2,308.8	2,459.5	2,610.8	2,763.0	2,916.0	3,070.2	700
	15.6	15.2	15.1	15.0	15.1	15.2	15.2	15.3	15.5	
800	1,868.0	2,021.7	2,173.3	2,323.8	2,474.6	2,626.0	2,778.2	2,931.3	3,085.7	800
	15.5	15.2	15.1	15.1	15.1	15.2	15.2	15.4	15.5	
900	1,883.5	2,036.9	2,188.4	2,338.9	2,489.7	2,641.2	2,793.4	2,946.7	3,101.2	900
	15.5	15.2	15.1	15.1	15.1	15.2	15.3	15.3	15.5	
1,000	1,899.0	2,052.1	2,203.5	2,354.0	2,504.8	2,656.4	2,808.7	2,962.0	3,116.7	1,000

REFERENCE TABLE FOR Pt TO Pt—13 PER CENT Rh THERMOCOUPLE

Emfs are expressed in microvolts and temperatures in °C.   Cold junctions at 0°C.

ROESER AND WENSEL, NATIONAL BUREAU OF STANDARDS

E(μv)	0	1,000	2,000	3,000	4,000	5,000	6,000	7,000	8,000	9,000	E(μv)
0	0	145.3	258.8	361.0	457.4	549.8	638.3	723.5	806.0	886.1	0
	17.9	12.2	10.6	9.5	9.0	8.7	8.4	8.1	7.9		
100	17.9	157.5	269.4	370.9	466.9	558.8	647.0	731.9	814.1	894.0	100
	16.7	12.0	10.5	9.4	9.0	8.6	8.4	8.1	7.8		
200	34.6	169.5	279.9	380.7	476.3	567.8	655.6	740.3	822.2	901.8	200
	15.8	11.7	10.4	9.8	9.4	8.6	8.3	8.1	7.9		
300	50.4	181.2	290.3	390.5	485.7	576.8	664.2	748.6	830.3	909.7	300
	15.1	11.5	10.3	9.7	9.3	8.9	8.6	8.3	8.0	7.8	
400	65.5	192.7	300.6	400.2	495.0	585.8	672.6	756.9	838.3	917.5	400
	14.5	11.4	10.2	9.7	9.3	8.9	8.5	8.2	8.0	7.8	
500	80.0	204.1	310.8	409.9	504.3	594.6	681.3	765.1	846.3	925.3	500
	13.9	11.2	10.2	9.6	9.2	8.8	8.5	8.2	8.0	7.8	
600	93.9	215.3	321.0	419.5	513.5	603.4	689.8	773.3	854.3	933.1	600
	13.4	11.1	10.1	9.5	9.1	8.8	8.5	8.2	8.0	7.8	
700	107.3	226.4	331.1	429.0	522.6	612.2	698.3	781.5	862.3	940.9	700
	13.0	10.9	10.0	9.5	9.1	8.7	8.4	8.2	8.0	7.8	
800	120.3	237.3	341.1	438.5	531.7	620.9	706.7	789.7	870.3	948.7	800
	12.6	10.8	10.0	9.3	9.1	8.7	8.4	8.1	7.9	7.7	
900	132.9	248.1	351.1	448.0	540.8	629.6	715.1	797.8	878.2	956.4	900
	12.4	10.7	9.9	9.4	9.0	8.7	8.4	8.2	7.9	7.7	
1,000	145.3	258.8	361.0	457.4	549.8	638.3	723.5	806.0	886.1	964.1	1,000

Emfs are expressed in microvolts and temperatures in °C.   Cold junctions at 0°C.

E(μv)	10,000	11,000	12,000	13,000	14,000	15,000	16,000	17,000	18,000	19,000	E(μv)
0	964.1	1,040.0	1,113.9	1,186.9	1,259.3	1,331.8	1,404.3	1,476.9	1,550.0	1,623.6	0
	7.6	7.4	7.3	7.3	7.2	7.2	7.3	7.3	7.4	7.4	
100	971.7	1,047.4	1,121.2	1,194.1	1,266.6	1,339.0	1,411.6	1,484.2	1,557.4	1,631.0	100
	7.7	7.5	7.4	7.3	7.2	7.2	7.3	7.3	7.4	7.4	
200	979.4	1,054.9	1,128.6	1,201.4	1,273.8	1,346.2	1,418.9	1,491.5	1,564.8	1,638.4	200
	7.6	7.4	7.3	7.3	7.3	7.3	7.2	7.3	7.3	7.4	
300	987.0	1,062.3	1,135.9	1,208.7	1,281.1	1,353.5	1,426.1	1,498.8	1,572.1	1,645.8	300
	7.7	7.4	7.3	7.2	7.2	7.3	7.2	7.3	7.4	7.4	
400	994.7	1,069.7	1,143.2	1,215.9	1,288.3	1,360.8	1,433.3	1,506.1	1,579.5	1,653.2	400
	7.6	7.4	7.3	7.3	7.2	7.2	7.2	7.3	7.3	7.4	
500	1,002.3	1,077.1	1,150.5	1,223.2	1,295.5	1,368.0	1,440.5	1,513.4	1,586.8	1,660.6	500
	7.6	7.3	7.3	7.2	7.2	7.3	7.2	7.3	7.4	7.4	
600	1,009.9	1,084.1	1,157.8	1,230.4	1,302.7	1,375.3	1,447.8	1,520.7	1,594.2	1,668.0	600
	7.6	7.4	7.3	7.2	7.2	7.2	7.3	7.3	7.3	7.4	
700	1,017.5	1,091.8	1,165.1	1,237.6	1,309.9	1,382.6	1,455.0	1,528.0	1,601.5	1,675.4	700
	7.5	7.4	7.2	7.2	7.3	7.2	7.3	7.3	7.3	7.4	
800	1,025.0	1,099.2	1,172.3	1,244.8	1,317.2	1,389.8	1,462.3	1,535.3	1,608.9	1,682.8	800
	7.5	7.3	7.3	7.3	7.3	7.3	7.3	7.4	7.3	7.4	
900	1,032.5	1,106.5	1,179.6	1,252.1	1,324.5	1,397.1	1,469.6	1,542.7	1,616.2	1,690.2	900
	7.5	7.4	7.3	7.2	7.3	7.2	7.3	7.3	7.4	7.4	
1,000	1,040.0	1,113.9	1,186.9	1,259.3	1,331.8	1,404.3	1,476.9	1,550.0	1,623.6	1,697.6	1,000

Emfs are expressed in microvolts and temperatures in °F.   Cold junctions at 32°F.

ROESER AND WENSEL, NATIONAL BUREAU OF STANDARDS

E(μv)	0	1,000	2,000	3,000	4,000	5,000	6,000	7,000	8,000	9,000	E(μv)
0	32.0	293.5	497.8	681.8	855.3	1,021.6	1,180.9	1,334.3	1,482.8	1,627.0	0
	32.2	22.0	19.1	17.8	17.0	16.2	15.6	15.1	14.6	14.2	
100	64.2	315.5	516.9	699.6	872.3	1,037.8	1,196.5	1,349.4	1,497.4	1,641.2	100
	30.1	21.6	18.9	17.7	17.0	16.2	15.6	15.1	14.6	14.1	
200	94.3	337.1	535.8	717.3	889.3	1,054.0	1,212.1	1,364.5	1,512.0	1,655.3	200
	28.4	21.1	18.7	17.6	16.9	16.2	15.5	15.0	14.5	14.1	
300	122.7	358.2	554.5	734.9	906.2	1,070.2	1,227.6	1,379.5	1,526.5	1,669.4	300
	27.2	20.7	18.6	17.5	16.8	16.1	15.4	14.9	14.4	14.1	
400	149.9	378.9	573.1	752.4	923.0	1,086.3	1,243.0	1,394.4	1,540.9	1,683.5	400
	26.1	20.4	18.4	17.4	16.7	16.0	15.3	14.8	14.4	14.0	
500	176.0	399.3	591.5	769.8	939.7	1,102.3	1,258.3	1,409.2	1,555.3	1,697.5	500
	25.0	20.2	18.3	17.3	16.6	15.9	15.3	14.8	14.4	14.1	
600	201.0	419.5	609.8	787.1	956.3	1,118.2	1,273.6	1,424.0	1,569.7	1,711.6	600
	24.1	20.0	18.2	17.2	16.4	15.8	15.2	14.8	14.4	14.0	
700	225.1	439.5	628.0	804.3	972.7	1,134.0	1,288.9	1,438.8	1,584.1	1,725.6	700
	23.4	19.7	18.0	17.1	16.4	15.7	15.2	14.7	14.4	14.0	
800	248.5	459.2	646.0	821.4	989.1	1,149.7	1,304.1	1,453.5	1,598.5	1,739.6	800
	22.7	19.4	18.0	17.0	16.3	15.6	15.1	14.6	14.3	13.9	
900	271.2	478.6	664.0	838.4	1,005.4	1,165.3	1,319.2	1,468.1	1,612.8	1,753.5	900
	22.3	19.2	17.8	16.9	16.2	15.6	15.1	14.7	14.2	13.9	
1,000	293.5	497.8	681.8	855.3	1,021.6	1,180.9	1,334.3	1,482.8	1,627.0	1,767.4	1,000

Emfs are expressed in microvolts and temperatures in °F.   Cold junctions at 32°F.

E(μv)	10,000	11,000	12,000	13,000	14,000	15,000	16,000	17,000	18,000	19,000	E(μv)
0	1,767.4	1,904.0	2,037.0	2,168.4	2,298.7	2,429.2	2,559.7	2,690.4	2,822.0	2,954.5	0
	13.8	13.4	13.2	13.0	13.1	13.0	13.1	13.2	13.3	13.3	
100	1,781.2	1,917.4	2,050.2	2,181.4	2,311.8	2,442.2	2,572.8	2,703.6	2,835.3	2,967.8	100
	13.7	13.4	13.2	13.1	13.0	13.0	13.1	13.1	13.3	13.3	
200	1,794.9	1,930.8	2,063.4	2,194.5	2,324.8	2,455.2	2,585.9	2,716.7	2,848.6	2,981.1	200
	13.7	13.3	13.2	13.1	13.1	13.1	13.0	13.1	13.2	13.3	
300	1,808.6	1,944.1	2,076.6	2,207.6	2,337.9	2,468.3	2,598.9	2,729.8	2,861.8	2,994.4	300
	13.8	13.3	13.2	13.0	13.0	13.1	13.0	13.1	13.3	13.4	
400	1,822.4	1,957.4	2,089.8	2,220.6	2,350.9	2,481.4	2,611.9	2,743.0	2,875.1	3,007.8	400
	13.7	13.3	13.1	13.1	13.0	13.0	13.1	13.1	13.2	13.3	
500	1,836.1	1,970.7	2,102.9	2,233.7	2,363.9	2,494.4	2,624.9	2,756.1	2,888.3	3,021.1	500
	13.6	13.3	13.1	13.0	13.0	13.1	13.1	13.2	13.3	13.3	
600	1,849.8	1,984.0	2,116.0	2,246.7	2,376.9	2,507.5	2,638.0	2,769.3	2,901.6	3,034.4	600
	13.6	13.3	13.1	13.0	13.0	13.1	13.0	13.1	13.2	13.3	
700	1,863.4	1,997.3	2,129.1	2,259.7	2,389.9	2,520.6	2,651.0	2,782.4	2,914.8	3,047.7	700
	13.6	13.3	13.1	13.0	13.1	13.0	13.1	13.2	13.2	13.3	
800	1,877.0	2,010.6	2,142.2	2,272.7	2,403.0	2,533.6	2,664.1	2,795.6	2,928.0	3,061.0	800
	13.5	13.2	13.1	13.0	13.1	13.1	13.1	13.2	13.2	13.4	
900	1,890.5	2,023.8	2,155.3	2,285.7	2,416.1	2,546.7	2,677.2	2,808.8	2,941.2	3,074.4	900
	13.5	13.2	13.1	13.0	13.1	13.0	13.2	13.2	13.3	13.3	
1,000	1,904.0	2,037.0	2,168.4	2,298.7	2,429.2	2,559.7	2,690.4	2,822.0	2,954.5	3,087.7	1,000

VALUES FOR THE LANGEVIN FUNCTION $\mathcal{L}(u)$

Compiled by Allen L. King

Because of random thermal rotations a dipole or dipole-like element ordinarily has an average dipole moment of zero. If it is placed in an orienting field F however it tends to align itself with the field so that the average component of the dipole moment parallel to the field equals $\bar{p}$. Classically, if the system is in thermal equilibrium,

$$\bar{p} = p_0(\coth u - 1/u) = p_0\mathcal{L}(u)$$

Here p_0 is the moment of the dipole itself and $\mathcal{L}(u)$ is the Langevin function of the argument u which equals Fp_0/kT.

$$\text{For } u \ll 1 \quad \mathcal{L}(u) = \frac{u}{3}$$

The Langevin function applies to permanent electric and magnetic dipoles.

(u)	0	1	2	3	4	5	6	7	8	9	10	Diff.
0.0	0000	0033	0066	0100	0133	0166	0200	0233	0266	0300	0333	33
0.1	0333	0366	0400	0433	0466	0499	0532	0565	0598	0631	0665	33
0.2	0665	0698	0731	0764	0797	0830	0862	0896	0929	0961	0994	33
0.3	0994	1027	1059	1092	1124	1157	1190	1222	1254	1287	1319	32
0.4	1319	1352	1384	1416	1448	1480	1512	1544	1576	1608	1640	32
0.5	1640	1671	1703	1734	1765	1797	1829	1860	1892	1923	1953	31
0.6	1953	1985	2016	2046	2077	2108	2138	2169	2200	2230	2260	31
0.7	2260	2290	2321	2351	2381	2411	2441	2471	2500	2530	2559	30
0.8	2559	2589	2618	2647	2676	2705	2734	2763	2792	2821	2850	29
0.9	2850	2878	2906	2934	2963	2991	3019	3047	3075	3103	3130	28
1.0	3130	3158	3185	3212	3240	3267	3294	3321	3348	3375	3401	27
1.1	3401	3428	3454	3480	3507	3533	3559	3585	3611	3637	3662	26
1.2	3662	3688	3713	3738	3763	3788	3813	3838	3863	3888	3913	25
1.3	3913	3937	3961	3985	4009	4033	4057	4081	4105	4129	4152	24
1.4	4152	4176	4199	4222	4245	4268	4291	4313	4336	4359	4381	23
1.5	4381	4403	4426	4448	4469	4491	4514	4536	4557	4579	4600	22
1.6	4600	4621	4642	4663	4684	4705	4726	4747	4768	4788	4808	21
1.7	4808	4828	4849	4869	4889	4909	4928	4948	4967	4987	5006	20
1.8	5006	5025	5044	5064	5083	5102	5121	5139	5158	5176	5195	19
1.9	5195	5213	5231	5249	5267	5285	5303	5321	5338	5356	5373	18
2.0	5373	5391	5408	5425	5442	5459	5476	5493	5509	5526	5542	17
2.1	5542	5559	5575	5591	5608	5624	5640	5656	5672	5688	5704	16
2.2	5704	5719	5734	5750	5765	5780	5795	5810	5825	5840	5855	15
2.3	5855	5870	5885	5899	5913	5928	5943	5957	5971	5985	6000	14
2.4	6000	6014	6027	6041	6055	6068	6082	6095	6109	6122	6136	13.5
2.5	6136	6149	6162	6175	6188	6201	6214	6227	6239	6252	6265	13
2.6	6265	6278	6290	6302	6314	6326	6339	6351	6363	6375	6387	12
2.7	6387	6399	6411	6422	6434	6446	6457	6469	6480	6492	6503	11.5
2.8	6503	6514	6525	6536	6548	6559	6570	6581	6591	6602	6613	11
2.9	6613	6624	6634	6644	6655	6665	6676	6686	6696	6707	6717	10
3.0	6717	6727	6737	6747	6757	6767	6777	6787	6796	6806	6815	10
3.1	6815	6825	6834	6844	6853	6862	6871	6880	6890	6899	6908	9
3.2	6908	6917	6926	6935	6944	6953	6962	6971	6979	6988	6997	9
3.3	6997	7006	7014	7023	7031	7040	7048	7056	7064	7073	7081	8.5
3.4	7081	7089	7097	7105	7113	7121	7129	7137	7145	7153	7161	8
3.5	7161	7169	7176	7184	7192	7200	7207	7215	7223	7230	7237	8
3.6	7237	7245	7252	7259	7267	7274	7281	7288	7295	7302	7309	7
3.7	7309	7317	7324	7330	7337	7344	7351	7358	7364	7371	7378	7
3.8	7378	7385	7392	7398	7405	7412	7418	7425	7431	7437	7444	6.5
3.9	7444	7450	7457	7463	7470	7476	7482	7488	7494	7501	7507	6

Note: Higher values of the Langevin function are nearly equal to $(u - 1)/u$.

Name	Composition,* Weight percent					Remanence, B_r (Gauss)	Coercive force H_c (Oersteds)	Maximum energy product, $(BH)_{max}$ (Gauss-Oersteds $\times 10^{-6}$)
	Al	Ni	Co	Cu	Other			
U.S.A.								
Alnico I	12	20–22	5	....	......	7,100	440	1.4
Alnico II	10	17	12.5	6	......	7,200	540	1.6
Alnico III	12	24–26	....	3	......	6,900	470	1.35
Alnico IV	12	27–28	5	....	......	5,500	700	1.3
Alnico V†	8	14	24	3	......	12,500	600	5.0
Alnico V DG†	8	14	24	3	......	13,100	640	6.0
Alnico VI†	8	15	24	3	1.25 Ti	10,500	750	3.75
Alnico VII†	8.5	18	24	3	5 Ti	7,200	1,050	2.75
Alnico XII	6	18	35	....	8 Ti	5,800	950	1.6
Carbon steel	....	....	....	....	1 Mn 0.9 C	10,000	50	0.2
Chromium steel	....	....	....	....	3.5 Cr 0.9 C 0.3 Mn	9,700	65	0.3
Cobalt steel	....	....	17	....	2.5 Cr 8 W 0.75 C	9,500	150	0.65
Cunico	....	21	29	50	.....	3,400	660	0.80
Cunife	....	20	....	60		5,400	550	1.5
Ferroxdur 1			$BaFe_{12}O_{19}$			2,200	1,800	1.0
Ferroxdur 2		$BaF_{12}O_{19}$ (oriented)				3,840	2,000	3.5
Platinum-Cobalt	....	....	23	....	77 Pt	6,000	4,300	7.5
Remalloy	....	....	12	....	17 Mo	10,500	250	1.1
Silmanol	4.4	....	....	....	86.6 Ag 8.8 Mn	550	6,000	0.075
Tungsten steel	....	....	....	....	5 W 0.3 Mn 0.7 C	10,300	70	0.32
Vicalloy I	....	....	52	....	10 V	8,800	300	1.0
Vicalloy II (wire)	....	....	52	....	14 V	10,000	510	3.5
Germany								
Alni 90	12	21	....	....	......	8,000	350	1.2
Alni 120	13	27	....	....	......	6,000	570	1.2
Alnico 130	12	23	5	....	......	6,300	620	1.4
Alnico 160	11	24	12	4	......	6,200	700	1.6
Alnico 190	12	21	15	4	......	7,000	700	1.8
Alnico 250	8	19	23	4	6 Ti	6,500	1,000	2.2
Alnico 400†	9	15	23	4	......	12,000	650	4.8
Alnico 580† (semicolumnar)	9	15	23	4	......	13,000	700	6.0
Oerstit 800	9	18	19	4	4 Ti	6,600	750	1.95
Great Britain								
Alcomax I	7.5	11	25	3	1.5 Ti	12,000	475	3.5
Alcomax II	8	11.5	24	4.5	......	12,400	575	4.7
Alcomax IISC (semicolumnar)	8	11	23	4.5	.....	12,800	600	5.15
Alcomax III	8	13.5	24	3	0.8 Nb	12,500	670	5.10
Alcomax IIISC (semicolumnar)	8	13.5	24	3	0.8 Nb	13,000	700	5.80
Alcomax IV	8	13.5	24	3	2.5 Nb	11,200	750	4.30

* Remainder of unlisted composition is either iron or iron plus trace impurities.

† Cast anisotropic. Unmarked ones are cast isotropic.

MAGNETIC PROPERTIES AND COMPOSITION OF
SOME PERMANENT MAGNETIC ALLOYS (Continued)

Name	Composition,* Weight percent					Remanence, B_r (Gauss)	Coercive force H_c (Oersteds)	Maximum energy product, $(BH)_{max}$ (Gauss-Oersteds $\times 10^{-6}$)
	Al	Ni	Co	Cu	Other			
Alcomax IVSC (semicolumnar)	8	13.5	24	3	2.5 Nb	11,700	780	5.10
Alni, high B_r	13	24	....	3.5	......	6,200	480	1.25
Alni, normal	....	....	....	....	......	5,600	580	1.25
Alni, high H_c	12	32	....	....	0–0.5 Ti	5,000	680	1.25
Alnico, high B_r	10	17	12	6	......	8,000	500	1.70
Alnico, normal	....	....	....	....	......	7,250	560	1.70
Alnico, high H_c	10	20	13.5	6	0.25 Ti	6,600	620	1.70
Columax (columnar)	similar to Alcomax III or IV					13,000–14,000	700–800	7.0–8.5
Hycomax	9	21	20	1.6	......	9,500	830	3.3

* Remainder of unlisted composition is either iron or iron plus trace impurities.
† Cast anisotropic. Unmarked ones are cast isotropic.

HIGH PERMEABILITY MAGNETIC ALLOYS
(See separate table for magnetic properties)

Name	Composition,* Weight percent	Sp. gr., gm. per cc	Tensile strength		Remark	Use
			Kg/mm²**	Form		
Silicon iron AISI M 15	Si 4	7.68–7.64	44.3	....	Annealed 4 hrs 802–1093°C	Low core losses
Silicon iron AISI M 8	Si 3	7.68–7.64	44.2	Grain oriented	Annealed 4 hrs 802–1204°C	
45 Permalloy	Ni 45; Mn 0.3	8.17	....	....	....	Audio transformer, coils, relays
Monimax	Ni 47; Mo 3	8.27	....	....		High frequency coils
4-79 Permalloy	Ni 79; Mo 4; Mn 0.3	8.74	55.4	....	H_2 annealed 1121°C	Audio coils, transformers, magnetic shields
Sinimax	Ni 43; Si 3	7.70	....	....	....	High frequency coils
Nu-metal	Ni 75; Cr 2; Cu 5	8.58	44.8	....	H_2 annealed 1221°C	Audio coils, magnetic shields, transformers
Supermalloy	Ni 79; Mo 5; Mn 0.3	8.77	....	....		Pulse transformers, magnetic amplifiers, coils
2-V Permendur	Co 40; V 2	8.15	46.3	....	....	D-c electromagnets, pole tips

* Iron is additional alloying metal.
** kg/mm² $\times$ 1422.33 = lbs/in.²

CAST PERMANENT MAGNETIC ALLOYS

(See separate table for magnetic properties)

Alloy name, country of manufacture*	Composition,** weight percent	Sp. gr., gm per cc	Thermal expansion		Tensile strength		Remark†	Use
			$\frac{Cm \times 10^{-6}}{cm \times °C}$	Between °C	***Kg/ mm²	Form		
Alnico I (USA)*	Al 12; Ni 20–22; Co 5	6.9	12.6	20–300	2.9	Cast	i.	Permanent magnets
Alnico II (USA)*	Al 10; Ni 17; Cu 6; Co 12.5	7.1	12.4	20–300	2.1 / 45.7	Cast / Sintered	i.	Temperature controls, magnetic toys and novelties
Alnico III (USA)*	Al 12; Ni 24–26; Cu 3	6.9	12	20–300	8.5	Cast	i.	Tractor magnetos
Alnico IV (USA)*	Al 12; Ni 27–28; Co 5	7.0	13.1	20–300	6.3 / 42.1	Cast / Sintered	i.	Application requiring high coercive force
Alnico V (USA)*	Al 8; Ni 14; Co 24; Cu 3	7.3	11.3	......	3.8 / 35	Cast / Sintered	a.	Application requiring high energy
Alnico V DG (USA)*	Al 8; Ni 14; Co 24; Cu 3	7.3	11.3	......	....	....	a., c.	
Alnico VI (USA)*	Al 8; Ni 15; Co 24; Cu 3; Ti 1.25	7.3	11.4	......	16.1	Cast	a.	Application requiring high energy
Alnico VII (USA)*	Al 8.5; Ni 18; Cu 3; Co 24; Ti 5	7.17	11.4	......	....	....	a.	
Alnico XII (USA)*	Al 6; Ni 18; Co 35; Ti 8	7.2	11	20–300	....	....	.....	Permanent magnets
Comol (USA)*	Co 12; Mo 17	8.16	9.3	20–300	88.6	....	.....	Permanent magnets
Cunife (USA)*	Cu 60; Ni 20	8.52	....	.....	70.3	....	.....	Permanent magnets
Cunico (USA)*	Cu 50; Ni 21	8.31	....	.....	70.3	....	.....	Permanent magnets
Barium ferrite Feroxdur (USA)*	Ba Fe₁₂O₁₉	4.7	10	......	70.3	....	....	Ceramics
Alcomax I (GB)*	Al 7.5; Ni 11; Co 25; Cu 3; Ti 1.5	....	......	......	....	....	a.	Permanent magnets
Alcomax II (GB)*	Al 8; Ni 11.5; Co 24; Cu 4.5	....	......	......	....	....	a.	Permanent magnets
Alcomax II SC(GB)*	Al 8; Ni 11; Co 22; Cu 4.5	7.3	....	......	....	....	a., sc.	
Alcomax III (GB)*	Al 8; Ni 13.5; Co 24; Nb 0.8	7.3	....	......	....	....	a.	Magnets for motors, loudspeakers
Alcomax IV (GB)*	Al 8; Ni 13.5; Cu 3; Co 24; Nb 2.5	....	......	......	....	....	.....	Magnets for cycle-dynamos
Columax (GB)*	Similar to Alcomax III or IV	....	....	......	....	....	a., sc.	Permanent magnets, heat treatable
Hycomax (GB)*	Al 9; Ni 21; Co 20; Cu 1.6	....	....	......	....	....	a.	Permanent magnets
Alnico (high H꜀) (GB)"	Al 10; Ni 20; Cu 13.5; Cu 6; Ti 0.25	7.3	....	......	....	....	i.	

* USA—United States; GB—Great Britain; Ger—Germany.

** Iron is the additional alloying metal for each of the magnets listed.

*** kg/mm × 1422.33 = lbs/in.²

† i. = isotropic; a. = anisotropic; c. = columnar; sc. = semicolumnar.

Alloy name, country of manufacture	Composition,** weight percent	Sp. gr., gm per cc	Thermal expansion		Tensile strength		Remark†	Use
			$\frac{Cm \times 10^{-6}}{cm \times °C}$	Between °C	*** Kg/mm²	Form		
Alnico (high B_r) (GB)*	Al 10; Ni 17; Co 12; Cu 6	7.3	....	......	....	....	i.	
Alni (high H_c) (GB)*	Al 12; Ni 32; Ti 0–0.5	6.9	....	......	....	....	i.	
Alni (high B_r) (GB)*	Al 13; Ni 24; Cu 3.5	....	....	......	....	....	i.	
Alnico 580 (Ger)*	Al 9; Ni 15; Co 23; Cu 4	....	....	......	....	....	i.	
Alnico 400 (Ger)*	Al 9; Ni 15; Co 23; Cu 4	....	....	......	....	....	a.	
Oerstit 800 (Ger)*	Al 9; Ni 18; Co 19; Cu 4; Ti 4	....	....	......	....	....	i.	Permanent magnets
Alnico 250 (Ger)*	Al 8; Ni 19; Co 23; Cu 4; Ti 6	....	....	......	....	....	i.	
Alnico 190 (Ger)*	Al 12; Ni 21; Cu 4; Co 15	....	....	......	....	....	i.	
Alnico 160 (Austria)	Al 11; Ni 24; Co 12; Cu 4	....	....	......	....	....	i.	Permanent magnets, sintered
Alnico 130 (Ger)*	Al 12; Ni 23; Co 5	....	....	......	....	....	i.	
Alni 120 (Ger)*	Al 13; Ni 27	....	....	......	....	....	i.	
Alni 90 (Ger)*	Al 12; Ni 21	....	....	......	....	....	i.	

* USA—United States; GB—Great Britain; Ger—Germany.

** Iron is the additional alloying metal for each of the magnets listed.

*** kg/mm × 1422.33 = lbs/in.²

† i. = isotropic; a. = anisotropic; c. = columnar; sc. = semicolumnar.

Properties of Antiferromagnetic Compounds

Compound	Crystal Symmetry	$\theta_N(°K)$	$\theta_P(°K)$	$(P_A)_{eff}$ μ_B	P_A μ_B
CoCl₂	Rhombohedral	25	−38.1	5.18	3.1 ± 0.6
CoF₂	Tetragonal	38	50	5.15	3.0
CoO	Tetragonal	291	330	5.1	3.8
Cr	Cubic	475			
Cr₂O₃	Rhombohedral	307	485	3.73	3.0
CrSb	Hexagonal	723	550	4.92	2.7
CuBr₂	Monoclinic	189	246	1.9	
CuCl₂·2H₂O	Orthorhombic	4.3	4–5	1.9	
CuCl₂	Monoclinic	~70	109	2.08	
FeCl₂	Hexagonal	24	−48	5.38	4.4 ± 0.7
FeF₂	Tetragonal	79–90	117	5.56	4.64
FeO	Rhombohedral	198	507	7.06	3.32
α-Fe₂O₃	Rhombohedral	953	2940	6.4	5.0
α-Mn	Cubic	95			
MnBr₂·4H₂O	Monoclinic	2.1	$\left\{\begin{matrix}2.5\\1.3\end{matrix}\right\}$	5.93	
MnCl₂·4H₂O	Monoclinic	1.66	1.8	5.94	
MnF₂	Tetragonal	72 75	113.2	5.71	5
MnO	Rhombohedral	122	610	5.95	5.0
β-MnS	Cubic	160	982	5.82	5.0
MnSe	Cubic	~173	361	5.67	
MnTe	Hexagonal	310–323	690	6.07	5.0
NiCl₂	Hexagonal	50	−68	3.32	
NiF₂	Tetragonal	78.5–83	115.6	3.5	2.0
NiO	Rhombohedral	533–650	~2000	4.6	2.0
TiCl₃		100			
V₂O₃		170			

1. θ_N = Néel temperature, determined from susceptibility maxima or from the disappearance of magnetic scattering.
2. θ_P = a constant in the Curie-Weiss law written in the form $\chi_A = C_A/(T + \theta_P)$, which is valid for antiferromagnetic material for $T > \theta_N$.
3. $(P_A)_{eff}$ = effective moment per atom, derived from the atomic Curie constant $C_A = (P_A)_{eff}^2(N^2/3R)$ and expressed in units of the Bohr magneton, $\mu_B = 0.9273 \times 10^{-20}$ erg gauss⁻¹.
4. P_A = magnetic moment per atom, obtained from neutron diffraction measurements in the ordered state.

SATURATION CONSTANTS AND CURIE POINTS OF FERROMAGNETIC ELEMENTS

Element	σ_s (20°C)	M_s (20°C)	σ_s (0°K)	n_B	Curie Point (°C)
Fe	218.0	1,714	221.9	2.219	770
Co	161	1,422	162.5	1.715	1,131
Ni	54.39	484.1	57.50	0.604	358
Gd	0	0	253.5	7.12	16

σ_s = saturation magnetic moment/gram; M_s = saturation magnetic moment/cm³, in cgs units. n_B = magnetic moment per atom in Bohr magnetons.

From American Institute of Physics Handbook, McGraw-Hill Company (1963) by permission.

MAGNETIC PROPERTIES OF TRANSFORMER STEELS

Ordinary Transformer Steel

B (Gauss)	H (Oersted)	Permeability = B/H
2,000	0.60	3,340
4,000	0.87	4,600
6,000	1.10	5,450
8,000	1.48	5,400
10,000	2.28	4,380
12,000	3.85	3,120
14,000	10.9	1,280
16,000	43.0	372
18,000	149	121

SATURATION CONSTANTS FOR MAGNETIC SUBSTANCES

Substance	Field intensity (For saturation)	Induced magnetization	Substance	Field intensity (For saturation)	Induced magnetization
Cobalt	9000	1300	Nickel, hard	8000	400
Iron, wrought	2000	1700	annealed	7000	515
cast	4000	1200	Vicker's steel	15000	1600
Manganese steel	7000	200			

High Silicon Transformer Steel

B	H	Permeability
2,000	0.50	4,000
4,000	0.70	5,720
6,000	0.90	6,670
8,000	1.28	6,250
10,000	1.99	5,020
12,000	3.60	3,340
14,000	9.80	1,430
16,000	47.4	338
18,000	165	109

INITIAL PERMEABILITY OF HIGH PURITY IRON FOR VARIOUS TEMPERATURES
L. Alberts and B. J. Shepstone

Temperature °C	Permeability (gauss/oersted)
0	920
200	1040
400	1440
600	2550
700	3900
770	12580

MAGNETIC MATERIALS
High-permeability Materials

Material	Form	Fe	Ni	Co	Mo	Other	Typical heat treatment °C	Permeability at $B = 20$ gausses	Maximum permeability	Saturation flux density B gausses	Hysteresis‡ loss, W_h ergs/cm³	Coercive‡ force H_c oersteds	Resistivity microhm-cm	Density, g/cm³
Cold rolled steel	Sheet	98.5	—	—	—	—	950 Anneal	180	2,000	21,000		1.8	10	7.88
Iron	Sheet	99.91	—	—	—	—	950 Anneal	200	5,000	21,500	5,000	1.0	10	7.88
Purified iron	Sheet	99.95	—	—	—	—	1480 H₂ + 880	5,000	180,000	21,500	300	.05	10	7.88
4% Silicon-iron	Sheet	96	—	—	—	4 Si	800 Anneal	500	7,000	19,700	3,500	.5	60	7.65
Grain oriented*	Sheet	97	—	—	—	3 Si	800 Anneal	1,500	30,000	20,000	—	.15	47	7.67
45 Permalloy	Sheet	54.7	45	—	—	.3 Mn	1050 Anneal	2,500	25,000	16,000	1,200	.3	45	8.17
45 Permalloy†	Sheet	54.7	45	—	—	.3 Mn	1200 H₂ Anneal	4,000	50,000	16,000	—	.07	45	8.17
Hipernik	Sheet	50	50	—	—	—	1200 H₂ Anneal	4,500	70,000	16,000	220	.05	50	8.25
Monimax	Sheet	—	—	—	—	—	1125 H₂ Anneal	2,000	35,000	15,000	—	.1	80	8.27
Sinimax	Sheet	—	—	—	—	—	1125 H₂ Anneal	3,000	35,000	11,000	—	—	90	—
78 Permalloy	Sheet	21.2	78.5	—	—	.3 Mn	1050 + 600 Q§	8,000	100,000	10,700	200	.05	16	8.60
4-79 Permalloy	Sheet	16.7	79	—	4	.3 Mn	1100 + Q	20,000	100,000	8,700	200	.05	55	8.72
Mu metal	Sheet	18	75	—	—	2 Cr, 5 Cu	1175 H₂	20,000	100,000	6,500	—	.05	62	8.58
Supermalloy	Sheet	15.7	79	—	5	.3 Mn	1300 H₂ + Q	100,000	800,000	8,000	—	.002	60	8.77
Permendur	Sheet	49.7	—	50	—	.3 Mn	800 Anneal	800	5,000	24,500	12,000	2.0	7	8.3
2V Permendur	Sheet	49	—	49	—	2 V	800 Anneal	800	4,500	24,000	6,000	2.0	26	8.2
Hiperco	Sheet	64	—	34	—	Cr	850 Anneal	650	10,000	24,200	—	1.0	25	8.0
2-81 Permalloy	Insulated powder	17	81	—	2	—	650 Anneal	125	130	8,000	—	<1.0	10⁶	7.8
Carbonyl iron	Insulated powder	99.9	—	—	—	—	—	55	132	—	—	—	—	7.86
Ferroxcube III	Sintered powder	MnFe₂O₄ + ZnFe₂O₄					—	1,000	1,500	2,500	—	.1	10⁸	5.0

* Properties in direction of rolling.
† Similar properties for Nicaloi, 4750 alloy, Carpenter 49, Armco 48.
‡ At saturation.
§ Q, quench or controlled cooling.

Permanent Magnet Alloys

Material	Percent composition (remainder Fe)	Heat treatment* (temperature, °C)	Magnetizing force H_{max} oersteds	Coercive force H_c oersteds	Residual induction B_r gausses	Energy product BH_{max} $\times 10^{-6}$	Method of fabrication†	Mechanical properties‡	Weight lb/in.³
Carbon steel.............	1 Mn, 0.9 C	Q 800	300	50	10,000	.20	HR, M, P	H, S	.280
Tungsten steel..........	5 W, 0.3 Mn, 0.7 C	Q 850	300	70	10,300	.32	HR, M, P	H, S	.292
Chromium steel........	3.5 Cr, 0.9 C, 0.3 Mn	Q 830	300	65	9,700	.30	HR, M, P	H, S	.280
17% Cobalt steel.......	17 Co, 0.75 C, 2.5 Cr, 8 W	—	1,000	150	9,500	.65	HR, M, P	H, S	—
36% Cobalt steel.......	36 Co, 0.7 C, 4 Cr, 5 W	Q 950	1,000	240	9,500	.97	HR, M, P	H, S	.296
Remalloy or Comol.....	17 Mo, 12 Co	Q 1200, B 700	1,000	250	10,500	1.1	HR, M, P	H	.295
Alnico I.............	12 Al, 20 Ni, 5 Co	A 1200, B 700	2,000	440	7,200	1.4	C, G	H, B	.249
Alnico II............	10 Al, 17 Ni, 2.5 Co, 6 Cu	A 1200, B 600	2,000	550	7,200	1.6	C, G	H, B	.256
Alnico II (sintered).....	10 Al, 17 Ni, 2.5 Co, 6 Cu	A 1300	2,000	520	6,900	1.4	Sn, G	H	.249
Alnico IV...........	12 Al, 28 Ni, 5 Co	Q 1200, B 650	3,000	700	5,500	1.3	Sn, C, G	H	.253
Alnico V...........	8 Al, 14 Ni, 24 Co, 3 Cu	AF 1300, B 600	2,000	550	12,500	4.5	C, G	H, B	.264
Alnico VI...........	8 Al, 15 Ni, 24 Co, 3 Cu, 1 Ti	—	3,000	750	10,000	3.5	C, G	H, B	.268
Alnico XII...........	6 Al, 18 Ni, 35 Co, 8 Ti	—	3,000	950	5,800	1.5	C, G	H, B	.26
Vicalloy I...........	52 Co, 10 V	B 600	1,000	300	8,800	1.0	C, CR, M, P	D	.295
Vicalloy II (wire)......	52 Co, 14 V	CW + B 600	2,000	510	10,000	3.5	C, CR, M, P	D	.292
Cunife (wire)..........	60 Cu, 20 Ni	CW + B 600	2,400	550	5,400	1.5	C, CR, M, P	D, M	.311
Cunico.............	50 Cu, 21 Ni, 29 Co	—	3,200	660	3,400	.80	C, CR, M, P	D, M	.300
Vectolite............	30 Fe₂O₃, 44 Fe₃O₄, 26 C₂O₃	—	3,000	1,000	1,600	.60	Sn, G	W	.113
Silmanal...........	86.8 Ag, 8.8 Mn, 4.4 Al	—	20,000	6,000ᵃ	550	.075	C, CR, M, P	D, M	.325
Platinum-cobalt........	77 Pt, 23 Co	Q 1200, B 650	15,000	3,600	5,900	6.5	C, CR, M	D	—
Hyflux...............	Fine powder	—	2,000	390	6,600	.97	—	—	.176

ᵃ Value given is intrinsic H_c.
* Q—Quenched in oil or water. A—Air cooled. B—Baked. F—Cooled in magnetic field. CW—Cold worked.
† HR—Hot rolled or forged. CR—Cold rolled or drawn. M—Machined. G—Must be ground. P—Punched. C—Cast. Sn—Sintered.
‡ H—Hard. B—Brittle. S—Strong. D—Ductile. M—Malleable. W—Weak.

MAGNETIC SUSCEPTIBILITY OF THE ELEMENTS AND INORGANIC COMPOUNDS

The following table lists the magnetic susceptibilities of one gram formula weight of a number of paramagnetic and diamagnetic inorganic compounds as well as the magnetic susceptibilities of the elements.

In each instance the magnetic moment is expressed in cgs units.

A more extensive listing of the magnetic susceptibilities of inorganic compounds as well as those for organic compounds may be found in Constantes Selectionnees Diamagnetisme et Paramagnetisme Relaxation Paramagnetique, Volume 7. This table is abridged from the above publication by permission of the publishers.

Substance	Formula	Temp. °K.	Susceptibility 10^{-6} cgs	Substance	Formula	Temp. °K.	Susceptibility 10^{-6} cgs
Aluminum (s).......	Al	ord.	+16.5	Barium (continued)			
" (l).......	Al	....	+12.0	Bromide.............	BaBr₂	ord.	−92.0
Fluoride..........	AlF₃	302	−13.4	"	BaBr₂·2H₂O	ord.	−119.0
Oxide............	Al₂O₃	ord.	−37.0	Carbonate...........	Ba(CO₃)	ord.	−58.9
Sulfate...........	Al₂(SO₄)₃	ord.	−93.0	Chlorate............	Ba(ClO₃)₂	ord.	−87.5
"	Al₂(SO₄)₃·18H₂O	ord.	−323.0	Chloride............	BaCl₂	ord.	−72.6
Ammonia (g)........	NH₃	ord.	−18.0	"	BaCl₂·2H₂O	ord.	−100.0
" (aq).......	NH₃	ord.	−17.0	Fluoride............	BaF₂	ord.	−51.0
Ammonium				Hydroxide...........	Ba(OH)₂	ord.	−53.2
Acetate...........	NH₄C₂H₃O₂	ord.	−41.1	"	Ba(OH)₂·8H₂O	ord.	−157.0
Bromide..........	NH₄Br	ord.	−47.0	Iodate..............	Ba(IO₃)₂	ord.	−122.5
Carbonate.........	(NH₄)₂CO₃	ord.	−42.50	Iodide..............	BaI₂	ord.	−124.0
Chlorate..........	NH₄ClO₃	ord.	−42.1	"	BaI₂·2H₂O	ord.	−163.0
Chloride..........	NH₄Cl	ord.	−36.7	Nitrate.............	Ba(NO₃)₂	ord.	−66.5
Fluoride..........	NH₄F	ord.	−23.0	Oxide..............	BaO	ord.	−29.1
Hydroxide (aq).....	NH₄OH	ord.	−31.5	"	BaO₂	ord.	−40.6
Iodate...........	NH₄IO₃	ord.	−62.3	Sulfate.............	BaSO₄	ord.	−71.3
Iodide...........	NH₄I	ord.	−66.0	Beryllium (s).........	Be	ord.	−9.0
Nitrate...........	NH₄NO₃	ord.	−33.6	Chloride............	BeCl₂	ord.	−26.5
Sulfate...........	(NH₄)₂SO₄	ord.	−67.0	Hydroxide...........	Be(OH)₂	ord.	−23.1
Thiocyanate.......	NH₄SCN	ord.	−48.1	Nitrate (aq).........	Be(NO₃)₂	298	−41.0
Americium (s).......	Am	300	+1000.0	Oxide..............	BeO	ord.	−11.9
Antimony (s)........	Sb	293	−99.0	Sulfate.............	BeSO₄	ord.	−37.0
" (l)..........	Sb	....	−2.5	Bismuth (s)..........	Bi	ord.	−280.1
Bromide..........	SbBr₃	ord.	−115.0	" (l)..........	Bi	....	−10.5
Chloride, tri......	SbCl₃	ord.	−86.7	Bromide............	BiBr₃	ord.	−147.0
Chloride, penta.....	SbCl₅	ord.	−120.0	Chloride............	BiCl₃	ord.	−26.5
Fluoride........	SbF₃	ord.	−46.0	Chromate............	Bi₂(CrO₄)₃	ord.	+154.0
Iodide...........	SbI₃	ord.	−147.0	Fluoride............	BiF₃	303	−61.0
Oxide...........	Sb₂O₃	ord.	−69.4	Hydroxide...........	Bi(OH)₃	ord.	−65.8
Sulfide..........	Sb₂S₃	ord.	−86.0	Iodide.............	BiI₃	ord.	−200.5
Argon (g)..........	A	ord.	−19.6	Nitrate.............	Bi(NO₃)₃	ord.	−91.0
Arsenic (α)........	As	293	−5.5	"	Bi(NO₃)₃·5H₂O	ord.	−159.0
" (β)........	As	293	−23.7	Oxide..............	BiO	ord.	−110.0
" (γ)........	As	293	−23.0	"	Bi₂O₃	ord.	−83.0
Bromide..........	AsBr₃	ord.	−106.0	Phosphate...........	BiPO₄	ord.	−77.0
Chloride..........	AsCl₃	ord.	−79.9	Sulfate.............	Bi₂(SO₄)₃	ord.	−199.0
Iodide...........	AsI₃	ord.	−142.0	Sulfide.............	Bi₂S₃	ord.	−123.0
Sulfide..........	As₂S₃	ord.	−70.0	Boric Acid...........	H₃BO₃	ord.	−34.1
Arsenious Acid......	H₃AsO₃	ord.	−51.2	Boron (s)...........	B	ord.	−6.7
Barium...........	Ba	ord.	+20.6	Chloride............	BCl₃	ord.	−59.9
Acetate...........	Ba(C₂H₃O₂)₂·H₂O	ord.	−100.1	Oxide..............	B₂O₃	ord.	−39.0
Bromate..........	Ba(BrO₃)₂	ord.	−105.8	Bromine (l)..........	Br₂		−56.4
				" (g)..........	Br₂	....	−73.5

Substance	Formula	Temp. °K.	Susceptibility 10⁻⁶ cgs	Substance	Formula	Temp. °K.	Susceptibility 10⁻⁶ cgs
Bromine (l) (continued)				Cobalt (continued)			
Fluoride.............	BrF₃	ord.	−33.9	Fluoride...........	CoF₂	293	+9490.0
"	BrF₅	ord.	−45.1	"	CoF₃	293	+1900.0
Cadmium (s).............	Cd	ord.	−19.8	Iodide.............	CoI₂	293	+10,760.0
" (l)	Cd	....	−18.0	Oxide.............	CoO	260	+4900.0
Acetate.............	Cd(C₂H₃O₂)₂	ord.	−83.7	"	Co₂O₃	ord.	+4560.0
Bromide.............	CdBr₂	ord.	−87.3	"	Co₃O₄	ord.	+7380.0
"	CdBr₂·4H₂O	ord.	−140.0	Phosphate.........	Co₃(PO₄)₂	291	+28,110.0
Carbonate.........	CdCO₃	ord.	−46.7	Sulfate.............	CoSO₄	293	+10,000.0
Chloride.............	CdCl₂	ord.	−68.7	"	Co₂(SO₄)₃	297	+1000.0
"	CdCl₂·2H₂O	ord.	−99.0	Sulfide.............	CoS	688	+251.0
Chromate.........	CdCrO₄	ord.	−16.8	"	CoS	293	+225.0
Cyanide.............	Cd(CN)₂	ord.	−54.0	Thiocyanate.......	Co(SCN)₂	303	+11,090.0
Fluoride.............	CdF₂	ord.	−40.6	Copper (s).........	Cu	296	−5.46
Hydroxide.........	Cd(OH)₂	ord.	−41.0	" (l)	Cu	....	−6.16
Iodate.............	Cd(IO₃)₂	ord.	−108.4	Bromide...........	CuBr	ord.	−49.0
Iodide.............	CdI₂	ord.	−117.2	"	CuBr₂	341.6	+653.3
Nitrate.............	Cd(NO₃)₂	ord.	−55.1	"	CuBr₂	292.7	+685.5
"	Cd(NO₃)₂·4H₂O	ord.	−140.0	"	CuBr₂	189	+736.9
Oxide.............	CdO	ord.	−30.0	"	CuBr₂	90	+658.7
Phosphate.........	Cd₃(PO₄)₂	ord.	−159.0	Chloride...........	CuCl	ord.	−40.0
Sulfate.............	CdSO₄	ord.	−59.2	"	CuCl₂	373.3	+1030.0
Sulfide.............	CdS	ord.	−50.0	"	CuCl₂	289	+1080.0
Calcium (s).........	Ca	....	+40.0	"	CuCl₂	170	+1815.0
Acetate.............	Ca(C₂H₃O₂)₂	ord.	−70.5	"	CuCl₂	69.25	+2370.0
Bromate...........	Ca(BrO₃)₂	ord.	−84.9	"	CuCl₂·2H₂O	293	+1420.0
Bromide...........	CaBr₂	ord.	−73.8	Cyanide...........	CuCN	ord.	−24.0
"	CaBr₂·3H₂O	ord.	−115.0	Fluoride...........	CuF₂	293	+1050.0
Carbonate.........	CaCO₃	ord.	−38.2	"	CuF₂	90	+1420.0
Chloride...........	CaCl₂	ord.	−54.7	"	CuF₂·2H₂O	293	+1600.0
Fluoride...........	CaF₂	ord.	−28.0	Hydroxide.........	Cu(OH)₂	292	+1170.0
Hydroxide.........	Ca(OH)₂	ord.	−22.0	Iodide.............	CuI	ord.	−63.0
Iodate.............	Ca(IO₃)₂	ord.	−101.4	Nitrate.............	Cu(NO₃)₂·3H₂O	293	+1570.0
Iodide.............	CaI₂	ord.	−109.0	"	Cu(NO₃)₂·6H₂O	293	+1625.0
Nitrate (aq).........	Ca(NO₃)₂	ord.	−45.9	Oxide.............	Cu₂O	293	−20.0
Oxide.............	CaO	ord.	−15.0	"	CuO	780	+259.6
"	CaO₂	ord.	−23.8	"	CuO	561	+267.3
Sulfate.............	CaSO₄	ord.	−49.7	"	CuO	397	+256.9
"	CaSO₄·2H₂O	ord.	−74.0	"	CuO	289.6	+238.9
Carbon (dia).........	C	ord.	−5.9	"	CuO	120	+156.2
" (graph)...........	C	ord.	−6.0	Phosphide.........	Cu₃P	ord.	−33.0
Dioxide.............	CO₂	ord.	−21.0	"	CuP₂	ord.	−35.0
Monoxide.........	CO	ord.	−9.8	Sulfate.............	CuSO₄	293	+1330.0
Cerium (α)...........	Ce	80.5	+5160.0	"	CuSO₄·H₂O	293	+1520.0
" (β)...........	Ce	293	+2450.0	"	CuSO₄·3H₂O	ord.	+1480.0
" (β)...........	Ce	80.5	+6230.0	"	CuSO₄·5H₂O	293	+1460.0
" (γ)...........	Ce	287.9	+2420.0	Sulfide.............	CuS	293	−2.0
" (γ)...........	Ce	125.6	+4640.0	Thiocyanate.......	CuSCN	ord.	−48.0
" (γ)...........	Ce	80.5	+5200.0	Dysprosium.........	Dy	293.2	103,500.0
Chloride...........	CeCl₃	287	+2490.0	Oxide.............	Dy₂O₃	287.2	+89,600.0
Fluoride...........	CeF₃	293	+2190.0	Sulfate.............	Dy₂(SO₄)₃	293	+91,400.0
Nitrate.............	Ce(NO₃)₃·5H₂O	292	+2310.0	"	Dy₂(SO₄)₃·8H₂O	291.2	+92,760.0
Oxide.............	CeO₂	293	+26.0	Sulfide.............	Dy₂S₃	292	+95,200.0
Sulfate.............	CeSO₄	ord.	+37.0	Erbium.............	Er	291	+44,300.0
"	Ce₂(SO₄)₃·5H₂O	293	+4540.0	Oxide.............	Er₂O₃	286	+73,920.0
"	Ce(SO₄)₂·4H₂O	293	−97.0	Sulfate.............	Er₂(SO₄)₃·8H₂O	293	+74,600.0
Sulfide.............	CeS	ord.	+2110.0	Sulfide.............	Er₂S₃	292	+77,200.0
"	Ce₂S₃	292	+5080.0	Europium...........	Eu	293	+34,000.0
Cesium (s)...........	Cs	ord.	+29.0	Bromide...........	EuBr₂	292	+26,800.0
" (l)	Cs	....	+26.5	Chloride...........	EuCl₂	292	+26,500.0
Bromate...........	CsBrO₃	ord.	−75.1	Fluoride...........	EuF₂	292	+23,750.0
Bromide...........	CsBr	ord.	−67.2	Iodide.............	EuI₂	292	+26,000.0
Carbonate.........	Cs₂CO₂	ord.	−103.6	Oxide.............	Eu₂O₃	298	+10,100.0
Chlorate...........	CsClO₃	ord.	−65.0	Sulfate.............	EuSO₄	293	+25,730.0
Chloride...........	CsCl	ord.	−86.7	"	Eu₂(SO₄)₃	293	+10,400.0
Fluoride...........	CsF	ord.	−44.5	"	Eu₂(SO₄)₃·8H₂O	293	+9,540.0
Iodate.............	CsIO₃	ord.	−83.1	Sulfide.............	EuS	293	+23,800.0
Iodide.............	CsI	ord.	−82.6	"	EuS	195	+35,400.0
Oxide.............	CsO₂	293	+1534.0	Gadolinium...........	Gd	300.6	+755,000.0
"	CsO₂	90	+4504.0	Chloride.............	GdCl₃	293	+27,930.0
Sulfate.............	Cs₂SO₄	ord.	−116.0	Oxide.............	Gd₂O₃	293	+53,200.0
Sulfide.............	Cs₂S	ord.	−104.0	Sulfate.............	Gd₂(SO₄)₃	285.5	+54,200.0
Chlorine (l).........	Cl₂	ord.	−40.5	"	Gd₂(SO₄)₃·8H₂O	293	+53,280.0
Fluoride, tri.........	ClF₃	ord.	−26.5	Sulfide.............	Gd₂S₃	292	+55,500.0
Chromium.........	Cr	273	+180.0	Gallium (s).........	Ga	80	−24.4
"	Cr	1713	+224.0	" (s)	Ga	290	−21.6
Acetate.............	Cr(C₂H₃O₂)₃	293	+5104.0	" (l)	Ga	313	+2.5
Chloride...........	CrCl₂	293	+7230.0	Chloride.............	GaCl₃	ord.	−63.0
"	CrCl₃	293	+6890.0	Iodide.............	GaI₃	ord.	−149.0
Fluoride...........	CrF₃	293	+4370.0	Oxide.............	Ga₂O	ord.	−34.0
Oxide.............	Cr₂O₃	300	+1960.0	Sulfide.............	Ga₂S	ord.	−36.0
"	CrO₃	ord.	+40.0	"	GaS	ord.	−23.0
Sulfate.............	Cr₂(SO₄)₃	293	+11,800.0	"	Ga₂S₃	ord.	−80.0
"	Cr₂(SO₄)₃·8H₂O	290	+12,700.0	Germanium.........	Ge	293	−76.84
"	Cr₂(SO₄)₃·10H₂O	290	+12,600.0	Chloride...........	GeCl₄	ord.	−72.0
"	Cr₂(SO₄)₃·14H₂O	290	+12,160.0	Fluoride...........	GeF₄	ord.	−50.0
"	CrSO₄·6H₂O	293	+9690.0	Iodide.............	GeI₄	ord.	−174.0
Sulfide.............	CrS	ord.	+2390.0	Oxide.............	GeO	ord.	−28.8
Cobalt.............	Co	....	ferro	"	GeO₂	ord.	−34.3
Acetate.............	Co(C₂H₃O₂)₂	293	+11,000.0	Sulfide.............	GeS	ord.	−40.9
Bromide.............	CoBr₂	293	+13,000.0	"	GeS₂	ord.	−53.3
Chloride...........	CoCl₂	293	+12,660.0	Gold (s)...........	Au	296	−28.0
"	CoCl₂·6H₂O	293	+9710.0	" (l)	Au	....	−34.0
Cyanide.............	Co(CN)₂	303	+3825.0				

Substance	Formula	Temp. °K.	Susceptibility 10⁻⁶ cgs	Substance	Formula	Temp. °K.	Susceptibility 10⁻⁶ cgs
Gold (continued)				Lead (s) (continued)			
Bromide	AuBr	ord.	−61.0	Thiocyanate	Pb(CNS)$_2$	ord.	−82.0
Chloride	AuCl	ord.	−67.0	Lithium	Li	ord.	+14.2
	AuCl$_3$	ord.	−112.0	Acetate	LiC$_2$H$_3$O$_2$	ord.	−34.0
Fluoride	AuF$_3$	ord.	+74.0	Bromate	LiBrO$_3$	ord.	−39.0
Iodide	AuI	ord.	−91.0	Bromide	LiBr	ord.	−34.7
Phosphide	AuP$_3$	ord.	−107.0	Carbonate	Li$_2$CO$_3$	ord.	−27.0
Hafnium (s)	Hf	298	+75.0	Chlorate (aq)	LiClO$_3$	ord.	−28.8
" (s)	Hf	1673	+104.0	Chloride	LiCl	ord.	−24.3
Oxide	HfO$_2$	ord.	−23.0	Fluoride	LiF	ord.	−10.1
Helium (g)	He	ord.	−1.88	Hydride	LiH	ord.	−4.6
Holmium	Ho			Hydroxide	LiOH	ord.	−12.3
Oxide	Ho$_2$O$_3$	293	+88,100.0	Iodate	LiIO$_3$	ord.	−47.0
Sulfate	Ho$_2$(SO$_4$)$_3$	293	+91,700.0	Iodide	LiI	ord.	−50.0
	Ho$_2$(SO$_4$)$_3$·8H$_2$O	293	+91,600.0	Nitrate	LiNO$_3$·3H$_2$O	ord.	−62.0
Hydrogen (g)	H$_2$		−3.98	Sulfate	Li$_2$SO$_4$	ord.	−40.0
Bromide (l)	HBr	273		Lutetium	Lu	ord.	>0.0
" (aq)	HBr	ord.		Magnesium	Mg	ord.	+13.1
Chloride (l)	HCl	273	−22.6	Acetate	Mg(C$_2$H$_3$O$_2$)$_2$·4H$_2$O	ord.	−116.0
" (aq)	HCl	300	−22.0	Bromide	MgBr$_2$	ord.	−72.0
Fluoride (l)	HF	287	−8.6	Carbonate	MgCO$_3$	ord.	−32.4
" (aq)	HF	ord.	−9.3	"	MgCO$_3$·3H$_2$O	ord.	−72.7
Iodide (l)	HI	281	−47.7	Chloride	MgCl$_2$	ord.	−47.4
" (l)	HI	233	−48.3	Fluoride	MgF$_2$	ord.	−22.7
" (s)	HI	195	−47.3	Hydroxide	Mg(OH)$_2$	288	−22.1
" (aq)	HI	ord.	−50.2	Iodide	MgI$_2$	ord.	−111.0
Oxide—See Water				Oxide	MgO	ord.	−10.2
Peroxide	H$_2$O$_2$	ord.	−17.7	Phosphate	Mg$_3$(PO$_4$)$_2$·4H$_2$O	ord.	−167.0
Sulfide	H$_2$S	ord.	−25.5	Sulfate	MgSO$_4$	294	−50.0
Indium	In	ord.	−64.0	"	MgSO$_4$·H$_2$O	ord.	−61.0
Bromide	InBr$_2$	ord.	−107.0	"	MgSO$_4$·5H$_2$O	ord.	−109.0
Chloride	InCl	ord.	−30.0	"	MgSO$_4$·7H$_2$O	ord.	−135.7
"	InCl$_2$	ord.	−56.0	Manganese (α)	Mn	293	+529.0
"	InCl$_3$	ord.	−86.0	(β)	Mn	293	+483.0
Fluoride	InF$_2$	ord.	−61.0	Acetate	Mn(C$_2$H$_3$O$_2$)$_2$	293	+13,650.0
Oxide	In$_2$O	ord.	−47.0	Bromide	MnBr$_2$	294	+13,900.0
"	In$_2$O$_3$	ord.	−56.0	Carbonate	MnCO$_3$	293	+11,400.0
Sulfide	In$_2$S	ord.	−50.0	Chloride	MnCl$_2$	293	+14,350.0
"	InS	ord.	−28.0	"	MnCl$_2$·4H$_2$O	293	+14,600.0
"	In$_2$S$_3$	ord.	−98.0	Fluoride	MnF$_2$	290	+10,700.0
Iodic Acid	HIO$_3$	ord.	−48.0	"	MnF$_3$	293	+10,500.0
metaper	HIO$_4$	ord.	−56.5	Hydroxide	Mn(OH)$_2$	293	+13,500.0
orthoparaper	H$_5$IO$_6$	ord.	−71.4	Iodide	MnI$_2$	293	+14,400.0
Iodine (s)	I$_2$	ord.	−88.7	Oxide	MnO	293	+1850.0
" (atomic)	I	1303	+869.0	"	Mn$_2$O$_3$	293	+14,100.0
" (atomic)	I	1400	+1120.0	"	MnO$_2$	293	+2280.0
Chloride	ICl	ord.	−54.6	"	Mn$_3$O$_4$	298	+12,400.0
"	ICl$_3$	ord.	−90.2	Sulfate	MnSO$_4$	293	+13,660.0
Fluoride	IF$_5$	ord.	−58.1	"	MnSO$_4$·H$_2$O	293	+14,200.0
Oxide	I$_2$O$_5$	ord.	−79.4	"	MnSO$_4$·4H$_2$O	293	+14,600.0
Iridium	Ir	298	+25.6	"	MnSO$_4$·5H$_2$O	293	+14,700.0
"	Ir	698	+32.1	Sulfide (α)	MnS	293	+5630.0
Chloride	IrCl$_3$	ord.	−14.4	" (β)	MnS	293	+3850.0
Oxide	IrO$_2$	298	+224.0	Mercury (s)	Hg		−24.1
Iron	Fe		ferro	" (l)	Hg	293	−33.44
Bromide	FeBr$_2$	ord.	+13,600.0	" (g)	Hg		−78.3
Carbonate	FeCO$_3$	293	+11,300.0	Acetate	HgC$_2$H$_3$O$_2$	ord.	−70.5
Chloride	FeCl$_2$	293	+14,750.0	"	Hg(C$_2$H$_3$O$_2$)$_2$	ord.	−100.0
"	FeCl$_2$·4H$_2$O	293	+12,900.0	Bromate	HgBrO$_3$	ord.	−57.7
"	FeCl$_3$	293	+13,450.0	Bromide	HgBr	ord.	−57.2
"	FeCl$_3$	398	+9,980.0	"	HgBr$_2$	ord.	−94.2
"	FeCl$_3$·6H$_2$O	290	+15,250.0	Chloride	HgCl	ord.	−52.0
Fluoride	FeF$_2$	293	+9,500.0	"	HgCl$_2$	ord.	−82.0
"	FeF$_3$	305	+13,760.0	Chromate	Hg$_2$CrO$_4$	ord.	−63.0
"	FeF$_3$·3H$_2$O	293	+7870.0	"	HgCrO$_4$	ord.	−12.5
Iodide	FeI$_2$	ord.	+13,600.0	Cyanide	Hg(CN)$_2$	ord.	−67.0
Nitrate	Fe(NO$_3$)$_3$·9H$_2$O	293	+15,200.0	Fluoride	HgF	ord.	−53.0
Oxide	FeO	293	+7200.0	"	HgF$_2$	302	−62.0
"	Fe$_2$O$_3$	1033	+3586.0	Hydroxide	Hg$_2$(OH)$_2$	ord.	−100.0
Phosphate	FePO$_4$	ord.	+11,500.0	Iodate	HgIO$_3$	ord.	−92.0
Sulfate	FeSO$_4$	293	+10,200.0	Iodide	HgI	ord.	−83.0
"	FeSO$_4$·H$_2$O	290	+10,500.0	"	HgI$_2$	ord.	−128.6
"	FeSO$_4$·7H$_2$O	293	+11,200.0	Nitrate	HgNO$_3$	ord.	−55.9
Sulfide	FeS	293	+1074.0	"	Hg(NO$_3$)$_2$	ord.	−74.0
Krypton	Kr		−28.8	Oxide	Hg$_2$O	ord.	−76.3
Lanthanum	La	ord.	+118.0	"	HgO	ord.	−44.0
Oxide	La$_2$O$_3$	ord.	−78.0	Sulfate	Hg$_2$SO$_4$	ord.	−123.0
Sulfate	La$_2$(SO$_4$)$_3$·9H$_2$O	293	−262.0	"	HgSO$_4$	ord.	−78.1
Sulfide	La$_2$S$_3$	292	−37.0	Sulfide	HgS	ord.	−55.4
"	La$_2$S$_4$	293	−100.0	Thiocyanate	Hg(SCN)$_2$	ord.	−96.5
Lead (s)	Pb	289	−23.0	Molybdenum	Mo	298	+89.0
" (l)	Pb	330	−15.5	"	Mo	63.8	+108.0
Acetate	Pb(C$_2$H$_3$O$_2$)$_2$	ord.	89.1	"	Mo	20.4	+149.2
Bromide	PbBr$_2$	ord.	−90.6	Bromide	MoBr$_3$	293	+525.0
Carbonate	PbCO$_3$	ord.	−61.2	"	MoBr$_4$	293	+520.0
Chloride	PbCl$_2$	ord.	−73.8	"	Mo$_3$Br$_6$	290.5	−46.0
Chromate	PbCrO$_4$	ord.	−18.0	Chloride	MoCl$_3$	290	+43.0
Fluoride	PbF$_2$	ord.	−58.1	"	MoCl$_4$	291	+1750.0
Iodate	Pb(IO$_3$)$_2$	ord.	−131.0	"	MoCl$_5$	289	+990.0
Iodide	PbI$_2$	ord.	−126.5	Fluoride	MoF$_6$	ord.	−26.0
Nitrate	Pb(NO$_3$)$_2$	ord.	−74.0	Oxide	Mo$_2$O$_3$	ord.	−42.0
Oxide	PbO	ord.	−42.0	"	MoO$_2$	289	+41.0
Phosphate	Pb$_3$(PO$_4$)$_2$	ord.	−182.0	"	MoO$_3$	292.5	+3.0
Sulfate	PbSO$_4$	ord.	−69.7	"	Mo$_3$O$_8$	ord.	+42.0
Sulfide	PbS	ord.	−84.0	Sulfide	MoS$_3$	289	−63.0

MAGNETIC SUSCEPTIBILITY OF THE ELEMENTS
AND INORGANIC COMPOUNDS (Continued)

Substance	Formula	Temp. °K.	Susceptibility 10^{-6} cgs
Neodymium	Nd	287.7	5628.0
Fluoride	NdF_3	293	+4980.0
Nitrate	$Nd(NO_3)_3$	293	+5020.0
Oxide	Nd_2O_3	292.0	+10,200.0
Sulfate	$Nd_2(SO_4)_3$	293	+9990.0
Sulfide	Nd_2S_3	292	+5550.0
Neon	Ne	ord.	−6.74
Nickel	Ni	......	ferro
Acetate	$Ni(C_2H_3O_2)_2$	293	+4690.0
Bromide	$NiBr_2$	293	+5600.0
Chloride	$NiCl_2$	293	+6145.0
"	$NiCl_2·6H_2O$	293	+4240.0
Fluoride	NiF_2	293	+2410.0
Hydroxide	$Ni(OH)_2$	ord.	+4500.0
Iodide	NiI_2	293	+3875.0
Nitrate	$Ni(NO_3)_2·6H_2O$	293.5	+4300.0
Oxide	NiO	293	+660.0
Sulfate	$NiSO_4$	293	+4005.0
Sulfide	NiS	293	+190.0
"	Ni_3S_2	ord.	+1030.0
Niobium	Nb	298	+195.0
Oxide	Nb_2O_5	ord.	−10.0
Nitric Acid	HNO_3	ord.	−19.9
Nitrogen	N_2	ord.	−12.0
Oxide	N_2O	285	−18.9
" (g)	NO	293	+1461.0
" (g)	NO	203.8	+1895.0
" (g)	NO	146.9	+2324.0
" (l)	NO	117.64	+114.2
" (s)	NO	90	+19.8
"	N_2O_3	291	−16.0
"	NO_2	408	+150.0
"	N_2O_4	303.6	−22.1
"	N_2O_4	295.1	−23.0
"	N_2O_4	257	−25.4
" (aq)	N_2O_5	289	−35.6
Osmium	Os	298	+9.9
Chloride	$OsCl_2$	ord.	+41.3
Oxygen (g)	O_2	293	+3449.0
" (l)	O_2	90.1	+7699.0
" (l)	O_2	70.8	+8685.0
" (s, γ)	O_2	54.3	+10,200.0
" (s, β)	O_2	......	......
" (s, α)	O_2	23.7	+1760.0
Ozone (l)	O_3	.....	+6.7
Palladium	Pd	288	+567.4
Chloride	$PdCl_2$	291.3	−38.0
Fluoride	PdF_3	293	+1760.0
Hydride	PdH	ord.	+1077.0
"	Pd_2H	ord.	+2353.0
Phosphoric Acid (aq)	H_3PO_4	ord.	−43.8
Phosphorous Acid (aq)	H_3PO_3	ord.	−42.5
Phosphorous (red)	P	......	−20.8
" (black)	P	ord.	−26.6
Chloride	PCl_3	...	−63.4
Platinum	Pt	290.3	+201.9
Chloride	$PtCl_2$	298	−54.0
"	$PtCl_3$	ord.	−66.7
"	$PtCl_4$	ord.	−93.0
Fluoride	PtF_4	293	+455.0
Oxide	Pt_2O_3	ord.	−37.70
Plutonium	Pu	293	+610.0
Fluoride	PuF_4	301	+1760.0
"	PuF_6	295	+173.0
Oxide	PuO_2	300	+730.0
Potassium	K	ord.	+20.8
Acetate (aq)	$KC_2H_3O_2$	28	−45.0
Bromate	$KBrO_3$	ord.	−52.6
Bromide	KBr	ord.	−49.1
Carbonate	K_2CO_3	ord.	−59.0
Chlorate	$KClO_3$	ord.	−42.8
Chloride	KCl	ord.	−39.0
Chromate	K_2CrO_4	ord.	−3.9
"	$K_2Cr_2O_7$	293	+29.4
Cyanide	KCN	ord.	−37.0
Ferricyanide	$K_3Fe(CN)_6$	297	+2290.0
Ferrocyanide	$K_4Fe(CN)_6$	ord.	−130.0
"	$K_4Fe(CN)_6·3H_2O$	ord.	−172.3
Fluoride	KF	ord.	−23.6
Hydroxide (aq)	KOH	ord.	−22.0
Iodate	KIO_3	ord.	−63.1
Iodide	KI	ord.	−63.8
Nitrate	KNO_3	ord.	−33.7
Nitrite	KNO_2	ord.	−23.3
Oxide	KO_2	293	+3230.0
"	KO_3	ord.	+1185.0
Permanganate	$KMnO_4$	ord.	+20.0
Sulfate	K_2SO_4	ord.	−67.0
"	$KHSO_4$	ord.	−49.8
Sulfide	K_2S	ord.	−60.0
"	K_2S_2	ord.	−71.0
"	K_2S_3	ord.	−80.0
"	K_2S_4	ord.	−89.0
"	K_2S_5	ord.	−98.0
Sulfite	K_2SO_3	ord.	−64.0
Potassium (continued)			
Thiocyanate	KSCN	ord.	−48.0
Praseodymium	Pr	293	+5010.0
Chloride	$PrCl_3$	307.1	+44.5
Oxide	PrO_2	293	+1930.0
"	Pr_2O_3	827	+4000.0
Oxide	Pr_2O_3	294.5	+8994.0
Sulfate	$Pr_2(SO_4)_3$	291	+9660.0
"	$Pr_2(SO_4)_3·8H_2O$	289	+9880.0
Sulfide	Pr_2S_3	292	+10,770.0
Rhenium	Re	293	+67.6
Chloride	$ReCl_5$	293	+1225.0
Oxide	ReO_2	ord.	+44.0
"	$ReO_2·2H_2O$	295	+74.0
"	ReO_3	ord.	+16.0
"	Re_2O_7	ord.	−16.0
Sulfide	ReS_2	ord.	+38.0
Rhodium	Rh	298	+111.0
"	Rh	723	+123.0
Chloride	$RhCl_3$	298	−7.5
Fluoride	RhF_4	293	+500.0
Oxide	Rh_2O_3	298	+104.0
Sulfate	$Rh_2(SO_4)_3·6H_2O$	298	+104.0
"	$Rh_2(SO_4)_3·14H_2O$	298	+149.0
Rubidium	Rb	303	+17.0
Bromide	RbBr	ord.	−56.4
Carbonate	Rb_2CO_3	ord.	−75.4
Chloride	RbCl	ord.	−46.0
Fluoride	RbF	ord.	−31.9
Iodide	RbI	ord.	−72.2
Nitrate	$RbNO_3$	ord.	−41.0
Oxide	RbO_2	293	+1527.0
Sulfate	Rb_2SO_4	ord.	−88.4
Sulfide	Rb_2S	ord.	−80.0
"	Rb_2S_2	ord.	−90.0
Ruthenium	Ru	298	+43.2
"	Ru	723	+50.2
Chloride	$RuCl_3$	290.9	+1998.0
Oxide	RuO_2	298	+162.0
Samarium	Sm	291	+1860.0
"	Sm	195	+2230.0
Bromide	$SmBr_2$	293	+5337.0
"	$SmBr_3$	293	+972.0
Oxide	Sm_2O_3	292	+1988.0
"	Sm_2O_3	170	+1960.0
"	Sm_2O_3	85	+2282.0
Sulfate	$Sm_2(SO_4)_3·8H_2O$	293	+1710.0
Sulfide	Sm_2S_3	292	+3300.0
Scandium	Sc	292	+315.0
Selenic Acid	H_2SeO_4	ord.	−51.2
Selenious Acid	H_2SeO_3	ord.	−45.4
Selenium (s)	Se	ord.	−25.0
" (l)	Se	900	−24.0
Bromide	Se_2Br_2	ord.	−113.0
Chloride	Se_2Cl_2	ord.	−94.8
Fluoride	SeF_6	ord.	−51.0
Oxide	SeO_2	ord.	−27.2
Silicon	Si	ord.	−3.9
Bromide	$SiBr_4$	ord.	−128.6
Carbide	SiC	ord.	−12.8
Chloride	$SiCl_4$	ord.	−88.3
Hydroxide	$Si(OH)_4$	ord.	−42.6
Oxide	SiO_2	ord.	−29.6
Silver (s)	Ag	296	−19.5
" (l)	Ag	......	−24.0
Acetate	$AgC_2H_3O_2$	ord.	−60.4
Bromide	AgBr	283	−59.7
Carbonate	Ag_2CO_3	ord.	−80.90
Chloride	AgCl	ord.	−49.0
Chromate	Ag_2CrO_4	ord.	−40.0
Cyanide	AgCN	ord.	−43.2
Fluoride	AgF	ord.	−36.5
Iodide	AgI	ord.	−80.0
Nitrate	$AgNO_3$	ord.	−45.7
Nitrite	$AgNO_2$	ord.	−42.0
Oxide	Ag_2O	ord.	−134.0
"	AgO	287	−19.6
Permanganate	$AgMnO_4$	300	−63.0
Phosphate	Ag_3PO_4	ord.	−120.0
Sulfate	Ag_2SO_4	ord.	−92.90
Thiocyanate	AgSCN	ord.	−61.8
Sodium	Na	ord.	+16.0
Acetate	$NaC_2H_3O_2$	ord.	−37.6
Borate, tetra	$Na_2B_4O_7$	ord.	−85.0
Bromate	$NaBrO_3$	ord.	−44.2
Bromide	NaBr	ord.	−41.0
Carbonate	Na_2CO_3	ord.	−41.0
Chlorate	$NaClO_3$	ord.	−34.7
Chloride	NaCl	ord.	−30.3
Chromate, di	$Na_2Cr_2O_7$	ord.	+55.0
Fluoride	NaF	ord.	−16.4
Hydroxide (aq)	NaOH	300	−16.0
Iodate	$NaIO_3$	ord.	−53.0
Iodide	NaI	ord.	−57.0
Nitrate	$NaNO_3$	ord.	−25.6

Substance	Formula	Temp. °K.	Susceptibility 10^{-6} cgs	Substance	Formula	Temp. °K.	Susceptibility 10^{-6} cgs
Sodium (continued)				Tin (continued)			
Nitrite	$NaNO_2$	ord.	−14.5	"	Sn	......	−4.5
Oxide	Na_2O	ord.	−19.8	Bromide	$SnBr_4$	ord.	−149.0
"	Na_2O_2	ord.	−28.10	Chloride	$SnCl_2$	ord.	−69.0
Phosphate, meta	$NaPO_3$	ord.	−42.5	"	$SnCl_2·2H_2O$	ord.	−91.4
"	Na_2HPO_4	ord.	−56.6	" (l)	$SnCl_4$	ord.	−115.0
Sulfate	Na_2SO_4	ord.	−52.0	Hydroxide	$Sn(OH)_4$	ord.	−60.0
"	$Na_2SO_4·10H_2O$	ord.	−184.0	Oxide	SnO	ord.	−19.0
Sulfide	Na_2S	ord.	−39.0	"	SnO_2	ord.	−41.0
"	Na_2S_2	ord.	−53.0	Titanium	Ti	293	+153.0
"	Na_2S_3	ord.	−68.0	"	Ti	90	+150.0
"	Na_2S_4	ord.	−84.0	Bromide	$TiBr_2$	288	+640.0
"	Na_2S_5	ord.	−99.0	"	$TiBr_3$	441	+520.0
Strontium	Sr	ord.	+92.0	"	$TiBr_3$	291	+660.0
Acetate	$Sr(C_2H_3O_2)_2$	ord.	−79.0	"	$TiBr_3$	195	+680.0
Bromate	$Sr(BrO_3)_2$	ord.	−93.5	"	$TiBr_3$	90	+220.0
Bromide	$SrBr_2$	ord.	−86.6	Carbide	TiC	ord.	+8.0
"	$SrBr_2·6H_2O$	ord.	−160.0	Chloride	$TiCl_2$	288	+570.0
Carbonate	$SrCO_3$	ord.	−47.0	"	$TiCl_3$	685	+705.0
Chlorate	$Sr(ClO_3)_2$	ord.	−73.0	"	$TiCl_3$	373	+1030.0
Chloride	$SrCl_2$	ord.	−63.0	"	$TiCl_3$	292	+1110.0
"	$SrCl_2·6H_2O$	ord.	−145.0	"	$TiCl_3$	212	+690.0
Chromate	$SrCrO_4$	ord.	−5.1	"	$TiCl_3$	90	+220.0
Fluoride	SrF_2	ord.	−37.2	"	$TiCl_4$	ord.	−54.0
Hydroxide	$Sr(OH)_2$	ord.	−40.0	Fluoride	TiF_3	293	+1300.0
"	$Sr(OH)_2·8H_2O$	ord.	−136.0	Iodide	TiI_2	288	+1790.0
Iodate	$Sr(IO_3)_2$	ord.	−108.0	"	TiI_3	434	+221.0
Iodide	SrI_2	ord.	−112.0	"	TiI_3	292	+160.0
Nitrate	$Sr(NO_3)_2$	ord.	−57.2	"	TiI_3	195	+159.0
"	$Sr(NO_3)_2·4H_2O$	ord.	−106.0	"	TiI_3	90	+167.0
Oxide	SrO	ord.	−35.0	Oxide	Ti_2O_3	382	+152.0
"	SrO_2	ord.	−32.3	"	Ti_2O_3	298	+125.6
Sulfate	$SrSO_4$	ord.	−57.9	"	TiO_3	248	+132.4
Sulfur (α)	S	ord.	−15.5	"	TiO_2	ord.	+5.9
" (β)	S	ord.	−14.9	Sulfide	TiS	ord.	+432.0
" (l)	S		−15.4	Tungsten	W	298	+59.0
" (g)	S	828	+700.0	Bromide	WBr_5	293	+250.0
" (g)	S	1023	+464.0	Carbide	WC	ord.	+10.0
Chloride	S_2Cl_2	ord.	−62.2	Chloride	WCl_2	293	−25.0
"	SCl_2	ord.	−49.4	"	WCl_5	293	+387.0
"	SCl_3	ord.	−49.4	"	WCl_6	ord.	−71.0
Fluoride	SF_6	ord.	−44.0	Fluoride	WF_6	ord.	−40.0
Iodide	SI	ord.	−52.7	Oxide	WO_2	ord.	+57.0
Oxide (l)	SO_2	ord.	−18.2	"	WO_3	ord.	−15.8
Sulfuric Acid	H_2SO_4	ord.	−39.8	Sulfide	WS_2	303	+5850.0
Tantalum	Ta	293	+154.0	Tungstic Acid, ortho.	H_2WO_4	ord.	−28.0
"	Ta	2143	+124.0	Uranium (α)	U	78	+395.0
Chloride	$TaCl_5$	304	+140.0	" (α)	U	298	+409.0
Fluoride	TaF_3	293	+795.0	" (α)	U	623	+440.0
Oxide	Ta_2O_5	ord.	−32.0	" (β)	U		
Technetium	Tc	402	250.0	" (γ)	U	1393	+514.0
"	Tc	298	270.0	Bromide	UBr_3	294	+4740.0
"	Tc	78	290.0	"	UBr_4	293	+3530.0
Oxide	$TcO_2·2H_2O$	300	+244.0	Chloride	UCl_3	300	+3460.0
"	Tc_2O_7	298	−40.0	"	UCl_4	294	+3680.0
Tellurium (s)	Te	ord.	−39.5	Fluoride	UF_4	300	+3530.0
" (l)	Te	......	−6.4	"	UF_6	ord.	+43.0
Bromide	$TeBr_2$	ord.	−106.0	Hydrides	UH_3	462	+2821.0
Chloride	$TeCl_2$	ord.	−94.0	"	UH_3	391	+3568.0
Fluoride	TeF_6	ord.	−66.0	"	UH_3	295	+6244.0
Terbium	Tb	273	+146,000.0	"	UH_3	255	+9306.0
Oxide	Tb_2O_3	288.1	+78,340.0	Iodide	UI_3	293	+4460.0
Sulfate	$Tb_2(SO_4)_3$	293	+78,200.0	Oxide	UO	293	+1600.0
"	$Tb_2(SO_4)_3·8H_2O$	293	+76,500.0	"	UO_2	293	+2360.0
Thallium (α)	Tl	ord.	−50.9	"	UO_3	ord.	+128.0
" (β)	Tl	>508	−32.3	Sulfate	$U(SO_4)_2$	ord.	+31.0
" (l)	Tl	573	−26.8	Sulfide (α)	US_2	290.5	+3137.0
Acetate	$TlC_2H_3O_2$	ord.	−69.0	" (β)	US_2	290.5	+3470.0
Bromate	$TlBrO_3$	ord.	−75.9	"	U_2S_3	ord.	+5206.0
Bromide	$TlBr$	ord.	−63.9	"	U_3S_5	ord.	+11,220.0
Carbonate	Tl_2CO_3	ord.	−101.6	Vanadium	V	298	+255.0
Chlorate	$TlClO_3$	ord.	−65.5	Bromide	VBr_2	293	+3230.0
Chloride	$TlCl$	ord.	−57.8	"	VBr_2	195	+3760.0
Chromate	Tl_2CrO_4	ord.	−39.3	"	VBr_2	90	+4470.0
Cyanide	$TlCN$	ord.	−49.0	"	VBr_3	293	+2890.0
Fluoride	TlF	ord.	−44.4	"	VBr_3	195	+4110.0
Iodate	$TlIO_3$	ord.	−86.8	"	VBr_3	90	+8540.0
Iodide	TlI	ord.	−82.2	Chloride	VCl_2	293	+2410.0
Nitrate	$TlNO_3$	ord.	−56.5	"	VCl_3	293	+3030.0
Nitrite	$TlNO_2$	ord.	−50.8	"	VCl_4	293	+1130.0
Oxide	Tl_2O_3	ord.	+76.0	"	VCl_4	195	+1700.0
Phosphate	Tl_3PO_4	ord.	−145.2	"	VCl_4	90	+4360.0
Sulfate	Tl_2SO_4	ord.	−112.6	Fluoride	VF_3	293	+2730.0
Sulfide	Tl_2S	ord.	−88.8	Oxide	VO_2	290	+270.0
Thiocyanate	$TlCNS$	ord.	−80.7	"	V_2O_3	293	+1976.0
Thorium	Th	293	+132.0	"	V_2O_5	ord.	−128.0
"	Th	90	+153.0	Sulfide	VS	ord.	+600.0
Chloride	$ThCl_4·8H_2O$	305.2	−180.0	"	V_2S_3	293	+1560.0
Nitrate	$Th(NO_3)_4$	ord.	−108.0	Water (g)	H_2O	>373	−13.1
Oxide	ThO_2	ord.	−16.0	" (l)	H_2O	373	−13.09
Thulium	Tm	291	+25,500.0	" (l)	H_2O	293	−12.97
Oxide	Tm_2O_3	296.5	+51,444.0	" (l)	H_2O	273	−12.93
Tin (white)	Sn	ord.	+3.1	" (s)	H_2O	273	−12.65
" (gray)	Sn	280	−37.0	" (s)	H_2O	223	−12.31
" (gray)	Sn	100	−31.7				

Substance	Formula	Temp. °K.	Susceptibility 10⁻⁶ cgs
Water (continued)			
" (l)	DHO	302	−12.97
" (l)	D₂O	293	−12.76
" (l)	D₂O	276.8	−12.66
" (s)	D₂O	276.8	−12.54
" (s)	D₂O	213	−12.41
Xenon	Xe	ord.	−43.9
Ytterbium	Yb	292	+249.0
"	Yb	90	+639.0
Sulfide	Yb₂S₃	292	+18,300.0
Yttrium	Y	292	+2.15
"	Y	90	+2.43
Oxide	Y₂O₃	293	+44.4
Sulfide	Y₂S₃	ord.	+100.0
Zinc (s)	Zn	ord.	−11.4
" (l)	Zn	......	−7.8
Acetate	Zn(C₂H₃O₂)₂·2H₂O	ord.	−101.0
Carbonate	ZnCO₃	ord.	−34.0
Chloride	ZnCl₂	296	−65.0
Cyanide	Zn(CN)₂	ord.	−46.0
Fluoride	ZnF₂	299.6	−38.2
Hydroxide	Zn(OH)₂	ord.	−67.0
Iodide	ZnI₂	ord.	−98.0
Nitrate (aq)	Zn(NO₃)₂	ord.	−63.0
Oxide	ZnO	ord.	−46.0
Phosphate	Zn₃(PO₄)₂	ord.	−141.0
Sulfate	ZnSO₄	ord.	−45.0
"	ZnSO₄·H₂O	ord.	−63.0
"	ZnSO₄·7H₂O	ord.	−143.0
Sulfide	ZnS	ord.	−25.0
Zirconium	Zr	293	+122.0
"	Zr	90	+119.0
Carbide	ZrC	ord.	−26.0
Nitrate	Zr(NO₃)₄·5H₂O	ord.	−77.0
Oxide	ZrO₂	ord.	−13.8

DIAMAGNETIC SUSCEPTIBILITIES OF ORGANIC COMPOUNDS

Compiled by George W. Smith

This table and its supplement contain values for the molar susceptibility of χ_M, specific susceptibility χ, and volumetric susceptibility K. The cgs Gaussian system of units is employed. In the Gaussian units the relation between magnetic induction B and magnetic field strength H is

$$B = H + 4\pi I \qquad (1)$$

where I is the magnetization or magnetic moment per unit volume. Actually, the quantities involved in equation (1) are all vectors, but one may assume that all three are collinear, a reasonable assumption for organic diamagnetic substances in the liquid state. For crystals I may vary with crystal orientation. Equation (1) may be written

$$B = H + 4\pi KH = (I + 4\pi K)H \qquad (2)$$

Here, K is the magnetic susceptibility, often called the volumetric susceptibility and is a unitless quantity.

Other susceptibilities of use to chemists and physicists are the specific or mass susceptibility which is defined

$$\chi = K/\rho \qquad (3)$$

where ρ is the density of the sample in grams per cc., and the molar susceptibility which is defined as

$$\chi_M = M\chi = MK/\rho \qquad (4)$$

where M is the molecular weight of the substance in grams.

Temperatures, when listed, are enclosed in parentheses and are listed in degrees C.

Literature references for values contained in this table may be found in General Motors Research Laboratories Bulletins GMR-317 and GMR-396.

Compound	$-\chi_M \times 10^6$	$-\chi \times 10^6$	$-K \times 10^6$
Acenaphthanthracene	184	.73	
Acenaphthene	109.3	(.709)	(.726) (99°)
Acetal	81.39	.688 (32°)	(.568) (32°)
Acetaldehyde	22.70	.515₃	(.403) (18°)
Acetamide	34.1	.577	(.618) (20°)
Acetic acid	31.54	.525 (32°)	(.551) (32°)
Acetic anhydride	(52.8)	.517	(.562) (15°)
Acetoaminofluorene	(141)	.63	
Acetone	33.7₈	.581₄	(.460) (20°)
Acetonitrile	28.0	(.682)	(.534) (20°)
Acetonylacetone	62.51	.547₆	(.531) (20°)
Acetophenone	72.05	.599₈	(.615) (20°)
Acetophenone oxime	79.9₀	.592₀	
Acetophenone oxime-O-methyl ether	92.3₁	.618₅	
Acetoxime	44.4₂	607₆	(.480) (20°)

Compound	$-\chi_M \times 10^6$	$-\chi \times 10^6$	$-K \times 10^6$
Acetoxime-O-benzyl ether	104.8₉	.642₇	
Acetoxime-O-methyl-ether	54.8₇	.629₈	
Acetylacetone	54.88	.548₁	(.535) (20°)
Acetyl chloride	38.9	.496	(.548) (20°)
Acetylene	12.5	(.480)	
Acetylphenylacetylene	86.9	.508	
Acetylthiophene	71.7	(.568)	
Acridine	(123.3)	.688	(.757) (20°)
Adonitol	91.30	.600	
Alanine	50.5	(.567)	
Allyl acetate	(56.7)	.566	(.525) (20°)
Allyl alcohol	36.70	.632	.540 (20°)
1-Allylpyrrole	73.80	.685 (20°)	
Aminoazobenzene	(118.3)	.600	
Aminoazotoluene	(142.2)	.631	
o-Aminoazotoluene	(138)	.61 ± .02	
α-Aminobutyric acid	62.1	(.602)	
Aminomethyldiethyldiazine	114.8	(.696)	
4-Aminostilbene	122.5	(.628)	
2-Aminothiazole	56.0	.564	
n-Amyl acetate	89.06	684₅	.5979 (20.7°)
iso-Amyl acetate	89.40	.687	.599 (20°)
n-Amyl alcohol	(67.5)	.766	(.624) (20°)
γ-Amyl alcohol	(71.0)	.8060	(.655) (25°)
Inactive Amyl alcohol	69.06	783₄ (25°)	
iso-Amyl alcohol	68.96	.782₃ (25°)	(.64) (15°)
sec-Amyl alcohol	69.1	.785	(.635) (20°)
tert-Amyl alcohol	(70.9)	.804	(.654) (15°)
n-Amylamine	69.4	(.796)	(.606) (20°)
iso-Amylamine	71.6	(.821)	(.616) (20°)
n-Amylbenzene	112.55	(.759)	(.652) (20°)
iso-Amyl bromide	(88.7)	.587	(.706) (20°)
iso-Amyl-n-butyrate	113.52	.717₄ (25°)	(.616) (25°)
iso-Amyl chloride	(79.0)	.741	(.662) (20°)
iso-Amyl cyanide	73.4	(.755)	(.609) (20°)
iso-Amylene	53.7	.766	
Amylene bromide	(114.5)	.498	
Amylene chloride	(95.2)	.675	
iso-Amyl ether	(129)	.813	(.635) (15°)
iso-Amyl formate	78.38	.674₈	(.591) (25°)
Amylidene chloride	(93.4)	.662	
Amyl iodide	(118.7)	.5996 (18°)	(.910) (20°)
n-Amyl methyl ketone	80.50	.705₃	(.580) (15°)
Amyl nitrate	(76.4)	.574	
iso-Amyl propionate	101.73	705₄ (25°)	(.609) (25°)
n-Amyl valerate	124.55	.723₉	(.638) (0°)
Anethole	(96.0)	.648	(.644) (15°)
Aniline	62.95	(.676)	(.691) (20°)
Anisidine	(80.5)	.654	(.72) (20°)
Anisole	72.79	(.673)	(.672) (15°)
Anthanthrene	204.2	.739	
Anthanthrone	178.1	.581	
Anthracene	(130)	.731	(.914) (27°)
Anthracenedinitrile	154.6	(.678)	
Anthracenonitrile	142.1	(.700)	
Anthraquinone	(119.6)	.575	(.825) (20°)
Anthrazine	245.7	.646	
Arabinose	85.70	.571	(.905) (20°)
Arbutoside	158.0	(.589)	
Asarone	131.4	(.631)	(.735) (18°)
Asparagine	69.5	(.526)	(.812) (15°)
Aspartic acid	64.2 ± .4	(.482)	(.800) (12°)
Aurin	(161.4)	.556	
p-Azoanisole	(147.7)	.610	
Azobenzene	(106.8)	.586	.611 (70.5°)
p-Azophenetole	(171.7)	.635	
m-Azotoluene	(127.8)	.608	.643 (58°)
Azulene	98.5	.768	
Barbituric acid (Anh.)	53.8	(.420)	
Barbituric acid (.2H₂O)	78.6	(4.79)	
Benzalazine	(123.7)	.594	
Benzaldehyde	60.78	(.573)	(.602) (15°)
Benzaldoxime	(69.8)	.576	(.639) (20°)
Benzamide	(72.3)	.597	(.801) (4°)
Benzanthrone	142.9	.620	
Benzene	54.84	.702 (32°)	.611
Benzidine	110.9	.603	(.754) (20°)
Benzil	(118.6)	.564	.616 (100°)
Benzoic acid	70.28	(.575)	(.728) (15°)
Benzoic anhydride	(124.9)	.552	(.662) (15°)
Benzonitrile	65.19	(.632)	(.638) (15°)
Benzophenone	109.60	.601₃	(.66) (50°)
3,4-Benzopyrene	135.7	.538	
Benzopyrene	194.0		
Benzoyl acetone	(95.0)	.586	(.639) (60°)
Benzoyl chloride	(75.8)	.539 (20°)	(.657) (15°)
Benzyl acetate	93.18	(.620)	(.655) (16°)
Benzyl alcohol	71.83	(.664)	(.697) (15°)
Benzylamine	75.26	(.702)	(.690) (19°)
Benzyl chloride	81.98	(.647)	(.713) (18°)
Benzyl formate	81.43	(.598)	(.646) (20°)
Benzylideneaniline	(100.4)	.554	
Benzylidene chloride	(97.9)	.608	(.763) (14°)
Benzylidenemethylamine	(73.1)	.613	
Benzyl methyl ketone	83.44	.621₉	(.624) (20°)
Bibenzyl	(126.8)	.696	.671 (54.5°)

Compound	$-\chi_M \times 10^6$	$-\chi \times 10^6$	$-K \times 10^6$	Compound	$-\chi_M \times 10^6$	$-\chi \times 10^6$	$-K \times 10^6$
3,4-Bis-(p-hydroxyphenyl)-2,4-hexadiene	(157)	.59		Chlorofumaric acid	67.02	(.445)	
m,m'-Bitolyl	(127.4)	.6993 (27.4°)	(.699) (16°)	p-Chloroiodo benzene	99.42	(.417)	(.786) (57°)
m,m'-Bitolyl sulfide	(140.0)	.6530 (27.4°)		Chloromaleic acid	67.36	(.448)	
Borneol	126.0	(.817)	(.826) (20°)	Chloromethylstilbene	144.8	(.633)	
Bromobenzene	78.92	.5030 (20°)	(.753) (20°)	α-Chloronaphthalene	107.60	.661	.789 (20°)
Bromobenzenediazocyanide	86.88	(.414)		m-Chloronitrobenzene	(74.8)	.475	.638 (48°)
Bromochloromethane	55.0 ± .6	(.425)	(.846) (19°)	o-Chlorophenol	77.4	(.602)	(.747) (18°)
Bromodichloromethane	66.3 ± .3	(.405)	(.812) (15°)	p-Chlorophenol	77.6	(.604)	(.789) (20°)
Bromoform	82.60	.327	.948 (20°)	1-(o-Chlorophenylazo)-2-naphthol	161.0	(.570)	
Bromonaphthalene	(123.8)	.598		1-(p-Chlorophenylazo)-2-naphthol	161.4	(.571)	
α-Bromonaphthalene	115.90	.560	.840 (20°)	Chlorotrifluoroethylene	49.1	.422	
m-Bromotoluene	(93.4)	.546	(.770) (20°)	Chlorotrifluoromethane	45.3 ± 1.5	(.434)	
Bromotrichloromethane	73.1 ± .7	(.369)	(.758) (0°)	Cholesterol	(284.2)	.735	(.784) (20°)
Butane	57.4	(.988)		Chrysene	166.67	.731	
iso-Butane	51.7	(.890)		Chrysoidine	(126.3)	.595	
1,4-Butanediol	61.5	(.682)	(.696) (20°)	Cinnamic acid	78.36	.529	(.660) (4°)
2-Butene (cis)	42.6	(.759)		Cinnamic acid (α-trans)	78.2	(.528)	
2-Butene (trans)	43.3	(.772)		Cinnamic acid (β-trans)	79.0	(.533)	
1-Butene-3,4-diacetate	95.5	(.555)		Cinnamic acid (cis-MP 68°)	77.6	(.524)	
2-Butene-1,4-diacetate (cis)	95.2	(.553)		Cinnamic acid (cis-MP 58°)	77.9	(.526)	
2-Butene-1,4-diacetate (trans)	95.1	(.552)		Cinnamic acid (cis-MP 42°)	83.2	(.562)	
2-Butene-1,4-diol (cis)	54.3	(.616)		Cinnamic aldehyde	(74.8)	.566	(.629) (15°)
2-Butene-1,4-diol (trans)	53.5	(.607)		Cinnamyl alcohol	(87.2)	.650	(.679) (20°)
n-Butyl acetate	77.47	$.666_9$ (25°)	(.583) (25°)	Cinnamylideneaniline	123.2	(.595)	
iso-Butyl acetate	78.52	$.676_9$	(.584) (25°)	Citral	(98.9)	.650	(.577) (20°)
n-Butyl alcohol	56.536 (20°)	(.7627)	(.6176) (20°)	Coronene	(243.3)	.810	
iso-Butyl alcohol	57.704 (20°)	(.7785)	(.624) (20°)	Coumarin	82.5	(.565)	(.528) (20°)
sec-Butyl alcohol	57.683 (20°)	(.7782)	(.629) (20°)	o-Cresol	72.90	.675	(.706) (20°)
tert-Butyl alcohol	57.42	$.774_7$ (25°)	(.611) (20°)	m-Cresol	72.02	.667 (26°)	(.690) (20°)
n-Butylamine	58.9	(.805)	(.596) (20°)	p-Cresol	72.1	.667 (26°)	(.690) (20°)
iso-Butylamine	59.8	(.818)	(.599) (20°)	o-Cresylmethyl ether	81.94	.671 (40°)	(.661) (15°)
9-Butyl anthracene	176.0	(.751)		m-Cresylmethyl ether	77.91	.638 (40°)	(.623) (15°)
n-Butylbenzene	100.79	(.751)	(.646) (20°)	p-Cresylmethyl ether	79.13	.648 (40°)	(.629) (19°)
iso-Butylbenzene	101.81	(.759)	(.648) (20°)	Cumene	89.53	$.744_9$	(.642)
tert-Butylbenzene	102.5	(.764)	(.662) (20°)	Cyamelide	(56.1)	.435	(.490) (15°)
n-Butyl benzoate	116.69	$.654_8$	(.656) (25°)	Cyameluric acid	101.1 (10°)	(.457)	
Butyl bromide	77.14	.563 (20°)	(.730) (20°)	9-Cyanoanthracene	142.1	(.699)	
iso-Butyl bromide	79.88	.583 (20°)	(.737) (20°)	Cyanogen	(21.6)	.415	(.359) (liq., 17°)
1-n-Butyl chloride	67.10	.725	.642 (20°)	Cyanuric acid	61.5	.476	(.842) (0°)
2-n-Butyl chloride	67.40	.728	.635 (20°)	Cyclobutanecarboxylic acid	58.16	.5816 (30°)	(.613) (30°)
n-Butyl cyanide	(62.8)	.7558 (27.4°)	(.606) (20°)	1,3-Cyclohexadiene	48.6	(.607)	(.510) (20°)
tert-Butyl cyclohexane	115.09	.8205	.6670 (20°)	1,4-Cyclohexadiene	48.7	(.608)	(.515) (20°)
1,4-Butyl diacetate	103.4	(.594)		Cyclohexane	68.13	.8100 (27.5°)	(.627) (20°)
n-Butyl ethyl ketone	80.73	$.707_2$	(.579) (20°)	Cyclohexanecarboxylic acid	83.24	.6499 (30°)	(.668) (30°)
n-Butyl formate	65.83	$.644_0$	(.571) (25°)	Cyclohexanol	73.40	.732	.694 (20°)
iso-Butyl formate	66.79	$.654_9$	(.574) (25°)	Cyclohexanone	62.0_4	$.632_3$	(.599) (20°)
iso-Butylideneazine	(95.8)	.683		Cyclohexanone oxime	71.5_2	$.632_1$	
Butyl iodide	(93.6)	.5086 (18°)	(.822) (20°)	Cyclohexanoneoxime-O-methyl ether	82.9_6	$.652_3$	
iso-Butyl methyl ketone	70.05	$.699_5$	(.561) (20°)	Cyclohexene	57.5	(.700)	(.567) (20°)
tert-Butyl methyl ketone	69.86	$.697_9$	(.558) (16°)	Cyclohexenol	64.1	(.653)	
n-Butyl perfluor-n-butyrate	126.7	(.469)		Cyclooctane	91.4	(.815)	(.684) (20°)
p-tert-Butylphenol	108.0	(.719)	(.653) (114°)	Cyclooctene	84.6	(.769)	(.654) (20°)
Butyl sulfide	(113.7)	.7774 (27.4°)	(.652) (16°)	Cyclooctatetraene	(53.9)	.518	
Butyl thiocyanate	(79.38)	.6891 (27.4°)	(.659) (25°)	Cyclopentane	59.18	.8439	.6290 (20°)
2-Butyne-1,4-diacetate	95.9	(.564)		Cyclopentanecarboxylic acid	73.48	.6446 (30°)	(.677) (30°)
2-Butyne-1,4-dibenzoate	169.0	(.561)		Cyclopentanone	51.63	.6141 (30°)	(.582) (30°)
2-Butyne-1,4-diol	50.3	(.584)		Cyclopropane	39.0	(.948)	(.683) (−79°)
n-Butyraldehyde	46.08	$.639_4$	(.522) (20°)	Cyclopropanecarboxylic acid	45.33	.5271 (30°)	(.569) (30°)
iso-Butyraldehyde	46.38	$.643_6$	(.511) (20°)	p-Cymene	102.8	.766 (20°)	(.656) (20°)
iso-Butyraldoxime	56.1_2	$.644_3$	(.576) (20°)	Decalin	106.70	.7718	.6814 (20°)
n-Butyric acid	55.10	.625	.598 (20°)	cis-Decalin	(107.0)	.774	(.686) (35°)
iso-Butyric acid	56.06	$.636_3$ (25°)	(.601) (25°)	trans-Decalin	(107.7)	.779	(.670) (35°)
Butyronitrile	49.4	(.715)	(.569) (15°)	n-Decane	119.74	(.8416)	(.6143) (20°)
Butyrylphenylacetylene	(106.4)	.618		l-Deuterio pyrrole	48.75	.716 (20°)	
Cacodyl	(99.9)	.476	(.689) (15°)	Deuteroindene	80.88	.690	(.692) (13°)
Cacodylic acid	(79.9)	.579		Diacetal	(153.8)	.668	
Camphor	(103)	.68	(.67) (25°)	Di-iso-amylamine	(133.1)	.846	(.049) (21°)
Camphoric acid	129.0	(.644)	(.791) (20°)	Diazoacetic ester	57	(.50)	(.54) (24°)
Camphoric anhydride	(113)	.620	(.740) (20°)	Dibenzocoronene	289.4	.778	
n-Caproic acid	78.55	$.676_2$	(.624) (25°)	1,2,5,6-Dibenzofluorene	184	.69 ± .03	
Caproylphenylacetylene	(130.4)	.651		3,4,5,6-Dibenzophenanthrene	(203)	.73 ± .03	
n-Caprylic acid	101.60	.7053	(.642) (20°)	Dibenzphenanthrene	200.5	.716	
Carbanilide	134.05	(.6316)	(.783) (20°)	Dibenzpyrene	213.6	.706	
Carbazole	117.4	(.702)		Dibenzpyrenequinone	183.1	.551	
Carbon disulfide	42.2	.554	(.699) (22°)	iso-Dibenzpyrenequinone	194.6	.586	
Carbon tetrabromide	93.73	.2826 (20°)	(.966)	Dibenzyl ketone	131.70	$.626_2$	
Carbon tetrachloride	66.60	.433	.691 (20°)	p-Dibromobenzene	(101.4)	.430	.786 (100°)
Carbon tetraiodide	(136)	.261	(1.13) (20°)	2,3-Dibromo-2-butene-1,4-diol	94.2	(.383)	
Carvacrol	(109.1)	.726	(.709) (20°)	Dibromodichloromethane	81.1 ± .4	(.334)	(.808) (25°)
Carvone	(92.2)	.614	(.590) (20°)	1,2-Dibromodiiodoethylene	(140.1)	.320	
Cetyl alcohol	(183.5)	.757 (17.5°)	(.619) (50°)	1,2-Dibromoethylene	(71.7)	.386	(.877) (17.5°)
Cetyl mercaptan	390.4	(1.510)		1,2-Dibromo-2-fluoroethane	(78.0)	.379	(.855) (17°)
Chloral	(67.7)	.459	(.694) (20°)	Dibromo-4-nitrophenol	(167.5)	.564	
Chloranil	(112.6)	.458		1,2-Dibromotetrachloroethane	(126.0)	.387	(1.049)
Chloracetic acid	48.1	(.509)	(.804) (20°)	Di-n-butylamine	103.7	(.802)	(.767) (20°)
Chloroacetone	(50.9)	.550	(.633) (20°)	Di-iso-butylamine	105.7	(.817)	(.009) (20°)
Chloroacetylchloride	53.7	(.475)	(.710) (0°)	Di-sec-butylamine	105.9	(.819)	(.641) (0°)
p-Chloranisole	89.1	(.605)		Di iso-butyl ketone	104.30	$.733_5$	(.591) (20°)
Chlorobenzene	69.97	(.6216)	(.688) (20°)	Di-tert-butyl ketone	104.06	$.732_1$	
Chlorobenzene diazocyanide	65.02	(.393)		2,6-Di-tert-butyl-4-methyl phenol	165.3	(.750)	
Chlorodibromomethane	75.1 ± .4	(.361)	(.883) (15°)	2,4-Di-tert-butyl phenol	155.6	(.754)	
Chlorodifluoromethane	38.6	.446		Dibutyl phthalate	175.1	(.629)	(.657) (21°)
1-Chloro-2,3-dihydroxypropane	(77.9)	.604		Di-iso-butylacetylene	(125.6)	.738	
Chlorodiphenylmethane	{131.9	(.651)		Dicetyl sulfide	401.7	(.832)	
Chloroethylene	35.9	.574	(.528) (liq., 15°)	Dichloroacetic acid	58.2	(.451)	(.705) (20°)
Chloroform	59.30	.497	.740 (20°)	Dichloroacetyl chloride	69.0	(.468)	

Compound	$-\chi_M \times 10^6$	$-\chi \times 10^6$	$-K \times 10^6$	Compound	$-\chi_M \times 10^6$	$-\chi \times 10^6$	$-K \times 10^6$
o-Dichlorobenzene	84.26	.5734	(.748) (20°)	2,5-Dimethylpyrrole	71.92	.756 (20°)	(.707) (20°)
m-Dichlorobenzene	83.19	.5661	(.729) (20°)	α,ω-Dimethyl styrene	(90.7)	.686	
p-Dichlorobenzene	82.93	.5644	(.823) (20.5°)	Dimethyl succinate	81.50	.5581	(.625) (18°)
1,4-Dichloro-2-butyne	74.2	(.603)		Dimethyl sulfate	(62.2)	.493	(.657) (20°)
1,2-Dichloro-1,2-dibromoethane	(108.6)	.423		Dimethyl sulfide	(44.9)	.723	(.612) (21°)
1,1-Dichloro-difluoroethylene	60.0	.451		Dimethyltrichloromethylcarbinol	(105)	.59	
Dichlorodifluoromethane	52.2	.432	(.642) (−30°)	N,N-Dimethyl urea	55.1	(.625)	(.784)
1,1-Dichloroethane	49.2	.508	(.635) (15°)	N,N′-Dimethyl urea	56.3	(.639)	(.730)
cis-1,2-Dichloroethylene	51.0	.526	(.679) (15°)	o-Dinitrobenzene	65.98	.3921	(.614) (17°)
trans-1,2-Dichloroethylene	48.9	.504	(.638) (15°)	m-Dinitrobenzene	70.53	.4197	(.659) (0°)
1,3-Dichloro-2-hydroxypropane	(80.1)	.621		p-Dinitrobenzene	68.30	.4064	(.660) (30°)
Dicyandiamide	44.55	(.530)	(.742) (14°)	2,4-Dinitrophenol	(73.1)	.397	(.668) (24°)
Dicyclohexanol acetylene	(151.6)	.682		Dinitroresorcinol	(62.4)	.312	
Dicyclohexyl	129.31	.7776	.6889 (20°)	1,4-Dioxane	52.16	.592 (32°)	(.606) (32°)
1,1-Dicyclohexylnonane	231.98	.7930	.7001 (20°)	Diphenyl	103.25	.6695	(.664) (73°)
Diethanolacetylene	(75.3)	.660		1,1-Diphenylallyl-3-chloride	146.1	(.639)	
Diethyl acetaldehyde	70.71	.705₉	(.576) (20°)	1,3-Diphenylallyl-3-chloride	140.7	(.615)	
Diethylallylacetophenone	146.2	(.676)	(.663) (16°)	Diphenylamine	(109.7)	.648	.686 (55.5°)
Diethyl allylmalonate	118.8	(.593)	(.602) (14°)	Diphenyl-bis-diazo cyanide	85.03	(.327)	
Diethylamine	56.8	(.777)	(.552) (18°)	Diphenylbutadiene	129.6	(.629)	
Diethylcyclohexylamine	(124.5)	.802	(.699) (0°)	Diphenylchloroarsine	(145.5)	.550	(.871) (40°)
Diethyl ethylmalonate	115.2	(.612)	(.614) (20°)	Diphenyldecapentaene	180.5	(.635)	
Diethyl ketone	58.1₄	.675₁	(.551) (19°)	Diphenyldiacetylene	(134.6)	.640	
Diethyl ketoxime	68.3₁	.6754		Diphenyldiazomethane	115	(.592)	
Diethyl malonate	(92.6)	.5782	(.611) (20°)	Diphenyldihydrotetrazine	129.9	(.545)	
Diethyl-3-(1-methyl butane) ethyl-malonate	175	(.677)		1,1-Diphenylethylene	(118.0)	.655	(.680) (14°)
Diethyl oxalate	81.71	.5595	(.603) (15°)	1,6-Diphenylhexane	171.81	.7208	.6877 (20°)
Diethyl phthalate	127.5	(.574)	(.645) (25°)	Diphenylhexatriene	146.9	(.632)	
Diethyl sebacate	(177.0)	.685	(.661) (20°)	Diphenylmethane	(115.7)	.688	.684 (35.5°)
Diethylstilbestrol	172.0	(.547)		Diphenylmethanol	119.1	.647	
Diethylstilbestrol dipropionate	265.2	.720		1,1-Diphenylnonane	206.32	.7357	.6935 (20°)
Diethyl succinate	105.07	.6035	(.628) (20°)	Diphenyloctatetraene	164.3	(.636)	
Diethyl sulfate	(86.8)	.563	(.667) (15°)	Diphenylphenoxyarsine	(225.2)	.567	
Diethyl sulfide	(67.9)	.753	(.630) (20°)	N,N-Diphenyl urea	126.3	(.595)	(.759)
Diethyl tartrate	(113.4)	.550	(.662) (20°)	N,N′-Diphenyl urea	127.5	(.600)	(.743) (20°)
Difluoroacetamide	(41.2)	.433		Di-n-propyl ketone	80.45	.705₀	(.576) (20°)
1-Difluoro-2-dibromoethane	(85.5)	.382	(.883) (20°)	Di-iso-propyl ketone	81.14	.711₀	(.573) (20°)
1,1-Difluoro-2,2-dichloroethyl amyl ether	129.84	(.587)	(.694) (20°)	Dipropyl oxalate	105.27	.6046	(.628) (0°)
1,1-Difluoro-2,2-dichloroethyl butyl ether	119.48	(.577)	(.703) (20°)	Di-iso-propyl oxalate	106.02	.6089	
1,1-Difluoro-2,2-dichloroethyl ethyl ether	96.13	(.537)	(.723) (20°)	Dodecyl alcohol	147.70	.7849 (20.7°)	(.652) (24°)
1,1-Difluoro-2,2-dichloroethyl methyl ether	80.68	(.489)	(.696) (20°)	Dulcitol	112.40	.617	(.905) (15°)
1,1-Difluoro-2,2-dichloroethyl propyl ether	107.19	(.555)	(.701) (20°)	Elaidic acid	204.8	(.725)	(.619) (79°)
Difluoroethanol	(41.3)	.503		Erythritol	73.80	.604	(.876) (20°)
Di-n-heptylamine	171.5	(.805)		Ethane	27.3₇	(.910)	(.511) (−100°)
Di-n-hexylamine	148.9	(.803)		4-Ethoxy-3-methoxybenzyl acetate	138.5	.619	
Dihydronaphthalene	(85.1)	.654	(.652) (12°)	4-Ethoxy-3-methoxybenzyl benzoate	177.3	.620	
o-Dimethoxybenzene	87.39	.6329	(.686) (25°)	1-Ethoxynaphthalene	119.9	(.696)	(.738) (20°)
m-Dimethoxybenzene	87.21	.6316	(.682) (0°)	2-Ethoxynaphthalene	119.2	(.692)	(.734) (25°)
p-Dimethoxybenzene	86.65	.6275	(.661) (55°)	Ethyl acetate	54.10	.614	.554 (20°)
o-(2,5-Dimethoxybenzoyl)-benzoic acid	161.0	(.562)		Ethyl acetoacetate	71.67	.550₈	(.565) (20°)
Dimethoxymethane	(47.3)	.621	(.532)	Ethylacetophenone	95.5	(.644)	(.639) (16°)
Dimethylacetophenone	96.8	(.653)	(.645) (16°)	Ethyl alcohol	33.60	.728	.575 (20°)
Dimethylallylacetophenone	122.4	(.650)	(.635) (16°)	Ethylally acetophenone	122.5	(.651)	(.634) (16°)
Dimethylaniline	89.66	(.740)		Ethyl amylpropiolate	(112.7)	.670	
2,2-Dimethylbutane	76.24	.8848	.5744 (20°)	Ethylaniline	89.30	(.737)	(.709)
2,3-Dimethylbutane	76.22	.8845	.5853 (20°)	9-Ethyl anthracene	153.0	(.741)	(.771) (99°)
2,3-Dimethyl-2-butene	65.9	(.783)	(.557)	Ethylbenzene	77.20	.7272	.6341 (20°)
Dimethylcyclohexanone	(84.8)	.672		Ethyl benzoate	93.32	.621₁	(.648) (25°)
1,2 and 1,3 Dimethylcyclopentanes	81.31	.8281	.6224 (20°)	Ethyl benzoylacetate	(115.3)	.600	(.673) (20°)
2,5-Dimethyl-2,5-dibromo-3-hexine	(135.6)	.506		Ethyl benzylidenecyanoacetate	(116.3)	.578	
Dimethyl diethylketo tetrahydro-furfurane	(116.2)	.753		Ethyl benzylmalonate	(154.5)	.6172	(.663) (20°)
2,5-Dimethyl-1-ethylpyrrole	94.61	.768 (20°)		Ethyl bromide	54.70	.502	.719 (20°)
2,5-Dimethyl-3-ethylpyrrole	93.87	.762 (20°)		Ethyl bromoacetate	(82.8)	.496	(.747) (20°)
2,5-Dimethylfuran	66.37	.687 (20°)	(.620) (18°)	Ethyl-1-isobutylacetoacetate	(121.4)	.652	
Dimethyl furazan	57.27	.584		Ethyl butylmalonate	139.3	.644₂	(.629) (20°)
2,5-Dimethyl-4-heptene	100.6	(.797)		Ethyl-n-butyrate	(77.7)	.6693	(.585) (25°)
2,4-Dimethyl-2,4-hexadiene	(78.7)	.714		Ethyl-iso-butyrate	78.32	.674₃	(.583) (25°)
2,3-Dimethylhexane	98.77	.8648	.6164 (20°)	Ethyl chloroacetate	(72.3)	.590	(.684) (20°)
2,5-Dimethylhexane	98.15	.8593	.5969 (20°)	Ethyl cinnamate	(107.5)	.610	(.640) (20°)
3,4-Dimethylhexane	99.06	.8673	.6240 (20°)	Ethyl-iso-cyanate	(45.6)	.642	(.582) (16°)
2,6-Dimethyl-4 hexanol	116.9	.812		Ethyl cyanoacetate	(67.3)	.595	(.632) (20°)
2,5-Dimethyl-3-hexine-2,5-diol	(103.0)	.724		Ethylcyclohexane	91.09	.8118	.6324 (20°)
Dimethyl isoxazole	59.7	(.615)		Ethyldiallylacetophenone	147.4	(.646)	(.636) (16°)
Dimethylketo tetrahydrofurfurane	(68.5)	.600		Ethyl dibromocinnamate	174.5	.519	
Dimethyl malonate	69.69	.5277	(.609) (20°)	Ethyl dichloroacetate	85.2	(.543)	(.696) (20°)
1,6-Dimethylnaphthalene	113.3	(.725)		Ethyl diethylacetoacetate	(117.9)	.6328	(.615) (20°)
2,4-Dimethylnonane	134.68	(.862)	(.636) (20°)	Ethyl diethylmalonate	(140.4)	.6492	(.641)(20°)
3,4-Dimethylnonane	134.70	(.862)	(.647) (20°)	Ethyl dithiolacetate	(71.0)	.5904 (27.4°)	
4,5-Dimethylnonane	134.52	(.861)	(.647) (20°)	Ethylene	12.0	(.428)	(.242) (−102°)
2,6-Dimethyl-2,6,8-nonatriene	(108.8)	.724		Ethylene	15.30	.546 (32°)	(.309) (−102°)
Dimethyl-2,4-nonatriene	(148.8)	.990		Ethylene bromide	78.80	.419	.915 (20°)
2,6-Dimethyloctane	122.54	(.861)	(.627) (20°)	Ethylene chloride	59.62	.602 (32°)	(.757) (20°)
3,4-Dimethyloxadiazole	57.17	.583		Ethylenediamine	46.26	.771 (32°)	(.686) (20°)
Dimethyl oxalate	(55.7)	.472	(.542) (54°)	Ethylene iodide	104.7	.371 (32°)	(.791) (10°)
Dimethyl oxamide	(63.2)	.544		Ethylene oxide	30.7	(.697)	(.618) (7°)
2,2-Dimethylpentane	86.97	.8680	.5849 (20°)	Ethyl ether	55.10	.743	(.534) (20°)
2,3-Dimethylpentane	87.51	.8733	.6070 (20°)	Ethyl ethylacetoacetate	93.9	.5937	(.582) (20°)
2,4-Dimethylpentane	87.48	.8732	.5876 (20°)	Ethyl ethylbutylmalonate	(163.3)	.6683	(.650) (20°)
2,2-Dimethylpropane	63.1	(.875)	(.536) (0°)	Ethyl ethylpropylmalonate	(152.4)	.6619	(.648) (20°)
2,5-Dimethyl-3-propyl-pyrrole	106.07	.773 (20°)		Ethyl formate	43.00	.580	.531 (20°)
2,4-Dimethylpyrrole	69.64	.732 (20°)	(.679) (14°)	Ethyl hexylpropiolate	129.9	.713	
				Ethyl hydroxylamine	(43.0)	.704	
				Ethylidene chloride	(57.4)	.580	(.681) (20°)
				Ethyl iodide	(69.7)	.4470 (17.5°)	(.864) (20°)
				Ethyl iodoacetate	(97.6)	.456	(.829) (13°)
				Ethyl lactate	(72.6)	.615	(.633) (25°)

Compound	$-\chi_M \times 10^6$	$-\chi \times 10^6$	$-K \times 10^6$	Compound	$-\chi_M \times 10^6$	$-\chi \times 10^6$	$-K \times 10^6$
Ethyl methylacetoacetate	(81.9)	.5684	(.569) (20°)	Indene (natural)	84.79	(.730)	(.723) 25°
Ethyl methyl ketoxime	57.3₂	.658₀	(.530) (20°)	Indene (synthetic)	80.89	(.696)	(.690) (25°)
Ethyl-1-methyl-2-oxocyclohexane-carboxylate	112.1	(.608)		Indole	85.0	(.726)	
				Iodobenzene	92.00	.451	.826 (20°)
Ethyl methylphenylmalonate	(153.2)	.6121	(.658) (20°)	Iodoform (in sol'n)	117.1	.2974 (20°)	(1.192) (17°)
Ethyl nitrophenylpropiolate	114.6	.523		1-Iodo-2-phenylacetylene	(110.1)	.483	
Ethyl oxamate	62.0	(.529)	(.427) (19°)	o-Iodotoluene	(112.2)	.5145 (30°)	(.874) (20°)
Ethyl perfluor-n-butyrate	103.5	(.427)		m-Iodotoluene	(112.3)	.5152 (30°)	(.875) (20°)
Ethyl phenylacetate	104.27	(.635)	(.656) (20°)	p-Iodotoluene	101.31	(.465)	(.780) (40°)
Ethyl phenylmalonate	(142.2)	.6017	(.659) (20°)	Leucine	84.9	(.647)	
Ethyl phenylpropiolate	(104.2)	.598	(.636) (13°)	iso-Leucine	84.9	(.647)	
Ethyl phosphate	(98.2)	.539	(.576) (25°)	Maleic acid	49.71	(.428)	
Ethyl propionate	(66.5)	.6514	(.584) (15°)	Maleic anhydride	(35.8)	.365	(.681) (20°)
Ethyl propylacetoacetate	(105.7)	.6135	(.593) (20°)	Malonic acid	(46.3)	.4453	(.341) (20°)
Ethyl-n-propyl ketone	69.03	.689₁	(.560) (22°)	Mannitol	111.20	.610	(.720) (15°)
Ethyl succinimide	(72.0)	.566		Mannose	102.90	.571	(.908) (20°)
Ethyl sulfine	(67.0)	.631		Mesitylene	92.32	.7682 (20°)	(.879)
Ethyl sulfite	(75.4)	.546	(.604) (0°)	Methane	12.2₇	(.765)	(.665) (20°)
Ethylsulfone ethyl ether	(81.8)	.592		Methione	91.0	(.610)	
Ethyl thiocyanate	(55.7)	.6392 (27.4°)	(.637) (25°)	p-Methoxyazobenzene	(118.9)	.560	
Ethyl isothiocyanate	(59.0)	.6772 (27.4°)	(.680) (15°)	o-Methoxybenzaldehyde	76.0	(.558)	(.632) (20°)
Ethyl thiolacetate	(62.7)	.6019 (27.4°)	(.586) (25°)	p-Methoxybenzaldehyde	78.0	(.572)	(.642) (20°)
Ethyl thionacetate	(63.5)	.6098 (27.4°)		o-Methoxybenzyl alcohol	87.9	.637	(.664) (25°)
Ethyl tribromoacetate	(119.5)	.368	(.821) (20°)	1-Methoxynaphthalene	107.0	(.676)	(.741) (14°)
Ethyl trichloroacetate	(99.6)	.520	(.719) (20°)	2-Methoxynaphthalene	107.6	(.680)	
N-Ethyl urea	55.5	(.630)	(.764) (18°)	1-(o-Methoxyphenylazo)-2-naphthol	163.6	(.588)	
Ethyl iso-valerate	(91.1)	.700	(.607) (20°)	Methoxysaligenin acetate	110.3	.613	
Eucalyptol	(116.3)	.754	(.699) (20°)	Methyl acetate	42.60	.575	.537 (20°)
Eugenol and iso-eugenol	(102.1)	.622	(.663) (20°)	Methyl acetoacetate	59.60	.513₂	(.553) (20°)
Flavanthrone	241.0	.590		Methylacetylacetone	(65.0)	.569	
Fluorene	110.5	.655		Methyl alcohol	21.40	.668	.530 (20°)
Fluorenone	99.4	.552	(.623) (100°)	Methylallylaketone	111.9	(1.330)	
Fluorobenzene	(58.4)	.608	(.623) (20°)	Methylamine	(27.0)	.870	(.608) (−11°)
Fluorobromoacetic acid	(59.5)	.379		N-Methylaniline	82.74	(.773)	(.762) (20°)
Fluorodichloromethane	48.8	.474	(.676) (0°)	9-Methylanthracene	146.5	.762)	(.812) (99°)
p-Fluorophenetole	(88.0)	.628		Methyl benzoate	81.59	.599₃	(.651) (25°)
Fluoro trichloroethylene	72.5	.485	(.742) (25°)	Methyl-o-benzoylbenzoate	139.4	(.580)	(.690) (19°)
Fluorotrichloromethane	58.7	.427	(.638) (17°)	Methylbenzylaniline	(132.2)	.670	
Formaldehyde	(18.6)	.62	(.51) (−20°)	Methyl bromide	42.8	.451	(1.044) (0°)
Formamide	(21.9)	.486	(.551) (20°)	2-Methylbutane	64.40	.8925	.5531 (20°)
Formic acid	19.90	.432	.527 (20°)	2-Methyl-2-butene	54.14	(.772)	(.516) (13°)
β-Formylpropionic acid	55.3	(.542)		Methyl butyl ketone	(69.1)	.690	(.563) (15°)
Fructose	102.60	.570		Methyl iso-butyl ketone	(69.3)	.692	(.554) (20°)
Fulvene (Benzene χ_M measured to be 49)	42.9	(.549)	(.452) (20°)	Methyl tert-butyl ketone	(70.4)	.703	(.562) (16°)
				p-Methyl-o-tert-butylphenol	120.3	(.732)	
Fulvene $\left(\times\dfrac{54.8}{49}\right)$	48.0	(.614)	(.505) (20°)	Methyl butyrate	(66.4)	.6498	(.588) (16°)
Fumaric acid	49.11	(.423)	(.692) (20°)	o-Methylcarbanilide	154.0	(.681)	
Furan	43.09	.633 (20°)	(.598) (15°)	Methyl chloride	(32.0)	.633	
Furfural	47.1	(.490)	(.568) (20°)	Methyl chloroacetate	58.1	(.535)	(.661) (20°)
Galactose	103.00	.572		Methylcholanthrene	(182)	.68 ± .04	
Gallic acid	90.0	(.529)	(.896) (4°)	3-Methylcholanthrene	194.0	(.723)	
Geraniol formate	(119.9)	.658	(.610) (20°)	Methylcyclohexane	78.91	.8038	.6181 (20°)
Glucose	102.60	.570		2-Methylcyclohexanone	(74.0)	.660	(.610) (18°)
D-Glucose	101.5	(.563)	(.869) (25°)	3-Methylcyclohexanone	(74.8)	.667	(.610) (20°)
Glutamic acid	78.5	(.533)		4-Methylcyclohexanone	(63.5)	.566	(.516) (24°)
Glycerol	57.06	.619	.779 (20°)	Methylcyclopentane	70.17	.8338	.6245 (20°)
Glycine	40.3	(.537)	(.846) (50°)	4-Methyl-2,6-di-tert-butylphenol	167.6	(.761)	
Glycol	38.80	.624	.698 (20°)	Methyl dichloroacetate	73.1	(.511)	
Guaiacol	(79.2)	.638	(.720) (21°)	Methyldiphenoxyphosphine oxide	(152.9)	.616	
Helianthrone	189.9	.497		Methyldiphenyltriazine	(155.1)	.627	
1,2-Heptadiene	73.5	(.764)		Methylene bromide	65.10	.375	.935 (20°)
2,3-Heptadiene	72.1	(.749)		Methylene chloride	(46.6)	.549	(.733) (20°)
Heptaldehyde	81.02	.709₆	(.603) (20°)	Methylene iodide	93.10	.348	1.156 (20°)
n-Heptane	85.24	.8507	.5817 (20°)	Methylene succinic acid	57.57	(.443)	(.723)
4-Heptanol	91.5	.789	(.647) (20°)	Methyl ether	26.3	.571	
n-Heptanoic acid	88.60	.680	.626 (20°)	Methylethylallylacetophenone	133.3	(.659)	(.643) (16°)
n-Heptyl amine	93.1	(.808)	(.628) (20°)	Methyl ethyl ketone	45.5₈	.632₂	(.509) (20°)
n-Heptyl benzene	134.41	.7625	.6528 (20°)	Methyl formate	(32.0)	.5327	(.519) (20°)
Heptyl cyclohexane	147.40	.8084	.6559 (20°)	Methylfumaric acid	56.98	(.438)	(.642)
n-Heptylic acid	89.74	.6900	(.630) (25°)	3-Methylheptane	97.99	.8580	.6056 (20°)
1-Heptyne	77.0	(.801)	(.584) (25°)	2-Methyl-4-heptene	88.0	(.784)	
2-Heptyne	79.5	(.826)	(.615) (25°)	5-Methyl-1,2-hexadiene	73.6	(.765)	(.553) (19°)
Hexabromoethane	(148.0)	.294	(1.124) (20°)	2-Methylhexane	86.24	.8607	.5841 (20°)
Hexachlorobenzene	(147.5)	.518	(1.059) (24°)	Methyl hexyl ketone	(93.3)	.728	(.596) (20°)
Hexachloroethane	(112.7)	.476	(.995) (20°)	Methyl-m-hydroxybenzoate	88.4	(.581)	
Hexachlorohexatrione	(145.0)	.433		Methyl-p-hydroxybenzoate	88.7	(.583)	
n-Hexadecane	187.63	.8286	.6421 (20°)	Methyl iodide	(57.2)	.403	(.918) (20°)
1,5-Hexadiene	(55.1)	.671	(.462) (20°)	Methylmaleic acid	57.84	(.446)	(.721)
2,3-Hexadiene	60.9	(.741)		9-Methyl-10-methoxyanthracene	158.1	(.711)	
n-Hexaldehyde	69.40	.693₀		Methyl-o-methoxybenzoate	95.6	(.575)	(.665) (19°)
2,2,4,7,9,9-Hexamethyldecane	191.52	.8458	.6596 (20°)	Methyl-p-methoxybenzoate	98.6	(.593)	
Hexamethyl disiloxane	118.9	.7324		Methyl-α-methoxy-isobutyrate	(81.9)	.620	
Hexamethylene glycol	84.30	.713		1-Methylnaphthalene	102.8	(.723)	(.741) (14°)
n-Hexane	(74.6)	.8654 (27.4°)	(.565)	2-Methylnaphthalene	102.6	(.722)	(.743) (20°)
Hexene	65.7	(.781)		4-Methylnonane	121.39	(.853)	(.625) (20°)
Hexestrol	(165)	.61 ± .02		5-Methyl-5-nonene	111.6	(.796)	
n-Hexyl alcohol	79.20	.774	.607 (20°)	4-Methyloctane	109.63	(.855)	(.618) (20°)
n-Hexyl benzene	124.23 (20°)	(.707)	(.668) (20°)	Methylol urea	48.3	(.493)	
n-Hexyl methyl ketone	91.4₂	.713₁	(.583)	2-Methylpentane	75.90	.8734	.5705 (20°)
n-Hexyl methyl ketoxime	102.5₈	.716₂	(.634) (20°)	3-Methylpentane	75.52	.8764	.5823 (20°)
Hexylpropiolamide	(103.7)	.677		4-Methyl-2-pentanol	80.4	.788	(.641) (20°)
Hydrindene	(78.5)	.664	(.639) (16°)	Methyl perfluor-n-butyrate	92.5	(.406)	
Hydroquinone	64.63	.587	(.797) (20°)	Methyl phenylacetate	92.73	(.618)	(.645) (16°)
Hydroxyazobenzene	(99.7)	.503		Methyl phenylpropiolate	95.6	.597	
p-Hydroxybenzaldehyde	66.8	(.547)	(.618) (130°)	2-Methylpropene	44.4	(.791)	
4-Hydroxy-2-butanone	48.5	.55	(.573) (14°)	Methyl propionate	(55.0)	.6240	(.571) (20°)

Compound	$-\chi_M \times 10^6$	$-\chi \times 10^6$	$-K \times 10^6$	Compound	$-\chi_M \times 10^6$	$-\chi \times 10^6$	$-K \times 10^6$
Methyl-n-propyl ketone	57.41	.666₄	(.541) (15°)	Pentachloroethane	(99.1)	.490	(.819) (25°)
Methyl-iso-propyl ketone	58.45	.679₀	(.545) (20°)	Pentachlorohexadione	(129.5)	.452	
1-Methylpyrrole	58.56	.722 (20°)	(.664) (10°)	2,3-Pentadiene	49.1	(.721)	(.501) (20°)
2-Methylpyrrole	60.10	.741 (20°)	(.700)	n-Pentane	63.05	.8739	.5472 (20°)
Methyl salicylate	86.30	.567	.668 (20°)	2,4-Pentanediol	70.4	.677	
Methyl silicone	(172.7)	.730		Perfluoroacetic acid	43.3	(.380)	
α-Methyl styrene	(80.1)	.678	(.620) (20°)	Perfluoro-n-butyric acid	81.0	(.378)	
2-Methylthiazole	59.56	.601 (20°)		Perfluorobutyric anhydride	149.4	(.387)	
2-Methylthiophene	66.35	.676 (20°)	(.689) (20°)	Perfluorocyclooctane oxide	157.6	(.379)	
Methyl trichloroacetate	84.2	(.475)	(.707) (19°)	Perfluoropropionic acid	61.0	(.372)	
N-Methyl urea	44.6	(.602)	(.725)	Perhydroanthracene	146.01	.7592	.7178 (20°)
Morpholine	55.0	(.631)	(.631)	Perylene	166.8	.662	
Myleran	169.7	.69	(.834) (4°)	Phenanthrene	(127.9)	.718	(.763) (100°)
Myristic acid	176.0	(.771)	(.661) (60°)	Phenanthrenequinone	104.5	.502	(.698)
Naphthalaldehydic acid	117.6	(.588)		Phenanthrenonitrile	139.0	(.685)	
Naphthalene	(91.9)	.717	(.821) (20°)	o-Phenetidine	(101.7)	.741 (25°)	
Naphthalene picrate	185.9	(.523)		p-Phenetidine	(96.8)	.706 (25°)	(.749) (15°)
2-Naphthalenesulfonylamine	127.6	(.616)		Phenetole	(84.5)	.692	(.689) (20°)
2-Naphthalenesulfonyl chloride	121.91	(.538)		Phenol	60.21	(.640)	(.675) (45°)
meso-Naphthodianthrene	214.6	.612		Phenothiazine	114.8	(.576)	
meso-Naphthodianthrone	221.8	.583		Phenylacetaldehyde	72.01	.599₄	(.614) (20°)
1-Naphthol	98.2	.681	(.834) (4°)	Phenyl acetate	82.04	(.603)	(.647) (25°)
	97.0	.673	(.819) (4°)	Phenylacetic acid	82.72	(.608)	(.657) (80°)
2-Naphthol	98.25	(.682)	(.829) (4°)	Phenylacetylene	72.01	(.705)	(.655) (20°)
α-Naphthonitrile	103.3	(.674)	(.753) (5°)	1-Phenylazo-2-naphthol	137.6	(.554)	
β-Naphthonitrile	101.0	(.659)	(.721) (60°)	2-Phenylbensofuran	130.5	(.672)	
α-Naphthoquinone	73.5	(.465)	(.661)	1-Phenyl-4-benzoyl-1,3-butadiene	(140.3)	.599	
β-Naphthoquinone	67.9	(.429)		Phenylbutadiene	(85.7)	.658	
N-1-Naphthylacetamide	117.8	(.636)		4-Phenyl-1-butene	93.49	(.7077)	(.6239) (20°)
N-2-Naphthylacetamide	117.8	(.636)		Phenylbutyl acetate	134.5	.653	
1-Naphthylamine	98.8	.690	.757 (54°)	Phenyl n-butyrate	105.46	(.643)	
2-Naphthylamine	98.00	(.684)	(.726) (98°)	Phenyl iso-cyanate	(72.7)	.610	(.699) (20°)
1-Naphthylamine hydrochloride	(127.6)	.710		o-Phenylenediamine	71.98	.6662	
Nicotine	113.328	(.699)	(.705) (20°)	m-Phenylenediamine	70.53	.6529	(.723) (58°)
o-Nitroaniline	66.47	(.481)	(.694) (15°)	p-Phenylenediamine	70.28	.6503	
m-Nitroaniline	70.09	(.507)	(.725) (20°)	Phenyl ether	(108.1)	.635	(.681) (20°)
p-Nitroaniline	66.43	(.481)	(.691) (14°)	Phenylethyl sulfide	(94.4)	.6826 (27.4°)	
o-Nitrobenzaldehyde	68.23	.4517		Phenylfluoroform	(77.3)	.529	
m-Nitrobenzaldehyde	68.55	.4538		Phenylhydrazine	67.82	(.627)	(.688) (23°)
p-Nitrobenzaldehyde	66.57	.4407	(.507) (0°)	Phenylhydroxylamine	(68.2)	.625	
Nitrobenzene	61.80	.502	.604 (20°)	Phenyl mercaptan	(70.8)	.6425 (27.4°)	(.693) (20°)
Nitrobenzene diazo cyanide	59.22	(.336)		1-Phenyl-2-Methylbutane	113.53	(.766)	(.660) (20°)
o-Nitrobenzoic acid	76.11	.4556	(.718) (4°)	Phenylmethyl sulfide	(83.2)	.6695 (27.4°)	
m-Nitrobenzoic acid	80.22	.4802	(.717) (4°)	Phenylpropiolamide	(83.3)	.574	
p-Nitrobenzoic acid	78.81	.4718	(.731) (32°)	Phenyl propionate	93.79	(.625)	(.654) (25°)
o-Nitrobromobenzene	87.3	(.432)	(.700) (80°)	Phenylsulfone	(129.0)	.591	(.740) (20°)
m-Nitrobromobenzene	89.5	(.443)	(.755) (20°)	Phenyl thiocyanate	(81.5)	.6027 (27.4°)	(.677) (24°)
p-Nitrobromobenzene	89.6	(.444)	(.859) (22°)	Phenyl isothiocyanate	(86.0)	.6365 (27.4°)	(.719) (24°)
m-Nitro carbanilide	148.1	(.576)		1-Phenyl-4,6,6-trimethylheptane	173.90	(.796)	(.682) (20°)
Nitroethane	(35.4)	.472	(.497) (20°)	N-Phenyl urea	82.1	(.603)	(.785)
Nitromethane	21.1	.3457	(.391) (25°)	Phloroglucinol	(73.4)	.582	
1-Nitronaphthalene	98.47	(.569)	(.696) (62°)	Phthalamide	(91.3)	.556	
o-Nitrophenol	73.3	.527 (24°)	(.873) (20°)	Phthalic acid	83.61	.5035	(.802) (20°)
m-Nitrophenol	70.8	.509 (25°)	(.756)	iso-Phthalic acid	84.64	.5097	
p-Nitrophenol	69.5	.500 (22°)	(.740)	tere-Phthalic acid	83.51	.5029	(.759)
1-(m-Nitrophenylazo)-2-naphthol	142.0	(.484)		Phthalic anhydride	67.31	(.454)	(.694) (4°)
1-(p-Nitrophenylazo)-2-naphthol	141.7	(.483)		Phthalimide	(78.4)	.533	
Nitrophenylfluoroform	(84.1)	.440		Picric acid	84.38	(.368)	(.649)
2-Nitropropane	45.73	.5135	(.509) (20°)	Piperazine	56.8	(.659)	
Nitrosobenzene	59.1	(.552)		Piperidine	64.2	(.754)	(.650) (20°)
N-Nitrosodiethylamine	59.3	(.580)	(.546) (20°)	Propane	40.5	.919	(.538) (−45°)
p-Nitrosodiethylaniline	92.6	(.520)	(.644) (15°)	Propene	31.5	(.749)	(.456) (−47°)
p-Nitrosodimethylaniline	73.3	(.488)		Propionaldehyde	34.32	.591₀	(.477) (20°)
N-Nitrosodiphenylamine	110.7	(.558)		Propionic acid	43.50	.586	.582 (20°)
1-Nitroso-2-naphthol	83.9	(.485)		Propionitrile	38.5	(.699)	(.547) (21°)
2-Nitroso-1-naphthol	82.7	(.478)		Propionylphenylacetylene	(95.1)	.601	
4-Nitroso-1-naphthol	91.8	(.530)		Propiophenone	83.73	.624₀	(.631) (20°)
m-Nitrosonitrobenzene	66.0	(.433)		n-Propyl acetate	65.91	.645₃ (25°)	(.569) (25°)
p-Nitrosonitrobenzene	65.8	(.433)		iso-Propyl acetate	67.04	.656₄	(.566) (25°)
p-Nitrosophenol	50.7	(.412)		n-Propyl alcohol	45.176 (20°)	(.7518)	(.6047) (20°)
Nitrosopiperidine	(63.4)	.555	(.590) (20°)	iso-Propyl alcohol	45.794 (20°)	(.7621)	(.5985) (20°)
p-Nitrosotoluene	70.4	(.581)		9-Propylanthracene	164.0	(.744)	
o-Nitrotoluene	72.28	.5272	(.613) (20°)	n-Propylbenzene	89.24	(.742)	(.640) (20°)
m-Nitrotoluene	72.71	.5304	(.614) (20°)	n-Propyl benzoate	105.00	(.640)	(.646) (25°)
p-Nitrotoluene (in sol'n)	72.06	.5257	(.676) (20°)	n-Propyl bromide	(65.6)	.533	(.721) (20°)
n-Nonane	108.13	.8431	.6057 (20°)	iso-Propyl bromide	(65.1)	.529	(.693) (20°)
1,2-Octadiene	83.6	(.759)		Propyl butyrate	(89.4)	.6867	(.604) (15°)
n-Octane	96.63	.8460	.5949 (20°)	prim-Propyl chloride	56.10	.715	(.633) (20°)
Octanonoxime	(102.7)	.717		iso-Propylcyclohexane	102.65	.8131	.6528 (20°)
Octyl alcohol	102.65	.7766 (20°)	(.640) (20°)	Propylenediamine	(58.1)	.784	(.688) (15°)
Octyl chloride	(114.9)	.773	(.676) (20°)	Propylene oxide	42.5	(.732)	(.629) (20°)
Octylcyclohexane	158.09	.8051	.6578 (20°)	Propyl formate	(55.0)	.6248	(.563) (20°)
Octylene	(89.5)	.798	(.576) (17°)	Propyl hexylpropiolate	(136.8)	.697	
Octylene bromide	(150.4)	.553		Propyl iodide	(84.3)	.4958 (30°)	(.864) (20°)
n-Octyl mercaptan	(115.1)	.7866 (27.4°)		Propyl propionate (extrap.)	(77.95)	.6711	(.593) (20°)
Oenanthylidene chloride	(116.5)	.689		Propyl sulfide	(92.1)	.7787 (27.4°)	(.634) (17°)
Oleic acid	208.5	(.738)	(.661) (18°)	N-Propyl urea	67.4	(.660)	
Opianic acid	111.5	(.530)		Pseudocumene	(101.6)	.815 (20°)	(.740) (20°)
Ovalene	353.8	.888		Pyramidone	149.0	(.645)	
Oxalic acid (anh.)	33.8	(.375)		Pyranthrene	266.9	.709	
Oxalic acid	60.05	(.4763)	(.787)	Pyranthrone	250.3	.616	
Oxamide	(39.0)	.443	(.738)	Pyrazine	37.6	(.469)	(.484) (61°)
Palmitic acid	198.6	(.775)	(.661) (62°)	Pyrene	147.9	.731	(.933) (0°)
Paraldehyde	(86.2)	.652	(.648) (20°)	Pyridine	49.21	(.622)	(.611) (20°)
Pentabromophenol	(194.0)	.397		Pyrocatechol	68.76	.6248	(.857) (15°)
Pentacene	(205.4)	.738		Pyrrole	47.6	(.709)	(.688) (20°)

DIAMAGNETIC SUSCEPTIBILITIES OF ORGANIC COMPOUNDS (Continued)

Compound	$-\chi_M \times 10^6$	$-\chi \times 10^6$	$-K \times 10^6$	Compound	$-\chi_M \times 10^6$	$-\chi \times 10^6$	$-K \times 10^6$
Pyrrolidine	54.8	(.771)	(.657) (23°)	Trianilinophosphine oxide	(201.7)	.624	
Quinoline	86.0	(.666)	(.729) (20°)	1,2,3-Tribromopropane	(117.9)	.420	(1.023) (23°)
Quinone	38.4	(.355)	(.468) (20°)	Tri-iso-butylamine	(156.8)	.846	(.646) (25°)
Quinonoxime	(50.4)	.409		Trichloroacetic acid (in sol'n)	73.0	(.44)	(.723) (46°)
Resorcinol	67.26	.6112	(.785) (15°)	Trichlorobenzene	(106.5)	.587	
Rhamnose	99.20	.605	(.890) (20°)	Trichloro-tert-butyl alcoho! (in sol'n)	98.01	.552	
Safrol and iso-Safro	(97.5)	.601	(.66) (20°)	Trichloroethylene	65.8	.501	(.734) (20°)
Salicylaldehyde	64.4	(.527)	(.615) (20°)	Trichloronitromethane	(75.3)	.458	(.756) (20°)
Salicylic acid	72.23	.523	(.755) (20°)	Triethylamine	81.4	(.804)	(.586) (20°)
Saligenin	76.9	.620	(.720) (25°)	Triethyl citrate	(161.9)	.586	(.666) (20°)
Salol	(123.2)	.575	.678 (45°)	Triethyl phosphate	(125.3)	.688	(.735) (20°)
Salvarsan dihydrochloride	(240.1)	.518		Triethylphosphine	(90.0)	.762	(.610) (15°)
Selenophene	66.82	.510		Triethylphosphine oxide	(91.6)	.683	
iso-Selenophene	110-111	.84-.85		Triethyl phosphite	(104.8)	.631	(.611) (20°)
trans-Selenophene	70-77	.53-.59		Triethyl triazinetricarbonate	(164.1)	.552	
Sorbitol	107.80	.592		Trifluorocresol	(83.8)	.517	
Stearic acid	220.8	(.776)	(.657) (69°)	Tri-n-heptylamine	251.3	(.806)	
Stilbene	(120.0)	.666	(.646) (125°)	Tri-n-hexylamine	221.7	(.823)	
Stilbestrol	(130)	.62, .63		Trimethylacetophenone	108.2	(.667)	(.648) (16°)
Styrene	(68.2)	.655	(.594) (20°)	2,2,3-Trimethylbutane	88.36	.8818	.6086 (20°)
Succinic acid	(57.9)	.4902	(.767) (15°)	2,2,3-Trimethylpentane	99.86	.8743	.6261 (20°)
Succinic anhydride	(47.5)	.475	(.524)	2,2,4-Trimethylpentane	98.34	.8610	.5958 (20°)
Succinimide	(47.3)	.477	(.674) (16°)	2,3,5-Trimethylpyrrole	82.31	.754 (20°)	
Sulfamide	44.4	(.462)	(.832)	1,3,5-Trinitrobenzene	74.55	(.350)	(.591) (20°)
p-Sulfanilamide	80.15	(.465)		Triperfluorobuty!amine	253.0	(.377)	
Terpineol	111.9	(.725)	(.678) (room temp.)	Triphenoxyarsine	(195.2)	.551	
				Triphenylarsine	(177.0)	.578	
Tetrabenzylmonosilane	266.2	(.678)		Triphenylarsine dihydroxide	(270.5)	.795	
1,1,2,2-Tetrabromoethane	(123.4)	.357	(1.058) (20°)	Triphenylarsine oxide	(199.1)	.618	
Tetrabromoethylene	(114.8)	.334		Triphenylbismuthine	(196.8)	.447	(.708) (20°)
Tetracene	(168.0)	.736		Triphenylbismuthine dinitrate	(254.5)	.451	
1,1,2,2-Tetrachloroethane	(89.8)	.535	(.856) (20°)	Triphenylcarbinol	(175.7)	.675	(.802) (20°)
Tetrachloroethylene	81.6	.492	(.802) (15°)	Triphenylmethane	(165.6)	.678	.686 (100°)
Tetrahydroquinoline	(89.0)	.668	(.715) (4°)	Triphenylphosphine	(166.8)	.636	(.759)
Tetraiodoethylene	(164.3)	.309	(.922) (20°)	Triphenyl phosphite	(183.7)	.592	(.701) (18°)
Tetraiodopyrrole	(188.9)	.331		Triphenylstibine	(182.2)	.516	
Tetramethylketotetrahydrofurfurane	(104.7)	.736		Triphenylstibine dihydroxide	(238.5)	.616	
Tetranitromethane	43.02	.2195	(.360) (20°)	N,N',N-Triphenyl urea	176.5	(.613)	
Tetraphenylbutadiene	228.0	(.636)		Triquinoyl	(133.0)	.426	
Tetraphenyldecapentaene	280.8	(.643)		Tropolone	61	.50	
Tetraphenylhexatriene	246.4	(.641)		Tryptophan	132.0	(.646)	
Tetraphenyloctatetraene	264.1	(.643)		Tyrosine	105.3	(.581)	
Tetraphenylrubene	344.0	(.646)		Undecane	131.84	(.8435)	(.6247) (20°)
Tetra-p-tolylmonosilane	276.4	(.704)		Urea	33.4	(.556)	(.742) (20°)
Tetrolic acetal	(97.8)	.688		Urethan	(57)	.64	(.63) (21°)
Tetronic acid	(52.5)	.525		iso-Valeraldehyde	(57.5)	.668	(.536) (17°)
Thiacoumerin	93.6	.577		n-Valeric acid	66.85	.6548	(.617) (20°)
Thiazole	50.55	.595 (20°)	(714) (17°)	iso-Valeric acid	(67.7)	.663	(.621) (15°)
Thiobarbituric acid	72.9	(.506)		Valerylphenylacetylene	(119.0)	.639	
Thiophene	57.38	.682 (20°)	(.726) (20°)	Valine	74.3	(.634)	
Tolane	(118.9)	.667	(.644) (100°)	Violanthrene	273.5	.641	
Toluene	66.11	.7176	.6179 (20°)	Violanthrone	204.8	.449	
o-Toluidine	76.0	.710 (24°)	(.709) (20°)	iso-Violanthrone	215.9	.473	
m-Toluidine	74.6	.697 (25°)	(.689) (20°)	Water	(13.00)	.7218 (20°)	(.7205) (20°)
p-Toluidine	72.1	.673 (25°)	(.704) (20°)	Water (value usually used as standard)	(12.97)	.720 (20°)	(.719) (20°)
α-Tolunitrile	76.87	(.656)	(.666) (18°)	Xanthone	(108.1)	.551	
1-(o-Tolylazo)-2-naphthol	148.7	(.567)		o-Xylene	77.78	.7327	.6440 (20°)
1-(p-Tolylazo)-2-naphthol	157.6	(.601)		m-Xylene	76.56	.7212	.6235 (20°)
Triallylacetophenone	152.5	(.634)		p-Xylene	76.78	.7232	.6226 (20°)
Tri-iso-amylamine	192	.845	(.647) (25°)	Xylose	84.80	.565	(.862) (20°)

DIAMAGNETIC SUSCEPTIBILITIES OF ORGANIC COMPOUNDS (Continued)

Supplementary Table

Formula	Compound	$-\chi_M \times 10^6$	$-\chi \times 10^6$	$-K \times 10^6$
$H_6N_3B_3$	Borazine	49.6	.616	
CO	Carbon monoxide	9.8	.350	
COS	Carbon oxysulfide	32.4	.539	
$COCl_2$	Phosgene	48	.485	(.675) (19°)
CO_2	Carbon dioxide	20	.45	
$CNCl$	Cyanogen chloride	32.4	.527	(.642) (4°)
CCl_2S	Thiophosgene	50.6	.440	(.664) (15°)
CH_2N_2	Cyanamide	24.8	.590	(.639)
CH_3SiCl_3	Methyl trichlorsilane	87.45	.584₈	
CH_4N_2S	Thiourea	42.4	.557	(.782) (20°)
C_2HF_3	Trifluoroethylene	32.2	.393	
$C_2HF_3Cl_2$	1,2-Dichloro-1,1,2-trifluoroethane	66.2	.433	
$C_2HF_3Br_2$	1,2-Dibromo-1,1,2-trifluoroethane	90.9	.376	
$C_2H_2O_2N_3$	Urazole	46.2	.456	
C_2H_4OS	Thioacetic acid	38.4	.505	(.542) (10°)
$C_2H_4O_2S$	Mercaptoacetic acid	50.0	.543	(.720) (20°)
C_2H_5NS	Thioacetamide	42.45	.565	
$C_2H_5SiCl_3$	Ethyl trichlorosilane	98.84	.604₆	
$C_2H_6O_2S_2$	Methyl thiosulfite	62.3	.494	
$C_2H_6O_2S$	Methyl sulfite	54.8	.490	
$C_2H_6N_2S$	N-Methyl thiourea	53.6	.595	
C_2H_6S	Ethyl mercaptan	47.0	.756	(.635)
$C_2H_6SiCl_2$	Dimethyl dichlorosilane	82.45	.639₂	
$C_2H_8N_2 \cdot HCl$	1,2-Diamino ethane hydrochloride	76.2	.789	
C_3H_3ON	Pyruvic nitrile	33.2	.481	
$C_3H_4OF_3$	1-Methoxy-1,1,2-trifluoroethane	55.9	.490	
C_3H_5OCl	Propionyl chloride	51	.55	(.59)

Formula	Compound	$-x_M \times 10^6$	$-x \times 10^6$	$-K \times 10^6$
$C_3H_5O_2Br$	Methylbromoacetate	71.1	.465	
C_3H_5Cl	1-Chloro-2-propene	47.8	.625	
C_3H_5Br	1-Bromo-2-propene	58.6	.484	
C_3H_5I	1-Iodo-2-propene	72.8	.433	
$C_3H_6N_6$	Melamine	61.8	.490	(.771) (250°)
C_3H_7N	1-Amino-2-propene	40.1	.702	
$C_3H_7SiCl_3$	n-Propyl trichlorosilane	110.2	.620$_0$	
$C_3H_8O_2N_2$	N-Hydroxymethyl-N-methylurea	68.0	.653	
$C_3H_8N_2S$	N,N-Dimethyl thiourea	64.2	.616	
$C_3H_8N_2S$	N,N'-Dimethyl thiourea	64.7	.621	
$C_3H_8N_2S$	N-Ethyl thiourea	62.8	.603	
C_3H_8S	Propyl mercaptan	58.5	.768	(.642) (25°)
C_3H_9SiCl	Trimethyl chlorosilane	77.36	.712$_2$	
$C_3H_{12}N_3B_3$	N-Trimethyl borazine	78.6	.641	
$C_4H_5ON_3$	Cytosine	55.8	.502	
$C_4H_6O_2$	Vinylacetate	46.4	.539	(.502)
$C_4H_6O_2NCl_3$	Nitro tri(chloromethyl) methane	107.8	.522	
$C_4H_6O_6$	Tartaric acid	67.5	.402	
C_4H_7OCl	Butyryl chloride	62.1	.582	(.598) (20°)
C_4H_7OCl	iso-Butyryl chloride	63.9	.599	
$C_4H_8N_2S$	N-Allyl thiourea	69.0	.595	(.725) (20°)
$C_4H_9ON_3$	Acetone semicarbazone	66.29	.575$_8$	(.716) (20°)
$C_4H_{10}O_2S_2$	Ethyl thiosulfite	86.2	.559	
$C_4H_{10}S_2$	Ethyl disulfide	83.6	.684	(.679) (20°)
$C_4H_{10}SiCl_2$	Diethyl dichlorosilane	105.80	.673$_5$	
$C_5H_4O_3N_4$	Uric acid	66.2	.394	(.746)
C_5H_6	Cyclopentadiene	44.5	.673	
$C_5H_6O_2N_2$	Thymine	57.1	.453	
$C_5H_8O_2$	Methyl methacrylate	57.3	.572	(.535) (20°)
$C_5H_8N_2$	3,5-Dimethyl pyrazole	56.2	.585	
$C_5H_8Cl_4$	Tetra (chloromethyl) methane	129	.652	
$C_5H_9S_3Na$	Sodium butyl thiocarbonate	104.5	.555	
$C_5H_9Cl_3$	1,1,1-Tri(chloromethyl) ethane	114	.650	
$C_5H_{10}O$	Cyclopentanol	64.0	.743	(.705) (20°)
$C_5H_{10}O_2$	Ethyl carbonate	75.4	.738	
$C_5H_{10}O_5$	D-Ribose	84.6	.564	
$C_5H_{10}NS_2Na$	Sodium diethyldithiocarbomate	99.2	.579	
$C_5H_{10}Cl_2$	2,2-Di-(Chloromethyl) propane	96.9	.687	
$C_5H_{11}ON$	Methyl n-propyl ketoxime	68.82	.679$_6$	(.618) (20°)
$C_5H_{11}ON_3$	Ethyl methyl ketone semicarbazone	77.93	.603$_4$	(.710) (20°)
$C_5H_{12}ON_2$	N,N'-Diethyl urea	74.1	.638	
$C_5H_{12}ON_2$	N,N,N',N'-Tetramethyl urea	75.7	.652	(.634) (15°)
$C_5H_{14}O_2Si$	Methyl diethoxysilane	92.99	.692$_4$	
$C_6H_3O_4N_2Cl$	1-Chloro-2,4-dinitrobenzene	84.4	.417	(.708) (22°)
$C_6H_3Cl_2I$	3,4-Dichloro-1-iodobenzene	118	.432	
$C_6H_5SiCl_3$	Phenyl trichlorosilane	120.4	.569$_4$	
C_6H_6NBr	o-Bromoaniline	87.32	.508	
C_6H_6NBr	m-Bromoaniline	84.89	.494	(.780) (20.4°)
C_6H_6NBr	p-Bromoaniline	84.06	.489	(.880)
$C_6H_7O_3NS . H_2O$	Sulfanilic acid	90.1	.471	
C_6H_7N	2-Methyl pyridine	60.3	.648	(.616) (15°)
C_6H_7N	3-Methyl pyridine	59.8	.642	(.617) (15°)
C_6H_7N	4-Methyl pyridine	59.8	.642	(.614) (15°)
$C_6H_7N . HI$	Aniline hydroiodide	113.6	.514	
C_6H_{10}	2,3-Dimethyl-1,3-butadiene	57.2	.696	(.539) (0°)
$C_6H_{11}OCl$	2-Ethyl butyryl chloride	87.2	.648	
$C_6H_{11}SiCl_3$	Cyclohexyltrichlorosilane	138.1	.634$_3$	
$C_6H_{12}N_2S_3$	Tetramethyl thiuram monosulfide	118.4	.568	(.795)
$C_6H_{12}N_2S_4$	Tetramethl thiuram disulfide	140.6	.585	(.755) (20°)
$C_6H_{13}ON$	Methyl-n-butyl ketoxime	79.97	.694$_2$	(.623) (20°)
$C_6H_{13}ON_3$	Methyl-n-propyl ketone semicarbazone	89.47	.624$_9$	(.669) (20°)
$C_6H_{13}ON_3$	Diethyl ketone semicarbazone	90.68	.633$_3$	(.730) (20°)
C_6H_{14}	3-Ethyl pentane	86.21	.861$_0$	(.601) (20°)
$C_6H_{14}O$	iso-Propyl ether	79.4	.777	(.564) (20°)
$C_6H_{14}S_2$	Propyl disulfide	106.2	.707	
$C_6H_{16}O_2Si$	Dimethyl diethoxysilane	104.6	.705$_2$	
$C_6H_{18}O_3Si_3$	Hexamethylcyclotrisiloxane	140.7	.632$_4$	
$C_6H_{18}N_3B_3$	Hexamethylborazine	119	.723	
$C_7H_5O_2Cl$	o-Chlorobenzoic acid	83.56	.534	(.824) (20°)
$C_7H_5O_4N$	Quinoleic acid	72.3	.433	
$C_7H_5NS_2$	2-Mercaptobenzothiazole	99.4	.594	(.843) (20°)
$C_7H_6F_2Cl$	Chlorodifluoromethylbenzene	87.2	.536	
$C_7H_7O_2N$	o-Aminobenzoic acid	77.18	.563	
C_7H_7Cl	o-Chlorotoluene	81.98	.648	(.701) (20°)
C_7H_7Cl	m-Chlorotoluene	80.07	.633	(.679) (20°)
C_7H_7Cl	p-Chlorotoluene	80.07	.633	(.677) (20°)
$C_7H_8N_2S$	N-phenylthiourea	87.4	.574	(.75)
C_7H_9ON	o-Anisidine	80.44	.654	(.714) (20°)
C_7H_9ON	m-Anisidine	79.95	.650	(.712) (20°)
C_7H_9ON	p-Anisidine	80.56	.655	(.702) (55°)
C_7H_9N	2,4-Dimethyl pyridine	71.50	.667	(.633) (0°)
C_7H_9N	2,6-Dimethyl pyridine	71.72	.669	(.630) (0°)
$C_7H_{15}ON$	Methyl amyl ketoxime	91.24	.706$_2$	(.630) (20°)
$C_7H_{15}ON_3$	Methyl-n-butyl ketone semicarbazone	100.40	.638$_6$	(.643) (20°)
$C_7H_{16}O$	1-Heptanol	91.7	.790	(.649) (20°)
$C_7H_{18}O_3Si$	Methyl triethoxysilane	120.6	.676$_2$	
C_8H_7OCl	Phenylacetyl chloride	88.5	.572	(.668) (20°)
$C_8H_8O_2$	o-Toluic acid	80.83	.594	(.626) (112°)
$C_8H_{10}ON_2$	N-Methyl, N'Phenyl urea	93.35	.622	
$C_8H_{10}O_4$	Butyne diacetate	95.9	.563	
$C_8H_{11}ON$	m-Phenetidine	90.28	.659	
$C_8H_{11}N$	2,4,6-Trimethyl pyridine	83.22	.687	(.630) (20°)
$C_8H_{16}O_2$	Hexylacetate	100.9	.700	(.623) (0°)
$C_8H_{17}ON_3$	Methyl amyl ketone semicarbazone	112.25	.655$_5$	(.687) (20°)
C_8H_{18}	3-Methyl-3-ethyl pentane	99.9	.875	(.623)
C_8H_{18}	4-Methyl heptane	97.30	.851$_7$	(.614)
C_8H_{18}	3-Ethyl hexane	97.76	.855$_8$	(.614) (20°)
C_8H_{18}	2,3,4-Trimethyl pentane	99.75	.872$_3$	

Formula	Compound	$-x_M \times 10^6$	$-x \times 10^6$	$-K \times 10^6$
$C_8H_{18}S_2$	Butyl disulfide	129.6	.727	
$C_8H_{18}S_3$	Butyl trisulfide	144.5	.687	
$C_8H_{18}S_4$	Butyl tetrasulfide	158.5	.653	
$C_8H_{20}O_4Si$	Tetraethoxysilane	137.1	.657$_9$	
$C_8H_{24}O_4Si_4$	Octamethyl cyclotetrasiloxane	187.4	.632$_2$	
C_9H_5N	Phenyl propionitrile	78.2	.615	
$C_9H_6O_2$	Phenyl propiolic acid	81.0	.554	
$C_9H_6O_3$	7-Hydroxycoumarin	88.22	.544$_9$	
C_9H_7N	iso-Quinoline	83.9	.650	(.714) (20°)
$C_9H_{10}O_4N_4$	Acetone-2,4-dinitrophenylhydrazone	110.62	.464$_4$	(.653) (20°)
$C_9H_{11}ON$	Benzylideneamino-1-hydroxyethane	91.0	.610	
$C_9H_{11}N$	Benzylideneaminoethane	85.5	.642	
$C_9H_{12}O_3S$	Ethyl p-toluene sulfonate	115	.574	
$C_9H_{12}O_6N_2$	Unidine	106.9	.438	
$C_9H_{13}O_5N_3$	Cytidine	123.7	.509	
$C_9H_{14}O_3$	1-Acetyl-1 ethoxycarbonyl cyclobutane	103.4	.608	
$C_9H_{14}O_4$	1,1-Di(ethoxycarbonyl) cyclopropane	110.4	.593	
$C_9H_{14}Si$	Trimethylphenylsilane	109.1	.726	
$C_9H_{19}ON_3$	Methyl-n-hexyl ketone semicarbazone	123.60	.666$_2$	(.716) (20°)
$C_9H_{20}O$	Di-isobutyl carbinol	116.9	.810	(.667) (0°)
$C_9H_{20}O_2N_2$	N,N,N,'N'-Tetraethylurea	122.4	.710	
$C_9H_{20}N_2S$	N,N,N',N'-Tetraethylthiourea	132.6	.704	
$C_9H_{24}N_3B_3$	B-Triethyl-N-Trimethyl borazine	146	.706	
$C_{10}H_6O_7N_2$	5,7-Dinitro-7-hydroxy-4-methylcoumarin	111.9	.420$_6$	
$C_{10}H_7O_3Br$	7-Hydroxy-4-methyl-3-bromocoumarin	127.3	.498$_7$	
$C_{10}H_7O_5N$	5-Nitro-6-hydroxy-4-methylcoumarin	105.6	.477$_9$	
$C_{10}H_7O_5N$	6-Nitro-7-hydroxy-4-methylcoumarin	105.5	.477$_5$	
$C_{10}H_7O_5N$	8-Nitro-7-hydroxy-4-methylcoumarin	106.0	.479$_8$	
$C_{10}H_8O_3$	6-Hydroxy-4-methylcoumarin	98.69	.560$_7$	
$C_{10}H_8O_3$	7-Hydroxy-4-methylcoumarin	99.96	.563$_7$	
$C_{10}H_8O_4$	Benzylidene malonic acid	97.5	.507	
$C_{10}H_8O_4$	5,7-Dihydroxy-4-methylcoumarin	106.9	.556$_7$	
$C_{10}H_8O_4$	7,8-Dihydroxy-4-methylcoumarin	105.1	.550$_4$	
$C_{10}H_8S$	1-Mercaptonaphthalene	109.5	.684	
$C_{10}H_8S_2$	1,8-Dimercaptonaphthalene	118.0	.614	
$C_{10}H_{10}O_4$	Methyl terephthalate	101.6	.523	
$C_{10}H_{10}Os$	Bis cyclopentadienyl osmium	193(20°)	.602	
$C_{10}H_{12}$	1,2,3,4-Tetrahydronaphthalene	93.3	.706	(.685)
$C_{10}H_{12}O_4N_4$	Ethyl methyl ketone-2,4-dinitrophenylhydrazone	124.11	.492$_1$	(.631) (20°)
$C_{10}H_{13}O_4N_5$	Adenosine	137.5	.514	
$C_{10}H_{13}O_5N_5$	Guanosine	149.1	.526	
$C_{10}H_{14}$	Durene	101.2	.754	(.632) (81°)
$C_{10}H_{14}$	sec-Butyl benzene	101.31	.754$_9$	(.651) (20°)
$C_{10}H_{16}O_4$	1,1-Di(ethoxycarbonyl) cyclobutane	118	.589	
$C_{10}H_{19}N$	Camphylamine	122.0	.796	
$C_{11}H_9BrS$	1-Bromo-4-Methylthionaphthalene	147.0	.581	
$C_{11}H_{10}O_2$	4,6-Dimethylcoumarin	106.2	.610$_3$	
$C_{11}H_{10}O_2$	4,7-Dimethylcoumarin	107.6	.610$_0$	
$C_{11}H_{10}O_3$	5-Hydroxy-4,7-dimethylcoumarin	113.5	.597$_3$	
$C_{11}H_{10}O_3$	6-Methoxy-4-methylcoumarin	109.5	.576$_3$	
$C_{11}H_{10}O_3$	7-Methoxy-4-methylcoumarin	110.5	.581$_4$	
$C_{11}H_{10}S$	Methyl-α-naphthyl sulfide	120.2	.690	
$C_{11}H_{14}O_2$	Benzyl butyrate	116.3	.653	(.663) (17.5°)
$C_{11}H_{14}O_4N_4$	Diethyl ketone-2,4-dinitrophenylhydrazone	135.16	.507$_6$	(.670) (20°)
$C_{11}H_{14}O_4N_4$	Methyl-n-propyl ketone-2,4-dinitrophenylhydrazone	135.70	.509$_7$	(.623) (20°)
$C_{11}H_{16}ON_2$	N,N-Diethyl-N'-phenyl urea	126.4	.657$_3$	
$C_{12}H_6O_4N_2Cl_2$	4,4'-Dichloro-2,2'-dinitro-1,1'-biphenyl	150	.479	
$C_{12}H_8$	Acenaphthylene	111.6	.733	(.659) (16°)
$C_{12}H_8O_4N_2$	2,4'-Dinitro-1,1'-biphenyl	116.5	.477	(.703) (20°)
$C_{12}H_8Cl_2$	4,4'-Dichloro-1,1'-biphenyl	133.1	.597	(.859) (20°)
$C_{12}H_8Br_2$	4,4'-Dibromo-1,1'-biphenyl	151.3	.485	(.920) (20°)
$C_{12}H_9O_2N$	2-Nitro-1,1'-biphenyl	109	.547	(.788) (20°)
$C_{12}H_9O_2N$	5-Nitroacenaphthene	116.0	.582	
$C_{12}H_{10}O_4$	Cinnamylidene malonic acid	105.4	.483	
$C_{12}H_{10}O_4$	Quinhydrone	105	.481	(.674) (20°)
$C_{12}H_{10}S$	Phenyl sulfide	119.2	.640	(.716) (20°)
$C_{12}H_{10}S_2$	Phenyl disulfide	122.5	.561	
$C_{12}H_{10}Cl_2Si$	Diphenyl dichlorosilane	153.5	.006$_3$	
$C_{12}H_{12}O_2Si$	Diphenyl silanediol	131.6	.608$_2$	
$C_{12}H_{16}O_2$	Amyl benzoate	128.5	.668	
$C_{12}H_{16}O_4N_4$	Methyl-n-butyl ketone-2,4-dinitrophenylhydrazone	147.65	.526$_8$	(.643) (20°)
$C_{12}H_{18}$	Hexamethyl benzene	122.5	.755	
$C_{12}H_{18}$	Diisopropyl benzene	124.77	.767$_1$	
$C_{12}H_{22}O_{11}$	Sucrose (saccharose)	189.1	.552	(.877) (15°)
$C_{12}H_{25}Cl_3Si$	Dodecyl trichlorosilane	209.2	.688$_9$	
$C_{12}H_{30}N_3B_3$	Hexaethylborazine	189	.759	
$C_{13}H_8OS$	Thioxanthone	130	.612	
$C_{13}H_{10}O_2$	Phenyl benzoate	117.3	.592	
$C_{13}H_{10}S$	Thiobenzophenone	118.1	.596	
$C_{13}H_{11}NS$	N-Thiobenzoyl aniline	123.0	.577	
$C_{13}H_{12}N_2S$	N,N'-Diphenyl thiourea	136.5	.598	
$C_{13}H_{12}N_2S$	N,N-Diphenyl thiourea	134.9	.591	
$C_{13}H_{18}O_4N_4$	Methyl amyl ketone-2,4-dinitrophenylhydrazone	156.84	.532$_9$	(.651) (20°)
$C_{14}H_8N_2S_4$	Di-2-benzothiazolyl disulfide	189.0	.568	
$C_{14}H_{10}O$	Anthrone	118	.608	
$C_{14}H_{12}O_2$	Benzyl benzoate	132.2	.622	(.693) (18°)
$C_{14}H_{12}O_2$	Diphenyl acetic acid	124.5	.587	
$C_{14}H_{14}O_3S$	p-Tolyl thiosulfonate	157	.564	
$C_{14}H_{14}N_2$	p-Azotoluene	135.1	.643	
$C_{14}H_{16}Si$	Dimethyl diphenyl silane	146.6	.690	
$C_{14}H_{20}O_4N_4$	Methyl n-hexyl ketone-2,4-dinitrophenylhydrazone	171.76	.55$_{1/2}$	(.655) (20°)
$C_{15}H_{10}O_2$	Flavone	120	.540	
$C_{15}H_{12}$	9-Ethylidene fluorene	124.8	.649	
$C_{15}H_{12}O$	Chalcone	125.7	.604	(.646) (62°)
$C_{15}H_{14}O_2$	Benzyl phenylacetate	143.7	.635	
$C_{15}H_{16}ON_2$	N,N'-Dimethyl-N,N'-Diphenyl urea	148.9	.620	
$C_{16}H_{10}$	Fluoranthene	138.0	.682	
$C_{16}H_{12}$	1-Benzylidene indene	130.5	.716	

DIAMAGNETIC SUSCEPTIBILITIES OF ORGANIC COMPOUNDS (Continued)

Formula	Compound	$-x_M \times 10^6$	$-x \times 10^6$	$-k \times 10^6$
$C_{16}H_{16}$	1,2-Dibenzylamine ethane	164	.787	
$C_{16}H_{33}SiCl_3$	Hexadecyl trichlorosilane	252.4	.701$_3$	
$C_{16}H_{48}O_6Si_7$	Hexadecamethyl heptasiloxane	351.1	.658$_8$	
$C_{17}H_{16}$	9-Butylidene fluorene	147.5	.670	
$C_{18}H_8S_4$	Tetrathiotetracene	202	.573	
$C_{18}H_{10}Cl_2$	5,11-Dichloro tetracene	202	.680	
$C_{18}H_{10}Br_2$	5,11-Dibromo tetracene	216	.559	
$C_{18}H_{12}$	Triphenylene	156.6	.686	
$C_{18}H_{14}$	o-Diphenyl benzene	150.4	.653	
$C_{18}H_{14}$	p-Diphenyl benzene (Terphenyl)	152	.660	
$C_{18}H_{15}SiCl$	Triphenyl chlorosilane	186.7	.633$_3$	(.814) (0°)
$C_{18}H_{16}OSi$	Triphenyl silanol	176.6	.634$_5$	
$C_{18}H_{16}Si$	Triphenylsilane	174	.668	
$C_{18}H_{20}$	5-Cyclohexyl acenaphthene	165.2	.699	
$C_{18}H_{22}$	Dimesitylene	171.8	.721	
$C_{18}H_{24}O_2$	Estradiol	186.6	.717	
$C_{18}H_{37}SiCl_3$	Octadecyl trichlorosilane	273.7	.705$_7$	
$C_{19}H_{14}O$	4-Benzoyl-1,1'-Biphenyl	158	.612	
$C_{19}H_{18}Si$	Methyl triphenyl silane	186	.678	
$C_{20}H_{14}O_2$	1,4-Dibenzoyl benzene	153	.534	
$C_{21}H_{24}N_3B_3$	B-Trimethyl-N-triphenylborazine	234	.667	
$C_{24}H_{18}$	4,4'-Diphenyl-1,1'-Biphenyl	201.3	.657	
$C_{24}H_{20}Si$	Tetraphenyl silane	224	.666	
$C_{24}H_{30}N_3B_3$	B-Triethyl-N-triphenylborazine	264	.693	
$C_{24}H_{40}O_4$	Desoxycholic acid	272.0	.715	
$C_{24}H_{40}O_5$	Cholic acid	282.3	.691	
$C_{25}H_{20}N_2S$	N,N,N',N'-Tetraphenylthiourea	229.7	.604	
$C_{26}H_{20}$	Tetraphenyl ethylene	217.4	.654	
$C_{28}H_{16}O_2$	Bianthrone (Dianthraquinone)	220	.572	
$C_{28}H_{18}O_2$	Dianthrone (Dianthronol)	229	.593	
$C_{28}H_{20}$	1,1,4,4-Tetraphenyl-1,2,3-butatriene	227	.659	
$C_{28}H_{44}O$	Calciferol	273.3	.689	
$C_{28}H_{44}O$	Ergosterol	279.6	.704	
$C_{36}H_{30}O_3Si_3$	Hexaphenyl cyclotrisiloxane	364.1	.612$_9$	
$C_{48}H_{40}O_4Si_4$	Octaphenyl cyclotetrasiloxane	485.3	.613$_2$	
$C_{60}H_{36}$	Hexabenzocoronene	346.0	.457	

MASS ATTENUATION COEFFICIENTS

Wavelength	Formvar $(C_5H_7O_2)_x$	Collodion $(C_{12}H_{11}O_{22}N_6)_x$	Polypropylene $(CH_2)_x$	Cellulose acetate $(C_{10}H_{21}O_{15})_x$	Mylar $(C_{10}H_8O_4)_x$	Teflon $(CF_2)_x$	Energy (eV)
2.0	14	20	8	19	14	28	6199.0
4.0	113	156	69	150	116	220	3099.5
6.0	372	510	234	489	384	700	2066.3
8.0	850	1140	550	1100	870	1540	1549.8
10.0	1580	2110	1040	2020	1630	2800	1239.8
12.0	2600	3450	1740	3310	2680	4520	1033.2
14.0	3920	5200	2660	4950	4040	6700	885.6
16.0	5600	7300	3830	7000	5800	9400	774.9
18.0	7500	9800	5200	9400	7800	12600	688.8
20.0	9900	12800	6900	12300	10200	2780	619.9
22.0	12500	16200	8800	15500	12900	3540	563.5
24.0	8200	6400	11000	4850	8500	4430	516.6
26.0	10100	7900	13500	5900	10400	5400	476.8
28.0	12000	9400	16200	7100	12400	6500	442.8
30.0	14300	11100	19200	8400	14700	7800	413.3
32.0	16700	8200	22400	9900	17200	9100	387.4
34.0	19300	9500	25900	11400	19900	10600	364.6
36.0	22100	10800	29600	13100	22800	12100	344.4
38.0	25000	12300	33600	14900	25800	13800	326.3
40.0	28200	13900	37800	16800	29100	15600	309.9
42.0	31500	15500	42200	18700	32500	17500	295.2
44.0	3250	4540	1940	4370	3350	6900	281.8
46.0	3640	5100	2180	4900	3760	7800	269.5
48.0	4050	5600	2430	5400	4170	8600	258.3
50.0	4450	6200	2690	6000	4590	9500	248.0
52.0	4910	6800	2960	6600	5100	10500	238.4
54.0	5400	7500	3240	7200	5600	11500	229.6
56.0	5900	8200	3540	7900	6100	12500	221.4
58.0	6400	8900	3860	8600	6600	13600	213.8
60.0	7000	9700	4190	9300	7200	14800	206.6
62.0	7500	10500	4540	10100	7800	16000	200.0
64.0	8100	11300	4880	10900	8400	17300	193.7
66.0	8700	12100	5200	11700	9000	18600	187.8
68.0	9400	13100	5700	12600	9700	19900	182.3
70.0	10000	14000	6000	13500	10300	21300	177.1
72.0	10700	14900	6400	14400	11100	22700	172.2
74.0	11400	15900	6800	15400	11800	24200	167.5
76.0	12200	17000	7300	16300	12500	25700	163.1
78.0	12900	18000	7700	17300	13300	27200	158.9
80.0	13600	19100	8100	18400	14100	28800	155.0
82.0	14500	20200	8600	19500	14900	30500	151.2
84.0	15300	21400	9100	20600	15800	32100	147.6
86.0	16100	22600	9600	21700	16600	33800	144.2
88.0	17000	23700	10100	22900	17500	35500	140.9
90.0	17800	25000	10600	24100	18400	37300	137.8
92.0	18800	26300	11100	25300	19400	39100	134.8
94.0	19700	27600	11700	26500	20300	40900	131.9
96.0	20600	28900	12200	27800	21300	43000	129.1
98.0	21600	30300	12800	29200	22300	44600	126.5
100.0	22600	31700	13400	30500	23300	46300	124.0
105.0	25200	35300	15000	34000	26000	51000	118.1
110.0	27900	39100	16600	37600	28800	56000	112.7
115.0	30700	43000	18200	41300	31600	61000	107.8
120.0	33600	47000	20000	45100	34600	67000	103.3
125.0	36800	52000	21900	49600	38000	72000	99.2
130.0	39800	56000	23900	53000	41100	78000	95.4
135.0	43200	60000	25900	58000	44600	83000	91.8
140.0	46700	65000	28100	63000	48200	89000	88.6
145.0	50000	70000	30300	67000	52000	95000	85.5
150.0	54000	75000	32600	72000	55000	101000	82.7
155.0	57000	80000	35000	76000	59000	106000	80.0
160.0	61000	85000	37600	82000	63000	112000	77.5
165.0	65000	90000	40200	87000	67000	118000	75.1
170.0	69000	96000	42800	92000	72000	124000	72.9
175.0	73000	101000	45400	97000	75000	130000	70.8
180.0	77000	107000	47900	102000	80000	136000	68.9
185.0	82000	113000	51000	108000	84000	141000	67.0
190.0	86000	118000	54000	112000	88000	147000	65.3
195.0	90000	124000	57000	118000	93000	153000	63.6
200.0	95000	130000	61000	124000	98000	159000	62.0

MASS ATTENUATION COEFFICIENTS (Continued)

Wavelength	Polystyrene (CH)$_x$	Nylon (C$_{12}$H$_{22}$O$_3$N$_2$)$_x$	Vyns (C$_{22}$H$_{33}$O$_2$Cl$_9$)$_x$	Saran (C$_2$H$_2$Cl$_2$)$_x$	Aluminum oxide Al$_2$O$_3$	Quartz (SiO$_2$)$_x$	Energy (eV)
2.0	9	12	114	164	68	77	6199.0
4.0	74	96	750	1070	480	530	3099.5
6.0	252	318	350	375	1440	1600	2066.3
8.0	590	730	780	820	860	980	1549.8
10.0	1120	1370	1440	1520	1580	1810	1239.8
12.0	1870	2270	2370	2490	2570	2950	1033.2
14.0	2870	3440	3590	3760	3840	4400	885.6
16.0	4120	4910	5100	5400	5500	6200	774.9
18.0	5600	6700	6900	7200	7300	8400	688.8
20.0	7500	8800	9000	9300	9600	11000	619.9
22.0	9500	11100	11400	11800	12100	13800	563.5
24.0	11900	10600	12800	14400	4290	4920	516.6
26.0	14600	13000	15500	17300	5200	6000	476.8
28.0	17400	15500	18400	20400	6300	7200	442.8
30.0	20700	18400	21400	23700	7500	8500	413.3
32.0	24200	17300	24700	27100	8700	9900	387.4
34.0	28000	20000	28100	30800	10100	11300	364.6
36.0	31900	22800	31600	34400	11500	12900	344.4
38.0	36200	25800	35400	38200	13100	14500	326.3
40.0	40700	29100	39100	42100	14700	16200	309.9
42.0	45500	32500	43100	46000	16300	18000	295.2
44.0	2090	2730	25700	37000	18100	19800	281.8
46.0	2350	3060	23600	33600	19900	21700	269.5
48.0	2620	3400	25300	36100	21800	23600	258.3
50.0	2900	3750	27300	38800	23700	25500	248.0
52.0	3190	4130	28900	41100	25700	27500	238.4
54.0	3500	4540	30600	43400	27700	29400	229.6
56.0	3820	4950	32200	45700	29800	31800	221.4
58.0	4160	5400	33900	47900	31800	33700	213.8
60.0	4510	5800	35100	49500	33900	35600	206.6
62.0	4890	6300			35900	37500	200.0
64.0	5300	6800			38000	39900	193.7
66.0	5600	7300			40600	41900	187.8
68.0	6100	7900			42800	44000	182.3
70.0	6500	8400			44900	46000	177.1
72.0	6900	9000			47100	48000	172.2
74.0	7400	9600			49300	50000	167.5
76.0	7800	10200			51000	52000	163.1
78.0	8300	10800			54000	54000	158.9
80.0	8800	11400			56000	56000	155.0
82.0	9300	12100			58000	52000	151.2
84.0	9800	12800			61000	53000	147.6
86.0	10300	13500			62000	56000	144.2
88.0	10900	14200			65000	57000	140.9
90.0	11400	15000			67000	59000	137.8
92.0	12000	15700			69000	61000	134.8
94.0	12600	16500			71000	63000	131.9
96.0	13200	17300			73000	65000	129.1
98.0	13800	18100			75000	67000	126.5
100.0	14500	19000			77000	69000	124.0
105.0	16100	21100			83000	73000	118.1
110.0	17900	23400			79000	78000	112.7
115.0	19600	25800			84000	82000	107.8
120.0	21600	28300			88000	86000	103.3
125.0	23600	31000			93000		99.2
130.0	25700	33600			97000		95.4
135.0	28000	36500			101000		91.8
140.0	30300	39400			106000		88.6
145.0	32700	42400			110000		85.5
150.0	35100	45600			114000		82.7
155.0	37700	48900			118000		80.0
160.0	40500	52000			122000		77.5
165.0	43300	56000			125000		75.1
170.0	46100	59000					72.9
175.0	48900	63000					70.8
180.0	52000	66000					68.9
185.0	55000	70000					67.0
190.0	58000	74000					65.3
195.0	62000	78000					63.6
200.0	65000	82000					62.0

MASS ATTENUATION COEFFICIENTS (Continued)

Wavelength	Stearate CH$_3$(CH$_2$)$_{16}$COO$^-$	Animal proteins C = 52.5% H = 7% S = 1.5% O = 22.5% N = 16.5%	Air O = 21% N = 78% Ar = 1%	P 10 CH$_4$ = 10% Ar = 90%	Methane CH$_4$	Q Gas C$_4$H$_{10}$ = 1.3% He = 98.7%	Energy (eV)
2.0	10	16	21	230	7	1	6199.0
4.0	84	126	148	162	60	12	3099.5
6.0	281	361	481	467	205	41	2066.3
8.0	650	820	1090	1020	479	97	1549.8
10.0	1220	1530	2020	1850	910	185	1239.8
12.0	2030	2530	3310	3010	1520	313	1033.2
14.0	3080	3830	4980	4500	2330	484	885.6
16.0	4410	5500	7100	6400	3350	700	774.9
18.0	6000	7400	9500	8400	4570	970	688.8
20.0	7900	9700	12400	10900	6100	1300	619.9
22.0	10100	12300	15700	13500	7700	1670	563.5
24.0	10000	10300	14100	16400	9700	2110	516.6
26.0	12200	12600	17100	19600	11800	2620	476.8
28.0	14600	15100	20400	22800	14100	3160	442.8
30.0	17300	17800	24000	26300	16800	3780	413.3
32.0	20300	15500	2290	29700	19600	4460	387.4
34.0	23400	17900	2650	33300	22700	5200	364.6
36.0	26800	20400	3040	36900	25900	6000	344.4
38.0	30300	23100	3460	40500	29300	6900	326.3
40.0	34100	26000	3810	37600	33000	7800	309.9
42.0	38200	29100	4270	40900	36900	8800	295.2
44.0	2390	3750	4780	42600	1700	2960	281.8
46.0	2680	4180	5300	45600	1910	3380	269.5
48.0	2980	4610	5900	48900	2130	3840	258.3
50.0	3290	5000	6400	52000	2350	4340	248.0
52.0	3620	5500	6300		2590	4910	238.4
54.0	3970	5900	7000		2840	5500	229.6
56.0	4340	6400	7600		3100	6100	221.4
58.0	4730	6900	8200		3380	6700	213.8
60.0	5100	7500	8900		3660	7400	206.6
62.0	5600	8100	9700		3970	8200	200.0
64.0	6000	8700	10400		4270	8900	193.7
66.0	6400	9300	11200		4570	9700	187.8
68.0	6900	10000	12100		4940	10600	182.3
70.0	7400	10600	12900		5200	11500	177.1
72.0	7900	11300	13800		5600	12500	172.2
74.0	8400	12000	14700		6000	13500	167.5
76.0	8900	11600	15600		6400	14600	163.1
78.0	9500	12300	16600		6700	15600	158.9
80.0	10000	13000	17600		7100	16800	155.0
82.0	10600	13800	18600		7600	18000	151.2
84.0	11200	14600	19700		7900	19300	147.6
86.0	11800	15400	20800		8400	20500	144.2
88.0	12400	16200	21900		8800	21900	140.9
90.0	13100	17000	23100		9300	23300	137.8
92.0	13700	17900	24200		9700	24700	134.8
94.0	14400	18800	25400		10300	26200	131.9
96.0	15100	19700	26700		10700	27800	129.1
98.0	15800	20700	28000		11200	29400	126.5
100.0	16600	21600	29200		11800	31000	124.0
105.0	18400	24100	32700		13100	35400	118.1
110.0	20400	26700	36200		14500	40100	112.7
115.0	22500	29300	39900		15900	44800	107.8
120.0	24600	32200	43800		17500	50000	103.3
125.0	27000	35300	48000		19200	56000	99.2
130.0	29300	38200	52000		20900	62000	95.4
135.0	31800	41500	57000		22700	68000	91.8
140.0	34400	44800	61000		24600	75000	88.6
145.0	37000	48200	65000		26500	82000	85.5
150.0	39800	52000	71000		28500	89000	82.7
155.0	42600	55000	76000		30600	96000	80.0
160.0	45700	59000	80000		32900	104000	77.5
165.0	48600	63000	86000		35100	112000	75.1
170.0	52000	67000	91000		37400	121000	72.9
175.0	55000	71000	96000		39700	130000	70.8
180.0	58000	75000	102000		41900	138000	68.9
185.0	62000	79000	108000		44900	147000	67.0
190.0	65000	83000	114000		47200	157000	65.3
195.0	68000	88000	119000		50000	167000	63.6
200.0	72000	92000	125000		53000	177000	62.0

INTRODUCTION TO X-RAY CROSS SECTIONS

Alex F. Burr

These tables are part of an extensive report published by W. H. McMaster, et al. as UCRL 50174 and available from the National Technical Information Service, Springfield, Va. 22151. Section I of UCRL 50174 describes the data base and the treatment given it, Section II contains the total cross sections between 1 and 1000 keV for all the elements, Section III contains results used in producing Section II, and Section IV contains total cross sections for selected energies and is reproduced in part here. To obtain these values existing experimental x-ray total cross section data and theoretical cross section calculations were surveyed. The coherent (Rayleigh) scattering cross sections and the incoherent (Compton) scattering cross sections were computed. The photo-electric cross sections were obtained by least squares fitting of experimental data, theory, and interpolation of experiment and theory. The following table contains cross sections interpolated from the basic compilation at those wavelengths of most use to x-ray crystallographers. The wavelengths chosen were selected to correspond to those given in the International Tables for X-Ray Crystallography. The energy-to-wavelength conversion is given below.

Table I. Energy-to-wavelength conversion

Target radiation	Å	keV	Target radiation	Å	keV
Ag Kᾱ	0.5608	22.105	Ni Kᾱ	1.6591	7.472
Kβ₁	0.4970	24.942	Kβ₁	1.5001	8.265
Pd Kᾱ	0.5869	21.125	Co Kᾱ	1.7902	6.925
Kβ₁	0.5205	23.819	Kβ₁	1.6208	7.649
Rh Kᾱ	0.6147	20.169	Fe Kᾱ	1.9373	6.400
Kβ₁	0.5456	22.724	Kβ₁	1.7565	7.058
Mo Kᾱ	0.7107	17.444	Mn Kᾱ	2.1031	5.895
Kβ₁	0.6323	19.608	Kβ₁	1.9102	6.490
Zn Kᾱ	1.4364	8.631	Cr Kᾱ	2.2909	5.412
Kβ₁	1.2952	9.572	Kβ₁	2.0848	5.947
Cu Kᾱ	1.5418	8.041	Ti Kᾱ	2.7496	4.509
Kβ₁	1.3922	8.905	Kβ₁	2.5138	4.932

Table II. Total Cross Section in cm²/g

Z KEV	1 H	2 He	3 Li	4 Be	5 B	6 C	7 N	8 O	9 F	10 Ne
4.51	.432	.661	2.10	5.63	12.9	25.6	43.0	64.8	91.8	125
4.93	.421	.550	1.62	4.25	9.69	19.4	32.6	49.4	70.3	95.9
5.41	.412	.465	1.24	3.18	7.23	14.5	24.4	37.2	53.1	72.7
5.90	.405	.405	.986	2.45	5.53	11.1	18.7	28.6	41.1	56.4
5.95	.405	.400	.964	2.39	5.39	10.8	18.2	27.9	40.0	54.9
6.40	.400	.362	.798	1.92	4.28	8.55	14.5	22.2	32.0	44.0
6.49	.400	.355	.770	1.84	4.10	8.18	13.9	21.3	30.6	42.2
6.93	.397	.329	.659	1.52	3.36	6.68	11.3	17.4	25.1	34.7
7.06	.396	.322	.631	1.44	3.17	6.30	10.7	16.5	23.7	32.8
7.47	.394	.303	.555	1.23	2.67	5.28	8.96	13.8	19.9	27.6
7.65	.393	.297	.528	1.15	2.49	4.92	8.33	12.9	18.6	25.7
8.04	.391	.284	.477	1.01	2.14	4.22	7.14	11.0	16.0	22.1
8.27	.390	.277	.452	.936	1.98	3.88	6.56	10.1	14.7	20.4
8.63	.389	.268	.417	.837	1.74	3.40	5.74	8.87	12.8	17.9
8.91	.388	.262	.394	.774	1.59	3.09	5.22	8.06	11.7	16.2
9.57	.386	.250	.349	.651	1.30	2.49	4.19	6.47	9.36	13.1
17.44	.373	.202	.197	.245	.345	.535	.790	1.15	1.58	2.21
19.61	.370	.197	.187	.222	.293	.429	.605	.855	1.15	1.60
20.17	.369	.196	.185	.217	.283	.408	.570	.799	1.07	1.48
21.13	.368	.195	.182	.210	.268	.379	.519	.717	.952	1.31
22.11	.366	.193	.179	.205	.256	.354	.476	.648	.851	1.16
22.72	.366	.192	.177	.201	.249	.340	.452	.610	.795	1.08
23.82	.364	.191	.175	.196	.239	.319	.416	.553	.711	.963
24.94	.363	.189	.173	.192	.229	.301	.385	.504	.640	.861

Table II. Total Cross Section in cm^2/g   (Continued)

Z KEV	11 Na	12 Mg	13 Al	14 Si	15 P	16 S	17 Cl	18 Ar	19 K	20 Ca
4.51	168	220	264	336	386	464	518	577	679	805
4.93	129	171	206	263	304	364	411	456	542	638
5.41	98.5	131	158	203	236	282	322	356	427	500
5.90	76.6	102	124	160	186	223	256	282	342	398
5.95	74.7	99.6	121	156	182	217	250	276	334	389
6.40	59.9	80.2	97.5	126	148	177	205	225	275	319
6.49	57.5	77	93.7	121	142	170	197	217	264	307
6.93	47.3	63.5	77.5	100	118	141	165	181	222	257
7.06	44.7	60.1	73.4	95.1	112	134	156	172	211	244
7.47	37.7	50.8	62.2	80.7	95.2	114	134	147	181	209
7.65	35.2	47.4	58.1	75.4	89.1	107	125	137	170	196
8.04	30.3	40.9	50.2	65.3	77.3	92.5	109	120	148	171
8.27	27.9	37.6	46.3	60.2	71.3	85.5	101	111	138	159
8.63	24.4	33.0	40.7	53.0	62.9	75.4	89.4	97.7	122	141
8.91	22.2	30.1	37.1	48.4	57.4	68.9	81.8	89.3	112	129
9.57	17.9	24.2	30.0	39.1	46.6	55.9	66.7	72.7	91.4	106
17.44	2.94	3.98	5.04	6.53	7.87	9.63	11.6	12.6	16.2	19
19.61	2.10	2.83	3.59	4.62	5.57	6.84	8.26	8.95	11.5	13.6
20.17	1.94	2.60	3.30	4.26	5.13	6.30	7.61	8.24	10.6	12.5
21.13	1.70	2.28	2.89	3.71	4.47	5.50	6.63	7.18	9.24	10.9
22.11	1.50	2.00	2.54	3.25	3.91	4.82	5.80	6.28	8.08	9.57
22.72	1.39	1.86	2.35	3.00	3.61	4.45	5.35	5.79	7.45	8.84
23.82	1.23	1.63	2.06	2.62	3.15	3.88	4.66	5.04	6.49	7.71
24.94	1.09	1.44	1.81	2.30	2.76	3.40	4.08	4.41	5.67	6.75

Z KEV	21 Sc	22 Ti	23 V	24 Cr	25 Mn	26 Fe	27 Co	28 Ni	29 Cu	30 Zn
4.51	819	111	125	143	160	188	206	240	257	280
4.93	658	86.8	97.3	111	125	147	161	188	201	220
5.41	521	571	75.1	85.7	96 1	113	125	146	155	172
5.90	420	459	513	67.4	75.6	88.9	98.4	115	123	137
5.95	411	449	501	65.8	73.8	86.8	96.1	113	120	134
6.40	339	370	411	462	59.9	70.4	78.3	91.8	97.4	110
6.49	327	357	396	445	57.6	67.7	75.3	88.3	93.6	106
6.93	276	301	333	375	405	56.3	62.9	73.8	78.1	88.7
7.06	262	286	316	357	385	53.3	59.6	70.0	74.1	84.3
7.47	226	246	271	307	331	367	50.9	59.8	63.2	72.4
7.65	212	231	255	288	311	346	47.7	56.1	59.2	68.0
8.04	186	202	223	252	273	304	339	48.8	51.5	59.5
8.27	173	188	206	234	253	283	315	45.2	47.7	55.3
8.63	153	167	183	208	225	253	281	306	42.3	49.2
8.91	141	153	168	191	207	234	259	283	38.7	45.3
9.57	116	126	138	157	170	194	214	236	245	37.4
17.44	21.0	23.3	25.2	29.3	31.9	37.7	41.0	47.2	49.3	55.5
19.61	15.0	16.7	18.1	21.0	22.9	27.2	29.5	34.2	35.8	40.3
20.17	13.8	15.4	16.7	19.4	21.1	25.1	27.2	31.6	33.1	37.2
21.13	12.1	13.4	14.6	17.0	18.5	22.0	23.8	27.7	29.0	32.7
22.11	10.5	11.8	12.8	14.9	16.2	19.3	20.9	24 3	25.5	28.7
22.72	9.72	10.9	11.8	13.7	15.0	17.8	19.3	22.5	23.6	26.6
23.82	8.47	9.48	10.3	12.0	13.1	15.6	16.9	19.7	20.7	23.3
24.94	7.40	8.30	9.02	10.5	11.5	13.7	14.8	17.3	18.2	20.4

Z KEV	31 Ga	32 Ge	33 As	34 Se	35 Br	36 Kr	37 Rb	38 Sr	39 Y	40 Zr
4.51	309	329	368	403	435	464	508	552	599	648
4.93	242	258	288	317	342	366	400	436	473	511
5.41	187	200	224	246	266	285	312	339	369	399
5.90	148	158	178	195	211	226	248	270	294	317
5.95	144	155	173	190	206	221	242	263	287	310
6.40	117	126	142	156	169	181	198	215	235	254
6.49	113	122	136	150	162	174	191	207	227	244
6.93	94.2	102	114	125	136	146	160	174	190	205
7.06	89.3	96.8	108	119	129	138	152	165	181	195
7.47	76.2	82.9	92.5	101	110	119	130	141	155	167
7.65	71.4	77.8	86.8	95.1	104	111	122	132	145	157
8.04	62.1	67.9	75.7	82.9	90.3	97	106	115	127	137
8.27	57.5	63.0	70.1	77.8	83.7	89.9	98.5	107	118	127
8.63	50.9	56.0	62.2	68.0	74.2	79.8	87.4	94.7	105	113
8.91	46.7	51.4	57.0	62.3	68.1	73.2	80.2	86.8	96.2	103
9.57	38.1	42.3	46.7	51.0	55.8	60.0	65.7	71.0	79.0	84.8
17.44	56.9	60.5	66.0	68.8	74.7	79.1	83.0	88.0	97.6	16.1
19.61	41.7	44.3	48.6	51.2	55.6	58.6	62.1	65.6	72.6	75.2
20.17	38.6	41.0	45.1	47.6	51.7	54.5	57.8	61.0	67.5	70.1
21.13	34.0	36.1	39.7	42.1	45.6	48.1	51.1	54.0	59.7	62.1
22.11	29.9	31.8	35.0	37.2	40.4	42.5	45.3	47.9	53.0	55.2
22.72	27.7	29.4	32.4	34.6	37.5	39.5	42.1	44.5	49.2	51.4
23.82	24.3	25.8	28.5	30.5	33.1	34.8	37.2	39.3	43.5	45.5
24.94	21.4	22.7	25.1	26.9	29.2	30.7	32.9	34.8	38.5	40.4

Z KEV	41 Nb	42 Mo	43 Te	44 Ru	45 Rh	46 Pd	47 Ag	48 Cd	49 In	50 Sn
4.51	697	738	786	832	892	928	987	1064	1151	1128
4.93	552	585	621	660	708	739	785	842	906	899
5.41	432	457	486	518	555	581	617	659	706	709
5.90	344	365	387	414	444	466	495	526	561	569
5.95	336	357	378	404	434	455	484	514	548	557
6.40	276	293	310	333	357	375	398	422	449	460
6.49	266	282	299	320	344	361	384	407	433	443
6.93	223	237	251	269	289	304	324	342	363	374
7.06	212	225	238	256	275	289	308	325	345	356
7.47	182	193	204	220	236	249	265	279	295	307
7.65	170	181	192	207	222	234	249	262	277	289
8.04	149	158	168	181	194	205	218	229	242	253
8.27	138	147	156	168	180	190	203	213	225	236
8.63	122	130	138	149	160	169	180	189	200	210
8.91	112	120	127	137	147	156	166	174	183	193
9.57	92.0	98.2	104	113	121	128	137	143	151	159
17.44	17.0	18.4	19.8	21.3	23.1	24.4	26.4	27.7	29.1	31.2
19.61	81.2	13.3	14.3	15.4	16.7	17.6	19.1	20.1	21.2	22.6
20.17	75.6	79.3	13.2	14.2	15.4	16.3	17.7	18.6	19.6	20.9
21.13	67.1	70.3	73.0	12.5	13.5	14.3	15.5	16.4	17.3	18.4
22.11	59.6	62.5	65.0	11.0	11.9	12.6	13.7	14.5	15.3	16.2
22.72	55.5	58.2	60.6	63.8	11.0	11.6	12.7	13.4	14.1	15.0
23.82	49.1	51.5	53.7	56.6	58.3	10.2	11.1	11.8	12.4	13.2
24.94	43.6	45.7	47.7	50.3	52.0	57.0	97.8	10.4	11.0	11.6

Table II. Total Cross Section in cm^2/g (Continued)

Z KEV	51 Sb	52 Te	53 I	54 Xe	55 Cs	56 Ba	57 La	58 Ce	59 Pr	60 Nd
4.51	997	753	293	300	324	334	355	383	414	433
4.93	926	843	921	683	259	266	282	304	330	344
5.41	733	769	835	755	803	587	223	240	261	271
5.90	592	617	666	701	742	660	677	521	210	218
5.95	579	603	651	685	725	645	662	509	205	213
6.40	479	497	535	565	597	615	636	592	450	464
6.49	462	479	516	545	575	593	613	571	610	447
6.93	391	404	434	459	484	499	519	559	596	532
7.06	373	385	413	437	460	475	494	532	567	506
7.47	322	331	355	376	395	408	427	459	488	506
7.65	303	312	333	353	372	384	402	432	459	476
8.04	267	273	292	310	325	336	354	379	402	418
8.27	248	254	271	288	302	312	329	352	374	389
8.63	221	226	241	256	269	278	294	314	333	347
8.91	204	208	222	236	248	256	271	290	307	320
9.57	168	172	183	195	204	211	224	240	253	265
17.44	33.0	33.9	36.3	38.3	40.4	42.4	45.3	48.6	50.8	53.3
19.61	23.9	24.7	26.5	27.9	29.5	31.0	33.1	35.5	37.1	38.9
20.17	22.1	22.8	24.6	25.8	27.3	28.7	30.7	33.0	34.4	36.0
21.13	19.4	20.1	21.7	22.7	24.1	25.4	27.0	29.1	30.3	31.7
22.11	17.1	17.7	19.2	20.0	21.3	22.5	23.9	25.7	26.8	28.0
22.72	15.8	16.4	17.8	18.6	19.8	20.9	22.1	23.9	24.9	26.0
23.82	13.8	14.4	15.7	16.3	17.4	18.4	19.5	21.0	21.9	22.9
24.94	12.1	12.7	13.9	14.4	15.4	16.3	17.2	18.6	19.3	20.2

Z KEV	61 Pm	62 Sm	63 Eu	64 Gd	65 Tb	66 Dy	67 Ho	68 Er	69 Tm	70 Yb
4.51	455	473	503	510	546	568	589	615	644	664
4.93	361	375	398	405	432	449	465	485	508	524
5.41	285	295	313	319	339	352	363	380	397	410
5.90	229	237	251	256	271	281	290	303	317	327
5.95	224	232	245	250	265	275	283	296	310	319
6.40	186	192	203	207	219	227	234	244	255	263
6.49	476	185	195	200	211	219	225	235	246	254
6.93	401	412	165	170	179	185	190	198	207	214
7.06	536	392	420	161	170	176	181	189	197	204
7.47	535	475	361	369	147	152	156	163	170	175
7.65	503	446	477	347	367	143	146	153	160	165
8.04	441	454	418	427	322	337	128	134	140	145
8.27	410	422	450	397	420	313	333	125	131	135
8.63	366	376	401	410	375	392	296	318	117	120
8.91	336	347	369	377	400	360	272	292	289	111
9.57	278	287	305	312	330	344	364	336	239	232
17.44	55.5	58.0	61.2	62.8	66.8	68.9	72.1	75.6	79.0	80.2
19.61	40.5	42.4	44.7	46.0	48.9	50.4	52.8	55.1	57.9	59.2
20.17	37.6	39.3	41.5	42.6	45.3	46.7	48.9	51.0	53.8	55.0
21.13	33.1	34.7	36.6	37.6	40.0	41.2	43.2	45.0	47.5	48.7
22.11	29.3	30.7	32.4	33.3	35.4	36.5	38.3	39.8	42.1	43.2
22.72	27.1	28.5	30.1	30.9	32.9	33.9	35.6	37.0	39.1	40.2
23.82	23.9	25.1	26.5	27.3	29.0	29.9	31.4	32.6	34.5	35.5
24.94	21.1	22.2	23.4	24.1	25.6	26.4	27.8	28.8	30.6	31.5

Z KEV	71 Lu	72 Hf	73 Ta	74 W	75 Re	76 Os	77 Ir	78 Pt	79 Au	80 Hg
4.51	696	720	736	753	796	824	871	934	906	958
4.93	549	568	581	598	631	653	688	734	720	760
5.41	430	445	455	470	496	512	540	572	568	598
5.90	343	355	363	378	397	410	431	455	457	480
5.95	335	347	355	369	388	401	422	444	447	469
6.40	276	286	293	306	321	332	348	365	371	388
6.49	266	276	282	295	310	320	336	351	358	375
6.93	225	233	238	250	262	270	283	295	303	317
7.06	214	222	227	238	249	257	270	281	289	302
7.47	184	191	195	206	215	222	233	241	250	261
7.65	173	180	184	194	203	209	219	226	236	246
8.04	152	158	162	171	178	184	192	198	208	216
8.27	142	147	150	159	166	171	179	184	194	202
8.63	126	131	134	142	149	153	160	164	174	180
8.91	117	121	124	132	137	141	148	151	161	167
9.57	247	236	103	110	114	118	123	125	134	139
17.44	84.2	86.3	89.5	95.8	98.7	100	103	109	111	115
19.61	62.0	64.2	66.1	70.6	72.5	74.1	77.2	80.2	82.3	85.3
20.17	57.6	59.7	61.4	65.5	67.3	68.9	71.9	74.6	76.5	79.4
21.13	51.0	52.9	54.4	58.0	59.5	61.1	63.8	66.0	67.8	70.4
22.11	45.3	46.9	48.3	51.4	52.8	54.2	56.8	58.6	60.2	62.6
22.72	42.1	43.7	44.9	47.8	49.1	50.5	52.9	54.5	56.0	58.3
23.82	37.2	38.6	39.7	42.2	43.3	44.6	46.8	48.2	49.5	51.7
24.94	33.0	34.2	35.2	37.4	38.4	39.6	41.6	42.7	43.9	45.9

Z KEV	81 Tl	82 Pb	83 Bi	86 Rn	90 Th	92 U	95 Pu
4.51	991	1035	1066	1174	1098	1084	960
4.93	785	820	847	930	993	862	1023
5.41	617	645	667	731	844	774	803
5.90	494	517	536	586	678	672	731
5.95	483	505	524	573	663	657	772
6.40	400	418	435	474	549	545	638
6.49	386	403	419	458	530	526	615
6.93	326	341	355	387	449	446	520
7.06	311	325	338	369	428	425	495
7.47	268	280	293	318	370	368	427
7.65	253	264	276	300	348	347	402
8.04	222	232	243	264	307	306	353
8.27	207	216	227	246	286	285	329
8.63	185	194	203	220	256	256	294
8.91	171	179	188	203	237	236	271
9.57	142	149	156	169	197	197	225
17.44	119	123	126	117	99.5	96.7	48.8
19.61	88.3	90.6	93.5	101	73.3	72.6	79.0
20.17	82.0	84.1	87.0	93.8	95.0	67.8	73.7
21.13	72.7	74.5	77.2	83.3	97.2	84.2	65.7
22.11	64.6	66.1	68.7	74.1	86.3	86.9	58.8
22.72	60.1	61.5	64.0	69.1	80.3	81.1	76.4
23.82	53.2	54.4	56.7	61.2	71.0	72.1	78.3
24.94	47.2	48.2	50.4	54.4	62.9	64.2	69.8

X-RAY WAVELENGTHS

J. A. Bearden

These tables were originally published as the final report to the U.S. Atomic Energy Commission as Report NYO-10586 in partial fulfillment of Contract AT(30-1)-2543. The tables were later reproduced in *Review of Modern Physics*. The data may also be obtained from the Superintendent of Documents, U.S. Government Printing Office, Washington, D. C. 20402 in the publication NSRDS-NBS 14. Persons seeking discussion of the experimental work, conventions, secondary standards, etc. will find these in *Review of Modern Physics*, Vol. 39, No. 1, 78-124, January 1967.

THE W $K\alpha_1$ WAVELENGTH STANDARD

A wavelength standard should possess characteristics which permit its ready redetermination in other laboratories by different techniques. Considering all of the factors involved in the selection of a wavelength standard, the W $K\alpha_1$ line is superior to any other x-ray or γ-ray wavelength. Its advantages as the x-ray wavelength standard are discussed in *Review of Modern Physics* Vol. 39, page 82 (1967).

$$\lambda W\ K\alpha_1 = 0.2090100\ \text{Å} \pm 5\ \text{ppm}.$$

This numerical value of the wavelength of the W $K\alpha_1$ line is used to define the *x-ray wavelength standard* by the relation

$$\lambda(W\ K\alpha_1) = 0.2090100\ \text{Å*}.$$

This is a new unit of length which may differ from the angstrom by ±5 ppm (probable error), *but as a wavelength standard it has no error*. In order to clearly indicate that this unit is not exactly an angstrom, it has been designated Å*.

Wavelengths tabulated normally refer to the pure element in its solid form. However, there are many instances in which such data are not available. For example, rare gases are of necessity almost always used in the gaseous form, while the rare-earth elements were customarily used in the form of salts.

In high precision work there is some ambiguity as to exactly what feature of a line profile should be taken to be the "true wavelength." In double-crystal work the line peak is usually employed. In crystallography the centroid is widely used; in photographic work with visual observation of the plates, there is involved some subjective criterion of the observer which is difficult to define precisely. In this survey the peak of the line profile has been adopted as the standard criterion.

X-ray wavelengths in Å* units and in keV. The probable error (p.e.) is the error in the last digit of wavelength. Designation indicates both conventional Siegbahn notation (if applicable) and transition, e.g., $\beta_1\ L_{II}M_{IV}$ denotes a transition between the L_{II} and M_{IV} levels, which is the $L\beta_1$ line in Siegbahn notation.

3 Lithium / 4 Beryllium

Designation	Å*	p.e.	keV	Å*	p.e.	keV
$\alpha\ KL$	228.	1	0.0543	114.	1	0.1085

5 Boron / 6 Carbon

Designation	Å*	p.e.	keV	Å*	p.e.	keV
$\alpha\ KL$	67.6	3	0.1833	44.7	3	0.277

7 Nitrogen / 8 Oxygen

Designation	Å*	p.e.	keV	Å*	p.e.	keV
$\alpha\ KL$	31.6	4	0.3924	23.62	3	0.5249

9 Fluorine / 10 Neon

Designation	Å*	p.e.	keV	Å*	p.e.	keV
$\alpha_{1,2}\ KL_{II,III}$	18.32	2	0.6768	14.610	3	0.8486
$\beta\ KM$				14.452	5	0.8579

11 Sodium / 12 Magnesium

Designation	Å*	p.e.	keV	Å*	p.e.	keV
$\alpha_{1,2}\ KL_{II,III}$	11.9101	9	1.0410	9.8900	2	1.25360
$\beta\ KM$	11.575	2	1.0711	9.521	2	1.3022
$L_{II,III}M$	407.1	5	0.03045	251.5	5	0.0493
$L_I L_{II,III}$	376	1	0.0330	317	1	0.0392

13 Aluminum / 14 Silicon

Designation	Å*	p.e.	keV	Å*	p.e.	keV
$\alpha_2\ KL_{II}$	8.34173	9	1.48627	7.12791	9	1.73938
$\alpha_1\ KL_{III}$	8.33934	9	1.48670	7.12542	9	1.73998
$\beta\ KM$	7.960	2	1.5574	6.753	1	1.8359
$L_{II,III}$	171.4	5	0.0724	135.5	4	0.0915
$L_I L_{II,III}$	290.	1	0.0428			

15 Phosphorus / 16 Sulfur

Designation	Å*	p.e.	keV	Å*	p.e.	keV
$\alpha_2\ KL_{II}$	6.160†	1	2.0127	5.37496	8	2.30664
$\alpha_1\ KL_{III}$	6.157†	1	2.0137	5.37216	7	2.30784
$\beta\ KM$	5.796	2	2.1390			
$\beta_1\ KM$				5.0316	2	2.4640
$\beta_x\ KM$				5.0233	3	2.4681
$L_{II,III}M$	103.8	4	0.1194			
$l,\eta\ L_{II,III}M_I$				83.4	3	0.1487

17 Chlorine / 18 Argon

Designation	Å*	p.e.	keV	Å*	p.e.	keV
$\alpha_2\ KL_{II}$	4.7307	1	2.62078	4.19474	5	2.95563
$\alpha_1\ KL_{III}$	4.7278	1	2.62239	4.19180	5	2.95770
$\beta\ KM$	4.4034	3	2.8156			
$\beta_{1,3}\ KM_{II,III}$				3.8860	2	3.1905
$\eta\ L_{II}M_I$	67.33	9	0.1841	55.9†	1	0.2217
$l\ L_{III}M_I$	67.90	9	0.1826	56.3†	1	0.2201

19 Potassium / 20 Calcium

Designation	Å*	p.e.	keV	Å*	p.e.	keV
$\alpha_2\ KL_{II}$	3.7445	2	3.3111	3.36166	3	3.68809
$\alpha_1\ KL_{III}$	3.7414	2	3.3138	3.35839	3	3.69168
$\beta_{1,3}\ KM_{II,III}$	3.4539	2	3.5896	3.0897	2	4.0127
$\beta_5\ KM_{IV,V}$	3.4413	4	3.6027	3.0746	3	4.0325

19 Potassium (Cont.) / 20 Calcium (Cont.)

Designation	Å*	p.e.	keV	Å*	p.e.	keV
$\eta\ L_{II}M_I$	47.24	2	0.2625	40.46	2	0.3064
β_1				35.94	2	0.3449
$l\ L_{III}M_I$	47.74	1	0.25971	40.96	2	0.3027
$\alpha_{1,2}\ L_{III}M_{IV,V}$				36.33	2	0.3413
$M_{II,III}N_I$	692	9	0.0179	525.	9	0.0236

21 Scandium / 22 Titanium

Designation	Å*	p.e.	keV	Å*	p.e.	keV
$\alpha_2\ KL_{II}$	3.0342	1	4.0861	2.75216	2	4.50486
$\alpha_1\ KL_{III}$	3.0309†	1	4.0906	2.74851	2	4.51084
$\beta_{1,3}\ KM_{II,III}$	2.7796	2	4.4605	2.51391	2	4.93181
$\beta_5\ KM_{IV,V}$	2.7634	3	4.4865	2.4985	2	4.9623
$\eta\ L_{II}M_I$	35.13	2	0.3529	30.89	3	0.4013
$\beta_1\ L_{II}M_{IV}$	31.02	2	0.3996	27.05	2	0.4584
$l\ L_{III}M_I$	35.59	3	0.3483	31.36	2	0.3953
$\alpha_{1,2}\ L_{III}M_{IV,V}$	31.35	3	0.3954	27.42	2	0.4522

23 Vanadium / 24 Chromium

Designation	Å*	p.e.	keV	Å*	p.e.	keV
$\alpha_2\ KL_{II}$	2.50738	2	4.94464	2.293606	3	5.40551
$\alpha_1\ KL_{III}$	2.50356	2	4.95220	2.28970	2	5.41472
$\beta_{1,3}\ KM_{II,III}$	2.28440	2	5.42729	2.08487	2	5.94671
$\beta_5\ KM_{IV,V}$	2.26951	6	5.4629	2.07087	6	5.9869
$\beta_{3,4}\ L_I M_{II,III}$	21.19†	9	0.585	18.96	2	0.654
$\eta\ L_{II}M_I$	27.34	3	0.4535	24.30	3	0.5102
$\beta_1\ L_{II}M_{IV}$	23.88	4	0.5192	21.27	1	0.5828
$l\ L_{III}M_I$	27.77	1	0.4465	24.78	1	0.5003
$\alpha_{1,2}\ L_{III}M_{IV,V}$	24.25	3	0.5113	21.64	3	0.5728
$M_{II,III}M_{IV,V}$	337.	9	0.037	309.	9	0.040

25 Manganese / 26 Iron

Designation	Å*	p.e.	keV	Å*	p.e.	keV
$\alpha_2\ KL_{II}$	2.10578	2	5.88765	1.939980	9	6.39084
$\alpha_1\ KL_{III}$	2.101820	9	5.89875	1.936042	9	6.40384
$\beta_{1,3}\ KM_{II,III}$	1.91021	2	6.49045	1.75661	2	7.05798
$\beta_5\ KM_{IV,V}$	1.8971	1	6.5352	1.7442	1	7.1081
$\beta_{3,4}\ L_I M_{II,III}$	17.19	2	0.721	15.65	2	0.792
$\eta\ L_{II}M_I$	21.85	2	0.5675	19.75	4	0.628
$\beta_1\ L_{II}M_{IV}$	19.11	2	0.6488	17.26	1	0.7185
$l\ L_{III}M_I$	22.29	1	0.5563	20.15	1	0.6152
$\alpha_{1,2}\ L_{III}M_{IV,V}$	19.45	1	0.6374	17.59	2	0.7050
$M_{II,III}M_{IV,V}$	273.	6	0.045	243.	5	0.051

27 Cobalt / 28 Nickel

Designation	Å*	p.e.	keV	Å*	p.e.	keV
$\alpha_2\ KL_{II}$	1.792850	9	6.91530	1.661747	8	7.46089
$\alpha_1\ KL_{III}$	1.788965	9	6.93032	1.657910	8	7.47815
$\beta_{1,3}\ KM_{II,III}$	1.62079	2	7.64943	1.500135	8	8.26466
$\beta_5\ KM_{IV,V}$	1.60891	3	7.7059	1.48862	4	8.3286
$\beta_{3,4}\ L_I M_{II,III}$	14.31	3	0.870	13.18	1	0.941
$\eta\ L_{II}M_I$	17.87	3	0.694	16.27	3	0.762
$\beta_1\ L_{II}M_{IV}$	15.666	8	0.7914	14.271	6	0.8688
$l\ L_{III}M_I$	18.292	9	0.6778	16.693	9	0.7427
$\alpha_{1,2}\ L_{III}M_{IV,V}$	15.972	6	0.7762	14.561	3	0.8515
$M_{II,III}M_{IV,V}$	214.	6	0.058	190.	2	0.0651

29 Copper / 30 Zinc

Designation	Å*	p.e.	keV	Å*	p.e.	keV
$\alpha_2\,KL_{II}$	1.544390	2	8.02783	1.439000	8	8.61578
$\alpha_1\,KL_{III}$	1.540562	2	8.04778	1.435155	7	8.63886
$\beta_3\,KM_{II}$	1.3926	1	8.9029			
$\beta_{1,3}\,KM_{II,III}$	1.392218	9	8.90529	1.29525	2	9.5720
$\beta_2\,KN_{II,III}$				1.28372	2	9.6580
$\beta_5\,KM_{IV,V}$	1.38109	3	8.9770	1.2848	1	9.6501
$\beta_{3,4}\,L_IM_{II,III}$	12.122	8	1.0228	11.200	7	1.1070
$\eta\,L_{II}M_I$	14.90	2	0.832	13.68	2	0.906
$\beta_1\,L_{II}M_{IV}$	13.053	3	0.9498	11.983	3	1.0347
$l\,L_{III}M_I$	15.286	9	0.8111	14.02	2	0.884
$\alpha_{1,2}\,L_{III}M_{IV,V}$	13.336	3	0.9297	12.254	3	1.0117
$M_{II,III}M_{V,V}$	173.	3	0.072	157.	3	0.079

31 Gallium / 32 Germanium

Designation	Å*	p.e.	keV	Å*	p.e.	keV
$\alpha_2\,KL_{II}$	1.34399	1	9.22482	1.258011	9	9.85532
$\alpha_1\,KL_{III}$	1.340083	9	9.25174	1.254054	9	9.88642
$\beta_3\,KM_{II}$	1.20835	5	10.2603	1.12936	9	10.9780
$\beta_1\,KM_{III}$	1.20789	2	10.2642	1.12894	2	10.9821
$\beta_2\,KN_{II,III}$	1.19600	2	10.3663	1.11686	2	11.1008
$\beta_5\,KM_{IV,V}$	1.1981	2	10.348	1.1195	1	11.0745
$\beta_4\,L_IM_{II}$				9.640	2	1.2861
$\beta_3\,L_IM_{III}$				9.581	2	1.2941
$\beta_{3,4}\,L_IM_{II,III}$	10.359†	8	1.197			
$\eta\,L_{II}M_I$	12.597	2	0.9842	11.609	2	1.0680
$\beta_1\,L_{II}M_{IV}$	11.023	2	1.1248	10.175	1	1.2185
$l\,L_{III}M_I$	12.953	2	0.9572	11.965	4	1.0362
$\alpha_{1,2}\,L_{III}M_{IV,V}$	11.292	1	1.09792	10.4361	8	1.18800

33 Arsenic / 34 Selenium

Designation	Å*	p.e.	keV	Å*	p.e.	keV
$\alpha_2\,KL_{II}$	1.17987	1	10.50799	1.10882	2	11.1814
$\alpha_1\,KL_{III}$	1.17588	1	10.54372	1.10477	2	11.2224
$\beta_3\,KM_{II}$	1.05783	5	11.7203	0.99268	5	12.4896
$\beta_1\,KM_{III}$	1.05730	2	11.7262	0.99218	3	12.4959
$\beta_2\,KN_{II,III}$	1.04500	3	11.8642	0.97992	5	12.6522
$\beta_5\,KM_{IV,V}$	1.0488	1	11.822	0.9843	1	12.595
$\beta_{3,4}\,L_IM_{II,III}$	8.929	1	1.3884	8.321†	9	1.490
$\eta\,L_{II}M_I$	10.734	1	1.1550	9.962	1	1.2446
$\beta_1\,L_{II}M_{IV}$	9.4141	8	1.3170	8.7358	5	1.41923
$l\,L_{III}M_I$	11.072	1	1.1198	10.294	1	1.2044
$\alpha_{1,2}\,L_{III}M_{IV,V}$	9.6709	8	1.2820	8.9900	5	1.37910
M_VN_{III}				230.	2	0.0538

35 Bromine / 36 Krypton

Designation	Å*	p.e.	keV	Å*	p.e.	keV
$\alpha_2\,KL_{II}$	1.04382	2	11.8776	0.9841	1	12.598
$\alpha_1\,KL_{III}$	1.03974	2	11.9242	0.9801	1	12.649
$\beta_3\,KM_{II}$	0.93327	5	13.2845	0.8790	1	14.104
$\beta_1\,KM_{III}$	0.93279	2	13.2914	0.8785	1	14.112
$\beta_2\,KN_{II,III}$	0.92046	2	13.4695	0.8661	1	14.315
$\beta_5\,KM_{IV,V}$	0.9255	1	13.396	0.8708	2	14.238
$\beta_4\,KN_{IV,V}$				0.8653	2	14.328
$\beta_4\,L_IM_{II}$				7.304	5	1.697
$\beta_3\,L_IM_{III}$				7.264	5	1.707

35 Bromine (*Cont.*) / 36 Krypton (*Cont.*)

Designation	Å*	p.e.	keV	Å*	p.e.	keV
$\beta_{3,4}\,L_IM_{II,III}$	7.767†	9	1.596			
$\eta\,L_{II}M_I$	9.255	1	1.3396			
$\beta_1\,L_{II}M_{IV}$	8.1251	5	1.52590	7.576†	3	1.6366
$\gamma_5\,L_{II}N_{IV}$				7.279	5	1.703
$l\,L_{III}M_I$	9.585	1	1.2935			
$\alpha_{1,2}\,L_{III}M_{IV,V}$	8.3746	5	1.48043	7.817†	3	1.5860
β_6				7.510	4	1.6510
$L_{II}N_{III}$				7.250	5	1.710
M_IM_{II}	184.6	3	0.0672			
M_IM_{III}	164.7	3	0.0753			
$M_{II}M_{IV}$	109.4	3	0.1133			
$M_{II}N_I$	76.9	2	0.1613			
$M_{III}M_{IV,V}$	113.8	3	0.1089			
	79.8	3	0.1554			
$\zeta_2\,M_{IV}N_{II}$	191.1	2	0.06488			
$M_{IV}N_{III}$	189.5	3	0.0654			
$\zeta_1\,M_VN_{III}$	192.6	2	0.06437			

37 Rubidium / 38 Strontium

Designation	Å*	p.e.	keV	Å*	p.e.	keV
$\alpha_2\,KL_{II}$	0.92969	1	13.3358	0.87943	1	14.0979
$\alpha_1\,KL_{III}$	0.925553	9	13.3953	0.87526	1	14.1650
$\beta_3\,KM_{II}$	0.82921	3	14.9517	0.78345	3	15.8249
$\beta_1\,KM_{III}$	0.82868	2	14.9613	0.78292	2	15.8357
$\beta_2\,KN_{II,III}$	0.81645	3	15.1854	0.77081	3	16.0846
$\beta_5\,KM_{IV,V}$	0.8219	1	15.085	0.7764	1	15.969
$\beta_4\,KN_{IV,V}$	0.8154	2	15.205	0.76989	5	16.104
$\beta_4\,L_IM_{II}$	6.8207	3	1.81771	6.4026	3	1.93643
$\beta_3\,L_IM_{III}$	6.7876	3	1.82659	6.3672	3	1.94719
$\gamma_{2,3}\,L_IN_{II,III}$	6.0458	3	2.0507	5.6445	3	2.1965
$\eta\,L_{II}M_I$	8.0415	4	1.54177	7.5171	3	1.64933
$\beta_1\,L_{II}M_{IV}$	7.0759	3	1.75217	6.6239	3	1.87172
$\gamma_5\,L_{II}N_{IV}$	6.7553	3	1.83532	6.2961	3	1.96916
$l\,L_{III}M_I$	8.3636	4	1.48238	7.8362	3	1.58215
$\alpha_2\,L_{III}M_{IV}$	7.3251	3	1.69256	6.8697	3	1.80474
$\alpha_1\,L_{III}M_V$	7.3183	2	1.69413	6.8628	2	1.80656
$\beta_6\,L_{III}N_I$	6.9842	3	1.77517	6.5191	3	1.90181
M_IM_{II}	144.4	3	0.0859			
$M_{II}M_{IV}$	91.5	2	0.1355	85.7	2	0.1447
$M_{II}N_I$	57.0	2	0.2174	51.3	1	0.2416
$M_{III}M_{IV,V}$	96.7	2	0.1282	91.4	2	0.1357
$M_{III}N_I$	59.5	2	0.2083	53.6	1	0.2313
$\zeta_2\,M_{IV}N_{II}$	127.8	2	0.0970			
$M_{IV}N_{III}$	126.8	2	0.0978			
$\zeta_2\,M_{IV}N_{II,III}$				108.0	2	0.1148
$\zeta_1\,M_VN_{III}$	128.7	2	0.0964	108.7	1	0.1140

39 Yttrium / 40 Zirconium

Designation	Å*	p.e.	keV	Å*	p.e.	keV
$\alpha_2\,KL_{II}$	0.83305	1	14.8829	0.79015	1	15.6909
$\alpha_1\,KL_{III}$	0.82884	1	14.9584	0.78593	1	15.7751
$\beta_3\,KM_{II}$	0.74126	3	16.7258	0.70228	4	17.654
$\beta_1\,KM_{III}$	0.74072	2	16.7378	0.70173	3	17.6678
$\beta_2\,KN_{II,III}$	0.72864	4	17.0154	0.68993	4	17.970
$\beta_5\,KM_{IV,V}$	0.7345	1	16.879	0.6959	1	17.815

Designation	Å*	p.e.	keV	Å*	p.e.	keV
	39 Yttrium (*Cont.*)			**40 Zirconium (*Cont.*)**		
$\beta_4\,KN_{IV,V}$	0.72776	5	17.036	0.68901	5	17.994
$\beta_4\,L_1M_{II}$	6.0186	3	2.0600	5.6681	3	2.1873
$\beta_3\,L_1M_{III}$	5.9832	3	2.0722	5.6330	3	2.2010
$\gamma_{2,3}\,L_1N_{II,III}$	5.2830	3	2.3468	4.9536	3	2.5029
$\eta\,L_1M_I$	7.0406	3	1.76095	6.6069	3	1.87654
$\beta_1\,L_{III}M_{IV}$	6.2120	3	1.99584	5.8360	3	2.1244
$\gamma_5\,L_{II}N_I$	5.8754	3	2.1102	5.4977	3	2.2551
$\gamma_1\,L_{II}N_{IV}$				5.3843	3	2.3027
$l\,L_{III}M_I$	7.3563	3	1.68536	6.9185	3	1.79201
$\alpha_2\,L_{III}M_{IV}$	6.4558	3	1.92047	6.0778	3	2.0399
$\alpha_1\,L_{III}M_V$	6.4488	2	1.92256	6.0705	2	2.04236
$\beta_6\,L_{III}N_I$	6.0942	3	2.0344	5.7101	3	2.1712
$\beta_{2,15}$				5.5863	3	2.2194
$M_{II}M_{IV}$	81.5	2	0.1522	76.7	2	0.1617
$M_{II}N_I$	46.48	9	0.267			
$M_{III}M_V$				80.9	2	0.1533
$M_{III}N_I$	48.5	2	0.256			
$M_{III}M_{IV,III}$	86.5	2	0.1434			
$\zeta\,M_{IV,V}N_{II,III}$	93.4	2	0.1328	82.1	2	0.1511
$M_{IV,V}O_{II,III}$				70.0	4	0.177

Designation	Å*	p.e.	keV	Å*	p.e.	keV
	41 Niobium			**42 Molybdenum**		
$\alpha_2\,KL_{II}$	0.75044	1	16.5210	0.713590	6	17.3743
$\alpha_1\,KL_{III}$	0.74620	1	16.6151	0.709300	1	17.47934
$\beta_3\,KM_{II}$	0.66634	3	18.6063	0.632872	9	19.5903
$\beta_1\,KM_{III}$	0.66576	2	18.6225	0.632288	9	19.6083
β_2^{II}				0.62107	5	19.963
$\beta_2\,KN_{II,III}$	0.65416	4	18.953	0.62099	2	19.9652
$\beta_4\,KN_{IV,V}$	0.65318	5	18.981			
$\beta_5^{II}\,KM_{IV}$				0.62708	5	19.771
$\beta_5^{I}\,KM_V$				0.62692	5	19.776
$\beta_4\,KN_{IV,V}$				0.62001	9	19.996
$\beta_4\,L_1M_{II}$	5.3455	3	2.3194	5.0488	3	2.4557
$\beta_3\,L_1M_{III}$	5.3102	3	2.3348	5.0133	3	2.4730
$\gamma_{2,3}\,L_1N_{II,III}$	4.6542	2	2.6638	4.3800	3	2.8306
$\eta\,L_{II}M_I$	6.2109	3	1.99620	5.8475	3	2.1202
$\beta_1\,L_{III}M_{IV}$	5.4923	3	2.2574	5.17708	8	2.39481
$\gamma_5\,L_{II}N_I$	5.1517	3	2.4066	4.8369	2	2.5632
$\gamma_1\,L_{II}N_{IV}$	5.0361	3	2.4618	4.7258	2	2.6235
$l\,L_{III}M_I$	6.5176	3	1.90225	6.1508	3	2.01568
$\alpha_2\,L_{III}M_{IV}$	5.7319	3	2.1630	5.41437	8	2.28985
$\alpha_1\,L_{III}M_V$	5.7243	2	2.16589	5.40655	8	2.29316
$\beta_6\,L_{III}N_I$	5.3613	3	2.3125	5.0488	2	2.4557
$\beta_{2,15}\,L_{III}N_{IV,V}$	5.2379	3	2.3670	4.9232	2	2.5183
$M_{II}M_{IV}$	72.1	3	0.1718	68.9	2	0.1798
$M_{II}N_I$	38.4	3	0.323	35.3	3	0.351
$M_{II}N_{IV}$	33.1	2	0.375			
$M_{III}M_V$	78.4	2	0.1582	74.9	1	0.1656
$M_{III}N_I$	40.7	2	0.305	37.5	2	0.331
$\gamma\,M_{III}N_{IV,V}$	34.9	2	0.356			
$\zeta\,M_{IV,V}N_{II,III}$	72.19	9	0.1717	64.38	7	0.1926
$M_{IV,V}O_{II,III}$	61.9	2	0.2002	54.8	2	0.2262

Designation	Å*	p.e.	keV	Å*	p.e.	keV
	43 Technetium			**44 Ruthenium**		
$\alpha_2\,KL_{II}$	0.67932†	3	18.2508	0.647408	5	19.1504
$\alpha_1\,KL_{III}$	0.67502†	3	18.3671	0.643083	4	19.2792
$\beta_3\,KM_{II}$	0.60188†	4	20.599	0.573067	4	21.6346
$\beta_1\,KM_{III}$	0.60130†	4	20.619	0.572482	4	21.6568
$\beta_2\,KN_{II,III}$	0.59024†	5	21.005	0.56166	3	22.074
$\beta_5^{II}\,KM_{IV}$				0.5680	2	21.829
$\beta_5^{I}\,KM_V$				0.56785	9	21.834
β_4				0.56089	9	22.104
$\beta_4\,L_{II}M_{IV}$				4.5230	2	2.7411
$\beta_3\,L_1M_{III}$				4.4866	3	2.7634
$\gamma_{2,3}\,L_1N_{II,III}$				3.8977	2	3.1809
$\eta\,L_{II}M_I$				5.2050	2	2.38197
$\beta_1\,L_{II}M_{IV}$	4.8873†	8	2.5368	4.62058	3	2.68323
$\gamma_5\,L_{II}N_I$				4.2873	2	2.8918
$\gamma_1\,L_{II}N_{IV}$				4.1822	2	2.9645
$l\,L_{III}M_I$				5.5035	3	2.2528
$\alpha_2\,L_{III}M_{IV}$				4.85381	7	2.55431
$\alpha_1\,L_{III}M_V$	5.1148†	3	2.4240	4.84575	5	2.55855
$\beta_6\,L_{III}N_I$				4.4866	3	2.7634
$\beta_{2,15}\,L_{III}N_{IV,V}$				4.3718	2	2.8360
$M_{II}M_{IV}$				62.2	1	0.1992
$M_{II}N_I$				32.3	2	0.384
$M_{II}N_{IV}$				25.50	9	0.486
$M_{III}M_V$				68.3	1	0.1814
$\gamma\,M_{III}N_{IV,V}$				26.9	1	0.462
$\zeta\,M_{IV,V}N_{II,III}$				52.34	7	0.2369
$M_{IV,V}O_{II,III}$				44.8	1	0.2768

Designation	Å*	p.e.	keV	Å*	p.e.	keV
	45 Rhodium			**46 Palladium**		
$\alpha_2\,KL_{II}$	0.617630	4	20.0737	0.589821	3	21.0201
$\alpha_1\,KL_{III}$	0.613279	4	20.2161	0.585448	3	21.1771
$\beta_3\,KM_{II}$	0.546200	4	22.6989	0.521123	4	23.7911
$\beta_1\,KM_{III}$	0.545605	4	22.7236	0.520520	4	23.8187
$\beta_2^{II}\,KN_{II}$	0.53513	5	23.168			
$\beta_2\,KN_{II,III}$	0.53503	2	23.1728	0.510228	4	24.2991
$\beta_5^{II}\,KM_{IV}$	0.54118	9	22.909			
$\beta_5^{I}\,KM_V$	0.54101	9	22.917			
$\beta_4\,KN_{IV,V}$	0.53401	9	23.217	0.5093	2	24.346
$\beta_5\,KM_{IV,V}$				0.51670	9	23.995
$\beta_4\,L_1M_{II}$	4.2888	2	2.8908	4.0711	2	3.0454
$\beta_3\,L_1M_{III}$	4.2522	2	2.9157	4.0346	2	3.0730
$\gamma_{2,3}\,L_1N_{II,III}$	3.6855	2	3.3640	3.4892	2	3.5533
$\eta\,L_{II}M_I$	4.9217	2	2.5191	4.6605	2	2.6603
$\beta_1\,L_{II}M_{IV}$	4.37414	4	2.83441	4.14622	5	2.99022
$\gamma_5\,L_{II}N_I$	4.0451	2	3.0650	3.8222	2	3.2437
$\gamma_1\,L_{II}N_{IV}$	3.9437	2	3.1438	3.7246	2	3.3287
$l\,L_{III}M_I$	5.2169	3	2.3765	4.9525	3	2.5034
$\alpha_2\,L_{III}M_{IV}$	4.60545	9	2.69205	4.37588	7	2.83329
$\alpha_1\,L_{III}M_V$	4.59743	9	2.69674	4.36767	5	2.83861
$\beta_6\,L_{III}N_I$	4.2417	2	2.9229	4.0162	2	3.0870
$\beta_{2,15}\,L_{III}N_{IV,V}$	4.1310	2	3.0013	3.90887	4	3.17179
$\beta_{10}\,L_1M_{IV}$				3.7988	2	3.2637

45 Rhodium (*Cont.*) / 46 Palladium (*Cont.*)

Designation	Å*	p.e.	keV	Å*	p.e.	keV
$\beta_9\ L_I M_V$				3.7920	2	3.2696
$M_I N_{II,III}$				20.1	2	0.616
$M_{II} M_{IV}$	59.3	1	0.2090	56.5	1	0.2194
$M_{II} N_I$	28.1	2	0.442	26.2	2	0.474
$M_{II} N_{IV}$				22.1	1	0.560
$M_{II} M_V$	65.5	1	0.1892	62.9	1	0.1970
$M_{II}' N_I$	29.8	1	0.417	27.9	1	0.445
$\gamma\ M_{III} N_{IV,V}$	25.01	9	0.496	23.3†	1	0.531
$\zeta\ M_{IV,V} N_{II,III}$	47.67	9	0.2601	43.6	1	0.2844
$M_{IV,V} O_{II,III}$	40.9	2	0.303	37.4	2	0.332

47 Silver / 48 Cadmium

Designation	Å*	p.e.	keV	Å*	p.e.	keV
$\alpha_2\ K L_{II}$	0.563798	4	21.9903	0.539422	3	22.9841
$\alpha_1\ K L_{III}$	0.5594075	6	22.16292	0.535010	3	23.1736
$\beta_3\ K M_{II}$	0.497685	4	24.9115	0.475730	5	26.0612
$\beta_1\ K M_{III}$	0.497069	4	24.9424	0.475105	6	26.0955
$\beta_2\ K N_{II,III}$	0.487032	4	25.4564	0.465328	7	26.6438
$\beta_5\ K M_{IV,V}$	0.49306	2	25.145			
$\beta_4\ K N_{IV,V}$	0.48598	3	25.512			
$\beta_4\ L_I M_{II}$	3.87023	5	3.20346	3.68203	9	3.36719
$\beta_3\ L_I M_{III}$	3.83313	9	3.23446	3.64495	9	3.40145
$\gamma_2\ L_I N_{II}$	3.31216	9	3.7432	3.1377	2	3.9513
$\gamma_3\ L_I N_{III}$	3.30635	9	3.7498			
$\eta\ L_{II} M_I$	4.4183	2	2.8061	4.19315	9	2.95675
$\beta_1\ L_{II} M_{IV}$	3.93473	3	3.15094	3.73823	4	3.31657
$\gamma_5\ L_{II} N_I$	3.61638	9	3.42832	3.42551	9	3.61935
$\gamma_1\ L_{III} N_{IV}$	3.52260	4	3.51959	3.33564	6	3.71686
$l\ L_{III} M_I$	4.7076	2	2.6337	4.48014	9	2.76735
$\alpha_2\ L_{III} M_{IV}$	4.16294	5	2.97821	3.96496	6	3.12691
$\alpha_1\ L_{III} M_V$	4.15443	3	2.98431	3.95635	4	3.13373
$\beta_6\ L_{III} N_I$	3.80774	9	3.25603	3.61467	9	3.42994
$\beta_{2,15}\ L_{III} N_{IV,V}$	3.70335	3	3.34781	3.51408	4	3.52812
$\beta_{10}\ L_I M_{IV}$	3.61158	9	3.43287	3.4367	2	3.6075
$\beta_9\ L_I M_V$	3.60497	9	3.43917	3.43015	9	3.61445
$M_I N_{II,III}$	18.8	2	0.658			
$M_{II} M_{IV}$	54.0	1	0.2295	52.0	2	0.2384
$M_{II} N_I$				22.9	2	0.540
$M_{II} N_{IV}$	20.66	7	0.600	19.40	7	0.639
$M_{III} M_V$	60.5	1	0.2048	58.7	2	0.2111
$M_{III} N_I$	26.0	1	0.478	24.5	1	0.507
$\gamma\ M_{III} N_{IV,V}$	21.82	7	0.568	20.47	7	0.606
$M_{IV} O_{II,III}$				30.4	1	0.408
$\zeta\ M_{IV,V} N_{II,III}$	39.77	7	0.3117	36.8	1	0.3371
$M_V N_I$	24.4	2	0.509			
$M_V O_{III}$				30.8	1	0.403
$M_{IV,V} O_{II,III}$	33.5	3	0.370			

49 Indium / 50 Tin

Designation	Å*	p.e.	keV	Å*	p.e.	keV
$\alpha_2\ K L_{II}$	0.516544	3	24.0020	0.495053	3	25.0440
$\alpha_1\ K L_{III}$	0.512113	3	24.2097	0.490599	3	25.2713
$\beta_3\ K M_{II}$	0.455181	4	27.2377	0.435877	5	28.4440

49 Indium (*Cont.*) / 50 Tin (*Cont.*)

Designation	Å*	p.e.	keV	Å*	p.e.	keV
$\beta_1\ K M_{III}$	0.454545	4	27.2759	0.435236	5	28.4860
$\beta_2\ K N_{II,III}$	0.44500	1	27.8608	0.425915	8	29.1093
$K O_{II,III}$	0.44374	3	27.940	0.42467	3	29.195
$\beta_5^{II}\ K M_{IV}$	0.45098	2	27.491	0.43184	3	28.710
$\beta_5^{I}\ K M_V$	0.45086	2	27.499	0.43175	3	28.716
$\beta_4\ K N_{IV,V}$	0.44393	4	27.928	0.42495	3	29.175
$\beta_4\ L_I M_{II}$	3.50697	9	3.5353	3.34335	9	3.7083
$\beta_3\ L_I M_{III}$	3.46984	9	3.5731	3.30585	3	3.7500
$\gamma_{2,3}\ L_I N_{II,III}$	2.9800	2	4.1605	2.8327	2	4.3768
$\gamma_4\ L_I O_{II,III}$	2.9264	2	4.2367	2.7775	2	4.4638
$\eta\ L_{II} M_I$	3.98327	9	3.11254	3.78876	9	3.27234
$\beta_1\ L_{II} M_{IV}$	3.55531	4	3.48721	3.38487	3	3.66280
$\gamma_5\ L_{II} N_I$	3.24907	9	3.8159	3.08475	3	4.0192
$\gamma_1\ L_{II} N_{IV}$	3.16213	4	3.92081	3.00115	3	4.13112
$l\ L_{III} M_I$	4.26873	9	2.90440	4.07165	9	3.04499
$\alpha_2\ L_{III} M_{IV}$	3.78073	6	3.27929	3.60891	4	3.43542
$\alpha_1\ L_{III} M_V$	3.77192	4	3.28694	3.59994	3	3.44398
$\beta_6\ L_{III} N_I$	3.43606	9	3.60823	3.26901	9	3.7926
$\beta_{2,15}\ L_{III} N_{IV,V}$	3.33838	3	3.71381	3.17505	3	3.90486
$l'\ L_{III} O_I$	3.324	4	3.730	3.1564	3	3.9279
$\beta_{10}\ L_I M_{IV}$	3.27404	9	3.7868	3.12170	3	3.9716
$\beta_9\ L_I M_V$	3.26763	9	3.7942	3.11513	9	3.9800
$M_{II} M_{IV}$				47.3	1	0.2621
$M_{II} N_I$				20.0	1	0.619
$M_{II} N_{IV}$				16.93*	5	0.733
$M_{III} M_V$				54.2	1	0.2287
$M_{III} N_I$				21.5	1	0.575
$\gamma\ M_{III} N_{IV,V}$				17.94	5	0.691
$M_{IV} O_{II,III}$				25.3	1	0.491
$\zeta\ M_{IV,V} N_{II,III}$				31.24	9	0.397
$M_V O_{III}$				25.7	1	0.483

51 Antimony / 52 Tellurium

Designation	Å*	p.e.	keV	Å*	p.e.	keV
$\alpha_2\ K L_{II}$	0.474827	3	26.1108	0.455784	3	27.2017
$\alpha_1\ K L_{III}$	0.470354	3	26.3591	0.451295	3	27.4723
$\beta_3\ K M_{II}$	0.417737	4	29.6792	0.400659	4	30.9443
$\beta_1\ K M_{III}$	0.417085	3	29.7256	0.399995	5	30.9957
$\beta_2\ K N_{II,III}$	0.407973	5	30.3895	0.391102	6	31.7004
$K O_{II,III}$	0.40666	1	30.4875	0.38974	1	31.8114
$\beta_5^{II}\ K M_{IV}$	0.41388	1	29.9560			
$\beta_5^{I}\ K M_V$	0.41378	1	29.9632			
$\beta_4\ K N_{IV,V}$	0.40702	1	30.4604			
$\beta_4\ L_I M_{II}$	3.19014	9	3.8864	3.04661	9	4.0695
$\beta_3\ L_I M_{III}$	3.15258	9	3.9327	3.00893	9	4.1204
$\gamma_{2,3}\ L_I N_{II,III}$	2.6953	2	4.5999	2.5674	2	4.8290
$\gamma_4\ L_I O_{II,III}$	2.6398	2	4.6967	2.5113	2	4.9369
$\eta\ L_{II} M_I$	3.60765	9	3.43661	3.43832	9	3.60586
$\beta_1\ L_{II} M_{IV}$	3.22567	4	3.84357	3.07677	6	4.02958
$\gamma_5\ L_{II} N_I$	2.93187	9	4.2287	2.79007	9	4.4437
$\gamma_1\ L_{II} N_{IV}$	2.85159	3	4.34779	2.71241	6	4.5709
$l\ L_{III} M_I$	3.88826	9	3.18860	3.71696	9	3.33555
$\alpha_2\ L_{III} M_{IV}$	3.44840	6	3.59532	3.29846	9	3.7588

Left columns

Designation	Å*	p.e.	keV	Å*	p.e.	keV
	51 Antimony (*Cont.*)			**52 Tellurium** (*Cont.*)		
$\alpha_1\,L_{III}M_V$	3.43941	4	3.60472	3.28920	6	3.76933
$\beta_6\,L_{III}N_I$	3.11513	9	3.9800	2.97088	9	4.1732
$\beta_{2,15}\,L_{III}N_{IV,V}$	3.02335	3	4.10078	2.88217	8	4.3017
$\beta_7\,L_{III}O_I$	3.0052	3	4.1255	2.8634	3	4.3298
$\beta_{10}\,L_I M_{IV}$	2.97917	9	4.1616	2.84679	9	4.3551
$\beta_9\,L_I M_V$	2.97261	9	4.1708	2.83897	9	4.3671
$M_{II}M_{IV}$	45.2	1	0.2743			
$M_{II}N_I$	18.8	1	0.658	17.6	1	0.703
$M_{II}N_{IV}$	15.98	5	0.776			
$M_{III}M_V$	52.2	1	0.2375	50.3	1	0.2465
$M_{III}N_I$	20.2	1	0.612	19.1	1	0.648
$\gamma\,M_{III}N_{IV,V}$	16.92	4	0.733	15.93	4	0.778
$M_{IV}O_{II,III}$				21.34	5	0.581
$\zeta\,M_{IV,V}N_{II,III}$	28.88	8	0.429	26.72	9	0.464
$M_V O_{III}$				21.78	5	0.569
	53 Iodine			**54 Xenon**		
$\alpha_2\,K L_{II}$	0.437829	7	28.3172	0.42087†	2	29.458
$\alpha_1\,K L_{III}$	0.433318	5	28.6120	0.41634†	2	29.779
$\beta_3\,K M_{II}$	0.384564	4	32.2394	0.36941†	2	33.562
$\beta_1\,K M_{III}$	0.383905	4	32.2947	0.36872†	2	33.624
$\beta_2\,K N_{II,III}$	0.37523†	2	33.042	0.36026†	3	34.415
$\beta_4\,L_I M_{II}$	2.91207	9	4.2575			
$\beta_3\,L_I M_{III}$	2.87429	9	4.3134			
$\gamma_{2,3}\,L_I N_{II,III}$	2.4475	2	5.0657			
$\gamma_4\,L_I O_{II,III}$	2.3913	2	5.1848			
$\eta\,L_{II}M_I$	3.27979	9	3.7801			
$\beta_1\,L_{II}M_{IV}$	2.93744	6	4.22072			
$\gamma_5\,L_{II}N_I$	2.65710	9	4.6660			
$\gamma_1\,L_{II}N_{IV}$	2.58244	8	4.8009			
$l\,L_{III}M_I$	3.55754	9	3.48502			
$\alpha_2\,L_{III}M_{IV}$	3.15791	6	3.92604			
$\alpha_1\,L_{III}M_V$	3.14860	6	3.93765	3.0166†	2	4.1099
$\beta_6\,L_{III}N_I$	2.83672	9	4.3706			
$\beta_{2,15}\,L_{III}N_{IV,V}$	2.75053	8	4.5075			
$\beta_7\,L_{III}O_I$	2.7288	3	4.5435			
$\beta_{10}\,L_I M_{IV}$	2.72104	9	4.5564			
$\beta_9\,L_I M_V$	2.71352	9	4.5690			
	55 Cesium			**56 Barium**		
$\alpha_2\,K L_{II}$	0.404835	4	30.6251	0.389668	5	31.8171
$\alpha_1\,K L_{III}$	0.400290	4	30.9728	0.385111	4	32.1936
$\beta_3\,K M_{II}$	0.355050	4	34.9194	0.341507	4	36.3040
$\beta_1\,K M_{III}$	0.354364	7	34.9869	0.340811	3	36.3782
$\beta_2\,K N_{II,III}$	0.34611	2	35.822	0.33277	1	37.257
$K O_{II,III}$				0.33127	2	37.426
$\beta_5^{II}\,K M_{IV}$				0.33835	2	36.643
$\beta_5^{I}\,K M_V$				0.33814	2	36.666
$\beta_4\,K N_{IV,V}$				0.33229	2	37.311
$\beta_4\,L_I M_{II}$	2.6666	2	4.6494	2.5553	2	4.8519
$\beta_3\,L_I M_{III}$	2.6285	2	4.7167	2.5164	2	4.9269
$\gamma_2\,L_I N_{II}$	2.2371	2	5.5420	2.1387	2	5.7969
$\gamma_3\,L_I N_{III}$	2.2328	2	5.5527	2.1342	2	5.8092

Right columns

Designation	Å*	p.e.	keV	Å*	p.e.	keV
	55 Cesium (*Cont.*)			**56 Barium** (*Cont.*)		
$\gamma_4\,L_I O_{II,III}$	2.1741	2	5.7026	2.0756	3	5.9733
$\eta\,L_{II}M_I$	2.9932	2	4.1421	2.8627	3	4.3309
$\beta_1\,L_{II}M_{IV}$	2.6837	2	4.6198	2.56821	5	4.82753
$\gamma_5\,L_{II}N_I$	2.4174	2	5.1287	2.3085	3	5.3707
$\gamma_1\,L_{II}N_{IV}$	2.3480	2	5.2804	2.2415	2	5.5311
$l\,L_{III}M_I$	3.2670	2	3.7950	3.1355	2	3.9541
$\alpha_2\,L_{III}M_{IV}$	2.9020	2	4.2722	2.78553	5	4.45090
$\alpha_1\,L_{III}M_V$	2.8924	2	4.2865	2.77595	5	4.46626
$\beta_6\,L_{III}N_I$	2.5932	2	4.7811	2.4826	2	4.9939
$\beta_{2,15}\,L_{III}N_{IV,V}$	2.5118	2	4.9359	2.40435	6	5.1565
$\beta_7\,L_{III}O_I$	2.4849	2	4.9893	2.3806	2	5.2079
$\beta_{10}\,L_I M_{IV}$	2.4920	2	4.9752	2.3869	2	5.1941
$\beta_9\,L_I M_V$	2.4783	2	5.0026	2.3764	2	5.2171
$\gamma\,M_{III}N_{IV,V}$				12.75	3	0.973
$M_{IV}O_{II}$				15.91	5	0.779
$M_{IV}O_{III}$				15.72	9	0.789
$\zeta\,M_V N_{III}$				20.64	4	0.601
$M_V O_{III}$				16.20	5	0.765
$N_{IV}O_{II}$	188.6	1	0.06574	163.3	2	0.07590
$N_{IV}O_{III}$	183.8	1	0.06746	159.0	2	0.07796
$N_V O_{III}$	190.3	1	0.06515	164.6	2	0.07530
	57 Lanthanum			**58 Cerium**		
$\alpha_2\,K L_{II}$	0.375313	2	33.0341	0.361683	2	34.2789
$\alpha_1\,K L_{III}$	0.370737	2	33.4418	0.357092	2	34.7197
$\beta_3\,K M_{II}$	0.328686	4	37.7202	0.316520	4	39.1701
$\beta_1\,K M_{III}$	0.327983	3	37.8010	0.315816	2	39.2573
$\beta_2\,K N_{II,III}$	0.320117	7	38.7299	0.30816	1	40.233
$K O_{II,III}$	0.31864	2	38.909	0.30668	2	40.427
$\beta_5^{II}\,K M_{IV}$	0.32563	2	38.074	0.31357	2	39.539
$\beta_5^{I}\,K M_V$	0.32546	2	38.094	0.31342	2	39.558
$\beta_4\,K N_{IV,V}$	0.31931	2	38.828	0.30737	2	40.337
$\beta_4\,L_I M_{II}$	2.4493	3	5.0620	2.3497	4	5.2765
$\beta_3\,L_I M_{III}$	2.4105	3	5.1434	2.3109	3	5.3651
$\gamma_2\,L_I N_{II}$	2.0460	4	6.060	1.9602	3	6.3250
$\gamma_3\,L_I N_{III}$	2.0410	4	6.074	1.9553	3	6.3409
$\gamma_4\,L_I O_{II,III}$	1.9830	4	6.252	1.8991	4	6.528
$\eta\,L_{II}M_I$	2.740	3	4.525	2.6203	4	4.7315
$\beta_1\,L_{II}M_{IV}$	2.45891	5	5.0421	2.3561	3	5.2622
$\gamma_5\,L_{II}N_I$	2.2056	4	5.621	2.1103	3	5.8751
$\gamma_1\,L_{II}N_{IV}$	2.1418	3	5.7885	2.0487	4	6.052
$\gamma_8\,L_{II}O_I$				2.0237	4	6.126
$l\,L_{III}M_I$	3.006	3	4.124	2.8917	4	4.2875
$\alpha_2\,L_{III}M_{IV}$	2.67533	5	4.63423	2.5706	3	4.8230
$\alpha_1\,L_{III}M_V$	2.66570	5	4.65097	2.5615	2	4.8402
$\beta_6\,L_{III}N_I$	2.3790	4	5.2114	2.2818	3	5.4334
$\beta_{2,15}\,L_{III}N_{IV,V}$	2.3030	3	5.3835	2.2087	2	5.6134
$\beta_7\,L_{III}O_I$	2.275	3	5.450	2.1701	2	5.7132
$\beta_{10}\,L_I M_{IV}$	2.290	3	5.415	2.1958	5	5.646
$\beta_9\,L_I M_V$	2.282	3	5.434	2.1885	3	5.6650
$\gamma\,M_{III}N_{IV,V}$	12.08	4	1.027	11.53	1	1.0749
$\beta\,M_{IV}N_{VI}$	14.51	5	0.854	13.75	4	0.902
$\zeta\,M_V N_{III}$	19.44	5	0.638	18.35	4	0.676
$\alpha\,M_V N_{VI,VII}$	14.88	5	0.833	14.04	2	0.883

Desig-nation	Å*	p.e.	keV	Å*	p.e.	keV
57 Lanthanum (*Cont.*)				**58 Cerium** (*Cont.*)		
$M_V O_{II,III}$				14.39	5	0.862
$N_{IV,V} O_{II,III}$	152.6	6	0.0812	144.4	6	0.0859
59 Praseodymium				**60 Neodymium**		
$\alpha_2 KL_{II}$	0.348749	2	35.5502	0.336472	2	36.8474
$\alpha_1 KL_{III}$	0.344140	2	36.0263	0.331846	2	37.3610
$\beta_3 KM_{II}$	0.304975	5	40.6529	0.294027	3	42.1665
$\beta_1 KM_{III}$	0.304261	4	40.7482	0.293299	2	42.2713
$\beta_2 KN_{II,III}$	0.29679	2	41.773	0.2861†	1	43.33
$\beta_4 L_I M_{II}$	2.2550	3	5.4981	2.1669	3	5.7216
$\beta_3 L_I M_{III}$	2.2172	3	5.5918	2.1268	2	5.8294
$\gamma_2 L_I N_{II}$	1.8791	4	6.598	1.8013	4	6.883
$\gamma_3 L_I N_{III}$	1.8740	4	6.616	1.7964	4	6.902
$\gamma_4 L_I O_{II,III}$	1.8193	4	6.815	1.7445	4	7.107
$\eta L_{II} M_I$	2.512	3	4.935	2.4094	4	5.1457
$\beta_1 L_{II} M_{IV}$	2.2588	3	5.4889	2.1669	2	5.7216
$\gamma_5 L_{II} N_I$	2.0205	4	6.136	1.9355	4	6.406
$\gamma_1 L_{II} N_{IV}$	1.9611	3	6.3221	1.8779	2	6.6021
$\gamma_8 L_{II} O_I$	1.9362	4	6.403	1.8552	5	6.683
$l L_{III} M_I$	2.7841	4	4.4532	2.6760	4	4.6330
$\alpha_2 L_{III} M_{IV}$	2.4729	3	5.0135	2.3807	3	5.2077
$\alpha_1 L_{III} M_V$	2.4630	2	5.0337	2.3704	3	5.2304
$\beta_6 L_{III} N_I$	2.1906	4	5.660	2.1039	3	5.8930
$\beta_{2,15} L_{III} N_{IV,V}$	2.1194	4	5.850	2.0360	3	6.0894
$\beta_7 L_{III} O_I$	2.0919	4	5.927	2.0092	3	6.1708
$\beta_{10} L_I M_{IV}$	2.1071	4	5.884	2.0237	3	6.1265
$\beta_9 L_I M_V$	2.1004	4	5.903	2.0165	3	6.1484
$\gamma M_{III} N_{IV,V}$	10.998	9	1.1273	10.505	9	1.180
$\beta M_{IV} N_{VI}$	13.06	2	0.950	12.44	2	0.997
$\zeta M_V N_{III}$	17.38	4	0.714	16.46	4	0.753
$\alpha M_V N_{VI,VII}$	13.343	5	0.9292	12.68	2	0.978
$N_{IV,V} N_{VI,VII}$	113.	1	0.1095	107.	1	0.116
$N_{IV,V} O_{II,III}$	136.5	4	0.0908	128.9	7	0.0962
61 Promethium				**62 Samarium**		
$\alpha_2 KL_{II}$	0.324803	4	38.1712	0.313698	2	39.5224
$\alpha_1 KL_{III}$	0.320160	4	38.7247	0.309040	2	40.1181
$\beta_3 KM_{II}$	0.28363†	4	43.713	0.27376	2	45.289
$\beta_1 KM_{III}$	0.28290†	3	43.826	0.27301	2	45.413
$\beta_2 KN_{II,III}$	0.2759†	1	44.94	0.2662	1	46.58
$KO_{II,III}$				0.26491	3	46.801
$\beta_5 KM_{IV,V}$				0.27111	3	45.731
$\beta_4 L_I M_{II}$				2.00095	6	6.1963
$\beta_3 L_I M_{III}$	2.0421	4	6.071	1.96241	3	6.3180
$\gamma_2 L_I N_{II}$				1.66044	6	7.4668
$\gamma_3 L_I N_{III}$				1.65601	3	7.4867
$\gamma_4 L_I O_{II,III}$				1.60728	3	7.7137
$\eta L_{II} M_I$				2.21824	3	5.5892
$\beta_1 L_{II} M_{IV}$	2.0797	4	5,961	1.99806	3	6.2051
$\gamma_5 L_{II} N_I$				1.77934	3	6.9678
$\gamma_1 L_{II} N_{IV}$	1.7989	9	6.892	1.72724	3	7.1780
$\gamma_8 L_{II} O_{IV}$				1.6966	9	7.3076
$l L_{III} M_I$				2.4823	4	4.9945

Desig-nation	Å*	p.e.	keV	Å*	p.e.	keV
61 Promethium (*Cont.*)				**62 Samarium** (*Cont.*)		
$\alpha_2 L_{III} M_{IV}$	2.2926	4	5.4078	2.21062	3	5.6084
$\alpha_1 L_{III} M_V$	2.2822	3	5.4325	2.1998	2	5.6361
$\beta_6 L_{III} N_I$				1.94643	3	6.3697
$\beta_{2,15} L_{III} N_{IV,V}$	1.9559	6	6.339	1.88221	3	6.5870
$\beta_7 L_{III} O_I$				1.85626	3	6.6791
$\beta_5 L_{III} O_{IV,V}$				1.84700	9	6.7126
$\beta_{10} L_I M_{IV}$				1.86990	3	6.6304
$\beta_9 L_I M_V$				1.86166	3	6.6597
$\gamma M_{III} N_{IV,V}$				9.600	9	1.291
$\beta M_{IV} N_{VI}$				11.27	1	1.0998
$\zeta M_V N_{III}$				14.91	4	0.831
$\alpha M_V N_{VI,VII}$				11.47	3	1.081
$N_{IV,V} N_{VI,VII}$				98.	1	0.126
$N_{IV,V} O_{II,III}$				117.4	4	0.1056
63 Europium				**64 Gadolinium**		
$\alpha_2 KL_{II}$	0.303118	2	40.9019	0.293038	2	42.3089
$\alpha_1 KL_{III}$	0.298446	2	41.5422	0.288353	2	42.9962
$\beta_3 KM_{II}$	0.264332	5	46.9036	0.25534	2	48.555
$\beta_1 KM_{III}$	0.263577	5	47.0379	0.25460	2	48.697
$\beta_2 KN_{II,III}$	0.256923	8	48.256	0.24816	3	49.959
$KO_{II,III}$	0.255645	7	48.497	0.24687	3	50.221
$\beta_5 KM_{IV,V}$				0.25275	2	49.052
$\beta_4 L_I M_{II}$	1.9255	2	6.4389	1.8540	2	6.6871
$\beta_3 L_I M_{III}$	1.8867	2	6.5713	1.8150	2	6.8311
$\gamma_2 L_I N_{II}$	1.5961	2	7.7677	1.5331	2	8.087
$\gamma_3 L_I N_{III}$	1.5903	2	7.7961	1.5297	2	8.105
$\gamma_4 L_I O_{II,III}$	1.5439	1	8.0304	1.4839	2	8.355
$\eta L_{II} M_I$	2.1315	2	5.8166	2.0494	1	6.0495
$\beta_1 L_{II} M_{IV}$	1.9203	2	6.4564	1.8468	2	6.7132
$\gamma_5 L_{II} N_I$	1.7085	2	7.2566	1.6412	2	7.5543
$\gamma_1 L_{II} N_{IV}$	1.6574	2	7.4803	1.5924	2	7.7858
$\gamma_8 L_{II} O_I$	1.6346	2	7.5849	1.5707	2	7.894
$\gamma_6 L_{II} O_{IV}$	1.6282	2	7.6147	1.5644	2	7.925
$l L_{III} M_I$	2.3948	2	5.1772	2.3122	2	5.3621
$\alpha_2 L_{III} M_{IV}$	2.1315	2	5.8166	2.0578	2	6.0250
$\alpha_1 L_{III} M_V$	2.1209	2	5.8457	2.0468	2	6.052
$\beta_6 L_{III} N_I$	1.8737	2	6.6170	1.8054	2	6.8671
$\beta_{2,15} L_{III} N_{IV,V}$	1.8118	2	6.8432	1.7455	2	7.1028
$\beta_7 L_{III} O_I$	1.7851	2	6.9453	1.7203	2	7.2071
$\beta_5 L_{III} O_{IV,V}$	1.7772	2	6.9763	1.7130	2	7.2374
$\beta_{10} L_I M_{IV}$	1.7993	3	6.890	1.7315	3	7.160
$\beta_9 L_I M_V$	1.7916	3	6.920	1.7240	3	7.192
$L_I O_{IV,V}$				1.4807	3	8.373
$\gamma M_{III} N_{IV,V}$	9.211	9	1.346	8.844	9	1.402
$\beta M_{IV} N_{VI}$	10.750	7	1.1533	10.254	6	1.2091
$\zeta M_V N_{III}$	14.22	2	0.872	13.57	2	0.914
$\alpha M_V N_{VI,VII}$	10.96	3	1.131	10.46	3	1.185
$N_{IV,V} O_{II,III}$	112.0	6	0.1107			
65 Terbium				**66 Dysprosium**		
$\alpha_2 KL_{II}$	0.283423	2	43.7441	0.274247	2	45.2078
$\alpha_1 KL_{III}$	0.278724	2	44.4816	0.269533	2	45.9984
$\beta_3 KM_{II}$	0.24603	3	50.779	0.23862	2	51.957

Designation	Å*	p.e.	keV	Å*	p.e.	keV
	65 Terbium (*Cont.*)			**66 Dysprosium** (*Cont.*)		
$\beta_1\,KM_{III}$	0.24608	2	50.382	0.23788	2	52.119
$\beta_2\,KN_{II,III}$	0.2397†	2	51.72	0.2317†	2	53.51
$KO_{II,III}$	0.23858	3	51.965	0.23056	3	53.774
$\beta_5\,KM_{IV,V}$				0.23618	3	52.494
$\beta_4\,L_I M_{II}$	1.7864	2	6.9403	1.72103	7	7.2039
$\beta_3\,L_I M_{III}$	1.7472	2	7.0959	1.6822	2	7.3702
$\gamma_2\,L_I N_{II}$	1.4764	2	8.398	1.42278	7	8.7140
$\gamma_3\,L_I N_{III}$	1.4718	2	8.423	1.41640	7	8.7532
$\gamma_4\,L_I O_{II,III}$	1.4276	2	8.685	1.37459	7	9.0195
$\eta\,L_{II} M_I$	1.9730	2	6.2839	1.89743	7	6.5342
$\beta_1\,L_{II} M_{IV}$	1.7768	3	6.978	1.71062	7	7.2477
$\gamma_5\,L_{II} N_I$	1.5787	2	7.8535	1.51824	7	8.1661
$\gamma_1\,L_{II} N_{IV}$	1.5303	2	8.102	1.47266	7	8.4188
$\gamma_8\,L_{II} O_I$	1.5097	2	8.212			
$\gamma_6\,L_{II} O_{IV}$	1.5035	2	8.246	1.44579	7	8.5753
$l\,L_{III} M_I$	2.2352	2	5.5467	2.15877	7	5.7431
$\alpha_2\,L_{III} M_{IV}$	1.9875	2	6.2380	1.91991	3	6.4577
$\alpha_1\,L_{II} M_V$	1.9765	2	6.2728	1.90881	3	6.4952
$\beta_6\,L_{III} N_I$	1.7422	2	7.1163	1.68213	7	7.3705
$\beta_{2,15}\,L_{III} N_{IV,V}$	1.6830	2	7.3667	1.62369	7	7.6357
$\beta_7\,L_{III} O_I$	1.6585	2	7.4753	1.60447	7	7.7272
$\beta_5\,L_{III} O_{IV,V}$	1.6510	2	7.5094	1.58837	7	7.8055
$\beta_{10}\,L_I M_{IV}$	1.6673	3	7.436	1.60743	9	7.7130
$\beta_9\,L_I M_V$				1.59973	9	7.7501
$L_I O_{IV,V}$	1.4228	3	8.714			
$\gamma\,M_{III} N_{IV,V}$	8.486	9	1.461	8.144	9	1.522
$\beta\,M_{IV} N_{VI}$	9.792	6	1.2661	9.357	6	1.3250
$\zeta\,M_V N_{III}$	12.98	2	0.955	12.43	2	0.998
$\alpha\,M_V N_{VI,VII}$	10.00	2	1.240	9.59	2	1.293
$N_{IV,V} N_{VI,VII}$	86.	1	0.144	83.	1	0.149
$N_{IV,V} O_{II,III}$	102.2	4	0.1213	97.2	8	0.128
	67 Holmium			**68 Erbium**		
$\alpha_2\,K L_{II}$	0.265486	2	46.6997	0.257110	2	48.2211
$\alpha_1\,K L_{III}$	0.260756	2	47.5467	0.252365	2	49.1277
$\beta_3\,KM_{II}$	0.23083	2	53.711	0.22341	2	55.494
$\beta_1\,KM_{III}$	0.23012	2	53.877	0.22266	2	55.681
$\beta_2\,KN_{II,III}$	0.2241†	2	55.32	0.2167†	2	57.21
$KO_{II,III}$	0.22305	3	55.584	0.21581	3	57.450
$\beta_5\,KM_{IV,V}$	0.22855	3	54.246	0.22124	3	56.040
$\beta_4\,L_I M_{II}$	1.6595	2	7.4708	1.6007	1	7.7453
$\beta_3\,L_I M_{III}$	1.6203	2	7.6519	1.5616	1	7.9392
$\gamma_2\,L_I N_{II}$	1.3698	2	9.051	1.3210	2	9.385
$\gamma_3\,L_I N_{III}$	1.3643	2	9.087	1.3146	1	9.4309
$\gamma_4\,L_I O_{II,III}$	1.3225	2	9.374	1.2752	2	9.722
$\eta\,L_{II} M_I$	1.8264	2	6.7883	1.7566	1	7.0579
$\beta_1\,L_{II} M_{IV}$	1.6475	2	7.5253	1.5873	1	7.8109
$\gamma_5\,L_{II} N_I$	1.4618	2	8.481	1.4067	3	8.814
$\gamma_1\,L_{II} N_{IV}$	1.4174	2	8.747	1.3641	2	9.089
$\gamma_8\,L_{II} O_I$	1.3983	2	8.867			
$\gamma_6\,L_{II} O_{IV}$	1.3923	2	8.905	1.3397	3	9.255
$l\,L_{III} M_I$	2.0860	2	5.9434	2.015	1	6.152
$\alpha_2\,L_{III} M_{IV}$	1.8561	2	6.6795	1.7955	2	6.9050
$\alpha_1\,L_{III} M_V$	1.8450	2	6.7198	1.78425	9	6.9487
$\beta_6\,L_{III} N_I$	1.6237	2	7.6359	1.5675	2	7.909
$\beta_{2,15}\,L_{III} N_{IV,V}$	1.5671	2	7.911	1.51399	9	8.1890
$\beta_7\,L_{III} O_I$				1.4941	3	8.298
$\beta_5\,L_{III} O_{IV,V}$	1.5378	2	8.062	1.4848	3	8.350

Designation	Å*	p.e.	keV	Å*	p.e.	keV
	67 Holmium (*Cont.*)			**68 Erbium** (*Cont.*)		
$\beta_{10}\,L_I M_{IV}$	1.5486	3	8.006	1.4941	3	8.298
$L_I O_{IV,V}$	1.3208	3	9.387			
$\beta_9\,L_I M_V$				1.4855	5	8.346
$M_{II} N_{IV}$				7.60	1	1.632
$\gamma\,M_{III} N_{IV,V}$	7.865	9	1.576			
$\gamma\,M_{III}\,v$				7.546	8	1.643
$\beta\,M_{IV} N_{VI}$	8.965	4	1.3830	8.592	3	1.4430
$\zeta\,M_V N_{III}$	11.86	1	1.0450	11.37	1	1.0901
$\alpha\,M_V N_{VI,VII}$	9.20	2	1.348	8.82	1	1.406
$N_{IV} N_{VI}$				72.7	9	0.171
$N_V N_{VI,VII}$				76.3	7	0.163
	69 Thulium			**70 Ytterbium**		
$\alpha_2\,K L_{II}$	0.249095	2	49.7726	0.241424	2	51.3540
$\alpha_1\,K L_{III}$	0.244338	2	50.7416	0.236655	2	52.3889
$\beta_3\,KM_{II}$	0.21636	2	57.304	0.2096†	1	59.14
$\beta_1\,KM_{III}$	0.21556	2	57.517	0.20884	8	59.37
$\beta_2\,KN_{II,III}$	0.2098†	2	59.09	0.2033†	2	60.98
$KO_{II,III}$	0.20891	2	59.346	0.20226	2	61.298
$\beta_5\,KM_{IV,V}$	0.21404	2	57.923	0.20739	2	59.782
$\beta_4\,L_I M_{II}$	1.5448	2	8.026	1.49138	3	8.3132
$\beta_3\,L_I M_{III}$	1.5063	2	8.231	1.45233	5	8.5367
$\gamma_2\,L_I N_{II}$	1.2742	2	9.730	1.22879	7	10.0897
$\gamma_3\,L_I N_{III}$	1.2678	2	9.779	1.22232	5	10.1431
$\gamma_4\,L_I O_{II,III}$	1.2294	2	10.084	1.1853	1	10.4603
$\eta\,L_{II} M_I$	1.6963	2	7.3088	1.63560	5	7.5802
$\beta_1\,L_{II} M_{IV}$	1.5304	2	8.101	1.47565	5	8.4018
$\gamma_5\,L_{II} N_I$	1.3558	2	9.144	1.3063	1	9.4910
$\gamma_1\,L_{II} N_{IV}$	1.3153	2	9.426	1.26769	5	9.8701
$\gamma_8\,L_{II} O_I$				1.24923	5	9.9246
$\gamma_6\,L_{II} O_{IV}$	1.2905	2	9.607	1.24271	3	9.9766
$l\,L_{III} M_I$	1.9550	2	6.3419	1.89415	5	6.5455
$\alpha_2\,L_{III} M_{IV}$	1.7381	2	7.1331	1.68285	5	7.3673
$\alpha_1\,L_{III} M_V$	1.7268†	2	7.1799	1.67189	4	7.4156
$\beta_6\,L_{III} N_I$	1.5162	2	8.177	1.4661	1	8.4563
$\beta_{2,15}\,L_{III} N_{IV,V}$	1.4640	2	8.468	1.41550	5	8.7588
$\beta_7\,L_{III} O_I$				1.3948	1	8.8889
$\beta_5\,L_{III} O_{IV,V}$	1.4349	2	8.641	1.38696	7	8.9390
$\beta_{10}\,L_I M_{IV}$	1.4410	3	8.604	1.3915	1	8.9100
$\beta_9\,L_I M_V$	1.4336	3	8.648	1.3838	1	8.9597
$L_I O_I$				1.1886	1	10.4312
$L_I O_{IV,V}$	1.2263	3	10.110	1.1827	1	10.4833
$L_{II} M_{II}$				1.58844	9	7.8052
$L_{II} O_{II,III}$				1.2453	1	9.9561
$t\,L_{III} M_{II}$				1.83091	9	6.7715
$L_{III} O_{II,III}$				1.3898	1	9.9209
$M_{III} N_I$				8.470	9	1.464
$\gamma\,M_{III} N_V$				7.024	8	1.765
$\beta\,M_{IV} N_{VI}$	8.249	7	1.503	7.909	2	1.5675
$\zeta\,M_V N_{III}$				10.48	1	1.183
$\alpha\,M_V N_{VI,VII}$	8.48	1	1.462	8.149	5	1.5214
$N_{IV} N_{VI}$				65.1	7	0.190
$N_V N_{VI,VII}$				69.3	5	0.179
	71 Lutetium			**72 Hafnium**		
$\alpha_2\,K L_{II}$	0.234081	2	52.9650	0.227024	3	54.6114
$\alpha_1\,K L_{III}$	0.229298	2	54.0698	0.222227	3	55.7902
$\beta_3\,KM_{II}$	0.20309†	4	61.05	0.19686†	4	62.98

Desig-nation	Å*	p.e.	keV	Å*	p.e.	keV
71 Lutetium (*Cont.*)				**72 Hafnium (*Cont.*)**		
$\beta_1\ KM_{III}$	0.20231†	3	61.283	0.19607†	3	63.234
$\beta_2\ KN_{II,III}$	0.1969†	2	62.97	0.1908†	2	64.98
$KO_{II,III}$	0.19589	2	63.293			
$\beta_5\ KM_{IV,V}$	0.20084	2	61.732			
$\beta_4\ L_I M_{II}$	1.44056	5	8.6064	1.39220	5	8.9054
$\beta_3\ L_I M_{III}$	1.40140	5	8.8469	1.35300	5	9.1634
$\gamma_2\ L_I N_{II}$	1.1853	2	10.460	1.14442	5	10.8335
$\gamma_3\ L_I N_{III}$	1.17953	4	10.5110	1.13841	5	10.8907
$\gamma'_4\ L_I O_{II}$				1.10376	5	11.2326
$\gamma_4\ L_I O_{II,III}$	1.1435	1	10.8425	1.10303	5	11.2401
$\eta\ L_{II} M_I$	1.5779	1	7.8575	1.52325	5	8.1393
$\beta_1\ L_{II} M_{IV}$	1.42359	3	8.7090	1.37410	5	9.0227
$\gamma_5\ L_{II} N_I$	1.2596	1	9.8428	1.21537	5	10.2011
$\gamma_1\ L_{II} N_{IV}$	1.22228	4	10.1434	1.17900	5	10.5158
$\gamma_8\ L_{II} O_I$	1.2047	1	10.2915	1.16138	5	10.6754
$\gamma_6\ L_{II} O_{IV}$	1.1987	1	10.3431	1.15519	5	10.7325
$l\ L_{III} M_I$	1.8360	1	6.7528	1.78145	5	6.9596
$\alpha_2\ L_{III} M_{IV}$	1.63029	5	7.6049	1.58046	5	7.8446
$\alpha_1\ L_{III} M_V$	1.61951	3	7.6555	1.56958	5	7.8990
$\beta_6\ L_{III} N_I$	1.4189	1	8.7376	1.37410	5	9.0227
$\beta_{15}\ L_{III} N_{IV}$	1.3715	1	9.0395	1.32783	5	9.3371
$\beta_2\ L_{III} N_V$	1.37012	3	9.0489	1.32639	5	9.3473
$\beta_7\ L_{III} O_I$	1.34949	5	9.1873	1.30564	5	9.4958
$\beta_5\ L_{III} O_{IV,V}$	1.34183	7	9.2397	1.29761	5	9.5546
$L_I M_I$				1.43025	9	8.6685
$\beta_{10}\ L_I M_{IV}$	1.3430	2	9.232	1.29819	9	9.5503
$\beta_9\ L_I M_V$	1.3358	1	9.2816	1.29025	9	9.6090
$L_I N_{IV}$	1.16227	9	10.6672	1.12250	9	11.0451
$\gamma_{11}\ L_I N_V$	1.16107	9	10.6782	1.12146	9	11.0553
$L_I O_I$				1.10664	9	11.2034
$L_I O_{IV}$				1.10086	9	11.2622
$L_{II} M_{II}$	1.53333	9	8.0858	1.48064	9	8.3735
$\beta_{17}\ L_{II} M_{III}$				1.43643	9	8.6312
$L_{II} N_V$				1.17788	9	10.5258
$v\ L_{II} N_{VI}$				1.15830	9	10.7037
$L_{II} O_{II,III}$	1.2014	1	10.3198			
$t\ L_{III} M_{II}$	1.7760	1	6.9810	1.72305	9	7.1954
$s\ L_{III} M_{III}$				1.66346	9	7.4532
$L_{III} N_{II}$				1.35887	9	9.1239
$L_{III} N_{III}$				1.35053	9	9.1802
$u\ L_{III} N_{VI,VII}$				1.30165	9	9.5249
$L_{III} O_{II,III}$	1.34524	9	9.2163			
$M_{III} N_I$				7.887	9	1.572
$\gamma\ M_{III} N_V$	6.768	6	1.832	6.544	4	1.895
ζ_2				9.686	7	1.2800
$\beta\ M_{IV} N_{VI}$	7.601	2	1.6312	7.303	1	1.6976
ζ_1				9.686	7	1.2800
$\alpha\ M_V N_{VI,VII}$	7.840	2	1.5813	7.539	1	1.6446
$N_{IV} N_{VI}$	63.0	5	0.197			
$N_V N_{VI,VII}$	65.7	2	0.1886			
73 Tantalum				**74 Tungsten**		
$\alpha_2\ KL_{II}$	0.220305	8	56.277	0.213828	2	57.9817
$\alpha_1\ KL_{III}$	0.215497	4	57.532	0.2090100	Std	59.31824
$\beta_3\ KM_{II}$	0.190890	2	64.9488	0.185181	2	66.9514
$\beta_1\ KM_{III}$	0.190089	4	65.223	0.184371	2	67.7443
$\beta_2^{II}\ KN_{II}$	0.185188	9	66.949	0.17960	1	69.031
$\beta_2^{I}\ KN_{III}$	0.185011	8	67.013	0.179421	7	69.101

Desig-nation	Å*	p.e.	keV	Å*	p.e.	keV
73 Tantalum (*Cont.*)				**74 Tungsten (*Cont.*)**		
$KO_{II,III}$	0.184031	7	67.370	0.178444	5	69.479
KL_I				0.21592	4	57.42
$\beta_5^{II}\ KM_{IV}$	0.188920	6	65.626	0.183264	5	67.652
$\beta_5^{I}\ KM_V$	0.188757	6	65.683	0.183092	7	67.715
$\beta_4\ KN_{IV,V}$	0.18451	1	67.194	0.17892	2	69.294
$\beta_4\ L_I M_{II}$	1.34581	3	9.2124	1.30162	5	9.5252
$\beta_3\ L_I M_{III}$	1.30678	3	9.4875	1.26269	5	9.8188
$\gamma_2\ L_I N_{II}$	1.1053	1	11.217	1.06806	3	11.6080
$\gamma_3\ L_I N_{III}$	1.09936	4	11.2776	1.06200	6	11.6743
$\gamma'_4\ L_I O_{II}$	1.06544	3	11.6366	1.02863	3	12.0530
$\gamma_4\ L_I O_{III}$	1.06467	3	11.6451	1.02775	5	12.0634
$\eta\ L_{II} M_I$	1.47106	5	8.4280	1.42110	3	8.7243
$\beta_1\ L_{II} M_{IV}$	1.32698	3	9.3431	1.281809	9	9.67235
$\gamma_5\ L_{II} N_I$	1.1729	1	10.5702	1.13235	3	10.9490
$\gamma_1\ L_{II} N_{IV}$	1.13794	3	10.8952	1.09855	3	11.2859
$\gamma_8\ L_{II} O_I$	1.1205	1	11.0646	1.08113	4	11.4677
$\gamma_6\ L_{II} O_{IV}$	1.11388	3	11.1306	1.07448	5	11.5387
$l\ L_{III} M_I$	1.72841	5	7.1731	1.6782	1	7.3878
$\alpha_2\ L_{III} M_{IV}$	1.53293	2	8.0879	1.48743	2	8.3352
$\alpha_1\ L_{III} M_V$	1.52197	2	8.1461	1.47639	2	8.3976
$\beta_6\ L_{III} N_I$	1.33094	8	9.3153	1.28989	7	9.6117
$\beta_{15}\ L_{III} N_{IV}$	1.28619	5	9.6394	1.24631	3	9.9478
$\beta_2\ L_{III} N_V$	1.28454	2	9.6518	1.24460	3	9.9615
$\beta_7\ L_{III} O_I$	1.26385	5	9.8098	1.22400	4	10.1292
$\beta_5\ L_{III} O_{IV,V}$	1.2555	1	9.8750	1.21545	3	10.2004
$L_I M_I$				1.3365	9	9.277
$\beta_{10}\ L_I M_{IV}$	1.2537	2	9.889	1.21218	3	10.2279
$\beta_9\ L_I M_V$	1.2466	2	9.946	1.20479	7	10.2907
$L_I N_I$	1.11521	9	11.1173			
$L_I N_{IV}$	1.08377	7	11.4398	1.0468	2	11.844
$\gamma_{11}\ L_I N_V$	1.08205	7	11.4580	1.0458	1	11.856
$L_I N_{VI,VII}$	1.06357	9	11.6570			
$L_I O_I$	1.06771	9	11.6118	1.0317	3	12.017
$L_I O_{IV,V}$	1.06192	9	11.6752	1.0250	2	12.095
$L_{II} M_{II}$	1.43048	9	8.6671			
$\beta_{17}\ L_{II} M_{III}$	1.3864	1	8.9428	1.3387	2	9.261
$L_{II} M_V$	1.31897	9	9.3998	1.2728	2	9.741
$L_{II} N_{II}$	1.1600	2	10.688	1.1218	3	11.052
$L_{II} N_{III}$	1.1553	1	10.7316	1.1149	2	11.120
$L_{II} N_V$	1.13687	9	10.9055			
$v\ L_{II} N_{VI}$	1.1158	1	11.1113	1.0771	1	11.510
$L_{II} O_{II}$	1.11789	9	11.0907			
$L_{II} O_{III}$	1.11693	9	11.1001	1.0792	2	11.488
$t\ L_{III} M_{II}$	1.67265	9	7.4123	1.6244	3	7.632
$s\ L_{III} M_{III}$	1.61264	9	7.6881	1.5642	3	7.926
$L_{III} N_{II}$	1.3167	1	9.4158	1.2765	2	9.712
$L_{III} N_{III}$	1.3086	1	9.4742	1.2672	2	9.784
$u\ L_{III} N_{VI,VII}$	1.25778	4	9.8572	1.21868	5	10.1733
$L_{III} O_{II,III}$	1.2601	3	9.839	1.2211	2	10.153
$M_I N_{III}$	5.40	2	2.295	5.172	9	2.397
$M_I O_{II,III}$				4.44	2	2.79
$M_{II} N_I$				6.28	2	1.973
$M_{II} N_{IV}$	5.570	4	2.226	5.357	4	2.314
$M_{III} N_I$	7.612	9	1.629	7.360	8	1.684
$M_{III} N_{IV}$	6.353	5	1.951	6.134	4	2.021
$\gamma\ M_{III} N_V$	6.312	4	1.964	6.092	3	2.035
$M_{III} O_I$	5.83	3	2.126	5.628	8	2.203
$M_{III} O_{IV,V}$	5.67	3	2.19			

Designation	Å*	p.e.	keV	Å*	p.e.	keV
73 Tantalum (Cont.)				**74 Tungsten (Cont.)**		
$\zeta_2\ M_{IV}N_{II}$	9.330	5	1.3288	8.993	5	1.3787
$M_{IV}N_{III}$	8.90	2	1.393	8.573	8	1.446
$\beta\ M_{IV}N_{VI}$	7.023	1	1.7655	6.757	1	1.8349
$M_{IV}O_{II}$	7.09	2	1.748	6.806	9	1.822
$\zeta_1\ M_{V}N_{III}$	9.316	4	1.3308	8.962	4	1.3835
$\alpha\ M_{V}N_{VI,VII}$	7.252	1	1.7096			
$\alpha_2\ M_{V}N_{VI}$				6.992	2	1.7731
$\alpha_1\ M_{V}N_{VII}$				6.983	1	1.7754
$M_{V}O_{III}$	7.30	2	1.700	7.005	9	1.770
$N_{II}N_{IV}$				54.0	2	0.2295
$N_{IV}N_{VI}$	58.2	1	0.2130	55.8	1	0.2221
$N_{V}N_{VI,VII}$	61.1	2	0.2028			
$N_{V}N_{VI}$				59.5	3	0.208
$N_{V}N_{VII}$				58.4	1	0.2122
75 Rhenium				**76 Osmium**		
$\alpha_2\ KL_{II}$	0.207611	1	59.7179	0.201639	2	61.4867
$\alpha_1\ KL_{III}$	0.202781	2	61.1403	0.196794	2	63.0005
$\beta_3\ KM_{II}$	0.179697	3	68.994	0.174431	3	71.077
$\beta_1\ KM_{III}$	0.178880	3	69.310	0.173611	3	71.413
$\beta_2^{II}\ KN_{II}$	0.17425	1	71.151	0.16910	1	73.318
$\beta_2^{I}\ KN_{III}$	0.174054	6	71.232	0.168906	6	73.402
$KO_{II,III}$	0.17308	1	71.633	0.16798	1	73.808
$\beta_5^{II}\ KM_{IV}$	0.17783	1	69.719	0.17262	1	71.824
$\beta_5^{I}\ KM_{V}$	0.17766	1	69.786	0.17245	1	71.895
$\beta_4\ KN_{IV,V}$	0.17362	2	71.410	0.16842	2	73.615
$\beta_4\ L_{I}M_{II}$	1.25917	5	9.8463	1.21844	5	10.1754
$\beta_3\ L_{I}M_{III}$	1.22031	5	10.1598	1.17955	7	10.5108
$\gamma_2\ L_{I}N_{II}$	1.03233	5	12.0098	0.99805	5	12.4224
$\gamma_3\ L_{I}N_{III}$	1.02613	7	12.0824	0.99186	5	12.4998
$\gamma'_4\ L_{I}O_{II}$	0.99334	5	12.4813	0.96033	8	12.910
$\gamma_4\ L_{I}O_{III}$	0.99249	5	12.4920	0.95938	8	12.923
$\eta\ L_{II}M_{I}$	1.37342	5	9.0272	1.32785	7	9.3370
$\beta_1\ L_{II}M_{IV}$	1.23858	2	10.0100	1.19727	7	10.3553
$\gamma_5\ L_{II}N_{I}$	1.09388	5	11.3341	1.05693	5	11.7303
$\gamma_1\ L_{II}N_{IV}$	1.06099	5	11.6854	1.02503	5	12.0953
$\gamma_8\ L_{II}O_{I}$	1.04398	5	11.8758	1.00788	5	12.3012
$\gamma_6\ L_{II}O_{IV}$	1.03699	9	11.956	1.00107	5	12.3848
$l\ L_{III}M_{I}$	1.63056	5	7.6036	1.58498	7	7.8222
$\alpha_2\ L_{III}M_{IV}$	1.44396	5	8.5862	1.40234	5	8.8410
$\alpha_1\ L_{III}M_{V}$	1.43290	4	8.6525	1.39121	5	8.9117
$\beta_6\ L_{III}N_{I}$	1.25100	5	9.9105	1.21349	5	10.2169
$\beta_{15}\ L_{III}N_{IV}$	1.20819	5	10.2617	1.17167	5	10.5816
$\beta_2\ L_{III}N_{V}$	1.20660	4	10.2752	1.16979	8	10.5985
$\beta_7\ L_{III}O_{I}$	1.18610	5	10.4529	1.14933	8	10.7872
$\beta_5\ L_{III}O_{IV,V}$	1.17721	5	10.5318	1.1405	1	10.8711
$\beta_{10}\ L_{I}M_{IV}$	1.17218	5	10.5770	1.13353	5	10.9376
$\beta_9\ L_{I}M_{V}$	1.16487	4	10.6433	1.12637	6	11.0071
$L_{I}N_{I}$	1.0420	1	11.899			
$L_{I}N_{IV}$	1.0119	1	12.252	0.9772	3	12.687
$\gamma_{11}\ L_{I}N_{V}$	1.0108	1	12.266	0.9765	3	12.696
$L_{I}O_{I}$	0.9965	1	12.442	0.96318	7	12.8721
$L_{I}O_{IV,V}$	0.9900	1	12.524	0.95603	5	12.9683
$L_{II}M_{II}$	1.3366	1	9.2761	1.2934	2	9.586
$\beta_{17}\ L_{II}M_{III}$	1.2927	1	9.5910	1.2480	2	9.934

Designation	Å*	p.e.	keV	Å*	p.e.	keV
75 Rhenium (Cont.)				**76 Osmium (Cont.)**		
$L_{II}M_{V}$	1.2305	1	10.0753	1.18977	7	10.4205
$L_{II}N_{II}$	1.0839	1	11.438			
$L_{II}N_{III}$	1.0767	1	11.515	1.03973	5	11.9243
$v\ L_{II}N_{VI}$	1.0404	1	11.917	1.0050	2	12.337
$L_{II}O_{III}$	1.0397	1	11.925	1.0047	2	12.340
$t\ L_{III}M_{II}$	1.5789	1	7.8525	1.5347	2	8.079
$s\ L_{III}M_{III}$	1.5178	1	8.1682	1.4735	2	8.414
$L_{III}N_{I}$				1.20086	7	10.3244
$L_{III}N_{III}$	1.2283	1	10.0933			
$u\ L_{III}N_{VI,VII}$	1.1815	1	10.4931	1.14537	7	10.8245
$M_{I}N_{III}$				4.79	2	2.59
$M_{I}N_{I}$				5.81	2	2.133
$M_{II}N_{IV}$				4.955	4	2.502
$M_{III}N_{I}$				6.89	2	1.798
$M_{III}N_{IV}$	5.931	5	2.090	5.724	2	2.166
$\gamma\ M_{III}N_{V}$	5.885	2	2.1067	5.682	4	2.182
$\zeta_2\ M_{IV}N_{II}$	8.664	5	1.4310	8.359	5	1.4831
$M_{IV}N_{III}$	8.239	8	1.505			
$\beta\ M_{IV}N_{VI}$	6.504	1	1.9061	6.267	1	1.9783
$\zeta_1\ M_{V}N_{III}$	8.629	4	1.4368	8.310	4	1.4919
$\alpha\ M_{V}N_{VI,VII}$	6.729	1	1.8425	6.490	1	1.9102
$N_{IV}N_{VI}$				51.9	1	0.2388
$N_{V}N_{VI,VII}$				54.7	2	0.2266
77 Iridium				**78 Platinum**		
$\alpha_2\ KL_{II}$	0.195904	2	63.2867	0.190381	4	65.122
$\alpha_1\ KL_{III}$	0.191047	2	64.8956	0.185511	4	66.832
$\beta_3\ KM_{II}$	0.169367	2	73.2027	0.164501	3	75.368
$\beta_1\ KM_{III}$	0.168542	2	73.5608	0.163675	3	75.748
$\beta_2^{II}\ KN_{II}$	0.16415	1	75.529	0.15939	1	77.785
$\beta_2^{I}\ KN_{III}$	0.163956	7	75.619	0.15920	1	77.878
$KO_{II,III}$	0.163019	5	76.053	0.15826	1	78.341
$\beta_5^{II}\ KM_{IV}$	0.16759	2	73.980	0.16271	2	76.199
$\beta_5^{I}\ KM_{V}$	0.167373	9	74.075	0.16255	3	76.27
$\beta_4\ KN_{IV,V}$	0.16352	2	75.821	0.15881	2	78.069
$\beta_4\ L_{I}M_{II}$	1.17958	3	10.5106	1.14223	5	10.8543
$\beta_3\ L_{I}M_{III}$	1.14085	3	10.8674	1.10394	5	11.2308
$\gamma_2\ L_{I}N_{II}$	0.96545	3	12.8418	0.93427	5	13.2704
$\gamma_3\ L_{I}N_{III}$	0.95931	5	12.9240	0.92791	5	13.3613
$\gamma'_4\ L_{I}O_{II}$	0.92831	3	13.3555	0.89747	4	13.8145
$\gamma_4\ L_{I}O_{III}$	0.92744	3	13.3681	0.89659	4	13.8281
$\eta\ L_{II}M_{I}$	1.28448	3	9.6522	1.2429	2	9.975
$\beta_1\ L_{II}M_{IV}$	1.15781	3	10.7083	1.11990	2	11.0707
$\gamma_5\ L_{II}N_{I}$	1.02175	5	12.1342	0.9877	2	12.552
$\gamma_1\ L_{II}N_{IV}$	0.99085	3	12.5126	0.95797	3	12.9420
$\gamma_8\ L_{II}O_{I}$	0.97409	3	12.7279	0.9411	1	13.173
$\gamma_6\ L_{II}O_{IV}$	0.96708	4	12.8201	0.9342	2	13.271
$l\ L_{III}M_{I}$	1.54094	3	8.0458	1.4995	2	8.268
$\alpha_2\ L_{III}M_{IV}$	1.36250	5	9.0995	1.32432	3	9.3618
$\alpha_1\ L_{III}M_{V}$	1.35128	3	9.1751	1.31304	3	9.4423
$\beta_6\ L_{III}N_{I}$	1.17796	3	10.5251	1.14355	5	10.8418
$\beta_{15}\ L_{III}N_{IV}$	1.13707	3	10.9036			
$\beta_2\ L_{III}N_{V}$	1.13532	3	10.9203	1.10200	3	11.2505
$\beta_7\ L_{III}O_{I}$	1.11489	3	11.1205	1.08168	3	11.4619

Designation	Å*	p.e.	keV	Å*	p.e.	keV	Designation	Å*	p.e.	keV	Å*	p.e.	keV
77 Iridium (*Cont.*)				**78 Platinum** (*Cont.*)			**79 Gold** (*Cont.*)				**80 Mercury** (*Cont.*)		
$\beta_5\ L_{III}O_{IV,V}$	1.10585	3	11.2114	1.0724	2	11.561	$\gamma_2\ L_I N_{II}$	0.90434	3	13.7095	0.87544	7	14.162
$L_I M_I$	1.2102	2	10.245	1.16962	9	10.6001	$\gamma_3\ L_I N_{III}$	0.89783	5	13.8090	0.86915	7	14.265
$\beta_{10}\ L_I M_{IV}$	1.09702	4	11.3016	1.06183	7	11.6762	$\gamma'_4\ L_I O_{II}$	0.86816	4	14.2809	0.84013	7	14.757
$\beta_9\ L_I M_V$	1.08975	5	11.3770	1.05446	5	11.7577	$\gamma_4\ L_I O_{III}$	0.86703	4	14.2996	0.83894	7	14.778
$L_I N_I$	0.9766	2	12.695	0.9455	2	13.113	$\eta\ L_{II}M_I$	1.20273	3	10.3083	1.1640	1	10.6512
$L_I N_{IV}$	0.9459	2	13.108				$\beta_1\ L_{II}M_{IV}$	1.08353	3	11.4423	1.04868	5	11.8226
$\gamma_{11}\ L_I N_V$	0.9446	2	13.126	0.9143	2	13.560	$\gamma_5\ L_{II}N_I$	0.95559	3	12.9743	0.92453	7	13.410
$L_I O_{IV,V}$	0.9243	3	13.413				$\gamma_1\ L_{II}N_{IV}$	0.92650	3	13.3817	0.89646	5	13.8301
$L_I O_I$				0.8995	2	13.784	$\gamma_8\ L_{II}O_I$	0.90989	5	13.6260	0.87995	7	14.090
$L_I O_{IV}$				0.8943	1	13.864	$\gamma_6\ L_{II}O_{IV}$	0.90297	3	13.7304	0.87319	7	14.199
$L_I O_V$				0.8934	1	13.878	$l\ L_{III}M_I$	1.45964	9	8.4939	1.4216	1	8.7210
$L_{II}M_{II}$	1.2502	3	9.917	1.213	1	10.225	$\alpha_2\ L_{III}M_{IV}$	1.28772	3	9.6280	1.25264	7	9.8976
$\beta_{17}\ L_{II}M_{III}$	1.2069	2	10.273	1.1667	1	10.6265	$\alpha_1\ L_{III}M_V$	1.27640	3	9.7133	1.24120	5	9.9888
$L_{II}M_V$	1.1489	2	10.791	1.1129	2	11.140	$\beta_6\ L_{III}N_I$	1.11092	3	11.1602	1.07975	7	11.4824
$L_{II}N_{II}$	1.0120	2	12.251	0.9792	2	12.661	$\beta_{15}\ L_{III}N_{IV}$	1.07188	5	11.5667	1.04151	7	11.9040
$L_{II}N_{III}$	1.0054	3	12.332	0.97173	4	12.7588	$\beta_2\ L_{III}N_V$	1.07022	3	11.5847	1.03975	7	11.9241
$v\ L_{II}N_{VI}$	0.97161	6	12.7603	0.93931	5	13.1992	$\beta_7\ L_{III}O_I$	1.04974	8	11.8106	1.01937	7	12.1625
$L_{II}O_{III}$	0.96979	5	12.7843				$\beta_5\ L_{III}O_{IV,V}$	1.04044	3	11.9163	1.00987	7	12.2769
$t\ L_{III}M_{II}$	1.4930	3	8.304	1.4530	2	8.533	$l_1 M_I$	1.13525	5	10.9210	1.0999	2	11.272
$s\ L_{III}M_{III}$	1.4318	2	8.659	1.3895	2	8.923	$\beta_{10}\ L_I M_{IV}$	1.02789	7	12.0617	0.9962	2	12.446
$L_{III}N_{II}$	1.16545	5	10.6380	1.1310	2	10.962	$\beta_9\ L_I M_V$	1.02063	7	12.1474	0.9871	2	12.560
$L_{III}N_{III}$	1.1560	3	10.725	1.1226	2	11.044	$L_I N_I$	0.9131	1	13.578	0.8827	2	14.045
$u\ L_{III}N_{VI,VII}$	1.11145	4	11.1549	1.07896	5	11.4908	$L_I N_{IV}$	0.88563	7	13.999			
$L_{III}O_{II,III}$	1.10923	6	11.1772	1.0761	3	11.521	$\gamma_{11}\ L_I N_V$	0.88433	7	14.020	0.85657	7	14.474
$M_I N_{III}$	4.631†	9	2.677	4.460	9	2.780	$L_I O_I$	0.87074	5	14.2385	0.8452	2	14.670
$M_{II}N_{IV}$	4.780	4	2.594	4.601	4	2.695	$L_I O_{IV,V}$	0.86400	5	14.3497	0.8350	2	14.847
$M_{III}N_I$	6.669	9	1.859	6.455	9	1.921	$L_{II}M_{II}$	1.1708	1	10.5892	1.1387	5	10.888
$M_{III}N_{IV}$	5.540	5	2.238	5.357	5	2.314	$\beta_{17}\ L_{II}M_{III}$	1.12798	5	10.9915	1.0916	5	11.358
$\gamma\ M_{II}N_V$	5.500	4	2.254	5.319	4	2.331	$L_{II}M_V$	1.0756	2	11.526			
$M_{III}O_I$				4.876	9	2.543	$L_{II}N_{III}$	0.9402	2	13.186	0.90894	7	13.640
$M_{III}O_{IV,V}$	4.869	9	2.546	4.694	8	2.641	$v\ L_{II}N_{VI}$	0.90837	5	13.6487	0.87885	7	14.107
$\zeta_2\ M_{IV}N_{II}$	8.065	5	1.5373	7.790	5	1.592	$L_{II}O_{II}$	0.90746	7	13.662	0.8784	1	14.114
$M_{IV}N_{III}$	7.645	8	1.622	7.371	8	1.682	$L_{II}O_{III}$	0.90638	7	13.679	0.8758	1	14.156
$\beta\ M_{IV}N_{VI}$	6.038	1	2.0535	5.828	1	2.1273	$t\ L_{III}M_I$	1.41366	7	8.7702	1.3746	2	9.019
$\zeta_1\ M_V N_{III}$	8.021	4	1.5458	7.738	4	1.6022	$s\ L_{III}M_{III}$	1.35131	7	9.1749	1.3112	2	9.455
$\alpha_2\ M_V N_{VI}$	6.275	3	1.9758	6.058	3	2.047	$L_{III}N_{II}$	1.09968	7	11.2743	1.0649	2	11.642
$\alpha_1\ M_V N_{VII}$	6.262	1	1.9799	6.047	1	2.0505	$L_{III}N_{III}$	1.09026	7	11.3717	1.0585	1	11.713
$M_V O_{III}$				5.987	9	2.071	$u\ L_{III}N_{VI,VII}$	1.04752	5	11.8357			
$N_{IV}N_{VI}$	50.2	1	0.2470	48.1	2	0.258	$u'\ L_{III}N_{VI}$				1.01769	7	12.1826
$N_V N_{VI,VII}$	52.8	1	0.2348	50.9	1	0.2436	$u\ L_{III}N_{VII}$				1.01674	7	12.1940
79 Gold				**80 Mercury**			$L_{III}O_{II,III}$	1.0450	2	11.865			
$\alpha_2\ K L_{II}$	0.185075	2	66.9895	0.179958	3	68.895	$L_{III}O_{II}$				1.01558	7	12.2079
$\alpha_1\ K L_{III}$	0.180195	2	68.8037	0.175068	3	70.819	$L_{III}O_{III}$				1.01404	7	12.2264
$\beta_2\ K M_{II}$	0.159810	2	77.580	0.155321	3	79.822	$L_{III}P_{II,III}$	1.03876	7	11.9355			
$\beta_1\ K M_{III}$	0.158982	3	77.984	0.154487	3	80.253	$M_I N_{III}$	4.300	9	2.883			
$\beta_2^{II}\ K N_{II}$	0.15483	2	80.08	0.15040	2	82.43	$M_{II}N_{IV}$	4.432	4	2.797			
$\beta_2^I\ K N_{III}$	0.154618	9	80.185	0.15020	2	82.54	$M_{III}N_I$	6.259	9	1.981	6.09	2	2.036
$K O_{II,III}$	0.153694	7	80.667	0.14931	2	83.04	$M_{III}N_{IV}$	5.186	5	2.391			
$K L_I$	0.18672	4	66.40				$\gamma\ M_{III}N_V$	5.145	4	2.410	4.984†	2	2.4875
$\beta_5^{II}\ K M_{IV}$	0.158062	7	78.438				$M_{III}O_I$	4.703	9	2.636			
$\beta_5^I\ K M_V$	0.157880	5	78.529				$M_{III}O_{IV,V}$	4.522	6	2.742			
$\beta_5\ K M_{IV,V}$				0.15353	2	80.75	$\zeta_2\ M_{IV}N_{II}$	7.523	5	1.648			
$\beta_4\ K N_{IV,V}$	0.154224	6	80.391	0.14978	2	82.78	$M_{IV}N_{III}$	7.101	8	1.746	6.87	2	1.805
$\beta_4\ L_I M_{II}$	1.10651	3	11.2047	1.07222	7	11.5630	$\beta\ M_{IV}N_{VI}$	5.624	1	2.2046	5.4318†	9	2.2825
$\beta_3\ L_I M_{III}$	1.06785	9	11.6103	1.03358	7	11.9953	$\zeta_1\ M_V N_{III}$	7.466	4	1.6605			
							$\alpha_2\ M_V N_{VI}$	5.854	3	2.118			

Desig-nation	Å*	p.e.	keV	Å*	p.e.	keV
	79 Gold (*Cont.*)			**80 Mercury** (*Cont.*)		
α_1 $M_V N_{VII}$	5.840	1	2.1229	5.6476†	9	2.1953
$M_V O_{III}$	5.767	9	2.150			
$N_{IV} N_{VI}$	46.8	2	0.265	45.2†	3	0.274
$N_V N_{VI,VII}$	49.4	1	0.2510	47.9†	3	0.259
	81 Thallium			**82 Lead**		
α_2 $K L_{II}$	0.175036	2	70.8319	0.170294	2	72.8042
α_1 $K L_{III}$	0.170136	2	72.8715	0.165376	2	74.9694
β_3 $K M_{II}$	0.150980	6	82.118	0.146810	4	84.450
β_1 $K M_{III}$	0.150142	5	82.576	0.145970	6	84.936
β_2^{II} $K N_{II}$	0.14614	1	84.836	0.14212	2	87.23
β_2^{I} $K N_{III}$	0.14595	1	84.946	0.14191	1	87.364
$K O_{II,III}$	0.14509	1	85.451	0.141012	8	87.922
$K P$				0.1408	1	88.06
β_5 $K M_{IV,V}$	0.14917	1	83.114			
β_5^{II} $K M_{IV}$				0.14512	2	85.43
β_5^{I} $K M_V$				0.14495	3	85.53
β_4 $K N_{IV,V}$	0.14553	2	85.19	0.14155	3	87.59
β_4 $L_1 M_{II}$	1.03918	3	11.9306	1.0075	1	12.306
β_3 $L_1 M_{III}$	1.00062	3	12.3904	0.96911	7	12.7933
γ_2 $L_1 N_{II}$	0.84773	5	14.6251	0.8210	2	15.101
γ_3 $L_1 N_{III}$	0.84130	4	14.7368	0.8147	1	15.218
γ'_4 $L_1 O_{II}$	0.81308	5	15.2482	0.78706	7	15.752
γ_4 $L_1 O_{III}$	0.81184	5	15.2716	0.7858	1	15.777
η $L_{II} M_I$	1.12769	3	10.9943	1.09241	7	11.3493
β_1 $L_{II} M_{IV}$	1.01513	4	12.2133	0.98291	3	12.6137
γ_5 $L_{II} N_I$	0.89500	4	13.8526	0.86655	5	14.3075
γ_1 $L_{II} N_{IV}$	0.86752	3	14.2915	0.83973	3	14.7644
γ_8 $L_{II} O_I$	0.8513	2	14.564	0.82365	5	15.0527
γ_6 $L_{II} O_{IV}$	0.8442	2	14.685	0.81683	5	15.1783
$L_{II} P_I$				0.81583	5	15.1969
l $L_{III} M_I$	1.38477	3	8.9532	1.34990	7	9.1845
α_2 $L_{III} M_{IV}$	1.21875	3	10.1728	1.18648	5	10.4495
α_1 $L_{III} M_V$	1.20739	4	10.2685	1.17501	2	10.5515
β_6 $L_{III} N_I$	1.04963	5	11.8118	1.0210	1	12.143
β_{15} $L_{III} N_{IV}$	1.01201	3	12.2510	0.98389	7	12.6011
β_2 $L_{III} N_V$	1.01031	3	12.2715	0.98221	7	12.6226
β_7 $L_{III} O_I$	0.99017	5	12.5212	0.9620	1	12.888
β_5 $L_{III} O_{IV,V}$	0.98058	3	12.6436	0.9526	1	13.015
$L_1 M_I$	1.0644	2	11.648	1.0323	2	12.010
β_{10} $L_1 M_{IV}$	0.96389	7	12.8626	0.9339	2	13.275
β_9 $L_1 M_V$	0.95675	7	12.9585	0.9268	1	13.377
$L_1 N_I$	0.8549	1	14.503	0.82859	7	14.963
$L_1 N_{IV}$	0.83001	7	14.937	0.80364	7	15.427
γ_{11} $L_1 N_V$	0.82879	5	14.9593	0.80233	9	15.453
$L_1 N_{VI,VII}$				0.7884	1	15.725
$L_1 O_I$	0.8158	1	15.198	0.7897	1	15.699
$L_1 O_{IV,V}$	0.80861	5	15.3327	0.78257	7	15.843
$L_{II} M_{II}$	1.0997	1	11.274	1.0644	2	11.648
β_{17} $L_{II} M_{III}$	1.05609	7	11.7397	1.0223	1	12.127
$L_{II} M_V$	1.00722	5	12.3093	0.9747	1	12.720
$L_{II} N_{II}$	0.882	2	14.057	0.8585	3	14.442

Desig-nation	Å*	p.e.	keV	Å*	p.e.	keV
	81 Thallium (*Cont.*)			**82 Lead** (*Cont.*)		
$L_{II} N_{III}$	0.87996	5	14.0893	0.85192	7	14.553
$L_{II} N_V$				0.8382	2	14.791
v $L_{II} N_{VI}$	0.85048	5	14.5777	0.82327	7	15.060
$L_{II} O_{II}$	0.8490	1	14.604			
$L_{II} O_{III}$				0.8200	1	15.120
t $L_{III} M_{II}$	1.34154	5	9.2417	1.30767	7	9.4811
s $L_{III} M_{III}$	1.27807	5	9.7007	1.24385	7	9.9675
$L_{III} N_{II}$				1.01040	7	12.2705
$L_{III} N_{III}$	1.0286	1	12.053	1.0005	1	12.392
u $L_{III} N_{VI,VII}$	0.9888	1	12.538	0.96133	7	12.8968
$L_{III} O_{II}$	0.98738	5	12.5566	0.9586	1	12.934
$L_{III} O_{III}$	0.98538	5	12.5820	0.9578	1	12.945
$L_{III} P_{II,III}$	0.97926	5	12.6607	0.95118	7	13.0344
$M_I N_{III}$	4.013	9	3.089	3.872	9	3.202
$M_{II} N_I$				4.655	8	2.664
$M_{II} N_{IV}$	4.116	4	3.013	3.968	5	3.124
$M_{III} N_I$	5.884	8	2.107	5.704	8	2.174
$M_{III} N_{IV}$	4.865	5	2.548	4.715	3	2.630
γ $M_{III} N_V$	4.823	4	2.571	4.674	1	2.6527
$M_{III} O_I$				4.244	9	2.921
$M_{II} O_{IV,V}$	4.216	6	2.941	4.069	6	3.047
ζ_2 $M_{IV} N_{II}$	7.032	5	1.763	6.802	5	1.823
$M_{IV} N_{III}$				6.384	7	1.942
β $M_{IV} N_{VI}$	5.249	1	2.3621	5.076	1	2.4427
$M_{IV} O_{II}$	5.196	9	2.386	5.004	9	2.477
ζ_1 $M_V N_{III}$	6.974	4	1.778	6.740	3	1.8395
α_2 $M_V N_{VI}$	5.472	2	2.2656	5.299	2	2.3397
α_1 $M_V N_{VII}$	5.460	1	2.2706	5.286	1	2.3455
$M_V O_{III}$				5.168	9	2.399
$N_{IV} N_{VI}$				42.3	2	0.293
$N_V N_{VI,VII}$	46.5	2	0.267	45.0	1	0.2756
$N_{VI} O_{IV}$	115.3	2	0.1075	102.4	1	0.1211
$N_{VI} O_V$	113.0	1	0.10968	100.2	2	0.1237
$N_{VII} O_V$	117.7	1	0.10530	104.3	1	0.1189
	83 Bismuth			**84 Polonium**		
α_2 $K L_{II}$	0.165717	2	74.8148	0.16130†	1	76.862
α_1 $K L_{III}$	0.160789	2	77.1079	0.15636†	1	79.290
β_3 $K M_{II}$	0.142779	7	86.834	0.13892†	2	89.25
β_1 $K M_{III}$	0.141948	3	87.343	0.13807†	2	89.80
β_2^{II} $K N_{II}$	0.13817	1	89.733	0.13438†	2	92.26
β_2^{I} $K N_{III}$	0.13797	1	89.864	0.13418†	2	92.40
$K O_{II,III}$	0.13709	1	90.435			
β_5 $K M_{IV,V}$	0.14111	1	87.860			
β_4 $K N_{IV,V}$	0.13759	2	90.11			
β_4 $L_1 M_{II}$	0.97690	4	12.6912	0.9475	3	13.086
β_3 $L_1 M_{III}$	0.93855	3	13.2098	0.9091	3	13.638
γ_2 $L_1 N_{II}$	0.79565	3	15.5824	0.772	1	16.07
γ_3 $L_1 N_{III}$	0.78917	5	15.7102			
γ'_4 $L_1 O_{II}$	0.76198	3	16.2709			
γ_4 $L_1 O_{III}$	0.76087	3	16.2947			
γ_{13} $L_1 P_{II,III}$	0.75690	3	16.3802			
η $L_{II} M_I$	1.05856	3	11.7122			
β_1 $L_{II} M_{IV}$	0.951978	9	13.0235	0.9220	2	13.447
γ_5 $L_{II} N_I$	0.83923	5	14.7732			

Desig-nation	Å*	p.e.	keV	Å*	p.e.	keV
83 Bismuth (*Cont.*)				**84 Polonium** (*Cont.*)		
$\gamma_1\ L_{II}N_{IV}$	0.81311	2	15.2477	0.78748	9	15.744
$\gamma_8\ L_{II}O_I$	0.7973	1	15.551			
$\gamma_6\ L_{II}O_{IV}$	0.79043	3	15.6853	0.7645	2	16.218
$l\ L_{III}M_I$	1.31610	7	9.4204	1.2829	5	9.664
$\alpha_2\ L_{III}M_{IV}$	1.15536	1	10.73091	1.12548†	5	11.0158
$\alpha_1\ L_{III}M_V$	1.14386	2	10.8388	1.11386	4	11.1308
$\beta_6\ L_{III}N_I$	0.99331	3	12.4816	0.9672	2	12.819
$\beta_{15}\ L_{III}N_{IV}$	0.95702	5	12.9549	0.9312	2	13.314
$\beta_2\ L_{III}N_V$	0.95518	4	12.9799	0.92937	5	13.3404
$\beta_7\ L_{III}O_I$	0.93505	5	13.2593			
$\beta_5\ L_{III}O_{IV,V}$	0.92556	3	13.3953	0.8996	2	13.782
L_1M_I	1.0005	9	12.39			
$\beta_{10}\ L_1M_{IV}$	0.90495	4	13.7002			
$\beta_9\ L_1M_V$	0.89791	3	13.8077			
L_1N_I	0.8022	1	15.456			
L_1N_{IV}	0.7795	5	15.904			
$\gamma_{11}\ L_1N_V$	0.77728	5	15.951			
$L_1N_{VI,VII}$	0.7641	5	16.23			
$L_1O_{IV,V}$	0.75791	5	16.358			
$L_{II}M_{II}$	1.0346	9	11.98			
$\beta_{17}\ L_{II}M_{III}$	0.98913	5	12.5344			
$L_{II}M_V$	0.94419	5	13.1310			
$L_{II}N_{II}$	0.8344	9	14.86			
$L_{II}N_{III}$	0.8248	1	15.031			
$v\ L_{II}N_{VI}$	0.79721	9	15.552			
$L_{II}O_{III}$	0.79384	5	15.6178			
$t\ L_{III}M_{II}$	1.2748	1	9.7252			
$s\ L_{III}M_{III}$	1.2105	1	10.2421			
$L_{III}N_{II}$	0.98280	5	12.6151			
$L_{III}N_{III}$	0.97321	5	12.7394			
$u\ L_{III}N_{VI,VII}$	0.93505	5	13.2593			
$L_{III}O_{II}$	0.9323	2	13.298			
$L_{III}O_{III}$	0.9302	2	13.328			
$L_{III}P_{II,III}$	0.92413	4	13.4159			
M_1N_{II}	3.892	9	3.185			
M_1N_{III}	3.740	9	3.315			
$M_{II}N_{IV}$	3.834	4	3.234			
$M_{III}N_I$	5.537	8	2.239			
$M_{III}N_{IV}$	4.571	5	2.712			
$\gamma\ M_{III}N_V$	4.532	2	2.735			
$M_{III}O_I$	4.105	9	3.021			
$M_{III}O_{IV,V}$	3.932	6	3.153			
$\zeta_2\ M_{IV}N_{II}$	6.585	1	1.883			
$M_{IV}N_{III}$	6.162	8	2.012			
$\beta\ M_{IV}N_{VI}$	4.909	1	2.5255			
$M_{IV}O_{II}$	4.823	3	2.571			
$M_{IV}P_{II,III}$	4.59	2	2.70			
$\zeta_1\ M_VN_{III}$	6.521	4	1.901			
$\alpha_2\ M_VN_{VI}$	5.130	2	2.4170			
$\alpha_1\ M_VN_{VII}$	5.118	1	2.4226			
$N_1P_{II,III}$	13.30	6	0.932			
$N_{VI}O_{IV}$	91.6	1	0.1354			
$N_{VII}O_V$	93.2	1	0.1330			

Desig-nation	Å*	p.e.	keV	Å*	p.e.	keV
	85 Astatine			**86 Radon**		
$\alpha_2\ KL_{II}$	0.15705†	2	78.95	0.15294†	3	81.07
$\alpha_1\ KL_{III}$	0.15210	2	81.52	0.14798†	3	83.78
$\beta_3\ KM_{II}$	0.13517†	4	91.72	0.13155†	5	94.24
$\beta_1\ KM_{III}$	0.13432†	4	92.30	0.13069†	5	94.87
$\beta_2^{II}\ KN_{II}$	0.13072†	4	94.84	0.12719†	5	97.47
$\beta_2^{I}\ KN_{III}$	0.13052†	4	94.99	0.12698†	5	97.64
$\beta_3\ L_1M_{III}$	0.88135†	9	14.067	0.85436†	9	14.512
$\beta_1\ L_{II}M_{IV}$	0.89349†	9	13.876	0.86605†	9	14.316
$\gamma_1\ L_{II}N_{IV}$	0.76289†	9	16.251	0.73928†	9	16.770
$\alpha_2\ L_{III}M_{IV}$	1.09671†	5	11.3048	1.06899†	5	11.5979
$\alpha_1\ L_{III}M_V$	1.08500†	5	11.4268	1.05723†	5	11.7270
	87 Francium			**88 Radium**		
$\alpha_2\ KL_{II}$	0.14896†	3	83.23	0.14512†	2	85.43
$\alpha_1\ KL_{III}$	0.14399†	3	86.10	0.14014†	2	88.47
$\beta_3\ KM_{II}$	0.12807†	5	96.81	0.12469†	3	99.43
$\beta_1\ KM_{III}$	0.12719†	5	97.47	0.12382†	3	100.13
$\beta_2^{II}\ KN_{II}$	0.12379†	5	100.16	0.12050†	3	102.89
$\beta_2^{I}\ KN_{III}$	0.12358†	5	100.33	0.12029†	3	103.07
$\beta_4\ L_1M_{II}$				0.84071	5	14.7472
$\beta_3\ L_1M_{III}$	0.82789†	9	14.976	0.80273	5	15.4449
$\gamma_2\ L_1N_{II}$				0.68199	5	18.179
$\gamma_3\ L_1N_{III}$				0.67538	5	18.357
$\gamma'_4\ L_1O_{II}$				0.65131	5	19.036
$\gamma_4\ L_1O_{III}$				0.64965	5	19.084
$\gamma_{13}\ L_1P_{II,III}$				0.64513	5	19.218
$\eta\ L_{II}M_I$				0.90742	5	13.6630
$\beta_1\ L_{II}M_{IV}$	0.83940†	9	14.770	0.81375	5	15.2358
$\gamma_5\ L_{II}N_I$				0.71774	5	17.274
$\gamma_1\ L_{II}N_{IV}$	0.71652†	9	17.303	0.69463	5	17.849
γ_8				0.6801	1	18.230
$\gamma_6\ L_{II}O_{IV}$				0.67328	5	18.414
$L_{II}P_I$				0.6724	1	18.439
$l\ L_{III}M_I$				1.16719	5	10.6222
$\alpha_2\ L_{III}M_{IV}$	1.04230	5	11.8950	1.01656	5	12.1962
$\alpha_1\ L_{III}M_V$	1.03049	5	12.0313	1.00473	5	12.3397
$\beta_6\ L_{III}N_I$				0.87088	5	14.2362
$\beta_{15}\ L_{III}N_{IV}$				0.83722	5	14.8086
$\beta_2\ L_{III}N_V$	0.858	2	14.45	0.83537	5	14.8414
$\beta_7\ L_{III}O_I$				0.8162	1	15.190
$\beta_5\ L_{III}O_{IV,V}$				0.80627	5	15.3771
$L_{III}P_I$				0.8050	1	15.402
$\beta_{10}\ L_1M_{IV}$				0.77546	5	15.988
$\beta_9\ L_1M_V$				0.76857	5	16.131
L_1N_I				0.6874	1	18.036
L_1N_{IV}				0.6666	1	18.600
$\gamma_{11}\ L_1N_V$				0.6654	1	18.633
$L_1O_{IV,V}$				0.6468	1	19.167
$\beta_{17}\ L_{II}M_{III}$				0.8438	1	14.692
$L_{II}N_{III}$				0.7043	1	17.604
$L_{II}N_V$				0.6884	1	17.884
$L_{II}O_{II}$				0.6780	1	18.286

87 Francium (Cont.) / 88 Radium (Cont.)

Designation	87 Francium Å*	p.e.	keV	88 Radium Å*	p.e.	keV
$L_{II}O_{III}$				0.6764	1	18.330
$L_{II}P_{II,III}$				0.6714	1	18.466
$L_{III}N_{II}$				0.8618	1	14.387
$L_{III}N_{III}$				0.8512	1	14.566
$u\ L_{III}N_{VI,VII}$				0.8186	1	15.146
$L_{III}P_{II,III}$				0.8038	1	15.425

89 Actinium / 90 Thorium

Designation	89 Actinium Å*	p.e.	keV	90 Thorium Å*	p.e.	keV
$\alpha_2\ KL_{II}$	0.14141†	2	87.67	0.137829	2	89.953
$\alpha_1\ KL_{III}$	0.136417†	8	90.884	0.132813	2	93.350
$\beta_3\ KM_{II}$	0.12143†	2	102.10	0.118268	3	104.831
$\beta_1\ KM_{III}$	0.12055†	2	102.85	0.117396	9	105.609
$\beta_2^{II}\ KN_{II}$	0.11732†	2	105.67	0.11426	1	108.511
$\beta_2^{I}\ KN_{III}$	0.11711†	2	105.86	0.114040	9	108.717
$KO_{II,III}$				0.11322	1	109.500
$\beta_5\ KM_{IV,V}$				0.116667	9	106.269
$\beta_4\ KN_{IV,V}$				0.11366	2	109.08
$\beta_4\ L_I M_{II}$				0.79257	4	15.6429
$\beta_3\ L_I M_{III}$	0.77822†	9	15.931	0.75479	3	16.4258
$\gamma_2\ L_I N_{II}$				0.64221	4	19.305
$\gamma_3\ L_I N_{III}$				0.63559	4	19.507
$\gamma'_4\ L_I O_{II}$				0.61251	4	20.242
$\gamma_4\ L_I O_{III}$				0.61098	4	20.292
$\gamma_{13}\ L_I P_{II,III}$				0.60705	8	20.424
$\eta\ L_{II}M_I$				0.85446	4	14.5099
$\beta_1\ L_{II}M_{IV}$	0.78903†	9	15.713	0.765210	9	16.2022
$\gamma_5\ L_{II}N_I$				0.67491	4	18.370
$\gamma_1\ L_{II}N_{IV}$	0.67351†	9	18.408	0.65313	3	18.9825
$\gamma_8\ L_{II}O_I$				0.63898	5	19.403
$\gamma_6\ L_{II}O_{IV}$				0.63258	4	19.599
$L_{II}P_I$				0.6316	1	19.629
$L_{II}P_{IV}$				0.62991	9	19.682
$l\ L_{III}M_I$				1.11508	4	11.1186
$\alpha_2\ L_{III}M_{IV}$	0.99178†	5	12.5008	0.96788	2	12.8096
$\alpha_1\ L_{III}M_V$	0.97993†	5	12.6520	0.95600	3	12.9687
$\beta_6\ L_{III}N_I$				0.82790	8	14.975
$\beta_{15}\ L_{III}N_{IV}$				0.79539	5	15.5875
$\beta_2\ L_{III}N_V$				0.79354	3	15.6237
$\beta_7\ L_{III}O_I$				0.77437	4	16.0105
$\beta_5\ L_{III}O_{IV,V}$				0.76468	5	16.213
$L_{III}P_I$				0.76338	5	16.241
$L_{III}P_{IV,V}$				0.76087	9	16.295
$\beta_{10}\ L_I M_{IV}$				0.7301	1	16.981
$\beta_9\ L_I M_V$				0.7234	1	17.139
$L_I N_I$				0.64755	5	19.146
$L_I N_{IV}$				0.6276	1	19.755
$\gamma_{11}\ L_I N_V$				0.62636	9	19.794
$L_I N_{VI,VII}$				0.6160	1	20.128
$L_I O_I$				0.6146	1	20.174
$L_I O_{IV,V}$				0.6083	1	20.383
$L_{II}M_{II}$				0.8338	1	14.869
$\beta_{17}\ L_{II}M_{III}$				0.79257	4	15.6429
$L_{II}M_V$				0.7579	1	16.359
$L_{II}N_{III}$				0.6620	1	18.729
$L_{II}N_V$				0.6521	1	19.014

89 Actinium (Cont.) / 90 Thorium (Cont.)

Designation	89 Actinium Å*	p.e.	keV	90 Thorium Å*	p.e.	keV
$v\ L_{II}N_{VI}$				0.64064	9	19.353
$L_{II}O_{II}$				0.6369	1	19.466
$L_{II}O_{III}$				0.6356	1	19.506
$L_{II}P_{II,III}$				0.6312	1	19.642
$t\ L_{III}M_I$				1.08009	9	11.4788
$s\ L_{III}M_{II}$				1.0112	1	12.261
$L_{III}N_{II}$				0.8190	2	15.138
$L_{III}N_{III}$				0.8082	1	15.341
$u\ L_{III}N_{VI,VII}$				0.77661	5	15.964
$L_{III}O_{II}$				0.7713	1	16.074
$L_{III}O_{III}$				0.7690	1	16.123
$L_{III}P_{II,III}$				0.7625	2	16.260
$M_I N_{III}$				2.934	8	4.23
$M_I O_{III}$				2.442	9	5.08
$M_{II}N_I$				3.537	9	3.505
$M_{II}N_{IV}$				3.011	2	4.117
$M_{II}O_{IV}$				2.618	5	4.735
$M_{III}N_I$				4.568	5	2.714
$M_{III}N_{IV}$				3.718	3	3.335
$\gamma\ M_{II}N_V$				3.679	2	3.370
$M_{III}O_I$				3.283	9	3.78
$M_{III}O_{IV,V}$				3.131	3	3.959
$\zeta_2\ M_V N_{II}$				5.340	5	2.322
$M_{IV}N_{III}$				4.911	5	2.524
$\beta\ M_{IV}N_{VI}$				3.941	1	3.1458
$M_{IV}O_{II}$				3.808	4	3.256
$\zeta_1\ M_V N_{III}$				5.245	5	2.364
$\alpha_2\ M_V N_{VI}$				4.151	2	2.987
$\alpha_1\ M_V N_{VII}$				4.1381	9	2.9961
$M_V P_{III}$				3.760	9	3.298
$N\ P_{II}$				9.44	7	1.313
$N\ P_{III}$				9.40	7	1.1319
$N_{II}O_{IV}$				11.56	5	1.072
$N_I P_I$				11.07	7	1.120
$N_{III}O_V$				13.8	1	0.897
$N_{IV}N_{VI}$				33.57	9	0.3693
$N_V N_{VI,VII}$				36.32	9	0.3414
$N_{VI}O_{IV}$				49.5	1	0.2505
$N_{VII}O_V$				48.2	1	0.2572
$N_{VII}O_V$				50.0	1	0.2479
$O_{III}P_{IV,V}$				68.2	3	0.1817
$O_{IV,V}Q_{II,III}$				181.	5	0.068

91 Protactinium / 92 Uranium

Designation	91 Protactinium Å*	p.e.	keV	92 Uranium Å*	p.e.	keV
$\alpha_2\ KL_{II}$	0.134343†	9	92.287	0.130968	4	94.665
$\alpha_1\ KL_{III}$	0.129325†	3	95.868	0.125947	3	98.439
$\beta_3\ KM_{II}$	0.11523†	2	107.60	0.112296	4	110.406
$\beta_1\ KM_{III}$	0.114345†	8	108.427	0.111394	5	111.300
$\beta_2^{II}\ KN_{II}$	0.11129†	2	111.40	0.10837	1	114.40
$\beta_2^{I}\ KN_{III}$	0.11107†	2	111.62	0.10818	1	114.60
$KO_{II,III}$				0.10744	1	115.39
$\beta_5\ KM_{IV,V}$				0.11069	1	112.01
$\beta_4\ KN_{IV,V}$				0.10780	2	115.01
$\beta_4\ L_I M_I$	0.7699	1	16.104	0.747985	9	16.5753
$\beta_3\ L_I M_{III}$	0.73230	5	16.930	0.71029	2	17.4550

91 Protactinium (*Cont.*) / 92 Uranium (*Cont.*)

Designation	Å*	p.e.	keV	Å*	p.e.	keV
$\gamma_2\ L_I N_{II}$	0.6239	1	19.872	0.605237	9	20.4847
$\gamma_3\ L_I N_{III}$	0.6169	1	20.098	0.598574	9	20.7127
$\gamma'_4\ L_I O_{II}$				0.576700	9	21.4984
$\gamma_4\ L_I O_{II,III}$	0.5937	1	20.882	0.57499	9	21.562
γ_8				0.5706	1	21.729
$\eta\ L_{II} M_I$	0.8295	1	14.946	0.80509	2	15.3997
$\beta_1\ L_{II} M_{IV}$	0.74232	5	16.702	0.719984	8	17.2200
$\gamma_5\ L_{II} N_I$	0.6550	1	18.930	0.63557	2	19.5072
$\gamma_1\ L_{II} N_{IV}$	0.63358†	9	19.568	0.614770	9	20.1671
$\gamma_8\ L_{II} O_I$				0.60125	5	20.621
$\gamma_6\ L_{II} O_{IV}$	0.6133	1	20.216	0.594845	9	20.8426
$L_{II} P_{IV}$				0.59203	5	20.942
$l\ L_{III} M_I$	1.0908	1	11.366	1.06712	2	11.6183
$\alpha_2\ L_{III} M_{IV}$	0.94482†	5	13.1222	0.922558	9	13.4388
$\alpha_1\ L_{III} M_V$	0.93284	5	13.2907	0.910639	9	13.6147
$\beta_6\ L_{III} N_I$	0.8079	1	15.347	0.78838	2	15.7260
$\beta_{15}\ L_{III} N_{IV}$				0.756642	9	16.3857
$\beta_2\ L_{III} N_V$	0.7737	1	16.024	0.754681	9	16.4283
$\beta_7\ L_{III} O_I$	0.7546	2	16.431	0.73602	6	16.845
$\beta_5\ L_{III} O_{IV,V}$	0.7452	2	16.636	0.726305	9	17.0701
$L_{III} P_I$				0.72521	5	17.096
$L_{III} P_{IV,V}$				0.72240	5	17.162
$\beta_{10}\ L_I M_V$	0.7088	2	17.492	0.68760	5	18.031
$\beta_9\ L_I M_V$	0.7018	1	17.667	0.681014	8	18.2054
$L_I N_{IV}$				0.59096	5	20.979
$\gamma_{11}\ L_I N_V$				0.58986	5	21.019
$L_I O_{IV,V}$				0.5725	1	21.657
$\beta_{17}\ L_{II} M_{III}$				0.74503	5	16.641
$L_{II} N_{III}$				0.6228	1	19.907
$v\ L_{II} N_{VI}$				0.6031	1	20.556
$L_{III} O_{III}$				0.59728	5	20.758
$L_{II} P_{II,III}$				0.5930	2	20.906
$t\ L_{III} M_{II}$				1.0347	1	11.982
$s\ L_{III} M_{III}$				0.9636	1	12.866
$L_{III} N_{II}$				0.78017	9	15.892
$L_{III} N_{III}$				0.7691	1	16.120
$u\ L_{III} N_{VI,VII}$				0.738603	9	16.7859
$L_{III} O_{II}$				0.7333	1	16.907
$L_{III} O_{III}$				0.7309	1	16.962
$L_{III} P_{II,III}$				0.72426	5	17.118
$M_I N_{II}$				2.92	2	4.25
$M_I N_{III}$				2.753	8	4.50
$M_I O_{III}$				2.304	7	5.38
$M_I P_{III}$				2.253	6	5.50
$M_{II} N_I$	3.441	5	3.603	3.329	4	3.724
$M_{II} N_{IV}$	2.910	2	4.260	2.817	2	4.401
$M_{II} O_{IV}$	2.527	4	4.906	2.443	4	5.075
$M_{III} N_I$	4.450	4	2.786	4.330	2	2.863
$M_{III} N_{IV}$	3.614	2	3.430	3.521	2	3.521
$\gamma\ M_{III} N_V$	3.577	1	3.4657	3.479	1	3.563
$M_{III} O_I$	3.245	9	3.82	3.115	7	3.980
$M_{III} O_{IV,V}$	3.038	2	4.081	2.948	2	4.205
$\zeta_2\ M_{IV} N_{II}$	5.193	2	2.3876	5.050	2	2.4548
$M_{IV} N_{III}$				4.625	5	2.681
$\beta\ M_{IV} N_{VI}$	3.827	1	3.2397	3.716	1	3.3367

91 Protactinium (*Cont.*) / 92 Uranium (*Cont.*)

Designation	Å*	p.e.	keV	Å*	p.e.	keV
$M_{IV} O_{II}$	3.691	2	3.359	3.576	1	3.4666
$\zeta_1\ M_V N_{III}$	5.092	2	2.4350	4.946	2	2.507
$\alpha_2\ M_V N_{VI}$	4.035	3	3.072	3.924	1	3.1595
$\alpha_1\ M_V N_{VII}$	4.022	1	3.0823	3.910	1	3.1708
$N_I O_{III}$				10.09	7	1.229
$N_I P_{II}$				8.81	7	1.41
$N_I P_{III}$				8.76	7	1.42
$N_{II} P_I$				10.40	7	1.192
$N_{III} O_V$				12.90	9	0.961
$N_{IV} N_{VI}$				31.8	1	0.390
$N_V N_{VI,VII}$				34.8	1	0.357
$N_{IV} O_{IV}$				43.3	2	0.286
$N_{VI} O_V$				42.1	2	0.295
$N_I P_{IV,V}$				8.60	7	1.44

93 Neptunium / 94 Plutonium

Designation	Å*	p.e.	keV	Å*	p.e.	keV
$\beta_4\ L_I M_{II}$	0.72671	2	17.0607	0.70620	2	17.5560
$\beta_3\ L_I M_{III}$	0.68920†	9	17.989	0.66871	2	18.5405
$\gamma_2\ L_I N_{II}$	0.5873	5	21.11	0.57068	2	21.7251
$\gamma_3\ L_I N_{III}$	0.5810	5	21.34	0.564001	9	21.9824
$\gamma'_4\ L_I O_{II}$				0.5432	1	22.823
$\gamma_4\ L_I O_{II,III}$	0.5585	5	22.20	0.5416	1	22.891
$\eta\ L_{II} M_I$	0.7809	2	15.876	0.7591	1	16.333
$\beta_1\ L_{II} M_{IV}$	0.698478	9	17.7502	0.67772	2	18.2937
$\gamma_5\ L_{II} N_I$	0.616	1	20.12	0.5988	1	20.704
$\gamma_1\ L_{II} N_{IV}$	0.596498	9	20.7848	0.578882	9	21.4173
γ_8				0.5658	1	21.914
$\gamma_6\ L_{II} O_{IV}$	0.57699	5	21.488	0.55973	2	22.1502
$l\ L_{III} M_I$	1.0428	6	11.890	1.0226	1	12.124
$\alpha_2\ L_{III} M_{IV}$	0.901045	9	13.7597	0.88028	2	14.0842
$\alpha_1\ L_{III} M_V$	0.889128	9	13.9441	0.86830	2	14.2786
$\beta_6\ L_{III} N_I$	0.769	1	16.13	0.75148	2	16.4983
$\beta_{15}\ L_{III} N_{IV}$				0.7205	1	17.208
$\beta_2\ L_{III} N_V$	0.736230	9	16.8400	0.71851	2	17.2553
$\beta_7\ L_{III} O_I$				0.7003	1	17.705
$\beta_5\ L_{III} O_{IV,V}$	0.70814	2	17.5081	0.69068	2	17.9506
$\beta_{10}\ L_I M_{IV}$				0.6482	1	19.126
$\beta_9\ L_I M_V$				0.6416	1	19.323
$u\ L_{III} N_{VI,VII}$				0.7031	1	17.635

95 Americium

Designation	Å*	p.e.	keV
$\beta_4\ L_I M_{II}$	0.68639	2	18.0627
$\beta_3\ L_I M_{III}$	0.64891	2	19.1059
$\gamma_2\ L_I N_{II}$	0.5544	2	22.361
$\beta_1\ L_{II} M_{IV}$	0.657655	9	18.8520
$\gamma_1\ L_{II} N_{IV}$	0.561886	9	22.0652
$\gamma_6\ L_{II} O_{IV}$	0.54311	2	22.8282
$l\ L_{III} M_I$	1.0012	6	12.384
$\alpha_2\ L_{III} M_{IV}$	0.860266	9	14.4119
$\alpha_1\ L_{III} M_V$	0.848187	9	14.6172
$\beta_6\ L_{III} N_I$	0.73418	2	16.8870
$\beta_{15}\ L_{III} N_{IV}$	0.70341	2	17.6258
$\beta_2\ L_{III} N_V$	0.701390	9	17.6765
$\beta_5\ L_{III} O_{IV,V}$	0.67383	2	18.3996

Wavelength Å*	p.e.	Element		Designation	keV
0.10723	1	92 U	K	Abs. Edge	115.62
0.10744	1	92 U		$KO_{II,III}$	115.39
0.10780	2	92 U	$K\beta_4$	$KN_{IV,V}$	115.01
0.10818	1	92 U	$K\beta_2^{I}$	KN_{III}	114.60
0.10837	1	92 U	$K\beta_2^{II}$	KN_{II}	114.40
0.11069	1	92 U	$K\beta_5$	$KM_{IV,V}$	112.01
0.11107	2	91 Pa	$K\beta_2^{I}$	KN_{III}	111.62
0.11129	2	91 Pa	$K\beta_2^{II}$	KN_{II}	111.40
0.111394	5	92 U	$K\beta_1$	KM_{III}	111.300
0.112296	4	92 U	$K\beta_3$	KM_{II}	110.406
0.11307	1	90 Th	K	Abs. Edge	109.646
0.11322	1	90 Th		$KO_{II,III}$	109.500
0.11366	2	90 Th	$K\beta_4$	$KN_{IV,V}$	109.08
0.114040	9	90 Th	$K\beta_2^{I}$	KN_{III}	108.717
0.11426	1	90 Th	$K\beta_2^{II}$	KN_{II}	108.511
0.114345	8	91 Pa	$K\beta_1$	KM_{III}	108.427
0.11523	2	91 Pa	$K\beta_3$	KM_{II}	107.60
0.116667	9	90 Th	$K\beta_5$	$KM_{IV,V}$	106.269
0.11711	2	89 Ac	$K\beta_2^{I}$	KN_{III}	105.86
0.11732	2	89 Ac	$K\beta_2^{II}$	KN_{II}	105.67
0.117396	9	90 Th	$K\beta_1$	KM_{III}	105.609
0.118268	3	90 Th	$K\beta_3$	KM_{II}	104.831
0.12029	3	88 Ra	$K\beta_2^{I}$	KN_{III}	103.07
0.12050	3	88 Ra	$K\beta_2^{II}$	KN_{II}	102.89
0.12055	2	89 Ac	$K\beta_1$	KM_{III}	102.85
0.12143	2	89 Ac	$K\beta_3$	KM_{II}	102.10
0.12358	5	87 Fr	$K\beta_2^{I}$	KN_{III}	100.33
0.12379	5	87 Fr	$K\beta_2^{II}$	KN_{II}	100.16
0.12382	3	88 Ra	$K\beta_1$	KM_{III}	100.13
0.12469	3	88 Ra	$K\beta_3$	KM_{II}	99.43
0.125947	3	92 U	$K\alpha_1$	KL_{III}	98.439
0.12698	5	86 Rn	$K\beta_2^{I}$	KN_{III}	97.64
0.12719	5	86 Rn	$K\beta_2^{II}$	KN_{II}	97.47
0.12719	5	87 Fr	$K\beta_1$	KM_{III}	97.47
0.12807	5	87 Fr	$K\beta_3$	KM_{II}	96.81
0.129325	3	91 Pa	$K\alpha_1$	KL_{III}	95.868
0.13052	4	85 At	$K\beta_2^{I}$	KN_{III}	94.99
0.13069	5	86 Rn	$K\beta_1$	KM_{III}	94.87
0.13072	4	85 At	$K\beta_2^{II}$	KN_{II}	94.84
0.130968	4	92 U	$K\alpha_2$	KL_{II}	94.665
0.13155	5	86 Rn	$K\beta_3$	KM_{II}	94.24
0.132813	2	90 Th	$K\alpha_1$	KL_{III}	93.350
0.13418	2	84 Po	$K\beta_2^{I}$	KN_{III}	92.40
0.13432	4	85 At	$K\beta_1$	KM_{III}	92.30
0.134343	9	91 Pa	$K\alpha_2$	KL_{II}	92.287
0.13438	2	84 Po	$K\beta_2^{II}$	KN_{II}	92.26
0.13517	4	85 At	$K\beta_3$	KM_{II}	91.72
0.136417	8	89 Ac	$K\alpha_1$	KL_{III}	90.884
0.13694	1	83 Bi	K	Abs. Edge	90.534
0.13709	1	83 Bi		$KO_{II,III}$	90.435
0.13759	2	83 Bi	$K\beta_4$	$KN_{IV,V}$	90.11
0.137829	2	90 Th	$K\alpha_2$	KL_{II}	89.953
0.13797	1	83 Bi	$K\beta_2^{I}$	KN_{III}	89.864
0.13807	2	84 Po	$K\beta_1$	KM_{III}	89.80
0.13817	1	83 Bi	$K\beta_2^{II}$	KN_{II}	89.733
0.13892	2	84 Po	$K\beta_3$	KM_{II}	89.25
0.14014	2	88 Ra	$K\alpha_1$	KL_{III}	88.47
0.1408	1	82 Pb		KP	88.06
0.140880	5	82 Pb	K	Abs. Edge	88.005
0.141012	8	82 Pb		$KO_{II,III}$	87.922
0.14111	1	83 Bi	$K\beta_5$	$KM_{IV,V}$	87.860
0.14141	2	89 Ac	$K\alpha_2$	KL_{II}	87.67
0.14155	3	82 Pb	$K\beta_4$	$KN_{IV,V}$	87.59
0.14191	1	82 Pb	$K\beta_2^{I}$	KN_{III}	87.364
0.141948	3	83 Bi	$K\beta_1$	KM_{III}	87.343
0.14212	2	82 Pb	$K\beta_2^{II}$	KN_{II}	87.23
0.142779	7	83 Bi	$K\beta_3$	KM_{II}	86.834
0.14399	3	87 Fr	$K\alpha_1$	KL_{III}	86.10
0.14495	1	81 Tl	K	Abs. Edge	85.533
0.14495	3	82 Pb	$K\beta_5^{I}$	KM_{V}	85.53
0.14509	1	81 Tl		$KO_{II,III}$	85.451
0.14512	2	82 Pb	$K\beta_5^{II}$	KM_{IV}	85.43
0.14512	2	88 Ra	$K\alpha_2$	KL_{II}	85.43
0.14553	2	81 Tl	$K\beta_4$	$KN_{IV,V}$	85.19
0.14595	1	81 Tl	$K\beta_2^{I}$	KN_{III}	84.946
0.145970	6	82 Pb	$K\beta_1$	KM_{III}	84.936
0.14614	1	81 Tl	$K\beta_2^{II}$	KN_{II}	84.836
0.146810	4	82 Pb	$K\beta_3$	KM_{II}	84.450
0.14798	3	86 Rn	$K\alpha_1$	KL_{III}	83.78
0.14896	3	87 Fr	$K\alpha_2$	KL_{II}	83.23
0.14917	1	81 Tl	$K\beta_5$	$KM_{IV,V}$	83.114
0.14918	1	80 Hg	K	Abs. Edge	83.109
0.14931	2	80 Hg		$KO_{II,III}$	83.04
0.14978	2	80 Hg	$K\beta_4$	$KN_{IV,V}$	82.78
0.150142	5	81 Tl	$K\beta_1$	KM_{III}	82.576
0.15020	2	80 Hg	$K\beta_2^{I}$	KN_{III}	82.54
0.15040	2	80 Hg	$K\beta_2^{II}$	KN_{II}	82.43
0.150980	6	81 Tl	$K\beta_3$	KM_{II}	82.118
0.15210	2	85 At	$K\alpha_1$	KL_{III}	81.52
0.15294	3	86 Rn	$K\alpha_2$	KL_{II}	81.07
0.15353	2	80 Hg	$K\beta_5$	$KM_{IV,V}$	80.75
0.153593	5	79 Au	K	Abs. Edge	80.720
0.153694	7	79 Au		$KO_{II,III}$	80.667
0.154224	5	79 Au	$K\beta_4$	$KN_{IV,V}$	80.391
0.154487	3	80 Hg	$K\beta_1$	KM_{III}	80.253
0.154618	9	79 Au	$K\beta_2^{I}$	KN_{III}	80.185
0.15483	2	79 Au	$K\beta_2^{II}$	KN_{II}	80.08
0.155321	3	80 Hg	$K\beta_3$	KM_{II}	79.822
0.15636	1	84 Po	$K\alpha_1$	KL_{III}	79.290
0.15705	2	85 At	$K\alpha_2$	KL_{II}	78.95
0.157880	5	79 Au	$K\beta_5^{I}$	KM_{V}	78.529
0.158062	7	79 Au	$K\beta_5^{II}$	KM_{IV}	78.438
0.15818	1	78 Pt	K	Abs. Edge	78.381
0.15826	1	78 Pt		$KO_{II,III}$	78.341
0.15881	2	78 Pt	$K\beta_4$	$KN_{IV,V}$	78.069
0.158982	3	79 Au	$K\beta_1$	KM_{III}	77.984
0.15920	1	78 Pt	$K\beta_2^{I}$	KN_{III}	77.878
0.15939	1	78 Pt	$K\beta_2^{II}$	KN_{II}	77.785
0.159810	2	79 Au	$K\beta_3$	KM_{II}	77.580
0.160789	2	83 Bi	$K\alpha_1$	KL_{III}	77.1079
0.16130	1	84 Po	$K\alpha_2$	KL_{II}	76.862
0.16255	3	78 Pt	$K\beta_5^{I}$	KM_{V}	76.27
0.16271	2	78 Pt	$K\beta_5^{II}$	KM_{IV}	76.199
0.16292	1	77 Ir	K	Abs. Edge	76.101

Wavelength Å*	p.e.	Element	Designation		keV	Wavelength Å*	p.e.	Element	Designation		keV
0.163019	5	77 Ir		$KO_{II,III}$	76.053	0.190381	4	78 Pt	$K\alpha_2$	KL_{II}	65.122
0.16352	2	77 Ir	$K\beta_4$	$KN_{IV,V}$	75.821	0.1908	2	72 Hf	$K\beta_2$	$KN_{II,III}$	64.98
0.163675	3	78 Pt	$K\beta_1$	KM_{III}	75.748	0.190890	2	73 Ta	$K\beta_3$	KM_{II}	64.9488
0.163956	7	77 Ir		KN_{III}	75.619	0.191047	2	77 Ir	$K\alpha_1$	KL_{III}	64.8956
0.16415	1	77 Ir	$K\beta_2{}^{II}$	KN_{II}	75.529	0.19585	5	71 Lu	K	Abs. Edge	63.31
0.164501	3	78 Pt	$K\beta_3$	KM_{II}	75.368	0.19589	2	71 Lu		$KO_{II,III}$	63.293
0.165376	2	82 Pb	$K\alpha_1$	KL_{III}	74.9694	0.195904	2	77 Ir	$K\alpha_2$	KL_{II}	63.2867
0.165717	2	83 Bi	$K\alpha_2$	KL_{II}	74.8148	0.19607	3	72 Hf	$K\beta_1$	KM_{III}	63.234
0.167373	9	77 Ir	$K\beta_5{}^I$	KM_V	74.075	0.196794	2	76 Os	$K\alpha_1$	KL_{III}	63.0005
0.16759	2	77 Ir	$K\beta_5{}^{II}$	KM_{IV}	73.980	0.19686	4	72 Hf	$K\beta_3$	KM_{II}	62.98
0.16787	1	76 Os	K	Abs. Edge	73.856	0.1969	2	71 Lu		$KN_{II,III}$	62.97
0.16798	1	76 Os		$KO_{II,III}$	73.808	0.20084	2	71 Lu	$K\beta_5$	$KM_{IV,V}$	61.732
0.16842	2	76 Os	$K\beta_4$	$KN_{IV,V}$	73.615	0.201639	2	76 Os	$K\alpha_2$	KL_{II}	61.4867
0.168542	2	77 Ir	$K\beta_1$	KM_{III}	73.5608	0.20224	5	70 Yb	K	Abs. Edge	61.30
0.168906	6	76 Os	$K\beta_2{}^I$	KN_{III}	73.402	0.20226	2	70 Yb		$KO_{II,III}$	61.298
0.16910	1	76 Os	$K\beta_2{}^{II}$	KN_{II}	73.318	0.20231	3	71 Lu	$K\beta_1$	KM_{III}	61.283
0.169367	2	77 Ir	$K\beta_3$	KM_{II}	73.2027	0.202781	2	75 Re	$K\alpha_1$	KL_{III}	61.1403
0.170136	2	81 Tl	$K\alpha_1$	KL_{III}	72.8715	0.20309	4	71 Lu	$K\beta_3$	KM_{II}	61.05
0.170294	2	82 Pb	$K\alpha_2$	KL_{II}	72.8042	0.2033	2	70 Yb		$KN_{II,III}$	60.89
0.17245	1	76 Os	$K\beta_5{}^I$	KM_V	71.895	0.20739	2	70 Yb	$K\beta_5$	$KM_{IV,V}$	59.782
0.17262	1	76 Os	$K\beta_5{}^{II}$	KM_{IV}	71.824	0.207611	1	75 Re	$K\alpha_2$	KL_{II}	59.7179
0.17302	1	75 Re	K	Abs. Edge	71.658	0.20880	5	69 Tm	K	Abs. Edge	59.38
0.17308	1	75 Re		$KO_{II,III}$	71.633	0.20884	8	70 Yb	$K\beta_1$	KM_{III}	59.37
0.173611	3	76 Os	$K\beta_1$	KM_{III}	71.413	0.20891	2	69 Tm		$KO_{II,III}$	59.346
0.17362	2	75 Re	$K\beta_4$	$KN_{IV,V}$	71.410	0.2090100	Std.	74 W	$K\alpha_1$	KL_{III}	59.31824
0.174054	6	75 Re	$K\beta_2{}^I$	KN_{III}	71.232	0.2096	1	70 Yb	$K\beta_3$	KM_{II}	59.14
0.17425	1	75 Re	$K\beta_2{}^{II}$	KN_{II}	71.151	0.2098	2	69 Tm	$K\alpha_2$	$KN_{II,III}$	59.09
0.174431	3	76 Os	$K\beta_3$	KM_{II}	71.077	0.213828	2	74 W	$K\alpha_2$	KL_{II}	57.9817
0.175036	2	81 Tl	$K\alpha_2$	KL_{II}	70.8319	0.21404	2	69 Tm	$K\beta_5$	$KM_{IV,V}$	57.923
0.175068	3	80 Hg	$K\alpha_1$	KL_{III}	70.819	0.215497	4	73 Ta	$K\alpha_1$	KL_{III}	57.532
0.17766	1	75 Re	$K\beta_5{}^I$	KM_V	69.786	0.21556	2	69 Tm	$K\beta_1$	KM_{III}	57.517
0.17783	1	75 Re	$K\beta_5{}^{II}$	KM_{IV}	69.719	0.21567	1	68 Er	K	Abs. Edge	57.487
0.17837	1	74 W	K	Abs. Edge	69.508	0.21581	3	68 Er		$KO_{II,III}$	57.450
0.178444	5	74 W		$KO_{II,III}$	69.479	0.21592	4	74 W		KL_I	57.42
0.178880	3	75 Re	$K\beta_1$	KM_{III}	69.310	0.21636	2	69 Tm	$K\beta_3$	KM_{II}	57.304
0.17892	2	74 W	$K\beta_4$	$KN_{IV,V}$	69.294	0.2167	2	68 Er	$K\beta_2$	$KN_{II,III}$	57.21
0.179421	7	74 W	$K\beta_2{}^I$	KN_{III}	69.101	0.220305	8	73 Ta	$K\alpha_2$	KL_{II}	56.277
0.17960	1	74 W	$K\beta_2{}^{II}$	KN_{II}	69.031	0.22124	3	68 Er	$K\beta_5$	$KM_{IV,V}$	56.040
0.179697	3	75 Re	$K\beta_3$	KM_{II}	68.994	0.222227	3	72 Hf	$K\alpha_1$	KL_{III}	55.7902
0.179958	3	80 Hg	$K\alpha_2$	KL_{II}	68.895	0.22266	2	68 Er	$K\beta_1$	KM_{III}	55.681
0.180195	2	79 Au	$K\alpha_1$	KL_{III}	68.8037	0.22291	1	67 Ho	K	Abs. Edge	55.619
0.183092	7	74 W	$K\beta_5{}^I$	KM_V	67.715	0.22305	3	67 Ho		$KO_{II,III}$	55.584
0.183264	5	74 W	$K\beta_5{}^{II}$	KM_{IV}	67.652	0.22341	2	68 Er	$K\beta_3$	KM_{II}	55.494
0.18394	1	73 Ta	K	Abs. Edge	67.403	0.2241	2	67 Ho	$K\beta_2$	$KN_{II,III}$	55.32
0.184031	7	73 Ta		$KO_{II,III}$	67.370	0.227024	3	72 Hf	$K\alpha_2$	KL_{II}	54.6114
0.184374	2	74 W	$K\beta_1$	KM_{III}	67.2443	0.22855	3	67 Ho	$K\beta_5$	$KM_{IV,V}$	54.246
0.18451	1	73 Ta	$K\beta_4$	$KN_{IV,V}$	67.194	0.229298	2	71 Lu	$K\alpha_1$	KL_{III}	54.0698
0.185011	8	73 Ta	$K\beta_2{}^I$	KN_{III}	67.013	0.23012	2	67 Ho	$K\beta_1$	KM_{III}	53.877
0.185075	2	79 Au	$K\alpha_2$	KL_{II}	66.9895	0.23048	1	66 Dy	K	Abs. Edge	53.793
0.185181	2	74 W	$K\beta_3$	KM_{II}	66.9514	0.23056	3	66 Dy		$KO_{II,III}$	53.774
0.185188	9	73 Ta	$K\beta_2{}^{II}$	KN_{II}	66.949	0.23083	2	67 Ho	$K\beta_3$	KM_{II}	53.711
0.185511	4	78 Pt	$K\alpha_1$	KL_{III}	66.832	0.2317	2	66 Dy	$K\beta_2$	$KN_{II,III}$	53.47
0.18672	4	79 Au		KL_I	66.40	0.234081	2	71 Lu	$K\alpha_2$	KL_{II}	52.9650
0.188757	6	73 Ta	$K\beta_5{}^I$	KM_V	65.683	0.23618	3	66 Dy	$K\beta_5$	$KM_{IV,V}$	52.494
0.188920	6	73 Ta	$K\beta_5{}^{II}$	KM_{IV}	65.626	0.236655	2	70 Yb	$K\alpha_1$	KL_{III}	52.3889
0.18982	5	72 Hf	K	Abs. Edge	65.31	0.23788	2	66 Dy	$K\beta_1$	KM_{III}	52.119
0.190089	4	73 Ta	$K\beta_1$	KM_{III}	65.223	0.23841	1	65 Tb	K	Abs. Edge	52.002

Wavelength Å*	p.e.	Element		Designation	keV	Wavelength Å*	p.e.	Element		Designation	keV
0.23858	3	65 Tb		$KO_{II,III}$	51.965	0.315816	2	58 Ce	$K\beta_1$	KM_{III}	39.2573
0.23862	2	66 Dy	$K\beta_3$	KM_{II}	51.957	0.316520	4	58 Ce	$K\beta_3$	KM_{II}	39.1701
0.2397	2	65 Tb	$K\beta_2$	$KN_{II,III}$	51.68	0.31844	5	57 La	K	Abs. Edge	38.934
0.241424	2	70 Yb	$K\alpha_2$	KL_{II}	51.3540	0.31864	2	57 La		$KO_{II,III}$	38.909
0.244338	2	69 Tm	$K\alpha_1$	KL_{III}	50.7416	0.31931	2	57 La	$K\beta_4{}^I$	$KN_{IV,V}$	38.828
0.24608	2	65 Tb	$K\beta_1$	KM_{III}	50.382	0.320117	7	57 La	$K\beta_2$	$KN_{II,III}$	38.7299
0.24681	1	64 Gd	K	Abs. Edge	50.233	0.320160	4	61 Pm	$K\alpha_1$	KL_{III}	38.7247
0.24683	2	65 Tb	$K\beta_3$	KM_{II}	50.229	0.324803	4	61 Pm	$K\alpha_2$	KL_{II}	38.1712
0.24687	3	64 Gd		$KO_{II,III}$	50.221	0.32546	2	57 La	$K\beta_5{}^I$	KM_V	38.094
0.24816	3	64 Gd	$K\beta_2$	$KN_{II,III}$	49.959	0.32563	2	57 La	$K\beta_5{}^{II}$	KM_{IV}	38.074
0.249095	2	69 Tm	$K\alpha_2$	KL_{II}	49.7726	0.327983	3	57 La	$K\beta_1$	KM_{III}	37.8010
0.252365	2	68 Er	$K\alpha_1$	KL_{III}	49.1277	0.328686	4	57 La	$K\beta_3$	KM_{II}	37.7202
0.25275	3	64 Gd	$K\beta_5$	$KM_{IV,V}$	49.052	0.33104	1	56 Ba	K	Abs. Edge	37.452
0.25460	2	64 Gd	$K\beta_1$	KM_{III}	48.697	0.33127	2	56 Ba		$KO_{II,III}$	37.426
0.25534	2	64 Gd	$K\beta_3$	KM_{II}	48.555	0.331846	2	60 Nd	$K\alpha_1$	KL_{III}	37.3610
0.25553	1	63 Eu	K	Abs. Edge	48.519	0.33229	2	56 Ba	$K\beta_4{}^{II}$	KN_{IV}	37.311
0.255645	7	63 Eu		$KO_{II,III}$	48.497	0.33277	1	56 Ba	$K\beta_2$	$KN_{II,III}$	37.257
0.256923	8	63 Eu	$K\beta_2{}^I$	$KN_{II,III}$	48.256	0.336472	2	60 Nd	$K\alpha_2$	KL_{II}	36.8474
0.257110	2	68 Er	$K\alpha_2$	KL_{II}	48.2211	0.33814	2	56 Ba	$K\beta_5{}^I$	KM_V	36.666
0.260756	2	67 Ho	$K\alpha_1$	KL_{III}	47.5467	0.33835	2	56 Ba	$K\beta_5{}^{II}$	KM_{IV}	36.643
0.263577	5	63 Eu	$K\beta_1$	KM_{III}	47.0379	0.340811	3	56 Ba	$K\beta_1$	KM_{III}	36.3782
0.264332	5	63 Eu	$K\beta_3$	KM_{II}	46.9036	0.341507	4	56 Ba	$K\beta_3$	KM_{II}	36.3040
0.26464	5	62 Sm	K	Abs. Edge	46.849	0.344140	2	59 Pr	$K\alpha_1$	KL_{III}	36.0263
0.26491	3	62 Sm		$KO_{II,III}$	46.801	0.34451	1	55 Cs	K	Abs. Edge	35.987
0.265486	2	67 Ho	$K\alpha_2$	KL_{II}	46.6997	0.34611	2	55 Cs	$K\beta_2$	$KN_{II,III}$	35.822
0.2662	1	62 Sm	$K\beta_2$	$KN_{II,III}$	46.57	0.348749	2	59 Pr	$K\alpha_2$	KL_{II}	35.5502
0.269533	2	66 Dy	$K\alpha_1$	KL_{III}	45.9984	0.354364	7	55 Cs	$K\beta_1$	KM_{III}	34.9869
0.27111	3	62 Sm	$K\beta_5$	$KM_{IV,V}$	45.731	0.355050	4	55 Cs	$K\beta_3$	KM_{II}	34.9194
0.27301	2	62 Sm	$K\beta_1$	KM_{III}	45.413	0.357092	2	58 Ce	$K\alpha_1$	KL_{III}	34.7197
0.27376	2	62 Sm	$K\beta_3$	KM_{II}	45.289	0.3584	5	54 Xe	K	Abs. Edge	34.59
0.274247	2	66 Dy	$K\alpha_2$	KL_{II}	45.2078	0.36026	3	54 Xe	$K\beta_2$	$KN_{II,III}$	34.415
0.27431	5	61 Pm	K	Abs. Edge	45.198	0.361683	2	58 Ce	$K\alpha_2$	KL_{II}	34.2789
0.2759	1	61 Pm	$K\beta_2$	$KN_{II,III}$	44.93	0.36872	2	54 Xe	$K\beta_1$	KM_{III}	33.624
0.278724	2	65 Tb	$K\alpha_1$	KL_{III}	44.4816	0.36941	2	54 Xe	$K\beta_3$	KM_{II}	33.562
0.28290	3	61 Pm	$K\beta_1$	KM_{III}	43.826	0.370737	2	57 La	$K\alpha_1$	KL_{III}	33.4418
0.283423	2	65 Tb	$K\alpha_2$	KL_{II}	43.7441	0.37381	1	53 I	K	Abs. Edge	33.1665
0.28363	4	61 Pm	$K\beta_3$	KM_{II}	43.713	0.37523	2	53 I	$K\beta_2$	$KN_{II,III}$	33.042
0.28453	5	60 Nd	K	Abs. Edge	43.574	0.375313	2	57 La	$K\alpha_2$	KL_{II}	33.0341
0.2861	1	60 Nd	$K\beta_2$	$KN_{II,III}$	43.32	0.383905	4	53 I	$K\beta_1$	KM_{III}	32.2947
0.288353	2	64 Gd	$K\alpha_1$	KL_{III}	42.9962	0.384564	4	53 I	$K\beta_3$	KM_{II}	32.2394
0.293038	2	64 Gd	$K\alpha_2$	KL_{II}	42.3089	0.385111	4	56 Ba	$K\alpha_1$	KL_{III}	32.1936
0.293299	2	60 Nd	$K\beta_1$	KM_{III}	42.2713	0.389668	5	56 Ba	$K\alpha_2$	KL_{II}	31.8171
0.294027	3	60 Nd	$K\beta_3$	KM_{II}	42.1665	0.38974	1	52 Te		$KO_{II,III}$	31.8114
0.29518	5	59 Pr	K	Abs. Edge	42.002	0.38974	1	52 Te	K	Abs. Edge	31.8114
0.29679	2	59 Pr	$K\beta_2$	$KN_{II,III}$	41.773	0.391102	6	52 Te	$K\beta_2$	$KN_{II,III}$	31.7004
0.298446	2	63 Eu	$K\alpha_1$	KL_{III}	41.5422	0.399995	5	52 Te	$K\beta_1$	KM_{III}	30.9957
0.303118	2	63 Eu	$K\alpha_2$	KL_{II}	40.9019	0.400290	4	55 Cs	$K\alpha_1$	KL_{III}	30.9728
0.304261	4	59 Pr	$K\beta_1$	KM_{III}	40.7482	0.400659	4	52 Te	$K\beta_3$	KM_{II}	30.9443
0.304975	5	59 Pr	$K\beta_3$	KM_{II}	40.6529	0.404835	4	55 Cs	$K\alpha_2$	KL_{II}	30.6251
0.30648	5	58 Ce	K	Abs. Edge	40.453	0.40666	1	51 Sb		$KO_{II,III}$	30.4875
0.30668	2	58 Ce		$KO_{II,III}$	40.427	0.40668	1	51 Sb	K	Abs. Edge	30.4860
0.30737	2	58 Ce	$K\beta_4{}^I$	$KN_{IV,V}$	40.337	0.40702	1	51 Sb	$K\beta_4{}^I$	$KN_{IV,V}$	30.4604
0.30816	1	58 Ce	$K\beta_2$	$KN_{II,III}$	40.233	0.407973	5	51 Sb	$K\beta_2$	$KN_{II,III}$	30.3895
0.309040	2	62 Sm	$K\alpha_1$	KL_{III}	40.1181	0.41378	1	51 Sb	$K\beta_5{}^I$	KM_V	29.9632
0.31342	2	58 Ce	$K\beta_5{}^I$	KM_V	39.558	0.41388	1	51 Sb	$K\beta_5{}^{II}$	KM_{IV}	29.9560
0.31357	2	58 Ce	$K\beta_5{}^{II}$	KM_{IV}	39.539	0.41634	2	54 Xe	$K\alpha_1$	KL_{III}	29.779
0.313698	2	62 Sm	$K\alpha_2$	KL_{II}	39.5224	0.417085	3	51 Sb	$K\beta_1$	KM_{III}	29.7256

Wavelength Å*	p.e.	Element	Designation		keV
0.417737	4	51 Sb	$K\beta_3$	KM_{II}	29.6792
0.42087	2	54 Xe	$K\alpha_2$	KL_{II}	29.458
0.42467	3	50 Sn		$KO_{II,III}$	29.195
0.42467	1	50 Sn	K	Abs. Edge	29.1947
0.42495	3	50 Sn	$K\beta_4{}^{I}$	$KN_{IV,V}$	29.175
0.425915	8	50 Sn	$K\beta_2{}^{I}$	$KN_{II,III}$	29.1093
0.43175	3	50 Sn	$K\beta_5{}^{I}$	KM_V	28.716
0.43184	3	50 Sn	$K\beta_5{}^{II}$	KM_{IV}	28.710
0.433318	5	53 I	$K\alpha_1$	KL_{III}	28.6120
0.435236	5	50 Sn	$K\beta_1$	KM_{III}	28.4860
0.435877	5	50 Sn	$K\beta_3$	KM_{II}	28.4440
0.437829	7	53 I	$K\alpha_2$	KL_{II}	28.3172
0.44371	1	49 In	K	Abs. Edge	27.9420
0.44374	3	49 In		$KO_{II,III}$	27.940
0.44393	4	49 In	$K\beta_4{}^{I}$	$KN_{IV,V}$	27.928
0.44500	1	49 In	$K\beta_2$	$KN_{II,III}$	27.8608
0.45086	2	49 In	$K\beta_5{}^{I}$	KM_V	27.499
0.45098	2	49 In	$K\beta_5{}^{II}$	KM_{IV}	27.491
0.451295	3	52 Te	$K\alpha_1$	KL_{III}	27.4723
0.454545	4	49 In	$K\beta_1$	KM_{III}	27.2759
0.455181	4	49 In	$K\beta_3$	KM_{II}	27.2377
0.455784	3	52 Te	$K\alpha_2$	KL_{II}	27.2017
0.46407	1	48 Cd	K	Abs. Edge	26.7159
0.465328	7	48 Cd	$K\beta_2$	$KN_{II,III}$	26.6438
0.470354	3	51 Sb	$K\alpha_1$	KL_{III}	26.3591
0.474827	3	51 Sb	$K\alpha_2$	KL_{II}	26.1108
0.475105	6	48 Cd	$K\beta_1$	KM_{III}	26.0955
0.475730	5	48 Cd	$K\beta_3$	KM_{II}	26.0612
0.48589	1	47 Ag	K	Abs. Edge	25.5165
0.4859	9	47 Ag	$K\beta_4$	$KN_{IV,V}$	25.512
0.487032	4	47 Ag	$K\beta_2$	$KN_{II,III}$	25.4564
0.490599	3	50 Sn	$K\alpha_1$	KL_{III}	25.2713
0.49306	2	47 Ag	$K\beta_5$	$KM_{IV,V}$	25.145
0.495053	3	50 Sn	$K\alpha_2$	KL_{II}	25.0440
0.497069	4	47 Ag	$K\beta_1$	KM_{III}	24.9424
0.497685	4	47 Ag	$K\beta_3$	KM_{II}	24.9115
0.5092	1	46 Pd	K	Abs. Edge	24.348
0.5093	2	46 Pd	$K\beta_4$	$KN_{IV,V}$	24.346
0.510228	4	46 Pd	$K\beta_2$	$KN_{II,III}$	24.2991
0.512113	3	49 In	$K\alpha_1$	KL_{III}	24.2097
0.516544	3	49 In	$K\alpha_2$	KL_{II}	24.0020
0.51670	9	46 Pd	$K\beta_5$	$KM_{IV,V}$	23.995
0.520520	4	46 Pd	$K\beta_1$	KM_{III}	23.8187
0.521123	4	46 Pd	$K\beta_3$	KM_{II}	23.7911
0.53395	1	45 Rh	K	Abs. Edge	23.2198
0.53401	9	45 Rh	$K\beta_4{}^{I}$	$KN_{IV,V}$	23.217
0.535010	3	48 Cd	$K\alpha_1$	KL_{III}	23.1736
0.53503	2	45 Rh	$K\beta_2$	$KN_{II,III}$	23.1728
0.53513	5	45 Rh	$K\beta_2{}^{II}$	KN_{II}	23.168
0.5365	1	94 Pu	L_I	Abs. Edge	23.109
0.539422	3	48 Cd	$K\alpha_2$	KL_{II}	22.9841
0.54101	9	45 Rh	$K\beta_5{}^{I}$	KM_V	22.917
0.54118	9	45 Rh	$K\beta_5{}^{II}$	KM_{IV}	22.909
0.5416	1	94 Pu	$L\gamma_4$	L_IO_{III}	22.891
0.54311	2	95 Am	$L\gamma_6$	$L_{II}O_{IV}$	22.8282
0.5432	1	94 Pu	$L\gamma_4'$	L_IO_{II}	22.823
0.545605	4	45 Rh	$K\beta_1$	KM_{III}	22.7236
0.546200	4	45 Rh	$K\beta_3$	KM_{II}	22.6989
0.5544	2	95 Am	$L\gamma_2$	L_IN_{II}	22.361
0.5572	1	94 Pu	L_{II}	Abs. Edge	22.253
0.5585	5	93 Np	$L\gamma_4$	$L_IO_{II,III}$	22.20
0.5594075	6	47 Ag	$K\alpha_1$	KL_{III}	22.16292
0.55973	2	94 Pu	$L\gamma_6$	$L_{II}O_{IV}$	22.1502
0.56051	1	44 Ru	K	Abs. Edge	22.1193
0.56089	9	44 Ru	$K\beta_4$	$KN_{IV,V}$	22.104
0.56166	3	44 Ru	$K\beta_2$	$KN_{II,III}$	22.074
0.561886	9	95 Am	$L\gamma_1$	$L_{II}N_{IV}$	22.0652
0.563798	4	47 Ag	$K\alpha_2$	KL_{II}	21.9903
0.564001	9	94 Pu	$L\gamma_3$	L_IN_{III}	21.9824
0.5658	1	94 Pu	$L\gamma_8$	$L_{II}O_I$	21.914
0.56785	9	44 Ru	$K\beta_5{}^{I}$	KM_V	21.834
0.5680	2	44 Ru	$K\beta_5{}^{II}$	KM_{IV}	21.829
0.5695	1	92 U	L_I	Abs. Edge	21.771
0.5706	1	92 U	$L\gamma_{13}$	$L_IP_{II,III}$	21.729
0.57068	2	94 Pu	$L\gamma_2$	L_IN_{II}	21.1251
0.572482	4	44 Ru	$K\beta_1$	KM_{III}	21.6568
0.5725	1	92 U		$L_IO_{IV,V}$	21.657
0.573067	4	44 Ru	$K\beta_3$	KM_{II}	21.6346
0.57499	9	92 U	$L\gamma_4$	L_IO_{III}	21.562
0.576700	9	92 U	$L\gamma_4'$	L_IO_{II}	21.4984
0.57699	5	93 Np	$L\gamma_6$	$L_{II}O_{IV}$	21.488
0.578882	9	94 Pu	$L\gamma_1$	$L_{II}N_{IV}$	21.4173
0.5810	5	93 Np	$L\gamma_3$	L_IN_{III}	21.34
0.585448	3	46 Pd	$K\alpha_1$	KL_{III}	21.1771
0.5873	5	93 Np	$L\gamma_2$	L_IN_{II}	21.11
0.58906	1	43 Te	K	Abs. Edge	21.0473
0.589821	3	46 Pd	$K\alpha_2$	KL_{II}	21.0201
0.58986	5	92 U	$L\gamma_{11}$	L_IN_V	21.019
0.59024	5	43 Tc	$K\beta_2$	$KN_{II,III}$	21.005
0.59096	5	92 U		L_IN_{IV}	20.979
0.5919	1	92 U	L_{II}	Abs. Edge	20.945
0.59203	5	92 U		$L_{II}P_{IV}$	20.942
0.5930	2	92 U		$L_{II}P_{II,III}$	20.906
0.5937	1	91 Pa	$L\gamma_4$	$L_IO_{II,III}$	20.882
0.594845	9	92 U	$L\gamma_6$	$L_{II}O_{IV}$	20.8426
0.596498	9	93 Np	$L\gamma_1$	$L_{II}N_{IV}$	20.7848
0.59728	5	92 U		$L_{II}O_{III}$	20.758
0.598574	9	92 U	$L\gamma_3$	L_IN_{III}	20.7127
0.5988	1	94 Pu	$L\gamma_5$	$L_{II}N_I$	20.704
0.60125	5	92 U	$L\gamma_8$	$L_{II}O_I$	20.621
0.60130	4	43 Tc	$K\beta_1$	KM_{III}	20.619
0.60188	4	43 Tc	$K\beta_3$	KM_{II}	20.599
0.6031	1	92 U	Lv	$L_{II}N_{VI}$	20.556
0.605237	9	92 U	$L\gamma_2$	L_IN_{II}	20.4847
0.6059	1	90 Th	L_I	Abs. Edge	20.464
0.60705	8	90 Th	$L\gamma_{13}$	$L_IP_{II,III}$	20.424
0.6083	1	90 Th		$L_IO_{IV,V}$	20.383
0.61098	4	90 Th	$L\gamma_4$	L_IO_{III}	20.292
0.61251	4	90 Th	$L\gamma_4'$	L_IO_{II}	20.242
0.6133	1	91 Pa	$L\gamma_6$	$L_{II}O_{IV}$	20.216
0.613279	4	45 Rh	$K\alpha_1$	KL_{III}	20.2161
0.6146	1	90 Th		L_IO_I	20.174
0.614770	9	92 U	$L\gamma_1$	$L_{II}N_{IV}$	20.1671
0.6160	1	90 Th		$L_IN_{VI,VII}$	20.128

Wavelength Å*	p.e.	Element	Designation		keV	Wavelength Å*	p.e.	Element	Designation		keV
0.616	1	93 Np	$L\gamma_5$	$L_{II}N_I$	20.12	0.67383	2	95 Am	$L\beta_5$	$L_{III}O_{IV,V}$	18.3996
0.6169	1	91 Pa	$L\gamma_3$	L_IN_{III}	20.098	0.67491	4	90 Th	$L\gamma_5$	$L_{II}N_I$	18.370
0.617630	4	45 Rh	$K\alpha_2$	KL_{II}	20.0737	0.67502	3	43 Tc	$K\alpha_1$	KL_{III}	18.3671
0.61978	1	42 Mo	K	Abs. Edge	20.0039	0.67538	5	88 Ra	$L\gamma_3$	L_IN_{III}	18.357
0.62001	9	42 Mo	$K\beta_4{}^I$	$KN_{IV,V}$	19.996	0.6764	1	88 Ra		$L_{II}O_{III}$	18.330
0.62099	2	42 Mo	$K\beta_2$	$KN_{II,III}$	19.9652	0.67772	2	94 Pu	$L\beta_1$	$L_{II}M_{IV}$	18.2937
0.62107	5	42 Mo	$K\beta_2{}^{II}$	KN_{II}	19.963	0.6780	1	88 Ra		$L_{II}O_{II}$	18.286
0.6228	1	92 U		$L_{II}N_{III}$	19.907	0.67932	3	43 Tc	$K\alpha_2$	KL_{II}	18.2508
0.6239	1	91 Pa	$L\gamma_2$	L_IN_{II}	19.872	0.6801	1	88 Ra	$L\gamma_8$	$L_{II}O_I$	18.230
0.62636	9	90 Th	$L\gamma_{11}$	L_IN_V	19.794	0.681014	8	92 U	$L\beta_9$	L_IM_V	18.2054
0.62692	5	42 No	$K\beta_5{}^I$	KM_V	19.776	0.68199	5	88 Ra	$L\gamma_2$	L_IN_{II}	18.179
0.62708	5	42 Mo	$K\beta_5{}^{II}$	KM_{IV}	19.771	0.68639	2	95 Am	$L\beta_4$	L_IM_{II}	18.0627
0.6276	1	90 Th		L_IN_{IV}	19.755	0.6867	1	94 Pu	L_{III}	Abs. Edge	18.054
0.6299	1	90 Th	L_{II}	Abs. Edge	19.683	0.6874	1	88 Ra		L_IN_I	18.036
0.62991	9	90 Th		$L_{II}P_{IV}$	19.682	0.68760	5	92 U	$L\beta_{10}$	L_IM_{IV}	18.031
0.6312	1	90 Th		$L_{II}P_{II,III}$	19.642	0.68883	1	40 Zr	K	Abs. Edge	17.9989
0.6316	1	90 Th		$L_{II}P_I$	19.629	0.68901	5	40 Zr	$K\beta_4$	$KN_{IV,V}$	17.994
0.632288	9	42 Mo	$K\beta_1$	KM_{III}	19.6083	0.68920	9	93 Np	$L\beta_3$	L_IM_{III}	17.989
0.63258	4	90 Th	$L\gamma_6$	$L_{II}O_{IV}$	19.599	0.68993	4	40 Zr	$K\beta_2$	$KN_{II,III}$	17.970
0.632872	2	42 Mo	$K\beta_3$	KM_{II}	19.5903	0.69068	2	94 Pu	$L\beta_5$	$L_{III}O_{IV,V}$	17.9506
0.63358	9	91 Pa	$L\gamma_1$	$L_{II}N_{IV}$	19.568	0.6932	1	88 Ra		$L_{II}N_V$	17.884
0.63557	2	92 U	$L\gamma_5$	$L_{II}N_I$	19.5072	0.69463	5	88 Ra	$L\gamma_1$	$L_{II}N_{IV}$	17.849
0.63559	4	90 Th	$L\gamma_3$	L_IN_{III}	19.507	0.6959	1	40 Zr	$K\beta_5$	$KM_{IV,V}$	17.815
0.6356	1	90 Th		$L_{II}O_{III}$	19.506	0.698478	9	93 Np	$L\beta_1$	$L_{II}M_{IV}$	17.7502
0.6369	1	90 Th		$L_{II}O_{II}$	19.466	0.7003	1	94 Pu	$L\beta_7$	$L_{III}O_I$	17.705
0.63898	5	90 Th	$L\gamma_8$	$L_{II}O_I$	19.403	0.701390	9	95 Am	$L\beta_2$	$L_{III}N_V$	17.6765
0.64064	9	90 Th	Lv	$L_{II}N_{VI}$	19.353	0.70173	3	40 Zr	$K\beta_1$	KM_{III}	17.6678
0.6416	1	94 Pu	$L\beta_9$	L_IM_V	19.323	0.7018	1	91 Pa	$L\beta_9$	L_IM_V	17.667
0.64221	4	90 Th	$L\gamma_2$	L_IN_{II}	19.305	0.70228	4	40 Zr	$K\beta_3$	KM_{II}	17.654
0.643083	4	44 Ru	$K\alpha_1$	KL_{III}	19.2792	0.7031	1	94 Pu	Lu	$L_{III}N_{VI,VII}$	17.635
0.6445	1	88 Ra	L_I	Abs. Edge	19.236	0.70341	2	95 Am	$L\beta_{15}$	$L_{III}N_{IV}$	17.6258
0.64513	5	88 Ra	$L\gamma_{13}$	$L_IP_{II,III}$	19.218	0.7043	1	88 Ra		$L_{II}N_{III}$	17.604
0.6468	1	88 Ra		$L_IO_{IV,V}$	19.167	0.70620	2	94 Pu	$L\beta_4$	L_IM_{II}	17.5560
0.647408	5	44 Ru	$K\alpha_2$	KL_{II}	19.1504	0.70814	2	93 Np	$L\beta_5$	$L_{III}O_{IV,V}$	17.5081
0.64755	5	90 Th		L_IN_I	19.146	0.7088	2	91 Pa	$L\beta_{10}$	L_IM_{IV}	17.492
0.6482	1	94 Pu	$L\beta_{10}$	L_IM_{IV}	19.126	0.709300	1	42 Mo	$K\alpha_1$	KL_{III}	17.47934
0.64891	2	95 Am	$L\beta_3$	L_IM_{III}	19.1059	0.71029	2	92 U	$L\beta_3$	L_IM_{III}	17.4550
0.64965	5	88 Ra	$L\gamma_4$	L_IO_{III}	19.084	0.713590	6	42 Mo	$K\alpha_2$	KL_{II}	17.3743
0.65131	5	88 Ra	$L\gamma_4'$	L_IO_{II}	19.036	0.71652	9	87 Fr	$L\gamma_1$	$L_{II}N_{IV}$	17.303
0.6521	1	90 Th		$L_{II}N_V$	19.014	0.71774	5	88 Ra	$L\gamma_5$	$L_{II}N_I$	17.274
0.65298	1	41 Nb	K	Abs. Edge	18.9869	0.71851	2	94 Pu	$L\beta_2$	$L_{III}N_V$	17.2553
0.65313	3	90 Th	$L\gamma_1$	$L_{II}N_{IV}$	18.9825	0.719984	8	92 U	$L\beta_1$	$L_{II}M_{IV}$	17.2200
0.65318	5	41 Nb	$K\beta_4$	$KN_{IV,V}$	18.981	0.7205	1	94 Pu	$L\beta_{15}$	$L_{III}N_{IV}$	17.208
0.65416	4	41 Nb	$K\beta_2$	$KN_{II,III}$	18.953	0.7223	1	92 U	L_{III}	Abs. Edge	17.165
0.6550	1	91 Pa	$L\gamma_5$	$L_{II}N_I$	18.930	0.72240	5	92 U		$L_{III}P_{IV,V}$	17.162
0.657655	9	95 Am	$L\beta_1$	$L_{II}M_{IV}$	18.8520	0.7234	1	90 Th	$L\beta_9$	L_IM_V	17.139
0.6620	1	90 Th		$L_{II}N_{III}$	18.729	0.72426	5	92 U		$L_{III}P_{II,III}$	17.118
0.6654	1	88 Ra	$L\gamma_{11}$	L_IN_V	18.633	0.72521	5	92 U		$L_{III}P_I$	17.096
0.66576	2	41 Nb	$K\beta_1$	KM_{III}	18.6225	0.726305	9	92 U	$L\beta_5$	$L_{III}O_{IV,V}$	17.0701
0.66634	3	41 Nb	$K\beta_3$	KM_{II}	18.6063	0.72671	2	93 Np	$L\beta_4$	L_IM_{II}	17.0607
0.6666	1	88 Ra		L_IN_{IV}	18.600	0.72766	5	39 Y	K	Abs. Edge	17.038
0.66871	2	94 Pu	$L\beta_3$	L_IM_{III}	18.5405	0.72776	5	39 Y	$K\beta_4$	$KN_{IV,V}$	17.036
0.6707	1	88 Ra	L_{II}	Abs. Edge	18.486	0.72864	4	39 Y	$K\beta_2$	$KN_{II,III}$	17.0154
0.6714	1	88 Ra		$L_{II}P_{II,III}$	18.466	0.7301	1	90 Th	$L\beta_{10}$	L_IM_{IV}	16.981
0.6724	1	88 Ra		$L_{II}P_I$	18.439	0.7309	1	92 U		$L_{III}O_{III}$	16.962
0.67328	5	88 Ra	$L\gamma_6$	$L_{II}O_{IV}$	18.414	0.73230	5	91 Pa	$L\beta_3$	L_IM_{III}	16.930
0.67351	9	89 Ac	$L\gamma_1$	$L_{II}N_{IV}$	18.408	0.7333	1	92 U		$L_{III}O_{II}$	16.907

Wavelength Å*	p.e.	Element		Designation	keV	Wavelength Å*	p.e.	Element		Designation	keV
0.73418	2	95 Am	$L\beta_6$	$L_{III}N_I$	16.8870	0.78292	2	38 Sr	$K\beta_1$	KM_{III}	15.8357
0.7345	1	39 Y	$K\beta_5$	$KM_{IV,V}$	16.879	0.78345	3	38 Sr	$K\beta_3$	KM_{II}	15.8249
0.73602	6	92 U	$L\beta_7$	$L_{III}O_I$	16.845	0.7858	1	82 Pb	$L\gamma_4$	L_IO_{III}	15.777
0.736230	9	93 Np	$L\beta_2$	$L_{III}N_V$	16.8400	0.78593	1	40 Zr	$K\alpha_1$	KL_{III}	15.7751
0.738603	9	92 U	Lu	$L_{III}N_{VI,VII}$	16.7859	0.78706	7	82 Pb	$L\gamma_4'$	L_IO_{II}	15.752
0.73928	9	86 Rn	$L\gamma_1$	$L_{II}N_{IV}$	16.770	0.78748	9	84 Po	$L\gamma_1$	$L_{II}N_{IV}$	15.744
0.74072	2	39 Y	$K\beta_1$	KM_{III}	16.7378	0.78838	2	92 U	$L\beta_6$	$L_{III}N_I$	15.7260
0.74126	3	39 Y	$K\beta_3$	KM_{II}	16.7258	0.7884	1	82 Pb		$L_IN_{VI,VII}$	15.725
0.74232	5	91 Pa	$L\beta_1$	$L_{II}M_{IV}$	16.702	0.7887	1	83 Bi	L_{II}	Abs. Edge	15.719
0.74503	5	92 U	$L\beta_{17}$	$L_{II}M_{III}$	16.641	0.78903	9	89 Ac	$L\beta_1$	$L_{III}M_{IV}$	15.713
0.7452	2	91 Pa	$L\beta_5$	$L_{III}O_{IV,V}$	16.636	0.78917	5	83 Bi	$L\gamma_3$	L_IN_{II}	15.7102
0.74620	1	41 Nb	$K\alpha_1$	KL_{III}	16.6151	0.7897	1	82 Pb		L_IO_I	15.699
0.747985	9	92 U	$L\beta_4$	L_IM_{II}	16.5753	0.79015	1	40 Zr	$K\alpha_2$	KL_{II}	15.6909
0.75044	1	41 Nb	$K\alpha_2$	KL_{II}	16.5210	0.79043	3	83 Bi	$L\gamma_6$	$L_{II}O_{IV}$	15.6853
0.75148	2	94 Pu	$L\beta_6$	$L_{III}N_I$	16.4983	0.79257	4	90 Th	$L\beta_4$	L_IM_{II}	15.6429
0.7546	2	91 Pa	$L\beta_7$	$L_{III}O_I$	16.431	0.79257	4	90 Th	$L\beta_{17}$	$L_{II}M_{III}$	15.6429
0.754681	9	92 U	$L\beta_2$	$L_{III}N_V$	16.4283	0.79354	3	90 Th	$L\beta_2$	$L_{III}M_V$	15.6237
0.75479	3	90 Th	$L\beta_8$	$L_{III}M_{III}$	16.4258	0.79384	5	83 Bi		$L_{II}O_{III}$	15.6178
0.756642	9	92 U	$L\beta_{15}$	$L_{III}N_{IV}$	16.3857	0.79539	5	90 Th	$L\beta_{15}$	$L_{III}N_{IV}$	15.5875
0.75690	3	83 Bi	$L\gamma_{13}$	$L_IP_{II,III}$	16.3802	0.79565	3	83 Bi	$L\gamma_2$	L_IN_{II}	15.5824
0.7571	1	83 Bi	L_I	Abs. Edge	16.376	0.79721	9	83 Bi	Lv	$L_{II}N_{VI}$	15.552
0.7579	1	90 Th		$L_{II}M_V$	16.359	0.7973	1	83 Bi	$L\gamma_8$	$L_{II}O_I$	15.551
0.75791	5	83 Bi		$L_IO_{IV,V}$	16.358	0.8022	1	83 Bi		L_IN_I	15.456
0.7591	1	94 Pu	$L\eta$	$L_{II}M_I$	16.333	0.80233	9	82 Pb	$L\gamma_{11}$	L_IN_V	15.453
0.7607	1	90 Th	L_{III}	Abs. Edge	16.299	0.80273	5	88 Ra	$L\beta_3$	L_IM_{III}	15.4449
0.76087	9	90 Th		$L_{III}P_{IV,V}$	16.295	0.8028	1	88 Ra	L_{III}	Abs. Edge	15.444
0.76087	3	83 Bi	$L\gamma_4$	L_IO_{III}	16.2947	0.80364	7	82 Pb		L_IN_{IV}	15.427
0.76198	3	83 Bi	$L\gamma_4'$	L_IO_{II}	16.2709	0.8038	1	88 Ra		$L_{III}P_{II,III}$	15.425
0.7625	2	90 Th		$L_{III}P_{II,III}$	16.260	0.8050	1	88 Ra		$L_{III}P_I$	15.402
0.76289	9	85 At	$L\gamma_1$	$L_{III}N_{IV}$	16.251	0.80509	2	92 U	$L\eta$	$L_{II}M_I$	15.3997
0.76338	5	90 Th		$L_{III}P_I$	16.241	0.80627	5	88 Ra	$L\beta_5$	$L_{III}O_{IV,V}$	15.3771
0.7641	5	83 Bi		$L_IN_{VI,VII}$	16.23	0.8079	1	91 Pa	$L\beta_6$	$L_{III}N_I$	15.347
0.7645	2	84 Po	$L\gamma_6$	$L_{II}O_{IV}$	16.218	0.8081	1	81 Tl	L_I	Abs. Edge	15.343
0.76468	5	90 Th	$L\beta_5$	$L_{III}O_{IV,V}$	16.213	0.8082	1	90 Th		$L_{III}N_{III}$	15.341
0.765210	9	90 Th	$L\beta_1$	$L_{II}M_{IV}$	16.2022	0.80861	5	81 Tl		$L_IO_{IV,V}$	15.3327
0.76857	5	88 Ra	$L\beta_9$	L_IM_V	16.131	0.81163	9	90 Th		L_IM_I	15.276
0.769	1	93 Np	$L\beta_6$	$L_{III}N_I$	16.13	0.81184	5	81 Tl	$L\gamma_4$	L_IO_{III}	15.2716
0.7690	1	90 Th		$L_{III}O_{III}$	16.123	0.81308	5	81 Tl	$L\gamma_4'$	L_IO_{II}	15.2482
0.7691	1	92 U		$L_{III}N_{III}$	16.120	0.81311	2	83 Bi	$L\gamma_1$	$L_{II}N_{IV}$	15.2477
0.76973	5	38 Sr	K	Abs. Edge	16.107	0.81375	5	88 Ra	$L\beta_1$	$L_{II}M_{IV}$	15.2358
0.7699	1	91 Pa	$L\beta_{10}$	L_IM_{IV}	16.104	0.8147	1	82 Pb	$L\gamma_3$	L_IN_{II}	15.218
0.76989	5	38 Sr	$K\beta_4$	$KN_{IV,V}$	16.104	0.81538	5	82 Pb	L_{II}	Abs. Edge	15.2053
0.77081	3	38 Sr	$K\beta_2$	$KN_{II,III}$	16.0846	0.8154	2	37 Rb	$K\beta_4$	$KN_{IV,V}$	15.205
0.7713	1	90 Th		$L_{III}O_{II}$	16.074	0.81554	5	37 Rb	K	Abs. Edge	15.2023
0.772	1	84 Po	$L\gamma_2$	L_IN_{II}	16.07	0.8158	1	81 Tl		L_IO_I	15.198
0.7737	1	91 Pa	$L\beta_2$	$L_{III}N_V$	16.024	0.81583	5	82 Pb		$L_{II}P_I$	15.1969
0.77437	4	90 Th	$L\beta_7$	$L_{III}O_I$	16.0105	0.8162	1	88 Ra	$L\beta_7$	$L_{III}O_I$	15.190
0.77546	5	88 Ra	$L\beta_{10}$	L_IM_{IV}	15.988	0.81645	3	37 Rb	$K\beta_2$	$KN_{II,III}$	15.1854
0.7764	1	38 Sr	$K\beta_5$	$KM_{IV,V}$	15.969	0.81683	5	82 Pb	$L\gamma_6$	$L_{II}O_{IV}$	15.1783
0.77661	5	90 Th	Lu	$L_{III}N_{VI,VII}$	15.964	0.8186	1	88 Ra	Lu	$L_{III}N_{VI,VII}$	15.146
0.77728	5	83 Bi	$L\gamma_{11}$	L_IN_V	15.951	0.8190	2	90 Th		$L_{III}N_{II}$	15.138
0.77822	9	89 Ac	$L\beta_3$	L_IM_{III}	15.931	0.8200	1	82 Pb		$L_{II}O_{III}$	15.120
0.77954	5	83 Bi		L_IN_{IV}	15.904	0.8210	2	82 Pb	$L\gamma_2$	L_IN_{II}	15.101
0.78017	9	92 U		$L_{III}N_{II}$	15.892	0.8219	1	37 Rb	$K\beta_5$	$KM_{IV,V}$	15.085
0.7809	2	93 Np	$L\eta$	$L_{II}M_I$	15.876	0.82327	7	82 Pb	Lv	$L_{II}N_{VI}$	15.060
0.78196	5	82 Pb	L_I	Abs. Edge	15.855	0.82365	5	82 Pb	$L\gamma_8$	$L_{II}O_I$	15.0527
0.78257	7	82 Pb		$L_IO_{IV,V}$	15.843	0.8248	1	83 Bi		$L_{II}N_{III}$	15.031

Wavelength Å*	p.e.	Element	Designation		keV	Wavelength Å*	p.e.	Element	Designation		keV
0.82789	9	87 Fr	$L\beta_3$	L_IM_{III}	14.976	0.87088	5	88 Ra	$L\beta_6$	$L_{III}N_I$	14.2362
0.82790	8	90 Th	$L\beta_6$	$L_{III}N_I$	14.975	0.8722	1	80 Hg	L_{II}	Abs. Edge	14.215
0.82859	7	82 Pb		L_IN_I	14.963	0.87319	7	80 Hg	$L\gamma_6$	$L_{II}O_{IV}$	14.199
0.82868	2	37 Rb	$K\beta_1$	KM_{III}	14.9613	0.87526	1	38 Sr	$K\alpha_1$	KL_{III}	14.1650
0.82879	5	81 Tl	$L\gamma_{11}$	L_IN_V	14.9593	0.87544	7	80 Hg	$L\gamma_2$	L_IN_{II}	14.162
0.82884	1	39 Y	$K\alpha_1$	KL_{III}	14.9584	0.8758	1	80 Hg		$L_{II}O_{III}$	14.156
0.82921	3	37 Rb	$K\beta_3$	KM_{II}	14.9517	0.8784	1	80 Hg		$L_{II}O_{II}$	14.114
0.8295	1	91 Pa	$L\eta$	$L_{II}M_I$	14.946	0.8785	1	36 Kr	$K\beta_1$	KM_{III}	14.112
0.83001	7	81 Tl		L_IN_{IV}	14.937	0.87885	7	80 Hg	Lv	$L_{III}N_{VI}$	14.107
0.83305	1	39 Y	$K\alpha_2$	KL_{II}	14.8829	0.8790	1	36 Kr	$K\beta_3$	KM_{II}	14.104
0.8338	1	90 Th		$L_{III}M_{II}$	14.869	0.87943	1	38 Sr	$K\alpha_2$	KL_{II}	14.0979
0.8344	9	83 Bi		$L_{III}N_{II}$	14.86	0.87995	7	80 Hg	$L\gamma_8$	$L_{II}O_I$	14.090
0.8350	2	80 Hg		$L_IO_{IV,V}$	14.847	0.87996	5	81 Tl		$L_{II}N_{III}$	14.0893
0.8353	1	80 Hg	L_I	Abs. Edge	14.842	0.88028	2	94 Pu	$L\alpha_2$	$L_{III}M_{IV}$	14.0842
0.83537	5	88 Ra	$L\beta_2$	$L_{III}N_V$	14.8414	0.88135	9	85 At	$L\beta_3$	L_IM_{III}	14.067
0.83722	5	88 Ra	$L\beta_{15}$	$L_{III}N_{IV}$	14.8086	0.8827	2	80 Hg		L_IN_I	14.045
0.8382	2	82 Pb		$L_{II}N_V$	14.791	0.88433	7	79 Au	$L\gamma_{11}$	L_IN_V	14.020
0.83894	7	80 Hg	$L\gamma_4$	L_IO_{III}	14.778	0.88563	7	79 Au		L_IN_{IV}	13.999
0.83923	5	83 Bi	$L\gamma_5$	$L_{II}N_I$	14.7732	0.8882	2	81 Tl		$L_{II}M_{II}$	13.959
0.83940	9	87 Fr	$L\beta_1$	$L_{II}M_{IV}$	14.770	0.889128	9	93 Np	$L\alpha_1$	$L_{III}M_V$	13.9441
0.83973	3	82 Pb	$L\gamma_1$	$L_{II}N_{IV}$	14.7644	0.8931	1	78 Pt	L_I	Abs. Edge	13.883
0.84013	7	80 Hg	$L\gamma_4'$	L_IO_{II}	14.757	0.8934	1	78 Pt		L_IO_V	13.878
0.84071	5	88 Ra	$L\beta_4$	L_IM_{II}	14.7472	0.89349	9	85 At	$L\beta_1$	$L_{II}M_{IV}$	13.876
0.84130	4	81 Tl	$L\gamma_3$	L_IN_{III}	14.7368	0.8943	1	78 Pt		L_IO_{IV}	13.864
0.8434	1	81 Tl	L_{II}	Abs. Edge	14.699	0.89500	4	81 Tl	$L\gamma_5$	$L_{III}N_I$	13.8526
0.8438	1	88 Ra	$L\beta_{17}$	$L_{II}M_{III}$	14.692	0.89646	5	80 Hg	$L\gamma_1$	$L_{II}N_{IV}$	13.8301
0.8442	2	81 Tl	$L\gamma_6$	$L_{II}O_{IV}$	14.685	0.89659	4	78 Pt	$L\gamma_4$	L_IO_{III}	13.8281
0.8452	2	80 Hg		L_IO_I	14.670	0.89747	4	78 Pt	$L\gamma_4'$	L_IO_{II}	13.8145
0.84773	5	81 Tl	$L\gamma_2$	L_IN_{II}	14.6251	0.89783	5	79 Au	$L\gamma_3$	L_IN_{III}	13.8090
0.848187	9	95 Am	$L\alpha_1$	$L_{III}M_V$	14.6172	0.89791	3	83 Bi	$L\beta_9$	L_IM_V	13.8077
0.8490	1	81 Tl		$L_{II}O_{II}$	14.604	0.8995	2	78 Pt		L_IO_I	13.784
0.85048	5	81 Tl	Lv	$L_{II}N_{VI}$	14.5777	0.8996	2	84 Po	$L\beta_6$	$L_{III}O_{IV,V}$	13.782
0.8512	1	88 Ra		$L_{III}N_{III}$	14.566	0.901045	9	93 Np	$L\alpha_2$	$L_{III}M_{IV}$	13.7597
0.8513	2	81 Tl	$L\gamma_8$	$L_{II}O_I$	14.564	0.90259	5	79 Au	L_{II}	Abs. Edge	13.7361
0.85192	7	82 Pb		$L_{II}N_{III}$	14.553	0.90297	3	79 Au	$L\gamma_6$	$L_{II}O_{IV}$	13.7304
0.85436	9	86 Rn	$L\beta_3$	L_IM_{III}	14.512	0.90434	3	79 Au	$L\gamma_2$	L_IN_{II}	13.7095
0.85446	4	90 Th	$L\eta$	$L_{II}M_I$	14.5099	0.90495	4	83 Bi	$L\beta_{10}$	L_IM_{IV}	13.7002
0.8549	1	81 Tl		L_IN_I	14.503	0.90638	7	79 Au		$L_{II}O_{III}$	13.679
0.85657	7	80 Hg	$L\gamma_{11}$	L_IN_V	14.474	0.90742	5	88 Ra	$L\eta$	$L_{II}M_I$	13.6630
0.858	2	87 Fr	$L\beta_2$	$L_{III}N_V$	14.45	0.90746	7	79 Au		$L_{II}O_{II}$	13.662
0.8585	3	82 Pb		$L_{II}N_{II}$	14.442	0.90837	5	79 Au	Lv	$L_{II}N_{VI}$	13.6487
0.860266	9	95 Am	$L\alpha_2$	$L_{III}M_{IV}$	14.4119	0.90894	7	80 Hg		$L_{II}N_{III}$	13.640
0.8618	1	88 Ra		$L_{III}N_{II}$	14.387	0.9091	3	84 Po	$L\beta_3$	L_IM_{III}	13.638
0.86376	5	79 Au	L_I	Abs. Edge	14.3537	0.90989	5	79 Au	$L\gamma_8$	$L_{II}O_I$	13.6260
0.86400	5	79 Au		$L_IO_{IV,V}$	14.3497	0.910639	9	92 U	$L\alpha_1$	$L_{III}M_V$	13.6147
0.8653	2	36 Kr	$K\beta_4$	$KN_{IV,V}$	14.328	0.9131	1	79 Au		L_IN_I	13.578
0.86552	1	36 Kr	K	Abs. Edge	14.3244	0.9143	2	78 Pt	$L\gamma_{11}$	L_IN_V	13.560
0.86605	9	86 Rn	$L\beta_1$	$L_{III}M_{IV}$	14.316	0.9204	1	35 Br	K	Abs. Edge	13.470
0.8661	1	36 Kr	$K\beta_2$	$KN_{II,III}$	14.315	0.92046	2	35 Br	$K\beta_2$	$KN_{II,III}$	13.4695
0.86655	5	82 Pb	$L\gamma_5$	$L_{II}N_I$	14.3075	0.9220	2	84 Po	$L\beta_1$	$L_{II}M_{IV}$	13.447
0.86703	4	79 Au	$L\gamma_4$	L_IO_{III}	14.2996	0.922558	9	92 U	$L\alpha_2$	$L_{III}M_{IV}$	13.4388
0.86752	3	81 Tl	$L\gamma_1$	$L_{II}N_{IV}$	14.2915	0.9234	1	83 Bi	L_{III}	Abs. Edge	13.426
0.86816	4	79 Au	$L\gamma_4'$	L_IO_{II}	14.2809	0.9236	1	77 Ir	L_I	Abs. Edge	13.423
0.86830	2	94 Pu	$L\alpha_1$	$L_{III}M_V$	14.2786	0.92413	4	83 Bi		$L_{III}P_{II,III}$	13.4159
0.86915	7	80 Hg	$L\gamma_3$	L_IN_{III}	14.265	0.9243	3	77 Ir		$L_IO_{IV,V}$	13.413
0.87074	5	79 Au		L_IO_I	14.2385	0.92453	7	80 Hg	$L\gamma_5$	$L_{II}N_I$	13.410
0.8708	2	36 Kr	$K\beta_5$	$KM_{IV,V}$	14.238	0.9255	1	35 Br	$K\beta_5$	$KM_{IV,V}$	13.396

Wavelength Å*	p.e.	Element	Designation		keV
0.925553	9	37 Rb	$K\alpha_1$	KL_{III}	13.3953
0.92556	3	83 Bi	$L\beta_5$	$L_{III}O_{IV,V}$	13.3953
0.92650	3	79 Au	$L\gamma_1$	$L_{II}N_{IV}$	13.3817
0.9268	1	82 Pb	$L\beta_9$	$L_{I}M_{V}$	13.377
0.92744	3	77 Ir	$L\gamma_4$	$L_{I}O_{III}$	13.3681
0.92791	5	78 Pt	$L\gamma_3$	$L_{I}N_{III}$	13.3613
0.92831	3	77 Ir	$L\gamma_4'$	$L_{I}O_{II}$	13.3555
0.92937	5	84 Po	$L\beta_2$	$L_{III}N_{V}$	13.3404
0.92969	1	37 Rb	$K\alpha_2$	KL_{II}	13.3358
0.9302	2	83 Bi		$L_{III}O_{III}$	13.328
0.9312	2	84 Po	$L\beta_{15}$	$L_{III}N_{IV}$	13.314
0.9323	2	83 Bi		$L_{III}O_{II}$	13.298
0.93279	2	35 Br	$K\beta_1$	KM_{III}	13.2914
0.93284	5	91 Pa	$L\alpha_1$	$L_{III}M_{V}$	13.2907
0.93327	5	35 Br	$K\beta_3$	KM_{II}	13.2845
0.9339	2	82 Pb	$L\beta_{10}$	$L_{I}M_{IV}$	13.275
0.93414	5	78 Pt	L_{II}	Abs. Edge	13.2723
0.9342	2	78 Pt	$L\gamma_6$	$L_{II}O_{IV}$	13.271
0.93427	5	78 Pt	$L\gamma_2$	$L_{I}N_{II}$	13.2704
0.93505	5	83 Bi	$L\beta_7$	$L_{III}O_{I}$	13.2593
0.93505	5	83 Bi	Lu	$L_{III}N_{VI,VII}$	13.2593
0.93855	3	83 Bi	$L\beta_3$	$L_{I}M_{III}$	13.2098
0.93931	5	78 Pt	Lv	$L_{II}N_{VI}$	13.1992
0.9402	2	79 Au		$L_{II}N_{III}$	13.186
0.9411	1	78 Pt	$L\gamma_8$	$L_{II}O_{I}$	13.173
0.94419	5	83 Bi		$L_{II}M_{V}$	13.1310
0.9446	2	77 Ir	$L\gamma_{11}$	$L_{I}N_{V}$	13.126
0.94482	5	91 Pa	$L\alpha_2$	$L_{III}M_{IV}$	13.1222
0.9455	2	78 Pt		$L_{I}N_{I}$	13.113
0.9459	2	77 Ir		$L_{I}N_{IV}$	13.108
0.9475	3	84 Po	$L\beta_4$	$L_{I}M_{II}$	13.086
0.95073	5	82 Pb	L_{III}	Abs. Edge	13.0406
0.95118	7	82 Pb		$L_{III}P_{II,III}$	13.0344
0.951978	9	83 Bi	$L\beta_1$	$L_{II}M_{IV}$	13.0235
0.9526	1	82 Pb	$L\beta_5$	$L_{III}O_{IV,V}$	13.015
0.95518	4	83 Bi	$L\beta_2$	$L_{III}N_{V}$	12.9799
0.95559	3	79 Au	$L\gamma_5$	$L_{II}N_{I}$	12.9743
0.9558	1	76 Os	L_{I}	Abs. Edge	12.972
0.95600	3	90 Th	$L\alpha_1$	$L_{III}M_{V}$	12.9687
0.95603	5	76 Os		$L_{I}O_{IV,V}$	12.9683
0.95675	7	81 Tl	$L\beta_9$	$L_{I}M_{V}$	12.9585
0.95702	5	83 Bi	$L\beta_{15}$	$L_{III}N_{IV}$	12.9549
0.9578	1	82 Pb		$L_{III}O_{III}$	12.945
0.95797	3	78 Pt	$L\gamma_1$	$L_{II}N_{IV}$	12.9420
0.9586	1	82 Pb		$L_{III}O_{II}$	12.934
0.95931	5	77 Ir	$L\gamma_3$	$L_{I}N_{III}$	12.9240
0.95938	8	76 Os	$L\gamma_4$	$L_{I}O_{III}$	12.923
0.96033	8	76 Os	$L\gamma_4'$	$L_{I}O_{II}$	12.910
0.96133	7	82 Pb	Lu	$L_{III}N_{VI,VII}$	12.8968
0.9620	1	82 Pb	$L\beta_7$	$L_{III}O_{I}$	12.888
0.96318	7	76 Os		$L_{I}O_{I}$	12.8721
0.9636	1	92 U	Ls	$L_{III}M_{III}$	12.866
0.96389	7	81 Tl	$L\beta_{10}$	$L_{I}M_{IV}$	12.8626
0.96545	3	77 Ir	$L\gamma_2$	$L_{I}N_{II}$	12.8418
0.96708	4	77 Ir	$L\gamma_6$	$L_{II}O_{IV}$	12.8201
0.9671	1	77 Ir	L_{II}	Abs. Edge	12.820
0.9672	2	84 Po	$L\beta_6$	$L_{III}N_{I}$	12.819
0.96788	2	90 Th	$L\alpha_2$	$L_{III}M_{IV}$	12.8096
0.96911	7	82 Pb	$L\beta_2$	$L_{I}M_{III}$	12.7933
0.96979	5	77 Ir		$L_{II}O_{III}$	12.7843
0.97161	6	77 Ir	Lv	$L_{II}N_{VI}$	12.7603
0.97173	4	78 Pt		$L_{II}N_{III}$	12.7588
0.97321	5	83 Bi		$L_{III}N_{III}$	12.7394
0.97409	3	77 Ir	$L\gamma_8$	$L_{II}O_{I}$	12.7279
0.9747	1	82 Pb		$L_{II}M_{V}$	12.720
0.9765	3	76 Os	$L\gamma_{11}$	$L_{I}N_{V}$	12.696
0.9766	2	77 Ir		$L_{I}N_{I}$	12.695
0.97690	4	83 Bi	$L\beta_4$	$L_{I}M_{II}$	12.6912
0.9772	3	76 Os		$L_{I}N_{IV}$	12.687
0.9792	2	78 Pt		$L_{II}N_{II}$	12.661
0.97926	5	81 Tl		$L_{III}P_{II,III}$	12.6607
0.9793	1	81 Tl	L_{III}	Abs. Edge	12.660
0.97974	1	34 Se	K	Abs. Edge	12.6545
0.97992	5	34 Se	$K\beta_2$	$KN_{II,III}$	12.6522
0.97993	5	89 Ac	$L\alpha_1$	$L_{III}M_{V}$	12.6520
0.9801	1	36 Kr	$K\alpha_1$	KL_{III}	12.649
0.98058	3	81 Tl	$L\beta_5$	$L_{III}O_{IV,V}$	12.6436
0.98221	7	82 Pb	$L\beta_2$	$L_{III}N_{V}$	12.6226
0.98280	5	83 Bi		$L_{III}N_{II}$	12.6151
0.98291	3	82 Pb	$L\beta_1$	$L_{II}M_{IV}$	12.6137
0.98389	7	82 Pb	$L\beta_{15}$	$L_{III}N_{IV}$	12.6011
0.9841	1	36 Kr	$K\alpha_2$	KL_{II}	12.598
0.9843	1	34 Se	$K\beta_5$	$KM_{IV,V}$	12.595
0.98538	5	81 Tl		$L_{III}O_{III}$	12.5820
0.9871	2	80 Hg	$L\beta_9$	$L_{I}M_{V}$	12.560
0.98738	5	81 Tl		$L_{III}O_{II}$	12.5566
0.9877	2	78 Pt	$L\gamma_6$	$L_{II}N_{I}$	12.552
0.9888	1	81 Tl	Lu	$L_{III}N_{VI,VII}$	12.538
0.98913	5	83 Bi	$L\beta_{17}$	$L_{II}M_{III}$	12.5344
0.9894	1	75 Re	L_{I}	Abs. Edge	12.530
0.9900	1	75 Re		$L_{I}O_{IV,V}$	12.524
0.99017	5	81 Tl	$L\beta_7$	$L_{III}O_{I}$	12.5212
0.99085	3	77 Ir	$L\gamma_1$	$L_{II}N_{IV}$	12.5126
0.99178	5	89 Ac	$L\alpha_2$	$L_{III}M_{IV}$	12.5008
0.99186	5	76 Os	$L\gamma_3$	$L_{I}N_{III}$	12.4998
0.99218	3	34 Se	$K\beta_1$	KM_{III}	12.4959
0.99249	5	75 Re	$L\gamma_4$	$L_{I}O_{III}$	12.4920
0.99268	5	34 Se	$K\beta_3$	KM_{II}	12.4896
0.99331	3	83 Bi	$L\beta_6$	$L_{III}N_{I}$	12.4816
0.99334	5	75 Re	$L\gamma_4'$	$L_{I}O_{II}$	12.4813
0.9962	2	80 Hg	$L\beta_{10}$	$L_{I}M_{IV}$	12.446
0.9965	1	75 Re		$L_{I}O_{I}$	12.442
0.99805	5	76 Os	$L\gamma_2$	$L_{I}N_{II}$	12.4224
1.0005	1	82 Pb		$L_{III}N_{III}$	12.392
1.0005	9	83 Bi		$L_{I}M_{I}$	12.39
1.00062	3	81 Tl	$L\beta_3$	$L_{I}M_{III}$	12.3904
1.00107	5	76 Os	$L\gamma_6$	$L_{II}O_{IV}$	12.3848
1.0012	6	95 Am	Ll	$L_{III}M_{I}$	12.384
1.0014	1	76 Os	L_{II}	Abs. Edge	12.381
1.0047	2	76 Os		$L_{II}O_{III}$	12.340
1.00473	5	88 Ra	$L\alpha_1$	$L_{III}M_{V}$	12.3397
1.0050	2	76 Os	Lv	$L_{II}N_{VI}$	12.337
1.0054	3	77 Ir		$L_{II}N_{III}$	12.332
1.00722	5	81 Tl		$L_{II}M_{V}$	12.3093

Wavelength Å*	p.e.	Element	Designation		keV	Wavelength Å*	p.e.	Element	Designation		keV
1.0075	1	82 Pb	$L\beta_4$	L_IM_{II}	12.306	1.04500	3	33 As	$K\beta_2$	$KN_{II,III}$	11.8642
1.00788	5	76 Os	$L\gamma_8$	$L_{II}O_I$	12.3012	1.0458	1	74 W	$L\gamma_{11}$	L_IN_V	11.856
1.0091	1	80 Hg	L_{III}	Abs. Edge	12.286	1.0468	2	74 W		L_IN_{IV}	11.844
1.00987	7	80 Hg	$L\beta_5$	$L_{III}O_{IV,V}$	12.2769	1.04752	5	79 Au	Lu	$L_{III}N_{VI,VII}$	11.8357
1.01031	3	81 Tl	$L\beta_2$	$L_{III}N_V$	12.2715	1.04868	5	80 Hg	$L\beta_1$	$L_{II}M_{IV}$	11.8226
1.01040	7	82 Pb		$L_{III}N_{II}$	12.2705	1.0488	1	33 As	$K\beta_5$	$KM_{IV,V}$	11.822
1.0108	1	75 Re	$L\gamma_{11}$	L_IN_V	12.266	1.04963	5	81 Tl	$L\beta_6$	$L_{III}N_I$	11.8118
1.0112	1	90 Th	Ls	$L_{III}M_{III}$	12.261	1.04974	8	79 Au	$L\beta_7$	$L_{III}O_I$	11.8106
1.0119	1	75 Re		L_IN_{IV}	12.252	1.05446	5	78 Pt	$L\beta_9$	L_IM_V	11.7577
1.0120	2	77 Ir		$L_{II}N_{II}$	12.251	1.05609	7	81 Tl	$L\beta_{17}$	$L_{II}M_{III}$	11.7397
1.01201	3	81 Tl	$L\beta_{15}$	$L_{III}N_{IV}$	12.2510	1.05693	5	76 Os	$L\gamma_5$	$L_{II}N_I$	11.7303
1.01404	7	80 Hg		$L_{III}O_{III}$	12.2264	1.05723	5	86 Rn	$L\alpha_1$	$L_{III}M_V$	11.7270
1.01513	4	81 Tl	$L\beta_1$	$L_{II}M_{IV}$	12.2133	1.05730	2	33 As	$K\beta_1$	KM_{III}	11.7262
1.01558	7	80 Hg		$L_{III}O_{II}$	12.2079	1.05783	5	33 As	$K\beta_3$	KM_{II}	11.7203
1.01656	5	88 Ra	$L\alpha_2$	$L_{III}M_{IV}$	12.1962	1.0585	1	80 Hg		$L_{III}N_{III}$	11.713
1.01674	7	80 Hg	Lu	$L_{III}N_{VII}$	12.1940	1.05856	3	83 Bi	$L\eta$	$L_{II}M_I$	11.7122
1.01769	7	80 Hg	Lu'	$L_{III}N_{VI}$	12.1826	1.06099	5	75 Re	$L\gamma_1$	$L_{II}N_{IV}$	11.6854
1.01937	7	80 Hg	$L\beta_7$	$L_{III}O_I$	12.1625	1.0613	1	73 Ta	L_I	Abs. Edge	11.682
1.02063	7	79 Au	$L\beta_9$	L_IM_V	12.1474	1.06183	7	78 Pt	$L\beta_{10}$	L_IM_{IV}	11.6762
1.0210	1	82 Pb	$L\beta_6$	$L_{III}N_I$	12.143	1.06192	9	73 Ta		$L_IO_{IV,V}$	11.6752
1.02175	5	77 Ir	$L\gamma_5$	$L_{II}N_I$	12.1342	1.06200	6	74 W	$L\gamma_3$	L_IN_{III}	11.6743
1.0223	1	82 Pb	$L\beta_{17}$	$L_{II}M_{III}$	12.127	1.06357	9	73 Ta		$L_IN_{VI,VII}$	11.6570
1.0226	1	94 Pu	Ll	$L_{III}M_I$	12.124	1.0644	2	82 Pb		$L_{II}M_{II}$	11.648
1.02467	5	74 W	L_I	Abs. Edge	12.0996	1.0644	2	81 Tl		L_IM_I	11.648
1.0250	2	74 W		$L_IO_{IV,V}$	12.095	1.06467	3	73 Ta	$L\gamma_4$	L_IO_{III}	11.6451
1.02503	5	76 Os	$L\gamma_1$	$L_{II}N_{IV}$	12.0953	1.0649	2	80 Hg		$L_{III}N_{II}$	11.642
1.02613	7	75 Re	$L\gamma_3$	L_IN_{III}	12.0824	1.06544	3	73 Ta	$L\gamma_4'$	L_IO_{II}	11.6366
1.02775	3	74 W	$L\gamma_4$	L_IO_{III}	12.0634	1.06712	2	92 U	Ll	$L_{III}M_I$	11.6183
1.02789	7	79 Au	$L\beta_{10}$	L_IM_{IV}	12.0617	1.06771	9	73 Ta		L_IO_I	11.6118
1.0286	1	81 Tl		$L_{III}N_{III}$	12.053	1.06785	9	79 Au	$L\beta_3$	L_IM_{III}	11.6103
1.02863	3	74 W	$L\gamma_4'$	L_IO_{II}	12.0530	1.06806	3	74 W	$L\gamma_2$	L_IN_{II}	11.6080
1.03049	5	87 Fr	$L\alpha_1$	$L_{III}M_V$	12.0313	1.06899	5	86 Rn	$L\alpha_2$	$L_{III}M_{IV}$	11.5979
1.0317	3	74 W		L_IO_I	12.017	1.07022	3	79 Au	$L\beta_2$	$L_{III}N_V$	11.5847
1.03233	5	75 Re	$L\gamma_2$	L_IN_{II}	12.0098	1.07188	5	79 Au	$L\beta_{15}$	$L_{III}N_{IV}$	11.5667
1.0323	2	82 Pb		L_IM_I	12.010	1.07222	7	80 Hg	$L\beta_4$	L_IM_{II}	11.5630
1.03358	7	80 Hg	$L\beta_3$	L_IM_{III}	11.9953	1.0723	1	78 Pt	L_{III}	Abs. Edge	11.562
1.0346	9	83 Bi		L_IM_{II}	11.98	1.0724	2	78 Pt	$L\beta_5$	$L_{III}O_{IV,V}$	11.561
1.0347	1	92 U	Lt	$L_{III}M_{II}$	11.982	1.07448	5	74 W	$L\gamma_6$	$L_{II}O_{IV}$	11.5387
1.03699	9	75 Re	$L\gamma_6$	$L_{II}O_{IV}$	11.956	1.0745	1	74 W	L_{II}	Abs. Edge	11.538
1.0371	1	75 Re	L_{II}	Abs. Edge	11.954	1.0756	2	79 Au		$L_{II}M_V$	11.526
1.03876	7	79 Au		$L_{III}P_{II,III}$	11.9355	1.0761	3	78 Pt		$L_{III}O_{II,III}$	11.521
1.03918	3	81 Tl	$L\beta_4$	$L_{II}M_{II}$	11.9306	1.0767	1	75 Re		$L_{III}N_{III}$	11.515
1.0397	1	75 Re		$L_{II}O_{III}$	11.925	1.0771	1	74 W	Lv	$L_{III}N_{VI}$	11.510
1.03973	5	76 Os		$L_{II}N_{III}$	11.9243	1.07896	5	78 Pt	Lu	$L_{III}N_{VI,VII}$	11.4908
1.03974	2	35 Br	$K\alpha_1$	KL_{III}	11.9242	1.0792	2	74 W		$L_{II}O_{III}$	11.488
1.03975	7	80 Hg	$L\beta_2$	$L_{III}N_V$	11.9241	1.07975	7	80 Hg	$L\beta_6$	$L_{III}N_I$	11.4824
1.04000	5	79 Au	L_{III}	Abs. Edge	11.9212	1.08009	9	90 Th	Lt	$L_{III}M_{II}$	11.4788
1.0404	1	75 Re	Lv	$L_{II}N_{VI}$	11.917	1.08113	4	74 W	$L\gamma_8$	$L_{II}O_I$	11.4677
1.04044	3	79 Au	$L\beta_5$	$L_{III}O_{IV,V}$	11.9163	1.08168	3	78 Pt	$L\beta_7$	$L_{III}O_I$	11.4619
1.04151	7	80 Hg	$L\beta_{15}$	$L_{III}N_{IV}$	11.9040	1.08205	7	73 Ta	$L\gamma_{11}$	L_IN_V	11.4580
1.0420	1	75 Re		L_IN_I	11.899	1.08353	3	79 Au	$L\beta_1$	$L_{II}M_{IV}$	11.4423
1.04230	5	87 Fr	$L\alpha_2$	$L_{III}M_{IV}$	11.8950	1.08377	7	73 Ta		L_IN_{IV}	11.4398
1.0428	6	93 Np	Ll	$L_{III}M_I$	11.890	1.0839	1	75 Re		$L_{II}N_{II}$	11.438
1.04382	2	35 Br	$K\alpha_2$	KL_{II}	11.8776	1.08500	5	85 At	$L\alpha_1$	$L_{III}M_V$	11.4268
1.04398	5	75 Re	$L\gamma_8$	$L_{II}O_I$	11.8758	1.08975	5	77 Ir	$L\beta_9$	L_IM_V	11.3770
1.0450	2	79 Au		$L_{III}O_{II,III}$	11.865	1.09026	7	79 Au		$L_{III}N_{III}$	11.3717
1.0450	1	33 As	K	Abs. Edge	11.865	1.0908	1	91 Pa	Ll	$L_{III}M_I$	11.366

Wavelength Å*	p.e.	Element		Designation	keV
1.0916	5	80 Hg	$L\beta_{17}$	$L_{II}M_{III}$	11.358
1.09241	7	82 Pb	$L\eta$	$L_{II}M_I$	11.3493
1.09388	5	75 Re	$L\gamma_5$	$L_{II}N_I$	11.3341
1.09671	5	85 At	$L\alpha_2$	$L_{III}M_{IV}$	11.3048
1.09702	4	77 Ir	$L\beta_{10}$	L_IM_{IV}	11.3016
1.09855	3	74 W	$L\gamma_1$	$L_{II}N_{IV}$	11.2859
1.09936	4	73 Ta	$L\gamma_3$	L_IN_{III}	11.2776
1.0997	1	81 Tl		$L_{II}M_{II}$	11.274
1.0997	1	72 Hf	L_I	Abs. Edge	11.274
1.09968	7	79 Au		$L_{III}N_{II}$	11.2743
1.0999	2	80 Hg		L_IM_I	11.272
1.10086	9	72 Hf		L_IO_{IV}	11.2622
1.10200	3	78 Pt	$L\beta_2$	$L_{III}N_V$	11.2505
1.10303	5	72 Hf	$L\gamma_4$	L_IO_{III}	11.2401
1.10376	5	72 Hf	$L\gamma_4'$	L_IO_{II}	11.2326
1.10394	5	78 Pt	$L\beta_3$	L_IM_{III}	11.2308
1.10477	2	34 Se	$K\alpha_1$	KL_{III}	11.2224
1.1053	1	73 Ta	$L\gamma_2$	L_IN_{II}	11.217
1.1058	1	77 Ir	L_{III}	Abs. Edge	11.212
1.10585	3	77 Ir	$L\beta_5$	$L_{III}O_{IV,V}$	11.2114
1.10651	3	79 Au	$L\beta_4$	L_IM_{II}	11.2047
1.10664	9	72 Hf		L_IO_I	11.2034
1.10882	2	34 Se	$K\alpha_2$	KL_{II}	11.1814
1.10923	6	77 Ir		$L_{III}O_{II,III}$	11.1772
1.11092	3	79 Au	$L\beta_6$	$L_{III}N_I$	11.1602
1.11145	4	77 Ir	Lu	$L_{III}N_{VI,VII}$	11.1549
1.1129	2	78 Pt		$L_{II}M_V$	11.140
1.1137	1	73 Ta	L_{II}	Abs. Edge	11.132
1.11386	4	84 Po	$L\alpha_1$	$L_{III}M_V$	11.1308
1.11388	3	73 Ta	$L\gamma_6$	$L_{II}O_{IV}$	11.1306
1.11489	3	77 Ir	$L\beta_7$	$L_{III}O_I$	11.1205
1.1149	2	74 W		$L_{II}N_{III}$	11.120
1.11508	4	90 Th	Ll	$L_{III}M_I$	11.1186
1.11521	9	73 Ta		L_IN_I	11.1173
1.1158	1	73 Ta	Lv	$L_{II}N_{VI}$	11.1113
1.11658	5	32 Ge	K	Abs. Edge	11.1036
1.11686	2	32 Ge	$K\beta_2$	$KN_{II,III}$	11.1008
1.11693	9	73 Ta		$L_{II}O_{III}$	11.1001
1.11789	9	73 Ta		$L_{II}O_{II}$	11.0907
1.1195	1	32 Ge	$K\beta_5$	$KM_{IV,V}$	11.0745
1.11990	2	78 Pt	$L\beta_1$	$L_{II}M_{IV}$	11.0707
1.1205	1	73 Ta	$L\gamma_8$	$L_{II}O_I$	11.0646
1.12146	9	72 Hf	$L\gamma_{11}$	L_IN_V	11.0553
1.1218	3	74 W		$L_{II}N_{II}$	11.052
1.12250	9	72 Hf		L_IN_{IV}	11.0451
1.1226	2	78 Pt		$L_{III}N_{III}$	11.044
1.12548	5	84 Po	$L\alpha_2$	$L_{III}M_{IV}$	11.0158
1.12637	6	76 Os	$L\beta_9$	L_IM_V	11.0071
1.12769	3	81 Tl	$L\eta$	$L_{II}M_I$	10.9943
1.12798	5	79 Au	$L\beta_{17}$	$L_{II}M_{III}$	10.9915
1.12894	2	32 Ge	$K\beta_1$	KM_{III}	10.9821
1.12936	9	32 Ge	$K\beta_3$	KM_{II}	10.9780
1.1310	2	78 Pt		$L_{III}N_{II}$	10.962
1.13235	3	74 W	$L\gamma_8$	$L_{II}N_I$	10.9490
1.13353	5	76 Os	$L\beta_{10}$	L_IM_{IV}	10.9376
1.13525	5	79 Au		L_IM_I	10.9210
1.13532	3	77 Ir	$L\beta_2$	$L_{III}N_V$	10.9203
1.13687	9	73 Ta		$L_{II}N_V$	10.9055
1.13707	3	77 Ir	$L\beta_{15}$	$L_{III}N_{IV}$	10.9036
1.13794	3	73 Ta	$L\gamma_1$	$L_{II}N_{IV}$	10.8952
1.13841	5	72 Hf	$L\gamma_3$	L_IN_{III}	10.8907
1.1387	5	80 Hg		$L_{II}M_{II}$	10.888
1.1402	1	71 Lu	L_I	Abs. Edge	10.8740
1.1405	1	76 Os	$L\beta_5$	$L_{III}O_{IV,V}$	10.8711
1.1408	1	76 Os	L_{III}	Abs. Edge	10.8683
1.14085	3	77 Ir	$L\beta_3$	L_IM_{III}	10.8674
1.14223	5	78 Pt	$L\beta_4$	L_IM_{II}	10.8543
1.1435	1	71 Lu	$L\gamma_4$	$L_IO_{II,III}$	10.8425
1.14355	5	78 Pt	$L\beta_6$	$L_{III}N_I$	10.8418
1.14386	2	83 Bi	$L\alpha_1$	$L_{III}M_V$	10.8388
1.14442	5	72 Hf	$L\gamma_2$	L_IN_{II}	10.8335
1.14537	7	76 Os	Lu	$L_{III}N_{VI,VII}$	10.8245
1.1489	2	77 Ir		$L_{II}M_V$	10.791
1.14933	8	76 Os	$L\beta_7$	$L_{III}O_I$	10.7872
1.1548	1	72 Hf	L_{II}	Abs. Edge	10.7362
1.15519	5	72 Hf	$L\gamma_6$	$L_{II}O_{IV}$	10.7325
1.1553	1	73 Ta		$L_{II}N_{III}$	10.7316
1.15536	1	83 Bi	$L\alpha_2$	$L_{III}M_{IV}$	10.73091
1.1560	3	77 Ir		$L_{III}N_{III}$	10.725
1.15781	3	77 Ir	$L\beta_1$	$L_{II}M_{IV}$	10.7083
1.15830	9	72 Hf	Lv	$L_{II}N_{VI}$	10.7037
1.1600	2	73 Ta		$L_{II}N_{II}$	10.688
1.16107	9	71 Lu	$L\gamma_{11}$	L_IN_V	10.6782
1.16138	5	72 Hf	$L\gamma_8$	$L_{II}O_I$	10.6754
1.16227	9	71 Lu		L_IN_{IV}	10.6672
1.1640	1	80 Hg	$L\eta$	$L_{II}M_I$	10.6512
1.16487	4	75 Re	$L\beta_9$	L_IM_V	10.6433
1.16545	5	77 Ir		$L_{III}N_{II}$	10.6380
1.1667	1	78 Pt	$L\beta_{17}$	$L_{II}M_{III}$	10.6265
1.16719	5	88 Ra	Ll	$L_{III}M_I$	10.6222
1.16962	9	78 Pt		L_IM_I	10.6001
1.16979	8	76 Os	$L\beta_2$	$L_{III}N_V$	10.5985
1.1708	1	79 Au		$L_{II}M_{II}$	10.5892
1.17167	5	76 Os	$L\beta_{15}$	$L_{III}N_{IV}$	10.5816
1.17218	5	75 Re	$L\beta_{10}$	L_IM_{IV}	10.5770
1.1729	1	73 Ta	$L\gamma_5$	$L_{II}N_I$	10.5702
1.17501	2	82 Pb	$L\alpha_1$	$L_{III}M_V$	10.5515
1.17588	1	33 As	$K\alpha_1$	KL_{III}	10.54372
1.17721	5	75 Re	$L\beta_5$	$L_{III}O_{IV,V}$	10.5318
1.1773	1	75 Re	L_{III}	Abs. Edge	10.5306
1.17788	9	72 Hf		$L_{II}N_V$	10.5258
1.17796	3	77 Ir	$L\beta_6$	$L_{III}N_I$	10.5251
1.17900	5	72 Hf	$L\gamma_1$	$L_{II}N_{IV}$	10.5158
1.17953	4	71 Lu	$L\gamma_3$	L_IN_{III}	10.5110
1.17955	7	76 Os	$L\beta_3$	L_IM_{III}	10.5108
1.17958	3	77 Ir	$L\beta_4$	L_IM_{II}	10.5106
1.17987	1	33 As	$K\alpha_2$	KL_{II}	10.50799
1.1815	1	75 Re	Lu	$L_{III}N_{VI,VII}$	10.4931
1.1818	1	70 Yb	L_I	Abs. Edge	10.4904
1.1827	1	70 Yb		$L_IO_{IV,V}$	10.4833
1.1853	1	70 Yb	$L\gamma_4$	$L_IO_{II,III}$	10.4603
1.1853	2	71 Lu	$L\gamma_2$	L_IN_{II}	10.460
1.18610	5	75 Re	$L\beta_7$	$L_{III}O_I$	10.4529
1.18648	5	82 Pb	$L\alpha_2$	$L_{III}M_{IV}$	10.4495

Wavelength Å*	p.e.	Element		Designation	keV	Wavelength Å*	p.e.	Element		Designation	keV
1.1886	1	70 Yb		L_IO_I	10.4312	1.254054	9	32 Ge	$K\alpha_1$	KL_{III}	9.88642
1.18977	7	76 Os		$L_{II}M_V$	10.4205	1.2553	1	73 Ta	L_{III}	Abs. Edge	9.8766
1.1958	1	31 Ga	K	Abs. Edge	10.3682	1.2555	1	73 Ta	$L\beta_5$	$L_{III}O_{IV,V}$	9.8750
1.19600	2	31 Ga	$K\beta_2$	$KN_{II,III}$	10.3663	1.25778	4	73 Ta	Lu	$L_{III}N_{VI,VII}$	9.8572
1.19727	7	76 Os	$L\beta_1$	$L_{II}M_{IV}$	10.3553	1.258011	9	32 Ge	$K\alpha_2$	KL_{II}	9.85532
1.1981	2	31 Ga	$K\beta_5$	$KM_{IV,V}$	10.348	1.25917	5	75 Re	$L\beta_4$	L_IM_{II}	9.8463
1.1985	1	71 Lu	L_{II}	Abs. Edge	10.3448	1.2596	1	71 Lu	$L\gamma_5$	$L_{II}N_I$	9.8428
1.1987	1	71 Lu	$L\gamma_6$	$L_{II}O_{IV}$	10.3431	1.2601	3	73 Ta		$L_{III}O_{II,III}$	9.839
1.20086	7	76 Os		$L_{III}N_{II}$	10.3244	1.26269	5	74 W	$L\beta_3$	L_IM_{III}	9.8188
1.2014	1	71 Lu		$L_{II}O_{II,III}$	10.3198	1.26385	5	73 Ta	$L\beta_7$	$L_{III}O_I$	9.8098
1.20273	3	79 Au	$L\eta$	$L_{II}M_I$	10.3083	1.2672	2	74 W		$L_{III}N_{III}$	9.784
1.2047	1	71 Lu	$L\gamma_8$	$L_{II}O_I$	10.2915	1.26769	5	70 Yb	$L\gamma_1$	$L_{II}N_{IV}$	9.7801
1.20479	7	74 W	$L\beta_9$	L_IM_V	10.2907	1.2678	2	69 Tm	$L\gamma_8$	L_IN_{III}	9.779
1.20660	4	75 Re	$L\beta_2$	$L_{III}N_V$	10.2752	1.2706	1	68 Er	L_I	Abs. Edge	9.7574
1.2069	2	77 Ir	$L\beta_{17}$		10.273	1.2728	2	74 W		$L_{II}M_V$	9.741
1.20739	4	81 Tl	$L\alpha_1$	$L_{III}M_V$	10.2685	1.2742	2	69 Tm	$L\gamma_2$	L_IN_{II}	9.730
1.20789	2	31 Ga	$K\beta_1$	KM_{III}	10.2642	1.2748	1	83 Bi	Lt	$L_{III}M_{II}$	9.7252
1.20819	5	75 Re	$L\beta_{15}$	$L_{III}N_{IV}$	10.2617	1.2752	2	68 Er	$L\gamma_4$	$L_IO_{II,III}$	9.722
1.20835	5	31 Ga	$K\beta_3$	KM_{II}	10.2603	1.27640	3	79 Au	$L\alpha_1$	$L_{III}M_V$	9.7133
1.2102	2	77 Ir		L_IM_I	10.245	1.2765	2	74 W		$L_{III}N_{II}$	9.712
1.2105	1	83 Bi	Ls	$L_{III}M_{III}$	10.2421	1.27807	5	81 Tl	Ls	$L_{III}M_{III}$	9.7007
1.21218	3	74 W	$L\beta_{10}$	L_IM_{IV}	10.2279	1.281809	9	74 W	$L\beta_1$	$L_{II}M_{IV}$	9.67235
1.213	1	78 Pt		$L_{II}M_I$	10.225	1.2829	5	84 Po	Ll	$L_{III}M_I$	9.664
1.21349	5	76 Os	$L\beta_6$	$L_{III}N_I$	10.2169	1.2834	1	30 Zn	K	Abs. Edge	9.6607
1.21537	5	72 Hf	$L\gamma_5$	$L_{II}N_I$	10.2011	1.28372	2	30 Zn	$K\beta_2$	$KN_{II,III}$	9.6580
1.21545	3	74 W	$L\beta_5$	$L_{III}O_{IV,V}$	10.2004	1.28448	3	77 Ir	$L\eta$	$L_{II}M_I$	9.6522
1.2155	1	74 W	L_{III}	Abs. Edge	10.1999	1.28454	2	73 Ta	$L\beta_2$	$L_{III}N_V$	9.6518
1.21844	5	76 Os	$L\beta_4$	L_IM_{II}	10.1754	1.2848	1	30 Zn	$K\beta_5$	$KM_{IV,V}$	9.6501
1.21868	5	74 W	Lu	$L_{III}N_{VI,VII}$	10.1733	1.28619	5	73 Ta	$L\beta_{15}$	$L_{III}N_{IV}$	9.6394
1.21875	3	81 Tl	$L\alpha_2$	$L_{III}M_{IV}$	10.1728	1.28772	3	79 Au	$L\alpha_2$	$L_{III}M_{IV}$	9.6280
1.22031	5	75 Re	$L\beta_3$	L_IM_{III}	10.1598	1.2892	1	69 Tm	L_{II}	Abs. Edge	9.6171
1.2211	2	74 W		$L_{III}O_{II,III}$	10.153	1.28989	7	74 W	$L\beta_6$	$L_{III}N_I$	9.6117
1.22228	4	71 Lu	$L\gamma_1$	$L_{II}N_{IV}$	10.1434	1.29025	9	72 Hf	$L\beta_9$	L_IM_V	9.6090
1.22232	5	70 Yb	$L\gamma_8$	L_IN_{III}	10.1431	1.2905	2	69 Tm	$L\gamma_6$	$L_{II}O_{IV}$	9.607
1.22400	4	74 W	$L\beta_7$	$L_{III}O_I$	10.1292	1.2927	1	75 Re	$L\beta_{17}$	$L_{II}M_{III}$	9.5910
1.2250	1	69 Tm	L_I	Abs. Edge	10.1206	1.2934	2	76 Os		$L_{II}M_{II}$	9.586
1.2263	3	69 Tm		$L_IO_{IV,V}$	10.110	1.29525	2	30 Zn	$K\beta_{1,3}$	$KM_{II,III}$	9.5720
1.2283	1	75 Re		$L_{III}N_{III}$	10.0933	1.2972	1	72 Hf	L_{III}	Abs. Edge	9.5577
1.22879	1	70 Yb	$L\gamma_2$	L_IN_{II}	10.0897	1.29761	5	72 Hf	$L\beta_5$	$L_{III}O_{IV,V}$	9.5546
1.2294	2	69 Tm	$L\gamma_4$	$L_IO_{II,III}$	10.084	1.29819	9	72 Hf	$L\beta_{10}$	L_IM_{IV}	9.5503
1.2305	1	75 Re		$L_{II}M_V$	10.0753	1.30162	5	74 W	$L\beta_4$	L_IM_{II}	9.5252
1.23858	2	75 Re	$L\beta_1$	$L_{II}M_{IV}$	10.0100	1.30165	9	72 Hf	Lu	$L_{III}N_{VI,VII}$	9.5249
1.24120	5	80 Hg	$L\alpha_1$	$L_{III}M_V$	9.9888	1.30564	5	72 Hf	$L\beta_7$	$L_{III}O_I$	9.4958
1.24271	3	70 Yb	$L\gamma_6$	$L_{II}O_{IV}$	9.9766	1.3063	1	70 Yb	$L\gamma_5$	$L_{II}N_I$	9.4910
1.2428	1	70 Yb	L_{II}	Abs. Edge	9.9761	1.30678	3	73 Ta	$L\beta_3$	L_IM_{III}	9.4875
1.2429	2	78 Pt	$L\eta$	$L_{II}M_I$	9.975	1.30767	7	82 Pb	Lt	$L_{III}M_{II}$	9.4811
1.24385	7	82 Pb	Ls	$L_{III}M_{III}$	9.9675	1.3086	1	73 Ta		$L_{III}N_{III}$	9.4742
1.24460	3	74 W	$L\beta_2$	$L_{III}N_V$	9.9615	1.3112	2	80 Hg	Ls	$L_{III}M_{III}$	9.455
1.2453	1	70 Yb		$L_{II}O_{II,III}$	9.9561	1.31304	3	78 Pt	$L\alpha_1$	$L_{III}M_V$	9.4423
1.24631	3	74 W	$L\beta_{15}$	$L_{III}N_{IV}$	9.9478	1.3146	1	68 Er	$L\gamma_8$	L_IN_{III}	9.4309
1.2466	2	73 Ta	$L\beta_9$	L_IM_V	9.946	1.3153	2	69 Tm	$L\gamma_1$	$L_{II}N_{IV}$	9.426
1.2480	2	76 Os	$L\beta_{17}$	$L_{II}M_{III}$	9.934	1.31610	7	83 Bi	Ll	$L_{III}M_I$	9.4204
1.24923	5	70 Yb	$L\gamma_8$	$L_{II}O_I$	9.9246	1.3167	1	73 Ta		$L_{III}N_{II}$	9.4158
1.2502	3	77 Ir		$L_{II}M_{II}$	9.917	1.31897	9	73 Ta		$L_{II}M_V$	9.3998
1.25100	5	75 Re	$L\beta_6$	$L_{III}N_I$	9.9105	1.3190	1	67 Ho	L_I	Abs. Edge	9.3994
1.25264	7	80 Hg	$L\alpha_2$	$L_{III}M_{IV}$	9.8976	1.3208	3	67 Ho		$L_IO_{IV,V}$	9.387
1.2537	2	73 Ta	$L\beta_{10}$	L_IM_{IV}	9.889	1.3210	2	68 Er	$L\gamma_2$	L_IN_{II}	9.385

Wavelength Å*	p.e.	Element	Designation		keV
1.3225	2	67 Ho	$L\gamma_4$	$L_I O_{II,III}$	9.374
1.32432	2	78 Pt	$L\alpha_2$	$L_{III} M_{IV}$	9.3618
1.32639	5	72 Hf	$L\beta_2$	$L_{II} N_V$	9.3473
1.32698	3	73 Ta	$L\beta_1$	$L_{II} M_{IV}$	9.3431
1.32783	5	72 Hf	$L\beta_{15}$	$L_{III} N_{IV}$	9.3371
1.32785	7	76 Os	$L\eta$	$L_{II} M_I$	9.3370
1.33094	8	73 Ta	$L\beta_6$	$L_{III} N_I$	9.3153
1.3358	1	71 Lu	$L\beta_9$	$L_I M_V$	9.2816
1.3365	3	74 W		$L_I M_I$	9.277
1.3366	1	75 Re		$L_{II} M_{II}$	9.2761
1.3386	1	68 Er	L_{II}	Abs. Edge	9.2622
1.3387	2	74 W	$L\beta_{17}$	$L_{II} M_{III}$	9.261
1.3397	3	68 Er	$L\gamma_6$	$L_{II} O_{IV}$	9.255
1.340083	9	31 Ga	$K\alpha_1$	$K L_{III}$	9.25174
1.3405	1	71 Lu	L_{III}	Abs. Edge	9.2490
1.34154	5	81 Tl	Lt	$L_{III} M_{II}$	9.2417
1.34183	7	71 Lu	$L\beta_5$	$L_{III} O_{IV,V}$	9.2397
1.3430	2	71 Lu	$L\beta_{10}$	$L_I M_{IV}$	9.232
1.34399	1	31 Ga	$K\alpha_2$	$K L_{II}$	9.22482
1.34524	9	71 Lu		$L_{III} O_{II,III}$	9.2163
1.34581	3	73 Ta	$L\beta_4$	$L_I M_{II}$	9.2124
1.34949	5	71 Lu	$L\beta_7$	$L_{III} O_I$	9.1873
1.34990	7	82 Pb	Ll	$L_{III} M_I$	9.1845
1.35053	9	72 Hf		$L_{II} N_{III}$	9.1802
1.35128	3	77 Ir	$L\alpha_1$	$L_{III} M_V$	9.1751
1.35131	7	79 Au	Ls	$L_{III} M_{III}$	9.1749
1.35300	5	72 Hf	$L\beta_3$	$L_I M_{III}$	9.1634
1.3558	2	69 Tm	$L\gamma_5$	$L_{II} N_I$	9.144
1.35887	9	72 Hf		$L_{III} N_{II}$	9.1239
1.36250	5	77 Ir	$L\alpha_2$	$L_{III} M_{IV}$	9.0995
1.3641	2	68 Er	$L\gamma_1$	$L_{II} N_{IV}$	9.089
1.3643	2	67 Ho	$L\gamma_2$	$L_I N_{II}$	9.087
1.3692	1	66 Dy	L_I	Abs. Edge	9.0548
1.3698	2	67 Ho	$L\gamma_2$	$L_I N_{II}$	9.051
1.37012	3	71 Lu	$L\beta_2$	$L_{III} N_V$	9.0489
1.3715	1	71 Lu	$L\beta_{15}$	$L_{III} N_{IV}$	9.0395
1.37342	5	75 Re	$L\eta$	$L_{II} M_I$	9.0272
1.37410	5	72 Hf	$L\beta_1$	$L_{II} M_{IV}$	9.0227
1.37410	5	72 Hf	$L\beta_6$	$L_{III} N_I$	9.0227
1.37459	7	66 Dy	$L\gamma_4$	$L_I O_{II,III}$	9.0195
1.3746	2	80 Hg	Lt	$L_{III} M_{II}$	9.019
1.38059	5	29 Cu	K	Abs. Edge	8.9803
1.38109	3	29 Cu	$K\beta_2$	$K M_{IV,V}$	8.9770
1.3838	1	70 Yb	$L\beta_9$	$L_I M_V$	8.9597
1.38477	3	81 Tl	Ll	$L_{III} M_I$	8.9532
1.3862	1	70 Yb	L_{III}	Abs. Edge	8.9441
1.3864	1	73 Ta	$L\beta_{17}$	$L_{II} M_{III}$	8.9428
1.38696	7	70 Yb	$L\beta_5$	$L_{III} O_{IV,V}$	8.9390
1.3895	2	78 Pt	Ls	$L_{III} M_{III}$	8.923
1.3898	1	70 Yb		$L_{III} O_{II,III}$	8.9209
1.3905	1	67 Ho	L_{II}	Abs. Edge	8.9164
1.39121	5	76 Os	$L\alpha_1$	$L_{III} M_V$	8.9117
1.3915	1	70 Yb	$L\beta_{10}$	$L_I M_{IV}$	8.9100
1.39220	5	72 Hf	$L\beta_4$	$L_I M_{II}$	8.9054
1.392218	9	29 Cu	$K\beta_{1,3}$	$K M_{II,III}$	8.90529
1.3923	2	67 Ho	$L\gamma_6$	$L_{II} O_{IV}$	8.905
1.3926	1	29 Cu	$K\beta_3$	$K M_{II}$	8.9029
1.3948	1	70 Yb	$L\beta_7$	$L_{III} O_I$	8.8889
1.3983	2	67 Ho	$L\gamma_8$	$L_{II} O_I$	8.867
1.40140	5	71 Lu	$L\beta_3$	$L_I M_{III}$	8.8469
1.40234	5	76 Os	$L\alpha_2$	$L_{III} M_{IV}$	8.8410
1.4067	3	68 Er	$L\gamma_5$	$L_{II} N_I$	8.814
1.41366	7	79 Au	Lt	$L_{III} M_{II}$	8.7702
1.41550	5	70 Yb	$L\beta_{2,15}$	$L_{III} N_{IV,V}$	8.7588
1.41640	7	66 Dy	$L\gamma_3$	$L_I N_{III}$	8.7532
1.4174	2	67 Ho	$L\gamma_1$	$L_{II} N_{IV}$	8.747
1.4189	1	71 Lu	$L\beta_6$	$L_{III} N_I$	8.7376
1.42110	3	74 W	$L\eta$	$L_{II} M_I$	8.7243
1.4216	1	80 Hg	Ll	$L_{III} M_I$	8.7210
1.4223	1	65 Tb	L_I	Abs. Edge	8.7167
1.42278	7	66 Dy	$L\gamma_2$	$L_I N_{II}$	8.7140
1.4228	3	65 Tb		$L_I O_{IV,V}$	8.714
1.42359	3	71 Lu	$L\beta_1$	$L_{II} M_{IV}$	8.7090
1.4276	2	65 Tb	$L\gamma_4$	$L_I O_{II,III}$	8.685
1.43025	9	72 Hf		$L_I M_I$	8.6685
1.43048	9	73 Ta		$L_{II} M_{II}$	8.6671
1.4318	2	77 Ir	Ls	$L_{III} M_{III}$	8.659
1.43290	4	75 Re	$L\alpha_1$	$L_{III} M_V$	8.6525
1.4334	1	69 Tm	L_{III}	Abs. Edge	8.6496
1.4336	3	69 Tm	$L\beta_9$	$L_I M_V$	8.648
1.4349	2	69 Tm	$L\beta_5$	$L_{III} O_{IV,V}$	8.641
1.435155	7	30 Zn	$K\alpha_1$	$K L_{III}$	8.63886
1.43643	9	72 Hf	$L\beta_{17}$	$L_{II} M_{III}$	8.6312
1.439000	8	30 Zn	$K\alpha_2$	$K L_{II}$	8.61578
1.44056	5	71 Lu	$L\beta_4$	$L_I M_{II}$	8.6064
1.4410	3	69 Tm	$L\beta_{10}$	$L_I M_{IV}$	8.604
1.44396	5	75 Re	$L\alpha_2$	$L_{III} M_{IV}$	8.5862
1.4445	1	66 Dy	L_{II}	Abs. Edge	8.5830
1.44579	7	66 Dy	$L\gamma_6$	$L_{II} O_{IV}$	8.5753
1.45233	5	70 Yb	$L\beta_3$	$L_I M_{III}$	8.5367
1.4530	2	78 Pt	Lt	$L_{III} M_{III}$	8.533
1.45964	9	79 Au	Ll	$L_{III} M_I$	8.4939
1.4618	2	67 Ho	$L\gamma_5$	$L_{II} N_I$	8.481
1.4640	2	69 Tm	$L\beta_{2,15}$	$L_{III} N_{IV,V}$	8.468
1.4661	1	70 Yb	$L\beta_6$	$L_{III} N_I$	8.4563
1.47106	5	73 Ta	$L\eta$	$L_{II} M_I$	8.4280
1.4718	2	65 Tb	$L\gamma_3$	$L_I N_{III}$	8.423
1.47266	7	66 Dy	$L\gamma_1$	$L_{II} N_{IV}$	8.4188
1.4735	2	76 Os	Ls	$L_{III} M_{III}$	8.414
1.47565	5	70 Yb	$L\beta_1$	$L_{II} M_{IV}$	8.4018
1.4764	2	65 Tb	$L\gamma_2$	$L_I N_{II}$	8.398
1.47639	2	74 W	$L\alpha_1$	$L_{III} M_V$	8.3976
1.4784	1	64 Gd	L_I	Abs. Edge	8.3864
1.48064	9	72 Hf		$L_{II} M_{II}$	8.3735
1.4807	3	64 Gd		$L_I O_{IV,V}$	8.373
1.4835	1	68 Er	L_{III}	Abs. Edge	8.3575
1.4839	2	64 Gd	$L\gamma_4$	$L_I O_{II,III}$	8.355
1.4848	3	68 Er	$L\beta_5$	$L_{III} O_{IV,V}$	8.350
1.4855	5	68 Er	$L\beta_9$	$L_I M_V$	8.346
1.48743	2	74 W	$L\alpha_2$	$L_{III} M_{IV}$	8.3352
1.48807	1	28 Ni	K	Abs. Edge	8.33165
1.48862	4	28 Ni	$K\beta_5$	$K M_{IV,V}$	8.3286
1.49138	3	70 Yb	$L\beta_4$	$L_I M_{II}$	8.3132
1.4930	3	77 Ir	Lt	$L_{III} M_{II}$	8.304

Wavelength Å*	p.e.	Element	Designation		keV
1.4941	3	68 Er	$L\beta_7$	$L_{III}O_I$	8.298
1.4941	3	68 Er	$L\beta_{10}$	$L_I M_{IV}$	8.298
1.4995	2	78 Pt	Ll	$L_{III}M_I$	8.268
1.500135	8	28 Ni	$K\beta_{1,3}$	$KM_{II,III}$	8.26466
1.5023	1	65 Tb	L_{II}	Abs. Edge	8.2527
1.5035	2	65 Tb	$L\gamma_6$	$L_{II}O_{IV}$	8.246
1.5063	2	69 Tm	$L\beta_2$	$L_I M_{III}$	8.231
1.5097	2	65 Tb	$L\gamma_8$	$L_{II}O_I$	8.212
1.51399	9	68 Er	$L\beta_{2,15}$	$L_{III}N_{IV,V}$	8.1890
1.5162	2	69 Tm	$L\beta_6$	$L_{III}N_I$	8.177
1.5178	1	75 Re	Ls	$L_{III}M_{III}$	8.1682
1.51824	7	66 Dy	$L\gamma_5$	$L_{II}N_I$	8.1661
1.52197	2	73 Ta	$L\alpha_1$	$L_{III}M_V$	8.1461
1.52325	5	72 Hf	$L\eta$	$L_{II}M_I$	8.1393
1.5297	2	64 Gd	$L\gamma_3$	$L_I N_{III}$	8.105
1.5303	2	65 Tb	$L\gamma_1$	$L_{II}N_{IV}$	8.102
1.5304	2	69 Tm	$L\beta_1$	$L_{II}M_{IV}$	8.101
1.53293	2	73 Ta	$L\alpha_2$	$L_{III}M_{IV}$	8.0879
1.5331	2	64 Gd	$L\gamma_2$	$L_I N_{II}$	8.087
1.53333	9	71 Lu		$L_{II}M_{II}$	8.0858
1.5347	2	76 Os	Ll	$L_{III}M_{II}$	8.079
1.5368	1	67 Ho	L_{III}	Abs. Edge	8.0676
1.5378	2	67 Ho	$L\beta_5$	$L_{III}O_{IV,V}$	8.062
1.5381	1	63 Eu	L_I	Abs. Edge	8.0607
1.540562	2	29 Cu	$K\alpha_1$	KL_{III}	8.04778
1.54094	3	77 Ir	Ll	$L_{III}M_I$	8.0458
1.5439	1	63 Eu	$L\gamma_4$	$L_I O_{II,III}$	8.0304
1.544390	9	29 Cu	$K\alpha_2$	KL_{II}	8.02783
1.5448	2	69 Tm	$L\beta_4$	$L_I M_{II}$	8.026
1.5486	3	67 Ho	$L\beta_{10}$	$L_I M_{IV}$	8.006
1.5616	1	68 Er	$L\beta_3$	$L_I M_{III}$	7.9392
1.5632	1	64 Gd	L_{II}	Abs. Edge	7.9310
1.5642	3	74 W	Ls	$L_{III}M_{III}$	7.926
1.5644	2	64 Gd	$L\gamma_6$	$L_{II}O_{IV}$	7.925
1.5671	2	67 Ho	$L\beta_{2,15}$	$L_{III}N_{IV,V}$	7.911
1.5675	2	68 Er	$L\beta_6$	$L_{III}N_I$	7.909
1.56958	5	72 Hf	$L\alpha_1$	$L_{III}M_V$	7.8990
1.5707	2	64 Gd	$L\gamma_8$	$L_{II}O_I$	7.894
1.5779	1	71 Lu	$L\eta$	$L_{II}M_I$	7.8575
1.5787	2	65 Tb	$L\gamma_5$	$L_{II}N_I$	7.8535
1.5789	1	75 Re	Ls	$L_{III}M_{II}$	7.8525
1.58046	5	72 Hf	$L\alpha_2$	$L_{III}M_{IV}$	7.8446
1.58498	7	76 Os	Ll	$L_{III}M_I$	7.8222
1.5873	1	68 Er	$L\beta_1$	$L_{III}M_{IV}$	7.8109
1.58837	7	66 Dy	$L\beta_5$	$L_{III}O_{IV,V}$	7.8055
1.58844	9	70 Yb		$L_{II}M_{II}$	7.8052
1.5903	2	63 Eu	$L\gamma_3$	$L_I N_{III}$	7.7961
1.5916	1	66 Dy	L_{III}	Abs. Edge	7.7897
1.5924	2	64 Gd	$L\gamma_1$	$L_{II}N_{IV}$	7.7858
1.5961	2	63 Eu	$L\gamma_2$	$L_I N_{II}$	7.7677
1.59973	9	66 Dy	$L\beta_9$	$L_I M_V$	7.7501
1.6002	1	62 Sm	L_I	Abs. Edge	7.7478
1.6007	1	68 Er	$L\beta_4$	$L_I M_{II}$	7.7453
1.60447	7	66 Dy	$L\beta_7$	$L_{III}O_I$	7.7272
1.60728	3	62 Sm	$L\gamma_4$	$L_I O_{II,III}$	7.714
1.60743	9	66 Dy	$L\beta_{10}$	$L_I M_{IV}$	7.7130
1.60815	1	27 Co	K	Abs. Edge	7.70954
1.60891	3	27 Co	$K\beta_5$	$KM_{IV,V}$	7.7059
1.61264	9	73 Ta	Ls	$L_{III}M_{III}$	7.6881
1.61951	3	71 Lu	$L\alpha_1$	$L_{III}M_V$	7.6555
1.6203	2	67 Ho	$L\beta_3$	$L_I M_{III}$	7.6519
1.62079	2	27 Co	$K\beta_{1,3}$	$KM_{II,III}$	7.64943
1.6237	2	67 Ho	$L\beta_6$	$L_{III}N_I$	7.6359
1.62369	7	66 Dy	$L\beta_{2,15}$	$L_{III}N_{IV,V}$	7.6357
1.6244	3	74 W	Ll	$L_{III}M_I$	7.6324
1.6271	1	63 Eu	L_{II}	Abs. Edge	7.6199
1.6282	2	63 Eu	$L\gamma_6$	$L_{II}O_{IV}$	7.6147
1.63029	5	71 Lu	$L\alpha_2$	$L_{III}M_{IV}$	7.6049
1.63056	5	75 Re	Ll	$L_{III}M_I$	7.6036
1.6346	2	63 Eu	$L\gamma_8$	$L_{II}O_I$	7.5849
1.63560	5	70 Yb	$L\eta$	$L_{II}M_I$	7.5802
1.6412	2	64 Gd	$L\gamma_5$	$L_{II}N_I$	7.5543
1.6475	2	67 Ho	$L\beta_1$	$L_{II}M_{IV}$	7.5253
1.6497	1	65 Tb	L_{III}	Abs. Edge	7.5153
1.6510	2	65 Tb	$L\beta_5$	$L_{III}O_{IV,V}$	7.5094
1.65601	3	62 Sm	$L\gamma_3$	$L_I N_{III}$	7.487
1.6574	2	63 Eu	$L\gamma_1$	$L_{II}N_{IV}$	7.4803
1.657910	8	28 Ni	$K\alpha_1$	KL_{III}	7.47815
1.6585	2	65 Tb	$L\beta_7$	$L_{III}O_I$	7.4753
1.6595	2	67 Ho	$L\beta_4$	$L_I M_{II}$	7.4708
1.66044	6	62 Sm	$L\gamma_2$	$L_I N_{II}$	7.467
1.661747	8	28 Ni	$K\alpha_2$	KL_{II}	7.46089
1.66346	9	72 Hf	Ls	$L_{III}M_{III}$	7.4532
1.6673	3	65 Tb	$L\beta_{10}$	$L_I M_{IV}$	7.436
1.6674	5	61 Pm	L_I	Abs. Edge	7.436
1.67189	4	70 Yb	$L\alpha_1$	$L_{III}M_V$	7.4156
1.67265	9	73 Ta	Ll	$L_{III}M_{II}$	7.4123
1.6782	1	74 W	Ll	$L_{III}M_I$	7.3878
1.68213	7	66 Dy	$L\beta_6$	$L_{III}N_I$	7.3705
1.6822	2	66 Dy	$L\beta_3$	$L_I M_{III}$	7.3702
1.68285	5	70 Yb	$L\alpha_2$	$L_{III}M_{IV}$	7.3673
1.6830	2	65 Tb	$L\beta_{2,15}$	$L_{III}N_{IV,V}$	7.3667
1.6953	1	62 Sm	L_{II}	Abs. Edge	7.3132
1.6963	2	69 Tm	$L\eta$	$L_{II}M_I$	7.3088
1.6966	9	62 Sm	$L\gamma_6$	$L_{II}O_{IV}$	7.308
1.7085	2	63 Eu	$L\gamma_5$	$L_{II}N_I$	7.2566
1.71062	7	66 Dy	$L\beta_1$	$L_{II}M_{IV}$	7.2477
1.7117	1	64 Gd	L_{III}	Abs. Edge	7.2430
1.7130	2	64 Gd	$L\beta_5$	$L_{III}O_{IV,V}$	7.2374
1.7203	2	64 Gd	$L\beta_7$	$L_{III}O_I$	7.2071
1.72103	7	66 Dy	$L\beta_4$	$L_I M_{II}$	7.2039
1.72305	9	72 Hf	Ll	$L_{III}M_{II}$	7.1954
1.7240	3	64 Gd	$L\beta_9$	$L_I M_V$	7.192
1.72724	3	62 Sm	$L\gamma_1$	$L_{II}N_{IV}$	7.178
1.7268	2	69 Tm	$L\alpha_1$	$L_{III}M_V$	7.1799
1.72841	5	73 Ta	Ll	$L_{III}M_I$	7.1731
1.7315	3	64 Gd	$L\beta_{10}$	$L_I M_{IV}$	7.160
1.7381	2	69 Tm	$L\alpha_2$	$L_{III}M_{IV}$	7.1331
1.7390	1	60 Nd	L_I	Abs. Edge	7.1294
1.7422	2	65 Tb	$L\beta_6$	$L_{III}N_I$	7.1163
1.74346	1	26 Fe	K	Abs. Edge	7.11120
1.7442	1	26 Fe	$K\beta_5$	$KM_{IV,V}$	7.1081
1.7445	4	60 Nd	$L\gamma_4$	$L_I O_{II,III}$	7.107
1.7455	2	64 Gd	$L\beta_{2,15}$	$L_{III}N_{IV,V}$	7.1028

Wavelength Å*	p.e.	Element	Designation		keV
1.7472	2	65 Tb	$L\beta_3$	$L_I M_{III}$	7.0959
1.75661	2	26 Fe	$K\beta_{1,3}$	$KM_{II,III}$	7.05798
1.7566	1	68 Er	$L\eta$	$L_{II} M_I$	7.0579
1.7676	5	61 Pm	L_{II}	Abs. Edge	7.014
1.7760	1	71 Lu	Ll	$L_{III} M_{II}$	6.9810
1.7761	1	63 Eu	L_{III}	Abs. Edge	6.9806
1.7768	3	65 Tb	$L\beta_1$	$L_{II} M_{IV}$	6.978
1.7772	2	63 Eu	$L\beta_5$	$L_{III} O_{IV,V}$	6.9763
1.77934	3	62 Sm	$L\gamma_5$	$L_{II} N_I$	6.968
1.78145	5	72 Hf	Ll	$L_{III} M_I$	6.9596
1.78425	9	68 Er	$L\alpha_1$	$L_{III} M_V$	6.9487
1.7851	2	63 Eu	$L\beta_7$	$L_{III} O_I$	6.9453
1.7864	2	65 Tb	$L\beta_4$	$L_I M_{II}$	6.9403
1.788965	9	27 Co	$K\alpha_1$	KL_{III}	6.93032
1.7916	3	63 Eu	$L\beta_9$	$L_I M_V$	6.920
1.792850	9	27 Co	$K\alpha_2$	KL_{II}	6.91530
1.7955	2	68 Er	$L\alpha_2$	$L_{III} M_{IV}$	6.9050
1.7964	4	60 Nd	$L\gamma_3$	$L_I N_{III}$	6.902
1.7989	9	61 Pm	$L\gamma_1$	$L_{II} N_{IV}$	6.892
1.7993	3	63 Eu	$L\beta_{10}$	$L_I M_{IV}$	6.890
1.8013	4	60 Nd	$L\gamma_2$	$L_I N_{II}$	6.883
1.8054	2	64 Gd	$L\beta_6$	$L_{III} N_I$	6.8671
1.8118	2	63 Eu	$L\beta_{2,15}$	$L_{III} N_{IV,V}$	6.8432
1.8141	5	59 Pr	L_I	Abs. Edge	6.834
1.8150	2	64 Gd	$L\beta_3$	$L_I M_{III}$	6.8311
1.8193	4	59 Pr	$L\gamma_4$	$L_I O_{II,III}$	6.815
1.8264	2	67 Ho	$L\eta$	$L_{II} M_I$	6.7883
1.83091	9	70 Yb	Ll	$L_{III} M_{II}$	6.7715
1.8360	1	71 Lu	Ll	$L_{III} M_I$	6.7528
1.8440	1	60 Nd	L_{II}	Abs. Edge	6.7234
1.8450	2	67 Ho	$L\alpha_1$	$L_{III} M_V$	6.7198
1.8457	1	62 Sm	L_{III}	Abs. Edge	6.7172
1.8468	2	64 Gd	$L\beta_1$	$L_{III} M_{IV}$	6.7132
1.84700	9	62 Sm	$L\beta_5$	$L_{III} O_{IV,V}$	6.7126
1.8540	2	64 Gd	$L\beta_4$	$L_I M_{II}$	6.6871
1.8552	5	60 Nd	$L\gamma_8$	$L_{II} O_I$	6.683
1.8561	2	67 Ho	$L\alpha_2$	$L_{III} M_{IV}$	6.6795
1.85626	3	62 Sm	$L\beta_7$	$L_{III} O_I$	6.679
1.86166	3	62 Sm	$L\beta_9$	$L_I M_V$	6.660
1.86990	3	62 Sm	$L\beta_{10}$	$L_I M_{IV}$	6.634
1.8737	2	63 Eu	$L\beta_6$	$L_{III} N_I$	6.6170
1.8740	4	59 Pr	$L\gamma_3$	$L_I N_{III}$	6.616
1.8779	2	60 Nd	$L\gamma_1$	$L_{II} N_{IV}$	6.6021
1.8791	4	59 Pr	$L\gamma_2$	$L_I N_{II}$	6.598
1.8821	3	62 Sm	$L\beta_{2,15}$	$L_{III} N_{IV,V}$	6.586
1.8867	2	63 Eu	$L\beta_3$	$L_I M_{III}$	6.5713
1.8934	5	58 Ce	L_I	Abs. Edge	6.548
1.89415	5	70 Yb	Ll	$L_{III} M_I$	6.5455
1.89643	5	25 Mn	K	Abs. Edge	6.5376
1.8971	1	25 Mn	$K\beta_5$	$KM_{IV,V}$	6.5352
1.89743	7	66 Dy	$L\eta$	$L_{II} M_I$	6.5342
1.8991	4	58 Ce	$L\gamma_4$	$L_I O_{II,III}$	6.528
1.90881	3	66 Dy	$L\alpha_1$	$L_{III} M_V$	6.4952
1.91021	2	25 Mn	$K\beta_{1,3}$	$KM_{II,III}$	6.49045
1.9191	1	61 Pm	L_{III}	Abs. Edge	6.4605
1.91991	3	66 Dy	$L\alpha_2$	$L_{III} M_{IV}$	6.4577
1.9203	2	63 Eu	$L\beta_1$	$L_{II} M_{IV}$	6.4564
1.9255	2	63 Eu	$L\beta_4$	$L_I M_{II}$	6.4389
1.9255	5	59 Pr	L_{II}	Abs. Edge	6.439
1.9355	4	60 Nd	$L\gamma_5$	$L_{II} N_I$	6.406
1.936042	9	26 Fe	$K\alpha_1$	KL_{III}	6.40384
1.9362	4	59 Pr	$L\gamma_8$	$L_{II} O_I$	6.403
1.939980	9	26 Fe	$K\alpha_2$	KL_{II}	6.39084
1.94643	3	62 Sm	$L\beta_6$	$L_{III} N_I$	6.3693
1.9550	2	69 Tm	Ll	$L_{III} M_I$	6.3419
1.9553	3	58 Ce	$L\gamma_3$	$L_I N_{III}$	6.3409
1.9559	6	61 Pm	$L\beta_{2,15}$	$L_{III} N_{IV,V}$	6.339
1.9602	3	58 Ce	$L\gamma_2$	$L_I N_{II}$	6.3250
1.9611	3	59 Pr	$L\gamma_1$	$L_{II} N_{IV}$	6.3221
1.96241	3	62 Sm	$L\beta_3$	$L_I M_{III}$	6.318
1.9730	2	65 Tb	$L\eta$	$L_{II} M_I$	6.2839
1.9765	2	65 Tb	$L\alpha_1$	$L_{III} M_V$	6.2728
1.9780	5	57 La	L_I	Abs. Edge	6.268
1.9830	4	57 La	$L\gamma_4$	$L_I O_{II,III}$	6.252
1.9875	2	65 Tb	$L\alpha_2$	$L_{III} M_{IV}$	6.2380
1.9967	1	60 Nd	L_{III}	Abs. Edge	6.2092
1.99806	3	62 Sm	$L\beta_1$	$L_{III} M_{IV}$	6.2051
2.00095	6	62 Sm	$L\beta_4$	$L_I M_{II}$	6.196
2.0092	3	60 Nd	$L\beta_7$	$L_{III} O_I$	6.1708
2.0124	5	58 Ce	L_{II}	Abs. Edge	6.161
2.015	1	68 Er	Ll	$L_{III} M_I$	6.152
2.0165	3	60 Nd	$L\beta_9$	$L_I M_V$	6.1484
2.0205	4	59 Pr	$L\gamma_5$	$L_{II} N_I$	6.136
2.0237	4	58 Ce	$L\gamma_8$	$L_{II} O_I$	6.126
2.0237	3	60 Nd	$L\beta_{10}$	$L_I M_{IV}$	6.1265
2.0360	3	60 Nd	$L\beta_{2,15}$	$L_{III} N_{IV,V}$	6.0894
2.0410	4	57 La	$L\gamma_3$	$L_I N_{III}$	6.074
2.0421	4	61 Pm	$L\beta_3$	$L_I M_{III}$	6.071
2.0460	4	57 La	$L\gamma_2$	$L_I N_{II}$	6.060
2.0468	2	64 Gd	$L\alpha_1$	$L_{III} M_V$	6.0572
2.0487	4	58 Ce	$L\gamma_1$	$L_{II} N_{IV}$	6.052
2.0494	1	64 Gd	$L\eta$	$L_{II} M_I$	6.0495
2.0578	2	64 Gd	$L\alpha_2$	$L_{III} M_{IV}$	6.0250
2.0678	5	56 Ba	L_I	Abs. Edge	5.996
2.07020	5	24 Cr	K	Abs. Edge	5.9888
2.07087	6	24 Cr	$K\beta_5$	$KM_{IV,V}$	5.9869
2.0756	3	56 Ba	$L\gamma_4$	$L_I O_{II,III}$	5.9733
2.0791	5	59 Pr	L_{III}	Abs. Edge	5.963
2.0797	4	61 Pm	$L\beta_1$	$L_{II} M_{IV}$	5.961
2.08487	2	24 Cr	$K\beta_{1,3}$	$KM_{II,III}$	5.94671
2.0860	2	67 Ho	Ll	$L_{III} M_I$	5.9434
2.0919	4	59 Pr	$L\beta_7$	$L_{III} O_I$	5.927
2.1004	4	59 Pr	$L\beta_9$	$L_I M_V$	5.903
2.101820	9	25 Mn	$K\alpha_1$	KL_{III}	5.89875
2.1039	3	60 Nd	$L\beta_6$	$L_{III} N_I$	5.8930
2.1053	5	57 La	L_{II}	Abs. Edge	5.889
2.10578	2	25 Mn	$K\alpha_2$	KL_{II}	5.88765
2.1071	4	59 Pr	$L\beta_{10}$	$L_I M_{IV}$	5.884
2.1103	3	58 Ce	$L\gamma_5$	$L_{II} N_I$	5.8751
2.1194	4	59 Pr	$L\beta_{2,15}$	$L_{III} N_{IV,V}$	5.850
2.1209	2	63 Eu	$L\alpha_1$	$L_{III} M_V$	5.8457
2.1268	2	60 Nd	$L\beta_3$	$L_I M_{III}$	5.8294
2.1315	2	63 Eu	$L\eta$	$L_{II} M_I$	5.8166
2.1315	2	63 Eu	$L\alpha_2$	$L_{III} M_{IV}$	5.8166

Wavelength Å*	p.e.	Element	Designation		keV	Wavelength Å*	p.e.	Element	Designation		keV
2.1342	2	56 Ba	$L\gamma_3$	$L_I N_{III}$	5.8092	2.3913	2	53 I	$L\gamma_4$	$L_I O_{II,III}$	5.1848
2.1387	2	56 Ba	$L\gamma_2$	$L_I N_{II}$	5.7969	2.3948	2	63 Eu	Ll	$L_{III} M_I$	5.1772
2.1418	3	57 La	$L\gamma_1$	$L_{II} N_{IV}$	5.7885	2.40435	6	56 Ba	$L\beta_{2,15}$	$L_{III} N_{IV,V}$	5.1565
2.15877	7	66 Dy	Ll	$L_{III} M_I$	5.7431	2.4094	4	60 Nd	$L\eta$	$L_{II} M_I$	5.1457
2.166	1	58 Ce	L_{III}	Abs. Edge	5.723	2.4105	3	57 La	$L\beta_3$	$L_I M_{III}$	5.1434
2.1669	3	60 Nd	$L\beta_4$	$L_I M_{II}$	5.7216	2.4174	2	55 Cs	$L\gamma_5$	$L_{II} N_I$	5.1287
2.1669	2	60 Nd	$L\beta_1$	$L_{II} M_{IV}$	5.7216	2.4292	1	54 Xe	L_{II}	Abs. Edge	5.1037
2.1673	5	55 Cs	L_I	Abs. Edge	5.721	2.442	9	90 Th		$M_I O_{III}$	5.08
2.1701	2	58 Ce	$L\beta_7$	$L_{III} O_I$	5.7132	2.443	4	92 U		$M_{II} O_{IV}$	5.075
2.1741	2	55 Cs	$L\gamma_4$	$L_I O_{II,III}$	5.7026	2.4475	2	53 I	$L\gamma_{2,3}$	$L_I N_{II,III}$	5.0657
2.1885	3	58 Ce	$L\beta_9$	$L_I M_V$	5.6650	2.4493	3	57 La	$L\beta_4$	$L_I M_{II}$	5.0620
2.1906	4	59 Pr	$L\beta_6$	$L_{III} N_I$	5.660	2.45891	5	57 La	$L\beta_1$	$L_{II} M_{IV}$	5.0421
2.1958	5	58 Ce	$L\beta_{10}$	$L_I M_{IV}$	5.646	2.4630	2	59 Pr	$L\alpha_1$	$L_{III} M_V$	5.0337
2.1998	2	62 Sm	$L\alpha_1$	$L_{III} M_V$	5.6361	2.4729	3	59 Pr	$L\alpha_2$	$L_{III} M_{IV}$	5.0135
2.2048	1	56 Ba	L_{II}	Abs. Edge	5.6233	2.4740	1	55 Cs	L_{III}	Abs. Edge	5.0113
2.2056	4	57 La	$L\gamma_5$	$L_{II} N_I$	5.621	2.4783	2	55 Cs	$L\beta_9$	$L_I M_V$	5.0026
2.2087	2	58 Ce	$L\beta_{2,15}$	$L_{III} N_{IV,V}$	5.6134	2.4823	4	62 Sm	Ll	$L_{III} M_I$	4.9945
2.21062	3	62 Sm	$L\alpha_2$	$L_{III} M_{IV}$	5.6090	2.4826	2	56 Ba	$L\beta_6$	$L_{III} N_I$	4.9939
2.2172	3	59 Pr	$L\beta_3$	$L_I M_{III}$	5.5918	2.4849	2	55 Cs	$L\beta_7$	$L_{III} O_I$	4.9893
2.21824	3	62 Sm	$L\eta$	$L_{II} M_I$	5.589	2.4920	2	55 Cs	$L\beta_{10}$	$L_I M_{IV}$	4.9752
2.2328	2	55 Cs	$L\gamma_3$	$L_I N_{III}$	5.5527	2.49734	5	22 Ti	K	Abs. Edge	4.96452
2.2352	2	65 Tb	Ll	$L_{III} M_I$	5.5467	2.4985	2	22 Ti	$K\beta_5$	$K M_{IV,V}$	4.9623
2.2371	2	55 Cs	$L\gamma_2$	$L_I N_{II}$	5.5420	2.50356	2	23 V	$K\alpha_1$	$K L_{III}$	4.95220
2.2415	2	56 Ba	$L\gamma_1$	$L_{II} N_{IV}$	5.5311	2.50738	2	23 V	$K\alpha_2$	$K L_{II}$	4.94464
2.253	6	92 U		$M_I P_{III}$	5.50	2.5099	1	52 Te	L_I	Abs. Edge	4.9397
2.2550	4	59 Pr	$L\beta_4$	$L_I M_{II}$	5.4981	2.5113	2	52 Te	$L\gamma_4$	$L_I O_{II,III}$	4.9369
2.2588	3	59 Pr	$L\beta_1$	$L_{II} M_{IV}$	5.4889	2.5118	2	55 Cs	$L\beta_{2,15}$	$L_{III} N_{IV,V}$	4.9359
2.261	1	57 La	L_{III}	Abs. Edge	5.484	2.512	3	59 Pr	$L\eta$	$L_{II} M_I$	4.935
2.2691	1	23 V	K	Abs. Edge	5.4639	2.51391	2	22 Ti	$K\beta_{1,3}$	$K M_{II,III}$	4.93181
2.26951	6	23 V	$K\beta_5$	$K M_{IV,V}$	5.4629	2.5164	2	56 Ba	$L\beta_3$	$L_I M_{III}$	4.9269
2.2737	1	54 Xe	L_I	Abs. Edge	5.4528	2.527	4	91 Pa		$M_{II} O_{IV}$	4.906
2.275	3	57 La	$L\beta_7$	$L_{III} O_I$	5.450	2.5542	5	53 I	L_{II}	Abs. Edge	4.8540
2.282	3	57 La	$L\beta_9$	$L_I M_V$	5.434	2.5553	2	56 Ba	$L\beta_4$	$L_I M_{II}$	4.8519
2.2818	3	58 Ce	$L\beta_6$	$L_{III} N_I$	5.4334	2.5615	2	58 Ce	$L\alpha_1$	$L_{III} M_V$	4.8402
2.2822	3	61 Pm	$L\alpha_1$	$L_{III} M_V$	5.4325	2.5674	2	52 Te	$L\gamma_{2,3}$	$L_I N_{II,III}$	4.8290
2.28440	2	23 V	$K\beta_{1,3}$	$K M_{II,III}$	5.42729	2.56821	5	56 Ba	$L\beta_1$	$L_{II} M_{IV}$	4.82753
2.28970	2	24 Cr	$K\alpha_1$	$K L_{III}$	5.41472	2.5706	3	58 Ce	$L\alpha_2$	$L_{III} M_{IV}$	4.8230
2.290	3	57 La	$L\beta_{10}$	$L_I M_{IV}$	5.415	2.58244	8	53 I	$L\gamma_1$	$L_{II} N_{IV}$	4.8009
2.2926	4	61 Pm	$L\alpha_2$	$L_{III} M_{IV}$	5.4078	2.5926	1	54 Xe	L_{III}	Abs. Edge	4.7822
2.293606	3	24 Cr	$K\alpha_2$	$K L_{II}$	5.405509	2.5932	2	55 Cs	$L\beta_6$	$L_{III} N_I$	4.7811
2.3030	3	57 La	$L\beta_{2,15}$	$L_{III} N_{IV,V}$	5.3835	2.618	5	90 Th		$M_{II} O_{IV}$	4.735
2.304	7	92 U		$M_I O_{III}$	5.38	2.6203	4	58 Ce	$L\eta$	$L_{II} M_I$	4.7315
2.3085	3	56 Ba	$L\gamma_5$	$L_{II} N_I$	5.3707	2.6285	2	55 Cs	$L\beta_3$	$L_I M_{III}$	4.7167
2.3109	3	58 Ce	$L\beta_3$	$L_I M_{III}$	5.3651	2.6388	1	51 Sb	L_I	Abs. Edge	4.6984
2.3122	2	64 Gd	Ll	$L_{III} M_I$	5.3621	2.6398	2	51 Sb	$L\gamma_4$	$L_I O_{II,III}$	4.6967
2.3139	1	55 Cs	L_{II}	Abs. Edge	5.3581	2.65710	9	53 I	$L\gamma_5$	$L_{II} N_I$	4.6660
2.3480	2	55 Cs	$L\gamma_1$	$L_{II} N_{IV}$	5.2804	2.66570	5	57 La	$L\alpha_1$	$L_{III} M_V$	4.65097
2.3497	4	58 Ce	$L\beta_4$	$L_I M_{II}$	5.2765	2.6666	2	55 Cs	$L\beta_4$	$L_I M_{II}$	4.6494
2.3561	3	58 Ce	$L\beta_1$	$L_{II} M_{IV}$	5.2622	2.67533	5	57 La	$L\alpha_2$	$L_{III} M_{IV}$	4.63423
2.3629	1	56 Ba	L_{III}	Abs. Edge	5.2470	2.6760	4	60 Nd	Ll	$L_{III} M_I$	4.6330
2.3704	2	60 Nd	$L\alpha_1$	$L_{III} M_V$	5.2304	2.6837	2	55 Cs	$L\beta_1$	$L_{II} M_{IV}$	4.6198
2.3764	2	56 Ba	$L\beta_9$	$L_I M_V$	5.2171	2.6879	1	52 Te	L_{II}	Abs. Edge	4.6126
2.3790	4	57 La	$L\beta_6$	$L_{III} N_I$	5.2114	2.6953	2	51 Sb	$L\gamma_{2,3}$	$L_I N_{II,III}$	4.5999
2.3806	2	56 Ba	$L\beta_7$	$L_{III} O_I$	5.2079	2.71241	6	52 Te	$L\gamma_1$	$L_{II} N_{IV}$	4.5709
2.3807	3	60 Nd	$L\alpha_2$	$L_{III} M_{IV}$	5.2077	2.71352	9	53 I	$L\beta_9$	$L_I M_V$	4.5690
2.3869	2	56 Ba	$L\beta_{10}$	$L_I M_{IV}$	5.1941	2.7196	5	53 I	L_{III}	Abs. Edge	4.5587
2.3880	5	53 I	L_I	Abs. Edge	5.192	2.72104	9	53 I	$L\beta_{10}$	$L_I M_{IV}$	4.5564

Wavelength Å*	p.e.	Element	Designation		keV	Wavelength Å*	p.e.	Element	Designation		keV
2.7288	3	53 I	$L\beta_7$	$L_{III}O_I$	4.5435	3.04661	9	52 Te	$L\beta_4$	L_IM_{II}	4.0695
2.740	3	57 La	$L\eta$	$L_{II}M_I$	4.525	3.068	5	90 Th	M_{III}	Abs. Edge	4.041
2.74851	2	22 Ti	$K\alpha_1$	KL_{III}	4.51084	3.0703	1	20 Ca	K	Abs. Edge	4.0381
2.75053	8	53 I	$L\beta_{2,15}$	$L_{III}N_{IV,V}$	4.5075	3.0746	3	20 Ca	$K\beta_5$	$KM_{IV,V}$	4.0325
2.75216	2	22 Ti	$K\alpha_2$	KL_{II}	4.50486	3.07677	6	52 Te	$L\beta_1$	$L_{II}M_{IV}$	4.02958
2.753	8	92 U		M_IN_{III}	4.50	3.08475	9	50 Sn	$L\gamma_5$	$L_{II}N_I$	4.0192
2.762	1	21 Sc	K	Abs. Edge	4.489	3.0849	1	48 Cd	L_I	Abs. Edge	4.0190
2.7634	3	21 Sc	$K\beta_5$	$KM_{IV,V}$	4.4865	3.0897	2	20 Ca	$K\beta_{1,3}$	$KM_{II,III}$	4.0127
2.77595	5	56 Ba	$L\alpha_1$	$L_{III}M_V$	4.46626	3.094	5	83 Bi	M_I	Abs. Edge	4.007
2.7769	1	50 Sn	L_I	Abs. Edge	4.4648	3.11513	9	50 Sn	$L\beta_9$	L_IM_V	3.9800
2.7775	2	50 Sn	$L\gamma_4$	$L_IO_{II,III}$	4.4638	3.11513	9	51 Sb	$L\beta_6$	$L_{III}N_I$	3.9800
2.7796	2	21 Sc	$K\beta_{1,3}$	$KM_{II,III}$	4.4605	3.115	7	92 U		$M_{III}O_I$	3.980
2.7841	4	59 Pr	Ll	$L_{III}M_I$	4.4532	3.12170	9	50 Sn	$L\beta_{10}$	L_IM_{IV}	3.9716
2.78553	5	56 Ba	$L\alpha_2$	$L_{III}M_{IV}$	4.45090	3.131	3	90 Th		$M_{III}O_{IV,V}$	3.959
2.79007	9	52 Te	$L\gamma_5$	$L_{II}N_I$	4.4437	3.1355	2	56 Ba	Ll	$L_{III}M_I$	3.9541
2.817	2	92 U		$M_{II}N_{IV}$	4.401	3.1377	2	48 Cd	$L\gamma_2$	L_IN_{II}	3.9513
2.8294	5	51 Sb	L_{II}	Abs. Edge	4.3819	3.1473	1	49 In	L_{II}	Abs. Edge	3.9393
2.8327	2	50 Sn	$L\gamma_{2,3}$	$L_IN_{II,III}$	4.3768	3.14860	6	53 I	$L\alpha_1$	$L_{III}M_V$	3.93765
2.83672	9	53 I	$L\beta_6$	$L_{III}N_I$	4.3706	3.15258	9	51 Sb	$L\beta_3$	L_IM_{III}	3.9327
2.83897	9	52 Te	$L\beta_9$	L_IM_V	4.3671	3.1557	1	50 Sn	L_{III}	Abs. Edge	3.9288
2.84679	9	52 Te	$L\beta_{10}$	L_IM_{IV}	4.3551	3.1564	3	50 Sn	$L\beta_7$	$L_{III}O_I$	3.9279
2.85159	3	51 Sb	$L\gamma_1$	$L_{II}N_{IV}$	4.34779	3.15791	6	53 I	$L\alpha_2$	$L_{III}M_{IV}$	3.92604
2.8555	1	52 Te	L_{III}	Abs. Edge	4.3418	3.16213	4	49 In	$L\gamma_1$	$L_{II}N_{IV}$	3.92081
2.8627	3	56 Ba	$L\eta$	$L_{II}M_I$	4.3309	3.17505	3	50 Sn	$L\beta_{2,15}$	$L_{III}N_{IV,V}$	3.90486
2.8634	3	52 Te	$L\beta_7$	$L_{III}O_I$	4.3298	3.19014	9	51 Sb	$L\beta_4$	L_IM_{II}	3.8364
2.87429	9	53 I	$L\beta_3$	L_IM_{III}	4.3134	3.217	5	82 Pb	M_I	Abs. Edge	3.854
2.88217	8	52 Te	$L\beta_{2,15}$	$L_{III}N_{IV,V}$	4.3017	3.22567	4	51 Sb	$L\beta_1$	$L_{II}M_{IV}$	3.84357
2.884	5	92 U	M_{III}	Abs. Edge	4.299	3.245	9	91 Pa		$M_{III}O_I$	3.82
2.8917	4	58 Ce	Ll	$L_{III}M_I$	4.2875	3.24907	9	49 In	$L\gamma_5$	$L_{II}N_I$	3.8159
2.8924	2	55 Cs	$L\alpha_1$	$L_{III}M_V$	4.2865	3.2564	1	47 Ag	L_I	Abs. Edge	3.8072
2.9020	2	55 Cs	$L\alpha_2$	$L_{III}M_{IV}$	4.2722	3.2670	2	55 Cs	Ll	$L_{III}M_I$	3.7950
2.910	2	91 Pa		$M_{II}N_{IV}$	4.260	3.26763	9	49 In	$L\beta_9$	L_IM_V	3.7942
2.91207	9	53 I	$L\beta_4$	L_IM_{II}	4.2575	3.26901	9	50 Sn	$L\beta_6$	$L_{III}N_I$	3.7926
2.92	2	92 U		M_IN_{II}	4.25	3.27404	9	49 In	$L\beta_{10}$	L_IM_{IV}	3.7868
2.9260	1	49 In	L_I	Abs. Edge	4.2373	3.27979	9	53 I	$L\eta$	$L_{II}M_I$	3.7801
2.9264	2	49 In	$L\gamma_4$	$L_IO_{II,III}$	4.2367	3.283	9	90 Th		$M_{III}O_I$	3.78
2.93187	9	51 Sb	$L\gamma_5$	$L_{II}N_I$	4.2287	3.28920	6	52 Te	$L\alpha_1$	$L_{III}M_V$	3.76933
2.934	8	90 Th		M_IN_{III}	4.23	3.29846	9	52 Te	$L\alpha_2$	$L_{III}M_{IV}$	3.7588
2.93744	6	53 I	$L\beta_1$	$L_{II}M_{IV}$	4.22072	3.30585	3	50 Sn	$L\beta_3$	L_IM_{III}	3.7500
2.948	2	92 U		$M_{III}O_{IV,V}$	4.205	3.30635	9	47 Ag	$L\gamma_3$	L_IN_{III}	3.7498
2.97088	9	52 Te	$L\beta_6$	$L_{III}N_I$	4.1732	3.31216	9	47 Ag	$L\gamma_2$	L_IN_{II}	3.7432
2.97261	9	51 Sb	$L\beta_9$	L_IM_V	4.1708	3.3237	1	49 In	L_{III}	Abs. Edge	3.7302
2.97917	9	51 Sb	$L\beta_{10}$	L_IM_{IV}	4.1616	3.324	4	49 In	$L\beta_7$	$L_{III}O_I$	3.730
2.9800	2	49 In	$L\gamma_{2,3}$	$L_IN_{II,III}$	4.1605	3.3257	1	48 Cd	L_{II}	Abs. Edge	3.7280
2.9823	1	50 Sn	L_{II}	Abs. Edge	4.1573	3.329	4	92 U		$M_{II}N_I$	3.724
2.9932	2	55 Cs	$L\eta$	$L_{II}M_I$	4.1421	3.333	5	92 U	M_{IV}	Abs. Edge	3.720
3.0003	1	51 Sb	L_{III}	Abs. Edge	4.1323	3.33564	6	48 Cd	$L\gamma_1$	$L_{II}N_{IV}$	3.71686
3.00115	3	50 Sn	$L\gamma_1$	$L_{II}N_{IV}$	4.13112	3.33838	3	49 In	$L\beta_{2,15}$	$L_{III}N_{IV,V}$	3.71381
3.0052	3	51 Sb	$L\beta_7$	$L_{III}O_I$	4.1255	3.34335	9	50 Sn	$L\beta_4$	L_IM_{II}	3.7083
3.006	3	57 La	Ll	$L_{III}M_I$	4.124	3.346	5	81 Tl	M_I	Abs. Edge	3.705
3.00893	9	52 Te	$L\beta_3$	L_IM_{III}	4.1204	3.35839	3	20 Ca	$K\alpha_1$	KL_{III}	3.69168
3.011	2	90 Th		$M_{II}N_{IV}$	4.117	3.359	5	83 Bi	M_{II}	Abs. Edge	3.691
3.0166	2	54 Xe	$L\alpha_1$	$L_{III}M_V$	4.1099	3.36166	3	20 Ca	$K\alpha_2$	KL_{II}	3.68809
3.02335	3	51 Sb	$L\beta_{2,15}$	$L_{III}N_{IV,V}$	4.10078	3.38487	3	50 Sn	$L\beta_1$	$L_{II}M_{IV}$	3.66280
3.0309	1	21 Sc	$K\alpha_1$	KL_{III}	4.0906	3.42551	9	48 Cd	$L\gamma_5$	$L_{II}N_I$	3.61935
3.0342	1	21 Sc	$K\alpha_2$	KL_{II}	4.0861	3.43015	9	48 Cd	$L\beta_9$	L_IM_V	3.61445
3.038	2	91 Pa		$M_{III}O_{IV,V}$	4.081	3.43606	9	49 In	$L\beta_6$	$L_{III}N_I$	3.60823

Wavelength Å*	p.e.	Element	Designation		keV	Wavelength Å*	p.e.	Element	Designation		keV
3.4365	1	19 K	K	Abs. Edge	3.6078	3.77192	4	49 In	$L\alpha_1$	$L_{III}M_V$	3.28694
3.4367	2	48 Cd	$L\beta_{10}$	L_IM_{IV}	3.6075	3.78073	6	49 In	$L\alpha_2$	$L_{III}M_{IV}$	3.27929
3.437	1	46 Pd	L_I	Abs. Edge	3.607	3.783	5	80 Hg	M_{II}	Abs. Edge	3.277
3.43832	9	52 Te	$L\eta$	$L_{II}M_I$	3.60586	3.78876	9	50 Sn	$L\eta$	$L_{II}M_I$	3.27234
3.43941	4	51 Sb	$L\alpha_1$	$L_{III}M_V$	3.60472	3.7920	2	46 Pd	$L\beta_9$	L_IM_V	3.2696
3.441	5	91 Pa		$M_{II}N_I$	3.603	3.7988	2	46 Pd	$L\beta_{10}$	L_IM_{IV}	3.2637
3.4413	4	19 K	$K\beta_5$	$KM_{IV,V}$	3.6027	3.80774	9	47 Ag	$L\beta_6$	$L_{III}N_I$	3.25603
3.44840	6	51 Sb	$L\alpha_2$	$L_{III}M_{IV}$	3.59532	3.808	4	90 Th		$M_{IV}O_{II}$	3.256
3.4539	2	19 K	$K\beta_{1,3}$	$KM_{II,III}$	3.5896	3.8222	2	46 Pd	$L\gamma_5$	$L_{II}N_I$	3.2437
3.46984	9	49 In	$L\beta_3$	L_IM_{III}	3.57311	3.827	1	91 Pa	$M\beta$	$M_{IV}N_{VI}$	3.2397
3.478	5	80 Hg	M_I	Abs. Edge	3.565	3.83313	9	47 Ag	$L\beta_3$	L_IM_{III}	3.23446
3.479	1	92 U	$M\gamma$	$M_{III}N_V$	3.563	3.834	4	83 Bi		$M_{II}N_{IV}$	3.234
3.4892	2	46 Pd	$L\gamma_{2,3}$	$L_IN_{II,III}$	3.5533	3.835	5	44 Ru	L_I	Abs. Edge	3.233
3.492	5	82 Pb	M_{II}	Abs. Edge	3.550	3.87023	5	47 Ag	$L\beta_4$	L_IM_{II}	3.20346
3.497	5	92 U	M_V	Abs. Edge	3.545	3.87090	5	18 A	K	Abs. Edge	3.20290
3.5047	1	48 Cd	L_{III}	Abs. Edge	3.5376	3.872	9	82 Pb		M_IN_{III}	3.202
3.50697	9	49 In	$L\beta_4$	L_IM_{II}	3.53528	3.8860	2	18 A	$K\beta_{1,3}$	$KM_{II,III}$	3.1905
3.51408	4	48 Cd	$L\beta_{2,15}$	$L_{III}N_{IV,V}$	3.52812	3.88826	9	51 Sb	Ll	$L_{III}M_I$	3.18860
3.5164	1	47 Ag	L_{II}	Abs. Edge	3.5258	3.892	9	83 Bi		M_IN_{II}	3.185
3.521	2	92 U		$M_{III}N_{IV}$	3.521	3.8977	2	44 Ru	$L\gamma_{2,3}$	$L_IN_{II,III}$	3.1809
3.52260	4	47 Ag	$L\gamma_1$	$L_{II}N_{IV}$	3.51959	3.904	5	83 Bi	M_{III}	Abs. Edge	3.176
3.537	9	90 Th		$M_{II}N_I$	3.505	3.9074	1	46 Pd	L_{III}	Abs. Edge	3.17298
3.55531	4	49 In	$L\beta_1$	$L_{II}M_{IV}$	3.48721	3.90887	4	46 Pd	$L\beta_{2,15}$	$L_{III}N_{IV,V}$	3.17179
3.557	5	90 Th	M_{IV}	Abs. Edge	3.485	3.910	1	92 U	$M\alpha_1$	M_VN_{VII}	3.1708
3.55754	9	53 I	Ll	$L_{III}M_I$	3.48502	3.915	5	77 Ir	M_I	Abs. Edge	3.167
3.576	1	92 U		$M_{IV}O_{II}$	3.4666	3.924	1	92 U	$M\alpha_2$	M_VN_{VI}	3.1595
3.577	1	91 Pa	$M\gamma$	$M_{III}N_V$	3.4657	3.932	6	83 Bi		$M_{III}O_{IV,V}$	3.153
3.59994	3	50 Sn	$L\alpha_1$	$L_{III}M_V$	3.44398	3.93473	3	47 Ag	$L\beta_1$	$L_{II}M_{IV}$	3.15094
3.60497	9	47 Ag	$L\beta_9$	L_IM_V	3.43917	3.936	5	79 Au	M_{II}	Abs. Edge	3.150
3.60765	9	51 Sb	$L\eta$	$L_{II}M_I$	3.43661	3.941	1	90 Th	$M\beta$	$M_{IV}N_{VI}$	3.1458
3.60891	4	50 Sn	$L\alpha_2$	$L_{III}M_{IV}$	3.43542	3.9425	5	45 Rh	L_{II}	Abs. Edge	3.1448
3.61158	9	47 Ag	$L\beta_{10}$	L_IM_{IV}	3.43287	3.9437	2	45 Rh	$L\gamma_1$	$L_{II}N_{IV}$	3.1438
3.614	2	91 Pa		$M_{III}N_{IV}$	3.430	3.95635	4	48 Cd	$L\alpha_1$	$L_{III}M_V$	3.13373
3.61467	9	48 Cd	$L\beta_6$	$L_{III}N_I$	3.42994	3.96496	6	48 Cd	$L\alpha_2$	$L_{III}M_{IV}$	3.12691
3.61638	9	47 Ag	$L\gamma_5$	$L_{II}N_I$	3.42832	3.968	5	82 Pb		$M_{II}N_{IV}$	3.124
3.616	5	79 Au	M_I	Abs. Edge	3.428	3.98327	9	49 In	$L\eta$	$L_{II}M_I$	3.11254
3.629	5	45 Rh	L_I	Abs. Edge	3.417	4.013	9	81 Tl		M_IN_{III}	3.089
3.634	5	81 Tl	M_{II}	Abs. Edge	3.412	4.0162	2	46 Pd	$L\beta_6$	$L_{III}N_I$	3.0870
3.64495	9	48 Cd	$L\beta_3$	L_IM_{III}	3.40145	4.022	1	91 Pa	$M\alpha_1$	M_VN_{VII}	3.0823
3.679	2	90 Th	$M\gamma$	$M_{III}N_V$	3.370	4.0346	2	46 Pd	$L\beta_3$	L_IM_{III}	3.0730
3.68203	9	48 Cd	$L\beta_4$	L_IM_{II}	3.36719	4.035	3	91 Pa	$M\alpha_2$	M_VN_{VI}	3.072
3.6855	2	45 Rh	$L\gamma_{2,3}$	$L_IN_{II,III}$	3.3640	4.0451	2	45 Rh	$L\gamma_5$	$L_{II}N_I$	3.0650
3.691	2	91 Pa		$M_{IV}O_{II}$	3.359	4.047	1	82 Pb	M_{III}	Abs. Edge	3.0632
3.6999	1	47 Ag	L_{III}	Abs. Edge	3.35096	4.058	5	43 Te	L_I	Abs. Edge	3.055
3.70335	3	47 Ag	$L\beta_{2,15}$	$L_{III}N_{IV,V}$	3.34781	4.069	6	82 Pb		$M_{III}O_{IV,V}$	3.047
3.716	1	92 U	$M\beta$	$M_{IV}N_{VI}$	3.3367	4.0711	2	46 Pd	$L\beta_4$	L_IM_{II}	3.0454
3.71696	9	52 Te	Ll	$L_{III}M_I$	3.33555	4.071	5	76 Os	M_I	Abs. Edge	3.045
3.718	3	90 Th		$M_{III}N_{IV}$	3.335	4.07165	9	50 Sn	Ll	$L_{III}M_I$	3.04499
3.7228	1	46 Pd	L_{II}	Abs. Edge	3.33031	4.093	5	78 Pt	M_{II}	Abs. Edge	3.029
3.7246	2	46 Pd	$L\gamma_1$	$L_{II}N_{IV}$	3.3287	4.105	9	83 Bi		$M_{III}O_I$	3.021
3.729	5	90 Th	M_V	Abs. Edge	3.325	4.116	4	81 Tl		$M_{II}N_{IV}$	3.013
3.73823	4	48 Cd	$L\beta_1$	$L_{II}M_{IV}$	3.31657	4.1299	5	45 Rh	L_{III}	Abs. Edge	**3.0021**
3.740	9	83 Bi		M_IN_{III}	3.315	4.1310	2	45 Rh	$L\beta_{2,15}$	$L_{III}N_{IV,V}$	3.0013
3.7414	2	19 K	$K\alpha_1$	KL_{III}	3.3138	4.1381	9	90 Th	$M\alpha_1$	M_VN_{VII}	2.9961
3.7445	2	19 K	$K\alpha_2$	KL_{II}	3.3111	4.14622	5	46 Pd	$L\beta_1$	$L_{II}M_{IV}$	2.99022
3.760	9	90 Th		M_VP_{III}	3.298	4.151	2	90 Th	$M\alpha_2$	M_VN_{VI}	2.987
3.762	5	78 Pt	M_I	Abs. Edge	3.296	4.15443	3	47 Ag	$L\alpha_1$	$L_{III}M_V$	2.98431

Wavelength Å*	p.e.	Element	Designation		keV
4.16294	5	47 Ag	$L\alpha_2$	$L_{III}M_{IV}$	2.97821
4.180	1	44 Ru	L_{II}	Abs. Edge	2.9663
4.1822	2	44 Ru	$L\gamma_1$	$L_{II}N_{IV}$	2.9645
4.19180	5	18 A	$K\alpha_1$	KL_{III}	2.95770
4.19315	9	48 Cd	$L\eta$	$L_{II}M_I$	2.95675
4.19474	5	18 A	$K\alpha_2$	KL_{II}	2.95563
4.198	1	81 Tl	M_{III}	Abs. Edge	2.9535
4.216	6	81 Tl		$M_{III}O_{IV,V}$	2.941
4.236	5	75 Re	M_I	Abs. Edge	2.927
4.2417	2	45 Rh	$L\beta_6$	$L_{III}N_I$	2.9229
4.244	9	82 Pb		$M_{III}O_I$	2.921
4.2522	2	45 Rh	$L\beta_3$	L_IM_{III}	2.9157
4.260	5	77 Ir	M_{II}	Abs. Edge	2.910
4.26873	9	49 In	Ll	$L_{III}M_I$	2.90440
4.2873	2	44 Ru	$L\gamma_5$	$L_{II}N_I$	2.8918
4.2888	2	45 Rh	$L\beta_4$	L_IM_{II}	2.8908
4.300	9	79 Au		M_IN_{III}	2.883
4.304	5	42 Mo	L_I	Abs. Edge	2.881
4.330	2	92 U		$M_{III}N_I$	2.863
4.355	1	80 Hg	M_{III}	Abs. Edge	2.8469
4.36767	5	46 Pd	$L\alpha_1$	$L_{III}M_V$	2.83861
4.369	1	44 Ru	L_{III}	Abs. Edge	2.8377
4.3718	2	44 Ru	$L\beta_{2,15}$	$L_{III}N_{IV,V}$	2.8360
4.37414	5	45 Rh	$L\beta_1$	$L_{II}M_{IV}$	2.83441
4.37588	7	46 Pd	$L\alpha_2$	$L_{III}M_{IV}$	2.83329
4.3800	2	42 Mo	$L\gamma_{2,3}$	$L_IN_{II,III}$	2.8306
4.3971	1	17 Cl	K	Abs. Edge	2.81960
4.4034	3	17 Cl	$K\beta$	KM	2.8156
4.407	5	74 W	M_I	Abs. Edge	2.813
4.4183	2	47 Ag	$L\eta$	$L_{II}M_I$	2.8061
4.432	4	79 Au		$M_{II}N_{IV}$	2.797
4.433	5	76 Os	M_{II}	Abs. Edge	2.797
4.436	1	43 Tc	L_{II}	Abs. Edge	2.7948
4.44	2	74 W		$M_IO_{II,III}$	2.79
4.450	4	91 Pa		$M_{III}N_I$	2.786
4.460	9	78 Pt		M_IN_{III}	2.780
4.48014	9	48 Cd	Ll	$L_{III}M_I$	2.76735
4.4866	3	44 Ru	$L\beta_3$	L_IM_{III}	2.7634
4.4866	3	44 Ru	$L\beta_6$	$L_{III}N_I$	2.7634
4.518	1	79 Au	M_{III}	Abs. Edge	2.7439
4.522	6	79 Au		$M_{III}O_{IV,V}$	2.742
4.5230	2	44 Ru	$L\beta_4$	L_IM_{II}	2.7411
4.532	2	83 Bi	$M\gamma$	$M_{III}N_V$	2.735
4.568	5	90 Th		$M_{III}N_I$	2.714
4.571	5	83 Bi		$M_{III}N_{IV}$	2.712
4.572	5	83 Bi	M_{IV}	Abs. Edge	2.711
4.575	5	41 Nb	L_I	Abs. Edge	2.710
4.585	5	73 Ta	M_I	Abs. Edge	2.704
4.59	2	83 Bi		$M_{IV}P_{II,III}$	2.70
4.59743	9	45 Rh	$L\alpha_1$	$L_{III}M_V$	2.69674
4.601	4	78 Pt		$M_{II}N_{IV}$	2.695
4.60545	9	45 Rh	$L\alpha_2$	$L_{III}M_{IV}$	2.69205
4.620	5	75 Re	M_{II}	Abs. Edge	2.684
4.62058	3	44 Ru	$L\beta_1$	$L_{II}M_{IV}$	2.68323
4.625	5	92 U		$M_{IV}N_{III}$	2.681
4.630	1	43 Tc	L_{III}	Abs. Edge	2.6780
4.631	9	77 Ir		M_IN_{III}	2.677
4.6542	2	41 Nb	$L\gamma_{2,3}$	$L_IN_{II,III}$	2.6638
4.655	8	82 Pb		$M_{III}N_I$	2.664
4.6605	2	46 Pd	$L\eta$	$L_{II}M_I$	2.6603
4.674	1	82 Pb	$M\gamma$	$M_{III}N_V$	2.6527
4.686	1	78 Pt	M_{III}	Abs. Edge	2.6459
4.694	8	78 Pt		$M_{III}O_{IV,V}$	2.641
4.703	9	79 Au		$M_{III}O_I$	2.636
4.7076	2	47 Ag	Ll	$L_{III}M_I$	2.6337
4.715	3	82 Pb		$M_{III}N_{IV}$	2.630
4.719	1	42 Mo	L_{II}	Abs. Edge	2.6274
4.7258	2	42 Mo	$L\gamma_1$	$L_{II}N_{IV}$	2.6235
4.7278	1	17 Cl	$K\alpha_1$	KL_{III}	2.62239
4.7307	1	17 Cl	$K\alpha_2$	KL_{II}	2.62078
4.757	5	82 Pb	M_{IV}	Abs. Edge	2.606
4.764	5	83 Bi	M_V	Abs. Edge	2.603
4.780	4	77 Ir		$M_{II}N_{IV}$	2.594
4.79	2	76 Os		M_IN_{III}	2.59
4.815	5	74 W	M_{II}	Abs. Edge	2.575
4.823	3	83 Bi		$M_{IV}O_{II}$	2.571
4.823	4	81 Tl	$M\gamma$	$M_{III}N_V$	2.571
4.8369	2	42 Mo	$L\gamma_5$	$L_{II}N_I$	2.5632
4.84575	5	44 Ru	$L\alpha_1$	$L_{III}M_V$	2.55855
4.85381	7	44 Ru	$L\alpha_2$	$L_{III}M_{IV}$	2.55431
4.861	1	77 Ir	M_{III}	Abs. Edge	2.5505
4.865	5	81 Tl		$M_{III}N_{IV}$	2.548
4.869	9	77 Ir		$M_{III}O_{IV,V}$	2.546
4.876	9	78 Pt		$M_{III}O_I$	2.543
4.879	5	40 Zr	L_I	Abs. Edge	2.541
4.8873	8	43 Tc	$L\beta_1$	$L_{II}M_{IV}$	2.5368
4.909	1	83 Bi	$M\beta$	$M_{IV}N_{VI}$	2.5255
4.911	5	90 Th		$M_{IV}N_{III}$	2.524
4.913	1	42 Mo	L_{III}	Abs. Edge	2.5234
4.9217	2	45 Rh	$L\eta$	$L_{II}M_I$	2.5191
4.9232	2	42 Mo	$L\beta_{2,15}$	$L_{III}N_{IV,V}$	2.5183
4.946	2	92 U	$M\zeta_1$	M_VN_{III}	2.507
4.952	5	81 Tl	M_{IV}	Abs. Edge	2.504
4.9525	3	46 Pd	Ll	$L_{III}M_I$	2.5034
4.9536	3	40 Zr	$L\gamma_{2,3}$	$L_IN_{II,III}$	2.5029
4.955	4	76 Os		$M_{II}N_{IV}$	2.502
4.955	5	82 Pb	M_V	Abs. Edge	2.502
4.984	2	80 Hg	$M\gamma$	$M_{III}N_V$	2.4875
5.004	9	82 Pb		$M_{IV}O_{II}$	2.477
5.0133	3	42 Mo	$L\beta_3$	L_IM_{III}	2.4730
5.0185	1	16 S	K	Abs. Edge	2.47048
5.020	5	73 Ta	M_{II}	Abs. Edge	2.470
5.0233	3	16 S	$K\beta_x$	KM	2.4681
5.031	1	41 Nb	L_{II}	Abs. Edge	2.4641
5.0316	2	16 S	$K\beta_1$	KM	2.46404
5.0361	3	41 Nb	$L\gamma_1$	$L_{II}N_{IV}$	2.4618
5.043	5	76 Os	M_{III}	Abs. Edge	2.458
5.0488	3	42 Mo	$L\beta_4$	L_IM_{II}	2.4557
5.0488	5	42 Mo	$L\beta_6$	$L_{III}N_I$	2.4557
5.050	2	92 U	$M\zeta_2$	$M_{IV}N_{II}$	2.4548
5.076	1	82 Pb	$M\beta$	$M_{IV}N_{VI}$	2.4427
5.092	2	91 Pa	$M\zeta_1$	M_VN_{III}	2.4350
5.1148	3	43 Tc	$L\alpha_1$	$L_{III}M_V$	2.4240
5.118	1	83 Bi	$M\alpha_1$	M_VN_{VII}	2.4226

Wavelength Å*	p.e.	Element	Designation		keV
5.130	2	83 Bi	$M\alpha_2$	$M_V N_{VI}$	2.4170
5.145	4	79 Au	$M\gamma$	$M_{III} N_V$	2.410
5.1517	3	41 Nb	$L\gamma_5$	$L_{II} N_I$	2.4066
5.153	5	81 Tl	M_V	Abs. Edge	2.406
5.157	5	80 Hg	M_{IV}	Abs. Edge	2.404
5.168	9	82 Pb		$M_V O_{III}$	2.399
5.172	9	74 W		$M_I N_{III}$	2.397
5.17708	8	42 Mo	$L\beta_1$	$L_{II} M_{IV}$	2.39481
5.186	5	79 Au		$M_{III} N_{IV}$	2.391
5.193	2	91 Pa	$M\zeta_2$	$M_{IV} N_{II}$	2.3876
5.196	9	81 Tl		$M_{IV} O_{II}$	2.386
5.2050	2	44 Ru	$L\eta$	$L_{II} M_I$	2.38197
5.217	5	39 Y	L_I	Abs. Edge	2.377
5.2169	3	45 Rh	Ll	$L_{III} M_I$	2.3765
5.230	1	41 Nb	L_{III}	Abs. Edge	2.3706
5.234	5	75 Re	M_{III}	Abs. Edge	2.369
5.2379	3	41 Nb	$L\beta_{2,15}$	$L_{III} N_{IV,V}$	2.3670
5.245	5	90 Th	$M\zeta_1$	$M_V N_{III}$	2.364
5.249	1	81 Tl	$M\beta$	$M_{IV} N_{VI}$	2.3621
5.2830	3	39 Y	$L\gamma_{2,3}$	$L_I N_{II,III}$	2.3468
5.286	1	82 Pb	$M\alpha_1$	$M_V N_{VII}$	2.3455
5.299	2	82 Pb	$M\alpha_2$	$M_V N_{VI}$	2.3397
5.3102	3	41 Nb	$L\beta_3$	$L_I M_{III}$	2.3348
5.319	4	78 Pt	$M\gamma$	$M_{III} N_V$	2.331
5.340	5	90 Th	$M\zeta_2$	$M_{IV} N_{II}$	2.322
5.3455	3	41 Nb	$L\beta_4$	$L_I M_{II}$	2.3194
5.357	4	74 W		$M_{II} N_{IV}$	2.314
5.357	5	78 Pt		$M_{III} N_{IV}$	2.314
5.36	1	80 Hg	M_V	Abs. Edge	2.313
5.3613	3	41 Nb	$L\beta_6$	$L_{III} N_I$	2.3125
5.37216	7	16 S	$K\alpha_1$	$K L_{III}$	2.30784
5.374	5	79 Au	M_{IV}	Abs. Edge	2.307
5.37496	8	16 S	$K\alpha_2$	$K L_{II}$	2.30664
5.378	1	40 Zr	L_{II}	Abs. Edge	2.3053
5.3843	3	40 Zr	$L\gamma_1$	$L_{II} N_{IV}$	2.3027
5.40	2	73 Ta		$M_I N_{III}$	2.295
5.40655	8	42 Mo	$L\alpha_1$	$L_{III} M_V$	2.29316
5.41437	8	42 Mo	$L\alpha_2$	$L_{III} M_{IV}$	2.28985
5.4318	9	80 Hg	$M\beta$	$M_{IV} N_{VI}$	2.2825
5.435	1	74 W	M_{III}	Abs. Edge	2.2811
5.460	1	81 Tl	$M\alpha_1$	$M_V N_{VII}$	2.2706
5.472	2	81 Tl	$M\alpha_2$	$M_V N_{VI}$	2.2656
5.4923	3	41 Nb	$L\beta_1$	$L_{II} M_{IV}$	2.2574
5.4977	3	40 Zr	$L\gamma_5$	$L_{II} N_I$	2.2551
5.500	4	77 Ir	$M\gamma$	$M_{III} N_V$	2.254
5.5035	3	44 Ru	Ll	$L_{III} M_I$	2.2528
5.537	8	83 Bi		$M_{III} N_I$	2.239
5.540	5	77 Ir		$M_{III} N_{IV}$	2.238
5.570	4	73 Ta		$M_{II} N_{IV}$	2.226
5.579	1	40 Zr	L_{III}	Abs. Edge	2.2225
5.584	5	79 Au	M_V	Abs. Edge	2.220
5.5863	3	40 Zr	$L\beta_{2,15}$	$L_{III} N_{IV,V}$	2.2194
5.59	1	78 Pt	M_{IV}	Abs. Edge	2.217
5.592	5	38 Sr	L_I	Abs. Edge	2.217
5.624	1	79 Au	$M\beta$	$M_{IV} N_{VI}$	2.2046
5.628	8	74 W		$M_{III} O_I$	2.203
5.6330	3	40 Zr	$L\beta_3$	$L_I M_{III}$	2.2010
5.6445	3	38 Sr	$L\gamma_{2,3}$	$L_I N_{II,III}$	2.1965
5.6476	9	80 Hg	$M\alpha_1$	$M_V N_{VII}$	2.1953
5.650	5	73 Ta	M_{III}	Abs. Edge	2.194
5.6681	3	40 Zr	$L\beta_4$	$L_I M_{II}$	2.1873
5.67	3	73 Ta		$M_{III} O_{IV,V}$	2.19
5.682	4	76 Os	$M\gamma$	$M_{III} N_V$	2.182
5.704	8	82 Pb		$M_{III} N_I$	2.174
5.7101	3	40 Zr	$L\beta_6$	$L_{III} N_I$	2.1712
5.724	5	76 Os		$M_{III} N_{IV}$	2.166
5.7243	2	41 Nb	$L\alpha_1$	$L_{III} M_V$	2.16589
5.7319	3	41 Nb	$L\alpha_2$	$L_{III} M_{IV}$	2.1630
5.756	1	39 Y	L_{II}	Abs. Edge	2.1540
5.767	9	79 Au		$M_V O_{III}$	2.150
5.784	1	15 P	K	Abs. Edge	2.1435
5.796	2	15 P	$K\beta$	KM	2.1391
5.81	2	76 Os		$M_{II} N_I$	2.133
5.81	1	78 Pt	M_V	Abs. Edge	2.133
5.828	1	78 Pt	$M\beta$	$M_{IV} N_{VI}$	2.1273
5.83	2	73 Ta		$M_{III} O_I$	2.126
5.83	1	77 Ir	M_{IV}	Abs. Edge	2.126
5.8360	3	40 Zr	$L\beta_1$	$L_{II} M_{IV}$	2.1244
5.840	1	79 Au	$M\alpha_1$	$M_V N_{VII}$	2.1229
5.8475	3	42 Mo	$L\eta$	$L_{II} M_I$	2.1202
5.854	3	79 Au	$M\alpha_2$	$M_V N_{VI}$	2.118
5.8754	3	39 Y	$L\gamma_5$	$L_{II} N_I$	2.1102
5.884	8	81 Tl		$M_{III} N_I$	2.107
5.885	2	75 Re	$M\gamma$	$M_{III} N_V$	2.1067
5.931	5	75 Re		$M_{III} N_{IV}$	2.090
5.962	1	39 Y	L_{III}	Abs. Edge	2.0794
5.9832	3	39 Y	$L\beta_3$	$L_I M_{III}$	2.0722
5.987	9	78 Pt		$M_V O_{III}$	2.071
6.008	5	37 Rb	L_I	Abs. Edge	2.063
6.0186	3	39 Y	$L\beta_4$	$L_I M_{II}$	2.0600
6.038	1	77 Ir	$M\beta$	$M_{IV} N_{VI}$	2.0535
6.0458	3	37 Rb	$L\gamma_{2,3}$	$L_I N_{II,III}$	2.0507
6.047	1	78 Pt	$M\alpha_1$	$M_V N_{VII}$	2.0505
6.05	1	77 Ir	M_V	Abs. Edge	2.048
6.058	3	78 Pt	$M\alpha_2$	$M_V N_{VI}$	2.047
6.0705	2	40 Zr	$L\alpha_1$	$L_{III} M_V$	2.04236
6.073	5	76 Os	M_{IV}	Abs. Edge	2.042
6.0778	3	40 Zr	$L\alpha_2$	$L_{III} M_{IV}$	2.0399
6.09	2	80 Hg		$M_{III} N_I$	2.036
6.092	3	74 W	$M\gamma$	$M_{III} N_V$	2.035
6.0942	3	39 Y	$L\beta_6$	$L_{III} N_I$	2.0344
6.134	4	74 W		$M_{III} N_{IV}$	2.021
6.1508	3	42 Mo	Ll	$L_{III} M_I$	2.01568
6.157	1	15 P	$K\alpha_1$	$K L_{III}$	2.0137
6.160	1	15 P	$K\alpha_2$	$K L_{II}$	2.0127
6.162	8	83 Bi		$M_{IV} N_{III}$	2.012
6.173	1	38 Sr	L_{II}	Abs. Edge	2.0085
6.2109	3	41 Nb	$L\eta$	$L_{II} M_I$	1.99620
6.2120	3	39 Y	$L\beta_1$	$L_{II} M_{IV}$	1.99584
6.259	9	79 Au		$M_{III} N_I$	1.981
6.262	1	77 Ir	$M\alpha_1$	$M_V N_{VII}$	1.9799
6.267	1	76 Os	$M\beta$	$M_{IV} N_{VI}$	1.9783
6.275	3	77 Ir	$M\alpha_2$	$M_V N_{VI}$	1.9758
6.28	2	74 W		$M_{II} N_I$	1.973

Wavelength Å*	p.e.	Element	Designation		keV	Wavelength Å*	p.e.	Element	Designation		keV
6.2961	3	38 Sr	$L\gamma_5$	$L_{II}N_I$	1.96916	7.101	8	79 Au		$M_{IV}N_{III}$	1.746
6.30	1	76 Os	M_V	Abs. Edge	1.967	7.11	1	73 Ta	M_V	Abs. Edge	1.743
6.312	4	73 Ta	$M\gamma$	$M_{III}N_V$	1.964	7.12542	9	14 Si	$K\alpha_1$	KL_{III}	1.73998
6.33	1	75 Re	M_{IV}	Abs. Edge	1.958	7.12791	9	14 Si	$K\alpha_2$	KL_{II}	1.73938
6.353	5	73 Ta		$M_{III}N_{IV}$	1.951	7.168	1	36 Kr	L_{II}	Abs. Edge	1.7297
6.3672	3	38 Sr	$L\beta_3$	L_IM_{III}	1.94719	7.250	5	36 Kr		$L_{II}N_{III}$	1.710
6.384	7	82 Pb		$M_{IV}N_{III}$	1.942	7.252	1	73 Ta	$M\alpha$	$M_VN_{VI,VII}$	1.7096
6.387	1	38 Sr	L_{III}	Abs. Edge	1.9411	7.264	5	36 Kr	$L\beta_3$	L_IM_{III}	1.707
6.4026	3	38 Sr	$L\beta_4$	L_IM_{II}	1.93643	7.279	5	36 Kr	$L\gamma_5$	$L_{II}N_I$	1.703
6.4488	2	39 Y	$L\alpha_1$	$L_{III}M_V$	1.92256	7.30	2	73 Ta		M_VO_{III}	1.700
6.455	9	78 Pt		$M_{III}N_I$	1.921	7.303	1	72 Hf	$M\beta$	$M_{IV}N_{VI}$	1.6976
6.4558	3	39 Y	$L\alpha_2$	$L_{III}M_{IV}$	1.92047	7.304	5	36 Kr	$L\beta_4$	L_IM_{II}	1.697
6.47	1	36 Kr	L_I	Abs. Edge	1.915	7.3183	2	37 Rb	$L\alpha_1$	$L_{III}M_V$	1.69413
6.490	1	76 Os	$M\alpha$	$M_VN_{VI,VII}$	1.9102	7.3251	3	37 Rb	$L\alpha_2$	$L_{III}M_{IV}$	1.69256
6.504	1	75 Re	$M\beta$	$M_{IV}N_{VI}$	1.9061	7.3563	3	39 Y	Ll	$L_{III}M_I$	1.68536
6.5176	3	41 Nb	Ll	$L_{III}M_I$	1.90225	7.360	8	74 W		$M_{III}N_I$	1.684
6.5191	3	38 Sr	$L\beta_6$	$L_{III}N_I$	1.90181	7.371	8	78 Pt		$M_{IV}N_{III}$	1.682
6.521	4	83 Bi	$M\zeta_1$	M_VN_{III}	1.901	7.392	1	36 Kr	L_{III}	Abs. Edge	1.6772
6.544	4	72 Hf	$M\gamma$	$M_{III}N_V$	1.895	7.466	4	79 Au	$M\zeta_1$	M_VN_{III}	1.6605
6.560	5	75 Re	M_V	Abs. Edge	1.890	7.503	1	34 Se	L_I	Abs. Edge	1.6525
6.585	5	83 Bi	$M\zeta_2$	$M_{IV}N_{II}$	1.883	7.510	4	36 Kr	$L\beta_6$	$L_{III}N_I$	1.6510
6.59	1	74 W	M_{IV}	Abs. Edge	1.880	7.5171	3	38 Sr	$L\eta$	$L_{II}M_I$	1.64933
6.6069	3	40 Zr	$L\eta$	$L_{II}M_I$	1.87654	7.523	5	79 Au	$M\zeta_2$	$M_{IV}N_{II}$	1.648
6.6239	3	38 Sr	$L\beta_1$	$L_{II}M_{IV}$	1.87172	7.539	1	72 Hf	$M\alpha$	$M_VN_{VI,VII}$	1.6446
6.644	1	37 Rb	L_{II}	Abs. Edge	1.8661	7.546	8	68 Er	$M\gamma$	$M_{III}N_V$	1.643
6.669	9	77 Ir		$M_{III}N_I$	1.859	7.576	3	36 Kr	$L\beta_1$	$L_{II}M_{IV}$	1.6366
6.729	1	75 Re	$M\alpha$	$M_VN_{VI,VII}$	1.8425	7.60	1	68 Er		$M_{III}N_{IV}$	1.632
6.738	1	14 Si	K	Abs. Edge	1.8400	7.601	2	71 Lu	$M\beta$	$M_{IV}N_{VI}$	1.6312
6.740	3	82 Pb	$M\zeta_1$	M_VN_{III}	1.8395	7.612	9	73 Ta		$M_{III}N_I$	1.629
6.7530	1	14 Si	$K\beta$	KM	1.83594	7.645	8	77 Ir		$M_{IV}N_{III}$	1.622
6.755	3	37 Rb	$L\gamma_5$	$L_{II}N_{IV}$	1.83532	7.738	4	78 Pt	$M\zeta_1$	M_VN_{III}	1.6022
6.757	1	74 W	$M\beta$	$M_{IV}N_{VI}$	1.8349	7.753	5	35 Br	L_{II}	Abs. Edge	1.599
6.768	6	71 Lu	$M\gamma$	$M_{III}N_V$	1.832	7.767	9	35 Br	$L\beta_{3,4}$	$L_IM_{II,III}$	1.596
6.7876	3	37 Rb	$L\beta_3$	L_IM_{III}	1.82659	7.790	5	78 Pt	$M\zeta_2$	$M_{IV}N_{II}$	1.592
6.802	5	82 Pb	$M\zeta_2$	$M_{IV}N_{II}$	1.823	7.817	3	36 Kr	$L\alpha_{1,2}$	$L_{III}M_{IV,V}$	1.5860
6.806	9	74 W		$M_{IV}O_{II}$	1.822	7.8362	3	38 Sr	Ll	$L_{III}M_I$	1.58215
6.8207	3	37 Rb	$L\beta_4$	L_IM_{II}	1.81771	7.840	2	71 Lu	$M\alpha$	$M_VN_{VI,VII}$	1.5813
6.83	1	74 W	M_V	Abs. Edge	1.814	7.865	9	67 Ho	$M\gamma$	$M_{III}N_{IV,V}$	1.576
6.862	1	37 Rb	L_{III}	Abs. Edge	1.8067	7.887	9	72 Hf		$M_{III}N_I$	1.572
6.8628	2	38 Sr	$L\alpha_1$	$L_{III}M_V$	1.80656	7.909	2	70 Yb	$M\beta$	$M_{IV}N_{VI}$	1.5675
6.8697	3	38 Sr	$L\alpha_2$	$L_{III}M_{IV}$	1.80474	7.94813	5	13 Al	K	Abs. Edge	1.55988
6.87	1	73 Ta	M_{IV}	Abs. Edge	1.805	7.960	2	13 Al	$K\beta$	KM	1.55745
6.87	2	80 Hg	δ	$M_{IV}N_{III}$	1.805	7.984	5	35 Br	L_{III}	Abs. Edge	1.5530
6.89	2	76 Os		$M_{III}N_I$	1.798	8.021	4	77 Ir	$M\zeta_1$	M_VN_{III}	1.5458
6.9185	3	40 Zr	Ll	$L_{III}M_I$	1.79201	8.0415	4	37 Rb	$L\eta$	$L_{II}M_I$	1.54177
6.959	5	35 Br	L_I	Abs. Edge	1.781	8.065	5	77 Ir	$M\zeta_2$	$M_{IV}N_{II}$	1.5373
6.974	4	81 Tl	$M\zeta_1$	M_VN_{III}	1.778	8.107	1	33 As	L_I	Abs. Edge	1.5293
6.983	1	74 W	$M\alpha_1$	M_VN_{VII}	1.7754	8.1251	5	35 Br	$L\beta_1$	$L_{II}M_{IV}$	1.52590
6.9842	3	37 Rb	$L\beta_6$	$L_{III}N_I$	1.77517	8.144	9	66 Dy	$M\gamma$	$M_{III}N_{IV,V}$	1.522
6.992	2	74 W	$M\alpha_2$	M_VN_{VI}	1.7731	8.149	5	70 Yb	$M\alpha$	$M_VN_{VI,VII}$	1.5214
7.005	9	74 W		M_VO_{III}	1.770	8.239	8	75 Re		$M_{IV}N_{III}$	1.505
7.023	1	73 Ta	$M\beta$	$M_{IV}N_{VI}$	1.7655	8.249	7	69 Tm	$M\beta$	$M_{IV}N_{VI}$	1.503
7.024	8	70 Yb	$M\gamma$	$M_{III}N_V$	1.765	8.310	4	76 Os	$M\zeta_1$	M_VN_{III}	1.4919
7.032	5	81 Tl	$M\zeta_2$	$M_{IV}N_{II}$	1.763	8.321	9	34 Se	$L\beta_{3,4}$	$L_IM_{II,III}$	1.490
7.0406	3	39 Y	$L\eta$	$L_{II}M_I$	1.76095	8.33934	9	13 Al	$K\alpha_1$	KL_{III}	1.48670
7.0759	3	37 Rb	$L\beta_1$	$L_{II}M_{IV}$	1.75217	8.34173	9	13 Al	$K\alpha_2$	KL_{II}	1.48627
7.09	2	73 Ta		$M_{IV}O_{II,III}$	1.748	8.359	5	76 Os	$M\zeta_2$	$M_{IV}N_{II}$	1.4831

Wavelength Å*	p.e.	Element	Designation		keV
8.3636	4	37 Rb	Ll	$L_{III}M_I$	1.48238
8.3746	5	35 Br	$L\alpha_{1,2}$	$L_{III}M_{IV,V}$	1.48043
8.407	1	34 Se	L_{II}	Abs. Edge	1.4747
8.470	9	70 Yb		$M_{III}N_I$	1.464
8.48	1	69 Tm	$M\alpha$	$M_VN_{VI,VII}$	1.462
8.486	9	65 Tb	$M\gamma$	$M_{III}N_{IV,V}$	1.461
8.487	5	69 Tm	M_V	Abs. Edge	1.4609
8.573	8	74 W		$M_{IV}N_{III}$	1.446
8.592	3	68 Er	$M\beta$	$M_{IV}N_{VI}$	1.4430
8.60	7	92 U		$N_IP_{IV,V}$	1.44
8.601	5	68 Er	M_{IV}	Abs. Edge	1.4415
8.629	4	75 Re	$M\zeta_1$	M_VN_{III}	1.4368
8.646	1	34 Se	L_{III}	Abs. Edge	1.4340
8.664	5	75 Re	$M\zeta_2$	$M_{IV}N_{II}$	1.4310
8.7358	5	34 Se	$L\beta_1$	$L_{II}M_{IV}$	1.41923
8.76	7	92 U		N_IP_{III}	1.42
8.773	1	32 Ge	L_I	Abs. Edge	1.4132
8.81	7	92 U		N_IP_{II}	1.41
8.82	1	68 Er	$M\alpha$	$M_VN_{VI,VII}$	1.406
8.844	9	64 Gd	$M\gamma$	$M_{III}N_{IV,V}$	1.402
8.847	5	68 Er	M_V	Abs. Edge	1.4013
8.90	2	73 Ta		$M_{IV}N_{III}$	1.393
8.929	1	33 As	$L\beta_{2,4}$	$L_IM_{II,III}$	1.3884
8.962	4	74 W	$M\zeta_1$	M_VN_{III}	1.3835
8.965	4	67 Ho	$M\beta$	$M_{IV}N_{VI}$	1.3830
8.9900	5	34 Se	$L\alpha_{1,2}$	$L_{III}M_{IV,V}$	1.37910
8.993	5	74 W	$M\zeta_2$	$M_{IV}N_{II}$	1.3787
9.125	1	33 As	L_{II}	Abs. Edge	1.3587
9.20	2	67 Ho	$M\alpha$	$M_VN_{VI,VII}$	1.348
9.211	9	63 Eu	$M\gamma$	$M_{III}N_{IV,V}$	1.346
9.255	1	35 Br	$L\eta$	$L_{II}M_I$	1.3396
9.316	4	73 Ta	$M\zeta_1$	M_VN_{III}	1.3308
9.330	5	73 Ta	$M\zeta_2$	$M_{IV}N_{II}$	1.3288
9.357	6	66 Dy	$M\beta$	$M_{IV}N_{VI}$	1.3250
9.367	1	33 As	L_{III}	Abs. Edge	1.3235
9.40	7	90 Th		N_IP_{III}	1.319
9.4141	8	33 As	$L\beta_1$	$L_{II}M_{IV}$	1.3170
9.44	7	90 Th		N_IP_{II}	1.313
9.5122	1	12 Mg	K	Abs. Edge	1.30339
9.517	5	31 Ga	L_I	Abs. Edge	1.3028
9.521	2	12 Mg	$K\beta$	KM	1.3022
9.581	2	32 Ge	$L\beta_3$	L_IM_{III}	1.2941
9.585	1	35 Br	Ll	$L_{III}M_I$	1.2935
9.59	2	66 Dy	$M\alpha$	$M_VN_{VI,VII}$	1.293
9.600	9	62 Sm	$M\gamma$	$M_{III}N_{IV,V}$	1.291
9.640	2	32 Ge	$L\beta_4$	L_IM_{II}	1.2861
9.6709	8	33 As	$L\alpha_{1,2}$	$L_{III}M_{IV,V}$	1.2820
9.686	7	72 Hf	$M\zeta_2$	$M_{IV}N_{II}$	1.2800
9.686	7	72 Hf	$M\zeta_1$	M_VN_{III}	1.2800
9.792	6	65 Tb	$M\beta$	$M_{IV}N_{VI}$	1.2661
9.8900	2	12 Mg	$K\alpha_{1,2}$	$KL_{II,III}$	1.25360
9.924	1	32 Ge	L_{II}	Abs. Edge	1.2494
9.962	1	34 Se	$L\eta$	$L_{II}M_I$	1.2446
10.00	2	65 Tb	$M\alpha$	$M_VN_{VI,VII}$	1.240
10.09	7	92 U		N_IO_{III}	1.229
10.175	1	32 Ge	$L\beta_1$	$L_{II}M_{IV}$	1.2185
10.187	1	32 Ge	L_{III}	Abs. Edge	1.2170
10.254	6	64 Gd	$M\beta$	$M_{IV}N_{VI}$	1.2091
10.294	1	34 Se	Ll	$L_{III}M_I$	1.2044
10.359	9	31 Ga	$L\beta_{3,4}$	$L_IM_{II,III}$	1.197
10.40	7	92 U		$N_{II}P_I$	1.192
10.4361	8	32 Ge	$L\alpha_{1,2}$	$L_{III}M_{IV,V}$	1.18800
10.46	3	64 Gd	$M\alpha$	$M_VN_{VI,VII}$	1.185
10.48	1	70 Yb	$M\zeta$	M_VN_{III}	1.183
10.505	9	60 Nd	$M\gamma$	$M_{III}N_{IV,V}$	1.180
10.711	5	63 Eu	M_{IV}	Abs. Edge	1.1575
10.734	1	33 As	$L\eta$	$L_{II}M_I$	1.1550
10.750	7	63 Eu	$M\beta$	$M_{IV}N_{VI}$	1.1533
10.828	5	31 Ga	L_{II}	Abs. Edge	1.1450
10.96	3	63 Eu	$M\alpha$	$M_VN_{VI,VII}$	1.131
10.998	9	59 Pr	$M\gamma$	$M_{III}N_{IV,V}$	1.1273
11.013	5	63 Eu	M_V	Abs. Edge	1.1258
11.023	2	31 Ga	$L\beta_1$	$L_{II}M_{IV}$	1.1248
11.072	1	33 As	Ll	$L_{III}M_I$	1.1198
11.07	7	90 Th		$N_{II}P_I$	1.120
11.100	1	31 Ga	L_{III}	Abs. Edge	1.1169
11.200	7	30 Zn	$L\beta_{3,4}$	$L_IM_{II,III}$	1.1070
11.27	1	62 Sm	$M\beta$	$M_{IV}N_{VI}$	1.0998
11.288	5	62 Sm	M_{IV}	Abs. Edge	1.0983
11.292	1	31 Ga	$L\alpha_{1,2}$	$L_{III}M_{IV,V}$	1.09792
11.37	1	68 Er	$M\zeta$	M_VN_{III}	1.0901
11.47	3	62 Sm	$M\alpha$	$M_VN_{VI,VII}$	1.081
11.53	1	58 Ce	$M\gamma$	$M_{III}N_{IV,V}$	1.0749
11.552	5	62 Sm	M_V	Abs. Edge	1.0732
11.56	5	90 Th		$N_{II}O_{IV}$	1.072
11.569	1	11 Na	K	Abs. Edge	1.07167
11.575	2	11 Na	$K\beta$	KM	1.0711
11.609	2	32 Ge	$L\eta$	$L_{II}M_I$	1.0680
11.862	1	30 Zn	L_{II}	Abs. Edge	1.04523
11.86	1	67 Ho	$M\zeta$	M_VN_{III}	1.0450
11.9101	9	11 Na	$K\alpha_{1,2}$	$KL_{II,III}$	1.04098
11.965	2	32 Ge	Ll	$L_{III}M_I$	1.0362
11.983	3	30 Zn	$L\beta_1$	$L_{II}M_{IV}$	1.0347
12.08	4	57 La	$M\gamma$	$M_{III}N_{IV,V}$	1.027
12.122	3	29 Cu	$L\beta_{3,4}$	$L_IM_{II,III}$	1.0228
12.131	1	30 Zn	L_{III}	Abs. Edge	1.02201
12.254	3	30 Zn	$L\alpha_{1,2}$	$L_{III}M_{IV,V}$	1.0117
12.43	2	66 Dy	$M\zeta$	M_VN_{III}	0.998
12.44	2	60 Nd	$M\beta$	$M_{IV}N_{VI}$	0.997
12.459	5	60 Nd	M_{IV}	Abs. Edge	0.9951
12.597	2	31 Ga	$L\eta$	$L_{II}M_I$	0.9842
12.68	2	60 Nd	$M\alpha$	$M_VN_{VI,VII}$	0.978
12.737	5	60 Nd	M_V	Abs. Edge	0.9734
12.75	3	56 Ba	$M\gamma$	$M_{III}N_{IV,V}$	0.973
12.90	9	92 U		$N_{III}O_V$	0.961
12.953	2	31 Ga	Ll	$L_{III}M_I$	0.9572
12.98	2	65 Tb	$M\zeta$	M_VN_{III}	0.955
13.014	1	29 Cu	L_{II}	Abs. Edge	0.95268
13.053	3	29 Cu	$L\beta_1$	$L_{II}M_{IV}$	0.9498
13.06	2	59 Pr	$M\beta$	$M_{IV}N_{VI}$	0.950
13.06	1	30 Zn	L_I	Abs. Edge	0.9495
13.122	5	59 Pr	M_{IV}	Abs. Edge	0.9448
13.18	2	28 Ni	$L\beta_{3,4}$	$L_IM_{II,III}$	0.941
13.288	1	29 Cu	L_{III}	Abs. Edge	0.93306

Wavelength Å*	p.e.	Element	Designation		keV	Wavelength Å*	p.e.	Element	Designation		keV
13.30	6	83 Bi		$N_IP_{II,III}$	0.932	18.8	2	47 Ag		$M_IN_{II,III}$	0.658
13.336	3	29 Cu	$L\alpha_{1,2}$	$L_{III}M_{IV,V}$	0.9297	18.96	4	24 Cr	$L\beta_{3,4}$	$L_IM_{II,III}$	0.654
13.343	5	59 Pr	$M\alpha$	$M_VN_{VI,VII}$	0.9292	19.11	2	25 Mn	$L\beta_1$	$L_{II}M_{IV}$	0.6488
13.394	5	59 Pr	M_V	Abs. Edge	0.9257	19.1	1	52 Te		$M_{III}N_I$	0.648
13.57	2	64 Gd	$M\zeta$	M_VN_{III}	0.914	19.40	7	48 Cd		$M_{II}N_{IV}$	0.639
13.68	2	30 Zn	$L\eta$	$L_{II}M_I$	0.906	19.44	5	57 La	$M\zeta$	M_VN_{III}	0.638
13.75	4	58 Ce	$M\beta$	$M_{IV}N_{VI}$	0.902	19.45	1	25 Mn	$L\alpha_{1,2}$	$L_{III}M_{IV,V}$	0.6374
13.8	1	90 Th		$N_{III}O_V$	0.897	19.66	5	53 I	$M_{IV,V}$	Abs. Edge	0.631
14.02	2	30 Zn	Ll	$L_{III}M_I$	0.884	19.75	4	26 Fe	$L\eta$	$L_{II}M_I$	0.628
14.04	2	58 Ce	$M\alpha$	$M_VN_{VI,VII}$	0.883	20.0	1	50 Sn		$M_{II}N_I$	0.619
14.22	2	63 Eu	$M\zeta$	M_VN_{III}	0.872	20.1	2	46 Pd		$M_IN_{II,III}$	0.616
14.242	5	28 Ni	L_{II}	Abs. Edge	0.8706	20.15	1	26 Fe	Ll	$L_{III}M_I$	0.6152
14.271	6	28 Ni	$L\beta_1$	$L_{II}M_{IV}$	0.8688	20.2	1	51 Sb		$M_{III}N_I$	0.612
14.3018	1	10 Ne	K	Abs. Edge	0.866889	20.47	7	48 Cd	$M\gamma$	$M_{III}N_{IV,V}$	0.606
14.31	3	27 Co	$L\beta_{3,4}$	$L_IM_{II,III}$	0.870	20.64	4	56 Ba	$M\zeta$	M_VN_{III}	0.601
14.39	5	58 Ce		$M_VO_{II,III}$	0.862	20.66	7	47 Ag		$M_{II}N_{IV}$	0.600
14.452	5	10 Ne	$K\beta$	KM	0.8579	20.7	1	24 Cr	L_{III}	Abs. Edge	0.598
14.51	5	57 La	$M\beta$	$M_{IV}N_{VI}$	0.854	21.19	5	23 Va	$L\beta_{3,4}$	$L_IM_{II,III}$	0.585
14.525	5	28 Ni	L_{III}	Abs. Edge	0.8536	21.27	1	24 Cr	$L\beta_1$	$L_{II}M_{IV}$	0.5828
14.561	3	28 Ni	$L\alpha_{1,2}$	$L_{III}M_{IV,V}$	0.8515	21.34	5	52 Te		$M_{IV}O_{II,III}$	0.581
14.610	3	10 Ne	$K\alpha_{1,2}$	$KL_{II,III}$	0.8486	21.5	1	50 Sn		$M_{III}N_I$	0.575
14.88	5	57 La	$M\alpha$	$M_VN_{VI,VII}$	0.833	21.64	3	24 Cr	$L\alpha_{1,2}$	$L_{III}M_{IV,V}$	0.5728
14.90	2	29 Cu	$L\eta$	$L_{II}M_I$	0.832	21.78	5	52 Te		M_VO_{III}	0.569
14.91	4	62 Sm	$M\zeta$	M_VN_{III}	0.831	21.82	7	47 Ag	$M\gamma$	$M_{III}N_{IV,V}$	0.568
15.286	9	29 Cu	Ll	$L_{III}M_I$	0.8111	21.85	2	25 Mn	$L\eta$	$L_{II}M_I$	0.5675
15.56	1	56 Ba	M_{IV}	Abs. Edge	0.7967	22.1	1	46 Pd		$M_{II}N_{IV}$	0.560
15.618	5	27 Co	L_{II}	Abs. Edge	0.7938	22.29	1	25 Mn	Ll	$L_{III}M_I$	0.5563
15.65	4	26 Fe	$L\beta_{3,4}$	$L_IM_{II,III}$	0.792	22.9	2	48 Cd		$M_{II}N_I$	0.540
15.666	8	27 Co	$L\beta_1$	$L_{II}M_{IV}$	0.7914	23.32	1	8 O	K	Abs. Edge	0.5317
15.72	9	56 Ba		$M_{IV}O_{III}$	0.789	23.3	1	46 Pd	$M\gamma$	$M_{III}N_{IV,V}$	0.531
15.89	1	56 Ba	M_V	Abs. Edge	0.7801	23.62	3	8 O	$K\alpha$	KL	0.5249
15.91	5	56 Ba		$M_{IV}O_{II}$	0.779	23.88	4	23 Va	$L\beta_1$	$L_{II}M_{IV}$	0.5192
15.915	5	27 Co	L_{III}	Abs. Edge	0.7790	24.25	3	23 Va	$L\alpha_{1,2}$	$L_{III}M_{IV,V}$	0.5113
15.93	4	52 Te	$M\gamma$	$M_{III}N_{IV,V}$	0.778	24.28	5	50 Sn	$M_{IV,V}$	Abs. Edge	0.511
15.972	6	27 Co	$L\alpha_{1,2}$	$L_{III}M_{IV,V}$	0.7762	24.30	3	24 Cr	$L\eta$	$L_{II}M_I$	0.5102
15.98	5	51 Sb		$M_{II}N_{IV}$	0.776	24.4	2	47 Ag		M_VN_I	0.509
16.20	5	56 Ba		M_VO_{III}	0.765	24.5	1	48 Cd		$M_{III}N_I$	0.507
16.27	3	28 Ni	$L\eta$	$L_{II}M_I$	0.762	24.78	1	24 Cr	Ll	$L_{III}M_I$	0.5003
16.46	4	60 Nd	$M\zeta$	M_VN_{III}	0.753	25.01	9	45 Rh	$M\gamma$	$M_{III}N_{IV,V}$	0.496
16.693	9	28 Ni	Ll	$L_{III}M_I$	0.7427	25.3	1	50 Sn		$M_{IV}O_{II,III}$	0.491
16.7	1	24 Cr	L_I	Abs. Edge	0.741	25.50	9	44 Ru		$M_{II}N_{IV}$	0.486
16.92	4	51 Sb	$M\gamma$	$M_{III}N_{IV,V}$	0.733	25.7	1	50 Sn		M_VO_{III}	0.483
16.93	5	50 Sn		$M_{II}N_{IV}$	0.733	26.0	1	47 Ag		$M_{III}N_I$	0.478
17.19	4	25 Mn	$L\beta_{3,4}$	$L_IM_{II,III}$	0.721	26.2	2	46 Pd		$M_{II}N_I$	0.474
17.202	5	26 Fe	L_{II}	Abs. Edge	0.7208	26.72	9	52 Te	$M\zeta$	$M_{IV,V}N_{II,III}$	0.464
17.26	1	26 Fe	$L\beta_1$	$L_{II}M_{IV}$	0.7185	26.9	1	44 Ru	$M\gamma$	$M_{III}N_{IV,V}$	0.462
17.38	4	59 Pr	$M\zeta$	M_VN_{III}	0.714	27.05	2	22 Ti	$L\beta_1$	$L_{II}M_{IV}$	0.4584
17.525	5	26 Fe	L_{III}	Abs. Edge	0.7074	27.29	1	22 Ti	$L_{II,III}$	Abs. Edge	0.4544
17.59	2	26 Fe	$L\alpha_{1,2}$	$L_{III}M_{IV,V}$	0.7050	27.34	3	23 Va	$L\eta$	$L_{II}M_I$	0.4535
17.6	1	52 Te		$M_{II}N_I$	0.703	27.42	2	22 Ti	$L\alpha_{1,2}$	$L_{III}M_{IV,V}$	0.4522
17.87	3	27 Co	$L\eta$	$L_{II}M_I$	0.694	27.77	1	23 Va	Ll	$L_{III}M_I$	0.4465
17.94	5	50 Sn	$M\gamma$	$M_{III}N_{IV,V}$	0.691	27.9	1	46 Pd		$M_{III}N_I$	0.445
17.9	1	24 Cr	L_{II}	Abs. Edge	0.691	28.1	2	45 Rh		$M_{II}N_I$	0.442
18.292	8	27 Co	Ll	$L_{III}M_I$	0.6778	28.13	5	48 Cd	$M_{IV,V}$	Abs. Edge	0.4408
18.32	2	9 F	$K\alpha$	KL	0.6768	28.88	8	51 Sb	$M\zeta$	$M_{IV,V}N_{II,III}$	0.429
18.35	4	58 Ce	$M\zeta$	M_VN_{III}	0.676	29.8	1	45 Rh		$M_{III}N_I$	0.417
18.8	1	51 Sb		$M_{II}N_I$	0.658	30.4	1	48 Cd		$M_{IV}O_{II,III}$	0.408

Wavelength Å*	p.e.	Element		Designation	keV	Wavelength Å*	p.e.	Element		Designation	keV
30.8	1	48 Cd		$M_V O_{III}$	0.403	49.4	1	79 Au		$N_V N_{VI,VII}$	0.2510
30.82	5	47 Ag	M_{IV}	Abs. Edge	0.4022	49.5	1	90 Th		$N_{VI} O_{IV}$	0.2505
30.89	3	22 Ti	$L\eta$	$L_{II} M_I$	0.4013	50.0	1	90 Th		$N_{VII} O_V$	0.2479
30.99	1	7 N	K	Abs. Edge	0.4000	50.2	1	77 Ir		$N_{IV} N_{VI}$	0.2470
31.02	2	21 Sc	$L\beta_1$	$L_{II} M_{IV}$	0.3996	50.3	1	52 Te		$M_{III} M_V$	0.2465
31.14	5	47 Ag	M_V	Abs. Edge	0.3981	50.9	1	78 Pt		$N_V N_{VI,VII}$	0.2436
31.24	9	50 Sn	$M\zeta$	$M_{IV,V} N_{II,III}$	0.397	51.3	1	38 Sr		$M_{II} N_I$	0.2416
31.35	3	21 Sc	$L\alpha_{1,2}$	$L_{III} M_{IV,V}$	0.3954	51.9	1	76 Os		$N_{IV} N_{VI}$	0.2388
31.36	2	22 Ti	Ll	$L_{III} M_I$	0.3953	52.0	2	48 Cd		$M_{II} M_{IV}$	0.2384
31.60	4	7 N	$K\alpha$	KL	0.3924	52.2	1	51 Sb		$M_{III} M_V$	0.2375
31.8	1	92 U		$N_{IV} N_{VI}$	0.390	52.34	7	44 Ru	$M\zeta$	$M_{IV,V} N_{II,III}$	0.2369
32.3	2	44 Ru		$M_{II} N_I$	0.384	52.8	1	77 Ir		$N_V N_{VI,VII}$	0.2348
33.1	2	41 Nb		$M_{III} N_{IV}$	0.375	53.6	1	38 Sr		$M_{III} N_I$	0.2313
33.5	3	47 Ag		$M_{IV,V} O_{II,III}$	0.370	54.0	2	74 W		$N_{II} N_{IV}$	0.2295
33.57	9	90 Th		$N_{IV} N_{VI}$	0.3693	54.0	1	47 Ag		$M_{II} M_{IV}$	0.2295
34.8	1	92 U		$N_V N_{VI,VII}$	0.357	54.2	1	50 Sn		$M_{III} M_V$	0.2287
34.9	2	41 Nb	$M\gamma$	$M_{III} N_{IV,V}$	0.356	54.7	2	76 Os		$N_V N_{VI,VII}$	0.2266
35.13	2	21 Sc	$L\eta$	$L_{II} M_I$	0.3529	54.8	2	42 Mo		$M_{IV,V} O_{II,III}$	0.2262
35.13	1	20 Ca	L_{II}	Abs. Edge	0.3529	55.8	1	74 W		$N_{IV} N_{VI}$	0.2221
35.3	3	42 Mo		$M_{II} N_I$	0.351	55.9	1	18 A	$L\eta$	$L_{II} M_I$	0.2217
35.49	1	20 Ca	L_{III}	Abs. Edge	0.34931	56.3	1	18 A	Ll	$L_{III} M_I$	0.2201
35.59	3	21 Sc	Ll	$L_{III} M_I$	0.3483	56.5	1	46 Pd		$M_{II} M_{IV}$	0.2194
35.63	1	20 Ca	$L_{II,III}$	Abs. Edge	0.34793	57.0	2	37 Rb		$M_{II} N_I$	0.2174
35.94	2	20 Ca	$L\beta_1$	$L_{II} M_{IV}$	0.3449	58.2	1	73 Ta		$N_{IV} N_{VI}$	0.2130
36.32	9	90 Th		$N_V N_{VI,VII}$	0.3414	58.4	1	74 W		$N_V N_{VII}$	0.2122
36.33	2	20 Ca	$L\alpha_{1,2}$	$L_{III} M_{IV,V}$	0.3413	58.7	2	48 Cd		$M_{III} M_V$	0.2111
36.8	1	48 Cd	$M\zeta$	$M_{IV,V} N_{II,III}$	0.3371	59.3	1	45 Rh		$M_{II} M_{IV}$	0.2090
37.4	2	46 Pd		$M_{IV,V} O_{II,III}$	0.332	59.5	3	74 W		$N_V N_{VI}$	0.208
37.5	2	42 Mo		$M_{III} N_I$	0.331	59.5	2	37 Rb		$M_{III} N_I$	0.2083
38.4	3	41 Nb		$M_{II} N_I$	0.323	60.5	1	47 Ag		$M_{III} M_V$	0.2048
39.77	7	47 Ag	$M\zeta$	$M_{IV,V} N_{II,III}$	0.3117	61.1	2	73 Ta		$N_V N_{VI,VII}$	0.2028
40.46	2	20 Ca	$L\eta$	$L_{II} M_I$	0.3064	61.9	2	41 Nb		$M_{IV,V} O_{II,III}$	0.2002
40.7	2	41 Nb		$M_{III} N_I$	0.305	62.2	1	44 Ru		$M_{II} M_{IV}$	0.1992
40.9	2	45 Rh		$M_{IV,V} O_{II,III}$	0.303	62.9	1	46 Pd		$M_{III} M_V$	0.1970
40.96	2	20 Ca	Ll	$L_{III} M_I$	0.3027	63.0	5	71 Lu		$N_{IV} N_{VI}$	0.197
42.1	2	92 U		$N_{VI} O_V$	0.295	64.38	7	42 Mo	$M\zeta$	$M_{IV,V} N_{II,III}$	0.1926
42.1	1	19 K	$L_{II,III}$	Abs. Edge	0.2946	65.1	7	70 Yb		$N_{IV} N_{VI}$	0.190
42.3	2	82 Pb		$N_{IV} N_{VI}$	0.293	65.5	1	45 Rh		$M_{III} M_V$	0.1892
43.3	2	92 U		$N_{VI} O_{IV}$	0.286	65.7	2	71 Lu		$N_V N_{VI,VII}$	0.1886
43.6	1	46 Pd	$M\zeta$	$M_{IV,V} N_{II,III}$	0.2844	67.33	9	17 Cl	$L\eta$	$L_{II} M_I$	0.1841
43.68	1	6 C	K	Abs. Edge	0.28384	67.6	3	5 B	$K\alpha$	KL	0.1833
44.7	3	6 C	$K\alpha$	KL	0.277	67.90	9	17 Cl	Ll	$L_{III} M_I$	0.1826
44.8	1	44 Ru		$M_{IV,V} O_{II,III}$	0.2768	68.2	3	90 Th		$O_{III} P_{IV,V}$	0.1817
45.0	1	82 Pb		$N_V N_{VI,VII}$	0.2756	68.3	1	44 Ru		$M_{III} M_V$	0.1814
45.2	3	80 Hg		$N_{IV} N_{VI}$	0.274	68.9	2	42 Mo		$M_{II} M_{IV}$	0.1798
45.2	1	51 Sb		$M_{II} M_{IV}$	0.2743	69.3	5	70 Yb		$N_V N_{VI,VII}$	0.179
46.48	9	39 Y		$M_{II} N_I$	0.267	70.0	4	40 Zr		$M_{IV,V} O_{II,III}$	0.177
46.5	2	81 Tl		$N_V N_{VI,VII}$	0.267	72.1	3	41 Nb		$M_{II} M_{IV}$	0.1718
46.8	2	79 Au		$N_{IV} N_{VI}$	0.265	72.19	9	41 Nb	$M\zeta$	$M_{IV,V} N_{II,III}$	0.1717
47.24	2	19 K	Ll	$L_{II} M_I$	0.2625	72.7	9	68 Er		$N_{IV} N_{VI}$	0.171
47.3	1	50 Sn		$M_{II} M_{IV}$	0.2621	74.9	1	42 Mo		$M_{III} M_V$	0.1656
47.67	9	45 Rh	$M\zeta$	$M_{IV,V} N_{II,III}$	0.2601	76.3	7	68 Er		$N_V N_{VI,VII}$	0.163
47.74	1	19 K	Ll	$L_{III} M_I$	0.25971	76.7	2	40 Zr		$M_{II} M_{IV}$	0.1617
47.9	3	80 Hg		$N_V N_{VI,VII}$	0.259	76.9	2	35 Br		$M_{II} N_I$	0.1613
48.1	2	78 Pt		$N_{IV} N_{VI}$	0.258	78.4	2	41 Nb		$M_{III} M_V$	0.1582
48.2	1	90 Th		$N_{VI} O_V$	0.2572	79.8	3	35 Br		$M_{III} N_I$	0.1554
48.5	2	39 Y		$M_{III} N_I$	0.256	80.9	3	40 Zr		$M_{III} M_V$	0.1533

Wavelength Å*	p.e.	Element	Designation		keV	Wavelength Å*	p.e.	Element	Designation		keV
81.5	2	39 Y		$M_{II}M_{IV}$	0.1522	157.	3	30 Zn		$M_{II,III}M_{IV,V}$	0.079
82.1	2	40 Zr	$M\zeta$	$M_{IV,V}N_{II,III}$	0.1511	159.0	2	56 Ba		$N_{IV}O_{III}$	0.07796
83.	1	66 Dy		$N_{IV,V}N_{VI,VII}$	0.149	159.5	5	29 Cu	M_{II}	Abs. Edge	0.0777
83.4	3	16 S	Ll, η	$L_{II,III}M_I$	0.1487	163.3	2	56 Ba		$N_{IV}O_{II}$	0.07590
85.7	2	38 Sr		$M_{II}M_{IV}$	0.1447	164.6	2	56 Ba		$N_V O_{III}$	0.07530
86.	1	65 Tb		$N_{IV,V}N_{VI,VII}$	0.144	164.7	3	35 Br		$M_I M_{III}$	0.0753
86.5	2	39 Y		$M_{III}M_{IV,V}$	0.1431	166.0	5	29 Cu	M_{III}	Abs. Edge	0.0747
91.4	2	38 Sr		$M_{III}M_{IV,V}$	0.1357	170.4	1	13 Al	$L_{II,III}$	Abs. Edge	0.07278
91.5	2	37 Rb		$M_{II}M_{IV}$	0.1355	171.4	5	13 Al		$L_{II,III}M$	0.0724
91.6	1	83 Bi		$N_{VI}O_{IV}$	0.1354	173.	3	29 Cu		$M_{II,III}M_{IV,V}$	0.072
93.2	1	83 Bi		$N_{VII}O_V$	0.1330	181.	5	90 Th		$O_{IV,V}O_{II,III}$	0.068
93.4	2	39 Y	$M\zeta$	$M_{IV,V}N_{II,III}$	0.1328	183.8	1	55 Cs		$N_{IV}O_{III}$	0.06746
94.	1	15 P	$L_{II,III}$	Abs. Edge	0.132	184.6	3	35 Br		$M_I M_{II}$	0.0672
96.7	2	37 Rb		$M_{III}M_{IV,V}$	0.1282	188.4	1	28 Ni	M_{III}	Abs. Edge	0.06581
97.2	8	66 Dy		$N_{IV,V}O_{II,III}$	0.128	188.6	1	55 Cs		$N_{IV}O_{II}$	0.06574
98.	1	62 Sm		$N_{IV,V}N_{VI,VII}$	0.126	189.5	3	35 Br		$M_{IV}N_{III}$	0.0654
100.2	2	82 Pb		$N_{VI}O_V$	0.1237	190.3	1	55 Cs		$N_V O_{III}$	0.06515
102.2	4	65 Tb		$N_{IV,V}O_{II,III}$	0.1213	190.	2	28 Ni		$M_{II,III}M_{IV,V}$	0.0651
102.4	1	82 Pb		$N_{VI}O_{IV}$	0.1211	191.1	2	35 Br	$M\zeta_2$	$M_{IV}N_{II}$	0.06488
103.8	4	15 P		$L_{II,III}M$	0.1194	192.6	2	35 Br	$M\zeta_1$	$M_V N_{III}$	0.06437
104.3	1	82 Pb		$N_{VII}O_V$	0.1189	197.3	1	12 Mg	L_I	Abs. Edge	0.06284
107.	1	60 Nd		$N_{IV,V}N_{VI,VII}$	0.116	202.	5	27 Co	$M_{II,III}$	Abs. Edge	0.061
108.0	2	38 Sr	$M\zeta_2$	$M_{IV}N_{II,III}$	0.1148	203.	1	16 S		$L_I L_{II,III}$	0.061
108.7	1	38 Sr	$M\zeta_1$	$M_V N_{III}$	0.1140	214.	6	27 Co		$M_{II,III}M_{IV,V}$	0.058
109.4	3	35 Br		$M_{II}M_{IV}$	0.1133	224.	1	53 I	$N_{IV,V}$	Abs. Edge	0.0552
110.6	5	29 Cu	M_I	Abs. Edge	0.1121	226.5	1	3 Li	K	Abs. Edge	0.05475
111.	1	4 Be	K	Abs. Edge	0.111	227.8	1	34 Se	M_V	Abs. Edge	0.05443
112.0	6	63 Eu		$N_{IV,V}O_{II,III}$	0.1107	228.	1	3 Li	$K\alpha$	KL	0.0543
113.0	1	81 Tl		$N_{VI}O_V$	0.10968	230.	2	34 Se		$M_V N_{III}$	0.0538
113.	1	59 Pr		$N_{IV,V}N_{VI,VII}$	0.1095	230.	1	26 Fe	$M_{II,III}$	Abs. Edge	0.0538
113.8	3	35 Br		$M_{III}M_{IV,V}$	0.1089	243.	5	26 Fe		$M_{II,III}M_{IV,V}$	0.051
114.	1	4 Be	$K\alpha$	KL	0.1085	249.3	1	12 Mg	L_{II}	Abs. Edge	0.04973
115.3	2	81 Tl		$N_{VI}O_{IV}$	0.1075	250.7	1	12 Mg	L_{III}	Abs. Edge	0.04945
117.4	4	62 Sm		$N_{IV,V}O_{II,III}$	0.1056	251.5	5	12 Mg		$L_{II,III}M$	0.04929
117.7	1	81 Tl		$N_{VII}O_V$	0.10530	273.	6	25 Mn		$M_{II,III}M_{IV,V}$	0.045
123.	1	14 Si	$L_{II,III}$	Abs. Edge	0.1006	290.	1	13 Al		$L_I L_{II,III}$	0.0428
126.8	2	37 Rb		$M_{IV}N_{III}$	0.0978	309.	9	24 Cr		$M_{II,III}M_{IV,V}$	0.040
127.8	2	37 Rb	$M\zeta_2$	$M_{IV}N_{II}$	0.0970	317.	1	12 Mg		$L_I L_{II,III}$	0.0392
128.7	2	37 Rb	$M\zeta_1$	$M_V N_{III}$	0.0964	337.	9	23 V		$M_{II,III}M_{IV,V}$	0.0368
128.9	7	60 Nd		$N_{IV,V}O_{II,III}$	0.0962	376.	1	11 Na		$L_I L_{II,III}$	0.03299
135.5	4	14 Si		$L_{II,III}M$	0.0915	399.	5	35 Br	N_I	Abs. Edge	0.0311
136.5	4	59 Pr		$N_{IV,V}O_{II,III}$	0.0908	405.	5	11 Na	$L_{II,III}$	Abs. Edge	0.0306
137.0	5	30 Zn	M_{II}	Abs. Edge	0.0905	407.1	5	11 Na		$L_{II,III}M$	0.03045
142.5	1	13 Al	L_I	Abs. Edge	0.08701	417.	5	17 Cl	M_I	Abs. Edge	0.0297
143.9	5	30 Zn	M_{III}	Abs. Edge	0.0862	444.	5	53 I	O_I	Abs. Edge	0.0279
144.4	6	58 Ce		$N_{IV,V}O_{II,III}$	0.0859	525.	9	20 Ca		$M_{II,III}N_I$	0.0236
144.4	3	37 Rb		$M_I M_{III}$	0.0859	692.	9	19 K		$M_{II,III}N_I$	0.0179
152.6	6	57 La		$N_{IV,V}O_{II,III}$	0.0812						

X-RAY ATOMIC ENERGY LEVELS

J. A. Bearden and A. F. Burr

These tables were originally published as the final report to the U.S. Atomic Energy Commission as Report NYO-2543-1 in partial fulfillment of Contract AT(30-1)-2543. The tables were later reproduced in *Review of Modern Physics*. The data may also be obtained from the Superintendent of Documents, U.S. Government Printing Office, Washington, D. C. 20402 in the publication NSRDS-NBS 14. Persons seeking discussion of the details of calculations, sources of energy level information and the problem of properly interpreting the experimental measurements should refer to the original publication or to *Review of Modern Physics*, Vol. 39, 125–142, January 1967.

All of the x-ray emission wavelengths have recently been reevaluated and placed on a consistent Å* scale. For most elements these data give a highly overdetermined set of equations for energy level differences, which have been solved by least-squares adjustment for each case. This procedure makes "best" use of all x-ray wavelength data, and also permits calculation of the probable error for each energy difference. Photoelectron measurements of absolute energy levels are more precise than x-ray absorption edge data. These have been used to establish the absolute scale for eighty-one elements and, in many cases, to provide additional energy level difference data. The x-ray absorption wavelengths were used for eight elements and ionization measurements for two; the remaining five were interpolated by a Moseley diagram involving the output values of energy levels from adjacent elements. Probable errors are listed on an absolute energy basis. In the original source of the present data, a table of energy levels in Rydberg units is given. Difference tables in volts, Rydbergs, and milli-Å* wavelength units, with the respective probable errors, are also included there.

X-Ray Atomic Energy Levels

Recommended values of the atomic energy levels, and probable errors in eV. Where available, photoelectron direct measurements are listed in brackets [ ] immediately under the recommended values. The measured values of the x-ray absorption energies are shown in parentheses ( ). Interpolated values are enclosed in angle brackets ⟨ ⟩.

Level	1 H	2 He	3 Li	4 Be	5 B	6 C	7 N	8 O
K	13.59811[a]	24.58678[b]	54.75±0.02 (54.75)	111.0±1.0 (111.0)	188.0±0.4 [188.0][c]	283.8±0.4 [283.8][c] (283.8)	401.6±0.4 [401.6][c]	532.0±0.4 [532.0][c]
L_I								23.7±0.4 [23.7][d]
$L_{II,III}$					4.7±0.9	6.4±1.9	9.2±0.6	7.1±0.8

Level	9 F	10 Ne	11 Na	12 Mg	13 Al	14 Si	15 P	16 S
K	685.4±0.4 [685.4][c]	866.9±0.3 (866.9)	1072.1±0.4 [1072.1][c] (1072.)	1305.0±0.4 [1305.0][c] (1303.)	1559.6±0.4 [1559.6][c] (1559.8)	1838.9±0.4 [1838.9][c] (1838.9)	2145.5±0.4 [2145.5][d]	2472.0±0.4 [2472.0][c] (2470.)
L_I	⟨31.⟩	⟨45.⟩	63.3±0.4 [63.3][d]	89.4±0.4 [89.4][d] (63.)	117.7±0.4 [117.7][d] (87.)	148.7±0.4 [148.7][d]	189.3±0.4 [189.3][d]	229.2±0.4 [229.2][d]
$L_{II,III}$	8.6±0.8	18.3±0.4	31.1±0.4 (31.)	51.4±0.5 (50.)	73.1±0.5 (72.8)	99.2±0.5 (100.6)	132.2±0.5 (132.)	164.8±0.7

Level	17 Cl	18 Ar	19 K	20 Ca	21 Sc	22 Ti	23 V	24 Cr
K	2822.4±0.3 [2822.4][c] (2820.)	3202.9±0.3 (3202.9)	3607.4±0.4 [3607.4][c] (3607.8)	4038.1±0.4 [4038.1][c] (4038.1)	4492.8±0.4 [4492.8][c]	4966.4±0.4 [4966.4][d] (4964.5)	5465.1±0.3 [5465.1][c] (5464.)	5989.2±0.3 [5989.2][c] (5989.)
L_I	270.2±0.4 [270.2][d]	320. ⟨320.⟩[d]	377.1±0.4 [377.1][d]	437.8±0.4 [437.8][d]	500.4±0.4 [500.4][d]	563.7±0.4 [563.7][d]	628.2±0.4 [628.2][d]	694.6±0.4 [694.6][d]
L_{II}	201.6±0.3	247.3±0.3	296.3±0.4	350.0±0.4	406.7±0.4	461.5±0.4	520.5±0.3	583.7±0.3
L_{III}	200.0±0.3	245.2±0.3	293.6±0.4	346.4±0.4	402.2±0.4	455.5±0.4	512.9±0.3	574.5±0.3
M_I	17.5±0.4	25.3±0.4	33.9±0.4	43.7±0.4	53.8±0.4	60.3±0.4	66.5±0.4	74.1±0.4
$M_{II,III}$	6.8±0.4	12.4±0.3	17.8±0.4	25.4±0.4	32.3±0.5	34.6±0.4	37.8±0.3	42.5±0.3
$M_{IV,V}$					6.6±0.5	3.7	2.2±0.3	2.3±0.4

X-Ray Atomic Energy Levels (*Continued*)

	25 Mn	26 Fe	27 Co	28 Ni	29 Cu	30 Zn	31 Ga	32 Ge
K	6539.0±0.4 [6539.0][e] (6538.)	7112.0±0.9 [7111.3][e,f] (7111.2)	7708.9±0.3 [7708.9][e] (7709.5)	8332.8±0.4 [8332.8][e] (8331.6)	8978.9±0.4 [8978.9][e,g] (8980.3)	9658.6±0.6 [9658.6][e] (9660.7)	10367.1±0.5 [10367.1][e] (10368.2)	11103.1±0.7 [11103.8][e] (11103.6)
L$_I$	769.0±0.4 [769.0][d]	846.1±0.4 [846.1][d]	925.6±0.4 [925.6][d]	1008.1±0.4 [1008.1][d]	1096.1±0.4 [1096.0][d]	1193.6±0.9	1297.7±1.1	1414.3±0.7 [1413.6][k]
L$_{II}$	651.4±0.4	721.1±0.9	793.6±0.3	871.9±0.4	951.0±0.4 [950.0][h] (953.)	1042.8±0.6 (1045.)	1142.3±0.5	1247.8±0.7 (1249.)
L$_{III}$	640.3±0.4	708.1±0.9	778.6±0.3	854.7±0.4	931.1±0.4 [931.4][h] (933.)	1019.7±0.6 (1022.)	1115.4±0.5 (1117.)	1216.7±0.7 (1217.0)
M$_I$	83.9±0.5	92.9±0.9	100.7±0.4	111.8±0.6	119.8±0.6	135.9±1.1	158.1±0.5	180.0±0.8
M$_{II}$	48.6±0.4	54.0±0.9	59.5±0.3	68.1±0.4	73.6±0.4	86.6±0.6	106.8±0.7	127.9±0.9
M$_{III}$	(54.)	(54.)	(61.)	(66.)	(75.)	(86.)	102.9±0.5	120.8±0.7
M$_{IV,V}$	3.3±0.5	3.6±0.9	2.9±0.3	3.6±0.4	1.6±0.4	8.1±0.6	17.4±0.5	28.7±0.7

	33 As	34 Se	35 Br	36 Kr	37 Rb	38 Sr	39 Y	40 Zr
K	11866.7±0.7 [11866.7][i] (11865.)	12657.8±0.7 [12657.8][i] (12654.5)	13473.7±0.4 (13470.)	14325.6±0.8 (14324.4)	15199.7±0.3 (15202.)	16104.6±0.3 (16107.)	17038.4±0.3 (17038.)	17997.6±0.4 (17999.)
L$_I$	1526.5±0.8 (1529.)	1653.9±3.5 (1652.5)	1782.0±0.4 [1782.0][j]	1921.0±0.6 [1921.2][k]	2065.1±0.3 [2065.4][j]	2216.3±0.3 [2216.2][j]	2372.5±0.3 [2372.7][j]	2531.6±0.3 [2531.6][j]
L$_{II}$	1358.6±0.7 (1358.7)	1476.2±0.7 (1474.7)	1596.0±0.4 [1596.2][j]	1727.2±0.5 [1727.2][k] (1730.)	1863.9±0.3 [1863.4][j]	2006.8±0.3 [2006.6][j] (2008.5)	2155.5±0.3 [2155.0][j] (2154.0)	2306.7±0.3 [2306.5][j] (2305.3)
L$_{III}$	1323.1±0.7 (1323.5)	1435.8±0.7 (1434.0)	1549.9±0.4 [1549.7][j]	1674.9±0.5 [1674.8][k] (1677.)	1804.4±0.3 [1804.6][j]	1939.6±0.3 [1939.9][j] (1941.)	2080.0±0.3 [2080.2][j] (2079.4)	2222.3±0.3 [2222.5][j] (2222.5)
M$_I$	203.5±0.7	231.5±0.7	256.5±0.4		322.1±0.3	357.5±0.3	393.6±0.3	430.3±0.3
M$_{II}$	146.4±1.2	168.2±1.3	189.3±0.4	222.7±1.1	247.4±0.3	279.8±0.3	312.4±0.4	344.2±0.4

X-Ray Atomic Energy Levels (Continued)

	33 As	34 Se	35 Br	36 Kr	37 Rb	38 Sr	39 Y	40 Zr
M_{III}	140.5±0.8	161.9±1.0	181.5±0.4	213.8±1.1	238.5±0.3	269.1±0.3	300.3±0.4	330.5±0.4
M_{IV}	41.2±0.7	56.7±0.8	70.1±0.4	88.9±0.8	111.8±0.3	135.0±0.3	159.6±0.3	182.4±0.3
M_{V}			69.0±0.4		110.3±0.3	133.1±0.3	157.4±0.3	180.0±0.3
N_{I}			27.3±0.5	24.0±0.8	29.3±0.3	37.7±0.3	45.4±0.3	51.3±0.3
N_{II}	2.5±1.0	5.6±1.3	5.2±0.4	10.6±1.9	14.8±0.4	19.9±0.3	25.6±0.4	28.7±0.4
N_{III}			4.6±0.4		14.0±0.3			

	41 Nb	42 Mo	43 Tc	44 Ru	45 Rh	46 Pd	47 Ag	48 Cd
K	18985.6±0.4 (18987.)	19999.5±0.3 (20004.)	21044.0±0.7	22117.2±0.3 (22119.)	23219.9±0.3 (23219.8)	24350.3±0.3 (24348.)	25514.0±0.3 (25516.)	26711.2±0.3 (26716.)
L_{I}	2697.7±0.3 [2697.7][l]	2865.5±0.3 [2866.0][l]	3042.5±0.4 [3042.5][l]	3224.0±0.3 [3224.3][l]	3411.9±0.3 [3412.0][l] (3417.)	3604.3±0.3 [3604.6][l] (3607.)	3805.8±0.3 [3806.2][m] (3807.)	4018.0±0.3 [4018.1][m] (4019.)
L_{II}	2464.7±0.3 [2464.7][l]	2625.1±0.3 [2624.5][l] (2627.)	2793.2±0.4 [2973.2][l]	2966.9±0.3 [2966.8][l] (2966.3)	3146.1±0.3 [3146.3][l] (3145.)	3330.3±0.3 [3330.3][l] (3330.3)	3523.7±0.3 [3523.6][x,m] (3526.)	3727.0±0.3 [3727.1][m] (3728.)
L_{III}	2370.5±0.3 [2370.6][l]	2520.2±0.3 [2520.2][l] (2523.2)	2676.9±0.4 [2676.9][l]	2837.9±0.3 [2837.7][l] (2837.7)	3003.8±0.3 [3003.5][x,l] (3002.)	3173.3±0.3 [3173.0][x,l] (3173.0)	3351.1±0.3 [3350.8][x] (3351.0)	3537.5±0.3 [3537.3][x] (3537.6)
M_{I}	468.4±0.3	504.6±0.3		585.0±0.3	627.1±0.3	669.9±0.3	717.5±0.3	770.2±0.3
M_{II}	378.4±0.4	409.7±0.4	444.9±1.5	482.8±0.3	521.0±0.3	559.1±0.3	602.4±0.3	650.7±0.3
M_{III}	363.0±0.4	392.3±0.3	425.0±1.5	460.6±0.3	496.2±0.3	531.5±0.3	571.4±0.3	616.5±0.3
M_{IV}	207.4±0.3	230.3±0.3	256.4±0.5	283.6±0.3	311.7±0.3	340.0±0.3	372.8±0.3	410.5±0.3
M_{V}	204.6±0.3	227.0±0.3	252.9±0.4	279.4±0.3	307.0±0.3	334.7±0.3	366.7±0.3	403.7±0.3
N_{I}	58.1±0.3	61.8±0.3		74.9±0.3	81.0±0.3	86.4±0.3	95.2±0.3	107.6±0.3
N_{II}	33.9±0.4	34.8±0.4	38.9±1.9	43.1±0.4	47.9±0.4	51.1±0.4	62.6±0.3	66.9±0.4
N_{III}							55.9±0.3	
$N_{IV,V}$	3.2±0.3	1.8±0.3		2.0±0.3	2.5±0.4	1.5±0.3	3.3±0.3	9.3±0.3

X-Ray Atomic Energy Levels (Continued)

	49 In	50 Sn	51 Sb	52 Te	53 I	54 Xe	55 Cs	56 Ba
K	27939.9±0.3	29200.1±0.4 (29195.)	30491.2±0.3 (30486.)	31813.8±0.3 (31811.)	33169.4±0.4 (33167.)	34561.4±1.1 (34590.)	35984.6±0.4 (35987.)	37440.6±0.4 (37452.)
L_I	4237.5±0.3 [4237.7][m] (4237.3)	4464.7±0.3 [4464.5][k] (4464.8)	4698.3±0.3 [4698.3][m] (4698.4)	4939.2±0.3 [4939.3][m] (4939.7)	5188.1±0.3 [5188.1][j]	5452.8±0.4 (5452.8)	5714.3±0.4 [5712.7][j] (5721.)	5988.8±0.4 [5986.8][j] (5996.)
L_{II}	3938.0±0.3 [3937.8][m] (3939.3)	4156.1±0.3 [4156.2][k] (4157.)	4380.4±0.3 [4380.6][m] (4382.)	4612.0±0.3 [4612.0][m] (4612.6)	4852.1±0.3 [4852.0][j]	5103.7±0.4 (5103.7)	5359.4±0.3 [5359.5][j] (5358.)	5623.6±0.3 [5623.6][j] (5623.3)
L_{III}	3730.1±0.3 [3730.0][k] (3730.2)	3928.8±0.3 [3928.8][k] (3928.8)	4132.2±0.3 [4132.2][k] (4132.3)	4341.4±0.3 [4341.2][k] (4341.8)	4557.1±0.3 [4557.1][j]	4782.2±0.4 (4782.2)	5011.9±0.3 [5012.0][j] (5011.3)	5247.0±0.3 [5247.3][j] (5247.0)
M_I	825.6±0.3	883.8±0.3	943.7±0.3	1006.0±0.3	1072.1±0.3		1217.1±0.4	1292.8±0.4
M_{II}	702.2±0.3	756.4±0.4	811.9±0.3	869.7±0.3	930.5±0.3	999.0±2.1	1065.0±0.5	1136.7±0.5
M_{III}	664.3±0.3	714.4±0.3	765.6±0.3	818.7±0.3	874.6±0.3	937.0±2.1	997.6±0.5	1062.2±0.5
M_{IV}	450.8±0.3	493.3±0.3	536.9±0.3	582.5±0.3	631.3±0.3		739.5±0.4	796.1±0.3
M_V	443.1±0.3	484.8±0.3	527.5±0.3	572.1±0.3	619.4±0.3	672.3±0.5	725.5±0.5	780.7±0.3
N_I	121.9±0.3	136.5±0.4	152.0±0.3	168.3±0.3	186.4±0.3		230.8±0.4	253.0±0.5
N_{II}	77.4±0.4	88.6±0.4	98.4±0.5	110.2±0.5	122.7±0.5	146.7±3.1	172.3±0.6	191.8±0.7
N_{III}							161.6±0.6	179.7±0.6
N_{IV}	16.2±0.3	23.9±0.3	31.4±0.3	39.8±0.3	49.6±0.3		78.8±0.5	92.5±0.5
N_V							76.5±0.5	89.9±0.5
O_I	0.1±4.5	0.9±0.5	6.7±0.5	11.6±0.6	13.6±0.6		22.7±0.5	39.1±0.6
O_{II}							13.1±0.5	16.6±0.5
O_{III}	0.8±0.4	1.1±0.5	2.1±0.4	2.3±0.5	3.3±0.5		11.4±0.5	14.6±0.5

	57 La	58 Ce	59 Pr	60 Nd	61 Pm	62 Sm	63 Eu	64 Gd
K	38924.6±0.4 (38934.)	40443.0±0.4 (40453.)	41990.6±0.5 (42002.)	43568.9±0.4 (43574.)	45184.0±0.7 (45198.)	46834.2±0.5 (46849.)	48519.0±0.4 (48519.)	50239.1±0.5 (50233.)

X-Ray Atomic Energy Levels (*Continued*)

	57 La	58 Ce	59 Pr	60 Nd	61 Pm	62 Sm	63 Eu	64 Gd
L_I	6266.3±0.5 [6266.3]^n	6548.8±0.5 [6548.5]^n	6834.8±0.5 [6834.9]^n	7126.0±0.4 [7125.8]^n (7129.)	7427.9±0.8 [7427.9]^o	7736.8±0.5 [7736.2]^n (7748.)	8052.0±0.4 [8051.7]^n (8061.)	8375.6±0.5 [8375.4]^n (8386.)
L_{II}	5890.6±0.4 [5890.7]^n	6164.2±0.4 [6164.3]^n	6440.4±0.5 [6440.2]^n	6721.5±0.4 [6721.8]^n (6723.)	7012.8±0.6 [7012.8]^o	7311.8±0.4 [7312.0]^n (7313.)	7617.1±0.4 [7617.6]^n (7620.)	7930.3±0.4 [7930.5]^n (7931.)
L_{III}	5482.7±0.4 [5482.6]^n	5723.4±0.4 [5723.6]^n	5964.3±0.4 [5964.3]^n	6207.9±0.4 [6208.0]^n (6209.)	6459.3±0.5 [6459.4]^o	6716.2±0.5 [6716.8]^n (6717.)	6976.9±0.4 [6976.7]^n (6981.)	7242.8±0.4 [7242.8]^n (7243.)
M_I	1361.3±0.3	1434.6±0.6	1511.0±0.8	1575.3±0.7		1722.8±0.8	1800.0±0.5	1880.8±0.5
M_{II}	1204.4±0.6	1272.8±0.6	1337.4±0.7	1402.8±0.6	1471.4±6.2	1540.7±1.2	1613.9±0.7	1688.3±0.7
M_{III}	1123.4±0.5	1185.4±0.5	1242.2±0.6	1297.4±0.5	1356.9±1.4	1419.8±1.1	1480.6±0.6	1544.0±0.8
M_{IV}	848.5±0.4	901.3±0.6	951.1±0.6	999.9±0.6	1051.5±0.9	1106.0±0.8	1160.6±0.6	1217.2±0.6
M_V	831.7±0.4	883.3±0.5	931.0±0.6	977.7±0.6	1026.9±1.0	1080.2±0.6	1130.9±0.6	1185.2±0.6
N_I	270.4±0.8	289.6±0.7	304.5±0.9	315.2±0.8		345.7±0.9	360.2±0.7	375.8±0.7
N_{II}	205.8±1.2	223.3±1.1	236.3±1.5	243.3±1.6	242.±16.	265.6±1.9	283.9±1.0	288.5±1.2
N_{III}	191.4±0.9	207.2±0.9	217.6±1.1	224.6±1.3		247.4±1.5	256.6±0.8	270.9±0.9
$N_{IV,V}$	98.9±0.8	110.0±0.6	113.2±0.7	117.5±0.7	120.4±2.0	129.0±1.2	133.2±0.6	140.5±0.8
$N_{VI,VII}$		0.1±1.2	2.0±0.6	1.5±0.9		5.5±1.1	0.0±3.2	0.1±3.5
O_I	32.3±7.2	37.8±1.3	37.4±1.0	37.5±0.9		37.4±1.5	31.8±0.7	36.1±0.8
$O_{II,III}$	14.4±1.2	19.8±1.2	22.3±0.7	21.1±0.8		21.3±1.5	22.0±0.6	20.3±1.2

(Note: the N_{II}/N_{III} value 242.±16. for 61 Pm is bracketed to span both levels.)

	65 Tb	66 Dy	67 Ho	68 Er	69 Tm	70 Yb	71 Lu	72 Hf
K	51995.7±0.5 (52002.)	53788.5±0.5 (53793.)	55617.7±0.5 (55619.)	57485.5±0.5 (57487.)	59389.6±0.5	61332.3±0.5 (61300.)	63313.8±0.5 (63310.)	65350.8±0.6 (65310.)
L_I	8708.0±0.5 [8707.6]^n (8717.)	9045.8±0.5 [9046.5]^n	9394.2±0.4 [9394.3]^n (9399.)	9751.3±0.4 [9751.5]^n (9757.)	10115.7±0.4 [10115.6]^n (10121.)	10486.4±0.4 [10487.3]^n (10490.)	10870.4±0.4 [10870.1]^n (10874.)	11270.7±0.4 [11271.6]^o (11274.)

X-Ray Atomic Energy Levels (Continued)

	65 Tb	66 Dy	67 Ho	68 Er	69 Tm	70 Yb	71 Lu	72 Hf
L_{II}	8251.6±0.4 [8251.8][n] (8253.)	8580.6±0.4 [8580.4][n] (8583.)	8917.8±0.4 [8918.2][n] (8916.)	9264.3±0.4 [9264.3][n] (9262.)	9616.9±0.4 [9617.1][n] (9617.1)	9978.2±0.4 [9977.9][n] (9976.)	10348.6±0.4 [10349.0][n] (10345.)	10739.4±0.4 [10738.9][b] (10736.)
L_{III}	7514.0±0.4 [7514.2][n] (7515.)	7790.1±0.4 [7789.6][n] (7789.7)	8071.1±0.4 [8070.6][n] (8068.)	8357.9±0.4 [8357.6][n] (8357.5)	8648.0±0.4 [8647.8][n] (8649.6)	8943.6±0.4 [8942.6][n] (8944.1)	9244.1±0.4 [9243.8][n] (9243.)	9560.7±0.4 [9560.4][b] (9558.)
M_I	1967.5±0.6	2046.8±0.4	2128.3±0.6	2206.5±0.6	2306.8±0.7	2398.1±0.4	2491.2±0.5	2600.9±0.4
M_{II}	1767.7±0.9	1841.8±0.5	1922.8±1.0	2005.8±0.6	2089.8±1.1	2173.0±0.4	2263.5±0.4	2365.4±0.4
M_{III}	1611.3±0.8	1675.6±0.9	1741.2±0.9	1811.8±0.6	1884.5±1.1	1949.8±0.5	2023.6±0.5	2107.6±0.4
M_{IV}	1275.0±0.6	1332.5±0.4	1391.5±0.7	1453.3±0.5	1514.6±0.7	1576.3±0.4	1639.4±0.4	1716.4±0.4
M_V	1241.2±0.7	1294.9±0.4	1351.4±0.8	1409.3±0.5	1467.7±0.9	1527.8±0.4	1588.5±0.4	1661.7±0.4
N_I	397.9±0.8	416.3±0.5	435.7±0.8	449.1±1.0	471.7±0.9	487.2±0.6	506.2±0.6	538.1±0.4
N_{II}	310.2±1.2	331.8±0.6	343.5±1.4	366.2±1.5	385.9±1.6	396.7±0.7	410.1±1.8	437.0±0.5
N_{III}	285.0±1.0	292.9±0.6	306.6±0.9	320.0±0.7	336.6±1.6	343.5±0.5	359.3±0.5	380.4±0.5
N_{IV}	147.0±0.8	154.2±0.5	161.0±1.0	176.7±1.2	179.6±1.2	198.1±0.5	204.8±0.5	223.8±0.4
N_V				167.6±1.5		184.9±1.3	195.0±0.4	213.7±0.5
$N_{VI,VII}$	2.6±1.5	4.2±1.6	3.7±3.0	4.3±1.4	5.3±1.9	6.3±1.0	6.9±0.5	17.1±0.5
O_I	39.0±0.8	62.9±0.5	51.2±1.3	59.8±1.7	53.2±3.0	54.1±0.5	56.8±0.5	64.9±0.4
O_{II}								38.1±0.6
O_{III}	25.4±0.8	26.3±0.6	20.3±1.5	29.4±1.6	32.3±1.6	23.4±0.6	28.0±0.6	30.6±0.6

	73 Ta	74 W	75 Re	76 Os	77 Ir	78 Pt	79 Au	80 Hg
K	67416.4±0.6 (67403.)	69525.0±0.3 (69508.)	71676.4±0.4 (71658.)	73870.8±0.5	76111.0±0.5	78394.8±0.7 (78381.)	80724.9±0.5 (80720.)	83102.3±0.8
L_I	11681.5±0.3 [11680.2][p] (11682.)	12099.8±0.3 [12098.2][p] (12099.6)	12526.7±0.4 (12530.)	12968.0±0.4 (12972.)	13418.5±0.3 (13423.)	13879.9±0.4 (13883.)	14352.8±0.4 (14353.7)	14839.3±1.0 (14842.)

X-Ray Atomic Energy Levels (Continued)

	73 Ta	74 W	75 Re	76 Os	77 Ir	78 Pt	79 Au	80 Hg
L_{II}	11136.1±0.3 [11136.1]^p (11132.)	11544.0±0.3 [11541.4]^p (11538.)	11958.7±0.3 [11956.9]^p (11954.)	12385.0±0.4 (12381.)	12824.1±0.3 [12824.0]^{e,p} (12820.)	13272.6±0.3 [13272.6]^{e,p} (13272.3)	13733.6±0.3 [13733.5]^{e,p} (13736.)	14208.7±0.7 (14215.)
L_{III}	9881.1±0.3 [9880.3]^p (9877.7)	10206.8±0.3 [10204.2]^p (10200.)	10535.3±0.3 [10534.2]^p (10531.)	10870.9±0.3 [10870.7]^p (10868.)	11215.2±0.3 [11215.1]^{e,p} (11212.)	11563.7±0.3 [11563.7]^{e,p} (11562.)	11918.7±0.3 [11918.2]^{e,p} (11921.)	12283.9±0.4 [12284.0]^{e,p} (12286.)
M_I	2708.0±0.4	2819.6±0.4	2931.7±0.4	3048.5±0.4	3173.7±1.7	3296.0±0.9	3424.9±0.3 [3424.8]^p	3561.6±1.1
M_{II}	2468.7±0.3 [2468.6]^p	2574.9±0.3 [2575.0]^p	2681.6±0.4	2792.2±0.3 [2791.9]^p	2908.7±0.3 [2909.1]^p	3026.5±0.4 [3026.5]^p (3029.)	3147.8±0.4 [3149.5]^p	3278.5±1.3
M_{III}	2194.0±0.3 [2194.1]^p	2281.0±0.3 [2281.0]^p	2367.3±0.3 [2367.3]^p	2457.2±0.4 [2457.4]^p	2550.7±0.3 [2550.5]^p (2550.5)	2645.4±0.4 [2645.5]^p (2645.9)	2743.0±0.3 [2743.1]^p (2744.0)	2847.1±0.4 [2847.1]^p
M_{IV}	1793.2±0.3 [1793.1]^p	1871.6±0.3 [1871.4]^p	1948.9±0.3 [1948.9]^p	2030.8±0.3 [2031.0]^p	2116.1±0.3 [2116.1]^p	2201.9±0.3 [2201.9]^p	2291.1±0.3 [2291.2]^p (2307.)	2384.9±0.3 [2384.9]^p
M_V	1735.1±0.3 [1735.2]^p	1809.2±0.3 [1809.3]^p	1882.9±0.3 [1882.9]^p	1960.1±0.3 [1960.2]^p	2040.4±0.3 [2040.5]^p	2121.6±0.3 [2121.6]^p	2205.7±0.3 [2206.1]^p (2220.)	2294.9±0.3 [2294.9]^p
N_I	565.5±0.5	595.0±0.4	625.0±0.4	654.3±0.5	690.1±0.4	722.0±0.6	758.8±0.4	800.3±1.0
N_{II}	464.8±0.5	491.6±0.4	517.9±0.5	546.5±0.5	577.1±0.4	609.2±0.6	643.7±0.5	676.9±2.4
N_{III}	404.5±0.4	425.3±0.5	444.4±0.5	468.2±0.6	494.3±0.6	519.0±0.6	545.4±0.5	571.0±1.4
N_{IV}	241.3±0.4	258.8±0.4	273.7±0.5	289.4±0.5	311.4±0.4	330.8±0.5	352.0±0.4	378.3±1.0
N_V	229.3±0.3	245.4±0.4	260.2±0.4	272.8±0.6	294.9±0.4	313.3±0.4	333.9±0.4	359.8±1.2
N_{VI}	25.0±0.4	36.5±0.4	40.6±0.4	46.3±0.6	63.4±0.4	74.3±0.4	86.4±0.4	102.2±0.5
N_{VII}	{25.0±0.4}	33.6±0.4	{40.6±0.4}	{46.3±0.6}	60.5±0.4	71.1±0.5	82.8±0.5	98.5±0.5
O_I	71.1±0.5	77.1±0.4	82.8±0.5	83.7±0.6	95.2±0.4	101.7±0.4	107.8±0.7	120.3±1.3
O_{II}	44.9±0.4	46.8±0.5	45.6±0.7	58.0±1.1	63.0±0.6	65.3±0.7	71.7±0.7	80.5±1.3
O_{III}	36.4±0.4	35.6±0.5	34.6±0.6	45.4±1.0	50.5±0.6	51.7±0.7	53.7±0.7	57.6±1.3
O_{IV}	5.7±0.4	6.1±0.4	3.5±0.5		3.8±0.4	2.2±1.3	2.5±0.5	6.4±1.4

X-Ray Atomic Energy Levels (Continued)

	81 Tl	82 Pb	83 Bi	84 Po	85 At	86 Rn	87 Fr	88 Ra
K	85530.4±0.6	88004.5±0.7 (88005.)	90525.9±0.7 (90534.)	93105.0±3.8	95729.9±7.7	98404.±12.	101137.±13.	103921.9±7.2
L_I	15346.7±0.4 (15343.)	15860.8±0.5 (15855.)	16387.5±0.4 (16376.)	16939.3±9.8	17493.±29.	18049.±38.	18639.±40.	19236.7±1.5 (19236.0)
L_{II}	14697.9±0.3 [14697.3]p (14699.)	15200.0±0.4 (15205.)	15711.1±0.3 [15708.4]p (15719.)	16244.3±2.4	16784.7±2.5	17337.1±3.4	17906.5±3.5	18484.3±1.5 (18486.0)
L_{III}	12657.5±0.3 [12656.3]e,p (12660.)	13035.2±0.3 [13034.9]e,p (13041.)	13418.6±0.3 [13418.3]e,p (13426.)	13813.8±1.0 (13813.8)	14213.5±2.0 ⟨14213.5⟩	14619.4±3.0 ⟨14619.4⟩	15031.2±3.0 ⟨15031.2⟩	15444.4±1.5 ⟨15444.0⟩
M_I	3704.1±0.4	3850.7±0.5	3999.1±0.3 [3999.1]p	4149.4±3.9	⟨4317.⟩	⟨4482.⟩	⟨4652.⟩	4822.0±1.5
M_{II}	3415.7±0.3 [3415.7]p	3554.2±0.3 [3554.2]p	3696.3±0.3 [3696.4]p	3854.1±9.8	4008.±28.	4159.±38.	4327.±40.	4489.5±1.8
M_{III}	2956.6±0.3 [2956.5]p	3066.4±0.4 [3066.3]p	3176.9±0.3 [3176.8]p	3301.9±9.9	3426.±29.	3538.±38.	3663.±40.	3791.8±1.7
M_{IV}	2485.1±0.3 [2485.2]p	2585.6±0.3 [2585.5]p (2606.)	2687.6±0.3 [2687.4]p	2798.0±1.2	2908.7±2.1	3021.5±3.1	3136.2±3.1	3248.4±1.6
M_V	2389.3±0.3 [2389.4]p	2484.0±0.3 [2484.2]p (2502.)	2579.6±0.3 [2579.5]p	2683.0±1.1	2786.7±2.1	2892.4±3.1	2999.9±3.1	3104.9±1.6
N_I	845.5±0.5	893.6±0.7	938.2±0.3 [938.7]p	995.3±2.9	⟨1042.⟩	⟨1097.⟩	⟨1153.⟩	1208.4±1.6
N_{II}	721.3±0.8	763.9±0.8	805.3±0.3 [805.3]p	851.±12.	886.±30.	929.±40.	980±42.	1057.6±1.8
N_{III}	609.0±0.5	644.5±0.6	678.9±0.3 [678.9]p	705.±14.	740.±30.	768.±40.	810±43.	879.1±1.8
N_{IV}	406.6±0.4	435.2±0.5	463.6±0.3 [463.6]p	500.2±2.4	533.2±3.2	566.6±4.0	603.3±4.1	635.9±1.6
N_V	386.2±0.5	412.9±0.6	440.0±0.3 [440.1]p	473.4±1.3			577.±34.	602.7±1.7

X-Ray Atomic Energy Levels (Continued)

	81 Tl	82 Pb	83 Bi	84 Po	85 At	86 Rn	87 Fr	88 Ra
N_{VI}	122.8±0.4	142.9±0.4	161.9±0.5					298.9±2.4
N_{VII}	118.5±0.4	138.1±0.4	157.4±0.6					254.4±2.1
O_I	136.3±0.7	147.3±0.8	159.3±0.7					200.4±2.0
O_{II}	99.6±0.6	104.8±1.0	116.8±0.7					152.8±2.0
O_{III}	75.4±0.6	86.0±1.0	92.8±0.6					
O_{IV}	15.3±0.4	21.8±0.4	26.5±0.5	{ 31.4±3.2				
O_V	13.1±0.4	19.2±0.4	24.4±0.6					67.2±1.7
P_I		3.1±1.0						43.5±2.2
$P_{II,III}$		0.7±1.0	2.7±0.7					18.8±1.8

	89 Ac	90 Th	91 Pa	92 U	93 Np	94 Pu	95 Am	96 Cm
K	106755.3±5.3	109650.9±0.9	112601.4±2.4	115606.1±1.6	118678.±33.	121818.±44.	125027.±55.	128220
L_I	19840.±18.	20472.1±0.5	21104.6±1.8	21757.4±0.3	22426.8±0.9	23097.2±1.6 (23109.)	23772.9±2.0 (23772.9)	24460
L_{II}	19083.2±2.8	19693.2±0.4 (19683.)	20313.7±1.5 (20319.)	20947.6±0.3 (20945.)	21600.5±0.4	22266.2±0.7 (22253.)	22944.0±1.0	23779
L_{III}	15871.0±2.0 ⟨15871.0⟩	16300.3±0.3 [16299.6]^a (16299.)	16733.1±1.4 (16733.)	17166.3±0.3 [17168.5]^r (17165.)	17610.0±0.4 (17606.2)	18056.8±0.6 (18053.1)	18504.1±0.9 (18504.1)	18930
M_I	⟨5002.⟩	5182.3±0.3 [5182.3]^a	5366.9±1.6	5548.0±0.4	5723.2±3.6	5932.9±1.4	6120.5±7.5	6288
M_{II}	4656.±18.	4830.4±0.4 [4830.6]^a	5000.9±2.3	5182.2±0.4 [5180.9]^r	5366.2±0.7 [5366.4]^e	5541.2±1.7	5710.2±2.1	5895
M_{III}	3909.±18.	4046.1±0.4 [4046.1]^a (4041.)	4173.8±1.8	4303.4±0.3 [4303.6]^r (4299.)	4434.7±0.5 [4434.6]^e	4556.6±1.5	4667.0±2.1	4797
M_{IV}	3370.2±2.1	3490.8±0.3 [3490.7]^a (3485.)	3611.2±1.4 (3608.)	3727.6±0.3 [3728.1]^r (3720.)	3850.3±0.4 [3849.8]^e	3972.6±0.6 [3972.7]^t	4092.1±1.0	4227

X-Ray Atomic Energy Levels (Continued)

	89 Ac	90 Th	91 Pa	92 U	93 Np	94 Pu	95 Am	96 Cm
M_V	3219.0±2.1	3332.0±0.3 [3332.1]a (3325.)	3441.8±1.4	3551.7±0.3 [3551.7]r (3545.)	3665.8±0.4 [3664.2]a	3778.1±0.6 [3778.0]b	3886.9±1.0	3971
N_I	⟨1269.⟩	1329.5±0.4 [1329.8]a	1387.1±1.9	1440.8±0.4 [1441.3]r	1500.7±0.8 [1500.7]a	1558.6±0.8	1617.1±1.1	1643
N_{II}	1080.±19.	1168.2±0.4 [1168.3]a	1224.3±1.6	1272.6±0.3 [1272.5]r	1327.7±0.8 [1327.7]a	1372.1±1.8	1411.8±8.3	1440
N_{III}	890.±19.	967.3±0.4 [967.6]a	1006.7±1.7	1044.9±0.3 [1044.9]r	1086.8±0.7 [1086.8]a	1114.8±1.6	⟨1135.7⟩	1154
N_{IV}	674.9±3.7	714.1±0.4 [714.4]a	743.4±2.1	780.4±0.3 [779.7]r	815.9±0.5 [817.1]a	848.9±0.6 [848.9]a	878.7±1.0	
N_V		676.4±0.4 [676.4]a	708.2±1.8	737.7±0.3 [737.6]r	770.3±0.4 [773.2]a	801.4±0.6 [801.4]b	827.6±1.0	
N_{VI}		344.4±0.3 [344.2]a	371.2±1.6	391.3±0.6	415.0±0.8 [415.0]a	445.8±1.7		
N_{VII}		335.2±0.4 [335.0]a	359.5±1.6	380.9±0.9	404.4±0.5 [404.4]a	432.4±2.1		
O_I		290.2±0.8	309.6±4.3	323.7±1.1		351.9±2.4		385
O_{II}		229.4±1.1	222.9±3.9	259.3±0.5	283.4±0.8 [283.4]a	274.1±4.7		
O_{III}		181.8±0.4 [181.8]a		195.1±1.3	206.1±0.7 [206.1]a	206.5±4.7		
O_{IV}		94.3±0.4 [94.4]a	94.1±2.8	105.0±0.5	109.3±0.7 [108.8]a	116.0±1.2	115.8±1.3	
O_V		87.9±0.3 [88.1]a		96.3±1.4	101.3±0.5 [101.4]a	105.4±1.0	103.3±1.1	
P_I		59.5±1.1		70.7±1.2				
P_{II}		49.0±2.5		42.3±9.0				
P_{III}		43.0±2.5		32.3±9.0				

X-Ray Atomic Energy Levels (Continued)

	97 Bk	98 Cf	99 Es	100 Fm	101 Md	102 No	103 Lw
K	[131590±40][u]	135960	139490	143090	146780	150540	154380
L_I	[25275±17][u]	26110	26900	27700	28530	29380	30240
L_{II}	[24385±17][u]	25250	26020	26810	27610	28440	29280
L_{III}	[19452±20][u]	19930	20410	20900	21390	21880	22360
M_I	[6556±21][u]	6754	6977	7205	7441	7675	7900
M_{II}	[6147±31][u]	6359	6574	6793	7019	7245	7460
M_{III}	[4977±31][u]	5109	5252	5397	5546	5688	5710
M_{IV}	4366	4497	4630	4766	4903	5037	5150
M_V	4132	4253	4374	4498	4622	4741	4860
N_I	[1755±22][u]	1799	1868	1937	2010	2078	2140
N_{II}	1554	1616	1680	1747	1814	1876	1930
N_{III}	1235	1279	1321	1366	1410	1448	1480
O_I	[398±22][u]	419	435	454	472	484	490

[a] J. E. Mack, 1949, as given in C. E. Moore, *Atomic Energy Levels* (U. S. National Bureau of Standards, Washington, D. C., 1949), Vol. 1, p. 1.

[b] G. Herzberg, 1957, as given in C. E. Moore, *Atomic Energy Levels* (U. S. National Bureau of Standards, Washington, D. C., 1958), Vol. 3, p. 238.

[c] See Ref. 18.

[d] A. Fahlman, D. Hamrin, R. Nordberg, C. Nordling, and K. Siegbahn, Phys. Rev. Letters **14**, 127 (1965).

[e] See Ref. 26.

[f] See Ref. 15.

[g] See Ref. 11.

[h] C. Nordling, Arkiv Fysik **15**, 397 (1959).

[i] E. Sokolowski, C. Nordling, and K. Siegbahn, Arkiv Fysik **12**, 301 (1957).

[j] C. Nordling and S. Hagström, Arkiv Fysik **16**, 515 (1960).

[j] J. Andersson and S. Hagström, Arkiv Fysik **27**, 161 (1964).

[k] M. O. Krause, Phys. Rev. **140**, A1845 (1965).

[l] A. Fahlman, O. Hörnfeldt, and C. Nordling, Arkiv Fysik **23**, 75 (1962).

[m] P. Bergvall, O. Hörnfeldt, and C. Nordling, Arkiv Fysik **17**, 113 (1960).

[n] P. Bergvall and S. Hagström, Arkiv Fysik **17**, 61 (1960).

[o] S. Hagström, Z. Physik **178**, 82 (1964).

[p] A. Fahlman and S. Hagström, Arkiv Fysik **27**, 69 (1964).

[q] C. Nordling and S. Hagström, Z. Physik **178**, 418 (1964).

[r] C. Nordling and S. Hagström, Arkiv Fysik **15**, 431 (1955).

[s] S. Hagström, Bull. Am. Phys. Soc. **11**, 389 (1966).

[t] A. Fahlman, K. Hamrin, R. Nordberg, C. Nordling, K. Siegbahn, and L. W. Holm, Phys. Letters **19**, 643 (1966).

[u] J. M. Hollander, M. D. Holtz, T. Novakov, and R. L. Graham, Arkiv Fysik **28**, 375 (1965).

LATTICE SPACING OF COMMON ANALYSING CRYSTALS

Crystal	Reflection plane	d Spacing	Crystal	Reflection plane	d Spacing
ADP[a]	101	5.31	Lead stearate		51
ADP[a]	110	5.325	LiF	200	2.014
ADP[a]	200	3.75	LiF	220	1.424
Beryl	1010	7.98	Mica	002	9.96
Calcite	100	3.036	NaCl	200	2.820
EDDT[b]	020	4.404	Oxalic acid	001	5.85
Germanium	111	3.265	PET[d]	002	4.371
Graphite	001	6.69	Quartz	10$\bar{1}$0	4.255
Gypsum	010	7.600	Quartz	10$\bar{1}$1	3.343
KAP[c]	001	13.32	Quartz	11$\bar{2}$0	2.456
KBr	200	3.29	Silicon	111	3.13
KCl	200	3.14	Topaz	303	1.356

While several of the above spacings have been measured to more than four significant figures, no more than four figures are given here because complications introduced by the index of refraction, anomalous dispersion, temperature coefficient of expansion, and crystal impurities must be considered before the additional figures are useful.

[a] Ammonium dihydrogen phosphate.
[b] Ethylenediamine d-tartrate.
[c] Potassium acid phthalate.
[d] Pentaerythritol.

RADIATIVE TRANSITION PROBABILITIES FOR K X-RAY LINES

Prepared by S. I. Salem and reproduced by permission of
the copyright owner, Academic Press.

$$K\beta'_1 = KM_2 + KM_3 + KM_{4,5} \qquad K\beta'_2 = KN_{2,3} + KO_{2,3}$$
$$K\alpha = K\alpha_1 + K\alpha_2 \qquad K\beta = K\beta'_1 + K\beta'_2$$

Element	$K\alpha_2/K\alpha_1$	$K\alpha_3/K\alpha_1$	$K\beta_1/K\alpha_1$	$K\beta'_2/K\alpha_1$	$K\beta_4/K\alpha_1$	$K\beta_5/K\alpha_1$	$K\beta_3/K\beta_1$	$K\beta/K\alpha$
12^{Mg}								0.013
14^{Si}								0.027
16^{S}								0.059
18^{Ar}								0.105
20^{Ca}	0.502							0.128
22^{Ti}	0.503							0.134
24^{Cr}	0.504							0.135
26^{Fe}	0.506							0.135
28^{Ni}	0.508							0.135
30^{Zn}	0.510							0.138
32^{Ge}	0.513							0.147
34^{Se}	0.515							0.157
36^{Kr}	0.517			0.019				0.172
38^{Sr}	0.520			0.030				0.180
40^{Br}	0.523			0.037				0.190
42^{Mo}	0.525			0.041				0.197
44^{Ru}	0.527			0.045				0.204
46^{Pd}	0.529			0.048				0.210
48^{Cd}	0.532			0.053			0.519	0.213
50^{Sn}	0.534			0.055			0.519	0.220
52^{Te}	0.537			0.058			0.519	0.225
54^{Xe}	0.539			0.064			0.518	0.232
56^{Ba}	0.543			0.070			0.518	0.237
58^{Ce}	0.546			0.076			0.518	0.242
60^{Nd}	0.549	0.11×10^{-3}		0.083			0.518	0.247
62^{Sm}	0.552	0.14×10^{-3}		0.086			0.517	0.250
64^{Gd}	0.556	0.17×10^{-3}	0.192	0.089	0.85×10^{-3}	3.02×10^{-3}	0.517	0.255
66^{Dy}	0.560	0.21×10^{-3}	0.198	0.089	0.92×10^{-3}	3.43×10^{-3}	0.517	0.257
68^{Er}	0.564	0.26×10^{-3}	0.202	0.088	0.96×10^{-3}	3.85×10^{-3}	0.518	0.260
70^{Yb}	0.567	0.30×10^{-3}	0.207	0.087	1.04×10^{-3}	4.23×10^{-3}	0.518	0.264
72^{Hf}	0.572	0.36×10^{-3}	0.212	0.085	1.16×10^{-3}	4.62×10^{-3}	0.518	0.267
74^{W}	0.576	0.43×10^{-3}	0.216	0.086	1.28×10^{-3}	5.04×10^{-3}	0.518	0.269
76^{Os}	0.580	0.51×10^{-3}	0.222	0.087	1.43×10^{-3}	5.44×10^{-3}	0.519	0.273
78^{Pt}	0.583	0.63×10^{-3}	0.226	0.091	1.61×10^{-3}	5.84×10^{-3}	0.520	0.275
80^{Hg}	0.588	0.76×10^{-3}	0.228	0.096	1.80×10^{-3}	6.24×10^{-3}	0.520	0.278
82^{Pb}	0.593	0.91×10^{-3}	0.228	0.102	2.02×10^{-3}	6.64×10^{-3}	0.521	0.280
84^{Po}	0.597	1.12×10^{-3}	0.228	0.108	2.26×10^{-3}	7.05×10^{-3}	0.522	0.283
86^{Rn}	0.602	1.32×10^{-3}	0.228	0.113	2.52×10^{-3}	7.48×10^{-3}	0.523	0.286
88^{Ra}	0.608	1.58×10^{-3}	0.230	0.117	2.80×10^{-3}	7.80×10^{-3}	0.524	0.287
90^{Th}	0.613	1.85×10^{-3}	0.232	0.120	3.13×10^{-3}	8.25×10^{-3}	0.525	0.288
92^{U}	0.619	2.15×10^{-3}	0.234	0.123	3.47×10^{-3}	8.65×10^{-3}	0.527	0.289
94^{Pu}	0.625		0.234	0.125			0.528	0.291
96^{Cm}	0.632		0.234	0.128			0.529	0.293
98^{Cf}	0.642		0.238	0.132			0.531	0.295
100^{Fm}	0.648		0.240	0.135			0.533	0.297

From Salem, S. I., Panossian, S. L., and Krause, R. A., *At. Data Nucl. Data Tables,* 14, 91, 1974. Reproduced by permission of the copyright owner, Academic Press.

RADIATIVE TRANSITION PROBABILITIES FOR
L X-RAY LINES

The following three tables present data for the radiative transition probabilities for the L_1, L_2, and L_3 X-ray lines. The data are normalized respectively to $L\beta_3 = 100$, $L\beta_1 = 100$ and $L\alpha_1 = 100$.

L_1 X-RAY LINES NORMALIZED TO $L\beta_3 = 100$

Element	$L\beta_3$	$L\beta_4$	$L\gamma_2$	$L\gamma_3$	Element	$L\beta_3$	$L\beta_4$	$L\gamma_2$	$L\gamma_3$
32^{Ge}	100			17.3	66^{Dy}	100	61.8	19.5	28.0
34^{Se}	100			18.0	68^{Er}	100	63.5	19.8	29.0
36^{Kr}	100			18.2	70^{Yb}	100	65.5	20.7	29.8
38^{Sr}	100			18.8	72^{Hf}	100	67.8	21.2	30.7
40^{Zr}	100			19.0	74^{W}	100	70.5	21.8	31.8
42^{Mo}	100	70.6		19.6	76^{Os}	100	73.2	23.0	32.8
44^{Ru}	100	67.8		20.2	78^{Pt}	100	76.5	24.5	33.8
46^{Pd}	100	65.5		20.6	80^{Hg}	100	80.3	26.3	35.0
48^{Cd}	100	63.5		21.3	82^{Pb}	100	84.2	28.6	36.0
50^{Sn}	100	62.1		22.0	84^{Po}	100	88.5	31.3	37.2
52^{Te}	100	60.7		22.6	86^{Rn}	100	93.4	34.2	38.2
54^{Xe}	100	59.8		23.3	88^{Ra}	100	98.9	37.5	39.6
56^{Ba}	100	59.5		24.0	90Th	100	104.5	41.2	41.0
58^{Ce}	100	59.2		24.6	92^{U}	100	110.2	45.0	42.6
60Nd	100	59.4		25.4	94^{Pu}	100	116.2	49.5	44.0
62^{Sm}	100	60.0		26.3	96^{Cm}	100	123.0	55.7	45.7
64^{Gd}	100	60.8	19.2	27.0					

L_2 X-RAY LINES NORMALIZED TO $L\beta_1 = 100$

Element	$L\beta_1$	L_η	$L\gamma_1$	$L\gamma_6$	Element	$L\beta_1$	L_η	$L\gamma_1$	$L\gamma_6$
28^{Ni}	100	7.60			64^{Gd}	100	2.35	17.00	
30^{Zn}	100	6.80			66^{Dy}	100	2.25	17.40	
32^{Ge}	100	6.28			68^{Er}	100	2.16	17.80	
34^{Se}	100	5.80			70^{Yb}	100	2.10	18.17	
36^{Kr}	100	5.35			72^{Hf}	100	2.08	18.43	
38^{Sr}	100	4.93			74^{W}	100	2.10	18.80	0.72
40^{Zr}	100	4.60	3.30		76^{Os}	100	2.12	19.34	1.65
42^{Mo}	100	4.30	5.50		78^{Pt}	100	2.18	19.73	2.40
44^{Ru}	100	4.00	7.33		80^{Hg}	100	2.25	20.35	3.10
46^{Pd}	100	3.75	10.67		82^{Pb}	100	2.30	20.93	3.65
48^{Cd}	100	3.55	10.60		84^{Po}	100	2.40	21.54	4.15
50^{Sn}	100	3.35	11.80		86^{Rn}	100	2.46	22.20	4.55
52^{Te}	100	3.20	12.70		88^{Ra}	100	2.50	22.87	4.87
54^{Xe}	100	3.00	14.00		90Th	100	2.60	23.43	5.02
56^{Ba}	100	2.85	14.50		92^{U}	100	2.65	24.10	5.12
58^{Ce}	100	2.70	15.30		94^{Pu}	100	2.70	24.40	5.16
60Nd	100	2.60	16.00		96^{Cm}	100	2.75	25.07	5.20
62^{Sn}	100	2.45	16.50						

RADIATIVE TRANSITION PROBABILITIES FOR
L X-RAY LINES (Continued)

L_3 X-RAY LINES NORMALIZED TO $L\alpha_1 = 100$

Element	$L_{\alpha 1}$	$L_{\beta 2,15}$	$L_{\alpha 2}$	$L_{\beta 5}$	$L_{\beta 6}$	L_ℓ
26 Fe	100					12.22
28 Ni	100					8.95
30 Zn	100					7.34
32 Ge	100					6.45
34 Se	100					7.76
36 Kr	100					5.28
38 Sr	100					4.92
40 Zr	100	0.70	11.10			4.67
42 Mo	100	5.17	11.10			4.45
44 Ru	100	9.30	11.12			4.28
46 Pd	100	11.80	11.12			4.11
48 Cd	100	14.33	11.12			4.07
50 Sn	100	16.00	11.13			4.00
52 Te	100	18.00	11.13			4.00
54 Xe	100	19.40	11.13			4.00
56 Ba	100	20.67	11.13			4.02
58 Ce	100	21.00	11.14			4.09
60 Nd	100	21.33	11.14		0.875	4.13
62 Sm	100	21.07	11.14		0.925	4.16
64 Gd	100	20.83	11.14		0.99	4.20
66 Dy	100	20.50	11.14		1.05	4.26
68 Er	100	20.04	11.15		1.12	4.33
70 Yb	100	19.40	11.15		1.17	4.47
72 Hf	100	21.33	11.15	0.30	1.21	4.59
74 W	100	22.74	11.16	0.50	1.25	4.76
76 Os	100	23.40	11.16	1.32	1.37	4.95
78 Pt	100	24.00	11.16	1.98	1.43	5.14
80 Hg	100	24.50	11.17	2.62	1.50	5.37
82 Pb	100	24.83	11.17	3.21	1.56	5.58
84 Po	100	25.13	11.17	3.73	1.62	5.80
86 Rn	100	25.60	11.18	4.25	1.68	6.00
88 Ra	100	25.92	11.18	4.73	1.76	6.26
90 Th	100	26.17	11.18	5.18	1.82	6.54
92 U	100	26.40	11.18	5.58	1.89	6.79
94 Pu	100	26.67	11.18	5.92	1.95	7.02
96 Cm	100	26.93	11.18	6.26	2.01	7.34

From Salem, S. I., Panossian, S. L., and Krause, R. A., *At. Data Nucl. Data Tables,* 14, 91, 1974. Reproduced by permission of the copyright owner. Academic Press.

K AND L X-RAY ABSORPTION EDGES

The wavelengths in Angstroms for the K absorption edge of elements having atomic numbers 3 to 11 and 83 to 100 were calculated from critical X-ray absorption energies listed in the Review of Scientific Instruments, **23,** 523–528. (1952.)

All wavelengths for the L absorption edges were calculated from absorption energies given in the above reference.

Values for the M, N, and O absorption edges are also listed in the above reference. The wavelengths in Angstroms for the K absorption edge of the elements having atomic numbers 12 to 82 are reproduced by permission from Structure of Metals, Barrett, 2nd edition, McGraw-Hill Book Company, Inc. (1952.)

ABSORPTION EDGES—ANGSTROMS

Atomic Number	Element	K	L_I	L_{II}	L_{III}
3	Li	226.62			
4	Be	110.68			
5	B	66.289			
6	C	43.648			
7	N	30.990			
8	O	23.301			
9	F	17.913			
10	Ne	14.183			
11	Na	11.478	197.39		
12	Mg	9.5117	142.48	247.92	
13	Al	7.9511	105.05	172.16	
14	Si	6.7446	81.02	126.48	
15	P	5.7866	64.228	96.843	
16	S	5.0182	52.084	76.049	76.519
17	Cl	4.3969	43.192	61.366	61.672
18	A	3.87068	36.352	50.390	50.803
19	K	3.43645		42.020	42.452
20	Ca	3.07016	31.068	35.417	35.827
21	Sc	2.7572	26.831	30.161	30.457
22	Ti	2.49730	23.389	26.831	27.184
23	Va	2.26902	20.523	23.702	24.0699
24	Cr	2.07012	18.256	21.226	21.5958
25	Mn	1.89636	16.268	18.896	19.2484
26	Fe	1.74344	14.601	17.169	17.4838
27	Co	1.60811	13.343	15.534	15.8314
28	Ni	1.48802	12.267	14.135	14.4476
29	Cu	1.38043	11.269	12.994	13.2578
30	Zn	1.2833	10.330	11.8395	12.1055
31	Ga	1.19567	9.535	10.6130	10.8546
32	Ge	1.11662	8.729	9.9646	10.2277
33	As	1.04497	8.107	9.1281	9.3767
34	Se	0.97978	7.467	8.4212	8.6624
35	Br	0.91994	6.925	7.7523	7.9871
36	Kr	0.86546	6.456	7.1653	7.4227
37	Rb	0.81549	6.006	6.6538	6.8752
38	Sr	0.76969	5.604	6.1856	6.3996
39	Y	0.72762	5.19312	5.70981	5.91412
40	Zr	0.68877	4.80380	5.37088	5.57374
41	Nb	0.65291	4.59111	5.02472	5.22596
42	Mo	0.61977	4.32066	4.71330	4.90930
43	Tc	0.58888	4.06426	4.42714	4.62537
44	Ru	0.56047	3.84133	4.17654	4.36632
45	Rh	0.53378	3.64159	3.94902	4.13889
46	Pd	0.50915	3.42999	3.71360	3.89688
47	Ag	0.48582	3.23824	3.49478	3.67288
48	Cd	0.46408	3.08434	3.32243	3.50070
49	In	0.44397	2.93327	3.15500	3.32154
50	Sn	0.42468	2.78875	2.99492	3.16952
51	Sb	0.40663	2.63296	2.82304	2.99637
52	Te	0.38972	2.50272	2.68253	2.85162
53	I	0.37379	2.38982	2.55324	2.71901
54	Xe	0.35849	2.27449	2.43058	2.59330
55	Cs	0.34473	2.17245	2.31268	2.47227
56	Ba	0.33137	2.08336	2.20216	2.36114
57	La	0.31842	1.97892	2.10030	2.25792
58	Ce	0.30647	1.89078	2.00940	2.16410
59	Pr	0.29517	1.81307	1.92305	2.07707
60	Nd	0.28451	1.73759	1.84244	1.99452
61	Pm	0.27425	1.66837	1.76581	1.91888
62	Sm	0.26462	1.60113	1.69436	1.84464
63	Eu	0.25552	1.53815	1.62591	1.77491
64	Gd	0.24680	1.47870	1.56081	1.70955
65	Tb	0.23840	1.42270	1.50108	1.64840
66	Dy	0.23046	1.36926	1.44357	1.59025
67	Ho	0.22290	1.31942	1.38999	1.53529
68	Er	0.21565	1.27086	1.33721	1.48242
69	Tm	0.2089	1.22708	1.28856	1.43140
70	Yb	0.20223	1.18136	1.24146	1.38518
71	Lu	0.19554	1.14007	1.19745	1.34039
72	Hf	0.18981	1.09864	1.15311	1.29570
73	Ta	0.18393	1.06084	1.11264	1.25427
74	W	0.17837	1.02497	1.07436	1.21529
75	Re	0.17311	0.99009	1.03645	1.17720
76	Os	0.16780	0.95374	1.00129	1.14143
77	Ir	0.16286	0.92425	0.96700	1.10599
78	Pt	0.15817	0.89405	0.93484	1.07306
79	Au	0.15344	0.86378	0.90277	1.04028
80	Hg	0.14923	0.83531	0.87790	1.00944
81	Tl	0.14470	0.80787	0.84355	0.97968
82	Pb	0.14077	0.78153	0.81552	0.95112
83	Bi	0.13691	0.75649	0.78910	0.92459
84	Po	0.13306	0.73219	0.76377	0.89761
85	At	0.12949	0.70915	0.73873	0.87234
86	Rn	0.12591	0.68675	0.71529	0.84845
87	Fr	0.12261	0.66537	0.69290	0.82529
88	Ra	0.11931	0.64461	0.67114	0.80284
89	Ac	0.11618	0.62479	0.65002	0.78158
90	Th	0.11290	0.60610	0.63010	0.76151
91	Pa	0.11028	0.58748	0.61064	0.74138
92	U	0.10775	0.56974	0.59186	0.72225
93	Np	0.10487	0.55314	0.57415	0.70391
94	Pu	0.10228	0.53662	0.55712	0.68637
95	Am	0.09972	0.52084	0.54036	0.66933
96	Cm	0.09674	0.50595	0.52458	0.65276
97	Bk	0.09506	0.49131	0.50928	0.63667
98	Cf	0.09278	0.47713	0.49445	0.62135
99		0.09068	0.46357	0.48009	0.60645
100		0.08861	0.45059	0.46654	0.59225

DIFFRACTION DATA FOR CUBIC ISOMORPHS

From Volume 14, pages 689, 690, and 691 of the Analytical Edition of Industrial and Engineering Chemistry. (With permission.)

X Units	Substance	X Units	Substance
A 4		4.82 **B 1** (Continued)	(Na_2CeO_3)
3.56	C (diamond)	4.84	(Na_2PrO_3)
5.42	Si	4.88	NaH
5.62	Ge	4.92	AgF
6.46	α-Sn	5.006	CaNH
A 1		5.13	SrO
3.517	Ni	5.14	LiCl
3.554	α-Co	5.14	NdN
3.60	Taenite (57.7 % Fe, 40.8 % Ni, 0.5 % P)	5.19	MgS
3.608	Cu	5.192	MnS (130°K.)
3.63	γ-Fe (1370°K.)	5.210	MnS (299°K.)
3.797	Rh	5.33	KF
3.831	Ir	5.45	MgSe
3.880	Pd	5.45	MnSe
3.88– 4.04	Pd-H	5.45	SrNH
3.912	Pt	5.49	LiBr
4.041	Al	5.52	BaO
4.070	Au	5.545	AgCl
4.077	Ag	5.55– 5.76	AgCl-AgBr
4.30	Co-N	5.627	NaCl
4.40– 4.46	Ti-H	5.63	RbF
4.52	Ne (4°K.)	5.68	CaS
4.66	Zr-H	5.69	SnAs
4.84	β-Tl	5.70	KH
4.939	Pb	5.755	AgBr
5.08	Th	5.76– 5.92	AgBr-AgI
5.14	α-Ce	5.83	NdP
5.296	β-La	5.83	NaCN
5.43	A (4°K.)	5.84	BaNH
5.56	Ca	5.87	SrS
5.59	Kr (20°K.)	5.91	CaSe
5.70	Kr (92°K.)	5.94	PbS
6.05	Sr	5.95	NaBr
6.20	X (88°K.)	5.957	EuS
A 2		5.96	NdAs
2.861	α-Fe	6.00	PrAs
2.875	α-Cr	6.00	LiI
2.90	β-Fe (1070°K.)	6.01	CsF
2.93	δ-Fe (1700°K.)	6.04	RbH
3.03	V	6.05	β-NaSH (>360°K.)
3.03– 3.41	V-C	6.06	CeAs
3.140	Mo	6.13	LaAs
3.157	W	6.14	PbSe
3.295	Cb	6.23	SrSe
3.30	Ta	6.278	KCl
3.32	β-Ti (1200°K.)	6.285	SnTe
3.46	Li (~80°K.)	6.31	NdSb
3.50	Li	6.345	CaTe
3.61	β-Zr (1120°K.)	6.35	PrSb
4.24	Na (~80°K.)	6.36	BaS
4.29	Na	6.38	CsH
5.02	Ba	6.40	CeSb
5.20	K (120°K.)	6.44	PbTe
5.33	K	6.462	NaI
5.62	Rb (~80°K.)	6.45	PrBi
6.05	Cs (~80°K.)	6.48	LaSb
B 1		6.49	CeBi
4.018	LiF	6.53	KCN
4.065	LiD	6.53	NH_4Cl (>457°K.)
4.08	VO	6.56	RbCl
4.09	LiH	6.57	LaBi
4.12	(Li_2TiO_3)	6.58	KBr
4.12– 4.20	$(Li_2TiO_3\text{-}MgO)$	6.59	BaSe
4.13	VN	6.60	β-KSH (>440°K.)
4.14	CrN	6.65	SrTe
4.14	VC	6.82	RbCN
4.142	$(63Li_2Fe_2O_4\cdot 37Li_2TiO_3)$	6.86	RbBr
4.173	NiO	6.90	NH_4Br (>411°K.)
4.207	MgO	6.93	β-RbSH (470°K.)
4.282	MgO (1570°K.)	6.99	BaTe
4.225	TiN	7.052	KI
4.235	TiO	7.10	β-CsCl (>730°K.)
4.24	80 TiN-20 TiC	7.24	NH_4I (>255°K.)
4.24	CoO	7.325	RbI
4.27	V-N	**H 0s**	
4.28	FeO (160°K.)	6.96 ± 0.04	$AgClO_4$ (453 ± 20°K.)
4.283	FeO (299°K.)	7.16 ± 0.10	$NaClO_4$ (618 ± 35°K.)
4.290	VC (ε-phase)	7.49 ± 0.02	$KClO_4$ (598 ± 15°K.)
4.30	TiC	7.65 ± 0.05	$TlClO_4$ (553°K.)
4.315	CbC	7.65 ± 0.02	NH_4ClO_4 (528 ± 15°K.)
4.40	CbN	7.68 ± 0.03	$RbClO_4$ (583 ± 10°K.)
4.41	MnO (117°K.)	7.97 ± 0.01	$CsClO_4$ (513 ± 10°K.)
4.426	MnO (299°K.)	**B 3**	
4.436	ScN	4.255	CuF
4.44	TaC	4.36	CSi IV
4.446	HfC	4.855	BeS
4.458	NaF	5.10	BeSe
4.615	ZrN	5.304	(Cu, Fe, Mo, Bu)₄(B, As, Te)₃₋₄, cousite
4.62	CdO	5.41	CuCl
4.69	ZrC	5.425	β-ZnS
4.69	CaO	5.43	AlP
4.80	CaO	5.44	GaP
		5.58	BeTe
		5.60	MnS (red)

X Units	Substance		X Units	Substance
B 3 (Continued)			4.33	**C 1** Be_2C
5.63	AlAs		4.619	Li_2O
5.635	GaAs		5.06	$(3ZrO_2 \cdot MgO)$
5.655	ZnSe		5.07	ZrO_2
5.68	CuBr		5.08	$(95ZrO_2 \cdot 5CeO_2)$
5.82	β-CdS		5.13	$(95HfO_2 \cdot 5CeO_2)$
5.84	HgS		5.38	PrO_2
5.86	InP		5.40	CeO_2
6.04	CdSe		5.40	CdF_2
6.04	InAs		5.406	CuF_2
6.05	CuI		5.45	CaF_2
6.07	HgSe		5.47	UO_2
6.08	ZnTe		5.526	$(66CaF_2 \cdot 33YF_3)$
6.103	α-Cu_2HgI_4		5.53	$(91CaF_2 \cdot 9ThF_4)$
6.12	AlSb		5.54	HgF_2
6.12	GaSb		5.55	Na_2O
6.13	SnSb		5.58	ThO_2
6.383	α-Ag_2HgI_4		5.59	Cu_2S
6.40	HgTe		5.704	Li_2S
6.43	CdTe		5.749	Cu_2Se
6.45	InSb		5.782	SrF_2
6.48	AgI		5.796	EuF_2
B 32			5.838	$(66SrF_2 \cdot 33LaF_3)$
6.195	LiGa		5.91	$PtAl_2$
6.209	LiZn		5.91	$PtGa_2$
6.36	LiAl		5.935	β-PbF_2 (520°K.)
6.687	LiCd		5.99	Al_2Au
6.786	LiIn		6.005	Li_2Se
7.297	NaIn		6.06	$AuGa_2$
7.373	($CeMg_3$)		6.19	BaF_2
7.373	($PrMg_3$)		6.34	Mg_2Si
7.473	NaTl		6.35	$PtIn_2$
B 20			6.368	RaF_2
4.437	NiSi		6.379	Mg_2Ge
4.438	FeSi		6.436	K_2O
4.438	CoSi		6.50	Li_2Te
4.548	MnSi		6.50	$AuIn_2$
4.620	CrSi		6.526	Na_2S
B 2			6.763	Mg_2Sn
2.603	NiBe		6.809	Na_2Se
2.606	CoBe		6.81	Mg_2Pb
2.69	CuBe		6.98	$SrCl_2$
2.813	PdBe		7.314	Na_2Te
2.82	AlNi		7.38	K_2S
2.945	CuZn		7.65	Rb_2S
2.989	CuPd		7.676	K_2Se
3.146	AuZn		8.152	K_2Te
3.156	AgZn			**C 15**
3.168	AgLi		5.94	Be_2Cu
3.259	AuMg		6.287	Be_2Ag
3.275	AgMg		6.435	Be_2Ti
3.287	HgLi		6.96	$MgNiZn$
3.325	AgCd		7.03	Cu_2Mg
3.34	AuCd (670°K.)		7.61	W_2Zr
3.424	LiTl		7.79	Au_2Na
3.442	HgMg		7.91	Au_2Pb
3.628	MgTl		7.94	Au_2Bi
3.67	PrZn		8.02	Al_2Ca
3.70	CeZn		8.04	Al_2Ce
3.73	AlNd		8.16	Al_2La
3.74	α-RbCl (83°K.)		9.50	Bi_2K
3.75	LaZn			**C 2**
3.82	TlCN		5.41	FeS_2
3.82	PrCd		5.42	(Fe, Ni)S_2 (6.5 % Ni)
3.84	TlSb		5.57	RbS_2
3.835	TlCl		5.57	RuS_2
3.847	CaTl		5.57	Bravoite (53.8 % NiS_2, 39.1 % FeS_2,
3.86	NH_4Cl (<457°K.)			7.1 % CoS_2)
3.86	CeCd		5.62	OsS_2
3.88	MgPr		5.64	CoS_2
3.90	LaCd		5.65	(Cu, Ni, Co, Fe)(S, Se)$_2$
3.97	TlBr		5.68	PtP_2
3.98	TlBi		5.74	NiS_2
4.024	SrTl		5.85	$CoSe_2$
4.05	NH_4Br (<411°K.)		5.92	$RuSe_2$
4.112	CsCl		5.93	$OsSe_2$
4.20	TlI		5.94	$PtAs_2$
4.20	CsCl (<720°K.)		5.97	$PdAs_2$
4.25	CsCN		6.02	$NiSe_2$
4.287	CsBr		6.096	MnS_2
4.29	CsSH		6.36	$RuTe_2$
4.37	NH_4I (290°K.)		6.37	$OsTe_2$
4.56	CsI		6.43	$PtSb_2$
D 2₁			6.44	$PdSb_2$
4.07	YB_6		6.64	$AuSb_2$
4.07	ErB_6		6.94	$MnTe_2$
4.10	NdB_6			**C 3**
4.12	GdB_6		4.25	Cu_2O
4.12	PrB_6		4.73	Ag_2O
4.13	CeB_6			**F 1**
4.13	YbB_6		5.55	CoAsS
4.14	CaB_6		5.68	NiAsS
4.15	LaB_6		5.90	NiSbS
4.15	ThB_6			(Ni, Fe)AsS, plessite
4.19	SrB_6			Ni(As, Sb)S, corynite
4.33	BaB_6			Ni(Sb, Bi)S, kallilite
				(Co, Ni)SbS, willyamite

DIFFRACTION DATA FOR CUBIC ISOMORPHS
(Continued)

X Units	Substance		X Units	Substance
	D 5₃			**H 1₁**
8.13	Be₃N₂		8.28	
9.37	(Mn, Fe)₂O₃		8.30	MgGa₂O₄
9.42	Mn₂O₃		8.30	NiCr₂O₄
9.74	Zn₃N₂		8.31	MgCr₂O₄
9.79	Sc₂O₃		8.32	ZnCr₂O₄
9.94	Mg₃N₂		8.32	CoCr₂O₄
10.12	In₂O₃		8.35	ZnGa₂O₄
10.15	Be₃P₂		8.35	NiFe₂O₄
10.37	Lu₂O₃		8.35	Cu₃Cr₂O₄
10.39	Yb₂O₃		8.36	FeCr₂O₄
10.52	Tm₂O₃		8.38	MgFe₂O₄
10.54	Er₂O₃		8.38	CoFe₂O₄
10.57	Tl₂O₃		8.40	NiMn₂O₄
10.58	Ho₂O₃		8.40	ZnFe₂O₄
10.60	Y₂O₃		8.42	FeFe₂O₄
10.63	Dy₂O₃		8.42	(Mn, Mg)Fe₂O₄
10.70	Tb₂O₃		8.43	TiCo₂O₄
10.79	Gd₂O₃		8.43	MnCr₂O₄
10.79	Cd₃N₂		8.43	TiMg₂O₄
10.84	Eu₂O₃		8.44	TiZn₂O₄
10.85	Sm₂O₃		8.47	CuFe₂O₄
11.05	Nd₂O₃		8.49	FeV₂O₄
11.40	α-Ca₃N₂		8.50	MnCr₂O₄
12.02	Mg₃P₂		8.54	TiFe₂O₄
12.33	Mg₃As₂		8.58	MnFe₂O₄
	D 6₁		8.58	CdCr₂O₄
11.05	As₄O₆		8.61	SnMg₂O₄
11.14	Sb₄O₆		8.63	SnCo₂O₄
	D 1₁		8.67	SnZn₂O₄
10.32	ZrCl₄		8.67	CdFe₂O₄
11.25	TiBr₄		8.81	TiMn₂O₄
(11.34)	(CBr₄) (>320°K.)		9.26	MgIn₂O₄
(11.62)	(CI₄)			Ag₂MoO₄
11.89	GeI₄		9.4	CoCo₂S₄
11.99	SiI₄		9.45	(Co, Ni)₃S₄
12.00	TiI₄		9.46	CuCo₂O₄
12.23	SnI₄		9.5	NiN₂S₄
	E 2₁		9.92	ZnCr₂S₄
3.67	YAlO₃		10.05	MnCr₂S₄
3.75	CdTiO₃		10.19	CdCr₂S₄
3.78	LaAlO₃		12.54	K₂Zn(Cn)₄
3.80	CaTiO₃		12.76	K₂Hg(CN)₄
3.83	NaWO₃		12.84	K₂Cd(CN)₄
3.85	(Na, Ce, Ca)(Ti, Cb)O₃ Loparite			**H 5₈**
3.88	NaTaO₃		10.08	2Na₂SO₄·NaCl·NaF
3.89	LaGaO₃			**H 4₁₃**
3.80	NaCbO₃		12.11	KCr(SO₄)₂·12H₂O
3.91	SrTiO₃		12.12	KAl(SO₄)₂·12H₂O
3.92	CaSnO₃		12.15	NH₄Al(SO₄)₂·12H₂O
3.97	BaTiO₃		12.15	NH₄Fe(SO₄)₂·12H₂O
3.98	KTaO₃		12.20	RbAl(SO₄)₂·12H₂O
3.99	CaZrO₃		12.21	TlAl(SO₄)₂·12H₂O
4.00	KMgF₃		12.31	CsAl(SO₄)₂·12H₂O
4.005	KNiF₃		12.44	NH₂·CH₃Al(SO₄)₂·12H₂O (β-alum)
4.01	KCbO₃			**Langbeinite**
4.03	SrSnO₃		9.93	K₂Mg(SO₄)₃
4.05	KZnF₃		10.2	K₂(Ca, Mg)(SO₃)₃
4.07	KCoF₃			**H 2₁**
4.07	SrHfO₃		6.00	Ag₃PO₄
4.09	SrZrO₃		6.120	Ag₃AsO₄ (90°K.)
4.18	BaZrO₃		6.130	Ag₃AsO₄ (380°K.)
4.35	BaPrO₃			**H 2₄**
4.38	BaCeO₃		5.37	Cu₃VS₄
4.46	KIO₃			**J 1₁**
4.48	BaThO₃		8.17	K₂SiF₆
4.5	NH₄IO₃		8.35	(NH₄)₂SiF₆
4.52	RbIO₃		8.38	Rb₂CrF₅H₂O
4.66	CsIO₃		8.41	Tl₂CrF₅H₂O
5.12	MgZrO₃		8.42	(NH₄)₂VF₅H₂O
5.20	CsCdCl₃		8.42	Rb₂VF₅H₂O
5.33	CsCdBr₃		8.45	Tl₂VF₅H₂O
5.44	CsHgCl₃		8.45	Rb₂SiF₆
5.77	CsHgBr₃		8.58	Tl₂SiF₆
	G 0₁		8.87	Cs₂SiF₆
6.57	NaClO₃		8.99	Cs₂GeF₆
6.71	NaBrO₃		9.73	K₂PtCl₆
	G 2₁		9.73	K₂OsCl₆
7.60	Ca(NO₃)₂		9.76	Tl₂PtCl₆
7.81	Sr(NO₃)₂		9.84	(NH₄)₂PtCl₆
7.84	Pb(NO₃)₂		9.86	K₂ReCl₆
8.11	Ba(NO₃)₂		9.88	Rb₂PtCl₆
	H 1₁		9.92	Rb₂TiCl₆
8.045	NiAl₂O₄		9.94	(NH₄)₂SeCl₆
8.07	CuAl₂O₄		9.97	K₂SnCl₆
8.07	CoCo₂O₄		9.97	Tl₂SnCl₆
8.07	MgAl₂O₄		9.98	Rb₂SeCl₆
8.08	CoAl₂O₄		10.02	Rb₂PdBr₆
8.08	ZnAl₂O₄		10.04	(NH₄)₂SnCl₆
8.10	FeAl₂O₄		10.08	Ni(NH₃)₆Cl₂
8.11	(Ni, Co)(Co, Ni)₂O₄		10.10	Rb₂SnCl₆
8.11	(Zn, Co)Co₂O₄		10.10	Co(NH₃)₆Cl₂
8.11	MgCo₂O₄		10.11	Tl₂TeCl₆
8.27	MnAl₂O₄		10.14	(NH₄)₂PbCl₆
8.27	(Mn, Co)(Co, Mn)₂O₄		10.14	K₂TeCl₆
			10.15	Fe(NH₃)₆Cl₂
			10.15	Mg(NH₃)₆Cl₂
			10.17	Cs₂PtCl₆

X Units	Substance	X Units	Substance
		10.25	$NaTl_2Co(NO_2)_6$
		10.28	$K_2CdNi(NO_2)_6$
	J 1₁	10.28	$(NH_4)_2CdFe(NO_2)_6$
10.18	Rb_2ZrCl_6	10.29	$K_2HgNi(NO_2)_6$
10.18	$(NH_4)_2TeCl_6$	10.30	$K_2SrFe(NO_2)_6$
10.20	$Mn(NH_3)_6Cl_2$	10.30	$Tl_2CaFe(NO_2)_6$
10.20	Rb_2PbCl_6	10.31	$K_2PbFe(NO_2)_6$
10.22	Cs_2TiCl_6	10.32	$K_2CaNi(NO_2)_6$
10.23	Rb_2TeCl_6	10.34	$(NH_4)_2SrFe(NO_2)_6$
10.25	$Zn(NH_3)_6(ClO_4)_2$	10.37	$(NH_4)_2PbFe(NO_2)_6$
10.26	Cs_2SeCl_6	10.37	$Tl_2CdNi(NO_2)_6$
10.30	K_2OSBr_6	10.39	$Tl_2PbFe(NO_2)_6$
10.35	Cs_2SnCl_6	10.39	$NaRb_2Co(NO_2)_6$
10.36	K_2SeBr_6	10.40	$Tl_2SrFe(NO_2)_6$
10.36	K_2PtBr_6	10.4	$K_2PbCo(NO_2)_6$
10.39	$Co(NH_3)_6Br_2$	10.41	$(NH_4)_2CdNi(NO_2)_6$
10.4	$Ni(NH_3)_6Br_2$	10.42	$Tl_2HgNi(NO_2)_6$
10.41	Cs_2ZrCl_6	10.43	$K_2BaFe(NO_2)_6$
10.42	Cs_2PbCl_6	10.45	$K_2BaCo(NO_2)_6$
10.45	Cs_2TeCl_6	10.45	$K_3Co(NO_2)_6$
10.45	$Co(NH_3)_5H_2OSO_4Br$	10.46	$(NH_4)_2HgNi(NO_2)_6$
10.45	$(NH_4)_2SeBr_6$	10.47	$Rb_2HgNi(NO_2)_6$
10.46	$Zn(NH_3)_6Br_2$	10.49	$K_2SrNi(NO_2)_6$
10.46	$Fe(NH_3)_6Br_2$	10.49	$K_4Ni(NO_2)_6$
10.47	$Mg(NH_3)_6Br_2$	10.50	$(NH_4)_2BaFe(NO_2)_6$
10.47	K_2SnBr_6	10.54	$K_2LiBi(NO_2)_6$
10.48	$Co(NH_3)_6SO_4Br$	10.55	$K_2PbNi(NO_2)_6$
10.51	$Mn(NH_3)_6Br_2$	10.55	$Tl_2BaFe(NO_2)_6$
10.52	$Sr_2Ni(NO_2)_6$	10.58	$Rb_2CdNi, Cd(NO_2)_6$
10.54	$Pb_2Ni(NO_2)_6$	10.58	$K_3Ir(NO_2)_6$
10.55	$(NH_4)_2SnBr_6$	10.59	$Rb_2LiBi(NO_2)_6$
10.57	Rb_2SnBr_6	10.6	$K_2PbCu(NO_2)_6$
10.58	$Co(NH_3)_5H_2OSO_4I$	10.63	$K_2Rh(NO_2)_6$
10.62	$Co(NH_3)_6SeO_4Br$	10.63	$(NH_4)_2LiBi(NO_2)_6$
10.63	$Ba_2Ni(NO_2)_6$	10.64	$Tl_2LiBi(NO_2)_6$
10.67	$Ca(NH_3)_6Br_2$	10.67	$K_2BaNi(NO_2)_6$
10.71	$Co(NH_3)_6SO_4I$	10.70	$NaCs_2Co(NO_2)_6$
10.71	Cs_2SnBr_6	10.70	$Ba_3[Rh(NO_2)_6]_2$
10.77	$Co(NH_3)_6SeO_4I$	10.72	$Tl_3Co(NO_2)_6$
10.79	$Ni(NH_3)_6I_2$	10.73	$Rb_3Co(NO_2)_6$
10.9	$Co(NH_3)_6I_2$	10.73	$(NH_4)_3Ir(NO_2)_6$
10.91	$Zn(NH_3)_6I_2$	10.73	$Tl_3Ir(NO_2)_6$
10.96	$Fe(NH_3)_6I_2$	10.77	$Rb_3Ir(NO_2)_6$
10.97	$Mg(NH_3)_6I_2$	10.8	$(NH_4)_3Co(NO_2)_6$
10.98	$Mn(NH_3)_6I_2$	10.81	$Cs_2Cd[Ni, Cd(NO_2)_6]$
11.04	$Cd(NH_3)_6I_2$	10.82	$Co(NH_3)_5H_2OI_3$
11.04	$Ca(NH_3)_6I_2$	10.83	$Rb_3Rh(NO_2)_6$
11.24	$Ni(NH_3)_6(BF_4)_2$	10.88	$K_2NaBi(NO_2)_6$
11.27	$Co(NH_3)_6(BF_4)_2$	10.89	$Co(NH_3)_6I_3$
11.3	$Zn(NH_3)_6(ClO_4)_2$	10.91	$Tl_3Rh(NO_2)_6$
(11.3)	$Mg(NH_3)_6(BF_4)_2$	10.91	$(NH_4)_3Rh(NO_2)_6$
11.34	$Fe(NH_3)_6(BF_4)_2$	10.94	$Cs_2LiBi(NO_2)_6$
11.34	$Mn(NH_3)_6(BF_4)_2$	10.95	$K_2AgBi(NO_2)_6$
11.37	$Cd(NH_3)_6(BF_4)_2$	10.98	$Rb_2NaBi(NO_2)_6$
11.38	$Ni(NH_3)_6(ClO_4)_2$	10.99	$(NH_4)_2NaBi(NO_2)_6$
11.41	$Co(NH_3)_6(ClO_4)_2$	11.01	$Tl_2NaBi(NO_2)_6$
11.43	$Ni(NH_3)_6(SO_3F)_2$	11.05	$Rb_2AgBi(NO_2)_6$
11.46	$Co(NH_3)_6(SO_3F)_2$	11.06	$Tl_2AgBi(NO_2)_6$
11.49	$Fe(NH_3)_6(ClO_4)_2$	11.10	$(NH_4)_2AgBi(NO_2)_6$
11.52	$Mg(NH_3)_6(ClO_4)_2$	11.15	$Cs_2NaBi(NO_2)_6$
11.53	$Cd(NH_3)_6Br_2$	11.15	$Cs_3Co(NO_2)_6$
11.54	$Fe(NH_3)_6(SO_3F)_2$	11.17	$Cs_3Ir(NO_2)_6$
11.54	$Mn(NH_3)_6(ClO_4)_2$	11.19	$Cs_3Bi(NO_2)_6$
11.58	$Cd(NH_3)_6(ClO_4)_2$	11.19	$Cs_2AgBi(NO_2)_6$
11.59	$Mn(NH_3)_6(SO_3F)_2$	11.21	$Co(NH_3)_6(BF_4)_3$
11.59	$Cd(NH_3)_6(SO_3F)_2$	11.30	$Cs_3Rh(NO_2)_6$
11.62	$Ni(NH_3)_6(PF_6)_2$	11.32	$[Co(NH_3)_5·H_2O](ClO_4)_3$
11.91	$Co(NH_3)_6(PF_6)_2$	11.39	$Co(NH_3)_6(ClO_4)_3$
11.94	$Ni(NH_2·CH_3)_6I_2$	11.67	$Co(NH_3)_6(PF_6)$
12.03	$Co(NH_2·CH_3)_6I_2$		**K 6₁**
12.05	$[NH(CH_3)_3]_2SnCl_6$	7.46	SiP_2O_7
12.19	$[S(CH_3)_3]_2SnCl_6$	7.80	TiP_2O_7
12.41	$[N(CH_3)_4]_2PtCl_6$	7.98	SnP_2O_7
12.65	$[S(CH_3)_2C_2H_5]_2SnCl_6$	8.18	HfP_2O_7
12.80	$[N(CH_3)_4]_2SnCl_6$	8.20	ZrP_2O_7
12.87	$[N(CH_3)_2C_2H_5]_2SnCl_6$	8.61	UP_2O_7
13.17	$[N(CH_2)(C_2H_5)_3]_2SnCl_6$		**S 1₄**
13.51	$[P(CH_3)(C_2H_5)_3]_2SnCl_6$	11.51	$Al_2(Mg, Fe)_3(SiO_4)_3$, pyrope
13.93		11.51	$Al_2Fe_3(SiO_4)_3$, almandite
	J 2₁ and Related Structures	11.60	$Al_2Mn_3(SiO_4)_3$, spessartite
8.88	Li_3FeF_6	11.87	$Al_2Ca_3(SiO_4)_3$, grossularite
8.90	$(NH_4)_3AlF_6$	11.89	$(Al, Fe)_2Ca_3(SiO_4)_3$, hessonite
9.01	$(NH_4)_3CrF_6$	11.95	$Cr_2Ca_3(SiO_4)_3$, uvarovite
9.04	$(NH_4)_3VF_6$	12.03	$Fe_2Ca_3(SiO_4)_3$, andradite
9.10	$(NH_4)_3FeF_6$	12.10	$(Na, Li)_3AlF_6$, cryolithionite
9.10	$(NH_4)MoO_3F_3$	12.35–	$(Mg, Mn)_2(Ca, Na)_3AsO_4)_3$, berzelite
9.26	Na_3FeF_6	12.46	
9.93	K_3FeF_6		**S 6₁**
9.96	$CuLi_2Fe(CN)_6$	13.68	$NaAlSi_2O_6H_2O$
10.0	$CuR_2Fe(CN)_6$		**S 0₈**
	$R = Na, K, Rb, NH_4, Tl$	13.82	$Al_{13}Si_5O_{20}(OH, F)_{18}Cl$, zunyite
10.15	$K_2CdFe(NO_2)_6$		**S 6₂**
10.17	$K_2CaCo(NO_2)_6$	8.87	$Na_4(AlSiO_4)_3Cl$, sodalite
10.19	$K_2CaFe(NO_2)_6$		**Tetrahedrite**
10.2	$Fe^{III}R^{II}(CN)_6$	10.19	$(Cu, Fe)_{12}As_4S_{13}$, binnite
	$R = Na, K, Rb, NH_4$	10.2–	$(Cu, Ag)_{10}(Zn, Fe)_2(Sb, As)_4S_{13}$
10.22	$K_2HgFe(NO_2)_6$	10.6	
10.23	$K_2SrCo(NO_2)_6$		
10.25	$(NH_4)_2CaFe(NO_2)_6$		

PHOTOMETRIC QUANTITIES, UNITS AND STANDARDS

Photometric quantities and units are also given in the section Quantities and Units under the sub-division Light.

Candela-cd (formerly candle): The International System (SI) unit of luminous intensity. One candela is defined as the luminous intensity of one sixtieth of one square centimeter of projected area of a black body radiator operating at the temperature of freezing platinum (2042K).

Footcandle-fc: The unit of illumination when a foot is the unit of length. Footcandle is the illumination on a surface one square foot in area on which there is a uniformly distributed flux of one lumen, or the illumination on a surface all points of which are at a distance of one foot from a directionally uniform point source of one candela. (1 footcandle = 10.76 lux.)

Lumen-lm: The unit of luminous flux. It is equal to the flux through a unit solid angle (steradian), from a uniform point source of one candela, or to the flux on a unit surface all points of which are at unit distance from a uniform source of one candela.

Lux-lx: The International System (SI) unit of illumination in which the meter is the unit of length. (See Footcandle above.) 1 Lux = 0.0929 footcandles.

Luminous Efficacy of a Source of Light: The quotient of the total luminous flux emitted by the total lamp power input. It is expressed in lumens per watt.

Luminance-L: The luminous intensity (photometric brightness) of any surface in a given direction per unit of projected area of the surface as viewed from that direction. In International System (SI) units the luminance of light sources is commonly expressed in candelas per square centimeter.

EFFICACIES OF ILLUMINANTS

The theoretical maximum efficacy of 680 lm/W is that which would be obtained if all the power input were emitted as green light at a wavelength of 555 nm (at which the eye is most sensitive). If all power could be emitted uniformly over the visible spectrum as white light, the efficacy would be of the order of 220 lm/W.

Fluorescent life-ratings are based upon 3 hr of operation per start. Life increases as lamps are burned for longer periods.

Lamp	Lamp watts	Rated average life, hours	Approximate initial lumens	Approximate initial efficacy, lm/lamp W
A. Tungsten filament (120 V)				
Vacuum	25	2,500	235	9.4
Gas filled	40	1,500	455	11.4
Gas filled	60	1,000	870	14.5
Gas filled	75	750	1,190	15.9
Gas filled	100	750	1,750	17.5
Gas filled	200	750	4,010	20.1
Gas filled	500	1,000	10,850	21.7
Gas filled	1,000	1,000	23,740	23.7
Gas filled (3,200 K)	5,000	150	145,000	29.0
Gas filled (3,200 K)	10,000	75	335,000	33.5
B. Fluorescent (cool white)				
Preheat (T12)	20	9,000	1,300	65.0
Rapid start (T12)	40	20,000	3,150	78.8
Rapid start (T12, shielded cathode)	40	15,000	3,250	81.3
Rapid start (T12, U shaped, 3 5/8-in. leg)	40	12,000	2,900	72.5
Slimline (96T12, 425 mA)	75	12,000	6,300	84.0
Preheat (T17)	90	9,000	6,400	71.1
High output (96T12, 800 mA)	110	12,000	9,200	83.6
Grooved lamp (96PG17, 1500 mA)	215	9,000	16,000	74.4
C. Fluorescent (other)				
Rapid start (T12, deluxe cool white)	40	20,000+	2,200	55.0
Rapid start (T12, white)	40	20,000+	3,200	80.0
Rapid start (T12, warm white)	40	20,000+	3,150	78.7
Rapid start (T12, deluxe warm-white)	40	20,000+	2,150	53.7
Rapid start (T12, daylight)	40	20,000+	2,600	65.0
Rapid start (T12, natural)	40	20,000+	2,100	52.5
Rapid start (T12, 5,000 K)	40	20,000+	2,200	55.0
Rapid start (T12, 7,500 K)	40	20,000+	2,000	50.0
Rapid start (T12, blue)	40	20,000+	1,160	29.0
Rapid start (T12, gold)	40	20,000+	2,400	60.0
Rapid start (T12, green)	40	20,000+	4,500	112.5
Rapid start (T12, pink)	40	20,000+	1,160	29.0
Rapid start (T12, red)	40	20,000+	200	5.0
D. High-intensity discharge (HID)				
1. Mercury vapor (E-37)				
Clear	400	24,000	21,000	52.5
Color improved	400	24,000	20,500	51.3
Deluxe white	400	24,000	22,500	56.3
Warm deluxe white	400	24,000	20,000	50.0
2. Mercury vapor (BT-56)				
Clear	1,000	24,000	57,000	57.4
Color improved	1,000	24,000	55,000	55.0
Deluxe white	1,000	24,000	63,000	63.0
Warm deluxe white	1,000	24,000	58,000	58.0
3. Metal halide				
E-37	400	10,000	34,000	85.0
BT-56	1,000	10,000	100,000	100.0
BT-56	1,500	1,500	155,000	103.3
4. High-pressure sodium (Lucalox®)				
	100	12,000	9,500	95.0
	150	12,000	16,000	106.7
	250	15,000	30,000	120.0
	400	20,000	50,000	125.0
	1,000	15,000	140,000	140.0
E. Electric arc				
High intensity	11,700		36,800	31.4

Table compiled by C. J. Allen and G. D. Rowe.

APPROXIMATE LUMINANCE
OF VARIOUS LIGHT SOURCES

Compiled by C.J. Allen and G.D. Rowe

Luminance of source is given in candelas per square centimeter

Source		Approx. avg. luminance* (Cd cm^{-2})
Natural sources		
Clear sky	Average luminance	0.8
Sun (as observed from earth's surface)	At meridian	160000
Sun (as observed from earth's surface)	Near horizon	600
Moon (as observed from earth's surface)	Bright spot	0.25
Combustion sources		
Candle flame (sperm)	Bright spot	1.0
Welsbach mantle	Bright spot	6.2
Acetylene flame	Mees burner	10.5
Photoflash lamps		16000-40000 peak
Incandescent electric lamps		
Carbon filament	3 Lumens per watt	52
Tungsten filament	Vacuum lamp— 10 lumens per watt	200
Tungsten filament	Gas-filled lamp— 20 lumens per watt	1200
Tungsten filament	750-watt projection lamp—26 lumens per watt	7500
Fluorescent lamps (cool white)		
Rapid start (40wT12)	430 mA	0.82
High-output (96T12)	800 mA	1.13
Grooved bulb (96T17)	1500 mA	1.50
Fluorescent lamps (other than cool white)		
Daylight (40wT12)	430 mA	0.62
Blue (40wT12)	430 mA	0.30
Green (40wT12)	430 mA	1.17
Red (40wT12)	430 mA	0.05
High-intensity discharge (HID)		
Mercury-vapor (E-37)		
Clear	400 watt	970
Color-improved	400 watt	11.0
Deluxe-white	400 watt	12.1
Mercury-vapor (BT-56)		
Clear	1000 watt	980
Color-improved	1000 watt	15.0
Deluxe-white	1000 watt	17.2
Metal halide (E-37)		
Clear	400 watt	810
Color-improved	1000 watt	930
Deluxe white	1500 watt	1620
High pressure sodium (Lucalox®)	250 watt	520
	400 watt	780
	1000 watt	810

®Registered trademark of the General Electric Company

*Luminance values perpendicular to lamp axis

FLAME STANDARDS

Value of Various Former Standards in International Candles

Standard Pentane lamp, burning pentane........	10.0 candles
Standard Hefner lamp, burning amyl acetate.....	0.9 candles
Standard Carcel lamp, burning colza oil.........	9.6 candles

The *Carcel unit* is the horizontal intensity of the carcel lamp, burning 42 grams of colza oil per hour. For a consumption between 38 and 46 grams per hour the intensity may be considered proportional to the consumption.

The *Hefner unit* is the horizontal intensity of the Hefner lamp burning amyl acetate, with a flame 4 cm. high. If the flame is l mm. high, the intensity $I = 1 + 0.027(l - 40)$.

WAVE LENGTHS OF VARIOUS RADIATIONS

	Ångstroms
Cosmic rays.....................................	0.0005
Gamma rays....................................	0.005–1.40
X-rays..	0.1–100
Ultra violet, below..............................	4000
Limit of sun's U.V. at earth's surface.................	2920
Visible spectrum................................	4000–7000
Violet, representative, 4100, limits...................	4000–4240
Blue, representative, 4700, limits....................	4240–4912
Green, representative, 5200, limits...................	4912–5750
Maximum visibility...............................	5560
Yellow, representative, 5800, limits..................	5750–5850
Orange, representative, 6000, limits..................	5850–6470
Red, representative, 6500, limits....................	6470–7000
Infra red, greater than..........................	7000
Hertzian waves, beyond..........................	2.20×10^6

WAVE LENGTHS OF THE FRAUNHOFER LINES

Sun's Spectrum

At 15°C and 76 cm pressure. Wave length in Ångström units (Fabry and Buisson system).

Line	Due to	Wave length	Line	Due to	Wave length
U	Fe	2947.9	h	H	4101.750
t	Fe	2994.4	g	Ca	4226.742
T	Fe	3021.067	G {	Fe	4307.914
s	Fe	3047.623	G {	Ca	4307.749
S_1 }	{ Fe	3100.683	G'	H	4340.477
S_2 }	{ Fe	3100.326	F	H	4861.344
	{ Fe	3099.943	b_4 {	Fe	5167.510
	{ Ca	3181.277	b_4 {	Mg	5167.330
R	{ Ca	3179.343	b_2	Mg	5172.700
Q	Fe	3286.773	b_1	Mg	5183.621
P	Ti	3361.194	E_2	Fe	5269.557
O	Fe	3441.020	D_2	Na	5889.977
N	Fe	3581.210	D_1	Na	5895.944
M	Fe	3727.636	C	H	6562.816
L	Fe	3820.438	B	O	6869.955
K	Ca	3933.684	A {	O	7621
H	Ca	3968.494	A {	O	7594
			Z	....	8228.5
			Y	....	8990.0

BRIGHTNESS OF TUNGSTEN

Characteristics of Straight Tungsten Wire in a Vacuum
(Forsythe and Worthing, 1924).

Temperature °K			Brightness candles/cm²	$\dfrac{B}{dB}\dfrac{dt}{T}$
Absolute	Brightness	Color		
1000	966	1006	0.00012	22.0
1200	1149	1210	0.006	20.0
1400	1330	1414	0.11	17.2
1600	1509	1619	0.92	15.2
1800	1684	1825	5.05	13.7
2000	1857	2033	20.0	12.3
2200	2026	2242	61.3	11.2
2400	2192	2452	157.0	10.3
2600	2356	2663	347.0	9.6
2800	2516	2878	694.0	8.9
3000	2673	3094	1257.0	8.3
3200	2827	3311	2110.0	7.8
3400	2978	3533	3370.0	7.6
3655*	3165	3817	5740.0	7.3

* Melting-point of tungsten.

WAVE LENGTHS FOR SPECTROSCOPE CALIBRATION

Source	Wave length	Source	Wave length
Potassium flame.........	0.7699μ	E, solar..............	0.5270μ
Potassium flame.........	0.7665	b_1, solar or magnesium	
Mercury I arc...........	0.6907	flame...............	0.5184
B, solar................	0.6869	b_2, solar or magnesium	
Lithium flame..........	0.6708	flame...............	0.5173
C, solar or hydrogen tube.	0.6563	Mercury I arc.........	0.4960
Mercury I arc...........	0.6234	Mercury I arc.........	0.4916
D_1, solar or sodium flame.	0.5896	F, solar or hydrogen tube	0.4861
D_2, solar or sodium flame.	0.5890	Strontium flame........	0.4608
Mercury I arc...........	0.5791	Mercury I arc.........	0.4358
Mercury I arc...........	0.5770	G', solar or hydrogen tube	0.4340
Mercury I arc...........	0.5461	Mercury I arc.........	0.4047
Thallium flame.........	0.5351	H_1, solar..............	0.3969
		K, solar..............	0.3934

STANDARD UNITS, SYMBOLS, AND DEFINING EQUATIONS FOR FUNDAMENTAL PHOTOMETRIC AND RADIOMETRIC QUANTITIES

Submitted by Abraham Abramowitz
from Z-7.1-1967

Radiometric Quantities
(See Note at bottom of page)

Quantity*	Symbol*	Defining Equation**	Commonly Used Units	Symbol
Radiant energy	$Q, (Q_e)$		erg	
			†joule	J
			kilowatt-hour	kWh
Radiant density	$w, (w_e)$	$w = dQ/dV$	†joule per cubic meter	J/m^3
			erg per cubic centimeter	erg/cm^3
Radiant flux	$\Phi, (\Phi_e)$	$\Phi = dQ/dt$	erg per second	erg/s
			†watt	W
Radiant flux density at a surface				
Radiant exitance (Radiant emittance)†	$M, (M_e)$	$M = d\Phi/dA$	watt per square centimeter	W/cm^2
Irradiance	$E, (E_e)$	$E = d\Phi/dA$	‡watt per square meter, etc.	W/m^2
Radiant intensity	$I, (I_e)$	$I = d\Phi/d\omega$ (ω = solid angle through which flux from point source is radiated)	‡watt per steradian	W/sr
Radiance	$L, (L_e)$	$L = d^2\Phi/d\omega/(dA \cos\theta)$ $= dI/(dA \cos\theta)$ (θ = angle between line of sight and normal to surface considered)	watt per steradian and square centimeter	$W \cdot sr^{-1} cm^{-2}$
			†watt per steradian and square meter	$W \cdot sr^{-1} m^{-2}$
Emissivity	ε	$\varepsilon = M/M_{blackbody}$ (M and $M_{blackbody}$ are respectively the radiant exitance of the measured specimen and that of a blackbody at the same temperature as the specimen)	one (numeric)	—

Note: The symbols for photometric quantities (see following table) are the same as those for the corresponding radiometric quantities (see above). When it is necessary to differentiate them the subscripts v and e respectively should be used, e.g., Q_v and Q_e.
  *Quantities may be restricted to a narrow wavelength band by adding the word spectral and indicating the wavelength. The corresponding symbols are changed by adding a subscript λ, e.g., Q_λ for a spectral concentration or a λ in parentheses, e.g., $K(\lambda)$, for a function of wavelength.
  **The equations in this column are given merely for identification.
  ***Φ_i = incident flux
    Φ_a = absorbed flux
    Φ_r = reflected flux
    Φ_t = transmitted flux
  †to be deprecated.
  ‡International System (SI) unit.

PHOTOMETRIC QUANTITIES

Quantity*	Symbol*	Defining Equation**	Commonly Used Units	Symbol
Absorptance	$\alpha, (\alpha_v, \alpha_e)$	$\alpha = \Phi_a/\Phi_i$***	one (numeric)	—
Reflectance	$\rho, (\rho_v, \rho_e)$	$\rho = \Phi_r/\Phi_i$***	one (numeric)	—
Transmittance	$\tau, (\tau_v, \tau_e)$	$\tau = \Phi_t/\Phi_i$***	one (numeric)	—
Luminous energy (quantity of light)	$Q, (Q_v)$	$Q_v = \int_{380}^{760} K(\lambda)\,Q_{e\lambda}\,d\lambda$	lumen-hour ‡lumen-second (talbot)	lm·h lm·s
Luminous density	$w, (w_v)$	$w = dQ/dV$	‡lumen-second per cubic meter	lm·s·m^{-3}
Luminous flux	$\Phi, (\Phi_v)$	$\Phi = dQ/dt$	‡lumen	lm
Luminous flux density at a surface				
Luminous exitance (Luminous emittance)†	$M, (M_v)$	$M = d\Phi/dA$	lumen per square foot	lm/ft^2
Illumination (illuminance)	$E, (E_v)$	$E = d\Phi/dA$	footcandle (lumen per square foot) ‡lux (lm/m^2) phot (lm/cm^2)	fc lx ph
Luminous intensity (candlepower)	$I, (I_v)$	$I = d\Phi/d\omega$ (ω = solid angle through which flux from point source is radiated)	‡candela (lumen per steradian)	cd
Luminance (photometric brightness)	$L, (L_v)$	$L = d^2\Phi/d\omega\,(dA\cos\theta)$ $= dI/(dA\cos\theta)$ (θ = angle between line of sight and normal to surface considered)	candela per unit area stilb (cd/cm^2) nit (†cd/m^2) footlambert (cd/πft^2) lambert (cd/πcm^2) apostilb (cd/πm^2)	cd/in^2, etc. sb nt fL L asb
Luminous efficacy	K	$K = \Phi_v/\Phi_e$	‡lumen per watt	lm/W
Luminous efficiency	V	$V = K/K_{maximum}$ ($K_{maximum}$ = maximum value of $K(\lambda)$ function)	one (numeric)	—

ILLUMINATION CONVERSION FACTORS

1 lumen = 1/680 lightwatt (sec 3.7.2)	1 watt-second = 1 joule = 10^7 ergs
1 lumen-hour = 60 lumen-minutes	1 phot = 1 lumen/cm^2
1 footcandle = 1 lumen/ft^2	1 lux = 1 lumen/m^2

Number of →
Multiplied by ↘

Equals Number of ↓	Footcandles	*Lux	Phots	Milliphots
Footcandles	1	0.0929	929	0.929
*Lux	10.76	1	10,000	10
Phot	0.00108	0.0001	1	0.001
Milliphot	1.076	0.1	1,000	1

*The International Standard (SI) unit.

Primary Standard

Wave length of the red cadmium line in air, 760 mm. pressure 15°C. measures of Benoit, Fabry and Perot 1907.

6438.4696 Ångström units

Secondary Standards
Lines of the Iron Arc

Selected lines from list by Ch. Fabry: *International Critical Tables*, 1929
Wave lengths in international Ångströms, atmospheric pressure, 15°C

Wave-length	Wave-length	Wave-length	Wave-length	Wave-length
3370.789	3935.816	4592.655	5232.948	6065.489
3399.337	3977.744	4602.945	5266.564	6137.697
3485.343	4021.870	4647.437	5371.493	6191.563
3513.821	4076.638	4691.414	5405.779	6230.729
3556.882	4118.549	4707.282	5434.527	6265.141
3606.682	4134.680	4736.782	5455.613	6318.023
3640.392	4147.673	4789.654	5497.520	6335.338
3676.314	4191.436	4878.219	5506.783	6393.606
3677.630	4233.609	4903.318	5569.626	6430.852
3724.381	4282.406	4919.001	5586.763	6494.985
3753.615	4315.087	5001.872	5615.652	6546.245
3805.346	4375.933	5012.072	5658.825	6592.920
3843.261	4427.313	5049.825	5709.396	6677.994
3850.820	4466.556	5083.343	5763.013	6750.157
3865.527	4494.568	5110.414	5857.759 Ni	
3906.482	4531.152	5167.491	5892.882 Ni	
3907.937	4547.851	5192.353	6027.058	

Iron, Wave Lengths in the Ultraviolet Spectrum

The following table presents the results of interferometer measurements made by Meggers and Humphreys and reported in the Jour. Research of B. of S. **18**, 543, 1937. The standard iron arc was used as a source and the wave lengths in air at 15°C. and 76 mm are given in international Ångströms.

λair A	λair A	λair A	λair A
2100.795	2265.053	2404.430	2735.473
2102.349	2270.8601	2406.6593	2739.5467
2108.955	2271.781	2410.5172	2746.4833
2110.233	2272.0670	2411.0663	2746.9823
2112.966	2274.0085	2413.3087	2749.325
2115.168	2276.0247	2431.025	2755.7366
2130.962	2277.098	2438.1811	2763.1078
2132.015	2279.922	2442.5674	2767.5208
2135.957	2283.653	2443.8707	2778.2205
2138.589	2284.087	2447.7086	2781.8347
2139.695	2287.2477	2453.4746	2797.7751
2141.715	2287.632	2457.5956	2804.5200
2145.188	2291.122	2465.1479	2806.9840
2147.787	2292.5227	2468.8782	2813.2861
2150.182	2293.8454	2474.8131	2823.2753
2151.099	2294.4059	2487.0643	2832.4350
2153.004	2296.9247	2496.5324	2838.1193
2154.458	2297.785	2507.8987	2845.5945
2157.792	2299.2180	2519.6279	2851.7970
2161.577	2300.1397	2530.6938	2863.864
2163.368	2301.6818	2542.1007	2869.3075
2163.860	2303.4225	2551.0936	2874.1722
2164.547	2303.579	2562.5348	2877.3005
2165.861	2308.9971	2575.7442	2894.5050
2172.581	2313.1022	2576.1033	2895.0352
2173.212	2320.3561	2584.5349	2899.4156
2176.837	2327.3940	2585.8753	2912.1581
2180.866	2331.3067	2598.3689	2920.6906
2183.979	2332.7972	2611.8725	2929.0081
2186.890	2338.0052	2613.8240	2941.3430
2187.192	2344.2802	2617.6160	2953.9400
2191.202	2354.8888	2621.6690	2957.3654
2196.040	2359.1039	2625.6663	2959.9924
2200.7227	2359.997	2628.2923	2965.2551
2201.117	2360.294	2635.8082	2981.4448
2207.068	2362.019	2643.9972	2987.2919
2210.686	2364.8269	2647.5576	2990.3923
2211.234	2366.592	2651.7059	2999.5123
2228.1704	2368.595	2662.0563	3003.0311
2231.211	2370.497	2673.2127	3009.5698
2240.627	2371.4285	2679.0608	3015.9129
2245.651	2374.517	2689.2117	3024.0330
2248.858	2375.193	2699.1060	3030.1491
2249.177	2379.2756	2706.5812	3037.3891
2253.1251	2380.7591	2711.6548	3040.4281
2255.861	2384.386	2714.413	3047.6059
2259.511	2388.6270	2718.4352	3055.2631
2260.079	2389.9713	2723.5770	3057.4452
2264.3894	2399.2396	2727.540	3059.0874

Iron, Wave Lengths in the Ultraviolet Spectrum (Continued)

λair A	λair A	λair A	λair A
3067.2433	3196.9288	3284.5892	3383.9808
3075.7204	3200.4741	3286.7538	3396.9772
3083.7419	3205.3992	3298.1328	3399.3343
3091.5777	3215.9398	3305.971	3401.5196
3116.6329	3217.3796	3306.356	3407.4608
3125.653	3222.0682	3314.7421	3413.1335
3134.1113	3225.7883	3323.7374	3427.1207
3143.9896	3236.2226	3328.8669	3443.8774
3157.0388	3239.4362	3337.6655	3445.1506
3160.6582	3244.1887	3340.5659	3465.8622
3175.4465	3254.3628	3347.9262	3476.7035
3178.0137	3257.5937	3355.2285	3485.3415
3184.8948	3271.0014	3370.7845	3490.5746
3191.6583	3280.2613	3380.1111	3497.8418

Iron, Wave Lengths in the Infrared

From interferometer measurements by Meggers. Jour. Research of B. of S. **14**, 33. 1935. The integrated light from the iron arc was used as a source. Wave lengths in air at 15°C and 760 mm are given as well as the intensity.

λair A	Intensity	λair A	Intensity	λair A	Intensity
7164.469	250	8096.874	10	8866.961	60
7187.341	800	8198.951	80	8945.204	10 n
7207.406	500	8207.767	40	8975.408	10
7389.425	80	8220.406	1500	8999.561	200
7401.689	4	8232.347	50	9012.098	10
7411.178	100	8239.130	8	9079.599	4
7418.674	5	8248.151	30	9088.326	50
7445.776	200	8293.527	20	9089.413	30
7495.088	400	8327.063	1200	9118.888	25
7511.045	800	8331.941	200	9147.800	2 n
7531.171	60	8339.431	80	9210.030	6
7568.925	30	8360.822	8	9258.30	10 n
7583.796	50	8365.642	25	9350.46	6
7586.044	150	8387.781	1200	9359.420	3
7620.538	25	8439.603	20	9362.370	4
7661.223	30	8468.413	300	9372.900	6
7664.302	80	8514.075	150	9430.08	3
7710.390	25	8526.685	8	9513.24	8 n
7748.281	125	8582.267	15	9569.960	15 n
7780.586	300	8611.807	40	9626.562	12 n
7832.224	400	8621.612	10	9653.143	15
7912.866	6	8661.908	600	9738.624	100
7937.166	700	8674.751	60	9753.129	10
7945.878	600	8688.633	1500	9763.450	10
7994.473	20	8757.192	25	9763.913	12
7998.972	700	8764.000	20 n	9800.335	8 n
8028.341	50	8793.376	25 n	9861.793	12
8046.073	600	8804.624	......	9889.082	15
8080.668	10 n	8824.227	250	10065.080	30
8085.200	500	8838.433	30	10145.601	40
				10216.351	50

Helium

Merrill, Bulletin 14, Bureau of Standards 1917.

λair	λair	λair	λair
2945.104	3888.646	4387.928	5047.736
3187.743	3964.727	4471.479	5875.620
3613.641	4026.189	4713.143	6678.149
3705.003	4120.812	4921.928	7065.188
3819.606	4143.759	5015.675	7281.349

From Meggers and Humphreys, Jour. Research of B. of S. **13**, 293. 1934.

λair A	λair A	λair A	λair A
10829.081	10830.250	10830.341	....

Neon

From Meggers and Humphreys, Jour. Research of B. of S. **13**, 293, 1934. The source was an "end on" Geissler tube. Values are given for the wave length in air at 15°C and 760 mm pressure, and referred to the primary standard (Cd 6438.4696 A) and also to the red lines of neon. For complex lines the value for the principal component is given.

λair A Ne Std.	λair A Cd Std.	λair A Ne Std.	λair A Cd Std	λair A Ne Std	λair A Cd Std
		4865.505		5906.429	
4334.125		4866.476	....	5913.633	
4363.524	......	4884.915	....		5944.8340
4381.220	......	4892.090	....		
4395.556	......	4928.235	....	5965.474	
4422.519	......	4939.041	....	5974.628	
4424.800	......	4944.987	....		5975.5345
4425.490	......	4957.0334	....	5987.9069	
4433.721	......	4957.122	....		6029.9968
4460.175	......	4994.930	....		6074.3376
4466.807	......	5005.160	....		6096.1630
4475.556	......	5011.003	....	6128.4513	6128.4502
4483.190	......	5022.870	....		6143.0627
4488.0928	......	5031.3484	....		6163.5937
4500.182	......	5037.7505	....	6182.146	
4517.736	......	5074.200	....		6217.2812
4525.764	......	5080.383	....		6266.4952
4537.751	......	5104.705	....		6304.7893
4540.376	......	5113.675	....		6334.4276
4552.598	......	5116.503	5116.501		6382.9914
4565.888	......	5122.257	....	6402.247	6402.248
4573.759	......	5144.9376	....		6506.5277
4575.060	......	5151.963	....		6532.8824
4582.035	......	5154.422	....		6598.9528
4582.450	......	5156.664	....		6678.2766
4609.910	......	5188.612	....		6717.0430
4614.391	......	5193.130	....		6929.4679
4617.837	......	5193.224	....	7024.0508	
4628.309	......	5203.8950	....	7032.4134	7032.4125
4630.125	......	5208.863	....	7059.109	7059.108
4636.634	......	5210.573	....	7173.9389	7173.9390
4645.416	......	5222.351	....	7245.1668	7245.1668
4649.904	......	5234.028	....	7438.8990	7438.8988
4656.3923	......	5298.190	....	7488.8722	7488.8717
4661.104	......	5304.756	....	7535.7750	7535.774
4670.884	......	5326.396	....	7544.046	
4678.218	......	5330.7766	5330.779	7943.1802	7943.1802
4679.135	......	5341.091	5341.093	8082.4580	8082.4585
4687.671	......	5343.284	....	8118.5495	8118.549
4704.395	......	5355.422	....	8136.4060	8136.4058
4708.854	......	5360.012	....	8259.380	....
4715.344	......	5374.975	....	8266.076	8266.077
4725.145	......	5400.5619	5400.5620	8300.3258	8300.3257
4749.572	......	5433.649	....	8377.6068	8377.6070
4752.7313	......	5448.508	....	8418.4274	8418.4275
4758.728	......	5562.769	....	8495.3600	8495.3604
4780.338	......	5656.6585	....	8591.2584	8591.2585
4788.9258	......	5662.547	....	8634.6480	8634.649
4790.218	......	5689.8164	5689.817	8654.3835	8654.383
4800.111	......	5719.2254	5719.224	8679.491	....
4810.0625	......	5748.299	5748.298	8681.920	....
4817.030	......	5764.418	5764.4182	8780.6223	8780.6220
4821.924	......	5804.4488	5804.450	8783.755	8783.755
4827.338	......	5820.1548	5820.1553	8853.867	8853.864
4827.587	......		5852.4878	8865.759	....
4837.3118	......	5872.828	....	9486.680	....
4852.655	......	....	5881.8950	9535.167	....
4863.074	......	5902.464	5902.4634	9665.424	....

Neon₁, Ultraviolet Lines

From Humphreys, Jour. Research of B. of S. **20**, 17, 1938. The source was an "end on" Geissler tube. Values are given for the wave length in dry air at 15°C and 760 mm of Hg pressure and referred to the Krypton secondary standards.

λair A	λair A	λair A	λair A
3369.8086	3450.7653	3501.2165	3609.1793
3369.9081	3454.1952	3510.7214	3633.6646
3375.6498	3460.5245	3515.1908	3682.2428
3417.9036	3464.3389	3520.4717	3685.7359
3418.0066	3466.5786	3593.5259	3701.2250
3423.9127	3472.5711	3593.6398	3754.2160
3447.7029	3498.0644	3600.1693	

Argon

From Meggers and Humphreys, Jour. Research of B. of S. **13**, 293, 1934.

λair A Ne Std.	λair A Cd Std.	λair A Ne Std.	λair A Cd Std.	λair A Ne Std.	λair A Cd Std.
3948.977		4887.9465		7030.262	
4044.4173	....	5162.2845		7067.2170	7067.2177
4054.5250	....	5187.7458		7147.0406	7147.0412
4158.5896	4158.5895	5221.270		7272.9357	7272.9356
4164.1788	4164.1789	5252.786		7372.117	
4181.8826	4181.8825	5421.346		7383.9800	7383.9800
	4190.7098	5451.650		7503.8676	7503.8667
	4191.0270	5495.8720		7514.6510	7514.653
4198.316	4198.3160	5506.112		7635.1053	7635.1055
4200.674	4200.6738	5558.702		7723.7597	7723.761
4251.1842		5572.548		7724.2064	7724.206
4259.3603	4259.3607	5606.732		7891.075	
4266.2853	4266.2855	5650.7034		7948.1754	7948.1756
4272.1680	4272.1678	5739.517		8006.1556	8006.155
4300.0995	4300.1000	5834.263		8014.7856	8014.785
4333.5595	4333.5601	5860.315		8053.307	
4335.3370	4335.3363	5888.592		8103.6922	8103.6922
4345.1666		5912.084		8115.3115	8115.3095
4363.7936		5928.805		8264.5209	8264.5210
4423.9936		6032.124		8408.208	8408.207
4510.7322	4510.7324	6043.230		8424.647	8424.646
4522.3216		6052.721		8521.4407	8521.4406
4589.2884		6059.373		8667.9430	8667.9435
4596.0964		6105.645		9122.9660	9122.9664
4628.4398		6170.183		9224.498	9224.498
4702.3151		6173.106		9354.218	....
4752.9381		6416.315		9657.7841	....
4768.6716		6752.832		9784.5010	....
4876.2596		6965.4302	6965.4304	10470.051	....

Argon₁

From Humphreys, Jour. Research of B. of S. **20**, 17, 1938. The source was an "end on" Geissler tube. Values are given for the wave length in dry air at 15°C and 760 mm of Hg pressure, referred to the Krypton secondary standards.

λair A	λair A	λair A	λair A
3319.3446	3690.8957	4158.5006	4272.1690
3373.481	3770.3688	4164.1800	4300.1011
3393.7517	3781.3609	4181.8838	4333.5612
3461.0780	3834.6785	4190.7127	4335.3380
3554.3061	3894.6602	4191.0296	4345.1682
3567.6565	3947.5043	4198.3170	4510.7333
3606.5224	3948.9788	4200.6751	4522.3238
3632.6837	4044.4182	4251.1852	4596.0970
3634.4605	4045.9658	4259.3618	4628.4410
3649.8324	4054.5254	4266.2867	4702.3164

Krypton

Meggers, Journal Optical Society of America, 1921.

λair A	λair A	λair A	λair A
4273.9696	4362.6422	4502.354	6456.290
4282.967	4376.120	4807.065	7587.414
4318.552	4399.969	5562.224	7601.544
4319.580	4453.9174	5570.2872	
4355.478	4463.690	5870.9137	

Krypton₁

From Humphreys, Jour. Research of B. of S. **20**, 17, 1938. The source was the "end on" Geissler tube. Values are given for the wave length in air at 15°C and 760 mm of Hg pressure.

λair A	λair A	λair A	λair A
3424.9433	3615.4755	3796.8839	4184.4726
3431.7217	3628.1570	3800.5437	4263.2881
3434.1423	3632.4896	3812.2155	4302.4455
3495.9900	3665.3259	3837.7028	4410.3685
3502.5537	3668.7363	3837.8162	4416.8838
3503.8981	3679.5609	3845.9778	4418.7626
3511.8963	3679.6111	3982.1699	4425.1908
3522.0747	3698.0459	3991.0707	4550.2085
3530.5116	3773.4241	3991.3581	4812.0307
3540.9538			

Titanium, Vacuum Arc Spectrum   Titanium, Vacuum Arc Spectrum (Continued)

From the measurements by Kiess. Jour. Research of B. of S. **1**, 75. 1928.
Wave lengths in air at 15°C. 760 mm.

λair A	Intensity	λair A	Intensity	λair A	Intensity	λair A	Intensity	λair A	Intensity	λair A	Intensity
2941.995	60 r	3929.875	40	4544.688	30	5689.465	10	5922.112	18	6258.103	40
2948.255	60 r	3947.770	40	4548.764	35	5715.123	9	5937.806	6	6258.706	50
2956.133	70 R	3948.679	60	4549.622	25	5739.464	9	5941.755	12	6261.101	35
3075.225	40	3956.336	60	4552.453	35	5766.330	4 n	5953.162	30	6303.754	10
3078.645	45	3958.206	80	4555.486	30	5774.037	5 n	5965.828	30	6312.240	10
3088.027	50	3962.851	35	4559.920	6	5785.979	5 n	5978.543	25	6336.104	8
3130.804	15	3964.269	35	4563.761	15	5804.265	5 n	5999.668	8	6366.354	8
3148.033	12	3981.761	70 R	4571.971	15	5866.453	35	6064.631	9	6546.276	20
3161.755	20	3989.758	80 R	4599.226	5	5899.295	25	6085.228	20	6554.226	30
3168.519	30	3998.635	100 R	4617.269	30	5903.317	5	6091.175	20	6556.066	25
3186.451	60 r	4008.926	35	4623.098	25	5918.548	10	6126.217	20	6743.124	10
3190.801	20	4013.587	12 n	4629.336	15						
3191.994	80 R	4015.377	12 n	4645.193	12						
3199.915	100 R	4017.771	15 n	4656.468	25						
3202.535	12	4024.573	35	4667.585	25						
3214.240	12	4026.539	25 n	4675.118	10						
3217.056	15	4030.512	25 n	4681.908	30						
3222.843	15	4035.828	10	4691.336	20						
3229.397	10	4055.011	20	4698.766	20						
3234.517	60	4058.139	7	4710.186	18						
3236.573	50	4060.263	20	4715.295	4						
3239.037	40	4065.094	15	4731.172	9						
3241.984	40	4078.471	30	4742.791	20						
3261.596	25	4082.456	20	4758.120	25						
3287.657	10	4099.166	8	4759.272	25						
3292.078	20	4112.708	20	4778.259	10						
3314.422	10	4122.143	10	4792.482	10						
3318.024	8	4127.531	15	4799.797	12						
3322.936	20	4137.284	10 n	4805.416	12						
3326.762	5	4150.963	10	4820.410	20						
3329.455	20	4159.634	9	4840.874	25						
3332.111	8	4163.644	8	4856.012	20						
3335.192	20	4171.897	5	4868.264	18						
3340.344	15	4186.119	25	4870.129	20						
3341.875	50 r	4237.889	7	4885.082	20						
3349.399	40	4249.114	5 n	4899.910	20						
3354.634	60 r	4256.025	8 n	4913.616	20						
3358.271	10	4258.523	4 n	4919.867	10						
3361.213	40	4263.134	15	4921.768	12						
3370.436	40 r	4274.584	15	4928.342	12						
3371.447	80 R	4281.371	10	4938.283	8						
3377.577	30 r	4282.702	12	4975.344	10						
3380.278	15	4286.006	25	4978.191	10						
3383.761	40	4287.405	22	4981.732	60						
3385.944	40 r	4289.068	25	4991.067	50						
3387.834	15	4294.101	8	4997.099	8						
3394.574	15	4295.751	22	4999.504	45						
3444.306	15	4298.664	40	5007.209	40						
3461.496	20	4305.910	60	5009.652	7						
3477.181	15	4307.900	12	5014.185	25						
3480.525	12	4312.861	7	5014.277	25						
3491.053	8	4314.801	25	5016.162	20						
3504.890	8	4318.631	10 n	5020.028	25						
3510.840	10	4321.655	8 n	5022.871	25						
3535.408	10	4325.134	9 n	5024.842	20						
3547.029	15	4337.916	10	5025.570	18						
3596.048	10	4346.104	5	5035.908	25						
3598.714	15	4360.487	4	5036.468	25						
3610.154	12	4369.682	5 n	5038.400	25						
3624.826	8	4372.383	3	5039.959	22						
3635.462	80 r	4393.325	8	5052.879	8						
3641.330	10	4395.031	25	5062.112	7						
3642.675	80 r	4399.767	6	5064.654	25						
3646.198	12	4417.274	15	5087.055	8						
3653.497	100 r	4421.754	6	5113.448	10						
3654.592	15	4422.823	10	5120.420	12						
3658.097	20	4426.054	10	5145.465	12						
3660.631	12	4427.098	40	5147.483	10						
3668.965	15	4430.366	7	5173.742	30						
3671.672	20	4434.003	15	5192.971	35						
3685.192	40	4436.586	4	5210.386	40						
3689.916	15	4440.345	10	5224.301	15						
3694.445	10	4443.802	25	5224.928	8						
3717.393	20	4449.143	30	5265.967	10						
3722.568	15	4450.896	25	5283.441	8						
3724.570	20	4453.312	30	5295.781	4						
3725.155	20	4453.708	20	5297.236	6						
3729.806	50 r	4455.321	30	5298.429	4						
3741.059	60 r	4457.428	40	5369.635	4						
3752.860	80 r	4465.807	20	5389.996	3						
3759.291	40	4468.493	25	5397.093	4						
3761.320	40	4471.238	20	5409.609	6						
3771.652	25	4474.852	8	5429.139	6						
3786.043	20	4481.261	30	5477.695	8						
3798.276	6	4482.688	10	5481.426	6						
3866.446	15 n	4489.089	20	5488.210	5						
3875.262	20 n	4496.146	20	5490.151	12						
3895.243	30 n	4501.270	25	5503.897	8						
3900.546	50	4503.762	4 n	5512.529	25						
3904.785	40 n	4512.734	40	5565.476	9						
3913.464	40	4518.022	50	5644.137	18						
3914.334	35	4522.798	40	5648.570	5						
3921.423	30	4527.305	35	5662.154	12						
3924.527	50	4533.238	80	5675.413	9						

Xenon

Meggers. Journal Optical Society of America. 1921

λair	λair	λair
4500.978	4624.275	4807.019
4524.680	4671.225	4829.705
4582.746	4697.020	4844.333
4603.028	4734.154	4923.246

Wave Lengths in the Vacuum Ultraviolet

J. C. Boyce, Rev. Med. Phys. 13, 34, (1941)

Copper (Shenstone, 1936)

λA	Intensity	P.E. in .001 A	λA	Intensity	P.E. in .001 A	λA	Intensity	P.E. in .001 A
685.139	8	2	1065.781	20	1	1393.126	10	2
685.396	2	2	1066.133	20	2	1399.355	3	2
724.487	15	2	1069.193	50	2	1402.776	15	2
735.519	20	2	1088.393	20	2	1442.136	15	2
736.031	25	2	1106.446	3	2	1444.131	2	2
810.997	15	2	1109.742	1	2	1473.976	25	2
813.882	20	2	1185.899	2	2	1496.686	35	4
826.995	30	2	1214.553	1	2	1517.630	20	2
866.440	5	2	1219.332	1	2	1519.491	50	2
876.719	20	2	1241.961	2	1	1535.004	25	2
883.837	5	2	1248.790	5	2	1540.391	30	2
884.824	5	2	1250.045	10	2	1541.701	75	2
911.654	1	2	1265.504	15	1	1558.344	30	2
912.022	0	2	1266.308	10	1	1565.925	40	2
992.951	25	1	1274.069	3	2	1566.411	40	2
1001.010	8	1	1274.463	3	2	1569.216	10	2
1004.053	30	1	1275.570	30	2	1590.164	40	3
1008.568	30	1	1281.458	8	4	1593.557	60	3
1011.433	2	1	1297.549	2	2	1598.402	40	3
1012.595	25	1	1298.394	15	2	1602.387	40	3
1018.705	20	1	1299.267	10	2	1604.848	20	3
1019.652	15	1	1308.296	30	2	1606.834	40	3
1022.100	5	1	1309.463	15	2	1608.638	25	3
1027.830	50	1	1314.147	15	2	1610.298	15	3
1028.326	25	1	1314.335	30	2	1617.914	20	3
1031.764	8	1	1325.511	3	2	1621.426	60	3
1035.160	8	1	1326.394	10	2	1649.457	25	3
1036.468	60	1	1350.592	15	2	1656.326	20	3
1039.345	60	2	1351.837	25	2	1660.005	20	3
1044.742	80	1	1355.304	15	2	1663.003	30	3
1049.363	20	2	1359.010	20	2	1944.586	25	4
1049.754	50	1	1359.935	5	2	1970.489	15	4
1054.690	60	1	1362.598	20	2	1979.947	50	4
1055.795	40	2	1363.501	5	2	1989.849	30	4
1058.796	40	2	1370.558	2	2	2000.339	60	4
1059.094	60	1	1371.840	20	2			

Iron (Green, 1939)

λA	Schüler tube	Spark	λA	Schüler tube	Spark	λA	Schüler tube	Spark
1550.273	1	..	1570.244	20	1	1584.949	15	
1559.084	20	2	1572.754	1	..	1612.805	20	8
1563.788	25	2	1573.826	5	..	1623.090	8	1
1566.821	20	1	1574.769	0	..	1625.520	20	8
1568.017	8	..	1574.921	20	1	1632.665	1	2
1569.674	12	..	1577.167	1	..	1633.906	15	2

λA	Schüler tube	Spark	λA	Schüler tube	Spark
1637.398	15	2	1702.044	25	25
1640.150	12	2	1709.551	0	..
1643.576	15	2	1712.998	20	25
1652.482	0	..	1718.100	2	..
1654.476	5	1	1720.611	20	20
1658.771	15	2	1724.962	8	1
1659.479	20	10	1726.391	12	8
1663.220	15	2	1815.411	0	1
1670.990	1	..	1818.516	2	1
1674.254	2	1	1826.994	1	1
1676.854	1	..	1833.073	0	..
1685.952	5	1	1842.283	0	..
1686.454	8	1	1848.771	12	2
1691.272	8	1	1851.526	1	..
1693.475	0	..	1859.744	15	10
1693.935	0	..	1898.535	10	2
1696.794	8	..	1903.384	1	..
1699.195	2	..	1904.785	15	5
			2001.025	30	30

Hydrogen (Paschen, 1929)

λA	λA
923.148	949.739
926.222	972.532
930.745	1025.717
937.799	1215.664

Helium (He II)(Paschen, 1929)

λA	λA	λA
234.3452	949.326	1084.940
237.3297	958.696	1215.129
243.0244	972.109	1640.409
256.3145	992.361	
303.7788	1025.270	

Carbon, Nitrogen, Oxygen (More and Rieke, 1936)

El.	λA	Int.	El.	λA	Int.	El.	λA	Int.
O II	832.764	0	N I	1176.502	1	C II	1335.703	18d
O II	833.332	1	N I	1199.550	7	N I	1494.670	4
O II	834.467	2	N I	1200.218	6	C I	1560.313	8d
O I	990.205	4d	N I	1200.707	5	C I	1560.702	15d
O I	990.794	3	O I	1217.643	2	C I	1656.271	8d
O I	999.493	2	O I	1302.174	8	C I	1656.994	15d
N II	1083.996	2	O I	1304.858	8	C I	1657.388	5d
N II	1084.582	3	O I	1306.023	6	C I	1657.908	8d
N I	1134.168	3	C I	1328.820	3	C I	1658.135	8d
N I	1134.417	3	C I	1329.099	5			
N I	1134.979	4	C II	1334.534	15d			

PERSISTENT LINES OF THE ELEMENTS

Spectra of the neutral atom, the singly ionized atom, and the doubly ionized atom are indicated by I, II, and III, respectively. The most sensitive lines are indicated by an asterisk (*). The symbol "D" preceding the intensity indicates the discharge-tube spectrum. Wave lengths are given in International Ångstrom units.
Wave lengths and intensities of lines between 2000 and 9000 ångstroms have been given according to the M.I.T. Wavelength Tables.

'ARRANGED BY ELEMENTS

Element	Wave length	Arc	Spark	Element	Wave length	Arc	Spark
A I	*1048.28			Al I	*2437.791	60	500
	1066.70				3082.155	800	800
	6965.430	....	D 400		3092.713	1000	1000
	7067.217	....	D 400		3944.032	2000	1000
	7500.067	....	D 700		*3961.527	5000	5000
	8115.311	....	D 5000	Al II	1671.0		
Ag I	*3280.683	2000	1000		1856.00		
	3382.891	1000	700		1858.13		
	5209.067	1500	1000		1862.48		
	5465.487	1000	500		2631.553	....	40
Ag II	2246.412	25	300		*2669.166	3	100

Element	Wave length	Arc	Spark	Element	Wave length	Arc	Spark
Al II	2816.179	10	100	Cd II	2265.017	25	300
	6231.76	....	30		2312.84	1	200
	6243.36	....	100		2573.09	3	150
Al III	1854.67				2748.58	5	200
	1862.90			Ce II	4012.388	60	20
As I	1889.9				4040.762	70	5
	*1890.5				4165.606	40	6
	1936.9				*4186.599	80	25
	1972.0			Cl I	1379.6		
	2288.12	250	5		1396.5		
	2349.84	250	18	Cl II	4794.54	....	D 250
	2309.07	40			4810.00	....	D 200
	2370.77	50	3		4819.46	....	D 200
	2456.53	100	8	Co I	*3453.505	3000	200
	2780.197	75	75		3465.800	2000	25
	2860.452	50	50		3529.813	1000	30
	2898.71	25	40	Co II	*2286.156	40	300
Au I	*2427.95	400	100		2307.857	25	50
	2675.95	250	100		2363.787	25	50
	2802.19	....	200		2378.622	25	50
B I	2496.778	300	300		2388.918	10	35
	*2497.733	500	400		2519.822	40	200
B II	1362.46			Cr I	3405.120	2000	150
	3451.41	5	30		*4254.346	5000	1000
	3452.33				4274.803	4000	800
Ba I	3071.591	100	50		4289.721	3000	800
	5424.616	100	30		5204.518	400	100
	5519.115	200	60		5206.039	500	200
	*5535.551	1000	200		5208.436	500	100
	5777.665	500	100	Cr II	*2835.633	100	400
Ba II	2304.235	60	80		2843.252	125	400
	2335.269	60	100		2849.838	80	150
	3891.785	18	25		2855.670	60	200
	4130.664	50	60		2860.934	60	100
	*4554.042	1000	200	Cs I	4555.355	2000	100
	4934.086	400	400		4593.177	1000	50
Be I	*2348.610	2000	50		*8521.10	5000	
	2650.781	25			8943.50	2000	
	3321.013	50		Cu I	*3247.540	5000	2000
	3321.086	100			3273.962	3000	1500
	3321.343	1000	30		5105.541	500	
Be II	*3130.416	200	200		5153.235	600	
	3131.072	200	150		5218.202	700	
Bi I	2061.70	300	100	Cu II	*2135.976	25	500
	2276.578	100	40		2192.260	25	500
	2780.521	200	100		2246.995	30	500
	2809.625	200	100	Dy I	4000.454	400	300
	2897.975	500	500		4045.983	150	12
	2938.298	300	300	Dy I	4077.974	150	100
	2989.029	250	100		4167.966	50	12
	*3067.716	3000	2000		4211.719	200	15
	4722.552	1000	100	Er I	3499.104	18	15
Bi II	1909.41				3692.652	20	12
Br I	1540.8				3906.316	25	12
	1633.8			Eu I	*4594.02		
Br II	*4704.86	....	D 250	Eu II	4129.737	150	50
	4785.50	....	D 400		*4205.046	200	50
	4816.71	....	D 300	F I	6856.02	....	D 1000
C I	*2478.573	400	D 400		6902.46	....	D 500
C II	1334.54			Fe I	3581.20		
	1335.72				*3719.935	1000	700
	2836.710	....	200		3737.133	1000	600
	2837.602	....	40		3745.564	500	500
	4267.02	....	350		3745.903	150	100
	4267.27	....	500		3748.264	500	200
C III	2296.89	....	200	Fe II	*2382.039	40	100
Ca I	*4226.728	500	50		2395.625	50	100
	4425.441	100			2404.882	50	100
	4434.960	150			2410.517	50	70
	4454.781	200			2413.309	60	100
	4455.880			Ga I	2874.244	10	15
	4456.62				2943.637	10	20
Ca II	3158.869	100	300		4032.982	1000	500
	3179.332	100	400		*4172.056	2000	1000
	*3933.666	600	600	Gd I	3646.196	200	150
	3968.468	500	500		3768.405	20	20
Cb I	4058.938	1000	400	Ge I	*2651.178	40	20
	4079.729	500	200		2651.575	30	20
	4100.923	300	200		2709.626	30	20
	4123.810	200	125		3039.064	1000	1000
	4137.095	100	60		3269.494	300	300
Cb II	3094.183	100	1000		4226.570	200	50
	3130.786	100	100	H I	1215.7		
	3163.402	15	8		4861.327	....	D 500
	3194.977	30	300		6562.79	....	D 3000
	3225.479	150	800	He I	584.4		
Cd I	3261.057	300	300		*.....440		D 1000
	3403.653	800	500		5875.618	....	D 1000
	3466.201	1000	500	He II	303.8		
	3610.510	1000	500		1640.5		
	6438.4696	2000	1000		4685.75	....	D 300
Cd II	*2144.382	50	200	Hf I	2898.259	50	12
					2904.408	30	6

Element	Wave length	Arc	Spark
Hf I	2916.481	50	15
	2940.772	60	12
	3072.877	80	18
	4093.161	25	20
Hf II	2513.028	25	70
	2516.881	35	100
	*2641.406	40	125
	2773.357	25	60
	2820.224	40	100
	3134.718	80	125
Hg I	*1849.68		
	2536.519	2000	1000
	3650.146	200	500
	3654.833	....	D 200
Hg I	3663.276	500	400
	4046.561	200	300
	4358.35	3000	500
	5460.740	....	D 2000
Hg II	1649.8		
	1942.3		
Ho I	3748 17	60	40
	3891.02	200	40
Ho II	2936.77	....	1000
I I	1782.9		
	2062.38	...	D 900
I II	5161.188	....	D 300
	5464 61	....	D 900
In I	3039.356	1000	500
	3256 090	1500	600
	3258.564	500	300
	4101.773	2000	1000
	*4511.323	5000	4000
Ir I	2543.97		
	2849.725	40	20
	2924.792	25	15
	*3220.780	100	30
	3437.015	20	15
	3513.645	100	100
K I	4044.140	800	400
	4047.201	400	200
	*7664.907	9000	
	7698.979	5000	
Kr I	5570.2895	....	D 2000
	5870.9158	....	D 3000
La I	5455.146	200	1
	5930.648	250	
	*6249.929	300	
La II	*3949.106	1000	800
	4077.340	600	400
	4123.228	500	500
Li I	3232.61	1000	500
	4603.00	800	
	6103.642	2000	300
	*6707.844	3000	200
Lu I	4518.57	300	40
Lu II	*2615.43		
	2894.84	60	200
	2911.39	100	300
	3397.07	50	20
	3472.48	50	150
	3554.43	50	150
Mg I	*2852.129	300	100
	3829.350	100	150
	3832.306	250	200
	3838.258	300	200
	5167.343	100	50
	5172.699	200	100
	5183.618	500	300
Mg II	*2795.53	150	300
	2802.695	150	300
Mn I	*4030.755	500	20
	4033.073	400	20
	4034.490	250	20
Mn II	*2576.104	300	2000
	2593.729	200	1000
	2605.688	100	500
Mo I	*3798.252	1000	1000
	3864.110	1000	500
	3902.963	1000	500
Mo II	*2816.154	200	300
	2848.232	125	200
	2871.508	100	100
	2890.994	30	50
	2909.116	25	40
N I	1199.5		
	1200.2		
	1200.7		
	*4099.94	....	D 150
	4109.98	....	D 1000
N II	5666.64	....	D 300
	5676.02	....	D 100
	5679.56	....	D 500
N III	989.8		

Element	Wave length	Arc	Spark
N III	991.6		
	4097.31	....	D 100
	4103.37	....	D 80
Na I	3302.323	600	300
	3302.988	300	150
	5682.657	80	
	5688.224	300	
	*5889.953	9000	1000
	5895.923	5000	500
Nd I	3951.154	40	30
	4177.321	15	25
	*4303.573	100	40
Ne I	735.95		
	743.73		
	5400.562	....	D 2000
	5832.488		
	5852.488	....	D 2000
	6402.246	....	D 2000
Ni I	*3414.765	1000	50
	3492.956	1000	100
	3515.054	1000	50
	3524.541	1000	100
Ni II	2216.47		
	2253.86	100	300
	2264.457	150	400
	2270.213	100	400
	*2287.084	100	500
O I	1302.27		
	1304.96		
	1306.12		
	*7771.928	....	D 1000
	7774.138	....	D 300
	7775.433	....	D 100
Os I	*2909.061	500	400
	3058.66	500	500
	3262.290	500	50
	3267.945	400	30
	3301.56		
	3752.54		
Os I	3782.20		
	4420.468	400	100
P I	1774.8		
	1782.7		
	1787.5		
	2136.8		
	2149.8		
	2534.01	50	D 20
	2535.65	100	D 30
	2536.38		
	2553.28	80	D 20
	2554.02		
	2554.93	60	D 20
Pb I	2169.994	1000	1000
	2614.178	200	80
	2833.069	500	80
	3639.580	300	50
	3683.471	300	50
	*4057.820	2000	300
Pb II	1682.4		
	*2203.505	50	5000
	5608.8	....	D 40
Pd I	*3404.580	2000	1000
	3421.24	2000	1000
	3516.943	1000	500
	3609.548	1000	700
	3634.695	2000	1000
Pd II	*2296.53		
	2488.921	10	30
	2498.784	4	150
	2505.739	3	30
	2658.722	20	300
	2854.581	4	500
Pr I	4062.817	150	50
Pr II	*4179.422	200	40
	4189.518	100	50
	4225.327	50	40
Pt I	2659.454	2000	500
	2830.295	1000	600
	2929.794	800	200
	2997.967	1000	200
	*3064.712	2000	300
Ra I	*4825.91	....	D
Ra II	*3814.42	....	D 2000
	4682.28	....	D 800
Rb I	4201.851	2000	500
	4215.556	1000	300
	*7800.227	9000	
	7947.60	5000	
Re I	*3460.47	1000	
	4889.17	2000	
Rh I	3323.092	1000	200
	3396.85	1000	500
	*3434.893	1000	200

Element	Wave length	Arc	Spark
Rh I	3657.987	500	200
	3692.357	500	150
Rn I	7055.42	....	D 400
	7450.00	....	D 600
Ru I	3436.737	300	150
	*3498.942	500	200
	3596.179	30	100
Ru II	2678.758	100	300
	2692.065	8	200
	2712.410	80	300
	2945.668	60	300
	2965.546	60	200
	2976.586	60	200
S I	1807.4		
	1820.5		
	1826.4		
	4694.13	....	D 500
	4695.45	....	D 30
	4696.25	....	D 15
	9212.91	....	D 200
	9228.11	....	D 200
	9237.49	....	D 200
Sb I	*2068.38	300	3
	2175.890	300	40
	2311.469	150	50
	2528.535	300	200
	2598.062	200	100
	2877.915	250	150
	3232.499	150	250
	3267.502	150	150
Sc I	3907.476	125	25
	*3911.810	150	30
	4020.399	50	20
	4023.688	100	25
	5671.80		
Sc II	*3613.836	40	70
	3630.740	50	70
	3642.785	60	50
Se I	*1960.2		
	2039.851	....	D 1000
	2062.788	....	D 800
	4730.78	....	D 1000
	4739.03	....	D 800
	4742.25	....	D 500
Si I	2506.899	300	200
	2516.123	500	500
	2528.516	400	500
	*2881.578	500	400
	3905.528	20	15
Si II	1526.83		
	*1533.55		
	*4296.75		
Sm I	3568.27		
Sm II	4390.865	150	150
	*4424.342	300	300
	4434.321	300	200
Sn I	*2839.989	300	300
	2863.327	300	300
	3009.147	300	200
	3034.121	200	150
	3175.019	500	400
	3262.328	400	300
	4524.741	500	50
Sn III	*2152.22		
Sr I	*4607.331	1000	50
	4832.075	200	8
	4872.493	25	
	4962.263	40	
Sr II	3380.711	150	200
	3464 57	200	200
	3474.887	80	50
	*4077.714	400	500
	4215.524	300	400
	4305.447	40	
Ta I	*3311.162	300	70
	3318.840	125	35
	3406.664	70	18
Tb I	3509.17	200	200
	3561.74	200	200
	3848.75	100	200
	3874.18	200	200
Te I	*2142.75	60	
	2383.25	500	D 300
	2385.76	600	D D 300
	2530.70	....	D 30
	2769.67	....	D 30
Th I	3538.75	....	50
	3601.040	8	10
	4019.137	8	8
Th II	3290.59	....	40
Ti I	3635.463	200	100
	3642.675	300	125
	3653.496	500	200

Element	Wave length	Arc	Spark
Ti I	*4981.733	300	125
	4991.066	200	100
	4999.510	200	80
	5007.213	200	40
	5014.25		
Ti II	*3349.035	125	800
	3361.213	100	600
	3372.800	80	400
	3383.761	70	300
Tl I	2767.87	400	300
	2918.32	400	200
	3229.75	2000	800
	3519.24	2000	1000
	3775.72	3000	1000
	*5350.46	5000	2000
Tm I	3462.21	200	100
	3761.333	250	150
	3761.917	200	120
Tm II	*3848.02		
U I	3552.172	8	12
	3672.579	8	15
	4241.669	40	50
V I	3183.406	200	100
	3183.982	500	400
	3185.396	500	400
	*4379.238	200	200
	4384.722	125	125
V I	4389.974	80	60
V II	*3093.108	100	400
	3102.299	70	300
	3110.706	70	300
	3118.383	70	200
	3125.284	80	200
W I	4008.753	45	45
	4294.614	50	50
	*4302.108	60	60
W II	*2204.49		
	2397.091	18	30
	2589.167	15	25
	3215.560	10	9
	3613.790	10	30
Xe I	1295.8		
	1469.9		
	4500.977	....	D 500
	4624.276	....	D 1000
	4671.226	....	D 2000
Y I	4643.695	50	100
	*4674.848	80	100
	5466.47		
Y II	3242.280	60	100
	3600.734	100	300
	3633.123	50	100
	*3710.290	80	150
	3774.332	12	100
	3788.697	30	30
Yb I	3289.37	500	1000
	*3987.994	1000	500
Yb II	*3694.203	500	1000
Zn I	*2138.56	800	500
	3282.333	500	300
	3302.588	800	300
	3345.020	800	300
	4680.138	300	200
	4722.159	400	300
	4810.534	400	300
	6362.347	1000	500
Zn II	*2025.51	200	200
	2061.91	100	100
	2502.001	20	400
	2557.958	10	300
Zr I	3519.605	100	10
	3547.682	200	12
	*3601.193	400	15
	4687.803	125	
	4710.075	60	
	4739.478	100	
	4772.312	100	
	4815.62		
Zr II	*3391.975	300	400
	3438.230	250	200
	3496.210	100	100
	3572.473	60	80

ARRANGED BY WAVE LENGTHS

Wave length	Element	Arc	Spark
303.8	He II		
584.4	He I		
735.95	Ne I		
743.73	Ne I		
989.8	N III		
991.6	N III		
*1048.26	A I		
1066.70	A I		
1199.5	N I		
1200.2	N I		
1200.7	N I		
1215.7	H I		
1295.8	Xe I		
1302.27	O I		
1304.96	O I		
1306.12	O I		
1334.54	C II		
1335.72	C II		
1362.46	B II		
1379.6	Cl I		
1396.5	Cl I		
1469.9	Xe I		
1526.83	Si II		
*1533.55	Si II		
1540.8	Br I		
1633.8	Br I		
1640.5	He II		
1649.8	Hg II		
1671.0	Al II		
1682.4	Pb II		
1774.8	P I		
1782.7	P I		
1782.9	I I		
1787.5	P I		
1807.4	S I		
1820.5	S I		
1826.4	S I		
*1849.6	Hg I		
1854.67	Al III		
1856.00	Al II		
1858.13	Al II		
1862.48	Al II		
1862.90	Al III		
1880.9	As I		
*1890.5	As I		
1909.41	Bi II		
1936.9	As I		
1942.3	Hg II		
*1960.2	Se I		
1972.0	As I		
*2025.51	Zn II	200	200
2039.851	Se I	....	D 1000
2061.70	Bi II	300	100
2061.91	Zn II	100	100
2062.38	I I	....	D 900
2062.788	Se I	....	D 800
*2068.38	Sb I	300	3
*2135.976	Cu II	25	500
2136.8	P I		
2138.56	Zn I	800	500
*2142.75	Te I	60	
*2144.382	Cd II	50	200
2149.8	P I		
*2152.22	Sn II		
2169.994	Pb II	1000	1000
2175.890	Sb I	300	40
2192.260	Cu II	25	500
*2203.505	Pb II	50	5000
2204.49	W II		
2216.47	Ni II		
2246.412	Ag II	25	300
2246.995	Cu II	30	500
2253.86	Ni II	100	300
2264.457	Ni II	150	400
2265.017	Cd II	25	300
2270.213	Ni II	100	300
2276.578	Bi II	100	40
*2286.156	Co II	40	300
*2287.084	Ni II	100	500
*2288.018	Cd I	1500	300
2288.12	As I	250	5
*2296.53	Pd II		
2296.89	C III	....	200
2304.235	Ba II	60	80
2307.857	Co II	25	50
2311.409	Bi I	100	50
2313.84	Cd II	1	200
2335.269	Ba II	60	100
*2348.610	Be II	2000	50
2349.84	As I	250	18
2363.787	Co II	25	50
2369.67	As I	40	
2370.77	As I	50	3
2378.622	Co II	25	50
*2382.039	Fe II	40	100
2383.25	Te I	500	D 300
2385.76	Te I	600	D 300
2388.918	Co II	10	35
2395.625	Fe II	50	100
2397.091	W II	18	30
2404.882	Fe II	50	100
2410.517	Fe II	50	70
2413.309	Fe II	60	100
*2427.95	Au I	400	100
2437.791	Ag II	60	500
2456.53	As I	100	8
*2478.573	C I	400	D 400
2488.921	Pd II	10	30
2496.778	B I	300	300
*2497.733	B I	500	400
2498.784	Pd II	4	150
2502.001	Zn II	20	400
2505.739	Pd II	3	30
2506.899	Si I	300	200
2513.028	Hf II	25	70
2516.123	Si I	500	500
2516.881	Hf II	35	100
2519.822	Co II	40	200
2528.516	Si I	400	500
2528.535	Sb I	300	200
2530.70	Te I	....	D 30
2534.01	P I	50	D 20
2535.65	P I	100	D 30
2536.38	P I		
2536.519	Hg I	2000	1000
2543.97	Ir I		
2553.28	P I	80	D 20
2554.02	P I		
2554.93	P I	60	D 20
2557.958	Zn I	10	300
2573.09	Cd II	3	150
*2576.104	Mn II	300	2000
2589.167	W II	15	25
2593.729	Mn II	200	1000
2598.062	Sb I	200	500
2605.688	Mn II	100	500
2614.178	Pb II	200	80
*2615.43	Lu II		
*2631.553	Al II	....	40
*2641.406	Hf II	40	125
2650.781	Be I	25	
*2651.178	Ge I	40	20
2651.575	Ge I	30	20
2658.722	Pd II	20	300
2659.454	Pt I	2000	300
*2669.166	Al II	3	100
2675.95	Au I	250	100
2678.758	Ru II	100	300
2692.065	Ru II	8	200
2709.626	Ge I	30	20
2712.410	Ru II	80	300
2748.58	Cd II	5	30
2767.87	Tl I	400	300
2769.67	Te I	....	D 30
2773.357	Hf II	25	60
2780.197	As I	75	75
2780.521	Bi I	200	100
*2795.53	Mg II	150	300
2802.19	Au I	....	
2802.695	Mg II	150	300
2809.625	Bi I	200	100
*2816.154	Mo II	200	200
2816.179	Al I	10	100
2820.224	Hf II	40	100
2830.295	Pt I	1000	600
2833.069	Pb I	500	80
*2835.633	Cr II	100	400
2836.710	C II	....	200
2837.602	C II	....	40
*2839.989	Sn I	300	300
2843.252	Cr II	125	400
2848.232	Mo II	125	200
2849.725	Ir I	40	20
2849.838	Cr II	80	150
*2852.129	Mg I	300	
2854.581	Pd II	4	500
2855.676	Cr II	60	200
2860.452	Ag I	50	50
2860.944	Cr II	80	100
2863.327	Sn I	300	300
2871.508	Mo II	100	100
2874.244	Ga I	10	15
2877.915	Sb I	250	150
*2881.578	Si I	500	400
2890.994	Mo II	30	50
2894.84	Lu II	60	200
2897.975	Bi I	500	500
2898.259	Hf I	50	12
2898.71	As I	25	40
2904.408	Hf I	30	6
*2909.061	Os I	500	400
2909.116	Mo II	25	40
2911.39	Lu II	100	300
2916.481	Hf I	50	15
2918.32	Tl I	400	200
2924.792	Ir I	25	15
2929.794	Pt I	800	200
2936.77	Ho II	....	1000
2938.298	Bi I	300	300
2940.772	Hf I	60	12
2943.637	Ga I	10	20
2945.668	Ru II	60	300
2965.546	Ru II	60	200
2976.586	Ru II	60	200
2989.029	Bi I	250	100
2997.967	Pt I	1000	200
3009.147	Sn I	300	200
3034.121	Sn I	200	150
3039.064	Ge I	1000	1000
3039.355	In I	1000	500
3058.66	Os I	500	500
*3064.712	Pt I	2000	300
*3067.716	Bi I	3000	2000
3071.591	Ba I	100	50
3072.877	Hf I	80	18
3082.155	Al I	800	800
3092.713	Al I	1000	1000
*3093.108	V II	100	400
*3094.183	Cb II	100	1000
3102.299	V II	70	300
3110.706	V II	70	300
3118.383	V II	70	200
3125.284	V II	80	200
*3130.416	Be II	200	200
3130.786	Cb II	100	100
3131.072	Be II	200	150
3134.718	Hf II	80	125
3158.869	Ca II	100	300
3163.402	Cb II	15	8
3175.019	Sn I	500	400
3179.332	Ca II	100	400
3183.406	V I	200	100
3183.982	V I	500	400
3185.396	V I	500	400
3194.977	Cb II	30	300
3215.560	W I	10	9
*3220.780	Ir I	100	30
3225.479	Cb II	150	800
3229.75	Tl I	2000	800
3232.499	Sb I	150	250
3232.61	Li I	1000	500
3242.280	Y II	60	100
*3247.540	Cu I	5000	2000
3256.090	In I	1500	600
3258.564	In I	500	300
3261.057	Cd I	300	50
3262.290	Os I	500	50
3262.328	Sn I	400	300
3267.502	Sb I	150	150
3267.945	Os I	400	30
3269.494	Ge I	300	300
3273.962	Cu I	3000	1500
*3280.683	Ag I	2000	1000
3282.333	Zn I	500	300
3289.37	Yb I	500	1000
3290.59	Th II	....	40
3301.56	Os I		
3302.323	Na I	600	300
3302.588	Zn I	800	300
3302.988	Na I	300	150
*3311.162	Ta I	300	70
3318.840	Ta I	125	35
3321.013	Be I	50	
3321.086	Be I	100	
3321.343	Be I	1000	30
3323.092	Rh I	1000	200
3345.020	Zn I	800	300
*3349.035	Ti II	125	800
3361.213	Ti II	100	600
3372.800	Ti II	80	100
3380.711	Sr II	150	200
3382.891	Ag I	1000	700
3383.761	Ti II	70	300
*3391.975	Zr II	300	400
3396.85	Rh I	1000	500
3397.07	Lu II	50	20
3403.653	Cd I	800	500
*3404.580	Pd I	2000	1000
3405.120	Co I	2000	150
3406.664	Ta I	70	18
*3414.765	Ni I	1000	50
3421.24	Pd I	2000	1000
3434.893	Rh I	1000	200
3436.737	Ru I	300	150
3437.015	Ir I	20	15
3438.230	Zr II	250	200
3451.41	B II	5	30
3452.33	B II		
*3453.505	Co I	3000	200
3460.47	Re I	1000	
3462.21	Tm I	200	100
3464.57	Sr II	200	200
3465.800	Co I	2000	25
3466.201	Cd I	1000	500
3472.48	Lu II	50	150
3474.887	Sr II	80	50
3492.956	Ni I	1000	100
3496.210	Zr II	100	100
*3498.942	Ru I	500	200
3499.104	Er I	18	15
3509.17	Tb I	200	200
3513.645	Ir I	100	100
3515.054	Ni I	1000	500
3516.943	Pd I	1000	500
3519.24	Tl I	2000	1000
3519.605	Zr I	100	10
3524.541	Ni I	1000	100
3529.813	Co I	1000	30
3538.75	Th I	....	50
3547.682	Zr I	200	12
3552.172	U I	8	12
3554.43	Lu II	50	150
3561.74	Tb I	200	200
3568.27	Sm II		
3572.473	Zr II	60	80
3581.20	Fe I		
3596.179	Ru I	30	100
3600.734	Y II	100	300
3601.040	Th II	8	10
*3601.103	Zr I	400	15
3609.548	Pd I	1000	700
3610.510	Cd I	1000	500
3613.790	W II	10	30
*3613.836	Sc II	40	70
3630.740	Sc II	50	70
3633.123	Y II	50	100
3634.695	Pd I	2000	1000
3635.463	Ti I	200	100
3639.580	Pb I	300	50
3642.675	Ti I	300	125
3642.785	Sc II	60	50
3646.196	Gd I	200	150
3650.146	Hg I	200	500
3653.496	Hg I	500	200
3654.833	Hg I	....	D 200
3657.987	Rh I	500	300
3663.276	Hg I	500	400
3672.579	U I	8	15
3683.471	Pb I	300	50
3692.357	Rh I	500	150
3692.652	Ir I	20	12
*3694.203	Yb II	500	1000
*3710.290	Y II	80	150
3719.935	Fe I	1000	700
3737.133	Fe I	1000	600
3745.564	Fe I	500	500
3745.903	Fe I	150	100
3748.17	Ho I	60	40
3748.264	Fe I	500	200
3752.54	Os I		
3761.333	Tm I	250	150
3761.917	Tm I	200	120
3768.405	Gd I	20	20
3774.332	Y II	12	100
3775.72	Tl I	3000	1000
3782.20	Os I		
3788.697	Y II	30	30
*3798.252	Mo I	1000	1000
*3814.42	Ra II	....	D 2000
3829.350	Mg I	100	150
3832.306	Mg I	250	200
3838.258	Mg I	300	200
*3848.02	Tl II	150	200
3848.75	Tb I	100	200
3864.110	Mo I	1000	600
3874.18	Tb I	200	200
*3888.646	He I	....	D 1000
3891.02	Ho I	200	40
3891.785	Ba II	18	25

Wave length	Element	Arc	Spark
3902.963	Mo I	1000	500
3905.528	Si I	20	15
3906.316	Er I	25	12
3907.476	Sc I	125	25
*3911.810	Sc I	150	30
*3933.666	Ca II	600	600
3944.032	Al I	2000	1000
*3949.106	La II	1000	800
3951.154	Nd I	40	30
*3961.527	Al I	3000	2000
3968.468	Ca II	500	500
*3987.994	Yb I	1000	500
4000.454	Dy I	400	300
4008.753	W I	45	45
4012.388	Ce II	60	20
4019.137	Th I	8	8
4020.399	Sc I	50	20
4023.688	Sc I	100	25
*4030.755	Mn I	500	20
4032.982	Ga I	1000	500
4033.073	Mn I	400	20
4034.490	Mn I	250	20
4040.762	Ce II	70	5
4044.140	K I	800	400
4045.983	Dy I	150	12
4046.561	Hg I	200	300
4047.201	K I	400	200
*4057.820	Pb I	2000	300
*4058.938	Cb I	1000	400
4062.817	Pr I	150	50
4077.340	La II	600	400
*4077.714	Sr II	400	500
4077.974	Dy I	150	100
4079.729	Cb I	500	200
4093.161	Hf II	25	20
4097.31	N III	....	D 100
*4099.94	N I	....	D 150
4100.923	Cb I	300	200
4101.773	In I	2000	1000
4103.37	N III	....	D 80
4109.98	N I	....	D 1000
4123.228	La II	500	500
4123.810	Cb I	200	125
4129.737	Eu II	150	50
4130.664	Ba II	.0	60
4137.095	Cb I	100	60
4165.606	Ce II	40	6
4167.966	Dy I	50	12
*4172.056	Ga I	2000	1000
4177.321	Nd I	15	25

Wave length	Element	Arc	Spark
*4179.422	Pr II	200	40
*4186.599	Ce II	80	25
4189.518	Pr II	100	50
4201.851	Rb I	2000	500
4205.046	Eu II	200	50
4211.719	Dy I	200	15
4215.524	Sr II	300	400
4215.556	Rb I	1000	300
4225.327	Pr II	50	40
4226.570	Ge I	200	50
*4226.728	Ca I	500	50
4241.669	U I	40	50
*4254.346	Cr I	5000	1000
4267.02	C II	....	350
4267.27	C II	....	500
4274.803	Cr I	4000	800
4289.721	Cr I	3000	800
4294.614	W I	50	50
*4296.75	Sm I		
*4302.108	W I	60	60
*4303.573	Nd I	100	40
4305.447	Sr II	40	
4358.35	Hg I	3000	500
*4379.238	V I	200	200
4384.722	V I	125	125
4389.974	V I	80	60
4390.865	Sm II	150	150
4420.468	Os I	400	100
*4424.342	Sm II	300	300
*4425.441	Ca I	100	50
4434.321	Sm II	200	200
4434.960	Ca I	150	
4454.781	Ca I	200	
4455.880	Ca I		
4456.62	Ca I		
4500.977	Xe I	....	D 500
*4511.323	In I	5000	4000
4518.57	Lu I	300	40
4524.741	Sn I	500	50
*4554.042	Ba II	1000	200
4555.355	Cs I	2000	100
4593.177	Cs I	1000	50
*4594.02	Eu I		
4603.00	Li I	800	
*4607.331	Sr I	1000	50
4624.276	Xe I	....	D 1000
4643.695	Y I	50	100
4671.226	Xe I	....	D 2000
*4674.848	Y I	80	100
4680.138	Zn I	300	200

Wave length	Element	Arc	Spark
4682.28	Ra II	....	D 800
4685.75	He II	....	D 300
4687.803	Zr I	125	
4694.13	S II	....	D 500
4695.45	S II	....	D 30
4696.25	S II	....	D 15
*4704.86	Br II	....	D 250
4710.075	Zr I	60	
4722.159	Zn I	400	300
4722.552	Bi I	1000	100
4730.78	Se I	....	D 1000
4739.03	Se I	....	D 800
4739.478	Zr I	100	
4742.25	Se I	....	D 500
4772.312	Zr I	100	
4785.50	Br II	....	D 400
4794.54	Cl II	....	D 250
4810.06	Cl II	....	D 200
4810.534	Zn I	400	300
4815.62	Zr I		
4816.71	Br II	....	D 300
4819.46	Cl II	....	D 200
*4825.91	Ra I	....	D 800
4832.075	Sr II	200	8
4861.327	H I	....	D 500
4872.493	Sr II	25	
4889.17	Re I	2000	
4934.086	Ba II	400	400
4962.263	Sr II	40	
*4981.733	Ti I	300	125
4991.066	Ti I	200	100
4999.510	Ti I	200	80
5007.213	Ti I	200	40
5014.25	Ti I		
5105.541	Cu I	500	
5153.235	Cu I	600	
5161.188	I II	....	D 300
5167.343	Mg I	100	50
5172.699	Mg I	200	100
5183.618	Mg I	500	300
5204.518	Cr I	400	100
5206.039	Cr I	500	200
5208.436	Cr I	500	100
5209.067	Ag I	1500	1000
5218.202	Cu I	700	
*5350.46	Tl I	5000	2000
5400.562	Ne I	....	D 2000
5424.616	Ba I	100	30
5455.146	La I	200	1
5460.740	Hg I	....	D 2000
5464.61	I II	....	D 900

Wave length	Element	Arc	Spark
5465.487	Ag I	1000	500
5466.47	Y I		
5519.115	Ba I	200	60
*5535.551	Ba I	1000	200
5570.2895	Kr I	....	D 2000
5608.8	Pb II	....	D 40
5666.64	N II	....	D 300
5671.80	Sc I		
5676.02	N II	....	D 100
5679.56	N II	....	D 500
5682.657	Na I	80	
5688.224	Na I	300	
5777.665	Ba I	500	100
5832.488	Ne I		
5852.488	Ne I	....	D 2000
5870.9158	Kr I	....	D 3000
5875.618	He I	....	D 1000
*5889.953	Na I	9000	1000
5895.923	Na I	5000	500
5930.648	La I	250	
6103.642	Li I	2000	.300
6231.76	Al II	....	30
6243.36	Al II	....	100
*6249.929	La I	300	
6362.347	Zn I	1000	500
6402.246	Ne I	....	D 2000
6438.4696	Cd I	2000	1000
6562.79	H I	....	D 3000
*6707.844	Li I	3000	200
6856.02	F I	....	D 1000
6902.46	F I	....	D 500
6965.430	A I	....	D 400
7055.42	A I	....	D 400
7067.217	A I	....	D 400
7450.00	Rn I	....	D 600
7503.867	A I	....	D 700
*7664.907	K I	9000	
7698.979	K I	5000	
*7771.928	O I	....	D 1000
7774.138	O I	....	D 300
7775.433	O I	....	D 100
*7800.227	Rb I	9000	
7947.60	Rb I	5000	
8115.311	A I	....	D 5000
*8521.10	Cs I	5000	
8943.50	Cs I	2000	
9212.91	S I	....	D 200
9228.11	S I	....	D 200
9237.49	S I	....	D 200

SECONDARY ELECTRON EMISSION

N. R. WHETTEN

General Electric Research Laboratory, Schenectady, New York

By permission from "Methods of Experimental Physics" Vol. IV (1962)
Academic Press

The secondary emission yield, or secondary emission ratio, δ, is the average number of secondary electrons emitted from a bombarded material for every incident primary electron. The secondary emission yield is a function of the primary electron energy. δ_{max} is the maximum yield corresponding to a primary electron energy $E_{p\,max}$ (see figure). The two primary electron energies corresponding to a yield of unity are denoted the first and second crossovers (E_I and E_{II}). An insulating target, or a conducting target that is electrically floating, will charge positively or negatively depending on the primary electron energy. For $E_I < E_p < E_{II}$, $\delta > 1$ and the surface charges positively provided there is a collector present that is positive with respect to the target. For $E_p < E_I$, $\delta < 1$, and the surface charges negatively towards the potential of the source of primary electrons. For $E_p > E_{II}$, $\delta < 1$, and the surface charges negatively to the second crossover.

The secondary emission yield is very sensitive to surface contamination, such as oxide films and carbon deposits. Whenever possible, yields believed to be most typical of clean surfaces have been selected. The yields are for measurements at room temperature and normal incidence of the primary electrons.

Table I

Secondary Electron Emission Properties of Elements and Compounds. δ_{max} is the maximum secondary emission yield, $E_{p\,max}$ the primary electron energy for maximum yield, and E_I and E_{II} are the first and second crossovers.

Elements	δ_{max}	$E_{p\,max}$ (ev)	E_I (ev)	E_{II} (ev)	Ref.
Ag	1.5	800	200	>2000	a, b, c
Al	1.0	300	300	300	b
Au	1.4	800	150	>2000	a, c, d
B	1.2	150	50	600	f
Ba	0.8	400	None	None	b
Bi	1.2	550			g, s
Be	0.5	200	None	None	b, h, i, d
C (diamond)	2.8	750		>5000	j
(graphite)	1.0	300	300	300	k
(soot)	0.45	500	None	None	l, d
Cd	1.1	450	300	700	m, n
Co	1.2	600	200	None	b, o
Cs	0.7	400	None	None	a, l, b
Cu	1.3	600	200	1500	n, c, p
Fe	1.3	400	120	1400	q
Ga	1.55	500	75	900	f, r, s
Ge	1.15	500	150	>1200	q
Hg	1.3	600	350	None	t, u
K	0.7	200	None	None	b
Li	0.5	85	None	None	o, b
Mg	0.95	300	None	1200	a, w, c, e, p
Mo	1.25	375	150	None	x
Na	0.82	300	None	1050	a, n, m, w, p
Nb	1.2	375	150	>1500	g, q
Ni	1.3	550	150	1000	v
Pb	1.1	500	250		c
Pd	>1.3	>250	120	3000	t
Pt	1.8	700	350	None	y
Rb	0.9	350	None	2000	f
Sb	1.3	600	250	500	g, x
Si	1.1	250	125		a
Sn	1.35	500		>2000	b
Ta	1.3	600	250		k
Th	1.1	800	None		s
Tl	0.9	280		>1500	z, a, a', e
W	1.7	650	70	>1500	k
Zr	1.4	350	250	1500	k

PRIMARY ELECTRON ENERGY (E_p)

SECONDARY ELECTRON EMISSION (Continued)

Table I (Continued)

Compounds	δ_{max}	$E_{p\,max}$ (ev)	Ref.
Alkali Halides			
CsCl	6.5	1800	b'
KBr (crystal)	14	1600	c', e'
KCl (crystal)	12.5	1200	b', d'
KI (layer)	7.5		b', f'
KI (crystal)	10	1600	c', d', e'
LiF (crystal)	5.6		b'
LiF (layer)	8.5	700	g', h', d'
NaBr (crystal)	24	1800	g', h', d'
NaBr (layer)	6.3		i', e', c', d', g'
NaCl (crystal)	14	1200	b', j'
NaCl (layer)	6.8	600	g'
NaF (crystal)	14	1200	g'
NaF (layer)	5.7		b'
NaI (crystal)	19	1300	g'
NaI (layer)	5.5		b'
RbCl (layer)	5.8		b'
Oxides			
Ag_2O	1.0		l'
Al_2O_3 (layer)	2 to 9	400	k', m', i', b
BaO (layer)	2.3 to 4.8	2000	m', b
BeO	3.4		m'
CaO	2.2	500	b', n'
Cu_2O	1.2	400	t', u', v'
MgO (crystal)	20 to 25	1500	w', m', r', s', t'
MgO (layer)	3 to 15	400 to 1500	l'
MoO_2	2.1 to 4	400	k', g'
SiO_2 (quartz)		640	o'
SnO_2	3.2		
Sulfides			
MoS_2	1.1		b'
PbS	1.2	500	p'
WS_2	1.0		p'
ZnS	1.8	350	q'
Others			
BaF_2 (layer)	4.5		b'
CaF_2 (layer)	3.2		b'
$BiCs_3$	6	1000	p'
BiCs	1.9	1000	p'
GeCs	7	700	p'
Rb_3Sb	7.1	450	p'
$SbCs_3$	6	700	p', x'
Mica	2.4	350	k'
Glasses	2 to 3	300 to 450	k', y'

References to Table I

a. R. Warnecke, J. phys. radium, 7, 270 (1936).
b. H. Bruining and J. H. deBoer, Physica, 5, 17 (1938).
c. R. Kollath, Physik. Z., 38, 202 (1937).
d. R. Suhrmann and W. Kundt, Z. Physik, 121, 118 (1943).
e. P. L. Copeland, J. Franklin Inst., 215, 593 (1933).
f. L. R. Koller and J. S. Burgess, Phys. Rev., 70, 571 (1946).
g. P. M. Morozov, J. Exptl. Theoret. Phys. USSR, 11, 410 (1941).
h. R. Kollath, Ann. Physik, 33, 285 (1938).
i. E. G. Schneider, Phys. Rev., 54, 185 (1938).
j. J. B. Johnson, Phys. Rev., 92, 843 (1953).
k. H. Bruining, Philips Tech. Rev., 3, 80 (1938).
l. R. Suhrmann and W. Kundt, Z. Physik, 120, 363 (1943).
m. D. E. Wooldridge, Phys. Rev., 56, 1062 (1939).
n. L. R. G. Treloar and D. H. Landon, Proc. Soc. (London), B50, 625 (1938).
o. N. S. Klebnikov, Tech. Phys. USSR, 5, 593 (1938).
p. R. L. Petry, Phys. Rev., 26, 346 (1925).
q. J. J. Brophy, Phys.Rev. 83, 534 (1951).
r. J. B. Johnson and K. G. McKay, Phys. Rev., 93, 668 (1954).
s. H. Gobrecht and F. Spear, Z. Physik, 135, 602 (1953).
t. A. Afanasjewa and P. W. Timofeew, Tech. Phys. USSR, 4, 953 (1937).
u. M. S. Joffe and I. V. Nechlaev, J. Exptl. Theoret. Phys. USSR, 11, 93 (1941).
v. H. E. Farnsworth, Phys. Rev., 25, 41 (1925).
w. G. Blankenfeld, Ann. Physik, 9, 48 (1951).
x. J. Woods, Proc. Phys. Soc. (London), B67, 843 (1954).
y. R. L. Petry, Phys. Rev., 28, 362 (1926).
z. R. Kollath, Handbuch der Physik, vol. 21 (1956), p. 232.
a'. E. A. Coomes, Phys. Rev., 55, 519 (1939).
b'. D. N Dobretzov and J H. deBoer, Physica, 6, 834 (1939).
c'. D. N Dobretzov and A. S. Titkow, Doklady Acad. Nauk USSR, 100, 33 (1955).
d'. N. R. Whetten, Bull. Am. Phys. Soc. Ser. II, 5, 347 (1960).
e'. A. R. Shulman and B. P. Dementyev, J. Tech. Phys. USSR, 25, 2256 (1955).
f'. M. Knoll, O. Hachenberg, and J. Randmer, Z. Physik, 122, 137 (1944).
g'. D. N. Dobretzov and T. L. Matskevich, J. Tech. Phys. USSR, 27, 734 (1957).
h'. T. L. Matskevich, J. Tech. Phys. USSR, 26, 2399 (1956).
i'. A. R. Shulman, W. L. Makedonsky, and J. D. Yaroshetsky, J. Tech. Phys. USSR, 23, 1152 (1953).
j'. M. M. Vudinsky, J. Tech. Phys. USSR, 9, 271 (1939).
k'. H. Salow, Z. Tech. Phys., 21, 8 (1940).
l'. A. Afanasjewa, P. Timofeew, and A. Ignaton, Phys. Z. Sowjet, 10, 831 (1936).
m'. K. H. Geyer, Ann Phys. 42, 241 (1942).
n'. N. B. Gornii, J. Exptl. Theoret. Phys. USSR, 26, 79 (1954).
o'. H. E. Mendenhall, Phys. Rev., 72, 532 (1947).
p'. O. Hachenberg and W. Brauer in Advances in Electronics and Electron Physics, Vol. XI, Academic Press, New York (1959), p. 438.
q'. N. B. Gornii, J. Exptl. Theoret. Phys. USSR, 26, 88 (1954).
r'. P. Wargo, B. V. Haxby, and W. G. Shepherd, J. Appl. Phys., 27, 1311 (1956).
s'. P. Rapnaport, J. Appl. Phys., 25, 288 (1954).
t'. N. R. Whetten and A. B. Laponsky, J Appl. Phys., 30, 432 (1959).
u'. J. B. Johnson and K. G. McKay, Phys. Rev., 91, 582 (1953).
v'. R. G. Lye, Phys. Rev., 99, 1647 (1955).
w'. N. R. Whetten and A. B. Laponsky, J. Appl. Phys., 28, 515 (1957).
x'. N. D. Morrulis and B. I. Djatlowitskaja, J. Tech. Phys. USSR, 10, 657 (1940).
y'. C. W. Mueller, J. Appl. Phys., 16, 453 (1945).

EMISSIVITY OF TUNGSTEN

Wavelengths in μ

Temperature °K	0.25	0.30	0.35	0.40	0.50	0.60	0.70
1600	.448*	.482	.478	.481	.469	.455	.444
1800	.442*	.478*	.476	.477	.465	.452	.44
2000	.436*	.474	.473	.474	.462	.448	.436
2200	.429*	.470	.470	.471	.458	.445	.431
2400	.422	.465	.466	.468	.455	.441	.427
2600	.418	.461	.464	.464	.451	.437	.423
2800	.411	.456	.461	.461	.448	.434	.419

Temperature °K	0.80	0.90	1.0	1.1	1.2	1.3	1.4
1600	.431	.413	.39	.366	.345	.322*	.300*
1800	.425	.407	.385	.364	.344	.323*	.302*
2000	.419	.401	.381	.361	.343	.323	.305
2200	.415	.396	.378	.359	.342	.324	.306
2400	.408	.391	.372	.355	.340	.324	.309
2600	.404	.386	.369	.352	.338	.325	.310
2800	.400	.383	.367	.352	.337	.325	.313

Temperature °K	1.5	1.6	1.8	2.0	2.2	2.4	2.6
1600	.279*	.263*	.234*	.210*	.19*	.175*	.164*
1800	.282	.267*	.241*	.218*	.20*	.182*	.174*
2000	.288	.273	.247	.227	.209	.197	.175
2200	.291	.278	.254	.235	.218	.205	.194
2400	.296	.283	.262	.244	.228	.215	.205
2600	.299	.288	.269	.251	.236	.224	.214
2800	.302	.292	.274	.259	.245	.233	.224

* Values by extrapolation.

LIQUIDS FOR INDEX BY IMMERSION METHOD

Liquid	N_D 24° C
Trimethylene chloride................	1.446
Cineole............................	1.456
Hexahydrophenol...................	1.466
Decahydronaphthalene..............	1.477
Isoamylphthalate..................	1.486
Tetrachloroethane.................	1.492
Pentachloroethane.................	1.501
Trimethylene bromide..............	1.513
Chlorobenzene.....................	1.523
Ethylene bromide + Chlorobenzene..	1.533
o-Nitrotoluene....................	1.544
Xylidine..........................	1.557
o-Toluidine.......................	1.570
Aniline...........................	1.584
Bromoform.........................	1.595
Iodobenzene + Bromobenzene........	1.603
Iodobenzene + Bromobenzene........	1.613
Quinoline.........................	1.622
α-Chloronaphthalene...............	1.633
α-Bromonaphthalene + α-Chloronaphthalene.......	1.640–1.650
α-Bromonaphthalene + α-Iodonaphthalene..........	1.660–1.690
Methylene iodide + Iodobenzene....	1.700–1.730
Methylene iodide..................	1.738
Methylene iodide saturated with sulfur........	1.78
Yellow phosphorus, sulfur and methylene iodide (8:1:1 by weight)................................	2.06

Can be diluted with methylene iodide to cover range 1.74–2.06. For precautions in use, cf. West, Am. Mineral, **21**, p. 245–9 (1936).

HEAVY LIQUIDS FOR MINERAL SEPARATION

Liquid	Density
Tetrabromoethane (sym.).....................	2.964, 20°/4°
Can be diluted with carbon tetrachloride (1.595) or benzene (0.894).	
Methylene iodide...........................	3.325, 20°/4°
Can be diluted with carbon tetrachloride or benzene.	
Thallium formate, aq......................	3.5
Can be diluted with water.	
Thallium malonate-thallium formate, aq......	4.9
Can be diluted with water.	

For preparation and recovery of these liquids, cf. U. S. Bureau Mines, Rept. Inv. #2897 (1928).

INDEX OF REFRACTION

Indices of refraction for elements, inorganic, metal-organic and organic compounds and minerals will be found in the tables of physical constants for the various classes of substances in the section Properties and Physical Constants.

Values for compounds not there listed and data subsequently collected are given below.

Indices not otherwise indicated are for sodium light, $\lambda = 589.3$ mμ. Other wave lengths are indicated by the value in millimicrons or symbol in parentheses which follows the index. Wave lengths are indicated as follows: He, $\lambda = 587.6$ mμ; Li, $\lambda = 670.8$ mμ; Hg, $\lambda = 579.1$ mμ; A, $\lambda = 759.4$ mμ; C, $\lambda = 656.3$ mμ; D, $\lambda = 589.3$ mμ; F, $\lambda = 486.1$ mμ.

Temperatures are understood to be 20°C for liquids, or ordinary room temperatures in the case of solids. Other temperatures appear as superior figures with the index.

Indices for the elements and inorganic compounds will be understood to be for the solid form except as indicated by the abbreviation liq.

See also under Physical Constants of Inorganic Compounds and index of Refraction of Gases.

ELEMENTS

Name	Formula	Index
Bromine (liq.).................	Br$_2$	1.661[15]
Cadmium (liq.)................	Cd	0.82 (579 mμ)
" (sol.)..................		1.13
Chlorine (liq.)...............	Cl$_2$	1.385
" (gas)...................		1.000768
Hydrogen (liq.)...............	H$_2$	1.10974[-252.83] (579 mμ)
Iodine (sol.).................	I$_2$	3.34
" (gas)...................		1.001920
Lead.........................	Pb	2.6 (579 mμ)
Mercury (liq.)................	Hg	1.6–1.9
Nitrogen (liq.)...............	N$_2$	1.2053[-190]

ELEMENTS

Name	Formula	Index
Oxygen (liq.).................	O$_2$	1.221[-181]
Phosphorus (yel.) (sol.).......		2.144[25]
Selenium......................	Se$_8$	3.00, 4.04
" (amor.) (sol.).........		2.92
Sodium........................	Na	0.0045
" (sol.).................		4.22
Sulfur (liq.).................	S$_8$	1.929[110]
" (amor.) (sol.).........		1.998
" (rhombic, α)..........		1.957, 2.0377, 2.2454
Tin (liq.)....................	Sn	2.1

INORGANIC COMPOUNDS
See also under Physical Constants of Inorganic Compounds.

Name	Formula	Index
Aluminum carbide............	Al$_4$C$_3$	2.7, 2.75 (700 mμ)
chloride..................	AlCl$_3$.6H$_2$O	1.560, 1.507
oxide.....................	Al$_2$O$_3$	1.665–1.680, 1.63–1.65
Alums. See under appropriate element.		
Ammonium antimonyl tartrate	2(NH$_4$.SbO.C$_4$H$_4$O$_6$).H$_2$O	β1.6229 (C)
orthoarsenate, di-H.......	NH$_4$H$_2$AsO$_4$	1.5766, 1.5217
bromide...................	NH$_4$Br	1.7108
perchlorate...............	NH$_4$ClO$_4$	1.4818, 1.4833, 1.4881
chloroplatinate..........	(NH$_4$)$_2$PtCl$_6$	1.8
fluoride..................	NH$_4$F	ω<1.328
" acid................	NH$_4$HF$_2$	1.385, 1.390, 1.394
hydrogen malate.(d).......	NH$_4$C$_4$H$_5$O$_5$	β1.503
nitrate...................	NH$_4$NO$_3$	1.413, 1.611(He), 1.63
Ammonium sulfate, acid....	NH$_4$HSO$_4$	1.463, 1.473, 1.510
tartrate (dl).............	(NH$_4$)$_2$C$_4$H$_4$O$_6$.2H$_2$O	β1.564
thiocyanate...............	NH$_4$CNS	1.546, 1.685, 1.692
uranyl acetate............	NH$_4$C$_2$H$_3$O$_2$.UO$_2$(C$_2$H$_3$O$_2$)$_2$	1.4808, 1.4933
Antimony bromide..........	SbBr$_3$	>1.74+
iodide, tri-..............	SbI$_3$	2.78 (Li), 2.36
Barium cadmium bromide.....	BaCdBr$_4$.4H$_2$O	β1.702
cadmium chloride..........	BaCdCl$_4$.4H$_2$O	β1.651
calcium propionate........	BaCa$_2$(C$_3$H$_5$O$_2$)$_6$	1.4442
fluochloride..............	BaCl$_2$.BaF$_2$	1.640, 1.633
fluoride..................	BaF$_2$	1.475 also 1.4741
Barium oxide..............	BaO	1.980
orthophosphate, di-.......	BaHPO$_4$	1.617, 1.63±, 1.635
propionate................	Ba(C$_2$H$_5$CO$_2$)$_2$.H$_2$O	β1.5175
sulfide, mono-............	BaS	2.155
Cadmium ammonium chloride..	CdCl$_2$.4NH$_4$Cl	1.6038, 1.6042
cesium sulfate............	CdSO$_4$.Cs$_2$SO$_4$.6H$_2$O	1.498, 1.500, 1.506
fluoride..................	CdF$_2$	1.56
magnesium chloride........	(CdCl$_2$)$_2$.MgCl$_2$.12H$_2$O	1.49, 1.5331, 1.5769
oxide.....................	CdO	2.49 (Li)
potassium chloride........	CdCl$_2$.4KCl	1.5906, 1.5907
" cyanide.............	Cd(CN)$_2$.2KCN	1.4213
rubidium sulfate..........	CdSO$_4$.Rb$_2$SO$_4$.6H$_2$O	1.4798, 1.4848, 1.4948
Calcium aluminate.........	Ca$_3$Al$_2$O$_6$	1.710
borate....................	CaO.B$_2$O$_3$	1.540, 1.656, 1.682
carbide...................	CaC$_2$	>1.75
copper acetate............	CaCu(C$_2$H$_3$O$_2$)$_4$.6H$_2$O	1.436, 1.478
cyanamide.................	CaCN$_2$	1.60, >1.95
dithionate................	CaS$_2$O$_6$.4H$_2$O	1.5516, 1.5414
pyrophosphate.............	Ca$_2$P$_2$O$_7$	1.585, 1.60±, 1.605
platinocyanide............	CaPt(CN)$_4$.5H$_2$O	1.623, 1.644, 1.767
strontium propionate......	Ca$_2$Sr(C$_3$H$_5$O$_2$)$_6$	1.4871, 1.4956
sulfide (oldhamite).......	CaS	2.137
sulfite...................	CaSO$_3$.2H$_2$O	1.590, 1.595, 1.628
thiosulfate...............	CaS$_2$O$_3$.6H$_2$O	1.545, 1.560, 1.605
Carbon dioxide (liq.)......	CO$_2$	1.195[15]
Cerium dithionate.........	Ce$_2$(S$_2$O$_6$)$_3$.15H$_2$O	β1.507
Cesium perchlorate........	CsClO$_4$	1.4752, 1.4788, 1.4804
nitrate...................	CsNO$_3$	1.55, 1.56
selenate..................	Cs$_2$SeO$_4$	1.5989, 1.5999, 1.6003
thallium chloride.........	Cs$_3$Tl$_2$Cl$_9$	1.784, 1.774
Chromium cesium sulfate....	CrCs(SO$_4$)$_2$.12H$_2$O	1.4810
oxide (ic)................	Cr$_2$O$_3$	2.5
potassium cyanide (ic)....	CrK$_3$(CN)$_6$	1.5221, 1.5244, 1.5373
sulfate (ic)..............	Cr$_2$(SO$_4$)$_3$.18H$_2$O	1.564
thallium sulfate..........	CrTl(SO$_4$)$_2$.12H$_2$O	1.5228
Cobalt acetate............	Co(C$_2$H$_3$O$_2$)$_2$.4H$_2$O	β1.542
aluminate (Thenard's Blue)	Co(AlO$_2$)$_2$	>1.78 (red), 1.74 (blue)
ammonium selenate.........	CoSeO$_4$.(NH$_4$)$_2$SeO$_4$.6H$_2$O	1.5246, 1.5311, 1.5396
cesium sulfate............	CoCs$_2$(SO$_4$)$_2$.6H$_2$O	1.5057, 1.5085, 1.5132
chloride (ous)............	CoCl$_2$.2H$_2$O	<1.625, <1.671, >1.67
potassium selenate........	CoSeO$_4$.K$_2$SeO$_4$.6H$_2$O	1.5135, 1.5195, 1.5358
rubidium sulfate..........	CoSO$_4$.Rb$_2$SO$_4$.6H$_2$O	1.4859, 1.4916, 1.5014
selenate..................	CoSeO$_4$.6H$_2$O	β1.5225, γ1.5227
Copper ammonium selenate..	CuSeO$_4$.(NH$_4$)$_2$SeO$_4$.6H$_2$O	1.5213, 1.5355, 1.5395
ammonium sulfate..........	CuSO$_4$.(NH$_4$)$_2$SO$_4$.6H$_2$O	1.4910, 1.5007, 1.5054
cesium sulfate............	CuSO$_4$.Cs$_2$SO$_4$.6H$_2$O	1.5048, 1.5061, 1.5153
chloride (ic).............	CuCl$_2$.2H$_2$O	1.644, 1.684, 1.742
formate...................	Cu(CHO$_2$)$_2$.4H$_2$O	1.4133, 1.5423, 1.5571

Name	Formula	Index	Name	Formula	Index
Copper oxide (ous) (cuprite).....	Cu_2O	2.705	Selenium oxide.............	SeO_2	>1.76
potassium chloride...........	$CuCl_2.2KCl.2H_2O$	1.6365, 1.6148	Silver cyanide.............	$AgCN$	1.685, 1.94
" cyanide (ous).......	$CuK_3(CN)_4$	1.5215	nitrate.............	$AgNO_3$	1.729, 1.744, 1.788
" selenate............	$CuSeO_4.K_2SeO_4.6H_2O$	1.5096, 1.5235, 1.5387	phosphate............	Ag_2HPO_4	1.8036, 1.7983
" sulfate............	$CuSO_4.K_2SO_4.6H_2O$	1.4836, 1.4864, 1.5020	potassium cyanide.......	$AgK(CN)_2$	1.625, 1.63
strontium formate............	$Cu(HCO_2)_2.2[Sr(HCO_2)_2]$ $8H_2O$	1.4995, 1.5199, 1.5801	Sodium ammonium tartrate (d)	$NaNH_4(C_4H_4O_6).4H_2O$	1.495, 1.498, 1.499
			ammonium tartrate (dl)....	$NaNH_4(C_4H_4O_6).H_2O$	β1.473 (red)
sulfate (ic)............	$CuSO_4$	1.724, 1.733, 1.739	orthoarsenate............	$NaH_2AsO_4.H_2O$	1.5382, 1.5535, 1.5607
Cyanogen................	C_2N_2	1.327^{15} (liq.)	"	$NaH_2AsO_4.2H_2O$	1.4794, 1.5021, 1.5265
Germanium bromide, tetra-	$GeBr_4$	1.6269	bromide............	$NaBr$	1.6412
Gold sodium chloride..........	$AuNaCl_4.2H_2O$	α1.545, γ1.75+	carbonate............	Na_2CO_3	1.415, 1.535, 1.546
Hafnium oxychloride..........	$HfOCl_2.8H_2O$	1.557, 1.543	Sodium carbonate, acid......	$NaHCO_3$	1.376, 1.500, 1.582
Ice....................	H_2O	1.3049, 1.3062 (A), 1.3091, 1.3104 (D), 1.3133, 1.3147 (F)	cyanide............	$NaCN$	1.452
			iodide............	NaI	1.7745
			molybdate............	$3Na_2O.7MoO_3.22H_2O$	β1.627
Iron ammonium chloride.......	$Fe(NH_4)_2Cl_4$	1.6439	nitrate............	$NaNO_3$	1.5874, 1.3361
ammonium selenate.........	$FeSeO_4.(NH_4)_2SeO_4.6H_2O$	1.5201, 1.5260, 1.5356	phosphate............	$NaH_2PO_4.2H_2O$	1.4401, 1.4629, 1.4815
cesium sulfate (ic).........	$FeCs_2(SO_4)_2.12H_2O$	1.4839	"	$Na_2HPO_4.7H_2O$	1.4412, 1.4424, 1.4526
" " (ous)......	$FeSO_4.Cs_2SO_4.6H_2O$	1.5003, 1.5035, 1.5094	hypophosphate............	$Na_4HP_2O_6.9H_2O$	1.4653, 1.4738, 1.4804
rubidium sulfate..........	$FeRb_2(SO_4)_2.12H_2O$	1.48234	silicate............	Na_2SiO_3	1.513, 1.520, 1.528
sulfate (ic)............	$Fe_2(SO_4)_3$	1.802, 1.814, 1.818	sulfate, acid............	$NaHSO_4.H_2O$	1.43, 1.46, 1.47
thallium sulfate...........	$FeTl(SO_4)_2.12H_2O$	1.52365	sulfite............	Na_2SO_3	1.565, 1.515
Lanthanum sulfate...........	$La_2(SO_4)_3.9H_2O$	1.564, 1.569	" acid............	$NaHSO_3$	1.474, 1.526, 1.685
Lead orthoarsenate, di-	$PbHAsO_4$	1.8903, 1.9097, 1.9765	tartrate, acid (d)............	$NaH(C_4H_4O_6).H_2O$	β1.533
nitrate............	$Pb(NO_3)_2$	1.782	thiocyanate............	$NaCNS$	1.545, 1.625, 1.695
Lithium ammonium sulfate......	$LiNH_4SO_4$	β1.437 (Li)	Sodium tungstate...........	$Na_2WO_4.2H_2O$	1.5526, 1.5533, 1.5695
ammonium tartrate (d)......	$LiNH_4(C_4H_4O_6).H_2O$	β1.567, γ1.5673	vanadate............	$Na_4VO_4.10H_2O$	1.5305; α1.5398, ϵ1.5475
" " (dl)......	$LiNH_4(C_4H_4O_6).H_2O$	β1.5287	"	$Na_3VO_4.12H_2O$	1.5095, 1.5232
bromide............	$LiBr$	1.784	Strontium dichromate...........	$SrCr_2O_7.3H_2O$	1.7146, 1.7174, 1.812
chloride............	$LiCl$	1.662	fluoride............	SrF_2	1.442 (1.438)
dithionate............	$Li_2S_2O_6.2H_2O$	1.5487, 1.5602, 1.5788	oxide............	SrO	1.870
oxide............	Li_2O	1.644	orthophosphate, acid......	$SrHPO_4$	1.608, 1.62±, 1.625
potassium sulfate..........	$LiKSO_4$	1.4723, 1.4717	sulfide, mono-............	SrS	2.107
" tartrate.........	$LiK(C_4H_4O_6).H_2O$	β1.5226 (red)	Sulfur nitride............	S_4N_4	α1.908, β2.046
rubidium tartrate (a).......	$LiRb(C_4H_4O_6).H_2O$	β1.552	Thallium chloride, mono-.....	$TlCl$	2.247
sodium tartrate (dl)........	$LiNa(C_4H_4O_6).2H_2O$	β1.4904	iodide, mono-............	TlI	2.78
Magnesium ammonium selenate	$MgSeO_4.(NH_4)_2SeO_4.6H_2O$	1.5070, 1.5093, 1.5169	Tin iodide (ic)............	SnI_4	2.106
ammonium sulfate..........	$Mg(NH_4)_2.(SO_4)_2.6H_2O$	1.4716, 1.4730, 1.4786	Uranyl potassium sulfate.......	$UO_2.SO_4.K_2SO_4.2H_2O$	1.5144, 1.5266, 1.5705 (580 mμ)
orthoborate............	$3MgO.B_2O_3$	1.6527, 1.6537, 1.6748			
cesium sulfate............	$MgCs_2(SO_4)_2.6H_2O$	1.4857, 1.4858, 1.4916	Vanadium ammonium sulfate..	$VNH_4(SO_4)_2.12H_2O$	1.475
chlorostannate............	$MgSnCl_6.6H_2O$	1.5885, 1.5970	Zinc ammonium selenate.....	$Zn(SeO_4).(NH_4)_2SeO_4.6H_2O$	1.5240, 1.5300, 1.5385
fluosilicate............	$MgSiF_6.6H_2O$	1.3439, 1.3602	bromate............	$Zn(BrO_3)_2.6H_2O$	1.5452
platinocyanide............	$MgPt(CN)_4.7H_2O$	1.5608, 1.91	cesium sulfate............	$ZnCs_2(SO_4)_2.6H_2O$	1.5022, 1.5048, 1.5093
Magnesium potassium selenate	$MgK_2(SeO_4)_2.6H_2O$	1.4969, 1.4991, 1.5139	chloride............	$ZnCl_2$	1.687, 1.713
potassium sulfate..........	$MgK_2(SO_4)_2.6H_2O$	1.4607, 1.4629, 1.4755	fluosilicate............	$ZnSiF_6.6H_2O$	1.3824, 1.3956
rubidium sulfate..........	$MgRb_2(SO_4)_2.6H_2O$	1.4672, 1.4689, 1.4779	potassium cyanide............	$ZnK_2(CN)_4$	1.4115
silicate............	$MgSiO_3$	1.651, 1.654 (calc.), 1.660	" selenate............	$ZnK_2(SeO_4)_2.6H_2O$	1.5121, 1.5181, 1.5335
sulfide............	MgS	2.271 also 2.268	" sulfate............	$ZnK_2(SO_4)_2.6H_2O$	1.4775, 1.4833, 1.4969
Manganese borate............	$Mn_3B_4O_9$	1.617, 1.738, 1.776	rubidium sulfate............	$ZnRb_2(SO_4)_2.6H_2O$	1.4833, 1.4884, 1.4975
cesium sulfate............	$MnCs_2(SO_4)_2.6H_2O$	1.4946, 1.4966, 1.5025	silicate............	$ZnSiO_3$	1.616, 1.62±, 1.623
chloride............	$MnCl_2.4H_2O$	1.555, 1.575, 1.607	Zirconium ammonium fluoride	$Zr(NH_4)_3F_7$	1.433
rubidium sulfate............	$MnRb_2(SO_4)_2.6H_2O$	1.4767, 1.4807, 1.4907			
sulfate (ous)............	$MnSO_4.4H_2O$	1.508, 1.518, 1.522			
"	$MnSO_4.5H_2O$	1.495, 1.508, 1.514			
Mercury chloride (ic)............	$HgCl_2$	1.725, 1.859, 1.965			
cyanide (ic)............	$Hg(CN)_2$	1.645, 1.492			
iodide (ic) (red)............	HgI_2	2.748, 2.455			
Nickel ammonium selenate......	$Ni(NH_4)_2.(SeO_4)_2.6H_2O$	1.5291, 1.5372, 1.5466			
cesium sulfate............	$NiCs_2(SO_4)_2.6H_2O$	1.5087, 1.5129, 1.5162			

Name	Index
Allontoln, solid............	α1.579, γ1.660
Dimethyl thiophene (α, α'), liq.	1.51693$^{13.4}$ (He)
" (β, β'), liq.	1.52217^{15} (He)
Ethyl carbylamine, liq.	1.36502^4
Ethylidene cyanhydrin, liq.	1.40582$^{18.6}$
Hexyl acetylene (n), liq............	1.42081$^{2.5}$

Continuing left column (Inorganic):

Name	Formula	Index
Nickel chloride............	$NiCl_2.6H_2O$	α1.535, γ1.61
fluoride, acid............	$NiF_2.5HF.6H_2O$	1.392, 1.408
potassium selenate............	$NiK_2(SeO_4)_2.6H_2O$	1.5199, 1.5248, 1.5339
rubidium sulfate............	$NiRb_2(SO_4)_2.6H_2O$	1.4895, 1.4961, 1.505+
selenate............	$NiSeO_4.6H_2O$	1.5393, 1.5125
Platinum potassium dibromo- nitrite............	$PtK_2(NO_2)_2Br_2.H_2O$	1.626, 1.6684, 1.757
Potassium carbonate............	K_2CO_3	1.426, 1.531, 1.541
carbonate, acid............	$KHCO_3$	1.380, 1.482, 1.578
perchlorate............	$KClO_4$	1.4731, 1.4737, 1.4769
chloroplatinate............	K_2PtCl_6	1.827 (577 mμ)
chloroplatinite............	K_2PtCl_4	1.64, 1.67
dichromate............	$K_2Cr_2O_7$	1.7202, 1.7380, 1.8197
cyanide............	KCN	1.410
fluoborate............	KBF_4	1.3239, 1.3245, 1.3247
fluoride............	KF	1.352 (1.361)
"	$KF.2H_2O$	1.345, 1.352, 1.363
fluosilicate............	K_2SiF_6	1.3391
periodate............	KIO_4	1.6205, 1.6479
lithium ferrocyanide............	$K_2Li_2Fe(CN)_6.3H_2O$	1.5883, 1.6007, 1.6316
hypophosphate............	$K_2H_2P_2O_6.2H_2O$	1.4893, 1.5314, 1.5363
"	$K_2H_2P_2O_6.3H_2O$	1.4768, 1.4843, 1.4870
ruthenium cyanide............	$K_4Ru(CN)_6.3H_2O$	β1.5837
silicate............	K_2SiO_3	1.520, 1.521, 1.528
thiocyanate............	$KCNS$	1.532, 1.660, 1.730
thionate, tetra-............	$K_2S_4O_6$	1.5896, 1.6057, 1.6435
" penta-............	$2K_2S_5O_6.3H_2O$	1.565, 1.63, 1.655
Rhodium cesium sulfate	$RhCs(SO_4)_2.12H_2O$	1.5077
Rubidium perchlorate............	$RbClO_4$	1.4692, 1.4701, 1.4731
chromate............	Rb_2CrO_4	β1.71, γ1.72
dithionate............	$Rb_2S_2O_6$	1.4574, 1.5078
fluoride............	RbF	1.396
selenate............	Rb_2SeO_4	1.5515, 1.5537, 1.5582
Ruthenium sodium nitrate.......	$RuNa_2(NO_2)_5.2H_2O$	1.5889, 1.5943, 1.7163

Name	Index	Name	Index
Albite glass............	1.4890	Magdala red....	1.90
Amber............	1.546	Obsidian........	1.482-1.496
Anorthite glass............	1.5755	Paraffin........	1.4329$^{53.3}$ (C)
Asphalt............	1.635	Quartz, fused.....	1.45640 (656 mμ)
Bell metal............	1.0052	"	1.45843 (589 mμ)
Borax, amorphous, fused	1.4630	"	1.46190 (509 mμ)
Canada balsam............	1.530	"	1.47503 (361 mμ)
Ebonite............	1.66 (red)	"	1.49634 (275 mμ)
Fuchsin	2.70	"	1.53386 (214 mμ)
Gelatin, Nelson's No. 1.	1.530	"	1.57464 (185 mμ)
Gelatin, various.........	1.516-1.534	Resin, aloes...	1.619 (red)
Gum Arabic............	1.480 (1.514)	colophony.......	1.548 (red)
"	(red)	copal............	1.528 (red)
Hoffman's violet............	2.20	mastic.........	1.535 (red)
Ivory............	1.539, 1.541	Peru balsam......	1.593

INDEX OF REFRACTION OF ORGANIC COMPOUNDS

(See also that section of this book which contains data of Physical Constants of Organic Compounds)
The following table contains a list of organic compounds arranged in order of increasing refractive index. Measurements were made at 25°C.

Compound	nD	Compound	nD
Trifluoroacetic acid	1.283	2,2,3-Trimethylpentane	1.401
2,2,2-Trifluoroethanol	1.290	1-Chlorobutane	1.401
Octofluoropentanol-1	1.316	β-Methoxypropionitrile	1.401
Dodecafluoroheptanol-1	1.316	3-Methyl butanoic acid	1.402
Methanol	1.326	n-Nonane	1.403
Acetonitrile	1.342	Dipropylamine	1.403
Ethyl ether	1.352	Isoamylacetate	1.403
Acetone	1.357	Cyclopentane	1.404
Ethyl formate	1.358	2-Methyl-2-butanol	1.404
Ethanol	1.359	3-Methyl-1-butanol	1.404
Methyl acetate	1.360	Tetrahydrofuran	1.404
Propionitrile	1.363	Capronitrile	1.405
2,2-Dimethylbutane	1.366	2-Pentanone	1.405
Isopropyl ether	1.367	2-Ethoxyethanol	1.405
2-methylpentane	1.369	2-Heptanone	1.406
Ethyl acetate	1.370	Valeric acid	1.406
Acetic acid	1.370	Diisobutylene	1.407
Propionaldehyde	1.371	Methylcyclopentane	1.407
n-Hexane	1.372	Isoamyl ether	1.407
2,3-Dimethylbutane	1.372	Methylpropyl carbinol	1.407
3-Methylpentane	1.374	Tributyl borate	1.407
2-Propanol	1.375	1-Pentanol	1.408
Isopropyl acetate	1.375	3-Methyl-2-butanol	1.408
Propyl formate	1.375	Diethyl oxalate	1.408
2-Chloropropane	1.376	n-Decane	1.409
2-Butanone	1.377	4-Methyl-2-pentanol	1.409
2-Chloropropane	1.377	3-Isopropyl-2-pentanone	1.409
Methylethyl ketone	1.377	2-Methyl-1-butanol	1.409
Butyraldehyde	1.378	Butyric acid anhydride	1.409
2,4-Dimethylpentane	1.379	Amyl ether	1.410
Propyl ether	1.379	Isoamyl isovalerate	1.410
Acetaldehyde-diethylacetal	1.379	1-Chloropentane	1.410
Butylethyl ether	1.380	2-Propene-1-ol	1.411
Nitromethane	1.380	2,4-Dimethyl dioxane	1.412
Trifluoropropanol	1.381	Ethyl lactate	1.412
2-Methylhexane	1.382	Diethyl malonate	1.412
Butyronitrile	1.382	3-Chloropropene	1.413
Propyl acetate	1.382	Ethyleneglycol diacetate	1.413
Ethyl propionate	1.382	2-Octanone	1.414
2-Methyl-2-propanol	1.383	3-Octanone	1.414
1-Propanol	1.383	3-Methyl-2-heptanone	1.415
Isobutyl formate	1.383	Caproic acid	1.415
Diethyl carbonate	1.383	4-Methyldioxane	1.415
Heptane	1.385	1,2-Propyleneglycol-1-monobutyl ether	1.415
2-Methyl-2-propanol	1.385	Ethylcyanoacetate	1.415
Propionic acid	1.385	Dibutylamine	1.416
3-Methylhexane	1.386	2-Pentanol	1.416
n-Propyl amine	1.386	1,1-Dichloroethane	1.416
1,1-Dimethyl-2-propanone	1.386	Heptachlorodiethyl ether	1.416
1-Chloropropane	1.386	1-Hexanol	1.416
2,2,3-Trimethylbutane	1.387	1-Amino-3-methoxy propane	1.417
Methylpropyl ketone	1.387	Octyl nitrile	1.418
sec-Butyl acetate	1.387	2-Heptanol	1.418
Butyl formate	1.387	2-Propenyl amine	1.419
β-Methylpropyl ethanoate	1.388	1,2-Propyleneglycol carbonate	1.419
2,2,4-Trimethyl pentane	1.389	Methylpentyl carbinol	1.420
2,3-Dimethyl pentane	1.389	2-Ethyl-1-butanol	1.420
Acetic anhydride	1.389	1-Chloro-2-methyl-1-propene	1.420
Diisopropyl amine	1.390	p-Dioxane	1.420
2-Aminobutane	1.390	Methylcyclohexane	1.421
2-Pentanone	1.390	4-Hydroxy-4-methyl-2-pentanone	1.421
3-Pentanone	1.390	1-Heptanol	1.422
Nitroethane	1.390	3-Isopropyl-2-heptanone	1.423
Methyl-b-butyrate	1.391	Cyclohexane	1.424
Butyl acetate	1.392	2-Bromopropane	1.424
2-Nitropropane	1.392	3-Chloro-2-methylprop-1-ene	1.425
4-Methyl-2-pentanone	1.394	Caproic acid	1.426
2-Methyl-1-propanol	1.394	Glycol carbonate	1.426
Octane	1.395	1-Octanol	1.427
1-Amino-2-methylpropane	1.395	1,1-Dimethylhexanol	1.427
Valeronitrile	1.395	N,N-Dimethylformamide	1.427
2-Butanol	1.395	Sulfuric acid	1.427
2-Hexanone	1.395	1-Chlorooctane	1.428
5-Methyl-3-hexanone	1.395	Triisobutylene	1.429
2-Chlorobutane	1.395	N-Methylaniline nitrile	1.429
Butyric acid	1.396	Ethylene glycol	1.429
2,2,2-Trimethylhexane	1.397	1-Chloro-2-ethylhexane	1.430
n-Dibutyl ether	1.397	Ethylcyclohexane	1.431
1-Butanol	1.397	1,2-Propanediol	1.431
Acrolein	1.397	1-Bromopropane	1.431
1-Chloro-2-methylpropane	1.397	2-Methyl-7-ethyl-4-nonanone	1.433
Methacrylonitrile	1.398	Ethyleneglycol-mono-allyl ether	1.434
3-Methyl-2-pentanone	1.398	Butyral lactone	1.434
Triethyl amine	1.399	2-Methyl-7-ethyl-4-undecanone	1.435
n-Butyl amine	1.399	4-n-Propyl-5-ethyldioxane	1.435
1,1,3,3-Tetramethyl-2-propanone	1.399	1,2-Dichloro-2-methylpropane	1.435
Isobutyl-n-butyrate	1.399	1,2-Propyleneglycol sulfite	1.435
1-Nitropropane	1.399	N-Methylmorpholine	1.436
n-Dodecane	1.400	1-Chloro-2-methyl-2-propanol	1.436
Amyl acetate	1.400	Epichlorohydrin	1.436
1-Chlorobutane	1.400	Triethyleneglycol-mono-butyl ether	1.437
2-Methoxy ethanol	1.400	4-Ethyl-7,7,7-trimethyl-1-heptanol	1.438
Propionic acid anhydride	1.400	1-Methyl-3-ethyloctan-1-ol	1.438

Compound	n_D	Compound	n_D
1-Ethyl-3-ethylhexan-1-ol	1.438	Furfuralcohol	1.489
Diethyl maleate	1.438	tert-Butylcumene	1.490
1-Butanethiol	1.440	n-Propylbenzene	1.490
2-Chloroethanal	1.440	sec-Butylbenzene	1.490
Dibutyl sebacate	1.440	tert-Butylbenzene	1.490
1-Ethyl-3-ethyloctan-1-ol	1.441	Dibutylphthalate	1.490
Dimethylmaleate	1.441	tert-Butyltoluene	1.491
3-Methylpentane-2,4-diol	1.441	1-Penyl-1-oxyphenylethane	1.491
Ethyl sulfide	1.442	n-Hexylcumene	1.492
Mesityl oxide	1.442	n-Octyltoluene	1.492
Butyl stearate	1.442	n-Octylcumene	1.492
		p-Xylene	1.493
1,2-Dichloroethane	1.444	1,31-Diethylbenzene	1.493
Chloroform	1.444	Ethylbenzene	1.493
trans-1,2-Dichloroethylene	1.444	1,3-Dimorpholylpropan-2-ol	1.493
Diethyleneglycol	1.445	1,12,2-Tetrachloroethane	1.493
cis-1,2-Dichloroethylene	1.445	Toluene	1.494
3-(α-Butyloctyl)-oxypropyl-1-amine	1.446	Benzylethyl ether	1.494
2-Methylmorpholine	1.446	m-Xylene	1.495
Dipropyleneglycol-monoethyl ether	1.446	1,4-Diethylbenzene	1.496
Formamide	1.446	2,3-Dichlorodioxane	1.496
3-Lauryloxypropyl-1-amine	1.447	Mesitylene	1.497
Cyclohexanone	1.448	2-Iodopropane	1.497
1-Aminopropan-1-ol	1.448	Benzene	1.498
Diethyleneglycol-mono-β-oxypropyl ether	1.448	Propyl benzoate	1.498
1-Amino-2-methylpentan-1-ol	1.449	α-Picoline	1.499
Tetrahydrofurfural alcohol	1.450	1,2-Diethylbenzene	1.501
2-Propylcyclohexa-1-one	1.452	Pentachloroethane	1.501
2-Aminoethanol	1.452	1-Iodopropane	1.502
2-Butylcyclohexan-1-one	1.453	1,2-Dimethylbenzene	1.503
Ethylenediamine	1.454	Ethyl benzoate	1.503
2-(β-Methyl)-propylcyclohexan-1-one	1.454	β-Picoline	1.504
4-Methylcyclohexanol	1.454	Tetrachloroethylene	1.504
3-Methylcyclohexanol	1.455	Phenetole	1.505
bis-2-Chloroethyl ether	1.455	Pyridine	1.507
Cyclohexylamine	1.456	Iodoethane	1.512
1,8-Cineol	1.456	Phenylmethallyl ether	1.514
2,2'-Dimethyl-2,2' dipropyldieththanol amine	1.456	Anisole	1.515
1,1',2,2'-Tetramethyldiethanol amine	1.459	Methyl benzoate	1.515
1-Aminopropan-3-ol	1.459	Diallylphthalate	1.517
Carbon tetrachloride	1.459	Benzylacetate	1.518
3-Methyl-5-ethylheptan-2,4-diol	1.459	2-Methyl-4-tertiarybutylphenetol	1.521
2-(β-Ethyl)-butylcyclohexan-1-one	1.461	Phenylacetonitrile	1.521
2-Methylcyclohexanol	1.461	Methyl salicylate	1.522
N-(n-Butyl)-diethanol amine	1.461	Chlorobenzene	1.523
4,5-Chloro-1,3-dioxolane-2	1.461	Fufural	1.524
2-Butylcyclohexan-1-ol	1.462	Benzonitrile	1.526
N-β-Oxypropyl morpholine	1.462	Thiophene	1.526
2-(β-Ethyl)-hexylcyclohexanone	1.463	Nonachlorodiethyl ether	1.529
2-Ethylcyclohexan-1-ol	1.463	Iodomethane	1.530
Fluorobenzene	1.463	4-Phenyldioxane	1.530
d-α-Pinene	1.464	3-Phenylpropan-1-ol	1.532
1-α-Pinene	1.465	Acetophenone	1.532
Cyclohexanol	1.465	Benzyl alcohol	1.538
m-Fluorotoluene	1.465	1,2-Dibromoethane	1.538
p-Fluorotoluene	1.467	1,2,3,4-Tetrahydronaphthalene	1.539
trans-Decahydronaphthalene	1.468	m-Cresol	1.542
o-Fluorotoluene	1.468	1,3-Dichlorobenzene	1.543
3-Alloxy-2-oxypropylamine-1	1.469	Benzaldehyde	1.544
Ethanol-1-methylisopropanol amine	1.470	Styrene	1.545
d-Limonene	1.471	Nitrobenzene	1.550
1,2,3-Trichloroisobutane	1.473	o-Dichlorobenzene	1.551
Decahydronaphthalene	1.474	Bromobenzene	1.557
1,2,3-Propanetriol	1.474	o-Nitroanisole	1.560
Trichloroethylene	1.475	m-Toluidine	1.566
N-β-Oxyethylmorpholine	1.476	Benzyl benzoate	1.568
Dimethylsulfoxide	1.476	o-Toluidine	1.570
cis-Decahydronaphthalene	1.479	1-Methoxyphenyl-1-phenyl-ethane	1.571
N-δ-Chlorallylmorpholine	1.481	Aniline	1.583
n-Dodecyl-4-tertiarybutylphenyl ether	1.482	o-Chloroaniline	1.586
n-Dodecylphenyl ether	1.482	Bromoform	1.587
n-Dodecyl-4-methylphenyl ether	1.483	Benzenethiol	1.588
2-Ethylidene cyclohexanone	1.486	2,4-Bis(β-phenylethyl)-phenylmethyl ether	1.590
n-Butylbenzene	1.487	Carbondisulfide	1.628
p-Cymene	1.488	1,12,2-Tetrabromomethane	1.633
iso-Propylbenzene	1.489	Diiodomethane	1.749

The molar refraction, R, is defined as:

$$R = \left(\frac{n^2 - 1}{n^2 + 2}\right)\left(\frac{M}{d}\right)$$

where n = refractive index; M = molecular weight; d = density in grams per cm³; and (M/d) is the volume occupied by 1 gram molecular weight of the compound. The units of R will then be cm⁻³.

R is, to a first approximation, independent of temperature or physical state, and it provides an approximate measure of the actual total volume (without free space) of the molecules in one gram mole.

For a very large number of compounds R is approximately additive for the bonds present in the molecule. Using R_D based on n_D (sodium light), the following atomic, group and structural contributions to R_D are based on Vogel's extensive modern measurements published in the Journal of the Chemical Society, 1948.

C	2.591	Cl	5.844	$=S$	7.921
H	1.028	Br	8.741	$C\equiv N$	5.459
$=O$	2.122	I	13.954	N (primary	
		C_6H_5	25.463	aliphatic)	2.376
O	1.643	$C_{10}H_7$	43.00	N (secondary	
				aliphatic)	2.582
OH	2.553	S	7.729		
F	0.81				

Ethylenic bond	1.575	Four membered ring	0.317
Acetylenic bond	1.977	Three membered ring	0.614
N (aromatic)	3.550		

Example:—For C_2H_5COOH: $R_{calc.} = 3(2.591) + 5(1.028)$
$$+ 2.122 + 2.553 = 17.588$$
$R_{obs.}$ for this compound is 17.51
For $C_6H_5NHCH_3$: $R_{calc.} = 25.463 + 3.550$
$$+ 2.591 + 4(1.028) = 35.716$$
$R_{obs.}$ for this compound is 35.67

INDEX OF REFRACTION OF WATER
Alcohol and Carbon Bisulfide
For sodium light, $\lambda = .5893$

Temp. °C	Water, pure relative to air	Ethyl Alcohol 99.8 relative to air	Carbon Bisulfide relative to air
14	1.33348	......	......
15	1.33341	......	1.62935
16	1.33333	1.36210	1.62858
18	1.33317	1.36129	1.62704
20	1.33299	1.36048	1.62546
22	1.33281	1.35967	1.62387
24	1.33262	1.35885	1.62226
26	1.33241	1.35803	1.62064
28	1.33219	1.35721	1.61902
30	1.33192	1.35639	1.61740
32	1.33164	1.35557	1.61577
34	1.33136	1.35474	1.61413
36	1.33107	1.35390	1.61247
38	1.33079	1.35306	1.61080
40	1.33051	1.35222	1.60914
42	1.33023	1.35138	1.60748
44	1.32992	1.35054	1.60582
46	1.32959	1.34969	......
48	1.32927	1.34885	......
50	1.32894	1.34800	......
52	1.32860	1.34715	......
54	1.32827	1.34629	......
56	1.32792	1.34543	......
58	1.32755	1.34456	......
60	1.32718	1.34368	......
62	1.32678	1.34279	......
64	1.32636	1.34189	......
66	1.32596	1.34096	......
68	1.32555	1.34004	......
70	1.32511	1.33912	......
72	1.32466	1.33820	......
74	1.32421	1.33728	......
76	1.32376	1.33626	......
78	1.32332	......	......
80	1.32287	......	......
82	1.32241	......	......
84	1.32195	......	......
86	1.32148	......	......
88	1.32100	......	......
90	1.32050	......	......
92	1.32000	......	......
94	1.31949	......	......
96	1.31897	......	......
98	1.31842	......	......
100	1.31783	......	......

ABSOLUTE INDEX FOR PURE WATER FOR SODIUM LIGHT

Temperature	Index	Temperature	Index
15° C.	1.33377	60° C.	1.32754
20	1.33335	65	1.32652
25	1.33287	70	1.32547
30	1.33228	75	1.32434
35	1.33157	80	1.32323
40	1.33087	85	1.32208
45	1.33011	90	1.32086
50	1.32930	95	1.31959
55	1.32846	100	1.31819

INDEX OF REFRACTION OF GLASS
RELATIVE TO AIR

Variety	Wave length in microns.							
	.361	.434	.486	.589 (Na)	.656	.768	1.20	2.00
Zinc crown	1.539	1.528	1.523	1.517	1.514	1.511	1.505	1.497
Higher dispersion crown	1.546	1.533	1.527	1.520	1.517	1.514	1.507	1.497
Light flint	1.614	1.594	1.585	1.575	1.571	1.567	1.559	1.549
Heavy flint	1.705	1.675	1.664	1.650	1.644	1.638	1.628	1.617
Heaviest flint	...	1.945	1.919	1.890	1.879	1.867	1.848	1.832

INDEX OF REFRACTION OF ROCK SALT, SYLVINE, CALCITE, FLUORITE AND QUARTZ
(Compiled from data of Martens, Paschen, and others.)

Wave length.	Rock salt.	Silvine, KCl.	Fluorite.	Calcspar, ordinary ray.	Calcspar, extraordinary ray.	Quartz, ordinary ray.	Quartz, extraordinary ray.
0.185	1.893	1.827	......	......	......	1.676	1.690
0.198	......	......	1.496	......	1.578	1.651	1.664
0.340	......	......	......	1.701	1.506	1.567	1.577
0.589	1.544	1.490	1.434	1.658	1.486	1.544	1.553
0.760	......	......	1.431	1.650	1.483	1.539	1.548
0.884	1.534	1.481	1.430	......	......	......	......
1.179	1.530	1.478	1.428	......	......	......	......
1.229	......	......	......	1.639	1.479	......	......
2.324	......	......	......	......	1.474	1.516	......
2.357	1.526	1.475	1.421	......	......	......	......
3.536	1.523	1.473	1.414	......	......	......	......
5.893	1.516	1.469	1.387	......	......	......	......
8.840	1.502	1.461	1.331	......	......	......	......

INDEX OF REFRACTION, AQUEOUS SOLUTIONS

Substance	Density	Temp. °C	Index for λ = .5893 (Na)	Observer
Ammonium chloride	1.067	27.05	1.379	Willigen
Ammonium chloride	1.025	29.75	1.351	Willigen
Calcium chloride	1.398	25.65	1.443	Willigen
Calcium chloride	1.215	22.9	1.397	Willigen
Calcium chloride	1.143	25.8	1.374	Willigen
Hydrochloric acid	1.166	20.75	1.411	Willigen
Nitric acid	1.359	18.75	1.402	Willigen
Potash (caustic)	1.416	11.0	1.403	Frauenhofer
Potassium chloride	Normal solution		1.343	Bender
Potassium chloride	Double normal		1.352	Bender
Potassium chloride	Triple normal		1.360	Bender
Soda (caustic)	1.376	21.6	1.413	Willigen
Sodium chloride	1.189	18.07	1.378	Schutt
Sodium chloride	1.109	18.07	1.360	Schutt
Sodium chloride	1.035	18.07	1.342	Schutt
Sodium nitrate	1.358	22.8	1.385	Willigen
Sulfuric acid	1.811	18.3	1.437	Willigen
Sulfuric acid	1.632	18.3	1.425	Willigen
Sulfuric acid	1.221	18.3	1.370	Willigen
Sulfuric acid	1.028	18.3	1.339	Willigen
Zinc chloride	1.359	26.6	1.402	Willigen
Zinc chloride	1.209	26.4	1.375	Willigen

INDEX OF REFRACTION OF FUSED QUARTZ

λ mµ, 15° C	n, 18° C	λ mµ, 15° C	n, 18° C
185.467	1.57436	434.047	1.46690
193.583	1.55999	435.834	1.46675
202.55	1.54727	467.815	1.46435
214.439	1.53386	479.991	1.46355
219.462	1.52907	486.133	1.46318
226.503	1.52308	508.582	1.46191
231.288	1.51941	533.85	1.46067
250.329	1.50745	546.072	1.46013
257.304	1.50379	589.29	1.45845
274.867	1.49617	643.847	1.45674
303.412	1.48594	650.278	1.45040
340.365	1.47867	706.520	1.45517
396.848	1.47061	794.763	1.45340
404.656	1.46968		

INDEX OF REFRACTION OF AIR (15°C, 76 cm Hg)

Corrections for reducing wavelengths and frequencies in air (15°C, 76 cm Hg) to vacuo

The indices were computed from the Cauchy formula $(n-1)10^7 = 2726.43 + 12.288/(\lambda^2 \times 10^{-8}) + 0.3555/(\lambda^4 \times 10^{-16})$. For 0°C and 76 cm Hg the constants of the equation become 2875.66, 13.412 and 0.3777 respectively, and for 30°C and 76 cm Hg 2589.72, 12.259 and 0.2576. Sellmeier's formula for but one absorption band closely fits the observations: $n^2 = 1 + 0.00057378\lambda^2/(\lambda^2 - 595260)$. If $n-1$ were strictly proportional to the density, then $(n-1)_0/(n-1)t$ would equal $1 + \alpha t$ where α should be 0.00367. The following values of α were found to hold:

λ	0.85µ	0.75µ	0.65µ	0.55µ	0.45µ	0.35µ	0.25µ
α	0.003672	0.003674	0.003678	0.003685	0.003700	0.003738	0.003872

The indices are for dry air (0.05 + % CO₂). Corrections to reduce to dry air the indices for moist air may be made for any wavelength by Lorenz's formula, $+0.000041(m/760)$, where m is the vapor pressure in mm. The corresponding frequencies in waves per cm and the corrections to reduce wavelengths and frequencies in air at 15°C and 76 cm Hg pressure to vacuo are given. E.g., a light wave of 5000 angstroms in dry air at 15°C, 76 cm Hg becomes 5001.391 A in vacuo; a frequency of 20.000 waves per cm correspondingly becomes 19994.44.

Wave-length, λ angstroms	Dry air (n−1) ×10^7 15°C 76 cm Hg	Vacuo correction for λ in air (nλ−λ) add	Frequency waves per cm 1/λ in air	Vacuo correction for 1/λ in air (1/nλ − 1/λ) subtract	Wave-length, λ angstroms	Dry air (n−1) ×10^7 15°C 76 cm Hg	Vacuo correction for λ in air (nλ−λ) add	Frequency waves per cm 1/λ in air	Vacuo correction for 1/λ in air (1/nλ − 1/λ) subtract
2000	3256	.651	50,000	16.27	3500	2850	.998	28,571	8.14
2100	3188	.670	47,619	15.18	3600	2842	1.023	27,777	7.89
2200	3132	.689	45,454	14.23	3700	2835	1.049	27,027	7.66
2300	3086	.710	43,478	13.41	3800	2829	1.075	26,315	7.44
2400	3047	.731	41,666	12.69	3900	2823	1.101	25,641	7.24
2500	3014	.754	40,000	12.05	4000	2817	1.127	25,000	7.04
2600	2986	.776	38,461	11.48	4100	2812	1.153	24,390	6.86
2700	2962	.800	37,037	10.97	4200	2808	1.179	23,809	6.68
2800	2941	.824	35,714	10.50	4300	2803	1.205	23,255	6.52
2900	2923	.848	34,482	10.08	4400	2799	1.232	22,727	6.36
3000	2907	.872	33,333	9.69	4500	2796	1.258	22,222	6.21
3100	2893	.897	32,258	9.33	4600	2792	1.284	21,739	6.07
3200	2880	.922	31,250	9.00	4700	2789	1.311	21,276	5.93
3300	2869	.947	30,303	8.69	4800	2786	1.338	20,833	5.80
3400	2859	.972	29,411	8.41	4900	2784	1.364	20,406	5.68

Wave-length, λ angstroms	Dry air (n−1) ×10^7 15°C 76 cm Hg	Vacuo correction for λ in air (nλ−λ) add	Frequency waves per cm 1/λ in air	Vacuo correction for 1/λ in air (1/nλ − 1/λ) subtract	Wave-length, λ angstroms	Dry air (n−1) ×10^7 15°C 76 cm Hg	Vacuo correction for λ in air (nλ−λ) add	Frequency waves per cm 1/λ in air	Vacuo correction for 1/λ in air (1/nλ − 1/λ) subtract
5000	2781	1.391	20,000	5.56	7000	2753	1.927	14,285	3.93
5100	2779	1.417	19,607	5.45	7100	2752	1.954	14,084	3.88
5200	2777	1.444	19,230	5.34	7200	2751	1.981	13,888	3.82
5300	2775	1.471	18,867	5.23	7300	2751	2.008	13,698	3.77
5400	2773	1.497	18,518	5.13	7400	2750	2.035	13,513	3.72
5500	2771	1.524	18,181	5.04	7500	2749	2.062	13,333	3.66
5600	2769	1.551	17,857	4.94	7600	2749	2.089	13,157	3.62
5700	2768	1.578	17,543	4.85	7700	2748	2.116	12,987	3.57
5800	2766	1.604	17,241	4.77	7800	2748	2.143	12,820	3.52
5900	2765	1.631	16,949	4.68	7900	2747	2.170	12,658	3.48
6000	2763	1.658	16,666	4.60	8000	2746	2.197	12,500	3.43
6100	2762	1.685	16,393	4.53	8100	2746	2.224	12,345	3.39
6200	2761	1.712	16,129	4.45	8250	2745	2.265	12,121	3.33
6300	2760	1.739	15,873	4.38	8500	2744	2.332	11,764	3.23
6400	2759	1.766	15,625	4.31	8750	2743	2.400	11,428	3.13
6500	2758	1.792	15,384	4.24	9000	2742	2.468	11,111	3.05
6600	2757	1.819	15,151	4.18	9250	2741	2.536	10,810	2.96
6700	2756	1.846	14,925	4.11	9500	2740	2.604	10,526	2.88
6800	2755	1.873	14,705	4.05	9750	2740	2.671	10,256	2.81
6900	2754	1.900	14,492	3.99	10000	2739	2.739	10,000	2.74

INDEX OF REFRACTION, GASES

Values are relative to a vacuum and for a Temp. of 0° C. and 760 mm. pressure.

(From Smithsonian Tables)

Substance	Kind of light	Indices of refraction	Observer
Acetone	D	1.001079–1.001100	
Air	D	1.0002926	Perreau
Ammonia	white	1.000381–1.000385	
Ammonia	D	1.000373–1.000379	Rayleigh
Argon	D	1.000281	
Benzene	D	1.001700–1.001823	
Bromine	D	1.001132	Mascart
Carbon dioxide	white	1.000449–1.000450	
dioxide	D	1.000448–1.000454	
disulfide	white	1.001500	Dulong
disulfide	D	1.001478–1.001485	
monoxide	white	1.000340	Dulong
monoxide	white	1.000335	Mascart
Chlorine	white	1.000772	Dulong
Chlorine	D	1.000773	Mascart
Chloroform	D	1.001436–1.001464	
Cyanogen	white	1.000834	Dulong
Cyanogen	D	1.000784–1.000825	
Ethyl alcohol	D	1.000871–1.000885	
ether	D	1.001521–1.001544	
Helium	D	1.000036	Ramsay
Hydrochloric acid	white	1.000449	Mascart
Hydrochloric acid	D	1.000447	Mascart
Hydrogen	white	1.000138–1.000143	
Hydrogen	D	1.000132	Burton
sulfide	D	1.000644	Dulong
sulfide	D	1.000623	Mascart
Methane	white	1.000443	Dulong
Methane	D	1.000444	Mascart
Methyl alcohol	D	1.000549–1.000623	
Methyl ether	D	1.000891	Marcast
Nitric oxide	white	1.000303	Dulong
Nitric oxide	D	1.000297	Mascart
Nitrogen	white	1.000295–1.000300	
Nitrogen	D	1.000296–1.000298	
Nitrous oxide	white	1.000503–1.000507	
Nitrous oxide	D	1.000516	Mascart
Oxygen	white	1.000272–1.000280	
Oxygen	D	1.000271–1.000272	
Pentane	D	1.001711	Mascart
Sulfur dioxide	white	1.000665	Dulong
Sulfur dioxide	D	1.000686	Ketteler
Water	white	1.000261	Jamin
Water	D	1.000249–1.000259	

COEFFICIENT OF TRANSPARENCY OF UVIOL GLASS FOR THE ULTRA-VIOLET

For a thickness of 1 mm.

Wave length, microns	0.280	0.309	0.325	0.346	0.361	0.383	0.397
Uviol crown	0.56	0.95	0.990	0.996	0.999	1.000	1.000

INDEX OF REFRACTION OF AQUEOUS SOLUTIONS OF SUCROSE (CANE SUGAR)

The table gives the index of refraction for $\lambda = 0.5893$ of aqueous sugar solutions at 20°C from 0–85 % sugar. Corrections for temperatures other than 20° are given at the end of the table.

Per cent sugar	.0	.1	.2	.3	.4	.5	.6	.7	.8	.9
00	1.3 330	331	333	334	336	337	338	340	341	342
1	344	345	347	348	350	351	353	355	356	357
2	359	361	362	363	365	367	368	369	371	373
3	374	375	377	378	380	381	382	384	385	387
4	388	389	391	393	394	395	397	399	400	401
5	403	405	406	407	409	411	412	413	415	417
6	418	419	421	423	424	425	427	429	430	431
7	433	435	436	437	439	441	442	443	445	447
8	448	450	451	453	454	456	458	459	461	462
9	464	465	467	469	470	471	473	475	476	477
10	479	481	482	483	485	487	488	489	491	493
11	494	496	497	499	500	502	504	505	507	508
12	510	512	513	515	516	518	520	521	523	524
13	526	527	529	531	532	533	535	537	538	539
14	541	543	544	546	547	549	551	552	554	555
15	557	559	560	562	563	565	567	568	570	571
16	573	575	576	578	580	582	583	585	587	588
17	590	592	593	595	596	598	600	601	603	604
18	606	608	609	611	612	614	616	617	619	620
19	622	624	625	627	629	631	632	634	636	637
20	639	641	642	644	645	647	649	650	652	653
21	655	657	658	660	662	663	665	667	669	670
22	672	674	675	677	679	681	682	684	686	687
23	689	691	692	694	696	698	699	701	703	704
24	706	708	709	711	713	715	716	718	720	721
25	723	725	726	728	730	731	733	735	737	738
26	740	742	744	745	747	749	751	753	754	756
27	758	760	761	763	765	767	768	770	772	773
28	775	777	779	780	782	784	786	788	789	791
29	793	795	797	798	800	802	804	806	807	809
30	811	813	815	816	818	820	822	824	825	827
31	829	831	833	834	836	838	840	842	843	845
32	847	849	851	852	854	856	858	860	861	863
33	865	867	869	870	872	874	876	878	879	881
34	883	885	887	889	891	893	894	896	898	900
35	902	904	906	907	909	911	913	915	916	918
36	920	922	924	926	928	929	931	933	935	937
37	939	941	943	945	947	949	950	952	954	956
38	958	960	962	964	966	968	970	972	974	976
39	978	980	982	984	986	987	989	991	993	995
40	997	999	*001	*003	*005	*007	*008	*010	*012	*014
41	1.4 016	018	020	022	024	026	028	030	032	034
42	036	038	040	042	044	046	048	050	052	054
43	056	058	060	062	064	066	068	070	072	074
44	076	078	080	082	084	086	088	090	092	094
45	096	098	100	102	104	107	109	111	113	115
46	117	119	121	123	125	127	129	131	133	135
47	137	139	141	143	145	147	150	152	154	156
48	158	160	162	164	166	169	171	173	175	177
49	179	181	183	185	187	189	192	194	196	198
50	200	202	204	206	208	211	213	215	217	219
51	221	223	225	227	229	231	234	236	238	240
52	242	244	246	249	251	253	255	257	260	262
53	264	266	268	270	272	275	277	279	281	283
54	285	287	289	292	294	296	298	300	303	305
55	307	309	311	313	316	318	320	322	325	327
56	329	331	333	336	338	340	342	344	347	349
57	351	353	355	358	360	362	364	366	369	371
58	373	375	378	380	382	385	387	389	391	394
59	396	398	400	403	405	407	409	411	414	416
60	418	420	423	425	427	429	432	434	436	439
61	441	443	446	448	450	453	455	457	459	462
62	464	466	468	471	473	475	477	479	482	484
63	486	488	491	493	495	497	500	502	504	507
64	509	511	514	516	518	521	523	525	527	530
65	532	534	537	539	541	544	546	548	550	553
66	558	561	563	565	567	570	572	574	577	579
67	581	584	586	588	591	593	595	598	600	602
68	605	607	609	612	614	616	619	621	623	625
69	628	630	632	635	637	639	642	644	646	649
70	651	653	656	658	661	663	666	668	671	673
71	676	678	681	683	685	688	690	693	695	698
72	700	703	705	708	710	713	715	717	720	722
73	725	727	730	732	735	737	740	742	744	747
74	749	752	754	757	759	762	764	767	769	772
75	774	777	779	782	784	787	789	792	794	797
76	799	802	804	807	810	812	815	817	820	822
77	825	827	830	832	835	838	840	843	845	848
78	850	853	855	858	860	863	865	868	871	873
79	876	878	881	883	886	888	891	893	896	898
80	901	904	906	909	912	914	917	919	922	925
81	927	930	933	935	938	941	943	946	949	951
82	954	956	959	962	964	967	970	972	975	978
83	980	983	985	988	991	993	996	999	*001	*004
84	1.5 007	009	012	015	017	020	022	025	028	030
85	033									

Correction table for determining the percentage of sucrose by means of the refractometer when the readings are made at temperatures other than 20° C[1]

Temperature	Percentage of sucrose—														
	0	5	10	15	20	25	30	35	40	45	50	55	60	65	70
Subtract from the percentage of sucrose															
°C.															
10	0.50	0.54	0.58	0.61	0.64	0.66	0.68	0.70	0.72	0.73	0.74	0.75	0.76	0.78	0.79
11	.46	.49	.53	.55	.58	.60	.62	.64	.65	.66	.67	.68	.69	.70	.71
12	.42	.45	.48	.50	.52	.54	.56	.57	.58	.59	.60	.61	.61	.63	.63
13	.37	.40	.42	.44	.46	.48	.49	.50	.51	.52	.53	.54	.54	.55	.55
14	.33	.35	.37	.39	.40	.41	.42	.43	.44	.45	.45	.46	.46	.47	.48
15	.27	.29	.31	.33	.34	.34	.35	.36	.37	.37	.38	.39	.39	.40	.40
16	.22	.24	.25	.26	.27	.28	.28	.29	.30	.30	.30	.31	.31	.32	.32
17	.17	.18	.19	.20	.21	.21	.21	.22	.22	.23	.23	.23	.23	.24	.24
18	.12	.13	.13	.14	.14	.14	.14	.15	.15	.15	.15	.16	.16	.16	.16
19	.06	.06	.06	.07	.07	.07	.07	.08	.08	.08	.08	.08	.08	.08	.08
Add to the percentage of sucrose															
21	0.06	0.07	0.07	0.07	0.07	0.08	0.08	0.08	0.08	0.08	0.08	0.08	0.08	0.08	0.08
22	.13	.13	.14	.14	.15	.15	.15	.15	.15	.16	.16	.16	.16	.16	.16
23	.19	.20	.21	.22	.22	.23	.23	.23	.23	.24	.24	.24	.24	.24	.24
24	.26	.27	.28	.29	.30	.30	.31	.31	.31	.31	.32	.32	.32	.32	.32
25	.33	.35	.36	.37	.38	.38	.39	.40	.40	.40	.40	.40	.40	.40	.40
26	.40	.42	.43	.44	.45	.46	.47	.48	.48	.48	.48	.48	.48	.48	.48
27	.48	.50	.52	.53	.54	.55	.55	.56	.56	.56	.56	.56	.56	.56	.56
28	.56	.57	.60	.61	.62	.63	.63	.64	.64	.64	.64	.64	.64	.64	.64
29	.64	.66	.68	.69	.71	.72	.72	.73	.73	.73	.73	.73	.73	.73	.73
30	.72	.74	.77	.78	.79	.80	.80	.81	.81	.81	.81	.81	.81	.81	.81

[1] International Temperature Correction Table, 1936, adopted by the International Commission for Uniform Methods of Sugar Analysis (Int. Sugar J. **39**, 24s, 1937).

INDEX OF REFRACTION OF MALTOSE HYDRATE SOLUTIONS

McDonald: Journal of Research of the National Bureau of Standards, Vol. **46**, 165, 1951.
The following table gives the refractive index of maltose solutions for λ = 5893 A at 20° and 25°C.

Percent	n_D^{20}	n_D^{25}	Δn	$\Delta n/\Delta t$	Percent	n_D^{20}	n_D^{25}	Δn	$\Delta n/\Delta t$
1	1.33438	1.33389	0.00049	0.00010	36	1.39004	1.38924	0.00080	0.00016
2	1.33579	1.33528	.00051	.00010	37	1.39185	1.39105	.00080	.00016
3	1.33720	1.33668	.00052	.00010	38	1.39367	1.39287	.00080	.00016
4	1.33862	1.33810	.00052	.00010	39	1.39551	1.39471	.00080	.00016
5	1.34006	1.33952	.00054	.00011	40	1.39735	1.39656	.00079	.00016
6	1.34150	1.34095	.00055	.00011	41	1.39922	1.39843	.00079	.00016
7	1.34295	1.34239	.00056	.00011	42	1.40109	1.40031	.00078	.00016
8	1.34442	1.34384	.00058	.00012	43	1.40298	1.40221	.00077	.00016
9	1.34589	1.34530	.00059	.00012	44	1.40488	1.40411	.00077	.00015
10	1.34738	1.34677	.00061	.00012	45	1.40680	1.40603	.00077	.00015
11	1.34887	1.34825	.00062	.00012	46	1.40873	1.40797	.00076	.00015
12	1.35039	1.34974	.00065	.00013	47	1.41067	1.40992	.00075	.00015
13	1.35190	1.35124	.00066	.00013	48	1.41263	1.41188	.00075	.00015
14	1.35343	1.35276	.00067	.00013	49	1.41460	1.41385	.00075	.00015
15	1.35497	1.35428	.00069	.00014	50	1.41658	1.41584	.00074	.00015
16	1.35652	1.35582	.00070	.00014	51	1.41858	1.41784	.00074	.00015
17	1.35808	1.35737	.00071	.00014	52	1.42059	1.41986	.00073	.00015
18	1.35965	1.35893	.00072	.00014	53	1.42262	1.42189	.00073	.00015
19	1.36124	1.36051	.00073	.00015	54	1.42466	1.42392	.00074	.00015
20	1.36283	1.36209	.00074	.00015	55	1.42672	1.42598	.00074	.00015
21	1.36444	1.36369	.00075	.00015	56	1.42878	1.42804	.00074	.00015
22	1.36606	1.36530	.00076	.00015	57	1.43087	1.43012	.00075	.00015
23	1.36770	1.36692	.00078	.00016	58	1.43296	1.43221	.00075	.00015
24	1.36934	1.36856	.00078	.00016	59	1.43508	1.43431	.00077	.00015
25	1.37100	1.37021	.00079	.00016	60	1.43720	1.43643	.00077	.00015
26	1.37267	1.37187	.00080	.00016	61	1.43934	1.43855	.00079	.00016
27	1.37435	1.37355	.00080	.00016	62	1.44150	1.44069	.00081	.00016
28	1.37604	1.37524	.00080	.00016	63	1.44367	1.44283	.00084	.00017
29	1.37775	1.37694	.00081	.00016	64	1.44585	1.44499	.00086	.00017
30	1.37946	1.37865	.00081	.00016	65	1.44805	1.44716	.00089	.00018
31	1.38120	1.38038	.00082	.00016					
32	1.38294	1.38213	.00082	.00016					
33	1.38470	1.38388	.00082	.00016					
34	1.38647	1.38565	.00081	.00016					
35	1.38825	1.38744	.00081	.00016					

RADIATION FROM AN IDEAL BLACK BODY

From NASA TT-F-783

Temperature dependence of the specific power radiated, Q_T, and of λ_{max} for an ideal black body according to Kirchhoff's law ($\sigma_O = 5.68 \cdot 10^{-8}$ W/m²·deg⁴ $= 4.88 \cdot 10^{-8}$ kcal/m²·deg⁴)

T, °K	t, °C	Q_T, W/cm²	Q_T kcal/m²·hr	λmax μ	T, °K	t, °C	Q_T W/cm²	Q_T kcal/m²·hr	λmax μ
100	−173	$5.680 \cdot 10^{-4}$	$4.880 \cdot 10^{0}$	28.96	730	457	$1.613 \cdot 10^{0}$	$1.386 \cdot 10^{1}$	3.967
200	−73	$9.088 \cdot 10^{-3}$	$7.808 \cdot 10^{1}$	14.48	740	467	1.703	1.463	3.914
273	0	$3.155 \cdot 10^{-2}$	$2.711 \cdot 10^{2}$	10.608	750	477	1.797	1.544	3.861
300	27	4.601	3.953	9.655	760	487	1.895	1.628	3.811
310	37	5.246	4.507	9.342	770	497	1.997	1.715	3.761
320	47	5.956	5.117	9.050	780	507	2.102	1.806	3.713
330	57	6.736	5.787	8.766	790	517	2.212	1.901	3.666
340	67	7.590	6.521	8.518	800	527	2.327	1.999	3.620
350	77	8.524	7.323	8.274	810	537	2.445	2.101	3.565
360	87	9.540	8.196	8.044	820	547	2.568	2.206	3.532
370	97	1.065	9.146	7.827	830	557	2.696	2.316	3.489
380	107	$1.184 \cdot 10^{-1}$	$1.018 \cdot 10^{3}$	7.621	840	567	2.828	2.430	3.448
390	117	1.314	1.128	7.426	850	577	2.965	2.547	3.407
400	127	1.454	1.249	7.270	860	587	3.107	2.670	3.367
410	137	1.605	1.379	7.053	870	597	3.254	2.796	3.329
420	147	1.76	1.519	6.865	880	607	3.406	2.927	3.291
430	157	1.942	1.668	6.735	890	617	3.564	3.062	3.254
440	167	2.129	1.829	6.562	900	627	3.727	3.202	3.218
450	177	2.329	2.001	6.436	910	637	3.895	3.346	3.162
460	187	2.543	2.185	6.266	920	647	4.069	3.496	3.148
470	197	2.772	2.381	6.162	930	657	4.249	3.650	3.114
480	207	3.015	2.591	6.033	940	667	4.435	3.810	3.081
490	217	3.274	2.813	5.910	950	677	4.626	3.975	3.048
500	227	3.550	3.05	5.792	960	687	4.824	4.145	3.017
510	237	3.843	3.301	5.668	970	697	5.028	4.320	2.986
520	247	4.163	3.568	5.559	980	707	5.239	4.501	2.955
530	257	4.482	3.851	5.454	990	717	5.456	4.688	2.925
540	267	4.830	4.150	5.363	1000	727	5.680	4.880	2.896
550	277	5.198		5.255	1010	737	5.909	5.07	2.866
560	287	5.586	4.799	5.161	1020	747	6.143	5.278	2.836
570	297	5.996	5.151	5.061	1030	757	6.394	5.494	2.812
580	307	6.428	5.522	4.963	1040	767	6.645	5.709	2.785
590	317	6.883	5.913	4.908	1050	777	6.904	5.932	2.758
600	327	7.361	6.324	4.827	1060	787	7.171	6.161	2.732
610	337	7.864	6.757	4.748	1070	797	7.445	6.397	2.707
620	347	8.393	7.211	4.671	1080	807	7.728	6.640	2.681
630	357	8.948	7.687	4.597	1090	817	8.018	6.888	2.657
640	367	9.529	8.187	4.525	1100	827	8.316	7.145	2.633
650	377	$1.014 \cdot 10^{0}$	8.711	4.455	1110	837	8.623	7.408	2.609
660	387	1.078	9.260	4.388	1120	847	8.937	7.679	2.586
670	397	1.145	9.831	4.322	1130	857	9.261	7.956	2.563
680	407	1.214	$1.013 \cdot 10^{4}$	4.259	1140	867	9.593	8.242	2.540
690	417	1.287	1.106	4.197	1150	877	9.934	8.535	2.516
700	427	1.364	1.172	4.137	1160	887	$1.028 \cdot 10^{1}$	8.836	2.497
710	437	1.443	1.240	4.069	1170	897	1.064	9.145	2.475
720	447	1.526	1.311	4.022	1180	907	1.101	9.461	2.454
1190	917	$1.139 \cdot 10^{1}$	$9.786 \cdot 10^{4}$	2.434	1640	1367	$4.109 \cdot 10^{1}$	$3.530 \cdot 10^{5}$	1.766
1200	927	1.178	$1.042 \cdot 10^{5}$	2.413	1650	1377	4.210	3.617	1.755
1210	937	1.218	1.046	2.393	1660	1387	4.313	3.706	1.745
1220	947	1.258	1.081	2.374	1670	1397	4.418	3.796	1.734
1230	957	1.300	1.117	2.354	1680	1407	4.525	3.887	1.724

T, °K	t, °C	Q_T, W/cm²	Q_T kcal/m²·hr	λmax μ	T, °K	t, °C	Q_T W/cm²	Q_T kcal/m²·hr	λmax μ
1240	967	1.343	1.154	2.335	1690	1417	4.633	3.981	1.714
1250	977	1.387	1.191	2.317	1700	1427	4.744	4.076	1.704
1260	987	1.431	1.230	2.298	1710	1437	4.858	4.183	1.694
1270	997	1.478	1.270	2.280	1720	1447	4.971	4.271	1.684
1280	1007	1.525	1.310	2.263	1730	1457	5.088	4.371	1.674
1290	1017	1.573	1.351	2.245	1740	1467	5.206	4.473	1.664
1300	1027	1.622	1.394	2.227	1750	1477	5.327	4.577	1.655
1310	1037	1.673	1.437	2.211	1760	1487	5.450	4.682	1.645
1320	1047	1.724	1.482	2.194	1770	1497	5.575	4.790	1.636
1330	1057	1.777	1.527	2.177	1780	1507	5.703	4.900	1.627
1340	1067	1.831	1.573	2.161	1790	1517	5.831	5.010	1.617
1350	1077	1.887	1.621	2.145	1800	1527	5.963	5.123	1.607
1360	1087	1.943	1.669	2.129	1810	1537	6.096	5.238	1.600
1370	1097	2.001	1.719	2.114	1820	1547	6.232	5.354	1.591
1380	1107	2.058	1.768	2.099	1830	1557	6.370	5.473	1.583
1390	1117	2.120	1.822	2.083	1840	1567	6.511	5.594	1.574
1400	1127	2.182	1.875	2.067	1850	1577	6.653	5.717	1.565
1410	1137	2.245	1.929	2.054	1860	1587	6.798	5.841	1.557
1420	1147	2.309	1.984	2.036	1870	1597	6.946	5.967	1.549
1430	1157	2.375	2.041	2.025	1880	1607	7.095	6.096	1.540
1440	1167	2.442	2.098	2.011	1890	1617	7.248	6.227	1.532
1450	1177	2.511	2.157	1.997	1900	1627	7.402	6.360	1.524
1460	1187	2.581	2.217	1.984	1910	1637	7.559	6.495	1.516
1470	1197	2.652	2.279	1.970	1920	1647	7.720	6.632	1.509
1480	1207	2.725	2.341	1.957	1930	1657	7.881	6.771	1.501
1490	1217	2.800	2.405	1.944	1940	1667	8.046	6.912	1.493
1500	1227	2.876	2.471	1.931	1950	1677	8.213	7.056	1.485
1510	1237	2.953	2.537	1.917	1960	1687	8.382	7.202	1.478
1520	1247	3.032	2.605	1.905	1970	1697	8.555	7.350	1.470
1530	1257	3.113	2.674	1.893	1980	1707	8.730	7.500	1.463
1540	1267	3.195	2.745	1.881	1990	1717	8.907	7.653	1.455
1550	1277	3.278	2.817	1.866	2000	1727	9.088	7.808	1.448
1560	1287	3.363	2.890	1.856	2500	2227	$2.219 \cdot 10^2$	$1.906 \cdot 10^6$	1.156
1570	1297	3.451	2.965	1.845	3000	2727	4.601	3.953	0.965
1580	1307	3.540	3.041	1.833	3500	3227	8.524	7.323	0.826
1590	1317	3.630	3.198	1.821	4000	3727	$1.454 \cdot 10^3$	1.249	0.722
1600	1327	3.722		1.810	4500	4227	2.329	2.001	0.644
1610	1337	3.816	3.279	1.797	5000	4727	3.550	3.050	0.579
1620	1347	3.912	3.361	1.787	5500	5227	5.198	4.465	0.527
1630	1357	4.010	3.445	1.777	6000	5727	7.361	6.324	0.483

REFLECTION COEFFICIENTS

Coefficients of Reflection of Miscellaneous Surfaces for Monochromatic Radiation in the Visible Spectrum
(J. L. Michaelson)

Material	Wave lengths (μ)			
	0.400	0.500	0.600	0.700
Carbon Black in Oil...............	0.003	0.003	0.003	0.003
Clay,				
Kaolin (treated)............	0.82	0.81	0.82	0.82
Kaolin (untreated)........	0.75	0.79	0.85	0.86
White Georgia............	0.94	0.92	0.93	0.94
Magnesium oxide..............	0.97	0.98	0.98	0.98
Paint,				
Lithopone............	0.95	0.98	0.98	0.98
MgCO₃-Vynal Acetate Lacquer....	0.90	0.88	0.88	0.88
ZnO-Milk............	0.74	0.84	0.85	0.86
Paper,				
Blotting............	0.64	0.72	0.79	0.79
Calendered............	0.64	0.69	0.73	0.76
Crepe, green............	0.23	0.49	0.19	0.48
Crepe, red............	0.03	0.02	0.21	0.69
Crepe, yellow............	0.17	0.44	0.75	0.79
News Print Stock........	0.38	0.61	0.63	0.78
Peach,				
Green............	0.18	0.17	0.62	0.63
Ripe............	0.10	0.10	0.41	0.42
Pear,				
Green............	0.04	0.12	0.29	0.41
Ripe............	0.08	0.19	0.46	0.53
Pigment,				
Chrome Yellow............	0.05	0.13	0.70	0.77
French Ochre............	0.06	0.14	0.50	0.56
Porcelain Enamel,				
Blue............	0.44	0.10	0.05	0.23
Orange............	0.09	0.09	0.59	0.69
Red............	0.05	0.03	0.08	0.62
White............	0.77	0.73	0.72	0.70
Yellow............	0.11	0.46	0.62	0.62
Talcum, Italian............	0.94	0.89	0.88	0.88
Wheat Flour............	0.75	0.87	0.94	0.97

REFLECTION COEFFICIENTS OF SURFACES FOR "INCANDESCENT" LIGHT

Material	Nature of Surface	Coefficient	Authority
Aluminum, "Alzak"........	Diffusing	0.77–0.81	3
"Alzak"............	Specular	0.79–0.83	3
on Glass............	First Surface	0.82–0.86	4
Polished............	Specular	0.69	3
Black Paper............	Diffusing	0.05–0.06	4
Chromium............	Specular	0.62	4
Copper............	Specular	0.63	4
Gold............	Specular	0.75	1
Magnesium oxide............	Diffusing	0.98	5
Nickel............	Specular	0.62–0.64	1, 3
Platinum............	Specular	0.62	1
Porcelain Enamel....	Glossy	0.76–0.79	3
Porcelain Enamel....	Ground	0.81	3
Porcelain Enamel....	Matt.	0.72–0.76	3
Silver............	Polished	0.93	1
Silvered Glass............	Second Surface	0.88–0.93	3
Snow............	Diffusing	0.93	2
Steel............	Specular	0.55	1
Stellite............	Specular	0.58–0.65	4

(1) Hagen and Rubens. (2) Nutting, Jones, and Elliot. (3) J. E. Bock. (4) Frank Benford. (5) J. L. Michaelson.

EMISSIVITY AND ABSORPTION

These data are the result of investigations made by the Bureau of Standards, the British National Physical Laboratory, General Electric Research Laboratories, and several eastern universities, and were collected by W. J. King of the General Electric Company.

Low Temperature Total Emissivities

Silver, highly polished..	0.02	Brass, polished........	0.60
Platinum " " ..	0.05	Oxidized copper.......	0.60
Zinc " " ..	0.05	Oxidized steel.........	0.70
Aluminum, " " ..	0.08	Bronze paint..........	0.80
*Monel metal, polished.	0.09	Black gloss paint.....	0.90
Nickel " ..	0.12	White lacquer........	0.95
Copper " ..	0.15	White vitreous enamel.	0.95
Stellite " ..	0.18	Asbestos paper........	0.95
Cast iron " ..	0.25	Green paint...........	0.95
Monel metal, oxidized..	0.43	Gray paint...........	0.95
Aluminum paint.......	0.55	Lamp black..........	0.95

Coefficient of Absorption of Solár Radiation

Silver, highly polished..	0.07	Stellite, polished.......	0.30
Platinum " " ..	0.10	Light cream paint.....	0.35
Nickel " " ..	0.15	Monel metal, polished.	0.40
*Aluminum............	0.15	Light yellow paint.....	0.45
Magnesium carbonate.	0.15	Light green paint......	0.50
Zinc oxide............	0.15	Aluminum paint.......	0.55
*Steel............	0.20	Zinc, polished metal...	0.55
Copper............	0.25	Gray paint...........	0.75
White lead paint......	0.25	Black matte..........	0.97
Zinc oxide paint......	0.30		

* Questionable because of scant or inconsistent data.

TOTAL EMISSIVITY
ROESER AND WENSEL, NATIONAL BUREAU OF STANDARDS

Material	Temp. °C	Emissivity	Material	Temp. °C	Emissivity
Alloys			Iron, rusted............	25	0.65
20Ni-25Cr-55Fe, oxidized	200	0.90	wrought, dull......	25	0.94
	500	0.97	oxidized..	350	0.94
60Ni-12Cr-28Fe, oxidized	270	0.89	Lead, unoxidized........	100	0.05
	560	0.82	oxidized........	200	0.63
80Ni-20Cr, oxidized......	100	0.87	Mercury, unoxidized.....	25	0.10
	600	0.87		100	0.12
	1300	0.89	Molybdenum, unoxidized.	1000	0.13
Aluminum, unoxidized......	25	0.022		1500	0.19
	100	0.028		2000	0.24
	500	0.060	Monel metal, oxidized...	200	0.43
oxidized........	200	0.11		600	0.43
	600	0.19	Nickel, unoxidized........	25	0.045
Bismuth, unoxidized.......	25	0.048		100	0.06
	100	0.061		500	0.12
Brass, oxidized.........	200	0.61		1000	0.19
	600	0.59	oxidized..........	200	0.37
unoxidized..........	25	0.035		1200	0.85
	100	0.035	Platinum, unoxidized....	25	0.037
Carbon, unoxidized......	25	0.81		100	0.047
	100	0.81		500	0.096
	500	0.81		1000	0.152
Chromium, unoxidized......	100	0.08		1500	0.191
Cobalt, unoxidized......	500	0.13	Silica brick............	1000	0.80
	1000	0.23		1100	0.85
Columbium, unoxidized....	1500	0.19	Silver, unoxidized........	100	0.02
	2000	0.24		500	0.035
Copper, unoxidized........	100	0.02	Steel, unoxidized........	100	0.08
	liquid	0.15		liquid	0.28
oxidized........	200	0.6	oxidized........	25	0.80
	1000	0.6		200	0.79
calorized........	100	0.26		600	0.79
	500	0.26	Steel plate, rough.......	40	0.94
calorized, oxidized..	200	0.18		400	0.97
	600	0.19	calorized, oxidized.	200	0.52
Fire brick............	1000	0.75		600	0.57
Gold, unoxidized............	100	0.02	Tantalum, unoxidized....	1500	0.21
	500	0.03		2000	0.26
Gold enamel.............	100	0.37	Tin, unoxidized........	25	0.043
Iron, unoxidized............	100	0.05		100	0.05
oxidized............	100	0.74	Tungsten, unoxidized....	25	0.024
	500	0.84		100	0.032
	1200	0.89		500	0.071
cast, unoxidized......	100	0.21		1000	0.15
	liquid	0.29		1500	0.23
cast, oxidized........	200	0.64		2000	0.28
	600	0.78	Zinc, unoxidized.........	300	0.05
cast, strongly oxidized.	40	0.95			
	250	0.95			

SPECTRAL EMISSIVITY

Prepared by Roeser and Wensel, National Bureau of Standards
Spectral Emissivity of Materials, Surface Unoxidized for 0.65μ

Element	Solid	Liquid	Element	Solid	Liquid
Beryllium......		0.61	Thorium.............	0.36	0.40
Carbon.........	0.80–0.93	0.61	Titanium...........	0.63	0.65
Chromium......	0.34	0.39	Tungsten...........	0.43	
Cobalt.........	0.36	0 37	Uranium...........	0.54	0.34
Columbium.....	0.37	0.40	Vanadium..........	0.35	0.32
Copper.........	0.10	0.15	Yttrium............	0.35	0.35
Erbium.........	0.55	0.38	Zirconium..........	0.32	0.30
Gold...........	0.14	0.22	Steel..............	0.35	0.37
Iridium........	0.30		Cast Iron..........	0.37	0.40
Iron...........	0.35	0.37	Constantan.........	0.35	
Manganese.....	0.59	0.59	Monel..............	0.37	
Molybdenum...	0.37	0.40	Chromel P (90Ni-10Cr)	0.35	
Nickel.........	0.36	0.37	80Ni-20Cr..........	0.35	
Palladium......	0.33	0.37	60Ni-24Fe-16Cr.....	0.36	
Platinum.......	0.30	0.38	Alumel (95Ni; Bal. Al,		
Rhodium.......	0.24	0.30	Mn, Si)..........		0.37
Silver.........	0.07	0.07	90Pt-10Rh..........		0.27
Tantalum......	0.49	....			

Spectral Emissivity of Oxides

The emissivity of oxides and oxidized metals depends to a large extent upon the roughness of the surface. In general, higher values of emissivity are obtained on the rougher surfaces.

Material	Range of observed values	Probable value for oxide formed on smooth metal	Material	Range of observed values	Probable value for oxide formed on smooth metal
Aluminum oxide..	0.22–0.40	0.30	Alumel (oxidized)..	....	0.87
Beryllium oxide....	0.07–0.37	0.35	Cast Iron (oxidized)...	....	0.70
Cerium oxide......	0.58–0.80	....	Chromel P (90Ni-10Cr)		
Chromium oxide...	0.60–0.80	0.70	(oxidized)....	....	0.87
Cobalt oxide.......		0.75	80Ni-20Cr (oxidized)..	....	0.90
Columbium oxide..	0.55–0.71	0.70	60Ni-24Fe-16Cr (oxi-		
Copper oxide......	0.60–0.80	0.70	dized)...........	....	0.83
Iron oxide........	0.63–0.98	0.70	55Fe-37.5Cr-7.5 Al (oxi-		
Magnesium oxide..	0.10–0.43	0.20	dized)...........	....	0.78
Nickel oxide......	0.85–0.96	0.90	70Fe-23Cr-5Al-2Co (oxi-		
Thorium oxide....	0 20–0.57	0.50	dized)...........	....	0.75
Tin oxide........	0.32–0.60	....	Constantan (55Cu-45Ni)		
Titanium oxide....	....	0.50	(oxidized).........	....	0.84
Uranium oxide.....	....	0 30	Carbon Steel (oxidized)..	....	0.80
Vanadium oxide....	....	0.70	Stainless Steel (18-8)		
Yttrium oxide.....	....	0.60	(oxidized).........	....	0.85
Zirconium oxide....	0.18–0.43	0.40	Porcelain............	0.25–0.50	

PROPERTIES OF TUNGSTEN

Jones and Langmuir, General Electric Review

Temp. °K	Resistivity microhm cm	Electron emission amp./cm²	Evaporation g/cm² sec	Vapor pressure dynes/cm²	Thermal expansion per cent l_0 at 293°	Atomic heat cal./g. atom./ °C.
300	5.65	....	....	....	.003	6.0
400	8.06	....	....	....	.044	6.0
500	10.56	....	....	....	.086	6.1
600	13.23	....	....	....	.130	6.1
700	16.09	....	....	....	.175	6.2
800	19.00	....	....	....	.222	6.2
900	21.94	....	....	....	.270	6.3
1000	24.93	1.07×10^{-15}	5.32×10^{-34}	1.98×10^{-29}	.320	6.4

PROPERTIES OF TUNGSTEN

Jones and Langmuir General Electric Review

Temp. °K	Resistivity microhm cm	Electron emission amp./cm²	Evaporation g/cm² sec	Vapor pressure dynes/cm²	Thermal expansion per cent l_0 at 293°	Atomic heat cal./g. atom./ °C.
1100	27.94	1.52×10^{-13}	2.17×10^{-30}	1.22×10^{-25}	.371	6.4
1200	30.98	9.73×10^{-12}	3.21×10^{-27}	1.87×10^{-22}	.424	6.5
1300	34.08	3.21×10^{-10}	1.35×10^{-24}	8.18×10^{-20}	.479	6.7
1400	37.19	6.62×10^{-9}	2.51×10^{-22}	1.62×10^{-17}	.535	6.8
1500	40.36	9.14×10^{-8}	2.37×10^{-20}	1.54×10^{-15}	.593	7.0
1600	43.55	9.27×10^{-7}	1.25×10^{-18}	8.43×10^{-14}	.652	7.1
1700	46.78	7.08×10^{-6}	4.17×10^{-17}	2.82×10^{-12}	.713	7.2
1800	50.05	4.47×10^{-5}	8.81×10^{-16}	6.31×10^{-11}	.775	7.4
1900	53.35	2.28×10^{-4}	1.41×10^{-14}	1.01×10^{-9}	.839	7.6
2000	56.67	1.00×10^{-3}	1.76×10^{-13}	1.33×10^{-8}	.904	7.7
2100	60.06	3.93×10^{-3}	1.66×10^{-12}	1.28×10^{-7}	.971	7.8
2200	63.48	1.33×10^{-2}	1.25×10^{-11}	9.88×10^{-7}	1.039	8.0
2300	66.91	4.07×10^{-2}	8.00×10^{-11}	6.47×10^{-6}	1.109	8.2
2400	70.39	1.16×10^{-1}	4.26×10^{-10}	3.52×10^{-5}	1.180	8.3
2500	73.91	2.98×10^{-1}	2.03×10^{-9}	1.71×10^{-4}	1.253	8.4
2600	77.49	7.16×10^{-1}	8.41×10^{-9}	7.24×10^{-4}	1.328	8.6
2700	81.04	1.63	3.19×10^{-8}	2.86×10^{-3}	1.404	8.7
2800	84.70	3.54	1.10×10^{-7}	9.84×10^{-3}	1.479	8.9
2900	88.33	7.31	3.30×10^{-7}	3.00×10^{-2}	1.561	9.0
3000	92.04	1.42×10	9.95×10^{-7}	9.20×10^{-2}	1.642	9.2
3100	95.76	2.64×10	2.60×10^{-6}	2.50×10^{-1}	1.724	9.4
3200	99.54	4.78×10	6.38×10^{-6}	6.13×10^{-1}	1.808	9.5
3300	103.3	8.44×10	1.56×10^{-5}	1.51	1.893	9.6
3400	107.2	1.42×10^2	3.47×10^{-5}	3.41	1.980	9.8
3500	111.1	2.33×10^2	7.54×10^{-5}	7.52	2.068	9.9
3000	115.0	3.73×10^2	1.51×10^{-4}	1.58×10	2.158	10.1
3655	117.1	4.79×10^2	2.28×10^{-4}	2.33×10	2.209	10.2

Roeser and Wensel, National Bureau of Standards

Temp. °K	Normal brightness new candles per cm²	Spectral emissivity 0.65μ	Spectral emissivity 0.467μ	Color emissivity	Total emissivity	Brightness temp. 0.65μ	Color temp.
300	....	0.472	0.505	.....	0.032		
400	....	....	....	.....	.042		
500	....	....	....	.....	.053		
600	....	....	....	.....	.064		
700	....	....	....	.....	.076		
800	....	....	....	.....	.088		
900	....	....	....	.....	.101		
1000	0.0001	.458	.486	.395	.114	966	1007
1100	0.001	.456	.484	.392	.128	1059	1108
1200	0.006	.454	.482	.390	.143	1151	1210
1300	0.029	.452	.480	.387	.158	1242	1312
1400	0.11	.450	.478	.385	.175	1332	1414
1500	0.33	.448	.476	.382	.192	1422	1516
1600	0.92	.446	.475	.380	.207	1511	1619
1700	2.3	.444	.473	.377	.222	1599	1722
1800	5.1	.442	.472	.374	.236	1687	1825
1900	10.4	.440	.470	.371	.249	1774	1928
2000	20.0	.438	.469	.368	.260	1861	2032
2100	36	.436	.467	.365	.270	1946	2136
2200	61	.434	.466	.362	.279	2031	2241
2300	101	.432	.464	.359	.288	2115	2345
2400	157	430	.463	.356	.296	2198	2451
2500	240	.428	.462	.353	.303	2280	2556
2600	350	.426	.460	.349	.311	2362	2662
2700	500	.424	.459	.346	.318	2443	2769
2800	690	.422	.458	.343	.323	2523	2876
2900	950	.420	.456	.340	.329	2602	2984
3000	1260	.418	.455	.336	.334	2681	3092
3100	1650	.416	.454	.333	.337	2759	3200
3200	2100	.414	.452	.330	.341	2837	3310
3300	2700	.412	.451	.326	.344	2913	3420
3400	3400	.410	.450	.323	.348	2989	3530
3500	4200	.408	.449	.320	.351	3063	3642
3600	5200	.406	.447	.317	.354	3137	3754

TRANSMISSION OF CORNING COLORED FILTERS

Supplied by R. G. Saxton

If I_o is the intensity of radiation entering a layer of some medium and I the intensity reaching the opposite surface, the ratio I/I_o is called the transmittance. In practice the ratio of intensity of radiation passing through a glass sample to that incident on its surface is often measured and plotted as transmission. The transmission is the result of two factors, the transmittance of the glass and the losses by reflection. These losses amount to about 4 % for each glass-air surface; the transmission of a sample is about 92 % of its transmittance. Since the reflection losses differ slightly with different samples, the correction is often determined and applied when the transmission is measured. Values in this table have been corrected for reflection losses.

The identifying glass number, CS number, color and properties, and nominal thickness for the Corning glasses in this table are:

Glass No.	CS	Color and properties	Nominal thickness
0160	0-54	Clear; Ultraviolet transmitting	2.0
2030	2-64	Red; Sharp cut	3.0
2403	2-58	Red; Sharp cut	3.0
2404	2-59	Red; Sharp cut	3.0
2408	2-60	Red; Sharp cut	3.0
2412	2-61	Red; Sharp cut	3.0
2418	2-62	Red; Sharp cut	3.0
2424	2-63	Red; Sharp cut	3.0
2434	2-73	Red; Sharp cut	3.0
2540	7-56	Black; IR transmitting; Visible absorbing	2.5
2550	7-57	Black; IR transmitting; Visible absorbing	2.0
2600	7-69	Black; IR transmitting; Visible absorbing	3.0
3060	3-75	Straw	2.0
3304	3-76	Dark amber	3.0
3307	3-77	Dark amber	3.0
3384	3-70	Yellow	3.0
3385	3-71	Yellow	3.0
3387	3-72	Straw	3.0
3389	3-73	Straw	3.0
3391	3-74	Straw	3.0
3480	3-66	Yellow; Sharp cut	3.0
3482	3-67	Yellow; Sharp cut	3.0
3484	3-68	Yellow; Sharp cut	3.0
3486	3-69	Yellow; Sharp cut	3.0
3718	3-94	Yellow	3.0
3750	3-79	Yellow; Yellow green fluorescing	5.0
3780	3-80	Yellow	2.0
3850	0-51	Clear; UV transmitting	4.0
3961	1-56	Bluish; IR absorbing; Visible transmitting	2.5
3962	1-57	Bluish; IR absorbing; Visible transmitting	2.5
3965	1-58	Bluish; IR absorbing; Visible transmitting	2.5
3966	1-59	Bluish; IR absorbing; Visible transmitting	2.5
4010	4-64	Green	4.0
4015	4-65	Yellow green	3.0
4060	4-67	Green	2.0
4084	4-68	Green	4.5
4303	4-72	Blue green	4.0
4305	4-71	Blue green	4.0
4308	4-70	Blue green	4.0
4309	4-69	Blue green	4.0
4445	4-74	Green	2.5
4602	1-75	Bluish; IR absorbing; Visible transmitting	3.0
4784	4-94	Blue green	5.0
5030	5-57	Blue	5.0
5031	5-56	Blue	4.5
5070	7-62	Amethyst	3.9
5071	7-63	Amethyst	3.9
5073	7-64	Amethyst	3.9
5113	5-58	Blue	4.0
5120	1-60	Smoky violet; Absorbs yellow	5.2
5300	4-106	Green	3.9
5330	1-64	Blue	4.5
5433	5-59	Blue	5.0
5543	5-60	Blue	5.0
5562	5-61	Blue	5.0
5572	1-61	Blue	5.0
5840	7-60	Black; UV transmitting; Visible absorbing	4.5
5850	7-59	Purple; UV transmitting; Visible absorbing	4.0
5860	7-37	Black; UV transmitting; Visible absorbing	5.0
5874	7-39	Black; UV transmitting; Visible absorbing	5.0
5900	1.62	Blue	5.5
5970	7-51	Black; UV transmitting; Visible absorbing	5.0
7380	0-52	Clear; UV transmitting	2.0
7740	0-53	Clear; UV transmitting	2.0
7905	9-30	Clear; UV transmitting; Long Range IR transmitting	2.0
7910	9-54	Clear; UV transmitting	2.0
8364	7-98	Gray	2.0
9780	4-76	Blue green	5.0
9782	4-96	Blue green	5.0
9788	4-97	Blue green	5.0
9830	4-77	Green	3.4
9863	7-54	Black; UV transmitting; Visible absorbing	3.0

						Transmittance						
						Corning Glass Number						
$\lambda(\mu)$	0160	2030	2403	2404	2408	2412	2418	2424	2434	2540	2550	2600
.22	.000	.000	.000	.000	.000	.000	.000	.000	.000	.000	.000	.000
.24	.000	.000	.000	.000	.000	.000	.000	.000	.000	.000	.000	.000
.26	.000	.000	.000	.000	.000	.000	.000	.000	.000	.000	.000	.000
.28	.000	.000	.000	.000	.000	.000	.000	.000	.000	.000	.000	.000
.30	.005	.000	.000	.000	.000	.000	.000	.000	.000	.000	.000	.000
.32	.642	.000	.000	.000	.000	.000	.000	.000	.000	.000	.000	.000
.34	.850	.000	.000	.000	.000	.000	.000	.000	.000	.000	.000	.000
.36	.882	.000	.000	.000	.000	.000	.000	.000	.000	.000	.000	.000
.38	.890	.000	.000	.000	.000	.000	.000	.000	.000	.000	.000	.000
.40	.892	.000	.000	.000	.000	.000	.000	.000	.000	.000	.000	.000
.41	.893	.000	.000	.000	.000	.000	.000	.000	.000	.000	.000	.000
.42	.896	.000	.000	.000	.000	.000	.000	.000	.000	.000	.000	.000
.43	.896	.000	.000	.000	.000	.000	.000	.000	.000	.000	.000	.000
.44	.898	.000	.000	.000	.000	.000	.000	.000	.000	.000	.000	.000
.45	.899	.000	.000	.000	.000	.000	.000	.000	.000	.000	.000	.000
.46	.900	.000	.000	.000	.000	.000	.000	.000	.000	.000	.000	.000
.47	.900	.000	.000	.000	.000	.000	.000	.000	.000	.000	.000	.000
.48	.900	.000	.000	.000	.000	.000	.000	.000	.000	.000	.000	.000
.49	.900	.000	.000	.000	.000	.000	.000	.000	.000	.000	.000	.000
.50	.900	.000	.000	.000	.000	.000	.000	.000	.000	.000	.000	.000
.51	.900	.000	.000	.000	.000	.000	.000	.000	.000	.000	.000	.000
.52	.900	.000	.000	.000	.000	.000	.000	.000	.000	.000	.000	.000
.53	.900	.000	.000	.000	.000	.000	.000	.000	.000	.000	.000	.000
.54	.900	.000	.000	.000	.000	.000	.000	.000	.000	.000	.000	.000
.55	.900	.000	.000	.000	.000	.000	.000	.000	.000	.000	.000	.000
.56	.901	.000	.000	.000	.000	.000	.000	.000	.000	.000	.000	.000
.57	.904	.000	.000	.000	.000	.000	.000	.000	.005	.000	.000	.000
.58	.904	.000	.000	.000	.000	.000	.000	.005	.200	.000	.000	.000
.59	.908	.000	.000	.000	.000	.000	.008	.170	.615	.000	.000	.000
.60	.910	.000	.000	.000	.000	.006	.250	.575	.808	.000	.000	.000
.61	.910	.000	.000	.000	.018	.190	.660	.790	.856	.000	.000	.000
.62	.910	.000	.000	.015	.265	.625	.822	.848	.872	.000	.000	.000
.63	.910	.000	.018	.295	.670	.828	.862	.870	.881	.000	.000	.000
.64	.910	.006	.260	.660	.828	.868	.874	.880	.887	.000	.001	.000
.65	.910	.028	.675	.796	.866	.881	.881	.887	.892	.000	.003	.000
.66	.910	.110	.838	.828	.877	.885	.885	.893	.895	.000	.005	.000
.67	.910	.305	.871	.842	.883	.887	.887	.897	.897	.000	.006	.000
.68	.910	.550	.880	.847	.886	.889	.889	.900	.899	.000	.009	.000
.69	.910	.735	.885	.851	.888	.900	.900	.901	.900	.000	.012	.000
.70	.910	.820	.886	.852	.888	.900	.900	.903	.900	.000	.017	.000
.71	.910	.853	.888	.854	.888	.889	.889	.903	.900	.000	.023	.000
.72	.910	.864	.889	.853	.888	.888	.888	.903	.899	.000	.031	.040
.73	.910	.867	.900	.851	.887	.887	.887	.903	.897	.000	.041	.175
.74	.910	.867	.900	.850	.885	.886	.886	.903	.896	.000	.055	.372
.75	.910	.866	.900	.849	.884	.885	.885	.902	.895	.000	.069	.547
.80	.910	.839	.875	.827	.870	.858	.857	.881	.866	.005	.225	.770
1.00	.912	.801	.840	.772	.840	.828	.822	.857	.842	.562	.780	.350
1.20	.908	.799	.845	.786	.845	.837	.827	.859	.849	.790	.870	.000
1.40	.909	.811	.854	.809	.854	.848	.840	.862	.857	.850	.895	.000
1.60	.913	.839	.873	.837	.873	.869	.858	.880	.879	.872	.904	.000
1.80	.909	.844	.870	.829	.870	.864	.854	.877	.872	.880	.900	.000
2.00	.904	.841	.868	.827	.868	.861	.851	.874	.871	.880	.897	.000
2.20	.888	.833	.820	.773	.825	.820	.810	.837	.835	.860	.875	.005
2.40	.875	.832	.803	.757	.809	.803	.792	.818	.812	.868	.870	.049
2.60	.868	.822	.750	.695	.754	.750	.723	.772	.767	.858	.850	.058
2.80	.690	.600	.100	.100	.100	.100	.050	.050	.260	.450	.480	.030
3.00	.630	.470	.070	.020	.070	.070	.072	.122	.400	.465	.383	.022
3.20	.500	.340	.140	.074	.150	.140	.142	.180	.470	.390	.330	.020
3.40	.379	.260	.140	.078	.140	.140	.120	.150	.350	.310	.245	.018
3.60	.320	.247	.000	.000	.000	.000	.000	.006	.015	.280	.220	.021
3.80	.310	.257	.000	.000	.000	.000	.000	.000	.020	.285	.250	.035
4.00	.311	.274	.000	.000	.000	.000	.000	.000	.015	.285	.275	.068
4.20	.251	.200	.000	.000	.000	.000	.000	.000	.017	.190	.190	.065
4.40	.110	.060	.000	.000	.000	.000	.000	.000	.002	.050	.100	.020
4.60	.012	.000	.000	.000	.000	.000	.000	.000	.000	.000	.000	.000
4.80	.004	.000	.000	.000	.000	.000	.000	.000	.000	.000	.000	.000
5.00	.000	.000	.000	.000	.000	.000	.000	.000	.000	.000	.000	.000

Transmittance

λ(μ)	3060	3304	3307	3384	3385	Corning Glass Number 3387	3389	3391	3480	3482	3484	3486
.22	.000	.000	.000	.000	.000	.000	.000	.000	.000	.000	.000	.000
.24	.000	.000	.000	.000	.000	.000	.000	.000	.000	.000	.000	.000
.26	.000	.000	.000	.000	.000	.000	.000	.000	.000	.000	.000	.000
.28	.000	.000	.000	.000	.000	.000	.000	.000	.000	.000	.000	.000
.30	.000	.000	.000	.000	.000	.000	.000	.000	.000	.000	.000	.000
.32	.000	.000	.000	.000	.000	.000	.005	.000	.000	.000	.000	.000
.34	.000	.000	.038	.000	.000	.000	.010	.000	.000	.000	.000	.000
.36	.000	.000	.050	.000	.005	.000	.015	.000	.000	.000	.000	.000
.38	.060	.000	.027	.005	.010	.010	.020	.000	.000	.000	.000	.000
.40	.410	.000	.016	.011	.016	.020	.026	.075	.000	.000	.000	.005
.41	.517	.000	.014	.011	.016	.020	.025	.425	.000	.000	.000	.005
.42	.604	.000	.014	.010	.015	.019	.105	.655	.000	.000	.000	.005
.43	.665	.000	.016	.009	.013	.017	.437	.747	.000	.000	.000	.005
.44	.710	.000	.022	.005	.011	.050	.620	.801	.000	.000	.000	.005
.45	.748	.000	.033	.003	.010	.325	.714	.838	.000	.000	.000	.005
.46	.778	.000	.049	.002	.008	.565	.780	.860	.000	.000	.000	.004
.47	.800	.000	.070	.001	.060	.690	.820	.874	.000	.000	.000	.003
.48	.819	.000	.101	.005	.410	.763	.848	.884	.000	.000	.000	.003
.49	.836	.003	.143	.088	.640	.803	.866	.890	.000	.000	.000	.002
.50	.850	.009	.193	.350	.727	.834	.878	.895	.000	.000	.000	.001
.51	.860	.019	.250	.595	.780	.854	.886	.898	.000	.000	.000	.045
.52	.870	.037	.315	.725	.817	.868	.890	.900	.000	.000	.003	.425
.53	.875	.063	.379	.789	.840	.876	.892	.901	.000	.000	.175	.710
.54	.881	.102	.447	.825	.856	.883	.894	.902	.000	.015	.600	.792
.55	.884	.146	.504	.846	.866	.887	.895	.903	.000	.230	.774	.823
.56	.886	.200	.560	.860	.873	.889	.894	.902	.020	.675	.818	.844
.57	.885	.255	.607	.869	.876	.890	.893	.901	.325	.850	.839	.859
.58	.883	.310	.648	.873	.878	.889	.892	.900	.710	.885	.854	.868
.59	.882	.360	.680	.876	.877	.887	.890	.898	.829	.894	.865	.876
.60	.882	.404	.705	.877	.877	.884	.886	.896	.858	.900	.873	.882
.61	.882	.438	.722	.877	.877	.881	.884	.893	.869	.903	.880	.886
.62	.882	.466	.735	.875	.876	.875	.880	.890	.876	.905	.885	.888
.63	.882	.488	.744	.871	.874	.871	.876	.886	.881	.906	.888	.889
.64	.883	.505	.748	.865	.872	.866	.872	.884	.884	.907	.890	.890
.65	.885	.519	.750	.860	.867	.860	.868	.881	.885	.908	.892	.890
.66	.886	.531	.750	.856	.863	.856	.865	.876	.886	.908	.893	.890
.67	.888	.543	.749	.850	.858	.851	.860	.873	.886	.908	.894	.890
.68	.890	.552	.745	.844	.853	.846	.856	.869	.886	.908	.893	.889
.69	.891	.561	.740	.837	.847	.839	.852	.865	.885	.907	.892	.887
.70	.892	.569	.734	.831	.842	.834	.847	.860	.884	.907	.891	.885
.71	.893	.574	.727	.825	.837	.827	.842	.856	.882	.906	.890	.883
.72	.893	.575	.720	.819	.831	.822	.837	.852	.880	.905	.888	.880
.73	.892	.576	.712	.813	.825	.816	.831	.848	.877	.905	.886	.877
.74	.891	.574	.702	.807	.820	.810	.826	.844	.874	.904	.885	.875
.75	.890	.570	.694	.800	.814	.805	.820	.840	.870	.903	.882	.873
.80	.871	.526	.642	.770	.865	.780	.775	.815	.837	.878	.846	.829
1.00	.830	.435	.516	.715	.830	.725	.716	.772	.801	.857	.811	.781
1.20	.860	.429	.500	.718	.858	.735	.730	.782	.807	.859	.819	.793
1.40	.901	.475	.540	.750	.900	.768	.768	.810	.828	.870	.837	.817
1.60	.917	.580	.635	.795	.918	.812	.812	.843	.852	.884	.856	.841
1.80	.916	.627	.675	.808	.915	.818	.820	.849	.847	.882	.852	.834
2.00	.908	.620	.668	.800	.909	.822	.817	.846	.847	.884	.852	.835
2.20	.900	.630	.675	.802	.900	.823	.810	.840	.805	.865	.829	.798
2.40	.885	.651	.690	.800	.885	.825	.811	.842	.787	.853	.817	.777
2.60	.860	.650	.690	.785	.858	.815	.800	.840	.725	.818	.757	.718
2.80	.550	.345	.390	.325	.670	.360	.340	.440	.050	.060	.110	.060
3.00	.379	.320	.360	.318	.348	.348	.322	.423	.080	.088	.190	.088
3.20	.315	.240	.290	.268	.332	.324	.290	.395	.150	.158	.270	.145
3.40	.250	.151	.190	.218	.289	.288	.255	.353	.120	.132	.140	.090
3.60	.231	.130	.150	.217	.266	.280	.249	.351	.000	.000	.000	.000
3.80	.258	.140	.160	.228	.270	.298	.267	.376	.000	.000	.000	.000
4.00	.283	.140	.175	.220	.280	.290	.260	.365	.000	.000	.000	.000
4.20	.200	.090	.125	.143	.210	.210	.178	.288	.000	.000	.000	.000
4.40	.100	.020	.030	.025	.080	.070	.040	.115	.000	.000	.000	.000
4.60	.008	.008	.010	.007	.002	.003	.000	.009	.000	.000	.000	.000
4.80	.000	.005	.009	.000	.000	.000	.000	.000	.000	.000	.000	.000
5.00	.000	.001	.008	.000	.000	.000	.000	.000	.000	.000	.000	.000

						Transmittance						
						Corning Glass Number						
λ(μ)	3718	3750	3780	3850	3961	3962	3965	3966	4010	4015	4060	4084
.22	.000	.000	.000	.000	.000	.000	.000	.000	.000	.000	.000	.000
.24	.000	.000	.000	.000	.000	.000	.000	.000	.000	.000	.000	.000
.26	.000	.000	.000	.000	.000	.000	.000	.000	.000	.000	.000	.000
.28	.000	.000	.000	.000	.000	.000	.000	.000	.000	.000	.000	.000
.30	.000	.000	.000	.000	.000	.000	.000	.000	.000	.000	.000	.000
.32	.004	.000	.000	.000	.000	.000	.018	.055	.000	.000	.000	.000
.34	.030	.000	.000	.000	.000	.018	.192	.375	.000	.000	.001	.018
.36	.550	.215	.000	.005	.020	.125	.430	.630	.000	.000	.021	.128
.38	.665	.327	.000	.350	.085	.270	.558	.710	.000	.000	.080	.248
.40	.480	.113	.000	.675	.185	.395	.636	.781	.000	.000	.178	.216
.41	.443	.088	.000	.749	.218	.426	.651	.788	.000	.000	.228	.180
.42	.465	.088	.000	.788	.248	.453	.666	.795	.000	.000	.281	.151
.43	.560	.135	.000	.812	.269	.474	.678	.800	.000	.000	.335	.136
.44	.675	.255	.006	.828	.290	.494	.693	.806	.000	.000	.388	.140
.45	.748	.410	.028	.841	.313	.519	.709	.816	.000	.005	.434	.163
.46	.780	.472	.058	.850	.331	.538	.724	.824	.006	.025	.473	.200
.47	.803	.570	.092	.858	.346	.556	.737	.831	.021	.073	.506	.247
.48	.800	.555	.088	.865	.361	.570	.748	.836	.050	.145	.527	.303
.49	.802	.550	.095	.870	.370	.582	.756	.840	.100	.245	.535	.370
.50	.824	.597	.152	.874	.376	.590	.762	.842	.160	.350	.528	.430
.51	.862	.720	.325	.878	.377	.594	.765	.843	.220	.455	.503	.465
.52	.894	.825	.595	.881	.373	.593	.765	.841	.252	.537	.460	.467
.53	.904	.853	.717	.883	.364	.588	.761	.838	.247	.582	.400	.438
.54	.905	.860	.763	.884	.354	.579	.764	.833	.207	.594	.325	.376
.55	.906	.864	.783	.884	.342	.569	.746	.827	.153	.572	.252	.303
.56	.907	.867	.795	.883	.331	.559	.736	.821	.096	.525	.183	.225
.57	.907	.869	.799	.882	.317	.547	.724	.813	.054	.457	.125	.157
.58	.907	.870	.804	.880	.298	.529	.706	.802	.026	.385	.083	.107
.59	.907	.870	.811	.877	.276	.508	.685	.790	.011	.311	.053	.073
.60	.908	.876	.826	.876	.251	.481	.662	.775	.004	.245	.033	.048
.61	.908	.880	.835	.875	.225	.452	.636	.757	.000	.190	.020	.034
.62	.909	.881	.842	.874	.299	.423	.610	.739	.000	.145	.012	.024
.63	.909	.884	.848	.875	.217	.392	.577	.719	.000	.115	.007	.018
.64	.910	.885	.854	.876	.147	.359	.546	.698	.000	.098	.004	.015
.65	.910	.887	.859	.877	.125	.326	.515	.675	.000	.084	.001	.012
.66	.911	.891	.864	.880	.104	.297	.482	.652	.000	.075	.000	.010
.67	.913	.896	.869	.883	.086	.265	.450	.630	.000	.075	.000	.009
.68	.914	.900	.873	.885	.063	.235	.418	.603	.000	.071	.000	.008
.69	.915	.901	.877	.887	.055	.206	.385	.576	.000	.065	.000	.007
.70	.915	.904	.880	.888	.042	.279	.352	.550	.000	.067	.000	.007
.71	.915	.905	.883	.888	.032	.155	.322	.524	.000	.070	.000	.007
.72	.915	.906	.885	.889	.025	.133	.294	.496	.000	.075	.000	.007
.73	.915	.907	.885	.888	.018	.114	.266	.472	.000	.080	.000	.007
.74	.915	.907	.882	.887	.014	.097	.242	.448	.000	.084	.000	.008
.75	.914	.906	.882	.886	.010	.084	.220	.424	.000	.086	.000	.008
.80	.902	.875	.855	.863	.000	.033	.120	.310	.000	.109	.000	.013
1.00	.899	.860	.882	.820	.000	.002	.038	.158	.000	.215	.018	.100
1.20	.898	.882	.898	.850	.000	.002	.040	.161	.007	.393	.158	.303
1.40	.880	.810	.855	.894	.002	.018	.100	.270	.058	.549	.404	.548
1.60	.882	.805	.855	.905	.007	.050	.190	.390	.162	.663	.612	.710
1.80	.900	.844	.907	.904	.008	.057	.201	.408	.299	.740	.740	.791
2.00	.897	.819	.909	.895	.011	.070	.228	.435	.422	.783	.817	.830
2.20	.888	.720	.900	.870	.021	.105	.277	.475	.518	.803	.840	.792
2.40	.865	.668	.890	.850	.037	.140	.320	.512	.597	.817	.862	.808
2.60	.840	.570	.860	.800	.050	.005	.339	.515	.634	.813	.870	.740
2.80	.460	.075	.620	.200	.022	.092	.135	.085	.270	.460	.520	.010
3.00	.282	.028	.465	.165	.033	.133	.200	.230	.260	.418	.620	.033
3.20	.252	.016	.420	.120	.054	.150	.247	.294	.204	.345	.642	.128
3.40	.175	.007	.370	.070	.048	.112	.165	.200	.131	.235	.631	.130
3.60	.150	.003	.351	.045	.003	.008	.016	.018	.121	.192	.634	.006
3.80	.168	.000	.368	.067	.007	.015	.035	.048	.125	.200	.600	.016
4.00	.182	.000	.370	.080	.006	.010	.020	.022	.123	.200	.557	.006
4.20	.120	.000	.300	.040	.005	.013	.022	.021	.070	.130	.422	.001
4.40	.020	.000	.140	.005	.001	.001	.000	.001	.002	.015	.135	.000
4.60	.002	.000	.010	.000	.000	.000	.000	.000	.000	.000	.012	.000
4.80	.000	.000	.000	.000	.000	.000	.000	.000	.000	.000	.002	.000
5.00	.000	.000	.000	.000	.000	.000	.000	.000	.000	.000	.000	.000

Transmittance

λ(μ)	Corning Glass Number											
	4303	4305	4308	4309	4445	4602	4784	5030	5031	5070	5071	5073
.22	.000	.000	.000	.000	.000	.000	.000	.000	.000	.000	.000	.000
.24	.000	.000	.000	.000	.000	.000	.000	.000	.000	.000	.000	.000
.26	.000	.000	.000	.000	.000	.000	.000	.000	.000	.000	.000	.000
.28	.000	.000	.000	.000	.000	.000	.000	.000	.000	.000	.000	.000
.30	.000	.000	.000	.000	.000	.001	.000	.000	.016	.000	.000	.000
.32	.000	.000	.000	.022	.001	.106	.000	.000	.145	.012	.045	.090
.34	.011	.060	.190	.394	.018	.505	.009	.038	.420	.310	.330	.540
.36	.188	.380	.580	.740	.114	.755	.200	.285	.685	.628	.340	.757
.38	.390	.590	.740	.831	.248	.827	.450	.595	.820	.745	.420	.810
.40	.545	.723	.826	.884	.400	.835	.596	.770	.884	.712	.665	.830
.41	.588	.750	.840	.887	.454	.845	.627	.799	.894	.600	.712	.786
.42	.624	.770	.850	.890	.505	.846	.648	.808	.895	.430	.716	.705
.43	.654	.786	.857	.892	.550	.851	.666	.797	.890	.290	.694	.620
.44	.680	.798	.862	.894	.593	.856	.680	.767	.872	.170	.655	.525
.45	.698	.809	.867	.897	.631	.857	.697	.738	.865	.097	.612	.436
.46	.712	.815	.869	.898	.659	.856	.717	.702	.864	.055	.568	.365
.47	.715	.814	.866	.897	.678	.861	.735	.628	.845	.035	.531	.313
.48	.705	.802	.856	.894	.689	.866	.750	.522	.805	.023	.501	.275
.49	.678	.780	.838	.885	.687	.869	.763	.406	.750	.017	.482	.252
.50	.636	.740	.810	.872	.673	.870	.768	.288	.684	.015	.469	.237
.51	.570	.685	.770	.850	.641	.869	.767	.186	.601	.013	.463	.231
.52	.480	.610	.714	.817	.586	.866	.753	.105	.495	.013	.461	.230
.53	.387	.525	.650	.781	.520	.863	.725	.053	.388	.014	.464	.235
.54	.288	.430	.576	.736	.437	.865	.676	.022	.295	.016	.473	.245
.55	.205	.340	.502	.683	.355	.869	.615	.007	.198	.018	.486	.260
.56	.132	.255	.422	.627	.275	.868	.525	.000	.113	.023	.502	.278
.57	.082	.184	.345	.565	.202	.863	.427	.000	.057	.030	.522	.300
.58	.047	.127	.277	.505	.144	.856	.328	.000	.025	.038	.540	.324
.59	.026	.087	.218	.447	.102	.848	.235	.000	.008	.048	.555	.348
.60	.013	.057	.170	.393	.068	.838	.157	.000	.000	.058	.571	.373
.61	.006	.036	.131	.341	.046	.824	.102	.000	.000	.070	.587	.395
.62	.001	.022	.100	.296	.031	.806	.058	.000	.000	.083	.600	.415
.63	.000	.013	.074	.256	.020	.787	.032	.000	.000	.096	.612	.435
.64	.000	.007	.056	.221	.013	.767	.017	.000	.000	.108	.622	.450
.65	.000	.004	.042	.191	.008	.745	.007	.000	.000	.120	.633	.466
.66	.000	.002	.033	.167	.006	.722	.002	.000	.000	.135	.644	.482
.67	.000	.001	.025	.146	.003	.695	.000	.000	.000	.148	.658	.498
.68	.000	.000	.020	.128	.001	.665	.000	.000	.000	.165	.674	.515
.69	.000	.000	.016	.116	.000	.634	.000	.000	.000	.182	.686	.531
.70	.000	.000	.013	.104	.000	.600	.000	.000	.000	.200	.700	.548
.71	.000	.000	.010	.096	.000	.565	.000	.000	.000	.220	.712	.566
.72	.000	.000	.009	.088	.000	.531	.000	.004	.024	.245	.725	.586
.73	.000	.000	.007	.083	.000	.496	.000	.047	.119	.268	.736	.606
.74	.000	.000	.006	.079	.000	.463	.000	.190	.330	.295	.749	.675
.75	.000	.000	.005	.075	.000	.430	.000	.440	.580	.323	.759	.642
.80	.000	.000	.008	.080	.003	.258	.000	.890	.917	.505	.815	.750
1.00	.000	.005	.045	.188	.056	.019	.000	.753	.868	.860	.885	.872
1.20	.013	.060	.166	.375	.269	.009	.000	.455	.720	.890	.897	.890
1.40	.080	.180	.342	.542	.527	.016	.003	.100	.285	.892	.902	.892
1.60	.210	.342	.500	.658	.701	.035	.038	.056	.162	.890	.902	.892
1.80	.350	.482	.617	.732	.792	.059	.142	.052	.140	.878	.890	.877
2.00	.475	.590	.690	.772	.839	.048	.275	.075	.175	.860	.865	.860
2.20	.560	.653	.720	.778	.850	.038	.345	.172	.295	.840	.830	.840
2.40	.635	.704	.752	.791	.870	.045	.404	.330	.483	.812	.795	.805
2.60	.663	.710	.748	.770	.861	.066	.340	.382	.530	.804	.752	.775
2.80	.260	.370	.370	.250	.280	.018	.045	.030	.030	.550	.500	.500
3.00	.249	.250	.203	.212	.395	.000	.000	.010	.001	.390	.308	.340
3.20	.202	.212	.145	.168	.451	.000	.000	.065	.026	.222	.145	.180
3.40	.135	.136	.084	.107	.449	.000	.000	.002	.006	.120	.070	.090
3.60	.124	.120	.078	.077	.470	.000	.000	.000	.000	.078	.032	.063
3.80	.132	.125	.082	.083	.470	.000	.000	.000	.000	.078	.029	.060
4.00	.132	.131	.094	.090	.448	.000	.000	.000	.000	.093	.037	.075
4.20	.078	.073	.050	.042	.320	.000	.000	.000	.000	.079	.020	.048
4.40	.008	.009	.008	.002	.100	.000	.000	.000	.000	.020	.004	.014
4.60	.000	.000	.000	.000	.007	.000	.000	.000	.000	.002	.000	.000
4.80	.000	.000	.000	.000	.000	.000	.000	.000	.000	.000	.000	.000
5.00	.000	.000	.000	.000	.000	.000	.000	.000	.000	.000	.000	.000

Transmittance

						Corning Glass Number						
λ(μ)	5113	5120	5300	5330	5433	5543	5562	5572	5840	5850	5860	5874
.22	.000	.000	.000	.000	.000	.000	.000	.000	.000	.000	.000	.000
.24	.000	.000	.000	.000	.000	.000	.000	.000	.000	.000	.000	.000
.26	.000	.000	.000	.000	.000	.000	.000	.000	.000	.000	.000	.000
.28	.000	.000	.000	.000	.000	.000	.000	.000	.000	.000	.000	.000
.30	.000	.000	.000	.002	.000	.000	.000	.000	.001	.039	.000	.000
.32	.000	.000	.000	.250	.000	.000	.000	.045	.242	.490	.008	.031
.34	.000	.000	.000	.622	.000	.000	.012	.325	.600	.790	.179	.228
.36	.035	.018	.000	.796	.100	.120	.205	.660	.682	.858	.340	.447
.38	.200	.540	.000	.835	.350	.380	.495	.805	.392	.850	.085	.378
.40	.371	.670	.000	.865	.585	.600	.717	.874	.000	.788	.000	.032
.41	.371	.790	.000	.850	.636	.635	.748	.873	.000	.720	.000	.004
.42	.337	.805	.000	.823	.665	.646	.761	.865	.000	.630	.000	.000
.43	.272	.560	.000	.783	.674	.635	.759	.857	.000	.522	.000	.000
.44	.198	.386	.000	.725	.665	.602	.742	.845	.000	.410	.000	.000
.45	.118	.485	.000	.650	.635	.550	.713	.832	.000	.290	.000	.000
.46	.055	.475	.000	.555	.577	.465	.662	.808	.000	.175	.000	.000
.47	.013	.370	.008	.455	.467	.335	.565	.765	.000	.125	.000	.000
.48	.000	.385	.026	.355	.327	.190	.435	.693	.000	.022	.000	.000
.49	.000	.685	.085	.270	.205	.090	.300	.605	.000	.005	.000	.000
.50	.000	.660	.125	.197	.120	.040	.197	.523	.000	.000	.000	.000
.51	.000	.390	.106	.145	.060	.013	.110	.430	.000	.000	.000	.000
.52	.000	.305	.094	.110	.024	.002	.051	.328	.000	.000	.000	.000
.53	.000	.175	.064	.085	.008	.000	.022	.247	.000	.000	.000	.000
.54	.000	.610	.149	.068	.005	.000	.012	.216	.000	.000	.000	.000
.55	.000	.817	.147	.055	.006	.000	.015	.246	.000	.000	.000	.000
.56	.000	.230	.087	.043	.007	.000	.018	.285	.000	.000	.000	.000
.57	.000	.125	.013	.032	.000	.000	.011	.258	.000	.000	.000	.000
.58	.000	.000	.000	.022	.000	.000	002	.175	.000	.000	.000	.000
.59	.000	.006	.000	.016	.000	.000	.000	.116	.000	.000	.000	.000
.60	.000	.180	.000	.012	.000	.000	.000	.113	.000	.000	.000	.000
.61	.000	.545	.000	.009	.000	.000	.000	.123	.000	.000	.000	.000
.62	.000	.825	.000	.010	.000	.000	.000	.126	.000	.000	.000	.000
.63	.000	.838	.000	.013	.000	.000	.000	.120	.000	.000	.000	.000
.64	.000	.878	.000	.015	.000	.000	.000	.111	.000	.000	.000	.000
.65	.000	.893	.000	.015	.000	.000	.000	.120	.000	.000	.000	.000
.66	.000	.883	.000	.014	.000	.000	.000	.165	.000	.000	.000	.000
.67	.000	.820	.000	.013	.000	.000	.000	.265	.000	.000	.000	.000
.68	.000	.705	.000	.015	.000	.000	.000	.425	.000	.000	.000	.000
.69	.000	.743	.000	.022	.000	.000	.001	.615	.000	.029	.000	.000
.70	.000	.860	.000	.041	.000	.000	.004	.756	.007	.160	.000	.017
.71	.000	.876	.000	.085	.000	.001	.004	.837	.020	.385	.000	.075
.72	.000	.815	.000	.165	.000	.002	.004	.874	.037	.615	.000	.168
.73	.000	.435	.000	.285	.000	.002	.002	.889	.060	.760	.000	.257
.74	.000	.045	.000	.460	.000	.002	.002	.895	.086	.843	.000	.320
.75	.000	.055	.000	.645	.000	.001	.001	.898	.080	.878	.000	.335
.80	.000	.030	.000	.900	.005	.002	.003	.895	.009	.890	.000	.218
1.00	.000	.860	.003	.800	.010	.015	.020	.880	.000	.716	.000	.050
1.20	.000	.770	.026	.570	.030	.020	.047	.690	.000	.169	.000	.011
1.40	.000	.550	.072	.410	.060	.040	.095	.640	.004	.042	.004	.012
1.60	.000	.620	.200	.405	.116	.060	.154	.625	.002	.036	.002	.010
1.80	.000	.580	.265	.425	.172	.090	.223	.635	.000	.048	.000	.010
2.00	.010	.580	.374	.476	.343	.247	.410	.750	.000	.168	.000	.018
2.20	.071	.747	.533	.535	475	.400	.528	.780	.000	.338	.000	.036
2.40	.190	.400	.370	.552	.575	.520	.600	.780	.000	.492	.000	.074
2.60	.203	.530	.523	.540	.580	.532	.603	.745	.000	.510	.000	.088
2.80	.100	.250	.265	.007	.162	.132	.360	.470	.000	.170	.000	.003
3.00	.080	.080	.202	.012	.195	.151	.280	.315	.000	.128	.000	.020
3.20	.068	.072	.180	.082	.131	.105	.172	.200	.000	.084	.000	.053
3.40	.030	.029	.131	.003	.079	.065	.100	.100	.000	.065	.000	.050
3.60	.021	.017	.103	.000	.061	.030	.053	.049	.002	.070	.000	.000
3.80	.023	.021	.093	.000	.068	.032	.040	.037	.001	.082	.000	.000
4.00	.040	.025	.112	.000	.071	.039	.050	.042	.005	.090	.000	.000
4.20	.019	.010	.069	.000	.020	.015	.017	.020	.002	.055	.000	.000
4.40	.001	.001	.007	.000	.000	.000	.000	.002	.000	.002	.000	.000
4.60	.000	.000	.000	.000	.000	.000	.000	.000	.000	.000	.000	.000
4.80	.000	.000	.000	.000	.000	.000	.000	.000	.000	.000	.000	.000
5.00	.000	.000	.000	.000	.000	.000	.000	.000	.000	.000	.000	.000

						Transmittance						
						Corning Glass Number						
λ (μ)	5900	5970	7380	7740	7905	7910	8364	9780	9782	9788	9830	9863
.22	.000	.000	.000	.000	.000	.012	.000	.000	.000	.000	.000	.000
.24	.000	.000	.000	.000	.360	.505	.000	.000	.000	.000	.000	.054
.26	.000	.000	.000	.000	.495	.780	.000	.000	.000	.000	.000	.482
.28	.000	.000	.000	.004	.590	.855	.000	.000	.000	.000	.000	.731
.30	.000	.000	.000	.321	.720	.877	.000	.000	.000	.000	.000	.831
.32	.000	.138	.000	.722	.825	.900	.000	.000	.000	.000	.000	.862
.34	.008	.600	.000	.851	.880	.903	.002	.015	.000	.060	.001	.854
.36	.150	.799	.440	.889	.910	.905	.083	.290	.060	.470	.059	.816
.38	.445	.742	.795	.900	.915	.906	.136	.590	.445	.770	.160	.620
.40	.678	.190	.892	.916	.920	.920	.296	.725	.747	.885	.130	.090
.41	.688	.029	.904	.915	.920	.920	.273	.705	.790	.895	.044	.018
.42	.635	.000	.910	.915	.920	.921	.232	.770	.818	.902	.004	.003
.43	.586	.000	.913	.914	.920	.923	.191	.778	.836	.905	.000	.000
.44	.522	.000	.915	.913	.920	.924	.157	.801	.847	.906	.000	.000
.45	.458	.000	.916	.913	.922	.925	.144	.814	.855	.906	.000	.000
.46	.400	.000	.917	.914	.922	.925	.140	.823	.860	.906	.000	.000
.47	.350	.000	.917	.915	.922	.925	.141	.832	.863	.906	.000	.000
.48	.306	.000	.917	.915	.923	.925	.146	.839	.863	.905	.000	.000
.49	.275	.000	.918	.915	.930	.926	.152	.843	.859	.904	.000	.000
.50	.246	.000	.918	.915	.925	.926	.166	.843	.848	.900	.014	.000
.51	.223	.000	.919	.915	.925	.927	.178	.838	.825	.893	.180	.000
.52	.196	.000	.919	.916	.925	.928	.190	.824	.784	.880	.175	.000
.53	.172	.000	.919	.916	.923	.928	.196	.798	.720	.862	.018	.000
.54	.154	.000	.919	.916	.926	.929	.198	.756	.627	.831	.000	.000
.55	.148	.000	.920	.917	.923	.929	.197	.697	.515	.787	.050	.000
.56	.151	.000	.920	.917	.925	.930	.199	.615	.380	.728	.265	.000
.57	.146	.000	.919	.918	.925	.930	.206	.518	.255	.655	.165	.000
.58	.125	.000	.918	.919	.925	.930	.217	.414	.150	.570	.035	.000
.59	.102	.000	.918	.920	.925	.930	.222	.302	.075	.475	.004	.000
.60	.093	.000	.920	.920	.925	.930	.215	.215	.032	.380	.000	.000
.61	.087	.000	.920	.920	.925	.930	.196	.135	.010	.290	.000	.000
.62	.081	.000	.920	.920	.925	.930	.175	.080	.002	.210	.000	.000
.63	.070	.000	.920	.919	.926	.930	.161	.042	.000	.145	.000	.000
.64	.061	.000	.920	.919	.927	.931	.156	.021	.000	.094	.000	.000
.65	.055	.000	.920	.918	.927	.931	.162	.008	.000	.059	.000	.000
.66	.055	.000	.920	.917	.927	.932	.176	.003	.000	.035	.000	.000
.67	.059	.000	.920	.916	.928	.932	.200	.000	.000	.020	.000	.000
.68	.065	.000	.920	.916	.927	.932	.228	.000	.000	.010	.075	.022
.69	.068	.007	.921	.915	.927	.932	.248	.000	.000	.005	.380	.106
.70	.068	.036	.921	.915	.928	.932	.251	.000	.000	.001	.642	.234
.71	.066	.085	.922	.914	.926	.933	.237	.000	.000	.000	.694	.332
.72	.064	.145	.922	.912	.926	.933	.223	.000	.000	.000	.666	.383
.73	.060	.222	.922	.910	.926	.933	.210	.000	.000	.000	.607	.384
.74	.057	.323	.921	.909	.927	.934	.197	.000	.000	.000	.531	.358
.75	.055	.385	.921	.907	.928	.934	.180	.000	.000	.000	.445	.322
.80	.050	.287	.918	.890	.930	.932	.110	.000	.000	.000	.045	.175
1.00	.085	.032	.910	.860	.930	.928	.032	.000	.000	.000	.000	.119
1.20	.180	.021	.910	.860	.925	.928	.032	.000	.000	.005	.007	.016
1.40	.295	.109	.906	.870	.925	.930	.062	.018	.000	.080	.000	.005
1.60	.405	.088	.910	.892	.931	.930	.137	.131	.011	.266	.000	.007
1.80	.495	.040	.903	.896	.931	.930	.182	.317	.085	.430	.157	.011
2.00	.590	.008	.900	.897	.934	.929	.171	.440	.216	.512	.041	.029
2.20	.628	.002	.898	.875	.934	.835	.184	.440	.278	.455	.000	.048
2.40	.640	.009	.890	.850	.930	.890	.225	.440	.325	.433	.000	.060
2.60	.630	.018	.860	.820	.920	.780	.258	.280	.212	.252	.057	.051
2.80	.470	.030	.375	.140	.908	.180	.145	.060	.040	.060	.020	.000
3.00	.248	.030	.425	.360	.880	.695	.130	.000	.000	.000	.000	.000
3.20	.121	.030	.380	.490	.861	.760	.125	.000	.000	.000	.000	.000
3.40	.032	.020	.310	.270	.670	.620	.099	.000	.000	.000	.000	.000
3.60	.010	.015	.270	.010	.111	.080	.115	.000	.000	.000	.000	.000
3.80	.010	.020	.275	.040	.270	.240	.142	.000	.000	.000	.000	.000
4.00	.010	.030	.260	.013	.170	.150	.172	.000	.000	.000	.000	.000
4.20	.006	.017	.180	.026	.250	.230	.158	.000	.000	.000	.000	.000
4.40	.001	.002	.040	.004	.085	.080	.078	.000	.000	.000	.000	.000
4.60	.000	.000	.000	.000	.050	.020	.010	.000	.000	.000	.000	.000
4.80	.000	.000	.000	.000	.000	.000	.003	.000	.000	.000	.000	.000
5.00	.000	.000	.000	.000	.000	.000	.000	.000	.000	.000	.000	.000

Compiled by Allie C. Peed, Jr. for The Eastman Kodak Company

Data condensed from Kodak Wratten Filters for Scientific and Technical Use published by the Eastman Kodak Company, manufacturers of the filters.

The following pages give (1) percentage luminous transmittance at wave lengths from 400 to 700μ at intervals of 10μ for the standard illuminant "C" adopted by the International Commission of Illumination, (2) dominant wave length in millimicrons, and (3) percentage of excitation purity. Values of wave length followed by "c" indicate the complementary wave lengths of purple filters which do not have a dominant wave length.

All colorimetric specifications are based on the 1931 standard ICI colorimetric and luminosity data.

The transmittance data are given as representing standard samples of the filters. They are intended only for the information of users in choosing filters which will meet their requirements. Values taken from the tables of data should not be used by research workers as representing precisely the absorption characteristics of a particular filter. If such precise data are needed, they should be determined for the particular filter being used.

Where the spectra extend into the ultraviolet this fact is indicated by an asterisk (*) in the transmission tables immediately beneath the filter number, and quantitative data are not given. The manufacturer should be consulted for this information. Transmission in the ultraviolet of wave lengths less than 330μ will be eliminated in the case of cemented filters, as glass absorbs ultraviolet radiation of wave lengths shorter than about 330μ.

Stability ratings are given as three letter combinations following the filter description in the table below. In establishing the stability classifications each filter is exposed to a selected light source for a specific time interval. The following grading system is used to describe the result:

Class A—stable
Class B—relatively stable
Class C—somewhat unstable
Class D—unstable

The classification letters, for example, AAA, describe the stability to the following three exposure tests in this order:
1. Two weeks' exposure to daylight in a south window
2. Twenty-four hours' exposure to a "Fade-Ometer"
3. Two weeks' exposure at two feet from a 1000-watt tungsten lamp.

Filters are supplied in two forms; as lacquered gelatin film, or as a gelatin film cemented between pieces of optical glass. Filters in glass are cemented between sheets of plane-parallel glass, which is surfaced in quantities and is of sufficient accuracy for general photographic work, and for most scientific purposes.

Most Wratten Gelatin Filters are stocked in 2- or 3-inch squares. Stocks of 2- or 3-inch square filters cemented in glass are maintained only in filters usually used for general photographic work.

The booklet "Kodak Filters and Lens Attachments" gives more valuable information on this subject.

FILTER DATA

No.	Description, use, and stability	No.	Description, use, and stability
	Colorless	26	Stereo red, AAA.
0	For compensating thickness of other gelatin filters in optical systems, AAA.	29	Red color separation from transparencies and for the Kodak Fluorescence Process. Strong contrast effects. Copying blueprints. Tungsten tricolor projection, AAA.
1	Absorbs ultraviolet below 360 mμ, DDD.		**Magentas and Violets**
1A	Kodak Skylight Filter—Reduces excess bluishness in outdoor color photographs in open shade under a clear, blue sky, ACA.	30	Green absorption, BBC.
	Yellows	31	Green absorption, CCA.
2B	Absorbs ultraviolet below 410 mμ, ACA.	32	Minus green, CCD.
3	Light yellow, CCD.	33	Strong green absorption, CCB.
3N5	No. 3 plus 0.5 neutral density, AAA.	34	Violet, CDD.
4	Light yellow—Approximate correction on panchromatic materials for outdoor scenes, including sky, CCC.	34A	Blue separation—Kodak Fluorescence Process, DCC.
6	K1—Light yellow—Partial correction outdoors, BBA.	35	Contrast in microscopy, CDD.
8	K2—Yellow—Full correction outdoors on Type B panchromatic materials. Widely used for proper sky, cloud, and foliage rendering. Green separation for Fluorescence Process, AAA.	36	Dark violet, CCC.
			Blues and Blue-greens
8N5	No. 8 plus 0.5 neutral density, AAA.	38	Red absorption, BCA.
9	K3—Deep yellow. Moderate contrast in outdoor photography (with black-and-white films), AAA.	38A	Red absorption. Increasing contrast in visual microscopy, BBB.
11	X1—Greenish yellow. Correction for tungsten light on Type B panchromatic materials; also for daylight correction with Type C panchromatic materials in making outdoor portraits, darkening skies, or lightening foliage, AAA.	39	Contrast control in printing motion-picture duplicates (glass), AAA.
		40	Green for two-color photography (tungsten), CBC.
12	Minus blue. Haze cutting in aerial photography, AAA.	44	Minus red—Two-color general viewing, DDD.
13	X2—Yellow green. Correction for Type C panchromatic materials in tungsten light, ABA.	44A	Minus red, DDD.
15	G—Deep yellow. Overcorrection in landscape photography. Contrast control in copying and in aerial infrared photography, AAA.	45	Contrast in microscopy, DDD.
		45A	Highest resolving power in visual microscopy, CDC.
16	Blue absorption, AAB.	46	Blue projection (experimental), DDD.
18A	Transmits ultraviolet and infrared only (glass), AAA.	47	Tricolor blue for direct color separation and from Kodak Ektacolor Film for Dye Transfer. Contrast effects in commercial photography. Tungsten and white-flame-arc tricolor projection, BBC.
	Oranges and Reds	47B	Tricolor blue for color separation from transparencies and from Kodak Ektacolor Film for Graphic Arts, BBB.
21	Blue and blue-green absorption, CBB.	48	Green and red absorption, CBC.
22	Yellow-orange. For increasing contrast in blue preparations in microscopy. Mercury yellow, BAC.	48	Green and red absorption, AAB.
23A	Light red. Two-color projection—contrast effects, BAB.	49	Dark blue, BCB.
24	Red for two-color photography (daylight or tungsten). White-flame-arc tricolor projection, AAB.	49B	Very dark blue, BBB.
25	A—Tricolor red for direct color separation. Contrast effects in commercial photography and in outdoor scenes. Two-color general viewing. Aerial infrared photography and haze cutting, AAA.	50	Very dark blue. Mercury violet, CCC.
			Greens
		52	Light green, AAB.
		53	Medium green, CCB.
		54	Very dark green, AAA.
		55	Stereo green, BBC.
		56	Very light green, CBC.

FILTER DATA

No.	Description, use, and stability	No.	Description, use, and stability
	Greens (Continued)		**Light Balancing**
57	Green for two-color photography (daylight), CBC.	80A	For Kodachrome Film, Daylight Type, and photographic flood lamps, ABA.
57A	Light green, BBC.	81	Yellowish. For warmer color rendering.
58	Tricolor green for direct color separation. Contrast effects in commercial photography and microscopy, BBC.	81A	Yellowish. For Kodak Ektachrome Film, Type B, with photographic flood lamps.
59	Green for tricolor projection (white-flame-arc), BBB.	81B	Yellowish. For warmer color rendering.
59A	Very light green, BBB.	81C	Yellowish. For Kodachrome Film, Type A, with flash lamps.
60	Green for two-color photography (tungsten), BDC.	81D	Yellowish. For Kodachrome Film, Type A, with flash lamps.
61	Green color separation from transparencies and Kodak Ekta-color Film. Tricolor projection (tungsten), ABC.	81EF	Yellowish. For Kodak Ektachrome Film, Type B, with flash lamps.
64	Red absorption (light), CDB.	82	Bluish. For cooler color rendering.
65	Red absorption, ADB.	82A	Bluish. For Kodachrome Film, Type A, with 3200 K lamps.
65A	Red absorption, CCD.	82B	Bluish. For cooler color rendering.
66	Contrast effects in microscopy and medical photography, DDD.	82C	Bluish. For cooler color rendering.
67A	Red absorption (light). Two-color projection, CDC.	83	Yellowish. For 16 mm Commercial Kodachrome Film and daylight exposure, BBB.
	Narrow-band	85	Orange. For Type A Kodak color films and daylight exposure, BAB.
70	Dark red. Infrared photography. Color separation for Kodak Ektacolor Film (with tungsten), ABC.	85B	Orange. For Kodak Ektachrome Film, Type B, and daylight exposure, BAB.
72B	Dark orange-yellow, CCC.		**Miscellaneous**
73	Dark yellow-green, ABB.	79	Photographic sensitometry. Corrects 2360 K to 5500 K, AAA.
74	Dark green. Mercury green, BBC.	87	For infrared photography. Absorbs visual.
75	Dark blue-green, ACC.	87C	Absorbs visual, transmits infrared.
76	Dark violet (compound filter), DDD.	88A	For infrared photography. Absorbs visual.
77	Transmits 546 mμ mercury line (glass plus gelatin), AAA.	89B	For infrared photography, AAA.
77A	Transmits 546 mμ mercury line (glass plus gelatin), AAA.	90	Narrow-band viewing filter for judging brightness scale of scenes, CCD.
	Photometrics	96	Neutral filters for controlling luminance, AAB.
78	Bluish. Photometric filter (visual), BAB.	97	Dichroic absorption, AAA.
78AA	Bluish. Photometric filter (visual), BAA.	102	Correction filter for Barrier-layer photocell, ABA.
78A	Bluish. Photometric filter (visual), AAA.	106	Correction filter for S-4 type photocell, AAA.
78B	Bluish. Photometric filter (visual), AAA.		
78C	Bluish. Photometric filter (visual), BAA.		
86	Yellowish. Photometric filter (visual), BBA.		
86A	Yellowish. Photometric filter (visual), AAA.		
†86B	Yellowish. Photometric filter (visual), BCA.		
*86C	Yellowish. Photometric filter (visual), AAA.		

Wave length	Percent transmittance												
	No. 0 *	No. 1 *	No. 1A *	No. 2B *	No. 3	No. 3N5 *	No. 4	No. 6 *	No. 8	No. 8N5	No. 9	No. 11 *	No. 12 *
400	88.0	85.0	59.0	19.0	.....	......	.....	7.40	......	......	......	......	......
10	88.5	85.5	76.0	48.0	.....	......	.....	8.32	......	......	......	0.16	......
20	88.9	86.0	82.0	67.0	.....	......	.....	10.4	......	......	......	0.29	......
30	89.3	86.5	84.6	75.3	0.36	......	.....	13.5	......	......	......	0.56	......
40	89.6	87.0	86.0	80.0	1.78	......	.....	18.9	......	......	......	1.32	......
50	89.8	87.4	86.8	83.0	11.5	1.59	.....	27.6	......	......	......	4.00	......
60	89.9	87.8	87.2	85.2	38.0	9.40	6.9	39.0	0.25	0.16	......	12.0	......
70	90.1	88.2	87.5	86.7	68.0	18.5	42.0	52.3	5.50	2.0	1.78	26.0	......
80	90.3	88.5	87.3	88.1	80.8	23.5	74.0	65.8	19.0	6.3	8.31	43.7	......
90	90.4	88.7	86.8	88.8	85.2	25.5	84.7	76.8	41.0	13.2	20.7	55.0	1.50
500	90.5	88.9	86.3	89.5	86.9	26.3	87.5	83.5	63.5	20.0	34.5	60.0	17.3
10	90.6	89.1	85.5	89.9	87.8	26.7	88.5	87.0	78.0	24.3	48.8	60.2	55.0
20	90.7	89.3	84.8	90.3	88.4	27.0	89.1	88.4	84.1	26.7	62.0	57.8	77.8
30	90.7	89.5	84.3	90.5	89.0	27.2	89.4	89.0	86.5	28.0	76.0	54.2	86.0
40	90.8	89.7	84.0	90.6	89.5	27.5	89.6	89.4	87.7	28.6	83.8	50.0	88.4
50	90.8	89.9	83.9	90.7	89.8	27.8	89.8	89.7	88.4	29.0	87.0	44.8	89.4
60	90.9	90.1	84.1	90.8	90.1	27.9	90.0	89.9	88.8	29.3	88.3	38.9	89.7
70	90.9	90.2	84.8	90.9	90.4	28.0	90.2	90.1	89.2	29.5	88.8	33.1	90.1
80	90.9	90.3	86.0	90.9	90.6	28.4	90.4	90.3	89.5	29.6	89.1	27.6	90.3
90	91.0	90.4	87.4	91.0	90.7	29.0	90.6	90.5	89.8	29.8	89.3	22.7	90.4
600	91.0	90.5	88.5	91.1	90.8	29.5	90.8	90.6	90.1	29.9	89.5	19.0	90.5
10	91.0	90.5	89.5	91.2	90.9	29.5	90.9	90.7	90.3	29.6	89.7	14.9	90.7
20	91.0	90.6	90.2	91.3	91.0	29.3	91.0	90.8	90.5	29.4	89.8	11.4	90.8
30	91.0	90.6	90.6	91.3	91.0	29.1	91.1	90.9	90.7	29.1	89.9	9.10	90.9
40	91.1	90.7	90.8	91.4	91.1	29.0	91.2	91.0	90.9	28.8	90.0	8.05	91.0
50	91.1	90.7	91.0	91.4	91.2	29.4	91.3	91.1	91.0	28.9	90.1	7.50	91.0
60	91.1	90.8	91.1	91.5	91.3	29.6	91.4	91.2	91.1	29.2	90.1	7.05	91.1
70	91.1	90.8	91.1	91.5	91.4	29.8	91.5	91.2	91.2	29.4	90.2	6.50	91.2
80	91.1	90.9	91.1	91.6	91.5	30.0	91.5	91.3	91.3	29.5	90.2	6.50	91.2
90	91.1	90.9	91.1	91.7	91.6	30.2	91.6	91.4	91.4	29.7	90.3	6.10	91.2
700	91.1	91.0	91.1	91.8	91.7	31.0	91.6	91.5	91.5	30.2	90.3	6.20	91.3
Luminous transmit.	90.8	89.9	85.9	90.5	88.3	27.4	87.8	87.5	82.7	27.0	76.6	40.2	73.8
Dominant wave lgth.	571.0	575.0	498.0	570.0	569.5	570.5	569.5	570.3	571.8	572.0	574.4	550.3	576.1
Excitation purity.	0.8	1.5	1.2	5.7	50.0	56.3	64.0	44.7	85.2	84.0	91.4	60.7	97.8

*Some transmission below 400 mμ. Consult the manufacturer.

TRANSMISSION OF WRATTEN FILTERS (Continued)

Wave length	No. 13 *	No. 15 *	No. 16	No. 18A *	No. 21	No. 22	No. 23A	No. 24	No. 25	No. 26	No. 29	No. 30 *	No. 31 *
400	.....	.....	.....	.....	.....	.....	.....	.....	.....	.....	.....	48.6	13.8
10	.....	.....	.....	.....	.....	.....	.....	.....	.....	.....	.....	47.4	14.5
20	.....	.....	.....	.....	.....	.....	.....	.....	.....	.....	.....	48.5	16.4
30	0.18	.....	.....	.....	.....	.....	.....	.....	.....	.....	.....	50.1	25.5
40	0.50	.....	.....	.....	.....	.....	.....	.....	.....	.....	.....	49.4	42.7
50	1.35	.....	.....	.....	.....	.....	.....	.....	.....	.....	.....	43.0	50.2
60	4.08	.....	.....	.....	.....	.....	.....	.....	.....	.....	.....	26.5	40.4
70	11.0	.....	.....	.....	.....	.....	.....	.....	.....	.....	.....	13.8	22.6
80	23.5	.....	.....	.....	.....	.....	.....	.....	.....	.....	.....	5.00	8.20
90	39.0	.....	.....	.....	.....	.....	.....	.....	.....	.....	.....	0.63	1.85
500	50.8	.....	.....	.....	.....	.....	.....	.....	.....	.....	.....	.....	0.12
10	55.2	1.00	.....	.....	.....	.....	.....	.....	.....	.....	.....	.....	.....
20	56.5	16.0	3.00	.....	.....	.....	.....	.....	.....	.....	.....	.....	.....
30	55.0	52.1	22.0	.....	.....	.....	.....	.....	.....	.....	.....	.....	.....
40	51.0	70.7	48.0	.....	2.50	.....	.....	.....	.....	.....	.....	.....	.....
50	46.0	84.3	69.5	.....	29.0	0.25	.....	.....	.....	.....	.....	.....	.....
60	39.2	87.5	79.5	.....	65.0	19.0	.....	.....	.....	.....	.....	0.10	.....
70	32.0	88.7	84.0	.....	80.6	60.0	11.0	.....	.....	.....	.....	10.0	.....
80	25.1	89.3	86.3	.....	85.4	81.0	47.0	4.55	.....	.....	.....	45.0	.....
90	18.2	89.7	87.8	.....	87.3	87.0	69.6	37.3	12.6	2.90	.....	76.0	0.63
600	13.5	90.0	89.0	.....	88.1	88.5	82.7	72.3	50.0	30.0	.....	87.4	26.0
10	9.60	90.1	89.6	.....	88.7	89.0	85.8	82.9	75.0	63.2	10.0	89.5	67.2
20	6.40	90.2	90.0	.....	89.0	89.5	87.2	86.4	82.6	78.9	45.3	90.2	84.0
30	3.66	90.3	90.2	.....	89.5	89.8	87.9	87.8	85.5	84.0	71.4	90.5	88.1
40	2.20	90.4	90.3	.....	89.9	90.0	88.5	88.5	86.7	86.1	82.7	90.7	89.8
50	1.58	90.5	90.4	.....	90.2	90.1	89.0	89.0	87.6	87.2	86.6	90.8	90.2
60	1.74	90.6	90.5	.....	90.4	90.2	89.4	89.3	88.2	88.1	88.4	90.9	90.4
70	2.62	90.6	90.6	.....	90.5	90.3	89.6	89.7	88.5	88.5	89.4	91.0	90.5
80	3.55	90.7	90.7	.....	90.5	90.4	89.8	89.9	89.0	88.9	90.0	91.1	90.7
90	4.48	90.7	90.8	0.25	90.6	90.5	90.0	90.2	89.2	89.2	90.3	91.1	90.8
700	5.25	90.8	90.8	1.20	90.6	90.6	90.2	90.3	89.5	89.5	90.4	91.1	91.0
Luminous transmit.	34.5	66.2	57.7	0.0014	45.6	35.8	25.0	17.8	14.0	11.7	6.3	26.6	12.9
Dominant wave lgth.	542.0	579.3	582.7	700.0	588.9	595.1	602.7	610.6	615.1	619.0	631.6	498.6c	513.1c
Excitation purity.	57.5	99.0	99.3	100.0	99.9	99.9	100.0	100.0	100.0	100.0	100.0	62.4	81.9

Wave length	No. 32 *	No. 33 *	No. 34 *	No. 34A *	No. 35 *	No. 36 *	No. 38 *	No. 38A *	No. 39 *	No. 40	No. 44 *	No. 44A *	No. 45
400	38.0	0.85	64.0	.....	48.0	36.5	60.5	33.4	85.2	.....	0.44	2.52	.....
10	37.9	0.71	70.1	0.1	57.0	45.5	66.5	41.2	78.2	.....	0.36	3.39	.....
20	40.0	1.17	72.0	40.0	57.6	45.5	72.5	53.0	70.5	.....	0.63	6.30	.....
30	43.0	1.69	68.4	69.7	47.5	32.7	75.3	58.0	63.3	.....	3.63	17.4	.....
40	55.5	5.36	58.2	68.7	29.5	15.2	76.2	58.8	53.6	.....	13.1	32.7	5.00
50	66.0	14.3	42.3	56.2	12.3	3.7	75.9	57.6	42.5	.....	25.4	41.8	19.0
60	66.0	12.4	25.2	40.5	3.5	0.35	74.8	55.2	28.5	3.16	36.5	48.1	29.5
70	57.0	5.00	12.1	23.8	0.25	....	73.4	51.9	17.3	21.6	46.5	51.7	34.4
80	40.0	0.50	2.7	9.2	.....	.....	71.6	48.5	10.2	44.7	53.6	52.9	35.7
90	21.0	.....	0.2	2.3	.....	.....	69.5	44.6	4.00	61.4	56.8	52.2	34.5
500	9.56	.....	.....	0.33	.....	.....	66.7	40.2	1.33	70.2	55.8	49.8	29.7
10	2.51	.....	.....	.....	.....	.....	63.9	35.8	0.35	72.4	50.9	44.8	21.5
20	0.13	.....	.....	.....	.....	.....	60.8	31.7	.....	70.5	42.1	36.8	11.5
30	.....	.....	.....	.....	.....	.....	57.0	27.2	.....	64.8	30.5	26.8	3.80
40	.....	.....	.....	.....	.....	.....	52.6	22.3	.....	55.5	18.6	16.8	0.85
50	.....	.....	.....	.....	.....	.....	48.0	17.6	.....	44.2	8.99	8.20	.....
60	.....	.....	.....	.....	.....	.....	42.8	12.9	.....	32.5	3.59	2.95	.....
70	.....	.....	.....	.....	.....	.....	37.0	8.78	.....	20.3	0.80	0.91	.....
80	.....	.....	.....	.....	.....	.....	30.6	5.65	.....	9.56	.....	0.10	.....
90	.....	.....	.....	.....	.....	.....	25.5	3.48	.....	3.20	.....	.....	.....
600	6.04	.....	.....	.....	.....	.....	20.9	2.09	.....	1.10	.....	.....	.....
10	41.0	0.80	.....	0.13	.....	.....	16.8	1.15	.....	0.32	.....	.....	.....
20	75.0	24.9	.....	1.0	.....	.....	12.9	0.59	.....	.....	.....	.....	.....
30	86.1	60.8	.....	6.3	.....	.....	10.0	0.28	.....	.....	.....	.....	.....
40	89.0	78.0	0.4	22.0	.....	.....	7.79	0.13	.....	.....	.....	.....	.....
50	90.0	85.0	4.0	45.0	0.1	.....	6.68	.....	.....	.....	.....	.....	.....
60	90.6	87.5	20.7	65.0	3.0	0.21	6.20	.....	.....	.....	.....	.....	.....
70	90.7	88.7	45.2	77.3	19.0	7.5	5.91	.....	.....	.....	.....	.....	.....
80	90.8	89.4	66.5	85.0	43.5	29.0	5.41	.....	.....	0.50	0.80	.....	.....
90	90.9	89.8	78.8	88.2	66.0	55.0	4.90	.....	.....	4.06	6.99	0.18	.....
700	91.0	90.0	85.0	89.8	77.7	71.3	5.00	.....	17.8	23.5	1.60	.....	1.00
Luminous transmit.	12.5	5.2	1.3	2.9	0.45	0.25	42.5	17.3	1.2	33.6	15.6	14.4	5.2
Dominant wave lgth.	551.7c	498.0c	424.0	564.8c	566.8c	566.4c	483.5	478.9	450.6	516.2	589.1	483.4	481.5
Excitation purity.	79.6	88.3	94.4	91.4	96.3	97.8	41.8	69.8	98.9	48.5	72.9	77.2	88.4

* Some transmission below 400 mμ. Consult the manufacturer.

Wave length	Percent transmittance												
	No. 45A	No. 46 *	No. 47 *	No. 47B *	No. 48 *	No. 48A	No. 49 *	No. 49B *	No. 50 *	No. 52 *	No. 53 *	No. 54	No. 55
400	.....	1.20	7.80	16.0	0.96	5.65	3.30	1.70	0.45	2.18	.....	.....	.....
10	.....	0.60	17.4	29.5	3.16	10.0	4.28	2.00	0.39	1.51	.....	.....	.....
20	.....	0.80	34.0	43.6	8.25	16.0	6.93	3.55	0.59	0.80	.....	.....	.....
30	1.00	5.98	47.0	50.0	15.0	21.0	11.2	7.00	2.63	0.44	.....	.....	.....
40	8.81	19.0	50.3	47.2	22.6	25.0	18.9	13.0	8.90	0.41	.....	.....	.....
50	17.4	30.1	48.3	36.0	30.3	26.2	25.6	17.4	14.0	0.69	.....	.....	.....
60	20.9	33.8	43.4	25.0	33.2	22.9	24.0	14.8	12.3	1.45	.....	.....	0.20
70	21.6	32.1	36.2	13.2	29.6	16.5	15.7	7.60	5.36	2.70	0.10	.....	2.90
80	20.5	27.0	28.5	4.5	22.4	9.55	6.93	2.76	1.55	4.90	0.71	.....	13.1
90	18.0	20.2	19.6	1.3	14.1	4.27	2.14	0.40	0.10	8.50	2.14	.....	34.2
500	14.4	11.1	11.3	0.17	7.30	1.58	0.46	.....	.....	13.3	4.47	.....	53.4
10	10.1	4.39	5.64	.....	2.64	0.48	.....	.....	.....	18.2	7.24	0.10	67.0
20	5.60	1.66	1.91	.....	0.50	.....	.....	.....	.....	23.7	10.7	0.31	69.3
30	2.52	0.35	0.36	.....	.....	.....	.....	.....	.....	28.5	14.0	0.64	65.1
40	0.64	.....	.....	.....	.....	.....	.....	.....	.....	32.1	16.6	0.89	56.7
50	0.10	.....	.....	.....	.....	.....	.....	.....	.....	33.1	17.3	0.93	45.0
60	.....	.....	.....	.....	.....	.....	.....	.....	.....	31.0	15.4	0.62	33.1
70	.....	.....	.....	.....	.....	.....	.....	.....	.....	25.6	11.4	0.21	20.7
80	.....	.....	.....	.....	.....	.....	.....	.....	.....	19.1	6.90	.....	9.00
90	.....	.....	.....	.....	.....	.....	.....	.....	.....	12.6	3.60	.....	2.70
600	.....	.....	.....	.....	.....	.....	.....	.....	.....	7.78	1.41	.....	0.40
10	.....	.....	.....	.....	.....	.....	.....	.....	.....	4.17	0.40	.....	.....
20	.....	.....	.....	.....	.....	.....	.....	.....	.....	2.34	0.15	.....	.....
30	.....	.....	.....	.....	.....	.....	.....	.....	.....	1.38	.....	.....	.....
40	.....	.....	.....	.....	.....	.....	.....	.....	.....	0.80	.....	.....	.....
50	.....	.....	.....	.....	.....	.....	.....	.....	.....	0.54	.....	.....	.....
60	.....	.....	.....	.....	.....	.....	.....	.....	.....	0.36	.....	.....	.....
70	.....	.....	.....	.....	.....	.....	.....	.....	.....	0.27	.....	.....	.....
80	.....	.....	.....	.....	.....	.....	.....	.....	.....	0.23	.....	.....	0.66
90	0.20	0.25	.....	.....	.....	.....	.....	.....	.....	0.19	.....	.....	6.90
700	2.24	0.85	.....	.....	.....	.....	.....	.....	.....	0.17	.....	.....	27.8
Luminous transmit.	2.8	2.4	2.8	0.78	1.86	0.88	0.69	0.36	0.26	20.1	9.0	0.032	31.4
Dominant wave lgth.	477.6	470.4	463.7	479.8	466.5	458.0	457.9	455.5	455.9	553.3	551.1	546.1	530.2
Excitation purity.	89.7	94.9	95.8	69.1	96.1	98.3	98.9	99.3	99.4	77.3	89.7	97.0	68.4

Wave length	Percent transmittance												
	No. 56	No. 57	No. 57A	No. 58	No. 59 *	No. 59A *	No. 60	No. 61	No. 64 *	No. 65	No. 65A *	No. 66 *	No. 67A *
400	.....	.....	.....	.....	.....	.....	.....	.....	9.00	.....	.....	12.3	1.10
10	.....	.....	.....	.....	.....	.....	.....	.....	9.20	.....	.....	13.0	0.93
20	.....	.....	.....	.....	.....	0.16	.....	.....	8.75	0.23	.....	15.0	1.28
30	.....	.....	.....	.....	.....	0.16	.....	.....	9.20	0.61	0.16	18.4	3.16
40	.....	.....	0.19	.....	.....	0.37	.....	.....	11.3	1.58	1.32	23.2	6.40
50	.....	.....	0.87	.....	0.40	1.26	0.19	.....	15.5	4.10	5.50	31.2	10.5
60	0.16	0.44	2.56	.....	1.90	4.57	1.38	.....	23.3	9.00	13.0	42.2	17.7
70	3.12	3.10	7.80	0.23	7.70	13.2	5.38	0.33	34.4	16.8	24.9	55.5	28.5
80	13.0	13.1	21.6	1.38	21.0	30.0	15.0	16.6	46.8	24.9	36.6	68.4	41.4
90	34.5	31.9	41.7	4.90	41.5	50.8	32.0	4.00	56.6	31.3	45.1	77.6	52.1
500	59.0	50.5	58.8	17.7	59.0	66.0	48.4	16.6	62.1	33.7	45.8	82.7	57.9
10	73.0	60.6	67.9	38.8	67.7	73.0	57.2	32.3	62.9	32.4	39.7	84.6	58.8
20	79.0	63.3	70.1	52.2	69.8	75.1	59.2	40.0	59.1	27.5	29.7	84.0	55.4
30	79.9	61.0	67.6	53.6	67.2	73.2	55.5	39.6	51.6	20.7	17.8	82.6	47.5
40	77.5	55.0	61.8	47.6	61.5	68.5	47.5	34.5	41.3	13.7	7.90	79.1	36.6
50	72.6	47.1	53.5	38.4	54.0	62.0	36.8	26.3	28.0	6.50	2.40	73.7	25.0
60	66.1	37.3	43.3	27.8	45.0	54.4	25.2	17.3	16.2	1.66	0.32	67.1	14.2
70	58.0	26.5	31.6	17.4	35.0	44.5	14.4	9.70	7.95	0.40	.....	58.8	5.50
80	46.1	16.6	19.4	9.0	24.0	33.0	6.3	4.40	3.10	.....	.....	47.2	1.40
90	33.8	8.69	9.70	3.50	14.0	22.0	1.82	1.66	0.80	.....	.....	34.5	0.28
600	24.0	3.70	4.50	1.50	7.95	14.6	0.48	0.38	.....	.....	.....	24.4	.....
10	18.7	1.60	2.00	0.41	4.90	10.5	0.10	.....	.....	.....	.....	18.5	.....
20	13.2	0.49	0.87	.....	2.70	6.92	.....	.....	.....	.....	.....	13.7	.....
30	7.22	.....	0.22	.....	1.00	3.16	.....	.....	.....	.....	.....	7.70	.....
40	3.02	.....	.....	.....	0.17	1.07	.....	.....	.....	.....	.....	3.00	.....
50	1.48	.....	.....	.....	.....	0.50	.....	.....	.....	.....	.....	1.46	.....
60	1.91	.....	.....	.....	.....	0.91	.....	.....	.....	.....	.....	1.91	.....
70	7.95	.....	.....	.....	0.63	3.00	.....	.....	.....	.....	.....	6.17	.....
80	23.0	.....	0.16	.....	4.00	10.0	.....	.....	.....	.....	.....	19.9	.....
90	44.1	.....	1.15	.....	12.0	20.0	2.10	.....	0.10	.....	0.20	42.6	.....
700	64.8	.....	3.17	0.53	22.6	30.0	8.70	.....	4.50	.....	2.18	63.1	0.40
Luminous transmit.	52.8	32.5	37.2	23.7	38.7	45.8	26.1	16.8	25.0	9.6	9.8	58.3	22.4
Dominant wave lgth.	552.3	536.4	534.0	540.2	538.3	541.4	525.7	536.8	497.3	496.6	492.7	512.3	499.8
Excitation purity.	78.2	69.2	62.1	88.1	66.0	59.3	62.2	85.4	55.0	67.8	77.4	21.5	55.8

* Some transmission below 400 mμ.   Consult the manufacturer.

Wave length	Percent transmittance											
	No. 70	No. 72B	No. 73	No. 74	No. 75	No. 76*	No. 77	No. 77A	No. 78*	No. 78AA	No. 78A*	No. 78B*
400	......	......	......	......	......	0.22	......	......	37.2	43.0	56.0	64.1
10	......	......	......	......	......	0.18	......	......	41.7	46.0	58.6	66.5
20	......	......	......	......	......	0.29	......	......	44.2	48.7	61.0	68.4
30	......	......	......	......	......	1.38	......	......	44.6	49.8	61.8	69.5
40	......	......	......	......	......	3.50	......	......	44.2	49.7	61.8	70.0
50	......	......	......	......	......	3.50	......	......	41.7	48.0	61.0	69.4
60	......	......	......	......	1.97	1.92	......	......	38.0	44.9	58.7	67.5
70	......	......	......	......	10.0	0.51	......	......	33.8	40.3	55.0	65.4
80	......	......	......	......	17.4	......	......	......	27.5	35.6	51.0	62.9
90	......	......	......	......	18.0	......	......	......	23.5	30.9	47.1	59.8
500	......	......	......	......	13.0	......	......	......	19.5	26.5	43.5	57.0
10	......	......	......	0.96	7.35	......	0.30	0.10	15.8	23.4	40.0	54.2
20	......	......	......	7.95	3.20	......	0.10	5.35	13.8	20.3	36.9	51.4
30	......	......	......	14.6	0.83	......	13.5	1.90	11.8	17.8	34.4	49.3
40	......	......	......	12.9	0.14	......	46.1	35.0	10.5	16.6	32.7	48.1
50	......	......	......	7.60	......	......	78.0	71.8	9.56	14.9	31.2	46.7
60	......	......	2.24	3.06	......	......	75.8	63.1	8.53	13.2	29.4	45.0
70	......	......	5.97	0.83	......	......	8.00	......	7.77	12.1	28.0	43.6
80	......	......	4.56	0.12	......	......	1.00	......	7.41	11.6	27.5	43.1
90	......	1.26	2.00	......	......	......	0.32	......	6.93	11.1	27.0	42.9
600	......	5.89	0.56	......	......	......	16.2	1.60	6.45	10.40	26.0	41.8
10	......	5.25	0.10	......	......	......	52.1	32.1	5.50	9.20	24.1	40.0
20	......	2.88	......	......	......	......	83.0	78.0	4.80	7.70	21.8	37.6
30	......	1.26	......	......	......	......	84.9	79.5	3.94	6.50	19.7	35.5
40	......	0.48	......	......	......	......	88.1	86.5	3.46	5.60	18.6	34.2
50	0.63	0.14	......	......	......	......	89.8	89.2	3.24	5.50	18.4	33.6
60	10.5	......	......	......	......	......	89.8	89.0	3.16	5.60	18.5	34.0
70	35.0	......	......	......	......	......	85.5	79.5	3.39	5.80	18.7	34.1
80	55.2	......	......	......	......	......	76.1	62.5	3.45	6.10	19.0	34.5
90	70.0	......	......	......	......	0.13	75.0	62.4	3.51	6.10	19.3	34.8
700	79.0	......	......	......	0.14	1.24	86.5	83.0	3.90	6.50	20.2	36.0
Luminous transmit.	0.31	0.74	1.3	4.0	1.9	0.046	32.3	25.5	10.7	15.8	31.6	46.7
Dominant wave lgth.	675.6	604.9	574.9	538.6	487.7	449.2	579.9	581.5	471.1	473.4	475.7	477.2
Excitation purity.	100.0	100.0	100.0	96.7	90.4	99.7	99.0	99.1	63.0	54.5	33.7	20.7

Wave length	Percent transmittance											
	No. 78C*	No. 79*	No. 80A*	No. 81*	No. 81A*	No. 81B*	No. 81C*	No. 81D*	No. 81EF*	No. 82*	No. 82A*	No. 82B*
400	74.9	24.0	67.6	77.7	65.1	55.1	46.1	38.2	30.7	83.0	80.1	76.7
10	76.6	26.0	73.1	78.1	65.9	55.8	46.6	38.4	31.5	83.7	80.8	78.0
20	77.9	29.0	76.8	79.0	67.6	57.7	49.0	41.0	34.3	84.6	81.6	79.2
30	78.9	31.0	7.77	80.5	70.2	61.0	52.5	45.5	38.6	85.1	82.2	79.7
40	79.4	32.2	76.5	81.9	72.8	64.5	57.2	50.0	43.2	85.4	82.4	79.7
50	79.5	32.7	73.0	83.0	74.8	67.2	60.5	53.9	47.4	85.4	82.4	79.2
60	79.3	31.4	69.0	83.7	76.0	69.1	63.0	56.5	50.2	85.0	81.7	78.0
70	78.6	28.8	63.6	84.3	77.1	70.6	64.2	58.1	52.0	84.6	80.7	76.3
80	77.8	25.6	57.6	84.6	77.8	71.3	65.0	59.0	53.0	84.0	79.3	74.4
90	76.7	22.2	51.3	84.9	78.3	71.8	65.7	60.0	54.0	83.3	78.0	72.1
500	75.5	19.3	45.2	85.3	78.6	72.6	66.4	60.8	55.4	82.6	76.6	70.2
10	74.2	16.8	39.4	85.4	79.0	72.9	66.5	61.1	56.2	82.0	75.3	68.3
20	73.0	14.2	34.2	85.5	79.5	73.2	67.0	61.6	57.0	81.4	74.0	66.5
30	72.1	12.7	30.0	86.0	80.4	74.5	68.8	62.5	59.5	81.0	73.1	65.5
40	71.5	11.8	27.1	86.5	81.5	76.0	71.0	66.1	62.7	80.8	72.7	65.0
50	70.7	11.0	24.8	86.8	82.3	77.0	72.0	67.3	64.5	80.6	72.4	64.5
60	69.8	9.76	23.5	87.0	82.6	77.6	72.5	68.0	65.3	80.4	71.8	63.8
70	69.0	8.81	22.6	87.1	82.7	77.8	72.7	68.3	65.8	80.2	71.5	63.2
80	68.8	8.50	22.6	87.1	82.8	78.0	73.0	68.5	66.0	80.2	71.5	63.2
90	68.6	8.29	23.2	87.4	83.1	78.2	74.0	69.5	66.5	80.3	71.7	63.4
600	68.0	7.56	23.7	87.6	84.0	79.1	75.6	72.0	68.1	80.2	71.5	63.0
10	66.7	6.45	23.2	88.1	85.0	81.0	78.5	75.0	71.6	79.3	70.3	61.5
20	65.0	5.13	21.0	88.8	86.1	83.1	80.8	78.0	74.7	78.4	68.5	59.0
30	63.8	4.17	18.2	89.2	87.0	84.2	82.1	79.8	77.0	77.5	66.9	56.9
40	63.0	3.47	15.8	89.4	87.4	85.1	83.0	80.8	78.4	76.8	65.5	55.0
50	62.7	3.16	14.5	89.5	87.7	85.6	83.5	81.5	79.2	76.5	64.8	54.1
60	63.0	3.09	13.8	89.8	88.0	86.0	84.1	82.1	80.1	76.2	64.6	53.7
70	63.3	3.16	13.4	90.0	88.2	86.5	84.8	83.0	80.9	76.1	64.5	53.7
80	63.4	3.16	12.7	90.1	88.5	87.0	85.5	83.7	81.8	76.1	64.4	53.5
90	63.6	3.16	11.7	90.3	89.0	87.5	86.1	84.6	82.9	76.2	64.2	53.4
700	65.0	3.31	11.5	90.5	89.2	88.0	86.8	85.5	84.0	77.1	64.6	54.1
Luminous transmit.	70.4	11.3	28.4	86.8	82.0	76.9	72.0	67.4	64.0	80.7	72.5	64.6
Dominant wave lgth.	479.8	474.8	471.7	576.7	577.5	577.8	577.4	579.5	579.0	477.5	476.6	475.6
Excitation purity.	6.8	52.8	45.9	2.9	6.0	8.7	10.7	14.7	19.0	3.0	6.3	10.2

* Some transmission below 400 mμ. Consult the manufacturer.

Wave length	Percent transmittance												
	No. 82C *	No. 83 *	No. 85 *	No. 85B *	No. 86 *	No. 86A *	No. 86B *	No. 86C *	No. 89B	No. 90	No. 96 *	No. 97	No. 102 *
400	73.4	13.5	6.0	1.59	0.50	8.00	20.0	44.0	....	....	4.28	...	1.12
10	75.0	13.1	18.0	9.32	0.81	12.2	26.1	55.0			4.91	....	0.96
20	76.4	13.5	28.4	15.5	1.55	16.7	31.6	62.0			5.50	....	0.89
30	77.2	14.1	33.4	19.0	2.88	21.5	37.5	66.6			6.17	....	0.96
40	77.2	15.6	36.2	20.8	5.50	27.8	44.0	70.8			6.92	....	1.23
50	76.6	17.8	38.1	22.1	9.10	34.2	50.1	74.3			7.50	....	1.86
60	75.2	21.0	40.4	24.3	13.5	40.4	55.4	76.8			7.81		3.23
70	73.2	25.5	43.0	27.5	17.8	45.0	59.5	78.7			8.15	0.22	6.45
80	70.7	30.2	45.3	30.9	21.3	48.7	62.5	80.2			8.47	0.43	14.0
90	68.1	35.8	47.2	34.3	24.5	51.2	64.6	81.2			8.60	0.39	21.6
500	65.7	43.5	48.9	38.3	26.8	52.8	66.0	81.7			8.73	0.15	30.7
10	63.5	46.3	49.2	40.7	27.9	53.4	66.4	81.9			8.85		41.4
20	61.5	47.2	48.2	40.6	28.6	53.7	66.6	82.0			8.90		51.3
30	59.9	48.3	48.3	40.7	30.4	55.0	67.6	82.4			9.01		59.4
40	59.1	49.6	49.2	41.6	32.5	56.5	69.0	83.0			9.07		64.2
50	58.3	51.8	51.0	43.2	35.0	58.5	70.2	83.5			9.20		66.7
60	57.2	56.5	55.8	47.1	41.2	63.0	73.0	84.6		9.00	9.30		66.3
70	56.2	65.0	64.5	56.0	53.0	70.9	78.1	86.8		30.5	9.20		63.0
80	56.1	75.5	75.0	68.1	67.5	79.0	84.0	88.9		34.3	9.19		58.0
90	56.0	83.0	83.0	78.1	76.5	85.2	87.5	89.9		25.2	9.54		51.9
600	55.0	87.3	87.2	85.0	85.0	88.1	89.3	90.6		16.1	9.64		45.2
10	53.0	89.3	88.9	88.0	88.1	89.8	90.3	91.0		11.3	9.73		37.8
20	50.2	90.4	90.0	89.6	89.6	90.5	90.7	91.1		7.40	9.56		30.5
30	47.4	90.8	90.5	90.3	90.4	90.8	90.9	91.2		2.94	9.27		25.0
40	45.2	91.0	90.7	90.7	90.7	91.1	91.1	91.3		0.76	9.10		20.6
50	44.1	91.1	90.9	90.9	91.0	91.2	91.2	91.4		0.29	9.07		17.5
60	43.6	91.3	91.0	91.0	91.1	91.3	91.3	91.5		0.41	9.00		15.2
70	43.5	91.5	91.0	91.2	91.2	91.4	91.4	91.6		2.30	9.13		13.7
80	43.1	91.5	91.0	91.3	91.3	91.4	91.5	91.6	0.10	9.52	9.08	0.44	12.8
90	42.8	91.5	91.0	91.3	91.3	91.5	91.6	91.6	1.58	28.5	9.21	5.02	12.1
700	43.5	91.5	91.0	91.3	91.3	91.5	91.6	91.6	11.2	51.9	9.52	18.7	12.0
Luminous transmit.	58.1	61.4	62.5	55.5	49.7	67.1	75.5	85.4	0.017	9.8	9.1	0.041	50.8
Dominant wave lgth.	477.2	581.5	587.7	585.7	585.7	581.7	579.6	577.6	700	583.1	572.4	555.0c	564.9
Excitation purity.	14.5	55.4	30.3	48.0	69.7	37.1	24.1	9.0	100	100.0	12.1	48.0	80.0

Wave length	Percent transmittance												
	No. 106	CC-05R *	CC-10R *	CC-20R *	CC-30R *	CC-40R *	CC-50R *	CC-05B *	CC-10B *	CC-20B *	CC-30B *	CC-40B *	CC-50B *
400	......	81.0	73.0	61.5	51.6	42.5	36.4	87.0	85.5	82.2	80.2	77.0	74.1
10	......	81.0	72.4	60.0	50.0	40.0	33.9	87.5	86.4	84.0	82.5	80.3	78.4
20	0.10	81.0	72.0	58.6	48.2	38.2	31.9	87.7	87.2	85.0	84.0	82.2	80.7
30	0.20	81.1	71.6	57.7	47.0	36.8	30.5	88.0	87.5	85.3	84.3	82.5	81.1
40	0.35	81.2	71.5	57.2	46.4	36.0	29.7	88.1	87.5	85.0	83.5	81.3	79.8
50	0.58	81.4	71.6	57.2	46.4	36.1	29.6	88.1	87.2	83.9	81.9	78.7	76.6
60	0.98	81.7	72.4	58.5	47.5	37.5	31.0	87.9	86.4	82.5	79.5	75.9	72.9
70	1.5	82.3	73.7	60.6	49.9	40.0	33.6	87.5	85.3	80.3	76.2	72.0	67.9
80	2.3	82.8	74.9	62.0	52.0	42.5	35.9	87.0	84.0	77.8	72.5	67.5	62.7
90	3.5	83.2	75.8	63.5	53.9	44.8	37.9	86.2	82.4	74.2	68.3	62.3	56.6
500	5.2	83.3	76.6	64.6	55.2	46.1	39.4	85.2	80.5	71.2	63.8	56.7	50.1
10	7.7	83.0	76.1	64.0	54.5	46.0	38.5	84.4	78.6	67.7	58.7	51.0	44.5
20	10.7	82.4	74.9	61.5	51.6	42.5	35.0	83.5	77.0	64.0	54.4	46.0	38.6
30	15.1	81.6	73.5	59.4	48.5	38.5	31.5	82.6	75.2	61.5	50.7	41.6	34.1
40	20.2	81.2	72.5	57.8	46.5	36.6	29.4	82.1	73.9	59.5	48.3	39.0	31.3
50	25.7	81.1	72.4	57.1	45.6	35.6	28.7	81.5	73.0	58.0	46.6	36.9	29.5
60	31.0	81.4	72.8	58.0	46.9	36.4	29.7	81.4	72.7	57.5	45.9	35.9	28.6
70	35.6	82.5	74.5	60.6	49.2	39.2	32.7	81.4	73.0	57.9	46.3	36.1	28.7
80	43.2	83.9	77.3	65.0	54.6	45.0	38.6	81.9	73.9	59.3	47.9	37.8	30.5
90	53.8	85.7	80.7	71.0	61.8	53.5	47.6	82.7	75.1	61.6	50.3	40.8	33.4
600	65.6	87.6	84.0	77.0	70.5	64.0	58.7	83.4	76.3	63.5	53.0	43.5	36.0
10	77.0	89.0	86.5	82.0	77.8	73.0	69.8	83.6	76.7	64.5	54.6	44.7	37.8
20	82.8	90.0	88.9	86.2	83.5	80.8	78.3	83.5	76.5	64.3	54.4	44.3	37.5
30	86.0	90.6	89.9	88.1	87.2	85.1	84.2	83.2	76.6	63.1	53.2	42.5	35.6
40	87.6	91.1	90.5	89.8	89.2	88.0	87.5	82.8	74.5	61.6	51.5	40.2	33.7
50	88.7	91.2	90.8	90.5	90.3	89.5	89.2	82.5	74.0	60.6	50.3	39.0	32.4
60	89.5	91.3	91.1	90.8	90.6	90.4	90.1	82.5	73.8	60.1	49.5	38.4	31.8
70	90.0	91.4	91.3	91.0	90.9	90.8	90.7	82.3	73.3	59.6	49.0	37.7	31.0
80	90.5	91.6	91.5	91.2	91.1	91.0	91.1	82.0	72.8	58.6	48.2	36.5	30.0
90	90.8	91.7	91.7	91.4	91.4	91.3	91.1	81.9	72.5	58.1	47.2	35.4	29.0
700	91.0	91.9	91.9	91.5	91.5	91.4	91.2	82.2	73.0	58.5	47.5	35.6	29.0
Luminous transmit.	34.6	83.7	77.0	65.3	55.9	47.3	41.3	82.8	75.5	62.3	52.0	42.8	35.7
Dominant wave lgth.	589.4	605.0	597.8	604.2	605.8	605.5	608.5	459.0	462.0	460.0	461.0	463.2	462.5
Excitation purity.	95.2	2.0	4.7	8.5	12.3	17.3	21.4	2.8	6.3	13.2	20.2	27.7	34.2

*Some transmission below 400 mμ.   Consult the manufacturer.

Wave length	Percent transmittance											
	CC-05G *	CC-10G *	CC-20G *	CC-30G *	CC-40G *	CC-50G *	CC-05Y *	CC-10Y *	CC-20Y *	CC-30Y *	CC-40Y *	CC-50Y *
400	80.0	73.1	58.8	48.0	39.7	32.0	81.0	74.5	61.3	50.5	43.9	34.5
10	80.7	72.9	57.8	46.5	38.1	30.3	80.6	73.2	59.0	47.4	39.5	30.5
20	81.0	72.8	57.3	45.8	37.3	29.5	80.4	72.6	57.8	46.0	37.5	29.0
30	81.4	72.7	57.0	45.5	36.5	29.0	80.4	72.5	57.5	45.6	36.5	28.7
40	81.6	73.0	57.3	45.8	36.6	29.1	80.6	72.8	57.8	46.5	36.8	29.5
50	82.1	73.9	58.4	46.9	38.1	30.6	81.2	74.0	59.5	48.5	38.5	31.5
60	83.0	75.5	61.4	50.3	41.5	34.3	82.5	76.0	63.0	52.5	42.5	36.2
70	84.4	78.0	65.4	55.8	47.0	40.5	83.9	78.5	67.5	58.2	48.8	43.5
80	85.6	80.4	70.0	61.8	53.5	47.8	85.3	81.2	72.3	64.9	56.2	54.0
90	86.8	83.0	75.2	68.9	61.3	57.0	87.0	84.4	78.0	72.4	66.0	64.0
500	87.9	85.9	80.3	76.4	70.7	68.0	88.4	87.2	84.0	81.0	77.0	75.5
10	88.7	87.5	83.8	80.9	77.8	75.3	89.5	89.0	88.0	86.6	85.5	84.2
20	89.0	88.1	84.9	82.3	79.5	77.5	90.0	90.0	89.6	89.1	89.0	88.5
30	89.0	88.0	84.0	81.7	79.4	77.0	90.4	90.4	90.0	89.7	89.9	89.6
40	89.0	87.6	83.7	80.5	77.8	74.8	90.7	90.7	90.6	90.4	90.2	90.0
50	88.6	87.1	82.4	78.6	75.8	72.2	90.9	90.9	90.8	90.6	90.4	90.3
60	88.1	86.3	80.9	76.2	72.9	68.8	91.0	91.0	90.9	90.8	90.7	90.6
70	87.5	85.3	79.0	73.5	69.3	64.8	91.3	91.3	91.0	90.9	90.8	90.7
80	87.0	84.1	77.0	70.4	65.3	60.3	91.4	91.4	91.1	91.0	90.8	90.7
90	86.4	82.8	74.5	67.2	61.9	55.9	91.4	91.4	91.2	91.1	90.9	90.8
600	85.7	81.5	72.0	64.1	57.7	51.7	91.4	91.4	91.3	91.2	90.9	90.8
10	85.0	80.0	69.5	60.7	53.7	47.3	91.4	91.4	91.3	91.2	90.9	90.9
20	84.0	78.5	66.5	57.2	49.8	42.5	91.4	91.4	91.3	91.2	91.0	90.9
30	83.0	76.9	63.8	53.7	45.5	38.0	91.5	91.5	91.4	91.3	91.0	91.0
40	82.2	75.6	61.5	50.8	42.0	34.6	91.5	91.5	91.4	91.3	91.0	91.0
50	81.9	74.9	60.1	49.1	40.2	32.5	91.5	91.5	91.4	91.3	91.1	91.1
60	81.5	74.4	59.4	48.1	39.5	31.5	91.5	91.5	91.4	91.3	91.1	91.1
70	81.4	74.0	58.8	47.5	38.5	31.0	91.5	91.5	91.4	91.4	91.2	91.2
80	81.1	73.5	58.1	46.6	37.6	29.9	91.5	91.5	91.4	91.4	91.2	91.2
90	81.1	73.2	57.6	46.0	36.6	28.9	91.5	91.5	91.4	91.4	91.3	91.3
700	81.5	73.5	58.0	46.4	36.5	28.7	91.5	91.5	91.4	91.4	91.3	91.3
Luminous transmit.	87.2	84.5	77.8	72.2	67.7	63.3	90.4	90.1	89.1	88.2	87.4	86.9
Dominant wave lgth.	553.0	555.5	555.0	554.0	554.3	553.4	572.0	571.3	571.4	571.3	571.3	571.2
Excitation purity	2.3	5.2	10.9	15.8	21.1	25.9	5.3	9.6	18.8	28.3	35.7	42.0

Wave length	Percent transmittance											
	CC-05M *	CC-10M *	CC-20M *	CC-30M *	CC-40M *	CC-50M *	CC-05C *	CC-10C *	CC-20C *	CC-30C *	CC-40C *	CC-50C *
400	87.6	86.6	85.6	84.2	82.3	80.9	87.3	86.0	83.9	82.3	80.4	78.8
10	88.2	87.7	86.6	85.7	84.6	83.6	88.2	87.5	85.2	84.5	83.4	82.7
20	88.6	88.0	87.0	85.9	85.2	84.4	88.7	88.1	86.5	86.0	85.3	84.8
30	88.7	88.0	86.9	85.6	84.4	83.6	89.0	88.6	87.5	87.0	86.3	85.9
40	88.7	87.9	86.0	84.7	82.5	81.4	89.3	89.0	87.7	87.3	86.6	86.1
50	88.6	87.5	84.9	82.8	80.0	78.1	89.5	89.1	87.8	87.5	86.6	86.0
60	88.4	86.5	83.1	80.0	76.1	73.7	89.6	89.1	87.7	87.3	86.4	85.7
70	87.8	85.2	80.8	76.4	71.3	68.0	89.7	89.0	87.5	87.0	85.8	85.2
80	87.0	83.6	77.9	72.1	65.8	61.7	89.7	89.0	87.2	86.5	85.3	84.3
90	86.0	81.8	74.4	67.0	60.0	55.0	89.7	89.0	87.0	86.0	84.4	83.4
500	85.0	79.7	70.5	61.7	53.7	48.1	89.6	89.0	86.5	85.2	83.5	82.3
10	83.8	77.5	66.7	56.5	47.7	41.6	89.6	88.7	86.0	84.4	82.4	80.8
20	82.7	75.3	63.4	52.0	42.8	36.3	89.5	88.5	85.2	83.5	81.1	79.2
30	81.8	73.7	60.5	48.6	39.0	31.9	89.4	88.0	84.3	82.4	79.6	77.3
40	81.3	72.5	58.6	46.6	36.7	29.8	89.2	87.5	83.4	81.0	77.7	75.0
50	81.2	72.2	58.0	46.0	36.0	29.1	88.9	87.0	82.3	79.0	75.3	72.2
60	81.5	72.8	58.3	46.5	36.7	29.7	88.5	86.1	80.5	76.7	72.7	69.0
70	82.5	74.6	60.5	49.8	40.2	32.3	88.0	85.0	78.5	74.0	69.3	65.0
80	84.0	77.3	64.9	55.6	46.2	39.0	87.5	83.8	76.1	70.9	65.4	60.5
90	85.8	80.8	70.6	63.3	54.9	48.7	87.0	82.5	73.9	67.5	61.6	55.8
600	88.0	84.5	77.1	71.6	64.9	59.9	86.4	81.0	71.2	64.1	57.6	51.3
10	89.3	87.0	82.2	79.2	74.9	70.7	85.5	79.5	68.5	60.4	53.4	46.2
20	90.2	88.9	86.1	84.1	81.4	79.2	84.5	77.9	65.5	56.7	49.2	42.3
30	90.6	90.0	88.7	87.4	86.0	84.5	83.8	76.3	62.7	53.1	45.0	38.0
40	90.8	90.5	90.0	89.3	88.7	87.6	83.3	75.1	60.8	50.4	42.0	34.9
50	91.0	90.7	90.5	90.2	90.0	89.7	82.8	74.4	59.5	48.8	40.2	32.9
60	91.1	91.0	90.8	90.8	90.4	90.4	82.5	74.0	58.5	48.0	39.4	32.0
70	91.2	91.2	91.0	91.0	90.7	90.7	82.4	73.6	57.9	47.2	38.6	31.0
80	91.3	91.3	91.2	91.1	91.0	91.0	82.0	73.0	57.5	46.0	37.5	29.9
90	91.4	91.4	91.4	91.3	91.3	91.3	82.0	72.8	57.4	45.5	36.7	29.1
700	91.5	91.5	91.5	91.5	91.5	91.5	82.5	74.0	58.5	46.4	37.3	29.8
Luminous transmit.	84.2	77.9	67.1	58.1	50.0	44.0	88.0	85.1	78.9	74.8	70.5	66.7
Dominant wave lgth.	541.0c	547.5c	551.2c	550.0c	550.3c	551.2c	489.2	487.5	486.5	486.2	486.1	485.5
Excitation purity	3.5	7.4	14.4	21.5	28.3	34.0	1.6	4.1	8.9	12.8	17.5	20.2

* Some transmission below 400 mμ.   Consult the manufacturer.

Wave length	Percent transmittance			
	No. 87	No. 87C	No. 88A	No. 89B
700	.....	.....	....	11.2
10	.....	.....	....	32.4
20	.....	.....	....	57.6
30	.....	.....	7.4	69.1
40	0.10	.....	32.8	77.6
50	2.19	.....	56.3	83.1
60	7.95	.....	69.2	85.0
70	17.4	.....	74.2	86.1
80	31.6	.....	77.6	87.0
90	43.7	.....	79.7	87.7
800	53.8	0.32	81.4	88.1
10	61.7	3.20	82.6	88.4
20	69.2	8.90	83.7	88.6
30	74.1	17.8	84.7	88.8
40	77.7	28.2	85.5	89.0
50	81.4	41.0	86.1	89.2
60	84.0	53.8	86.6	89.4
70	85.4	61.6	87.2	89.6
80	86.8	69.2	87.5	89.8
90	87.8	74.1	87.8	89.9
900	88.4	78.5	88.0	90.0
10	88.8	81.5	88.2	90.1
20	89.1	83.6	88.4	90.2
30	89.1	85.1	88.6	90.3
40	89.1	86.0	88.8	90.4
50	89.1	87.0	89.0	90.5

* Some transmission below 400 mμ.   Consult the manufacturer.

Ratio of the transmitted light to the incident light for a definite thickness of the substance, usually 1 cm.

GLASS.

Glass in general is opaque to the ultra-violet and infra-red. Uviol glass is transparent to the longer radiations of the ultra-violet.

Coefficient of transparency of glass for visible and ultra-violet radiations.

	Normal incidence, thickness 1 cm.								
Wave length microns.......	0.309	0.330	0.347	0.357	0.361	0.375	0.384	0.388	0.396
Crown, ordinary..	...	...	...	...	...	.947			
Crown, borosilicate.........	0.08	0.65	0.88	0.72	0.95	...	0.972	0.975	0.986
Flint, ordinary...	...	...	0.01	...	0.16	...	...	0.904	
Flint, heavy.....	...	...		...		...	0.58		

	Normal incidence, thickness 1 cm.								
Wave length, microns.......	0.400	0.415	0.419	0.425	0.434	0.455	0.500	0.580	0.677
Crown, ordinary..	0.964	...	0.952	...	0.960	0.981	...	0.986	0.990
Crown, borosilicate..........	...	0.985	...	0.993	...	...	0.993		
Flint, ordinary...	...	0.959	...	...	...	...	1.00		
Flint, heavy.....	...	...	...	0.905					

QUARTZ

Quartz is very transparent to the ultra-violet and to the visible spectrum, but opaque for the infra-red beyond 7.0μ.

(Pflüger.)

Wave length, microns.........	0.19	0.20	0.21	0.22
Transmission for 1 mm.........	.67	.84	.92	.94

FLUORITE

Fluorite is very transparent to the ultra-violet, nearly to 0.10μ. Coefficient of transparency at λ = 186 is found by Pflüger to be 0.80.

For the infra-red the values are given in a table below.

ROCK SALT AND SYLVINE AND FLUORITE

TRANSPARENCY FOR THE INFRA-RED.

Thickness 1 cm.

Wave length, microns.	Rock salt	Sylvine KCl	Fluorite
8.	....	....	.844
9.	0.995	1.000	.543
10.	.995	.988	.164
12.	.993	.995	.010
14.	.931	.975	.000
16.	.661	.936	
18.	.275	.862	
19.	.096	.758	
20.7	.006	.585	
23.7	.000	.155	

COLORIMETRY

Selected from Judd, Jour. Opt. Soc. Amer. **23**, 359 (1933)

Recommendations of the International Commission on Illumination

Standard Illuminants

A. Gas-filled tungsten incandescent lamp of color temperature 2848° K.

B. Noon Sunlight. Lamp as above in combination with the Davis-Gibson filter for converting color temperature 2848° to 4800° K.

The filter is to be composed of a layer one centimeter thick of each of two separate solutions B₁ and B₂, contained in a double cell of colorless optical glass.

Solution B₁

Copper sulfate (CuSO₄·5H₂O)	2.452 g
Mannite (C₆H₈(OH)₆)	2.452 g
Pyridine (C₅H₅N)	30.0 cc
Distilled water to make	1000 cc

Solution B₂

Cobalt ammonium sulfate (CoSO₄·(NH₄)₂SO₄·6H₂O)	21.71 g
Copper sulfate (CuSO₄·5H₂O)	16.11 g
Sulfuric acid (density 1.835)	10.0 cc
Distilled water to make	1000 cc

C. Average Daylight. Lamp as in A in combination with Davis-Gibson filter for converting color temperature 2848° to 6500° K.

The filter is composed of a layer one centimeter thick of each of two separate solutions C₁ and C₂, contained in a double cell made of colorless optical glass.

Solution C₁

Copper sulfate (CuSO₄·5H₂O)	3.412 g
Mannite (C₆H₈(OH)₆)	3.412 g
Pyridine (C₅H₅N)	30.0 cc
Distilled water to make	1000 cc

Solution C₂

Cobalt ammonium sulfate (CoSO₄·(NH₄)₂SO₄·6H₂O)	30.580 g
Copper sulfate (CuSO₄·5H₂O)	22.520 g
Sulfuric acid (density 1.835)	10.0 cc
Distilled water to make	1000 cc

See R. Davis and K. S. Gibson Bur. Stds. Misc. Pub. No. 114, Jan. 1931 or Bur. Stds. Jour. Research **7**, 796 (1931).

Standard Coordinate System

The tristimulus system of color specification is based on four chosen stimuli consisting of homogeneous radiant energy of wave lengths

700.0   546.1   435.8

mµ and of standard illuminant B (see above).

To establish the system of specification coordinates are assigned as follows:

Stimulus	x	y	z
700.0 mµ	0.73467	0.26533	0.00000
546.1 mµ	0.27376	0.71741	0.00883
435.8 mµ	0.16658	0.00886	0.82456
Standard illuminant B:	0.34842	0.35161	0.29997

The Standard Observer

The "standard observer" is determined below by the specification for the equal energy spectrum both in fractions, x, y, z of the total amount for each wave length interval of 5 mµ and directly $\bar{x}$, $\bar{y}$, $\bar{z}$. The fractional values are known as the **trilinear coordinates** or **trichromatic coefficients** of the spectrum; the direct values as the **distribution functions** or coefficients. The sum of the trichromatic coefficients is unity, that is $x + y + z = 1$. Therefore the value of z may be and often is omitted from a specification.

Relative Visibility

The value of $\bar{y}$ given in the table is the standard visibility function or relative visibility.

Wave length mµ	Trichromatic coefficients			Distribution coefficients for equal energy			Wave length mµ
	x	y	z	$\bar{x}$	$\bar{y}$ (Rel. Vis.)	$\bar{z}$	
380	0.1741	0.0050	0.8209	0.0014	0.0000	0.0065	380
385	0.1740	0.0050	0.8210	0.0022	0.0001	0.0105	385
390	0.1738	0.0049	0.8213	0.0042	0.0001	0.0201	390
395	0.1736	0.0049	0.8215	0.0076	0.0002	0.0362	395
400	0.1733	0.0048	0.8219	0.0143	0.0004	0.0679	400
405	0.1730	0.0048	0.8222	0.0232	0.0006	0.1102	405
410	0.1726	0.0048	0.8226	0.0435	0.0012	0.2074	410
415	0.1721	0.0048	0.8231	0.0776	0.0022	0.3713	415
420	0.1714	0.0051	0.8235	0.1344	0.0040	0.6456	420

The Standard Observer (Continued)

Wave length mµ	Trichromatic coefficients			Distribution coefficients for equal energy			Wave length mµ
	x	y	z	$\bar{x}$	$\bar{y}$ (Rel. Vis.)	$\bar{z}$	
425	0.1703	0.0058	0.8239	0.2148	0.0073	1.0391	425
430	0.1689	0.0069	0.8242	0.2839	0.0116	1.3856	430
435	0.1669	0.0086	0.8245	0.3285	0.0168	1.6230	435
440	0.1644	0.0109	0.8247	0.3483	0.0230	1.7471	440
445	0.1611	0.0138	0.8251	0.3481	0.0298	1.7826	445
450	0.1566	0.0177	0.8257	0.3362	0.0380	1.7721	450
455	0.1510	0.0227	0.8263	0.3187	0.0480	1.7441	455
460	0.1440	0.0297	0.8263	0.2908	0.0600	1.6692	460
465	0.1355	0.0399	0.8246	0.2511	0.0739	1.5281	465
470	0.1241	0.0578	0.8181	0.1954	0.0910	1.2876	470
475	0.1096	0.0868	0.8036	0.1421	0.1126	1.0419	475
480	0.0913	0.1327	0.7760	0.0956	0.1390	0.8130	480
485	0.0687	0.2007	0.7306	0.0580	0.1693	0.6162	485
490	0.0454	0.2950	0.6596	0.0320	0.2080	0.4652	490
495	0.0235	0.4127	0.5638	0.0147	0.2586	0.3533	495
500	0.0082	0.5384	0.4534	0.0049	0.3230	0.2720	500
505	0.0039	0.6548	0.3413	0.0024	0.4073	0.2123	505
510	0.0139	0.7502	0.2359	0.0093	0.5030	0.1582	510
515	0.0389	0.8120	0.1491	0.0291	0.6082	0.1117	515
520	0.0743	0.8338	0.0919	0.0633	0.7100	0.0782	520
525	0.1142	0.8262	0.0596	0.1096	0.7932	0.0573	525
530	0.1547	0.8059	0.0394	0.1655	0.8620	0.0422	530
535	0.1929	0.7816	0.0255	0.2257	0.9149	0.0298	535
540	0.2296	0.7543	0.0161	0.2904	0.9540	0.0203	540
545	0.2658	0.7243	0.0099	0.3597	0.9803	0.0134	545
550	0.3016	0.6923	0.0061	0.4334	0.9950	0.0087	550
555	0.3373	0.6589	0.0038	0.5121	1.0002	0.0057	555
560	0.3731	0.6245	0.0024	0.5945	0.9950	0.0039	560
565	0.4087	0.5896	0.0017	0.6784	0.9786	0.0027	565
570	0.4441	0.5547	0.0012	0.7621	0.9520	0.0021	570
575	0.4788	0.5202	0.0010	0.8425	0.9154	0.0018	575
580	0.5125	0.4866	0.0009	0.9163	0.8700	0.0017	580
585	0.5448	0.4544	0.0008	0.9786	0.8163	0.0014	585
590	0.5752	0.4242	0.0006	1.0263	0.7570	0.0011	590
595	0.6029	0.3965	0.0006	1.0567	0.6949	0.0010	595
600	0.6270	0.3725	0.0005	1.0622	0.6310	0.0008	600
605	0.6482	0.3514	0.0004	1.0456	0.5668	0.0006	605
610	0.6658	0.3340	0.0002	1.0026	0.5030	0.0003	610
615	0.6801	0.3197	0.0002	0.9384	0.4412	0.0002	615
620	0.6915	0.3083	0.0002	0.8544	0.3810	0.0002	620
625	0.7006	0.2993	0.0001	0.7514	0.3210	0.0001	625
630	0.7079	0.2920	0.0001	0.6424	0.2650	0.0000	630
635	0.7140	0.2859	0.0001	0.5419	0.2170	0.0000	635
640	0.7190	0.2809	0.0001	0.4479	0.1750	0.0000	640
645	0.7230	0.2770	0.0000	0.3608	0.1382	0.0000	645
650	0.7260	0.2740	0.0000	0.2835	0.1070	0.0000	650
655	0.7283	0.2717	0.0000	0.2187	0.0816	0.0000	655
660	0.7300	0.2700	0.0000	0.1649	0.0610	0.0000	660
665	0.7311	0.2689	0.0000	0.1212	0.0446	0.0000	665
670	0.7320	0.2680	0.0000	0.0874	0.0320	0.0000	670
675	0.7327	0.2673	0.0000	0.0636	0.0232	0.0000	675
680	0.7334	0.2666	0.0000	0.0468	0.0170	0.0000	680
685	0.7340	0.2660	0.0000	0.0329	0.0119	0.0000	685
690	0.7344	0.2656	0.0000	0.0227	0.0082	0.0000	690
695	0.7346	0.2654	0.0000	0.0158	0.0057	0.0000	695
700	0.7347	0.2653	0.0000	0.0114	0.0041	0.0000	700
705	0.7347	0.2653	0.0000	0.0081	0.0029	0.0000	705
710	0.7347	0.2653	0.0000	0.0058	0.0021	0.0000	710
715	0.7347	0.2653	0.0000	0.0041	0.0015	0.0000	715
720	0.7347	0.2653	0.0000	0.0029	0.0010	0.0000	720
725	0.7347	0.2653	0.0000	0.0020	0.0007	0.0000	725
730	0.7347	0.2653	0.0000	0.0014	0.0005	0.0000	730
735	0.7347	0.2653	0.0000	0.0010	0.0004	0.0000	735
740	0.7347	0.2653	0.0000	0.0007	0.0003	0.0000	740
745	0.7347	0.2653	0.0000	0.0005	0.0002	0.0000	745
750	0.7347	0.2653	0.0000	0.0003	0.0001	0.0000	750
755	0.7347	0.2653	0.0000	0.0002	0.0001	0.0000	755
760	0.7347	0.2653	0.0000	0.0002	0.0001	0.0000	760
765	0.7347	0.2653	0.0000	0.0001	0.0000	0.0000	765
770	0.7347	0.2653	0.0000	0.0001	0.0000	0.0000	770
775	0.7347	0.2653	0.0000	0.0000	0.0000	0.0000	775
780	0.7347	0.2653	0.0000	0.0000	0.0000	0.0000	780
Totals				21.3713	21.3714	21.3715	

SPECIFIC ROTATION

Specific rotation or rotatory power is given in degrees per decimeter for liquids and solutions and in degrees per millimeter for solids; + signifies right handed rotation, − left. Specific rotation varies with the wave length of light used, with temperature and, in the case of solutions, with the concentration. When sodium light is used, indicated by D in the wave length column, a value of $\lambda = 0.5893$ may be assumed.

Optical rotatory power for a large number of organic compounds will be found in the International Critical Tables, Vol. VII; for sugars, Vol. II.

SOLIDS

Substance	Wave length μ	Rotation deg./mm	Substance	Wave length μ	Rotation deg./mm
Cinnabar (HgS)...	D	+32.5	Quartz (continued)..........	0.3609	+63.628
Lead hyposulfate..	D	5.5		0.3582	64.459
Potassium hyposulphate........	D	8.4		0.3466	69.454
Quartz...........	0.7604	12.668		0.3441	70.587
	0.7184	14.304		0.3402	72.448
	0.6867	15.746		0.3360	74.571
	0.6562	17.318		0.3286	78.579
	0.5895	21.684		0.3247	80.459
	0.5889	21.727		0.3180	84.972
	0.5269	27.543		0.2747	121.052
	0.4861	32.773		0.2571	143.266
	0.4307	42.604		0.2313	190.426
	0.4101	47.481		0.2265	201.824
	0.3968	51.193		0.2194	220.731
	0.3933	52.155		0.2143	235.972
	0.3820	55.625	Sodium bromate	D	2.8
	0.3726	58.894	Sodium chlorate	D	3.13

LIQUID

Liquid	Temp. °C	Wave length μ	Specific rotation deg./dm
Amyl alcohol..............	......	D	− 5.7
Camphor....................	204	D	+ 70.33
Cedar oil..................	15	D	− 30 to −40
Citron oil.................	15	D	+ 62
Ethyl malate (C_2H_5)$_2C_4H_4O_5$..	11	D	− 10.3 to −12.4
Menthol....................	35.2	D	− 49.7
Nicotine $C_{10}H_{14}N_2$..............	10–30	D	−162
	20	0.6563	−126
	20	0.5351	−207.5
	20	0.4861	−253.5
Turpentine $C_{10}H_6$................	20	D	− 37
	20	0.6563	− 29.5
	20	0.5351	− 45
	20	0.4861	− 54.5

SOLUTIONS

Corrections for values of the specific rotation for concentration are given in the last column. c indicates concentration in grams per 100 milliliters of solution; d indicates the concentration in grams per 100 grams of solution.

Substance	Solvent	Temp. °C	Wave length μ	Specific rotation deg./dm	Correction for concentration or temperature
Albumen.............	water	..	D	− 25 to −38	
Arabinose...........	water	20	D	− 105.0	
Camphor............	alcohol	20	D	+ 54.4 − .135d for d = 45–91	
	benzene	20	D	+ 56 − .166d for d = 47–90	
	ether	..	D	+ 57	
Dextrose d-glucose $C_6H_{12}O_6$	water	20	D	+ 52.5 + .025d for d = 1–18	
			.5461	+ 62.03 + .04257c for c = 6–32	
Galactose..........	water	..	D	+ 83.9 + .078d − .91t for d = 1–36 and t = 10–40°C	
l-Glucose (β)........	water	20	D	− 51.4	
Invert sugar $C_6H_{12}O_6$	water	20	D	− 19.7 − .036c for c = 9–35	
				$\alpha_t = \alpha_{20} + .304(t − 20) + .00165 (t − 20)^2$ for t = 3–30°C	
		25	5461	− 21.5	
Lactose.............	water	20	D	+ 52.4 + .072 (20° − t) for c = 5	
			.5461	+ 61.9 + .085(20° − t) for c = 5	
Levulose fruit sugar...	water	25	D	− 88.5 − .145d for d = 2.6–18.6	
		25	.5461	− 105.30	

Substance	Solvent	Temp °C	Wave length μ	Specific rotation deg./dm	Correction for concentration or temperature
Maltose.............	water	20	D	+ 138.48 − .01837d for d = 5–35	
		25	5461	+ 153.75	
Mannose............	water	20	D	+ 14.1 c = 10.2	
Nicotine............	water	20	D	− 77 for d = 1–16	
	benzene	20	D	− 164 for d = 8–100	
Potassium tartrate...	water	20	D	+ 27.14 + .0992c − .00094c² for c = 8–50	
Quinine sulfate......	water	17	D	− 214	
Santonin...........	alcohol	20	D	− 161.0 c = 1.78	
		20	D	+ 693 c = 4.05	
	chloroform	20	D	− 202.7 + .309d for d = 75–96.5	
	alcohol	20	.6867	+ 442 c = 4.05	
			.5269	+ 991 c = 4.05	
			.4861	+1323 c = 4.05	
Sodium potassium tartrate (Rochelle salt)	water	20	D	+ 29.75 − .0078c	
Sucrose (cane sugar) $C_{12}H_{22}O_{11}$	water	20	D	+ 66.412 + .01267d − .000376d² for d = 0–50	
				$\alpha_t = \alpha_{20}[1 − .00037 (t − 20)]$ for t = 14–30°C	

Sucrose dissolved in water, 20°C.

μ	Spec. rot.	μ	Spec. rot.	μ	Spec. rot.
670.8 (Li)	+50.51	510.6 (Cu)	+90.46	435.3 (Fe)	+128.5
643.8 (Cd)	55.04	508.6 (Cd)	91.16	433.7 (Fe)	129.8
636.2 (Zn)	56.51	481.1 (Zn)	103.07	431.5 (Fe)	130.7
589.3 (Na)	66.45	480.0 (Cd)	103.62	428.2 (Fe)	133.6
578.2 (Cu)	69.10	472.2 (Zn)	107.38	427.2 (Fe)	134.2
578.0 (Hg)	69.22	468.0 (Zn)	109.49	426.1 (Fe)	134.9
570.0 (Cu)	71.24	467.8 (Cd)	109.69	419.1 (Fe)	140.0
546.1 (Hg)	78.16	438.4 (Fe)	126.5	414.4 (Fe)	144.2
521.8 (Cu)	86.21	437.6 (Fe)	127.2	388.9 (Fe)	166.7
515.3 (Cu)	88.68	435.8 (Hg)	128.49	383.3 (Fe)	171.8
				382.6 (Fe)	173.1

Substance	Solvent	°C	μ	Spec. rot.	Correct.
Tartaric acid (ord.)...	water	20	D	+15.06 − .131c	
		20	.6563	7.75	
		20	D	8.86	for d = 41
		20	.5351	9.65	
		20	.4861	9.37	
Turpentine..........	alcohol	20	D	−37 − .00482d − .00013d² for d = 0–90	
	benzene	20	D	−37 − .0265d for d = 0–91	
Xylose..............	water	20	D	+19.13	d = 2.7

OPTICAL ROTATION OF ACIDS AND BASES

Optical rotation of acids and bases commonly used in the resolution of racemic substances. Compiled by F. E. Ray.

Name	Formula	Solvent	Conc. %	a_D
Bromocamphor-sulfonic acid. K salt.	$C_{10}H_{15}O_4BrS$	H_2O	....	72.1
Camphorsulfonic acid...	$C_{10}H_{16}O_4S$	H_2O	....	23.9
Chlorocamphor-sulfonic acid.	$C_{10}H_{15}ClO_4S$	H_2O	....	49.6
Codeinesulfonic acid.....	$C_{18}H_{21}NO_6S$	H_2O	3	− 190.1
Hydroxybutyric acid.....	$C_4H_8O_3$	H_2O	3.3	− 24.8
Lactic acid..............	$C_3H_6O_3$	H_2O	10.5	3.8
Malic acid..............	$C_4H_6O_5$	H_2O	....	2.4
Mandelic acid...........	$C_8H_8O_3$	H_2O	2.01	155.5
Methylene-camphor.....	$C_{11}H_{16}O$	C_2H_5OH	....	127
Phenylsuccinic acid.....	$C_{10}H_{10}O_4$	C_2H_5OH	1.5	148
Tartaric acid...........	$C_4H_6O_5$	C_2H_5OH and H_2O	....	3 to 25*
Brucine...............	$C_{23}H_{26}N_2O_4$	C_2H_5OH	5.4	− 85
Cinchonidine..........	$C_{19}H_{22}N_2O$	C_2H_5OH	1.0	−111.0
Cinchonine...........	$C_{19}H_{22}N_2O$	C_2H_5OH	0.6	+209.0
Cocaine..............	$C_{17}H_{21}NO_4$	50 % C_2H_5OH	1.1	− 35.4
Coniine..............	$C_8H_{17}N$	$CHCl_3$	4	8.6
Codeine..............	$C_{18}H_{21}NO_3$	C_2H_5OH	5	−135.8
Hydrastine...........	$C_{21}H_{21}NO_6$	50 % C_2H_5OH	0.2	115
Menthol.............	$C_{10}H_{20}O$	C_2H_5OH	9.6	− 50.6
Menthylamine........	$C_{10}H_{21}N$	C_2H_5OH	11.3	− 31.9
Narcotine............	$C_{22}H_{23}NO_7$	$CHCl_3$	2.6	+200.0
Quinidine............	$C_{20}H_{24}N_2O_2$	C_2H_5OH	1.0	+233.6
Quinine..............	$C_{20}H_{24}N_2O_2$	C_6H_6	0.6	− 136
Thebaine............	$C_{19}H_{21}NO_3$	$CHCl_3$	5	−229.5
Strychnine...........	$C_{21}H_{22}N_2O_2$	C_2H_5OH	0.9	− 128

* Varies greatly with temperature, solvent, and conc.

The rotation of the plane of polarization of light by transparent substances subjected to a magnetic field may be applied to problems of molecular structure. This rotatory effect is known as the Faraday effect. Investigations of this effect by E. Verdet showed the angle of rotation (a) to depend on the nature of the substance and to be proportional to the length (l) of the column of the substance which the light traverses and to the strength (H) of the magnetic field. Thus

$$a = \Lambda l H$$

where Λ is the Verdet constant for the experimental material. Other symbols in the table have the following significance:

λ = Wavelength in μ
t = Degrees centigrade
ρ_M = Molecular magnetic rotation of the substance under consideration compared to that of water determined in the same apparatus in the same magnetic field.

Thus

$$\rho_M = M' a' \rho' / M' a' \rho$$

where M is the molecular weight, a the angle of rotation and ρ the density of the given substance, and M', a', and ρ' are the same quantities of water.

$[\Lambda]_M^{\lambda, t}$ = Molecular rotatory value of the substance at the given temperature and at the wavelength λ. Values are in (radians)(gauss^{-1})(cm^{-1}).

$\Lambda^{\lambda, t}$ = Verdet constant at the temperature t and at the wavelength λ. Values are in (minutes)(gauss^{-1}) (cm^{-1}).

Values in this table are reproduced by permission from Volume 3, Tables de Constantes et Donnees Nuimeriques, "Pouvoir Rotatorie Magnetique, Effet Magneto-Optique de Kerr."
A much greater listing of values for both organic and inorganic compounds is in the above publication.

Formula	Name	λ	t	ρ_M	$10^5[\Lambda]_M^{\lambda, t}$	$10^5\Lambda^{\lambda, t}$ Verdet
CH₄	Methane	578	0	......	......	*17.4
CCl₄	Tetrachloromethane	589	25.1	6.58	45.3	1.60
CHCl₃	Trichloromethane	589	20.0	5.535	37.98	1.60
CHBr₃	Tribromomethane	589	17.9	11.63	80.00	3.13
CH₂O₂	Formic acid	589	20.8	1.671	11.50	1.046
CH₂Cl₂	Dichloromethane	589	11.9	4.31	29.7	1.60
CH₂Br₂	Dibromomethane	589	15.9	8.11	55.8	2.74
CH₂I₂	Diiodomethane	589	15.0	10.83	129.5	1.51
CH₃Cl	Monochloromethane	589	23.0	2.99	20.5	1.37
CH₃Br	Monobromomethane	589	1.5	4.64	31.9	2.04
CH₃I	Monoiodomethane	589	19.5	9.01	63.2	3.35
CH₄O	Methylalcohol	589	18.7	1.640	11.28	0.958
CH₅N	Methylamine	578	......	......	......	*22.7
CF₂Cl₂	Difluorodichloromethane (Freon)	....	......	......	......	*32.7
CH₃O₂N	Mononitromethane	589	9.9	1.86	12.8	0.826
CH₄ON₂	Urea (carbamide) 40 % aqueous solution	578	20.0	2.38	22.7	......
C₂H₂	Acetylene (ethyne)	578	......	......	......	*33.0
C₂H₄	Ethylene (ethene)	578	......	......	......	*34.5
C₂H₆	Ethane	578	......	......	......	*23.5
C₂N₂	Cyanogen	578	......	......	......	......
C₂H₂O₄	Oxalic acid (aqueous sol. 8.3 %)	578	20	2.88	20.6	......
C₂H₂O₄·2H₂O	Oxalic acid (alcohol sol. 16.5 %)	578	24	2.82	20.2	......
C₂H₃Br	Vinylbromide	589	7.8	6.22	42.8	2.10
C₂H₃N	Acetonitrile (ethanonitrile)	589	25.0	2.32	16.0	*21.0
C₂H₄O	Ethyleneoxide (1,2-epoxyethane)	589	8.0	1.935	13.3	0.92
C₂H₄O	Acetaldehyde (ethanal)	589	16.3	2.38	16.4	1.00
C₂H₄O₂	Acetic acid	589	21.0	2.525	17.37	1.044
C₂H₄O₂	Formic acid methylester (methylformate)	589	16.5	2.49	17.1	0.96
C₂H₄Cl₂	Ethylidenechloride (1,1-dichloroethane)	589	14.4	5.33	36.7	1.51
C₂H₄Cl₂	Ethylenechloride (1,2-dichloroethane)	589	14.4	5.49	37.7	1.65
C₂H₄Br₂	Ethylenebromide (1,2-dibromoethane)	589	15.2	9.70	66.7	2.66
C₂H₅Cl	Monochloroethane	589	5.0	4.04	27.8	1.36
C₂H₅Br	Monobromoethane	589	19.7	5.85	40.2	1.82
C₂H₅I	Monoiodoethane	589	18.1	10.07	69.3	2.95
C₂H₆O	Ethylalcohol (ethanol)	589	16.8	2.780	19.13	1.131
C₂H₆O₂	Glycol (1,2-ethanediol)	589	15.1	2.94	20.2	1.25
C₂H₆S	Ethylmercaptan	578	16.0	5.52	39.5	1.85
C₂H₇N	Ethylamine (aminoethane)	589	5.8	3.61	24.8	*34.5
C₂H₂O₂Cl₂	Dichloroacetic acid (dichloroethanoic acid)	589	13.5	5.30	3.65	1.52
C₂H₃O₂Cl	Chloroacetic acid (chloroethanoic acid)	589	64.5	3.89	26.7	1.33
C₂H₃O₂Cl₃	Chloralhydrate (2-2-2-trichloro-1,1-ethanediol)	589	54.6	7.10	48.8	1.65
C₂H₅O₂N	Mononitroethane	589	10.2	2.84	19.5	0.946
C₃H₃	Propane	578	......	......	......	*34.0
C₃H₄O	Acrolein (propenal)	578	20.0	4.74	34.0	1.76
C₃H₄O₃	Pyruvic acid (2-oxopropanoic acid)	589	14.5	3.56	24.2	1.21
C₃H₄O₄	Malonic acid (propandioic acid) 2n-aqueous sol.	589	23.0	3.47	......	......
C₃H₆O	Allyl alcohol	589	18.3	4.68	32.2	1.60
C₃H₆O	Propyl alcohol (1-propanol)	589	13.6	3.33	22.9	1.09
C₃H₆O	Acetone (2-propanone)	589	20.0	3.472	23.89	1.1136
C₃H₆O₂	Propionic acid (propanoic acid)	589	20.3	3.462	23.82	1.10
C₃H₆O₂	Formic acid ethylester (ethylmethanoate)	589	18.8	3.56	24.5	1.05
C₃H₆O₂	Acetic acid methylester (methylacetate)	589	20.0	3.42	23.5	1.03
C₃H₇Cl	Propylchloride (1-chloropropane)	589	16.1	5.04	34.7	1.34
C₃H₇Cl	Isopropylchloride (2-chloropropane)	589	17.2	5.16	35.5	1.34
C₃H₇Br	Propylbromide (1-bromopropane)	589	19.2	6.88	47.8	1.79
C₃H₇Br	Isopropylbromide (2-bromopropane)	589	17.1	7.00	48.2	1.77
C₃H₇I	Propyliodide (1-iodopropane)	589	18.1	11.08	76.2	2.69
C₃H₇I	Isopropyliodide (2-iodopropane)	589	26.3	11.18	76.9	2.63
C₃H₈O	n-Propyl alcohol (1-propanol)	589	15.6	3.77	25.9	1.20
C₃H₈O	Isopropyl alcohol (2-propanol)	589	20.0	3.90	26.8	1.23
C₃H₈O₃	Glycerine (1,2,3-propanetriol)	589	16.0	4.11	28.3	1.33
C₃H₉N	n-Propylamine	589	9.6	4.56	31.4	1.33
C₃H₅O₉N₃	Nitroglycerine	589	13.5	5.405	37.2	0.900

* Verdet constant factor = 10⁶.

Formula	Name	λ	t	ρ_M	$10^5[A]_M^{\lambda,t}$	$10^5\Lambda^{\lambda,t}$ Verdet
$C_3H_7O_2N$	1-Nitropropane	589	18.9	3.82	26.3	1.018
C_4H_6	1,3-Butadiene (erythrene)	589	15.0	7.94	54.6	2.16
C_4H_8	1-Butene (α-butylene)	589	15.0	5.53	38.0	1.39
C_4H_8	cis-2-Butene (β-butylene)	589	15.0	5.27	36.3	1.38
C_4H_8	trans-2-Butene	589	15.0	5.07	34.9	1.29
C_4H_{10}	Butane	589	15.0	4.59	31.6	1.09
C_4H_{10}	Isobutane (2-methylpropane)	589	15.0	4.87	33.5	1.11
$C_4H_2O_3$	Maleic anhydride (cis-butenedioic anhydride)	589	25.0	4.5	31.0	....
C_4H_4O	Furan (furfuran)	589	20.0	5.48	37.7	1.78
$C_4H_4O_4$	Maleic acid (cis-butenedioic acid) $2n$ aqueous solution	589	25.0	5.63	38.7	....
C_4H_4S	Thiophene (thiofuran)	589	20.0	9.40	64.7	2.83
$C_4H_6O_3$	Acetic anhydride (ethanoic anhydride)	589	20.0	4.28	29.5	1.115
$C_4H_6O_4$	Succinic acid (butanedioic acid) 5.9 % aqueous sol.	578	20.0	4.68	33.5	....
$C_4H_6O_6$	Tartaric acid (47.8 % aqueous sol.)	578	20.0	4.79	34.3	....
$C_4H_8O_2$	n-Butyric acid (butanoic acid)	589	18.8	4.47	30.8	1.15
$C_4H_8O_2$	Ethylacetate (ethyl ethanoate)	589	20.0	4.47	30.8	1.08
$C_4H_8O_2$	Propionic acid methylester (methylpropanoate)	589	20.0	4.37	30.1	1.07
$C_4H_8O_3$	Lactic acid methylester (methyl 2-hydroxypropanoate)	589	.....	4.66	32.1	
$C_4H_{10}O$	Ethyl ether (ethoxyethane)	589	20.0	4.78	32.9	1.09
$C_4H_{10}O$	n-Butyl alcohol (1-butanol)	589	20.0	4.60	31.6	1.23
$C_4H_{10}O$	Isobutyl alcohol (2-methyl-1-propanol)	589	17.7	4.94	34.0	1.27
$C_4H_{10}O$	sec-Butyl alcohol (methylethylcarbinol)	589	20.0	4.91	33.8	1.27
C_5H_6	Cyclopentadiene	589	15.0	7.03	48.8	2.02
C_5H_8	1,3-Pentadiene	589	15.0	8.80	60.5	2.08
C_5H_8	Isoprene (2-methyl-1,3-butadiene)	589	15.0	8.80	60.5	2.08
C_5H_8	Cyclopentene	589	15.0	5.69	39.1	1.52
C_5H_{10}	1-Pentene	589	15.0	6.45	44.4	1.39
C_5H_{10}	Isopentane (2-methyl-1-butane)	589	15.0	6.36	43.8	1.39
C_5H_{10}	Cyclopentane	589	20.0	4.89	33.6	1.23
C_5H_{12}	Pentane	589	15.0	5.00	38.5	1.15
C_5H_{12}	Isopentane (2-methylbutane)	589	15.0	5.75	39.6	1.17
$C_5H_4O_2$	Furfural (2-furancarbonal)	578	20.0	7.01	50.2	2.06
C_5H_5N	Pyridine	589	11.9	8.76	60.3	2.58
$C_5H_8O_4$	Glutaric acid (pentanedioic acid) 2 N aqueous sol.	589	16.0	5.48	37.7	....
$C_5H_{10}O_2$	Propionic acid ethylester	589	20.0	5.46	37.6	1.13
$C_5H_{10}O_2$	Acetic acid propylester	589	15.7	5.45	37.5	1.13
$C_5H_{14}N_2$	Cadaverine (1,5-pentanediamine)	589	14.7	7.49	51.6	1.53
C_6H_6	Benzene	589	15.0	11.27	77.5	3.00
C_6H_{12}	Cyclohexane	589	20.0	5.00	39.0	1.24
C_6H_{14}	Hexane	589	15.0	6.62	45.5	1.20
$C_6H_4Cl_2$	1,4-Dichlorobenzene (p-dichlorobenzene)	589	64.5	13.55	93.2	2.69
C_6H_5F	Fluorobenzene (phenylfluoride)	589	19.0	9.96	68.5	2.51
C_6H_5Cl	Chlorobenzene (phenylchloride)	589	15.0	12.51	86.1	2.92
C_6H_5Br	Bromobenzene (phenylbromide)	589	15.0	14.51	99.8	3.26
C_6H_5I	Iodobenzene (phenyliodide)	589	15.0	19.11	131.4	4.06
C_6H_6O	Phenol (hydroxybenzene)	589	39.0	12.07	83.5	3.21
C_6H_7N	Aniline (aminobenzene)	589	15.0	16.08	110.6	4.18
$C_6H_{11}Cl$	Chlorocyclohexane (cyclohexylchloride)	589	13.0	7.50	51.6	1.46
$C_6H_{12}O_3$	Paraldehyde (paraacetaldehyde)	589	17.3	6.66	45.8	1.19
$C_6H_{12}O_6$	Glucose 11H$_2$O (dextrose) (1 M aqueous sol.)	589	15.0	6.72	46.2	....
$C_6H_{12}O_6$	Galactose 10H$_2$O (1 M aqueous sol.)	589	15.0	6.89	47.4	....
$C_6H_{12}O_6$	Fructose 10H$_2$O (levulose) (1 M aqueous sol.)	589	15.0	6.73	46.3	....
$C_6H_{14}O$	2-Hexanol (butylmethylcarbinol)	589	20.0	6.89	47.4	1.31
$C_6H_{14}O$	3-Hexanol (ethylpropylcarbinol)	589	20.0	6.85	47.1	1.30
$C_6H_{14}O$	2-Methyl-3-Pentanol (ethylisopropylcarbinol)	589	20.0	6.90	47.5	1.32
$C_6H_4O_4N_2$	1,3-Dinitrobenzene (m-Dinitrobenzene)	589	17.1	9.65	66.4	2.17
$C_6H_5O_2N$	Nitrobenzene	589	15.0	9.36	64.4	2.17
C_7H_8	Toluene (methylbenzene)	589	15.0	12.16	83.7	2.71
C_7H_{14}	1-Heptene (α-heptylene)	589	18.0	8.48	58.3	1.43
C_7H_{16}	Heptane	589	15.0	7.61	52.7	1.23
C_7H_5N	Benzonitrile (benzenecarbonitrile)	589	15.7	11.85	81.5	2.74
$C_7H_6O_2$	Benzoic acid (20 % alcohol sol.)	578	20.0	11.8	84.7	....
C_7H_7Cl	o-Chlorotoluene (2-chloro-1-methylbenzene)	589	15.4	13.72	94.3	2.95
C_7H_7Cl	p-Chlorotoluene (4-chloro-1-methylbenzene)	589	15.2	13.25	90.8	2.65
C_7H_7Br	o-Bromotoluene (2-bromo-1-methylbenzene)	589	16.7	15.67	107.3	3.08
C_7H_7Br	p-Bromotoluene (4-bromo-1-methylbenzene)	589	39.0	15.09	103.6	2.88
C_7H_8O	o-Cresol (o-methylphenol)	589	16.0	13.38	92.1	3.07
C_7H_8O	m-Cresol (m-methylphenol)	589	17.9	12.77	87.6	2.89
C_7H_8O	p-Cresol (p-methylphenol)	589	17.0	12.86	88.5	2.91
C_7H_9N	o-Toluidine (o-methylaniline)	589	17.3	17.18	118.2	3.79
C_7H_9N	m-Toluidine (m-methylaniline)	589	15.0	16.21	111.5	3.56
C_7H_9N	p-Toluidine (p-methylaniline)	589	50.0	15.92	109.5	3.37
$C_7H_{14}O$	Enanthaldehyde (heptanal)	589	16.2	7.42	51.1	1.26
$C_7H_{16}O$	1-Heptanol (n-heptylalcohol)	589	12.6	7.85	54.0	1.33
$C_7H_{16}O$	2-Heptanol (amylmethylcarbinol)	589	20.0	7.94	54.6	1.32
$C_7H_{16}O$	3-Heptanol (butylethylcarbinol)	589	20.0	7.86	54.1	1.37
$C_7H_7O_2N$	o-Nitrotoluene	589	18.0	10.80	74.3	2.16
$C_7H_7O_2N$	p-Nitrotoluene	589	54.3	10.20	70.2	1.97
C_8H_{10}	Ethylbenzene (phenylethane)	589	15.0	13.41	92.3	2.80
C_8H_{10}	o-Xylene (1,2-dimethylbenzene)	589	15.0	13.36	91.9	2.62
C_8H_{10}	m-Xylene (1,3-dimethylbenzene)	589	15.0	12.82	88.2	2.47
C_8H_{10}	p-Xylene (1,4-dimethylbenzene)	589	15.0	12.80	88.1	2.46
C_8H_{16}	1-Octene (α-octylene)	589	15.0	9.00	65.5	1.44
C_8H_{16}	2-Octene (β-octylene)	589	15.0	9.33	64.2	1.43
C_8H_{18}	Octane	589	15.0	8.65	59.5	1.26
$C_8H_{18}O$	1-Octanol (n-octylalcohol)	589	20.0	8.88	61.1	1.33
$C_8H_{18}O$	2-Octanol (methylhexylcarbinol)	589	20.0	9.00	61.8	1.34
$C_8H_{18}O$	3-Octanol (ethylamylcarbinol)	589	20.0	8.90	61.2	1.33
C_9H_{12}	o-Ethyltoluene (1-ethyl-2-ethylbenzene)	589	15.0	14.56	100.2	2.32
C_9H_{12}	m-Ethyltoluene (1-ethyl-3-ethylbenzene)	589	15.0	14.18	97.6	2.91
C_9H_{12}	p-Ethylbenzene (1-ethyl-4-ethylbenzene)	589	15.0	13.98	96.2	2.37
C_9H_{12}	Mesitylene (1-3-5-trimethylbenzene)	589	15.0	13.36	91.9	2.28
C_9H_{20}	Nonane	589	15.0	9.70	66.7	1.28
$C_{10}H_8$	Naphthalene	589	89.5	24.98	171.8	4.47
$C_{10}H_{20}$	1-Decene (n-decylene)	589	21.0	11.65	80.1	1.45
$C_{10}H_{22}$	Decane	589	15.0	10.70	73.6	1.30

Formula	Name	λ	t	ρ_M	$10^5[\Delta]_M^{\lambda,t}$	$10^5\Lambda^{\lambda,t}$ Verdet
$C_{10}H_7Cl$	1-Chloronaphthalene (α-chloronaphthalene)	578	18.0	28.15	201.5	4.91
$C_{10}H_7Br$	1-Bromonaphthalene (α-bromonaphthalene)	578	20.0	31.05	222.0	5.19
$C_{10}H_8O$	β-Naphthol (2-hydroxynaphthalene)	578	136.0	27.1	194.0	4.80
$C_{10}H_9N$	1-Naphthylamine (α-naphthylamine)	589	32.6	37.23	256.1	6.84
$C_{10}H_{12}O_2$	Isoeugenol (4-propenylguaiacol)	589	19.3	21.44	147.5	3.55
$C_{10}H_{12}O_2$	Eugenol (4-allylguaiacol)	589	15.4	18.72	128.8	2.88
$C_{10}H_{12}O_2$	Benzoic acid propylester (n-propylbenzoate)	589	15.4	14.87	102.3	2.20
$C_{10}H_{12}O_2$	o-Toluic acid ethylester	589	15.2	15.06	103.6	2.25
$C_{10}H_{12}O_2$	p-Toluic acid ethylester	589	15.0	14.74	101.4	2.18
$C_{10}H_{12}O_2$	α-Toluic acid ethylester (ethylphenylacetate)	589	14.0	14.99	103.1	2.25
$C_{10}H_{12}O_3$	Methylsalicylic acid ethylester	589	18.6	17.14	117.9	2.50
$C_{10}H_{15}N$	N,N-Diethylaniline (N-phenyldiethylamine)	589	15.3	25.16	173.1	3.74
$C_{10}H_{16}O$	Camphor	589	14.0	9.26	63.7	......
$C_{10}H_{18}O$	α-Terpineol	589	16.0	10.84	74.6	1.56
$C_{10}H_{18}O$	Citronellal	589	14.5	11.48	79.0	1.51
$C_{10}H_{18}O_4$	Dipropylsuccinate	589	11.4	10.36	71.3	1.22
$C_{10}H_{18}O_6$	Tartaric acid dipropylester (propyltartrate)	589	20.5	10.83	74.5	1.24
$C_{10}H_{20}O$	Menthol	589	45.2	10.51	72.3	1.40
$C_{11}H_{24}$	Undecane	589	20.5	11.65	80.1	1.31
$C_{12}H_{26}$	Dodecane	589	21.5	12.71	87.4	1.32
$C_{12}H_{22}O_{11}$	Saccharose 19H_2O (1 M aqueous sol.)	589	15.0	12.59	86.6	......
$C_{12}H_{22}O_{11}$	Maltose 20H_2O (1 M aqueous sol.)	589	15.0	12.69	87.3	......
$C_{12}H_{22}O_{11}$	Lactose 41H_2O (1 M aqueous sol.)	589	18.4	12.71	87.5	......
$C_{14}H_{10}$	Phenanthrene	578	100.0	39.7	284.0	5.84
$C_{16}H_{34}$	Hexadecane	589	15.0	16.8	115.6	1.35
$C_{18}H_{14}$	1,2-Diphenylbenzene	589	15.0	40.2	276.3	4.70
$C_{18}H_{14}$	1,3-Diphenylbenzene (m-phenyldiphenyl)	589	15.0	41.0	282.4	......
$C_{18}H_{22}$	1,6-Diphenylhexane	589	20.0	......	......	2.75

TRANSPARENCY TO OPTICAL DENSITY CONVERSION TABLE

Transparency of a layer of material is defined as the ratio of the intensity of the transmitted light to that of the incident light. Opacity is the reciprocal of the transparency. Optical density is the common logarithm of the opacity.

Thus,

$$\text{Transparency} = \frac{I_t}{I_i}$$

$$\text{Opacity} = \frac{1}{\text{Transparency}} = \frac{I_i}{I_t}$$

$$\text{Optical density} = \log_{10}\left(\frac{I_i}{I_t}\right)$$

where I_i = Intensity of incident light
I_t = Intensity of transmitted light.

Trans.	Density	Trans.	Density	Trans.	Density	Trans.	Density	Trans.	Density	Trans.	Density	Trans.	Density	Trans.	Density
0.000	—	**.030**	1.523	**.060**	1.222	**.090**	1.046	**.120**	.9208	**.150**	.8239	**.180**	.7447	**.210**	.6778
.001	3.000	.031	1.509	.061	1.215	.091	1.041	.121	.9172	.151	.8210	.181	.7423	.211	.6757
.002	2.699	.032	1.495	.062	1.208	.092	1.036	.122	.9137	.152	.8182	.182	.7399	.212	.6737
.003	2.523	.033	1.482	.063	1.201	.093	1.032	.123	.9101	.153	.8153	.183	.7375	.213	.6716
.004	2.398	.034	1.469	.064	1.194	.094	1.027	.124	.9066	.154	.8125	.184	.7352	.214	.6696
.005	2.301	.035	1.456	.065	1.187	.095	1.022	.125	.9031	.155	.8097	.185	.7328	.215	.6676
.006	2.222	.036	1.444	.066	1.180	.096	1.018	.126	.8996	.156	.8069	.186	.7305	.216	.6655
.007	2.155	.037	1.432	.067	1.174	.097	1.013	.127	.8962	.157	.8041	.187	.7282	.217	.6635
.008	2.097	.038	1.420	.068	1.168	.098	1.009	.128	.8928	.158	.8013	.188	.7258	.218	.6615
.009	2.046	.039	1.409	.069	1.161	.099	1.004	.129	.8894	.159	.7986	.189	.7235	.219	.6596
.010	2.000	**.040**	1.398	**.070**	1.155	**.100**	1.000	**.130**	.8861	**.160**	.7959	**.190**	.7212	**.220**	.6576
.011	1.959	.041	1.387	.071	1.149	.101	.9957	.131	.8827	.161	.7932	.191	.7190	.221	.6556
.012	1.921	.042	1.377	.072	1.143	.102	.9914	.132	.8794	.162	.7905	.192	.7167	.222	.6536
.013	1.886	.043	1.367	.073	1.137	.103	.9872	.133	.8761	.163	.7878	.193	.7144	.223	.6517
.014	1.854	.044	1.357	.074	1.131	.104	.9830	.134	.8729	.164	.7852	.194	.7122	.224	.6498
.015	1.824	.045	1.347	.075	1.125	.105	.9788	.135	.8697	.165	.7825	.195	.7100	.225	.6478
.016	1.796	.046	1.337	.076	1.119	.106	.9747	.136	.8665	.166	.7799	.196	.7077	.226	.6459
.017	1.770	.047	1.328	.077	1.114	.107	.9706	.137	.8633	.167	.7773	.197	.7055	.227	.6440
.018	1.745	.048	1.319	.078	1.108	.108	.9666	.138	.8601	.168	.7747	.198	.7033	.228	.6421
.019	1.721	.049	1.310	.079	1.102	.109	.9626	.139	.8570	.169	.7721	.199	.7011	.229	.6402
.020	1.699	**.050**	1.301	**.080**	1.097	**.110**	.9586	**.140**	.8539	**.170**	.7696	**.200**	.6990	**.230**	.6383
.021	1.678	.051	1.292	.081	1.092	.111	.9547	.141	.8508	.171	.7670	.201	.6968	.231	.6364
.022	1.658	.052	1.284	.082	1.086	.112	.9508	.142	.8477	.172	.7645	.202	.6946	.232	.6345
.023	1.638	.053	1.276	.083	1.081	.113	.9469	.143	.8447	.173	.7620	.203	.6925	.233	.6326
.024	1.620	.054	1.268	.084	1.076	.114	.9431	.144	.8416	.174	.7594	.204	.6904	.234	.6308
.025	1.602	.055	1.260	.085	1.071	.115	.9393	.145	.8386	.175	.7570	.205	.6882	.235	.6289
.026	1.585	.056	1.252	.086	1.066	.116	.9356	.146	.8356	.176	.7545	.206	.6861	.236	.6271
.027	1.569	.057	1.244	.087	1.060	.117	.9318	.147	.8327	.177	.7520	.207	.6840	.237	.6253
.028	1.553	.058	1.237	.088	1.055	.118	.9281	.148	.8297	.178	.7496	.208	.6819	.238	.6234
.029	1.538	.059	1.229	.089	1.051	.119	.9244	.149	.8268	.179	.7471	.209	.6799	.239	.6216

Trans.	Density	Trans.	Density	Trans.	Density	Trans.	Density	Trans.	Density
.240	.6198	.315	.5017	.390	.4089	.465	.3325	.540	.2676
.241	.6180	.316	.5003	.391	.4078	.466	.3316	.541	.2668
.242	.6162	.317	.4989	.392	.4067	.467	.3307	.542	2660
.243	.6144	.318	.4976	.393	.4056	.468	.3298	.543	.2652
.244	.6126	.319	.4962	.394	.4045	.469	.3288	.544	.2644
.245	.6108	.320	.4949	.395	.4034	.470	.3279	.545	.2636
.246	.6091	.321	.4935	.396	.4023	.471	.3270	.546	.2628
.247	.6073	.322	.4921	.397	.4012	.472	.3260	.547	.2620
.248	.6056	.323	.4908	.398	.4001	.473	.3251	.548	.2612
.249	.6038	.324	.4895	.399	.3990	.474	.3242	.549	.2604
.250	.6021	.325	.4881	.400	.3979	.475	.3233	.550	.2596
.251	.6003	.326	.4868	.401	.3969	.476	.3224	.551	.2589
.252	.5986	.327	.4855	.402	.3958	.477	.3215	.552	.2581
.253	.5969	.328	.4841	.403	.3947	.478	.3206	.553	.2573
.254	.5952	.329	.4828	.404	.3936	.479	.3197	.554	.2565
.255	.5935	.330	.4815	.405	.3925	.480	.3188	.555	.2557
.256	.5918	.331	.4802	.406	.3915	.481	.3179	.556	.2549
.257	.5901	.332	.4789	.407	.3904	.482	.3170	.557	.2541
.258	.5884	.333	.4776	.408	.3893	.483	.3161	.558	.2534
.259	.5867	.334	.1763	.409	.3883	.484	.3152	.559	.2526
.260	.5850	.335	.4750	.410	.3872	.485	.3143	.560	.2518
.261	.5834	.336	.4737	.411	.3862	.486	.3134	.561	.2510
.262	.5817	.337	.4724	.412	.3851	.487	.3125	.562	.2503
.263	.5800	.338	.4711	.413	.3840	.488	.3116	.563	.2495
.264	.5784	.339	.4698	.414	.3830	.489	.3107	.564	.2487
.265	.5768	.340	.4685	.415	.3819	.490	.3098	.565	.2479
.266	.5751	.341	.4673	.416	.3809	.491	.3089	.566	.2472
.267	.5735	.342	.4660	.417	.3799	.492	.3080	.567	.2464
.268	.5719	.343	.4647	.418	.3788	.493	.3072	.568	.2457
.209	.5702	.344	.4634	.419	.3778	.494	.3063	.569	.2449
.270	.5686	.345	.4622	.420	.3768	.495	.3054	.570	.2441
.271	.5670	.346	.4609	.421	.3757	.496	.3045	.571	.2434
.272	.5654	.347	.4597	.422	.3747	.497	.3036	.572	.2426
.273	.5638	.348	.4584	.423	.3737	.498	.3028	.573	.2418
.274	.5622	.349	.4572	.424	.3726	.499	.3019	.574	.2411
275	.5607	.350	.4559	.425	.3716	.500	.3010	.575	.2403
.276	.5591	.351	.4547	.426	.3706	.501	.3002	.576	.2396
.277	.5575	.352	.4535	.427	.3696	.502	.2993	.577	.2388
.278	.5560	.353	.4522	.428	.3685	.503	.2984	.578	.2381
.279	.5544	.354	.4510	.429	.3675	.504	.2975	.579	.2373
.280	.5528	.355	.4498	.430	.3665	.505	.2967	.580	.2366
.281	.5513	.356	.4486	.431	.3655	.506	.2959	.581	.2358
282	.5498	.357	.4473	.432	.3645	.507	.2950	.582	.2351
283	.5482	.358	.4461	.433	.3635	.508	.2941	.583	.2343
284	.5467	.359	.4449	.434	.3625	.509	.2933	.584	.2336
.285	.5452	.360	.4437	.435	.3615	.510	.2924	.585	.2328
.286	.5436	.361	.4425	.436	.3605	.511	.2916	.586	.2321
.287	.5421	.362	.4413	.437	.3595	.512	.2907	.587	.2314
.288	.5406	.363	.4401	.438	.3585	.513	.2899	.588	.2306
.289	.5391	.364	.4389	.439	.3575	.514	.2890	.589	.2299
.290	.5376	.365	.4377	.440	.3565	.515	.2882	.590	.2291
.291	.5361	.366	.4365	.441	.3556	.516	.2873	.591	.2284
.292	.5346	.367	.4353	.442	.3546	.517	.2865	.592	.2277
.293	.5331	.368	.4342	.443	.3536	.518	.2857	.593	.2269
.294	.5317	.369	.4330	.444	.3526	.519	.2848	.594	.2262
295	.5302	.370	.4318	.445	.3516	.520	.2840	.595	.2255
296	.5287	.371	.4306	.446	.3507	.521	.2831	.596	.2248
297	.5272	.372	.4295	.447	.3497	.522	.2823	.597	.2240
298	.5258	.373	.4283	.448	.3487	.523	.2815	.598	.2233
299	.5243	.374	.4271	.449	.3478	.524	.2807	.599	.2226
.300	.5229	.375	.4260	.450	.3468	.525	.2798	.600	.2219
.301	.5215	.376	.4248	.451	.3458	.526	.2790	.601	.2211
.302	.5200	.377	.4237	.452	.3449	.527	.2782	.602	.2204
.303	.5186	.378	.4225	.453	.3439	.528	.2774	.603	.2197
.304	.5171	.379	.4214	.454	.3429	.529	.2766	.604	.2190
.305	.5157	.380	.4202	.455	.3420	.530	.2757	.605	.2182
.306	.5143	.381	.4191	.456	.3410	.531	.2749	.606	.2175
.307	.5128	.382	.4179	.457	.3401	.532	.2741	.607	.2168
.308	.5114	.383	.4168	.458	.3391	.533	.2733	.608	.2161
.309	.5100	.384	.4157	.459	.3382	.534	.2725	.609	.2154
.310	.5086	.385	.4145	.460	.3372	.535	.2717	.610	.2147
.311	.5072	.386	.4134	.461	.3363	.536	.2708	.611	.2140
.312	.5058	.387	.4123	.462	.3354	.537	.2700	.612	.2132
.313	.5045	.388	.4112	.463	.3344	.538	.2692	.613	.2125
.314	.5031	.389	.4101	.464	.3335	.539	.2684	.614	.2118

Trans.	Density	Trans.	Density	Trans.	Density	Trans.	Density	Trans.	Density
.615	.2111	.695	.1580	.775	.1107	.855	.0680	.935	.0292
.616	.2104	.696	.1574	.776	.1102	.856	.0675	.936	.0287
.617	.2097	.697	.1568	.777	.1096	.857	.0670	.937	.0282
.618	.2090	.698	.1562	.778	.1090	.858	.0665	.938	.0278
.619	.2083	.699	.1555	.779	.1085	.859	.0660	.939	.0273
.620	.2076	.700	.1549	.780	.1079	.860	.0655	.940	.0269
.621	.2069	.701	.1543	.781	.1073	.861	.0650	.941	.0264
.622	.2062	.702	.1537	.782	.1068	.862	.0645	.942	.0260
.623	.2055	.703	.1531	.783	.1062	.863	.0640	.943	.0255
.624	.2048	.704	.1524	.784	.1057	.864	.0635	.944	.0250
.625	.2041	.705	.1518	.785	.1051	.865	.0630	.945	.0246
.626	.2034	.706	.1512	.786	.1046	.866	.0625	.946	.0241
.627	.2027	.707	.1506	.787	.1040	.867	.0620	.947	.0237
.628	.2020	.708	.1500	.788	.1035	.868	.0615	.948	.0232
.629	.2013	.709	.1493	.789	.1029	.869	.0610	.949	.0227
.630	.2007	.710	.1487	.790	.1024	.870	.0605	.950	.0223
.631	.2000	.711	.1481	.791	.1018	.871	.0600	.951	.0218
.632	.1993	.712	.1475	.792	.1013	.872	.0595	.952	.0214
.633	.1986	.713	.1469	.793	.1007	.873	.0590	.953	.0209
.634	.1979	.714	.1463	.794	.1002	.874	.0585	.954	.0204
.635	.1972	.715	.1457	.795	.0996	.875	.0580	.955	.0200
.636	.1965	.716	.1451	.796	.0991	.876	.0575	.956	.0195
.637	.1959	.717	.1445	.797	.0985	.877	.0570	.957	.0191
.638	.1952	.718	.1439	.798	.0980	.878	.0565	.958	.0186
.639	.1945	.719	.1433	.799	.0975	.879	.0560	.959	.0182
.640	.1938	.720	.1427	.800	.0969	.880	.0555	.960	.0177
.641	.1932	.721	.1421	.801	.0964	.881	.0550	.961	.0173
.642	.1925	.722	.1415	.802	.0958	.882	.0545	.962	.0168
.643	.1918	.723	.1409	.803	.0953	.883	.0540	.963	.0164
.644	.1911	.724	.1403	.804	.0948	.884	.0535	.964	.0159
.645	.1904	.725	.1397	.805	.0942	.885	.0530	.965	.0155
.646	.1898	.726	.1391	.806	.0937	.886	.0526	.966	.0150
.647	.1891	.727	.1385	.807	.0931	.887	.0521	.967	.0146
.648	.1884	.728	.1379	.808	.0926	.888	.0516	.968	.0141
.649	.1877	.729	.1373	.809	.0921	.889	.0511	.969	.0137
.650	.1871	.730	.1367	.810	.0915	.890	.0506	.970	.0132
.651	.1864	.731	.1361	.811	.0910	.891	.0501	.971	.0128
.652	.1857	.732	.1355	.812	.0904	.892	.0496	.972	.0123
653	.1851	.733	.1349	.813	.0899	.893	.0491	.973	.0119
.654	.1844	.734	.1343	.814	.0894	.894	.0487	.974	.0114
.655	.1838	.735	.1337	.815	.0888	.895	.0482	.975	.0110
.656	.1831	.736	.1331	.816	.0883	.896	.0477	.976	.0106
.657	.1824	.737	.1325	.817	.0878	.897	.0472	.977	.0101
.658	.1818	.738	.1319	.818	.0872	.898	.0467	.978	.0097
.659	.1811	.739	.1314	.819	.0867	.899	.0462	.979	.0092
.660	.1805	.740	.1308	.820	.0862	.900	.0458	.980	.0088
.661	.1798	.741	.1302	.821	.0856	.901	.0453	.981	.0083
.662	.1791	.742	.1296	.822	.0851	.902	.0448	.982	.0079
.663	.1785	.743	.1290	.823	.0846	.903	.0443	.983	.0074
.664	.1778	.744	.1284	.824	.0841	.904	.0438	.984	.0070
.665	.1772	.745	.1278	.825	.0835	.905	.0434	.985	.0066
.666	.1765	.746	.1273	.826	.0830	.906	.0429	.986	.0061
.667	.1759	.747	.1267	.827	.0825	.907	.0424	.987	.0057
.668	.1752	.748	.1261	.828	.0820	.908	.0419	.988	.0052
.669	.1746	.749	.1255	.829	.0815	.909	.0414	.989	.0048
.670	.1739	.750	.1249	.830	.0809	.910	.0410	.990	.0044
.671	.1733	.751	.1244	.831	.0804	.911	.0405	.991	.0039
.672	.1726	.752	.1238	.832	.0799	.912	.0400	.992	.0035
.673	.1720	.753	.1232	.833	.0794	.913	.0395	.993	.0030
.674	.1713	.754	.1226	.834	.0788	.914	.0391	.994	.0026
.675	.1707	.755	.1221	.835	.0783	.915	.0386	.995	.0022
.676	.1701	.756	.1215	.836	.0778	.916	.0381	.996	.0017
.677	.1694	.757	.1209	.837	.0773	.917	.0376	.997	.0013
.678	.1688	.758	.1203	.838	.0767	.918	.0371	.998	.0009
.679	.1681	.759	.1198	.839	.0762	.919	.0367	.999	.0004
.680	.1675	.760	.1192	.840	.0757	.920	.0362	1.000	.0000
.681	.1668	.761	.1186	.841	.0752	.921	.0357		
.682	.1662	.762	.1180	.842	.0747	.922	.0353		
.683	.1655	.763	.1175	.843	.0742	.923	.0348		
.684	.1649	.764	.1169	.844	.0736	.924	.0343		
.685	.1643	.765	.1163	.845	.0731	.925	.0339		
.686	.1637	.766	.1158	.846	.0726	.926	.0334		
.687	.1630	.767	.1152	.847	.0721	.927	.0329		
.688	.1624	.768	.1146	.848	.0716	.928	.0325		
.689	.1618	.769	.1141	.849	.0711	.929	.0320		
.690	.1612	.770	.1135	.850	.0706	.930	.0315		
.691	.1605	.771	.1129	.851	.0701	.931	.0310		
.692	.1599	.772	.1124	.852	.0696	.932	.0306		
.693	.1593	.773	.1118	.853	.0690	.933	.0301		
.694	.1586	.774	.1113	.854	.0685	.934	.0296		

DENSITY OF VARIOUS SOLIDS

The approximate density of various solids at ordinary atmospheric temperature.
In the case of substances with voids such as paper or leather the bulk density is indicated rather than the density of the solid portion.

(Selected principally from the Smithsonian Tables.)

Substance	Grams per cu. cm	Pounds per cu. ft.	Substance	Grams per cu. cm	Pound per cu. ft.	Substance	Grams per cu. cm	Pounds per cu. ft.
Agate	2.5–2.7	156–168	Glass, common	2.4–2.8	150–175	Tallow, beef	0.94	59
Alabaster, carbonate	2.69–2.78	168–173	flint	2.9–5.9	180–370	mutton	0.94	59
sulfate	2.26–2.32	141–145	Glue	1.27	79	Tar	1.02	66
Albite	2.62–2.65	163–165	Granite	2.64–2.76	165–172	Topaz	3.5–3.6	219–223
Amber	1.06–1.11	66–69	Graphite*	2.30–2.72	144–170	Tourmaline	3.0–3.2	190–200
Amphiboles	2.9–3.2	180–200	Gum arabic	1.3–1.4	81–87	Wax, sealing	1.8	112
Anorthite	2.74–2.76	171–172	Gypsum	2.31–2.33	144–145	Wood (seasoned)		
Asbestos	2.0–2.8	125–175	Hematite	4.9–5.3	306–330	alder	0.42–0.68	26–42
Asbestos slate	1.8	112	Hornblende	3.0	187	apple	0.66–0.84	41–52
Asphalt	1.1–1.5	69–94	Ice	0.917	57.2	ash	0.65–0.85	40–53
Basalt	2.4–3.1	150–190	Ivory	1.83–1.92	114–120	balsa	0.11–0.14	7–9
Beeswax	0.96–0.97	60–61	Leather, dry	0.86	54	bamboo	0.31–0.40	19–25
Beryl	2.69–2.7	168–169	Lime, slaked	1.3–1.4	81–87	basswood	0.32–0.59	20–37
Biotite	2.7–3.1	170–190	Limestone	2.68–2.76	167–171	beech	0.70–0.90	43–56
Bone	1.7–2.0	106–125	Linoleum	1.18	74	birch	0.51–0.77	32–48
Brick	1.4–2.2	87–137	Magnetite	4.9–5.2	306–324	blue gum	1.00	62
Butter	0.86–0.87	53–54	Malachite	3.7–4.1	231–256	box	0.95–1.16	59–72
Calamine	4.1–4.5	255–280	Marble	2.6–2.84	160–177	butternut	0.38	24
Calcspar	2.6–2.8	162–175	Meerschaum	0.99–1.28	62–80	cedar	0.49–0.57	30–35
Camphor	0.99	62	Mica	2.6–3.2	165–200	cherry	0.70–0.90	43–56
Caoutchouc	0.92–0.99	57–62	Muscovite	2.76–3.00	172–187	dogwood	0.76	47
Cardboard	0.69	43	Ochre	3.5	218	ebony	1.11–1.33	69–83
Celluloid	1.4	87	Opal	2.2	137	elm	0.54–0.60	34–37
Cement, set	2.7–3.0	170.190	Paper	0.7–1.15	44–72	hickory	0.60–0.93	37–58
Chalk	1.9–2.8	118–175	Paraffin	0.87–0.91	54–57	holly	0.76	47
Charcoal, oak	0.57	35	Peat blocks	0.84	52	juniper	0.56	35
pine	0.28–0.44	18–28	Pitch	1.07	67	larch	0.50–0.56	31–35
Cinnabar	8.12	507	Porcelain	2.3–2.5	143–156	lignum vitae	1.17–1.33	73–83
Clay	1.8–2.6	112–162	Porphyry	2.6–2.9	162–181	locust	0.67–0.71	42–44
Coal, anthracite	1.4–1.8	87–112	Pressed wood pulp board	0.19	12	logwood	0.91	57
bituminous	1.2–1.5	75–94	Pyrite	4.95–5.1	309–318	mahogany		
Cocoa butter	0.89–0.91	56–57	Quartz	2.65	165	Honduras	0.66	41
Coke	1.0–1.7	62–105	Resin	1.07	67	Spanish	0.85	53
Copal	1.04–1.14	65–71	Rock salt	2.18	136	maple	0.62–0.75	39–47
Cork	0.22–0.26	14–16	Rubber, hard	1.19	74	oak	0.60–0.90	37–56
Cork linoleum	0.54	34	Rubber, soft			pear	0.61–0.73	38–45
Corundum	3.9–4.0	245–250	commercial	1.1	69	pine, pitch	0.83–0.85	52–53
Diamond	3.01–3.52	188–220	pure gum	0.91–0.93	57–58	white	0.35–0.50	22–31
Dolomite	2.84	177	Sandstone	2.14–2.36	134–147	yellow	0.37–0.60	23–37
Ebonite	1.15	72	Serpentine	2.50–2.65	156–165	plum	0.66–0.78	41–49
Emery	4.0	250	Silica, fused transparent	2.21	138	poplar	0.35–0.5	22–31
Epidote	3.25–3.50	203–218	translucent	2.07	129	satinwood	0.95	59
Feldspar	2.55–2.75	159–172	Slag	2.0–3.9	125–240	spruce	0.48–0.70	30–44
Flint	2.63	164	Slate	2.6–3.3	162–205	sycamore	0.40–0.60	24–37
Fluorite	3.18	198				teak, Indian	0.66–0.88	41–55
						African	0.98	61
Galena	7.3–7.6	460–470	Soapstone	2.6–2.8	162–175	walnut	0.64–0.70	40–43
Gamboge	1.2	75	Spermacéti	0.95	59	water gum	1.00	62
Garnet	3.15–4.3	197–268	Starch	1.53	95	willow	0.40–0.60	24–37
Gas carbon	1.88	117	Sugar	1.59	99			
Gelatin	1.27	79	Talc	2.7–2.8	168–174			

* Some values reported as low as 1.6.

WEIGHT OF 1 GALLON OF WATER (U.S. Gallon)

The weights in air are for dry air at the same temperature as the water up to 40°C. and at a (corrected) barometric pressure of 760 mm and against brass weights of 8.4 density at 0°C. Above 40°C. the temperature of the air is assumed to be 20°C., i. e., the water is allowed to cool to 20°C. before the weighings are made. The volumetric computations are based on the relation that 1 liter = 1.000027 cubic decimeters and 1 cubic decimeter = 61.023378 cubic inches.

Temperature °C.	Weight in vacuo		Weight in air		Temperature °C.	Weight in vacuo		Weight in air	
	Grams	Pounds	Grams	Pounds		Grams	Pounds	Grams	Pounds
0	3784.833	8.34412	3780.520	8.33461	24	5.220	.32293	1.256	.31419
1	5.055	.34461	0.758	.33513	25	4.268	.32083	0.317	.31212
2	5.211	.34495	0.930	.33551	26	3.279	.31865	3769.341	.30996
3	5.303	.34515	1.037	.33575	27	2.254	.31639	8.329	.30773
4	5.332	.34522	1.082	.33585	28	1.195	.31405	7.283	.30543
5	5.302	.34515	1.067	.33582	29	0.100	.31164	6.201	.30304
6	5.212	.34495	0.992	.33565	30	3768.972	.30915	5.086	.30058
7	5.066	.34463	0.861	.33536	31	7.812	.30659	3.938	.29805
8	4.864	.34419	0.675	.33495	32	6.618	.30396	2.757	.29545
9	4.610	.34363	0.435	.33442	33	5.393	.30126	1.545	.29278
10	4.303	.34295	0.144	.33378	34	4.137	.29849	0.301	.29003
11	3.943	.34216	3779.798	.33302	35	2.851	.29566	3759.027	.28723
12	3.534	.34125	9.403	.33215	40	3755.995	.28054	2.232	.27225
13	3.076	.34025	8.960	.33117	45	3748.39	.2638	3744.40	.2550
14	2.574	.33914	8.472	.33009	50	3740.17	8.2457	3736.20	8.2369
15	2.026	.33793	7.939	.32892	55	3731.32	.2261	3727.35	.2174
(15½) 60° F.	(3781.703)	(8.33722)	(3777.623)	(8.32823)	60	3721.89	.2054	3717.93	.1966
16	1.435	.33663	7.362	.32765	65	3711.86	.1832	3707.91	.1745
(16⅔) 62° F.	(3781.017)	(8.33571)	(3776.953)	(8.32675)	70	3701.33	.1600	3697.40	.1514
17	0.801	.33523	6.741	.32628	75	3690.28	.1357	3686.36	.1270
18	0.125	.33374	6.080	.32482	80	3678.70	.1101	3674.79	.1015
19	3779.407	.33216	5.375	.32327	85	3666.66	.0836	3662.76	.0750
20	8.649	.33049	4.630	.32162	90	3654.13	.0560	3650.25	.0474
21	7.850	.32872	3.845	.31989	95	3641.19	.0274	3637.32	.0189
22	7.012	.32688	3.021	.31808	100	3627.79	7.9979	3623.93	7.9894
23	6.135	.32494	2.157	.31617					

TEMPERATURE CORRECTION FOR VOLUMETRIC SOLUTIONS

This table gives the correction to various observed volumes of water, measured at the designated temperatures to give the volume at the standard temperature, 20°C. Conversely, by subtracting the corrections from the volume desired at 20°C., the volume that must be measured out at the designated temperatures in order to give the desired volume at 20°C., will be obtained. It is assumed that the volumes are measured in glass apparatus having a coefficient of cubical expansion of 0.000025 per degree centigrade. The table is applicable to dilute aqueous solutions having the same coefficient of expansion as water.

Temperature of measurement, °C.	Capacity of apparatus in milliliters at 20°C.							Temperature of measurement, °C.	Capacity of apparatus in milliliters at 20°C.						
	2,000	1,000	500	400	300	250	150		2,000	1,000	500	400	300	250	150
	Correction in milliliters to give volume of water at 20°C.								Correction in milliliters to give volume of water at 20°C.						
								23	−1.18	−.59	−.30	−.24	−.18	−.15	−.09
15	+1.54	+0.77	+0.38	+0.31	+0.23	+0.19	+0.12	24	−1.61	−.81	−.40	−.32	−.24	−.20	−.12
16	+1.28	+.64	+.32	+.26	+.19	+.16	+.10	25	−2.07	−1.03	−.52	−.41	−.31	−.26	−.15
17	+.99	+.50	+.25	+.20	+.15	+.12	+.07								
18	+.68	+.34	+.17	+.14	+.10	+.08	+.05	26	−2.54	−1.27	−.64	−.51	−.38	−.32	−.19
19	+.35	+.18	+.09	+.07	+.05	+.04	+.03	27	−3.03	−1.52	−.76	−.61	−.46	−.38	−.23
								28	−3.55	−1.77	−.89	−.71	−.53	−.44	−.27
21	−.37	−.18	−.09	−.07	−.06	−.05	−.03	29	−4.08	−2.04	−1.02	−.82	−.61	−.51	−.31
22	−.77	−.38	−.19	−.15	−.12	−.10	−.06	30	−4.62	−2.31	−1.16	−.92	−.69	−.58	−.35

In using the above table to correct the volume of certain standard solutions to 20°C. more accurate results will be obtained if the numerical values of the corrections are increased by the percentages given below:

Solution	Normality		
	N	N/2	N/10
HNO_3	50	25	6
H_2SO_4	45	25	5
NaOH	40	25	5
KOH	40	20	4

TEMPERATURE CORRECTION FOR GLASS VOLUMETRIC APPARATUS

This table gives the correction to be added to actual capacity (determined at certain temperatures) to give the capacity at the standard temperature, 20°C. Conversely, by subtracting the corrections from the indicated capacity of an instrument standard at 20°C. the corresponding capacity at other temperatures is obtained. The table assumes for the cubical coefficient of expansion of glass 0.000025 per degree centigrade. The coefficients of expansion of glasses used for volumetric instruments vary from 0.000023 to 0.000028.

Temperature in degrees C.	2,000 ml	1,000 ml	500 ml	400 ml	300 ml	250 ml	Temperature in degrees C.	2,000 ml	1,000 ml	500 ml	400 ml	300 ml	250 ml
15	+0.25	+0.12	+0.06	+0.05	+0.04	+0.031	23	− .15	− .08	− .04	− .03	− .02	− .019
16	+ .20	+ .10	+ .05	+0.04	+ .03	+ .025	24	− .20	− .10	− .05	− .04	− .03	− .025
17	+ .15	+ .08	+ .04	+ .03	+ .02	+ .019	25	− .25	− .12	− .06	− .05	− .04	− .031
18	+ .10	+ .05	+ .02	+ .02	+ .02	+ .012	26	− .30	− .15	− .08	− .06	− .04	− .038
19	+ .05	+ .02	+ .01	+ .01	+ .01	+ .006	27	− .35	− .18	− .09	− .07	− .05	− .044
							28	− .40	− .20	− .10	− .08	− .06	− .050
21	− .05	− .02	− .01	− .01	− .01	− .006	29	− .45	− .22	− .11	− .09	− .07	− .056
22	− .10	− .05	− .02	− .02	− .02	− .012	30	− .50	− .25	− .12	− .10	− .08	− .062

DENSITY OF VARIOUS LIQUIDS

(Selected from Smithsonian Tables.)

Liquid	Grams per cu. cm	Pounds per cu. ft.	Temp ° C	Liquid	Grams per cu. cm	Pounds per cu. ft.	Temp. ° C
Acetone	0.792	49.4	20°	Milk	1.028–1.035	64.2–64.6	
Alcohol, ethyl	0.791	49.4	20	Naphtha, petroleum ether	0.665	41.5	15
methyl	0.810	50.5	0	wood	0.848–0.810	52.9–50.5	0
Benzene	0.899	56.1	0	Oils:			
Carbolic acid	0.950–0.965	59.2–60.2	15	castor	0.969	60.5	15
Carbon disulfide	1.293	80.7	0	cocoanut	0.925	57.7	15
tetrachloride	1.595	99.6	20	cotton seed	0.926	57.8	16
Chloroform	1.489	93.0	20	creosote	1.040–1.100	64.9–68.6	15
Ether	0.736	45.9	0	linseed, boiled	0.942	58.8	15
Gasoline	0.66–0.69	41.0–43.0		olive	0.918	57.3	15
Glycerin	1.260	78.6	0	Sea water	1.025	63.99	15
Kerosene	0.82	51.2		Turpentine (spirits)	0.87	54.3	
Mercury	13.6	849.0		Water	1.00	62.43	4

DENSITY OF ALCOHOL

DENSITY OF ETHYL ALCOHOL IN GRAMS PER CUBIC CENTIMETER, COMPUTED FROM MENDELEEFF'S FORMULA

(Selected from Smithsonian Tables.)

Temp. ° C	0	1	2	3	4	5	6	7	8	9
0	.80625	.80541	.80457	.80374	.80290	.80207	.80123	.80039	.79956	.79872
10	.79788	.79704	.79620	.79535	.79451	.79367	.79283	.79198	.79114	.79029
20	.78945	.78860	.78775	.78691	.78606	.78522	.78437	.78352	.78267	.78182
30	.78097	.78012	.77927	.77841	.77756	.77671	.77585	.77500	.77414	.77329

HYDROMETERS AND DENSITY UNITS

Alcoholometer. — For testing alcoholic solutions; the scale shows the per cent of alcohol by volume; 0°-100° is the per cent.

Ammoniameter. — For testing ammonia solutions; scale 0°-40°; to convert to sp. gr. multiply by 3 and deduct from 1000.

Barktrometer or *Barkometer.* — For testing tanning liquor; scale 0°-80° Bk; the number to the right of the decimal point of the sp. gr. is the degree Bk; thus, 1.025 sp. gr. is 25° Bk.

Baumé. — There are two kinds in use; heavy Bé, for liquids heavier than water and light Bé for liquids lighter than water. In the former, 0° corresponds to a sp. gr. 1.000 (water at 4°C.) and 66° corresponds to a sp. gr. 1.842; in the lighter than water scale, 0° Bé is equivalent to the gravity of a 10% solution of sodium chloride and 60° Bé corresponds to a sp. gr. of 0.745. For Baumé degrees on the scale of densities greater than unity, the following equation gives the means of conversion:

$$\text{Sp. gr.} = \frac{m}{m - d}$$ where m = 145 (in the United States)
m = 144 (old scale used in Holland)
m = 146.78 (New scale or Gerlach scale)
d = Baumé reading

Beck's Hydrometer has 0° corresponding to sp. gr. 1.000 and 30° to sp. gr. 0.850; equal divisions on the scale are continued as far as required in both directions.

Brix Saccharometer or *Balling Saccharometer* shows directly the per cent of sugar (sucrose) by weight at the temperature indicated on the instrument, usually 17.5°C.; i.e., degrees Brix is the per cent sugar.

Cartier's Hydrometer floats in water at the 10° scale division and at 30° corresponds to 32° Bé.

Oleometer.—For vegetable and sperm oils; scale 50°-0° corresponds to sp. gr. 0.870–0.970.

Soxhlet's Lactometer, for determining the density of milk, has a scale from 25° (sp. gr. 1.025) to 35° (sp. gr. 1.035) divided into suitable scale divisions.

Twaddell Hydrometers have the scale so arranged that the reading multiplied by 5 and added to 1000 gives the sp. gr. with reference to water as 1000; it is always used for densities greater than water.

HYDROMETER CONVERSION TABLES

SHOWING THE RELATION BETWEEN DENSITY (C. G. S.) AND DEGREES BAUMÉ FOR DENSITIES LESS THAN UNITY.

Density.	Degrees Baumé.				
	.00	.01	.02	.03	.04
0.60	103.33	99.51	95.81	92.22	88.75
.70	70.00	67.18	64.44	61.78	59.19
.80	45.00	42.84	40.73	38.68	36.67
.90	25.56	23.85	22.17	20.54	18.94
1.00	10.00	.....	.....	.....	.....

Density.	Degrees Baumé.				
	.05	.06	.07	.08	.09
0.60	85.38	82.12	78.95	75.88	72.90
.70	56.67	54.21	51.82	49.49	47.22
.80	34.71	32.79	30.92	29.09	27.30
.90	17.37	15.83	14.33	12.86	11.41
1.00	.....	.....	.....	.....	.....

HYDROMETER CONVERSION TABLES
(Continued)
Showing the Relation between Density (C. G. S.) and Baumé and Twaddell Scales for Densities above Unity.

Density	Degrees Baume.	Degrees Twaddell.	Density.	Degrees Baume.	Degrees Twaddell.	Density	Degrees Baumé.	Degrees Twaddell.	Density.	Degrees Baume.	Degrees Twaddell.
1.00	0.00	0	1.20	24.17	40	1.41	42.16	82	1.61	54.94	122
1.01	1.44	2	1.21	25.16	42	1.42	42.89	84	1.62	55.49	124
1.02	2.84	4	1.22	26.15	44	1.43	43.60	86	1.63	56.04	126
1.03	4.22	6	1.23	27.11	46	1.44	44.31	88	1.64	56.58	128
1.04	5.58	8	1.24	28.06	48	1.45	45.00	90	1.65	57.12	130
1.05	6.91	10	1.25	29.00	50	1.46	45.68	92	1.66	57.65	132
1.06	8.21	12	1.26	29.92	52	1.47	46.36	94	1.67	58.17	134
1.07	9.49	14	1.27	30.83	54	1.48	47.03	96	1.68	58.69	136
1.08	10.74	16	1.28	31.72	56	1.49	47.68	98	1.69	59.20	138
1.09	11.97	18	1.29	32.60	58	1.50	48.33	100	1.70	59.71	140
1.10	13.18	20	1.30	33.46	60	1.51	48.97	102	1.71	60.20	142
1.11	14.37	22	1.31	34.31	62	1.52	49.60	104	1.72	60.70	144
1.12	15.54	24	1.32	35.15	64	1.53	50.23	106	1.73	61.18	146
1.13	16.68	26	1.33	35.98	66	1.54	50.84	108	1.74	61.67	148
1.14	17.81	28	1.34	36.79	68	1.55	51.45	110	1.75	62.14	150
1.15	18.91	30	1.35	37.59	70	1.56	52.05	112	1.76	62.61	152
1.16	20.00	32	1.36	38.38	72	1.57	52.64	114	1.77	63.08	154
1.17	21.07	34	1.37	39.16	74	1.58	53.23	116	1.78	63.54	156
1.18	22.12	36	1.38	39.93	76	1.59	53.80	118	1.79	63.99	158
1.19	23.15	38	1.39	40.68	78	1.60	54.38	120	1.80	64.44	160
			1.40	41.43	80				....	.....	...

DENSITY OF D_2O
G. S. Kell

t, ° C.	ρ, G./Cc.	t, ° C.	ρ, G./Cc.	t, ° C.	ρ, G./Cc.	t, ° C.	ρ, G./Cc.
0	1.10469	20	1.10534	50	1.09570	80	1.07824
3.813	1.10546	25	1.10445	55	1.09325	85	1.07475
5	1.10562	30	1.10323	60	1.09060	90	1.07112
10	1.10599	35	1.10173	65	1.08777	95	1.06736
11.185	1.10600	40	1.09996	70	1.08475	100	1.06346
15	1.10587	45	1.09794	75	1.08158	101.431	1.06232

VOLUME PROPERTIES OF ORDINARY WATER

G. S. Kell

Reprinted by permission of the American Chemical Society, publishers of Journal of Chemical and Engineering Data, **12**, 67–68 (1967)

(Specific volume v, density ρ, thermal expansivity $\alpha = \mathrm{d}\ln v/\mathrm{d}t$
$= -\,\mathrm{d}\ln\rho/\mathrm{d}t$, compressibility $\kappa = -\,\mathrm{d}\ln v/\mathrm{d}p = \mathrm{d}\ln\rho/\mathrm{d}p$)

t, °C.	v, Cc./G.	ρ, G./Ml.	$10^6\alpha$, Deg.$^{-1}$	$10^6\kappa$, Bar^{-1}
−20	1.00658	0.99349	−678.48	61.94
−18	1.00532	0.99474	−580.83	60.48
−16	1.00424	0.99581	−495.74	59.11
−14	1.00332	0.99672	−420.85	57.83
−12	1.00254	0.99749	−354.33	56.64
−10	1.001895	0.998137	−294.73	55.52
−9	1.001614	0.998417	−267.18	54.99
−8	1.001359	0.998671	−240.95	54.48
−7	1.001131	0.998899	−215.94	53.98
−6	1.000926	0.999102	−192.06	53.50
−5	1.000746	0.999283	−169.22	53.04
−4	1.000587	0.999441	−147.34	52.60
−3	1.000451	0.999578	−126.36	52.17
−2	1.000334	0.999694	−106.20	51.76
−1	1.000238	9.999790	−86.81	51.36
0	1.000160	0.999868	−68.14	50.98
1	1.000101	0.999927	−50.14	50.61
2	1.000060	0.999968	−32.77	50.26
3	1.000036	0.999992	−15.98	49.92
4	1.000028	1.000000	0.26	49.59
5	1.000036	0.999992	15.98	49.28
6	1.000060	0.999968	31.23	48.98
7	1.000098	0.999930	46.01	48.69
8	1.000151	0.999877	60.37	48.41
9	1.000219	0.999809	74.33	48.15
10	1.000300	0.999728	87.90	47.89
11	1.000395	0.999634	101.12	47.65
12	1.000502	0.999526	113.99	47.42
13	1.000623	0.999406	126.54	47.19
14	1.000755	0.999273	138.78	46.98
15	1.000900	0.999129	150.73	46.78
16	1.001057	0.998972	162.41	46.59
17	1.001225	0.998804	173.82	46.40
18	1.001405	0.998625	184.99	46.23
19	1.001596	0.998435	195.91	46.06
20	1.001797	0.998234	206.61	45.91
21	1.002010	0.998022	217.10	45.76
22	1.002232	0.997801	227.37	45.62
23	1.002465	0.997569	237.45	45.48
24	1.002708	0.997327	247.34	45.36
25	1.002961	0.997075	257.05	45.24
26	1.003224	0.996814	266.59	45.13
27	1.003496	0.996544	275.96	45.02
28	1.003778	0.996264	285.17	44.93
29	1.004069	0.995976	294.23	44.84
30	1.004369	0.995678	303.14	44.75
31	1.004678	0.995372	311.92	44.67
32	1.004995	0.995057	320.55	44.60
33	1.005322	0.994734	329.06	44.54
34	1.005657	0.994403	337.44	44.48
35	1.006000	0.994063	345.71	44.42
36	1.006352	0.993716	353.85	44.37
37	1.006713	0.993360	361.89	44.33
38	1.007081	0.992997	369.81	44.29
39	1.007457	0.992626	377.64	44.25
40	1.007842	0.992247	385.36	44.22
41	1.008234	0.991861	392.99	44.20
42	1.008634	0.991467	400.52	44.18
43	1.009042	0.991067	407.97	44.16
44	1.009458	0.990659	415.33	44.15
45	1.009881	0.990244	422.60	44.15
46	1.010311	0.989822	429.80	44.14
47	1.010749	0.989393	436.91	44.15
48	1.011194	0.988957	443.95	44.15
49	1.011647	0.988515	450.92	44.16
50	1.012107	0.988066	457.81	44.17
51	1.012574	0.987610	464.64	44.19
52	1.013048	0.987148	471.40	44.21
53	1.013529	0.986680	478.10	44.24
54	1.014017	0.986205	484.74	44.26
55	1.014512	0.985723	491.32	44.29
56	1.015014	0.985236	497.84	44.33
57	1.015522	0.984743	504.30	44.37
58	1.016038	0.984243	510.71	44.41
59	1.016560	0.983737	517.07	44.45
60	1.017089	0.983226	523.38	44.50
61	1.017625	0.982708	529.64	44.55
62	1.018167	0.982185	535.85	44.61
63	1.018716	0.981655	542.02	44.66
64	1.019271	0.981120	548.14	44.72
65	1.019833	0.980580	554.22	44.79
66	1.020402	0.980034	560.26	44.85
67	1.020977	0.979482	566.26	44.92
68	1.021558	0.978924	572.22	45.00
69	1.022146	0.978361	578.15	45.07
70	1.022740	0.977793	584.04	45.15
71	1.023340	0.977219	589.89	45.23
72	1.023947	0.976640	595.72	45.32
73	1.024560	0.976056	601.51	45.40
74	1.025180	0.975466	607.27	45.49
75	1.025805	0.974871	613.00	45.59
76	1.026437	0.974271	618.71	45.68
77	1.027076	0.973665	624.39	45.78
78	1.027720	0.973055	630.04	45.88
79	1.028371	0.972439	635.67	45.99
80	1.029027	0.971819	641.27	46.10
81	1.029690	0.971193	646.86	46.21
82	1.030360	0.970562	652.42	46.32
83	1.031035	0.969926	657.96	46.44
84	1.031716	0.969286	663.48	46.56
85	1.032404	0.968640	668.98	46.68
86	1.033098	0.967990	674.47	46.81
87	1.033797	0.967335	679.94	46.94
88	1.034503	0.966674	685.40	47.07
89	1.035216	0.966009	690.84	47.20
90	1.035934	0.965340	696.26	47.34
91	1.036658	0.964665	701.68	47.48
92	1.037389	0.963986	707.08	47.63
93	1.038125	0.963302	712.48	47.77
94	1.038868	0.962613	717.86	47.93
95	1.039617	0.961920	723.24	48.08
96	1.040372	0.961222	728.60	48.24
97	1.041133	0.960519	733.96	48.40
98	1.041900	0.959812	739.32	48.56
99	1.042673	0.959100	744.67	48.73
100	1.043453	0.958384	750.01	48.90
101	1.044239	0.957662	755.36	49.07
102	1.045030	0.956937	760.70	49.25
103	1.045828	0.956207	766.03	49.43
104	1.046633	0.955472	771.37	49.62
105	1.047443	0.954733	776.71	49.80
106	1.048260	0.953989	782.05	50.00
107	1.049083	0.953240	787.39	50.19
108	1.049912	0.952488	792.73	50.39
109	1.050747	0.951730	798.07	50.59
110	1.051589	0.950968	803.42	50.80

DENSITY AND VOLUME OF MERCURY

BASED ON THE DENSITY OF MERCURY AT 0° C. BY THIESEN AND SCHEEL

(Selected from Smithsonian Tables.)

Temp. °C.	Mass in gr. per ml.	Vol. of 1 gr. in ml.	Temp. °C.	Mass in gr. per ml.	Vol. of 1 gr. in ml.	Temp. °C.	Mass in gr. per ml.	Vol. of 1 gr. in ml.	Temp. °C.	Mass in gr. per ml.	Vol. of 1 gr. in ml.
−10	13.6202	0.0734205	11	5684	7011	30°	13.5217	0.0739552	150	2330	5688
−9	6177	4338	12	5659	7145	31	5193	9686	160	2093	7044
−8	6152	4472	13	5634	7278	32	5168	9820	170	1856	8402
−7	6128	4606	14	5610	7412	33	5144	9953	180	1620	9764
−6	6103	4739	15	13.5585	0.0737546	34	5119	40087	190	13.1384	0.0761128
−5	13.6078	0.0734873	16	5561	7680	35	13.5095	0.0740221	200	1148	2495
−4	6053	5006	17	5536	7813	36	5070	0354	210	0913	3865
−3	6029	5140	18	5512	7947	37	5046	0488	220	0678	5239
−2	6004	5273	19	5487	8081	38	5021	0622	230	0443	6616
−1	5979	5407	20	13.5462	0.0738215	39	4997	0756	240	13.0209	0.0767996
0	13.5955	0.0735540	21	5438	8348	40	13.4973	0.0740891	250	12.9975	9381
1	5930	5674	22	5413	8482	50	4729	2229	260	9741	70769
2	5906	5808	23	5389	8616	60	4486	3569	270	9507	2161
3	5881	5941	24	5364	8750	70	4244	4910	280	9273	3558
4	5856	6075	25	13.5340	0.0738883	80	4003	6252	290	12.9039	0.0774958
5	13.5832	0.0736209	26	5315	9017	90	13.3762	0.0747594	300	8806	6364
6	5807	6342	27	5291	9151	100	3522	8939	310	8572	7774
7	5782	6476	28	5266	9285	110	3283	50285	320	8339	9189
8	5758	6610	29	5242	9419	120	3044	1633	330	8105	80609
9	5733	6744	30	13.5217	0.0739552	130	2805	2982	340	12.7872	0.0782033
10	13.5708	0.0736877				140	13.2567	0.0754334	350	7638	3464
									360	7405	4900

SULFURIC ACID

Specific Gravity of Aqueous Sulfuric Acid Solutions

AT $\frac{20°}{4°}$ C.

Be.	Sp. gr.	Per cent H$_2$SO$_4$	G. per liter	Lbs. per cu. ft.	Lbs. per gal.	Be.	Sp. gr.	Per cent H$_2$SO$_4$	G. per liter	Lbs. per cu. ft.	Lbs. per gal.
0.7	1.0051	1	10.05	0.6275	0.0839	41.8	1.4049	51	716.5	44.73	5.979
1.7	1.0118	2	20.24	1.263	0.1689	42.5	1.4148	52	735.7	45.93	6.140
2.6	1.0184	3	30.55	1.907	0.2550	43.2	1.4248	53	755.1	47.14	6.302
3.5	1.0250	4	41.00	2.560	0.3422	44.0	1.4350	54	774.9	48.37	6.467
4.5	1.0317	5	51.59	3.220	0.4305	44.7	1.4453	55	794.9	49.62	6.634
5.4	1.0385	6	62.31	3.890	0.5200	45.4	1.4557	56	815.2	50.89	6.803
6.3	1.0453	7	73.17	4.568	0.6106	46.1	1.4662	57	835.7	52.17	6.974
7.2	1.0522	8	84.18	5.255	0.7025	46.8	1.4768	58	856.5	53.47	7.148
8.1	1.0591	9	95.32	5.950	0.7955	47.5	1.4875	59	877.6	54.79	7.324
9.0	1.0661	10	106.6	6.655	0.8897	48.2	1.4983	60	899.0	56.12	7.502
9.9	1.0731	11	118.0	7.369	0.9851	48.9	1.5091	61	920.6	57.47	7.682
10.8	1.0802	12	129.6	8.092	1.082	49.6	1.5200	62	942.4	58.83	7.865
11.7	1.0874	13	141.4	8.825	1.180	50.3	1.5310	63	964.5	60.21	8.049
12.5	1.0947	14	153.3	9.567	1.279	51.0	1.5421	64	986.9	61.61	8.236
13.4	1.1020	15	165.3	10.32	1.379	51.7	1.5533	65	1010	63.03	8.426
14.3	1.1094	16	177.5	11.08	1.481	52.3	1.5646	66	1033	64.46	8.618
15.2	1.1168	17	189.9	11.85	1.584	53.0	1.5760	67	1056	65.92	8.812
16.0	1.1243	18	202.4	12.63	1.689	53.7	1.5874	68	1079	67.39	9.008
16.9	1.1318	19	215.0	13.42	1.795	54.3	1.5989	69	1103	68.87	9.207
17.7	1.1394	20	227.9	14.23	1.902	55.0	1.6105	70	1127	70.38	9.408
18.6	1.1471	21	240.9	15.04	2.010	55.6	1.6221	71	1152	71.90	9.611
19.4	1.1548	22	254.1	15.86	2.120	56.3	1.6338	72	1176	73.44	9.817
20.3	1.1626	23	267.4	16.69	2.231	56.9	1.6456	73	1201	74.99	10.02
21.1	1.1704	24	280.9	17.54	2.344	57.5	1.6574	74	1226	76.57	10.24
21.9	1.1783	25	294.6	18.39	2.458	58.1	1.6692	75	1252	78.15	10.45
22.8	1.1862	26	308.4	19.25	2.574	58.7	1.6810	76	1278	79.75	10.66
23.6	1.1942	27	322.4	20.13	2.691	59.3	1.6927	77	1303	81.37	10.88
24.4	1.2023	28	336.6	21.02	2.809	59.9	1.7043	78	1329	82.99	11.09
25.2	1.2104	29	351.0	21.91	2.929	60.5	1.7158	79	1355	84.62	11.31
26.0	1.2185	30	365.6	22.82	3.051	61.1	1.7272	80	1382	86.26	11.53
26.8	1.2267	31	380.3	23.74	3.173	61.6	1.7380	81	1408	87.90	11.75
27.6	1.2349	32	395.2	24.67	3.298	62.1	1.7491	82	1434	89.54	11.97
28.4	1.2432	33	110.3	25.61	3.424	62.6	1.7594	83	1460	91.16	12.19
29.1	1.2515	34	425.5	26.56	3.551	63.0	1.7693	84	1486	92.78	12.40
29.9	1.2599	35	441.0	27.53	3.680	63.5	1.7786	85	1512	94.38	12.62
30.7	1.2684	36	456.6	28.51	3.811	63.9	1.7872	86	1537	95.95	12.83
31.4	1.2769	37	472.5	29.49	3.943	64.2	1.7951	87	1562	97.49	13.03
32.2	1.2855	38	488.5	30.49	4.077	64.5	1.8022	88	1586	99.01	13.23
33.0	1.2941	39	504.7	31.51	4.212	64.8	1.8087	89	1610	100.5	13.42
33.7	1.3028	40	521.1	32.53	4.349	65.1	1.8144	90	1633	101.9	13.63
34.5	1.3116	41	537.8	33.57	4.488	65.3	1.8195	91	1656	103.4	13.82
35.2	1.3205	42	554.6	34.62	4.628	65.5	1.8240	92	1678	104.8	14.00
35.9	1.3294	43	571.6	35.69	4.770	65.7	1.8279	93	1700	106.1	14.19
36.7	1.3384	44	588.9	36.76	4.914	65.8	1.8312	94	1721	107.5	14.36
37.4	1.3476	45	606.4	37.86	5.061	65.9	1.8337	95	1742	108.7	14.54
38.1	1.3569	46	624.2	38.97	5.209	66.0	1.8355	96	1762	110.0	14.70
38.9	1.3663	47	642.2	40.09	5.359	66.0	1.8364	97	1781	111.2	14.87
39.6	1.3758	48	660.4	41.23	5.511	66.0	1.8361	98	1799	112.3	15.02
40.3	1.3854	49	678.8	42.38	5.665	65.9	1.8342	99	1816	113.4	15.15
41.1	1.3951	50	697.6	43.55	5.821	65.8	1.8305	100	1831	114.3	15.28

DENSITY AND COMPOSITION OF FUMING SULFURIC ACID

Actual H₂SO₄, %	Specific gravity	Equiv. H₂SO₄, %	Weight, lb./cu. ft.	Weight, lb. per U.S. gal.	Comb. H₂O, %	Free SO₃, %	Total SO₃, %	SO₃, lb./cu. ft.
100	1.839	100.00	114.70	15.33	18.37	0	81.63	93.63
99	1.845	100.22	115.07	15.38	18.19	1	81.81	94.14
98	1.851	100.45	115.33	15.41	18.00	2	82.00	94.57
97	1.855	100.67	115.70	15.46	17.82	3	82.18	95.08
96	1.858	100.89	115.88	15.49	17.64	4	82.36	95.44
95	1.862	101.13	116.13	15.52	17.45	5	82.55	95.87
94	1.865	101.35	116.32	15.55	17.27	6	82.73	96.23
93	1.869	101.58	116.57	15.58	17.08	7	82.92	96.66
92	1.873	101.80	116.82	15.61	16.90	8	83.10	97.12
91	1.877	102.02	117.07	15.64	16.72	9	83.28	97.50
90	1.880	102.25	117.26	15.67	16.57	10	83.47	97.88
89	1.884	102.47	117.51	15.70	16.35	11	83.65	98.30
88	1.887	102.71	117.69	15.73	16.17	12	83.83	98.66
87	1.891	102.92	117.94	15.76	15.98	13	84.02	99.09
86	1.895	103.15	118.19	15.79	15.80	14	84.20	99.52
85	1.899	103.38	118.44	15.82	15.61	15	84.39	99.95
84	1.902	103.60	118.63	15.86	15.43	16	84.57	100.33
83	1.905	103.82	118.81	15.89	15.25	17	84.75	100.69
82	1.909	104.05	119.06	15.92	15.06	18	84.94	101.13
81	1.911	104.28	119.28	15.95	14.88	19	85.12	101.45
80	1.915	104.50	119.50	15.98	14.70	20	85.30	101.93
79	1.920	104.73	119.75	16.01	14.51	21	85.49	102.37
78	1.923	104.95	119.94	16.04	14.33	22	85.67	102.75
77	1.927	105.18	120.19	16.07	14.14	23	85.86	103.20
76	1.931	105.40	120.44	16.10	13.96	24	86.04	103.63
75	1.934	105.62	120.62	16.12	13.78	25	86.22	104.00
74	1.939	105.85	120.94	16.16	13.59	26	86.41	104.50
73	1.943	106.08	121.18	16.19	13.41	27	86.59	104.93
72	1.946	106.29	121.37	16.22	13.28	28	86.72	105.31
71	1.949	106.53	121.56	16.25	13.04	29	86.96	105.71
70	1.952	106.75	121.75	16.28	12.86	30	87.14	106.09
69	1.955	106.97	121.93	16.30	12.68	31	87.32	106.47
68	1.958	107.20	122.12	16.33	12.49	32	87.51	106.87
67	1.961	107.42	122.31	16.35	12.31	33	87.69	107.25
66	1.965	107.65	122.56	16.38	12.12	34	87.88	107.71
65	1.968	107.87	122.74	16.40	11.94	35	88.06	108.08
64	1.972	108.10	122.99	16.43	11.76	36	88.24	108.53
63	1.976	108.33	123.24	16.46	11.57	37	88.43	108.98
62	1.979	108.55	123.43	16.50	11.39	38	88.61	109.37
61	1.981	108.77	123.55	16.52	11.21	39	88.79	109.70
60	1.983	109.00	123.74	16.54	11.02	40	88.98	110.10
59	1.985	109.22	123.80	16.55	10.84	41	89.16	110.38
58	1.987	109.45	123.93	16.56	10.65	42	89.35	110.83
57	1.989	109.68	124.05	16.58	10.47	43	89.53	111.06
56	1.991	109.90	124.18	16.60	10.29	44	89.71	111.40
55	1.993	110.13	124.30	16.62	10.10	45	89.90	111.75
50	2.001	111.25	124.80	16.68	9.18	50	90.72	113.34
40	2.102	113.50	131.10	17.53	7.35	60	92.65	121.46
30	1.982	115.75	123.62	16.50	5.51	70	94.49	116.81
20	1.949	118.00	121.56	16.25	3.67	80	96.33	117.10
10	1.911	120.25	119.19	15.92	1.84	90	98.16	117.00
0	1.857	122.50	115.83	15.50	0.00	100	100.00	115.83

* By permission from the 7th edition of Chemical Plant Control Data, Chemical Construction Corporation (1957).

DENSITY OF MOIST AIR

The density of dry air may be determined by computation from the general relation $D = D_0(T_0/T)(P/P_0)$ where D_0 represents a known density at absolute temperature T_0 and pressure P_0 and D, the density at absolute temperature T and pressure P.

The density of **moist** air may be determined by a similar relation:
$D = 1.2929\ (273.13/T)\ [(B - 0.3783e)/760]$ where T is the absolute temperature; B, the barometric pressure in mm, and e the vapor pressure of the moisture in the air in mm. The density will then be the product of two terms, each of which may be found by use of the tables which follow.

The **first factor**, $1.2929\ (273.13/T)$, may be found directly in Table I for various temperatures. For convenience, temperatures are given in the table in °C although the values of the factor have been computed with absolute temperatures. The tabular values actually represent the density of dry air at various temperatures and 760 mm pressure.

The **second factor**, $[(B - 0.3783e)/760]$, must be obtained in two steps: First—the numerator of the expression is obtained by subtracting $0.3783e$ from the barometric pressure. The quantity $0.3783e$ may be found directly from the dew point in Table II. If the wet and dry bulb thermometer readings are known e may be found in the table Reduction of Psychrometric Observations given in the section Hygrometric and Barometric Tables. $0.3783e$ may then be found by calculation or read from the table. Second—the value of the whole factor for any value of $B - 0.3783e$ may be obtained from Table III.

The product of the above two factors will give the required density in **g/l**.

To facilitate obtaining **approximate values** of the density for ordinary pressures and temperatures, a table of products is given which may be entered with the temperature in °C and the corrected (for moisture) value of the barometric pressure in mm to obtain density.

As an illustration of the use of the tables, let it be desired to find the density of air for a barometric pressure of 750 mm, a dew point of 10° C, and air temperature of 20° C.

From the dew point, the value of $0.3783e$ is found in Table II to be 3.48 mm. $750 - 3.48 = 746.52$, the corrected pressure. The pressure factor for this value found in Table III by interpolation is 0.98226. The temperature factor from Table I is 1.2047.

$$1.2047 \times 0.98224 = 1.1833\ \text{g/l}.$$

To obtain the value directly from Table IV, enter it for 20° C and 746.5 mm which gives by interpolation 1.183 g/l.

TABLE I

$(1.2929 \times 273.13/T)$

(Besides being a necessary part of the determination of the density of moist air, the values in this table are actually the density of dry air in g/l at 760 mm pressure for various temperatures.)

Temp. °C	0	1	2	3	4	5	6	7	8	9
−50	1.5 826	897	969	*042	*115	*189	*264	*339	*415	*491
−40	1.5 147	213	278	345	412	479	547	616	686	756
−30	1.4 524	584	645	706	767	829	892	955	*019	*083
−20	1.3 951	*006	*062	*118	*175	*232	*289	*347	*406	*465
−10	1.3 420	472	523	575	628	680	734	787	841	896
− 0	1.2 929	977	*024	*073	*121	*170	*219	*269	*319	*370
+ 0	1.2 929	882	835	789	742	697	651	606	561	517
10	1.2 472	428	385	342	299	256	214	171	130	088
20	1.2 047	*006	*965	*925	*885	*845	*805	*766	*727	*688
30	1.1 649	611	573	535	498	460	423	387	350	314
40	1.1 277	242	206	170	135	100	065	031	*006	*962
50	1.0 928	895	861	828	795	702	729	697	664	632
60	1.0 600	569	537	506	475	444	413	382	352	322

TABLE II

Vapor Pressure—Value of $0.3783e$

Dew point °C	Vap. press. e mm (ice)	0.3783e	Dew point °C	Vap. press. e mm (water)	0.3783e	Dew point °C	Vap. press. e mm (water)	0.3783e	Dew point °C	Vap. press. e mm (ice)	0.3783e	Dew point °C	Vap. press. e mm (water)	0.3783e	Dew point °C	Vap. press. e mm (water)	0.3783e
−50	0.029	0.01	−15	1.252	0.47	0	4.58	1.73	15	12.79	4.84	30	31.86	12.05	45	71.97	27.23
−45	.054	.02	−14	1.373	.52	1	4.92	1.86	16	13.64	5.16	31	33.74	12.76	46	75.75	28.66
−40	.096	.04	−13	1.503	.57	2	5.29	2.00	17	14.54	5.50	32	35.70	13.51	47	79.70	30.15
−35	.169	.06	−12	1.644	.62	3	5.68	2.15	18	15.49	5.86	33	37.78	14.29	48	83.83	31.71
−30	.288	.11	−11	1.798	.68	4	6.10	2.31	19	16.49	6.24	34	39.95	15.11	49	88.14	33.34
−25	0.480	0.18	−10	1.964	0.74	5	6.54	2.47	20	17.55	6.64	35	42.23	15.98	50	92.6	35.03
−24	.530	.20	− 9	2.144	.81	6	7.01	2.65	21	18.66	7.06	36	44.62	16.88	51	97.3	36.81
−23	.585	.22	− 8	2.340	.89	7	7.51	2.84	22	19.84	7.51	37	47.13	17.83	52	102.2	38.66
−22	.646	.24	− 7	2.550	.96	8	8.04	3.04	23	21.09	7.98	38	49.76	18.82	53	107.3	40.59
−21	.712	.27	− 6	2.778	1.05	9	8.61	3.26	24	22.40	8.47	39	52.51	19.86	54	112.7	42.63
−20	0.783	0.30	− 5	3.025	1.14	10	9.21	3.48	25	23.78	9.00	40	55.40	20.96	55	118.2	44.72
−19	.862	.33	− 4	3.291	1.24	11	9.85	3.73	26	25.24	9.55	41	58.42	22.10	56	124.0	46.91
−18	.947	.36	− 3	3.578	1.35	12	10.52	3.98	27	26.77	10.13	42	61.58	23.30	57	130.0	49.18
−17	1.041	.39	− 2	3.887	1.47	13	11.24	4.25	28	28.38	10.74	43	64.89	24.55	58	136.3	51.56
−16	1.142	.43	− 1	4.220	1.60	14	11.99	4.54	29	30.08	11.38	44	68.35	25.86	59	142.8	54.02
														60	149.6	56.59

TABLE III

Pressure Factor.—$[(B - 0.3783e)/760]$

The figures in the body of the table give values of the whole term $(B - 0.3783e)/760$ for various values of the numerator $(B - 0.3783e)$ expressed at the left and top.

Press. mm corr.	0	1	2	3	4	5	6	7	8	9	Press. mm corr.	0	1	2	3	4	5	6	7	8	9
80	.10526	.10658	.10789	.10921	.11053	.11184	.11316	.11447	.11579	.11711	...	.....	.....	.....	.....	.....	.....	.....	.....	.....	.....
90	.11842	.11974	.12105	.12237	.12368	.12500	.12632	.12763	.12895	.13026	...	.....	.....	.....	.....	.....	.....	.....	.....	.....	.....
100	.13158	.13289	.13421	.13553	.13684	.13816	.13947	.14079	.14211	.14342	200	.26316	.26447	.26579	.26711	.26842	.26974	.27105	.27237	.27368	.27500
110	.14474	.14605	.14737	.14868	.15000	.15132	.15263	.15395	.15526	.15658	210	.27632	.27763	.27895	.28026	.28158	.28289	.28421	.28553	.28684	.28816
120	.15789	.15921	.16053	.16184	.16316	.16447	.16579	.16711	.16842	.16974	220	.28947	.29079	.29211	.29342	.29474	.29605	.29737	.29868	.30000	.30132
130	.17105	.17237	.17368	.17500	.17632	.17763	.17895	.18026	.18158	.18289	230	.30263	.30395	.30526	.30658	.30789	.30921	.31053	.31184	.31316	.31447
140	.18421	.18553	.18684	.18816	.18947	.19079	.19211	.19342	.19474	.19605	240	.31579	.31711	.31842	.31974	.32105	.32237	.32368	.32500	.32632	.32763
150	.19737	.19868	.20000	.20132	.20263	.20395	.20526	.20658	.20789	.20921	250	.32895	.33026	.33158	.33289	.33421	.33553	.33684	.33816	.33947	.34079
160	.21053	.21184	.21316	.21447	.21579	.21711	.21842	.21974	.22105	.22237	260	.34211	.34342	.34474	.34605	.34737	.34868	.35000	.35132	.35263	.35395
170	.22368	.22500	.22632	.22763	.22895	.23026	.23158	.23289	.23421	.23553	270	.35526	.35658	.35789	.35921	.36053	.36184	.36316	.36447	.36579	.36711
180	.23684	.23816	.23947	.24079	.24211	.24342	.24474	.24605	.24737	.24868	280	.36842	.36974	.37105	.37237	.37368	.37500	.37632	.37763	.37895	.38026
190	.25000	.25132	.25263	.25395	.25526	.25658	.25789	.25921	.26053	.26184	290	.38158	.38289	.38421	.38553	.38684	.38816	.38947	.39079	.39211	.39342

TABLE III (Continued)

Press. mm corr.	0	1	2	3	4	5	6	7	8	9
300	.39474	.39605	.39737	.39868	.40000	.40132	.40263	.40395	.40526	.40658
310	.40789	.40921	.41053	.41184	.41316	.41447	.41579	.41711	.41842	.41974
320	.42105	.42237	.42368	.42500	.42632	.42763	.42895	.43026	.43158	.43289
330	.43421	.43553	.43684	.43816	.43947	.44079	.44211	.44342	.44474	.44605
340	.44737	.44868	.45000	.45132	.45263	.45395	.45526	.45658	.45789	.45921
350	.46053	.46184	.46316	.46447	.46579	.46711	.46842	.46974	.47105	.47237
360	.47368	.47500	.47632	.47763	.47895	.48026	.48158	.48289	.48421	.48553
370	.48684	.48816	.48947	.49079	.49211	.49342	.49474	.49605	.49737	.49868
380	.50000	.50132	.50263	.50395	.50526	.50658	.50789	.50921	.51053	.51184
390	.51316	.51447	.51579	.51711	.51842	.51974	.52105	.52237	.52368	.52500
400	.52632	.52763	.52895	.53026	.53158	.53289	.53421	.53553	.53684	.53816
410	.53947	.54079	.54211	.54342	.54474	.54605	.54737	.54868	.55000	.55132
420	.55263	.55395	.55526	.55658	.55789	.55921	.56053	.56184	.56316	.56447
430	.56579	.56711	.56842	.56974	.57105	.57237	.57368	.57500	.57632	.57763
440	.57895	.58026	.58158	.58289	.58421	.58553	.58684	.58816	.58947	.59079
450	.59211	.59342	.59474	.59605	.59737	.59868	.60000	.60132	.60263	.60395
460	.60526	.60658	.60789	.60921	.61053	.61184	.61316	.61447	.61579	.61711
470	.61842	.61974	.62105	.62237	.62368	.62500	.62632	.62763	.62895	.63026
480	.63158	.63289	.63421	.63553	.63684	.63816	.63947	.64079	.64211	.64342
490	.64474	.64605	.64737	.64868	.65000	.65132	.65263	.65395	.65526	.65658
500	.65790	.65921	.66053	.66184	.66316	.66447	.66579	.66711	.66842	.66974
510	.67105	.67237	.67368	.67500	.67632	.67763	.67895	.68026	.68158	.68290
520	.68421	.68553	.68684	.68816	.68947	.69079	.69211	.69342	.69474	.69605
530	.69737	.69868	.70000	.70132	.70263	.70395	.70526	.70658	.70790	.70921
540	.71053	.71184	.71316	.71447	.71579	.71711	.71842	.71974	.72105	.72237
550	.72368	.72500	.72632	.72763	.72895	.73026	.73158	.73290	.73421	.73553
560	.73684	.73816	.73947	.74079	.74211	.74342	.74474	.74605	.74737	.74868
570	.75000	.75132	.75263	.75395	.75526	.75658	.75790	.75921	.76053	.76184
580	.76316	.76447	.76579	.76711	.76842	.76974	.77105	.77237	.77368	.77500
590	.77632	.77763	.77895	.78026	.78158	.78290	.78421	.78553	.78684	.78816
600	.78947	.79079	.79211	.79342	.79474	.79605	.79737	.79868	.80000	.80132
610	.80263	.80395	.80526	.80658	.80790	.80921	.81053	.81184	.81316	.81447
620	.81579	.81711	.81842	.81974	.82105	.82237	.82368	.82500	.82632	.82763
630	.82895	.83026	.83158	.83290	.83421	.83553	.83684	.83816	.83947	.84079
640	.84211	.84342	.84474	.84605	.84737	.84868	.85000	.85132	.85263	.85395
650	.85526	.85658	.85790	.85921	.86053	.86184	.86316	.86447	.86579	.86711
660	.86842	.86974	.87105	.87237	.87368	.87500	.87632	.87763	.87895	.88026
670	.88158	.88290	.88421	.88553	.88684	.88816	.88947	.89079	.89211	.89342
680	.89474	.89605	.89737	.89868	.90000	.90132	.90263	.90395	.90526	.90658
690	.90790	.90921	.91053	.91184	.91316	.91447	.91579	.91711	.91842	.91974
700	.92105	.92237	.92368	.92500	.92632	.92763	.92895	.93026	.93158	.93290
710	.93421	.93553	.93684	.93816	.93947	.94079	.94211	.94342	.94474	.94605
720	.94737	.94868	.95000	.95132	.95263	.95395	.95526	.95658	.95790	.95921
730	.96053	.96184	.96316	.96447	.96579	.96711	.96842	.96974	.97105	.97237
740	.97368	.97500	.97632	.97763	.97895	.98026	.98158	.98290	.98421	.98553
750	.98684	.98816	.98947	.99079	.99211	.99342	.99474	.99605	.99737	.99868
760	1.0000	1.0013	1.0026	1.0039	1.0053	1.0066	1.0079	1.0092	1.0105	1.0118
770	1.0132	1.0145	1.0158	1.0171	1.0184	1.0197	1.0211	1.0224	1.0237	1.0250
780	1.0263	1.0276	1.0289	1.0303	1.0316	1.0329	1.0342	1.0355	1.0368	1.0382
790	1.0395	1.0408	1.0421	1.0434	1.0447	1.0461	1.0474	1.0487	1.0500	1.0513

TABLE IV

Density of Moist Air
Values in the body of the table give the density of moist air in g/l for a limited range of temperatures and corrected pressure values $(B - 0.3783e)$. The latter may be obtained by use of Table II.

°C	600	610	620	630	640	650	660	670	680	690	700	710	720	730	740	750	760	770	780	790
5	1.0024	1.0191	1.0358	1.0525	1.0692	1.0859	1.1026	1.1193	1.1361	1.1528	1.1695	1.1862	1.2029	1.2196	1.2363	1.2530	1.2697	1.2864	1.3031	1.3198
6	.99876	1.0154	1.0321	1.0487	1.0654	1.0820	1.0986	1.1153	1.1319	1.1486	1.1652	1.1819	1.1985	1.2152	1.2318	1.2485	1.2651	1.2817	1.2984	1.3150
7	.99521	1.0118	1.0284	1.0450	1.0616	1.0781	1.0947	1.1113	1.1279	1.1445	1.1611	1.1777	1.1943	1.2108	1.2274	1.2440	1.2606	1.2772	1.2938	1.3104
8	.99165	1.0082	1.0247	1.0412	1.0578	1.0743	1.0908	1.1074	1.1239	1.1404	1.1569	1.1735	1.1900	1.2065	1.2230	1.2396	1.2561	1.2726	1.2892	1.3057
9	.98818	1.0047	1.0211	1.0376	1.0541	1.0705	1.0870	1.1035	1.1199	1.1364	1.1529	1.1694	1.1858	1.2023	1.2188	1.2352	1.2517	1.2682	1.2846	1.3011
10	.98463	1.0010	1.0175	1.0339	1.0503	1.0667	1.0831	1.0995	1.1159	1.1323	1.1487	1.1651	1.1816	1.1980	1.2144	1.2308	1.2472	1.2636	1.2800	1.2964
11	.98115	.99751	1.0139	1.0302	1.0466	1.0629	1.0793	1.0956	1.1120	1.1283	1.1447	1.1610	1.1774	1.1937	1.2101	1.2264	1.2428	1.2592	1.2755	1.2919
12	.97776	.99406	1.0104	1.0267	1.0430	1.0592	1.0755	1.0918	1.1081	1.1244	1.1407	1.1570	1.1733	1.1896	1.2059	1.2222	1.2385	1.2548	1.2711	1.2874
13	.97436	.99061	1.0068	1.0231	1.0393	1.0556	1.0718	1.0880	1.1043	1.1205	1.1368	1.1530	1.1692	1.1855	1.2017	1.2180	1.2342	1.2504	1.2667	1.2829
14	.97097	.98715	1.0033	1.0195	1.0357	1.0519	1.0681	1.0843	1.1004	1.1166	1.1328	1.1490	1.1652	1.1814	1.1975	1.2137	1.2299	1.2461	1.2623	1.2784
15	.96757	.98370	.99983	1.0160	1.0321	1.0482	1.0643	1.0805	1.0966	1.1127	1.1288	1.1450	1.1611	1.1772	1.1933	1.2095	1.2256	1.2417	1.2579	1.2740
16	.96426	.98033	.99641	1.0125	1.0286	1.0446	1.0607	1.0768	1.0928	1.1089	1.1250	1.1410	1.1571	1.1732	1.1893	1.2053	1.2214	1.2375	1.2535	1.2696
17	.96086	.97688	.99290	1.0089	1.0249	1.0409	1.0570	1.0730	1.0890	1.1050	1.1210	1.1370	1.1530	1.1691	1.1851	1.2011	1.2171	1.2331	1.2491	1.2651
18	.95763	.97359	.98955	1.0055	1.0215	1.0374	1.0534	1.0694	1.0853	1.1013	1.1172	1.1332	1.1492	1.1651	1.1811	1.1970	1.2130	1.2290	1.2449	1.2609
19	.95431	.97022	.98613	1.0020	1.0179	1.0338	1.0497	1.0656	1.0816	1.0975	1.1134	1.1293	1.1452	1.1611	1.1770	1.1929	1.2088	1.2247	1.2406	1.2565
20	.95107	.96693	.98278	.99864	1.0145	1.0303	1.0462	1.0620	1.0779	1.0937	1.1096	1.1254	1.1413	1.1572	1.1730	1.1888	1.2047	1.2206	1.2364	1.2522
21	.94784	.96364	.97944	.99524	1.0110	1.0294	1.0426	1.0584	1.0742	1.0900	1.1058	1.1216	1.1374	1.1532	1.1690	1.1848	1.2006	1.2164	1.2322	1.2480
22	.94460	.96035	.97609	.99184	1.0076	1.0233	1.0391	1.0548	1.0706	1.0863	1.1020	1.1178	1.1335	1.1493	1.1650	1.1808	1.1965	1.2122	1.2280	1.2437
23	.94144	.95714	.97283	.98852	1.0042	1.0199	1.0356	1.0513	1.0670	1.0827	1.0984	1.1140	1.1297	1.1454	1.1611	1.1768	1.1925	1.2082	1.2239	1.2396
24	.93829	.95393	.96957	.98521	1.0008	1.0165	1.0321	1.0478	1.0634	1.0790	1.0947	1.1103	1.1259	1.1416	1.1572	1.1729	1.1885	1.2041	1.2198	1.2354
25	.93513	.95072	.96630	.98189	.99748	1.0131	1.0286	1.0442	1.0598	1.0754	1.0910	1.1066	1.1222	1.1377	1.1533	1.1689	1.1845	1.2001	1.2157	1.2313
26	.93197	.94750	.96304	.97858	.99411	1.0096	1.0252	1.0407	1.0562	1.0718	1.0873	1.1028	1.1184	1.1339	1.1494	1.1650	1.1805	1.1960	1.2116	1.2271
27	.92889	.94437	.95986	.97534	.99083	1.0063	1.0218	1.0373	1.0528	1.0682	1.0837	1.0992	1.1147	1.1302	1.1456	1.1611	1.1766	1.1921	1.2076	1.2230
28	.92581	.94124	.95668	.97211	.98754	1.0030	1.0184	1.0338	1.0493	1.0647	1.0801	1.0955	1.1110	1.1264	1.1418	1.1573	1.1727	1.1881	1.2036	1.2190
29	.92273	.93811	.95350	.96888	.98426	.99963	1.0150	1.0304	1.0458	1.0612	1.0765	1.0919	1.1073	1.1227	1.1380	1.1534	1.1688	1.1842	1.1996	1.2149
30	.91965	.93498	.95031	.96564	.98097	.99629	1.0116	1.0270	1.0423	1.0576	1.0729	1.0883	1.1036	1.1189	1.1342	1.1496	1.1649	1.1802	1.1956	1.2109
31	.91665	.93193	.94721	.96249	.97777	.99304	1.0083	1.0236	1.0389	1.0542	1.0694	1.0847	1.1000	1.1153	1.1305	1.1458	1.1611	1.1764	1.1917	1.2069
32	.91365	.92888	.94411	.95934	.97457	.98979	1.0050	1.0203	1.0355	1.0507	1.0659	1.0812	1.0964	1.1116	1.1268	1.1421	1.1573	1.1725	1.1878	1.2030
33	.91065	.92583	.94101	.95619	.97137	.98651	1.0017	1.0169	1.0321	1.0473	1.0624	1.0776	1.0928	1.1080	1.1231	1.1383	1.1535	1.1687	1.1839	1.1990
34	.90773	.92286	.93800	.95313	.96826	.98338	.99851	1.0136	1.0288	1.0439	1.0590	1.0742	1.0893	1.1044	1.1195	1.1347	1.1498	1.1649	1.1801	1.1952
35	.90473	.91981	.93490	.94998	.96506	.98013	.99521	1.0103	1.0254	1.0405	1.0555	1.0706	1.0857	1.1008	1.1158	1.1309	1.1460	1.1611	1.1762	1.1912

DENSITY OF DRY AIR

At the Temperature t, and under the Pressure H cm of Mercury the Density of Air

$$= \frac{0.001293}{1+0.00367\,t}\,\frac{H}{76}.$$

Units of this table are grams per milliliter
(From Miller's Laboratory Physics, Ginn & Co., publishers, by permission.)

t	Pressure H in Centimeters						Proportional Parts	
	72.0	73.0	74.0	75.0	76.0	77.0		
°								17
10	0.001182	0.001198	0.001215	0.001231	0.001247	0.001264	cm	
11	178	193	210	227	243	259	0.1	2
12	173	190	206	222	239	255	0.2	3
13	169	186	202	218	234	251	0.3	5
14	165	181	198	214	230	246	0.4	7
							0.5	8
							0.6	10
							0.7	12
15	0.001161	0.001177	0.001193	0.001210	0.001226	0.001242	0.8	14
16	157	173	189	205	221	238	0.9	15
17	153	169	185	201	217	233		16
18	149	165	181	197	213	229	cm	
19	145	161	177	193	209	225	0.1	2
							0.2	3
							0.3	5
							0.4	6
20	0.001141	0.001157	0.001173	0.001189	0.001205	0.001221	0.5	8
21	137	153	169	185	201	216	0.6	10
22	134	149	165	181	197	212	0.7	11
23	130	145	161	177	193	208	0.8	13
24	126	142	157	173	189	204	0.9	14
								15
25	0.001122	0.001138	0.001153	0.001169	0.001185	0.001200	cm	
26	118	134	149	165	181	196	0.1	1
27	115	130	146	161	177	192	0.2	3
28	111	126	142	157	173	188	0.3	4
29	107	123	138	153	169	184	0.4	6
							0.5	7
							0.6	9
							0.7	10
							0.8	12
30	0.001104	0.001119	0.001134	0.001150	0.001165	0.001180	0.9	13

DENSITY OF WATER

The temperature of maximum density for pure water, free from air = 3.98C (277.13K)

t, °C	d, gm/ml	t, °C	d, gm/ml
0	0.99987	40	0.99224
3.98	1.00000	45	0.99025
5	0.99999	50	0.98807
10	0.99973	55	0.98573
15	0.99913	60	0.98324
18	0.99862	65	0.98059
20	0.99823	70	0.97781
25	0.99707	75	0.97489
30	0.99567	80	0.97183
35	0.99406	85	0.96865
38	0.99299	90	0.96534
		95	0.96192
		100	0.95838

THERMODYNAMIC AND TRANSPORT PROPERTIES OF AIR

From NASA Technical Note D-7488 by David J. Poferl and Roger Svehla (1973). The following three tables list the thermodynamic and transport properties of air over the temperature range of 300-2800K at pressures of 20, 30, and 40 atm. Factors for converting viscosity, specific heat at constant pressure, thermal conductivity, and enthalpy from cgs units to SI and English units are

Viscosity:

$$1 \frac{g}{(cm)(sec)} = 0.1 \frac{(N)(sec)}{m^2}$$

$$= 6.72 \times 10^{-2} \frac{lbm}{(ft)(sec)}$$

$$= 241.9 \frac{lbm}{(ft)(hr)}$$

$$= 2.089 \times 10^{-3} \frac{(lbf)(sec)}{ft^2}$$

Thermal conductivity:

$$1 \frac{cal}{(cm)(sec)(K)} = 418.4 \frac{W}{(m)(K)}$$

$$= 0.8064 \frac{Btu}{(ft)^2(sec)(^\circ F/in.)}$$

$$= 6.72 \times 10^{-2} \frac{Btu}{(ft^2)(sec)(^\circ F/ft)}$$

$$= 241.9 \frac{Btu}{(ft)^2(hr)(^\circ F/ft)}$$

Specific heat at constant pressure:

$$1 \frac{cal}{(g)(K)} = 4.184 \frac{J}{(g)(K)}$$

$$= 1 \frac{Btu}{(lbm)(^\circ F)}$$

Enthalpy:

$$1 \frac{cal}{g} = 4.184 \frac{J}{g}$$

$$= 1.8 \frac{Btu}{lbm}$$

THERMODYNAMIC AND TRANSPORT PROPERTIES OF AIR *(Continued)*

PROPERTIES AT 20 ATM

Temperature, T, K	Isentropic exponent, γ	Molecular weight, m	Viscosity, μ g/(cm)(sec)	Specific heat at constant pressure, c_p, cal/(g)(K)	Thermal conductivity, k, cal/(cm)(sec)(K)	Prandtl number, Pr	Enthalpy, h, cal/g
2800	1.2309	28.890	821×10^{-6}	0.3850	473×10^{-6}	0.669	747.0
2700	1.2374	28.915	800	.3707	439	.676	709.2
2600	1.2437	28.933	779	.3588	409	.683	672.7
2500	1.2498	28.945	758	.3488	384	.688	637.4
2400	1.2556	28.953	736	.3404	362	.692	602.9
2300	1.2612	28.958	715	.3332	343	.696	569.3
2200	1.2666	28.961	694	.3270	325	.698	536.2
2100	1.2719	28.963	672	.3214	309	.699	503.8
2000	1.2772	28.964	651	.3163	294	.700	471.9
1900	1.2825	28.965	629	.3115	280	.701	440.6
1800	1.2879		607	.3070	266	.702	409.6
1700	1.2933		585	.3025	252	.702	379.2
1600	1.2989		563	.2981	239	.703	349.1
1500	1.3045		540	.2939	226	.703	319.5
1400	1.3103		517	.2897	213	.704	290.3
1300	1.3162		494	.2855	200	.704	261.6
1200	1.3224		470	.2814	188	.705	233.2
1100	1.3288		445	.2773	175	.705	205.3
1000	1.3356		419	.2730	162	.705	177.8
900	1.3439	28.964	391	.2681	148	.706	150.7
800	1.3537		362	.2626	135		124.2
700	1.3646		331	.2568	121		98.2
600	1.3759		299	.2511	106		72.8
500	1.3865		265	.2461	92		48.0
400	1.3951		227	.2422	78		23.6
300	1.4000		184	.2401	63		−.5

PROPERTIES AT 30 ATM

Temperature, T, K	Isentropic exponent, γ	Molecular weight, m	Viscosity, μ, g/(cm)(sec)	Specific heat at constant pressure, c_p, cal/(g)(K)	Thermal conductivity, k, cal/(cm)(sec)(K)	Prandtl number, Pr	Enthalpy, h, cal/g
2800	1.2340	28.904	821×10^{-6}	0.3773	460×10^{-6}	0.674	745.0
2700	1.2399	28.924	800	.3652	430	.680	707.9
2600	1.2456	28.939	779	.3548	403	.686	671.9
2500	1.2512	28.949	758	.3462	380	.690	636.8
2400	1.2566	28.956	736	.3387	359	.694	602.6
2300	1.2619	28.960	715	.3321	341	.696	569.1
2200	1.2671	28.962	694	.3263	324	.698	536.1
2100	1.2722	28.964	672	.3211	309	.699	503.8
2000	1.2773	28.965	651	.3161	294	.700	471.9
1900	1.2826		629	.3115	280	.701	440.5
1800	1.2879		607	.3069	266	.702	409.6
1700	1.2933		585	.3025	252	.702	379.2
1600	1.2988		563	.2981	239	.703	349.1
1500	1.3045		540	.2939	226	.703	319.5
1400	1.3103		517	.2897	213	.704	290.3
1300	1.3162		494	.2855	200	.704	261.6
1200	1.3223		470	.2814	188	.705	233.2
1100	1.3288		445	.2773	175	.705	205.3
1000	1.3356		419	.2730	162	.705	177.8
900	1.3439	28.964	391	.2681	148	.706	150.7
800	1.3537		362	.2626	135		124.2
700	1.3646		331	.2568	121		98.2
600	1.3759		299	.2511	106		72.8
500	1.3865		265	.2461	92		48.0
400	1.3951		227	.2422	78		23.6
300	1.4000		184	.2401	63		−.5

THERMODYNAMIC AND TRANSPORT PROPERTIES OF AIR *(Continued)*

PROPERTIES AT 40 ATM

Temperature, T, K	Isentropic exponent, γ	Molecular weight, m	Viscosity, μ, g/(cm)(sec)	Specific heat at constant pressure, c_p, cal/(g)(K)	Thermal conductivity, k, cal/(cm)(sec)(K)	Prandtl number, Pr	Enthalpy, h, cal/g
2800	1.2360	28.913	821 x 10⁻⁶	0.3727	452 x 10⁻⁶	0.677	743.8
2700	1.2414	28.930	800	.3619	424	.683	707.1
2600	1.2468	28.943	779	.3526	399	.688	671.4
2500	1.2521	28.951	758	.3446	377	.692	636.5
2400	1.2573	28.957	736	.3376	358	.695	602.4
2300	1.2623	28.961	715	.3315	340	.697	569.0
2200	1.2673	28.963	694	.3260	324	.699	536.1
2100	1.2724	28.964	672	.3209	308	.700	503.8
2000	1.2774	28.965	651	.3160	294	.700	471.9
1900	1.2826		629	.3114	279	.701	440.5
1800	1.2879		607	.3069	266	.702	409.6
1700	1.2933		585	.3025	252	.702	379.2
1600	1.2988		563	.2981	239	.703	349.1
1500	1.3045		540	.2939	226	.703	319.5
1400	1.3103		517	.2897	213	.704	290.4
1300	1.3162		494	.2855	200	.704	261.6
1200	1.3223		470	.2814	188	.705	233.2
1100	1.3288		445	.2773	175	.705	205.3
1000	1.3356		419	.2730	162	.705	177.8
900	1.3439		391	.2681	148	.706	150.7
800	1.3537	28.964	362	.2626	135		124.2
700	1.3646		331	.2568	121		98.2
600	1.3759		299	.2511	106		72.8
500	1.3865		265	.2461	92		48.0
400	1.3951		227	.2422	78		23.6
300	1.4000		184	.2401	63		−.5

ISOTHERMAL COMPRESSIBILITY OF LIQUIDS

Compiled by John C. McGowan

The figures in this table are for isothermal compressibilities in c.g.s. units. The compiler suggests, that provided the pressure is not too high, the reciprocal of the isothermal compressibility varies linearly with the pressure. This suggestion also appears in papers by J. R. Macdonald, Reviews of Modern Physics **38**, 669, (1966) and O. L. Anderson, J. Phys. Chem. Solids **27**, 547, (1966). The papers vary somewhat as to how far this linearity persists.

Liquid	Temp. °C*	Isothermal Compressibility x 10^{10} m^2N^{-1} at 1 atm (or 1.013 x 10^5 Nm^2)	at 1000 atm (or 1.013 x 10^8 Nm^2)	Ref.
Acetic Acid	15	8.75	....	1
	20	9.08	....	1
	30	9.72	....	1
	40	10.37	....	1
	50	11.11	....	1
	60	11.91	....	1
	70	12.77	....	1
	80	13.68	....	1
Acetic acid, ethyl ester	0	9.78	....	1
	10	10.36	....	1
	20	11.32	....	1
	30	12.37	....	1
	40	13.52	....	1
	50	14.78	....	1
	60	16.21	....	1
	70	17.90	....	1
Acetone	20	12.75	....	3
	20	12.29	....	10
	25	12.39	6.02	4
	30	13.34	....	10
	40	15.61	....	3
	40	14.64	....	10
	50	16.03	....	10
Aniline	0	4.08	....	1
	10	4.30	....	1
	20	4.53	....	1
	25	4.67	3.23	5
	40	5.04	....	1
	45	5.22	3.48	5
	50	5.33	....	1
	60	5.64	....	1
	65	5.84	3.76	5
	70	5.97	....	1
	80	6.32	....	1
	85	6.56	4.04	5
	90	6.70	....	1
Anisole	21	6.67	....	2
	30	7.04	....	2
	45	7.72	....	2
	60	8.50	....	2
	81	9.79	....	2
	100	11.25	....	2
	120	13.07	....	2
	140	15.45	....	2
Benzene	0	8.09	....	1
	10	8.73	....	1
	10	8.64	....	3
	20	9.44	....	1
	20	9.37	....	3
	20	9.54	....	10
	25	9.67	5.07	6
	25	9.7	....	15
	30	10.27	....	10
	30	10.18	....	1
	30	10.12	....	3
	35	10.43	5.28	6
	39.5	10.91	....	15
	40	11.05	....	10
	40	11.00	....	1
	40	10.96	....	3
	45	11.32	5.50	6
	50	11.90	....	10
	50	11.89	....	1
	50	11.83	....	3
	50.1	11.91	....	15
	55	12.29	5.73	6
	60	12.78	....	10
	60	12.83	....	1
	60	12.96	....	15
	65	13.39	5.98	6
	70	13.72	....	10
	70	14.13	....	1
	75.9	14.95	....	15
	80	15.44	....	1
Benzene, bromo-	25	6.68	4.09	5
	45	7.52	4.39	5
	65	8.50	4.72	5
	85	9.65	5.06	5

Liquid	Temp. °C*	Isothermal Compressibility x 10^{10} m^2N^{-1} at 1 atm (or 1.013 x 10^5 Nm^2)	at 1000 atm (or 1.013 x 10^8 Nm^2)	Ref.
Benzene, chloro-	0	6.61	....	1
	10	7.02	....	1
	20	7.45	....	1
	20	7.38	....	3
	25	7.51	4.39	5
	30	7.89	....	1
	30	7.84	....	3
	40	8.39	....	1
	40	8.32	....	3
	45	8.55	4.73	5
	50	8.92	....	1
	50	8.83	....	3
	60	9.50	....	1
	65	9.76	5.10	5
	70	10.13	....	1
	80	10.79	....	1
	85	11.23	5.49	5
Benzene, nitro-	0	4.41	....	1
	10	4.67	....	1
	20	4.93	....	1
	25	5.03	3.39	5
	30	5.23	....	1
	40	5.49	....	1
	45	5.59	3.64	5
	65	6.24	3.91	5
	85	6.99	4.20	5
n-Butyl alcohol	0	8.10	....	11
Carbon disulphide	0	8.04	....	1
	0	7.95	....	3
	10	8.64	....	1
	10	8.54	....	3
	20	9.13	....	10
	20	9.26	....	1
	20	9.19	....	3
	30	9.72	....	10
	30	9.92	....	1
	30	9.96	....	3
	40	10.65	....	1
	40	10.57	....	10
	40	10.89	....	3
	50	11.48	....	1
	50	11.95	....	3
Carbon tetrachloride	−22.9	7.84	....	12
	−13.1	8.31	....	12
	−3.1	8.87	....	12
	0	8.98	....	1
	0	8.85	....	3
	6.9	9.59	....	12
	10	9.70	....	1
	10	9.57	....	3
	10	9.45	....	16
	16.9	10.35	....	12
	20	10.46	....	1
	20	10.34	....	3
	20	10.40	....	10
	25	10.67	5.30	7
	25	10.77	....	15
	25	10.58	....	16
	26.9	11.15	....	12
	30	11.28	....	10
	30	11.29	....	1
	30	11.18	....	3
	35	11.95	5.52	7
	37.5	11.99	....	15
	40	12.20	....	10
	40	12.23	....	1
	40	12.16	....	3
	40	11.96	....	16
	45	12.54	5.75	7
	50	13.20	....	10
	50	13.32	....	1
	50	13.26	....	3
	50.3	13.28	....	15
	55	13.63	5.97	7
	55	13.51	....	15
	60	14.26	....	10
	60	14.52	....	1
	62.6	14.84	....	15
	65	14.87	6.22	7
	70	15.43	....	10
	70	15.77	....	1
	75	16.70	....	15

*K = 273.15 + C

*K = 273.15 + C

Liquid	Temp. °C*	Isothermal Compressibility x 10^10 m^2N^{-1}		Ref.
		at 1 atm (or 1.013 x 10^5 Nm²)	at 1000 atm (or 1.013 x 10^8 Nm²)	
Chloroform.........	−33.1	7.13	....	12
	−23.1	7.61	....	12
	−13.1	8.12	....	12
	− 3.1	8.66	....	12
	0	8.48	....	1
	0	8.55	....	3
	6.9	9.30	....	12
	10	9.17	....	1
	10	9.19	....	3
	16.9	10.35	....	12
	20	9.98	....	1
	20	9.94	....	3
	20	10.15	....	10
	25	9.74	5.34	4
	26.9	11.15	....	12
	30	10.86	....	1
	30	10.81	....	3
	30	10.99	....	10
	40	11.84	....	1
	40	11.79	....	3
	40	11.94	....	10
	50	12.90	....	1
	50	12.99	....	10
	60	14.06	....	1
Cyclohexane........	10	9.88	....	16
	25	11.10	....	16
	25	11.40	....	15
	35	12.02	....	16
	37.6	12.67	....	15
	40	12.56	....	16
	45	13.14	....	16
	50.1	14.15	....	15
	55	14.35	....	16
	60	14.88	....	16
	62.4	15.76	....	15
	75	17.84	....	15
Dodecane..........	37.8	9.9	5.3	13
	60.0	11.3	5.7	13
	79.4	12.8	6.1	13
	98.9	14.4	6.4	13
	115.0	16.1	6.8	13
	135.0	18.3	7.3	13
Ethane 1,1,2,2-tetrachloro-......	25	6.17	3.88	4
Ethyl alcohol........	0	9.87	....	1
	0	9.87	....	11
	0	9.63	....	3
	10	10.49	....	1
	10	10.30	....	3
	20	11.19	....	1
	20	10.98	....	3
	30	11.91	....	1
	30	11.80	....	3
	40	12.74	....	1
	40	12.61	....	3
	50	13.70	....	1
	50	13.60	....	3
	60	14.74	....	1
	70	15.93	....	1
	75	16.67	....	1
Ethyl bromide.......	0	10.76	....	1
	10	11.78	....	1
	20	12.94	....	1
	30	14.23	....	1
	40	15.52	....	1
Ethylene, 1,2-dichloro-(trans)....	25	11.19	5.62	4
Ethylene, tetrachloro-	25	7.56	4.45	4
Ethylene, trichloro-...	25	8.57	4.99	4
Ethylene chloride....	0	6.91	....	1
	10	7.42	....	1
	20	7.97	....	1
	20	7.82	....	10
	25	7.78	4.54	4
	30	8.41	....	10
	30	8.58	....	1
	40	9.09	....	10
	40	9.25	....	1
	50	9.86	....	10
	50	9.99	....	1
	60	10.66	....	10
	60	10.83	....	1
	70	11.54	....	10
	70	11.76	....	1
	80	12.79	....	1

Liquid	Temp. °C*	Isothermal Compressibility x 10^10 m^2N^{-1}		Ref.
		at 1 atm (or 1.013 x 10^5 Nm²)	at 1000 atm (or 1.013 x 10^8 Nm²)	
Ethyl ether..........	0	15.10	....	1
	0	15.07	....	3
	10	16.81	....	1
	10	16.52	....	3
	20	18.65	....	1
	20	18.44	....	3
	30	20.90	....	1
	30	20.80	....	3
	35	24.15	....	1
Ethyl iodide.........	0	8.45	....	1
	10	9.12	....	1
	20	9.82	....	1
	30	10.59	....	1
	40	11.44	....	1
	50	12.38	....	1
	60	13.40	....	1
	70	14.49	....	1
Glycol.............	25	3.72	2.73	7
	45	4.00	2.89	7
	65	4.32	3.05	7
	85	4.70	3.24	7
	105	5.14	3.44	7
n-Heptane..........	0	11.80	5.64	8
	25	14.24	6.18	8
	40	15.96	6.50	8
	60	18.67	6.94	8
1-Heptanol..........	0	7.05	....	11
n-Hexane...........	0	13.04	5.92	8
	25	16.06	6.51	8
	40	18.31	6.89	8
	60	21.93	8.87	8
1-Hexanol..........	0	7.47	....	11
Mercury............	0	0.40	....	14
	20	0.40	0.39	14
	40	0.41	....	14
	80	0.42	....	14
	120	0.44	....	14
	160	0.46	....	14
Methanol...........	0	10.62	....	1
	0	10.68	....	11
	0	10.78	....	3
	10	11.34	....	1
	10	11.45	....	3
	20	12.11	....	1
	20	12.18	....	3
	30	12.93	....	1
	30	12.98	....	3
	40	13.85	....	1
	40	13.82	....	3
	50	14.76	....	3
Methylene bromide...	−33.1	4.95	....	12
	−23.1	5.11	....	12
	−13.1	5.50	....	12
	− 3.1	5.81	....	12
	6.9	6.13	....	12
	16.9	6.47	....	12
	26.9	6.85	....	12
Methylene chloride...	25	9.74	5.31	4
Methyl iodide........	−33.1	6.86	....	12
	−23.1	7.41	....	12
	−13.1	7.97	....	12
	− 3.1	8.55	....	12
	6.9	9.13	....	12
	16.9	9.71	....	12
	26.9	10.33	....	12
n-Octadecane.......	60	9.4	5.1	13
	79.4	10.4	5.5	13
	98.9	11.6	5.8	13
	115.0	12.8	6.1	13
	135	14.4	6.4	13
n-Octane...........	0	9.99	5.11	8
	25	11.98	5.69	8
	40	13.36	6.00	8
	60	15.53	6.40	8
1-Octanol..........	0	6.82	....	11
n-Pentadecane.......	37.8	9.1	....	13
	60	10.2	5.0	13
	79.4	11.7	5.5	13

*K = 273.15 + C

*K = 273.15 + C

Liquid	Temp. °C*	Isothermal Compressibility x 10^10 m²N⁻¹		Ref.
		at 1 atm (or 1.013 x 10⁵ Nm²)	at 1000 atm (or 1.013 x 10⁸ Nm²)	
n-Pentadecane.......	98.9	13.2	5.8	13
(cont.)...........	115	14.7	6.1	13
	135	16.8	6.4	13
Pentanol............	0	7.71	....	11
Phenol.............	46	5.61	....	2
	60	6.05	....	2
	80	6.78	....	2
	110	8.12	....	2
	125	8.88	....	2
	150	10.30	....	2
	175	12.35	....	2
n-Propyl alcohol.....	0	8.43	....	11
Toluene............	−59.3	5.27	....	9
	−41.1	5.93	....	9
	−19.2	6.87	....	9
	0	7.83	....	1
	0	7.97	....	3
	0	7.84	....	9
	10	8.38	....	1
	10	8.44	....	3
	20	8.96	....	1
	20	8.94	....	3
	30	9.60	....	1
	30	9.49	....	3
	40	10.33	....	1
	40	10.14	....	3
	50	11.13	....	1
	50	10.90	....	3
	60	11.99	....	1
	70	12.95	....	1
Water.............	0	5.01	....	1
	0	5.04	....	9
	10	4.78	....	1
	20	4.58	....	1
	25	4.57	3.48	7
	30	4.46	....	1
	34.8	4.41	....	9
	35	4.48	3.42	7
	40	4.41	....	1
	45	4.44	3.40	7
	50	4.40	....	1
	55	4.44	3.40	7
	60	4.43	....	1
	65	4.48	3.42	7
	70	4.49	....	1
	75	4.55	3.47	7
	80	4.57	....	1
	85	4.65	3.53	7
	90	4.68	....	1
	100	4.80	....	1
m-Xylene..........	0	7.44	....	1
	10	7.94	....	1
	20	8.46	....	1
	30	9.03	....	1
	40	9.63	....	1
	50	10.25	....	1
	60	11.01	....	1
	70	11.77	....	1
	80	12.56	....	1

*K = 273.15 + C

References
(1) D. Tyrer, J. Chem. Soc. **105**, 2534, 1914.
(2) A. E. Lutskii and V. N. Solon ko, Russian Journal of Physical Chemistry **38**, 602, 1964.
(3) E. B. Fryer, J. C. Hubbard and D. H. Andrews, J. Amer. Chem. Soc. **51**, 759, 1929.
(4) D. M. Newitt and K. E. Weale, J. Chem. Soc., 3092, 1951.
(5) R. E. Gibson and O. H. Loeffler, J. Amer. Chem. Soc. **61**, 2515, 1939.
(6) R. E. Gibson and J. F. Kincaid, J. Amer. Chem. Soc. **60**, 511, 1938.
(7) R. E. Gibson and O. H. Loeffler, J. Amer. Chem. Soc. **63**, 898, 1941.
(8) H. E. Eduljee, D. M. Newitt and K. E. Weale, J. Chem. Soc. 3086, 1951.
(9) J. G. Marshall, L. A. K. Staveley and K. R. Hart, Trans. Farad. Soc. **52**, 23, 1956.
(10) L. A. K. Staveley, W. I. Tupman and K. R. Hart, Trans. Farad. Soc. **51**, 323, 1955.
(11) W. P. McKinney, G. F. Skinner and L. A. K. Staveley, J. Chem. Soc. 2415, 1959.
(12) D. Harrison and E. A. Moelwyn-Hughes, Proceedings of the Royal Society, **239A**, 230, 1957.
(13) W. G. Cutler, R. H. McMickle, W. Webb and R. W. Schiessler, Journal Chemical Phys. **29**, 727, 1958.
(14) E. A. Moelwyn-Hughes, Journal Physical and Colloid Chemistry, **55**, 1246, 1951.
(15) G. A. Holder and E. Whalley, Trans. Faraday Soc. **58**, 2095, 1962.
(16) M. Diaz Pena and M. L. McGlashan. Trans. Faraday Soc. **57**, 1511, 1961.

COEFFICIENT OF FRICTION

Compiled by Harold Minshall

The coefficient of friction between two surfaces is the ratio of the force required to move one over the other to the total force pressing the two together. If F is the force required to move one surface over another and W, the force pressing the surfaces together, the coefficient of friction,

$$\mu = \frac{F}{W}$$

Materials	Condition	Temperature °C	μ (Static)
A. STATIC FRICTION			
Non Metals			
Glass on glass	clean	—	0.9 1.0
,, ,, ,,	lubricated with paraffin oil	—	0.5–0.6
,, ,, ,,	,, ,, liquid fatty acids	—	0.3–0.6
,, ,, ,,	,, ,, solid hydrocarbons, alcohols or fatty acids	—	0.1
,, ,, metal	clean	—	0.5–0.7
,, ,, ,,	lubricated	—	0.2–0.3
Diamond on diamond	clean	—	0.1
,, ,, ,,	lubricated	—	0.05–0.1
,, ,, metal	clean	—	0.1–0.15
,, ,, ,,	lubricated	—	0.1
Sapphire on sapphire	clean or lubricated	—	0.2
,, ,, steel	,, ,, ,,	—	0.15
Hard carbon on carbon	clean	—	0.16
,, ,, ,,	lubricated	—	0.12–0.14
Graphite on graphite	clean or lubricated	—	0.1
,, ,, ,,	outgassed	—	0.5–0.8
,, ,, steel	clean or lubricated	—	0.1
Mica on mica	freshly cleaved	—	1.0
,, ,, ,,	contaminated	—	0.2–0.4
Crystals of $NaNO_3$, KNO_3, NH_4Cl on self	clean	—	0.5
,, ,, ,,	lubricated with long chain polar compounds	—	0.12
Tungsten carbide on tungsten carbide	clean	room	0.17
Tungsten carbide on tungsten carbide	outgassed	room	0.58
,, ,, ,, ,, ,,	clean	820	0.35
,, ,, ,, ,, ,,	,,	970	0.40
,, ,, ,, ,, ,,	,,	1010	0.45
,, ,, ,, ,, ,,	,,	1160	0.5
,, ,, ,, ,, ,,	,,	1220	0.7
,, ,, ,, ,, ,,	,,	1440	1.2
,, ,, ,, ,, ,,	,,	1600	1.8
,, ,, ,, graphite	outgassed	room	0.62
,, ,, ,, ,,	clean	,,	0.15
,, ,, ,, ,,	,,	800	0.32
,, ,, ,, ,,	,,	910	0.30
,, ,, ,, ,,	,,	1000	0.25
,, ,, ,, ,,	,,	1120	0.29
,, ,, ,, ,,	,,	1220	0.26
,, ,, ,, ,,	,,	1300	0.25
,, ,, ,, ,,	,,	1410	0.25
,, ,, ,, ,,	,,	1800	0.24
,, ,, ,, ,,	,,	2030	0.25
,, ,, ,, steel	,,	—	0.4–0.6
,, ,, ,, ,,	lubricated	—	0.1–0.2
Polymethyl methacrylate on self	clean	—	0.8
,, ,, ,, steel	,,	—	0.4–0.5
Polystyrene on self	,,	—	0.5
,, ,, steel	,,	—	0.3–0.35
Polyethylene on self	,,	—	0.2
,, ,, steel	,,	—	0.2
Polytetrafluoroethylene on self	,,	—	0.04
,, ,, steel	,,	—	0.04
Nylon on nylon[1]		—	0.15–0.25
Silk on silk	commercially clean	—	0.2–0.3
Cotton on cotton (thread)	,, ,,	—	0.3
,, ,, ,, (from cotton wool)	,, ,,	—	0.6
Rubber on solids	,, ,,	—	1–4
Wood on wood	,, ,, and dry	—	0.25–0.5
,, ,, ,,	,, ,, ,, wet	—	0.2
,, ,, metals	,, ,, ,, dry	—	0.2–0.6
,, ,, ,,	,, ,, ,, wet	—	0.2
,, ,, brick	,, ,,	—	0.6
,, ,, leather	,, ,,	—	0.3–0.4
Leather on metal	,, ,,	—	0.6
,, ,, ,,	,, ,, and wet	—	0.4
,, ,, ,,	greasy	—	0.2
Brake material on cast iron	commercially clean	—	0.4
,, ,, ,, ,, ,,	,, ,, and wet	—	0.2
,, ,, ,, ,, ,,	lubricated with mineral oil	—	0.1
Wool fiber on horn	clean (against scales)	—	0.8–1.0
,, ,, ,, ,,	,, (with scales)	—	0.4–0.6
,, ,, ,, ,,	greasy (against scales)	—	0.5–0.8
,, ,, ,, ,,	,, (with scales)	—	0.3–0.4
Metals			
Steel on steel	clean	20	0.58
,, ,, ,,	vegetable oil lubricant (a) castor oil	20	0.095
,, ,, ,,		100	0.105
,, ,, ,,	(b) rape	20	0.105
,, ,, ,,		100	0.105
,, ,, ,,	(c) olive	20	0.105
,, ,, ,,		100	0.105
,, ,, ,,	(d) coconut	20	0.08
,, ,, ,,		100	0.08

[1] Registered trade name.

Materials	Condition	Temperature °C	μ (Static)
A. STATIC FRICTION (Cont.)			
Metals (Cont.)			
Steel on steel	Animal oil lubricant		
„ „ „	(a) sperm	20	0.10
		100	0.10
„ „ „	(b) pale whale	20	0.095
		100	0.095
„ „ „	(c) neatsfoot	20	0.095
		100	0.095
„ „ „	(d) lard	20	0.085
		100	0.085
„ „ „	Mineral oil lubricant		
„ „ „	(a) light machine	20	0.16
		100	0.19
„ „ „	(b) thick gear	20	0.125
		100	0.15
„ „ „	(c) solvent refined	20	0.15
		100	0.20
„ „ „	(d) heavy motor	20	0.195
		100	0.205
„ „ „	(e) extreme pressure	20	0.09–0.1
		100	0.09–0.1
„ „ „	(f) graphited oil	20	0.13
		100	0.15
„ „ „	(g) B.P. Paraffin	20	0.18
		100	0.22
„ „ „	lubricated with trichloroethylene	20	0.33
„ „ „	„ „ benzene	20	0.48
„ „ „	„ „ glycerol	20	0.2
„ „ „	„ „ ethyl alcohol	20	0.43
„ „ „	„ „ butyl alcohol	room	0.3
„ „ „	„ „ octyl	„	0.23
„ „ „	„ „ decyl	„	0.16
„ „ „	„ „ cetyl	„	0.10
„ „ „	lubricated with nonane	room	0.26
„ „ „	„ „ decane	„	0.23
„ „ „	„ „ acetic acid	„	0.5
„ „ „	„ „ proprionic acid	„	0.4
„ „ „	„ „ valeric acid	„	0.17
„ „ „	„ „ caproic acid	„	0.12
„ „ „	„ „ pelargonic acid	„	0.11
„ „ „	„ „ capric acid	„	0.11
„ „ „	„ „ lauric acid	„	0.11
„ „ „	„ „ myristic acid	„	0.11
„ „ „	„ „ oleic acid	20–100	0.08
„ „ „	„ „ palmitic acid	room	0.11
„ „ „	„ „ stearic acid	„	0.10
„ „ hard steel	„ „ rape oil	—	0.14
„ „ „	„ „ castor oil	—	0.12
„ „ „	„ „ mineral oil	—	0.16
„ „ „	„ „ long chain fatty acid	—	0.09
„ „ cast iron	„ „ rape oil	—	0.11
„ „ „	„ „ castor oil	—	0.15
„ „ „	„ „ mineral oil	—	0.21
„ „ „	clean	—	0.4
„ „ gun metal	lubricated with rape oil	—	0.15
„ „ „	„ „ castor oil	—	0.16
„ „ „	„ „ mineral oil	—	0.21
„ „ bronze	„ „ rape oil	—	0.12
„ „ „	„ „ caster oil	—	0.12
„ „ „	„ „ mineral oil	—	0.16
„ „ lead	„ „ „ „	—	0.5
„ „ „	„ „ long chain fatty acid	—	0.22
„ „ base white metal	„ „ mineral oil	—	0.1
„ „ „ „	„ „ long chain fatty acid	—	0.08
„ „ „	clean	—	0.55
„ „ tin	lubricated with mineral oil	—	0.6
„ „ „	„ „ long chain fatty acid	—	0.21
„ „ white metal, tin base	„ „ mineral oil	—	0.1
„ „ „ „ „ „	„ „ long chain fatty acid	—	0.07
„ „ „ „ „ „	clean	—	0.8
„ „ sintered bronze	lubricated with mineral oil	—	0.13
„ „ brass	„ „ „ „	—	0.19
„ „ „	„ „ castor oil	—	0.11
„ „ „	„ „ long chain fatty acid	—	0.13
„ „ „	clean	—	0.35
„ „ copper–lead alloy	„	—	0.22
„ „ Wood's alloy	„	—	0.7
„ „ phosphor bronze	„	—	0.35
„ „ aluminum bronze	„	—	0.45
„ „ constantan	„	—	0.4
[2] „ „ indium film deposited on steel	4 kg load, clean	—	0.08
[2] „ „ „ „ „ „ „	8 kg „ „ „	—	0.04
[2] „ „ „ „ „ „ „ silver	4 kg „ „	—	0.1
[2] „ „ „ „ „ „ „	8 kg „ „ „	—	0.07
[2] „ „ lead film deposited on copper	4 kg „ „ „	—	0.18
[2] „ „ „ „ „ „ „	8 kg „ „ „	—	0.12
[2] „ „ copper film deposited on steel	4 kg „ „ „	—	0.3
[2] „ „ „ „ „ „ „	8 kg „ „ „	—	0.2
[2]Al on Al	in air or O_2	—	1.9
	„ H_2O vapor	—	1.1
[3]Cu on Cu	„ H_2 or N_2	—	4.0
„ „ „	„ air or O_2	—	1.6

[2] Hemispherical steel slider having 0.6 cm. diameter. The thin, 10^{-3} to 10^{-4} cm., thin metallic films were deposited on various substrates as indicated. Amonton's Law is not obeyed in this case.

[3] The metals which were spectroscopically pure were outgassed in a vacuum prior to other gases being admitted. When clean and in vacuum there is gross seizure.

Materials	Condition	Temperature °C	μ (Static)
A. STATIC FRICTION (Cont.)			
Metals (Cont.)			
[3]Au on Au	in H_2 or N_2	—	4.0
,, ,, ,,	,, air or O_2	—	2.8
,, ,, ,,	,, H_2O vapor	—	2.5
[3]Fe on Fe	,, in air or O_2	—	1.2
,, ,, ,,	,, H_2O vapor	—	1.2
[3]Mo on Mo	,, air or O_2	—	0.8
,, ,, ,,	,, H_2O vapor	—	0.8
[3]Ni on Ni	,, H_2 or N_2	—	5.0
,, ,, ,,	,, air or O_2	—	3.0
,, ,, ,,	,, H_2O vapor	—	1.6
[3]Pt on Pt	,, air or O_2	—	3.0
,, ,, ,,	,, H_2O vapor	—	3.0
[3]Ag on Ag	,, air or O_2	—	1.5
,, ,, ,,	,, H_2O vapor	—	1.5
Various Materials on Snow and Ice			
Ice on ice	clean	0	0.05–0.15
,, ,, ,,	,,	−12	0.3
,, ,, ,,	,,	−71	0.5
,, ,, ,,	,,	−82	0.5
,, ,, ,,	,,	−110	0.5
Polymethylmethylacrylate	on wet snow	0	0.5
,,	,, dry ,,	0	0.3
,,	,, ,, ,,	−10	0.34
,,	,, ,, ,,	−32	0.4
Polyester of teraphthalic acid and ethylene glycol	,, wet ,,	0	0.5
Polyester of teraphthalic acid and ethylene glycol	,, dry ,,	0	0.35
Polyester of teraphthalic acid and ethylene glycol	,, ,, ,,	−10	0.38
[1]Nylon	on wet snow	0	0.4
,,	,, dry ,,	0	0.3
,,	,, ,, ,,	−10	0.3
Polytetrafluoroethylene	,, wet ,,	0	0.05
,,	,, dry ,,	0	0.02
,,	,, ,, ,,	−10	0.08
,,	,, ,, ,,	−32	0.1
Paraffin wax	,, wet ,,	0	0.06
,, ,,	,, dry ,,	0	0.06
,, ,,	,, ,, ,,	−10	0.35
,, ,,	,, ,, ,,	−32	0.4
Swiss wax	,, wet ,,	0	0.05
,, ,,	,, dry ,,	0	0.03
,, ,,	,, ,, ,,	−10	0.2
,, ,,	,, ,, ,,	−32	0.2
Ski wax	,, wet ,,	0	0.1
,, ,,	,, dry ,,	0	0.04
,, ,,	,, ,, ,,	−10	0.2
,, ,,	,, ,, ,,	−32	0.2
,, laquer	,, wet ,,	0	0.2
,, ,,	,, dry ,,	0	0.1
,, ,,	,, ,, ,,	−10	0.4
,, ,,	,, ,, ,,	−32	0.4
Aluminum	,, wet ,,	0	0.4
,,	,, dry ,,	0	0.35
,,	,, ,, ,,	−10	0.38

Materials	Condition	Temperature °C	μ (Kinetic)
B. KINETIC FRICTION Various Materials			
Unwaxed hickory	4 m/sec on dry snow	−3	0.08
Waxed ,,	0.1 m/sec ,, wet ,,	0	0.14
,, ,,	0.1 m/sec ,, dry ,,	0	0.04
,, ,,	0.1 m/sec ,, ,, ,,	−3	0.09
,, ,,	4 m/sec ,, ,, ,,	−3	0.03
Waxed hickory	0.1 m/sec on dry snow	−10	0.18
,, ,,	0.1 m/sec ,, ,, ,,	−40	0.4
Ice on ice	4 m/sec, clean	0	0.02
,, ,, ,,	,, ,, ,,	−10	0.035
,, ,, ,,	,, ,, ,,	−20	0.050
,, ,, ,,	,, ,, ,,	−40	0.075
,, ,, ,,	,, ,, ,,	−60	0.085
,, ,, ,,	,, ,, ,,	−80	0.09
Ebonite	4 m/sec on ice	0	0.02
,,	,, ,, ,,	−10	0.05
,,	,, ,, ,,	−20	0.065
,,	,, ,, ,,	−40	0.085
,,	,, ,, ,,	−60	0.10
,,	,, ,, ,,	−80	0.11
Brass	4 m/sec on ice	0	0.02
,,	,, ,, ,,	−10	0.075
,,	,, ,, ,,	−20	0.085
,,	,, ,, ,,	−40	0.115
,,	,, ,, ,,	−60	0.14
,,	,, ,, ,,	−80	0.15
Natural rubber, vulcanized	100m/min on ground glass, clean	—	1.07
,, ,, , ,,	100m/min ,, ,, ,, , wetted with water	—	0.94
,, ,, , ,,	100m/min on concrete, clean	—	1.02
,, ,, , ,,	100m/min ,, ,, , wetted with water	—	0.97
,, ,, , ,,	100m/min on bitumen, clean	—	1.07
,, ,, , ,,	100m/min ,, ,, , wetted with water	—	0.95
,, ,, , ,,	100m/min on rubber flooring or rubber tread vulcanisate. clean	—	1.16
,, ,, , ,,	100m/min on bitumen containing rubber powder, clean	—	1.15 (Varies with quantity of powder)
,, ,, , ,,	100m/min on bitumen containing rubber powder, wetted with water	—	1.03

[1]Registered trade name. [3] The metals which were spectroscopically pure were outgassed in a vacuum prior to other gases being admitted. When clean and in vacuum there is gross seizure.

LOW MELTING POINT ALLOYS

Melting point °C	Name	Composition, wt %				
−48	Binary Eutectic	Cs 77.0	K 23.0			
−40	Binary Eutectic	Cs 87.0	Rb 13.0			
−30	Binary Eutectic	Cs 95.0	Na 5.0			
−11	Binary Eutectic	K 78.0	Na 22.0			
−8	Binary Eutectic	Rb 92.0	Na 8.0			
10.7	Ternary Eutectic	Ga 62.5	In 21.5	Sn 16.0		
10.8	Ternary Eutectic	Ga 69.8	In 17.6	Sn 12.5		
17	Ternary Eutectic	Ga 82.0	Sn 12.0	Zn 6.0		
33	Binary Eutectic	Rb 68.0	K 32.0			
46.5	Quinternary Eutectic	Sn 10.65	Bi 40.63	Pb 22.11	In 18.1	Cd 8.2
47	Quinternary Eutectic	Bi 44.7	Pb 22.6	Sn 8.3	Cd 5.3	In 19.1
58.2	Quaternary Eutectic	Bi 49.5	Pb 17.6	Sn 11.6	In 21.3	
60.5	Ternary Eutectic	In 51.0	Bi 32.5	Sn 16.5		
70	Wood's Metal	Bi 50.0	Pb 25.0	Sn 12.5	Cd 12.5	
70	Lipowitz's Metal	Bi 50.0	Pb 26.7	Sn 13.3	Cd 10.0	
70	Binary Eutectic	In 67.0	Bi 33.0			
91.5	Ternary Eutectic	Bi 51.6	Pb 40.2	Cd 8.2		
95	Ternary Eutectic	Bi 52.5	Pb 32.0	Sn 15.5		
97	Newton's Metal	Bi 50.0	Sn 18.8	Pb 31.2		
98	D'Arcet's Metal	Bi 50.0	Sn 25.0	Pb 25.0		
100	Onion's or Lichtenberg's Metal	Bi 50.0	Sn 20.0	Pb 30.0		
102.5	Ternary Eutectic	Bi 54.0	Sn 26.0	Cd 20.0		
109	Rose's Metal	Bi 50.0	Pb 28.0	Sn 22.0		
117	Binary Eutectic	In 52.0	Sn 48.0			
120	Binary Eutectic	In 75.0	Cd 25.0			
123	Malotte's Metal	Bi 46.1	Sn 34.2	Pb 19.7		
124	Binary Eutectic	Bi 55.5	Pb 44.5			
130	Ternary Eutectic	Bi 56.0	Sn 40.0	Zn 4.0		
140	Binary Eutectic	Bi 58.0	Sn 42.0			
140	Binary Eutectic	Bi 60.0	Cd 40.0			
183	Eutectic solder	Sn 63.0	Pb 37.0			
185	Binary Eutectic	Tl 52.0	Bi 48.0			
192	Soft solder	Sn 70.0	Pb 30.0			
198	Binary Eutectic	Sn 91.0	Zn 9.0			
199	Tin foil	Sn 92.0	Zn 8.0			
199	White Metal	Sn 92.0	Sb 8.0			
221	Binary Eutectic	Sn 96.5	Ag 3.5			
226	Matrix	Bi 48.0	Pb 28.5	Sn 14.5	Sb 9.0	
227	Binary Eutectic	Sn 99.25	Cu 0.75			
240	Antimonial Tin solder	Sn 95.0	Sb 5.0			
245	Tin-silver solder	Sn 95.0	Ag 5.0			

HARDNESS OF MATERIALS

Material	Value	Material	Value
Agate	6–7	Indium	1.2
Alabaster	1.7	Iridium	6–6.5
Alum	2–2.5	Iridosmium	7
Aluminum	2–2.9	Iron	4–5
Alundum	9+	Kaolinite	2.0–2.5
Amber	2–2.5	Lead	1.5
Andalusite	7.5	Lithium	0.6
Anthracite	2.2	Loess (0°)	0.3
Antimony	3.0–3.3	Magnesium	2.0
Apatite	5	Magnetite	6
Aragonite	3.5	Manganese	5.0
Arsenic	3.5	Marble	3–4
Asbestos	5	Meerschaum	2–3
Asphalt	1–2	Mica	2.8
Augite	6	Opal	4–6
Barite	3.3	Orthoclase	6
Bell-metal	4	Osmium	7.0
Beryl	7.8	Palladium	4.8
Bismuth	2.5	Phosphorus	0.5
Boric acid	3	Phosphorbronze	4
Boron	9.5	Platinum	4.3
Brass	3–4	Plat-iridium	6.5
Cadmium	2.0	Potassium	0.5
Calamine	5	Pumice	6
Calcite	3	Pyrite	6.3
Calcium	1.5	Quartz	7
Carbon	10.0	Rock salt (halite)	2
Carborundum	9–10	Ross' metal	2.5–3.0
Cesium	0.2	Rubidium	0.3
Chromium	9.0	Ruthenium	6.5
Copper	2.5–3	Selenium	2.0
Corundum	9	Serpentine	3–4
Diamond	10	Silicon	7.0
Diatomaceous earth	1–1.5	Silver	2.5–4
Dolomite	3.5–4	Silver chloride	1.3
Emery	7–9	Sodium	0.4
Feldspar	6	Steel	5–8.5
Flint	7	Stibnite	2
Fluorite	4	Strontium	1.8
Galena	2.5	Sulfur	1.5–2.5
Gallium	1.5	Talc	1
Garnet	6.5–7	Tellurium	2.3
Glass	4.5–6.5	Tin	1.5–1.8
Gold	2.5–3	Topaz	8
Graphite	0.5–1	Tourmaline	7.3
Gypsum	1.6–2	Wax (0°)	0.2
Hematite	6	Wood's metal	3
Hornblende	5.5	Zinc	2.5

COMPARISON OF HARDNESS VALUES OF VARIOUS MATERIALS ON MOHS AND KNOOP SCALES*

Compiled by Laurence S. Foster

Substance	Formula	Mohs value	Knoop value
Talc	$3MgO·4SiO_2·H_2O$	1	
Gypsum	$CaSO_4·2H_2O$	2	32
Cadmium	Cd	..	37
Silver	Ag	..	60
Zinc	Zn	..	119
Calcite	$CaCO_3$	3	135
Fluorite	CaF_2	4	163
Copper	Cu	..	163
Magnesia	MgO	..	370
Apatite	$CaF_2·3Ca_3(PO_4)_2$	5	430
Nickel	Ni	..	557
Glass (soda lime)		..	530
Feldspar (orthoclase)	$K_2O·Al_2O_3·6SiO_2$	6	560
Quartz	SiO_2	7	820
Chromium	Cr	..	935
Zirconia	ZrO_2	..	1160
Beryllia	BeO	..	1250
Topaz	$(AlF)_2SiO_4$	8	1340
Garnet	$Al_2O_3·3FeO·3SiO_2$	..	1360
Tungsten carbide alloy	WC, Co	..	1400–1800
Zirconium boride	ZrB_2	..	1550
Titanium nitride	TiN	9	1800
Tungsten carbide	WC	..	1880
Tantalum carbide	TaC	..	2000
Zirconium carbide	ZrC	..	2100
Alumina	Al_2O_3	..	2100
Beryllium carbide	Be_2C	..	2410
Titanium carbide	TiC	..	2470
Silicon carbide	SiC	..	2480
Aluminum boride	AlB	..	2500
Boron carbide	B_4C	..	2750
Diamond	C	10	7000

MOHS HARDNESS SCALE

Hardness number	Original scale	Modified scale
1	Talc	Talc
2	Gypsum	Gypsum
3	Calcite	Calcite
4	Fluorite	Fluorite
5	Apatite	Apatite
6	Orthoclase	Orthoclase
7	Quartz	Vitreous silica
8	Topaz	Quartz or Stellite
9	Corundum	Topaz
10	Diamond	Garnet
11	....	Fused Zirconia
12	....	Fused Alumina
13	....	Silicon Carbide
14	....	Boron Carbide
15	....	Diamond

* Acknowledgment is made to N. W. Thibault, Norton Company, Worcester, Massachusetts, for many of Knoop hardness values. Cf. R. F. Geller, "A Study of Ceramics for Nuclear Reactors," Nucleonics, Vol. 7, No. 4, Table 1, pp. 8–9 (Oct. 1950). V. E. Lysaght, Indentation Hardness Testing, Reinhold 1949.

SURFACE TENSION OF LIQUID ELEMENTS

Gernot Lang

The following data were collected from many sources. As a result their accuracy varies. Users of data in this table are advised that:

1. As a rule, results from the "sessile drop" and "maximum bubble pressure" as well as from the "pendant drop" methods are preferable to results obtained from other methods for metals with very high melting points.
2. Values of single measurements are usually not as well supported by experiments as those of serial measurements at various temperatures.
3. Values in parentheses can be considered improbable.

Element	Purity (wt.%)	σ_{mp} (dyn/cm)	Atm.	t_1 °C	σ_{t1} (dyn/cm)	t_2 °C	σ_{t2} (dyn/cm)	t_5 °C	σ_{t3} (dyn/cm)	Method	Ref.
Ag	99.99		H_2	1000	916					Bubble pressure	134
	–	(785)	vac.							Pendant drop	182
	99.96		H_2	1000	893	1150	862	1250	849	Bubble pressure	127
	–		vac.	1000	908					Sessile drop	51
	99.995		H_2	1000	907	1100	894	1200	876	Bubble pressure	128
	99.999	(828)	vac.							Pendant drop	65
	99.99		Ar, H_2	1000	890					Bubble pressure	169
	spect. pure	921	–	$\sigma = 1136-0.174\ T\ (°K)$ (1300–2200°K)						Bubble pressure	26
		918		$\sigma = 918-0.149\ (t-t_{mp})\ (t°C)$						Bubble pressure	204
	99.999		Ar	980	905±10	1108	890±10			Sessile drop	Z3
Al	99.99	860±20	Ar	950	840					Bubble pressure	102
	99.72		vac.							Bubble pressure	46
	99.7	863±25	Ar	$\sigma_t = (863\pm25)-0.33\ (t-t_{mp})\ (t°C)$						Bubble pressure	113
	99.99	865	vac.	$\sigma_t = 865-0.14\ (t-t_{mp})\ (t°C)$						Sessile drop	137, 56
	99.99	825	Ar	$(\sigma_t = 825-0.05\ (T-993))\ (T°K)$						Bubble pressure	38
	99.99	866	He	$\sigma_t = 866-0.15\ (t-t_{mp})\ (t°C)$						Sessile drop	10
	99.999	873	He	1600 $\quad$ 725 $\quad \sigma_t = 873-0.15\ (t-t_{mp})\ (t°C)$						Sessile drop	199
	99.99	(760)	vac.	$(\sigma_t = 948-0.202T)\ (T°K, 980-1090°K)\ (t°C)$						Sessile drop	Z4
	99.998	(915)	Ar	$(\sigma_t = 915-0.51\ (t-t_{mp}))\ (t°C)$ (660–800°C)						Sessile drop	Z6
	99.996	855±6	Ar	$\sigma_t = 855-0.104\ (t-t_{mp})\ (t°C)$ (660–911°C)						Bubble pressure	Z13

SURFACE TENSION OF LIQUID ELEMENTS (Continued)

Element	Purity (wt.–%)	σ_{mp} (dyn/cm)	Atm.	σ_{t1} t_1 °C	σ_{t1} σ (dyn/cm)	σ_{t2} t_2 °C	σ_{t2} σ (dyn/cm)	σ_{t3} t_3 °C	σ_{t3} σ (dyn/cm)	Method	Ref.
Au	99.999	(754)	vac.							Pendant drop	182
	99.999	1130	He	1200	1070	1300	1020			Sessile drop	86
	99.999	(731)	vac.							Pendant drop	65
			Ar	1108	1130±10					Sessile drop	Z3
B	99.8	1060±50	vac.							Sessile & pendant drop	187
Ba	–		Ar	720	224					Bubble pressure	3
	99.5	276		$\sigma = 351-0.075\ T$ (°K) (1410–1880°K)						Bubble pressure	25
Be	99.98		vac.	1500	1100					Sessile drop	58
Bi	99.99	376	vac.							Drop pressure	155
	99.99	376	vac.							Drop pressure	156
	99.90		H_2	800	343	1000	328			Bubble pressure	134
			vac.	450	(382)					Electro-capillarity	118
	99.9	380±10	Ar							Bubble pressure	103
			–	350	362					Drop pressure	76
			vac.	700	350					Sessile drop	29
	99.98	380±10	Ar	450	380					Bubble pressure	105
			–	300	379					Drop pressure	120
			vac.							Sessile drop	64
		378	vac., Ar, H_2							Drop weight	4
	99.99995	375		$\sigma = 423-0.088\ T\ (T°K)\ (1352-1555°K)$						Bubble pressure	26
	99.999	380±3	Ar	$\sigma_t = 380-0.142\ (t-t_{mp})\ (MP-555°C)\ (t°C)$						Bubble pressure	Z13a
Ca	–	360	Ar	850	337					Bubble pressure	3
	p.a.			$\sigma = 472-0.100\ T\ (T°K)\ (1445-1655°K)$						Bubble pressure	25
Cd			–	450	600					Drop pressure	119
			–	400	600					Bubble pressure	13
			–	350	586					Drop pressure	69
	99.9	(550±10)	Ar							Bubble pressure	103

SURFACE TENSION OF LIQUID ELEMENTS (Continued)

Element	Purity (wt.-%)	σ_{mp} (dyn/cm)	Atm.	t₁ °C	σ_{t1} (dyn/cm)	t₂ °C	σ_{t2} (dyn/cm)	t₃ °C	σ_{t3} (dyn/cm)	Method	Ref.
		(525±30)	H₂	390	604					Bubble pressure	1
		590±5	—							Solid state curvature	Z8
	99.9999		—		(non linear)					Sessile drop	Z12
Co	99.99		Ar	1550	1836					Sessile drop	108
	99.99		vac., Al₂O₃	1520	1800					Sessile drop	46
	99.99		He, Al₂O₃	1520	(1630)					Sessile drop	46
	99.99		He, BeO	1520	(1640)					Sessile drop	46
	99.99		He, MgO	1520	(1560)					Sessile drop	46
	99.99		H₂, Al₂O₃	1520	1780					Sessile drop	46
	99.99		He	1520	(1620)					Bubble pressure	46
	99.99		H₂	1520	(1590)					Bubble pressure	46
			vac.	1500	1870					Sessile drop	7
				1600	(1640)					Sessile drop	135
				1600	(1600)					Sessile drop	135
	99.99		vac.	1600	1815					Sessile drop	53
	99.99	(1520)	vac., Al₂O₃	1600	1812					Sessile drop	54
	99.99		H₂, He	1550	1845					Bubble pressure	61
	99.99		H₂, He							Bubble pressure	63
	99.9983	1880	vac.	1550	1780					Pendant drop	5
	99.99		vac.							Bubble pressure	59
Cr	—	1700±50	vac.	1950	1590±50					Sessile drop	47
	99.9997		Ar							Dynam. drop weight	6
Cs			Ar	62	68.4					Pendant drop	195
			Ar	62	67.5	146	62.9			Bubble pressure	193
	99.95		Ar	39	69.5	494	42.8	642	34.6	Bubble pressure	24
	99.99	73.74	Ar	$\sigma = 73.74 - 1.791 \cdot 10^{-2}(t-t_{mp}) - 9.610 \cdot 10^{-5}(t-t_{mp})^2 + 6.629 \cdot 10^{-8}(t-t_{mp})^3$ (t°C) (71–1011°C)						Bubble pressure	26
	99.995	58.6	He	$\sigma = 68.6 - 0.047(t-t_{mp})$ (t°C) (52–1100°C)						Bubble pressure	121
Cu	—		Ar	1120	1269±20					Sessile drop	11
		(1150)	vac.							Pendant drop	35
	—		Ar	1120	1285±10					Sessile drop	108

SURFACE TENSION OF LIQUID ELEMENTS (Continued)

Element	Purity (wt.-%)	σ_{mp} (dyn/cm)	Atm.	t_1 °C	σ_{t1} (dyn/cm)	t_2 °C	σ_{t2} (dyn/cm)	t_3 °C	σ_{t3} (dyn/cm)	Method	Ref.
	99.98		H_2	1100	1301	1165	1295	1255	1287	Bubble pressure	134
		1270	vac.							Sessile drop	7
			vac.	1120	1285					Sessile drop	198
		(1085)		1440	1298					Bubble pressure	129
			vac.							Pendant drop	182
	99.99		He	1250	1290					Bubble pressure	62
	99.99		H_2	1250	1300					Bubble pressure	62
	99.9	(1180±40)	Ar							Bubble pressure	103
	—			1100	1220					Sessile drop	136
	—			1183	(1130)					Sessile drop	200
	—		vac.	1150	1370					Sessile drop	52
	99.997	1355	He, H_2							Sessile drop + Bubble pressure	138
	99.997	1352	vac.		$\sigma_t = 1352-0.17\,(t-t_{mp})$	(t°C)	(t°C)			Sessile drop	137
	99.997	1358	Ar		$\sigma_t = 1358-0.20\,(t-t_{mp})$	(t°C)	(t°C)			Bubble pressure	137
	99.99		Ar, He	1120	1285±10					Sessile drop	110
			H_2, He	1550	1265					Bubble pressure	63
	99.99999	1300	vac.							Pendant drop	5
	99.98		vac.	1130	1268±60					Sessile drop	15
	99.999		Ar	1600	1230					Bubble pressure	205
	99.9		N_2	1100	1341	1150	1338			Bubble pressure	128
		(1127)	vac.							Pendant drop	65
	99.99		Ar, H_2	1100	1320			1200	1335	Bubble pressure	169
Fe	—	1720	He	1570	(1731)					Sessile drop	95
				1550	1860					Sessile drop	74
										Sessile drop	74
	99.99			1580–1760	(880)					Bubble pressure	100
				1570	(1632)					Sessile drop	93
	99.99		He	1650	(1610)					Sessile drop	46
	99.99		He	1650	(1430)					Sessile drop	46
	99.99		H_2	1650	(1400)					Sessile drop	46
		(1384)	vac.							Pendant drop	182
		(1700)	vac.							Sessile drop	7
	—		vac., He	1550	1865					Sessile drop	209

SURFACE TENSION OF LIQUID ELEMENTS (Continued)

Element	Purity (wt.—%)	σ_{mp} (dyn/cm)	Atm.	t_1,°C	σ_{t1} (dyn/cm)	t_2,°C	σ_{t2} (dyn/cm)	t_3,°C	σ_{t3} (dyn/cm)	Method	Ref.
	99.99	(1650)	He	1650	(1430)					Bubble pressure	62
	99.99		H₂	1650	(1400)					Bubble pressure	62
			He, H₂	1650	(1640)					Sessile drop	136
	99.985	(1560)	Ar	1550	1788					Bubble pressure	61
	—		vac., Al₂O₃	1560	(1710)					Sessile drop	110
	99.94		vac.							Sessile drop	68
	99.9998	1880	He							Sessile drop	207
	99.93	1860±40	He							Pendant drop	5
			vac.							Sessile drop	116
		(1510)	vac.							Drop weight	139
	99.97		vac., BeO	1550	1830±6					Sessile drop	45
	Armco		Ar, N₂	1550	1795					Bubble pressure	164
			vac.	1550	1754					Sessile drop	42
	99.987		vac.	1550	(1730)					Sessile drop	159
	99.85	(1619)	vac.							Pendant drop	65
	99.69		He, Al₂O₃	1550	(1727)					Sessile drop	158
	99.69		H₂, Al₂O₃	1550	(1734)					Sessile drop	158
		1760±20	He, H₂		$\sigma = 1760 - 0.35\,(t - t_{mp})$ (t°C)					Sessile drop	157
	99.9992	1773	He, H₂		$\sigma = 773 + 0.65\; t$ (t°C) (1550–1780°C)					Oscillating drop	Z2
			—	1550	1780					Sessile drop	Z11
Fr	—		—	100	58.4					calculated	145
Ga	—	704	Ar, He							Bubble pressure	197
	—	725±10	Ar							Bubble pressure	104
	—		vac.	350	718					Sessile drop	64
			He, Al₂O₃	1500	559					Sessile drop	57
	99.9998	718	vac., Al₂O₃		$\sigma = 718 - 0.101\,(t - t_{mp})$ (t°C)					Sessile drop	85
Ge		621.4	vac.							Drop weight	126
		650	vac.	1200	530					Sessile drop	99
			vac.	1000	650					Sessile drop	Z5
		632±5	N₂, He							Solid state curvature	Z8

SURFACE TENSION OF LIQUID ELEMENTS (Continued)

Element	Purity (wt.–%)	σ_{mp} (dyn/cm)	Atm.	σ_{t1}		σ_{t2}		σ_{t3}		Method	Ref.
				t_1 °C	σ (dyn/cm)	t_2 °C	σ (dyn/cm)	t_3 °C	σ (dyn/cm)		
Hf	97.5+2.5 Zr	(1460)	vac.							Pendant drop	151
		1630	vac.							Pendant drop	5
Hg			H_2	20	(542)					Pendant drop	165
			air	16	(410)					Sessile drop	181
			air	20	(435.5)					Oscillating jet	175
			vac.	20	472					Oscillating jet	73
			vac.	20	(402)					Drop pressure	146
				25	476					Drop weight	75
			vac.	20	(436)					Sessile drop	160
			vac.	20	(432)					Sessile drop	170
			H_2	25	476					Drop pressure	78
				25	472					Drop weight	81
				25	(464)					Sessile drop	82
			H_2	19	473					Bubble pressure	173
				20	(437)					Capillary depression	144
			vac.	20	480					Drop weight	21
				25	(516)					Sessile drop	37
				25	(435)					Sessile drop	91
			vac.	25	473					Drop weight†	31
				25	488					Sessile drop	32
				25	(498)					Sessile drop	30
			vac.	20	(420)					Sessile drop	174
				25	476					Sessile drop	90
			vac.	20	(410)					Drop pressure	178
			vac.	20	(455)					Drop pressure	39
				25	484±1.5					Sessile drop	89
			vac.	22	(468)					Drop pressure	162
			vac.	20	(465.2)	103	449.7	350	387.1	Drop pressure	162
				25	484.9±1.8					Sessile drop	27
			vac.	20	485.5±1.0	$\sigma_t = 489.5 - 0.20 \ (t°C)$				Drop pressure	17
			Ar	20	(454.7)					Bubble pressure	188
				21	(350.5)					Bubble pressure	23

SURFACE TENSION OF LIQUID ELEMENTS (Continued)

Element	Purity (wt.-%)	σ_{mp} (dyn/cm)	Atm.	t_1°C	σ_{t1} (dyn/cm)	t_2°C	σ_{t2} (dyn/cm)	t_3°C	σ_{t3} (dyn/cm)	Method	Ref.
	99.99		He, H_2	20	475					Bubble pressure	62
	99.9		Ar	20	(500±15)					Bubble pressure	103
			vac.	-10	487					Drop pressure	69
			vac.	25	483.5±1.0					Sessile drop	140
				22	(465)					Bubble pressure	194
				25	485.1					Sessile drop	142
				16.5	487.3	25	485.4±1.2			Pendant drop	171
				23–25	482.8±9.7					Contact angle	18
				span: $\sigma_t = 468.7 - 1.61 \cdot 10^{-1} \cdot t - 1.815 \cdot 10^{-4} t^2$ (t°C)							206
			vac.	20	484.6±1.3					Pendant drop	132
			Ar	25	480					Bubble pressure	172
			vac.	20	482.5±3.0					Bubble pressure	177
					$\sigma_t = 485.5 - 0.149t - 2.84 \cdot 10^{-4} t^2$ (t°C)						
			Ar	21.5	484.9±0.3					Bubble pressure	Z13a
In	99.95	559	H_2	600	515					Capillary method	133
	99.995	556.0	Ar, He	623	540					Capillary method	77
			vac.	185	592					Bubble pressure	69
			H_2	600	514					Drop pressure	16
				300	541					Sessile drop	83
	99.999		Ar	200	556	400	535	550	527.8	Bubble pressure	123
	99.9994		vac.	350	539					Drop pressure	106
	99.9999	560±5	–	$\sigma = 568.0 - 0.04t - 7.08 \cdot 10^{-5} t^2$ (t°C)						Sessile drop	Z12
Ir	99.9980	2250	vac.							Pendant drop	5
K	99.895	101	Ar	$\sigma = 117 - 0.66 (t - t_{mp})$						Bubble pressure	189
	1±0.3±1		–							–	84
	1±7		vac.	87	112	457	80	677	64.8	Drop weight	185
	–		Ar							Bubble pressure	24
	99.986	116.95	Ar	$\sigma = 116.95 - 6.742 \cdot 10^{-2} (t - t_{mp}) - 3.836 \cdot 10^{-5} (t - t_{mp})^2 + 3.707 \cdot 10^{-8} (t - t_{mp})^3$ (t°C) (77–983°C)						Bubble pressure	172

SURFACE TENSION OF LIQUID ELEMENTS (Continued)

Element	Purity (wt.-%)	σ_{mp} (dyn/cm)	Atm.	t_1°C	σ_{t1} (dyn/cm)	t_2°C	σ_{t2} (dyn/cm)	t_3°C	σ_{t3} (dyn/cm)	Method	Ref.
	99.936	(79.2)	He		$(\sigma = 76.8 - 70.3 \cdot 10^{-4}(t-400))$ (t°C) (600–1126°C)					Bubble pressure	121
	99.97	95±9.5	–							Drop weight	Z9
		111.35 ±0.64	He		$\sigma = 115.51 - 0.0653 \cdot$ (t°C) (70–713°C)					Bubble pressure	Z10
Li	99.95		Ar	180	397.5	300	380	500	351.5	Bubble pressure	189
	99.98		Ar	287	386	922	275	1077	253	Bubble pressure	24
Mg	99.8		Ar	681	563	789	532	894	502	Bubble pressure	208
	99.9		N₂	670	552	700	542	740	528	Bubble pressure	149
	99.91	(525±10)	Ar	700	550±15					Bubble pressure	114
	99.5	583	Ar							Bubble pressure	105
			Ar		$\sigma = 721 - 0.149\,T$ (T°K) (1125–1326°K)					Bubble pressure	25
Mn	99.9985	1100 ± 50	Ar							Dynam. drop weight	6
	99.94		vac.	1550	1030					Sessile drop	159
	–		–	1550	1010					Sessile drop	Z11
Mo	99.7	(1915)	vac.							Pendant drop	148
		2080	vac.							Drop weight	139
	99.9996	2250	vac.							Pendant drop	5
	99.98	2049	vac.							Pendant drop	65
	–	2130	vac.							Pendant drop	Z1
Na	99.995	191	Ar	110	205.7	263	198.2			Bubble pressure	208
			Ar	123	198	129	198.5			Bubble pressure	188
			vac.	140	190					Drop volume	2
		200.2±0.6	vac.							Sessile drop	28
		202	vac.		$\sigma = 202 - 0.092(t-t_{mp})$; 100–1000C					–	84
			vac.	617	144	764	130	855	120.4	Drop weight	185
	p.a.	210.12	Ar		$\sigma = 210.12 - 8.105 \cdot 10^{-2}(t-t_{mp}) - 8.064 \cdot 10^{-5}(t-t_{mp})^2 + 3.380 \cdot 10^{-8}(t-t_{mp})^3$ (t°C) (141–992°C)					Bubble pressure	24
	99.96		Ar							Bubble pressure	172
	99.982	187.4	He		$\sigma = 144 - 0.108(t-500)$ (t°C) (400–1125°C)					Bubble pressure	121
Nb, Cb	99.9986	1900	vac.							Pendant drop	5
	99.99	(1827)	vac.							Pendant drop	65
	–	2020	vac.							Pendant drop	Z1

SURFACE TENSION OF LIQUID ELEMENTS (Continued)

Element	Purity (wt.–%)	σ_{mp} (dyn/cm)	Atm.	t_1 °C	σ_{t1} (dyn/cm)	t_2 °C	σ_{t2} (dyn/cm)	t_3 °C	σ_{t3} (dyn/cm)	Method	Ref.
Nd		688	Ar	1186	674					Bubble pressure	124
Ni	99.7		He	1470	(1615)					Sessile drop	94
	99.7		H$_2$	1470	(1570)					Sessile drop	94
	99.7	1725	vac.	1470	1735					Sessile drop	94
			vac.	1475	1725					Sessile drop	141
	99.99		vac.	1550	(1934)					Sessile drop	115
	–		Ar							Sessile drop	108
	99.99		vac., Al$_2$O$_3$	1520	1740					Sessile drop	46
	99.99		He, Ar, Al$_2$O$_3$	1520	1770					Sessile drop	46
	99.99		H$_2$, Al$_2$O$_3$	1520	(1600)					Sessile drop	46
	99.99		He, MgO	1470	(1530)					Sessile drop	46
	99.99		He, BeO	1470	(1500)					Sessile drop	46
	99.99		H$_2$	1530	(1650)					Bubble pressure	46
	99.99		H$_2$	1470	(1530)					Bubble pressure	46
	99.99		He	1470	(1490)					Bubble pressure	46
	99.99	1725	vac.	1600	(1600)					Sessile drop	7
	99.99		vac.	1500	1720					Sessile drop	135
	99.99		vac.	1550	1780					Sessile drop	50
	99.99		vac., Al$_2$O$_3$	1550	1735					Sessile drop	54
	99.99		H$_2$, He	1470	1700					Bubble pressure	60
	99.99		vac.	1640	1705					Bubble pressure	61
	99.99		vac., Al$_2$O$_3$	1560	1810					Sessile drop	56
	–		vac.							Sessile drop	207
	99.9991	1770±13	vac.							Drop weight	5
	99.9991	1728±10	vac.							Drop weight	5
	99.9991	1822±8	vac.							Pendant drop	5
		(1670)	vac.							Drop weight	139
		1760	vac.							Sessile drop	55
		(1687)	vac.							Pendant drop	65
	–		He	1500	1745	$\sigma = 1770-0.39\,(t-1550)\ (t°C)$				Sessile drop	57
	–	1809±20	H$_2$, He / Al$_2$O$_3$		$\sigma = 1665+0.215t\ (t°C)\ (1475-1650°C)$					Sessile drop	157
	99.99975	(1977)	He							Oscillating drop	Z2

SURFACE TENSION OF LIQUID ELEMENTS (Continued)

Element	Purity (wt.–%)	σ_{mp} (dyn/cm)	Atm.	t_1 °C	σ_{t1} (dyn/cm)	t_2 °C	σ_{t2} (dyn/cm)	t_3 °C	σ_{t3} (dyn/cm)	Method	Ref.
Os	99.9998	2500	vac.							Pendant drop	5
P(white)				50	69.7	68.7	64.95			Bubble pressure	80
Pb	99.98		H$_2$, N$_2$	340	448					Bubble pressure	71
			air	360	452	390	442	440	439	Ring removal	97
		451	vac.	425	440					Drop pressure	101
		450	He	350–450	450					Pendant drop	87
	99.998	480	H$_2$	623	474					Ring removal	13
				362	455					Capillary method	133
				700	428					Capillary method	77
			vac.	1000	388					Drop pressure	69
	99.9									Sessile drop	27
			H$_2$	350	445					Bubble pressure	134
	99.9	(410±5)	Ar	340	442					Bubble pressure	104
			vac.			400	435			Drop pressure	153
	99.98		vac.							Drop pressure	70
	99.9995	470	vac.	$\sigma = 538 - 0.114\,T\ (T°K)\ (1440\text{–}1970°K)$						Bubble pressure	26
	99.9994		vac.	450	438					Drop pressure	107
	99.999		He	1600	310					Sessile drop	199
				390	456					Bubble pressure	1
				$\sigma_t = 470 - 0.164\,(t - t_{mp})\ (MP\text{–}535°C)\ (t°C)$						Solid state curvature	Z8
		424±10	Air							Bubble pressure	Z13a
	99.999	470	Ar							Sessile drop	50
Pd	99.998	1470	vac.							Pendant drop	5
	99.998	1500	vac.							Sessile drop	199
		1460	He								
Pt	99.84	1869	CO$_2$	1800	(1699±20)					Drop weight	167
		(1740±20)	vac.							Drop volume	48
	99.999	1865	Ar							Sessile drop	109
	99.9980		vac.							Pendant drop	5
Pu		550±55								—	186
Rb		(77±5)	vac.							Drop diffusion in quartz tube	201

SURFACE TENSION OF LIQUID ELEMENTS (Continued)

Element	Purity (wt.-%)	σ_{mp} (dyn/cm)	Atm.	t_1 °C	σ_{t1} (dyn/cm)	t_2 °C	σ_{t2} (dyn/cm)	t_3 °C	σ_{t3} (dyn/cm)	Method	Ref.
	99.8		Ar	52	84	477	55	632	46.8	Bubble pressure	24
	99.92	91.17	Ar	$\sigma = 91.17 - 9.189 \cdot 10^{-2}(t-t_{mp}) + 7.228 \cdot 10^{-5}(t-t_{mp})^2 - 3.830 \cdot 10^{-8}(t-t_{mp})^3$ (t°C) (104–1006°C)						Bubble pressure	172
	99.997	85.7	He	$\sigma = 85.7 - 0.054(t-t_{mp})$ (t°C) (53–1115°C)						Bubble pressure	121
Re	99.4	2610	vac.							Pendant drop	148
	99.9999	2700	vac.							Pendant drop	5
Ru	99.9980	2250	vac.							Pendant drop	5
Rh	99.9975	1940	vac.							Sessile drop	50
		2000	vac.							Pendant drop	5
S	—	60.9	vac.	250	51.1					Pendant drop	143
Sb			H₂	640	349	700	349	974	342	Drop weight	20
			H₂	750	368	900	361	1100	348	Bubble pressure	40
			vac.	640	367.9	762	364.9			Drop weight	131
	99.5	383	H₂, N₂	675	384	800	380			Bubble pressure	71
	99.99	395±20	Ar							Bubble pressure	104
	99.15	395±20	Ar							Bubble pressure	105
	99.999		N₂	800	359	1000	351	1100	345	Bubble pressure	128
	99.995		Ar	650	350.2	700	347.6	800	345.0	Bubble pressure	123
	99.999		He	1600	320					Sessile drop	199
Se	—		Ar	230–250	88.0±5					Bubble pressure	105
Si			He	1450	725					Pendant drop	87
			vac.	1550	720					Sessile drop	68
	99.99		vac.	1550	750					Sessile drop	41
	99.9999		Ar	1500	825					Pendant drop	43
Sn	—		N₂	275	612	500	572	800	520	Bubble pressure	149
	—		air	280	523	340	520			Ring removal	97

SURFACE TENSION OF LIQUID ELEMENTS (Continued)

Element	Purity (wt.-%)	σ_{mp} (dyn/cm)	Atm.	t_1 °C	σ_{t1} (dyn/cm)	t_2 °C	σ_{t2} (dyn/cm)	t_3 °C	σ_{t3} (dyn/cm)	Method	Ref.
	99.99	537	vac.	500	524	600	508			Drop pressure	154
		530	He							Pendant drop	87
			H₂	489	543	572	528	692	503	Conical capillaries	9
			—	250	536					Drop pressure	179
			—	450	530					Drop pressure	119
			—	250	545					Drop pressure	112
	99.93		vac.	250	549	400	539	600	526	Drop pressure	156
	99.998	566	H₂	623	559					Capillary method	133
			—							Capillary method	77
		610	vac.							Pendant drop	182
			—	800	500					Sessile drop	7
			—	300	538					Drop pressure	190
			—	300	(527)					Drop pressure	76
			—	290	546					Sessile drop	190
	99.99	(526±10)	H₂, He	600	530					Bubble pressure	62
	99.9		Ar	290	600					Bubble pressure	104
			vac.							Sessile drop	147
	99.965	543.7	H₂	740	508	950	489.5	1115	479.5	Bubble pressure	127
	99.89	562	vac.							Bubble pressure	33
			vac.	300	554					Sessile drop	55
			vac.							Sessile drop	64
	99.999	590	H₂							Sessile drop	86
	99.9999		H₂	290	(520)					Sessile drop	67
	99.9994		vac.	246	552.7	290	(524)	(vac.)		Sessile drop	203
				350	537					Drop pressure	106
Sr	99.999	555.8±1.9	vac.	1000	470					Bubble pressure	176
	99.96	552	vac.		$\sigma = 566.84 - 4.76 \cdot 10^{-2}\,t$ (t°C)					Sessile drop	Z5
	99.96	552	Ar		$\sigma_t = 552 - 0.167\,(t - t_{mp})$ (MP−500°C) (t°C)					Bubble pressure	Z13a
			Ar	775	288	830	282	893	282	Bubble pressure	125
	99.5	303	Ar		$\sigma = 392 - 0.085\,T$ (T°K) (1152−1602°K)					Bubble pressure	25
Ta		2360	vac.							Pendant drop	88
		2030	vac.							Pendant drop	88
		1910	vac.							Drop weight	139
	99.9983	2150	vac.							Pendant drop	5
	99.9	(1884)	vac.							Pendant drop	65

SURFACE TENSION OF LIQUID ELEMENTS

SURFACE TENSION OF LIQUID ELEMENTS (Continued)

Element	Purity (wt-%)	σ_{mp} (dyn/cm)	Atm.	σ_{t1}		σ_{t2}		σ_{t3}		Method	Ref.
				t_1 °C	σ (dyn/cm)	t_2 °C	σ (dyn/cm)	t_3 °C	σ (dyn/cm)		
Te	99.4	186±2	Ar							Bubble pressure	105
	–		vac.	460	178±1.5					Capillary method	184
			vac.	475	(162)					Electro-capillarity	117
		178	vac.		$\sigma = 178-0.024\,(t-t_{mp})$ (t°C)					Bubble pressure	204
Ti	98.7	1510	vac.							Capillary method	44
	99.92	1390	Ar							Pendant drop	151
	99.9551	1460	vac.							Drop weight	139
	99.0	1650	vac.							Pendant drop	5
	99.99999		vac.	1680	1576					Drop weight	191
			vac.	1680	1588					Drop weight	191
	99.85	(1880)	vac.							Pendant drop	65
	99.69	1402	vac.							Pendant drop	65
Tl		464.5	Ar	450	452					Bubble pressure	192
	–		–	450	450					Drop pressure	119
			vac.							Electro-capillarity	117
	99.999	467	vac.	450	450					Bubble pressure	26
	99.999		vac.		$\sigma = 536-0.119T$ (T°K) (1270–1695°K)					Drop pressure	107
U		1500±75	Ar							Bubble pressure	186
	99.94	1550	vac.							Pendant drop	34
		(1294)	vac.							Pendant drop	65
V	99.9977	1950	vac.							Pendant drop	5
	–	(1760)	vac.							Pendant drop	Z1
W		2310	vac.							Pendant drop	35
	99.9999	2500	vac.							Pendant drop	5
	99.8	2220	vac.							Pendant drop	148
	99.9	(2000)	vac.							Pendant drop	65

SURFACE TENSION OF LIQUID ELEMENTS (Continued)

Element	Purity (wt.-%)	σ_{mp} (dyn/cm)	Atm.	t_1 °C	σ_{t1} (dyn/cm)	t_2 °C	σ_{t2} (dyn/cm)	t_3 °C	σ_{t3} (dyn/cm)	Method	Ref.
Zn	99.9	750 ± 20	Ar							Bubble pressure	104
	99.99	757.0 ± 5	vac.							Sessile drop	202
	99.999	761.0	vac.							Sessile drop	202
	99.9999	767.5	vac.							Sessile drop	202
Zr	99.5	1400	Ar							Drop weight	151
	99.9998	1411 ± 70	vac.							Drop weight	180
	99.7	1480	vac.							Pendant drop	5
		(1533)	vac.							Pendant drop	65

SURFACE TENSION OF LIQUID HALOGENS

John Fredrickson

Element	Purity (wt.-%)	σ_{mp} (dyn/cm)	Atm.	t_1 °C	σ_{t1} (dyn/cm)	t_2 °C	σ_{t2} (dyn/cm)	t_3 °C	σ_{t3} (dyn/cm)	Method	Ref.
F			Vac.	-203.16	17.9	-197.86	16.2	-192.16	14.6	Capillary method	210
		22.33	Vac.		$\sigma = -39.10 - 0.2797(t°C)$					Calculated	211
Cl			Air	-61.5	31.61	-44.5	28.38	-28.7	25.23	Capillary method	212
		39.19	Air		$\sigma = 19.736 - 0.1927(t°C)$					Calculated	211
Br	99.999		Air	0	45.5	25	40.9	50	36.4	Capillary method	213
		46.8	Air		$\sigma = 45.5 - 0.182(t°C)$					Calculated	213
I	99.98		N_2	130	53.1	150	50.1	170	47.7	Bubble pressure	211
		55.7			$\sigma = 70.74 - 0.135(t°C)$					Calculated	211

References

1. Abdel-Aziz Abol Hassan, Neue Hütte, 15, 304 (1970).
2. Addison, Addison, Kerridge and Lewis, J. Chem. Soc., 2262 (1955).
3. Addison, Coldrey and Pulham, J. Chem. Soc., 1227 (1963).
4. Addison and Raynor, J. Chem. Soc., 965 (1966).
5. Allen, Trans. AIME, 227, 1175 (1963).
6. Allen, Trans. AIME, 230, 1357 (1964).
7. Allen and Kingery, Trans. AIME, 215, 30 (1959).
8. Astakhov, Penin and Dobkina, Zh. Fiz. Khim., 20, 403 (1946).
9. Atterton and Hoar, J. Inst. Met., 81, 541 (1953).
10. Ayushina, Levin and Geld, Zh. Fiz. Khim., 42, 2799 (1968).
11. Baes and Kellogg, J. Metals, 15, 643 (1953).
12. Baker and Gilbert, J. Amer. Chem. Soc., 62, 2479 (1940).
13. Bakradse and Pines, Zh. Tekhn. Fiz., 23, 1548 (1953).
14. Becker, Harders and Kornfeld, Arch. f. Eisenh., 20, 363 (1949).
15. Belforti and Lepie, Trans. AIME, 227, 80 (1963).
16. Bergh, J. Electrochem. S., 109, 1199 (1962).
17. Bering and Ioileva, Doklady A.N., 93, 85 (1953).
18. Biery and Oblak, Ind. Eng. Chem., Fund., 5, 121 (1966).
19. Bircumshaw, Phil. Mag., 2, 341 (1926).
20. Bircumshaw, Phil. Mag., 3, 1286 (1927).
21. Bircumshaw, Phil. Mag., 6, 510 (1928).
22. Bircumshaw, Phil. Mag., 12, 596 (1931).
23. Bobyk, Przemysl Chem., 39, 423 (1960).
24. Bohdanski and Schins, J. Inorg. Nucl. Chem., 29, 2173 (1967).
25. Bohdanski and Schins, J. Inorg. Nucl. Chem., 30, 2331 (1968).
26. Bohdanski and Schins, J. Inorg. Nucl. Chem., 30, 3362 (1968).
27. Bradhurst and Buchanan, J. Phys. Chem., 63, 1486 (1959).
28. Bradhurst and Buchanan, Austral. J. Chem., 14, 397 (1961).
29. Bradhurst and Buchanan, Austral. J. Chem., 14, 409 (1961).
30. Bradley, J. Phys. Chem., 38, 234 (1934).
31. Brown, Phil. Mag., 13, 578 (1932).
32. Burdon, Trans. Farad. Soc., 28, 866 (1932).
33. Cahill and Kirshenbaum, J. Inorg. Nucl. Chem., 26, 206 (1964).
34. Cahill and Kirshenbaum, J. Inorg. Nucl. Chem., 27, 73 (1965).
35. Calverley, Proc. Phys. Soc., 70, 1040 (1957).
36. Coffman and Parr, Ind. Eng. Chem., 19, 1308 (1927).
37. Cook, Phys. Review, 34, 513 (1929).
38. de L. Davies and West, J. Inst. Met., 92, 208 (1964).
39. Didenko and Pokrovski, Doklady A.N., 31, 233 (1941).
40. Drath and Sauerwald, Z. allg. anorg. Chem., 162, 301 (1927).
41. Dshemilev, Popel and Zarevski, Fiz. Met.i Met., 18, 83 (1964).
42. Dyson, Trans. AIME, 227, 1098 (1963).
43. Eljutin, Kostikov and Levin, Izv. Vys. Uch. Sav., Tsvetn. Met., 2, 131 (1970).
44. Eljutin and Maurakh, Izv. A.N., OTN, 4, 129 (1956).
45. Eremenko, Ivashchenko and Bogatyrenko, The Role of Surface Phenomena in Metallurgy, 37 (1963).
46. Eremenko, Ivashchenko, Fessenko and Nishenko, Izv. A.N., OTN, 7, 144 (1958).
47. Eremenko and Naidich, Izv. A.N., OTN, 2, 111 (1959).
48. Eremenko and Naidich, Izv. A.N., OTN, 6, 129 (1959).
49. Eremenko and Naidich, Izv. A.N., OTN, 6, 100 (1961)
50. Eremenko and Naidich, Izv. A.N., OTN, 2, 53 (1960).
51. Eremenko and Naidich, The Role of Surface Phenomena in Metallurgy, 65 (1963).
52. Eremenko, Naidich and Nossonovich, Zh. Fiz. Khim., 34, 1018 (1960).
53. Eremenko and Nishenko, Ukr. Khim. Zh., 26, 423 (1960).
54. Eremenko and Nishenko, Zh. Fiz. Khim., 35, 1301 (1961).
55. Eremenko and Nishenko, Ukr. Khim. Zh., 30, 125 (1964).
56. Eremenko, Nishenko and Naidich, Izv. A.N., OTN, 3, 150 (1961).
57. Eremenko, Nishenko and Skljarenko, Izv. A. N., OTN, 2, 188 (1966).

References (Continued)

58. Eremenko, Nishenko and Taj-Shou-Vej., Izv. A.N., OTN, **3**, 116 (1960).
59. Eremenko and Vassiliu, Ukr. Khim. Zh., **31**, 557 (1965).
60. Eremenko, Vassiliu and Fessenko, Zh. Fiz. Khim., **35**, 1750 (1961).
61. Fessenko, Zh. Fiz. Khim., **35**, 707 (1961).
62. Fessenko and Eremenko, Ukr. Khim. Zh., **26**, 198 (1960).
63. Fessenko, Vassiliu and Eremenko, Zh. Fiz. Khim., **36**, 518 (1962).
64. Flechsig, Thesis, Techn. Univ. Berlin, (1964).
65. Flint, J. Nucl. Mat., **16**, 260 (1965).
66. Gans, Pawlek and Roepenack, Z. Metallkunde, **54**, 147 (1963).
67. Gans and Parthey, Z. Metallkunde, **57**, 19 (1966).
68. Geld and Petrushevski, Izv. A.N., OTN, **3**, 160 (1961).
69. Gratzianski and Rjabov, Zh. Fiz. Khim., **33**, 487, 1253 (1959).
70. Gratzianski, Rjabov and Tobolich, Ukr. Khim. Zh., **29**, 1219 (1963).
71. Greenaway, J. Inst. Met., **74**, 133 (1947).
72. Grunmach, Ann.d. Physik, **3**, 660 (1900).
73. Hagemann, Thesis, Univ. of Freiburg/Br., (1914).
74. Halden and Kingery, J. Phys. Chem., **59**, 557 (1955).
75. Harkins and Ewing, J. Amer. Chem., Soc., **42**, 2539 (1920).
76. Herczynska, Z. Phys. Chem., **214**, 355 (1960).
77. Hoar and Melford, Trans. Farad. Soc., **53**, 315 (1957).
78. Hogness, J. Amer. Chem. Soc., **43**, 1621 (1921).
79. Humenik and Kingery, J. Amer. Ceram. Soc., **37**, 18 (1954).
80. Hutchinson, Trans. Farad. Soc., **39**, 229 (1943).
81. Iredale, Phil. Mag., **45**, 1088 (1923).
82. Iredale, Phil. Mag., **48**, 177 (1924).
83. Jacobj, Thesis, Univ. of Braunschweig, (1962).
84. Jordan and Lane, Austral. J. Chem., **18**, 1711 (1965).
85. Karasaev, Sadunıkin and Kukhno, Zh. Fiz. Khim., **41**, 654 (1967).
86. Kaufman and Whalen, Acta Metallurg., **13**, 797 (1965).
87. Keck and van Horn, Phys. Review, **91**, 512 (1953).
88. Kelly and Calverley, SERL-Report, **80**, 53 (1959).
89. Kemball, Trans. Farad. Soc., **42**, 526 (1946).
90. Kernaghan, Phys. Review, **37**, 990 (1931).
91. Kernaghan, Phys. Review, **49**, 414 (1936).
92. Kingery, J. Amer. Ceram. Soc., **37**, 42 (1954).
93. Kingery, Kolloid-Z., **161**, 95 (1958).
94. Kingery and Humenik, J. Phys. Chem., **57**, 359 (1953).
95. Kingery and Norton, AEC-Progr. Rep., **NYO-6296**, (1954).
96. Klyachko, Zavodskaja Labor., **6**, 1376 (1937).
97. Klyachko and Kunin, Zavodskaja Labor., **14**, 66 (1948).
98. Klyachko and Kunin, Doklady A.N., **64**, 64 (1949).
99. Kolesnikova, Izv. Vys. Uch. Sav., Tsvetn. Met., **9** (1960).
100. Kolesnikova and Samarin, Izv. A.N., OTN, **5**, 63 (1956).
101. Konstantinov, Thesis, State Univ. Moscow, (1950).
102. Korolkov, Izv. A.N., OTN, **2**, 35 (1956).
103. Korolkov: Litein'e Svojstva Metallov i Splavov, Isdatelstvo, A.N., SSSR, 37 (1960).
104. Korolkov and Bychkova, Issled. Splav. Tsvetn. Met., **2**, 122 (1960).
105. Korolkov and Igumnova, Izv. A.N., OTN, **6**, 95 (1961).
106. Kovalchuk, Kusnezov and Kotlovanova, Zh. Fiz. Khim., **42**, 1754 (1968).
107. Kovalchuk, Kusnezov and Butuzova, Zh. Fiz. Khim., **42**, 2265 (1968).
108. Kozakevitch and Urbain, J. Iron-& Steel-Inst., **186**, 167 (1957).
109. Kozakevitch and Urbain, C.R., Paris, **253**, 2229 (1961).
110. Kozakevitch and Urbain, Mém. Sci. Rev. Met., **58**, 401, 517, 931 (1961).
111. Krause, Sauerwald and Michalke, Z. anorg. allg. Chem., **181**, 353 (1929).
112. Kristian, Thesis, State Univ. Moscow, (1954).
113. Kubichek, Izv. A.N., OTN, **2**, 96 (1959).
114. Kubichek and Malzev, Izv. A.N., OTN, **3**, 144 (1959).
115. Kurkjian and Kingery, J. Phys. Chem., **60**, 961 (1956).
116. Kurochkin, Baum and Borodulin, Fiz. Met.i Met., **15**, 461 (1963).

117. Kusnezov, The Role of Surface Phenomena in Metallurgy, 72 (1963).
118. Kusnezov, Djakova and Malzeva, Zh. Fiz. Khim., **33**, 1551 (1959).
119. Kusnezov, Kochergin, Tishchenko and Posdynshcva, Doklady A.N., **92**, 1197 (1953).
120. Kusnezov, Popova and Duplina, Zh. Fiz. Khim., **36**, 880 (1962).
121. Kyrianenko and Solovev, Teplofiz. Vysok. Temp., **8**, 537 (1970).
122. Lasarev, Zh. Fiz. Khim., **36**, 405 (1962).
123. Lasarev, Zh. Fiz. Khim., **38**, 325 (1964).
124. Lasarev and Pershikov, Doklady A.N., **146**, 143 (1962).
125. Lasarev and Pershikov, Zh. Fiz. Khim., **37**, 907 (1963).
126. Lasarev and Pugachevich, Doklady A.N., **134**, 132 (1960).
127. Lauermann, Metzger and Sauerwald, Z. Phys. Chem., **216**, 42 (1961).
128. Lauermann and Sauerwald, Z. Metallkunde, **55**, 605 (1964).
129. Lucas, C.R., Paris, **248**, 2336 (1959).
130. Mack, Davis and Bartell, J. Phys. Chem., **45**, 846 (1941).
131. Matuyama, Sci. Rep. RITU, **16**, 555 (1927).
132. Melik-Gajkazan, Woronchikhina and Sakharova, Elektrokhim., **4**, 1420 (1968).
133. Melford and Hoar, J. Inst. Met., **85**, 197 (1957).
134. Metzger, Z. Phys. Chem., **211**, 1 (1959).
135. Monma and Suto, J. Jap. Inst. Met., **24**, 167 (1960).
136. Monma and Suto, J. Inst. Met., **1**, 69 (1960).
137. Naidich and Eremenko, Fiz. Met.i Met., **11**, 883 (1961).
138. Naidich, Eremenko, Fessenko, Vassiliu and Kirichenko, Zh. Fiz. Khim., **35**, 694 (1961).
139. Namba and Isobe, Sci. Pap. Inst. Phys. Chem. Res., Tokyo, **57**, 5154 (1963).
140. Nicholas, Joyner, Tessem and Olson, J. Phys. Chem., **65**, 1375 (1961).
141. Norton and Kingery, AEC-Progr. Rep., NYO 4632, (1955).
142. Olson and Johnson, J. Phys. Chem., **67**, 2529 (1963).
143. Ono and Matsushima, Sci. Rep. RITU, **9**, 309 (1957).
144. Oppenheimer, Z. anorg. allg. Chem., **171**, 98 (1928).
145. Osminin, Zh. Fiz. Khim., **43**, 2610 (1969).
146. Palacios, An. Soc. Esp. Fis., **18**, 294 (1920).
147. Parthey, Thesis, Techn. Univ. Berlin, (1961).
148. Pekarev, Izv. Vys. Uch. Sav., Tsvetn. Met., **6**, 111 (1963).
149. Pelzel, Berg-u. Hütt. Mon. Hefte, Leoben, **93**, 248 (1948).
150. Pelzel, Berg-u. Hütt. Mon. Hefte, Leoben, **94**, 10 (1949).
151. Peterson, Kedesdy, Keck and Schwarz, J. Appl. Phys., **29**, 213 (1958).
152. Poindexter, Phys. Review, **27**, 820 (1926).
153. Pokrovski, Ukr. Khim. Zh., **7**, 845 (1962).
154. Pokrovski and Galanina, Zh. Fiz. Khim., **23**, 324 (1949).
155. Pokrovski and Kristian, Zh. Fiz. Khim., **28**, (1954).
156. Pokrovski and Saidov, Fiz. Met.i Met., **2**, 546 (1956).
157. Popel, Shergin and Zarevski, Zh. Fiz. Khim., **43**, 2365 (1969).
158. Popel, Smirnov, Zarevski, Dshemilev and Pastukhov, Izv. A.N., **1**, 62 (1965).
159. Popel, Zarevski and Dshemilev, Fiz. Met.i Met., **18**, 468 (1964).
160. Popesco, C.R., Paris, **172**, 1474 (1921).
161. Portevin and Bastien, C.R., Paris, **202**, 1072 (1936).
162. Pugachevich, Zh. Fiz. Khim., **25**, 1365 (1951).
163. Pugachevich and Altynov, Doklady A.N., **86**, 117 (1952).
164. Pugachevich and Yashkichev, The Role of Surface Phenomena in Metallurgy, 46 (1963).
165. Quincke, Ann. d. Physik, **134**, 356 (1868).
166. Quincke, Ann. d. Physik, **135**, 621 (1868).
167. Quincke, Ann. d. Physik, **138**, 141 (1869).
168. Quincke, Ann. d. Physik, **61**, 267 (1897).
169. Raue, Metzger and Sauerwald, Metall, **20**, 1040 (1966).
170. Richards and Boyer, J. Amer. Chem. Soc., **43**, 290 (1921).
171. Roberts, J. Chem. Soc., 1907 (1964).
172. Roehlich jun., Tepper and Rankin, J. Chem. Eng. Data, **13**, 518 (1968).
173. Sauerwald and Drath, Z. anorg. allg. Chem., **154**, 79 (1926).
174. Sauerwald, Schmidt and Pelka, Z. anorg. allg. Chem., **223**, 84 (1935).

References (Continued)

175. Schmidt, Ann. d. Physik, **39**, 1108 (1912).
176. Schwaneke and Falke, US-Bur. Min., Inv. Rep. No. 7372, (1970).
177. Schwaneke, Falke and Miller, US-Bur. Min., Inv. Rep. No. 7340, (1970).
178. Semenchenko and Pokrovski, Uspekhii Khim., **6**, 945 (1937).
179. Semenchenko, Pokrovski and Lasarev, Doklady A.N., **89**, 1021 (1953).
180. Shunk and Burr, Trans. ASM, **55**, 786 (1962).
181. Siedentopf, Ann. d. Physik, **61**, 235 (1897).
182. Smirnova and Ormont, Zh. Fiz. Khim., **33**, 771 (1959).
183. Smith, J. Inst. Met., **12**, 168, 20 (1914).
184. Smith and Spitzer, J. Phys. Chem., **66**, 946 (1962).
185. Solovev and Makarova, Teplofiz. Vysok. Temp., **4**, 189 (1966).
186. Spriet, Mém. Sci. Rev. Mét., **60**, 531 (1963).
187. Tavadse, Bairamashvili, Khantadse and Zagareishvili, Doklady A.N., **150**, 544 (1963).
188. Taylor, J. Inst. Met., **83**, 143 (1954).
189. Taylor, Phil. Mag., **46**, 867 (1955).
190. Thyssen, Thesis, Humboldt-Univ. Berlin, (1960).
191. Tille and Kelly, Brit. J. Appl. Phys., **146**, 717 (1963).
192. Timofeyevicheva and Lasarev, Doklady A.N., **138**, 412 (1961).
193. Timofeyevicheva and Lasarev, Doklady A.N., 358 (1962).
194. Timofeyevicheva and Lasarev, Kolloidnyi-Zh., **24**, 227 (1962).
195. Timofeyevicheva, Lasarev and Pershikov, Doklady A.N., **143**, 618 (1962).
196. Timofeyevicheva and Pugachevich, Doklady A.N., **124**, 1093 (1959).
197. Timofeyevicheva and Pugachevich, Doklady A.N., **134**, 840 (1960).
198. Urbain and Lucas, Proc. N.P.L., Teddington, **9**, Pap. 4E (1959).
199. Watolin, Esin, Ukhov and Dubinin, Trudy Inst. Met., Sverdlovsk, **18**, 73 (1969).
200. Whalen and Humenik, Trans. AIME, **218**, 952 (1960).
201. Wegener, Z. Physik, **143**, 548 (1956).
202. White, Trans. AIME, **236**, 796 (1966).
203. White, Met. Review, **124**, 73 (1968).
204. Wobst and Rentzsch, Z. Phys. Chem., **240**, 36 (1969).
205. Yashkichevich and Lasarev, Izv. A.N., OTN, **1**, 170 (1964).
206. Yung Lee, Ind. Eng. Chem., Prod. Res. Dev., **7**, 66 (1968).
207. Zarevski and Popel, Fiz. Met.i Met., **13**, 451 (1962).
208. Zhivov, Trudy WAMI, SSSR, **14**, 99 (1937).
209. Zsin-Tan Wan, Karassev and Samarin, Izv. A.N., OTN, **1**, 30, 49 (1960).
210. Elverum and Doescher, J. Chem. Phys., **20**, 1834 (1952).
211. Fredrickson, J. Colloid Interfac. Sci., **48**, 506 (1974).
212. Johnson and McIntosh, J. Am. Chem. Soc., **31**, 1138 (1909).
213. Chao and Stenger, Talanta, **11**, 271 (1963).

Addendum

Z1. Eljutin, Kostikow and Penkow, Poroshk. Met., **9**, 46 (1970).
Z2. Fraser, Lu, Hamielec and Murarka, Met. Trans., **2**, 817 (1971).
Z3. Bernard and Lupis, Met. Trans., **2**, 555 (1971).
Z4. Rhee, J. Am. Ceram. Soc., **53**, 386 (1970).
Z5. Naidich, Perevertailo and Shuravlev, Zh. Fiz. Chim., **45**, 991 (1971). ·
Z6. Körber and Löhberg, Gießereiforschung, **23**, 173 (1971).
Z7. Ziesing, Austral. J. Phys., **6**, 86 (1953).
Z8. Sangster and Carman, J. Chem. Phys., **23**, 1142 (1955).
Z9. Primak and Quarterman, J. Phys. Chem., **58**, 1051 (1954).
Z10. Cooke, HTLMHTTM, Oak Ridge, Vol. I, p. 66, (Nov. 1964).
Z11. Ofizerow, Izv. A.N., Metally, **4**, 91 (1971).
Z12. White, Met. Trans., **3**, 1933 (1972).
Z13. Lang, Aluminum (Germany), **49**, 231 (1972).
Z13a. Lang, J. Inst. Met. (to be published).

SURFACE TENSION

SURFACE TENSION OF INORGANIC SOLUTES IN WATER

% = Weight % of solute
γ = Surface tension in dynes/cm.

Solute	T°C	%/γ							
HCl	20	%	1.78	3.52	6.78	12.81	16.97	23.74	35.29
		γ	72.55	72.45	72.25	71.85	71.75	70.55	65.75
HNO₃	20	%	4.21	8.64	14.99	34.87			
		γ	72.15	71.65	70.95	68.75			
H₂SO₄	25	%	4.11	8.26	12.18	17.66	21.88	29.07	33.63
		γ	72.21	72.55	72.80	73.36	73.91	74.80	75.29
HClO₄	25	%	4.86	10.01	20.38	30.36	53.74	63.47	72.25
		γ	71.18	70.34	69.21	68.57	69.02	69.73	69.01
KOH	18	%	2.73	5.31	10.08	17.57			
		γ	73.95	74.85	76.55	79.75			
NaOH	18	%	2.72	5.66	16.66	30.56	35.90		
		γ	74.35	75.85	83.05	96.05	101.05		
NH₄OH	18	%	1.72	3.39	4.99	9.51	17.37	34.47	54.37
		γ	71.65	70.65	69.95	67.85	65.25	61.05	57.05
KCl	20	%	0.74	3.60	6.93	13.88	18.77	22.97	24.70
		γ	72.99	73.45	74.15	75.55	76.95	78.25	78.75
LiCl	25	%	5.46	7.37	10.17	13.95			
		γ	74.23	75.10	76.30	78.10			

Solute	T°C	%/γ							
NaCl	20	%	0.58	2.84	5.43	10.46	14.92	22.62	25.92
		γ	72.92	73.75	74.39	76.05	77.65	80.95	82.55
PbCl	25	%	21.57	28.52	37.74				
		γ	75.20	76.80	79.20				
BaCl₂	25	%	9.26	16.73	25.58				
		γ	73.50	74.93	76.38				
MgCl₂	20	%	0.94	4.55	8.69	16.00	22.30	25.44	
		γ	73.07	74.00	75.75	79.15	82.95	85.75	
NaBr	20	%	4.89	9.33	13.37	23.00			
		γ	73.45	74.05	74.75	76.55			
Al₂(SO₄)₃	25	%	2.54	4.06	9.40	14.60	19.32	23.54	25.50
		γ	72.32	72.92	73.51	74.71	76.06	78.30	79.73
MgSO₄	20	%	1.19	5.68	10.75	19.41	24.53		
		γ	73.01	73.78	74.85	77.35	79.25		
Na₂SO₄	20	%	2.76	6.63	12.44				
		γ	73.25	74.15	75.45				
Na₂CO₃	20	%	2.58	5.03	9.50	13.72			
		γ	73.45	74.05	75.45	76.75			
NaNO₃	20	%	0.85	4.08	7.84	14.53	29.82	37.30	47.06
		γ	72.87	73.75	73.95	75.15	78.35	80.25	87.05

SURFACE TENSION OF INORGANIC SOLUTES IN ORGANIC SOLVENTS

% = Mol %
γ = Surface tension in dynes/cm.

Solute	Solvent	T°C	%/γ						
LiCl	Ethyl alcohol	14	%	0.72	2.30	4.62			
			γ	22.90	23.17	23.26			
LiBr	Ethyl alcohol	14	%	0.95	2.60				
			γ	23.08	23.35				
LiI	Ethyl alcohol	14	%	1.43	2.87	5.08	10.21	19.47	26.92
			γ	23.11	23.56	24.39	26.03	28.87	31.95
KI	Methyl alcohol	14	%	0.81	1.52	2.68			
			γ	23.76	24.11	24.71			
CaCl₂	Ethyl alcohol	24	%	0.94	1.98	3.79	7.47		
			γ	22.62	22.58	23.23	23.97		
NaI	Methyl alcohol	14	%	0.76	1.48	4.33	8.55	12.53	
			γ	22.83	23.29	24.85	27.41	29.75	

Solute	Solvent	T°C	%/γ						
NaI	Ethyl alcohol	24	%	0.45	1.80	3.63	4.54	6.02	10.46
			γ	22.47	22.82	23.41	23.52	24.00	25.07
NaI	Acetone	14	%	0.93	2.08	5.07	6.53		
			γ	24.22	24.40	25.04	25.12		
ZnI₂	Methyl alcohol	22	%	0.90	2.79	5.07			
			γ	22.97	24.23	25.84			
ZnI₂	Ethyl alcohol	24	%	0.41	1.72	3.42	6.90		
			γ	22.70	22.90	23.71	25.49		
H₂SO₄	Ethyl ether	17	%	3	10	40	75	90	
			γ	17.30	19.55	32.50	46.30	46.83	
H₂SO₄	Nitrobenzene	17	%	3	10	40	75	90	
			γ	42.73	43.96	46.05	47.52	48.25	

SURFACE TENSION OF ORGANIC COMPOUNDS IN WATER

% = Weight % of solute
γ = Surface tension in dynes/cm.

Solute	T°C	%/γ							
Acetic acid	30	%	1.00	2.475	5.001	10.01	30.09	49.96	69.91
		γ	68.00	64.40	60.10	54.60	43.60	38.40	34.30
Acetone	25	%	5.00	10.00	20.00	50.00	75.00	95.00	100.00
		γ	55.50	48.90	41.10	30.40	26.80	24.20	23.00
Acetonitrile	20	%	1.13	3.95	11.77	20.20	37.58	61.33	81.22
		γ	69.02	63.03	47.61	39.06	31.84	30.02	29.02
o-Aminobenzoic acid	25	%	12.35	22.36	30.45	37.44			
		γ	71.90	73.23	74.54	75.79			
m-Aminobenzoic acid	25	%	12.35	22.36	30.45	37.44			
		γ	73.30	74.59	76.16	77.89			

Solute	T°C	%/γ							
p-Aminobenzoic acid	25	%	12.35	22.36	30.45	37.44			
		γ	73.38	74.79	76.32	78.20			
Aminobutyric acid	25	%	4.96	9.34	13.43				
		γ	71.91	71.67	71.40				
Ammonium lactate	29	%	30.00	50.00	60.00	70.00	80.00	90.00	
		γ	35.40	34.40	35.40	35.60	38.20	44.50	
n-Butanol	30	%	0.04	0.41	9.53	80.44	86.05	94.20	97.40
		γ	69.33	60.38	26.97	23.69	23.47	23.29	22.25
n-Butyric acid	25	%	0.14	0.31	1.05	8.60	25.00	79.00	100.00
		γ	69.00	65.00	56.00	33.00	28.00	27.00	26.00

SURFACE TENSION OF ORGANIC COMPOUNDS
IN WATER (Continued)

Solute	T°C	%/γ								Solute	T°C	%/γ							
Dioxan	26	%	0.44	2.20	4.70	11.14	20.17	35.20	55.00	Morpholine	20	%	8.56	19.39	30.41	50.45	69.93	80.14	92.00
		γ	69.83	65.64	62.45	56.90	51.57	45.30	39.27			γ	67.80	62.62	59.15	52.85	47.05	43.62	41.60
Dioxan	26	%	67.68	76.45	83.02	91.90	95.60	97.77		Potassium lactate	29	%	40.00	50.00	60.00	70.00			
		γ	36.95	35.80	35.00	33.95	33.60	33.10				γ	66.40	66.40	65.40	63.40			
Formic acid	30	%	1.00	5.00	10.00	25.00	50.00	75.00	100.00	Phenol	20	%	0.024	0.047	0.118	0.417	0.941	3.76	5.62
		γ	70.07	66.20	62.78	56.29	49.50	43.40	36.51			γ	72.60	72.20	71.30	66.50	61.10	46.00	42.30
Glycerol	18	%	5.00	10.00	20.00	30.00	50.00	85.00	100.00	n-Propanol	25	%	0.1	0.5	1.0	5.0	60.0	80.0	90.0
		γ	72.90	72.90	72.40	72.00	70.00	66.00	63.00			γ	67.10	56.18	49.30	24.34	24.15	23.66	23.41
Glycine	25	%	3.62	6.98	10.12	13.10				Propionic acid	25	%	1.91	5.84	9.80	21.70	49.80	73.90	100.00
		γ	72.54	73.11	73.74	74.18						γ	60.00	49.00	44.00	36.00	32.00	30.00	26.00
Hydrocinnamic acid	21.5	%	7.02	12.62	18.39	26.09	31.06	38.25	47.93	Sodium lactate	29	%	1.00	10.00	30.00	40.00	50.00	60.00	70.00
		γ	69.08	66.49	63.63	59.25	56.14	52.96	47.24			γ	70.40	69.60	68.50	64.80	45.40	56.70	60.70
Methyl acetate	25	%	0.66	1.29	2.29	3.56				Sucrose	25	%	10.00	20.00	30.00	40.00	55.00		
		γ	66.33	62.92	58.22	55.08						γ	72.50	73.00	73.40	74.10	75.70		

SURFACE TENSION OF ORGANIC COMPOUNDS
IN ORGANIC SOLVENTS

% = Weight % of solvent
γ = Surface tension dynes/cm.

Solute	Solvent	T°C	%/γ					
Acetic acid	Benzene	35	%	10.45	25.53	34.28	43.93	68.77
			γ	25.40	25.21	25.32	25.43	25.99
Acetic acid	Acetone	25	%	25.63	50.83	75.62		
			γ	27.50	26.61	24.90		
Acetone	Ethyl ether	30	%	21.83	40.98	61.29	75.69	89.03
			γ	16.75	17.49	19.15	19.80	21.00
Acetonitrile	Ethyl alcohol	20	%	10.83	32.42	49.90	69.78	80.19
			γ	22.92	23.92	24.36	25.08	26.51
Aniline	Cyclohexane	32	%	14.35	37.65	50.67	72.28	96.46
			γ	24.21	24.51	24.50	25.61	37.45
Carbontetrachloride	Benzene	50	%	30.40	51.69	62.38	78.29	88.62
			γ	24.39	24.09	23.78	23.47	23.21
Cyclohexane	Nitrobenzene	15	%	5.00	10.00			
			γ	37.59	33.03			
Naphthalene	Benzene	79.5	%	20.00	40.00	50.00	60.00	80.00
			γ	23.42	26.70	27.80	29.20	31.70
Naphthalene	p-Nitrophenol	121	%	10.21	29.74	45.94	58.01	67.57
			γ	29.90	31.80	33.70	34.80	41.80

SURFACE TENSION OF METHYL ALCOHOL
IN WATER

% = Volume % of alcohol
γ = Surface tension dynes/cm.

T°C	%	7.5	10.00	25.0	50.0	60.0	80.0	90.0	100.0
20	γ	60.90	59.04	46.38	35.31	32.95	27.26	25.36	22.65
30	γ	59.33	57.27	45.30	34.52	32.26	26.48	24.42	21.58
50	γ	56.19	55.01	43.24	32.95	30.79	25.01	22.55	19.52

SURFACE TENSION OF ETHYL ALCOHOL IN WATER

% = Volume % of alcohol
γ = Surface tension dynes/cm.

T°C	%	5.00	10.00	24.00	34.00	48.00	60.00	72.00	80.00	96.00
20	γ	...	...	...	33.24	30.10	27.56	26.28	24.91	23.04
40	γ	54.92	48.25	35.50	31.58	28.93	26.18	24.91	23.43	21.38
50	γ	53.35	40.77	34.32	30.70	28.24	25.50	24.12	22.56	20.40

WATER AGAINST AIR

Temperature °C	Surface tension dynes/cm.	Temperature °C	Surface tension dynes/cm.	Temperature °C	Surface tension dynes/cm.
−8	77.0	15	73.49	40	69.56
−5	76.4	18	73.05	50	67.91
0	75.6	20	72.75	60	66.18
5	74.9	25	71.97	70	64.4
10	74.22	30	71.18	80	62.6
				100	58.9

INTERFACIAL TENSION

Surface Tension at the Interface Between Two Liquids
(Each liquid saturated with the other)

Liquids	Temperature °C	γ	Liquids	Temperature °C	γ
Benzene--Mercury...	20	357	Water--Heptylic acid	20	7.0
Ethyl ether--Mercury	20	379	Water--n-Hexane....	20	51.1
Water--Benzene.....	20	35.00	Water--Mercury.....	20	375.
Water--Carbon tetra- chloride	20	45.	Water-n-Octane......	20	50.8
Water--Ethyl ether ..	20	10.7	Water-n-Octyl alcohol	20	8.5

Substance		In contact with	Temperature °C	Surface tension dynes/cm.	References
Name	Formula				
Acetaldehyde	C_2H_4O	--vapor	20	21.2	AC(12)
Acetaldoxime	C_2H_5NO	--vapor	35	30.1	JP(1); JSG(1)
Acetamide	C_2H_5NO	--vapor	85	39.3	JS(3)
Acetanilide	C_2H_5NO	--vapor	120	35.6	JS(3)
Acetic acid	$C_2H_4O_2$	--vapor	10	28.8	AC(22, 23, 25); GC(1); JS(14);
" "	C_2H_4O	--vapor	20	27.8	tPRS(1); ZC(1, 6)
" "	C_2H_4O	--vapor	50	24.8	
Acetic anhydride	$C_4H_6O_3$	--vapor	20	32.7	GC(1); JS(4)
Acetone	C_3H_6O	--air or vapor	0	26.21	AC(20, 24, 25); AdC(1); BF(1);
"	C_3H_6O	--air or vapor	20	23.70	JP(5); JS(4, 14); ZC(3)
"	C_3H_6O	--air or vapor	40	21.16	
Acetonitrile	C_2H_3N	--vapor	20	29.30	AC(16); BF(1); GC(1); JP(5)
Acetophenone	C_8H_8O	--vapor	20	39.8	AC(27); AS(1); JP(2)
Acetyl chloride	C_2H_3ClO	--vapor	14.8	26.7	JS(4)
Acetylene	C_2H_2	--vapor	−70.5	16.4	AC(14)
Acetylsalicylic acid (in aq. sol.)	$C_9H_8O_4$	--vapor	25.9	60.06	GC(2)
Allyl alcohol	C_3H_6O	--air or vapor	20	25.8	AC(27); AdC(1); JS(4)
Allyl isothiocyanate	C_4H_5NS	--air or vapor	20	34.5	AC(16); GC(1)
Ammonia	NH_3	--vapor	11.1	23.4	JP(7)
"	NH_3	--vapor	34.1	18.1	JP(7)
Aniline	C_6H_7N	--air	10	44.10	AC(6, 17, 28); GC(1); JP(5); JS(12)
"	C_6H_7N	--vapor	20	42.9	
"	C_6H_7N	--air	50	39.4	
Argon	A	--vapor	−188	13.2	JS(15)
Azoxybenzene	$C_{12}H_{10}N_2O$	--vapor	51	43.34	JS(5)
Benzaldehyde	C_7H_6O	--air	20	40.04	AC(6, 24)
Benzene	C_6H_6	--air	10	30.22	AC(3, 5, 31, 32, 34); BF(2); JP(5);
"	C_6H_6	--air	20	28.85	JS(4, 9, 10, 11, 14); PRS(2); tRIA(1);
"	C_6H_6	--saturated with vapor	20	28.89	tPRS(1); ZC(4, 5)
"	C_6H_6	--air	30	27.56	
Benzonitrile	C_7H_5N	--air	20	39.05	AC(28); AS(2); GC(1); JP(5); JS(3)
Benzophenone	$C_{13}H_{10}O$	--air or vapor	20	45.1	AC(27); AS(1); ZC(5)
Benzylamine	C_7H_9N	--vapor	20	39.5	JS(3)
Benzyl alcohol	C_7H_8O	--air or vapor	20	39.0	AC(33); JS(6); PRS(1)
Bromine	Br_2	--air or vapor	20	41.5	AC(17); AdP(3); GC(1)
Bromobenzene	C_6H_5Br	--air	20	36.5	AC(8, 17); GC(1); JS(12)
Bromoform	$CHBr_3$	--vapor	20	41.53	AC(8); JP(2)
p-Bromophenol	C_6H_5BrO	--vapor	74.4	42.36	JS(6)
d-sec-Butyl alcohol	$C_4H_{10}O$	--vapor	10	23.5	JS(7)
n-Butyl alcohol	$C_4H_{10}O$	--air or vapor	0	26.2	AC(27, 33); JS(4)
" "	$C_4H_{10}O$	--air or vapor	20	24.6	AC(27, 33); JS(4)
" "	$C_4H_{10}O$	--air or vapor	50	22.1	AC(27, 33); JS(4)
tert-Butyl alcohol	$C_4H_{10}O$	--air or vapor	20	20.7	AC(33); JS(8)
n-Butylamine	$C_4H_{11}N$	--nitrogen	41	19.7	ZA(1)
n-Butyric acid	$C_4H_8O_2$	--air	20	26.8	AC(27); GC(1); JS(4)
Carbon bisulfide	CS_2	--vapor	20	32.33	AC(17, 28); GC(1); BF(2); JS(14); PRS(2); ZC(6)
Carbon dioxide	CO_2	--vapor	20	1.16	VK(1, 2)
"	CO_2	--vapor	−25	9.13	VK(1, 2)
Carbon tetrachloride	CCl_4	--vapor	20	26.95	AC(3, 5, 6, 28, 31); PRS(1, 2); ZC(5)
" "	CCl_4	--vapor	100	17.26	
" "	CCl_4	--vapor	200	6.53	
Carbon monoxide	CO	--vapor	−193	9.8	JS(15)
" "	CO	--vapor	−203	12.1	JS(15)
Chloral	C_2HCl_3O	--vapor	19.4	25.34	JS(4)
Chlorine	Cl_2	--chlorine	20	18.4	AC(11); JP(3)
"	Cl_2	--vapor	−30	25.4	AC(11); JP(3)
"	Cl_2	--vapor	−40	27.3	AC(11); JP(3)
"	Cl_2	--vapor	−50	29.2	AC(11); JP(3)
"	Cl_2	--vapor	−60	31.2	AC(11); JP(3)
Chloroacetic acid	$C_2H_2Cl_2O_2$	--nitrogen	25.7	35.4	ZA(1)
Chlorobenzene	C_4H_5Cl	--vapor	20	33.56	AC(6, 20, 28); JP(5); JS(11); PRS(2); tRIA(1); tPRS(1); ZC(6)
Chloroform	$CHCl_3$	--air	20	27.14	AC(6, 28, 31); AdC(1); PRS(2); tRIA(1); ZC(6)
o-Chlorophenol	C_6H_5ClO	--vapor	12.7	42.25	JS(6)
Cyclohexane	C_6H_{12}	--air	20	25.5	PRS(1); ZA(1)
Dichloroacetic acid	$C_2H_2Cl_2O_2$	--nitrogen	25.7	35.4	ZA(1)
Dichloroethane	$C_2H_4Cl_2$	--air	35.0	23.4	AC(17); AdC(1)
Diethylamine	$C_4H_{11}N$	--air	56	16.4	GC(1)
Diethylaniline	$C_{10}H_{15}N$	--vapor	20	34.2	AC(31); AS(1); MfC(1)
Diethyl carbonate	$C_5H_{10}O$	--air	20	26.31	AC(4); JS(5)
Diethyl oxalate	$C_6H_{10}O_4$	--vapor	20	32.0	AC(16); GC(1)
Diethyl phthalate	$C_{12}H_{14}O_4$	--vapor	20	37.5	AC(21); PRS(1)
Diethyl sulfate	$C_4H_{12}O_4S$	--air	13	34.61	JS(5)
Dimethylamine	C_2H_7N	--nitrogen	0	18.1	ZA(1)
"	C_2H_7N	--nitrogen	5	17.7	ZA(1)
Dimethylaniline	C_8H_{11}	--air or vapor	20	36.6	AC(4, 17, 31); JP(5)
1,5-Dimethyl-2-phenyl-3-pyrazolone	$C_{11}H_{12}N_2O$	--vapor	25.9	63.63	GC(2)
Dimethyl sulfate	$C_2H_6O_4S$	--air	18	40.12	JS(5)
Diphenylamine	$C_{12}H_{11}N$	--air or vapor	80	37.7	JP(2, 9); JS(3); ZA(1)
Ethyl acetate	$C_4H_8O_2$	--air	0	26.5	AC(26, 33); AdC(1); AS(2); JP(5); tPRS(1); ZC(6)
" "	$C_4H_8O_2$	--air	20	23.9	
" "	$C_4H_8O_2$	--air	50	20.2	
Ethyl acetoacetate	$C_6H_{10}O_3$	--air or vapor	20	32.51	AC(16); BD(2); GC(1); JS(4)
Ethyl alcohol	C_2H_6O	--air	0	24.05	AC(22, 23, 25, 32); BF(2); JP(5); tRIA(1); tPRS(1)
" "	C_2H_6O	--vapor	10	23.61	
" "	C_2H_6O	--vapor	20	22.75	
" "	C_2H_6O	--vapor	30	21.89	
Ethylamine	C_2H_7N	--nitrogen	0	21.3	PRA(4); ZA(1)
"	C_2H_7N	--nitrogen	9.9	20.4	PRA(4); ZA(1)
Ethylaniline	$C_8H_{11}N$	--air or vapor	20	36.6	AC(17, 33); AS(1); MfC(1)

Substance		In contact with	Temperature °C	Surface tension dynes/cm.	References
Name	Formula				
Ethylbenzene	C_8H_{10}	--vapor	20	29.20	AC(**17, 33, 34**); AdC(**1**); PRS(**1**)
Ethylbenzoate	$C_9H_{10}O_2$	--vapor	20	35.5	GC(**1**); ZA(**1**); MfC(**1**)
Ethyl bromide	C_2H_5Br	--vapor	20	24.15	AC(**6, 33**); GC(**1**)
Ethyl chloroformate	$C_3H_5ClO_2$	--vapor	15.1	27.5	JS(**4**)
Ethyl Cinnamate	$C_{11}H_{12}O_2$	--air	20	38.37	AC(**16**); PRS(**1**); ZC(**5**)
Ethylene bromide	$C_2H_4Br_2$	--vapor	20	38.37	AC(**5, 28, 33**); GC(**1**); JP(**2**); PRS(**2**); tRIA(**1**)
Ethylene chloride	$C_2H_4Cl_2$	--air	20	24.15	AC(**17, 33**); AdC(**1**); JS(**14**); ZC(**6**)
Ethylene oxide	C_2H_4O	--vapor	−20	30.8	
"	C_2H_4O	--vapor	0.0	27.6	
"	C_7H_7O	--vapor	20	24.3	
Ethyl ether	$C_4H_{10}O$	--vapor	20	17.01	} AC(**4, 15, 28, 31**); AdC(**1**); tPRS(**1**)
	$C_4H_{10}O$	--vapor	50	13.47	
Ethyl formate	$C_3H_6O_2$	--air or vapor	20	23.6	AC(**20, 26**); AdC(**1**); PRS(**2**)
Ethyl iodide	C_2H_5I	--vapor	20	29.4	AC(**33**); GC(**1**); JS(**4**); PRS(**1**); ZC(**6**)
Ethyl nitrate	$C_2H_5NO_3$	--air or vapor	20	28.7	AC(**27**); GC(**1**)
dl-Ethyl lactate	$C_5H_{10}O_3$	--air	20	29.9	AC(**20, 21**); JP(**8**)
Ethyl mercaptan	C_2H_6S	--air or vapor	20	22.5	AC(**4, 16**); JS(**4**)
Ethyl salicylate	$C_9H_{10}O_3$	--vapor	20.5	38.33	JS(**6**)
Formamide	CH_3NO	--vapor	20	58.2	AC(**27**); JS(**3**); ZC(**4**)
Formic acid	CH_2O_2	--air	20	37.6	AC(**23, 27**); GC(**1**); JS(**4**); MfC(**1**); ZA(**1**)
Furfural	$C_5H_4O_2$	--air or vapor	20	43.5	AC(**27**); GC(**1**)
Gelatin solution (1 %)		--water	2.85	8.3	ZK(**1**)
Glycerol	$C_3H_8O_3$	--air	20	63.4	
"	$C_3H_8O_3$	--air	90	58.6	} JR(**1**); MB(**1**); ZA(**1**); ZC(**3**)
"	$C_3H_8O_3$	--air	150	51.9	
Glycol	$C_2H_6O_2$	--air or vapor	20	47.7	AC(**29**); JS(**4**)
Helium	He	--vapor	−269	.12	cUL(**2**); PRA(**2**)
"	He	--vapor	−270	.239	cUL(**2**); PRA(**2**)
"	He	--vapor	−271.5	.353	cUL(**2**); PRA(**2**)
n-Hexane	C_6H_{14}	--air	20	18.43	AC(**5, 6, 16**); AdC(**1**); AS(**1**)
Hydrazine	N_2H_4	--vapor	25	91.5	AC(**1**)
Hydrogen	H_2	--vapor	−255	2.31	cUL(**1**); PRA(**1**)
Hydrogen cyanide	HCN	--vapor	17	18.2	ZE(**1**)
Hydrogen peroxide	H_2O_2	--vapor	18.2	76.1	AC(**13**)
Isobutyl alcohol	$C_4H_{10}O$	--vapor	20	23.0	AC(**4, 27, 32**); AdC(**1**); JP(**5**); JS(**4**)
Isobutylamine	$C_4H_{11}N$	--air	68	17.6	GC(**1**)
Isobutyl chloride	C_4H_9Cl	--air	20	21.94	AC(**6**); GC(**1**)
Isobutyric acid	$C_4H_8O_2$	--air or vapor	20	25.2	AC(**27**); GC(**1**); JS(**4**)
Isopentane	C_5H_{12}	--air	20	13.72	AC(**6**)
Isopropyl alcohol	C_3H_8O	--air or vapor	20	21.7	JS(**4**); AdC(**1**)
Methyl acetate	$C_3H_6O_2$	--air or vapor	20	24.6	AC(**26, 33**); AdC(**1**); PRS(**2**)
Methyl alcohol	CH_4O	--air	0	24.49	
" "	CH_4O	--air	20	22.61	} AC(**22, 23, 25, 32**); tPRS(**1**)
" "	CH_4O	--vapor	50	20.14	
Methylamine	CH_3NH_2	--nitrogen	−12	22.2	PRA(**1**); ZA(**1**)
"	CH_3NH_2	--vapor	−20	23.0	PRA(**1**); ZA(**1**)
"	CH_3NH_2	--nitrogen	−70	29.2	PRA(**1**); ZA(**1**)
N-Methylaniline	C_7H_9N	--air or vapor	20	39.6	AC(**17, 32**); AS(**1**)
Methyl benzoate	$C_8H_8O_2$	--air or vapor	20	37.6	GC(**1**); JP(**5**)
Methyl chloride	CH_3Cl	--air	20	16.2	WN(**1**)
Methyl ether	C_2H_6O	--vapor	−10	16.4	AC(**12**)
" "	C_2H_6O	--vapor	−40	21	AC(**12**)
Methylene chloride	CH_2Cl_2	--air	20	26.52	AC(**6**)
Methylene iodide	CH_2I_2	--air	20	50.76	AC(**8**)
Methyl ethyl ketone	C_4H_8O	--air	20	24.6	AC(**24**); AS(**1**)
Methyl formate	$C_2H_4O_2$	--vapor	20	25.08	AC(**26**); tPRS(**1**); GC(**1**)
Methyl iodide	CH_3I	--air	43.5	25.8	GC(**1**)
Methyl propionate	$C_4H_8O_2$	--air or vapor	20	24.9	AC(**20, 26**); AdC(**1**); PRS(**2**)
Methyl salicylate	$C_8H_8O_3$	--nitrogen	94	31.9	ZA(**1**)
Methyl sulfide	C_2H_6S	--vapor	11.1	26.50	JP(**6**)
Naphthalene	$C_{10}H_8$	--air or vapor	127	28.8	AS(**1**); JP(**2**)
Neon	Ne	--vapor	−248	5.50	cUL(**3**); PRA(**3**)
Nitric acid (98.8%)	HNO_3	--air	11.6	42.7	JS(**2**)
Nitrobenzene	$C_6H_5NO_2$	--air or vapor	20	43.9	AC(**6, 23**); AS(**2**); BF(**2**); GC(**1**); JS(**4, 12**)
Nitroethane	$C_2H_5NO_2$	--air or vapor	20	32.2	GC(**1**); JS(**4**)
Nitrogen	N_2	--vapor	−183	6.6	JS(**15**)
"	N_2	--vapor	−193	8.27	JS(**15**)
"	N_2	--vapor	−203	10.53	JS(**15**)
Nitrogen tetra oxide	N_2O_4	--vapor	19.8	27.5	JS(**4**)
Nitromethane	CH_3NO_2	--vapor	20	36.82	AC(**6, 27**); GC(**1**)
Nitrous oxide	N_2O	--vapor	20	1.75	VK(**1**)
n-Octane	C_8H_{18}	--vapor	20	21.80	AC(**4, 5, 34**); JS(**4**)
n-Octyl alcohol	$C_8H_{18}O$	--air	20	27.53	AC(**4, 5**)
Oleic acid	$C_{18}H_{34}O_2$	--air	20	32.50	PRS(**1**); AC(**4**)
Oxygen	O_2	--vapor	−183	13.2	JS(**15**)
Oxygen (65 %)	O_2	--air	−190.5	12.2	AD(**1**)
"	O_2	--vapor	−193	15.7	JS(**15**)
"	O_2	--vapor	−203	18.3	JS(**15**)
Paraldehyde	$C_6H_{12}O_3$	--air	20	25.9	AC(**27**); AdC(**1**)
Phenetole	$C_8H_{10}O$	--vapor	20	32.74	AC(**6, 28**); GC(**1**); JP(**5**)
Phenol	C_6H_6O	--air or vapor	20	40.9	} AC(**18, 19, 75**); JS(**2, 6, 13**); JP(**4**)
	C_6H_6O	--air or vapor	50	39.88	
Phenylhydrazine	$C_6H_8N_2$	--vapor	20	46.1	JS(**3**)
Phosphorus tribromide	PBr_3	--air	24	45.8	JS(**5**)
Phosphorus trichloride	PCl_3	--vapor	20	29.1	AC(**17**); GC(**1**); JP(**2**); JS(**4**)
Phosphorus triiodide	PI_3	--vapor	75.3	56.5	ZA(**1**)
Propionic acid	$C_3H_6O_2$	--vapor	20	26.7	AC(**27**); GC(**1**); JS(**4**)
n-Propyl acetate	$C_5H_{10}O_2$	--air or vapor	20	24.3	AC(**20, 26**); AdC(**1**); PRS(**2**)
n-Propyl alcohol	C_3H_8O	--vapor	20	23.78	AC(**24, 33**); AdC(**1**); JP(**5**); JS(**4**)
n-Propylamine	C_3H_9N	--air	20	22.4	GC(**1**); JS(**3**)

Substance Name	Formula	In contact with	Temperature °C	Surface tension dynes/cm.	References
n-Propyl bromide	C_3H_7Br	-vapor	71	19.65	GC(1)
n-Propyl chloride	C_3H_7Cl	-air	47	18.2	AdC(1)
n-Propyl formate	$C_4H_8O_2$	-vapor	20	24.5	AC(26, 33); AdC(1); PRS(2)
Pyridine	C_5H_5N	-air	20	38.0	AC(17, 26, 28); GC(1); JP(5); JS(4, 14)
Quinoline	C_9H_7N	-air	20	45.0	AC(17, 22); GC(1); JP(4, 5)
Ricinoleic acid	$C_{18}H_{34}O_3$	-air	16	35.81	PRS(1)
Selenium	Se	-air	217	92.4	AdP(3)
Styrene	C_8H_8	-air	19	32.14	PRS(1)
Sulfuric acid (98.5 %)	H_2SO_4	-air or vapor	20	55.1	AC(17a); AdP(7); JS(2)
Tetrabromoethane 1,1,2,2-	$C_2H_2Br_4$	-air	20	49.67	AC(6); ZC(2)
Tetrachloroethane 1,1,2,2-	$C_2H_2Cl_4$	-air	22.5	36.03	ZC(2)
Tetrachloroethylene	C_2Cl_4	-vapor	20	31.74	AC(8); GC(1)
Toluene	C_7H_8	-vapor	10	27.7	AC(4, 17, 20, 31
"	C_7H_8	-vapor	20	28.5	AdC(1); BF(2)
"	C_7H_8	-vapor	30	27.4	JP(5); PRS(2); ZC(5, 6)
m-Toluidine	C_7H_9N	-vapor	20	36.9	AC(33)
o-Toluidine	C_7H_9N	-air or vapor	20	40.0	AC(27, 33); AS(1, 3); ZA(1)
p-Toluidine	C_7H_9N	-air	50	34.6	AC(27); AS(1); JS(12)
Trichloroacetic acid	$C_2HCl_3O_2$	-nitrogen	80.2	27.8	ZA(1)
Trichloroethane 1,1,2-	$C_2H_3Cl_3$	-air	114	22.0	GC(1)
Triethyl phosphate	$C_6H_{15}O_4P$	-air	15.5	30.61	JS(5)
Trimethylamine	C_3H_9N	-nitrogen	−4	17.3	ZA(1)
Triphenylcarbinol	$C_{19}H_{16}O$	-air	165.8	30.38	JS(6)
Vinyl acetate	$C_4H_6O_2$	-vapor	20	23.95	
"	$C_4H_6O_2$	-vapor	25	23.16	
"	$C_4H_6O_2$	-vapor	30	22.54	
Water	H_2O	-air	18	73.05	
m-Xylene	C_8H_{10}	-vapor	20	28.9	AC(4, 33, 34); AdC(1); JP(5); ZC(5)
o-Xylene	C_8H_{10}	-vapor	20	30.10	AC(6, 17, 34)
p-Xylene	C_8H_{10}	-vapor	20	28.37	AC(6, 17, 33, 34); AdC(1)

REFERENCE KEY

AC—
Journal of the American Chemical Society. (1) Baker and Gilbert, 62: 2479–2480; 40. (2) H. Brown, 56: 2564–2568; 38. (3) Harkins and Brown, 41: 449; 19. (4) Harkins, Brown and Davies, 39: 354; 17. (5) Harkins and Cheng, 43: 35; 21. (6) Harkins, Clark and Roberts, 42: 700; 20. (7) Harkins and Ewing, 42: 2539; 20. (8) Harkins and Feldman, 44: 2665; 22. (9) Harkins and Grafton, 42: 2534; 20. (10) Hogness, 43: 1621; 21. (11) Johnson and McIntosh, 31: 1139; 09. (12) Maass and Boomer, 44: 1709; 22. (13) Maass and Hatcher, 42: 2548; 20. (14) Maass and McIntosh, 36, 741 (1914). (15) Maass and Wright, 43: 1098; 21. (16) Morgan and Chazel, 35: 1821, 13. (17) Morgan and Daghlian, 33: 672; 11. (17a) Morgan and Davis, 38: 555; 16. (18) Morgan and Egloff, 38; 844: 16. (19) Morgan and Evans, 39: 2151; 17. (20) Morgan and Griggs, 39: 2261; 17. (21) Morgan and Kramer, 35: 1834; 13. (22) Morgan and McAfee, 33: 1275; 11. (23) Morgan and Neidle, 35: 1856; 13. (24) Morgan and Owen, 35: 1713; 11. (25) Morgan and Scarlett, 39, 2275; 17. (26) Morgan and Schartz, 33: 1041; 11. (27) Morgan and Stone, 35: 1505; 13. (28) Morgan and Thomssen, 33: 657; 11. (29) Morgan and Woodward, 35: 1249; 13. (30) Richards and Boyer, 43: 274; 21. (31) Richards and Carver 43: 827; 21. (32) Richards and Coombs, 37: 1656; 15. (33) Richards and Matthews, 30: 8; 08. (34) Richards, Speyers and Carver, 46: 1196; 24.

AD—
Atti della reale accademia nazionale dei Lincei. (1) Magini, 19 II: 184; 10.

AdC—Annalen der Chemie, Justus Liebig's. (1) Schiff. 223: 47; 84

AdP—
Annalen der Physik. (1) Heydweiller, 62: 694; 97. (2) Quincke, 134: 356; 68. (3) Quincke, 135: 621; 68. (4) Gradenwitz, 67: 467; 99. (5) Meyer, 66: 523; 98. (6) Stöckle 66: 499; 98. (7) Rontgen and Schneider, 29: 165; 86.

AS—
Archives des sciences physicques at naturelles. (1) Dutoit and Friederich, 9: 105; 00. (2) Guye and Baud, 11: 449; 01. (3) Herzen, 14: 232; 02.

BD—
Berichte der deutschen Chemischen Gesellschaft. (1) Lorenz and Kauffler, 41: 3727; 08. (2) Schenck and Ellenberger, 37: 3443; 04.

BF—
Bulletin de la société Chimique de France. (1) Dutoit and Frederich, 19: 321; 98. (2) Sentis Ann. Univ. Grenoble, 27: 593; 04.

CR—
Comptes Rendus. (1) A Portevin and P. Bastien, 202; 1072–1074; 36. (2) Popesco, 172: 1474; 21.

cUL—
Communications from the Physical Laboratory at the University of Leiden. (1) No. 142. (2) No. 179a. (3) No. 182b.

GC—
Gazzetta chimica italiana. (1) Schiff, 14: 368; 84. (2) A. Giacolone and D. DiMaggio, 3: 198–206; 39

JI—
Journal of the Institute of Metals, London. (1) Smith, 12: 168; 14.

JP—
Journal de Chimie physique. (1) Dutoit and Fath, 1: 358; 03. (2) Dutoit and Mojoiu, 7: 169; 09. (3) Marchand, 11: 573; 13. (4) Bolle and Guye, 3: 38; 05. (5) Renard and Guye, 5: 81; 07. (6) Berthoud, 21: 143; 24. (7) Berthoud, 16: 429; 18. (8) Homfray and Guye, 1: 505; 03. (9) Przyluska. 7: 511; 09.

JR—
Journal of the Russian Physico Chem. Soc. (Chem. part). (1) Elisseev and Kurbatov, 41: 1426; 09.

JS—
Journal of the Chemical Society of London. (1) Kellas, 113: 903; 18. (2) Aston and Ramsay, 65: 167; 94. (3) Turner and Merry, 97: 2069; 10. (4) Ramsay and Shields, 63: 1089; 93. (5) Sugden, Reed and Wilkins, 127: 1525; 25. (6) Hewitt and Winmill, 91: 441; 07. (7) Smith, 105: 1703; 14. (8) Atkins, 99: 10; 11. (9) Sugden, 119: 1483; 21. (10) Sugden, 121: 858, 22. (11) Sugden, 125: 32; 24. (12) Sugden, 125: 1167; 24. (13) Worley, 105: 260; 14. (14) Worley, 105: 273; 14. (15) Baly and Donnan, 81: 907; 02.

JSG—Jahresb. Schles. Ges. Vaterl. Kultur. (1) Wilborn, 1912: 56.
MB—Metron. Beit. (1) Weinstein, No. 6: 89.

MfC—
Monatshefte für Chemie und verwandte Teile anderer Wissenschaften. (1) Kremann and Meingast, 35: 1323; 14.

PM—
Philosophical Magazine and Journal of Science, Lond, Edinburg and Dublin. (1) Bircumshaw, 2: 341; 26. 3: 1286; 27. (2) R. C. Brown. 13: 578–584; 32. (3) A. E. Bate, 28: 252–255; 39.

PR—The Physical Review. (1) Poindexter, 27: 820; 26.

PRA—
Proceedings of the Royal Academy of Sciences of Amsterdam. (1) Kamerlingh Onnes and Kuypers, 17: 528; 14. (2) Van Urk, Keesom and Onnes, 28: 958; 25. (3) Van Urk, Keesom and Nijhoff 29: 914; 26. (4) Jaeger and Kahn, 18: 75; 15.

PRS—
Proceedings of the Royal Society, London. (1) Hardy 88: 303; 13. (2) Ramsay and Aston, 56: 162; 182; 94.

tPRS—
Philosophical Transactions Royal Society of London, Series A. (1) Ramsay and Shields, 184: 647; 93.

tRIA—
Royal Irish Academy Transactions. (1) Ramsay and Aston, 32A: 93; 02.

VK—
Verslag koninklijke Academie van Wetenschappen te Amsterdam. (1) Verschaffelt, No. 18: 1895; 74. (2) Verschaffelt, No. 28, 1896: 94.

WN—
Wissenschaftliche Natuurk. Tydschr. (1) Verschaffelt, 2: 231, 25.

ZA—
Zeitschrift fur anorganische ana allgemeine Chemie. (1) Jaeger, 101: 1; 17. (2) Motylewski, 38: 410, 04. (3) Lorenz, Liebmann and Hochberg, 94: 301; 16. (4) Sauerwald and Drath 154: 79; 26.

ZC—
Zeitschrift für physikalische Chemie. (1) Bennett and Mitchell, 84: 475; 13. (2) Walden and Swinne, 82: 271; 13. (3) Drucker, 52: 641; 05. (4) Walden, 75: 555; 10. (5) Walden and Swinne, 79: 700; 12. (6) Whatmough, 39: 129; 02.

ZE—
Zeitschrift fur Elektrochemie und angewandte physikalische Chemie. (1) Bredig and Tiechmann. 31: 449; 25.

ZK—
Zeitschrift Kolloid. (1) N. Jermolanko, 48: 14–146; 29.

VISCOSITY

Viscosity.—All fluids possess a definite resistance to change of form and many solids show a gradual yielding to forces tending to change their form. This property, a sort of internal friction, is called viscosity; it is expressed in dyne-seconds per cm² or poises. Dimensions,—$[m\ l^{-1}\ t^{-1}]$. If the tangential force per unit area, exerted by a layer of fluid upon one adjacent is one dyne for a space rate of variation of the tangential velocity of unity, the viscosity is one poise.

Kinematic viscosity is the ratio of viscosity to density. The c. g. s. unit of kinematic viscosity is the **stoke.**

Flow of liquids through a tube; where l is the length of the tube, r its radius, p the difference of pressure at the ends, η the coefficient of viscosity, the volume escaping per second,

$$v = \frac{\pi p r^4}{8l\eta} \text{ (Poiseuille).}$$

The volume will be given in cm³ per second if l and r are in cm, p in dynes per cm² and η in poises or dyne-seconds per cm².

VISCOSITY OF WATER BELOW 0°C
White-Twining 1914

Temperature	Viscosity centipoises	Temperature	Viscosity centipoises
0°C	1.708	−7.23	2.341
−2.10	1.930	−8.48	2.458
−4.70	2.121	−9.30	2.549
−6.20	2.250		

ABSOLUTE VISCOSITY OF WATER AT 20°C
Swindells, J. R. Coe, Jr., and T. B. Godfrey, Journal of Research, National Bureau of Standards **48**, 1, 1952.

The value found for the viscosity of water at 20°C was 0.010010 ± 0.000003 poise.

The value **0.01002** poise is to be used as the absolute value of the viscosity of water for calibration purposes.

VISCOSITY CONVERSION TABLE

Poise = c.g.s. unit of absolute viscosity = $\dfrac{gm}{sec \times cm}$

Stoke = c.g.s. unit of kinematic viscosity = $\dfrac{gm}{sec \times cm \times density_{(t°F)}}$

Centipoise = 0.01 poise
Centistoke = 0.01 stoke
Centipoises = Centistokes × density (at given temperature)

To convert poises to $\dfrac{lb}{sec \times ft}$ or $\dfrac{lb}{hr \times ft}$ multiply by **0.0672 or 242** respectively.

Centi-stokes	Saybolt Seconds at			Redwood Seconds at			Engler Degrees at all temps.	Centi-stokes	Saybolt Seconds at			Redwood Seconds at			Engler Degrees at all temps.
	100°F	130°F	210°F	70°F	140°F	200°F			100°F	130°F	210°F	70°F	140°F	200°F	
2.0	32.6	32.7	32.8	30.2	31.0	31.2	1.14	28.0	132.1	132.4	133.0	115.3	116.5	118.0	3.82
3.0	36.0	36.1	36.3	32.7	33.5	33.7	1.22	30.0	140.9	141.2	141.9	123.1	124.4	126.0	4.07
4.0	39.1	39.2	39.4	35.3	36.0	36.3	1.31	32.0	149.7	150.0	150.8	131.0	132.3	134.1	4.32
5.0	42.3	42.4	42.6	37.9	38.5	38.9	1.40	34.0	158.7	159.0	159.8	138.9	140.2	142.2	4.57
6.0	45.5	45.6	45.8	40.5	41.0	41.5	1.48	36.0	167.7	168.0	168.9	146.9	148.2	150.3	4.83
7.0	48.7	48.8	49.0	43.2	43.7	44.2	1.56	38.0	176.7	177.0	177.9	155.0	156.2	158.3	5.08
8.0	52.0	52.1	52.4	46.0	46.4	46.9	1.65	40.0	185.7	186.0	187.0	163.0	164.3	166.7	5.34
9.0	55.4	55.5	55.8	48.9	49.1	49.7	1.75	42.0	194.7	195.:	196.1	171.0	172.3	175.0	5.59
10.0	58.8	58.9	59.2	51.7	52.0	52.6	1.84	44.0	203.8	204.2	205.2	179.1	180.4	183.3	5.85
11.0	62.3	62.4	62.7	54.8	55.0	55.6	1.93	46.0	213.0	213.4	214.5	187.1	188.5	191.7	6.11
12.0	65.9	66.0	66.4	57.9	58.1	58.8	2.02	48.0	222.2	222.6	223.8	195.2	196.6	200.0	6.37
14.0	73.4	73.5	73.9	64.4	64.6	65.3	2.22	50.0	231.4	231.8	233.0	203.3	204.7	208.3	6.63
16.0	81.1	81.3	81.7	71.0	71.4	72.2	2.43	60.0	277.4	277.9	279.3	243.5	245.3	250.0	7.90
18.0	89.2	89.4	89.8	77.9	78.5	79.4	2.64	70.0	323.4	324.0	325.7	283.9	286.0	291.7	9.21
20.0	97.5	97.7	98.2	85.0	85.8	86.9	2.87	80.0	369.6	370.3	372.2	323.9	326.6	333.4	10.53
22.0	106.0	106.2	106.7	92.4	93.3	94.5	3.10	90.0	415.8	416.6	418.7	364.4	367.4	375.0	11.84
24.0	114.0	114.8	115.4	99.9	100.9	102.2	3.34	*100.0	462.0	462.0	465.2	404.0	408.2	416.7	13.16
26.0	123.3	123.6	124.2	107.8	108.6	110.0	3.55								

* At higher values use the same ratio as above for 100 centistokes; e.g., 110 centistokes = 110 × 4.620 Saybolt seconds at 100°F.

To obtain the Saybolt Universal viscosity equivalent to a kinematic viscosity determined at t°F, multiply the equivalent Saybolt Universal viscosity at 100°F by $1 + (t - 100)0.000064$; e.g., 10 centistokes at 210°F are equivalent to 58.8 × 1.0070, or 59.2 Saybolt Universal seconds at 210°F.

To convert from	To	Multiply by
cm²/sec (Stokes)	Centistokes	10^2
	ft²/hr.	3.875
	ft²/sec.	1.076×10^{-3}
	in.²/sec.	1.550×10^{-1}
	m²/hr.	3.600×10^{-1}
cm²/sec × 10² (Centistokes)	cm²/sec. (Stokes)	1×10^{-2}
	ft²/hr.	3.875×10^{-2}
	ft²/sec.	1.076×10^{-5}
	in.²/sec.	1.550×10^{-3}
	m²/hr.	3.600×10^{-3}
ft²/hr	cm²/sec (Stokes)	2.581×10^{-1}
	cm/sec × 10² (centistokes)	2.581×10
	ft²/sec.	2.778×10^{-4}
	in.²/sec.	4.00×10^{-2}
	m²/hr.	9.290×10^{-2}
ft²/sec	cm²/sec. (Stokes)	9.29×10^2
	cm²/sec.×10² (centistokes)	9.29×10^4
	ft²/hr	3.60×10^3
	in.²/sec.	1.44×10^2
	m²/hr.	3.345×10^2
in.²/sec	cm²/sec. (Stokes)	6.452
	cm²/sec.×10² (centistokes)	6.452×10^2
	ft²/hr.	2.50×10
	ft²/sec.	6.944×10^{-3}
	m²/hr.	2.323
m²/hr	cm²/sec. (Stokes)	2.778
	cm²/sec.×10² (centistokes)	2.778×10^2
	ft²/hr.	1.076×10
	ft²/sec.	2.990×10^{-3}
	in.²/sec.	4.306×10^{-1}

VISCOSITY CONVERSION
Absolute

Absolute viscosity = kinematic viscosity × density; lb = mass pounds; lb$_F$ = force pounds

To convert from	To	Multiply by
gm/(cm)(sec) [Poise]	gm/(cm)(sec)(10²) [Centipoise]	10^2
	kg/(m)(hr)	3.6×10^2
	lb/(ft)(sec)	6.72×10^{-2}
	lb/(ft)(hr)	2.419×10^2
	lb/(in.)(sec)	5.6×10^{-3}
	(gm$_F$)(sec)/cm²	1.02×10^{-3}
	(lb$_F$)(sec)/in.² [Reyn]	1.45×10^{-5}
	(lb$_F$)(sec)/ft²	2.089×10^{-3}
gm/(cm)(sec)(10²) [Centipoise]	gm/(cm)(sec) [Poise]	10^{-2}
	kg/(m)(hr)	3.6
	lb/(ft)(sec)	6.72×10^{-4}
	lb/(ft)(hr)	2.419
	lb/(in.)(sec)	5.60×10^{-5}
	(gm$_F$)(sec)/cm²	1.02×10^{-5}
	(lb$_F$)(sec)/in.² [Reyn]	1.45×10^{-7}
	(lb$_F$)(sec)/ft²	2.089×10^{-5}
kg/(m)(hr)	gm/(cm)(sec)	2.778×10^{-3}
	gm/(cm)(sec)(10²) [Centipoise]	2.778×10^{-1}
	lb/(ft)(sec)	1.867×10^{-4}
	lb/(ft)(hr)	6.720×10^{-1}
	lb/(in.)(sec)	1.555×10^{-5}
	(gm$_F$)(sec)/cm²	2.833×10^{-4}

To convert from	To	Multiply by
kg/(m)(hr) (Cont.)	(lb$_F$)(sec)/in.² [Reyn]	4.029×10^{-8}
	(lb$_F$)(sec)/ft²	5.801×10^{-6}
lb/(ft)(sec)	gm/(cm)(sec) [Poise]	1.488×10^1
	gm/(cm)(sec)(10²) [Centipoise]	1.488×10^3
	kg/(m)(hr)	5.357×10^3
	lb/(ft)(hr)	3.60×10^3
	lb/(in.)(sec)	8.333×10^{-2}
	(gm$_F$)(sec)/cm²	1.518×10^{-1}
	(lb$_F$)(sec)/in.² [Reyn]	2.158×10^{-4}
	(lb$_F$)(sec)/ft²	3.108×10^{-2}
lb/(ft)(hr)	gm/(cm)(sec) [Poise]	4.134×10^{-3}
	gm/(cm)(sec)(10²) [Centipoise]	4.134×10^{-1}
	kg/(m)(hr)	1.488
	lb/(ft)(sec)	2.778×10^{-4}
	lb/(in.)(sec)	2.315×10^{-5}
	(gm$_F$)(sec)/cm²	4.215×10^{-6}
	(lb$_F$)(sec)/in.² [Reyn]	5.996×10^{-8}
	(lb$_F$)(sec)/ft²	8.634×10^{-6}
lb/(in.)(sec)	gm/(cm)(sec) [Poise]	1.786×10^2
	gm/(cm)(sec)(10²) [Centipoise]	1.786×10^4
	kg/(m)(hr)	6.429×10^4
	lb/(ft)(sec)	1.20×10
	lb/(ft)(hr)	4.32×10^4
	(gm$_F$)(sec)/cm²	1.821×10^{-1}
	(lb$_F$)(sec)/in.² [Reyn]	2.590×10^{-3}
	(lb$_F$)(sec)/ft²	3.73×10^{-1}
(gm$_F$)(sec)/cm²	gm/(cm)(sec)	9.807×10^2
	gm/(cm)(sec)(10²) [Centipoise]	9.807×10^4
	kg/(m)(hr)	3.530×10^5
	lb/(ft)(sec)	6.590×10
	lb/(ft)(hr)	2.372×10^5
	lb/(in.)(sec)	5.492
	(lb$_F$)(sec)/in.² [Reyn]	1.422×10^{-2}
	(lb$_F$)(sec)/ft²	2.048
(lb$_F$)(sec)/in.² [Reyn]	gm/(cm)(sec) [Poise]	6.895×10^4
	gm/(cm)(sec)(10²) [Centipoise]	6.895×10^6
	kg/(m)(hr)	2.482×10^7
	lb/(ft)(sec)	4.633×10^3
	lb/(ft)(hr)	1.668×10^7
	lb/(in.)(sec)	3.861×10^2
	(gm$_F$)(sec)/cm²	7.031×10
	(lb$_F$)(sec)/ft²	1.440×10^2
(lb$_F$)(sec)/ft²	gm/(cm)(sec) [Poise]	4.788×10^2
	gm/(cm)(sec)(10²) [Centipoise]	4.788×10^4
	kg/(m)(hr)	1.724×10^5
	lb/(ft)(sec)	3.217×10
	lb/(ft)(hr)	1.158×10^5
	lb/(in.)(sec)	2.681
	(gm$_F$)(sec)/cm²	4.882×10^{-1}
	(lb$_F$)(sec)/in.² [Reyn]	6.944×10^{-3}

THE VISCOSITY OF WATER 0°C TO 100°C

Contribution from the National Bureau of Standards, not subject to copyright.

°C	η(cp)	°C	η(cp)	°C	η(cp)	°C	η(cp)
0	1.787	26	0.8705	52	0.5290	78	0.3638
1	1.728	27	.8513	53	.5204	79	.3592
2	1.671	28	.8327	54	.5121	80	.3547
3	1.618	29	.8148	55	.5040	81	.3503
4	1.567	30	.7975	56	.4961	82	.3460
5	1.519	31	.7808	57	.4884	83	.3418
6	1.472	32	.7647	58	.4809	84	.3377
7	1.428	33	.7491	59	.4736	85	.3337
8	1.386	34	.7340	60	.4665	86	.3297
9	1.340	35	.7194	61	.4596	87	.3259
10	1.307	36	.7052	62	.4528	88	.3221
11	1.271	37	.6915	63	.4462	89	.3184
12	1.235	38	.6783	64	.4398	90	.3147
13	1.202	39	.6654	65	.4335	91	.3111
14	1.169	40	.6529	66	.4273	92	.3076
15	1.139	41	.6408	67	.4213	93	.3042
16	1.109	42	.6291	68	.4155	94	.3008
17	1.081	43	.6178	69	.4098	95	.2975
18	1.053	44	.6067	70	.4042	96	.2942
19	1.027	45	.5960	71	.3987	97	.2911
20	1.002	46	.5856	72	.3934	98	.2879
21	0.9779	47	.5755	73	.3882	99	.2848
22	.9548	48	.5656	74	.3831	100	.2818
23	.9325	49	.5561	75	.3781		
24	.9111	50	.5468	76	.3732		
25	.8904	51	.5378	77	.3684		

The above table was calculated from the following empirical relationships derived from measurements in viscometers calibrated with water at 20°C (and one atmosphere), modified to agree with the currently accepted value for the viscosity at 20° of 1.002 cp:

$$0° \text{ to } 20°C: \log_{10} \eta_T = \frac{1301}{998.333 + 8.1855(T-20) + 0.00585(T-20)^2} - 3.30233$$

(R. C. Hardy and R. L. Cottington, J.Res.NBS *42*, 573 (1949).)

$$20° \text{ to } 100°C: \log_{10} \frac{\eta_T}{\eta_{20}} = \frac{1.3272(20-T) - 0.001053(T-20)^2}{T + 105}$$

(J. F. Swindells, NBS, unpublished results.)

VISCOSITY OF LIQUIDS

Viscosity of liquids in centipoises (cp) including elements, inorganic and organic compounds and mixtures.

Liquid	Temp. °C	Viscosity cp	Liquid	Temp. °C	Viscosity cp
Acetaldehyde............	0	.2797	n-Amyl acetate............	11	1.58
	10	.2557		45	.805
	20	.22	alcohol...............	15	4.65
Acetanilide..............	120	2.22		30	2.99
	130	1.90	ether.................	15	1.188
Acetic acid..............	15	1.31	Aniline..................	−6	13.8
	18	1.30		0	10.2
	25.2	1.155		5	8.06
	30	1.04		10	6.50
	41	1.00		15	5.31
	59	.70		20	4.40
	70	.60		25	3.71
	100	.43		30	3.16
anhydride.............	0	1.24		35	2.71
	15	.971		40	2.37
	18	.90		50	1.85
	30	.783		60	1.51
	100	.49		70	1.27
Acetone.................	−92.5	2.148		80	1.09
	−80.0	1.487		90	.935
	−59.6	.932		100	.825
	−42.5	.695	Anisol..................	0	1.78
	−30.0	.575		20	1.32
	−20.9	.510		40	1.12
	−13.0	.470	Antimony, liq............	645	1.55
	−10.0	.450		700	1.26
	0	.399		800	1.08
	15	.337		850	1.05
	25	.316	Benzaldehyde.............	25	1.39
	30	.295	Benzene.................	0	.912
	41	.280		10	.758
Acetonitrile..............	0	.442		20	.652
	15	.375		30	.564
	25	.345		40	.503
Acetophenone............	11.9	2.28		50	.442
	23.5	1.59		60	.392
	25.0	1.617		70	.358
	50.0	1.246		80	.329
	80.0	.734	Benzonitrile..............	25	1.24
Air, liq.................	−192.3	.172	Benzophenone............	55	4.79
Alcohol. See *Ethyl, Methyl*, etc.				120	1.38
			Benzyl alcohol...........	20	5.8
Allyl alcohol..............	0	2.145	Benzylamine.............	25	1.59
	15	1.49	Benzylaniline............	33	2.18
	20	1.363		130	1.20
	30	1.07	Benzyl ether.............	0	10.5
	40	.914		20	5.33
	70	.553		40	3.21
Allylamine..............	130	.506	Bismuth.................	285	1.61
Allyl chloride............	15	.347		304	1.662
	30	.300		365	1.46
Ammonia................	−69	.475		451	1.280
	−50	.317		600	.998
	−40	.276	Bromine, liq.............	−4.3	1.31
	−33.5	.255		0	1.241

Liquid	Temp. °C	Viscosity cp	Liquid	Temp. °C	Viscosity cp
Bromine, liq.............	12.6	1.07	Carbon tetrachloride.......	20	.969
	16	1.0		30	.843
	19.5	.995		40	.739
	28.9	.911		50	.651
o-Bromoaniline...........	40	3.19		60	.585
m-Bromoaniline..........	20	6.81		70	.524
	40	3.70		80	.468
	80	1.70		90	.426
p-Bromoaniline...........	80	1.81		100	.384
Bromobenzene...........	15	1.196	Cetyl alcohol...........	50	13.4
	30	.985	Chlorine, liq.............	−76.5	.729
Bromoform..............	15	2.152		−70.5	.680
	25	1.89		−60.2	.616
	30	1.741		−52.4	.566
Butyl acetate...........	0	1.004		−35.4	.494
	20	.732		0	.385
	40	.563	Chlorobenzene...........	15	.900
n-Butyl alcohol...........	−50.9	36.1		20	.799
	−30.1	14.7		40	.631
	−22.4	11.1		80	.431
	−14.1	8.38		100	.367
	0	5.186	Chloroform..............	−13	.855
	15	3.379		0	.700
	20	2.948		8.1	.643
	30	2.30		15	.596
	40	1.782		20	.58
	50	1.411		25	.542
	70	.930		30	.514
	100	.540		39	.500
sec-Butyl alcohol.........	15	4.21	o-Chlorophenol...........	25	4.11
n-Butyl bromide..........	15	.626		50	2.015
n-Butyl chloride..........	15	.469	m-Chlorophenol..........	25	11.55
Butyl chloride, tertiary.....	15	.543	p-Chlorophenol..........	50	4.99
n-Butyl formate..........	0	.940	Copper, liq.............	1,085	3.36
	20	.689		1,100	3.33
Butyric acid.............	0	2.286		1,150	3.22
	15	1.81		1,200	3.12
	20	1.540	o-Cresol.............	40	4.49
	40	1.120	m-Cresol.............	10	43.9
	50	.975		20	20.8
	70	.760		40	6.18
	100	.551	p-Cresol.............	40	7.00
Cadmium, liq.............	349	1.44	Creosote.............	20	12.0
	506	1.18	Cycloheptane............	13.5	1.64
	603	1.10	Cyclohexane.............	17	1.02
Carbolic acid. See *Phenol*.			Cyclohexanol............	20	68
Carbon dioxide, liq., pressure that of saturated vapor	0	.099	Cyclohexene............	13.5	.696
	10	.085		20	.66
	20	.071	Cyclooctane............	13.5	2.35
	30	.053	Cyclopentane............	13.5	.493
disulfide..............	−13	.514	nDecane................	20	.92
	−10	.495	Diethylamine...........	25	.340
	0	.436		25	.367
	5	.380	Diethylaniline............	.5	3.84
	20	.363		20.0	2.18
	40	.330		25.0	1.95
Carbon tetrachloride.......	0	1.329	Diethylcarbinol...........	15.0	7.34
	15	1.038	Diethylketone...........	15	.493

Liquid	Temp. °C	Viscosity cp	Liquid	Temp. °C	Viscosity cp
Dimethylaniline...........	10	1.69	Ethylbenzene, bromide....	−80	1.81
	20	1.41		0	.487
	25	1.285		10	.441
	30	1.17		15	.418
	40	1.04		20	.402
	50	.91		30	.348
Dimethyl-α-naphthylamine.	130	.868	n-Ethyl butyrate..........	15	.711
Dimethyl-β-naphthylamine.	130	.952	Ethyl carbonate..........	15	.868
Diphenyl.................	70	1.49	Ethylene bromide.........	0	2.438
	100	.97		17	1.95
Diphenylamine...........	130	1.04		20	1.721
Dodecane................	25	1.35		40	1.286
Ether (diethyl-)..........	−100	1.69		67.3	.922
	−80	.958		70	.903
	−60	.637		82.2	.750
	−40	.461		99.0	.648
	−20	.362	chloride...............	0	1.077
	0	.2842		15	.887
	17	.240		19.4	.800
	20	.2332		40	.652
	25	.222		50	.565
	40	.197		70	.479
	60	.166	glycol.................	20	19.9
	80	.140		40	9.13
	100	.118		60	4.95
Ethyl acetate............	0	.582		80	3.02
	8.96	.516		100	1.99
	10	.512	oxide.................	−49.8	.577
	15	.473		−38.2	.488
	20	.455		−21.0	.394
	25	.441		0	.320
	30	.400	Ethyl formate............	20	.402
	50	.345	iodide.................	0	.727
	75	.283		15	.617
alcohol.................	−98.11	44.0		20	.592
	−89.8	28.4		40	.495
	−71.5	13.2		70	.391
	−59.42	8.41	malate.................	24.7	3.016
	−52.58	6.87	oxalate................	15	2.31
	−32.01	3.84	propionate.............	15	.564
	−17.59	2.68	Eugenol.................	0	29.9
	−.30	1.80		20	9.22
	0	1.773		40	4.22
	10	1.466	Fluorobenzene............	20	.598
	20	1.200		40	.478
	30	1.003		60	.389
	40	.834		80	.329
	50	.702		100	.275
	60	.592	Formamide..............	0	7.55
	70	.504		25	3.30
alcohol, anh.............	−148	8,470	Formic acid..............	7.59	2.3868
	−146	5,990		10	2.262
	−130	467		20	1.804
aniline.................	25	2.04		30	1.465
Ethylbenzene............	17	.691		40	1.219
benzoate..............	20	2.24		70	.780
bromide..............	−120	5.6		100	.549
	−100	2.89			

Liquid	Temp. °C	Viscosity cp	Liquid	Temp. °C	Viscosity cp
Furfurol................	0	2.48	Isoheptane.............	40	.315
	25	1.49	Isohexane...............	0	.376
Glucose................	22	9.1×10^{15}		20	.306
	30	6.6×10^{13}		40	.254
	40	2.8×10^{11}	Isopentane.............	0	.273
	60	9.3×10^{7}		20	.223
	80	6.6×10^{5}	Isopropyl alcohol.........	15	2.86
	100	2.5×10^{4}		30	1.77
Glycerin...............	−42	6.71×10^{6}	Isoquinoline.............	25	3.57
	−36	2.05×10^{6}	Isosafrol................	25	3.981
	−25	2.62×10^{5}	Lead, liq...............	350	2.58
	−20	1.34×10^{5}		400	2.33
	−15.4	6.65×10^{4}		441	2.116
	−10.8	3.55×10^{4}		500	1.84
	−4.2	1.49×10^{4}		551	1.70
	0	12,110		600	1.38
	6	6,260		703	1.349
	15	2,330		844	1.185
	20	1,490	Menthol, liq.............	55.6	6.29
	25	954		74.6	2.47
	30	629		99.0	1.04
Glycerin trinitrate........	10	69.2	Mercury.................	−20	1.855
	20	36.0		−10	1.764
	30	21.0		0	1.685
	40	13.6		10	1.615
	60	6.8		19.02	1.56
Heptane................	0	.524		20	1.554
	17	.461		20.2	1.55
	20	.409		30	1.499
	25	.386		40	1.450
	40	.341		40.8	1.45
	70	.262		41.86	1.44
n-Heptyl alcohol..........	15	8.53		50	1.407
Hexadecane..............	20	3.34		60	1.367
Hexane.................	0	.401		70	1.331
	17	.374		80	1.298
	20	.326		90	1.268
	25	.294		100	1.240
	40	.271		150	1.130
	50	.248		200	1.052
Hydrazine..............	1	1.29		250	.995
	10	1.12		300	.950
	20	.97		340	.921
Hydrogen, liq............	....	.011	Methyl acetate...........	0	.484
Iodine, liq..............	116	2.27		20	.381
Iodobenzene............	15	1.74		40	.320
Iron, 2.5% carbon, liq......	1,400	2.25	Methyl alcohol............	−98.30	13.9
Isoamyl acetate..........	8.97	1.030	(Methanol)	−84.23	6.8
	19.91	.872		−72.55	4.36
alcohol..............	10	6.20		−44.53	1.98
amine.............	25	.724		−22.29	1.22
Isobutyl alcohol..........	15	4.703		0	.82
amine.............	25	.553		15	.623
Isobutyric acid...........	15	1.44		20	.597
	30	1.13		25	.547
Isoeugenol..............	25	26.72		30	.510
Isoheptane..............	0	.481		40	.456
	20	.384		50	.403

Liquid	Temp. °C	Viscosity cp	Liquid	Temp. °C	Viscosity cp
Methyl amine.............	0	.236	Oil, olive................	10	138.0
aniline.................	25	2.02		20	84.0
	30	1.55		40	36.3
chloride.............	20	.1834		70	12.4
Methylene bromide........	15	1.09	rape.................	0	2,530
	30	0.92		10	385
chloride.............	15	.449		20	163
	30	.393		30	96
Methyl iodide.............	0	.606	soya bean..............	20	69.3
	15	.518		30	40.6
	20	.500		50	20.6
	30	.460		90	7.8
	40	.424	sperm.................	15.6	42.0
Naphthalene.............	80	.967		37.8	18.5
	100	.776		100.0	4.6
Nitric acid...............	0	2.275	Oleic acid...............	30	25.6
	10	1.770	Pentadecane..............	22	2.81
Nitrobenzene.............	2.95	2.91	Pentane.................	0	.289
	5.69	2.71		20	.240
	5.94	2.71	o-Phenetidine.............	0	16.5
	9.92	2.48		20	6.08
	14.94	2.24		30	4.22
	20.00	2.03	m-Phenetidine.............	30	12.9
Nitromethane.............	0	.853	p-Phenetidine.............	20	12.9
	25	.620		30	8.3
o-Nitrotoluene.............	0	3.83	Phenol..................	18.3	12.7
	20	2.37		50	3.49
	40	1.63		60	2.61
	60	1.21		70	2.03
m-Nitrotoluene............	20	2.33		90	1.26
	40	1.60	Phenylcyanide............	.28	1.96
	60	1.18		20.0	1.33
p-Nitrotoluene.............	60	1.20	Phosphorus, liq...........	21.5	2.34
n-Nonane.................	20	.711		31.2	2.01
n-Octane.................	0	.706		43.2	1.73
	16	.574		50.5	1.60
	20	.542		60.2	1.45
	40	.433		69.7	1.32
Octodecane..............	40	2.86		79.9	1.21
n-Octylalcohol.............	15	10.6	Potassium bromide, liq.....	745	1.48
Oil, castor................	10	2,420		775	1.34
	20	986		805	1.19
	30	451	nitrate, liq..............	334	2.1
	40	231		358	1.7
	100	16.9		333	2.97
cottonseed..............	20	70.4		418	2.00
cylinder, filtered........	37.8	240.6	Propionic acid............	10	1.289
	100	18.7		15	1.18
cylinder, dark..........	37.8	422.4		20	1.102
	100	24.0		40	.845
linseed.................	30	33.1	Propyl acetate............	10	.66
	50	17.6		20	.59
	90	7.1		40	.44
machine, light..........	15.6	113.8	n-Propyl alcohol..........	0	3.883
	37.8	34.2		15	2.52
	100	4.9		20	2.256
machine, heavy	15.6	660.6		30	1.72
	37.8	127.4		40	1.405

Liquid	Temp. °C	Viscosity cp	Liquid	Temp. °C	Viscosity cp
n-Propyl alcohol..........	50	1.130	Sulfuric acid.............	50	8.82
	70	.760		60	7.22
Propyl aldehyde...........	10	.47		70	6.09
	20	.41		80	5.19
	40	.33	Tetrachloroethane........	15	1.844
bromide...............	0	.651	Tetradecane.............	20	2.18
	20	.524	Tin, liq.................	240	2.12
	40	.433		280	1.678
chloride..............	0	.436		300	1.73
	20	.352		301	1.680
	40	.291		400	1.43
n-Propyl ether...........	15	.448		450	1.270
Pyridine.................	20	.974		500	1.20
Salicylic acid.............	10	3.20		600	1.08
	20	2.71		604	1.045
	40	1.81		750	.905
Salol....................	45	.746	Toluene.................	0	.772
Sodium bromide..........	762	1.42		17	.61
	780	1.28		20	.590
chloride, liq............	841	1.30		30	.526
	896	1.01		40	.471
	924	.97		70	.354
nitrate, liq.............	308	2.919	o-Toluidine..............	20	4.39
	348	2.439	m-Toluidine..............	20	3.81
	398	1.977	p-Toluidine..............	50	1.80
	418	1.828	Triacetin................	17	28.0
Stearic acid..............	70	11.6	Tributyrin...............	20	11.6
Sucrose (cane sugar).......	109	2.8×10^6	Trichlorethane...........	20	1.2
	124.6	1.9×10^5	Tridecane................	23.3	1.55
Sulfur (gas free)...........	123.0	10.94	Triethylcarbinol..........	20	6.75
	135.5	8.66	Tripalmitin..............	70	16.8
	149.5	7.09	Tristearin...............	75	18.5
	156.3	7.19	Turpentine..............	0	2.248
	158.2	7.59		10	1.783
	159.2	9.48		20	1.487
	159.5	14.45		30	1.272
	160.0	22.83		40	1.071
	160.3	77.32		70	.728
	165.0	500.0	Turpentine, Venice........	17.3	1.3×10^5
	171.0	4,500.0	n-Undecane..............	20	1.17
	184.0	16,000.00	o-Xylene (xylol)..........	0	1.105
	190.5	19,700.0		16	.876
	197.5	21,300.0		20	.810
	200.0	21,500.0		40	.627
	210.0	20,500.0	m-Xylene (xylol)..........	0	.806
	217.0	19,100.0		15	.650
	220.0	18,600.0		20	.620
Sulfur dioxide, liq..........	−33.5	.5508		40	.497
	−10.5	.4285	p-Xylene (xylol)..........	16	.696
	0.1	.3936		20	.648
Sulfuric acid.............	0	48.4		40	.513
	15	32.8	Zinc, liq.................	280	1.68
	20	25.4		357	1.42
	30	15.7		389	1.31
	40	11.5			

VISCOSITY OF GASES

Gas or vapor	Temp. °C	Viscosity micropoises	Gas or vapor	Temp. °C	Viscosity micropoises
Acetic acid, vap............	119.1	107.0	Benzene, vap..............	14.2	73.8
Acetone, vap..............	100	93.1		131.2	103.1
	119.0	99.1		194.6	119.8
	190.4	118.6		252.5	134.3
	247.7	133.4		312.8	148.4
	306.4	148.1	Bromine, vap..............	12.8	151
Acetylene.................	0	93.5		65.7	170
Air.....................	−194.2	55.1		99.7	188
	−183.1	62.7		139.7	208
	−104.0	113.0		179.7	227
	−69.4	133.3		220.3	248
	−31.6	153.9	Bromoform, vap............	151.2	253.0
	0	170.8	Butyl alcohol, n, vap........	116.9	143
	18	182.7	tert, vap..............	82.9	160
	40	190.4	chloride, n, vap..........	78	149.5
	54	195.8	iodide, vap..............	130	202
	74	210.2	β-Butylene.................	18.8	74.4
	229	263.8		100.4	94.5
	334	312.3		200	119.2
	357	317.5	Butyric acid, vap...........	161.7	130.0
	409	341.3	Carbon dioxide.............	−97.8	89.6
	466	350.1		−78.2	97.2
	481	358.3		−60.0	106.1
	537	368.6		−40.2	115.5
	565	375.0		−21	129.4
	620	391.6		−19.4	126.0
	638	401.4		0	139.0
	750	426.3		15	145.7
	810	441.9		19	149.9
	923	464.3		20	148.0
	1034	490.6		30	153
	1134	520.6		32	155
				35	156
Alcohol. See Ethyl, Methyl, etc.				40	157
Ammonia.................	−78.5	67.2		99.1	186.1
	0	91.8		104	188.9
	20	98.2		182.4	222.1
	50	109.2		235	241.5
	100	127.9		302.0	268.2
	132.9	139.9		490	330.0
	150	146.3		685	380.0
	200	164.6		850	435.8
	250	181.4		1052	478.6
	300	198.7	disulfide, vap.............	0	91.1
Argon....................	0	209.6		14.2	96.4
	20	221.7		114.3	130.3
	100	269.5		190.2	156.1
	200	322.3		309.8	196.6
	302	368.5	monoxide.................	−191.5	56.1
	401	411.5		−78.5	127
	493	448.4		0	166
	584	481.5		15	172
	714	525.7		21.7	175.3
	827	563.2		126.7	218.3
Arsenic hydride (Arsine)	0	145.8		227.0	254.8
	15	114.0		276.9	271.4
	100	198.1	tetrachloride, vap.........	76.7	195.0

Gas or vapor	Temp. °C	Viscosity micropoises	Gas or vapor	Temp. °C	Viscosity micropoises
Carbon tetrachloride, vap.............	127.9	133.4	Ethylene.................	50	110.3
	200.2	156.2		100	125.7
	314.9	190.2		150	140.3
Chlorine.................	12.7	129.7		200	154.1
	20	132.7		250	166.6
	50	146.9	bromide, vap............	131.6	221.0
	100	167.9	chloride, vap............	83.5	168.0
	150	187.5	Ethyl formate, vap........	99.8	92
	200	208.5	iodide, vap..............	72.3	216.0
	250	227.6	Helium....................	−257.4	27.0
Chloroform, vap...........	0	93.6		−252.6	35.0
	14.2	98.9		−191.6	87.1
	100	129		0	186.0
	121.3	135.7		20	194.1
	189.1	157.9		100	228.1
	250.0	177.6		200	267.2
	307.5	194.7		250	285.3
Cyanogen.................	0	92.8		282	299.2
	17	98.7		407	343.6
	100	127.1		486	370.6
Ethane..................	−78.5	63.4		606	408.7
	0	84.8		676	430.3
	17.2	90.1		817	471.3
	50.8	100.1	Hydrogen.................	−257.7	5.7
	100.4	114.3		−252.5	8.5
	200.3	140.9		−198.4	33.6
Ether (diethyl), vap........	0	67.8		−183.4	38.8
	14.2	71.6		−113.5	57.2
	100	95.5		−97.5	61.5
	121.8	98.3		−31.6	76.7
	159.4	107.9		0	83.5
	189.9	115.2		20.7	87.6
	251.0	130.0		28.1	89.2
	277.8	135.8		129.4	108.6
Ethyl acetate, vap..........	0	68.4		229.1	126.0
	100	94.3		299	138.1
	128.1	101.8		412	155.4
	158.6	109.8		490	167.2
	192.9	119.5		601	182.9
	212.5	126		713	198.2
alcohol, vap.............	100	108		825	213.7
	130.2	117.3	bromide.................	18.7	181.9
	170.7	129.3		100.2	234.4
	191.8	135.5	chloride.................	12.5	138.5
	212.5	140		16.5	140.7
	251.7	151.9		18	142.6
	308.7	167.0		100.3	182.2
bromide, vap............	38.4	186.5	iodide...................	20	165.5
butyrate, vap............	119.8	160.0		50	201.8
chloride, vap............	0	93.7		100	231.6
Ethylene.................	−78.7	69.9		150	262.7
	−44.1	76.9		200	292.4
	−38.6	78.5		250	318.9
	0	90.7	phosphide..............	0	106.1
	13.8	95.4		15	112.0
	20	100.8		100	143.8
			sulfide.................	0	116.6

Gas or vapor	Temp. °C	Viscosity micropoises	Gas or vapor	Temp. °C	Viscosity micropoises
Hydrogen sulfide...........	17	124.1	Neon.....................	285	470.8
	100	158.7		429	545.4
Iodine, vap...............	124.0	184		502	580.2
	170.0	204		594	623.0
	205.4	220		686	662.6
	247.1	240		827	721.0
Isobutyl acetate, vap........	16.1	76.4	Nitric oxide (NO)..........	0	178
	116.4	155.0		20	187.6
alcohol, vap..............	108.4	144.5		100	227.2
bromide, vap.............	92.3	179.5		200	268.2
butyrate, vap............	156.9	167.0	Nitrogen..................	−21.5	156.3
chloride, vap............	68.5	150.0		10.9	170.7
iodide, vap..............	120	204.7		27.4	178.1
Isopentane, vap............	25	69.5		127.2	219.1
	100	86.0		226.7	255.9
Isopropyl alcohol, vap.......	99.8	109		299	279.7
	120.3	103.1		490	337.4
	198.4	124.8		825	419.2
	293.1	148.8	Nitrosyl chloride..........	15	113.9
bromide, vap.............	60	176.0		100	150.4
chloride, vap............	37.0	148.5		200	192.0
iodide, vap..............	89.3	201.5	Nitrous oxide (N_2O)........	0	135
Krypton..................	0	232.7		26.9	148.8
	15	246		126.9	194.3
Mercury, vap..............	273	494	n-Nonane, vap............	100.3	63.3
	313	551		202.1	78.1
	369	641	n-Octane, vap.............	100.4	67.5
	380	654		202.2	84.8
Methane..................	−181.6	34.8	Oxygen...................	0	189
	−78.5	76.0		19.1	201.8
	0	102.6		127.7	256.8
	20	108.7		227.0	301.7
	100.0	133.1		283	323.3
	200.5	160.5		402	369.3
	284	181.3		496	401.3
	380	202.6		608	437.0
	499	226.4		690	461.2
Methyl acetate, vap........	99.8	98		829	501.2
	100	100	n-Pentane, vap............	25	67.6
	143.3	113.9		100	84.1
	218.5	134.8	Propane..................	17.9	79.5
alcohol, vap..............	66.8	135.0		100.4	100.9
	111.3	125.9		199.3	125.1
	217.5	162.0	n-Propyl alcohol, vap.......	99.9	93
	311.5	192.1		121.7	102.5
chloride.................	−15.3	92		209.7	126.7
	0	96.9		273.0	143.4
	15.0	104	bromide, vap.............	99.8	119
	99.1	137	Propylene.................	16.7	83.4
	182.4	168		49.9	93.5
	302.0	211		100.1	107.6
iodide, vap..............	44	232		199.4	133.8
Neon.....................	0	297.3	Propyl iodide, vap..........	102	210.0
	20	311.1	Sulfur dioxide.............	−75.0	85.8
	100	364.6		−20.0	107.8
	200	424.8		0	115.8
	250	453.2		0	117

Gas or vapor	Temp. °C	Viscosity micro-poises	Gas or vapor	Temp. °C	Viscosity micro-poises
Sulfur dioxide.............	18	124.2	Water, vap...............	150	144.5
	20.5	125.4		200	163.5
	100.4	161.2		250	182.7
	199.4	203.8		300	202.4
	293	244.7		350	221.8
	490	311.5		400	241.2
Trimethylbutane. (2,2,3-),			Xenon..................	0	210.1
vap...................	70.3	73.4		16.5	223.5
	132.2	82.7		20	226.0
	262.1	104.8		127	300.9
Trimethylethylene, vap.....	25	70.1		177	335.1
	100	86.9		227	365.2
Water, vap...............	100	125.5		277	395.4

DIFFUSIVITIES OF GASES IN LIQUIDS

Solute	Solvent	Temp., °C	Diffusivity x 10^5, cm^2/sec
H_2	n-Hexane	25.4	16.36
H_2	Cyclohexane	25.4	7.08
H_2	Ethylene glycol	25.4	0.75
H_2	Carbon tetrachloride	0	6.28
O_2	Cyclohexane	29.6	5.31
O_2	Carbon tetrachloride	25.4	3.71
O_2	Ethanol	29.6	2.64
N_2	Carbon tetrachloride	0	2.44
CH_4	Glycerol	25.4	0.95
C_2H_6	n-Hexane	30	6.00
C_2H_6	n-Heptane	30	5.60
C_2H_2	Water	0	1.10
H_2S	Water	16	1.77
CO_2	Amyl alcohol	25	1.91
CO_2	Isobutyl alcohol	25	2.20
SO_2	n-Heptane	20	2.70
SO_2	n-Nonane	20	2.50
SO_2	n-Decane	20	2.40

DIFFUSION COEFFICIENTS IN AQUEOUS SOLUTIONS AT 25°

The diffusion coefficient D may be defined by either of the equations

$$J = -D \frac{\partial c}{\partial x}$$

or

$$\frac{\partial c}{\partial t} = D \frac{\partial^2 c}{\partial x^2}$$

when diffusion occurs in the x-direction only. Here J is the diffusion-flux across unit area normal to the x-direction, $\frac{\partial c}{\partial x}$ is the concentration-gradient at a fixed time, $\frac{\partial c}{\partial t}$ is the rate of change of concentration with time at a fixed distance. If J is expressed in mole cm^{-2} sec^{-1} and c in mole cm^{-3}, x in cm, and t in sec, D will be given in units of cm^2 sec^{-1}. In general D varies somewhat with concentration. The values below are a selection from measurements by modern high-precision methods, mainly by H. S. Harned and collaborators, R. H. Stokes and collaborators, L. J. Gosting and collaborators, and L. G. Longsworth.

For strong electrolytes at infinite dilution, limiting diffusion coefficients may be calculated by the Nernst relation:

$$D = \frac{RT}{F^2} \left[\frac{(\nu_1 + \nu_2)(\lambda_1^0 \lambda_2^0)}{\nu_1 |Z_1| (\lambda_1^0 + \lambda_2^0)} \right]$$

where R = gas constant, F = Faraday, T = absolute temperature, λ_1^0 and λ_2^0 are cation and anion limiting equivalent conductances, ν_1 and ν_2 are the numbers of cations and anions formed from one "molecule" of electrolyte, and Z_1 is the cation valency. Concentrations, unless expressed otherwise are as molarities and the diffusion coefficients are expressed as $10^5 D/cm^2$ sec^{-1} at 25°C.

DIFFUSION COEFFICIENTS OF STRONG ELECTROLYTES
Molarity

Solute	0.01	0.1	1.0
HCL	....	3.050	3.436
HBr	....	3.156	3.87
LiCl	1.312	1.269	1.302
LiBr	....	1.279	1.404
LiNO$_3$	1.276	1.240	1.293
NaCl	1.545	1.483	1.484
NaBr	....	1.517	1.596
NaI	....	1.520	1.662
KCl	1.917	1.844	1.892
KBr	....	1.874	1.975
KI	....	1.865	2.065
KNO$_3$	1.846	....	....
KClO$_4$	1.790	....	....
CaCl$_2$	1.188	1.110	1.203

C = 0.005M

Solute	0.01	0.1	1.0
BaCl$_2$	1.265	1.159	1.179
Na$_2$SO$_4$	1.123	....	....
MgSO$_4$	0.710	....	....
LaCl$_3$	1.105	....	....
K$_4$Fe(CN)$_6$	1.183	....	....

DIFFUSION COEFFICIENTS OF WEAK AND NON-ELECTROLYTES
Concentration

Solute	Concentration	Coefficient
Glucose	0.39%	0.673
Sucrose	0.38%	0.521
Raffinose	0.38%	0.434
Sucrose	Zero	0.5226
Mannitol	Zero	0.682
Penta-erythritol	Zero	0.761
Glycolamide	Zero	1.142
Glycine	Zero	1.064
α-alanine	0.32%	0.910
β-alanine	0.31%	0.933
Amino-benzoic acid ortho	0.24%	0.840
Amino-benzoic acid meta	0.24%	0.774
Amino-benzoic acid para	0.23%	0.843
Citric acid	0.1 M	0.661

DIFFUSION OF GASES INTO AIR

Gas or vapor	Temp. °C	Coefficient of diffusion, sq. cm/sec	Observer
Alcohol, vapor..........	40.4	0.137	Winkelmann
Carbon dioxide..........	0.0	0.139	Mean of various
Carbon disulfide........	19.9	0.102	Winkelmann
Ether, vapor............	19.9	0.089	Winkelmann
Hydrogen...............	0.0	0.634	Obermayer
Oxygen.................	0.0	0.178	Obermayer
Water, vapor...........	8.0	0.239	Guglielmo

RADIOACTIVE TRACER DIFFUSION DATA FOR PURE METALS

John Askill

The data in these tables are the most reliable set of radioactive tracer diffusion data for pure metals published in the literature from 1938 through December, 1970. For a complete listing of all published data on this subject up to December 1968 see "Tracer Diffusion Data for Metals, Alloys and Simple Oxides" by John Askill, published by Plenum Press, New York, 1970.

The diffusion coefficient D_T at a temperature $T(°K)$ is given by the following relation:

$$D_T = D_0 e^{-Q/RT}$$

Abbreviations used in the tables are:

A.R.G. = Autoradiography
R.A. = Residual Activity
S.D. = Surface Decrease
S.S. = Serial Sectioning
P. = Polycrystalline
S. = Single Crystal
⊥c. = Perpendicular to c Direction
∥c. = Parallel to c Direction
99.95 = 99.95 %

Solute (tracer)	Material (metal, crystalline form and purity)		Temperature range, °C	Form of analysis	Activation energy, Q, Kcal/mole	Frequency factor, D_0, cm²/sec	Reference
Aluminum							
Ag[110]	S	99.999	371–655	S.S.	27.83	0.118	1
Al[27]	S		450–650	S.S.	34.0	1.71	2
Au[198]	S	99.999	423–609	S.S.	27.0	0.077	3
Cd[115]	S	99.999	441–631	S.S.	29.7	1.04	3
Ce[141]	P	99.995	450–630	R.A.	26.60	1.9×10^{-6}	5
Co[60]	S	99.999	369–655	S.S.	27.79	0.131	1
Cr[51]	S	99.999	422–654	S.S.	41.74	464	1
Cu[64]	S	99.999	433–652	S.S.	32.27	0.647	1
Fe[59]	S	99.99	550–636	S.S.	46.0	135	3
Ga[72]	S	99.999	406–652	S.S.	29.24	0.49	1
Ge[71]	S	99.999	401–653	S.S.	28.98	0.481	1
In[114]	P	99.99	400–600	S.S., R.A.	27.6	0.123	4
La[140]	P	99.995	500–630	R.A.	27.0	1.4×10^{-6}	5
Mn[54]	P	99.99	450–650	S.S.	28.8	0.22	2
Mo[99]	P	99.995	400–630	R.A.	13.1	1.04×10^{-9}	6
Nb[95]	P	99.95	350–480	R.A.	19.65	1.66×10^{-7}	7
Nd[147]	P	99.995	450–630	R.A.	25.0	4.8×10^{-7}	5
Ni[63]	P	99.99	360–630	R.A.	15.7	2.9×10^{-8}	8
Pd[103]	P	99.995	400 630	R.A.	20.2	1.92×10^{-7}	9
Pr[142]	P	99.995	520–630	R.A.	23.87	3.58×10^{-7}	5
Sb[124]	P		448–620	R.A.	29.1	0.09	10
Sm[153]	P	99.995	450–630	R.A.	22.88	3.45×10^{-7}	5
Sn[113]	P		400–600	S.S., R.A.	28.5	0.245	4
V[48]	P	99.995	400–630	R.A.	19.6	6.05×10^{-8}	11
Zn[65]	S	99.999	357–653	S.S.	28.86	0.259	1
Beryllium							
Ag[110]	S⊥c	99.75	650–900	R.A.	43.2	1.76	12
Ag[110]	S∥c	99.75	650–900	R.A.	39.3	0.43	12
Be[7]	S⊥c	99.75	565–1065	R.A.	37.6	0.52	13
Be[7]	S∥c	99.75	565–1065	R.A.	39.4	0.62	13
Fe[59]	S	99.75	700–1076	R.A.	51.6	0.67	12
Ni[63]	P		800–1250	R.A.	58.0	0.2	14
Cadmium							
Ag[110]	S	99.99	180–300	—	25.4	2.21	15
Cd[115]	S	99.95	110–283	R.A.	19.3	0.14	16
Zn[65]	S	99.99	180–300	—	19.0	0.0016	15
Calcium							
C[14]		99.95	550–800	R.A.	29.8	3.2×10^{-5}	17
Ca[45]		99.95	500–800	R.A.	38.5	8.3	17

Solute (tracer)	Material (metal, crystalline form and purity)		Temperature range, °C	Form of analysis	Activation energy, Q, Kcal/mole	Frequency factor, D_0, cm^2/sec	Reference
Fe^{59}		99.95	500–800	R.A.	23.3	2.7×10^{-3}	17
Ni^{63}		99.95	550–800	—	28.9	1.0×10^{-5}	17
U^{235}		99.95	500–700	R.A.	34.8	1.1×10^{-5}	17
Carbon							
Ag^{110}	$\perp$c		750–1050	R.A.	64.3	9280	18
C^{14}			2000–2200	—	163	5	19
Ni^{63}	$\perp$c		540–920	R.A.	47.2	102	18
Ni^{63}	$\parallel$c		750–1060	R.A.	53.3	2.2	18
Th^{228}	$\perp$c		1400–2200	R.A.	145.4	1.33×10^{-5}	18
Th^{228}	$\parallel$c		1800–2200	R.A.	114.7	2.48	18
U^{232}	$\perp$c		1400–2200	R.A.	115.0	6760	18
U^{232}	$\parallel$c		1400–1820	R.A.	129.5	385	18
Chromium							
C^{14}	P		1200–1500	R.A.	26.5	9.0×10^{-3}	20
Cr^{51}	P	99.98	1030–1545	S.S.	73.7	0.2	21
Fe^{59}	P	99.8	980–1420	R.A.	79.3	0.47	22
Mo^{99}	P		1100–1420	R.A.	58.0	2.7×10^{-3}	20
Cobalt							
C^{14}	P	99.82	600–1400	R.A.	34.0	0.21	23
Co^{60}	P	99.9	1100–1405	S.S.	67.7	0.83	24
Fe^{59}	P	99.9	1104–1303	S.S.	62.7	0.21	24
Ni^{63}	P		1192–1297	R.A.	60.2	0.10	25
S^{35}	P	99.99	1150–1250	R.A.	5.4	1.3	26
Copper							
Ag^{110}	S, P		580–980	R.A.	46.5	0.61	27
As^{76}	P		810–1075	R.A.	42.13	0.20	28
Au^{198}	S, P		400–1050	S.S.	42.6	0.03	29
Cd^{115}	S	99.98	725–950	S.S.	45.7	0.935	30
Ce^{141}	P	99.999	766–947	R.A.	27.6	2.17×10^{-8}	31
Cr^{51}	S, P		800–1070	R.A.	53.5	1.02	32
Co^{60}	S	99.998	701–1077	S.S.	54.1	1.93	33
Cu^{67}	S	99.999	698–1061	S.S.	50.5	0.78	34
Eu^{152}	P	99.999	750–970	S.S., R.A.	26.85	1.17×10^{-7}	31
Fe^{59}	S, P		460–1070	R.A.	52.0	1.36	32
Ga^{72}			—	—	45.90	0.55	35
Ge^{68}	S	99.998	653–1015	S.S.	44.76	0.397	36
Hg^{203}	P		—	—	44.0	0.35	35
Lu^{177}	P	99.999	857–1010	R.A.	26.15	4.3×10^{-9}	31
Mn^{54}	S	99.99	754–950	S.S.	91.4	10^7	37
Nb^{95}	P	99.999	807–906	R.A.	60.06	2.04	38
Ni^{63}	P		620–1080	R.A.	53.8	1.1	39
Pd^{102}	S	99.999	807–1056	S.S.	54.37	1.71	40
Pm^{147}	P	99.999	720–955	R.A.	27.5	3.62×10^{-8}	31
Pt^{195}	P		843–997	S.S.	37.5	4.8×10^{-4}	41
S^{35}	S	99.999	800–1000	R.A.	49.2	23	42
Sb^{124}	S	99.999	600–1000	S.S.	42.0	0.34	43
Sn^{113}	P		680–910	—	45.0	0.11	44
Tb^{160}	P	99.999	770–980	R.A.	27.45	8.96×10^{-9}	31
Tl^{204}	S	99.999	785–996	S.S.	43.3	0.71	45
Tm^{170}	P	99.999	705–950	R.A.	24.15	7.28×10^{-9}	31
Zn^{65}	P	99.999	890–1000	S.S.	47.50	0.73	46
Germanium							
Cd^{115}	S		750–950	R.A.	102.0	1.75×10^9	47
Fe^{59}	S		775–930	R.A.	24.8	0.13	48
Ge^{71}	S		766–928	S.S.	68.5	7.8	49
In^{114}	S		600–920	—	39.9	2.9×10^{-4}	50
Sb^{124}	S		720–900	—	50.2	0.22	51
Te^{125}	S		770–900	S.S.	56.0	2.0	52
Tl^{204}	S		800–930	S.S.	78.4	1700	53

Solute (tracer)	Material (metal, crystalline form and purity)		Temperature range, °C	Form of analysis	Activation energy, Q, Kcal/mole	Frequency factor, D_0, cm²/sec	Reference
Gold							
Ag[110]	S	99.99	699–1007	S.S.	40.2	0.072	54
Au[198]	S	99.97	850–1050	S.S.	42.26	0.107	224
Co[60]	P	99.93	702–948	R.A.	41.6	0.068	55
Fe[59]	P	99.93	701–948	R.A.	41.6	0.082	55
Hg[203]	S	99.994	600–1027	—	37.38	0.116	56
Ni[63]	P	99.96	880–940	S.S.	46.0	0.30	57
Pt[195]	P, S	99.98	800–1060	S.S.	60.9	7.6	58
β-Hafnium							
Hf[181]	P	97.9	1795–1995	S.S.	38.7	1.2×10^{-3}	59
Indium							
Ag[110]	S⊥c	99.99	25–140	S.S.	12.8	0.52	60
Ag[110]	S∥c	99.99	25–140	S.S.	11.5	0.11	60
Au[198]	S	99.99	25–140	S.S.	6.7	9×10^{-3}	60
In[114]	S⊥c	99.99	44–144	S.S.	18.7	3.7	61
In[114]	S∥c	99.99	44–144	S.S.	18.7	2.7	61
Tl[204]	S	99.99	49–157	S.S.	15.5	0.049	62
α-Iron							
Ag[110]	P		748–888	S.S.	69.0	1950	63
Au[198]	P	99.999	800–900	R.A.	62.4	31	64
C[14]	P	99.98	616–844	R.A.	29.3	2.2	65
Co[60]	P	99.995	638–768	R.A.	62.2	7.19	62
Cr[51]	P	99.95	775–875	R.A.	57.5	2.53	66
Cu[64]	P	99.9	800–1050	R.A.	57.0	0.57	67
Fe[55]	P	99.92	809–889	—	60.3	5.4	68
K[42]	P	99.92	500–800	R.A.	42.3	0.036	69
Mn[54]	P	99.97	800–900	R.A.	52.5	0.35	70
Mo[99]	P		750–875	R.A.	73.0	7800	71
Ni[63]	P	99.97	680–800	R.A.	56.0	1.3	72
P[32]	P		860–900	R.A.	55.0	2.9	73
Sb[124]	P		800–900	R.A.	66.6	1100	74
V[48]	P		755–875	R.A.	55.4	1.43	75
W[185]	P		755–875	R.A.	55.1	0.29	75
γ-Iron							
Be[7]	P	99.9	1100–1350	R.A.	57.6	0.1	76
C[14]	P	99.34	800–1400	—	34.0	0.15	23
Co[60]	P	99.98	1138–1340	S.S.	72.9	1.25	77
Cr[51]	P	99.99	950–1400	R.A.	69.7	10.8	78
Fe[59]	P	99.98	1171–1361	S.S.	67.86	0.49	79
Hf[181]	P	99.99	1110–1360	R.A.	97.3	3600	78
Mn[54]	P	99.97	920–1280	R.A.	62.5	0.16	70
Ni[63]	P	99.97	930–2050	R.A.	67.0	0.77	72
P[32]	P	99.99	950–1200	R.A.	43.7	0.01	80
S[35]	P		900–1250	R.A.	53.0	1.7	81
V[48]	P	99.99	1120–1380	R.A.	69.3	0.28	78
W[185]	P	99.5	1050–1250	R.A.	90.0	1000	82
δ-Iron							
Co[60]	P	99.995	1428–1521	R.A.	61.4	6.38	83
Fe[59]	P	99.95	1428–1492	S.S.	57.5	2.01	83
P[32]	P	99.99	1370–1460	R.A.	55.0	2.9	73
Lanthanum							
Au[198]	P	99.97	600–800	S.S.	45.1	1.5	84
La[140]	P	99.97	690–850	S.S.	18.1	2.2×10^{-2}	84
Lead							
Ag[110]	P	99.9	200–310	R.A.	14.4	0.064	85
Au[198]	S	99.999	190–320	S.S.	10.0	8.7×10^{-3}	86

Solute (tracer)	Material (metal, crystalline form and purity)		Temperature range, °C	Form of analysis	Activation energy, Q, Kcal/mole	Frequency factor, D_0, cm²/sec	Reference
Cd¹¹⁵	S	99.999	150–320	S.S.	21.23	0.409	87
Cu⁶⁴	S		150–320	S.S.	14.44	0.046	88
Pb²⁰⁴	S	99.999	150–320	S.S.	25.52	0.887	87
Tl²⁰⁵	P	99.999	207–322	S.S.	24.33	0.511	89
Lithium							
Ag¹¹⁰	P	92.5	65–161	S.S.	12.83	0.37	90
Au¹⁹⁵	P	92.5	47–153	S.S.	10.49	0.21	90
Bi	P	99.95	141–177	S.S.	47.3	5.3×10^{13}	91
Cd¹¹⁵	P	92.5	80–174	S.S.	16.05	2.35	90
Cu⁶⁴	P	99.98	51–120	S.S.	9.22	0.47	93
Ga⁷²	P	99.98	58–173	S.S.	12.9	0.21	93
Hg²⁰³	P	99.98	58–173	S.S.	14.18	1.04	93
In¹¹⁴	P	92.5	80–175	S.S.	15.87	0.39	90
Li⁶	P	99.98	35–178	S.S.	12.60	0.14	94
Na²²	P	92.5	52–176	S.S.	12.61	0.41	90
Pb²⁰⁴	P	99.95	129–169	S.S.	25.2	160	91
Sb¹²⁴	P	99.95	141–176	S.S.	41.5	1.6×10^{10}	91
Sn¹¹³	P	99.95	108–174	S.S.	15.0	0.62	91
Zn⁶⁵	P	92.5	60–175	S.S.	12.98	0.57	92
Magnesium							
Ag¹¹⁰	P	99.9	476–621	S.S.	28.50	0.34	95
Fe⁵⁹	P	99.95	400–600	R.A.	21.2	4×10^{-6}	96
In¹¹⁴	P	99.9	472–610	S.S.	28.4	5.2×10^{-2}	95
Mg²⁸	S⊥c		467–635	S.S.	32.5	1.5	97
Mg²⁸	S∥c		467–635	S.S.	32.2	1.0	97
Ni⁶³	P	99.95	400–600	R.A.	22.9	1.2×10^{-5}	96
U²³⁵	P	99.95	500–620	R.A.	27.4	1.6×10^{-5}	96
Zn⁶⁵	P	99.9	467–620	S.S.	28.6	0.41	95
Molybdenum							
C¹⁴	P	99.98	1200–1600	R.A.	41.0	2.04×10^{-2}	99
Co⁶⁰	P	99.98	1850–2350	S.S.	106.7	18	100
Cr⁵¹	P		1000–1500	R.A.	54.0	2.5×10^{-4}	20
Cs¹³⁴	S	99.99	1000–1470	R.A., A.R.G.	28.0	8.7×10^{-11}	101
K⁴²	S		800–1100	R.A.	25.04	5.5×10^{-9}	102
Mo⁹⁹	P		1850–2350	S.S.	96.9	0.5	103
Na²⁴	S		800–1100	R.A.	21.25	2.95×10^{-9}	102
Nb⁹⁵	P	99.98	1850–2350	S.S.	108.1	14	100
P³²	P	99.97	2000–2200	S.S.	80.5	0.19	104
Re¹⁸⁶	P		1700–2100	A.R.G.	94.7	0.097	105
S³⁵	S	99.97	2220–2470	S.S.	101.0	320	106
Ta¹⁸²	P		1700–2150	R.A.	83.0	3.5×10^{-4}	20
U²³⁵	P	99.98	1500–2000	R.A.	76.4	7.6×10^{-3}	107
W¹⁸⁵	P	99.98	1700–2260	S.S.	110	1.7	108
Nickel							
Au¹⁹⁸	S, P	99.999	700–1075	S.S.	55.0	0.02	109
Be⁷	P	99.9	1020–1400	R.A.	46.2	0.019	76
C¹⁴	P	99.86	600–1400	—	34.0	0.012	23
Co⁶⁰	P	99.97	1149–1390	R.A.	65.9	1.39	110
Cr⁵¹	P	99.95	1100–1270	S.S.	65.1	1.1	111
Cu⁶⁴	P	99.95	1050–1360	S.S.	61.7	0.57	111
Fe⁵⁹	P		1020–1263	S.S.	58.6	0.074	112
Mo⁹⁹	P		900–1200	R.A.	51.0	1.6×10^{-3}	20
Ni⁶³	P	99.95	1042–1404	S.S.	68.0	1.9	111
Pu²³⁸	P		1025–1125	A.R.G.	51.0	0.5	113
Sb¹²⁴	P	99.97	1020–1220	—	27.0	1.8×10^{-5}	114
Sn¹¹³	P	99.8	700–1350	A.R.G.	58.0	0.83	115
V⁴⁸	P	99.99	800–1300	R.A.	66.5	0.87	11
W¹⁸⁵	P	99.95	1100–1300	S.S.	71.5	2.0	116

Solute (tracer)	Material (metal, crystalline form and purity)		Temperature range, °C	Form of analysis	Activation energy, Q, Kcal/mole	Frequency factor, D_0, cm²/sec	Reference
Niobium							
C^{14}	P		800–1250	R.A.	32.0	1.09×10^{-5}	117
Co^{60}	P	99.85	1500–2100	A.R.G.	70.5	0.74	118
Cr^{51}	S		943–1435	S.S.	83.5	0.30	119
Fe^{55}	P	99.85	1400–2100	A.R.G.	77.7	1.5	118
K^{42}	S		900–1100	R.A.	22.10	2.38×10^{-7}	102
Nb^{95}	P, S	99.99	878–2395	S.S.	96.0	1.1	120
P^{32}	P	99.0	1300–1800	S.S.	51.5	5.1×10^{-2}	104
S^{35}	S	99.9	1100–1500	R.A.	73.1	2600	121
Sn^{113}	P	99.85	1850–2400	S.S.	78.9	0.14	122
Ta^{182}	P, S	99.997	878–2395	S.S.	99.3	1.0	120
Ti^{44}	S		994–1492	S.S.	86.9	0.099	123
U^{235}	P	99.55	1500–2000	R.A.	76.8	8.9×10^{-3}	107
V^{48}	S	99.99	1000–1400	R.A.	85.0	2.21	124
W^{185}	P	99.8	1800–2200	R.A.	91.7	5×10^{-4}	125
Palladium							
Pd^{103}	S	99.999	1060–1500	S.S.	63.6	0.205	126
Phosphorus							
P^{32}	P		0–44	S.S.	9.4	1.07×10^{-3}	127
Platinum							
Co^{60}	P	99.99	900–1050	—	74.2	19.6	129
Cu^{64}	P		1098–1375	S.S.	59.5	0.074	41
Pt^{195}	P	99.99	1325–1600	S.S.	68.2	0.33	130
Potassium							
Au^{198}	P	99.95	5.6–52.5	S.S.	3.23	1.29×10^{-3}	131
K^{42}	S	99.7	−52–61	S.S.	9.36	0.16	132
Na^{22}	P	99.7	0–62	S.S.	7.45	0.058	133
Rb^{86}	P	99.95	0.1–59.9	S.S.	8.78	0.090	134
γ-Plutonium							
Pu^{238}	P		190–310	S.S.	16.7	2.1×10^{-5}	135
δ-Plutonium							
Pu^{238}	P		350–440	S.S.	23.8	4.5×10^{-3}	136
ε-Plutonium							
Pu^{238}	P		500–612	R.A.	18.5	2.0×10^{-2}	137
α-Praseodymium							
Ag^{110}	P	99.93	610–730	S.S.	25.4	0.14	138
Au^{195}	P	99.93	650–780	S.S.	19.7	4.3×10^{-2}	138
Co^{60}	P	99.93	660–780	S.S.	16.4	4.7×10^{-2}	138
Zn^{65}	P	99.96	766–603	S.S.	24.8	0.18	139
β-Praseodymium							
Ag^{110}	P	99.93	800–900	S.S.	21.5	3.2×10^{-2}	138
Au^{195}	P	99.93	800–910	S.S.	20.1	3.3×10^{-2}	138
Ho^{166}	P	99.96	800–930	S.S.	26.3	9.5	140
In^{114}	P	99.96	800–930	S.S.	28.9	9.6	140
La^{140}	P	99.96	800–930	S.S.	25.7	1.8	140
Pr^{142}	P	99.93	800–900	S.S.	29.4	8.7	140
Zn^{65}	P	99.96	822–921	S.S.	27.0	0.63	139
Selenium							
Fe^{59}	P		40–100	R.A.	8.88	—	141
Hg^{203}	P	99.996	25–100	R.A.	1.2	—	141
S^{35}	S⊥c		60–90	S.D.	29.9	1700	142

Solute (tracer)	Material (metal, crystalline form and purity)		Temperature range, °C	Form of analysis	Activation energy, Q, Kcal/mole	Frequency factor, D_0, cm^2/sec	Reference
S^{35}	S∥c		60–90	S.D.	15.6	1100	142
Se^{75}	P		35–140	—	11.7	1.4×10^{-4}	143
Silicon							
Au^{198}	S		700–1300	S.S.	47.0	2.75×10^{-3}	145
C^{14}	P		1070–1400	R.A.	67.2	0.33	146
Cu^{64}	P		800–1100	R.A.	23.0	4×10^{-2}	147
Fe^{59}	S		1000–1200	R.A.	20.0	6.2×10^{-3}	148
Ni^{63}	P		450–800	—	97.5	1000	149
P^{32}	S		1100–1250	R.A.	41.5	—	150
Sb^{124}	S		1190–1398	R.A.	91.7	12.9	151
Si^{31}	S	99.99999	1225–1400	S.S.	110.0	1800	146
Silver							
Au^{198}	P	99.99	718–942	S.S.	48.28	0.85	54
Ag^{110}	S	99.999	640–955	S.S.	45.2	0.67	152
Cd^{115}	S	99.99	592–937	S.S.	41.69	0.44	153
Co^{60}	S	99.999	700–940	—	48.75	1.9	154
Cu^{64}	P	99.99	717–945	S.S.	46.1	1.23	155
Fe^{59}	S	99.99	720–930	S.S.	49.04	2.42	156
Ge^{77}	P		640–870	S.S.	36.5	0.084	157
Hg^{203}	P	99.99	653–948	S.S.	38.1	0.079	155
In^{114}	S	99.99	592–937	S.S.	40.80	0.41	153
Ni^{63}	S	99.99	749–950	S.S.	54.8	21.9	158
Pb^{210}	P		700–865	S.S.	38.1	0.22	159
Pd^{102}	S	99.999	736–939	S.S.	56.75	9.56	140
Ru^{103}	S	99.99	793–945	S.S.	65.8	180	160
S^{35}	S	99.999	600–900	R.A.	40.0	1.65	161
Sb^{124}	P	99.999	780–950	S.S., R.A.	39.07	0.234	162
Sn^{113}	S	99.99	592–937	S.S.	39.30	0.255	153
Te^{125}	P		770–940	R.A.	38.90	0.47	163
Tl^{204}	P		640–870	S.S.	37.9	0.15	157
Zn^{65}	S	99.99	640–925	S.S.	41.7	0.54	164
Sodium							
Au^{198}	P	99.99	1.0–77	S.S.	2.21	3.34×10^{-4}	165
K^{42}	P	99.99	0–91	S.S.	8.43	0.08	133
Na^{22}	P	99.99	0–98	S.S.	10.09	0.145	166
Rb^{86}	P	99.99	0–85	S.S.	8.49	0.15	133
Tantalum							
C^{14}	P		1450–2200	S.S.	40.3	1.2×10^{-2}	167
Fe^{59}	P		930–1240	—	71.4	0.505	168
Mo^{99}	P		1750–2220	R.A.	81.0	1.8×10^{-3}	20
Nb^{95}	P, S	99.996	921–2484	S.S.	98.7	0.23	169
S^{35}	P	99.0	1970–2110	R.A.	70.0	100	170
Ta^{182}	P, S	99.996	1250–2200	S.S.	98.7	1.24	226
Tellurium							
Hg^{203}	P		270–440	—	18.7	3.14×10^{-5}	171
Se^{75}	P		320–440	—	28.6	2.6×10^{-2}	171
Tl^{204}	P		360–430	—	41.0	320	172
Te^{127}	S⊥c	99.9999	300–400	S.S.	46.7	3.91×10^4	173
Te^{127}	S∥c	99.9999	300–400	S.S.	35.5	130	173
α-Thallium							
Ag^{110}	P⊥c	99.999	80–250	S.S.	11.8	3.8×10^{-2}	174
Ag^{110}	P∥c	99.999	80–250	S.S.	11.2	2.7×10^{-2}	174
Au^{198}	P⊥c	99.999	110–260	S.S.	2.8	2.0×10^{-5}	174
Au^{198}	P∥c	99.999	110–260	S.S.	5.2	5.3×10^{-4}	174
Tl^{204}	S⊥c	99.9	135–230	S.S.	22.6	0.4	175
Tl^{204}	S∥c	99.9	135–230	S.S.	22.9	0.4	175

Solute (tracer)	Material (metal, crystalline form and purity)		Temperature range, °C	Form of analysis	Activation energy, Q, Kcal/mole	Frequency factor, D_0, cm²/sec	Reference
β-Thallium							
Ag[110]	P	99.999	230–310	S.S.	11.9	4.2×10^{-2}	174
Au[198]	P	99.999	230–310	S.S.	6.0	5.2×10^{-4}	174
Tl[204]	S	99.9	230–280	S.S.	20.7	0.7	175
α-Thorium							
Pa[231]	P	99.85	770–910	—	74.7	126	176
Th[228]	P	99.85	720–880	—	71.6	395	176
U[233]	P	99.85	700–880	—	79.3	2210	176
Tin							
Ag[110]	S⊥c		135–225	S.S.	18.4	0.18	177
Ag[110]	S∥c		135–225	S.S	12.3	7.1×10^{-3}	177
Au[198]	S⊥c		135–225	S.S.	17.7	0.16	177
Au[198]	S∥c		135–225	S.S.	11.0	5.8×10^{-3}	177
Co[60]	S, P		140–217	R.A.	22.0	5.5	178
In[114]	S⊥c	99.998	181–221	S.S.	25.8	34.1	179
In[114]	S∥c	99.998	181–221	S.S.	25.6	12.2	179
Sn[113]	S⊥c	99.999	160–226	S.S.	25.1	10.7	180
Sn[113]	S∥c	99.999	160–226	S.S.	25.6	7.7	180
Tl[204]	P	99.999	137–216	S.S.	14.7	1.2×10^{-3}	181
α-Titanium							
Ti[44]	P	99.99	700–850	R.A.	35.9	8.6×10^{-6}	182
β-Titanium							
Ag[110]	P	99.95	940–1570	S.S.	43.2	3×10^{-3}	183
Be[7]	P	99.96	915–1300	R.A.	40.2	0.8	184
C[14]	P	99.62	1100–1600	R.A.	20.0	3.02×10^{-3}	185
Cr[51]	P	99.7	950–1600	A.R.G.	35.1 / 61.0	5×10^{-3} / 4.9	186
Co[60]	P	99.7	900–1600	S.S.	30.6 / 52.5	1.2×10^{-2} / 2.0	186
Fe[59]	P	99.7	900–1600	A.R.G.	31.6 / 55.0	7.8×10^{-3} / 2.7	186
Mo[99]	P	99.7	900–1600	S.S.	43.0 / 73.0	8.0×10^{-3} / 20	186
Mn[54]	P	99.7	900–1600	S.S.	33.7 / 58.0	6.1×10^{-3} / 20	186
Nb[95]	P	99.7	1000–1600	A.R.G.	39.3 / 73.0	5.0×10^{-3} / 20	186
Ni[63]	P	99.7	925–1600	A.R.G.	29.6 / 52.5	9.2×10^{-3} / 2.0	186
P[32]	P	99.7	950–1600	S.S.	24.1 / 56.5	3.62×10^{-3} / 5	187
Sc[46]	P	99.95	940–1590	S.S.	32.4	4.0×10^{-3}	183
Sn[113]	P	99.7	950–1600	S.S.	31.6 / 69.2	3.8×10^{-4} / 10	187
Ti[44]	P	99.95	900–1540	S.S.	31.2 / 60.0	3.58×10^{-4} / 1.09	188
U[235]	P	99.9	900–1400	R.A.	29.3	5.1×10^{-4}	189
V[48]	P	99.95	900–1545	S.S.	32.2 / 57.2	3.1×10^{-4} / 1.4	190
W[185]	P	99.94	900–1250	R.A.	43.9	3.6×10^{-3}	191
Zr[95]	P	98.94	920–1500	R.A.	35.4	4.7×10^{-3}	191
Tungsten							
C[14]	P	99.51	1200–1600	R.A.	53.5	8.91×10^{-3}	99
Fe[59]	P		940–1240	—	66.0	1.4×10^{-2}	168
Mo[99]	P		1700–2100	R.A.	101.0	0.3	20
Nb[95]	P	99.99	1305–2367	S.S.	137.6	3.01	192
Re[186]	S		2100–2400	R.A.	141.0	19.5	193

Solute (tracer)	Material (metal, crystalline form and purity)		Temperature range, °C	Form of analysis	Activation energy, Q, Kcal/mole	Frequency factor, D_0, cm²/sec	Reference
Ta[182]	P	99.99	1305–2375	S.S.	139.9	3.05	192
W[185]	P	99.99	1800–2403	S.S.	140.3	1.88	192
α-Uranium							
U[234]	P		580–650	—	40.0	2×10^{-3}	194
β-Uranium							
Co[60]	P	99.999	692–763	S.S.	27.45	1.5×10^{-2}	195
U[235]	P		690–750	R.A.	44.2	2.8×10^{-3}	196
γ-Uranium							
Au[195]	P	99.99	785–1007	S.S.	30.4	4.86×10^{-3}	197
Co[60]	P	99.99	783–989	S.S.	12.57	3.51×10^{-4}	198
Cr[51]	P	99.99	797–1037	S.S.	24.46	5.37×10^{-3}	198
Cu[64]	P	99.99	787–1039	S.S.	24.06	1.96×10^{-3}	198
Fe[55]	P	99.99	787–990	S.S.	12.0	2.69×10^{-4}	198
Mn[54]	P	99.99	787–939	S.S.	13.88	1.81×10^{-4}	198
Nb[95]	P	99.99	791–1102	S.S.	39.65	4.87×10^{-2}	198
Ni[63]	P	99.99	787–1039	S.S.	15.66	5.36×10^{-4}	198
U[233]	P	99.99	800–1070	S.S.	28.5	2.33×10^{-3}	227
Zr[95]	P		800–1000	R.A.	16.5	3.9×10^{-4}	228
Vanadium							
C[14]	P	99.7	845–1130	S.S.	27.3	4.9×10^{-3}	199
Cr[51]	P	99.8	960–1200	R.A.	64.6	9.54×10^{-3}	200
Fe[59]	P		960–1350	S.S.	71.0	0.373	201
P[32]	P	99.8	1200–1450	R.A.	49.8	2.45×10^{-2}	202
S[35]	P	99.8	1320–1520	R.A.	34.0	3.1×10^{-2}	184
V[48]	S, P	99.99	880–1360	S.S.	73.65	0.36	203
V[48]	S, P	99.99	1360–1830	S.S.	94.14	214.0	203
Yttrium							
Y[90]	S⊥c		900–1300	R.A.	67.1	5.2	204
Y[90]	S∥c		900–1300	R.A.	60.3	0.82	204
Zinc							
Ag[110]	S⊥c	99.999	271–413	S.S.	27.6	0.45	205
Ag[110]	S∥c	99.999	271–413	S.S.	26.0	0.32	205
Au[198]	S⊥c	99.999	315–415	S.S.	29.72	0.29	206
Au[198]	S∥c	99.999	315–415	S.S.	29.73	0.97	206
Cd[115]	S⊥c	99.999	225–416	S.S.	20.12	0.117	206
Cd[115]	S∥c	99.999	225–416	S.S.	20.54	0.114	206
Cu[64]	S⊥c	99.999	338–415	S.S.	29.92	2.0	206
Cu[64]	S∥c	99.999	338–415	S.S.	29.53	2.22	207
Ga[72]	S⊥c		240–403	S.S.	18.15	0.018	207
Ga[72]	S∥c		240–403	S.S.	18.4	0.016	207
Hg[203]	S⊥c		260–413	S.S.	20.18	0.073	208
Hg[203]	S∥c		260–413	S.S.	19.70	0 056	208
In[114]	S⊥c		271–413	S.S.	19.60	0.14	205
In[114]	S∥c		271–413	S.S.	19.10	0.062	205
Sn[113]	S⊥c		298–400	S.S.	18.4	0.13	209
Sn[113]	S∥c		298–400	S.S.	19.4	0.15	209
Zn[65]	S⊥c	99.999	240–418	S.S.	23.0	0.18	210
Zn[65]	S∥c	99.999	240–418	S.S.	21.9	0.13	210
α-Zirconium							
Cr[51]	P	99.9	700–850	R.A.	18.0	1.19×10^{-8}	211
Fe[55]	P		750–840	—	48.0	2.5×10^{-2}	212
Mo[99]	P		600–850	R.A.	24.76	6.22×10^{-8}	213
Nb[95]	P	99.99	740–857	R.A.	31.5	6.6×10^{-6}	182
Sn[113]	P		300–700	A.R.G.	22.0	1.0×10^{-8}	214
Ta[182]	P	99.6	700–800	R.A.	70.0	100	215

Solute (tracer)	Material (metal, crystalline form and purity)	Temperature range, °C	Form of analysis	Activation energy, Q, Kcal/mole	Frequency factor, D_0, cm²/sec	Reference
V^{48}	P 99.99	600–850	R.A.	22.9	1.12×10^{-8}	124
Zr^{95}	P 99.95	750–850	S.S.	45.5	5.6×10^{-4}	216
β-Zirconium						
Be^7	P 99.7	915–1300	R.A.	31.1	8.33×10^{-2}	184
C^{14}	P 96.6	1100–1600	R.A.	34.2	3.57×10^{-2}	217
Ce^{141}	P	880–1600	R.A.	41.4	3.16	218
				74.1	42.17	
Co^{60}	P 99.99	920–1600	S.S.	21.82	3.26×10^{-3}	219
Cr^{51}	P 99.9	700–850	R.A.	18.0	1.19×10^{-8}	211
Fe^{55}	P	750–840	—	48.0	2.5×10^{-2}	212
Mo^{99}	P	900–1635	R.A.	35.2	1.99×10^{-6}	218
				68.55	2.63	
Nb^{95}	P	1230–1635	R.A.	36.6	7.8×10^{-4}	220
P^{32}	P 99.94	950–1200	R.A.	33.3	0.33	221
Sn^{113}	P	300–700	A.R.G.	22.0	1×10^{-8}	214
Ta^{182}	P 99.6	900–1200	R.A.	27.0	5.5×10^{-5}	215
U^{235}	P	900–1065	S.S.	30.5	5.7×10^{-4}	222
V^{48}	P 99.99	870–1200	R.A.	45.8	7.59×10^{-3}	223
V^{48}	P 99.99	1200–1400	R.A.	57.7	0.32	223
W^{185}	P 99.7	900–1250	R.A.	55.8	0.41	223
Zr^{95}	P	1100–1500	S.S.	30.1	2.4×10^{-4}	225

REFERENCES

1. N. L. Peterson and S. J. Rothman, *Phys. Rev.* **B1** (8), 3264 (1970).
2. T. S. Lundy and J. F. Murdock, *J. Appl. Phys.* **33** (5), 1671 (1962).
3. W. B. Alexander and L. M. Slifkin, *Phys. Rev.* **B1** (8), 3274 (1970).
4. M. S. Anand and R. P. Agarwala *Phys. Stat. Solidi* **A1** (1), 41K (1970).
5. S. P. Murarka and R. P. Agarwala, *Indian At. Energy Comm.* **Report BARC-368** (1968).
6. A. R. Paul and R. P. Agarwala, *J. Appl. Phys.* **38** (9), 3790 (1967).
7. G. P. Tiwari and B. D. Sharma, *Trans. Indian Inst. Metals* **20**, 83 (1967).
8. K. Hirano, R. P. Agarwala, and M. Cohen, *Acta Met.* **10** (9), 857 (1962).
9. M. S. Anand and R. P. Agarwala, *Trans. AIME* **239** (11), 1848 (1967).
10. S. Badrinarayanan and H. B. Mathers, *Int. J. Appl. Radiat. Isotopes* **19** (4), 353 (1968).
11. S. P. Murarka, M. S. Anand, and R. P. Agarwala, *Acta Met.* **16** (1), 69 (1968).
12. M. C. Naik, J. M. Dupony, and Y. Adda, *Mem. Sci. Rev. Met.* **63**, 488 (1966).
13. J. M. Dupony, J. Mathie, and Y. Adda, *Mem. Sci. Rev. Met.* **63**, 481 (1966).
14. V. M. Ananyn, V. P. Gladkov, V. S. Zotov, and D. M. Skorov, *At. Energ;* **29** (3), 220 (1970).
15. W. Hirschwald and W. Schroedter, *Z. Physik. Chem. N.F.* **53**, 392 (1967).
16. W. Chomka, *Zess. Nauk Politech Gdansk Fizyka* **1**, 39 (1967).
17. L. V. Pavlinov, A. M. Gladyshev, and V. N. Bikov, *Fiz. Metal Metalloved.* **26** (5), 823 (1968).
18. J. R. Wolfe, D. R. McKenzie, and R. J. Borg, *J. Appl. Phys.* **36** (6), 1906 (1965).
19. M. A. Kanter, *Phys. Rev.* **107**, 655 (1957).
20. E. V. Borisov, P. L. Gruzin, and S. V. Zemskii, *Zashch Pokryt Metal* **2**, 104 (1968).
21. J. Askill and D. H. Tomlin, *Phil. Mag.* **11** (111), 467 (1965).
22. H. W. Paxton and R. A. Wolfe, *Trans. AIME* **230**, 1426 (1964).
23. I. I. Kovenskii, *Fiz. Metal. i Metalloved.* **16**, 613 (1963).
24. H. W. Mead and C. E. Birchenall, *Trans. Met. Soc. AIME* **203** (9), 994 (1955).
25. K. Hirano, R. P. Agarwala, B. L. Averbach, and M. Cohen, *J. Appl. Phys.* **33** (10), 3049 (1962).
26. M. M. Pavlyuchenko and I. F. Kononyuk, *Dokl. Akad. Nauk Belorusskoi SSR* **8**, 157 (1964).
27. G. Barreau, G. Brunel, G. Azeron, P. Lacombe, *C. R. Acad. Sci. Paris* Ser C **270** (6), 514 (1970).
28. S. M. Klotsman, A. Ya Rabovskii, V. K. Talinskii, and A. N. Timofeeu, *Fiz. Met. Metalloved* **29** (4), 803 (1970).
29. A. Chatterjee and D. J. Fabian, *Acta Met.* **17** (9), 1141 (1969).
30. T. Hirone, N. Kunitomi, M. Sakamoto, and H. Yamaki, *J. Phys. Soc. Japan* **13** (8), 838 (1958).
31. S. Badrinarayanan and H. B. Mathur, *Indian J. Pure Appl. Phys.* **8** (6), 324 (1970).
32. G. Barreau, G. Brunel, and G. Cizeron, *C. R. Acad. Sci.* **Ser. C 272** (7), 618 (1971).
33. C. A. Machiet, *Phys. Rev.* **109** (6), 1964 (1958).
34. S. J. Rothman and N. L. Peterson, *Phys. Stat. Solidi* **35**, 305 (1969).
35. C. T. Tomizuka, cited by D. Lazarus, *Solid State Phys.* **Vol. 10** (1960).
36. F. D. Reinke and C. E. Dahlstrom, *Phil. Mag.* **22** (175), 57 (1970).
37. A. Ikushima, *J. Phys. Soc. Japan* **14**, 111 (1959).
38. M. C. Saxena and B. D. Sharma, *Trans. Indian Inst. Metals* **23** (3), 16 (1970).
39. G. Brunel, G. Cizeron, P. Lacombe, *C. R. Acad. Sci. Paris* Ser. C **270** (4), 393 (1970).
40. N. L. Peterson, *Phys. Rev.* **132** (6), 2471 (1963).
41. R. D. Johnson and B. H. Faulkenberry, *ASD-TDR-63-625* (July 1963).
42. F. Moya, G. E. Moya-Gontier and F. Cabane-Brouty, *Phys. Stat. Solidi* **35** (2), 893 (1969).
43. M. C. Inman and L. W. Barr, *Acta Met.* **8** (2), 112 (1960).
44. P. P. Kuzmenko, L. F. Ostrovskii, and V. S. Kovalchuk, *Fiz. Tverd. Tela* **4**, 490 (1962).
45. S. Komura and N. Kunitomi, *J. Phys. Soc. Japan* **18** (Suppl. 2), 208 (1963).
46. S. M. Klotsman, Ya A. Rabovskii, V. K. Talinskii, and A. N. Timofeev, *Fiz. Metal. Metalloved.* **28** (6), 1025 (1969).
47. V. E. Kosenko, *Fiz. Tverd. Tela* **1**:1622 (1959); *Soviet Phys.—Solid State (English transl.)* **1**, 1481 (1959).
48. A. A. Bugai, V. E. Kosenko, and E. G. Miselynuk, *Sh. Tekhn. Fiz.* **27** (1), 207 (1957); *NP-tr-448*, **P.** 219 (1960).
49. H. Letaw, W. M. Portnoy, and L. Slifkin, *Phys. Rev.* **102**, 636 (1956).
50. A. V. Sandulova, M. I. Droniuk, and V. M. P'dak, *Fiz. Tverd. Tela* **3**, 2913 (1961).
51. B. I. Boltaks, V. P. Grabtchak, and T. D. Dzafarov, *Fiz. Tverd. Tela* **6**, 3181 (1964).
52. V. D. Ignatkov and V. E. Kosenko, *Fiz. Tverd. Tela* **4** (6), 1627 (1962): *Soviet Phys.—Solid State (Eng. transl.)* **4** (6), 1627 (1962).
53. V. I. Tagirov and A. A. Kuliev, *Fiz. Tverd. Tela* **4** (1), 272 (1962) *Soviet Phys.—Solid State (Eng. transl.)* **4** (1), 196 (1962).
54. W. C. Mallard, A. B. Gardner, R. F. Bass, and L. M. Slifkin, *Phys. Rev.* **129** (2), 617 (1963).
55. D. Duhl, K. Hirano, and M. Cohen, *Acta Met.* **11** (1), 1 (1963).
56. A. J. Mortlock and A. H. Rowe, *Phil. Mag.* **11** (114), 115 (1965).
57. J. E. Reynolds, B. L. Averbach, and M. Cohen, *Acta Met.* **5**, 29 (1957).
58. A. J. Mortlock, A. H. Rowe, and A. D. LeClaire, *Phil. Mag.* **5**, 803 (1960).

59. F. R. Winslow and T. S. Lundy, *Trans. Met. Soc. AIME* **233**, 1790 (1965).
60. T. R. Anthony and D. Turnbull, *Phys. Rev.* **151**, 495 (1966).
61. V. M. Amonenko, A. M. Blinkin, and I. G. Ivantsov, *Fiz. Metal. i Metalloved.* **17** (1), 56 (1964); *Phys. Metals Metallog.* (*USSR*) (*Eng. transl.*) **17** (1), 54 (1964).
62. D. W. James and G. M. Leak, *Phil. Mag.* **14**, 701 (1966).
63. A. Bondy and V. Levy, *C. R. Acad. Sci. Ser C* **272** (1), 19 (1971).
64. R. J. Borg and D. Y. F. Lai, *Acta Met.* **11** (8), 861 (1963).
65. C. G. Homan, *Acta Met.* **12**, 1071 (1964).
66. A. M. Huntz, M. Aucouturier, and P. Lacombe, *C. R. Acad. Sci. Paris Ser. C* **265** (10), 554 (1967).
67. M. S. Anand and R. P. Agarwala, *J. Appl. Phys.* **37**, 4248 (1966).
68. R. Angers and F. Claisse, *Can. Met. Quart.* **7** (2), 73 (1968).
69. A. V. Tomilov and G. V. Shcherbedinskii, *Fiz. Khim. Met. Mater.* **3** (3), 261 (1967).
70. K. Nohara and K. Hirano, *Proc. Intl. Conf. Sci. Technol. Iron Steel Tokyo*, Sept 1970.
71. V. T. Borisov, V. M. Golikov, and G. V. Shcherbedinskii, *Fiz. Metal. i Metalloved.* **22** (1), 159 (1966).
72. K. Hirano, M. Cohen, and B. L. Averbach, *Acta Met.* **9** (5), 440 (1961).
73. G. Seibel, *Compt. Rend.* **256** (22), 4661 (1963).
74. G. Bruggeman and J. Roberts, *J. Met.* **20** (8), 54 (1968).
75. V. D. Lyubimov, *Izv. Akad. Nauk. SSSR. Met.* **3** 201 (1969); V. D. Lyubimov, V. A. Tskhai, and G. B. Bogomolov, *Trudy Inst. Khim. Akad. Nauk. SSSR Ural Filial* **17**, 44, 48 (1970).
76. G. V. Grigorev and L. V. Pavlinov, *Fiz. Metal. i Metalloved.* **25** (5), 836 (1968).
77. T. Suzuoka, *Japan. Inst. Metals* **2**, 176 (1961).
78. A. W. Bowen and G. M. Leak, *Met. Trans.* **1** (6), 1695 (1970).
79. Th. Heumann and R. Imm, *J. Phys. Chem. Solids* **29** (9), 1613 (1968).
80. P. L. Gruzin and V. V. Mural, *Fiz. Metal. i Metalloved.* **16** (4), 551 (1963); *Phys. Metals Metallog.* (*USSR*) (*Eng. transl.*) **16** (4), 50 (1963).
81. A. Hoshino and R. Ataki, *Tetsu to Hagane* **56** (2), 252 (1970).
82. K. Sato, *Trans. Japan Inst. Metals* **5**, 91 (1964).
83. D. W. James and G. M. Leak, *Phil. Mag.* **14**, 701 (1966).
84. M. P. Dariel, G. Erez, and G. M. J. Schmidt, *Phil. Mag.* **19** (161), 1053 (1969).
85. P. P. Kuzmenko, G. P. Grinevich and B. A. Danilchenko, *Fiz. Met. Metalloved* **29** (2), 318 (1970).
86. G. V. Kidson, *Phil. Mag.* **13**, 247 (1966).
87. J. W. Miller, *Phys. Rev.* **181** (3), 1095 (1969).
88. B. F. Dyson, T. Anthony, and D. Turnbull, *J. Appl. Phys.* **37**, 2370 (1966).
89. H. A. Resing and N. H. Nachtrieb, *Phys. Chem. Solids* **21** (1/2), 40 (1961).
90. A. Ott and A. Lodding, *Int. Conf. Vac. and Interstitials in metals.* **Julich 1**, 43 (1968); *Z. Naturforsch* **23A**, 1683 (1968), 2126 (1968).
91. A. Ott, A. Lodding, and D. Lazarus, *Phys. Rev.* **188** (3), 1088 (1969).
92. A. Ott, *J. Appl. Phys.* **40** (6), 2395 (1969); J. N. Mundy, A. Ott, L. Lowenberg, and A. Lodding, *Phys. Stat. Solidi.* **35** (1), 359 (1969).
93. A. Ott, *Z. Naturforschg* **25a** (10), 1477 (1970).
94. A. Lodding, J. N. Mundy, and A. Ott, *Phys. Stat. Solidi* **38** (2), 559 (1970).
95. K. Lal, *Commis. Energ. At. Report.* **CEA-R** 3136 (1967).
96. L. V. Pavlinov, A. M. Gladyshev, and V. N. Bikov, *Fiz. Metal Metalloved* **26** (5), 823 (1968).
97. P. G. Shewmon, *Trans. Met. Soc. AIME* **206**, 918 (1956).
98. Y. V. Borisov, P. L. Gruzin, and L. V. Pavlinov, *Met. i Metalloved. Chistykh Metal.* **1** 213 (1959), translated in *JPRS-5195*.
99. A. Y. Nakonechnikov, L. V. Pavlinov, and V. N. Bikov, *Fiz. Metal i Metalloved.* **22**, 234 (1966).
100. J. Askill, *Phys. Status Solidi* **9** (2), K113 (1965).
101. L. V. Pavlinov and A. A. Kordev, *Fiz. Metal. Metalloved.* **29** (6), 1326 (1970).
102. G. N. Dubinin, G. P. Benediktova, M. G. Karpman, and G. V. Shcherbedinskii, *Khim—Term Obrab Stali Splavov* **6**, 129 (1969).
103. J. Askill and D. H. Tomlin, *Phil. Mag.* **8** (90), 997 (1963).
104. B. A. Vandyshev and A. S. Panov, *Fiz. Met. Metalloved.* **26** (3), 517 (1968).
105. S. Z. Benediktova, G. N. Dubinin, M. G. Kapman, and G. V. Shcherbedinskii, *Metalloved. i Term. Obrabotka Metal.* **5**, 5 (1966).
106. B. A. Vandyshev and A. S. Panov, *Fiz. Metal. i Metalloved.* **25** (2), 321 (1968).
107. L. V. Pavlinov, A. Y. Nakonechnikov, and V. N. Bikov, *At. Energ.* (*USSR*) **19** 521 (1965).
108. J. Askill, *Phys. Status Solidi* **23**, K21 (1967).
109. A. Chatterjee and D. J. Fabian, *J. Inst. Metals* **96** (6), 186 (1968).
110. A. Hassner and W. Lange, *Phys. Status Solidi* **8**, 77 (1965).
111. K. Monma, H. Suto, and H. Oikawa, *J. Japan Inst. Metals* **28**, 188 (1964).
112. A. Ya. Shinyaev, *Izv. Akad. Nauk. S.S.S.R. Metl.* **4**, 182 (1969).
113. J. J. Blechet, A. VanGryeynest, and D. Calais, *J. Nucl. Mater.* **28** (1), 177 (1968).
114. P. P. Kuzmenko and G. P. Grinevich, *Fiz. Tverd. Tela.* **4** (11), 3266 (1962); *Soviet Physics—Solid State* **4** (11), 2390 (1962).

115. S. Z. Bokshtein, S. T. Kishkin, and L. M. Moroz, *Investigation of the Structure of Metals by Radioactive Isotope Methods; State Publishing House of the Ministry of Defense Industry, Moscow* (1959); *AEC-tr-4505* (1961).
116. M. S. Anand, S. P. Murarka, and R. P. Agarwala, *J. Appl. Phys.* **36** (12), 3860 (1965).
117. V. D. Lyubimov, *Izv. Akad. Nauk. S.S.S.R. Metal* **3**, 201 (1969); V. D. Lyubimov, V. A. Tskhai, and G. B. Bogmolov, *Toudy Inst. Khim. Akad. Nauk. S.S.S.R. Ural Filial* **17**, 44, 48 (1970).
118. R. F. Peart, D. Graham, and D. H. Tomlin, *Acta Met.* **10**, 519 (1962).
119. J. Pelleg, *J. Metals* **20** (8), 54 (1968); *J. Less Common Metals* **17**, 319 (1969); *Phil. Mag.* **19** (157), 25 (1969).
120. T. S. Lundy, F. E. Winslow, R. E. Pawel, and C. J. McHargue, *Trans. Met. Soc. AIME* **223**, 1533 (1965).
121. B. A. Vandyshev and A. S. Panov, *Izv. Akad. Nauk. S.S.S.R.* **1**, 206 (1968).
122. J. Askill, *Phys. Status Solidi* **9** (3), K167 (1965).
123. J. Pelleg, *Phil. Mag.* **21** (172), 735 (1970).
124. R. P. Agarwala, S. P. Murarka, and M. S. Anand, *Acta Met.* **16** (1), 61 (1968).
125. G. B. Fedorov, F. I. Zhomov, and E. A. Smirnov, *Met. Metalloved. Chist. Metal* **8**, 145 (1969).
126. N. L. Peterson, *Phys. Rev.* **136** (2A), A568 (1964).
127. N. H. Nachtrieb and G. S. Handler, *J. Chem. Phys.* **23**, 1187 (1955).
129. J. Kucera and T. Zemcik, *Can. Met. Quart.* **7** (2), 83 (1968).
130. G. V. Kidson and R. Ross, *Proc. 1st UNESCO Int. Conf. Radio-isotopes in Scientific Res.*, p. 185 (1958).
131. F. A. Smith and L. W. Barr, *Phil. Mag.* **21** (171), 633 (1970).
132. J. N. Mundy, T. E. Miller, and R. J. Porte, *Phys. Rev.* **B3** (8), 2445 (1971).
133. L. W. Barr, J. N. Mundy, and F. A. Smith, *Phil. Mag.* **16**, 1139 (1967).
134. F. A. Smith and L. W. Barr, *Phil. Mag.* **20** (163), 205 (1969).
135. R. E. Tate and G. R. Edwards, *Symposium on Thermodynamics with Emphasis on Nuclear Materials and Atomic Solids*, **pp. 105–113 in IAEA Symposium Vol. II,** International Atomic Energy Agcy., Vienna (1966).
136. R. E. Tate and E. M. Cramer, *Trans. Met. Soc. AIME* **230**, 639 (1964).
137. M. Dupuy and D. Calais, *Trans. AIME* **242**, 1679 (1968).
138. M. P. Dariel, G. Erez, and G. M. J. Schmidt, *J. Appl. Phys.* **40** (7), 2746 (1969).
139. M. P. Dariel, *Phil. Mag.* **22** (177), 653 (1970).
140. M. P. Dariel, G. Erez, and G. M. J. Schmidt, *Phil. Mag.* **18** (161), 1045 (1969).
141. A. A. Kuliev and D. N. Nasledov, *Zh. Tekhn. Fiz.* **28** (2), 259 (1958); *Soviet Phys.—Tech. Phys.* (*Eng. transl.*) **3** (2), 235 (1958).
142. P. Braetter and H. Gobrecht, *Phys. Stat. Sol* **41** (2), 631 (1970).
143. B. I. Boltaks, and B. T. Plachenov, *Soviet Phys.—Tech. Phys.* (*Eng. transl.*) **27** (10), 2071 (1957).
144. R. F. Peart, *Phys. Status Solidi* **15**, K119 (1966).
145. W. R. Wilcox and T. J. LaChapelle, *J. Appl. Phys.* **35** (1) 240 (1964).
146. R. C. Newman and J. Wakefield, *Phys. Chem. Solids* **19** (3), 230 (1961).
147. B. I. Boltaks and I. I. Sozinov, *Zh. Tekhn. Fiz.* **28** (3), 679 (1958); *Soviet Phys.—Tech. Phys.* (*Eng. transl.*) **3** (3), 636 (1958).
148. J. D. Struthers, *J. Appl. Phys.* **27** (12), 1560 (1958); errata **28** (4), 516 (1957).
149. H. P. Bonzel, *Phys. Status Solidi* **20**, 493 (1967).
150. S. Mackawa, *J. Phys. Soc. Japan* **17** (10), 1592 (1962).
151. J. J. Rahan, M. E. Pickering, and J. Kennedy, *J. Electrochem. Soc.* **106** (8), 705 (1959).
152. S. J. Rothman, N. L. Peterson, and J. T. Robinson, *Phys. Stat. Sol.* **39** (2), 635 (1970).
153. C. T. Tomizuka and L. M. Slifkin, *Phys. Rev.* **96**, 610 (1954).
154. J. Bernardini, A. Combe-Brun, and J. Cabane, *Ser. Met.* **4** (12), 985 (1970).
155. A. Sawatskii and F. E. Jaumot, *Trans. AIME* **209**, 1207 (1957).
156. J. G. Mullen, *Phys. Rev.* **121**, 1649 (1961).
157. R. E. Hoffman, *Acta Met.* **6**, 95 (1958).
158. T. Hirone, S. Miura, and T. Suzuoka, *J. Phys. Soc. Japan* **16** (12), 2456 (1961).
159. R. E. Hoffman, D. Turnbull, and E. W. Hart, *Acta Met.* **3**, 417 (1955).
160. C. B. Pierce and D. Lazarus, *Phys. Rev.* **114**, 686 (1959).
161. N. Barbouth, J. Ouder, and J. Cabane, *C. R. Acad. Sci. Paris Ser. C* **264** (12), 1029 (1967).
162. V. N. Kaigorodov, Ya. A. Rabovskii, and V. K. Talinskii, *Fiz. Metal. i Metalloved.* **24** (4), 661 (1967).
163. V. N. Kaigorodov, S. M. Klotsman, A. N. Timofeev, and I. Sh. Traktenberg, *Fiz. Metal. Metalloved.* **28** (1), 120 (1969).
164. A. Sawatskii and F. E. Jaumot, *Phys. Rev.* **100**, 1627 (1955).
165. L. W. Barr, J. N. Mundy, and F. A. Smith, *Phil. Mag.* **20** (164), 389 (1969).
166. J. N. Mundy, L. W. Barr, and F. A. Smith, *Phil. Mag.* **14**, 785 (1966).
167. P. Son, S. Ihara, M. Miyake, and T. Sano, *J. Japan Inst. Met.* **33** (1), 1 (1969).
168. V. P. Vasilev, I. F. Kamardin, V. I. Skatskill, S. G. Chernomorchenko, and G. N. Shuppe, *Trudy Sred. Gos. Uni. im V.I. Lenina* **65**, 47 (1955); *Translation AEC-tr-4272.*
169. R. E. Pawel and T. S. Lundy, *J. Phys. Chem. Solids* **26**, 937 (1965).

170. B. A. Vandyshev and A. S. Panov, *Izv. Akad. Nauk. SSSR Metal* **1**, 244 (1969).
171. Sh. Movalanov and A. A. Kuliev, *Fiz. Tverd. Tela* **4** (2), 542 (1962).
172. N. I. Ibraginov, M. G. Shachtachtinskii, and A. A. Kuliev, *Fiz. Tverd. Tela* **4**, 3321 (1962).
173. R. N. Ghoshtagore, *Phys. Rev.* **155** (3), 698 (1967).
174. T. R. Anthony, B. F. Dyson, and D. Turnbull, *J. Appl. Phys.* **39** (3), 1391 (1968).
175. G. A. Shirn, *Acta Met.* **3**, 87 (1955).
176. F. Schmitz and M. Fock, *J. Nucl. Materials* **21**, 317 (1967).
177. B. F. Dyson, *J. Appl. Phys.* **37**, 2375 (1966).
178. W. Chomka and J. Andruszkiewicz, *Nukleonika* **5** (10), 611 (1960).
179. A. Sawatskii, *J. Appl. Phys.* **29** (9), 1303 (1958).
180. D. Yolokoff, S. May, and Y. Adda, *Compt. Rend.* **251** (3), 2341 (1960).
181. L. Bartha and T. Szalay, *Int. J. Appl. Radiat. Isotopes* **20** (2), 825 (1969).
182. F. Dyment and C. M. Libanati, *J. Mager. Sci.* **3** (4), 349 (1968).
183. J. Askill, *Phys. Stat Sol.* **B43** (1), K1 (1971).
184. L. V. Pavlinov, G. V. Grigorev, and G. O. Gromyko, *Izv. Akad. Nauk. SSSR Metal* **3**, 207 (1969).
185. A. Y. Nakonechnikov, L. V. Pavlinov, and V. N. Bikov, *Fiz. Metal i Metalloved* **22**, 234 (1966).
186. G. B. Gibbs, D. Graham, and D. H. Tomlin, *Phil. Mag.* **8** (92), 1269 (1963).
187. J. Askill and G. B. Gibbs, *Phys. Status Solidi* **11**, 557 (1965).
188. J. F. Murdock, T. S. Lundy, and E. E. Stansbury, *Acta Met.* **12** (9), 1033 (1964).
189. L. V. Pavlinov, *Fiz. Metal Metalloved* **30** (4), 800 (1970).
190. J. F. Murdock, T. S. Lundy, and E. E. Stansbury, *Acta Met.* **12** (9), 1033 (1964).
191. L. V. Pavlinov, *Fiz. Metal. i Metalloved.* **24** (2), 272 (1967).
192. R. E. Pawel and T. S. Lundy, *Acta Met.* **17** (8), 979 (1969).
193. L. N. Larikov, V. M. Tyshkevich, and L. F. Chorna, *Ukr. Fiz. Zh.* **12** (6), 983 (1967).
194. Y. Adda, A. Kirianenko, and C. Mairy, *Compt. Rend.* **253**, 445 (1961); *J. Nucl. Mater.* **6** (1), 130 (1962).
195. M. P. Dariel, M. Blumenfeld, and G. Kimmel, *J. Appl. Phys.* **41** (4), 1480 (1970).
196. G. B. Federov, E. A. Smirnov, and S. S. Moiseenko, *Met. Metalloved. Chist. Metal.* **7**, 124 (1968).
197. S. J. Rothman, *J. Nucl. Mater.* **3** (1), 77 (1961).
198. N. L. Peterson and S. J. Rothman, *Phys. Rev.* **136** (3A), A842 (1964).
199. P. Son, S. Ihara, M. Miyake, and T. Sano, *J. Japan Inst. Met.* **33** (1), 1 (1969).
200. H. W. Paxton and R. A. Wolfe, *Trans. AIME* **230**, 1426 (1964).
201. M. G. Coleman, *Ph.D. Thesis Univ. of Illinois* (1967); *Univ. Microf.* **68–1725** (1968).
202. B. A. Vandychev and A. S. Panov, *Izv. Akad. Nauk SSSR Metal* **2**, 231 (1970).
203. R. F. Peart, *J. Phys. Chem. Solids* **26**, 1853 (1965).
204. D. S. Gorney and R. M. Altovskii, *Fiz. Metal Metalloved* **30** (1), 85 (1970).
205. J. H. Rosolowski, *Phys. Rev.* **124** (6), 1828 (1961).
206. P. B. Ghate, *Phys. Rev.* **130** (1), 174 (1963).
207. A. P. Batra and H. B. Huntington, *Phys. Rev.* **145**, 542 (1966).
208. A. P. Batra and H. B. Huntington, *Phys. Rev.* **154** (3), 569 (1967).
209. J. S. Warford and M. B. Huntington, *Phys. Rev.* **B1** (4), 1867 (1970).
210. N. L. Peterson and S. J. Rothman, *Phys. Rev.* **163** (3), 645 (1967).
211. R. P. Agarwala, S. P. Murarka, and M. S. Anand, *Trans. Met. Soc. AIME* **233**, 986 (1965).
212. A. M. Blinkin and V. V. Vorobiov, *Ukr. Fiz. Zh.* **9** (1), 91 (1964).
213. R. P. Agarwala and A. R. Paul, *Proc. Nucl. Rad. Chem. Symp. Poona, India* p. **542** (1967).
214. P. L. Gruzin, V. S. Emelyanov, G. G. Ryabova, and G. B. Federov, *Proc. 2nd Intern. Conf. Peaceful Uses At. Energy*, **19**:187 (1958).
215. Y. V. Borisov, Y. G. Godin, P. L. Gruzin, A. I. Evstyukhin, and V. S. Yemelyanov, *Met. i Met. Izdatel. Akad. Nauk. SSSR Moscow 1958. Translation NP-TR-448* p. 196 (1960).
216. P. Flubacher, *E. I. R. Bericht* **49**, May (1963).
217. R. A. Andriyevskii, V. N. Zagraykin, and G. Ya. Meshcheryakov, *Phys. Met. Metalloved.* **19** (3), 146 (1966).
218. R. P. Agarwala and A. R. Paul, Report CONF-670335, *Int. Conf. Vacancies and Interstitials in Metals*, Julich (1968) **1**, 105 (1968), *Report BARC*-377 (1968).
219. G. V. Kidson and G. J. Young, *Phil. Mag.* **20** (167), 1047 (1969).
220. G. B. Federov, E. A. Smirnov, and S. M. Novikov, *Met. Metalloved Chist. Metal* **8**, 41 (1969).
221. B. A. Vandychev and A. S. Panov, *Izv. Akad. Nauk. SSSR Metal* **2**, 231 (1970).
222. G. B. Federov, E. A. Smirnov, and F. I. Zhomov, *Met. Metalloved. Chist. Metal.* **7**, 116 (1968).
223. L. V. Pavlinov, *Fiz. Metal i Metalloved* **24** (2), 272 (1967).
224. H. M. Gilder and D. Lazarus, *J. Phys. Chem. Solids* **26**, 2081 (1965).
225. G. V. Kidson and J. McGurn, *Can. J. Phys.* **39** (8), 1146 (1961).
226. R. E. Pawel and T. S. Lundy, *J. Phys. Chem. Solids* **26**, 937 (1965).
227. S. J. Rothman, L. T. Lloyd, and A. L. Harkness, *Trans. Met. Soc. AIME* **218** (4), 605 (1960).
228. G. B. Federov, E. A. Smirnov, and V. N. Gusev, *At. Energ.* **27** (2), 149 (1969).

VISCOSITY AND THERMAL CONDUCTIVITY
OF OXYGEN AS A
FUNCTION OF TEMPERATURE

Conversion Factors

$T, °K$	$\rightarrow$ T, °F: multiply by (9/5) then subtract 459.67
$T, °K$	$\rightarrow$ T, °C: subtract 273.15
$T, °K$	$\rightarrow$ T, °R: multiply by (9/5)
P, atm	$\rightarrow$ P, psia: multiply by 14.69595
P, atm	$\rightarrow$ p, N/m^2: multiply by 1.01325×10^5
η, g/cm-s	$\rightarrow$ η, N-s/m^2
η, g/cm-s	$\rightarrow$ η, lb$_m$/ft-s
λ, W/m-°K	$\rightarrow$ λ, cal/cm-s-°K
λ, W/m-°K	$\rightarrow$ λ, Btu ft-hr-°R

Temperature, °K	Viscosity, g/cm-s $10^3 \eta_0$	Thermal conductivity, W/m-K $10^3 \lambda_0$
80	0.0585	6.94
90	0.0663	7.95
100	0.0740	8.96
110	0.0818	9.96
120	0.0894	10.94
130	0.0970	11.92
140	0.1045	12.89
150	0.1118	13.85
160	0.1191	14.78
170	0.1261	15.70
180	0.1331	16.60
190	0.1399	17.48
200	0.1465	18.35
210	0.1530	19.21
220	0.1595	20.05
230	0.1658	20.88
240	0.1719	21.69
250	0.1780	22.49
260	0.1840	23.29
270	0.1898	24.08
280	0.1955	24.86
290	0.2012	25.62
300	0.2068	26.38
310	0.2122	27.14
320	0.2176	27.89
330	0.2230	28.62
340	0.2282	29.36
350	0.2334	30.10
360	0.2385	30.85
370	0.2435	31.58

[a]Data for all temperatures in excess of 1,000 K are extrapolated.

VISCOSITY AND THERMAL CONDUCTIVITY
OF OXYGEN AS A
FUNCTION OF TEMPERATURE (Continued)

Temperature, °K	Viscosity, g/cm-s $10^3 \eta_0$	Thermal conductivity, W/m-K $10^3 \lambda_0$
380	0.2485	32.32
390	0.2534	33.06
400	0.2583	33.79
410	0.2631	34.54
420	0.2678	35.28
430	0.2725	36.02
450	0.2818	37.49
470	0.2908	38.95
490	0.2997	40.41
510	0.3085	41.86
530	0.3170	43.29
550	0.3255	44.72
570	0.3338	46.14
590	0.3420	47.56
610	0.3501	48.97
630	0.3580	50.37
650	0.3659	51.77
670	0.3736	53.16
690	0.3813	54.54
710	0.3888	55.89
730	0.3963	57.25
750	0.4037	58.59
770	0.4110	59.90
790	0.4183	61.22
820	0.4290	63.16
850	0.4396	65.09
880	0.4500	66.98
910	0.4603	68.89
940	0.4705	70.72
970	0.4805	72.52
1,000	0.4905	74.32
1,030[a]	0.5002	76.07
1,060	0.5100	77.84
1,090	0.5196	79.56
1,120	0.5291	81.27
1,150	0.5384	82.97
1,180	0.5478	84.66
1,210	0.5571	86.32
1,240	0.5662	89.97
1,270	0.5753	89.61
1,300	0.5843	91.24
1,330	0.5932	92.85
1,360	0.6021	94.45
1,390	0.6109	96.06
1,420	0.6196	97.64

VISCOSITY AND THERMAL CONDUCTIVITY
OF OXYGEN AS A
FUNCTION OF TEMPERATURE (Continued)

Temperature, °K	Viscosity, g/cm-s $10^3 \eta_0$	Thermal conductivity, W/m-K $10^3 \lambda_0$
1,450	0.6282	99.22
1,480	0.6368	100.78
1,510	0.6454	102.35
1,540	0.6538	103.90
1,570	0.6622	105.45
1,600	0.6706	106.98
1,630	0.6789	108.52
1,660	0.6871	110.05
1,690	0.6953	111.58
1,720	0.7034	113.09
1,750	0.7116	114.61
1,780	0.7196	116.12
1,810	0.7276	117.63
1,840	0.7355	119.12
1,870	0.7435	120.63
1,900	0.7514	122.13
1,930	0.7592	123.62
1,960	0.7670	125.11
1,980	0.7721	126.11
2,000	0.7773	127.10

From Hanley, H. J. M., McCarty, R. D., and Sengers, J. V., *Viscosity and Thermal Conductivity Coefficients of Gaseous and Liquid Oxygen,* NASA CR-2440, National Aeronautics and Space Administration, Washington, D.C., August 1974 (available from National Technical Information Service, Springfield, Va. 22151).

THERMAL CONDUCTIVITY OF COMPRESSED OXYGEN

In this table, thermal conductivity, λ, is in the unit milliwatt/m-K.

Conversion Factors

T, °K → T, °F: multiply by (9/5) then subtract 459.67
T, °K → T, °C: subtract 273.15
T, °K → T, °R: multiply by (9/5)
P, atm → P, psia: multiply by 14.69595
P, atm → P, N/m^2: multiply by 1.01325×10^5
η, g/cm-s → η, Ns/m^2: multiply by 10^{-1}
η, g/cm-s → η, lb$_m$/ft-s: multiply by 0.0671969
λ, W/m-K → λ, cal/cm-s-K: multiply by (1/418.4)
λ, W/m-K → λ, Btu/ft-hr-°R: multiply by 0.578176

T, °K \ P, atm	1	5	10	15	20	25	30	35	40	45	50	55
80	164.7	164.9	165.2	165.4	165.7	165.9	166.2	166.4	166.7	166.9	167.1	167.4
90	151.7	152.0	152.3	152.6	152.9	153.3	153.6	153.9	154.2	154.5	154.8	155.1
100	9.5	138.4	138.8	139.2	139.6	140.0	140.4	140.8	141.1	141.5	141.9	142.3
110	10.4	11.4	124.9	125.3	125.8	126.3	126.8	127.3	127.7	128.2	128.6	129.1
120	11.4	12.2	13.5	110.9	111.5	112.1	112.8	113.3	113.9	114.5	115.1	115.6
130	12.3	13.1	14.2	15.6	96.3	97.1	98.0	98.8	99.6	100.3	101.1	101.8
140	13.2	14.0	15.0	16.1	17.5	19.3	81.6	82.9	84.1	85.2	86.3	87.3
150	14.1	14.8	15.7	16.7	17.9	19.2	20.9	23.3	27.8	68.4	70.4	72.1
160	15.8	15.7	16.5	17.4	18.4	19.5	20.7	22.3	24.2	26.7	30.5	37.3
170	15.9	16.5	17.3	18.1	19.0	19.9	20.9	22.1	23.4	24.9	26.8	29.0
180	16.8	17.4	18.1	18.8	19.6	20.4	21.3	22.3	23.3	24.4	25.7	27.1
190	17.7	18.2	18.9	19.5	20.3	21.0	21.8	22.6	23.5	24.4	25.4	26.4
200	18.5	19.0	19.6	20.3	20.9	21.6	22.3	23.0	23.8	24.6	25.4	26.3
210	19.3	19.8	20.4	21.0	21.6	22.3	22.9	23.6	24.2	24.9	25.7	26.4
220	20.2	20.6	21.2	21.7	22.3	22.9	23.5	24.1	24.7	25.4	26.0	26.7
230	21.0	21.4	21.9	22.5	23.0	23.6	24.1	24.7	25.3	25.9	26.5	27.1
240	21.7	22.2	22.7	23.2	23.7	24.2	24.8	25.3	25.8	26.4	26.9	27.5
250	22.5	22.9	23.4	23.9	24.4	24.9	25.4	25.9	26.4	26.9	27.5	28.0
260	23.3	23.7	24.1	24.6	25.1	25.6	26.0	26.5	27.0	27.5	28.0	28.5
270	24.0	24.4	24.9	25.3	25.8	26.2	26.7	27.1	27.6	28.1	28.5	29.0
280	24.8	25.1	25.6	26.0	26.4	26.9	27.3	27.8	28.2	28.6	29.1	29.5
290	25.5	25.9	26.3	26.7	27.1	27.5	28.0	28.4	28.8	29.2	29.6	30.1
300	26.2	26.6	27.0	27.4	27.8	28.2	28.6	29.0	29.4	29.8	30.2	30.6
310	27.0	27.3	27.7	28.1	28.5	28.8	29.2	29.6	30.0	30.4	30.8	31.2
320	27.7	28.0	28.4	28.7	29.1	29.5	29.9	30.2	30.6	31.0	31.4	31.7
330	28.4	28.7	29.0	29.4	29.8	30.1	30.5	30.9	31.2	31.6	31.9	32.3
340	29.1	29.3	29.7	30.1	30.4	30.8	31.1	31.5	31.8	32.2	32.5	32.9
350	29.7	30.0	30.4	30.7	31.1	31.4	31.7	32.1	32.4	32.8	33.1	33.4
360	30.4	30.7	31.0	31.4	31.7	32.0	32.4	32.7	33.0	33.3	33.7	34.0
370	31.1	31.4	31.7	32.0	32.3	32.7	33.0	33.3	33.6	33.9	34.3	34.6
380	31.8	32.0	32.3	32.7	33.0	33.3	33.6	33.9	34.2	34.5	34.8	35.1
390	32.4	32.7	33.0	33.3	33.6	33.9	34.2	34.5	34.8	35.1	35.4	35.7
400	33.1	33.3	33.6	33.9	34.2	34.5	34.8	35.1	35.4	35.7	36.0	36.3

THERMAL CONDUCTIVITY OF COMPRESSED OXYGEN (Continued)

T,°K \ P, atm	60	65	70	80	90	100	110	120	130	150	175
80	167.6	167.9	168.1	168.6	169.1	169.5	170.0	170.4	170.9	171.8	172.8
90	155.4	155.7	156.0	156.6	157.1	157.7	158.3	158.8	159.4	160.4	161.8
100	142.6	143.0	143.3	144.0	144.7	145.4	146.1	146.8	147.4	148.7	150.3
110	129.5	130.0	130.4	131.2	132.1	132.9	133.7	134.5	135.3	136.8	138.6
120	116.2	115.7	117.2	118.3	119.3	120.3	121.2	122.2	123.1	124.9	127.0
130	102.5	103.2	103.9	105.2	106.4	107.6	108.8	109.9	111.0	113.1	115.6
140	88.3	89.2	90.1	91.8	93.4	95.0	96.4	97.8	99.1	101.6	104.5
150	73.5	74.9	76.2	78.5	80.5	82.5	84.2	85.9	87.5	90.5	93.8
160	50.2	57.8	61.3	65.6	68.6	71.0	73.1	75.1	76.9	80.2	83.9
170	31.7	35.1	39.2	47.9	54.7	59.3	62.7	65.3	67.6	71.3	75.3
180	26.7	38.4	32.4	36.9	42.0	47.0	51.3	55.0	58.1	63.0	67.7
190	27.8	28.8	30.1	33.0	36.2	39.6	43.2	46.5	49.7	55.1	60.5
200	27.2	28.1	29.1	31.3	33.6	36.1	38.7	41.4	44.0	48.9	54.3
210	27.2	28.0	28.8	30.5	32.4	34.4	36.4	38.5	40.6	44.9	49.8
220	27.4	28.1	28.8	30.3	31.9	33.5	35.2	36.9	38.7	42.3	46.6
230	27.7	28.3	29.0	30.3	31.7	33.1	34.6	36.1	37.6	40.7	44.5
240	28.1	28.7	29.2	30.5	31.7	33.0	34.3	35.6	36.9	39.7	43.1
250	28.5	29.1	29.6	30.7	31.8	33.0	34.2	35.4	36.6	39.0	42.1
260	29.0	29.5	30.0	31.0	32.1	33.1	34.2	35.3	36.4	38.7	41.5
270	29.5	29.9	30.4	31.4	32.4	33.3	34.4	35.4	36.4	38.4	41.0
280	30.0	30.4	30.9	31.8	32.7	33.6	34.6	35.5	36.5	38.4	40.8
290	30.5	30.9	31.3	32.2	33.1	33.9	34.8	35.7	36.6	38.4	40.6
300	31.0	31.4	31.8	32.7	33.5	34.3	35.1	36.0	36.8	38.5	40.6
310	31.6	31.9	32.3	33.1	33.9	34.7	35.5	36.3	37.1	38.7	40.6
320	32.1	32.5	32.8	33.6	34.3	35.1	35.8	36.6	37.4	38.9	40.8
330	32.7	33.0	33.4	34.1	34.8	35.5	36.2	37.0	37.7	39.1	40.9
340	33.2	33.5	33.9	34.6	35.3	36.0	36.7	37.3	38.0	39.4	41.1
350	33.8	34.1	34.4	35.1	35.8	36.4	37.1	37.7	38.4	39.7	41.4
360	34.3	34.6	35.0	35.6	36.2	36.9	37.5	38.2	38.6	40.1	41.7
370	34.9	35.2	35.5	36.1	36.7	37.9	38.0	38.6	39.2	40.4	42.0
380	35.4	35.7	36.0	36.6	37.2	37.8	38.4	39.0	39.6	40.8	42.3
390	36.0	36.3	36.6	37.2	37.8	38.3	38.9	39.5	40.1	41.2	42.6
400	36.6	36.9	37.1	37.7	38.3	38.8	39.4	40.0	40.5	41.6	43.0

From Hanley, H. J. M., McCarty, R. D., and Sengers, J. V., *Viscosity and Thermal Conductivity Coefficients of Gaseous and Liquid Oxygen,* NASA CR-2440, National Aeronautics and Space Administration, Washington, D.C., August 1974 (available from National Technical Information Service, Springfield, Va. 22151).

TRANSPORT PROPERTIES OF OXYGEN AT SATURATION

Conversion Factors

T, °K → T, °F: multiply by (9/5) then subtract 459.67
T, °K → T, °C: subtract 273.15
T, °K → T, °R: multiply by (9/5)
P, atm → P,psia: multiply by 14.69595
P, atm → P, N/m²: multiply by 1.01325×10^5
η, g/cm-s → η, Ns/m²: multiply by 10^{-1}
η, g/cm-s → η, lb$_m$/ft-s: multiply by 0.0671969
λ, W/m-K → λ, cal/cm-s-K: multiply by (1/418.4)
λ, W/m-K → λ, Btu/ft-hr-°R: multiply by 0.578176

Temperature, °K	Pressure, atm	Viscosity, mg/cm-s		Thermal conductivity, mW/m-K	
		Vapor	Liquid	Vapor	Liquid
80	0.30	0.059	2.652	7.4	164.7
90	0.98	0.068	1.971	8.5	151.8
100	2.51	0.079	1.504	9.9	138.2
110	5.36	0.092	1.188	11.5	124.3
120	10.09	0.108	0.971	13.6	110.3
130	17.26	0.129	0.824	16.3	95.9
140	27.52	0.158	0.696	20.1	80.6
142	30.00	0.166	0.668	21.1	77.4
144	32.64	0.175	0.638	22.3	74.0
146	35.45	0.185	0.607	23.6	70.6
148	38.44	0.197	0.574	25.2	67.0
150	41.61	0.211	0.537	27.2	63.2
152	45.00	0.231	0.494	29.9	58.7
154	48.65	0.269	0.424	35.2	52.0

From Hanley, H. J. M., McCarty, R. D., and Sengers, J. V., *Viscosity and Thermal Conductivity Coefficients of Gaseous and Liquid Oxygen,* NASA CR-2440, National Aeronautics and Space Administration, Washington, D.C., August 1974 (available from National Technical Information Service, Springfield, Va. 22151).

Physical Constant	Ozone (O₃)	Oxygen (O₂)
Molecular Weight	47.9982 g/g-mol	31.9988 g/g-mol
Boiling Point (760 mm)	$-111.9 \pm 0.3°C$	$-182.97°C$
Melting Point	$-192.7 \pm 0.2°C$	$-218.4°C$
Critical Temperature	$-12.1 \pm 0.1°C$	$-118.574°C$
Critical Pressure	54.6 atm	49.77 atm
Critical Density	0.437 g/cc	0.436 g/cc
Critical Volume	147.1 cc/mol	73.37 cc/mol
Gas Density (0°C) (760 mm pressure)	2.144 g/liter	1.429 g/liter
Liquid Density		
$-112°C$	1.358 g/cc	
$-183°C$	1.571 g/cc	1.14 g/cc
$-195.4°C$	1.614 g/cc	1.201 g/cc
Surface Tension		
$-195°C$	43.8 ± 0.1 dyne/cm	
$-182.7°C$	38.1 ± 0.2 dyne/cm	
$-183.0°C$	38.4 ± 0.7 dyne/cm	13.2 dyne/cm
Heat Capacity of Liquid		
-183 to $-145°C$	0.45 cal/g°C	
Heat Capacity of Gas		
$-173°C$	7.95 cal/g mol°C	
0°C	9.10 cal/g mol°C	
25°C	9.37 cal/g mol°C	
100°C		6.979 cal/g mol°C
127°C	10.44 cal/g mol°C	
Viscosity of Liquid		
$-195.6°C$	4.14 ± 0.05 cp	
$-183.0°C$	1.57 ± 0.02 cp	0.1958 cp
Heat of Vaporization		
$-112°C$	75.6 cal/g	
$-182.9°C$		50.9 cal/g
Heat of Formation		
25°C	-34.4 Kg cal/mol	
Free Energy		
25°C	32.4 Kg cal/mol	
Van der Waals Constant (a)	3.545 atm liter²/mol²	1.36 atm liter²/mol²
Van der Waals Constant (b)	0.04903 liter/mol	0.03803 liter/mol
Magnetic Susceptibility		
gas ($\times 10^{-6}$)	0.002 cgs units	10.6.2 cgs units
liq ($\times 10^{-6}$)	0.150 cgs units	260.0 cgs units
Thermal Conductivity of Liquid		
$-195.8°C$	5.21 cal/sec cm°C $\times 10^4$	
$-183.0°C$	5.31 cal/sec cm°C $\times 10^4$	
$-165.0°C$	5.42 cal/sec cm°C $\times 10^4$	
$-128.0°C$	5.52 cal/sec cm°C $\times 10^4$	

Phase Boundaries—Ozone-Oxygen System
$-183°C$ 29.8 and 72.4 wt % O₃
$-195.4°C$ 9   and 90.8 wt %O₃
Consolute Temperature—Ozone-Oxygen System
$-180 \pm 0.5°C$
Coefficient of Thermal Expansion for Liquid Ozone

Temp. °C	α
-195.6	1.62
-183.0	1.58
-148.0	1.47
-123.0	1.41
-112.0	1.35
-98.8	1.31

PHYSICAL CONSTANTS OF CLEAR FUSED QUARTZ

Based on information contained in Fused Quartz Catalogue Q-7A General Electric Company.

Property	Clear fused quartz	Property	Clear fused quartz
Density	2.2 g./c.c.	Annealing Point	(approx.) 1140°C
Hardness	4.9 (Mohs')	Strain Point	1070°C
Tensile Strength	7,000 p.s.i.	Electrical Resistance	9.5 log₁₀ R for cm.³ at 350°C
Compressive Strength	>160,000 p.s.i.	Dielectric Constant	3.75 at 20°C. 1 Mc.
Bulk Modulus	(approx.) 5.3×10^6 p.s.i.	Dielectric Loss Factor	less than .0004 at 20°C. 1 Mc.
Rigidity Modulus	4.5×10^6 p.s.i.	Dissipation Factor	less than .0001 at 20°C. 1 Mc.
Young's Modulus	10.4×10^6 p.s.i.	Index of Refraction	1.4585
Poisson's Ratio	.16	Velocity of Sound—Shear Wave	3.75×10^5 cm./sec.
Coefficient of Thermal Expansion	(av.) 5.5×10^{-7} cm./cm./°C $\{ 20°C / 320°C$		
Thermal Conductivity	.0033 g. cal./cm.²/sec./°C/cm.	Velocity of Sound—Compressional Wave	5.90×10^5 cm./sec.
Specific Heat	.18 g. cal./gm.		
Softening Point	(approx.) 1665°C	Sonic Attenuation	less than .033 db/ft./mc.

FIXED POINT PROPERTIES OF OXYGEN

From NASA SP-3071, "ASRDI Oxygen Technology Survey, Thermophysical Properties", Volume I (1972), edited by Hans M. Roder and Lloyd A. Weber. This NASA publication contains an extensive bibliography and a discussion of basis for selection of these data for oxygen. The publication is available from the National Technical Information Service, Springfield, Virginia 22151.

PROPERTIES / CONDITIONS →	Triple Point			Normal Boiling Point		Critical Point ††	Standard Conditions	
	Solid	Liquid	Vapor	Liquid	Vapor		STP (0°C)	NTP (20°C)
Temperature (K)		54.351		90.180		154.576	273.15	293.15
Pressure (mmHg)		1.138		760		37,823	760	760
Density (mole/cm³) x 10⁻³	42.46	40.83	0.000336	35.65	0.1399	13.63	0.04466	0.04160
Specific Volume (cm³/mole) x 10⁻³	0.02355	0.02449	2975	0.028047	7.1501	0.07337	22.392	24.038
Compressibility Factor, $Z = \frac{PV}{RT}$		0.0000082	0.9986	0.00379	0.9662	0.2879	0.9990	0.9992
Heats of Fusion & Vaporization (J/mole)	444.8	7761.4		6812.3		0	–	–
Specific Heat C_s, @saturation	46.07	53.313	-108.7	54.14	-53.2	(very large)	29.33	29.40
(J/mole-K) C_p, @ constant pressure	–	53.27	29.13	54.28	30.77	(very large)	29.33	29.40
C_v, @ constant volume	–	35.65	20.81	29.64	21.28	(38.7)	20.96	21.04
Specific Heat Ratio, $\gamma = C_p/C_v$	–	1.494	1.400	1.832	1.446	(large)	1.40	1.40
Enthalpy (J/mole)	-6634.4	-6189.6	1571.8	-4270.3	2542.0	1032.2	7937.8	8525.1
Internal Energy (J/mole)	-6634.4	-6189.6	1120.0	-4273.1	1817.5	662.3	5668.9	6089.5
Entropy (J/mole-K)	58.92	67.11	209.54	94.17	169.68	134.42	202.4	204.5
Velocity of Sound (m/sec)		1159	141	903	178	164	315	326
Viscosity, μ, (N-sec/m³) x 10³	–	0.6194	0.003914	0.1958	0.00685	(0.031)	0.01924	0.02036
(centipoise)‡‡	–	0.6194	0.003914	0.1958	0.00685	(0.031)	0.01924	0.02036
Thermal Conductivity (mW/cm-K), k	–	1.929	0.04826	1.515	0.08544	(*)	0.2428	0.2575
Prandtl Number, $N_{pr} = \mu C_p/k$		5.344	0.7392	2.193	0.7714		0.7259	0.7265
Dielectric Constant, ϵ	(1.614)	1.5687	1.000004	1.4870	1.00166	1.17082	1.00053	1.00049
Index of Refraction, $n = \sqrt{\epsilon}$ †	(1.271)	1.2525	1.000002	1.219	1.00083	1.0820	1.00027	1.00025
Surface Tension (N/m) x 10³	–	22.65		13.20		0	–	–
Equiv. Vol./Vol. Liquid at NBT	0.8397	0.8732	106,068	1	254.9	2.616	798.4	857.1

† Long Wavelengths
* Anomalously Large

Gas Constant: R = 62, 365.4 cm³-mm Hg/mole-K[1]
†† Values in parenthesis are estimates

Molecular Weight = 31.9988[3]
"mole" = gram mole
‡‡ Units for poise are: g/cm-sec

PHYSICAL PROPERTIES OF SODIUM, POTASSIUM AND Na-K ALLOYS

Temperature °C	Density (g/cm³) Na (a)	(b)	(c)	K	Alloys (wt % K) 43.4 Experimental	(d) Calculated	78.6 Experimental	(d) Calculated	Viscosity (centipoise) Na	Alloys (wt % K) 43.3	66.0
100	.927	.927	.9265	.819	.887	.890	.847	.850	.705	.540	.529
200	.904	.904	.9037	.795	.862	.867	.823	.827	.450	.379	.354
300	.882	.880	.8805	.771	.838	.843	.799	.802	.345	.299	.276
400	.859	.856	.8570	.747	.814	.818	.775	.778	.284	.245	.229
500	.834	.831	.8331	.723	.789	.794	.751	.754	.234	.207	.195[e]
600	.809	.808	.8089	.701	.765	.771	.727	.732	.210	.178[e]	.168[e]
700	.783	.784	.....	.676	.740	.745	.703	.705	.186[e]	.257[e]	.146[e]
800	.757	.760	.....	....	....	....	....	....	.165[e]	......	......
900	....	....	.....	....	....	....	....	....	.150[e]	......	......

Temperature, °C	Thermal conductivity (watts/cm²-°C/cm) Na Experimental	Calculated	Alloy (wt % K) 56.5	77.0	Electrical resistivity (microohms) Na[f]	Alloy (wt % K) 56.5	78.0	Heat capacity[g] (cal/°C-g) K	Alloy (wt % K) 44.8	78.26
100	......	....	....	.238[h]	8.99	41.61	45.63	.1940	.2690	.2248
200	.815	.808	.249	.247	13.52	47.23	51.33	.1887	.2612	.2169
300	.757	.755	.262	.259	17.52	54.33	58.58	.1894	.2553	.2122
400	.712	.710	.269	.262	21.93	62.21	65.65	.126	.2512	.2097
500	.668	.672	.271	.259	26.96	69.37	73.48	.1818	.2498	.2088
600	.627[e]	.639	....	.255	32.65	78.29	82.61	.1825	.2484	.2092
700	.590[e]	.610	....	......	39.05	88.23	91.76	.1846	.2497	.2108
800	.547[e]	.583	....	......	46.15	99.68	104.51	.1883	.2529	.2133
900	......	....	....	......	......	......	......	......	......	......

Vapor Pressure, mm Hg

Temperature °C	Na	K	Alloys (wt % K)	
			56	78
127	2.23×10^{-6}	. . . .	. . . .	. . . .
227	1.15×10^{-3}	2.88×10^{-2}	1.57×10^{-3}	1.81×10^{-3}
327	5.03×10^{-2}	9.27×10^{-1}	5.73×10^{-2}	6.14×10^{-2}
427	.881	9.26	3.53	5.06
527	7.53	52.22	23.0	31.87
627	39.98	201.25	101.35	136.50
727	148.5	588.62	328.7	431.85
827	453.7	1421.0	864.2	1099.52
927	1127.8	. . . .	. . . .	. . . .
1027	2522.4	. . . .	. . . .	. . . .
1127	4696.8	. . . .	. . . .	. . . .

NOTES: (a) From plotted data.

(b) Epstein equation: $d_t = 0.9514 - 2.392 \times 10^{-4}\, t°C$.

(c) Thomson and Garelis: $d_t = 0.9490 - 22.3 \times 10^{-5} t°C - 1.75 \times 10^{-8} t^2 °C$.

(d) Formula to calculate density: $V = M_K \cdot V_K + M_{Na} \cdot V_{Na}$ (where V, V_K and V_{Na} are the specific volumes (reciprocal of density) of the alloy, K and Na respectively, M_K and M_{Na} the mole fraction of the elements).

(e) Extrapolated by calculation, Epstein equation:

$$K = \frac{2.433 \times 10^{-2}(t + 273.16)}{6.8393 + 3.3873 \times 10^{-2}t + 1.7235 \times 10^{-5}t^2}$$

(f) Epstein equation: $r_t = 10.892 + 0.015272t + 3.6746 \times 10^{-5}t^2 - \dfrac{379.26}{t}$.

(g) Formula to calculate heat capacity: $C = W_{Na} \cdot C_{Na} + W_K \cdot C_K$ (where C, C_{Na} and C_K are the heat capacity of the alloy, Na and K respectively, W_{Na} and W_{Ka} the weight fractions of Na and K respectively in the alloy).

(h) 150°C.

MECHANICAL AND PHYSICAL PROPERTIES OF WHISKERS

From NASA SP-5055

This table lists some nominal values for physical and mechanical properties of some whiskers. The strength of whiskers is influenced by temperature, time, surface conditions, surface films or corrosion, crystallographic orientation, impurities and testing techniques.

Material	Tensile Strength (σt) lb/in.$^2 \times 10^{-6}$	Young's Modulus (E) lb/in.$^2 \times 10^{-6}$	Specific Gravity (S) lb/in.$^2 \times 10^{-6}$	$\dfrac{(\sigma t)}{(S)}$ inch	$\dfrac{(E)}{(S)}$ inch
Graphite	3.0	. .	137	21,700	. . . .
Al$_2$O$_3$	3.0	76	250	12,000	300,000
Iron	1.8	28	485	3,700	58,000
Si$_3$N$_4$	2.0	55	193	10,000	285,000
SiC	3.0	70	187	16,000	380,000
Si	1.1	26	143	7,000	182,000

ABSOLUTE VISCOSITY OF LIQUID SODIUM AND POTASSIUM

Sodium

T (°K)	η (10^{-2} poise)	ν (cm^3/g)	$\eta \nu^{1/3}$ (10^3 poise cm/g$^{-1/3}$)	$1/T\nu$ [10^3g/ (cm$^3 \cdot$ °K)]
Experimental range				
371.00	0.690	1.078,75	7.0766	2.4987
473	.450	1.106,56	4.6544	1.9106
573	.010	1.136,70	0.6100	1.5000
673	.278	1.166,86	2.9268	1.2734
773	.239	1.200,34	2.54057	1.0776
873	.212	1.236,25	2.2754	0.9266
973	.193	1.274,37	2.0925	.8065
1073	.179	1.315,79	1.9615	.7083
1173	.167	1.360,54	1.8505	.6266
1203	.164	1.373,62	1.8230	.6052

Potassium

T (°K)	η (10^{-2} poise)	ν (cm^3/g)	$\eta \nu^{1/3}$ (10^3 poise cm/g$^{-1/3}$)	$1/T\nu$ [10^3g/ (cm$^3 \cdot$ °K)]
Experimental range				
336.9	0.560	1.2062$_7$	5.961$_2$	2.4606
400	.384	1.22911	4.113$_4$	2.0340
500	.070	1.00711	0.000$_1$	1.5504
600	.221	1.3075$_3$	2.416$_6$	1.2747
700	.185	1.3506$_2$	2.045$_0$	1.0577
800	.162	1.3966$_5$	1.810$_8$	0.8049$_7$
900	.147	1.4459$_2$	1.6623	.7684$_6$
1000	.132	1.4988$_0$	1.5106	.6672$_0$
1100	.121	1.5556$_9$	1.4020	.5843$_5$
1200	.113	1.6170$_7$	1.3264	.5153$_3$
1300	.106	1.6835$_0$	1.2610	.4569$_1$
1400	.100	1.7556$_1$	1.2064	.4068$_7$

PHYSICAL PROPERTIES OF PIGMENTS

From Rutherford J. Gettens and George L. Stout. *Painting Materials*, Dover Publications, Inc., New York, 1966. Reprinted by permission of the Publisher.

OPAQUE WHITE PIGMENTS

Pigment Name and Chemical Composition[1]	Specific Gravity[2]	Particle Characteristics[3]	Refractive Index[4]
Titanium calcium white, TiO_2 (25%) + $CaSO_4$ (75%)	3.10	prism. or ragged gr.	mostly 1.8–2.0 (irr.) (bi.) [M*]
Titanium dioxide (rutile) + $CaSO_4$	3.25	...	Av. 1.98 [TPC]
Titanium barium white, TiO_2 (25%) + $BaSO_4$ (75%)	4.30	min. round. gr.	$n_{\Sigma c}$ 1.7–2.5 [M*]
White lead (basic sulfate) $PbSO_4 \cdot PbO$	6.46	...	Av. 1.93 [TPC]
Lithopone	4.3	...	Av. 1.84 [TPC]
Lithopone (regular), ZnS (28–30%), $BaSO_4$ (72–70%)	4.30	fine comp. gr.	2.3 (ZnS)–1.64 ($BaSO_4$) [M]
Zinc white (ordinary), ZnO	5.65	v. fine cryst. gr.	ϵ2.02, ω2.00 [M]
(acicular), ZnO	...	spicules, fourlets	ϵ2.02, ω2.00 [M*]
White lead (basic carbonate), $2PbCO_3 \cdot Pb(OH)_2$	6.70	v. fine cryst.	ϵ1.94, ω2.09 [M]
Antimony oxide, Sb_2O_3	5.75	v. fine cryst.	valentinite, α2.18, γ and β2.35 [LB, M*] senarmonite, 2.09 (isot.)
Zirconium oxide (baddeleyite), ZrO_2	5.69	...	χ2.13, γ2.20, β2.19 [LB], Av. 2.40 [TPC]
Titanium dioxide (anatase), TiO_2	3.9	min. round. gr.	ϵ and ω 2.5 (w. bi.) [M*]
(rutile), TiO_2	4.2	round. or prism. gr.	ϵ2.9, ω2.6 [M*]

TRANSPARENT WHITE PIGMENTS†

Pigment Name and Chemical Composition[1]	Specific Gravity[2]	Particle Characteristics[3]	Refractive Index[4]
Diatomaceous earth, SiO_2	2.31	min. fossil forms	n mostly 1.435, some 1.40 [M*]
Aluminum stearate, $Al(C_{18}H_{35}O_2)_3$	0.99	agg. of spher. gr.	1.49 (w. bi.) [W]
Pumice (volcanic glass), Na, K, Al, silicate	...	vesicular vitr. frag.	c 1.50 (isot.) [M*]
Aluminum hydrate, $Al(OH)_3$	2.45	v. fine amorph. part.	$n_{\Sigma c}$ 1.50–1.56 [M*]
Gypsum, $CaSO_4 \cdot 2H_2O$	2.36	fine cryst. gr.	α1.520, γ1.530, β1.523 [LB]
Silica quartz), SiO_2	2.66	cryst. frag.	ϵ1.553, ω1.544 [LB]
(chalcedony), SiO_2	2.6	crypt. agg.	ϵ, ω1.54 [LB, M*]
China clay (kaolinite), $Al_2O_3 \cdot 2SiO_2 \cdot 2H_2O$	2.60	fine, vermicular cryst.	α1.558, γ1.565, β1.564 (all ± .005) [LB, M*]
Talc, $3MgO \cdot 4SiO_2 \cdot H_2O$	2.77	platy frag.	α1.539, γ1.589, β1.589 [LB]
Mica (muscovite), $H_2KAl_3(SiO_4)_3$	2.89	platy frag.	α1.563, γ1.604, β1.599 [LB]
Anhydrite, $CaSO_4$	2.93	cryst. frag.	α1.570, γ1.614, β1.575 [LB]
Chalk (whiting), $CaCO_3$	2.70	hollow spherulites	$\epsilon_{\Sigma c}$ 1.510, $\omega_{\Sigma c}$ 1.645 [M*]
Barytes (barite, nat.), $BaSO_4$	4.45	cryst. frag.	α1.636, γ1.648, β1.637 [LB]
(blanc fixe, art.), $BaSO_4$	4.36	v. fine cryst. agg.	1.62–1.64 [M*]
Barium carbonate, $BaCO_3$ (witherite)	4.3	...	α1.529, γ1.677, β1.676 [LB]

†Also called "Extender" or "Inert" White Pigments.

IRON OXIDE PIGMENTS

Pigment Name and Chemical Composition[1]	Specific Gravity[2]	Particle Characteristics[3]	Refractive Index[4]
Ochre, yellow (goethite), $Fe_2O_3 \cdot H_2O$, clay, etc.	2.9–4.0	irr. spherulites	n_Σ2.0 (isot. part); $(\alpha, \beta)_\Sigma$ 2.05–2.31; γ_Σ 2.08–2.40 (bi. part) [M*]
Sienna, raw (goethite), $Fe_2O_3 \cdot H_2O$, clay, etc.	3.14	uneven spherulites	1.87–2.17 (mostly 2.06) (isot.) [M*]
Sienna, burnt, Fe_2O_3, clay, etc.	3.56	uneven, round. part.	c1.85 (var.) (isot.) [M]
Umber, raw, $Fe_2O_3 + MnO_2 + H_2O$, clay, etc.	3.20	uneven, round. gr.	mostly 1.87–2.17 [M*]
Umber, burnt, $Fe_2O_3 + MnO_2$, clay, etc.	3.64	uneven, round. gr.	mostly 2.2–2.3 [M*]
Iron oxide red (haematite), Fe_2O_3	5.2	min. cryst.	ϵ_{Li} 2.78, ω_{Li} 3.01 [M]

RED AND ORANGE PIGMENTS

Pigment Name and Chemical Composition[1]	Specific Gravity[2]	Particle Characteristics[3]	Refractive Index[4]
Red lead, Pb_3O_4 ($c95\%$)	8.73	crypt. agg.	2.42_{Li} (w. bi.; pleo.) [M]
**Realgar, As_2S_2	3.56	cryst. frag.	α_{Li} 2.46, γ_{Li} 2.61, β_{Li} 2.59 [LB]
Molybdate orange, $Pb(Mo,S,Cr,P)O_4$	...	min. round. gr.	β_{Li} 2.55 (s. bi.) [M*]
Chrome orange, $PbCrO_4 \cdot Pb(OH)_2$	6.7	tabular cryst.	α2.42, γ2.7 +, β2.7 [M*]
Cadmium red lithopone, $CdS(Se) + BaSO_4$	4.30	min. round. gr.	2.50–2.76 (for CdS(Se)part) (isot.) [M*]
Cadmium red, $CdS(Se)$	4.5	min. round. gr.	2.64 (bright red)–2.77 (deep red) (isot.) [M*]
Antimony vermilion, Sb_2S_3	...	v. fine red glob.	n_{Li} 2.65 (isot.) [M*]
Vermilion (art.), HgS	8.09	hexagonal gr. and prisms	ϵ_{Li} 3.14, ω_{Li} 2.81 [M]
**(nat., cinnabar), HgS	8.1	cryst. frag.	ϵ_{Li} 3.146, ω_{Li} 2.819 [LB]
Quinacridone red, $C_{20}H_{12}O_2N_2$ (gamma)	1.5	thin plates	n_{Na} Av. 2.04 [Du P]

YELLOW PIGMENTS

**Gamboge, organic resin	...	irr. amorph. part.	1.582–1.586 [W]
**Indian yellow, $C_{19}H_{18}O_{11}Mg \cdot 5H_2O$	...	prisms, plates	1.67 (w. bi.) [M*]
Cobalt yellow, $CoK_3(NO_2)_6 \cdot H_2O$	...	fine dendritic cryst.	1.72–1.76 (isot.) [W]
Zinc yellow, $4ZnO \cdot 4CrO_3 \cdot K_2O \cdot 3H_2O$	3.46	min. spher. gr.	1.84–1.9 (irr.; bi.) [M*]
Strontium yellow, $SrCrO_4$	...	small needles	α, β (or ω) 1.92, γ (or ϵ) 2.01 (‖ext.) [M*]
Barium yellow, $BaCrO_4$	4.49	v. fine cryst. gr.	1.94–1.98 (bi.) [M]
**Naples yellow, $Pb_3(SbO_4)_2$	...	round. gr.	2.01–2.28 (isot.) [M*]
Chrome yellow (med.), $PbCrO_4$	5.96	fine prism. gr.	$\alpha_{620m\mu} < 2.31$, $\gamma_{650m\mu}$ 2.49 [M]
Cadmium yellow lithopone, $CdS + BaSO_4$	4.25	fine comp. gr.	2.39–2.40 (for CdS part) [M*]
Cadmium yellow, CdS	4.35	min. round. gr.	2.35–2.48 (isot.) [M*]
Massicot (litharge), PbO	9.40	min. flakes	α_{Li} 2.51, γ_{Li} 2.71, β_{Li} 2.61 [M]
**Orpiment, As_2S_3	3.4	min. flakes	α_{Li} 2.4 ±, γ_{Li} 3.02, β_{Li} 2.81 [LB]

GREEN PIGMENTS

Phthalocyanine green, chloro-copper phthalocyanine	2.1	laths	$n_{580m\mu}$ 1.40 [ACC]
**Verdigris (copper basic acetate), $Cu(C_2H_3O_2)_2 \cdot 2Cu(OH)_2$	...	cryst. frag.	α1.53, γ1.56 [M]
**Chrysocolla, $CuSiO_3 \cdot \eta H_2O$	2.4	crypt. agg.	α1.575, γ1.598, β1.597 [LB]
Green earth (celadonite and glauconite), Fe, Mg, Al, K, hydrosilicate	2.5–2.7	round. irr. gr.	n var. c 1.62, (porous) [M*]
Emerald green (Paris green), $Cu(C_2H_3O_2)_2 \cdot 3Cu(AsO_2)_2$	3.27	spherulites and disks	α_Σ1.71, γ_Σ1.78 (w. pleo.) [M*]
**Malachite, $CuCO_3 \cdot Cu(OH)_2$	4.0	cryst. frag.	α1.655, γ1.909, β1.875 [LB]
Cobalt green, $CoO \cdot \eta ZnO$	...	spher. gr.	1.94–2.0 (w. bi.) [M*]
Viridian (chromium oxide, transparent), $Cr_2O_3 \cdot 2H_2O$	3.32	spherul. gr.	α, β_Σ 1.82, γ_Σ 2.12 [M*]
Chrome green (med.), $Fe_4[Fe(CN)_6]_3 + PbCrO_4$	4.06	fine green agg.	c 2.4 (cf. Prussian blue and chrome yellow)
Chromium oxide green, opaque, Cr_2O_3	5.10	fine cryst. agg.	n_{Li} 2.5 [M]

BLUE PIGMENTS

Pigment Name and Chemical Composition[1]	Specific Gravity[2]	Particle Characteristics[3]	Refractive Index[4]
Phthalocyanine blue, copper phthalocyanine	1.6	laths	Av. 1.38 [DuP]
Ultramarine blue (art.), $Na_{8-10}Al_6Si_6O_{24}S_{2-4}$	2.34	uniform small round. gr.	n 1.51 green, 1.63 red (isot.) [M]
**(nat., lazurite), $3Na_2O \cdot 3Al_2O_3 \cdot 6SiO_2 \cdot 2Na_2S$	2.4	angular, broken frag.	1.50± (isot.) [LB]
**Maya blue, Fe, Mg, Ca, Al, silicate (?)	. . .	porous irr. agg.	$\beta\Sigma$1.54 (irr.; bi. and pleo.) [M*]
Smalt, K, Co(Al), silicate (glass)	. . .	splintery, vitr. frag.	1.49–1.52 [M*]
Prussian blue, $Fe_4[Fe(CN)_6]_3$	1.83	colloidal agg.	$1.56_{460m\mu}$ [M*]
**Egyptian blue, $CaO \cdot CuO \cdot 4SiO_2$	. . .	cryst. frag.	ϵ1.605, ω1.635 [APL]
Manganese blue, $BaMnO_4 + BaSO_4$	. . .	gr. and stubby prisms	c 1.65 [W]
**Blue verditer, $2CuCO_3 \cdot Cu(OH)_2$	. . .	fibrous agg.	$a\Sigma$1.72, $\gamma\Sigma$slightly > 1.74 [M*]
Cobalt blue, $CoO \cdot Al_2O_3$	3.83	round. gr.	n var.; max. c 1.74_{blue} (isot.) [M]
**Azurite, $2CuCO_3 \cdot Cu(OH)_2$	3.80	cryst. frag.	a1.730, γ1.838, β1.758 [LB]
Cerulean blue, $CoO \cdot \eta SnO_2$	. . .	round gr.	1.84 (isot.) [M*]

VIOLET PIGMENTS

Ultramarine violet	. . .	round. gr. (blue, rose and violet)	c 1.56 (isot.) [M*]
Cobalt violet, $Co_3(PO_4)_2$	. . .	round. gr.	ϵ1.65–1.79 (dull violet), ω1.68–1.81 (salmon) (s. bi.) [M*]
Manganese violet, $(NH_4)_2Mn_2(P_2O_7)_2$	. . .	fine cryst. gr.	a1.67, γ1.75, β1.72 (for violet) [M]
Quinacridone violet, $C_{20}H_{12}O_2N_2$ (beta)	1.5	thin plates	Av. 2.02 [DuP]

BROWN PIGMENTS

Sepia (organic)	. . .	angular frag.	(opaque) [M*]
Asphaltum (bitumen)	. . .	irr. amorph. part.	1.64–1.66 [M*]
Van Dyke brown (bituminous earth)	1.66	irr. amorph. part.	1.62–1.69 [M*]

BLACK PIGMENTS

Bone black, $C + Ca_3(PO_4)_2$	2.29	irr. coarse grains	1.65–1.70 (for larger translucent gr.) [M]
Lamp black, C	1.77	min. round. part.	(opaque)
Charcoal black, C	. . .	irr. splintery part.	(opaque)
Graphite, C	2.36	irr. plates	(opaque) [M]

[1]Abbreviations: art. = artificial; med. = medium; nat. = natural. The chemical formulas are those commonly accepted in chemical and mineralogical literature, but they may not compare exactly with structural formulas based on x-ray diffraction data or even on critical chemical analysis.

[2]The figures for specific gravity of the artificial pigments are mainly from H. A. Gardner, pp. 710–712, and those on the mineral pigments are chiefly from E. S. Larsen and H. Berman.

[3]Symmetry terms (monoclinic, orthorhombic, etc.) are omitted because pigments are so finely divided that it is rare when observations on crystal symmetry can be made. The term "spherulitic," as used here means aggregates that tend toward radial structure and spherical shape. "Amorphous" describes materials that are microscopically formless but may be truly crystalline on the basis of x-ray diffraction data. Abbreviations: agg. = aggregate(s); amorph. = amorphous; comp. = composite; crypt. = cryptocrystalline; cryst. = crystal(s); frag. = fragment(s); glob. = globule(s); gr. = grain(s); irr. = irregular; min. = minute; part. = particle(s); prism. = prismatic; round. = rounded; spher. = spheroidal; spherul. = spherulitic; var. = variable; v. = very; vitr. = vitreous.

[4]Unless otherwise indicated, all refractive index measurements are by sodium light. Σ is the symbol used by H. E. Merwin to indicate greater or less indefiniteness or irregularity in the case of aggregates, especially in respect to refractive index. Abbreviations: bi. = birefringent; c = circa; ext. = extinction; isot. = isotropic; ‖ = parallel; pleo. = pleochroic; s. = strongly; w. = weakly. The letters in brackets refer to the authorities for the refractive index data: M = H. E. Merwin; M* = H. E. Merwin, data by private communication, hitherto unpublished; W = C. D. West data by private communication, hitherto unpublished; LB = E. S. Larsen and H. Berman; APL = A. P. Laurie and co-authors; ACC = A. C. Cooper, "The refractive index of organic pigments. Its determination and significance," *Journal Oil & Colour Chemists Association*, Vol. 31 (1948), pp. 343–357; TPC = Titanium Pigment Corporation; Du P = E. I. Du Pont de Nemours & Co.

**Chiefly of historical interest.

Compiled by Rudolf Loebel

Table I —Organic compounds
Table II—Inorganic compounds

Table I

Formula	Name	Critical temp. T_c °C	Critical press. P_c atm.
$CHClF_2$	Methane, monochlorodifluoro-	96	48.5
$CHCl_2F$	Methane, dichloromonofluoro-	178.5	51
$CHCl_3$	Methane, trichloro- (Chloroform)	263	54
CHF_3	Methane, trifluoro- (Fluoroform)	25.9	46.9
CH_2Cl_2	Methylene chloride	237	60
CH_2NO_2	Methane, nitro-	314.8	62.3
CH_3Br	Methane, monobromide-	194	83.4
CH_3Cl	Methane, monochloro-	143.8	65.9
CH_3F	Methane, monofluoro-	44.6	58
CH_3I	Methane, monoiodo-	254.8	72.7
CH_4	Methane	−82.1	45.8
CH_4O	Methanol (Methyl alcohol)	240	78.5
CH_4S	Methylmercaptan	196.8	71.4
CH_5N	Methylamine	156.9	40.2
$CBrF_3$	Methane, monobromotrifluoro-	67	50.3
$CClF_3$	Methane, monochlorotrifluoro-	28.85	38.2
CCl_2F_2	Methane, dichlorodifluoro-	111.5	39.6
CCl_3F	Methane, trichloromonofluoro-	198	43.2
CCl_4	Methane, tetrachloro- (Carbon tetrachloride)	283.1	45
CF_4	Methane, tetrafluoro-	−45.7	41.4
C_2H_2	Acetylene	35.5	61.6
C_2H_2	Ethyne (see Acetylene)	35.5	61.6
$C_2H_2F_2$	Ethylene, 1,1-difluoro-	30.1	—
C_2H_3N	Acetonitrile	274.7	47.7
$C_2H_3F_3$	Ethane, 1,1,1-trifluoro-	73.1	—
C_2H_4	Ethene	9.9	50.5
C_2H_4	Ethylene (see Ethene)	9.9	50.5
C_2H_4O	Acetaldehyde	187.8	54.7
C_2H_4O	Ethylene oxide	195.8	71
$C_2H_4O_2$	Acetic acid	321.6	57.1
$C_2H_4O_2$	Formic acid, methyl- (Methyl formate)	214	59.2
$C_2H_4Cl_2$	Ethane, 1,1-dichloro-	249.8	50
$C_2H_4F_2$	Ethane, 1,1-difluoro-	386.7	—
C_2H_5Br	Ethane, monobromo-	230.8	61.5
C_2H_5Cl	Ethane, monochloro-	187.2	52
C_2H_5F	Ethane, monofluoro-	102.16	49.6
C_2H_6	Ethane	32.2	48.2
C_2H_6O	Ether, dimethyl-	127	52.6
C_2H_6O	Ethanol (Ethyl alcohol)	243	63
C_2H_6O	Glycol, ethylene-	(374)*	—
C_2H_6S	Dimethylsulfide	229.9	54.5
C_2H_6S	Ethylmercaptan	225.5	54.2
C_2H_7N	Dimethylamine	164.6	52.4
C_2H_7N	Ethylamine	183.2	55.5
$C_2Br_2F_4$	Ethane, dibromotetrafluoro-	214.5	—
C_2ClF_5	Ethane, chloropentafluoro-	80	—
$C_2Cl_2F_4$	Ethane, 1,2-dichlorotetrafluoro-	145.7	—
$C_2Cl_3F_3$	Ethane, trichlorotrifluoro-	214.2	33.7
$C_2Cl_4F_2$	Ethane, tetrachlorodifluoro-	278	32.9
C_2F_6	Ethane, hexafluoro-	24.3	—
C_3H_4	Propadiene	120	43.6
C_3H_4	Allene (see Propadiene)	120	43.6
C_3H_4	Acetylene, methyl-	127.8	52.8
C_3H_4	Propyne (see Acetylene, methyl-)	127.8	52.8
C_3H_5N	Ethyl cyanide	290.8	41.3
C_3H_5N	Propionitrile (see Ethyl cyanide)	290.8	41.3
C_3H_5OCl	Epichlorohydrin	(323)	—
C_3H_5Cl	Propene, 3-chloro- (allyl chloride)	240.3	46.5
C_3H_6	Propylene	91.9	45.4
C_3H_6	Cyclopropane	124.7	—
C_3H_6O	Acetone	235.5	47
C_3H_6O	Allylalcohol	272	55.5
C_3H_6O	Propylene oxide	209	48.6
$C_3H_6O_2$	Formic acid, ethyl- (Ethyl formate)	235.3	46.3
$C_3H_6O_2$	Acetic acid, methyl- (Methyl acetate)	233.7	46.3
$C_3H_6O_2$	Propanoic acid	337.6	53
C_3H_7Cl	n-Propane, monochloro-	230	45.2
C_3H_8	Propane	96.8	42
C_3H_8O	Ether, ethyl methyl- (Methoxyethane)	161.7	40.4
C_3H_8O	Glycol, 1,2-propylene-	351	—
C_3H_8O	Isopropyl alcohol	235	47
C_3H_8O	n-Propyl alcohol	263.6	51
$C_3H_8O_3$	Glycerol	(452)	—
C_3H_9N	Isopropylamine	209.7	—
C_3H_9N	n-Propylamine	223.8	46.8
C_4H_4O	Furan	213.8	52.5
C_4H_4S	Thiophene	307	56.2
C_4H_6	1,2-Butadiene	171	44.4
C_4H_6	1,3-Butadiene	152	42.7
C_4H_8	n-Butene	146	39.7
C_4H_8	2-Butene, cis-	160	40.5
C_4H_8	2-Butene, trans-	155	41.5
C_4H_8O	1,2-Butylene oxide	243	—
C_4H_8O	Ketone, ethyl methyl- (2-Butanone)	262	41
$C_4H_8O_2$	Butanoic acid	355	52
$C_4H_8O_2$	p-Dioxane	314.8	51.4
$C_4H_8O_2$	Acetic acid, ethyl- (Ethyl acetate)	250.4	37.8
$C_4H_8O_2$	Propanoic acid, methyl- (Methyl propionate)	257.4	39.3
$C_4H_8O_2$	Formic acid, propyl- (Propyl formate)	264.9	40.1
C_4H_9Cl	n-Butane, monochloride-	269	—
C_4H_{10}	n-Butane	152	37.5
C_4H_{10}	Isobutane	135	36
$C_4H_{10}O$	Butanol (n-Butyl alcohol)	289.8	43.6
$C_4H_{10}O$	sec-Butyl alcohol	263	41.4
$C_4H_{10}O$	tert-Butyl alcohol	235	39.2
$C_4H_{10}O$	Ether, diethyl-	192.6	35.6
$C_4H_{10}O$	Isobutyl alcohol	277	42.4
$C_4H_{10}O_2$	Glycol, diethylene-	407	—
$C_4H_{10}S$	Diethyl sulfide	283.8	39.1
$C_4H_{11}N$	Butyl amine	287.9	—
$C_4H_{11}N$	Diethyl amine	223.3	36.6
$C_4H_{11}N$	Isobutyl amine	266.7	—
C_4F_{10}	Butane, perfluoro-	113.2	23
C_5H_5N	Pyridine	346.8	—
C_5H_8	Cyclopentene	232.94	47.2
C_5H_{10}	Cyclopentane	238.6	44.6
C_5H_{10}	1-Pentene	191	39.9
$C_5H_{10}O$	Ketone, diethyl-	287.8	36.9
$C_5H_{10}O_2$	Propanoic acid, ethyl- (Ethyl propionate)	272.9	33
$C_5H_{10}O_2$	n-Butanoic acid, methyl- (n-Methyl butyrate)	281.3	34.3
$C_5H_{10}O_2$	Acetic acid, n-propyl (n-Propyl acetate)	276	32.9
$C_5H_{10}O_2$	n-Valeric acid	378	37.6
$C_5H_{11}N$	Piperidine	320.8	44.1
C_5H_{12}	Butane, 2-methyl- (See Isopentane)	187.8	32.9
C_5H_{12}	Isopentane	187.8	32.9
C_5H_{12}	Neopentane	160.6	31.6
C_5H_{12}	n-Pentane	196.6	33.3
C_5H_{12}	Propane, 2,2-dimethyl (see Neopentane)	160.6	31.6
$C_5H_{12}O$	Isoamyl alcohol	309.77	—
C_6H_5Br	Benzene, bromo-	397	44.6
C_6H_5Cl	Benzene, chloro-	359.2	44.6
C_6H_5F	Benzene, fluoro-	286.95	44.6
C_6H_6	Benzene	288.0	48.6
C_6H_6O	Phenol	421.1	60.5
C_6H_7N	Aniline	425.6	52.3
C_6H_7N	α-Picoline	348	—
C_6H_7N	β-Picoline	371.7	—
C_6H_7N	γ-Picoline	372.5	—
C_6H_{10}	Cyclohexene	287.3	—
C_6H_{10}	1,5-Hexadiene	234.4	32.6
C_6H_{12}	Cyclohexane	280.4	40
C_6H_{12}	Cyclopentane, methyl-	259.5	37.4
C_6H_{12}	1-Hexene	231	31.1
$C_6H_{12}O_2$	Formic acid, n-amyl (n-Amyl formate)	302.6	34.1
$C_6H_{12}O_2$	Acetic acid, n-butyl (n-Butyl acetate)	305.9	30.7
$C_6H_{12}O_2$	Butanoic acid, ethyl- (Ethyl butyrate)	293	30.2
$C_6H_{12}O_2$	Propanoic acid, propyl- (Propyl propionate)	304.8	30.7
$C_6H_{12}O_3$	Paraldehyde	290	—
C_6H_{14}	Butane, 2,3-dimethyl-	226.8	30.9
C_6H_{14}	n-Hexane	234.2	29.9
C_6H_{14}	Pentane, 2-methyl-	224.3	30
$C_6H_{14}O$	Ether, isopropyl-	226.9	28.4
$C_6H_{14}O$	1-Hexyl alcohol	313.5	—
$C_6H_{14}O_4$	Glycol, triethylene-	(437)	—
$C_6H_{15}N$	Dipropyl amine	277	31
$C_6H_{15}N$	Hexyl amine	318.8	—
$C_6H_{15}N$	Triethyl amine	258.9	30
C_7H_5N	Benzonitrile	426.2	41.6
C_7H_8	Benzene, methyl- (see Toluene)	320.8	41.6

*( ) uncertain

Table I (Continued)

Formula	Name	Critical temp. T_c °C	Critical press. P_c atm.	Formula	Name	Critical temp. T_c °C	Critical press. P_c atm.
C_7H_8	Toluene	320.8	41.6	C_8H_{18}	Butane, 2,2,3,3-tetramethyl-	270.8	24.5
C_7H_8O	Anisole, (see Benzene, methoxy-)	368.5	41.3	C_8H_{18}	Heptane, 4-methyl-	290	25.6
C_7H_8O	Benzene, methoxy-	368.5	41.3	C_8H_{18}	Hexane, 2,4-dimethyl-	282	25.8
C_7H_8O	o-Cresol	424.4	49.4	C_8H_{18}	n-Octane	296	24.8
C_7H_8O	m-Cresol	432	45	C_8H_{18}	Pentane, 2,2,3-trimethyl-	294	28.2
C_7H_8O	p-Cresol	431.4	50.8	$C_8H_{18}O$	1-Octyl alcohol	385.5	26.5
C_7H_9N	Aniline, methyl-	428.4	51.3	$C_8H_{19}N$	Dibutyl amine	322.6	—
C_7H_9N	2,3-Lutidine	382.3	—	C_9H_7N	Quinoline	508.8	—
C_7H_9N	2,4-Lutidine	374	—	C_9H_{12}	Benzene, n-propyl-	365	31.2
C_7H_9N	2,6-Lutidine	350.6	—	C_9H_{12}	Benzene, 1,2,3-trimethyl-	391.3	31
C_7H_9N	3,4-Lutidine	410.6	—	C_9H_{12}	Cumene (see Benzene, isopropyl-)	362.7	31.2
C_7H_9N	3,5-Lutidine	394.1	—	C_9H_{12}	Benzene, isopropyl-	362.7	31.2
C_7H_{14}	Cyclohexane, methyl-	299.1	34.3	C_9H_{20}	n-Nonane	321	22.5
C_7H_{14}	Cyclopentane, ethyl-	296.3	33.5	C_9H_{21}	Tripropyl amine	304.3	—
C_7H_{14}	1-Heptene	264.1	—	$C_{10}H_8$	Naphthalene	474.8	40.6
$C_7H_{14}O_2$	Acetic acid, isoamyl- (Isoamyl acetate)	326.1	28	$C_{10}H_{12}O$	Ether, diphenyl-	494	30.9
C_7H_{16}	Butane, 2,2,3-trimethyl-	258.3	29.8	$C_{10}H_{14}$	Benzene, 1-isopropyl-4-methyl-	385.5	27.7
C_7H_{16}	n-Heptane	267.1	27	$C_{10}H_{14}$	Benzene, 1,2,3,5-tetramethyl-	402.8	28.6
C_7H_{16}	Hexane, 2-methyl-	257.9	27.2	$C_{10}H_{14}$	p-Cymene, (see Benzene, 1-isopropyl-4-methyl-)	—	—
C_7H_{16}	Pentane, 3-ethyl-	267.6	28.6	$C_{10}H_{14}$	Isodurene, (see Benzene, 1,2,3,5-tetramethyl-)	—	—
C_7H_{16}	Pentane, 2,4-dimethyl-	247.1	27.4	$C_{10}H_{14}O$	3-p-Cymenol	425.1	33
$C_7H_{16}O$	1-Heptyl alcohol	365.3	29.4	$C_{10}H_{14}O$	Thymol, (see 3-p-Cymenol)	425.1	33
C_7F_{16}	n-Heptane, perfluoro-	201.7	16	$C_{10}H_{18}$	Decalin, cis-	418	28.7
C_8H_8	Styrene	374.4	39.4	$C_{10}H_{18}$	Decalin, trans-	408	28.7
C_8H_{10}	Benzene, ethyl-	343.9	36.9	$C_{10}H_{22}$	n-Decane	344.4	20.8
C_8H_{10}	o-Xylene	359	35.7	$C_{11}H_{10}$	Naphthalene, 1-methyl-	498.8	32.1
C_8H_{10}	m-Xylene	346	34.7	$C_{12}H_{10}$	Biphenyl	495	31.8
C_8H_{10}	p-Xylene	345	33.9	$C_{12}H_{11}N$	Diphenylamine	615.5	—
$C_8H_{10}O$	Xylenol	449.7	56.4	$C_{12}H_{18}$	Benzene, hexamethyl-	494	23.5
$C_8H_{10}O$	Phenetol (see Benzene, ethoxy-)	374	33.8	$C_{12}H_{18}$	Mellitine, (see Benzene, hexamethyl-)	—	—
$C_8H_{10}O$	Benzene, ethoxy-	374	33.8	$C_{12}H_{26}$	n-Dodecane	386	17.9
$C_8H_{11}N$	Aniline, N,N-dimethyl-	414.4	35.8	$C_{12}H_{27}N$	Tributyl amine	365.2	—
$C_8H_{11}N$	Aniline, N-ethyl-	425.4	—				
C_8H_{16}	n-Octene	305	25.5				

Table II

Name	Formula	Critical temp. T_c °C	Critical press. P_c atm.	Name	Formula	Critical temp. T_c °C	Critical press. P_c atm.
Ammonia	NH_3	132.5	112.5	Hydrogen iodide	HI	150	81.9
Argon	A	−122.3	48	Hydrogen sulfide	H_2S	100.4	88.9
Boron tribromide	BBr_3	300	—	Hydrazine	N_2H_2	380	—
Boron trichloride	BCl_3	178.8	38.2	Iodine	I_2	512	116
Boron trifluoride	BF_3	−12.26	49.2	Krypton	Kr	−63.8	54.3
Carbon dioxide	CO_2	31	72.9	Neon	Ne	−228.7	26.9
Carbon disulfide	CS_2	279	78	Nitric oxide	NO	−93	64
Carbon monoxide	CO	−140	34.5	Nitrogen dioxide	NO_2	157.8	100
Carbonyl sulfide	COS	104.8	65	Nitrogen	N_2	−147	33.5
Chlorine	Cl_2	144	76.1	Nitrous oxide	N_2O	36.5	71.7
Cyanogen	C_2N_2	126.6	—	Oxygen	O_2	−118.4	50.1
Deuterium	D_2	−234.8	16.4	Ozone	O_3	−5.16	67
Fluorine	F_2	−129	55	Phosphine	PH_3	51.3	64.5
Germanium tetrachloride	$GeCl_4$	276.9	38	Radon	Rn	104.04	62
Helium	He	−267.9	2.26	Silane, chlorotrifluoro-	$SiClF_3$	34.5	34.2
Hydrogen	H_2	−239.9	12.8	Silane	SiH_4	−3.46	47.8
Hydrogen bromide	HBr	90	84.5	Silicon tetrachloride	$SiCl_4$	232.8	—
Hydrogen chloride	HCl	51.4	82.1	Silicon tetrafluoride	SiF_4	−14.06	36.7
Hydrogen deuteride	HD	237.3	14.6	Sulfur dioxide	SO_2	157.8	77.7
Hydrogen cyanide	HCN	183.5	48.9	Stannic chloride	$SnCl_4$	318.7	37
Hydrogen fluoride	HF	188	64	Water	H_2O	374.1	218.3
				Xenon	Xe	16.6	58

DISSOCIATION PRESSURE OF CALCIUM CARBONATE

Temp. °C	mm/Hg	Temp. °C	mm/Hg	Temp. °C	mm/Hg	Temp. °C	mm/Hg
550	0.41	727	44	819	235	894	716
587	1.0	736	54	830	255	898	760 atm.
605	2.3	743	60	840	311	906.5	1.151
671	13.5	748	70	852	381	937	1.770
680	15.8	749	72	857	420	1082.5	8.892
691	19.0	777	105	871	537	1157.7	18.687
701	23.0	786	134	881	603	1226.3	34.333
703	25.5	795	150	891	684	1241	39.094
711	32.7	800	183				

DEFINITIONS AND FORMULAS
The chemical terms have been compiled with the collaboration of
B. Clifford Hendricks

DEFINITIONS AND FORMULAS
The chemical terms have been compiled with the collaboration of
B. Clifford Hendricks

AB.—A prefix attached to the names of the practical electric units to indicate the corresponding unit in the cgs electromagnetic system (emu), e.g. abampere, abvolt.

Abcoulomb.—The abcoulomb, the emu of charge, is defined as the charge which passes a given surface in one second if a steady current of one abampere flows across the surface. Its dimensions are, therefore, $cm^{\frac{1}{2}} gm^{\frac{1}{2}}$ which differ from the dimensions of the statcoulomb by a factor which has the dimensions of a speed. This relationship is connected with the fact that the ratio $2K_e/K_m$ must have the value of the square of the speed of light in any consistent system of units. It follows further that

1 abcoulomb = 2.99793×10^{10} statcoulomb,

the speed of light in vacuo being $(2.99793 \pm 0.000003) \times 10^{10}$ cm/sec.

Abegg's rule.—For use in regard to a helical periodic system. If the maximum positive valence exhibited by an element be numerically added to its maximum negative valence, there is evidently a tendency for the sum to equal 8. This tendency is exhibited especially by the elements of the 4th, 5th, 6th and 7th groups and is known as Abegg's rule.

Absolute humidity.—See Humidity

Absolute pressure.—See Pressure

Absolute temperature.—Temperature reckoned from the absolute zero. See Temperature

Absolute units.—A system of units based on the smallest possible number of independent units. Specifically, units of force, work, energy and power not derived from or dependent on gravitation.

Absolute zero.—The temperature at which a gas would show no pressure if the general law for gases would hold for all temperatures. It is equal to $-273.15°C$ or $-459.67°F$.

Absorption.—1. Penetration of a substance into the body of another. 2. Transformation into other forms suffered by radiant energy passing through a material substance.

Absorption coefficient.—See Absorption factor

Absorption factor.—The ratio of the intensity loss by absorption to the total original intensity of radiation. If I_o represents the original intensity, I_r, the intensity of reflected radiation, I_t, the intensity of the transmitted radiation, the absorption factor is given by the expression

$$\frac{I_o - (I_r + I_t)}{I_o}$$

Also called coefficient of absorption.

Permission was granted by D. Van Nostrand Company, Inc., publishers of The Dictionary of Physics and Electronics for the inclusion of 18 definitions in this section.

Absorption, Lambert's law.—If I_0 is the original intensity, I the intensity after passing through a thickness x of a material whose absorption coefficient is k,

$$I = I_0 e^{-kx}$$

The **index of absorption** k' is given by the relation $\bar{k} = (4\pi k'n)/\lambda$ where n is the index of refraction and λ the wave length in vacuo. The **mass absorption** is given by k/d when d is the density. The transmission factor is given by I/I_0.

Absorption spectrum.—The spectrum obtained by the examination of light from a source, itself giving a continuous spectrum, after this light has passed through an absorbing medium in the gaseous state. The absorption spectrum will consist of dark lines or bands, being the reverse of the emission spectrum of the absorbing substance.

When the absorbing medium is in the solid or liquid state the spectrum of the transmitted light shows broad dark regions which are not resolvable into lines and have no sharp or distinct edges.

Absorptive power or absorptivity for any body is measured by the fraction of the radiant energy falling upon the body which is absorbed or transformed into heat. This ratio varies with the character of the surface and the wave length of the incident energy. It is the ratio of the radiation absorbed by any substance to that absorbed under the same conditions by a black body.

Abvolt.—The cgs electromagnetic unit of potential difference and electromotive force. It is the potential difference that must exist between two points in order that one erg of work be done when one abcoulomb of charge is moved from one point to the other. One abvolt is 10^{-8} volt.

Acceleration.—The time rate of change of velocity in either speed or direction. Cgs unit, one centimeter per second per second. Dimensions, $-[l\ t^{-2}]$.—See Angular acceleration

Acceleration due to gravity.—The acceleration of a body freely falling in a vacuum. The International Committee on Weights and Measures has adopted as a standard or accepted value, 980.665 cm/sec² or 32.174 ft/sec².

Acceleration due to gravity at any latitude and elevation.—If ϕ is the latitude and H the elevation in centimeters the acceleration in cgs units is, $g = 980.616 - 2.5928 \cos 2\phi + 0.0069 \cos^2 2\phi - 3.086 \times 10^{-6} H$. (Helmert's equation)

Accelerators.—Machines for speeding up subatomic particles to energies running into millions of electron volts.—See Betatron, cyclotron, etc.

Achromatic.—A term applied to lenses signifying their more or less complete correction for chromatic aberration.

Acid.—For many purposes it is sufficient to say that an acid is a hydrogen-containing substance which dissociates on solution in water to produce one or more hydrogen ions. More generally, however, acids are defined according to other concepts. The Brönsted concept states that an acid is any compound which can furnish a proton. Thus NH_4^+ is an acid since it can give up a proton:

$$NH_4^+ \rightleftharpoons NH_3 + H^+$$

and NH_3 is a base since it accepts a proton.

A still more general concept is that of G. N. Lewis which defines an acid as anything which can attach itself to something with an unshared pair of electrons. Thus in the reaction

$$H^+ + :N\underset{\underset{H}{|}}{\overset{\overset{H}{|}}{-}}H \rightleftharpoons NH_4^+$$

the NH_3 is a base because it possesses an unshared pair of electrons. This latter concept explains many phenomena, such as the effect of certain substances other than hydrogen ions in the changing of the color of indicators. It also explains acids and bases in non-aqueous sytems as liquid NH_3 and SO_2.

Actinide Series.—Elements of atomic numbers 89 to 103 analogous to the lanthanide series of the so-called rare earths.

Action is measured by the product of work by time. Cgs units of action are the erg-second and the joule-second. Dimensions, $[m \, l^2 \, t^{-1}]$. Planck's quantum or constant of action is $(6.62517 - 0.00023) \times 10^{-27}$ erg-sec.

Active mass of a substance is the number of gram molecular weights per liter in solution, or in gaseous form.

Activity coefficient.—A factor which, when multiplied by the molecular concentration yields the active mass. The activity coefficient is evaluated by thermodynamic calculations, usually from data on the emf of certain cells, or the lowering of the freezing point of certain solutions. It is a correction factor which makes the thermodynamic calculations correct.

Adiabatic.—A body is said to undergo an adiabatic change when its condition is altered without gain or loss of heat. The line on the pressure volume diagram representing the above change is called an adiabatic line.

Adsorption.—The condensation of gases, liquids, or dissolved substances on the surfaces of solids is called adsorption.

Air columns, frequency of vibration in.—See *Organ pipes*

Albedo. — The fraction of electromagnetic radiation reflected by a surface.

Allobar.—A form of an element differing in isotopic composition from the naturally occurring form.

Allotropy.—The property shown by certain elements or being capable of existence in more than one form, due to

differences in the arrangement of atoms or molecules.—See *Monotropic* and *Enantiotropic*

Alpha (α)-particle, or alpha-ray.—One of the particles emitted in radioactive decay. It is identical with the nucleus of the helium atom and consists, therefore, of two protons plus two neutrons bound together. A moving alpha particle is strongly ionizing and so loses energy rapidly in traversing through matter. Natural alpha particles will traverse only a few centimeters of air before coming to rest.

Alternating current, (A-C).—Current in which the charge-flow periodically reverses, as opposed to direct current, and whose average value is zero. Alternating current usually implies a sinusoidal variation of current and voltage. This behavior is represented mathematically in various ways:

$$I = I_0 \cos{(2\pi f t + \phi)}$$
$$\dot{I} = I_0 \angle \phi$$
$$I = I_e{}^{j\omega t}$$

where f is the frequency; $\omega = 2\pi f$, the pulsatance, or radian frequency; ϕ the phase angle; I_0 the amplitude; and I, the complex amplitude. In the complex rotation, it is understood that the actual current is the real part of I. For circuits involving also a capacitance C in farads and L in henrys, the impedance becomes,

$$\sqrt{R^2 + \left(2\pi f L - \frac{1}{2\pi f C}\right)^2}$$

Altitudes with the barometer.—If b_1 and b_2 denote the corrected barometer readings at two stations, t the mean of the temperatures, t_1 and t_2 of the air at the two stations, e_1 and e_2 the tension of water vapor at the two stations, h the mean height above sea level, ϕ the latitude; then the difference in elevation in centimeters is $H = 1,843,000 \, (\log b_1 - \log b_2) \, (1 + 0.00367t) \, (1 + 0.0026 \cos 2\phi + 0.00002h + \frac{3}{8}k)$, where

$$k = \frac{1}{2}\left(\frac{e_1}{b_1} + \frac{e_2}{b_2}\right)$$

An approximate formula, sufficient for differences not over 1000 meters is

$$H = 1,600,000 \frac{b_1 - b_2}{b_1 + b_2}(1 + 0.004t).$$

Amorphous.—Without definite form, not crystallized.

Ampere's rule.—A positive charge moving horizontally is deflected by a force to the right if it is moving in a region where the magnetic field is vertically upward. This may be generalized to currents in wires by recalling that a current in a certain direction is equivalent to the motion of positive charges in that direction. The force felt by a negative charge is opposite to that felt by a positive charge.

Amplitude.—The maximum value of the displacement in an oscillatory motion.

AMU.—The atomic mass unit (amu), a unit of mass equal to 1,12 the mass of the carbon atom of mass number 12. On the atomic mass scale $^{12}C=12$.

$$1 \text{ amu} = 931.4812(52) \text{ MeV}$$
$$= 1.660531(11) \ 10^{-27} \text{ kg (SI units)}$$
$$= 1.660531(11) \ 10^{-24} \text{ g (cgs units)}$$

The numbers in parentheses are the standard deviation uncertainties in the last digits of the quoted value, computed on the basis of internal consistency.

Angle.—The ratio between the arc and the radius of the arc. Units of angle,—the radian, the angle subtended by an arc equal to the radius; the degree, $\frac{1}{360}$ part of the total angle about a point. Dimensions,—a numeric.

Angstrom.—A unit of length, used especially in expressing the length of light waves, equal to one ten-thousandth of a micron, or one hundred-millionth of a centimeter (1×10^{-8} cm).

Angular acceleration.—The time rate of change of angular velocity either in angular speed or in direction of the axis of rotation (precession). Cgs unit,—one radian per second per second. Dimensions,—$[t^{-2}]$.

If the initial angular velocity is ω_o, and the velocity after time t is ω_t, the angular acceleration,

$$\alpha = \frac{\omega_t - \omega_o}{t}$$

The angular velocity after time t,

$$\omega_t = \omega_o + \alpha t$$

The angle swept out in time t,

$$\theta = \omega_o t + \tfrac{1}{2}\alpha t^2$$

The angular velocity after movement through the arc θ,

$$\omega = \sqrt{\omega_o{}^2 + 2\alpha\theta}$$

In the above equations, for angular displacement in radians, angular velocity will be in radians per second and angular acceleration in radians per second per second.

Angular aperture of an objective is the largest angular extent of wave surface which it can transmit.

Angular harmonic motion or harmonic motion of rotation.—Periodic, oscillatory angular motion in which the restoring torque is proportional to the angular displacement. Torsional vibration.

Angular momentum or moment of momentum.—Quantity of angular motion measured by the product of the angular velocity and the moment of inertia. Cgs unit,—unnamed, its nature is expressed by g-cm²/sec. Dimensions,—$[m, l^2 t^{-1}]$.

The angular momentum of a mass whose moment of inertia is I, rotating with angular velocity ω, is $I\omega$.

Angular velocity.—Time rate of angular motion about an axis. Cgs unit,—one radian per second. Dimensions,—$[t^{-1}]$. If the angle described in time t is θ, the angular velocity,

$$\omega = \frac{\theta}{t}$$

θ in radians and t in seconds gives ω in radians per second.

Anhydride (of acid or base).—An oxide which when combined with water gives an acid or base.

Anion.—A negatively charged ion.

Anode.—The electrode at which oxidation occurs in a cell. It is also the electrode toward which anions travel due to the electrical potential. In spontaneous cells the anode is considered negative. In non-spontaneous or electrolytic cells the anode is considered positive.

Apochromat.—A term applied to photographic and microscope objectives indicating the highest degree of color correction.

Archimedes principle.—A body wholly or partly immersed in a fluid is buoyed up by a force equal to the weight of the fluid displaced. A body of volume V cm³ immersed in a fluid of density ρ grams per cm³ is buoyed up by a force in dynes,

$$F = \rho g V$$

where g is the acceleration due to gravity.

A floating body displaces its own weight of liquid.

Area, unit of.—The square centimeter. The area of a square whose sides are one centimeter in length. Other units of area are similarly derived. Dimensions,—$[l^2]$.

Arrhenius theory of electrolytic dissociation states that the molecule of an electrolyte can enter into two or more electrically charged atoms or ions.

Astigmatism is an error of spherical lenses peculiar to the formation of images by oblique pencils. The image of a point when astigmatism is present will consist of two focal lines at right angles to each other and separated by a measurable distance along the axis of the pencil. The error is not eliminated by reduction of aperture as is spherical aberration.

Atom.—The smallest particle of an element which can enter into a chemical *combination*. All chemical compounds are formed of atoms, the difference between compounds being attributable to the nature, number, and arrangement of their constituent atoms.—See *isotopes, nuclear atom*.

Atomic bomb.—An explosive that derives its energy from the fission or fusion of atomic nuclei.

Atomic energy.—1. The constitutive internal energy of the atom which was absorbed when it was formed. 2. Energy derived from the mass converted into energy in nuclear transformations.—See *Einstein's formula*

Atomic mass (atomic weight).—The mass of a neutral atom of a nuclide. It is usually expressed in terms of the physical scale of atomic masses, that is, in atomic mass units (amu). See AMU

Atomic number.—The number (Z) of protons within the atomic nucleus. The electrical charge of these protons determines the number and arrangement of the outer electrons of the

DEFINITIONS AND FORMULAS (Continued)

atom, and thereby the chemical and physical properties of the element.

Atomic structure.—According to the currently accepted view, the atom consists of a central part, called nucleus, and a number of *electrons* (called orbital or planetary electrons) circling about the latter, like planets about the sun. The nucleus is of a high specific weight; it contains most of the mass of the entire atom (its mass is considered equal to the atomic mass) and is composed of positively charged particles, called *protons* (the number of which always equals the atomic number, (Z), and particles of 0 charge, called neutrons (the number of which equals the difference between the atomic weight and the atomic number, $A - Z$). The diameter of the nucleus is between 10^{-13} and 10^{-12} cm, and the relatively vast distance in which the orbital electrons circle about it is illustrated by the fact that this nuclear diameter is only 10^{-4} to 10^{-5} of the entire atomic diameter. While the nucleus carries an integral number of positive charges (an integral number of protons) each of $1 \cdot 6 \times 10^{-19}$ coulomb, each electron carries one negative charge of $1 \cdot 6 \times 10^{-19}$ coulomb, and the number of orbital electrons is equal to the number of protons in the nucleus (i.e. to the atomic number, Z), so that the atom as a whole has a net charge of 0. The electrons are arranged in successive shells (q.v.) around the nucleus; the maximum number of electrons in each shell is determined by natural laws, and the extranuclear electronic structure of the atom is characteristic of the element. The electrons in the inner shells are tightly bound to the nucleus; this inner structure can be altered by high-energy particles, γ-rays of radium, or x-rays. The electrons in the outer shells are responsible for the chemical properties of the element.—See *Bohr's atomic theory, Heisenberg's theory, shell and subshell*

Atomic theory.—All elementary forms of matter are composed of very small unit quantities called atoms. The atoms of a given element all have the same size and weight. The atoms of different elements have different sizes and weights. Atoms of the same or different elements unite with each other to form very small unit quantities of compound substances called molecules.

Atomic weight.—Atomic weight is the relative weight of the atom on the basis of $^{12}\text{C} = 12$. For a pure isotope, the atomic weight rounded off to the nearest integer gives the total number of nucleons (neutrons and protons) making up the atomic nucleus. If these weights are expressed in grams they are called gram atomic weights.—See *Isotopes and Atomic Mass*

Avogadro's law.—Equal volumes of different gases at the same pressure and temperature contain the same number of molecules.

Avogadro's number.—The number of molecules in one mole or gram-molecular weight of a substance. A number of values of the Avogadro number, which is usually denoted by N, have been found by various methods, generally lying within a range of 1% about the value 6.02252×10^{23} per gram mole.

Avogadro's principle (or theory).—The numbers of molecules present in equal volumes of gases at the same temperature and pressure are equal.

Babo's law.—The addition of a non-volatile solid to a liquid in which it is soluble lowers the vapor pressure of the solvent in proportion to the amount of substance dissolved.

Balmer series of spectral lines. The wave lengths of a series of lines in the spectrum of hydrogen are given in angstroms by the equation

$$\lambda = 3646 \, \frac{N^2}{N^2 - 4}$$

where N is an integer having values greater than 2.

Bar.—International unit of pressure 10^6 dyne/cm². Unfortunately some writers have used this term for 1 dyne/cm². 1 bar = 0.987 atmosphere.

Barn.—Unit for measuring capture cross sections (q.v.) of elements. One barn = 10^{-24} cm² per nucleus.

Barye.—Cgs pressure unit = one dyne/cm².

Bases.—For many purposes it is sufficient to say that a base is a substance which dissociates on solution in water to produce one or more hydroxyl ions. More generally, however, bases are defined according to other concepts. The Brönsted concept states that a base is any compound which can accept a proton. Thus NH_3 is a base since it can accept a proton to form ammonium ions.

$$NH_3 + H^+ \rightleftharpoons NH_4^+$$

A still more general concept is that of G. N. Lewis which defines a base as anything which has an unshared pair of electrons. Thus in the reaction

$$H^+ + \ :\!N\!-\!H \rightleftharpoons NH_4^+$$

the NH_3 is a base because it possesses an unshared pair of electrons. This latter concept explains many phenomena, such as the effect of certain substances other than hydrogen ions in the changing of the color of indicators. It also explains acids and bases in non-aqueous systems as liquid NH_3 and SO_2.

Beat(s).—Two vibrations of slightly different frequencies f_1 and f_2 when added together, produce in a detector sensitive to both these frequencies, a regularly varying response which rises and falls at the "beat" frequency $f_b = |f_1 - f_2|$. It is important to note that a resonator which is sharply tuned to f_b alone will not resound at all in the presence of these two beating frequencies.—See *Combination Frequencies*

DEFINITIONS AND FORMULAS (Continued)

electronic orbits, i.e., by definite energy levels of their extra-nuclear electrons, and in these stationary states they do not emit radiation; the jump of an electron from an orbit to another of a smaller radius is accompanied by monochromatic radiation.

Boyle's law for gases.—At a constant temperature the volume of a given quantity of any gas varies inversely as the pressure to which the gas is subjected. For a perfect gas, changing from pressure p and volume v to pressure p' and volume v' without change of temperature,

$$pv = p'v'$$

Breeder, Reactor (Breeder pile).—A nuclear chain reactor in which transmutation produces a greater number of fissionable atoms than the number of parent atoms consumed.

Brewster's law.—The tangent of the polarizing angle for a substance is equal to the index of refraction. The polarizing angle is that angle of incidence for which the reflected polarized ray is at right angles to the refracted ray. If n is the index of refraction and θ the polarizing angle, $n = \tan \theta$.

Brightness is measured by the flux emitted per unit emissive area as projected on a plane normal to the line of sight. The unit of brightness is that of a perfectly diffusing surface giving out one lumen per square centimeter of projected surface and is called the lambert. The millilambert (0.001 lambert) is a more convenient unit. **Candle per square centimeter** is the brightness of a surface which has, in the direction considered, a luminous intensity of one candle per cm².

British thermal unit.—The quantity of heat required to raise the temperature of one pound of water one degree Fahrenheit at, or near, its point of maximum density (39.1°F). The Btu is equivalent to 0.252 kilogram-calorie.

Brownian movement.—A continuous agitation of particles in a colloidal solution caused by unbalanced impacts with molecules of the surrounding medium. The motion may be observed with a microscope when a strong beam of light is caused to traverse the solution across the line of sight.

Bulk modulus.—The modulus of volume elasticity,

$$M_B = \frac{p_2 - p_1}{\dfrac{v_1 - v_2}{v_1}}$$

where $p_1, p_2; v_1, v_2$ are the initial and final pressure and volume respectively.

Calorie.—The amount of heat necessary to raise 1 gram of water at 15°C, 1°C. There are various calories depending upon the interval chosen. Sometimes the unit is written as the gram-calorie or the kilogram calorie, the meaning of which is evident. The calorie may be defined in terms of its mechanical equivalent. The National Bureau of Standards defines the calorie as

Beat frequencies.—The beat of two different frequencies of signals on a non-linear circuit when they combine or beat together. It has a frequency equal to the difference of the two applied frequencies.

Beer's law.—If two solutions of the same colored compound be made in the same solvent, one of which is, say, twice the concentration of the other, the absorption due to a given thickness of the first solution should be equal to that of twice the thickness of the second.

Mathematically this may be expressed $l_{c_1} = l_{2c_2}$ when the intensity of light passing through the two solutions is a constant and if the intensity and wave length of light incident upon each solution are the same.

Bernoulli's theorem.—At any point in a tube through which a liquid is flowing the sum of the pressure energy, potential energy, and kinetic energy is constant. If p is pressure; h, height above a reference plane; d, density of the liquid, and v, velocity of flow,

$$p + hdg + \tfrac{1}{2} dv^2 = a \text{ constant.}$$

Berthelot principle of maximum work.—Of all possible chemical processes which can proceed without the aid of external energy, that process always takes place which is accompanied by the greatest evolution of heat. This law holds good for low temperatures only and does not account for endothermic reactions.

Beta (β)-particle, (Beta ray).—One of the particles which can be emitted by a radioactive atomic nucleus. It has a mass about $1/1837$ that of the proton. The negatively charged beta-particle is identical with the ordinary electron, while the positively charged type (positron) differs from the electron in having equal but opposite electrical properties. The emission of an electron entails the change of a neutron into a proton inside the nucleus. The emission of a positron is similarly associated with the change of a proton into a neutron. Beta particles have no independent existance inside the nucleus, but are created at the instant of emission.—See Neutrino

Betatron.—An accelerator used to impart high velocities to electrons (beta particles). Propellant is an electromagnetic field. A five to six Mev betatron can produce X-rays equivalent to the gamma readiation of 10 to 20 grams of radium.

Bevatron.—A six or more billion electron volt accelerator of protons and other atomic particles. Makes use of a Cockeroft-Walton transformer cascade accelerator and a linear (q.v.) as well as an electromagnetic field in the build-up.

Black body.—If, for all values of the wave length of the incident radiant energy, all of the energy is absorbed the body is called a black body.

Bohr's atomic theory.—The theory that atoms can exist for a duration solely in certain states, characterized by definite

4.18400 joules. At the International Steam Table Conference held in London in 1929 the international calorie was defined at $\frac{1}{860}$ of the international watt hour, which makes it equal to 4.1860 international joules.

With the adoption of the absolute sytem of electrical units, this becomes 1/859.858 watt hours or 4.18674 joules. The Btu was defined at the same time as 251.996 international calories.

Calutron.—An apparatus operating on the principle of the mass spectrograph and used for separating U^{235} from U^{238}.

Candela.—The candela is the luminous intensity, in the direction of the normal, of a black body surface 1/600,000 square meter in area, at the temperature of the solidification of platinum (2042K) under a pressure of 101,325 newtons per square meter.

Candle (new unit).—$\frac{1}{60}$ of the intensity of one square centimeter of a blackbody radiator at the temperature of solidification of platinum (2042K).

Capacitance is measured by the charge which must be communicated to a body to raise its potential one unit. Electrostatic unit capacitance is that which requires one electrostatic unit of charge to raise the potential one electrostatic unit. The farad $= 9 \times 10^{11}$ electrostatic units. A capacitance of one farad requires one coulomb of electricity to raise its potential one volt. Dimensions,—$[\epsilon l]$; $[\mu^{-1} l^{-1} t^2]$.

A conductor charged with a quantity Q to a potential V has a capacitance,

$$C = \frac{Q}{V}$$

Capacitance of a spherical conductor of radius r,

$$C = Kr$$

Capacitance of two concentric spheres of radii r and r'

$$C = K\frac{rr'}{r - r'}$$

Capacitance of a parallel plate condenser, the area of whose plates is A and the distance between them d,

$$C = \frac{KA}{4\pi d}$$

Capacitances will be given in electrostatic units if the dimensions of condensers are substituted in cm. K is the dielectric constant of the medium.

Capillary constant or specific cohesion,

$$a^2 = \frac{2T}{(d_1 - d_2)g} = hr$$

where T is surface tension, d_1 and d_2, the densities of the two fluids, g the acceleration due to gravity, h the height of rise in a capillary tube of radius r.—See *Surface tension*

Carnot cycle.—A sequence of operations forming the working cycle of an ideal heat engine of maximum thermal efficiency.

It consists of isothermal expansion, adiabatic expansion, isothermal compression, and adiabatic compression to the initial state.

Catalytic agent.—A substance which by its mere presence alters the velocity of a reaction, and may be recovered unaltered in nature or amount at the end of the reaction.

Cathode.—The electrode at which reduction occurs. It is the negative electrode in a cell through which current is being forced, but it is the positive pole of a battery. In a vacuum tube, the cathode is the electrode from which electrons are liberated.—See *Anode*

Cation.—A positively charged ion.

Cauchy's dispersion formula.

$$n = A + \frac{B}{\lambda^2} + \frac{C}{\lambda^4} + \cdots$$

An empirical expression giving an approximate relation between the refractive index n of a medium and the wavelength λ of the light; A, B, and C being constants for a given medium.

Celsius.—See temperature, Celsius, in this section.

Centipoise.—A standard unit of *viscosity*, equal to 0.01 poise, the c.g.s. unit of viscosity. Water at 20°C has a viscosity of 1.002.

Centripetal force.—The force required to keep a moving mass in a circular path. Centrifugal force is the name given to the reaction against centripetal force.

Chain reaction.—In general, any self-sustaining process, whether molecular or nuclear, the products of which are instrumental in, and directly contribute to the propagation of the process. Specifically, a *fission chain reaction*, where the energy liberated or particles produced (fission products) by the fission of an atom cause the fission of other atomic nuclei, which in turn propagate the fission reaction in the same manner.

Charles' law or Gay-Lussac's law.—The volumes assumed by a given mass of a gas at different temperatures, the pressure remaining constant, are, within moderate ranges of temperature, directly proportional to the corresponding absolute temperatures.

Chemiluminescence.—Emission of light during a chemical reaction.

Christiansen effect.—When finely powdered substances, such as glass or quartz, are immersed in a liquid of the same index of refraction complete transparency can only be obtained for monochromatic light. If white light is employed the transmitted color corresponds to the particular wave-length for which the two substances, solid and liquid have exactly the same index of refraction. Due to differences in dispersion the indices of refraction will match for only a narrow band of the spectrum.

DEFINITIONS AND FORMULAS (Continued)

Chromatic aberration.—Due to the difference in the index of refraction for different wave lengths, light of various wave lengths from the same source cannot be focused at a point by a simple lens. This is called chromatic aberration.

Cloud chamber.—An apparatus containing moist air or other gas which on sudden expansion condenses moisture to droplets on dust particles or other nuclei. Thus charged particles or ions in the space become nuclei and their numbers and behavior, when properly illuminated, may be studied.

Colligative property.—A property numerically the same for a group of substances, independent of their chemical nature.

Colloid.—A phase dispersed to such a degree that the surface forces become an important factor in determining its properties.

In general particles of colloidal dimensions are approximately 10 angstroms to 1 micron in size. Colloidal particles are often best distinguished from ordinary molecules due to the fact that colloidal particles cannot diffuse through membranes which do allow ordinary molecules and ions to pass freely.

Coma.—An aberration of spherical lenses, occurring in the case of oblique incidence, when the bundle of rays forming the image is unsymmetrical. The image of a point is comet shaped, hence the name.

Combination frequencies.—Two vibrations of arbitrary frequencies f_1 and f_2 when applied simultaneously to a nonlinear (distorting) device will excite it to a motion containing not only the original frequencies, but also members of a set of "combination" frequencies given by $f_c = mf_1 + nf_2$ where m and n are integers. A resonator sharply tuned to any one of these frequencies which may be produced in the nonlinear device will respond to it with an amplitude depending on the type of nonlinearity. The superheterodyne radio receiver depends on this phenomenon.

Combining volumes.—Under comparable conditions of pressure and temperature the volume ratios of gases involved in chemical reactions are simple whole numbers.

Combining weight of an element or radical is its atomic weight divided by its valence.

Combining weights, law of.—If the weights of elements which combine with each other be called their "combining weights," then elements always combine either in the ratio of their combining weights or of simple multiples of these weights.

Component substances, law of.—Every material consists of one substance, or is a mixture of two or more substances, each of which exhibits a specific set of properties, independent of the other substances.

Compounds are substances containing more than one constituent element and having properties, on the whole, different from those which their constituents had as elementary substances. The composition of a given pure compound is perfectly definite, and is always the same no matter how that compound may have been formed.

Compressibility.—Reciprocal of the bulk modulus.

Compton effect, (Compton recoil effect).—Elastic scattering of photons by electrons results in decrease in frequency and increase of wave length of x-rays and gamma-rays when scattered by free electrons.

Concentration.—The amount of a substance in weight, moles, or equivalents contained in unit volume.

Condensers in parallel and series.—If c_1, c_2, c_3, etc. represent the capacitances of a series of condensers and C their combined capacitance,—

when in parallel, $C = c_1 + c_2 + c_3 \cdots$

when in series, $\dfrac{1}{C} = \dfrac{1}{c_1} + \dfrac{1}{c_2} + \dfrac{1}{c_3} \cdots$

Conductance, the reciprocal of resistance, is measured by the ratio of the current flowing through a conductor to the difference of potential between its ends. The practical unit of conductance, the mho, the conductance of a body through which one ampere of current flows when the potential difference is one volt. The conductance of a body in mho is the reciprocal of the value of its resistance in ohms. Dimensions,—$[\epsilon\, l^{-1}\, t^{-1}]$.

Conductivity, electrical, is measured by the quantity of electricity transferred across unit area, per unit potential gradient per unit time. Reciprocal of resistivity. **Volume conductivity** or specific conductance, $k = 1/\rho$ where ρ is the volume resistivity. **Mass conductivity** $= k/d$ where d is density. **Equivalent conductivity** $\Lambda = k/c$ where c is the number of equivalents per unit volume of solution. **Molecular conductivity** $\mu = k/m$ where m is the number of moles per unit volume of solution. Dimensions: volume conductivity,—$[\epsilon\, l^{-1}]; [\mu^{-1}\, l^{-2}\, t]$, mass conductivity,—$[\epsilon\, m^{-1}\, l^s\, t^{-1}]; [\mu^{-1}\, m^{-1}\, l\, t]$.

Conductivity, thermal.—Time rate of transfer of heat by conduction, through unit thickness, across unit area for unit difference of temperature. It is measured as calories per second per square centimeter for a thickness of one centimeter and a difference of temperature of 1°C. Dimensions,— W/m K.

If the two opposite faces of a rectangular solid are maintained at temperatures t_1 and t_2 the heat conducted across the solid of section a and thickness d in a time T will be,

$$Q = \frac{K(t_2 - t_1)aT}{d}$$

K is a constant depending on the nature of the substance, designated as the specific heat conductivity. K is usually given for Q in calories, t_1 and t_2 in °C, a in cm², T in sec, and d in cm.—See *Heat conductivity*

DEFINITIONS AND FORMULAS (Continued)

Conductors.—A class of bodies which are incapable of supporting electric strain. A charge given to a conductor spread to all parts of the body.

Conjugate foci.—Under proper conditions light divergent from a point on or near the axis of a lens or spherical mirror is focused at another point. The point of convergence and the position of the source are interchangeable and are called conjugate foci.

Conservation of energy, (Chem).—In a chemical change there is no loss or gain but merely a transformation of energy from one form to another.

Conservation of energy, law of.—Energy can neither be created nor destroyed and therefore the total amount of energy in the universe remains constant.

Conservation of mass.—In all ordinary chemical changes, the total of the reactants is always equal to the total mass of the products.

Conservation of momentum, law of.—For any collision, the vector sum of the momenta of the colliding bodies after collison equals the vector sum of their momenta before collision. If two bodies of masses m_1 and m_2 have, before impact velocities v_1 and v_2 and after impact velocities u_1 and u_2

$$m_1 u_1 + m_2 u_2 = m_1 v_1 + m_2 v_2$$

Constitutive property.—A property which depends on the constitution or structure of the molecule.

Cooling.—Processing highly radioactive materials to attain lesser radioactivity for subsequent use or handling.

Cosmic rays.—Highly penetrating radiations which strike the earth, assumed to originate in interstellar space. They are classed as: primary, coming from the assumed source, and secondary, those induced in upper atmospheric nuclei by collisions with primary cosmic rays.

Cosmotron.—A particle accelerator capable of giving them energies to billions of electron volts.

Coulomb.—A unit quantity of electricity. It is the quantity of electricity which must pass through a circuit to deposit 0.0011180 grams of silver from a solution of silver nitrate. An ampere is one coulomb per second. A coulomb is also the quantity of electricity on the positive plate of a condenser of one-farad capacity when the electromotive force is one volt.

Couple.—Two equal and oppositely directed parallel but not colinear forces acting upon a body form a couple. The moment of the couple or torque is given by the product of one of the forces by the perpendicular distance between them. Dimension, —[m l^2 t^{-2}].

Couple acting on a magnet of magnetic moment ml in a field of strength H. If the magnet is perpendicular to the direction of the field

$$C = Hml = HM$$

If the angle between the magnet and the field is θ

$$C = Hml \sin \theta$$

The couple will be in dyne-cm for cgs electromagnetic units of H, m and l.

Critical mass.—The minimum mass the fissile material must have in order to maintain a spontaneous fission chain reaction. For pure U^{235} it is computed to be about 20 pounds.

Critical temperature is that temperature above which a gas cannot be liquefied by pressure alone. The pressure under which a substance may exist as a gas in equilibrium with the liquid at the critical temperature is the **critical pressure.**

Cross section, (Nuclear cross section).—A measure of the probability of a particular process. The nuclear cross section is expressed by a/bc, where a is the number of processes occurring, b the number of incident particles, and c the number of target nuclei per cm^2. There are nuclear cross sections for fission, for slow neutron capture, for Compton collision, and for ionization by electron impact.

Cryohydrate.—The solid which separates when a saturated solution freezes. It contains the solvent and the solute in the same proportions as they were in the saturated solution.

Crystal.—The "ideal crystal" is a homogeneous portion of crystalline matter, (q.v.) whether bounded by faces or not. Crystalline matter is matter that possesses a triperiodic structure on the atomic scale. It is characterized by discontinuous vectorial properties that give rise to "crystal planes" [(1) crystal growth (faces); (2) cohesion (cleavage planes); (3) twinning (twin planes); (4) gliding (gliding planes); (5) x-ray, electron, or neutron diffraction ("reflecting" planes); all of which are parallel to lattice planes.]

Curie.—Unit for measuring radioactivity. One Curie = that quantity of any radioactive isotope undergoing 3.7×10^{10} disintegrations per second.

Curie's law.—The intensity of magnetization,

$$I = \frac{AH}{T}$$

where H, is the magnetic field strength, T the absolute temperature and A Curie's constant. Used for paramagnetic substances.

Curie point.—All ferro-magnetic substances have a definite temperature of transition at which the phenomena of ferromagnetism disappear and the substances become merely paramagnetic. This temperature is called the "Curie Point," and is usually lower than the melting point.

Curie-Weiss law.—The Curie law was modifed by Weiss to state that the susceptibility of a paramagnetic substance above the Curie point varies inversely as the excess of the temperature above that point.

This law is not valid at or below the Curie point.

DEFINITIONS AND FORMULAS (Continued)

Current (electric).—The rate of transfer of electricity. The transfer at the rate of one electrostatic unit of electricity in one second is the electrostatic unit of current. The electromagnetic unit of current is a current of such strength that one centimeter of the wire in which it flows is pushed sideways with a force of one dyne when the wire is at right angles to a magnetic field of unit intensity. The practical unit of current is the **ampere**, a transfer of one coulomb per second, which is one tenth the electromagnetic unit. The **international ampere** is the unvarying electric current which, when passed through a solution of silver nitrate in accordance with certain specifications, deposits silver at the rate of 0.00111800 gram per second. The international ampere is equivalent to 0.999835 absolute ampere. The **ampere-turn** is the magnetic potential produced between the two faces of a coil of one turn carrying one ampere. Dimensions, —[$e^{\frac{1}{2}} m^{\frac{1}{2}} l^{\frac{1}{2}} t^{-2}$]; [$\mu^{-\frac{1}{2}} m^{\frac{1}{2}} l^{\frac{1}{2}} t^{-1}$].

Current in a simple circuit.—The current in a circuit including an external resistance R and a cell of electromotive force E and internal resistance r,

$$I = \frac{E}{R + r}$$

If E is in volts and r and R in ohms the current will be in amperes.

For two cells in parallel,

$$I = \frac{E}{R + \frac{r}{2}}$$

For two cells in series,

$$I = \frac{2E}{R + 2r}$$

Cyclotron.—The magnetic resonance accelerator for imparting very great velocities to heavier nuclear particles without the use of excessive voltages.

Dalton's law of partial pressures.—The pressure exerted by a mixture of gases is equal to the sum of the separate pressures which each gas would exert if it alone occupied the whole volume. This fact is expressed in the following formula:

$$PV = V(p_1 + p_2 + p_3, \text{ etc.})$$

Decay.—Diminution of a radioactive substance due to nuclear emission of alpha or beta particles, gamma rays or positrons.

Declination.—The angle between the vertical plane containing the direction of the earth's field at any point and a plane containing the geographic north and south meridian.

Decomposition is the chemical separation of a substance into two or more substances, which may differ from each other and from the original substances.

Definite proportions, law of.—In every sample of each compound substance the proportions by weight of the constituent elements are always the same.

Degree of freedom.—The number of the variables determining the state of a system (usually pressure, temperature, and concentrations of the components) to which arbitrary values can be assigned.

Density.—Concentration of matter, measured by the mass per unit volume. Dimensions, —[$m\,l^{-3}$].

Deuteron.—Nucleus of the deuterium atom or the ion of deuterium. Its structure—one neutron and one proton.

Dew point.—The temperature at which condensation of water vapor in the air takes place.

Diamagnetic materials.—Are those within which an externally applied magnetic field is slightly reduced because of an alteration of the atomic electron orbits produced by the field. Diamagnetism is an atomic-scale consequence of the Lenz law of induction. The permeability of diamagnetic materials is slightly less than that of empty space.

Dielectric constant of a medium is defined by ϵ in the equation

$$F = \frac{QQ'}{\epsilon r^2}$$

where F is the force of attraction between two charges Q and Q' separated by a distance r in a uniform medium.

Dielectrics or insulators or non-conductors.—A class of bodies supporting an electric strain. A charge on one part of a non-conductor is not communicated to any other part.

Diffraction.—That phenomena produced by the spreading of waves around and past obstacles which are comparable in size to their wavelength.

Diffraction grating.—If s is the distance between the rulings, d the angle of diffraction, then the wave length where the angle of incidence is 90° is (for the nth order spectrum),

$$\lambda = \frac{s \sin d}{n}$$

If i is the angle of incidence, d the angle of diffraction, s the distance between the rulings, n the order of the spectrum, the wave length is,

$$\lambda = \frac{s}{n}(\sin i + \sin d).$$

Diffusion.—If the concentration (mass of solid per unit volume of solution) at one surface of a layer of liquid is d_1 and at the other surface d_2, the thickness of the layer h and the area under consideration A, then the mass of the substance which diffuses through the cross-section A in time t is,

$$m = \Delta A \frac{(d_2 - d_1)t}{h}$$

where Δ is the coefficient of diffusion.

Diffusivity or coefficient of diffusion is also given by Δ in the equation

$$\frac{dQ}{dt} = -\Delta \left(\frac{dc}{dx}\right) dy\, dz$$

where dQ is the amount passing through an area $dy\, dz$ in the direction of x in a time dt where dc/dx is the rate of increase of volume concentration in the direction of x. Dimensions, $[l^2\, t^{-1}]$.

Diffusivity of heat is given by Δ in the equation

$$\frac{dH}{dt} = -\Delta s d\, \frac{dT}{dx}\, dy\, dz$$

where dH is the quantity of heat passing through the area $dy\, dz$ in the direction of x in a time dt. The rate of variation of temperature along x is given by dT/dx, s is specific heat and d, density. Dimensions, $[l^2\, t^{-1}]$.

Dimensional formulae.—If mass, length, and time are considered fundamental quantities, the relation of other physical quantities and their units to these three may be expressed by a formula involving the symbols l, m and t respectively, with appropriate exponents. For example, the dimensional formula for volume would be expressed, $[l^3]$; velocity, $[l t^{-1}]$; force $[m\, l t^{-2}]$. Other fundamental quantities used in dimensional formulae may be indicated as follows: θ, temperature, ϵ the dielectric constant of a vacuum; μ, the magnetic permeability of a vacuum.

Diminution of pressure at the side of a moving stream. If a fluid of density d moves with a velocity v, the diminution of pressure due to the motion is (neglecting viscosity),

$$p = \tfrac{1}{2} dv^2$$

Dip.—The angle measured in a vertical plane between the direction of the earth's magnetic field and the horizontal.

Dipole.—(1) A combination of two electrically or magnetically charged particles of opposite sign which are separated by a very small distance. (2) Any system of charges, such as a circulating current, which has the properties that: (a) no forces act on it in a uniform field; (b) a torque proportional to $\sin\theta$, where θ is the angle between the dipole axis and a uniform field, does act on it; (c) it produces a potential which is proportional to the inverse square of the distance from it.

Dipole moment.—A mathematical entity; the product of one of the charges of a dipole unit by the distance separating the two dipolar charges. In terms of the definition of a dipole (2), the dipole moment p is related to the torque T, and the field strength E (or B) through the equation:

$$T = p \times E.$$

Dipole moment, molecular.—It is found from measurements of dielectric constant (i.e. by its temperature dependence, as in the **Debye equation for total polarization**) that certain molecules have permanent dipole moments. These moments are associated with transfer of charge within the molecule, and provide valuable information as to the molecular structure.

Dispersion.—The difference between the index of refraction of any substance for any two wave lengths is a measure of the dispersion for these wave lengths, called the coefficient of dispersion.

Dispersion forces.—The force of attraction between molecules possessing no permanent **dipole**. The interaction energy is given by

$$U_D = -\frac{3}{4} h\, \frac{V_0 \alpha^2}{r^6}$$

where h is Planck's constant, V_0 a characteristic frequency of the molecule, r the distance between the molecules, and α the polarizability.

Dispersive power.—If n_1 and n_2 are the indices of refraction for wave lengths λ_1 and λ_2 and n the mean index or that for sodium light, the dispersive power for the specified wave length is,

$$\omega = \frac{n_2 - n_1}{n - 1}$$

Displacement is a reaction in which an elementary substance displaces and sets free a constituent element from a compound.

Displacement or elongation at any instant. The distance of a vibrating or oscillating particle from its position of equilibrium.

Distribution law.—A substance distributes itself between two immiscible solvents so that the ratio of its concentrations in the two solvents is approximately a constant (and equal to the ratio of the solubilities of the substance in each solvent). The above statement requires modification if more than one molecular species is formed.

Doppler effect, (Light).—The apparent change in the wave-length of light produced by the motion in the line of sight of either the observer or the source of light.

Doppler effects.—Effects on the apparent frequency of a wave train produced (1) by motion of the source toward or away from the stationary observer, and (2) by motion of the observer toward or from the stationary source; the motion in each case being with reference to the (supposedly stationary) medium.

For sound waves, the observed frequency f_0, in cycles/sec., is given by

$$f_0 = \frac{v + w - v_0}{v + w - v_s} f_s$$

where v is the velocity of sound in the medium, v_0 is the velocity of the observer, v_s is the velocity of the source, w is the velocity of the wind in the direction of sound propagation, and f_s is the frequency of source.

For optical waves

$$f_0 = f_s \sqrt{\frac{c + v_r}{c - v_r}}$$

where v_r is the velocity of the source relative to the observer and c is the speed of light.

Dosimeter.—A gadget worn by those who work about radioactive sources to record the amount of exposure the wearer has had to radioactivity.

Double decomposition consists of a simple exchange of the parts of two substances to form two new substances.

Dulong and Petit, law of.—The specific heats of the several elements are inversely proportional to their atomic weights. The atomic heats of solid elements are constant and approximately equal to 6.3. Certain elements of low atomic weight and high melting point have, however, much lower atomic heats at ordinary temperatures.

Dyne.—The force necessary to give acceleration of one centimeter per second per second to one gram of mass.

Eddy current.—A current induced in a mass of conducting material by a varying magnetic field. Also called *Foucault current.*

Einstein theory for mass-energy equivalence.—The equivalence of a quantity of mass m and a quantity of energy E by the formula $E = mc^2$. The conversion factor c^2 is the square of the velocity of light.

Elasticity.—The property by virtue of which a body resists and recovers from deformation produced by force.

Elastic limit.—The smallest value of the stress producing permanent alteration.

Elastic moduli.

Young's modulus by stretching.—If an elongation s is produced by the weight of the mass m, in a wire of length l, and radius r, the modulus,

$$M = \frac{mgl}{\pi r^2 s}$$

Young's modulus by bending, bar supported at both ends. If a flexure s is produced by the weight of mass m, added midway between the supports separated by a distance l, for a rectangular bar with vertical dimensions of cross-section a and horizontal dimension b, the modulus is,

$$M = \frac{mgl^3}{4sa^3b}$$

For a cylindrical bar of radius r,

$$M = \frac{mgl^3}{12\pi r^4 s}$$

For a bar supported at one end. In the case of a rectangular bar as described above,

$$M = \frac{4mgl^3}{sa^3b}$$

For a round bar supported at one end,

$$M = \frac{4mgl^3}{3\pi r^4 s}$$

Modulus of rigidity.—If a couple C ($= mgx$) produces a twist of θ radians in a bar of length l and radius r, the modulus is

$$M = \frac{2Cl}{\pi r^4 \theta}$$

The substitution in the above formulae for the elastic coefficients of m in grams, g in cm per sec^2, l, a, b, and r in cm, s in cm, and C in dyne-cm will give moduli in dynes per cm^2. The dimensions of elastic moduli are the same as of stress,— $[m\ l^{-1}\ t^{-2}]$.

Coefficient of restitution.—Two bodies moving in the same straight line, with velocities v_1 and v_2 respectively, collide and after impact move with velocities v_3 and v_4. The coefficient of restitution is

$$C = \frac{v_4 - v_3}{v_2 - v_1}$$

Electric field intensity is measured by the force exerted on unit charge. Unit field intensity is the field which exerts the force of one dyne on unit positive charge. Dimensions,— $[\epsilon^{-\frac{1}{2}} m^{\frac{1}{2}} l^{-\frac{1}{2}} t^{-1}]; [\mu^{\frac{1}{2}} m^{\frac{1}{2}} l^{\frac{1}{2}} t^{-2}]$.

The field intensity or force exerted on unit charge at a point distant r from a charge q in a vacuum

$$H = \frac{q}{r^2}$$

If the dielectric in the above cases is not a vacuum the dielectric constant ϵ must be introduced. The formula becomes

$$H = \frac{q}{\epsilon r^2}$$

The value of ϵ is frequently considered unity for air. If the dielectric constant of a vacuum is considered unity the value for air at 0°C and 760 mm pressure is 1.000576.

Electrochemical equivalent of an ion is the mass liberated by the passage of unit quantity of electricity.

DEFINITIONS AND FORMULAS (Continued)

Electrolysis.—If a current i flows for a time t and deposits a metal whose electrochemical equivalent is e, the mass deposited is

$$m = eit$$

The value of e is usually given for mass in grams, i in amperes and t in seconds.

Electrolytic dissociation or ionization theory.—When an acid, base or salt is dissolved in water or any other dissociating solvent, a part or all of the molecules of the dissolved substance are broken up into parts called ions, some of which are charged with positive electricity and are called cations, and an equivalent number of which are charged with negative electricity and are called anions.

Electrolytic solution tension theory (or the Helmholtz double layer theory).—When a metal, or any other substance capable of existing in solution as ions, is placed in water or any other dissociating solvent, a part of the metal or other substances passes into solution in the form of ions, thus leaving the remainder of the metal or substances charged with an equivalent amount of electricity of opposite sign from that carried by the ions. This establishes a difference in potential between the metal and the solvent in which it is immersed.

Electromotive force is defined as that which causes a flow of current. The electromotive force of a cell is measured by the maximum difference of potential between its plates. The electromagnetic unit of potential difference is that against which one erg of work is done in the transfer of electromagnetic unit quantity. The **volt** is that potential difference against which one joule of work is done in the transfer of one coulomb. One volt is equivalent to 10^8 electromagnetic units of potential. The **international** volt is the electrical potential which when steadily applied to a conductor whose resistance is one international ohm will cause a current of one international ampere to flow. The international volt = 1.00033 absolute volts. The electromotive force of a Weston standard cell is 1.0183 int. volts at 20°C. Dimensions,—[e^{-1} $m^{\frac{1}{2}}$ $l^{\frac{3}{2}}$ t^{-1}], [$\mu^{\frac{1}{2}}$ $m^{\frac{1}{2}}$ $l^{\frac{3}{2}}$ t^{-1}].

Electromotive series is a list of the metals arranged in the decreasing order of their tendencies to pass into ionic form by losing electrons.

Electron.—The electron is a small particle having a unit negative electrical charge, a small mass, and a small diameter. Its charge is $(4.80294 \pm .00008) \times 10^{-10}$ absolute electrostatic units, its mass $\frac{1}{1837}$ that of the hydrogen nucleus, and its diameter about 10^{-12} cm. Every atom consists of one nucleus and one or more electrons. Cathode rays and Beta rays are electrons.

Electron-volt (ev).—Energy acquired by any charged particle carrying unit electronic charge when it falls through a potential difference of one volt. 1 electron-volt = $(1.60207 \pm .00007) \times 10^{-12}$ erg. Multiples of this unit are also in common use: the kilo-, million-, and billion electron-volt. 1 kev = 10^3 ev; 1 mev = 10^6 ev; and 1 bev = 10^9 ev. An ev is associated through the Planck constant with a photon of wave length 1.2395 microns.

Elements are substances which cannot be decomposed by the ordinary types of chemical change, or made by chemical union.

Emissive power or emissivity is measured by the energy radiated from unit area of a surface in unit time for unit difference of temperature between the surface in question and surrounding bodies. For the cgs system the emissive power is given in ergs per second per square centimeter with the radiating surface at 1° absolute and the surroundings at absolute zero.—See *Radiation formula*

Enantiotropic.—Crystal forms capable of existing in reversible equilibrium with each other.

Energy.—The capability of doing work. **Potential energy** is energy due to position of one body with respect to another or to the relative parts of the same body. **Kinetic energy** is energy due to motion. Cgs units,—the erg, the energy expended when a force of one dyne acts through a distance of one centimeter; the joule is 1×10^7 ergs. Dimensions,—[m l^2 t^{-2}].

The potential energy of a mass m, raised through a distance h, where g is the acceleration due to gravity is

$$E = mgh.$$

The kinetic energy of mass m, moving with a velocity v, is

$$E = \tfrac{1}{2}mv^2$$

Energy will be given in ergs if m is in grams, g in cm per sec^2, h in cm and v in cm per sec.

Energy of a charge in ergs where Q is the charge and V the potential in electrostatic units.

$$E = \tfrac{1}{2}QV.$$

Energy of the electric field.—If H is the electric field intensity in electrostatic units and K the specific inductive capacity, the energy of the field in ergs per cm^3 is

$$E = \frac{KH^2}{8\pi}$$

Energy of rotation.—If a mass whose moment of inertia about an axis is I, rotates with angular velocity ω about this axis, the kinetic energy of rotation will be,

$$E = \tfrac{1}{2}I\omega^2$$

Energy will be given in ergs if I is in g-cm^2 and ω in radians per sec.

Enthalpy, or heat content, is a thermodynamic quantity. It is equal to the sum of the internal energy of a system plus the product of the pressure-volume work done on the system. Thus

$$H = E + pv$$

where H = enthalpy or heat content
E = internal energy of the system
p = pressure
v = volume.

Entropy.—Entropy is the capacity factor for isothermally unavailable energy. The increase in the entropy of a body during an infinitesimal stage of a reversible process is equal to the infinitesimal amount of heat absorbed divided by the absolute temperature of the body. Thus for a reversible process

$$dS = \frac{Q}{T}$$

Every spontaneous process in nature is characterized by an increase in the total entropy of the bodies concerned in the process.

Equilibrium, chemical.—A state of affairs in which a chemical reaction and its reverse reaction are taking place at equal velocities, so that the concentrations of reacting substances remain constant.

Equilibrium constant.—The product of the concentrations (or activities) of the substances produced at equilibrium in a chemical reaction divided by the product of concentrations of the reacting substances, each concentration raised to that power which is the coefficient of the substance in the chemical equation.

Equivalent conductance of an electrolyte is defined as the conductance of a volume of solution containing one equivalent weight of dissolved substance when placed between two parallel electrodes 1 cm apart, and large enough to contain between them all of the solution. Λ is never determined directly, but is calculated from the specific conductance. If C is the concentration of a solution in gram equivalents per liter, then the concentration per cubic centimeter is $C/1000$, and the volume containing one equivalent of the solute is, therefore, $1000/C$. Since L_s is the conductance of a centimeter cube of the solution, the conductance of $1000/C$ cc, and hence Λ will be

$$\Lambda = \frac{1000 L_s}{C}$$

Equivalent weight or combining weight of an element or ion is its atomic or formula weight divided by its valence. Elements entering into combination always do so in quantities proportional to their equivalent weights.

In oxidation-reduction reactions the equivalent weight of the reacting substances is dependent upon the change in oxidation number of the particular substance.

Ettinghausen's effect (Von Ettinghausen's).—When an electric current flows across the lines of force of a magnetic field an electromotive force is observed which is at right angles to both the primary current and the magnetic field; a temperature gradient is observed which has the opposite direction to the Hall electromotive force.

Eutectic.—A term applied to the mixture of two or more substances which has the lowest melting point.

Expansion of gases.

Charles' law or Gay-Lussac's law.—The volume of a gas at constant pressure increases proportionally to the absolute temperature. If V_1 and V_2 are volumes of the same mass of gas at absolute temperatures, T_1 and T_3,

$$\frac{V_1}{V_2} = \frac{T_1}{T_2}$$

For an original volume V_o at 0°C the volume at t°C (at constant pressure) is

$$V_t = V_o(1 + 0.00367t).$$

General law for gases.

$$pv_t = p_o v_o \left(1 + \frac{t}{273}\right)$$

where p_2, v_o, p_t, v_t represent the pressure and volume at 0° and t°C or

$$\frac{p_t v_1}{T_1} = \frac{p_2 v_2}{T_2}$$

where p_1, v_1, and T_1 represent pressure, volume and absolute temperature in one case and p_2, v_2 and T_2 the same quantities for the same mass of gas in another.
The law may also be expressed:

$$pv = RmT$$

where m is the mass of gas at absolute temperature T. R is the **gas constant** which depends on the units used. **Boltzmann's molecular gas constant** is obtained by expressing m in terms of the number of molecules.
For volume in cm³ pressure in dynes per cm² and temperature in Centigrade degrees on the absolute scale $R = 8.3136 \times 10^7$.

Reduction of a gas volume to 0°C, 760 mm pressure.—If V is the original volume of a gas at temperature t and pressure H, the volume at 0°C and 760 mm pressure will be,

$$V_o = \frac{V}{(1 + \alpha t)} \cdot \frac{H}{760}$$

If d is the original density the density at 0°C and 760 mm pressure will be

$$d_o = d(1 + \alpha t) \frac{760}{H}$$

$$\alpha = 0.00367 \text{ approximately.}$$

Falling bodies.—For bodies falling from rest conditions are as for uniformly accelerated motion except that $v_0 = O$ and g is the acceleration due to gravity. The formulae become,— air resistance neglected,

$$v_t = gt, \quad s = \tfrac{1}{2}gt^2, \quad v_s = \sqrt{2gs}.$$

For bodies projected vertically upward,—if v is the velocity of projection, the time to reach greatest height, neglecting the resistance of the air,

$$t = \frac{v}{g}$$

Greatest height,

$$h = \frac{v^2}{2g}$$

—See *Projectiles*

Faraday's laws.—In the process of electrolytic changes equal quantities of electricity charge or discharge equivalent quantities of ions at each electrode. One gram equivalent weight of matter is chemically altered at each electrode for 96,487 int. coulombs, or one faraday, of electricity passed through the electrolyte.

Faraday effect.—The rotation of the plane of polarization produced when plane-polarized light is passed through a substance in a magnetic field, the light traveling in a direction parallel to the lines of force. For a given substance, the rotation is proportional to the thickness traversed by the light and to the magnetic field strength.

Faraday, new determination of (1960).—By the National Bureau of Standards which uses an electrochemical method that dissolves, rather than deposits, silver from a solution. The new value, 96,516 ± 2 coulombs (physical scale) or 96,489 ± 2 coulombs (chemical scale). NBS used its mass, time, and electrical standards in measuring the faraday, and have found that its value agreed within 22 p.p.m. with the one obtained by an independent physical method using the omegatron.

Fermat's principle.—The path followed by light (or other waves) passing through any collection of media from one specified point to another, is that path for which the time of travel is least.

Fission.—A nuclear reaction from which the atoms produced are each approximately half the mass of the parent nucleus. In other words, the atom is split into two approximately equal masses. There is also the emission of extremely great quantities of energy since the sum of the masses of the two new atoms is less than the mass of the parent heavy atom. The energy released is expressed by Einstein's equation.

Fleming's rule.—A simple rule for relating the directions of the flux, motion, and e.m.f. in an electric machine. The forefinger, second finger and thumb, placed at right-angles to each other, represent respectively the directions of flux, e.m.f., and motion or torque. If the right hand is used the conditions are those obtaining in a generator and if the left hand is used the conditions are those obtaining in a motor.

Fluidity.—The reciprocal of viscosity. The cgs unit is the rhe, the reciprocal of the poise. Dimensions,—$[m^{-1}\,lt]$.

Fluorescence.—The property of emitting radiation as the result of absorption of radiation from some other source. The emitted radiation persists only as long as the exposure is subjected to radiation which may be either electrified particles or waves. The fluorescent radiation generally has a longer wave length than that of the absorbed radiation. If the fluorescent radiation includes waves of the same length as that of the absorbed radiation it is termed resonance radiation.

Foot-candle.—Foot-candle = 1 lumen incident per foot² = 1.076 milliphots = 10.76 lux.

Foot-lambert is the unit of photometric brightness (luminance) equal to $1/\pi$ candle per square foot.

Force.—That which changes the state of rest or motion in matter, measured by the rate of change of momentum. Absolute unit,—the **dyne**, the force which will produce an acceleration of one centimeter per second per second in a gram mass. The gram weight or weight of a gram mass is the cgs gravitational unit. The poundal is that force which will give an acceleration of one foot per second per second to a pound mass. Dimensions,—$[m\,l\,t^{-2}]$.

The force F required to produce an acceleration a in a mass m is given by

$$F = ma.$$

If m is substituted in grams and a in cm per sec², F will be given in dynes.

Force between two charges, Coulomb's law.—If two charges q and q' are at a distance r in a vacuum, the force between them is,

$$F = \frac{qq'}{r^2}$$

The force will be given in dynes if q and q' are in electrostatic units and r in cm.

Force between two magnetic poles.—If two poles of strength m and m' are separated by a distance r in a medium whose permeability is μ (unity for a vacuum), the force between them is,

$$F = \frac{mm'}{\mu r^2}$$

Force will be given in dynes if r is in cm and m and m' are in cgs units of pole strength.

DEFINITIONS AND FORMULAS (Continued)

The strength of a magnetic field at a point distance r from an isolated pole of strength m is

$$H = \frac{m}{\mu r^2}$$

The field will be given in gauss if m and r are in cgs units.

Formula, chemical.—A combination of symbols with their subscripts representing the constituents of a substance and their proportions by weight.

Fraunhofer's lines.—When sunlight is examined through a spectroscope it is found that the spectrum is traversed by an enormous number of dark lines parallel to the length of the slit. These dark lines are known as Fraunhofer's lines. Kirchoff conceived the idea that the sun is surrounded by layers of vapors which act as filters of the white light arising from incandescent solids within and which abstract those rays which correspond in their periods of vibration to those of the components of the vapors. Thus reversed or dark lines are obtained due to the absorption by the vapor envelop, in place of the bright lines found in the emission spectrum.

Frequency in uniform circular motion or in any periodic motion is the number of revolutions or cycles completed in unit time. Cgs units,—cycles per second. Dimension,—$[t^{-1}]$.

Frequency of vibrating strings.—The fundamental frequency of a stretched string is given by

$$n = \frac{1}{2l}\sqrt{\frac{T}{m}}$$

where l is the length, T, the tension and m the mass per unit length.

For a string or wire of circular section of length l, tension T, density d, and radius r, the frequency of the fundamental is

$$n = \frac{1}{2rl}\sqrt{\frac{T}{\pi d}}$$

The frequency in vibrations per second will be given if T is in dynes, r and l in cm and d in g per cm³.

Friction, coefficient of.—The coefficient of friction between two surfaces is the ratio of the force required to move one over the other to the total force pressing the two together. If F is the force required to move one surface over another and W, the force pressing the surfaces together, the coefficient of friction,

$$k = \frac{F}{W}$$

Fundamental units.—See *Mass, Length and Time*

Fusion (atomic).—A nuclear reaction involving the combination of smaller atomic nuclei or particles into larger ones with the release of energy from mass transformation. This is also called a thermo-nuclear reaction by reason of the extremely high temperature required to initiate it.

Gal.—1 gal = cm/sec./sec. Therefore, where the value of gravity is 980 this is the same as 980 gals. The milligal is now quite commonly used since it is approximately one part in a thousand of the normal gravity of the earth.

Gamma (γ) rays (nuclear x-rays).—May be emitted from radioactive substances. They are quanta of electromagnetic wave energy similar to but of much higher energy than ordinary x-rays. The energy of a quantum is equal to $h\nu$ ergs, where h is Planck's constant (6.6254×10^{-27} erg sec) and ν is the frequency of the radiation. Gamma rays are highly penetrating, an appreciable fraction being able to traverse several centimeters of lead.

Gas.—A state of matter in which the molecules are practically unrestricted by cohesive forces. A gas has neither definite shape nor volume.

Gas thermometer.—Where P_o, P_s and P_x represent the total pressure with the bulb at 0°C, at the boiling-point of water and at the unknown temperature respectively, t_s the temperature of steam and t_x the unknown temperature,

$$t_x = t_s \frac{P_x - P_o}{P_s - P_o}$$

(approximately). The total pressure on the gas in the bulb is the algebraic sum of barometric pressure at the time and that measured by the manometer.

Gauss.—The cgs emu of magnetic induction (flux density). It is equal to 1 maxwell per cm². It has such a value that if a conductor 1 cm long moves through a magnetic field at a velocity of 1 cm, in an induction mutually perpendicular, the induced emf is one abvolt.

Gay-Lussac's law.—See *Charles' law*

Gay-Lussac's law of combining volumes.—If gases interact and form a gaseous product, the volumes of the reacting gases and the volumes of the gaseous products are to each other in simple proportions, which can be expressed by small whole numbers.

Geiger counter.—Detector for radioactivity depending upon ionized particles that affect its mechanism. As its name indicates, it both detects and makes a count of them possible.

Geopotential. — The geopotential, Φ, of a point at a height z above mean sea level is the work which must be accomplished against gravity in elevating a unit mass from sea level to the height z.

$$\Phi = \int_o^z g \, dz$$

where g is the local acceleration of gravity at height z. For most metrological work geopotential is given in the units geopotential meter (gpm). By definition, 1 gpm = 9.8 ×

10^4 cm² sec⁻². For most purposes the geopotential can be assumed to equal the geometric height.

Gibbs' phase rule.—$F = C + 2 - P$, F, the number of degrees of freedom of a system, is the number of variable factors (temperature, pressure and concentration) of the components, which must be arbitrarily fixed in order that the condition of the system may be perfectly defined. C, the number of the components of the system, is chosen equal to the smallest number of independently variable constituents by means of which the composition of each phase participating in the state of equilibrium can be expressed in the form of a chemical equation; the components must be chosen from among the constituents which are present when the system is in a state of true equilibrium and which take part in that equilibrium; as components are chosen the smallest number of such constituents necessary to express the composition of each phase participating in the equilibrium, zero and negative quantities of components being permissible; in any system the number of components is definite, but may alter with changes in conditions of experiment; a qualitative but not quantitative freedom of selection of components is allowed, the choice being influenced by suitability and simplicity of application. P, the number of phases of the system, are the homogeneous, mechanically separable and physically distinct portions of a heterogeneous system; the number of phases capable of existence varies greatly in different systems; there can never be more than one gas or vapor phase since all gases are miscible in all proportions, a heterogeneous mixture of solid substances forms as many phases as there are substances present.

Gilbert.—The cgs emu of magnetomotive force. 1 gilbert = $10/4\pi$ ampere-turns.

Graham's law.—The relative rates of diffusion of gases under the same conditions are inversely proportional to the square roots of the densities of those gases.

Gram atom or gram atomic weight.—The mass in grams numerically equal to the atomic weight.

Gram equivalent of a substance is the weight of a substance displacing or otherwise reacting with 1.008 grams of hydrogen or combining with one-half of a gram atomic weight (8.00 grams) of oxygen.

Gram mole, gram formula weight, gram equivalent.—Mass in grams numerically equal to the molecular weight, formula weight or chemical equivalent, respectively.

Gram molecular weight or gram molecule.—A mass in grams of a substance numerically equal to its molecular weight. Gram mole.

Gravitation.—The universal attraction existing between all material bodies. The force of attraction between two masses m and m', separated by a distance r, k being the constant of gravitation,

$$F = k \frac{mm'}{r^2}$$

(If m and m' are given in grams, and r in centimeters, F will be in dynes if $k = 6.670 \times 10^{-8}$.)

Half-life.—Used to measure the rate of radioactive decay of disintegration. The time lapse during which a radioactive mass loses one half of its radioactivity.

Hall effect.—When a steady current is flowing in a steady magnetic field, electromotive forces are developed which are at right angles both to the magnetic force and to the current and are proportional to the product of the intensity of the current, the magnetic force and the sine of the angle between the directions of these quantities.

Hardness.—Property of substances determined by their ability to abrade or indent one another. An arbitrary scale of hardness is based upon ten selected minerals. For metals the diameter of the indentation made by a hardened steel sphere (Brinnell) or the height of rebound of a small drop hammer (Shore Scleroscope) serve to measure hardness.

Harmonic motion.—See *Simple harmonic motion and Angular harmonic motion*

Heat capacity.—That quantity of heat required to increase the temperature of a system or substance one degree of temperature. It is usually expressed in calories per degree centigrade. Molar heat capacity is the quantity of heat necessary to raise the temperature of one molecular weight of the substance one degree.

Heat effect.—The heat in calories developed in a circuit by an electric current of I amperes flowing through a resistance of R ohms, with a difference of potential E volts for a time t seconds.

$$H = \frac{RI^2t}{4.18} = \frac{Eit}{4.18}$$

Heat equivalent, or latent heat, of fusion.—The quantity of heat necessary to change one gram of solid to a liquid with no temperature change. Dimensions,—$[l^2 t^{-2}]$.

Heat of combustion of a substance is the amount of heat evolved by the combustion of 1 gram molecular weight of the substance.

Heat quantity.—The cgs unit of heat is the **calorie**, the quantity of heat necessary to change the temperature of one gram of water from 3.5°C to 4.5°C (called a small calorie). If the temperature change involved is from 14.5 to 15.5°C, the unit is the normal calorie. The mean calorie is $\frac{1}{100}$ the quantity of heat necessary to raise one gram of water from 0°C to 100°C. The large calorie is equal to 1000 small calories. The British thermal unit is the heat required to raise the temperature of one pound of water at its maximum density, 1°F. It is equal to about 252 calories. Dimensions of energy,—$[m\, l^2\, t^{-2}]$.

Hehner number (value).—A number expressing the percentage (i.e. grams per hundred grams) of water-insoluble fatty acids in an oil or fat.

Heisenberg's theory of atomic structure.—The currently accepted view of the structure of atom, formulated by

DEFINITIONS AND FORMULAS (Continued)

Heisenberg in 1934, according to which the atomic nuclei are built of nucleons, which may be protons or neutrons, while the extranuclear shells consist of electrons only. The nucleons are held together by nuclear forces of attraction, with exchange forces operating between them. The number of protons is equal to the atomic number (Z) of the element; the number of neutrons is equal to the difference between the mass number and the atomic number ($A - Z$). The number of excess neutrons, i.e. the excess of neutrons over protons, is of paramount importance for the radioactive properties or stability of the element.

Henry's law.—The mass of a slightly soluble gas that dissolves in a definite mass of a liquid at a given temperature is very nearly directly proportional to the partial pressure of that gas. This holds for gases which do not unite chemically with the solvent.

Hess' law of constant heat summation.—The amount of heat generated by a chemical reaction is the same whether reaction takes place in one step or in several steps, or all chemical reactions which start with the same original substances and end with the same final substances liberate the same amounts of heat, irrespective of the process by which the final state is reached.

Hooke's law.—Within the elastic limit of any body the ratio of the stress to the strain produced is constant.

Humidity, absolute.—Mass of water vapor present in unit volume of the atmosphere, usually measured as grams per cubic meter. It may also be expressed in terms of the actual pressure of the water vapor present.

Huygens' theory of light.—This theory states that light is a disturbance traveling through some medium, such as the ether. Thus light is due to wave motion in ether. Every vibrating point on the wave-front is regarded as the center of a new disturbance. These secondary disturbances traveling with equal velocity, are enveloped by a surface identical in its properties with the surface from which the secondary disturbances start and this surface forms the new wave-front.

Hydrogen equivalent of a substance is the number of replaceable hydrogen atoms in 1 molecule or the number of atoms of hydrogen with which 1 molecule could react.

Hydrogen ion concentration.—The concentration of hydrogen ions in solution when the concentration is expressed as gram-ionic weights per liter. A convenient form of expressing hydrogen ion concentration is in terms of the negative logarithm of this concentration. The negative logarithm of the hydrogen ion concentration is called pH. The significance of pH is still in dispute (ref. J. Am. Chem. Soc. 60, 1094 (1938)). Water at 25°C has a concentration of H ion of 10^{-7} and of OH ion of 10^{-7} moles per liter. Thus the pH of water is 7 at 24°C. A greater accuracy is obtained if one substitutes the thermodynamic activity of the ion for its concentration.

Hydrolysis is a double decomposition reaction involving the splitting of water into its ions and the formation of a weak acid or base or both.

Hydrostatic pressure at a distance h from the surface of a liquid of density d,

$$P = hdg.$$

The total force on an area A due to hydrostatic pressure,

$$F = PA = Ahdg.$$

Hyperon.—Any article with mass intermediate between that of the neutron and the deuteron.—See *Meson*

Hysteresis.—The magnetization of a sample of iron or steel due to a magnetic field which is made to vary through a cycle of values, lags behind the field. This phenomenon is called hysteresis.

Steinmetz' equation for hysteresis gives the loss of energy in ergs per cycle per cm³,

$$W = \eta B^{1.6}$$

where B is the maximum induction in maxwells per cm² and η the coefficient of hysteresis.

Illumination on any surface is measured by the luminous flux incident on unit area. The units in use are: the **lux**, (abbreviation lx) one lumen per square meter; the **phot**, (abbreviation ph) one lumen per square centimeter; the **footcandle**, (abbreviation fc) one lumen per square foot.

Indeterminacy principle (Uncertainty principle).—The postulate that it is impossible to determine simultaneously both the exact position and the exact momentum of an electron. So this aspect of electronics can only be expressed as a probability.

Index of refraction for any substance is the ratio of the velocity of light in a vacuum to its velocity in the substance. It is also the ratio of the sine of the angle of incidence to the sine of the angle of refraction. In general, the index of refraction for any substance varies with the wave length of the refracted light.

Indicators are substances which change from one color to another when the hydrogen ion concentration reaches a certain value, different for each indicator.

Induced electromotive force in a circuit is proportional to the rate of change of magnetic flux through the circuit.

$$E = -\frac{d\phi}{dt}$$

where $d\phi$ is the change of magnetic flux in a time dt. The induced current will be given by

$$I = \frac{d\phi}{Rdt}$$

where R is the resistance of the circuit.

Inductance.—The change in magnetic field due to the variation of a current in a conducting circuit causes an induced counter electromotive force in the circuit itself. This phenomenon is known as **self-induction.** If an electromotive force is induced in a neighboring circuit the term mutual induction is used. Inductance may thus be distinguished as self- or mutual and is measured by the electromotive force produced in a conductor by unit rate of variation of the current. Units of inductance are the centimeter (absolute electromagnetic) and the henry, which is equal to 10^9 centimeters of inductance. The **henry** is that inductance in which an induced electromotive force of one volt is produced when the inducing current is changed at the rate of one ampere per second. Dimensions,—$[\epsilon^{-1} l^{-1} t^2]$; $[\mu l]$.

Induction.—Any change in the intensity or direction of a magnetic field causes an electromotive force in any conductor in the field. The induced electromotive force generates an induced current if the conductor forms a closed circuit.

Inertia.—The resistance offered by a body to a change of its state of rest or motion, a fundamental property of matter. Dimension,—$[m]$.

Intensity of Illumination (Properly called **Illumination**). Illumination in lux of a screen by a source of illuminating power P at a distance r meters, for normal incidence,

$$I = \frac{P}{r^2}$$

If two sources of illuminating power P_1 and P_2 produce equal illumination on a screen when at distances r_1 and r_2 respectively,

$$\frac{P_1}{r_1^2} = \frac{P_2}{r_2^2} \quad \text{or} \quad \frac{P_1}{P_2} = \frac{r_1^2}{r_2^2}$$

If I_o is the illumination when the screen is normal to the incident light, then I is the illumination when the screen is at an angle θ. Thus,

$$I = I_o \cos \theta$$

Intensity of magnetization is given by the quotient of the magnetic moment of a magnet by its volume. Unit intensity of magnetization is the intensity of a magnet which has unit magnetic moment per cubic centimeter. Dimensions,—$[\epsilon^{-\frac{1}{2}} m^{\frac{1}{2}} l^{-2}]$; $[\mu^{\frac{1}{2}} m^{\frac{1}{2}} l^{-\frac{1}{2}} t^{-1}]$.

Intensity of radiation is the rate of transfer of energy across unit areas by the radiation. In all forms of energy transfer by waves (radiation) the intensity I is given by $I = Uv$

where U is the energy density of the wave in the medium, and v is the velocity of propagation of the wave. The energy density U is always proportional to the square of the wave amplitude.

Intensity of sound depends upon the energy of the wave motion. The intensity is measured by the energy in ergs transmitted per second through one square centimeter of surface. The energy in ergs per cm³ in a sound wave is given by

$$E = 2\pi^2 dn^2 a^2$$

where d is density in g per cm³, n is frequency in vib. per sec and a is amplitude in cm. The energy reaching the ear in unit time will also be proportional to the velocity of propagation.

Iodine number (value).—A number expressing the percentage (i.e. grams per 100 grams) of iodine absorbed by a substance. It is a measure of the proportion of unsaturated linkages present and is usually determined in the analysis of oils and fats.

Ion.—An ion is an atom or group of atoms that is not electrically neutral but instead carries a positive or negative electric charge. Positive ions are formed when neutral atoms or molecules lose valence electrons; negative ions are those which have gained electrons.

Ionization potential.—The work (expressed in electron volts) required to remove a given electron from its atomic orbit and place it at rest at an infinite distance. It is customary to list values in electron volts (ev.) 1 ev. = 23,053 calories per mole.

Isobars.—For chemistry, elements of the same atomic mass but of different atomic numbers. The sum of their nucleons is the same but there are more protons in one than in the other.

Isomerism.—Existence of molecules having the same number and kinds of atoms but in different configurations.

Isothermal.—When a gas passes through a series of pressure and volume variations without change of temperature the changes are called isothermal. A line on a pressure-volume diagram representing these changes is called an isothermal line.

Isotopes.—Two or more nuclides having the same atomic number, hence constituting the same element, but differing in mass number. Isotopes of a given element have the same number of nuclear protons but differing numbers of neutrons. Naturally occurring chemical elements are usually mixtures of isotopes so that observed (non-integer) atomic weights are average values for the mixture.—See *Atomic number*

Joule-Thomson effect.—The cooling which occurs when a highly compressed gas is allowed to expand in such a way that no external work is done is known as the Joule-Thomson effect. This cooling is inversely proportional to the square of the absolute temperature.

Kepler's laws.

I. The planets move about the sun in ellipses, at one focus of which the sun is situated.

II. The radius vector joining each planet with the sun describes equal areas in equal times.

III. The cubes of the mean distances of the planets from the sun are proportional to the squares of their times of revolution about the sun.

Kerr effect.—When plane polarized light is incident on the pole of an electromagnet, polished so as to act like a mirror, the plane of polarization of the reflected light is not the same when the magnet is "on" as when it is "off." It was found that the direction of rotation was opposite to that of the currents exciting the pole from which the light was reflected.

Kinetic theory, expression for pressure.

$$P = \tfrac{1}{3}Nmv^2$$

where N is the number of molecules in unit volume, m the mass of each molecule and v^2 the mean square of the velocity of the molecules.

Kinetic theory of gases.—Gases are considered to be made up of minute, perfectly elastic particles which are ceaselessly moving about with high velocities, colliding with each other and with the walls of the containing vessel. The pressure exerted by a gas is due to the combined effect of the impacts of the moving molecules upon the walls of the containing vessel, the magnitude of the pressure being dependent upon the kinetic energy of the molecules and their number.

Kirchhoff's laws.

I. The algebraic sum of the currents which meet at any point is zero.

II. In any closed circuit the algebraic sum of the products of the current and the resistance in each conductor in the circuit is equal to the electromotive force in the circuit.

Kirchhoff's laws of radiation.—The relation between the powers of emission and the powers of absorption for rays of the same wave-length is constant for all bodies at the same temperature. First, a substance when excited by some means or other possess a certain power of emission; it tends to emit definite rays, whose wave-lengths depend upon the nature of the substance and upon the temperature. Second, the substance exerts a definite absorptive power, which is a maximum for the rays it tends to emit. Third, at a given temperature the ratio between the emissive and the absorptive power for a given wave-length is the same for all bodies, and is equal to the emissive power of a perfectly black body.

Kohlrausch's law.—When ionization is complete, the conductivity of an electrolyte is equal to the sum of the conductivities of the ions into which the substance dissociates.

Kundt's law.—On approaching an absorption band from the red side of the spectrum the refractive index is abnormally increased by the presence of the band, while the approach is from the blue side and the index is abnormally decreased.

Lambert is the unit of brightness equal to $1/\pi$ candle per square centimeter.

Lambert's law of absorption.—Each layer of equal thickness absorbs an equal fraction of the light which traverses it.

Lambert's law of illumination.—The illumination of a surface on which the light falls normally from a point source is inversely proportional to the square of the distance of the surface from the source. If the normal to the surface makes an angle with the direction of the rays, the illumination is proportional to the cosine of that angle.

Lanthanide series (Lanthanides).—Rare earth elements of atomic numbers 57 through 71, which have chemical properties similar to lanthanum (#57).

Latent heat of vaporization.—The quantity of heat necessary to change one gram of liquid to vapor without change of temperature, measured as calories per gram. Dimensions,— $[l^2 t^{-2}]$.

Lattice energy.—The energy required to separate the ions of a crystal to an infinite distance from each other.

LeChatelier's principle.—If some stress is brought to bear upon a system in equilibrium, a change occurs, such that the equilibrium is displaced in a direction which tends to undo the effect of the stress.

Length, units of.—Meter.1. (Abbr m) The basic unit of length of the metric system, defined as $1,650,763.73$ wavelengths in vacuo of the unperturbed transition $2p_{10}5d_5$ in krypton^{86}. Effective 1 July 1959 in the U. S. system of measures, 1 yard = 0.9144 meter, exactly, or 1 meter = 1.094 yards = 39.37 inches. The standard inch is exactly 25.4 millimeters.

Lenses.—For a single thin lens whose surfaces have radii of curvature r_1 and r_2 whose principal focus is F, the index of refraction n, and conjugate focal distances f_1 and f_2,

$$\frac{1}{F} = \frac{1}{f_1} + \frac{1}{f_2} = (n-1)\left(\frac{1}{r_1} + \frac{1}{r_2}\right)$$

For a thick lens, of thickness t,

$$F = \frac{nr_1r_2}{(n-1)[n(r_1+r_2) - t(n-1)]}$$

Combinations of lenses.—If f_1 and f_2 are the focal lengths of two thin lenses separated by a distance d the focal length of the system,

$$F = \frac{f_1f_2}{f_1 + f - d}$$

DEFINITIONS AND FORMULAS (Continued)

Lenz's law.—When an electromotive force is induced in a conductor by any change in the relation between the conductor and the magnetic field, the direction of the electromotive force is such as to produce a current whose magnetic field will oppose the change.

Line of force.—A term employed in the description of an electric or magnetic field. A line such that its direction at every point is the same as the direction of the force which would act on a small positive charge (or pole) placed at that point. A line of force is defined as starting from a positive charge (or pole) and ending on a negative charge (or pole).

The line (of force) is also used as a unit of magnetic flux, equivalent to the maxwell.

Lissajous figures.—The path described by a particle which is simultaneously displaced by two simple harmonic motions at right angles, when the periods of the two motions are in the ratio of two small whole numbers, shows a variety of characteristic curves called Lissajous figures.

Liquid.—A state of matter in which the molecules are relatively free to change their positions with respect to each other but restricted by cohesive forces so as to maintain a relatively fixed volume.

Loschmidt's number.—The number of molecules per unit volume of an ideal gas at 0°C and normal atmospheric pressure.

$$n_0 = (2.68719 \pm 0.0001) \times 10^{19} \text{ cm}^{-3}$$

Loudness.—The psychological response of the ear which is related to the physical quantity *intensity*. The loudness of a sound depends on frequency also since the ear responds more strongly to some frequency bands than to others. The loudness is roughly related to the cube root of the intensity, and for many purposes it is convenient to represent loudness as proportional to the logarithm of the intensity.

Lumen.—The lumen is the unit of luminous flux. It is equal to the luminous flux through a unit-solid angle (steradian) from a uniform point source of one candle, or to the flux on a unit surface all points of which are at unit distance from a uniform point source of one candle.

Luminous flux.—The total visible energy emitted by a source per unit time is called the total luminous flux from the source. The unit of flux, the **lumen,** is the flux emitted in unit solid angle (steradian) by a point source of one candle luminous intensity. A uniform point source of one candle intensity thus emits 4π lumens.

Luminous intensity or candle-power is the property of a source of emitting luminous flux and may be measured by the luminous flux emitted per unit solid angle. The accepted unit of luminous intensity is the **international candle.** The **Hefner unit,** which is equivalent to 0.9 international candles,

is the intensity of a lamp of specified design burning amyl acetate, called the Hefner lamp.

The mean horizontal candle-power is the average intensity measured in a horizontal plane passing through the source. The mean spherical candle-power is the average candle-power measured in all directions and is equal to the total luminous flux in lumens divided by 4π.

Magnetic field due to a current.—The intensity of the magnetic field in oersted at the center of a circular conductor of radius r in which a current I in absolute electromagnetic units is flowing,

$$H = \frac{2\pi I}{r}$$

If the circular coil has n turns the magnetic intensity at the center is,

$$H = \frac{2\pi n I}{r}$$

The magnetic field in a long solenoid of n turns per centimeter carrying a current I in absolute electromagnetic units

$$H = 4\pi n I$$

If I is given in amperes the above formulae become,—

$$H = \frac{2\pi I}{10r}, \qquad H = \frac{2\pi n I}{10r}, \qquad H = \frac{4\pi n I}{10}$$

Magnetic field due to a magnet.—At a point on the magnetic axis prolonged, at a distance r cm from the center of the magnet of length $2l$ whose poles are $+m$ and $-m$ and magnetic moment M, the field strength in oersted is,

$$H = \frac{4mlr}{(r^2 - l^2)^2}$$

If r is large compared with l,

$$H = \frac{2M}{r^3}$$

At a point on a line bisecting the magnet at right angles, with corresponding symbols,

$$H = \frac{2ml}{(r^2 + l^2)^{\frac{3}{2}}}$$

For large value of r,

$$H = \frac{M}{r^3}$$

Magnetic field intensity or magnetizing force.—Is measured by the force acting on unit pole. Unit field intensity, the oersted, is that field which exerts a force of one dyne on unit magnetic pole. The field intensity is also specified by the number of lines of force intersecting unit area normal to the field, equal numerically to the field strength in oersted. Magnetizing force is measured by the space rate of variation of magnetic potential and as such its unit may be the **gilbert per centimeter.** The gamma (γ) is equivalent to 0.00001 oersted. Dimensions,—$[\epsilon^{\frac{1}{2}} m^{\frac{1}{2}} l^{\frac{1}{2}} t^{-1}]$; $[\mu^{-\frac{1}{2}} m^{\frac{1}{2}} l^{-\frac{1}{2}} t^{-1}]$.

Magnetic flux through any area perpendicular to a magnetic field is measured as the product of the area by the field strength. The units of magnetic flux, the **maxwell** is the flux through a square centimeter normal to a field of one gauss. The **line** is also a unit of flux. It is equivalent to the maxwell. Dimensions,—$[\epsilon^{-\frac{1}{2}} m^{\frac{1}{2}} l^{\frac{1}{2}}]$; $[\mu^{\frac{1}{2}} m^{\frac{1}{2}} l^{\frac{3}{2}} t^{-1}]$.

Magnetic induction resulting when any substance is subjected to a magnetic field is measured as the magnetic flux per unit area taken perpendicular to the direction of the flux. The unit is the maxwell per square centimeter or its equivalent, the gauss. Dimensions,—$[\epsilon^{-\frac{1}{2}} m^{\frac{1}{2}} l^{-\frac{1}{2}}]$; $[\mu^{\frac{1}{2}} m^{\frac{1}{2}} l^{-\frac{1}{2}} t^{-1}]$.

If a substance of permeability μ is placed in a magnetic field H the magnetic induction in the substance,

$$M = \mu H.$$

If I is the magnetic moment for unit volume, or intensity of magnetization,

$$M = H + 4\pi I.$$

The susceptibility,

$$\kappa = \frac{I}{H} \qquad \mu = 1 + 4\pi\kappa.$$

Magnetic moment of a magnet is measured by the torque experienced when it is at right angles to a uniform field of unit intensity. The value of the magnetic moment is given by the product of the magnetic pole strength by the distance between the poles. Unit magnetic moment is that possessed by a magnet formed by two poles of opposite sign and of unit strength, one centimeter apart. Dimensions,—$[\mu^{\frac{1}{2}} m^{\frac{1}{2}} l^{\frac{3}{2}} t^{-1}]$; $[\epsilon^{-\frac{1}{2}} m^{\frac{1}{2}} l^{\frac{3}{2}}]$.

If the poles are separated by a distance which is great compared with the dimensions of the magnet, the magnetic moment of a magnet of length 1 whose poles have values of $+m$ and $-m$ is,

$$m = ml.$$

Magnetic permeability is a property of materials modifying the action of magnetic poles placed therein and modifying the magnetic induction resulting when the material is subjected to a magnetic field or magnetizing force. The permeability of a substance may be defined as the ratio of the magnetic induction in the substance to the magnetizing field to which it is subjected. The permeability of a vacuum is unity. Dimensions,—$[\epsilon^{-1} l^{-2} t^2]$; $[\mu]$.

Magnetic pole or quantity of magnetism.—Two unit quantities of magnetism concentrated at points unit distance apart in a vacuum repel each other with unit force. If the distance involved is one centimeter and the force one dyne, the quantity of magnetism at each point is one cgs unit of magnetism. Dimensions,—$[\epsilon^{-\frac{1}{2}} m^{\frac{1}{2}} l^{\frac{3}{2}}]$; $[\mu^{\frac{1}{2}} m^{\frac{1}{2}} l^{\frac{1}{2}} t^{-1}]$.

Magnetic potential or magnetomotive force at a point is measured by the work required to bring unit positive pole from an infinite distance (zero potential) to the point. The unit is the *gilbert*, that magnetic potential against which an erg of work is done when unit magnetic pole is transferred. Dimensions,—$[\epsilon^{\frac{1}{2}} m^{\frac{1}{2}} l\, t^{-2}]$; $[\mu^{-\frac{1}{2}} m^{\frac{1}{2}} l\, t^{-1}]$.

Magnifying power of an optical instrument is the ratio of the angle subtended by the image of the object seen through the instrument to the angle subtended by the object when seen by the unaided eye. In the case of the microscope or simple magnifier the object as viewed by the unaided eye is supposed to be a distance of 25 cm (10 in.).

Mass.—Quantity of matter. **Units of mass**—the gram is $\frac{1}{1000}$ the quantity of matter in the International Prototype Kilogram; one of the three fundamental units of the cgs system. The British standard of mass is the pound, of which a standard is preserved by the government. The United States standard mass is the avoirdupois pound defined as 1/2.20462 kilogram.

Mass action, law of.—At a constant temperature the product of the active masses on one side of a chemical equation when divided by the product of the active masses on the other side of the chemical equation is a constant, regardless of the amounts of each substance present at the beginning of the action.

At constant temperature the rate of the reaction is proportional to the concentration of each kind of substance taking part in the reaction.

Mass by weighing on a balance with unequal arms.—If W_1 is the value for one side, W_2 the value for the other, the true mass,

$$W = \sqrt{W_1 W_2}.$$

Mass defect.—Difference between atomic mass and mass number of a nuclide.—See *Packing fraction.*

Mass-energy equivalence.—The equivalence of a quantity of mass and a quantity of energy when the two quantities are related by the equation $E = mc^2$. The conversion factor c^2 is the square of the velocity of light. The relationship was developed from **relativity theory,** but has been experimentally confirmed.

Maxwell.—The cgs emu magnetic flux is the flux through a cm² normal to a field at 1 cm from a unit magnetic pole.

Maxwell's rule.—A law stating that every part of an electric circuit is acted upon by a force tending to move it in such a direction as to enclose the maximum amount of magnetic flux.

Mechanical equivalent of heat is the quantity of energy which, when transformed into heat, is equivalent to unit quantity of heat; 4.18×10^7 ergs = 1 calorie (20°C).

Meson.—Two types of particles of mass intermediate between that of the electron and proton have been discovered in cosmic radiation and in the laboratory. The one particle with mass about $215m_e$ is called μ-meson, the other with about $280m_e$, π-meson. Mesons of both positive and negative charge have been found and there is now reasonably good evidence for neutral mesons. Both types of mesons decay spontaneously. Some evidence exists for a meson of mass about $1000m_e$.

Metallic elements in general are distinguished from the non-metallic elements by their lustre, malleability, conductivity and usual ability to form positive ions. **Non-metallic** elements are not malleable, have low conductivity and never form positive ions.

Mev. = million electron volts.

Minimum deviation.—The deviation or change of direction of light passing through a prism is a minimum when the angle of incidence is equal to the angle of emergence. If D is the angle of minimum deviation and A the angle of the prism, the index of refraction of the prism for the wave length used is,

$$n = \frac{\sin \frac{1}{2}(A + D)}{\sin \frac{1}{2}A}$$

Mixtures consist of two or more substances intermingled with no constant percentage composition, and with each component retaining its essential original properties.

Moderator.—A material used for slowing down neutrons in an atomic pile or reactor. Usually graphite or "heavy water" (deuterium oxide).

Modulus of elasticity.—The stress required to produce unit strain, which may be a change of length (Young's modulus); a twist or shear (modulus of rigidity or modulus of torsion) or a change of volume (bulk modulus), expressed in dynes per square centimeter. Dimensions,—the same as of stress, $[m\,l^{-1}\,t^{-2}]$.

Mol volume.—The volume occupied by a mol or a gram molecular weight of any gas measured at standard conditions is 22.414 liters.

A **molal solution** contains one mole per 1000 grams of solvent.

A **molar solution** contains one mole or gram molecular weight of the solute in one liter of solution.

Mole.—Mass numerically equal to the molecular weight. It is most frequently expressed as the gram molecular weight, i. e. as the weight of one mole expressed in grams.

Molecular volume.—Volume occupied by one mole. Numerically equal to the molecular weight divided by the density.

Molecular weight.—The sum of the atomic weights of all the atoms in a molecule.

Molecule.—The smallest unit quantity of matter which can exist by itself and retain all the properties of the original substance.

Moment of force or torque.—The effectiveness of a force to produce rotation about an axis, measured by the product of the force and the perpendicular distance from the line of action of the force to the axis. Cgs unit—the dyne-centimeter. Dimensions,—$[m\,l^2\,t^{-2}]$. If a force F acts to produce rotation about a center at a distance d from the line in which the force acts, the force has a torque,

$$L = Fd.$$

Moment of inertia.—A measure of the effectiveness of mass in rotation. In the rotation of a rigid body not only the body's mass, but the distribution of the mass about the axis of rotation determines the change in the angular velocity resulting from the action of a given torque for a given time. Moment of inertia in rotation is analogous to mass (inertia) in simple translation. The cgs unit is g-cm². Dimensions,—$[m\,l^2]$.

If m_1, m_2, m_3, etc. represent the masses of infinitely small particles of a body; r_1, r_2, r_3, etc. their respective distances from an axis of rotation, the moment of inertia about this axis will be

$$I = (m_1 r_1^2 + m_2 r_2^2 + m_3 r_3^2 + \cdots)$$

or

$$I = \Sigma(mr^2)$$

Momentum.—Quantity of motion measured by the product of mass and velocity. Cgs unit—, one gram-centimeter per second. Dimensions,—$[m\,l\,t^{-1}]$.

A mass m moving with velocity v has a momentum,

$$M = mv.$$

If a mass m has its velocity changed from v_1 to v_2 by the action of a force F for a time t,

$$mv_2 - mv_1 = Ft.$$

Monochromatic emissive power is the ratio of the energy of certain defined wave lengths radiated at definite temperatures to the energy of the same wave lengths radiated by a black body at the same temperature and under the same conditions.

Monotropic.—Crystal forms one of which is always metastable with respect to the other.

Mosley's law.—The frequencies of the characteristic X-rays of the elements show a strict linear relationship with the square of the atomic number.

Motion, laws of.—See *Newton's law of motion*

Multiple proportions, law of.—If two elements form more than one compound, the weights of the first element which combine with a fixed weight of the second element are in the ratio of integers to each other.

Negatron.—1. A term used for electron when it is necessary to distinguish between (negative) electrons and positrons. 2. A four element vacuum tube which displays a negative resistance characteristic.

Nernst effect.—When heat flows across the lines of magnetic force, there is observed an electromotive force in the mutually perpendicular direction.

Neutralization is a reaction in which the hydrogen ion of an acid and the hydroxyl ion of a base unite to form water, the other product being a salt.

Neutrino.—An electrically neutral particle of very small (probably zero) rest mass and of spin quantum number $\frac{1}{2}$. When the spin is oriented parallel to the linear momentum the particle is the antineutrino. When the spin is oriented antiparallel to the linear momentum the particle is the neutrino. Postulated by Pauli in explaining the beta decay process. Whenever a beta (positron) particle is created in a radioactive decay so is an antineutrino (neutrino). The two particles and the parent nucleus share between them the available energy and momentum. Neutrinos and antineutrinos can penetrate amounts of matter measured in light years without appreciable attenuation. Detected by Reines and Cowan using antineutrinos from fission reactors and large scintillation detectors.

Neutron.—A neutral elementary particle of mass number 1. It is believed to be a constituent particle of all nuclei of mass number greater than 1. It is unstable with respect to beta-decay, with a half life of about 12 minutes. It produces no detectable primary ionization in its passage through matter, but interacts with matter predominantly by collisions and, to a lesser extent, magnetically. Some properties of the neutron are: rest mass, 1.00894 atomic mass unit; charge, 0; spin quantum number, $\frac{1}{2}$; magnetic moment, -1.9125 nuclear Bohr magnetrons.

Neutron cross section.—See *cross section*

Newton.—The force necessary to give acceleration of one meter per second per second to one kilogram of mass.

Newton's law of cooling.—The rate of cooling of a body under given conditions is proportional to the temperature difference between the body and its surroundings.

Newton's law of motion.

I Every body continues in its state of rest or of uniform motion in a straight line except in so far as it may be compelled to change that state by the action of some outside force.

II. Change of motion is proportional to force applied and takes place in the direction of the line of action of the force. III. To every action there is always an equal and opposite reaction.

Nodal points.—Two points on the axis of a lens such that a ray entering the lens in the direction of one, leaves as if from the other and parallel to the original direction.

A **normal salt** is an ionic compound containing neither replaceable hydrogen nor hydroxyl ions.

A **normal solution** contains one gram molecular weight of the dissolved substance divided by the hydrogen equivalent of the substance (that is, one gram equivalent) per liter of solution.

Nuclear atom.—The atom of each element consists of a small dense nucleus which includes most of the mass of the atom. The nucleus is made up of roughly equal numbers of neutrons and protons. The positive charges of the protons enables the nucleus to surround itself with a set of negatively charged electrons which move around the nucleus in complicated orbits with well defined energies. The outermost electrons which are least tightly bound to the nucleus play the dominant part in determining the physical and chemical properties of the atom. There are as many electrons in orbits as there are protons in the nucleus.

Nuclear fusion.—See *fusion*

Nuclear isomers.—Isotopes of elements having the same mass number and atomic number but differing in radioactive properties such as half-life period.

Nucleon.—Any particle found in the structure of an atom's nucleus. The most plentiful ones are neutrons and protons.

Nucleus.—The dense central core of the atom, in which most of the mass and all of the positive charge is concentrated. The charge on the nucleus, an integral multiple of Z of the electronic charge, is the essential factor which distinguishes one element from another. Z is called the atomic number and gives the number of protons in the nucleus, which includes a roughly equal number of neutrons. The mass number A gives the total number of neutrons plus protons.—See *Isotopes and Nuclear Atom*

Nuclide.—A species of atom distinguished by the constitution of its nucleus. The nuclear constitution is specified by the number of protons, Z; number of neutrons, N; and energy content. (Or, by the atomic number, Z; mass number A ($= N + Z$) and atomic mass.)

Numerical aperture is the sine of half the angular aperture, used as a measure of the optical power of an objective.

Oersted.—The cgs emu of magnetic intensity exists at a point where a force of 1 dyne acts upon a unit magnetic pole at that point, i.e., the intensity 1 cm from a unit magnetic pole.

Ohm's law.—Current in terms of electromotive force E and resistance R.

$$I = \frac{E}{R}.$$

The current is given in amperes when E is in volts and R in ohms.

Organ pipes.—The frequency of vibration of a closed pipe or other air column of length l, where V is the velocity of sound in air, for the fundamental and first three overtones respectively is,

$$n_o = \frac{V}{4l}, \quad n_1 = \frac{3V}{4l}, \quad n_2 = \frac{5V}{4l}, \quad n_3 = \frac{7V}{4l}$$

For an open pipe,

$$n_o = \frac{V}{2l}, \quad n_1 = \frac{2V}{2l}, \quad n_2 = \frac{3V}{2l}, \quad n_3 = \frac{4V}{2l}$$

Oxidation is any process which increases the proportion of oxygen or acid-forming element or radical in a compound.

Packing fraction.—Packing fraction is the difference between the actual mass of the isotope and the nearest whole number divided by the mass number. Thus the packing fraction is equal to $(M - A)/A$ where M is the actual mass and A is the mass number. For example, one of the chlorine isotopes has a mass of 32.9860. The packing fraction for this isotope is

$$\frac{32.9860 - 33.0000}{33.0000} = -0.00042$$

Packing fractions are usually expressed as parts per 10,000 and so the packing fraction for this isotope of chlorine is written as -4.2. Since oxygen is taken as the standard, elements with positive packing fractions are less stable than oxygen, those with negative packing fractions are more stable.

It is positive for nuclides with mass number less than 16 or greater than 180, and negative for most others.

Paramagnetic materials.—Those within which an applied magnetic field is slightly increased by the alignment of electron orbits. The slight diamagnetic effect in materials having magnetic dipole moments is overshadowed by this paramagnetic alignment. As the temperature increases this paramagnetism disappears leaving only diamagnetism. The permeability of paramagnetic materials is slightly greater than that of empty space.

Pascal's law.—Pressure exerted at any point upon a confined liquid is transmitted undiminished in all directions.

Peltier effect.—When a current flows across the junction of two unlike metals it gives rise to an absorption or liberation of heat. If the current flows in the same direction as the current at the hot junction in a thermoelectric circuit of the two metals, heat is absorbed; if it flows in the same direction as the current at the cold junction of the thermoelectric circuit heat is liberated.

Pendulum.—For a simple pendulum of length l, for a small amplitude, the complete period,

$$T = 2\pi \sqrt{\frac{l}{g}} \quad \text{or} \quad g = 4\pi^2 \frac{l}{T^2}$$

T will be given in seconds if l is in cm and g in cm per sec². For a sphere suspended by a wire of negligible mass where d is the distance from the knife edge to the center of the sphere whose radius is r, the length of the equivalent simple pendulum,

$$l = d + \frac{2r^2}{5d}$$

If the period is P for an arc θ, the time of vibration in an infinitely small arc is approximately

$$T = \frac{P}{1 + \frac{1}{4}\sin^2 \frac{\theta}{4}}$$

For a compound pendulum, if a body of mass m be suspended from a point about which its moment of inertia is I with its center of gravity a distance h below the point of suspension, the period

$$T = 2\pi \sqrt{\frac{I}{mgh}}$$

Period in uniform circular motion is the time of one complete revolution. In any oscillatory motion it is the time of a complete oscillation. Dimension,—$[t]$.

Periodic law.—Elements when arranged in the order of their atomic weights or atomic numbers show regular variations in most of their physical and chemical properties.

Permeance, the reciprocal of reluctance. Unit permeance is the permeance of a cylinder one square centimeter cross-section and one centimeter length taken in a vacuum. Dimensions—$[\epsilon^{-1} l^{-1} t^2]; [\mu l]$.

Phase of oscillatory motion.—The fraction of a whole period which has elapsed since the moving particle last passed through its middle position in a positive direction.

Photographic density.—The density D of silver deposit on a photographic plate or film is defined by the relation

$$D = \log O$$

where O is the opacity. If I_o and I are the incident and transmitted intensities respectively the opacity is given by I_o/I. The transparency is the reciprocal of the opacity or I/I_o.

Photon.—A photon (or γ-ray) is a quantum of electromagnetic radiation which has zero rest mass and an energy of h

Planck's constant) times the frequency of the radiation. Photons are generated in collisions between nuclei or electrons and in any other process in which an electrically charged particle changes its momentum. Conversely photons can be absorbed (i.e., annihilated) by any charged particle.

Piezo-electric effect.—The phenomenon exhibited by certain crystals of expansion along one axis and contraction along another when subjected to an electric field. Conversely compression of certain crystals generate an electrostatic voltage across the crystal. Piezoelectricity is only possible in crystal classes which do not possess a center of symmetry.

Pinch effect.—When an electric current, either direct or alternating, passes through a liquid conductor, that conductor tends to contract in cross-section, due to *electromagnetic* forces.

Pitch.—Psychological response of the ear, primarily dependent upon the frequency of vibration of the air. The intensity of the sound also has a certain effect on the pitch. Pitch of a screw is the axial distance between adjacent turns of a single thread on the screw.

Planck's constant (h).—A universal constant of nature which relates the energy of a quantum of radiation to the frequency of the oscillator which emitted it. It has the dimensions of action (energy × time). Expressed by $E = h\nu$ where E is the energy of the quantum and ν is its frequency. Its numerical value is $6.626196\ (.50) \times 10^{-27}$ erg sec.

Plutonium.—A fissile element, artificially produced in the pile by neutron bombardment of U^{238}.

Poise.—A unit of coefficient of viscosity, defined as the tangential force per unit area (dynes/cm²) required to maintain unit difference in velocity (1 cm/sec) between two parallel planes separated by 1 cm of fluid;

1 poise = 1 dyne sec/cm² = 1 gm/cm sec.

Poisson's ratio is the ratio of the transverse contraction per unit dimension of a bar of uniform cross-section to its elongation per unit length, when subjected to a tensile stress.

Polarized light.—Light which exhibits different properties in different directions at right angles to the line of propagation is said to be polarized. Specific rotation is the power of liquids to rotate the plane of polarization. It is stated in terms of specific rotation or the rotation in degrees per decimeter per unit density.

Polymorphism.—The ability to exist in two or more crystalline forms.

Positron.—A particle of the same mass M_e, as an ordinary electron. It has a positive electrical charge of exactly the same amount as that of an ordinary electron (which is sometimes called negatron). Positrons are created either by the radioactive decay of certain unstable nuclei or, together with a negatron, in a collision between an energetic (more than one Mev) photon and an electrically charged particle (or another photon). A positron does not decay spontaneously but on passing through matter it sooner or later collides with an ordinary electron and in this collision the positron-negatron pair is annihilated. The rest energy of the two particles, which is given by Einstein's relation $E = mc^2$ and amounts to 1.0216 mev altogether, is converted into electromagnetic radiation in the form of one or more photons.

Potential (electric) at any point is measured by the work necessary to bring unit positive charge from an infinite distance. Difference of potential between two points is measured by the work necessary to carry unit positive charge from one to the other. If the work involved is one erg we have the electrostatic unit of potential. Dimensions,—$[\epsilon^{-\frac{1}{2}} m^{\frac{1}{2}} l^{\frac{1}{2}} t^{-1}]$, $[\mu^{\frac{1}{2}} m^{\frac{1}{2}} l^{\frac{3}{2}} t^{-2}]$.

The potential at a point due to a charge q at a distance r in a medium whose dielectric constant is ϵ is,

$$V = \frac{q}{\epsilon r}$$

Power.—The time rate at which work is done. Units of power,—the watt, one joule (ten million ergs) per second; the kilowatt is equal to 1000 watts; the horse-power, 33,000 foot-pounds per minute, is equal to 746 watts. Dimensions,—$[m\ l^2\ t^{-3}]$.

If an amount of work W is done in time t the power or rate of doing work is

$$P = \frac{W}{t}$$

Power will be obtained in watts if W is expressed in joules (10^7 ergs) and t in sec.

Power in watts for alternating current,

$$P = EI \cos \phi$$

where E and I are the effective values of the electromotive force and current in volts and amperes respectively and ϕ the phase angle between the current and the impressed electromotive force. The ratio,

$$\frac{P}{EI} = \cos \phi$$

is called the power factor.

Power developed by a direct current.—The power in watts developed by an electric current flowing in a conductor, where E is the difference of potential at its terminals in volts, R its resistance in ohms, and I the current in amperes,

$$P = EI = RI^2$$

The work done in joules in a time t sec is,

$$W = EIt = RI^2t.$$

Power ratios in telephone engineering are measured in **decibels.** The gain or loss of power expressed in decibels is ten times the logarithm of the power ratio. By reference to an arbitrarily chosen "power level" the actual power may be expressed in decibels. The numerical values thus used will not be proportional to the actual power level but roughly to the sensation on the ear produced when the electrical power is converted into sound. A difference of 1 decibel in the power supply to a telephone receiver produces approximately the smallest change in volume of sound which a normal ear can detect.

Pressure.—Force applied to, or distributed, over a surface; measured as force per unit area. Cgs unit,—the barye, one dyne per square centimeter. The megabarye is equal to 10^6 dynes per square centimeter. Pressure is also measured by the height of the column of mercury or water which it supports. Dimensions,—$[m\ l^{-1}\ t^{-2}]$.

The pressure due to a force F distributed over an area A,

$$P = \frac{F}{A}$$

Absolute pressure.—Pressure measured with respect to zero pressure. *Gauge pressure*—pressure measured with respect to that of the atmosphere.

Principal focus of a lens or spherical mirror is the point of convergence of light coming from a source at an infinite distance.

Projectiles.—For bodies projected with velocity v at an angle a above the horizontal, the time to highest point of flight.

$$t = \frac{v \sin a}{g}$$

Total time of flight to reach the original horizontal plane,

$$T = \frac{2v \sin a}{g}$$

Maximum height,

$$h = \frac{v^2 \sin^2 a}{2g}$$

Horizontal range,

$$R = \frac{v^2 \sin 2a}{g}$$

In the above equations the resistance of the air is neglected. g is the acceleration due to gravity.

Proton.—An elementary particle having a positive charge equivalent to the negative charge of the electron but possessing a mass approximately 1837 times as great. The proton is in effect the positive nucleus of the hydrogen atom.

Purkinje effect.—A phenomenon associated with the human eye, making it more sensitive to blue light when the illumination is poor (less than about 0.1 lumen per sq. ft.) and to yellow light when the illumination is good.

Quality or timbre of a sound depends on the coexistence with the fundamental of other vibrations of various frequencies and amplitudes.

Quantity of electricity or charge.—The electrostatic unit of charge, the quantity which when concentrated at a point and placed at unit distance from an equal and similarly concentrated quantity, is repelled with unit force. If the distance is one centimeter and force of repulsion one dyne and the surrounding medium a vacuum, we have the electrostatic unity of quantity. The electrostatic unit of quantity may be defined as that transferred by electrostatic unit current in unit time. The quantity transferred by one ampere in one second is the coulomb, the practical unit. The faraday is the electrical charge carried by one gram equivalent. The coulomb = 3×10^9 electrostatic units. Dimensions,—

$$[e^{\frac{1}{2}}\ m^{\frac{1}{2}}\ l^{\frac{3}{2}}\ t^{-1}];\ [\mu^{-\frac{1}{2}}\ m^{\frac{1}{2}}\ l^{\frac{1}{2}}].$$

Quantum.—Unit quantity of energy postulated in the quantum theory. The *photon* is a quantum of the electromagnetic field, and in nuclear field theories, the *meson* is considered to be the quantum of the nuclear field.

Radiation.—The emission and propagation of energy through space or through a material medium in the form of waves.

The term may be extended to include streams of sub-atomic particles as alpha-rays, or beta-rays, and cosmic rays as well as electromagnetic radiation. Often used to designate the energy alone without reference to its character. In the case of light this energy is transmitted in bundles (photons).

Radiation formula, Planck's.—The emissive power of a black body at wave length λ may be written

$$E_\lambda = \frac{c_1 \lambda^{-5}}{e^{c_2/\lambda T} - 1}$$

where c_1 and c_2 are constants with c_1 being 3.7403×10^{10} microwatts microns^4 per cm^2 or 3.7403×10^{-12} watt cm^2, c_2 being 14384 micron degrees and T the absolute temperature.

Radioactive nuclides.—Atoms that disintegrate by emission of corpuscular or electromagnetic radiations. The rays most commonly emitted are alpha or beta or gamma rays. The three classes are:

1. Primary, which have half-life times exceeding 10^8 years. These may be alpha-emitters or beta-emitters.

2. Secondary, which are formed in radioactive transformations starting with U^{238}, U^{235}, or Th^{232}.

3. Induced, having geologically short lifetimes and formed by induced nuclear reactions occurring in nature. All these reactions result in transmutation.

Radius of gyration may be defined as the distance from the axis of rotation at which the total mass of a body might be concentrated without changing its moment of inertia. The product of total mass and the square of the radius of gyration will give (the) moment of inertia.

Rankine scale of temperature.—The absolute Fahrenheit scale.

°F + 459.69 = °R; thus 0°F Rankine = −459.69°F.

Raoult's law.—Molar weights of non-volatile non-electrolytes when dissolved in a definite weight of a given solvent under the same conditions lower the solvent's freezing point, elevate its boiling point and reduce its vapor pressure equally for all such solutes.

Reduction is any process which increases the proportion of hydrogen or base-forming elements or radicals in a compound. Reduction is also the gaining of electrons by an atom, an ion, or an element thereby reducing the positive valence of that which gained the electron.

Reflection coefficient or reflectivity is the ratio of the light reflected from a surface to the total incident light. The coefficient may refer to diffuse or to specular reflection. In general it varies with the angle of incidence and with the wavelength of the light.

Reflection of light by a transparent medium in air (Fresnel's formulae).—If i is the angle of incidence, r the angle of refraction, n_1 the index of refraction for air (nearly equal to unity), n_2 index of refraction for a medium, then the ratio of the reflected light to the incident light is,

$$R = \frac{1}{2}\left(\frac{\sin^2(i-r)}{\sin^2(i+r)} + \frac{\tan^2(i-r)}{\tan^2(i+r)}\right)$$

If $i = 0$ (normal incidence), and $n_1 = 1$ (approximate for air),

$$R = \left(\frac{n_2-1}{n_2+1}\right)^2$$

Refraction.—See *Index of refraction; Snell's law.*

Refraction at a spherical surface.—If u be the distance of a point source, v the distance of the point image or the intersection of the refracted ray with the axis, n_1 and n_2 the indices of refraction of the first and second medium, and r the radius of curvature of the separating surface,

$$\frac{n_2}{v} + \frac{n_1}{u} = \frac{n_2 - n_1}{r}$$

If the first medium is air the equation becomes,

$$\frac{n}{v} + \frac{1}{u} = \frac{n-1}{r}$$

Refractivity is given by $(n-1)$ when n is the index of refraction; the **specific refractivity** is given by $\frac{n-1}{d}$ where d is the density. **Molecular refractivity** is the product of specific refractivity by the molecular weight.

Relative humidity.—The ratio of the quantity of water vapor present in the atmosphere to the quantity which would saturate at the existing temperature. It is also the ratio of the pressure of water vapor present to the pressure of saturated water vapor at the same temperature.

Reluctance is that property of a magnetic circuit which determines the total magnetic flux in the circuit when a given magnetomotive force is applied. Unit, the reluctance of one centimeter length and one square centimeter cross-section of space taken in a vacuum. Dimensions,—$[\epsilon l t^{-2}]$; $[\mu^{-1} l^{-1}]$.

Reluctivity or specific reluctance is the reciprocal of magnetic permeability. The reluctivity of empty space is taken as unity. Dimensions,—$[\epsilon l^2 t^{-2}]$; $[\mu^{-1}]$.

Resistance is a property of conductors depending on their dimensions, material and temperature which determines the current produced by a given difference of potential. The practical unit of resistance, the **ohm** is that resistance through which a difference of potential of one volt will produce a current of one ampere. The **international ohm** is the resistance offered to an unvarying current by a column of mercury at 0°C, 14.4521 grams in mass, of constant cross-sectional area and 106.300 centimeters in length, sometimes called the legal ohm. Dimensions,—$[\epsilon^{-1} l^{-1} t]$; $[\mu l t^{-1}]$.

Resistance of a conductor at 0°C, of length l, cross-section s and specific resistance ρ

$$R_o = \rho \frac{l}{s}$$

The resistivity may be expressed as ohm-cm when R is in ohms, l in cm and s in cm².

Resistance of a conductor at a temperature t whose resistance at 0°C is R_o and whose temperature resistance coefficient is α

$$R_t = R_o(1 + \alpha t)$$

Resistance of conductors in series and parallel.—The total resistance of any number of resistances joined in series is the sum of the separate resistances. The total resistance of conductors in parallel whose separate resistances are r_1, r_2, $r_3 \ldots r_n$ is given by the formula

$$\frac{1}{R} = \frac{1}{r_1} + \frac{1}{r_2} + \frac{1}{r_3} + \ldots + \frac{1}{r_n}$$

Where R is the total resistance. For two terms this becomes,

$$R = \frac{r_1 r_2}{r_1 + r_2}$$

Resistance, specific (Resistivity).—A proportionality factor characteristic of different substances equal to the **resistance** that a centimeter cube of the substance offers to the passage of electricity, the current being perpendicular to two parallel faces. It is defined by the expression:

$$R = \rho \frac{l}{A}$$

where R is the resistance of a uniform conductor, l is its length, A is its cross sectional area, and ρ is its resistivity. Resistivity is usually expressed in ohm-centimeters.

Resolving power of a telescope or microscope is indicated by the minimum separation of two objects for which they appear distinct and separate when viewed through the instrument.

Resonance (chemical).—The moving of electrons from one atom of a molecule or ion to another atom of that molecule or ion. It is simply the oriented movement of the bonds between atoms.

Restitution, coefficient of, for two bodies on impact.—The ratio of the difference in velocity, after impact to the difference before impact.

Reversible reaction.—One which can be caused to proceed in either direction by suitable variation in the conditions of temperature, volume, pressure or of the quantities of reacting substances.

Roentgen.—A radiation unit, that amount of radiation that will produce one electrostatic unit of ions per cubic centimeter volume.

Rotatory power is the power of rotating the plane of polarized light, given in general by θ/l where θ is the total rotation which occurs in a distance l.

The **molecular or atomic rotatory power** is the product of the specific rotatory power by the molecular or atomic weight. Magnetic rotatory power is given by

$$\theta / e \, H \cos \alpha$$

where H the intensity of the magnetic field, and α the angle between the field and the direction of the light.

Rydberg formula.—A formula, similar to that of Balmer, for expressing the wave-numbers (ν) of the lines in a spectral series:

$$\nu = R \left[\frac{1}{(n+a)^2} - \frac{1}{(m+b)^2} \right]$$

where n and m are integers and $m > n$, a and b are constants for a particular series, and R is the *Rydberg constant,* 109737.3 cm^{-1} for hydrogen.

Salt.—Any substance which yields ions, other than hydrogen or hydroxyl ions. A salt is obtained by displacing the hydrogen of an acid by a metal.

Scintillometer.—An instrument which detects radiation by emitting flashes of light.

Seebeck effect.—If a circuit consists of two metals, one junction hotter than the other, a current flows in the circuit. The direction of the flow depends on the metals and the temperature of the junctions.

Sensitiveness of a balance.—Assuming the three knife edges of a balance to lie on a straight line,—if M is the weight of the beam, h the distance of the center of gravity below the knife edge, L the length of the balance arms and m a small mass added to one pan, the deflection θ produced is given by

$$\tan \theta = \frac{mL}{Mh}$$

Shell.—According to *Pauli's exclusion principle* (q.v.), the extranuclear electrons do not circle around the nucleus all in orbits of the same radius, but are arranged in orbits at various distances from the nucleus. The extranuclear orbital electrons are thus assumed to be arranged in a series of concentric spheres, called *shells,* which are designated, in the order of increasing distance from the nucleus, as K, L, M, N, O, P, and Q shells. The number of the electrons which each of these shells can contain is limited. All electrons arranged in the same shell have the same principal quantum number. The electrons in the same shell are grouped into various subshells (q.v.), and all the electrons in the same subshell have the same orbital angular momentum.—See *Subshell.*

Simple harmonic motion.—Periodic oscillatory motion in a straight line in which the restoring force is proportional to the displacement. If a point moves uniformly in a circle, the motion of its projection on the diameter (or any straight line in the same plane) is simple harmonic motion.

If r is the radius of the reference circle, ω the angular velocity of the point in the circle, θ the angular displacement at the time t after the particle passes the mid-point of its path, the linear displacement,

$$x = r \sin \theta = r \sin \omega t.$$

The velocity at the same instant,

$$v = r\omega \cos \theta = \omega \sqrt{r^2 - x^2}$$

The acceleration,

$$a = -\omega^2 x.$$

The force for a mass m,

$$F = m\omega^2 x = -\frac{4\pi^2 m x}{T^2}$$

The period,

$$T = 2\pi \sqrt{\frac{x}{a}}$$

In the above equations the cgs system calls for x and r in cm, v in cm per sec, a in cm per sec², T in sec, m in grams, F in dynes, θ in radians and ω in radians per sec.

Simple machine.—A contrivance for the transfer of energy and for increased convenience in the performance of work.

Mechanical advantage is the ratio of the resistance overcome to the force applied. *Velocity ratio* is the ratio of the distance through which force is applied to the distance through which resistance is overcome.

Efficiency is the ratio of the work done by a machine to the work done upon it.

If a force f applied to a machine through a distance s results in a force F exerted by the machine through a distance s, neglecting friction,

$$fS = Fs.$$

The theoretical mechanical advantage or velocity ratio in the above case is,

$$\frac{S}{s}$$

Actually the force obtained from the machine will have a smaller value than will satisfy the equation above. If F' be the actual force obtained, the practical mechanical advantage will be,

$$\frac{F'}{f}$$

The efficiency of the machine,

$$E = \frac{F's}{fS}.$$

Snell's law of refraction.—If i is the angle of incidence, r the angle of refraction, v the velocity of light in the first medium, v' the velocity in the second medium, the index of refraction n,

$$n = \frac{\sin i}{\sin r} = \frac{v}{v'}.$$

Solid.—A state of matter in which the relative motion of the molecules is restricted and they tend to retain a definite fixed position relative to each other, giving rise to crystal structure. A solid may be said to have a definite shape and volume.

Solid angle.—Measured by the ratio of the surface of the portion of a sphere enclosed by the conical surface forming the angle, to the square of the radius of the sphere. Unit of solid angle,—the steradian, the solid angle which encloses a surface on the sphere equivalent to the square of the radius. Dimensions,—unity.

Solubility of one liquid or solid in another is the mass of a substance contained in a solution which is in equilibrium with an excess of the substance. Under these conditions the solution is said to be saturated. Solubility of a gas is the ratio of concentration of gas in the solution to the concentration of gas above the solution.

Solubility product or precipitation value is the product of the concentrations of the ions of a substance in a saturated solution of the substance. These concentrations are frequently expressed as moles of solute per liter of solution.

Solute.—That constituent of a solution which is considered to be dissolved in the other, the solvent. The solvent is usually present in larger amount than the solute.

A **solution** is **saturated** if it contains at given temperature as much of a solute as it can retain in the presence of an excess of that solute.

A **true solution** is a mixture, liquid, solid or gaseous, in which the components are uniformly distributed throughout the mixture. The proportion of the constituents may be varied within certain limits.

Solvent.—That constituent of a solution which is present in larger amount; or, the constituent which is liquid in the pure state, in the case of solutions of solids or gases in liquids.

Specific gravity.—The ratio of the mass of a body to the mass of an equal volume of water at 4°C or other specified temperature. Dimensions,—unity.

Specific heat of a substance is the ratio of its thermal capacity to that of water at 15°C. Dimensions,—unity.

If a quantity of heat H calories is necessary to raise the temperature of m grams of a substance from t_1 to t_2°C, the specific heat, or more properly, thermal capacity of the substance,

$$s = \frac{H}{m(t_2 - t_1)}.$$

Specific heat by the method of mixtures.—Where a mass m_1 of the substance is heated to a temperature t_1, then placed in a mass of water m_2 at a temperature t_2 contained in a calorimeter with stirrer (of same material) of mass m_3, specific heat of the calorimeter c, t_3 the final temperature

$$m_1s(t_1 - t_3) = (m_2c + m_2)(t_3 - t_2).$$

Black's ice calorimeter.—If a body of mass m and temperature t melts a mass m' of ice, its temperature being reduced to 0°C, the specific heat of the substance is,

$$s = \frac{80.1m'}{mt}.$$

Bunsen's ice calorimeter.—A body of mass m at temperature t causes a motion of the mercury column of l centimeters in a tube whose volume per unit length is v. The specific heat is

$$s = \frac{884lv}{mt}.$$

Specific inductive capacity.—The ratio of the capacitance of a condenser with a given substance as dielectric to the capacitance of the same condenser with air or a vacuum as dielectric is called the specific inductive capacity. The ratio of the dielectric constant of a substance to that of a vacuum.

Specific rotation.—If there are n grams of active substance in v cubic centimeters of solution and the light passes through l decimeters, r being the observed rotation in degrees, the specific rotation (for 1 centimeter),

$$[\alpha] = \frac{rv}{nl}$$

Specific volume is the reciprocal of density. Dimensions,—$[m^{-1} l^3]$.

Spectral series are spectral lines or groups of lines which occur in an orderly sequence.

Speed.—Time rate of motion measured by the distance moved over in unit time. Cgs unit,—one centimeter per second. Dimension,—$[l\,t^{-1}]$.

Spherical aberration.—When large surfaces of spherical mirrors or lenses are used the light divergent from a point source is not exactly focused at a point. The phenomenon is known as spherical aberration. For axial pencils the error is known as axial spherical aberration; for oblique pencils, coma.

Spherical mirrors.—If R is the radius of curvature, F principal focus, and f_1 and f_2 any two conjugate focal distances,

$$\frac{1}{f_1} + \frac{1}{f_2} = \frac{1}{F} = \frac{2}{R}$$

If the linear dimensions of the object and image be O and I respectively and u and v their distances from the mirror,

$$\frac{O}{I} = \frac{u}{v}$$

Spin.—In nuclear physics, used to describe the angular momentum of elementary particles or of nuclei.

Standard conditions for gases.—Measured volumes of gases are quite generally recalculated to 0 degrees C temperature and 760 mm pressure, which have been arbitrarily chosen as standard conditions.

Stark effect.—The splitting of a single spectrum line into multiple lines which occurs when the emitting material is placed in a strong electric field. The observed effect depends on the angle between the direction of the field and the direction of observation. The effect is due to the shifting of the energy states of certain orbits which all have the same energy in zero field.

Statcoulomb.—The unit of electric charge in the metric system. 3×10^9 statcoulombs = 1 coulomb.

Stationary or standing waves are produced in a medium by the simultaneous transmission, in opposite directions of two similar wave motions. Fixed points of minimum amplitude are called **nodes**. A **segment** extends from one node to the next. An **antinode** or **loop** is the point of maximum amplitude between two nodes.

Stefan-Boltzmann law of radiation.—The energy radiated in unit time by a black body is given by, $E = K(T^4 - T_0^4)$, where T is the absolute temperature of the body, T_0 the absolute temperature of the surroundings, and K a constant.

Stoichiometric.—Pertaining to weight relations in chemical reactions.

Stoke.—See under viscosity.

Stokes' law.—1. Gives the rate of fall of a small sphere in a viscous fluid. When a small sphere falls under the action of gravity through a viscous medium it ultimately acquires a constant velocity,

$$V = \frac{2ga^2(d_1 - d_2)}{9\eta}$$

where a is the radius of the sphere, d_1 and d_2 the densities of the sphere and the medium respectively, and η the coefficient of viscosity. V will be in cm per sec if g is in cm per sec², a in cm, d_1 and d_2 in g per cm³ and η in dyne-sec per cm² or poises.

2. The empirical law stating that the wavelength of light emitted by a fluorescent material is longer than that of the radiation used to excite the fluorescence. In modern language the emitted photons carry off less energy than is brought in by the exciting photons; the details accord with the energy conservation principle.

Strain.—The deformation resulting from a stress measured by the ratio of the change to the total value of the dimension in which the change occurred. Dimensions,—unity.

Stress.—The force producing or tending to produce deformation in a body measured by the force applied per unit area. Cgs units,—one dyne per square centimeter. Dimensions,—$[m\,l^{-1}\,t^{-2}]$.

Subshell.—The electrons within the same shell (energy level) of the atom are characterized by the same principal quantum number (n), and are further divided into groups according to the value of their azimuthal quantum numbers (l); the electrons which possess the same azimuthal quantum number for the same principal quantum number are considered to occupy the same subshell (or sublevel). The individual subshells are designated with the letters s, p, d, f, g, and h, as follows:

l value	designation of subshell
0	s
1	p
2	d
3	f
4	g
5	h

An electron assigned to the s-subshell is called an s-electron, one assigned to the p-subshell is referred to as a p-electron, etc. In formulae of electron structure, the value of the principal quantum number (n) is prefixed to the letter indicating the azimuthal quantum number (l) of the electron; thus, e.g., a 4f-electron is an electron which has the principal quantum number 4 (i.e. assigned to the N-shell) and the orbital angular momentum 3 (f-subshell).

Surface density of electricity.—Quantity of electricity per unit area. Dimensions,—$[\epsilon^{\frac{1}{2}} m^{\frac{1}{2}} l^{-\frac{1}{2}} t^{-1}]$; $[\mu^{-\frac{1}{2}} m^{\frac{1}{2}} l^{-\frac{3}{2}}]$.

Surface density of magnetism.—Quantity of magnetism per unit area. Dimensions,—$[\epsilon^{-1} m^{\frac{1}{2}} l^{-\frac{1}{2}}]$, $[\mu^{\frac{1}{2}} m^{\frac{1}{2}} l^{-\frac{1}{2}} t^{-1}]$.

Surface tension.—Two fluids in contact exhibit phenomena, due to molecular attractions which appear to arise from a tension in the surface of separation. It may be expressed as dynes per cm or as ergs per square centimeter. Dimensions, —$[m t^{-2}]$.

The total force along a line of length l on the surface of a liquid whose surface tension is T,

$$F = lT.$$

Capillary tubes.—If a liquid of density d rises a height h in a tube of internal radius r the surface tension is,

$$T = \frac{rhdg}{2}$$

The tension will be in dynes per cm if r and h are in cm, d in g per cm³ and g in cm per sec².

Drops and bubbles.—Pressure in dynes per cm² due to surface tension on a drop of radius r cm for a liquid whose surface tension is T dynes per cm,

$$P = \frac{2T}{r}$$

For a bubble of mean radius r cm,

$$P = \frac{4T}{r}.$$

Susceptibility (magnetic) is measured by the ratio of the intensity of magnetization produced in a substance to the magnetizing force or intensity of field to which it is subjected. The susceptibility of a substance will be unity when unit intensity of magnetization is produced by a field of one gauss. Dimensions,—$[\epsilon^{-1} l^{-2} t^2]$, $[\mu]$.

Tangent galvanometer.—A tangent galvanometer with n turns, of radius r, in the earth's field H, has a deflection θ. The current flowing is,

$$i = \frac{Hr}{2\pi n} \tan \theta$$

If $\frac{2\pi n}{r} = G$ (the galvanometer constant).

$$i = \frac{H}{G} \tan \theta$$

Temperature may be defined as the condition of a body which determines the transfer of heat to or from other bodies. Particularly it is a manifestation of the average translational kinetic energy of the molecules of a substance due to heat agitation. The customary unit of temperature is the **Centigrade** degree, $\frac{1}{100}$ the difference between the temperature of melting ice and that of water boiling under standard atmospheric pressure. **Celsius scale.**—The Celsius temperature scale is a designation of the scale also known as the centigrade scale. The degree **Fahrenheit** is $\frac{1}{180}$, and the degree **Beaumur** $\frac{1}{80}$ the same difference of temperature.

The fundamental temperature scale is the absolute, thermodynamic or **Kelvin scale** in which the temperature measure is based on the average kinetic energy per molecule of a perfect gas. The zero of the Kelvin scale is −273.15°C. The temperature scale adopted by the International Bureau of Weights and Measures is that of the constant volume hydrogen gas thermometer. The magnitude of the degree in both these scales is defined as $\frac{1}{100}$ the difference between the temperature of melting ice and that of boiling water at 760 mm pressure. Frequently the Kelvin scale is defined as degrees C + 273.15 and the Rankine scale as degrees F + 459.67°F.

The fundamental temperature scale is now defined by means of the equation

$$\theta(X) = 273.15°K \frac{X}{X_3}$$

where θ denotes the temperature; X the thermometric property $(P, V, \ldots)$; the subscript 3 refers to the triple point of water, and 273.16°K is the arbitrary fixed point for the temperature associated with the triple point of water.

The ideal gas temperature θ, (numerically equal to the Kelvin temperature), in particular, is defined by either of the two equations:

$$273.15° \lim_{P_3 \to 0} \frac{P}{P_3}, \text{ const. V}$$

$$\theta =$$

$$273.15° \lim_{P \to 0} \frac{V}{V_3}, \text{ const. P}$$

Temperature resistance coefficient.—The ratio of the change of resistance in a wire due to a change of temperature of 1°C to its resistance at 0°C. Dimension,—$[\theta^{-1}]$.

Thermal capacity of a substance is the quantity of heat necessary to produce unit change of temperature in unit mass.

It is ordinarily expressed as calories per gram per degree Centigrade. Numerically equivalent to specific heat.

Thermal capacity or water equivalent.—The total quantity of heat necessary to raise any body or system unit temperature, measured as calories per degree centigrade in the cgs system. Dimension,—$[m]$.

Thermal expansion.—The coefficient of linear expansion or expansivity is the ratio of the change in length per degree C to the length at 0°C. The coefficient of volume expansion (for solids) is approximately three times the linear coefficient. The coefficient of volume expansion for liquids is the ratio of the change in volume per degree to the volume at 0°C. The value of the coefficient varies with temperature. The coefficient of volume expansion for a gas under constant pressure is nearly the same for all gases and temperatures and is equal to 0.00367 for 1°C. Dimension,—$[\theta^{-1}]$.

If l_t is the length at 0°C, α the coefficient of linear expansion, the length at t°C is,

$$l_t = l_o(1 + \alpha t).$$

General formula for thermal expansion.—The rate of thermal expansion varies with the temperature. The general equation giving the magnitude m_t (length or volume) at a temperature t, where m_o is the magnitude at 0°C, is

$$m_t = m_o(1 + \alpha t + \beta t^2 + \gamma t^3 \cdots)$$

where α, β, γ, etc. are empirically determined coefficients.
Volume expansion.—If V represents volume and β the coefficient of expansion,

$$V_t = V_o(1 + \beta t).$$

For solids, $\beta = 3\alpha$ (approximately).

Thermal neutrons.—Neutrons slowed down by a moderator to an energy of a fraction of an electron volt—about 0.025 ev. at 15°.

Thermionic emission.—Electron or ion emission due to the temperature of the emitter. The rate of emission increases rapidly with the increase of temperature. It is also very sensitive to the state of the surface.

Thermodynamics, law of.
I. When mechanical work is transformed into heat or heat into work, the amount of work is always equivalent to the quantity of heat.
II. It is impossible by any continuous self-sustaining process for heat to be transferred from a colder to a hotter body.

Thermoelectric power is measured by the electromotive force produced by a thermocouple for unit difference of temperature between the two junctions. It varies with the average temperature and is usually expressed in microvolts per degree C. It is customary to list the thermoelectric power of the various metals with respect to lead. Dimensions,— $[\epsilon^{-\frac{1}{2}} m^{\frac{1}{2}} l^{\frac{1}{2}} t^{-1} \theta^{-1}]$; $[\mu^{\frac{1}{2}} m^{\frac{1}{2}} l^{\frac{1}{2}} t^{-1} \theta^{-1}]$.

Thomson thermoelectric effect is the designation of the potential gradient along a conductor which accompanies a temperature gradient. The magnitude and direction of the potential varies with the substance.

The coefficient of the Thomson effect or specific heat of electricity is expressed in joules per coulomb per degree Centigrade. Dimensions,—$[\epsilon^{-\frac{1}{2}} m^{\frac{1}{2}} l^{\frac{1}{2}} t^{-1} \theta^{-1}]$, $[\mu^{\frac{1}{2}} m^{\frac{1}{2}} l^{\frac{1}{2}} t^{-2} \theta^{-1}]$.

Time, unit of.—The fundamental invariable unit of time is the ephemeris second, which is defined as 1/31,556,925.9747 of the tropical year for 1900 January 0ᵈ12ʰ ephemeris time. The ephemeris day is 86,400 ephemeris seconds.
The former unit of time was the mean solar second, defined as 1/86,400 of the mean solar day. (See supplementary list).

Torque produced by the action of one magnet on another.—The turning moment experienced by a magnet of pole strength m' and length $2l'$ placed at a distance r from another magnet of length $2l$ and pole strength m, where the center of the first magnet is on the axis (extended) of the second and the axis of the first is perpendicular to the axis of the second,

$$C = 8\frac{mm'll'}{r^3} = \frac{2MM'}{r^3}$$

If the first magnet is deflected through an angle θ, the expression becomes,

$$C = \frac{2MM'}{r^3}\cos\theta$$

Torsional vibration.—See *Angular harmonic motion*
Total reflection.—When light passes from any medium to one in which the velocity is greater, refraction ceases and total reflection begins at a certain critical angle of incidence θ such that

$$\sin\theta = \frac{1}{n}$$

where n is the index of the first medium with respect to the second. If the second medium is air n has the ordinary value for the first medium. For any other second medium,

$$n = \frac{n_1}{n_2}$$

where n_1 and n_2 are the ordinary indices of refraction for the first and second medium respectively.

Tractive force of a magnet.—If a magnet with induction B has a pole face of area A the force, is,

$$F = \frac{B^2A}{8\pi}$$

If B and A are in cgs units, F will be in dynes.

Transmutation.—A nuclear change producing a new element from an old one.

Transuranic elements.—Elements of atomic numbers above 92. All of them are radioactive and are products of artificial nuclear changes. All are members of the actinide group.

Triangle or polygon of forces.—If three or more forces acting on the same point are in equilibrium, the vectors representing them form, when added, a closed figure.

Tritium.—An isotope of hydrogen with a mass of three, structure, two neutrons, and one proton in its nucleus.

Uncertainty principle.—See *Indeterminancy*

Uniform circular motion.—If r is the radius of a circle, v the linear speed in the arc, ω the angular velocity and T the period or time of one revolution,

$$\omega = \frac{v}{r} = \frac{2\pi}{T}$$

The acceleration toward the center is

$$a = \frac{v^2}{r} = \omega^2 r = \frac{4\pi^2 r}{T^2}$$

The centrifugal force for a mass m,

$$F = \frac{mv^2}{r} = m\omega^2 r = \frac{4\pi^2 mr}{T^2}$$

In the above equations ω will be in radians per second and a in cm per sec² if r is in cm, v in cm per sec and T in sec. F will be in dynes if mass is in grams and other units as above.

Application to the solar system.—If M is the mass of the sun, G the constant of gravitation, P the period of the planet and r the distance of the planet from the sun, then the mass of the sun

$$M = \frac{4\pi^2 r^3}{GP^2}, \ (G = 6.670 \times 10^{-8} \text{ for cgs units}).$$

If P is the period and r the distance of a satellite revolving around the planet, the above expression for M gives the mass of the planet. The formula is written on the assumption that the orbit of the planet or satellite is circular, which is only approximately true.

Uniformly accelerated rectilinear motion.—If v_o is the initial velocity, v_t the velocity after time t, the acceleration,

$$a = \frac{v_t - v_o}{t}$$

The velocity after time t,

$$v_t = v_o + at$$

Space passed over in time t,

$$s = v_o t + \tfrac{1}{2}at^2$$

Velocity after passing over space s,

$$v = \sqrt{v_o^2 + 2as}$$

Space passed over in the nth second

$$s = v_o + \tfrac{1}{2}a(2n - 1).$$

In the above and following similar equations the values of the space, velocity, and acceleration must be substituted in the same system. For space in cm, velocity will be in cm per sec and acceleration in cm per sec per sec.

Unit.—Specific magnitude of a quantity, set apart by appropriate definition, which is to serve as a basis of comparison or measurement for other quantities of the same nature.

Valence of an atom of an element is that property which is measured by the number of atoms of hydrogen (or its equivalent) one atom of that element can hold in combination if negative, or can displace in a reaction if it is positive.

Valence electrons of the atom are electrons which are gained, lost or shared in chemical reactions.

Van der Waals' equation of state.—This equation is expressed by:

$$\left(p + \frac{a}{v^2}\right)(v - b) = RT$$

It makes allowance both for the volume occupied by the molecules and for the attractive force between the molecules. b is the effective volume of molecules in one mole of gas. a is a measure of the attractive force between the molecules. For values of R, a, and b see index for table of Van der Waal's constants for gasses.

Van't Hoff's principle.—If the temperature of interacting substances in equilibrium is raised, the equilibrium concentrations of the reaction are changed so that the products of that reaction which absorb heat are increased in quantity, or if the temperature for such an equilibrium is lowered, the products which evolve heat in their formation are increased in amounts.

Vapor.—The words **vapor** and **gas** are often used interchangeably. **Vapor** is more frequently used for a substance which, though present in the gaseous phase, generally exists as a liquid or solid at room temperature. **Gas** is more frequently used for a substance that generally exists in the gaseous phase at room temperature. Thus one would speak of iodine or carbon tetrachloride vapors and of oxygen gas.

Vapor pressure.—The pressure exerted when a solid or liquid is in equilibrium with its own vapor. The vapor pressure is a function of the substance and of the temperature.

Vectors, composition of.—If the angle between two vectors is A, and their magnitude a and b, their resultant, Cgs

$$C = \sqrt{a^2 + b^2 - 2ab \cos A}$$

Velocity.—Time rate of motion in a fixed direction. Dimensions,—$[l\,t^{-1}]$. units,—one centimeter per second. If s is space passed over in time t, the velocity,

$$\bar{v} = \frac{s}{t}$$

Velocity of a compressional wave.—The velocity of a compressional wave in an elastic medium, in terms of elasticity E (bulk modulus) and density d,

$$V = \sqrt{\frac{E}{d}}$$

For the velocity of sound in air, where p is the pressure and d the density,

$$V = \sqrt{\frac{1.4p}{d}}$$

Velocity of efflux of a liquid.—If h is the distance from the opening to the free surface of the liquid, the velocity of efflux is

$$V = \sqrt{2gh}$$

The above is the theoretical discharge velocity disregarding friction and the shape of orifice. For water issuing through a circular opening with sharp edges of area, A, the volume discharged per second is given approximately by,

$$Q = 0.62A\sqrt{2gh}$$

Velocity of sound, variation with temperature.—The velocity in meters per sec at any temperature t in °C is given approximately by

$$V = V_0\sqrt{1 + \frac{t}{273}}$$

$$V = 331.5 + .607t$$

The **variation with humidity** is given by the equation

$$V_d = V_h\sqrt{1 - \frac{e}{p}\left(\frac{\gamma_\omega}{\gamma_a} - \frac{5}{8}\right)}$$

where V_d is the velocity in dry air, V_h that in air at barometric pressure p in which the pressure of water vapor is e. γ_ω and γ_a are the specific heat ratios for water vapor and for air respectively.

Velocity of a transverse wave in a stretched cord. If T is the tension of the cord and m the mass per unit length,

$$V = \sqrt{\frac{T}{m}}$$

Velocity of water waves.—If the depth h is small compared with the wave length, the velocity,

$$V = \sqrt{gh}$$

In deep water for a wave length λ,

$$V = \sqrt{\frac{g\lambda}{2\pi}}$$

If the wavelength is very small, less than about 1.6 cm, the velocity increases as the wave length decreases and is expressed by the following,

$$V = \sqrt{\frac{2\pi T}{\lambda d} + \frac{g\lambda}{2\pi}}$$

where T is the surface tension and d the density of the liquid V will be given in cm per sec if h and λ are in cm, g in cm per sec², T in dynes per cm and d in g per cm³.

Velocity of a wave.—The velocity of propagation in terms of wavelength λ and the period T or frequency n is,

$$V = \frac{\lambda}{T} = n\lambda$$

Viscosity.—All fluids possess a definite resistance to change of form and many solids show a gradual yielding to forces tending to change their form. This property, a sort of internal friction, is called viscosity; it is expressed in dyne-seconds per cm² or poises. Dimensions,—$[m\,l^{-1}\,t^{-1}]$. If the tangential force per unit area, exerted by a layer of fluid upon one adjacent is one dyne for a space rate of variation of the tangential velocity of unity, the viscosity is one poise. The

Kinematic viscosity is the ratio of viscosity to density. The c. g. s. unit of kinematic viscosity is the **stoke**.

Flow of liquids through a tube; where l is the length of the tube, r its radius, p the difference of pressure at the ends, η the coefficient of viscosity, the volume escaping per second,

$$v = \frac{\pi p r^4}{8l\eta} \quad \text{(Poiseuille)}.$$

The volume will be given in cm³ per second if l and r are in cm, p in dynes per cm² and η in poises or dyne-seconds per cm².

Visibility is measured by the ratio of the luminous flux in lumens to the total radiant energy in ergs per second or in watts.

If a force F act through a space s, the work done is

$$W = Fs$$

Work will be given in ergs if F is in dynes and s in cm. Work done in rotation. If a torque L dyne-cm acts through an angle θ radians, the work done in ergs is

$$W = L\theta$$

X-rays.—A type of radiation of higher frequency than visible light but lower than gamma rays. Usually produced by high energy electrons impinging upon a metal target.

X units.—X-ray wavelengths have been measured in two kinds of units. The older measurements are given in X units (XU) which are based on the effective lattice constant of rock salt being 2,814.00 XU. More recently X-ray wavelengths have been directly connected, through measurements with ruled gratings, to the wavelengths in the optical region and through them to the standard meter. It turned out that the XU which was originally intended as 10^{-11} cm was 0.202 per cent larger than this value. It has become customary to give X-ray wavelengths in Angstrom units (Å) when the absolute scale is used (1 Å $= 10^{-8}$ cm). The two are related by

$$1{,}000 \text{ XU} = 1.00202 \pm 0.00003) \text{ Å}$$

and wavelengths given in XU must be multiplied by 1.00202 and then divided by 1,000 in order to convert them into Angstrom units.

Zeeman effect.—The splitting of a spectrum line into several symmetrically disposed components, which occurs when the source of light is placed in a strong magnetic field. The components are polarized, the directions of polarization and the appearance of the effect depending on the direction from which the source is viewed relative to the lines of force.

Volt.—The unit of electromotive force. It is the difference in potential required to make a current of one ampere flow through a resistance of one ohm.

Volume, unit of.—The cubic centimeter, the volume of a cube whose edges are one centimeter in length. Other units of volume are derived in a similar manner. Dimension,—$[l^3]$.

Wave motion.—A progressive disturbance propagated in a medium by the periodic vibration of the particles of the medium. Transverse wave motion is that in which the vibration of the particles is perpendicular to the direction of propagation. Longitudinal wave motion is that in which the vibration of the particles is parallel to the direction of propagation.

Weight.—The force with which a body is attracted toward the earth. Cgs unit,—the dyne. Dimensions,—$[m\,l\,t^{-2}]$. Although the weight of a body varies with its location, the weights of various standards of mass are often used as units of force as,—pound weight, or pound force, gram weight, etc. The weight of mass m, where g is the acceleration due to gravity,

$$W = mg.$$

The weight will be given in dynes when m is in grams and g in cm per sec².

Wheatstone's bridge.—If the resistances r_1, r_2, r_3, and r_4 form the arms of a Wheatstone's bridge in order as the circuit (omitting cell and galvanometer connections) is traced, when the bridge is balanced,

$$\frac{r_1}{r_2} = \frac{r_4}{r_3} \quad \text{or} \quad \frac{r_1}{r_4} = \frac{r_2}{r_3}$$

Wien's displacement law.—When the temperature of a radiating black body increases, the wave length corresponding to maximum energy decreases in such a way that the product of the absolute temperature and wave length is constant.

$$\lambda_{max}T = w$$

w is known as **Wien's displacement constant.**

Work.—When a force acts against resistance to produce motion in a body the force is said to do work. Work is measured by the product of the force acting and the distance moved through against the resistance. Cgs units of work,—the erg, a force of one dyne acting through a distance of one centimeter. The joule is 1×10^7 ergs. Dimensions,—$[m\,l^2\,t^{-2}]$. The foot-pound is the work required to raise a mass of one pound a vertical distance of one foot where $g = 32.174$ ft./sec². The foot-poundal is the work done by a force of one poundal acting through a distance of one foot. The International joule, a unit of electrical energy, is the work expended per second by a current of one International ampere flowing through one International ohm. The kilowatt-hour is the total amount of energy developed in one hour by a power of one kilowatt.

Supplementary Tables

Units for a System of Measures for International Relations

Length	meter	m
Mass	kilogram	kg
Time	second	s
Electric current	ampere	A
Temperature	Kelvin	K
Luminous intensity	candela	cd

Prefix Names of Multiples and Submultiples of Units

Factor by which unit is multiplied	Prefix	Symbol	Factor by which unit is multiplied	Prefix	Symbol
10^{12}	tera	T	10^{-2}	centi	c
10^{9}	giga	G	10^{-3}	milli	m
10^{6}	mega	M	10^{-6}	micro	μ
10^{3}	kilo	k	10^{-9}	nano	n
10^{2}	hecto	h	10^{-12}	pico	p
10	deka	da	10^{-15}	femto	f
10^{-1}	deci	d	10^{-18}	atto	a

Derived Units

Acceleration	meter per second squared	m/s^2	
Activity (of radioactive source)	1 per second	s^{-1}	
Angular acceleration	radian per second squared	rad/s^2	
Angular velocity	radian per second	rad/s	
Area	square meter	m^2	
Density	kilogram per cubic meter	kg/m^3	
Dynamic viscosity	newton-second per sq meter	$N \cdot s/m^2$	
Electric capacitance	farad	F	$(A \cdot s/V)$
Electric charge	coulomb	C	$(A \cdot s)$
Electric field strength	volt per meter	V/m	
Electric resistance	ohm		(V/A)
Entropy	joule per kelvin	J/K	
Force	newton	N	$(kg \cdot m/s^2)$
Frequency	hertz	Hz	(s^{-1})
Illumination	lux	lx	(lm/m^2)
Inductance	henry	H	$(V \cdot s/A)$
Kinematic viscosity	sq meter per second	m^2/s	
Luminance	candela per sq meter	cd/m^2	
Luminous flux	lumen	lm	$(cd \cdot sr)$
Magnetomotive force	ampere	A	
Magnetic field strength	ampere per meter	A/m	
Magnetic flux	weber	Wb	$(V \cdot s)$
Magnetic flux density	tesla	T	(Wb/m^2)
Power	watt	W	(J/s)
Pressure	newton per square meter (Pascal)	N/m^2	
Radiant intensity	watt per steradian	W/sr	
Specific heat	joule per kilogram kelvin	J/kg K	
Thermal conductivity	watt per meter kelvin	W/m K	
Velocity	meter per second	m/s	
Volume	cubic meter	m^3	
Voltage, Potential difference, Electromotive force	volt	V	(W/A)
Wave number	1 per meter	m^{-1}	
Work, energy, quantity of heat	joule	J	$(N \cdot m)$

Supplementary Tables

Definition of Most Important International System (SI) Units

The *ampere* (unit of electric current) is the constant current which, if maintained in two straight parallel conductors of infinite length, of negligible circular sections, and placed 1 meter apart in a vacuum, will produce between these conductors a force equal to 2×10^{-7} newton per meter of length.

Antiferromagnetic Materials: Those in which the magnetic moments of atoms or ions tend to assume an ordered arrangement in zero applied field, such that the vector sum of the moments is zero, below a characteristic temperature called the Néel Point. The permeability of antiferromagnetic materials is comparable to that of paramagnetic materials. Above the Néel Point, these materials become paramagnetic.

Candela. The candela is the luminous intensity, in the direction of the normal, of a black body surface 1/600,000 square meter in area, at the temperature of solidification of platinum under a pressure of 101,325 newtons per square meter.

Compensation Point: The temperature (below the Néel Point) at which, in some ferrimagnetic compounds, the saturation magnetization becomes zero.

The *coulomb* (unit of quantity of electricity) is the quantity of electricity transported in 1 second by a current of 1 ampere.

Diamagnetic Materials: Those within which the magnetic induction is slightly less than the applied magnetic field. Diamagnetism is an atomic scale consequence of the Lenz law of induction. For diamagnetic materials, the permeability is slightly less than that of empty space, and the magnetic susceptibility is negative and small.

The ephemeris *second* (unit of time) is exactly 1/31 556 925.974 7 of the tropical year of 1900, January, 0 days, and 12 hours ephemeris time.

The *farad* (unit of electric capacitance) is the capacitance of a capacitor between the plates of which there appears a difference of potential of 1 volt when it is charged by a quantity of electricity equal to 1 coulomb.

Ferrimagnetic Materials: Those in which the magnetic moments of atoms or ions tend to assume an ordered but nonparallel arrangement in zero applied field, below a characteristic temperature called the Néel Point. In the usual case, within a magnetic domain, a substantial net magnetization results from the antiparallel alignment of neighboring *nonequivalent* sublattices. The macroscopic behavior is similar to that in ferromagnetism. Above the Néel Point, these materials become paramagnetic.

Ferromagnetic Materials: Those in which the magnetic moments of atoms or ions in a magnetic domain tend to be aligned parallel to one another in zero applied field, below a characteristic temperature called the Curie Point. Complete ordering is achieved only at the absolute zero of temperature. Within a magnetic domain, at absolute zero, the magnetization is equal to the sum of the magnetic moments of the atoms or ions per unit volume. Bulk matter, consisting of many small magnetic domains, has a net magnetization which depends upon the magnetic history of the specimen (hysteresis effect). The permeability depends on the magnetic field, and can reach values of the order of 10^6 times that of free space. Above the Curie Point, these materials become paramagnetic.

The *henry* (unit of electric inductance) is the inductance of a closed circuit in which an electromotive force of 1 volt is produced when the electric current in the circuit varies uniformly at a rate of 1 ampere per second.

International Practical Kelvin Temperature Scale of 1960 and the *International Practical Celsius Temperature Scale* of 1960 are defined by a set of interpolation equations based on the following reference temperatures:

	°K	°C
Oxygen, liquid-gas equilibrium	90.18	−182.97
Water, solid-liquid equilibrium	273.15	0.00
Water, solid-liquid-gas equilibrium	273.16	0.01
Water, liquid-gas equilibrium	373.15	100.00
Zinc, solid-liquid equilibrium	692.655	419.505
Sulphur, liquid-gas equilibrium	717.75	444.6
Silver, solid-liquid equilibrium	1233.95	960.8
Gold, solid-liquid equilibrium	1336.15	1063.0

The *joule* (unit of energy) is the work done when the point of application of 1 newton is displaced a distance of 1 meter in the direction of the force.

Kelvin: The kelvin, the unit of thermodynamic temperature, is the fraction 1/273.16 of the thermodynamic temperature of the triple point of water. The decision was made at the 13th General Conference on Weights and Measures on October 13, 1967 that the name of the unit of thermodynamic temperature would be changed from *degree Kelvin* (symbol: °K) to *kelvin* (symbol: K). The name (*kelvin*) and symbol (K) are to be used for expressing temperature intervals. The former convention which expressed a temperature interval in *degrees Kelvin* or, abbreviated, *deg. K* is dropped. However, the old designations are acceptable temporarily as alternatives to the new ones. One may also express temperature intervals in *degrees Celsius*.

The *kilogram* (unit of mass) is the mass of a particular cylinder of platinum- iridium alloy, called the International Prototype Kilogram, which is preserved in a vault at Sèvres, France, by the International Bureau of Weights and Measures.

Length: The name "micron", for a unit of length equal to 10^{-6} meter, and the symbol "μ" which has been used for it were dropped by action of the 13th General Conference on Weights and Measures on October 13, 1967. The symbol "μ" is to be used solely as an abbreviation for the prefix "micro-", standing for the multiplication by 10^{-6}. Thus the length previously designated as 1 micron, should be designated 1 μm.

The *lumin* (unit of luminous flux) is the luminous flux emitted in a solid angle of 1 steradian by a uniform point source having an intensity of 1 candela.

Magnetic Anisotropy: In ferro- or ferrimagnetic crystals, it is found that the magnetization prefers to lie along certain crystal directions. These are termed *easy directions* of magnetization. Work must be expended to turn the magnetization away from these easy directions. That work as a function of crystal direction defines the *anisotropy energy surface*. Directions associated with a maximum of the anisotropy energy are termed *hard directions* of magnetization. In general, the energy difference between easy and hard directions decreases as the temperature is increased, and vanishes at the Curie or Néel point.

Magnetic Domains: The magnetization of a ferromagnetic or a ferrimagnetic material tends to break up into regions called *domains* separated by thin transition regions called *domain walls*. Within the volume of a domain, the magnetization has its saturation value, and is directed along a single direction. The magnetizations of other domains are directed along different directions in such a way that the net magnetization of the whole sample may be zero. The application of an external magnetic field first causes some domains to grow by the motion of their walls. At higher fields, the magnetizations of the resulting domains rotate toward parallelism with the field.

Magnetostriction: Change in sample dimensions as the magnitude or the direction of the magnetization in a crystal is changed.

Metamagnetic Materials: Those which are antiferromagnetic in weak fields, but which become ferromagnetically ordered in strong applied fields.

The *meter* (unit of length) is the length of exactly 1 650 763.73 wavelengths of the radiation in vacuum corresponding to the unperturbed transition between the levels $2p_{10}$ and $5d_5$ of the atom of Krypton 86, the orange-red line.

Néel Point: The temperature at which ferrimagnetic and antiferromagnetic materials become paramagnetic.

The **newton** (unit of force) is that force which gives to a mass of 1 kilogram an acceleration of 1 meter per second (m/sec). 1 newton/m^2 = 1 pascal.

The *ohm* (unit of electric resistance) is the electric resistance between two points of a conductor when a constant difference of potential of 1 volt, applied between these two points, produces in this conductor a current of 1 ampere, this conductor not being the source of any electromotive force.

Paramagnetic Materials: Those within which the magnetic induction is slightly greater than the applied magnetic field. Paramagnetism arises from the partial alignment of the permanent magnetic dipole moments of atoms or ions. The permeability is slightly greater than that of empty space, and the magnetic susceptibility is positive and small.

Second: The second is the unit of time of the International System of Units. The definition adopted at the October 13, 1967 meeting of the 13th General Conference on Weights and Measures is: "The second is the duration of 9,192,631,770 periods of the radiation corresponding to the transition between the two hyperfine levels of the fundamental state of the atom of cesium 133." The frequency (9,192,631,770 Hz) which the definition assigns to the cesium radiation was carefully chosen to make it impossible, by any existing experimental evidence, to distinguish the new second from the "ephemeris second" based on the earth's motion. Therefor no changes need to be made in data stated in terms of the old standard in order to convert them to the new one. The atomic definition has two important advantages over the previous definition: (1) it can be realized (i.e., generated by a suitable clock) with sufficient precision, ± 1 part per hundred billion (10^{11}) or better, to meet the most exacting demands of modern metrology; and (2) it is available to anyone who has access to or who can build an atomic clock controlled by the specified cesium radiation. (A description of such clocks is given in "Atomic Frequency Standards," *NBS Tech. News Bull.* 45, 8–11 (Jan., 1961). For more recent developments and technical details, see R. E. Beehler, R. C. Mockler, and J. M. Richardson, "Cesium Beam Atomic Time and Frequency Standards," *Metrologia* 1, 114–131 (July, 1965)). In addition one can compare other high-precision clocks directly with such a standard in a relatively short time—an hour or so compared against years with the astronomical standard. Laboratory-type atomic clocks are complex and expensive, so that most clocks and frequency generators will continue to be calibrated against a standard such as the NBS Frequency Standard, controlled by a cesium atomic beam, at the Radio Standards Laboratory in Boulder, Colorado. In most cases the comparison will be by way of the standard-frequency and time-interval signals broadcast by NBS radio stations WWV, WWVH, WWVB, and WWVL.

The *volt* (unit of electric potential difference and electromotive force) is the difference of electric potential between two points of a conducting wire carrying a constant current of 1 ampere, when the power dissipated between these points is equal to 1 watt.

The *watt* (unit of power) is the power which gives rise to the production of energy at the rate of 1 joule per second.

The *weber* (unit of magnetic flux) is the magnetic flux which, linking a circuit of one turn, produces in it an electromotive force of 1 volt as it is reduced to zero at a uniform rate in 1 second.

Definitions of the most important SI Units are given in the above Supplementary Tables. These definitions have been extracted from the records of the International Committee and the General Conferences.

Conductance, σ. — The conductance of a conductor of electricity is the reciprocal of its electrical resistance (R) and its unit is the reciprocal "absolute" ohm, ohm^{-1}, or mho.

Debye-Falkenhagen effect. — The increase in the conductance of an electrolytic solution produced by alternating currents of sufficiently high frequencies over that observed with low frequencies or with direct current.

Degree of association, $(1 - \alpha)$. — The degree of association of an electrolytic solution is the percentage of ions associated into nonconducting species, such as ion-pairs. (See ionophores).

Degree of dissociation (or ionization) in general, α. — The degree of dissociation (or ionization) of an electrolytic solution is the percentage of solute (or electrolyte) in the dissociated (or ionized) state in solution. Classically this degree is obtained from conductance measurements from the ratio, Λ/Λ_i where Λ_i is the equivalent conductance an electrolytic solution would have at some *finite* concentration if it were completely dissociated into ions at that concentration. (See ionogens). This symbol is also used to denote the fraction of free ions in a solution when simple ions, ion pairs, and clusters higher than ion pairs are present. (See ionophores).

Dissociation-field effect. — The increased dissociation (or ionization) of the molecules of weak electrolytes under the influence of high electrical fields (potential gradients).

Electrolytic cell constant, J_c. — The cell constant of an electrolytic cell is the resistance in ohms of that cell when filled with a liquid of unit resistance.

Electrophoretic effect. — The slowing down, owing to interionic attraction and repulsion, of the movement of an ion with its solvent molecules in the forward direction by ions of opposite charge with their solvent molecules moving in the reverse direction under an applied electrical field (potential gradient).

Equivalent conductance, Λ. — The equivalent conductance of an electrolytic solution is the conductance of the amount of solution that contains one gram-equivalent of a solute (or electrolyte) when measured between parallel electrodes which are one centimeter apart and large enough in area to include the necessary volume of solution. Equivalent conductance is numerically equal to the conductivity multiplied by the volume in cubic centimeters containing one gram-equivalent of the electrolyte. The unit of equivalent conductance is ohm^{-1} cm^2 equiv^{-1} (frequently, in the literature the unit is given simply, although incorrectly, as ohm^{-1}, so that it may be comparable to the unit for conductance, in general).

Interionic attraction. — The electrostatic attraction between ions of unlike charge (sign).

Interionic repulsion. — The electrostatic repulsion between ions of like charge (sign).

Ion atmosphere (or continuous charge distribution). — In the electrostatic effects between ions the term ion atmosphere denotes a continuous charge distribution, or charge density, ρ (r), which is a continuous function of r, the distance from the reference ion, rather than a discrete or discontinuous charge distribution. The ion atmosphere extends from $r = a$ to $r = 0(V^{1/3}) \approx \infty$, where V is the volume of the system, and acts electrostatically somewhat like a sphere of charge $-e$ at a distance, κ^{-1}, from the reference ion of charge $+e$ (see below for definition of κ^{-1}).

Ion size or "ion-size" parameter, a (or a_i). — The ion size is formally considered to be the sum of the ionic radii of the oppositely charged ions in contact. The ion size is also called the "distance of closest approach" of the ions, or the "ion-size" parameter. Generally the ion size is greater than the sum of the crystal radii, and the "ion-size" parameter may include several factors which contribute to its numerical value.

Ionic equivalent conductance, λ. — The ionic equivalent conductance is the equivalent conductance of an individual ion constituent of the solute (or electrolyte) of an electrolytic solution. This symbol is also used to designate the equivalent conductance of complex ions, ion pairs, ion clusters, etc., in combination with simple ions.

Ionic mobility, u. — The mobility of an ion at any finite equivalent concentration is the velocity with which the ion moves under unit potential gradient. Its unit is cm^2 sec^{-1} volt^{-1} equiv^{-1} or cm^2 ohm^{-1} F^{-1} where F is the Faraday expressed in coulombs (or ampere seconds) equiv^{-1}.

Ionogens. — Substances, like acetic acid (HAc), which, although in the pure state are nonelectrolytic neutral molecules, can react with certain solvents to form products which rearrange to ion pairs which then dissociate to give conducting solutions. As an example:

$$\text{HAc} + \text{H}_2\text{O} \rightleftharpoons \text{HAc} \cdot \text{H}_2\text{O} \rightleftharpoons \text{H}_3\text{O}^+ \cdot \text{Ac}^- \rightleftharpoons \text{H}_3\text{O}^+ + \text{Ac}^-$$

Ionophores. — Substances, like sodium chloride, which exist only as ionic lattices in the pure crystalline form, and which when dissolved in an appropriate solvent give conductances which change according to some fractional power of the concentration. Such solutions possess no neutral molecules which can dissociate, but may contain associated ions.

Kohlrausch law of independent migration of ions. — The value of the equivalent conductance, as the concentration approaches zero, is equal to the sum of the limiting ionic equivalent conductances of the ions constituting the solute of the electrolytic solution.

Limiting equivalent conductance, Λ_0. — The limiting equivalent conductance of an electrolytic solution, Λ_0, is expressed by $\Lambda_0 \equiv \lim\limits_{c \to 0} (\sigma_{corr}/c)$ where σ_{corr} is solution conductance corrected for solvent conductance and c is the equivalent concentration. Λ_0 is the value which Λ approaches as the solution is diluted so far that the effects of interionic forces become negligible (and dissociation, in the case of ionogens, is essentially complete).

Limiting ionic equivalent conductance, λ_0.—The limiting ionic equivalent conductance of an individual ion constituent of the solute (or electrolyte) of an electrolytic solution is given by $\lambda_0 \equiv \lim_{c \to 0} (\lambda/c)$. This symbol is also used to designate the limiting equivalent conductances of complex ions, ion pairs, ion clusters, etc., in combination with simple ions.

Limiting ionic mobility, u^0.—The limiting mobility of an individual ion of a solute (or electrolyte) is given by $u^0 \equiv \lim_{c \to 0} u$.

Limiting molar conductance, Λ_0^m.—The limiting molar conductance of an electrolytic solution, Λ_0^m, is expressed by $\Lambda_0^m \equiv \lim_{m \to 0} (\sigma_{corr}/m)$ where σ_{corr} is solution conductance corrected for solvent conductance and m is the molar concentration. Λ_0^m is the value which Λ^m approaches as the solution is diluted so far that the effects of interionic forces become negligible. Seldomly used.

Molar conductance, Λ^m.—The molar conductance of an electrolytic solution is the conductance of a solution containing one gram mole of the solute (or electrolyte) when measured in a like manner to equivalent conductance. Seldomly used.

Osmotic-pressure effect.—An enhancement in the velocity of the central ion, in the direction of the applied external field, as a result of more collisions on the central ion from ions behind the central ion than from ions in front of it.

Relaxation-field effect.—The delay in the ion atmosphere in maintaining its symmetry around a central ion as the central ion moves in the forward direction under an applied electrical field (potential gradient).

Specific conductance, σ_{sp}.—The specific conductance, or conductivity, of a conductor of electricity is the conductance of the material between opposite sides of a cube, one centimeter in each direction. The unit of specific conductance is ohm^{-1} cm^{-1} or mho cm^{-1}

Thickness or average radius of ion atmosphere, κ^{-1}.—The average distance of the ion atmosphere from the reference ion in angstrom units. This average distance decreases in magnitude with the square root of the ionic concentration. Mathematically, κ^{-1} is the distance at which the average charge, dq, in a spherical shell of volume $4\pi r^2 dr$ reaches a maximum using the continuous density, $\rho(r)$, approximation.

Transference (or transport) number, t.—The transference number of each ion of a solute (or electrolyte) in an electrolytic solution is the fraction of the total current carried by that ion, and is given by the ratio of the mobility of the ion to the sum of the mobilities of the ions of the solute constituting the electrolytic solution.

Viscosity effect.—An alteration in the velocity of a given ion as a result of the contribution to the bulk viscosity owing to the ions of opposite charge. This effect applies to ions of large size.

Walden's rule, $\Lambda_0 \eta_0$.—Walden's rule states that the product of the limiting equivalent conductance of an electrolytic solution, Λ_0, and the viscosity of the solvent, η_0, in which the solute (or electrolyte) is dissolved is a constant at a particular temperature. Walden's rule is an approximation which would be valid only for ions which behave hydrodynamically like Stokes spheres in a continuum.

Wien effect.—The increase in the conductance of an electrolytic solution produced by high electrical fields (potential gradients).

PRIMARY FIXED POINTS OF INTERNATIONAL PRACTICAL TEMPERATURE SCALE-68 (IPTS-68)

Primary fixed points of IPTS-68 are given in degrees Celsius and kelvin. Also shown are the comparative values from previous international temperature scales.

Fixed point	ITS-27, °C	ITS-48, °C	IPTS-48, °C	IPTS-68		
				°C	K	Uncertainty (K)
Equilibrium between the liquid and vapor phases of water (boiling point of water)	100.000	100	100	100	373.15	0.005
Equilibrium between the solid and liquid phases of zinc (freezing point of zinc)				419.58	692.73	0.03
Equilibrium between the liquid and vapor phases of sulfur (boiling point of sulfur)	444.60	444.600	444.6			
Equilibrium between the solid and liquid phases of silver (freezing point of silver)	960.5	960.8	960.8	961.93	1,235.08	0.2
Equilibrium between the solid and liquid phases of gold (freezing point of gold)	1,063	1,063.0	1,063	1,064.43	1,337.58	0.2

From Sparks, L. L., *ASRDI Oxygen Technology Survey*, Vol. 4, Scientific and Technical Information Office, National Aeronautics and Space Administration, Washington, D. C., 1974.

TEMPERATURE CONVERSION TABLE

This table permits one to convert from degrees Celsius to degrees Fahrenheit or from degrees Fahrenheit to degrees Celsius. The conversion is accomplished by first locating in a column printed in bold face type the number that is to be converted. If the number to be converted is in degrees Fahrenheit, one may find its equivalent in degrees Celsius by reading to the left. If the number to be converted is in degrees Celsius, one may find its equivalent in degrees Fahrenheit by reading to the right. Degrees Celsius are identical to degrees Centigrade. However, the word Celsius is preferred for international use.

The approved international symbolic abbreviation for degrees Celsius is °C, whereas for degrees Fahrenheit it is °F. Absolute zero on the Celsius scale is –273.15°C; on the Fahrenheit scale it is –459.67°F. The relation between degrees Fahrenheit and degrees Celsius may be expressed by

$$°C = 5/9(°F - 32) \text{ or}$$
$$°F = 9/5(°C) + 32.$$

To °C	←°F or °C→	To °F	To °C	←°F or °C→	To °F	To °C	←°F or °C→	To °F
−273.15	−459.67	—	−245.56	−410	—	−217.78	−360	—
−272.78	−459	—	−245	−409	—	−217.22	−359	—
−272.22	−458	—	−244.44	−408	—	−216.67	−358	—
−271.67	−457	—	−243.89	−407	—	−216.11	−357	—
−271.11	−456	—	−243.33	−406	—	−215.56	−356	—
−270.56	−455	—	−242.78	−405	—	−215	−355	—
−270	−454	—	−242.22	−404	—	−214.44	−354	—
−269.44	−453	—	−241.67	−403	—	−213.89	−353	—
−268.89	−452	—	−241.11	−402	—	−213.33	−352	—
−268.33	−451	—	−240.56	−401	—	−212.78	−351	—
−267.78	−450	—	−240	−400	—	−212.22	−350	—
−267.22	−449	—	−239.44	−399	—	−211.67	−349	—
−266.67	−448	—	−238.89	−398	—	−211.11	−348	—
−266.11	−447	—	−238.33	−397	—	−210.56	−347	—
−265.56	−446	—	−237.78	−396	—	−210	−346	—
−265	−445	—	−237.22	−395	—	−209.44	−345	—
−264.44	−444	—	−236.67	−394	—	−208.89	−344	—
−263.89	−443	—	−236.11	−393	—	−208.33	−343	—
−263.33	−442	—	−235.56	−392	—	−207.78	−342	—
−262.78	−441	—	−235	−391	—	−207.22	−341	—
−262.22	−440	—	−234.44	−390	—	−206.67	−340	—
−261.67	−439	—	−233.89	−389	—	−206.11	−339	—
−261.11	−438	—	−233.33	−388	—	−205.56	−338	—
−260.56	−437	—	−232.78	−387	—	−205	−337	—
−260	−436	—	−232.22	−386	—	−204.44	−336	—
−259.44	−435	—	−231.67	−385	—	−203.89	−335	—
−258.89	−434	—	−231.11	−384	—	−203.33	−334	—
−258.33	−433	—	−230.56	−383	—	−202.78	−333	—
−257.78	−432	—	−230	−382	—	−202.22	−332	—
−257.22	−431	—	−229.44	−381	—	−201.67	−331	—
−256.67	−430	—	−228.89	−380	—	−201.11	−330	—
−256.11	−429	—	−228.33	−379	—	−200.56	−329	—
−255.56	−428	—	−227.78	−378	—	−200	−328	—
−255	−427	—	−227.22	−377	—	−199.44	−327	—
−254.44	−426	—	−226.67	−376	—	−198.89	−326	—
−253.89	−425	—	−226.11	−375	—	−198.33	−325	—
−253.33	−424	—	−225.56	−374	—	−197.78	−324	—
−252.78	−423	—	−225	−373	—	−197.22	−323	—
−252.22	−422	—	−224.44	−372	—	−196.67	−322	—
−251.67	−421	—	−223.89	−371	—	−196.11	−321	—
−251.11	−420	—	−223.33	−370	—	−195.56	−320	—
−250.56	−419	—	−222.78	−369	—	−195	−319	—
−250	−418	—	−222.22	−368	—	−194.44	−318	—
−249.44	−417	—	−221.67	−367	—	−193.89	−317	—
−248.89	−416	—	−221.11	−366	—	−193.33	−316	—
−248.33	−415	—	−220.56	−365	—	−192.78	−315	—
−247.78	−414	—	−220	−364	—	−192.22	−314	—
−247.22	−413	—	−219.44	−363	—	−191.67	−313	—
−246.67	−412	—	−218.89	−362	—	−191.11	−312	—
−246.11	−411	—	−218.33	−361	—	−190.56	−311	—

To Convert			To Convert			To Convert		
To °C	←°F or °C→	To °F	To °C	←°F or °C→	To °F	To °C	←°F or °C→	To °F
−190	−310	—	−156.67	−250	−418	−123.33	−190	−310
−189.44	−309	—	−156.11	−249	−416.2	−122.78	−189	−308.2
−188.89	−308	—	−155.56	−248	−414.4	−122.22	−188	−306.4
−188.33	−307	—	−155	−247	−412.6	−121.67	−187	−304.6
−187.78	−306	—	−154.44	−246	−410.8	−121.11	−186	−302.8
−187.22	−305	—	−153.89	−245	−409	−120.56	−185	−301
−186.67	−304	—	−153.33	−244	−407.2	−120	−184	−299.2
−186.11	−303	—	−152.78	−243	−405.4	−119.44	−183	−297.4
−185.56	−302	—	−152.22	−242	−403.6	−118.89	−182	−295.6
−185	−301	—	−151.67	−241	−401.8	−118.33	−181	−293.8
−184.44	−300	—	−151.11	−240	−400	−117.78	−180	−292
−183.89	−299	—	−150.56	−239	−398.2	−117.22	−179	−290.2
−183.33	−298	—	−150	−238	−396.4	−116.67	−178	−288.4
−182.78	−297	—	−149.44	−237	−394.6	−116.11	−177	−286.6
−182.22	−296	—	−148.89	−236	−392.8	−115.56	−176	−284.8
−181.67	−295	—	−148.33	−235	−391	−115	−175	−283
−181.11	−294	—	−147.78	−234	−389.2	−114.44	−174	−281.2
−180.56	−293	—	−147.22	−233	−387.4	−113.89	−173	−279.4
−180	−292	—	−146.67	−232	−385.6	−113.33	−172	−277.6
−179.44	−291	—	−146.11	−231	−383.8	−112.78	−171	−275.8
−178.89	−290	—	−145.56	−230	−382	−112.22	−170	−274
−178.33	−289	—	−145	−229	−380.2	−111.67	−169	−272.2
−177.78	−288	—	−144.44	−228	−378.4	−111.11	−168	−270.4
−177.22	−287	—	−143.89	−227	−376.6	−110.56	−167	−268.6
−176.67	−286	—	−143.33	−226	−374.8	−110	−166	−266.8
−176.11	−285	—	−142.78	−225	−373	−109.44	−165	−265
−175.56	−284	—	−142.22	−224	−371.2	−108.89	−164	−263.2
−175	−283	—	−141.67	−223	−369.4	−108.33	−163	−261.4
−174.44	−282	—	−141.11	−222	−367.6	−107.78	−162	−259.6
−173.89	−281	—	−140.56	−221	−365.8	−107.22	−161	−257.8
−173.33	−280	—	−140	−220	−364	−106.67	−160	−256
−172.78	−279	—	−139.44	−219	−362.2	−106.11	−159	−254.2
−172.22	−278	—	−138.89	−218	−360.4	−105.56	−158	−252.4
−171.67	−277	—	−138.33	−217	−358.6	−105	−157	−250.6
−171.11	−276	—	−137.78	−216	−356.8	−104.44	−156	−248.8
−170.56	−275	—						
−170	−274	—	−137.22	−215	−355	−103.89	−155	−247
—	−273.15	−459.67	−136.67	−214	−353.2	−103.33	−154	−245.2
−169.44	−273	−459.4	−136.11	−213	−351.4	−102.78	−153	−243.4
−168.89	−272	−457.6	−135.56	−212	−349.6	−102.22	−152	−241.6
−168.33	−271	−455.8	−135	−211	−347.8	−101.67	−151	−239.8
−167.78	−270	−454	−134.44	−210	−346	−101.11	−150	−238
−167.22	−269	−452.2	−133.89	−209	−344.2	−100.56	−149	−236.2
−166.67	−268	−450.4	−133.33	−208	−342.4	−100	−148	−234.4
−166.11	−267	−448.6	−132.78	−207	−340.6	−99.44	−147	−232.6
−165.56	−266	−446.8	−132.22	−206	−338.8	−98.89	−146	−230.8
−165	−265	−445	−131.67	−205	−337	−98.33	−145	−229
−164.44	−264	−443.2	−131.11	−204	−335.2	−97.78	−144	−227.2
−163.89	−263	−441.4	−130.56	−203	−333.4	−97.22	−143	−225.4
−163.33	−262	−439.6	−130	−202	−331.6	−96.67	−142	−223.6
−162.78	−261	−437.8	−129.44	−201	−329.8	−96.11	−141	−221.8
−162.22	−260	−436	−128.89	−200	−328	−95.56	−140	−220
−161.67	−259	−434.2	−128.33	−199	−326.2	−95	−139	−218.2
−161.11	−258	−432.4	−127.78	−198	−324.4	−94.44	−138	−216.4
−160.56	−257	−430.6	−127.22	−197	−322.6	−93.89	−137	−214.6
−160	−256	−428.8	−126.67	−196	−320.8	−93.33	−136	−212.8
−159.44	−255	−427	−126.11	−195	−319	−92.78	−135	−211
−158.89	−254	−425.2	−125.56	−194	−317.2	−92.22	−134	−209.2
−158.33	−253	−423.4	−125	−193	−315.4	−91.67	−133	−207.4
−157.78	−252	−421.6	−124.44	−192	−313.6	−91.11	−132	−205.6
−157.22	−251	−419.8	−123.89	−191	−311.8	−90.56	−131	−203.8

To Convert			To Convert			To Convert		
To °C	←°F or °C→	To °F	To °C	←°F or °C→	To °F	To °C	←°F or °C→	To °F
−90	−130	−202	−56.67	−70	−94	−23.33	−10	14
−89.44	−129	−200.2	−56.11	−69	−92.2	−22.78	−9	15.8
−88.89	−128	−198.4	−55.56	−68	−90.4	−22.22	−8	17.6
−88.33	−127	−196.6	−55	−67	−88.6	−21.67	−7	19.4
−87.78	−126	−194.8	−54.44	−66	−86.8	−21.11	−6	21.2
−87.22	−125	−193	−53.89	−65	−85	−20.56	−5	23
−86.67	−124	−191.2	−53.33	−64	−83.2	−20	−4	24.8
−86.11	−123	−189.4	−52.78	−63	−81.4	−19.44	−3	26.6
−85.56	−122	−187.6	−52.22	−62	−79.6	−18.89	−2	28.4
−85	−121	−185.8	−51.67	−61	−77.8	−18.33	−1	30.2
−84.44	−120	−184	−51.11	−60	−76	−17.78	0	32
−83.89	−119	−182.2	−50.56	−59	−74.2	−17.22	1	33.8
−83.33	−118	−180.4	−50	−58	−72.4	−16.67	2	35.6
−82.78	−117	−178.6	−49.44	−57	−70.6	−16.11	3	37.4
−82.22	−116	−176.8	−48.89	−56	−68.8	−15.56	4	39.2
−81.67	−115	−175	−48.33	−55	−67	−15	5	41
−81.11	−114	−173.2	−47.78	−54	−65.2	−14.44	6	42.8
−80.56	−113	−171.4	−47.22	−53	−63.4	−13.89	7	44.6
−80	−112	−169.6	−46.67	−52	−61.6	−13.33	8	46.4
−79.44	−111	−167.8	−46.11	−51	−59.8	−12.78	9	48.2
−78.89	−110	−166	−45.56	−50	−58	−12.22	10	50
−78.33	−109	−164.2	−45	−49	−56.2	−11.67	11	51.8
−77.78	−108	−162.4	−44.44	−48	−54.4	−11.11	12	53.6
−77.22	−107	−160.6	−43.89	−47	−52.6	−10.56	13	55.4
−76.67	−106	−158.8	−43.33	−46	−50.8	−10	14	57.2
−76.11	−105	−157	−42.78	−45	−49	−9.44	15	59
−75.56	−104	−155.2	−42.22	−44	−47.2	−8.89	16	60.8
−75	−103	−153.4	−41.67	−43	−45.4	−8.33	17	62.6
−74.44	−102	−151.6	−41.11	−42	−43.6	−7.78	18	64.4
−73.89	−101	−149.8	−40.56	−41	−41.8	−7.22	19	66.2
−73.33	−100	−148	−40	−40	−40	−6.67	20	68
−72.78	−99	−146.2	−39.44	−39	−38.2	−6.11	21	69.8
−72.22	−98	−144.4	−38.89	−38	−36.4	−5.56	22	71.6
−71.67	−97	−142.6	−38.33	−37	−34.6	−5	23	73.4
−71.11	−96	−140.8	−37.78	−36	−32.8	−4.44	24	75.2
−70.56	−95	−139	−37.22	−35	−31	−3.89	25	77
−70	−94	−137.2	−36.67	−34	−29.2	−3.33	26	78.8
−69.44	−93	−135.4	−36.11	−33	−27.4	−2.78	27	80.6
−68.89	−92	−133.6	−35.56	−32	−25.6	−2.22	28	82.4
−68.33	−91	−131.8	−35	−31	−23.8	−1.67	29	84.2
−67.78	−90	−130	−34.44	−30	−22	−1.11	30	86
−67.22	−89	−128.2	−33.89	−29	−20.2	−0.56	31	87.8
−66.67	−88	−126.4	−33.33	−28	−18.4	0	32	89.6
−66.11	−87	−124.6	−32.78	−27	−16.6	.56	33	91.4
−65.56	−86	−122.8	−32.22	−26	−14.8	1.11	34	93.2
−65	−85	−121	−31.67	−25	−13	1.67	35	95
−64.44	−84	−119.2	−31.11	−24	−11.2	2.22	36	96.8
−63.89	−83	−117.4	−30.56	−23	−9.4	2.78	37	98.6
−63.33	−82	−115.6	−30	−22	−7.6	3.33	38	100.4
−62.78	−81	−113.8	−29.44	−21	−5.8	3.89	39	102.2
−62.22	−80	−112	−28.89	−20	−4	4.44	40	104
−61.67	−79	−110.2	−28.33	−19	−2.2	5	41	105.8
−61.11	−78	−108.4	−27.78	−18	−0.4	5.56	42	107.6
−60.56	−77	−106.6	−27.22	−17	1.4	6.11	43	109.4
−60	−76	−104.8	−26.67	−16	3.2	6.67	44	111.2
−59.44	−75	−103	−26.11	−15	5	7.22	45	113
−58.89	−74	−101.2	−25.56	−14	6.8	7.78	46	114.8
−58.33	−73	−99.4	−25	−13	8.6	8.33	47	116.6
−57.78	−72	−97.6	−24.44	−12	10.4	8.89	48	118.4
−57.22	−71	−95.8	−23.89	−11	12.2	9.44	49	120.2

To Convert			To Convert			To Convert		
To °C	←°F or °C→	To °F	To °C	←°F or °C→	To °F	To °C	←°F or °C→	To °F
10	50	122	43.33	110	230	76.67	170	338
10.56	51	123.8	43.89	111	231.8	77.22	171	339.8
11.11	52	125.6	44.44	112	233.6	77.78	172	341.6
11.67	53	127.4	45	113	235.4	78.33	173	343.4
12.22	54	129.2	45.56	114	237.2	78.89	174	345.2
12.78	55	131	46.11	115	239	79.44	175	347
13.33	56	132.8	46.67	116	240.8	80	176	348.8
13.89	57	134.6	47.22	117	242.6	80.56	177	350.6
14.44	58	136.4	47.78	118	244.4	81.11	178	352.4
15	59	138.2	48.33	119	246.2	81.67	179	354.2
15.56	60	140	48.89	120	248	82.22	180	356
16.11	61	141.8	49.44	121	249.8	82.78	181	357.8
16.67	62	143.6	50	122	251.6	83.33	182	359.6
17.22	63	145.4	50.56	123	253.4	83.89	183	361.4
17.78	64	147.2	51.11	124	255.2	84.44	184	363.2
18.33	65	149	51.67	125	257	85	185	365
18.89	66	150.8	52.22	126	258.8	85.56	186	366.8
19.44	67	152.6	52.78	127	260.6	86.11	187	368.6
20	68	154.4	53.33	128	262.4	86.67	188	370.4
20.56	69	156.2	53.89	129	264.2	87.22	189	372.2
21.11	70	158	54.44	130	266	87.78	190	374
21.67	71	159.8	55	131	267.8	88.33	191	375.8
22.22	72	161.6	55.56	132	269.6	88.89	192	377.6
22.78	73	163.4	56.11	133	271.4	89.44	193	379.4
23.33	74	165.2	56.67	134	273.2	90	194	381.2
23.89	75	167	57.22	135	275	90.56	195	383
24.44	76	168.8	57.78	136	276.8	91.11	196	384.8
25	77	170.6	58.33	137	278.6	91.67	197	386.6
25.56	78	172.4	58.89	138	280.4	92.22	198	388.4
26.11	79	174.2	59.44	139	282.2	92.78	199	390.2
26.67	80	176	60	140	284	93.33	200	392
27.22	81	177.8	60.56	141	285.8	93.89	201	393.8
27.78	82	179.6	61.11	142	287.6	94.44	202	395.6
28.33	83	181.4	61.67	143	289.4	95	203	397.4
28.89	84	183.2	62.22	144	291.2	95.56	204	399.2
29.44	85	185	62.78	145	293	96.11	205	401
30	86	186.8	63.33	146	294.8	96.67	206	402.8
30.56	87	188.6	63.89	147	296.6	97.22	207	404.6
31.11	88	190.4	64.44	148	298.4	97.78	208	406.4
31.67	89	192.2	65	149	300.2	98.33	209	408.2
32.22	90	194	65.56	150	302	98.89	210	410
32.78	91	195.8	66.11	151	303.8	99.44	211	411.8
33.33	92	197.6	66.67	152	305.6	100	212	413.6
33.89	93	199.4	67.22	153	307.4	100.56	213	415.4
34.44	94	201.2	67.78	154	309.2	101.11	214	417.2
35	95	203	68.33	155	311	101.67	215	419
35.56	96	204.8	68.89	156	312.8	102.22	216	420.8
36.11	97	206.6	69.44	157	314.6	102.78	217	422.6
36.67	98	208.4	70	158	316.4	103.33	218	424.4
37.22	99	210.2	70.56	159	318.2	103.89	219	426.2
37.78	100	212	71.11	160	320	104.44	220	428
38.33	101	213.8	71.67	161	321.8	105	221	429.8
38.89	102	215.6	72.22	162	323.6	105.56	222	431.6
39.44	103	217.4	72.78	163	325.4	106.11	223	433.4
40	104	219.2	73.33	164	327.2	106.67	224	435.2
40.56	105	221	73.89	165	329	107.22	225	437
41.11	106	222.8	74.44	166	330.8	107.78	226	438.8
41.67	107	224.6	75	167	332.6	108.33	227	440.6
42.22	108	226.4	75.56	168	334.4	108.89	228	442.4
42.78	109	228.2	76.11	169	336.2	109.44	229	444.2

To Convert			To Convert			To Convert		
To °C	←°F or °C→	To °F	To °C	←°F or °C→	To °F	To °C	←°F or °C→	To °F
110	230	446	143.33	290	554	176.67	350	662
110.56	231	447.8	143.89	291	555.8	177.22	351	663.8
111.11	232	449.6	144.44	292	557.6	177.78	352	665.6
111.67	233	451.4	145	293	559.4	178.33	353	667.4
112.22	234	453.2	145.56	294	561.2	178.89	354	669.2
112.78	235	455	146.11	295	563	179.44	355	671
113.33	236	456.8	146.67	296	564.8	180	356	672.8
113.89	237	458.6	147.22	297	566.6	180.56	357	674.6
114.44	238	460.4	147.78	298	568.4	181.11	358	676.4
115	239	462.2	148.33	299	570.2	181.67	359	678.2
115.56	240	404	148.89	300	572	182.22	360	680
116.11	241	465.8	149.44	301	573.8	182.78	361	681.8
116.67	242	467.6	150	302	575.6	183.33	362	683.6
117.22	243	469.4	150.56	303	577.4	183.89	363	685.4
117.78	244	471.2	151.11	304	579.2	184.44	364	687.2
118.33	245	473	151.67	305	581	185	365	689
118.89	246	474.8	152.22	306	582.8	185.56	366	690.8
119.44	247	476.6	152.78	307	584.6	186.11	367	692.6
120	248	478.4	153.33	308	586.4	186.67	368	694.4
120.56	249	480.2	153.89	309	588.2	187.22	369	696.2
121.11	250	482	154.44	310	590	187.78	370	698
121.67	251	483.8	155	311	591.8	188.33	371	699.8
122.22	252	485.6	155.56	312	593.6	188.89	372	701.6
122.78	253	487.4	156.11	313	595.4	189.44	373	703.4
123.33	254	489.2	156.67	314	597.2	190	374	705.2
123.89	255	491	157.22	315	599	190.56	375	707
124.44	256	492.8	157.78	316	600.8	191.11	376	708.8
125	257	494.6	158.33	317	602.6	191.67	377	710.6
125.56	258	496.4	158.89	318	604.4	192.22	378	712.4
126.11	259	498.2	159.44	319	606.2	192.78	379	714.2
126.67	260	500	160	320	608	193.33	380	716
127.22	261	501.8	160.56	321	609.8	193.89	381	717.8
127.78	262	503.6	161.11	322	611.6	194.44	382	719.6
128.33	263	505.4	161.67	323	613.4	195	383	721.4
128.89	264	507.2	162.22	324	615.2	195.56	384	723.2
129.44	265	509	162.78	325	617	196.11	385	725
130	266	510.8	163.33	326	618.8	196.67	386	726.8
130.56	267	512.6	163.89	327	620.6	197.22	387	728.6
131.11	268	514.4	164.44	328	622.4	197.78	388	730.4
131.67	269	516.2	165	329	624.2	198.33	389	732.2
132.22	270	518	165.56	330	626	198.89	390	734
132.78	271	519.8	166.11	331	627.8	199.44	391	735.8
133.33	272	521.6	166.67	332	629.6	200	392	737.6
133.89	273	523.4	167.22	333	631.4	200.56	393	739.4
134.44	274	525.2	167.78	334	633.2	201.11	394	741.2
135	275	527	168.33	335	635	201.67	395	743
135.56	276	528.8	168.89	336	636.8	202.22	396	744.8
136.11	277	530.6	169.44	337	638.6	202.78	397	746.6
136.67	278	532.4	170	338	640.4	203.33	398	748.4
137.22	279	534.2	170.56	339	642.2	203.89	399	750.2
137.78	280	536	171.11	340	644	204.44	400	752
138.33	281	537.8	171.67	341	645.8	205	401	753.8
138.89	282	539.6	172.22	342	647.6	205.56	402	755.6
139.44	283	541.4	172.78	343	649.4	206.11	403	757.4
140	284	543.2	173.33	344	651.2	206.67	404	759.2
140.56	285	545	173.89	345	653	207.22	405	761
141.11	286	546.8	174.44	346	654.8	207.78	406	762.8
141.67	287	548.6	175	347	656.6	208.33	407	764.6
142.22	288	550.4	175.56	348	658.4	208.89	408	766.4
142.78	289	552.2	176.11	349	660.2	209.44	409	768.2

To °C	←°F or °C→	To °F	To °C	←°F or °C→	To °F	To °C	←°F or °C→	To °F
	To Convert			To Convert			To Convert	
210	410	770	243.33	470	878	276.67	530	986
210.56	411	771.8	243.89	471	879.8	277.22	531	987.8
211.11	412	773.6	244.44	472	881.6	277.78	532	989.6
211.67	413	775.4	245	473	883.4	278.33	533	991.4
212.22	414	777.2	245.56	474	885.2	278.89	534	993.2
212.78	415	779	246.11	475	887	279.44	535	995
213.33	416	780.8	246.67	476	888.8	280	536	996.8
213.89	417	782.6	247.22	477	890.6	280.56	537	998.6
214.44	418	784.4	247.78	478	892.4	281.11	538	1000.4
215	419	786.2	248.33	479	894.2	281.67	539	1002.2
215.56	420	788	248.89	480	896	282.22	540	1004
216.11	421	789.8	249.44	481	897.8	282.78	541	1005.8
216.67	422	791.6	250	482	899.6	283.33	542	1007.6
217.22	423	793.4	250.56	483	901.4	283.89	543	1009.4
217.78	424	795.2	251.11	484	903.2	284.44	544	1011.2
218.33	425	797	251.67	485	905	285	545	1013
218.89	426	798.8	252.22	486	906.8	285.56	546	1014.8
219.44	427	800.6	252.78	487	908.6	286.11	547	1016.6
220	428	802.4	253.33	488	910.4	286.67	548	1018.4
220.56	429	804.2	253.89	489	912.2	287.22	549	1020.2
221.11	430	806	254.44	490	914	287.78	550	1022
221.67	431	807.8	255	491	915.8	288.33	551	1023.8
222.22	432	809.6	255.56	492	917.6	288.89	552	1025.6
222.78	433	811.4	256.11	493	919.4	289.44	553	1027.4
223.33	434	813.2	256.67	494	921.2	290	554	1029.2
223.89	435	815	257.22	495	923	290.56	555	1031
224.44	436	816.8	257.78	496	924.8	291.11	556	1032.8
225	437	818.6	258.33	497	926.6	291.67	557	1034.6
225.56	438	820.4	258.89	498	928.4	292.22	558	1036.4
226.11	439	822.2	259.44	499	930.2	292.78	559	1038.2
226.67	440	824	260	500	932	293.33	560	1040
227.22	441	825.8	260.56	501	933.8	293.89	561	1041.8
227.78	442	827.6	261.11	502	935.6	294.44	562	1043.6
228.33	443	829.4	261.67	503	937.4	295	563	1045.4
228.89	444	831.2	262.22	504	939.2	295.56	564	1047.2
229.44	445	833	262.78	505	941	296.11	565	1049
230	446	834.8	263.33	506	942.8	296.67	566	1050.8
230.56	447	836.6	263.89	507	944.6	297.22	567	1052.6
231.11	448	838.4	264.44	508	946.4	297.78	568	1054.4
231.67	449	840.2	265	509	948.2	298.33	569	1056.2
232.22	450	842	265.56	510	950	298.89	570	1058
232.78	451	843.8	266.11	511	951.8	299.44	571	1059.8
233.33	452	845.6	266.67	512	953.6	300	572	1061.6
233.89	453	847.4	267.22	513	955.4	300.56	573	1063.4
234.44	454	849.2	267.78	514	957.2	301.11	574	1065.2
235	455	851	268.33	515	959	301.67	575	1067
235.56	456	852.8	268.89	516	960.8	302.22	576	1068.8
236.11	457	854.6	269.44	517	962.6	302.78	577	1070.6
236.67	458	856.4	270	518	964.4	303.33	578	1072.4
237.22	459	858.2	270.56	519	966.2	303.89	579	1074.2
237.78	460	860	271.11	520	968	304.44	580	1076
238.33	461	861.8	271.67	521	969.8	305	581	1077.8
238.89	462	863.6	272.22	522	971.6	305.56	582	1079.6
239.44	463	865.4	272.78	523	973.4	306.11	583	1081.4
240	464	867.2	273.33	524	975.2	306.67	584	1083.2
240.56	465	869	273.89	525	977	307.22	585	1085
241.11	466	870.8	274.44	526	978.8	307.78	586	1086.8
241.67	467	872.6	275	527	980.6	308.33	587	1088.6
242.22	468	874.4	275.56	528	982.4	308.89	588	1090.4
242.78	469	876.2	276.11	529	984.2	309.44	589	1092.2

| To Convert | | | To Convert | | | To Convert | | |
To °C	←°F or °C→	To °F	To °C	←°F or °C→	To °F	To °C	←°F or °C→	To °F
310	590	1094	343.33	650	1202	376.67	710	1310
310.56	591	1095.8	343.89	651	1203.8	377.22	711	1311.8
311.11	592	1097.6	344.44	652	1205.6	377.78	712	1313.6
311.67	593	1099.4	345	653	1207.4	378.33	713	1315.4
312.22	594	1101.2	345.56	654	1209.2	378.89	714	1317.2
312.78	595	1103	346.11	655	1211	379.44	715	1319
313.33	596	1104.8	346.67	656	1212.8	380	716	1320.8
313.89	597	1106.6	347.22	657	1214.6	380.56	717	1322.6
314.44	598	1108.4	347.78	658	1216.4	381.11	718	1324.4
315	599	1110.2	348.33	659	1218.2	381.67	719	1326.2
315.56	600	1112	348.89	660	1220	382.22	720	1328
316.11	601	1113.8	349.44	661	1221.8	382.78	721	1329.8
316.67	602	1115.6	350	662	1223.6	383.33	722	1331.6
317.22	603	1117.4	350.56	663	1225.4	383.89	723	1333.4
317.78	604	1119.2	351.11	664	1227.2	384.44	724	1335.2
318.33	605	1121	351.67	665	1229	385	725	1337
318.89	606	1122.8	352.22	666	1230.8	385.56	726	1338.8
319.44	607	1124.6	352.78	667	1232.6	386.11	727	1340.6
320	608	1126.4	353.33	668	1234.4	386.67	728	1342.4
320.56	609	1128.2	353.89	669	1236.2	387.22	729	1344.2
321.11	610	1130	354.44	670	1238	387.78	730	1346
321.67	611	1131.8	355	671	1239.8	388.33	731	1347.8
322.22	612	1133.6	355.56	672	1241.6	388.89	732	1349.6
322.78	613	1135.4	356.11	673	1243.4	389.44	733	1351.4
323.33	614	1137.2	356.67	674	1245.2	390	734	1353.2
323.89	615	1139	357.22	675	1247	390.56	735	1355
324.44	616	1140.8	357.78	676	1248.8	391.11	736	1356.8
325	617	1142.6	358.33	677	1250.6	391.67	737	1358.6
325.56	618	1144.4	358.89	678	1252.4	392.22	738	1360.4
326.11	619	1146.2	359.44	679	1254.2	392.78	739	1362.2
326.67	620	1148	360	680	1256	393.33	740	1364
327.22	621	1149.8	360.56	681	1257.8	393.89	741	1365.8
327.78	622	1151.6	361.11	682	1259.6	394.44	742	1367.6
328.33	623	1153.4	361.67	683	1261.4	395	743	1369.4
328.89	624	1155.2	362.22	684	1263.2	395.56	744	1371.2
329.44	625	1157	362.78	685	1265	396.11	745	1373
330	626	1158.8	363.33	686	1266.8	396.67	746	1374.8
330.56	627	1160.6	363.89	687	1268.6	397.22	747	1376.6
331.11	628	1162.4	364.44	688	1270.4	397.78	748	1378.4
331.67	629	1164.2	365	689	1272.2	398.33	749	1380.2
332.22	630	1166	365.56	690	1274	398.89	750	1382
332.78	631	1167.8	366.11	691	1275.8	399.44	751	1383.8
333.33	632	1169.6	366.67	692	1277.6	400	752	1385.6
333.89	633	1171.4	367.22	693	1279.4	400.56	753	1387.4
334.44	634	1173.2	367.78	694	1281.2	401.11	754	1389.2
335	635	1175	368.33	695	1283	401.67	755	1391
335.56	636	1176.8	368.89	696	1284.8	402.22	756	1392.8
336.11	637	1178.6	369.44	697	1286.6	402.78	757	1394.6
336.67	638	1180.4	370	698	1288.4	403.33	758	1396.4
337.22	639	1182.2	370.56	699	1290.2	403.89	759	1398.2
337.78	640	1184	371.11	700	1292	404.44	760	1400
338.33	641	1185.8	371.67	701	1293.8	405	761	1401.8
338.89	642	1187.6	372.22	702	1295.6	405.56	762	1403.6
339.44	643	1189.4	372.78	703	1297.4	406.11	763	1405.4
340	644	1191.2	373.33	704	1299.2	406.67	764	1407.2
340.56	645	1193	373.89	705	1301	407.22	765	1409
341.11	646	1194.8	374.44	706	1302.8	407.78	766	1410.8
341.67	647	1196.6	375	707	1304.6	408.33	767	1412.6
342.22	648	1198.4	375.56	708	1306.4	408.89	768	1414.4
342.78	649	1200.2	376.11	709	1308.2	409.44	769	1416.2

To Convert			To Convert			To Convert		
To °C	←°F or °C→	To °F	To °C	←°F or °C→	To °F	To °C	←°F or °C→	To °F
410	770	1418	443.33	830	1526	476.67	890	1634
410.56	771	1419.8	443.89	831	1527.8	477.22	891	1635.8
411.11	772	1421.6	444.44	832	1529.6	477.78	892	1637.6
411.67	773	1423.4	445	833	1531.4	478.33	893	1639.4
412.22	774	1425.2	445.56	834	1533.2	478.89	894	1641.2
412.78	775	1427	446.11	835	1535	479.44	895	1643
413.33	776	1428.8	446.67	836	1536.8	480	896	1644.8
413.89	777	1430.6	447.22	837	1538.6	480.56	897	1646.6
414.44	778	1432.4	447.78	838	1540.4	481.11	898	1648.4
415	779	1434.2	448.33	839	1542.2	481.67	899	1650.2
415.56	780	1436	448.89	840	1544	482.22	900	1652
416.11	781	1437.8	449.44	841	1545.8	482.78	901	1653.8
416.67	782	1439.6	450	842	1547.6	483.33	902	1655.6
417.22	783	1441.4	450.56	843	1549.4	483.89	903	1657.4
417.78	784	1443.2	451.11	844	1551.2	484.44	904	1659.2
418.33	785	1445	451.67	845	1553	485	905	1661
418.89	786	1446.8	452.22	846	1554.8	485.56	906	1662.8
419.44	787	1448.6	452.78	847	1556.6	486.11	907	1664.6
420	788	1450.4	453.33	848	1558.4	486.67	908	1666.4
420.56	789	1452.2	453.89	849	1560.2	487.22	909	1668.2
421.11	790	1454	454.44	850	1562	487.78	910	1670
421.67	791	1455.8	455	851	1563.8	488.33	911	1671.8
422.22	792	1457.6	455.56	852	1565.6	488.89	912	1673.6
422.78	793	1459.4	456.11	853	1567.4	489.44	913	1675.4
423.33	794	1461.2	456.67	854	1569.2	490	914	1677.2
423.89	795	1463	457.22	855	1571	490.56	915	1679
424.44	796	1464.8	457.78	856	1572.8	491.11	916	1680.8
425	797	1466.6	458.33	857	1574.6	491.67	917	1682.6
425.56	798	1468.4	458.89	858	1576.4	492.22	918	1684.4
426.11	799	1470.2	459.44	859	1578.2	492.78	919	1686.2
426.67	800	1472	460	860	1580	493.33	920	1688
427.22	801	1473.8	460.56	861	1581.8	493.89	921	1689.8
427.78	802	1475.6	461.11	862	1583.6	494.44	922	1691.6
428.33	803	1477.4	461.67	863	1585.4	495	923	1693.4
428.89	804	1479.2	462.22	864	1587.2	495.56	924	1695.2
429.44	805	1481	462.78	865	1589	496.11	925	1697
430	806	1482.8	463.33	866	1590.8	496.67	926	1698.8
430.56	807	1484.6	463.89	867	1592.6	497.22	927	1700.6
431.11	808	1486.4	464.44	868	1594.4	497.78	928	1702.4
431.67	809	1488.2	465	869	1596.2	498.33	929	1704.2
432.22	810	1490	465.56	870	1598	498.89	930	1706
432.78	811	1491.8	466.11	871	1599.8	499.44	931	1707.8
433.33	812	1493.6	466.67	872	1601.6	500	932	1709.6
433.89	813	1495.4	467.22	873	1603.4	500.56	933	1711.4
434.44	814	1497.2	467.78	874	1605.2	501.11	934	1713.2
435	815	1499	468.33	875	1607	501.67	935	1715
435.56	816	1500.8	468.89	876	1608.8	502.22	936	1716.8
436.11	817	1502.6	469.44	877	1610.6	502.78	937	1718.6
436.67	818	1504.4	470	878	1612.4	503.33	938	1720.4
437.22	819	1506.2	470.56	879	1614.2	503.89	939	1722.2
437.78	820	1508	471.11	880	1616	504.44	940	1724
438.33	821	1509.8	471.67	881	1617.8	505	941	1725.8
438.89	822	1511.6	472.22	882	1619.6	505.56	942	1727.6
439.44	823	1513.4	472.78	883	1621.4	506.11	943	1729.4
440	824	1515.2	473.33	884	1623.2	506.67	944	1731.2
440.56	825	1517	473.89	885	1625	507.22	945	1733
441.11	826	1518.8	474.44	886	1626.8	507.78	946	1734.8
441.67	827	1520.6	475	887	1628.6	508.33	947	1736.6
442.22	828	1522.4	475.56	888	1630.4	508.89	948	1738.4
442.78	829	1524.2	476.11	889	1632.2	509.44	949	1740.2

To Convert			To Convert			To Convert		
To °C	←°F or °C→	To °F	To °C	←°F or °C→	To °F	To °C	←°F or °C→	To °F
510	950	1742	543.33	1010	1850	576.67	1070	1958
510.56	951	1743.8	543.89	1011	1851.8	577.22	1071	1959.8
511.11	952	1745.6	544.44	1012	1853.6	577.78	1072	1961.6
511.67	953	1747.4	545	1013	1855.4	578.33	1073	1963.4
512.22	954	1749.2	545.56	1014	1857.2	578.89	1074	1965.2
512.78	955	1751	546.11	1015	1859	579.44	1075	1967
513.33	956	1752.8	546.67	1016	1860.8	580	1076	1968.8
513.89	957	1754.6	547.22	1017	1862.6	580.56	1077	1970.6
514.44	958	1756.4	547.78	1018	1864.4	581.11	1078	1972.4
515	959	1758.2	548.33	1019	1866.2	581.67	1079	1974.2
515.56	960	1760	548.89	1020	1868	582.22	1080	1976
516.11	961	1761.8	549.44	1021	1869.8	582.78	1081	1977.8
516.67	962	1763.6	550	1022	1871.6	583.33	1082	1979.6
517.22	963	1765.4	550.56	1023	1873.4	583.89	1083	1981.4
517.78	964	1767.2	551.11	1024	1875.2	584.44	1084	1983.2
518.33	965	1769	551.67	1025	1877	585	1085	1985
518.89	966	1770.8	552.22	1026	1878.8	585.56	1086	1986.8
519.44	967	1772.6	552.78	1027	1880.6	586.11	1087	1988.6
520	968	1774.4	553.33	1028	1882.4	586.67	1088	1990.4
520.56	969	1776.2	553.89	1029	1884.2	587.22	1089	1992.2
521.11	970	1778	554.44	1030	1886	587.78	1090	1994
521.67	971	1779.8	555	1031	1887.8	588.33	1091	1995.8
522.22	972	1781.6	555.56	1032	1889.6	588.89	1092	1997.6
522.78	973	1783.4	556.11	1033	1891.4	589.44	1093	1999.4
523.33	974	1785.2	556.67	1034	1893.2	590	1094	2001.2
523.89	975	1787	557.22	1035	1895	590.56	1095	2003
524.44	976	1788.8	557.78	1036	1896.8	591.11	1096	2004.8
525	977	1790.6	558.33	1037	1898.6	591.67	1097	2006.6
525.56	978	1792.4	558.89	1038	1900.4	592.22	1098	2008.4
526.11	979	1794.2	559.44	1039	1902.2	592.78	1099	2010.2
526.67	980	1796	560	1040	1904	593.33	1100	2012
527.22	981	1797.8	560.56	1041	1905.8	593.89	1101	2013.8
527.78	982	1799.6	561.11	1042	1907.6	594.44	1102	2015.6
528.33	983	1801.4	561.67	1043	1909.4	595	1103	2017.4
528.89	984	1803.2	562.22	1044	1911.2	595.56	1104	2019.2
529.44	985	1805	562.78	1045	1913	596.11	1105	2021
530	986	1806.8	563.33	1046	1914.8	596.67	1106	2022.8
530.56	987	1808.6	563.89	1047	1916.6	597.22	1107	2024.6
531.11	988	1810.4	564.44	1048	1918.4	597.78	1108	2026.4
531.67	989	1812.2	565	1049	1920.2	598.33	1109	2028.2
532.22	990	1814	565.56	1050	1922	598.89	1110	2030
532.78	991	1815.8	566.11	1051	1923.8	599.44	1111	2031.8
533.33	992	1817.6	566.67	1052	1925.6	600	1112	2033.6
533.89	993	1819.4	567.22	1053	1927.4	600.56	1113	2035.4
534.44	994	1821.2	567.78	1054	1929.2	601.11	1114	2037.2
535	995	1823	568.33	1055	1931	601.67	1115	2039
535.56	996	1824.8	568.89	1056	1932.8	602.22	1116	2040.8
536.11	997	1826.6	569.44	1057	1934.6	602.78	1117	2042.6
536.67	998	1828.4	570	1058	1936.4	603.33	1118	2044.4
537.22	999	1830.2	570.56	1059	1938.2	603.89	1119	2046.4
537.78	1000	1832	571.11	1060	1940	604.44	1120	2048
538.33	1001	1833.8	571.67	1061	1941.8	605	1121	2049.8
538.89	1002	1835.6	572.22	1062	1943.6	605.56	1122	2051.6
539.44	1003	1837.4	572.78	1063	1945.4	606.11	1123	2053.4
540	1004	1839.2	573.33	1064	1947.2	606.67	1124	2055.2
540.56	1005	1841	573.89	1065	1949	607.22	1125	2057
541.11	1006	1842.8	574.44	1066	1950.8	607.78	1126	2058.8
541.67	1007	1844.6	575	1067	1952.6	608.33	1127	2060.6
542.22	1008	1846.4	575.56	1068	1954.4	608.89	1128	2062.4
542.78	1009	1848.2	576.11	1069	1956.2	609.44	1129	2064.2

To °C	←°F or °C→	To °F	To °C	←°F or °C→	To °F	To °C	←°F or °C→	To °F
610	1130	2066	643.33	1190	2174	676.67	1250	2282
610.56	1131	2067.8	643.89	1191	2175.8	677.22	1251	2283.8
611.11	1132	2069.6	644.44	1192	2177.6	677.78	1252	2285.6
611.67	1133	2071.4	645	1193	2179.4	678.33	1253	2287.4
612.22	1134	2073.2	645.56	1194	2181.2	678.89	1254	2289.2
612.78	1135	2075	646.11	1195	2183	679.44	1255	2291
613.33	1136	2076.8	646.67	1196	2184.8	680	1256	2292.8
613.89	1137	2078.6	647.22	1197	2186.6	680.56	1257	2294.6
614.44	1138	2080.4	647.78	1198	2188.4	681.11	1258	2296.4
615	1139	2082.2	648.33	1199	2190.2	681.67	1259	2298.2
615.56	1140	2084	648.89	1200	2192	682.22	1260	2300
616.11	1141	2085.8	649.44	1201	2193.8	682.78	1261	2301.8
616.67	1142	2087.6	650	1202	2195.6	683.33	1262	2303.6
617.22	1143	2089.4	650.56	1203	2197.4	683.89	1263	2305.4
617.78	1144	2091.2	651.11	1204	2199.2	684.44	1264	2307.2
618.33	1145	2093	651.67	1205	2201	685	1265	2309
618.89	1146	2094.8	652.22	1206	2202.8	685.56	1266	2310.8
619.44	1147	2096.6	652.78	1207	2204.6	686.11	1267	2312.6
620	1148	2098.4	653.33	1208	2206.4	686.67	1268	2314.4
620.56	1149	2100.2	653.89	1209	2208.2	687.22	1269	2316.2
621.11	1150	2102	654.44	1210	2210	687.78	1270	2318
621.67	1151	2103.8	655	1211	2211.8	688.33	1271	2319.8
622.22	1152	2105.6	655.56	1212	2213.6	688.89	1272	2321.6
622.78	1153	2107.4	656.11	1213	2215.4	689.44	1273	2323.4
623.33	1154	2109.2	656.67	1214	2217.2	690	1274	2325.2
623.89	1155	2111	657.22	1215	2219	690.56	1275	2327
624.44	1156	2112.8	657.78	1216	2220.8	691.11	1276	2328.8
625	1157	2114.6	658.33	1217	2222.6	691.67	1277	2330.6
625.56	1158	2116.4	658.89	1218	2224.4	692.22	1278	2332.4
626.11	1159	2118.2	659.44	1219	2226.2	692.78	1279	2334.2
626.67	1160	2120	660	1220	2228	693.33	1280	2336
627.22	1161	2121.8	660.56	1221	2229.8	693.89	1281	2337.8
627.78	1162	2123.6	661.11	1222	2231.6	694.44	1282	2339.6
628.33	1163	2125.4	661.67	1223	2233.4	695	1283	2341.4
628.89	1164	2127.2	662.22	1224	2235.2	695.56	1284	2343.2
629.44	1165	2129	662.78	1225	2237	696.11	1285	2345
630	1166	2130.8	663.33	1226	2238.8	696.67	1286	2346.8
630.56	1167	2132.6	663.89	1227	2240.6	697.22	1287	2348.6
631.11	1168	2134.4	664.44	1228	2242.4	697.78	1288	2350.4
631.67	1169	2136.2	665	1229	2244.2	698.33	1289	2352.2
632.22	1170	2138	665.56	1230	2246	698.89	1290	2354
632.78	1171	2139.8	666.11	1231	2247.8	699.44	1291	2355.8
633.33	1172	2141.6	666.67	1232	2249.6	700	1292	2357.6
633.89	1173	2143.4	667.22	1233	2251.4	700.56	1293	2359.4
634.44	1174	2145.2	667.78	1234	2253.2	701.11	1294	2361.2
635	1175	2147	668.33	1235	2255	701.67	1295	2363
635.56	1176	2148.8	668.89	1236	2256.8	702.22	1296	2364.8
636.11	1177	2150.6	669.44	1237	2258.6	702.78	1297	2366.6
636.67	1178	2152.4	670	1238	2260.4	703.33	1298	2368.4
637.22	1179	2154.2	670.56	1239	2262.2	703.89	1299	2370.2
637.78	1180	2156	671.11	1240	2264	704.44	1300	2372
638.33	1181	2157.8	671.67	1241	2265.8	705	1301	2373.8
638.89	1182	2159.6	672.22	1242	2267.6	705.56	1302	2375.6
639.44	1183	2161.4	672.78	1243	2269.4	706.11	1303	2377.4
640	1184	2163.2	673.33	1244	2271.2	706.67	1304	2379.2
640.56	1185	2165	673.89	1245	2273	707.22	1305	2381
641.11	1186	2166.8	674.44	1246	2274.8	707.78	1306	2382.8
641.67	1187	2168.6	675	1247	2276.6	708.33	1307	2384.6
642.22	1188	2170.4	675.56	1248	2278.4	708.89	1308	2386.4
642.78	1189	2172.2	676.11	1249	2280.2	709.44	1309	2388.2

To °C	←°F or °C→	To °F	To °C	←°F or °C→	To °F	To °C	←°F or °C→	To °F
710	1310	2390	743.33	1370	2498	776.67	1430	2606
710.56	1311	2391.8	743.89	1371	2499.8	777.22	1431	2607.8
711.11	1312	2393.6	744.44	1372	2501.6	777.78	1432	2609.6
711.67	1313	2395.4	745	1373	2503.4	778.33	1433	2611.4
712.22	1314	2397.2	745.56	1374	2505.2	778.89	1434	2613.2
712.78	1315	2399	746.11	1375	2507	779.44	1435	2615
713.33	1316	2400.8	746.67	1376	2508.8	780	1436	2616.8
713.89	1317	2402.6	747.22	1377	2510.6	780.56	1437	2618.6
714.44	1318	2404.4	747.78	1378	2512.4	781.11	1438	2620.4
715	1319	2406.2	748.33	1379	2514.2	781.67	1439	2622.2
715.56	1320	2408	748.89	1380	2516	782.22	1440	2624
716.11	1321	2409.8	749.44	1381	2517.8	782.78	1441	2625.8
716.67	1322	2411.6	750	1382	2519.6	783.33	1442	2627.6
717.22	1323	2413.4	750.56	1383	2521.4	783.89	1443	2629.4
717.78	1324	2415.2	751.11	1384	2523.2	784.44	1444	2631.2
718.33	1325	2417	751.67	1385	2525	785	1445	2633
718.89	1326	2418.8	752.22	1386	2526.8	785.56	1446	2634.8
719.44	1327	2420.6	752.78	1387	2528.6	786.11	1447	2636.6
720	1328	2422.4	753.33	1388	2530.4	786.67	1448	2638.4
720.56	1329	2424.2	753.89	1389	2532.2	787.22	1449	2640.2
721.11	1330	2426	754.44	1390	2534	787.78	1450	2642
721.67	1331	2427.8	755	1391	2535.8	788.33	1451	2443.8
722.22	1332	2429.6	755.56	1392	2537.6	788.89	1452	2645.6
722.78	1333	2431.4	756.11	1393	2539.4	789.44	1453	2647.4
723.33	1334	2433.2	756.67	1394	2541.2	790	1454	2649.2
723.89	1335	2435	757.22	1395	2543	790.56	1455	2651
724.44	1336	2436.8	757.78	1396	2544.8	791.11	1456	2652.8
725	1337	2438.6	758.33	1397	2546.6	791.67	1457	2654.6
725.56	1338	2440.4	758.89	1398	2548.4	792.22	1458	2656.4
726.11	1339	2442.2	759.44	1399	2550.2	792.78	1459	2658.2
726.67	1340	2444	760	1400	2552	793.33	1460	2660
727.22	1341	2445.8	760.56	1401	2553.8	793.89	1461	2661.8
727.78	1342	2447.6	761.11	1402	2555.6	794.44	1462	2663.6
728.33	1343	2449.4	761.67	1403	2557.4	795	1463	2665.4
728.89	1344	2451.2	762.22	1404	2559.2	795.56	1464	2667.2
729.44	1345	2453	762.78	1405	2561	796.11	1465	2669
730	1346	2454.8	763.33	1406	2562.8	796.67	1466	2670.8
730.56	1347	2456.6	763.89	1407	2564.6	797.22	1467	2672.6
731.11	1348	2458.4	764.44	1408	2566.4	797.78	1468	2674.4
731.67	1349	2460.2	765	1409	2568.2	798.33	1469	2676.2
732.22	1350	2462	765.56	1410	2570	798.89	1470	2678
732.78	1351	2463.8	766.11	1411	2571.8	799.44	1471	2679.8
733.33	1352	2465.6	766.67	1412	2573.6	800	1472	2681.6
733.89	1353	2467.4	767.22	1413	2575.4	800.56	1473	2683.4
734.44	1354	2469.2	767.78	1414	2577.2	801.11	1474	2685.2
735	1355	2471	768.33	1415	2579	801.67	1475	2687
735.56	1356	2472.8	768.89	1416	2580.8	802.22	1476	2688.8
736.11	1357	2474.6	769.44	1417	2582.6	802.78	1477	2690.6
736.67	1358	2476.4	770	1418	2584.4	803.33	1478	2692.4
737.22	1359	2478.2	770.56	1419	2586.2	803.89	1479	2694.2
737.78	1360	2480	771.11	1420	2588	804.44	1480	2696
738.33	1361	2481.8	771.67	1421	2589.8	805	1481	2697.8
738.89	1362	2483.6	772.22	1422	2591.6	805.56	1482	2699.6
739.44	1363	2485.4	772.78	1423	2593.4	806.11	1483	2701.4
740	1364	2487.2	773.33	1424	2595.2	806.67	1484	2703.2
740.56	1365	2489	773.89	1425	2597	807.22	1485	2705
741.11	1366	2490.8	774.44	1426	2598.8	807.78	1486	2706.8
741.67	1367	2492.6	775	1427	2600.6	808.33	1487	2708.6
742.22	1368	2494.4	775.56	1428	2602.4	808.89	1488	2710.4
742.78	1369	2496.2	776.11	1429	2604.2	809.44	1489	2712.2

To °C	←°F or °C→	To °F	To °C	←°F or °C→	To °F	To °C	←°F or °C→	To °F
810	**1490**	2714	843.33	**1550**	2822	876.67	**1610**	2930
810.56	**1491**	2715.8	843.89	**1551**	2823.8	877.22	**1611**	2931.8
811.11	**1492**	2717.6	844.44	**1552**	2825.6	877.78	**1612**	2933.6
811.67	**1493**	2719.4	845	**1553**	2827.4	878.33	**1613**	2935.4
812.22	**1494**	2721.2	845.56	**1554**	2829.2	878.89	**1614**	2937.2
812.78	**1495**	2723	846.11	**1555**	2831	879.44	**1615**	2939
813.33	**1496**	2724.8	846.67	**1556**	2832.8	880	**1616**	2940.8
813.89	**1497**	2726.6	847.22	**1557**	2834.6	880.56	**1617**	2942.6
814.44	**1498**	2728.4	847.78	**1558**	2836.4	881.11	**1618**	2944.4
815	**1499**	2730.2	848.33	**1559**	2838.2	881.67	**1619**	2946.2
815.56	**1500**	2732	848.89	**1560**	2840	882.22	**1620**	2948
816.11	**1501**	2733.8	849.44	**1561**	2841.8	882.78	**1621**	2949.8
816.67	**1502**	2735.6	850	**1562**	2843.6	883.33	**1622**	2951.6
817.22	**1503**	2737.4	850.56	**1563**	2845.4	883.89	**1623**	2953.4
817.78	**1504**	2739.2	851.11	**1564**	2847.2	884.44	**1624**	2955.2
818.33	**1505**	2741	851.67	**1565**	2849	885	**1625**	2957
818.89	**1506**	2742.8	852.22	**1566**	2850.8	885.56	**1626**	2958.8
819.44	**1507**	2744.6	852.78	**1567**	2852.6	886.11	**1627**	2960.6
820	**1508**	2746.4	853.33	**1568**	2854.4	886.67	**1628**	2962.4
820.56	**1509**	2748.2	853.89	**1569**	2856.2	887.22	**1629**	2964.2
821.11	**1510**	2750	854.44	**1570**	2858	887.78	**1630**	2966
821.67	**1511**	2751.8	855	**1571**	2859.8	888.33	**1631**	2967.8
822.22	**1512**	2753.6	855.56	**1572**	2861.6	888.89	**1632**	2969.6
822.78	**1513**	2755.4	856.11	**1573**	2863.4	889.44	**1633**	2971.4
823.33	**1514**	2757.2	856.67	**1574**	2865.2	890	**1634**	2973.2
823.89	**1515**	2759	857.22	**1575**	2867	890.56	**1635**	2975
824.44	**1516**	2760.8	857.78	**1576**	2868.8	891.11	**1636**	2976.8
825	**1517**	2762.6	858.33	**1577**	2870.6	891.67	**1637**	2978.6
825.56	**1518**	2764.4	858.89	**1578**	2872.4	892.22	**1638**	2980.4
826.11	**1519**	2766.2	859.44	**1579**	2874.2	892.78	**1639**	2982.2
826.67	**1520**	2768	860	**1580**	2876	893.33	**1640**	2984
827.22	**1521**	2769.8	860.56	**1581**	2877.8	893.89	**1641**	2985.8
827.78	**1522**	2771.6	861.11	**1582**	2879.6	894.44	**1642**	2987.6
828.33	**1523**	2773.4	861.67	**1583**	2881.4	895	**1643**	2989.4
828.89	**1524**	2775.2	862.22	**1584**	2883.2	895.56	**1644**	2991.2
829.44	**1525**	2777	862.78	**1585**	2885	896.11	**1645**	2993
830	**1526**	2778.8	863.33	**1586**	2886.8	896.67	**1646**	2994.8
830.56	**1527**	2780.6	863.89	**1587**	2888.6	897.22	**1647**	2996.6
831.11	**1528**	2782.4	864.44	**1588**	2890.4	897.78	**1648**	2998.4
831.67	**1529**	2784.2	865	**1589**	2892.2	898.33	**1649**	3000.2
832.22	**1530**	2786	865.56	**1590**	2894	898.89	**1650**	3002
832.78	**1531**	2787.8	866.11	**1591**	2895.8	899.44	**1651**	3003.8
833.33	**1532**	2789.6	866.67	**1592**	2897.6	900	**1652**	3005.6
833.89	**1533**	2791.4	867.22	**1593**	2899.4	900.56	**1653**	3007.4
834.44	**1534**	2793.2	867.78	**1594**	2901.2	901.11	**1654**	3009.2
835	**1535**	2795	868.33	**1595**	2903	901.67	**1655**	3011
835.56	**1536**	2796.8	868.89	**1596**	2904.8	902.22	**1656**	3012.8
836.11	**1537**	2798.6	869.44	**1597**	2906.6	902.78	**1657**	3014.6
836.67	**1538**	2800.4	870	**1598**	2908.4	903.33	**1658**	3016.4
837.22	**1539**	2802.2	870.56	**1599**	2910.2	903.89	**1659**	3018.2
837.78	**1540**	2804	871.11	**1600**	2912	904.44	**1660**	3020
838.33	**1541**	2805.8	871.67	**1601**	2913.8	905	**1661**	3021.8
838.89	**1542**	2807.6	872.22	**1602**	2915.6	905.56	**1662**	3023.6
839.44	**1543**	2809.4	872.78	**1603**	2917.4	906.11	**1663**	3025.4
840	**1544**	2811.2	873.33	**1604**	2919.2	906.67	**1664**	3027.2
840.56	**1545**	2813	873.89	**1605**	2921	907.22	**1665**	3029
841.11	**1546**	2814.8	874.44	**1606**	2922.8	907.78	**1666**	3030.8
841.67	**1547**	2816.6	875	**1607**	2924.6	908.33	**1667**	3032.6
842.22	**1548**	2818.4	875.56	**1608**	2926.4	908.89	**1668**	3034.4
842.78	**1549**	2820.2	876.11	**1609**	2928.2	909.44	**1669**	3036.2

To Convert			To Convert			To Convert		
To °C	←°F or °C→	To °F	To °C	←°F or °C→	To °F	To °C	←°F or °C→	To °F
910	1670	3038	943.33	1730	3146	976.67	1790	3254
910.56	1671	3039.8	943.89	1731	3147.8	977.22	1791	3255.8
911.11	1672	3041.6	944.44	1732	3149.6	977.78	1792	3257.6
911.67	1673	3043.4	945	1733	3151.4	978.33	1793	3259.4
912.22	1674	3045.2	945.56	1734	3153.2	978.89	1794	3261.2
912.78	1675	3047	946.11	1735	3155	979.44	1795	3263
913.33	1676	3048.8	946.67	1736	3156.8	980	1796	3264.8
913.89	1677	3050.6	947.22	1737	3158.6	980.56	1797	3266.6
914.44	1678	3052.4	947.78	1738	3160.4	981.11	1798	3268.4
915	1679	3054.2	948.33	1739	3162.2	981.67	1799	3270.2
915.56	1680	3056	948.89	1740	3164	982.22	1800	3272
916.11	1681	3057.8	949.44	1741	3165.8	982.78	1801	3273.8
916.67	1682	3059.6	950	1742	3167.6	983.33	1802	3275.6
917.22	1683	3061.4	950.56	1743	3169.4	983.89	1803	3277.4
917.78	1684	3063.2	951.11	1744	3171.2	984.44	1804	3279.2
918.33	1685	3065	951.67	1745	3173	985	1805	3281
918.89	1686	3066.8	952.22	1746	3174.8	985.56	1806	3282.8
919.44	1687	3068.6	952.78	1747	3176.6	986.11	1807	3284.6
920	1688	3070.4	953.33	1748	3178.4	986.67	1808	3286.4
920.56	1689	3072.2	953.89	1749	3180.2	987.22	1809	3288.2
921.11	1690	3074	954.44	1750	3182	987.78	1810	3290
921.67	1691	3075.8	955	1751	3183.8	988.33	1811	3291.8
922.22	1692	3077.6	955.56	1752	3185.6	988.89	1812	3293.6
022.78	1693	3079.4	956.11	1753	3187.4	989.44	1813	3295.4
923.33	1694	3081.2	956.67	1754	3189.2	990	1814	3297.2
923.89	1695	3083	957.22	1755	3191	990.56	1815	3299
924.44	1696	3084.8	957.78	1756	3192.8	991.11	1816	3300.8
925	1697	3086.6	958.33	1757	3194.6	991.67	1817	3302.6
925.56	1698	3088.4	958.89	1758	3196.4	992.22	1818	3304.4
926.11	1699	3090.2	959.44	1759	3198.2	992.78	1819	3306.2
926.67	1700	3092	960	1760	3200	993.33	1820	3308
927.22	1701	3093.8	960.56	1761	3201.8	993.89	1821	3309.8
927.78	1702	3095.6	961.11	1762	3203.6	994.44	1822	3311.6
928.33	1703	3097.4	961.67	1763	3205.4	995	1823	3313.4
928.89	1704	3099.2	962.22	1764	3207.2	995.56	1824	3315.2
929.44	1705	3101	962.78	1765	3209	996.11	1825	3317
930	1706	3102.8	963.33	1766	3210.8	996.67	1826	3318.8
930.56	1707	3104.6	963.89	1767	3212.6	997.22	1827	3320.6
931.11	1708	3106.4	964.44	1768	3214.4	997.78	1828	3322.4
931.67	1709	3108.2	965	1769	3216.2	998.33	1829	3324.2
932.22	1710	3110	965.56	1770	3218	998.89	1830	3326
932.78	1711	3111.8	966.11	1771	3219.8	999.44	1831	3327.8
933.33	1712	3113.6	966.67	1772	3221.6	1000	1832	3329.6
933.89	1713	3115.4	967.22	1773	3223.4	1000.56	1833	3331.4
934.44	1714	3117.2	967.78	1774	3225.2	1001.11	1834	3333.2
935	1715	3119	968.33	1775	3227	1001.67	1835	3335
935.56	1716	3120.8	968.89	1776	3228.8	1002.22	1836	3336.8
936.11	1717	3122.6	969.44	1777	3230.6	1002.78	1837	3338.6
936.67	1718	3124.4	970	1778	3232.4	1003.33	1838	3340.4
937.22	1719	3126.2	970.56	1779	3234.2	1003.89	1839	3342.2
937.78	1720	3128	971.11	1780	3236	1004.44	1840	3344
938.33	1721	3129.8	971.67	1781	3237.8	1005	1841	3345.8
938.89	1722	3131.6	972.22	1782	3239.6	1005.56	1842	3347.6
939.44	1723	3133.4	972.78	1783	3241.4	1006.11	1843	3349.4
940	1724	3135.2	973.33	1784	3243.2	1006.67	1844	3351.2
940.56	1725	3137	973.89	1785	3245	1007.22	1845	3353
941.11	1726	3138.8	974.44	1786	3246.8	1007.78	1846	3354.8
941.07	1727	3140.0	975	1787	3248.0	1008.33	1847	3356.0
942.22	1728	3142.4	975.56	1788	3250.4	1008.89	1848	3358.4
942.78	1729	3144.2	976.11	1789	3252.2	1009.44	1849	3360.2

To °C	←°F or °C→	To °F	To °C	←°F or °C→	To °F	To °C	←°F or °C→	To °F
1010	1850	3362	1043.33	1910	3470	1076.67	1970	3578
1010.56	1851	3363.8	1043.89	1911	3471.8	1077.22	1971	3579.8
1011.11	1852	3365.6	1044.44	1912	3473.6	1077.78	1972	3581.6
1011.67	1853	3367.4	1045	1913	3475.4	1078.33	1973	3583.4
1012.22	1854	3369.2	1045.56	1914	3477.2	1078.89	1974	3585.2
1012.78	1855	3371	1046.11	1915	3479	1079.44	1975	3587
1013.33	1856	3372.8	1046.67	1916	3480.8	1080	1976	3588.8
1013.89	1857	3374.6	1047.22	1917	3482.6	1080.56	1977	3590.6
1014.44	1858	3376.4	1047.78	1918	3484.4	1081.11	1978	3592.4
1015	1859	3378.2	1048.33	1919	3486.2	1081.67	1979	3594.2
1015.56	1860	3380	1048.89	1920	3488	1082.22	1980	3596
1016.11	1861	3381.8	1049.44	1921	3489.8	1082.78	1981	3597.8
1016.67	1862	3383.6	1050	1922	3491.6	1083.33	1982	3599.6
1017.22	1863	3385.4	1050.56	1923	3493.4	1083.89	1983	3601.4
1017.78	1864	3387.2	1051.11	1924	3495.2	1084.44	1984	3603.2
1018.33	1865	3389	1051.67	1925	3497	1085	1985	3605
1018.89	1866	3390.8	1052.22	1926	3498.8	1085.56	1986	3606.8
1019.44	1867	3392.6	1052.78	1927	3500.6	1086.11	1987	3608.6
1020.	1868	3394.4	1053.33	1928	3502.4	1086.67	1988	3610.4
1020.56	1869	3396.2	1053.89	1929	3504.2	1087.22	1989	3612.2
1021.11	1870	3398	1054.44	1930	3506	1087.78	1990	3614
1021.67	1871	3399.8	1055	1931	3507.8	1088.33	1991	3615.8
1022.22	1872	3401.6	1055.56	1932	3509.6	1088.89	1992	3617.6
1022.78	1873	3403.4	1056.11	1933	3511.4	1089.44	1993	3619.4
1023.33	1874	3405.2	1056.67	1934	3513.2	1090	1994	3621.2
1023.89	1875	3407	1057.22	1935	3515	1090.56	1995	3623
1024.44	1876	3408.8	1057.78	1936	3516.8	1091.11	1996	3624.8
1025	1877	3410.6	1058.33	1937	3518.6	1091.67	1997	3626.6
1025.56	1878	3412.4	1058.89	1938	3520.4	1092.22	1998	3628.4
1026.11	1879	3414.2	1059.44	1939	3522.2	1092.78	1999	3630.2
1026.67	1880	3416	1060	1940	3524	1093.33	2000	3632
1027.22	1881	3417.8	1060.56	1941	3525.8	1093.89	2001	3633.8
1027.78	1882	3419.6	1061.11	1942	3527.6	1094.44	2002	3635.6
1028.33	1883	3421.4	1061.67	1943	3529.4	1095	2003	3637.4
1028.89	1884	3423.2	1062.22	1944	3531.2	1095.56	2004	3639.2
1029.44	1885	3425	1062.78	1945	3533	1096.11	2005	3641
1030	1886	3426.8	1063.33	1946	3534.8	1096.67	2006	3642.8
1030.56	1887	3428.6	1063.89	1947	3536.6	1097.22	2007	3644.6
1031.11	1888	3430.4	1064.44	1948	3538.4	1097.78	2008	3646.4
1031.67	1889	3432.2	1065	1949	3540.2	1098.33	2009	3648.2
1032.22	1890	3434	1065.56	1950	3542	1098.89	2010	3650
1032.78	1891	3435.8	1066.11	1951	3543.8	1099.44	2011	3651.8
1033.33	1892	3437.6	1066.67	1952	3545.6	1100	2012	3653.6
1033.89	1893	3439.4	1067.22	1953	3547.4	1100.56	2013	3655.4
1034.44	1894	3441.2	1067.78	1954	3549.2	1101.11	2014	3657.2
1035	1895	3443	1068.33	1955	3551	1101.67	2015	3659
1035.56	1896	3444.8	1068.89	1956	3552.8	1102.22	2016	3660.8
1036.11	1897	3446.6	1069.44	1957	3554.6	1102.78	2017	3662.6
1036.67	1898	3448.4	1070	1958	3556.4	1103.33	2018	3664.4
1037.22	1899	3450.2	1070.56	1959	3558.2	1103.89	2019	3666.2
1037.78	1900	3452	1071.11	1960	3560	1104.44	2020	3668
1038.33	1901	3453.8	1071.67	1961	3561.8	1105	2021	3669.8
1038.89	1902	3455.6	1072.22	1962	3563.6	1105.56	2022	3671.6
1039.44	1903	3457.4	1072.78	1963	3565.4	1106.11	2023	3673.4
1040	1904	3459.2	1073.33	1964	3567.2	1106.67	2024	3675.2
1040.56	1905	3461	1073.89	1965	3569	1107.22	2025	3677
1041.11	1906	3462.8	1074.44	1966	3570.8	1107.78	2026	3678.8
1041.67	1907	3464.6	1075	1967	3572.6	1108.33	2027	3680.6
1042.22	1908	3466.4	1075.56	1968	3574.4	1108.89	2028	3682.4
1042.78	1909	3468.2	1076.11	1969	3576.2	1109.44	2029	3684.2

To Convert			To Convert			To Convert		
To °C	←°F or °C→	To °F	To °C	←°F or °C→	To °F	To °C	←°F or °C→	To °F
1110	2030	3686	1143.33	2090	3794	1176.67	2150	3902
1110.56	2031	3687.8	1143.89	2091	3795.8	1177.22	2151	3903.8
1111.11	2032	3689.6	1144.44	2092	3797.6	1177.78	2152	3905.6
1111.67	2033	3691.4	1145	2093	3799.4	1178.33	2153	3907.4
1112.22	2034	3693.2	1145.56	2094	3801.2	1178.89	2154	3909.2
1112.78	2035	3695	1146.11	2095	3803	1179.44	2155	3911
1113.33	2036	3696.8	1146.67	2096	3804.8	1180	2156	3912.8
1113.89	2037	3698.6	1147.22	2097	3806.6	1180.56	2157	3914.6
1114.44	2038	3700.4	1147.78	2098	3808.4	1181.11	2158	3916.4
1115	2039	3702.2	1148.33	2099	3810.2	1181.67	2159	3918.2
1115.56	2040	3704	1148.89	2100	3812	1182.22	2160	3920
1116.11	2041	3705.8	1149.44	2101	3813.8	1182.78	2161	3921.8
1116.67	2042	3707.6	1150	2102	3815.6	1183.33	2162	3923.6
1117.22	2043	3709.4	1150.56	2103	3817.4	1183.89	2163	3925.4
1117.78	2044	3711.2	1151.11	2104	3819.2	1184.44	2164	3927.2
1118.33	2045	3713	1151.67	2105	3821	1185	2165	3929
1118.89	2046	3714.8	1152.22	2106	3822.8	1185.56	2166	3930.8
1119.44	2047	3716.6	1152.78	2107	3824.6	1186.11	2167	3932.6
1120	2048	3718.4	1153.33	2108	3826.4	1186.67	2168	3934.4
1120.56	2049	3720.2	1153.89	2109	3828.2	1187.22	2169	3936.2
1121.11	2050	3722	1154.44	2110	3830	1187.78	2170	3938
1121.67	2051	3723.8	1155	2111	3831.8	1188.33	2171	3939.8
1122.22	2052	3725.6	1155.56	2112	3833.6	1188.89	2172	3941.6
1122.78	2053	3727.4	1156.11	2113	3835.4	1189.44	2173	3943.4
1123.33	2054	3729.2	1156.67	2114	3837.2	1190	2174	3945.2
1123.89	2055	3731	1157.22	2115	3839	1190.56	2175	3947
1124.44	2056	3732.8	1157.78	2116	3840.8	1191.11	2176	3948.8
1125	2057	3734.6	1158.33	2117	3842.6	1191.67	2177	3950.6
1125.56	2058	3736.4	1158.89	2118	3844.4	1192.22	2178	3952.4
1126.11	2059	3738.2	1159.44	2119	3846.2	1192.78	2179	3954.2
1126.67	2060	3740	1160	2120	3848	1193.33	2180	3956
1127.22	2061	3741.8	1160.56	2121	3849.8	1193.89	2181	3957.8
1127.78	2062	3743.6	1161.11	2122	3851.6	1194.44	2182	3959.6
1128.33	2063	3745.4	1161.67	2123	3853.4	1195	2183	3961.4
1128.89	2064	3747.2	1162.22	2124	3855.2	1195.56	2184	3963.2
1129.44	2065	3749	1162.78	2125	3857	1196.11	2185	3965
1130	2066	3750.8	1163.33	2126	3858.8	1196.67	2186	3966.8
1130.56	2067	3752.6	1163.89	2127	3860.6	1197.22	2187	3968.6
1131.11	2068	3754.4	1164.44	2128	3862.4	1197.78	2188	3970.4
1131.67	2069	3756.2	1165	2129	3864.2	1198.33	2189	3972.2
1132.22	2070	3758	1165.56	2130	3866	1198.89	2190	3974
1132.78	2071	3759.8	1166.11	2131	3867.8	1199.44	2191	3975.8
1133.33	2072	3761.6	1166.67	2132	3869.6	1200	2192	3977.6
1133.89	2073	3763.4	1167.22	2133	3871.4	1200.56	2193	3979.4
1134.44	2074	3765.2	1167.78	2134	3873.2	1201.11	2194	3981.2
1135	2075	3767	1168.33	2135	3875	1201.67	2195	3983
1135.56	2076	3768.8	1168.89	2136	3876.8	1202.22	2196	3984.8
1136.11	2077	3770.6	1169.44	2137	3878.6	1202.78	2197	3986.6
1136.67	2078	3772.4	1170	2138	3880.4	1203.33	2198	3988.4
1137.22	2079	3774.2	1170.56	2139	3882.2	1203.89	2199	3990.2
1137.78	2080	3776	1171.11	2140	3884	1204.44	2200	3992
1138.33	2081	3777.8	1171.67	2141	3885.8	1205	2201	3993.8
1138.89	2082	3779.6	1172.22	2142	3887.6	1205.56	2202	3995.6
1139.44	2083	3781.4	1172.78	2143	3889.4	1206.11	2203	3997.4
1140	2084	3783.2	1173.33	2144	3891.2	1206.67	2204	3999.2
1140.56	2085	3785	1173.89	2145	3893	1207.22	2205	4001
1141.11	2086	3786.8	1174.44	2146	3894.8	1207.78	2206	4002.8
1141.67	2087	3788.6	1175	2147	3896.6	1208.33	2207	4004.0
1142.22	2088	3790.4	1175.56	2148	3898.4	1208.89	2208	4006.4
1142.78	2089	3792.2	1176.11	2149	3900.2	1209.44	2209	4008.2

To °C	←°F or °C→	To °F	To °C	←°F or °C→	To °F	To °C	←°F or °C→	To °F
1210	2210	4010	1243.33	2270	4118	1276.67	2330	4226
1210.56	2211	4011.8	1243.89	2271	4119.8	1277.22	2331	4227.8
1211.11	2212	4013.6	1244.44	2272	4121.6	1277.78	2332	4229.6
1211.67	2213	4015.4	1245	2273	4123.4	1278.33	2333	4231.4
1212.22	2214	4017.2	1245.56	2274	4125.2	1278.89	2334	4233.2
1212.78	2215	4019	1246.11	2275	4127	1279.44	2335	4235
1213.33	2216	4020.8	1246.67	2276	4128.8	1280	2336	4236.8
1213.89	2217	4022.6	1247.22	2277	4130.6	1280.56	2337	4238.6
1214.44	2218	4024.4	1247.78	2278	4132.4	1281.11	2338	4240.4
1215	2219	4026.2	1248.33	2279	4134.2	1281.67	2339	4242.2
1215.56	2220	4028	1248.89	2280	4136	1282.22	2340	4244
1216.11	2221	4029.8	1249.44	2281	4137.8	1282.78	2341	4245.8
1216.67	2222	4031.6	1250	2282	4139.6	1283.33	2342	4247.6
1217.22	2223	4033.4	1250.56	2283	4141.4	1283.89	2343	4249.4
1217.78	2224	4035.2	1251.11	2284	4143.2	1284.44	2344	4251.2
1218.33	2225	4037	1251.67	2285	4145	1285	2345	4253
1218.89	2226	4038.8	1252.22	2286	4146.8	1285.56	2346	4254.8
1219.44	2227	4040.6	1252.78	2287	4148.6	1286.11	2347	4256.6
1220	2228	4042.4	1253.33	2288	4150.4	1286.67	2348	4258.4
1220.56	2229	4044.2	1253.89	2289	4152.2	1287.22	2349	4260.2
1221.11	2230	4046	1254.44	2290	4154	1287.78	2350	4262
1221.67	2231	4047.8	1255	2291	4155.8	1288.33	2351	4263.8
1222.22	2232	4049.6	1255.56	2292	4157.6	1288.89	2352	4265.6
1222.78	2233	4051.4	1256.11	2293	4159.4	1289.44	2353	4267.4
1223.33	2234	4053.2	1256.67	2294	4161.2	1290	2354	4269.2
1223.89	2235	4055	1257.22	2295	4163	1290.56	2355	4271
1224.44	2236	4056.8	1257.78	2296	4164.8	1291.11	2356	4272.8
1225	2237	4058.6	1258.33	2297	4166.6	1291.67	2357	4274.6
1225.56	2238	4060.4	1258.89	2298	4168.4	1292.22	2358	4276.4
1226.11	2239	4062.2	1259.44	2299	4170.2	1292.78	2359	4278.2
1226.67	2240	4064	1260	2300	4172	1293.33	2360	4280
1227.22	2241	4065.8	1260.56	2301	4173.8	1293.89	2361	4281.8
1227.78	2242	4067.6	1261.11	2302	4175.6	1294.44	2362	4283.6
1228.33	2243	4069.4	1261.67	2303	4177.4	1295	2363	4285.4
1228.89	2244	4071.2	1262.22	2304	4179.2	1295.56	2364	4287.2
1229.44	2245	4073	1262.78	2305	4181	1296.11	2365	4289
1230	2246	4074.8	1263.33	2306	4182.8	1296.67	2366	4290.8
1230.56	2247	4076.6	1263.89	2307	4184.6	1297.22	2367	4292.6
1231.11	2248	4078.4	1264.44	2308	4186.4	1297.78	2368	4294.4
1231.67	2249	4080.2	1265	2309	4188.2	1298.33	2369	4296.2
1232.22	2250	4082	1265.56	2310	4190	1298.89	2370	4298
1232.78	2251	4083.8	1266.11	2311	4191.8	1299.44	2371	4299.8
1233.33	2252	4085.6	1266.67	2312	4193.6	1300	2372	4301.6
1233.89	2253	4087.4	1267.22	2313	4195.4	1300.56	2373	4303.4
1234.44	2254	4089.2	1267.78	2314	4197.2	1301.11	2374	4305.2
1235	2255	4091	1268.33	2315	4199	1301.67	2375	4307
1235.56	2256	4092.8	1268.89	2316	4200.8	1302.22	2376	4308.8
1236.11	2257	4094.6	1269.44	2317	4202.6	1302.78	2377	4310.6
1236.67	2258	4096.4	1270	2318	4204.4	1303.33	2378	4312.4
1237.22	2259	4098.2	1270.56	2319	4206.2	1303.89	2379	4314.2
1237.78	2260	4100	1271.11	2320	4208	1304.44	2380	4316
1238.33	2261	4101.8	1271.67	2321	4209.8	1305	2381	4317.8
1238.89	2262	4103.6	1272.22	2322	4211.6	1305.56	2382	4319.6
1239.44	2263	4105.4	1272.78	2323	4213.4	1306.11	2383	4321.4
1240	2264	4107.2	1273.33	2324	4215.2	1306.67	2384	4323.2
1240.56	2265	4109	1273.89	2325	4217	1307.22	2385	4325
1241.11	2267	4110.8	1274.44	2326	4218.8	1307.78	2386	4326.8
1241.67	2267	4112.6	1275	2327	4220.6	1308.33	2387	4328.6
1242.22	2268	4114.4	1275.56	2328	4222.4	1308.89	2388	4330.4
1242.78	2269	4116.2	1276.11	2329	4224.2	1309.44	2389	4332.2

To Convert			To Convert			To Convert		
To °C	←°F or °C→	To °F	To °C	←°F or °C→	To °F	To °C	←°F or °C→	To °F
1310	2390	4334	1343.33	2450	4442	1376.67	2510	4550
1310.56	2391	4335.8	1343.89	2451	4443.8	1377.22	2511	4551.8
1311.11	2392	4337.6	1344.44	2452	4445.6	1377.78	2512	4553.6
1311.67	2393	4339.4	1345	2453	4447.4	1378.33	2513	4555.4
1312.22	2394	4341.2	1345.56	2454	4449.2	1378.89	2514	4557.2
1312.78	2395	4343	1346.11	2455	4451	1379.44	2515	4559
1313.33	2396	4344.8	1346.67	2456	4452.8	1380	2516	4560.8
1313.89	2397	4346.6	1347.22	2457	4454.6	1380.56	2517	4562.6
1314.44	2398	4348.4	1347.78	2458	4456.4	1381.11	2518	4564.4
1315	2399	4350.2	1348.33	2459	4458.2	1381.67	2519	4566.2
1315.56	2400	4352	1348.89	2460	4460	1382.22	2520	4568
1316.11	2401	4353.8	1349.44	2461	4461.8	1382.78	2521	4569.8
1316.67	2402	4355.6	1350	2462	4463.6	1383.33	2522	4571.6
1317.22	2403	4357.4	1350.56	2463	4465.4	1383.89	2523	4573.4
1317.78	2404	4359.2	1351.11	2464	4467.2	1384.44	2524	4575.2
1318.33	2405	4361	1351.67	2465	4469	1385	2525	4577
1318.89	2406	4362.8	1352.22	2466	4470.8	1385.56	2526	4578.8
1319.44	2407	4364.6	1352.78	2467	4472.6	1386.11	2527	4580.6
1320	2408	4366.4	1353.33	2468	4474.4	1386.67	2528	4582.4
1320.56	2409	4368.2	1353.89	2469	4476.2	1387.22	2529	4584.2
1321.11	2410	4370	1354.44	2470	4478	1387.78	2530	4586
1321.67	2411	4371.8	1355	2471	4479.8	1388.33	2531	4587.8
1322.22	2412	4373.6	1355.56	2472	4481.6	1388.89	2532	4589.6
1322.78	2413	4375.4	1356.11	2473	4483.4	1380.44	2533	4591.4
1323.33	2414	4377.2	1356.67	2474	4485.2	1390	2534	4593.2
1323.89	2415	4379	1357.22	2475	4487	1390.56	2535	4595
1324.44	2416	4380.8	1357.78	2476	4488.8	1391.11	2536	4596.8
1325	2417	4382.6	1358.33	2477	4490.6	1391.67	2537	4598.6
1325.56	2418	4384.4	1358.89	2478	4492.4	1392.22	2538	4600.4
1326.11	2419	4386.2	1359.44	2479	4494.2	1392.78	2539	4602.2
1326.67	2420	4388	1360	2480	4496	1393.33	2540	4604
1327.22	2421	4389.8	1360.56	2481	4497.8	1393.89	2541	4605.8
1327.78	2422	4391.6	1361.11	2482	4499.6	1394.44	2542	4607.6
1328.33	2423	4393.4	1361.67	2483	4501.4	1395	2543	4609.4
1328.89	2424	4395.2	1362.22	2484	4503.2	1395.56	2544	4611.2
1329.44	2425	4397	1362.78	2485	4505	1396.11	2545	4613
1330	2426	4398.8	1363.33	2486	4506.8	1396.67	2546	4614.8
1330.56	2427	4400.6	1363.89	2487	4508.6	1397.22	2547	4616.6
1331.11	2428	4402.4	1364.44	2488	4510.4	1397.78	2548	4618.4
1331.67	2429	4404.2	1365	2489	4512.2	1398.33	2549	4620.2
1332.22	2430	4406	1365.56	2490	4514	1398.89	2550	4622
1332.78	2431	4407.8	1366.11	2491	4515.8	1399.44	2551	4623.8
1333.33	2432	4409.6	1366.67	2492	4517.6	1400	2552	4625.6
1333.89	2433	4411.4	1367.22	2493	4519.4	1400.56	2553	4627.4
1334.44	2434	4413.2	1367.78	2494	4521.2	1401.11	2554	4629.2
1335	2435	4415	1368.33	2495	4523	1401.67	2555	4631
1335.56	2436	4416.8	1368.89	2496	4524.8	1402.22	2556	4632.8
1336.11	2437	4418.6	1369.44	2497	4526.6	1402.78	2557	4634.6
1336.67	2438	4420.4	1370	2498	4528.4	1403.33	2558	4636.4
1337.22	2439	4422.2	1370.56	2499	4530.2	1403.89	2559	4638.2
1337.78	2440	4424	1371.11	2500	4532	1404.44	2560	4640
1338.33	2441	4425.8	1371.67	2501	4533.8	1405	2561	4641.8
1338.89	2442	4427.6	1372.22	2502	4535.6	1405.56	2562	4643.6
1339.44	2443	4429.4	1372.78	2503	4537.4	1406.11	2563	4645.4
1340	2444	4431.2	1373.33	2504	4539.2	1406.67	2564	4647.2
1340.56	2445	4433	1373.89	2505	4541	1407.22	2565	4649
1341.11	2446	4434.8	1374.44	2506	4542.8	1407.78	2566	4650.8
1341.67	2447	4436.6	1375	2507	4544.6	1408.33	2567	4652.0
1342.22	2448	4438.4	1375.56	2508	4546.4	1408.89	2568	4654.4
1342.78	2449	4440.2	1376.11	2509	4548.2	1409.44	2569	4656.2

To Convert			To Convert			To Convert		
To °C	←°F or °C→	To °F	To °C	←°F or °C→	To °F	To °C	←°F or °C→	To °F
1410	2570	4658	1443.33	2630	4766	1476.67	2690	4874
1410.56	2571	4659.8	1443.89	2631	4767.8	1477.22	2691	4875.8
1411.11	2572	4661.6	1444.44	2632	4769.6	1477.78	2692	4877.6
1411.67	2573	4663.4	1445	2633	4771.4	1478.33	2693	4879.4
1412.22	2574	4665.2	1445.56	2634	4773.2	1478.89	2694	4881.2
1412.78	2575	4667	1446.11	2635	4775	1479.44	2695	4883
1413.33	2576	4668.8	1446.67	2636	4776.8	1480	2696	4884.8
1413.89	2577	4670.6	1447.22	2637	4778.6	1480.56	2697	4886.6
1414.44	2578	4672.4	1447.78	2638	4780.4	1481.11	2698	4888.4
1415	2579	4674.2	1448.33	2639	4782.2	1481.67	2699	4890.2
1415.56	2580	4676	1448.89	2640	4784	1482.22	2700	4892
1416.11	2581	4677.8	1449.44	2641	4785.8	1482.78	2701	4893.8
1416.67	2582	4679.6	1450	2642	4787.6	1483.33	2702	4895.6
1417.22	2583	4681.4	1450.56	2643	4789.4	1483.89	2703	4897.4
1417.78	2584	4683.2	1451.11	2644	4791.2	1484.44	2704	4899.2
1418.33	2585	4685	1451.67	2645	4793	1485	2705	4901
1418.89	2586	4686.8	1452.22	2646	4794.8	1485.56	2706	4902.8
1419.44	2587	4688.6	1452.78	2647	4796.6	1486.11	2707	4904.6
1420	2588	4690.4	1453.33	2648	4798.4	1486.67	2708	4906.4
1420.56	2589	4692.2	1453.89	2649	4800.2	1487.22	2709	4908.2
1421.11	2590	4694	1454.44	2650	4802	1487.78	2710	4910
1421.67	2591	4695.8	1455	2651	4803.8	1488.33	2711	4911.8
1422.22	2592	4697.6	1455.56	2652	4805.6	1488.89	2712	4913.6
1422.78	2593	4699.4	1456.11	2653	4807.4	1489.44	2713	4915.4
1423.33	2594	4701.2	1456.67	2654	4809.2	1490	2714	4917.2
1423.89	2595	4703	1457.22	2655	4811	1490.56	2715	4919
1424.44	2596	4704.8	1457.78	2656	4812.8	1491.11	2716	4920.8
1425	2597	4706.6	1458.33	2657	4814.6	1491.67	2717	4922.6
1425.56	2598	4708.4	1458.89	2658	4816.4	1492.22	2718	4924.4
1426.11	2599	4710.2	1459.44	2659	4818.2	1492.78	2719	4926.2
1426.67	2600	4712	1460	2660	4820	1493.33	2720	4928
1427.22	2601	4713.8	1460.56	2661	4821.8	1493.89	2721	4929.8
1427.78	2602	4715.6	1461.11	2662	4823.6	1494.44	2722	4931.6
1428.33	2603	4717.4	1461.67	2663	4825.4	1495	2723	4933.4
1428.89	2604	4719.2	1462.22	2664	4827.2	1495.56	2724	4935.2
1429.44	2605	4721	1462.78	2665	4829	1496.11	2725	4937
1430	2606	4722.8	1463.33	2666	4830.8	1496.67	2726	4938.8
1430.56	2607	4724.6	1463.89	2667	4832.6	1497.22	2727	4940.6
1431.11	2608	4726.4	1464.44	2668	4834.4	1497.78	2728	4942.4
1431.67	2609	4728.2	1465	2669	4836.2	1498.33	2729	4944.2
1432.22	2610	4730	1465.56	2670	4838	1498.89	2730	4946
1432.78	2611	4731.8	1466.11	2671	4839.8	1499.44	2731	4947.8
1433.33	2612	4733.6	1466.67	2672	4841.6	1500	2732	4949.6
1433.89	2613	4735.4	1467.22	2673	4843.4	1500.56	2733	4951.4
1434.44	2614	4737.2	1467.78	2674	4845.2	1501.11	2734	4953.2
1435	2615	4739	1468.33	2675	4847	1501.67	2735	4955
1435.56	2616	4740.8	1468.89	2676	4848.8	1502.22	2736	4956.8
1436.11	2617	4742.6	1469.44	2677	4850.6	1502.78	2737	4958.6
1436.67	2618	4744.4	1470	2678	4852.4	1503.33	2738	4960.4
1437.22	2619	4746.2	1470.56	2679	4854.2	1503.89	2739	4962.2
1437.78	2620	4748	1471.11	2680	4856	1504.44	2740	4964
1438.33	2621	4749.8	1471.67	2681	4857.8	1505	2741	4965.8
1438.89	2622	4751.6	1472.22	2682	4859.6	1505.56	2742	4967.6
1439.44	2623	4753.4	1472.78	2683	4861.4	1506.11	2743	4969.4
1440	2624	4755.2	1473.33	2684	4863.2	1506.67	2744	4971.2
1440.56	2625	4757	1473.89	2685	4865	1507.22	2745	4973
1441.11	2626	4758.8	1474.44	2686	4866.8	1507.78	2746	4974.8
1441.67	2627	4760.6	1475	2687	4868.6	1508.33	2747	4976.6
1442.22	2628	4762.4	1475.56	2688	4870.4	1508.89	2748	4978.4
1442.78	2629	4764.2	1476.11	2689	4872.2	1509.44	2749	4980.2

To Convert			To Convert			To Convert		
To °C	←°F or °C→	To °F	To °C	←°F or °C→	To °F	To °C	←°F or °C→	To °F
1510	2750	4982	1543.33	2810	5090	1576.67	2870	5198
1510.56	2751	4983.8	1543.89	2811	5091.8	1577.22	2871	5199.8
1511.11	2752	4985.6	1544.44	2812	5093.6	1577.78	2872	5201.6
1511.67	2753	4987.4	1545	2813	5095.4	1578.33	2873	5203.4
1512.22	2754	4989.2	1545.56	2814	5097.2	1578.89	2874	5205.2
1512.78	2755	4991	1546.11	2815	5099	1579.44	2875	5207
1513.33	2756	4992.8	1546.67	2816	5100.8	1580	2876	5208.8
1513.89	2757	4994.6	1547.22	2817	5102.6	1580.56	2877	5210.6
1514.44	2758	4996.4	1547.78	2818	5104.4	1581.11	2878	5212.4
1515	2759	4998.2	1548.33	2819	5106.2	1581.67	2879	5214.2
1515.56	2760	5000	1548.89	2820	5108	1582.22	2880	5216
1516.11	2761	5001.8	1549.44	2821	5109.8	1582.78	2881	5217.8
1516.67	2762	5003.6	1550	2822	5111.6	1583.33	2882	5219.6
1517.22	2763	5005.4	1550.56	2823	5113.4	1583.89	2883	5221.4
1517.78	2764	5007.2	1551.11	2824	5115.2	1584.44	2884	5223.2
1518.33	2765	5009	1551.67	2825	5117	1585	2885	5225
1518.89	2766	5010.8	1552.22	2826	5118.8	1585.56	2886	5226.8
1519.44	2767	5012.6	1552.78	2827	5120.6	1586.11	2887	5228.6
1520	2768	5014.4	1553.33	2828	5122.4	1586.67	2888	5230.4
1520.56	2769	5016.2	1553.89	2829	5124.2	1587.22	2889	5232.2
1521.11	2770	5018	1554.44	2830	5126	1587.78	2890	5234
1521.67	2771	5019.8	1555	2831	5127.8	1588.33	2891	5235.8
1522.22	2772	5021.6	1555.56	2832	5129.6	1588.89	2892	5237.6
1522.78	2773	5023.4	1556.11	2833	5131.4	1589.44	2893	5239.4
1523.33	2774	5025.2	1556.67	2834	5133.2	1590	2894	5241.2
1523.89	2775	5027	1557.22	2835	5135	1590.56	2895	5243
1524.44	2776	5028.8	1557.78	2836	5136.8	1591.11	2896	5244.8
1525	2777	5030.6	1558.33	2837	5138.6	1591.67	2897	5246.6
1525.56	2778	5032.4	1558.89	2838	5140.4	1592.22	2898	5248.4
1526.11	2779	5034.2	1559.44	2839	5142.2	1592.78	2899	5250.2
1526.67	2780	5036	1560	2840	5144	1593.33	2900	5252
1527.22	2781	5037.8	1560.56	2841	5145.8	1593.89	2901	5253.8
1527.78	2782	5039.6	1561.11	2842	5147.6	1594.44	2902	5255.6
1528.33	2783	5041.4	1561.67	2843	5149.4	1595	2903	5257.4
1528.89	2784	5043.2	1562.22	2844	5151.2	1595.56	2904	5259.2
1529.44	2785	5045	1562.78	2845	5153	1596.11	2905	5261
1530	2786	5046.8	1563.33	2846	5154.8	1596.67	2906	5262.8
1530.56	2787	5048.6	1563.89	2847	5156.6	1597.22	2907	5264.6
1531.11	2788	5050.4	1564.44	2848	5158.4	1597.78	2908	5266.4
1531.67	2789	5052.2	1565	2849	5160.2	1598.33	2909	5268.2
1532.22	2790	5054	1565.56	2850	5162	1598.89	2910	5270
1532.78	2791	5055.8	1566.11	2851	5163.8	1599.44	2911	5271.8
1533.33	2792	5057.6	1566.67	2852	5165.6	1600	2912	5273.6
1533.89	2793	5059.4	1567.22	2853	5167.4	1600.56	2913	5275.4
1534.44	2794	5061.2	1567.78	2854	5169.2	1601.11	2914	5277.2
1535	2795	5063	1568.33	2855	5171	1601.67	2915	5279
1535.56	2796	5064.8	1568.89	2856	5172.8	1602.22	2916	5280.8
1536.11	2797	5066.6	1569.44	2857	5174.6	1602.78	2917	5282.6
1536.67	2798	5068.4	1570	2858	5776.4	1603.33	2918	5284.4
1537.22	2799	5070.2	1570.56	2859	5178.2	1603.89	2919	5286.2
1537.78	2800	5072	1571.11	2860	5180	1604.44	2920	5288
1538.33	2801	5073.8	1571.67	2861	5181.8	1605	2921	5289.8
1538.89	2802	5075.6	1572.22	2862	5183.6	1605.56	2922	5291.6
1539.44	2803	5077.4	1572.78	2863	5185.4	1606.11	2923	5293.4
1540	2804	5079.2	1573.33	2864	5187.2	1606.67	2924	5295.2
1540.56	2805	5081	1573.89	2865	5189	1607.22	2925	5297
1541.11	2806	5082.8	1574.44	2866	5190.8	1607.78	2926	5298.8
1541.67	2807	5084.6	1575	2867	5192.6	1608.33	2927	5300.0
1542.22	2808	5086.4	1575.56	2868	5194.4	1608.89	2928	5302.4
1542.78	2809	5088.2	1576.11	2869	5196.2	1609.44	2929	5304.2

To Convert			To Convert			To Convert		
To °C	←°F or °C→	To °F	To °C	←°F or °C→	To °F	To °C	←°F or °C→	To °F
1610	2930	5306	1643.33	2990	5414	1676.67	3050	5522
1610.56	2931	5307.8	1643.89	2991	5415.8	1677.22	3051	5523.8
1611.11	2932	5309.6	1644.44	2992	5417.6	1677.78	3052	5525.6
1611.67	2933	5311.4	1645	2993	5419.4	1678.33	3053	5527.4
1612.22	2934	5313.2	1645.56	2994	5421.2	1678.89	3054	5529.2
1612.78	2935	5315	1646.11	2995	5423	1679.44	3055	5531
1613.33	2936	5316.8	1646.67	2996	5424.8	1680	3056	5532.8
1613.89	2937	5318.6	1647.22	2997	5426.6	1680.56	3057	5534.6
1614.44	2938	5320.4	1647.78	2998	5428.4	1681.11	3058	5536.4
1615	2939	5322.2	1648.33	2999	5430.2	1681.67	3059	5538.2
1615.56	2940	5324	1648.89	3000	5432	1682.22	3060	5540
1616.11	2941	5325.8	1649.44	3001	5433.8	1682.78	3061	5541.8
1616.67	2942	5327.6	1650	3002	5435.6	1683.33	3062	5543.6
1617.22	2943	5329.4	1650.56	3003	5437.4	1683.89	3063	5545.4
1617.78	2944	5331.2	1651.11	3004	5439.2	1684.44	3064	5547.2
1618.33	2945	5333	1651.67	3005	5441	1685	3065	5549
1618.89	2946	5334.8	1652.22	3006	5442.8	1685.56	3066	5550.8
1619.44	2947	5336.6	1652.78	3007	5444.6	1686.11	3067	5552.6
1620	2948	5338.4	1653.33	3008	5446.4	1686.67	3068	5554.4
1620.56	2949	5340.2	1653.89	3009	5448.2	1687.22	3069	5556.2
1621.11	2950	5342	1654.44	3010	5450	1687.78	3070	5558
1621.67	2951	5343.8	1655	3011	5451.8	1688.33	3071	5559.8
1622.22	2952	5345.6	1655.56	3012	5453.6	1688.89	3072	5561.6
1622.78	2953	5347.4	1656.11	3013	5455.4	1689.44	3073	5563.4
1623.33	2954	5349.2	1656.67	3014	5457.2	1690	3074	5565.2
1623.89	2955	5351	1657.22	3015	5459	1690.56	3075	5567
1624.44	2956	5352.8	1657.78	3016	5460.8	1691.11	3076	5568.8
1625	2957	5354.6	1658.33	3017	5462.6	1691.67	3077	5570.6
1625.56	2958	5356.4	1658.89	3018	5464.4	1692.22	3078	5572.4
1626.11	2959	5358.2	1659.44	3019	5466.2	1692.78	3079	5574.2
1626.67	2960	5360	1660	3020	5468	1693.33	3080	5576
1627.22	2961	5361.8	1660.56	3021	5469.8	1693.89	3081	5577.8
1627.78	2962	5363.6	1661.11	3022	5471.6	1694.44	3082	5579.6
1628.33	2963	5365.4	1661.67	3023	5473.4	1695	3083	5581.4
1628.89	2964	5367.2	1662.22	3024	5475.2	1695.56	3084	5583.2
1629.44	2965	5369	1662.78	3025	5477	1696.11	3085	5585
1630	2966	5370.8	1663.33	3026	5478.8	1696.67	3086	5586.8
1630.56	2967	5372.6	1663.89	3027	5480.6	1697.22	3087	5588.6
1631.11	2968	5374.4	1664.44	3028	5482.4	1697.78	3088	5590.4
1631.67	2969	5376.2	1665	3029	5484.2	1698.33	3089	5592.2
1632.22	2970	5378	1665.56	3030	5486	1698.89	3090	5594
1632.78	2971	5379.8	1666.11	3031	5487.8	1699.44	3091	5595.8
1633.33	2972	5381.6	1666.67	3032	5489.6	1700	3092	5597.6
1633.89	2973	5383.4	1667.22	3033	5491.4	1700.56	3093	5599.4
1634.44	2974	5385.2	1667.78	3034	5493.2	1701.11	3094	5601.2
1635	2975	5387	1668.33	3035	5495	1701.67	3095	5603
1635.56	2976	5388.8	1668.89	3036	5496.8	1702.22	3096	5604.8
1636.11	2977	5390.6	1669.44	3037	5498.6	1702.78	3097	5606.6
1636.67	2978	5392.4	1670	3038	5500.4	1703.33	3098	5608.4
1637.22	2979	5394.2	1670.56	3039	5502.2	1703.89	3099	5610.2
1637.78	2980	5396	1671.11	3040	5504	1704.44	3100	5612
1638.33	2981	5397.8	1671.67	3041	5505.8	1705	3101	5613.8
1638.89	2982	5399.6	1672.22	3042	5507.6	1705.56	3102	5615.6
1639.44	2983	5401.4	1672.78	3043	5509.4	1706.11	3103	5617.4
1640	2984	5403.2	1673.33	3044	5511.2	1706.67	3104	5619.2
1640.56	2985	5405	1673.89	3045	5513	1707.22	3105	5621
1641.11	2986	5406.8	1674.44	3046	5514.8	1707.78	3106	5622.8
1641.67	2987	5408.6	1675	3047	5516.6	1708.33	3107	5624.6
1642.22	2988	5410.4	1675.56	3048	5518.4	1708.89	3108	5626.4
1642.78	2989	5412.2	1676.11	3049	5520.2	1709.44	3109	5628.2

To °C	←°F or °C→	To °F	To °C	←°F or °C→	To °F	To °C	←°F or °C→	To °F
	To Convert			To Convert			To Convert	
1710	3110	5630	1743.33	3170	5738	1776.67	3230	5846
1710.56	3111	5631.8	1743.89	3171	5739.8	1777.22	3231	5847.8
1711.11	3112	5633.6	1744.44	3172	5741.6	1777.78	3232	5849.6
1711.67	3113	5635.4	1745	3173	5743.4	1778.33	3233	5851.4
1712.22	3114	5637.2	1745.56	3174	5745.2	1778.89	3234	5853.2
1712.78	3115	5639	1746.11	3175	5747	1779.44	3235	5855
1713.33	3116	5640.8	1746.67	3176	5748.8	1780	3236	5856.8
1713.89	3117	5642.6	1747.22	3177	5750.6	1780.56	3237	5858.6
1714.44	3118	5644.4	1747.78	3178	5752.4	1781.11	3238	5860.4
1715	3119	5646.2	1748.33	3179	5754.2	1781.67	3239	5862.2
1715.56	3120	5648	1748.89	3180	5756	1782.22	3240	5864
1716.11	3121	5649.8	1749.44	3181	5757.8	1782.78	3241	5865.8
1716.67	3122	5651.6	1750	3182	5759.6	1783.33	3242	5867.6
1717.22	3123	5653.4	1750.56	3183	5761.4	1783.89	3243	5869.4
1717.78	3124	5655.2	1751.11	3184	5763.2	1784.44	3244	5871.2
1718.33	3125	5657	1751.67	3185	5765	1785	3245	5873
1718.89	3126	5658.8	1752.22	3186	5766.8	1785.56	3246	5874.8
1719.44	3127	5660.6	1752.78	3187	5768.6	1786.11	3247	5876.6
1720	3128	5662.4	1753.33	3188	5770.4	1786.67	3248	5878.4
1720.56	3129	5664.2	1753.89	3189	5772.2	1787.22	3249	5880.2
1721.11	3130	5666	1754.44	3190	5774	1787.78	3250	5882
1721.67	3131	5667.8	1755	3191	5775.8	1788.33	3251	5883.8
1722.22	3132	5669.6	1755.56	3192	5777.6	1788.89	3252	5885.6
1722.78	3133	5671.4	1756.11	3193	5779.4	1789.44	3253	5887.4
1723.33	3134	5673.2	1756.67	3194	5781.2	1790	3254	5889.2
1723.89	3135	5675	1757.22	3195	5783	1790.56	3255	5891
1724.44	3136	5676.8	1757.78	3196	5784.8	1791.11	3256	5892.8
1725	3137	5678.6	1758.33	3197	5786.6	1791.67	3257	5894.6
1725.56	3138	5680.4	1758.89	3198	5788.4	1792.22	3258	5896.4
1726.11	3139	5682.2	1759.44	3199	5790.2	1792.78	3259	5898.2
1726.67	3140	5684	1760	3200	5792	1793.33	3260	5900
1727.22	3141	5685.8	1760.56	3201	5793.8	1793.89	3261	5901.8
1727.78	3142	5687.6	1761.11	3202	5795.6	1794.44	3262	5903.6
1728.33	3143	5689.4	1761.67	3203	5797.4	1795	3263	5905.4
1728.89	3144	5691.2	1762.22	3204	5799.2	1795.56	3264	5907.2
1729.44	3145	5693	1762.78	3205	5801	1796.11	3265	5909
1730	3146	5694.8	1763.33	3206	5802.8	1796.67	3266	5910.8
1730.56	3147	5696.6	1763.89	3207	5804.6	1797.22	3267	5912.6
1731.11	3148	5698.4	1764.44	3208	5806.4	1797.78	3268	5914.4
1731.67	3149	5700.2	1765	3209	5808.2	1798.33	3269	5916.2
1732.22	3150	5702	1765.56	3210	5810	1798.89	3270	5918
1732.78	3151	5703.8	1766.11	3211	5811.8	1799.44	3271	5919.8
1733.33	3152	5705.6	1766.67	3212	5813.6	1800	3272	5921.6
1733.89	3153	5707.4	1767.22	3213	5815.4	1800.56	3273	5923.4
1734.44	3154	5709.2	1767.78	3214	5817.2	1801.11	3274	5925.2
1735	3155	5711	1768.33	3215	5819	1801.67	3275	5927
1735.56	3156	5712.8	1768.89	3216	5820.8	1802.22	3276	5928.8
1736.11	3157	5714.6	1769.44	3217	5822.6	1802.78	3277	5930.6
1736.67	3158	5716.4	1770	3218	5824.4	1803.33	3278	5932.4
1737.22	3159	5718.2	1770.56	3219	5826.2	1803.89	3279	5934.2
1737.78	3160	5720	1771.11	3220	5828	1804.44	3280	5936
1738.33	3161	5721.8	1771.67	3221	5829.8	1805	3281	5937.8
1738.89	3162	5723.6	1772.22	3222	5831.6	1805.56	3282	5939.6
1739.44	3163	5725.4	1772.78	3223	5833.4	1806.11	3283	5941.4
1740	3164	5727.2	1773.33	3224	5835.2	1806.67	3284	5943.2
1740.56	3165	5729	1773.89	3225	5837	1807.22	3285	5945
1741.11	3166	5730.8	1774.44	3226	5838.8	1807.78	3286	5946.8
1741.67	3167	5732.6	1775	3227	5840.6	1808.33	3287	5948.6
1742.22	3168	5734.4	1775.56	3228	5842.4	1808.89	3288	5950.4
1742.78	3169	5736.2	1776.11	3229	5844.2	1809.44	3289	5952.2

To Convert			To Convert			To Convert		
To °C	←°F or °C→	To °F	To °C	←°F or °C→	To °F	To °C	←°F or °C→	To °F
1810	3290	5954	1954.44	3550	6422	2121.11	3850	6962
1810.56	3291	5955.8	1957.22	3555	6431	2123.89	3855	6971
1811.11	3292	5957.6	1960.00	3560	6440	2126.67	3860	6980
1811.67	3293	5959.4	1962.78	3565	6449	2129.44	3865	6989
1812.22	3294	5961.2	1965.56	3570	6458	2132.22	3870	6998
1812.78	3295	5963	1968.33	3575	6467	2135.00	3875	7007
1813.33	3296	5964.8	1971.11	3580	6476	2137.78	3880	7016
1813.89	3297	5966.6	1973.89	3585	6485	2140.56	3885	7025
1814.44	3298	5968.4	1976.67	3590	6494	2143.33	3890	7034
1815	3299	5970.2	1979.44	3595	6503	2145.11	3895	7043
1815.56	3300	5972	1982.22	3600	6512	2148.89	3900	7052
1818.33	3305	5981	1985.00	3605	6521	2151.67	3905	7061
1821.11	3310	5990	1987.78	3610	6530	2154.44	3910	7070
1823.89	3315	5999	1990.56	3615	6539	2157.22	3915	7079
1826.67	3320	6008	1993.33	3620	6548	2160.00	3920	7088
1829.44	3325	6017	1996.11	3625	6557	2162.78	3925	7097
1832.22	3330	6026	1998.89	3630	6566	2165.56	3930	7106
1835.00	3335	6035	2001.67	3635	6575	2168.33	3935	7115
1837.78	3340	6044	2004.44	3640	6584	2171.11	3940	7124
1840.56	3345	6053	2007.22	3645	6593	2173.89	3945	7133
1843.33	3350	6062	2010.00	3650	6602	2176.67	3950	7142
1846.11	3355	6071	2012.78	3655	6611	2179.44	3955	7151
1848.89	3360	6080	2015.56	3660	6620	2182.22	3960	7160
1851.67	3365	6089	2018.33	3665	6629	2185.00	3965	7169
1854.44	3370	6098	2021.11	3670	6638	2187.78	3970	7178
1857.22	3375	6107	2023.89	3675	6647	2190.56	3975	7187
1860.00	3380	6116	2026.67	3680	6656	2193.33	3980	7196
1862.78	3385	6125	2029.44	3685	6665	2196.11	3985	7205
1865.56	3390	6134	2032.22	3690	6674	2198.89	3990	7214
1868.33	3395	6143	2035.00	3695	6683	2201.67	3995	7223
1871.11	3400	6152	2037.78	3700	6692	2204.44	4000	7232
1873.89	3405	6161	2040.56	3705	6701	2207.22	4005	7241
1876.67	3410	6170	2043.33	3710	6710	2210.00	4010	7250
1879.44	3415	6179	2046.11	3715	6719	2212.78	4015	7259
1882.22	3420	6188	2048.89	3720	6728	2215.56	4020	7268
1885.00	3425	6197	2051.67	3725	6737	2218.33	4025	7277
1887.78	3430	6206	2054.44	3730	6746	2221.11	4030	7286
1890.56	3435	6215	2057.22	3735	6755	2223.89	4035	7295
1893.33	3440	6224	2060.00	3740	6764	2226.67	4040	7304
1896.11	3445	6233	2062.78	3745	6773	2229.44	4045	7313
1898.89	3450	6242	2065.56	3750	6782	2232.22	4050	7322
1901.67	3455	6251	2068.33	3755	6791	2235.00	4055	7331
1904.44	3460	6260	2071.11	3760	6800	2237.78	4060	7340
1907.22	3465	6269	2073.89	3765	6809	2240.56	4065	7349
1910.00	3470	6278	2076.67	3770	6818	2243.33	4070	7358
1912.78	3475	6287	2079.44	3775	6827	2246.11	4075	7367
1915.56	3480	6296	2082.22	3780	6836	2248.89	4080	7376
1918.33	3485	6305	2085.00	3785	6845	2251.67	4085	7385
1921.11	3490	6314	2087.78	3790	6854	2254.44	4090	7394
1923.89	3495	6323	2090.56	3795	6863	2257.22	4095	7403
1926.67	3500	6332	2093.33	3800	6872	2260.00	4100	7412
1929.44	3505	6341	2096.11	3805	6881	2262.78	4105	7421
1932.22	3510	6350	2098.89	3810	6890	2265.56	4110	7430
1935.00	3515	6359	2101.67	3815	6899	2268.33	4115	7439
1937.78	3520	6368	2104.44	3820	6908	2271.11	4120	7448
1940.56	3525	6377	2107.22	3825	6917	2273.89	4125	7457
1943.33	3530	6386	2110.00	3830	6926	2276.67	4130	7466
1946.11	3535	6395	2112.78	3835	6935	2279.44	4135	7475
1948.89	3540	6404	2115.56	3840	6944	2282.22	4140	7484
1951.67	3545	6413	2118.33	3845	6953	2285.00	4145	7493

To Convert			To Convert			To Convert		
To °C	←°F or °C→	To °F	To °C	←°F or °C→	To °F	To °C	←°F or °C→	To °F
2287.78	4150	7502	2354.44	4270	7718	2421.11	4390	7934
2290.56	4155	7511	2357.22	4275	7727	2423.89	4395	7943
2293.33	4160	7520	2360.00	4280	7736	2426.67	4400	7952
2296.11	4165	7529	2362.78	4285	7745	2429.44	4405	7961
2298.89	4170	7538	2365.56	4290	7754	2432.22	4410	7970
2301.67	4175	7547	2368.33	4295	7763	2435.00	4415	7979
2304.44	4180	7556	2371.11	4300	7772	2437.78	4420	7988
2307.22	4185	7565	2373.89	4305	7781	2440.56	4425	7997
2310.00	4190	7574	2376.67	4310	7790	2443.33	4430	8006
2312.78	4195	7583	2379.44	4315	7799	2446.11	4435	8015
2315.56	4200	7592	2382.22	4320	7808	2448.89	4440	8024
2318.33	4205	7601	2385.00	4325	7817	2451.67	4445	8033
2321.11	4210	7610	2387.78	4330	7826	2454.44	4450	8042
2323.89	4215	7619	2390.56	4335	7835	2457.22	4455	8051
2326.67	4220	7628	2393.33	4340	7844	2460.00	4460	8060
2329.44	4225	7637	2396.11	4345	7853	2462.78	4465	8069
2332.22	4230	7646	2398.89	4350	7862	2465.56	4470	8078
2335.00	4235	7655	2401.67	4355	7871	2468.33	4475	8087
2337.78	4240	7664	2404.44	4360	7880	2471.11	4480	8096
2340.56	4245	7673	2407.22	4365	7889	2473.89	4485	8105
2343.33	4250	7682	2410.00	4370	7898	2476.67	4490	8114
2346.11	4255	7691	2412.78	4375	7907	2479.44	4495	8123
2348.89	4260	7700	2415.56	4380	7916	2482.22	4500	8132
2351.67	4265	7709	2418.33	4385	7925			

STANDARD TYPES OF STAINLESS AND HEAT RESISTING STEELS
Chemical Ranges and Limits
Subject to Tolerances for Check Analyses
By permission of American Iron and Steel Institute

						Chemical Composition, per cent								
Type Number	C	Mn Max.	P Max.	S Max.	Si Max.	Cr	Ni	Mo	Zr	Se	Cb-Ta	Ta	Al	N
⁻201	0.15 Max.	5.50/ 7.50	0.060	0.030	1.00	16.00/ 18.00	3.50/ 5.50							0.25 Max.
⁻202	0.15 Max.	7.50/ 10.00	0.060	0.030	1.00	17.00/ 19.00	4.00/ 6.00							0.25 Max.
⁻301	0.15 Max.	2.00	0.045	0.030	1.00	16.00/ 18.00	6.00/ 8.00							
⁻302	0.15 Max.	2.00	0.045	0.030	1.00	17.00/ 19.00	8.00/ 10.00							
⁻302B	0.15 Max.	2.00	0.045	0.030	2.00/ 3.00	17.00/ 19.00	8.00/ 10.00							
⁻303	0.15 Max.	2.00	0.20	0.15 Min.	1.00	17.00/ 19.00	8.00/ 10.00	0.60* Max.	0.60* Max.					
⁻303 Se	0.15 Max.	2.00	0.20	0.06	1.00	17.00/ 19.00	8.00/ 10.00			0.15 Min.				
⁻304	0.08 Max	2.00	0.045	0.030	1.00	18.00/ 20.00	8.00/ 12.00							
⁻304L	0.03 Max.	2.00	0.045	0.030	1.00	18.00/ 20.00	8.00/ 12.00							
⁻305	0.12 Max.	2.00	0.045	0.030	1.00	17.00/ 19.00	10.00/ 13.00							
⁻308	0.08 Max.	2.00	0.045	0.030	1.00	19.00/ 21.00	10.00/ 12.00							
⁻309	0.20 Max.	2.00	0.045	0.030	1.00	22.00/ 24.00	12.00/ 15.00							
⁻309S	0.08 Max.	2.00	0.045	0.030	1.00	22.00/ 24.00	12.00/ 15.00							
⁻310	0.25 Max.	2.00	0.045	0.030	1.50	24.00/ 26.00	19.00/ 22.00							
⁻310S	0.08 Max.	2.00	0.045	0.030	1.50	24.00/ 26.00	19.00/ 22.00							
⁻314	0.25 Max.	2.00	0.045	0.030	1.50/ 3.00	23.00/ 26.00	19.00/ 22.00							
⁻316	0.08 Max.	2.00	0.045	0.030	1.00	16.00/ 18.00	10.00/ 14.00	2.00/ 3.00						
⁻316L	0.03 Max.	2.00	0.045	0.030	1.00	16.00/ 18.00	10.00/ 14.00	2.00/ 3.00						
⁻317	0.08 Max.	2.00	0.045	0.030	1.00	18.00/ 20.00	11.00/ 15.00	3.00/ 4.00						
⁻321	0.08 Max.	2.00	0.045	0.030	1.00	17.00/ 19.00	9.00/ 12.00				5 × C Min.			
⁻347	0.08 Max.	2.00	0.045	0.030	1.00	17.00/ 19.00	9.00/ 13.00					10 × C Min.		
⁻348	0.08 Max.	2.00	0.045	0.030	1.00	17.00/ 19.00	9.00/ 13.00				10 × C Min.	0.10 Max.		
**403	0.15 Max.	1.00	0.040	0.030	0.50	11.50/ 13.00								
°405	0.08 Max.	1.00	0.040	0.030	1.00	11.50/ 14.50							0.10/ 0.30	
**410	0.15 Max.	1.00	0.040	0.030	1.00	11.50/ 13.50								
**414	0.15 Max.	1.00	0.040	0.030	1.00	11.50/ 13.50	1.25/ 2.50							
**416	0.15 Max.	1.25	0.06	0.15 Min.	1.00	12.00/ 14.00		0.60* Max.	0.60* Max.					
**416 Se	0.15 Max.	1.25	0.06	0.06	1.00	12.00/ 14.00				0.15 Min.				
**420	Over 0.15	1.00	0.040	0.030	1.00	12.00/ 14.00								

* At producer's option; reported only when intentionally added.
** Heat treatable.
⁻ Not heat treatable.
° Essentially not heat treatable.

Chemical Composition, per cent

Type Number	C	Mn Max.	P Max.	S Max.	Si Max.	Cr	Ni	Mo	Zr	Se	Cb-Ta	Ta	Al	N
°430	0.12 Max.	1.00	0.040	0.030	1.00	14.00/ 18.00								
°430F	0.12 Max.	1.25	0.06	0.15 Min.	1.00	14.00/ 18.00		0.60* Max.	0.60* Max.					
°430F Se	0.12 Max.	1.25	0.06	0.06	1.00	14.00/ 18.00				0.15 Min.				
**431	0.20 Max.	1.00	0.040	0.030	1.00	15.00/ 17.00	1.25/ 2.50							
**440A	0.60/ 0.75	1.00	0.040	0.030	1.00	16.00/ 18.00		0.75 Max.						
**400B	0.75/ 0.95	1.00	0.040	0.030	1.00	16.00/ 18.00		0.75 Max.						
**440C	0.95/ 1.20	1.00	0.040	0.030	1.00	16.00/ 18.00		0.75 Max.						
°446	0.20 Max.	1.50	0.040	0.030	1.00	23.00/ 27.00								0.25 Max.
**501	Over 0.10	1.00	0.040	0.030	1.00	4.00/ 6.00		0.40/ 0.65						
**502	0.10 Max.	1.00	0.040	0.030	1.00	4.00/ 6.00		0.40/ 0.65						

* At producer's option; reported only when intentionally added.
** Heat treatable.
– Not heat treatable.
° Essentially not heat treatable.

STANDARD TEST SIEVES (WIRE CLOTH)

Sieve Designation		Nominal Sieve Opening in	Permissible Variation of Average Opening from the Standard Sieve Designation	Maximum Opening Size for Not More than 5 percent of Openings	Maximum Individual Opening	Nominal Wire Diameter, mm[a]
Standard	Alternative					
(1)	(2)	(3)	(4)	(5)	(6)	(7)
125 mm	5 in.	5	±3.7 mm	130.0 mm	130.9 mm	8.0
106 mm	4.24 in.	4.24	±3.2 mm	110.2 mm	111.1 mm	6.40
100 mm	4 in.	4	±3.0 mm	104.0 mm	104.8 mm	6.30
90 mm	3½ in.	3.5	±2.7 mm	93.6 mm	94.4 mm	6.08
75 mm	3 in.	3	±2.2 mm	78.1 mm	78.7 mm	5.80
63 mm	2½ in.	2.5	±1.9 mm	65.6 mm	66.2 mm	5.50
53 mm	2.12 in.	2.12	±1.6 mm	55.2 mm	55.7 mm	5.15
50 mm	2 in.	2	±1.5 mm	52.1 mm	52.6 mm	5.05
45 mm	1¾ in.	1.75	±1.4 mm	46.9 mm	47.4 mm	4.85
37.5 mm	1½ in.	1.5	±1.1 mm	39.1 mm	39.5 mm	4.59
31.5 mm	1¼ in.	1.25	±1.0 mm	32.9 mm	33.2 mm	4.23
26.5 mm	1.06 in.	1.06	±0.8 mm	27.7 mm	28.0 mm	3.90
25.0 mm	1 in.	1	±0.8 mm	26.1 mm	26.4 mm	3.80
22.4 mm	⅞ in.	0.875	±0.7 mm	23.4 mm	23.7 mm	3.50
19.0 mm	¾ in.	0.750	±0.6 mm	19.9 mm	20.1 mm	3.30
16.0 mm	⅝ in.	0.625	±0.5 mm	16.7 mm	17.0 mm	3.00
13.2 mm	0.530 in.	0.530	±0.41 mm	13.83 mm	14.05 mm	2.75
12.5 mm	½ in.	0.500	±0.39 mm	13.10 mm	13.31 mm	2.67
11.2 mm	⁷⁄₁₆ in.	0.438	±0.35 mm	11.75 mm	11.94 mm	2.45
9.5 mm	⅜ in.	0.375	±0.30 mm	9.97 mm	10.16 mm	2.27
8.0 mm	⁵⁄₁₆ in.	0.312	±0.25 mm	8.41 mm	8.58 mm	2.07
6.7 mm	0.265 in.	0.265	±0.21 mm	7.05 mm	7.20 mm	1.87
6.3 mm	¼ in.	0.250	±0.20 mm	6.64 mm	6.78 mm	1.82
5.6 mm	No. 3½	0.223	±0.18 mm	5.90 mm	6.04 mm	1.68
4.75 mm	No. 4	0.187	±0.15 mm	5.02 mm	5.14 mm	1.54
4.00 mm	No. 5	0.157	±0.13 mm	4.23 mm	4.35 mm	1.37
3.35 mm	No. 6	0.132	±0.11 mm	3.55 mm	3.66 mm	1.23
2.80 mm	No. 7	0.111	±0.095 mm	2.975 mm	3.070 mm	1.10
2.36 mm	No. 8	0.0937	±0.080 mm	2.515 mm	2.600 mm	1.00
2.00 mm	No. 10	0.0787	±0.070 mm	2.135 mm	2.215 mm	0.900
1.70 mm	No. 12	0.0661	±0.060 mm	1.820 mm	1.890 mm	0.810
1.40 mm	No. 14	0.0555	±0.050 mm	1.505 mm	1.565 mm	0.725
1.18 mm	No. 16	0.0469	±0.045 mm	1.270 mm	1.330 mm	0.650
1.00 mm	No. 18	0.0394	±0.040 mm	1.080 mm	1.135 mm	0.580
850 μm	No. 20	0.0331	±35 μm	925 μm	970 μm	0.510
710 μm	No. 25	0.0278	±30 μm	775 μm	815 μm	0.450
600 μm	No. 30	0.0234	±25 μm	660 μm	695 μm	0.390
500 μm	No. 35	0.0197	±20 μm	550 μm	585 μm	0.340
425 μm	No. 40	0.0165	±19 μm	471 μm	502 μm	0.290
355 μm	No. 45	0.0139	±16 μm	396 μm	425 μm	0.247
300 μm	No. 50	0.0117	±14 μm	337 μm	363 μm	0.215
250 μm	No. 60	0.0098	±12 μm	283 μm	306 μm	0.180
212 μm	No. 70	0.0083	±10 μm	242 μm	263 μm	0.152
180 μm	No. 80	0.0070	±9 μm	207 μm	227 μm	0.131
150 μm	No. 100	0.0059	±8 μm	174 μm	192 μm	0.110
125 μm	No. 120	0.0049	±7 μm	147 μm	163 μm	0.091
106 μm	No. 140	0.0041	±6 μm	126 μm	141 μm	0.076
90 μm	No. 170	0.0035	±5 μm	108 μm	122 μm	0.064
75 μm	No. 200	0.0029	±5 μm	91 μm	103 μm	0.053
63 μm	No. 230	0.0025	±4 μm	77 μm	89 μm	0.044
53 μm	No. 270	0.0021	±4 μm	66 μm	76 μm	0.037
45 μm	No. 325	0.0017	±3 μm	57 μm	66 μm	0.030
38 μm	No. 400	0.0015	±3 μm	48 μm	57 μm	0.025

[a] The average diameter of the warp and of the shoot wires, taken separately, of the cloth of any sieve shall not deviate from the nominal values by more than the following:

Sieves coarser than 600 μm	5 percent
Sieves 600 to 125 μm	7½ percent
Sieves finer than 125 μm	10 percent

PHYSICAL PROPERTIES OF GLASS SEALING AND LEAD WIRE MATERIALS

From General Electric Company

	Copper OFC	Copper 0.02P	Dumet	42 Ni	Gas Free 42% Ni	42-6 Ni Cr.	46 Ni	52 Ni.	27 Cr.	® Kovar	W	Mo	Nickel 200
Analysis: Carbon				0.10	0.05	0.10	0.10	0.10	0.15	0.02			0.06
Manganese				0.50	0.50	0.50	0.50	0.50	0.60	0.30			0.25
Silicon			*Copper Clad*	0.25	0.25	0.25	0.25	0.25	0.40	0.20			0.05
Chromium			*42% Nickel*	—	—	5.75	—	—	28.00	—			
Nickel	99.95	99.90	*Iron*	42	42	42.5	46	51	0.50	29			99.5
Copper		P	*See GE Spec.*	—	—	—	—	—	—	—			0.05
		0.02	*DS 8311-01*		Ti0.4		Ti0.4			Co 17			
Other				Bal.Fe	Bal.Fe	Bal.Fe	Bal.Fe	Bal.Fe	Bal.Fe	Bal.Fe			
Density: grams/cc	8.94	8.94	8.26 to 8.32	8.12	8.12	8.12	8.17	8.30	7.60	8.36	19.3	10.2	8.89
lbs. per cu. in.	0.323	0.323	0.298—0.301	0.293	0.293	0.293	0.295	0.300	0.274	0.302	0.697	0.369	0.321
Thermal Conductivity 20-100°/C													
Cal/cm/sec/cm²/°C	0.948	0.8	0.2—0.3	0.025	0.025	0.029	0.028	0.032	0.054	0.04	0.31	0.34	0.15
Btu/in/hr/sq. ft/°F	2750	2320	580—870	74	74	84	81	93	158	116	900	1000	435
Electrical Resistivity (20°C)													
Microhm—cm	1.71	2.03	7.3 to 12.0	72	72	95	46	43	63	49	5.5	5.2	9.5
Ohm per cir. mil ft.	10.3	12.2	44 to 72	430	430	570	275	258	380	294	33	31	57
Elec. Cond. % IACS	101	85	23 to 14	2.3	2.3	1.8	3.6	3.9	2.8	3.4	31	33	18
Curie Temperature °C	—	—	380	380	380	295	460	530	610	435			360
Melting Temperature °C	1083	1083	— —	1425	1425	1425	1425	1425	1425	1450	3410	2610	1455
°F	1981	1981	— —	2597	2597	2597	2597	2597	2597	2642	6170	4730	2651
Specific Heat cal/gr.	0.092	0.092	0.11	0.12	0.12	0.12	0.12	0.12	0.14	0.11	0.033	0.066	0.13
Thermal Expansion in/in/°C x10⁷			*Radial*										
25-100°C	168	168	60 to 80	50.1	43.4	65.5	71.0	99.5	94.6	58.6	45	51	133
25-200°C	172	172		47.1	44.1	70.8	73.7	101.0	100.5	52.0	46		139
25-300°C	177	177	60 to 80	47.6	46.1	82.6	75.0	101.0	105.3	51.3	46		144
25-350°C	178	178	65 to 85	50.5		90.4	74.4	100.0	107.0	48.9	46		146
25-400°C	181	181	80 to 100	62.5	64.1	100.0	74.3	100.0	107.8	50.6	46		148
25-500°C	183	183	100 to 140	83.2	85.6	115.0	86.8	102.1	111.2	61.5	46	57	172
25-600°C	188	188		99.0	100.1	125.8	100.2	110.0	112.6	78.0			
Mechanical Properties (Annealed)													
Ultimate Str. (1000 psi)	35	35	74	82	80	80	82	80	85	75	490	120	70
Yield Str. (1000 psi)			50	34	34	40	34	40	55	50	360	110	25
% Elong. (2")			30	30	30	30	27	35	25	30	8	30	45
Rockwell Hardness				B76	B76	B80	B76	B83	B85	B68	C25	B88	B62
Elastic Modulus (10⁶ psi)	16	16		21.5	21.0	23	23	24	30	20	50	47	30

	Metal Alloy Lead Wires								Clad Materials (Also see Dumet)			Pure Metals (Also see W and Mo glass sealing materials)						
Nickel 211	AISI Type 302	AISI Type 316	AISI Type 430	400 Monel	600 Inconel	Advance ®	CDA 752	70-30 Brass	Kulgrid ®	40% CCFe	30% CCFe	Au	Ag	Al	Pt	Ta	Fe	Ti
0.10	0.15 Max	0.08 Max	0.12 Max	0.12	0.04		0.50 Max											
4.75	2.00 Max	2.00 Max	1.00 Max	0.90	0.20													
0.05	1.00 Max	1.00 Max	1.00 Max	0.15														
	17–19	16–18	14–18		16				27									
95.0	8–10	10–14	0.50 Max	66	76	43	18	70		37.5	26							
		—		31.5		Bal.	65											
		Mo 2–3			Fe 7.20		Bal. Zn	Bal. Zn	Cu Core	Fe Core	Fe Core							
8.72	7.9	7.9	7.7	8.84	8.41	8.9	8.73	8.53	8.89	8.15	8.15	19.3	10.5	2.69	21.45	16.6	7.87	4.51
0.315	0.285	0.285	0.278	0.319	0.304	0.322	0.316	0.308	0.321	0.294	0.294	0.698	0.379	0.097	0.775	0.600	0.284	0.163
0.12	0.04	0.04	0.05	0.062	0.036	0.051	0.08	0.29		0.46	0.38	0.71	1.00	0.57	0.165	0.13	0.18	0.43
350	116	116	145	180	104	148	232	845		1330	1100	2050	2900	1650	480	380	520	1250
18.3	72	74	60	48.2	98.1	49	28.7	6.16	2.3	4.4	5.9	2.19	1.629	2.65	9.83	12.45	9.71	7.0
110	433	445	361	290	590	294	173	37	14	26.4	35.3	13	9.8	16	59	75	58	42
9	2.3	2.3	2.9	3.6	1.7	3.5	6	28	70	40	30	78	105	65	16	14	18	25
352			610	43/60	−125	—	—	—		770	770						770	
1427	1421	1399	1510	1349	1427	1210	1110	954				1063	960	660	1769	3000	1536	1668
2600	2590	2550	2750	2460	2600	2210	2030	1750				1945	1760	1220	3217	5425	2797	3035
0.13	0.12	0.12	0.11	0.102	0.109	0.094	0.09	0.09		0.10	0.10	0.031	0.056	0.225	0.031	0.034	0.11	0.124
133	166	166	101	140	115	149						142	196	239	91	65	122	88
139					145									243			129	91
144	171	175	110	150			160	199						253				
146																		
148				155													138	94
153	180	180	120	160		163						152	206		96	66	145	97
				165										287				
	90	85	75	85	100	60	60	50				20	22	13	40	55	40	
	37	35	45	40	45		30	—					8	5	12		20	
	55	55	30	40	40		40	60				45	48	40	30	30	45	
	B82	B80	B82	B68	B74		—	—										
30	29	29	29	26	31	18	18	16		24	24	11.6	11	9	21.3	27	30	16.8

WIRE TABLES
COMPARISON OF WIRE GAUGES
DIAMETER OF WIRE IN INCHES

Gauge No.	Brown & Sharpe	Birmingham or Stubs',	Washburn & Moen	Imperial or Brit. Std.	Stubs' Steel	U.S. Std. plate	Gauge No.	Brown & Sharpe	Birmingham or Stubs'.	Washburn & Moen	Imperial or Brit. Std.	Stubs' steel	U.S. Std. plate
00000000	....	....	....	....	....	....	25	0.01790	0.020	0.0204	0.020	0.148	0.021875
0000000	....	....	....	.500	....	....	26	0.01594	0.018	0.0181	0.018	0.146	0.01875
000000	....	....	....	.464	....	.46875	27	0.01419	0.016	0.0173	0.016	0.143	0.0171875
00000	....	....	....	.432	....	.4375	28	0.01264	0.014	0.0162	0.0149	0.139	0.015625
0000	.4600	.454	.3938	.400	....	.40625	29	0.01126	0.013	0.0150	0.0136	0.134	0.0140625
000	.4096	.425	.3625	.372	....	.375							
00	.3648	.380	.3310	.348	....	.34375	30	0.01003	0.012	0.0140	0.0124	0.127	0.0125
0	.3249	.340	.3065	.324	....	.3125	31	0.008928	0.010	0.0132	0.0116	0.120	0.0109375
1	.2893	.300	.2830	.300	.227	.28125	32	0.007950	0.009	0.0128	0.0108	0.115	0.01015625
2	.2576	.284	.2625	.276	.219	.265625	33	0.007080	0.008	0.0118	0.0100	0.112	0.009375
3	.2294	.259	.2437	.252	.212	.25	34	0.006304	0.007	0.0104	0.0092	0.110	0.00859375
4	.2043	.238	.2253	.232	.207	.234375							
5	.1819	.220	.2070	.212	.204	.21875	35	0.005614	0.005	0.0095	0.0084	0.108	0.0078125
6	.1620	.203	.1920	.192	.201	.203125	36	0.005000	0.004	0.0090	0.0076	0.106	0.00703125
7	.1443	.180	.1770	.176	.199	.1875	37	0.004453	....	0.0085	0.0068	0.103	0.006640625
8	.1285	.165	.1620	.160	.197	.171875	38	0.003965	....	0.0080	0.0060	0.101	0.00625
9	.1144	.148	.1483	.144	.194	.15625	39	0.003531	....	0.0075	0.0052	0.099	....
10	.1019	.134	.1350	.128	.191	.140625							
11	.09074	.120	.1205	.116	.188	.125	40	0.003145	....	0.0070	0.0048	0.097	....
12	.08081	.109	.1055	.104	.185	.109375	41	....	....	0.0066	0.0044	0.095	....
13	.07196	.095	.0915	.092	.182	.09375	42	....	....	0.0062	0.0040	0.092	....
14	.06408	.083	.0800	.080	.180	.078125	43	....	....	0.0060	0.0036	0.088	....
15	.05707	.072	.0720	.072	.178	.0703125	44	....	....	0.0058	0.0032	0.085	....
16	.05082	.065	.0625	.064	.175	.0625							
17	.04526	.058	.0540	.056	.172	.05625	45	....	....	0.0055	0.0028	0.081	....
18	.04030	.049	.0475	.048	.168	.05	46	....	....	0.0052	0.0024	0.079	....
19	.03589	.042	.0410	.040	.164	.04375	47	....	....	0.0050	0.0020	0.077	....
20	.03196	.035	.0348	.036	.161	.0375	48	....	....	0.0048	0.0016	0.075	....
21	.02846	.032	.0318	.032	.157	.034375	49	....	....	0.0046	0.0012	0.072	....
22	.02535	.028	.0286	.028	.155	.03125							
23	.02257	.025	.0258	.024	.153	.028125	50	....	....	0.0044	0.0010	0.069	....
24	.02010	.022	.0230	.022	.151	.025							

DIAMETER OF WIRE IN CENTIMETERS

Gauge No.	Brown & Sharpe	Birmingham or Stubs.	Washburn & Moen	Imperial or Brit. Std.	Stubs' steel	U.S. Std. plate	Gauge No.	Brown & Sharpe	Birmingham or Stubs'.	Washburn & Moen	Imperial or Brit. Std.	Stubs' steel	U.S. Std. plate
0000000	....	....	....	....	....	....	25	0.04547	0.051	0.0518	0.0508	0.376	0.05556
0000000	....	....	1.245	1.27	....	1.27	26	0.04049	0.046	0.0460	0.0457	0.371	0.04763
000000	....	....	1.172	1.18	....	1.191	27	0.03604	0.041	0.0439	0.0417	0.363	0.04366
00000	....	....	1.093	1.10	....	1.111	28	0.03211	0.036	0.0411	0.0378	0.353	0.03969
0000	1.168	1.15	1.000	1.02	....	1.032	29	0.02860	0.033	0.0381	0.0345	0.340	0.03572
000	1.040	1.08	0.9208	0.945	....	0.9525							
00	0.9266	0.965	0.8407	0.884	....	0.8731	30	0.02548	0.030	0.0356	0.0315	0.323	0.03175
0	0.8252	0.864	0.7785	0.823	....	0.7938	31	0.02268	0.025	0.0335	0.0295	0.305	0.02778
1	0.7348	0.762	0.7188	0.762	0.577	0.7144	32	0.02019	0.023	0.0325	0.0274	0.292	0.02580
2	0.6543	0.721	0.6668	0.701	0.556	0.6747	33	0.01798	0.020	0.0300	0.0254	0.284	0.02381
3	0.5827	0.658	0.6190	0.640	0.538	0.6350	34	0.01601	0.018	0.0264	0.0234	0.279	0.02183
4	0.5189	0.605	0.5723	0.589	0.526	0.5953							
5	0.4620	0.559	0.5258	0.538	0.518	0.5556	35	0.01426	0.013	0.024	0.0213	0.274	0.01984
6	0.4115	0.516	0.4877	0.488	0.511	0.5159	36	0.01270	0.010	0.023	0.0193	0.269	0.01786
7	0.3665	0.457	0.4496	0.447	0.505	0.4763	37	0.01131	....	0.022	0.0173	0.262	0.01687
8	0.3264	0.419	0.4115	0.406	0.500	0.4366	38	0.01007	....	0.020	0.0152	0.257	0.01588
9	0.2906	0.376	0.3767	0.366	0.493	0.3969	39	0.008969	....	0.019	0.0132	0.251	....
10	0.2588	0.340	0.3429	0.325	0.485	0.3572							
11	0.2305	0.305	0.3061	0.295	0.478	0.3175	40	0.007988	....	0.018	0.0122	0.246	....
12	0.2053	0.277	0.2680	0.264	0.470	0.2778	41	....	....	0.017	0.0112	0.241	....
13	0.1828	0.241	0.232	0.234	0.462	0.2381	42	....	....	0.016	0.0102	0.234	....
14	0.1628	0.211	0.203	0.203	0.457	0.1984	43	....	....	0.015	0.0091	0.224	....
15	0.1450	0.183	0.183	0.183	0.452	0.1786	44	....	....	0.015	0.0081	0.216	....
16	0.1291	0.165	0.159	0.163	0.445	0.1588							
17	0.1150	0.147	0.137	0.142	0.437	0.1429	45	....	....	0.014	0.0071	0.206	....
18	0.1024	0.124	0.121	0.122	0.427	0.1270	46	....	....	0.013	0.0061	0.201	....
19	0.09116	0.107	0.104	0.102	0.417	0.1111	47	....	....	0.013	0.0051	0.196	....
20	0.08118	0.089	0.0884	0.0914	0.409	0.09525	48	....	....	0.012	0.0041	0.191	....
21	0.07229	0.081	0.0808	0.0813	0.399	0.08731	49	....	....	0.012	0.0030	0.183	....
22	0.06439	0.071	0.0726	0.0711	0.394	0.07938							
23	0.05733	0.064	0.0655	0.0610	0.389	0.07144	50	....	....	0.011	0.0025	0.175	....
24	0.05105	0.056	0.0584	0.0559	0.384	0.06350							

TWIST DRILL AND STEEL WIRE GAUGE

No.	Size	No.	Size	No.	Size	No.	Size	No.	Size
1	0.2280	17	0.1730	33	0.1130	49	0.0730	65	0.0350
2	0.2210	18	0.1695	34	0.1110	50	0.0700	66	0.0330
3	0.2130	19	0.1660	35	0.1100	51	0.0670	67	0.0320
4	0.2090	20	0.1610	36	0.1065	52	0.0635	68	0.0310
5	0.2055	21	0.1590	37	0.1040	53	0.0595	69	0.02925
6	0.2040	22	0.1570	38	0.1015	54	0.0550	70	0.0280
7	0.2010	23	0.1540	39	0.0995	55	0.0520	71	0.0260
8	0.1990	24	0.1520	40	0.0980	56	0.0465	72	0.0250
9	0.1960	25	0.1495	41	0.0960	57	0.0430	73	0.0240
10	0.1935	26	0.1470	42	0.0935	58	0.0420	74	0.0225
11	0.1910	27	0.1440	43	0.0890	59	0.0410	75	0.0210
12	0.1890	28	0.1405	44	0.0860	60	0.0400	76	0.0200
13	0.1850	29	0.1360	45	0.0820	61	0.0390	77	0.0180
14	0.1820	30	0.1285	46	0.0810	62	0.0380	78	0.0160
15	0.1800	31	0.1200	47	0.0785	63	0.0370	79	0.0145
16	0.1770	32	0.1160	48	0.0760	64	0.0360	80	0.0135

No.	Size	No.	Size	No.	Size	No.	Size	No.	Size
1	0.5791	17	0.4394	33	0.2870	49	0.1854	65	0.0889
2	0.5613	18	0.4305	34	0.2819	50	0.1778	66	0.0838
3	0.5410	19	0.4216	35	0.2794	51	0.1702	67	0.0813
4	0.5309	20	0.4089	36	0.2705	52	0.1613	68	0.0787
5	0.5220	21	0.4039	37	0.2642	53	0.1511	69	0.0743
6	0.5182	22	0.3988	38	0.2578	54	0.1397	70	0.0711
7	0.5105	23	0.3912	39	0.2527	55	0.1321	71	0.0660
8	0.5055	24	0.3861	40	0.2489	56	0.1181	72	0.0635
9	0.4978	25	0.3797	41	0.2438	57	0.1092	73	0.0610
10	0.4915	26	0.3734	42	0.2375	58	0.1067	74	0.0572
11	0.4851	27	0.3658	43	0.2261	59	0.1041	75	0.0533
12	0.4801	28	0.3569	44	0.2184	60	0.1016	76	0.0508
13	0.4699	29	0.3454	45	0.2083	61	0.0991	77	0.0457
14	0.4623	30	0.3264	46	0.2057	62	0.0965	78	0.0406
15	0.4572	31	0.3048	47	0.1994	63	0.0940	79	0.0368
16	0.4496	32	0.2946	48	0.1930	64	0.0914	80	0.0343

DIMENSIONS OF WIRE

STUBS' GAUGE

Giving the diameter and cross-section in English and metric system for the Birmingham or Stubs' gauge.

Gauge No.	Diameter in in.	Section in sq. in.	Diameter in cm	Section in sq. cm
0000	0.454	0.16188	1.1532	1.0444
000	.425	.14186	1.0795	.9152
00	.380	.11341	0.9652	.7317
0	0.340	0.09079	0.8636	0.5858
1	.300	.07069	.7620	.4560
2	.284	.06335	.7214	.4087
3	.259	.05269	.6579	.3399
4	.238	.04449	.6045	.2870
5	0.220	0.03801	0.5588	0.2452
6	.203	.03237	.5156	.20881
7	.180	.02545	.4572	.16147
8	.165	.02138	.4191	.13795
9	.148	.01720	.3759	.11099
10	0.134	0.01410	0.3404	0.09098
11	.120	.011310	.3048	.07297
12	.109	.009331	.2769	.06160
13	.095	.007088	.2413	.04573
14	.083	.005411	.2108	.03491
15	0.072	0.004072	0.1829	0.02627
16	.065	.0033183	.16510	.021409
17	.058	.0026421	.14732	.017046
18	.049	.0018857	.12446	.012166
19	.042	.0013854	.10668	.008938
20	0.035	0.0009621	0.08890	0.006207
21	.032	.0008042	.08128	.005189
22	.028	.0006158	.07112	.003973
23	.025	.0004909	.06350	.003167
24	.022	.0003801	.05588	.002452
25	0.020	0.0003142	0.05080	0.002027
26	.018	.0002545	.04572	.0016417
27	.016	.0002011	.04064	.0012972
28	.014	.0001539	.03556	.0009932
29	.013	.0001327	.03302	.0008563
30	0.012	0.0001181	0.03048	0.0007297
31	.010	.00007854	.02540	.0005067
32	.009	.00006362	.02286	.0004104
33	.008	.00005027	.02032	.0003243
34	.007	.00003848	.01778	.0002483
35	0.005	0.00001963	0.01270	0.0001267
36	.004	.00001257	.01016	.0000811

BRITISH STANDARD GAUGE

Giving the diameter and cross-section in English and metric system for the British Standard Gauge.

Gauge No.	Diameter in in.	Section in sq. in.	Diameter in cm	Section in sq. cm
0000000	0.500	0.1963	1.2700	1.267
000000	.464	.1691	1.1786	1.091
00000	0.432	0.1466	1.0973	0.9456
0000	.400	.1257	1.0160	.8107
000	.372	.1087	0.9449	.7012
00	.348	.0951	.8839	.6136
0	.324	.0825	.8230	.5319
1	.300	.07069	.7620	.4560
2	.276	.05983	.7010	.3858
3	.252	.04988	.6401	.3218
4	.232	.04227	.5893	.2727
5	.212	.03530	.5385	.2277
6	.192	.02895	.4877	.18679
7	.176	.02433	.4470	.15696
8	.160	.02010	.4064	.12973
9	.144	.01629	.3658	.10507
10	.128	.01287	.3251	.08302
11	.116	.010568	.2946	.06818
12	.104	.008495	.2642	.05480
13	.092	.006648	.2337	.04289
14	.080	.005027	.2032	.03243
15	0.072	0.004071	0.1829	0.02627
16	.064	.003217	.16256	.020755
17	.056	.002463	.14224	.015890
18	.048	.001810	.12192	.011675
19	.040	.001257	.10160	.008107
20	0.036	0.001018	0.09144	0.006567
21	.032	.0008042	.08128	.005189
22	.028	.0006158	.07112	.003973
23	.024	.0004524	.06096	.002922
24	.022	.0003801	.05588	.002452
25	0.020	0.0003142	0.05080	0.002027
26	.0180	.0002545	.04572	.0016417
27	.0164	.0002112	.04166	.0013628
28	.0148	.0001728	.03759	.0011099
29	.0136	.0001453	.03454	.0009363
30	0.0124	0.0001208	0.03150	0.0007791
31	.0116	.00010568	.02946	.0006818
32	.0108	.00009161	.02743	.0005910
33	.0100	.00007854	.02540	.0005067
34	.0092	.00006648	.02337	.0004289
35	0.0084	0.00005542	0.02134	0.0003575
36	.0076	.00004536	.01930	.0002927
37	.0068	.00003632	.01727	.0002343
38	.0060	.00002827	.01524	.0001824
39	.0052	.00002124	.01321	.0001370
40	0.0048	0.00001810	0.01219	0.0001167
41	.0044	.00001521	.01118	.0000982
42	.0040	.00001257	.01016	.0000811
43	.0036	.00001018	.00914	.0000656
44	.0032	.00000804	.00813	.0000519
45	0.0028	0.00000616	0.00711	0.0000397
46	.0024	.00000452	.00610	.0000212
47	.0020	.00000314	.00508	.0000203
48	.0016	.00000201	.00406	.0000129
49	.0012	.00000113	.00305	.0000073
50	0.0010	0.00000079	0.00254	0.0000051

PLATINUM WIRE

Mass in Grams per Foot

B. & S. Gauge	Diameter, inches	Mass, g per ft.	B. & S. Gauge	Diameter, inches	Mass, g per ft.
10	.1019	37.5	23	.02257	1.8
11	.09074	28.0	24	.02010	1.4
12	.08081	22.0	25	.01790	1.1
13	.07196	17.5	26	.01594	0.9
14	.06408	14.0	27	.01420	0.7
15	.05707	11.0	28	.01264	0.6
16	.05082	9.0	29	.01126	0.45
17	.04526	7.0	30	.01003	0.35
18	.04030	5.7	31	.008928	0.28
19	.03589	4.4	32	.007950	0.22
20	.03196	3.4	33	.007080	0.17
21	.02846	2.9	34	.006305	0.15
22	.02535	2.3	35	.005615	0.11

ALLOWABLE CARRYING CAPACITIES OF CONDUCTORS
(National Electrical Code)

The ratings in the following tabulation are those permitted by the National Electrical Code for flexible cords and for interior wiring of houses, hotels, office buildings, industrial plants, and other buildings.

The values are for copper wire. For aluminum wire the allowable carrying capacities shall be taken as 84 % of those given in the table for the respective sizes of copper wire with the same kind of covering.

Size A.W.G.	Area Circular Mils	Diameter of Solid Wires Mils	Rubber Insulation Amperes	Varnished Cambric Insulation Amperes	Other Insulations and Bare Conductors Amperes
18	1,624.	40.3	3*	. . .	6†
16	2,583.	50.8	6*	. . .	10†
14	4,107.	64.1	15	18	20
12	6,530.	80.8	20	25	30
10	10,380.	101.9	25	30	35
8	16,510.	128.5	35	40	50
6	26,250.	162.0	50	60	70
5	33,100.	181.9	55	65	80
4	41,740.	204.3	70	85	90
3	52,630.	229.4	80	95	100
2	66,370.	257.6	90	110	125
1	83,690.	289.3	100	120	150
0	105,500.	325.0	125	150	200
00	135,100.	364.8	150	180	225
000	167,800.	409.6	175	210	275
0000	211,600.	460	225	270	325

1 Mil = 0.001 inch.
* The allowable carrying capacities of No. 18 and 16 are 5 and 7 amperes respectively, when in flexible cords.
† The allowable carrying capacities of No. 18 and 16 are 10 and 15 amperes respectively, when in cords for portable heaters. Types AFS, AFSJ, HC, HPD, and HSJ.

WIRE TABLE, STANDARD ANNEALED COPPER
American Wire Gauge (B. & S.) English Units

Gauge No.	Diameter in mils at 20°C	Circular mils	Sq. inches	0°C (32°F)	20°C (68°F)	50°C (122°F)	75°C (107°F)
		Cross section at 20°C		Ohms per 1000 feet*			
0000	460.0	211600	0.1662	0.04516	0.04901	0.05479	0.05961
000	409.6	167800	.1318	.05695	.06180	.06909	.07516
00	364.8	133100	.1045	.07181	.07793	.08712	.09478
0	324.9	105500	.08289	.09055	.09827	.1009	.1195
1	289.3	83690	.06573	.1142	.1239	.1385	.1507
2	257.6	66370	.05213	.1440	.1563	.1747	.1900
3	229.4	52640	.04134	.1816	.1970	.2203	.2396
4	204.3	41740	.03278	.2289	.2485	.2778	.3022
5	181.9	33100	.02600	.2887	.3133	.3502	.3810
6	162.0	26250	.02062	.3640	.3951	.4416	.4805
7	144.3	20820	.01635	.4590	.4982	.5569	.6059
8	128.5	16510	.01297	.5788	.6282	.7023	.7640
9	114.4	13090	.01028	.7299	.7921	.8855	.9633
10	101.9	10380	.008155	.9203	.9989	1.117	1.215
11	90.74	8234	.006467	1.161	1.260	1.408	1.532
12	80.81	6530	.005129	1.463	1.588	1.775	1.931
13	71.96	5178	.004067	1.845	2.003	2.239	2.436
14	64.08	4107	.003225	2.327	2.525	2.823	3.071
15	57.07	3257	.002558	2.934	3.184	3.560	3.873
16	50.82	2583	.002028	3.700	4.016	4.489	4.884
17	45.26	2048	.001609	4.666	5.064	5.660	6.158
18	40.30	1624	.001276	5.883	6.385	7.138	7.765
19	35.89	1288	.001012	7.418	8.051	9.001	9.792
20	31.96	1022	.0008023	9.355	10.15	11.35	12.35
21	28.45	810.1	.0006363	11.80	12.80	14.31	15.57
22	25.35	642.4	.0005046	14.87	16.14	18.05	19.63
23	22.57	509.5	.0004002	18.76	20.36	22.76	24.76
24	20.10	404.0	.0003173	23.65	25.67	28.70	31.22
25	17.90	320.4	.0002517	29.82	32.37	36.18	39.36
26	15.94	254.1	.0001996	37.61	40.81	45.63	49.64
27	14.20	201.5	.0001583	47.42	51.47	57.53	62.59
28	12.64	159.8	.0001255	59.80	64.90	72.55	78.93
29	11.26	126.7	.00009953	75.40	81.83	91.48	99.52
30	10.03	100.5	.00007894	95.08	103.2	115.4	125.5
31	8.928	79.70	.00006260	119.9	130.1	145.5	158.2
32	7.950	63.21	.00004964	151.2	164.1	183.4	199.5
33	7.080	50.13	.00003937	190.6	206.9	231.3	251.6
34	6.305	39.75	.00003122	240.4	260.9	291.7	317.3
35	5.615	31.52	.00002476	303.1	329.0	367.8	400.1
36	5.000	25.00	.00001964	382.2	414.8	463.7	504.5
37	4.453	19.83	.00001557	482.0	523.1	584.8	636.2
38	3.965	15.72	.00001235	607.8	659.6	737.4	802.2
39	3.531	12.47	.000009793	766.4	831.8	929.8	1012
40	3.145	9.888	.000007766	966.5	1049	1173	1276

* Resistance at the stated temperatures of a wire whose length is 1000 feet at 20°C.

WIRE TABLE, STANDARD ANNEALED COPPER
American Wire Gauge (B. & S.) English Units (Continued)

Gauge No.	Pounds per 1000 feet	Feet per pound	0°C (32°F)	20°C (68°F)	50°C (122°F)	75°C (107°F)
			Feet per ohm*			
0000	640.5	1.561	22140	20400	18250	16780
000	507.9	1.968	17560	16180	14470	13300
00	402.8	2.482	13930	12830	11480	10550
0	319.5	3.130	11040	10180	9103	8367
1	253.3	3.947	8758	8070	7219	6636
2	200.9	4.977	6946	6400	5725	5262
3	159.3	6.276	5508	5075	4540	4173
4	126.4	7.914	4368	4025	3600	3309
5	100.2	9.980	3464	3192	2855	2625
6	79.46	12.58	2747	2531	2264	2081
7	63.02	15.87	2179	2007	1796	1651
8	49.98	20.01	1728	1592	1424	1309
9	39.63	25.23	1370	1262	1129	1038
10	31.43	31.82	1087	1001	895.6	823.2
11	24.92	40.12	861.7	794.0	710.2	652.8
12	19.77	50.59	683.3	629.6	563.2	517.7
13	15.68	63.80	541.9	499.3	446.7	410.6
14	12.43	80.44	429.8	396.0	354.2	325.6
15	9.858	101.4	340.8	314.0	280.9	258.2
16	7.818	127.9	270.3	249.0	222.8	204.8
17	6.200	161.3	214.3	197.5	176.7	162.4
18	4.917	203.4	170.0	156.6	140.1	128.8
19	3.899	256.5	134.8	124.2	111.1	102.1
20	3.092	323.4	106.9	98.50	88.11	80.99
21	2.452	407.8	84.78	78.11	69.87	64.23
22	1.945	514.2	67.23	61.95	55.41	50.94
23	1.542	648.4	53.32	49.13	43.94	40.39
24	1.223	817.7	42.28	38.96	34.85	32.03
25	0.9699	1031	33.53	30.90	27.64	25.40
26	.7692	1300	26.59	24.50	21.92	20.15
27	.6100	1639	21.09	19.43	17.38	15.98
28	.4837	2067	16.72	15.41	13.78	12.67
29	.3836	2607	13.26	12.22	10.93	10.05
30	.3042	3287	10.52	9.691	8.669	7.968
31	.2413	4145	8.341	7.685	6.875	6.319
32	.1913	5227	6.614	6.095	5.452	5.011
33	.1517	6591	5.245	4.833	4.323	3.974
34	.1203	8310	4.160	3.833	3.429	3.152
35	.09542	10480	3.299	3.040	2.719	2.499
36	.07568	13210	2.616	2.411	2.156	1.982
37	.06001	16660	2.075	1.912	1.710	1.572
38	.04759	21010	1.645	1.516	1.356	1.247
39	.03774	26500	1.305	1.202	1.075	0.9886
40	.02993	33410	1.035	0.9534	0.8529	.7840

* Length at 20°C of a wire whose resistance is 1 ohm at the stated temperatures.

Gauge No.	Diameter in mils at 20°C	Ohms per pound 0°C (32°F)	Ohms per pound 20°C (68°F)	Ohms per pound 50°C (122°F)	Lbs. per ohm 20°C (68°F)
0000	460.0	0.00007051	0.00007652	0.00008554	13070
000	409.6	.0001121	.0001217	.0001360	8219
00	364.8	.0001783	.0001935	.0002163	5169
0	324.9	.0002835	.0003076	.0003439	3251
1	289.3	.0004507	.0004891	.0005468	2044
2	257.6	.0007166	.0007778	.0008695	1286
3	229.4	.001140	.001237	.001383	808.6
4	204.3	.001812	.001966	.002198	508.5
5	181.9	.002881	.003127	.003495	319.8
6	162.0	.004581	.004972	.005558	201.1
7	144.3	.007284	.007905	.008838	126.5
8	128.5	.01158	.01257	.01405	79.55
9	114.4	.01842	.01999	.02234	50.03
10	101.9	.02928	.03178	.03553	31.47
11	90.74	.04656	.05053	.05649	19.79
12	80.81	.07404	.08035	.08983	12.45
13	71.96	.1177	.1278	.1428	7.827
14	64.08	.1872	.2032	.2271	4.922
15	57.07	.2976	.3230	.3611	3.096
16	50.82	.4733	.5136	.5742	1.947
17	45.26	.7525	.8167	.9130	1.224
18	40.30	1.197	1.299	1.452	.7700
19	35.89	1.903	2.065	2.308	.4843
20	31.96	3.025	3.283	3.670	.3046
21	28.46	4.810	5.221	5.836	.1915
22	25.35	7.649	8.301	9.280	.1205
23	22.57	12.16	13.20	14.76	.07576
24	20.10	19.34	20.99	23.46	.04765
25	17.90	30.75	33.37	37.31	.02997
26	15.94	48.89	53.06	59.32	.01885
27	14.20	77.74	84.37	94.32	.01185
28	12.64	123.6	134.2	150.0	.007454
29	11.26	196.6	213.3	238.5	.004688
30	10.03	312.5	339.2	379.2	.002948
31	8.928	497.0	539.3	602.9	.001854
32	7.950	790.2	857.6	958.7	.001166
33	7.080	1256	1364	1524	.0007333
34	6.305	1998	2168	2424	.0004612
35	5.615	3177	3448	3854	.0002901
36	5.000	5051	5482	6128	.0001824
37	4.453	8032	8717	9744	.0001147
38	3.965	12770	13860	15490	.00007215
39	3.531	20310	22040	24640	.00004538
40	3.145	32290	35040	39170	.00002854

Gauge No.	Diameter in mm at 20°C	Cross section in mm² at 20°C	Ohms per kilometer* 0°C	20°C	50°C	75°C
20	.8118	.5176	30.69	33.31	37.24	40.51
21	.7230	.4105	38.70	42.00	46.95	51.08
22	.6438	.3255	48.80	52.96	59.21	64.41
23	.5733	.2582	61.54	66.79	74.66	81.22
24	.5106	.2047	77.60	84.21	94.14	102.4
25	.4547	.1624	97.85	106.2	118.7	129.1
26	.4049	.1288	123.4	133.9	149.7	162.9
27	.3606	.1021	155.6	168.9	188.8	205.4
28	.3211	.08098	196.2	212.9	238.0	258.9
29	.2859	.06422	247.4	268.5	300.1	326.5
30	.2546	.05093	311.9	338.6	378.5	411.7
31	.2268	.04039	393.4	426.9	477.2	519.2
32	.2019	.03203	496.0	538.3	601.8	654.7
33	.1798	.02540	625.5	678.8	758.8	825.5
34	.1601	.02014	788.7	856.0	956.9	1041
35	.1426	.01597	994.5	1079	1207	1313
36	.1270	.01267	1254	1361	1522	1655
37	.1131	.01005	1581	1716	1919	2087
38	.1007	.007967	1994	2164	2419	2632
39	.08969	.006318	2514	2729	3051	3319
40	.07987	.005010	3171	3441	3847	4185

* Resistance at the stated temperatures of a wire whose length is 1 kilometer at 20°C.

Gauge No.	Diameter in mm at 20°C	Cross section in mm² at 20°C	Ohms per kilometer* 0°C	20°C	50°C	75°C
0000	11.68	107.2	0.1482	0.1608	0.1798	0.1956
000	10.40	85.03	.1868	.2028	.2267	.2466
00	9.266	67.43	.2356	.2557	.2858	.3110
0	8.252	53.48	.2971	.3224	.3604	.3921
1	7.348	42.41	.3746	.4066	.4545	.4944
2	6.544	33.63	.4724	.5127	.5731	.6235
3	5.827	26.67	.5956	.6465	.7227	.7862
4	5.189	21.15	.7511	.8152	.9113	.9914
5	4.621	16.77	.9471	1.028	1.149	1.250
6	4.115	13.30	1.194	1.296	1.449	1.576
7	3.665	10.55	1.506	1.634	1.827	1.988
8	3.264	8.366	1.899	2.061	2.304	2.506
9	2.906	6.634	2.395	2.599	2.905	3.161
10	2.588	5.261	3.020	3.277	3.663	3.985
11	2.305	4.172	3.807	4.132	4.619	5.025
12	2.053	3.309	4.801	5.211	5.825	6.337
13	1.828	2.624	6.054	6.571	7.345	7.991
14	1.628	2.081	7.634	8.285	9.262	10.08
15	1.450	1.650	9.627	10.45	11.68	12.71
16	1.291	1.309	12.14	13.17	14.73	16.02
17	1.150	1.038	15.31	16.61	18.57	20.20
18	1.024	0.8231	19.30	20.95	23.42	25.48
19	0.9116	.6527	24.34	26.42	29.53	32.12

Gauge No.	Diameter in mm at 20°C	Kilograms per kilometer	Meters per gram	Meters per ohm* 0°C	20°C	50°C	75°C
0000	11.68	953.2	0.001049	6749	6219	5563	5113
000	10.40	755.9	.001323	5352	4932	4412	4055
00	9.266	599.5	.001668	4245	3911	3499	3216
0	8.252	475.4	.002103	3366	3102	2774	2550
1	7.348	377.0	.002652	2669	2460	2200	2022
2	6.544	299.0	.003345	2117	1951	1745	1604
3	5.827	237.1	.004217	1679	1547	1384	1272
4	5.189	188.0	.005318	1331	1227	1097	1009
5	4.621	149.1	.006706	1056	972.9	870.2	799.9
6	4.115	118.2	.008457	837.3	771.5	690.1	634.4
7	3.665	93.78	.01066	664.0	611.8	547.3	503.1
8	3.264	74.37	.01345	526.6	485.2	434.0	399.0
9	2.906	58.98	.01696	417.6	384.8	344.2	316.4
10	2.588	46.77	.02138	331.2	305.1	273.0	250.9
11	2.305	37.09	.02696	262.6	242.0	216.5	199.0
12	2.053	29.42	.03400	208.3	191.9	171.7	157.8
13	1.828	23.33	.04287	165.2	152.2	136.1	125.1
14	1.628	18.50	.05406	131.0	120.7	108.0	99.24
15	1.450	14.67	.06816	103.9	95.71	85.62	78.70
16	1.291	11.63	.08595	82.38	75.90	67.90	62.41
17	1.150	9.226	.1084	65.33	60.20	53.85	49.50
18	1.024	7.317	.1367	51.81	47.74	42.70	39.25
19	0.9116	5.803	.1723	41.09	37.86	33.86	31.13
20	.8118	4.602	.2173	32.58	30.02	26.86	24.69
21	.7230	3.649	.2740	25.84	23.81	21.30	19.58
22	.6438	2.894	.3455	20.49	18.88	16.89	15.53
23	.5733	2.295	.4357	16.25	14.97	13.39	12.31
24	.5106	1.820	.5494	12.89	11.87	10.62	9.764
25	.4547	1.443	.6928	10.22	9.417	8.424	7.743
26	.4049	1.145	.8736	8.105	7.468	6.680	6.141
27	.3606	.9078	1.102	6.428	5.922	5.298	4.870
28	.3211	.7199	1.389	5.097	4.697	4.201	3.862
29	.2859	.5709	1.752	4.042	3.725	3.332	3.063
30	.2546	.4527	2.209	3.206	2.954	2.642	2.429
31	.2268	.3590	2.785	2.542	2.342	2.095	1.926
32	.2019	.2847	3.512	2.016	1.858	1.662	1.527
33	.1798	.2258	4.429	1.599	1.473	1.318	1.211
34	.1601	.1791	5.584	1.268	1.168	1.045	.9606
35	.1426	.1420	7.042	1.006	.9265	.8288	.7618
36	.1270	.1126	8.879	.7974	.7347	.6572	.6041
37	.1131	.08931	11.20	.6324	.5827	.5212	.4791
38	.1007	.07083	14.12	.5015	.4621	.4133	.3799
39	.08969	.05617	17.80	.3977	.3664	.3278	.3013
40	.07987	.04454	22.45	.3154	.2906	.2600	.2390

° Length at 20°C of a wire whose resistance is 1 ohm at the stated temperatures.

WIRE TABLE, STANDARD ANNEALED COPPER
(Continued)

American Wire Gauge (B. & S.) Metric Units

Gauge No.	Ohms per kilogram			Grams per ohm
	0°C	20°C	50°C	20°C
0000	0.0001554	0.0001687	0.0001886	5928000
000	.0002472	.0002682	.0002999	3728000
00	.0003930	.0004265	.0004768	2344000
0	.0006249	.0006782	.0007582	1474000
1	.0009936	.001078	.001206	927300
2	.001580	.001715	.001917	583200
3	.002512	.002726	.003048	366800
4	.003995	.004335	.004846	230700
5	.006352	.006893	.007706	145100
6	.01010	.01096	.01225	91230
7	.01606	.01743	.01948	57380
8	.02553	.02771	.03098	36080
9	.04060	.04406	.04926	22690
10	.06456	.07007	.07833	14270
11	.1026	.1114	.1245	8976
12	.1632	.1771	.1980	5645
13	.2595	.2817	.3149	3550
14	.4127	.4479	.5007	2233
15	.6562	.7122	.7961	1404
16	1.043	1.132	1.266	883.1
17	1.659	1.801	2.013	555.4
18	2.638	2.863	3.201	349.3
19	4.194	4.552	5.089	219.7
20	6.670	7.238	8.092	138.2
21	10.60	11.51	12.87	86.88
22	16.86	18.30	20.46	54.64
23	26.81	29.10	32.53	34.36
24	42.63	46.27	51.73	21.61
25	67.79	73.57	82.25	13.59
26	107.8	117.0	130.8	8.548
27	171.4	186.0	207.9	5.376
28	272.5	295.8	330.6	3.381
29	433.3	470.3	525.7	2.126
30	689.0	747.8	836.0	1.337
31	1096	1189	1329	0.8410
32	1742	1891	2114	.5289
33	2770	3006	3361	.3326
34	4404	4780	5344	.2092
35	7003	7601	8497	.1316
36	11140	12090	13510	.08274
37	17710	19220	21480	.05204
38	28150	30500	34160	.03273
39	44770	48590	54310	.02058
40	71180	77260	86360	.01294

ALUMINUM WIRE TABLE
Hard-Drawn Aluminum Wire at 20°C (or, 68°F)
American Wire Gauge (B. & S.) English Units

Gauge No.	Diameter in mils	Cross section Circular mils	Cross section Square inches	Ohms per 1000 ft.	Pounds per 1000 ft.	Pounds per ohm	Feet per ohm
0000	460	212000	0.166	0.0804	195	2420	12400
000	410	168000	.132	.101	154	1520	9860
00	365	133000	.105	.128	122	957	7820
0	325	106000	.0829	.161	97.0	602	6200
1	289	83700	.0657	.203	76.9	379	4920
2	258	66400	.0521	.256	61.0	238	3900
3	229	52600	.0413	.323	48.4	150	3090
4	204	41700	.0328	.408	38.4	94.2	2450
5	182	33100	.0260	.514	30.4	59.0	1950
6	162	26300	.0206	.648	24.1	37.2	1540
7	144	20800	.0164	.817	19.1	23.4	1220
8	128	16500	.0130	1.03	15.2	14.7	970
9	114	13100	.0103	1.30	12.0	9.26	770

ALUMINUM WIRE TABLE (Continued)

Gauge No.	Diameter in mils	Cross section Circular mils	Cross section Square inches	Ohms per 1000 ft.	Pounds per 1000 ft.	Pounds per ohm	Feet per ohm
10	102	10400	.00815	1.64	9.55	5.83	610
11	91	8230	.00647	2.07	7.57	3.66	484
12	81	6530	.00513	2.61	6.00	2.30	384
13	72	5180	.00407	3.29	4.76	1.45	304
14	64	4110	.00323	4.14	3.78	0.911	241
15	57	3260	.00256	5.22	2.99	.573	191
16	51	2580	.00203	6.59	2.37	.360	152
17	45	2050	.00161	8.31	1.88	.227	120
18	40	1620	.00128	10.5	1.49	.143	95.5
19	36	1290	.00101	13.2	1.18	.0897	75.7
20	32	1020	.000802	16.7	0.939	.0564	60.0
21	28.5	810	.000636	21.0	.745	.0355	47.6
22	25.3	642	.000505	26.5	.591	.0223	37.8
23	22.6	509	.000400	33.4	.468	.0140	29.9
24	20.1	404	.000317	42.1	.371	.00882	23.7
25	17.9	320	.000252	53.1	.295	.00555	18.8
26	15.9	254	.000200	67.0	.234	.00349	14.9
27	14.2	202	.000158	84.4	.185	.00219	11.8
28	12.6	160	.000126	106.	.147	.00138	9.39
29	11.3	127	.0000995	134.	.117	.000868	7.45
30	10.0	101	.0000789	169.	.0924	.000546	5.91
31	8.9	79.7	.0000626	213.	.0733	.000343	4.68
32	8.0	63.2	.0000496	269.	.0581	.000216	3.72
33	7.1	50.1	.0000394	339.	.0461	.000136	2.95
34	6.3	39.8	.0000312	428.	.0365	.0000854	2.34
35	5.6	31.5	.0000248	540.	.0290	.0000537	1.85
36	5.0	25.0	.0000196	681.	.0230	.0000338	1.47
37	4.5	19.8	.0000156	858.	.0182	.0000212	1.17
38	4.0	15.7	.0000123	1080.	.0145	.0000134	0.924
39	3.5	12.5	.00000979	1360.	.0115	.00000840	.733
40	3.1	9.9	.00000777	1720.	.00913	.00000528	.581

Gauge No.	Diameter in mm	Cross section in mm²	Ohms per kilometer	Kilograms per kilometer	Grams per ohm	Meters per ohm
0000	11.7	107	0.264	289	1100000	3790
000	10.4	85.0	.333	230	690000	3010
00	9.3	67.4	.419	182	434000	2380
0	8.3	53.5	.529	144	273000	1890
1	7.3	42.4	.667	114	172000	1500
2	6.5	33.6	.841	90.8	108000	1190
3	5.8	26.7	1.06	72.0	67900	943
4	5.2	21.2	1.34	57.1	42700	748
5	4.6	16.8	1.69	45.3	26900	593
6	4.1	13.3	2.13	35.9	16900	470
7	3.7	10.5	2.68	28.5	10600	373
8	3.3	8.37	3.38	22.6	6680	296
9	2.91	6.63	4.26	17.9	4200	235
10	2.59	5.26	5.38	14.2	2640	186
11	2.30	4.17	6.78	11.3	1660	148
12	2.05	3.31	8.55	8.93	1050	117
13	1.83	2.62	10.8	7.08	657	92.8
14	1.63	2.08	13.6	5.62	413	73.6
15	1.45	1.65	17.1	4.46	260	58.4
16	1.29	1.31	21.6	3.53	164	46.3
17	1.15	1.04	27.3	2.80	103	36.7
18	1.02	0.823	34.4	2.22	64.7	29.1
19	0.91	.653	43.3	1.76	40.7	23.1
20	.81	.518	54.6	1.40	25.6	18.3
21	.72	.411	68.9	1.11	16.1	14.5
22	.64	.326	86.9	0.879	10.1	11.5
23	.57	.258	110	.697	6.36	9.13
24	.51	.205	138	.553	4.00	7.24
25	.45	.162	174	.438	2.52	5.74
26	.40	.129	220	.348	1.58	4.55
27	.36	.102	277	.276	0.995	3.61
28	.32	.0810	349	.219	.626	2.86
29	.29	.0642	440	.173	.394	2.27
30	.25	.0509	555	.138	.248	1.80
31	.227	.0404	700	.109	.156	1.43
32	.202	.0320	883	.0865	.0979	1.13
33	.180	.0254	1110	.0686	.0616	0.899
34	.160	.0201	1400	.0544	.0387	.712
35	.143	.0160	1770	.0431	.0244	.565
36	.127	.0127	2230	.0342	.0153	.448
37	.113	.0100	2820	.0271	.00963	.355
38	.101	.0080	3550	.0215	.00606	.282
39	.090	.0063	4480	.0171	.00381	.223
40	.080	.0050	5640	.0135	.00240	.177

CROSS-SECTION AND MASS OF WIRES
U. S. Measure

Diameters are given in mils (1 mil = .001 in.), and area in square mils (1 sq. mil = .000001 sq. in.). For sections and masses for one-tenth the diameters given, divide by 100 and for sections and masses for ten times the diameter multiply by 100.

Diam. in mils	Cross-sec. in sq. mils	Pounds per foot				Diam. in mils	Cross-sec. in sq. mils	Pounds per foot			
		Copper, density 8.90	Iron, density 7.80	Brass, density 8.56	Aluminum, density 2.67			Copper, density 8.90	Iron, density 7.80	Brass, density 8.56	Aluminum, density 2.67
10	78.54	0.000303	0.0002656	0.0002915	0.0000909	85	5674.50	0.02189	0.01919	0.02106	0.006568
11	95.03	0367	03214	03527	01100	86	5808.80	2241	1964	2156	6724
12	113.10	0436	03825	04197	01309	87	5944.68	2294	2010	2206	6881
13	132.73	0512	04488	04926	01536	88	6082.12	2347	2057	2257	7040
14	153.94	0594	05206	05713	01782	89	6221.14	2400	2104	2309	7201
15	176.71	0.000682	0.0005976	0.0006558	0.0002045	90	6361.73	0.02455	0.02151	0.02360	0.007364
16	201.06	0776	06799	07461	02327	91	6503.88	2509	2199	2414	7528
17	226.98	0876	07675	08423	02627	92	6647.61	2565	2248	2467	7695
18	254.47	0982	08605	09443	02946	93	6792.91	2621	2297	2521	7863
19	283.53	1094	09588	10522	03282	94	6939.78	2678	2347	2575	8033
20	314.16	0.001212	0.001062	0.001166	0.0003636	95	7088.22	0.02735	0.02397	0.02630	0.008205
21	346.36	1336	1171	1285	04009	96	7238.23	2793	2448	2686	8378
22	380.13	1467	1286	1411	04400	97	7389.81	2851	2499	2742	8554
23	415.48	1603	1405	1542	04809	98	7542.96	2910	2551	2799	8731
24	452.39	1746	1530	1679	05237	99	7697.69	2970	2603	2857	8910
25	490.87	0.001894	0.001660	0.001822	0.0005682	100	7853.98	0.03030	0.02656	0.02915	0.009091
26	530.93	2046	1795	1970	06147						
27	572.56	2209	1936	2125	06628						
28	615.75	2376	2082	2285	07127						
29	660.52	2549	2234	2451	07646						
30	706.86	0.002727	0.002390	0.002623	0.0008182						
31	754.77	2912	2552	2801	08737						
32	804.25	3103	2720	2985	09309						
33	855.30	3300	2892	3174	09900						
34	907.92	3503	3070	3369	10509						

CROSS-SECTION AND MASS OF WIRES (Continued)
Metric Measure

Diameters are given in thousandths of a centimeter and area of section in square thousandths of a centimeter. 1 (cm/1000)^2 = .000001 sq. cm For sections and masses for diameters 1/10 or 10 times those of the table, divide or multiply by 100.

Diam. in mils	Cross-sec. in sq. mils	Copper, 8.90	Iron, 7.80	Brass, 8.56	Aluminum, 2.67	Diam. in thousandths of a cm	Cross-section in square thousandths of a cm	Grams per meter			
								Copper, density 8.90	Iron, density 7.80	Brass, density 8.56	Aluminum, density 2.67
35	962.11	0.003712	0.003253	0.003570	0.001114	10	78.54	0.06990	0.06126	0.06723	0.02097
36	1017.88	3927	3442	3777	1178	11	95.03	.08458	.07412	.08135	.02537
37	1075.21	4149	3636	3990	1245	12	113.10	.10065	.08822	.09681	.03020
38	1134.11	4376	3844	4218	1316	13	132.73	.11813	.10353	.11362	.03544
39	1194.59	4609	4040	4433	1383	14	153.94	.13701	.12008	.13177	.04110
40	1256.64	0.004849	0.004249	0.004664	0.001455	15	176.71	0.1573	0.1378	0.1513	0.04718
41	1320.25	5094	4465	4900	1528	16	201.06	.1789	.1568	.1721	.05368
42	1385.44	5346	4685	5141	1604	17	226.98	.2020	.1770	.1943	.06060
43	1452.20	5603	4911	5389	1681	18	254.47	.2265	.1985	.2178	.06794
44	1520.53	5867	5142	5643	1760	19	283.53	.2523	.2212	.2427	.07570
45	1590.43	0.006137	0.005378	0.005902	0.001841	20	314.16	0.2796	0.2450	0.2689	0.08388
46	1661.90	6412	5620	6167	1924	21	346.36	.3083	.2702	.2965	.09248
47	1734.94	6694	5867	6438	2008	22	380.13	.3383	.2965	.3254	.10149
48	1809.56	6982	6119	6715	2095	23	415.48	.3698	.3241	.3557	.11093
49	1885.74	7276	6377	6998	2183	24	452.39	.4026	.3529	.3872	.12079
50	1963.50	0.007576	0.006640	0.007287	0.002273	25	490.87	0.4369	0.3829	0.4202	0.1311
51	2042.82	7882	6908	7581	2365	26	530.93	.4725	.4141	.4545	.1418
52	2123.72	8194	7181	7881	2458	27	572.56	.5096	.4466	.4901	.1529
53	2206.18	8512	7460	8187	2554	28	615.75	.5480	.4803	.5271	.1644
54	2290.22	8837	7744	8499	2651	29	660.52	.5879	.5152	.5654	.1764
55	2375.83	0.009167	0.008034	0.008817	0.002750	30	706.86	0.6291	0.5514	0.6051	0.1887
56	2463.01	09504	08329	09140	2851	31	754.77	.6717	.5887	.6461	.2015
57	2551.76	09846	08629	09470	2954	32	804.25	.7158	.6273	.6884	.2147
58	2642.08	10195	08934	09805	3058	33	855.30	.7612	.6671	.7321	.2284
59	2733.97	10549	09245	10146	3165	34	907.92	.8081	.7082	.7772	.2424
60	2827.43	0.01091	0.00956	0.01049	0.003273	35	962.11	0.856	0.7504	0.8236	0.2569
61	2922.47	1128	0988	1085	3383	36	1017.88	.906	.7939	.8713	.2718
62	3019.07	1165	1021	1120	3495	37	1075.21	.957	.8387	.9204	.2871
63	3117.25	1203	1054	1157	3608	38	1134.11	1.012	.8866	.9730	.3035
64	3216.99	1241	1088	1194	3724	39	1194.59	.063	.9318	1.0230	.3190
65	3318.31	0.01280	0.01122	0.01231	0.003841	40	1256.64	1.118	0.980	1.076	0.3355
66	3421.19	1320	1157	1270	3960	41	1320.25	.175	1.030	.130	.3525
67	3525.65	1360	1192	1308	4081	42	1385.44	.233	.081	.186	.3699
68	3631.68	1401	1228	1348	4204	43	1452.20	.292	.133	.243	.3877
69	3739.28	1443	1264	1388	4328	44	1520.53	.353	.186	.302	.4060
70	3848.45	0.01485	0.01302	0.01429	0.004456	45	1590.43	1.415	1.241	1.361	0.4246
71	3959.19	1528	1339	1469	4583	46	1661.90	.479	.296	.423	.4437
72	4071.50	1571	1377	1511	4713	47	1734.94	.544	.353	.485	.4632
73	4185.39	1615	1415	1553	4845	48	1809.56	.611	.411	.549	.4832
74	4300.84	1660	1454	1596	4978	49	1885.74	.678	.471	.614	.5035
75	4417.86	0.01705	0.01494	0.01639	0.005114	50	1963.50	1.748	1.532	1.681	0.5243
76	4536.46	1751	1534	1684	5251	51	2042.82	.818	.593	.753	.5454
77	4656.63	1797	1575	1728	5390	52	2123.72	.890	.657	.818	.5670
78	4778.36	1844	1616	1773	5531	53	2206.18	.964	.721	.888	.5891
79	4901.67	1892	1658	1819	5674	54	2290.22	2.038	.786	.960	.6115
80	5026.55	0.01939	0.01700	0.01865	0.005818						
81	5153.00	1988	1743	1912	5965						
82	5281.02	2038	1786	1960	6113						
83	5410.61	2088	1830	2008	6263						
84	5541.77	2138	1874	2057	6415						

Diameters are given in thousandths of a centimeter and area of section in square thousandths of a centimeter. 1 (cm/1000)^2 = .000001 sq. cm. For sections and masses for diameters 1/10 or 10 times those of the table, divide or multiply by 100.

Diam. in thousandths of a cm	Cross-section in square thousandths of a cm	Grams per meter				Diam. in thousandths of a cm	Cross-section in square thousandths of a cm	Grams per meter			
		Copper, density 8.90	Iron, density 7.80	Brass, density 8.56	Aluminum, density 2.67			Copper, density 8.90	Iron, density 7.80	Brass, density 8.56	Aluminum, density 2.67
55	2375.83	2.114	1.853	2.034	0.6343	75	4417.86	3.932	3.446	3.782	1.180
56	2463.01	.192	.921	.108	.6576	76	4536.46	4.037	.538	.883	.211
57	2551.76	.271	.990	.184	.6813	77	4656.63	.144	.632	.986	.243
58	2642.08	.351	2.061	.262	.7054	78	4778.36	.253	.727	4.090	.276
59	2733.97	.433	.132	.340	.7300	79	4901.67	.362	.823	.177	.309
60	2827.43	2.516	2.205	2.420	0.7549	80	5026.55	4.474	3.921	4.303	1.342
61	2922.47	.601	.280	.502	.7803	81	5153.00	.586	4.019	.411	.376
62	3019.07	.687	.355	.584	.8061	82	5281.02	.700	.119	.521	.410
63	3117.25	.774	.431	.668	.8323	83	5410.61	.815	.220	.631	.445
64	3216.99	.863	.509	.760	.8589	84	5541.77	.932	.323	.744	.480
65	3318.31	2.953	2.588	2.840	0.8860	85	5674.50	5.050	4.426	4.857	1.515
66	3421.19	3.045	.669	.929	.9135	86	5808.80	.170	.531	.972	.551
67	3525.65	.138	.750	3.018	.9413	87	5944.68	.291	.637	5.089	.587
68	3631.68	.232	.833	.109	.9697	88	6082.12	.413	.744	.206	.624
69	3739.28	.328	.917	.201	.9984	89	6221.14	.537	.852	.325	.661
70	3848.45	3.426	3.003	3.295	1.028	90	6361.73	5.662	4.962	5.446	1.699
71	3959.19	.524	.088	.389	.057	91	6503.88	.788	5.073	.567	.737
72	4071.50	.624	.176	.485	.087	92	6647.61	.916	.185	.690	.775
73	4185.39	.725	.265	.583	.117	93	6792.91	6.046	.298	.815	.814
74	4300.84	.828	.355	.682	148	94	6939.78	.176	.413	.940	.853
						95	7088.22	6.309	5.529	6.068	1.893
						96	7238.23	.442	.646	.196	.933
						97	7389.81	.577	.764	.326	.973
						98	7542.96	.713	.884	.457	2.014
						99	7697.69	.851	6.004	.589	.055
						100	7853.98	6.990	6.126	6.723	2.097

RESISTANCE OF WIRES

The following table gives the approximate resistance of various metallic conductors. The values have been computed from the resistivities at 20°C, except as otherwise stated, and for the dimensions of wire indicated. Owing to differences in purity in the case of elements and of composition in alloys, the values can be considered only as approximations.

RESISTANCE OF WIRES

The following dimensions have been adopted in the computations.

B. & S. gauge	Diameter		B. & S. gauge	Diameter	
	mm	mils 1 mil = .001 in.		mm	mils 1 mil = .001 in.
10	2.588	101.9	26	0.4049	15.94
12	2.053	80.81	27	0.3606	14.20
14	1.628	64.08	28	0.3211	12.64
16	1.291	50.82	30	0.2546	10.03
18	1.024	40.30	32	0.2019	7.950
20	0.8118	31.96	34	0.1601	6.305
22	0.6438	25.35	36	0.1270	5.000
24	0.5106	20.10	40	0.07987	3.145

B. & S. No.	Ohms per cm	Ohms per ft.	B. & S. No.	Ohms per cm	Ohms per ft.
*Advance (0°C) ρ = 48. × 10^{-6} ohm cm			Aluminum ρ = 2.828 × 10^{-6} ohm cm		
10	.000912	.0278	10	.0000538	.00164
12	.00145	.0442	12	.0000855	.00260
14	.00231	.0703	14	.000136	.00414
16	.00367	.112	16	.000216	.00658
18	.00583	.178	18	.000344	.0105
20	.00927	.283	20	.000546	.0167
22	.0147	.449	22	.000869	.0265
24	.0234	.715	24	.00138	.0421
26	.0373	1.14	26	.00220	.0669
27	.0470	1.43	27	.00277	.0844
28	.0593	1.81	28	.00349	.106
30	.0942	2.87	30	.00555	.169
32	.150	4.57	32	.00883	.269
34	.238	7.26	34	.0140	.428
36	.379	11.5	36	.0223	.680
40	.605	20.2	40	.0564	1.70

B. & S. No.	Ohms per cm	Ohms per ft.	B. & S. No.	Ohms per cm	Ohms per ft.
Brass ρ = 7.00 × 10^{-6} ohm cm			Climax ρ = 87. × 10^{-6} ohm cm		
10	.000133	.00406	10	.00165	.0504
12	.000212	.00645	12	.00263	.0801
14	.000336	.0103	14	.00418	.127
16	.000535	.0163	16	.00665	.203
18	.000850	.0259	18	.0106	.322
20	.00135	.0412	20	.0168	.512
22	.00215	.0655	22	.0267	.815
24	.00342	.104	24	.0425	1.30
26	.00543	.166	26	.0675	2.06
27	.00686	.209	27	.0852	2.60
28	.00864	.263	28	.107	3.27
30	.0137	.419	30	.171	5.21
32	.0219	.666	32	.272	8.28
34	.0348	1.06	34	.432	13.2
36	.0552	1.68	36	.687	20.9
40	.140	4.26	40	1.74	52.9
Constantan (0°C) ρ = 44.1 × 10^{-6} ohm cm			Copper, annealed ρ = 1.724 × 10^{-6} ohm cm		
10	.000838	.0255	10	.0000328	.000999
12	.00133	.0406	12	.0000521	.00159
14	.00212	.0646	14	.0000828	.00253
16	.00337	.103	16	.000132	.00401
18	.00536	.163	18	.000209	.00638
20	.00852	.260	20	.000333	.0102
22	.0135	.413	22	.000530	.0161
24	.0215	.657	24	.000842	.0257
26	.0342	1.04	26	.00134	.0408
27	.0432	1.32	27	.00169	.0515
28	.0545	1.66	28	.00213	.0649
30	.0866	2.64	30	.00339	.103
32	.138	4.20	32	.00538	.164
34	.219	6.67	34	.00856	.261
36	.348	10.6	36	.0136	.415
40	.880	26.8	40	.0344	1.05

* Trade mark.

Eureka (0°C) ρ = 47. × 10⁻⁶ ohm cm

B. & S. No	Ohms per cm	Ohms per ft.
10	.000893	.0272
12	.00142	.0433
14	.00226	.0688
16	.00359	.109
18	.00571	.174
20	.00908	.277
22	.0144	.440
24	.0230	.700
26	.0365	1.11
27	.0460	1.40
28	.0580	1.77
30	.0923	2.81
32	.147	4.47
34	.233	7.11
36	.371	11.3
40	.938	28.6

German silver ρ = 33. × 10⁻⁶ ohm cm

B. & S. No	Ohms per cm	Ohms per ft.
10	.000627	.0191
12	.000997	.0304
14	.00159	.0483
16	.00252	.0768
18	.00401	.122
20	.00638	.194
22	.0101	.309
24	.0161	.491
26	.0256	.781
27	.0323	.985
28	.0408	1.24
30	.0648	1.97
32	.103	3.14
34	.164	4.99
36	.260	7.94
40	.659	20.1

Iron ρ = 10. × 10⁻⁶ ohm cm

B. & S. No	Ohms per cm	Ohms per ft.
10	.000190	.00579
12	.000302	.00921
14	.000481	.0146
16	.000764	.0233
18	.00121	.0370
20	.00193	.0589
22	.00307	.0936
24	.00489	.149
26	.00776	.237
27	.00979	.299
28	.0123	.376
30	.0196	.598
32	.0312	.952
34	.0497	1.51
36	.0789	2.41
40	.200	6.08

Magnesium ρ = 4.6 × 10⁻⁶ ohm cm

B. & S. No	Ohms per cm	Ohms per ft.
10	.0000874	.00267
12	.000139	.00424
14	.000221	.00674
16	.000351	.0107
18	.000559	.0170
20	.000889	.0271
22	.00141	.0431
24	.00225	.0685
26	.00357	.109
27	.00451	.137
28	.00568	.173
30	.00903	.275
32	.0144	.438
34	.0228	.696
36	.0363	1.11
40	.0918	2.80

Molybdenum ρ = 5.7 × 10⁻⁶ ohm cm

B. & S. No	Ohms per cm	Ohms per ft.
10	.000108	.00330
12	.000172	.00525
14	.000274	.00835
16	.000435	.0133
18	.000693	.0211
20	.00110	.0336
22	.00175	.0534

Excello ρ = 92. × 10⁻⁶ ohm cm

B. & S. No.	Ohms per cm	Ohms per ft.
10	.00175	.0533
12	.00278	.0847
14	.00442	.135
16	.00703	.214
18	.0112	.341
20	.0178	.542
22	.0283	.861
24	.0449	1.37
26	.0714	2.18
27	.0901	2.75
28	.114	3.46
30	.181	5.51
32	.287	8.75
34	.457	13.9
36	.726	22.1
40	1.84	56.0

Gold ρ = 2.44 × 10⁻⁶ ohm cm

B. & S. No.	Ohms per cm	Ohms per ft.
10	.0000464	.00141
12	.0000737	.00225
14	.000117	.00357
16	.000186	.00568
18	.000296	.00904
20	.000471	.0144
22	.000750	.0228
24	.00119	.0363
26	.00189	.0577
27	.00239	.0728
28	.00301	.0918
30	.00479	.146
32	.00762	.232
34	.0121	.369
36	.0193	.587
40	.0487	1.48

Lead ρ = 22. × 10⁻⁶ ohm cm

B. & S. No.	Ohms per cm	Ohms per ft.
10	.000418	.0127
12	.000665	.0203
14	.00106	.0322
16	.00168	.0512
18	.00267	.0815
20	.00425	.130
22	.00676	.206
24	.0107	.328
26	.0171	.521
27	.0215	.657
28	.0272	.828
30	.0432	1.32
32	.0687	2.09
34	.109	3.33
36	.174	5.29
40	.439	13.4

Manganin ρ = 44. × 10⁻⁶ ohm cm

B. & S. No.	Ohms per cm	Ohms per ft.
10	.000836	.0255
12	.00133	.0405
14	.00211	.0644
16	.00336	.102
18	.00535	.163
20	.00850	.259
22	.0135	.412
24	.0215	.655
26	.0342	1.04
27	.0431	1.31
28	.0543	1.66
30	.0864	2.63
32	.137	4.19
34	.218	6.66
36	.347	10.6
40	.878	26.8

Monel Metal ρ = 42. × 10⁻⁶ ohm cm

B. & S. No.	Ohms per cm	Ohms per ft.
10	.000798	.0243
12	.00127	.0387
14	.00202	.0615
16	.00321	.0978
18	.00510	.156
20	.00811	.247
22	.0129	.393

Molybdenum ρ = 5.7 × 10⁻⁶ ohm cm

B. & S. No.	Ohms per cm	Ohms per ft.
24	.00278	.0849
26	.00443	.135
27	.00558	.170
28	.00704	.215
30	.0112	.341
32	.0178	.542
34	.0283	.863
36	.0450	1.37
40	.114	3.47

*Nichrome ρ = 115. × 10⁻⁶ ohm cm

B. & S. No.	Ohms per cm	Ohms per ft.
10	.0021281	.06488
12	.0033751	.1029
14	.0054054	.1648
16	.0085116	.2595
18	.0138383	.4219
20	.0216218	.6592
22	.0346040	1.055
24	.0548088	1.671
26	.0875760	2.670
28	.1394328	4.251
30	.2214000	6.750
32	.346040	10.55
34	.557600	17.00
36	.885600	27.00
38	1.383832	42.19
40	2.303872	70.24

Platinum ρ = 10. × 10⁻⁶ ohm cm

B. & S. No.	Ohms per cm	Ohms per ft.
10	.000190	.00579
12	.000302	.00921
14	.000481	.0146
16	.000764	.0233
18	.00121	.0370
20	.00193	.0589
22	.00307	.0936
24	.00489	.149
26	.00776	.237
27	.00979	.299
28	.0123	.376
30	.0196	.598
32	.0312	.952
34	.0497	1.51
36	.0789	2.41
40	.200	6.08

Steel, piano wire (0°C) ρ = 11.8 × 10⁻⁶ ohm cm

B. & S. No.	Ohms per cm	Ohms per ft.
10	.000224	.00684
12	.000357	.0109
14	.000567	.0173
16	.000901	.0275
18	.00143	.0437
20	.00228	.0695
22	.00363	.110
24	.00576	.176
26	.00916	.279
27	.0116	.352
28	.0146	.444
30	.0232	.706
32	.0368	1.12
34	.0586	1.79
36	.0931	2.84
40	.236	7.18

Tantalum ρ = 15.5 × 10⁻⁶ ohm cm

B. & S. No.	Ohms per cm	Ohms per ft.
10	.000295	.00898
12	.000468	.0143
14	.000745	.0227
16	.00118	.0361
18	.00188	.0574
20	.00299	.0913
22	.00476	.145
24	.00757	.231
26	.0120	.367
27	.0152	.463
28	.0191	.583
30	.0304	.928
32	.0484	1.47
34	.0770	2.35
36	.122	3.73
40	.309	9.43

Monel Metal ρ = 42. × 10⁻⁶ ohm cm

B. & S. No.	Ohms per cm	Ohms per ft.
24	.0205	.625
26	.0326	.994
27	.0411	1.25
28	.0519	1.58
30	.0825	2.51
32	.131	4.00
34	.209	6.36
36	.331	10.1
40	.838	25.6

Nickel ρ = 7.8 × 10⁻⁶ ohm cm

B. & S. No.	Ohms per cm	Ohms per ft.
10	.000148	.00452
12	.000236	.00718
14	.000375	.0114
16	.000596	.0182
18	.000948	.0289
20	.00151	.0459
22	.00240	.0730
24	.00381	.116
26	.00606	.185
27	.00764	.233
28	.00963	.294
30	.0153	.467
32	.0244	.742
34	.0387	1.18
36	.0616	1.88
40	.156	4.75

Silver (18°C) ρ = 1.629 × 10⁻⁶ ohm cm

B. & S. No.	Ohms per cm	Ohms per ft.
10	.0000310	.000944
12	.0000492	.00150
14	.0000783	.00239
16	.000124	.00379
18	.000198	.00603
20	.000315	.00959
22	.000500	.0153
24	.000796	.0243
26	.00126	.0386
27	.00160	.0486
28	.00201	.0613
30	.00320	.0975
32	.00509	.155
34	.00809	.247
36	.0129	.392
40	.0325	.991

Steel, invar (35 % Ni) ρ = 81. × 10⁻⁶ ohm cm

B. & S. No.	Ohms per cm	Ohms per ft.
10	.00154	.0469
12	.00245	.0746
14	.00389	.119
16	.00619	.189
18	.00984	.300
20	.0156	.477
22	.0249	.758
24	.0396	1.21
26	.0629	1.92
27	.0793	2.42
28	.100	3.05
30	.159	4.85
32	.253	7.71
34	.402	12.3
36	.639	19.5
40	1.62	49.3

Tin ρ = 11.5 × 10⁻⁶ ohm cm

B. & S. No.	Ohms per cm	Ohms per ft.
10	.000219	.00666
12	.000348	.0106
14	.000553	.0168
16	.000879	.0268
18	.00140	.0426
20	.00222	.0677
22	.00353	.108
24	.00562	.171
26	.00893	.272
27	.0113	.343
28	.0142	.433
30	.0226	.688
32	.0359	1.09
34	.0571	1.74
36	.0908	2.77
40	.230	7.00

B. & S. No.	Ohms per cm	Ohms per ft.	B. & S. No.	Ohms per cm	Ohms per ft.
Tungsten $\rho = 5.51 \times 10^{-6}$ ohm cm			Zinc (0°C) $\rho = 5.75 \times 10^{-6}$ ohm cm		
10	.000105	.00319	10	.000109	.00333
12	.000167	.00508	12	.000174	.00530
14	.000265	.00807	14	.000276	.00842
16	.000421	.0128	16	.000439	.0134
18	.000669	.0204	18	.000699	.0213
20	.00106	.0324	20	.00111	.0339
22	.00169	.0516	22	.00177	.0538
24	.00269	.0820	24	.00281	.0856
26	.00428	.130	26	.00446	.136
27	.00540	.164	27	.00563	.172
28	.00680	.207	28	.00710	.216
30	.0108	.330	30	.0113	.344
32	.0172	.524	32	.0180	.547
34	.0274	.834	34	.0286	.870
36	.0435	1.33	36	.0454	1.38
40	.110	3.35	40	.115	3.50

COLOR CODE FOR RESISTORS

COLOR CODE FOR RESISTORS

GENERAL REQUIREMENTS

Code Colors. Colors used for color coding shall conform to Standard MIL–STD–174, and shall be permanent and nonfading. The color-code marking shall remain legible after the resistor has been subjected to all the tests specified in the individual resistor specification.

Body Colors (Background). The exterior body color of resistors shall be any color other than black; for composition-type resistors, tan is preferred, for wire-wound-type resistors, brown is preferred.

Conflict of Colors. When the body color is the same as any of the band colors, then either the body color or the band color shall be differentiated by shade or gloss.

Band A		Band B		Band C		Band D	
Color	First significant figure	Color	Second significant figure	Color	Multiplier	Color	Resistance tolerance (per cent)
Black..	0	Black.....	0	Black...	1	Silver..	±10
Brown..	1	Brown....	1	Brown...	10	Gold...	±5
Red....	2	Red......	2	Red....	100		
Orange..	3	Orange...	3	Orange..	1,000		
Yellow..	4	Yellow...	4	Yellow..	10,000		
Green...	5	Green....	5	Green...	100,000		
Blue....	6	Blue.....	6	Blue....	1,000,000		
Purple (viole.	7	Purple (violet)..	7	...	...		
Gray....	8	Gray.....	8	Silver...	0.01		
White..	9	White....	9	Gold....	0.1		

COLOR CODE FOR RESISTORS (Not wire wound)

FIRST SIGNIFICANT FIGURE
SECOND SIGNIFICANT FIGURE
TOLERANCE
MULTIPLIER

Band A—The first significant figure of the resistance value. (For composition-type resistors, all bands shall be of equal width. For wire-wound-type resistors, band A shall be double width.)

Band B—The second significant figure of the resistance value.

Band C—The multiplier. (The multiplier is the factor by which the two significant figures are multiplied to yield the nominal resistance value.)

Band D—The resistance tolerance.

COLOR CODE FOR RESISTORS (Wire wound)

FIRST SIGNIFICANT FIGURE (DOUBLE-WIDTH SIGNIFIES WIREWOUND-TYPE RESISTORS)
SECOND SIGNIFICANT FIGURE
TOLERANCE
MULTIPLIER

Examples of color coding

3,900 ohms ±10 percent—Band A. orange; band B. white; band C, red; band D, silver.

43,000 ohms ±5 percent—Band A, yellow; band B, orange; band C orange; band D, gold.

ELECTRICAL RESISTIVITY AND TEMPERATURE COEFFICIENTS OF ELEMENTS

Element	Temperature °C	Microhm-Cm	Temperature Coefficient per °C
Aluminum, 99.996%	20	2.6548	0.00429[20][z]
Antimony	0	39.0	
Arsenic	20	33.3	
Beryllium[a]	20	4.0	0.025[20][z]
Bismuth	0	106.8	
Boron	0	1.8×10^{12}	
Cadmium	0	6.83	0.0042[0][z]
Calcium	0	3.91	0.00416[0][z]
Carbon[b]	0	1375.0	
Cerium	25	75.0	0.00087[0-25]
Cesium	20	20	
Chromium	0	12.9	0.003[0][z]
Cobalt	20	6.24	0.00604[0-100]
Copper	20	1.6730	0.0068[20][z]
Dysprosium[c]	25	57.0	0.00119[0-25]
Erbium	25	107.0	0.00201[0-25]
Europium	25	90.0	
Gadolinium	25	140.5	0.00176[0-25]
Gallium[d]	20	17.4	
Germanium[e]	22	46×10^6	
Gold	20	2.35	0.004[0-100]
Hafnium	25	35.1	0.0038[25][z]
Holmium	25	87.0	0.00171[0-25]
Indium	20	8.37	
Iodine	20	1.3×10^{15}	
Iridium	20	5.3	0.003925[0-100]
Iron, 99.99%	20	9.71	0.00651[20][z]
Lanthanum	25	5.70	0.00218[0-25]
Lead	20	20.648	0.00336[20-40]
Lithium	0	8.55	
Lutetium	25	79.0	0.00240[0-25]
Magnesium[f]	20	4.45	0.0165[20][z]
Manganese α	23–100	185.0	
Mercury	50	98.4	
Molybdenum	0	5.2	
Neodymium	25	64.0	0.00164[0-25]
Nickel	20	6.84	0.0069[0-100]
Niobium (Columbium)[g]	0	12.5	
Osmium	20	9.5	0.0042[0-100]
Palladium	20	10.8	0.00377[0-100]
Phosphorus, white	11	1×10^{17}	
Platinum, 99.85%	20	10.6	0.003927[0-100]
Plutonium	107	141.4	
Potassium	0	6.15	
Praseodymium	25	68	0.00171[0-25]
Rhenium	20	19.3	0.00395[0-100]
Rhodium	20	4.51	0.0042[0-100]
Rubidium	20	12.5	
Ruthenium	0	7.6	
Samarium	25	88.0	0.00184[0-25]
Scandium[h]	22	61.0	0.00282[0-25]
Selenium	0	12.0	
Silicon	0	10.0	
Silver	20	1.59	0.0041[0-100]
Sodium	0	4.2	
Strontium	20	23.0	
Sulfur, yellow	20	2×10^{23}	
Tantalum	25	12.45	0.00383[0-100]

ELECTRICAL RESISTIVITY AND TEMPERATURE COEFFICIENTS OF ELEMENTS
(Continued)

Element	Temperature °C	Microhm-Cm	Temperature Coefficient per °C
Tellurium	25	4.36×10^5	
Thallium	0	18.0	
Thorium	0	13.0	0.0038^{0-100}
Thulium	25	79.0	0.00195^{0-25}
Tin	0	11.0	0.0047^{0-100}
Titanium	20	42.0	
Tungsten	27	5.65	
Uranium		30.0	
Vanadium	20	24.8–26.0	
Ytterbium	25	29.0	0.0013^{0-25}
Yttrium	25	57.0	0.0027^{0-25}
Zinc	20	5.916	0.00419^{0-100}
Zirconium	20	40.0	$0.0044^{20\,z}$

[a] Annealed, comm. pure.
[b] Graphite.
[c] Polycrystalline.
[d] Hard Wire.
[e] Intrinsic Ge.
[f] Polycrystalline.
[g] High Purity.
[h] Zone refined bar.
[z] Data not available to indicate range over which coefficient is valid.

ELECTRICAL RESISTIVITY OF THE ALKALI METALS

Metal	At. No.	At. Wt.	Sp. Gr.	M.P., °C	Resistivity μ-ohm cm at °C	
Li	3	6.939	0.534^{20}	179	12.17	86.6
					13.36	120.5
					14.73	153.3
					15.54	178.2
Na	11	22.9898	0.971^{20}	97.81	5.23	29.4
					5.72	50.6
					6.53	83.3
					6.71	91.6
					6.83	97.1
K	19	39.102	0.86^{20}	63.65	7.01	22.8
					7.32	35.5
					7.54	41.1
					8.05	56.1
Rb	37	85.47	$1.475^{38.89}$	38.89	11.28	0
					12.52	53
Cs	55	132.905	1.8785^{15}	28.5	20.29	18.2
					37.39	28.1

LOW MELTING POINT SOLDERS
(From N.B.S. Circular 492)

Nominal Composition, Weight Percent			Liquidus Temperature, °F
Pb	Sn	Bi	
25	25	50	266
50	37.5	12.5	374
25	50	25	336

AWS-ASTM Classification	Solidus, °F	Liquidus, °F	Brazing Temperature Range, °F	Ag	Al	As	Au	B	Be	Bi	C	Cd	Cr	Cu	Fe	Li	Mg	Mn	Ni	P	Pb	Sb	Si	Sn	Ti	Zn	Other Each	Other Total	AWS-ASTM Classification
ALUMINUM-SILICON																													
BAlSi-2	1070	1135	1110-1150		Bal.									0.25	0.8			0.10					6.8-8.2			0.20	0.05	0.15	BAlSi-2
BAlSi-3	970	1085	1060-1120		Bal.								0.15	3.3-4.7	0.8		0.15	0.15					9.3-10.7			0.20	0.05	0.15	BAlSi-3
BAlSi-4	1070	1080	1080-1120		Bal.									0.30	0.8		0.10	0.15					11.0-13.0			0.20	0.05	0.15	BAlSi-4
BAlSi-5	1070	1095	1090-1120		Bal.									0.30	0.8		0.05	0.05					9.0-11.0		0.20	0.10	0.05	0.15	BAlSi-5
COPPER-PHOSPHORUS																													
BCuP-1	1310	1650	1450-1700											Bal.						4.75-5.25								0.15	BCuP-1
BCuP-2	1310	1460	1350-1550											Bal.						7.00-7.25								0.15	BCuP-2
BCuP-3	1190	1485	1300-1500	4.75-5.25										Bal.						5.75-6.25								0.15	BCuP-3
BCuP-4	1190	1335	1300-1450	5.75-6.25										Bal.						7.00-7.50								0.15	BCuP-4
BCuP-5	1190	1475	1300-1500	14.50-15.50										Bal.						4.75-5.25								0.15	BCuP-5
SILVER																													
BAg-1	1125	1145	1145-1400	44-46								23-25		14-16												14-18		0.15	BAg-1
BAg-1a	1160	1175	1175-1400	49-51								17-19		14.5-16.5												14.5-18.5		0.15	BAg-1a
BAg-2	1125	1295	1295-1550	34-36								17-19		25-27												19-23		0.15	BAg-2
BAg-3	1170	1270	1270-1500	49-51								15-17		14.5-16.5					2.5-3.5							13.5-17.5		0.15	BAg-3
BAg-4	1240	1435	1435-1650	39-41										29-31					1.5-2.5							26-30		0.15	BAg-4
BAg-5	1250	1370	1370-1550	44-46										29-31												23-27		0.15	BAg-5
BAg-6	1270	1425	1425-1600	49-51										33-35												14-18		0.15	BAg-6
BAg-7	1145	1205	1205-1400	55-57										21-23										4.5-5.5		15-19		0.15	BAg-7
BAg-8	1435	1435	1435-1650	71-73										Bal.														0.15	BAg-8
BAg-8a	1410	1410	1410-1600	71-73										Bal.														0.15	BAg-8a
BAg-13	1325	1575	1575-1775	53-55										Bal.												4.0-6.0		0.15	BAg-13
BAg-18	1115	1125	1325-1550	59-61										Bal.	0.15-0.3									9.5-10.5				0.15	BAg-18
BAg-19	1435	1635	1610-1800	92-93										Bal.	0.15-0.3						0.025							0.15	BAg-19
PRECIOUS METALS																													
BAu-1	1815	1860	1860-2000				37.0+1 −0							Bal.														0.15	BAu-1
BAu-2	1635	1635	1635-1850				79.5+1 −0							Bal.														0.15	BAu-2
BAu-3	1785	1885	1885-1995				34.5+1 −0							Bal.					2.5-3.5									0.15	BAu-3
BAu-4	1740	1740	1740-1840				81.5+1 −0							Bal.														0.15	BAu-4
COPPER AND COPPER-ZINC																													
BCu-1	1980	1980	2000-2100		0.01									99.90 min.						0.075	0.02							0.10	BCu-1
BCu-1a	1980	1980	2000-2100											99.0 min.														0.30[a]	BCu-1a
BCu-2	1980	1980	2000-2100											86.5 min.														0.50[c]	BCu-2[b]
RBCuZn-A	1630	1650	1670-1750		0.01*									57-61	*			*			0.05*		*	0.25-1.00		Bal.		0.50[d]	RBCuZn-A[e]
RBCuZn-D	1690	1715	1720-1800		0.01*									46-50					9.0-11.0	0.25	0.05*			0.04-0.25		Bal.		0.50[d]	RBCuZn-D[e]
MAGNESIUM																													
BMg-1	830	1110	1120-1160		8.3-9.7				0.0002-0.0008					0.05	0.005		Bal.	0.15 min.	0.005					0.05			1.7-2.3		0.30	BMg-1
BMg-2	770	1050	1080-1130		11.0-13.0												Bal.										4.5-5.5		0.30	BMg-2
BMg-2a	770	1050	1080-1130		11.0-13.0				0.0002-0.0008								Bal.										4.5-5.5		0.30	BMg-2a

[a] Total other elements requirement pertains only to the metallic elements for this filler metal.

[b] These chemical requirements pertain only to the copper oxide and do not include requirements for the organic vehicle in which the copper oxide is suspended.

[c] Total other elements requirement pertains only to metallic elements for this filler metal. The following limitations are placed on the nonmetallic elements:

Constituent	per cent (max)
Chlorides	0.4
Sulfates	0.1
Oxygen	remainder
Nitric acid insoluble	0.3
Acetone soluble matter	0.5

[d] Total other elements, including the elements marked with an asterisk (*), shall not exceed the value specified.

[e] This AWS-ASTM classification is intended to be identical with the same classification that appears in the Specification for Copper and Copper-Alloy Welding Rods (AWS Designation A5.7; ASTM Designation B 259).[3]

BRAZING FILLER METALS (SOLDERS) (Continued)

AWS-ASTM Classification	Solidus, °F	Liquidus, °F	Brazing Temperature Range, °F	Ag	Al	As	Au	B	Be	Bi	C	Cd	Cr	Cu	Fe	Li	Mg	Mn	Ni	P	Pb	Sb	Si	Sn	Ti	Zn	Other Each	Other Total	AWS-ASTM Classification
NICKEL																													
BNi-1	1790	1900	1950-2200					2.75-4.00			0.6-0.9		13.0-15.0		4.0-5.0				Bal.				3.0-5.0					0.50	BNi-1
BNi-2	1780	1830	1850-2150					2.75-3.5			0.15		6.0-8.0		2.0-4.0				Bal.				4.0-5.0					0.50	BNi-2
BNi-3	1800	1900	1850-2150					2.75-3.5			0.06				1.5				Bal.				4.0-5.0					0.50	BNi-3
BNi-4	1800	1950	1850-2150					1.0-2.2			0.06				1.5				Bal.				3.0-4.0					0.50	BNi-4
BNi-5	1975	2075	2100-2200								0.15		18.0-20.0						Bal.				9.75-10.5					0.50	BNi-5
BNi-6	1610	1610	1700-1875								0.15								Bal.	10.0-12.0								0.50	BNi-6
BNi-7	1630	1630	1700-1900										11.0-15.0						Bal.	9.0-11.0								0.50	BNi-7
SOLDERS—ASTM DESIGNATION B-32-60T, REVISED 1966																													
70A	361	378		0.005 max	0.03 max					0.25 max				0.08 max	0.02 max						30			70		0.005 max			70A
70B				0.005 max	0.03 max					0.25 max				0.08 max	0.02 max						30	0.2-0.5		70		0.005 max			70B
63A	361	361		0.005 max	0.03 max					0.25 max				0.08 max	0.02 max						37	0.12 max		63		0.005 max			63A
63B				0.005 max	0.03 max					0.25 max				0.08 max	0.02 max						37	0.2-0.5		63		0.005 max			63B
60A	361	374		0.005 max	0.03 max					0.25 max				0.08 max	0.02 max						40	0.12 max		60		0.005 max			60A
60B				0.005 max	0.03 max					0.25 max				0.08 max	0.02 max						40	0.2-0.5		60		0.005 max			60B
50A	361	421		0.005 max	0.03 max					0.25 max				0.08 max	0.02 max						50	0.12 max		50		0.005 max			50A
50B	360	420		0.005 max	0.03 max					0.25 max				0.08 max	0.02 max						50	0.2-0.5		50		0.005 max			50B
45A	361	441		0.005 max	0.03 max					0.25 max				0.08 max	0.02 max						55	0.12 max		45		0.005 max			45A
45B				0.005 max	0.03 max					0.25 max				0.08 max	0.02 max						55	0.2-0.5		45		0.005 max			45B
40A	361	460		0.005 max	0.03 max					0.25 max				0.08 max	0.02 max						60	0.12 max		40		0.005 max			40A
40B	360	460		0.005 max	0.03 max					0.25 max				0.08 max	0.02 max						60	0.2-0.5		40		0.005 max			40B
40C	365	448		0.005 max	0.03 max					0.25 max				0.08 max	0.02 max						58	1.8-2.4		40		0.005 max			40C
35A	361	477		0.005 max	0.03 max					0.25 max				0.08 max	0.02 max						65	0.25 max		35		0.005 max			35A
35B				0.005 max	0.03 max					0.25 max				0.08 max	0.02 max						65	0.2-0.5		35		0.005 max			35B
35C	365	470		0.005 max	0.03 max					0.25 max				0.08 max	0.02 max						63.2	1.6-2.0		35		0.005 max			35C
30A	361	491		0.005 max	0.03 max					0.25 max				0.08 max	0.02 max						70	0.25 max		30		0.005 max			30A
30B				0.005 max	0.03 max					0.25 max				0.08 max	0.02 max						70	0.2-0.5		30		0.005 max			30B
30C	364	482		0.005 max	0.03 max					0.25 max				0.08 max	0.02 max						68.4	1.4-1.8		30		0.005 max			30C
25A	361	511		0.005 max	0.03 max					0.25 max				0.08 max	0.02 max						75	0.25 max		25		0.005 max			25A
25B	360	510		0.005 max	0.03 max					0.25 max				0.08 max	0.02 max						75	0.2-0.5		25		0.005 max			25B
25C				0.005 max	0.03 max					0.25 max				0.08 max	0.02 max						73.7	1.1-1.5		25		0.005 max			25C
20B	361	531		0.005 max	0.03 max					0.25 max				0.08 max	0.02 max						80	0.2-0.5		20		0.005 max			20B
20C	363	517		0.005 max	0.03 max					0.25 max				0.08 max	0.02 max						79	0.8-1.2		20		0.005 max			20C
15B	440	550		0.005 max	0.03 max					0.25 max				0.08 max	0.02 max						85	0.2-0.5		15		0.005 max			15B
10B				0.005 max	0.03 max					0.25 max				0.08 max	0.02 max						90	0.2-0.5		10		0.005 max			10B
5A	518	594		0.005 max	0.03 max					0.25 max				0.08 max	0.02 max						95	0.12 max		5*		0.005 max			5A
5B				0.005 max	0.03 max					0.25 max				0.08 max	0.02 max						95	0.2-0.5		5*		0.005 max			5B
2A				0.005 max	0.03 max					0.25 max				0.08 max	0.02 max						98	0.12 max		2**		0.005 max			2A
2B				0.005 max	0.03 max					0.25 max				0.08 max	0.02 max						98	0.2-0.5		2**		0.005 max			2B
2.5S	579	579		0.005 max	0.03 max					0.25 max				0.08 max	0.02 max						97.5	0.4 max		0***		0.005 max			2.5S
1.5S	588	588		2.3-2.7	0.03 max					0.25 max				0.08 max	0.02 max						97.5	0.4 max		1****		0.005 max			1.5S
95TA	452	464		1.3-1.7	0.03 max					0.25 max				0.08 max	0.02 max						0.2	4.5-5.5		95		0.005 max			95TA
96.5TS				3.7-4.4	0.03 max					0.25 max				0.08 max	0.02 max						0.2	0.5 max		96.5		0.005 max			96.5TS

* Permissible tin range, 4.5-5.5%.
** Permissible tin range, 1.5-2.5%.
*** Tin maximum, 0.25%.
**** Permissible tin range, 0.75-1.25%.

PHYSICAL DATA FOR THE PLANETS, THEIR SATELLITES AND SOME ASTEROIDS

Compiled by W. Joseph Armento, 1970

Data was gathered for inclusion in this table from some of the latest available references. Calculations were performed to verify the internal consistency of the interrelated quantities. The deviations are based on the spread of the data as gathered from the selected references and their respective uncertainties.

Certain data which were calculated include the length of the solar day, rotational velocity, centrifical force, isosynchronous satellite data, escape velocity, orbital velocity, synodic period, equilibrium temperature, solar constant, gravitational constant, and all conversions to "earth" units. In the last calculations, a standard deviation is carried in the data to indicate the error arising from the uncertainties in the Earth measurements.

Sidereal time is the time required for the body to return to the equivalent position as defined by the stars. An isosynchronous satellite placed over a point on an equator with no perturbations in the orbit, no eccentricity, and no deflection from the equator will appear to remain stationary in the sky (or remain over the same position on the body); the angular velocity of the body equals the angular velocity of the satellite. The synodic period is the time from conjunction to conjunction. The letter "R" indicates a retrograde or opposite motion to that of the Sun/Earth system.

The exponents for large numbers are expressed in the following form:

$$N \times 10^m = N\,EM$$
i.e. $1.991 \pm 0.002\,E^{30}$ is equivalent
to $1.991 \times 10^{30} \pm 0.002 \times 10^{30}$

Body	Radius of Body (km)			Ellipticity (Oblateness)	Mass (kg)	Average Density (g/cc.)
	Average	Equatorial	Polar			
Sun (Sol)	695950.0 ± 810.0	695950.0 ± 810.0	695950.0 ± 810.0	⩽ 0.0017	1.991 ± 0.002 E30	1.410 ± 0.002
Mercury	2433.0 ± 35.0	2433.0 ± 35.0	Unknown	⩽ 0.0292	3.181 ± 0.110 E23	5.431 ± 0.300
Venus	6053.0 ± 7.8	6053.0 ± 7.8	6053.0 ± 7.8	0.0000 ± 0.0018	4.883 ± 0.034 E24	5.256 ± 0.043
Earth (Terra)	6371.315 ± 0.437	6378.533 ± 0.437	6356.912 ± 0.437	0.003393 ± 0.000097	5.979 ± 0.004 E24	5.519 ± 0.004
Moon (Luna)	1738.3 ± 1.1	1738.7 ± 1.1	1737.6 ± 1.1	0.006327 ± 0.008947	7.354 ± 0.066 E22	3.342 ± 0.031
Mars	3380.0 ± 20.0	3386.0 ± 20.0	3369.0 ± 20.0	0.0050 ± 0.0084	6.418 ± 0.024 E23	3.907 ± 0.079
Phobos	10.4 ± 5.0	11.3 ± 5.0	8.8 ± 5.0	0.22 ± 0.63	2.72 E16†	3.5 est.
Deimos	5.0 ± 4.0	5.0 ± 4.0	Unknown	—	1.83 E15†	3.5 est.
Jupiter	69758.0 ± 139.0	71370.0 ± 254	66644.0 ± 42.0	0.0662 ± 0.0036	1.901 ± 0.003 E27	1.337 ± 0.015
Io	1726.0 ± 109.0	1726.0 ± 109.0	Unknown	—	7.87 ± 0.15 E22	3.654 ± 0.696
Europa	1488.0 ± 70.0	1488.0 ± 70.0	Unknown	—	4.78 ± 0.15 E22	3.464 ± 0.501
Ganymede	2529.0 ± 54.0	2529.0 ± 54.0	Unknown	—	1.54 ± 0.03 E23	2.273 ± 0.152
Callisto	2416.0 ± 137.0	2416.0 ± 137.0	Unknown	—	7.35 ± 2.65 E22	1.244 ± 0.496
V (Amalthea)	87.0 ± 23.0	87.0 ± 23.0	Unknown	—	8.3 E18†	3.0 est.
VI (Hestia)	67.0 ± 16.0	67.0 ± 16.0	Unknown	—	3.8 E18†	3.0 est.
VII (Hera)	20.0 ± 9.0	20.0 ± 9.0	Unknown	—	1.0 E17†	3.0 est.
VIII (Poseidon)	18.0 ± 8.0	18.0 ± 8.0	Unknown	—	7.3 E16†	3.0 est.
IX (Hades)	12.0 ± 3.0	12.0 ± 3.0	Unknown	—	2.2 E16†	3.0 est.
X (Demeter)	9.0 ± 3.0	9.0 ± 3.0	Unknown	—	9.2 E15†	3.0 est.
XI (Pan)	12.0 ± 4.0	12.0 ± 4.0	Unknown	—	2.2 E16†	3.0 est.
XII (Adrastea)	10.0 ± 2.0	10.0 ± 2.0	Unknown	—	1.3 E16†	3.0 est.
Saturn	58219.0 ± 262.0	60369.0 ± 218.0	54148.0 ± 379.0	0.1030 ± 0.0073	5.684 ± 0.022 E26	0.688 ± 0.010
Mimas	272.0 ± 23.0	272.0 ± 23.0	Unknown	—	3.7 ± 2.0 E19	0.439 ± 0.262
Enceladus	299.0 ± 21.0	299.0 ± 21.0	Unknown	—	7.4 ± 3.0 E19	0.661 ± 0.302
Tethys	581.0 ± 74.0	581.0 ± 74.0	Unknown	—	4.9 E20†	0.6 est.
Dione	598.0 ± 86.0	598.0 ± 86.0	Unknown	—	5.4 E20†	0.6 est.
Rhea	890.0 ± 37.0	890.0 ± 37.0	Unknown	—	1.8 E21†	0.6 est.
Titan	2379.0 ± 194.0	2379.0 ± 194.0	Unknown	—	1.19 ± 0.55 E23	2.110 ± 1.103
Hyperion	201.0 ± 17.0	201.0 ± 17.0	Unknown	—	6.8 E19†	2.0 est.
Iapetus	647.0 ± 166.0	647.0 ± 166.0	Unknown	—	2.3 E21†	2.0 est.
Phoebe	132.0 ± 23.0	132.0 ± 23.0	Unknown	—	1.9 E19†	2.0 est.
X (Themis/Janus)	241.0 ± 16.0	241.0 ± 16.0	Unknown	—	1.2 E20†	2.0 est.
Uranus	23470.0 ± 732.0	24045.0 ± 559.0	22362.0 ± 1254.0	0.0700 ± 0.0572	8.682 ± 0.031 E25	1.603 ± 0.149
Ariel	311.0 ± 25.0	311.0 ± 25.0	Unknown	—	5.0 E20†	4.0 est.
Umbriel	201.0 ± 20.0	201.0 ± 20.0	Unknown	—	1.4 E20†	4.0 est.
Titania	500.0 ± 32.0	500.0 ± 32.0	Unknown	—	2.1 E21†	4.0 est.
Oberon	401.0 ± 28.0	401.0 ± 28.0	Unknown	—	1.1 E21†	4.0 est.
Miranda	121.0 ± 11.0	121.0 ± 11.0	Unknown	—	3.0 E19†	4.0 est.
Neptune	22716.0 ± 869.0	22716.0 ± 869.0	Unknown	⩽ 0.0796	1.027 ± 0.014 E26	2.272 ± 0.263
Triton	2008.0 ± 55.0	2008.0 ± 55.0	Unknown	—	1.46 ± 0.05 E23	4.305 ± 0.383
Nereid	136.0 ± 34.0	136.0 ± 34.0	Unknown	—	5.0 ± 3.0 E19	4.7 ± 4.6
Pluto	5700.0 ± 413.0	5700.0 ± 413.0	Unknown	⩽ 0.1562	1.08 ± 1.00 E24	1.65 ± 1.57
Typical Asteroid	20.0 ± 10.0	20.0 ± 10.0	Unknown	—	1.17 E17†	3.5 est.
1—Ceres	372.0 ± 22.0	372.0 ± 22.0	Unknown	—	6.0 ± 3.0 E20	2.8 ± 1.5
2—Pallas	238.0 ± 22.0	238.0 ± 22.0	Unknown	—	1.8 ± ? E20	3.2 ± ?
3—Juno	103.0 ± 14.0	103.0 ± 14.0	Unknown	—	2.0 ± ? E19	4.4 ± ?
4—Vesta	195.0 ± 100.0	195.0 ± 100.0	Unknown	—	1.0 ± ? E20	3.2 ± ?
5—Astraea	Unknown	Unknown	Unknown	—	Unknown	3.5 est.
6—Hebe	110.0 ± 10.0	110.0 ± 10.0	Unknown	—	2.0 ± ? E19	3.6 ± ?
7—Iris	100.0 ± 10.0	100.0 ± 10.0	Unknown	—	1.5 ± ? E19	3.6 ± ?
10—Hygiea	160.0 ± 13.0	160.0 ± 13.0	Unknown	—	6.0 ± ? E19	3.5 ± ?
15—Eunomia	140.0 ± 12.0	140.0 ± 12.0	Unknown	—	4.0 ± ? E19	3.5 ± ?
16—Psyche	140.0 ± 12.0	140.0 ± 12.0	Unknown	—	4.0 ± ? E19	3.5 ± ?
51—Nemansa	40.0 ± 6.0	40.0 ± 6.0	Unknown	—	9.0 ± ? E17	3.4 ± ?
323—Brucia	Unknown	Unknown	Unknown	—	Unknown	3.5 est.
433—Eros	12.0 ± 5.0	12.0 ± 5.0	Unknown	—	5.0 ± ? E15	0.7 ± ?
511—Davida	130.0 ± 11.0	130.0 ± 11.0	Unknown	—	3.0 ± ? E19	3.3 ± ?
588—Achilles	28.0 ± 5.0	28.0 ± 5.0	Unknown	—	3.22 E14†	3.5 est.
617—Patrochus	Unknown	Unknown	Unknown	—	Unknown	3.5 est.
744—Hidalgo	18.0 ± 8.0	18.0 ± 8.0	Unknown	—	3.96 E14†	3.5 est.
1048—Feodosia	Unknown	Unknown	Unknown	—	Unknown	3.5 est.
1221—Amor	3.0 ± 1.5	3.0 ± 1.5	Unknown	—	3.96 E14†	3.5 est.
1566—Icarus	0.53 ± 0.13	0.7 ± 0.1	0.3 ± 0.2	0.57 ± 0.36	5.0 ± ? E12	8.1 ± ?
1620—Geographos	1.5 ± 0.8	1.5 ± 0.8	Unknown	—	5.0 ± ? E13	3.5 ± ?
—Adonis	1.0 ± 0.5	1.0 ± 0.5	Unknown	—	1.47 E13†	3.5 est.
—Apollo	2.0 ± 1.0	2.0 ± 1.0	Unknown	—	1.17 E14†	3.5 est.
—Hermes	1.0 ± 0.5	1.0 ± 0.5	Unknown	—	1.47 E13†	3.5 est.

† Value of mass calculated from an estimated density.

Body	Semimajor axis of Revolution (km) a	Eccentricity (x/a)	Aphelion (km) (a + x)	Perhelion (km) (a − x)	Longitude of Perhelion (Deg.)	Longitude of Ascending Node (Deg.)
Sun (Sol)	—	—	—	—	—	—
Mercury	5.795 ± 0.013 E7	0.2056 ± 0.0002	6.986 ± 0.016 E7	4.604 ± 0.010 E7	76.583	47.667
Venus	1.0811 ± 0.0010 E8	0.0068 ± 0.0001	1.0885 ± 0.0010 E8	1.0737 ± 0.0010 E8	130.783	76.183
Earth (Terra)	1.4957 ± 0.0007 E8	0.0167 ± 0.0001	1.5207 ± 0.0007 E8	1.4707 ± 0.0007 E8	101.983	—
Moon (Luna)	3.84403 ± 0.00006 E5	0.0549 ± 0.0000	4.05506 ± 0.00006 E5	3.63299 ± 0.00006 E5	Not tabulated	Unknown
Mars	2.2784 ± 0.0022 E8	0.0934 ± 0.0002	2.4912 ± 0.0024 E8	2.0656 ± 0.0020 E8	335.033	49.133
Phobos	9.408 ± 0.034 E3	Unknown	—	—	Not tabulated	None*
Deimos	2.3457 ± 0.0265 E4	Unknown	—	—	Not tabulated	None*
Jupiter	7.7814 ± 0.0017 E8	0.0484 ± 0.0002	8.1580 ± 0.0024 E8	7.4048 ± 0.0022 E8	13.417	99.883
Io	4.219 ± 0.003 E5	Unknown	—	—	Not tabulated	None*
Europa	6.712 ± 0.002 E5	Unknown	—	—	Not tabulated	None*
Ganymede	1.071 ± 0.001 E6	Unknown	—	—	Not tabulated	None*
Callisto	1.8830 ± 0.005 E6	Unknown	—	—	Not tabulated	None*
V (Amalthea)	1.814 ± 0.005 E5	Unknown	—	—	Not tabulated	None*
VI (Hestia)	1.14 ± 0.02 E7	Unknown	—	—	Not tabulated	Unknown
VII (Hera)	1.16 ± 0.04 E7	Unknown	—	—	Not tabulated	Unknown
VIII (Poseidon)	2.35 ± 0.01 E7	Unknown	—	—	Not tabulated	Unknown
IX (Hades)	2.37 ± 0.02 E7	Unknown	—	—	Not tabulated	Unknown
X (Demeter)	1.178 ± 0.005 E7	Unknown	—	—	Not tabulated	Unknown
XI (Pan)	2.26 ± 0.02 E7	Unknown	—	—	Not tabulated	Unknown
XII (Adrastea)	2.11 ± 0.01 E7	Unknown	—	—	Not tabulated	Unknown
Saturn	1.4270 ± 0.0009 E9	0.0543 ± 0.0021	1.5045 ± 0.0031 E9	1.3495 ± 0.0031 E9	91.950	113.167
Mimas	1.816 ± 0.007 E5	Unknown	—	—	Not tabulated	Unknown
Enceladus	2.394 ± 0.016 E5	Unknown	—	—	Not tabulated	Unknown
Tethys	2.952 ± 0.004 E5	Unknown	—	—	Not tabulated	Unknown
Dione	3.781 ± 0.015 E5	Unknown	—	—	Not tabulated	Unknown
Rhea	5.284 ± 0.019 E5	Unknown	—	—	Not tabulated	Unknown
Titan	1.227 ± 0.007 E6	Unknown	—	—	Not tabulated	Unknown
Hyperion	1.4873 ± 0.0066 E6	Unknown	—	—	Not tabulated	Unknown
Iapetus	3.571 ± 0.019 E6	Unknown	—	—	Not tabulated	Unknown
Phoebe	1.2983 ± 0.0072 E7	0.17 ± 0.01	1.5190 ± 0.0155 E7	1.0776 ± 0.0143 E9	Not tabulated	Unknown
X (Themis/Janus)	1.58 ± 0.15 E5	Unknown	—	—	Not tabulated	Unknown
Uranus	2.8703 ± 0.0015 E9	0.0460 ± 0.0015	3.0023 ± 0.0046 E9	2.7383 ± 0.0045 E9	169.75	73.717
Ariel	1.918 ± 0.003 E5	Unknown	—	—	Not tabulated	None*
Umbriel	2.672 ± 0.002 E5	Unknown	—	—	Not tabulated	None*
Titania	4.386 ± 0.009 E5	Unknown	—	—	Not tabulated	None*
Oberon	5.861 ± 0.006 E5	Unknown	—	—	Not tabulated	None*
Miranda	1.294 ± 0.014 E5	Unknown	—	—	Not tabulated	None*
Neptune	4.4999 ± 0.0038 E9	0.0082 ± 0.0007	4.5368 ± 0.0050 E9	4.4630 ± 0.0049 E9	44.117	131.167
Triton	3.531 ± 0.004 E5	Unknown	—	—	Not tabulated	Unknown
Nereid	5.9 ± 0.2 E6	Unknown	—	—	Not tabulated	Unknown
Pluto	5.909 ± 0.019 E9	0.2481 ± 0.0006	7.375 ± 0.024 E9	4.443 ± 0.015 E9	270.059	131.278
Typical Asteroid	2.9 ± 1.5 E8	0.10 ± 0.05	3.2 ± 1.7 E8	2.6 ± 1.4 E8	Unknown	Unknown
1—Ceres	4.141 ± 0.003 E8	0.079 ± 0.002	4.468 ± 0.009 E8	3.814 ± 0.009 E8	Unknown	Unknown
2—Pallas	4.141 ± 0.003 E8	0.236 ± 0.003	5.118 ± 0.013 E8	3.164 ± 0.013 E8	Unknown	Unknown
3—Juno	3.994 ± 0.001 E8	0.259 ± 0.001	5.028 ± 0.004 E8	2.920 ± 0.004 E8	Unknown	Unknown
4—Vesta	3.531 ± 0.001 E8	0.089 ± 0.001	3.845 ± 0.004 E8	3.217 ± 0.004 E8	Unknown	Unknown
5—Astraea	3.848 ± ? E8	0.190 ± ?	4.580 ± ? E8	3.117 ± ? E8	Unknown	Unknown
6—Hebe	3.629 ± ? E8	0.20 ± ?	4.35 ± ? E8	2.90 ± ? E8	Unknown	Unknown
7—Iris	3.567 ± ? E8	0.23 ± ?	4.39 ± ? E8	2.75 ± ? E8	Unknown	Unknown
10—Hygiea	4.173 ± ? E8	0.10 ± ?	4.59 ± ? E8	3.76 ± ? E8	Unknown	Unknown
15—Eunomia	3.956 ± ? E8	0.18 ± ?	4.67 ± ? E8	3.24 ± ? E8	Unknown	Unknown
16—Psyche	4.392 ± ? E8	0.14 ± ?	4.98 ± ? E8	3.76 ± ? E8	Unknown	Unknown
51—Nemansa	3.539 ± ? E8	0.06 ± ?	3.75 ± ? E8	3.33 ± ? E8	Unknown	Unknown
323—Brucia	3.564 ± ? E8	0.301 ± ?	4.637 ± ? E8	2.491 ± ? E8	Unknown	Unknown
433—Eros	2.179 ± 0.004 E8	0.222 ± 0.002	2.663 ± 0.007 E8	1.695 ± 0.005 E8	Unknown	Unknown
511—Davida	4.759 ± ? E8	0.18 ± ?	5.616 ± ? E8	3.902 ± ? E8	Unknown	Unknown
588—Achilles	7.793 ± 0.005 E8	0.148 ± 0.001	8.946 ± 0.010 E8	6.640 ± 0.009 E8	Unknown	Unknown
617—Patrochus	7.785 ± 0.005 E8	0.141 ± 0.002	8.883 ± 0.017 E8	6.687 ± 0.016 E8	Unknown	Unknown
744—Hidalgo	8.660 ± 0.004 E8	0.656 ± 0.001	1.4341 ± 0.0011 E9	2.979 ± 0.009 E8	Unknown	Unknown
1048—Feodosia	4.088 ± ? E8	0.180 ± ?	4.824 ± ? E8	3.352 ± ? E8	Unknown	Unknown
1221—Amor	2.878 ± ? E8	0.437 ± ?	4.135 ± ? E8	1.620 ± ? E8	Unknown	Unknown
1566—Icarus	1.613 ± 0.003 E8	0.828 ± 0.002	2.949 ± 0.006 E8	2.77 ± 0.03 E7	Unknown	Unknown
1620—Geographos	1.861 ± ? E8	0.34 ± ?	2.494 ± ? E8	1.228 ± ? E8	Unknown	Unknown
—Adonis	2.942 ± ? E8	0.779 ± ?	5.234 ± ? E8	6.50 ± ? E7	Unknown	Unknown
—Apollo	2.221 ± 0.005 E8	0.566 ± 0.001	3.473 ± 0.008 E8	9.64 ± 0.03 E7	Unknown	Unknown
—Hermes	1.934 ± ? E8	0.630 ± ?	3.152 ± ? E8	7.15 ± ? E7	Unknown	Unknown

* To equator of primary.

PHYSICAL DATA FOR THE PLANETS, THEIR SATELLITES AND SOME ASTEROIDS (Continued)

Body	Sidereal Period of Revolution (Solar Seconds)	Equatorial Rotation Period (Solar Seconds)	Average Solar Day (Solar Seconds)	Rotational Velocity at Equator (km/sec)	Centrifical Force at Equator (cm/sec²)	Altitude of an Isosynchronous Satellite (km)
Sun (Sol)	—	2.125 ± ? E6†	—	2.0578 ± 0.0024	0.6085 ± 0.0016	24054600.0 ± 1100.0
Mercury	7.60234 ± 0.00173 E6	5.06775 ± 0.00020 E6	1.52004 ± 0.00110 E8	0.0030 ± 0.0000	0.00037 ± 0.00001	237298.0 ± 49.0
Venus	1.94141 ± 0.00017 E7	R 2.10747 ± 0.09243 E7	R 1.01052 ± 0.04996 E7	0.0018 ± 0.0000	0.0000538 ± 0.0000001	1534693.0 ± 11.0
Earth (Terra)	3.1558150 ± 0.0000000 E7	8.616406 ± 0.000001 E4	8.639588 ± 0.000010 E4	0.4651 ± 0.0000	3.39177 ± 0.00052	35767.0 ± 0.6
Moon (Luna)	2.36055 ± 0.0009 E6	2.36055 ± 0.00009 E6	2.55139 ± 0.00010 E6	0.0046 ± 0.0000	0.0012319 ± 0.0000017	86673.1 ± 1.6
Mars	5.93553 ± 0.00016 E7	8.86427 ± 0.00001 E4	8.87753 ± 0.00034 E4	0.2400 ± 0.0014	1.70126 ± 0.02247	17049.4 ± 6.4
Phobos	2.75468 ± 0.00097 E4	*	2.75596 ± 0.00098 E4	0.0029 ± 0.0011	0.05879 ± 0.05817	232.0 ± ?
Deimos	1.09077 ± 0.00009 E5	*	1.09278 ± 0.00010 E5	0.00029 ± 0.00023	0.00166 ± 0.00297	283.0 ± ?
Jupiter	3.74320 ± 0.00037 E8	3.54300 ± 0.00000 E4‡	3.54334 ± 0.00050 E4	12.6568 ± 0.0450	224.46 ± 1.79	87688.0 ± 359.0
Io	1.52859 ± 0.00009 E5	*	1.52922 ± 0.00023 E5	0.0709 ± 0.0045	0.2916 ± 0.0412	12860.0 ± 1718.0
Europa	3.06824 ± 0.00017 E5	*	3.07076 ± 0.00046 E5	0.0305 ± 0.0014	0.0624 ± 0.0066	18175.0 ± 2226.0
Ganymede	6.18175 ± 0.00017 E5	*	6.19198 ± 0.00088 E5	0.02570 ± 0.00055	0.0262 ± 0.0012	43740.0 ± 4155.0
Callisto	1.44193 ± 0.00000 E6	*	1.44751 ± 0.00020 E6	0.01053 ± 0.00060	0.00459 ± 0.00058	61263.0 ± 19485.0
V (Amalthea)	4.30358 ± 0.00000 E4	*	4.30408 ± 0.00060 E4	0.01270 ± 0.00336	0.1854 ± 0.1096	2087.0 ± ?
VI (Hestia)	2.16639 ± 0.00199 E7	Unknown	—	Unknown	Unknown	Unknown
VII (Hera)	2.24467 ± 0.00173 E7	Unknown	—	Unknown	Unknown	Unknown
VIII (Poseidon)	R 6.38496 ± 0.00086 E7	Unknown	—	Unknown	Unknown	Unknown
IX (Hades)	R 6.54048 ± 0.01469 E7	Unknown	—	Unknown	Unknown	Unknown
X (Demeter)	2.23085 ± 0.03110 E7	Unknown	—	Unknown	Unknown	Unknown
XI (Pan)	R 6.03677 ± 0.01987 E7	Unknown	—	Unknown	Unknown	Unknown
XII (Adrastea)	R 5.4000 ± 0.01296 E7	Unknown	—	Unknown	Unknown	Unknown
Saturn	9.29604 ± 0.00035 E8	3.68400 ± 0.00000 E4§	3.6414 ± 0.00020 E4	10.2961 ± 0.0372	175.60 ± 1.42	48797.0 ± 308.0
Mimas	8.17603 ± 0.06912 E4	*	8.17674 ± 0.06913 E4	0.0209 ± 0.0018	0.1606 ± 0.0305	475.0 ± 297.0
Enceladus	1.18515 ± 0.00242 E5	*	1.18530 ± 0.00242 E5	0.0159 ± 0.0011	0.0840 ± 0.0132	907.0 ± 397.0
Tethys	1.62743 ± 0.00639 E5	*	1.62772 ± 0.00639 E5	0.0224 ± 0.0029	0.0866 ± 0.0241	2222.0 ± ?
Dione	2.36848 ± 0.00648 E5	*	2.36905 ± 0.00648 E5	0.0158 ± 0.0023	0.0421 ± 0.0135	3107.0 ± ?
Rhea	3.89820 ± 0.00890 E5	*	3.89983 ± 0.00891 E5	0.0143 ± 0.0006	0.0231 ± 0.0022	6796.0 ± ?
Titan	1.37912 ± 0.00225 E6	*	1.38117 ± 0.00225 E6	0.0108 ± 0.0009	0.00494 ± 0.00090	70161.0 ± 22891.0
Hyperion	1.83876 ± 0.00078 E6	*	1.84240 ± 0.00079 E6	0.000687 ± 0.000058	0.000235 ± 0.000044	7092.0 ± ?
Iapetus	6.84720 ± 0.01469 E6	Unknown	—	Unknown	Unknown	Unknown
Phoebe	R 4.74509 ± 0.1814 E7	Unknown	—	Unknown	Unknown	Unknown
X (Themis/Janus)	6.4145 ± ? E4	Unknown	—	Unknown	Unknown	Unknown
Uranus	2.65114 ± 0.00026 E9	R 3.88080 ± 0.01920	R 3.88074 ± 0.01921 E4	3.8930 ± 0.0901	63.03 ± 3.26	36370.0 ± 791.0
Ariel	R 2.17745 ± 0.00017 E5	*	R 2.17727 ± 0.00035 E5	0.00897 ± 0.00072	0.0259 ± 0.0047	3117.0 ± ?
Umbriel	R 3.58050 ± 0.00000 E5	*	R 3.58002 ± 0.00050 E5	0.00353 ± 0.00035	0.0062 ± 0.0014	2886.0 ± ?
Titania	R 7.52189 ± 0.00000 E5	*	R 7.51976 ± 0.00104 E5	0.00418 ± 0.00027	0.00349 ± 0.00050	?
Oberon	R 1.16321 ± 0.00001 E6	*	R 1.16270 ± 0.00116 E6	0.00217 ± 0.00018	0.00117 ± 0.00018	?
Miranda	R 1.22169 ± 0.00120 E5	*	R 1.22163 ± 0.00121 E5	0.00622 ± 0.00057	0.03201 ± 0.00651	?
Neptune	5.20027 ± 0.00037 E9	5.66520 ± 0.02410 E4	5.66526 ± 0.00241 E4	2.5194 ± 0.0968	27.94 ± 2.40	59506.0 ± 1229.0
Triton	R 5.07712 ± 0.00095 E5	Unknown	R 5.07663 ± 0.00108 E5	Unknown	Unknown	Unknown
Nereid	3.91390 ± 0.69980 E7	Unknown	3.94358 ± 0.70513 E7	Unknown	Unknown	Unknown
Pluto	7.83735 ± 0.01058 E9	5.52320 ± 0.00430 E5	5.52349 ± 0.01139 E5	0.0648 ± 0.0047	0.0738 ± 0.0120	76510.0 ± 584.0
Typical Asteroid						
1—Ceres	8.5224 ± ? E7	3.96 ± 3.60 E4	4.0 ± 3.8 E4	0.0032 ± 0.0030	0.0503 ± 0.0994	11259.0 ± 11019.0
2—Pallas	1.4515 ± 0.0009 E8	Unknown	—	Unknown	Unknown	Unknown
3—Juno	1.4558 ± 0.0017 E8	Unknown	—	Unknown	Unknown	Unknown
4—Vesta	1.3772 ± 0.0009 E8	1.92 ± 0.06 E4	1.92	0.0635 ± 0.0337	2.088 ± 2.455	130109.0 ± 119463.0
5—Astraea	1.1457 ± 0.0009 E8	Unknown	—	Unknown	Unknown	Unknown
6—Hebe	1.3029 ± 0.0035 E8	Unknown	—	Unknown	Unknown	Unknown
7—Iris	1.1923 ± 0.0009 E8	Unknown	—	Unknown	Unknown	Unknown
10—Hygiea	1.1612 ± 0.0009 E8	Unknown	—	Unknown	Unknown	Unknown
15—Eunomia	1.7643 ± 0.0009 E8	Unknown	—	Unknown	Unknown	Unknown
16—Psyche	1.3556 ± 0.0009 E8	Unknown	—	Unknown	Unknown	Unknown
	1.5777 ± 0.0009 E8	Unknown	—	Unknown	Unknown	Unknown

PHYSICAL DATA FOR THE PLANETS, THEIR SATELLITES AND SOME ASTEROIDS (Continued)

Body	Sidereal Period of Revolution (Solar Seconds)	Equatorial Rotation Period (Solar Seconds)	Average Solar Day (Solar Seconds)	Rotational Velocity at Equator (km/sec)	Centrifical Force at Equator (cm/sec²)	Altitude of an Isosynchronous Satellite (km)
51 — Nemansa	1.1491 ± 0.0009 E8	Unknown	—	Unknown	Unknown	Unknown
323 — Brucia	1.1612 ± 0.0035 E8	Unknown	—	Unknown	Unknown	Unknown
433 — Eros	5.5556 ± 0.0086 E7	Unknown	—	Unknown	Unknown	Unknown
511 — Davida	1.7902 ± 0.0009 E8	Unknown	—	Unknown	Unknown	Unknown
588 — Achilles	3.7688 ± 0.0190 E8	Unknown	—	Unknown	Unknown	Unknown
617 — Patrochus	3.7489 ± 0.0035 E8	Unknown	—	Unknown	Unknown	Unknown
744 — Hidalgo	4.3943 ± 0.0112 E8	Unknown	—	Unknown	Unknown	Unknown
1048 — Feodosia	1.4265 ± 0.0035 E8	Unknown	—	Unknown	Unknown	Unknown
1221 — Amor	8.4240 ± 0.0346 E7	Unknown	—	Unknown	Unknown	Unknown
1566 — Icarus	3.5338 ± 0.0086 E7	9.72 ± 3.51 E4	9.72 ± 3.51 E4	0.0000453 ± 0.0000088	0.000287 ± 0.000144	264.0 ± 186.0
1620 — Geographos	4.3805 ± 0.0086 E7	Unknown	—	Unknown	Unknown	Unknown
— Adonis	8.7091 ± 0.0346 E7	Unknown	—	Unknown	Unknown	Unknown
— Apollo	5.7110 ± 0.0346 E7	Unknown	—	Unknown	Unknown	Unknown
— Hermes	4.6397 ± 0.0346 E7	Unknown	—	Unknown	Unknown	Unknown

* Estimated to be equal to the period of revolution (shows same face to primary).
†At latitude 30°—2.290 E6; 60°—2.678 ± 6; 90°—2.851 E6.
‡ Polar—3.5741 E4.
§ Polar—3.8280 E4.

PHYSICAL DATA FOR THE PLANETS, THEIR SATELLITES AND SOME ASTEROIDS (Continued)

Body	Gravity (cm/sec²)				Escape Velocity (km/sec)	Orbital Velocity (km/sec)		
	Mean	Polar	Equatorial	Equatorial—Uncorrected		Semimajor	Perihelion	Aphelion
Sun (Sol)	27372.0 ± 7.0	27370.0 ± 11.0	27369.0 ± 116.0	27369.0 ± 116.0	617.23 ± 0.44	—	—	—
Mercury	357.8 ± 16.1	357.8 ± 19.1	357.8 ± 21.7	357.8 ± 21.7	4.1725 ± 0.0493	47.828 ± 0.566	58.921 ± 0.697	38.824 ± 0.460
Venus	887.4 ± 6.6	887.4 ± 7.4	887.4 ± 7.4	887.4 ± 7.4	10.365 ± 0.020	35.017 ± 0.066	35.256 ± 0.067	34.780 ± 0.066
Earth (Terra)	980.7 ± 0.9	985.1 ± 1.0	975.0 ± 1.0	978.4 ± 1.0	11.179 ± 0.003	29.771 ± 0.007	30.272 ± 0.008	29.278 ± 0.007
Moon (Luna)	162.0 ± 1.5	162.2 ± 1.5	162.0 ± 1.5	162.0 ± 1.5	2.3735 ± 0.0054	1.0176 ± 0.0023	1.0751 ± 0.0024	0.9632 ± 0.0022
Mars	374.0 ± 4.6	376.5 ± 7.8	355.7 ± 7.8	372.7 ± 7.8	5.0282 ± 0.0173	24.121 ± 0.083	26.490 ± 0.091	21.964 ± 0.076
Phobos	1.67 ± ?	2.33 ± ?	Unknown	1.41 ± ?	0.01865 ± 0.00501	0.6739 ± 0.1818	Unknown	Unknown
Deimos	0.49 ± ?	Unknown	Unknown	Unknown	0.00699 ± 0.00312	0.4268 ± 0.2156	Unknown	Unknown
Jupiter	2601.0 ± 11.0	2850.0 ± 17.0	2260.0 ± 23.0	2485.0 ± 23.0	60.238 ± 0.007	13.052 ± 0.016	13.700 ± 0.017	12.435 ± 0.015
Io	176.0 ± 22.0	Unknown	Unknown	Unknown	2.464 ± 0.088	17.320 ± 0.617	Unknown	Unknown
Europa	144.0 ± 14.0	Unknown	Unknown	Unknown	2.068 ± 0.057	13.732 ± 0.377	Unknown	Unknown
Ganymede	160.0 ± 8.0	Unknown	Unknown	Unknown	0.900 ± 0.012	10.871 ± 0.140	Unknown	Unknown
Callisto	84.0 ± 32.0	Unknown	Unknown	Unknown	2.013 ± 0.192	8.194 ± 0.783	Unknown	Unknown
V (Amalthea)	7.28 ± ?	Unknown	Unknown	Unknown	0.1125 ± ?	26.414 ± 3.914	Unknown	Unknown
VI (Hestia)	5.61 ± ?	Unknown	Unknown	Unknown	0.08666 ± ?	3.332 ± 0.453	Unknown	Unknown
VII (Hera)	1.67 ± ?	Unknown	Unknown	Unknown	0.02587 ± ?	3.303 ± 0.860	Unknown	Unknown
VIII (Poseidon)	1.51 ± ?	Unknown	Unknown	Unknown	0.02329 ± ?	2.321 ± 0.579	Unknown	Unknown
IX (Hades)	1.00 ± ?	Unknown	Unknown	Unknown	0.01552 ± ?	2.311 ± 0.326	Unknown	Unknown
X (Demeter)	0.73 ± ?	Unknown	Unknown	Unknown	0.01164 ± ?	3.278 ± 0.613	Unknown	Unknown
XI (Pan)	1.00 ± ?	Unknown	Unknown	Unknown	0.01552 ± ?	2.366 ± 0.445	Unknown	Unknown
XII (Adrastea)	0.84 ± ?	Unknown	Unknown	Unknown	0.01294 ± ?	2.449 ± 0.275	Unknown	Unknown
Saturn	1117.0 ± 11.0	1291.0 ± 25.0	863.0 ± 16.0	1038.0 ± 16.0	36.056 ± 0.097	9.6383 ± 0.0261	10.177 ± 0.031	9.1284 ± 0.0282
Mimas	3.33 ± 1.89	Unknown	Unknown	Unknown	0.1346 ± 0.0193	14.436 ± 2.075	Unknown	Unknown
Enceladus	5.51 ± 2.36	Unknown	Unknown	Unknown	0.1815 ± 0.0197	12.573 ± 1.376	Unknown	Unknown
Tethys	9.72 ± ?	Unknown	Unknown	Unknown	0.3361 ± ?	11.322 ± 0.807	Unknown	Unknown
Dione	10.01 ± ?	Unknown	Unknown	Unknown	0.3460 ± ?	10.004 ± 0.807	Unknown	Unknown
Rhea	14.89 ± ?	Unknown	Unknown	Unknown	0.5149 ± ?	8.4628 ± 0.1974	Unknown	Unknown
Titan	140.0 ± 69.0	Unknown	Unknown	Unknown	0.8161 ± 0.1014	5.5536 ± 0.6938	Unknown	Unknown
Hyperion	11.21 ± ?	Unknown	Unknown	Unknown	0.2123 ± ?	5.0442 ± 0.2396	Unknown	Unknown
Iapetus	36.09 ± ?	Unknown	Unknown	Unknown	0.6834 ± ?	3.2554 ± 0.4694	Unknown	Unknown
Phoebe	7.36 ± ?	Unknown	Unknown	Unknown	0.1394 ± ?	1.7073 ± 0.1672	2.0270 ± 0.1991	1.4380 + 0.1412
X (Themis/Janus)	13.45 ± ?	Unknown	Unknown	Unknown	0.2546 ± ?	1.5476 ± 0.0575	Unknown	Unknown
Uranus	1049.0 ± 66.0	1156.0 + 164.0	937.0 ± 101.0	1000.0 ± 101.0	22.194 ± 0.387	6.7951 ± 0.1187	7.1161 ± 0.1245	6.4902 ± 0.1135
Ariel	34.69 ± ?	Unknown	Unknown	Unknown	0.4645 ± ?	5.4898 ± 0.2471	Unknown	Unknown
Umbriel	22.43 ± ?	Unknown	Unknown	Unknown	0.3003 ± ?	4.6512 ± 0.2589	Unknown	Unknown
Titania	55.77 ± ?	Unknown	Unknown	Unknown	0.7468 ± ?	3.6304 ± 0.1302	Unknown	Unknown
Oberon	44.72 ± ?	Unknown	Unknown	Unknown	0.5989 ± ?	3.1405 ± 0.1227	Unknown	Unknown
Miranda	13.50 ± ?	Unknown	Unknown	Unknown	0.1807 ± ?	6.6837 ± 0.3433	Unknown	Unknown
Neptune	1325.0 ± 103.0	1325.0 ± 145.0	1297.0 ± 177.0	1325.0 ± 177.0	24.536 ± 0.531	5.4276 ± 0.1176	5.4723 ± 0.1186	5.3833 ± 0.1167
Triton	241.0 ± 16.0	Unknown	Unknown	Unknown	3.1116 ± 0.0546	4.4006 ± 0.0773	Unknown	Unknown
Nereid	18.0 ± 14.0	Unknown	Unknown	Unknown	0.2213 ± 0.0454	1.0765 ± 0.2282	Unknown	Unknown
Pluto	221.0 ± 207.0	221.0 ± 210.0	221.0 ± 212.0	221.0 ± 212.0	5.0230 ± 1.1804	4.7365 ± 1.1166	6.1024 ± 1.4387	3.6763 ± 0.86670
Typical Asteroid	1.95 ± 1.95	1.95 ± 2.76	1.95 ± 3.38	1.95 ± 3.38	0.02795 ± 0.00781	21.380 ± 9.067	23.637 ± 10.060	19.339 ± 8.231
1—Ceres	28.9 ± 14.8	Unknown	Unknown	Unknown	0.4634 ± 0.0599	17.892 ± 2.315	19.366 ± 2.506	16.530 ± 2.139
2—Pallas	21.2 ± ?	Unknown	Unknown	Unknown	0.3174 ± ?	17.892 ± 0.925	22.757 ± 1.178	14.067 ± 0.728
3—Juno	12.6 ± ?	Unknown	Unknown	Unknown	0.1608 ± ?	18.218 ± 1.385	23.747 ± 1.805	13.977 ± 1.062
4—Vesta	17.5 ± ?	17.5 ± ?	15.4 ± ?	17.5 ± ?	0.2613 ± ?	19.376 ± 5.556	21.184 ± 6.075	17.722 ± 5.082
5—Astraea	Unknown	Unknown	Unknown	Unknown	Unknown	Unknown	Unknown	Unknown
6—Hebe	11.0 ± ?	Unknown	Unknown	Unknown	0.1556 ± ?	19.113 ± 0.971	23.408 ± 1.190	15.605 ± 0.793
7—Iris	10.0 ± ?	Unknown	Unknown	Unknown	0.1413 ± ?	19.278 ± 1.078	24.365 ± 1.362	15.233 ± 0.853
10—Hygiea	15.6 ± ?	Unknown	Unknown	Unknown	0.2235 ± ?	17.823 ± 0.810	19.704 ± 0.895	16.122 ± 0.732
15—Eunomia	13.6 ± ?	Unknown	Unknown	Unknown	0.1951 ± ?	18.306 ± 0.877	21.959 ± 1.052	15.260 ± 0.731
16—Psyche	13.6 ± ?	Unknown	Unknown	Unknown	0.1951 ± ?	17.413 ± 0.834	20.048 ± 0.961	15.124 ± 0.725
51—Nemansa	37.5 ± ?	Unknown	Unknown	Unknown	0.1731 ± ?	19.354 ± 1.623	20.552 ± 1.723	18.226 ± 1.528
323—Brucia	Unknown	Unknown	Unknown	Unknown	Unknown	Unknown	Unknown	Unknown
433—Eros	0.0172 ± ?	Unknown	Unknown	Unknown	0.00203 ± ?	24.665 ± 5.756	30.912 ± 7.214	19.681 ± 4.593
511—Davida	0.880 ± ?	Unknown	Unknown	Unknown	0.0478 ± ?	16.690 ± 0.789	20.021 ± 0.947	13.913 ± 0.658
588—Achilles	0.204 ± ?	Unknown	Unknown	Unknown	0.0107 ± ?	13.042 ± 1.303	15.139 ± 1.512	11.236 ± 1.122
617—Patrochus	Unknown	Unknown	Unknown	Unknown	Unknown	Unknown	Unknown	Unknown
744—Hidalgo	0.606 ± ?	Unknown	Unknown	Unknown	0.0148 ± ?	12.372 ± 3.075	27.146 ± 6.748	5.639 ± 1.402
1048—Feodosia	Unknown	Unknown	Unknown	Unknown	Unknown	Unknown	Unknown	Unknown
1221—Amor	0.29 ± ?	Unknown	Unknown	Unknown	0.1325 ± ?	21.46 ± ?	34.29 ± ?	13.43 ± ?
1566—Icarus	0.120 ± ?	0.357 ± ?	0.069 ± ?	0.069 ± ?	0.00112 ± ?	28.668 ± 3.833	93.458 ± 12.507	8.794 ± 1.177
1620—Geographos	0.015 ± ?	Unknown	Unknown	Unknown	0.00067 ± ?	26.689 ± 7.957	38.029 ± 11.337	18.731 ± 5.584
—Adonis	0.098 ± ?	Unknown	Unknown	Unknown	0.0441 ± ?	21.23 ± ?	60.23 ± ?	7.483 ± ?
—Apollo	0.29 ± ?	Unknown	Unknown	Unknown	0.1073 ± ?	24.431 ± 6.844	46.408 ± 13.001	12.861 ± 3.603
—Hermes	0.098 ± ?	Unknown	Unknown	Unknown	0.0441 ± ?	26.18 ± ?	54.95 ± ?	12.47 ± ?

PHYSICAL DATA FOR THE PLANETS, THEIR SATELLITES AND SOME ASTEROIDS (Continued)

Body	Inclination of Equator to Orbit (Deg.)	Inclination of Orbit to Ecliptic (Deg.)	Inclination of Equator to Ecliptic (Deg.)	Inclination of Orbit to Equator of Primary (Deg.)	Inclination of Orbit to Orbit of Primary (Deg.)	Average Synodic Period (Solar Seconds)	Albedo	Average Temperatures (°K)			Solar Constant (cal/cm²/min)	Surface Pressure (atmospheres)	Atmospheric Composition (in cm-atm) (1 cm-atm = 2.69 E19 molecules per cm³)
								Night	Day	Equilibrium			
Sun (Sol)	—	7.0	—	—	—	—	—	—	—	5776	88682.0 (est.)	Unknown	H_2/He major
Mercury	R 179.0 ± 1.0	7.0028	Unknown	—	—	1.00149 E7	0.076 ± 0.022	13	683	633	12.79	1 E-4 (est.)	150–3550 CO_2 (surface outgassings) SO_2?, Ar?
Venus	—	3.40	Unknown	—	—	5.04505 E7	0.76	233	720	463	3.675	10–25‡	90% CO_2, 0.4% H_2O, 0.4% O_2, balance N_2 + inerts
Earth (Terra)	23.45	—	23.45	—	—	—	0.36 ± 0.06	275	295	394	1.920	1.0	78% N_2, 21% O_2, 1% Ar (see supplementary tables)
Moon (Luna)	6.683	5.12	1.533	Unknown	Unknown	—	0.086 ± 0.025	100	365	394	1.920	~0	small amounts of outgassing. SO_2?, Ar?, Xe?
Mars	25.20	1.850	Unknown	—	—	6.73861 E7	0.152 ± 0.003	170	300	319	0.827	0.006–0.009	8300 ± 800 CO_2, 3900 CO, 4.35 ± 1.87 H_2O, ≤20. O_2, bal N_2
Phobos	0.0*	Unknown	Unknown	2.0	Unknown	Not tabulated	0.065	Unknown	Unknown	319	0.827	None	—
Deimos	0.0*	Unknown	Unknown	2.0	Unknown	Not tabulated	Unknown	Unknown	Unknown	319	0.827	None	—
Jupiter	3.117	1.309	Unknown	—	—	3.44637 E7	0.54 ± 0.04	123	313	173	0.0709	10^4–10^5	1.20 E7 H_2, 2.35 E6 He, 1.5 E4 CH_4, 7 E2 NH_3, 0.198 H_2O, no O_2/N_2 ? (CH_4 likely)
Io	0.0*	Unknown	Unknown	0.0	3.1	Not tabulated	0.37	Unknown	Unknown	173	0.0709	Trace	—
Europa	0.0*	Unknown	Unknown	0.0	3.1	Not tabulated	0.39	Unknown	Unknown	173	0.0709	None?	None detected
Ganymede	0.0*	Unknown	Unknown	0.0	3.1	Not tabulated	0.20	Unknown	Unknown	173	0.0709	None?	None detected
Callisto	0.0*	Unknown	Unknown	0.0	3.1	Not tabulated	0.03	Unknown	Unknown	173	0.0709	None?	None detected
V (Amalthea)	0.0*	Unknown	Unknown	0.0	3.1	Not tabulated	Unknown	Unknown	Unknown	173	0.0709	None	
VI (Hestia)	Unknown	Unknown	Unknown	28.5	Unknown	Not tabulated	Unknown	Unknown	Unknown	173	0.0709	None	
VII (Hera)	Unknown	Unknown	Unknown	28.0	Unknown	Not tabulated	Unknown	Unknown	Unknown	173	0.0709	None	
VIII (Poseidon)	Unknown	Unknown	Unknown	R 147.5 ± 1.0	Unknown	Not tabulated	Unknown	Unknown	Unknown	173	0.0709	None	
IX (Hades)	Unknown	Unknown	Unknown	R 156.5 ± 1.0	Unknown	Not tabulated	Unknown	Unknown	Unknown	173	0.0709	None	
X (Demeter)	Unknown	Unknown	Unknown	28.3	Unknown	Not tabulated	Unknown	Unknown	Unknown	173	0.0709	None	
XI (Pan)	Unknown	Unknown	Unknown	R 163.4	Unknown	Not tabulated	Unknown	Unknown	Unknown	173	0.0709	None	
XII (Adrastea)	Unknown	Unknown	Unknown	R ?	Unknown	Not tabulated	Unknown	Unknown	Unknown	173	0.0709	None	
Saturn	26.75	2.493	Unknown	—	—	3.26671 E7	0.57 ± 0.09	103	223	128	0.0211	10^2–10^4	H_2/He major, 2.5 E4 CH_4, 2.5 E2 NH_3
Mimas	0.0*	Unknown	Unknown	1.5	27 ± 2	Not tabulated	Unknown	Unknown	Unknown	128	0.0211	None	—
Enceladus	0.0*	Unknown	Unknown	0.0	26.8	Not tabulated	Unknown	Unknown	Unknown	128	0.0211	None	—
Tethys	0.0*	Unknown	Unknown	1.1	27 ± 1	Not tabulated	Unknown	Unknown	Unknown	128	0.0211	None	—
Dione	0.0*	Unknown	Unknown	0.0	26.8	Not tabulated	Unknown	Unknown	Unknown	128	0.0211	None	—
Rhea	0.0*	Unknown	Unknown	0.3	26.8 ± 0.3	Not tabulated	Unknown	Unknown	Unknown	128	0.0211	None	—
Titan	0.0*	Unknown	Unknown	0.3	26.8 ± 0.6	Not tabulated	Unknown	Unknown	Unknown	128	0.0211	?	traces NH_3, CH_4 (est. at 2 E4)
Hyperion	0.0*	Unknown	Unknown	0.6	27.0 ± 1.0	Not tabulated	Unknown	Unknown	Unknown	128	0.0211	None	—
Iapetus	Unknown	Unknown	Unknown	14.7	Unknown	Not tabulated	Unknown	Unknown	Unknown	128	0.0211	None	—
Phoebe	0.0*	Unknown	Unknown	R 174.7	R 150.0	Not tabulated	Unknown	Unknown	Unknown	128	0.0211	None	—
X (Themis/Janus)	Unknown	Unknown	Unknown	Unknown	Unknown	Not tabulated	Unknown	Unknown	Unknown	128	0.0211	None	—
Uranus	R 97.983	0.773	R ?	—	—	3.19383 E7	0.65 ± 0.03	103	123	90	0.0052	2–3	H_2/He major, 1.5 E5 CH_4, trace NH_3 (?)
Ariel	0.0*	R ?	R ?	0.0	98.0	Not tabulated	Unknown	Unknown	Unknown	90	0.0052	None	—
Umbriel	0.0*	R ?	R ?	0.0	98.0	Not tabulated	Unknown	Unknown	Unknown	90	0.0052	None	—
Titania	0.0*	R ?	R ?	0.0	98.0	Not tabulated	Unknown	Unknown	Unknown	90	0.0052	None	—
Oberon	0.0*	R ?	R ?	0.0	98.0	Not tabulated	Unknown	Unknown	Unknown	90	0.0052	None	—
Miranda	0.0*	R ?	R ?	0.0	98.0	Not tabulated	Unknown	Unknown	Unknown	90	0.0052	None	—
Neptune	29.0	1.779	Unknown	—	—	3.17508 E7	0.68 ± 0.08	103	123	72	0.0021	5–10 (est.)	H_2/He major, 2.5 E5 CH_4, trace NH_3 (?)
Triton	Unknown	Unknown	Unknown	R 150.0 ± 10.0	Unknown	Not tabulated	Unknown	Unknown	Unknown	72	0.0021	Trace?	trace CH_4 (at <8 E2)
Nereid	Unknown	Unknown	Unknown	Unknown	Unknown	Not tabulated	Unknown	Unknown	Unknown	72	0.0021	None	—
Pluto	90.0 (?)	17.146	Unknown	—	—	3.16857 E7	0.13 ± 0.05	43	63	63	0.0012	Unknown	None detected

PHYSICAL DATA FOR THE PLANETS, THEIR SATELLITES AND SOME ASTEROIDS (Continued)

Body	Inclination of Equator to Orbit (Deg.)	Inclination of Orbit to Ecliptic (Deg.)	Inclination of Equator to Ecliptic (Deg.)	Inclination of Orbit to Equator of Primary (Deg.)	Inclination of Orbit to Orbit of Primary (Deg.)	Average Synodic Period (Solar Seconds)	Albedo	Night	Day	Equilibrium	Solar Constant (cal/cm²/min)	Surface Pressure (atmospheres)	Atmospheric Composition (in cm-atm) (1 cm-atm = 2.69 E19 molecules per cm²)
Typical Asteroid	Unknown	10.0	Unknown	—	—	5.01157 E7	Unknown	Unknown	Unknown	283	0.275	None	—
1—Ceres	Unknown	10.4 ± 0.3	Unknown	—	—	4.03256 E7	Unknown	Unknown	Unknown	237	0.250	None	—
2—Pallas	Unknown	34.8 ± 0.1	Unknown	—	—	4.02926 E7	Unknown	Unknown	Unknown	237	0.250	None	—
3—Juno	Unknown	13.0 ± 0.1	Unknown	—	—	4.09392 E7	Unknown	Unknown	Unknown	241	0.269	None	—
4—Vesta	Unknown	7.11 ± 0.03	Unknown	—	—	4.35554 E7	0.20 ± 0.11	Unknown	Unknown	256	0.345	None	—
5—Astraea	Unknown	5.33 ± ?	Unknown	—	—	4.16452 E7	Unknown	Unknown	Unknown	246	0.290	None	—
6—Hebe	Unknown	14.8 ± ?	Unknown	—	—	4.29177 E7	Unknown	Unknown	Unknown	253	0.326	None	—
7—Iris	Unknown	5.5 ± ?	Unknown	—	—	4.33355 E7	Unknown	Unknown	Unknown	255	0.338	None	—
10—Hygiea	Unknown	3.8 ± ?	Unknown	—	—	3.84326 E7	Unknown	Unknown	Unknown	236	0.247	None	—
15—Eunomia	Unknown	11.8 ± ?	Unknown	—	—	4.11341 E7	Unknown	Unknown	Unknown	242	0.274	None	—
16—Psyche	Unknown	3.1 ± ?	Unknown	—	—	3.94490 E7	Unknown	Unknown	Unknown	230	0.225	None	—
51—Nemausa	Unknown	9.9 ± ?	Unknown	—	—	4.35065 E7	Unknown	Unknown	Unknown	256	0.343	None	—
323—Bruce	Unknown	24.2 ± ?	Unknown	—	—	4.33355 E7	Unknown	Unknown	Unknown	255	0.338	None	—
433—Eros	Unknown	10.8 ± 0.1	Unknown	—	—	7.30584 E7	Unknown	Unknown	Unknown	326	0.905	None	—
511—Davida	Unknown	15.7 ± ?	Unknown	—	—	3.83119 E7	Unknown	Unknown	Unknown	221	0.190	None	—
588—Achilles	Unknown	10.3 ± 0.1	Unknown	—	—	3.44422 E7	Unknown	Unknown	Unknown	173	0.071	None	—
617—Patroclus	Unknown	22.1 ± ?	Unknown	—	—	3.44589 E7	Unknown	Unknown	Unknown	173	0.071	None	—
744—Hidalgo	Unknown	42.5 ± 0.1	Unknown	—	—	3.39999 E7	Unknown	Unknown	Unknown	164	0.058	None	—
1048—Feodosia	Unknown	53.8 ± ?	Unknown	—	—	4.05229 E7	Unknown	Unknown	Unknown	238	0.257	None	—
1221—Amor	Unknown	11.9 ± ?	Unknown	—	—	5.04625 E7	Unknown	Unknown	Unknown	284	0.519	None	—
1566—Icarus	Unknown	23.0 ± 0.1	Unknown	—	—	2.95038 E8	Unknown	Unknown	Unknown	377	1.651	None	—
1620—Geographos	Unknown	13.3 ± ?	Unknown	—	—	1.12878 E8	Unknown	Unknown	Unknown	353	1.240	None	—
—Adonis	Unknown	1.5 ± ?	Unknown	—	—	4.94920 E7	Unknown	Unknown	Unknown	281	0.496	None	—
—Apollo	Unknown	6.4 ± 0.1	Unknown	—	—	7.05344 E7	Unknown	Unknown	Unknown	323	0.871	None	—
—Hermes	Unknown	6.2 ± ?	Unknown	—	—	9.86736 E7	Unknown	Unknown	Unknown	346	1.140	None	—

*Assumed value.
‡Conflicting satellite data.

PHYSICAL DATA FOR THE PLANETS, THEIR SATELLITES AND SOME ASTEROIDS (Continued)

Body	Radius of Body (Earth Radii)			Period of Rotation (Sidereal Days)	Mass (in Earth Masses)	Density (in Earth Units)	Gravitational Constant (gR²)	
	Mean	Equatorial	Polar				km³/sec²	in Earth Units
Sun (Sol)	109.227 ± 0.128	109.232 ± 0.127	109.232 ± 0.129	24.66225 ± 0.00003	332999.0 ± 402.0	0.2555 ± 0.0009	1.3256 ± 0.0047 E + 11	3.330 ± 0.012 E + 5
Mercury	0.3819 ± 0.0055	0.3819 ± 0.0055	Unknown	58.8151 ± 0.0023	0.0532 ± 0.0018	0.9554 ± 0.0528	2.118 ± 0.113 E + 4	5.32 ± 0.28 E - 2
Venus	0.9500 ± 0.0012	0.9500 ± 0.0012	0.9500 ± 0.0012	R 224.588 ± 10.727	0.8167 ± 0.0057	0.9524 ± 0.0076	3.251 ± 0.026 E + 5	0.817 ± 0.006
Earth (Terra)	1.00000 ± 0.00010	1.00114 ± 0.00010	0.99774 ± 0.00010	1.000000 ± 0.000002	1.0000 ± 0.0009	1.0000 ± 0.0010	3.981 ± 0.004 E + 5	1.000 ± 0.001
Moon (Luna)	0.27283 ± 0.00017	0.27290 ± 0.00017	0.27272 ± 0.00017	27.3960 ± 0.0010	0.01230 ± 0.00011	0.6056 ± 0.0056	4.896 ± 0.045 E + 3	0.0123 ± 0.0001
Mars	0.5306 ± 0.0031	0.5314 ± 0.031	0.5288 ± 0.0031	1.028766 ± 0.000002	0.10734 ± 0.00041	0.7188 ± 0.0130	4.273 ± 0.073 E + 4	0.1073 ± 0.00018
Phobos	0.0016 ± 0.0008	0.0018 ± 0.0008	0.0014 ± 0.0008	0.319702 ± 0.000113	4.5426 ± ? E - 9	0.63 ± ?	1.81 ± ? E - 3	4.54 ± ? E - 9
Deimos	0.0008 ± 0.0006	0.0008 ± 0.0006	Unknown	1.26592 ± 0.00005	3.0657 ± ? E - 10	0.63 ± ?	0.12 ± ? E - 4	3.07 ± ? E - 10
Jupiter	10.949 ± 0.022	11.202 ± 0.040	10.460 ± 0.007	0.411192 ± 0.000000	317.929 ± 0.545	0.2422 ± 0.0015	1.266 ± 0.007 E + 8	317.9 ± 1.9
Io	0.2709 ± 0.0171	0.2709 ± 0.0171	Unknown	1.77405 ± 0.00010	0.01316 ± 0.00025	0.662 ± 0.126	5.240 ± 0.941 E + 3	0.0132 ± 0.0024
Europa	0.2335 ± 0.0110	0.2335 ± 0.0110	Unknown	3.56093 ± 0.00020	0.00799 ± 0.00025	0.628 ± 0.091	3.183 ± 0.435 E + 3	0.0080 ± 0.0011
Ganymede	0.3969 ± 0.0085	0.3969 ± 0.0085	Unknown	7.17440 ± 0.00020	0.02580 ± 0.00052	0.412 ± 0.003	1.025 ± 0.065 E + 3	0.0026 ± 0.0002
Callisto	0.3792 ± 0.0215	0.3792 ± 0.0215	Unknown	16.7347 ± 0.0000	0.01239 ± 0.00443	0.225 ± 0.090	4.894 ± 1.931 E + 3	0.0123 ± 0.0049
V (Amalthea)	0.0137 ± 0.0036	0.0137 ± 0.0036	Unknown	0.499463 ± 0.000000	1.3840 ± ? E - 6	0.5 ± ?	0.551 ± ?	1.38 ± ? E - 6
VI (Hestia)	0.0105 ± 0.0025	0.0105 ± 0.0025	Unknown	Unknown	6.3205 ± ? E - 7	0.5 ± ?	0.252 ± ?	6.32 ± ? E - 7
VII (Hera)	0.0031 ± 0.0014	0.0031 ± 0.0014	Unknown	R ?	1.6809 ± ? E - 8	0.5 ± ?	6.69 ± ? E - 3	1.68 ± ? E - 8
VIII (Poseidon)	0.0028 ± 0.0013	0.0028 ± 0.0013	Unknown	R ?	1.2258 ± ? E - 8	0.5 ± ?	4.88 ± ? E - 3	1.23 ± ? E - 8
IX (Hades)	0.0019 ± 0.0005	0.0019 ± 0.0005	Unknown	R ?	3.6310 ± ? E - 9	0.5 ± ?	1.45 ± ? E - 3	3.63 ± ? E - 9
X (Demeter)	0.0014 ± 0.0005	0.0014 ± 0.0005	Unknown	Unknown	1.5322 ± ? E - 9	0.5 ± ?	6.10 ± ? E - 4	1.53 ± ? E - 9
XI (Pan)	0.0019 ± 0.0006	0.0019 ± 0.0006	Unknown	R ?	3.6310 ± ? E - 9	0.5 ± ?	1.45 ± ? E - 3	3.63 ± ? E - 9
XII (Adrastea)	0.0016 ± 0.0003	0.0016 ± 0.0003	Unknown	R ?	2.1024 ± ? E - 9	0.5 ± ?	8.37 ± ? E - 4	2.10 ± ? E - 9
Saturn	9.1377 ± 0.0411	9.4751 ± 0.0342	8.4987 ± 0.0595	0.427556 ± 0.000000	95.0661 ± 0.3734	0.1246 ± 0.0018	3.784 ± 0.050 E + 7	95.06 ± 1.27
Mimas	0.0427 ± 0.0036	0.0427 ± 0.0036	Unknown	0.948890 ± 0.008022	6.188 ± 3.345 E - 6	0.080 ± 0.047	2.464 ± 1.456	6.188 ± 3.658 E - 6
Enceladus	0.0469 ± 0.0033	0.0469 ± 0.0033	Unknown	1.37546 ± 0.00281	1.238 ± 0.502 E - 5	0.120 ± 0.055	4.927 ± 2.224	1.238 ± 0.559 E - 5
Tethys	0.0912 ± 0.0116	0.0912 ± 0.0116	Unknown	1.88876 ± 0.00742	8.244 ± ? E - 5	0.11 ± ?	3.282 ± ? E + 1	8.24 ± ? E - 5
Dione	0.0939 ± 0.0135	0.0939 ± 0.0135	Unknown	2.74880 ± 0.00752	8.990 ± ? E - 4	0.11 ± ?	3.579 ± ? E + 1	8.99 ± ? E - 5
Rhea	0.1397 ± 0.0058	0.1397 ± 0.0058	Unknown	4.52416 ± 0.00453	2.964 ± ? E - 4	0.11 ± ?	1.180 ± ? E + 2	2.96 ± ? E - 4
Titan	0.3734 ± 0.0304	0.3734 ± 0.0304	Unknown	16.0057 ± 0.0261	0.01991 ± 0.00092	**0.382** ± 0.020	7.923 ± 4.093 E + 3	1.990 ± 1.028 E - 2
Hyperion	0.0315 ± 0.0027	0.0315 ± 0.0027	Unknown	21.3402 ± 0.0091	1.138 ± ? E - 5	0.36 ± ?	4.53 ± ?	1.14 ± ? E - 5
Iapetus	0.1015 ± 0.0261	0.1015 ± 0.0261	Unknown	R ?	3.795 ± ? E - 4	0.36 ± ?	1.51 ± ? E + 2	3.79 ± ? E - 4
Phoebe	0.0207 ± 0.0036	0.0207 ± 0.0036	Unknown	R ?	3.223 ± ? E - 6	0.36 ± ?	1.78 ± ?	3.22 ± ? E - 6
X (Themis/Janus)	0.0378 ± **0.0025**	0.0378 ± 0.0025	Unknown	Unknown	1.962 ± ? E - 5	0.36 ± ?	7.81 ± ?	1.96 ± ? E - 5
Uranus	3.6837 ± 0.1149	3.7740 ± 0.0877	3.5098 ± 0.1968	R 0.450397 ± 0.002228	14.521 ± 0.053	0.2905 ± **0.0272**	5.781 ± 0.510 E + 6	14.52 ± 1.28
Ariel	0.0488 ± 0.0039	0.0488 ± 0.0039	Unknown	R 25.2710 ± 0.0002	8.430 ± ? E - 5	0.72 ± ?	3.36 ± ? E + 1	8.43 ± ? E - 5
Umbriel	0.0315 ± 0.0031	0.0315 ± 0.0031	Unknown	R 4.15544 ± 0.00000	2.276 ± ? E - 4	0.72 ± ?	9.06 ± ?	2.28 ± ? E - 4
Titania	0.0785 ± 0.0050	0.0785 ± 0.0050	Unknown	R 8.72973 ± 0.00000	3.502 ± ? E - 4	0.72 ± ?	1.39 ± ? E + 2	3.50 ± ? E - 4
Oberon	0.0629 ± **0.0044**	0.0629 ± 0.0044	Unknown	R 13.4999 ± 0.0001	1.806 ± ? E - 4	0.72 ± ?	7.19 ± ? E + 1	1.81 ± ? E - 4
Miranda	0.0190 ± 0.0017	0.0190 ± 0.0017	Unknown	R 1.41787 ± 0.00139	4.964 ± ? E - 6	0.72 ± ?	1.98 ± ?	4.96 ± ? E - 6
Neptune	3.5654 ± 0.1364	3.5654 ± 0.1364	Unknown	0.657490 ± 0.002797	17.177 ± 0.234	0.3790 ± 0.0438	6.838 ± 0.746 E + 6	17.18 ± 1.87
Triton	0.3152 ± 0.0086	0.3152 ± 0.0086	Unknown	Unknown	0.02442 ± 0.00084	0.780 ± 0.069	9.721 ± 0.823 E + 3	2.442 ± 0.207 E - 2
Nereid	0.0213 ± 0.0053	0.0213 ± 0.0053	Unknown	Unknown	8.363 ± 5.018 E - 6	0.860 ± 0.826	3.329 ± 3.087	8.363 ± 7.755 E - 6
Pluto	0.8946 ± 0.0648	0.8946 ± 0.0648	Unknown	6.4101 ± 0.0050	0.1806 ± 0.1673	0.2523 ± 0.2399	7.191 ± 6.819 E + 4	0.1806 ± 0.1713
Typical Asteroid	0.0031 ± 0.0016	0.0031 ± 0.0016	Unknown		1.962 ± ? E - 8	0.63 ± ?	7.81 ± ? E - 3	1.96 ± ? E - 8
1—Ceres	0.0584 ± 0.0035	0.0584 ± 0.0035	Unknown	0.4596 ± 0.4178	1.004 ± 0.502 E - 5	0.504 ± **0.267**	3.995 ± 2.106	1.004 ± 0.529 E - 5
2—Pallas	0.0374 ± 0.0035	0.0374 ± 0.0035	Unknown	Unknown	3.011 ± ? E - 6	0.58 ± ?	1.20 ± ?	3.01 ± ? E - 6
3—Juno	0.0162 ± 0.0022	0.0162 ± 0.0022	Unknown	Unknown	3.345 ± ? E - 6	0.79 ± ?	1.33 ± ?	3.35 ± ? E - 6
4—Vesta	0.0306 ± 0.0157	0.0306 ± 0.0157	Unknown	0.2228 ± 0.0070	1.673 ± ? E - 5	0.58 ± ?	6.66 ± ?	1.67 ± ? E - 5
5—Astraea	Unknown	Unknown	Unknown	Unknown	Unknown	Unknown	Unknown	Unknown
6—Hebe	0.0173 ± ?	0.0173 ± ?	Unknown	Unknown	3.345 ± ? E - 6	0.65 ± ?	1.33 ± ?	3.35 ± ? E - 6
7—Iris	0.0153 ± ?	0.0153 ± ?	Unknown	Unknown	2.509 ± ? E - 6	0.65 ± ?	1.00 ± ?	2.51 ± ? E - 6
10—**Hygiea**	0.0251 ± ?	0.0251 ± ?	Unknown	Unknown	1.004 ± ? E - 5	0.63 ± ?	3.99 ± ?	1.00 ± ? E - 5
15—Eunomia	0.0220 ± ?	0.0220 ± ?	Unknown	Unknown	6.690 ± ? E - 6	0.63 ± ?	2.66 ± ?	6.69 ± ? E - 6

PHYSICAL DATA FOR THE PLANETS, THEIR SATELLITES AND SOME ASTEROIDS (Continued)

Body	Radius of Body (Earth Radii)			Period of Rotation (Sidereal Days)	Mass (in Earth Masses)	Density (in Earth Units)	Gravitational Constant (gR^2)	
	Mean	Equatorial	Polar				km^3/sec^2	in Earth Units
16—Psyche	0.0220 ± ?	0.0220 ± ?	Unknown	Unknown	6.690 ± ?E − 6	0.63 ± ?	2.66 ± ?	6.69 ± ?E − 6
51—Nemausa	0.0063 ± ?	0.0063 ± ?	Unknown	Unknown	1.505 ± ?E − 7	0.61 ± ?	0.060 ± ?	1.51 ± ?E − 7
323—Brucia	Unknown	Unknown	Unknown	Unknown	Unknown	Unknown	Unknown	Unknown
433—Eros	0.0019 ± 0.0008	0.0019 ± 0.0008	Unknown	Unknown	8.363 ± ?E − 10	0.13 ± ?	3.33 ± ?E − 4	8.36 ± ?E − 10
511—Davida	0.0204 ± ?	0.0204 ± ?	Unknown	Unknown	5.018 ± ?E − 6	0.59 ± ?	2.00 ± ?	5.02 ± ?E − 6
588—Achilles	0.0044 ± 0.0008	0.0044 ± 0.0008	Unknown	Unknown	5.382 ± ?E − 11	0.63 ± ?	2.14 ± ?E − 5	5.38 ± ?E − 11
617—Patrochus	Unknown	Unknown	Unknown	Unknown	Unknown	Unknown	Unknown	Unknown
744—Hidalgo	0.0028 ± 0.0013	0.0028 ± 0.0013	Unknown	Unknown	6.620 ± ?E − 11	0.63 ± ?	2.64 ± ?E − 5	6.62 ± ?E − 11
1048—Feodosia	Unknown	Unknown	Unknown	Unknown	Unknown	Unknown	Unknown	Unknown
1221—Amor	0.00047 ± ?	0.00047 ± ?	Unknown	Unknown	6.620 ± ?E − 11	0.63 ± ?	2.64 ± ?E − 5	6.67 ± ?E − 11
1566—Icarus	0.00008 ± 0.00002	0.00011 ± 0.00002	0.00005 ± 0.00003	1.128 ± 0.407	8.363 ± ?E − 13	1.47 ± ?	3.33 ± ?E − 7	8.36 ± ?E − 13
1520—Geographos	0.00024 ± ?	0.00024 ± ?	Unknown	Unknown	8.363 ± ?E − 12	0.64 ± ?	3.33 ± ?E − 6	8.36 ± ?E − 12
—Adonis	0.00016 ± ?	0.00016 ± ?	Unknown	Unknown	2.452 − ?E − 12	0.63 ± ?	9.76 ± ?E − 7	2.45 ± ?E − 12
—Apollo	0.00031 ± 0.00016	0.00031 ± 0.00016	Unknown	Unknown	2.892 ± ?E − 11	0.63 ± ?	1.15 ± ?E − 5	2.89 ± ?E − 11
—Hermes	0.00016 ± ?	0.00016 ± ?	Unknown	Unknown	2.452 ± ?E − 12	0.63 ± ?	9.76 ± ?E − 7	2.45 ± ?E − 12

PHYSICAL DATA FOR THE PLANETS, THEIR SATELLITES AND SOME ASTEROIDS (Continued)

Body	Radius of Orbit (Au) — Mean	Aphelion	Perihelion	Period of Revolution (Sidereal Years)	Velocity (Earth Units) — Rotational	Orbital	Escape	Gravity (g-s) — Polar	Equatorial	Volume (in Earth Units)
Sun (Sol)	—				4.4241		55.089	27.915	27.908	1303150.0 ± 4580.0
Mercury	0.38744 ± 0.00049	0.46710 ± 0.00107	0.30779 ± 0.00071	0.240899 ± 0.000055	0.00649	1.6040	0.3723	Unknown	0.3648	0.0557 ± 0.0024
Venus	0.72281 ± 0.00075	0.72772 ± 0.00076	0.71789 ± 0.00075	0.615185 ± 0.000005	R 0.00388	1.1745	0.9286	0.9049	0.9049	**0.8575** ± 0.0033
Earth (Terra)	1.00000 ± 0.00066	1.01670 ± 0.00068	0.98330 ± 0.00066	1.000000 ± 0.000000	1.0000	1.0000	1.0000	1.005	0.9942	1.0000 ± 0.0003
Moon (Luna)	0.0025701 ± 0.0000012	0.0027111 ± 0.0000013	0.0024290 ± 0.0000011	0.074800 ± 0.000003	0.00995	0.03423	0.2116	0.1654	0.1652	0.02031 ± 0.00004
Mars	1.5233 ± 0.0016	1.6656 ± 0.0018	1.3810 ± 0.0015	1.88082 ± 0.00005	0.5160	0.8087	0.4489	0.3839	0.3627	0.1493 ± 0.0027
Phobos	0.0000629 ± 0.0000002	Unknown	Unknown	0.0008729 ± 0.0000003	0.00554	0.02262	0.001666	Unknown	Unknown	4.344 ± 6.268 E − 9
Deimos	0.000157 ± 0.000001	Unknown	Unknown	0.0034564 ± 0.0000001	0.00062	0.01433	0.000624	Unknown	Unknown	4.833 ± 11.599 E − 10
Jupiter	5.2025 ± 0.0027	5.4543 ± 0.0030	4.9507 ± 0.0028	11.8613 ± 0.0117	27.212	0.4396	5.375	2.906	2.305	1312.5 ± 7.9
Io	0.002821 ± 0.000002	Unknown	Unknown	0.0048437 ± 0.0000003	0.1525	0.5805	0.2196	Unknown	Unknown	0.01988 ± 0.00377
Europa	0.004488 ± 0.000002	Unknown	Unknown	0.0097225 ± 0.0000005	0.0655	0.4597	0.1848	Unknown	Unknown	0.0127 ± 0.0018
Ganymede	0.007161 ± 0.000007	Unknown	Unknown	0.0195884 ± 0.0000005	0.0553	0.3658	0.0804	Unknown	Unknown	0.0625 ± 0.0040
Callisto	0.012589 ± 0.000007	Unknown	Unknown	0.0456912 ± 0.0000007	0.0226	0.2752	0.1795	Unknown	Unknown	0.0545 ± 0.0093
V (Amalthea)	0.001213 ± 0.000003	Unknown	Unknown	0.0013637 ± 0.000005	0.0273	0.8860	0.01005	Unknown	Unknown	2.546 ± 2.019 E − 6
VI (Hestia)	0.07622 ± 0.00134	Unknown	Unknown	0.686475 ± 0.000631	Unknown	0.1117	0.00774	Unknown	Unknown	1.163 ± 0.833 E − 6
VII (Hera)	0.07756 ± 0.00267	Unknown	Unknown	0.711280 ± 0.000548	Unknown	0.1107	0.00231	Unknown	Unknown	3.093 ± 4.176 E − 8
VIII (Poseidon)	0.15712 ± 0.00067	Unknown	Unknown	R 2.02324 ± 0.00027	R ?	R 0.0779	0.00208	Unknown	Unknown	2.255 ± 3.007 E − 8
IX (Hades)	0.15845 ± 0.00134	Unknown	Unknown	R 2.07252 ± 0.00465	R ?	R 0.0775	0.00139	Unknown	Unknown	**6.681** ± 5.011 E − 9
X (Demeter)	0.07876 ± 0.00034	Unknown	Unknown	0.706901 ± 0.009855	Unknown	0.1101	0.00104	Unknown	Unknown	2.819 ± 2.819 E − 9
XI (Pan)	0.1151 ± 0.0013	Unknown	Unknown	R 1.91290 ± 0.00630	R ?	R 0.0795	0.00139	Unknown	Unknown	6.681 ± 6.681 E − 9
XII (Adrastea)	1.14107 ± 0.00067	Unknown	Unknown	R 1.71113 ± 0.00411	Unknown	R 0.0822	0.00115	Unknown	Unknown	3.866 ± 2.320 E − 9
Saturn	9.5407 ± 0.0075	10.0587 ± 0.0215	9.0226 ± 0.0213	29.4568 ± 0.0111	22.136	0.3235	3.2232	1.316	0.8800	763.0 ± 10.3
Mimas	0.001214 ± 0.000005	Unknown	Unknown	0.0025908 ± 0.0000219	0.0449	0.4832	0.0121	Unknown	Unknown	7.781 ± 1.974 E − 5
Enceladus	0.001601 ± 0.000011	Unknown	Unknown	0.0037534 ± 0.0000077	0.0341	0.4228	0.0162	Unknown	Unknown	1.034 ± 0.218 E − 4
Tethys	0.001874 ± 0.000003	Unknown	Unknown	0.0051569 ± 0.0000202	0.0482	0.3792	0.02873	Unknown	Unknown	7.584 ± 2.897 E − 4
Dione	0.002528 ± 0.000010	Unknown	Unknown	0.0075051 ± 0.0000205	0.0341	0.3365	0.03078	Unknown	Unknown	8.268 ± 3.567 E − 4
Rhea	0.003533 ± 0.000013	Unknown	Unknown	0.0123524 ± 0.0000124	0.0308	0.2839	0.04602	Unknown	Unknown	2.726 ± 0.340 E − 3
Titan	0.008204 ± 0.000047	Unknown	Unknown	0.0437009 ± 0.0000713	0.0233	0.1862	0.0729	Unknown	Unknown	5.206 ± 1.274 E − 2
Hyperion	0.009944 ± 0.000044	Unknown	Unknown	0.0582658 ± 0.0000247	0.00148	0.1691	0.01895	Unknown	Unknown	3.140 ± 0.797 E − 3
Iapetus	0.02388 ± 0.00013	Unknown	Unknown	0.216971 ± 0.000466	Unknown	0.1094	0.06099	Unknown	Unknown	1.047 ± 0.806 E − 2
Phoebe	0.08680 ± 0.00048	Unknown	Unknown	R 1.50360 ± 0.00575	R ?	R 0.0574	0.01245	Unknown	Unknown	8.893 ± 4.648 E − 6
X (Themis/Janus)	0.001056 ± 0.000001	Unknown	Unknown	0.002033 ± ?	Unknown	0.5201	0.02273	Unknown	Unknown	5.412 ± 1.078 E − 5
Uranus	19.190 ± 0.013	20.073 ± 0.032	18.308 ± 0.032	84.0081 ± 0.0824	R 8.3697	0.2282	1.9821	1.179 ± 0.168	0.9554 ± 0.168	49.987 ± 4.676
Ariel	0.001282 ± 0.000002	Unknown	Unknown	R 0.0068998 ± 0.0000005	R 0.01929	R 0.1842	0.04150	Unknown	Unknown	1.163 ± 0.280 E − 4
Umbriel	0.001786 ± 0.000002	Unknown	Unknown	R 0.0113457 ± 0.0000005	R 0.0075	R 0.1560	0.02682	Unknown	Unknown	3.140 ± 0.937 E − 5
Titania	0.002932 ± 0.000006	Unknown	Unknown	R 0.0238350 ± 0.0000005	R 0.00898	R 0.1218	0.06663	Unknown	Unknown	4.833 ± 0.928 E − 4
Oberon	0.003919 ± 0.000004	Unknown	Unknown	R 0.0368593 ± 0.0000003	R 0.00466	R 0.1054	0.05336	Unknown	Unknown	2.493 ± 0.522 E − 4
Miranda	0.0008651 ± 0.0000094	Unknown	Unknown	R 0.0038712 ± 0.0000038	R 0.01338	R 0.2242	0.01615	Unknown	Unknown	6.850 ± 1.868 E − 6
Neptune	30.086 ± 0.029	30.332 ± 0.036	29.839 ± 0.036	164.784 ± 0.012	5.4166	0.1822	2.1875	Unknown	1.323 ± 0.210	45.322 ± 5.201
Triton	0.002361 ± 0.000003	Unknown	Unknown	0.0160881 ± 0.000030	Unknown	0.1477	0.2777	Unknown	Unknown	3.130 ± 0.257 E − 2
Nereid	0.03945 ± 0.00134	Unknown	Unknown	1.24022 ± 0.22175	Unknown	0.0362	0.0197	Unknown	Unknown	9.726 ± 7.294 E − 6
Pluto	39.507 ± 0.128	49.308 ± 0.162	29.705 ± 0.099	248.35 ± 0.34	0.1394	0.1591	0.4482	Unknown	0.225 ± 0.217	0.7160 ± 0.1556
Typical Asteroid	1.94 ± 1.00	2.13 ± 1.11	1.75 ± 0.91	2.70 ± ?	0.00682	0.7181	0.00250	Unknown	Unknown	3.093 ± 4.640 E − 8
1 — Ceres	2.7686 ± 0.0024	2.9873 ± 0.0061	2.5499 ± 0.0060	4.5994 ± 0.0029	Unknown	0.6007	0.0413	Unknown	Unknown	1.990 ± 0.353 E − 4
2 — Pallas	2.7686 ± 0.0024	3.4220 ± 0.0088	2.1152 ± 0.0085	4.6131 ± 0.0054	Unknown	0.6007	0.0283	Unknown	Unknown	5.213 ± 1.445 E − 5
3 — Juno	2.6703 ± 0.0014	3.3619 ± 0.0032	1.9787 ± 0.0029	4.3640 ± 0.0054	0.0610	0.6107	0.0144	Unknown	Unknown	4.225 ± 1.723 E − 5
4 — Vesta	2.3608 ± 0.0013	2.5709 ± 0.0027	2.1507 ± 0.0026	3.6304 ± 0.0029	0.1372	0.6510	0.0233	Unknown	Unknown	2.867 ± 4.411 E − 5
5 — Astraea	2.57 ± ?	3.06 ± ?	2.08 ± ?	3.5816 ± 0.0111	Unknown	0.6229	Unknown	Unknown	Unknown	Unknown
6 — Hebe	2.43 ± ?	2.91 ± ?	1.94 ± ?	3.7781 ± 0.0029	Unknown	0.6409	0.0139	Unknown	Unknown	5.146 ± 1.404 E − 6
7 — Iris	2.38 ± ?	2.93 ± ?	1.84 ± ?	3.6796 ± 0.0029	Unknown	0.6477	0.0126	Unknown	Unknown	3.866 ± 1.160 E − 6
10 — Hygiea	2.79 ± ?	3.07 ± ?	2.51 ± ?	5.5906 ± 0.0029	Unknown	0.5973	0.0199	Unknown	Unknown	1.584 ± 0.386 E − 5
15 — Eunomia	2.64 ± ?	3.12 ± ?	2.17 ± ?	4.2956 ± 0.0029	Unknown	0.6141	0.0174	Unknown	Unknown	1.061 ± 0.273 E − 5

PHYSICAL DATA FOR THE PLANETS, THEIR SATELLITES AND SOME ASTEROIDS (Continued)

Body	Radius of Orbit (Au)			Period of Revolution (Sidereal Years)	Velocity (in Earth Units)			Gravity (in g-s)		Volume (in Earth Units)
	Mean	Aphelion	Perhelion		Rotational	Orbital	Escape	Polar	Equatorial	
16—Psyche	2.92 ± ?	3.33 ± ?	2.51 ± ?	4.9993 ± 0.0029	Unknown	0.5839	0.0174	Unknown	Unknown	1.061 ± 0.273 E − 5
51—Nemansa	2.37 ± ?	2.51 ± ?	2.22 ± ?	3.6412 ± 0.0029	Unknown	0.6510	0.0154	Unknown	Unknown	2.475 ± 1.114 E − 7
323—Brucia	2.38 ± ?	3.10 ± ?	1.67 ± ?	3.6796 ± 0.0111	Unknown	0.6473	Unknown	Unknown	Unknown	Unknown
433—Eros	1.4568 ± 0.0028	1.7803 ± 0.0045	1.1334 ± 0.0036	1.7604 ± 0.0027	Unknown	0.8289	0.000210	Unknown	Unknown	6.681 ± 8.351 E − 9
511—Davida	3.18 ± ?	3.75 ± ?	2.61 ± ?	5.6727 ± 0.0029	Unknown	0.5604	0.00495	Unknown	Unknown	8.495 ± 2.156 E − 6
588—Achilles	5.2103 ± 0.0041	5.9814 ± 0.0071	4.4391 ± 0.0063	11.942 ± 0.060	Unknown	0.4362	0.00111	Unknown	Unknown	8.488 ± 4.547 E − 8
617—Patrochus	5.2049 ± 0.0041	5.9388 ± 0.0114	4.4710 ± 0.0110	11.879 ± 0.011	Unknown	0.4362	Unknown	Unknown	Unknown	Unknown
744—Hidalgo	5.7899 ± 0.0038	9.5881 ± 0.0086	1.9917 ± 0.0059	13.924 ± 0.035	Unknown	0.4161	0.0015	Unknown	Unknown	2.255 ± 3.007 E − 8
1048—Feodosia	2.73 ± ?	3.23 ± ?	2.24 ± ?	4.5202 ± 0.0111	Unknown	0.6038	Unknown	Unknown	Unknown	Unknown
1221—Amor	1.92 ± ?	2.77 ± ?	1.08 ± ?	2.6694 ± 0.0110	Unknown	0.7205	0.0119	Unknown	Unknown	1.044 ± 1.566 E − 10
1566—Icarus	1.0784 ± 0.0021	1.9714 ± 0.0044	0.1855 ± 0.0022	1.1198 ± 0.0027	0.000098	0.9631	0.0001	Unknown	3.772 ± 5.637 E − 4	5.684 ± 4.070 E − 13
1620—Geographos	1.24 ± ?	1.67 ± ?	0.82 ± ?	1.3881 ± 0.0027	Unknown	0.8960	0.000059	Unknown	Unknown	1.305 ± 2.088 E − 11
—Adonis	1.97 ± ?	3.50 ± ?	0.43 ± ?	2.7597 ± 0.0110	Unknown	0.7120	0.0039	Unknown	Unknown	3.866 ± 5.800 E − 12
—Apollo	1.4849 ± 0.0034	2.3254 ± 0.0055	0.6445 ± 0.0071	1.3097 ± 0.0110	Unknown	0.8188	0.0096	Unknown	Unknown	3.093 ± 4.640 E − 11
—Hermes	1.29 ± ?	2.11 ± ?	0.48 ± ?	1.4702 ± 0.0110	Unknown	0.7205	0.0039	Unknown	Unknown	3.866 ± 5.800 E − 12

PHYSICAL DATA FOR THE PLANETS, THEIR SATELLITES AND SOME ASTEROIDS (Continued)

| Body | Symbol | Escape Velocity | | | | | Mean Orbital Velocity km/sec | Mean Rotational Velocity km/sec | Isosynchronous Satellite Data | | | |
| | | Solar Escape from Position of | | Solar Escape from Surface of | | Mean Escape Velocity km/sec | | | | | | |
		km/sec	in Earth Units	km/sec	in Earth Units				Altitude (km)	Orbital Velocity (km/sec)	Escape Velocity from (km/sec)	Solar Escape from (km/sec)
Sun	⊙	—	—	617.2 ± 0.9	14.17 ± 0.02	617.2 ± 0.9	—	2.058 ± 0.002	24055600.0 ± 29000.0	73.19 ± 0.43	103.5 ± 0.6	—
Mercury	☿	67.64 ± 0.10	1.607 ± 0.002	67.77 ± 0.14	1.556 ± 0.003	4.173 ± 0.070	47.83 ± 0.10	0.0030 ± 0.0000	237301.0 ± 4268.0	0.297 ± 0.003	0.420 ± 0.004	67.64 ± 0.14
Venus	♀	49.52 ± 0.06	1.176 ± 0.001	50.60 ± 0.06	1.161 ± 0.001	10.36 ± 0.03	35.02 ± 0.04	0.0018 ± 0.0000	1534720.0 ± 45230.0	0.459 ± 0.017	0.650 ± 0.024	49.53 ± 0.31
Earth	⊕ or ♁	42.10 ± 0.05	1.000 ± 0.001	43.56 ± 0.04	1.000 ± 0.001	11.18 ± 0.00	29.77 ± 0.01	0.4651 ± 0.0000	35775.0 ± 13.0	3.073 ± 0.002	4.346 ± 0.003	42.33 ± 0.05
Moon*	☾	1.439 ± 0.000	0.0342 ± 0.0000	2.775 ± 0.001	0.0637 ± 0.0000	2.373 ± 0.011	1.018 ± 0.002	0.0046 ± 0.0000	86667.0 ± 275.0	0.235 ± 0.002	0.333 ± 0.003	1.477 ± 0.002*
Mars	♂	34.11 ± 0.04	0.8102 ± 0.0009	34.48 ± 0.05	0.7915 ± 0.0011	5.028 ± 0.024	24.12 ± 0.044	0.2400 ± 0.0014	17032.0 ± 118.0	1.447 ± 0.012	2.046 ± 0.017	34.18 ± 0.08
Jupiter	♃	18.46 ± 0.02	0.4384 ± 0.0004	63.00 ± 0.17	1.446 ± 0.004	60.24 ± 0.10	13.05 ± 0.03	12.66 ± 0.05	89304.0 ± 338.0	28.21 ± 0.26	39.89 ± 0.37	43.96 ± 2.92
Saturn	♄	13.63 ± 0.02	0.3238 ± 0.0004	38.55 ± 0.14	0.8850 ± 0.0032	36.06 ± 0.14	9.639 ± 0.017	10.30 ± 0.04	50964.0 ± 552.0	18.62 ± 0.34	26.33 ± 0.49	29.65 ± 2.56
Uranus	♅	9.611 ± 0.012	0.2283 ± 0.0002	24.18 ± 0.35	0.5551 ± 0.0080	22.19 ± 0.55	6.796 ± 0.012	3.893 ± 0.091	36938.0 ± 1939.0	9.780 ± 0.825	13.83 ± 1.17	16.84 ± 3.23
Neptune	♆	7.676 ± 0.010	0.1823 ± 0.0002	25.71 ± 0.52	0.5901 ± 0.0119	24.54 ± 0.75	5.428 ± 0.010	2.519 ± 0.096	59504.0 ± 3122.0	9.119 ± 1.031	12.82 ± 1.46	15.01 ± 3.76
Pluto	♇	6.699 ± 0.011	0.1591 ± 0.0002	8.371 ± 0.237	0.1921 ± 0.0054	5.019 ± 1.67	4.737 ± 0.011	0.0648 ± 0.0047	76470.0 ± 25960.0	0.935 ± 0.847	1.322 ± 1.198	6.828 ± 0.317

*Escape from Earth

*Earth Escape from

HOHMANN ELLIPSE TRANSFER DATA (MINIMUM ENERGY OF TRANSFER)

W. Joseph Armento

The "from" body is the body of departure and the "to" body is the body of arrival. The three lines of data for each planetary entry are:

    top—from perhelion of inner planet to aphelion of outer planet
    middle—from mean of inner planet to mean of outer planet
    bottom—from aphelion of inner planet to perhelion of outer planet

The orbital parameters and velocities are given for the transfer orbit. The orbital velocity, change in velocity necessary to reach the new Hohmann orbital velocity, and the maximum change in velocity to reach the Hohmann orbital velocity are given for departure. For arrival data, look in the table listing the arrival planet as "from" and the departure planet as "to". The maximum Hohmann velocity change is assumed to be a single impulse to overcome the necessary energy for change in velocity and escape velocity from the surface of the departure planet.

Body	Mean orbital Semimajor axis (km × 10^{-6})	Eccentricity ε	Aphelion (km × 10^{-6})	Perhelion (km × 10^{-6})	Orbital Velocity (km/sec) Mean	Aphelion	Perhelion	Orbital Velocity of Departure Body (km/sec)	Time of one way trip (½ orbit) (Solar Seconds)	Departure Δ$_v$ orbit (km/sec)	Maximum Δ$_v$ (km/sec)
From Mercury to:											
Venus	77.440	0.4055	103.85	46.035	41.38	26.91	63.62	58.92	5.880 E6	4.699	6.284
	83.030	0.3021	108.11	57.950	39.96	29.26	54.58	47.83	6.528 E6	6.748	7.934
	88.620	0.2116	107.37	69.864	38.68	31.20	47.95	38.83	7.198 E6	9.124	10.03
Earth	99.052	0.5352	152.07	46.035	36.58	20.13	66.49	58.92	8.506 E6	7.569	8.643
	103.76	0.4415	149.57	57.950	35.75	22.25	57.43	47.83	9.119 E6	9.596	10.46
	108.47	0.3559	147.07	69.864	34.96	24.10	50.72	38.83	9.747 E6	11.90	12.61
Mars	147.58	0.6881	249.12	46.035	29.97	12.88	69.72	58.92	1.547 E7	10.80	11.58
	142.89	0.5945	227.84	57.950	30.46	15.36	60.40	47.83	1.474 E7	12.57	13.24
	138.21	0.4945	206.56	69.864	30.97	18.01	53.25	38.83	1.402 E7	14.43	15.02
Jupiter	430.92	0.8932	815.80	46.035	17.54	4.167	73.84	58.92	7.718 E7	14.91	15.49
	418.04	0.8614	778.14	57.950	17.81	4.860	65.26	47.83	7.375 E7	17.43	17.92
	405.17	0.8276	740.48	69.864	18.09	5.556	58.89	38.83	7.037 E7	20.06	20.49
Saturn	775.26	0.9406	1504.5	46.035	13.08	2.287	74.76	58.92	1.862 E8	15.83	16.37
	742.47	0.9220	1427.0	57.950	13.36	2.693	66.31	47.83	1.746 E8	18.48	18.94
	709.69	0.9016	1349.5	69.864	13.67	3.110	60.07	38.83	1.631 E8	21.24	21.65
Uranus	1524.2	0.9698	3002.3	46.035	9.326	1.155	75.32	58.92	5.134 E8	16.39	16.92
	1464.1	0.9604	2870.3	57.950	9.515	1.352	66.97	47.83	4.834 E8	19.14	19.59
	1404.1	0.9502	2738.3	69.864	9.717	1.552	60.83	38.83	4.539 E8	22.01	22.40
Neptune	2291.4	0.9799	4536.8	46.035	7.606	0.7662	75.51	58.92	9.464 E8	16.59	17.10
	2278.9	0.9746	4499.9	57.950	7.627	0.8655	67.21	47.83	9.337 E8	19.38	19.83
	2266.4	0.9692	4463.0	69.864	7.648	0.9569	61.13	38.83	9.310 E8	22.30	22.69
Pluto	3710.5	0.9876	7375.0	46.035	5.977	0.4723	75.66	58.92	1.950 E9	16.73	17.24
	2983.5	0.9806	5909.0	57.950	6.666	0.6601	67.31	47.83	1.406 E9	19.48	19.93
	2256.4	0.9690	4443.0	69.864	7.665	0.9612	61.13	38.83	9.248 E8	22.30	22.69
From Venus to:											
Mercury	77.440	0.4055	108.85	46.035	41.38	26.91	63.62	34.78	5.880 E6	7.873	13.02
	83.030	0.3021	108.11	57.950	39.96	29.26	54.59	35.02	6.528 E6	5.763	11.86
	88.620	0.2116	107.37	69.864	38.68	31.20	47.95	35.26	7.198 E6	4.058	11.13
Earth	129.72	0.1723	152.07	107.37	31.97	26.86	38.04	35.26	1.275 E7	2.787	10.73
	128.84	0.1609	149.57	108.11	32.08	27.27	37.73	35.02	1.262 E7	2.712	10.71
	127.96	0.1494	147.07	108.85	32.19	27.69	37.42	34.78	1.249 E7	2.635	10.69
Mars	178.25	0.3976	249.12	107.37	27.27	17.90	41.54	35.26	2.053 E7	6.283	12.12
	167.97	0.3564	227.84	108.11	28.09	19.35	40.78	35.02	1.878 E7	5.766	11.86
	157.70	0.3098	206.56	108.85	28.99	21.05	39.94	34.78	1.709 E7	5.161	11.58
Jupiter	461.59	0.7674	815.80	107.37	16.95	6.148	46.71	35.26	8.557 E7	11.46	15.45
	443.12	0.7560	778.14	108.11	17.30	6.447	46.40	35.02	8.048 E7	11.39	15.40
	424.66	0.7437	740.48	108.85	17.67	6.774	46.09	34.78	7.551 E7	11.30	15.34
Saturn	805.93	0.8668	1504.5	107.37	12.83	3.426	48.01	35.26	1.974 E8	12.75	16.43
	767.55	0.8592	1427.0	108.11	13.14	3.617	47.75	35.02	1.835 E8	12.73	16.42
	729.18	0.8507	1349.5	108.85	13.48	3.829	47.48	34.78	1.699 E8	12.70	16.39
Uranus	1554.9	0.9309	3002.3	107.37	9.234	1.746	48.83	35.26	5.290 E8	13.57	17.08
	1489.2	0.9274	2870.3	108.11	9.435	1.831	48.62	35.02	4.958 E8	13.60	17.10
	1423.6	0.9235	2738.3	108.85	9.650	1.924	48.40	34.78	4.634 E8	13.62	17.12
Neptune	2322.6	0.9538	4536.8	107.37	7.556	1.162	49.12	35.26	9.655 E8	13.86	17.31
	2304.0	0.9531	4499.9	108.11	7.586	1.176	48.94	35.02	9.542 E8	13.92	17.36
	2285.9	0.9524	4463.0	108.85	7.616	1.189	48.77	34.78	9.430 E8	13.98	17.41
Pluto	3741.2	0.9713	7375.0	107.37	5.953	0.7183	49.34	35.26	1.974 E9	14.08	17.48
	3008.6	0.9641	5909.0	108.11	6.638	0.8979	49.08	35.02	1.424 E9	14.06	17.47
	2275.9	0.9522	4443.0	108.85	7.632	1.195	48.76	34.78	9.368 E8	13.98	17.40

Body	Mean orbital Semimajor axis (km × 10⁻⁶)	Eccentricity ε	Aphelion (km × 10⁻⁶)	Perhelion (km × 10⁻⁶)	Orbital Velocity (km/sec)			Orbital Velocity of Departure Body (km/sec)	Time of one way trip (½ orbit) (Solar Seconds)	Departure Δᵥ orbit (km/sec)	Maximum Δᵥ (km/sec)
					Mean	Aphelion	Perhelion				
From Earth to:											
Mercury	99.052	0.5352	152.07	46.035	36.58	20.13	66.49	29.28	8.506 E6	9.150	14.45
	103.76	0.4415	149.57	57.950	35.75	22.25	57.43	29.77	9.119 E6	7.523	13.47
	108.47	0.3559	147.07	69.864	34.96	24.10	50.72	30.27	9.747 E6	6.178	12.77
Venus	129.72	0.1723	152.07	107.37	31.97	26.86	38.04	29.28	1.275 E7	2.416	11.44
	128.84	0.1609	149.57	108.11	32.08	27.27	37.73	29.77	1.262 E7	2.500	11.46
	127.96	0.1494	147.07	108.85	32.19	27.69	37.42	30.27	1.249 E7	2.583	11.47
Mars	198.10	0.2576	249.12	147.07	25.87	19.88	33.67	30.27	2.406 E7	3.396	11.68
	188.70	0.2074	227.84	149.57	26.51	21.48	32.71	29.77	2.237 E7	2.942	11.56
	179.31	0.1519	206.56	152.07	27.19	23.33	31.69	29.28	2.072 E7	2.411	11.44
Jupiter	481.44	0.6945	815.80	147.07	16.59	7.046	39.08	30.27	9.114 E7	8.810	14.23
	463.85	0.6776	778.14	149.57	16.91	7.412	38.56	29.77	8.620 E7	8.789	14.22
	446.27	0.6592	740.48	152.07	17.24	7.811	38.03	29.28	8.134 E7	8.755	14.20
Saturn	825.78	0.8219	1504.5	147.07	12.67	3.962	40.53	30.27	2.047 E8	10.25	15.17
	788.28	0.8103	1427.0	149.57	12.97	4.199	40.06	29.77	1.910 E8	10.29	15.19
	750.79	0.7975	1349.5	152.07	13.29	4.461	39.59	29.28	1.775 E8	10.31	15.21
Uranus	1574.7	0.9066	3002.3	147.07	9.176	2.031	41.46	30.27	5.392 E8	11.18	15.81
	1509.9	0.9009	2870.3	149.57	9.370	2.139	41.05	29.77	5.062 E8	11.28	15.88
	1445.2	0.8948	2738.3	152.07	9.578	2.257	40.64	29.28	4.740 E8	11.36	15.94
Neptune	2341.9	0.9372	4536.8	147.07	7.524	1.355	41.79	30.27	9.779 E8	11.51	16.05
	2324.7	0.9357	4499.9	149.57	7.552	1.377	41.42	29.77	9.671 E8	11.65	16.15
	2307.5	0.9341	4463.0	152.07	7.580	1.399	41.06	29.28	9.564 E8	11.78	16.24
Pluto	3761.0	0.9609	7375.0	147.07	5.937	0.8384	42.04	30.27	1.990 E9	11.77	16.23
	3029.3	0.9506	5909.0	149.57	6.615	1.053	41.58	29.77	1.439 E9	11.81	16.26
	2297.5	0.9338	4443.0	152.07	7.596	1.405	41.06	29.28	9.502 E8	11.78	16.24
From Mars to:											
Mercury	147.58	0.6881	249.12	46.035	29.97	12.88	69.72	21.97	1.547 E7	9.081	10.38
	142.89	0.5945	227.84	57.950	30.46	15.36	60.40	24.12	1.474 E7	8.761	10.10
	138.21	0.4945	206.56	69.864	30.97	18.01	53.25	26.49	1.402 E7	8.479	9.858
Venus	178.25	0.3976	249.12	107.37	27.27	17.90	41.54	21.97	2.053 E7	4.060	6.463
	167.97	0.3564	227.84	108.11	28.09	19.35	40.78	24.12	1.878 E7	4.770	6.931
	157.70	0.3098	206.56	108.85	28.99	21.05	39.94	26.49	1.709 E7	5.444	7.411
Earth	198.10	0.2576	249.12	147.07	25.87	19.88	33.67	21.97	2.406 E7	2.088	5.444
	188.70	0.2074	227.84	149.57	26.51	21.48	32.71	24.12	2.237 E7	2.646	5.682
	179.31	0.1519	206.56	152.07	27.19	23.33	31.69	26.49	2.072 E7	3.161	5.939
Jupiter	511.18	0.5959	815.80	206.56	16.10	8.104	32.00	26.49	9.972 E7	5.514	7.462
	502.99	0.5470	778.14	227.84	16.23	8.785	30.00	24.12	9.733 E7	5.881	7.737
	494.80	0.4965	740.48	249.12	16.37	9.494	28.22	21.97	9.496 E7	6.256	8.026
Saturn	855.52	0.7586	1504.5	206.56	12.45	4.613	33.60	26.49	2.159 E8	7.105	8.704
	827.42	0.7246	1427.0	227.84	12.66	5.058	31.68	24.12	2.054 E8	7.556	9.076
	799.32	0.6883	1349.5	249.12	12.38	5.533	29.97	21.97	1.950 E8	8.010	9.457
Uranus	1604.4	0.8713	3002.3	206.56	9.090	2.384	34.66	26.49	5.545 E8	8.165	9.589
	1549.1	0.8529	2870.3	227.84	9.251	2.606	32.84	24.12	5.260 E8	8.713	10.06
	1493.7	0.8332	2738.3	249.12	9.421	2.842	31.23	21.97	4.981 E8	9.269	10.55
Neptune	2371.7	0.9129	4536.8	206.56	7.477	1.595	35.04	26.49	9.966 E8	8.548	9.917
	2363.9	0.9036	4499.9	227.84	7.489	1.685	33.28	24.12	9.916 E8	9.160	10.45
	2356.1	0.8943	4463.0	249.12	7.501	1.772	31.75	21.97	9.867 E8	9.785	11.00
Pluto	3790.8	0.9455	7375.0	206.56	5.914	0.9897	35.34	26.49	2.014 E9	8.846	10.17
	3068.4	0.9257	5909.0	227.84	6.573	1.291	33.47	24.12	1.467 E9	9.352	10.62
	2346.0	0.8938	4443.0	249.12	7.517	1.780	31.75	21.97	9.804 E8	9.781	11.00
From Jupiter to:											
Mercury	430.92	0.8932	815.80	46.036	17.54	4.167	73.84	12.44	7.718 E7	8.269	60.80
	418.04	0.8614	778.14	57.950	17.81	4.860	65.26	13.05	7.375 E7	8.193	60.79
	405.17	0.8276	740.48	69.865	18.09	5.556	58.89	13.70	7.037 E7	8.144	60.79
Venus	461.59	0.7674	815.80	107.37	16.95	6.148	46.71	12.44	8.557 E7	6.287	60.57
	443.12	0.7560	778.14	108.11	17.30	6.447	46.40	13.05	8.048 E7	6.606	60.60
	424.66	0.7437	740.48	108.85	17.67	6.774	46.09	13.70	7.551 E7	6.926	60.64
Earth	481.44	0.6945	815.80	147.07	16.59	7.046	39.08	12.44	9.114 E7	5.390	60.48
	463.85	0.6776	778.14	149.57	16.91	7.412	38.56	13.05	8.620 E7	5.641	60.50
	446.27	0.6592	740.48	152.07	17.24	7.811	38.03	13.70	8.134 E7	5.890	60.53
Mars	511.18	0.5959	815.80	206.56	16.10	8.104	32.00	12.44	9.972 E7	4.332	60.40
	502.99	0.5470	778.14	227.84	16.23	8.785	30.00	13.05	9.733 E7	4.268	60.39
	494.80	0.4965	740.48	249.12	16.37	9.494	28.22	13.70	9.496 E7	4.206	60.39
Saturn	1122.5	0.3403	1504.5	740.48	10.87	7.624	15.49	13.70	3.245 E8	1.790	60.27
	1102.6	0.2942	1427.0	778.14	10.97	8.097	14.85	13.05	3.159 E8	1.797	60.27
	1082.7	0.2465	1349.5	815.80	11.07	8.604	14.23	12.44	3.074 E8	1.797	60.27
Uranus	1871.4	0.6043	3007.3	740.48	8.417	4.180	16.95	13.70	6.985 E8	3.248	60.33
	1824.2	0.5743	2870.3	778.14	8.525	4.439	16.37	13.05	6.723 E8	3.320	60.33
	1777.0	0.5409	2738.3	815.80	8.637	4.715	15.82	12.44	6.463 E8	3.389	60.33
Neptune	2638.6	0.7194	4536.8	740.48	7.088	2.864	17.55	13.70	1.169 E9	3.845	60.36
	2639.0	0.7051	4499.9	778.14	7.088	2.947	17.04	13.05	1.170 E9	3.992	60.37
	2639.4	0.6909	4463.0	815.80	7.087	3.030	16.58	12.44	1.170 E9	4.141	60.38

Body	Mean orbital Semimajor axis (km × 10⁻⁶)	Eccentricity ε	Aphelion (km × 10⁻⁶)	Perhelion (km × 10⁻⁶)	Orbital Velocity (km/sec)			Orbital Velocity of Departure Body (km/sec)	Time of one way trip (½ orbit) (Solar Seconds)	Departure	
					Mean	Aphelion	Perhelion			Δ_v orbit (km/sec)	Maximum Δ_v (km/sec)
	4057.7	0.8175	7375.0	740.48	5.716	1.811	18.04	13.70	2.230 E9	4.339	60.40
Pluto	3343.6	0.7673	5909.0	778.14	6.297	2.285	17.35	13.05	1.668 E9	4.299	60.39
	2629.4	0.6897	4443.0	815.80	7.101	3.043	16.57	12.44	1.163 E9	4.135	60.38
From Saturn to:											
	775.26	0.9406	1504.5	46.036	13.08	2.287	74.76	9.129	1.862 E8	6.841	36.71
Mercury	742.47	0.9220	1427.0	57.950	13.36	2.693	66.31	9.639	1.746 E8	6.946	36.73
	709.69	0.9016	1349.5	69.860	13.67	3.110	60.07	10.18	1.631 E8	7.067	36.75
	805.93	0.8668	1504.5	107.37	12.83	3.426	45.01	9.129	1.974 E8	5.702	36.51
Venus	767.55	0.8592	1427.0	108.11	13.14	3.617	47.75	9.639	1.835 E8	6.021	36.56
	729.18	0.8507	1349.5	108.85	13.48	3.829	47.48	10.18	1.699 E8	6.348	36.62
	825.78	0.8219	1504.5	147.07	12.67	3.962	40.53	9.129	2.047 E8	5.167	36.43
Earth	788.28	0.8103	1427.0	149.57	12.97	4.199	40.06	9.639	1.910 E8	5.440	36.47
	750.79	0.7975	1349.5	152.07	13.29	4.461	39.59	10.18	1.775 E8	5.716	36.51
	855.52	0.7586	1504.5	206.56	12.45	4.613	33.60	9.129	2.159 E8	4.516	36.35
Mars	827.42	0.7246	1427.0	227.84	12.66	5.058	31.68	9.639	2.054 E8	4.581	36.35
	799.32	0.6883	1349.5	249.12	12.88	5.533	29.97	10.18	1.950 E8	4.644	36.36
	1122.5	0.3403	1504.5	740.48	10.87	7.624	15.49	9.129	3.245 E8	1.504	36.10
Jupiter	1102.6	0.2942	1427.0	778.14	10.97	8.097	14.85	9.639	3.159 E8	1.541	36.10
	1082.7	0.2465	1349.5	815.80	11.07	8.604	14.23	10.18	3.074 E8	1.573	36.10
	2175.9	0.3798	3002.3	1349.5	7.806	5.233	11.64	10.18	8.758 E8	1.465	36.09
Uranus	2148.6	0.3359	2870.3	1427.0	7.855	5.539	11.14	9.639	8.593 E8	1.502	36.10
	2121.4	0.2908	2738.3	1504.5	7.905	5.860	10.67	9.129	8.430 E8	1.536	36.10
	2943.2	0.5415	4536.8	1349.5	6.712	3.660	12.31	10.18	1.378 E9	2.129	36.13
Neptune	2963.4	0.5185	4499.9	1427.0	6.689	3.767	11.88	9.639	1.392 E9	2.239	36.13
	2983.7	0.4958	4463.0	1504.5	6.666	3.870	11.48	9.129	1.406 E9	2.352	36.14
	4362.3	0.6906	7375.0	1349.5	5.513	2.358	12.89	10.18	2.486 E9	2.710	36.17
Pluto	3668.0	0.6110	5909.0	1427.0	6.012	2.954	12.23	9.639	1.917 E9	2.595	36.16
	2973.7	0.4941	4443.0	1504.5	6.677	3.885	11.47	9.129	1.399 E9	2.345	36.14
From Uranus to:											
	1524.2	0.9698	3002.3	46.036	9.326	1.155	75.32	6.490	5.134 E8	5.336	22.82
Mercury	1464.1	0.9604	2870.3	57.950	9.516	1.352	66.97	6.796	4.834 E8	5.444	22.85
	1404.1	0.9502	2738.3	69.865	9.717	1.552	60.83	7.116	4.539 E8	5.564	22.88
	1554.9	0.9309	3002.3	107.37	9.234	1.746	48.83	6.490	5.290 E8	4.744	22.69
Venus	1489.2	0.9274	2870.3	108.11	9.435	1.831	48.62	6.796	4.958 E8	4.965	22.74
	1423.6	0.9235	2738.3	108.85	9.650	1.924	48.40	7.116	4.634 E8	5.192	22.69
	1574.7	0.9066	3002.3	147.07	9.176	2.031	41.46	6.490	5.392 E8	4.460	22.63
Earth	1509.9	0.9009	2870.3	149.57	9.370	2.139	41.05	6.796	5.062 E8	4.657	22.67
	1445.2	0.8948	2738.3	152.07	9.578	2.257	40.64	7.116	4.740 E8	4.859	22.72
	1604.4	0.8813	3002.3	206.56	9.090	2.384	34.66	6.490	5.545 E8	4.106	22.57
Mars	1549.1	0.8529	2870.3	227.84	9.251	2.606	32.84	6.796	5.260 E8	4.190	22.58
	1493.7	0.8332	2738.3	249.12	9.421	2.842	31.23	7.116	4.981 E8	4.275	22.60
	1817.4	0.6043	3002.3	740.48	8.417	4.180	16.95	6.490	6.985 E8	2.310	22.31
Jupiter	1824.2	0.5743	2870.3	778.14	8.525	4.439	16.37	6.796	6.723 E8	2.358	22.31
	1777.0	0.5409	2738.3	815.80	8.637	4.715	15.82	7.116	6.463 E8	2.402	22.32
	2175.9	0.3798	3002.3	1349.5	7.806	5.233	11.64	6.490	8.758 E8	1.257	22.23
Saturn	2148.6	0.3359	2870.3	1427.0	7.855	5.539	11.14	6.796	8.593 E8	1.258	22.23
	2121.4	0.2908	2738.3	1504.5	7.905	5.860	10.67	7.116	8.430 E8	1.257	22.23
	3637.5	0.2472	4536.8	2738.3	6.037	4.690	7.771	7.116	1.893 E9	0.6544	22.20
Neptune	3685.1	0.2211	4499.9	2870.3	5.998	4.790	7.510	6.796	1.930 E9	0.7139	22.20
	3732.7	0.1957	4463.0	3002.3	5.960	4.888	7.266	6.490	1.968 E9	0.7757	22.20
	5056.6	0.4585	7375.0	2738.3	5.120	3.120	8.403	7.116	3.102 E9	1.287	22.23
Pluto	4389.6	0.3461	5909.0	2870.3	5.496	3.830	7.885	6.796	2.509 E9	1.089	22.22
	3722.7	0.1935	4443.0	3002.3	5.968	4.906	7.260	6.490	1.960 E9	0.7691	22.20
From Neptune to:											
	2291.4	0.9799	4536.8	46.037	7.606	0.7662	75.51	5.384	9.464 E8	4.617	24.97
Mercury	2278.9	0.9746	4499.9	57.948	7.627	0.8655	67.21	5.428	9.387 E8	4.562	24.96
	2266.4	0.9692	4463.0	69.864	7.648	0.9569	61.13	5.473	9.310 E8	4.516	24.95
	2322.1	0.9538	4536.8	107.37	7.556	1.162	49.12	5.384	9.655 E8	4.221	24.90
Venus	2304.0	0.9531	4499.9	108.11	7.586	1.176	48.94	5.428	9.542 E8	4.252	24.90
	2285.9	0.9524	4463.0	108.85	7.616	1.189	48.77	5.473	9.430 E8	4.283	24.91
	2341.9	0.9372	4536.8	147.07	7.524	1.355	41.79	5.384	9.779 E8	4.029	24.86
Earth	2324.7	0.9357	4499.9	149.57	7.552	1.377	41.42	5.428	9.667 E8	4.051	24.87
	2307.5	0.9341	4463.0	152.07	7.580	1.399	41.06	5.473	9.564 E8	4.073	24.87
	2371.7	0.9129	4536.8	206.56	7.477	1.595	35.04	5.384	9.966 E8	3.788	24.83
Mars	2363.9	0.9036	4499.9	227.84	7.489	1.685	33.28	5.428	9.916 E8	3.743	24.82
	2356.1	0.8943	4463.0	249.12	7.501	1.772	31.75	5.473	9.867 E8	3.700	24.81
	2638.6	0.7194	4536.8	740.48	7.088	2.864	17.55	5.384	1.169 E9	2.520	24.66
Jupiter	2639.0	0.7051	4499.9	778.14	7.088	2.947	17.04	5.428	1.170 E9	2.480	24.66
	2639.4	0.6909	4463.0	815.80	7.088	3.030	16.58	5.473	1.170 E9	2.442	24.66

Body	Mean orbital Semimajor axis (km × 10⁻⁶)	Eccentricity ε	Aphelion (km × 10⁻⁶)	Perhelion (km × 10⁻⁶)	Orbital Velocity (km/sec)			Orbital Velocity of Departure Body (km/sec)	Time of one way trip (½ orbit) (Solar Seconds)	Departure Δᵥ orbit (km/sec)	Maximum Δᵥ (km/sec)
					Mean	Aphelion	Perhelion				
Saturn	2943.2	0.5415	4536.8	1349.5	6.712	3.660	12.31	5.384	1.378 E9	1.723	24.60
	2963.4	0.5185	4499.9	1427.0	6.689	3.767	11.88	5.428	1.392 E9	1.661	24.59
	2983.7	0.4958	4463.0	1504.5	6.666	3.870	11.48	5.473	1.406 E9	1.602	24.59
Uranus	3637.5	0.2472	4536.8	2738.3	6.037	4.690	7.771	5.384	1.893 E9	0.6933	24.54
	3685.1	0.2211	4499.9	2870.3	5.998	4.790	7.510	5.428	1.930 E9	0.6375	24.54
	3732.7	0.1957	4463.0	3002.3	5.960	4.888	7.266	5.473	1.968 E9	0.5845	24.54
Pluto	5919.0	0.2460	7375.0	4463.0	4.733	3.682	6.084	5.473	3.929 E9	0.6112	24.54
	5204.4	0.1354	5909.0	4499.9	5.047	4.404	5.784	5.428	3.240 E9	0.3557	24.54
	4489.9	−0.1045	4443.0	4536.8	5.434	5.491	5.377	5.384	2.596 E9	−0.0061	24.54
From Pluto to:											
Mercury	3710.5	0.9876	7375.0	46.037	5.977	0.4723	75.66	3.676	1.950 E9	3.204	5.955
	2983.5	0.9806	5909.0	57.948	6.666	0.6601	67.31	4.737	1.406 E9	4.077	6.466
	2256.4	0.9690	4443.0	69.864	7.665	0.9612	67.13	6.103	9.248 E8	5.141	7.185
Venus	3741.2	0.9713	7375.0	107.37	5.953	0.7183	49.34	3.676	1.974 E9	2.958	5.826
	3008.6	0.9641	5909.0	108.11	6.638	0.8979	49.08	4.737	1.424 E9	3.839	6.319
	2275.9	0.9522	4443.0	108.85	7.632	1.195	48.76	6.103	9.368 E8	4.908	7.020
Earth	3761.0	0.9609	7375.0	147.07	5.937	0.8384	42.04	3.676	1.990 E9	2.838	5.766
	3029.3	0.9506	5909.0	149.57	6.615	1.053	41.58	4.737	1.439 E9	3.684	6.226
	2297.5	0.9338	4443.0	152.07	7.596	1.405	41.06	6.103	9.502 E8	4.697	6.874
Mars	3790.8	0.9455	7375.0	206.56	5.914	0.9897	35.34	3.676	2.014 E9	2.687	5.693
	3068.4	0.9257	5909.0	227.84	6.573	1.291	33.47	4.737	1.467 E9	3.446	6.088
	2346.0	0.8938	4443.0	249.12	7.517	1.780	31.75	6.103	9.804 E8	4.323	6.624
Jupiter	4057.7	0.8175	7375.0	740.48	5.716	1.811	18.04	3.676	2.230 E9	1.865	5.355
	3343.6	0.7673	5909.0	778.14	6.297	2.285	17.35	4.737	1.668 E9	2.452	5.586
	2629.4	0.6897	4443.0	815.80	7.101	3.043	16.57	6.103	1.163 E9	3.060	5.879
Saturn	4362.3	0.6906	7375.0	1349.5	5.513	2.358	12.89	3.676	2.486 E9	1.318	5.190
	3668.0	0.6110	5909.0	1427.0	6.012	2.954	12.23	4.737	1.917 E9	1.782	5.326
	2973.7	0.4941	4443.0	1504.5	6.677	3.885	11.47	6.103	1.399 E9	2.217	5.487
Uranus	5056.6	0.4585	7375.0	2738.3	5.120	3.120	8.403	3.676	3.102 E9	0.5564	5.050
	4389.6	0.3461	5909.0	2870.3	5.496	3.830	7.885	4.737	2.509 E9	0.9065	5.101
	3722.7	0.1935	4443.0	3002.3	5.968	4.906	7.260	6.103	1.960 E9	1.197	5.160
Neptune	5919.0	0.2460	7375.0	4463.0	4.733	3.682	6.084	3.676	3.929 E9	−5.164	5.019
	5204.4	0.1354	5909.0	4499.9	5.047	4.404	5.784	4.737	3.240 E9	0.3323	5.030
	4489.9	−0.1045	4443.0	4536.8	5.434	5.491	5.377	6.103	2.596 E9	0.6117	5.056

CONSTANTS FOR SATELLITE GEODESY

Defining Constants

1. Number of ephemeris seconds in 1 tropical year (1900) . . . .s $= 31\ 556\ 925.9747$
2. Gaussian gravitational constant, defining the a. u. . . . .k $= 0.017\ 202\ 09895$

Primary Constants

3. Velocity of light in meters per second . . . .c $= 299\ 792.5 \times 10^3$
4. Dynamical form-factor for Earth . . . .J_2 $= 0.001\ 082\ 7$
5. Sidereal mean motion of Moon in radians per second (1900). . . . .$n_{\mathbb{C}}{}^*$ $= 2.661\ 699\ 489 \times 10^{-6}$
6. General precession in longitude per tropical century (1900). . . . . .p $= 5025''.64$
7. Constant of nutation (1900) . . . .N $= 9''.210$

Auxiliary Constants and Factors

$k/86400$, for use when the unit of time is 1 second . . . .k' $= 1.990\ 983\ 675 \times 10^{-7}$

Number of seconds of arc in 1 radian. . . . . $= 206\ 264.806$

Factor for constant of aberration (note 10) . . . .F_1 $= 1.000\ 142$

Factor for mean distance of Moon (note 12) . . . .F_2 $= 0.999\ 093\ 142$

Factor for parallactic inequality (note 15) . . . .F_3 $= 49853''.2$

Derived Constants

8. Solar parallax. . . . . $\arcsin(\alpha_e/A) = \pi.$ $= 8''.79405\ (8''.794)$
9. Light-time for unit distance . . . . $A/c' = \tau_A$ $= 499^s.012$
   $= 1^s/0.002\ 003\ 96$
10. Constant of aberration . . . . $F_1 k' \tau_A = \kappa$ $= 20''.4958\ (20''.496)$
11. Ratio of masses of Sun and Earth + Moon . . . . $S/E(1 + \mu)$ $= 328\ 912$
12. Perturbed mean distance of Moon, in meters . . . . $F_2(GE(1 + \mu)/n_{\mathbb{C}}{}^{*2})^{\frac{1}{3}} = \alpha_{\mathbb{C}}$ $= 384\ 400 \times 10^3$
13. Constant of sine parallax for Moon. . . . . $\alpha_c/\alpha_{\mathbb{C}} = \sin \pi_{\mathbb{C}}$ $= 3422''.451$

14. Constant of lunar inequality . . . . $\dfrac{\mu}{1 + \mu}\dfrac{\alpha_{\mathbb{C}}}{A} = L = 6''.43987\ (6''.440)$

15. Constant of parallactic inequality. . . . . $F_3\dfrac{1 - \mu}{1 + \mu}\dfrac{\alpha_{\mathbb{C}}}{A} = P_{\mathbb{C}} = 124''.986$

THE EARTH: ITS MASS, DIMENSIONS AND OTHER RELATED QUANTITIES

From NASA Technical Translation NASA TT-F-533

TABLE A

Quantity	Unit of Measurement	Symbol	Numerical Value	Sources; Remarks[1]
Mass	Proportion of the mass of the sun	M	$5.9763 \cdot 10^{27}$ $1/331950$	I. D. Zhongolovich, 1952
Major Orbital semi-axis	Astr. Unit in km	a_{orb}	149,457,000 1.000000	1961 data of Soviet radar determinations
Distance from sun at perihelion	a.u.	r_{π}	0.983298	for 1962
Distance from sun at aphelion	a.u.	r_{α}	1.016744	for 1962
Moment of perihelion passage		T_{π}	Jan. 2, $4^{hr}52^{m}$	for 1962 USSR Astron. Yearbook for 1962
Moment of aphelion passage		T_{α}	Jul 4 $5^{hr}05^{m}$	for 1962
Siderial rotation period around sun	sec	P_{orb}	$31.558 \cdot 10^{6}$	
Mean rotational velocity	km/sec	U_{orb}	29.8	
Mean equatorial radius	km	$\bar{a}$	6,378.245 6,378.077	A. A. Izotov, 1950 I. D. Zhongolovich, 1956
Mean polar compression		α	1/298.3 1/296.6 1/298.2	A. A. Izotov, 1950 I. D. Zhongolovich, 1952 D. G. King-Hele, R. Merson, 1959. On observations on the movements of artificial earth satellites.
Difference in equatorial and polar semi-axes	km	$a - c$	21.382 21.500	A. A. Izotov, 1950 I. D. Zhongolovich, 1956
Compression of meridian of major equatorial axis		α_a	1/295.2	I. D. Zhongolovich, 1952
Compression of meridian of minor equatorial axis		α_b	1/298.0	I. D. Zhongolovich, 1952
Equatorial compression		ϵ	1/30 000 1/32 000	A. A. Izotov, 1950 I. D. Zhongolovich, 1952

[1] The source does not indicate whether the value given is generally accepted or has merely been calculated by the author, G. N. Katterfel'd.

THE EARTH: ITS MASS, DIMENSIONS AND OTHER RELATED QUANTITIES (*Continued*)

TABLE A Continued

Quantity	Unit of Measurement	Symbol	Numerical Value	Sources; Remarks[1]
Difference in equatorial semi-axes	m	$a - b$	213 199	A. A. Izotov, 1950 I. D. Zhongolovich, 1952
Meridian of longitude of minor equatorial semi-axis		λ_a	15°E - 6°W	A. A. Izotov, 1950 I. D. Zhongolovich, 1952
Meridian of longitude of minor equatorial axis		λ_b	105°E - 75° W; 84°E - 96°W	A. A. Izotov, 1950 I. D. Zhongolovich, 1952
Difference in polar semi-axes	m	$C_N - C_S$	~ 70 <100	I. D. Zhongolovich, 1952 Based on observations of artificial satellites[1]
Polar asymmetry		η	$\sim 1.10^{-5}$	
Mean acceleration of gravity at equator		g_e	978,057.3	I. D. Zhongolovich, 1952
Mean acceleration of gravity at poles	milligals (mgl)	g_ρ	983,225.1	
Difference in acceleration of gravity at pole and at equator		$g_p - g_e$	+5,167.8	
Difference in acceleration of gravity at equator	mgl	$g_a - g_b$	+30.2	I. D. Zhongolovich, 1952
Difference in acceleration of gravity at poles		$g_N - g_S$	+30	I. D. Zhongolovich, 1952
Mean acceleration of gravity for entire surface of terrestrial ellipsoid	mgl	g	979,783.0	I. D. Zhongolovich, 1952
Mean radius	km	R	6,370.949	
Area of surface	km²	S	$510.0501 \cdot 10^6$	
Volume	km³	V	$1,083.1579 \cdot 10^9$	
Mean density	gr/cm³	δ	5.5170	I. D. Zhongolovich, 1952
Siderial rotational period	sec	P	86,164.09	
Angular rotational velocity	rad/sec	ω	$7.292116 \cdot 10^{-5}$	
Mean equatorial rotational velocity	km/sec	v	0.465	

TABLE A Continued

Quantity	Unit of Measurement	Symbol	Numerical Value	Sources; Remarks[1]
Ratio of centrifugal force to attractive force at equator		q	$\dfrac{1}{289}$	
Ratio of centrifugal force to force of gravity at equator		q_c	$0.0034677 = \dfrac{1}{288}$	I. D. Zhongolovich, 1952
Coefficients characterizing the radial distribution of densities within the earth		κ_1 κ	0.966 0.331	Based on observations of artificial satellites; several larger values were given earlier[1]
Radius of inertia	km; proportion of mean radius	R_i	3,674.735 0.5768	
Geocentric latitude of inertial parallel		ϕ_i	$54°47'$	
Moment of inertia	gr · cm^2	I	$8.070 \cdot 10^{44}$	
Moment of rotation	gr · cm^2/sec	L	$5.885 \cdot 10^{40}$	
Relative true secular braking of earth's rotation due to tidal friction		$\dfrac{\Delta\omega_e}{\omega}$	$-4.2 \cdot 10^{-8}$ per century	
Relative proper secular acceleration of earth's rotation		$\dfrac{\Delta\omega_i}{\omega}$	$+1.4 \cdot 10^{-8}$ per century	N. N. Pariyskiy, 1955
Relative observed secular braking of earth's rotation		$\dfrac{\Delta\omega}{\omega}$	$-2.8 \cdot 10^{-8}$ per century	
Mean rotational velocity of terrestrial radius due to abyssal compression	cm/century	$\dfrac{\Delta R}{\Delta t}$	~5 Assumed invariability of mass (M) 4.5 and distribution of masses (κ)	B. Meyermann, 1928, 1928a N. N. Pariyskiy, 1955
Secular variation in potential gravitational energy of earth accompanying reduction of terrestrial radius by 5 cm and corresponding increase in earth's kinetic energy	erg/century	ΔE	$\sim 17 \cdot 10^{30}$	Assumed uniformity of compression of entire planet. P. N. Kropotkin, 1948 and A. T. Aslanyan, 1955

[1] On the basis of materials published in the Astron. J., Vol. 64, 1272, 1959.

TABLE A Continued

Quantity	Unit of Measurement	Symbol	Numerical Value	Sources; Remarks[1]
Probable value of total energy of tectonic deformation of earth	erg/century	E_t	$\sim 1 \cdot 10^{30}$	With allowance for earthquakes, volcanic eruptions and other forms of tectonic activity P. N. Kropotkin, 1948
Secular loss of heat of earth through radiation into space	erg/century cal/century	$\Delta' E_k$	$1 \cdot 10^{30}$ $2.4 \cdot 10^{22}$	P. N. Kropotkin, 1948
Portion of earth's kinetic energy transformed into heat as a result of lunar and solar tides in the hydrosphere	erg/century cal/century	$\Delta'' E_k$	$0.11 \cdot 10^{30}$ $0.26 \cdot 10^{22}$	Heiskanen, 1922 and de Sitter, 1927
Difference in duration of days in March and August	sec	ΔP	0.0025 (March-Aug.)	N. N. Pariyskiy, 1955
Corresponding relative annual variation in earth's rotational velocity		$\dfrac{\Delta^* \omega}{\omega}$	$2.9 \cdot 10^{-8}$ (Aug.-March)	N. N. Pariyskiy, 1955
Presumed variation in earth's radius between August and March	cm	$\Delta^* R$	−9.2 (Aug.-March)	
Annual variation in level of world ocean	cm	Δh_0	~ 10 (Sept.-March)	N. N. Pariyskiy, 1955

The Earth's Lithosphere, Hydrosphere, Atmosphere and Biosphere

TABLE B

Quantity	Unit of Measurement	Symbol	Numerical Value	Source
Area of continents	km²; in % of area of surface of earth	S_C	$149 \cdot 10^6$ 29.2	E. Kossina, 1933
Area of world ocean	km²; in % of area of surface of earth	S_O	$361 \cdot 10^6$ 70.8	E. Kossina, 1933
Mean height of continents above sea level	m	h_C	875	E. Kossina, 1933
Mean depth of world ocean	m	h_O	$=3794$	Morskoy Atlas, Vol. II, 1953
Mean position of earth's surface with respect to sea level	m	h_m	$=2430$	E. Kossina, 1933
Mean thickness of lithosphere within the limits of the continents	km	$h_{c.l.}$	35	M. Yuing and F. Press, 1955
Mean thickness of lithosphere within the limits of the ocean	km	$h_{o.l.}$	4.7	Kh. Khess, 1955
Mean rate of thickening of continental lithosphere	m/10⁶ yr	$\frac{\Delta h}{\Delta t}$	10 – 40	V. I. Popov, 1955
Mean rate of horizontal extension of continental lithosphere	km/10⁶ yr	$\frac{\Delta l}{\Delta t}$	0.75 – 20	V. I. Popov, 1955
Mass of lithosphere	gr	m_l	$2.367 \cdot 10^{25}$	A. Poldervart, 1955
Amount of water released from the mantle and core in the course of geological time	gr		$3.400 \cdot 10^{24}$	Kalp, 1951
Total reserve of water in the mantle	gr		$2 \cdot 10^{26}$	A. P. Vinogradov, 1959
Present day content of free and bound water in the earth's lithosphere	gr		$2.2 – 2.6 \cdot 10^{24}$ $1.8 – 2.7 \cdot 10^{24}$	Kalp, 1951 A. Poldervart, 1955
Mass of hydrosphere	gr	m_h	$1.664 \cdot 10^{24}$	A. Poldervart, 1955
Amount of oxygen bound in the earth's crust	gr		$1.300 \cdot 10^{24}$	A. Poldervart, 1955
Amount of free oxygen	gr		$1.5 \cdot 10^{21}$	A. Poldervart, 1955

TABLE B Continued

Quantity	Unit of Measurement	Symbol	Numerical Value	Source
Mass of atmosphere	gr	m_a	$5.136 \cdot 10^{21}$	A. Poldervart, 1955
Mass of biosphere	gr	m_b	$1.148 \cdot 10^{19}$	A. Poldervart, 1955
Mass of living matter in the biosphere	gr		$3.6 \cdot 10^{17}$	A. Poldervart, 1955
Density of living matter on dry land	gr/cm^2		0.1	A. Poldervart, 1955
Density of living matter in ocean	gr/cm^3		$15 \cdot 10^{-8}$	A. Poldervart, 1955

ESTIMATED AGE OF EARTH

TABLE C

Object of Study	Age in billions of years	Source
Fossils of the most ancient organisms	2.7	L. Arens, 1955
Most ancient known terrestrial rocks: Mica (biotite) found within migmatites on the Kola Peninsula and at the Great Rapids of the Voron'ya River in 1958;	3.6	A. A. Polkanov and E. K. Gerling, 1961
Rock found in South Africa	4	A. L. Heils, 1960[1]
Lithosphere	~4	V. I. Baranov, 1958
Earth	~5	A. P. Vinogradov, 1959 and others

[1] See *Priroda*, No. 11, 1960, p. 113.

Approximate Scale of Geologic Time,[1]
Based on the Data of Soviet Research, 1960.

TABLE D

Era	Period or Epoch	Beginning and end, in millions of years	Approximate Duration, in millions of years
Cenozoic	**Quaternian** Contemporary	0 – 10,000 yrs ± 2,000 yrs	8 – 12,000 years
	Pleistocene	10,000 – 1,000,000 yrs ± 50,000 yrs	1
	Tertiary Pliocene	1 – 10	9
	Miocene	10 – 25	15
	Oligocene	25 – 40	15 } 69
	Eocene	40 – 60	20
	Paleocene	60 – 70	10
Mesozoic	Cretaceous	70 – 140	70
	Jurassic	140 – 185	45
	Triassic	185 – 225	40
Paleozoic	Permian	225 – 270	45
	Carboniferous	270 – 320	50
	Devonian	320 – 400	80
	Silurian	400 – 420	20
	Ordovician	420 – 480	60
	Cambrian	480 – 570	90
	Pre-Cambrian IV (Riphean)[2]	570 – 1,200	630
	Pre-Cambrian III (Proterozoic)[3]	1,200 – 1,900	700
	Pre-Cambrian II (Archean)	1,900 – 2,700	800
	Pre-Cambrian I (Catarchean)	2,700 – 3,500	800
	Pregeological era	3,500 – 5,000	1,500

(570 indicated at right of Cenozoic bracket)

[1] Based on the geochronological scale of the Commission for Determining the Absolute Age of Geological Formations, published in *Izv. AN SSSR*, Geological series, No. 10, 1960.

[2] Proterozoic II.

[3] Proterozoic I.

ACCELERATION DUE TO GRAVITY AND LENGTH OF THE SECONDS PENDULUM

FOR SEA LEVEL AT VARIOUS LATITUDES

Based on the formula of the U. S. Coast and Geodetic Survey. The length of the simple pendulum whose period is two seconds, that is which beats seconds, is computed in each case from the corresponding value of the acceleration.

Latitude	Acceleration due to gravity		Length of seconds pendulum	
•	cm/sec.^{2}	ft./sec.^{2}	cm	in.
0	978.039	32.0878	99.0961	39.0141
5	978.078	32.0891	99.1000	39.0157
10	978.195	32.0929	99.1119	39.0204
15	978.384	32.0991	99.1310	39.0279
20	978.641	32.1076	99.1571	39.0382
25	978.960	32.1180	99.1894	39.0509
30	979.329	32.1302	99.2268	39.0656
31	979.407	32.1327		
32	979.487	32.1353		
33	979.569	32.1380		
34	979.652	32.1407		
35	979.737	32.1435	99.2681	39.0819
36	979.822	32.1463		
37	979.908	32.1491		
38	979.995	32.1520		
39	980.083	32.1549		
40	980.171	32.1578	99.3121	39.0992
41	980.261	32.1607		
42	980.350	32.1636		
43	980.440	32.1666		
44	980.531	32.1696		
45	980.621	32.1725	99.3577	39.1171
46	980.711	32.1755		
47	980.802	32.1785		
48	980.892	32.1814		
49	980.981	32.1844		
50	981.071	32.1873	99.4033	39.1351
51	981.159	32.1902		
52	981.247	32.1931		
53	981.336	32.1960		
54	981.422	32.1988		
55	981.507	32.2016	99.4475	39.1525
56	981.592	32.2044		
57	981.675	32.2071		
58	981.757	32.2098		
59	981.839	32.2125		
60	981.918	32.2151	99.4891	39.1689
65	982.288	32.2272	99.5266	39.1836
70	982.608	32.2377	99.5590	39.1964
75	982.868	32.2463	99.5854	39.2068
80	983.059	32.2525	99.6047	39.2144
85	983.178	32.2564	99.6168	39.2191
90	983.217	32.2577	99.6207	39.2207

FREE AIR CORRECTION FOR ALTITUDE

−0.0003086 cm/sec.^{2}/m for altitude in meters.
−0.000003086 ft./sec.^{2}/ft. for altitude in feet.

Altitude meters	Correction cm/sec.^{2}	Altitude feet	Correction ft./sec.^{2}
200	−0.0617	200	−0.000617
300	0.0926	300	0.000926
400	0.1234	400	0.001234
500	0.1543	500	0.001543
600	0.1852	600	0.001852
700	0.2160	700	0.002160
800	0.2469	800	0.002469
900	0.2777	900	0.002777

DATA IN REGARD TO THE EARTH

Quadrant of the equator, 10,019,150 meters, 6,225.60 miles.
Quadrant of the meridian, 10,002,290 meters, 6,215.12 miles.
1° latitude at the equator = 69.41 miles.
1° latitude at the pole = 68.70 miles.
Mean surface density of the continents, 2.67 g/cm^3, 166.7 lb./ft.^{3}
Land area, 148.847 × 10^6 km^2, 57.470 × 10^6 sq. mi.
Ocean area, 361.254 × 10^6 km^2, 139.480 × 10^6 sq. mi.

DATA IN REGARD TO THE EARTH
(Continued)

Highest mountain, Everest, 8,840 meters, 29,003 ft.
Greatest sea depth, 10,430 meters, 34,219 ft.
Thermal gradient of the earth, higher at increasing depths, 30°C per km, 48°C per mi. (uncertain).

THE COMMONER CHEMICAL ELEMENTS IN THE EARTH'S CRUST

Reprinted from "Principles of Geochemistry" (1952) with the permission of Brian Mason, author, and John Wiley and Sons, publishers.
The "Earth's Crust" refers to the rocks only and does not include atmosphere or the oceans. The atom percent column is obtained by dividing the weight percent by the atomic weights and reducing to 100%. The radius is the ionic radius. The volume percent is the atomic percent multiplied by $\frac{4}{3}\pi r^3$ and reducing to 100%.

Element	Weight %	Atom %	Ion Radius (Å)	Volume %
O	46.60	62.55	1.32	91.97
Si	27.72	21.22	0.39	0.80
Al	8.13	6.47	0.57	0.77
Fe	5.00	1.92	0.82	0.68
Mg	2.09	1.84	0.78	0.56
Ca	3.63	1.94	1.06	1.48
Na	2.83	2.64	0.98	1.60
K	2.59	1.42	1.33	2.14

THE AVERAGE AMOUNTS OF THE ELEMENTS IN EARTH'S CRUST IN GRAMS PER METRIC TON OR PARTS PER MILLION

Reprinted from "Principles of Geochemistry" (1952) with the permission of Brian Mason, author, and John Wiley and Sons, publishers.

O	466,000	N	46			Br	1.6
Si	277,200	Cc	46			Ho	1.2
Al	81,300	Sn	40			Eu	1.1
Fe	50,000	Y	28			Sb	1?
Ca	36,300	Nd	24			Tb	0.9
Na	28,300	Nb	24			Lu	0.8
K	25,900	Co	23			Tl	0.6
Mg	20,900	La	18			Hg	0.5
Ti	4,400	Pb	16			I	0.3
H	1,400	Ga	15			Bi	0.2
P	1,180	Mo	15			Tm	0.2
Mn	1,000	Th	12			Cd	0.15
S	520	Cs	7			Ag	0.1
C	320	Ge	7			In	0.1
Cl	314	Sm	6.5			Se	0.09
Rb	310	Gd	6.4			A	0.04
F	300	Be	6			Pd	0.01
Sr	300	Pr	5.5			Pt	0.005
Ba	250	Sc	5			Au	0.005
Zr	220	As	5			He	0.003
Cr	200	Hf	4.5			Te	0.002?
V	150	Dy	4.5			Rh	0.001
Zn	132	U	4			Re	0.001
Ni	80	B	3			Ir	0.001
Cu	70	Yb	2.7			Os	0.001?
W	69	Er	2.5			Ru	0.001?
Li	65	Ta	2.1				

CHEMICAL COMPOSITION OF ROCKS

Reprinted from "Sedimentary Rocks" (1948) with the permission of F. J. Pettijohn, author, and Harper Brothers, publishers.

Element	Average igneous rock	Average shale	Average sandstone	Average limestone	Average sediment
SiO_2	59.14	58.10	78.33	5.19	57.95
TiO_2	1.05	0.65	0.25	0.06	0.57
Al_2O_3	15.34	15.40	4.77	0.81	13.39
Fe_2O_3	3.08	4.02	1.07	0.54	3.47
FeO	3.80	2.45	0.30		2.08
MgO	3.49	2.44	1.16	7.89	2.65
CaO	5.08	3.11	5.50	42.57	5.89
Na_2O	3.84	1.30	0.45	0.05	1.13
K_2O	3.13	3.24	1.31	0.33	2.86
H_2O	1.15	5.00	1.63	0.77	3.23
P_2O_5	0.30	0.17	0.08	0.04	0.13
CO_2	0.10	2.63	5.03	41.54	5.38
SO_3		0.64	0.07	0.05	0.54
BaO	0.06	0.05	0.05		
C		0.80			0.66
	99.56	100.00	100.00	99.84	99.93

SOLAR SPECTRAL IRRADIANCE

From NASA Technical Report R-351, "The Solar Constant and the Solar Spectrum Measured from a Research Aircraft". Report edited by Matthew P. Thekaekara, Goddard Space Flight Center, Greenbelt, Maryland 20771. Discussion of previously reported values and of measurements and calculations leading to the following table are contained in the NASA Technical Report R-351.

SOLAR SPECTRAL IRRADIANCE—PROPOSED STANDARD CURVE

λ —Wavelength in microns
P_λ —Solar spectral irradiance averaged over small bandwidth centered at λ, in Watts cm$^{-2}\mu^{-1}$
A_λ—Area under the solar spectral irradiance curve in the wavelength range 0 to λ, mW cm^{-2}
D_λ—Percentage of the solar constant associated with wavelengths shorter than λ
Solar Constant—135.30 mW cm^{-2}, or 1.940 cal min^{-1} cm^{-2}

λ	P_λ	A_λ	D_λ	λ	P_λ	A_λ	D_λ	λ	P_λ	A_λ	D_λ
0.120	0.000010	0.00059992	0.00044	0.475	0.2044	25.6001	18.921	2.4	0.0064	129.695	95.858
0.140	0.000003	0.00072999	0.00053	0.480	0.2074	26.6296	19.681	2.5	0.0054	130.285	96.294
0.150	0.000007	0.00077999	0.00057	0.485	0.1976	27.6421	20.430	2.6	0.0048	130.795	96.671
0.160	0.000023	0.00092999	0.00068	0.490	0.1950	28.6236	21.155	2.7	0.0043	131.250	97.007
0.170	0.000063	0.00135999	0.00100	0.495	0.1960	29.6011	21.878	2.8	0.00390	131.660	97.3103
0.180	0.000125	0.00229999	0.00169	0.500	0.1942	30.5766	22.599	2.9	0.00350	132.030	97.5838
0.190	0.000271	0.00427999	0.00316	0.505	0.1920	31.5421	23.312	3.0	0.00310	132.360	97.8277
0.200	0.00107	0.010984	0.0081	0.510	0.1882	32.4926	24.015	3.1	0.00260	132.645	98.0383
0.210	0.00229	0.027784	0.0205	0.515	0.1833	33.4214	24.701	3.2	0.00226	132.888	98.2179
0.220	0.00575	0.067984	0.0502	0.520	0.1833	34.3379	25.379	3.3	0.00192	133.097	98.3724
0.225	0.00649	0.098584	0.0728	0.525	0.1852	35.2591	26.059	3.4	0.00166	133.276	98.5047
0.230	0.00667	0.131484	0.0971	0.530	0.1842	36.1826	26.742	3.5	0.00146	133.432	98.6200
0.235	0.00593	0.162984	0.1204	0.535	0.1818	37.0976	27.418	3.6	0.00135	133.573	98.7238
0.240	0.00630	0.193559	0.1430	0.540	0.1783	37.9979	28.084	3.7	0.00123	133.702	98.8192
0.245	0.00723	0.227384	0.1680	0.545	0.1754	38.8821	28.737	3.8	0.00111	133.819	98.9056
0.250	0.00704	0.263059	0.1944	0.550	0.1725	39.7519	29.380	3.9	0.00103	133.926	98.9847
0.255	0.0104	0.306659	0.226	0.555	0.1720	40.6131	30.017	4.0	0.00095	134.025	99.0579
0.260	0.0130	0.365159	0.269	0.560	0.1695	41.4669	30.648	4.1	0.00087	134.116	99.1252
0.265	0.0185	0.443909	0.328	0.565	0.1705	42.3169	31.276	4.2	0.00078	134.198	99.1861
0.270	0.0232	0.548159	0.405	0.570	0.1712	43.1711	31.907	4.3	0.00071	134.273	99.2412
0.275	0.0204	0.657159	0.485	0.575	0.1719	44.0289	32.541	4.4	0.00065	134.341	99.2915
0.280	0.0222	0.763659	0.564	0.580	0.1715	44.8874	33.176	4.5	0.00059	134.403	99.3373
0.285	0.0315	0.897909	0.663	0.585	0.1712	45.7441	33.809	4.6	0.00053	134.459	99.3787
0.290	0.0482	1.09715	0.810	0.590	0.1700	46.5971	34.439	4.7	0.00048	134.509	99.4160
0.295	0.0584	1.36365	1.007	0.595	0.1682	47.4426	35.064	4.8	0.00045	134.556	99.4504
0.300	0.0514	1.63815	1.210	0.600	0.1666	48.2796	35.683	4.9	0.00041	134.599	99.482195
0.305	0.0603	1.91740	1.417	0.605	0.1647	49.1079	36.295	5.0	0.0003830	134.63905	99.511500
0.310	0.0689	2.24040	1.655	0.610	0.1635	49.9284	36.902	6.0	0.0001750	134.91805	99.717708
0.315	0.0764	2.60365	1.924	0.620	0.1602	51.5469	38.098	7.0	0.0000990	135.05505	99.818965
0.320	0.0830	3.00215	2.218	0.630	0.1570	53.1329	39.270	8.0	0.0000600	135.13455	99.877723
0.325	0.0975	3.45340	2.552	0.640	0.1544	54.6899	40.421	9.0	0.0000380	135.18355	99.913939
0.330	0.1059	3.96190	2.928	0.650	0.1511	56.2174	41.550	10.0	0.0000250	135.21505	99.937220
0.335	0.1081	4.49690	3.323	0.660	0.1486	57.7159	42.657	11.0	0.0000170	135.23605	99.952742
0.340	0.1074	5.03565	3.721	0.670	0.1456	59.1869	43.744	12.0	0.0000120	135.25055	99.963458
0.345	0.1069	5.57140	4.117	0.680	0.1427	60.6284	44.810	13.0	0.0000087	135.26090	99.971108
0.350	0.1093	6.11190	4.517	0.690	0.1402	62.0429	45.855	14.0	0.0000055	135.26800	99.976356
0.355	0.1083	6.65590	4.919	0.700	0.1369	63.4284	46.879	15.0	0.0000049	135.27320	99.980199
0.360	0.1068	7.19365	5.316	0.710	0.1344	64.7849	47.882	16.0	0.0000038	135.27755	99.983414
0.365	0.1132	7.74365	5.723	0.720	0.1314	66.1139	48.864	17.0	0.0000031	135.28100	99.985964
0.370	0.1181	8.32190	6.150	0.730	0.1290	67.4159	49.826	18.0	0.0000024	135.28375	99.987997
0.375	0.1157	8.90640	6.582	0.740	0.1260	68.6909	50.769	19.0	0.0000020	135.28595	99.989623
0.380	0.1120	9.47565	7.003	0.750	0.1235	69.9384	51.691	20.0	0.0000016	135.28775	99.990953
0.385	0.1098	10.0301	7.413	0.800	0.1107	75.7934	56.018	25.0	0.000000610	135.29328	99.995036
0.390	0.1098	10.5791	7.819	0.850	0.0988	81.0309	59.889	30.0	0.000000300	135.29555	99.996718
0.395	0.1189	11.1509	8.241	0.900	0.0889	85.7234	63.358	35.0	0.000000160	135.29670	99.997568
0.400	0.1429	11.8054	8.725	0.950	0.0835	90.0334	66.543	40.0	0.000000094	135.29734	99.998037
0.405	0.1644	12.5736	9.293	1.000	0.0746	93.9859	69.464	50.0	0.000000038	135.29800	99.998525
0.410	0.1751	13.4224	9.920	1.100	0.0592	100.675	74.409	60.0	0.000000019	135.29828	99.998736
0.415	0.1774	14.3036	10.571	1.200	0.0484	106.055	78.385	80.0	0.000000007	135.29854	99.998928
0.420	0.1747	15.1839	11.222	1.300	0.0396	110.455	81.637	100.0	0.000000003	135.29864	99.999002
0.425	0.1693	16.0439	11.858	1.400	0.0336	114.115	84.342	1000.0	0	135.30000	100.000000
0.430	0.1639	16.8769	12.473	1.500	0.0287	117.230	86.645				
0.435	0.1663	17.7024	13.083	1.600	0.0244	119.885	88.607				
0.440	0.1810	18.5706	13.725	1.700	0.0202	122.115	90.255				
0.445	0.1922	19.5036	14.415	1.800	0.0159	123.920	91.589				
0.450	0.2006	20.4856	15.140	1.900	0.0126	125.345	92.642				
0.455	0.2057	21.5014	15.891	2.000	0.0103	126.490	93.489				
0.460	0.2066	22.5321	16.653	2.100	0.0090	127.455	94.202				
0.465	0.2048	23.5606	17.413	2.200	0.0079	128.300	94.826				
0.470	0.2033	24.5809	18.167	2.300	0.0068	129.035	95.370				

TOTAL MONTHLY SOLAR RADIATION IN A CLOUDLESS SKY

Total radiation is the sum of the direct and scattered radiation that strikes the earth's surface. It is influenced by the degree of cloudiness, atmospheric transparency, duration of sunshine, and height of elevation at which the measurements are taken. Deviations from values in this table are bound to occur; however, it is believed that the deviations do not exceed ±10% for the summer months and ±15% for the winter months. The radiation units in this table are kcal/cm².

$\phi°$	January	February	March	April	May	June	July	August	September	October	November	December
90 N	0	0	0.1	10.0	21.9	26.0	23.8	12.9	2.4	0	0	0
85	0	0	0.7	10.2	21.8	25.8	23.4	13.1	3.0	0	0	0
80	0	0	2.4	10.8	21.4	25.2	23.0	13.4	4.3	0.5	0	0
75	0	0.5	4.0	11.7	21.0	24.5	22.2	13.8	5.8	1.3	0	0
70	0	1.6	6.0	13.1	20.5	23.6	21.2	14.6	7.5	2.7	0.5	0
65	0.7	2.8	8.0	14.5	20.1	22.8	21.0	15.6	9.5	4.3	1.4	0.2
60	1.8	4.3	9.9	16.0	20.8	22.9	21.4	16.7	11.3	6.1	2.6	1.1
55	3.1	6.2	11.7	17.3	21.4	23.4	21.9	17.9	12.9	7.8	4.0	2.3
50	4.8	8.2	13.3	18.5	22.2	23.7	22.6	19.1	14.4	9.7	5.8	3.9
45	6.7	10.3	14.8	19.5	22.6	23.9	23.2	20.1	15.8	11.5	7.8	5.9
40	8.8	12.2	16.4	20.3	23.0	24.0	23.4	20.9	17.0	13.2	9.7	7.7
35	10.7	14.0	17.6	21.0	23.0	24.0	23.6	21.6	18.1	14.7	11.4	9.7
30	12.5	15.5	18.6	21.4	23.0	23.8	23.4	21.8	19.1	16.1	13.1	11.5
25	14.1	16.8	19.5	21.6	23.0	23.4	23.1	21.8	19.8	17.4	14.6	13.1
20	15.5	17.9	20.2	21.6	22.5	22.8	22.6	21.6	20.4	18.5	16.1	14.7
15	16.9	19.0	20.8	21.4	21.9	22.0	21.9	21.2	20.9	19.3	17.4	16.1
10	18.1	19.8	21.1	21.2	21.2	21.0	21.1	20.6	21.2	20.1	18.5	17.5
5	19.3	20.4	21.4	21.0	20.2	19.9	20.0	20.0	21.3	20.6	19.5	18.8
0	20.2	20.9	21.5	20.4	19.3	18.8	19.1	19.3	21.2	21.2	20.4	19.2
5 S	20.1	21.4	21.4	19.9	18.3	17.6	17.9	18.3	20.8	21.4	21.8	21.0
10	22.0	21.8	21.1	19.2	17.7	16.3	16.3	17.3	20.4	21.4	21.8	22.0
15	22.6	22.0	20.6	18.3	16.0	14.9	15.4	16.1	19.7	21.3	22.4	22.9
20	23.2	22.0	20.0	17.2	14.7	13.4	13.8	14.9	18.9	21.0	22.6	23.6
25	23.6	22.0	19.4	16.0	13.0	12.0	12.6	13.6	18.0	20.6	23.0	24.1
30	23.9	21.8	18.6	14.9	11.9	10.6	11.1	12.1	17.0	20.1	23.0	24.6
35	24.0	21.3	17.6	13.6	10.4	9.0	9.6	10.6	15.9	19.5	23.0	25.0
40	24.0	20.6	16.4	12.2	8.7	7.3	8.1	9.0	14.3	18.7	22.8	25.2
45	24.0	19.9	15.2	10.7	7.1	5.5	6.3	7.3	13.4	17.7	22.4	25.2
50	23.6	18.9	13.8	9.2	5.4	3.8	4.6	5.5	12.0	16.6	21.8	25.0
55	23.2	17.8	12.3	7.5	3.8	2.3	3.0	3.8	10.3	15.4	21.2	24.6

TOTAL MONTHLY SOLAR RADIATION IN A CLOUDLESS SKY (Continued)

$\varphi°$	January	February	March	April	May	June	July	August	September	October	November	December
60	22.6	16.6	10.8	5.6	2.4	1.0	1.6	2.3	8.5	14.1	21.0	24.4
65	22.4	15.3	9.1	3.9	1.1	0.1	0.4	1.0	6.7	12.6	20.8	24.5
70	22.6	14.2	7.3	2.2	0.1	0	0	0	5.0	11.4	21.0	24.9
75	23.2	13.4	5.7	0.9	0	0	0	0	3.5	10.4	21.2	25.4
80	24.0	12.8	4.3	0	0	0	0	0	2.1	9.7	21.9	26.0
85	24.6	12.4	2.9	0	0	0	0	0	0.9	9.2	22.4	26.6
90	24.9	12.3	1.7	0	0	0	0	0	0	9.0	22.6	27.0

ELEMENTS PRESENT IN SOLUTION IN SEA WATER EXCLUDING DISSOLVED GASES

Reprinted by permission of the publishers from "The Oceans" by Sverdrup, Johnson, and Fleming. Copyright, 1942, by Prentice-Hall, Inc.

Element	Concentration (grams/metric ton) or parts per million
Cl	18,980
Na	10,561
Mg	1,272
S	884
Ca	400
K	380
Br	65
C (inorganic)	28
Sr	13
(SiO_2)	0.01–7.0
B	4.6
Si	0.02–4.0
C (organic)	1.2–3.0
Al	0.16–1.9
F	1.4
N (as nitrate)	0.001–0.7
N (as organic nitrogen)	0.03–0.2
Rb	0.2
Li	0.1
P (as phosphate)	>0.001–0.10
Ba	0.05
I	0.05
N (as nitrite)	0.0001–0.05
N (as ammonia)	>0.005–0.05
As (as arsenite)	0.003–0.024
Fe	0.002–0.02
P (as organic phosphorus)	0–0.016
Zn	0.005–0.014
Cu	0.001–0.09
Mn	0.001–0.01
Pb	0.004–0.005
Se	0.004
Sn	0.003
Cs	0.002 (approximate)
U	0.00015–0.0016
Mo	0.0003–0.002
Ga	0.0005
Ni	0.0001–0.0005
Th	<0.0005
Ce	0.0004
V	0.0003
La	0.0003
Y	0.0003
Hg	0.00003
Ag	0.00015–0.0003
Bi	0.0002
Co	0.0001
Sc	0.00004
Au	0.000004–0.000008
Fe (in true solution)	$<10^{-9}$
Ra	2.10^{-11}–3.10^{-10}
Ge	Present
Ti	Present
W	Present
Cd	Present in marine organisms
Cr	Present in marine organisms
Tl	Present in marine organisms
Sb	Present in marine organisms
Zr	Present in marine organisms
Pt	Present in marine organisms

THE pH OF NATURAL MEDIA AND ITS RELATION TO THE PRECIPITATION OF HYDROXIDES

Reprinted from "Principles of Geochemistry" (1952) with the permission of Brian Mason, author, and John Wiley and Sons, publishers.

pH	Precipitation of hydroxides	Natural media	pH
11 ⎫	Magnesium		11
10 ⎭		Alkali soils	10
9 ⎫	Bivalent manganese		⎰9
8 ⎭		Seawater	⎱8
7	Bivalent iron	River water	7
6	Zinc copper	Rain water	6
5	Aluminum		5
4		Peat water	4
3 ⎫	Trivalent iron	Mine waters	3
2 ⎭		Acid thermal springs	⎰2
1			⎱1

PROPERTIES OF THE EARTH'S ATMOSPHERE AT ELEVATIONS UP TO 160 KILOMETERS

The average atmosphere up to 160 km based on pressure and density data obtained on rocket flights above White Sands, New Mexico.
Havens, Koll, and LaGow, Journal of Geophysical Research, March, 1952.

Altitude km above sea level	Pressure mm Hg	Density gm/meters³	Temperatures °K (N_2, O_2) M = 29	Temperatures °K (N_2, O) M = 24	Velocity of Sound m. sec	Mean Free Path cm (N_2)
0	760	1220	290		345	6.5×10^{-6}
10	210	425	230		310	1.9×10^{-5}
20	42	92	210		295	8.6×10^{-5}
30	9.5	19	235		315	4.2×10^{-4}
40	2.4	4.3	260		325	1.8×10^{-3}
50	7.5×10^{-1}	1.3	270		330	6.1×10^{-3}
60	2.1×10^{-1}	3.8×10^{-1}	260		325	2.1×10^{-2}
70	5.4×10^{-2}	1.2×10^{-1}	210		295	6.6×10^{-1}
80	1.0×10^{-2}	2.5×10^{-2}	190		280	3.2×10^{-1}
90	1.9×10^{-3}	4.0×10^{-3}	210		295	2.0
100	4.2×10^{-4}	8.0×10^{-4}	240		315	10.0
110	1.2×10^{-4}	2.0×10^{-4}	270	220	330	40.0
120	3.5×10^{-5}	5.0×10^{-5}	330	270	370	1.5×10^2
130	1.5×10^{-5}	2.0×10^{-5}	390	320	400	4.0×10^2
140	7×10^{-6}	7.0×10^{-6}	450	370	430	1.0×10^3
150	3×10^{-6}	3.0×10^{-6}	510	420	460	2.5×10^3
160	2×10^{-6}	1.5×10^{-6}	570	470	480	5.0×10^3

VELOCITY OF SEISMIC WAVES

Depth km	Longitudinal or condensational km/sec.	Transverse or distortional km/sec.
0–20	5.4 –5.6	3.2
20–45	6.25–6.75	3.5
1300	12.5	6.9
2400	13.5	7.5

ATMOSPHERIC AND METEOROLOGICAL DATA

Total mass of the atmosphere, estimated by Ekholm, 5.2×10^{21} g, 11.4×10^{18} pounds, 5.70×10^{16} tons.
Evidence of extent: twilight, 63 km, 39 mi.: meteors, 200 km, 124 mi.: aurora 44–360 km, 27–224 mi.

*Distance to Earth.

STANDARD ATMOSPHERE

U. S. Extension to International Civil Aviation Organization Standard Atmosphere, 1958

The atmosphere was classified in 1958 into three altitude regions designated as

a. Standard   0 to 32   standard geopotential kilometers
b. Tentative   32 to 75   „   „   „
c. Speculative 75 to 300   „   „   „

Properties of the atmosphere were calculated as functions of geometric altitude as well as geopotential, the potential being established for the latitude where the acceleration of gravity has a sea-level value of 9.80665 meters per second per second. Symbols and abbreviations used in these tables are as follows:

H – Altitude in geopotential measure
L_M = Molecular-scale-temperature gradient
M = Mean molecular weight of air
m = Meter
m' = Standard geopotential meter
P = Pressure
ρ = Mass density
T = Temperature in absolute thermodynamic scales
T_M = Molecular-scale temperature in absolute thermodynamic scales
Z = Altitude in geometric measure

Relationship between Geopotential and Geometric Altitude

The concept originally introduced by Bjerknes expresses vertical displacement in units of geopotential. Geopotential at an altitude Z is the potential energy of a unit mass at that altitude relative to the potential energy of that same unit mass at sea level. *Geopotential H* of a point at altitude Z may be rigorously defined as the increase in potential energy of a unit mass lifted from mean sea level to Z against the local force of gravity. Mathematically this definition becomes,

$$GH = \frac{\Delta E}{m} = \int_o^Z g(Z)\mathrm{d}Z$$

where
- ΔE = increase in potential energy in joules,
- m = mass of the body in kilograms,
- $g(Z)$ = acceleration of gravity in m sec^{-2} expressed as a function of Z,
- H = geopotential of a point at altitude Z,
- G = proportionality factor depending on the units of H.

Solving this equation for H in terms of Z yields:

$$H = \frac{1}{G} \int_o^Z g(Z)\mathrm{d}Z.$$

The differential form of this relationship to be used later is

$$G\mathrm{d}H = g(Z)\mathrm{d}Z.$$

The basic unit of geopotential in these tables is one *standard geopotential* meter, m', which is defined as 9.80665 m^2 sec^{-2} and which is equal to the vertical distance through which a one-kilogram mass must be lifted against the local force of gravity to increase its potential energy by 9.80665 joules. If the acceleration of gravity were constant at 9.80665 m sec^{-2} over an altitude interval of one geometric meter, one *standard geopotential* meter would be exactly equal to one geometric meter; this condition is true within two parts in a million at 45° 32′ 33″ at sea level, where g is equal to 9.80665 m sec^{-2}.

Relationship between Temperature and Molecular-scale Temperature

The molecular-scale temperature introduced by Minzner and Ripley is the defining atmospheric property of this Extension. This property is a composite of temperature and molecular weight, and is defined by the equation:

$$T_M = \left(\frac{T}{M} \right) M_o$$

where
- T = temperature in the absolute thermodynamic scales,
- T_M = molecular-scale temperature in the absolute thermodynamic scales,
- M = molecular weight (nondimensional),
- M_o = sea-level value of molecular weight.

No direct measurements of temperature have been made at altitudes above those which are reached by balloons; instead, the temperature is derived from values of the velocity of sound, or by substitution of measured pressures or densities into the barometric equation. The molecular-scale temperature can be derived in this way without specifying the molecular weight, whereas the temperature can be derived only if the molecular weight is known. Since the molecular weight is not well known at altitudes above 90 km, the molecular-scale temperature is more precisely known than temperature. Thus, the introduction of molecular-scale temperature increases the validity of some of the tabulated properties while simultaneously decreasing the complexity of the mathematics relating the basic atmospheric properties. The use of molecular-scale temperature also avoids the necessity for changing the defined atmosphere each time new values for the inadequately known molecular-weight distribution may be adopted.

SEA LEVEL ATMOSPHERIC COMPOSITION FOR
A DRY ATMOSPHERE[a]

Constituent gas	Molecular fraction, %	Molecular weight $(0 = 15.999_4)$
Nitrogen (N_2)	78.09	14.0067
Oxygen (O_2)	20.95	31.998_8
Argon (A)	0.93	39.94_8
Carbon dioxide (CO_2)	0.03	44.01
Neon (Ne)	1.8×10^{-3}	20.117_9
Helium (He)	5.24×10^{-4}	4.00260
Krypton (Kr)	1.0×10^{-4}	83.80
Hydrogen (H_2)	5.0×10^{-5}	2.016
Xenon (Xe)	8.0×10^{-6}	131.30
Ozone (O_3)	1.0×10^{-6}	47.999_4
Radon (Rn)	6.0×10^{-18}	222

[a]These values are taken as standard and do not necessarily indicate the exact condition of the atmosphere. Ozone and radon particularly are known to vary at sea level and above, but these variations would not appreciably affect the value of M_O.

SEA LEVEL VALUES OF ICAO ATMOSPHERE

Property	Metric units
Collision frequency	6.9204049×10^9 sec^{-1}
Conductivity, thermal	2.5339053×10^{-2} J m^{-1} sec^{-1} ($^\circ$K)$^{-1}$
Conductivity, thermal	6.0532182×10^{-6} kcal m^{-1} sec^{-1} ($^\circ$K)$^{-1}$
Conductivity, thermal	2.5838643×10^{-3} kgf[a] sec^{-1} ($^\circ$K)$^{-1}$
Density, mass	1.2250140 kg m^{-3}
Density, mass	0.12491666 kgf sec^2 m^{-4}
Gravitational acceleration	9.80665 m sec^{-2}
Kinematic viscosity	1.4607413×10^{-5} m^2 sec^{-1}
Mean free path	6.6317223×10^{-8} m
Molar volume	23.645444 m^3 (kg-mol)$^{-1}$
Molar volume	231.88259 m^3 [(kgf sec^2 m^{-1})-mol]
Molecular weight	28.966 (dimensionless)
Number density	2.5475521×10^{25} m^{-3}
Particle speed	458.94204 m sec^{-1}
Pressure	0.760 m Hg
Pressure	1,013.2500 mbar
Pressure	101,325.00 nt m^{-2}
Pressure	10,332.275 kgf m^{-2}
Scale height	8,434.4134 m
Sound speed	340,29205 m sec^{-1}
Specific weight	12.013284 kg m^{-2} sec^{-2}
Specific weight	1.2250140 kgf m^{-3}
Temperature	15.0°C
Temperature, absolute	288.16 K
Temperature, molecular scale	288.16 K
Viscosity, coefficient of	1.7894285×10^{-5} kg m^{-1} sec^{-1}
Viscosity, coefficient of	1.8247093×10^{-6} kgf sec m^{-2}

[a]kgf = kilogram (force)

STANDARD ATMOSPHERE

Nature of Ions in Unpolluted Air

Initially, all molecules are ionized with equal probability according to their abundance. After a sequence of charge transfer, molecular switching reactions, etc., these ions transform within less than 1 μs into the "fast ions" with the following "core composition:"

Dominant positive ions: $(NH_4)^+ \cdot (NH_3)_l \cdot (H_2O)_n$ $0 < H \gtrsim 25$ km

                              $(H_3O)^+ \cdot (H_2O)_n$ $25 \gtrsim H < 90$ km

the n, l depending on atmospheric temperature, water vapor concentration, and ammonia concentration;

Dominant negative ions: $O_2^- \cdot (H_2O)_m$ and $CO_4^- \cdot (H_2O)_m$ $H < 25$ km

the m depending on temperature and the ratio of water vapor to carbon dioxide concentration. Collisional interaction of these ions with atmospheric trace gases (with permanent dipoles or high polarizability) will lead to larger cluster ions through attachment and detachment reactions around the "core ion."

Compiled by V. A. Mohnen.

STANDARD ATMOSPHERE (Continued)

Abbreviated Metric Table of the U. S. Extension to the ICAO Standard Atmosphere

H m'	Z m	L_M °K m'$^{-1}$	T_M °K	T °K	M	P mb	ρ kg m^{-3}
−5,000	−4,996.070		320.66	320.66	28.966	1.7776 × 10³	1.9312
		−0.0065					
0	0		288.16	288.16	28.966	1.01325 × 10³	1.2250
		−0.0065					
11,000	11,019.067		216.66	216.66	28.966	2.2632 × 10²	3.6391 × 10⁻¹
		zero					
20,000	20,063.124		216.66	216.66	28.966	5.4748 × 10¹	8.8034 × 10⁻²
		zero					
25,000	25,098.710		216.66	216.66	28.966	2.4886 × 10¹	4.0016 × 10⁻²
		+0.0030					
32,000	32,161.906		237.66	237.66	28.966	8.6776 × 10⁰	1.2721 × 10⁻²
		+0.0030					
47,000	47,350.101		282.66	282.66	28.966	1.2044 × 10⁰	1.4845 × 10⁻³
		zero					
53,000	53,445.620		282.66	282.66	28.966	5.8320 × 10⁻¹	7.1881 × 10⁻⁴
		−0.0039					
75,000	75,895.488		196.86	196.86	28.966	2.452 × 10⁻²	4.339 × 10⁻⁵
		zero					
90,000	91,292.601		196.86	196.86	28.966	1.815 × 10⁻³	3.213 × 10⁻⁶
		+0.0035					
126,000	128,548.193		322.86	273.6	24.54	1.451 × 10⁻⁵	1.566 × 10⁻⁸
		+0.0100					
175,000	179,954.614		812.86	669.0	23 34	6.190 × 10⁻⁷	2.655 × 10⁻¹⁰
		+0.0058					
300,000	314,862.257		1,537.86	973.5	18.34	1.447 × 10⁻⁸	3.279 × 10⁻¹²

Abbreviated English Table of the U. S. Extension to the ICAO Standard Atmosphere

H ft'	Z ft	L_M °R ft'$^{-1}$	T_M °R	T °R	M	P lb ft^{-2}	ρ slugs ft^{-3}
−16,404.199	−16,391.307		577.188	577.188	28.966	3.7110 × 10³	3.7457 × 10⁻³
		−0.003566160					
0	0		518.688	518.688	28.966	2.1162 × 10³	2.3769 × 10⁻³
		−0.003566160					
36,089.239	36,151.798		389.988	389.988	28.966	4.7268 × 10²	7.0611 × 10⁻⁴
		zero					
65,616.798	65,823.897		389.988	389.988	28.966	1.1548 × 10²	1.7251 × 10⁻⁴
		zero					
82,020.997	82,344.849		389.988	389.988	28.966	3.1975 × 10¹	7.7644 × 10⁻⁵
		+0.001645920					
104,986.877	105,518.055		427.788	427.788	28.966	1.8124 × 10¹	2.4682 × 10⁻⁵
		+0.001645920					
154,199.475	155,348.103		508.788	508.788	28.966	2.5155 × 10⁰	2.8803 × 10⁻⁶
		zero					
173,884.514	175,346.523		508.788	508.788	28.966	1.2180 × 10⁰	1.3947 × 10⁻⁶
		−0.002139696					
246,062.992	249,000.945		354.348	354.348	28.966	5.121 × 10⁻²	8.420 × 10⁻⁸
		zero					
295,275.591	299,516.408		354.348	354.348	28.966	3.792 × 10⁻³	6.234 × 10⁻⁹
		+0.001920240					
413,385.827	421,746.041		581.148	492.4	24.54	3.031 × 10⁻⁵	3.038 × 10⁻¹¹
		+0.005486400					
574,146.982	590,402.278		1,463.148	1,204.000	23.84	1.293 × 10⁻⁶	5.147 × 10⁻¹³
		+0.003182112					
984,251.969	1,033,012.654		2,768.148	1,752.000	18.3	3.023 × 10⁻⁸	6.362 × 10⁻¹⁵

TEMPERATURE VS ALTITUDE

MEAN MOLECULAR WEIGHT VS ALTITUDE

PRESSURE VS. ALTITUDE

DENSITY VS. ALTITUDE

SPEED OF SOUND VS. ALTITUDE

MEAN FREE PATH VS. ALTITUDE

COLLISION FREQUENCY VS ALTITUDE

MEAN PARTICLE SPEED
VS. ALTITUDE

ACCELERATION OF GRAVITY
VS. ALTITUDE

Angular Radius of Halos and Rainbows

Coronae due to small water drops................. 1° to 10°
Small halo, due to 60° angles of ice crystals....... 22°
Large halo, due to 90° angles of ice crystals....... 46°
Rainbow, primary.................................... 41° 20′
Rainbow, secondary.................................. 52° 15′

Solar Constant

The energy falling on one sq. cm. area at normal incidence, outside the earth's atmosphere, at the mean distance of the earth from the sun equals 2.00 small calories per minute. This value varies ±2%.

COMPONENTS OF ATMOSPHERIC AIR
(Exclusive of water vapor)

Constituent	Content (per cent) by volume	Content (ppm) by volume
N_2	78.084 ± 0.004	
O_2	20.946 ± 0.002	
CO_2	0.033 ± 0.001	
A	0.934 ± 0.001	
Ne		18.18 ± 0.04
He		5.24 ± 0.004
Kr		1.14 ± 0.01
Xe		0.087 ± 0.001
H_2		0.5
CH_4		2
N_2O		0.5 ± 0.1

MOLECULAR CONSTANTS

The following gives the arithmetical average velocity, the mean free path, molecular diameter and collision frequency for the temperatures indicated and at standard pressure, 760 mm Hg. except as otherwise stated.

Gas	Average velocity in cm/sec.		Mean free path in cm at 75 cm Hg.		
			Boltzmann		Meyer
	0° C	20° C	0° C	20° C	20° C
Air...........	447×10^2	463×10^2			
Ammonia...........	583	604	5.92×10^{-6}	6.60×10^{-6}	5.83×10^{-6}
Argon...........	381	395	8.98	9.88	8.73
Carbon monoxide......	454	471	8.46	9.23	8.16
Carbon dioxide......	362	376	5.56	6.15	5.44
Helium...........	1208	1252	25.25	27.45	33.10
Hydrogen...........	1696	1755	16.00	17.44	15.40
Krypton...........	263	272	9.5		
Mercury...........	170	176	(14.70)	(13.0)	
Neon...........	538	557			
Nitrogen...........	454	471	8.50	9.29	8.21
Oxygen...........	425	440	9.05	9.93	8.78
Water vapor........	566	587			
Xenon...........	210	218	5.6		

Gas	Collision frequency 20° C	Molecular diameter, cm		
		From viscosity	From van der Waal's equation	From heat conductivity
Ammonia...............	9150×10^6	2.97×10^{-8}	3.08×10^{-8}	
Argon...............	4000	2.88	2.94	2.86×10^{-8}
Carbon monoxide...........	5100	3.19	3.12	
Carbon dioxide...........	6120	3.34	3.23	3.40
Helium...............	4540	1.90	2.65	2.30
Hydrogen...............	10060	2.40	2.34	2.32
Krypton...............			(3.69)	3.14
Mercury...............			3.01	
Nitrogen...............	5070	3.15	3.15	3.53
Oxygen...............	4430	2.98	2.92	
Xenon...............			4.02	3.42

ATMOSPHERIC ELECTRICITY

HANS DOLEZALEK

Fair-weather electricity. Electrically, a fair-weather situation is given when the activity of local generators is low. Usually, this is supposed to be the case when there are no hydrometeors (rain, snow, hail, fog, droplets) and no highly charged dust in the air, cloudiness not more than 3/10 and not concentrated overhead, wind speed below 5 m/s (no white caps on sea). Under these conditions the atmospheric electric parameters over land have the average or typical values as shown in the table.

The "Classical Picture" is a group of hypotheses to explain the electrification of the atmosphere, the main hypothesis assuming that the ionosphere is charged by the thunderstorms to a high positive potential everywhere the same but varying in time. The classical picture is probably fundamentally correct but it has never been proven and probably requires supplements and corrections. In particular, extraterrestrial influences probably have to be admitted.

ELECTRICAL PARAMETERS OF THE CLEAR (FAIR-WEATHER) ATMOSPHERE, PERTINENT TO THE CLASSICAL PICTURE OF ATM. ELECTRICITY

All currents and fields listed are part of the global circuit, i.e., circuits of local generators are not included. Values are subject to variations due to latitude and altitude of the point of observation above sea level, locality with respect to sources of disturbances, meteorological and climatological factors, and man-made changes.

Part of atmosphere for which the values are calculated (Elements are in free, cloudless atmosphere):	Currents, I, in A, and current densities, i, in A/m²	Potential Differences, U, in V; field strength E in V/m; U = 0 at sea level	Resistances, R, in Ω; Columnar resistances, R_c, in Ω m²; and resistivities, ρ, in Ω m	Conductances, G, in Ω^{-1}; Columnar conductances G_c, in $\Omega^{-1} m^{-2}$; total conductivities, γ, in $\Omega^{-1} m^{-1}$	Capacitances, C, in F; Columnar capacitances, C_c, in F m^{-2} and capacitivities, ε, in F m^{-1}	Time constants τ, in seconds
Volume element at about sea level, one cubic meter	$i = 3 \times 10^{-12}$*	$E_0 = 1.2 \times 10^2$*	$\rho_0 = 4 \times 10^{13}$	$\gamma_0 = 2.5 \times 10^{-14}$	$\varepsilon_0 = 8.9 \times 10^{-12}$*	$\tau_0 = 3.6 \times 10^2$
Lower column of 1 m² cross section from sea level to 2 km height	same as above	at upper end: $U_l = 1.8 \times 10^5$	$R_{cl} = 6 \times 10^{16}$	$G_{cl} = 1.7 \times 10^{-17}$	$C_{cl} = 4.4 \times 10^{-15}$	$\tau_{cl} = 2.6 \times 10^2$
Volume element at about 2 km height, 1 m³	same as above	$E_2 = 6.6 \times 10^1$	$\rho_2 = 2.2 \times 10^{13(*)}$	$\gamma_2 = 4.5 \times 10^{-14}$	$\varepsilon_2 = 8.9 \times 10^{-12}$	$\tau_2 = 2 \times 10^2$
Center column of 1 m² cross section from 2 to 12 km	same as above	at upper end: $U_m = 3.15 \times 10^5$	$R_{cm} = 4.5 \times 10^{16}$	$G_{cm} = 5 \times 10^{-17}$	$C_{cm} = 8.8 \times 10^{-16}$	$\tau_{cm} = 1.8 \times 10^1$
Volume element at about 12 km height, 1 m³	same as above	$E_{12} = 4.2 \times 10^0$	$\rho_{12} = 1.3 \times 10^{12(*)}$	$\gamma_{12} = 4.0 \times 10^{-13}$	$\varepsilon_{12} = 8.9 \times 10^{-12}$	$\tau_{12} = 1.2 \times 10^1$
Upper column of 1 m² cross section from 12 to 65 km height	same as above	at upper end: $U_u = 3.5 \times 10^5$	$R_{cu} = 1.5 \times 10^{16}$	$G_{cu} = 2.5 \times 10^{-17}$	$C_{cu} = 1.67 \times 10^{-16}$	$\tau_{cu} = 6.7 \times 10^0$
Whole column of 1 m² cross section from 0 to 65 km height	same as above	at upper end: $U = 3.5 \times 10^5$	$R_c = 1.2 \times 10^{17}$	$G_c = 8.3 \times 10^{-18}$	$C_c = 1.36 \times 10^{-16}$	$\tau_c = 1.64 \times 10^1$
Total spherical capacitor area: 5×10^{14} m²	$1 = 1.5 \times 10^3$	$U = 3.5 \times 10^5$*	$R = 2.4 \times 10^2$	$G = 4.2 \times 10^{-3}$	$C = 6.8 \times 10^{-2}$	$\tau = 1.64 \times 10^1$

Values with a star, *, are rough average values from measurement. A star in parentheses, (*), points to a typical value from one or a few measurements. All other values have been calculated from starred values, under the assumption, that at 2 km 50% and at 12 km 90% of the columnar resistance is reached. Voltage drop along one of the partial columns can be calculated by subtracting the value for the lower column from that of the upper one. Columnar resistances, conductances, and capacitances are valid for that particular part of the column which is indicated at left. Capacitances are calculated with the formula for plate capacitors, and this fact must be considered also for the time constants for columns.

According to measurements, U, the potential difference between 0 m and 65 km may vary by a factor of approx. 2 (two). The total columnar resistance, R_c, is estimated to vary up to a factor of 3 (three), the variation being due to either reduction of conductivity in the exchange layer (about lowest 2 km of this table) or to the presence of high mountains, in both cases the variation is caused in the troposphere. Smaller variations in the stratosphere and mesosphere discussed because of aerosol there. The air-earth current density in fair-weather varies by a factor of 3 to 6 accordingly. Conductivity near the ground varies by a factor of about 3 (three) but only decreasing, increase of conductivity due to extraordinary radioactivity is a singular event. The field strength near the ground varies as a consequence of variations of air-earth current density and conductivity from about 1/3 to about 10 of the value quoted in the table. Conductivity near the ground shows a diurnal and an annual variation which depends strongly on the locality; air-earth current density shows a diurnal and annual variation because the earth-ionosphere potential difference undergoes such variations, and because also the columnar resistance is supposed to have a diurnal and probably an annual variation.

Conductivities and air-earth current densities on high mountains are by factors of up to 10 greater than at sea level. Conductivity decreases when atmospheric humidity increases. Values for space charges not quoted because measurements are too few to allow calculation of average values. Values of parameters over the oceans still rather uncertain.

Ions. Ionization rate at ground level over land: from radioactive substances in the ground: 4.0; from radioactive substances in the air: 4.6; from cosmic radiation 1.5–1.8, total (10.1–10.4) × 10⁶ ion pairs per m³ and sec. Over ocean far from shore: cosmic radiation only, but in spite of smaller ionization over the ocean conductivity is nearly equal to that over land because of longer ion life time (a consequence of smaller aerosol density).

Contribution from radioactive material over land decreases with altitude in the free air, from cosmic radiation increases (up to a certain level) and depends on latitude. Number densities of fast ions over land and ocean average at $(4–5) \times 10^8$ m^{-3}, varying with height by only about one order of magnitude up to ionospheric C-layer. Their life time varies from about 10 s in aerosol-rich air to 300 s in pure air. All values quoted are approximate averages.

Ion classes in lower atmosphere	Designation	Mobilities in m²/(Vs)	Size ranges, radii in m
Primary atmospheric ions:	Fast ions (also called small or light ions)	$k > 10^{-4}$	$r < 6.6 \times 10^{-10}$
Secondary atmospheric ions: slow ions (also called large or heavy ions	Fast intermediate ions	$10^{-4} > k \geq 10^{-2}$	$6.6 \times 10^{-10} < r < 7.8 \times 10^{-9}$
	Slow intermediate ions	$10^{-2} > k \geq 10^{-1}$	$7.8 \times 10^{-9} < r < 2.5 \times 10^{-8}$
	Langevin ions	$10^{-1} > k \geq 2.5$	$2.5 \times 10^{-8} < r < 5.7 \times 10^{-8}$
	Ultralarge ions	$k < 2.5$	$5.7 \times 10^{-8} < r < 10^{-7}$

Electric conduction current in atmosphere carried nearly exclusively by the fast ions because number densities of the intermediate ions generally one order of magnitude smaller.

Nature of ions in pure air ("Standard Atmosphere"): initially all molecules are ionized with equal probability according to their abundance, but within nanoseconds these ions transform into the "fast ions" with the following composition:

positive ions: $(H_3O)^+(H_2O)_n$

negative ions: $O_2^-(H_2O)_n$, or $CO_4^-(H_2O)_n$;

the n depending on atmospheric temperature and water vapor pressure, varies very often in the life time of an ion. Most probable values of n for positive ions: troposphere 6 or 7, stratosphere 4, mesosphere 3 or 2.

Thunderstorm electricity. Clouds are generally more or less electrified. In thunderstorms, mechanical, thermodynamical and maybe chemical energy is transformed into electrical energy (generator) with separate poles. Most thunderstorms have during most of their life time (phases: development 10–20, mature 15–30, decay 30 min) a positive charge center above and a negative one below, probably another positive one near the base. Electrification occurs (according to processes not yet fully understood) in periods of tens of minutes and spaces of about 1 km³, and there may be several such centers in a cloud. Thunderclouds mostly reach beyond freezing level, in moderate latitudes from about 3 to 10 km, in the tropics often up to 16–20 km, seldom more. 1000 to 2000 thunderstorms active at any time. Updrafts in storms up to 30 m/s. Water content 10^8–10^9 kg. Total energy about 10^{15} joule, electric energy 10^{12}–10^{13} J. Electric potential vs. ground at negative and positive charge centers: minus and plus 10–100 MV, resp.; field strength not yet measured reliably. Electric resistances of an atmospheric vertical column of 50 km² cross section: several 100 MΩ each between ground and negative center, negative and positive center, and positive center and ionosphere. Total current flowing upwards towards ionosphere derived from (still unsufficient) measurements of current densities: 0.5–2 A per thunderstorm cell. Current below cloud carried by conduction by fair-weather ions, conduction by corona ions, convection by vertical winds, precipitation, and lightning. Field strength at ground under storm: varying in strength and polarity, often 10 kV/m and more.

Atmospheric Electricity by H. Israël. Tabular material reproduced from this publication. Permission received from Israel Program for Scientific Translations.

Lightning, during its life time of up to a second, undergoes numerous variations and all its parameters change by orders of magnitude in these. Also, there are many different forms of lightning. Even disregarding particular forms such as ball lightning, we find at least four classification criteria which, taken together, give a great number of differences: intercloud, intracloud, and cloud-to-ground discharges and combinations of these: short high-current and long low-current flashes; lightnings beginning in the cloud and moving towards ground, and lightnings moving upwards; lightnings lowering positive and lightnings lowering negative charges, and those which do first the one and then the other. The usual cloud-to-ground lightning begins with a stepped leader of low luminosity, probably a meter or so in diameter, followed by a return stroke with a diameter in the order of centimeters, temperatures of about 30,000 K, and pressures of up to a MN/m². After this, a dart leader may again move downwards causing a second return stroke. This may repeat several times (multiple stroke flash).

Typical voltage drop in ground or other conductors after lightning impact in the neighborhood: 10 kV/m (dangerous!).

Intracloud lightnings observed with up to 100 km length.

There are probably about 100 lightnings occurring on earth at any time. Lightning frequency over oceans only about 1/10 from that over continents. Diurnal variations on continents show maximum in late afternoon and early evening, over oceans late evening until after midnight.

Energy delivered to a stroke about 100 kJ/m.

Upward lightnings initiated mostly from high masts and towers and mountains. Over flat terrain mostly downward flashes, probably generally met by short (decameters) upwards moving darts.

Height from which a lightning points at a target probably several decameters, depending on conductivity distribution in ground.

Long-lasting low-current (hundreds of amperes) flashes more dangerous to man and more damaging to objects (forest fires) than short high-current flashes.

Sferics, etc. Lightning generates a sudden variation of electric field (decreasing with r^{-3}), a quickly varying magnetic field (r^{-2}) and an electromagnetic radiation (r^{-1}) from a few hertz (in case of excitation of ionosphere-earth resonance range around the globe) through VLF (maximum intensity, range up to 10 Mm and more depending on direction and time of day) into VHF. Main frequency of thunder about 200 Hz.

Data for a normal cloud-to-ground lightning discharge bringing negative charge to earth. The values listed are intended to convey a rough feeling for the various physical parameters of lightning. No great accuracy is claimed since the results of different investigators are often not in good agreement. These values may in fact, depend on the particular environment in which the lightning discharge is generated. The choice of some of the entries in the table is arbitrary.

	Minimum*	Representative	Maximum*
Stepped leader			
Length of step, m	3	50	200
Time interval between steps, μsec	30	50	125
Average velocity of propagation of stepped leader, m/sec†	1.0×10^5	1.5×10^5	2.6×10^6
Charge deposited on stepped-leader channel, coulombs	3	5	20
Dart leader			
Velocity of propagation, m/sec†	1.0×10^6	2.0×10^6	2.1×10^7
Charge deposited on dart-leader channel, coulombs	0.2	1	6
Return stroke‡			
Velocity of propagation, m/sec†	2.0×10^7	5.0×10^7	1.4×10^8
Current rate of increase, kA/μsec§	<1	10	>80
Time to peak current, μsec§	<1	2	30
Peak current, kA§		10–20	110
Time to half of peak current μsec	10	40	250
Charge transferred excluding continuing current, coulombs	0.2	2.5	20
Channel length, km	2	5	14
Lightning flash			
Number of strokes per flash	1	3–4	26
Time interval between strokes in absence of continuing current, msec	3	40	100
Time duration of flash, sec	10^{-2}	0.2	2¶
Charge transferred including continuing current, coulombs	3	25	90

* The words maximum and minimum are used in the sense that most measured values fall between these limits.

† Velocities of propagation are generally determined from photographic data and thus represent "two-dimensional" velocities. Since many lightning flashes are not vertical, values stated are probably slight underestimates of actual values.

‡ First return strokes have slower average velocities of propagation, slower current rates of increase, longer times to current peak, and generally larger charge transfer than subsequent return strokes in a flash.

§ Current measurements are made at the ground.

¶ A lightning flash lasting 15 to 20 sec has been reported by Godlonton (1896).

Lightning by M. A. Uman, Table 1.1, page 4. Tabular material reproduced from this publication. Permission received from McGraw-Hill Book Company.

CRYSTAL IONIC RADII OF THE ELEMENTS

Numerical values of the radii of the ions may vary depending on how they were measured. They may have been calculated from wavefunctions and determined from the lattice spacings or crystal structure of various salts. Different values are obtained depending on the kind of salt used or the method of calculating. Data for many of the rare-earth ions were furnished by F. H. Spedding and K. Gschneidner.

Element	Charge	Atomic number	Radius in A	Element	Charge	Atomic number	Radius in A	Element	Charge	Atomic number	Radius in A
Ac	+3	89	1.18	Fe	+2	26	0.74	Os	+4	76	0.88
Ag	+1	47	1.26		+3		0.64		+6		0.69
	+2		0.89	Fr	+1	87	1.80	P	−3	15	2.12
Al	+3	13	0.51	Ga	+1	31	0.81		+3		0.44
Am	+3	95	1.07		+3		0.62		+5		0.35
	+4		0.92	Gd	+3	64	0.938	Pa	+3	91	1.13
Ar	+1	18	1.54	Ge	−4	32	2.72		+4		0.98
As	−3	33	2.22		+2		0.73		+5		0.89
	+3		0.58		+4		0.53	Pb	+2	82	1.20
	+5		0.46	H	−1	1	1.54		+4		0.84
At	+7	85	0.62	Hf	+4	72	0.78	Pd	+2	46	0.80
Au	+1	79	1.37	Hg	+1	80	1.27		+4		0.65
	+3		0.85		+2		1.10	Pm	+3	61	0.979
B	+1	5	0.35	Ho	+3	67	0.894	Po	+6	84	0.67
	+3		0.23	I	−1	53	2.20	Pr	+3	59	1.013
Ba	+1	56	1.53		+5		0.62		+4		0.90
	+2		1.34		+7		0.50	Pt	+2	78	0.80
Be	+1	4	0.44	In	+3	49	0.81		+4		0.65
	+2		0.35	Ir	+4	77	0.68	Pu	+3	94	1.08
Bi	+1	83	0.98	K	+1	19	1.33		+4		0.93
	+3		0.96	La	+1	57	1.39	Ra	+2	88	1.43
	+5		0.74		+3		1.016	Rb	+1	37	1.47
Br	−1	35	1.96	Li	+1	3	0.68	Re	+4	75	0.72
	+5		0.47	Lu	+3	71	0.85		+7		0.56
	+7		0.39	Mg	+1	12	0.82	Rh	+3	45	0.68
C	−4	6	2.60		+2		0.66	Ru	+4	44	0.67
	+4		0.16	Mn	+2	25	0.80	S	−2	16	1.84
Ca	+1	20	1.18		+3		0.66		+2		2.19
	+2		0.99		+4		0.60		+4		0.37
Cd	+1	48	1.14		+7		0.46		+6		0.30
	+2		0.97	Mo	+1	42	0.93	Sb	−3	51	2.45
Ce	+1	58	1.27		+4		0.70		+3		0.76
	+3		1.034		+6		0.62		+5		0.62
	+4		0.92	N	−3	7	1.71	Sc	+3	21	0.732
Cl	−1	17	1.81		+1		0.25	Se	−2	34	1.91
	+5		0.34		+3		0.16		−1		2.32
	+7		0.27		+5		0.13		+1		0.66
Co	+2	27	0.72	NH₄	+1		1.43		+4		0.50
	+3		0.63	Na	+1	11	0.97		+6		0.42
Cr	+1	24	0.81	Nb	+1	41	1.00	Si	−4	14	2.71
	+2		0.89		+4		0.74		−1		3.84
	+3		0.63		+5		0.69		+1		0.65
	+6		0.52	Nd	+3	60	0.995		+4		0.42
Cs	+1	55	1.67	Ne	+1	10	1.12	Sm	+3	62	0.964
Cu	+1	29	0.96	Ni	+2	28	0.69	Sn	−4	50	2.94
	+2		0.72	Np	+3	93	1.10		−1		3.70
Dy	+3	66	0.908		+4		0.95		+2		0.93
Er	+3	68	0.881		+7		0.71		+4		0.71
Eu	+3	63	0.950	O	−2	8	1.32	Sr	+2	38	1.12
	+2		1.09		−1		1.76	Ta	+5	73	0.68
F	−1	9	1.33		+1		0.22	Tb	+3	65	0.923
	+7		0.08		+6		0.09		+4		0.84

Ele-ment	Charge	Atomic number	Radius in A	Ele-ment	Charge	Atomic number	Radius in A	Ele-ment	Charge	Atomic number	Radius in A
Tc	+7	43	0.979	Ti	+4		0.68	W	+4	74	0.70
Te	−2	52	2.11	Tl	+1	81	1.47		+6		0.62
	−1		2.50		+3		0.95	Y	+3	39	0.893
	+1		0.82	Tm	+3	69	0.87	Yb	+2	70	0.93
	+4		0.70	U	+4	92	0.97		+3		0.858
	+6		0.56		+6		0.80	Zn	+1	30	0.88
Th	+4	90	1.02	V	+2	23	0.88		+2		0.74
Ti	+1	22	0.96		+3		0.74	Zr	+1	40	1.09
	+2		0.94		+4		0.63		+4		0.79
	+3		0.76		+5		0.59				

BOND LENGTHS BETWEEN CARBON AND OTHER ELEMENTS

Prepared by Olga Kennard.

The tables are based on bond distance determinations, by experimental methods, mainly X-ray and electron diffraction, and include values published up to January 1, 1956. In the present tables, for the sake of completeness individual values of bond distances of lower accuracy are quoted with limits of error indicated where possible. Values for tungsten and bismuth should be treated with particular caution.

According to the statistical theory of errors if an average quantity μ and a standard deviation σ can be evaluated there is a 95% probability that the true value lies within the interval $\mu \pm 2\sigma$. Too much reliance should, however, not be placed on σ values in bond distance determinations since the derivation of these certain sources of error may have been neglected.

Values of the bond lengths and the limits of error are each given in Angstrom units.

Reproduced by permission from International Tables for X-ray Crystallography.

BOND LENGTHS BETWEEN CARBON AND OTHER ELEMENTS
Reference: HCP and "Tables of interatomic distances" Chem. Soc. of London, 1958

Group	Bond type	Element				
I	All types	H** 1.056 — 1.115				
II		Be 1.93	Hg 2.07 ± 0.01			
III		B 1.56 ± 0.01	Al 2.24 ± 0.04	In 2.16 ± 0.04		
IV	All types Alkyls (CH₃XH₃) Aryl (C₆H₅XH₃) Neg. Subst. (CH₃XCl₃)	C** 1.54 — 1.20	Ge 1.98 ± 0.03	Si 1.865 ± 0.008 1.84 ± 0.01 1.88 ± 0.01	Sn 2.143 ± 0.008 2.18 ± 0.02	Pb 2.29 ± 0.05
V	All types Paraffinic (CH₃)₃X	N** 1.47 — 1.1	P 1.87 ± 0.02	As 1.98 ± 0.02	Sb 2.202 ± 0.016	Bi 2.30*
VI		O** 1.43 — 1.15	S** 1.81 — 1.55	Cr 1.92 ± 0.04	Se 1.98 — 1.71	Te 2.05 ± 0.14	Mo 2.08 ± 0.04	W 2.06 ± 0.01*
VII	Paraffinic (monosubstituted) (CH₃X) Paraffinic (disubstituted) (CH₂X₂) Olefinic (CH₂:CHX) Aromatic (C₆H₅X) Acetylenic (HC:CX)	F 1.381 ± 0.005 1.334 ± 0.004 1.32₅ ± 0.1 1.30 ± 0.01	Cl 1.767 ± 0.002 1.767 ± 0.002 1.72 ± 0.01 1.70 ± 0.01 1.635 ± 0.004	Br 1.937 ± 0.003 1.937 ± 0.003 1.89 ± 0.01 1.85 ± 0.01 1.79₅ ± 0.01	I 2.13₅ ± 0.01 2.13₅ ± 0.1 2.092 ± 0.005 2.05 ± 0.01 1.99 ± 0.02	
VIII		Fe 1.84 ± 0.02	Co 1.83 ± 0.02	Ni 1.82 ± 0.03	Pd 2.27 ± 0.04	

* Error uncertain.
** See following individual tables.

CARBON-CARBON

Single Bond

Paraffinic	1.541 ± 0.003
In diamond (18°C)	1.54452 ± 0.00014

Partial Double Bond

(1) Shortening of single bond in presence of carbon carbon double bond, e.g. $(CH_3)_2$-$C:CH_2$; or of aromatic ring e.g. C_6H_5.-CH_3 1.53 ± 0.01
(2) Shortening in presence of a carbon oxygen double bond e.g. CH_3CHO 1.516 ± 0.005
(3) Shortening in presence of two carbon-oxygen double bonds, e.g. $(CO_2H)_2$ 1.49 ± 0.01
(4) Shortening in presence of one carbon-carbon triple bond, e.g. $CH_3.C:CH$ 1.460 ± 0.003
(5) In compounds with tendency to dipole formation, e.g. $C:C.C:N$ 1.44 ± 0.01
(6) In graphite (at 15°C) 1.4210 ± 0.0001
(7) In aromatic compounds 1.395 ± 0.003
(8) In presence of two carbon carbon triple bonds, e.g. $HC:C.C:CH$ 1.373 ± 0.004

Double Bond

(1) Simple 1.337 ± 0.006
(2) Partial triple bond, e.g. $CH_2:C:CH_2$ 1.309 ± 0.005

Triple Bond

(1) Simple, e.g. C_2H_2 1.204 ± 0.002
(2) Conjugated, e.g. $CH_3.(C:C)_2.H$ 1.206 ± 0.004

CARBON-HYDROGEN

(1) Paraffinic (a) in methane 1.091
    (b) in monosubstituted carbon 1.101 ± 0.003
    (c) in disubstituted carbon 1.073 ± 0.004
    (d) in trisubstituted carbon 1.070 ± 0.007
(2) Olefinic, e.g. $CH_2:CH_2$ 1.07 ± 0.01
(3) Aromatic in C_6H_6 1.084 ± 0.006
(4) Acetylenic, e.g. $CH:C.X$ 1.056 ± 0.003
(5) Shortening in presence of a carbon triple bond, e.g. CH_3CN 1.115 ± 0.004
(6) In small rings, e.g. $(CH_2)_2S$ 1.081 ± 0.007

CARBON-NITROGEN

Single Bond

(1) Paraffinic (a) 4 co-valent nitrogen   1.479 ± 0.005
          (b) 3 co-valent nitrogen   1.472 ± 0.005
(2) In C—N= e.g. CH_3NO_2 1.475 ± 0.010
(3) Aromatic in $C_6H_5NHCOCH_3$ 1.426 ± 0.012
(4) Snortened (partial double bond) in heterocyclic systems, e.g. C_5H_5N 1.352 ± 0.005
(5) Shortened (partial double bond) in N—C=O e.g. $HCONH_2$ 1.322 ± 0.003

Triple Bond

(1) In R.C:N   1.158 ± 0.002

CARBON-OXYGEN

Single Bond

(1) Paraffinic   1.43 ± 0.01
(2) Strained e.g. epoxides   1.47 ± 0.01
(3) Shortened (partial double bond) as in carboxylic acids or through influence of aromatic ring, e.g. salicylic acid   1.36 ± 0.01

Double Bond

(1) In aldehydes, ketones, carboxylic acids, esters   1.23 ± 0.01
(2) In zwitterion forms, e.g. DL serine   1.26 ± 0.01
(3) Shortened (partial triple bond) as in conjugated systems   1.207 ± 0.006
(4) Partial triple bond as in acyl halides or isocyanates   1.17 ± 0.01

CARBON-SULPHUR

Single Bond

(1) Paraffinic, e.g. CH_3SH 1.81(5) ± 0.01
(2) Lengthened in presence of fluorine, e.g. $(CF_3)_2S$ 1.83(5) ± 0.01
(3) Shortened (partial double bond) as in heterocyclic systems, e.g. C_4H_4S 1.73 ± 0.01

Double Bond

(1) In ethylene thiourea   1.71 ± 0.02
(2) Shortened (partial triple bond) in presence of second carbon double bond, e.g. COS   1.558 ± 0.003

BOND LENGTHS OF ELEMENTS

Element	Bond	Å
Ac	Ac—Ac	3.756
Ag (25°C)	Ag—Ag	2.8894
Al (25°C)	Al—Al	2.863
As	As—As	2.49
As_4	As—As	2.44 ± 0.03
Au (25°C)	Au—Au	2.8841
B_2	B—B	1.589
Ba (room temp.)	Ba—Ba	4.347
Be (α-form, 20°C)	Be—Be	2.2260
Bi (25°C)	Bi—Bi	3.09
Br_2	Br—Br	2.290
Ca (α-form, 18°C)	Ca—Ca	3.947 (f.c.c.)
(β-form, 500°C		3.877 (b.c.c.)
Cd (21°C)	Cd—Cd	2.9788
Cl_2	Cl—Cl	1.988
Ce	Ce—Ce	3.650
Co (18°C)	Co—Co	2.5061
Cr (α-form, 20°C)	Cr—Cr	2.4980
(β-form, >1850°C		2.61
Cs (−10°C)	Cs—Cs	5.309
Cu (20°C)	Cu—Cu	2.5560
Dy	Dy—Dy	3.503

Element	Bond	Å
Er	Er—Er	3.468
Eu	Eu—Eu	3.989
F_2	F—F	1.417 ± 0.001
Fe (α-form, 20°C)	Fe—Fe	2.4823 (b.c.c.)
(γ-form, 916°C)		2.578 (f.c.c.)
(δ-form, 1394°C)		2.539 (b.c.c.)
Ga (20°C)	Ga—Ga	2.442
Gd (20°C)	Gd—Gd	3.573
Ge (20°C)	Ge—Ge	2.4498
H_2	H—H in H_2	0.74611
	H—D in HD	0.74136
	D—D in D_2	0.74164
He	He—He in $[He_2]^+$	1.08₀
Hf (α-form, 24°C)	Hf—Hf	3.1273 (h.c.p.)
Hg (−46°C)	Hg—Hg	3.005
Ho	Ho—Ho	3.486
I_2	I—I	2.662
In (20°C)	In—In	3.2511
Ir (room temp.)	Ir—Ir	2.714
K (78°K)	K—K	4.544
La (α-form)	La—La	3.739 (h.c.p.)
(β-form)		3.745 (f.c.c.)
Li (20°C)	Li—Li	3.0390
Lu	Lu—Lu	3.435
Mg (25°C)	Mg—Mg	3.1971
Mn (γ-form, 1095°C)	Mn—Mn	2.7311 (f.c.c.)
(δ-form, 1134°C)		2.6679 (b.c.c.)
Mo (20°C)	Mo—Mo	2.7251
N_2	N—N	1.0975₈ ± 0.0001
Na (20°C)	Na—Na	3.7157
Nb (20°C)	Nb—Nb	2.8584
Nd	Nd—Nd	3.628
Ni (18°C)	Ni—Ni	2.4916
Np (α-form, 20°C)	Np—Np	2.60 (orthorhombic)
(β-form, 313°C)		2.76 (tetragon.)
(γ-form, 600°C)		3.05 (b.c.c.)
O_2	O—O	1.208
O_3 angle 116.8 ± 0.5°		1.278 ± 0.003
Os (20°C)	Os—Os	2.6754
P black		2.18
P_4	P—P	2.21 ± 0.02
Pa	Pa—Pa	3.212
Pb (25°C)	Pb—Pb	3.5003
Pd (25°C)	Pd—Pd	2.7511
Po (α-form, 10°C)	Po—Po	3.345 (cubic)
(β-form, 75°C)		3.359 (rh. hedr.)
Pr (α-form)	Pr—Pr	3.640 (tetrag.)
(β-form)		3.649 (f.c.c.)
Pt (20°C)	Pt—Pt	2.746
Pu (γ-form, 235°C)	Pu—Pu	3.026 (f.c.c.)
(δ-form, 313°C)		3.279 (f.c.c.)
(ε-form, 500°C)		3.150 (b.c.c.)
Rb (20°C)	Rb—Rb	4.95
Re (room temp.)	Re—Re	2.741
Rh (20°C)	Rh—Rh	2.6901
Ru (25°C)	Ru—Ru	2.6502
S_2	S—S	1.887
S_8	S—S	2.07 ± 0.02
Sb (25°C)	Sb—Sb	2.90
Sc (room temp.)	Sc—Sc	3.212
Se (20°C)	Se—Se	2.321
Se_2	Se—Se	2.152 ± 0.003
Se_8	Se—Se	2.32 ± 0.003
Si (20°C)	Si—Si	2.3517
Sn (α-form, 20°C)	Sn—Sn diamond type lattice	2.8099
(β-form, 25°C)		3.022 (tetrag.)
Sr (α-form, 25°C)	Sr—Sr	4.302 (f.c.c.)
(β-form, 248°C)		4.32 (h.c.p.)
(γ-form, 614°C)		4.20 (b.c.c.)
Ta (20°C)	Ta—Ta	2.86
Tb	Tb—Tb	3.525
Tc (room temp.)	Tc—Tc	2.703
Te (25°C)	Te—Te	2.864
Th (α-form, 25°C)	Th—Th	3.595 (f.c.c.)
(β-form, 1450°C)		3.56 (b.c.c.)
Ti (α-form, 25°C)	Ti—Ti	2.8956 (h.c.p.)
(β-form, 900°C)		2.8636 (b.c.c.)
Tl (α-form, 18°C)	Tl—Tl	3.4076 (h.c.p.)
(β-form, 262°C)		3.362 (b.c.c.)
Tm	Tm—Tm	3.447
U (α-form)	U—U	2.77
(β-form, 805°C)		3.058 (b.c.c.)
V (30°C)	V—V	2.6224
W (25°C)	W—W	2.7409
Y	Y—Y	3.551
Yb	Yb—Yb	3.880
Zn (25°C)	Zn—Zn	2.6694
Zr	Zr—Zr	3.179

BOND LENGTH AND ANGLE VALUES BETWEEN ELEMENTS

Elements	In	Bond length (Å)	Bond angle (°)
Boron			
B—B	B_2H_6	1.770 ± 0.013	H—B—H 121.5 ± 7.5
B—Br	BBr	1.88₇	
B—Br	BBr₃	1.87 ± 0.02	Br—B—Br 120 ± 6
B—Cl	BCl₃	1.715₇	
	BCl₃	1.72 ± 0.01	Cl—B—Cl 120 ± 3
B—F	BF	1.262	
	BF₃	1.29₅ ± 0.01	F—B—F 120
B—H	Hydrides	1.21 ± 0.02	
B—H Bridge	Hydrides	1.39 ± 0.02	
B—N	(BClNH)₃	1.42 ± 0.01	B—N—B 121
B—O	BO	1.2049	
	B(OH)₃	1.362 ± 0.005 (av.)	O—B—O 119.7
Nitrogen			
N—Cl	NO₂Cl	1.79 ± 0.02	
N—F	NF₃	1.36 ± 0.02	F—N—F 102.5 ± 1.5
N—H	[NH₄]⁺	1.034 ± 0.003	
	NH	1.038	
	HNCS	1.041	
	N₃H	1.013 ± 0.005	H—N—C 130.25 ± 0.25
N—N	N₃H	1.02 ± 0.01	H—N—N 112.65 ± 0.5
	[N₂]⁺	1.126 ± 0.002	
N—O	N₂O	1.116₂	
	NO₂Cl	1.24 ± 0.01	O—N—O 126 ± 2
N=O	N₂O₂	1.188 ± 0.005	O—N—O 134.1 ± 0.25
	[NO]⁺	1.186 ± 0.002	
N—Si	SiN	1.572	
Oxygen			
O—H	[OH]⁺	1.0289	
	OD	0.9699	
	H₂O₂	0.960 ± 0.005	O—O—H 100 ± 2
O—O	H₂O₂	1.227	
	[O₂]⁺	1.26 ± 0.02	
	[O₂]⁻⁻	1.49 ± 0.02	
Phosphorus			
P—D	PD	1.429	
P—H	[PH₄]⁺	1.42 ± 0.02	
P—N	PN	1.4910	
P—S	PSBr₃(Cl₃, F₃)	1.86 ± 0.02	
Sulfur			
S—Br	SOBr₂	2.27 ± 0.02	Br—S—Br 96 ± 2
S—F	SOF₂	1.585 ± 0.005	F—S—F 92.8 ± 1
S—D	SD	1.3473	
	SD₂	1.345	
S—O	SO₂	1.4321	O—S—O 119.54
	SOCl₂	1.45 ± 0.02	
S—S	S₂Cl₂	2.04 ± 0.01	
Silicon			
Si—Br	SiBr₄	2.17 ± 1.01	
Si—Cl	SiCl₄	2.03 ± 1.01 (av.)	
Si—F	SiF₄	1.561 ± 0.003 (av.)	
Si—H	SiH₄	1.480 ± 0.005	
Si—O	[SiOl]⁺	1.504	
Si—Si	Si₂Cl₂	2.30 ± 0.02	

BOND LENGTHS AND ANGLES OF CHEMICAL COMPOUNDS

A. Inorganic Compounds

Compound	Formula	Bond lengths in Å	Bond angles (°)
Ammonia	NH₃	N—H 1.008 ± 0.004	H—N—H 107.3 ± 0.2
Antimony tribromide	SbBr₃	Sb—Br 2.51 ± 0.02	Br—Sb—Br 97 ± 2
Antimony trichloride	SbCl₃	Sb—Cl 2.352 ± 0.005	Cl—Sb—Cl 99.5 ± 1.5
Antimony triiodide	SbI₃	Sb—I 2.67 ± 0.03	I—Sb—I 99.0 ± 1
Arsenic tribromide	AsBr₃	As—Br 2.33 ± 0.02	Br—As—Br 100.5 ± 1.5
Arsenic trichloride	AsCl₃	As—Cl 2.161 ± 0.004	Cl—As—Cl 98.4 ± 0.5
Arsenic trifluoride	AsF₃	As—F 1.712 ± 0.005	F—As—F 102.0 ± 2
Arsenic triiodide	AsI₃	As—I 2.55 ± 0.03	I—As—I 101.0 ± 1.5
Arsenic trioxide	As₄O₆	As—O 1.78 ± 0.02	As—O—As 99.0
Arsine	AsH₃	As—H 1.5192 ± 0.002	As—O—As 128.0 ± 2
Bismuthum tribromide	BiBr₃	Bi—Br 2.63 ± 0.02	H—As—H 91.83 ± 0.33
Bismuthum trichloride	BiCl₃	Bi—Cl 2.48 ± 0.02	Br—Bi—Br 100.0 ± 4
Bromosilane	SiH₃Br	Si—H 1.57 ± 0.03	Cl—Bi—Cl 100.0 ± 6
Chlorine dioxide	ClO₂	Cl—O 1.49	H—Si—H 111.3 ± 1
Chlorogermane	GeH₃Cl	Ge—H 1.52 ± 0.03	O—Cl—O 118.5
Chlorosilane	SiH₃Cl	Si—Cl 1.483 ± 0.001	Ge—H 110.9 ± 1.5
Chromium oxychloride	Cr(OCl)₂	Cr—O 2.047 ± 0.0007	H—Si—H 110 ± 0.03
		Cr—O 1.57 ± 0.03	O—Cr—O 105 ± 4
		Cr—Cl 2.12 ± 0.02	Cl—Cr—O 113 ± 3
Cyanuric triazide	C₃N₁₂	C—N 1.38	Cl—Cr—Cl 109 ± 3
Dichlorosilane	SiH₂Cl₂	Si—H 1.46	C—N—C 113.0
		SiCl 2.02 ± 0.03	
Difluorodiazine	N₂F₂	N—F 1.44 ± 0.04	Cl—Si—Cl 110 ± 1
Difluoromethylsilane	CH₃SiHF₂	N—N 1.25 ± 0.02	F—N=N 115 ± 5
			H—Si—F 106 ± 0.5
Disilicon hexachloride (hexachlorosilane)	Si₂Cl₆	Si—Cl 2.02 ± 0.02	C—Si—F 116.2 ± 1
		Si—Si 2.34 ± 0.06	C—Si—H 109.8 ± 0.5
Fluorosilane	SiH₃F	Si—F 1.595 ± 0.002	C—Si—Cl 109.5 ± 1
Hydrogen phosphide	PH₃	P—H 1.415 ± 0.003	H—Si—H 109.3 ± 0.3
Hydrogen selenide	SeH₂	Se—H 1.47	H—P—H 93.3 ± 0.2
Hydrogen sulfide	SH₂	S—H 1.3455	H—Se—H 91.0
Hydrogen telluride	Te—H₂		H—S—H 93.3
Iodo silane	Si—H₃I	Si—H 1.48 ± 0.01	H—Te—H 89.5 ± 0.4
		Si—I 2.45 ± 0.09	H—Si—H 109.9 ± 0.4
Methylgermane	CH₃GeH₃		H—C—H 108.2 ± 0.5
			H—Ge—H 108.6 ± 0.5
Nitrosyl bromide	NOBr	O—N 1.15 ± 0.04	Br—N=O 117 ± 3
		N—Br 2.14 ± 0.02	
Nitrosyl chloride	NOCl	N—Cl 1.14 ± 0.02	Cl—N=O 113.0 ± 2
		N—O 1.97 ± 0.01	
Nitrosyl fluoride	NOF	N—F 1.13	F—N=O 110.0
		H—O 1.52	
cis-Nitrous acid	NO(OH)	H—O 0.98	O—N=O 114 ± 2
		N—O 1.46	
		N—O' 1.20	
trans-Nitrous acid	NO(OH)	O—N 0.98	O—N=O 118 ± 2
		H—O—N 1.20	
		NO' 1.46	
Oxygen chloride	OCl₂	O—Cl 1.701 ± 0.02	Cl—O—Cl 110.8 ± 1
Oxygen fluoride	OF₂	O—F 1.418	F—O—F 103.2
Phosphorus oxychloride	POCl₃	Cl—P 1.99₄ ± 0.02	Cl—P—Cl 103.5 ± 1
Phosphorus oxysulfide	P₄O₆S₄	P—O 1.61 ± 0.02	P—O 128.5 ± 1.5
			O—P—S 101.5 ± 1
Phosphorus pentoxide	P₄O₁₀	P—S 1.85 ± 0.02	O—P—S 116.5 ± 1
		P—O 1.62 ± 0.02	O—P—O' 101.5 ± 1
		P—O' 1.38 ± 0.02	O—P—O' 116.5 ± 1
			P—O—P 123.5 ± 1

BOND LENGTHS AND ANGLES OF CHEMICAL COMPOUNDS (Continued)

A. Inorganic Compounds (Continued)

Compound	Formula	Bond lengths in Å	Bond angles (°)
Phosphorus tribromide	PBr_3	P—Br 2.18 ± 0.03	Br—P—Br 101.5 ± 1.5
Phosphorus trichloride	PCl_3	P—Cl 2.043 ± 0.003	Cl—P—Cl 100.1 ± 0.3
Phosphorus trifluoride	PF_3	P—F 1.535	F—P—F 100.0
Phosphorus trioxide	P_4O_6	P—O 1.65 ± 0.02	O—P—O 99.0 ± 1; P—O—P 127.5 ± 1
Stibine	SbH_3	Sb—H 1.7073 ± 0.0025	H—Sb—H 91.3 ± 0.33
Sulfur dichloride	SCl_2	S—Cl 1.99 ± 0.03	Cl—S—Cl 101.0 ± 4
Sulfur dioxide	SO_2	S—O 1.4321	O—S—O 119.536
Sulfur monochloride	S_2Cl_2	S—Cl 2.01 ± 0.07; S—S 1.43 ± 0.02	Cl—S—S 104.5 ± 0.25; S—S—Cl 119.75 ± 5
Sulfuryl chloride	SO_2Cl_2	S—Cl 1.99 ± 0.02	Cl—S—Cl 111.20 ± 2; Cl—S—O 106.5 ± 2
Tellurium bromide	$TeBr_2$	Te—Br 2.51 ± 0.02	Br—Te—Br 98.0 ± 3
Tribromo silane	$SiHBr_3$	Si—Br 2.16 ± 0.03	Br—Si—Br 110.5 ± 1.5
Trichloro germane	$GeHCl_3$	Ge—Cl 2.16 ± 0.04	Cl—Ge—Cl 108.3 ± 0.2
Trichloro silane	$SiHCl_3$	Si—H 1.47	F—Si—Cl 109.4 ± 1
Trifluorochlorosilane	$SiClF_3$	Si—Cl 1.560 ± 0.005; Si—F 1.989 ± 0.018	F—Si—F 108.5 ± 1
Trifluorochlorogermane	$GeClF_3$	Gr—F 1.688 ± 0.0017; Gr—Cl 2.067 ± 0.005	F—Ge—F 107.7 ± 1.5
Trifluorosilane	$SiHF_3$	Si—H 1.455 ± 0.01; Si—F 1.565 ± 0.005	F—Si—F 108.3 ± 0.5
Vanadium oxytrichloride	$VOCl_3$	V—O 1.56 ± 0.04; V—Cl 2.12 ± 0.03	Cl—V—Cl 111.2 ± 2; Cl—V—O 108.2 ± 2
Water	H_2O	O—H 0.9584	H—O—H 104.45

B. Organic Compounds

Compound	Formula	Bond lengths in Å	Bond angles (°)
Acetaldehyde	CH_3COH	C—H 1.09; C—C 1.50 ± 0.02	C—C=O 121 ± 2
Bromomethane	CH_3Br	C—H 1.22 ± 0.02; C—Br 1.929	H—C—H 111.2 ± 0.5
Carbon tetrachloride	CCl_4	C—Cl 1.766 ± 0.003; Cl—Cl 2.887 ± 0.004	Cl—C—Cl 109.5
Chloromethane	CH_3Cl	C—H 1.11 ± 0.01; C—Cl 1.784 ± 0.003	H—C—H 110 ± 2
Dichloromethane	CH_2Cl_2	C—H 1.068 ± 0.005; C—Cl 1.7724 ± 0.0005	H—C—H 112 ± 0.3; Cl—C—Cl 111.8
Difluorochloromethane	$CHClF_2$	C—H 1.06; C—Cl 1.73 ± 0.03; C—F 1.36 ± 0.03	F—C—F 110.5 ± 1; Cl—C—F 110.5 ± 1
1,1-Difluoroethylene	$C_2H_2F_2$	C—F 1.321 ± 0.015	F—C=C 125.2 ± 0.2; H—C—H 117 ± 7
Difluoromethane	CH_2F_2	C—F 1.311 ± 0.035	F—C—F 108.2 ± 0.8; H—C—H 112.5 ± 6
p-Dinitrobenzene	$C_6H_4(NO_2)_2$	C—C 1.360 ± 0.005; N—O 1.38	O—N=O 124.0
Dithio oxamide	$NH_2CSCSNH_2$	N—C 1.21; N—C 1.54; S—C 1.30	N=C—S 124.8; N—C—C 124.87; S—C—C 115.25
Ethane	C_2H_6	C—S 1.66; C—C 1.107	H—C—H 109.3
Ethylidene fluoride	CH_3CHF_2	C—C 1.536; C—F 1.345 ± 0.001; C—F 1.540; C—H 1.100	F—C—F 109.15 ± 0.001; F—C—C 109.4; H—C—C 110.2

BOND LENGTHS AND ANGLES OF CHEMICAL COMPOUNDS (Continued)

B. Organic Compounds (Continued)

Compound	Formula	Bond lengths in Å	Bond angles (°)
Fluorochloromethane	CH_2ClF	C—H 1.078 ± 0.005; C—Cl 1.759 ± 0.003; C—F 1.378 ± 0.006	Cl—C—F 100.0 ± 0.1
Fluorotrichloromethane	$CFCl_3$	C—Cl 1.76 ± 0.02; C—F 1.44 ± 0.04	Cl—C—Cl 113 ± 3
Formaldehyde	CH_2O	C—H 1.060 ± 0.038; C—O 1.230 ± 0.017	H—C—H 125.8 ± 7
Formamide	$HCONH_2$	C—N 1.25_8; C—O 1.300; C—N 1.245	N—C=O 121.5
Formic acid	$HCOOH$	C—O 1.312; C—H 1.085; C—O 0.95	O—C=O' 124.3; H—C=O' 117.8; C—O—H 107.8
Glycine	NH_2CH_2COOH	C—H 1.52; C—O 1.27	C—C—O 119.0; O—C—O 122.0; C—C=O 112.0
Hexachloroethane	C_2Cl_6	C—C 1.39; C—Cl 1.74 ± 0.01	Cl—C—Cl 109.3 ± 0.01
Iodomethane	CH_3I	C—I 1.57 ± 0.06; C—H 1.11 ± 0.01	H—C—H 111.4 ± 0.1
Methane	CH_4	C—H 2.139; C—H 1.091	
Methanethiol	CH_3SH	C—S 1.1039 ± 0.002; S—H 1.8177 ± 0.0002	H—S—C 110.3 ± 0.2; H—C—H 100.3 ± 0.2
Methanol	CH_3OH	C—O 1.329 ± 0.004; C—H 1.427 ± 0.007; O—H 0.956 ± 0.015	H—C—H 109.3 ± 0.75; C—O—H 108.9 ± 2
Methylamine	CH_3NH_2	C—N 1.093; C—H 1.474 ± 0.005; N—H 1.014	H—C—H 109.5 ± 1; H—N—H 105.8 ± 1
Methylether	$(CH_2)_2O$	C—H 1.00; C—N 1.43 ± 0.03	C—O—C 110.0 ± 3
Methylnitrite	CH_3NO_2	N—O 1.49 ± 0.02; N=O 1.22 ± 0.1	O—N=O 127 ± 4
Methylsulfide	$(CH_3)_2S$	N—S 1.82 ± 0.01; C—C 1.06	C—S—C 105 ± 3; H—C—H 109.5
Oxamide	$NH_2COCONH_2$	C—N 1.32; C—O 1.24	C—C=O 125.7 ± 0.3
Phosgene	CCl_2O	C—Cl 1.746 ± 0.004; C—O 1.166 ± 0.002	Cl—C—Cl 124.3 ± 0.1; C—C—Cl 111.3 ± 0.1
Propylene / Propynal	C_3H_6 / $CHC.COH$	Cl—C₂ 1.204; C—C₂ 1.46; C—O 1.21; C—H 1.08	C—C—O 124.75 ± 0.3; C—C—O 123.0; C—C—H 120.0
Tribromomethane	$CHBr_3$	C—H 1.068 ± 0.01; C—Br 1.930 ± 0.003	Br—C—Br 110.8 ± 0.3
Trichlorobromomethane	$CBrCl_3$	C—Br 1.936; C—Cl 1.764	Cl—C—Cl 111.2 ± 1
Trifluorochloromethane	$CClF_3$	C—Cl 1.751 ± 0.004; C—F 1.328 ± 0.02	F—C—F 108.6 ± 0.4
Trifluoromethane	CHF_3	C—F 1.332 ± 0.008; C—F 1.098	F—C—F 108 ± 0.75
Triiodomethane	CHI_3	C—I 2.12 ± 0.04	I—C—I 113.0 ± 1
Trimethylamine	$(CH_3)_3N$	C—N 1.47 ± 0.01; C—H 1.06	C—N—C 108.0 ± 4
Trimethylarsine	$(CH_3)_3As$	C—H 1.09	C—As—C 96 ± 5
Trimethylphosphine	$(CH_3)_3P$	C—As 1.98 ± 0.02; C—P 1.09; C—P 1.87 ± 0.02	C—P—C 100.0 ± 4

STRENGTHS OF CHEMICAL BONDS

J. A. Kerr, M. J. Parsonage
The University, Birmingham, 15, U.K.
and
A. F. Trotman-Dickenson
Institute of Technology, Cardiff, U.K.
(Revised to 1 January 1974)

The strength of a chemical bond, $D(R - X)$, often known as the bond dissociation energy, is defined as the heat of the reaction: $RX \rightarrow R + X$. It is given by: $D(R - X) = \Delta Hf^\circ(R) + \Delta Hf^\circ(X) - \Delta Hf^\circ(RX)$. Some authors list bond strengths for $0^\circ K$ but here the values for 298 K are given because more thermodynamic data are available for this temperature. Bond strengths, or bond dissociation energies, are not equal to, and may differ considerably from, mean bond energies derived solely from thermochemical data on molecules and atoms.

BOND STRENGTHS IN DIATOMIC MOLECULES

These have usually been measured spectroscopically or by mass spectrometric analysis of hot gases effusing from a Knudsen cell. Excellent accounts of these and other methods are given in Reference 58. The errors quoted are those given in the original paper or review article. The references have been chosen primarily as a key to the literature. It should not be assumed that the author referred to was responsible for the determination quoted, as the reference may be only to a review article.

Molecule	kcal mol^{-1}	Ref.	Molecule	kcal mol^{-1}	Ref.
H–H	104.207 ± 0.001	67	H–Sn	63 ± 1	89
H–D	105.030 ± 0.001	67	H–Te	64 ± 1	63
D–D	106.010 ± 0.001	67	H–I	71.4 ± 0.2	51
H–Li	56.91 ± 0.01	125	H–Cs	42.6 ± 0.9	107
H–Be	54	66	H–Ba	42 ± 4	51
H–B	79 ± 1	74	H–Yb	38 ± 1	64
H–C	80.9	66	H–Pt	84 ± 9	51
H–N	75 ± 4	51	H–Au	75 ± 3	106
H–O	102.34 ± 0.30	19	H–Hg	9.5	51
H–F	135.9 ± 0.3	51	H–Tl	45 ± 2	51
H–Na	48 ± 5	51	H–Pb	42 ± 5	51
H–Mg	47 ± 12	46, 51	H–Bi	59 ± 7	51
H–Al	68 ± 2	51	Li–Li	24.55 ± 0.14	126
H–Si	71.4 ± 1.2	51	Li–O	78 ± 6	19
H–P	82 ± 7	51	Li–F	137.5 ± 1	18
H–S	82.3 ± 2.9	75	Li–Cl	111.9 ± 2	18
H–Cl	103.1	51	Li–Br	100.2 ± 2	18
H–K	43.8 ± 3.5	51	Li–I	84.6 ± 2	18
H–Ca	40.1	51	Be–Be	17	45
H–Cr	67 ± 12	51	Be–O	98 ± 7	19
H–Mn	56 ± 7	51	Be–F	136 ± 2	70
H–Ni	61 ± 7	51	Be–S	89 ± 14	51
H–Cu	67 ± 2	23	Be–Cl	92.8 ± 2.2	73
H–Zn	20.5 ± 0.5	51	Be–Au	∿67	11
H–Ga	68 ± 5	51	B–B	∿67 ± 5	112
H–Ge	76.8 ± 0.2	10	B–N	93 ± 12	51
H–As	65 ± 3	41	B–O	192.7 ± 1.2	120
H–Se	73 ± 1	63	B–F	180 ± 3	100
H–Br	87.4 ± 0.5	51	B–S	138.8 ± 2.2	120
H–Rb	40 ± 5	51	B–Cl	119	51
H–Sr	39 ± 2	51	B–Se	110 ± 4	130
H–Ag	59 ± 1	108	B–Br	101 ± 5	51
H–Cd	16.5 ± 0.1	51	B–Ru	107 ± 5	124
H–In	59 ± 2	51	B–Rh	114 ± 5	124

BOND STRENGTHS IN DIATOMIC MOLECULES (*Continued*)

Molecule	kcal mol^{-1}	Ref.	Molecule	kcal mol^{-1}	Ref.
B–Pd	79 ± 5	124	O–Sc	155 ± 5	19
B–Te	85 ± 5	120	O–Ti	158 ± 8	19
B–Ce	$\sim$100	118	O–V	154 ± 5	19
B–Ir	123 ± 4	124	O–Cr	110 ± 10	19
B–Pt	114 ± 4	95	O–Mn	96 ± 8	19
B–Au	82 ± 4	124	O–Fe	96 ± 5	19
B–Th	71	55	O–Co	88 ± 5	19
C–C	144 ± 5	45	O–Ni	89 ± 5	19
C–N	184 ± 1	35	O–Cu	82 ± 15	19
C–O	257.26 ± 0.77	19	O–Zn	⩽66	19
C–F	128 ± 5	51	O–Ga	68 ± 15	19
C–Si	104 ± 5	43	O–Ge	158.2 ± 3	19
C–P	139 ± 23	51	O–As	115 ± 3	19
C–S	175 ± 7	92	O–Se	101	44
C–Cl	93	102	O–Br	56.2 ± 0.6	19
C–Ti	128?	51	O–Rb	(61) ± 20	19
C–V	133	50	O–Sr	93 ± 6	19
C–Ge	110 ± 5	51	O–Y	162 ± 5	19
C–Se	139 ± 23	51	O–Zr	181 ± 10	19
C–Br	67 ± 5	51	O–Nb	189 ± 10	19
C–Ru	152 ± 3	95	O–Mo	115 ± 12	19
C–Rh	139 ± 2	122	O–Ru	115 ± 15	19
C–I	50 ± 5	51	O–Rh	90 ± 15	19
C–Ce	109 ± 7	56	O–Pd	56 ± 7	19
C–Ir	149 ± 3	95	O–Ag	51 ± 20	19
C–Pt	146 ± 2	122	O–Cd	⩽67	19
C–U	111 ± 7	56	O–In	⩽77	19
N–N	226.8 ± 1.5	49	O–Sn	127 ± 2	19
N–O	150.8 ± 0.2	19	O–Sb	89 ± 20	19
N–F	62.6 ± 0.8	5	O–Te	93.4 ± 2	99
N–Al	71 ± 23	51	O–I	47 ± 7	19
N–Si	105 ± 9	51	O–Xe	9 ± 5	19
N–P	148 ± 5	57	O–Cs	67 ± 8	19
N–S	$\sim$120 ± 6	101	O–Ba	131 ± 6	19
N–Cl	93 ± 12	51	O–La	188 ± 5	19
N–Ti	111	116	O–Ce	188 ± 6	19
N–As	116 ± 23	51	O–Pr	183.7	48
N–Se	105 ± 23	51	O–Nd	168 ± 8	19
N–Br	67 ± 5	97	O–Sm	134 ± 8	19
N–Sb	72 ± 12	51	O–Eu	130 ± 10	19
N–I	$\sim$38	104	O–Gd	162 ± 6	19
N–Xe	55	65	O–Tb	165 ± 8	19
N–Th	138 ± 1	54	O–Dy	146 ± 10	19
N–U	127 ± 1	53	O–Ho	149 ± 10	19
O–O	118.86 ± 0.04	20	O–Er	147 ± 10	19
O–F	56 ± 9	51	O–Tm	122 ± 15	19
O–Na	61 ± 4	72	O–Yb	98 ± 15	19
O–Mg	79 ± 7	19	O–Lu	159 ± 8	19
O–Al	116 ± 5	19	O–Hf	185 ± 10	19
O–Si	184 ± 3	71	O–Ta	183 ± 15	19
O–P	119.6 ± 3	19	O–W	156 ± 6	19
O–S	124.69 ± 0.03	19	O–Os	<142	19
O–Cl	64.29 ± 0.03	19	O–Ir	⩽94	19
O–K	57 ± 8	19	O–Pt	83 ± 8	19
O–Ca	84 ± 7	19	O–Pb	90.3 ± 1.0	119

BOND STRENGTHS IN DIATOMIC MOLECULES (*Continued*)

Molecule	kcal mol^{-1}	Ref.	Molecule	kcal mol^{-1}	Ref.
O–Bi	81.9 ± 1.5	119	Mg–I	∿68	14
O–Th	192 ± 10	19	Mg–Au	59 ± 23	51
O–U	182 ± 8	19	Al–Al	44	62
O–Np	172 ± 7	4	Al–P	52 ± 3	38
O–Pu	163 ± 15	19	Al–S	79	91
O–Cm	≼134	113	Al–Cl	119.0 ± 1	73
F–F	37.5 ± 2.3	36	Al–Br	103.1	8
F–Na	114 ± 1	18	Al–I	88	7
F–Mg	110 ± 1	68	Al–Au	65	12
F–Al	159 ± 3	100	Al–U	78 ± 7	59
F–Si	116 ± 12	51	Si–Si	76 ± 5	43
F–P	105 ± 23	51	Si–S	148 ± 3	51
F–Cl	59.9 ± 0.1	51	Si–Cl	105 ± 12	51
F–K	118.9 ± 0.6	9	Si–Fe	71 ± 6	123
F–Ca	125 ± 5	17	Si–Co	66 ± 4	123
F–Sc	141 ± 3	136	Si–Ni	76 ± 4	123
F–Ti	136 ± 8	137	Si–Ge	72 ± 5	51
F–Cr	104.5 ± 4.7	88	Si–Se	127 ± 6	51
F–Mn	101.2 ± 3.5	86	Si–Br	82 ± 12	51
F–Ni	89 ± 4	51	Si–Ru	95 ± 5	124
F–Cu	88 ± 9	87	Si–Rh	95 ± 5	124
F–Ga	138 ± 4	100	Si–Pd	75 ± 4	124
F–Ge	116 ± 5	47	Si–Te	121 ± 9	51
F–Br	55.9	21	Si–Ir	110 ± 5	124
F–Rb	116.1 ± 1	18	Si–Pt	120 ± 5	124
F–Sr	129.5 ± 1.6	68	Si–Au	75 ± 3	124
F–Y	144 ± 5	136	P–P	117 ± 3	57
F–Ag	84.7 ± 3.9	51	P–S	70	98
F–Cd	73 ± 5	16	P–Ga	56	61
F–In	121 ± 4	100	P–W	73 ± 1	52
F–Sn	111.5 ± 3	133	P–Th	90	55
F–Sb	105 ± 23	51	S–S	101.9 ± 2.5	44
F–I	67?	51	S–Ca	75 ± 5	29
F–Xe	11	76	S–Sc	114 ± 3	30
F–Cs	119.6 ± 1	18	S–Mn	72 ± 4	130
F–Ba	140.3 ± 1.6	68	S–Fe	78	96
F–Nd	130 ± 3	134	S–Cu	72 ± 12	51
F–Sm	126.9 ± 4.4	135	S–Zn	49 ± 3	39
F–Eu	126.1 ± 4.4	135	S–Ge	131.7 ± 0.6	30, 44
F–Gd	141.1 ± 6.5	135	S–Se	91 ± 5	44
F–Hg	31 ± 9	51	S–Sr	75 ± 5	29
F–Tl	106.4 ± 4.6	15	S–Y	127 ± 3	30
F–Pb	85 ± 2	133	S–Cd	48	96
F–Bi	62 ± 7	51	S–In	69 ± 4	28
F–Pu	129 ± 7	85	S–Sn	111 ± 1	44
Na–Na	18.4	112	S–Te	81 ± 5	44
Na–Cl	97.5 ± 0.5	18	S–Ba	96 ± 5	29
Na–K	15.2 ± 0.7	51	S–La	137 ± 3	26, 30
Na–Br	86.7 ± 1	18	S–Ce	137 ± 3	30
Na–Rb	14 ± 1	51	S–Pr	122.7	48
Na–I	72.7 ± 1	18	S–Nd	113 ± 4	114
Mg–Mg	8?	51	S–Eu	87 ± 4	114
Mg–S	56?	51	S–Gd	126 ± 4	114
Mg–Cl	76 ± 3	69	S–Ho	102 ± 4	114
Mg–Br	75 ± 23	51	S–Lu	121 ± 4	114

Molecule	kcal mol^{-1}	Ref.	Molecule	kcal mol^{-1}	Ref.
S–Au	100 ± 6	58	Mn–Au	44 ± 3	115
S–Hg	51	96	Fe–Fe	24 ± 5	94
S–Pb	82.7 ± 0.4	119	Fe–Ge	50 ± 7	83
S–Bi	75.4 ± 1.1	119	Fe–Br	59 ± 23	51
S–U	135 ± 2	25	Fe–Au	45 ± 4	79
Cl–Cl	58.066 ± 0.001	93	Co–Co	40 ± 6	82
Cl–K	101.3 ± 0.5	18	Co–Cu	39 ± 5	84
Cl–Ca	95 ± 3	69	Co–Ge	57 ± 6	83
Cl–Sc	79	111	Co–Au	51 ± 3	79
Cl–Ti	26 ± 2	51	Ni–Ni	55.5 ± 5	77
Cl–Cr	87.5 ± 5.8	51	Ni–Cu	48 ± 5	84
Cl–Mn	86.2 ± 2.3	51	Ni–Ge	67.3 ± 4	51
Cl–Fe	84?	51	Ni–Br	86 ± 3	51
Cl–Ni	89 ± 5	51	Ni–I	70 ± 5	51
Cl–Cu	84 ± 6	51	Ni–Au	59 ± 5	79
Cl–Zn	54.7 ± 4.7	31	Cu–Cu	46.6 ± 2.2	2
Cl–Ga	114.5	7	Cu–Ge	49 ± 5	83
Cl–Ge	82?	51	Cu–Se	70 ± 9	51
Cl–Br	52.3 ± 0.2	51	Cu–Br	79 ± 6	51
Cl–Rb	100.7 ± 1	18	Cu–Ag	41.6 ± 2.2	2
Cl–Sr	97 ± 3	69	Cu–Sn	42.3 ± 4	1
Cl–Y	82 ± 23	51	Cu–Te	42 ± 9	51
Cl–Ag	75 ± 9	51	Cu–I	47?	51
Cl–Cd	49.9	22	Cu–Au	55.4 ± 2.2	2
Cl–In	103.3	7	Zn–Zn	7	112
Cl–Sn	75?	51	Zn–Se	33 ± 3	39
Cl–Sb	86 ± 12	51	Zn–Te	49?	51
Cl–I	50.5 ± 0.1	51	Zn–I	33 ± 7	51
Cl–Cs	106.2 ± 1	18	Ga–Ga	∿33	112
Cl–Ba	106 ± 3	69	Ga–As	50.1 ± 0.3	40
Cl–Au	82 ± 2	51	Ga–Br	101 ± 4	51
Cl–Hg	24 ± 2	51	Ga–Ag	43	24
Cl–Tl	89.0 ± 0.5	15	Ga–Te	60 ± 6	121
Cl–Pb	72 ± 7	51	Ga–I	81 ± 2	51
Cl–Bi	72 ± 1	32	Ga–Au	51 ± 23	51
Cl–Ra	82 ± 18	51	Ge–Ge	65.8 ± 3	78
Ar–Ar	0.2	117	Ge–Se	114 ± 5	51
K–K	12.8	112	Ge–Br	61 ± 7	51
K–Br	90.9 ± 0.5	18	Ge–Te	93 ± 2	51
K–I	76.8 ± 0.5	18	Ge–Au	70 ± 23	51
Ca–I	70 ± 23	51	As–As	91.7	51
Ca–Au	18	109	As–Se	23	103
Sc–Sc	25.9 ± 5	129	Se–Se	79.5 ± 0.1	119
Ti–Ti	34 ± 5	80	Se–Cd	75?	51
V–V	58 ± 5	80	Se–In	59 ± 4	28
Cr–Cr	<37	127	Se–Sn	95.9 ± 1.4	27
Cr–Cu	37 ± 5	84	Se–Te	64 ± 2	44
Cr–Ge	41 ± 7	83	Se–La	114 ± 4	13
Cr–Br	78.4 ± 5.8	51	Se–Nd	92 ± 4	13
Cr–I	68.6 ± 5.8	51	Se–Eu	72 ± 4	13
Cr–Au	51.3 ± 3.5	3	Se–Gd	103 ± 4	13
Mn–Mn	4 ± 3	81	Se–Ho	80 ± 4	13
Mn–Se	48 ± 3	131	Se–Lu	100 ± 4	13
Mn–Br	75.1 ± 23	51	Se–Pb	72.4 ± 1	119
Mn–I	67.6 ± 2.3	51	Se–Bi	67.0 ± 1.5	119

Molecule	kcal mol^{-1}	Ref.	Molecule	kcal mol^{-1}	Ref.
Br–Br	46.336 ± 0.001	93	Te–Te	63.2 ± 0.2	119
Br–Rb	90.4 ± 1	18	Te–La	91 ± 4	13
Br–Ag	70 ± 7	51	Te–Nd	73 ± 4	13
Br–Cd	38?	51	Te–Eu	58 ± 4	13
Br–In	93	7	Te–Gd	82 ± 4	13
Br–Sn	47 ± 23	51	Te–Ho	62 ± 4	13
Br–Sb	75 ± 14	51	Te Lu	78 ± 4	13
Br–I	42.8 ± 0.1	51	Te–Au	59 ± 16	51
Br–Cs	96.5 ± 1	18	Te–Pb	60 ± 3	119
Br–Hg	17.3	132	Te–Bi	56 ± 3	119
Br–Tl	79.8 ± 0.4	15	I–I	36.460 ± 0.002	93
Br–Pb	59 ± 9	51	I–Cs	82.4 ± 1	18
Br–Bi	63.9 ± 1	33	I–Hg	9	132
Rb–Rb	12.2	112	I–Tl	65 ± 2	14
Rb–I	76.7 ± 1	18	I–Pb	47 ± 9	51
Sr–Au	63 ± 23	51	I–Bi	52 ± 1	34
Y–Y	38.3	128	Xe–Xe	∿0.7	110
Y–La	48.3	128	Cs–Cs	11.3	112
Pd–Pd	33?	51	Ba–Au	38 ± 14	51
Pd–Au	34.2 ± 5	3	La–La	58.6	128
Ag–Ag	41 ± 2	51	La–Au	80 ± 5	60
Ag–Sn	32.5 ± 5	1	Ce–Ce	66 ± 1	6
Ag–Te	70 ± 23	51	Ce–Au	76 ± 4	60
Ag–I	56 ± 7	51	Pr–Au	74 ± 5	60
Ag–Au	48.5 ± 2.2	2	Nd–Au	70 ± 6	60
Cd–Cd	2.7 ± 0.2	51	Au–Au	52.4 ± 2.2	2
Cd–I	33 ± 5	51	Au–Pb	31 ± 23	51
In–In	23.3 ± 2.5	37	Au–U	76 ± 7	59
In–Sb	36.3 ± 2.5	37	Hg–Hg	4.1 ± 0.5	51
In–Te	52 ± 4	28	Hg–Tl	1	66
In–I	80	7	Tl–Tl	15?	45
Sn–Sn	46.7 ± 4	1	Pb–Pb	24 ± 5	45
Sn–Te	76 ± 1	51	Pb–Bi	32 ± 5	42
Sn–Au	58.4 ± 4	1	Bi–Bi	45 ± 2	42
Sb–Sb	71.5 ± 1.5	37	Po–Po	44.4 ± 2.3	51
Sb–Te	61 ± 4	105	At–At	19	45
Sb–Bi	60 ± 1	90	Th–Th	≤69	55

References

1. Ackerman, M., Drowart, J., Stafford, F. E., and Verhaegen, G., *J. Chem. Phys.,* 36, 1557, 1962.
2. Ackerman, M., Stafford, F. E., and Drowart, J., *J. Chem. Phys.,* 33, 1784, 1960.
3. Ackermann, M., Stafford, F. E., and Verhaegen, G., *J. Chem. Phys.,* 36, 1560, 1962.
4. Ackermann, R. J., Faircloth, R. F., Rauh, E. G., and Thorn, R. J., *J. Inorg. Nucl. Chem.,* 28, 111, 1966.
5. Armstrong, D. R., Marantz, S., and Coyle, C. E., *J. Am. Chem. Soc.,* 81, 3798, 1959.
6. Balducci, G., De Maria, G., and Guido, M., *J. Chem. Phys.,* 50, 5424, 1969.
7. Balfour, W. J. and Whitlock, R. E., *J. Chem. Soc., D,* 1231, 1971.
8. Barrow, R. E., *Trans. Faraday Soc.,* 56, 952, 1960.
9. Barrow, R. E., *Nature,* 189, 480, 1961.
10. Barrow, R. F. and Caunt, A. D., *Proc. R. Soc., Ser. A,* 219, 120, 1953.
11. Barrow, R. F. and Deutsch, E. W., *Proc. Chem. Soc.,* 122, 1960.
12. Barrow, R. F., Gissane, W. J. M., and Travis, D. N., *Proc. R. Soc., Ser. A,* 287, 240, 1965.
13. Barrow, R. F. and Travis, D. N., *Proc. R. Soc., Ser. A,* 273, 133, 1963.

14. Bergman, C., Coppens, P., Drowart, J., and Smoes, S., *Trans. Faraday Soc.*, 66, 800, 1970.
15. Berkowitz, J. and Chupka, W. A., *J. Chem. Phys.*, 45, 1287, 1966.
16. Berkowitz, J. and Walter, T., *J. Chem. Phys.*, 49, 1184, 1968.
17. Besenbruch, G., Kana'an, A. S., and Margrave, J. L., *J. Phys. Chem.*, 69, 3174, 1965.
18. Blue, G. D., Green, J. W., Bautista, R. G., and Margrave, J. L., *J. Phys. Chem.*, 67, 877, 1963.
19. Brewer, L. and Brackett, E., *Chem. Rev.*, 61, 425, 1961.
20. Brewer, L. and Rosenblatt, G. M., *Adv. High Temp. Sci.*, 2, 1, 1969.
21. Brix, P. and Herzberg, G., *J. Chem. Phys.*, 21, 2240, 1953.
22. Broderson, P. H. and Sicre, J. E., *Z. Phys.*, 141, 515, 1955.
23. Bruner, B. L. and Corbett, J. D., *U.S.A.E.C.I.S.*, 739, 1963.
24. Bulewicz, E. M. and Sugden, T. M., *Trans. Faraday Soc.*, 52, 1475, 1956.
25. Carbonel, M. and Laffitte, M., *C.R. Acad. Sci., Paris, Ser. C*, 270, 2105, 1970.
26. Cater, E. D., Rauh, E. G., and Thorn, R. J., *J. Chem. Phys.*, 44, 3106, 1966.
27. Cater, E. D. and Steiger, R. P., *J. Phys. Chem.*, 72, 2231, 1968.
28. Cocke, D. L. and Gingerich, K. A., *J. Phys. Chem.*, 75, 3264, 1971.
29. Cocke, D. L. and Gingerich, K. A., *J. Phys. Chem.*, 76, 2332, 1972.
30. Colin, R. and Drowart, J., *Trans. Faraday Soc.*, 60, 673, 1964.
31. Colin, R. and Drowart, J., *Trans. Faraday Soc.*, 64, 2611, 1968.
32. Colin, R., Goldfinger, P., and Jeunehomme, M., *Trans. Faraday Soc.*, 60, 306, 1964.
33. Coppens, P., Smoes, S., and Drowart, J., *Trans. Faraday Soc.*, 63, 2140, 1967.
34. Corbett, J. D. and Lynde, R. A., *Inorg. Chem.*, 6, 2199, 1967.
35. Cubicciotti, D., *J. Phys. Chem.*, 71, 3066, 1967.
36. Cubicciotti, D., *Inorg. Chem.*, 7, 208, 1968.
37. Cubicciotti, D., *Inorg. Chem.*, 7, 211, 1968.
38. Davis, D. D. and Okabe, H., *J. Chem. Phys.*, 49, 5526, 1968.
39. De Corpo, J. J., Steiger, R. P., Franklin, J. L., and Margrave, J. L., *J. Chem. Phys.*, 53, 936, 1970.
40. De Maria, G., Drowart, J., and Inghram, M. G., *J. Chem. Phys.*, 31, 1076, 1959.
41. De Maria, G., Gingerich, K. A., Malaspina, L., and Piacente, V., *J. Chem. Phys.*, 44, 2531, 1966.
42. De Maria, G., Goldfinger, P., Malaspina, L., and Piacente, V., *Trans. Faraday Soc.*, 61, 2146, 1965.
43. De Maria, G., Malaspina, L., and Piacente, V., *J. Chem. Phys.*, 52, 1019, 1970.
44. De Maria, G., Malaspina, L., and Piacente, V., *J. Chem. Phys.*, 56, 1978, 1972.
45. Dixon, R. N. and Lambertson, H. M., *J. Mol. Spectrosc.*, 25, 12, 1968.
46. Drowart, J., *Phase Stabil. Metals Alloys*, 305, 1967.
47. Drowart, J., De Maria, G., and Inghram, M. G., *J. Chem. Phys.*, 29, 1015, 1958.
48. Drowart, J. and Goldfinger, P., *Q. Rev.* (London), 20, 545, 1966.
49. Drowart, J. and Honig, R. E., *J. Phys. Chem.*, 61, 980, 1957.
50. Drowart, J., Myers, C. E., Szwarc, R., Vander Auwera-Mahieu, A., and Uy, O. M., *J. Chem. Soc. Faraday Trans. II*, 68, 1749, 1972.
51. Edwards, J. G., Franklin, H. F., and Gilles, P. W., *J. Chem. Phys.*, 54, 545, 1971.
52. Ehlert, T. C., Hilmer, R. M., and Beauchamp, E. A., *J. Inorg. Nucl. Chem.*, 30, 3112, 1968.
53. Ehlert, T. C. and Margrave, J. L., *J. Chem. Phys.*, 41, 1066, 1964.
54. Faure, F. M., Mitchell, M. J., and Bartlett, R. W., *High Temp. Sci.*, 4, 181, 1972.
55. Fries, J. A. and Cater, E. D., Report COO-1182-27, supported under USAEC Contract AT(11-1)-1182.
56. Frost, D. C. and McDowell, C. A., *Proc. R. Soc., Ser. A*, 236, 278, 1956.
57. Fujishiro, S., *Trans. Jap. Inst. Metals*, 1, 125, 1960.
58. Gaydon, A. G., *Dissociation Energies and Spectra of Diatomic Molecules*, 3rd ed., Chapman and Hall, London, 1968.
59. Gingerich, K. A., *J. Phys. Chem.*, 68, 768, 1964.
60. Gingerich, K. A., *J. Chem. Phys.*, 47, 2192, 1967.
61. Gingerich, K. A., *J. Chem. Phys.*, 49, 19, 1968.
62. Gingerich, K. A., *High Temp. Sci.*, 1, 258, 1969.
63. Gingerich, K. A., *J. Chem. Phys.*, 50, 2255, 1969.
64. Gingerich, K. A., *J. Phys. Chem.*, 73, 2734, 1969.
65. Gingerich, K. A., *Chem. Commun.*, 10, 580, 1970.
66. Gingerich, K. A., *J. Chem. Phys.*, 54, 2646, 1971.
67. Gingerich, K. A., *J. Chem. Phys.*, 54, 3720, 1971.

68. Gingerich, K. A., *High Temp. Sci.*, 3, 415, 1971.
69. Gingerich, K. A., *J. Chem. Phys.*, 56, 4239, 1972.
70. Gingerich, K. A. and Blue, G. D., *J. Chem. Phys.*, 47, 5447, 1967.
71. Gingerich, K. A. and Cocke, D. L., *J. Chem. Soc. Chem. Commun.*, 536, 1972.
72. Gingerich, K. A. and Finkbeiner, H. C., *Proc. Rare Earth Res. Conf. 9th*, 2, 795, 1971.
73. Gingerich, K. A. and Finkbeiner, H. C., *J. Chem. Phys.*, 54, 2621, 1971.
74. Gingerich, K. A. and Piacente, V., *J. Chem. Phys.*, 54, 2498, 1971.
75. Ginter, D. S., Ginter, M. L., and Innes, K. K., *Astrophys. J.*, 139, 365, 1964.
76. Graeber, P. and Weil, K. G., *Ber. Bunsenges. Phys. Chem.*, 76, 417, 1972.
77. Guido, M., Gigli, G., and Balducci, G., *J. Chem. Phys.*, 57, 3731, 1972.
78. Gunn, S. R., *J. Phys. Chem.*, 68, 949, 1964.
79. Hagland, I., Kopp, I., and Auslund, N., *Ark. Fys.*, 32, 321, 1966.
80. Herman, R. and Herman, L., *J. Phys. Radium*, 24, 73, 1963.
81. Herzberg, G., *Molecular Spectra and Molecular Structure. I. Spectra of Diatomic Molecules*, 2nd ed., Van Nostrand, New York, 1950.
82. Herzberg, G., *J. Mol. Spectrosc.*, 33, 147, 1970.
83. Hildenbrand, D. L., *J. Chem. Phys.*, 48, 3657, 1968.
84. Hildenbrand, D. L., *J. Chem. Phys.*, 52, 5751, 1970.
85. Hildenbrand, D. L., *Chem. Phys. Lett.*, 15, 379, 1972.
86. Hildenbrand, D. L. and Murad, E., *J. Chem. Phys.*, 44, 1524, 1966.
87. Hildenbrand, D. L. and Murad, E., *J. Chem. Phys.*, 53, 3403, 1970.
88. Hildenbrand, D. L. and Theard, L. P., *J. Chem. Phys.*, 50, 5350, 1969.
89. Hurley, A. C., *Proc. R. Soc., Ser. A*, 261, 237, 1961.
90. Johns, J. W. C. and Ramsey, D. A., *Can. J. Phys.*, 39, 210, 1961.
91. Johnston, H. S. and Woolfolk, R., *J. Chem. Phys.*, 41, 269, 1964.
92. Kant, A., *J. Chem. Phys.*, 41, 1872, 1964.
93. Kant, A., *J. Chem. Phys.*, 49, 5144, 1968.
94. Kant, A. and Lin, S-S., *J. Chem. Phys.*, 51, 1644, 1969.
95. Kant, A., Lin, S-S., and Strauss, B., *J. Chem. Phys.*, 49, 1983, 1968.
96. Kant, A. and Strauss, B. H., *J. Chem. Phys.*, 41, 3806, 1964.
97. Kant, A. and Strauss, B., *J. Chem. Phys.*, 49, 3579, 1968.
98. Kant, A., Strauss, B., and Lin, S-S., *J. Chem. Phys.*, 52, 2384, 1970.
99. Kent, R. A., *J. Am. Chem. Soc.*, 90, 5657, 1968.
100. Kent, R. A., Ehlert, T. C., and Margrave, J. L., *J. Am. Chem. Soc.*, 86, 5090, 1964.
101. Kent, R. A., McDonald, J. D., and Margrave, J. L., *J. Phys. Chem.*, 70, 874, 1966.
102. Kent, R. A. and Margrave, J. L., *J. Am. Chem. Soc.*, 87, 5382, 1965.
103. Klynning, L., Lundgrew, B., and Auslund, N., *Ark. Fys.*, 30, 141, 1965.
104. Kohl, F. J. and Carlson, K. D., *J. Am. Chem. Soc.*, 90, 4814, 1968.
105. Kordis, J. and Gingerich, K. A., *J. Phys. Chem.*, 76, 2336, 1972.
106. Kronekvist, M. and Lagerqvist, A., *Ark. Fys.*, 39, 133, 1969.
107. Kronekvist, M., Lagerqvist, A., and Neuhaus, H., *J. Mol. Spectrosc.*, 39, 516, 1971.
108. LeRoy, R. J., *J. Chem. Phys.*, 57, 573, 1972.
109. LeRoy, R. J. and Bernstein, R. B., *Chem. Phys. Lett.*, 5, 42, 1970.
110. Lin, S-S. and Kant, A., *J. Phys. Chem.*, 73, 2450, 1969.
111. Liu, B., *Phys. Rev. Lett.*, 27, 1251, 1971.
112. McIntyre, N. S., Vander Auwera-Mahieu, A., and Drowart, J., *Trans. Faraday Soc.*, 64, 3006, 1968.
113. Marquart, J. R. and Berkowitz, J., *J. Chem. Phys.*, 39, 283, 1963.
114. Milton, E. R. V., Dunford, H. B., and Douglas, A. E., *J. Chem. Phys.*, 35, 1202, 1961.
115. Mole, M. F. and McCoubrey, J. C., *Nature*, 202, 450, 1964.
116. Muenow, D. W., Hastie, J. W., Hauge, R., Bautista, R., and Margrave, J. L., *Trans. Faraday Soc.*, 65, 3210, 1969.
117. Murad, E., Hildenbrand, D. L., and Main, R. P., *J. Chem. Phys.*, 45, 263, 1966.
118. Neckel, A. and Sodeck, G., *Monatsh. Chem.*, 103, 367, 1972.
119. O'Hare, P. A. G., *J. Chem. Phys.*, 52, 2992, 1970.
120. Ovcharenko, I. E., Ya. Kuzyankov, Y., and Tatevaskii, V. M., *Opt. Spektrosk.*, 19, 528, 1965.
121. Peeters, R., Vander Auwera-Mahieu, A., and Drowart, J., *Z. Naturforsch.*, 4, 26, 327, 1971.
122. Pelevin, O. V., Mil'vidskii, M. G., Belyaev, A. I., and Khotin, B. A., *Izv. Akad. Nauk SSSR Neorgan. Mat.*, 2, 942, 1966.
123. Phillips, L. F., *Can. J. Chem.*, 46, 1429, 1968.

124. Piacente, V. and Desideri, A., *J. Chem. Phys.*, 57, 2213, 1972.
125. Piacente, V. and Gingerich, K. A., *High Temp. Sci.*, 4, 312, 1972.
126. Piacente, V. and Malaspina, L., *J. Chem. Phys.*, 56, 1780, 1972.
127. Porter, R. F. and Spencer, C. W. J., *J. Chem. Phys.*, 32, 943, 1960.
128. Ringstrom, U., *Ark. Fys.*, 27, 227, 1964.
129. Ringstrom, U., *J. Mol. Spectrosc.*, 36, 232, 1970.
130. Ringstrom, U. and Auslund, N., *Ark. Fys.*, 32, 19, 1966.
131. Schultz, J., *Compt. Rend.*, 252, 1750, 1961.
132. Shardanand, *Phys. Rev.*, 160, 67, 1967.
133. Shenyavskaya, E. A., Mal'tsev, A. A., Kataev, D. I., and Gurvich, L. V., *Opt. Spektrosk.*, 26, 937, 1969.
134. Siegel, B., *Q. Rev.* (London), 19, 77, 1965.
135. Smith, P. K. and Peterson, D. E., U.S.A.E.C. 1968 DM-MS-67-110.
136. Smoes, S., Coppens, P., Bergman, C., and Drowart, J., *Trans. Faraday Soc.*, 65, 682, 1969.
137. Smoes, S. and Drowart, J., *Chem. Commun.*, 534, 1968.
138. Smoes, S., Huguet, R., and Drowart, J., *Z. Naturforsch. A.*, 26, 1934, 1971.
139. Smoes, S., Myers, C. E., and Drowart, J., *Chem. Phys. Lett.*, 8, 10, 1971.
140. Stearns, C. A. and Kohl, F. J., *High Temp. Sci.*, 2, 146, 1970; NASA Tech. Note 1969 NASA-TN-D-5027.
141. Torshina, V. V., Smolina, G. N., and Dobychin, S. L., *Zh. Prikl. Khim.*, 39, 1468, 1966.
142. Uy, O. M. and Drowart, J., *Trans. Faraday Soc.*, 65, 3221, 1969.
143. Uy, O. M. and Drowart, J., *High Temp. Sci.*, 2, 293, 1970.
144. Uy, O. M., Muenow, D. W., Ficalora, P. J., and Margrave, J. L., *Trans. Faraday Soc.*, 64, 2998, 1968.
145. Vander Auwera-Mahieu, A. and Drowart, J., *Chem. Phys. Lett.*, 1, 311, 1967.
146. Vander Auwera-Mahieu, A., McIntyre, N. S., and Drowart, J., *Chem. Phys. Lett.*, 4, 198, 1969.
147. Vander Auwera-Mahieu, A., Peeters, R., McIntyre, N. S., and Drowart, J., *Trans. Faraday Soc.*, 66, 809, 1970.
148. Velasco, R., *Can. J. Phys.*, 35, 1204, 1957.
149. Velasco, R., Ottinger, C., and Zare, R. N., *J. Chem. Phys.*, 51, 5522, 1969.
150. Verhaegen, G., Ph.D. thesis, University of Brussels, 1965.
151. Verhaegen, G., Smoes, S., and Drowart, J., U.S.A.E.C. WADD TR60-782, Part 19, 1963.
152. Verhaegen, G., Smoes, S., and Drowart, J., *J. Chem. Phys.*, 40, 239, 1964.
153. Wiedemeier, H. and Gilles, P. W., *J. Chem. Phys.*, 42, 2765, 1965.
154. Wiedemeier, H. and Goyette, W. J., *J. Chem. Phys.*, 48, 2936, 1968.
155. Wieland, Von K., *Z. Elektrochem.*, 64, 761, 1960.
156. Wu, Y. H. and Wahlbeck, P. G., *J. Chem. Phys.*, 56, 4534, 1972.
157. Zmbov, K. F., Hastie, J. W., and Margrave, J. L., *Trans. Faraday Soc.*, 64, 861, 1968.
158. Zmbov, K. F. and Margrave, J. L., *J. Chem. Phys.*, 45, 3167, 1966.
159. Zmbov, K. F. and Margrave, J. L., *J. Inorg. Nucl. Chem.*, 29, 59, 1976.
160. Zmbov, K. F. and Margrave, J. L., *J. Phys. Chem.*, 47, 3122, 1967.
161. Zmbov, K. F. and Margrave, J. L., *J. Phys. Chem.*, 71, 2893, 1967.

STRENGTHS OF CHEMICAL BONDS (*Continued*)

HEATS OF FORMATION OF GASEOUS ATOMS FROM ELEMENTS IN THEIR STANDARD STATES

J. A. Kerr, M. J. Parsonage, and A. F. Trotman-Dickenson

For elements that are diatomic gases in their standard states these are readily obtained from the bond strength. For elements that are crystalline in their standard states they are derived from vapor pressure data. All values are given in kcal mol^{-1} at 298 K.

Element	kcal mol^{-1}	Ref.	Element	kcal mol^{-1}	Ref.
H$_2$(g)	52.104 ± 0.001	1	Zr(c)	145.5 ± 1	2
Li(c)	38.6 ± 0.4	2	Nb(c)	172.4 ± 1	2
Be(c)	77.5 ± 1.5	2	Mo(c)	157.3 ± 0.5	2
B(c)	136.5 ± 3	2	Ru(c)	155.5 ± 1.5	2
C(c)	171.29 ± 0.11	1	Rh(c)	133 ± 1	2
N$_2$(g)	112.97 ± 0.10	1	Pd(c)	90.0 ± 0.5	2
O$_2$(g)	59.553 ± 0.024	1	Ag(c)	67.9 ± 0.2	2
F$_2$(g)	18.9	2	Cd(c)	26.72 ± 0.15	2
Na(c)	25.85 ± 0.15	2	In(c)	58 ± 1	2
Mg(c)	35.0 ± 0.3	2	Sn(c)	72.2 ± 0.5	2
Al(c)	78.7 ± 0.5	2	Sb(c)	63.2 ± 0.6	2
Si(c)	108.9 ± 1	2	Te(c)	47.0 ± 0.5	2
P(c) yellow	79.4 ± 10	2	I$_2$(c)	25.517 ± 0.010	1
S(c)	66.2 ± 2	2	Cs(c)	18.7 ± 0.1	2
Cl$_2$(g)	28.989 ± 0.002	1	Ba(c)	42.5 ± 1	2
K(c)	21.42 ± 0.05	2	Ce(c)	101 ± 3	2
Ca(c)	42.6 ± 0.4	2	Sm(c)	49.4 ± 0.5	2
Sc(c)	90.3 ± 1	2	Er(c)	75.8 ± 1	2
Ti(c)	112.3 ± 0.5	2	Yb	36.35 ± 0.2	2
V(c)	122.9 ± 0.3	2	Hf(c)	148 ± 1	2
Cr(c)	95 ± 1	2	Ta(c)	186.9 ± 0.6	2
Mn(c)	67.7 ± 1	2	W(c)	203.1 ± 1	2
Fe(c)	99.3 ± 0.3	2	Re(c)	185 ± 1.5	2
Co(c)	102.4 ± 1	2	Os(c)	188 ± 1.5	2
Ni(c)	102.8 ± 0.5	2	Ir(c)	160 ± 1	2
Cu(c)	80.7 ± 0.3	2	Pt(c)	135.2 ± 0.3	2
Zn(c)	31.25 ± 0.1	2	Au(c)	88.0 ± 0.5	2
Ga(c)	65.4 ± 0.5	2	Hg(c)	14.69 ± 0.03	2
Ge(c)	89.5 ± 0.5	2	Tl(c)	43.55 ± 0.1	2
As(c)	72.3 ± 3	2	Pb(c)	46.62 ± 0.3	2
Se(c)	54.3 ± 1	2	Bi(c)	50.1 ± 0.5	2
Br$_2$(e)	26.730 ± 0.029	1	U(c)	126 ± 3	2
Rb(c)	19.6 ± 0.1	2	Th(c)	137.5 ± 0.5	2
Sr(c)	39.1 ± 0.5	2	Pu(c)	87.1 ± 4	2
Y(c)	101.5 ± 0.5	2			

References

1. *Tentative Set of Key Values for Thermodynamics — Part 1*, International Council of Scientific Unions, Committee on Data for Science and Technology, CODATA Bulletin No. 2, November 1970.
2. **Brewer, L. and Rosenblatt, G. M.**, *Adv. High Temp. Chem.*, 2, 1, 1969.

STRENGTHS OF CHEMICAL BONDS (*Continued*)

BOND STRENGTHS IN POLYATOMIC MOLECULES

J. A. Kerr, M. J. Parsonage, and A. F. Trotman-Dickenson

The values below refer to a temperature of 298 K and have mostly been determined by kinetic methods (see References 8 and 44 for a full discussion of the methods).

Some have been calculated from the heats of formation of the species involved according to the equations:

$$D(R-X) = \Delta H_f^\circ(\dot{R}) + \Delta H_f^\circ(\dot{X}) - \Delta H_f^\circ(RX)$$

or

$$D(R-R) = 2\Delta H_f^\circ(\dot{R}) - \Delta H_f^\circ(RR)$$

The sources of the data on the heats of formation are given in the references.

An attempt has been made to list all the important values obtained by methods that are considered to be valid. The references are intended to serve as a guide to the literature.

Bond	kcal mol^{-1}	Ref.
H–CH	102 ± 2	15, 71
H–CH$_2$	110 ± 2	15, 71
H–CH$_3$	104 ± 1	39
H-ethynyl	128 ± 5	79
H-vinyl	⩾108 ± 2	39
H–C$_2$H$_5$	98 ± 1	39
H–propargyl	93.9 ± 1.2	76
H–allyl	89 ± 1	39
H–cyclopropyl	100.7 ± 1	27
H–n-C$_3$H$_7$	98 ± 1	39
H–i-C$_3$H$_7$	95 ± 1	39
H–cyclobutyl	96.5 ± 1	27, 56
H–cyclopropylcarbinyl	97.4 ± 1.6	55
H–methallyl	83 ± 1	39
H–s-C$_4$H$_9$	95 ± 1	39
H–t-C$_4$H$_9$	92 ± 1	39
H–cyclopentadien-1,3-yl–5	81.2 ± 1.2	37
H–pentadien–1,4-yl-3	80 ± 1	39
H–cyclopentenyl-3	82.3 ± 1	36
H–spiropentyl	98.8 ± 1	27
H–cyclopentyl	94.5 ± 1	27, 35
H–dimethylallyl	77.2 ± 1.5	72
H–neo-C$_5$H$_{11}$	100.3 ± 1	51
H–C$_6$H$_5$	110.2 ± 2.0	14
H–cyclohexadieny-1,3-yl-5	70 ± 5	42
H–cyclohexyl	95.5 ± 1	27
H–CH$_2$C$_6$H$_5$	85 ± 1	39
H–cycloheptatrien-1,3-yl-7	73.4	73
H–norbornyl	96.7 ± 2.5	57
H–cycloheptyl	92.5 ± 1	27
H–CN	120 ± 1	23
H–CHO	87 ± 1	39
H–CH$_2$OH	94 ± 2	39
H–COCH$_3$	86.0 ± 0.8	24
H–CH$_2$OCH$_3$	93 ± 1	39

Bond	kcal mol^{-1}	Ref.
H–CH(CH$_3$)OH	93.0 ± 1.0	1
H COCH:CH$_2$	87.1 ± 1.0	2
H–CH$_2$COCH$_3$	98.3 ± 1.8	46, 69
H–COC$_2$H$_5$	87.4 ± 1.0	78
H–CH(OH)CH:CH$_2$	81.6 ± 1.8	4
H–C(CH$_3$)$_2$OH	91 ± 1	39
H–tetrahydrofuran-2-yl	92 + 1	39
H–CH(CH$_3$)COCH$_3$	92.3 ± 1.4	70
H–COC$_6$H$_5$	86.9 ± 1	68
H–COOCH$_3$	92.7 ± 1	66
H–CH$_2$OCOC$_6$H$_5$	100.2 ± 1.3	67
H–COCF$_3$	91.0 ± 2	5
H–CH$_2$F	101 ± 2	45
H–CHF$_2$	101 ± 2	45
H–CF$_3$	106 ± 1	39
H–CF$_2$Cl	104 ± 1	54
H–CH$_2$Cl	100.9	34
H–CHCl$_2$	99.0	34
H–CCl$_3$	95.7 ± 1	44
H–CH$_2$Br	102.0	34
H–CHBr$_2$	103.7	34
H–CBr$_3$	96.0 ± 1.6	47
H–CH$_2$I	103 ± 2	39
H–CHI$_2$	103 ± 2	39
H–C$_2$F$_5$	103.1 ± 1.5	7
H–CCl$_2$CHCl$_2$	94 ± 2	33, 71
H–C$_2$Cl$_5$	95 ± 2	32, 71
H–*n*-C$_3$F$_7$	104 ± 2	44
H–CHClCH:CH$_2$	88.6	3
H–NH$_2$	110 ± 2	40
H–NHCH$_3$	103 ± 2	40
H–N(CH$_3$)$_2$	95 ± 2	40
H–NHC$_6$H$_5$	80 ± 3	10, 44
H–N(CH$_3$)C$_6$H$_5$	74 ± 3	10, 44
H–NO	≤ 49.5	16
H–NF$_2$	75.7 ± 2.5	59, 71
H–N$_3$	85	41
H–OH	119 ± 1	44
H–OCH$_3$	103.6 ± 1	6, 10, 19, 71
H–OC$_2$H$_5$	103.9 ± 1	6, 10, 19, 71
H–OC(CH$_3$)$_3$	104.7 ± 1	6, 10, 19, 71
H–OC$_6$H$_5$	88 ± 5	13
H–O$_2$H	90 ± 2	44
H–O$_2$CCH$_3$	112 ± 4	44
H–O$_2$CC$_2$H$_5$	110 ± 4	44
H–O$_2$C*n*-C$_3$H$_7$	103 ± 4	44
H–ONO	78.3 ± 0.5	9, 71
H–ONO$_2$	101.2 ± 0.5	9, 71
H–SH	90 ± 2	44
H–SCH$_3$	≥ 88	44
H–SiH$_3$	94 ± 3	64
H–Si(CH$_3$)$_3$	90 ± 3	77
BH$_3$–BH$_3$	35	10
HC≡CH	230 ± 2	15, 71
H$_2$C–CH$_2$	172 ± 2	15, 71

Bond	kcal mol^{-1}	Ref.
H_3C-CH_3	88 ± 2	44
$CH_3-C(CH_3)_2CH:CH_2$	69.4	10
$C_6H_5CH_2-C_2H_5$	69 ± 2	44
$C_6H_5CH(CH_3)-CH_3$	71	10
$C_6H_5CH_2-n-C_3H_7$	67 ± 2	44
CH_3-CH_2CN	72.7 ± 2	10, 44
$CH_3-C(CH_3)_2CN$	70.2 ± 2	10, 44
$C_6H_5C(CH_3)(CN)-CH_3$	59.9	10
$NC-CN$	128 ± 1	23
$C_6H_5CH_2CO-CH_2C_6H_5$	65.4	10
$C_6H_5CO-CF_3$	73.8	10
$CH_3CO-COCH_3$	67.4 ± 2.3	48
$C_6H_5CH_2-COOH$	68.1	10
$C_6H_5CH_2-O_2CCH_3$	67	10
$C_6H_5CO-COC_6H_5$	66.4	10
$C_6H_5CH_2-O_2CC_6H_5$	69	10
$(C_6H_5CH_2)_2CH-COOH$	59.4	10
CH_2F-CH_2F	88 ± 2	45
$CF_2=CF_2$	76.3 ± 3	80
CF_3-CF_3	96.9 ± 2	17
$C_6H_5CH_2-NH_2$	71.9 ± 1	40
$C_6H_5NH-CH_3$	67.7	10
$C_6H_5CH_2-NHCH_3$	68.7 ± 1	40
$C_6H_5N(CH_3)-CH_3$	65.2	10
$C_6H_5CH_2-N(CH_3)_2$	60.9 ± 1	40
CF_3-NF_2	65 ± 2.5	71, 74
$CH_2=N_2$	$\leqslant 41.7 \pm 1$	52
$CH_3N:N-CH_3$	52.5	10, 58
$C_2H_5N:N-C_2H_5$	50.0	10, 58
$i-C_3H_7N:N-i-C_3H_7$	47.5	10, 58
$n-C_4H_9N:N-n-C_4H_9$	50.0	10, 58
$i-C_4H_9N:N-i-C_4H_9$	49.0	10, 58
$s-C_4H_9N:N-s-C_4H_9$	46.7	10, 58
$t-C_4H_9N:N-t-C_4H_9$	43.5	10, 58
$C_6H_5CH_2N:N-CH_2C_6H_5$	37.6	10, 58
$CF_3N:N-CF_3$	55.2	10, 58
$C_2H_5-NO_2$	62	65, 71
$O=CO$	127.2 ± 0.1	21
$CH_3-O_2SCH_3$	66.8	10, 44
$Allyl-O_2SCH_3$	49.6	10, 44
$C_6H_5CH_2-O_2SCH_3$	52.9	10, 44
$C_6H_5S-CH_3$	60	44
$C_6H_5CH_2-SCH_3$	53.8	10
$F-CH_3$	103 ± 3	25, 44
$Cl-CN$	97 ± 1	23
$Cl-COC_6H_5$	74 ± 3	44
$Cl-CF_3$	86.1 ± 0.8	18
$Cl-CCl_2F$	73 ± 2	31
$Cl-C_2F_5$	82.7 ± 1.7	18
$Br-CH_3$	70.0 ± 1.2	26
$Br-CN$	83 ± 1	23
$Br-COC_6H_5$	64.2	10
$Br-CF_3$	70.6 ± 1.0	28, 30
$Br-CBr_3$	56.2 ± 1.8	47
$Br-C_2F_5$	68.7 ± 1.5	18, 29, 30

BOND STRENGTHS IN POLYATOMIC MOLECULES (*Continued*)

Bond	kcal mol^{-1}	Ref.
Br$-n-$C$_3$F$-$	66.5 ± 2.5	18
I$-$CH$_3$	56.3 ± 1	44
I$-$norbornyl	62.5 ± 2.5	57
I$-$CN	73 ± 1	23
I$-$CF$_3$	53.5 ± 2	12
CH$_3$$-$Ga(CH$_3$)$_2$	59.5	10, 58
CH$_3$$-$CdCH$_3$	54.4	10, 58
CH$_3$ HgCH$_3$	57.5	49
C$_2$H$_5$ HgC$_2$H$_5$	43.7 ± 1	50
n-C$_3$H$_7$$-Hgn$-C$_3H_7$	47.1	10, 58
i-C$_3$H$_7$$-Hgi$-C$_3H_7$	40.7	10, 58
C$_6$H$_5$$-HgC_6H_5$	68	10, 58
CH$_3$$-$Tl(CH$_3$)$_2$	36.4 ± 0.6	63
CH$_3$$-$Pb(CH$_3$)$_3$	49.4 ± 1	38
NH$_2$$-NH_2$	70.8 ± 2	10, 58
NH$_2$$-$NHCH$_3$	64.8	10, 58
NH$_2$$-$N(CH$_3$)$_2$	62.7	10, 58
NH$_2$$-NHC_6H_5$	51.1	10, 58
NO$-$NO$_2$	9.5 ± 0.5	44
NO$_2$$-NO_2$	12.9 ± 0.5	44
NF$_2$$-NF_2$	21 ± 1	21
O$-$N$_2$	40	9, 71
O$-$NO	73	8, 71
HO$-$N:CHCH$_3$	49.7	10, 58
Cl$-$NF$_2$	$\sim$ 32	61, 71
HO$-$OH	51 ± 1	44
CH$_3$O$-$OCH$_3$	36.9 ± 1	10, 58
HO$-$OC(CH$_3$)$_3$	42.5	10, 11
C$_2$H$_5$O$-$OC$_2$H$_5$	37.3 ± 1.2	53
n-C$_3$H$_7$O$-$On-C$_3$H$_7$	37.2 ± 1	10, 58
i-C$_3$H$_7$O$-$Oi-C$_3$H$_7$	37.0 ± 1	43
s-C$_4$H$_9$O$-$Os-C$_4$H$_9$	36.4 ± 1	75
t-C$_4$H$_9$O$-$Ot-C$_4$H$_9$	37.4 ± 1	10, 44
(CH$_3$)$_3$CCH$_2$O$-$OCH$_2$C(CH$_3$)$_3$	36.4 ± 1	60
O$-$O$_2$ClF	58.4	10, 58
CH$_3$CO$_2$$-O_2CCH_3$	30.4 ± 2	10, 44
C$_2$H$_5$CO$_2$$-O_2CC_2H_5$	30.4 ± 2	10, 44
n-C$_3$H$_7$CO$_2$$-O_2Cn$-C$_3H_7$	30.4 ± 2	10, 44
O$-$SO	132 ± 2	21
F$-$OCF$_3$	43.5 ± 0.5	20
Cl$-$OH	60 ± 3	44
O$-$ClO	59 ± 3	21
Br$-$OH	56 ± 3	44
I$-$OH	56 ± 3	44
ClO$_3$$-ClO_4$	58.4	10, 58
O=PF$_3$	130 ± 5	44
O=PCl$_3$	122 ± 5	44
O=PBr$_3$	119 ± 5	44
SiH$_3$$-SiH_3$	81 ± 4	62, 64
(CH$_3$)$_3$Si$-$Si(CH$_3$)$_3$	80.5	22

References

1. Alfassi, Z. B. and Golden, D. M., *J. Phys. Chem.,* 76, 3314, 1972.
2. Alfassi, Z. B. and Golden, D. M., *J. Am. Chem. Soc.,* 95, 319, 1973.
3. Alfassi, Z. B., Golden, D. M., and Benson, S. W., *Int. J. Chem. Kinet.,* 5, 155, 1973; Trenwith, A. B., *Int. J. Chem. Kinet.,* 5, 67, 1973.
4. Alfassi, Z. B. and Golden, D. M., *Int. J. Chem. Kinet.,* 5, 295, 1973; Trenwith, A. B., *J. Chem. Soc. Faraday Trans. I,* 69, 1737, 1973.
5. Amphlett J. C. and Whittle, E., *Trans. Faraday Soc.,* 66, 2016, 1970.
6. Baker, G., Littlefair J. H., Shaw, R., and Thynne, J. C. J., *J. Chem. Soc.,* 6970, 1965.
7. Bassett J. E. and Whittle, E., *J. Chem. Soc. Faraday Trans. I,* 68, 492, 1972.
8. Benson, S. W., *J. Chem. Educ.,* 42, 502, 1965.
9. Benson, S. W., *Thermochemical Kinetics,* John Wiley and Sons, New York, 1968.
10. Benson, S. W. and O'Neal, H. E., *Kinetic Data on Gas Phase Unimolecular Reactions,* NSRDS-NBS 21, 1970.
11. Benson, S. W. and Spokes, G. N., *J. Phys. Chem.,* 72, 1182, 1968.
12. Boyd, R. K., Downs, G. W., Gow, J. S., and Horrex, C., *J. Phys. Chem.,* 67, 719, 1963.
13. Carson, A. S., Fine, D. H., Gray, P., and Laye, P. G., *J. Chem. Soc., B,* 1611, 1971.
14. Chamberlain, G. A. and Whittle, E., *Trans. Faraday Soc.,* 67, 2077, 1971.
15. Chupka, W. A. and Lifshitz, C., *J. Chem. Phys.,* 48, 1109, 1968.
16. Clement, M. J. Y. and Ramsay, D. A., *Can. J. Phys.,* 39, 205, 1961.
17. Coomber, J. W. and Whittle, E., *Trans. Faraday Soc.,* 63, 1394, 1967.
18. Coomber, J. W. and Whittle, E., *Trans. Faraday Soc.,* 63, 2656, 1967.
19. Cox, J. D. and Pilcher, G., *Thermochemistry of Organic and Organometallic Compounds,* Academic Press, New York, 1970.
20. Czarnarski, J., Castellano, E., and Shumacher, H. J., *Chem. Commun.,* 1255, 1968.
21. Darwent, B. de B., *Bond Dissociation Energies in Simple Molecules,* NSRDS-NBS, 31, 1970.
22. Davidson, I. M. T. and Howard, A. B., *J. Chem. Soc. Chem. Commun.,* 323, 1973.
23. Davis, D. D. and Okabe, H., *J. Chem. Phys.,* 49, 5526, 1968.
24. Devore, J. A. and O'Neal, H. E., *J. Phys. Chem.,* 73, 2644, 1969.
25. Dibeler, V. H. and Reese, R. M., *J. Res. Nat. Bur. Stand.,* 54, 127, 1955.
26. Ferguson, K. C., Okafo, E. N., and Whittle, E., *J. Chem. Soc. Faraday Trans. I,* 69, 295, 1973.
27. Ferguson, K. C. and Whittle, E., *Trans. Faraday Soc.,* 67, 2618, 1971; Jones, S. H. and Whittle E., *Int. J. Chem. Kinet.,* 2, 479, 1970.
28. Ferguson, K. C. and Whittle, E., *J. Chem. Soc. Faraday Trans. I,* 68, 295, 1972.
29. Ferguson, K. C. and Whittle, E., *J. Chem. Soc. Faraday Trans. I,* 68, 306, 1972.
30. Ferguson, K. C. and Whittle, E., *J. Chem. Soc. Faraday Trans. I,* 68, 641, 1972.
31. Foon, R. and Tait, K. B., *J. Chem. Soc. Faraday Trans. I,* 68, 104, 1972.
32. Franklin, J. A., Huybrechts, G. H., and Cillien, C., *Trans. Faraday Soc.,* 65, 2094, 1969.
33. Franklin, J. A. and Huybrechts, G. H., *Int. J. Chem. Kinet.,* 1, 1, 1969.
34. Furuyama, S., Golden, D. M., and Benson, S. W., *J. Am. Chem. Soc.,* 91, 7564, 1969.
35. Furuyama, S., Golden, D. M., and Benson, S. W., *Int. J. Chem. Kinet.,* 2, 83, 1970.
36. Furuyama, S., Golden, D. M., and Benson, S. W., *Int. J. Chem. Kinet.,* 2, 93, 1970.
37. Furuyama, S., Golden, D. M., and Benson, S. W., *Int. J. Chem. Kinet.,* 3, 237, 1971.
38. Gilroy, K. M., Price, S. J., and Webster, N. J., *Can. J. Chem.,* 50, 2639, 1972.

39. Golden, D. M. and Benson, S. W., *Chem. Rev.,* 69, 125, 1969.
40. Golden, D. M., Solly, R. K., Gac, N. A., and Benson, S. W., *J. Am. Chem. Soc.,* 94, 363, 1972.
41. Gray, P., *Q. Rev.* (London), 17, 441, 1963.
42. James, D. G. L. and Suart, R. D., *Trans. Faraday Soc.,* 64, 2752, 1968.
43. Kerr, J. A., *Ann. Rep. Chem. Soc., A,* 64, 73, 1967.
44. Kerr, J. A., *Chem. Rev.,* 66, 465, 1966.
45. Kerr, J. A. and Timlin, D. M., *Int. J. Chem. Kinet.,* 3, 427, 1971.
46. King, K. D., Golden, D. M., and Benson, S. W., *J. Am. Chem. Soc.,* 92, 5541, 1970.
47. King, K. D., Golden, D. M., and Benson, S. W., *J. Phys. Chem.,* 75, 987, 1971.
48. Knoll, H., Scherker, K., and Geiseler, G., *Int. J. Chem. Kinet.,* 5, 271, 1973.
49. Kominar, R. J. and Price, S. J., *Can. J. Chem.,* 47, 991, 1969.
50. LaLonde, A. C. and Price, S. J. W., *Can. J. Chem.,* 49, 3367, 1971.
51. Larson, C. W., Hardwidge, E. A., and Rabinovitch, B. S., *J. Chem. Phys.,* 50, 2769, 1969.
52. Laufer, A. H. and Okabe, H., *J. Am. Chem. Soc.,* 93, 4137, 1971.
53. Leggett, C. and Thynne, J. C. J., *Trans. Faraday Soc.,* 63, 2504, 1967.
54. Leyland, L. M., Majer, J. R., and Robb, J. C., *Trans. Faraday Soc.,* 66, 898, 1970.
55. McMillen, D. F., Golden, D. M., and Benson, S. W., *Int. J. Chem. Kinet.,* 3, 359, 1971.
56. McMillen, D. F., Golden, D. M., and Benson, S. W., *Int. J. Chem. Kinet.,* 4, 487, 1972.
57. O'Neal, H. E., Bagg, J. W., and Richardson, W. H., *Int. J. Chem. Kinet.,* 2, 493, 1970.
58. O'Neal, H. E. and Benson, S. W., in *Free Radicals,* Kochi, J. K., Ed., John Wiley and Sons, New York, 1973, 275.
59. Pankratov, A. V., Zercheninov, A. N., Chesnokov, V. I., and Zhdanova, N. N., *Zh. Fiz. Khim.,* 43, 394, 1969.
60. Perona, M. J. and Golden, D. M., *Int. J. Chem. Kinet.,* 5, 55, 1973.
61. Petry, R. C., *J. Am. Chem. Soc.,* 89, 4600, 1967.
62. Potzinger, P. and Lampe, F. W., *J. Phys. Chem.,* 74, 719, 1970.
63. Price, S. J., Richard, J. P., Rufeldt, R. C., and Jacko, M. G., *Can J. Chem.,* 51, 1397, 1973.
64. Ring, M. A., Puentes, M. J., and O'Neal, H. E., *J. Am. Chem. Soc.,* 92, 4845, 1970; Steele, W. C. and Stone, F. G. A., *J. Am. Chem. Soc.,* 84, 3599, 1962; Steele, W. C., Nichols, L. D., and Stone, F. G. A., *J. Am. Chem. Soc.,* 84, 441, 1962.
65. Shaw, R., *Int. J. Chem. Kinet.,* 5, 261, 1973.
66. Solly, R. K. and Benson, S. W., *Int. J. Chem. Kinet.,* 1, 427, 1969.
67. Solly, R. K. and Benson, S. W., *Int. J. Chem. Kinet.,* 3, 509, 1971.
68. Solly, R. K. and Benson, S. W., *J. Am. Chem. Soc.,* 93, 1592, 1971.
69. Solly, R. K., Golden, D. M., and Benson, S. W., *Int. J. Chem. Kinet.,* 2, 11, 1970.
70. Solly, R. K., Golden, D. M., and Benson, S. W., *Int. J. Chem. Kinet.,* 2, 381, 1970.
71. Thermochemical calculation.
72. Trenwith, A. B., *Trans. Faraday Soc.,* 66, 2805, 1970.
73. Vincow, G., Dauben, H. J., Hunter, F. R., and Volland, W. V., *J. Am. Chem. Soc.,* 91, 2823, 1969.
74. Walker, L. C., *J. Chem. Thermodynamics,* 4, 219, 1972.
75. Walker, R. F. and Phillips, L., *J. Chem. Soc., A,* 2103, 1968.
76. Walsh, R., *Trans. Faraday Soc.,* 67, 2085, 1971.
77. Walsh, R. and Wells, J. M., *J. Chem. Soc. Chem. Commun.,* 513, 1973.
78. Watkins, K. W. and Thompson, W. W., *Int. J. Chem. Kinet.,* 5, 791, 1973.
79. Wyatt, J. R. and Stafford, F. E., *J. Phys. Chem.,* 76, 1913, 1972.
80. Zmbov, K. F., Uy, O. M., and Margrave, J. L., *J. Am. Chem. Soc.,* 90, 5090, 1968.

HEATS OF FORMATION OF FREE RADICALS

J. A. Kerr, M. J. Parsonage, and A. F. Trotman-Dickenson

The values are given in kcal mol^{-1} at 298 K. They are related to the corresponding bond strengths by the equations

$$D(R-X) = \Delta H_f^{\circ}(\dot{R}) + \Delta H_f^{\circ}(\dot{X}) - \Delta H_f^{\circ}(RX)$$

or

$$D(R-R) = 2\Delta H_f^{\circ}(\dot{R}) - \Delta H_f^{\circ}(RR)$$

For an excellent review of the methods of determining the heats of formation of free radicals the reader is referred to "Thermochemistry of Free Radicals" by H. E. O'Neal and S. W. Benson, in *Free Radicals*, Kochi, J. K., Ed., John Wiley and Sons, New York, 1973, 275.

The references are those given for the preceding table (Bond Strengths in Polyatomic Molecules).

Radical	ΔH_f°	Ref.
$\ddot{C}H$	142 ± 1	15, 71
$\ddot{C}H_2$	92 ± 1	15, 71
$\dot{C}H_3$	34.0 ± 1.2	39
Ethynyl	130 ± 5	79
Vinyl	⩾ 68 ± 2	39
C_2H_5	25.9 ± 1.3	39
Propargyl	86.5 ± 1.2	76
Allyl	41.4 ± 1.1	39
Cyclopropyl	61.3 ± 1	19, 27
$n\text{-}\dot{C}_3H_7$	22.6 ± 1.8	39
$i\text{-}\dot{C}_3H_7$	18.2 ± 1.5	39
Methallyl	30.4 ± 1.3	39
Cyclopropylcarbinyl	51.5 ± 1.6	55
Cyclobutyl	51.2 ± 1.0	27, 56
$s\text{-}\dot{C}_4H_9$	13.0 ± 2	39
$t\text{-}\dot{C}_4H_9$	7.6 ± 1.2	39
Cyclopentadien-1,3-yl-5	60.9 ± 1.2	37
Pentadien-1,4-yl-3	52.9 ± 1.2	39
Cyclopentenyl-3	38.4 ± 1	36
Spiropentyl	91.0 ± 1	19, 27
Dimethylallyl	18.3 ± 1.5	72
Cyclopentyl	24.3 ± 1.0	27, 35
$neo\text{-}\dot{C}_5H_{11}$	7.6 ± 1	19, 51
Phenyl	77.7 ± 2.0	14
Cyclohexadien-1,3-yl-5	44 ± 5	42
Cyclohexyl	13.9 ± 1	19, 27
Benzyl	45.1 ± 1	39
Cycloheptatrien-1,3,5-yl-7	64.8	73
Norbornyl	32.6 ± 2.5	57
Cycloheptyl	12.2 ± 1	19, 27
$C_6H_5\dot{C}HCH_3$	38	10, 58
$\dot{C}N$	101 ± 1	23
$CH_3\dot{N}H$	45.4 ± 1	40
CH_2CN	51.1	10, 58
$(CH_3)_2\dot{N}$	38.5 ± 1	40

Radical	ΔH_f°	Ref.
$(CH_3)_2\dot{C}CN$	36.7	10, 58
$C_6H_5\ddot{N}H$	55.0	10, 58
$C_6H_5\dot{N}CH_3$	53.5	10, 58
$C_6H_5\dot{C}(CH_3)CN$	54.4	10, 58
$\dot{C}HO$	7.7 ± 1.2	39, 58
$\dot{C}H_2OH$	-4.2 ± 1.5	39, 58
$CH_3\dot{O}$	3.5 ± 1	6, 10, 71
$CH_3\dot{C}O$	-5.8 ± 0.4	39, 58
$CH_3\dot{C}HOH$	-15.2 ± 1.0	1
$CH_3O\dot{C}H_2$	-2.8 ± 1.2	39, 58
$C_2H_5\dot{O}$	-4.4 ± 1	6, 10, 71
$CH_3CO\dot{C}H_2$	-5.7 ± 2.6	46, 49
$(CH_3)_2\dot{C}OH$	-26.6 ± 1.1	39, 58
$CH_3CO\dot{C}HCH_3$	-16.8 ± 1.7	70
$n\text{-}C_3H_7\dot{O}$	-9.7	58
$i\text{-}C_3H_7\dot{O}$	-12.4	58
Tetrahydrofuran-2-yl	-4.3 ± 1.5	39, 58
$n\text{-}C_4H_9\dot{O}$	-14.7	58
$(CH_3)_3\dot{C}O$	-22.1 ± 1	6, 10, 71
$C_6H_5\dot{O}$	13 ± 5	13
$C_6H_5\dot{C}O$	26.1 ± 2	58, 68
$\dot{C}OOH$	-53.3	10, 68
$\dot{C}OOCH_3$	-40.4 ± 1	58, 66
$CH_3C\dot{O}_2$	-49.6 ± 1	58
$C_2H_5C\dot{O}_2$	-54.6 ± 1	58
$n\text{-}C_3H_7C\dot{O}_2$	-59.6 ± 1	58
$C_6H_5CO_2\dot{C}H_2$	-16.7 ± 2.0	58, 67
$\dot{C}FO$	⩽-44	58
$CH_3\dot{S}$	30.5 ± 1	44
$C_6H_5\dot{S}$	49.5	58
$CH_3\dot{S}O_2$	-57.2	58
$\dot{C}H_2F$	-7.8 ± 2	45
$\dot{C}HF_2$	-59.2 ± 2	45
$\dot{C}F_2$	-39.7	58, 80
$\dot{C}F_3$	-112.0 ± 3.6	39, 58
$\dot{C}H_2Cl$	28.1	34
$\dot{C}Cl_2$	57	58
$\dot{C}HCl_2$	24.1	34
$\dot{C}F_2Cl$	-64.3 ± 2	54
$\dot{C}FCl_2$	-23	31
$\dot{C}Cl_3$	18.7	44, 58
$\dot{C}H_2Br$	41.5	34
$\dot{C}HBr_2$	54.3	34
$\dot{C}H_2I$	55.0 ± 1.6	39, 58
$\dot{C}HI_2$	79.8 ± 2.2	39, 58
$\dot{C}_2F_5$	-217.3 ± 1	58
$CHCl_2\dot{C}Cl_2$	5.5 ± 2	33, 71
$CCl_3\dot{C}Cl_2$	8.4 ± 2	33, 71
$\dot{N}H$	86	58
$\dot{N}H_2$	47.2 ± 1	40, 58
$\dot{N}_2H_3$	3.1	58
$\dot{N}F_2$	8 ± 1	9, 21, 71
$\dot{P}H_2$	33 ± 2	58
$H\dot{O}$	9.2 ± 1	44

To convert from	To	Multiply by	To convert from	To	Multiply by
Pounds (avdp.)	Pennyweights	291.6666	Quarterns (Brit., liq.)	Gallons (Brit.)	0.03125
"	Poundals	32.1740	"	Liters	0.1420613
"	Pounds (apoth. *or* troy)	1.215277	Quarters (U.S., long)	Kilograms	254.0117272
"	Scruples (apoth.)	350	"	Pounds (avdp.)	560
"	Slugs	0.0310810	Quarters (U.S., short)	Kilograms	226.796185
"	Tons (long)	0.00044642857	"	Pounds	500
"	Tons (metric)	0.00045359237	Quarts (Brit.)	Cu. cm	1136.522
"	Tons (short)	0.0005	"	Cu. inches	69.35482
Pounds of H$_2$O evap. from and at 212°F.	B.t.u.	970.9	"	Gallons (Brit.)	0.25
"	B.t.u. (IST.)	970.2	"	Gallons (U.S., liq.)	0.3002373
"	B.t.u. (mean)	969.4	"	Liters	1.136490
"	Joules	1.0237×10^6	"	Quarts (U.S., dry)	1.032056
"	Joules (Int.)	1.0234×10^6	"	Quarts (U.S., liq.)	1.200949
Pounds/cu. ft.	Grams/cu. cm	0.016018463	Quarts (U.S., dry)	Bushels (U.S.)	0.03125
"	Kg./cu. meter	16.018463	"	Cu. cm	1101.2209
Pounds/cu. inch	Grams/cu. cm	27.679905	"	Cu. feet	0.038889251
"	Grams/liter	27.68068	"	Cu. inches	67.200625
"	Kg./cu. meter	27679.905	"	Gallons (U.S., dry)	0.25
Pounds/gal. (Brit.)	Pounds/cu. ft.	6.228839	"	Gallons (U.S., liq.)	0.29091180
Pounds/gal. (U.S., liq.)	Grams/cu. cm	0.11982643	"	Liters	1.1011901
"	Pounds/cu. ft.	7.4805195	"	Pecks (U.S.)	0.125
Pounds/inch	Grams/cm	178.57967	"	Pints (U.S., dry)	2
"	Grams/ft.	5443.1084	Quarts (U.S., liq.)	Cu. cm	946.35295
"	Grams/inch	453.59237	"	Cu. feet	0.033420136
"	Ounces/cm	6.2992	"	Cu. inches	57.75
"	Ounces/inch	16	"	Drams (U.S., fluid)	256
"	Pounds/meter	39.370079	"	Gallons (U.S., dry)	0.21484175
Pounds/minute	Kilograms/hr	27.2155422	"	Gallons (U.S., liq.)	0.25
"	Kilograms/min	0.45359237	"	Gills (U.S.)	8
Pounds of H$_2$O (30.2°F.)/min	Cu. ft./min	0.01601891	"	Liters	0.9463264
"	Gal. (U.S.)/min	0.1198298	"	Ounces (U.S., fluid)	32
"	Liters/min	0.45359237	"	Pints (U.S., liq.)	2
Pounds/sq. ft.	Atmospheres	0.000472541	"	Quarts (Brit.)	0.8326747
"	Bars	0.000478803	"	Quarts (U.S., dry)	0.8593670
"	Cm. of Hg (0°C.)	0.0359131	Quintals (metric)	Grams	100000
"	Dynes/sq. cm	478.803	"	Hundredweights (long)	1.9684131
"	Ft. of air (1 atm., 60°F.)	13.096	"	Kilograms	100
"	Grams/sq. cm	0.48824276	"	Pounds (avdp.)	220.46226
"	In. of Hg (32°F.)	0.0141390			
"	In. of H$_2$O (39.2°F.)	0.192227	Radians	Circumferences	0.15915494
"	Kg./sq. meter	4.8824276	"	Degrees	57.295779
"	Mm. of Hg (0°C.)	0.359131	"	Minutes	3437.7468
Pounds/sq. inch	Atmospheres	0.0680460	"	Quadrants	0.63661977
"	Bars	0.0689476	"	Revolutions	0.15915494
"	Cm. of Hg (0°C.)	5.17149	"	Seconds	206264.81
"	Cm. of H$_2$O (4°C.)	70.3089	Radians/cm	Degrees/cm	57.295779
"	Dynes/sq. cm	68947.6	"	Degrees/ft.	1746.3754
"	Grams/sq. cm	70.306958	"	Degrees/inch	145.53128
"	In. of Hg (32°F.)	2.03602	"	Minutes/cm	3437.7468
"	In. of H$_2$O (39.2°F.)	27.6807	Radians/sec.	Degrees/sec.	57.295779
"	Kg./sq. cm	0.070306958	"	Revolutions/min	9.5492966
"	Mm. of Hg (0°C.)	51.7149	"	Revolutions/sec.	0.15915494
Pound wt.-sec./sq. ft.	Poises	478.803	Radians/(sec. × sec.)	Revolutions/(min. × min.)	572.95779
Pound wt.-sec./sq. in.	Poises	68947.6	"	Revolutions/(min. × sec.)	9.5492966
Puncheons (Brit.)	Cu. meters	0.31797510	"	Revolutions/(sec. × sec.)	0.15915494
"	Gallons (Brit.)	69.94467	Register tons	Cu. feet	100
"	Gallons (U.S.)	84	"	Cu. meters	2.8316847
			Revolutions	Degrees	360
Quadrants	Minutes	5400	"	Grades	400
"	Radians	1.5707963	"	Quadrants	4
Quarterns (Brit., dry)	Buckets (Brit.)	0.125	"	Radians	6.2831853
"	Bushels (Brit.)	0.0625	Reyns*	Centipoises	6.89476×10^6
"	Cu. cm	2273.044	Rhes	Poises^{-1}	1
"	Gallons (Brit.)	0.5	Rods	Centimeters	502.92
"	Liters	2.272980	"	Chains (Gunter's)	0.25
"	Pecks (Brit.)	0.25	"	Chains (Ramden's)	0.165
Quarterns (Brit., liq.)	Cu. cm	142.0652	"	Feet	16.5
			"	Feet (U.S. Survey)	16.499967
			"	Furlongs	0.025
			"	Inches	198
			"	Links (Gunter's)	25

* See also separate table of "viscosity conversion factors".

To convert from	To	Multiply by	To convert from	To	Multiply by
Ounces/sq. inch......	Pounds/sq. ft..........	9	Pints (Brit.).........	Minims (Brit.)...........	9600
"	Pounds/sq. inch......	0.0625	"	Ounces (Brit., fluid).......	20
Ounces (avdp.)/ton...			"	Pints (U.S., dry).......	1.032056
(long)........	Milligrams/kg...........	27.901786	"	Pints (U.S., liq.).......	1.200949
Ounces (avdp.)/ton			"	Quarts (Brit.)........	0.5
(short)...........	Milligrams/kg...........	31.25	"	Scruples (Brit., fluid).....	480
Paces.............	Centimeters...........	76.2	Pints (U.S., dry)....	Bushels (U.S.)........	0.015625
"	Chains (Gunter's)........	0.0378788	"	Cu. cm...........	550.61047
"	Chains (Ramden's)........	0.025	"	Cu. inches........	33.6003125
"	Feet................	2.5	"	Gallons, (U.S., dry)........	0.125
"	Hands...............	7.5	"	Gallons (U.S., liq.)........	0.14545590
"	Inches...............	30	"	Liters...........	0.5505951
"	Ropes (Brit.)........	0.125	"	Pecks (U.S.)........	0.0625
Palms.............	Centimeters...........	7.62	"	Quarts (U.S., dry).......	0.5
"	Chains (Ramden's)........	0.0025	Pints (U.S., liq.)....	Cu. cm...........	473.17647
"	Cubits................	0.1666666	"	Cu. feet........	0.016710069
"	Feet................	0.25	"	Cu. inches........	28.875
"	Hands...............	0.75	"	Cu. yards........	0.00061889146
"	Inches...............	3	"	Drams (U.S., fluid)....	128
Parsecs.............	Kilometers...........	3.08572×10^{13}	"	Gallons (U.S., liq.)........	0.125
"	Miles (statute.......	1.91738×10^{13}	"	Gills (U.S.)...........	4
Parts/million*......	Grains/gal. (Brit.).....	0.07015488	"	Liters...........	0.4731632
"	Grains/gal. (U.S.)......	0.05841620	"	Milliliters........	473.1632
"	Grams/liter........	0.001	"	Minims (U.S.)........	7680
"	Milligrams/liter.......	1	"	Ounces (U.S., fluid).......	16
Pecks (Brit.)......	Bushels (Brit.).......	0.25	"	Pints (Brit.)........	0.8326747
"	Coombs (Brit.).......	0.0625	"	Quarts (U.S., liq.).........	0.5
"	Cu. cm...........	9092.175	Planck's constant....	Erg-seconds.............	6.6255×10^{-27}
"	Cu. inches........	554.8385	"	Joule-seconds...........	6.6255×10^{-34}
"	Gallons (Brit.).......	2	"	Joule-sec./Avog. No.	
"	Gills (Brit.).......	64		(chem.)...........	3.9905×10^{-10}
"	Hogsheads.........	0.03812537	Points (printer's).....	Centimeters...........	0.03514598
"	Kilderkins (Brit.).......	0.111111	"	Inches...........	0.013837
"	Liters...........	9.091920	"	Picas...........	0.0833333
"	Pints (Brit.)........	16	Poises**.............	Cgs. units of absolute	
"	Quarterns (Brit., dry)...	4		viscosity...........	1
"	Quarters (Brit., dry)....	0.03125	"	Grams/(cm. $\times$ sec.)....	1
"	Quarts (Brit.).......	8	Poise-cu. cm./gram...	Sq. cm./sec.........	1
"	Quarts (U.S., dry).....	8.256449	Poise-cu. ft./lb.....	Sq. cm./sec.........	62.427960
Pecks (U.S.)......	Barrels (U.S., dry)......	0.076191185	Poise-cu. in./gram...	Sq. cm./sec.........	16.387064
"	Bushels (U.S.).......	0.25	Poles/sq. cm........	E.M. cgs. units of	
"	Cu. cm...........	8809.7675		magnetization..........	1
"	Cu. feet...........	0.311114005	Pottles (Brit.)........	Gallons (Brit.)..........	0.5
"	Cu. inches........	537.605	"	Liters............	2.272980
"	Gallons (U.S., dry).......	2	Poundals...........	Dynes...........	13825.50
"	Gallons (U.S., liq.)........	2.3272944	"	Grams...........	14.09808
"	Liters...........	8.809521	"	Pounds (avdp.)........	0.0310810
"	Pints (U.S., dry)........	16	Pounds (apoth. or	
"	Quarts (U.S., dry).....	8	troy).............	Drams (apoth. or troy)....	96
Pennyweights........	Drams (apoth. or troy)....	0.4	"	Drams (avdp.)..........	210.65143
"	Drams (avdp.)..........	0.87771429	"	Grains...........	5760
"	Grains...........	24	"	Grams...........	373.24172
"	Grams	1.55517384	"	Kilograms...........	0.37324172
"	Ounces (apoth. or troy)...	0.05	"	Ounces (apoth. or troy)...	12
"	Ounces (avdp.)........	0.054857143	"	Ounces (avdp.).......	13.165714
"	Pounds (apoth. or troy)...	0.0041666	"	Pennyweights...........	240
"	Pounds (avdp.).......	0.0034285714	"	Pounds (avdp.)........	0.8228571
Perches (masonry)....	Cu. feet............	24.75	"	Scruples (apoth.).......	288
Phots.............	Foot-candles........	929.0304	"	Tons (long)...........	0.00036734694
"	Lumens/sq. cm........	1	"	Tons (metric).........	0.00037324172
"	Lumens/sq. meter........	10000	"	Tons (short)..........	0.00041142857
"	Lux..............	10000	Pounds (avdp.)......	Drams (apoth. or troy)...	116.6666
Picas (printer's)......	Centimeters...........	0.42175176	"	Drams (avdp.)........	256
"	Inches................	0.166044	"	Grains...........	7000
Pints (Brit.).........	Cu. cm...........	568.26092	"	Grams...........	453.59237
"	Gallons (Brit.)............	0.125	"	Hundredweights (long)....	0.00892857
"	Gills (Brit.)...........	4	"	Hundredweights (short)...	0.01
"	Gills (U.S.)........	4.803797	"	Kilograms...........	0.45359237
"	Liters................	0.5682450	"	Ounces (apoth. or troy)...	14.583333
			"	Ounces (avdp.)...........	16

* Based on density of 1 gram/ml. for the solvent.
** See separate table of "viscosity conversion factors".

To convert from	To	Multiply by	To convert from	To	Multiply by
Millimicrons	Ångström units	10	Oersteds	Gilberts/cm	1
"	Centimeters	1×10^{-7}	"	Oersteds (Int.)	1.000165
"	Inches	3.9370079×10^{-8}	Oersteds (Int.)	Oersteds	0.999835
"	Microns	0.001	Ohms	Abohms	1×10^9
"	Millimeters	1×10^{-6}	"	Cgs. units of resistance	1
Milliphots	Foot-candles	0.9290304	"	Megohms	1×10^{-6}
"	Lumens/sq. ft	0.9290304	"	Microhms	1×10^6
"	Lumens/sq. meter	10	"	Ohms (Int.)	0.999505
"	Lux	10	"	Statohms	1.112646×10^{-12}
"	Phots	0.001	Ohms (Int.)	Ohms	1.000495
Millivolts	Statvolts	3.335635×10^{-6}	Ohms (mil, foot)	Circ. mil-ohms/ft	1
"	Volts	0.001	"	Ohm-cm	1.6624261×10^{-7}
Minims (Brit.)	Cu. cm	0.05919385	Ohm-cm	Circ. mil-ohms/ft	6.0153049×10^6
"	Cu. inches	0.003612230	"	Microhm-cm	1×10^6
"	Milliliters	0.05919219	"	Ohm inches	0.39370079
"	Ounces (Brit., fluid)	0.0020833333	Ohm-inches	Ohm-cm	2.54
"	Scruples (Brit., fluid)	0.05	Ohm-meters	Abohm-cm	1×10^{11}
Minims (U.S.)	Cu. cm	0.061611520	"	E.M. cgs. units	1×10^{11}
"	Cu. inches	0.0037597656	"	E.S. cgs. units	1.112646×10^{-10}
"	Drams (U.S., fluid)	0.0166666	"	Mks. units	1
"	Gallons (U.S., liq.)	1.6276042×10^{-5}	"	Statohm-cm	1.112646×10^{-10}
"	Gills (U.S.)	0.0005208333	Ounces (apoth. or troy)	Dekagrams	3.1103486
"	Liters	6.160979×10^{-5}	"	Drams (apoth. or troy)	8
"	Milliliters	0.06160979	"	Drams (avdp.)	17.554286
"	Ounces (U.S., fluid)	0.002083333	"	Grains	480
"	Pints (U.S., liq.)	0.0001302083	"	Grams	31.103486
Minutes (angular)	Degrees	0.0166666	"	Milligrams	31103.486
"	Quadrants	0.000185185	"	Ounces (avdp.)	1.0971429
"	Radians	0.00029088821	"	Pennyweights	20
"	Seconds (angular)	60	"	Pounds (apoth. or troy)	0.0833333
Minutes (mean solar)	Days (mean solar)	0.0006944444	"	Pounds (avdp.)	0.068571429
"	Days (sidereal)	0.00069634577	"	Scruples (apoth.)	24
"	Hours (mean solar)	0.0166666	"	Tons (short)	3.4285714×10^{-5}
"	Hours (sidereal)	0.016712298	Ounces (avdp.)	Drams (apoth. or troy)	7.291666
"	Minutes (sidereal)	1.00273791	"	Drams (avdp.)	16
Minutes (sidereal)	Days (mean solar)	0.00069254831	"	Grains	437.5
"	Minutes (mean solar)	0.99726957	"	Grams	28.349523
"	Months (mean calendar)	2.2768712×10^{-5}	"	Hundredweights (long)	0.00055803571
"	Seconds (sidereal)	60	"	Hundredweights (short)	0.000625
Minutes/cm	Radians/cm	0.00029088821	"	Ounces (apoth. or troy)	0.9114583
Months (lunar)	Days (mean solar)	29.530588	"	Pennyweights	18.229166
"	Hours (mean solar)	708.73411	"	Pounds (apoth. or troy)	0.075954861
"	Minutes (mean solar)	42524.047	"	Pounds (avdp.)	0.0625
"	Second (mean solar)	2.5514428×10^6	"	Scruples (apoth.)	21.875
"	Weeks (mean calendar)	4.2186554	"	Tons (long)	2.7901786×10^{-5}
Months (mean calendar)	Days (mean solar)	30.416666	"	Tons (metric)	2.8349527×10^{-5}
"	Hours (mean solar)	730	"	Tons (short)	3.125×10^{-5}
"	Months (lunar)	1.0300055	Ounces (Brit., fluid)	Cu. cm	28.41305
"	Weeks (mean calendar)	4.3452381	"	Cu. inches	1.733870
"	Years (calendar)	0.08333333	"	Drachms (Brit., fluid)	8
"	Years (sidereal)	0.083274845	"	Drams (U.S., fluid)	7.686075
"	Years (tropical)	0.083278075	"	Gallons (Brit.)	0.00625
Myriagrams	Grams	10000	"	Milliliters	28.41225
"	Kilograms	10	"	Minims (Brit.)	480
"	Pounds (avdp.)	22.046226	"	Ounces (U.S., fluid)	0.9607594
Newtons	Dynes	100000	Ounces (U.S., fluid)	Cu. cm	29.573730
"	Pounds	0.22480894	"	Cu. inches	1.8046875
Newton-meters	Dyne-cm	1×10^7	"	Cu. meters	2.9573730×10^{-5}
"	Gram-cm	10197.162	"	Drams (U.S., fluid)	8
"	Kg.-meters	0.10197162	"	Gallons (U.S., dry)	0.0067138047
"	Pound-feet	0.73756215	"	Gallons (U.S., liq.)	0.0078125
Noggins (Brit.)	Cu. cm	142.0652	"	Gills (U.S.)	0.25
"	Gallons (Brit.)	0.03125	"	Liters	0.029572702
"	Gills (Brit.)	1	"	Minims (U.S.)	480
Oersteds	Ampere-turns/inch	2.0212678	"	Ounces (Brit., fluid)	**1.040843**
"	Ampere-turns/meter	79.577472	"	Pints (U.S., liq.)	**0.0625**
"	E.M. cgs. units of magnetic field intensity	1	"	Quarts (U.S., liq.)	**0.03125**
"	E.S. cgs. units	2.997930×10^{10}	Ounces/sq. inch	Dynes/sq. cm	4309.22
			"	Grams/sq. cm	4.3941849
			"	In. of H_2O (39.2°F.)	1.73004
			"	In. of H_2O (60°F.)	1.73100

To convert from	To	Multiply by	To convert from	To	Multiply by
Microns..........	Centimeters..........	0.0001	Milligrams..........	Grains..........	0.015432358
"	Feet..........	3.2808399×10^{-6}	"	Grams..........	0.001
"	Inches..........	3.9370079×10^{-5}	"	Ounces (apoth. or troy)....	3.2150737×10^{-5}
"	Meters..........	1×10^{-6}	"	Ounces (avdp.)..........	3.5273962×10^{-5}
"	Millimeters..........	0.001	"	Pennyweights..........	0.00064301493
"	Millimicrons..........	1000	"	Pounds (apoth. or troy)....	2.6792289×10^{-6}
Miles (naut., Brit.)....	Cable lengths (Brit.)....	8.4444	"	Pounds (avdp.)..........	2.2046226×10^{-6}
"	Fathoms..........	1013.333	"	Scruples (apoth.)..........	0.00077161792
"	Feet..........	6080	Milligrams/assay ton.	Milligrams/kg..........	34.285714
"	Meters..........	1853.184	"	Ounces (troy)/ton (avdp.).	1
"	Miles (Adm., Brit.)....	1	Milligrams/gm........	Dynes/cm..........	0.980665
"	Miles (naut., Int.)....	1.0006393	"	Pounds/inch..........	5.5997415×10^{-6}
"	Miles (statute)....	1.151515	Milligrams/gram......	Carats (parts gold per 24 of mixture)	0.024
Miles (naut., Int.)....	Cable lengths..........	8.4390493	"	Grams/ton (short)..........	907.18474
"	Fathoms..........	1012.6859	"	Milligrams/assay ton......	29.166666
"	Feet..........	6076.1155	"	Ounces (avdp.)/ton (long)..	35.84
"	Feet (U.S. Survey).......	6076.1033	"	Ounces (avdp.)/ton (short).	32
"	Kilometers..........	1.852	"	Ounces (troy)/ton (long)...	32.6666
"	Leagues (naut., Int.).....	0.333333	"	Ounces (troy)/ton (short).	29.1666
"	Meters..........	1852	Milligrams/inch.......	Dynes/cm..........	0.386089
"	Miles (geographical)......	1	"	Dynes/inch..........	0.980665
"	Miles (naut. Brit.).......	0.99936110	"	Grams/cm..........	0.00039370079
"	Miles (statute)...........	1.1507794	"	Grams/inch..........	0.0001
Miles (statute).......	Centimeters..........	160934.4	Milligrams/kg........	Pounds (avdp.)/ton (short)	0.002
"	Chains (Gunter's)........	80	Milligrams/liter......	Grains/gal. (U.S.).........	0.05841620
"	Chains (Ramden's)........	52.8	"	Grams/liter..........	0.001
"	Feet..........	5280	"	Parts/million*..........	1
"	Feet (U.S. Survey).......	5279.9894	"	Lb./cu. ft..........	6.242621×10^{-5}
"	Furlongs..........	8	Milligrams/mm......	Dynes/cm..........	9.80665
"	Inches..........	63360	Millihenries..........	Abhenries..........	1×10^{6}
"	Kilometers..........	1.609344	"	Henries..........	0.001
"	Light years..........	1.70111×10^{-13}	"	Stathenries..........	1.112646×10^{-15}
"	Links (Gunter's)..........	8000	Millilamberts.......	Candles/sq. cm..........	0.00031830989
"	Meters..........	1609.344	"	Candles/sq. inch..........	0.0020536081
"	Miles (naut., Brit.).......	0.86842105	"	Foot-lamberts..........	0.9290304
"	Miles (naut., Int.).......	0.86897624	"	Lamberts..........	0.001
"	Myriameters..........	0.1609344	"	Lumens/sq. cm..........	0.001
"	Rods..........	320	"	Lumens/sq. ft..........	0.9290304
"	Yards..........	1760	Milliliters..........	Cu. cm..........	1
Miles/hr..........	Cm./sec..........	44.704	"	Cu. inches..........	0.06102545
"	Feet/hr..........	5280	"	Drams (U.S., fluid)........	0.2705198
"	Feet/min..........	88	"	Gills (U.S.)..........	0.008453742
"	Feet/sec..........	1.466666	"	Liters..........	0.001
"	Kilometers/hr..........	1.609344	"	Minims (U.S.)..........	16.23119
"	Knots (Int.)..........	0.86897624	"	Ounces (Brit., fluid).......	0.03519609
"	Meters/min..........	26.8224	"	Ounces (U.S., fluid).......	0.03381497
"	Miles/min..........	0.0166666	"	Pints (Brit.)..........	0.001759804
Miles/(hr. × min.)..	Cm./(sec. × sec.)........	0.7450666	"	Pints (U.S., liq.)..........	0.002113436
Miles/(hr. × sec.)..	Cm./(sec. × sec.)........	44.704	Millimeters..........	Ångström units..........	1×10^{7}
"	Ft./(sec. × sec.)........	1.466666	"	Centimeters..........	0.1
"	Kilometers/(hr. × sec.)....	1.609344	"	Decimeters..........	0.01
"	Meters/(sec. × sec.).......	0.44704	"	Dekameters..........	0.0001
Miles/min..........	Cm./sec..........	2682.24	"	Feet..........	0.0032808399
"	Feet/hr..........	316800	"	Inches..........	0.039370079
"	Feet/sec..........	88	"	Meters..........	0.001
"	Kilometers/min..........	1.609344	"	Microns..........	1000
"	Knots (Int.)..........	52.138574	"	Mils..........	39.370079
"	Meters/min..........	1609.344	"	Wave length of orange-red line of krypton 86	1650.76373
"	Miles/hr..........	60	"	Wave length of red line of cadmium	1553.16413
Millibars..........	Atmospheres..........	0.000986923	Millimeters of Hg (0°C.)..........	Atmospheres..........	0.0013157895
"	Bars..........	0.001	"	Bars..........	0.00133322
"	Baryes..........	1000	"	Dynes/sq. cm..........	1333.224
"	Dynes/sq. cm..........	1000	"	Grams/sq. cm..........	1.35951
"	Grams/sq. cm..........	1.019716	"	Kg./sq. meter..........	13,5951
"	In. of Hg (32°F.).........	0.0295300	"	Pounds/sq. ft..........	2.78450
"	Pounds/sq. ft..........	2.088543	"	Pounds/sq. inch..........	0.0193368
"	Pounds/sq. inch..........	0.0145038	"	Torrs..........	1
Milligrams..........	Carats (1877)..........	0.004871			
"	Carats (metric)..........	0.005			
"	Drams (apoth. or troy)....	0.00025720597			
"	Drams (advp.)..........	0.00056438339			

* Density of 1 gram per milliliter of solvent.

To convert from	To	Multiply by	To convert from	To	Multiply by
Liters/sec	Cu. yards/min	0.0784771	Meters	Links (Ramden's)	3.2808399
"	Gal. (U.S., liq.)/min	15.850342	"	Megameters	1×10^{-6}
"	Gal. (U.S., liq.)/sec	9.2641723	"	Miles (naut., Brit.)	0.00053961182
Liter-atm	B.t.u.	0.0961045	"	Miles (naut., Int.)	0.00053995080
"	B.t.u. (IST.)	0.0960417	"	Miles (statute)	0.00062137119
"	B.t.u. (mean)	0.0959664	"	Millimeters	1000
"	Cal., gm	24.2179	"	Millimicrons	1×10^{9}
"	Cal., gm (IST.)	24.2021	"	Mils	39370.079
"	Cal., gm (mean)	24.1831	"	Rods	0.19883878
"	Cu. ft.-atm	0.0353157	"	Yards	1.0936133
"	Foot-poundals	2404.55	Meters of Hg (0°C.)	Atmospheres	1.3157895
"	Foot-pounds	74.7356	"	Ft. of H_2O (60°F.)	44.6474
"	Hp.-hours	3.77452×10^{-5}	"	In. of Hg (32°F.)	39.370079
"	Joules	101.328	"	Kg./sq. cm	1.35951
"	Joules (Int.)	101.311	"	Pounds/sq. inch	19.3368
"	Kg.-meters	10.3320	Meters/hr	Feet/hr	3.2808399
"	Kw.-hours	2.81466×10^{-5}	"	Feet/min	0.054680665
Liter-atm. (lat. 45°)	Joules	101.323	"	Knots (Int.)	0.00053995680
Lumens	Candle power (spher.)	0.079577472	"	Miles (statute)/hr	0.00062137119
Lumens (at 5550 Å)	Watts	0.0014705882	Meters/min	Cm./sec	1.666666
Lumens/sq. cm	Lamberts	1	"	Feet/min	3.2808399
"	Phots	1	"	Feet/sec	0.054680665
Lumens/(sq. cm × steradian)	Lamberts	3.1415927	"	Kilometers/hr	0.06
Lumens/sq. ft	Foot-candles	1	"	Knots (Int.)	0.032397408
"	Foot-lamberts	1	"	Miles (statute)/hr	0.037282272
"	Lumens/sq. meter	10.763910	Meters/sec	Feet/min	196.85039
Lumens/(sq. ft. × steradian)	Millilamberts	3.3815822	"	Feet/sec	3.2808399
Lumens/sq. meter	Foot-candles	0.09290304	"	Kilometers/hr	3.6
"	Lumens/sq. ft	0.09290304	"	Kilometers/min	0.06
"	Phots	0.0001	"	Miles (statute)/hr	2.2369363
Lux	Foot-candles	0.09290304	Meters/(sec. × sec.)	Kilometers/(hr. × sec.)	3.6
"	Lumens/sq. meter	1	"	Miles/(hr. × sec.)	2.2369363
"	Phots	0.0001	Meter-candles	Lumens/sq. meter	1
Maxwells	E.M. cgs. units of induction flux	1	Mhos	Abmhos	1×10^{-9}
"	E.S. cgs. units	3.335635×10^{-11}	"	Cgs. units of conductance	1
"	Gauss-sq. cm	1	"	E.M. cgs. units	1×10^{-9}
"	Lines	1	"	E.S. cgs. units	8.987584×10^{11}
"	Maxwells (Int.)	0.999670	"	Mhos (Int.)	1.000495
"	Volt-seconds	1×10^{-8}	"	Mks. (r or nr) units	1
"	Webers	1×10^{-8}	"	Ohms^{-1}	1
Maxwells (Int.)	Maxwells	1.000330	"	Siemen's units	1
Maxwells/sq. cm	Maxwells/sq. in	6.4516	"	Statmhos	8.987584×10^{11}
"	Maxwells (Int.)/sq. cm	0.999670	Mhos (Int.)	Abmhos	9.99505×10^{-10}
Maxwells (Int.)/sq. cm	Maxwells/sq. cm	1.000330	"	Mhos	0.999505
Maxwells/sq. inch	Maxwells/sq. cm	0.15500031	Mhos/meter	Abmhos/cm	1×10^{-11}
Megalines	Maxwells	1×10^{6}	"	Mhos (Int.)/meter	1.000495
Megmhos/cm	Abmhos/cm	0.001	Mho-ft./circ. mil	Mhos/cm	6.0153049×10^{6}
"	Megmhos/inch cube	2.54	Microfarads	Abfarads	1×10^{-15}
"	(Microhm-cm.)$^{-1}$	1	"	Farads	1×10^{-6}
Megmhos/inch	Megmhos/cm	0.39370079	"	Statfarads	8.987584×10^{5}
"	(Microhm-inches)$^{-1}$	1	Micrograms	Grams	1×10^{-6}
Megohms	Microhms	1×10^{12}	"	Milligrams	0.001
"	Ohms	1×10^{6}	Microhenries	Henries	1×10^{-6}
"	Statohms	1.112646×10^{-6}	"	Stathenries	1.112646×10^{-18}
Megohms^{-1}	Micromhos	1	Microhms	Abohms	1000
Meters	Ångström units	1×10^{10}	"	Megohms	1×10^{-12}
"	Centimeters	100	"	Ohms	1×10^{-6}
"	Chains (Gunter's)	0.049709695	"	Statohms	1.112646×10^{-18}
"	Chains (Ramden's)	0.032808399	Microhm-cm	Abohm-cm	1000
"	Fathoms	0.54680665	"	Circ. mil-ohms/ft	6.0153049
"	Feet	3.2808399	"	Microhm-inches	0.39370079
"	Feet (U.S. Survey)	3.280833	"	Ohm-cm	1×10^{-6}
"	Furlongs	0.0049700695	Microhm-inches	Circ. mil-ohms/ft	15.278875
"	Inches	39.370079	"	Michrom-cm	2.54
"	Kilometers	0.001	Micromicrofarads	Farads	1×10^{-12}
"	Links (Gunter's)	4.9709695	Micromicrons	Ångström units	0.01
			"	Centimeters	1×10^{-10}
			"	Inches	$3.9370079 \times 10^{-11}$
			"	Meters	1×10^{-12}
			"	Microns	1×10^{-6}
			Microns	Ångström units	10000

To convert from	To	Multiply by
Kilowatts	Horsepower (boiler)	0.101942
"	Horsepower (electric)	1.34048
"	Horsepower (metric)	1.35962
"	Joules/hr	3.6×10^6
"	Joules (IST.)/hr	3.59941×10^6
"	Joules/sec	1000
"	Kg.-meters/hr	3.67098×10^5
"	Kilowatts (Int.)	0.999835
"	Watts (Int.)	999.835
Kilowatts (Int.)	B.t.u./hr	3414.99
"	B.t.u. (IST.)/hr	3412.76
"	B.t.u. (mean)/hr	3410.08
"	B.t.u. (mean)/min	56.8347
"	B.t.u. (mean)/sec	0.947244
"	Cal., gm. (mean)/hr	859326
"	Cal., gm. (mean)/min	14322.1
"	Cal., kg./hr	860.563
"	Cal., kg. (IST.)/hr	860
"	Cal., kg. (mean)/hr	859.326
"	Cu. cm.-atm./hr	3.55351×10^7
"	Cu. ft.-atm./hr	1254.91
"	Ergs/sec	1.000165×10^{10}
"	Foot-poundals/min	1.42406×10^6
"	Foot-pounds/min	44261.0
"	Foot-pounds/sec	737.684
"	Gram-cm./sec	1.01988×10^7
"	Horsepower	1.34124
"	Horsepower (boiler)	0.101959
"	Horsepower (electric)	1.34070
"	Horsepower (metric)	1.35985
"	Joules/hr	3.60059×10^6
"	Joules (Int.)/hr	3.6×10^6
"	Kg.-meters/hr	367158
"	Kilowatts	1.000165
Kilowatt-hours	B.t.u. (mean)	3409.52
"	Cal., gm. (mean)	859184
"	Foot-pounds	2.65522×10^6
"	Hp.-hours	1.34102
"	Joules	3.6×10^6
"	Kg.-meters	367098
"	Lb. H$_2$O evap. from and at 212°F	3.5168
"	Watt-hours	1000
"	Watt-hours (Int.)	999.835
Kilowatt-hours (Int.)	B.t.u. (mean)	3410.08
"	Cal., gm. (IST.)	860000
"	Cal., gm. (mean)	859326
"	Cu. cm.-atm	3.55351×10^7
"	Cu. ft.-atm	1254.91
"	Foot-pounds	2.65566×10^6
"	Hp.-hours	1.34124
"	Joules	3.60059×10^6
"	Joules (Int.)	3.6×10^6
"	Kg.-meters	367158
Kw.-hr./gram	B.t.u./(lb.)	1.54876×10^6
"	B.t.u. (IST.)/lb	1.54774×10^6
"	B.t.u. (mean)/lb	1.54653×10^6
"	Cal., gm./gram	860421
"	Cal., gm. (mean)/gram	859184
"	Cu. cm.-atm./gram	3.55292×10^7
"	Cu. ft.-atm./lb	569124
"	Hp.-hr./lb	608.277
"	Joules/gram	3.6×10^6
Knots (Int.)	Cm./sec	51.4444
"	Feet/hr	6076.1155
"	Feet/min	101.26859
"	Feet/sec	1.6878099
"	Kilometers/hr	1.852
"	Meters/min	30.8666
"	Meters/sec	0.514444
"	Miles (naut., Int.)/hr	1
"	Miles (statute)/hr	1.1507794

To convert from	To	Multiply by
Lamberts	Candles/sq. cm	0.31830989
"	Candles/sq. ft	295.71956
"	Candles/sq. inch	2.0536081
"	Foot-lamberts	929.0304
"	Lumens/sq. cm	1
Lasts (Brit.)	Liters	2909.414
Leagues (naut., Brit.)	Feet	18240
"	Kilometers	5.559552
"	Leagues (naut., Int.)	1.0006393
"	Leagues (statute)	1.151515
"	Miles (statute)	3.454545
Leagues (naut., Int.)	Fathoms	3038.0577
"	Feet	18228.346
"	Kilometers	5.556
"	Leagues (statute)	1.1507794
"	Miles (statute)	3.4523383
Leagues (statute)	Fathoms	2640
"	Feet	15840
"	Kilometers	4.828032
"	Leagues (naut., Int.)	0.86897625
"	Miles (naut., Int.)	2.6069287
"	Miles (statute)	3
Light years	Astronomical units	63279.5
"	Kilometers	9.46055×10^{12}
"	Miles (statute)	5.87851×10^{12}
Lines	Maxwells	1
Lines (Brit.)	Centimeters	0.211666
"	Inches	0.083333
Lines/sq. cm	Gausses	1
Lines/sq. inch	Gausses	0.15500031
"	Webers/sq. inch	1×10^{-8}
Links (Gunter's)	Chains (Gunter's)	0.01
"	Feet	0.66
"	Feet (U.S. Survey)	0.65999868
"	Inches	7.92
"	Meters	0.201168
"	Miles (statute)	0.000125
"	Rods	0.04
Links (Ramden's)	Centimeters	30.48
"	Chains (Ramdens)	0.01
"	Feet	1
"	Inches	12
Liters	Bushels (Brit.)	0.02749617
"	Bushels (U.S.)	0.02837759
"	Cu. centimeters	1000
"	Cu. feet	0.035314667
"	Cu. inches	61.023744
"	Cu. meters	0.001
"	Cu. yards	0.0013079506
"	Drams (U.S., fluid)	270.51218
"	Gallons (Brit.)	0.2199694
"	Gallons (U.S., dry)	0.22702075
"	Gallons (U.S., liq.)	0.26417205
"	Gills (Brit.)	7.039020
"	Gills (U.S.)	8.4535058
"	Hogsheads	0.004193212
"	Minims (U.S.)	16320.75
"	Ounces (Brit., fluid)	35.19510
"	Ounces (U.S., fluid)	33.814023
"	Pecks (Brit.)	0.1099848
"	Pecks (U.S.)	0.1135105
"	Pints (Brit.)	1.795756
"	Pints (U.S., dry)	1.8161660
"	Pints (U.S., liq.)	2.1133764
"	Quarts. (Brit.)	0.8798775
"	Quarts (U.S., dry)	0.90808298
"	Quarts (U.S., liq.)	1.0566882
Liters/min	Cu. ft./min	0.0353147
"	Cu. ft./sec	0.000588578
"	Gal. (U.S., liq.)/min	0.26417226
Liters/sec	Cu. ft./min	2.118880
"	Cu. ft./sec	0.0353147

To convert from	To	Multiply by	To convert from	To	Multiply by
Joules (Int.)/sec	B.t.u. (mean)/min	0.0568347	Kilogram-meters	Hp.-hours	3.65304 × 10⁻⁶
"	Cal., gm./min	14.3427	"	Joules	9.80665
"	Cal., kg./min	0.0143427	"	Joules (Int.)	9.80503
"	Dyne-cm./sec	1.000165 × 10⁷	"	Kw.-hours	2.72407 × 10⁻⁶
"	Ergs/sec	1.000165 × 10⁷	"	Liter-atm	0.0967814
"	Foot-pounds/min	44.2610	"	Newton-meters	9.80665
"	Foot-pounds/sec	0.737684	"	Watt-hours	0.00272407
"	Gram-cm./sec	10198.8	"	Watt-hours (Int.)	0.00272362
"	Horsepower	0.00134124	Kilogram-meters/sec.	Watts	9.80665
"	Watts	1.000165	Kilolines	Maxwells	1000
"	Watts (Int.)	1	"	Webers	1 × 10⁻⁵
Kilderkins (Brit.)	Cu. cm	81829.57	Kiloliters	Cu. centimeters	1 × 10⁶
"	Cu. feet	2.889784	"	Cu. feet	35.31566
"	Cu. inches	4993.55	"	Cu. inches	61025.45
"	Cu. meters	0.08182957	"	Cu. meters	1.000028
"	Gallons (Brit.)	18	"	Cu. yards	1.307987
Kilograms	Drams (apoth. or troy)	257.20597	"	Gallons (Brit.)	219.9755
"	Drams (avdp.)	564.38339	"	Gallons (U.S., dry)	227.0271
"	Dynes	980665	"	Gallons (U.S., liq.)	264.1794
"	Grains	15432.358	"	Liters	1000
"	Hundredweights (long)	0.019684131	Kilometers	Astronomical units	6.68878 × 10⁻⁹
"	Hundredweights (short)	0.022046226	"	Centimeters	100000
"	Ounces (apoth. or troy)	32.150737	"	Feet	3280.8399
"	Ounces (avdp.)	35.273962	"	Feet (U.S. Survey)	3280.833
"	Pennyweights	643.01493	"	Light years	1.05702 × 10⁻¹³
"	Poundals	70.931635	"	Meters	1000
"	Pounds (apoth. or troy)	2.6792289	"	Miles (naut., Int.)	0.53995680
"	Pounds (avdp.)	2.2046226	"	Miles (statute	0.62137119
"	Quarters (Brit., long)	0.078736522	"	Myriameters	0.1
"	Quarters (U.S. long)	0.0039368261	"	Rods	198.83878
"	Scruples (apoth.)	771.61792	"	Yards	1093.6133
"	Slugs	0.06852177	Kilometers/hr.	Cm./sec	27.7777
"	Tons (long)	0.00098420653	"	Feet/hr	3280.8399
"	Tons (metric)	0.001	"	Feet/min	54.680665
"	Tons (short)	0.0011023113	"	Knots (Int.)	0.53995680
Kilograms/cu. meter	Grams/cu. cm	0.001	"	Meters/sec	0.277777
"	Lb./cu. ft	0.062427961	"	Miles (statute)/hr.	0.62137119
"	Lb./cu. inch	3.0127292 × 10⁻⁵	Kilometers/(hr. × sec.)	Cm./(sec. × sec.)	27.7777
Kg. of ice melted/hr.	Tons of refrig. (U.S., comm.)	0.026336	"	Ft./(sec. × sec.)	0.91134442
Kilograms/sq. cm	Atmospheres	0.967841	"	Meters/(sec. × sec.)	0.277777
"	Bars	0.980665	Kilometers/min	Cm./sec	1666.666
"	Cm. of Hg (0°C.)	73.5559	"	Feet/min	3280.8399
"	Dynes/sq. cm	980665	"	Kilometers/hr	60
"	Ft. of H₂O (39.2°F.)	32.8093	"	Knots (Int.)	32.397408
"	In. of Hg (32°F.)	28.9590	"	Miles/hr	37.282272
"	Pounds/sq. inch	14.223343	"	Miles/min	0.62137119
Kilograms/sq. meter	Atmospheres	9.67841 × 10⁻⁵	Kilovolts/cm	Abvolts/cm	1 × 10¹¹
"	Bars	9.80665 × 10⁻⁵	"	Microvolts/meter	1 × 10¹¹
"	Dynes/sq. cm	98.0665	"	Millivolts/meter	1 × 10⁸
"	Ft. of H₂O (39.2°F.)	0.00328093	"	Statvolts/cm	3.335635
"	Grams/sq. cm	0.1	"	Volts/inch	2540
"	In. of Hg (32°F.)	0.00289590	Kilowatts	B.t.u./hr	3414.43
"	Mm. of Hg (0°C.)	0.0735559	"	B.t.u. (IST.)/hr	3412.19
"	Pounds/sq. ft	0.20481614	"	B.t.u. (mean)/hr	3409.52
"	Pounds/sq. in	0.0014223343	"	B.t.u. (mean)/min	56.8253
Kilograms/sq. mm	Pounds/sq. ft	204816.14	"	B.t.u. (mean)/sec	0.947088
"	Pounds/sq. in	1422.3343	"	Cal., gm. (mean)/hr	859184
"	Tons (short)/sq. in	0.71116716	"	Cal., gm. (mean)/min	14319.7
Kilogram sq. cm	Pounds sq. ft	0.0023730360	"	Cal., gm. (mean)/sec	238.662
"	Pounds sq. in	0.34171719	"	Cal., kg. (mean)/hr	859.184
Kilogram-meters	B.t.u. (mean)	0.00928776	"	Cal., kg. (mean)/min	14.3197
"	Cal., gm. (mean)	2.34048	"	Cal., kg. (mean)/sec	0.238662
"	Cal., kg. (mean)	0.00234048	"	Cu. ft.-atm./hr	1254.70
"	Cu. ft.-atm	0.00341790	"	Ergs/sec	1 × 10¹⁰
"	Dynes-cm	9.80665 × 10⁷	"	Foot-poundals/min	1.42382 × 10⁶
"	Ergs	9.80665 × 10⁷	"	Foot-pounds/hr	2.65522 × 10⁶
"	Foot-poundals	232.715	"	Foot-pounds/min	44253.7
"	Foot-pounds	7.23301	"	Foot-pounds/sec	737.562
"	Gram-cm	100000	"	Gram-cm./sec	1.019710 × 10⁷
			"	Horsepower	1.34102

To convert from	To	Multiply by	To convert from	To	Multiply by
Hours (sidereal)	Minutes (sidereal)	60	Joules (abs)	Cal., kg. (mean)	0.000238662
Hundredweights (long)	Kilograms	50.802345	" "	Cu. ft.-atm	0.000348529
"	Pounds	112	" "	Ergs	1×10^7
"	Quarters (Brit., long)	4	" "	Foot-poundals	23.730360
"	Quarters (U.S., long)	0.2	" "	Foot-pounds	0.737562
"	Tons (long)	0.05	" "	Gram-cm	10197.16
Hundredweights (short)	Kilograms	45.359237	" "	Hp.-hours	3.72506×10^{-7}
"	Pounds (advp.)	100	" "	Joules (Int.)	0.999835
"	Quarters (Brit., short)	4	" "	Kg.-meters	0.1019716
"	Quarters (U.S., short)	0.2	" "	Kw.-hours	2.7777×10^{-7}
"	Tons (long)	0.044642857	" "	Liter-atm	0.00986895
"	Tons (metric)	0.045359237	" "	Volt-coulombs (Int.)	0.999835
"	Tons (short)	0.05	" "	Watt-hours (abs.)	0.0002777777
Inches	Ångström units	2.54×10^8	" "	Watt-hours (Int.)	0.000277732
"	Centimeters	2.54	" "	Watt-sec.	1
"	Chains (Gunter's)	0.00126262	" "	Watt-sec. (Int.)	0.999835
"	Cubits	0.055555	Joules (Int.)	B.t.u	0.000948608
"	Fathoms	0.013888	"	B.t.u. (IST.)	0.000947988
"	Feet	0.083333	"	B.t.u. (mean)	0.000947244
"	Feet (U.S. Survey)	0.083333167	"	Cal. gm	0.239045
"	Links (Gunter's)	0.126262	"	Cal., gm. (IST.)	0.238888
"	Links (Ramden's)	0.083333	"	Cal., gm. (mean)	0.238702
"	Meters	0.0254	"	C.h.u.	0.000527004
"	Mils	1000	"	C.h.u. (IST.)	0.000526660
"	Picas (printer's)	6.0225	"	C.h.u. (mean)	0.000526247
"	Points (printer's)	72.27000	"	Cu. cm.-atm	9.87086
"	Wave length of orange-red line of krypton 86	41929.399	"	Cu. ft.-atm	0.000348586
"	Wave length of the red line of cadmium	39450.369	"	Dyne-cm	1.000165×10^7
"	Yards	0.027777	"	Ergs	1.000165×10^7
Inches of Hg (32°F.)	Atmospheres	0.0334211	"	Foot-poundals	23.73428
"	Bars	0.0338639	"	Foot-pounds	0.737684
"	Dynes/sq. cm.	33863.9	"	Gram-cm	10198.8
"	Ft. of air (1 atm., 60°F.)	926.24	"	Joules (abs.)	1.000165
"	Ft. of H_2O (39.2°F.)	1.132957	"	Kw.-hours	2.77824×10^{-7}
"	Grams/sq. cm.	34.5316	"	Liter-atm	0.00987058
"	Kg./sq. meter	345.316	"	Volt-coulombs	1.000165
"	Mm. of Hg (60°C.)	25.4	"	Volt-coulombs (Int.)	1
"	Ounces/sq. inch	7.85847	"	Watt-sec	1.000165
Inches of Hg (32°F.)	Pounds/sq. ft.	70.7262	"	Watt-sec. (Int.)	1
Inches of Hg (60°F.)	Atmospheres	0.0333269	Joules/(abcoulomb × °F.)	Joules/(coulomb × °C.)	0.18
"	Dynes/sq. cm.	39768.5	Joules/amp.-hr	Joules/abcoulomb	0.002777
"	Grams/sq. cm.	34.4343	"	Joules/statcoulomb	9.265653×10^{-14}
"	Mm. of Hg (60°F.)	25.4	Joules/coulomb	Joules/abcoulomb	10
"	Ounces/sq. inch	7.83633	"	Volts	1
"	Pounds/sq. ft.	70.5269	Joules/(coulomb × °F.)	Joules/(coulomb × °C.)	1.8
Inches of H_2O(4°C.)	Atmospheres	0.0024582	Joules/°C	B.t.u./°F	0.000526917
"	Dynes/sq. cm.	2490.82	"	Cal., gm./°C	0.239006
"	In. of Hg (32°F.)	0.0735539	"	Cal., gm. (mean)/°C	0.238662
"	Kg./sq. meter	25.3993	Joules/electronic charge	Joules/abcoulomb	6.24196×10^{19}
"	Ounces/sq. ft.	83.2350	Joules/(electronic charge × °C.)	Joules/(coulomb × °C.)	6.24196×10^{18}
"	Ounces/sq. inch	0.578020	Joules/(gram × °C.)	B.t.u./(lb. × °F.)	0.239006
"	Pounds/sq. ft.	5.20218	"	Cal., gm./(gram × °C.)	0.239006
"	Pounds/sq. inch	0.03612628	Joules (Int.)/(gram °C.)	B.t.u./(lb. × °F.)	0.239045
Inches/hr	Cm./hr	2.54	"	Cal., gm. (mean)/(gram × °C.)	0.238702
"	Feet/hr	0.0833333	Joules/sec. (abs.)	B.t.u./min	0.0569071
"	Miles/hr	1.578282×10^{-5}	"	Cal., gm./min	14.3403
Inches/min	Cm./hr	152.4	"	Cal., kg./min	0.0143403
"	Feet/hr	5	"	Cal., kg. (mean)/min	0.0143197
"	Miles/hr	0.000946969	"	Dyne-cm./sec	1×10^7
Joules (abs.)	B.t.u.	0.000948451	"	Ergs/sec	1×10^7
" "	B.t.u. (IST.)	0.000947831	"	Foot-pounds/sec	0.737562
" "	B.t.u. (mean)	0.000947088	"	Gram-cm./sec	10197.16
" "	Cal., gm	0.239006	"	Horsepower	0.00134102
" "	Cal., gm. (IST.)	0.238849	"	Watts	1
" "	Cal., gm. (mean)	0.238662	"	Watts (Int.)	0.999835
" "	Cal., gm. (15°C.)	0.238903	Joules (Int.)/sec	B.t.u./min	0.0569165
" "	Cal., gm. (20°C.)	0.239126			

To convert from	To	Multiply by	To convert from	To	Multiply by
Hectoliters	Cu. cm	1.00028×10^5	Horsepower (boiler)	Horsepower (metric)	13.3372
"	Cu. feet	3.531566	"	Horsepower (water)	13.1487
"	Gallons (U.S., liq.)	26.41794	"	Joules/sec	9809.50
"	Liters	100	"	Kilowatts	9.80950
"	Ounces (U.S.) fluid	3381.497	"	Lb. H_2O evap. per hr. from and at 212°F	34.5
"	Pecks (U.S.)	11.35136	Horsepower (electric)	B.t.u./hr	2547.16
Hectometers	Centimeters	10000	"	B.t.u. (IST.)/hr	2545.50
"	Decimeters	1000	"	B.t.u. (mean)/hr	2543.50
"	Dekameters	10	"	Cal., gm./sec	178.298
"	Feet	328.08399	"	Cal., kg./hr	641.874
"	Meters	100	"	Ergs/sec	7.46×10^9
"	Rods	19.883878	"	Foot-pounds/min	33013.3
"	Yards	109.3613	"	Foot-pounds/sec	550.221
Hectowatts	Watts	100	"	Horsepower	1.00040
Hefner units	Candles (English)	0.86	"	Horsepower (boiler)	0.0760487
"	Candles (German)	0.85	"	Horsepower (metric)	1.0142777
"	Candles (Int.)	0.90	"	Horsepower (water)	0.999942
"	10-cp. pentane candles	0.090	"	Joules/sec	746
Henries	Abhenries	1×10^9	"	Kilowatts	0.746
"	E.M. cgs. units	1×10^9	"	Watts	746
"	E.S. cgs. units	1.112646×10^{-12}	Horsepower (metric)	B.t.u./hr	2511.31
"	Henries (Int.)	0.999505	"	B.t.u. (IST.)/hr	2509.66
"	Millihenries	1000	"	B.t.u. (mean)/hr	2507.70
"	Mks. (r or nr) units	1	"	Cal., gm./hr	6.32838×10^5
"	Stathenries	1.112646×10^{-12}	"	Cal., gm. (IST.)/hr	6.32425×10^5
Henries (Int.)	Henries	1.000495	"	Cal., gm. (mean)/hr	6.31929×10^5
Henries/meter	Cgs. units of permeability	795774.72	"	Ergs/sec	7.35499×10^9
"	E.M. cgs. units	795774.72	"	Foot-pounds/min	32548.6
"	E.S. cgs. units	8.854156×10^{-16}	"	Foot-pounds/sec	542.476
"	Gausses/oersted	795774.72	"	Horsepower	0.986320
"	Mks. (nr) units	0.079577472	"	Horsepower (boiler)	0.0749782
"	Mks. (r) units	1	"	Horsepower (electric)	0.985923
Hogsheads	Butts (Brit.)	0.5	"	Horsepower (water)	0.985866
"	Cu. feet	8.421875	"	Kg.-meters/sec	75
"	Cu. inches	14553	"	Kilowatts	0.735499
"	Cu. meters	0.23848094	"	Watts	735.499
"	Gallons (Brit.)	52.458505	Horsepower (water)	Foot-pounds/min	33015.2
"	Gallons (U.S.)	63	"	Horsepower	1.00046
"	Gallons (wine)	63	"	Horsepower (boiler)	0.0760531
"	Liters	238.47427	"	Horsepower (electric)	1.00006
Horsepower*	B.t.u. (mean)/hr	2542.48	"	Horsepower (metric)	1.01434
"	B.t.u./min	42.4356	"	Kilowatts	0.746043
"	B.t.u. (mean)/sec	0.706243	Horsepower-hours	B.t.u	2546.14
"	Cal., gm./hr	6.41616×10^5	"	B.t.u. (IST.)	2544.47
"	Cal., gm. (IST.)/hr	6.41196×10^5	"	B.t.u. (mean)	2542.48
"	Cal., gm. (mean)/hr	6.40693×10^5	"	Cal., gm	641616
"	Cal., gm./min	10693.6	"	Cal., gm. (IST.)	641196
"	Cal., gm. (IST.)/min	10686.6	"	Cal., gm. (mean)	640693
"	Cal., gm. (mean)/min	10678.2	"	Foot-pounds	1.98×10^6
"	Ergs/sec	7.45700×10^9	"	Joules	2.68452×10^6
"	Foot-pounds/hr	1980000	"	Kg.-meters	273745
"	Foot-pounds/min	33000	"	Kw.-hours	0.745700
"	Foot-pounds/sec	550	"	Watt-hours	745.700
"	Horsepower (boiler)	0.0760181	Hp.-hr./lb.	B.t.u./lb	2546.14
"	Horsepower (electric)	0.999598	"	Cal., gm./gram	1414.52
"	Horsepower (metric)	1.01387	"	Cu. ft.-(lb./sq. in.)/lb	13750
"	Joules/sec	745.700	"	Foot-pounds/lb	1980000
"	Kilowatts	0.745700	"	Joules/gram	5918.35
"	Kilowatts (Int.)	0.745577	Hours (mean solar)	Days (mean solar)	0.0416666
"	Tons of refrig. (U.S., comm.)	0.21204	"	Days (sidereal)	0.041780746
"	Watts	745.700	"	Hours (sidereal)	1.00273791
Horsepower (boiler)	B.t.u. (mean)/hr	33445.7	"	Minutes (mean solar)	60
"	Cal., gm./min	140671.6	"	Minutes (sidereal)	60.164275
"	Cal., gm. (mean)/min	140469.4	"	Seconds (mean solar)	3600
"	Cal., gm. (15°C.)/min	140611.1	"	Seconds (sidereal)	3609.8565
"	Cal., gm., (20°C.)/min	140742.2	"	Weeks (mean calendar)	0.0059523809
"	Ergs/sec	9.80950×10^{10}	Hours (sidereal)	Days (mean solar)	0.41552899
"	Foot-pounds/min	434107	"	Days (sidereal)	0.0416666
"	Horsepower	13.1548	"	Hours (mean solar)	0.99726957
"	Horsepower (electric)	13.1105	"	Minutes (mean solar)	59.83617

* Mechanical horsepower, equal to 550 ft.-lb./sec.

To convert from	To	Multiply by	To convert from	To	Multiply by
Gills (Brit.)	Ounces (U.S., fluid)	4.803764	Grams/cu. cm	Pounds/gal. (U.S., dry)	9.7111064
"	Pints (Brit.)	0.25	"	Pounds/gal. (U.S., liq.)	8.3454044
Gills (U.S.)	Cu. cm	118.29412	Grams/cu. meter	Grains/cu. ft.	0.43699572
"	Cu. inches	7.21875	Grams/liter	Parts/million*	1000
"	Drams (U.S., fluid)	32	"	Lb./cu. ft.	0.06242621
"	Gallons (U.S., liq.)	0.03125	"	Lb./gal. (U.S.)	8.345171×10^{-3}
"	Gills (Brit.)	0.8326747	Grams/milliliter	Grams/cu. cm	1
"	Liters	0.1182908	"	Pounds/cu. ft.	62.42621
"	Minims (U.S.)	1920	"	Pounds/gallon (U.S.)	8.345171
"	Ounces (U.S., fluid)	4	Grams/sq. cm	Atmospheres	0.000967841
"	Pints (U.S., liq.)	0.25	"	Bars	0.000980665
"	Quarts (U.S., liq.)	0.125	"	Cm. of Hg. (0°C.)	0.0735559
Grades	Circles	0.0025	"	Dynes/sq. cm	980.665
"	Circumferences	0.0025	"	In. of Hg (32°F.)	0.0289590
"	Degrees	0.9	"	Kg./sq. meter	10
"	Minutes	54	"	Mm. of Hg (0°C.)	0.735559
"	Radians	0.015707963	"	Poundals/sq. inch	0.457623
"	Revolutions	0.0025	"	Pounds/sq. inch	0.014223343
"	Seconds	3240	Grams/ton (long)	Milligrams/kg.	0.98420653
Grains	Carats (metric)	0.32399455	Grams/ton (short)	Milligrams/kg.	1.1023113
"	Drams (apoth. or troy)	0.016666	Grams-cm	B.t.u.	9.30113×10^{-8}
"	Drams (avdp.)	0.036571429	"	B.t.u. (IST.)	9.29505×10^{-8}
"	Dynes	63.5460	"	B.t.u. (mean)	9.28776×10^{-8}
"	Grams	0.06479891	"	Cal., gm.	2.34385×10^{-5}
"	Milligrams	64.79891	"	Cal., gm. (IST.)	2.34231×10^{-5}
"	Ounces (apoth. or troy)	0.0020833	"	Cal., gm. (mean)	2.34048×10^{-5}
"	Ounces (avdp.)	0.0022857143	"	Cal., gm. (15°C.)	2.34284×10^{-5}
"	Pennyweights	0.041666	"	Cal., gm. (20°C.)	2.34502×10^{-5}
"	Pounds (apoth. or troy)	0.000173611	"	Cal., kg.	2.34385×10^{-8}
"	Pounds (avdp.)	0.00014285714	"	Cal., kg. (IST.)	2.34231×10^{-8}
"	Scruples (apoth.)	0.05	"	Cal., kg. (mean)	2.34048×10^{-8}
"	Tons (metric)	6.479891×10^{-8}	"	Dyne-cm	980.665
Grains/cu. ft.	Grams/cu. meter	2.2883519	"	Ergs	980.665
Grains/gal. (U.S.)	Parts/million*	17.11854	"	Foot-poundals	0.00232715
"	Pounds/million gal.	142.8571	"	Foot-pounds	7.2330138×10^{-5}
Grams	Carats (metric)	5	"	Hp.-hours	3.65303×10^{-11}
"	Decigrams	10	"	Joules	9.80665×10^{-5}
"	Dekagrams	0.1	"	Kw.-hours	2.72407×10^{-11}
"	Drams (apoth. or troy)	0.25720597	"	Kw.-hours (Int.)	2.72362×10^{-11}
"	Drams (avdp.)	0.56438339	"	Newton-meters	9.80665×10^{-5}
"	Dynes	980.665	"	Watt-hours	2.72407×10^{-8}
"	Grains	15.432358	Gram-cm./sec.	B.t.u./sec.	9.30113×10^{-8}
"	Kilograms	0.001	"	Cal., gm./sec.	2.34385×10^{-5}
"	Micrograms	1×10^{6}	"	Ergs-sec.	980.665
"	Myriagrams	0.0001	"	Foot-pounds/sec.	7.2330138×10^{-5}
"	Ounces (apoth. or troy)	0.032150737	"	Horsepower	1.31509×10^{-7}
"	Ounces (avdp.)	0.035273962	"	Joules/sec.	9.80665×10^{-5}
"	Pennyweights	0.64301493	"	Kilowatts	9.80665×10^{-8}
"	Poundals	0.0709316	"	Kilowatts (Int.)	9.80503×10^{-8}
"	Pounds (apoth. or troy)	0.0026792289	"	Watts	9.80665×10^{-5}
"	Pounds (avdp.)	0.0022046226	Gram/sq. cm	Pounds/sq. inch	0.000341717
"	Scruples (apoth.)	0.77161792	Gram wt.-sec./sq. cm	Poises	980.665
"	Tons (metric)	1×10^{-6}	Gravitational constants	Cm./(sec. × sec.)	980.621
Grams/cm	Dynes/cm	980.665	"	Ft./(sec. × sec.)	32.1725
"	Grams/inch	2.54			
"	Kg./km	100	Hands	Centimeters	10.16
"	Kg./meter	0.1	"	Inches	4
"	Poundals/inch	0.180166	Hectares	Acres	2.4710538
"	Pounds/ft	0.067196898	"	Ares	100
"	Pounds/inch	0.0055997415	"	Sq. cm	1×10^{8}
"	Tons (metric)/km	0.1	"	Sq. feet	107639.10
Grams/(cm. × sec.)	Poises	1	"	Sq. meters	10000
"	Lb./(ft. × sec.)	0.06719690	"	Sq. miles	0.0038610216
Grams/cu. cm	Dynes/cu. cm	980.665	"	Sq. rods	395.36861
"	Grains/milliliter	15.43279	Hectograms	Grams	100
"	Grams/milliliter	1	"	Poundals	7.09316
"	Poundals/cu. inch	1.16236	"	Pounds (apoth or troy)	0.26792289
"	Pounds/circ. mil-ft	3.4049170×10^{-7}	"	Pounds (avdp.)	0.22046226
"	Pounds/cu. ft	62.427961	Hectoliters	Bushels (Brit.)	2.749694
"	Pounds/cu. inch	0.036127292	"	Bushels (U.S.)	2.837839
"	Pounds/gal. (Brit.)	10.02241			

* Based on density of 1 gram/ml.

To convert from	To	Multiply by	To convert from	To	Multiply by
Foot-pounds/hr	Foot-pounds/min	0.0166666	Gallons (U.S., dry)	Cu. inches	268.8025
"	Horsepower	5.050505×10^{-7}	"	Gallons (U.S., liq.)	1.16364719
"	Horsepower (metric)	5.12055×10^{-7}	"	Liters	4.404760
"	Kilowatts	3.76616×10^{-7}	Gallons (U.S., liq.)	Acre-feet	3.0688833×10^{-6}
"	Watts	0.000376616	"	Barrels (U.S., liq.)	0.031746032
"	Watts (Int.)	0.000376554	"	Barrels (petroleum, U.S.)	0.023809524
Foot-pounds/min	B.t.u./sec	2.14321×10^{-5}	"	Bushels (U.S.)	0.10742088
"	B.t.u. (mean)/sec	2.14013×10^{-5}	"	Cu. centimeters	3785.4118
"	Cal., gm./sec	0.00540080	"	Cu. feet	0.133680555
"	Cal., gm. (mean)/sec	0.00539304	"	Cu. inches	231
"	Ergs/sec	2.25970×10^{5}	"	Cu. meters	0.0037854118
"	Foot-pounds/sec	0.0166666	"	Cu. yards	0.0049511317
"	Horsepower	3.030303×10^{-5}	"	Gallons (Brit.)	0.8326747
"	Horsepower (metric)	3.07233×10^{-5}	"	Gallons (U.S., dry)	0.85936701
"	Joules/sec	0.0225970	"	Gallons (wine)	1
"	Joules (Int.)/sec	0.0225932	"	Gills (U.S.)	32
"	Kilowatts	2.25970×10^{-5}	"	Liters	3.7854118
"	Watts	0.0225970	"	Minims (U.S.)	61440
Foot-pounds/lb	B.t.u./lb	0.00128593	"	Ounces (U.S., fluid)	128
"	B.t.u. (IST.)/lb	0.00128509	"	Pints (U.S., liq.)	8
"	B.t.u. (mean)/lb	0.00128408	"	Quarts (U.S., liq.)	4
"	Cal., gm./gm	0.000714404	Gallons (U.S.) of H_2O (4°C.) in air	Lb. of H_2O	8.33585
"	Cal., gm. (IST.)/gram	0.000713937	Gallons (U.S.) of H_2O (60°F.) in air	Lb. of H_2O	8.32823
"	Cal., gm. (mean)/gram	0.000713377	Gallons (U.S.)/day	Cu. ft./min	0.0055700231
"	Hp.-hr./lb	5.05050×10^{-7}	"	Cu. meters/min	7.576812×10^{-5}
"	Joules/gram	0.00298907	Gallons (Brit.)/hr	Cu. meters/min	7.576812×10^{-5}
"	Kg.-meters/gram	0.000304800	Gallons (U.S.)/hr	Acre-feet/hr	3.0688833×10^{-6}
"	Kw.-hr./gram	8.30296×10^{-10}	"	Cu. ft./hr	0.1336805
Foot-pounds/sec	B.t.u./min	0.0771556	"	Cu. meters/min	6.3090197×10^{-5}
"	B.t.u. (mean)/min	0.0770447	"	Cu. yd./min	8.2518861×10^{-5}
"	B.t.u./sec	0.00128593	"	Liters/hr	3.7854118
"	B.t.u. (mean)/sec	0.00128408	Gal. (Brit.)/sec	Cu. cm./sec	4546.087
"	Cal., gm./sec	0.324048	Gal. (U.S.)/sec	Cu. cm./sec	3785.4118
"	Cal., gm. (mean)/sec	0.323582	"	Cu. ft./sec	8.020833
"	Ergs/sec	1.35582×10^{7}	"	Cu. yd./min	0.29706790
"	Gram-cm./sec	13825.5	"	Liters/min	227.1183
"	Horsepower	0.00181818	Gammas	Grams	1×10^{-6}
"	Joules/sec	1.35582	"	Micrograms	1
"	Kilowatts	0.00135582	Gausses	E.M. cgs. units of magnetic flux density	1
"	Watts	1.35582	"	E.S. cgs. units	3.335635×10^{-11}
"	Watts (Int.)	1.35559	"	Gausses (Int.)	0.999670
Furlongs	Centimeters	20116.8	"	Maxwells/sq. cm	1
"	Chains (Gunter's)	10	"	Lines/sq. cm	1
"	Chains (Ramden's)	6.6	"	Lines/sq. inch	6.4516
"	Feet	660	Gausses (Int.)	Gausses	1.000330
"	Inches	7920	Gausses/oersted	E.M. cgs. units of permeability	1
"	Meters	201.168	"	E.S. cgs. units	1.112646×10^{-21}
"	Miles (naut., Int.)	0.10862203	Geepounds	Slugs	1
"	Miles (statute)	0.125	"	Kilograms	14.5939
"	Rods	40	Gigameters	Meters	1×10^{9}
"	Yards	220	Gilberts	Abampere-turns	0.079577472
Gallons (Brit.)	Barrels (Brit.)	0.027777	"	Ampere-turns	0.79577472
"	Bushels (Brit.)	0.125	"	E.M. cgs. units of mmf., or magnetic potential	1
"	Cu. centimeters	4546.087	"	E.S. cgs. units	2.997930×10^{10}
"	Cu. feet	0.1605436	"	Gilberts (Int.)	1.000165
"	Cu. inches	277.4193	Gilberts (Int.)	Gilberts	0.999835
"	Drachms (Brit. fluid)	1280	Gilberts/cm	Ampere-turns/cm	0.79577472
"	Firkins (Brit.)	0.111111	"	Ampere-turns/in	2.0212678
"	Gallons (U.S., liq.)	1.200949	"	Oersteds	1
"	Gills (Brit.)	32	Gilberts/maxwell	Ampere-turns/weber	7.957747×10^{7}
"	Liters	4.545960	"	E.M. cgs. units of reluctance	1
"	Minims (Brit.)	76800	"	E.S. cgs. units	8.987584×10^{20}
"	Ounces (Brit., fluid)	160	Gills (Brit.)	Cu. cm	142.0652
"	Ounces (U.S., fluid)	153.7215	"	Gallons (Brit.)	0.03125
"	Pecks (Brit.)	0.5	"	Gills (U.S.)	1.000949
"	Lb. of H_2O (62°F.)	10	"	Liters	0.1420613
Gallons (U.S., dry)	Barrels (U.S., dry)	0.038095592	"	Ounces (Brit., fluid)	5
"	Barrels (U.S., liq.)	0.036941181			
"	Bushels (U.S.)	0.125			
"	Cu. centimeters	4404.9825			
"	Cu. feet	0.15555700			

To convert from	To	Multiply by	To convert from	To	Multiply by
Fathoms	Feet	6	Feet/(sec. × sec.)	Meters/(sec. × sec.)	0.3048
"	Inches	72	"	Miles/(hr. × sec.)	0.68181818
"	Meters	1.8288	Firkins (Brit.)	Bushels (Brit.)	1.125
"	Miles (naut., Int.)	0.00098747300	"	Cu. cm	40914.79
"	Miles (statute)	0.001136363	"	Cu. feet	1.444892
"	Yards	2	"	Firkins (U.S.)	1.200949
Feet	Centimeters	30.48	"	Gallons (Brit.)	9
"	Chains (Gunter's)	0.01515151	"	Liters	40.91364
"	Fathoms	0.166666	"	Pints (Brit.)	72
"	Feet (U.S. Survey)	0.99999800	Firkins (U.S.)	Barrels (U.S., dry)	0.29464286
"	Furlongs	0.00151515	"	Barrels (U.S., liq.)	0.28571429
"	Inches	12	"	Bushels (U.S.)	0.96678788
"	Meters	0.3048	"	Cu. feet	1.203125
"	Microns	304800	"	Firkins (Brit.)	0.8326747
"	Miles (naut., Int.)	0.00016457883	"	Liters	34.06775
"	Miles (statute)	0.000189393	"	Pints (U.S., liq.)	72
"	Rods	0.060606	Foot-candles	Lumens/sq. ft	1
"	Ropes (Brit.)	0.05	"	Lumens/sq. meter	10.763910
"	Yards	0.333333	"	Lux	10.763910
Feet (U.S. Survey)	Centimeters	30.480061	"	Milliphots	1.0763910
"	Chains (Gunter's)	0.015151545	Foot-lamberts	Candles/sq. cm	0.00034262591
"	Chains (Ramden's)	0.010000020	"	Candles/sq. ft	0.31830989
"	Feet	1.0000020	"	Millilamberts	1.0763910
"	Inches	12.000024	"	Lamberts	0.0010763910
"	Links (Gunter's)	1.5151545	"	Lumens/sq. ft	1
"	Links (Ramden's)	1.0000020	Foot-poundals	B.t.u.	3.99678×10^{-5}
"	Meters	0.30480061	"	B.t.u. (IST.)	3.99417×10^{-5}
"	Miles (statute)	0.00018939432	"	B.t.u. (mean)	3.99104×10^{-5}
"	Rods	0.060606182	"	Cal., gm	0.0100717
"	Yards	0.33333400	"	Cal., gm (IST.)	0.0100651
Feet of air (1 atm., 60°F.)	Atmospheres	3.6083×10^{-5}	"	Cal., gm (mean)	0.0100573
"	Ft. of Hg (32°F.)	0.00089970	"	Cu. cm.-atm	0.415890
"	Ft. of H$_2$O (60°F.)	0.0012244	"	Cu. ft.-atm	1.46870×10^{-5}
"	In. of Hg (32°F.)	0.0010796	"	Dyne-cm	4.2140110×10^{5}
"	Pounds/sq. inch	0.00053027	"	Ergs	4.2140110×10^{5}
Feet of Hg (32°F.)	Cm. of Hg (0°C.)	30.48	"	Foot-pounds	0.0310810
"	Ft. of H$_2$O (60°F.)	13.6085	"	Hp.-hours	1.56974×10^{-8}
"	In. of H$_2$O (60°F.)	163.302	"	Joules	0.042140110
"	Ounces/sq. inch	94.3016	"	Joules (Int.)	0.0421332
"	Pounds/sq. inch	5.89385	"	Kg.-meters	0.00429710
Feet of H$_2$O (4°C.)	Atmospheres	0.0294990	"	Kw.-hours	1.17056×10^{-8}
"	Cm. of Hg (0°C.)	2.24192	"	Liter-atm	0.000415879
"	Dynes/sq. cm	29889.8	"	B.t.u.	0.00128593
"	Grams/sq. cm	30.4791	Foot-pounds	B.t.u. (IST.)	0.00128509
"	In. of Hg (32°F.)	0.882646	"	B.t.u. (mean)	0.00128408
"	Kg./sq. meter	304.791	"	Cal., gm	0.324048
"	Pounds/sq. inch	0.433515	"	Cal., gm (IST.)	0.323836
Feet/hour	Cm./hr	30.48	"	Cal., gm (mean)	0.323582
"	Cm./min	0.508	"	Cal., gm (20°C.)	0.324211
"	Cm./sec	0.0084666	"	Cal., kg	0.000324048
"	Feet/min	0.0166666	"	Cal., kg (IST.)	0.000323836
"	Inches/hr	12	"	Cal., kg (mean)	0.000323582
"	Kilometers/hr	0.0003048	"	Cu. ft.-atm	0.000472541
"	Kilometers/min	5.08×10^{-6}	"	Dyne-cm	1.35582×10^{7}
"	Knots (Int.)	0.0001645788	"	Ergs	1.35582×10^{7}
"	Miles/hr	0.000189393	"	Foot-poundals	32.1740
"	Miles/min	3.156565×10^{-6}	"	Gram-cm	13825.5
"	Miles/sec	5.2609428×10^{-8}	"	Hp.-hours	5.05050×10^{-7}
Feet/minute	Cm./sec	0.508	"	Joules	1.35582
"	Feet/sec	0.0166666	"	Kg.-meters	0.138255
"	Kilometers/hr	0.018288	"	Kw.-hours	3.76616×10^{-7}
"	Meters/min	0.3048	"	Kw.-hours (Int.)	3.76554×10^{-7}
"	Meters/sec	0.00508	"	Liter-atm	0.0133805
"	Miles/hr	0.01136363	"	Newton-meters	1.3558180
Feet/second	Cm./sec	30.48	"	Lb. H$_2$O evap. from and at 212°F	1.3245×10^{-6}
"	Kilometers/hr	1.09728	"	Watt-hours	0.000376616
"	Kilometers/min	0.018288	Foot-pounds/hr	B.t.u./min	2.14321×10^{-5}
"	Meters/min	18.288	"	B.t.u. (mean)/min	2.14013×10^{-5}
"	Miles/hr	0.68181818	"	Cal., gm./min	0.00540080
"	Miles/min	0.01136363	"	Cal., gm. (mean)/min	0.00539304
Feet/(sec. × sec.)	Kilometers/(hr. × sec.)	1.09728	"	Ergs/min	2.25970×10^{5}

To convert from	To	Multiply by	To convert from	To	Multiply by
Decimeters	Feet	0.32808399	Dynes/sq. cm	Cm. of H₂O (4°C.)	0.001019745
"	Feet (U.S. Survey)	9.328083333	"	Grams/sq. cm	0.001019716
"	Inches	3.9370079	"	In. of Hg (32°F.)	2.95300×10^{-5}
"	Meters	0.1	"	In. of H₂O (4°C.)	0.000401474
Decisteres	Cu. meters	0.1	"	Kg./sq. meter	0.01019716
Degrees	Circles	0.0027777	"	Poundals/sq. in.	0.00046664510
"	Minutes	60	"	Pounds/sq. in.	1.450377×10^{-5}
"	Quadrants	0.0111111	Dyne-centimeters	Ergs	1
"	Radians	0.017453293	"	Foot-poundals	2.3730360×10^{-6}
"	Seconds	3600	"	Foot-pounds	7.37562×10^{-8}
Degrees/cm	Radians/cm	0.017453293	"	Gram-cm	0.001019716
Degrees/foot	Radians/cm	0.00057261158	"	Inch-pounds	8.85075×10^{-7}
Degrees/inch	Radian/cm	0.0068713750	"	Kg.-meters	1.019716×10^{-8}
Degrees/min	Degrees/sec	0.0166666	"	Newton-meters	1×10^{-7}
"	Radians/sec	0.00029088821			
"	Revolutions/sec	4.629629×10^{-5}	Electron volts	Ergs	1.60219×10^{-12}
Degrees/sec	Radians/sec	0.017453293	"	Grams	1.78253×10^{-33}
"	Revolutions/min	0.166666	Electronic charges	Abcoulombs	1.60209×10^{-20}
"	Revolutions/sec	0.0027777	"	Coulombs	1.60209×10^{-19}
Dekaliters	Pecks (U.S.)	1.135136	"	Statcoulombs	4.80296×10^{-10}
"	Pints (U.S., dry)	18.16217	Electronic charges/kg.	Statcoulombs/dyne	4.89766×10^{-16}
Dekameters	Centimeters	1000	E.S. cgs. units of induction flux	E.M. cgs. units	2.997930×10^{10}
"	Feet	32.808399	E.S. cgs. units of magnetic charge	E.M. cgs. units	2.997930×10^{10}
"	Feet (U.S. Survey)	32.808333	E.S. cgs. units of magnetic field intensity	E.M. cgs. units	3.335635×10^{-11}
"	Inches	393.70079	Ells	Centimeters	114.3
"	Kilometers	0.01	"	Inches	45
"	Meters	10	Ergs	B.t.u.	9.48451×10^{-11}
"	Yards	10.93613	"	Cal., gm	2.39006×10^{-8}
Demals	Gram-equiv./cu. decimeter	1	"	Cal., kg	2.39006×10^{-11}
Drachms (Brit., fluid)	Cu. cm	3.551631	"	Cal., kg. (20°C.)	2.39126×10^{-11}
"	Cu. inches	0.2167338	"	Cu. cm.-atm	9.86923×10^{-7}
"	Drams (U.S., fluid)	0.9607594	"	Cu. ft.-atm	3.48529×10^{-11}
"	Milliliters	3.551531	"	Cu. ft.-(lb./sq. in.)	5.12196×10^{-10}
Drams (apoth. or troy)	Drams (avdp.)	2.1942857	"	Dyne-cm	1
"	Grains	60	"	Electron volts	6.24145×10^{11}
"	Grams	3887.9346	"	Foot-poundals	2.3730360×10^{-6}
"	Ounces (apoth. or troy)	0.125	"	Foot-pounds	7.37562×10^{-8}
"	Ounces (avdp.)	0.13714286	"	Gram-cm	0.001019716
"	Scruples (apoth.)	3	"	Joules	1×10^{-7}
Drams (avdp.)	Drams (apoth. or troy)	0.455729166	"	Joules (Int.)	9.99835×10^{-8}
"	Grains	27.34375	"	Kw.-hours	2.777777×10^{-14}
"	Grams	1.7718452	"	Kg.-meters	1.019716×10^{-8}
"	Ounces (apoth. or troy)	0.056966146	"	Liter-atm	9.86895×10^{-10}
"	Ounces (avdp.)	0.0625	"	Watt-sec	1×10^{-7}
"	Pennyweights	1.1393229	Ergs/(gram-mol. × °C.)	Foot-pounds/(lb.-mol. × °F.)	1.85863×10^{-5}
"	Pounds (apoth. or troy)	0.0047471788	Ergs/sec	B.t.u./min	5.69071×10^{-9}
"	Pounds (avdp.)	0.00390625	"	Cal., gm./min	1.43403×10^{-6}
"	Scruples (apoth.)	1.3671875	"	Dyne-cm./sec	1
Drams (U.S., fluid)	Cu. cm	3.6967162	"	Foot-pounds/min	4.42537×10^{-6}
"	Cu. inches	0.22558504	"	Gram-cm./sec	0.001019716
"	Drachms (Brit., fluid)	1.040843	"	Horsepower	1.34102×10^{-10}
"	Gills (U.S.)	0.03125	"	Joules/sec	1×10^{-7}
"	Milliliters	3.696588	"	Kilowatts	1×10^{-10}
"	Minims (U.S.)	60	"	Watts	1×10^{-7}
"	Ounces (U.S., fluid)	0.125	Ergs/sq. cm	Dynes/cm	1
"	Pints (U.S., liq.)	0.0078125	"	Ergs/sq. mm	0.01
Dynes	Grains	0.01573663	Ergs/sq. mm	Dynes/cm	100
"	Grams	0.001019716	"	Ergs/sq. cm	100
"	Newtons	0.00001	Erg-sec	Planck's constant	1.50932×10^{26}
"	Poundals	7.2330138×10^{-5}			
"	Pounds	2.248089×10^{-6}	Farads	Abfarads	1×10^{-9}
Dynes/cm	Ergs/sq. cm	1	"	E.M. cgs. units	1×10^{-9}
"	Ergs/sq. mm	0.01	"	E.S. cgs. units	8.987584×10^{11}
"	Grams/cm	0.001019716	"	Farad (Int.)	1.000495
"	Poundals/inch	0.00018371855	"	Microfarads	1×10^{6}
Dynes/cu. cm	Grams/cu. cm	0.001019716	"	Statfarads	8.98758×10^{11}
"	Poundals/cu. inch	0.0011852786	Farads (Int.)	Farads	0.999505
Dynes/sq. cm	Atmospheres	9.80923×10^{-7}	Fathoms	Centimeters	182.88
"	Bars	1×10^{-6}			
"	Baryes	1			
"	Cm. of Hg (0°C.)	7.50062×10^{-5}			

To convert from	To	Multiply by	To convert from	To	Multiply by
Cubic decimeters.....	Cu. yards.............	0.0013079506	Cubic inches.........	Ounces (U.S., fluid)......	0.55411255
"	Liters...............	1	"	Pecks (U.S.)............	0.0018601017
Cubic dekameters....	Cu. decimeters.......	1×10^6	"	Pints (U.S., dry)........	0.029761628
"	Cu. feet.............	35314.667	"	Pints (U.S., liq.)........	0.034632035
"	Cu. inches...........	6.1023744×10^7	"	Quarts (U.S., dry).......	0.014880814
"	Cu. meters...........	1000	"	Quarts (U.S., liq.).......	0.017316017
"	Liters...............	999972	Cu. in. of H_2O (4°C.)..	Pounds of H_2O.......	0.0361263
Cubic feet...........	Acre-feet............	2.2956841×10^{-5}	Cu. in. of H_2O (60°F.).	Pounds of H_2O.......	0.0360916
"	Board feet...........	12	Cubic meters.........	Acre-feet............	0.00081071319
"	Bushels (Brit.).......	0.7786049	"	Barrels (Brit.)........	6.110261
"	Bushels (U.S.).......	0.80356395	"	Barrels (U.S., dry).....	8.648490
"	Cords (wood)........	0.0078125	"	Barrels (U.S., liq.).....	8.3864145
"	Cord-feet...........	0.0625	"	Bushels (Brit.).......	27.49617
"	Cu. centimeters......	28316.847	"	Bushels (U.S.).......	28.377593
"	Cu. meters...........	0.028316847	"	Cu. cm.............	1×10^6
"	Gallons (U.S., dry)...	6.4285116	"	Cu. feet.............	35.314667
"	Gallons (U.S., liq.)...	7.4805195	"	Cu. inches...........	61023.74
"	Liters...............	28.316847	"	Cu. yards............	1.3079506
"	Ounces (Brit., fluid)..	996.6143	"	Gallons (Brit.).......	219.9694
"	Ounces (U.S., fluid)..	957.50649	"	Gallons (U.S., liq.)...	264.17205
"	Pints (U.S., liq.).....	59.844156	"	Hogshead...........	4.1932072
"	Quarts (U.S., dry)....	25.714047	"	Liters...............	1000
"	Quarts (U.S., liq.)....	29.922078	"	Pints (U.S., liq.).....	2113.3764
Cu. ft. of H_2O			"	Quarts (U.S., liq.)....	1056.6882
(39.2°F.)	Pounds of H_2O....	62.4262	"	Steres..............	1
Cu. ft. ot H_2O (60°F.)	Pounds of H_2O....	62.3663	Cu. meters/min.....	Gal. (Brit.)/min......	219.9694
Cu. ft./hr	Acre-feet/hr.........	2.2956841×10^{-5}	"	Gal. (U.S.)/min......	264.1721
"	Cu. cm./sec.........	7.8657907	"	Liters/min...........	999.972
"	Cu. ft./day..........	24	Cu. millimeters.....	Cu. cm.............	0.001
"	Gal. (U.S.)/hr.......	7.4805195	"	Cu. inches...........	6.1023744×10^{-5}
"	Liters/hr............	28.31605	"	Cu. meters...........	1×10^{-9}
Cu. ft./min..........	Acre-feet/hr.........	0.0013774105	"	Minims (Brit.).......	0.01689365
"	Acre-feet/min........	2.2956841×10^{-5}	"	Minims (U.S.).......	0.016230731
"	Cu. cm./sec.........	471.94744	Cu. yards...........	Bushels (Brit.).......	21.02233
"	Cu. ft./hr...........	60	"	Bushels (U.S.).......	21.696227
"	Gal. (U.S.)/min......	7.4805195	"	Cu. cm.............	764554.86
"	Liters/sec...........	0.4719342	"	Cu. feet.............	27
Cu. ft./lb	Cu. cm./gram........	62.427961	"	Cu. inches...........	46656
"	Millimeters/gram.....	62.42621	"	Cu. meters...........	0.76455486
Cu. ft./sec..........	Acre-inches/hr........	0.99173553	"	Gallons (Brit.).......	168.1787
"	Cu. cm./sec.........	28316.847	"	Gallons (U.S., dry)...	173.56981
"	Cu. yards/min.......	2.222222	"	Gallons (U.S., liq.)...	201.97403
"	Gal. (U.S.)/min......	448.83117	"	Liters...............	764.55486
"	Liters/min...........	1698.963	"	Quarts (Brit.)........	672.7146
"	Liters/sec...........	28.31605	"	Quarts (U.S., dry)....	694.27926
Cu. ft. of H_2O			"	Quarts (U.S., liq.)....	807.89610
(60°F.)/sec........	Lb. of H_2O/min....	3741.98	Cu. yd./min........	Cu. ft./sec..........	0.45
Cu. ft.-atm.........	B.t.u...............	2.72130	"	Gal. (U.S.)/sec......	3.3662338
"	Cal., *gm*...........	685.756	"	Liters/sec...........	12.74222
"	Cu. cm.-atm.........	28316.847	Cubits..............	Centimeters.........	45.72
"	Cu. ft.-(lb/sq. in.)...	14.6960	"	Feet................	1.5
"	Foot-pounds.........	2116.22	"	Inches..............	18
"	Hp.-hours...........	0.00106880			
"	Joules..............	2869.20	Daltons (chem.)......	Grams..............	1.66024×10^{-24}
"	Kg-meters...........	292.577	Daltons (phys.)......	Grams..............	1.65979×10^{-24}
"	Kw.-hours...........	0.000797001	Days (mean solar)....	Days (sidereal)......	1.00273791
Cubic inches.........	Barrels (Brit.).......	0.0001001292	"	Hours (mean solar)...	24
"	Barrels (U.S., dry)...	0.00014172336	"	Hours (sidereal).....	24.065710
"	Board feet...........	0.0069444	"	Years (calendar).....	0.0027397260
"	Bushels (Brit.).......	0.0004505815	"	Years (sidereal).....	0.0027378031
"	Bushels (U.S.).......	0.00046502544	"	Years (tropical).....	0.0027379093
"	Cu. cm.............	16.387064	Days (sidereal)......	Days (mean solar)....	0.99726957
"	Cu. feet.............	0.00057870370	"	Hours (mean solar)...	23.934470
"	Cu. meters...........	1.6387064×10^{-5}	"	Hours (sidereal).....	24
"	Cu. yards............	2.1433470×10^{-5}	"	Minutes (mean solar)...	1436.0682
"	Drams (U.S., fluid)...	4.4329004	"	Minute (sidereal).....	1440
"	Gallons (Brit.).......	0.003604652	"	Second (sidereal).....	86400
"	Gallons (U.S., dry)...	0.0037202035	"	Years (calendar).....	0.0027322454
"	Gallons (U.S., liq.)...	0.0043290043	"	Years (sidereal).....	0.0027303277
"	Liters...............	0.016387064	"	Years (tropical).....	0.0027304336
"	Milliliters...........	16.387064	Decibels............	Bels................	0.1
"	Ounces (Brit., fluid)...	0.5767444	Decimeters..........	Centimeters.........	10

To convert from	To	Multiply by	To convert from	To	Multiply by
Centimeters	Rods	0.0019883878	Circumferences	Minutes	21600
"	Wave length of orange-red line of krypton 86	16507.6373	"	Radians	6.2831853
			"	Seconds	1296000
"	Wave length of red line of cadmium	15531.6413	Cords	Cord-feet	8
"	Yards	0.010936133	"	Cu. feet	128
Cm. of Hg (0°C.)	Atmospheres	0.013157895	"	Cu. meters	3.6245734
"	Bars	0.0133322	Cord-feet	Cords	0.125
"	Dynes/sq. cm	13332.2	"	Cu. feet	16
"	Ft. of H_2O (4°C.)	0.446050	Coulombs	Abcoulombs	0.1
"	Ft. of H_2O (60°F.)	0.446474	"	Ampere-hours	0.0002777
"	In. of Hg (0°C.)	0.39370079	"	Ampere-seconds	1
"	Kg./sq. meter	135.951	"	Coulombs (Int.)	1.000165
"	Pounds/sq. ft	27.8450	"	Electronic charge	6.24196×10^{18}
"	Pounds/sq. inch	0.193368	"	E.M. cgs. units of electric charge	0.1
"	Torrs	10	"	E.S. cgs. units of electric charge	2.997930×10^9
Cm. of H_2O (4°C.)	Atmospheres	0.000967814	"	Faradays (chem.)	1.036377×10^{-5}
"	Dynes/sq. cm	980.638	"	Faradays (phys.)	1.036086×10^{-5}
"	Pounds/sq. inch	0.0142229	"	Mks. units of electric charge	1
Centimeters/sec	Feet/min	1.9685039	"	Statcoulombs	2.997930×10^9
"	Feet/sec	0.032808399	Coulombs/cu. meter	E.M. cgs. units of volume charge density	1×10^{-7}
"	Kilometers/hr	0.036	"	E.S. cgs. units	2997.930
"	Kilometers/min	0.0006	Coulombs/sq. cm	Abcoulombs/sq. cm	0.1
"	Knots (Int.)	0.019438445	"	Cgs. units of polarization, and surface charge density	1
"	Meters/min	0.6	Cubic centimeters	Board feet	0.00042377600
"	Miles/hr	0.022369363	"	Bushels (Brit.)	2.749617×10^{-5}
"	Miles/min	0.00037282272	"	Bushels (U.S.)	2.837759×10^{-5}
Cm./(sec. $\times$ sec.)	Kilometers/(hr. $\times$ sec.)	0.036	"	Cu. feet	3.5314667×10^{-5}
"	Miles/(hr. $\times$ sec.)	0.022369363	"	Cu. inches	0.061023744
Centimeters/year	Inches/year	0.39370079	"	Cu. meters	1×10^{-6}
Centipoise*	Grams/(cm. $\times$ sec.)	0.01	"	Cu. yards	1.3079506×10^{-6}
"	Poises	0.01	"	Drachms (Brit., fluid)	0.28156080
"	Pound/(ft. $\times$ hr.)	2.4190883	"	Drams (U.S., fluid)	0.27051218
"	Pounds/(ft. $\times$ sec.)	0.00067196898	"	Gallons (Brit.)	0.0002199694
Centistokes*	Stokes	0.01	"	Gallons (U.S., dry)	0.00022702075
Chains (Gunter's)	Centimeters	2011.68	"	Gallons (U.S., liq.)	0.00026417205
"	Chains (Ramden's)	0.66	"	Gills (Brit.)	0.007039020
"	Feet	66	"	Gills (U.S.)	0.0084535058
"	Feet (U.S. Survey)	65.999868	"	Liters	0.001
"	Furlongs	0.1	"	Ounces (Brit., fluid)	0.03519510
"	Inches	792	"	Ounces (U.S., fluid)	0.033814023
"	Links (Gunter's)	100	"	Pints (U.S., dry)	0.0018161660
"	Links (Ramden's)	66	"	Pints (U.S., liq.)	0.0021133764
"	Meters	20.1168	"	Quarts (Brit.)	0.0008798775
"	Miles (statute)	0.0125	"	Quarts (U.S., dry)	0.00090808298
"	Rods	4	"	Quarts (U.S., liq.)	0.0010566882
"	Yards	22	Cu. cm./gram	Cu. ft./lb	0.016018463
Chains (Ramden's)	Centimeters	3048	Cu. cm./sec	Cu. ft./min	0.0021188800
"	Chains (Gunter's)	1.515151	"	Gal. (U.S.)/min	0.015850323
"	Feet	100	"	Gal. (U.S.)/sec	0.00026417205
"	Feet (U.S. Survey)	99.999800	Cu. cm.-atm	B.t.u.	9.61019×10^{-5}
Cheval-vapeur	Horsepower (metric)	1	"	B.t.u. (mean)	9.59637×10^{-5}
Cheval-vapeur-heures	Joules	2647795	"	Cal., gm.	0.0242173
Circles	Degrees	360	"	Cal., gm. (mean)	0.0241824
"	Grades	400	"	Cu. ft.-atm	3.5314667×10^{-5}
"	Minutes	21600	"	Joules	0.101325
"	Radians	6.2831853	"	Watt-hours	2.81458×10^{-5}
"	Signs	12	Cu. cm.-atm./gram	B.t.u./lb	0.0435911
Circular inches	Circular mm	645.16	"	Cal., gm./gram	0.0242173
"	Sq. cm	5.0670748	"	Cu. ft.-(lb./sq. in.)/lb	0.235406
"	Sq. inches	0.78539816	"	Ft.-lb./lb	33.8985
Circular mm	Sq. cm	0.0078539816	"	Joules/gram	0.101325
"	Sq. inches	0.0012173696	"	Kg.-meters/gram	0.0103323
"	Sq. mm	0.78539816	"	Kw.-hr./gram	2.81458×10^{-8}
Circular mils	Circular inches	1×10^{-6}	Cubic decimeters	Cu. cm	1000
"	Sq. cm	5.0670748×10^{-6}	"	Cu. feet	0.035316667
"	Sq. inches	7.8539816×10^{-7}	"	Cu. inches	61.023744
"	Sq. mm	0.00050670748	"	Cu. meters	0.001
"	Sq. mils	0.78539816			
Circumferences	Degrees	360			
"	Grades	400			

* See also special table on viscosity.

To convert from	To	Multiply by	To convert from	To	Multiply by
Calories, *kg*	Ergs	4.184×10^{10}	Cal., *gm*.-cm. $\overline{\text{(hr.} \times \text{sq. cm.} \times °\text{C.)}}$	B.t.u.-ft. $\overline{\text{(hr.} \times \text{sq. ft.} \times °\text{F.)}}$	0.0671969
"	Foot-poundals	99287.8			
"	Foot-pounds	3085.96	"	B.t.u.-inch $\overline{\text{(hr.} \times \text{sq. ft.} \times °\text{F.)}}$	0.806363
"	Gram-cm	4.26649×10^7			
"	Hp.-hours	0.00155857	Cal., *gm*.-cm./sq. cm.	B.t.u.-inch/sq. ft.	1.4514530
"	Joules	4184	Cal., *gm*.-sec.	Planck's constant	6.31531×10^{33}
"	Kw.-hours	0.001162222	Cal., *gm*.-sec./Avog. No. (chem.)*	Planck's constant	1.04849×10^{10}
"	Liter-atm	41.2917			
"	Watt-hours	1.162222	Cal., *gm*.-sec./Avog. No. (phys.)*	Planck's constant	1.04821×10^{10}
Calories, *kg*. (mean)	B.t.u.	3.97403			
"	B.t.u. (IST.)	3.97144	Candles (English)	Candles (Int.)	1.04
"	B.t.u. (mean)	3.9683207	"	Hefner units	1.16
"	B.t.u. (60°F.)	3.97280	Candles (German)	Candles (English)	1.01
"	Cal., *gm*	1001.44	"	Candles (Int.)	1.05
"	Cal., *gm*. (IST.)	1000.78	"	Hefner units	1.17
"	Cal., *gm*. (mean)	1000	Candles (Int.)	Candles (English)	0.96
"	Cal., *gm*. (15°C.)	1000.10	"	Candles (German)	0.95
"	Cal., *gm*. (20°C.)	1001.94	"	Candles (pentane)	1.00
"	Ergs	4.19002×10^{10}	"	Hefner units	1.11
"	Foot-poundals	99430.8	"	Lumens (Int.)/steradian	1
"	Foot-pounds	3090.40	Candles (pentane)	Candles (Int.)	1.00
"	Gram-cm	4.27263×10^7	Candles/sq. cm	Candles/sq. inch	6.4516
"	Hp.-hours	0.00156081	"	Candles/sq. meter	10000
"	Joules	4190.02	"	Foot-lamberts	2918.6351
"	Kg.-meters	427.263	"	Lamberts	3.1415927
"	Kw.-hours (Int.)	0.00116370	Candles/sq. ft	Candles/sq. inch	0.0069444
"	Liter-atm	41.3511	"	Candles/sq. meter	10.763910
"	Watt-hours	1.16390	"	Foot-lamberts	3.1415927
Cal., *gm*./°C	B.t.u./°F	0.00220462	"	Lamberts	0.0033815822
"	Joules/°F	2.324444	Candles/sq. inch	Candles/sq. cm.	0.15500031
"	Joules (Int.)/°F	2.32406	"	Candles/sq. foot	144
Cal., *gm*./gram	B.t.u./lb	1.8	"	Foot-lamberts	452.38934
"	Foot-pounds/lb	1399.77	"	Lamberts	0.48694784
"	Joules/gram	4.184	Candle power (spher.)	Lumens	12.566370
"	Watt-hours/gram	0.001162222	Carats (parts of gold per 24 of mixture)	Milligrams/gram	41.6666
Cal., *gm*./(gram × °C)	B.t.u./(lb. × °C.)	1.8			
"	B.t.u./(lb, × °F.)	1	Carats (1877)	Grains	3.168
"	Cal., *kg*./(kg. × °C.)	1	"	Milligrams	205.3
"	Joules/(gram × °C.)	4.184	Carats (metric)	Grains	3.08647
"	Joules/(lb. × °F.)	1054.35	"	Grams	0.2
Cal., *gm*./hr	B.t.u./hr	0.0039683207	"	Milligrams	200
"	Ergs/sec	11622.222	Carcel units	Candles (Int.)	9.61
"	Watts	0.001162222	Centals	Kilograms	45.359237
Cal., *gm*. (mean)/hr	B.t.u. (mean)/hr	0.0039683207	"	Pounds	100
"	Ergs/sec	11639.0	Centares	Ares	0.01
"	Watts	0.00116390	"	Sq. feet	10.763910
Cal., *kg*./hr	Watts	1.162222	"	Sq. inches	1550.0031
Cal., *gm*./min	B.t.u./min	0.0039683207	"	Sq. meters	1
"	Ergs/sec	697333.3	"	Sq. yards	1.1959900
"	Watts	0.069733	Centigrams	Grains	0.15432358
Cal., *gm*. (mean)/min	B.t.u. (mean)/min	0.0039683207	"	Grams	0.01
"	Ergs/sec	698337	Centiliters	Cu. cm	10
"	Joules/sec	0.0698337	"	Cu. inches	0.6102545
"	Watts	0.0698337	"	Liters	0.01
Cal., *kg*./min	Kg. ice melted/min	0.012548	"	Ounces (U.S., fluid)	0.3381497
"	Lb. ice melted/min	0.027665	Centimeters	Ångström units	1×10^8
"	Watts	69.7333	"	Feet	0.032808399
Cal., *gm*./sec	B.t.u./sec	0.0039683207	"	Feet (U.S. Survey)	0.032808333
"	Ergs/sec	4.184×10^7	"	Hands	0.098425197
"	Foot-pounds/sec	3.08596	"	Inches	0.39370079
"	Horsepower	0.00561084	"	Links (Gunter's)	0.049709695
"	Watts	4.184	"	Links (Ramden's)	0.032808399
Cal., *gm*. (mean)/sec	Ergs/sec	4.19002×10^7	"	Meters	0.01
"	Watts	4.19002	"	Microns	10000
Cal., *gm*./(sec. × sq. cm.)	B.t.u./(hr. × sq. ft.)	13272.1	"	Miles (naut., Int.)	5.3995680×10^{-6}
"	Cal., *gm*./(hr. × sq. cm.)	3600	"	Miles (statute)	6.2137119×10^{-6}
"	Watts/sq. cm	4.184	"	Millimeters	10
Cal., *gm*./(sec. × sq. cm. × °C.)	B.t.u./(hr. × sq. ft. × °F.)	7373.38	"	Millimicrons	1×10^7
			"	Mils	393.70079
Cal., *gm*./sq. cm	B.t.u./sq. ft	3.68669	"	Picas (printer's)	2.3710630
			"	Points (printer's)	28.452756

* For factors for C = 12 scale or those which can be derived from same table on Values for General Physical Constants.

To convert from	To	Multiply by	To convert from	To	Multiply by
B.t.u./lb	Joules/gram	2.32444	Calories, gm.**	B.t.u.	0.0039683207
B.t.u. (mean)/lb	Cal., gm. (mean)/gram	0.555555	"	B.t.u. (IST.)	0.00396573
"	Cu. cm.-atm./gram	22.9735	"	B.t.u. (mean)	0.00396262
"	Foot-pounds/lb	778.768	"	B.t.u. (39°F.)	0.00394841
"	Hp.-hr./lb	0.000393317	"	B.t.u. (60°F.)	0.00396709
"	Joules/gram	2.32779	"	Cal., gm. (IST.)	0.999346
B.t.u./sec	B.t.u./hr	3600	"	Cal., gm. (mean)	0.998563
"	B.t.u./min	60	"	Cal., gm. (15°C.)	0.999570
"	Cal., kg./hr	907.185	"	Cal., gm. (20°C.)	1.00050
"	Cal., kg./min	15.1197	"	Cal., kg	0.001
"	Cheval-vapeur	1.43352	"	Cal., kg. (IST.)	0.000999346
"	Ergs/sec	1.05435×10^{10}	"	Cal., kg. (mean)	0.000998563
"	Foot-pounds/sec	777.649	"	Cal., kg. (15°C.)	0.000999570
"	Horsepower	1.41391	"	Cal., kg. (20°C.)	0.00100050
"	Horsepower (boiler)	0.107483	"	Cu. cm.-atm	41.2929
"	Horsepower (electric)	1.41334	"	Cu. ft.-atm	0.00145824
"	Horsepower (metric)	1.43352	"	Ergs	4.184×10^7
"	Kg.-meters/sec	107.514	"	Foot-poundals	99.2878
"	Kilowatts	1.05435	"	Foot-pounds	3.08596
"	Kilowatts (Int.)	1.05418	"	Gram-cm	42664.9
"	Watts	1054.35	"	Hp.-hours	1.55857×10^{-6}
"	Watts (Int.)	1054.18	"	Joules	4.184
B.t.u. (mean)/sec	Ergs/sec	1.05587×10^{10}	"	Joules (Int.)	4.18331
"	Foot-pounds/sec	778.768	"	Kg.-meters	0.426649
"	Horsepower	1.41594	"	Kw.-hours	1.162222×10^{-6}
"	Horsepower (boiler)	0.107637	"	Liter-atm	0.0412917
"	Horsepower (electric)	1.41537	"	Watt-hours	0.001162222
"	Horsepower (metric)	1.43558	"	Watt-hours (Int.)	0.00116203
"	Watts	1055.87	"	Watt-seconds	4.184
B.t.u./sq. ft	Cal., gm./sq. cm	0.271246	Calories, gm. (mean)	B.t.u.	0.00397103
B.t.u./sq.ft. × min.)			"	Cal., gm	1.00144
"	Hp./sq. ft	0.0235651	"	Cal., gm. (IST.)	1.00078
"	Kw./sq. ft	0.0175725	"	Cal., gm. (20°C.)	1.00194
"	Watts/sq. in	0.122031	"	Cal., kg. (mean)	0.001
Buckets (Brit.)	Cu. cm	18184.35	"	Cu. cm.-atm	41.3523
"	Gallons (Brit.)	4	"	Cu. ft.-atm	0.00146034
Bushels (Brit.)	Bags (Brit.)	0.333333	"	Ergs	4.19002×10^7
"	Bushels (U.S.)	1.032056	"	Foot-poundals	99.4308
"	Cu. cm	36368.70	"	Foot-pounds	3.09040
"	Cu. feet	1.284348	"	Hp.-hours	1.56081×10^{-6}
"	Cu. inches	2219.354	"	Joules	4.19002
"	Dekaliters	3.636768	"	Joules (Int.)	4.18933
"	Gallons (Brit.)	8	"	Kg.-meters	0.427263
"	Hectoliters	0.3636768	"	Kw.-hours	1.16390×10^{-6}
"	Liters	36.36768	"	Liter-atm	0.0413511
Bushels (U.S.)*	Barrels (U.S.), dry	0.3047647	"	Watt-seconds	4.19002
"	Bushels (Brit.)	0.9689395	Calories, gm. (15°C.)	B.t.u	0.00397003
"	Cu. cm	35239.07	"	Cal., gm	1.00043
"	Cu. feet	1.244456	"	Cal., gm. (IST.)	0.999776
"	Cu. inches	2150.42	"	Cal., gm. (mean)	0.998992
"	Cu. meters	0.03523907	"	Cal., gm. (20°C.)	1.00093
"	Cu. yards	0.04609096	"	Joules	4.18580
"	Gallons (U.S., dry)	8	"	Joules (Int.)	4.18511
"	Gallons (U.S., liq.)	9.309177	Calories, gm. (20°C.)	B.t.u	0.00396633
"	Liters	35.23907	"	Cal., gm	0.999498
"	Ounces (U.S., fluid)	1191.575	"	Cal., gm. (IST.)	0.998845
"	Pecks (U.S.)	4	"	Cal., gm. (mean)	0.998061
"	Pints (U.S., dry)	64	"	Cal., gm. (15°C.)	0.999068
"	Quarts (U.S., dry)	32	"	Joules	4.18190
"	Quarts (U.S., liq.)	37.23671	"	Joules (Int.)	4.18121
Butts (Brit.)	Bushels (U.S.)	13.53503	Calories, kg	B.t.u	3.9683207
"	Cu. feet	16.84375	"	B.t.u. (IST.)	3.96573
"	Cu. meters	0.4769619	"	B.t.u. (mean)	3.96262
"	Gallons (U.S.)	126	"	B.t.u. (60°F.)	3.96709
			"	Cal., gm	1000
			"	Cal., kg. (mean)	0.998563
Cable lengths	Fathoms	120	"	Cal., kg. (15°C.)	0.999570
"	Feet	720	"	Cal., kg. (20°C.)	1.00050
"	Meters	219.456	"	Cu. cm.-atm	41292.86

* Stricken or struck bushel. A heaped bushel for apples of 2747.715 cu. inches was established by the U.S. Court of Customs Appeals on Feb. 15, 1912. A heaped bushel equal to 1¼ stricken bushels is also known.

** This is the calorie as defined by the U.S. National Bureau of Standards and is equal to 4.18400 joules.

To convert from	To	Multiply by	To convert from	To	Multiply by
Bags (Brit.)	Bushels (Brit.)	3	B.t.u.	Kw.-hours (Int.)	0.000292827
Barns	Sq. cm	1×10^{-24}	"	Liter-atm	10.4053
Barrels (Brit.)*	Bags (Brit.)	1.5	"	Tons of refrig. (U.S. std.)	3.46995×10^{-6}
"	Barrels (U.S., dry)	1.415404	"	Watt-seconds	1054.35
"	Barrels (U.S., liq.)	1.372513	"	Watt-seconds (Int.)	1054.18
"	Bushels (Brit.)	4.5	B.t.u. (IST.)	B.t.u.	1.00065
"	Bushels (U.S.)	4.644253	B.t.u. (mean)	B.t.u.	1.00144
"	Cu. feet	5.779568	"	B.t.u. (IST.)	1.00078
"	Cu. meters	0.1636591	"	B.t.u. (39°F.)	0.996415
"	Gallons (Brit.)	36	"	B.t.u. (60°F.)	1.00113
"	Liters	163.6546	"	Hp.-hours	0.000393317
Barrels (petroleum, U.S.)	Cu. feet	5.614583	"	Joules	1055.87
"	Gallons (U.S.)	42	"	Kg.-meters	107.669
"	Liters	158.98284	"	Kw.-hours	0.000293297
Barrels (U.S., dry)	Barrels (U.S. liq.)	0.969696	"	Kw.-hours (Int.)	0.000293248
"	Bushels (U.S.)	3.2812195	"	Liter-atm	10.4203
"	Cu. feet	4.083333	"	Watt-hours	0.293297
"	Cu. inches	7056	"	Watt-hours (Int.)	0.293248
"	Cu. meters	0.11562712	B.t.u. (39°F.)	B.t.u.	1.00504
"	Quarts (U.S., dry)	105	"	B.t.u. (IST.)	1.00439
Barrels (U.S., liq.)	Barrels (U.S., dry)	1.03125	"	B.t.u. (mean)	1.00360
"	Barrels (wine)	1	"	B.t.u. (60°F)	1.00473
"	Cu. feet	4.2109375	"	Joules	1059.67
"	Cu. inches	7276.5	B.t.u. (60°F.)	B.t.u.	1.00031
"	Cu. meters	0.11924047	"	B.t.u. (IST.)	0.999657
"	Gallons (Brit.)	26.22925	"	B.t.u. (mean)	0.998873
"	Gallons (U.S., liq.)	31.5	"	B.t.u. (39°F.)	0.995291
"	Liters	119.23713	B.t.u./hr	Cal., kg./hr.	0.251996
Bars	Atmospheres	0.986923	"	Ergs/sec.	2.928751×10^{6}
"	Baryes	1×10^{6}	"	Foot-pounds/hr	777.649
"	Cm. of Hg (0°C.)	75.0062	"	Horsepower	0.000392752
"	Dynes/sq. cm	1×10^{6}	"	Horsepower (boiler)	2.98563×10^{-5}
"	Ft. of H_2O (60°F.)	33.4883	"	Horsepower (electric)	0.000392594
"	Grams/sq. cm	1019.716	"	Horsepower (metric)	0.000398199
"	In. of Hg (32°F.)	29.5300	"	Kilowatts	0.000292875
"	Kg./sq. cm	1.019716	"	Lb. ice melted/hr.	0.0069714
"	Millibars	1000	"	Tons of refrig. (U.S. comm.)	8.32789×10^{-5}
"	Pounds/sq. inch	14.5038	"	Watts	0.292875
Baryes	Atmospheres	9.86923×10^{-7}	B.t.u./min	Cal., kg./min	0.251996
"	Bars	1×10^{-6}	"	Ergs/sec.	1.75725×10^{8}
"	Dynes/sq. cm	1	"	Foot-pounds/min	777.649
"	Grams/sq. cm	0.001019716	"	Horsepower	0.0235651
"	Millibars	0.001	"	Horsepower (boiler)	0.00179138
Bels	Decibels	10	"	Horsepower (electric)	0.0235556
Board feet	Cu. cm	2359.7372	"	Horsepower (metric)	0.0238920
"	Cu. feet	0.083333	"	Joules/sec.	17.5725
"	Cu. inches	144	"	Kg.-meters/min	107.514
Bolts of cloth	Linear feet	120	"	Kilowatts	0.0175725
"	Meters	36.576	"	Lb. ice melted/hr.	0.41828
Bougie decimales	Candles (Int.)	1.00	"	Tons of refrig. (U.S. comm.)	0.00499673
B.t.u.	B.t.u. (IST.)**	0.999346	"	Watts	17.5725
"	B.t.u. (mean)	0.998563	B.t.u. (mean)/min	B.t.u. (mean)/hr.	60
"	B.t.u. (39°F.)	0.994982	"	Cal., kg. (mean)/hr.	15.1197
"	B.t.u. (60°F.)	0.999689	"	Cal., kg. (mean)/min	0.251996
"	Cal. gm	251.99576	"	Ergs/sec.	1.75978×10^{8}
"	Cal., gm. (IST.)	251.831	"	Foot-pounds/min	778.768
"	Cal., gm. (mean)	251.634	"	Horsepower	0.0235990
"	Cal., gm. (20°C.)	252.122	"	Horsepower (boiler)	0.00179396
"	Cu. cm.-atm	10405.6	"	Horsepower (electric)	0.0235895
"	Ergs	1.05435×10^{10}	"	Horsepower (metric)	0.0239264
"	Foot-poundals	25020.1	"	Joules/sec.	17.5978
"	Foot-pounds	777.649	"	Kg.-meters/min	107.669
"	Gram-cm	1.07514×10^{7}	"	Kilowatts	0.0175978
"	Hp.-hours	0.000392752	"	Lb. ice-melted/hr.	0.41888
"	Hp.-years	4.48347×10^{-8}	B.t.u./lb	Cal., gm./gram	0.555555
"	Joules	1054.35	"	Cu. cm.-atm./gram	22.9405
"	Joules (Int.)	1054.18	"	Cu. ft.-atm./lb	0.367471
"	Kg.-meters	107.514	"	Cu. ft.-(lb./sq. in.)/lb	5.40034
"	Kw.-hours	0.000292875	"	Foot-pounds/lb	777.649
			"	Hp.-hr./lb	0.000392752

* Barrel (Brit., liq.) = Barrel (Brit., dry)
** International Steam Table.

CONVERSION FACTORS

(From various U. S. Government and IUPAC publications and from calculations based on values given in these publications)

To convert from	To	Multiply by	To convert from	To	Multiply by
Abamperes	Amperes	10	Acre-inches	Gallons (U.S.)	27154.286
"	E.M. cgs. units of current	1	Amperes	Abamperes	0.1
"	E.S. cgs. units	2.997930×10^{10}	"	Amperes (Int.)	1.000165
"	Faradays (chem.)/sec	1.036377×10^{-4}	"	Cgs. units of current	1
"	Faradays (phys.)/sec	1.036086×10^{-4}	"	Mks. units of current	1
"	Statamperes	2.997930×10^{10}	"	Coulombs/sec	1
Abamperes/cm	E.M. cgs. units of surface charge density	1	"	Coulombs (Int.)/sec	1.000165
"	E.S. cgs. units	2.997930×10^{10}	"	Faradays (chem.)/sec	1.036377×10^{-5}
Abamperes/sq. cm	Amperes/circ. mil	5.0670748×10^{-5}	"	Faradays (phys.)/sec	1.036086×10^{-5}
"	Amperes/sq. cm	10	"	Statamperes	2.997930×10^{9}
"	Amperes/sq. inch	64.516	Amperes (Int.)	Amperes	0.999835
Abampere-turns	Ampere-turns	10	"	Coulombs/sec	0.999835
Abampere-turns/cm	Ampere-turns/cm	10	"	Coulombs (Int.)/sec	1
Abcoulombs	Ampere-hours	0.0027777	"	Faradays (chem.)/sec*	1.03623×10^{-5}
"	Coulombs	10	"	Faradays (phys.)/sec*	1.03592×10^{-5}
"	Electronic charges	6.24196×10^{19}	Amperes/meter	Cgs. units of surface current density	0.01
"	E.M. cgs. units of charge	1	"	E.M. cgs. units	0.001
"	E.S. cgs. units	2.997930×10^{10}	"	E.S. cgs. units	2.997930×10^{7}
"	Faradays (chem.)	1.036377×10^{-4}	"	Mks. units	1
"	Faradays (phys.)	1.036086×10^{-4}	Amperes/sq. meter	Cgs. units of volume current density	0.0001
"	Statcoulombs	2.997930×10^{10}	"	E.M. cgs. units	1×10^{-5}
Abfarads	E.M. cgs. units of capacitance	1	"	E.S. cgs. units	299793.0
"	E.S. cgs. units	8.987584×10^{20}	"	Mks. units	1
"	Farads	1×10^{9}	Amperes/sq. mil	Abamperes/sq. cm	15500.031
"	Microfarads	1×10^{15}	"	Amperes/sq. cm	1.5500031×10^{5}
"	Statfarads	8.987584×10^{20}	Ampere-hours	Abcoulombs	360
Abhenries	E.M. cgs. units of induction	1	"	Coulombs	3600
"	E.S. cgs. units	1.112646×10^{-21}	"	Faradays (chem.)*	0.0373096
"	Henries	1×10^{-9}	"	Faradays (phys.)*	0.0372991
Abmhos	E.M. cgs. units of conductance	1	Ampere-turns	Cgs. units of magnetomotive force	1.2566371
"	E.S. cgs. units	8.987584×10^{20}	"	E.M. cgs. units	1.2566371
"	Megamhos	1000	"	E.S. cgs. units	3.767310×10^{10}
"	Mhos	1×10^{9}	"	Gilberts	1.2566371
"	Statmhos	8.987584×10^{20}	Ampere-turns/weber	Cgs. units of reluctance	1.256637×10^{-8}
Abohms	E.M. cgs. units of resistance	1	"	E.M. cgs. units	1.256637×10^{-8}
"	Megohms	1×10^{-15}	"	E.S. cgs. units	1.129413×10^{13}
"	Microhms	0.001	"	Gilberts/maxwell	1.256637×10^{-8}
"	Ohms	1×10^{-9}	Ångström units	Centimeters	1×10^{-8}
"	Statohms	1.112646×10^{-21}	"	Inches	3.9370079×10^{-9}
Abohm-cm	Circ. mil-ohms/ft	0.0060153049	"	Microns	0.0001
"	E.M. cgs. units of resistivity	1	"	Millimicrons	0.1
"	Microhm-inches	0.00039370079	"	Wave length of orange-red line of krypton 86	0.000165076373
"	Ohm-cm	1×10^{-9}	"	Wave length of red line of cadmium	0.000155316413
Abvolts	Microvolts	0.01	Ares	Acres	0.024710538
"	Millivolts	1×10^{-5}	"	Sq. dekameters	1
"	Volts	1×10^{-8}	"	Sq. feet	1076.3910
"	Volts (Int.)	9.99670×10^{-9}	"	Sq. ft. (U.S. Survey)	1076.3867
Abvolts/cm	E.M. cgs. units of electric field intensity	1	"	Sq. meters	100
"	E.S. cgs. units	3.335635×10^{-11}	"	Sq. miles	3.8610216×10^{-5}
"	Volts/cm	1×10^{-8}	Atmospheres	Bars	1.01325
"	Volts/inch	2.54×10^{-8}	"	Cm. of Hg (0°C.)	76
"	Volts/meter	1×10^{-6}	"	Cm. of H_2O (4°C.)	1033.26
Acres	Sq. cm	40468564	"	Dynes/sq. cm	1.01325×10^{6}
"	Sq. ft.	43560	"	Ft. of H_2O (39.2°F.)	33.8995
"	Sq. ft. (U.S. Survey)	43559.826	"	Grams/sq. cm	1033.23
"	Sq. inches	6272640	"	In. of Hg (32°F.)	29.9213
"	Sq. kilometers	0.0040468564	"	Kg./sq. cm	1.03323
"	Sq. links (Gunter's)	1×10^{5}	"	Mm. of Hg (0°C.)	760
"	Sq. meters	4046.8564	"	Pounds/sq. inch	14.6960
"	Sq. miles (statute)	0.0015625	"	Tons (short)/sq. ft.	1.05811
"	Sq. perches	160	"	Torrs	760
"	Sq. rods	160	Atomic mass units (chem.)*	Electron volts	9.31395×10^{8}
"	Sq. yards	4840	"	Grams*	1.66024×10^{-24}
Acre-feet	Cu. feet	43560	Atomic mass units (phys.)*	Electron volts	9.31141×10^{8}
"	Cu. meters	1233.4818	"	Grams*	1.65979×10^{-24}
"	Cu. yards	1613.333			
Acre-inches	Cu. feet	3630			
"	Cu. meters	102.79033			

* For factors for C = 12 scale or those which can be derived from same see table on Value for General Physical Constants.

ounce-inch................................oz-in.
outside diameter.........................OD

parts per million.........................ppm
peck......................................pk
penny (pence – new British)..............p.
pennyweight..............................dwt
per......................(See Fundamental Rules)
peso..................................spell out
pint......................................pt
potential.............................spell out
potential difference..................spell out
pound.....................................lb
pound-foot...............................lb-ft
pound-inch...............................lb-in.
pound sterling.............................£
pounds per brake horsepower-hour....lb per bhp-hr
pounds per cubic foot................lb per cu ft
pounds per square foot...................psf
pounds per square inch...................psi
pounds per square inch absolute..........psia
power factor...................spell out or pf

quart.....................................qt

radian................................spell out
reactive kilovolt-ampere.................kvar
reactive volt-ampere......................var
revolutions per minute...................rpm
revolutions per second...................rps
rod...................................spell out
root mean square.........................rms

secant...................................sec
second...................................sec
second (angular measure)..................."
second-foot (see cubic feet per second)
second (time)(in astronomical tables).....s
shaft horsepower.........................shp
shilling...................................s
sine.....................................sin
sine of the amplitude, an elliptic function.......sn
specific gravity........................sp gr
specific heat...........................sp ht
spherical candle power...................scp
square....................................sq
square centimeter...............sq cm or cm²
square foot...........................sq ft
square inch...........................sq in.
square kilometer...............sq km or km²
square meter...................sq m or m²
square micron...........sq μ or sq mu or μ²
square millimeter.............sq mm or mm²
square root of mean square...............rms
standard.................................std
stere......................................s

tangent..................................tan
temperature.............................temp
tensile strength..........................ts
thousand...................................M
thousand foot-pounds...................kip-ft
thousand pound...........................kip
ton...................................spell out
ton-mile..............................spell out

versed sine.............................vers
volt.......................................v
volt-ampere...............................va
volt-coulomb..........................spell out

watt.......................................w
watthour.................................whr
watts per candle.........................wpc
week..................................spell out
weight....................................wt

yard......................................yd
year......................................yr

From NBS Miscellaneous Publication No. 233.

Spelling and Abbreviations of Units

The spelling of the names of units as adopted by the National Bureau of Standards is that given in the list below. The spelling of the metric units is in accordance with that given in the law of July 28, 1866, legalizing the metric system in the United States.

Following the name of each unit in the list below is given the abbreviation which the Bureau has adopted. Attention is particularly called to the following principles:

1. The period is omitted after all abbreviations of units, except where the abbreviation forms an English word.

2. The exponents "2" and "3" are used to signify "square" and "cubic," respectively, instead of the abbreviations "sq" or "cu," which are, however, frequently used in technical literature for the United States customary units. In conformity with this principle the abbreviation for cubic centimeter is "cm³" (instead of "cc" or "c cm"). The term "cubic centimeter," as used in chemical work, is, in fact, a misnomer, since the unit actually used is the "milliliter" of which "ml" is the correct abbreviation.

3. The use of the same abbreviation for both singular and plural is recommended. This practice is already established in expressing metric units and is in accordance with the spirit and chief purpose of abbreviations.

4. It is also suggested that, unless all the text is printed in capital letters, only small letters be used for abbreviations, except in such case as, A for angstrom, etc., where the use of capital letters is general.

LIST OF THE MOST COMMON UNITS OF WEIGHT AND MEASURE AND THEIR ABBREVIATIONS

Unit	Abbreviation	Unit	Abbreviation
acre	acre	kiloliter	kl
angstrom	A	kilometer	km
are	a	link	li
avoirdupois	avdp	liquid	liq
barrel	bbl	liter	liter
board foot	fbm	meter	m
bushel	bu	metric ton	t
carat	c	microgram*	μg
centare	ca	microinch	μin.
centigram	cg	microliter*	μl
centiliter	cl	micron	μ
centimeter	cm	mile	mi
chain	ch	milligram	mg
cubic centimeter	cm³	milliliter	ml
cubic decimeter	dm³	millimeter	mm
cubic dekameter	dkm³	millimicron	mμ
cubic foot	ft³	minim	min or m̨
cubic hectometer	hm³	ounce	oz
cubic inch	in.³	ounce, apothecaries	oz ap or ℥
cubic kilometer	km³	ounce, avoirdupois	oz avdp
cubic meter	m³	ounce, fluid	fl oz
cubic mile	mi³	ounce, troy	oz t
cubic millimeter	mm³	peck	pk
cubic yard	yd³	pennyweight	dwt
decigram	dg	pint	pt
deciliter	dl	pound	lb
decimeter	dm	pound, apothecaries	lb ap
decistere	ds	pound, avoirdupois	lb avdp
dekagram	dkg	pound, troy	lb t
dekaliter	dkl	quart	qt
dekameter	dkm	rod	rd
dekastere	dks	scruple, apothecaries	s ap or ℈
dram	dr	square centimeter	cm²
dram, apothecaries	dr ap or ʒ	square chain	ch²
dram, avoirdupois	dr avdp	square decimeter	dm²
dram, fluid	fl dr	square dekameter	dkm²
fathom	fath	square foot	ft²
foot	ft	square hectometer	hm²
furlong	fur.	square inch	in.²
gallon	gal	square kilometer	km²
grain	grain	square link	li²
gram	g	square meter	m²
hectare	ha	square mile	mi²
hectogram	hg	square millimeter	mm²
hectoliter	hl	square rod	rd²
hectometer	hm	square yard	yd²
hogshead	hhd	stere	s
hundredweight	cwt	ton	ton
inch	in.	ton, metric	t
kilogram	kg	troy	t
		yard	yd

* The abbreviations γ and λ for microgram and microliter, respectively, have been advocated by some authorities.

efficiency	eff
electric	elec
electromotive force	emf
elevation	el
equation	eq
external	ext
farad	spell out or f
feet board measure (board feet)	fbm
feet per minute	fpm
feet per second	fps
fluid	fl
foot	ft
foot-candle	ft-c
foot-Lambert	ft-L
foot-pound	ft-lb
foot-pound-second (system)	fps
foot-second (see cubic feet per second)	
franc	fr
free aboard ship	spell out
free alongside ship	spell out
free on board	fob
freezing point	fp
frequency	spell out
fusion point	fnp
gallon	gal
gallons per minute	gpm
gallons per second	gps
grain	spell out
gram	g
gram-calorie	g-cal
greatest common divisor	gcd
haversine	hav
hectare	ha
henry	H
high-pressure (adjective)	h-p
hogshead	hhd
horsepower	hp
horsepower-hour	hp-hr
hour	hr
hour (in astronomical tables)	h
hundred	C
hundredweight (112 lb)	cwt
hyperbolic cosine	cosh
hyperbolic sine	sinh
hyperbolic tangent	tanh
inch	in.
inch-pound	in-lb
inches per second	ips
indicated horsepower	ihp
indicated horsepower-hour	ihp-hr
inside diameter	ID
intermediate-pressure (adjective)	i-p
internal	int
joule	J
kilocalorie	kcal
kilocycles per second	kc
kilogram	kg
kilogram-calorie	kg-cal
kilogram-meter	kg-m
kilograms per cubic meter or kg/m³	kg per cu m
kilograms per second	kgps

kiloliter	kl
kilometer	km
kilometers per second	kmps
kilovolt	kv
kilovolt-ampere	kva
kilowatt	kw
kilowatthour	kwhr
lambert	L
latitude	lat or ϕ
least common multiple	lcm
linear foot	lin ft
liquid	liq
lira	spell out
liter	l
logarithm (common)	log
logarithm (natural)	$\log_e$ or ln
longitude	long. or λ
low-pressure (as adjective)	l-p
lumen	l*
lumen-hour	l-hr*
lumens per watt	lpw
mass	spell out
mathematics (ical)	math
maximum	max
mean effective pressure	mep
mean horizontal candlepower	mhcp
megacycle	spell out
megohm	spell out
melting point	mp
meter	m
meter-kilogram	m-kg
mho	spell out
microampere	μa or mu a
microfarad	μf
microinch	μin.
micromicrofarad	$\mu\mu$f
micromicron	$\mu\mu$ or mu mu
micron	μ or mu
microvolt	μv
microwatt	μw or mu w
mile	spell out
miles per hour	mph
miles per hour per second	mphps
milliampere	ma
milligram	mg
millihenry	mh
millilambert	mL
milliliter	ml
millimeter	mm
millimicron	mμ or m mu
million	spell out
million gallons per day	mgd
millivolt	mv
minimum	min
minute	min
minute (angular measure)	'
minute (time)(in astronomical tables)	m
mole	spell out
molecular weight	mol. wt
month	spell out
National Electrical Code	NEC
ohm	spell out or Ω
ohm-centimeter	ohm-cm
ounce	oz
ounce-foot	oz-ft

[1] There are circumstances under which one or the other of these forms is preferred. In general the sign ° is used where space conditions make it necessary, as in tabular matter, and when abbreviations are cumbersome, as in some angular measurements, i.e., 59° 23′ 42″. In the interest of simplicity and clarity the Committee has recommended that the abbreviation for the temperature scale, F, C, K, etc., always be included in expressions for numerical temperatures, but, wherever feasible, the abbreviation for "degree" be omitted; as 69 F.

* The International Commission on Illumination has changed the symbol for lumen to lm, and the symbol for lumen-hour to lm-hr. This nomenclature is used in American Standard for Illuminating Engineering Nomenclature and Photometric Standards (ASA Z7.1–1942).

AMERICAN STANDARD
ABBREVIATIONS FOR SCIENTIFIC AND
ENGINEERING TERMS

Reproduced by permission of The American Society of Mechanical Engineers

Introductory Notes

SCOPE AND PURPOSE

1. The Executive Committee of the Sectional Committee on Scientific and Engineering Symbols and Abbreviations has made the following distinction between symbols and abbreviations: Letter symbols are letters used to represent magnitudes of physical quantities in equations and mathematical formulas. Abbreviations are shortened forms of names or expressions employed in texts and tabulations, and should not be used in equations.

FUNDAMENTAL RULES

2. Abbreviations should be used sparingly in text and with due regard to the context and to the training of the reader. Terms denoting units of measurement should be abbreviated in the text only when preceded by the amounts indicated in numerals; thus "several inches," "one inch," "12 in." In tabular matter, specifications, maps, drawings, and texts for special purposes, the use of abbreviations should be governed only by the desirability of conserving space.

3. Short words such as ton, day, and mile should be spelled out.

4. Abbreviations should not be used where the meaning will not be clear. In case of doubt, spell out.

5. The same abbreviation is used for both singular and plural, as "bbl" for barrel and barrels.

6. The use of conventional signs for abbreviations in text is not recommended; thus "per," not /; "lb," not #; "in," not ". Such signs may be used sparingly in tables and similar places for conserving space.

7. The period should be omitted except in cases where the omission would result in confusion.

8. The letters of such abbreviations as ASA should not be spaced (not A S A).

9. The use in text of exponents for the abbreviations of square and cube and of the negative exponents for terms involving "per" is not recommended. The superior figures are usually not available on the keyboards of typesetting and linotype machines and composition is therefore delayed. There is also the likelihood of confusion with footnote reference numbers. These shorter forms are permissible in tables and are sometimes difficult to avoid in text.

10. A sentence should not begin with a numeral followed by an abbreviation. Abbreviations for names of units are to be used only after numerical values, such as 25 ft or 110 v.

Abbreviations*

absolute	abs
acre	spell out
acre-foot	acre-ft
air horsepower	air hp
alternating-current (as adjective)	a-c
ampere	amp
ampere-hour	amp-hr
amplitude, an elliptic function	am
Angstrom unit	A
antilogarithm	antilog
atmosphere	atm
atomic weight	at. wt
average	avg
avoirdupois	avdp
azimuth	az or α
barometer	bar.
barrel	bbl
Baumé	Bé
board feet (feet board measure)	fbm
boiler pressure	spell out

boiling point	bp
brake horsepower	bhp
brake horsepower-hour	bhp-hr
Brinell hardness number	Bhn
British thermal unit[1]	Btu or B
bushel	bu
calorie	cal
candle	c
candle-hour	c-hr
candlepower	cp
cent	c or ¢
center to center	c to c
centigram	cg
centiliter	cl
centimeter	cm
centimeter-gram-second (system)	cgs
chemical	chem
chemically pure	cp
circular	cir
circular mils	cir mils
coefficient	coef
cologarithm	colog
concentrate	conc
conductivity	cond
constant	const
continental horsepower	cont hp
cord	cd
cosecant	csc
cosine	cos
cosine of the amplitude, an elliptic function	cn
cost, insurance, and freight	cif
cotangent	cot
coulomb	spell out
counter electromotive force	cemf
cubic	cu
cubic centimeter	cu cm, cm³ (liquid, meaning milliliter. ml)
cubic foot	cu ft
cubic feet per minute	cfm
cubic feet per second	cfs
cubic inch	cu in.
cubic meter	cu m or m³
cubic micron	cu μ or cu mu or μ³
cubic millimeter	cu mm or mm³
cubic yard	cu yd
current density	spell out
cycles per second	spell out or c
cylinder	cyl
day	spell out
decibel	db
degree[1]	deg or °
degree centigrade	C
degree Fahrenheit	F
degree Kelvin	K
degree Réaumur	R
delta amplitude, an elliptic function	dn
diameter	diam
direct-current (as adjective)	d-c
dollar	$
dozen	doz
dram	dr

* These forms are recommended for readers whose familiarity with the terms used makes possible a maximum of abbreviations. For other classes of readers editors may wish to use less contracted combinations made up from this list. For example, the list gives the abbreviation of the term "feet per second" as "fps." To some readers ft per sec will be more easily understood. [1] Abbreviation recommended by the A.S.M.E. Power Test Codes Committee. B = 1 Btu, kB = 1000 Btu, mB = 1,000,000 Btu. The A.S.H. &V.E. recommends the use of Mb = 1000 Btu and Mbh = 1000 Btu per hr.

ALPHABET TABLE

Greek letter	Greek name	English equivalent	RUSSIAN letter	English equivalent
A α	Alpha	(ä)	А а	(ä)
B β	Beta	(b)	Б б	(b)
Γ γ	Gamma	(g)	В в	(v)
Δ δ	Delta	(d)	Г г	(g)
E ε	Epsilon	(e)	Д д	(d)
Z ζ	Zeta	(z)	Е е	(ye)
H η	Eta	(ā)	Ж ж	(zh)
Θ θ	Theta	(th)	З з	(z)
I ι	Iota	(ē)	И и	(i, ē)
K κ	Kappa	(k)	Й й	(ē) 7
Λ λ	Lambda	(l)	К к	(k)
M μ	Mu	(m)	Л л	(l)
N ν	Nu	(n)	М м	(m)
Ξ ξ	Xi	(ks)	Н н	(n)
O o	Omicron	(ɑ)	О о	(ô, o)
Π π	Pi	(p)	П п	(p)
P ρ	Rho	(r)	Р р	(r)
Σ σ ς	Sigma	(s)	С с	(s)
T τ	Tau	(t)	Т т	(t)
Υ υ	Upsilon	(ü, ōō)	У у	(ōō)
Φ φ	Phi	(f)	Ф ф	(f)
X χ	Chi	(H)	Х х	(kh)
Ψ ψ	Psi	(ps)	Ц ц	(ts)
Ω ω	Omega	(ō)	Ч ч	(ch)
			Ш ш	(sh)
			Щ щ	(shch)
			Ъ ъ	8
			Ы ы	(ē)
			Ь ь	9
			Э э	(e)
			Ю ю	(ū)
			Я я	(yä)

For that reason several investigators have advocated the introduction of a four-dimensional system of units, which is a generalization of the CGS system. This unit-system is chosen so that to any unit of the CGS system (with three basic units) there corresponds one particular unit of this "generalized CGS system" (with four basic units), such that the *numerical* values of the physical quantities in the field of electricity are invariant.

The introduction of such a "generalized CGS system" has the advantage that the relation between the units of this "generalized CGS system" and the units of the MKSA system can be expressed by ordinary conversion equations.

The use of the four-dimensional system of equations (with four basic quantities) accompanied by the usage of such a "generalized CGS system" of units (with four basic units) is therefore of advantage as an intermediate representation in this period of coexistence of the CGS system and the MKSA system, where transitions from one system to the other often have to be made.

As a result of all these considerations the General Assembly of the IUPAP, Copenhagen, 1951, approved by its resolution 5 the introduction of the following two "generalized CGS systems" based on four basic units:

(5.a) The system with the *centimetre, gramme, second* and the charge corresponding to one *electrostatic unit*, as basic units, being a 4-dimensional generalization of the electrostatic CGS system (3.a)

(5.b) The system with the *centimetre, gramme second* and the current corresponding to one *electromagnetic unit* or deca-ampere, as basic units, being a 4-dimensional generalization of the electromagnetic CGS system (3.b)

In practical applications of these systems it is of advantage to indicate the *basic electrical unit* in each of these two systems with a name and symbol.

The name franklin was proposed in 1941 for the electrostatic unit of electric charge considered as a basic unit of the system (5.a). The franklin, symbol: Fr, is thus defined as:

The *franklin* is that charge, which exerts on an equal charge at a distance of 1 centimetre in vacuo a force of 1 dyne.

According to this definition 1 franklin $= (10/\zeta)$ coulomb, where $\zeta = 2.997925 \times 10^{10}$ is the numerical value of the velocity of light in vacuum, measured in cm/s.

For the electromagnetic unit of electric current, considered as a basic unit of the system (5.b), the name biot has been used. The biot, symbol: Bi, is thus defined as:

The *biot* is that constant current intensity, which, when maintained in two parallel infinitely long rectilinear conductors of infinite length and of negligible circular section, placed at a mutual distance of 1 centimetre apart in vacuo, would produce between these conductors a force of 2 dyne per centimetre length.

According to this definition 1 biot = 10 ampere).

These unit systems (5.a) and (5.b) are referred to as cm-g-s-Fr system and cm-g-s-Bi system respectively.

The definitions of the franklin in the system (5.a) and that of the biot in the system (5.b) which closely correspond to the electrostatic CGS unit of charge and the electromagnetic CGS unit of current respectively, ensure that the quantities of the *non-rationalized* four-dimensional system of equations (second column, table p. 27), when expressed in these units, have the same numerical value as the corresponding quantities of the non-rationalized three-dimensional system of equations (first column, table p. 27), when expressed in the corresponding CGS units.

Some of the units of the three-dimensional CGS system and the corresponding units of the two four-dimensional systems are given in the table:

	three-dimensional unit of mixed CGS system		corresponding four-dimensional unit of generalized CGS system
Q^*	$\mathrm{erg}^{\frac{1}{2}} \cdot \mathrm{cm}^{\frac{1}{2}}$	Q	Fr
I^*	$\mathrm{erg}^{\frac{1}{2}} \cdot \mathrm{cm}^{\frac{1}{2}} \mathrm{s}^{-1\frac{1}{2}}$	I	Fr/s
V^*	$\mathrm{erg}^{\frac{1}{2}} \cdot \mathrm{cm}^{-\frac{1}{2}}$	V	erg/Fr
$\boldsymbol{E}^*$	$\mathrm{erg}^{\frac{1}{2}} \cdot \mathrm{cm}^{-\frac{3}{2}}$	$\boldsymbol{E}$	dyn/Fr
$\boldsymbol{D}^*$	$\mathrm{erg}^{\frac{1}{2}} \cdot \mathrm{cm}^{-\frac{3}{2}}$	$\boldsymbol{D}'$	Fr/cm^2
C^*	cm	C	Fr^2/erg
ϵ_r	1	ϵ'	Fr^2/erg $\cdot$ cm
$\boldsymbol{B}^*$	G	$\boldsymbol{B}$	dyn/Bi $\cdot$ cm
$\boldsymbol{H}^*$	Oe	$\boldsymbol{H}'$	Bi/cm
μ_r	1	μ'	dyn/Bi^2

Two different sets of equations are in use:

(2.a) The *"non-rationalized system"* of equations, in which the factors 4π and 2π often appear at unexpected places.

(2.b) The *"rationalized system"* of equations, in which these factors only appear in those equations, where they could be expected from the geometry.

When four-dimensional equations are used, one commonly writes these equations in the rationalized form (2.b).

Some characteristic expressions of the non rationalized three-dimensional "symmetrical system" (1.c) and the corresponding four-dimensional equations in the non-rationalized form (2.a) and the rationalized form (2.b) are given in the table. The quantities of the three-dimensional "symmetrical system" of equations (1.c) have been indicated with an asterisk (*), those of the non-rationalized four-dimensional equations (2.a) with a prime ('), as far as they are different from those of the system (2.b).

Non-rationalized symmetric system with 3 basic quantities	Non-rational. system with 4 basic quantities	Rationalized system with 4 basic quantities
$c \operatorname{rot} \boldsymbol{E}^* = -\partial \boldsymbol{B}^*/\partial t$	$\operatorname{rot} \boldsymbol{E} = -\partial \boldsymbol{B}/\partial t$	$\operatorname{rot} \boldsymbol{E} = -\partial \boldsymbol{B}/\partial t$
$\operatorname{div} \boldsymbol{D}^* = 4\pi\rho$	$\operatorname{div} \boldsymbol{D}' = 4\pi\rho$	$\operatorname{div} \boldsymbol{D} = \rho$
$\operatorname{div} \boldsymbol{B}^* = 0$	$\operatorname{div} \boldsymbol{B} = 0$	$\operatorname{div} \boldsymbol{B} = 0$
$c \operatorname{rot} \boldsymbol{H}^* = 4\pi\boldsymbol{j}^* + \partial \boldsymbol{D}^*/\partial t$	$\operatorname{rot} \boldsymbol{H}' = 4\pi\boldsymbol{j} + \partial \boldsymbol{D}'/\partial t$	$\operatorname{rot} \boldsymbol{H} = \boldsymbol{j} + \partial \boldsymbol{D}/\partial t$
$\boldsymbol{F} = Q^*\boldsymbol{E}^* + Q^*\boldsymbol{v} \times \boldsymbol{B}^*/c$	$\boldsymbol{F} = Q\boldsymbol{E} + Q\boldsymbol{v} \times \boldsymbol{B}$	$\boldsymbol{F} = Q\boldsymbol{E} + Q\boldsymbol{v} \times \boldsymbol{B}.$
$w = (\boldsymbol{E}^*.\boldsymbol{D}^* + \boldsymbol{B}^*.\boldsymbol{H}^*)/8\pi$	$w = (\boldsymbol{E}.\boldsymbol{D}' + \boldsymbol{B}.\boldsymbol{H}')/8\pi$	$w = (\boldsymbol{E}.\boldsymbol{D} + \boldsymbol{B}.\boldsymbol{H})/2$
$\boldsymbol{S} = c(\boldsymbol{E}^* \times \boldsymbol{H}^*)/4\pi$	$\boldsymbol{S} = (\boldsymbol{E} \times \boldsymbol{H}')/4\pi$	$\boldsymbol{S} = \boldsymbol{E} \times \boldsymbol{H}$
$\boldsymbol{E}^* = -\operatorname{grad} V^* - (1/c)\partial \boldsymbol{A}^*/\partial t$	$\boldsymbol{E} = -\operatorname{grad} V - \partial \boldsymbol{A}/\partial t$	$\boldsymbol{E} = -\operatorname{grad} V - \partial \boldsymbol{A}/\partial t$
$\boldsymbol{B}^* = \operatorname{rot} \boldsymbol{A}^*$	$\boldsymbol{B} = \operatorname{rot} \boldsymbol{A}$	$\boldsymbol{B} = \operatorname{rot} \boldsymbol{A}$
$\epsilon_r \boldsymbol{E}^* = \boldsymbol{D}^*$	$\epsilon_0' \epsilon_r \boldsymbol{E} = \epsilon' \boldsymbol{E} = \boldsymbol{D}'$	$\epsilon_0 \epsilon_r \boldsymbol{E} = \epsilon \boldsymbol{E} = \boldsymbol{D}$
$\boldsymbol{E}^* = \boldsymbol{D}^* - 4\pi\boldsymbol{P}^*$	$\epsilon_0' \boldsymbol{E} = \boldsymbol{D}' - 4\pi\boldsymbol{P}$	$\epsilon_0 \boldsymbol{E} = \boldsymbol{D} - \boldsymbol{P}$
$\boldsymbol{B}^* = \mu_r \boldsymbol{H}^*$	$\boldsymbol{B} = \mu'\boldsymbol{H}' = \mu_0'\mu_r\boldsymbol{H}'$	$\boldsymbol{B} = \mu\boldsymbol{H} = \mu_0\mu_r\boldsymbol{H}$
$\boldsymbol{B}^* = \boldsymbol{H}^* + 4\pi\boldsymbol{M}^*$	$\boldsymbol{B} = \mu_0'(\boldsymbol{H}' + 4\pi\boldsymbol{M})$	$\boldsymbol{B} = \mu_0(\boldsymbol{H} + \boldsymbol{M})$
$a_0 = \hbar^2/me^{*2}$	$a_0 = \hbar^2\epsilon_0'/me^2$	$a_0 = \hbar^2 4\pi\epsilon_0/me^2$
$hcR_\infty = e^{*2}/2a_0$	$hcR_\infty = e^2/2\epsilon_0'a_0$	$hcR_\infty = e^2/8\pi\epsilon_0'a_0$
$\mu_B^* = e^*\hbar/2mc$	$\mu_B = e\hbar/2m$	$\mu_B = e\hbar/2m$
$\gamma^* = g(e^*/2mc)$	$\gamma = g(e/2m)$	$\gamma = g(\epsilon/2m)$
$\omega_L = (e^*/2mc)B^*$ $= \mu_B^* B^*/\hbar$	$\omega_L = (e/2m)B =$ $= \mu_B B/\hbar$	$\omega_L = (e/2m)B =$ $= \mu_B B/\hbar$
$\alpha = e^{*2}/\hbar c$	$\alpha = e^2/\epsilon_0'\hbar c$	$\alpha = e^2/4\pi\epsilon_0\hbar c$
$r_e = e^{*2}/mc^2$	$r_e = e^2/\epsilon_0'mc^2$	$r_e = e^2/4\pi\epsilon_0 mc^2$

Remark on rationalization:

The basis of these considerations in which the rationalization is connected with the writing of the equations between physical quantities is in agreement with the resolution accepted by the I.U.P.A.P. in 1951 in Copenhagen:

"The General Assembly of the Union of Physics considers that, in the case that the equations are rationalized, the rationalization should be effected by the introduction of new quantities."

("L'Assemblée Générale de l'Union de Physique considère que, dans le cas où les équations sont rationalisées, la rationalisation doit être obtenue par l'introduction de grandeurs nouvelles.")

3. CGS system of units.

(3.a) The *electrostatic CGS system of units* forms a coherent system of units in combination with the three-dimensional "electrostatic system" of equations (1.a).

(3.b) The *electromagnetic CGS system of units* forms a coherent system of units in combination with the three-dimensional "electromagnetic system" of equations (1.b).

(3.c) The *mixed CGS system of units*, called *Gaussian units*, consisting of the set of electric units of the electrostatic CGS system on the one hand and the set of magnetic units of the electromagnetic CGS system on the other hand, form together also a coherent system of units, when used in combination with the three-dimensional "symmetrical system" of equations (1.c).

4. MKSA system of units.

The MKSA system of units forms a coherent system of units in either of the four-dimensional systems of equations mentioned under 2.

The MKSA system is, however, most commonly used together with the rationalized (four-dimensional) equations (2.b).

5. centimetre-gramme-second-franklin system and centimetre-gramme-second-biot system

Several investigators have pointed out over many years the advantages, which result from the use of the four-dimensional equations, i.e. equations with four basic quantities from which at least one is of electrical nature. These advantages are partly of a didactical nature, but many investigators consider the usage of four basic quantities also important for developing a clear representation of the field of electricity and magnetism.

It has often been considered as a disadvantage that the transition from the three- to the four-dimensional system of equations should be tied to the transition from the CGS system of units to the MKSA system of units as explained under 3, and 4, which as a consequence leads to a change in the numerical value of many well known physical quantities.

6. The *International System of Units.* For the coherent system based on the six basic units:

metre	m	ampere	A
kilogramme	kg	degree Kelvin	°K
second	s	candela	cd

the name *International System of Units* has been recommended by the Conférence Générale des Poids et Mesures in 1960. The units of this system are called: *SI-units*

7. The *mole.*

In the field of *chemical and molecular physics*, in addition to the basic quantities defined above having units defined by the Conférence Générale des Poids et Mesures, *amount of substance* is also treated as a basic quantity. The recommended basic unit is the mole, symbol: mol. The mole is defined as the amount of substance of a system, which contains the same number of molecules (or ions, or atoms, or electrons, as the case may be), as there are atoms in exactly 12 gramme of the pure carbon nuclide ^{12}C.

9.2 Other units.

l	angström; *angström*	Å
σ	barn; *barn* $(= 10^{-24}$ cm$^2)$	b
V	litre; *litre*	l
$t, \tau, T_{\frac{1}{2}}$	minute; *minute*	min
$t, \tau, T_{\frac{1}{2}}$	hour; *heure*	h
$t, \tau, T_{\frac{1}{2}}$	day; *jour*	d
$t, \tau, T_{\frac{1}{2}}$	year; *année*	a
p	atmosphere; *atmosphère*	atm
E	kilowatt-hour; *kilowatt-heure*	kWh
Q	calorie; *calorie*	cal
E, Q	electronvolt; *électronvolt*	eV
m	tonne; *tonne* $(= 1000$ kg$)$	t
m_a	(unified) atomic mass unit;	
	unité de masse atomique (unifiée)	u
p	bar; *bar* $(= 10^6$ dyn/cm$^2)$	bar
A	curie, *curie*	Ci

Remark: The (unified) atomic mass unit is defined as $\frac{1}{12}$th of the mass of an atom of the ^{12}C nuclide.

APPENDIX*). SYSTEMS OF QUANTITIES AND UNITS IN ELECTRICITY AND MAGNETISM.

The CGS unit system with three basic units and the MKSA unit system with four basic units correspond respectively to two different sets of equations in the field of electricity and magnetism, which are developed starting from three and from four basic quantities respectively. These systems are denoted as three and four "dimensional" systems of equations respectively.

1. Systems of equations with 3 basic quantities.

Three distinct sets of equations with three basic quantities**) have been developed in the field of electricity and magnetism. These are:

(1.a) *The "electrostatic system" of equations*, defining the electric charge on the basis of Coulomb laws for the force between two electric charges, by taking the permittivity in vacuo equal to a dimensionless quantity, the number unity.

(1.b) *The "electromagnetic system" of equations*, defining the electric current on the basis of the interaction law for the force between two electric current elements, by taking the permeability in vacuo equal to a dimensionless quantity, the number unity.

(1.c) *The "symmetrical system" or Gaussian system of equations*, using the electric quantities from system (1.a) and the magnetic quantities from system (1.b). As a result of combining the two sets of quantities the velocity of light in vacuo appears explicitly in some of the equations interrelating electric and magnetic quantities.

The equations in these three systems are usually written in the *"non-rationalized"* form, which is called "non-rationalized," because in these equations often factors 2π or 4π appear in situations not involving circular or spherical symmetry respectively. These equations are sometimes written in a *"rationalized"* form, in which these factors appear only in those equations, where they could be expected from the geometry of the system. When three dimensional equations are used (e.g. in theoretical physics), one commonly uses those of the *non-rationalized symmetrical system.*

2. Systems of equations with 4 basic quantities.

In the equations with four basic quantities at least one quantity of electric or magnetic nature is included in the basic set. In such a system the permittivity and the permeability in vacuo appear explicitly as physical quantities with dimension in the relevant equations.

* The S.U.N. commission, after reproducing in the previous chapters all the recommendations on symbols, units and nomenclature approved by the I.U.P.A.P., gives in this Appendix some factual information about existing systems of quantities and units in the field of electricity and magnetism.

** Often length, time and mass are chosen as basic quantities, but also other choices, e.g. length, time and energy or length, time and force have been used.

In the field of *mechanics* the following units of this system have special names and symbols, which have been approved by the Conférence Générale des Poids et Mesures:

l, b, h	centimetre; *centimètre*	cm
t	second; *seconde*	s
m	gramme; *gramme*	g
f, v	hertz; *hertz* $(= s^{-1})$	Hz
F	dyne; *dyne* $(= g.cm/s^2)$	dyn
E, U, W, A	erg; *erg* $(= g.cm^2/s^2)$	erg
p	microbar; *microbar* $(= dyn/cm^2)$	μbar
η	poise; *poise* $(= dyn. s/cm^2)$	P

In the field of *electricity and magnetism* several variants of the CGS unit system have been developed, in particular the *electrostatic CGS system* and *electromagnetic CGS system*. Special names and symbols for some of the units of the second system are:*)

$H*$	oersted; *oersted* $(= cm^{-}.g^{\frac{1}{2}}.s^{-1})$	Oe
$B*$	gauss; *gauss* $(= cm^{-\frac{1}{2}}.g^{\frac{1}{2}}.s^{-1})$	G
$\Phi*$	maxwell; *maxwell* $(= cm^{\frac{1}{2}}.g^{\frac{1}{2}}s^{-1})$	Mx

For further information about the units and unit systems in electricity and magnetism see appendix, section 2.

3. The **MKSA system** or m-kg-s-A system is a coherent system of units for mechanics, electricity and magnetism, based on *four basic units* for the four basic quantities length, mass, time and electric current intensity:

metre	m
kilogramme	kg
second	s
ampere	A

Remark: The system based on these four units has been given the name *Giorgi system* by the International Electrotechenical Committee in 1958. The subsystem for mechanics, which is based on the first three units only, has the name *MKS system*.

The following units of the MKSA system have special names and symbols, which have been approved by the Conférence Générale des Poids et Measures:

l, b, h	metre; *mètre*	m
t	second; *seconde*	s
m	kilogramme; *kilogramme*	kg
v, f	hertz; *hertz* $(- s^{-1})$	Hz
F	newton; *newton* $(= kg.m/s^2)$	N
E	joule; *joule* $(= kg.m^2/s^2)$	J
P	watt; *watt* $(= J/s)$	W

I	ampere; *ampère*	A
Q	coulomb; *coulomb* $(= A.s)$	C
V	volt; *volt* $(= W/A)$	V
C	farad; *farad* $(= C/V)$	F
R	ohm; *ohm* $(= V/A)$	Ω
L	henry; *henry* $(= V.s/A)$	H
Φ	weber; *weber* $(= V.s)$	Wb
B	tesla; *tesla* $(= Wb/m^2)$	T

4. The **degree Kelvin.** In the field of *thermodynamics* one introduces an additional basic unit, corresponding to the basic quantity:

thermodynamic temperature, the unit being the degree Kelvin, symbol: °K
When the *customary temperature* is used, defined by $t = T - T_0$, where $T_0 = 273.15°K$, this is usually expressed in degree Celsius symbol: °C. For *temperature interval* the name degree, symbol: deg is often used, the indications "Kelvin" or "Celsius," indicating the zeropoint of the temperature scale used, being irrelevant in this case.

5. The **candela.**

In the field of *photometry* one introduces an additional basic unit, corresponding to the basic quantity: *luminous intensity*, this unit being the candela, symbol: cd. Special names and symbols for units in this field are:

I	candela; *candéla*	cd
Φ	lumen; *lumen*	lm
E	lux; *lux* $(= lm/m^2)$	lx

*) See also Appendix.

8.5 Symbols for special values of periodic quantities.

	Normal case		Exceptional case	
instantaneous value	x	x	x	x
r.m.s. value	x_{eff}	$\tilde{x}$	X	X
maximum value	x_{m}	$\hat{x}$	$x_{\text{m}}, X_{\text{m}}$	$\hat{x}, \hat{X}$
average value	x_{av}	$\bar{x}, \langle x \rangle$	x_{av}	$\bar{x}, \langle x \rangle$

Remarks:

a. The "normal" case is the case in which only a small or only a capital letter may be used for the quantity. The "exceptional" case is the case in which both small and capital letters may be used for the same quantity.

b. The minimum value of x may be indicated by x_{min} or $\check{x}$.

c. The r.m.s. value is defined as $\tilde{x}^2 = T^{-1} \int_0^T x(t)^2 dt$.

d. The average value is defined as $\bar{x} = T^{-1} \int_0^T x(t) dt$.

8.6 Vector calculus. (see also 1.2.3)

absolute value; *valeur absolue* $\qquad$ $|A|, A$

differential vector operator; *vecteur opérateur différentiel* $\qquad$ $\partial/\partial r, \nabla$

gradient; *gradient* $\qquad$ grad $\varphi, \nabla\varphi$

divergence; *divergence* $\qquad$ div $A, \nabla \cdot A$

curl; *rotationnel* $\qquad$ curl A, rot $A, \nabla \times A$

Laplacian; *Laplacien* $\qquad$ $\triangle\varphi, \nabla^2\varphi$

Dalembertian; *Dalembertien* $\qquad$ $\square\varphi$

8.7 Matrix calculus.

transpose of matrix A; *matrice transposée de A*: $A_{ij} = A_{ji}$ $\qquad$ $\tilde{A}$

complex conjugate of A; *matrice complexe conjugueé de A*: $A^*_{ij} = (A_{ij})^*$ $\qquad$ A^*

Hermitian conjugate of A; *matrice conjugueé Hermitienne de A*: $A\dagger_{ji} = A_{ji}^*$ $\qquad$ $A\dagger$

Pauli matrices; *matrices de Pauli*: $\qquad$ $\sigma,$
$\qquad$ $\sigma_x, \sigma_y, \sigma_s$

$$\sigma_x = \begin{vmatrix} 0 & 1 \\ 1 & 0 \end{vmatrix} \qquad \sigma_y = \begin{vmatrix} 0 & -i \\ i & 0 \end{vmatrix} \qquad \sigma_z = \begin{vmatrix} 1 & 0 \\ 0 & -1 \end{vmatrix}$$
$\qquad$ $\sigma_1, \sigma_2, \sigma_3$

unit matrix; *matrice unité*: $I = \begin{vmatrix} 1 & 0 \\ 0 & 1 \end{vmatrix}$ $\qquad$ I

Dirac (4×4) matrices; (4×4) *matrices de Dirac* *)

$$\alpha_x = \begin{vmatrix} 0 & \sigma_x \\ \sigma_x & 0 \end{vmatrix} \qquad x_y = \begin{vmatrix} 0 & \sigma_y \\ \sigma_y & 0 \end{vmatrix} \qquad \alpha_z = \begin{vmatrix} 0 & \sigma_z \\ \sigma_s & 0 \end{vmatrix}$$
$\qquad$ $\alpha, \alpha_x, \alpha_y, \alpha_s$

$$\beta = \begin{vmatrix} I & 0 \\ 0 & -I \end{vmatrix}$$
$\qquad$ β

9. INTERNATIONAL SYMBOLS FOR UNITS.

9.1 Unit systems.

1. A *coherent system of units* is a system based on a certain set of "basic units" from which all "derived units" are obtained by multiplication or division without introducing numerical factors. In addition there are "dimensionless units," in particular the radian, symbol: rad, for plane angle and the steradian, symbol: sr, for solid angle.

2. The *CGS system* or cm-g-s system is a coherent system of units based on *three basic units* for the three basic quantities length, mass and time respectively:

centimetre $\qquad$ cm
gramme $\qquad$ g
second $\qquad$ s

*) Sometimes a different representation is used.

approximately equal to; *égal environ à*	$\approx$
asymptotically equal to; *asymptotiquement égal à*	$\simeq$
proportional to; *proportionnel à*	$\sim$ $\propto$
approaches; *tend vers*	$\to$
larger than; *supérieur á*	$>$
smaller than; *inférieur á*	$<$
much larger than; *très supérieur á*	$\gg$
much smaller than; *très inférieur á*	$\ll$
larger than or equal to; *supérieur ou égal á*	$\geqq$
smaller than or equal to; *inférieur ou égal á*	$\leqq$
plus; *plus*	$+$
minus; *moins*	$-$
plus or minus; *plus ou moins*	$\pm$
a multiplied by b; *a multiplié par b*	$ab,\ a.b,\ a \cdot b,\ a \times b$
a divided by b; *a divisé par b*	$a/b,\ \dfrac{a}{b},\ ab^{-1}$
a raised to the power n; *a puissance n*	a^n
magnitude of a; *valeur absolue de a*	$\lvert a \rvert$
square root of a; *racine carrée de a*	$\sqrt{a},\ \surd a,\ a^{\frac{1}{2}}$
mean value of a; *valeur moyenne de a*	$\bar{a}\ \langle a \rangle$
factorial p; *factorielle p*	$p!$
binomial coefficient; *coefficient binomial*: $n!/p!(n - p)!$	$\dbinom{n}{p}$
infinity; *infini*	∞

8.2 Letter symbols and letter expressions for *mathematical operations* should be written in *roman (or upright)* type

exponential of x; *exponentielle de x*	$\exp x,\ \mathrm{e}^x$	
base of natural logarithms; *base des logarithmes népériens*	e	
logarithm to the base a of x; *logarithme de base a de x*	$\log_a x$	
natural logarithm of x; *logarithme népérien de x*	$\ln x$	
common logarithm of x; *logarithme décimal de x*	$\lg x,\ \log x$	*)
binary logarithm of x; *logarithme binaire de x*	$\mathrm{lb}\ x\ \log_2 x$	
summation; *somme*	Σ	
product; *produit*	Π	
finite increase of x; *accroissement fini de x*	Δx	**)
variation of x; *variation de x*	δx	
total differential of x; *différentielle totale de x*	$\mathrm{d}x$	
function of x; *fonction de x*	$f(x),\ \mathrm{f}(x)$	
limit of $f(x)$; *limite de f(x)*	$\lim f(x)$	
Dirac delta function; *fonction delta de Dirac* $\delta(\boldsymbol{r}) = \delta(\mathrm{x})\delta(\mathrm{y})\delta(\mathrm{z})$	$\delta(x),\ \delta(\boldsymbol{r})$	
Kronecker delta symbol; *symbole delta de Kronecker*	δ_{ij}	
Unit step function; *fonction unité*($\epsilon(x) = 1$ for $x > 0$, $\epsilon(x) = 0$ for $x < 0$)	$\epsilon(x)$	†)

8.3 Trigonometric functions.

sine of x, *sinus x*	$\sin x$
cosine of, *cosinus x*	$\cos x$
tangent of x, *tangente x*	$\tan x,\ \mathrm{tg}\ x$
cotangent of x, *cotangente x*	$\cot x,\ \mathrm{ctg}\ x$
secant of x, *sécante x*	$\sec x$
cosecant of x, *cosécante x*	$\operatorname{cosec} x$

Remarks:

a. It is recommended to use for the *inverse circular functions* the symbolic expressions for the corresponding circular function preceded by the letters: arc.
   Examples: arcsin x, arccos x, arctan x or arctg x, etc. Sometimes the notation $\sin^{-1} x$, $\tan^{-1} x$, etc. is used.
b. It is recommended to use for the *hyperbolic functions* the symbolic expression for the corresponding circular function, followed by the letter: h.
   Examples: sinh x, cosh x, tanh x or tgh x, etc.
c. It is recommended to use for the *inverse hyperbolic functions* the symbolic expression for the corresponding hyperbolic function preceded by the letters: ar.

   Example: arsinh x, arcosh x, etc.

8.4 Complex quantities.

imaginary unit; *unité imaginaire* ($\mathrm{i}^2 = -1$)	$\mathrm{i},\ \mathrm{j}$
real part of z; *partie réelle de z*	$\operatorname{Re} z,\ z$
imaginary part of z; *partie imaginaire de z*	$\operatorname{Im} z,\ z''$
modulus of z; *module de z*	$\lvert z \rvert$
argument of z; *argument de z* : $z = \lvert z \rvert \exp \mathrm{i}\varphi$	$\arg z,\quad \varphi$
complex conjugate of z, conjugate of z; *complexe conjugué de z, conjugué de z*	z^*
Remark: Sometimes the notation $\bar{z}$ is used for the complex conjugate of z.	

*) In case of ambiguity $\log_{10} x$.   **) Greek capital delta, not triangle.
†) $\Theta(t)$ is used for unit step function of time.

qu.n. of component of S in direction of external field; *n.qu. de la composante de S dans la direction du champ extérieur* — M_S

qu.n. of total angular momentum; *n.qu. du moment angulaire total* (including nuclear spin) $F = J + I$ — F

qu.n. of component of F in direction of external field; *n.qu. de la composante de F dans la direction du champ extérieur* — M_F

qu.n. of component of I in direction of external field; *n.qu. de la composante de I dans la direction du champ extérieur* — M_I

qu.n. of component of angular momentum along axis; *n.qu. de la composante du moment angulaire suivant l'axe* (L.M. and S.T.M.; excluding electron- and nuclear spin; for L.M.: $(K = |\Lambda + l|)$ — K

qu.n. of total angular momentum; *n.qu. du moment angulaire total* (L.M. and S.T.M.; excluding electron and nuclear spin: $J = N + S*$) — N

qu.n. of component of angular momentum along symmetry axis; *n.qu. de la composante du moment angulaire suivant l'axe de symétrie* (L.M. and S.T.M., excluding nuclear spin; for L.M.: $P = |K + \Sigma|**$) — P

electronic term; *terme électronique*: $T_e = E_e/hc†$ — T_e

vibrational term; *terme de vibration*: $G = E_{vibr}/hc$ — G

coefficients in expression for vibrational term (for D.M.); *coefficients de l'expression d'un terme de vibration*:
$G = \sigma_e(v + \frac{1}{2}) - x\sigma_e(v + \frac{1}{2})^2$ — $\sigma_e, x\sigma_e$

coefficients in expression for vibrational term (for P.M.) *coefficients de l'expression d'un terme de vibration*:
$G = \Sigma\sigma_i(v_i + \frac{1}{2}d_i) + \frac{1}{2}\Sigma\Sigma x_{jk}(v_i + \frac{1}{2}d_i)(v_k + \frac{1}{2}d_k)$ — σ_i, x_{jk}

rotational term; *terme de rotation*: $F = E_{rot}/hc$ — F

principal moments of inertia; *moments principaux d'inertie*:
$I_A \leqq I_B \leqq I_C††$ — I_A, I_B, I_C

rotational constants; *constants de rotation*: $A = h/8\pi^2cI_A$, etc.†† — A, B, C

total term; *terme total*: $T = T_e + G + F$ — T

Remark: L.M. = linear molecules. *S.T.M.* = symmetric top molecules. D.M. = diatomic molecules. P.M. = polyatomic molecules.

See for further details: Report on Notation for the Spectra of Polyatomic Molecules (Joint Commission for Spectroscopy of I.U.P.A.P. and I.A.U. 1954) J. Chem. Phys. **23** (1955) 1997.

7.12 Chemical physics.

amount of substance; *quantité de substance* — ν, n *)

molar mass of substance B; *masse molaire de la substance B* — M_B

molarity of subst. B; *molarité de la subst. B* — c_B

mole fraction of subst. B; *fraction molaire de la subst. B* — x_B

mass fraction of subst. B; *fraction massique de la subst. B* — w_B

volume fraction of subst. B; *fraction volumique de la subst. B* — φ_B

mole ratio of solution; *rapport molaire d'une solution* — r

molality of solution; *molalité d'une solution* — m

chemical potential of subst. B; *potentiel chimique de la subst. B* — μ_B

absolute activity of subst. B (dimensionless); *activité absolue de la subst. B (sans dimension)* $\lambda_B = \exp(\mu_B/kT)$ — λ_B

relative activity; *activité relative* — a_B

activity coefficients; *coefficients d'activité* — γ_B, f_B

osmotic pressure; *pression osmotique* — Π

osmotic coefficient; *coefficient osmotique* — g, φ

stoichiometric number of molec. B; *coeff. stœchiométrique de moléc. B* — v_B

affinity; *affinité* — A

extent of reaction; *état d'avancement d'une réaction* — ξ

equilibrium constant; *constante d'équilibre* — K

charge number of ion; *électrovalence d'un ion* — z

Faraday constant; *constante de Faraday* — F

ionic strength; *force ionique* — I

activity of substance B; *activité de la substance B*: $z_B = (2\pi mkT/h^2)^{3/2}\lambda_B$ — z_B

8. RECOMMENDED MATHEMATICAL SYMBOLS.

8.1 General symbols.

equal to; *égal à* — $=$

not equal to; *différent de* — $\neq$

identically equal to; *égal identiquement à* — $\equiv$

corresponds to; *correspond à* — $\geqq$

*) case of loosely coupled electron spin. **) case of tightly coupled electron spin.

†) All energies are taken here with respect to the ground state as reference level.

††) For diatomic molecules use I and $A = h/8\pi^2cI$.

*) n is used in chemistry, but v may be used as an alternative to n, when n is used for number density of particles.

mean life; *vie moyenne*	τ
reaction energy; *énergie de réaction*	Q
cross section; *section efficace*	σ
macroscopic cross section; *section efficace macroscopique:* $\Sigma = n\sigma$	Σ
impact parameter; *paramètre de collision*	b
scattering angle; *angle de diffusion*	$\vartheta, \theta, \varphi$
internal conversion coefficient; *coefficient de conversion interne*	α
disintegration energy; *énergie de désintégration*	Q
half life; *demi-vie*	$T_{\frac{1}{2}}$
reduced half life; *demi-vie réduite*	$fT_{\frac{1}{2}}$
decay constant, disintegration constant; *constante de désintégration*	λ
activity; *activité*	A
Compton wavelength; *longueur d'onde de Compton:* $\lambda_C = h/mc$	λ_C
electron radius; *rayon de l'électron***)	r_e
linear attenuation coefficient; *coeff. d'atténuation linéaire*	μ, μ_1
atomic attenuation coefficient; *coeff. d'atténuation atomique*	μ_a
mass attenuation coefficient; *coeff. d' atténuation massique*	μ_m
linear stopping power; *pouvoir d' arrêt linéaire*	S, S_1
atomic stopping power; *pouvoir d' arrêt atomique*	S_a
linear range; *distance de pénétration linéaire*	R, R_1
recombination coefficient; *coefficient de recombinaison*	α

7.10 Solid state physics.

fundamental translations for lattice; *translations fondamentales d'un réseau*	$\boldsymbol{a}, \boldsymbol{b}, \boldsymbol{c}$ $\boldsymbol{a}_1, \boldsymbol{a}_2, \boldsymbol{a}_3$
Miller indices; *indices de Miller*	h, k, l h_1, h_2, h_3
plane in lattice; *plan d'un réseau**)	(h, k, l) (h_1, h_2, h_3)
direction in lattice; *direction dans un réseau**)	$[h, k, l]$ $[h_1, h_2, h_3]$
fundamental translations in reciprocal lattice; *translations fondamentales de reseau réciproque*	$\boldsymbol{a}^*, \boldsymbol{b}^*, \boldsymbol{c}^*$
vector in crystal lattice; *vecteur dans un réseau*	$\boldsymbol{b}_1, \boldsymbol{b}_2, \boldsymbol{b}_3$ r
distance between successive lattice planes; *distance de plans successifs d'un réseau*	d
Bragg angle; *angle de Bragg*	θ, ϑ
order of reflexion; *ordre du réflexion*	n
short range order parameter; *paramètre d'ordre (proche voisin)*	σ
long range order parameter; *paramètre d'ordre (longue distance)*	s
Burgers vector; *vecteur de Burgers*	$\boldsymbol{b}$
circular wave vector; propagation vector (of phonons); *vecteur d'onde circulaire, vecteur de propagation (de phonons)*	$\boldsymbol{q}$
circular wave vector, propagation vector (of particles); *vecteur d'onde circulaire, vecteur de propagation (de particules)*	$\boldsymbol{k}$
effective mass of electron; *masse effective d'une électron*	m^*, m_{eff}
Fermi energy; *énergie de Fermi*	E_F, ϵ_F
Fermi circular wave vector; *vecteur d'onde circulaire de Fermi*	$\boldsymbol{k}_F$
work function; *fonction de travail*	Φ
differential thermoelectric power; *force thermoélectrique différentielle*	$S, (\Sigma)$
Peltier coefficient; *coefficient de Peltier*	Π
Thomson coefficient; *coefficient de Thomson*	μ
piezoelectric coefficient; *coefficient piézoélectrique:* (polarization/stress)	d_{mn}
characteristic (Weiss) temperature; *température caractéristique (de Weiss)*	Θ, Θ_w
Curie temperature; *température de Curie*	T_C
Neel temperature; *température de Néel*	T_N
Hall coefficient; *coefficient de Hall*	R_H

7.11 Molecular spectroscopy.

qu.n. of component of electronic orbital angular momentum vector along symmetry axis; *n.qu. de la composante du moment angulaire orbital électronique suivant l'axe de symétrie*	Λ, λ_i
qu.n. of component of electronic spin along symmetry axis; *n.qu. de la composante du spin électronique suivant l'axe de symétrie*	Σ, σ_i
qu.n. of total electronic angular momentum vector along symmetry axis; *n.qu. du moment angulaire total électronique suivant l'axe de symétrie*	Ω, ω_i
qu.n. of electronic spin; *n.qu. du spin électronique*	S
qu.n. of nuclear spin; *n.qu. du spin nucléaire*	I
qu.n. of vibrational mode; *n.qu. d'un mode de vibration*	v
degeneracy of vibrational mode; *degré de dégénérescance d'une mode de vibration*	d
qu.n. of vibrational angular momentum; *n.qu. de moment angulaire vibrationnel* (L.M.)	l
qu.n. of total angular momentum; *n.qu. de moment angulaire total* (excluding nuclear spin)	J
qu.n. of component of *J* in direction of external field; *n.qu. de la composante de J dans la direction du champ extérieur*	M, M_J

*) Instead of the ordinary brackets ( ) and square brackets [ ], curly brackets { } and diamond brackets ⟨ ⟩ are also used respectively.

7.7 Acoustics.

velocity of sound; *vitesse du son* — c
velocity of longitudinal waves; *vitesse d'ondes longitudinale* — c_1
velocity of transversal waves; *vitesse d'ondes transversale* — c_t
group velocity; *vitesse de groupe* — c_g
sound energy flux; *flux énergétique du son* — P
reflexion factor; *facteur de réflexion:* P_r/P_0 — ρ
acoustic absorption factor; *facteur d'absorption acoustique* $1 - \rho$ — α_a (α)
transmission factor; *facteur de transmission:* P_{tr}/P_c — τ
dissipation factor; *facteur de dissipation:* $\alpha_a - \tau$ — δ
loudness level; *niveau d'isosonie* — L_N, (Λ)

7.8 Quantum mechanics.

complexe conjugate of Ψ; *complexe conjugué de* Ψ — Ψ^*
probability density; *densité de probabilité:* $P = \Psi^*\Psi$ — P
probability current density: *densité de courant de probabilité:*
  $S = (\hbar/2im)(\Psi^*\Delta\Psi - \Psi\Delta\Psi^*)$ — S
charge density of electrons; *charge volumique d'électrons:* $\rho = -eP$ — ρ
electric current density of electrons; *densité de courant électrique d'électrons:*
  $j = -eS$ — j
expectation value of A; *valeur moyenne de* A — $\langle A \rangle$, $\bar{A}$
commutator of A and B, *commutateur de* A *et* B: $[A,B] = AB - BA$ — $[A,B]$, $[A,B]$
anticommutator of A and B; *anticommutateur de* A *et* B: $[A,B]_+ = AB + BA$ — $[A,B]_+$
matrix element; *élément de matrice:* $A_{ij} = \int \psi_i^*(A\psi_j)\,d\tau$ — A_{ij}
Hermitian conjugate of operator A; *conjugué Hermitien de l'opérateur* A — $A\dagger$
momentum operator in coordinate representation; *opérateur de quantité de mouvement* — $+(\hbar/i)\Delta$
annihilation operators; *opérateurs d'annihilation* — a, b, α, β
creation operators; *opérateurs de création* — a^+, $b\dagger$, $\alpha\dagger$ $\beta\dagger$

7.9 Atomic and nuclear physics.

mass number, nucleon number; *nombre de masse, nombre de nucléons* — A
atomic number, proton number; *nombre atomique, nombre de protons* — Z
neutron number; *nombre de neutrons:* $N = A - Z$ — N
elementary charge (of position); *charge élémentaire (du position)* — e
electron mass; *masse de l'électron* — m, m_e
proton mass; *masse du proton* — m_p
neutron mass; *masse du neutron* — m_n
meson mass; *masse du méson* — m_π,
nuclear mass; *masse nucléaire* (of nucleus: ^AX) — m_N, m_N (^AX)
atomic; mass; *masse atomique* (of nuclide: ^AX) — m_a, m_a (^AX)
(unified) atomic mass constant; *constante (unifiée) de masse atomique:*
  $m_u = m_a(^{12}C)/12$ — m_u
relative atomic mass; *masse atomique relative:* m_a/m_u — A_r
Planck constant; *constante de Planck* $(\hbar = h/2\pi)$ — h
principal quantum number; *nombre quantique principal* — n, n_i
orbital angular momentum quantum number; *nombre quantique de moment angulaire*
  orbital — L, l_i
spin quantum number; *nombre quantique de spin* — S, s_i
angular momentum quantum number; *nombre quantique de moment angulaire*
  (including electron spin) — J, j_i
magnetic quantum number; — — *magnétique* — M, m_i
nuclear spin quantum number; — — *de spin nucléaire* — I, J — *)
hyperfine quantum number; — — *hyperfin* — F
rotational quantum number; — — *de rotation* — J, K
vibrational quantum number; — — *de vibration* — v
quadrupole moment; *moment quadripolaire* — Q
Rydberg constant; *constante de Rydberg***) — $R\infty$
Bohr radius; *rayon de Bohr***) — a_0
fine structure constant; *constante de structure fine***) — α
mass excess; *excès de masse:* $m_a - Am_u$ — Δ
packing fraction; *packing fraction:* Δ/Am_u — f
nuclear radius; *rayon nucléaire:* $R = r_0 A^{1/3}$ — R
magnetic moment of particle: *moment magnétique d'une particule* — μ
magnetic moment of proton; *moment magnétique du proton* — μ_p
magnetic moment of neutron; *moment magnétique du neutron* — μ_n
magnetic moment of electron; *moment magnétique électronique* — μ_e
Bohr magneton; *magnéton de Bohr***) — μ_B
nuclear magneton; *magnéton nucléaire* — μ_N
g-factor; *facteur g:* e.g. $g = \mu/I\mu_N$ — g
gyromagnetic ratio; *rapport gyromagnétique***) — γ
Larmor (angular) frequency; *fréquence (angulaire) de Larmor***) — ω_L
level width; *largeur d'un niveau* — Γ

*) I is used in atomic physics. J in nuclear physics.
**) See for definition: Appendix, section 2.

7.5 Electricity and magnetism.††)

quantity of electricity; *quantité d' électricité*	Q
charge density; *charge volumique*	ρ
surface charge density; *charge surfacique*	σ
electric potential; *potentiel électrique*	V, φ
potential difference, tension; *différence de potentiel, tension*	U, V
electromotive force; *force électromotrice*	E
electric field strength; *champ électrique*	$\mathbf{E}$
electric flux; *flux électrique*	Ψ
electric displacement; *déplacement électrique*	$\mathbf{D}$
capacitance; *capacité*	C
permittivity; *permittivité:* $\mathbf{D} = \epsilon \mathbf{E}$	ϵ
permittivity of vacuum; *permittivité du vide*	ϵ_0
relative permittivity; *permittivité relative* $\epsilon_r = \epsilon/\epsilon_0$	ϵ_r
dielectric polarization: *polarisation diélectrique:* $\mathbf{D} = \epsilon_0 \mathbf{E} + \mathbf{P}$	$\mathbf{P}$
electric susceptibility; *susceptibilité électrique*	χ_e
polarizability; *polarisabilité*	α, γ
electric dipole moment; *moment dipolaire électrique*	$\mathbf{p}$
electric current; *courant électrique*	I
electric current density; *densité de courant électrique*	$\mathbf{j}$
magnetic field strength; *champ magnétique*	$\mathbf{H}$
magnetic potential difference; *différence de potentiel magnétique*	U_m
magnetomotive force; *force magnétomotrice:* $F_m = \oint H_s ds$	F_m
magnetic induction, magnetic flux density; *induction magnétique, densité de flux magnétique*	$\mathbf{B}$
magnetic flux; *flux magnétique*	Φ
permeability; *perméabilité:* $\mathbf{B} = \mu \mathbf{H}$	μ
permeability of vacuum; *perméabilité du vide*	μ_0
relative permeability; *perméabilité relative:* $\mu_r = \mu/\mu_0$	μ_r
magnetization; *aimantation:* $\mathbf{B} = \mu_0(\mathbf{H} + \mathbf{M})$	$\mathbf{M}$
magnetic susceptibility; *susceptibilité magnétique*	χ_m
electromagnetic moment; *moment électromagnétique:* $E_p = -\mathbf{m}.\,\mathbf{B}$	$\mu, \mathbf{m}$
magnetic polarization; *polarisation magnétique:* $\mathbf{B} = \mu_0 \mathbf{H} + \mathbf{J}$	$\mathbf{J}$
resistance; *résistance*	R
reactance; *réactance*	X
quality factor: *facteur de qualité:* $Q = |X|/R$	Q
impedance; *impédance:* $Z = R + i\,X$	Z
admittance; *admittance:* $Y = 1/Z = G + iB$	Y
conductance; *conductance*	G
susceptance; *susceptance*	B
resistivity; *résistivité*	ρ
conductivity; *conductivité* $\gamma = 1/\rho$	γ, σ
self inductance; *inductance propre*	L
mutual inductance; *inductance mutuelle*	M, L_{12}
coupling coefficient; *coefficient de couplage:* $k = L_{12}/(L_1 L_2)^{1/2}$	k
phase number; *nombre de phases*	m
loss angle; *angle de pertes*	δ
number of turns; *nombre de tours*	N
power; *puissance*	P
electromagnetic energy density; *énergie électromagnetique volumique*	w
Poynting vector; *vecteur de Poynting*	$\mathbf{S}$
magnetic vector potential; *potentiel vecteur magnétique*	$\mathbf{A}$

7.6 Radiation, light.†)

radiant energy; *énergie rayonnante*	$Q, (Q_e), W$
radiant flux, radiant power; *flux énergétique, puissance rayonnante*	$\Phi, (\Phi_e), P$
radiant intensity; *intensité énergétique*	$I, (I_e)$
irradiance; *irradiance, éclairement énergétique*	$E, (E_e)$
radiance; *luminance énergétique, radiance*	$L, (L_e)$
radiant emittance; *émittance énergétique*	$M, (M_e)$
quantity of light; *quantité de lumière*	$Q, (Q_V)$
luminous flux; *flux lumineux*	$\Phi, (\Phi_V)$
luminous intensity; *intensité lumineuse:* $d\Phi/d\omega$	$I, (I_V)$
illuminance, illumination; *éclairement lumineux:* $d\Phi/dS$	$E, (E_V)$
luminance; *luminance:* $dI/dS \cos \vartheta$	$L, (L_V)$
luminous emittance; *émittance lumineuse:* $d\Phi/dS$	$M, (M_V)$
absorption factor; *facteur d'absorption:* Φ_a/Φ_0	α
reflection factor; *facteur de réflexion* Φ_r/Φ_0	ρ
transmission factor; *facteur de transmission* Φ_{tr}/Φ_0	τ
(linear) absorption coefficient; *coefficient d'absorption (linéique)*	a
(linear) extinction coefficient; *coefficient d'atténuation (linéique)*	μ
speed of light in empty space; *vitesse de la lumière dans le vide*	c
refractive index; *indice de réfraction:* $n = c/c_n$	n

††) Written in rationalized, 4-dimensional form. See Appendix, section 2.
†) The symbols between brackets are reserve symbols and are to be used whenever it is necessary to distinguish between radiation and light quantities.

power; *puissance*	P
efficiency; *rendement*	η
Hamiltonian function; *fonction de Hamilton*	H
Lagrangian function; *fonction de Lagrange*	L
principal function of Hamilton; *fonction principale de Hamilton*: $W = \int L \mathrm{d}t$	W, S_p
characteristic function of Hamilton; *fonction caractéristique de Hamilton*: $S = 2\int T \mathrm{d}t$	S
generalized coordinate; *coordonnée généralisée*	q, q_i
generalized momentum; *moment généralisé*	p, p_i
action integral; *intégrale d'action*: $J = \oint p \mathrm{d}q$	J

7.3 Molecular physics.

number of molecules; *nombre de molécules*	N
number density of molecules; *nombre volumique de molécules* $n = N/V$	n
Avogadro constant; *constante d'Avogadro*	L, N_A
molecular mass; *masse moléculaire*	m
molecular velocity vector with components; *vecteur vitesse moléculaire et ses composantes*	$\boldsymbol{c}, (c_x, c_y, c_z)$ $\boldsymbol{u}, (u_x, u_y, u_z)$
molecular position vector with components; *vecteur position moléculaire et ses composantes*	$\boldsymbol{r}, (x, y, z)$
molecular momentum vector with components; *vecteur quantité de mouvement moléculaire et ses composantes*	$\boldsymbol{p}, (p_x, p_y, p_z)$
average velocity; *vitesse moyenne*	$c_0, u_0, \langle c \rangle, \langle u \rangle$
average speed; *vitesse moyenne*	$\bar{c}, \bar{u}, \langle c \rangle, \langle u \rangle$
most probable speed; *vitesse la plus probable*	$\hat{c}, \hat{u}$
mean free path; *libre parcours moyen*	l
molecular attraction energy; *énergie d'attraction moléculaire*	ϵ
interaction energy between molecules i and j; *énergie d'interaction entre les molécules i et j*	φ_{ij}, V_{ij}
velocity distribution function; *fonction de distribution des vitesses*: $n = \int f \, \mathrm{d}c_x \mathrm{d}c_y \mathrm{d}c_z$	$f(c)$
Boltzmann function; *fonction de Boltzman*	H
generalized coordinate; *coordonnée généralisée*	q
generalized momentum; *moment généralisé*	p
volume in γ phase space; *volume dans l'espace γ*	Ω
thermodynamic temperature; *température thermodynamique*	T
Boltzmann constant; *constante de Boltzmann*	k
$1/kT$ (in exponential functions; *dans les fonctions exponentielles*)	β
molar gas constant; *constante molaire des gaz*	R
partition function; *fonction de partitions*	Q, Z
symmetry number; *facteur de symétrie*	s
diffusion coefficient; *coefficient de diffusion*	D
thermal diffusion coefficient; *coefficient de thermodiffusion*	D_T
thermal diffusion ratio; *rapport de thermodiffusion*	K_T
thermal diffusion factor; *facteur de thermodiffusion*	α_T
characteristic temperature; *température caractéristique*	Θ
Debye temperature; *température de Debye*: $\Theta_D = h\nu_D/k$	Θ_D
Einstein temperature; *température d'Einstein*: $\Theta_E = h\nu_E/k$	Θ_E
rotational temperature; *température de rotation*: $\Theta_r = h^2/8\pi^2 Ik$	Θ_r
vibrational temperature; *température de vibration*: $\Theta_v = h\nu/k$	Θ_v

7.4 Thermodynamics.*)

quantity of heat; *quantité de chaleur*	Q
work; *travail*	W, A
temperature; *température*	$t, (\vartheta)$ *)
thermodynamic temperature; *température thermodynamique*	$T, (\Theta)$ **)
entropy; *entropie*	S
internal energy; *énergie interne*	U
Helmholtz function; *fonction de Helmholtz, énergie libre*: $F = U - TS$	F
enthalpy; *enthalpie*: $H = U + pV$	H
Gibbs function; *fonction de Gibbs, enthalpie libre*: $G = H - TS$	G
pressure coefficient; *coefficient d'augmentation de pression*: $\beta = (1/p)(\partial p/\partial T)_V$	β
compressibility; *compressibilité*: $\kappa = -(1/V)(\partial V/\partial p)_T$	κ
linear expansion coefficient; *coefficient de dilatation linéique*	α
cubic expansion coefficient; *coefficient de dilatation volumique*	γ
thermal conductivity; *conductivité thermique*	λ
specific heat capacity; *chaleur massique*: $c = C/m$	c_p, c_v
heat capacity; *capacité thermique*	C_p, C_v
Joule-Thomson coefficient; *coefficient de Joule-Thomson*	μ
ratio of specific heat capacities; *rapport des chaleurs massiques*	κ, γ
heat flow rate; *flux thermique*	$\Phi, (q)$
heat current density; *densité de flux thermique*	$\boldsymbol{q}, (\varphi)$
thermal diffusivity; *diffusivité thermique*: $a = \lambda/\rho c_p$	a

†) The index m is added in the case of molar quantities, if needed, to distinguish them from quantities referring to the whole system. For specific quantities (see 6.1) lower case letters are used.

*) Preferred symbol: t.   **) Preferred symbol: T.

7.1 Space and time.

space coordinates; *coordonnées d'espace*	(x, y, z)
position vector; *vecteur de position*	$\boldsymbol{r}$
length; *longueur*	l
breadth; *largeur*	b
height; *hauteur*	h
radius; *rayon*	r
thickness; *épaisseur*	d, δ
diameter; *diamètre: d = 2r*	d
path; *parcours: $L = \int ds$*	L, s
area; *aire; superficie*	A, S
volume; *volume*	$V, (v)$
plane angle, *angle plan*	$\alpha, \beta, \gamma, \theta, \vartheta, \varphi$
solid angle; *angle solide*	ω, Ω
wave length; *longueur d'onde*	λ
wave number; *nombre d'onde* $\sigma = 1/\lambda$	σ *)
wave vector; *vecteur d'onde*	σ
circular wave number; *nombre d'onde circulaire: $k = 2\pi/\lambda$*	k
circular wave vector; *vecteur d'onde circulaire*	$\boldsymbol{k}$
attenuation coefficient; *constante d'affaiblissement: $F(x) = \exp(-\alpha x)\cos\beta x$*	α
phase coefficient; *constante de phase*	β
propagation coefficient; *constante de propagation: $\gamma = \alpha + i\beta$*	γ
time; *temps*	t
period; *période*	T
frequency; *fréquence: $\nu = 1/T$*	ν, f
pulsatance; *pulsation: $\omega = 2\pi\nu$*	ω **)
relaxation time; *temps de relaxation: $F(t) = \exp(-t/\tau)$*	τ
damping coefficient; *coefficient d'amortissement: $F(t) = \exp(-\delta t)\sin\omega t$*	δ
logarithmic decrement; *décrément logarithmique: $\Lambda = T\delta = T/\tau$*	Λ
velocity; *vitesse: $v = ds/dt$*	u, v
angular velocity; *vitesse angulaire: $\omega = d\varphi/dt$*	ω
acceleration; *accélération: $a = dv/dt$*	a
angular acceleration; *accélération angulaire: $\alpha = d\omega/dt$*	α
acceleration of free fall; *accélération de la pesanteur*	g
standard — —; *— — normale*	g_n
speed of light in empty space; *vitesse de la lumière dans le vide*	c
v/c	β
relativistic coordinates; *coordonnées relativistes:* $x_0 = ct, x_1 = x, x_2 = y, x_3 = z, x_4 = ict$	$(x_0 x_1 x_2 x_3)$ $(x_1 x_2 x_3 x_4)$

7.2 Mechanics.

mass; *masse*	m
(mass) density; *masse volumique: $\rho = m/V$*	ρ
relative density; *densité relative: $d = \rho/\rho(H_2O)$*	d
specific volume; *volume massique: $v = V/m = 1/\rho$*	v
reduced mass; *masse réduite: $\mu = m_1 m_2/(m_1 + m_2)$*	μ
momentum; *quantité de mouvement: $\boldsymbol{p} = mv$*	$\boldsymbol{P}$
angular momentum; *moment cinétique: $\boldsymbol{L} = \boldsymbol{r} \times \boldsymbol{p}$*	$\boldsymbol{L}$
second moment of plane area; *moment quadratique d'une aire plane: $I_{a,y} = \int x^2 dx dy$*	I_a
second polar moment of plane area; *moment quadratique polaire d'une aire plane:* $I_p = \int(x^2 + y^2)\, dx dy$	I_p
moment of inertia; *moment d'inertie: $I_z = \int(x^2 + y^2)\, dm$*	I, J
force; *force*	$\boldsymbol{F}$
torque, moment of a couple; *torque, moment d'un couple*	$\boldsymbol{T}$
weight; *poids*	$G, (W, P)$
moment of force; *moment d'une force*	$\boldsymbol{M}$
pressure; *pression*	p
normal stress; *tension normale*	σ
shear stress; *tension de cisaillement*	τ
gravitational constant; *constante de gravitation: $F(r) = G\, m_1 m_2/r^2$*	G
linear strain, relative elongation; *dilation linéaire relative: $\epsilon = \Delta l/l_0$*	ϵ
modulus of elasticity, Young's modulus; *module d'élasticité: $\sigma = E\,\epsilon$*	E
shear strain; shear angle; *glissement unitaire*	γ
shear modulus; *module de torsion: $\tau = G \, \mathrm{tg}\, \gamma$*	G
volume strain, bulk strain; *dilation volumique relative: $\theta = \Delta V/V_0$*	θ
bulk modulus; *module de compression: $p = -K\theta$*	K
Poisson ratio, *rapport de Poisson*	μ, ν
viscosity; *viscosité*	$\eta, (\mu)$
kinematic viscosity; *viscosité cinématique: $\nu = \eta/\rho$*	ν
friction coefficient; *coefficient de frottement*	$\mu, (f)$
surface tension; *tension superficielle*	γ, σ
energy; *énergie*	E, W
potential energy; *énergie potentielle*	E_p, V, Φ
kinetic energy; *énergie cinétique*	E_k, T, K
work; *travail*	W, A

*) In molecular spectroscopy: $\bar{\nu}$.   **) Also called angular frequency.

2. A spectroscopic transition should be indicated by writing the upper state first and the lower state second, connected by a dash inbetween.

Examples:

$$^2P_{1/2} - {}^2S_{1/2}$$ for an electronic transition
$$(J', K') - (J'', K'')$$ for a rotational transition
$$v' - v''$$ for a vibrational transition.

3. Absorption transition and emission transition may be indicated by arrows $\leftarrow$ and $\rightarrow$ respectively.

Examples:

$$^2P_{1/2} \rightarrow {}^2S_{1/2} \text{ emission from } {}^2P_{1/2} \text{ to } {}^2S_{1/2}$$
$$(J', K') \leftarrow (J'', K'') \text{ absorption from } (J'', K'') \text{ to } (J', K')$$

4. The difference Δ between two quantum numbers should be that of the upper state minus that of the lower state.

Example:

$$\Delta J = J' - J''$$

5. The indications of the branches of the rotation band should be as follows:

$$\Delta J = J' - J'' = -2: \quad \text{O — branch}$$
$$= -1: \quad \text{P — branch}$$
$$= 0: \quad \text{Q — branch}$$
$$= +1: \quad \text{R — branch}$$
$$= +2: \quad \text{S — branch}$$

6. NOMENCLATURE.

1. *Use of the word specific.*

The word 'specific' in English names for physical quantities should be restricted to the meaning 'divided by mass'. *Examples:*

specific volume   volume/mass
specific energy   energy/mass
specific heat capacity   heat capacity/mass

2. *Notation for covariant character of coupling.*

S	Scalar coupling	A	Axial vector coupling
V	Vector coupling	P	Psuedoscalar coupling
T	Tensor coupling		

3. *Abbreviated notation for a nuclear reaction.*

The meaning of the symbolic expression indicating a nuclear reaction should be the following:
initial (incoming particle(s), outgoing particle(s)) final
nuclide (or quanta   or quanta) nuclide

Examples: $^{14}N(\alpha,p)^{17}O$ $^{59}Co(n,\gamma)^{60}Co$
$^{23}Na(\gamma,3n)^{20}Na$ $^{31}P(\gamma,pn)^{29}Si$

4. *Character of transitions.*

Multipolarity of transition:

electric or magnetic	monopole	E0 or M0
" " "	dipole	E1 or M1
" " "	quadrupole	E2 or M2
" " "	octupole	E3 or M3
" " "	2^n-pole	En or Mn

parity change in transition:

transition *with* parity change: yes
transition *without* parity change: no

5. *Nuclide:* A species of *atoms*, identical as regards atomic number (proton number) and mass number (nucleon number) should be indicated by the word *nuclide*, not the word isotope.
Different nuclides having the same atomic number should be indicated as *isotopes* or *isotopic nuclides*.
Different nuclides having the same mass number should be indicated as *isobars* or *isobaric nuclides*.

6. *Sign of polarization vector (Basel Convention).*

In nuclear interactions the positive polarization of particles with spin $\frac{1}{2}$ is taken in the direction of the vector product

$$\boldsymbol{k}_i \times \boldsymbol{k}_0,$$

where $\boldsymbol{k}_i$ and $\boldsymbol{k}_0$ are the circular wave vectors of the incoming and outgoing particles respectively.

7. RECOMMENDED SYMBOLS FOR PHYSICAL QUANTITIES.

Remark:
(1) Where several symbols are given for one quantity, and no special indication is made, they are on equal footing.
(2) In general, no special attention is paid to the name of the quantity.

If in connection with the symbols p and e no charge is indicated, these symbols should refer to the positive proton and the negative electron respectively.

The tilde $\sim$ above the symbol of a particle is used to indicate the corresponding anti-particle.

Examples:

$$\tilde{n}, \nu, \sim\!p, \tilde{\tilde{N}}$$

5. QUANTUM STATES.

5.1 General rules.

A letter-symbol indicating the quantum state of a *system* should be printed in capital upright type.

A letter-symbol indicating the quantum state of a *single particle* should be printed in lower case upright type.

5.2 Atomic spectroscopy.

The letter-symbols indicating atomic quantum states are:

$L, l = 0$: S, s	$L, l = 4$: G, g	$L, l = 8$: L, l
$= 1$: P, p	$= 5$: H, h	$= 9$: M, m
$= 2$: D, d	$= 6$: I, i	$= 10$: N, n
$= 3$: F, f	$= 7$: K, k	$= 11$: O, o

A right hand subscript indicates the total angular momentum quantum number J or j.

A left hand superscript indicates the spin multiplicity $2S + 1$.

Example: $^2\mathrm{P}_{3/2}$—state   ($J = 3/2$, multiplicity 2)

$\mathrm{p}_{3/2}$—electron ($j = 3/2$)

An atomic electron configuration is indicated symbolically by:

$$(nl)^\kappa \quad (n'l')^{\kappa'} \ldots$$

Instead of $l = 0, 1, 2, 3 \ldots$ one uses the quantum state symbol s, p, d, f, $\ldots$

Example: the atomic configuration: $(1\mathrm{s})^2 \, (2\mathrm{s})^2 \, (2\mathrm{p})^3$.

5.3 Molecular spectroscopy.

The letter symbols, indicating molecular electronic quantum states are in the case of *linear molecules*:

$$\Lambda, \lambda = 0: \Sigma, \sigma$$
$$= 1: \Pi, \pi$$
$$= 2: \Delta, \delta$$

and for *non-linear molecules*

$$\mathrm{A, a} \; ; \quad \mathrm{B, b} \; ; \quad \mathrm{E, e} \; ; \quad \text{etc.}$$

Remarks: A left hand superscript indicates the spin multiplicity. For molecules having a symmetry center the parity symbol g or u, indicating respectively symmetric or antisymmetric behaviour on inversion, is attached as a right hand subscript. A + or − sign attached as a right hand superscript indicates the symmetry as regards reflection in any plane through the symmetry axis of the molecules.

Examples: Σ_g^+, Π_u, $^2\Sigma$, $^3\Pi$,   etc.

The letter symbols indicating the vibrational angular momentum states in the case of *linear molecules* are

$$l = 0: \Sigma$$
$$= 1: \Pi$$
$$= 2: \Delta$$

5.4 Nuclear spectroscopy.

The spin and parity assignment of a nuclear state is

$$J^\pi$$

where the parity symbol π is + for even and − for odd parity.

Examples: 3^+, 2^-,   etc.

A shell model configuration is indicated symbolically by:

$$(nlj)^\kappa \quad (n'l'j')^{\kappa'}$$

where the first bracket refers to the proton shell and the second to the neutron shell. Negative values of κ or κ' indicate holes in a completed shell. Instead of $l = 0, 1, 2, 3, \ldots$ one uses the quantum state symbols s, p, d, f, $\ldots$

Example: the nuclear configuration: $(1 \, \mathrm{d} \, 3/2)^3 \, (1 \, \mathrm{f} \, 7/2)^2$

5.5 Spectroscopic transitions.

1. The upper level and the lower level are indicated by ′ and ″ respectively.

Examples: $h\nu = E' - E''$ $\sigma = T' - T''$

2.3 Mathematical operations.

1. *Multiplication* of two units may be indicated in one of the following ways:

$$\text{Nm} \qquad \text{N m} \qquad \text{N} \cdot \text{m} \qquad \text{N . m}$$

2. *Division* of one unit by another unit may be indicated in one of the following ways:

$$\frac{\text{m}}{\text{s}} \qquad \text{m/s} \qquad \text{m s}^{-1}$$

or by any other way of writing the product of m and s^{-1}.
Not more than one solidus should be used. *Examples:*

Not: cm/s/s,	*but:* cm/s² = cm s⁻²
	1 gm sec⁻¹ cm⁻¹
	J°K⁻¹ mol⁻¹

Not: cm/s/s,	*but:* cm/s^2 = cm s^{-2}
Not: 1 poise = 1 g/s/cm,	*but:* 1 poise = 1 g/s cm = $\quad$ 1 gm sec^{-1} cm^{-1}
Not: J/°K/mol,	*but:* J/°K mol = $\quad$ J°K^{-1} mol^{-1}

3. NUMBERS.

1. *Numbers* should be printed in *upright type.*

2. The *decimal sign* between digits in a number should be a comma (,) or (but *only* in *English* texts) a point (.).

3. The *multiplication* sign between numbers should be a cross ($\times$) or (but *only in non-English* texts) a centered dot, e.g. 2.3×3.4 or $2,3 \cdot 3,4$.

4. *Division* of one number by another number may be indicated in the following ways:

$$\frac{136}{273.15} \qquad\qquad 136/273.15$$

or by writing it as the product of numerator and the inverse first power of the denominator. In such cases the number under the inverse power should always be placed between brackets.

Remark: When the solidus is used and when there is any doubt where the numerator starts or the denominator ends, brackets should be used, as in the case of quantities (see 1.3.3).

5. To facilitate the reading of *long numbers*, the digits may be grouped in *groups of three*, but *no* comma or point should be used except for the decimal sign.
Example: 2 573. 421 736.

4. SYMBOLS FOR CHEMICAL ELEMENTS, NUCLIDES AND PARTICLES.

1. *Symbols for chemical elements* should be written in *roman* (upright) *type*. The symbol is not followed by full stop.
Examples: $\quad$ Ca $\quad$ C $\quad$ H $\quad$ He

2. The attached numerals specifying a *nuclide* are:

$$\text{mass number } {}^{14}\text{N}_2 \text{ atoms/molecule}$$

Remark: The atomic number may be placed as a left subscript, if desired. The right superscript position should be used, if required, for indicating a state of ionisation (e.g. Ca^{2+}, PO_4^{3-}) or an excited state (e.g. ${}^{110}\text{Ag}^m$, He*).

3. *Symbols for particles and quanta.*
It is recommended that the following notation be used:

proton:	p	pion	π
neutron:	n	K-meson	K
Λ-particle	Λ	electron	e
Σ-particle	Σ	muon	μ
Ξ-particle	Ξ	neutrino	ν
deuteron	d		
triton	t	photon	γ
α-particle	α		

A nucleon (proton or neutron) is indicated by N
It is recommended that the charge of particles may be indicated by adding the superscript $+$, $-$ or 0.
Examples:

$$\pi^+ \ \pi^- \ \pi^0, \ \text{p}^+ \ \text{p}^-, \ \text{e}^+ \ \text{e}^-.$$

These procedures can be extended to cases where one of the quantities or both are themselves products, quotients, sums or differences of other quantities.

If necessary brackets have to be used in accordance with the rules of mathematics. If the solidus is used to separate the numerator from the denominator and if there is any doubt where the numerator starts or where the denominator ends, brackets should be used.

Examples:

Expressions with a horizontal bar:	Same expressions with a solidus:
$\dfrac{a}{bcd}$	a/bcd
$\dfrac{2}{9}\sin kx,\ \dfrac{1}{2}RT$	$(2/9)\sin kx,\ (1/2)RT$ or $RT/2$
$\dfrac{a}{b}-c$	$a/b-c$
$\dfrac{a}{b-c}$	$a/(b-c)$
$\dfrac{a-b}{c-d}$	$(a-b)/(c-d)$
$\dfrac{a}{c}-\dfrac{b}{d}$	$a/c-b/d$

Remark: It is recommended that in expressions like:

$$\sin\{2\pi(x-x_0)/\lambda\} \qquad \exp\{(r-r_0)/\sigma\}$$
$$\exp\{-V(r)/kT\} \qquad \sqrt{(\epsilon/c^2)}$$

the argument should always be placed between brackets, except when the argument is a simple product of two quantities: e.g. $\sin kx$. When the horizontal bar above the square root is used no brackets are needed.

2. UNITS—GENERAL RECOMMENDATIONS.

2.1 Symbols for units—General rules.

1. *Symbols for units* of physical quantities should be printed in *roman (upright) type.*

2. *Symbols for units* should not contain a final full stop and should remain unaltered in the plural, e.g.: 7 cm and *not* 7 cms.

3. *Symbols for units* should be printed in *lower case* roman (upright) type. However, the symbol for a unit, derived from a proper name, should start with a capital roman letter, e.g.: m (metre); A (ampere); Wb (weber); Hz (hertz).

2.2 Prefixes—General rules.

1. The following *prefixes* should be used to indicate decimal fractions or multiples of a unit

deci; *déci*	$(=10^{-1})$	d					
centi; *centi*	$(=10^{-2})$	c					
milli; *milli*	$(=10^{-3})$	m	kilo; *kilo*	$(=10^{3})$	k		
micro; *micro*	$(=10^{-6})$	μ	mega; *méga*	$(=10^{6})$	M		
nano; *nano*	$(=10^{-9})$	n	giga; *giga*	$(=10^{9})$	G		
pico; *pico*	$(=10^{-12})$	p	tera; *téra*	$(=10^{12})$	T		
femto; *femto*	$(=10^{-15})$	f					
atto; *atto*	$(=10^{-18})$	a					

2. The use of *double prefixes* should be avoided when single prefixes are available.

Not: mμs,	*but:* ns	(nanosecond)
Not: kMW	*but:* GW	(gigawatt)
Not: $\mu\mu$F,	*but:* pF	(picofarad)

3. When a prefix is placed before the symbol of a unit, the *combination of prefix and symbol* should be considered as *one new symbol*, which can be raised to a positive or negative power without using brackets.

Examples:

$$cm^3 \qquad , \qquad mA^2 \qquad , \qquad \mu s^{-1}$$

Remark:

cm^3 *means always* $(0.01\ m)^3$ *but never* $0.01\ m^3$
μs^{-1} *means always* $(10^{-6}\ s)^{-1}$ *but never* $10^{-6}\ s^{-1}$

From Document U.I.P. 11 (S.U.N. 65–3)
International Union of Pure and Applied Physics
Used by permission of the Secretary

1. PHYSICAL QUANTITIES—GENERAL RECOMMENDATIONS.

1.1 The symbol for a ***physical quantity*** (french: 'grandeur physique', german: 'physikalische Grösse', american sometimes: 'physical magnitude') is equivalent to the product of the *numerical value* (or the measure), a pure number, and a *unit*, i.e.

physical quantity = numerical value × unit.

For dimensionless physical quantities the unit often has no name or symbol and is not explicitly indicated.

Examples:

$E = 200$ erg $n = 1.55$ (for quartz)
$F = 27$ N $\nu = 3 \times 10^8$ s^{-1}

1.2 Symbols for physical quantities—General rules.

1. *Symbols for physical quantities* should be *single letters* of the latin or greek alphabet with or without modifying signs: subscripts, superscripts, dashes, etc.

   Remark:

   a. An exception to this rule consists of the two letter symbols, which are sometimes used to represent dimensionless combinations of physical quantities. If such a symbol, composed of two letters, appears as a factor in a product, it is recommended to separate this symbol from the other symbols by a dot or by brackets or by a space.

   b. Abbreviations, i.e. shortened forms of names or expressions, such as p.f. for partition function, should not be used in physical equations. These abbreviations in the text should be written in ordinary roman type.

2. *Symbols for physical quantities* should be printed in *italic* (or *sloping*) *type*.

   Remark:

   It is recommended to consider as a guiding principle for the printing of indices the criterion: only indices which are symbols for physical quantities should be printed in italic (sloping) type. *Examples:*

Upright indices:	Sloping indices:
C_g (g = gas)	p in C_p
g_n (n = normal)	n in $\Sigma_n a_n \varphi_n$
μ_r (r = relative)	x in $\Sigma_x a_x b_x$
E_k (k = kinetic)	i, k in g_{ik}
χ_e (e = electric)	x in p_x

3. *Symbols for vectors and tensors:* To avoid the usage of subscripts it is often convenient to indicate vectors and tensors of the second rank by letters of a special type. The following choice is recommended:
   a. Vectors should be printed in bold type, by preference bold italic (sloping) type, e.g. ***A, a***.
   b. Tensors of the second rank should be printed in bold face sans serif type, e.g. **S, T**.

   Remark:

   When this is not available, vectors may be indicated by an arrow and tensors by a double arrow on top of the symbol.

1.3 Simple mathematical operations.

1. *Addition and subtraction* of two physical quantities are indicated by:

   $a + b$ and $a - b$

2. *Multiplication* of two physical quantities may be indicated in one of the following ways:

   ab $a\ b$ $a . b$ $a \cdot b$ $a \times b$

   Remark: The various products of vectors and tensors may be written in the following ways:

   scalar product of vectors A and B: ***A . B***   ***A · B***
   vector product of vectors A and B: ***A ∧ B***   ***A × B***
   dyadic product of vectors A and B: ***AB***

   scalar product of tensors **S** and **T** ($\Sigma_{i,k} S_{ik} T_{ki}$)   **S : T**
   tensor product of tensors **S** and **T** ($\Sigma_k S_{ik} T_{kl}$)   **S · T**   **S . T**
   product of tensor **S** and vector A ($\Sigma_k S_{ik} A_k$)   **S · A**   **S . A**

3. *Division* of one quantity by another quantity may be indicated in one of the following ways:

   $$\frac{a}{b} \qquad a/b \qquad a\ b^{-1}$$

or in any other way of writing the product of a and b^{-1}.

SPELLING AND SYMBOLS FOR UNITS

From "Units of Weight and Measure"
L. B. Chisholm, National Bureau of Standards
Miscellaneous Publication 286 (May, 1967)

The spelling of the names of units as adopted by the National Bureau of Standards is that given in the list below. The spelling of the metric units is in accordance with that given in the law of July 28, 1866, legalizing the Metric System in the United States.

Following the name of each unit in the list below is given the symbol that the Bureau has adopted. Attention is particularly called to the following principles:

1. No period is used with symbols for units. Whenever "in" for inch might be confused with the preposition "in", "inch" should be spelled out.

2. The exponents "2" and "3" are used to signify "square" and "cubic," respectively, instead of the symbols "sq" or "cu," which are, however, frequently used in technical literature for the U. S. Customary units.

3. The same symbol is used for both singular and plural.

Some Units and Their Symbols

Unit	Symbol	Unit	Symbol	Unit	Symbol
acre	acre	fathom	fath	millimeter	mm
are	a	foot	ft	minim	minim
barrel	bbl	furlong	furlong	ounce	oz
board foot	fbm	gallon	gal	ounce, avoirdupois	oz avdp
bushel	bu	grain	grain	ounce, liquid	liq oz
carat	c	gram	g	ounce, troy	oz tr
Celsius, degree	°C	hectare	ha	peck	peck
centare	ca	hectogram	hg	pennyweight	dwt
centigram	cg	hectoliter	hl	pint, liquid	liq pt
centiliter	cl	hectometer	hm	pound	lb
centimeter	cm	hogshead	hhd	pound, avoirdupois	lb avdp
chain	ch	hundredweight	cwt	pound, troy	lb tr
cubic centimeter	cm³	inch	in	quart, liquid	liq qt
cubic decimeter	dm³	International		rod	rod
cubic dekameter	dam³	Nautical Mile	INM	second	s
cubic foot	ft³	Kelvin, degree	°K	square centimeter	cm²
cubic hectometer	hm³	kilogram	kg	square decimeter	dm²
cubic inch	in³	kiloliter	kl	square dekameter	dam²
cubic kilometer	km³	kilometer	km	square foot	ft²
cubic meter	m³	link	link	square hectometer	hm²
cubic mile	mi³	liquid	liq	square inch	in²
cubic millimeter	mm³	liter	liter	square kilometer	km²
cubic yard	yd³	meter	m	square meter	m²
decigram	dg	microgram	μg	square mile	mi²
deciliter	dl	microinch	μin	square millimeter	mm²
decimeter	dm	microliter	μl	square yard	yd²
dekagram	dag	micron	μm	stere	stere
dekaliter	dal	mile	mi	ton, long	long ton
dekameter	dam	milligram	mg	ton, metric	t
dram, avoirdupois	dr avdp	milliliter	ml	ton, short	short ton
				yard	yd

Abbreviations

The following list of abbreviations is intended to cover those in common use in chemistry and physics. Symbols are presented in a separate list following the abbreviations.

Abbr.	Meaning
A.	Acre
Å	Ångström unit
a	Are
a.	Acid
abs.	Absolute
abt.	About
a.c.	Alternating current
acet.	Acetone
acet. a.	Acetic acid
al.	Alcohol
alk.	Alkali
alt.	Altitude
amal.	Amalgam; amalgamated
amor. or amorph.	Amorphous
amp.	Ampere
anh.	Anhydrous
antilog	Antilogarithm
ap.	Apothecaries'
appr.	Approximately
aq.	Aqua; aqueous; water
aq. reg.	Aqua regia
asym.	Asymmetrical
atm. or atmos.	Atmosphere (atmospheric)
At. No.	Atomic number
At. Wt.	Atomic weight
aux.	Auxiliary
Av.	Average
av. or avoir.	Avoirdupois
bar.	Barometer
bbl.	Barrel
bd.	Board
Bé	Beaumé (degrees)
B.G.	Birmingham gauge (hoop and sheet)
b.h.p.	Brake horse power
bl.	Blue
blk.	Black
B.M.	Board measure
b.p.	Boiling point
br.	Brown
BTU	British thermal unit
bu.	Bushel
B.W.G.	Birmingham wire gauge
bz.	Benzene
C	Centigrade
c.	Carat; centi-
c.	Cold
ca	Candle
ca.	*Circa*, about; approximately
cal.	Calorie (gram)
cc. or c.c.	Cubic centimeter
cd.	Cord
c. cm	Cubic centimeter
Cent.	Centigrade
centi-	Prefix meaning 1/100
cf.	*Confer*, compare
c.f.m.	Cubic foot per minute
cgs	Centimeter-gram-second system of units
cgse	Cgs electrostatic system
cgsm	Cgs electromagnetic system
ch.	Chain
chl.	Chloroform
cir.	Circular
circum.	Cirumference
cl	Centiliter
cm	Centimeter
cm^2	Square centimeter
cm^3	Cubic centimeter
c.m.	Circular mil
coef.	Coefficient
colog	Cologarithm
colorl.	Colorless
comm'l	Commercial
conc.	Concentrated
cond.	Condensing
const.	Constant
cos	Cosine
cos^{-1}	Arc or angle whose cosine is...; anti-cosine of; inverse cosine of
cosec	Cosecant
cosh	Hyperbolic cosine
$cosh^{-1}$	Inverse hyperbolic cosine
cot	Cotangent
cot^{-1}	Arc or angle whose cotangent is...
coth	Hyperbolic cotangent
$coth^{-1}$	Inverse hyperbolic cotangent
covers	Coversed sine
c.p.	Candle power; circular pitch; center of pressure
cry. or cryst.	Crystalline; crystals
csc	Cosecant
csc^{-1}	Arc or angle whose cosecant is...
csch	Hyperbolic cosecant
$csch^{-1}$	Inverse hyperbolic cosecant
CTU	Centigrade thermal unit
cu.	Cubic
cu. cm	Cubic centimeter
cu. ft.	Cubic foot
cu. in.	Cubic inch
cu. m	Cubic meter
cu. yd.	Cubic yard
cwt.	Hundredweight
cyl.	Cylinder
d.	Derivative; deci-
d.	Decomposes; day
d.	Dextrorotary
d.c.	Direct current
dec.	Decomposes
deci-	Prefix meaning 1/10
def.	Definition(s)
deg	Thermometric degree; absolute C unless contrary is indicated
deka-	Prefix meaning 10
deliq.	Deliquescent
den. or dens.	Density
dg	Decigram
diam.	Diameter
dil.	Dilute
dissd.	Dissolved
dk.	Deka-
dk.	Dark
dkg.	Dekagram
dkl	Dekaliter
dkm	Dekameter
dkm^2	Square dekameter
dkm^3	Cubic dekameter
dks	Dekastere
dl	Deciliter
dm	Decimeter
dm^2	Square decimeter
dm^3	Cubic decimeter
d.p.	Diametral pitch; double pole
dr.	Dram
dr. ap. or ʒ ap.	Dram, apothecaries'
dr. av. or ʒ av.	Dram, avoirdupois
dr. fl. or ʒ fl.	Dram, fluid
dr. t. or ʒ t.	Dram, troy
ds	Decistere
dwt.	Pennyweight
efflor.	Efflorescent
e.g.	*Exempli gratia*, for example
e.h.p.	Effective horse power
E.L.	Elastic limit
em	Cgsm unit of quantity of electricity
emf or e.m.f.	Electromotive force
es	Electrostatic or cgse unit of quantity of electricity
etc.	*Et cetera*, and so forth
eth.	Ether
eth. acet.	Ethyl acetate
et. seq.	*Et sequentes*, and the following
evap.	Evaporation
ex.	Excess
exp	Exponential function
exp.	Explodes
exsec	Exterior secant
F	Fahrenheit
f.	From
fahr.	Fahrenheit
fath.	Fathom
feath.	Feathery
f.h.p.	Friction horse power
fir.	Firkin
fl.	Fluid
fl. dr.	Dram, fluid
fl. oz.	Ounce, fluid
fluores.	Fluorescent
fps	Foot-pound-second system of units
fpse	Foot-pound-second electrostatic system
fpsm	Foot-pound-second electromagnetic system
fpsm	Foot-pound-second electromotagnetic system
F.S.	Factor of safety
ft.	Foot
$ft.^2$	Square foot
$ft.^3$	Cubic foot
ft.-lb.	Foot-pound
fur.	Furlong
G	Gravitation constant
g	Gram
g-cal. or g.-cal.	Gram calorie
gal.	Gallon
gel.	Gelatinous
gi.	Gill
glac.	Glacial
glit.	Glittering
glyc.	Glycerine
gm.	Gram
gr.	Gray; grain
grn.	Green
gyr.	Gyration
h.	Hecto-
h.	Hot; hour
ha	Hectare
hecto-	Prefix meaning 100
hex.	Hexagonal
hg	Hectogram
hhd.	Hogshead
hl	Hectoliter
hm	Hectometer
hm^2	Square hectometer
hm^3	Cubic hectometer
hor. or horiz.	Horizontal
h.-p.	High-Pressure
HP or HP	Horse power
h.p.	Horse power-
h.p.-hr.	Horse power-hour
hr.	Hour
hyg.	Hygroscopic
ibid.	*Ibidem*, in the same place
i.e.	*Id est*, that is
ign.	Ignites
i.h.p.	Indicated horse power
in.	Indigo; inch
$in.^2$	Square inch
$in.^3$	Cubic inch
inc.	Inclusive
in.-lb.	Inch-pound
insol.	Insoluble
Int.	International
iso.	Isotropic
isom.	Isometric
isoth.	Isothermal
k	Kilo-
kg	Kilogram
kg-cal.	Kilogram-calorie
kg-m	Kilogram-meter
kilo-	Prefix meaning 1,000
kl	Kiloliter
km	Kilometer
km^2	Square kilometer
km^3	Cubic kilometer
kva.	Kilovolt-ampere
kw	Kilowatt
kw.-hr.	Kilowatt-hour
l	Liter
l.	Long
l	Laevorotary
lat.	Latitude
lb.	Pound
lb. ap.	Pound, apothecaries'
lb. av.	Pound, avoirdupois
lb. t.	Pound, troy
leaf.	Leaflets
lgr.	Ligroin
li.	Link
lin.	Linear
liq.	Liquid
lim.	Limit
ln	Natural hyperbolic or Napierian logarithm
log or log.	Logarithm
log_e	Logarithm to the base e; natural, hyperbolic or Napierian logarithm
log_{10}	Common logarithm; logarithm to the base 10
long.	Longitude
lng.	Long
l.-p.	Low-pressure
lt.	Light
lust.	Lustrous
♏	Minim or drop
m	Meter; milli-
m^2	Square meter
m^3	Cubic meter
m.	Minute
m.	Meta-
max.	Maximum
med.	Medium
meth.	Methyl
meth. al.	Methyl alcohol
m.e.p.	Mean effective pressure
met.	Metallic
mg	Milligram
m.h.c.p.	Mean horizontal candle power
mi.	Mile
mic.	Microscopic
micro-	Prefix meaning 1/1,000,000 or 10^{-6}
micromicro	Prefix meaning 10^{-12}
milli-	Prefix meaning 1/1,000
millimicro-	Prefix meaning 10^{-9}
min or min.	Minute
min.	Minim; minimum; mineral
ml	Milliliter
m.l.h.c.p.	Mean lower hemispherical candle power
mm	Millimeter
mm^2	Square millimeter
mm^3	Cubic millimeter
mmf or m.m.f.	Magnetomotive force
mol.	Molecule
Mol. Wt.	Molecular weight
monocl.	Monoclinic
m.p.	Melting point
m.s.c.p.	Mean spherical candle power
myria-	Prefix meaning 10,000 or 10^4
$m\mu$	Millimicron; millimicro-
N	Numeric; number (in mathematical tables)
n.	Normal
n	Refractive index
need.	Needles
o	Ortho-
Obs.	Observer
octahdr.	Octahedral
oil	Oil of turpentine
or.	Orange
oz.	Ounce
oz. ap. or ʒ ap.	Ounce, apothecaries'
oz. av. or ʒ av.	Ounce, avoirdupois
oz. fl. or ʒ fl.	Ounce, fluid
oz. t. or ʒ t.	Ounce, troy
p	Para-
pa.	Pale
p. ct.	Per cent
perp.	Perpendicular
p.f.	Power factor
pk.	Peck
pl.	Plates
powd.	Powder
pr.	Prisms
precip. or p'p't'd	Precipitated
p. sol.	Partly soluble
pt.	Point; pint
purp.	Purple
pyr.	Pyridine
Q	Quantity
q	Quintal
qt.	Quart
q.v.	*Quod vide*, which see
R	Réaumur; radioactive mineral
rac	Racemic
rad	Radian, measure of angle
rad.	Radius
rd.	Rod
reg.	Regular
rev.	Revolution
rhbdr.	Rhombohedral
rhomb.	Rhombic or orthorhombic
R.M.S.	Square root of mean square
r.p.m.	Revolutions per minute
s	Stere
s.	Scruple; soluble; second
s. ap. or ℈	Scruple, apothecaries'
sat. or sat'd	Saturated
sc	Scales
S.E.	Siemens unit
sec or sec.	Second (mean solar unless contrary is stated)
sec	Secant
sec^{-1}	Arc or angle whose secant is...
sech	Hyperbolic secant
$sech^{-1}$	Inverse hyperbolic secant
segm.	Segment
sh.	Short
sin	Sine
sin^{-1}	Arc or angle whose sine is...
sinh	Hyperbolic sine
$sinh^{-1}$	Inverse hyperbolic sine
sl.	Slightly
sm.	Small
sol.	Solution; soluble
soln.	Solution
sp.	Specific
specif.	Specification
sp. gr.	Specific gravity
sq.	Square
sq. ch.	Square chain
sq. ft.	Square foot
sq. in.	Square inch
sq. mi.	Square mile
sq. rd.	Square rod
sq. yd.	Square yard
std.	Standard
subl.	Sublimes
sym.	Symmetrical
t	Metric ton
t.	Troy
t.	Tablets
tab. or tabl.	Tablets
tan	Tangent
tan^{-1}	Arc or angle whose tangent is...
tanh	Hyperbolic tangent
$tanh^{-1}$	Inverse hyperbolic tangent
temp.	Temperature
tetr. or tetrag.	Tetragonal
tn.	Ton
tr.	Transition
tricl.	Triclinic
trig.	Trigonal
trim.	Trimetric
T.S.	Tensile strength
turp.	Turpentine
Tw.°	Degrees Twaddell, hydrometer scale
ult.	Ultimate
uns.	Unsymmetrical
U.S.	United States of America; universal system of lens apertures
v.	Very
v.	*Vide*, see
vel. or veloc.	Velocity
vers	Versed sine
vert	Vertical
visc.	Viscous
vol.	Volume
volt.	Volatilizes
w.	Water
wh.	White
wt.	Weight
yd.	Yard
yel.	Yellow
yr.	Year
μ	Micron; micro-
$\mu\mu$	Micromicron; micromicro-

CHARACTERISTICS OF PARTICLES AND PARTICLE DISPERSOIDS

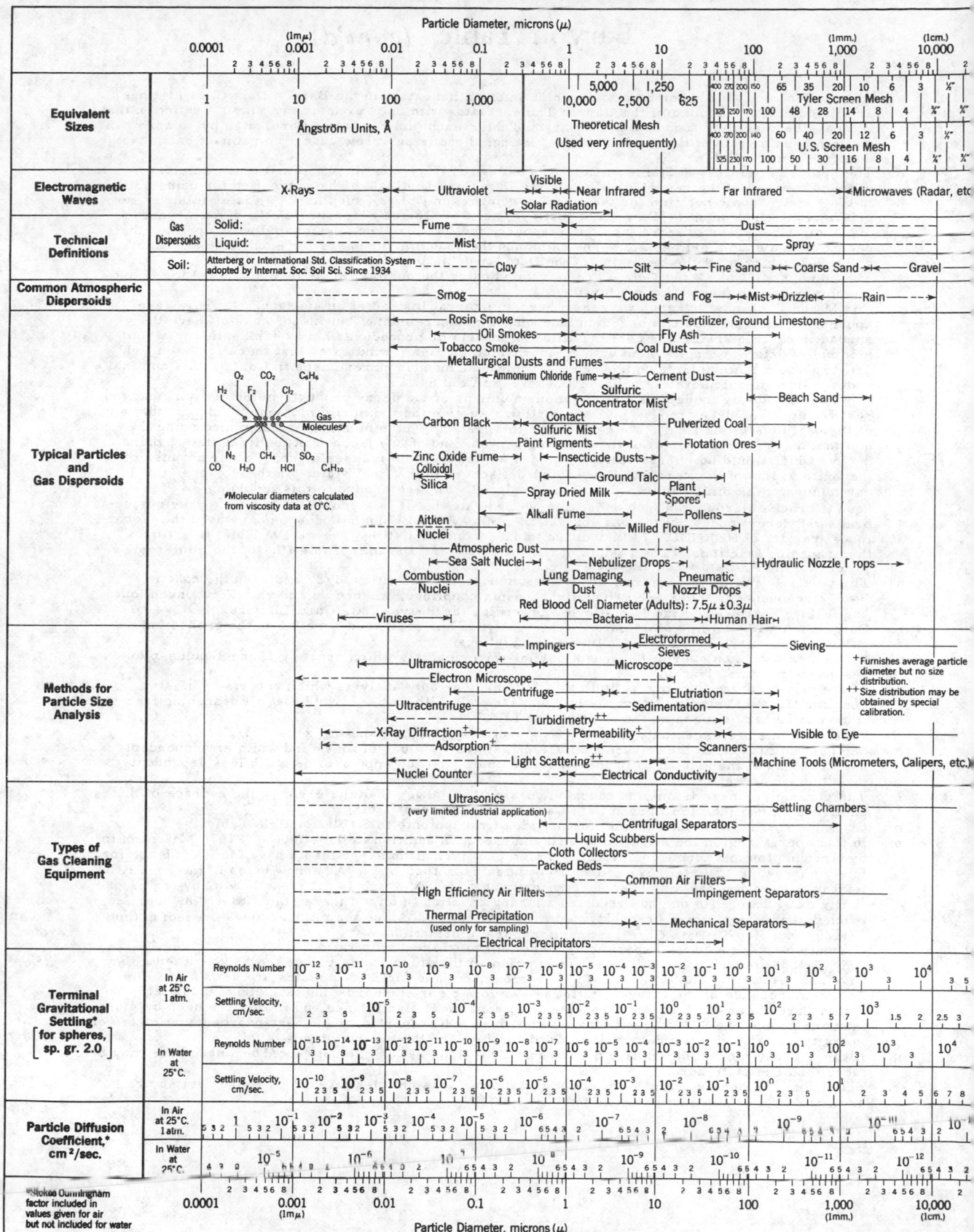

→   For convenience all Baryon States for which information exists in the Baryon Data Card Listings are listed at the beginning of the Baryon Table. States with only a one or two star (*) rating in that list have been omitted from the main Baryon Table; each omitted state is indicated by an arrow in the left-hand margin of the Table. In the Listings there is an arrow under the name of each state omitted from the Table.

a.   The names of the Baryon States in Col. 1 [such as N(1470)] contain a nominal mass which is a rounded average of the reported values in the Data Card Listings. The convention for using primes in the spectroscopic notation for the quantum numbers in Col. 2 [such as P'_{11}] is as follows: no prime is attached when the Data Card Listings include only one resonance on the given Argand diagram; when there is more than one resonance the first has been designated with a prime, the second with a double prime, etc. The name and the quantum numbers for each state are also given in large print at the beginning of the Data Card Listings for that state.

b.   The numbers in Col. 3 and Col. 6 are calculated using the nominal mass (see a. above) for M and the nominal width (see c. below) for Γ.

c.   For M and Γ of most baryons we report here an interval instead of an average. Averages are appropriate if each result is based on independent measurements, but inappropriate where the spread in parameters arises because different models or procedures have been applied to a common set of data. A single value with an approximation sign (~) indicates that there is not enough data to give a meaningful interval. A nominal width is included in parentheses in Col. 5; this nominal width is used to calculate the value of ΓM given in Col. 6.

d.   For two body decay modes we give the momentum, p, of the decay products in the decaying baryon rest frame. For decay modes into ≥ 3 particles we give the maximum momentum, p_{max}, that any of the particles in the final state can have in this frame. The momenta are calculated using the nominal mass (see a. above) of the decaying baryon, and of any isobars in the final state. Some decays which would be energetically forbidden for the nominal masses actually occur because of the finite widths of the decaying Baryon and/or isobars in the final state. In these cases, the decay momentum is omitted from Col. 9 and replaced with a reference to this footnote.

e.   Square brackets around an isobar decay mode indicate that it is a sub-reaction of the previous unbracketed decay mode. In the case of N* and Δ decays into isobar modes we have used the isobar model results of HERNDON 74 in addition to data from the listings (where available) to estimate the branching fractions. The results of HERNDON 74 are shown in Table III.1 of the mini-review preceding the N* Data Card Listings.

f.   The tabulated radiative fractions involve a sum over two helicities (1/2, 3/2). In the case of I = 1/2 resonances, there are two distinct isospin couplings, whence γp and γn. For conventions and further details, see the Mini-Review preceding the Baryon Data Card Listings.

g.   Only information coming from partial-wave analyses has been used here. For the production experiments results see the Baryon Data Card Listings.

h.   Value obtained in an energy-dependent partial-wave analysis which uses a t-channel-poles-plus-resonance parametrization.

i.   There may be more than one state in this region. The only analysis which reports an elastic coupling (LEA 73) also finds unusually low mass and width values. Note that all branching fractions quoted here depend on the elasticity of LEA 73.

j.   This state has been seen only in total cross sections. J is not known; x is Γ_{el}/Γ.

k.   See note on $\Delta(1232)$ in the Baryon Data Card Listings. Values of mass and width are dependent upon resonance shape used to fit the data. The pole position appear to be much less dependent upon the parametrization used.

ℓ.   The error given here is only an educated guess; it is larger than the error of the average of the published values (see the Baryon Data Card Listings for the latter).

m.   Quoted error includes an S (scale) factor. See first footnote to Stable Particle Table.

n.   In this energy region the situation is still confused. In addition to the effect at ~ 1670 MeV seen in both production and formation experiments, recent formation experiments have found evidence for fairly narrow (Γ ~ 50 MeV) S_{11} and/or P_{11} states near 1620 MeV. A narrow bump in the I = 1 $\overline{K}N$ total cross section has also been seen recently at ~ 1590 MeV. It is not clear how many states really exist here. No one has reported a strong coupling of any of these states to $\overline{K}N$ but there is much disagreement about branching ratios into $\pi\Lambda$ and $\pi\Sigma$. See the mini-reviews preceding the $\Sigma(1620)$ and $\Sigma(1670)$ Data Card Listings for more information.

o.   Formation and production experiments do not agree on the $\Sigma\pi/\Lambda\pi$ ratio.

p.   Only $\Xi(1530)$ is firmly established; information on the other states comes from experiments that have poor statistics due to the fact that the cross sections for S = -2 states are very low. For Ξ states, because of the meager statistics, we lower our standards and tabulate resonant effects if they have at least a four-standard-deviation statistical significance and if they are seen by more than one group. So $\Xi(2030)$, with main decay mode $\Sigma\overline{K}$, reported as a 3.5-standard-deviation effect, is not tabulated. See the Baryon Data Card Listings for the other states.

q.   All four decay modes shown have been seen. Branching ratios are not quoted because there may be more than one state here.

r.   This bump has been seen in both final states shown; it is not clear if one, or more, states are present.

Baryon Table *(cont'd)*

Particle[a]	I ——— estab.	(J^P)[a]	$\dfrac{\pi \text{ or } K \text{ Beam}}{P_{beam}(\text{GeV/c})}$ $\sigma = 4\pi \lambda^2$ (mb)	Mass M^c (MeV)	Full Width Γ^c (MeV)	$M^2 \pm \Gamma M$[b] (GeV^2)	Mode	Partial decay mode Fraction %	p or p_{max} (MeV/c) [d]
$\Lambda(2350)$	0(?)		p = 2.29 σ = 5.85	~2350	140 to 320 (240)	5.52 ±0.56	$N\overline{K}$	(J+1/2)x ~ 0.9[j]	913
$\Lambda(2585)$	0(?)		p = 2.91 σ = 4.37	~2585	~300 (300)	6.68 ±0.78	$N\overline{K}$	(J+1/2)x ~1.0[j]	1058
Σ	1(1/2$^+$)			(+)1189.4 (0)1192.5 (-)1197.4		1.415 1.422 1.434	See Stable Particle Table		
$\Sigma(1385)$	1(3/2$^+$)P$'_{13}$		below K$^-$p threshold	(+)1383±1 S=1.2[m] (-)1387±1 S=2.4[m]	(+)35±2 S=2.0[m] (-)42±5 S=3.5[m] (35)	1.92 ±0.05	$\Lambda\pi$ $\Sigma\pi$	88±2 12±2	208 117
$\Sigma(1670)$[n]	1(3/2$^-$)D$'_{13}$		p = 0.74 σ = 28.5	1670 ±10[l]	35 to 60 (50)	2.79 ±0.08	$N\overline{K}$ $\Sigma\pi$ $\Lambda\pi$	~8 30-60 ~12	410 387 447
$\Sigma(1750)$	1(1/2$^-$)S$'_{11}$		p = 0.91 σ = 20.7	1700 to 1790	50 to 100 (75)	3.06 ±0.13	$N\overline{K}$ $\Lambda\pi$ $\Sigma\pi$ $\Sigma\eta$	12-45 5-18 6-19 11-44	483 507 450 54
$\Sigma(1765)$	1(5/2$^-$)D$_{15}$		p = 0.94 σ = 19.6	1765 ±5[l]	~120 (120)	3.12 ±0.21	$N\overline{K}$ $\Lambda\pi$ $\Lambda(1520)\pi$ $\Sigma(1385)\pi$ $\Sigma\pi$	~41 ~13 ~15 ~10 ~1	496 518 187 315 461
$\Sigma(1915)$[g, o]	1(5/2$^+$)F$'_{15}$		p = 1.25 σ = 13.0	1900 to 1930	50 to 120 (80)	3.67 ±0.15	$N\overline{K}$ $\Lambda\pi$ $\Sigma\pi$	~14 ~6 ~6	612 619 568
$\Sigma(1940)$[i]	1(3/2$^-$)D$''_{13}$		p = 1.32 σ = 12.0	1865 to 1950	110 to 280 (220)	3.76 ±0.43	$N\overline{K}$ $\Lambda\pi$ $\Sigma\pi$	~21 ~4 < 7	678 680 589
$\Sigma(2030)$	1(7/2$^+$)F$_{17}$		p = 1.52 σ = 9.93	2020 to 2040	120 to 170 (140)	4.12 ±0.28	$N\overline{K}$ $\Lambda\pi$ $\Sigma\pi$ ΞK	~20 ~20 ~4 < 2	700 700 652 412
$\Sigma(2250)$	1(?) —		p = 2.04 σ = 6.76	2245 to 2280	100 to 230 (160)	5.06 ±0.36	$N\overline{K}$	(J+1/2)x ~0.3[j]	849
$\Sigma(2455)$	1(?)		p = 2.57 σ = 5.09	~2455	~120 (120)	6.03 ±0.29	$N\overline{K}$	(J+1/2)x ~0.2[j]	979
$\Sigma(2620)$	1(?) —		p = 2.95 σ = 4.30	~2620	~ 175 (175)	6.86 ±0.46	$N\overline{K}$	(J+1/2)x ~0.3[j]	1064
Ξ	1/2(1/2$^+$)			(0)1314.9 (-)1321.3		1.729 1.746	See Stable Particle Table		
$\Xi(1530)$[p]	1/2(3/2$^+$)P$_{13}$			(0)1531.8±0.3 S=1.3[m] (-)1535.1±0.7	(0) 9.1±0.5 (-) 10.6±2.6 (10)	2.34 ±0.02	$\Xi\pi$	100	144
$\Xi(1820)$[p, q]	1/2(?)			1795 to 1870	12 to 100 (60)	3.31 ±0.11	$\Lambda\overline{K}$ $\Sigma\overline{K}$ $\Xi\pi$ $\Xi(1530)\pi$	seen seen seen seen	396 306 413 234
$\Xi(1940)$[p, r]	1/2(?)			1920 to 1960	40 to 140 (90)	3.76 ±0.17	$\Xi\pi$ $\Xi(1530)\pi$	seen seen	499 336
Ω^-	0(3/2$^+$)			1672.2		2.796	See Stable Particle Table		

Baryon Table *(cont'd)*

Particle[a]	I $(J^P)^{[a]}$ estab.	$\frac{\pi \text{ or } K \text{ Beam}^{[b]}}{p_{beam}(\text{GeV/c})}$ $\sigma = 4\pi\lambda^2$ (mb)	Mass $M^{[c]}$ (MeV)	Full Width $\Gamma^{[c]}$ (MeV)	M^2 $\pm\Gamma M^{[b]}$ (GeV^2)	Mode	Fraction %	p or p_{max}[d] (MeV/c)
$\Delta(1670)$	$3/2(3/2^-)D_{33}$	$p = 1.00$ $\sigma = 15.6$	1650 to 1720	190 to 270 (260)	2.79 ±0.43	$N\pi$ $N\pi\pi$ $[N\rho$ $[\Delta\pi_f$ $p\gamma^f$	~15 >60 ~30]^e ~40]^e 0.1-0.7	560 525 d 361 572
$\Delta(1890)$	$3/2(5/2^+)F_{35}$	$p = 1.42$ $\sigma = 9.88$	1840 to 1920	140 to 350 (250)	3.57 ±0.47	$N\pi$ $N\pi\pi$ $[N\rho$ $[\Delta\pi$ ΣK $p\gamma^f$	~17 >50 40-60]^e 8-20]^e <3 <0.3	704 677 403 531 400 712
$\Delta(1910)$	$3/2(1/2^+)P_{31}$	$p = 1.46$ $\sigma = 9.54$	1780 to 1935	200 to 340 (300)	3.65 ±0.57	$N\pi$ $N\pi\pi$ $[N\rho$ $[\Delta\pi$ ΣK	~25 ? small]^e small]^e ~6	716 691 429 545 420
$\Delta(1950)$	$3/2(7/2^+)F_{37}$	$p = 1.54$ $\sigma = 8.90$	1930 to 1980	170 to 270 (230)	3.80 ±0.45	$N\pi$ $N\pi\pi$ $[N\rho$ $[\Delta\pi$ ΣK $\Sigma(1385)K$ $p\gamma^f$	~40 >25 8-14]^e 16-26]^e ~2 ~1.4 0.16-0.34	741 716 471 574 460 232 749
$\Delta(2420)$	$3/2(11/2^+)$	$p = 2.64$ $\sigma = 4.68$	2320 to 2450	250 to 350 (300)	5.86 ±0.73	$N\pi$ $N\pi\pi$	~11 >20	1023 1006
$\Delta(2850)$	$3/2(?^+)$	$p = 3.85$ $\sigma = 3.05$	~2850	~400 (400)	8.12 ±1.14	$N\pi$	$(J+1/2)x$ ~ 0.25^j	1266
$\Delta(3230)$	$3/2(?)$	$p = 5.08$ $\sigma = 2.25$	~3230	~440 (440)	10.43 ±1.42	$N\pi$	$(J+1/2)x$ ~ 0.05^j	1475
Z^*	Evidence for states with strangeness +1 is controversial. See the Baryon Data Card listings for discussion and display of data.							
Λ	$0(1/2^+)$		1115.6		1.245	See Stable Particle Table		
$\Lambda(1405)$	$0(1/2^-)S'_{01}$	below K^-p threshold	1405 $\pm5^l$	40$\pm10^l$ (40)	1.97 ±0.06	$\Sigma\pi$	100	142
$\Lambda(1520)$	$0(3/2^-)D'_{03}$	$p = 0.389$ $\sigma = 84.5$	1518 $\pm2^l$	16 $\pm2^l$ (16)	2.31 ±0.02	$N\overline{K}$ $\Sigma\pi$ $\Lambda\pi\pi$ $\Sigma\pi\pi$	45±1 41±1 10$\pm.5$ .8$\pm.1$	234 258 250 140
$\Lambda(1670)$	$0(1/2^-)S''_{01}$	$p = 0.74$ $\sigma = 28.5$	1660 to 1680	23 to 40 (35)	2.79 ±0.06	$N\overline{K}$ $\Lambda\eta$ $\Sigma\pi$	15-35 15-25 30-50	410 64 393
$\Lambda(1690)$	$0(3/2^-)D''_{03}$	$p = 0.78$ $\sigma = 26.1$	1690 $\pm10^l$	30 to 70 (60)	2.86 ±0.10	$N\overline{K}$ $\Sigma\pi$ $\Lambda\pi\pi$ $\Sigma\pi\pi$	20-30 30-50 <25 <25	429 409 415 352
$\Lambda(1815)$	$0(5/2^+)F'_{05}$	$p = 1.05$ $\sigma = 16.7$	1820 $\pm5^l$	70 to 100 (85)	3.29 ±0.15	$N\overline{K}$ $\Sigma\pi$ $\Sigma(1385)\pi$	~61 ~11 15-20	542 508 362
$\Lambda(1830)$	$0(5/2^-)D'_{05}$	$p = 1.09$ $\sigma = 15.8$	1810 to 1840	70 to 120 (95)	3.35 ±0.17	$N\overline{K}$ $\Sigma\pi$ $\Lambda\eta$	~10 20-60 ~2	554 519 367
$\Lambda(2100)$	$0(7/2^-)G_{07}$	$p = 1.68$ $\sigma = 8.68$	2090 to 2120	80 to 140 (120)	4.41 ±0.25	$N\overline{K}$ $\Sigma\pi$ $\Lambda\eta$ ΞK $\Lambda\omega$	~30 ~5 <3 <3 <3	748 699 617 483 443

Particle[a]	I (J^P)[a] ___ estab.	$\frac{\pi \text{ or K Beam}^b}{p_{beam}\text{(GeV/c)}}$ $\sigma = 4\pi\lambda^2$ (mb)	Mass M^c (MeV)	Full Width Γ^c (MeV)	M^2 $\pm\Gamma M^b$ (GeV²)	Mode	Fraction %	p or p_{max}[d] (MeV/c)
N(1670)[g]	1/2(5/2⁻)D'₁₅	p = 1.00 σ = 15.6	1670 to 1685	115 to 175 (140)	2.79 ±0.23	Nπ Nππ [Δπ ΛK Nη pγ[f] nγ[f]	~40 ~60 ~50][e] <1 <1[h] <0.04 0.01-0.13	560 525 360 200 368 572 572
N(1688)[g]	1/2(5/2⁺)F'₁₅	p = 1.03 σ = 14.9	1680 to 1690	105 to 180 (140)	2.85 ±0.24	Nπ Nππ [Nε [Nρ [Δπ ΛK Nη pγ[f] nγ[f]	~60 ~40 ~13][e] ~12][e] ~11][e] <0.1 <0.3[h] 0.20-0.44 <0.04	572 538 340 d 375 231 388 583 583
N(1700)[g]	1/2(1/2⁻)S''₁₁	p = 1.05 σ = 14.3	1665 to 1765	100 to 300 (200)	2.89 ±0.34	Nπ Nππ [Nε [Nρ [Δπ ΛK ΣK Nη pγ[f] nγ[f]	~55 ~25 ~10][e] ~10][e] ~7][e] ~5 <3 ~3[h] <0.24 <0.24	580 547 355 d 385 250 109 340 591 591
N(1780)[g]	1/2(1/2⁺)P''₁₁	p = 1.20 σ = 12.2	1650 to 1860	50 to 350 (200)	3.17 ±0.36	Nπ Nππ [Nε [Nρ [Δπ ΛK ΣK Nη pγ[f] nγ[f]	~20 >40 16-40][e] 20-45][e] 8-20][e] <7 ~7 2-20[h] <0.08 <0.08	633 603 440 249 448 353 267 476 643 643
N(1810)	1/2(3/2⁺)P₁₃	p = 1.26 σ = 11.5	1770 to 1860	180 to 330 (250)	3.28 ±0.45	Nπ Nππ [Nρ ΛK Nη	~25 >50 45-55][e] ~5 ~4[h]	652 624 297 386 503
N(2190)	1/2(7/2⁻)G₁₇	p = 2.07 σ = 6.21	2000 to 2260	150 to 325 (250)	4.80 ±0.55	Nπ	~25	888
N(2220)	1/2(9/2⁺)H₁₉	p = 2.14 σ = 5.97	2200 to 2245	260 to 330 (300)	4.93 ±0.67	Nπ	~15	905
N(2650)	1/2(?⁻)	p = 3.26 σ = 3.67	~2650	~360 (360)	7.02 ±0.95	Nπ	(J+1/2)x ~0.45[j]	1154
N(3030)	1/2(?)	p = 4.41 σ = 2.62	~3030	~400 (400)	9.18 ±1.21	Nπ	(J+1/2)x ~0.05[j]	1366
Δ(1232)[k]	3/2(3/2⁺)P'₃₃	p = 0.30 σ = 94.3	1230 to 1236	110 to 122 (110)	1.52 ±0.14	Nπ Nπ⁺π⁻ pγ[f]	~99.4 ~0 0.70-0.74	227 80 259

Δ(++) Pole position:[k] $M - i\Gamma/2 = (1211.6\pm0.7) - i(49.1\pm1.7)$

Λ(1650)	1/2(1/2⁻)S'₃₁	p=0.96 σ =16.4	1615 to 1695	140 to 200 (140)	2.72 ±0.23	Nπ Nππ [Nρ [Δπ pγ[f]	~30 ~70 10-26][e] ~50][e] 0.02-0.034	547 511 d 344 558

Baryon Table

April 1974

The following short list gives the status of all the Baryon States in the Data Card Listings. In addition to the status, the name, the nominal mass, and the quantum numbers (where known) are shown. States with three or four star status are included in the main Baryon Table, the others have been omitted because the evidence for the existence of the effect and/or for its interpretation as a resonance is open to considerable question.

N		Δ / Z		Λ		Σ		Ξ / Ω	
N(939) P11	****	Δ(1232) P33	****	Λ(1116) P01	****	Σ(1193) P11	****	Ξ(1317) P11	****
N(1470) P11	****	Δ(1650) S31	****	Λ(1330)	Dead	Σ(1385) P13	****	Ξ(1530) P13	****
N(1520) D13	****	Δ(1670) D33	***	Λ(1405) S01	****	Σ(1440)	Dead	Ξ(1630)	**
N(1535) S11	****	Δ(1690) P33	*	Λ(1520) D03	****	Σ(1480)	*	Ξ(1820)	***
N(1670) D15	****	Δ(1890) F35	***	Λ(1670) S01	****	Σ(1620) S11	**	Ξ(1940)	***
N(1688) F15	****	Δ(1900) S31	*	Λ(1690) D03	****	Σ(1620) P11	**	Ξ(2030)	**
N(1700) S11	****	Δ(1910) P31	***	Λ(1750) P01	**	Σ(1670) D13	****	Ξ(2250)	*
N(1700) D13	**	Δ(1950) F37	****	Λ(1815) F05	****	Σ(1670)	**	Ξ(2500)	**
N(1780) P11	***	Δ(1960) D35	**	Λ(1830) D05	***	Σ(1690)	**		
N(1810) P13	***	Δ(2160)	**	Λ(1860) P03	**	Σ(1750) S11	***	Ω(1672) P03	****
N(1990) F17	**	Δ(2420) H311	***	Λ(1870) S01	**	Σ(1765) D15	****		
N(2000) F15	**	Δ(2850)	***	Λ(2010) D03	**	Σ(1840) P13	*		
N(2040) D13	**	Δ(3230)	***	Λ(2020) F07	**	Σ(1880) P11	**		
N(2100) S11	*			Λ(2100) G07	****	Σ(1915) F15	****		
N(2100) D15	*	Z0(1780) P01	*	Λ(2110) ?05	*	Σ(1940) D13	***		
N(2190) G17	***	Z0(1865) D03	*	Λ(2350)	****	Σ(2000) S11	*		
N(2220) H19	***	Z1(1900) P13	*	Λ(2585)	***	Σ(2030) F17	****		
N(2650)	***	Z1(2150)	*			Σ(2070) F15	*		
N(3030)	***	Z1(2500)	*			Σ(2080) P13	**		
N(3245)	*					Σ(2100) G17	**		
N(3690)	*					Σ(2250)	****		
N(3755)	*					Σ(2455)	***		
						Σ(2620)	***		
						Σ(3000)	**		

**** Good, clear, and unmistakable.   *** Good, but in need of clarification or not absolutely certain.
** Needs confirmation.   * Weak.

[See notes on N's and Δ's, on possible Z*'s, and on Y*'s and Ξ*'s at the beginning of those sections in the Baryon Data Card Listings; also see notes on individual resonances in the Baryon Data Card Listings.]

Particle[a]	$I\ (J^P)$[a] estab.	π or K Beam[b] p_{beam}(GeV/c) $\sigma = 4\pi\lambda^2$ (mb)	Mass M^c (MeV)	Full Width Γ^c (MeV)	M^2 $\pm\Gamma M$[b] (GeV^2)	Mode	Fraction %	p or p_{max}[d] (MeV/c)
p	$1/2(1/2^+)$		938.3		0.880	See Stable Particle Table		
n			939.6		0.883			
N(1470)	$1/2(1/2^+)$ P'$_{11}$	p = 0.66 σ = 27.8	1400 to 1470	165 to 300 (250)	2.16 ±0.37	Nπ	~60	420
						Nη	~9	d
						N$\pi\pi$	~35	368
						[Nϵ	~6]e	d
						[Δπ	~16]e	177
						[Nρ	<5]e	d
						pγ[f]	0.12-0.32	435
						nγ[f]	<0.24	435
N(1520)	$1/2(3/2^-)$ D'$_{13}$	p = 0.74 σ = 23.5	1510 to 1540	105 to 150 (125)	2.31 ±0.19	Nπ	~55	456
						N$\pi\pi$	~45	410
						[Nϵ	<5]e	d
						[Nρ	~18]e	d
						[Δπ	~23]e	228
						Nη	0.2-1.4	d
						pγ[f]	0.57-0.79	471
						nγ[f]	0.36-0.56	471
N(1535)	$1/2(1/2^-)$ S'$_{11}$	p = 0.76 σ = 22.5	1500 to 1600	50 to 160 (100)	2.36 ±0.15	Nπ	~35	467
						Nη	~55	182
						N$\pi\pi$	~10	422
						[Nρ	~2]e	d
						[Nϵ	~2]e	d
						pγ[f]	0.04-0.32	481
						nγ	0.04-0.12	481

Meson Table *(cont'd)*

→   indicates an entry in Meson Data Card Listings not entered in the Meson Table. We do not regard these as established resonances.

¶   See Meson Data Card Listings.

*   Quoted error includes scale factor $S = \sqrt{\chi^2/(N-1)}$. See footnote to Stable Particle Table.

†   Square brackets indicate a subreaction of the previous (unbracketed) decay mode(s).

§   This is only an educated guess; the error given is larger than the error of the average of the published values. (See Meson Data Card Listings for the latter.)

(a) ΓM is approximately the half-width of the resonance when plotted against M^2.

(b)   For decay modes into ≥ 3 particles, p_{max} is the maximum momentum that any of the particles in the final state can have. The momenta have been calculated by using the averaged central mass values, without taking into account the widths of the resonances.

(c)   From pole position $(M - i\Gamma/2)$. For both ε and S^* the pole is on Riemann Sheet 2.

(d)   The e^+e^- branching ratio is from $e^+e^- \to \pi^+\pi^-$ experiments only. The $\omega\rho$ interference is then due to $\omega\rho$ mixing only, and is expected to be small. See note in Meson Data Card Listings. The $\mu^+\mu^-$ branching ratio is compiled from 3 experiments; each possibly with substantial $\omega\rho$ interference. The error reflects this uncertainty; see notes in Meson Data Card Listings. If eμ universality holds, $\Gamma(\rho^0 \to \mu^+\mu^-) = \Gamma(\rho^0 \to e^+e^-) \times$ phase space correction.

(e)   Empirical limits on fractions for other decay modes of $\rho(765)$ are $\pi^\pm\gamma < 0.5\%$, $\pi^\pm\eta < 0.8\%$, $\pi^+\pi^+\pi^-\pi^- < 0.15\%$, $\pi^\pm\pi^+\pi^-\pi^0 < 0.2\%$.

(f)   Empirical limits on fractions for other decay modes of $f(1270)$ are $\eta\pi\pi < 15\%$; $K^0K^-\pi^+ +$ c.c. $< 6\%$.

(g)   Empirical limits on fractions for other decay modes of $\omega(783)$ are $\pi^+\pi^-\gamma < 5\%$. $\pi^0\pi^0\gamma < 1\%$, $\eta +$ neutral(s) $< 1.5\%$, $\mu^+\mu^- < 0.02\%$, $\pi^0\mu^+\mu^- < 0.2\%$, $\eta\gamma < 0.5\%$.

(h)   Empirical limits on fractions for other decay modes of $\eta'(958)$: $\pi^+\pi^- < 2\%$, $\pi^+\pi^-\pi^0 < 5\%$, $\pi^+\pi^+\pi^-\pi^- < 1\%$, $\pi^+\pi^+\pi^-\pi^-\pi^0 < 1\%$, $6\pi < 1\%$, $\pi^+\pi^-e^+e^- < 0.6\%$, $\pi^0e^+e^- < 1.3\%$, $\eta e^+e^- < 1.1\%$, $\pi^0\rho^0 < 4\%$, $\pi^0\omega + \gamma\omega < 8\%$.

(i)   Empirical limits on fractions for other decay modes of $\varphi(1019)$ are $\pi^+\pi^- < 0.03\%$, $\pi^+\pi^-\gamma < 0.7\%$, $\omega\gamma < 5\%$, $\rho\gamma < 2\%$, $\pi^0\gamma < 0.35\%$, $2\pi^+2\pi^-\pi^0 < 1\%$.

(j)   Empirical limits on fractions for other decay modes of $B(1235)$: $\pi\pi < 15\%$, $K\bar{K} < 2\%$, $4\pi < 50\%$, $\phi\pi < 1.5\%$, $\eta\pi < 25\%$, $(\bar{K}K)^\pm\pi^0 < 8\%$, $K_SK_S \pi^\pm < 2\%$, $K_SK_L \pi^\pm < 6\%$.

(k)   Empirical limits on fractions for other decay modes of $f'(1514)$ are $\pi^+\pi^- < 20\%$, $\eta\eta < 50\%$, $\eta\pi\pi < 30\%$, $K\bar{K}\pi + K^*\bar{K} < 35\%$, $2\pi^+2\pi^- < 32\%$.

(ℓ)   We assume as a working hypothesis that peaks with $I^G = 1^+$ observed around 1.7 GeV all come from $g(1680)$. For indications to the contrary see Meson Data Card Listings.

(m)   See Q-region note in Meson Data Card Listings. Some investigators see a broad enhancement in mass ($K\pi\pi$) from 1250-1400 MeV (the Q region), and others see structure. The $K\eta$, $K\omega$, and $K\pi$ modes are less than a few percent.

(n)   The tabulated mass of 1421 MeV comes from the $K\pi$ mode; the $K\pi\pi$ mode can be contaminated with diffractively produced $Q^\pm$.

Established Nonets, and octet-singlet mixing angles from Appendix IIB, Eq. (2'). Of the two isosinglets, the "mainly octet" one is written first, followed by a semicolon.

$(J^P)C_n$	Nonet members	$\theta_{lin.}$	$\theta_{quadr.}$
$(0^-)+$ or: $(0^-)+$	π, K, η; η' π, K, η; E	$24 \pm 1°$ $16 \pm 1°$	$10 \pm 1°$ $6 \pm 1°$
$(1^-)-$	ρ, K^*, ϕ; ω	$36 \pm 1°$	$39 \pm 1°$
$(2^+)+$	A_2, $K^*(1420)$, f'; f	$29 \pm 2°$	$31 \pm 2°$

Name		Mass M (MeV)	Full Width Γ (MeV)	$\pm\Gamma M^{(a)}$ $(GeV)^2$	Partial decay mode		
$\begin{array}{c c c}\hline G & I & 0 & 1 \\ \hline - & \omega/\phi & \pi \\ \hline + & \eta & \rho \end{array}$	$I^G(J^P)C_n$ ├──estab.				Mode	Fraction (%) [Upper limits are 1σ (%)]	p or $p_{max}^{(b)}$ (MeV/c)

κ $1/2(0^+)$ δ_0^1 goes slowly through 90° near 1300 MeV.
See note on Kπ S wave¶.
→ ──

Q	$\begin{cases} K_A(1240)1/2(1^+) \\ \text{or C} \end{cases}$	1242 ±10	127 ±25 .seen in p̄p at rest	1.54 ±.16	Kππ	only mode seen	
					†[K*π	large]	
	$\begin{array}{l} K_A(1280\ 1/2(1^+) \\ \text{to 1400}) \end{array}$	1280 to 1400			†[Kρ	seen]	
	See note (m).				†[K(ππ)$_{\ell=0}$	possibly seen]	

K*(1420)	$1/2(2^+)$	1421$_\S$ ±5§	100$_\S$ ±10§	2.02 ±.14	Kπ	55.0±2.7	616
					K*π	29.5±2.5	414
			See note (n).		Kρ	9.2±2.4	319
					Kω	4.4±1.7	306
					Kη	2.0±2.0	482

→ ──

L(1770)	$1/2(A)$	1765$_\S$ ±10§	140$_\S$ ±50§	3.11 ±.25	Kππ	dominant	788
					Kπππ	seen	757
					†[K*(1420)π and other subreactions¶]		

      $J^P=2^-$ favoured, 1^+ and 3^+ not excluded.

→ ──

See note (1) for possible heavier states.

═══

(1)   Contents of Meson Data Card Listings

Non-strange (Y = 0)						Strange (|Y| = 1)	
entry	$I^G(J^P)C_n$	entry	$I^G(J^P)C_n$	entry	$I^G(J^P)C_n$	entry	$I\ (J^P)$
π (140)	$1^-(0^-)+$	→ η_N (1080)	$0^+(N)+$	ρ′ (1600)	$1^+(1^-)-$	K (494)	$1/2(0^-)$
η (549)	$0^+(0^-)^+$	A_1 (1100)	$1^-(1^+)+$	A_3 (1640)	$1^-(2^-)+$	K* (892)	$1/2(1^-)$
ε (600)	$0^+(0^+)+$	→ M (1150)		ω (1675)	$0^-(N)-$	κ	$1/2(0^+)$
ρ (770)	$1^+(1^-)-$	→ $A_{1.5}$(1170)	1^-	g (1680)	$1^+(3^-)-$	Q	$1/2(1^+)$
ω (783)	$0^-(1^-)-$	B (1235)	$1^+(1^+)-$	→ X (1690)	$^-$	K* (1420)	$1/2(2^+)$
→ M (940)		→ ρ′ (1250)	$1^+(1^-)-$	→ X (1795)	1	→ K_N(1660)	1/2
→ M (953)	$^+$	f (1270)	$0^+(2^+)+$	→ S (1930)	1	→ K_N(1760)	1/2
η′ (958)	$0^+(0^-)+$	D (1285)	$0^+(A)+$	→ A_4 (1960)	1^-	L (1770)	$1/2(A)$
δ (970)	$1^-(0^+)+$	A_2 (1310)	$1^-(2^+)+$	→ ρ (2100)	1^+	→ K_N(1850)	
→ H (990)	$0^-(A)-$	E (1420)	$0^+(A)+$	→ T (2200)	1	→ K* (2200)	
S^* (993)	$0^+(0^+)+$	→ X (1430)	0	→ ρ (2275)	1^+	→ K* (2800)	
φ (1019)	$0^-(1^-)-$	→ X (1440)	1	→ U (2360)	1		
→ M (1033)		f′ (1514)	$0^+(2^+)+$	→ N̄N (2375)	0	→ Exotics	
→ B_1(1040)	1^+	F_1 (1540)	1 (A)	→ X(2500-3600)			

Name	$I^G(J^P)C_n$ estab.	Mass M (MeV)	Full Width Γ (MeV)	$\pm \Gamma M^{(a)}$ (GeV)^2	Partial decay mode Mode	Fraction (%) [Upper limits are 1σ (%)]	p or Pmax$^{(b)}$ (MeV/c)
f(1270)	$\underline{0^+(2^+)+}$	1270§ ±10§	170§ ±30§	1.61 ±.22	ππ	83±5§	619
					$2\pi^+2\pi^-$	4±1§	556
					$K\bar{K}$	4±3 S=1.5*	394
					For upper limits, see footnote (f)		
D(1285)	$\underline{0^+(A)\pm}$	1286§ ±10§	30§ ±20§	1.65 +.03	$K\bar{K}\pi$	seen	305
					$\eta\pi\pi$	seen	484
					†[δ(970)π	seen]	245
	$J^P = 0^-,\ 1^+,\ 2^-$, with 1^+ favoured				$2\pi^+2\pi^-$ (prob. $\rho^0\pi^+\pi^-$)	seen	565
A$_2$(1310)	$\underline{1^-(2^+)+}$	1310§ ±10§	100§ ±10§	1.72 ±.13	ρπ	71.5±1.8 S=1.2*	413
					ηπ	15.2±1.2	529
					ωππ	8.6±1.8 S=1.3*	354
					$K\bar{K}$	4.7±0.6	428
					η′(958)π	<1	280
E(1420)	$\underline{0^+(A)\pm}$	1416§ ±10§	60§ ±20§	2.01 ±.08	$K\bar{K}\pi$	∼ 40	421
					†[$K^*\bar{K} + \bar{K}^*K$	∼ 20]	130
					ηππ	∼ 60	564
					†[δ(970)π	possibly seen]	352
f′(1514)	$\underline{0^+(2^+)+}$	1516 ±3	40 ±10	2.29 ±.06	$K\bar{K}$	only mode seen	572
					For upper limits, see footnote (k)		
F$_1$(1540)	$\underline{1}$ (A)	1540 ±5	40 ±15	2.37 ±.06	$K^*\bar{K} + \bar{K}^*K$	only mode seen	321
	Evidence based on only one experiment						
ρ′(1600)	$\underline{1^+(1^-)-}$	∼ 1600	∼ 400	2.56 ±.64	4π	dominant	738
					†[$\rho\pi^+\pi^-$	seen with $\pi^+\pi^-$ in S-wave]	575
					ππ	possibly seen	788
					$K\bar{K}$	< 8	629
A$_3$(1640)	$\underline{1^-(2^-)+}$	∼ 1640	∼ 300	2.69 ±.49	fπ		305
	Broad enhancement in the $J^P = 2^-$ fπ partial wave; not a Breit-Wigner resonance.¶						
ω(1675)	$\underline{0^-(N)-}$	1666§ ±10§	142§ ±20§	2.78 ±.24	ρπ	seen	647
					3π	possibly seen	805
					5π	possibly seen	778
					†[ωππ	possibly seen]	614
g(1680)	$\underline{1^+(3^-)-}$	1686§ ±20§	180§ ±30§	2.84 ±.30	2π	26±5§	831
					4π (incl. ππρ,ρρ,A$_2$π,ωπ)	∼ 70	784
					$K\bar{K}$	∼ 2 }(ℓ)	680
	J^P, M and Γ from the 2π mode$^{(ℓ)}$.				$K\bar{K}\pi$ (incl. $K^*\bar{K}$)	∼ 3	621
	See note (1) for possible heavier states.						
K$^+$(494) K^0(498)	$\underline{1/2(0^-)}$	493.71 497.70		0.244 0.248	See Stable Particle Table		
K*(892)	$\underline{1/2(1^-)}$	892.2 ±0.5	49.8 ±1.1	0.796 ±.044	Kπ	≈ 100	288
					Kππ	< 0.2	216
					Kγ	< 0.16	310
	(Charged mode; $m^0 - m^\pm = 6.1\pm1.5$ MeV)						

Meson Table

April 1974

In addition to the entries in the Meson Table, the Meson Data Card Listings contain all substantial claims for meson resonances. See Contents of Meson Data Card Listings[1].

Quantities in italics have changed by more than one (old) standard deviation since April 1973.

Name $\frac{\bar{G}}{+}\frac{I|0|1}{\omega/\phi|\pi}$ $I^G(J^P)C_n$ estab.	Mass M (MeV)	Full Width Γ (MeV)	M^2 $\pm\Gamma M^{(a)}$ $(GeV)^2$	Partial decay mode				p or $p_{max}^{(b)}$ (MeV/c)
				Mode	Fraction (%) [Upper limits are 1σ (%)]			
$\pi^\pm(140)$ $\underline{1^-(0^-)+}$	139.57	0.0	0.019483	See Stable Particle Table				
$\pi^0(135)$	134.96	7.8 eV ±.9 eV	0.018217					
$\eta(549)$ $\underline{0^+(0^-)+}$	548.8 ±0.6	2.63 keV ±.58 keV	0.301 ±.000	All neutral $\pi^+\pi^-\pi^0$ + $\pi^+\pi^-\gamma$	71 29	See Stable Particle Table		
ϵ $\underline{0^+(0^+)+}$	$\lesssim 700^{(c)}$	$\gtrsim 600^{(c)}$		$\pi\pi$				
Existence of pole not established. See note on $\pi\pi$ S wave¶.								
$\rho(770)$ $\underline{1^+(1^-)-}$	$770_\S$ ±10§	$150_\S$ ±10§	0.593 ±.116	$\pi\pi$ e^+e^- $\mu^+\mu^-$ For upper limits, see footnote (e)	≈100 0.0043±.0005 (d) 0.0067±.0012 (d)		359 385 370
$\omega(783)$ $\underline{0^-(1^-)-}$	$782.7_\S$ ±0.6§	10.0 ±.4	0.613 ±.008	$\pi^+\pi^-\pi^0$ $\pi^+\pi^-$ $\pi^0\gamma$ e^+e^- For upper limits, see footnote (g)	90.0±0.6 1.3±0.3 8.7±0.5 0.0076±.0017	S=1.2* S=1.5* S=1.9*	327 366 380 391
$\eta'(958)$ or X^0 $\underline{0^+(\ ^-)+}$ J=0 or 2	957.6 ±0.3	< 1	0.917 <.001	$\eta\pi\pi$ $\rho^0\gamma$ $\gamma\gamma$ For upper limits, see footnote (h)	70.6±2.5 27.4±2.2 1.9±0.3	S=1.4* S=1.6*	234 458 479
$\delta(970)$ $\underline{1^-(0^+)+}$	$976_\S$ ±10§	$50_\S$ ±20§	0.953 ±.049	$\eta\pi$ $\rho\pi$	seen < 25		315 139
Possibly a virtual bound state of the I = 1 $K\bar{K}$ system¶.								
$S^*(993)$ $\underline{0^+(0^+)+}$	$\sim 993^{(c)}$ ±5	$40^{(c)}$ ±8	0.986 ±.040	$K\bar{K}$ $\pi\pi$		near threshold	479
See notes on $\pi\pi$ and $K\bar{K}$ S wave¶.								
$\Phi(1019)$ $\underline{0^-(1^-)-}$	1019.7 ±0.3 S=1.9*	4.2 ±.2	1.040 ±.004	K^+K^- $K_L K_S$ $\pi^+\pi^-\pi^0$ (incl. $\rho\pi$) $\eta\gamma$ e^+e^- $\mu^+\mu^-$ For upper limits, see footnote (i)	46.6±2.5 34.6±2.2 15.8±1.5 3.0±1.1 .032±.002 .025±.003	S=1.6* S=1.6* S=1.2* S=1.6* S=1.4*	127 111 462 362 510 499
$A_1(1100)$ $\underline{1^-(1^+)+}$	~ 1100	~ 300	1.21 ±.33	$\rho\pi$	~ 100		253
Broad enhancement in the $J^P=1^+$ $\rho\pi$ partial wave; not a Breit-Wigner resonance¶.								
$B(1235)$ $\underline{1^+(1^+)-}$	$1237_\S$ ±10§	$120_\S$ ±20§	1.53 ±.12	$\omega\pi$ [D/S amplitude ratio = .24±.06] For upper limits, see footnote (j)	only mode seen		352

Stable Particle Table *(cont'd)*

S = Scale factor = $\sqrt{\chi^2/(N-1)}$, where $N \approx$ number of experiments. S should be ≈ 1. If $S > 1$, we have enlarged the error of the mean, δx, i.e., $\delta x \to S\delta x$. This convention is still inadequate, since if $S \gg 1$, the experiments are probably inconsistent, and therefore the real uncertainty is probably even greater than $S\delta x$. See text and ideogram in Stable Particle Data Card Listings.

a. Quoted upper limits correspond to a 90% confidence level.

b. In decays with more than two bodies, p_{max} is the maximum momentum that any particle can have.

c. See Stable Particle Data Card Listings for energy limits used in this measurement.

d. Theoretical value; see also Stable Particle Data Card Listings.

e. See note in Stable Particle Data Card Listings.

f. P for Ξ and J^P for Ω^- not yet measured. Values reported are SU(3) predictions.

g. Assumes rate for $\Xi^- \to \Sigma^0 e^- \nu$ small compared with $\Xi^- \to \Lambda e^- \nu$.

h. The direct emission branching ratio is $(1.56 \pm .35) \times 10^{-5}$.

i. This upper limit is above the contradictory results of Carithers et al. $(1.0^{+.7}_{-.35}) \times 10^{-8}$, and Clark et al. $(< 0.19) \times 10^{-8}$. See note in Stable Particle Data Card Listings.

j. $|g_A/g_V|$ defined by $g_A^2 = |C_A|^2 + |C'_A|^2$, $g_V^2 = |C_V|^2 + |C'_V|^2$, and $\Sigma \langle \overline{e}\,|\Gamma_i|\mu\rangle \langle \overline{\nu}\,|\Gamma_i(C_i + C'_i\gamma_5)|\nu\rangle$;
ϕ defined by $\cos\phi = -R_e(C^*_A C'_V + C'_A C^*_V)/g_A g_V$ [for more details, see text Section VI A].

k. The definition of the slope parameter of the Dalitz plot is as follows [see also text Section VI B.1]: $|M|^2 = 1 + g\left(\dfrac{s_3 - s_0}{m_{\pi^+}^2}\right)$.

ℓ. The definition for the CP violation parameters is as follows [see also text Section VI B.3]:
$$\delta = \frac{\Gamma(K_L^0 \to \ell^+) - \Gamma(K_L^0 \to \ell^-)}{\Gamma(K_L^0 \to \ell^+) + \Gamma(K_L^0 \to \ell^-)} \qquad |\eta_{+-0}|^2 = \frac{\Gamma(K_S^0 \to \pi^+\pi^-\pi^0)}{\Gamma(K_L^0 \to \pi^+\pi^-\pi^0)} \qquad |\eta_{000}|^2 = \frac{\Gamma(K_S^0 \to \pi^0\pi^0\pi^0)}{\Gamma(K_L^0 \to \pi^0\pi^0\pi^0)}$$

m The definition of these quantities is as follows [for more details on sign convention, see text Section VI B]:

$\alpha = \dfrac{2|s||p|\cos\Delta}{|s|^2 + |p|^2}$; $\qquad\qquad \beta = \sqrt{1 - \alpha^2}\sin\phi$; $\qquad\qquad g_A/g_V$ defined by $\langle B_f|\gamma_\lambda(g_V - g_A\gamma_5)|B_i\rangle$;

$\beta = \dfrac{-2|s||p|\sin\Delta}{|s|^2 + |p|^2}$ $\qquad\qquad \gamma = \sqrt{1 - \alpha^2}\cos\phi$. $\qquad\qquad \delta$ defined by $g_A/g_V = |g_A/g_V|e^{i\delta}$.

n. The $K_S^0 \to \pi\pi$ and $K_L^0 \to \pi\pi$ rates (and branching fractions) are from independent fits and do not include results of K_L^0-K_S^0 interference experiments. The $|\eta_{+-}|$ and $|\eta_{00}|$ values given in the addendum are these rates combined with the $|\eta_{+-}|$ and $|\eta_{00}|$ results from interference experiments.

Stable Particle Table

	Magnetic moment		
e	1.001 159 6567 $\frac{e\hbar}{2m_ec}$ ±.000 000 0035		
μ	1.001 166 16 $\frac{e\hbar}{2m_\mu c}$ ±.000 000 31		

μ Decay parameters[j]

$\rho = 0.752 \pm 0.003$ $\eta = -0.12 \pm 0.21$
$\xi = 0.972 \pm 0.013$ $\delta = 0.755 \pm 0.009$ $h = 1.00 \pm 0.13$
$|g_A/g_V| = 0.86^{+0.33}_{-0.11}$ $\phi = 180° \pm 15°$

$K^\pm$

Mode	Partial rate (sec^{-1})	
$\mu\nu$	$(51.36 \pm 0.19)10^6$	S=1.2*
$\pi\pi^0$	$(17.07 \pm 0.15)10^6$	S=1.1*
$\pi\pi^+\pi^-$	$(4.52 \pm 0.02)10^6$	S=1.1*
$\pi\pi^0\pi^0$	$(1.40 \pm 0.04)10^6$	S=1.4*
$\mu\pi^0\nu$	$(2.58 \pm 0.07)10^6$	S=1.7*
$e\pi^0\nu$	$(3.90 \pm 0.04)10^6$	S=1.1*

$\Delta I = \frac{1}{2}$ rule for $K \to 3\pi$ [k]

$K^+ \to \pi^+\pi^+\pi^-$	$g = -.214 \pm .005$	S=1.7*
$K^- \to \pi^-\pi^+\pi^-$	$g = -.214 \pm .007$	S=2.7*
$K^\pm \to \pi^\pm\pi^0\pi^0$	$g = .522 \pm .020$	S=1.3*
$K^0_L \to \pi^0\pi^+\pi^-$	$g = .610 \pm .021$	S=2.6*

K^0_S

Mode	Partial rate	
$\pi^+\pi^-$	$^n(0.776 \pm .006)10^{10}$	S=1.8*
$\pi^0\pi^0$	$^n(0.352 \pm .004)10^{10}$	S=1.3*

Form factors for $K_{\ell 3}$ decays (see Data Card Listings for ξ, λ^μ_+ and λ^μ_0)

K^+_{e3} $\lambda^e_+ = .029 \pm .004$ K^0_{e3} $\lambda^e_+ = .026 \pm .004$

K^0_L

Mode	Partial rate	
$\pi^0\pi^0\pi^0$	$(4.11 \pm 0.13)10^6$	S=1.1*
$\pi^+\pi^-\pi^0$	$(2.31 \pm 0.07)10^6$	S=2.0*
$\pi\mu\nu$	$(5.31 \pm 0.11)10^6$	S=1.1*
$\pi e\nu$	$(7.53 \pm 0.12)10^6$	S=1.1*
$\pi^+\pi^-$	$^n(3.42 \pm 0.36)10^4$	S=4.6*
$\pi^0\pi^0$	$^n(1.80 \pm 0.36)10^4$	S=1.5*

CP violation parameters [ℓ,n]

$|\eta_{+-}| = (2.17 \pm .07)10^{-3}$ S=3.4* $|\eta_{00}| = (2.25 \pm .09)10^{-3}$ S=1.1*
$\phi_{+-} = (46.6 \pm 2.5)°$ S=1.5* $\phi_{00} = (49 \pm 13)°$
$|\eta_{+-0}|^2 < 0.12$ $|\eta_{000}|^2 < 1.2$ $\delta = (.34 \pm .01)10^{-2}$ S=1.1*

$\Delta S = -\Delta Q$
Re x = .000 ± .022 S=1.5*   Im x = .012 ± .030 S=1.2*

η

Mode	Asymmetry parameter
$\pi^+\pi^-\pi^0$	$(0.12 \pm .17)\%$
$\pi^+\pi^-\gamma$	$(0.88 \pm .40)\%$

	Magnetic moment ($e\hbar/2m_pc$)	Decay parameters[m] Measured		Derived		g_A/g_V	g_V/g_A
		α	ϕ(degree)	γ	Δ(degree)		
p	2.7928456 ±.0000011						
n	-1.913148 ±.000066	$pe^-\nu$				-1.250±.09 $\delta=(181.1\pm1.3)°$	
Λ	-0.67 ±.06	$p\pi^-$ 0.647±0.013 $n\pi^0$ 0.651±0.045 $pe\nu$	$(-6.5\pm3.5)°$	0.76	$\left(7.6^{+4.0}_{-4.1}\right)°$	-0.66±0.05 S=1.2*	
Σ$^+$	2.62 ±.41	$p\pi^0$ -0.979±0.016 $n\pi^+$ +0.066±0.016 $p\gamma$ $-1.03^{+.52}_{-.42}$	$(36\pm34)°$ $(167\pm20)°$ S=1.1*	0.17 -0.97	$(187\pm6)°$ $\left(-73^{+136}_{-10}\right)°$		
Σ$^-$	-1.6 to 0.8	$n\pi^-$ -0.069±0.008 $ne^-\nu$ $\Lambda e^-\nu$	$(10\pm15)°$	0.98	$\left(249^{+12}_{-115}\right)°$	See Data Cds. 0.37±0.20	
Ξ^0		$\Lambda\pi^0$ -0.44±0.08 S=1.3*	$(21\pm12)°$	0.84	$\left(216^{+13}_{-19}\right)°$		
Ξ$^-$	-1.93 ±.75	$\Lambda\pi^-$ -0.393±0.023 S=1.2*	$(2\pm7)°$	0.92	$\left(184\pm15\right)°$		

Stable Particle Table (cont'd)

Particle	$I^G(J^P)C_n$	Mass (MeV) Mass^2 $(\text{GeV})^2$	Mean Life (sec) $c\tau$ (cm)	Mode	Fraction[a]	p or p_{max}[b] (MeV/c)
p	$\frac{1}{2}(\frac{1}{2}^+)$	938.2796 ± 0.0027 $m^2 = 0.8804$	stable $(> 2 \times 10^{28} y)$			
n	$\frac{1}{2}(\frac{1}{2}^+)$	939.5731 ± 0.0027 $m^2 = 0.8828$ $m_p - m_n = -1.29344$ ± 0.00007	918 ± 14 $c\tau = 2.75 \times 10^{13}$	$pe\,\nu$	100 %	1
Λ	$0(\frac{1}{2}^+)$	1115.60 ± 0.05 $S = 1.2^*$ $m^2 = 1.245$	2.578×10^{-10} $\pm.021$ $S = 1.6^*$ $c\tau = 7.73$	$p\pi^-$ $n\pi^0$ $pe\,\nu$ $p\mu\,\nu$ $p\pi^-\gamma$	$(\ 64.2 \pm 0.5\ )\%$ $(\ 35.8 \pm 0.5\ )\%$ $(\ 8.13 \pm 0.29)10^{-4}$ $(\ 1.57 \pm 0.35)10^{-4}$ $c(\ 0.85 \pm 0.14)10^{-3}$	100 104 163 131 100
Σ^+	$1(\frac{1}{2}^+)$	1189.37 ± 0.06 $S = 1.8^*$ $m^2 = 1.415$ $m_{\Sigma^+} - m_{\Sigma^-} = -7.99$ $\pm.08$ $S = 1.2^*$	0.800×10^{-10} $\pm.006$ $c\tau = 2.40$ $\frac{\Gamma(\Sigma^+ \to \ell^+ n\,\nu)}{\Gamma(\Sigma^- \to \ell^- n\,\nu)} < .035$	$p\pi^0$ $n\pi^+$ $p\gamma$ $n\pi^+\gamma$ $\Lambda e^+\nu$ $n\mu^+\nu$ $ne^+\nu$ pe^+e^-	$(\ 51.6\ \ \ \ \ )\%$ $(\ 48.4 \pm 0.7\ )\%$ $(\ 1.24 \pm 0.18)10^{-3}\ S=1.4^*$ $c(\ 0.93 \pm 0.10)10^{-3}$ $(\ 2.02 \pm 0.47)10^{-5}$ $(< 2.4\ \ \ \ )10^{-5}$ $(< 1.0\ \ \ \ )10^{-5}$ $(< 7\ \ \ \ )10^{-6}$	189 185 225 185 72 202 224 225
Σ^0	$1(\frac{1}{2}^+)$	1192.48 ± 0.08 $m^2 = 1.422$	$< 1.0 \times 10^{-14}$ $c\tau < 3 \times 10^{-4}$	$\Lambda\gamma$ $\Lambda e^+ e^-$	100 % $d(\ 5.45\ \ \ )10^{-3}$	74 74
Σ^-	$1(\frac{1}{2}^+)$	1197.35 ± 0.06 $m^2 = 1.434$ $m_{\Sigma^0} - m_{\Sigma^-} = -4.87$ $\pm.06$	1.482×10^{-10} $\pm.017$ $S = 1.5^*$ $c\tau = 4.44$	$n\pi^-$ $ne^-\nu$ $n\mu^-\nu$ $\Lambda e^-\nu$ $n\pi^-\gamma$	100 % $(\ 1.08 \pm 0.04)10^{-3}$ $(\ 0.45 \pm 0.04)10^{-3}$ $(\ 0.60 \pm 0.06)10^{-4}$ $c(\ 1.0 \pm 0.2\ )10^{-4}$	193 230 210 79 193
Ξ^0	$\frac{1}{2}(\frac{1}{2}^+)^f$	1314.9 ± 0.6 $m^2 = 1.729$ $m_{\Xi^0} - m_{\Xi^-} = -6.4$ $\pm.6$	2.96×10^{-10} $\pm.12$ $c\tau = 8.93$	$\Lambda\pi^0$ $p\pi^-$ $pe^-\nu$ $\Sigma^- e^+\nu$ $\Sigma^+ e^-\nu$ $\Sigma^- \mu^+\nu$ $\Sigma^+ \mu^-\nu$ $p\mu^-\nu$	100 % $(< 0.9\ \ \ )10^{-3}$ $(< 1.3\ \ \ )10^{-3}$ $(< 1.5\ \ \ )10^{-3}$ $(< 1.5\ \ \ )10^{-3}$ $(< 1.5\ \ \ )10^{-3}$ $(< 1.5\ \ \ )10^{-3}$ $(< 1.3\ \ \ )10^{-3}$	135 299 323 119 112 64 49 309
Ξ^-	$\frac{1}{2}(\frac{1}{2}^+)^f$	1321.29 ± 0.14 $m^2 = 1.746$	1.652×10^{-10} $\pm.023$ $S = 1.1^*$ $c\tau = 4.95$	$\Lambda\pi^-$ $\Lambda e^-\nu$ $\Sigma^0 e^-\nu$ $\Lambda\mu^-\nu$ $\Sigma^0\mu^-\nu$ $n\pi^-$ $ne^-\nu$	100 % $g(\ 0.70 \pm 0.21)10^{-3}$ $(< 0.5\ \ \ )10^{-3}$ $(< 1.3\ \ \ )10^{-3}$ $(< 0.5\ \ \ )\%$ $(< 1.1\ \ \ )10^{-3}$ $(< 1.0\ \ \ )\%$	139 190 123 163 70 303 327
Ω^-	$0(\frac{3}{2}^+)^f$	$1672.2 \pm .4$ $m^2 = 2.797$	$1.3^{+0.3}_{-0.2} \times 10^{-10}$ $c\tau = 3.9$	$\left.\begin{array}{l}\Xi^0\pi^- \\ \Xi^-\pi^0 \\ \Lambda K^-\end{array}\right\}$	Total of 41 events seen	293 290

Stable Particle Table *(cont'd)*

Particle	$I^G(J^P)C_n$	Mass (MeV) Mass^2 (GeV)^2	Mean life (sec) $c\tau$ (cm)	Mode	Fraction[a]	p or p_{max}[b] (MeV/c)
$K^\pm$	$\frac{1}{2}(0^-)$	493.707 ±0.037 $m^2=0.244$	1.2371×10^{-8} ±.0026 S=1.9* $c\tau$=370.8 $(\tau^+-\tau^-)/\overline{\tau}=$ (.11±.09)% (test of CPT) S=1.2*	$\mu\nu$	(63.54±0.19)%	236
				$\pi\pi^0$	(21.12±0.17)%	205
				$\pi\pi^-\pi^+$	(5.59±0.03)% S=1.1*	125
				$\pi\pi^0\pi^0$	(1.73±0.05)% S=1.4*	133
				$\mu\pi^0\nu$	(3.20±0.09)% S=1.7*	215
				$e\pi^0\nu$	(4.82±0.05)% S=1.1*	228
				$e\pi^0\pi^0\nu$	($1.8^{+6.4}_{-0.6}$) 10^{-5}	207
				$\pi\pi^\mp e^\pm\nu$	(3.7 ±0.2) 10^{-5}	203
				$\pi\pi^\pm e^\mp\nu$	(< 5) 10^{-7}	203
				$\pi\pi^\mp\mu^\pm\nu$	(0.9 ±0.4) 10^{-5}	151
				$\pi\pi^\pm\mu^\mp\nu$	(< 3) 10^{-6}	151
	$m_{K\pm}-m_{K^0}=-3.99$ ±0.13 S=1.1*			$e\nu$	(1.38±0.20) 10^{-5}	247
				$e\nu\gamma$	c(< 7) 10^{-5}	247
				$\pi\pi^0\gamma$	h,c(2.71±0.19) 10^{-4}	205
				$\pi\pi^+\pi^-\gamma$	c(10 ±4) 10^{-5}	125
				$\mu\pi^0\nu\gamma$	c(< 6) 10^{-5}	215
				$e\pi^0\nu\gamma$	c(3.7 ±1.4) 10^{-4}	228
				πe^+e^-	(< 0.26) 10^{-6}	227
				$\pi^\mp e^\pm e^\pm$	(< 1.5) 10^{-5}	227
				$\pi\mu^+\mu^-$	(< 2.4) 10^{-6}	172
				$\pi\gamma\gamma$	c(< 3.5) 10^{-5}	227
				$\pi\gamma\gamma\gamma$	c(< 3) 10^{-4}	227
				$\pi\nu\overline{\nu}$	(< 0.6) 10^{-6}	227
				$\pi\gamma$	(< 4) 10^{-6}	227
				$e\pi^\mp\mu^\pm$	(< 3) 10^{-8}	214
				$e\pi^\pm\mu^\mp$	(< 1.4) 10^{-8}	214
				$\mu\nu\nu\overline{\nu}$	c(< 6) 10^{-6}	236

Particle	$I^G(J^P)C_n$	Mass (MeV) Mass^2 (GeV)^2	Mean life (sec) $c\tau$ (cm)	Mode	Fraction[a]	p or p_{max}[b] (MeV/c)
K^0	$\frac{1}{2}(0^-)$	497.70 ±0.13 S=1.1* $m^2=0.248$	50% K_{Short}, 50% K_{Long}			
K^0_S	$\frac{1}{2}(0^-)$		0.886×10^{-10} ±.007 S=2.4* $c\tau$=2.66	$\pi^+\pi^-$	(68.77±0.26)% S=1.1*	206
				$\pi^0\pi^0$	(31.23±0.26)% S=1.1*	209
				$\mu^+\mu^-$	(< 0.3) 10^{-6}	225
				e^+e^-	(<35) 10^{-5}	249
				$\pi^+\pi^-\gamma$	c(2.0 ±0.4) 10^{-3}	206
				$\gamma\gamma$	(< 0.4) 10^{-3}	249

Particle	$I^G(J^P)C_n$	Mass (MeV) Mass^2 (GeV)^2	Mean life (sec) $c\tau$ (cm)	Mode	Fraction[a]	p or p_{max}[b] (MeV/c)
K^0_L	$\frac{1}{2}(0^-)$		5.179×10^{-8} ±0.040 $c\tau$=1553	$\pi^0\pi^0\pi^0$	(21.3 ±0.6)% S=1.1*	139
				$\pi^+\pi^-\pi^0$	(11.9 ±0.4)% S=2.2*	133
				$\pi\mu\nu$	(27.5 ±0.5)% S=1.1*	216
				$\pi e\nu$	(39.0 ±0.6)% S=1.1*	229
				$\pi e\nu\gamma$	c(1.3 ±0.8)%	229
	$m_{K_L}-m_{K_S}=0.5403\times10^{10}\,\hbar\,sec^{-1}$ ±0.0035			$\pi^+\pi^-$	(0.177±0.018)%S=4.9*	206
				$\pi^0\pi^0$	(0.093±0.019)%S=1.5*	209
				$\pi^+\pi^-\gamma$	c(< 0.4) 10^{-3}	206
				$\pi^0\gamma\gamma$	(< 2.4) 10^{-4}	231
				$\gamma\gamma$	(4.9± 0.4) 10^{-4}	249
				$e\mu$	(< 1.6) 10^{-9}	238
				$\mu^+\mu^-$	i(< 1.6) 10^{-8}	225
				e^+e^-	(< 1.6) 10^{-9}	249
				$e^+e^-\gamma$	(< 2.8) 10^{-5}	249

Particle	$I^G(J^P)C_n$	Mass (MeV) Mass^2 (GeV)^2	Mean life (sec) $c\tau$ (cm)	Mode	Fraction[a]	p or p_{max}[b] (MeV/c)
η	$0^+(0^-)^+$	548.8 ±0.6 S=1.4* $m^2=0.301$	$e\Gamma$=(2.63±0.58)keV Neutral decays 71.1%	$\gamma\gamma$	(38.0 ±1.0)% S=1.2*	274
				$\pi^0\gamma\gamma$	e(3.1 ±1.1)% S=1.2*	258
				$3\pi^0$	(30.0 ±1.1)% S=1.1*	180
				$\pi^+\pi^-\pi^0$	(23.9 ±0.6)% S=1.1*	175
				$\pi^+\pi^-\gamma$	(5.0 ±0.1)%	236
				$\pi^0 e^+e^-$	(< 0.04)%	258
		Charged decays 28.9%		$\pi^+\pi^-$	(< 0.15)%	236
				$\pi^+\pi^-e^+e^-$	(0.1 ±0.1)%	236
				$\pi^+\pi^-\pi^0\gamma$	(< 6) 10^{-4}	175
				$\pi^+\pi^-\gamma\gamma$	(< 0.2)%	236
				$\mu^+\mu^-$	(2.2 ±0.8) 10^{-5}	253
				$\mu^+\mu^-\pi^0$	(< 5) 10^{-4}	211

TABLES OF PARTICLE PROPERTIES

April 1974

N. Barash-Schmidt, A. Barbaro-Galtieri, C. Bricman, V. Chaloupka, D. M. Chew,

R. L. Kelly, T. A. Lasinski, A. Rittenberg, M. Roos, A. H. Rosenfeld

P. Söding, T. G. Trippe, and F. Uchiyama

Reprinted from Physics Letters, Vol. 50B, No. 1, April 1974.

An updated version of this table is published every April —
in odd-numbered years in Reviews of Modern Physics, and
in even-numbered years in Physics Letters B.

(Closing date for data: Feb. 1, 1974)

Stable Particle Table

For additional parameters, see Addendum to this table.

Quantities in italics have changed by more than one (old) standard deviation since April 1973.

Particle	$I^G(J^P)C_n$	Mass (MeV) Mass^2 (GeV)^2	Mean Life (sec) $c\tau$ (cm)	Partial decay mode		
				Mode	Fraction[a]	p or p_{max}[b] (MeV/c)
γ	$0, 1(1^-)^-$	$0(< 2)10^{-21}$	stable	stable		
ν ν_e ν_μ	$J = \frac{1}{2}$	$0(< 60 \text{ eV})$ $0(< 1.2)$	stable	stable		
e	$J = \frac{1}{2}$	0.5110034 $\pm.0000014$	stable $(>2\times10^{21}\text{y})$	stable		
μ	$J = \frac{1}{2}$ $m^2 = 0.01116$ $m_\mu - m_{\pi^\pm} = -33.909$ $\pm.006$	105.65948 $\pm.00035$ $c\tau = 6.593\times10^4$	2.1994×10^{-6} $\pm.0006$ S=1.1*	$e\nu\bar{\nu}$ $e\gamma\gamma$ $3e$ $e\gamma$	100 % $(<1.6)10^{-5}$ $(<6)10^{-9}$ $(<2.2)10^{-8}$	53 53 53 53
$\pi^\pm$	$1^-(0^-)$ $m^2 = 0.0195$	139.5688 $\pm.0064$ $c\tau = 780.4$ $(\tau^+ - \tau^-)/\bar{\tau} =$ $(0.05\pm0.07)\%$ (test of CPT)	2.6030×10^{-8} $\pm.0023$	$\mu\nu$ $e\nu$ $\mu\nu\gamma$ $\pi^0 e\nu$ $e\nu\gamma$ $e\nu e^+ e^-$	100 % $_c(1.24\pm0.03)10^{-4}$ $_c(1.24\pm0.25)10^{-4}$ $(1.02\pm0.07)10^{-8}$ $_c(3.0 \pm0.5)10^{-8}$ $(<3.4)10^{-8}$	30 70 30 5 70 70
π^0	$1^-(0^-)^+$ $m^2 = 0.0182$ $m_{\pi^\pm} - m_{\pi^0} = 4.6043$ $\pm.0037$	134.9645 $\pm.0074$ $c\tau = 2.5\times10^{-6}$	0.84×10^{-16} $\pm.10$ S=2.1*	$\gamma\gamma$ $\gamma e^+ e^-$ $\gamma\gamma\gamma$ $e^+ e^- e^+ e^-$ $\gamma\gamma\gamma\gamma$	$(98.83\pm0.05)\%$ $(1.17\pm0.05)\%$ $(<5)10^{-6}$ $_d(3.47)10^{-5}$ $(<6.1)10^{-5}$	67 67 67 67 67

CHARACTERISTIC NMR SPECTRAL POSITIONS
FOR HYDROGEN IN ORGANIC STRUCTURES

By permission from Erno Mohacsi, J. of Chemical Education, 41, 38 (1964)

This table is useful for quick qualitative determination of proton spectrum lines by providing a tabulation of line positions obtained using tetramethylsilane as an internal reference. The listing has been kept as simple as possible for this purpose. The proton spectrum lines are arranged according to the chemical shift relative to tetramethylsilane and are given in values of τ and δ. The purpose of this table is to supplement tables available in standard references and to summarize information available in the literature.

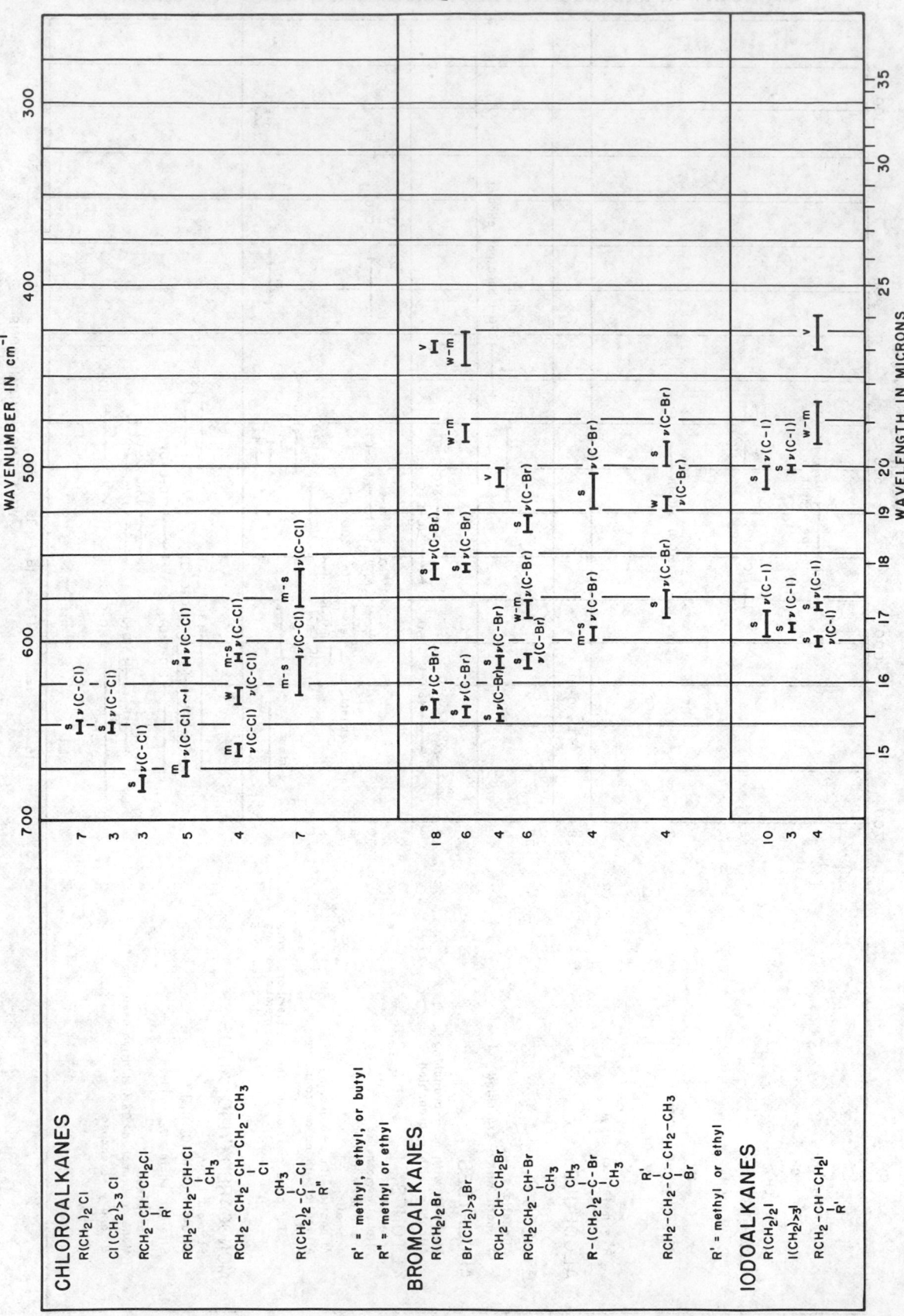

CHART OF CHARACTERISTIC FREQUENCIES BETWEEN ~ 700–300 cm⁻¹

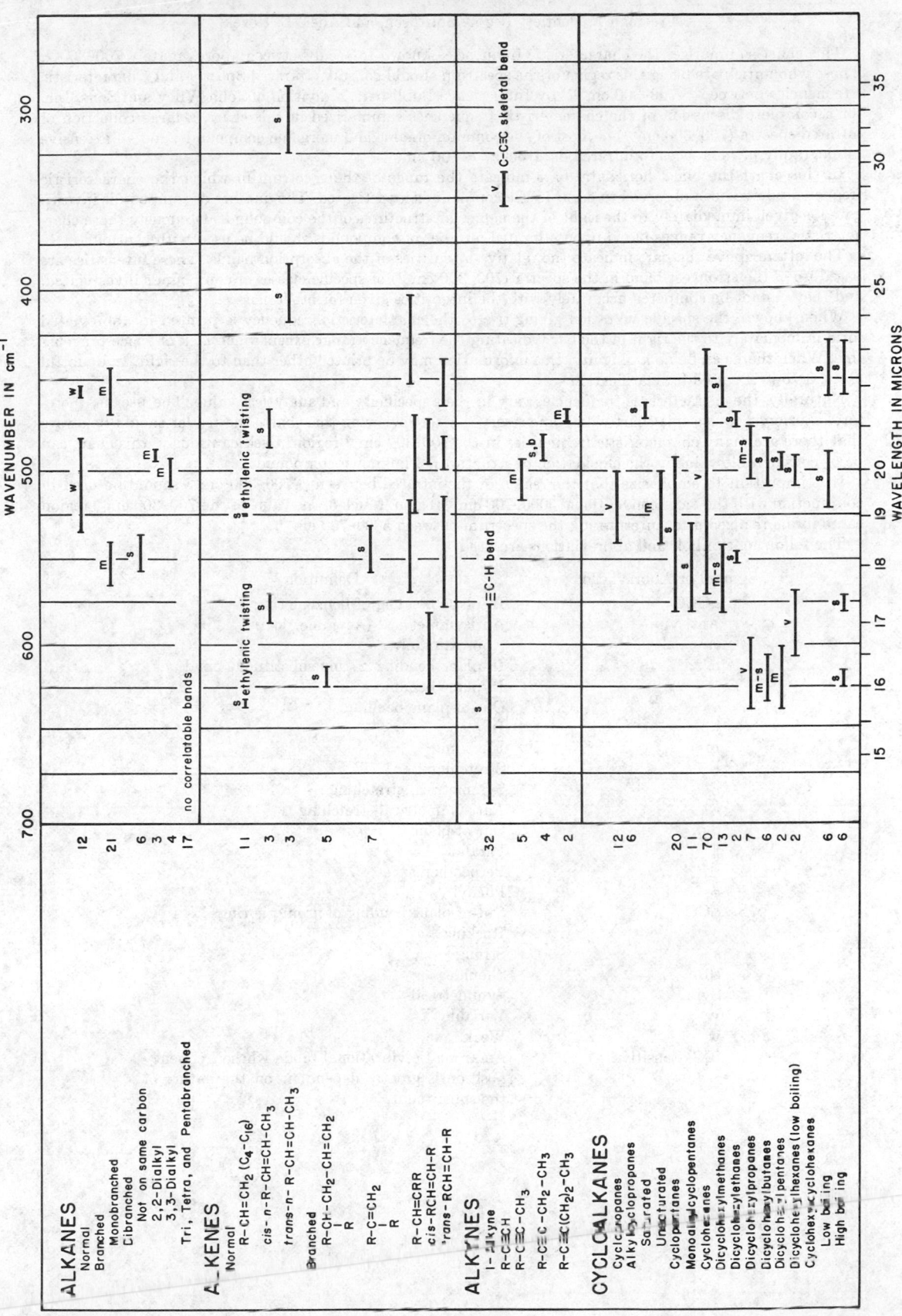

CHART OF CHARACTERISTIC FREQUENCIES BETWEEN ∼ 700–300 cm⁻¹

Freeman F. Bentley, Lee D. Smithson, and Adele L. Rozek

This chart summarizes the characteristic frequencies known to occur between approximately 700–300⁻¹. Those who anticipate using this region of the spectrum should consult "Infrared Spectra and Characteristic Frequencies between ∼700–300 cm⁻¹" by Interscience Publishers, a division of John Wiley and Sons, Inc. for a complete discussion of the characteristic frequencies summarized in this chart, a large collection of infrared spectra (700–300 cm⁻¹) of most of the common organic and inorganic compounds, and an extensive bibliography of references to infrared data below ∼700 cm⁻¹.

In this chart the black horizontal bars indicate the range of the spectrum in which the characteristic frequencies have been observed to occur in the compounds investigated. The number of compounds investigated is given immediately to the right of the names or structures of the compounds. Obviously those characteristic frequency ranges based upon a limited number of compounds should be used with caution.

The letters above the bars indicate the relative intensities of the absorption bands. These intensities are based upon the strongest band in the spectra (700–300 cm⁻¹) of specific classes of compounds investigated, and they cannot be compared accurately with the intensities given for other classes.

When known, the specific vibration giving rise to the characteristic frequency is printed in abbreviated form immediately to the right of the bar indicating the frequency range except when lack of space prevents this. When there can be no ambiguity, this information may be printed other than to the right. In doubtful cases, arrows are used for clarification.

Naturally, the characteristic frequencies vary in their specificity and analytical value. The user is, therefore, cautioned to use this chart with some reserve. After reviewing this chart, the reader should be aware that there are many characteristic frequencies in the 700–300 cm⁻¹ region. Used cautiously, this chart can be of considerable value in the elucidation of structures of unknown compounds.

It is important to emphasize that the region of the infrared between ∼700–300 cm⁻¹ should be used in conjunction with the more conventional 5000–700 cm⁻¹ region. Much of the value of the 700–300 cm⁻¹ region can only be realized after interpreting the spectrum between 5000–700 cm⁻¹.

The following symbols and abbreviations are used:

Symbol or Abbreviation	Definition
αCCC	In-plane bending of benzene ring
Antisym.	Antisymmetrical (Asymmetrical)
∼	Approximately
β	In-plane bending of ring substituent bond
δ	In-plane bending
γ	Out-of-plane bending
i.p.	In-plane
m	Medium
ν	Stretching
ν_s	Symmetrical stretching
ν_{as}	Antisymmetrical stretching
o.p.	Out-of-plane
$\parallel$	Parallel
$\perp$	Perpendicular
ϕ	Phenyl
ϕCC	Out-of-plane bending of aromatic ring
r	Rocking
s	Strong
sh	Shoulder
Sym.	Symmetrical
v	Variable
w	Weak
"X" Sensitive	An aromatic vibrational mode whose frequency position is greatly dependent on the nature of the substituent.

FAR INFRARED VIBRATIONAL FREQUENCY CORRELATION CHART (Con't.)

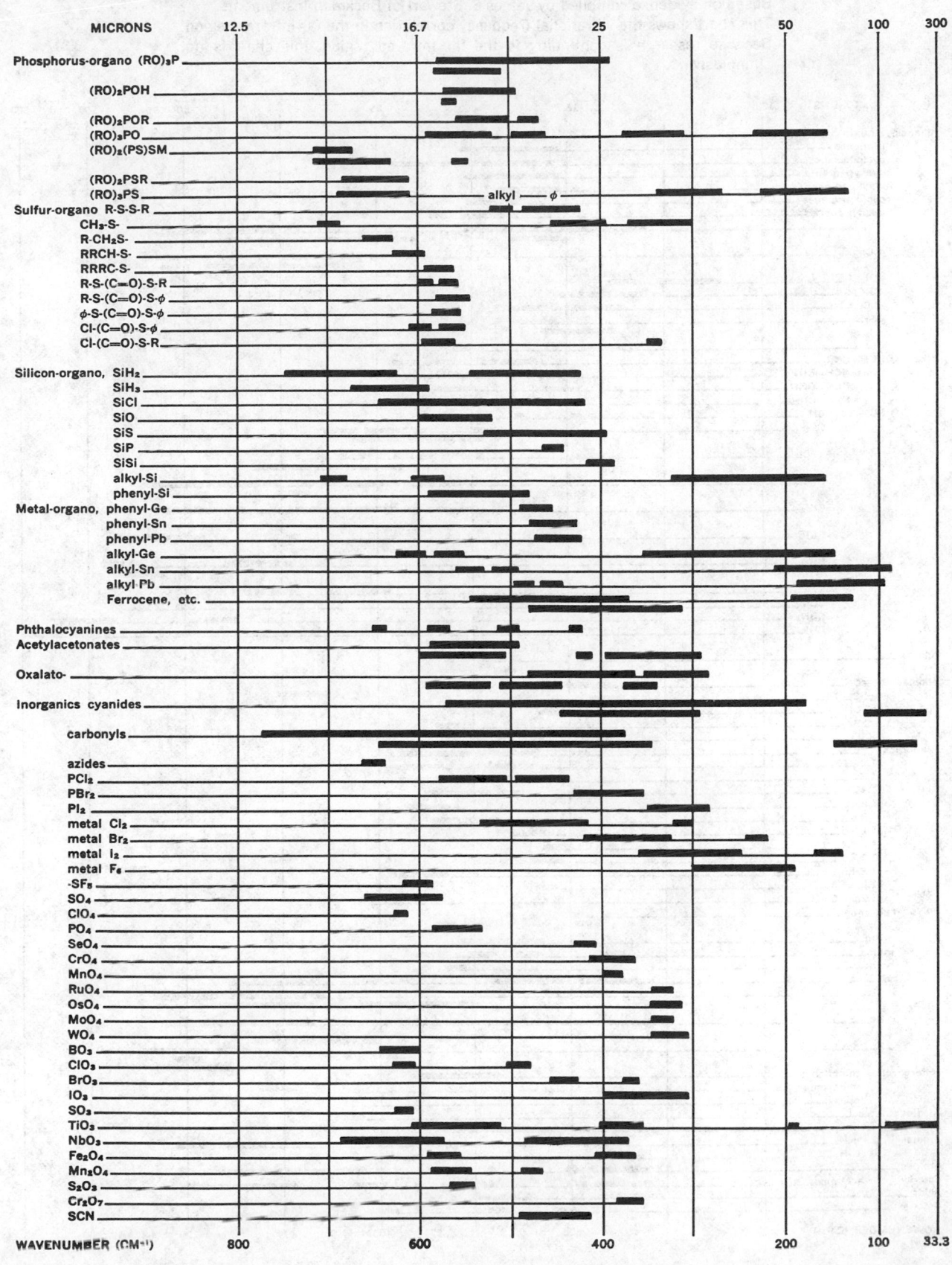

FAR INFRARED VIBRATIONAL FREQUENCY CORRELATION CHART

Based on evidence compiled by James E. Stewart of Beckman Instruments.
This chart shows the vibrational frequency correlation in the far infrared region.
Because research is continuing in the far infrared region, this chart is not
all-inclusive.

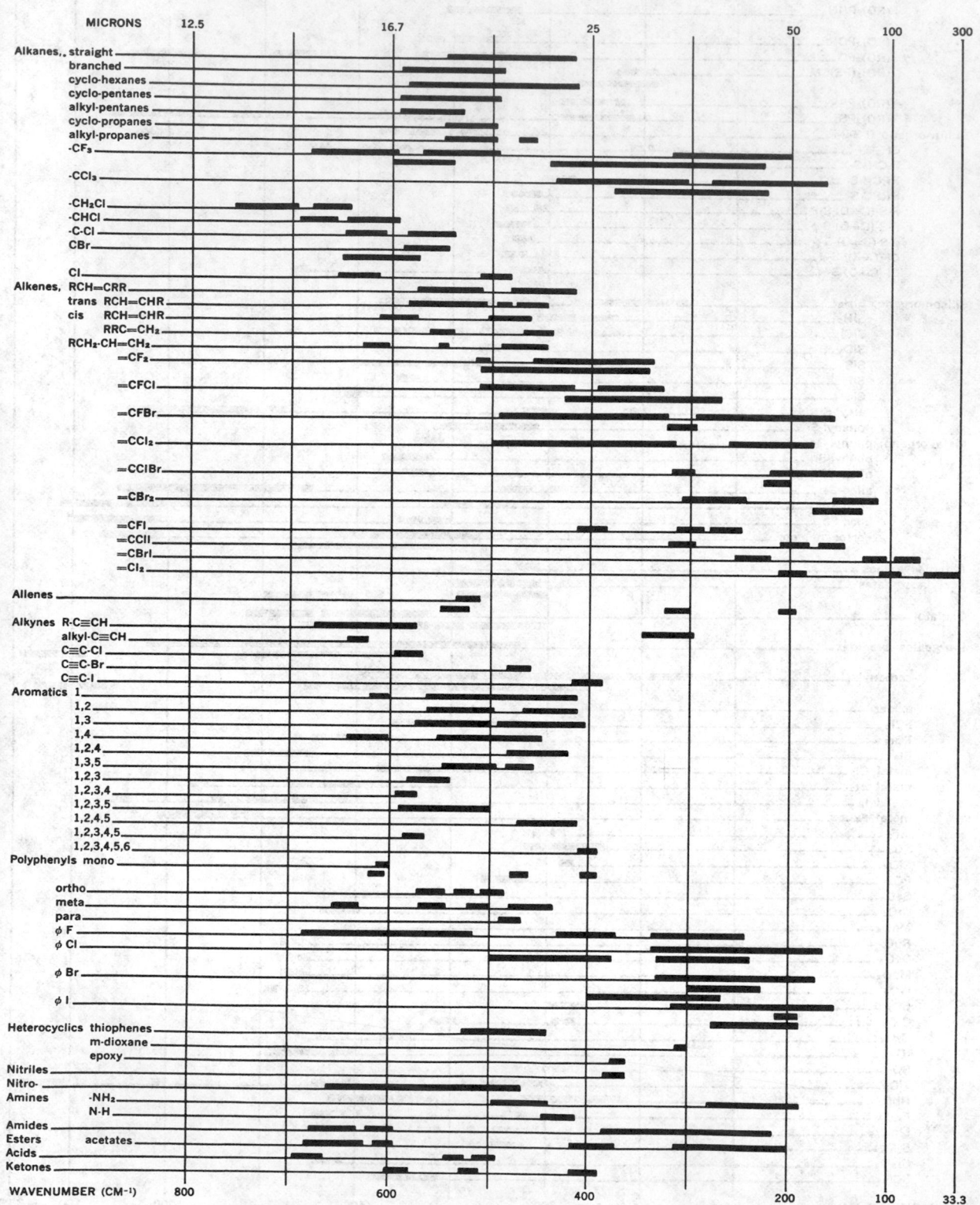

INFRARED CORRELATION CHART No. 4 (Con't.)

Prepared from information supplied by Beckman Instruments

This chart presents some correlations between structure and single-bond vibrations for a number of classes of compounds having absorption between 1500-650 cm⁻¹.

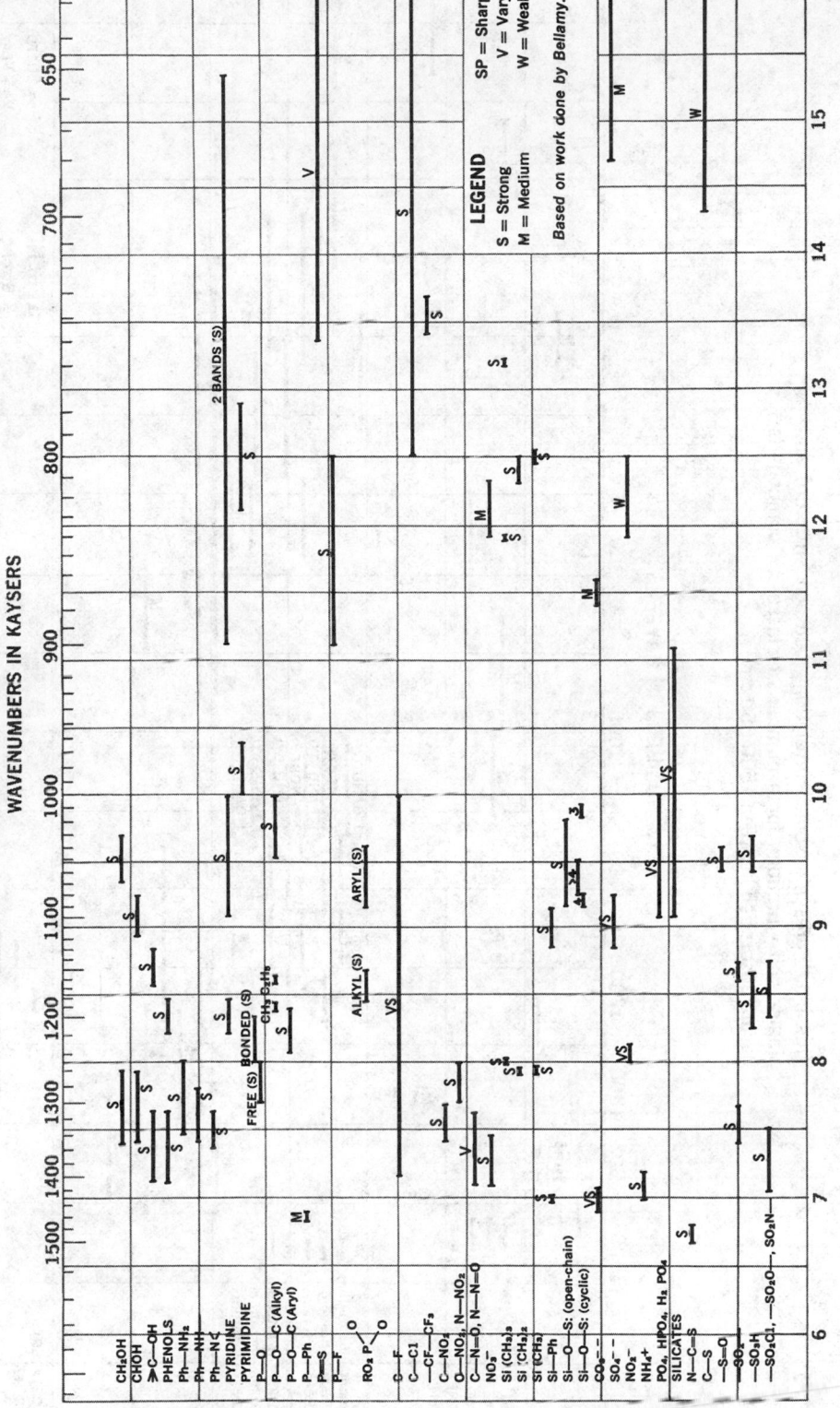

INFRARED CORRELATION CHART No. 4

Prepared from information supplied by Beckman Instruments

This chart presents some correlations between structure and single-bond vibrations for a number of classes of compounds having absorption between 1500-650 cm⁻¹

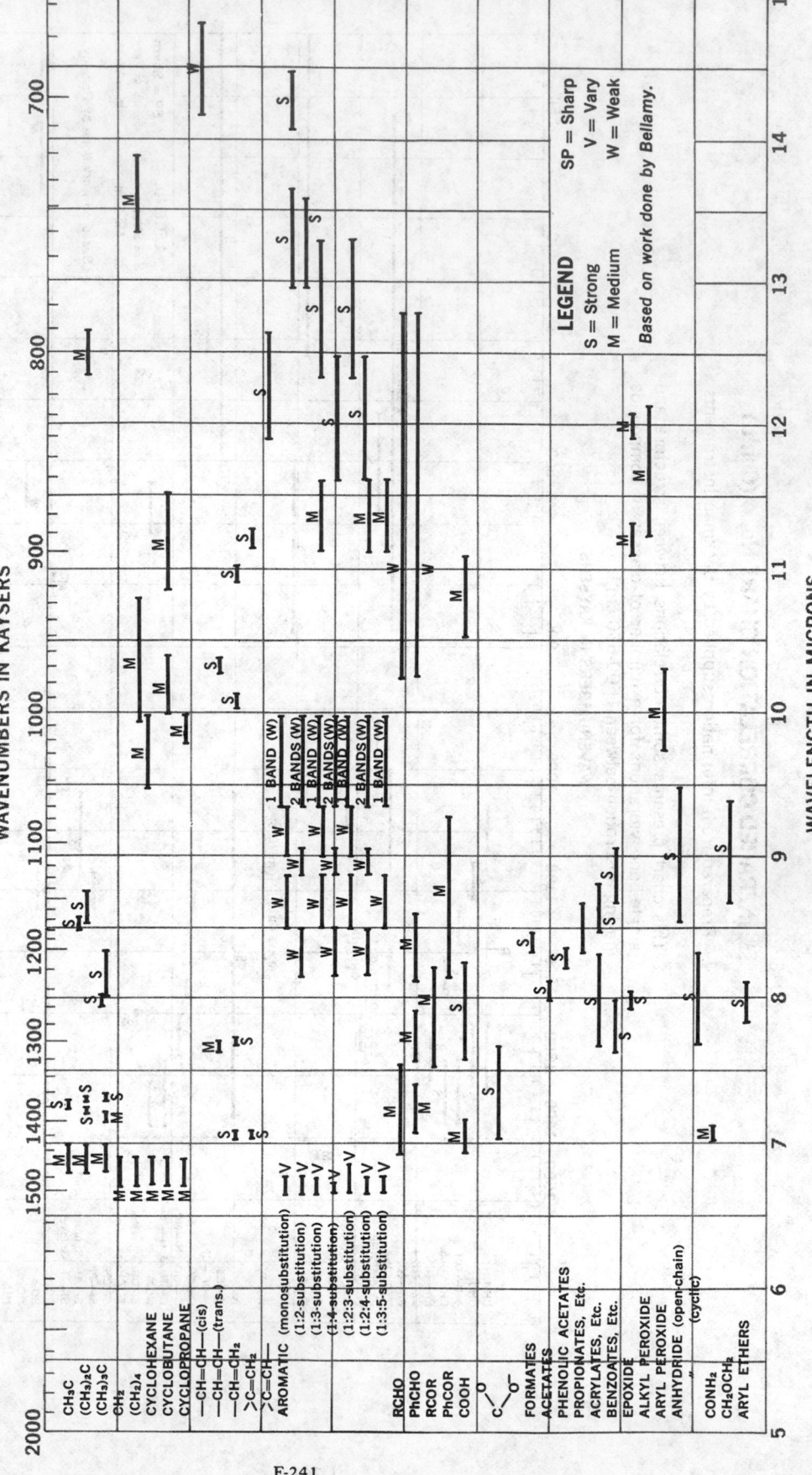

INFRARED CORRELATION CHART No. 3

Prepared from information supplied by Beckman Instruments

This chart presents some correlations between structure and the carbonyl vibrations of some classes of organic compounds. In all cases the absorption bands are strong and fall within the range of 1900-1500 cm⁻¹.

WAVENUMBERS IN KAYSERS

4000   3000   2500   2000   1500   1400

SATURATED KETONES AND ACIDS
$\alpha\beta$—UNSATURATED KETONES
ARYL KETONES
$\alpha\beta$—,$\alpha'\beta'$—UNSATURATED AND DIARYL KETONES
α—HALOGEN KETONES
$\alpha\alpha'$—HALOGEN KETONES
CHELATED KETONES

6-MEMBERED RING KETONES
5-MEMBERED RING KETONES
4-MEMBERED RING KETONES
SATURATED ALDEHYDES

$\alpha\beta$—UNSATURATED ALDEHYDES
$\alpha\beta$—,$\alpha'\beta'$—UNSATURATED ALDEHYDES
CHELATED ALDEHYDES
$\alpha\beta$—UNSATURATED ACIDS

α—HALOGEN ACIDS
ARYL ACIDS
INTRAMOLECULARLY BONDED ACIDS
IONISED ACIDS

SATURATED ESTERS 6- AND 7-RING LACTONES
$\alpha\beta$—UNSATURATED AND ARYL ESTERS
VINYL ESTERS, α—HALOGEN ESTERS
SALICYLATES AND ANTHRANILATES

CHELATED ESTERS
5-RING LACTONES
$\alpha\beta$—UNSATURATED 5-RING LACTONES
THIOL ESTERS

ACID HALIDES
CHLOROCARBONATES
ANHYDRIDES (open-chain)   SEPARATION 60 CM⁻¹
ANHYDRIDES (cyclic)   SEPARATION 60 CM⁻¹

ALKYL PEROXIDES   SEPARATION 25 CM⁻¹
ARYL PEROXIDES   SEPARATION 25 CM⁻¹
PRIMARY AMIDES (CO)   FREE BONDED
SECONDARY AMIDES AND —δ LACTAMS (CO)   FREE BONDED

TERTIARY AMIDES (CO)
γ—LACTAMS   FUSED RINGS ⊢——⊣ UNFUSED
β—LACTAMS   FUSED ⊢—⊣ ⊢—⊣ UNFUSED RINGS

3   4   5   6   7

WAVELENGTH IN MICRONS

INFRARED CORRELATION CHART No. 2

Prepared from information supplied by Beckman Instruments

This chart presents some information regarding structure, double-bond vibrations, hydrogen stretching and triple-bond vibrations.

HYDROGEN STRETCHING AND TRIPLE-BOND VIBRATIONS, 3750-2000 CM.⁻¹   DOUBLE-BOND VIBRATIONS, ETC. 2000-1500 CM.⁻¹

WAVENUMBERS IN KAYSERS

WAVELENGTH IN MICRONS

LEGEND

S = Strong   SP = Sharp
M = Medium   V = Vary   Based on work done by Bellamy.
W = Weak

Row labels (hydrogen stretching / triple-bond section):
CH₃
CH₂
CH
CH=CH
CH=CH₂
>C=CH₂
CH≡CR
RC≡CR¹
CHO
AROMATIC CH
COOH
OH
C=O
NH₂
NH
=NH
CONH₂
CONH (open-chain)
CONH (lactams)
NH₃⁺RCOOH
NH₄⁺CLRCOOH
NH₂ RCOO—X⁺
PYRIDINE, Etc.
AZIDES
C≡N
α,β— UNSATURATED NITRILES
C≡N—
P—H
NH₄⁺
CN⁻, OCN⁻, Etc.
P—OH
SH
Si H

Annotations: (MONOMER) M POLYMERS (V) FREE (V) SINGLE BRIDGE (V) CHELATES (W) w-BROAD DIMER 2 BANDS(S) FREE 2 BANDS (M) BONDED (S) FREE BAND (M) BONDED (S) FREE (M) BONDED (S) FREE (M) BONDED (M) FREE (M) BONDED (M) (w) MOST CONTINUOUS M BAND SERIES VS

Right-hand section labels (double-bond vibrations):
ALLENES
—CH=CH₂
>C=CH₂
C=C
C=C (conjugated)
AROMATIC (all types of substitution except as below)
AROMATIC (para- and unsymmetrical trisubstitution)
AROMATIC (vicinal trisubstitution)
AROMATIC (conjugated)
AROMATIC (all types)
C=N
C=N (conjugated or cyclic)
N=N
CONH₂ (see chart 4 for CO)
CDNH (open-chains only)
NH₂
NH
NH₃⁺
NH₄⁺CLR
COO⁻
C—NO₂
O—NO₂
N—NO₂
—O—N=O
PYRIDINE, Etc.
PYRIMIDINE, Etc.
TROPOLONES

CHARACTERISTIC BAND PATTERNS FOR VARIOUS TYPES OF SUBSTITUTION

BONDED (S) FREE (S) BONDED(S) FREE (S)

F-239

INFRARED CORRELATION CHART No. 1 (Con't.)

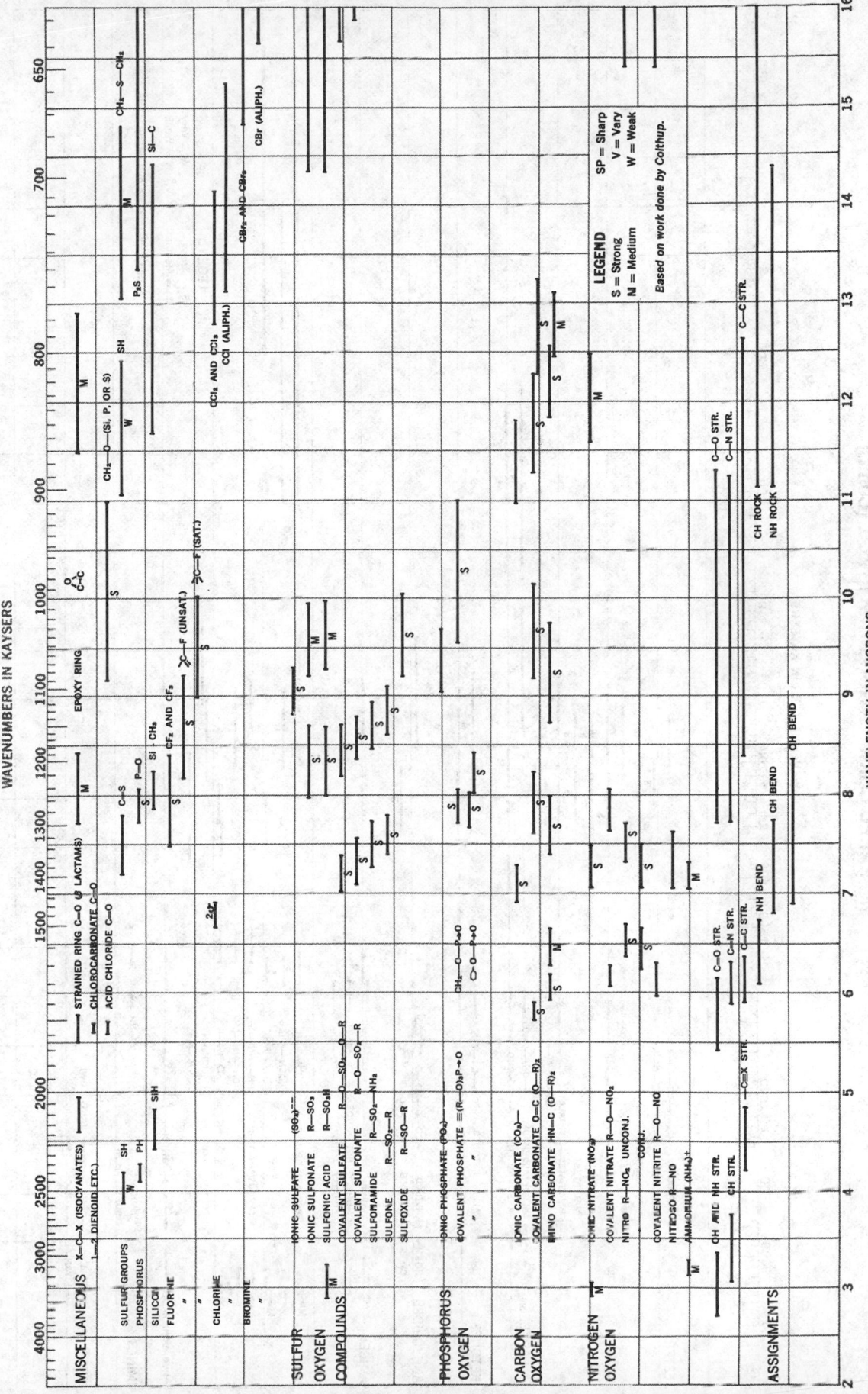

INFRARED CORRELATION CHART No. 1 (Con't.)

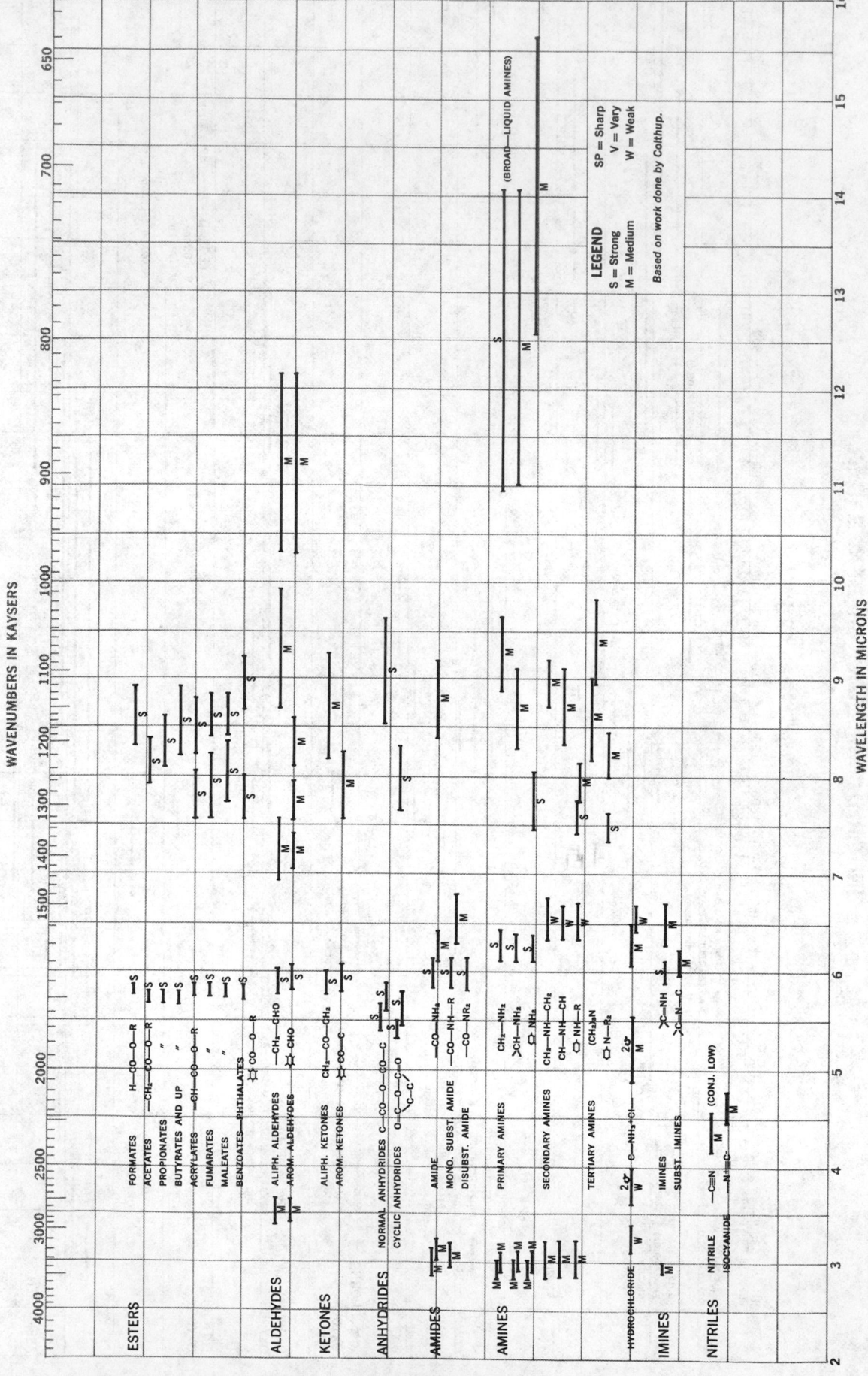

WAVENUMBERS IN KAYSERS

WAVELENGTH IN MICRONS

INFRARED CORRELATION CHART No. 1

Prepared from information supplied by Beckman Instruments

ENERGY CONVERSION FACTORS

Quantity	Value	Unit	Error (ppm)
1 kg	5.609538(24)	10^{29} MeV	4.4
1 amu	931.4812(52)	MeV	5.5
Electron mass	0.5110041(16)	MeV	3.1
Proton mass	938.2592(52)	MeV	5.5
Neutron mass	939.5527(52)	MeV	5.5
1 electron volt	1.6021917(70)	10^{-19} J 10^{-12} erg	4.4
	2.4179659(81)	10^{14} Hz	3.3
	8.065465(27)	10^{5} m^{-1} 10^{3} cm^{-1}	3.3
	1.160485(49)	10^{4} K	42
Energy–wavelength conversion	1.2398541(41)	10^{-6} eV·m 10^{-4} eV·cm	3.3
Rydberg constant, R_{∞}	2.179914(17)	10^{-18} J 10^{-11} erg	7.6
	13.605826(45)	eV	3.3
	3.2898423(11)	10^{15} Hz	0.35
	1.578936(67)	10^{5} K	43
Bohr magneton, μ_B	5.788381(18)	10^{-5} eV T^{-1}	3.1
	1.3996108(43)	10^{10} Hz T^{-1}	3.1
	46.68598(14)	m^{-1}·T^{-1} 10^{-2} cm^{-1}·T^{-1}	3.1
	0.671733(29)	K T^{-1}	43
Nuclear magneton, μ_n	3.152526(21)	10^{-8} eV T^{-1}	6.8
	7.622700(42)	10^{6} Hz T^{-1}	5.5
	2.542659(14)	10^{-2} m^{-1}·T^{-1} 10^{-4} cm^{-1}·T^{-1}	5.5
	3.65846(16)	10^{-4} K·T^{-1}	44
Gas constant, R_0	8.20562(35)	10^{-2} m^3·atm kmole^{-1}·K^{-1}	42
Standard volume of ideal gas, V_0	22.4136	m^3 kmole^{-1}	

RECOMMENDED CONSISTENT VALUES OF THE FUNDAMENTAL PHYSICAL CONSTANTS (Continued)

Quantity	Symbol	Value	Uncertainty, ppm
26. Proton Moment in Nuclear Magnetons	μ_p/μ_N	$2.7928456(11)$	0.38
27. Bohr Magneton	$\mu_B = e\hbar/2m_e$	$9.274078(36) \times 10^{-24}$ J T^{-1}	3.9
28. Nuclear Magneton	$\mu_N = e\hbar/2m_p$	$5.050824(20) \times 10^{-27}$ J T^{-1}	3.9
29. Electron Magnetic Moment	μ_e	$9.28432(36) \times 10^{-24}$ J T^{-1}	3.9
30. Proton Magnetic Moment	μ_p	$1.4106171(55) \times 10^{-26}$ J T^{-1}	3.9
31. Proton Magnetic Moment in Bohr Magnetons	μ_p/μ_B	$1.521032209(16) \times 10^{-3}$	0.011
32. Ratio, Electron to Proton Magnetic Moments	μ_e/μ_p	$658.210688(66)$	0.010
33. Ratio, Muon Moment to Proton Moment	μ_μ/μ_p	$3.1833402(72)$	2.3
34. Muon Magnetic Moment	μ_μ	$4.490474(18) \times 10^{-25}$ J T^{-1}	3.9
35. Proton Gyromagnetic Ratio	γ_p	$2.6751987(75) \times 10^{8}$ s^{-1} T^{-1}	2.8
36. Diamagnetic Shielding Factor, Spherical H$_2$O Sample	$1 + \sigma(\mathrm{H_2O})$	$1.000025637(67)$	0.067
37. Proton Gyromagnetic Ratio (uncorrected)	$\gamma'_p/2\pi$	$2.6751301(75) \times 10^{8}$ s^{-1} T^{-1}	2.8
	$\gamma'_p/2\pi$	$42.57602(12)$ MHz T^{-1}	2.8
38. Proton Moment in Nuclear Magnetons (uncorrected)	μ'_p/μ_N	$2.7927740(11)$	0.38
39. Proton Compton Wavelength	$\lambda_{C,p} = h/m_p c$	$1.3214099(22) \times 10^{-15}$ m	1.7
	$\hbar_{C,p} = \lambda_{C,p}/2\pi$	$2.103092(36) \times 10^{-16}$ m	1.7
40. Neutron Compton Wavelength	$\lambda_{C,n} = \hbar/m_n c$	$1.3195909(22) \times 10^{-15}$ m	1.7
	$\hbar_{C,n} = \lambda_{C,n}/2\pi$	$2.1001941(35) \times 10^{-16}$ m	1.7
41. Molar Gas Constant	R	$8.31441(26)$ J mol^{-1} K^{-1}	31
42. Molar Volume, Ideal Gas ($T_0 = 273.15$ K, $p_0 = 1$ atm)	$V_m = RT_0/p_0$	$0.02241383(70)$ m^3 mol^{-1}	31
43. Boltzmann Constant	$k = R/N_A$	$1.380662(44) \times 10^{-23}$ J K^{-1}	32
44. Stefan-Boltzmann Constant	$\sigma = (\pi^2/60)k^4/\hbar^3 c^2$	$5.67032(71) \times 10^{-8}$ W m^{-2} K^{-4}	125
45. First Radiation Constant	$c_1 = 2\pi hc^2$	$3.741832(20) \times 10^{-16}$ W m^2	5.4
46. Second Radiation Constant	$c_2 = hc/k$	$0.01438786(45)$ m K	31
47. Gravitational Constant	G	$6.6720(41) \times 10^{-11}$ N m^2 kg^{-2}	615

Data from CODATA Bulletin No. 11, ICSU CODATA Central Office, 19 Westendstrasse, 6 Frankfurt/Main, German Federal Republic (copies of this bulletin are available at no cost from this office).

RECOMMENDED CONSISTENT VALUES OF THE FUNDAMENTAL PHYSICAL CONSTANTS

Quantity	Symbol	Value	Uncertainty, ppm
1. Permeability of Vacuum	μ_0	$4\pi \times 10^{-7}$ H m^{-1} $= 12.5663706144 \times 10^{-7}$ H m^{-1}	
2. Speed of Light in Vacuum	c	$2.99792458(1.2)$ m s^{-1}	0.004
3. Permittivity of Vacuum	$\epsilon_0 = (\mu_0 c^2)^{-1}$	$8.85418782(7) \times 10^{-12}$ F m^{-1}	0.008
4. Fine Structure Constant, $\mu_0 c e^2 / 2h$	α	$0.0072973506(60)$	0.82
	α^{-1}	$137.03604(11)$	0.82
5. Elementary Charge	e	$1.6021892(46) \times 10^{-19}$ C	2.9
6. Planck Constant	h	$6.626176(36) \times 10^{-34}$ J Hz^{-1}	5.4
	$\hbar = h/2\pi$	$1.0545887(57) \times 10^{-34}$ J s	5.4
7. Avogadro Constant	N_A	$6.022045(31) \times 10^{23}$ mol^{-1}	5.1
8. Atomic Mass Unit	$1u = (10^{-3}\ \text{kg mol}^{-1})/N_A$	$1.6605655(86) \times 10^{-27}$ kg	5.1
9. Electron Rest Mass	m_e	$0.9109534(47) \times 10^{-30}$ kg	5.1
		$5.485026(21) \times 10^{-4}$ u	0.38
10. Muon Rest Mass	m_μ	$1.883566(11) \times 10^{-28}$ kg	5.6
		$0.11342920(26)$ u	2.3
11. Proton Rest Mass	m_p	$1.6726485(86) \times 10^{-27}$ kg	5.1
		$1.007276470(11)$ u	0.011
12. Neutron Rest Mass	m_n	$1.6749543(86) \times 10^{-27}$ kg	5.1
		$1.00865012(37)$ u	0.037
13. Ratio, Proton Mass to Electron Mass	m_p/m_e	$1,836.15152(70)$	0.38
14. Ratio, Muon Mass to Electron Mass	m_μ/m_e	$206.76865(47)$	2.3
15. Specific Electron Charge	e/m_e	$1.7588047(49) \times 10^{11}$ C kg^{-1}	2.8
16. Faraday Constant	$\mathcal{F} = N_A e$	$9.64856(27) \times 10^4$ C mol^{-1}	2.8
17. Magnetic Flux Quantum	$\Phi_0 = h/2e$	$2.0678506(54) \times 10^{-15}$ Wb	2.6
	h/e	$4.135701(11) \times 10^{-15}$ J Hz^{-1} C^{-1}	2.6
18. Josephson Frequency-Voltage Ratio	$2e/h$	$483.5939(13)$ THz V^{-1}	2.6
19. Quantum of Circulation	$h/2m_e$	$3.6369455(60) \times 10^{-4}$ J Hz^{-1} kg^{-1}	1.6
	h/m_e	$7.273891(12) \times 10^{-4}$ J Hz^{-1} kg^{-1}	1.6
20. Rydberg Constant	R_∞	$1.097373177(83) \times 10^7$ m^{-1}	0.075
21. Bohr Radius	$a_0 = \alpha/4\pi R_\infty$	$0.52917706(44) \times 10^{-10}$ m	0.82
22. Electron Compton Wavelength	$\lambda_c = \alpha^2/2R_\infty$	$2.4263089(40) \times 10^{-12}$ m	1.6
23. Classical Electron Radius	$\lambdabar_c = \lambda_c/2\pi = \alpha a_0$	$3.8615905(64) \times 10^{-13}$ m	1.6
	$r_e = \mu_0 e^2/4\pi m_e = \alpha \lambdabar_c$	$2.8179380(70) \times 10^{-15}$ m	2.5
24. Electron g-Factor	$\tfrac{1}{2}g_e = \mu_e/\mu_B$	$1.0011596567(35)$	0.0035
25. Muon g-Factor	$\tfrac{1}{2}g_\mu$	$1.0011616(31)$	0.31

VALUES OF THE GAS CONSTANT, R

Coleman J. Major

The numerical value of the gas constant, R, defined by the equation PV = nRT, depends upon the units of P, V, n, and T. A large number of values of the constant may be calculated. The accompanying table gives 84 values of R in a convenient form using the most common units of pressure and volume. It also incorporates both the pound and gram mole and both Rankine and Kelvin temperature scales. Various combinations of metric and English units may, therefore, be used without the necessity of converting each variable to a common system of units. Conversion factors and constants used for computing the values of R are listed at the bottom of the table.

The following example illustrates the use of the table:

Calculate: The volume in ft³ occupied by 2 lb. moles of a gas at 15°C at a pressure of 32.2 ft. of water, assuming the ideal gas law.

Solution: 15°C + 273.2 = 288.2°K

Enter the top of the table under the column headed "ft H₂O" and proceed downward to the value of 44.6 for R. (Note that this lines up horizontally with the desired units of ft³, °K, and lb. moles shown on the left side of the table)

$$V = \frac{nRT}{P} = \frac{2 \times 44.6 \times 288.2}{32.2} = 798 \text{ ft}^3$$

$$\text{Values of Gas Constant, } R = \frac{PV}{nT}$$

Absolute Pressure

Volume	Temp.	moles	Atm	psia	mm Hg	cm Hg	in Hg	in H₂O	ft H₂O
ft³	°K	gm	0.00290	0.0426	2.20	0.220	0.0867	1.18	0.0982
		lb	1.31	19.31	999	99.9	39.3	535	44.6
	°R	gm	0.00161	0.02366	1.22	0.122	0.0482	0.655	0.0546
		lb	0.730	10.73	555	55.5	21.8	297	24.8
cm³	°K	gm	82.05	1206	62,400	6240	2450	33,400	2780
		lb	37,200	547,000	2.83×10^7	2.83×10^6	1.11×10^6	1.51×10^7	1.26×10^6
	°R	gm	45.6	670	34,600	3460	1360	18,500	1550
		lb	20,700	304,000	1.57×10^7	1.57×10^6	619,000	8.41×10^6	701,000
liters	°K	gm	0.08205	1.206	62.4	6.24	2.45	33.4	2.78
		lb	37.2	547	28,300	2830	1113	15,140	1262
	°R	gm	0.0456	0.670	34.6	3.46	1.36	18.5	1.55
		lb	20.7	304	15,700	1570	619	8410	701

Conversion Factors and Constants

1 lb. = 453.59 gm
1 atm = 14.696 psia
1 atm = 760 mm Hg
1 atm = 76 cm Hg
1 atm = 29.921 in Hg
1 atm = 406.79 in H₂O
1 atm = 33.90 ft H₂O

359.0 ft³/lb mole
22.414 cm³/gm mole
1 inch = 2.54 cm
Std. temp. = 273.16°K or 491.69°R
28.31605 liters = 1 ft³
$R = 8.31432 \pm 0.00034 \times 10^7$ erg °K⁻¹ mol⁻¹

HEATS OF FORMATION OF FREE RADICALS

Radical	ΔH_f°	Ref.
$H\dot{O}_2$	5.3 ± 2	44
HS	33.1 ± 2	44
SiH_3	49.1 ± 3	62, 64
$C_6H_5Si(CH_3)_2$	39	58
$(C_6H_5)_2SiCH_3$	78	58
$(C_6H_5)_3Si$	116.2	58
GeH_3	57	58

STRENGTHS OF CHEMICAL BONDS (*Continued*)

BOND STRENGTHS OF SOME ORGANIC MOLECULES

Bond strengths at 298 K expressed in kcal mol^{-1} for some organic molecules of the general formula R—X are presented below. Some are experimental values taken from the preceding tables; the remainder are calculated from the heats of formation of the radicals, listed above, and the heats of formation of the parent compounds from sources indicated by the references below. The table also includes the bond strengths for ammonia, water, and the hydrogen halides.

X R	H	F	Cl	Br	I	OH	NH_2	OCH_3	CH_3	CH_3CO
H	104.207	135.8	103.1	87.4	71.4	119	110	104	104	86
CH_3	104	109b	84a	70a	56a	91a	87a	81a	88a	80a
C_2H_5	98	–	81a	68a	53a	91a	84a	81a	85a	77a
i-C_3H_7	95	106a	81a	68a	53a	92a	85a	81a	84a	75a
t-C_4H_9	92	–	81a	67a	50a	91a	84a	81a	82a	71a
C_6H_5	110	125a	95a	80	64a	110a	104a	98a	100a	93a
$C_6H_5CH_2$	85	–	69a	55a	45a	78a	–	–	72a	63a
CCl_3	96	102a	73a	55a	–	–	–	–	88d	–
CF_3	106	130a	86a	71a	54	–	–	–	99a	–
CH_3CO	86	119a	81a	67a	50a	106a	99c	97	80a	66a
CN	120	–	97	83	73	–	–	–	–	–

References

a. **Cox, J. D. and Pilcher, G.**, *Thermochemistry of Organic and Organometallic Compounds,* Academic Press, London, 1970.
b. **Lacher, J. R. and Skinner, H. A.,** *J. Chem. Soc., A,* 1034, 1968.
c. **Benson, S. W. et al.,** *Chem. Rev.,* 69, 279, 1969.
d. **Hu, A. T., Sinke, G. C., and Mintz, M. J.,** *J. Chem. Thermodynamics,* 4, 239, 1972.

To convert from	To	Multiply by
Rods	Links (Ramden's)	16.5
"	Meters	5.0292
"	Miles (statute)	0.003125
"	Perches	1
"	Yards	5.5
Rods (Brit., volume)	Cu. feet	1000
"	Cu. meters	28.316847
Roods (Brit.)	Acres	0.25
"	Ares	10.117141
"	Sq. perches	40
"	Sq. yards	1210
Ropes (Brit.)	Feet	20
"	Meters	6.096
"	Yards	6.6666666
Scruples (apoth.)	Drams (apoth. or troy)	0.333333
"	Drams (avdp.)	0.73142857
"	Grains	20
"	Grams	1.2959782
"	Ounces (apoth. or troy)	0.041666
"	Ounces (avdp.)	0.045714286
"	Pennyweights	0.833333
"	Pounds (apoth. or troy)	0.003472222
"	Pounds (avdp.)	0.0028571429
Scruples (Brit., fluid)	Minims (Brit.)	20
Seams (Brit.)	Bushels (Brit.)	8
"	Cu. feet	10.27479
"	Liters	290.9414
Seconds (angular)	Degrees	0.000277777
"	Minutes	0.0166666
"	Radians	4.8481368×10^{-6}
Seconds (mean solar)	Days (mean solar)	1.1574074×10^{-5}
"	Days (sidereal)	1.1605763×10^{-5}
"	Hours (mean solar)	0.0002777777
"	Hours (sidereal)	0.00027853831
"	Minutes (mean solar)	0.0166666
"	Minutes (sidereal)	0.016712298
"	Seconds (sidereal)	1.00273791
Seconds (sidereal)	Days (mean solar)	1.1542472×10^{-5}
"	Days (sidereal)	1.1574074×10^{-5}
"	Hours (mean solar)	0.00027701932
"	Hours (sidereal)	0.000277777
"	Minutes (mean solar)	0.016621159
"	Minutes (sidereal)	0.0166666
"	Seconds (mean solar)	0.99726957
Siemen's units	*Same as Mhos*	
Skeins	Feet	360
"	Meters	109.728
Slugs	Geepounds	1
"	Kilograms	14.5939
"	Pounds (avdp.)	32.1740
Slugs/cu. ft.	Grams/cu. cm.	0.515379
Space (entire)	Hemispheres	2
"	Steradians	12.566371
Spans	Centimeters	22.86
"	Fathoms	0.125
"	Feet	0.75
"	Inches	9
"	Quarters (Brit. linear)	1
Spherical right angles	Hemispheres	0.25
"	Spheres	0.125
"	Steradians	1.5707963
Sq. centimeters	Ares	1×10^{-6}
"	Circ. mm	127.32395
"	Circ. mils	197352.52
"	Sq. chains (Gunter's)	2.4710538×10^{-7}
"	Sq. chains (Ramden's)	1.0763910×10^{-7}
"	Sq. decimeters	0.01
"	Sq. feet	0.0010703910
"	Sq. ft. (U.S. Survey)	0.0010763867
"	Sq. inches	0.15500031
"	Sq. meters	0.0001

To convert from	To	Multiply by
Sq. centimeters	Sq. mm	100
"	Sq. mils	155000.31
"	Sq. rods	3.9536861×10^{-6}
"	Sq. yards	0.00011959900
Sq. chains (Gunter's)	Acres	0.1
"	Sq. feet	4356
"	Sq. ft. (U.S. Survey)	4355.9826
"	Sq. inches	627264
"	Sq. links (Gunter's)	10000
"	Sq. meters	404.68564
"	Sq. miles	0.00015625
"	Sq. rods	16
"	Sq. yards	484
Sq. chains (Ramden's)	Acres	0.22956841
"	Sq. feet	10000
"	Sq. ft. (U.S. Survey)	9999.9600
"	Sq. inches	1.44×10^{6}
"	Sq. links (Ramden's)	10000
"	Sq. meters	929.0304
"	Sq. miles	0.00035870064
"	Sq. rods	36.730946
"	Sq. yards	1111.111
Sq. decimeters	Sq. cm	100
"	Sq. inches	15.500031
Square degrees	Steradians	0.00030461742
Sq. dekameters	Acres	0.024710538
"	Ares	1
"	Sq. meters	100
"	Sq. yards	119.59900
Sq. feet	Acres	2.295684×10^{-5}
"	Ares	0.0009290304
"	Sq. cm	929.0304
"	Sq. chains (Gunter's)	0.00022956841
"	Sq. ft. (U.S. Survey)	0.99999600
"	Sq. inches	144
"	Sq. links (Gunter's)	2.2956841
"	Sq. meters	0.09290304
"	Sq. miles	3.5870064×10^{-8}
"	Sq. rods	0.0036730946
"	Sq. yards	0.111111
Sq. feet (U.S. Survey)	Acres	$2.29569330 \times 10^{-5}$
"	Sq. centimeters	929.03412
"	Sq. chains (Ramden's)	0.00010000040
"	Sq. feet	1.0000040
Sq. hectometers	Sq. meters	10000
Sq. inches	Circ. mils	1273239.5
"	Sq. cm	6.4516
"	Sq. chains (Gunter's)	1.5942251×10^{-6}
"	Sq. decimeters	0.064516
"	Sq. feet	0.0069444
"	Sq. ft. (U.S. Survey)	0.0069444167
"	Sq. links (Gunter's)	0.01594225
"	Sq. meters	0.00064516
"	Sq. miles	$2.4909767 \times 10^{-10}$
"	Sq. mm	645.16
"	Sq. mils	1×10^{6}
Sq. inches/sec.	Sq. cm./hr.	23225.76
"	Sq. cm./sec.	6.4516
"	Sq. ft./min.	0.416666
Sq. kilometers	Acres	247.10538
"	Sq. feet	1.0763910×10^{7}
"	Sq. ft. (U.S. Survey)	1.0763867×10^{7}
"	Sq. inches	1.5500031×10^{9}
"	Sq. meters	1×10^{6}
"	Sq. miles	0.38610216
"	Sq. yards	1.1959900×10^{6}
Sq. links (Gunter's)	Acres	1×10^{-5}
"	Sq. cm	404.68564
"	Sq. chains (Gunter's)	0.0001
"	Sq. feet	0.4356
"	Sq. ft. (U.S. Survey)	0.43559826
"	Sq. Inches	62.7264

To convert from	To	Multiply by
Sq. links (Ramden's)..	Acres	2.2956841×10^{-5}
"	Sq. feet	1
Sq. meters	Acres	0.00024710538
"	Ares	0.01
"	Hectares	0.0001
"	Sq. cm	10000
"	Sq. feet	10.763910
"	Sq. inches	1550.0031
"	Sq. kilometers	1×10^{-6}
"	Sq. links (Gunter's)	24.710538
"	Sq. links (Ramden's)	10.763910
"	Sq. miles	3.8610216×10^{-7}
"	Sq. mm	1×10^{6}
"	Sq. rods	0.039536861
"	Sq. yards	1.1959900
Sq. miles	Acres	640
"	Hectares	258.99881
"	Sq. chains (Gunter's)	6400
"	Sq. feet	2.7878288×10^{7}
"	Sq. ft. (U.S. Survey)	2.78288×10^{7}
"	Sq. kilometers	2.5899881
"	Sq. meters	2589988.1
"	Sq. rods	102400
"	Sq. yards	3.0976×10^{6}
Sq. millimeters	Circ. mm	1.2732395
"	Circ. mils	1973.5252
"	Sq. cm	0.01
"	Sq. inches	0.0015500031
"	Sq. meters	1×10^{-6}
Sq. mils	Circ. mils	1.2732395
"	Sq. cm	6.4516×10^{-6}
"	Sq. inches	1×10^{-6}
"	Sq. mm	0.00064516
Sq. rods	Acres	0.00625
"	Ares	0.2529285264
"	Hectares	0.002529285264
"	Sq. cm	252928.5264
"	Sq. feet	272.25
"	Sq. ft. (U.S. Survey)	272.24891
"	Sq. inches	39204
"	Sq. links (Gunter's)	625
"	Sq. links (Ramden's)	272.25
"	Sq. meters	25.29285264
"	Sq. miles	9.765625×10^{-6}
"	Sq. yards	30.25
Sq. yards	Acres	0.00020661157
"	Ares	0.0083612736
"	Hectares	8.3612736×10^{-5}
"	Sq. cm	8361.2736
"	Sq. chains (Gunter's)	0.0020661157
"	Sq. chains (Ramden's)	0.0009
"	Sq. feet	9
"	Sq. ft. (U.S. Survey)	8.9999640
"	Sq. inches	1296
"	Sq. links (Gunter's)	20.661157
"	Sq. links (Ramden's)	9
"	Sq. meters	0.83612736
"	Sq. miles	$3.228305785 \times 10^{-7}$
"	Sq. perches (Brit.)	0.033057851
"	Sq. rods	0.033057851
Statamperes	Abamperes	3.335635×10^{-11}
"	Amperes	3.335635×10^{-10}
"	E.M. cgs. units of current	3.335635×10^{-11}
"	E.S. cgs. units	1
Statcoulombs	Ampere-hours	9.265653×10^{-14}
"	Coulombs	3.335635×10^{-10}
"	Electronic charges	2.082093×10^{9}
"	E.M. cgs. units of electric charge	3.335635×10^{-11}
Statfarads	E.M. cgs. units of capacitance	1.112646×10^{-21}
"	E.S. cgs. units	1

To convert from	To	Multiply by
Statfarads	Farads	1.112646×10^{-12}
"	Microfarads	1.112646×10^{-6}
Stathenries	Abhenries	8.987584×10^{20}
"	E.M. cgs. units of inductance	8.987584×10^{20}
"	E.S. cgs. units	1
"	Henries	8.987584×10^{11}
"	Millihenries	8.987584×10^{14}
Statohms	Abohms	8.987584×10^{20}
"	E.S. cgs. units	1
"	Ohms	8.987584×10^{11}
Statvolts	Abvolts	2.997930×10^{10}
"	Volts	299.7930
Statvolts/cm	Volts/cm	299.7930
"	Volts/inch	761.4742
Statvolts/inch	Volts/cm	118.0287
Steradians	Hemispheres	0.15915494
"	Solid angles	0.079577472
"	Spheres	0.079577472
"	Spher. right angles	0.63661977
"	Square degrees	3282.8063
Steres	Cubic meters	1
"	Decisteres	10
"	Dekasteres	0.1
"	Liters	999.972
Stilbs	Candles/sq. cm	1
"	Candles/sq. inch	6.4516
"	Lamberts	3.1415927
Stokes*	Cgs. units of kinematic viscosity	1
"	Sq. cm./sec	1
"	Sq. inches/sec	0.15500031
"	Poise cu. cm./gram	1
Stones (Brit., legal)	Centals (Brit.)	0.14
Tons (long)	Dynes	9.96402×10^{8}
"	Hundredweights (long)	20
"	Hundredweights (short)	22.4
"	Kilograms	1016.0469
"	Ounces (avdp.)	35840
"	Pounds (apoth. or troy)	2722.22
"	Pounds (avdp.)	2240
"	Tons (metric)	1.0160469
"	Tons (short)	1.12
Tons (metric)	Dynes	9.80665×10^{8}
"	Grams	1×10^{6}
"	Hundredweights (short)	22.046226
"	Kilograms	1000
"	Ounces (avdp.)	35273.962
"	Pounds (apoth. or troy)	2679.2289
"	Pounds (avdp.)	2204.6226
"	Tons (long)	0.98420653
"	Tons (short)	1.1023113
Tons (short)	Dynes	8.89644×10^{8}
"	Hundredweights (short)	20
"	Kilograms	907.18474
"	Ounces (avdp.)	32000
"	Pounds (apoth. or troy)	2430.555
"	Pounds (avdp.)	2000
"	Tons (long)	0.89285714
"	Tons (metric)	0.90718474
Tons of refrig. (U.S., comm.)	B.t.u. (IST.)/hr	12000
"	B.t.u. (IST.)/min	200
"	Cal., kg. (IST.)/hr	3023.949
"	Horsepower	4.71611
"	Kg. of ice melted/hr	37.971
"	Lb. of ice melted/hr	83.711
Tons of refrig. (U.S., std.)	B.t.u. (IST.)	288000
"	B.t.u. (mean)	287774
"	Cal., kg. (IST.)	72574.8

* See also separate table of "viscosity conversion factors".

To convert from	To	Multiply by
Tons of refrig. (U.S., std.)	Cal., *kg.* (mean)	72517.9
"	Lb. of ice melted	2009.1
Tons (long)/sq. ft.	Atmospheres	1.05849
"	Dynes/sq. cm.	1.07252×10^6
"	Grams/sq. cm.	1093.6638
"	Pounds/sq. ft.	2240
Tons (short)/sq. ft.	Atmospheres	0.945082
"	Dynes/sq. cm.	957.605
"	Grams/sq. cm.	976.486
"	Pounds/sq. inch	13.8888
Tons (long)/sq. in.	Atmospheres	152.423
"	Dynes/sq. cm.	1.54443×10^8
"	Grams/sq. cm.	157487.59
Tons (short)/sq. in.	Dynes/sq. cm.	1.37895×10^8
"	Kg./sq. mm.	1406.139
"	Pounds/sq. inch	2000
Torrs (*or* Tors)	Millimeters of Hg (0°C.)	1
Townships (U.S.)	Acres	23040
"	Sections	36
"	Sq. miles	36
Tuns	Gallons (U.S.)	252
"	Hogsheads	4
Volts	Abvolts	1×10^8
"	Mks. (r *or* nr) units	1
"	Statvolts	0.003335635
"	Volts (Int.)	0.999670
Volts (Int.)	Volts	1.000330
Volts/°C.	Joules/(coulomb × °C.)	1
Volt-coulombs	Joules (Int.)	0.999835
Volt-coulombs (Int.)	Joules	1.000165
Volt-electronic charge-seconds	Planck's constant*	2.41814×10^{14}
Volt-faraday (chem.)-seconds	Planck's constant*	1.45650×10^{38}
Volt-faraday (phys.)-seconds	Planck's constant	1.45690×10^{38}
Volt-seconds	Maxwells	1×10^8
Watts	B.t.u./hr.	3.41443
"	B.t.u. (mean)/hr.	3.40952
"	B.t.u. (mean)/min.	0.0568253
"	B.t.u./sec.	0.000948451
"	B.t.u. (mean)/sec.	0.000947088
"	Cal., *gm.*/hr.	860.421
"	Cal., *gm.* (mean)/hr.	859.184
"	Cal., *gm.* (20°C.)/hr.	860.853
"	Cal., *gm.*/min.	14.3403
"	Cal., *gm.* (IST.)/min.	14.3310
"	Cal., *gm.* (mean)/min.	14.3197
"	Cal., *kh.*/min.	0.0143403
"	Cal., *kg.* (IST.)/min.	0.0143310
"	Cal., *kg.* (mean)/min.	0.0143197
"	Ergs/sec.	1×10^7
"	Foot-pounds/min.	44.2537
"	Horsepower	0.00134102
"	Horsepower (boiler)	0.000101942
"	Horsepower (elec.)	0.00134048
"	Horsepower (metric)	0.00135962
"	Joules/sec.	1
"	Kilowatts	0.001
"	Liter-atm./hr.	35.5282
Watts (Int.)	B.t.u./hr.	3.41499
"	B.t.u. (mean)/hr.	3.41008
"	B.t.u./min.	0.569165
"	B.t.u. (mean)/min.	0.0568347
"	Cal., *gm.*/hr.	860.563
"	Cal., *gm.* (mean)/hr.	859.326
"	Cal., *kg.*/min.	0.0143427
"	Cal., *kg.* (IST.)/min.	0.0143333
"	Cal., *kg.* (mean)/min.	0.0143221

To convert from	To	Multiply by
Watts (Int.)	Ergs/sec.	1.000165×10^7
"	Joules (Int.)/sec.	1
"	Watts	1.000165
Watts/sq. cm.	B.t.u./(hr. × sq. ft.)	3172.10
"	Cal., *ym.*/(hr. × sq. cm.)	860.421
"	Ft.-lb./(min. × sq. ft.)	41113.1
Watts/sq. in.	B.t.u./(hr. × sq. ft.)	491.677
"	Cal., *gm.*/(hr. × sq. cm.)	133.365
"	Ft.-lb./(min. × sq. ft.)	6372.54
Watt-hours	B.t.u.	3.41443
"	B.t.u. (mean)	3.40952
"	Cal., *gm.*	860.421
Watt-hours	Cal., *kg.* (mean)	0.859184
"	Cal., *gm.* (mean)	859.184
"	Foot-pounds	2655.22
"	Hp.-hours	0.00134102
"	Joules	3600
"	Joules (Int.)	3599.41
"	Kg.-meters	367.098
"	Kw.-hours	0.001
"	Watt-hours (Int.)	0.999835
Watt-sec.	Foot-pounds	0.737562
"	Gram-cm.	10197.16
"	Joules	1
"	Liter-atm.	0.00986895
"	Volt-coulombs	1
Wave length of orange-red line of krypton 86	Ångström units	6057.80211
"	Millimeters	0.000605780211
Wave length of red line of cadmium	Ångström units	6438.4696
"	Millimeters	0.00064384696
Webers	Cgs. units of induction flux	1×10^8
"	E.M. cgs. units of induction flux	1×10^8
"	Lines	1×10^8
"	Maxwells	1×10^8
"	Mks. units of induction flux	1
"	Mks. nr units of magnetic charge	0.079577472
"	Mks. r units of magnetic charge	1
"	Volt-seconds	1
Webers/sq. cm.	Gausses	1×10^8
"	Lines/sq. cm.	1×10^8
"	Lines/sq. inch	6.4516×10^8
Webers/sq. in.	Gausses	1.5500031×10^7
Weeks (mean calendar)	Days (mean solar)	7
"	Days (sidereal)	7.0191654
"	Hours (mean solar)	168
"	Hours (sidereal)	168.45997
"	Minutes (mean solar)	10080
"	Minutes (sidereal)	10107.598
"	Months (lunar)	0.23704235
"	Months (mean calendar)	0.23013699
"	Years (calendar)	0.019178082
"	Years (sidereal)	0.019164622
"	Years (tropical)	0.019165365
Weys (Brit., mass.)	Pounds (avdp.)	252
Yards	Centimeters	91.44
"	Chains (Gunter's)	0.4545454
"	Chains (Ramden's)	0.03
"	Cubits	2
"	Fathoms	0.5
"	Feet	3
"	Feet (U.S. Survey)	2.9999940
"	Furlongs	0.00454545
"	Inches	36
"	Meters	0.9144
"	Poles (Brit.)	0.181818

* For factors for C = 12 scale or those which can be derived from same see table on Values for General Physical Constants.

CONVERSION FACTORS (Continued)

To convert from	To	Multiply by	To convert from	To	Multiply by
Yards.............	Quarters (Brit., linear)....	4	Years (sidereal)......	Days (sidereal).........	366.25640
"	Rods...................	0.181818	"	Years (calendar)..........	1.0007024
"	Spans.................	4	"	Years (tropical)..........	1.0000388
Years (calendar).....	Days (mean solar)........	365	Years (tropical).....	Days (mean solar).......	365.24219
"	Hours (mean solar).......	8760	"	Days (sidereal)..........	366.24219
"	Minutes (mean solar)......	525600	"	Hours (mean solar).......	8765.8126
"	Months (lunar)..........	12.360065	"	Hours (sidereal).........	8789.8126
"	Months (mean calendar)...	12	"	Months (mean calendar)...	12.007963
"	Seconds (mean solar).....	3.1536×10^7	"	Seconds (mean solar).....	3.1556926×10^7
"	Weeks (mean calendar)....	52.142857	"	Seconds (sidereal)........	3.1643326×10^7
"	Years (sidereal)..........	0.99929814	"	Weeks (mean calendar)....	52.177456
"	Years (tropical)..........	0.99933690	"	Years (calendar)..........	1.0006635
Years (leap)........	Days (mean solar).......	366	"	Years (sidereal)..........	0.99996121
Years (sidereal)......	Days (mean solar).......	365.25636			

DEFINED VALUES AND EQUIVALENTS

Meter..	(m)	1 650 763.73 wave lengths in vacuo of the unperturbed transition $2p_{10} - 5d_5$ in ^{86}Kr
Kilogram..	(kg)	mass of the international kilogram at Sèvres, France
Second..	(s)	1/31 556 925.974 7 of the tropical year at 12^h ET, 0 January 1900
Degree Kelvin...................................	(°K)	defined in the thermodynamic scale by assigning 273.16 °K to the triple point of water (freezing point, 273.15 °K = 0 °C)
Unified atomic mass unit........................	(u)	1/12 the mass of an atom of the ^{12}C nuclide
Mole..	(mol)	amount of substance containing the same number of atoms as 12 g of pure ^{12}C
Standard acceleration of free fall................	(gₙ)	9.806 65 m s^{-2}, 980.665 cm s^{-2}
Normal atmospheric pressure.....................	(atm)	101 325 N m^{-2}, 1 013 250 dyn cm^{-2}
Thermochemical calorie.........................	(cal$_{th}$)	4.1840 J, 4.1840×10^7 erg
International Steam Table calorie................	(cal$_{IT}$)	4.1868 J, 4.1868×10^7 erg
Liter..	(l)	0.001 m³, 1000 cm³ (recommended by GCWM, 1964)
Inch..	(in)	0.0254 m. 2.54 cm
Pound (avdp)...................................	(lb)	0.453 592 37 kg, 453.592 37 g

FACTORS FOR THE CONVERSION OF ($LOG_{10}X$) TO ($RT LOG_eX$)

Units are in Calories

t°C	0	1	2	3	4	5	6	7	8	9	Differences		
											Tenths	Units	Tens
0	1249.4	1254.0	1258.6	1263.2	1267.7	1272.3	1276.9	1281.45	1286.0	1290.6			
10	1295.2	1299.8	1304.3	1308.9	1313.5	1318.0	1322.6	1327.2	1331.8	1336.3			
20	1340.9	1345.5	1350.1	1354.6	1359.2	1363.8	1368.4	1372.9	1377.5	1382.1			
30	1386.7	1391.2	1395.8	1400.4	1405.0	1409.5	1414.1	1418.7	1423.2	1427.8	1 .5	4.6	45.7
40	1432.4	1437.0	1441.5	1446.1	1450.7	1455.3	1459.8	1464.4	1469.0	1473.6	2 .9	9.1	91.5
50	1478.1	1482.7	1487.3	1491.9	1496.4	1501.0	1505.6	1510.2	1514.7	1519.3	3 1.4	13.7	137.2
60	1523.9	1528.5	1533.0	1537.6	1542.2	1546.7	1551.3	1555.9	1560.5	1565.0	4 1.8	18.3	183.0
70	1569.6	1574.2	1578.8	1583.3	1587.9	1592.5	1597.1	1601.6	1606.2	1610.8	5 2.3	22.9	228.7
80	1615.4	1619.9	1624.5	1629.1	1633.7	1638.2	1642.8	1647.4	1651.9	1656.5	6 2.7	27.4	274.4
90	1661.1	1665.7	1670.2	1674.8	1679.4	1684.0	1688.5	1693.1	1697.7	1702.3			
100	1706.8	1711.4	1716.0	1720.6	1725.1	1729.7	1734.3	1738.9	1743.4	1748.0	7 3.2	32.0	320.2
											8 3.7	36.6	365.9
110	1752.6	1757.2	1761.7	1766.3	1770.9	1775.4	1780.0	1784.6	1789.2	1793.7	9 4.1	41.2	411.7
120	1798.3	1802.9	1807.5	1812.0	1816.6	1821.2	1825.8	1830.3	1834.9	1839.5			
130	1844.1	1848.6	1853.2	1857.8	1862.4	1866.9	1871.5	1876.1	1880.6	1885.2			
140	1889.8	1894.4	1898.9	1903.5	1908.1	1912.7	1917.2	1921.8	1926.4	1931.0			
150	1935.5	1940.1	1944.7	1949.3	1953.8	1958.4	1963.0	1967.6	1972.1	1976.7			
160	1981.3	1985.9	1990.4	1995.0	1999.6	2004.1	2008.7	2013.3	2017.9	2022.4			
170	2027.0	2031.6	2036.2	2040.7	2045.3	2049.9	2054.5	2059.0	2063.6	2068.2			
180	2072.8	2077.3	2081.9	2086.5	2091.1	2095.6	2100.2	2104.8	2109.4	2113.9			
190	2118.5	2123.1	2127.6	2132.2	2136.8	2141.4	2145.9	2150.5	2155.1	2159.7			
200	2164.2	2168.8	2173.4	2178.0	2182.5	2187.1	2191.7	2196.3	2200.8	2205.4			

DIMENSIONLESS GROUPS

John P. Catchpole and George Fulford

Reprinted from Industrial & Engineering Chemistry, Vol. 58, No. 3, pp. 47 to 60. Copyright 1966 by the American Chemical Society and reprinted by permission of the copyright owners and the authors. See also the Supplementary Table which follows this table.

Dimensionless groups are frequently generated in the analysis of a complex engineering problem. The more common groups thus generated are easily recognized, while the less common ones are not. Unless the less common existing groups are recognized, an already named group could unknowingly be renamed. Table A provides a tool that may be used to avoid this occurrence, by listing the groups by the variables of which they consist. These variables—i.e., length, density, diffusivity, viscosity, etc.—are further subdivided into their exponents to which they are raised in the groups in question. Thus, Reynolds number is listed under the exponent +1 for the variables, length, fluid velocity, and density, and the exponent −1 for viscosity.

To illustrate the use of the tables in the analysis of a problem, the group $(kE/\eta\sigma T^3)$ might be generated in the solution of a complex heat transfer problem. From Table A the groups containing the constituent variables are checked and the groups are listed:

Thermal conductivity	(k^{+1})	F11, L7, R1
Modulus of elasticity	(E^{+1})	C1, E13, R1
Stefan-Boltzmann coefficient	(η^{-1})	R1, T6
Surface tension	(σ^{-1})	B9, C3, E8, L6, R1, W1
Temperature	(T^{-3})	R1, T6

It is immediately apparent that the only group common to all the categories listed is the Radiation number, R1, which is equivalent to the previously unidentified group.

The symbol assigned to a dimensionless group is usually the first two letters of its names. Several groups, however, have nonstandard symbols, particularly in the groups which are named after persons. These symbols are listed in the nomenclature.

NOMENCLATURE

a	=	annulus or clearance width, L
A	=	area, L^2
A^*	=	cooling area/unit volume, $1/L$
b	=	bearing breadth, L
B	=	groups B6, B11
c	=	specific heat, $L^2/\theta^2 T$
c_A	=	concentration, M/L^3
c_b	=	specific vapor capacity (mass/unit mass/unit pressure change), $L\theta^2/M$
$\left.\begin{array}{l}c_d\\c_D\end{array}\right\}$	=	group D13
c_f	=	group R9
c_H	=	group H4
c_m	=	mass capacity, L^3/M
$\left.\begin{array}{l}c_P\\c_v\end{array}\right\}$	=	specific heats at constant pressure and volume, $L^2/\theta^2 T$
c_q	=	heat capacity, $L^2/\theta^2 T$
c_Q	=	group F9
c_S	=	group S11
C	=	group C10, dimensional concentration, M/L^3
C_a	=	groups C11, C4
d	=	diameter, L
d_e	=	equivalent diameter (of particles, etc.), L
d_h	=	hydraulic diameter, L
D	=	diffusivity (molecular, unless noted otherwise), L^2/θ
D_{AB}	=	binary bulk diffusion coefficient, L^2/θ
D_{KA}	=	Knudsen diffusion coefficient, L^2/θ
e	=	voidage; porosity (⁻)
e^*	=	surface emissivity (⁻)
E	=	modulus of elasticity, $M/L\theta^2$
E_a	=	activation energy, L^2/θ^2
E_b	=	bulk modulus, $M/L\theta^2$
f	=	frequency, $1/\theta$, or Group F1
$f(M)$	=	group F11
F	=	force, ML/θ^2
F_b	=	force per unit length of bearing, M/θ^2
$F(M)$	=	group F6
F_R	=	resistance force in flow, ML/θ^2
g	=	acceleration due to gravity, L/θ^2
G	=	mass velocity (mass flux density; mass transfer coefficient), $M/\theta L^2$
h	=	heat transfer coefficient, $M/T\theta^3$
h_c	=	convective heat transfer coefficient, $M/T\theta^3$
H	=	energy change per unit mass (= $g \times$ head), L^2/θ^2
H'	=	fluid head, L
H_e	=	field strength, $Q/L\theta$
H_0	=	homochronicity number
$I(M)$	=	group F8
j	=	heat liberated per unit volume per unit time, $M/L\theta^3$
j_H, j_M	=	groups J2, J3
J	=	average free path/average velocity, θ, or group L6
k	=	thermal conductivity, $ML/T\theta^3$
k_c	=	mass transfer coefficient, L/θ
K	=	groups K2, K10, N5
K_1	=	group A4
K_E	=	group E4
K_F	=	group C2
K_P	=	group P13
K_Q	=	group H5
K_r	=	group E11
K_g	=	group A1
K_E	=	group E4
K_r	=	group E12
K_{rE}	=	group E13
K_s	=	group R1
K_σ	=	group C1
$K_{\sigma g}$	=	group C2
L	=	characteristic dimension (except as noted), L
L_m	=	distance from midpoint to surface, L
m_T	=	group T3
M	=	group M10
M_H	=	group H2
n^*	=	concentration, wt./wt. (⁻)
n^*	=	specific mass content, mass/mass (⁻)
n_m	=	moisture content, wt./wt. bone dry gas (⁻)
N	=	rate of rotation, $1/\theta$, and groups M3, N4
N_{B_o}	=	groups B7, B8
N_c	=	group C5
N_{cv}	=	group C10
N_D	=	groups D7, D14
N_E	=	group E1
N_F	=	group F4
N_H	=	groups H1, H9
N_K	=	group K1
N_{KnA}	=	Knudsen number for diffusion (see Addendum)
N_1	=	group N2
N_P	=	group P7
N_{rf}	=	group R7
N_{s1}	=	group S8
N_{s1}	=	group S9
N_{s2}	=	group S9
N_T	=	group N9
P	=	pressure, $M/L\theta^2$
P	=	plasticity number (see Addendum)
p_b	=	bearing pressure, $M/L\theta^2$
p_s	=	static pressure, $M/L\theta^2$
p_v	=	vapor pressure, $M/L\theta^2$
p_σ	=	capillary pressure, $M/L\theta^2$
Δp_F	=	frictional pressure drop, $M/L\theta^2$
q	=	heat flux (heat flow/unit time), ML^2/θ^3
q^*	=	heat flux density (heat flux/unit area), M/θ^3
Q	=	heat liberated/unit mass, L^2/θ^2
r	=	latent heat of phase change, L^2/θ^2
r_v	=	heat of vaporization, L^2/θ^2
R	=	radius, L
R_H	=	hydraulic radius, L
R_2'	=	group R5
R_M	=	group M7
R_V	=	group V3
$\mathscr{R}$	=	gas constant, $L^2/\theta^2 T$
s	=	humid heat, $L^2/\theta^2 T$
S	=	particle area/particle volume, L^2/L^3, and group M6
$\overline{St}$	=	group S14
t	=	temperature, T
T	=	absolute temperature, T
$\Delta t, \Delta T$	=	temperature difference, T
U^+	=	group P10
U	=	reaction rate, $M/L^3\theta$
v_s	=	velocity of surface (solid), L/θ
V	=	fluid velocity, L/θ, and group V1
V_A	=	velocity of Alfven magnetic waves, L/θ
V_f	=	volumetric flow rate, L^3/θ
V_l	=	velocity of light, L/θ
V_m	=	mass flow rate, M/θ
V_s	=	velocity of sound, L/θ
w	=	circumferential velocity, L/θ
W	=	volume of system, L^3
W^*	=	gross volume, L^3
x	=	entry length; distance from entrance, L
y^+	=	group P11
Z	=	group O2
α	=	thermal diffusivity (temperature conductivity), L^2/θ

β	= coefficient of bulk expansion, $1/T$, and group **D12**
β^*	= Dufour coefficient, T
γ	= specific gravity ($^-$) and group **R3**
$\dot{\gamma}$	= rate of shear, $1/\theta$
Γ	= rate of change of temperature of medium, T/θ
δ	= Soret or thermogradient coefficient, $1/T$, and group **D11**
Δ	= difference in quantity
ε	= height of roughness, L and group **A3**
ε_D	= eddy mass diffusivity, L^2/θ
ζ	= diffusion tortuosity ($^-$)
η	= radiation coefficient (Stefan-Boltzmann coefficient), $M/T^4\theta^3$
θ	= time, θ
θ_r	= relaxation time, θ
λ	= mean free path, L
μ	= dynamic viscosity, $M/L\theta$
μ_e	= magnetic permeability, ML/Q^2
μ_p	= rigidity coefficient, $M/L\theta$
ξ	= permeability, L^2

π	= 3.1416. . . .
Π	= power to agitator or impeller, ML^2/θ^3
ρ	= density, M/L^3
ρ_n	= group **P3**
σ	= surface tension, M/θ^2 and group **S12**
σ_c	= group **C6**
σ_e	= electrical conductivity, $Q^2\theta/L^3M$
σ_t	= group **T4**
τ	= group **T8**
τ_w	= wall shear stress, $M/L\theta^2$
τ_y	= yield stress, $M/L\theta^2$
φ	= group **D9**
ψ	= groups **N8, P14, R10**
ω	= angular velocity (of fluid, unless noted otherwise), $1/\theta$
Ω	= mass transfer potential (concn.), M/L^3
— (bar over)	= mean value
N.B.: (F)	$= \left|\dfrac{ML}{\theta^2}\right|$; $(H) = \left(\dfrac{ML^2}{\theta^2}\right)$

TABLES FOR IDENTIFYING DIMENSIONLESS GROUPS
TABLE A

PHYSICAL PROPERTIES
General Physical Properties

Parameter	Symbol	Dimensions	Exponent	Group
Coefficient of bulk expansion	β	$1/T$	-1	E4, 12, G2
			$+1$	G5, R5, K9, 6
Density	ρ	M/L^3	-2	M1
			-1	A1, B1, 10, C1, 2, 6, D3, 13, E3, 9, 10, 13, F1, 11, H5, J1, K4, K10, L7, M3, 6, N2, 3, 4, P7, 9, R10, 13, S4, 13, 15
			$-\frac{2}{3}$	C9, J3
			$-\frac{1}{3}$	E2, L11, O2, P13
			$+\frac{1}{3}$	J3, K5, 53
			$+\frac{1}{2}$	D10, G3, P10, 11, R4, W2
			$+\frac{2}{3}$	F2, N8, S2
			$+1$	A5, B1, B6, 9, C5, 7, D5, 7, 13, E4, 6, 7, 8, H6, 11, J1, 3, 4, K1, L9, P1, R5, 11, 13, S17, T1, T6, V1, W1, W3
			$+2$	C10, G1, 5, K9, R5, 6, T2
Density gradient	$d\rho/dL$	M/L^4	$+1$	R13
Diffusivity (molecular unless noted otherwise)	D, a_m, ε_D	L^2/θ	-1	B5, B7[4], D2, K4[1], K7[2], L2, 7, 10, N7, P2, P9, S4, 13
			$-\frac{2}{3}$	J3
			$-\frac{1}{3}$	T3
			$+1$	D12, F12[1], K7[3], L2[4], L9[1]
Diffusivity (surface)	D_s	ML/θ^2	$+1$	S18
Diffusion tortuosity	ζ	—	-1	K7
Molecular weight	M	—	-1	D14, K9, S6
			$+1$	D14
Permeability (packed bed)	ξ	L^2	$+\frac{1}{2}$	L6
Porosity (voidage)	e	—	-1	B4
			$-\frac{1}{2}$	L6
			$+1$	K7
Specific weight	γ	—	$\pm\frac{1}{2}$	F2
Surface tension	σ	M/θ^2	-3	C2
			-2	C1
			-1	B9, C3, 13, E8, L6, R1, W1, 3
			$-\frac{1}{2}$	D10, G3, O2, P13, R4, W2
			$+1$	M9, S17, 18

(1) Coefficient of potential diffusion in mass transfer.
(2) Knudsen diffusion coefficient.
(3) Binary bulk diffusion coefficient.
(4) Effective diffusivity $(D + \varepsilon_D)$ (molecular + eddy transfer).

PHYSICAL PROPERTIES
Electrical and Magnetic Properties

Parameter	Symbol	Dimensions	Exponent	Group
Current density	I	$Q/L^2\theta$	$+1$	K10
Electrical conductivity	σ_e	$Q^2\theta/L^3M$	-1	E6
			$+\frac{1}{2}$	H2
			$+1$	L11, M3, 7
Field strength	H_e	$Q/L\theta$	-2	J4
			$+1$	H2, L11
			$+2$	K9, M3, 6, S6
Magnetic permeability	μ_e	ML/Q^2	-1	E5, J4
			$+1$	H2, M6, 7
			$+\frac{1}{2}$	L11
			$+2$	M3
Voltage	E	$ML/Q\theta^2$	$+1$	K10

Thermal Properties

Parameter	Symbol	Dimensions	Exponent	Group
Humid heat	S	L^2/θ^2T	-1	P15
Latent heats of phase change	λ, r	L^2/θ^2	-1	A3, E11, 12, 13, J1, K10, M1
			$+1$	B13, C9, K8, 11, N5
Ratio of specific heats	γ	—	$\pm\frac{1}{2}$	L5
Specific heat	C, c	L^2/θ^2T	-1	B2, 13, D3, 15, E1, F11, J2, K8, 11, L7, M10, N5, R3, S13
			$-\frac{1}{3}$	J2
			$+\frac{1}{2}$	F6, 7, 8
			$+\frac{2}{3}$	J2
			$+1$	A3, E4, 12, G4, J1, 4, L9, P1, 8, R3, 5, 6, 7
Surface emissivity	e^*	—	-1	T6
Temperature conductivity (thermal diffusivity)	α	L^2/θ	-1	L9, P1, 12, R5
			$+1$	C13, L7, 10
Thermal conductivity	k or λ	$ML/T\theta^3$	-3	M1
			-2	R6
			-1	B4, 12, C7, 9, 10, D4, G4, K3, L9, N6, P1, 5, 8, R5, S14

Rheological and Elastic Behavior

Parameter	Symbol	Dimensions	Exponent	Group
Modulus of elasticity	E	$M/L\theta^2$	-1	C5, E4, H11
			$+1$	C1, E13, R1
			$+3$	A1
Rate of shear	$\dot{\gamma}$	$1/\theta$	$+1$	T8
Rigidity coefficient	μ_p	$M/L\theta$	-2	H6
			-1	B3
			-1	E5
Shear stress	τ	$M/L\theta^2$	$-\frac{1}{2}$	P10
			$+\frac{1}{2}$	P11
Viscosity (in all cases kinematic viscosity has been written as μ/ρ)	μ	$M/L\theta$	-2	A1, 5, G1, 5, K1, 9, S17, T2
			-1	B6, C10, D5, 7, E6, 7, H8, L1, 3, 9, O1, P4, 11, R5, 6, 11, S9, 19, T1, V1

Rheological and Elastic Behavior

Parameter	Symbol	Dimensions	Exponent	Group
			$-\frac{2}{3}$	F2, K5, N8
			$-\frac{1}{2}$	H2
			$-\frac{1}{3}$	S2, 3
			$+\frac{1}{2}$	E2
			$+\frac{2}{3}$	C9, J2, 3
			$+1$	B12, C3, 13, E3, 5, M1, O2, P8, 9, S4, 8, 15, T8
			$+2$	C1
			$+4$	C2
Viscosity (surface)	μ_s	M/θ	$+1$	S19
Yield stress	τ_y	$M/L\theta^2$	$+1$	B3, H6

LENGTHS, AREAS AND VOLUMES
Characteristic Linear Dimensions
(In all cases kinematic viscosity has been written as μ/ρ)

Parameter	Symbol	Dimensions	Exponent	Group
General characteristic linear dimension	Various	L	-5	P7
			-3	F9, L1
			-2	D9, 12, E3, F11, 12, H4, 5, N2, 3, 4, O1, R9, S8, 9, 15
			-1	B1, 10, E2, 5, 10, F1, 13, G4, H10, K6, L4, R6, 10, 15, 16, S6, 19, T5, W4
			$-\frac{1}{2}$	B11, D7, F14, O2
			$+\frac{1}{2}$	R4, T1, W2
			$+1$	B3, 4, 5, 7, 10, C7, D1, 3, 5, 11, 13, E7, 10, F1, 2, 5, G3, H2, K3, 4, 6, 10, L3, 4, 9, 11, M1, 3, 7, N6, 7, 8, O1, P1, 2, 11, R8, 10, 11, 16, S2, 7, 14, 16, 17, 18, 13, W1
			$+\frac{3}{2}$	D7, H7, T1
			$+2$	B9, D2, 4, E8, H6, K9, O1, P4, 5, 12, S8, 9, V1
			$+3$	A5, C10, G1, 5, K1, R5
			$+4$	T2
			$+5$	R6
Dimension of agitator, impeller, etc.	Various	L	-5	P7
			-3	F9
			-2	D7, H4
			$+1$	D11, F15
			$+3$	W3
Film thickness	L_f	L	$+1$	N8
Furnace half-width	L	L	-1	T7
Larmor radius	L_L	L	$+1$	L4
Mean free path	λ	L	$+1$	K6
Particle dimension	d_e	L	-2	S15
			$+1$	F2
			$+3$	A5, G1
Pore or nozzle radius	R	L	$+1$	M12, T7
Reactor length	L	L	$+1$	B7
			-1	C3, L9
Thickness of liquid layer	L	L	$+1$	H2, L11
			$+2$	L9
			$+3$	R5
			$+4$	T2

Areas

Parameter	Symbol	Dimensions	Exponent	Group
Area	A	L^2	-1	D9, F6, 7, 8
			$+1$	B2
Area/unit volume	S, A^*	$1/L$	-1	B6
			$+1$	M11, 12

Volumes

Parameter	Symbol	Dimensions	Exponent	Group
Volume	—	L^3	$+$	A5, H9, M11

TIMES AND FREQUENCIES

Parameter	Symbol	Dimensions	Exponent	Group
			-1	D8
Time	θ	θ	$+1$	D8, 12, E3, F11, 12, H1, 10, S15, T5
Frequency	f'	$1/\theta$	$+1$	H1, 10, S16, V1

TEMPERATURES AND CONCENTRATIONS (DRIVING FORCES)
Concentrations and Related Quantities

Parameter	Symbol	Dimensions	Exponent	Group
Dimensional concentration	C, c_A	M/L^3	-1	D1, 2, R2
			$-\frac{1}{2}$	T3
			$+1$	B10
Dimensionless concentration—e.g., wt./wt. inert material, etc.	n	—	-1	P6
			$+1$	A4, K8
Mass capacity	C_m	L^3/M	-1	R2
Mole fraction	Y, Z	—	±1	D14
Specific mass content, mass/unit mass	n^*	—	-1	K4
Surface concentration	Γ'	M/L^2	±1	S18
Vapor capacity (porous body)	C_b	$L\theta^2/M$	$+1$	B13, R2

Temperatures, Temperature Differences

Parameter	Symbol	Dimensions	Exponent	Group
Temperature, temperature difference	$T, \Delta T$	T	-3	R1*, T6*
			-1	A4, 6*, B12, 13, C4*, 7, 10, D3*, 4*, 15, E1, G2, 6*, K3, 8, 9, 11, L9, N5, P5*, 12*, R14*, S6
			$-\frac{1}{2}$	L5
			$+\frac{1}{2}$	F6*, 7*, 8*
			$+1$	C4, G5, 6, J1, 4, L9, M1, P6, R5, 7, 14*
			$+3$	S14*
Rate of temperature change	—	T/θ	$+1$	P12

* Absolute temperature; others—temperature differences.

VELOCITIES, RATES, FLUXES, TRANSFER COEFFICIENTS
Velocities

Parameter	Symbol	Dimensions	Exponent	Group
Angular velocity (rate of rotation)	N	$1/\theta$	-3	P7
			-2	H4, L1
			-1	F9, R15
			$-\frac{1}{2}$	E2
			$+1$	S8, 11, 12, T1
			$+2$	F15, T2, W3
Fluid velocity	V	L/θ	-3	H5
			-2	C6, 11, D13, E9, 10, F1, M6, N2, 3, 4, R7, 8, 9, 10
			-1	A2, B3, C12, 14, D1, 3, F10, H7, 8, K10, L3, M3, P4, S13, 16
			$+1$	A2, B6, 7, 11, C3, 12, 14, D5, 7, E5, 7, F10, 14, H10, K2, L5, 8, M2, 4, 7, P1, 2, 3, 10, R4, 11, 15, S1, 2, 3, T5, 6, V2, W2, 4,
			$+2$	B1, 12, C5, 11, D15, E1, 11, F13, H11, W1
			$+3$	C7
Impeller or agitator circumference	U_s	L/θ	-2	P14
			-1	D9
Light	V_l	L/θ	-1	L8
Sound	V_s	L/θ	-1	M2, N1, S1
Waves	V_w	L/θ	-1	V1
			-1	P3
Velocity gradient	dV/dL	$1/\theta$	-2	R12
Velocity of Alfven waves	V_A	L/θ	-1	A2, K2, M4
			$+1$	A2, N1
			$+2$	C11
Velocity of bearing surface	v_s	L/θ	$+1$	H8, O1, S9

Flow Rates (Mass Fluxes)

Parameter	Symbol	Dimensions	Exponent	Group
Mass flow rate (mass flux)	V_m	M/θ	-1	B2, M11, T7
			$+1$	F6, 7, 8, G4, T
Mass flux density (mass flux/unit area)	G	$M/L^2\theta$	-1	J1, 3, P15, S13
			$+1$	K4, M11

Flow Rates (Mass Fluxes)

Parameter	Symbol	Dimensions	Exponent	Group
Mass flux/unit volume (reaction rate)	U	$M/L^3\theta$	$+\frac{1}{2}$	T3
Reaction rate constant	K	L/θ	-1	S5
Volumetric flow rate	V_f	L^3/θ	$+1$	D1, 2, 3, 4
			-1	H9
			$-\frac{1}{2}$	D11
			$+\frac{1}{2}$	S11, 12
			$+1$	D9, F9

Heat Fluxes

Parameter	Symbol	Dimensions	Exponent	Group
Heat flux (heat flow/unit time)	q	ML^2/θ^3	$+1$	H5
Heat flux/unit area	q^*	M/θ^3	$+1$	K3, R6
Heat liberated/unit mass	Q	L^2/θ^2 (H/M)	$+1$	D3, 4
Rate of heat liberation/unit volume (heat source power)	j	$M/L\theta^3$	$+1$	P5

Transfer Coefficients

Parameter	Symbol	Dimensions	Exponent	Group
Heat transfer coefficient	h	$M/T\theta^3$	$+1$	B2, 4, C9, J2, N6, P15, S13
		$(H/L^2T\theta)$	$+4$	M1
Mass transfer coefficient	k_c	L/θ	$+1$	B5, J3, L9, N7, S5, 7

FORCE, HEAD, POWER, PRESSURE
Forces

Parameter	Symbol	Dimensions	Exponent	Group
Force (resistance)	F, F_R	ML/θ^2	$-\frac{1}{3}$	S2
			$+\frac{1}{3}$	K5
			$+1$	N2, 3, 4, R9
Force/unit length	F_b	M/θ^2	$+1$	H8, O1, S9

Heads, Power

Parameter	Symbol	Dimensions	Exponent	Group
Fluid head	H'	L	$-\frac{3}{4}$	S11
			$+1$	H4

Heads, Power

Parameter	Symbol	Dimensions	Exponent	Group
Head (energy per unit mass of fluid $= gH'$)	H	L^2/θ^2	-1	P3, T4
			$-\frac{3}{4}$	S12
			$+\frac{1}{4}$	D11
			$+1$	A6, P14, T4
Power	π	ML^2/θ^3 (LF/θ)	$+1$	L1, P7

Pressures

Parameter	Symbol	Dimensions	Exponent	Group
Pressure	P	$M/L\theta^2$	-1	F6, 7, 8, H9, S8, T8
			$+1$	B13, C6, L6, P13, R2
Pressure drop	$\Delta P, dP$	$M/L\theta$	$+1$	E9, 10, F1, H9, L3, R10
Pressure gradient	$\Delta P/L$	$M/L^2\theta^2$	$+1$	E10, F1, K1, P4, R10

CONSTANTS AND MISCELLANEOUS QUANTITIES
Gravity Acceleration

Parameter	Symbol	Dimensions	Exponent	Group
Gravity acceleration	—	L/θ^2	-2	A1
			-1	B1, F13, 15, M1, S6
			$-\frac{3}{4}$	S11
			$-\frac{1}{2}$	B11, F14, P13
			$-\frac{1}{3}$	C9, S3
			$+\frac{1}{3}$	F2, N8
			$+1$	A5, B9, C2, 10, D13, E8, G1, 5, H4, R5, 6, 8, 13

Other Quantities

Parameter	Symbol	Dimensions	Exponent	Group
Avogadro's number	N	$1/M$	$+1$	K9, S6
Boltzmann's constant	k	—	-1	K9, S6
Dufour coefficient	β	T	$+1$	A3, 4, F3
Energy of activation	E_a	L^2/θ^2	$+1$	A6
Gas constant	$\mathcal{R}$	$L^2/\theta^2 T$	-1	A6
			$-\frac{1}{2}$	L5
Shape factor	ξ^*	—	$+1$	V2
Soret coefficient	δ	$1/T$	$+1$	F3, P6
Stefan constant	η	$M/T^4\theta^3$	-1	R1, T6
			$+1$	S14

Serial No.	Name	Symbol	Definition	Significance	Field of Use	Reference
A1	Acceleration number	K_g	$E^3/\rho g^2 \mu^2 = (N_{Re}N_{Fr1})^2/(H_0)^3$	Group dependent only on physical properties	Accelerated flow	25
A2	Alfven number	N_{Al}	V_A/V (or V/V_A) [cf. Cowling No. Kármán No. (2), magnetic mach number]	Ratio of Alfven wave velocity/fluid velocity	Magneto-fluid dynamics	5, 6
A3	Anonymous group (1)	ε	$\beta^* c/r$ [see also Fedorov No. (2)]		Transfer processes	39
A4	Anonymous group (2)	K_1	$\beta^* \Delta n/\Delta t$; Δt = temp. diff. $[T]$; Δn = conc. diff. $[\quad]$		Transfer processes	67
A5	Archimedes number	N_{Ar}	$\dfrac{gL^3\rho}{\mu^2}{}_0$ $(\rho-\rho_o)$; ρ_o = fluid density; ρ = particle density (cf. N_{Ga1})	N_{Re}, gravitational force/viscous force	Fluidization, motion of liquids due to density differences	6, 13
A6	Arrhenius group	—	$E_a/\mathscr{R}T$	Activation energy/potential energy of fluid	Reaction rates	5
B1	Bagnold number	B	$3c\alpha\rho_g V^2/4d\rho_p g$, ρ_g = gas density ρ_p = particle density	Drag force/gravitational force	Saltation studies	12
B2	Bansen number	N_{Ba}	$h_r A_w/V_{mc}$; h_r = radiant heat transfer coefficient; A_w = wall area of channel; (cf. N_{St})	Heat transferred by radiation/thermal capacity of fluid	Radiation	1
B3	Bingham number	N_{Bm}	$\tau_y L/\mu_p V$ (L = channel width)	Ratio of yield stress/viscous stress	Flow of Bingham plastics	5
B4	Biot number (heat transfer)	N_{Bih}	hL_m/k (in French literature, "Biot No." $= N_{Nu}$)	Midplane thermal internal resistance/surface film resistance	Unsteady state heat transfer	5, 6, 13
B5	Biot number (mass transfer)	N_{Bim}	$k_c L/D_{int}$; L = thickness of layer, D_{int} = diffusivity at interface	Mass transfer rate at interface/mass transfer rate in interior of solid wall thickness L	Mass transfer between fluid and solid	13
B6	Blake number	B	$V\rho/[\mu(1-e)S]$	Inertial force/viscous force	Beds of particles	6
B7	Bodenstein number	N_{Bo}	$VL/D_a = N_{Pe_m}$; L = reactor length, D_a = axial diffusivity (effective) (L^2/θ) $\equiv$ Thring radiation group		Diffusion in reactors	6
B8	Boltzmann number	N_{Bo}				1
B9	Bond number	N_{Bo}	$(\rho-\rho')L^2 g/\sigma = N_{We_1}/N_{Fr_1}$ if $\rho-\rho' \cong \rho$ (gas in liq.); ρ = drop or bubble density; ρ' = medium density	Gravitational force/surface tension force	Atomization, motion of bubbles and drops	5
B10	Bouguer number	N_{Bu}, B	$3C_D\lambda_r/4\rho DR$; C_D = wt. dust/unit bed volume (M/L^3), λ_r = mean path for radiation (L), ρ_D = dust density, R = mean particle radius. Also $N_{Bu} = kL$; L = characteristic dimension, k = absorption coefficient of medium		Radiant heat transfer to dust—gas streams	66
B11	Boussinesq number	B	$V/(2gR_H)^{1/2}$ (cf. N_{Fr2})	(Inertia force/gravitational force)$^{1/2}$	Wave behavior in open channels	6
B12	Brinkman number	N_{Br}	$\mu V^2/k\Delta t$; Δt = temp. diff.	Heat generation/heat transferred	Viscous flow	6
B13	Bulygin number	N_{Bu}	$r \cdot \dfrac{C_b}{C_a} \cdot \dfrac{P}{t_m-t_o} t_m$ = temp. of medium, medium, t_o = init. temp. of body	Heat for vaporization/heat to bring liquid to boiling point	Heat transfer during evaporation	6, 13, 14
C1	Capillary number	$K\sigma$	$\mu^2 E/\rho\sigma^2 = (N/_{We_1})^2/H_o \cdot (N_{Re})^2$	Depends only on physical properties	Action of surface tension in flowing media	25
C2	Capillarity-buoyancy number (physical properties group) (film No.)[a]	$K\sigma_g, K_F$	$g\mu^4/\rho\sigma^3 \cdot = \sqrt{K\sigma/Kg} = (N_{We_1})^3/(N_{Fr_1})(N_{Re})^4$	Depends only on physical properties and g	Effects of surface tension and acceleration in flowing media (two-phase flow)	21, 25
C3	Capillary number	Ca	$\mu V/\sigma = N_{We}/N_{Re}$	Viscous force/surface-tension force	Atomization, two-phase flow	6
C4	Carnot number	Ca, N_{Ca}	$(T_2-T_1)/(T_2)$; T_1, T_2 = abs. temp. of two heat sources or sinks	Theoretical efficiency of Carnot cycle operating between T_1 and T_2		21
C5	Cauchy number	N_c	$\rho V^2/E_b = (N_{Ma})^2$ = Hooke No.	Inertia force/compressibility force	Compressible flow	5, 25
C6	Cavitation number	σ_c	$[(p-P_o)/\rho]/(V^2/2)p$ = local static pressure (abs.); P_v = vapor pressure	Excess of local static head over vapor pressure head/velocity head	Cavitation	5
C7	Clausius number	Cl, N_{Cl}	$V^3L\rho/k\Delta T$; ΔT = temp. diff.		Heat conduction in forced flows	25
C8	Colburn number	—	Same as Schmidt number			5
C9	Condensation number (1)	N_{Co}	$(h/k)(\mu^2/\rho^2 g)^{1/3}$	$N_{Co} = N_{Nu}\left[\dfrac{(\text{viscous force})}{(\text{gravity force})} \times \dfrac{1}{Re}\right]^{1/3}$	Condensation	5
C10	Condensation number (2)	N_{Cv}	$L^3\rho^2 gr/k\mu\Delta t$; r = latent heat of condensation		Condensation on vertical walls	5
C11	Cowling number	C	$(V_A/V)^2 \equiv$ (Alfven number)^2		Magneto-fluid dynamics	6
C12	Craya-Curtet number	C_t	$V_k/(V_d^2 - V_k^2/2)^{1/2}$; V_k = kinematic mean velocity, V_d = dynamic mean velocity		Radiant heat transfer	3, 27

[a] Very similar to Hu and Kintner's pH factor for drops and bubbles [A.I.Ch.E. J. 1, 42 (1955)].

Serial No.	Name	Symbol	Definition	Significance	Field of Use	Reference
C13	Crispation group	N_{Cr}	$\mu\alpha/\sigma^*L$; σ^* = undisturbed surface tension; L = layer thickness		Convection currents	55
C14	Crocco number	N_{Cr}	$V/V_{max} = \left[1 + \dfrac{2}{(\gamma-1)(N_{Ma})^2}\right]^{-1/2}$ V_{max} = maximum velocity of gas expanding adiabatically	Velocity/maximum velocity	Compressible flow	5
D1	Damköhler group I	DaI	UL/V_{cA}	Chemical reaction rate/bulk mass flow rate	Chemical reaction, momentum, and heat transfer	5
D2	Damköhler group II	DaII	UL^2/D_{cA}	Chemical reaction rate/molecular diffusion rate	Chemical reaction, momentum, and heat transfer	5
D3	Damköhler group III	DaIII	$QUL/C_p\rho Vt$	Heat liberated/bulk transport of heat	Chemical reaction, momentum, and heat transfer	5
D4	Damköhler group IV	DaIV	QUL^2/kt	Heat liberated/conductive heat transfer	Chemical reaction, momentum, and heat transfer	5
D5	Damköhler group V	DaV	$= (N_{Re})$			5
D6	Darcy number		$4f$; see Fanning friction factor			5
D7	Dean number	N_D	$(VL\rho/\mu)(L/2R)^{1/2}$; L = pipe diam.; R = radius of curvature of bend	N_{Re} (centrifugal force/inertial force)	Flow in curved channels	5, 6
D8	Deborah number	D	θ_r/θ_o; θ_o = observation time	Relaxation time/observation time	Rheology	49
D9	Delivery number	ϕ	V_f/Aw; A = impeller area = $\pi d^2/4 \equiv$ [Diameter No.]$^{-3}$ [Speed No.]$^{-1}$		Flow machines	25
D10	Deryagin number	De	$L(\rho g/2\sigma)^{1/2}$; L = film thickness	Film thickness/capillary length	Coating	58
D11	Diameter group	δ	$(\pi/4)^{1/2}(2H)^{1/4}d/(V_f)^{1/2}$, d = impeller diam. = [pressure No.]$^{1/4}$ × [delivery No.]$^{-1/2}$		Flow machines	25
D12	Diffusion group	β	$D\theta/L_m^2$; D = diffusivity of solute through stationary solution contained in solid; cf. N_{Fom}		Mass transfer	37
D13	Drag coefficient	$C_d = C_D$	$(\rho-\rho')L_g/\rho V^2$; ρ = density of object; ρ' = density of medium; cf. f, ψ, N_e	Gravity force/inertial force	Free settling velocities, etc.	5
D14	Drew number	N_D	$\dfrac{Z_A(M_A - M_B) + M_B}{(Z_A - Y_{AW})(M_B - M_A)}\ln\dfrac{M_V}{M_W}$: M_A, M_B = mol. wt. of components A and B; M_V, M_W = mol. wt. of mixture in vapor and at wall; Y_{AW} = mole fraction of A at wall; Z_A = mole fraction of A in diffusing stream		Boundary layer mass transfer rates; velocity profile distortion; drag coefficients for binary system	22
D15	Dulong number	Du, N_{Du}	$V^2/C_p\Delta T$ = Eckert No.			25
E1	Eckert number	N_E	$V_\infty^2/C_p\Delta T$, V_∞ = velocity of fluid far from body ($= 2$/recovery factor, q.v. $\equiv$ Dulong No.)		Compressible flow	5, 24
E2	Ekman number		$(\mu/2\rho\omega L^2)^{1/2} = (N_{Ro}/N_{Re})^{1/2}$	(Viscous force/Coriolis force)$^{1/2}$	Magneto-fluid dynamics	6
E3	Elasticity number (1)	N_{El_1}	$\theta_r\mu/\rho L^2$ = pipe radius	Elastic force/inertial force	Viscoelastic flow	5
E4	Elasticity number (2)	$\overline{K}_E$	$\rho C_p/\beta E \equiv$ [Gay Lussac No.] × [Hooke No.] ÷ [Dulong No.]	Depends on physical properties only	Effect of elasticity in flow processes	25
E5	Ellis number	N_{El}	$\mu_o V/2\tau_{1/2}R$; μ_0 = zero shear viscosity, $\tau_{1/2}$ = shear stress when $\mu = \mu_o/2[M/L\theta^2]$; R = tube radius		Flow of non-Newtonian liquids	38
E6	Elsasser number	N_{El}	$\rho/\mu\sigma_e\mu_e \equiv N_{Re}/$[magnetic Reynolds No.]		Magneto-fluid dynamics	6
E7	Entry Reynolds Number	K_E	$\chi/d_h \cdot N_{Re} = \dfrac{\chi V\rho}{\mu}$; χ = entry length	As N_{Re}	Entry or inlet processes	25
E8	Eötvös number	N_{Eo}	$(\rho-\rho')L^2g/\sigma \equiv$ Bond No., q.v.			6
E9	Euler number (1)	N_{Eu_1}	$\Delta P_F/\rho V^2$; ΔP_F = pressure drop due to friction	Friction head/2 × velocity head	Fluid friction in conduits	5, 13, 25
E10	Euler number (2)	N_{Eu_2}	$d(-dp/dL)\rho V^2$; d = pipe diam., dp/dL = pressure gradient $\equiv 2 ×$ Fanning friction factor		Fluid friction in conduits	
E11	Evaporation number	K_r	V^2/r [r = heat of vaporization (L^2/θ^2)]		Evaporation processes	25
E12	Evaporation number (2)	$\overline{K}_r$	$C_p/r\beta$ (r as in E11) $\equiv$ (Gay Lussac No.) × (E11)/(Dulong No.)		Evaporation processes	25
E13	Evaporation-elasticity number	K_{rE}	$E/r\rho = K_r/$Hooke number		Evaporation processes	25
F1	Fanning friction factor	f	$d\Delta p_F/2\rho V^2L$, d = dimension of cross section; L = length (cf. resistance coeff., Ne)	Shear stress at wall expressed as number of velocity heads	Fluid friction in conduits	5
F2	Fedorov number (1)	F_{e_1}, N_{Fe_1}	$d\sqrt[3]{\dfrac{4g\rho^2}{3\mu^2}\left(\dfrac{\gamma M}{\gamma g} - 1\right)}d_e$ = equiv. particle diam.; γM = sp. gr. of particles; γg = sp. gr. of gas (cf. N_{Ar})		Fluidized beds	6, 13

Serial No.	Name	Symbol	Definition	Significance	Field of Use	Reference
F3	Fedorov number (2)	F_{e_2}, N_{Fe_2}	$\delta\beta^* = K_1 Pn = \varepsilon \times K_a Pn$	Mass transfer analogy of Posnov number	Transport processes	39, 67
F4	Fenske number	N_F		Number of stages in separation process		6
F5	Fineness coefficient	ψ	$L/W_D^{1/3}$; W_D = volume displacement $[L^3]$		Ship modeling	26, 43
F6, F7, F8	Fliegner numbers	$F(M_a)$ $f(M_a)$ $I(M_a)$	$\left\{\begin{array}{l}\text{Functions of ratio of specific heats and}\\ \text{mach number}\end{array}\right.$ $V_m(cT)^{1/2}/A(p_s + \rho V^2) = [\gamma M_a/(\gamma-1)^{1/2}]$ $\left[1 + \dfrac{(\gamma-1)Ma^2}{2}\right]^{1/2}$ = impulse Fliegner number; γ = ratio of specific heats, Ma = mach number, A = flow area			43
F9	Flow coefficient	C_Q	V_f/Nd, d = impeller diam.		Power required by fans, etc.	32
F10	Fluidization number		V/V_{init}, V_{init} = velocity for initial fluidization	Fluid velocity in fluidized bed/that at start of fluidization	Fluidization	59
F11	Fourier number (heat transfer)	N_{Foh}	$k\theta/\rho C_p L_m^2$	Unsteady state heat transfer		5, 13, 14, 25
F12	Fourier number (mass transfer)	N_{Fom}	$D\theta/L^2 = k_c\theta/L$ (cf. **D12**)		Unsteady state mass transfer	13
F13	Froude number (1)	N_{Fr_1}	$V^2/gL \equiv (N_{Fr_2})^2$ (cf. Reech No., Boussinesq No., Vedernikov No.)	Inertial force/gravitational force	Wave and surface behavior	5, 13, 25
F14	Froude number (2)	N_{Fr_2}	$V/\sqrt{gL} \equiv (N_{Fr_1})^{1/2}$ (cf. Boussinesq No.)	Velocity of open channel flow/speed of very small gravity wave	Open channel flow; free surfaces	7, 50
F15	Froude No. (rotating)	Fr	DN^2/g; D = impeller diam.		Agitation	64
G1	Galileo number	N_{Ga_1}	$L^3 g\rho^2/\mu^2$ (cf. N_{Ar}, Nusselt thickness group)	$N_{Ga_1} = N_{Re} \times$ gravity force/viscous force	Circulation of viscous liquid, thermal expansion	5, 13
G2	Gay Lussac number	Ga, N_{Ga_2}	$1/\beta\Delta T$		Thermal expansion processes	25
G3	Goucher number	N_{Go}	$R(\rho g/2\sigma)^{1/2}$; R = wall or wire radius	Gravitational force/surface tension force$^{1/2}$	Coating	24
G4	Graetz (Grätz) number	N_{Gz}	$V_m c_p/kL$	Thermal capacity fluid/convective heat transfer	Streamline flow	5, 25
G5	Grashof number	N_{Gr}	$L^3\rho^2 g\beta\Delta t/\mu^2 \equiv N_{Ga_1}/N_{Ga_2} \equiv (N_{Re})^2/(N_{Ga_2})(N_{Fr_1})$	$N_{Gr} = N_{Re}$ (buoyancy force/viscous force)	Free convection	5, 13, 25
G6	Gukhman number	Gu, N_{Gu}	$(t_o - t_m)/T_o$; t_o, T_o = temp. (°C., °K.) of hot gas stream, t_m = temp. of moist surface (wet bulb temp.)	Thermodynamic criterion of evaporation under isobaric adiabatic conditions	Convective heat transfer in evaporation	6, 23, 17, 53
G7	Guldberg-Waage group	N_{Gw}	Given by equation relating volumes of reacting gases and reaction products		Chemical reaction in blast furnaces	5
H1	Hall coefficient	N_H	$f_c J$ (f_c = cyclotron frequency, J = av. free path/av. veloc.)		Magneto-fluid dynamics	7
H2	Hartmann number	M_H	$(\mu_e^2 H_e^2\sigma_e L^2/\mu)^{1/2} = (SR_M N_{Re})^{1/2} \equiv (N_{Re}N)^{1/2}$	Magnetically induced stress/hydrodynamic shear stress (magnetic body force/viscous force)$^{1/2}$	Magneto-fluid dynamics	5, 6
H3	Hatta number	β	$\gamma/\tanh \gamma$; $\gamma = (rCD)^{1/2}/k_c$, r = reaction rate constant $[L^3/M\theta]$ [a modified Hatta number has also been defined 35)]		Gas absorption with chemical reaction	41
H4	Head coefficient	C_H	$gH'/N^2 d^2$ (d = impeller diam.)		Flow in pumps and fans	32
H5	Heat transfer number	K_Q	$q/V^3 L^2\rho$		Heat transfer in stream	25
H6	Hedstrom number	N_{He}	$\tau_y L^2\rho/\mu_p^2 \equiv (N_{Re}) \times (N_{Bm})$		Flow of Bingham plastics	5
H7	Helmholtz resonator group		$(d^3/W)^{1/2}/Ma$	Proportional to frequency × residence time	Pulsating combustion	28
H8	Hersey number		$F_b/\mu v_s$ (cf. truncation number)	Load force/viscous force	Lubrication	6
H9	Hodgson number	N_H	$Wf\Delta\rho_f/\overline{V}_{f.p_s}$	Time constant of system/period of pulsation	Pulsating gas flow	5
H10	Homochronous number	H_{o_1}	$V\theta/L$ (θ = time for liquid to move characteristic distance L)	Duration of process/time for liquid to move through L	Choice of time scales	13
H11	Hooke number	H_{o_2}	$\rho V^2/E \equiv$ Vauchy No., q.v.		Elasticity of flowing media	25
J1	Jakob modulus	Ja	$C_P\rho_L\Delta t/r\rho_v$ (ρ_L, ρ_v = densities of liquid and vapor; Δt = liquid superheat temperature diff.)	Maximum bubble radius/thickness of superheated film	Boiling	6
J2	J-factor (heat transfer)	j_H	$(h/c_p G)(c_p\mu/k)^{2/3} \equiv (N_{Nu})/(N_{Re})(N_{Pr})^{1/3}$		Heat, mass and momentum transfer theory	5
J3	J-factor (mass transfer)	j_M	$(k_c\rho/G)(\mu/\rho D)^{2/3} \equiv (k_c\rho/G)(N_{Sc})^{2/3}$			5
J4	Joule number	J	$2\rho C_p\Delta t/\mu_e H_e^2 \equiv 2(N_{Re})(R_M)/(M_H)^2(N_E)$	Joule heating energy/magnetic field energy	Magneto-fluid dynamics	6
K1	Kármán number (1)	N_K	$\rho d^3(-dp/dL)/\mu^2$ (d = pipe diam., dp/dL = pressure gradient) $\equiv 2(N_{Re})^2 f^{1/2}$		Fluid friction in conduits	5

Serial No.	Name	Symbol	Definition	Significance	Field of Use	Reference
K2	Kármán number (2)	K	V/V_A (see Alfven No.)		Magneto-fluid dynamics	6
K3	Kirpichev number for heat transfer	Ki_q, N_{Ki_q}	$q^* L/k \Delta t$ (cf. N_{Bih}, N_{Nu})	Intensity external heat transfer/internal heat transfer intensity	Heat transfer	6, 14
K4	Kirpichev number for mass transfer	Ki_m	$GL/D \rho n^*$ (cf. N_{Pem}, N_{Bim})	Intensity external mass transfer/internal mass transfer intensity	Mass transfer	13, 14
K5	Kirpitcheff number		$(\rho F_R/\mu^2)^{1/3} = [(N_{Re})^2 cf]^{1/3}$		Flow around obstacles	34
K6	Knudsen number (1)	N_{Kn}	λ/L	Length of mean free path/characteristic dimension	Low pressure gas flow	5
K7	Knudsen number (2)	N_{KnA}	$\rho D/_{AB} D_{KA} \zeta$	Bulk diffusion/Knudsen diffusion	Gaseous diffusion in packed beds	6
K8	Kossovich number	K_o, N_{Ko}	$r_v \Delta n_m/c \Delta t$	Heat used for evaporation/heat used in raising temperature of body	Convective heat transfer during evaporation	6, 14
K9	Kronig number	Kr	$4L^2 \beta \rho^2 \Delta t E_S^2 N[\alpha + 2/3(p_o^2/kT)]/u^2 M$ E_S = electric field at surface, N = Avogadro's Number, α = polarization coefficient, p_o = molecular dipole moment, k = Boltzmann's constant, M = molecular weight	(N_{Re}) (electrostatic force/viscous force)	Convective heat transfer	6, 44
K10	Kutateladze number (1)	Ku	$IEL/\rho V u'$; I = current density $[Q/L^2 \theta]$, E = voltage $[ML/Q\theta^2]$, u' = enthalpy $[L^2/\theta^2]$		Electric arcs in gas streams	65
K11	Kutateladze number (2)	K	$r_v/c_p(t_o - t_w)$, $(t_o, t_w$ = stream, wall temp.)		Combined heat and mass transfer in evaporation	17
L1	Lagrange group (1)	La_1	$\Pi/\mu L^3 N^2$; L = characteristic dimension of agitator = $N_{Re}.N_p$		Agitation	6
L2	Lagrange number (2)	La_2	$(D + \varepsilon_D)/D$	Combined molecular and eddy mass transfer rate/molecular mass transfer rate	Mass transfer in turbulent systems	31
L3	Lagrange number (3)	La_3	$\Delta PR/\mu V$		Magneto-fluid dynamics	6
L4	Larmor number	R_{La}	L_L/L; (L_L = Larmor radius)		Magneto-fluid dynamics	23
L5	Laval number	La	$V \Big/ \left(\dfrac{2\gamma}{\gamma + 1} RT\right)^{1/2}$; γ = ratio of specific heats	Linear velocity/critical velocity of sound	Compressible flow	56
L6	Leverett function	J	$(\xi/e)^{1/2}(P\sigma/\sigma$	Characteristic dimension of surface curvature/characteristic dimension of pores	Two-phase flow in porous media	6
L7	Lewis No.	N_{Le}	$k/\rho c_p D = \alpha/D \equiv N_{Sc}/N_{Pr}$ (N.B.: Lewis number is sometimes defined as reciprocal of this quantity)		Combined heat and mass transfer	5, 25
L8	Lorentz number	N_{Lo}	V/V_1; (V_1 = velocity of light)	Fluid velocity/velocity of light	Magneto-fluid dynamics	6
L9	Luikov (Lỹkov) number	Lu	$k_c L/\alpha = k_c L_\rho C_p/k$	Mass diffusivity/thermal diffusivity; rate of extension of mass transfer field/rate of extension of heat transfer field	Combined heat and transfer	6, 13
L10	Lukomskii number	Lu	α/a_m; a_m = potential conductivity of mass transfer $[L^2/\theta]$		Combined heat and mass transfer	36
L11	Lundquist number	N_{Lu}	$\sigma_e H_e \mu^{3/2} L/\rho^{1/2} = M_H (R_M/N_{Re})^{1/2}$ (L = thickness of fluid layer)		Magneto-fluid dynamics	6
L12	Lyashchenko number	Ly	$\equiv N_{Re}^3/N_{Ar}$		Fluidization	19
L13	Lykoudis number	N_{Ly}	$(\mu_e H_e)^2 \dfrac{\sigma_e}{\rho} \left[\dfrac{L}{g \beta \Delta t}\right]^{1/2} \equiv (M_H)^2/(N_{Gr})^{1/2}$		Magneto-fluid dynamics	6
M1	McAdams group		$h^4 L \mu \Delta t/k^3 \rho^2 gr$	Constant for given surface orientation	Condensation	5
M2	Mach number	N_{Ma}, Ma	V/V_s; (V_s = velocity of sound in fluid) $\equiv$ $v/\sqrt{E_b/\rho}$; (E_b = bulk modulus of fluid) (cf. Sarrau number)	Linear velocity/sonic velocity	Compressible flow	5–7, 25, 50
M3	Magnetic force parameter	N	$\mu_e^2 H_e^2 \sigma_e L/\rho V$	Magnetic body force/inertia force; resistance time of fluid in field/relaxation time of lines force	Magnetic-fluid dynamics	6
M4	Magnetic mach number	M_{Ma}	V/V_a (see Alfven number)		Magneto-fluid dynamics	6
M5	Magnetic Oseen number	k	$\frac{1}{2}(1 - N_{Al}^2) R_M$	Magnetic force/inertia force	Magneto-fluid dynamics	2
M6	Magnetic pressure number	S	$\mu_e H_e^2/\rho V^2$	Magnetic pressure/2 × dynamic pressure	Magneto-fluid dynamics	5
M7	Magnetic Reynolds number	R_M	$\sigma_e \mu_e LV$ (cf. velocity number)	Mass transport diffusivity/magnetic diffusivity	Magneto-fluid dynamics	5
M8	Maievskii number		$\equiv Ma$		Compressible flow	12
M9	Marangoni number	N_{Ma}	$\dfrac{\Delta \sigma}{\Delta t} \dfrac{\Delta t}{\Delta L} L^2/\mu\alpha$; L = layer thickness		Cellular convection	46

Serial No.	Name	Symbol	Definition	Significance	Field of Use	Reference
M10	Margoulis number	M	$\equiv N_{st}$		Forced convection	6, 7
M11	Merkel number	N_{Me}	$GA^*W^*/(V_m)$ gas	Mass of water transferred in cooling per unit humidity difference/ mass of dry gas	Cooling towers, liquid-gas contact	5
M12	Miniovich number	Mn	SR/e; R = pore radius		Drying	36
M13	Mondt number	N_{Mo}		Convective/conductive heat transfer	Heat transfer	6
N1	Naze number	N_a	$V_A/V_s \equiv (N_{Ma}.N_{A1})$	Velocity Alfven wave/ velocity of sound	Magneto-fluid dynamics	6
N2	Newton inertial force group	N_I	$F/\rho V^2 L^2$	Imposed force/inertial group	Agitation	5
N3	Newton number	N_e	$F_R/\rho V^2 L^2$; (cf. f, ψ)	Resistance force/inertia force	Friction in fluid flow	25
N4	Number of velocity heads	N	$(F/\rho L^2)/(V^2/2)$	Imposed head/velocity head	Friction in conduits	6
N5	Number for similarity of phys. and chem. changes	K	$r/C_p \Delta t$	Heat flow for phase change/superheat (supercooling) of one of the phases	Changes of phase	14
N6	Nusselt number	N_{Nu}	$hL/k \equiv (N_{Re} N_{St})$ (cf. N_{Bi_h}, Ki_g)	Total heat transfer/conductive heat transfer	Forced convection	5, 13, 25
N7	Nusselt number for mass transfer	Nu_m, N_{Nu_m}	$k_c L/D = N_{Sh}$	Intensity of mass flux at interface/specific flux by pure molecular diffusion in layer of thickness, L	Mass transfer	13, 20
N8	Nusselt film thickness group	ψ, N_T	$L_f(\rho^2 g/\mu^2)^{1/3} \equiv (N_{Ga})^{1/3}$; ($L_f$ = film thickness)	= $(N_{Re})^{1/3}$ (gravitational force/viscous force)$^{1/3}$	Falling films	6
O1	Ocvirk number		$(F_b/\mu V_s)(a/R)^2(D/b)^2$; ($v_s$ = shaft surface velocity; R = shaft radius; D = shaft diam.) (cf. N_S)	Load force/viscous force	Lubrication	6
O2	Ohnesorge number	Z	$\mu/(\rho L\sigma)^{1/2} = (N_{We_1})^{1/2}/(N_{Re})$	Viscous force/(inertia force × surface tension force)$^{1/2}$	Atomization	5
P1	Péclet number (heat)	Pe, N_{Pe_h}	$LV\rho C_p/k = LV/\alpha = (N_{Re}.N_{Pr})$	Bulk heat transfer/conductive heat transfer	Forced convection	5, 13, 25
P2	Péclet number (mass)	N_{Pe_m}	$LV/D = (N_{Re} N_{Sc})$	Bulk mass transfer/diffusive mass transfer	Mass transfer	5
P3	Pipeline parameter	ρn	$V_w V_o/2H'_s$; (V_w = velocity water-hammer wave, V_o = initial velocity H'_s = static head × $g[L^2/\theta^2]$	Maximum pressure rise in water hammer/2 × static pressure	Water hammer	5
P4	Poiseuille number		$D^2(-dp/dL)/\mu V(D$ = pipe diam., dp/dL = pressure gradient)	= 32 for laminar flow in round pipe	Laminar fluid friction	5
P5	Pomerantsev number	P_o	$jL^2/k(t_m - t_o)(t_m, t_o$ = temp. of medium, initial temp. of body) cf. Damköhler Group IV		Heat transfer with heat sources in medium	6, 14, 60
P6	Posnov number	Pn	$\delta \Delta t/(\Delta n_m)$ (cf. Fe_2)		Combined heat and mass transfer	13, 14, 67
P7	Power number	N_P	$\Pi/L^5\rho N^3$	Drag on (agitator impeller) or inertial force	Power consumption by agitators, fans, pumps, etc	5, 32
P8	Prandtl number	N_{Pr}	$C_p\mu/k$ = Da IV/Da III × Da V	Momentum diffusivity/ thermal diffusivity	Forced and free convection	5, 13, 25
P9	Prandtl number (mass transfer)	Pr_m	$\mu/\rho D = N_{Sc}$, v (used in Russian, German literature)	See Schmidt number		13
P10	Prandtl velocity ratio	u^+	$V/(r_w/\rho)^{1/2}$ (V = local fluid velocity)	Inertial force/wall shear force$^{1/2}$	Turbulence studies	5
P11	Prandtl dimensionless	y^+	$L(\rho r_w)^{1/2}/\mu$ (L = distance from wall, etc.)		Turbulence studies	
P12	Predvoditelev number	Pd	$\Gamma L^2/\alpha t_o = \left(\dfrac{dt^*}{\alpha(N_{Fo})}\right)_{max}$ where t_o = init. temp. of body, t^* = temp. of medium relative to its initial temp.	Rate of change of temp. of medium/rate of change of temp. of body	Heat transfer	13, 14, 60
P13	Pressure number (1)	K_P	$P/\{g\sigma(\rho' - \rho'')\}^{1/2}(\rho', \rho''$ = density of liquid gas)	Absolute pressure in system (pressure jump on interface)		14
P14	Pressure number (2)		$H/\frac{1}{2}/_2 U_s^2(U_s$ = circumferential velocity) $\equiv$ [diameter No.]$^{-2}$ × [Speed No.]$^{-2}$		Flow machines (turbines, pumps, etc.)	25
P15	Psychrometric ratio		h_c/Gs	Heat transfer by convection/heat transfer by mass transfer	Wet and dry bulb thermometry	5
R1	Radiation number	$\bar{K}_s$	$kE/\eta\sigma T^3 = (N_{We_1})/(\text{Hooke No.})$ × (Stefan No.)		Radiant transfer	25
R2	Ramzin number	Ra	$\dfrac{C_b P}{C_m(\Delta\Omega)} = \dfrac{(\text{Bulygin No.})}{(\text{Kosovich No.})}$		Molar mass transfer	40
R3	Ratio of specific heats	γ	C_p/C_v (specific heats at constant pressure, volume)		Compressible flow	5
R4	Rayleigh number (1)	N_{Ra_1}	$V(\rho L/\sigma)^{1/2} = N_{We_2}$ (q.v.)	See N_{We_1}	Breakup of liquid jets	5
R5	Rayleigh number (2)	R'_2	$L^3\rho^2 g\beta c_p \Delta t/\mu k = L^3\rho g\beta \Delta t/\mu\alpha = (N_{Gr}) \cdot (N_{Pr})$		Free convection	5, 25

Serial No.	Name	Symbol	Definition	Significance	Field of Use	Reference
R6	Rayleigh number (3)	Ra_3	$q^* L^5 \rho^2 g \beta C_p / \mu k^2 x = (N_{Gr})(N_{Pr})$ $(N_{Nu})(L/x)$; (L = pipe diam.)		Combined free and forced convection in vertical tubes	6
R7	Recovery factor	N_{rf}	$C_p(t_{aw} - t_m)/V^2$; t_{aw} = attained adiabatic wall temp. t_m = temp. of moving medium (cf. Eckert No.)	Actual temp. recovery/ theoretical temp. recovery	Convective heat transfer in compressible flow	5
R8	Reech number		$= 1/(N_{Fr_1})$ q.v.		Wave and surface behavior	6
R9	Resistance coefficient (1)	C_f	$F_R/\frac{1}{2}\rho V^2 L^2$ (cf. drag coeff., Newton number, Fanning factor)		Flow resistance	25
R10	Resistance coefficient (2)	ψ	$\Delta p . D_H/\frac{1}{2}\rho V^2 L$ (Δp = pressure drop over length, L) (cf. R9)		Fluid friction in conduits	25
R11	Reynolds number	N_{Re}	$LV\rho/\mu$	Inertia force/viscous force	Dynamic similarity	5, 25
R12	Reynolds number (rotating)	Re	$L^2 N\rho/\mu$; L = impeller diam.		Agitation	45
R13	Richardson number	N_{Ri}	$-(g/\rho)(d\rho/dL)/(dV/dL)_w^2$ [L = height of liquid layer, $(dV/dL)_w$ = velocity gradient at wall]	Gravity force/inertial force	Stratified flow of multi-layer systems	54
R14	Romankov number	R'_o	T_D/T_{PROD}	Dry bulb temperature (abs.)/(product temperature (abs.)	Drying	6, 52
R15	Rossby number	N_{Ro}	$V/2\omega_e L \sin \Lambda$ (ω_e = angular velocity of earth's rotation [$1/\theta$]; Λ = angle between axis of earth's rotation and direction of fluid motion [$^-$])	Inertia force/Coriolis force	Effect of earth's rotation on flow in pipes	5
R16	Roughness factor		ε/L		Fluid friction	5
S1	Sarrau number		$\equiv$ mach number, q.v.		Compressible flow	6
S2	Schiller number (1)		$LV(\rho^2/\mu F_R)^{1/3}$		Flow around obstacles	34
S3	Schiller number (2)	Sch	$V\left[\frac{3}{4} \cdot \frac{\rho \gamma_m}{g\mu(\gamma_M - \gamma_m)}\right]^{1/3}$; V = velocity in fluidized bed; γ_m, γ_M = specific gravity of medium and material in bed		Fluidization	66
S4	Schmidt number	N_{Sc}	$\mu/\rho D$ (cf. N_{Pr_m}) (= Da II/Da I Da V)	Kinetic viscosity/molecular diffusivity	Diffusion in flowing	5, 25
S5	Semenov number	Sm	k_c/K; K = reaction rate constant [L/θ]		Reaction kinetics	11
S6	Senftleben number	S_e	$NE_a^2[\alpha + 2/3(\rho_o^2/kT)] \cdot [1/4LM_g]$ Kronig number, q.v.		Convective heat transfer	6
S7	Sherwood number	N_{Sh}	$k_c L/D = Nu_m$ (also termed Taylor number)	Mass diffusivity/molecular diffusivity	Mass transfer	5
S8	Sommerfeld number (1)	N_{S_1}	$(\mu N/P_b)(D/a)^2$ (D = shaft diam., (cf.) Ocvirk number)	Viscous force/load force	Lubrication	5
S9	Sommerfeld number (2)	N_{S_2}	$(F_b/\mu V_s)(a/R)^2$ (V_s = veloc. of shaft surface; R = shaft radius) ($N_{S_2} = 4/\pi N_{S_1}$)	Viscous force/load force	Lubrication	6
S10	Spalding function	Sp	$-\left(\frac{\delta\theta}{\partial u^+}\right)_{u^+ = 0}$; $\theta = (T - T_\infty)/(T_w - T_\infty)$, T_w = wall temperature, T_∞ = free stream temp., u^+ = Prandtl velocity ratio	Dimensionless temp. gradient at wall	Convection	18, 33
S11	Specific speed	C_s	$N(V_f)^{1/2}/(gH')^{3/4}$ (H' = head of liquid produced by one stage) (cf. speed number)		Pumps and compressors	8, 32
S12	Speed number	σ	$(4\pi)^{1/2}(V_f)^{1/2} N/(2H)^{3/4}$ = (delivery number)$^{1/2}$ × pressure number)$^{-3/4}$ (cf. specific speed)		Flow machines	25
S13	Stanton number	N_{St}	$h/C_p \rho V = h/C_p G = (N_{Nu})/(N_{Re})(N_{Pr})$	Heat transferred/thermal capacity of fluid	Forced convection	5, 6, 13, 25
S14	Stefan number	$\check{S}t$	$\eta L T^3/k$		Heat radiation	25
S15	Stokes number	St	$\mu\theta_v/\rho L^2$ (θ_v = vibration time) $\equiv (N_{S_1})^{-1}(N_{Re})^{-1}$		Particle dynamics	6
S16	Strouhal number	N_{S_1}, Sr	fL/V (cf. N_{Th})		Vortex streets; unsteady-state flow	6, 25
S17	Suratman number	Su	$\rho L\sigma/\mu^2 = (N_{Re})^2/(N_{We_1}) = (Z)^{-2}$		Particle dynamics	6
S18	Surface elasticity number	N_{El}	$-\frac{\Gamma'}{D_S}L\frac{(\partial\sigma)}{(\partial\Gamma')}$; Γ' = surface concentration of surfactant in undisturbed state, D_S = surface diffusivity, L = film thickness		Convection cells	10
S19	Surface viscosity number	N_{Vi}	$\mu_S/\mu L$; μ_S = surface viscosity, [M/θ], L = film thickness		Convection cells	10
T1	Taylor number (1)	N_{Ta_1}	$\omega_c(R_a)^{1/2}a^{3/2}\rho/\mu$; ($\omega_c$ = angular velocity of cylinder; R_a = mean radius of annulus)		Stability of flow pattern in annulus with rotating cylinder	5
T2	Taylor number (2)	N_{Ta_2}	$(2\omega L^2\rho/\mu)^2[\omega$ = rate of spin $(1/\theta)$; L = height of fluid layer]	α(Coriolis force/viscous force)^2	Effect of rotation on free convection	6
T3	Thiele modulus	m_T	$Q^{1/2}U^{1/2}L/k^{1/2}t^{1/2} = (Da IV)^{1/2}$		Diffusion in porous catalysts	5
T4	Thoma number	σ_T	$(H_a - H_s - H_v)/H$ (H = total head; H_a = atm. pressure head; H_s = suction head; H_v = vapor pressure head)	Net positive suction head/total head	Cavitation in pumps	5
T5	Thomson number	N_{Th}	$\theta V/L$; θ = characteristic time (cf. N_{S_1})		Fluid flow	6
T6	Thring radiation group		$\rho C_p V/e^* \eta T^3$ (cf. Boltzmann number)	Bulk heat transport/heat transport by radiation	Radiation	5

Serial No.	Name	Symbol	Definition	Significance	Field of Use	Reference
T7	Thring-Newby criterion	θ	$[(V_{m_1}+V_{m_0})/V_{m_0}](R/L)$; V_{m_0}, V_{u_1} = mass flow rates of nozzle fluid and surrounding fluid $[M/\theta]$; R = equivalent nozzle radius; L = furnace half width		Combustion of fuels	4
T8	Truncation number	r	$\mu\gamma/P$ (cf. Hersey number)	Shear stress/normal stress	Viscous flow	6
V1	Valensi number	V	$\omega L^2 \rho/\mu$; ω = circular oscillation frequency when $\mu = 0$ $[1/\theta]$		Oscillations of drops and bubble-	57
V2	Vedernikov number	V	$\zeta^* \xi^* \bar{V}/(V_w - \bar{V}) \equiv \zeta^* \xi^* (N_{Fr_2})$ (ζ^* = exponent of hydraulic radius in formula $[^-]$; ζ^* = shape factor of channel section; V_w = absolute velocity of disturbance wave)	Generalized Froude number	Instability of open-channel flow	6, 61
V3	Velocity number	R_v	$\equiv$ Magnetic Reynolds number, q.v.			5, 6
W1	Weber number (1)	N_{We_1}	$V^2 \rho L/\sigma = (N_{We_2})^2$	Inertia force/surface tension force	Bubble formation, etc.	2, 25
W2	Weber number (2)	N_{We_2}	$V(\rho L/\sigma)^{1/2} = (N_{We_1})^{1/2}$			
W3	Weber number (rotating)	W_e	$L^3 N^2 \rho/\sigma$; L = impeller diameter		Agitation	64
W4	Weissenberg number	N_{We}	$\omega_3 V/\omega_1 L$; $\omega_3 = \int_0^\infty sG(s)\,ds$, $\omega_1 = \int_0^\infty G(s)\,ds$, G = relaxation modulus of linear viscoelasticity, s = recoverable elastic strain	Viscoelastic force/viscous force	Viscoelastic flow	63

REFERENCES

1. Adrianov, V. N., Shorin, S. N., *AIAA J.* 1, 1729 (1963).
2. Ahlstrom, H. G., *J. Fluid Mech.* 15, 205 (1963).
3. Becker, H. A., Hottel, H. C., Williams, G. C., "Ninth Symposium (International) on Combustion," p. 7, Academic Press, New York, 1963.
4. Beer, J. M., Chigier, N. A., Lee, K. B., *Ibid.*, p. 892.
5. Boucher, D. F., Alves, G. E., *Chem. Eng. Progr.* 55 (9), 55 (1959).
6. *Ibid.*, 59 (8), 75 (1963).
7. British Standard 1991, "Recommendations for Letter Symbols, Signs and Abbreviations. Part 2. Chemical Engineering, Nuclear Science, and Applied Chemistry," British Standards Institution, London, 1961.
8. Brown, G. G., *et al.*, "Unit Operations," Wiley, New York, 1950.
9. Buckingham, E., *Phys. Rev.* 4, 345 (1914).
10. Berg, J. C., Acrivos, A., *Chem. Eng. Sci.* 20, 737 (1965).
11. Chukhanov, Z. F., *Intern. J. Heat Mass Transfer* 6, 691 (1963).
12. Dallavalle, J. M., "Micromeritics," 2nd ed., Pitman, New York, 1948.
13. El'perin, I. T., *Inzh. Fiz. Zh. Akad. Nauk Belorussk. SSR* 4 (1), 131 (1963).
14. El'perin, I. T., *Intern. J. Heat Mass Transfer* 5, 349 (1962).
15. Engel, F. V. A, *Z.V.D.I.* 107, 671, 793 (1965).
16. Faller, A. J., *J. Fluid Mech.* 15, 560 (1963).
17. Fedorov, B. I., *Inzh. Fiz. Zh. Akad. Nauk Belorussk. SSR* 7 (1), 21 (1964).
18. Gardner, G. O., Kestin, J., *Intern. J. Heat Mass Transfer* 6, 289 (1963).
19. Gel'perin, I. T., Ainshtein, V. G., Goĭkhman, I. D., *Inzh. Fiz. Zh. Akad. Nauk Belorussk. SSR* 7 (7), 15 (1964).
20. Grassmann, P., *Chem. Ing.-Tech.* 31, 148 (1959).
21. Grassman, P., Lemaire, L. H., *Ibid.*, 30, 450 (1958).
22. Greene, D. F., Ph.D. Thesis, Columbia Univ., 1961 [*Dissertation Abstr.* 24 (8), 3248 (1964)].
23. Gukhman, A. A., "Introduction to the Theory of Similarity," Academic Press, New York, 1965.
24. Gutfinger, C., Tallmadge, J. A., *A.I.Ch.E. J.* 10, 774 (1965).
25. Hahnemann, H. W., "Die Umstellung auf das internationale Einheitensystem in Mechanik und Wärmetechnik," VDI-Verlag, Düsseldorf, 1959.
26. Holt, M., "Dimensional Analysis" in "Handbook of Fluid Dynamics," V. L. Streeter, ed., McGraw-Hill, New York, 1961.
27. Hottel, H. C., Sarofim, A. F., *Intern. J. Heat Mass Transfer* 8, 1153 (1965).
28. Hottel, H. C., Williams, G. C., Jensen, W. P., Tobey, A. C., Burrage, P. M. R., p. 923 in "Ninth Symposium (International) on Combustion," Academic Press, New York, 1963.
29. Huntley, H. E., "Dimensional Analysis," MacDonald & Co., London, 1952.
30. Johnson, S. P., "Survey of Flow Calculation Methods," p. 98, Pre-printed Papers & Program, Aeronautic & Hydraulic Divisions, A.S.M.E. Summer Meeting, June 19–21, Univ. of Calif. and Stanford Univ., 1934.
31. Kafarov, V. V., *Zh. Prikl. Khim.* 29, 40 (1956).
32. Kay, J. M., "An Introduction to Fluid Mechanics & Heat Transfer," Cambridge Univ. Press, 1957.
33. Kestin, J., Persen, L. N., *Intern. J. Heat Mass Transfer* 5, 143 (1962).
34. Klinkenberg, A., Mooy, H. H., *Chem. Eng. Progr.* 44, 17 (1948).
35. Koide, K., Kubota, H., Shindo, M., *Chem. Eng.* (Japan), 28 (8), 657 (1964).
36. Lỹkov, A. V., Mikhaĭlov, Yu. A., "Theory of Energy & Mass Transfer," Prentice-Hall, Englewood Cliffs, N J., 1961.
37. McCabe, W. L., Smith, J. C., "Unit Operations of Chemical Engineering," McGraw-Hill, New York, 1956.
38. Matsuhisa, S., Bird, R. B., *A.I.Ch.E. J.* 11, 588 (1965).
39. Mikhaĭlov, Yu. A., Bornikova, R. M., *Inzh. Fiz. Zh. Akad. Nauk Belorussk. SSR* 6 (10), 45 (1963).
40. Mikhaĭlov, Yu. A., Romanina, I. V., *Ibid.*, 7 (1), 49 (1964).
41. Miyauchi, T., Nakano, K., Obata, K., Kimura, S., *Chem. Eng.* (Japan) 26 (9), 999 (1962).
42. Mkhitaryan, A. M., "Hydraulics & Fundamentals of Gas Dynamics," Israel Program for Scientific Translations, Jerusalem, 1964.
43. Mordell, D. L., Wu, J. H. T., *Can. Aeronaut. Space J.* 9 (4), 117 (1963).
44. Motulevich, V. P., Eroshenko, V. M., Petrov, Yu. P., in "Physics of Heat Exchange & Gas Dynamics," A. S. Predvoditelev, ed., Consultants Bureau, New York, 1963.
45. Nagata, S., *Chem. Eng.* (Japan) 27 (8), 592 (1962).
46. Nield, D. A., *J. Fluid Mech.* 19, 341 (1964).
47. Potter, J. M. F., B.Sc. Thesis, Dept. of Chem. Engrg., Univ. of Birmingham, England, 1959.
48. Rayleigh, Lord, *Phil. Mag.* 48, 321 (1899).
49. Reiner, M., *Phys. Today* 17 (1), 62 (1964).
50. Rouse, H. (ed.), "Engineering Hydraulics," Wiley, New York, 1950.
51. Rouse, H., Ince, S., "History of Hydraulics," Iowa Institute of Hydraulic Research, State University of Iowa, 1957.
52. Sazhin, B. S., *Inzh. Fiz. Zh. Akad. Nauk Belorussk. SSR* 5 (6), 13 (1962).
53. Sazhin, B. S., Miklin, Yu. A., *Ibid.*, 6 (10), 57 (1963).
54. Schlichting, H., "Boundary Layer Theory," 4th ed., McGraw-Hill, New York, 1960.
55. Scriven, L. E., Sternling, C. V., *J. Fluid Mech.* 19, 321 (1964).
56. Sillem, H., *Z.V.D.I.* 106, 398 (1964).
57. Szebehely, V. G., p. 771 in "Proc. 2nd U.S. Nat. Congress of Appl. Mech.," Ann Arbor, Mich., June 1954; A.S.M.E., New York, 1955.
58. Tallmadge, J. A., Labine, R. A., Wood, B. H., *Ind. Eng. Chem. Fundamentals* 4, 400 (1965).
59. Tamarin, A. I., *Inzh. Fiz. Zh. Akad. Nauk Belorussk. SSR* 6 (7), 19 (1963).
60. Tartakovskii, D. F., *Ibid.*, 7 (1), 71 (1964).
61. Vedernikov, V. V., *Compt. Rend. Acad. Sci. U.R.S.S.* 48, 239 (1945); 52, 207 (1946).
62. Weber, M., *Jahrb. Schiffbautechn. Ges.* 20, 355 (1919).
63. White, J. L., *J. Appl. Polymer. Sci.* 8, 2339 (1964).
64. Yamaguchi, I., Yabuta, S., Nagata, S., *Chem. Eng.* (Japan) 27 (8), 576 (1963).
65. Yas'ko, O. I., *Inzh.-Fiz. Zh. Akad. Nauk Belorussk. SSR* 7 (12), 112 (1964).
66. Zabrodskii, S. S., "Flow & Heat Transfer in Fluidized Beds," to be published shortly by M.I.T. Press.
67. Zhuravleva, V. P., *Inzh.-Fiz. Zh. Akad. Nauk Belorussk. SSR* 6 (9), 73 (1963).

George D. Fulford and John P. Catchpole

Reprinted from Industrial and Engineering Chemistry, Vol. 60, No. 3, pp. 71 to 78. Copyright 1968 by the American Chemical Society and reprinted by permission of the copyright owners and the authors.

TABLE II. ALPHABETICAL
LIST OF NEW GROUPS

Serial No.	Name	Symbol	Definition	Significance	Field of Use	Reference
A0	Absorption No.	Ab	$kc_L \sqrt{\dfrac{xL_f}{DV_f'}}$ kc_L = liquid side mass transfer coefficient; x = length of wetted surface; L_f = film thickness; V_f = volume flow rate per wetted perimeter $[L^2/\theta]$	Dimensionless mass transfer coefficient	Gas absorption in wetted wall column	40
A1a	Advance ratio	J	V/ND V = forward speed; D = propeller diameter	Special form of Strouhal No.	Propeller studies	27
A1b	Aeroelasticity parameter	—	$\equiv$ Cauchy No., $q.v.$	Inertia force/compressibility force	Compressible flow	27
A4a	Anonymous group 3	ε	$Dx/V_f'L_f$ (symbols as in Absorption No.). $\varepsilon = (Ab)^2/(N_{Sh})^2$	Dimensionless diffusivity	Gas absorption in wetted wall column	40
A4b	Anonymous group 4	$1/\alpha$ $(1/\beta)$	$\tau_w R/V_\infty \mu$; R = cylinder radius; V_∞ = velocity outside boundary layer	Frictional force/ viscous force dimensionless skin friction)	Laminar boundary layer flow	12, 28, 35
B1a	Bairstow No.	—	$V/V_{s.w}$ $V_{s w}$ = velocity of sound at wall ($cf.$ Mach. No.)	Previously used for Mach No., now largely obsolete	—	27
B2a	Batchelor No.	—	$VL\sigma_e/V_t^2\varepsilon_e$ ε_e = electrical permittivity $[Q^2\theta^2/L^3M]$	—	Magnetofluid dynamics	27
B13a	Buoyancy parameter	—	$\dfrac{\Delta T}{T}\dfrac{gL}{V^2} = (N_{Gr})/(N_{Re})^2 = \dfrac{\Delta T}{T}\left(\dfrac{1}{N_{Fr_1}}\right)$	Buoyancy force/ inertia force	Free convection	27
D6a	Darcy No. (2)	Da_2	VL/D'; D' = permeability coefficient of porous medium $[L^2/\theta]$	Inertia force/permeation force	Flow in porous media	19
D8a	Generalized Deborah No.	N_2	$\sqrt{I_e - I_w} \cdot \theta_n$ I_e = invariant of rate of strain tensor (sec.$^{-2}$); I_w = invariant of vorticity tensor (sec.$^{-2}$); θ_n = natural time (sec.)	Generalization of group D8	Rheology	2
D14a	Dufour No.	Du_2	$\mathscr{R}\Theta n'_{10}/c_p$ Θ = thermodiffusion constant = $(D_T/D)/n_{10}n_{20}$ $[-]$; D_T = thermal diffusion coefficient $[L^2/\theta]$; $n'_{10}, n'_{20} = n'_1/n'$, n'_2/n'; n' = total No. of molecules = $n'_1 + n'_2$; n'_1, n'_2 = No. of molecules of components 1, 2, in binary mixture; also $Du_2 = (D_T/D)p/\rho c_p Tn_{20}$	Heat of isothermal mass transfer/enthalpy of unit mass of mixture	Thermodiffusion	22
E1a	Einstein No.	—	V/V_t (V_t = speed of light) ($cf.$ Lorentz No.)	Fluid velocity/ velocity of light	Magnetofluid dynamics	27
E4a	Electric field parameter	R_E	$E/V\mu_e H_e$		Magnetohydro-dynamics	26
E4b	Electrical characteristic No.	El	$\rho(d\chi/dT)L^2 \cdot \Delta T \cdot E_1^2/\mu^2$ E_1 = electrical field strength $[ML/Q\theta^2]$; χ = dielectric susceptibility $[Q^2\theta^2/ML^3]$		Electrical effects on transfer processes	6
E4c	Electrical Nusselt No.	N_u	VL/D^*; $D^* = \frac{1}{2}(D^+ + D^-)$ $[L^2/\theta]$ D^+, D^- = diffusion coefficients of ions ($cf.$ group P2)	Convection current/ diffusion current	Electrochemistry	10
E4d	Electrical Reynolds No. (1)	—	$\varepsilon_e V/Q'Lb'$ ε_e = electrical permittivity $[Q^2\theta^2/L^3M]$; Q' = space charge density $[Q/L^3]$; b' = carrier mobility $[Q\theta/M]$		Electrical effects in flow	27
E4e	Electrical Reynolds No. (2)	—	Alternate name for group E4c, $q.v.$			10
E10a	Modified Euler No.	Eu'	$H_L'\rho_L g/V_G^2\rho_G$ H_L' = head of liquid on tray $[L]$; ρ_L, ρ_G = densities of liquid, vapor; V_G = vapor velocity based on free area, $[L/\theta]$	Friction head/ velocity head	Flow of vapor across mass transfer trays	13
E13a	Expansion No.	Ex	$\left(\dfrac{gd}{V^2}\right)\left(\dfrac{\rho_L - \rho_G}{\rho_L}\right)$ d = bubble diam., V = bubble veloc., ρ_L, ρ_G = densities of liquid, gas	$1/N_{Fr_1} \times$ density ratio	Rise of bubbles	13
F12a	Fourier No. (flow)	Fo	$\mu\theta/\rho L^2$		Unsteady state flow problems	17
F12b	Frank-Kamenetskii No.	δ	$\dfrac{Q''}{k}\dfrac{E_a}{\mathscr{R}T_o^2}L^2 k_o \exp(-E_a/\mathscr{R}T)$ Q'' = heat liberated per unit mass of material reacting/unit volume $[1/L\theta^2]$; k = thermal conductivity of reacting mixture $[ML/T\theta^3]$; k_o = preexponential constant in Arrhenius equation $[M/\theta]$	Dimensionless heat effect of reaction	Heat transfer in reacting systems	24
F12c	Frequency parameter	—	$\omega'L/V = 2\pi \times$ Strouhal No.; $2\pi/\omega'$ = period of motion $[\theta]$	Special form of Strouhal No. ($cf.$ also T5)	Unsteady state flow, etc.	27
F12d	Frequency No. (2)	N_f	$\omega_r L/V$; L = packing element diameter $[L]$; V = interstitial fluid velocity $[L/\theta]$; ω_r = radial frequency (radians/sec.) $[1/\theta]$ ($cf.$ groups H10, S16, T5)	Special form of group F12c	Flow in packed or fluidized beds	23, 29

TABLE II. ALPHABETICAL LIST OF NEW GROUPS (Continued)

Serial No.	Name	Symbol	Definition	Significance	Field of Use	Reference
F12e	Frössling No. (heat transfer)	Fs_h	$(N_{Nu} - 2)/(N_{Re}^{1/2} N_{Pr}^{1/3})$	Special dimensionless heat transfer coefficient	Heat transfer to spheres in turbulent streams	8a
F12f	Frössling No. (mass transfer)	Fs_m	$(N_{Sh} - 2)/(N_{Re}^{1/2} N_{Sc}^{1/3})$	Special dimensionless mass transfer coefficient	Mass transfer to spheres in turbulent streams	8a
G2a	Geometric No.	Ge	h^*/H^*; $h^* = $ surface area of packing element/perimeter $[L]$; $H = $ height of packing $[L]$.	Dimensionless packed bed height	Mass transfer in packed beds	5a
G2b	Goertler parameter	—	$\dfrac{VL_b\rho}{\mu}\left(\dfrac{L_b}{R_c}\right)^{1/2}$ $L_b = $ boundary layer momentum thickness, $[L]$; $R_c = $ radius of curvature $[L]$	Modified Reynolds No.	Boundary layer flow on curved surfaces	27
G5a	Diffusional Grashof No.	Gr_{AB}	$L^3\rho^2 g\beta'_A \Delta n'_A/\mu^2$ $n'_A = $ mass fraction of species A, $[-]$; $\beta'_A = $ coefficient of density change with n'_A, $[-]$	Buoyant forces × inertia forces/ (viscous forces)^2	Interphase transfer by free convection (density changes caused by concentration differences)	37
H8a	Hess No.	Ge	$(KL^2/a_m)(C_o)^{n-1}$ $n = $ order of reaction $[-]$; $C_o = $ initial concn. $[M/L^3]$; $a_m = $ mass transfer conductivity of reaction products $[L^2/\theta]$; $K = $ reaction rate constant, $\left[\dfrac{1}{\theta}\dfrac{L^{3n-3}}{M^{n-1}}\right]$		Heat and mass transfer with chemical and phase changes	22
H9a	Homochronicity No.	Ho_3	$N\theta$ ($N = $ mixer r.p.m., $\theta = $ mixing time)		Mixing, agitation	31
H11a	Hydraulic resistance group	Γc	$\Delta p_p/\rho_L gL = We_4 \times$ Laplace No. $= N_{Eu_1} \times N_{Fr_1}$ $\Delta p_p = $ pressure drop across liquid on tray $[M/L\theta^2]$; $\rho_L = $ liquid density; $L = $ depth of liquid on tray	Characterizes development of interfacial area per unit area of tray	Pressure drop in distillation columns	15
I1	Ilyushin No.	I	$(Vd\rho/\mu) \cdot 4\tau_D/3V^2\rho = 4\tau_D/3V^2\rho \cdot N_{Re}$; $\tau_D = $ max. dynamic slip resistance $[M/L\theta^2]$		Flow of viscoplastic fluids	20a
K7a	Knudsen No. for diffusion	$N_{Kn_{A2}}$	$3eD_{AB}/4\zeta K_{oA}\bar{u}_A$ $K_{oA} = $ Knudsen flow permeability constant; $\bar{u}_A = $ equilibrium mean molecular speed of species A	Differs from K7 by numerical constant	Gaseous diffusion in packed beds	34
K7b	Kondrat'ev No.	Kn	ΨN_{Bih}; $N_{Bih} = $ heat transfer Biot No.; $\Psi = $ temp. field nonuniformity parameter = $(t_s - t_a)/(\bar{t} - t_a)$; $t_a = $ temp. of surrounding medium; $t_s = $ body surface temp.; $\bar{t} = $ body mean temp.		Heat transfer between fluid and body	21
L3a	Laplace No.	La_4	$\Delta p_p \cdot L/\sigma = \Gamma c/We_4$ $\Delta p_p = $ pressure drop across liquid on tray $[M/L\theta^2]$; $L = $ depth of liquid on tray		Interfacial behavior on distillation trays	32
L5a	Lebedev No.	Le_2	$eb_T(t_a - t_o)/c_b\rho\rho_s$ $b_T = $ intensity of vapor expansion in capillaries of body on heating $[M/L^3 T]$; $t_a = $ temp. of surrounding medium; $t_o = $ initial temp.; $\rho_s = $ density of solid $[M/L^3]$	Molar expansion flux/ molar vapor transfer flux	Drying of porous materials	22
L5b	Leroux No.	—	$\equiv$ cavitation No. C6			27
L7a	Turbulent Lewis No.	Le_T	$c_p\rho\varepsilon_D/k_T = l_D/l_T = \varepsilon_D/\varepsilon_T$ $k_T = $ eddy thermal conductivity $[LM/T\theta^3]$; $l_D, l_T = $ mixing lengths for mass, heat transfer $[L]$; $\varepsilon_T = $ eddy thermal diffusivity $[L^2/\theta]$		Combined turbulent heat and mass transfer	11
L7b	Lewis-Semenov No.	—	$\equiv 1/N_{Le}$; $N_{Le} = $ group L7			27
L7c	Lock No.	—	$\rho R^4 ia'/I$ $\rho = $ fluid density; $a' = $ rotor lift curve slope $[L^2/M]$; $i = $ blade chord $[L]$; $R = $ rotor radius $[L]$; $I = $ moment of inertia of blade about hinge $[L^4]$		Rotor blade dynamics	27
M3a	Magnetic Grashof No.	—	$4\pi\sigma_e\mu_e(\mu/\rho) \cdot N_{Gr}$ $N_{Gr} = $ group G5		Magnetofluid dynamics	7
M4a	Magnetic No.	R_m	$\mu_e H_e(\sigma_e L/\rho V)^{1/2} = $ (magnetic force parameter)$^{1/2}$	See group M3	Magnetohydrodynamics	26
M5a	Magnetic Prandtl No.	—	$\sigma_e\mu_e\dfrac{\mu}{\rho}$ cf. Magnetic Grashof No., group M3a	Magnetic Reynolds No./Reynolds No. (properties of fluid)	Magnetofluid dynamics	27
P3a	Plasticity No.	P	$\equiv$ Bingham No.			41
P7a	Modified Power No.	N'_P	$\dfrac{\Pi}{L^5\rho N^3}\left(\dfrac{D'_e}{L'}\right)(\Delta\omega)^{-1/2}(N_bN_s)^{0.67}$ $D'_e = $ effective agitator diameter $[L]$; $L'_e = $ effective agitator height; $\Delta\omega = $ wall proximity factor; $N_b = $ No. of blades on agitator; $N_s = $ effective No. of blade edges		Agitation	36
P8a	Total Prandtl No.	Pr	$\dfrac{\varepsilon_M + (\mu/\rho)}{\varepsilon_T + \alpha}$ $\varepsilon_M, \varepsilon_T = $ eddy transfer coefficient for momentum, heat $[L^2/\theta]$	Total momentum diffusivity/total thermal diffusivity	Heat transfer in combined turbulent and laminar flows	25
P8b	Turbulent Prandtl No.	Pr_T	$\varepsilon_M/\varepsilon_T = l/l_T$ $\varepsilon_M, \varepsilon_T = $ eddy viscosity, eddy thermal diffusivity $[L^2/\theta]$; $l, l_T = $ mixing lengths for momentum, heat transfer	Eddy momentum diffusivity/eddy thermal diffusivity	Heat transfer in turbulent flow	9, 25

TABLE II. ALPHABETICAL LIST OF NEW GROUPS (Continued)

Serial No.	Name	Symbol	Definition	Significance	Field of Use	Reference
P12a	Predvoditelev No. (mass transfer)	Pd_m	$(\Gamma_m L^2/a_m)(N_{Fo_m})$ Γ_m = rate of change of mass transfer potential of medium, (mass/unit mass)/time $[1/\theta]$; a_m = mass conductivity of material $[L^2/\theta]$; N_{Fo_m} = group F12	Rate of change of concn. of medium/rate of change of concn. of body	Mass transfer	22
P15a	Pulsation No.	N_{Pu}	$fd_e\rho/G$ d_e = equiv. diam. of channel		Transfer to pulsed fluid	20
R0a	Radial frequency parameter (1)	—	$\omega_r D/V^2$, $\omega_r\alpha/V^2$ D = diffusivity or dispersion coefficient of packed bed $[L^2/\theta]$, ω_r = radial frequency (radians/sec.) $[1/\theta]$		Packed and fluidized beds	18, 33, 39
R0b	Radial frequency parameter (2)	—	$\omega_r L^2/\alpha$ ω_r as in group R0a; L = tube radius $[L]$		Packed and fluidized beds	29, 39
R0c	Radial frequency parameter (3)	—	$\omega_r^2 DL/V^3$ (Quantities as in groups R0a and R0b)	(Group R0a)^2 (Group P2)	Packed and fluidized beds	18, 33, 39
R0d	Radial frequency parameter (4)	—	$L(\omega_r/2D)^{1/2} \equiv [\frac{1}{2}(\text{group R0b})^{1/2}$ (quantities as in groups R0a and R0b)	Analog of Wave No.	Packed and fluidized beds	39
R1a	Radiation parameter	Φ	$e^+\eta T_w^3 d_h/k$ e^+ = function of mean surface emissivity of walls, $[-]$; T_w = wall temp. (abs.) $[T]$		Effect of radiation on convective mass transfer	14
R6a	Reaction enthalpy No.	N_H	$(\Delta u)_A(\Delta n_A)/C_p(\Delta T)$ $(\Delta u)_A$ = enthalpy of reaction per unit mass of A produced $[L^2/\theta^2]$, n_A = mass fraction of species A $[-]$	Change in reaction energy/change in sensible energy	Interphase transfer with chemical reaction	37
R15a	Rossby No.	—	$V/\omega L$	More general form of group R15		27
S4a	Schmidt No. (2)	—	$\equiv$ Semenov No. (2)	No longer used		27
S4b	Schmidt No. (3)	$(Sc)_3$	$\mu\chi/\rho\sigma_e L^2$ χ as in group E4b	Diffusivity of vorticity/mass diffusivity of ions	Electrochemistry	10
S4c	Total Schmidt No.	Sc	$\dfrac{\varepsilon_M + (\mu/\rho)}{\varepsilon_D + D}$ ε_M = eddy viscosity $[L^2/\theta]$	Total momentum diffusivity/total mass diffusivity	Mass transfer in combined laminar and turbulent flows	25
S4d	Turbulent Schmidt No.	Sc_T	$\varepsilon_M/\varepsilon D = l/l_D$ ε_M = eddy viscosity, $[L^2/\theta]$, l, l_D = mixing lengths for momentum, mass transfer $[L]$	Eddy momentum diffusivity/eddy mass diffusivity	Mass transfer in turbulent flow	25
S5a	Semenov No. (2)	—	$\equiv 1/N_{Le}$ (see group L7)			27
S7a	Smoluchowski No.	—	$L/\lambda \equiv 1/N_{Kn}$ N_{Kn} = group K6	See group K6		27
S9a	Soret No.	S_o	$\Theta n'_{20}$ (definitions as group D14a)	Dimensionless thermodiffusion coefficient	Coupled heat and mass transfer	22
S10a	Spalding No.	B'	$c_p\Delta T/(r_v - q_r/V_m)$; q_r = radiant heat flux $[ML^2/\theta^3]$; V_m = rate of mass transfer $[M/\theta]$	Ratio (sensible heat/latent heat) for evaporated material	Droplet evaporation	33a
S13a	Stark No.	Sk	$\eta T^3 L/k$ L = thickness of layer $[L]$; ($\equiv$ Stefan No.)		Radiant heat transfer	1, 30
S14a	Stewart No.	—	$\mu_e^2 H_e^2\sigma_e L/V\rho$	(Hartmann No.)^2/Reynolds No.	Magnetofluid dynamics	38
S15a	Stokes No. (2)	St_2	$1.042\, m_f g\rho(1 - \rho/\rho_f)R^{*3}/\mu^2$; ρ, μ = density, viscosity of fluid; m_f, ρ_f = mass, density of float; R^* = tube radius/float radius $[-]$		Calibration of rotameters	10a
S18a	Surface tension No.	T_s	$\mu^2/h^*\sigma\rho$; h^* = surface area of packing element/perimeter $[L]$		Mass transfer in packed columns	5a
T5a	Thompson No.	N_{Th_2}	$\dfrac{-\Delta t}{\Delta L}L^2\left(\dfrac{d\sigma}{dT}\right)/\mu\alpha$ (cf. Marangoni No.)		Cellular convection	3
T7a	Thrust coefficient	T_c	$F_T/\rho V^2 d^2$ F_T = thrust force $[ML/\theta^2]$; V = forward speed $[L/\theta]$; d = tip diameter $[L]$		Propeller studies	27
T7b	Torque coefficient	Q_c	$F'/\rho V^2 d^3$ F' = propeller torque $[ML^2/\theta^2]$		Propeller studies	27
T7c	Transiency groups	K_p	$\dfrac{1}{\left[\dfrac{\partial p}{\partial L}\right]}\cdot\dfrac{\partial\left(\dfrac{\partial p}{\partial L}\right)}{\partial(Fo_f)}$		Transient flow behavior	17
		K_Q	$\dfrac{1}{(N_{Re})}\cdot\dfrac{\partial(N_{Re})}{\partial(Fo_f)}$ $\partial p/\partial L$ = pressure gradient in flow direction $[M/L^2\theta^2]$; Fo_f = group F12a			
W0a	Wave No.	k	$L(\omega_r/2\alpha)^{1/2}$ w_r = radial frequency (radians/sec.) $[1/\theta]$	Heat transfer analog group R0d	Cyclic heat transfer	4
W3a	Weber No. (3)	We_3	$\sigma/\rho_L g L^2$ ρ_L = liquid density $[M/L^3]$; L = depth of liquid on tray $[L]$	Surface tension force/gravity force	Interfacial area determination in distillation equipment	32
W4a	Generalized Weissenberg No.	N_1	$\sqrt{I_e}\,\theta_n$ (definitions as group D8a)	Generalization of group W4	Rheology	2

TABLE III. TABLES FOR IDENTIFYING DIMENSIONLESS GROUPS

These tables incorporate those from the earlier publication (5)

Basic dimensions are taken to be: Length [L]
Mass [M]
Electrical charge [Q]
Temperature [T]
Time [θ]

PHYSICAL PROPERTIES

General Physical Properties

Parameter	Symbol	Dimensions	Exponent	Groups
Coefficient of thermal bulk expansion	β	$1/T$	−1	E4, E12, G2
			+1	G5, K9, M3a, R5, R6
Coefficient of density change with concn. n_A	$\beta_{A'}$	—	+1	G5a
Density	ρ	M/L^3	−2	M1
			−1	A1, B1, B10, C1, C2, C6, D3, D13, D14a, E3, E9, E10, E10a, E13, E13a, F1, F11, F12a, H5, H11a, I1, J1, K4, K10, L5a, L5b, L7, M3, M3a, M5a, M6, N2, N3, N4, P7, P8a, P9, R0a, R9, R10, R13, S4, S4b, S4c, S13, S14a, S15, S15a, S18a, T7a, T7b, T7c, W3a
			$-\frac{2}{3}$	C9, J3
			$-\frac{1}{2}$	E2, L11, M4a, O2, P13
			$+\frac{1}{3}$	J3, K5, S3
			$+\frac{1}{2}$	D10, G3, P10, P11, R4, W0a, W2
			$+\frac{2}{3}$	F2, N8, S2
			+1	A1b, B1, B6, B9, C5, C7, D5, D7, D13, E4, E4b, E6, E7, E8, E10a, E13a, G2b, H6, H11, I1, J1, J3, J4, K1, L7a, L7b, L7c, L9, M3a, P1, P8a, P15a, R0b, R5, R11, R13, S4a, S5a, S15a, S17, T1, T5a, T6, T7c, V1, W1, W3
			+2	A5, C10, G1, G5, G5a, K9, R5, R6, S15a, T2
Density gradient	$d\rho/dL$	M/L^4	+1	R13
Diffusivity (molecular unless noted otherwise)	D, a_m	L^2/θ	−1	B5, B7[4], D2, D14a, E4c, E4e, H8a[1], K4[1], K7[2], L2, L7, L10, N7, P2, P9, P12a[1], S4, S4c, S9a
			$-\frac{2}{3}$	J3
			$-\frac{1}{2}$	A0, R0d
			+1	A4a, F12[1], K7[3], K7a, L2[4], L7b, L9[1], R0a, R0c, S4a, S5a
Diffusivity (eddy)	E_D, ε_D	L^2/θ	−1	S4c, S4d
			+1	L2, L7a
Diffusivity (surface)	D_S	ML/θ^2	−1	S18
Diffusion tortuosity	ζ	—	−1	K7, K7a
Dispersion (permeability) coefficient	D'	L^2/θ	−1	D6a
			+1	R0a, R0c
Molecular weight	M	M	−1	D14, K9, S6
			+1	D14
Permeability (packed bed)	ξ	L^2	$+\frac{1}{2}$	L6
Porosity (voidage)	e	—	−1	B6, M12
			$-\frac{1}{2}$	L6
			+1	K7, K7a, L5a
Specific gravity	γ	—	$\pm\frac{1}{2}$	F2
Surface tension	σ	M/θ^2	−3	C2
			−2	C1
			−1	B9, C3, C13, E8, L3a, L6, R1, S18a, W1, W3
			$-\frac{1}{2}$	D10, G3, O2, P13, R4, W2
			+1	M9, S17, S18, T5a, W3a

PHYSICAL PROPERTIES

General Physical Properties

Parameter	Symbol	Dimensions	Exponent	Groups
Thermal diffusion coefficient	D_T	L^2/θ	+1	D14a, S9a

[1] Coefficient of potential diffusion in mass transfer.
[2] Knudsen diffusion coefficient.
[3] Binary bulk diffusion coefficient.
[4] Effective diffusivity (molecular and eddy) = $D + \varepsilon_D$.

Electrical and Magnetic Properties

Parameter	Symbol	Dimensions	Exponent	Groups
Carrier suspectibility	b'	$Q\theta/M$	−1	E4d
Current density	I	$Q/L^2\theta$	+1	K10
Dielectric suscepti-bility	χ	$Q^2\theta^2/L^3M$	+1	E4b, S4b
Electrical conductivity	σ_e	$Q^2\theta/L^3M$	−1	E6, S4b
			$+\frac{1}{2}$	H2, M4a
			+1	B2a, L11, M3, M3a, M5a, M7, S14a
Electrical permittivity	ε_e	$Q^2\theta^2/L^3\theta$	−1	B2a
			+1	E4d
Field strength	H_e	$Q/L\theta$	−2	J4
			−1	E4a
			+1	H2, L11, M4a
			+2	K9, M3, M6, S6, S14a
Magnetic perme-ability	μ_e	ML/Q^2	−1	E4a, E6, J4
			+1	H2, M3a, M4a, M5a, M6, M7
			$+\frac{1}{3}$	L11
			+2	M3, S14a
Space charge density	Q	Q/L^3	−1	E4d
Voltage	E	ML/θ^2Q	+1	E4a, K10
			+2	E4b

Thermal Properties

Parameter	Symbol	Dimensions	Exponent	Groups
Eddy thermal conductivity	k_T	$ML/T\theta^3$	−1	L7a
Eddy thermal diffusivity	ε_T	L^2/θ	−1	L7a, P8a, P8b
Humid heat	s	L^2/θ^2T	−1	P15
Latent heats of phase change	λ, r	L^2/θ^2	−1	A3, E11, E12, E13, J1, M1, S10a
			+1	B13, C10, K8, K11, N5
Ratio of specific heats	γ	—	$\pm\frac{1}{2}$	L5
Specific heat	C, c_p	L^2/θ^2T	−1	B2, B13, D3, D14a, D15, E1, F11, J2, K8, K11, L7, M10, N5, R0a, R3, R6a, S13
			$-\frac{1}{3}$	J2
			$+\frac{1}{2}$	F6, F7, F8, W0a
			$+\frac{2}{3}$	J2
			+1	A3, E4, E12, G4, J1, J4, L7a, L7b, L9, P1, P8, P8a, R0b, R3, R5, R6, R7, S5a, S10a, T5a
Surface emissivity	e^*	—	−1	T6
			+1	R1a
Temperature conductivity (thermal diffusivity)	$\alpha = \dfrac{k}{\rho c_p}$	L^2/θ	−1	L7b, L9, P1, P8a, P12, R0b, R5, S5a, T5a
			$-\frac{1}{2}$	W0a
			+1	C13, L7, L10, R0a
Thermal conductivity	k, λ	$ML/T\theta^3$	−3	M1
			−2	R6
			−1	B4, B12, C7, C9, C10, D4, F12b, G4, K3, K7b, L7b, L9, N6, P1, P5,

TABLE III. TABLES FOR IDENTIFYING DIMENSIONLESS GROUPS (Co...

Thermal Properties

Parameter	Symbol	Dimensions	Exponent	Groups
			$-\frac{2}{3}$	P8, R0b, R1a, R5, S4a, S5a, S13a, S14, T5a, J2
			$-\frac{1}{2}$	T3, W0a
			$+1$	F11, L7, R0a, R1

Rheological and Elastic Behavior

Parameter	Symbol	Dimensions	Exponent	Groups
Eddy viscosity	e_M	L^2/θ	$+1$	P8a, P8b, S4c, S4d
Invariants of rate-of-strain and vorticity tensors	I_e, I_w	θ^{-2}	$+\frac{1}{2}$	D8a, W4a
Maximum dynamic slip resistance	τ_D	$M/L\theta^2$	$+1$	I1
Modulus of elasticity	E	$M/L\theta^2$	-1	A1b, C5, E4, H11
			$+1$	C1, E13, R1
			$+3$	A1
Rate of shear	$\dot\gamma$	$1/\theta$	$+1$	T8
Rigidity coefficient	μ_p	$M/L\theta$	-2	H6
			-1	B3, P3a
Shear stress	τ	$M/L\theta^2$	-1	E5
			$-\frac{1}{2}$	P10
			$+\frac{1}{2}$	P11
			$+1$	A4b
Viscosity (in all cases, kinematic viscosity has been written as μ/ρ)	μ	$M/L\theta$	-2	A1, A5, E4b, G1, G5, G5a, K1, K9, S15a, S17, T2
			-1	A4b, B6, C10, D5, D7, E6, E7, G2b, H8, I1, L1, L3, M3a, O1, P4, P11, R5, R6, R11, S9, S19, T1, T5a, T7c, V1
			$-\frac{2}{3}$	F2, K5, N8
			$-\frac{1}{2}$	H2
			$-\frac{1}{3}$	S2, S3
			$+\frac{1}{2}$	E2
			$+\frac{2}{3}$	C9, J2, J3
			$+1$	B12, C3, C13, E3, E5, F12a, M1, M3a, M5a, O2, P8, P8a, P9, S4, S4b, S4c, S8, S15, T7c, T8
			$+2$	C1, S18a
			$+4$	C2
Viscosity (surface)	μ_s	M/θ	$+1$	S19
Yield stress	τ_y	$M/L\theta^2$	$+1$	B3, H6, P3a

LENGTHS, AREAS, AND VOLUMES

Characteristic Lengths

Parameter	Symbol	Dimensions	Exponent	Groups
General length dimension	Various	L	-5	P7, P7a
			-3	F9, L1, S15a, T7b
			-2	D9, D12, E3, F11, F12, F12a, H4, H5, N2, N3, N4, O1, R9, S4b, S8, S9, S15, T7a, W3a
			-1	A1a, B1, B10, E2, E4d, E5, E10, F1, F13, G2a, G4, H10, H11a, K6, L4, P7a, R6, R10, R15, R15a, R16, S6, S7a, S18a, S19, T5, T5a, T7, T7c, W4
			$-\frac{1}{2}$	B11, D7, F14, G2b, O2
			$+\frac{1}{2}$	A0, G2b, M4a, R4, T1, W2
			$+1$	A4a, A4b, B2a, B3, B4, B5, B7, B10, B13a, C7, D1, D3, D5, D6a, D11, D13, E4c, E4e, E7, E10, E13a, F1, F2, F5, F12c, F12d, F15, G2a, G2b, G3, H2, I1, K3, K4, K6, K7b, K10, L3, L3a, L4, L7c, L9, L11, M1, M3, M7, N6, N7, N8, P1, P2, P3a, P7a, P11, P15a, R0c, R0d, R1a, R8, R10,

Characteristic Lengths

Parameter	Symbol	Dimensions	Exponent	Groups
				R11, R16, S2, S7, S7a, S13a, S14, S14a, S16, S17, S18, T3, T7c, W0a, W1
			$+\frac{1}{2}$	D7, H7, T1
			$+2$	B9, D2, D4, E4b, E8, F12b, H6, H8a, K9, O1, P4, P5, P12, P12a, R0b, S8, S9, T5a, T7c, V1
			$+3$	A5, C10, G1, G5, G5a, K1, M3a, R5, S15a, W3
			$+4$	L7c, T2
			$+5$	R6
Dimension of agitator, propeller, etc.	Various	L	-5	P7, P7a
			-3	F9, T7b
			-2	H4, T7a
			-1	A1a, P7a
			$+1$	D11, F15, L7c, P7a
			$+3$	W3
			$+4$	L7c
Film thickness	L_f	L	-1	A4a
			$+1$	N8
Furnace half-width	L	L	-1	T7
Larmor radius	L_L	L	$+1$	L4
Mean free path	λ	L	-1	S7a
Mixing length-mass	l_D	L	$+1$	K6
			-1	S4d
Mixing length-heat	l_T	L	$+1$	L7a
Mixing length-momentum	l	L	-1	L7a, P8b
			$+1$	P8b, S4d
Particle dimension	d_e	L	-2	S15
			$+1$	F2, F12d
			$+3$	A5, G1
Pore or nozzle radius	R	L	$+1$	B7
Thickness of liquid layer	L	L	-1	C13, M9, T5a
			$+1$	H2, L11
			$+2$	M9, T5a
			$+3$	R5
			$+4$	T2

Areas

Parameter	Symbol	Dimensions	Exponent	Groups
Area	A	L^2	-1	D9, F6, F7, F8
			$+1$	B2
Area/unit volume	S, A^*	L^{-1}	-1	B6
			$+1$	M11, M12

Volumes

Parameter	Symbol	Dimensions	Exponent	Groups
Volume	W, W^*	L^3	$+1$	A5, H9, M11

TIMES AND FREQUENCIES

Parameter	Symbol	Dimensions	Exponent	Groups
Time	θ	θ	-1	D8, T7c
			$+1$	D8, D8a, D12, E3, F11, F12, F12a, H1, H9a, H10, P12a, S15, T5, W4a
Frequency	f', ω'	$1/\theta$	$+1$	F12c, H1, P15a, S16, V1
Radial frequency[1]	ω_r (radians/time)	$1/\theta$	$+\frac{1}{2}$	R0d, W0a
($= 2\pi f'$)			$+1$	F12d, R0a, R0b
[1] Also see angular velocity.			$+2$	R0c

TEMPERATURES AND CONCENTRATIONS (DRIVING FORCES)

Concentrations and Related Quantities

Parameter	Symbol	Dimensions	Exponent	Groups
Dimensional concentration	C, c_A	M/L^3	$(n-1)$	H8a (nth order reaction)
			-1	D1, D2, R2
			$+1$	B10
Dimensionless concentration (e.g., wt./wt., mass fraction)	n	—	-1	D14a, P6, S9a
			$+1$	A4, D14a, G5a, K8, R6a, S9a

TABLE III. TABLES FOR IDENTIFYING DIMENSIONLESS GROUPS (Continued)

Concentrations and Related Quantities

Parameter	Symbol	Dimensions	Exponent	Groups
Mole fraction	Y, Z	—	± 1	D14
Rate of change of mass transfer potential (mass per unit mass/time)	Γ_m	$1/\theta$	$+1$	P12a
Specific mass content (mass/unit mass)	n^*	—	-1	K4
Surface concentration	Γ'	M/L^2	± 1	S18
$\{$ Vapor capacity $\}$ $\{$ Mass capacity $\}$ (porous body)	c_b	$L\theta^2/M$	-1 $+1$	L5a B13, R2
Vapor expansion intensity on heating	b_T	$M/L^3 T$	$+1$	L5a

Temperatures, Temperature Differences

Parameter	Symbol	Dimensions	Exponent	Groups
Dimensional temperature, temperature difference	$T, \Delta T$	T	-3	R1*, T6*
			-2	F12b*
			-1	A4, A6*, B12, B13, B13a*, C4*, C7, C10, D3*, D4*, D14a*, D15, E1, E4b*, F12b*, G2, G6*, K3, K7b, K8, K9, K11, N5, P5*, P12*, R6a, R14*, S6, T5a
			$-\frac{1}{2}$	L5
			$+\frac{1}{2}$	F6*, F7*, F8*
			$+1$	B13a, C4, E4b, G5, G6, J1, J4, K7b, L5a, M1, M3a, P6, R5, R7, R14*, S10a, T5a
			$+3$	R1a*, S13a*, S14*
Dimensionless temperature difference	Ψ	—	$+1$	K7b
Rate of temperature change	Γ	T/θ	$+1$	P12

* Absolute temperature.

VELOCITIES, RATES, FLUXES, TRANSFER COEFFICIENTS

Velocities

Parameter	Symbol	Dimensions	Exponent	Groups
Angular velocity (rate of rotation) (see also frequency)	N, ω	$1/\theta$	-3	P7, P7a
			-2	H4, L1
			-1	A1a, F9, R15, R15a
			$-\frac{1}{2}$	E2
			$+1$	H9a, S8, S11, S12, T1
			$+2$	F15, T2, W3
Equilibrium molecular speed of A	u_A	L/θ	-1	K7a
General velocity (usually of fluid)	V	L/θ	-3	H5, R0c
			-2	B13a, C6, C11, D13, E9, E10, E13a, F1, I1, L5b, M6, N2, N3, N4, R0a, R7, R8, R9, R10, T7a, T7b
			-1	A2, A4b, B3, C12, C14, D1, D3, E4a, F10, F12c, F12d, H7, H8, I1, K10, L3, M3, P3a, P4, S13, S14a, S16, T7c, V2
			$-\frac{1}{2}$	M4a
			$+1$	A1a, A2, B1a, B2a, B6, B7, B11, C3, C12, C14, D5, D6a, D7, E1a, E4c, E4d, E4e, E5, E7, F10, F14, G2b, H7, H10, I1, K2, L5, L8, M2, M4, M7, P1, P2, P3, P10, R4, R11, R13, R15a, S1,

Velocities

Parameter	Symbol	Dimensions	Exponent	Groups
			$+2$	S2, S3, T5, T6, T7c, V2, W2, W4
				A1b, B1, B12, C5, C11, D15, E1, E11, F13, H11, P3, W1
Velocity of impeller or agitator periphery	U_s	L/θ	-2	P14
			-1	D9
Velocity of light	V_l	L/θ	-2	B2a
			-1	E1a, L8
Velocity of sound	V_s	L/θ	-1	B1a, M2, N1, S1
Velocity of waves	V_w	L/θ	-1	V2
			$+1$	P3
Velocity of Alfven waves	V_A	L/θ	-1	A2, K2, M4
			$+1$	A2, N1
			$+2$	C11
Velocity of bearing surface	v_s	L/θ	-1	H8, O1, S9
Velocity gradient	dV/dL	$1/\theta$	-2	R13

Flow Rates, Mass Fluxes, etc.

Parameter	Symbol	Dimensions	Exponent	Groups
Mass flow rate (mass flux)	V_m	M/θ	-1	B2, M11, T7
			$+1$	F6, F7, F8, G4, S10a, T7
Mass flow rate/unit area (mass flux density)	G	$M/L^2\theta$	-1	J2, J3, P15, P15a, S13
			$+1$	K4, M11
Mass flux/unit volume (reaction rate)	U	$M/L^2\theta$	$+\frac{1}{2}$	T3
			$+1$	D1, D2, D3, D4
Reaction rate constant (first order)	K	L/θ	-1	S5
Reaction rate constant (nth order)	K_n	$\dfrac{1}{\theta} \cdot \dfrac{L^{3n-3}}{M^{n-1}}$	$+1$	H8a
Volumetric flow rate	V_f	L^3/θ	-1	H9
			$-\frac{1}{2}$	D11
			$+\frac{1}{2}$	S11, S12
			$+1$	D9, F9
Volumetric flow rate/wetted perimeter	$V_{f'}$	L^2/θ	-1	A4a
			$-\frac{1}{2}$	A0

Heat Fluxes and Related Quantities

Parameter	Symbol	Dimensions	Exponent	Groups
Heat flux (heat flow/unit time)	q	ML^2/θ^3	-1	S10a
			$+1$	H5
Heat flux/unit area	q^*	M/θ^2	$+1$	K3, R6
Heat of reaction/unit mass of material reacting	Δu	L^2/θ^2	$+1$	R6a
Heat liberated/unit mass	Q	L^2/θ^2	$+1$	D3, D4
Heat liberated per unit mass of material reacting/unit volume	Q''	$1/L\theta^2$	$+1$	F12b
Heat liberated/unit volume (heat source power)	j	$M/L\theta^3$	$+1$	P5

Transfer Coefficients

Parameter	Symbol	Dimensions	Exponent	Groups
Heat transfer coefficient	h	$M/T\theta^3$	$+1$	B2, B4, C9, J2, K7b, N6, P15, S13
			$+4$	M1
Mass transfer coefficient	k_c	L/θ	$+1$	A0, B5, J3, L9, N7, S5, S7

FORCE, TORQUE, POWER, PRESSURE, HEAD

Force, Torque, Power

Parameter	Symbol	Dimensions	Exponent	Groups
Force	F, F_R	ML/θ^2	$-\frac{1}{2}$	S2
			$+\frac{1}{4}$	K5
			$+1$	N1, N3, N4, R9, T7a
Force/unit length	F_u	M/θ^2	$+1$	H8, O1, S9
Torque	F	ML^2/θ^2	$+1$	T7b
Power	Π	ML^2/θ^3	$+1$	L1, P7, P7a

TABLE III. TABLES FOR IDENTIFYING DIMENSIONLESS GROUPS (Continued)

Head, Pressure

Parameter	Symbol	Dimensions	Exponent	Groups
Fluid head (ft. fluid)	H'	L	$-\frac{3}{4}$	S12
			$+1$	E10a, H4
Head (energy/unit mass of fluid = gH')	H	L^2/θ^2	-1	P3, T4
			$-\frac{3}{4}$	S11
			$+\frac{1}{4}$	D11
			$+1$	P14, T4
Pressure	P, p	$M/L\theta^2$	-1	F6, F7, F8, H9, L5a, S8, T8
			$+1$	B13, C6, D14a, L5b, L6, P13, R2
Pressure drop	$\Delta P, dP$	$M/L\theta^2$	$+1$	E9, E10, F1, H9, H11a, K1, L3, L3a, R10
Pressure gradient	$\Delta P/L$	$M/L^2\theta^2$	-1	T7c
			$+1$	E10, F1, H11a, K1, P4, R10, T7c

Other Quantities

Parameter	Symbol	Dimensions	Exponent	Groups
Arrhenius pre-exponential factor	k_0	M/θ	$+1$	F12b
Avogadro's No.	N	$1/M$	$+1$	K9, S6
Boltzmann's constant	k	$ML^2/\theta^2 T$	-1	K9, S6
Dufour coefficient	β^*	T	$+1$	A3, A4, F3
Energy of activation/unit mass	E_a	L^2/θ^2	$+1$	A6, F12b
Gas constant/unit mass	$\mathscr{R}$	$L^2/\theta^2 T$	-1	A6, F12b
			$-\frac{1}{2}$	L5
			$+1$	D14a
Knudsen flow permeability	K_{oA}	L	-1	K7a
Mass of float	m_f	M	$+1$	S15a
Moment of inertia	I	L^4	-1	L7c
Rotor lift curve slope	a'	L^2/M	$+1$	L7c
Shape factor	ξ^*	—	$+1$	V2
Soret coefficient	δ	$1/T$	$+1$	F3, P6
Stefan-Boltzmann coefficient	η	$M/T^4\theta^3$	$+1$	R1, T6
(radiation coefficient)	—		$+1$	R1a, S13a, S14
Thermodiffusion constant	Θ	—	$+1$	D14a, S9a

CONSTANTS AND MISCELLANEOUS QUANTITIES

Gravity Acceleration

Parameter	Symbol	Dimensions	Exponent	Groups
Gravity acceleration	g	L/θ^2	-2	A1
			-1	B1, F13, F15, H11a, M1, S6, W3a
			$-\frac{3}{4}$	S11
			$-\frac{1}{2}$	B11, F14, P13
			$-\frac{1}{3}$	C9, S3
			$+\frac{1}{3}$	F2, N8
			$+1$	A5, B9, B13a, C2, C10, D13, E8, E10a, E13a, G1, G5, G5a, H4, M3a, R5, R6, R8, R13, S15a

REFERENCES

1. Adrianov, V. N., "Radiation-Conductive and Radiation-Convective Heat Transfer," in "Teplo- i Massoperenos," A. V. Lȳkov and B. M. Smol'skii, Eds., Vol. II, pp. 92–102, Nauka i Tekhnika, Minsk, 1965.
2. Astarita, G., *Ind. Eng. Chem. Fundamentals* 6, 257 (1967).
3. Berg, J. C., Acrivos, A., Boudart, M., "Evaporative Convection," in "Advances in Chemical Engineering," T. B. Drew *et al.*, Eds., Vol. 6, pp. 61–123, Academic Press, New York, 1966.
4. Carslaw, H. S., Jaeger, J. C., "Conduction of Heat in Solids," 2nd ed., Oxford University Press, 1959.
5. Catchpole, J. P., Fulford, G., *Ind. Eng. Chem.* 58 (3), 46 (1966).
5a. Costa Novella, E., Costa Lopez, J., *An. Real. Soc. Espan. Fis. Quim., Ser. B,* 63 (2), 145 (1967).
6. Coulson, J. M., Porter, J. E., *Trans. Inst. Chem. Engrs.* 44, T388 (1966).
7. Ede, A. J., *Intern. J. Heat Mass Transfer* 9, 837 (1966).
8. Gall, C. E., Hudgins, R. R., *J. Chem. Educ.* 42, 611 (1965).
8a. Galloway, T. R., Sage, B. H., *Int. J. Heat Mass Transfer* 10, 1195 (1967).
9. Gardner, G. O., Kestin, J., *Ibid.*, 6, 289 (1963).
10. Gibbins, J. C., Hignett, E. T., *Electrochim. Acta* 11, 815 (1966).
10a. Gilmont, R., Maurer, P. W., *Instr. Control Systems* 34, 2070 (1961).
11. Ginzburg, I. P., "Heat and Mass Transfer from Bodies Interacting with Gas and Liquid Streams," in "Teplo- i Massoperenos," A. V. Lȳkov and B. M. Smol'skii, Eds., Vol. II, pp. 3–26, Nauka i Tekhnika, Minsk, 1965.
12. Glauert, M. B., Lighthill, M. J., *Proc. Roy. Soc.* 230A, 188 (1955).
13. Hobler, T., "Mass Transfer and Absorbers," Pergamon Press, New York, 1966.
14. Irvine, T. F., Stein, R. P., Simon, G. A., "Effect of Radiation on Convection in a Flat Channel," in "Teplo- i Massoperenos," A. V. Lȳkov and B. M. Smol'skii, Eds., Vol. II, pp. 78–91, Nauka i Tekhnika, Minsk, 1965.
15. Kasatkin, A. G., Dȳtnerskii, Yu. N., Kochergin, N. V., "Mass and Heat Transfer in Tray Columns," in "Teplo- i Massoperenos," A. V. Lȳkov and B. M. Smol'skii, Eds., Vol. II, pp. 12–17, Nauka i Tekhnika, Minsk, 1966.
16. Kerber, R., *Chem.-Ing.-Technik* 38, 1133 (1966).
17. Kochenov, I. S., Kuznetsov, Yu. N., "Unsteady Flow in Pipes," in "Teplo- Massoperenos," A. V. Lȳkov and B. M. Smol'skii, Eds., Vol. II, pp. 306–314, Nauka i Tekhnika, Minsk, 1965.
18. Kramers, H., Alberda, G., *Chem. Eng. Sci.* 2, 173 (1953).
19. Laslo, A., *Inzh.-Fiz. Zh.* 10 (1), 60 (1966).
20. Lemlich, R., Armour, J. C., *Chem. Engr. Progr. Symp. Ser.* 61 (57), 83 (1965).
20a. Leshchii, N. P., Mochernyuk, D. Yu, *Izv. Vysshikh Uchebn. Zavedenii, Nefti Gaz* 10 (2), 77 (1967).
21. Luikov (Lȳkov), A. V., "Heat and Mass Transfer in Capillary-Porous Bodies," Pergamon Press, New York, 1966.
22. Luikov (Lȳkov), A. V., Mikhailov, Yu. A., "Theory of Energy and Mass Transfer," revised Engl. ed., Pergamon Press, New York, 1965.
23. McHenry, K. W., Wilhelm, R. H., *A.I.Ch.E. J.* 3, 83 (1957).
24. Merzhanov, A. G., "Problems of Heat Transfer in the Theory of Thermal Detonation," in "Teplo- i Massoperenos," A. V. Lȳkov and B. M. Smol'skii, Eds., Vol. IV, pp. 259–72, Nauka i Tekhnika, Minsk, 1966.
25. Opfell, J. B., Sage, B. H., "Turbulence in Thermal and Material Transport," in "Advances in Chemical Engineering," T. B. Drew *et al.*, Ed., Vol. I, pp. 241–88, Academic Press, New York, 1961.
26. Pai, Shih-I., "Magnetohydrodynamics of Channel Flow," in "Advances in Hydroscience," Ven Te Chow, Ed., Vol. III, pp. 63–110, Academic Press, New York, 1966.
27. Pankhurst, R. C., "Dimensional Analysis and Scale Factors," Chapman and Hall, London, 1964.
28. Pechoč, V., Research Institute of Chemical Fibers, Svit, Czechoslovakia, private communication, 1966.
29. Philip, J. R., *Austral. J. Phys.* 16 (4), 454 (1963).
30. Postolnik, Yu. S., *Inzh.-Fiz. Zh.* 8 (1), 64 (1965).
31. Prochazka, J., Landau, J., *Collection Czech. Chem. Commun.* 26, 2961 (1961).
32. Rodionov, A. I., Kashnikov, A. M., Radikovskii, V. M., "Determination of Interfacial Contact Areas and Heat and Mass Transfer Coefficients on Sieve Trays," in "Teplo- i Massoperenos," A. V. Lȳkov, B. M. Smol'skii, Eds., Vol., IV, pp. 28–37, Nauka i Tekhnika, Minsk, 1966.
33. Rosen, J. B., Winsche, W. E., *J. Chem. Phys.* 18, 1587 (1950).
33a. Ross, L. L., Hoffman, T. W., Proc. 3rd Internat. Heat Transfer Conference, Chicago, August 1966, 5, 50 (A.I.Ch.E., New York, 1966).
34. Rothfield, L. B., *A.I.Ch.E. J.* 9, 19 (1963).
35. Sakiadis, B. S., *Ibid.*, 7, 467 (1961).
36. Skelland, A. H. P., "Non-Newtonian Flow and Heat Transfer," Wiley, New York, 1967.
37. Stewart, W. E., *Chem. Eng. Progr. Symp. Ser.* 61 (58), 16 (1965).
38. Tsinober, A. B., *Appl. Mech. Rev.* 18, 3751 (1965).
39. Turner, G. A., Dept. of Chemical Engineering, University of Waterloo, Waterloo, Ontario, private communication, 1967.
40. Vyazovov, V. V., *Zh. Tekhn. Fiz.* 10, 1519 (1940).
41. Wilkinson, W. L., "Non-Newtonian Fluids," Pergamon Press, London, 1960.

NUMERICAL DATA PROJECTS

SOURCES OF CRITICAL DATA

The following is abstracted from *Continuing Numerical Data Projects, A Survey and Analysis*. This publication was prepared under the auspices of the Office of Critical Tables, National Academy of Sciences and National Research Council. Persons requesting further information and details regarding the projects listed may obtain the publication from Printing and Publishing Office, National Academy of Sciences, 2101 Constitution Avenue, Washington, D. C., 20418. Price $5.00.

THERMODYNAMIC PROJECTS

Selected Values of Chemical Thermodynamic Properties, NBS Circular 500, F. D. Rossini, D. D. Wagman, W. H. Evans, S. Levine, and I. Jaffe, Government Printing Office, Washington, D.C. 20402, 1952, iv + 1268 pp, $7.25 (out of print). Paperback reprint issued in two parts: I. Tables; and II. References; Government Printing Office, Washington, D.C. 20402, 1961 (out of print). Revisions of C500 are being issued provisionally as NBS Technical Notes, listed below.

Selected Values of Chemical Thermodynamic Properties

Part 1: Tables for the First Twenty-three Elements in the Standard Order of Arrangement, NBS Technical Note 270-1, D. D. Wagman, W. H. Evans, I. Halow, V. B. Parker, S. M. Bailey, and R. H. Schumm, U.S. Government Printing Office, Washington, D.C. 20402, October 1965, iv + 124 pp, $0.65.

Part 2: Tables for the Elements Twenty-four through Thirty-two in the Standard Order of Arrangement, NBS Technical Note 270-2, D. D. Wagman, W. H. Evans, I. Halow, V. B. Parker, S. M. Bailey, and R. H. Schumm, U.S. Government Printing Office, Washington, D.C. 20402, May 1966, iv + 62 pp, $0.40.

Selected Values of Properties of Hydrocarbons and Related Compounds, American Petroleum Institute Research Project 44, J. B. Zwolinski, dir., Texas A&M Research Foundation, College Station, Texas. As of June 1966 there were 2391 valid data sheets, complete set 6 volumes at $0.30 per sheet.

Selected Values of Properties of Chemical Compounds, Thermodynamics Research Center, B. J. Zwolinski, dir., Texas A&M Research Foundation, College Station, Texas. As of June 1966 there were 754 valid data sheets, complete set 2 volumes at $0.30 per sheet.

JANAF (Joint Army-Navy-Air Force) Thermochemical Tables, PB 168 370, D. R. Stull, dir., Clearinghouse for Federal Scientific and Technical Information, Springfield, Virg., 1965, 945 pp, $10.00.

First Addendum, PB 168 370-1, D. R. Stull, dir., Clearinghouse for Federal Scientific and Technical Information, Springfield, Virg., 1966, vii + 197 pp, $4.00 (Supplements 18, 19, 20, and 21).

Information on further supplements is available from Dr. D. R. Stull, dir., Thermal Research Laboratory, Dow Chemical Company, Midland, Michigan.

Contributions to the Data on Theoretical Metallurgy, I–XV, published as Bureau of Mines bulletins between 1932 and 1962. Many bulletins were superceded; six are revisions and Bulletin 601 is a reprinting of four previous bulletins and out of print for some years, but still in demand as essential in present-day research. The ones currently available are listed below.

Contributions to the Data on Theoretical Metallurgy

XIII High-Temperature Heat-Content, Heat Capacity, and Entropy Data for the Elements and Inorganic Compounds, K. K. Kelley, Bulletin 584 (Bureau of Mines), U.S. Government Printing Office, Washington, D.C. 20402, 1960, 232 pp, $1.25.

XIV Entropies of Elements and Inorganic Compounds, K. K. Kelley and E. G. King, Bulletin 592 (Bureau of Mines), U.S. Government Printing Office, Washington, D.C. 20402, 1961, 149 pp, $0.75.

XV A Reprint of Bulletins 383, 384, 393, and 406 (III, IV, V, and VII), Bulletin 601, Bureau of Mines (Publications Distribution Section, 4800 Forbes Avenue), Pittsburgh, Penna., 1962, 525 pp, single copies free.

383: The Free Energies of Vaporization and Vapor Pressures of Inorganic Substances, K. K. Kelley, 1935.

384: Metal Carbonates, Correlation and Applications of Thermodynamic Data, K. K. Kelley and C. T. Anderson, 1935.

393: Heats of Fusion of Inorganic Substances, K. K. Kelley, 1936.

406: The Thermodynamic Properties of Sulphur and Its Inorganic Compounds, K. K. Kelley, 1937.

Thermodynamic Properties of Chemical Substances, V. P. Glushko et al, eds, Vol. I, 1164 pp, and Vol. II, 916 pp, USSR Academy of Sciences, Moscow, 1962, approx $16.00.

Thermodynamic Constants of Substances, Handbook in 10 parts, V. P. Glushko, ed, USSR Academy of Sciences, All-Union Institute of Scientific and Technological Information, Moscow: Part I, 1965, 146 pp, 72 kopecks ($1.75); Part II, 1966, 96 pp, 52 kopecks ($1.40). Available in the United States from Victor Kamkin, Inc., Bookstore, 1410 Columbia Rd. N.W., Washington, D.C. 20009.

Chemical Thermodynamics in Non-Ferrous Metallurgy, J. I. Gerassimov, A. N. Krestovnikov, and A. S. Shakhov, Metallurgical Publishing House, Moscow.

Vol. I: Theoretical Introduction, Thermodynamic Properties of Important Gases, Thermodynamics of Zinc and Its Important Compounds, 1960, 231 pp.

Vol. II: Thermodynamics of Copper, Lead, Tin, Silver, and Their Important Compounds, 1960, 231 pp.

Vol. III: Thermodynamics of Tungsten, Molybdenum, Titanium, Zirconium, Niobium, Tantalum, and Their Important Compounds, 1963, 283 pp. English translation available as NASA-TT-F-285 or CFSTI-TT-65-50111, $6.00, from the Clearinghouse for Federal Scientific and Technical Information, Springfield, Virg. 22151.

Vol. IV: Thermodynamics of Aluminum, Antimony, Magnesium, Nickel, Bismuth, Cadmium, and Their Important Compounds, 1966, 428 pp.

Selected Values for the Thermodynamic Properties of Metals and Alloys, Ralph Hultgren, Raymond L. Orr, Philip D. Anderson, and Kenneth K. Kelley, John Wiley & Sons, Inc., New York, N.Y. 10016, 1963, xi + 963 pp, $12.50.

Thermochemistry for Steelmaking, Vol. I, J. F. Elliott and M. Gleiser, Addison-Wesley Publishing Co., Reading, Mass. 01867, 1960, viii + 296 pp, $17.50.

Thermochemistry for Steelmaking, Vol. II: Thermodynamics and Transport Properties, J. F. Elliott, M. Gleiser, and V. Ramakrishna, Addison-Wesley Publishing Co., Reading, Mass. 01867, 1963, xvi + 550 pp (pp 297–846), $25.00.

Thermodynamic Functions of Gases, F. Din, ed, Butterworth & Co. (Publishers) Ltd., 88 Kingsway, London, W.C.2, England, $12.50 per volume.

Vol. 1: Ammonia, Carbon Dioxide, Carbon Monoxide, 1956, viii + 175 pp.

Vol. 2: Air, Acetylene, Ethylene, Propane and Argon, 1956, vi + 201 pp.

Vol. 3: Methane, Nitrogen, Ethane, 1961, vi + 218 pp.

THERMOPHYSICAL PROJECTS

A Compendium of the Properties of Materials at Low Temperatures, V. J. Johnson, ed. Available from Clearinghouse for Federal Scientific and Technical Information, Springfield, Virg. 22151.

Phase I, Part I, Properties of Fluids, July 1960, 489 pp, WADD Technical Report 60-56, Part I (PB-171-618), $6.00.

Phase I, Part II, Properties of Solids, Oct. 1960, 330 pp, WADD Technical Report 60-56, Part II (PB-171-619), $4.00.

Phase I, Part III, Bibliography of References (cross-indexed), Oct. 1960, 161 pp, WADD Technical Report 60-56, Part III (PB-171-620), $3.00.

Phase II, R. B. Stewart and V. J. Johnson, eds, Dec. 1961, 501 pp, WADD Technical Report 60-56, Part IV (AD-272-769), $8.10.

Thermophysical Properties Research Center Data Book. Issued as loose-leaf sheets; sold on subscription basis at $0.10 per sheet, Thermophysical Properties Research Center, Purdue University, Research Park, 2595 Yeager Rd., West Lafayette, Ind. 47906.

Vol. I: Metallic Elements and Their Alloys.

Vol. II: Nonmetallic Elements, Compounds and Mixtures (In Liquid and Gaseous States at Normal Temperature and Pressure).

Vol. III: Nonmetallic Elements, Compounds and Mixtures (In the Solid State at Normal Temperature and Pressure).

Handbook of Thermophysical Properties of Solid Materials, A. Goldsmith, T. E. Waterman, and H. J. Hirschorn, revised edition, 1961 (8½″ × 11¼″), The Macmillan Co., 60 Fifth Ave., New York, N.Y. 10011, $90.00 per set.

Vol. I: Elements, vi + 752 pp.

Vol. II: Alloys, vi + 1,270 pp.

Vol. III: Ceramics, vi + 1,162 pp.

Vol. IV: Cermets, Intermetallics, Polymerics and Composites, vi + 798 pp.

Vol. V: Appendix (includes materials, author indexes, and a list of references), 286 pp.

PHYSICOCHEMICAL PROJECTS

Tables of Chemical Kinetics, Homogeneous Reactions, NBS Circular 510, U.S. Government Printing Office, Washington, D.C. 20402, 1951, xxiv + 732 pp (out of print).

Tables of Chemical Kinetics, Homogeneous Reactions, NBS Circular 510, Supplement 1, U.S. Government Printing Office, Washington, D.C. 20402, 1956, xiv + 422 pp (out of print).

Alphabetical Index to Tables of Chemical Kinetics, Homogeneous Reactions, NBS Circular 510, Supplement 2, U.S. Government Printing Office, Washington, D.C. 20402, 1960, iv + 37 pp, $0.35.

Tables of Chemical Kinetics, Homogeneous Reactions, Supplementary Tables, To Accompany Circular 510 and Supplements 1 and 2, NBS Monograph 34, U.S. Government Printing Office, Washington, D.C. 20402, 1961, $2.75.

Tables of Chemical Kinetics, Homogeneous Reactions, Supplementary Tables, NBS Monograph 34, Vol. 2, U.S. Government Printing Office, Washington, D.C. 20402, 1964, $2.00.

Phase Diagrams for Ceramists, E. M. Levin, H. F. McMurdie, and F. P. Hall, The American Ceramic Society, 4055 N. High St., Columbus, Ohio 43214, 1956, 286 pp (811 phase diagrams).

Phase Diagrams for Ceramists, Part II, E. M. Levin and H. F. McMurdie, The American Ceramic Society, 4055 N. High St., Columbus, Ohio 43214, 1959, 153 pp (462 phase diagrams).

Phase Diagrams for Ceramists, E. M. Levin, C. R. Robbins, and H. F. McMurdie (7th compilation), The American Ceramic Society, 4055 N. High St., Columbus, Ohio 43214, 1964, 601 pp (2064 phase diagrams), $18.00 (discount to members).

Phase Equilibrium Diagrams of Oxide Systems, revised and redrawn by E. F. Osborn and A. Muan, The American Ceramic Society, 4055 N. High St., Columbus, Ohio 43214, (Ten 19″ × 23″ plates for three-oxide systems containing SiO_2, four of them for oxide phases in equilibrium with metallic iron. Reproductions of these plates appear in the 1964 compilation).

Constitution of Binary Alloys, M. Hansen and K. Anderko, McGraw-Hill Book Company, New York, N.Y. 10036, 1958, xix + 1305 pp, $39.50.

Constitution of Binary Alloys, First Supplement, R. P. Elliott, McGraw-Hill Book Company, New York, N.Y. 10036, 1965, xxxii + 877 pp, $35.00.

Stability Constants of Metal-Ion Complexes, Section I: Inorganic Ligands, compiled by Lars Gunnar Sillen; Section II: Organic Ligands, compiled by Arthur E. Martell; Special Publication No. 17, The Chemical Society, London, 1964, xviii + 754 pp, $23.00.

Solubilities of Inorganic and Metal Organic Compounds, A compilation of Solubility Data from the Periodical Literature, A. Seidell, 4th ed., W. F. Linke, American Chemical Society, 1155 16th St. N.W., Washington, D.C. 20036.

> Vol. I, 1958, iv + 1287 pp, $32.50.
> Vol. II, 1965, iv + 1914 pp, $32.50.

INDEXES

Consolidated Index of Selected Property Values: Physical Chemistry and Thermodynamics, Prepared by the Office of Critical Tables. A key to the contents of six compilations that present critically evaluated numerical property values. Publication 976, National Academy of Sciences—National Research Council Printing and Publishing Office, 2101 Constitution Ave., N.W., Washington, D.C. 20418, 1962, xxiii + 274 pp, $6.00.

CRYSTALLOGRAPHIC PROJECTS

Crystal Data, Classification of Substances by Space Groups and their Identification from Cell Dimensions, J. D. H. Donnay and Werner Nowacki, Memoir 60 of the Geological Society of America, 1954, ix + 719 pp, Geological Society of America, 419 W. 117 St., New York, N.Y. 10027 (out of print).

Crystal Data, Determinative Tables, second edition, J. D. H. Donnay, General Editor; Gabrielle Donnay, Assistant Editor; E. G. Cox, Inorganic Compounds; Olga Kennard, Organic Compounds; Murray Vernon King, Proteins; Monograph 5 of the American Crystallographic Association, 1963, x + 1,302 pp, $20.00. Polycrystal Book Service, P.O. Box 11567, Pittsburgh, Pa. 15238.

Crystal Structures, first edition, Ralph W. C. Wyckoff, Interscience Publishers, John Wiley & Sons, New York.

> Section I: Chapters I to VIII, 1948, 378 pp, $13.50.
> Section II: Chapters VIII–X, XIII, 1951, 509 pp, $17.00.
> Section III: Chapters XIV, XV, Organic Index, 1953, 465 pp, $25.00.
> Section IV: Chapters XI and XII, 1957, 261 pp, $8.00.
> Supplement I: Additions to Chapters II to VII, 1951, 143 pp, $5.00.
> Supplement II: Additions to Chapter XIII, 1953, 85 pp, $8.50.
> Supplement III: Additions to Chapters II to VIII, 1958, 311 pp, $20.00.
> Supplement IV: Additions to Chapters IX, X, XIII–XV, 1959, 509 pp, $22.00.
> Supplement V: Additions to Chapters II to XV, Indexes, 1960, 513 pp, $26.50.

Crystal Structures, 2nd ed., Ralph W. C. Wyckoff, Interscience Publishers, John Wiley & Sons, New York.

> Vol. I: Chapters I–IV, 1963, 467 pp, $17.50.
> Vol. II: Chapters V–VII, 1964, 588 pp, $24.00.
> Vol. III: Chapters VIII–X, 1965, 981 pp, $27.50.

Powder Diffraction Data File (PD-1), 16 Sets, American Society for Testing and Materials, 1916 Race St., Philadelphia, Pa. 19103.

Sets	Indexes	Cards		
		Plain ($)	Keysort ($)	IBM ($)
1–16	Organic	715	1,125	300
	Inorganic	1,280	1,855	
16 only	Organic	60	95	25
	Inorganic	140	220	
Book Form				
1–5	Organic	25		
	Inorganic	45		
	Both	60		

Structure Reports, Vols. 8–16 and Vol. 18, A. J. C. Wilson, General Editor; Vol. 17 and Vols. 19–23, W. B. Pearson, General Editor; published for the International Union of Crystallography by N. V. A. Oosthoek's Uitgevers, Mij, Utrecht, the Netherlands. Agent in the U.S.—Polycrystal Book Service, Box 11567, Pittsburgh, Pa. 15238.

The years covered, year published, and price of each volume are as follows:

Volume	Years Covered	Year Published	Price	
			Dutch florin	$
8	1940–1941	1956	80	22.50
9	1942–1944	1955	70	19.50
10	1945–1946	1953	55	15.50
11	1947–1948	1951	100	28.00
12	1949	1952	70	19.50
13	1950	1954	100	28.00
14[a]	1940–1950	1959	35	10.00
15	1951	1957	110	31.00
16	1952	1959	120	33.50
17	1953	1963	125	35.00
18	1954	1961	120	33.50
19	1955	1963	100	28.00
20	1956	1963	100	28.00
21	1957	1964	100	28.00
22	1958	In preparation	...	.....
23	1959	1965	120	33.50

[a]Index.

A Handbook of Lattice Spacings and Structures of Metals and Alloys, No. 4 of Pergamon Press series of monographs on Metal Physics and Physical Metallurgy. W. B. Pearson, Pergamon Press, Ltd., Headington Hill Hall, Oxford, England, also London, Edinburgh, New York, Paris, and Frankfurt, 1958, x + 1044 pp, $38.00.

International Tables for X-Ray Crystallography, Kathleen Lonsdale, general editor, Published for the International Union of Crystallography by the Kynoch Press, Witton, Birmingham 6, England. Also available from Polycrystal Book Service, P.O. Box 11567, Pittsburgh, Pa. 15238.

Vol. I: Symmetry Groups, Norman F. M. Henry and Kathleen Lonsdale, eds, 1952, xii + 558 pp, £5.5.0. ($14.70).

Vol. II: Mathematical Tables, John S. Kasper and Kathleen Lonsdale, eds, 1959, xviii + 444 pp, £5.15.0. ($16.50).

Vol. III: Physical and Chemical Tables, Caroline H. MacGillavry and Gerard D. Rieck, eds, 1962, xvi + 362 pp, £5.15.0. ($16.10).

The Barker Index of Crystals, A Method for the Identification of Crystalline Substances, Published for the Barker Index Committee by W. Heffer & Sons, Ltd., Cambridge, England.

Vol. I, Crystals of the Tetragonal, Hexagonal, Trigonal and Orthorhombic Systems, M. W. Porter and R. C. Spiller, 1951.

Part 1: Introduction and Tables, ix + 350 pp, £1.10.0. net ($4.20).

Part 2: Crystal Descriptions, x + 1,086 pp, £4.10.0. net ($12.60).
 The two parts—£6.0.0. net ($16.80).

Vol. II, Crystals of the Monoclinic System, M. W. Porter and R. C. Spiller, 1956.

Part 1: Introduction and Tables, v + 383 pp.

Part 2: Crystal Descriptions, M.1 to M.1800, viii + 760 pp.

Part 3: Crystal Descriptions, M.1801 to M.3572, viii + 688 pp.
 The three parts—£10.0.0. net ($28.00).

Vol. III, Crystals of the Anorthic System, M. W. Porter and L. W. Codd, 1964.

Part 1: Introduction and Tables, vi + 50 pp., and unpaginated tables.

Part 2: Crystal Descriptions, A.1 to A.831 and Atlas of Configurations, vii pp + unpaginated descriptions.
   The two parts—£12.0.0. net ($33.60).

MINERALOGICAL PROJECTS

The System of Mineralogy of James Dwight Dana and Edward Salibury Dana, Yale University, 1837–1892, 7th edition, John Wiley & Sons, Inc., 605 Third Ave., New York, N.Y. 10016; and Glen House, Stag Place, London, S.W.1., England.

Vol.   I: Elements, Sulfides, Sulfosalts, Oxides; Charles Palache, Harry Berman, and Clifford Frondel, 1944, xiii + 834 pp, $14.00.

Vol. II: Halides, Nitrates, Borates, Carbonates, Sulfates, Phosphates, Arsenates, Tungstates, Molybdates, etc.; C. Palache, H. Berman, and C. Frondel, 1951 xi + 1124 pp, $16.00

Vol. III: Silica Minerals, C. Frondel, 1962, xii + 334 pp, $7.95.

Rock-Forming Minerals, W. A. Deer, J. Zussman, and R. A. Howie, Longmans, Green and Co., Ltd., 48 Grosvenor St., London, W.1, England. Rights in USA, Philippines, and Central America—John Wiley & Sons, Inc., 605 Third Ave., New York, N.Y. 10016.

Vol.   I: 1962, 333 pp, $16.50.

Vol. II: 1963, 379 pp, $19.50.

Vol. III: 1962, 270 pp, $16.50.

Vol. IV: 1963, 435 pp, $16.50.

Vol. V: 1962, 371 pp, $16.50.

INDEXES

Indexes to Crystallographic Data Compilations. The American Society for Testing and Materials publishes the following indexes to the Powder Diffraction File (see p. 278). All ASTM publications are available from the American Society for Testing and Materials, 1916 Race St., Philadelphia, Pa. 19103.

   a. Index to the Powder Diffraction File; Organic (Hanawalt), includes Section 1–16, PDIS–15o, bound, $15.00.

   b. Index to the Powder Diffraction File; Inorganic (Hanawalt), includes Section 1–15, PDIS–16i, bound, $20.00.

   c. Fink Inorganic Index to the Powder Diffraction File, PDIS–16f, bound, $15.00.

   d. Matthews Coordinate Index to the Powder Diffraction File, Inorganic: Termatrex Cards, $675.00; Negative-Line Cards, $185.00.

GENERAL NUCLEAR PROPERTIES PROJECTS

Nuclear Data Sheets, Jan. 1958—. Vols. 5, and 6, 1958, 1959, 1960, 1961, published by the National Academy of Sciences—National Research Council, 2101 Constitution Avenue, Washington, D.C. 20418. Section B of the new journal "Nuclear Data" will be devoted to Nuclear Data Sheets. Vol. 1, No. 1, containing sheets for A-chains from $A=182$ through $A=185$, was issued in Feb. 1966.

1959 Nuclear Data Tables, U.S. Government Printing Office, Washington, D.C. 20402, April 1959, viii + 151 pp, $1.00.

1960 Nuclear Data Tables, U.S. Government Printing Office, Washington, D.C. 20402.

   Part 1: Consistent Set of Q Values, $A \leq 66$, 1961, 214 pp, $1.50.

   Part 2: Consistent Set of Q Values, $67 \leq A \leq 199$, 1961, 456 pp, $2.75.

   Part 3: Nuclear Reaction Graphs, 1960 (out of print).

   Part 4: Short Tables, 249 pp, 1961, $1.50.

Energy Levels of Light Nuclei, May 1962, T. Lauritsen and F. Ajzenberg, issued as Sets 5 and 6 of the 1961 Nuclear Data Sheets, essentially an addendum to a review article in **Nucl. Phys., 11,** 1–340 (1959).

Members of the Nuclear Data Project contributed the section **Energy Levels of Nuclei,** $A=21$ to $A=212$ of Group I, Vol. 1 of the New Series of Landolt-Börnstein, **Numerical Data and Functional Relationships in Science and Technology.**

Table of Isotopes, J. J. Livingood and G. T. Seaborg, **Rev. Mod. Phys., 12,** 30–47 (1940).

Table of Isotopes, G. T. Seaborg and I. Perlman, **Rev. Mod. Phys., 16,** 1–32 (1944).

GENERAL NUCLEAR PROPERTIES PROJECTS (Continued)

Table of Isotopes, G. T. Seaborg and I. Perlman, **Rev. Mod. Phys., 20,** 585–666 (1948).

Table of Isotopes, J. M. Hollander, I. Perlman, and G. T. Seaborg, **Rev. Mod. Phys., 25,** 469–650 (1953).

Table of Isotopes, D. Strominger, J. M. Hollander, and G. T. Seaborg, **Rev. Mod. Phys., 30,** No. 2, Part 2, 585–904 (1958). Also available from the American Institute of Physics, 335 E. 45th St., New York, N.Y. 10017.

Tabellen der Atomkerne (Nuclear Tables), W. Kunz and J. Schintlmeister. Teil (Part) I, Eigenschaften der Atomkerne (Nuclear Properties); Band (Volume) 1, Die Elemente Neutron bis Zinn (The Elements Neutron to Tin), 1958, xliv + 465 pp, Akademie-Verlag, G.m.b.H., Berlin W.8, Mohrenstrasse 39, Germany, price, 105 DM ($26.25). Teil I, Band 2, Eigenschaften der Atomkerne, Die Elemente Antimon bis Nobelium (Antimony to Nobelium), 1959, xliv + 641 pp (466–1107), price, 130 DM ($32.50). Akademie-Verlag, Berlin. (Also available from Pergamon Press, Headington Hill Hall, Oxford, England; 4/5 Fitzroy Square, London, W.1, England; 122 E. 55th St., New York, N.Y. 10022, £20.0.0 per set.)

Part II, Nuclear Reactions, Vol. 1, The Elements from Neutron to Magnesium, Text Volume, xliv + 700 pp. Table Volume, 36 tables (five of which require 2 or 3 sheets), 1965. Price £25.0.0. ($75.00) for the two volumes.

CROSS-SECTION PROJECTS

Neutron Cross Sections, BNL (Brookhaven National Laboratory) 325, 2nd ed, U.S. Government Printing Office, Washington, D.C. 20402, July 1958, v + 373 pp, $4.50.

Supplement 1, U.S. Government Printing Office, Washington, D.C. 20402, January 1960, iv + 129 pp, $2.00.

Supplement 2, Vol. I, $Z=1$ to 20, U.S. Government Printing Office, Washington, D.C. 20402, May 1964, Sectional pagination, $2.50.

Supplement 2, Vol. IIA, $Z=21$ to 40, Clearinghouse for Federal Scientific and Technical Information, Springfield, Virg. 22151, February 1966, sectional pagination, $4.00.

Supplement 2, Vol. III, $Z=88$ to 98, Clearinghouse for Federal Scientific and Technical Information, Springfield, Virg. 22151, February 1965, sectional pagination, $3.00.

Neutron Cross Sections—Angular Distributions, BNL 400, Clearinghouse for Federal Scientific and Technical Information, Virg. 22151, June 1956, 102 pp.
2nd ed, Angular Distributions in Neutron-Induced Reactions, Vol. I, $Z=1$ to 22; Vol. II, $Z=23$ to 94, Clearinghouse for Federal Scientific and Technical Information, Springfield, Virg. 22151, October 1962, 804 pp, sectional pagination, $8.50.

Part I, **Tabulated Neutron Cross Sections,** 0.001–14.5 MeV., R. J. Howerton, Vol. I, $_1$H–$_{22}$Ti; Vol. II, $_{23}$V–$_{50}$Sn; Vol. III, $_{51}$Sb–$_{95}$Am; UCRL-5226, first edition, May 1958. UCRL-5226, revised, 1959; Vol. I, $5.00, Vol. II, $5.00, Vol. III, $4.00, Clearinghouse for Federal Scientific and Technical Information, Springfield, Virg. 22151.

Part II, **Semi-Empirical Neutron Cross Sections,** 0.5–15 MeV., $_1$H–$_{94}$Pu, R. J. Howerton, Vol. I, Nov. 1958, UCRL-5351. (Photostat copy, $37.80, Microfilm copy, $11.10, available from the Library of Congress.)

Part III, **Tabulated Differential Neutron Cross Sections,** $_1$H–$_{94}$Pu, R. J. Howerton, Vol. I, Jan. 1961, UCRL-5573, Clearinghouse for Federal Scientific and Technical Information, Springfield, Virg. 22151, $5.00.

Charged Particle Cross Sections, LA-2014, Nelson Jarmie and John D. Seagrave, eds, Clearinghouse for Federal Scientific and Technical Information, Springfield, Virg. 22151, Feb. 1957, 234 pp, $1.25.

Charged Particle Cross Sections, LA-2424, Neon to Chromium, Darryl B. Smith, Compiler and ed, Nelson Jarmie and John D. Seagrave, associate eds, Clearinghouse for Scientific and Technical Information, Springfield, Virg. 22151, Jan. 1961, iii + 137 pp, $2.50.

Nuclear Cross Sections for Charged-Particle Induced Reactions, ORNL-CPX-1, Mn, Fe, Co, F. K. McGowan, W. T. Milner, and H. J. Kim, compilers, Oak Ridge National Laboratory, P.O. Box X, Oak Ridge, Tenn. 37831, July 1964, 443 pp.

Nuclear Cross Sections for Charged-Particle Induced Reactions, ORNL-CPX-2, Ni, Cu, F. K. McGowan, W. T. Milner, and H. J. Kim, compilers, Oak Ridge National Laboratory, P.O. Box X, Oak Ridge, Tenn. 37831, Sept. 1964, iii + 511 pp.

ENERGY LEVEL PROJECTS

Energy Levels of Light Nuclei

III: W. F. Hornyak, Thomas Lauritsen, P. Morrison, and H. A. Fowler, **Rev. Mod. Phys., 22,** 291–372, (1950).

IV: F. Ajzenberg and T. Lauritsen, **Rev. Mod. Phys., 24,** 321–402 (1952).

V: F. Ajzenberg and T. Lauritsen, **Rev. Mod. Phys. 27,** 77–166 (1955).

VI: F. Ajzenberg-Selove and T. Lauritsen, **Nucl. Phys., 11,** 1–340 (1959). This report may be obtained for $10.00 from North Holland Publishing Company, P.O. Box 103, Amsterdam, the Netherlands.

Energy Levels of Light Nuclei, Z=11 to Z=20

I: P. M. Endt and J. C. Kluyver, **Rev. Mod. Phys., 26,** 95–166, (1954).

II: P. M. Endt and C. M. Braams, **Rev. Mod. Phys., 29,** 683–756 (1957).

III: P. M. Endt and C. van der Leun, **Nucl. Phys., 34,** 1–324 (1962). Reprints of this paper are obtainable for $10.00 from North Holland Publishing Company, P.O. Box 103, Amsterdam, the Netherlands.

Decay Schemes of Radioactive Nuclei, B. S. Dzhelepov and L. K. Peker, 1958, viii + 787 pp, USSR Academy of Sciences Press, Moscow and Leningrad. English translation of above, 1961, vi + 786 pp, Pergamon Press, New York, Oxford, London, Paris.

Decay Schemes of Radioactive Nuclei, A ≥ 100, B. S. Dzhelepov, L. K. Peker, and V. O. Sergejev, 1963, 1060 pp, USSR Academy of Sciences Press, Moscow and Leningrad.

ATOMIC SPECTRA

Atomic Energy Levels As Derived from the Analyses of Optical Spectra, Charlotte E. Moore, NBS Circular 467, U.S. Government Printing Office, Washington, D.C. 20402.

Vol.   I: Hydrogen to Vanadium (Z=1–23), 1949, 309 pp, $5.50.

Vol. II: Chromium to Niobium (Z=24–41), 1952, 227 pp, $4.00.

Vol. III: Molybdenum to Lanthanum (Z=42–57) and Hafnium to Actinium (Z=72–89), 1958, 245 pp, $3.00.

Vol. IV: Lanthanide and Actinide groups; in preparation.

An Ultraviolet Multiplet Table, Charlotte E. Moore, NBS Circular 488, U.S. Government Printing Office, Washington, D.C. 20402.

Section 1, 1950, 85 pp, reprinted 1956.

Section 2, 1952, 120 pp, reprinted 1956.
Combined Sections 1 and 2, reprinted 1963, $1.25;

Section 3, 1962, 98 pp, 60 cents.
The first three sections include spectra of the elements in the corresponding volumes of Circular 467.

Section 4, 1962, 70 pp, 45 cents.
A Finding List for spectra of elements in Sections 1 and 2.

Section 5, 1962, 34 pp, 30 cents.
A Finding List for spectra of elements in Section 3.

Selected Tables of Atomic Spectra, Atomic Energy Levels and Multiplet Tables Si ii, Si iii, Si iv. NSRDS-NBS 3, Section 1, Charlotte E. Moore, U.S. Government Printing Office, Washington, D.C. 20402, June 1965, 40 pp, $0.35.

Atomic Transition Probabilities, A Critical Data Compilation; Vol. I, Hydrogen Through Neon, W. L. Wiese, M. W. Smith, and B. M. Glennon (NSRDS-NBS 4, Vol. I), U.S. Government Printing Office, Washington, D.C. 20402, May 1966, xi + 154 pp, $2.50.

INFRARED AND MICROWAVE SPECTRA

Selected Infrared Spectral Data, American Petroleum Institute Research Project 44, current loose-leaf sheets. As of June 30, 1966, there were 2813 valid sheets; sold as complete set 7 volumes at $0.30 per sheet, Texas A&M Research Foundation, College Station, Texas.

Selected Infrared Spectral Data, Thermodynamics Research Center, current loose-leaf sheets. As of June 30, 1966, there were 342 valid sheets. Sold as complete sets at $0.30 per sheet, Texas A&M Research Foundation, College Station, Texas.

Coblentz Society Spectra, set of 4,000 spectra, 1964, $115 per 1000. Indexes: Alphabetical Index, Molecular Formula Index, Chemical Classes Index, Numerical Index, $5.00 each, set of four, $10.00. Available from Sadtler Research Laboratories, Inc., 1517 Vine St., Philadelphia, Pa. 19102, to whom orders may be sent.

DMS (Documentation of Molecular Spectroscopy) Spectral Cards. The DMS card service is obtained by subscription from Butterworth & Co. (Publishers) Ltd., London, W.C.2, England, from Verlag Chemie, G.m.b.H., Weinheim an der Bergstrasse, West Germany. Volumes 1 through 6 contain 2000 cards, about 80 percent spectral and 20 percent literature. The spectral cards are supplied slotted or unslotted, the unslotted being marked according to the DMS code. The subscription includes a current literature list in a ring binder, the Junior Index, codes for the literature list, instruction and coding manual for the spectral cards, a formula list for each issue and the newsletters. Literature lists for nuclear magnetic resonance were begun in 1965. The prices for the DMS Spectral and Index cards are as follows:

	Price		
Cards	U.K. (£)	U.S. ($)	W. Germany (DM)
Spectral[a]			
(volume, each)			
1–4 (unslotted)	67. 0.0.	187.50	750.00
5–8 (unslotted)	75. 0.0.	210.00	840.00
1–4 (slotted)	80. 5.0.	225.00	900.00
5–8 (slotted)	88. 0.0.	247.00	988.00
9– (unslotted)	112.10.0.	315.00	1,260.00
9– (slotted)	130.10.0.	365.00	1,460.00
Index			
(sets)			
S-1 (1–4999) single	22. 5.0.	62.50	250.00
S-1 (1–4999) multiple	18. 0.0.	50.00	200.00
S-2 (5000–9999) single	26. 5.0.	73.50	295.00
S-2 (5000–9999) multiple	21. 0.0.	59.00	236.00

[a]Each volume consists of four issues, each issue containing about 400 spectral cards (pink) and 100 literature cards (yellow). From Issue 17 (beginning of Vol. 5), spectral cards for inorganic compounds (blue) are included and from Issue 25, the literature cards are replaced by literature lists.

The Infrared Data Committee of Japan Infrared Data Cards, published by Nankodo Co., Ltd., Harukicho, Bunkyo-ku, Tokyo, Japan. They are sold on a subscription basis at $238.00 for 1200 cards (postage included). Asian subscribers receive a special price of $150.00. Export agency is Sanyo Shuppan Bocki Co., Inc., P.O. Box 1705, Tokyo, Central Japan. The agent in the United States is the Preston Technical Abstracts Co., 909 Pitner Ave., Evanston, Ill. 60202. The agent in Europe is Heyden & Son Ltd., Spectrum House, Alderton Crescent, Hendon, London, N.W.4, England.

Standard Infrared Spectra (pure substances), Sadtler Research Laboratories, Inc., 3316 Spring Garden St., Philadelphia, Pa. 19104.

27 volumes of 1000 spectra each (complete through 1965), include alphabetical name, molecular formula, chemical classes, numerical, and commercial alphabetical indexes, $3,500.00 (or each volume $125.00, or indexes, set of five, $50.00).

1966 spectra by subscription, includes 2 volumes of 1000 spectra each, Nos. 27,001—29,000, five indexes and Spec-Finder, $350.00.

Standard spectra on 16-mm microfilm, prices same as above.

Sadtler Standard Grating Spectra, Sadtler Research Laboratories, Inc., 3316 Spring Garden St., Philadelphia, Pa. 19104.

Near Infrared Spectra
Completed set of 2000 spectra in 9 volumes, prices available upon request.

Far Infrared Spectra
Completed set of 500 spectra in 2 volumes, prices available upon request.

Commercial Spectra
Groups priced separately, prices available upon request.
Commercial Spec-Finder, $25.00.

The Red System ($A^2\pi - X^2\Sigma$) **of the CN Molecule,** Sumner P. Davis and John G. Phillips, University of California Press, Berkeley and Los Angeles, 1963, x + 214 pp, $9.50.

Spectral Data and Physical Constants of Alkaloids, J. Holubek and O. Štrouf, eds. Published by Heyden & Sons, Ltd., London, in cooperation with The Publishing House of the Czechoslovakia Academy of Sciences. Available in Western Europe and the Western Hemisphere from Heyden & Sons, Ltd., Spectrum House, Alderton Crescent, Hendon, London, N.W.4, England.

Vol. I, 1965, spectral cards 1–30 issued in two binders to take Vols. I and II, £23.0.0. ($69.00).

Vol. II, 1966, spectral cards 301–400, punched cards to be inserted in second binder, £7.0.0. ($21.00).

Microwave Spectral Tables, NBS Monograph 70, U.S. Government Printing Office, Washington, D.C. 20402.

Vol. I: Diatomic Molecules, Paul F. Wacker, Masataka Mizushima, Jean D. Peterson, and Joe R. Ballard, Dec. 1, 1964, xviii + 146 pp, 8″ × 10½″, $2.00.

Vol. II: Line Strengths of Asymmetric Rotors, Paul F. Wacker and Marlene R. Pratto, Dec. 15, 1964, xii + 340 pp, 8″ × 10½″, $3.00.

ELECTRONIC SPECTRA (ULTRAVIOLET AND VISIBLE)

Selected Ultraviolet Spectral Data, American Petroleum Institute Research Project 44, current loose-leaf sheets. As of June 30, 1966, there were 1076 valid sheets. Sold in complete sets, 3 volumes, at $0.30 per sheet. Texas A&M Research Foundation, College Station, Texas.

Selected Ultraviolet Spectral Data, Thermodynamics Research Center, current loose-leaf sheets. As of June 30, 1966, there were 126 valid sheets. Sold in complete sets at $0.30 per sheet. Texas A&M Research Foundation, College Station, Texas.

Organic Electronic Spectral Data, Interscience Publishers, a division of John Wiley & Sons, Inc., New York, London, and Sydney.

> Vol. I, 1946–1952, M. J. Kamlet, ed, 1961, pp xiii + 1244, $25.00.

> Vol. II, 1953–1955, H. E. Ungnade, ed, 1960, pp x + 919, $15.00.

> Vol. III, 1956–1957, O. H. Wheeler and L. A. Kaplan, eds, 1966, xii + 1210 pp, $25.00.

> Vol. IV, 1958–1959, J. P. Phillips and F. C. Nachod, eds, 1963, viii + 1179 pp, $20.00.

The "Sadtler Standard Ultraviolet Spectra" including alphabetical and numerical indexes are available on a subscription basis—$560.00 for the 1965 subscription (5000 spectra). The 11000 bound spectra previously issued sell for $1,265.00 including indexes. Individual spectra are priced at $0.15 each. The spectra are also available on 16-mm microfilm at the same price.

Orders and inquiries should be sent to Sadtler Research Laboratories, Inc., 3314–3320 Spring Garden St., Philadelphia, Pa. 19104.

Absorption Spectra in the Ultraviolet and Visible Region (a Theoretical and Technical Introduction), elaborated and edited by Dr. L. Láng; published in German and English in 1959, 2nd edition, 1961, 3rd edition, 1963, 80 pp, Co-production of the Academic Press, New York and London, and the Publishing House of the Hungarian Academy of Sciences, Budapest. Printed in English in Hungary. Available in both continents of America from Academic Press, Publishers, 111 Fifth Ave., New York, N.Y. 10003.

Absorption Spectra in the Ultraviolet and Visible Region, L. Láng, ed, Co-production of the Academic Press, New York and London, and the Publishing House of the Hungarian Academy of Sciences, Budapest Printed in English in Hungary. Available in both continents of America from Academic Press, Publishers, 111 Fifth Ave., New York, N.Y. 10003.

> Vol. 1: Substances, 170, 1959, 414 pp + Index pamphlet, 24, 2nd edition, 1961, 3rd edition, 1963. Combined introduction and Vol. 1, $18.00.

> Vol. 2: Substances, 179, 1961, 408 pp + Index pamphlet, 31, 2nd edition, 1964, $18.00.

> Vol. 3: Substances, 172, 1962, 424 pp + Index pamphlet, 24, $20.00.

> Vol. 4: Substances, 185, 1963, 414 pp + Index pamphlet, 24, $20.00.

> Vol. 5: Substances, 192, 1965, 416 pp + Index pamphlet, 28. Cumulative Index, Vols. 1–5, 1965, 112 pp, $23.00.

> Vol. 6: Substances, 197, 1966, 412 pp + Index pamphlet, 30, $23.00.

RAMAN SPECTRA

Selected Raman Spectral Data, American Petroleum Institute Research Project 44, current loose-leaf sheets. As of June 30, 1966, there were 501 valid data sheets. Sold in complete sets, 2 volumes, at $0.30 per sheet, Texas A&M Research Foundation, College Station, Texas.

Selected Raman Spectral Data, Thermodynamics Research Center, current loose-leaf sheets. As of June 30, 1966, there were 40 valid sheets. Sold as complete sets at $0.30 per sheet. Texas A&M Research Foundation, College Station, Texas.

MASS SPECTRA

Selected Mass Spectral Data, American Petroleum Institute Research Project 44, current loose-leaf sheets. As of June 30, 1966, there were 2342 valid sheets in the catalog. Sold as complete sets, 6 volumes, at $0.30 per sheet. Texas A&M Research Foundation, College Station, Texas.

Selected Mass Spectral Data, Thermodynamics Research Center, current loose-leaf sheets. As of June 30, 1966, there were 168 valid sheets. Sold as complete sets at $0.30 per sheet. Texas A&M Research Foundation, College Station, Texas.

Compilation of Mass Spectral Data (Index de Spectres de Masse), A. Cornu and R. Massot, 1966, xv + 617 pp, $8\frac{1}{2}'' \times 11''$. Published by Heyden & Sons Ltd., in cooperation with Presses Universitaires de France. Distributed by Heyden & Sons Ltd., Spectrum House, Alderton Crescent, London, N.W.4, England; $42.00.

NUCLEAR MAGNETIC RESONANCE SPECTRA

Selected Nuclear Magnetic Resonance Spectral Data, American Petroleum Institute Research Project 44, current loose-leaf sheets. As of June 30, 1966, there were 649 valid sheets. Sold as complete sets, 2 volumes, at $0.30 per sheet. Texas A&M Research Foundation, College Station, Texas.

Selected Nuclear Magnetic Resonance Spectral Data, Thermodynamics Research Center, current loose-leaf sheets. As of June 30, 1966, there were 551 valid sheets. Sold as complete sets, 2 volumes, at $0.30 per sheet. Texas A&M Research Foundation, College Station, Texas.

High Resolution NMR Spectra Catalog, Vol. I, 1962, N. S. Bhacca, L. F. Johnson, and J. N. Shoolery, compilers, Varian Associates, Instrument Division, Palo Alto, Calif. 94303, 43 pp + 368 spectra, $6.00; 10 or more copies, $4.50 each; student price, $5.00.

High Resolution NMR Spectra Catalog, Vol. II, 1963, N. S. Bhacca, D. P. Hollis, L. F. Johnson, and E. A. Pier, compilers, Varian Associates, Instrument Division, Palo Alto, Calif. 94303, x + 62 pp + 332 spectra; price same as Vol. I; combined edition, Vols. I and II, hard cover, $20.00.

LANDOLT-BÖRNSTEIN

Landolt-Börnstein: Zahlenwerte und Funktionen àus Physik, Chemie, Astronomie, Geophysik und Technik, sixth edition.

Volumes Published

Vol. I: Atom—und Molekularphysik

Part 1, Atome und Ionen, 1950, xii + 441 pp., DM 126 ($31.50).
Part 2, Molekeln I: Kerngerüst, 1951, viii + 571 pp., DM 168 ($42.00).
Part 3, Molekeln II: Elektronenhülle, 1951, xi + 724 pp., DM 218 ($54.50).
Part 4, Kristalle, 1955, xi + 1,007 pp., DM 318 ($79.50).
Part 5, Atomkerne und Elementarteilchen, 1952, viii + 470 pp., DM 148 ($37.00).

Vol. II: Eigenschaften der Materie in Ihren Aggregatzuständen

Part 2, Gleichgewichte ausser Schmelzgleichgewichten.
2a, Gleichgewichte Dampf-Kondensat und Osmotische Phänomene, 1960, xi + 974 pp., DM 448 ($112.00).
2b, Lösungsgleichgewichte I, 1962, x + 983 pp., DM 510 ($127.50).
2c, Lösungsgleichgewichte II, 1964, viii + 731 pp., DM 403.5 ($100.88).
Part 3, Schmelzgleichgewichte und Grenzflächenerscheinungen, 1956, xi + 535 pp., DM 198 ($49.50).
Part 4, Kalorische Zustandsgrössen, 1961, xii + 863 pp., DM 438 ($109.50).
Part 6, Elektrische Eigenschaften I, 1959, xv + 1,018 pp., DM 448 ($112.00).
Part 7, Elektrische Eigenschaften II, 1960, xii + 959 pp., DM 478 ($119.50).
Part 8, Optische Konstanten, 1962, xv + 901 pp., DM 476 ($119.00).
Part 9, Magnetische Eigenschaften I, 1962, xxv + 1,934 pp., DM 496 ($124.00).

Vol. III: Astronomie und Geophysik, 1952, xviii + 795 pp., DM 248 ($62.00).

Vol. IV: Technik

Part 1, Stoffwerte und mechanisches Verhalten von Nichtmetallen, 1955, xvi + 881 pp., DM 288 ($72.00).
Part 2, Stoffwerte und Verhalten von metallischen Werkstoffen.
2a, Grundlagen, Prüfverfahren, Eisenwerkstoffe, 1963, xii + 888 pp., DM 468 ($117.00).
2b, Sinterwerkstoffe, Schwermetalle (ohne Sonderwerkstoffe), 1964, xx + 1,000 pp., DM 530 ($132.50).
2c, Leichtmetalle, Sonderwerkstoffe, Halbleiter, Korrosion, 1965, xx + 976 pp., DM 518 ($129.50).
Part 3, Elektrotechnik, Lichttechnik, Röntgentechnik, 1957, xv + 1,076 pp., DM 396 ($99.00).

Volumes in Preparation

Vol. II: Eigenschaften der Materie in Ihren Aggregatzuständen

Part 1, Mechanisch-thermische Zustandgrössen.
Part 5, Physikalische und chemische Kinetik.
Part 10, Magnetische Eigenschaften II.

Vol. IV: Technik
Part 4, Wärmetechnik.

Landolt-Börnstein: Zahlenwerte und Functionen aus Naturwissenschaften und Technik, Neue Serie—Numerical Data and Functional Relationships in Science and Technology, New Series, K. H. Hellwege, editor-in-chief.

Volumes Published

Group I: Kernphysik und Kerntechnik—Nuclear Physics and Technology
   Vol. I, Energy Levels of Nuclei: A = 5 to A = 257, A. M. Hellwege and K. H. Hellwege, eds., 1961, xii + 813 pp., DM 212 ($53.00).

Group II: Atom und Molekularphysik—Atomic and Molecular Physics
   Vol. I, Magnetische Eigenschaften Freier Radikale—Magnetic Properties of Free Radicals, K. H. Hellwege and A. M. Hellwege, eds., 1965, x + 154 pp., DM 68 ($17.00).

Group VI: Astronomie, Astrophysik und Weltraum-Forschung—Astronomy, Astrophysics and Space Research
   Vol. I, Astronomie und Astrophysik—Astronomy and Astrophysics, H. H. Voigt, ed., 1965, xxxix + 711 pp., DM 314 ($78.50).

Other groups planned and volumes expected to be published in 1966 or 1967:

Group I: Nuclear Physics and Technology
   Hilfstabellen für α-, β-, γ- Spektroskopie—Auxiliary Tables for α-, β-, γ- Spectroscopy.
   Ladungs-und Dichteverteilung im Kern- -Charge and Density Distribution in the Nucleus.

Group II: Atomic and Molecular Physics
   Vol. I, Lumineszenz organischer Molekeln—Luminescence of Organic Molecules.
   Mikrowellenspektroskopie von Molekeln—Microwave Spectroscopy of Molecules.
   Molekularakustik—Molecular Acoustics.
   Vol. II, Magnetische Eigenschaften der Koordinations und metallorganischen Verbindungen der Übergangselemente—Magnetic Properties of Co-ordination and Organo-metallic Compounds of Transition Elements.

Group III: Crystal and Solid State Physics
   Elastische, elastooptische, piezoelektrische und andere Eigenschaften von Einkristallen—Elastic, Elasto-optic, Piezoelectric and Other Properties of Single Crystals.

Group IV: Macroscopic and Technical Properties of Matter
   Phosphoreszenz anorganischer Substanzen—Phosphorescence (Luminescence) of Inorganic Substances.

Group V: Geophysics and Space Research
   Aeronomy; Cosmic Radiation.

Published by Springer-Verlag, Berlin, Heidelberg, and New York. Also available from Walter J. Johnson, Inc., 111 Fifth Ave., New York, N.Y. 10003, and Stechert-Hafner, Inc., 31 E. 10th St., New York, N.Y. 10003.

TABLES DE CONSTANTES SELECTIONNEES—TABLES OF SELECTED CONSTANTS

Tables de Constantes Sélectionnées—Tables of Selected Constants

Vol. 1. Longueurs d'Onde d'Emissions X et des Ciscontinuités d'Absorption X-Wavelengths of Emission and Discontinuities in Absorption of X-Rays, Y. Cauchois and H. Hulubei, 1947, 199 pp. (out of print).

Vol. 2. Physique Nucléaire—Nuclear Physics, R. Grégoire, F. Joliot-Curie, and I. Joliot-Curie, 1948, 131 pp. (out of print).

Vol. 3. Pouvoir Rotatoire Magnétique (Effet Faraday)—Magnetic Rotatory Power (Faraday Effect); R. de Mallemann, Effet Magnéto-Optique de Kerr—Magneto-Optic Effect (Kerr), F. Suhner, 1951, 137 pp., 15 F, £1.10.0. ($4.50).

Vol. 4. Données Spectroscopiques Concernant les Molécules Diatomiques—Spectroscopic Data for Diatomic Molecules, B. Rosen, R. F. Barrow, A. D. Caunt, A. R. Downie, R. Herman, E. Huldt, A. MacKellar, E. Miescher, and K. Wieland, 1951, 361 pp., 48 F, £5.0.0. ($15.00).

Vol. 5. Atlas des Longueurs d'Onde Caractéristiques des Bandes d'Emission et d'Absorption des Molécules Diatomiques—Atlas of Characteristic Wavelengths for Emission and Absorption Bands of Diatomic Molecules (a continuation of Vol. 4 by the same authors), 1952, 389 pp., 56 F, £5.15.0 ($17.50).

Vol. 6. Pouvoir Rotatoire Naturel I-Steroïdes—Optical Rotatory Powers I-Steroids, J.-P. Mathieu and A. Petit, 1956, 507 pp. (out of print).

Vol. 7. Diamagnétisme et Paramagnétisme—Diamagnetism and Paramagnetism, G. Foëx; Relaxation Paramagnétique—Paramagnetic Relaxation, C. J. Gorter and L. J. Smits, 1957, 317 pp., 97 F, £9.15.9. ($29.00).

Vol. 8. Potentiels d'Oxydo-Réduction—Oxidation-Reduction Potentials, G. Charlot, D. Bézier, and J. Courtot, 1958, 41 pp., 21.60 F, £1.10.0 ($5.00).

Vol. 9. Pouvoir Rotatoire Naturel II-Triterpénoïdes—Optical Rotatory Power II-Triterpenoids, J.-P. Mathieu and G. Ourisson, 1958, 302 pp., 93.60F, £7.0.0. ($21.00)

Vol. 10. Pouvoir Rotatoire Naturel III-Amino-acides—Optical Rotatory Power III-Amino Acids, J.-P. Mathieu, J. Roche, and P. Desnuelle, 1959, 61 pp., 28 F, £2.0.0. ($6.50).

Vol. 11. Pouvoir Rotatoire Naturel IV-Alcaloïdes—Optical Rotatory Power IV-Alkaloids, J.-P. Mathieu and M. M. Janot, 1959, 211 pp., 110.40 F, £8.0.0. ($24.00).

Vol. 12. Semi-Conducteurs—Semi-Conductors, P. Aigrain and J. Balkanski, 1961, 78 pp., 27 F, £2.0.0. ($6.50).

Vol. 13. Rendements Radiolytiques—Radiolytic Yields, M. Haïssinsky and M. Magat, 1963, 230 pp., 114 F, £8.10.0. ($25.50).

Vol. 14. Pouvoir Rotatoire Naturel Ia-Stéroïdes—Optical Rotatory Power Ia-Steroids, J. Jacques, H. Kagan, G. Ourisson, and S. Allard, 1965, 1,046 pp., 258 F.

Vol. 15. Données Relatives aux Sesquiterpenoïdes—Data Relative to Sesquiter-penoids, G. Ourisson, S. Munavalli, and C. Éhret, 1966, 70 pp.

In Preparation

Metals of High Purity, 1967

Refractory Compounds

There have been several publishers for the present series. Volume 8 and later volumes have been published by Pergamon Press from whom the earlier volumes as well as the titles, availability, and prices of the 40 installments of Tables Annuelles, covering the period 1931–1936, may be obtained.

Published by Pergamon Press, 4 and 5 Fitzroy Square, London, W.1, England; 122 E. 55th St., New York, N.Y., U.S.; and 24 rue des Ecoles, Paris Vᵉ, France.

INTERNATIONAL CRITICAL TABLES

International Critical Tables of Numerical Data, Physics, Chemistry and Technology, published for the National Academy of Sciences—National Research Council, by McGraw-Hill Book Co., 330 W. 42nd St., New York, N. Y. 10036.

Vol. I, 1926, xx + 415 pp.	Vol. II, 1927, xviii + 616 pp.
Vol. III, 1928, xiv + 444 pp.	Vol. IV, 1928, viii + 481 pp.
Vol. V, 1929, ix + 465 pp.	Vol. VI, 1929, x + 471 pp.
Vol. VII, 1930, ix + 507 pp.	Index, 1933, vii + 321 pp.

Seven volumes and Index, $250.00; Vols. I-VII and Index, each $35.00.

NATIONAL STANDARD REFERENCE DATA SYSTEM PUBLICATIONS

U.S. Department of Commerce, National Bureau of Standards, Office of Standard Reference Data,
Washington, D.C. 20234

The NSRDS provides the quantitative data of physical science, critically evaluated and compiled for convenience. The technical scope of the NSRDS is indicated by the principal categories of data compilation projects now active or being planned: nuclear properties, atomic and molecular properties, thermodynamic and transport properties, solid state properties, chemical kinetics, colloid and surface properties and mechanical properties.
The NSRDS–NBS series of publications is intended primarily to include evaluated reference data and critical review of long-term interest to the scientific and technical community.

Beginning in 1972, the major portion of the output of the National Standard Reference Data System has been presented in a new quarterly, *Journal of Physical and Chemical Reference Data,* jointly published by the American Institute of Physics, the American Chemical Society, and the National Bureau of Standards. Bound reprint copies of each of the 16 papers appearing in the four issues of Volume 1, 1972 of the *Journal of Physical and Chemical Reference Data* are available for purchase from the American Chemical Society, 1155 16th Street, N.W., Washington, D.C. 20036, for the price indicated. Cost of requested reprints must accompany all orders. The other listed publications have been printed by the U.S. Government Printing Office except as noted and may be ordered from the Superintendent of Documents, U.S. Government Printing Office, Washington, D.C. 20402 for the price indicated.

Cost of requested publications must accompany order. No charge is made for postage to destinations in the United States and possessions, Canada, Mexico, and certain Central and South American countries. To other countries, payments for documents must cover postage. Therefore, one fourth of the price of the publication should be added for postage.

Reprints from the *Journal of Physical and Chemical Reference Data*

1. **Gaseous Diffusion Coefficients,** T. R. Marrero and E. A. Mason, Vol. 1, No. 1, pp. 1–118, 1972 ($6).
2. **Selected Values of Critical Supersaturation for Nucleation of Liquids from the Vapor,** G. M. Pound, Vol. 1, No. 1, pp. 119–134, 1972 ($3).
3. **Selected Values of Evaporation and Condensation Coefficients of Simple Substances,** G. M. Pound, Vol. 1, No. 1, pp. 135–146, 1972 ($3).
4. **Atlas of the Observed Absorption Spectrum of Carbon Monoxide between 1060 and 1900 Å,** S. G. Tilford and J. D. Simmons, Vol. 1, No. 1, pp. 147–188, 1972 ($4).
5. **Tables of Molecular Vibrational Frequencies, Part 5,** T. Shimanouchi, Vol. 1, No. 1, pp. 189–216, 1972 ($3.50).
6. **Selected Values of Heats of Combustion and Heats of Formation of Organic Compounds Containing the Elements C, H, N, O, P, and S,** E. S. Domalski, Vol. 1, No. 2, pp. 221–278, 1972 ($4.50).
7. **Thermal Conductivity of the Elements,** C. Y. Ho, R. W. Powell, and P. E. Liley, Vol. 1, No. 2, pp. 279–422, 1972 ($7).
8. **The Spectrum of Molecular Oxygen,** P. H. Krupenie, Vol. 1, No. 2, pp. 423–534, 1972 ($6).
9. **A Critical Review of the Gas-Phase Reaction Kinetics of the Hydroxyl Radical,** W. E. Wilson, Jr., Vol. 1, No. 2, pp. 535-574, 1972 ($4).
10. **Molten Salts: Volume 3, Nitrates, Nitrites, and Mixtures, Electrical Conductance, Density, Viscosity, and Surface Tension Data,** G. J. Janz, U. Krebs, H. F. Siegenthaler, and R. P. T. Tomkins, Vol. 1, No. 3, pp. 581–746, 1972 ($8).
11. **High Temperature Properties and Decomposition of Inorganic Salts—Part 3, Nitrates and Nitrites,** K. H. Stern, Vol. 1, No. 3, pp. 747–772, 1972 ($3.50).

12. **High-Pressure Calibration: A Critical Review,** D. L. Decker, W. A. Bassett, L. Merrill, H. T. Hall, and J. D. Barnett, Vol. 1, No. 3, pp. 773–836, 1972 ($4.50).
13. **The Surface Tension of Pure Liquid Compounds,** J. J. Jasper, Vol. 1, No. 4, pp. 841–1009, 1972 ($8).
14. **Microwave Spectra of Molecules of Astrophysical Interest. I. Formaldehyde, Formamide, and Thioformaldehyde,** D. R. Johnson, F. J. Lovas, and W. H. Kirchhoff, Vol. 1, No. 4, pp. 1011–1045, 1972 ($4).
15. **Osmotic Coefficients and Mean Activity Coefficients of Uni-univalent Electrolytes in Water at 25°C,** W. J. Hamer and Y. C. Wu, Vol. 1, No. 4, pp. 1047–1099, 1972 ($4.50).
16. **The Viscosity and Thermal Conductivity Coefficients of Gaseous and Liquid Fluorine,** H. J. M. Hanley and R. Prydz, Vol. 1, No. 4, pp. 1101–1113, 1972 ($3).

Publications Issued in the NSRDS Series

NBS-NSRDS-1, (C13.48:1) National Standard Reference Data System—Plan of Operation, by E. L. Brady and M. B. Wallenstein, 1964 (15 cents).
NBS-NSRDS-2, (C13.48:2) Thermal Properties of Aqueous Uni-univalent Electrolytes, by V. B. Parker, 1965 (45 cents).
NBS-NSRDS-3, Sec. 1, (C13.48:3/Sec. 1) Selected Tables of Atomic Spectra, Atomic Energy Levels and Multiplet Tables, Si II, Si III, Si IV, by C. E. Moore, 1965 (35 cents).
NBS-NSRDS-3, Sec. 2, (C13.48:3/Sec. 2) Selected Tables of Atomic Spectra, Atomic Energy Levels and Multiplet Tables, Si I, by C. E. Moore, 1967 (20 cents).
NBS-NSRDS-3, Sec. 3, (C13.48:3/Sec. 3) Selected Tables of Atomic Spectra, Atomic Energy Levels and Multiplet Tables, C I, C II, C III, C IV, C V, C VI, by C. E. Moore, 1970 ($1).
NBS-NSRDS-3, Sec. 4, (C13.48:3/Sec. 4) Selected Tables

of Atomic Spectra, Atomic Energy Levels and Multiplet Tables, N IV, N V, N VI, N VII, by C. E. Moore, 1971 (55 cents).

NSRDS-NBS-3, Section 6 (C13.48:3/Sec. 6) Selected Tables of Atomic Spectra, Atomic Energy Levels and Multiplet Tables, H I, D, T, by C. E. Moore, 1972 (40 cents).

NBS-NSRDS-4, (C13.48:4/Vol. I) Atomic Transition Probabilities, Vol. I, Hydrogen Through Neon, by W. L. Wiese, M. W. Smith, and B. M. Glennon, 1966 ($2.50).

NBS-NSRDS-5, (C13.48:5) The Band Spectrum of Carbon Monoxide, by P. H. Krupenie, 1966 (70 cents).

NBS-NSRDS-6, (C13.48:6/Pt. 1) Tables of Molecular Vibrational Frequencies, Part 1, by T. Shimanouchi, 1967. Superseded by NBS-NSRDS 39.

NBS-NSRDS-7, (C13.48:7/Pt. 1) High Temperature Properties and Decomposition of Inorganic Salts, Part 1. Sulfates, by K. H. Stern and E. L. Weise, 1966 (35 cents).

NBS-NSRDS-8, (PB189698) Thermal Conductivity of Selected Materials, by R. W. Powell, C. Y. Ho, and P. E. Liley, 1966 ($3).

NBS-NSRDS-9, (C13.48:9) Tables of Bimolecular Gas Reactions, by A. F. Trotman-Dickenson and G. S. Milne, 1967 ($2).

NBS-NSRDS-10, (C13.48:10) Selected Values of Electric Dipole Moments for Molecules in the Gas Phase, by R. D. Nelson, Jr., D. R. Lide, Jr., and A. A. Maryott, 1967 (40 cents).

NBS-NSRDS-11, (C13.48:11/Pt. 2) Tables of Molecular Vibrational Frequencies, Part 2, by T. Shimanouchi, 1967. Superseded by NBS-NSRDS 39.

NBS-NSRDS-12, (C13.48:12) Tables for the Rigid Asymmetric Rotor: Transformation Coefficients From Symmetric to Asymmetric Bases and Expectation Values of P_z^2, P_z^4, and P_z^6, by R. H. Schwendeman, 1968 (60 cents).

NBS-NSRDS-13, (C13.48:13) Hydrogenation of Ethylene on Metallic Catalysts, by J. Horiuti and K. Miyahara, 1968 ($1).

NBS-NSRDS-14, (C13.48:14) X-Ray Wavelengths and X-Ray Atomic Energy Levels, by J. A. Bearden, 1967 (40 cents).

NBS-NSRDS-15, (C13.48:15/Vol. 1) Molten Salts: Vol. 1, Electrical Conductance, Density, and Viscosity Data, by G. J. Janz, F. W. Dampier, G. R. Lakshminarayanan, P. K. Lorenz, and R. P. T. Tomkins, 1968 ($3).

NBS-NSRDS-16, (C13.48:16/Pt. 2) Thermal Conductivity of Selected Materials, Part 2, by C. Y. Ho, R. W. Powell, and P. E. Liley, 1968 ($2).

NBS-NSRDS-17, (C13.48:17/Pt. 3) Tables of Molecular Vibrational Frequencies, Part 3, by T. Shimanouchi, 1968. Superseded by NBS-NSRDS 39.

NBS-NSRDS-18, (C13.48:18) Critical Analysis of the Heat-Capacity Data of the Literature and Evaluation of Thermodynamic Properties of Copper, Silver, and Gold from 0 to 300°K, by G. T. Furukawa, W. G. Saba, and M. L. Reilly, 1968 (40 cents).

NBS-NSRDS-19, (C13.48:19) Thermodynamic Properties of Ammonia as an Ideal Gas, by L. Haar, 1968 (20 cents).

NBS-NSRDS-20, (C13.48:20) Gas Phase Reaction Kinetics of Neutral Oxygen Species, by H. S. Johnston, 1968 (45 cents).

NBS-NSRDS-21, (C13.48:21) Kinetic Data on Gas Phase Unimolecular Reactions, by S. W. Benson and H. E. O'Neal, 1970 ($7).

NBS-NSRDS-22, (C13.48:22/Vol. II) Atomic Transition Probabilities, Vol. II, Sodium Through Calcium, by W. L. Wiese, M. W. Smith, and B. M. Miles, 1969 ($4.50).

NBS-NSRDS-23, (C13.48:23) Partial Grotrian Diagrams of Astrophysical Interest, by C. E. Moore and P. W. Merrill, 1968 (55 cents).

NBS-NSRDS-24 (C13.48:24) Theoretical Mean Activity Coefficients of Strong Electrolytes in Aqueous Solutions from 0 to 100°C, by Walter J. Hamer, 1968 ($4.25).

NBS-NSRDS-25, (C13.48:25) Electron Impact Excitation of Atoms, by B. L. Moiseiwitsch and S. J. Smith, 1968 ($2).

NBS-NSRDS-26, (C13.48:26) Ionization Potentials, Appearance Potentials, and Heats of Formation of Gaseous Positive Ions, by J. L. Franklin, J. G. Dillard, H. M. Rosenstock, J. T. Herron, K. Draxl, and F. H. Field, 1969 ($4).

NBS-NSRDS-27, (C13.48:27) Thermodynamic Properties of Argon From the Triple Point to 300 K at Pressures to 1000 Atmospheres, by A. L. Gosman, R. D. McCarty, and J. G. Hust, 1969 ($1.25).

NBS-NSRDS-28, (C13.48:28/Vol. 2) Molten Salts: Vol. 2, Section 1. Electrochemistry of Molten Salts: Gibbs Free Energies and Excess Free Energies From Equilibrium-Type Cells, by G. J. Janz and Chr. G. M. Dijkhuis; Section 2. Surface Tension Data, by G. J. Janz, G. R. Lakshminarayanan, R. P. T. Tomkins, and J. Wong, 1969 ($2.75).

NBS-NSRDS-29, (C13.48:29) Photon Cross Sections, Attenuation Coefficients, and Energy Absorption Coefficients From 10 keV to 100 GeV, by J. H. Hubbell, 1969 (75 cents).

NBS-NSRDS-30, (C13.48:30/Pt. 2) High Temperature Properties and Decomposition of Inorganic Salts, Part 2. Carbonates, by K. H. Stern and E. L. Weise, 1969 (45 cents).

NBS-NSRDS-31, (C13.48:31) Bond Dissociation Energies in Simple Molecules, by B. deB. Darwent, 1970 (55 cents).

NBS-NSRDS-32, (C13.48:32) Phase Behavior in Binary and Multicomponent Systems at Elevated Pressures: n-Pentane and Methane-n-Pentane, by V. M. Berry and B. H. Sage, 1970 (70 cents).

NBS-NSRDS-33, (C13.48:33) Electrolytic Conductance and the Conductances of the Halogen Acids in Water, by W. J. Hamer and H. J. DeWane, 1970 (50 cents).

NBS-NSRDS-34, (C13.48:34) Ionization Potentials and Ionization Limits Derived From the Analyses of Optical Spectra, by C. E. Moore, 1970 (75 cents).

NBS-NSRDS-35, (C13.48:35/Vols. I, II, and III) Atomic Energy Levels as Derived From the Analyses of Optical Spectra. Vol. I, ^{1}H to [23]V; Vol. II, [24]Cr to [41]Nb; Vol. III, [42]Mo to [57]La, [72]Hf to [89]Ac, by C. E. Moore, 1972 (Vol. I, $5; Vol. II, $4.25; Vol. III, $4.50).

NBS-NSRDS-36, (C13.48:36) Critical Micelle Concentrations of Aqueous Surfactant Systems, by P. Mukerjee and K. J. Mysels, 1971 ($3.75).

NBS-NSRDS-37, (C13.48:37) JANAF Thermochemical Tables, 2d Edition, by D. R. Stull, H. Prophet, et al., 1971 ($9.75).

NBS-NSRDS-38, (C13.48:38) Critical Review of Ultraviolet Photoabsorption Cross Sections for Molecules of Astrophysical and Aeronomic Interest, by R. D. Hudson, 1970 ($1).

NBS-NSRDS-39, (C13.48:39) Tables of Molecular Vibrational Frequencies, Consolidated Volume, by T. Shimanouchi, 1972 ($3.00).

NBS-NSRDS-40, (C13.48:40) A Multiplet Table of Astrophysical Interest, by C. E. Moore, 1972 ($2.00).

NSRDS-NBS-41, (C13.48:41) Crystal Structure Transformations in Binary Halides, by C. N. R. Rao and M. Natarajan, 1972 (55 cents).

NSRDS NBS-42, (C13.48:42) Selected Specific Rates of Reactions of the Solvated Electron in Alcohols, by E. Watson, Jr. and S. Roy, 1972 (30 cents).

McDaniel, E. W., Cermák, V., Dalgarno, A., Ferguson, E. E., and Friedman, L., Ion-Molecule Reactions, published by Wiley-Interscience Series in Atomic and Molecular Collisional Processes, 1970 ($19.25).

NSRDS-UCRL-20000 YN, A Compilation of YN Reactions, by the Berkeley Particle Data Group, January 1970.

NSRDS-UCRL-20030 πN, πN Partial-Wave Amplitudes, by the Berkeley Particle Data Group, February 1970.

NSRDS-UCRL-20000 NN, NN and ND Interactions [above 0.5 GeV/c] – A Compilation, by the Berkeley Particle Data Group, August 1970.

NSRDS-LBL-55, K_L^0N Interactions–A Compilation, by the Berkeley Particle Data Group, March 1972.

NSRDS-LBL-100, Review of Particle Properties, by the Berkeley Particle Data Group, April 1972.

NSRDS-LBL-58, $\overline{N}$N and $\overline{N}$D Interactions–A Compilation, by the Berkeley Particle Data Group, May 1972.

UCRL-8030, Review of Particle Properties, by the Berkeley Particle Data Group, August 1970.

McDaniel, E. W., Cermák, V., Dalgarno, A., Ferguson, E. E., and Friedman, L., Ion-Molecule Reactions, published by Wiley-Interscience Series in Atomic and Molecular Collisional Processes, 1970 ($19.25).

Mapleton, Robert A., Theory of Charge Exchange, published by Wiley-Interscience Series in Atomic and Molecular Collisional Processes, 1971 ($19.95).

McClure, Gordon W. and Peek, James, M., Dissociation in Heavy Particle Collisions, published by Wiley-Interscience Series in Atomic and Molecular Collisional Processes, 1972 ($13.95).

Thomas, E. W., Excitation in Heavy Particle Collisions, published by Wiley-Interscience Series in Atomic and Molecular Collisional Processes, 1972 ($22.50).

Donnay, J. D. H. and Ondik, Helen M., Crystal Data, Determinative Tables, Third Edition, Volume I: Organic Compounds, published jointly by the U.S. Department of Commerce-National Bureau of Standards and the Joint Committee on Powder Diffraction Standards, 1972 ($30).

Other NBS Compilations of Data

NBS Tech Note 270-3, (C13.46:270-3) Selected Values of Chemical Thermodynamic Properties, Tables for the First Thirty-Four Elements in the Standard Order of Arrangement, by D. D. Wagman, W. H. Evans, V. B. Parker, I. Halow, S. M. Bailey, and R. H. Schumm, 1968 ($1.25).

NBS Tech Note 270-4, (C13.46:270-4) Selected Values of Chemical Thermodynamic Properties, Tables for Elements 35 Through 53 in the Standard Order of Arrangement, by D. D. Wagman, W. H. Evans, V. B. Parker, I. Halow, S. M. Bailey, and R. H. Schumm, 1969 ($1.25).

NBS Tech Note 270-5, (C13.46:270-5) Selected Values of Chemical Thermodynamic Properties, Tables for Elements 54 Through 61 in the Standard Order of Arrangement, by D. D. Wagman, W. H. Evans, et al., 1971 (55 cents).

NBS Tech Note 384, (C13.46:384) Thermophysical Properties of Oxygen from the Freezing Liquid Line to 600 R for Pressures to 5000 Psia, by Robert D. McCarty and Lloyd A. Weber, 1971 ($1.50).

NBS Tech Note 724, (C13.46:724) Properties of Selected Superconductive Materials, by B. W. Roberts, 1972 ($1).

Bederson, Benjamin and Kieffer, L. J., Total Electron-Atom Collision Cross Sections at Low Energies–A Critical Review, *Rev. Mod. Phys.*, 43, No. 4, 601-641 (1971).

NBS Tech Note 270-6, (C13.46:270-6) Selected Values of Chemical Thermodynamic Properties, Tables for the Alkaline Earth Elements [Elements 92 through 97 in the Standard Order of Arrangement], by V. B. Parker, D. D. Wagman, and W. H. Evans, 1971 ($1.25).

NBS Tech Note 438, (C13.46:438) Compendium of *ab-initio* Calculations of Molecular Energies and Properties, by M. Krauss, 1967 (70 cents).

NBS Tech Note 474, (C13.46:474) Critically Evaluated Transition Probabilities for Ba I and II, by B. M. Miles and W. L. Wiese, 1969 (30 cents).

NBS Tech Note 482, (C13.46:482) Superconductive Materials and Some of Their Properties, by B. W. Roberts, 1969 ($1.25).

NBS Tech Note 484, (C13.46:484) A Review of Rate Constants of Selected Reactions of Interest in Re-Entry Flow Fields in the Atmosphere, by M. H. Bortner, 1969 (60 cents).

NBS Monograph 94, (C13.44:94) Thermodynamic and Related Properties of Parahydrogen From the Triple Point to 100°K at Pressures to 340 Atmospheres, by H. M. Roder, L. A. Weber, and R. D. Goodwin, 1965 (75 cents).

NBS Monograph 70, Vol. I, (PB168072) Microwave Spectral Tables, Diatomic Molecules, by P. F. Wacker, M. Mizushima, J. D. Petersen, and J. R. Ballard, 1964 ($6).

NBS Monograph 70, Vol. II, (PB189714) Microwave Spectral Tables, Line Strengths of Asymmetric Rotors, by P. F. Wacker and M. R. Pratto, 1964 ($6).

NBS Monograph 70, Vol. III, (C13.44:70/Vol. III) Microwave Spectral Tables, Polyatomic Molecules With Internal Rotation, by P. F. Wacker, M. S. Cord, D. G. Burkhard, J. D. Petersen, and R. F. Kukol, 1969 ($4.25).

NBS Monograph 70, Vol. IV, (C13.44:70/Vol. IV) Microwave Spectral Tables, Polyatomic Molecules Without

Internal Rotation, by M. S. Cord, J. D. Petersen, M. S. Lojko, and R. H. Haas, 1968 ($5.50).

NBS Monograph 70, Vol. V, (C13.44:70/Vol. V) Microwave Spectral Tables, Spectral Line Listing, by M. S. Cord, M. S. Lojko, and J. D. Petersen, 1968 ($4.75).

NBS Monograph 115, (C13.44:115) The Calculation of Rotational Energy Levels and Rotational Line Intensities in Diatomic Molecules, by Jon T. Hougen, 1970 (55 cents).

COM-72-10014, Rate Constants of Gas Phase Reactions, by V. N. Kondratiev. Translated by L. Holtschlag and R. Fristrom, 1972 ($8.50).

Nondata Publications from NSRDS Related Projects

NBS Misc. Publ. 277, (PB191754) Photonuclear Data Index, prepared by the Photonuclear Data Group, NBS Radiation Physics Division, 1966 (55 cents).

NBS Special Publication 320, (C13.10:320) Bibliography on Atomic Transition Probabilities, Jan. 1916 through June 1969, by B. M. Miles and W. L. Wiese, 1970 ($1.25).

NBS Misc. Publ. 281, (C13.10:281) Bibliography on Flame Spectroscopy, Analytical Applications, 1800 to 1966, by R. Mavrodineanu, 1967 ($2).

NBS Misc. Publ. 289, (C13.10:289) Bibliography of Low Energy Electron Collision Cross Section Data, by L. J. Kieffer, 1967 (50 cents).

NBS Tech Note 290, (C13.46:290) Information Handling in the National Standard Reference Data System, by F. L. Alt, 1966 (25 cents).

NBS Tech Note 291, (C13.46:291) A Bibliography on Ion-Molecule Reactions, January 1900 to March 1966, by F. N. Harllee, H. M. Rosenstock, and J. T. Herron, 1966 (30 cents).

NBS Tech Note 444, (TN444) Reform: A General-Purpose Program for Manipulating Formatted Data Files, by Robert C. McClenon and Joseph Hilsenrath, 1968 ($3).

NBS Tech Note 446, (C13.46:446) PRECISE: A Multiple Precision Version of Omnitab, by Alfred E. Beam and Joseph Hilsenrath, 1968 (55 cents).

NBS Tech Note 448, (C13.46:448) Status Report—National Standard Reference Data System, April 1968, E. L. Brady, Editor, 1968 (70 cents).

NBS Tech Note 464, (C13.46:464) The NBS Alloy Data Center: Function, Bibliographic System, Related Data Centers, and Reference Books, by G. C. Carter, L. H. Bennett, J. R. Cuthill, and D. J. Kahan, 1968 ($1.25).

NBS Tech Note 470, (C13.46:470) Edpac: Utility Programs for Computer-Assisted Editing, Copy-Production, and Data Retrieval, by Carla G. Messina and Joseph Hilsenrath, 1969 (75 cents).

NBS Tech Note 500, (C13.46:500) Edit-Insertion Programs for Automatic Typesetting of Computer Print-out, by C. G. Messina and J. Hilsenrath, 1970 (60 cents).

NBS Tech Note 553, (C13.46:553) Critical Evaluation of Data in the Physical Sciences—A Status Report on the National Standard Reference Data System, by David R. Lide, Jr., 1970 (70 cents).

NBS Tech Note 554, (C13.46:554) Annotated Accession List of Data Compilations of the NBS Office of Standard Reference Data, by H. M. Weisman and G. B. Sherwood, 1970 ($1.50).

NBS Tech Note 700, (C13.46:700) COMBO: A General-Purpose Program for Searching, Annotating, Encoding-Decoding, and Reformatting Data Files, by Robert McClenon and Joseph Hilsenrath, 1972 (75 cents).

NBS Tech Note 747, (C13.46:747) Critical Evaluation of Data in the Physical Sciences—A Status Report on the National Standard Reference Data System, June 1972, by S. A. Rossmassier, 1972 ($1.25).

NBS Special Publication 306-1, (C13.10:306-1) Bibliography on the Analyses of Optical Atomic Spectra, Section 1 ^1H-^{23}V, by Charlotte E. Moore, 1968 ($1).

NBS Special Publication 306-2, (C13.10:306-2) Bibliography on the Analyses of Optical Atomic Spectra, Section 2 ^{24}Cr-^{41}Nb, by Charlotte E. Moore, 1969 (60 cents).

NBS Special Publication 306-3, (C13.10:306-3) Bibliography on the Analyses of Optical Atomic Spectra, Section 3 ^{42}Mo-^{57}La ^{72}Hf-^{89}Ac, by Charlotte E. Moore, 1969 (50 cents).

NBS Special Publication 306-4, (C13.10:306-4) Bibliography on the Analyses of Optical Atomic Spectra, Section 4 ^{57}La-^{71}Lu ^{89}Ac-^{99}Es, by Charlotte E. Moore, 1969 (55 cents).

NBS Special Publication 320, Supplement I, (C13.10:320/Suppl. I) Bibliography on Atomic Transition Probabilities, July 1969 through June 1971, by J. R. Fuhr and W. L. Wiese, 1971 (65 cents).

NBS Special Publication 322, (C13.10:322) Photonuclear Data Index, January 1965 through January 1970, prepared by the Photonuclear Data Group, 1970 (75 cents). Supersedes NBS Misc. Publ. 277, Supplement 1.

NBS Special Publication 324, (C13.10:324) The NBS Alloy Data Center: Permuted Materials Index, by G. C. Carter, D. J. Kahan, L. H. Bennett, J. R. Cuthill, and R. C. Dobbyn, 1971 ($7).

NBS Special Publication 349, (C13.10:349) Heavy-Atom Kinetic Isotope Effects, by M. J. Stern and M. Wolfsberg, 1972 (45 cents).

NBS Special Publication 362, (C13.10:362) Chemical Kinetics in the C–O–S and H–N–O–S Systems: A Bibliography–1899 through June 1971, by Francis Westley, 1972 (70 cents).

NBS Special Publication 363, (C13.10:363) Bibliography on Atomic Energy Levels and Spectra, July 1968 through June 1971, by L. Hagen and W. C. Martin, 1972 ($1).

NBS Special Publication 366, (C13.10:366) Bibliography on Atomic Line Shapes and Shifts (1889 through March 1972), by J. R. Fuhr, W. L. Wiese, and L. J. Roszinan, 1972 ($1.75).

NBS HANDBOOK 101, (C13.11:101) OMNITAB–A Computer Program for Statistical and Numerical Analysis, by Joseph Hilsenrath, Guy G. Ziegler, Carla G. Messina, Philip J. Walsh, and Robert J. Herbold, Revised January 1968 ($3).

Coblentz Society Specifications for Evaluation of Infrared

Index

A

Reference Spectra, by Board of Managers, Coblentz Society, Analytical Chemistry 38, No. 9 (August 1966).

Kieffer, L. J. and Dunn, Gordon H., Electron Impact Ionization Cross-Section Data for Atoms, Atomic Ions, and Diatomic Molecules: I. Experimental Data, Rev. Mod. Phys., 38, No. 1, 1-35 (1966).

Rudge, M. R. H., Theory of the Ionization of Atoms by Electron Impact, Rev. Mod. Phys., 40, No. 3, 564-90 (1968).

Coblentz Society Evaluated Infrared Reference Spectra, by the American Society for Testing and Materials' Joint Committee on Atomic and Molecular Physical Data, 1969. Vol. 6, 1000 Spectra ($225). Vol. 7, 1000 Spectra ($225). Vol. 8, 1000 Spectra ($225). Index to Vols. 1-8 ($40).

Publications in the OSRD Bibliography Series

NBS-OSRDB-70-1-V1, (PB191174) High Pressure Bibliography 1900-1968, Vol. I, Section I–Bibliography. Section II–Author Index, by L. Merrill, 1970 ($7).

NBS-OSRDB-70-1-V2, (PB191175) High Pressure Bibliography 1900-1968, Vol. II–Subject Index, by L. Merrill, 1970 ($7).

NBS-OSRDB-70-2, (COM-71-00722) The NBS Alloy Data Center: Author Index, by G. C. Carter, D. J. Kahan, L. H. Bennett, J. R. Cuthill, and R. C. Dobbyn, 1970 ($10).

NBS-OSRDB-70-3, (AD705110) Semiempirical and Approximate Methods for Molecular Calculations–Bibliography and KWIC Index, by G. A. Henderson and S. Frattali, 1969 ($3).

NBS-OSRDB-70-4, (COM-71-00025) Bibliography of Photoabsorption Cross Section Data, by R. D. Hudson and L. J. Kieffer, 1970 ($4).

NBS-OSRDB 71-1, (COM-71-00248) Bibliography on Properties of Defect Centers in Alkali Halides, by S. C. Jain, S. A. Khan, H. K. Sehgal, V. K. Garg, and R. K. Jain, 1971 ($3).

NBS-OSRDB-71-2, (COM-71-00841) Bibliography of Kinetic Data on Gas Phase Reactions of Nitrogen, Oxygen, and Nitrogen Oxides, by F. Westley, 1971 ($3).

Publications of the Atomic and Molecular Processes Information Center
Oak Ridge National Laboratory
Oak Ridge, Tennessee

ORNL-AMPIC-1, Bibliography of Atomic and Molecular Processes for 1963, compiled by the Atomic and Molecular Processes Information Center (July 1965).

ORNL-AMPIC-2, Directory of International Workers in the Field of Atomic and Molecular Collisions, September 1965 (October 1965).

ORNL-AMPIC-3, Bibliography of Atomic and Molecular Processes for 1964, compiled by the Atomic and Molecular Processes Information Center (March 1966).

ORNL-AMPIC-6, Bibliography of Atomic and Molecular Processes for July-December 1965, compiled by the Atomic and Molecular Processes Information Center (September 1967).

ORNL-AMPIC-7, Bibliography of Atomic and Molecular Processes for January-June 1966, compiled by the Atomic and Molecular Processes Information Center (October 1967).

ORNL-AMPIC-8, Bibliography of Atomic and Molecular Processes for July-December 1966, compiled by the Atomic and Molecular Processes Information Center (October 1967).

ORNL-AMPIC-9, Bibliography of Atomic and Molecular Processes for January-June 1967, compiled by the Atomic and Molecular Processes Information Center (January 1968).

ORNL-AMPIC-10, Bibliography of Atomic and Molecular Processes for July-December 1967, compiled by the Atomic and Molecular Processes Information Center (June 1968).

ORNL-AMPIC-11, Bibliography of Atomic and Molecular Processes for January-June 1968, compiled by the Atomic and Molecular Processes Information Center (January 1969).

ORNL-AMPIC-12, Bibliography of Atomic and Molecular Processes for July-December 1968, compiled by the Atomic and Molecular Processes Information Center (June 1969).

ORNL-AMPIC-13, Bibliography of Atomic and Molecular Processes for January-December 1969, compiled by the Atomic and Molecular Processes Information Center (November 1970).

Publications of the Joint Institute for Laboratory Astrophysics, NBS
Boulder, Colorado

PB189132, Kieffer, L. J., Bibliography of Photoabsorption Cross Section Data, JILA Information Center Report #5, 32 pages (April 1968).

PB189127, Kieffer, L. J., Compilation of Low Energy Electron Collision Cross Section Data, Part I, JILA Information Center Report #6, 95 pages (January 1969).

AD695692, Sinnott, George A., Bibliography of Ion-Molecule Reaction Rate Data, JILA Information Center Report #9, 80 pages (August 1969).

AD696467, Kieffer, L. J., Compilation of Low Energy Electron Collision Cross Section Data, Part II, JILA Information Center Report #7, 167 pages (September 1969).

Chamberlain, G. E., and Kieffer, L. J., Bibliography of Low Energy Electron Collision Cross Section Data (1967-1969), JILA Information Center Report #10, 44 pages (February 1970).

Publications of the Radiation Chemistry Data Center
University of Notre Dame
Notre Dame, Indiana

COO-38-595, Bibliography on Electron Spin Resonance of Radiation Produced Radicals (November 1967).

COO-38-641, Bibliography on the Radiation Chemistry of Aqueous Solutions. I. Amino Acids, November 1968 (Revised, August 1969).

COO-38-642, Bibliography on the Radiation Chemistry of Aqueous Solutions. II. Carbohydrates, December 1968 (Revised, August 1969).

COO-38-643, Bibliography on Radiation Chemistry of Alcohols and Phenols (November 1968).

COO-38-621, Thesaurus for Radiation Chemistry, May 1968 (Revised, August 1969).

COO-38-661, Bibliography on Radiation Chemistry of Alkanes (May 1969).

COM-71-01103, Weekly List of Papers on Radiation Chemistry, Index and Cumulation, Vol. IV, Nos. 1-26, Jan. through June 1971, August 1971 ($6).

COM-72-10266, Index and Cumulative List of Papers on Radiation Chemistry, Vol. IV, Nos. 27-52, July through December 1971, January 1972 ($6).

E

INDEX

dielectric constants, tables, E-58—59
diffusion, coefficient of, into air, F-60
diffusion, Graham's law, F-102
diffusivity of, in liquids, F-59
dispersoids, F-270
expansion of, laws and equations, F-99
general law, equation, F-99
Gay-Lussac's law of combining volumes, F-101
heat capacity
organic gases at 300° and 800°C, table, D-162—164
organic vapors at 25°C, table, D-160—161
hydrogen, wave lengths, vacuum, UV, E-212
ideal, Loschmidt's number for, F-106
ideal, temperature, equations, F-117
index of refraction of several organic and inorganic, E-224
inert, wave lengths of, E-209—212
inflammability
in air, limits of, D-106
in oxygen, limits of, D-106—107
kinetic theory, F-105
liquid state, surface tension of several, F-44—46
low boiling elements, boiling and triple points °K, D-174
mass attenuation coefficients of several, E-138
Meyer constant for several, F-206
molecular constants for several, F-206
molecular diameter of several, F-206
nitrogen, viscosity and thermal conductivity at cryogenic
temperatures, B-421
nitrogen, wave length, vacuum, UV, E-212
oxygen, fixed point properties of, F-79
oxygen, wave lengths, vacuum, UV, E-212
ozone and oxygen, physical constants for liquid and
gaseous, F-78
reference, dielectric constants, E-58
refrigerants, thermodynamic properties, E-27—33
standard conditions for, F-116
thermal conductivities of helium, nitrogen, and water, E-3
thermal conductivities of various, E-2—4
Underwriters' Laboratories' classification, comparative
life hazard of gases and vapors, E-36
Van der Waals' constant, table, D-178
Van der Waals' equation, D-178
Van der Waals' equation of state, F-119
Van der Waals' radii in A, D-178
vapor pressure of some elements that are gaseous at
standard conditions, D-212—214
velocity of sound in various, E-47
viscosity, table, F-56—59
volume, reduction to 0°C, 760 mm pressure, F-99
Gauge pressure, definition, F-112
Gauges, wire, comparison of, F-157
Gauss, definition, F-101
Gaussian gravitational constant, defining the a.u., F-187
Gay-Lussac's law, see Charles' law
Gay-Lussac's law of combining volumes, F-101
Gay Lussac number, definition, F-323
Geiger counter, definition, F-101
Geodesy, satellite, constants for, F-180
Geologic time, approximate scale, F-194
Geometric number, definition, F-329
Geopotential and geometric altitude relationship, F-200
Germanium (Ge 32)

atomic number, B-1
atomic weight, B-1
boiling point, B-1
electronic configuration, B-3
gravimetric factors, logs of, B-173
history, B-16—17
melting point, B-1
periodic table, B-4
price, approximate, B-17
production, general methods, B-16—17
properties in general, B-16—17
properties specific, see under Elements, Inorganic
compounds
specific gravity, B-16
symbol, B-1
uses, B-16—17
valence, B-16
Gibbs energy function, alkane hydrocarbons, D-87—100
Gibbs energy of formation, alkane hydrocarbons, D-87—100
Gibbs' phase rule, F-101
Gilbert, definition, F-102
Gills, conversion factors for, F-302
Glass
dielectric constants of various, E-60
filters, Corning, transmission of, E-231—237
friction, coefficient of, static, F-19
index of refraction of several types, E-223
quartz
physical constants for clear, fused, F-78
refraction, index of, for fused, E-224
transmissibility for radiations, E-246
thermal conductivities of various, E-6—9
transmissibility for radiations of several, E-246
values of F for various, D-179
velocity of sound in various, E-47
Glass scale, temperature correction, metric units, E-41
Glass sealing materials, physical properties, F-155—156
Glassware, calibration of volumetric, D-130
Glucose (Dextrose), see also Organic compounds
concentrative properties of, in varying concentration, D-230
Glycerol, see also Organic compounds
concentrative properties of, in varying concentration,
D-230—231
Goertler parameter, definition, F-329
Gold (Au 79)
atomic number, B-1
atomic weight, B-1
aqua regia reagent, preparation, D-116
boiling point, B-1
electronic configuration, B-3
gravimetric factors, logs of, B-173
history, B-17—18
melting point, B-1
periodic table, B-4
prices, history of, B-17—18
production, general methods, B-17—18
properties in general, B-17—18
properties specific, see under Elements, Inorganic
compounds
specific gravity, B-17
symbol, B-1
uses, B-17—18

MELTING AND BOILING POINTS, AND ATOMIC WEIGHTS OF THE ELEMENTS

Based on the Assigned Relative Atomic Mass of $^{12}C = 12$

The following values apply to elements as they exist in materials of terrestrial origin and to certain artificial elements. When used with the footnotes, they are reliable to ±1 in the last digit, or ±3 if that digit is in small type.

Name	Symbol	Atomic number	Atomic weight	Melting point, °C	Boiling point, °C
Actinum	Ac	89	(227)	1,050	3,200 ± 300
Aluminum	Al	13	26.98154[a]	660.37	2,467
Americium	Am	95	(243)	994 ± 4	2,607
Antimony	Sb	51	121.75	630.74	1,750
Argon	Ar	18	39.948[b,c,d,g]	−189.2	−185.7
Arsenic (gray)	As	33	74.9216[a]	817(28 atm)	613(sub.)
Astatine	At	85	~210	302	337
Barium	Ba	56	137.34	725	1,640
Berkelium	Bk	97	(247)	—	—
Beryllium	Be	4	9.01218[a]	1,278 ± 5	2,970(5 mm)
Bismuth	Bi	83	208.9808[a]	271.3	1,560 ± 5
Boron	B	5	10.81[c,d,e]	2,300	2,550(sub.)
Bromine	Br	35	79.904[c]	−7.2	58.78
Cadmium	Cd	48	112.40	320.9	765
Calcium	Ca	20	40.08	839 ± 2	1,484
Californium	Cf	98	(251)	—	—
Carbon	C	6	12.011[b,d]	~3,550	4,827
Cerium	Ce	58	140.12	798 ± 3	3,257
Cesium	Cs	55	132.9054[c]	28.40 ± 0.01	678.4
Chlorine	Cl	17	35.453[c]	−100.98	−34.6
Chromium	Cr	24	51.996[c]	1,857 ± 20	2,672
Cobalt	Co	27	58.9332[a]	1,495	2,870
Copper	Cu	29	63.546[c,d]	1,083.4 ± 0.2	2,567
Curium	Cm	96	(247)	1,340 ± 40	
Dysprosium	Dy	66	162.50	1,409	2,335
Einsteinium	Es	99	(254)	—	
Erbium	Er	68	167.26	1,522	2,510
Europium	Eu	63	151.96	822 ± 5	1,597
Fermium	Fm	100	(257)	—	
Fluorine	F	9	18.99840[a]	−219.62	−188.14
Francium	Fr	87	(223)	(27)	(677)
Gadolinium	Gd	64	157.25	1,311 ± 1	3,233
Gallium	Ga	31	69.72	29.78	2,403
Germanium	Ge	32	72.59	937.4	2,830
Gold	Au	79	196.9665[a]	1,064.43	2,807
Hafnium	Hf	72	178.49	2,227 ± 20	4,602
Helium	He	2	4.00260[b]	−272.2[26 atm]	−268.934
Holmium	Ho	67	164.9304[a]	1,470	2,720
Hydrogen	H	1	1.0079[b,d]	−259.14	−252.87
Indium	In	49	114.82	156.61	2,080
Iodine	I	53	126.9045[a]	113.5	184.35
Iridium	Ir	77	192.22	2,410	4,130
Iron	Fe	26	55.847	1,535	2,750
Krypton	Kr	36	83.80	−156.6	−152.30 ± 0.10
Lanthanum	La	57	138.9055[b]	920 ± 5	3,454
Lawrencium	Lr	103	(260)	—	
Lead	Pb	82	207.2[d,g]	327.502	1,740
Lithium	Li	3	6.941[c,d,e]	180.54	1,347
Lutetium	Lu	71	174.97	1,656 ± 5	3,315
Magnesium	Mg	12	24.305[c]	648.8 ± 0.5	1,090
Manganese	Mn	25	54.9380[a]	1,244 ± 3	1,962
Mendelevium	Md	101	(258)	—	
Mercury	Hg	80	200.59	−38.87	356.58
Molybdenum	Mo	42	95.94	2,617	4,612

Note: See end of table for footnotes.

W

S